PESTLINE

PESTLINE

Material Safety Data Sheets for Pesticides and Related Chemicals

VOLUME II

Occupational Health Services Inc.

VNR VAN NOSTRAND REINHOLD
New York

DISCLAIMER

Although great care has been taken by OHS in compiling and checking the information and data contained in Pestline™ to insure that it is current and accurate, OHS disclaims any and all liability for any errors, omissions, or inaccuracies in such information and data, whether attributable to inadvertence or otherwise, and for any consequences arising therefrom. The data provided hereunder neither purports to be nor constitutes legal or medical advice. It is further understood that OHS MAKES NO REPRESENTATIONS OR WARRANTIES OF ANY KIND INCLUDING BUT NOT LIMITED TO THE WARRANTIES OF FITNESS FOR A PARTICULAR PURPOSE OR MERCHANTABILITY, NOR ARE ANY SUCH REPRESENTATIONS OR WARRANTIES TO BE IMPLIED WITH RESPECT TO THE DATA FURNISHED, AND OHS ASSUMES NO RESPONSIBILITY WITH RESPECT TO CUSTOMERS, ITS EMPLOYEES, OR CLIENTS. OHS SHALL NOT BE LIABLE FOR ANY INCIDENTAL, SPECIAL, CONSEQUENTIAL, OR EXEMPLARY DAMAGES (INCLUDING DAMAGES FOR LOSS OF BUSINESS PROFITS, AND THE LIKE) RESULTING IN WHOLE OR IN PART, FROM CUSTOMERS USE OF DATA, EVEN IF OHS HAS BEEN ADVISED OF THE POSSIBILITY OF SUCH DAMAGES.

WARNING

Library of Congress Catalog Card Number 90-48902
ISBN 0-442-00698-5

Manufactured in the United States of America

Published by Van Nostrand Reinhold
115 Fifth Avenue
New York, New York 10003

Chapman and Hall
2-6 Boundary Row
London, SEJ 8HN

Thomas Nelson Australia
102 Dodds Street
South Melbourne 3205
Victoria, Australia

Nelson Canada
1120 Birchmount Road
Scarborough, Ontario MIK 5G4, Canada

16 15 14 13 12 11 10 9 8 7 6 5 4 3 2 1

Library of Congress Cataloging-in-Publication Data
Pestline: material safety data sheets for pesticides and related chemicals/by Occupational Health Services, Inc.
p. cm.
Includes bibliographical references and indexes.
"Volume 1 contains chemicals with PST numbers ranging from PST00020 through PST18670. Volume 2 contains PST18690 through PST86204"—Vol. 2, p.
ISBN 0-442-00697-7 (v. 1).—ISBN 0-442-00698-5 (v. 2)
1. Pesticides—Safety measures. 2. Agricultural chemicals—Safety measures. 3. Pesticides—Toxicology. 4. Agricultural chemicals—Toxicology. I. Occupational Health Services. II. Title: Pestline.
SB952.5. P48 1990
632'.95'0289—dc20

CONTENTS

PREFACE

The potential health and environmental risks associated with exposure to agricultural chemicals became evident during the 1970s with the banning of DDT, a potent insecticide that devastated some wildlife while persisting for years in the environment. Recent events, such as the cancer scare related to the growth regulator Alar, have heightened public awareness of the risks associated with pesticides. Government and industry have come to recognize the need to better communicate risk information to workers and the public.

Today, the Material Safety Data Sheet (MSDS) has become the most widely accepted means of communicating risk information. In response to the growing demand for technical information on pesticides, OHS created *Pestline*, a two-volume collection of MSDSs for more than 1000 pesticides and related chemicals. The MSDS is the culmination of an evolutionary process that has its roots in the eighteenth century.

During the late eighteenth century, the English developed the concept of "Failure to Warn," which today remains in various forms a part of all legal systems that subsequently sprang from English Common Law. "Failure to Warn" is a concept of liability that requires the innocent to be adequately warned when they may be subjected to one or more than one condition that might cause them injury, death, or both. The principle has been finely honed in recent years to include subjects other than physical dangers, such as can be found in financial transactions, investments, the transferring of properties, and even marriage contracts. Of the many nations and societies that have descended from England, none has come near to the extremes to which the United States legal system has raised this principle of law, to the point that it impinges daily upon the lives and activities of every citizen.

THE DESCENDENT VARIATIONS OF "FAILURE TO WARN"

"Failure to Warn" litigation has come to be a civilian enforcement tool that punishes through "Punitive Damages" the alleged wrongdoings of the financially influential when governmental inactions fail to fulfill those needs. The principle variations of the doctrine of "Failure to Warn" include:

1. "Right-To-Know"
2. "Full Disclosure"
3. "Punitive Damages"

The "Right-To-Know" and "Full Disclosure" doctrines or principles, at first glance, might seem the same or just different ways of saying the same thing. Though related to one another, they are treated entirely differently in the courts. Thus, corporations and other entities are required to build different defenses in structuring themselves for survival in this litigious society. "Right-To-Know" has, very recently (within the past 10 years), come to mean that anyone who is subject to any potentially harmful event or agent under the control of another must have been adequately and fully apprised of the dangers in a manner that can be proven to have been available to the injured party prior to the fact of the injury itself. The single greatest example of this principle at work can be found in tobacco products, where clear health warnings are and have been printed on each package for decades. These labels have effectively preempted personal injury suits by plaintiffs who claim tobacco companies failed to warn them of the risks associated with smoking. In such cases, the courts have presumed that the plaintiffs proceeded to use the products with full knowledge before the fact and did so willingly.

"Full Disclosure" goes beyond simple "Right-To-Know." Under this principle, a person or corporation who provides a service to the public is under a much broader requirement to disclose in advance to the purchaser all aspects of using the product or service, and it must be provable that such disclosure was made readily available to the purchaser. Many thousands of examples of this "Full Disclosure" doctrine or principle can be found in the securities industry. It might fairly be said that they have become legion.

As mentioned previously, "Failure to Warn" can result in civil litigation seeking "Punitive Damages." Such damages go beyond the normal compensation awarded the plaintiff and are designed to punish the defendant for a serious wrong. "Failure to Warn" the innocent of a condition that results in death or injury is, under the United States legal system, usually considered a serious wrong and grounds for "Punitive Damages."

PESTLINE AND THE DISCLOSURE DOCTRINES

Pestline is, to some degree, a product that fulfills the disclosure requirements of the principles outlined above. Its primary function is, however, rooted in the laws of nearly all of the 50 states and all of the Canadian Provinces. Nearly all such political subdivisions have passed laws requiring the existence of "Right-to-Know" documents of disclosure and warning for persons exposed to hazardous substances or conditions. It should be noted that of all chemical compounds, pesticides and drugs are the two most traditionally dangerous found in human society.

In addition to state and provincial laws requiring "Right-to-Know" documentation, there are powerful federal agencies, with overlapping powers and unclear lines of authority, that also require these same "Disclosure" documents.

Some of these agencies include:

1. Occupational Safety and Health Administration (OSHA)
2. Environmental Protection Agency (EPA)
3. United States Department of Agriculture (USDA)
4. Food and Drug Administration (FDA)
5. United States Department of Transportation (DOT)

It should be remembered that the legislative authority for all of the regulations promulgated by each of these agencies and departments has previously been enacted into law by the Congress of the United States.

OSHA created the progenitor Material Safety Data Sheet (MSDS) in the 1970s, with the original Form Number 20. In November of 1983, OSHA published the Hazard Communication standard, requiring chemical manufacturers to access the hazards of their chemicals and disclose this information to employees and downstream users via MSDS. The standard, which became effective in 1985, has since been expanded to cover all employers whose employees may be potentially exposed to hazardous chemicals. By act of congress, OSHA's authority is limited to the workplace; it does not have authority in the areas in which the EPA, USDA, and to some degree the FDA administer their respective controls over pesticides. There remain today many unanswered questions of jurisdiction, such as whether OSHA, the EPA, or the USDA have authority over worker exposures of hired employees on large farms who may be engaged in the mixing and application of pesticides.

The EPA is responsible for the regulation of the chemical pesticides listed in *Pestline* from two separate lines of legislative authority: the Federal Insecticide, Fungicide and Rodenticide Act (FIFRA) and the Superfund Amendments and Reauthorization Act (SARA).

Under FIFRA, the EPA carries the burden of governing all aspects of pesticides, with the exception of manufacturing worker occupational health conditions. These responsibilities include administration, mixing, labeling, disposal, registration, and toxicity review of manufacturer-provided data and licensing. Under SARA Title III, the EPA has promulgated regulations that require the states and their constituent political subdivisions to maintain MSDSs on the local inventory of hazardous chemicals that reside within their local boundaries. These local organizations are called LEPCs, or Local Emergency Planning Committees.

The FDA and USDA are responsible for enforcing pesticide tolerance levels set by EPA. These tolerances specify an upper limit of allowable pesticide residues on crops. The USDA enforces tolerances for residues found in meat, poultry, and dairy products. All other pesticide tolerances are enforced by the FDA.

DOT has promulgated certain regulations for the movement of pesticides or their hazardous wastes that require the labeling and classification of pesticide hazards. Further, DOT requires stringent packaging regulations on all goods shipped via air, rail, truck, or water. DOT also requires that shipping papers containing certain specific information accompany the pesticides, of which data is usually supplied from the MSDS, as presented in *Pestline*. In addition to the traditional shipping papers, DOT now requires that certain emergency response information accompany a hazardous shipment. Presently, the MSDS is the only document that fulfills that requirement.

The MSDS itself has become the principal instrument of data transmission for virtually all state and federal agencies. and that information is provided in unabridged form in Pestline.

We wish to acknowledge, with great appreciation, the dedicated work by the OHS research staff in Nashville, TN, especially Alison Barrett, Eric Boehme, Gerry Crownover, Scott Eckert, Ron Kirsch, and Linda Moore. Without their contributions this book would not have been possible. Special thanks go to John Bransford, President of OHS, and Jeff Hale, CEO of OHS, for their support and insight in the development of this project.

GUIDELINES FOR USING THE PESTLINE MSDS

This first edition of *Pestline* contains Material Safety Data Sheets (MSDSs) on more than 1000 agrochemicals. Most of these chemicals are registered as active pesticide ingredients with the Environmental Protection Agency (EPA) under the Federal Insecticide, Fungicide and Rodenticide Act (FIFRA). Some of the substances contained in the *Pestline* database are no longer registered for agricultural use in the United States. However, several U.S. companies continue to manufacture these chemicals, exporting them to other nations for use as pesticides.

Occupational Health Services, Inc. (OHS) produces and constantly updates thousands of MSDSs yearly. *Pestline* is a subset of that larger MSDS database. The MSDSs contained in *Pestline* are identified by a unique numbering system called the PST number. Two extensive indexes aid in finding a chemical of interest. The first index is organized alphabetically by chemical name, trade name, and synonym. The second index is organized by Chemical Abstract Service (CAS) number. Each index provides the appropriate PST number. Volume 1 contains chemicals with PST numbers ranging from PST00020 through PST18670. Volume 2 contains PST18690 through PST86204.

All of the MSDSs created by OHS, including those contained in *Pestline*, utilize a format based on the MSDS provisions of the Occupational Safety and Health Administration (OSHA) Hazard Communication Standard (HCS) 29 CFR 1910.1200. The following guidelines describe each section within the *Pestline* MSDS.

The first section of each MSDS always provides the name, address, and telephone number of the issuer of the MSDS.

SUBSTANCE IDENTIFICATION

SUBSTANCE/CHEMICAL NAME - OHS policy follows that of the HCS, which requires that chemicals be designated according to the nomenclature system developed by the International Union of Pure and Applied Chemistry (IUPAC), the CAS rules of nomenclature, or a name that will clearly identify the chemical for the purpose of conducting an evaluation. The CAS assigns a unique multidigit number to each chemical. OHS includes that number in this section.

SYNONYMS/COMMON NAMES - Designation or identification such as code name, code number, trade name, brand name, or generic name used to identify a chemical other than by its chemical name. OHS includes as many synonyms as possible, including the base name for all hydrates, salts, and isomers. The empirical formula is included when applicable. Code numbers include:

RCRA waste number (EPA)
UN and NA number (DOT)
STCC number (Standard Transportation Commodity Code)
PST number (A unique five-digit number assigned by OHS)

CHEMICAL FAMILY - Identifies the main functional groups of the chemical, as well as secondary functional groups.

MOLECULAR FORMULA - Structurally represents the substance, where space allows.

MOLECULAR WEIGHT - Supplies the weight of the substance in Daltons (atomic mass units).

CERCLA RATINGS - Quick reference indicator as to the severity of the hazards of the substance. Ratings are listed for health, fire, reactivity, and persistency on a scale of O to 3, 3 being the most hazardous, with U being unknown.

NFPA RATINGS - National Fire Protection Association quick reference indicators as to the severity of the hazards of the substance. Ratings, on a scale of O to 4, are listed for health, fire, and reactivity based on NFPA definitions in 704, 49, or 325 M.

COMPONENTS/CONTAMINANTS

COMPONENTS - Indicates the constituents of the material/substance that may pose a significant hazard. Single substances are generally listed as 100%. Components in mixtures are listed, and their percentages and CAS numbers included, if available.

CONTAMINANTS - Present in the substance in very small amounts, usually in parts per million (ppm) or less. Stabilizers and inhibitors are also included in this section.

EXPOSURE LIMITS - Established limits of an air contaminant to control potential exposure. The HCS requires the OSHA permissible exposure limit (PEL), the American Conference of Governmental Industrial Hygienists (ACGIH) threshold limit value (TLV), and any other exposure limits used or recommended by the chemical manufacturer, importer, or employer preparing the MSDS. In addition to the HCS requirements, OHS also includes National Institute for Occupational Safety and Health (NIOSH)-recommended exposure limits (RELs). Manufacturer exposure limits, industry consensus standards, and American Industrial Hygiene Association (AIHA) Workplace Environmental Exposure Levels (WEELs) are included only if the substance is not regulated or if the recommended limits are lower than those of OSHA, ACGIH, and NIOSH.

The following are other regulatory concerns covered under this category:

- CERCLA Reportable Quantities (RQs) - Environmental Exposure Limits;
- SARA Threshold Planning Quantities (TPQs), (RQs) - Environmental Exposure Limits;
- SARA Section 313 - Annual reporting on environmental releases; and
- California Proposition 65 - Environmental Health Warning requirements.

PHYSICAL DATA

OHS includes the following sections when information is available. If information is not available, NO DATA AVAILABLE is inserted in the categories.

DESCRIPTION - physical state, color, etc.

BOILING POINT - The temperature in degrees Fahrenheit and/or Centigrade at which a liquid boils (is converted to a gas).

MELTING POINT (FREEZING POINT) - The temperature at which conversion of a solid to a liquid (or liquid to a solid) begins.

SPECIFIC GRAVITY - The ratio of the weight of a volume of a substance to the weight of an equal volume of water. If the substance has a specific gravity greater than 1.0, it will sink in water; if less than 1.0, it will float in water.

VISCOSITY - A measure of the internal resistance to flow exhibited by a fluid.

VAPOR PRESSURE - The pressure (often expressed in millimeters of mercury - mmHg) characteristic at any given temperature of a vapor in equilibrium with its liquid or solid form. A high vapor pressure indicates that a liquid will evaporate readily (volatility). Materials with high vapor pressures can be especially dangerous when used in an enclosed area with poor ventilation. Materials with low vapor pressures may pose an inhalation hazard when sprayed. Also listed is the temperature at which the substance may become volatile.

EVAPORATION RATE - A value denoting the rate at which the substance evaporates compared to a standard such as ether (which evaporates very quickly) or to butyl acetate (which evaporates very slowly). The chemical used as the standard (either ether, butyl acetate, carbon tetrachloride, etc.) is listed.

PH - A value taken to represent the acidity or alkalinity of a substance. The pH of strong acids is 1-3; the pH of strong bases is 12-13. Neutrality is equal to a pH of 7.

WATER SOLUBILITY - The ability or tendency of the substance to blend uniformily with water.

ODOR THRESHOLD - The concentration, usually in ppm, at which an odor is detected.

VAPOR DENSITY - The relative weight or density of a vapor or gas compared with an equal volume of dry air.

SOLVENT SOLUBILITY - The ability or tendency of the substance to blend uniformily with another.

OTHER - This category is designed to include any special or extraordinary physical characteristics or properties of the substance.

FIRE AND EXPLOSION DATA

This section contains the physical hazards of the chemical, including the potential for fire, explosion, and reactivity.

FIRE AND EXPLOSION HAZARD - Qualifies the CERCLA and NFPA fire ratings utilizing the physical properties of the substance. Explains any other extraneous circumstances that could cause problems or hazards.

FLASH POINT - The lowest temperature, reported in degrees Fahrenheit and Centigrade, at which a liquid gives off enough vapor to ignite in air in the presence of an ignition source.

UPPER EXPLOSIVE LIMIT - Maximum concentration at which the substance will form a flammable (explosive) mixture with air. Above this level there will be too much fuel to support combustion.

LOWER EXPLOSIVE LIMIT - Minimum concentration at which the substance will form a flammable (explosive) mixture with air. Below this level there will be too little fuel to support combustion.

AUTOIGNITION TEMPERATURE - The lowest temperature at which the substance will ignite without an ignition source.

FLAMMABILITY CLASS - Based on OSHA 29 CFR 1910. 106 - Classification of flammable liquids. I to IIIB.

FIREFIGHTING MEDIA - A list of agents used to extinguish a fire involving the substance.

FIREFIGHTING PROCEDURES - Instructions on how to use the agents listed in firefighting media; steps to take, steps not to take.

TRANSPORTATION DATA

Provides DOT information on assigning hazard classifications, labeling requirements, and references for packaging requirements. Aids in completing shipping papers and choosing placards.

TOXICITY

This section is intended for the health professional/toxicologist and provides the following information, when available:

IRRITATION DATA - Compiled from the Registry of Toxic Effects of Chemical Substances (RTECS) animal irritancy testing data and, if available, the level of severity of irritation. Other sources of information may also be included.

TOXICITY DATA - Compiled from RTECS, journals, abstracts, and manufacturer animal toxicity testing data and, if available, any human data. This information determines whether the chemical is labeled toxic or highly toxic in the health effects section of the MSDS.

CARCINOGEN STATUS - OHS policy follows the HCS requirements. Under the HCS, a chemical is considered a carcinogen if it has been evaluated by the International Agency for Research on Cancer (IARC) and found to be a carcinogen or potential carcinogen; or it is listed as a carcinogen or potential carcinogen in the Annual Report on Carcinogens published by the National Toxicology Program (NTP); or it is regulated by OSHA as a carcinogen. If the NTP has published a technical report indicating some degree of carcinogenicity, but has not included this information in its annual report, OHS will summarize this information.

LOCAL EFFECTS - A list of the local effects labels used in the health effects section and by which route these labels have been assigned.

ACUTE TOXICITY LEVEL - An assessment by occupational exposure route of the available toxicity data.

TARGET EFFECTS - A list of all target organ labels used in the health effects section. A statement may also be made about other organs affected, but not affected severely enough to warrant a label.

AT INCREASED RISK - Lists medical conditions that are generally recognized as being aggravated by exposure to the chemical.

ADDITIONAL DATA - This is an optional category intended for significant information of which either a route of exposure is not known or the route is nonoccupational.

HEALTH EFFECTS AND FIRST AID

INHALATION/SKIN/EYE/INGESTION - This section contains health effects and first aid information on the primary routes of exposure. OHS reports the information in the following order:

1. **Label** - A word designating the significant toxicologic or characteristic effects of the substance (e.g., corrosive/toxic).
2. **Immediately Dangerous to Life or Health (IDLH) level** - A concentration in air at which an immediate danger to the life or health of an individual can occur within 30 minutes. Reported in inhalation only for purposes of respirator selection.
3. **Acute Exposure** - Effects that occur during an 8-hour workday or from a single exposure.
4. **Chronic Exposure** - Effects that occur from repeated or more than one exposure.
5. **First Aid** - Provides information on emergency and first aid procedures.

ANTIDOTE - Designed to inform trained personnel of substances that, when administered to an individual, have an antagonistic effect on the substance or chemical reaction brought about by the substance to which that individual has been exposed.

REACTIVITY

Qualifies the assigned CERCLA/NFPA reactivity rating. Explains the hazards due to exposure to natural forces (e.g., water, air, light, heat, shock, friction).

INCOMPATIBILITY - A list of substances that, when in the presence of the chemical, react dangerously. Includes a summary of the dangerous reaction.

DECOMPOSITION - A list of hazardous products that will evolve when the substance is exposed to heat.

POLYMERIZATION - A chemical reaction usually carried out with a catalyst, heat, or light, and often under high pressure, in which a large number of relatively simple molecules combine to form a chain-like macromolecule. OHS is primarily concerned with hazardous polymerizations (e.g., violent, explosive, exothermic).

STORAGE AND DISPOSAL

This section lists the general precautions to take when storing or disposing of the substance. RCRA waste numbers are included to aid in meeting disposal regulations governed by the EPA.

CONDITIONS TO AVOID

This section lists the general precautions that should be taken when handling the substance.

SPILL AND LEAK PROCEDURES

WATER RELEASE - Steps to be taken when the substance has spilled into a water supply. If applicable, the California Proposition 65 warning requirement is noted in this section.

AIR RELEASE - Steps to be taken when the substance has been released into the air.

SOIL RELEASE - Steps to be taken when the substance has spilled onto the ground.

OCCUPATIONAL SPILL - Steps to be taken when the substance has spilled in the workplace. If applicable, EPA reporting information (CERCLA/SARA RQs) is included to help comply with CERCLA and SARA notification requirements.

PROTECTIVE EQUIPMENT

VENTILATION - Recommends engineering controls (e.g., local exhaust) based on the toxicological and physical hazards of the substance.

RESPIRATORY PROTECTION - Includes OSHA requirements, when regulated, and NIOSH and ACGIH recommendations. If none of these apply, OHS makes a recommendation based on the toxicological and physical characteristics of the substance.

CLOTHING - Includes OSHA requirements, if regulated. If not, OHS recommends appropriate protective clothing based on the physical characteristics and toxicological and local effects of the substance.

GLOVES - Includes OSHA requirements, if regulated. If not, OHS recommends appropriate protective gloves based on the physical characteristics and toxicological and local effects of the substance.

EYE PROTECTION - Includes OSHA requirements, if regulated. If not, OHS recommends eye protection based on the physical characteristics and local effects of the substance.

CREATION DATE/REVISION DATE

This final section provides the original creation date for the MSDS, as well as the date of the last revision.

KEY TO ABBREVIATIONS

AAOHN	American Association of Occupational Health Nurses
AAP	Asbestos Action Program
ACFM	Asbestos-Containing Friable Materials
ACGIH	American Conference of Governmental Industrial Hygienists
ACS	American Chemical Society
ADI	Acceptable Daily Intake
ADN	European agreement concerning international carriage of dangerous goods by inland waterways
ADNR ***and*** ADN /Rhine	Regulations for the carriage of dangerous goods on the Rhine river
ADR	European agreement concerning the international carriage of dangerous goods by road
AEA	Atomic Energy Act
AFGE	American Federation of Government Employees
AFL-CIO	American Federation of Labor and Congress of Industrial Organizations
AHA	American Heart Association
AHERA	Asbestos Hazard Emergency Response Act
AIHA	American Industrial Hygiene Association
AIHC	American Industrial Health Council
AIMS	American Institute of Merchant Shipping
ALJ	Administrative Law Judge
AMA	American Medical Association
ANPRM	Advanced Notice of Proposed Rule Making
ANSI	American National Standards Institute
AOMA	American Occupational Medical Association
APHIS	Animal and Plant Health Inspection Service
API	American Petroleum Institute
ARDS	Adult Respiratory Distress Syndrome
ASTM	American Society for Testing Materials
AT	Advanced Technology
ATSDR	Agency for Toxic Substances and Disease Registry
BAT	Best Available Technology
BDAT	Best Demonstrated Available Technology
BCT	Best Conventional Technology
BNA	Bureau of National Affairs, Inc.
BOD	Biochemical Oxygen Demand
BOS	Bureau Of Standards
BPT	Best Practical Technology
BSCC	Biotechnology Science Coordinating Committee
CAA	Clean Air Act (EPA)
CAER	Community Awareness Emergency Response
CAMEO	Computer-Aided Management of Emergency Operations
CAS	Chemical Abstracts Service
CASN	Chemical Abstracts Service Number
CBI	Confidential Business Information
CD-ROM	Compact Disc - Read Only Memory
CDC	Centers for Disease Control
CEFIC	Conseil European des Federations d'Industries Chemiques (European council of chemical manufacturers federations)
CEPP	Community Emergency Preparedness Program
CEQ	Council on Environmental Quality
CERCLA	Comprehensive, Environmental Response, Compensation and Liability Act (Superfund, EPA)
CFR	Code of Federal Regulations
CGL	Comprehensive General Liability
CHIB	Chemical Hazard Identification Branch
CHIP	Chemical Hazard Information Profile
CHRIS	Chemical Hazard Response Information System
CI	Color Index
CIM	International convention concerning the carriage of goods by rail
CISN	Chemical Information Screening Network
CMA	Chemical Manufacturers Association
COE	Corps Of Engineers
COETDG	Committee Of Experts on the Transport of Dangerous Goods, United Nations
COTR	Contracting Officer's Technical Representative
CPSA	Consumer Product Safety Act
CPSC	Consumer Product Safety Commission
CRT	Cathode Ray Tube
CSB	Chemical Screening Branch
CUFT	Center for the Utilization of Federal Technology
CWA	Clean Water Act (EPA)
DAWN	Drug Alert Warning Network
DEA	Drug Enforcement Administration
DGP	Dangerous Goods Panel
DHHS	Department of Health and Human Services
DLA	Defense Logistics Agency
DOD	Department Of Defense
DOE	Department Of Energy
DOI	Department Of the Interior
DOJ	Department Of Justice
DOL	Department Of Labor
DOT	Department Of Transportation
DRR	Division of Research Resources (DHHS)
ECA	Economic Commission for Africa
ECAD	Existing Chemical Assessment Division

KEY TO ABBREVIATIONS

ECE	Economic Commission for Europe
ECLAC	Economic Commission for Latin America and the Carribean
ECMT	European Conference of Ministers of Transport
ECOSOC	Economic and Social Council, United Nations
ECTF	Existing Chemicals Task Force
EEC	European Economic Community
EEGL	Emergency Exposure Guidance Levels
EEL	Emergency Exposure Levels
EDF	Environmental Defense Fund
EHC	Environmental Health Committee
EHN	Environmental Health News
EIL	Environmental Impairment Liability
EIS	Environmental Impact Statement
EMS	Emergency procedures for ships carrying dangerous goods
ENT	ENTomology number
EP	Extraction Procedures
EPA	Environmental Protection Agency
EPCRA	Emergency Planning and Community Right-to-know Act
EPI	Environmental Policy Institute
ERCS	Emergency Response Cleanup Services
ERTKA	Employee Right-To-Know Act (state level)
ESCAP	Economic and Social Commission for Asia and the Pacific
ESCWA	Economic and Social Commission for Western Asia
ETS	Emergency Temporary Standard
FAA	Federal Aviation Administration
FACOSH	Federal Advisory Council on Occupational Safety and Health
FCCSET	Federal Coordinating Council for Science, Engineering and Technology
FDA	Food and Drug Administration
FDCA	Federal Food, Drug and Cosmetic Act
FEMA	Federal Emergency Management Agency
FEV	Forced Expiratory Volume
FFDCA	Federal Food, Drug and Cosmetic Act
FHCP	Federal Hazard Communication Program
FHSA	Federal Hazardous Substances Act
FIATA	International federation of forwarding agents
FIFRA	Federal Insecticide, Fungicide and Rodenticide Act (EPA)
FMCSR	Federal Motor Carrier Safety Regulations
FOET	Foundation On Economic Trends
FOIA	Freedom Of Information Act
FR	Federal Register
FLSA	Fair Labor Standards Act
FTCA	Federal Tort Claims Act
FSN	Federal Stock Number
FWPCA	Federal Water Pollution Control Act
FVC	Forced Vital Capacity
FYI	For Your Information
GAO	General Accounting Office
GE-15	Group of experts, economic commission for Europe
GPO	Government Printing Office
GRAS	Generally Recognized As Safe (FDA)
GRASP	Government Relations And Science Policy
HATS	Human Adipose Tissue Survey (EPA)
HAZBATE	HAZard aBATEment file (OSHA)
HAZCAP	HAZard communication Compliance Assistance Program
HHS	Health and Human Services
HMAC	Hazardous Materials Advisory Council
HMIS	Hazardous Materials Information System
HMTA	Hazardous Materials Transportation Act
HMTC	Hazardous Materials Technical Center
HSDB	Hazardous Substances Data Bank (NLM)
HSIA	Halogenated Solvents Industry Alliance
HSWA	Hazardous and Solid Waste Amendments
HUD	Housing and Urban Development
IAEA	International Atomic Energy Agency
IAFF	International Association of Fire Fighters
IAO	Industrial Assistance Office
IARC	International Agency for Research on Cancer
IATA	International Air Transportation Association
IBM	International Business Machines corp.
ICAO	International Civil Aviation Organization
ICSC	International Chemical Safety Card
IDLH	Immediately Dangerous to Life or Health
IISRP	International Institute for Synthetic Rubber Producers
ILO	International Labour Organization
IMDG	International Maritime Dangerous Goods code (IMO)
IMGS	International Medical Guide for Ships
IMIS	Integrated Management Information System (OSHA)
IMO	International Maritime Organization
INS	Immigration and Naturalization Service
IPM	Integrated Pest Management
IPSC	International Programme for Safety in Chemicals
IRCA	Immigration Reform and Control Act
ITC	Interagency Testing Committee (TSCA)
IUPAC	International Union of Pure and Applied Chemistry
KB	KiloByte
KG	KiloGram
L	Liter
LC5O	Lethal Concentration-5O
LCLO	Lethal Concentration-LOw

LD50	Lethal Dose-50
LDLO	Lethal Dose-LOw
LEA	Local Education Agencies
LEL	Lower Exposure Limit
LEPC	Local Emergency Planning Committee
LEPD	Local Emergency Planning District
LFG	Liquified Flammable Gas
LUST	Leaking Underground Storage Tank
MAC	Maximum Allowable Concentration
MOTC	Ministry Of Transport, Canada
MOTJ	Ministry Of Transport, Japan
MS	Mail Stock
MAK	Maximum Allowable concentration (German)
MB	MegaByte
MCL	Maximum Contaminant Level
MCLG	Maximum Contaminant Level Goals
MCSAP	Motor Carrier Safety Assistance Program
MFAG	Medical First Aid Guide
MG	MilliGram
MPU	MicroProcessing Unit
MPRSA	Marine Protection, Research and Sanctuaries Act
MSDS	Material Safety Data Sheet
MSHA	Mine Safety and Health Administration
MSHACT	Mine Safety and Health ACT
MTB	Materials Transportation Bureau
NA	North American
NAAQS	National Ambient Air Quality Standards
NACE	National Association of Corrosion Engineers and health
NAS	National Academy of Sciences
NASA	National Aeronautics and Space Administration
NCI	National Cancer Institute
NCP	National Contingency Plan (Superfund)
NEI	National Eye Institute
NEPA	National Environmental Policy Act
NFFE	National Federation of Federal Employees
NFPA	National Fire Protection Agency
NHLBI	National Heart, Lung and Blood Institute
NIDA	National Institute of Drug Abuse
NIDR	National Institute of Dental Research
NIEHS	National Institute of Environmental Health Sciences
NIH	National Institute of Health
NINCDS	National Institute of Neurological and Communicative Disorders and Stroke
NIOSH	National Institute for Occupational Safety and Health
NLM	National Library of Medicine
NLRB	National Labor Relations Board
NLS	Noxious Liquid Substances
NOAA	National Oceanic and Atmospheric Administration
NOEL	No Observed Effect Level
NOES	National Occupational Exposure Survey (NIOSH)
NOS	Not Otherwise Specified
NPDES	National Pollutant Discharge Elimination System
NPIRS	National Pesticide Information and Retrieval System
NPL	National Priorities List (Superfund)
NPRM	Notice of Proposed Rule Making
NRC	Nuclear Regulatory Commission
NRDC	National Resources Defense Council
NSC	National Safety Council
NSF	National Science Foundation
NSPS	New Source Performance Standard
NSTA	National Science Teachers Association
NTP	National Toxicology Program
OCIS	OSHA Computerized Information System
OCM	Office of Compliance Monitoring
OECD	Organization for Economic Cooperative Development, Paris
OECM	Office of Enforcement and Compliance Monitoring
OGC	Office of General Council
OHEA	Office of Health and Environmental Assessment
OHMR	Office of Hazardous Material Regulation
OHMTADS	Oil and Hazardous Materials/Technical Assistance Data System (EPA)
OHS	Occupational Health Services, Inc.
OMB	Office of Management and Budget
OPP	Office of Pesticide Programs
OPTS	Office of Pesticides and Toxic Substances
ORM	Other Regulated Material
OSC	On-Scene Coordinator
OSHA	Occupational Safety and Health Administration
OSHACT	Occupational Safety and Health ACT
OSHSPA	Occupational Safety and Health State Plan Association
OSTP	Office of Science and Technology Policy
OSW	Office of Solid Waste
OTS	Office of Toxic Substances
OWPE	Office of Waste Programs Enforcement
PCL	Permissible Concentration Limits
PEF	Peak Expiratory Flowrate
PEL	Permissible Exposure Limit
PMN	PreManufacture Notification
POTW	Publicly Owned Treatment Work
PPM	Parts Per Million
PSC	Public Service Commission

KEY TO ABBREVIATIONS

PSD	Prevention of Significant Deterioration
PSES	Pretreatment Standards for Existing Sources
PSNS	Pretreatment Standards for New Sources
QSAR	Quantitative Structure-Activity Relationship
RAB	Risk Analysis Branch
RAM	Random Access Memory
RCRA	Resource Conservation and Recovery Act (EPA)
RI/FS	Remedial Investigation / Feasibility Study (Superfund)
RIN	Regulatory Information Number
RMCL	Recommended Maximum Contaminant Level
RPAR	Rebuttable Presumption Against Registration
RPDB	Regulatory Program Development Branch
RP	Reportable Quantity
RSPA	Research and Special Programs Administration
RTECS	Registry of Toxic Effects of Chemical Substances
SAB	Scientific Advisory Board
SAP	Scientific Advisory Panel
SARA	Superfund Amendments and Reauthorization Act
SDWA	Safe Drinking Water Act
SERC	State Emergency Response Commission
SIC	Standard Industrial Classification
SIP	State Implementation Plan
SNUR	Significant New Use Rule
SODA	State Occupational Directors Association
SOLAS	Safety Of Life At Sea convention
SPEGLS	Short-term Public Emergency Guidance LevelS
STCC	Standard Transportation Commodity Code
STEL	Short-Term Exposure Limit
STLC	Soluble Threshold Limit Concentration
TAO	TSCA Assistance Office
TCLO	Toxic Concentration-LOw
TDLO	Toxic Dose-LOw
TLM	Threshold Limit Median
TLV	Threshold Limit Value
TPQ	Threshold Planning Quantity
TRDB	Test Rules Development Branch
TRI	Toxic Release Inventory (SARA Title III)
TSCA	Toxic Substances Control Act (EPA)
TSDF	Treatment, Storage and Disposal Facility
TSP	Total Suspended Particles
TSS	Total Suspended Solids
TTLC	Total Threshold Limit Concentration
TWA	Time-Weighted Average
UAW	United Auto Workers
UEL	Upper Exposure Limit
UG/M3	MicroGram per Cubic Meter
UIC	Underground Injection Control
UICPC	Underground Injection Control Practices Panel
UN	United Nations
UNEP	United Nations Environment Program
URW	United Rubber Workers
USCG	United States Coast Guard
USDA	United States Department of Agriculture
USDI	United States Department of the Interior
USWA	United Steel Workers of America
VA	Veterans Administration
VDT	Video Display Terminal
VFW	Veterans of Foreign Wars
VOC	Volatile Organic Chemical
VSD	Virtually Safe Dose
WHD	Wage and Hour Division (DOL)
WEEL	Workplace Environmental Exposure Level
WIPP	Waste Isolation Pilot Plant (DOE)
WHMIS	Workplace Hazardous Materials Information System (Canada)
WHO	World Health Organization
WQA	Water Quality Act

PESTLINE

MATERIAL SAFETY DATA SHEET

OCCUPATIONAL HEALTH SERVICES, INC.
AGRICULTURE AND PESTICIDE DIVISION
450 SEVENTH AVENUE, SUITE 2407
NEW YORK, NEW YORK 10123
1-800-445-MSDS OR (212) 967-1100

EMERGENCY CONTACT:
JOHN S. BRANSFORD, JR. (615) 292-1180

SUBSTANCE IDENTIFICATION

CAS-NUMBER 7664-38-2
SUBSTANCE: **PHOSPHORIC ACID, SOLID**
TRADE NAMES/SYNONYMS: WHITE PHOSPHORIC ACID; ORTHOPHOSPHORIC ACID; PHOSPHORIC ACID; SONAC; WC-REINIGER; SUPERPHOS-105 (M & T CHEMICALS); STCC 4930248; UN 1805; H3PO4; PST18690
CHEMICAL FAMILY: INORGANIC ACID
MOLECULAR FORMULA: H3-P-O4
MOLECULAR WEIGHT: 98.00
CERCLA RATINGS (SCALE 0-3): HEALTH=2 FIRE=0 REACTIVITY=1 PERSISTENCE=0
NFPA RATINGS (SCALE 0-4): HEALTH=2 FIRE=0 REACTIVITY=0

COMPONENTS AND CONTAMINANTS

COMPONENT: PHOSPHORIC ACID ***PERCENT:*** 100.0
CAS# 7664-38-2
OTHER CONTAMINANTS: NONE
EXPOSURE LIMITS: PHOSPHORIC ACID: 1 MG/M3 OSHA TWA; 3 MG/M3 OSHA STEL 1 MG/M3 ACGIH TWA; 3 MG/M3 ACGIH STEL
5000 POUNDS CERCLA SECTION 103 REPORTABLE QUANTITY SUBJECT TO SARA SECTION 313 ANNUAL TOXIC CHEMICAL RELEASE REPORTING

PHYSICAL DATA

DESCRIPTION: ODORLESS, COLORLESS TRANSPARENT CRYSTALLINE SOLID.
MELTING POINT: 108 F (42 C) ***SPECIFIC GRAVITY:*** 1.834 @ 18 C
VAPOR PRESSURE: 0.0285 MMHG @ 20 C ***PH:*** 1.5 @ 0.1N SOLN
SOLUBILITY IN WATER: 548%
SOLVENT SOLUBILITY: SOLUBLE IN ALCOHOL.
LOSES WATER ABOVE 415 F (213 C) TO FORM PYROPHOSPHORIC ACID; ABOVE 572 F (300 C) FORMS METAPHOSPHORIC ACID.

FIRE AND EXPLOSION DATA

FIRE AND EXPLOSION HAZARD: NEGLIGIBLE FIRE HAZARD WHEN EXPOSED TO HEAT OR FLAME.
FIREFIGHTING MEDIA: DRY CHEMICAL, CARBON DIOXIDE, HALON, WATER SPRAY OR STANDARD FOAM (1987 EMERGENCY RESPONSE GUIDEBOOK, DOT P 5800.4).
FOR LARGER FIRES, USE WATER SPRAY, FOG OR STANDARD FOAM (1987 EMERGENCY RESPONSE GUIDEBOOK, DOT P 5800.4).
FIREFIGHTING: MOVE CONTAINERS FROM FIRE AREA IF POSSIBLE. COOL CONTAINERS EXPOSED TO FLAMES WITH WATER FROM SIDE UNTIL WELL AFTER FIRE IS OUT. STAY AWAY FROM STORAGE TANK ENDS (1987 EMERGENCY RESPONSE GUIDEBOOK, DOT P 5800.4, GUIDE PAGE 60).
USE AGENT SUITABLE FOR TYPE OF FIRE. USE WATER IN FLOODING QUANTITIES AS FOG. COOL CONTAINERS WITH FLOODING AMOUNTS OF WATER, APPLY FROM AS FAR A DISTANCE AS POSSIBLE. AVOID BREATHING CORROSIVE VAPORS, KEEP UPWIND.

TRANSPORTATION DATA

DEPARTMENT OF TRANSPORTATION HAZARD CLASSIFICATION 49 CFR 172.101: CORROSIVE MATERIAL
DEPARTMENT OF TRANSPORTATION LABELING REQUIREMENTS 49 CFR 172.101 AND SUBPART E: CORROSIVE
DEPARTMENT OF TRANSPORTATION PACKAGING REQUIREMENTS: 49 CFR 173.245 EXCEPTIONS: 49 CFR 173.244

TOXICITY

PHOSPHORIC ACID: IRRITATION DATA: 595 MG/24 HOURS SKIN-RABBIT SEVERE; 119 MG EYE-RABBIT SEVERE. TOXICITY DATA: 2740 MG/KG SKIN-RABBIT LD50; 1530 MG/KG ORAL-RAT LD50; 220 MG/KG UNREPORTED-MAN LDLO. CARCINOGEN STATUS: NONE. LOCAL EFFECTS: CORROSIVE- INHALATION, SKIN, EYE, INGESTION. ACUTE TOXICITY LEVEL: MODERATELY TOXIC BY INGESTION; SLIGHTLY TOXIC BY DERMAL ABSORPTION. TARGET EFFECTS: NO DATA AVAILABLE. AT INCREASED RISK FROM EXPOSURE: PERSONS WITH PRE-EXISTING RESPIRATORY OR SKIN DISEASE.

HEALTH EFFECTS AND FIRST AID

INHALATION: PHOSPHORIC ACID: CORROSIVE. SEE INFORMATION ON ACIDIC CORROSIVE COMPOUNDS.
ACIDIC CORROSIVES: **ACUTE EXPOSURE-** MAY CAUSE RESPIRATORY TRACT IRRITATION WITH COUGHING, CHOKING, AND POSSIBLY BURNS OF THE MUCOUS MEMBRANES. OTHER INITIAL SYMPTOMS MAY INCLUDE DIZZINESS, HEADACHE, NAUSEA AND WEAKNESS. IN SOME CASES PULMONARY EDEMA MAY DEVELOP, EITHER IMMEDIATELY IN SEVERE CASES, OR MORE LIKELY AFTER A LATENT PERIOD OF 5-72 HOURS. THE SYMPTOMS MAY INCLUDE TIGHTNESS IN THE CHEST, DYSPNEA, FROTHY SPUTUM, AND CYANOSIS. PHYSICAL FINDINGS MAY INCLUDE HYPOTENSION, WEAK, RAPID PULSE AND MOIST RALES. RECOVERY MAY BE PROLONGED AND RELAPSES ARE POSSIBLE. IN SEVERE EXPOSURES, DEATH DUE TO ANOXIA MAY OCCUR WITHIN A FEW HOURS AFTER ONSET OF PULMONARY EDEMA SYMPTOMS OR FOLLOWING A RELAPSE. **CHRONIC EXPOSURE-** DEPENDING ON THE CONCENTRATION AND DURATION OF EXPOSURE, REPEATED OR PROLONGED EXPOSURE MAY CAUSE EROSION OF THE TEETH, INFLAMMATORY AND ULCERATIVE CHANGES IN THE MOUTH, AND POSSIBLY JAW NECROSIS. BRONCHIAL IRRITATION WITH COUGH AND FREQUENT ATTACKS OF BRONCHIAL PNEUMONIA MAY OCCUR. GASTROINTESTINAL DISTURBANCES ARE ALSO POSSIBLE.
FIRST AID- REMOVE FROM EXPOSURE AREA TO FRESH AIR IMMEDIATELY. IF BREATHING HAS STOPPED, GIVE ARTIFICIAL RESPIRATION. MAINTAIN AIRWAY AND BLOOD PRESSURE AND ADMINISTER OXYGEN IF AVAILABLE. KEEP AFFECTED PERSON WARM AND AT REST. TREAT SYMPTOMATICALLY AND SUPPORTIVELY. ADMINISTRATION OF OXYGEN SHOULD BE PERFORMED BY QUALIFIED PERSONNEL. GET MEDICAL ATTENTION IMMEDIATELY.

SKIN CONTACT: PHOSPHORIC ACID: CORROSIVE. SEE INFORMATION ON ACIDIC CORROSIVE COMPOUNDS.
ACIDIC CORROSIVES: **ACUTE EXPOSURE-** DIRECT CONTACT MAY CAUSE SEVERE PAIN, BURNS AND POSSIBLY BROWNISH OR YELLOWISH STAINS. BURNS MAY BE DEEP WITH SHARP EDGES AND HEAL SLOWLY WITH SCAR TISSUE FORMATION. **CHRONIC EXPOSURE-** EFFECTS DEPEND ON THE CONCENTRATION AND DURATION OF EXPOSURE. REPEATED OR PROLONGED CONTACT MAY RESULT IN DERMATITIS OR EFFECTS SIMILAR TO ACUTE EXPOSURE.
FIRST AID- REMOVE CONTAMINATED CLOTHING AND SHOES IMMEDIATELY. WASH AFFECTED AREA WITH SOAP OR MILD DETERGENT AND LARGE AMOUNTS OF WATER UNTIL NO EVIDENCE OF CHEMICAL REMAINS (AT LEAST 15-20 MINUTES). IN CASE OF CHEMICAL BURNS, COVER AREA WITH STERILE, DRY DRESSING. BANDAGE SECURELY, BUT NOT TOO TIGHTLY. GET MEDICAL ATTENTION IMMEDIATELY.

EYE CONTACT: PHOSPHORIC ACID: CORROSIVE. DIRECT CONTACT WITH A 0.16M SOLUTION BUFFERED TO PH 2.5 CAUSED A MODERATE, BRIEF STINGING SENSATION, BUT NO INJURY WHEN APPLIED AS A SINGLE DROP IN HUMAN EYES. WHEN ADJUSTED TO PH 3.4, A DROP OF THE SOLUTION CAUSED NO DISCOMFORT. IRRIGATION OF RABBIT EYES FOR 5 MINUTES WITH PH 3.8 SOLUTION CAUSED SLIGHT TRANSIENT EPITHELIAL EDEMA AND CONJUNCTIVAL HYPEREMIA, BUT THE EYE WAS NORMAL WITHIN 24 HOURS. WHEN INJECTED INTO THE CORNEAL STROMA OR APPLIED TO THE CORNEA AFTER REMOVAL OF THE EPITHELIUM, IT CAUSED DETECTABLE INJURY BELOW PH 5.5. EYE BURNS MAY RESULT FROM SPLASHES OF CONCENTRATED SOLUTIONS. SEE INFORMATION ON ACIDIC CORROSIVE COMPOUNDS.
ACIDIC CORROSIVES: **ACUTE EXPOSURE-** DIRECT CONTACT MAY CAUSE PAIN, LACRIMATION, PHOTOPHOBIA AND AND BURNS. IN MILD BURNS, THE EPITHELIUM REGENERATES RAPIDLY AND THE EYE RECOVERS COMPLETELY. IN SEVERE CASES, THE EXTENT OF INJURY MAY NOT BE FULLY APPARENT FOR SEVERAL WEEKS. ULTIMATELY, THE WHOLE CORNEA MAY BECOME DEEPLY VASCULARIZED AND OPAQUE RESULTING IN BLINDNESS. IN THE WORST CASES, THE EYE MAY BE TOTALLY DESTROYED. **CHRONIC EXPOSURE-** EFFECTS DEPEND ON THE CONCENTRATION AND DURATION OF EXPOSURE. REPEATED OR PROLONGED CONTACT MAY CAUSE CONJUNCTIVITIS OR EFFECTS AS IN ACUTE EXPOSURE.
FIRST AID- WASH EYES IMMEDIATELY WITH LARGE AMOUNTS OF WATER, OCCASIONALLY LIFTING UPPER AND LOWER LIDS, UNTIL NO EVIDENCE OF CHEMICAL REMAINS (AT LEAST 15-20 MINUTES). CONTINUE IRRIGATING WITH NORMAL SALINE UNTIL THE PH HAS RETURNED TO NORMAL (30-60 MINUTES). COVER WITH STERILE BANDAGES. GET MEDICAL ATTENTION IMMEDIATELY.

INGESTION: PHOSPHORIC ACID: CORROSIVE. SEE INFORMATION ON ACIDIC CORROSIVE COMPOUNDS.
ACIDIC CORROSIVES: **ACUTE EXPOSURE-** MAY CAUSE CIRCUMORAL BURNS WITH DISCOLORATION AND CORROSION OF THE MUCOUS MEMBRANES OF THE MOUTH, THROAT AND ESOPHAGUS. THERE MAY BE IMMEDIATE PAIN AND DIFFICULTY OR INABILITY TO SWALLOW OR SPEAK. EPIGLOTTAL EDEMA MAY RESULT IN RESPIRATORY DISTRESS AND POSSIBLY ASPHYXIA. MARKED THIRST, NAUSEA,

VOMITING AND DIARRHEA MAY OCCUR. DEPENDING ON THE AREA AND DEGREE OF CORROSION, THE VOMITUS MAY CONTAIN FRESH OR DARK BLOOD AND LARGE SHREDS OF MUCOSA. SHOCK MAY OCCUR WITH MARKED HYPOTENSION, WEAK AND RAPID PULSE, SHALLOW RESPIRATION, AND CLAMMY SKIN. CIRCULATORY COLLAPSE MAY DEVELOP AND IF UNCORRECTED, LEAD TO RENAL FAILURE. IN SEVERE CASES, GASTRIC AND, TO A LESSER DEGREE, ESOPHAGEAL PERFORATION MAY OCCUR WITH PERITONITIS ACCOMPANIED BY FEVER AND ABDOMINAL RIGIDITY. ESOPHAGEAL, GASTRIC OR PYLORIC STRICTURE MAY OCCUR WITHIN A FEW WEEKS, OR MAY BE DELAYED FOR MONTHS OR EVEN YEARS. DEATH MAY RESULT WITHIN A SHORT TIME FROM ASPHYXIA, CIRCULATORY COLLAPSE OR ASPIRATION OF EVEN MINUTE AMOUNTS. IF DEATH IS DELAYED, IT MAY BE DUE TO PERITONITIS, SEVERE NEPHRITIS OR PNEUMONIA. COMA AND CONVULSIONS SOMETIMES OCCUR TERMINALLY. **CHRONIC EXPOSURE-** DEPENDING ON THE CONCENTRATION, REPEATED INGESTION MAY RESULT IN INFLAMMATORY AND ULCERATIVE CHANGES IN THE MUCOUS MEMBRANES OF THE MOUTH AND OTHER EFFECTS AS IN ACUTE INGESTION.

FIRST AID- DO NOT USE GASTRIC LAVAGE OR EMESIS. DILUTE THE ACID IMMEDIATELY BY DRINKING LARGE QUANTITIES OF WATER OR MILK. IF VOMITING PERSISTS, ADMINISTER FLUIDS REPEATEDLY. INGESTED ACID MUST BE DILUTED APPROXIMATELY 100 FOLD TO RENDER IT HARMLESS TO TISSUES. MAINTAIN AIRWAY AND TREAT SHOCK (DREISBACH, HANDBOOK OF POISONING, 12TH ED.). GET MEDICAL ATTENTION IMMEDIATELY. IF VOMITING OCCURS, KEEP HEAD BELOW HIPS TO HELP PREVENT ASPIRATION.

ANTIDOTE: NO SPECIFIC ANTIDOTE. TREAT SYMPTOMATICALLY AND SUPPORTIVELY.

REACTIVITY

REACTIVITY: REACTS MILDLY WITH WATER AND EVOLVES HEAT.

INCOMPATIBILITIES: PHOSPHORIC ACID: BASES: VIOLENT REACTION. FERROUS METALS AND ALLOYS: VERY CORROSIVE, EXPECIALLY WHEN HEATED. GRANITE: ATTACKED BY HOT CONCENTRATED ACID. METALS: REACTS WITH LIBERATION OF EXPLOSIVE HYDROGEN GAS. NITROMETHANE: FORMS DETONABLE MIXTURE. PLASTICS, RUBBER, COATINGS: MAY BE ATTACKED. PORCELAIN: ATTACKED BY HOT CONCENTRATED ACID. SODIUM TETRAHYDROBORATE: GENERATES HEAT AND MAY BE EXPLOSIVE ON RAPID MIXING.

DECOMPOSITION: THERMAL DECOMPOSITION PRODUCTS MAY INCLUDE TOXIC OXIDES OF PHOSPHOROUS AND PHOSPHORIC ACID FUMES.

POLYMERIZATION: HAZARDOUS POLYMERIZATION HAS NOT BEEN REPORTED TO OCCUR UNDER NORMAL TEMPERATURES AND PRESSURES.

STORAGE AND DISPOSAL

OBSERVE ALL FEDERAL, STATE AND LOCAL REGULATIONS WHEN STORING OR DISPOSING OF THIS SUBSTANCE. FOR ASSISTANCE, CONTACT THE DISTRICT DIRECTOR OF THE ENVIRONMENTAL PROTECTION AGENCY.

STORAGE

PROTECT AGAINST PHYSICAL DAMAGE. STORE IN COOL, DRY, WELL VENTILATED LOCATION, AWAY FROM ANY AREA WHERE THE FIRE HAZARD MAY BE ACUTE (NFPA 49, HAZARDOUS CHEMICALS DATA, 1975).

STORE AWAY FROM INCOMPATIBLE SUBSTANCES.

CONDITIONS TO AVOID

MAY BURN BUT DOES NOT IGNITE READILY. FLAMMABLE, POISONOUS GASES MAY ACCUMULATE IN TANKS AND HOPPER CARS. MAY IGNITE COMBUSTIBLES (WOOD, PAPER, OIL, ETC.).

SPILL AND LEAK PROCEDURES

SOIL SPILL: DIG A HOLDING AREA SUCH AS A PIT, POND OR LAGOON TO CONTAIN SPILL AND DIKE SURFACE FLOW USING BARRIER OF SOIL, SANDBAGS, FOAMED POLYURETHANE OR FOAMED CONCRETE. ABSORB LIQUID MASS WITH FLY ASH OR CEMENT POWDER.

NEUTRALIZE SPILL WITH SLAKED LIME, SODIUM BICARBONATE OR CRUSHED LIMESTONE.

AIR SPILL: APPLY WATER SPRAY TO KNOCK DOWN AND REDUCE VAPORS. KNOCK-DOWN WATER IS CORROSIVE AND TOXIC AND SHOULD BE DIKED FOR CONTAINMENT AND LATER DISPOSAL.

WATER SPILL: NEUTRALIZE WITH AGRICULTURAL LIME, SLAKED LIME, CRUSHED LIMESTONE, OR SODIUM BICARBONATE.

ADD CALCIUM HYPOCHLORITE TO SPILL.

USE MECHANICAL DREDGES OR LIFTS TO EXTRACT IMMOBILIZED MASSES OF POLLUTION AND PRECIPITATES.

OCCUPATIONAL SPILL: DO NOT TOUCH SPILLED MATERIAL. STOP LEAK IF YOU CAN DO IT WITHOUT RISK. FOR SMALL SPILLS, TAKE UP WITH SAND OR OTHER ABSORBENT MATERIAL AND PLACE INTO CONTAINERS FOR LATER DISPOSAL. FOR SMALL DRY SPILLS, WITH CLEAN SHOVEL PLACE MATERIAL INTO CLEAN, DRY CONTAINER AND COVER. MOVE CONTAINERS FROM SPILL AREA. FOR LARGER SPILLS, DIKE FAR AHEAD OF SPILL FOR LATER DISPOSAL. KEEP UNNECESSARY PEOPLE AWAY. ISOLATE HAZARD AREA AND DENY ENTRY.

REPORTABLE QUANTITY (RQ): 5000 POUNDS THE SUPERFUND AMENDMENTS AND REAUTHORIZATION ACT (SARA) SECTION 304 REQUIRES THAT A RELEASE EQUAL TO OR GREATER THAN THE REPORTABLE QUANTITY FOR THIS SUBSTANCE BE IMMEDIATELY REPORTED TO THE LOCAL EMERGENCY PLANNING COMMITTEE AND THE STATE EMERGENCY RESPONSE COMMISSION (40 CFR 355.40). IF THE RELEASE OF THIS SUBSTANCE IS REPORTABLE UNDER CERCLA SECTION 103, THE NATIONAL RESPONSE CENTER MUST BE NOTIFIED IMMEDIATELY AT (800) 424-8802 OR (202) 426-2675 IN THE METROPOLITAN WASHINGTON, D.C. AREA (40 CFR 302.6).

PROTECTIVE EQUIPMENT

VENTILATION: PROVIDE LOCAL EXHAUST VENTILATION AND/OR GENERAL DILUTION VENTILATION TO MEET PUBLISHED EXPOSURE LIMITS.

RESPIRATOR: THE FOLLOWING RESPIRATORS AND MAXIMUM USE CONCENTRATIONS ARE RECOMMENDATIONS BY THE U.S. DEPARTMENT OF HEALTH AND HUMAN SERVICES, NIOSH POCKET GUIDE TO CHEMICAL HAZARDS; NIOSH CRITERIA DOCUMENTS OR BY THE U.S. DEPARTMENT OF LABOR, 29 CFR 1910 SUBPART Z. THE SPECIFIC RESPIRATOR SELECTED MUST BE BASED ON CONTAMINATION LEVELS FOUND IN THE WORK PLACE, MUST NOT EXCEED THE WORKING LIMITS OF THE RESPIRATOR AND BE JOINTLY APPROVED BY THE NATIONAL INSTITUTE FOR OCCUPATIONAL SAFETY AND HEALTH AND THE MINE SAFETY AND HEALTH ADMINISTRATION (NIOSH-MSHA).

PHOSPHORIC ACID: 25 MG/M3- ANY SUPPLIED-AIR RESPIRATOR OPERATED IN A CONTINUOUS FLOW MODE.

50 MG/M3- ANY SUPPLIED-AIR RESPIRATOR WITH A FULL FACEPIECE. ANY SELF-CONTAINED BREATHING APPARATUS WITH A FULL FACEPIECE. ANY AIR-PURIFYING FULL FACEPIECE RESPIRATOR WITH A HIGH-EFFICIENCY PARTICULATE FILTER.

2000 MG/M3- ANY SUPPLIED-AIR RESPIRATOR WITH FULL FACEPIECE AND OPERATED IN A PRESSURE-DEMAND OR OTHER POSITIVE PRESSURE MODE.

ESCAPE- ANY AIR-PURIFYING FULL FACEPIECE RESPIRATOR (GAS MASK) WITH A CHIN-STYLE OR FRONT- OR BACK-MOUNTED CANISTER WITH A HIGH-EFFICIENCY PARTICULATE FILTER. ANY ESCAPE-TYPE SELF-CONTAINED BREATHING APPARATUS.

FOR FIREFIGHTING AND OTHER IMMEDIATELY DANGEROUS TO LIFE OR HEALTH CONDITIONS:

SELF-CONTAINED BREATHING APPARATUS WITH FULL FACEPIECE OPERATED IN PRESSURE-DEMAND OR OTHER POSITIVE PRESSURE MODE.

SUPPLIED-AIR RESPIRATOR WITH FULL FACEPIECE AND OPERATED IN PRESSURE-DEMAND OR OTHER POSITIVE PRESSURE MODE IN COMBINATION WITH AN AUXILIARY SELF-CONTAINED BREATHING APPARATUS OPERATED IN PRESSURE-DEMAND OR OTHER POSITIVE PRESSURE MODE.

CLOTHING: EMPLOYEE MUST WEAR APPROPRIATE PROTECTIVE (IMPERVIOUS) CLOTHING AND EQUIPMENT TO PREVENT ANY POSSIBILITY OF SKIN CONTACT WITH THIS SUBSTANCE.

GLOVES: EMPLOYEE MUST WEAR APPROPRIATE PROTECTIVE GLOVES TO PREVENT CONTACT WITH THIS SUBSTANCE.

EYE PROTECTION: EMPLOYEE MUST WEAR SPLASH-PROOF OR DUST-RESISTANT SAFETY GOGGLES AND A FACESHIELD TO PREVENT CONTACT WITH THIS SUBSTANCE.

EMERGENCY WASH FACILITIES: WHERE THERE IS ANY POSSIBILITY THAT AN EMPLOYEE'S EYES AND/OR SKIN MAY BE EXPOSED TO THIS SUBSTANCE, THE EMPLOYER SHOULD PROVIDE AN EYE WASH FOUNTAIN AND QUICK DRENCH SHOWER WITHIN THE IMMEDIATE WORK AREA FOR EMERGENCY USE.

AUTHORIZED BY- OCCUPATIONAL HEALTH SERVICES, INC.

CREATION DATE: 11/17/89 ***REVISION DATE:*** 05/16/90

MATERIAL SAFETY DATA SHEET

OCCUPATIONAL HEALTH SERVICES, INC.
AGRICULTURE AND PESTICIDE DIVISION
450 SEVENTH AVENUE, SUITE 2407
NEW YORK, NEW YORK 10123
1-800-445-MSDS OR (212) 967-1100

EMERGENCY CONTACT:
JOHN S. BRANSFORD, JR. (615) 292-1180

SUBSTANCE IDENTIFICATION

CAS-NUMBER 7723-14-0

SUBSTANCE: **PHOSPHORUS, RED**

TRADE NAMES/SYNONYMS: RED PHOSPHOROUS; PHOSPHORUS; PHOSPHOROUS; AMORPHOUS, RED PHOSPHORUS; PHOSPHORUS-31; STCC 4916725; UN 1338; P-103; PST18790

CHEMICAL FAMILY: PHOSPHORUS

MOLECULAR FORMULA: P4
MOLECULAR WEIGHT: 123.89
CERCLA RATINGS (SCALE 0-3): HEALTH = U FIRE = 1 REACTIVITY = 1 PERSISTENCE = 3
NFPA RATINGS (SCALE 0-4): HEALTH = U FIRE = 1 REACTIVITY = 1

COMPONENTS AND CONTAMINANTS

COMPONENT: PHOSPHORUS, RED ***PERCENT:*** 100
CAS# 7723-14-0
OTHER CONTAMINANTS: NONE, MAYBE CONTAMINATED WITH HIGHLY TOXIC WHITE PHOSPHORUS.
EXPOSURE LIMITS: NO OCCUPATIONAL EXPOSURE LIMITS ESTABLISHED BY OSHA, ACGIH, OR NIOSH.
PHOSPHORUS, RED: 100 POUNDS SARA SECTION 302 THRESHOLD PLANNING QUANTITY 1 POUND SARA SECTION 304 REPORTABLE QUANTITY 1 POUND CERCLA SECTION 103 REPORTABLE QUANTITY SUBJECT TO SARA SECTION 313 ANNUAL TOXIC CHEMICAL RELEASE REPORTING

PHYSICAL DATA

DESCRIPTION: ODORLESS, RED TO REDDISH-BROWN TO VIOLET CUBIC OR AMORPHOUS POWDER OR LUMPS WHICH DOES NOT PHOSPHORESCE IN AIR.
MELTING POINT: 781 F (416 C) SUBLIMES ***SPECIFIC GRAVITY:*** 2.340
VAPOR PRESSURE: 760 MMHG @ 417 C ***SOLUBILITY IN WATER:*** INSOLUBLE
VAPOR DENSITY: 4.77
SOLVENT SOLUBILITY: SOLUBLE IN PHOSPHORUS TRIBROMIDE, ABSOLUTE ALCOHOL; INSOLUBLE IN ORGANIC SOLVENTS, CAUSTIC ALKALI, CARBON BISULFIDE, ETHER, AMMONIA SOLUTION

FIRE AND EXPLOSION DATA

FIRE AND EXPLOSION HAZARD: SLIGHT FIRE HAZARD WHEN EXPOSED TO HEAT OR FLAME.
DUST-AIR MIXTURES MAY IGNITE OR EXPLODE.
OXIDIZER: OXIDIZERS DECOMPOSE, ESPECIALLY WHEN HEATED, TO YIELD OXYGEN OR OTHER GASES WHICH WILL INCREASE THE BURNING RATE OF COMBUSTIBLE MATTER. CONTACT WITH EASILY OXIDIZABLE, ORGANIC, OR OTHER COMBUSTIBLE MATERIALS MAY RESULT IN IGNITION, VIOLENT COMBUSTION OR EXPLOSION.
FLASH POINT: FLAMMABLE SOLID ***AUTOIGNITION TEMP.:*** 500 F (260 C)
FIREFIGHTING MEDIA: DRY CHEMICAL, SAND, WATER SPRAY OR FOAM (1987 EMERGENCY RESPONSE GUIDEBOOK, DOT P 5800.4).
FOR LARGER FIRES, USE WATER SPRAY, FOG OR STANDARD FOAM (1987 EMERGENCY RESPONSE GUIDEBOOK, DOT P 5800.4).
FIREFIGHTING: MOVE CONTAINER FROM FIRE AREA IF POSSIBLE. COOL CONTAINERS EXPOSED TO FLAME WITH WATER FROM SIDE UNTIL WELL AFTER FIRE IS OUT. STAY AWAY FROM STORAGE TANK ENDS. FOR MASSIVE FIRE IN CARGO AREA, USE UNMANNED HOSE HOLDER OR MONITOR NOZZLES; ELSE WITHDRAW AND LET FIRE BURN (1987 EMERGENCY RESPONSE GUIDEBOOK, DOT P 5800.4, GUIDE PAGE 32).
FLOOD WITH WATER. WHEN FIRE IS OUT COVER WITH WET DIRT OR SAND, UNTIL MATERIAL CAN BE PERMAMENTLY DISPOSED OF. AVOID BREATHING TOXIC VAPORS, KEEP UPWIND.
FIRE FIGHTING PHASES: FLOOD WITH WATER AND WHEN FIRE IS EXTINGUISHED COVER WITH WET SAND OR DIRT. EXTEME CAUTION SHOULD BE USED DURING CLEANUP SINCE REIGNITION MAY OCCUR. UNDER CERTIAN CONDITIONS AT HIGH TEMPERATURES, RED PHOSPHORUS REVERTS TO THE MORE HAZARDOUS WHITE PHOSPHORUS.

TRANSPORTATION DATA

DEPARTMENT OF TRANSPORTATION HAZARD CLASSIFICATION 49 CFR 172.101: FLAMMABLE SOLID
DEPARTMENT OF TRANSPORTATION LABELING REQUIREMENTS 49 CFR 172.101 AND SUBPART E: FLAMMABLE SOLID
DEPARTMENT OF TRANSPORTATION PACKAGING REQUIREMENTS: 49 CFR 173.189 EXCEPTIONS: NONE

TOXICITY

RED PHOSPHORUS: TOXICITY DATA: 4412 UG/KG UNREPORTED-MAN LDLO.
CARCINOGEN STATUS: NONE. ACUTE TOXICITY LEVEL: INSUFFICIENT DATA.
TARGET EFFECTS: POISONING MAY AFFECT THE HEART, LIVER AND KIDNEYS.

HEALTH EFFECTS AND FIRST AID

INHALATION: RED PHOSPHORUS: **ACUTE EXPOSURE-** INHALATION OF RED PHOSPHORUS DUST MAY CAUSE ACUTE CHEMICAL PNEUMONIA. RED PHOSPHORUS REACTS WITH OXYGEN AND WATER VAPOR TO EVOLVE HIGHLY TOXIC PHOSPHINE. PHOSPHINE POISONING MAY CAUSE WIDELY DILATED PUPILS, CHEST PRESSURE, CHILLS AND CARDIAC ARRHYTHMIAS. DEATH USUALLY OCCURS WITHIN 4 DAYS BUT MAY BE DELAYED 1-2 WEEKS. **CHRONIC EXPOSURE-** NO DATA AVAILABLE.
FIRST AID- REMOVE FROM EXPOSURE AREA TO FRESH AIR IMMEDIATELY. IF BREATHING HAS STOPPED, PERFORM ARTIFICIAL RESPIRATION. KEEP PERSON WARM AND AT REST. TREAT SYMPTOMATICALLY AND SUPPORTIVELY. GET MEDICAL ATTENTION IMMEDIATELY.

SKIN CONTACT: RED PHOSPHORUS: **ACUTE EXPOSURE-** NO DATA AVAILABLE. **CHRONIC EXPOSURE-** NO DATA AVAILABLE.
FIRST AID- REMOVE CONTAMINATED CLOTHING AND SHOES IMMEDIATELY. WASH AFFECTED AREA WITH SOAP OR MILD DETERGENT AND LARGE AMOUNTS OF WATER UNTIL NO EVIDENCE OF CHEMICAL REMAINS (APPROXIMATELY 15-20 MINUTES). GET MEDICAL ATTENTION IMMEDIATELY.

EYE CONTACT: RED PHOSPHORUS: **ACUTE EXPOSURE-** NO DATA AVAILABLE. **CHRONIC EXPOSURE-** NO DATA AVAILABLE.
FIRST AID- WASH EYES IMMEDIATELY WITH LARGE AMOUNTS OF WATER OR NORMAL SALINE, OCCASIONALLY LIFTING UPPER AND LOWER LIDS, UNTIL NO EVIDENCE OF CHEMICAL REMAINS (APPROXIMATELY 15-20 MINUTES). GET MEDICAL ATTENTION IMMEDIATELY.

INGESTION: RED PHOSPHORUS: **ACUTE EXPOSURE-** RED PHOSPHORUS IS INSOLUBLE, UNABSORBED AND ESSENTIALLY NON-TOXIC IN SINGLE DOSES. **CHRONIC EXPOSURE-** REPEATED EXPOSURE MAY INDUCE SYSTEMIC PHOSPHORUS POISONING WITH GASTROINTESTINAL UPSET, AN ASYMPTOMATIC PERIOD, THEN ACUTE DEGENERATION AND FATTY INFILTRATION OF THE LIVER WITH ACCOMPANYING METABOLIC DISTURBANCES. HEMORRHAGES MAY OCCUR AT MANY SITES. PHOSPHORUS MAY ALSO ACT DIRECTLY TO INHIBIT PROTEIN SYNTHESIS IN THE LIVER. DEATH MAY OCCUR FROM MYOCARDIAL DAMAGE, ACUTE RENAL FAILURE, OR CORTICAL NECROSIS.
FIRST AID- TREAT SYMPTOMATICALLY AND SUPPORTIVELY. GET MEDICAL ATTENTION IMMEDIATELY. IF VOMITING OCCURS, KEEP HEAD LOWER THAN HIPS TO PREVENT ASPIRATION.
ANTIDOTE: NO SPECIFIC ANTIDOTE. TREAT SYMPTOMATICALLY AND SUPPORTIVELY.

REACTIVITY

REACTIVITY: IGNITES READILY BY FRICTION OR STATIC ELECTRICITY.
REACTS WITH OXYGEN AND WATER VAPOR TO EVOLVE HIGHLY TOXIC PHOSPHINE GAS.
INCOMPATIBILITIES: RED PHOSPHORUS: CHLORINE: IGNITES ON CONTACT. COMBUSTIBLE MATERIALS: READILY IGNITABLE WHEN CONTAMINATED. FLUORINE: IGNITES ON CONTACT. HEATING AGENTS: MAY IGNITE. HEPTANE SOLUTION OF CHLORINE AT 0 C: IGNITES. HYDRIODIC ACID: EXPLODES. LIQUID BROMINE: IGNITES. METAL HALOGENATES: EXPLODE ON INITIATION BY FRICTION, IMPACT OR HEAT. METAL OXIDES: REACTS VIGOROUSLY. METAL PEROXIDES: IGNITES. METAL SULFATES: BURNS. NON-METAL HALIDES: REACTS. ORGANIC MATERIALS: EXPLODES. OXIDES: IGNITES AT LOW HUMIDITY. OXIDIZING MATERIALS: EXPLOSIVE. PEROXIDES: INCOMPATIBLE. POTASSIUM CHLORATE: INCOMPATIBLE. POTASSIUM PERMANGANATE: INCOMPATIBLE. REDUCING MATERIALS: MAY REACT. STRONG ALKALINE HYDROXIDES: INCOMPATIBLE. PHOSPHORUS (FORM UNSPECIFIED): ALKALIES: EVOLVES FLAMMABLE PHOSPHINE. ANTIMONY PENTACHLORIDE: IGNITES. CALCIUM HYDROXIDE (HOT): EVOLVES FLAMMABLE PHOSPHINE. CHROMYL CHLORIDE: EXPLODES IN PRESENCE OF MOISTURE. HALOGEN AZIDES: INCOMPATIBLE. HALOGEN OXIDES: INCOMPATIBLE. HALOGENS: IGNITES. HEXALITHIUM DISILICIDE: INCANDESCES. HYDROGEN PEROXIDE: INCOMPATIBLE. INTERHALOGENS: IGNITES. MAGNESIUM PERCHLORATE: EXPLODES VIOLENTLY. METAL ACETYLIDES: INCANDESCES. METAL HALOGENATES: EXPLODE ON INITIATION BY FRICTION, IMPACT OR HEAT. METAL PEROXIDES: EXPLODES. METALS: INCOMPATIBLE. NITRATES: IGNITES. NITRIC ACID: INCOMPATIBLE. NITROGEN HALIDES: INCOMPATIBLE. NITRYL FLUORIDE: INCOMPATIBLE. NON-METAL HALIDES: INCANDESCES. NON-METAL OXIDES: DELAYED IGNITION. PEROXYFORMIC ACID: INCOMPATIBLE. POTASSIUM NITRIDE: INCOMPATIBLE. POTASSIUM PERMANGANATE: INCOMPATIBLE. SELENIUM: INCOMPATIBLE. SODIUM CHLORITE: INCOMPATIBLE. SULFUR: INCOMPATIBLE. SULFURIC ACID: INCOMPATIBLE.
DECOMPOSITION: THERMAL DECOMPOSITION MAY RELEASE TOXIC OXIDES OF PHOSPHORUS.
POLYMERIZATION: HAZARDOUS POLYMERIZATION HAS NOT BEEN REPORTED TO OCCUR UNDER NORMAL TEMPERATURES AND PRESSURES.

STORAGE AND DISPOSAL

OBSERVE ALL FEDERAL, STATE AND LOCAL REGULATIONS WHEN STORING OR DISPOSING OF THIS SUBSTANCE. FOR ASSISTANCE, CONTACT THE DISTRICT DIRECTOR OF THE ENVIRONMENTAL PROTECTION AGENCY.

****STORAGE****

THRESHOLD PLANNING QUANTITY (TPQ): THE SUPERFUND AMENDMENTS AND REAUTHORIZATION ACT (SARA) SECTION 302 REQUIRES THAT EACH FACILITY

WHERE ANY EXTREMELY HAZARDOUS SUBSTANCE IS PRESENT IN A QUANTITY EQUAL TO OR GREATER THAN THE TPQ ESTABLISHED FOR THAT SUBSTANCE NOTIFY THE STATE EMERGENCY RESPONSE COMMISSION FOR THE STATE IN WHICH IT IS LOCATED. SECTION 303 OF SARA REQUIRES THESE FACILITIES TO PARTICIPATE IN LOCAL EMERGENCY RESPONSE PLANNING (40 CFR 355.30).
STORE AWAY FROM INCOMPATIBLE SUBSTANCES.
PROTECT AGAINST PHYSICAL DAMAGE. STORE IN COOL PLACE WITH ADEQUATE VENTILATION AND AVOID OVERHEATING. SEPARATE FROM OTHER MATERIALS (NFPA 49, HAZARDOUS CHEMICALS DATA, 1975).

CONDITIONS TO AVOID

AVOID CONTACT WITH HEAT, SPARKS, FLAMES OR OTHER SOURCES OF IGNITION. MATERIAL IS EXTREMELY FLAMMABLE AND MAY BURN RAPIDLY WITH FLARE-BURNING EFFECT.

SPILL AND LEAK PROCEDURES

SOIL SPILL: DIG A HOLDING AREA SUCH AS PIT, POND OR LAGOON TO CONTAIN SPILLED MATERIAL. USE PROTECTIVE COVER SUCH AS A PLASTIC SHEET TO PREVENT DISSOLVING IN FIREFIGHTING WATER OR RAIN.

WATER SPILL: TRAP SPILLED MATERIAL AT BOTTOM IN DEEP WATER POCKETS, EXCAVATED HOLDING AREAS OR WITHIN SAND BAG BARRIERS.
USE SUCTION HOSES TO REMOVE TRAPPED SPILL MATERIAL. USE MECHANICAL DREDGES OR LIFTS TO EXTRACT IMMOBILIZED MASSES OF POLLUTION AND PRECIPITATES.

OCCUPATIONAL SPILL: SHUT OFF IGNITION SOURCES. DO NOT TOUCH SPILLED MATERIAL. FOR SMALL SPILLS, WITH CLEAN SHOVEL, PLACE MATERIAL INTO CLEAN, DRY CONTAINER AND COVER; MOVE CONTAINERS FROM SPILL AREA. FOR LARGER SPILLS, WET DOWN WITH WATER AND DIKE FOR LATER DISPOSAL. NO SMOKING, FLAMES OR FLARES IN HAZARD AREA! KEEP UNNECESSARY PEOPLE AWAY. ISOLATE HAZARD AREA AND DENY ENTRY.
REPORTABLE QUANTITY (RQ): 1 POUND THE SUPERFUND AMENDMENTS AND REAUTHORIZATION ACT (SARA) SECTION 304 REQUIRES THAT A RELEASE EQUAL TO OR GREATER THAN THE REPORTABLE QUANTITY FOR THIS SUBSTANCE BE IMMEDIATELY REPORTED TO THE LOCAL EMERGENCY PLANNING COMMITTEE AND THE STATE EMERGENCY RESPONSE COMMISSION (40 CFR 355.40). IF THE RELEASE OF THIS SUBSTANCE IS REPORTABLE UNDER CERCLA SECTION 103, THE NATIONAL RESPONSE CENTER MUST BE NOTIFIED IMMEDIATELY AT (800) 424-8802 OR (202) 426-2675 IN THE METROPOLITAN WASHINGTON, D.C. AREA (40 CFR 302.6).

PROTECTIVE EQUIPMENT

VENTILATION: PROVIDE LOCAL EXHAUST OR GENERAL DILUTION VENTILATION SYSTEM.

RESPIRATOR: THE FOLLOWING RESPIRATORS ARE RECOMMENDED BASED ON INFORMATION FOUND IN THE PHYSICAL DATA, TOXICITY AND HEALTH EFFECTS SECTIONS. THEY ARE RANKED IN ORDER FROM MINIMUM TO MAXIMUM RESPIRATORY PROTECTION. THE SPECIFIC RESPIRATOR SELECTED MUST BE BASED ON CONTAMINATION LEVELS FOUND IN THE WORK PLACE, MUST NOT EXCEED THE WORKING LIMITS OF THE RESPIRATOR AND BE JOINTLY APPROVED BY THE NATIONAL INSTITUTE FOR OCCUPATIONAL SAFETY AND HEALTH AND THE MINE SAFETY AND HEALTH ADMINISTRATION (NIOSH-MSHA).
DUST AND MIST RESPIRATOR WITH A FULL FACEPIECE.
AIR-PURIFYING FULL FACEPIECE RESPIRATOR WITH A HIGH-EFFICIENCY PARTICULATE FILTER.
POWERED AIR-PURIFYING RESPIRATOR WITH A TIGHT-FITTING FACEPIECE AND HIGH-EFFICIENCY PARTICULATE FILTER.
TYPE 'C' SUPPLIED-AIR RESPIRATOR WITH A FULL FACEPIECE OPERATED IN PRESSURE-DEMAND OR OTHER POSITIVE PRESSURE MODE OR WITH A FULL FACEPIECE, HELMET OR HOOD OPERATED IN CONTINUOUS-FLOW MODE.
SELF-CONTAINED BREATHING APPARATUS WITH A FULL FACEPIECE OPERATED IN PRESSURE-DEMAND OR OTHER POSITIVE PRESSURE MODE.
FOR FIREFIGHTING AND OTHER IMMEDIATELY DANGEROUS TO LIFE OR HEALTH CONDITIONS:
SELF-CONTAINED BREATHING APPARATUS WITH FULL FACEPIECE OPERATED IN PRESSURE-DEMAND OR OTHER POSITIVE PRESSURE MODE.
SUPPLIED-AIR RESPIRATOR WITH FULL FACEPIECE AND OPERATED IN PRESSURE-DEMAND OR OTHER POSITIVE PRESSURE MODE IN COMBINATION WITH AN AUXILIARY SELF-CONTAINED BREATHING APPARATUS OPERATED IN PRESSURE-DEMAND OR OTHER POSITIVE PRESSURE MODE.

CLOTHING: EMPLOYEE MUST WEAR APPROPRIATE PROTECTIVE (IMPERVIOUS) CLOTHING AND EQUIPMENT TO PREVENT REPEATED OR PROLONGED SKIN CONTACT WITH THIS SUBSTANCE.

GLOVES: EMPLOYEE MUST WEAR APPROPRIATE PROTECTIVE GLOVES TO PREVENT CONTACT WITH THIS SUBSTANCE.

EYE PROTECTION: EMPLOYEE MUST WEAR SPLASH-PROOF OR DUST-RESISTANT SAFETY GOGGLES TO PREVENT EYE CONTACT WITH THIS SUBSTANCE.
EMERGENCY EYE WASH: WHERE THERE IS ANY POSSIBILITY THAT AN EMPLOYEE'S EYES MAY BE EXPOSED TO THIS SUBSTANCE, THE EMPLOYER SHOULD PROVIDE AN EYE WASH FOUNTAIN WITHIN THE IMMEDIATE WORK AREA FOR EMERGENCY USE.

AUTHORIZED BY- OCCUPATIONAL HEALTH SERVICES, INC.
CREATION DATE: 10/04/89 ***REVISION DATE:*** 05/16/90

MATERIAL SAFETY DATA SHEET

OCCUPATIONAL HEALTH SERVICES, INC.
AGRICULTURE AND PESTICIDE DIVISION
450 SEVENTH AVENUE, SUITE 2407
NEW YORK, NEW YORK 10123
1-800-445-MSDS OR (212) 967-1100

EMERGENCY CONTACT:
JOHN S. BRANSFORD, JR. (615) 292-1180

SUBSTANCE IDENTIFICATION

CAS-NUMBER 7723-14-0

SUBSTANCE: PHOSPHORUS, WHITE

TRADE NAMES/SYNONYMS: YELLOW PHOSPHORUS; YELLOW PHOSPHOROUS; PHOSPHOROUS; WHITE PHOSPHOROUS; PHOSPHORUS YELLOW DRY; PHOSPHORUS YELLOW; PHOSPHORUS (WHITE); PHOSPHOROUS WHITE DRY; PHOSPHORUS; WHITE PHOSPHORUS; RAT-NIP; WP; STCC 4916140; UN 1381; P-104; PST18800

CHEMICAL FAMILY: PHOSPHORUS

MOLECULAR FORMULA: P4

MOLECULAR WEIGHT: 123.89

CERCLA RATINGS (SCALE 0-3): HEALTH=3 FIRE=3 REACTIVITY=2 PERSISTENCE=3

NFPA RATINGS (SCALE 0-4): HEALTH=3 FIRE=3 REACTIVITY=1

COMPONENTS AND CONTAMINANTS

COMPONENT: PHOSPHORUS, WHITE ***PERCENT:*** 100
CAS# 7723-14-0

OTHER CONTAMINANTS: NONE

EXPOSURE LIMITS: PHOSPHOROUS, WHITE: 0.1 MG/M3 OSHA TWA 0.1 MG/M3 ACGIH TWA
100 POUNDS SARA SECTION 302 THRESHOLD PLANNING QUANTITY 1 POUND SARA SECTION 304 REPORTABLE QUANTITY 1 POUND CERCLA SECTION 103 REPORTABLE QUANTITY SUBJECT TO SARA SECTION 313 ANNUAL TOXIC CHEMICAL RELEASE REPORTING

PHYSICAL DATA

DESCRIPTION: WHITE, YELLOW, OR COLORLESS, TRANSPARENT, SOFT, WAXY, CUBIC, CRYSTALLINE SOLID WITH A PUNGENT ODOR; DARKENS ON EXPOSURE TO LIGHT; GLOWS IN THE DARK WITH A GREENISH LIGHT. ***BOILING POINT:*** 536 F (280 C)

MELTING POINT: 111 F (44 C) ***SPECIFIC GRAVITY:*** 1.82

VAPOR PRESSURE: 0.028 MMHG @ 21 C ***PH:*** ACIDIC IN SOLUTION

SOLUBILITY IN WATER: 0.0003% ***VAPOR DENSITY:*** 4.4

SOLVENT SOLUBILITY: CARBON DISULFIDE, BENZENE, ALKALIES, TOLUENE, ABSOLUTE ALCOHOL, ABSOLUTE ETHER, CHLOROFORM, OLIVE OIL, OIL OF TURPENTINE, ALMOND OIL, CASTOR OIL, AMMONIA

HARDNESS (MOHS): 0.5

FIRE AND EXPLOSION DATA

FIRE AND EXPLOSION HAZARD: DANGEROUS FIRE HAZARD WHEN EXPOSED TO HEAT OR FLAME.
MAY IGNITE SPONTANEOUSLY ON EXPOSURE TO AIR.

AUTOIGNITION TEMP.: 86 F (30 C)

FIREFIGHTING MEDIA: COVER WITH SAND, EARTH OR WATER SPRAY AND KEEP WET WITH WATER. (1987 EMERGENCY RESPONSE GUIDEBOOK, DOT P 5800.4).
FOR LARGER FIRES, USE WATER SPRAY OR FOG (1987 EMERGENCY RESPONSE GUIDEBOOK, DOT P 5800.4).

FIREFIGHTING: MOVE CONTAINERS FROM FIRE AREA IF POSSIBLE. DO NOT SCATTER SPILLED MATERIAL WITH HIGH-PRESSURE WATER STREAMS. COOL CONTAINERS EXPOSED TO FLAMES WITH WATER FROM SIDE UNTIL WELL AFTER FIRE IS OUT. STAY AWAY FROM STORAGE TANK ENDS. FOR MASSIVE FIRE IN STORAGE AREA, USE UNMANNED HOSE HOLDER OR MONITOR NOZZLES; ELSE WITHDRAW FROM AREA AND LET FIRE BURN (1987 EMERGENCY RESPONSE GUIDEBOOK, DOT P 5800.4, GUIDE PAGE 38).
FLOOD WITH WATER. WHEN FIRE IS OUT, COVER WITH WET DIRT OR SAND UNTIL DISPOSAL OF MATERIAL. AVOID BREATHING POISONOUS FUMES, KEEP UPWIND.

TRANSPORTATION DATA

DEPARTMENT OF TRANSPORTATION HAZARD CLASSIFICATION 49 CFR 172.101: FLAMMABLE SOLID
DEPARTMENT OF TRANSPORTATION LABELING REQUIREMENTS 49 CFR 172.101 AND SUBPART E: FLAMMABLE SOLID AND POISON
DEPARTMENT OF TRANSPORTATION PACKAGING REQUIREMENTS: 49 CFR 173.190 EXCEPTIONS: NONE

TOXICITY

PHOSPHORUS, WHITE (PHOSPHORUS, YELLOW): TOXICITY DATA: 22 MG/KG ORAL-WOMAN LDLO; 11 MG/KG ORAL-WOMAN TDLO; 4600 UG/KG ORAL-WOMAN LDLO; 1400 UG/KG ORAL-HUMAN LDLO; 2600 UG/KG ORAL-WOMAN TDLO; 3030 UG/KG ORAL-RAT LD50; 4820 UG/KG ORAL-MOUSE LD50; 10 MG/KG ORAL-DOG LDLO; 4 MG/KG ORAL-CAT LDLO; 160 MG/KG ORAL-PIG LDLO; 200 MG/KG ORAL-MAMMAL LDLO; 2 MG/KG SUBCUTANEOUS-DOG LDLO; 10 MG/KG SUBCUTA NEOUS-RABBIT LDLO; REPRODUCTIVE EFFECTS DATA (RTECS). CARCINOGEN STATUS: NONE. LOCAL EFFECTS: CORROSIVE: INHALATION, SKIN, AND EYE. ACUTE TOXICITY LEVEL: HIGHLY TOXIC BY INGESTION. TARGET EFFECTS: POISONING MAY AFFECT THE LIVER, KIDNEYS, BRAIN, TEETH AND BONES. AT INCREASED RISK FROM EXPOSURE: PERSONS WITH CARIOUS TEETH AND POOR DENTAL HYGIENE. ADDITIONAL DATA: ENHANCED TOXICITY MAY OCCUR WITH CONCURRENT ADMINISTRATION OF WHITE PHOSPHORUS WITH ALCOHOL, DIGESTIBLE FATS AND OILS.

HEALTH EFFECTS AND FIRST AID

INHALATION: PHOSPHORUS, WHITE (PHOSPHORUS, YELLOW): CORROSIVE. **ACUTE EXPOSURE-** THE VAPORS OF BURNING WHITE PHOSPHORUS ARE IRRITATING TO THE NOSE, THROAT AND LUNGS AND MAY CAUSE COUGHING, DYSPNEA, GARLIC ODOR OF BREATH, PULMONARY EDEMA, ABDOMINAL PAIN, NAUSEA, VOMITING, DIARRHEA AND UNCONSCIOUSNESS. PHOTOPHOBIA WITH MYOSIS, DILATION OF PUPILS, RETINAL HEMORRHAGE, CONGESTION OF THE BLOOD VESSELS AND RARELY OPTIC NEURITIS HAVE BEEN REPORTED FOLLOWING INHALATION. BONE NECROSIS, FATTY DEGENERATION OF THE VISCERA, LIVER AND KIDNEY INJURY MAY OCCUR. **CHRONIC EXPOSURE-** REPEATED OR PROLONGED EXPOSURE MAY CAUSE A DULL RED APPEARANCE OF THE ORAL MUCOSA, WEAKNESS, ANEMIA, ANOREXIA, STOMACH COMPLAINTS, BRONCHITIS, CACHEXIA AND PALENESS. PHOSPHORUS EXERTS A SOLVENT ACTION ON THE TEETH. AN INCREASE IN BONE FORMATION UNDER EPIPHYSEAL CARTILAGE MAY OCCUR AND IMPAIR BLOOD CIRCULATION IN THE BONE. THESE CHANGES LEAD TO BONE DESTRUCTION AND NECROSIS RESULTING IN SEVERE DEFORMITY OF THE MANDIBLE, AND LESS OFTEN THE MAXILLA, KNOWN AS PHOSSY JAW. THIS IS CHARACTERIZED BY PERIOSTITIS WITH SUPPURATION, ULCERATION, AND THE PRESENCE OF PUS WITH A FOUL, FETID ODOR EXUDING BOTH INTERNALLY AND EXTERNALLY. SEQUESTRATION OF BONE MAY OCCUR. THE SHORTEST PERIOD OF EXPOSURE RESULTING IN BONE NECROSIS IS REPORTED TO BE 10 MONTHS. POLYMORPHIC LEUKOPENIA, SUSCEPTIBILITY TO BONE FRACTURES AND FAILURE OF THE ALVEOLAR BONE TO RESORB FOLLOWING EXTRACTION HAVE BEEN REPORTED. INHALATION OF MORE THAN 20 PPM BY RATS FOR 7 HOURS/DAY FOR 5 DAYS/WEEK RESULTED IN SEVERE RESPIRATORY IRRITATION AND IN A HIGH MORTALITY RATE PRIMARILY DUE TO EDEMA OF LUNGS AND BRONCHOPNEUMONIA WITH HYALINE MEMBRANE FORMATION.

FIRST AID- REMOVE FROM EXPOSURE AREA TO FRESH AIR IMMEDIATELY. IF BREATHING HAS STOPPED, GIVE ARTIFICIAL RESPIRATION. MAINTAIN AIRWAY AND BLOOD PRESSURE AND ADMINISTER OXYGEN IF AVAILABLE. KEEP AFFECTED PERSON WARM AND AT REST. TREAT SYMPTOMATICALLY AND SUPPORTIVELY. ADMINISTRATION OF OXYGEN SHOULD BE PERFORMED BY QUALIFIED PERSONNEL. GET MEDICAL ATTENTION IMMEDIATELY.

SKIN CONTACT: PHOSPHORUS, WHITE (PHOSPHORUS, YELLOW): CORROSIVE. **ACUTE EXPOSURE-** ON CONTACT WITH THE SKIN, SOLID PHOSPHORUS MAY IGNITE AND PRODUCE SEVERE YELLOWISH NECROTIC THERMAL BURNS WITH REDNESS, PAIN AND BLISTERING. THE BURNS MAY BE FLUORESCENT UNDER ULTRA VIOLET LIGHT AND HAVE A GARLIC-LIKE ODOR. OFTEN A FIRM GRAYISH-WHITE ESCHAR IS PRODUCED AND IS SURROUNDED BY VESICULATION AND INFECTION ENSUES. ANIMAL STUDIES INDICATE THAT PHOSPHORUS IS ABSORBED THROUGH BURNED SKIN TO PRODUCE SYSTEMIC POISONING WITH LIVER AND KIDNEY DAMAGE AND A MARKED REVERSAL OF THE SERUM CALCIUM-PHOSPHORUS RATIO AND ECG CHANGES. SHOCK MAY ENSUE RAPIDLY AND DEATH MAY OCCUR IMMEDIATELY. **CHRONIC EXPOSURE-** EFFECTS ARE DEPENDENT UPON CONCENTRATION AND DURATION OF EXPOSURE. DERMATITIS OR EFFECTS SIMILAR TO THOSE FOR ACUTE EXPOSURE MAY OCCUR.

FIRST AID- PHOSPHORUS BURNS SHOULD BE IMMERSED IMMEDIATELY IN WATER TO AVOID CONTACT WITH AIR. PHOSPHORUS PARTICLES ARE REMOVED GENTLY UNDER WATER AND THE WOUND IS WASHED WITH 1% COPPER SULFATE SOLUTION TO COAT THE RESIDUAL PARTICLES WITH A PROTECTIVE FILM OF COPPER PHOSPHIDE; THESE FLUORESCE AND CAN BE READILY REMOVED IN A DARKENED ROOM. FOLLOWING INITIAL TREATMENT, CHEMICAL BURNS SHOULD BE TREATED AS THERMAL BURNS OF COMPARABLE SIZE AND EXTENT. (MERCK MANUAL 14 ED) FOR BURNS, COVER AREA WITH STERILE, DRY DRESSING. BANDAGE SECURELY, BUT NOT TOO TIGHTLY. GET MEDICAL ATTENTION IMMEDIATELY.

EYE CONTACT: PHOSPHORUS, WHITE (PHOSPHORUS, YELLOW): CORROSIVE. **ACUTE EXPOSURE-** CONTACT WITH FUMES MAY CAUSE SEVERE EYE IRRITATION WITH BLEPHAROSPASM, PHOTOPHOBIA AND LACRIMATION. CONTACT WITH THE SOLID MAY CAUSE SEVERE BURNS WITH REDNESS AND PAIN. **CHRONIC EXPOSURE-** IN HUMANS, CHRONIC SYSTEMIC POISONING HAS CAUSED A YELLOW DISCOLORATION OF THE CONJUNCTIVA IN ASSOCIATION WITH JAUNDICE FROM LIVER DAMAGE. ISOLATED INSTANCES OF RETINAL EDEMA, RETINAL HEMORRHAGES AND NEURITIC AND EDEMATOUS CHANGES IN THE OPTIC NERVEHEADS HAVE BEEN REPORTED.

FIRST AID- WASH EYES IMMEDIATELY WITH LARGE AMOUNTS OF WATER, OCCASIONALLY LIFTING UPPER AND LOWER LIDS, UNTIL NO EVIDENCE OF CHEMICAL REMAINS (AT LEAST 15-20 MINUTES). CONTINUE IRRIGATING WITH NORMAL SALINE UNTIL THE PH HAS RETURNED TO NORMAL (30-60 MINUTES). COVER WITH STERILE BANDAGES. GET MEDICAL ATTENTION IMMEDIATELY.

INGESTION: PHOSPHORUS, WHITE (PHOSPHORUS, YELLOW): CORROSIVE/HIGHLY TOXIC. **ACUTE EXPOSURE-** MAY CAUSE WARMTH OR BURNING PAIN IN THE THROAT AND ABDOMEN WITH INTENSE THIRST. NAUSEA, VOMITING, HEMATEMESIS, GARLIC ODOR, LUMENESCENCE, OR FUMING OF BREATH OR EXCRETA, BLOODY DIARRHEA, OLIGURIA, ANURIA, AND CARDIAC ARRHYTHMIA MAY OCCUR WITHIN 1-2 HOURS. DEATH IN COMA FROM PERIPHERAL VASCULAR COLLAPSE OR CARDIAC ARREST MAY OCCUR IN 24-48 HOURS, OR SYMPTOMS MAY SUBSIDE AND RECUR IN SEVERAL DAYS MORE INTENSELY. DELAYED SYMPTOMS MAY INCLUDE NAUSEA, BLOODY DIARRHEA, LOSS OF MUCOSAL SURFACES OF THE STOMACH AND INTESTINES, MARKED THIRST, SKIN ERUPTIONS, INCREASED BLOOD COAGULATION TIME, RESTLESSNESS, DEPRESSION, DELIRIUM, FALL IN BLOOD PRESSURE, CYANOSIS, HYPOGLYCEMIA, FATTY INFILTRATION OF THE VITAL ORGANS, KIDNEY DAMAGE WITH OLIGURIA AND ALBUMIN AND CASTS IN THE URINE, OR ANURIA, LIVER DAMAGE WITH ENLARGEMENT, TENDERNESS, JAUNDICE, PETECHIAL HEMORRHAGES INTO THE SKIN, MUCOUS MEMBRANES AND VISCERA, TETANY (HYPOCALCEMIC), PROSTRATION AND SHOCK. PHOSPHORUS MAY CAUSE ABNORMAL ELECTROCARDIOGRAMS, ABNORMAL URINARY AND SERUM CALCIUM AND PHOSPHATE LEVELS, PROTEINURIA, AMINOACIDURIA AND ELEVATED SERUM SGPT LEVELS. IT MAY CAUSE DAMAGE TO PERIPHERAL NERVES WITH WEAKNESS OF THE LOWER EXTREMITIES, ABNORMAL LIMB SENSATIONS, VISUAL AND HEARING DISTURBANCES, IRRITABILITY AND LOSS OF COORDINATION. ONSET OF CHEYNE-STOKES RESPIRATION FOLLOWED BY CONVULSIONS, COMA, AND DEATH DUE TO CARDIAC OR HEPATIC FAILURE MAY OCCUR UP TO 3 WEEKS AFTER POISONING. **CHRONIC EXPOSURE-** REPEATED OR PROLONGED EXPOSURE MAY CAUSE A DULL RED APPEARANCE OF THE ORAL MUCOSA, ULCERATIVE STOMATITIS, SALIVATION, TOOTHACHE, BONY NECROSIS, ESPECIALLY OF THE MANDIBLE AND MAXILLA WITH LOOSENING AND LOSS OF TEETH, SPONTANEOUS FRACTURES, ANOREXIA, WEIGHT LOSS, WEAKNESS, CACHEXIA, ANEMIA, BRONCHITIS, AND JAUNDICE. A FEW MILLIGRAMS MAY CAUSE ACUTE HEPATIC DAMAGE WITH RENAL PATHOLOGIC CHANGES, HEPATIC ENCEPHALOPATHY, OR DEATH DUE TO ACUTE YELLOW ATROPHY OF THE LIVER. HEPATIC DEGENERATION LEADING TO CIRRHOSIS HAS BEEN PRODUCED IN EXPERIMENTAL ANIMALS.

FIRST AID- REMOVE POISON BY GASTRIC LAVAGE WITH 5-10 L OF TAP WATER. IF A GASTRIC TUBE IS NOT IMMEDIATELY AVAILABLE, REPEAT THE ADMINISTRATION OF 1 LITER OF WATER FOLLOWED BY THE STIMULATION OF VOMITING AT LEAST 3 TIMES. GIVE 120 MG/ML (4 OZ) OF MINERAL OIL, FOLLOWED BY 30-60 ML OF FLEET'S PHOSPHOSODA DILUTED 1:4 IN WATER. REPEAT AFTER 2 HOURS. TREATMENT MUST BE PERFORMED BY QUALIFIED MEDICAL PERSONNEL. (DREISBACH, HANDBOOK OF POISONING, 11TH EDITION). GET MEDICAL ATTENTION IMMEDIATELY.

ANTIDOTE: NO SPECIFIC ANTIDOTE. TREAT SYMPTOMATICALLY AND SUPPORTIVELY.

REACTIVITY

REACTIVITY: IGNITES SPONTANEOUSLY ON CONTACT WITH MOIST AIR AT OR ABOVE 86 F (30 C) AND BURNS WITH A BLUE FLAME PRODUCING ACRID FUMES.

INCOMPATIBILITIES: PHOSPHOROUS, WHITE (PHOSPHOROUS, YELLOW): AIR: SPONTANEOUS IGNITION @ 86 F. ALKALI METAL NITRIDES: FORMATION OF HIGHLY FLAMMABLE COMPOUND. ALKALINE HYDROXIDES: FORMATION OF PYROTECHNIC COMPOUND ON BOILING. AMMONIUM NITRATE: EXPLOSION ON IMPACT. ANIMAL CHARCOAL: IGNITION REACTION. ANTIMONY PENTACHLORIDE: IGNITES ON CONTACT. ANTIMONY PENTAFLUORIDE: IGNITION REACTION ON CONTACT. BARIUM BROMATE: EXPLOSIVE REACTION BY HEAT, PERCUSSION, OR LIGHT FRICTION. BARIUM CHLORATE: EXPLOSIVE REACTION BY HEAT, PERCUSSION, OR LIGHT FRICTION. BARIUM IODATE: EXPLOSIVE REACTION BY HEAT, PERCUSSION,

OR LIGHT FRICTION. BERYLLIUM: INCANDESCENT REACTION IN PHOSPHOROUS VAPORS. BORON TRIFLUORIDE: INCANDESCENT REACTION. BORON TRIIODIDE: INCANDESCENT REACTION. BROMATES: EXPLOSION BY HEAT, IMPACT OR FRICTION. BROMINE (GAS, VAPOR): IGNITION REACTION. BROMINE (LIQUID): EXPLOSIVE REACTION. BROMINE, CARBON DISULFIDE: YIELDS SLIMY BY-PRODUCT THAT EXPLODES VIOLENTLY ON HEATING. BROMINE TRIFLUORIDE: INCANDESCENT REACTION. BROMOAZIDE: EXPLOSIVE REACTION. CALCIUM BROMATE: EXPLOSIVE REACTION BY HEAT, PERCUSSION, OR LIGHT FRICTION. CALCIUM CHLORATE: EXPLOSIVE REACTION BY HEAT, PERCUSSION, OR LIGHT FRICTION. CALCIUM HYDROXIDE (HOT): EVOLVES PHOSPHINE, WHICH MAY IGNITE IN AIR. CALCIUM IODATE: EXPLOSIVE REACTION BY HEAT, PERCUSSION, OR LIGHT FRICTION. CAUSTIC ALKALIES (BOILING): EVOLVES PHOSPHINE, WHICH MAY IGNITE IN AIR. CARBON, AIR: IGNITION AT ROOM TEMPERATURE. CERIUM: VIOLENT REACTION ON HEATING. CESIUM: VIGOROUS REACTION BELOW 250 C. CESIUM ACETYLENE CARBIDE: INCANDESCENT REACTION ON HEATING. CESIUM NITRIDE: VIGOROUS REACTION. CHLORATES (MOIST): EXPLOSIVE REACTION ON CONTACT. CHLORINE (GAS): IGNITION REACTION. CHLORINE (LIQUID): EXPLOSIVE REACTION. CHLORINE DIOXIDE: IGNITION AND POSSIBLE EXPLOSION. CHLORINE MONOXIDE: EXPLOSIVE REACTION. CHLORINE TRIFLUORIDE: VIGOROUS REACTION. CHLORINE TRIOXIDE: EXPLOSIVE REACTION. CHLOROSULFONIC ACID: EXPLOSIVE REACTION @ 25-30 C. CHROMIC ANHYDRIDE: EXPLOSIVE REACTION. CHROMIC ACID: EXPLOSIVE REACTION. CHROMIUM TRIOXIDE (MOLTEN): EXPLOSIVE REACTION. CHROMYL CHLORIDE (MOIST): EXPLOSIVE REACTION. COPPER: INCANDESCENT REACTION ON HEATING. CYANOGEN IODIDE: INCANDESCENT REACTION WITH MOLTEN PHOSPHOROUS. DICHLORINE OXIDE: EXPLOSION ON CONTACT. DINITROGEN PENTAOXIDE: IGNITION ON HEATING. DINITROGEN TETROXIDE: VIOLENT COMBUSTION. FLUORINE: IGNITES ON CONTACT. HALIDES (NON-METAL): POSSIBLE VIOLENT REACTION. HALOGENS OR INTERHALOGENS: IGNITION OR INCANDESCENT REACTION. HALOGEN AZIDES: EXPLOSIVE REACTION. HEPTASILVER NITRATE OCTAOXIDE: EXPLOSION ON IMPACT. HEXALITHIUM DISILICIDE: INCANDESCENT REACTION. HYDROGEN IODIDE: FORMATION OF EXPLOSIVE PRODUCT. HYDROGEN PEROXIDE: VIOLENT REACTION WHEN HEATING IN AIR. IODINE: IGNITES ON CONTACT. IODINE, CARBON DISULFIDE: VIGOROUS REACTION. IODINE MONOCHLORIDE: VIOLENT REACTION. IODINE MONOBROMIDE (MOLTEN): VIOLENT REACTION. IODINE PENTAFLUORIDE: EXPLOSIVE REACTION. IRON: INCANDESCENT REACTION ON HEATING. LANTHANUM: VIOLENT REACTION ON HEATING. LEAD OXIDES: EXPLOSION ON GRINDING. LEAD PEROXIDES: EXPLOSIVE REACTION. LITHIUM: VIOLENT REACTION ON HEATING. LITHIUM CARBIDE: COMBUSTION ON HEATING. LITHIUM SILICIDE: INCANDESCENT REACTION. LYE: REACTS TO FORM HIGHLY TOXIC PHOSPHINE GAS. MAGNESIUM BROMATE: EXPLOSIVE REACTION BY HEAT, PERCUSSION OR LIGHT FRICTION. MAGNESIUM CHLORATE: EXPLOSIVE REACTION BY HEAT, PERCUSSION, LIGHT FRICTION. MAGNESIUM IODATE: EXPLOSIVE REACTION BY HEAT, PERCUSSION, OR LIGHT FRICTION. MAGNESIUM PERCHLORATE: EXPLOSIVE REACTION ON MIXING. MANGANESE: INCANDESCENT REACTION IN PHOSPHOROUS VAPOR. MANGANESE OXIDE: VIOLENT REACTION ON HEATING. METAL ACETYLIDES: INCANDESCES WITH WARM PHOSPHORUS. MERCURIC NITRATE: EXPLOSION ON PERCUSSION. MERCURIC OXIDE: EXPLOSION ON PERCUSSION. NEODYMIUM: VIOLENT REACTION ON HEATING. NICKEL: INCANDESCENT REACTION ON HEATING. NITRATES: POSSIBLE EXPLOSION. NITRIC ACID VAPOR: IGNITION REACTION. NITROGEN BROMIDE: VIOLENT EXPLOSION ON CONTACT. NITROGEN DIOXIDE: IGNITION REACTION ON HEATING. NITROGEN OXIDE: IGNITION REACTION ON HEATING. NITROGEN TRIBROMIDE: POSSIBLE EXPLOSION. NITROGEN TRIBROMIDE HEXAAMMONIATE: EXPLOSIVE REACTION. NITROGEN TRICHLORIDE: EXPLOSIVE REACTION. NITROSYL FLUORIDE: INCANDESCENT REACTION. OIL OF TURPENTINE: INCOMPATIBLE. OSMIUM: INCANDESCENT REACTION IN PHOSPHOROUS VAPOR. OXIDIZING MATERIALS: EXPLOSIVE REACTION. OXYGEN: VIGOROUS REACTION AT ROOM TEMPERATURE. OXYGEN DIFLUORIDE: IGNITION REACTION. PERCHLORATES: EXPLOSION ON HEAT, IMPACT OR FRICTION. PERFORMIC ACID: EXPLOSIVE REACTION. PERIODATES: EXPLOSION ON HEAT, IMPACT OR FRICTION. PEROXYFORMIC ACID: EXPLOSIVE REACTION. PLATINUM: BURNS VIVIDLY BELOW RED-HEAT. PRASEODYMIUM: VIOLENT REACTION ON HEATING. POTASSIUM: EXPLOSIVE REACTION. POTASSIUM BROMATE: EXPLOSIVE REACTION BY HEAT, PERCUSSION OR LIGHT FRICTION. POTASSIUM CHLORATE: EXPLOSIVE REACTION BY HEAT, PERCUSSION, LIGHT FRICTION, EVOLVES SPONTANEOUSLY FLAMMABLE PHOSPHINE ON BOILING. POTASSUM HYDROXIDE: EXPLOSIVE REACTION. POTASSIUM IODATE: EXPLOSIVE REACTION BY HEAT, PERCUSSION, OR LIGHT FRICTION. POTASSIUM IODATE, WATER: VIOLENT REACTION AND POSSIBLE EXPLOSION. POTASSIUM NITRATE: VIOLENT OXIDATION ON HEATING. POTASSIUM NITRIDE: FORMATION OF HIGHLY FLAMMABLE COMPOUND ON HEATING. POTASSIUM PERMANGANATE: EXPLOSION ON GRINDING. POTASSIUM PEROXIDE: IGNITION AND POSSIBLE EXPLOSION. RUBIDIUM: VIGOROUS REACTION. RUBIDIUM ACETYLENE CARBIDE: INCANDESCENT REACTION ON HEATING. SELENINYL CHLORIDE: POSSIBLE EXPLOSION. SELENIUM MONOCHLORIDE: EXPLOSION ON MIXING. SELENIUM OXYCHLORIDE: POSSIBLE EXPLOSION. SELENIUM OXYFLUORIDE: SPONTANEOUS IGNITION REACTION. SELENIUM TETRAFLUORIDE: VIOLENT REACTION. SILVER NITRATE: EXPLOSIVE REACTION BY HEAT, PERCUSSION, OR LIGHT FRICTION. SILVER OXIDE: IGNITION ON IMPACT. SODIUM: EXPLOSIVE REACTION. SODIUM BROMATE: EXPLOSIVE REACTION BY HEAT, PERCUSSION, OR LIGHT FRICTION. SODIUM CARBIDE: IGNITION REACTION IN PHOSPHORUS VAPOR. SODIUM CHLORATE: EXPLOSIVE REACTION BY HEAT, PERCUSSION, OR LIGHT FRICTION. SODIUM HYDRIDE: IGNITION REACTION. SODIUM HYDROXIDE: EXPLOSIVE REACTION. SODIUM IODATE: EXPLOSIVE REACTION BY HEAT, PERCUSSION, OR LIGHT FRICTION. SODIUM PEROXIDE: EXPLOSIVE REACTION. SULFUR: IGNITION AND EXPLOSION ON WARMING. SULFURIC ACID (BOILING, CONCENTRATED): IGNITION. SULFUR PEROXIDE: IGNITION AND POSSIBLE EXPLOSION. SULFUR TRIOXIDE (LIQUID): IMMEDIATE IGNITION ON CONTACT. SULFUR TRIOXIDE (VAPOR): IGNITION REACTION, WHICH MAY BE DELAYED. SULFURYL CHLORIDE: POSSIBLE EXPLOSIVE REACTION. TELLURIUM: INCANDESCENT REACTION. THORIUM: INCANDESCENT REACTION ON HEATING. TRIOXYGEN DIFLUORIDE: IGNITION REACTION. VANADIUM OXYTRICHLORIDE: POSSIBLE EXPLOSION. ZINC BROMATE: EXPLOSIVE REACTION BY HEAT, PERCUSSION, OR LIGHT FRICTION. ZINC CHLORATE: EXPLOSIVE REACTION BY HEAT, PERCUSSION, OR LIGHT FRICTION. ZINC IODATE: EXPLOSIVE REACTION BY HEAT, PERCUSSION, OR LIGHT FRICTION. ZIRCONIUM (IN VACUUM): INCANDESCENT REACTION ON HEATING.

DECOMPOSITION: THERMAL DECOMPOSITION MAY RELEASE HIGHLY TOXIC FUMES OF PHOSPHORUS OXIDES.

POLYMERIZATION: HAZARDOUS POLYMERIZATION HAS NOT BEEN REPORTED TO OCCUR UNDER NORMAL TEMPERATURES AND PRESSURES.

STORAGE AND DISPOSAL

OBSERVE ALL FEDERAL, STATE AND LOCAL REGULATIONS WHEN STORING OR DISPOSING OF THIS SUBSTANCE. FOR ASSISTANCE, CONTACT THE DISTRICT DIRECTOR OF THE ENVIRONMENTAL PROTECTION AGENCY.

STORAGE

STORAGE: PROTECT AGAINST PHYSICAL DAMAGE. ALWAYS KEEP UNDER WATER, OR IN INERT ATMOSPHERE, SEPARATED FROM OTHER MATERIALS (NFPA 49, HAZARDOUS CHEMICALS DATA, 1975).

STORE AWAY FROM INCOMPATIBLE SUBSTANCES.

THRESHOLD PLANNING QUANTITY (TPQ): THE SUPERFUND AMENDMENTS AND REAUTHORIZATION ACT (SARA) SECTION 302 REQUIRES THAT EACH FACILITY WHERE ANY EXTREMELY HAZARDOUS SUBSTANCE IS PRESENT IN A QUANTITY EQUAL TO OR GREATER THAN THE TPQ ESTABLISHED FOR THAT SUBSTANCE NOTIFY THE STATE EMERGENCY RESPONSE COMMISSION FOR THE STATE IN WHICH IT IS LOCATED. SECTION 303 OF SARA REQUIRES THESE FACILITIES TO PARTICIPATE IN LOCAL EMERGENCY RESPONSE PLANNING (40 CFR 355.30).

CONDITIONS TO AVOID

WILL IGNITE ITSELF IF EXPOSED TO AIR AND WILL RE-IGNITE ITSELF AFTER FIRE IS EXTINGUISHED. BURNS RAPIDLY, RELEASING DENSE WHITE FUMES. RUNOFF TO SEWER MAY CREATE FIRE OR EXPLOSION HAZARD.

SPILL AND LEAK PROCEDURES

SOIL SPILL: DIG HOLDING AREA SUCH AS LAGOON, POND OR PIT FOR CONTAINMENT. COVER WITH WATER OR WET SAND.

AIR SPILL: KNOCK DOWN VAPORS WITH WATER SPRAY. KEEP UPWIND. COMBUSTION PRODUCTS INCLUDE CORROSIVE OR TOXIC VAPORS.

WATER SPILL: TRAP SPILLED MATERIAL AT BOTTOM IN DEEP WATER POCKETS, EXCAVATED HOLDING AREAS OR WITHIN SAND BAG BARRIERS.

OCCUPATIONAL SPILL: DO NOT TOUCH SPILLED MATERIAL. STOP LEAK IF YOU CAN DO IT WITHOUT RISK. USE WATER SPRAY TO REDUCE VAPORS. FOR SMALL SPILLS, COVER WITH WATER, SAND OR EARTH. SHOVEL INTO METAL CONTAINER AND KEEP MATERIAL UNDER WATER. CLEAN UP ONLY UNDER SUPERVISION OF AN EXPERT. FOR LARGER SPILLS, DIKE FOR LATER DISPOSAL AND COVER WITH WATER OR WET SAND. KEEP UNNECESSARY PEOPLE AWAY. ISOLATE HAZARD AREA AND DENY ENTRY.

REPORTABLE QUANTITY (RQ): 1 POUND THE SUPERFUND AMENDMENTS AND REAUTHORIZATION ACT (SARA) SECTION 304 REQUIRES THAT A RELEASE EQUAL TO OR GREATER THAN THE REPORTABLE QUANTITY FOR THIS SUBSTANCE BE IMMEDIATELY REPORTED TO THE LOCAL EMERGENCY PLANNING COMMITTEE AND THE STATE EMERGENCY RESPONSE COMMISSION (40 CFR 355.40). IF THE RELEASE OF THIS SUBSTANCE IS REPORTABLE UNDER CERCLA SECTION 103, THE NATIONAL RESPONSE CENTER MUST BE NOTIFIED IMMEDIATELY AT (800) 424-8802 OR (202) 426-2675 IN THE METROPOLITAN WASHINGTON, D.C. AREA (40 CFR 302.6).

PROTECTIVE EQUIPMENT

VENTILATION: PROVIDE LOCAL EXHAUST OR PROCESS ENCLOSURE VENTILATION TO MEET THE PUBLISHED EXPOSURE LIMITS. VENTILATION EQUIPMENT MUST BE EXPLOSION-PROOF.

RESPIRATOR: THE FOLLOWING RESPIRATORS AND MAXIMUM USE CONCENTRATIONS ARE RECOMMENDATIONS BY THE U.S. DEPARTMENT OF HEALTH AND HUMAN SERVICES, NIOSH POCKET GUIDE TO CHEMICAL HAZARDS; NIOSH CRITERIA

DOCUMENTS OR BY THE U.S. DEPARTMENT OF LABOR, 29 CFR 1910 SUBPART Z. THE SPECIFIC RESPIRATOR SELECTED MUST BE BASED ON CONTAMINATION LEVELS FOUND IN THE WORK PLACE, MUST NOT EXCEED THE WORKING LIMITS OF THE RESPIRATOR AND BE JOINTLY APPROVED BY THE NATIONAL INSTITUTE FOR OCCUPATIONAL SAFETY AND HEALTH AND THE MINE SAFETY AND HEALTH ADMINISTRATION (NIOSH-MSHA).

PHOSPHOROUS, WHITE:

1.0 MG/M3- ANY DUST AND MIST RESPIRATOR WITH FULL FACEPIECE.

2.5 MG/M3- ANY POWERED AIR-PURIFYING RESPIRATOR WITH HIGH-EFFICIENCY PARTICULATE FILTER. ANY SUPPLIED-AIR RESPIRATOR OPERATED IN CONTINUOUS FLOW MODE.

5.0 MG/M3- ANY SELF-CONTAINED BREATHING APPARATUS WITH FULL FACEPIECE. ANY SUPPLIED-AIR RESPIRATOR WITH FULL FACEPIECE. ANY AIR-PURIFYING FULL FACEPIECE RESPIRATOR WITH A HIGH-EFFICIENCY PARTICULATE FILTER.

200.0 MG/M3- ANY SUPPLIED-AIR RESPIRATOR WITH FULL FACEPIECE OPERATED IN PRESSURE-DEMAND OR OTHER POSITIVE PRESSURE MODE.

ESCAPE- AIR-PURIFYING FULL FACEPIECE RESPIRATOR WITH HIGH-EFFICIENCY PARTICULATE FILTER. ESCAPE-TYPE SELF-CONTAINED BREATHING APPARATUS.

FOR FIREFIGHTING AND OTHER IMMEDIATELY DANGEROUS TO LIFE OR HEALTH CONDITIONS:

SELF-CONTAINED BREATHING APPARATUS WITH FULL FACEPIECE OPERATED IN PRESSURE-DEMAND OR OTHER POSITIVE PRESSURE MODE. SUPPLIED-AIR RESPIRATOR WITH FULL FACEPIECE AND OPERATED IN PRESSURE-DEMAND OR OTHER POSITIVE PRESSURE MODE IN COMBINATION WITH AN AUXILIARY SELF-CONTAINED BREATHING APPARATUS OPERATED IN PRESSURE-DEMAND OR OTHER POSITIVE PRESSURE MODE.

CLOTHING: EMPLOYEE MUST WEAR APPROPRIATE PROTECTIVE (IMPERVIOUS) CLOTHING AND EQUIPMENT TO PREVENT ANY POSSIBILITY OF SKIN CONTACT WITH THIS SUBSTANCE.

GLOVES: EMPLOYEE MUST WEAR APPROPRIATE PROTECTIVE GLOVES TO PREVENT CONTACT WITH THIS SUBSTANCE.

EYE PROTECTION: EMPLOYEE MUST WEAR SPLASH-PROOF OR DUST-RESISTANT SAFETY GOGGLES AND A FACESHIELD TO PREVENT CONTACT WITH THIS SUBSTANCE.

EMERGENCY WASH FACILITIES: WHERE THERE IS ANY POSSIBILITY THAT AN EMPLOYEE'S EYES AND/OR SKIN MAY BE EXPOSED TO THIS SUBSTANCE, THE EMPLOYER SHOULD PROVIDE AN EYE WASH FOUNTAIN AND QUICK DRENCH SHOWER WITHIN THE IMMEDIATE WORK AREA FOR EMERGENCY USE.

AUTHORIZED BY- OCCUPATIONAL HEALTH SERVICES, INC.

CREATION DATE: 10/04/89 ***REVISION DATE:*** 05/16/90

MATERIAL SAFETY DATA SHEET

OCCUPATIONAL HEALTH SERVICES, INC.
AGRICULTURE AND PESTICIDE DIVISION
450 SEVENTH AVENUE, SUITE 2407
NEW YORK, NEW YORK 10123
1-800-445-MSDS OR (212) 967-1100

EMERGENCY CONTACT:
JOHN S. BRANSFORD, JR. (615) 292-1180

SUBSTANCE IDENTIFICATION

CAS-NUMBER 37333-40-7

SUBSTANCE: PHOSTEX

TRADE NAMES/SYNONYMS: THIOPEROXYDIPHOSPHORIC ACID ((HO)2P(S))2S2), ETHYL TRIS(1-METHYL ETHYL) ESTER MIXTURE WITH THIOPEROXYDIPHOSPHORIC ACID (((HO)2P(S))2S2) TRIETHYL 1-METHYLETHYL ESTER; BIS(DIALKYLPHOSPHINOTHIOYL) DISULFIDE; C20H48O8P4S8; PST18807

CHEMICAL FAMILY: ORGANOPHOSPHATE THIO

MOLECULAR FORMULA: C11-H26-O4-P2-S4.C9-H22-O4-P2-S4

MOLECULAR WEIGHT: 797.04

CERCLA RATINGS (SCALE 0-3): HEALTH=3 FIRE=U REACTIVITY=0 PERSISTENCE=1

NFPA RATINGS (SCALE 0-4): HEALTH=3 FIRE=U REACTIVITY=0

COMPONENTS AND CONTAMINANTS

COMPONENT: PHOSTEX ***PERCENT:*** 100.0
CAS# 37333-40-7

OTHER CONTAMINANTS: NONE

EXPOSURE LIMITS: NO OCCUPATIONAL EXPOSURE LIMITS ESTABLISHED BY OSHA, ACGIH, OR NIOSH.

PHYSICAL DATA

DESCRIPTION: PALE YELLOW LIQUID. ***BOILING POINT:*** NOT AVAILABLE
SPECIFIC GRAVITY: NOT AVAILABLE ***VAPOR PRESSURE:*** NOT AVAILABLE
EVAPORATION RATE: NOT AVAILABLE ***SOLUBILITY IN WATER:*** SLIGHTLY SOLUBLE
SOLVENT SOLUBILITY: SOLUBLE IN MOST ORGANIC SOLVENTS.

FIRE AND EXPLOSION DATA

FIRE AND EXPLOSION HAZARD: UNKNOWN FIRE AND EXPLOSION HAZARD. ***FLASH POINT:*** NOT AVAILABLE

FIREFIGHTING MEDIA: DRY CHEMICAL, CARBON DIOXIDE, HALON, WATER SPRAY OR STANDARD FOAM (1987 EMERGENCY RESPONSE GUIDEBOOK, DOT P 5800.4). FOR LARGER FIRES, USE WATER SPRAY, FOG OR STANDARD FOAM (1987 EMERGENCY RESPONSE GUIDEBOOK, DOT P 5800.4).

FIREFIGHTING: MOVE CONTAINERS FROM FIRE AREA IF POSSIBLE. FIGHT FIRE FROM MAXIMUM DISTANCE. STAY AWAY FROM STORAGE TANK ENDS. DIKE FIRE CONTROL WATER FOR LATER DISPOSAL. DO NOT SCATTER MATERIAL (1987 EMERGENCY RESPONSE GUIDEBOOK, DOT P 5800.4, GUIDE PAGE 55). EXTINGUISH ONLY IF FLOW CAN BE STOPPED. EXTINGUISH USING AGENT INDICATED. USE FLOODING AMOUNTS OF WATER AS A FOG. COOL CONTAINERS WITH FLOODING AMOUNTS OF WATER FROM AS FAR A DISTANCE AS POSSIBLE. AVOID BREATHING POISONOUS VAPORS, KEEP UPWIND. CONSIDER EVACUATION OF DOWNWIND AREA IF MATERIAL IS LEAKING.

TOXICITY

PHOSTEX: TOXICITY DATA: 480 MG/KG SKIN-RAT LD50; 265 MG/KG ORAL-RAT LD50. CARCINOGEN STATUS: NONE. ACUTE TOXICITY LEVEL: TOXIC BY DERMAL ABSORPTION, INGESTION. TARGET EFFECTS: CHOLINESTERASE INHIBITOR. POISONING MAY AFFECT THE HEART AND THE RESPIRATORY, MUSCULAR, SECRETORY, AND CENTRAL NERVOUS SYSTEMS.* AT INCREASED RISK FROM EXPOSURE: PERSONS WITH RESPIRATORY AILMENTS, IMPAIRED CHOLINESTERASE PRODUCTION, OR LIVER MALFUNCTION.* ADDITIONAL DATA: MAY CROSS THE PLACENTA. HIGH ENVIRONMENTAL TEMPERATURES OR EXPOSURE OF THE CHEMICAL TO VISIBLE OR ULTRAVIOLET LIGHT MAY ENHANCE THE TOXICITY.

* MAY BE BASED ON GENERAL INFORMATION ON ORGANOPHOSPHATES.

HEALTH EFFECTS AND FIRST AID

INHALATION: PHOSTEX: SEE INFORMATION ON ORGANOPHOSPHATES.

ORGANOPHOSPHATES: CHOLINESTERASE INHIBITOR. **ACUTE EXPOSURE-** WHEN INHALED, THE FIRST EFFECTS OF CHOLINESTERASE INHIBITORS ARE USUALLY RESPIRATORY AND MAY INCLUDE NASAL HYPEREMIA AND WATERY DISCHARGE, COUGH, CHEST DISCOMFORT, DYSPNEA, AND WHEEZING DUE TO INCREASED BRONCHIAL SECRETIONS AND BRONCHOCONSTRICTION. IF SUFFICIENT AMOUNTS ARE ABSORBED, OTHER SYSTEMIC EFFECTS MAY BEGIN WITHIN A FEW MINUTES OR BE DELAYED FOR UP TO 12 HOURS. SYMPTOMS MAY INCLUDE PALLOR, NAUSEA, VOMITING, DIARRHEA, ABDOMINAL CRAMPS, HEADACHE, DIZZINESS, OCULAR PAIN, BLURRED VISION, MIOSIS OR IN SOME CASES, ESPECIALLY INITIALLY, MYDRIASIS, LACRIMATION, SALIVATION, SWEATING, AND CONFUSION. OTHER REPORTED CENTRAL NERVOUS SYSTEM OR NEUROMUSCULAR EFFECTS MAY INCLUDE ATAXIA, SLURRED SPEECH, AREFLEXIA, WEAKNESS, FATIGUE, FASCICULATIONS, TWITCHING, TREMORS POSSIBLY OF THE TONGUE AND EYELIDS, AND EVENTUALLY PARALYSIS OF THE EXTREMITIES AND POSSIBLY OF THE RESPIRATORY MUSCLES. IN SEVERE CASES THERE MAY ALSO BE INVOLUNTARY DEFECATION AND URINATION, CYANOSIS, PSYCHOSIS, HYPERGLYCEMIA, ACUTE PANCREATITIS, CARDIAC IRREGULARITIES, PULMONARY EDEMA, UNCONSCIOUSNESS, CONVULSIONS, AND COMA. DEATH IS PRIMARILY DUE TO RESPIRATORY FAILURE, ALTHOUGH CARDIOVASCULAR EFFECTS INCLUDING CARDIAC ARREST MAY ALSO BE IMPLICATED. LONG TERM SEQUELAE ARE RARE BUT MAY INCLUDE NEUROPSYCHIATRIC DISORDERS AND MYOPATHY WITH MUSCLE TENDERNESS. SOME ORGANOPHOSPHATES MAY CAUSE A DELAYED NEUROPATHY BEGINNING 1-4 WEEKS AFTER AN ACUTE EXPOSURE WHICH MAY OR MAY NOT HAVE CAUSED ACUTE CHOLINERGIC EFFECTS. NUMBNESS, TINGLING, WEAKNESS AND CRAMPING BEGINNING SYMMETRICALLY IN THE LOWER LIMBS MAY PROGRESS TO ATAXIA AND PARALYSIS. IN SEVERE CASES, UPPER LIMB INVOLVEMENT IS POSSIBLE AND FLACCID PARALYSIS MAY PROGRESS TO SPASTIC PARALYSIS WITH EXAGGERATED REFLEXES. IMPROVEMENT MAY OCCUR OVER MONTHS TO YEARS, BUT SOME RESIDUAL IMPAIRMENT USUALLY REMAINS.

CHRONIC EXPOSURE- REPEATED OR PROLONGED EXPOSURE MAY RESULT IN THE EFFECTS OF ACUTE EXPOSURE INCLUDING THE DELAYED NEUROPATHY. OTHER EFFECTS REPORTED IN WORKERS REPEATEDLY EXPOSED INCLUDE IMPAIRED MEMORY AND CONCENTRATION, ACUTE PSYCHOSIS, SEVERE DEPRESSIONS, IRRITABILTY, CONFUSION, APATHY, EMOTIONAL LABILITY, SOCIAL WITHDRAWAL, CONFUSION, HEADACHE, SPEECH DIFFICULTIES, DELAYED REACTION TIMES, SPATIAL DISORIENTATION, NIGHTMARES, SLEEPWALKING, AND DROWSINESS OR INSOMNIA. AN INFLUENZA-LIKE CONDITION WITH HEADACHE, NAUSEA, WEAKNESS, ANOREXIA AND MALAISE HAS ALSO BEEN REPORTED.

FIRST AID- REMOVE FROM EXPOSURE AREA TO FRESH AIR IMMEDIATELY. IF BREATHING HAS STOPPED, GIVE ARTIFICIAL RESPIRATION. MAINTAIN AIRWAY AND BLOOD PRESSURE AND ADMINISTER OXYGEN IF AVAILABLE. KEEP AFFECTED PERSON WARM AND AT REST. TREAT SYMPTOMATICALLY AND SUPPORTIVELY. ADMINISTRATION OF OXYGEN SHOULD BE PERFORMED BY QUALIFIED PERSONNEL. GET MEDICAL ATTENTION IMMEDIATELY.

SKIN CONTACT: PHOSTEX: TOXIC. THE LETHAL DOSE REPORTED IN RATS WAS 480 MG/KG. THE SYMPTOMS WERE NOT REPORTED. SEE INFORMATION ON ORGANOPHOSPHATES.
ORGANOPHOSPHATES: CHOLINESTERASE INHIBITOR. **ACUTE EXPOSURE**- LOCALIZED SWEATING AND FASCICULATIONS MAY OCCUR AT THE SITE OF CONTACT. IF SUFFICIENT AMOUNTS ARE ABSORBED, OTHER EFFECTS OF CHOLINESTERASE INHIBITION AS DESCRIBED IN ACUTE INHALATION MAY OCCUR. SYMPTOMS MAY BE DELAYED 2-3 HOURS, BUT USUALLY NO MORE THAN 12 HOURS. THE RATE OF ABSORPTION IS INCREASED BY THE PRESENCE OF DERMATITIS OR HIGH AMBIENT TEMPERATURES. DELAYED NEUROPATHY IS ALSO POSSIBLE. **CHRONIC EXPOSURE**- REPEATED OR PROLONGED EXPOSURE MAY CAUSE EFFECTS AS DESCRIBED IN ACUTE EXPOSURE. SOME ORGANOPHOSPHATES MAY CAUSE SENSITIZATION.
FIRST AID- REMOVE CONTAMINATED CLOTHING IMMEDIATELY. WASH CONTAMINATED AREAS WITH SOAP AND WATER FOLLOWED BY ALCOHOL (ARENA, POISONING, 4TH ED.). EMERGENCY PERSONNEL SHOULD WEAR GLOVES AND AVOID CONTAMINATION. TREAT RESPIRATORY DIFFICULTY WITH ARTIFICIAL RESPIRATION. GET MEDICAL ATTENTION IMMEDIATELY.

EYE CONTACT: PHOSTEX: SEE INFORMATION ON ORGANOPHOSPHATES.
ORGANOPHOSPHATES: CHOLINESTERASE INHIBITOR. **ACUTE EXPOSURE**- DIRECT CONTACT MAY CAUSE PAIN, HYPEREMIA, LACRIMATION, TWITCHING OF THE EYELIDS, MIOSIS, AND CILIARY MUSCLE SPASM WITH LOSS OF ACCOMODATION, BLURRED OR DIMMED VISION AND BROWACHE. SOMETIMES MYDRIASIS MAY OCCUR INSTEAD OF MIOSIS. WITH SUFFICIENT EXPOSURE, OTHER SYMPTOMS OF CHOLINESTERASE INHIBITION AS DESCRIBED IN ACUTE INHALATION MAY OCCUR. **CHRONIC EXPOSURE**- REPEATED OR PROLONGED EXPOSURE MAY CAUSE EFFECTS AS DESCRIBED IN ACUTE EXPOSURE. SOME COMPOUNDS HAVE CAUSED TOXIC EFFECTS ON THE CRYSTALLINE LENS, CONJUNCTIVAL THICKENING AND OBSTRUCTION OF THE NASOLACRIMAL CANALS WHEN USED AS MIOTIC EYEDROPS.
FIRST AID- IRRIGATE EYES WITH WATER OR SALINE SOLUTION. IF SYMPTOMS OF POISONING OCCUR, TREAT RESPIRATORY DIFFICULTY WITH ARTIFICIAL RESPIRATION AND OXYGEN. OBSERVE PATIENT FOR AT LEAST 24-36 HOURS (GOSSELIN, CLINICAL TOXICOLOGY OF COMMERCIAL PRODUCTS, 5TH ED.). GET MEDICAL ATTENTION IMMEDIATELY. OXYGEN SHOULD BE ADMINISTERED BY QUALIFIED MEDICAL PERSONNEL.

INGESTION: PHOSTEX: TOXIC. THE LETHAL DOSE REPORTED IN RATS WAS 265 MG/KG. THE SYMPTOMS WERE NOT REPORTED. SEE INFORMATION ON ORGANOPHOSPHATES.
ORGANOPHOSPHATES: CHOLINESTERASE INHIBITOR. **ACUTE EXPOSURE**- WHEN INGESTED, THE FIRST EFFECTS MAY BE NAUSEA, VOMITING, ANOREXIA, ABDOMINAL CRAMPS AND DIARRHEA. GASTROINTESTINAL ABSORPTION MAY CAUSE SYMPTOMS OF CHOLINESTERASE INHIBITION AS DESCRIBED IN ACUTE INHALATION. SYMPTOMS MAY BEGIN WITHIN MINUTES OR BE DELAYED FOR HOURS. DELAYED EFFECTS INCLUDING NEUROPATHY MAY ALSO OCCUR. **CHRONIC EXPOSURE**- REPEATED INGESTION MAY CAUSE EFFECTS AS DESCRIBED IN ACUTE EXPOSURE.
FIRST AID- IF PERSON IS ALERT AND RESPIRATION IS NOT DEPRESSED, GIVE SYRUP OF IPECAC FOLLOWED BY WATER (IF VOMITING OCCURS, KEEP HEAD BELOW HIPS TO PREVENT ASPIRATION). IF CONSCIOUSNESS LEVEL DECLINES OR VOMITING HAS NOT OCCURRED IN 15 MINUTES EMPTY STOMACH BY GASTRIC LAVAGE WITH THE AID OF CUFFED ENDOTRACHEAL TUBE USING ISOTONIC SALINE OR 5% SODIUM BICARBONATE FOLLOW WITH ACTIVATED CHARCOAL. ESTABLISH AND MAINTAIN AIRWAY. TREAT RESPIRATORY DIFFICULTY WITH ARTIFICIAL RESPIRATION AND OXYGEN. DO NOT GIVE MORPHINE, AMINOPHYLLINE, PHENOTHIAZINES, RESERPINE, FUROSEMIDE, OR ETHACRYNIC ACID (MORGAN, RECOGNITION AND MANAGEMENT OF PESTICIDE POISONINGS, 3RD ED.). TREAT SYMPTOMATICALLY AND SUPPORTIVELY. ADMINISTRATION OF OXYGEN AND LAVAGE MUST BE PERFORMED BY QUALIFIED MEDICAL PERSONNEL. GET MEDICAL ATTENTION IMMEDIATELY.
ANTIDOTE: THE FOLLOWING ANTIDOTE(S) HAVE BEEN RECOMMENDED. HOWEVER, THE DECISION AS TO WHETHER THE SEVERITY OF POISONING REQUIRES ADMINISTRATION OF ANY ANTIDOTE AND ACTUAL DOSE REQUIRED SHOULD BE MADE BY QUALIFIED MEDICAL PERSONNEL.
FOR CHOLINESTERASE INHIBITORS: ESTABLISH CLEAR AIRWAY AND TISSUE OXYGENATION BY ASPIRATION OF SECRETIONS, AND IF NECESSARY, BY ASSISTED PULMONARY VENTILATION WITH OXYGEN. IMPROVE TISSUE OXYGENATION AS MUCH AS POSSIBLE BEFORE ADMINISTERING ATROPINE TO MINIMIZE THE RISK OF VENTRICULAR FIBRILLATION. ADMINISTER ATROPINE SULFATE INTRAVENOUSLY, OR INTRAMUSCULARLY IF IV INJECTION IS NOT POSSIBLE. IN MODERATELY SEVERE POISONING ADMINISTER ATROPINE SULFATE, 0.4-2.0 MG REPEATED EVERY 15 MINUTES UNTIL ATROPINIZATION IS ACHIEVED (TACHYCARDIA, FLUSHING, DRY MOUTH, MYDRIASIS). MAINTAIN ATROPINIZATION BY REPEATED DOSES FOR 2-12 HOURS, OR LONGER, DEPENDING ON THE SEVERITY OF POISONING. THE APPEARANCE OF RALES IN THE LUNG BASES, MIOSIS, SALIVATION, NAUSEA, BRADYCARDIA, ARE ALL INDICATIONS OF INADEQUATE ATROPINIZATION. SEVERELY POISONED INDIVIDUALS MAY EXHIBIT REMARKABLE TOLERANCE TO ATROPINE; TWO OR MORE TIMES THE DOSAGES SUGGESTED ABOVE MAY BE NEEDED. PERSONS NOT POISONED OR ONLY SLIGHTLY POISONED, HOWEVER, MAY DEVELOP SIGNS OF ATROPINE TOXICITY FROM SUCH LARGE DOSAGES: FEVER, MUSCLE FIBRILLATIONS, AND DELIRIUM ARE THE MAIN SIGNS OF ATROPINE TOXICITY. IF THESE SIGNS APPEAR WHILE THE PATIENT IS FULLY ATROPINIZED, ATROPINE ADMINISTRATION SHOULD BE DISCONTINUED, AT LEAST TEMPORARILY. OBSERVE TREATED PATIENTS CLOSELY AT LEAST 24 HOURS TO INSURE THAT SYMPTOMS (POSSIBLY PULMONARY EDEMA) DO NOT RECUR AS ATROPINIZATION WEARS OFF. IN VERY SEVERE POISONINGS, METABOLIC DISPOSITION OF TOXICANT MAY REQUIRE SEVERAL HOURS OR DAYS DURING WHICH ATROPINIZATION MUST BE MAINTAINED. MARKEDLY LOWER LEVELS OF URINARY METABOLITES INDICATE THAT ATROPINE DOSAGE CAN BE TAPERED OFF. AS DOSAGE IS REDUCED, CHECK THE LUNG BASES FREQUENTLY FOR RALES. IF RALES ARE HEARD OR OTHER SYMPTOMS RETURN, RE-ESTABLISH ATROPINIZATION PROMPTLY (MORGAN, RECOGNITION AND MANAGEMENT OF PESTICIDE POISONINGS, 3RD ED.). ADMINISTRATION OF ANTIDOTE MUST BE PERFORMED BY QUALIFIED MEDICAL PERSONNEL.
IN CASES OF SEVERE POISONING BY ORGANOPHOSPHATE PESTICIDES IN WHICH RESPIRATORY DEPRESSION, MUSCLE WEAKNESS AND TWITCHINGS ARE SEVERE, GIVE PRALIDOXIME (PROTOPAM-AYERST, 2-PAM), 1.0 GRAM INTRAVENOUSLY AT NO MORE THAN 0.5 GRAM PER MINUTE. DOSAGE OF PRALIDOXIME MAY BE REPEATED IN 1-2 HOURS, THEN AT 10-12 HOUR INTERVALS IF NEEDED. IN VERY SEVERE POISONINGS, DOSAGE RATES MAY BE DOUBLED. TREATMENT WITH PRALIDOXIME WILL BE MOST EFFECTIVE IF GIVEN WITHIN THIRTY-SIX HOURS AFTER POISONING (MORGAN, RECOGNITION AND MANAGEMENT OF PESTICIDE POISONINGS, 3RD ED.). ANTIDOTE SHOULD BE ADMINISTERED BY QUALIFIED MEDICAL PERSONNEL.

REACTIVITY

REACTIVITY: STABLE UNDER NORMAL TEMPERATURES AND PRESSURES.
INCOMPATIBILITIES: PHOSTEX: OXIDIZERS (STRONG): FIRE AND EXPLOSION HAZARD.
DECOMPOSITION: THERMAL DECOMPOSITION PRODUCTS MAY INCLUDE TOXIC OXIDES OF CARBON, SULFUR, AND PHOSPHORUS.
POLYMERIZATION: HAZARDOUS POLYMERIZATION HAS NOT BEEN REPORTED TO OCCUR UNDER NORMAL TEMPERATURES AND PRESSURES.

STORAGE AND DISPOSAL

OBSERVE ALL FEDERAL, STATE AND LOCAL REGULATIONS WHEN STORING OR DISPOSING OF THIS SUBSTANCE. FOR ASSISTANCE, CONTACT THE DISTRICT DIRECTOR OF THE ENVIRONMENTAL PROTECTION AGENCY.

****STORAGE****

STORE IN ACCORDANCE WITH 40 CFR 165 RECOMMENDED PROCEDURES FOR THE DISPOSAL AND STORAGE OF PESTICIDES AND PESTICIDE CONTAINERS.
STORE AWAY FROM INCOMPATIBLE SUBSTANCES.

****DISPOSAL****

DISPOSAL MUST BE IN ACCORDANCE WITH 40 CFR 165 RECOMMENDED PROCEDURES FOR THE DISPOSAL AND STORAGE OF PESTICIDES AND PESTICIDE CONTAINERS.

CONDITIONS TO AVOID

MAY BURN BUT DOES NOT IGNITE READILY. CONTAINERS MAY EXPLODE IN HEAT OF FIRE.

SPILL AND LEAK PROCEDURES

OCCUPATIONAL SPILL: DO NOT TOUCH SPILLED MATERIAL. STOP LEAK IF YOU CAN DO IT WITHOUT RISK. USE WATER SPRAY TO REDUCE VAPORS. FOR SMALL SPILLS, TAKE UP WITH SAND OR OTHER ABSORBENT MATERIAL AND PLACE INTO CONTAINERS FOR LATER DISPOSAL. FOR SMALL DRY SPILLS, WITH A CLEAN SHOVEL PLACE MATERIAL INTO CLEAN, DRY CONTAINERS AND COVER. MOVE CONTAINERS FROM SPILL AREA. FOR LARGER SPILLS, DIKE FAR AHEAD OF SPILL FOR LATER DISPOSAL. KEEP UNNECESSARY PEOPLE AWAY. ISOLATE HAZARD AREA AND DENY ENTRY. VENTILATE CLOSED SPACES BEFORE ENTERING.

PROTECTIVE EQUIPMENT

VENTILATION: PROVIDE LOCAL EXHAUST OR PROCESS ENCLOSURE VENTILATION. VENTILATION EQUIPMENT MUST BE EXPLOSION-PROOF.

RESPIRATOR: THE FOLLOWING RESPIRATORS ARE RECOMMENDED BASED ON INFORMATION FOUND IN THE PHYSICAL DATA, TOXICITY AND HEALTH EFFECTS SECTIONS. THEY ARE RANKED IN ORDER FROM MINIMUM TO MAXIMUM RESPIRATORY PROTECTION. THE SPECIFIC RESPIRATOR SELECTED MUST BE BASED ON CONTAMINATION LEVELS FOUND IN THE WORK PLACE, MUST NOT EXCEED THE WORKING LIMITS OF THE RESPIRATOR AND BE JOINTLY APPROVED BY THE NATIONAL INSTITUTE FOR OCCUPATIONAL SAFETY AND HEALTH AND THE MINE SAFETY AND HEALTH ADMINISTRATION (NIOSH-MSHA).

TYPE 'C' SUPPLIED-AIR RESPIRATOR WITH A FULL FACEPIECE OPERATED IN PRESSURE-DEMAND OR OTHER POSITIVE PRESSURE MODE OR WITH A FULL FACEPIECE, HELMET OR HOOD OPERATED IN CONTINOUS-FLOW MODE. SELF-CONTAINED BREATHING APPARATUS WITH A FULL FACEPIECE OPERATED IN PRESSURE-DEMAND OR OTHER POSITIVE PRESSURE MODE.

FOR FIREFIGHTING AND OTHER IMMEDIATELY DANGEROUS TO LIFE OR HEALTH CONDITIONS:

SELF-CONTAINED BREATHING APPARATUS WITH FULL FACEPIECE OPERATED IN PRESSURE-DEMAND OR OTHER POSITIVE PRESSURE MODE.

SUPPLIED-AIR RESPIRATOR WITH FULL FACEPIECE AND OPERATED IN PRESSURE-DEMAND OR OTHER POSITIVE PRESSURE MODE IN COMBINATION WITH AN AUXILIARY SELF-CONTAINED BREATHING APPARATUS OPERATED IN PRESSURE-DEMAND OR OTHER POSITIVE PRESSURE MODE.

CLOTHING: EMPLOYEE MUST WEAR APPROPRIATE PROTECTIVE (IMPERVIOUS) CLOTHING AND EQUIPMENT TO PREVENT ANY POSSIBILITY OF SKIN CONTACT WITH THIS SUBSTANCE.

GLOVES: EMPLOYEE MUST WEAR APPROPRIATE PROTECTIVE GLOVES TO PREVENT CONTACT WITH THIS SUBSTANCE.

EYE PROTECTION: EMPLOYEE MUST WEAR SPLASH-PROOF OR DUST-RESISTANT SAFETY GOGGLES AND A FACESHIELD TO PREVENT CONTACT WITH THIS SUBSTANCE.

EMERGENCY WASH FACILITIES: WHERE THERE IS ANY POSSIBILITY THAT AN EMPLOYEE'S EYES AND/OR SKIN MAY BE EXPOSED TO THIS SUBSTANCE, THE EMPLOYER SHOULD PROVIDE AN EYE WASH FOUNTAIN AND QUICK DRENCH SHOWER WITHIN THE IMMEDIATE WORK AREA FOR EMERGENCY USE.

AUTHORIZED BY- OCCUPATIONAL HEALTH SERVICES, INC.

CREATION DATE: 05/18/90 ***REVISION DATE:*** 05/18/90

MATERIAL SAFETY DATA SHEET

OCCUPATIONAL HEALTH SERVICES, INC.
AGRICULTURE AND PESTICIDE DIVISION
450 SEVENTH AVENUE, SUITE 2407
NEW YORK, NEW YORK 10123
1-800-445-MSDS OR (212) 967-1100

EMERGENCY CONTACT:
JOHN S. BRANSFORD, JR. (615) 292-1180

SUBSTANCE IDENTIFICATION

CAS-NUMBER 1918-02-1

SUBSTANCE: PICLORAM

TRADE NAMES/SYNONYMS: 4-AMINO-3,5,6-TRICHLORO-2-PYRIDINECARBOXYLIC ACID; 4-AMINO-3,5,6-TRICHLOROPICOLINIC ACID; 4-AMINOTRICHLOROPICOLINIC ACID; 4-AMINO-3,5,6-TRICHLORO-2-PICOLINIC ACID; 3,5,6-TRICHLORO-4-AMINOPICOLINIC ACID; 4-AMINO-3,5,6-TRICHLOROPYRIDINE-2-CARBOXYLIC ACID; 2-PYRIDINECARBOXYLIC ACID, 4-AMINO-2,5,6-TRICHLORO-; PICOLINIC ACID, 4-AMINO-3,5,6-TRICHLORO-; ATCP; TORDON; GRAZON; NCI-C00237; AMDON; C6H3CL3N2O2; PST18840

CHEMICAL FAMILY: PYRIDINE
HALOGEN

MOLECULAR FORMULA: C6-H3-CL3-N2-O2

MOLECULAR WEIGHT: 241.46

CERCLA RATINGS (SCALE 0-3): HEALTH=2 FIRE=0 REACTIVITY=0 PERSISTENCE=3

NFPA RATINGS (SCALE 0-4): HEALTH=2 FIRE=0 REACTIVITY=0

COMPONENTS AND CONTAMINANTS

COMPONENT: PICLORAM ***PERCENT:*** 100
CAS# 1918-02-1

OTHER CONTAMINANTS: MAY CONTAIN 200 PPM HEXACHLOROBENZENE

EXPOSURE LIMITS: PICLORAM: 5 MG/M3 OSHA TWA (RESPIRABLE FRACTION); 10 MG/M3 OSHA TWA (TOTAL DUST) 10 MG/M3 ACGIH TWA; 20 MG/M3 ACGIH STEL (NOTICE OF INTENDED CHANGES 1988-89)

PHYSICAL DATA

DESCRIPTION: WHITE POWDER WITH A CHLORINE-LIKE ODOR ***BOILING POINT:*** DECOMPOSES

MELTING POINT: 424-426 F (218-219 C) DECOMPOSES ***SPECIFIC GRAVITY:*** NOT AVAILABLE

VAPOR PRESSURE: NEGLIGIBLE ***EVAPORATION RATE:*** NOT AVAILABLE

SOLUBILITY IN WATER: 430 PPM

SOLVENT SOLUBILITY: ACETONE, 2-PROPANOL, DICHLOROMETHANE, DIMETHYL SULFOXIDE, ALCOHOL, ETHER, KEROSENE, AND MOST ORGANIC SOLVENTS

FIRE AND EXPLOSION DATA

FIRE AND EXPLOSION HAZARD: NEGLIGIBLE FIRE HAZARD WHEN EXPOSED TO HEAT OR FLAME.

FIREFIGHTING MEDIA: DRY CHEMICAL, CARBON DIOXIDE, HALON, WATER SPRAY OR STANDARD FOAM (1987 EMERGENCY RESPONSE GUIDEBOOK, DOT P 5800.4). FOR LARGER FIRES, USE WATER SPRAY, FOG OR STANDARD FOAM (1987 EMERGENCY RESPONSE GUIDEBOOK, DOT P 5800.4).

FIREFIGHTING: MOVE CONTAINER FROM FIRE AREA IF POSSIBLE. DO NOT SCATTER SPILLED MATERIAL WITH HIGH PRESSURE WATER STREAMS. DIKE FIRE CONTROL WATER FOR LATER DISPOSAL (1987 EMERGENCY RESPONSE GUIDEBOOK, DOT P 5800.4, GUIDE PAGE 31).

USE AGENTS SUITABLE FOR TYPE OF SURROUNDING FIRE. AVOID BREATHING HAZARDOUS VAPORS, KEEP UPWIND.

TOXICITY

PICLORAM: TOXICITY DATA: 2898 MG/KG ORAL-RAT LD50; 1061 MG/KG ORAL-MOUSE LD50; 2000 MG/KG ORAL-RABBIT LD50; 1922 MG/KG ORAL-GUINEA PIG LD50; MUTAGENIC DATA (RTECS); REPRODUCTIVE EFFECTS DATA (RTECS); TUMORIGENIC DATA (RTECS). CARCINOGEN STATUS: NONE. ACUTE EFFECTS: MODERATELY TOXIC BY INGESTION. TARGET EFFECTS: NO DATA AVAILABLE.

HEALTH EFFECTS AND FIRST AID

INHALATION: PICLORAM: **ACUTE EXPOSURE-** MAY CAUSE IRRITATION. **CHRONIC EXPOSURE-** PROLONGED OR REPEATED EXPOSURE MAY CAUSE IRRITATION.

FIRST AID- REMOVE FROM EXPOSURE AREA TO FRESH AIR IMMEDIATELY. IF BREATHING HAS STOPPED, PERFORM ARTIFICIAL RESPIRATION. KEEP PERSON WARM AND AT REST. TREAT SYMPTOMATICALLY AND SUPPORTIVELY. GET MEDICAL ATTENTION IMMEDIATELY.

SKIN CONTACT: PICLORAM: **ACUTE EXPOSURE-** MAY CAUSE IRRITATION. A LETHAL DOSE IN RABBITS BY DERMAL ABSORPTION WAS GREATER THAN 4000 MG/KG. **CHRONIC EXPOSURE-** PROLONGED OR REPEATED EXPOSURE MAY CAUSE DERMATITIS.

FIRST AID- REMOVE CONTAMINATED CLOTHING AND SHOES IMMEDIATELY. WASH AFFECTED AREA WITH SOAP OR MILD DETERGENT AND LARGE AMOUNTS OF WATER UNTIL NO EVIDENCE OF CHEMICAL REMAINS (APPROXIMATELY 15-20 MINUTES). GET MEDICAL ATTENTION IMMEDIATELY.

EYE CONTACT: PICLORAM: **ACUTE EXPOSURE-** MAY CAUSE IRRITATION. **CHRONIC EXPOSURE-** PROLONGED OR REPEATED EXPOSURE MAY CAUSE CONJUNCTIVITIS.

FIRST AID- WASH EYES IMMEDIATELY WITH LARGE AMOUNTS OF WATER OR NORMAL SALINE, OCCASIONALLY LIFTING UPPER AND LOWER LIDS, UNTIL NO EVIDENCE OF CHEMICAL REMAINS (APPROXIMATELY 15-20 MINUTES). GET MEDICAL ATTENTION IMMEDIATELY.

INGESTION: PICLORAM: **ACUTE EXPOSURE-** A LETHAL DOSE IN RATS WAS 2898 MG/KG; SYMPTOMS WERE NOT REPORTED. **CHRONIC EXPOSURE-** AN INCREASED INCIDENCE OF DERMATITIS, ALOPECIA, TACHYPNEA, DIARRHEA AND VAGINAL BLEEDING WAS OBSERVED IN A PROLONGED STUDY OF MICE AND RATS. REPRODUCTIVE EFFECTS HAVE BEEN REPORTED IN ANIMALS. CHRONIC ADMINISTRATION OF PICLORAM TO MICE AND RATS PRODUCED FOLLICULAR HYPERPLASIA, C-CELL HYPERPLASIA, AND C-CELL ADENOMA OF THE THYROID. HOWEVER, THE STATISTICAL TESTS FOR ADENOMA DID NOT SHOW SUFFICIENT EVIDENCE FOR ASSOCIATION OF THE TUMOR WITH PICLORAM ADMINISTRATION. IN FEMALE RATS, TREATMENT WITH PICLORAM WAS ASSOCIATED WITH THE DEVELOPMENT OF BENIGN TUMORS OF THE LIVER.

FIRST AID- REMOVE BY GASTRIC LAVAGE AND CATHARSIS. MAINTAIN BLOOD PRESSURE AND AIRWAY. GIVE OXYGEN IF RESPIRATION IS DEPRESSED. DO NOT PERFORM GASTRIC LAVAGE IF VICTIM IS UNCONSCIOUS. GET MEDICAL ATTENTION IMMEDIATELY (DREISBACH, HANDBOOK OF POISONING, 12TH ED.). ADMINISTRATION OF LAVAGE OR OXYGEN SHOULD BE PERFORMED BY QUALIFIED MEDICAL PERSONNEL.

ANTIDOTE: NO SPECIFIC ANTIDOTE. TREAT SYMPTOMATICALLY AND SUPPORTIVELY.

REACTIVITY

REACTIVITY: STABLE UNDER NORMAL TEMPERATURES AND PRESSURES.

INCOMPATIBILITIES: PICLORAM: NO DATA AVAILABLE.
DECOMPOSITION: THERMAL DECOMPOSITION MAY RELEASE HIGHLY TOXIC AND HAZARDOUS FUMES OF CHLORINE AND OXIDES OF NITROGEN.
POLYMERIZATION: HAZARDOUS POLYMERIZATION HAS NOT BEEN REPORTED TO OCCUR UNDER NORMAL TEMPERATURES AND PRESSURES.

STORAGE AND DISPOSAL

OBSERVE ALL FEDERAL, STATE AND LOCAL REGULATIONS WHEN STORING OR DISPOSING OF THIS SUBSTANCE. FOR ASSISTANCE, CONTACT THE DISTRICT DIRECTOR OF THE ENVIRONMENTAL PROTECTION AGENCY.

STORAGE

STORE IN ACCORDANCE WITH 40 CFR 165 RECOMMENDED PROCEDURES FOR THE DISPOSAL AND STORAGE OF PESTICIDES AND PESTICIDE CONTAINERS.

DISPOSAL

DISPOSAL MUST BE IN ACCORDANCE WITH 40 CFR 165 RECOMMENDED PROCEDURES FOR THE DISPOSAL AND STORAGE OF PESTICIDES AND PESTICIDE CONTAINERS.

CONDITIONS TO AVOID

MAY BURN BUT DOES NOT IGNITE READILY. AVOID CONTACT WITH STRONG OXIDIZERS, EXCESSIVE HEAT, SPARKS, OR OPEN FLAME.

SPILL AND LEAK PROCEDURES

OCCUPATIONAL SPILL: SWEEP UP AND PLACE IN SUITABLE CLEAN, DRY CONTAINERS FOR RECLAMATION OR LATER DISPOSAL. DO NOT FLUSH SPILLED MATERIAL INTO SEWER. KEEP UNNECESSARY PEOPLE AWAY.

PROTECTIVE EQUIPMENT

VENTILATION: PROVIDE LOCAL EXHAUST VENTILATION AND/OR GENERAL DILUTION VENTILATION TO MEET PUBLISHED EXPOSURE LIMITS.
RESPIRATOR: THE FOLLOWING RESPIRATORS ARE RECOMMENDED BASED ON INFORMATION FOUND IN THE PHYSICAL DATA, TOXICITY AND HEALTH EFFECTS SECTIONS. THEY ARE RANKED IN ORDER FROM MINIMUM TO MAXIMUM RESPIRATORY PROTECTION. THE SPECIFIC RESPIRATOR SELECTED MUST BE BASED ON CONTAMINATION LEVELS FOUND IN THE WORK PLACE, MUST NOT EXCEED THE WORKING LIMITS OF THE RESPIRATOR AND BE JOINTLY APPROVED BY THE NATIONAL INSTITUTE FOR OCCUPATIONAL SAFETY AND HEALTH AND THE MINE SAFETY AND HEALTH ADMINISTRATION (NIOSH-MSHA).
CHEMICAL CARTRIDGE RESPIRATOR WITH FULL FACEPIECE AND PESTICIDE CARTRIDGE.
TYPE 'C' SUPPLIED-AIR RESPIRATOR WITH A FULL FACEPIECE OPERATED IN PRESSURE-DEMAND OR OTHER POSITIVE PRESSURE MODE OR WITH A FULL FACEPIECE, HELMET OR HOOD OPERATED IN CONTINUOUS-FLOW MODE.
SELF-CONTAINED BREATHING APPARATUS OPERATED IN PRESSURE-DEMAND OR OTHER POSITIVE PRESSURE MODE.
FOR FIREFIGHTING AND OTHER IMMEDIATELY DANGEROUS TO LIFE OR HEALTH CONDITIONS:
SELF-CONTAINED BREATHING APPARATUS WITH FULL FACEPIECE OPERATED IN PRESSURE-DEMAND OR OTHER POSITIVE PRESSURE MODE. SUPPLIED-AIR RESPIRATOR WITH FULL FACEPIECE AND OPERATED IN PRESSURE-DEMAND OR OTHER POSITIVE PRESSURE MODE IN COMBINATION WITH AN AUXILIARY SELF-CONTAINED BREATHING APPARATUS OPERATED IN PRESSURE-DEMAND OR OTHER POSITIVE PRESSURE MODE.
CLOTHING: EMPLOYEE MUST WEAR APPROPRIATE PROTECTIVE (IMPERVIOUS) CLOTHING AND EQUIPMENT TO PREVENT REPEATED OR PROLONGED SKIN CONTACT WITH THIS SUBSTANCE.
GLOVES: EMPLOYEE MUST WEAR APPROPRIATE PROTECTIVE GLOVES TO PREVENT CONTACT WITH THIS SUBSTANCE.
EYE PROTECTION: EMPLOYEE MUST WEAR SPLASH-PROOF OR DUST-RESISTANT SAFETY GOGGLES TO PREVENT EYE CONTACT WITH THIS SUBSTANCE.
EMERGENCY EYE WASH: WHERE THERE IS ANY POSSIBILITY THAT AN EMPLOYEE'S EYES MAY BE EXPOSED TO THIS SUBSTANCE, THE EMPLOYER SHOULD PROVIDE AN EYE WASH FOUNTAIN WITHIN THE IMMEDIATE WORK AREA FOR EMERGENCY USE.

AUTHORIZED BY- OCCUPATIONAL HEALTH SERVICES, INC.
CREATION DATE: 10/04/89 ***REVISION DATE:*** 05/31/90

MATERIAL SAFETY DATA SHEET

OCCUPATIONAL HEALTH SERVICES, INC. EMERGENCY CONTACT:
AGRICULTURE AND PESTICIDE DIVISION JOHN S. BRANSFORD, JR. (615) 292-1180
450 SEVENTH AVENUE, SUITE 2407
NEW YORK, NEW YORK 10123
1-800-445-MSDS OR (212) 967-1100

SUBSTANCE IDENTIFICATION

CAS-NUMBER 8002-09-3
SUBSTANCE: PINE OIL
TRADE NAMES/SYNONYMS: OIL OF PINE; OILS, PINE; YARMOR; HERCO AND YARMOR 80 PINE OIL (HERCULES, INC.); PINE NEEDLE OIL; STCC 4915170; UN 1272; PST18900
CHEMICAL FAMILY: ESSENTIAL OIL
CERCLA RATINGS (SCALE 0-3): HEALTH=2 FIRE=2 REACTIVITY=0 PERSISTENCE=3
NFPA RATINGS (SCALE 0-4): HEALTH=0 FIRE=2 REACTIVITY=0

COMPONENTS AND CONTAMINANTS

COMPONENT: PINE OIL ***PERCENT:*** 100.0
CAS# 8002-09-3
OTHER CONTAMINANTS: NONE
EXPOSURE LIMITS: NO OCCUPATIONAL EXPOSURE LIMITS ESTABLISHED BY OSHA, ACGIH, OR NIOSH.

PHYSICAL DATA

DESCRIPTION: COLORLESS TO PALE YELLOW LIQUID WITH A PENETRATING PINE ODOR.
BOILING POINT: 392-428 F (200-220 C) ***MELTING POINT:*** <50 F (<10 C)
SPECIFIC GRAVITY: 0.85-0.95 ***VAPOR PRESSURE:*** 1 MMHG @ 20 C
EVAPORATION RATE: (BUTYL ACETATE=1) <1 ***SOLUBILITY IN WATER:*** INSOLUBLE
VAPOR DENSITY: 5.3
SOLVENT SOLUBILITY: SOLUBLE IN MOST ORGANIC SOLVENTS.

FIRE AND EXPLOSION DATA

FIRE AND EXPLOSION HAZARD: MODERATE FIRE HAZARD WHEN EXPOSED TO HEAT OR FLAME.
VAPORS ARE HEAVIER THAN AIR AND MAY TRAVEL A CONSIDERABLE DISTANCE TO A SOURCE OF IGNITION AND FLASH BACK. VAPOR-AIR MIXTURES ARE EXPLOSIVE ABOVE FLASH POINT.
FLASH POINT: 138-172 F (59-78 C) (CC) ***FLAMMABILITY CLASS(OSHA):*** II
FIREFIGHTING MEDIA: DRY CHEMICAL, CARBON DIOXIDE, HALON, WATER SPRAY OR ALCOHOL FOAM (1987 EMERGENCY RESPONSE GUIDEBOOK, DOT P 5800.4).
FOR LARGER FIRES, USE WATER SPRAY, FOG OR ALCOHOL FOAM (1987 EMERGENCY RESPONSE GUIDEBOOK, DOT P 5800.4).
FIREFIGHTING: MOVE CONTAINER FROM FIRE AREA IF POSSIBLE. COOL FIRE-EXPOSED CONTAINERS WITH WATER FROM SIDE UNTIL WELL AFTER FIRE IS OUT. STAY AWAY FROM STORAGE TANK ENDS. FOR MASSIVE FIRE IN STORAGE AREA, USE UNMANNED HOSE HOLDER OR MONITOR NOZZLES, ELSE WITHDRAW FROM AREA AND LET FIRE BURN. WITHDRAW IMMEDIATELY IN CASE OF RISING SOUND FROM VENTING SAFETY DEVICE OR ANY DISCOLORATION OF STORAGE TANK DUE TO FIRE (1987 EMERGENCY RESPONSE GUIDEBOOK, DOT P 5800.4, GUIDE PAGE 26). EXTINGUISH ONLY IF FLOW CAN BE STOPPED. USE WATER IN FLOODING QUANTITIES AS FOG, SOLID STREAMS MAY SPREAD FIRE. COOL CONTAINERS WITH FLOODING AMOUNTS OF WATER, APPLY FROM AS FAR A DISTANCE AS POSSIBLE. AVOID BREATHING TOXIC VAPORS, KEEP UPWIND.

TRANSPORTATION DATA

DEPARTMENT OF TRANSPORTATION HAZARD CLASSIFICATION 49 CFR 172.101: COMBUSTIBLE LIQUID
DEPARTMENT OF TRANSPORTATION LABELING REQUIREMENTS 49 CFR 172.101 AND SUBPART E: NONE
DEPARTMENT OF TRANSPORTATION PACKAGING REQUIREMENTS: NONE
EXCEPTIONS: 49 CFR 173.118A

TOXICITY

PINE OIL: IRRITATION DATA: 500 MG/24 HOURS SKIN-RABBIT SEVERE. TOXICITY DATA: 5 GM/KG SKIN-RABBIT LD50; 4700 MG/KG ORAL-MAN TDLO; 3200 MG/KG ORAL-RAT LD50. CARCINOGEN STATUS: NONE. LOCAL EFFECTS: IRRITANT-INHALATION, SKIN, EYE. ACUTE TOXICITY LEVEL: MODERATELY TOXIC BY INGESTION; SLIGHTLY TOXIC BY DERMAL ABSORPTION. TARGET EFFECTS: CENTRAL NERVOUS SYSTEM DEPRESSANT.

HEALTH EFFECTS AND FIRST AID

INHALATION: PINE OIL: IRRITANT. INHALATION OF MIST MAY RESULT IN IRRITATION OF THE MUCOUS MEMBRANES. A CASE OF ASTHMA WITH UNPRODUCTIVE COUGH, WHEEZE, PROGRESSIVE DYSPNEA, AND POSITIVE ALLERGIC TEST RESPONSE TO PINE OIL HAS BEEN REPORTED. SEE INFORMATION ON VOLATILE OILS.

VOLATILE/ESSENTIAL OILS: **ACUTE EXPOSURE-** INHALATION OF VOLATILE OILS MAY CAUSE DIZZINESS, RAPID, SHALLOW BREATHING, TACHYCARDIA, BRONCHIAL IRRITATION AND UNCONSCIOUSNESS OR CONVULSIONS. COMPLICATIONS MAY INCLUDE ANURIA, PULMONARY EDEMA, AND BRONCHIAL PNEUMONIA. **CHRONIC EXPOSURE-** NO DATA AVAILABLE.

FIRST AID- REMOVE FROM EXPOSURE AREA TO FRESH AIR IMMEDIATELY. IF BREATHING HAS STOPPED, PERFORM ARTIFICIAL RESPIRATION. KEEP PERSON WARM AND AT REST. TREAT SYMPTOMATICALLY AND SUPPORTIVELY. GET MEDICAL ATTENTION IMMEDIATELY.

SKIN CONTACT: PINE OIL: IRRITANT. **ACUTE EXPOSURE-** APPLICATION OF 500 MG TO RABBIT SKIN FOR 24 HOURS CAUSED SEVERE IRRITATION. **CHRONIC EXPOSURE-** REPEATED OR PROLONGED CONTACT WITH IRRITANTS MAY CAUSE DERMATITIS. A CASE OF ALLERGIC CONTACT DERMATITIS HAS BEEN REPORTED.

FIRST AID- REMOVE CONTAMINATED CLOTHING AND SHOES IMMEDIATELY. WASH AFFECTED AREA WITH SOAP OR MILD DETERGENT AND LARGE AMOUNTS OF WATER UNTIL NO EVIDENCE OF CHEMICAL REMAINS (APPROXIMATELY 15-20 MINUTES). GET MEDICAL ATTENTION IMMEDIATELY.

EYE CONTACT: PINE OIL: IRRITANT. **ACUTE EXPOSURE-** CONTACT MAY CAUSE MARKED IRRITATION. **CHRONIC EXPOSURE-** REPEATED OR PROLONGED CONTACT WITH IRRITANTS MAY CAUSE CONJUNCTIVITIS.

FIRST AID- WASH EYES IMMEDIATELY WITH LARGE AMOUNTS OF WATER OR NORMAL SALINE, OCCASIONALLY LIFTING UPPER AND LOWER LIDS, UNTIL NO EVIDENCE OF CHEMICAL REMAINS (APPROXIMATELY 15-20 MINUTES). GET MEDICAL ATTENTION IMMEDIATELY.

INGESTION: PINE OIL: NARCOTIC. **ACUTE EXPOSURE-** A 49 YEAR OLD MALE INGESTED 400 TO 500 MILLILITERS OF PINE OIL. SYMPTOMS INCLUDED ERYTHEMA OF THE MOUTH AND LARYNX, FLUSHED FACE, ATAXIA, HYPERVENTILATION, AND DELAYED SOMNOLENCE WITH RETROGRADE AMNESIA. RECOVERY WAS COMPLETE IN 3 DAYS. ADDITIONAL EFFECTS FROM PINE OIL INGESTION MAY INCLUDE HEADACHE, DELIRIUM, HEMORRHAGIC GASTRITIS, SUBSTERNAL CHEST PAIN, NAUSEA, VOMITING, DIARRHEA, WEAKNESS, AGITATION, CENTRAL NERVOUS SYSTEM DEPRESSION WITH HYPOTHERMIA, COMA, AND RESPIRATORY FAILURE. RENAL FAILURE IS POSSIBLE, HOWEVER, DEATH IS RARE. CHEMICAL PNEUMONITIS FROM GASTROINTESTINAL ABSORPTION AND DEPOSITION IN LUNG TISSUE, OR ASPIRATION PNEUMONITIS MAY ALSO OCCUR. **CHRONIC EXPOSURE-** NO DATA AVAILABLE.

FIRST AID- GIVE 120-240 ML OF MILK; THEN REMOVE BY GASTRIC LAVAGE OR EMESIS, TAKING CARE TO PREVENT ASPIRATION. FOLLOW THESE PROCEDURES BY ADMINISTERING 30-60 ML OF FLEET'S PHOSPHO-SODA DILUTED 1:4 IN WATER. PERFORM ARTIFICIAL RESPIRATION IF NECESSARY. GET MEDICAL ATTENTION (DREISBACH, HANDBOOK OF POISONING, 12TH ED.). FIRST AID SHOULD BE PERFORMED BY QUALIFIED MEDICAL PERSONNEL.

ANTIDOTE: NO SPECIFIC ANTIDOTE. TREAT SYMPTOMATICALLY AND SUPPORTIVELY.

REACTIVITY

REACTIVITY: STABLE UNDER NORMAL TEMPERATURES AND PRESSURES.

INCOMPATIBILITIES: PINE OIL: ACIDS (STRONG): POSSIBLE EXOTHERMIC POLYMERIZATION. OXIDIZERS (STRONG): FIRE AND EXPLOSION HAZARD. SEE ALSO ALCOHOLS.

ALCOHOLS: ACETALDEHYDE: VIOLENT CONDENSATION REACTION. BARIUM PERCHLORATE: FORMATION OF HIGHLY EXPLOSIVE PERCHLORIC ESTER ON REFLUXING. CHLORINE: FORMATION OF HIGHLY EXPLOSIVE ALKYL HYPOCHLORITES. DIETHYL ALUMINUM BROMIDE: SPONTANEOUS IGNITION. ETHYLENE OXIDE: POSSIBLE EXPLOSION. HEXAMETHYLENE DIISOCYANATE: POSSIBLE EXPLOSION IN ABSENCE OF SOLVENT. HYDROGEN PEROXIDE + SULFURIC ACID: POSSIBLE EXPLOSION. HYPOCHLOROUS ACID: FORMATION OF HIGHLY EXPLOSIVE ALKYL HYPOCHLORITES. ISOCYANATES: POSSIBLE EXPLOSION IN ABSENCE OF SOLVENT. LITHIUM ALUMINUM HYDRIDE: VIGOROUS REACTION. NITROGEN TETROXIDE: POSSIBLE EXPLOSION. PERCHLORIC ACID (HOT): DANGEROUS INTERACTION. PERMONOSULFURIC ACID: POSSIBLE EXPLOSION ON CONTACT WITH PRIMARY OR SECONDARY ALCOHOLS. TRI-ISO-BUTYL ALUMINUM: VIOLENT REACTION.

DECOMPOSITION: THERMAL DECOMPOSITION PRODUCTS MAY INCLUDE TOXIC OXIDES OF CARBON.

POLYMERIZATION: HAZARDOUS POLYMERIZATION HAS NOT BEEN REPORTED TO OCCUR UNDER NORMAL TEMPERATURES AND PRESSURES.

STORAGE AND DISPOSAL

OBSERVE ALL FEDERAL, STATE AND LOCAL REGULATIONS WHEN STORING OR DISPOSING OF THIS SUBSTANCE. FOR ASSISTANCE, CONTACT THE DISTRICT DIRECTOR OF THE ENVIRONMENTAL PROTECTION AGENCY.

STORAGE

STORE IN ACCORDANCE WITH 29 CFR 1910.106.

BONDING AND GROUNDING: SUBSTANCES WITH LOW ELECTROCONDUCTIVITY, WHICH MAY BE IGNITED BY ELECTROSTATIC SPARKS, SHOULD BE STORED IN CONTAINERS WHICH MEET THE BONDING AND GROUNDING GUIDELINES SPECIFIED IN NFPA 77-1983, RECOMMENDED PRACTICE ON STATIC ELECTRICITY.

STORE AWAY FROM INCOMPATIBLE SUBSTANCES.

DISPOSAL

DISPOSAL MUST BE IN ACCORDANCE WITH STANDARDS APPLICABLE TO GENERATORS OF HAZARDOUS WASTE, 40 CFR 262. EPA HAZARDOUS WASTE NUMBER D001. 100 POUND CERCLA SECTION 103 REPORTABLE QUANTITY.

CONDITIONS TO AVOID

AVOID CONTACT WITH HEAT, SPARKS, FLAMES, OR OTHER SOURCES OF IGNITION. VAPORS MAY BE EXPLOSIVE AND POISONOUS; DO NOT ALLOW UNNECESSARY PERSONNEL IN AREA. DO NOT OVERHEAT CONTAINERS; CONTAINERS MAY VIOLENTLY RUPTURE AND TRAVEL A CONSIDERABLE DISTANCE IN HEAT OF FIRE.

SPILL AND LEAK PROCEDURES

OCCUPATIONAL SPILL: SHUT OFF IGNITION SOURCES. STOP LEAK IF YOU CAN DO IT WITHOUT RISK. USE WATER SPRAY TO REDUCE VAPORS. FOR SMALL SPILLS, TAKE UP WITH SAND OR OTHER ABSORBENT MATERIAL AND PLACE INTO CONTAINERS FOR LATER DISPOSAL. FOR LARGER SPILLS, DIKE FAR AHEAD OF SPILL FOR LATER DISPOSAL. NO SMOKING, FLAMES OR FLARES IN HAZARD AREA. KEEP UNNECESSARY PEOPLE AWAY; ISOLATE HAZARD AREA AND DENY ENTRY.

PROTECTIVE EQUIPMENT

VENTILATION: PROVIDE LOCAL EXHAUST VENTILATION SYSTEM.

RESPIRATOR: THE FOLLOWING RESPIRATORS ARE RECOMMENDED BASED ON INFORMATION FOUND IN THE PHYSICAL DATA, TOXICITY AND HEALTH EFFECTS SECTIONS. THEY ARE RANKED IN ORDER FROM MINIMUM TO MAXIMUM RESPIRATORY PROTECTION. THE SPECIFIC RESPIRATOR SELECTED MUST BE BASED ON CONTAMINATION LEVELS FOUND IN THE WORK PLACE, MUST NOT EXCEED THE WORKING LIMITS OF THE RESPIRATOR AND BE JOINTLY APPROVED BY THE NATIONAL INSTITUTE FOR OCCUPATIONAL SAFETY AND HEALTH AND THE MINE SAFETY AND HEALTH ADMINISTRATION (NIOSH-MSHA).

TYPE 'C' SUPPLIED-AIR RESPIRATOR WITH A FULL FACEPIECE OPERATED IN PRESSURE-DEMAND OR OTHER POSITIVE PRESSURE MODE OR WITH A FULL FACEPIECE, HELMET OR HOOD OPERATED IN CONTINOUS-FLOW MODE.

SELF-CONTAINED BREATHING APPARATUS WITH A FULL FACEPIECE OPERATED IN PRESSURE-DEMAND OR OTHER POSITIVE PRESSURE MODE.

FOR FIREFIGHTING AND OTHER IMMEDIATELY DANGEROUS TO LIFE OR HEALTH CONDITIONS:

SELF-CONTAINED BREATHING APPARATUS WITH FULL FACEPIECE OPERATED IN PRESSURE-DEMAND OR OTHER POSITIVE PRESSURE MODE.

SUPPLIED-AIR RESPIRATOR WITH FULL FACEPIECE AND OPERATED IN PRESSURE-DEMAND OR OTHER POSITIVE PRESSURE MODE IN COMBINATION WITH AN AUXILIARY SELF-CONTAINED BREATHING APPARATUS OPERATED IN PRESSURE-DEMAND OR OTHER POSITIVE PRESSURE MODE.

CLOTHING: EMPLOYEE MUST WEAR APPROPRIATE PROTECTIVE (IMPERVIOUS) CLOTHING AND EQUIPMENT TO PREVENT REPEATED OR PROLONGED SKIN CONTACT WITH THIS SUBSTANCE.

GLOVES: EMPLOYEE MUST WEAR APPROPRIATE PROTECTIVE GLOVES TO PREVENT CONTACT WITH THIS SUBSTANCE.

EYE PROTECTION: EMPLOYEE MUST WEAR SPLASH-PROOF OR DUST-RESISTANT SAFETY GOGGLES TO PREVENT EYE CONTACT WITH THIS SUBSTANCE.

EMERGENCY EYE WASH: WHERE THERE IS ANY POSSIBILITY THAT AN EMPLOYEE'S EYES MAY BE EXPOSED TO THIS SUBSTANCE, THE EMPLOYER SHOULD PROVIDE AN EYE WASH FOUNTAIN WITHIN THE IMMEDIATE WORK AREA FOR EMERGENCY USE.

AUTHORIZED BY- OCCUPATIONAL HEALTH SERVICES, INC.

CREATION DATE: 10/04/89 ***REVISION DATE:*** 04/05/90

MATERIAL SAFETY DATA SHEET

OCCUPATIONAL HEALTH SERVICES, INC.
AGRICULTURE AND PESTICIDE DIVISION
450 SEVENTH AVENUE, SUITE 2407
NEW YORK, NEW YORK 10123
1-800-445-MSDS OR (212) 967-1100

EMERGENCY CONTACT:
JOHN S. BRANSFORD, JR. (615) 292-1180

SUBSTANCE IDENTIFICATION

CAS-NUMBER 83-26-1

***SUBSTANCE:* PIVAL**

TRADE NAMES/SYNONYMS: 1H-INDENE-1,3(2H)-DIONE, 2-(2,2-DIMETHYL-1-OXOPROPYL)-; 2-(2,2-DIMETHYL-1-OXOPROPYL)-1H-INDENE-1,3(2H)-DIONE; 1,3-INDANDIONE, 2-PIVALOYL-; 2-PIVALOYL-1,3-INDANDIONE; 2-PIVALOYLINDAN-1,3-DIONE; 2-PIVALYL-1,3-INDANDIONE; 2-TRIMETHYLACETYL-1,3-INDANDIONE; PIVALYLINDAN-1,3-DIONE; PINDONE; PIVALYN; PIVALYL; PIVALYLINDANDIONE; PIVALYL VALONE; PIVALDIONE; TRIBAN; UN 2472; C14H14O3; PST18970

CHEMICAL FAMILY: INDANDIONE

MOLECULAR FORMULA: C6-H4-C3-O2-C-O-C(C-H3)3

MOLECULAR WEIGHT: 230.25

CERCLA RATINGS (SCALE 0-3): HEALTH = 3 FIRE = 1 REACTIVITY = 0 PERSISTENCE = 3

NFPA RATINGS (SCALE 0-4): HEALTH = U FIRE = 1 REACTIVITY = 0

COMPONENTS AND CONTAMINANTS

COMPONENT: PIVAL ***PERCENT:*** 100

CAS# 83-26-1

OTHER CONTAMINANTS: NONE

EXPOSURE LIMITS: PIVAL: 0.1 MG/M3 OSHA TWA 0.1 MG/M3 ACGIH TWA

PHYSICAL DATA

DESCRIPTION: BRIGHT YELLOW CRYSTALS OR POWDER

MELTING POINT: 228-232 F (109-111 C) ***SPECIFIC GRAVITY:*** 1.06

SOLUBILITY IN WATER: 18 PPM

SOLVENT SOLUBILITY: SOLUBLE IN ALCOHOL, ETHER, ACETONE, AQUEOUS ALKALI, AMMONIA, MOST ORGANIC SOLVENTS.

FIRE AND EXPLOSION DATA

FIRE AND EXPLOSION HAZARD: SLIGHT FIRE HAZARD WHEN EXPOSED TO HEAT OR FLAME.

FIREFIGHTING MEDIA: DRY CHEMICAL, CARBON DIOXIDE, HALON, WATER SPRAY OR STANDARD FOAM (1987 EMERGENCY RESPONSE GUIDEBOOK, DOT P 5800.4). FOR LARGER FIRES, USE WATER SPRAY, FOG OR STANDARD FOAM (1987 EMERGENCY RESPONSE GUIDEBOOK, DOT P 5800.4).

FIREFIGHTING: MOVE CONTAINERS FROM FIRE AREA IF POSSIBLE (1987 EMERGENCY RESPONSE GUIDEBOOK, DOT P 5800.4, GUIDE PAGE 53).
EXTINGUISH ONLY IF FLOW CAN BE STOPPED. EXTINGUISH USING AGENT INDICATED. USE FLOODING AMOUNTS OF WATER AS A FOG. COOL CONTAINERS WITH FLOODING AMOUNTS OF WATER FROM AS FAR A DISTANCE AS POSSIBLE. AVOID BREATHING POISONOUS VAPORS, KEEP UPWIND. CONSIDER EVACUATION OF DOWNWIND AREA IF MATERIAL IS LEAKING.

TOXICITY

PIVAL: TOXICITY DATA: 280 MG/KG ORAL-RAT LD50; 150 MG/KG ORAL-RABBIT LD50; 75 MG/KG ORAL-DOG LD50; 75 MG/KG ORAL-DOMESTIC ANIMAL LDLO; 50 MG/KG PARENTERAL-RAT LD50; 50 MG/KG INTRAVENOUS-RAT LD50. CARCINOGEN STAGUS: NONE. ACUTE TOXICITY LEVEL: TOXIC BY INGESTION. TARGET EFFECTS: HEMORRHAGIC AGENT. AT INCREASED RISK FROM EXPOSURE: PERSONS WITH BLOOD DYSCRASIAS, BLEEDING TENDENCIES, LIVER OR KIDNEY DISEASE, ULCERS OF THE GASTROINTESTINAL TRACT, OR HYPERTENSION.*

* MAY BE BASED ON GENERAL INFORMATION ON INDANDIONE DERIVATIVES.

HEALTH EFFECTS AND FIRST AID

INHALATION: PIVAL: 200 MG/M3 IMMEDIATELY DANGEROUS TO LIFE OR HEALTH. SEE INFORMATION ON INDANDIONE DERIVATIVES.
INDANDIONE DERIVATIVES: HEMORRHAGIC AGENT. **ACUTE EXPOSURE-** ABSORPTION BY THE LUNGS MAY RESULT IN HEMORRHAGIC EFFECTS AS DESCRIBED IN CHRONIC EXPOSURE. SEVERE CASES MAY BE FATAL. **CHRONIC EXPOSURE-** REPEATED ABSORPTION MAY CAUSE THE INHIBITION OF PROTHROMBIN SYNTHESIS AND DAMAGE TO CAPILLARY PERMEABILITY RESULTING IN WIDESPREAD INTERNAL HEMORRHAGE WITH ASSOCIATED EFFECTS OF NOSEBLEED, HEMATOMA, HEMATURIA, WIDESPREAD BRUISING, AND ANEMIA.

FIRST AID- REMOVE FROM EXPOSURE AREA TO FRESH AIR IMMEDIATELY. IF BREATHING HAS STOPPED, PERFORM ARTIFICIAL RESPIRATION. KEEP PERSON WARM AND AT REST. TREAT SYMPTOMATICALLY AND SUPPORTIVELY. GET MEDICAL ATTENTION IMMEDIATELY.

SKIN CONTACT: PIVAL: SEE INFORMATION ON INDANDIONE DERIVATIVES.
INDANDIONE DERIVATIVES: HEMORRHAGIC AGENT. **ACUTE EXPOSURE-** ABSORPTION THROUGH THE SKIN MAY RESULT IN HEMORRHAGIC EFFECTS AS DESCRIBED IN CHRONIC EXPOSURE. SEVERE CASES MAY BE FATAL. **CHRONIC EXPOSURE-** REPEATED ABSORPTION MAY CAUSE THE INHIBITION OF PROTHROMBIN SYNTHESIS AND DAMAGE TO CAPILLARY PERMEABILITY RESULTING IN WIDESPREAD INTERNAL HEMORRHAGE WITH ASSOCIATED EFFECTS OF NOSEBLEED, HEMATOMA, HEMATURIA, WIDESPREAD BRUISING, AND ANEMIA.

FIRST AID- REMOVE CONTAMINATED CLOTHING AND SHOES IMMEDIATELY. WASH AFFECTED AREA WITH SOAP OR MILD DETERGENT AND LARGE AMOUNTS OF WATER UNTIL NO EVIDENCE OF CHEMICAL REMAINS (APPROXIMATELY 15-20 MINUTES). GET MEDICAL ATTENTION IMMEDIATELY.

EYE CONTACT: PIVAL: **ACUTE EXPOSURE-** NO DATA AVAILABLE. **CHRONIC EXPOSURE-** NO DATA AVAILABLE.

FIRST AID- WASH EYES IMMEDIATELY WITH LARGE AMOUNTS OF WATER OR NORMAL SALINE, OCCASIONALLY LIFTING UPPER AND LOWER LIDS, UNTIL NO EVIDENCE OF CHEMICAL REMAINS (APPROXIMATELY 15-20 MINUTES). GET MEDICAL ATTENTION IMMEDIATELY.

INGESTION: PIVAL: TOXIC. SEE INFORMATION ON INDANDIONE DERIVATIVES.
INDANDIONE DERIVATIVES: HEMORRHAGIC AGENT. **ACUTE EXPOSURE-** LETHAL DOSES IN ANIMALS HAVE PRODUCED LABORED BREATHING, PROGRESSIVE MUSCULAR WEAKNESS, HYPEREXCITABILITY, PULMONARY CONGESTION, VENOUS ENGORGEMENT, AND CARDIAC STANDSTILL. **CHRONIC EXPOSURE-** MAY BE READILY ABSORBED FROM THE GASTROINTESTINAL TRACT AND CAUSE THE INHIBITION OF PROTHROMBIN SYNTHESIS AND DAMAGE TO CAPILLARY PERMEABILITY. HEMORRHAGIC EFFECTS FROM SYSTEMIC ABSORPTION MAY INCLUDE NOSEBLEED, BLEEDING GUMS AND PHARYNX, PETECHIAL RASH, WIDESPREAD BRUISING, HEMATOMA, HEMOPTYSIS, HEMATEMESIS, HEMATURIA, BLOODY STOOLS, BLEEDING INTO THE ORGANS, GASTROINTESTINAL TRACT, JOINTS, ABDOMINAL OR RETROPERITONEAL AREA WITH ABDOMINAL, BACK, JOINT AND LIMB PAIN AND CEREBROVASCULAR ACCIDENT. ANEMIA ACCOMPANIED BY WEAKNESS, PALLOR, AND SHOCK MAY OCCUR. SEVERE HEMORRHAGING MAY CAUSE DEATH. THERAPEUTIC USE OF SOME INDANDIONE DERIVATIVES HAS PRODUCED SIDE EFFECTS OF AGRANULOCYTOSIS, THROMBOCYTOPENIA, PYREXIA, DIARRHEA, STEATORRHEA, HEPATITIS, RENAL TUBULAR NECROSIS, EXFOLIATIVE DERMATITIS AND PARALYSIS OF ACCOMMODATION.

FIRST AID- IF ONLY A FEW GRAINS OF ANTICOAGULANT BAIT HAVE BEEN INGESTED BY AN ADULT OR CHILD HAVING NO ANTECEDENT LIVER OR BLOOD CLOTTING DISEASE, TREATMENT IS PROBABLY UNNECESSARY. IF LARGE AMOUNTS OF ANTICOAGULANT WERE INGESTED IN THE PRECEDING 2-3 HOURS, INDUCE VOMITING WITH SYRUP OF IPECAC, FOLLOWED BY 1-2 GLASSES OF WATER. FOLLOWING EMESIS, GIVE ACTIVATED CHARCOAL IN 4-6 OUNCES OF WATER TO LIMIT ABSORPTION OF ANTICOAGULANT REMAINING IN THE GUT. OBSERVE PATIENT 4-5 DAYS AFTER INGESTION. (MORGAN, RECOGNITION AND MANAGEMENT OF PESTICIDE POISONINGS, THIRD EDITION). GET MEDICAL ATTENTION.

ANTIDOTE: THE FOLLOWING ANTIDOTE HAS BEEN RECOMMENDED. HOWEVER, THE DECISION AS TO WHETHER THE SEVERITY OF POISONING REQUIRES ADMINISTRATION OF ANY ANTIDOTE AND ACTUAL DOSE REQUIRED SHOULD BE MADE BY QUALIFIED MEDICAL PERSONNEL.
OVERDOSE OF ANTICOAGULANTS: VITAMIN K IS A SPECIFIC ANTIDOTE. VITAMIN K1 EMULSION IS THE PREFERRED FORM. THE INITIAL SUBCUTANEOUS OR INTRAMUSCULAR DOSE IN ADULTS IS 5 TO 10 MG (UP TO 25 MG), REPEATED ONCE IF NECESSARY. ONLY IN VICTIMS WHO ARE BLEEDING SEVERLY OR OTHERWISE IN SERIOUS DISTRESS SHOULD THE DRUG BE GIVEN INTRAVENOUSLY AND THEN AT A RATE NO FASTER THAN 1 MG/MINUTE. IF NECESSARY, ON SUBSEQUENT DAYS, VITAMIN K1 SHOULD BE CONTINUED AT A REDUCED LEVEL UNTIL THE PROTHROMBIN TIME RETURNS TO NORMAL. VITAMIN K1 IS PREFERABLE TO K1 OXIDE (DOSE 0.5-2.5) AND CERTAINLY PREFERABLE TO MENADIONE OR MENADIONE SODIUM BISULFITE (GOSSELIN, CLINICAL TOXICOLOGY OF COMMERCIAL PRODUCTS, 5TH ED.). ANTIDOTE SHOULD BE ADMINISTERED BY QUALIFIED MEDICAL PERSONNEL.

REACTIVITY

REACTIVITY: STABLE UNDER NORMAL TEMPERATURES AND PRESSURES.

INCOMPATIBILITIES: PIVAL: OXIDIZERS (STRONG): FIRE AND EXPLOSION HAZARD.

DECOMPOSITION: THERMAL DECOMPOSITION MAY YIELD ACRID SMOKE AND IRRITATING FUMES.

POLYMERIZATION: HAZARDOUS POLYMERIZATION HAS NOT BEEN REPORTED TO OCCUR UNDER NORMAL TEMPERATURES AND PRESSURES.

STORAGE AND DISPOSAL

OBSERVE ALL FEDERAL, STATE AND LOCAL REGULATIONS WHEN STORING OR DISPOSING OF THIS SUBSTANCE. FOR ASSISTANCE, CONTACT THE DISTRICT DIRECTOR OF THE ENVIRONMENTAL PROTECTION AGENCY.

STORAGE

STORE IN ACCORDANCE WITH 40 CFR 165 RECOMMENDED PROCEDURES FOR THE DISPOSAL AND STORAGE OF PESTICIDES AND PESTICIDE CONTAINERS.
STORE AWAY FROM INCOMPATIBLE SUBSTANCES.

DISPOSAL

DISPOSAL MUST BE IN ACCORDANCE WITH 40 CFR 165 RECOMMENDED

PROCEDURES FOR THE DISPOSAL AND STORAGE OF PESTICIDES AND PESTICIDE CONTAINERS.

CONDITIONS TO AVOID

MAY BURN BUT DOES NOT IGNITE READILY.

SPILL AND LEAK PROCEDURES

OCCUPATIONAL SPILL: DO NOT TOUCH SPILLED MATERIAL. STOP LEAK IF YOU CAN DO IT WITHOUT RISK. FOR SMALL SPILLS, TAKE UP WITH SAND OR OTHER ABSORBENT MATERIAL AND PLACE INTO CONTAINERS FOR LATER DISPOSAL. FOR SMALL DRY SPILLS, WITH A CLEAN SHOVEL PLACE MATERIAL INTO CLEAN, DRY CONTAINER AND COVER. MOVE CONTAINERS FROM SPILL AREA. FOR LARGER SPILLS, DIKE FAR AHEAD OF SPILL FOR LATER DISPOSAL. KEEP UNNECESSARY PEOPLE AWAY. ISOLATE HAZARD AREA AND DENY ENTRY.

PROTECTIVE EQUIPMENT

VENTILATION: PROVIDE LOCAL EXHAUST VENTILATION SYSTEM TO MEET PUBLISHED EXPOSURE LIMITS.

RESPIRATOR: THE FOLLOWING RESPIRATORS AND MAXIMUM USE CONCENTRATIONS ARE RECOMMENDATIONS BY THE U.S. DEPARTMENT OF HEALTH AND HUMAN SERVICES, NIOSH POCKET GUIDE TO CHEMICAL HAZARDS; NIOSH CRITERIA DOCUMENTS OR BY THE U.S. DEPARTMENT OF LABOR, 29 CFR 1910 SUBPART Z. THE SPECIFIC RESPIRATOR SELECTED MUST BE BASED ON CONTAMINATION LEVELS FOUND IN THE WORK PLACE, MUST NOT EXCEED THE WORKING LIMITS OF THE RESPIRATOR AND BE JOINTLY APPROVED BY THE NATIONAL INSTITUTE FOR OCCUPATIONAL SAFETY AND HEALTH AND THE MINE SAFETY AND HEALTH ADMINISTRATION (NIOSH-MSHA).

PIVAL: 0.5 MG/M3- ANY DUST AND MIST RESPIRATOR EXCEPT SINGLE-USE RESPIRATORS.

1 MG/M3- ANY DUST AND MIST RESPIRATOR EXCEPT SINGLE-USE AND QUARTER-MASK RESPIRATORS. ANY SUPPLIED-AIR RESPIRATOR. ANY SELF-CONTAINED BREATHING APPARATUS.

2.5 MG/M3- ANY POWERED AIR-PURIFYING RESPIRATOR WITH A DUST AND MIST FILTER. ANY SUPPLIED-AIR RESPIRATOR OPERATED IN A CONTINUOUS FLOW MODE.

5 MG/M3- ANY POWERED AIR-PURIFYING RESPIRATOR WITH A TIGHT-FITTING FACEPIECE AND A HIGH-EFFICIENCY PARTICULATE FILTER. ANY SELF-CONTAINED BREATHING APPARATUS WITH A FULL FACEPIECE. ANY SUPPLIED-AIR RESPIRATOR WITH A FULL FACEPIECE. ANY AIR-PURIFYING FULL FACEPIECE RESPIRATOR WITH A HIGH-EFFICIENCY PARTICULATE FILTER. ANY SUPPLIED-AIR RESPIRATOR WITH A TIGHT-FITTING FACEPIECE OPERATED IN A CONTINUOUS FLOW MODE.

100 MG/M3- ANY SUPPLIED-AIR RESPIRATOR WITH A HALF-MASK AND OPERATED IN A PRESSURE-DEMAND OR OTHER POSITIVE PRESSURE MODE.

200 MG/M3- ANY SUPPLIED-AIR RESPIRATOR WITH A FULL FACEPIECE AND OPERATED IN A PRESSURE-DEMAND OR OTHER POSITIVE PRESSURE MODE.

ESCAPE- ANY AIR-PURIFYING FULL FACEPIECE RESPIRATOR WITH A HIGH-EFFICIENCY PARTICULATE FILTER. ANY APPROPRIATE ESCAPE-TYPE SELF-CONTAINED BREATHING APPARATUS.

FOR FIREFIGHTING AND OTHER IMMEDIATELY DANGEROUS TO LIFE OR HEALTH CONDITIONS:

SELF-CONTAINED BREATHING APPARATUS WITH FULL FACEPIECE OPERATED IN PRESSURE-DEMAND OR OTHER POSITIVE PRESSURE MODE.

SUPPLIED-AIR RESPIRATOR WITH FULL FACEPIECE AND OPERATED IN PRESSURE-DEMAND OR OTHER POSITIVE PRESSURE MODE IN COMBINATION WITH AN AUXILIARY SELF-CONTAINED BREATHING APPARATUS OPERATED IN PRESSURE-DEMAND OR OTHER POSITIVE PRESSURE MODE.

CLOTHING: EMPLOYEE MUST WEAR APPROPRIATE PROTECTIVE (IMPERVIOUS) CLOTHING AND EQUIPMENT TO PREVENT ANY POSSIBILITY OF SKIN CONTACT WITH THIS SUBSTANCE.

GLOVES: EMPLOYEE MUST WEAR APPROPRIATE PROTECTIVE GLOVES TO PREVENT CONTACT WITH THIS SUBSTANCE.

EYE PROTECTION: EMPLOYEE MUST WEAR SPLASH-PROOF OR DUST-RESISTANT SAFETY GOGGLES WITH OR WITHOUT A FACESHIELD TO PREVENT CONTACT WITH THIS SUBSTANCE.

EMERGENCY EYE WASH: WHERE THERE IS ANY POSSIBILITY THAT AN EMPLOYEE'S EYES MAY BE EXPOSED TO THIS SUBSTANCE, THE EMPLOYER SHOULD PROVIDE AN EYE WASH FOUNTAIN WITHIN THE IMMEDIATE WORK AREA FOR EMERGENCY USE.

AUTHORIZED BY- OCCUPATIONAL HEALTH SERVICES, INC.

CREATION DATE: 10/04/89 ***REVISION DATE:*** 11/02/89

MATERIAL SAFETY DATA SHEET

OCCUPATIONAL HEALTH SERVICES, INC.
AGRICULTURE AND PESTICIDE DIVISION
450 SEVENTH AVENUE, SUITE 2407
NEW YORK, NEW YORK 10123
1-800-445-MSDS OR (212) 967-1100

EMERGENCY CONTACT:
JOHN S. BRANSFORD, JR. (615) 292-1180

SUBSTANCE IDENTIFICATION

CAS-NUMBER 9002-88-4

SUBSTANCE: POLYETHYLENE

TRADE NAMES/SYNONYMS: ETHENE, HOMOPOLYMER; ETHYLENE, POLYMERS; POLYETHENE; PST19119

CHEMICAL FAMILY: POLYMER HYDROCARBON, ALIPHATIC

MOLECULAR FORMULA: (C2-H4)X

MOLECULAR WEIGHT: (26.02)X

CERCLA RATINGS (SCALE 0-3): HEALTH=3 FIRE=1 REACTIVITY=0 PERSISTENCE=3

NFPA RATINGS (SCALE 0-4): HEALTH=U FIRE=1 REACTIVITY=0

COMPONENTS AND CONTAMINANTS

COMPONENT: POLYETHYLENE ***PERCENT:*** 100.0
CAS# 9002-88-4

OTHER CONTAMINANTS: NONE

EXPOSURE LIMITS: NO OCCUPATIONAL EXPOSURE LIMITS ESTABLISHED BY OSHA, ACGIH, OR NIOSH.

PHYSICAL DATA

DESCRIPTION: WHITE, PLASTIC SOLID WITH A MILKY TRANSPARENCY. DARKENS ON EXPOSURE TO LIGHT. ***MELTING POINT:*** 185-230 F (85-110 C)

SPECIFIC GRAVITY: 0.91-0.96 ***SOLUBILITY IN WATER:*** INSOLUBLE

SOLVENT SOLUBILITY: SOLUBLE IN TURPENTINE, PETROLEUM NAPHTHA, XYLENE, AND TOLUENE, HOT TRICHLOROETHYLENE, AND HOT MINERAL OILS; SLIGHTLY SOLUBLE IN METHYL ACETATE AND ACETONE.

FIRE AND EXPLOSION DATA

FIRE AND EXPLOSION HAZARD: SLIGHT FIRE HAZARD WHEN EXPOSED TO HEAT OR FLAME.

AUTOIGNITION TEMP.: 660 F (349 C)

FIREFIGHTING MEDIA: DRY CHEMICAL, CARBON DIOXIDE, HALON, WATER SPRAY OR STANDARD FOAM (1987 EMERGENCY RESPONSE GUIDEBOOK, DOT P 5800.4). FOR LARGER FIRES, USE WATER SPRAY, FOG OR STANDARD FOAM (1987 EMERGENCY RESPONSE GUIDEBOOK, DOT P 5800.4).

FIREFIGHTING: MOVE CONTAINER FROM FIRE AREA IF POSSIBLE. DO NOT SCATTER SPILLED MATERIAL WITH HIGH PRESSURE WATER STREAMS. DIKE FIRE CONTROL WATER FOR LATER DISPOSAL (1987 EMERGENCY RESPONSE GUIDEBOOK, DOT P 5800.4, GUIDE PAGE 31).

USE AGENTS SUITABLE FOR TYPE OF SURROUNDING FIRE. AVOID BREATHING HAZARDOUS VAPORS, KEEP UPWIND.

TOXICITY

POLYETHYLENE: TOXICITY DATA: TUMORIGENIC DATA (RTECS). CARCINOGEN STATUS: ANIMAL INADEQUATE EVIDENCE (IARC GROUP-3). ACUTE TOXICITY LEVEL: NO DATA AVAILABLE. TARGET EFFECTS: NO DATA AVAILABLE.

HEALTH EFFECTS AND FIRST AID

INHALATION: POLYETHYLENE: **ACUTE EXPOSURE-** NO EVIDENCE HAS BEEN FOUND TO SHOW THAT POLYETHYLENE PRODUCES TOXIC SYMPTOMS WHEN INHALED. **CHRONIC EXPOSURE-** NO DATA AVAILABLE.

FIRST AID- REMOVE FROM EXPOSURE AREA TO FRESH AIR IMMEDIATELY. IF BREATHING HAS STOPPED, PERFORM ARTIFICIAL RESPIRATION. KEEP PERSON WARM AND AT REST. TREAT SYMPTOMATICALLY AND SUPPORTIVELY. GET MEDICAL ATTENTION IMMEDIATELY.

SKIN CONTACT: POLYETHYLENE: **ACUTE EXPOSURE-** POLYETHYLENES ARE NEITHER IRRITANTS OR SENSITIZERS TO THE SKIN. DERMATITIS RESULTING FROM HEAT-SEALING OF POLYETHYLENE BAGS WAS ATTRIBUTED TO THERMAL DECOMPOSITION PRODUCTS, FORMALDEHYDE AND ACROLEIN. **CHRONIC EXPOSURE-** NO DATA AVAILABLE.

FIRST AID- REMOVE CONTAMINATED CLOTHING AND SHOES IMMEDIATELY. WASH AFFECTED AREA WITH SOAP OR MILD DETERGENT AND LARGE AMOUNTS OF WATER UNTIL NO EVIDENCE OF CHEMICAL REMAINS (APPROXIMATELY 15-20 MINUTES). GET MEDICAL ATTENTION IMMEDIATELY.

EYE PROTECTION: EYE PROTECTION NOT REQUIRED, BUT ADVISABLE.

AUTHORIZED BY- OCCUPATIONAL HEALTH SERVICES, INC.
CREATION DATE: 11/17/89 *REVISION DATE:* 07/10/90

MATERIAL SAFETY DATA SHEET

OCCUPATIONAL HEALTH SERVICES, INC.
AGRICULTURE AND PESTICIDE DIVISION
450 SEVENTH AVENUE, SUITE 2407
NEW YORK, NEW YORK 10123
1-800-445-MSDS OR (212) 967-1100

EMERGENCY CONTACT:
JOHN S. BRANSFORD, JR. (615) 292-1180

SUBSTANCE IDENTIFICATION

CAS-NUMBER 25322-69-4
SUBSTANCE: **POLYPROPYLENE GLYCOLS**
TRADE NAMES/SYNONYMS: PPG; POLYOXYPROPYLENE GLYCOL; 1,2-EPOXYPROPANE POLYMER; ALPHA-HYDRO-OMEGA-HYDROXY-POLY(OXY(METHYL-1,2-ETHANEDIYL)); LAPROL; NIAX; PLURACOL; POLYGLYCOL TYPE P; PROPYLAN; VORANOL P; PST19140
CHEMICAL FAMILY: GLYCOL POLYMER
MOLECULAR FORMULA: (C3-H6-O)XH2-O
MOLECULAR WEIGHT: 400-2000
CERCLA RATINGS (SCALE 0-3): HEALTH=2 FIRE=1 REACTIVITY=0 PERSISTENCE=0
NFPA RATINGS (SCALE 0-4): HEALTH=0 FIRE=1 REACTIVITY=0

COMPONENTS AND CONTAMINANTS

COMPONENT: POLYPROPYLENE GLYCOL *PERCENT:* 100
CAS# 25322-69-4
EXPOSURE LIMITS: NO OCCUPATIONAL EXPOSURE LIMITS ESTABLISHED BY OSHA, ACGIH, OR NIOSH.

PHYSICAL DATA

DESCRIPTION: CLEAR, LIGHTLY COLORED, SLIGHTLY OILY, VISCOUS LIQUIDS WITH A SLIGHTLY SWEET OR FAINT ETHER-LIKE ODOR *BOILING POINT:* DECOMPOSES
MELTING POINT: -22 F (-30 C) *SPECIFIC GRAVITY:* 1.0 *VAPOR PRESSURE:* LOW
EVAPORATION RATE: NOT AVAILABLE *SOLUBILITY IN WATER:* LOW MOL WT: SOLUBLE
SOLVENT SOLUBILITY: OILS

FIRE AND EXPLOSION DATA

FIRE AND EXPLOSION HAZARD: SLIGHT FIRE HAZARD WHEN EXPOSED TO HEAT OR FLAME.
FLASH POINT: 360-550 F (182-287 C) (OC) *FLAMMABILITY CLASS(OSHA):* IIIB
FIREFIGHTING MEDIA: DRY CHEMICAL, CARBON DIOXIDE, HALON, WATER SPRAY OR STANDARD FOAM (1987 EMERGENCY RESPONSE GUIDEBOOK, DOT P 5800.4).
FOR LARGER FIRES, USE WATER SPRAY, FOG OR STANDARD FOAM (1987 EMERGENCY RESPONSE GUIDEBOOK, DOT P 5800.4).
ALCOHOL FOAM (NFPA 325M, FIRE HAZARD PROPERTIES OF FLAMMABLE LIQUIDS, GASES, AND VOLATILE SOLIDS, 1984).
FIREFIGHTING: MOVE CONTAINER FROM FIRE AREA IF POSSIBLE. DO NOT SCATTER SPILLED MATERIAL WITH HIGH PRESSURE WATER STREAMS. DIKE FIRE CONTROL WATER FOR LATER DISPOSAL (1987 EMERGENCY RESPONSE GUIDEBOOK, DOT P 5800.4, GUIDE PAGE 31).
USE AGENTS SUITABLE FOR TYPE OF SURROUNDING FIRE. AVOID BREATHING HAZARDOUS VAPORS, KEEP UPWIND.
WATER OR FOAM MAY CAUSE FROTHING (NFPA 325M, FIRE HAZARD PROPERTIES OF FLAMMABLE LIQUIDS, GASES, AND VOLATILE SOLIDS, 1984)

TOXICITY

POLYPROPYLENE GLYCOLS: IRRITATION DATA: 500 MG/24 HOURS SKIN-RABBIT; 500 MG EYE-RABBIT; 500 MG/24 HOURS EYE-RABBIT MILD. TOXICITY DATA: 4190 MG/KG ORAL-RAT LD50. CARCINOGEN STATUS: NONE. ACUTE TOXICITY LEVEL: MODERATELY TOXIC BY INGESTION. TARGET EFFECTS: POISONING MAY AFFECT THE HEART AND CENTRAL NERVOUS SYSTEM.

HEALTH EFFECTS AND FIRST AID

INHALATION: POLYPROPYLENE GLYCOLS: **ACUTE EXPOSURE-** THE VERY LOW VOLATILITY OF THESE MATERIALS MAKES INHALATION IMPROBABLE EXCEPT WHEN MISTS ARE FORMED FROM VIOLENT AGITATION OR HIGH TEMPERATURES.

EYE CONTACT: POLYETHYLENE: **ACUTE EXPOSURE-** NO DATA AVAILABLE. **CHRONIC EXPOSURE-** NO DATA AVAILABLE.
FIRST AID- WASH EYES IMMEDIATELY WITH LARGE AMOUNTS OF WATER OR NORMAL SALINE, OCCASIONALLY LIFTING UPPER AND LOWER LIDS, UNTIL NO EVIDENCE OF CHEMICAL REMAINS (APPROXIMATELY 15-20 MINUTES). GET MEDICAL ATTENTION IMMEDIATELY.

INGESTION: POLYETHYLENE: **ACUTE EXPOSURE-** NO EVIDENCE HAS BEEN FOUND TO SHOW THAT POLYETHYLENE PRODUCES TOXIC SYMPTOMS WHEN INGESTED. A DOSE OF 7000 MG/KG WAS NOT LETHAL TO MICE. **CHRONIC EXPOSURE-** RATS FED 8 GM/KG DAILY SHOWED NO TOXIC REACTIONS AND GAINED WEIGHT NORMALLY.
FIRST AID- TREAT SYMPTOMATICALLY AND SUPPORTIVELY. GET MEDICAL ATTENTION IMMEDIATELY. IF VOMITING OCCURS, KEEP HEAD LOWER THAN HIPS TO PREVENT ASPIRATION.
ANTIDOTE: NO SPECIFIC ANTIDOTE. TREAT SYMPTOMATICALLY AND SUPPORTIVELY.

REACTIVITY

REACTIVITY: STABLE UNDER NORMAL TEMPERATURES AND PRESSURES.
INCOMPATIBILITIES: POLYETHYLENE: AROMATIC HYDROCARBONS: MAY ATTACK POLYMER. BENZENE: MAY ATTACK POLYMER. CHLORINATED HYDROCARBONS: MAY ATTACK POLYMER. FLUORINE: REACTS VIOLENTLY. FREE HALOGENS: MAY ATTACK POLYMER. GASOLINE: MAY ATTACK POLYMER. LUBRICATING OILS: MAY ATTACK POLYMER. NITRIC ACID: MAY ATTACK POLYMER. OXIDIZING AGENTS: MAY SLOWLY ATTACK POLYMER. PERCHLORIC ACID: MAY ATTACK POLYMER. PETROLEUM ETHER: MAY ATTACK POLYMER. GASEOUS OR LIQUID FLUORINE-OXYGEN: VIOLENT REACTION. SULFURIC ACID (FUMING): MAY SLOWLY ATTACK POLYMER.
DECOMPOSITION: THERMAL DECOMPOSITION PRODUCTS MAY INCLUDE TOXIC AND HAZARDOUS ACROLEIN AND FORMALDEHYDE AND OXIDES OF CARBON.
POLYMERIZATION: HAZARDOUS POLYMERIZATION HAS NOT BEEN REPORTED TO OCCUR UNDER NORMAL TEMPERATURES AND PRESSURES.

STORAGE AND DISPOSAL

OBSERVE ALL FEDERAL, STATE AND LOCAL REGULATIONS WHEN STORING OR DISPOSING OF THIS SUBSTANCE. FOR ASSISTANCE, CONTACT THE DISTRICT DIRECTOR OF THE ENVIRONMENTAL PROTECTION AGENCY.

CONDITIONS TO AVOID

MAY BURN BUT DOES NOT IGNITE READILY. AVOID CONTACT WITH STRONG OXIDIZERS, EXCESSIVE HEAT, SPARKS, OR OPEN FLAME.

SPILL AND LEAK PROCEDURES

OCCUPATIONAL SPILL: SWEEP UP AND PLACE IN SUITABLE CLEAN, DRY CONTAINERS FOR RECLAMATION OR LATER DISPOSAL. DO NOT FLUSH SPILLED MATERIAL INTO SEWER. KEEP UNNECESSARY PEOPLE AWAY.

PROTECTIVE EQUIPMENT

VENTILATION: PROVIDE LOCAL EXHAUST OR GENERAL DILUTION VENTILATION SYSTEM.
RESPIRATOR: THE FOLLOWING RESPIRATORS ARE RECOMMENDED BASED ON INFORMATION FOUND IN THE PHYSICAL DATA, TOXICITY AND HEALTH EFFECTS SECTIONS. THEY ARE RANKED IN ORDER FROM MINIMUM TO MAXIMUM RESPIRATORY PROTECTION. THE SPECIFIC RESPIRATOR SELECTED MUST BE BASED ON CONTAMINATION LEVELS FOUND IN THE WORK PLACE, MUST NOT EXCEED THE WORKING LIMITS OF THE RESPIRATOR AND BE JOINTLY APPROVED BY THE NATIONAL INSTITUTE FOR OCCUPATIONAL SAFETY AND HEALTH AND THE MINE SAFETY AND HEALTH ADMINISTRATION (NIOSH-MSHA).
DUST AND MIST RESPIRATOR.
AIR-PURIFYING RESPIRATOR WITH A HIGH-EFFICIENCY PARTICULATE FILTER.
POWERED AIR-PURIFYING RESPIRATOR WITH A DUST AND MIST FILTER.
POWERED AIR-PURIFYING RESPIRATOR WITH A HIGH-EFFICIENCY PARTICULATE FILTER.
TYPE 'C' SUPPLIED-AIR RESPIRATOR OPERATED IN THE PRESSURE-DEMAND OR OTHER POSITIVE PRESSURE OR CONTINUOUS-FLOW MODE.
SELF-CONTAINED BREATHING APPARATUS.
FOR FIREFIGHTING AND OTHER IMMEDIATELY DANGEROUS TO LIFE OR HEALTH CONDITIONS:
SELF-CONTAINED BREATHING APPARATUS WITH FULL FACEPIECE OPERATED IN PRESSURE-DEMAND OR OTHER POSITIVE PRESSURE MODE.
SUPPLIED-AIR RESPIRATOR WITH FULL FACEPIECE AND OPERATED IN PRESSURE-DEMAND OR OTHER POSITIVE PRESSURE MODE IN COMBINATION WITH AN AUXILIARY SELF-CONTAINED BREATHING APPARATUS OPERATED IN PRESSURE-DEMAND OR OTHER POSITIVE PRESSURE MODE.
CLOTHING: PROTECTIVE CLOTHING NOT REQUIRED. AVOID REPEATED OR PROLONGED CONTACT WITH THIS SUBSTANCE.
GLOVES: PROTECTIVE GLOVES ARE NOT REQUIRED BUT RECOMMENDED.

SYMPTOMS OF POISONING HAVE NOT BEEN REPORTED. **CHRONIC EXPOSURE**- NO DATA AVAILABLE.

FIRST AID- REMOVE FROM EXPOSURE AREA TO FRESH AIR IMMEDIATELY. IF BREATHING HAS STOPPED, PERFORM ARTIFICIAL RESPIRATION. KEEP PERSON WARM AND AT REST. TREAT SYMPTOMATICALLY AND SUPPORTIVELY. GET MEDICAL ATTENTION IMMEDIATELY.

SKIN CONTACT: POLYPROPYLENE GLYCOLS: **ACUTE EXPOSURE**- ANIMAL STUDIES INDICATE THESE MATERIALS ARE NOT SIGNIFICANTLY IRRITATING TO THE SKIN. SKIN ABSORPTION MAY OCCUR AND CAUSE SYSTEMIC TOXICITY, HOWEVER SUCH HIGH LEVELS ARE REQUIRED THAT THIS ROUTE DOES NOT PRESENT A SERIOUS INDUSTRIAL HAZARD. **CHRONIC EXPOSURE**- TESTS CONDUCTED ON RABBITS INDICATE POLYPROPYLENE GLYCOLS ARE NOT SIGNIFICANTLY IRRITATING TO THE SKIN EVEN WHEN EXPOSURES ARE PROLONGED AND REPEATED. WHEN TESTED ON 50 HUMAN VOLUNTEERS FOR SENSITIZATION PROPERTIES, POLYPROPYLENE GLYCOL (M.W. OF 425) CAUSED NO RESPONSES. 5 AND 10 MG/KG OF POLYPROPYLENE GLYCOL (M.W. OF 2000) FOR 24 HOURS/DAY, 5 DAY/WEEK FOR 3 MONTHS BY SKIN POULTICE CAUSED DEPRESSED GROWTH IN RABBITS AND RESPIRATORY FAILURE IN SOME ANIMALS AT HIGHER DOSES.

FIRST AID- REMOVE CONTAMINATED CLOTHING AND SHOES IMMEDIATELY. WASH AFFECTED AREA WITH SOAP OR MILD DETERGENT AND LARGE AMOUNTS OF WATER UNTIL NO EVIDENCE OF CHEMICAL REMAINS (APPROXIMATELY 15-20 MINUTES). GET MEDICAL ATTENTION IMMEDIATELY.

EYE CONTACT: POLYPROPYLENE GLYCOLS: **ACUTE EXPOSURE**- DIRECT CONTACT WITH THE EYES MAY CAUSE SLIGHT TRANSIENT PAIN AND CONJUNCTIVAL IRRITATION BUT NO CORNEAL DAMAGE. THE RESPONSE IS SIMILAR TO THAT CAUSED BY MILD SOAP. **CHRONIC EXPOSURE**- NO DATA AVAILABLE.

FIRST AID- WASH EYES IMMEDIATELY WITH LARGE AMOUNTS OF WATER OR NORMAL SALINE, OCCASIONALLY LIFTING UPPER AND LOWER LIDS, UNTIL NO EVIDENCE OF CHEMICAL REMAINS (APPROXIMATELY 15-20 MINUTES). GET MEDICAL ATTENTION IMMEDIATELY.

INGESTION: POLYPROPYLENE GLYCOLS: **ACUTE EXPOSURE**- THE LOW MOLECULAR WEIGHT POLYPROPYLENE GLYCOLS (400 TO 1200) ARE RAPIDLY ABSORBED FROM THE GASTROINTESTINAL TRACT AND ARE POTENT CENTRAL NERVOUS SYSTEM STIMULANTS. EXCITEMENT AND CONVULSIONS APPEAR WITHIN MINUTES AFTER ADMINISTRATION. CARDIAC ARRHYTHMIAS OCCUR READILY. IN DOGS, VENTRICULAR EXTRASYSTOLES HAVE BEEN REPORTED. **CHRONIC EXPOSURE**- IN ANIMAL FEEDING STUDIES, 3% OF POLYPROPYLENE GLYCOL (M.W. OF 2000) IN THE DIET OF RATS CAUSED SLIGHT GROWTH DEPRESSION. NO EFFECTS HAVE BEEN REPORTED FOR OTHER POLYPROPYLENE GLYCOLS TESTED.

FIRST AID- TREAT SYMPTOMATICALLY AND SUPPORTIVELY. GET MEDICAL ATTENTION IMMEDIATELY. IF VOMITING OCCURS, KEEP HEAD LOWER THAN HIPS TO PREVENT ASPIRATION.

ANTIDOTE: NO SPECIFIC ANTIDOTE. TREAT SYMPTOMATICALLY AND SUPPORTIVELY.

REACTIVITY

REACTIVITY: STABLE UNDER NORMAL TEMPERATURES AND PRESSURES.

INCOMPATIBILITIES: POLYPROPYLENE GLYCOL: STRONG OXIDIZERS: FIRE AND EXPLOSION HAZARD.

DECOMPOSITION: THERMAL DECOMPOSITION PRODUCTS MAY INCLUDE TOXIC OXIDES OF CARBON.

POLYMERIZATION: HAZARDOUS POLYMERIZATION HAS NOT BEEN REPORTED TO OCCUR UNDER NORMAL TEMPERATURES AND PRESSURES.

STORAGE AND DISPOSAL

OBSERVE ALL FEDERAL, STATE AND LOCAL REGULATIONS WHEN STORING OR DISPOSING OF THIS SUBSTANCE. FOR ASSISTANCE, CONTACT THE DISTRICT DIRECTOR OF THE ENVIRONMENTAL PROTECTION AGENCY.

STORAGE

STORE AWAY FROM INCOMPATIBLE SUBSTANCES.

CONDITIONS TO AVOID

MAY BURN BUT DOES NOT IGNITE READILY. AVOID CONTACT WITH STRONG OXIDIZERS, EXCESSIVE HEAT, SPARKS, OR OPEN FLAME.

SPILL AND LEAK PROCEDURES

OCCUPATIONAL SPILL: SWEEP UP AND PLACE IN SUITABLE CLEAN, DRY CONTAINERS FOR RECLAMATION OR LATER DISPOSAL. DO NOT FLUSH SPILLED MATERIAL INTO SEWER. KEEP UNNECESSARY PEOPLE AWAY.

PROTECTIVE EQUIPMENT

VENTILATION: PROVIDE GENERAL DILUTION VENTILATION.

RESPIRATOR: THE FOLLOWING RESPIRATORS ARE RECOMMENDED BASED ON INFORMATION FOUND IN THE PHYSICAL DATA, TOXICITY AND HEALTH EFFECTS SECTIONS. THEY ARE RANKED IN ORDER FROM MINIMUM TO MAXIMUM RESPIRATORY PROTECTION. THE SPECIFIC RESPIRATOR SELECTED MUST BE BASED ON CONTAMINATION LEVELS FOUND IN THE WORK PLACE, MUST NOT EXCEED THE WORKING LIMITS OF THE RESPIRATOR AND BE JOINTLY APPROVED BY THE NATIONAL INSTITUTE FOR OCCUPATIONAL SAFETY AND HEALTH AND THE MINE SAFETY AND HEALTH ADMINISTRATION (NIOSH-MSHA).

CHEMICAL CARTRIDGE RESPIRATOR WITH AN ORGANIC VAPOR CARTRIDGE(S) WITH A FULL FACEPIECE.

GAS MASK WITH ORGANIC VAPOR CANISTER (CHIN-STYLE OR FRONT- OR BACK-MOUNTED CANISTER) WITH A FULL FACEPIECE.

TYPE 'C' SUPPLIED-AIR RESPIRATOR WITH A FULL FACEPIECE OPERATED IN PRESSURE-DEMAND OR OTHER POSITIVE PRESSURE MODE OR WITH A FULL FACEPIECE, HELMET OR HOOD OPERATED IN CONTINUOUS-FLOW MODE.

SELF-CONTAINED BREATHING APPARATUS WITH A FULL FACEPIECE OPERATED IN PRESSURE-DEMAND OR OTHER POSITIVE PRESSURE MODE.

FOR FIREFIGHTING AND OTHER IMMEDIATELY DANGEROUS TO LIFE OR HEALTH CONDITIONS:

SELF-CONTAINED BREATHING APPARATUS WITH FULL FACEPIECE OPERATED IN PRESSURE-DEMAND OR OTHER POSITIVE PRESSURE MODE.

SUPPLIED-AIR RESPIRATOR WITH FULL FACEPIECE AND OPERATED IN PRESSURE-DEMAND OR OTHER POSITIVE PRESSURE MODE IN COMBINATION WITH AN AUXILIARY SELF-CONTAINED BREATHING APPARATUS OPERATED IN PRESSURE-DEMAND OR OTHER POSITIVE PRESSURE MODE.

CLOTHING: EMPLOYEE MUST WEAR APPROPRIATE PROTECTIVE (IMPERVIOUS) CLOTHING AND EQUIPMENT TO PREVENT REPEATED OR PROLONGED SKIN CONTACT WITH THIS SUBSTANCE.

GLOVES: EMPLOYEE MUST WEAR APPROPRIATE PROTECTIVE GLOVES TO PREVENT CONTACT WITH THIS SUBSTANCE.

EYE PROTECTION: EMPLOYEE MUST WEAR SPLASH-PROOF OR DUST-RESISTANT SAFETY GOGGLES TO PREVENT EYE CONTACT WITH THIS SUBSTANCE.

EMERGENCY EYE WASH: WHERE THERE IS ANY POSSIBILITY THAT AN EMPLOYEE'S EYES MAY BE EXPOSED TO THIS SUBSTANCE, THE EMPLOYER SHOULD PROVIDE AN EYE WASH FOUNTAIN WITHIN THE IMMEDIATE WORK AREA FOR EMERGENCY USE.

AUTHORIZED BY- OCCUPATIONAL HEALTH SERVICES, INC.

CREATION DATE: 10/04/89 ***REVISION DATE:*** 05/31/90

MATERIAL SAFETY DATA SHEET

OCCUPATIONAL HEALTH SERVICES, INC.
AGRICULTURE AND PESTICIDE DIVISION
450 SEVENTH AVENUE, SUITE 2407
NEW YORK, NEW YORK 10123
1-800-445-MSDS OR (212) 967-1100

EMERGENCY CONTACT:
JOHN S. BRANSFORD, JR. (615) 292-1180

SUBSTANCE IDENTIFICATION

CAS-NUMBER 7646-93-7

SUBSTANCE: **POTASSIUM BISULFATE**

TRADE NAMES/SYNONYMS: ACID POTASSIUM SULFATE; MONOPOTASSIUM SULFATE; POTASSIUM BISULPHATE; POTASSIUM HYDROGEN SULFATE, SOLID; SAL ENIXUM; SULFURIC ACID, MONOPOTASSIUM SALT; SULFURIC ACID, POTASSIUM SALT (1:1); POTASSIUM SULFATE (KHSO4); POTASSIUM ACID SULFATE; HYDROGEN POTASSIUM SULFATE; POTASSIUM HYDROGEN SULFATE; POTASSIUM SULFATE; UN 2509; STCC 4944148; HKO4S; PST19255

CHEMICAL FAMILY: INORGANIC SALT

MOLECULAR FORMULA: K-H-S-O4

MOLECULAR WEIGHT: 136.17

CERCLA RATINGS (SCALE 0-3): HEALTH=2 FIRE=0 REACTIVITY=0 PERSISTENCE=0

NFPA RATINGS (SCALE 0-4): HEALTH=2 FIRE=0 REACTIVITY=0

COMPONENTS AND CONTAMINANTS

COMPONENT: POTASSIUM BISULFATE ***PERCENT:*** 100
CAS# 7646-93-7

EXPOSURE LIMITS: NO OCCUPATIONAL EXPOSURE LIMITS ESTABLISHED BY OSHA, ACGIH, OR NIOSH.

PHYSICAL DATA

DESCRIPTION: COLORLESS CRYSTALLINE SOLID WITH SULFUR ODOR.

BOILING POINT: DECOMPOSES ***MELTING POINT:*** 417 F (214 C)

SPECIFIC GRAVITY: 2.322 ***VAPOR PRESSURE:*** NEGLIGIBLE
PH: ACIDIC IN SOLUTION ***SOLUBILITY IN WATER:*** 36.3% @ 0 C
SOLVENT SOLUBILITY: INSOLUBLE IN ACETONE; DECOMPOSES IN ALCOHOL

FIRE AND EXPLOSION DATA

FIRE AND EXPLOSION HAZARD: NEGLIGIBLE FIRE HAZARD WHEN EXPOSED TO HEAT OR FLAME.

FIREFIGHTING MEDIA: DRY CHEMICAL, CARBON DIOXIDE, HALON, WATER SPRAY OR STANDARD FOAM (1987 EMERGENCY RESPONSE GUIDEBOOK, DOT P 5800.4). FOR LARGER FIRES, USE WATER SPRAY, FOG OR STANDARD FOAM (1987 EMERGENCY RESPONSE GUIDEBOOK, DOT P 5800.4).

FIREFIGHTING: MOVE CONTAINERS FROM FIRE AREA IF POSSIBLE. COOL CONTAINERS EXPOSED TO FLAMES WITH WATER FROM SIDE UNTIL WELL AFTER FIRE IS OUT. STAY AWAY FROM STORAGE TANK ENDS (1987 EMERGENCY RESPONSE GUIDEBOOK, DOT P 5800.4, GUIDE PAGE 60).
EXTINGUISH USING AGENT INDICATED; DO NOT USE WATER DIRECTLY ON MATERIAL. IF LARGE AMOUNTS OF COMBUSTIBLE MATERIALS ARE INVOLVED, USE WATER SPRAY OR FOG IN FLOODING AMOUNTS. AVOID BREATHING CORROSIVE DUSTS AND FUMES FROM BURNING MATERIAL, KEEP UPWIND.

TRANSPORTATION DATA

DEPARTMENT OF TRANSPORTATION HAZARD CLASSIFICATION 49 CFR 172.101: ORM-B
DEPARTMENT OF TRANSPORTATION LABELING REQUIREMENTS 49 CFR 172.101 AND SUBPART E: NONE
DEPARTMENT OF TRANSPORTATION PACKAGING REQUIREMENTS: 49 CFR 173.800 EXCEPTIONS: 49 CFR 173.505

TOXICITY

POTASSIUM BISULFATE: TOXICITY DATA: 2340 MG/KG ORAL-RAT LD50.
CARCINOGEN STATUS: NONE LOCAL EFFECTS: CORROSIVE- INHALATION, SKIN, AND EYES. ACUTE TOXICITY LEVEL: MODERATELY TOXIC BY INGESTION. TARGET EFFECTS: NO DATA AVAILABLE.

HEALTH EFFECTS AND FIRST AID

INHALATION: POTASSIUM BISULFATE: CORROSIVE. **ACUTE EXPOSURE-** INHALATION OF CORROSIVE SUBSTANCES MAY CAUSE SYMPTOMS OF RESPIRATORY TRACT IRRITATION POSSIBLY INCLUDING COUGHING, CHOKING, PAIN IN THE NOSE, MOUTH AND THROAT AND BURNS OF THE MUCOUS MEMBRANES. IF SUFFICIENT QUANTITIES ARE INHALED, PULMONARY EDEMA MAY DEVELOP, OFTEN WITH A LATENT PERIOD OF 5-72 HOURS. THE SYMPTOMS MAY INCLUDE TIGHTNESS IN THE CHEST, DYSPNEA, FROTHY SPUTUM, CYANOSIS, AND DIZZINESS. PHYSICAL FINDINGS MAY INCLUDE WEAK, RAPID PULSE, HYPOTENSION, HEMOCONCENTRATION AND MOIST RALES. **CHRONIC EXPOSURE-** DEPENDING ON THE CONCENTRATION AND DURATION OF EXPOSURE, REPEATED OR PROLONGED EXPOSURE TO CORROSIVE SUBSTANCES MAY CAUSE INFLAMMATORY AND ULCERATIVE CHANGES IN THE MOUTH AND POSSIBLY BRONCHIAL AND GASTROINTESTINAL DISTURBANCES.

FIRST AID- REMOVE FROM EXPOSURE AREA TO FRESH AIR IMMEDIATELY. IF BREATHING HAS STOPPED, GIVE ARTIFICIAL RESPIRATION. MAINTAIN AIRWAY AND BLOOD PRESSURE AND ADMINISTER OXYGEN IF AVAILABLE. KEEP AFFECTED PERSON WARM AND AT REST. TREAT SYMPTOMATICALLY AND SUPPORTIVELY. ADMINISTRATION OF OXYGEN SHOULD BE PERFORMED BY QUALIFIED PERSONNEL. GET MEDICAL ATTENTION IMMEDIATELY.

SKIN CONTACT: POTASSIUM BISULFATE: CORROSIVE. **ACUTE EXPOSURE-** DIRECT CONTACT WITH CORROSIVE SUBSTANCES MAY CAUSE SEVERE IRRITATION, PAIN AND POSSIBLY BURNS. **CHRONIC EXPOSURE-** EFFECTS DEPEND ON CONCENTRATION AND DURATION OF EXPOSURE. REPEATED OR PROLONGED CONTACT WITH CORROSIVE SUBSTANCES MAY RESULT IN DERMATITIS OR EFFECTS SIMILAR TO ACUTE EXPOSURE.

FIRST AID- REMOVE CONTAMINATED CLOTHING AND SHOES IMMEDIATELY. WASH AFFECTED AREA WITH SOAP OR MILD DETERGENT AND LARGE AMOUNTS OF WATER UNTIL NO EVIDENCE OF CHEMICAL REMAINS (AT LEAST 15-20 MINUTES). IN CASE OF CHEMICAL BURNS, COVER AREA WITH STERILE, DRY DRESSING. BANDAGE SECURELY, BUT NOT TOO TIGHTLY. GET MEDICAL ATTENTION IMMEDIATELY.

EYE CONTACT: POTASSIUM BISULFATE: CORROSIVE. **ACUTE EXPOSURE-** DIRECT CONTACT WITH CORROSIVE SUBSTANCES MAY CAUSE SEVERE IRRITATION, PAIN, AND BURNS, POSSIBLY SEVERE. THE DEGREE OF INJURY DEPENDS ON THE CONCENTRATION AND DURATION OF CONTACT. THE FULL EXTENT OF THE INJURY MAY NOT BE IMMEDIATELY APPARENT. **CHRONIC EXPOSURE-** EFFECTS DEPEND ON CONCENTRATION AND DURATION OF EXPOSURE. REPEATED OR PROLONGED CONTACT WITH CORROSIVE SUBSTANCES MAY RESULT IN CONJUNCTIVITIS OR EFFECTS AS IN ACUTE EXPOSURE.

FIRST AID- WASH EYES IMMEDIATELY WITH LARGE AMOUNTS OF WATER, OCCASIONALLY LIFTING UPPER AND LOWER LIDS, UNTIL NO EVIDENCE OF CHEMICAL REMAINS (AT LEAST 15-20 MINUTES). CONTINUE IRRIGATING WITH NORMAL SALINE UNTIL THE PH HAS RETURNED TO NORMAL (30-60 MINUTES). COVER WITH STERILE BANDAGES. GET MEDICAL ATTENTION IMMEDIATELY.

INGESTION: POTASSIUM BISULFATE: CORROSIVE. **ACUTE EXPOSURE-** CORROSIVE SUBSTANCES MAY CAUSE IMMEDIATE PAIN AND SEVERE BURNS OF THE MUCOUS MEMBRANES. THERE MAY BE DISCOLORATION OF THE TISSUES. SWALLOWING AND SPEECH MAY BE DIFFICULT AT FIRST AND THEN ALMOST IMPOSSIBLE. THE EFFECTS ON THE ESOPHAGUS AND GASTROINTESTINAL TRACT MAY RANGE FROM IRRITATION TO SEVERE CORROSION. EDEMA OF THE EPIGLOTTIS AND SHOCK MAY OCCUR. **CHRONIC EXPOSURE-** DEPENDING ON THE CONCENTRATION, REPEATED INGESTION OF CORROSIVE SUBSTANCES MAY RESULT IN EFFECTS AS WITH ACUTE INGESTION.

FIRST AID- DO NOT USE GASTRIC LAVAGE OR EMESIS. DILUTE IMMEDIATELY BY DRINKING LARGE QUANTITIES OF WATER OR MILK. IF VOMITING PERSISTS, ADMINISTER FLUIDS REPEATEDLY. MAINTAIN AIRWAY AND TREAT SHOCK. IF VOMITING OCCURS, KEEP HEAD BELOW HIPS TO HELP PREVENT ASPIRATION. GET MEDICAL ATTENTION IMMEDIATELY.

ANTIDOTE: NO SPECIFIC ANTIDOTE. TREAT SYMPTOMATICALLY AND SUPPORTIVELY.

REACTIVITY

REACTIVITY: STABLE UNDER NORMAL TEMPERATURES AND PRESSURES IN A CLOSED CONTAINER.

INCOMPATIBILITIES: POTASSIUM BISULFATE: ALKALI: INCOMPATIBLE. BASES (STRONG): INCOMPATIBLE. METALS: CORROSIVE IN THE PRESENCE OF MOISTURE. OXIDIZERS (STRONG): INCOMPATIBLE. SEE ALSO METAL SULFATES.
METAL SULFATES: ALUMINUM: POSSIBLE EXPLOSION ON MELTING. MAGNESIUM: POSSIBLE EXPLOSION.

DECOMPOSITION: THERMAL DECOMPOSITION MAY RELEASE HIGHLY TOXIC FUMES OF OXIDES OF SULFUR AND POTASSIUM OXIDE.

POLYMERIZATION: HAZARDOUS POLYMERIZATION HAS NOT BEEN REPORTED TO OCCUR UNDER NORMAL TEMPERATURES AND PRESSURES.

STORAGE AND DISPOSAL

OBSERVE ALL FEDERAL, STATE AND LOCAL REGULATIONS WHEN STORING OR DISPOSING OF THIS SUBSTANCE. FOR ASSISTANCE, CONTACT THE DISTRICT DIRECTOR OF THE ENVIRONMENTAL PROTECTION AGENCY.

****STORAGE****

STORE AWAY FROM INCOMPATIBLE SUBSTANCES.

CONDITIONS TO AVOID

MAY BURN BUT DOES NOT IGNITE READILY. FLAMMABLE, POISONOUS GASES MAY ACCUMULATE IN TANKS AND HOPPER CARS. MAY IGNITE COMBUSTIBLES (WOOD, PAPER, OIL, ETC.).

SPILL AND LEAK PROCEDURES

OCCUPATIONAL SPILL: DO NOT TOUCH SPILLED MATERIAL. STOP LEAK IF YOU CAN DO IT WITHOUT RISK. FOR SMALL SPILLS, TAKE UP WITH SAND OR OTHER ABSORBENT MATERIAL AND PLACE INTO CONTAINERS FOR LATER DISPOSAL. FOR SMALL DRY SPILLS, WITH CLEAN SHOVEL PLACE MATERIAL INTO CLEAN, DRY CONTAINER AND COVER. MOVE CONTAINERS FROM SPILL AREA. FOR LARGER SPILLS, DIKE FAR AHEAD OF SPILL FOR LATER DISPOSAL. KEEP UNNECESSARY PEOPLE AWAY. ISOLATE HAZARD AREA AND DENY ENTRY.

PROTECTIVE EQUIPMENT

VENTILATION: PROVIDE LOCAL EXHAUST OR GENERAL DILUTION VENTILATION SYSTEM.

RESPIRATOR: THE FOLLOWING RESPIRATORS ARE RECOMMENDED BASED ON INFORMATION FOUND IN THE PHYSICAL DATA, TOXICITY AND HEALTH EFFECTS SECTIONS. THEY ARE RANKED IN ORDER FROM MINIMUM TO MAXIMUM RESPIRATORY PROTECTION. THE SPECIFIC RESPIRATOR SELECTED MUST BE BASED ON CONTAMINATION LEVELS FOUND IN THE WORK PLACE, MUST NOT EXCEED THE WORKING LIMITS OF THE RESPIRATOR AND BE JOINTLY APPROVED BY THE NATIONAL INSTITUTE FOR OCCUPATIONAL SAFETY AND HEALTH AND THE MINE SAFETY AND HEALTH ADMINISTRATION (NIOSH-MSHA).
DUST AND MIST RESPIRATOR WITH A FULL FACEPIECE.
AIR-PURIFYING FULL FACEPIECE RESPIRATOR WITH A HIGH-EFFICIENCY PARTICULATE FILTER.
POWERED AIR-PURIFYING RESPIRATOR WITH A TIGHT-FITTING FACEPIECE AND HIGH-EFFICIENCY PARTICULATE FILTER.
TYPE 'C' SUPPLIED-AIR RESPIRATOR WITH A FULL FACEPIECE OPERATED IN PRESSURE-DEMAND OR OTHER POSITIVE PRESSURE MODE OR WITH A FULL FACEPIECE, HELMET OR HOOD OPERATED IN CONTINUOUS-FLOW MODE.

SELF-CONTAINED BREATHING APPARATUS WITH A FULL FACEPIECE OPERATED IN PRESSURE-DEMAND OR OTHER POSITIVE PRESSURE MODE.
FOR FIREFIGHTING AND OTHER IMMEDIATELY DANGEROUS TO LIFE OR HEALTH CONDITIONS:
SELF-CONTAINED BREATHING APPARATUS WITH FULL FACEPIECE OPERATED IN PRESSURE-DEMAND OR OTHER POSITIVE PRESSURE MODE.
SUPPLIED-AIR RESPIRATOR WITH FULL FACEPIECE AND OPERATED IN PRESSURE-DEMAND OR OTHER POSITIVE PRESSURE MODE IN COMBINATION WITH AN AUXILIARY SELF-CONTAINED BREATHING APPARATUS OPERATED IN PRESSURE-DEMAND OR OTHER POSITIVE PRESSURE MODE.

CLOTHING: EMPLOYEE MUST WEAR APPROPRIATE PROTECTIVE (IMPERVIOUS) CLOTHING AND EQUIPMENT TO PREVENT ANY POSSIBILITY OF SKIN CONTACT WITH THIS SUBSTANCE.

GLOVES: EMPLOYEE MUST WEAR APPROPRIATE PROTECTIVE GLOVES TO PREVENT CONTACT WITH THIS SUBSTANCE.

EYE PROTECTION: EMPLOYEE MUST WEAR SPLASH-PROOF OR DUST-RESISTANT SAFETY GOGGLES AND A FACESHIELD TO PREVENT CONTACT WITH THIS SUBSTANCE.
EMERGENCY WASH FACILITIES: WHERE THERE IS ANY POSSIBILITY THAT AN EMPLOYEE'S EYES AND/OR SKIN MAY BE EXPOSED TO THIS SUBSTANCE, THE EMPLOYER SHOULD PROVIDE AN EYE WASH FOUNTAIN AND QUICK DRENCH SHOWER WITHIN THE IMMEDIATE WORK AREA FOR EMERGENCY USE.

AUTHORIZED BY- OCCUPATIONAL HEALTH SERVICES, INC.
CREATION DATE: 11/17/89 ***REVISION DATE:*** 05/16/90

MATERIAL SAFETY DATA SHEET

OCCUPATIONAL HEALTH SERVICES, INC.
AGRICULTURE AND PESTICIDE DIVISION
450 SEVENTH AVENUE, SUITE 2407
NEW YORK, NEW YORK 10123
1-800-445-MSDS OR (212) 967-1100

EMERGENCY CONTACT:
JOHN S. BRANSFORD, JR. (615) 292-1180

SUBSTANCE IDENTIFICATION

CAS-NUMBER 7758-02-3
SUBSTANCE: POTASSIUM BROMIDE
TRADE NAMES/SYNONYMS: BROMIDE SALT OF POTASSIUM; TRIPOTASSIUM TRIBROMIDE; KALII; PST19280
CHEMICAL FAMILY: INORGANIC SALT
MOLECULAR FORMULA: K-BR
MOLECULAR WEIGHT: 119.01
CERCLA RATINGS (SCALE 0-3): HEALTH=2 FIRE=0 REACTIVITY=0 PERSISTENCE=0
NFPA RATINGS (SCALE 0-4): HEALTH=2 FIRE=0 REACTIVITY=0

COMPONENTS AND CONTAMINANTS

COMPONENT: POTASSIUM BROMIDE ***PERCENT:*** 100
CAS# 7758-02-3
OTHER CONTAMINANTS: NONE
EXPOSURE LIMITS: NO OCCUPATIONAL EXPOSURE LIMITS ESTABLISHED BY OSHA, ACGIH, OR NIOSH.

PHYSICAL DATA

DESCRIPTION: COLORLESS, HYGROSCOPIC CRYSTALS OR WHITE GRANULES OR POWDER WITH A BITTER, SALINE TASTE. ***BOILING POINT:*** 2615 F (1435 C)
MELTING POINT: 1345 F (730 C) ***SPECIFIC GRAVITY:*** 2.8
VAPOR PRESSURE: 1 MMHG @ 795 C ***PH:*** NEUTRAL IN SOLUTION
SOLUBILITY IN WATER: 53.48%
SOLVENT SOLUBILITY: GLYCERIN, ALCOHOL

FIRE AND EXPLOSION DATA

FIRE AND EXPLOSION HAZARD: NEGLIGIBLE FIRE HAZARD WHEN EXPOSED TO HEAT OR FLAME.

FIREFIGHTING MEDIA: DRY CHEMICAL, CARBON DIOXIDE, HALON, WATER SPRAY OR ALCOHOL FOAM (1987 EMERGENCY RESPONSE GUIDEBOOK, DOT P 5800.4).
FOR LARGER FIRES, USE WATER SPRAY, FOG OR ALCOHOL FOAM (1987 EMERGENCY RESPONSE GUIDEBOOK, DOT P 5800.4).

FIREFIGHTING: NO ACUTE HAZARD. MOVE CONTAINER FROM FIRE AREA IF POSSIBLE. AVOID BREATHING VAPORS OR DUSTS; KEEP UPWIND.

TOXICITY

POTASSIUM BROMIDE: TOXICITY DATA: MUTAGENIC DATA (RTECS). CARCINOGEN STATUS: NONE. LOCAL EFFECTS: IRRITANT- INHALATION, SKIN, AND EYES. ACUTE TOXICITY LEVEL: NO DATA AVAILABLE. TARGET EFFECTS: POISONING USUALLY AFFECTS THE CENTRAL NERVOUS SYSTEM.

HEALTH EFFECTS AND FIRST AID

INHALATION: POTASSIUM BROMIDE: IRRITANT. **ACUTE EXPOSURE-** MAY CAUSE SORE THROAT, COUGHING, DYSPNEA, NAUSEA, VOMITING, DELAYED PULMONARY EDEMA, PNEUMONIA, CONFUSION, COMA AND PARALYSIS. **CHRONIC EXPOSURE-** REPEATED OR PROLONGED EXPOSURE MAY CAUSE HEADACHE, CONFUSION, AND ACNEFORM PAPULAR RASHES OF THE HANDS AND FACE.

FIRST AID- REMOVE FROM EXPOSURE AREA TO FRESH AIR IMMEDIATELY. IF BREATHING HAS STOPPED, PERFORM ARTIFICIAL RESPIRATION. KEEP PERSON WARM AND AT REST. TREAT SYMPTOMATICALLY AND SUPPORTIVELY. GET MEDICAL ATTENTION IMMEDIATELY.

SKIN CONTACT: POTASSIUM BROMIDE: IRRITANT. **ACUTE EXPOSURE-** DIRECT CONTACT MAY CAUSE IRRITATION, SKIN RASHES AND PIGMENTATION. **CHRONIC EXPOSURE-** REPEATED OR PROLONGED EXPOSURE MAY CAUSE DERMATITIS, USUALLY WITH AN ACNEFORM PAPULAR RASH OF THE HANDS AND FACE, PIGMENTATION, NODULAR LESIONS ON THE LEGS, AND PUSTULAR NODULES.

FIRST AID- REMOVE CONTAMINATED CLOTHING AND SHOES IMMEDIATELY. WASH AFFECTED AREA WITH SOAP OR MILD DETERGENT AND LARGE AMOUNTS OF WATER UNTIL NO EVIDENCE OF CHEMICAL REMAINS (APPROXIMATELY 15-20 MINUTES). GET MEDICAL ATTENTION IMMEDIATELY.

EYE CONTACT: POTASSIUM BROMIDE: IRRITANT. **ACUTE EXPOSURE-** DIRECT CONTACT MAY CAUSE IRRITATION, REDNESS, PAIN. **CHRONIC EXPOSURE-** REPEATED OR PROLONGED EXPOSURE MAY CAUSE CONJUNCTIVITIS.

FIRST AID- WASH EYES IMMEDIATELY WITH LARGE AMOUNTS OF WATER OR NORMAL SALINE, OCCASIONALLY LIFTING UPPER AND LOWER LIDS, UNTIL NO EVIDENCE OF CHEMICAL REMAINS (APPROXIMATELY 15-20 MINUTES). GET MEDICAL ATTENTION IMMEDIATELY.

INGESTION: POTASSIUM BROMIDE: NARCOTIC. **ACUTE EXPOSURE-** MAY CAUSE NAUSEA, VOMITING, ABDOMINAL PAIN, CONFUSION, DROWSINESS, PULMONARY EDEMA, COMA AND PARALYSIS; HOWEVER, DOSES THAT WOULD BE SUFFICIENT TO CAUSE ACUTE POISONING ARE SO IRRITATING TO THE STOMACH THAT NAUSEA AND VOMITING OCCUR ALMOST IMMEDIATELY. **CHRONIC EXPOSURE-** REPEATED OR PROLONGED EXPOSURE MAY CAUSE ANOREXIA, FURRED TONGUE, CONSTIPATION, FOUL BREATH, CONFUSION, IMPAIRED MEMORY, HALLUCINATIONS, AND DISTURBANCES OF COLOR VISION, DROWSINESS, EXTREME EXCITEMENT, PARANOIA, OCULAR BOBBING, HEADACHE, WEAKNESS, FATIGUE, IRRITABILITY, ATAXIA, VERTIGO, CONFUSION, SLUGGISHNESS, THICKENED SPEECH, COMA, TREMORS, INCOORDINATION, A STAGGERING GAIT, POSITIVE BABINSKI TEST (WEAK ACHILLES TENDON REFLEX), HYPERACTIVE OF HYPOACTIVE DEEP TENDON REFLEX, PAPILLEDEMA AND INCREASED SPINAL FLUID PRESSURES. THE MENTAL AND NEUROLOGICAL EFFECTS ARE EXTREMELY VARIABLE, RANGING FROM MERE ACCENTUATION OF THE SEDATIVE EFFECTS OF THE DRUG TO OVERT MANIA, DELIRIUM, HALLUCINATIONS AND COMA. TRANSITORY SCHIZOPHRENIA HAS BEEN REPORTED DURING BROMIDE INTOXICATION.

FIRST AID- REMOVE BY EMESIS. MAINTAIN BLOOD PRESSURE AND AIRWAY. GIVE OXYGEN IF RESPIRATION IS DEPRESSED. DO NOT INDUCE VOMITING IN AN UNCONSCIOUS PERSON. GET MEDICAL ATTENTION IMMEDIATELY. OXYGEN MUST BE ADMINISTERED BY QUALIFIED MEDICAL PERSONNEL. (DREISBACH, HANDBOOK OF POISONING, 11TH ED.)

ANTIDOTE: THE FOLLOWING ANTIDOTE HAS BEEN RECOMMENDED. HOWEVER, THE DECISION AS TO WHETHER THE SEVERITY OF POISONING REQUIRES ADMINISTRATION OF ANY ANTIDOTE AND ACTUAL DOSE REQUIRED SHOULD BE MADE BY QUALIFIED MEDICAL PERSONNEL.
BROMIDE POISONING: GIVE SODIUM CHLORIDE, 1 GRAM ORALLY EVERY HOUR IN WATER OR AS SALT TABLETS; FOR MORE SEVERE INVOLVEMENT IN WHICH ORAL MEDICATION IS IMPOSSIBLE, GIVE NORMAL SALINE, 1 LITER EVERY 8 HOURS INTRAVENOUSLY TO A MAXIMUM OF 2 LITERS DAILY. SODIUM CHLORIDE THERAPY MUST BE CONTINUED UNTIL THE BLOOD BROMIDE LEVEL DROPS BELOW 50 MG/DL. SIMULTANEOUS ADMINISTRATION OF DIURETICS IS ALSO USEFUL (DREISBACH, HANDBOOK OF POISONING, 11TH ED.). ANTIDOTE SHOULD BE ADMINISTERED BY QUALIFIED MEDICAL PERSONNEL.

REACTIVITY

REACTIVITY: STABLE UNDER NORMAL TEMPERATURES AND PRESSURES.
INCOMPATIBILITIES: POTASSIUM BROMIDE: BROMINE TRIFLUORIDE: REACTS VIOLENTLY. STRONG ACIDS: REACT TO FORM CORROSIVE HYDROGEN BROMIDE.

DECOMPOSITION: THERMAL DECOMPOSITION EMITS TOXIC FUMES OF BROMINE.
POLYMERIZATION: HAZARDOUS POLYMERIZATION HAS NOT BEEN REPORTED TO OCCUR UNDER NORMAL TEMPERATURES AND PRESSURES.

CONDITIONS TO AVOID

NONE REPORTED.

SPILL AND LEAK PROCEDURES

OCCUPATIONAL SPILL: NO SPECIAL PRECAUTIONS INDICATED.

PROTECTIVE EQUIPMENT

VENTILATION: PROVIDE LOCAL EXHAUST OR GENERAL DILUTION VENTILATION SYSTEM.
RESPIRATOR: THE FOLLOWING RESPIRATORS ARE RECOMMENDED BASED ON INFORMATION FOUND IN THE PHYSICAL DATA, TOXICITY AND HEALTH EFFECTS SECTIONS. THEY ARE RANKED IN ORDER FROM MINIMUM TO MAXIMUM RESPIRATORY PROTECTION. THE SPECIFIC RESPIRATOR SELECTED MUST BE BASED ON CONTAMINATION LEVELS FOUND IN THE WORK PLACE, MUST NOT EXCEED THE WORKING LIMITS OF THE RESPIRATOR AND BE JOINTLY APPROVED BY THE NATIONAL INSTITUTE FOR OCCUPATIONAL SAFETY AND HEALTH AND THE MINE SAFETY AND HEALTH ADMINISTRATION (NIOSH-MSHA).
DUST AND MIST RESPIRATOR WITH A FULL FACEPIECE.
AIR-PURIFYING FULL FACEPIECE RESPIRATOR WITH A HIGH-EFFICIENCY PARTICULATE FILTER.
POWERED AIR-PURIFYING RESPIRATOR WITH A TIGHT-FITTING FACEPIECE AND HIGH-EFFICIENCY PARTICULATE FILTER.
TYPE 'C' SUPPLIED-AIR RESPIRATOR WITH A FULL FACEPIECE OPERATED IN PRESSURE-DEMAND OR OTHER POSITIVE PRESSURE MODE OR WITH A FULL FACEPIECE, HELMET OR HOOD OPERATED IN CONTINUOUS-FLOW MODE.
SELF-CONTAINED BREATHING APPARATUS WITH A FULL FACEPIECE OPERATED IN PRESSURE-DEMAND OR OTHER POSITIVE PRESSURE MODE.
FOR FIREFIGHTING AND OTHER IMMEDIATELY DANGEROUS TO LIFE OR HEALTH CONDITIONS:
SELF-CONTAINED BREATHING APPARATUS WITH FULL FACEPIECE OPERATED IN PRESSURE-DEMAND OR OTHER POSITIVE PRESSURE MODE.
SUPPLIED-AIR RESPIRATOR WITH FULL FACEPIECE AND OPERATED IN PRESSURE-DEMAND OR OTHER POSITIVE PRESSURE MODE IN COMBINATION WITH AN AUXILIARY SELF-CONTAINED BREATHING APPARATUS OPERATED IN PRESSURE-DEMAND OR OTHER POSITIVE PRESSURE MODE.
CLOTHING: EMPLOYEE MUST WEAR APPROPRIATE PROTECTIVE (IMPERVIOUS) CLOTHING AND EQUIPMENT TO PREVENT REPEATED OR PROLONGED SKIN CONTACT WITH THIS SUBSTANCE.
GLOVES: EMPLOYEE MUST WEAR APPROPRIATE PROTECTIVE GLOVES TO PREVENT CONTACT WITH THIS SUBSTANCE.
EYE PROTECTION: EMPLOYEE MUST WEAR SPLASH-PROOF OR DUST-RESISTANT SAFETY GOGGLES TO PREVENT EYE CONTACT WITH THIS SUBSTANCE.
EMERGENCY EYE WASH: WHERE THERE IS ANY POSSIBILITY THAT AN EMPLOYEE'S EYES MAY BE EXPOSED TO THIS SUBSTANCE, THE EMPLOYER SHOULD PROVIDE AN EYE WASH FOUNTAIN WITHIN THE IMMEDIATE WORK AREA FOR EMERGENCY USE.

AUTHORIZED BY- OCCUPATIONAL HEALTH SERVICES, INC.
CREATION DATE: 10/04/89 ***REVISION DATE:*** 05/18/90

MATERIAL SAFETY DATA SHEET

OCCUPATIONAL HEALTH SERVICES, INC.
AGRICULTURE AND PESTICIDE DIVISION
450 SEVENTH AVENUE, SUITE 2407
NEW YORK, NEW YORK 10123
1-800-445-MSDS OR (212) 967-1100

EMERGENCY CONTACT:
JOHN S. BRANSFORD, JR. (615) 292-1180

SUBSTANCE IDENTIFICATION

CAS-NUMBER 584-08-7
SUBSTANCE: POTASSIUM CARBONATE
TRADE NAMES/SYNONYMS: CARBONIC ACID, DIPOTASSIUM SALT; SALT OF TARTAR; POTASH; PEARL ASH; DIPOTASSIUM CARBONATE; PST19290
CHEMICAL FAMILY: INORGANIC SALT
MOLECULAR FORMULA: C-O3.2K
MOLECULAR WEIGHT: 138.21
CERCLA RATINGS (SCALE 0-3): HEALTH=2 FIRE=0 REACTIVITY=1
PERSISTENCE=0
NFPA RATINGS (SCALE 0-4): HEALTH=2 FIRE=0 REACTIVITY=1

COMPONENTS AND CONTAMINANTS

COMPONENT: POTASSIUM CARBONATE ***PERCENT:*** 100
CAS# 584-08-7
OTHER CONTAMINANTS: NONE
EXPOSURE LIMITS: NO OCCUPATIONAL EXPOSURE LIMITS ESTABLISHED BY OSHA, ACGIH, OR NIOSH.

PHYSICAL DATA

DESCRIPTION: ODORLESS, COLORLESS, HYGROSCOPIC, MONOCLINIC CRYSTALS, GRANULES OR POWDER WITH A STRONG ALKALINE TASTE. ***BOILING POINT:*** DECOMPOSES
MELTING POINT: 1636 F (891 C) ***SPECIFIC GRAVITY:*** 2.428 ***PH:*** 11.6
SOLUBILITY IN WATER: 112% @ 20 C
SOLVENT SOLUBILITY: INSOLUBLE IN ALCOHOL, ACETONE, ETHYL ALCOHOL

FIRE AND EXPLOSION DATA

FIRE AND EXPLOSION HAZARD: NEGLIGIBLE FIRE HAZARD WHEN EXPOSED TO HEAT OR FLAME.
FIREFIGHTING MEDIA: DRY CHEMICAL, CARBON DIOXIDE, WATER SPRAY OR FOAM FOR LARGER FIRES, USE WATER SPRAY, FOG OR ALCOHOL FOAM
FIREFIGHTING: MOVE CONTAINER FROM FIRE AREA IF POSSIBLE. DO NOT SCATTER SPILLED MATERIAL WITH MORE WATER THAN NEEDED FOR FIRE CONTROL. DIKE FIRE CONTROL WATER FOR LATER DISPOSAL
USE AGENTS SUITABLE FOR TYPE OF SURROUNDING FIRE. AVOID BREATHING HAZARDOUS VAPORS, KEEP UPWIND.

TOXICITY

POTASSIUM CARBONATE: TOXICITY DATA: ANHYDROUS: 1870 MG/KG ORAL-RAT LD50. SESQUIHYDRATE: NO DATA AVAILABLE. CARCINOGEN STATUS: NONE. LOCAL EFFECTS: IRRITANT- INHALATION, SKIN, EYES. ACUTE TOXICITY LEVEL: MODERATELY TOXIC BY INGESTION. TARGET EFFECTS: NO DATA AVAILABLE.

HEALTH EFFECTS AND FIRST AID

INHALATION: POTASSIUM CARBONATE: IRRITANT. **ACUTE EXPOSURE-** INHALATION OF DUSTS MAY CAUSE MUCOUS MEMBRANE EFFECTS INCLUDING COUGH, PAINFUL THROAT AND NASAL IRRITATION. SUPERFICIAL DESTRUCTION OF THE MUCOUS MEMBRANES MAY OCCUR. **CHRONIC EXPOSURE-** PROLONGED INHALATION OF ALKALINE MATERIALS MAY PRODUCE LESIONS OF THE NASAL SEPTUM.
FIRST AID- REMOVE FROM EXPOSURE AREA TO FRESH AIR IMMEDIATELY. IF BREATHING HAS STOPPED, GIVE ARTIFICIAL RESPIRATION. MAINTAIN AIRWAY AND BLOOD PRESSURE AND ADMINISTER OXYGEN IF AVAILABLE. KEEP AFFECTED PERSON WARM AND AT REST. TREAT SYMPTOMATICALLY AND SUPPORTIVELY. ADMINISTRATION OF OXYGEN SHOULD BE PERFORMED BY QUALIFIED PERSONNEL. GET MEDICAL ATTENTION IMMEDIATELY.

SKIN CONTACT: POTASSIUM CARBONATE: IRRITANT. **ACUTE EXPOSURE-** DIRECT CONTACT MAY PRODUCE STRONG IRRITATION AND SUPERFICIAL DESTRUCTION OF THE SKIN. DEPENDING UPON THE DURATION OF CONTACT; BURNS MAY OCCUR. **CHRONIC EXPOSURE-** PROLONGED CONTACT WITH CARBONATE SOLUTIONS MAY CAUSE ECZEMA, DERMATITIS AND ULCERATION. CONTACT WITH BAGGED CARBONATES MAY CAUSE CHERRY-SIZED NECROTIC PORTIONS OF THE SKIN. SUBSEQUENT DEEP ULCERATED PITTING OF THE SKIN IS SOMETIMES OBSERVED.
FIRST AID- REMOVE CONTAMINATED CLOTHING AND SHOES IMMEDIATELY. WASH AFFECTED AREA WITH SOAP OR MILD DETERGENT AND LARGE AMOUNTS OF WATER UNTIL NO EVIDENCE OF CHEMICAL REMAINS (AT LEAST 15-20 MINUTES). IN CASE OF CHEMICAL BURNS, COVER AREA WITH STERILE, DRY DRESSING. BANDAGE SECURELY, BUT NOT TOO TIGHTLY. GET MEDICAL ATTENTION IMMEDIATELY.

EYE CONTACT: POTASSIUM CARBONATE: IRRITANT. **ACUTE EXPOSURE-** CONTACT WITH DUSTS MAY CAUSE IRRITATION. EXPERIMENTAL IRRIGATION OF THE SURFACE OF THE EYES OF RABBITS WITH A 10% SOLUTION AT PH 11.6 FOR 30 SECONDS CAUSED PAIN AND VERY SLIGHT TRANSIENT OPTICAL IRREGULARITY OF THE EPITHELIUM. HOWEVER, 1 TO 2 HOURS LATER THE CORNEAS AND CONJUNCTIVA APPEARED NORMAL UPON EXAMINATION. CONCENTRATED ALKALIES MAY CAUSE CONJUNCTIVAL EDEMA AND CORNEAL DESTRUCTION. **CHRONIC EXPOSURE-** REPEATED OR PROLONGED EXPOSURE TO IRRITANTS MAY CAUSE CONJUNCTIVITIS.
FIRST AID- WASH EYES IMMEDIATELY WITH LARGE AMOUNTS OF WATER, OCCASIONALLY LIFTING UPPER AND LOWER LIDS, UNTIL NO EVIDENCE OF CHEMICAL REMAINS (AT LEAST 15-20 MINUTES). CONTINUE IRRIGATING WITH NORMAL SALINE UNTIL THE PH HAS RETURNED TO NORMAL (30-60 MINUTES). COVER WITH STERILE BANDAGES. GET MEDICAL ATTENTION IMMEDIATELY.

INGESTION: POTASSIUM CARBONATE: **ACUTE EXPOSURE-** THE ESTIMATED FATAL DOSE FOR POTASSIUM CARBONATE IS 20 GRAMS. INGESTION OF A STRONG ALKALI MAY CAUSE SEVERE PAIN, VOMITING, DIARRHEA, AND COLLAPSE. THE VOMITUS MAY CONTAIN BLOOD AND DESQUAMATED MUCOSAL LINING. IF DEATH DOES NOT OCCUR IN THE FIRST 24 HOURS, THE PATIENT MAY IMPROVE FOR 2-4 DAYS AND THEN HAVE A SUDDEN ONSET OF SEVERE ABDOMINAL PAIN, BOARDLIKE ABDOMINAL RIGIDITY, AND RAPID FALL OF BLOOD PRESSURE INDICATING DELAYED GASTRIC OR ESOPHAGEAL PERFORATION. EVEN THOUGH THE PATIENT RECOVERS FROM THE IMMEDIATE DAMAGE, ESOPHAGEAL STRICTURE CAN OCCUR WEEKS, MONTHS, OR EVEN YEARS LATER TO MAKE SWALLOWING DIFFICULT. APPROXIMATELY 25% OF THOSE WHO INGEST STRONG ALKALI DIE FROM THE IMMEDIATE EFFECTS. DAMAGE TO THE ESOPHAGUS AND STOMACH AFTER INGESTION MAY PROGRESS FOR 2-3 WEEKS. DEATH FROM PERITONITIS MAY OCCUR AS LATE AS 1 MONTH AFTER INGESTION. APPROXIMATELY 95% OF THOSE WHO INGEST STRONG ALKALI AND RECOVER FROM THE IMMEDIATE EFFECTS HAVE PERSISTENT ESOPHAGEAL STRICTURE. **CHRONIC EXPOSURE-** IN A STUDY FOR THE FOOD AND DRUG ADMINISTRATION, POTASSIUM CARBONATE WAS FOUND TO BE NONTERATOGENIC IN MICE WHEN THEY WERE GIVEN DAILY ORAL INTUBATIONS OF UP TO 290 MG/KG ON DAYS 6-15 OF GESTATION.

FIRST AID- DILUTE THE ALKALI BY GIVING WATER OR MILK IMMEDIATELY AND ALLOW VOMITING TO OCCUR. AVOID GASTRIC LAVAGE OR EMETICS. ESOPHAGOSCOPY IS THE ONLY WAY TO EXCLUDE THE POSSIBLITY OF CORROSION IN THE UPPER GASTROINTESTINAL TRACT; IF CORROSION IS SUSPECTED, ESOPHAGOSCOPY SHOULD USUALLY BE PERFORMED WITHIN 24 HOURS (DREISBACH, HANDBOOK OF POISONING, 12TH ED.). MAINTAIN AIRWAY AND TREAT SHOCK. IF VOMITING OCCURS, KEEP HEAD BELOW HIPS TO HELP PREVENT ASPIRATION. GET MEDICAL ATTENTION IMMEDIATELY.

ANTIDOTE: NO SPECIFIC ANTIDOTE. TREAT SYMPTOMATICALLY AND SUPPORTIVELY.

REACTIVITY

REACTIVITY: REACTS WITH WATER WITH THE EVOLUTION OF HEAT.

INCOMPATIBILITIES: POTASSIUM CARBONATE: ACIDS: EXOTHERMIC REACTION. CARBON: POSSIBLE EXPLOSION ON HEATING. CHLORINE TRIFLUORIDE: VIOLENT REACTION WITH IGNITION. MAGNESIUM: FORMATION OF EXPLOSIVE COMPOUND ON HEATING.

DECOMPOSITION: THERMAL DECOMPOSITION PRODUCTS MAY INCLUDE TOXIC OXIDES OF CARBON.

POLYMERIZATION: HAZARDOUS POLYMERIZATION HAS NOT BEEN REPORTED TO OCCUR UNDER NORMAL TEMPERATURES AND PRESSURES.

STORAGE AND DISPOSAL

OBSERVE ALL FEDERAL, STATE AND LOCAL REGULATIONS WHEN STORING OR DISPOSING OF THIS SUBSTANCE. FOR ASSISTANCE, CONTACT THE DISTRICT DIRECTOR OF THE ENVIRONMENTAL PROTECTION AGENCY.

STORAGE

STORE AWAY FROM INCOMPATIBLE SUBSTANCES.

CONDITIONS TO AVOID

NONE REPORTED.

SPILL AND LEAK PROCEDURES

OCCUPATIONAL SPILL: NO SPECIAL PRECAUTIONS INDICATED.

PROTECTIVE EQUIPMENT

VENTILATION: PROVIDE LOCAL EXHAUST OR GENERAL DILUTION VENTILATION SYSTEM.

RESPIRATOR: THE FOLLOWING RESPIRATORS ARE RECOMMENDED BASED ON INFORMATION FOUND IN THE PHYSICAL DATA, TOXICITY AND HEALTH EFFECTS SECTIONS. THEY ARE RANKED IN ORDER FROM MINIMUM TO MAXIMUM RESPIRATORY PROTECTION. THE SPECIFIC RESPIRATOR SELECTED MUST BE BASED ON CONTAMINATION LEVELS FOUND IN THE WORK PLACE, MUST NOT EXCEED THE WORKING LIMITS OF THE RESPIRATOR AND BE JOINTLY APPROVED BY THE NATIONAL INSTITUTE FOR OCCUPATIONAL SAFETY AND HEALTH AND THE MINE SAFETY AND HEALTH ADMINISTRATION (NIOSH-MSHA).

DUST AND MIST RESPIRATOR WITH A FULL FACEPIECE.

AIR-PURIFYING FULL FACEPIECE RESPIRATOR WITH A HIGH-EFFICIENCY PARTICULATE FILTER.

POWERED AIR-PURIFYING RESPIRATOR WITH A TIGHT-FITTING FACEPIECE AND HIGH-EFFICIENCY PARTICULATE FILTER.

TYPE 'C' SUPPLIED-AIR RESPIRATOR WITH A FULL FACEPIECE OPERATED IN PRESSURE-DEMAND OR OTHER POSITIVE PRESSURE MODE OR WITH A FULL FACEPIECE, HELMET OR HOOD OPERATED IN CONTINUOUS-FLOW MODE.

SELF-CONTAINED BREATHING APPARATUS WITH A FULL FACEPIECE OPERATED IN PRESSURE-DEMAND OR OTHER POSITIVE PRESSURE MODE.

FOR FIREFIGHTING AND OTHER IMMEDIATELY DANGEROUS TO LIFE OR HEALTH CONDITIONS:

SELF-CONTAINED BREATHING APPARATUS WITH FULL FACEPIECE OPERATED IN PRESSURE-DEMAND OR OTHER POSITIVE PRESSURE MODE.

SUPPLIED-AIR RESPIRATOR WITH FULL FACEPIECE AND OPERATED IN PRESSURE-DEMAND OR OTHER POSITIVE PRESSURE MODE IN COMBINATION WITH AN AUXILIARY SELF-CONTAINED BREATHING APPARATUS OPERATED IN PRESSURE-DEMAND OR OTHER POSITIVE PRESSURE MODE.

CLOTHING: EMPLOYEE MUST WEAR APPROPRIATE PROTECTIVE (IMPERVIOUS) CLOTHING AND EQUIPMENT TO PREVENT ANY POSSIBILITY OF SKIN CONTACT WITH THIS SUBSTANCE.

GLOVES: EMPLOYEE MUST WEAR APPROPRIATE PROTECTIVE GLOVES TO PREVENT CONTACT WITH THIS SUBSTANCE.

EYE PROTECTION: EMPLOYEE MUST WEAR SPLASH-PROOF OR DUST-RESISTANT SAFETY GOGGLES AND A FACESHIELD TO PREVENT CONTACT WITH THIS SUBSTANCE.

EMERGENCY WASH FACILITIES: WHERE THERE IS ANY POSSIBILITY THAT AN EMPLOYEE'S EYES AND/OR SKIN MAY BE EXPOSED TO THIS SUBSTANCE, THE EMPLOYER SHOULD PROVIDE AN EYE WASH FOUNTAIN AND QUICK DRENCH SHOWER WITHIN THE IMMEDIATE WORK AREA FOR EMERGENCY USE.

AUTHORIZED BY- OCCUPATIONAL HEALTH SERVICES, INC.

CREATION DATE: 11/17/89 ***REVISION DATE:*** 05/15/90

MATERIAL SAFETY DATA SHEET

OCCUPATIONAL HEALTH SERVICES, INC.
AGRICULTURE AND PESTICIDE DIVISION
450 SEVENTH AVENUE, SUITE 2407
NEW YORK, NEW YORK 10123
1-800-445-MSDS OR (212) 967-1100

EMERGENCY CONTACT:
JOHN S. BRANSFORD, JR. (615) 292-1180

SUBSTANCE IDENTIFICATION

CAS-NUMBER 151-50-8

SUBSTANCE: **POTASSIUM CYANIDE, SOLID**

TRADE NAMES/SYNONYMS: HYDROCYANIC ACID, POTASSIUM SALT; POTASSIUM CYANIDE (K(CN)); RCRA P098; STCC 4923226; UN 1680; POTASSIUM CYANIDE; CYANIDE OF POTASSIUM; P-225I; P-226I; CKN; PST19350

CHEMICAL FAMILY: CYANIDE

MOLECULAR FORMULA: K-C-N

MOLECULAR WEIGHT: 65.12

CERCLA RATINGS (SCALE 0-3): HEALTH=3 FIRE=0 REACTIVITY=0 PERSISTENCE=0

NFPA RATINGS (SCALE 0-4): HEALTH=3 FIRE=0 REACTIVITY=0

COMPONENTS AND CONTAMINANTS

COMPONENT: POTASSIUM CYANIDE ***PERCENT:*** 100
CAS# 151-50-8

OTHER CONTAMINANTS: NONE

EXPOSURE LIMITS: POTASSIUM CYANIDE: 5 MG(CN)/M3 OSHA TWA (SKIN) 5 MG(CN)/M3 ACGIH TWA (SKIN) 5 MG(CN)/M3/10 MINUTES NIOSH RECOMMENDED CEILING

100 POUNDS SARA SECTION 302 THRESHOLD PLANNING QUANTITY 10 POUNDS SARA SECTION 304 REPORTABLE QUANTITY 10 POUNDS CERLCA SECTION 103 REPORTABLE QUANTITY SUBJECT TO SARA SECTION 313 ANNUAL TOXIC CHEMICAL RELEASE REPORTING

PHYSICAL DATA

DESCRIPTION: COLORLESS DELIQUESCENT CUBES OR WHITE GRANULES WITH A FAINT ODOR OF BITTER ALMONDS WHEN MOIST. ***BOILING POINT:*** 2957 F (1625 C)

MELTING POINT: 1175 F (635 C) ***SPECIFIC GRAVITY:*** 1.52 @ 16 C

VAPOR PRESSURE: <0.1 MMHG @ 20 C ***PH:*** 11 @ 0.1N SOLN.

SOLUBILITY IN WATER: 72%

SOLVENT SOLUBILITY: SOLUBLE IN GLYCEROL; SLIGHTLY SOLUBLE IN METHANOL; ALMOST INSOLUBLE IN ETHANOL.

FIRE AND EXPLOSION DATA

FIRE AND EXPLOSION HAZARD: NEGLIGIBLE FIRE HAZARD WHEN EXPOSED TO HEAT OR FLAME.

FIREFIGHTING MEDIA: DRY CHEMICAL, CARBON DIOXIDE, HALON, WATER SPRAY OR STANDARD FOAM (1987 EMERGENCY RESPONSE GUIDEBOOK, DOT P 5800.4).

FOR LARGER FIRES, USE WATER SPRAY, FOG OR STANDARD FOAM (1987 EMERGENCY RESPONSE GUIDEBOOK, DOT P 5800.4).

FIREFIGHTING: MOVE CONTAINERS FROM FIRE AREA IF POSSIBLE. FIGHT FIRE FROM MAXIMUM DISTANCE. STAY AWAY FROM STORAGE TANK ENDS. DIKE FIRE CONTROL WATER FOR LATER DISPOSAL. DO NOT SCATTER MATERIAL (1987 EMERGENCY RESPONSE GUIDEBOOK, DOT P 5800.4, GUIDE PAGE 55).
USE AGENT SUITABLE FOR TYPE OF FIRE. USE WATER IN FLOODING AMOUNTS AS FOG. COOL CONTAINERS WITH FLOODING QUANTITIES OF WATER, APPLY FROM AS FAR A DISTANCE AS POSSIBLE. AVOID BREATHING POISONOUS VAPORS, KEEP UPWIND.

TRANSPORTATION DATA

DEPARTMENT OF TRANSPORTATION HAZARD CLASSIFICATION 49 CFR 172.101: POISON B
DEPARTMENT OF TRANSPORTATION LABELING REQUIREMENTS 49 CFR 172.101 AND SUBPART E: POISON
DEPARTMENT OF TRANSPORTATION PACKAGING REQUIREMENTS: 49 CFR 173.370 EXCEPTIONS: 49 CFR 173.370

TOXICITY

POTASSIUM CYANIDE: TOXICITY DATA: 7870 UG/KG OCULAR-RABBIT LD50; 2857 UG/KG ORAL-HUMAN LDLO; 14 MG/KG ORAL-MAN TDLO; 5 MG/KG ORAL-RAT LD50; 8500 UG/KG ORAL-MOUSE LD50; 5 MG/KG ORAL-RABBIT LD50; 9 MG/KG SUBCUTANEOUS-RAT LD50; 6500 UG/KG SUBCUTANEOUS-MOUSE LD50; 4 MG/KG SUBCUTANEOUS-RABBIT LD50; 8 MG/KG SUBCUTANEOUS-GUINEA PIG LDLO; 3600 UG/KG INTRAVENOUS-RAT LD50; 2600 UG/KG INTRAVENOUS-MOUSE LD50; 5 MG/KG INTRAVENOUS-GUINEA PIG LDLO; 4 MG/KG INTRAPERITONEAL-RAT LD50; 5991 UG/KG INTRAPERITONEAL-MOUSE LD50; 8 MG/KG INTRAMUSCULAR-RAT LDLO; 3256 UG/KG INTRAMUSCULAR-RABBIT LD50; 5 MG/KG INTRAARTERIAL-GUINEA PIG LDLO; MUTAGENIC DATA (RTECS); REPRODUCTIVE EFFECTS DATA (RTECS). CARCINOGEN STATUS: NONE. LOCAL EFFECTS: CORROSIVE- INHALATION, SKIN, AND EYES. ACUTE TOXICITY LEVEL: HIGHLY TOXIC BY INGESTION. TARGET EFFECTS: CHEMICAL ASPHYXIANT. POISONING MAY AFFECT THE RESPIRATORY, CARDIOVASCULAR, AND CENTRAL NERVOUS SYSTEMS. AT INCREASED RISK FROM EXPOSURE: PERSONS WITH A HISTORY OF FANTING SPELLS (SYMPTOMS OF VARIOUS TYPES OF CARDIOVASCULAR AND NERVOUS DISORDERS), UNUSUAL SUSCEPTIBILITY TO EFFECTS OF ANOXIA OR WITH ANEMIA, PRE-EXISTING SKIN DISORDERS AND/OR IMPAIRED PULMONARY FUNCTION.

HEALTH EFFECTS AND FIRST AID

INHALATION: POTASSIUM CYANIDE, SOLID: IRRITANT/CHEMICAL ASPHYXIANT. 50 MG/M3 IMMEDIATELY DANGEROUS TO LIFE OR HEALTH. **ACUTE EXPOSURE**- MAY CAUSE IRRITATION TO THE NOSE AND MUCOUS MEMBRANES. MISTS OF ALKALI CYANIDES, IN CONCENTRATIONS SLIGHTLY MORE THAN 5 MG/M3 HAVE BEEN REPORTED TO CAUSE NOSEBLEED AND NASAL ULCERATION. IF SUFFICIENT AMOUNTS ARE ABSORBED, SYSTEMIC EFFECTS MAY OCCUR, AS IN ACUTE INGESTION. **CHRONIC EXPOSURE**- EXPOSURE TO LOW LEVELS OF CYANIDE COMPOUNDS OVER LONG PERIODS OF TIME, IS REPORTED TO CAUSE LOSS OF APPETITE, HEADACHE, WEAKNESS, NAUSEA, DIZZINESS AND SYMPTOMS OF UPPER RESPIRATORY TRACT IRRITATION.

FIRST AID- REMOVE FROM EXPOSURE. IF BREATHING HAS STOPPED OR IS DEPRESSED, GIVE ARTIFICIAL RESPIRATION. MAINTAIN AIRWAY AND ADMINISTER OXYGEN TO MAINTAIN HIGH BLOOD/OXYGEN TENSION. GET MEDICAL ATTENTION IMMEDIATELY. (DREISBACH, HANDBOOK OF POISONING, 11TH ED.).

SKIN CONTACT: POTASSIUM CYANIDE, SOLID: CORROSIVE/ASPHYXIANT. **ACUTE EXPOSURE**- DIRECT CONTACT WITH AQUEOUS SOLUTIONS OR SOLID ON MOIST SKIN MAY CAUSE REDNESS, PAIN, BURNS, CONTACT DERMATITIS AND ULCERS WHICH ARE SLOW TO HEAL. A SOLUTION CAUSED SEVERE PRURITIS AND BROWNISH-RED PIGMENTATION ON THE FOREARMS. IT MAY BE ABSORBED THROUGH THE SKIN, ESPECIALLY IF OPEN WOUNDS ARE PRESENT. IF SUFFICIENT AMOUNTS ARE ABSORBED, SYSTEMIC EFFECTS MAY OCCUR, AS IN ACUTE INGESTION. **CHRONIC EXPOSURE**- PROLONGED AND REPEATED EXPOSURE MAY CAUSE DERMATITIS AND "CYANIDE RASH", CHARACTERIZED BY ITCHING, MACULAR, PAPULAR AND VESICULAR ERUPTIONS. EXPOSURE TO LOW LEVELS OF CYANIDE COMPOUNDS OVER LONG PERIODS OF TIME IS REPORTED TO CAUSE LOSS OF APPETITE, HEADACHE, WEAKNESS, NAUSEA, AND DIZZINESS.

FIRST AID- REMOVE CONTAMINATED CLOTHING AND SHOES AND WASH AFFECTED AREAS WITH SOAP OR MILD DETERGENT AND LARGE AMOUNTS OF WATER, TAKING CARE NOT TO CONTACT THE CHEMICAL. GET MEDICAL ATTENTION IMMEDIATELY. (CAIN, EMERGENCY TREATMENT AND MANAGEMENT, 7TH ED.).

EYE CONTACT: POTASSIUM CYANIDE, SOLID: CORROSIVE/CHEMICAL ASPHYXIANT/HIGHLY TOXIC. **ACUTE EXPOSURE**- DUST MAY CAUSE IRRITATION . SOLUTIONS ARE CORROSIVE AND MAY CAUSE REDNESS, PAIN, BLURRED VISION, AND SERIOUS CORNEAL BURNS. THE LETHAL DOSE FOR RABBITS IS 7870 UG/KG. IN THE PRESENCE OF TEARS, SYSTEMIC INTOXICATION MAY OCCUR, DEMONSTRATING SYMPTOMS SIMILAR TO THOSE DESCRIBED IN ACUTE INGESTION SECTION. **CHRONIC EXPOSURE**- EFFECTS DEPEND ON CONCENTRATION AND DURATION OF EXPOSURE. REPEATED OR PROLONGED CONTACT WITH CORROSIVE SUBSTANCES MAY RESULT IN CONJUNCTIVITIS OR EFFECTS AS IN ACUTE EXPOSURE.

FIRST AID- WASH EYES IMMEDIATELY WITH LARGE AMOUNTS OF WATER, OCCASIONALLY LIFTING UPPER AND LOWER LIDS, UNTIL NO EVIDENCE OF CHEMICAL REMAINS (AT LEAST 15-20 MINUTES). CONTINUE IRRIGATING WITH NORMAL SALINE UNTIL THE PH HAS RETURNED TO NORMAL (30-60 MINUTES). COVER WITH STERILE BANDAGES. GET MEDICAL ATTENTION IMMEDIATELY.

INGESTION: POTASSIUM CYANIDE, SOLID: CORROSIVE/CHEMICAL ASPHYXIANT/ HIGHLY TOXIC. **ACUTE EXPOSURE**- DEATH HAS BEEN REPORTED IN A HUMAN FROM A DOSE AS LOW AS 2857 UG/KG. MASSIVE DOSES MAY RESULT IN IMMEDIATE UNCONSCIOUSNESS, OFTEN WITH CONVULSIONS AND DEATH, USUALLY WITHIN 1-15 MINUTES. LOWER LEVELS MAY RESULT IN CORROSION OF THE GASTRIC MUCOSA, A BITTER ALMOND ODOR ON THE BREATH, A BURNING TASTE, FEELING OF CONSTRICTION OF THE THROAT, BLOTCHY SKIN ERUPTIONS ON THE FACE, SALIVATION, NAUSEA WITH OR WITHOUT VOMITING, ANXIETY, CONFUSION, VERTIGO, GIDDINESS, WEAKNESS, HEADACHE, RAPID PULSE, PALPITATIONS, LOWER JAW STIFFNESS, AND OPISTHOTONOS. RESPIRATORY RATE AND DEPTH USUALLY INCREASE INITIALLY, BECOMING SLOW AND GASPING. CYANOSIS, COMA, CONVULSIONS, AND BRADYCARDIA OCCUR IN SOME CASES. INVOLUNTARY MICTURITION AND DEFECATION MAY OCCUR. PARALYSIS MAY FOLLOW THE CONVULSIVE STAGE. THE EYEBALLS MAY PROTRUDE AND THE PUPILS MAY BE UNREACTIVE. DAMAGE TO THE OPTIC NERVES AND RETINA AND BLINDNESS ARE POSSIBLE. THE MOUTH MAY BE COVERED WITH FOAM, WHICH IS SOMETIMES BLOOD-STAINED, INDICATIVE OF PULMONARY EDEMA. IF DEATH OCCURS IT IS USUALLY WITHIN 4 HOURS AND MAY BE DUE TO RESPIRATORY ARREST OR TISSUE ANOXIA. OTHER SYMPTOMS MAY INCLUDE CHEST PAIN, CHERRY-RED COLORING, IRREGULAR SPEECH, AND A TRANSIENT STAGE OF CENTRAL NERVOUS SYSTEM STIMULATION WITH HYPERPNEA AND HEADACHE. **CHRONIC EXPOSURE**- EXPOSURE TO LOW LEVELS OF CYANIDE COMPOUNDS OVER LONG PERIODS OF TIME, IS REPORTED TO CAUSE LOSS OF APPETITE, HEADACHE, WEAKNESS, NAUSEA, AND DIZZINESS.

FIRST AID- IF PATIENT IS ASYMPTOMATIC ADMINISTER SYRUP OF IPECAC AND/OR PERFORM GASTRIC LAVAGE, USING TAP WATER, DILUTE SODIUM BICARBONATE SOLUTION OR PREFERABLY, IF AVAILABLE, DILUTE POTASSIUM PERMANGANATE SOLUTION (1:5000). ACTIVATED CHARCOAL IS INEFFECTIVE. IF BREATHING HAS STOPPED, GIVE ARTIFICIAL RESPIRATION. MAINTAIN AIRWAY. OXYGEN THERAPY MAY BE OF VALUE IN COMBINATION WITH THE ANTIDOTE (GOSSELIN, CLINICAL TOXICOLOGY OF COMMERCIAL PRODUCTS, 5TH ED.). TREATMENT SHOULD BE PERFORMED BY QUALIFIED MEDICAL PERSONNEL. GET MEDICAL ATTENTION IMMEDIATELY.

ANTIDOTE: THE FOLLOWING ANTIDOTE HAS BEEN RECOMMENDED. HOWEVER, THE DECISION AS TO WHETHER THE SEVERITY OF POISONING REQUIRES ADMINISTRATION OF ANY ANTIDOTE AND ACTUAL DOSE REQUIRED SHOULD BE MADE BY QUALIFIED MEDICAL PERSONNEL.
FOR CYANIDE POISONING: IF SYMPTOMS OF CYANIDE POISONING ARE EVIDENT, ADMINISTER IMMEDIATELY BEFORE ANY OTHER FIRST AID MEASURES. ADMINISTER AMYL NITRITE (AMYL NITRITE PERLES) BY INHALATION FOR 15 TO 30 SECONDS OF EVERY MINUTE, WHILE SODIUM NITRITE SOLUTION IS BEING PREPARED. DISCONTINUE AMYL NITRITE AND IMMEDIATELY INJECT 10 ML OF A 3% SOLUTION OF SODIUM NITRITE INTRAVENOUSLY OVER A PERIOD OF 2 TO 4 MINUTES. IF NECESSARY, INJECT A NON-STERILE SOLUTION. DO NOT REMOVE THE NEEDLE. CAUTION: APPROPRIATE ADJUSTMENTS IN THE DOSE SHOULD BE MADE ON A BODY WEIGHT BASIS. THROUGH THE SAME NEEDLE, INFUSE INTRAVENOUSLY 50 ML OF A 25% AQUEOUS SOLUTION OF SODIUM THIOSULFATE. THE INJECTION SHOULD TAKE ABOUT 10 MINUTES. OTHER CONCENTRATIONS (5 TO 50%) ARE PERMISSIBLE IF THE TOTAL DOSE IS HELD AT APPROXIMATELY 12 GRAMS. OXYGEN THERAPY MAY BE OF VALUE IN COMBINATION WITH NITRITE AND SODIUM THIOSULFATE THERAPY. IF SYMPTOMS RECUR, THE INJECTIONS OF NITRITE AND THIOSULFATE MAY BE REPEATED AT HALF THE ABOVE DOSES. IN VERY SEVERE POISONINGS IT IS SAFER AND PERHAPS MORE EFFICIENT TO KEEP REPEATING THE THIOSULFATE INJECTIONS INSTEAD OF THE NITRITE (GOSSELIN, SMITH, HODGE, CLINICAL TOXICOLOGY OF COMMERCIAL PRODUCTS, 5TH ED.). ANTIDOTE SHOULD BE ADMINISTERED BY QUALIFIED MEDICAL PERSONNEL.

REACTIVITY

REACTIVITY: MAY BE SLOWLY DECOMPOSED BY MOISTURE OR CARBON DIOXIDE RELEASING HIGHLY TOXIC HYDROGEN CYANIDE GAS.

INCOMPATIBILITIES: POTASSIUM CYANIDE: ACIDS: VIOLENT REACTION WITH RELEASE OF HIGHLY TOXIC AND FLAMMABLE HYDROGEN CYANIDE. ALKALOIDS: INCOMPATIBLE. ALUMINUM: CORRODES. CHLORAL HYDRATE: INCOMPATIBLE. CHLORATES: EXPLOSIVE REACTION WHEN HEATED. IODINE: INCOMPATIBLE.

MERCURY(II) NITRATE: POSSIBLE EXPLOSION WHEN HEATED UNDER CONFINMENT. METAL SALTS: INCOMPATIBLE. NITRATES: FIRE AND EXPLOSION HAZARD. NITRITES: POSSIBLE EXPLOSIVE REACTION. NITROGEN TRICHLORIDE: EXPLOSIVE DECOMPOSITION REACTION. OXIDIZERS (STRONG): FIRE AND EXPLOSION HAZARD. PERCHLORYL FLUORIDE: POSSIBLE EXPLOSION WHEN HEATED. PERMANGANATES: INCOMPATIBLE. PEROXIDES: INCOMPATIBLE. SODIUM CHLORATE: EXPLOSIVE REACTION WHEN HEATED. SODIUM NITRITE: EXPLOSIVE REACTION WHEN HEATED. ZINC: CORRODES. SEE ALSO CYANIDE SALTS.

CYANIDE SALTS: ACIDS, ACID SALTS: FORM TOXIC AND FLAMMABLE HYDROGEN GAS. CHLORATES: POSSIBLE EXPLOSION ON HEATING. FLUORINE: VIGOROUS REACTION. MAGNESIUM: POSSIBLE INCANDESCENT REACTION. NITRATES (MOLTEN): POSSIBLE EXPLOSIVE REACTION. NITRIC ACID: POSSIBLE EXPLOSIVE REACTION. NITRITES: POSSIBLE EXPLOSION ON HEATING. OXIDIZERS (STRONG): FIRE AND EXPLOSION HAZARD.

DECOMPOSITION: THERMAL DECOMPOSITION PRODUCTS MAY INCLUDE HIGHLY TOXIC FUMES OF HYDROGEN CYANIDE.

POLYMERIZATION: HAZARDOUS POLYMERIZATION HAS NOT BEEN REPORTED TO OCCUR UNDER NORMAL TEMPERATURES AND PRESSURES.

STORAGE AND DISPOSAL

OBSERVE ALL FEDERAL, STATE AND LOCAL REGULATIONS WHEN STORING OR DISPOSING OF THIS SUBSTANCE. FOR ASSISTANCE, CONTACT THE DISTRICT DIRECTOR OF THE ENVIRONMENTAL PROTECTION AGENCY.

STORAGE

PROTECT AGAINST PHYSICAL DAMAGE. STORE IN A COOL, DRY PLACE. SEPARATE FROM OTHER STORAGE AND PROTECT FROM ACIDS AND OXIDIZING MATERIALS (NFPA 49, HAZARDOUS CHEMICALS DATA, 1975).

STORE AWAY FROM INCOMPATIBLE SUBSTANCES.

THRESHOLD PLANNING QUANTITY (TPQ): THE SUPERFUND AMENDMENTS AND REAUTHORIZATION ACT (SARA) SECTION 302 REQUIRES THAT EACH FACILITY WHERE ANY EXTREMELY HAZARDOUS SUBSTANCE IS PRESENT IN A QUANTITY EQUAL TO OR GREATER THAN THE TPQ ESTABLISHED FOR THAT SUBSTANCE NOTIFY THE STATE EMERGENCY RESPONSE COMMISSION FOR THE STATE IN WHICH IT IS LOCATED. SECTION 303 OF SARA REQUIRES THESE FACILITIES TO PARTICIPATE IN LOCAL EMERGENCY RESPONSE PLANNING (40 CFR 355.30).

DISPOSAL

DISPOSAL MUST BE IN ACCORDANCE WITH STANDARDS APPLICABLE TO GENERATORS OF HAZARDOUS WASTE, 40CFR 262. EPA HAZARDOUS WASTE NUMBER P098.

CONDITIONS TO AVOID

MAY BURN BUT DOES NOT IGNITE READILY. CONTAINERS MAY EXPLODE IN HEAT OF FIRE.

SPILL AND LEAK PROCEDURES

SOIL SPILL: DIG A HOLDING AREA SUCH AS PIT, POND OR LAGOON TO CONTAIN SPILLED MATERIAL. USE PROTECTIVE COVER SUCH AS A PLASTIC SHEET TO PREVENT DISSOLVING IN FIREFIGHTING WATER OR RAIN.

AIR SPILL: APPLY WATER SPRAY TO KNOCK DOWN AND REDUCE VAPORS. KNOCK-DOWN WATER IS CORROSIVE AND TOXIC AND SHOULD BE DIKED FOR CONTAINMENT.

WATER SPILL: NEUTRALIZE WITH CAUSTIC SODA.

ADD CALCIUM HYPOCHLORITE TO SPILL.

ADD SUITABLE AGENT TO NEUTRALIZE SPILLED MATERIAL TO PH-7.

OCCUPATIONAL SPILL: DO NOT TOUCH SPILLED MATERIAL. STOP LEAK IF YOU CAN DO IT WITHOUT RISK. USE WATER SPRAY TO REDUCE VAPORS. FOR SMALL SPILLS, TAKE UP WITH SAND OR OTHER ABSORBENT MATERIAL AND PLACE INTO CONTAINERS FOR LATER DISPOSAL. FOR SMALL DRY SPILLS, WITH A CLEAN SHOVEL PLACE MATERIAL INTO CLEAN, DRY CONTAINERS AND COVER. MOVE CONTAINERS FROM SPILL AREA. FOR LARGER SPILLS, DIKE FAR AHEAD OF SPILL FOR LATER DISPOSAL. KEEP UNNECESSARY PEOPLE AWAY. ISOLATE HAZARD AREA AND DENY ENTRY. VENTILATE CLOSED SPACES BEFORE ENTERING.

REPORTABLE QUANTITY (RQ): 10 POUNDS THE SUPERFUND AMENDMENTS AND REAUTHORIZATION ACT (SARA) SECTION 304 REQUIRES THAT A RELEASE EQUAL TO OR GREATER THAN THE REPORTABLE QUANTITY FOR THIS SUBSTANCE BE IMMEDIATELY REPORTED TO THE LOCAL EMERGENCY PLANNING COMMITTEE AND THE STATE EMERGENCY RESPONSE COMMISSION (40 CFR 355.40). IF THE RELEASE OF THIS SUBSTANCE IS REPORTABLE UNDER CERCLA SECTION 103, THE NATIONAL RESPONSE CENTER MUST BE NOTIFIED IMMEDIATELY AT (800) 424-8802 OR (202) 426-2675 IN THE METROPOLITAN WASHINGTON, D.C. AREA (40 CFR 302.6).

PROTECTIVE EQUIPMENT

VENTILATION: PROVIDE LOCAL EXHAUST OR PROCESS ENCLOSURE VENTILATION TO MEET PUBLISHED EXPOSURE LIMITS.

RESPIRATOR: THE FOLLOWING RESPIRATORS AND MAXIMUM USE CONCENTRATIONS ARE RECOMMENDATIONS BY THE U.S. DEPARTMENT OF HEALTH AND HUMAN SERVICES, NIOSH POCKET GUIDE TO CHEMICAL HAZARDS; NIOSH CRITERIA DOCUMENTS OR BY THE U.S. DEPARTMENT OF LABOR, 29 CFR 1910 SUBPART Z. THE SPECIFIC RESPIRATOR SELECTED MUST BE BASED ON CONTAMINATION LEVELS FOUND IN THE WORK PLACE, MUST NOT EXCEED THE WORKING LIMITS OF THE RESPIRATOR AND BE JOINTLY APPROVED BY THE NATIONAL INSTITUTE FOR OCCUPATIONAL SAFETY AND HEALTH AND THE MINE SAFETY AND HEALTH ADMINISTRATION (NIOSH-MSHA).

CYANIDES (AS CN):

50 MG(CN)/M3- SUPPLIED-AIR RESPIRATOR. SELF-CONTAINED BREATHING APPARATUS.

ESCAPE- AIR-PURIFYING FULL FACEPIECE RESPIRATOR (GAS MASK) WITH CHIN-STYLE OR FRONT- OR BACK-MOUNTED CANISTER PROVIDING PROTECTION AGAINST CYANIDE AND HAVING A HIGH-EFFICIENCY PARTICULATE FILTER.

APPROPRIATE ESCAPE-TYPE SELF-CONTAINED BREATHING APPARATUS.

FOR FIREFIGHTING AND OTHER IMMEDIATELY DANGEROUS TO LIFE OR HEALTH CONDITIONS:

SELF-CONTAINED BREATHING APPARATUS WITH FULL FACEPIECE OPERATED IN PRESSURE-DEMAND OR OTHER POSITIVE PRESSURE MODE.

SUPPLIED-AIR RESPIRATOR WITH FULL FACEPIECE AND OPERATED IN PRESSURE-DEMAND OR OTHER POSITIVE PRESSURE MODE IN COMBINATION WITH AN AUXILIARY SELF-CONTAINED BREATHING APPARATUS OPERATED IN PRESSURE-DEMAND OR OTHER POSITIVE PRESSURE MODE.

CLOTHING: EMPLOYEE MUST WEAR APPROPRIATE PROTECTIVE (IMPERVIOUS) CLOTHING AND EQUIPMENT TO PREVENT ANY POSSIBILITY OF SKIN CONTACT WITH THIS SUBSTANCE.

GLOVES: EMPLOYEE MUST WEAR APPROPRIATE PROTECTIVE GLOVES TO PREVENT CONTACT WITH THIS SUBSTANCE.

EYE PROTECTION: EMPLOYEE MUST WEAR SPLASH-PROOF OR DUST-RESISTANT SAFETY GOGGLES AND A FACESHIELD TO PREVENT CONTACT WITH THIS SUBSTANCE.

EMERGENCY WASH FACILITIES: WHERE THERE IS ANY POSSIBILITY THAT AN EMPLOYEE'S EYES AND/OR SKIN MAY BE EXPOSED TO THIS SUBSTANCE, THE EMPLOYER SHOULD PROVIDE AN EYE WASH FOUNTAIN AND QUICK DRENCH SHOWER WITHIN THE IMMEDIATE WORK AREA FOR EMERGENCY USE.

AUTHORIZED BY- OCCUPATIONAL HEALTH SERVICES, INC.

CREATION DATE: 10/04/89 ***REVISION DATE:*** 06/25/90

MATERIAL SAFETY DATA SHEET

OCCUPATIONAL HEALTH SERVICES, INC.
AGRICULTURE AND PESTICIDE DIVISION
450 SEVENTH AVENUE, SUITE 2407
NEW YORK, NEW YORK 10123
1-800-445-MSDS OR (212) 967-1100

EMERGENCY CONTACT:
JOHN S. BRANSFORD, JR. (615) 292-1180

SUBSTANCE IDENTIFICATION

CAS-NUMBER 2244-21-5

SUBSTANCE: POTASSIUM DICHLOROISOCYANURATE

TRADE NAMES/SYNONYMS: DICHLORO-S-TRIAZINE-2,4,6(1H,3H,5H)-TRIONE POTASSIUM DERIVATIVE; 1,3-DICHLORO-1,3,5-TRIAZINE-2,4,6(1H,3H,5H)-TRIONE POTASSIUM SALT; DICHLOROISOCYANURIC ACID POTASSIUM SALT; TROCLOSENE POTASSIUM; 1,3-DICHLORO-S-TRIAZINE-2,4,6(1H,3H,5H)-TRIONE POTASSIUM SALT; POTASSIUM DICHLOROCYANURATE; POTASSIUM DICHLORO-S-TRIAZINETRIONE; ACL 59; NEOCHLOR 59; NA 2465; PST19360

CHEMICAL FAMILY: ISOCYANATE

MOLECULAR FORMULA: C3-H-CL2-N3-O3.K

MOLECULAR WEIGHT: 237.07

CERCLA RATINGS (SCALE 0-3): HEALTH=2 FIRE=0 REACTIVITY=2 PERSISTENCE=0

NFPA RATINGS (SCALE 0-4): HEALTH=3 FIRE=0 REACTIVITY=2

COMPONENTS AND CONTAMINANTS

COMPONENT: POTASSIUM DICHLOROISOCYANURATE ***PERCENT:*** 100
CAS# 2244-21-5

OTHER CONTAMINANTS: NONE

EXPOSURE LIMITS: NO OCCUPATIONAL EXPOSURE LIMITS ESTABLISHED BY OSHA, ACGIH, OR NIOSH.

PHYSICAL DATA

DESCRIPTION: SLIGHTLY HYGROSCOPIC, WHITE CRYSTALLINE SOLID WITH STRONG CHLORINE ODOR ***BOILING POINT:*** DECOMPOSES
MELTING POINT: 482 F (250 C) DECOMPOSES ***SPECIFIC GRAVITY:*** 0.96
EVAPORATION RATE: NOT AVAILABLE ***SOLUBILITY IN WATER:*** SOLUBLE

FIRE AND EXPLOSION DATA

FIRE AND EXPLOSION HAZARD: NEGLIGIBLE FIRE HAZARD WHEN EXPOSED TO HEAT OR FLAME. OXIDIZER: OXIDIZERS DECOMPOSE, ESPECIALLY WHEN HEATED, TO YIELD OXYGEN OR OTHER GASES WHICH WILL INCREASE THE BURNING RATE OF COMBUSTIBLE MATTER. CONTACT WITH EASILY OXIDIZABLE, ORGANIC, OR OTHER COMBUSTIBLE MATERIALS MAY RESULT IN IGNITION, VIOLENT COMBUSTION OR EXPLOSION.

FIREFIGHTING MEDIA: DRY CHEMICAL, CARBON DIOXIDE, HALON OR WATER SPRAY (1987 EMERGENCY RESPONSE GUIDEBOOK, DOT P 5800.4).
FOR LARGER FIRES, USE WATER SPRAY OR FOG (1987 EMERGENCY RESPONSE GUIDEBOOK, DOT P 5800.4).

FIREFIGHTING: MOVE CONTAINERS FROM FIRE AREA IF POSSIBLE. COOL CONTAINERS EXPOSED TO FLAME WITH WATER FROM SIDE UNTIL WELL AFTER FIRE IS OUT. KEEP AWAY FROM STORAGE TANK ENDS. FOR MASSIVE FIRE IN STORAGE AREA, USE UNMANNED HOSE HOLDER OR MONITOR NOZZLES (1987 EMERGENCY RESPONSE GUIDEBOOK, DOT 5800.4, GUIDE PAGE 42).
FLOOD WITH WATER. COOL CONTAINERS WITH FLOODING AMOUNTS OF WATER,APPLY FROM AS FAR A DISTANCE AS POSSIBLE. AVOID BREATHING TOXIC VAPORS, KEEP UPWIND. EVACUATE TO A RADIUS OF 2500 FEET FOR UNCONTROLLABLE FIRES.

TRANSPORTATION DATA

DEPARTMENT OF TRANSPORTATION HAZARD CLASSIFICATION 49 CFR 172.101: OXIDIZER
DEPARTMENT OF TRANSPORTATION LABELING REQUIREMENTS 49 CFR 172.101 AND SUBPART E: OXIDIZER
DEPARTMENT OF TRANSPORTATION PACKAGING REQUIREMENTS: 49 CFR 173.217 EXCEPTIONS: 49 CFR 173.153

TOXICITY

POTASSIUM DICHLOROISOCYANURATE: IRRITATION DATA: 500 MG/24 HOURS SKIN-RABBIT MODERATE; 500 MG SKIN-RABBIT SEVERE; 10 MG/24 HOURS EYE-RABBIT SEVERE. TOXICITY DATA: 3570 MG/KG ORAL-HUMAN LDLO. CARCINOGEN STATUS: NONE. LOCAL EFFECTS: CORROSIVE- INGESTION; IRRITANT- INHALATION, SKIN, AND EYES. ACUTE TOXICITY LEVEL: INSUFFICIENT DATA. TARGET EFFECTS: NO DATA AVAILABLE.

HEALTH EFFECTS AND FIRST AID

INHALATION: POTASSIUM DICHLOROISOCYANURATE: IRRITANT. **ACUTE EXPOSURE-** THE CHEMICAL MAY IRRITATE THE UPPER RESPIRATORY TRACT. INHALATION OF DUST MAY CAUSE COUGHING, SNEEZING, DIFFICULTY IN BREATHING AND BRONCHITIS. **CHRONIC EXPOSURE-** NO DATA AVAILABLE.

FIRST AID- REMOVE FROM EXPOSURE AREA TO FRESH AIR IMMEDIATELY. IF BREATHING HAS STOPPED, PERFORM ARTIFICIAL RESPIRATION. KEEP PERSON WARM AND AT REST. TREAT SYMPTOMATICALLY AND SUPPORTIVELY. GET MEDICAL ATTENTION IMMEDIATELY.

SKIN CONTACT: POTASSIUM DICHLOROISOCYANURATE: IRRITANT. **ACUTE EXPOSURE-** CYANURATES GENERALLY DO NOT IRRITATE INTACT SKIN BUT ARE LIKELY TO IRRITATE ABRADED AND MOIST SKIN. POTASSIUM DICHLOROISOCYANURATE MAY CAUSE REDNESS AND PAIN. **CHRONIC EXPOSURE-** REPEATED OR PROLONGED EXPOSURE WITH IRRITANTS MAY LEAD TO DERMATITIS.

FIRST AID- REMOVE CONTAMINATED CLOTHING AND SHOES IMMEDIATELY. WASH AFFECTED AREA WITH SOAP OR MILD DETERGENT AND LARGE AMOUNTS OF WATER UNTIL NO EVIDENCE OF CHEMICAL REMAINS (APPROXIMATELY 15-20 MINUTES). GET MEDICAL ATTENTION IMMEDIATELY.

EYE CONTACT: POTASSIUM DICHLOROISOCYANURATE: IRRITANT. **ACUTE EXPOSURE-** THE CHEMICAL MAY BE MODERATELY TO HIGHLY IRRITATING. DUST MAY IRRITATE THE EYES. 10 MG CAUSED SEVERE IRRITATION TO THE EYES OF RABBITS. **CHRONIC EXPOSURE-** REPEATED OR PROLONGED EXPOSURE WITH IRRITANTS MAY LEAD TO CONJUNCTIVITIS.

FIRST AID- WASH EYES IMMEDIATELY WITH LARGE AMOUNTS OF WATER OR NORMAL SALINE, OCCASIONALLY LIFTING UPPER AND LOWER LIDS, UNTIL NO EVIDENCE OF CHEMICAL REMAINS (APPROXIMATELY 15-20 MINUTES). GET MEDICAL ATTENTION IMMEDIATELY.

INGESTION: POTASSIUM DICHLOROISOCYANURATE: CORROSIVE. **ACUTE EXPOSURE-** INGESTION MAY CAUSE BURNS OF THE MOUTH AND STOMACH. CHLORINATED CYANURATES MAY CAUSE CORROSION TO THE STOMACH LINING. SYMPTOMS OF INTOXICATION MAY INCLUDE WEAKNESS, LETHARGY, TREMORS, SALIVATION, LACRIMATION, DYSPNEA, AND COMA. THE PATHOLOGICAL FINDINGS CONSIST OF GASTROINTESTINAL IRRITATION AND INFLAMMATION, TISSUE EDEMA, AND LIVER AND KIDNEY CONGESTION. **CHRONIC EXPOSURE-** DEPENDING ON THE CONCENTRATION, REPEATED INGESTION MAY RESULT IN EFFECTS AS IN ACUTE INGESTION.

FIRST AID- TREAT SYMPTOMATICALLY AND SUPPORTIVELY. IF PERSON IS CONSCIOUS AND ABLE TO SWALLOW, GIVE LARGE AMOUNTS OF WATER OR MILK TO DILUTE SUBSTANCE. GET MEDICAL ATTENTION IMMEDIATELY. GASTRIC LAVAGE PERFORMED BY QUALIFIED MEDICAL PERSONNEL MIGHT BE ADVISABLE IF THERE ARE NO SIGNS OF PERFORATION FROM THE INGESTION OF A CORROSIVE SUBSTANCE. IF VOMITING OCCURS, KEEP HEAD BELOW HIPS TO HELP PREVENT ASPIRATION.

ANTIDOTE: NO SPECIFIC ANTIDOTE. TREAT SYMPTOMATICALLY AND SUPPORTIVELY.

REACTIVITY

REACTIVITY: ACCELERATES THE BURNING RATE OF COMBUSTIBLE MATERIALS AND VIGOROUSLY REACTS WITH WATER YIELDING CHLORINE GAS.

INCOMPATIBILITIES: POTASSIUM DICHLOROISOCYANURATE: AMMONIA: EXPLOSIVE. AMMONIUM SALTS: EXPLOSIVE. EASILY CHLORINATED SUBSTANCES: FIRE MAY RESULT. HYDRATED SALTS: EXOTHERMIC REACTION. NITROGEN CONTAINING COMPOUNDS WHICH MAY FORM NITROGEN TRICHLORIDE: EXPLOSIVE. NON-IONIC SURFACTANT: STRONG EXOTHERMIC REACTION THAT MAY RESULT IN FIRE OR EXPLOSION ORGANIC SUBSTANCES: FIRE RISK UPON CONTACT. UREA: EXPLOSIVE.

DECOMPOSITION: THERMAL DECOMPOSITION PRODUCTS MAY INCLUDE TOXIC AND CORROSIVE FUMES OF CHLORIDES AND TOXIC OXIDES OF NITROGEN.
THERMAL DECOMPOSITION PRODUCTS MAY INCLUDE TOXIC OXIDES OF CARBON.

POLYMERIZATION: HAZARDOUS POLYMERIZATION HAS NOT BEEN REPORTED TO OCCUR UNDER NORMAL TEMPERATURES AND PRESSURES.

STORAGE AND DISPOSAL

OBSERVE ALL FEDERAL, STATE AND LOCAL REGULATIONS WHEN STORING OR DISPOSING OF THIS SUBSTANCE. FOR ASSISTANCE, CONTACT THE DISTRICT DIRECTOR OF THE ENVIRONMENTAL PROTECTION AGENCY.

STORAGE

PROTECT AGAINST PHYSICAL DAMAGE. STORE IN COOL, DRY, WELL-VENTILATED PLACE AWAY FROM FLAMMABLE LIQUIDS, COMBUSTIBLE MATERIALS, AND OXIDIZABLE MATERIALS. DRUMS MAY RUPTURE IF THE CONTENTS ARE EXPOSED TO HEAT OR BECOME CONTAMINATED OR WET. DRUMS SHOULD BE PALLETIZED TO PREVENT WETTING FROM FLOOR WASHINGS OR DRAINAGE. AVOID PROLONGED STORAGE IN UNVENTILATED AREAS AT SUMMER TEMPERATURES. (NFPA49, HAZARDOUS CHEMICALS DATA, 1975).
STORE AWAY FROM INCOMPATIBLE SUBSTANCES.

CONDITIONS TO AVOID

AVOID CONTACT WITH OTHER COMBUSTIBLE MATERIALS (WOOD, PAPER, OIL, ETC.). AVOID CONTACT WITH EYES AND SKIN; MATERIAL MAY BE POISONOUS OR CORROSIVE.

SPILL AND LEAK PROCEDURES

OCCUPATIONAL SPILL: KEEP COMBUSTIBLES (WOOD, PAPER, OIL, ETC.) AWAY FROM SPILLED MATERIAL. DO NOT TOUCH SPILLED MATERIAL. FOR SMALL DRY SPILLS, WITH CLEAN SHOVEL PLACE MATERIAL INTO CLEAN, DRY CONTAINER AND COVER; MOVE CONTAINERS FROM SPILL AREA. FOR LARGER SPILLS, DIKE FAR AHEAD OF SPILL FOR LATER DISPOSAL. KEEP UNNECESSARY PEOPLE AWAY. ISOLATE HAZARD AREA AND DENY ENTRY.

PROTECTIVE EQUIPMENT

VENTILATION: PROVIDE LOCAL EXHAUST OR PROCESS ENCLOSURE VENTILATION SYSTEM.

RESPIRATOR: THE FOLLOWING RESPIRATORS ARE RECOMMENDED BASED ON INFORMATION FOUND IN THE PHYSICAL DATA, TOXICITY AND HEALTH EFFECTS SECTIONS. THEY ARE RANKED IN ORDER FROM MINIMUM TO MAXIMUM RESPIRATORY PROTECTION. THE SPECIFIC RESPIRATOR SELECTED MUST BE BASED ON CONTAMINATION LEVELS FOUND IN THE WORK PLACE, MUST NOT EXCEED THE WORKING LIMITS OF THE RESPIRATOR AND BE JOINTLY APPROVED BY THE NATIONAL INSTITUTE FOR OCCUPATIONAL SAFETY AND HEALTH AND THE MINE SAFETY AND HEALTH ADMINISTRATION (NIOSH-MSHA).
DUST AND MIST RESPIRATOR WITH A FULL FACEPIECE.
AIR-PURIFYING FULL FACEPIECE RESPIRATOR WITH A HIGH-EFFICIENCY PARTICULATE FILTER.
POWERED AIR-PURIFYING RESPIRATOR WITH A TIGHT-FITTING FACEPIECE AND HIGH-EFFICIENCY PARTICULATE FILTER.
TYPE 'C' SUPPLIED-AIR RESPIRATOR WITH A FULL FACEPIECE OPERATED IN PRESSURE-DEMAND OR OTHER POSITIVE PRESSURE MODE OR WITH A FULL FACEPIECE, HELMET OR HOOD OPERATED IN CONTINUOUS-FLOW MODE.

SELF-CONTAINED BREATHING APPARATUS WITH A FULL FACEPIECE OPERATED IN PRESSURE-DEMAND OR OTHER POSITIVE PRESSURE MODE.
FOR FIREFIGHTING AND OTHER IMMEDIATELY DANGEROUS TO LIFE OR HEALTH CONDITIONS:
SELF-CONTAINED BREATHING APPARATUS WITH FULL FACEPIECE OPERATED IN PRESSURE-DEMAND OR OTHER POSITIVE PRESSURE MODE.
SUPPLIED-AIR RESPIRATOR WITH FULL FACEPIECE AND OPERATED IN PRESSURE-DEMAND OR OTHER POSITIVE PRESSURE MODE IN COMBINATION WITH AN AUXILIARY SELF-CONTAINED BREATHING APPARATUS OPERATED IN PRESSURE-DEMAND OR OTHER POSITIVE PRESSURE MODE.

CLOTHING: EMPLOYEE MUST WEAR APPROPRIATE PROTECTIVE (IMPERVIOUS) CLOTHING AND EQUIPMENT TO PREVENT REPEATED OR PROLONGED SKIN CONTACT WITH THIS SUBSTANCE.

GLOVES: EMPLOYEE MUST WEAR APPROPRIATE PROTECTIVE GLOVES TO PREVENT CONTACT WITH THIS SUBSTANCE.

EYE PROTECTION: EMPLOYEE MUST WEAR SPLASH-PROOF OR DUST-RESISTANT SAFETY GOGGLES TO PREVENT EYE CONTACT WITH THIS SUBSTANCE.
EMERGENCY EYE WASH: WHERE THERE IS ANY POSSIBILITY THAT AN EMPLOYEE'S EYES MAY BE EXPOSED TO THIS SUBSTANCE, THE EMPLOYER SHOULD PROVIDE AN EYE WASH FOUNTAIN WITHIN THE IMMEDIATE WORK AREA FOR EMERGENCY USE.

AUTHORIZED BY- OCCUPATIONAL HEALTH SERVICES, INC.
CREATION DATE: 10/04/89 ***REVISION DATE:*** 05/25/90

MATERIAL SAFETY DATA SHEET

OCCUPATIONAL HEALTH SERVICES, INC.
AGRICULTURE AND PESTICIDE DIVISION
450 SEVENTH AVENUE, SUITE 2407
NEW YORK, NEW YORK 10123
1-800-445-MSDS OR (212) 967-1100

EMERGENCY CONTACT:
JOHN S. BRANSFORD, JR. (615) 292-1180

SUBSTANCE IDENTIFICATION

CAS-NUMBER 7778-50-9

SUBSTANCE: POTASSIUM DICHROMATE

TRADE NAMES/SYNONYMS: DICHROMIC ACID; DIPOTASSIUM SALT; POTASSIUM BICHROMATE; DIPOTASSIUM DICHROMATE; BICHROMATE OF POTASH; POTASSIUM DICHROMATE (VI); RED POTASSIUM CHROMATE; IOPEZITE; CHROMIC ACID, DIPOTASSIUM SALT; P-186; P-188; PST19370

CHEMICAL FAMILY: INORGANIC SALT

MOLECULAR FORMULA: CR2-K2-O7

MOLECULAR WEIGHT: 294.20

CERCLA RATINGS (SCALE 0-3): HEALTH=3 FIRE=0 REACTIVITY=1 PERSISTENCE=3

NFPA RATINGS (SCALE 0-4): HEALTH=1 FIRE=0 REACTIVITY=1

COMPONENTS AND CONTAMINANTS

COMPONENT: POTASSIUM DICHROMATE ***PERCENT:*** 100
CAS# 7778-50-9

OTHER CONTAMINANTS: NONE

EXPOSURE LIMITS: CHROMIC ACID AND CHROMATES: 0.1 MG(CRO3)/M3 OSHA CEILING 0.05 MG(CR)/M3 ACGIH TWA 25 UG(CR(VI))/M3 NIOSH RECOMMENDED 10 HOUR TWA; 50 UG(CR(VI))/M3 NIOSH RECOMMENDED 15 MINUTE CEILING
SUBJECT TO SARA SECTION 313 ANNUAL TOXIC CHEMICAL RELEASE REPORTING
SUBJECT TO CALIFORNIA PROPOSITION 65 CANCER AND/OR REPRODUCTIVE TOXICITY WARNING AND RELEASE REQUIREMENTS (HEXAVALENT CHROMIUM COMPOUNDS) (FEBRUARY 27, 1987)
POTASSIUM DICHROMATE: 10 POUNDS CERCLA SECTION 103 REPORTABLE QUANTITY

PHYSICAL DATA

DESCRIPTION: ODORLESS, BRIGHT ORANGE-RED CRYSTALS, WITH BITTER, METALLIC TASTE

BOILING POINT: 932 F (500 C) DECOMPOSES ***MELTING POINT:*** 748 F (398 C)

SPECIFIC GRAVITY: 2.68 @ 25 C ***PH:*** (1% SOLUTION) 4.04

SOLUBILITY IN WATER: 4.9% @ 0 C

FIRE AND EXPLOSION DATA

FIRE AND EXPLOSION HAZARD: NEGLIGIBLE FIRE HAZARD WHEN EXPOSED TO HEAT OR FLAME.
OXIDIZER: OXIDIZERS DECOMPOSE, ESPECIALLY WHEN HEATED, TO YIELD OXYGEN OR OTHER GASES WHICH WILL INCREASE THE BURNING RATE OF COMBUSTIBLE MATTER. CONTACT WITH EASILY OXIDIZABLE, ORGANIC, OR OTHER COMBUSTIBLE MATERIALS MAY RESULT IN IGNITION, VIOLENT COMBUSTION OR EXPLOSION.

FIREFIGHTING MEDIA: DRY CHEMICAL, CARBON DIOXIDE, HALON OR WATER SPRAY (1987 EMERGENCY RESPONSE GUIDEBOOK, DOT P 5800.4).
FOR LARGER FIRES, USE WATER SPRAY OR FOG (1987 EMERGENCY RESPONSE GUIDEBOOK, DOT P 5800.4).

FIREFIGHTING: MOVE CONTAINER FROM FIRE AREA IF POSSIBLE. DO NOT SCATTER SPILLED MATERIAL WITH HIGH PRESSURE WATER STREAMS. DIKE FIRE CONTROL WATER FOR LATER DISPOSAL (1987 EMERGENCY RESPONSE GUIDEBOOK, DOT P 5800.4, GUIDE PAGE 31).
USE AGENTS SUITABLE FOR TYPE OF SURROUNDING FIRE. AVOID BREATHING HAZARDOUS VAPORS, KEEP UPWIND.

TRANSPORTATION DATA

DEPARTMENT OF TRANSPORTATION HAZARD CLASSIFICATION 49 CFR 172.101: ORM-A
DEPARTMENT OF TRANSPORTATION LABELING REQUIREMENTS 49 CFR 172.101 AND SUBPART E: NONE
DEPARTMENT OF TRANSPORTATION PACKAGING REQUIREMENTS: 49 CFR 173.510 EXCEPTIONS: 49 CFR 173.505

TOXICITY

POTASSIUM DICHROMATE: TOXICITY DATA: 26 MG/KG ORAL-CHILD LDLO; 190 MG/KG ORAL-MOUSE LD50; 2829 MG/KG ORAL-DOG LDLO; 163 MG/KG ORAL-GUINEA PIG LDLO; 27900 UG/KG INTRAVENOUS-RABBIT LDLO; 100 MG/KG SUBCUTANEOUS-MOUSE LDLO; 10 MG/KG SUBCUTANEOUS-RABBIT LDLO; 29400 UG/KG SUBCUTANEOUS-GUINEA PIG LDLO; 37 MG/KG INTRAPERITONEAL-MOUSE LD50; 40 MG/KG SUBCUTANEOUS-MONKEY LDLO; MUTAGENIC DATA (RTECS); REPRODUCTIVE EFFECTS DATA (RTECS). CARCINOGEN STATUS: KNOWN HUMAN CARCINOGEN (NTP); ANIMAL INADEQUATE EVIDENCE (FOR POTASSIUM DICHROMATE), HUMAN SUFFICIENT EVIDENCE, ANIMAL SUFFICIENT EVIDENCE (IARC GROUP-1 FOR HEXAVALENT CHROMIUM COMPOUNDS). AN INCREASED INCIDENCE OF LUNG CANCER IN PERSONS OCCUPATIONALLY EXPOSED DURING CHROMATE PRODUCTION, PIGMENT MANUFACTURING AND PLATING AND ALLOYING PROCESSES. INCIDENCES OF CANCERS AT OTHER SITES MAY ALSO BE INCREASED IN SUCH PERSONS. HOWEVER, A CLEAR DISTINCTION BETWEEN THE RELATIVE CARCINOGENICITY OF CHROMIUM COMPOUNDS OF DIFFERENT OXIDATION STATES OR SOLUBILITIES HAS BEEN DIFFICULT TO ACHIEVE. LOCAL EFFECTS: CORROSIVE- INHALATION, SKIN, EYES, AND INGESTION. ACUTE TOXICITY LEVEL: TOXIC BY INGESTION. TARGET EFFECTS: SENSITIZER- SKIN.

HEALTH EFFECTS AND FIRST AID

INHALATION: POTASSIUM DICHROMATE: CORROSIVE. 30 MG(CRO3)/M3 IMMEDIATELY DANGEROUS TO LIFE OR HEALTH. **ACUTE EXPOSURE-** EXPOSURE TO CHROMIUM DUST AND/OR VAPORS MAY CAUSE NASAL IRRITATION, LUNG IRRITATION, COUGHING, LABORED BREATHING, WHEEZING, CHEST PAIN, ULCERATION AND PERFORATION OF THE NASAL SEPTUM, PULMONARY EDEMA, JAUNDICE, AND LIVER AND KIDNEY DAMAGE. **CHRONIC EXPOSURE-** EROSION AND DISCOLORATION OF THE TEETH, PAINLESS ULCERATION OF THE NASAL SEPTUM, NOSE BLEEDS AND FOUL NASAL DISCHANGE MAY OCCUR. PERFORATED EARDRUMS, KIDNEY DAMAGE, HEPATITIS WITH JAUNDICE AND LUNG CANCER MAY ALSO OCCUR.

FIRST AID- REMOVE FROM EXPOSURE AREA TO FRESH AIR IMMEDIATELY. IF BREATHING HAS STOPPED, PERFORM ARTIFICIAL RESPIRATION. KEEP PERSON WARM AND AT REST. TREAT SYMPTOMATICALLY AND SUPPORTIVELY. GET MEDICAL ATTENTION IMMEDIATELY.

SKIN CONTACT: POTASSIUM DICHROMATE: CORROSIVE/SENSITIZER. **ACUTE EXPOSURE-** CONTACT MAY CAUSE PAINLESS, PENETRATING, SLOW HEALING LESIONS. SENSITIZATION DERMATITIS HAS BEEN REPORTED, POSSIBLY DUE TO THE PRESENCE OF CHROMIUM. **CHRONIC EXPOSURE-** PROLONGED OR REPEATED EXPOSURE MAY CAUSE ECZEMATOUS DERMATITIS WITH EDEMA AND ULCERATION THAT HEALS SLOWLY. PROLONGED OR REPEATED CONTACT WITH CHROMATE MAY INDUCE SENSITIZATION TO CHROMIUM.

FIRST AID- REMOVE CONTAMINATED CLOTHING AND SHOES IMMEDIATELY. WASH AFFECTED AREA WITH SOAP OR MILD DETERGENT AND LARGE AMOUNTS OF WATER UNTIL NO EVIDENCE OF CHEMICAL REMAINS (AT LEAST 15-20 MINUTES). IN CASE OF CHEMICAL BURNS, COVER AREA WITH STERILE, DRY DRESSING. BANDAGE SECURELY, BUT NOT TOO TIGHTLY. GET MEDICAL ATTENTION IMMEDIATELY.

EYE CONTACT: POTASSIUM DICHROMATE: CORROSIVE. **ACUTE EXPOSURE-** CONTACT WITH VAPORS/ AND OR FUMES OF CHROMIUM MAY CAUSE IRRITATION, REDNESS, PAIN, TEARING, CONJUNCTIVITIS, BLURRED VISION, AND INFLAMMATION.

CHRONIC EXPOSURE- PROLONGED EXPOSURE TO VAPORS AND/ OR FUMES MAY CAUSE CONJUNCTIVITIS.

FIRST AID- WASH EYES IMMEDIATELY WITH LARGE AMOUNTS OF WATER, OCCASIONALLY LIFTING UPPER AND LOWER LIDS, UNTIL NO EVIDENCE OF CHEMICAL REMAINS (AT LEAST 15-20 MINUTES). CONTINUE IRRIGATING WITH NORMAL SALINE UNTIL THE PH HAS RETURNED TO NORMAL (30-60 MINUTES). COVER WITH STERILE BANDAGES. GET MEDICAL ATTENTION IMMEDIATELY.

INGESTION: POTASSIUM DICHROMATE: CORROSIVE. **ACUTE EXPOSURE-** INGESTION OF SOLUBLE DICHROMATE SALTS MAY CAUSE VIOLENT GASTROENTERITIS, DIARRHEA, PERIPHERAL VASCULAR COLLAPSE, VERTIGO, MUSCLE CRAMPS, COMA, HEMORRHAGIC DIATHESIS, FEVER, LIVER DAMAGE, HEMORRHAGIC NEPHRITIS, AND ACUTE RENAL FAILURE. **CHRONIC EXPOSURE-** PROLONGED OR REPEATED INGESTION IS NOT LIKELY TO OCCUR, BUT MAY CAUSE LIVER AND KIDNEY DAMAGE.

FIRST AID- REMOVE BY GASTRIC LAVAGE OR EMESIS. MAINTAIN BLOOD PRESSURE AND AIRWAY. GIVE OXYGEN IF RESPIRATION IS DEPRESSED. DO NOT PERFORM GASTRIC LAVAGE OR EMESIS IF VICTIM IS UNCONSCIOUS. GET MEDICAL ATTENTION IMMEDIATELY (DREISBACH, HANDBOOK OF POISONING, 11TH ED.). ADMINISTRATION OF GASTRIC LAVAGE OR OXYGEN SHOULD BE PERFORMED BY QUALIFIED MEDICAL PERSONNEL.

ANTIDOTE: NO SPECIFIC ANTIDOTE. TREAT SYMPTOMATICALLY AND SUPPORTIVELY.

REACTIVITY

REACTIVITY: STABLE UNDER NORMAL TEMPERATURES AND PRESSURES.

INCOMPATIBILITIES: POTASSIUM DICHROMATE: ACETONE AND SULFURIC ACID: ACETONE IGNITED IN SOLUTION OF SULFURIC ACID AND POTASSIUM DICHROMATE. ALUMINUM (FINELY DIVIDED): COMBUSTIBLE REACTION. FLAMMABLE MATERIALS: HEATING MAY CAUSE IGNITION. HYDRAZINES AND THEIR SALTS: EXPLOSIVE REACTION WITH IGNITION POSSIBLE. HYDROXYLAMINES AND THEIR SALTS: EXPLOSIVE REACTION WITH IGNITION POSSIBLE. MERCURY CYANIDES: FRICTION MAY CAUSE IGNITION. OXIDIZABLE SUBSTANCES: RAPID REACTION WITH IGNITION POSSIBLE. OXIDIZABLE SUBSTANCES (FINELY DIVIDED): VIOLENT REACTION WITH COMBUSTION. PAPER: COMBUSTIBLE REACTION. PLASTICS: COMBUSTIBLE REACTION. SLAKED LIME: MIXING MAY CAUSE EXPLOSION. SULFUR: COMBUSTIBLE REACTION. WOOD: COMBUSTIBLE REACTION.

DECOMPOSITION: THERMAL DECOMPOSITION MAY RELEASE TOXIC AND/OR HAZARDOUS GASES.

POLYMERIZATION: HAZARDOUS POLYMERIZATION HAS NOT BEEN REPORTED TO OCCUR UNDER NORMAL TEMPERATURES AND PRESSURES.

STORAGE AND DISPOSAL

OBSERVE ALL FEDERAL, STATE AND LOCAL REGULATIONS WHEN STORING OR DISPOSING OF THIS SUBSTANCE. FOR ASSISTANCE, CONTACT THE DISTRICT DIRECTOR OF THE ENVIRONMENTAL PROTECTION AGENCY.

DISPOSAL

CHROMIUM - REGULATORY LEVEL: 5.0 MG/L MATERIALS WHICH CONTAIN THE ABOVE SUBSTANCE AT OR ABOVE THE REGULATORY LEVEL MEET THE EPA CHARACTERISTIC OF TOXICITY, AND MUST BE DISPOSED OF IN ACCORDANCE WITH 40 CFR PART 262. EPA HAZARDOUS WASTE NUMBER D007.

CONDITIONS TO AVOID

AVOID CONTACT WITH COMBUSTIBLE MATERIALS (WOOD, PAPER, FUEL, OILS, ETC); IGNITION OR EXPLOSION MAY RESULT. AVOID CONTAMINATION OF WATER SOURCES.

SPILL AND LEAK PROCEDURES

SOIL SPILL: DIG HOLDING AREA SUCH AS LAGOON, POND OR PIT FOR CONTAINMENT. USE PROTECTIVE COVER SUCH AS A PLASTIC SHEET TO PREVENT MATERIAL FROM DISSOLVING IN FIRE EXTINGUISHING WATER OR RAIN.

WATER SPILL: ADD SODIUM BISULFITE.

NEUTRALIZE WITH AGRICULTURAL LIME, SLAKED LIME, CRUSHED LIMESTONE OR SODIUM BICARBONATE.

NEUTRALIZE WITH DILUTE ACID OR REMOVABLE STRONG ACID.

ADD SUITABLE AGENT TO NEUTRALIZE SPILLED MATERIAL TO PH-7.

USE MECHANICAL DREDGES OR LIFTS TO EXTRACT IMMOBILIZED MASSES OF POLLUTION AND PRECIPITATES.

THE CALIFORNIA SAFE DRINKING WATER AND TOXIC ENFORCEMENT ACT OF 1986 (PROPOSITION 65) PROHIBITS CONTAMINATING ANY KNOWN SOURCE OF DRINKING WATER WITH SUBSTANCES KNOWN TO CAUSE CANCER AND/OR REPRODUCTIVE TOXICITY.

OCCUPATIONAL SPILL: KEEP COMBUSTIBLES (WOOD, PAPER, OIL, ETC) AWAY FROM SPILLED MATERIAL. DO NOT TOUCH SPILLED MATERIAL. FOR SMALL DRY SPILLS, WITH CLEAN SHOVEL PLACE MATERIAL INTO CLEAN, DRY CONTAINER AND COVER; MOVE CONTAINERS FROM SPILL AREA. FOR SMALL LIQUID SPILLS, TAKE UP WITH SAND, EARTH OR OTHER ABSORBENT MATERIAL AND PLACE INTO CONTAINERS FOR LATER DISPOSAL. FOR LARGER SPILLS, DIKE FAR AHEAD OF SPILL FOR LATER DISPOSAL. KEEP UNNECESSARY PEOPLE AWAY. ISOLATE HAZARD AREA AND DENY ENTRY.

REPORTABLE QUANTITY (RQ): 10 POUNDS THE SUPERFUND AMENDMENTS AND REAUTHORIZATION ACT (SARA) SECTION 304 REQUIRES THAT A RELEASE EQUAL TO OR GREATER THAN THE REPORTABLE QUANTITY FOR THIS SUBSTANCE BE IMMEDIATELY REPORTED TO THE LOCAL EMERGENCY PLANNING COMMITTEE AND THE STATE EMERGENCY RESPONSE COMMISSION (40 CFR 355.40). IF THE RELEASE OF THIS SUBSTANCE IS REPORTABLE UNDER CERCLA SECTION 103, THE NATIONAL RESPONSE CENTER MUST BE NOTIFIED IMMEDIATELY AT (800) 424-8802 OR (202) 426-2675 IN THE METROPOLITAN WASHINGTON, D.C. AREA (40 CFR 302.6).

PROTECTIVE EQUIPMENT

VENTILATION: PROVIDE LOCAL EXHAUST OR PROCESS ENCLOSURE VENTILATION TO MEET PUBLISHED EXPOSURE LIMITS.

RESPIRATOR: THE FOLLOWING RESPIRATORS AND MAXIMUM USE CONCENTRATIONS ARE RECOMMENDATIONS BY THE U.S. DEPARTMENT OF HEALTH AND HUMAN SERVICES, NIOSH POCKET GUIDE TO CHEMICAL HAZARDS; NIOSH CRITERIA DOCUMENTS OR BY THE U.S. DEPARTMENT OF LABOR, 29 CFR 1910 SUBPART Z. THE SPECIFIC RESPIRATOR SELECTED MUST BE BASED ON CONTAMINATION LEVELS FOUND IN THE WORK PLACE, MUST NOT EXCEED THE WORKING LIMITS OF THE RESPIRATOR AND BE JOINTLY APPROVED BY THE NATIONAL INSTITUTE FOR OCCUPATIONAL SAFETY AND HEALTH AND THE MINE SAFETY AND HEALTH ADMINISTRATION (NIOSH-MSHA).

HEXAVALENT CHROMIUM COMPOUNDS:

0.25 MG/M3- ANY SUPPLIED-AIR RESPIRATOR. ANY SELF-CONTAINED BREATHING APPARATUS. ANY DUST AND MIST RESPIRATOR EXCEPT SINGLE-USE AND QUARTER-MASK RESPIRATORS.

0.625 MG/M3- ANY POWERED AIR-PURIFYING RESPIRATOR WITH A HIGH-EFFICIENCY PARTICULATE FILTER. ANY SUPPLIED-AIR RESPIRATOR OPERATED IN A CONTINUOUS FLOW MODE.

1.25 MG/M3- ANY AIR-PURIFYING FULL FACEPIECE RESPIRATOR WITH A HIGH-EFFICIENCY PARTICULATE FILTER. ANY POWERED AIR-PURIFYING RESPIRATOR WITH A TIGHT-FITTING FACEPIECE AND A HIGH-EFFICIENCY PARTICULATE FILTER. ANY SELF-CONTAINED BREATHING APPARATUS WITH A FULL FACEPIECE. ANY SUPPLIED-AIR RESPIRATOR WITH A FULL FACEPIECE.

25 MG/M3- ANY SUPPLIED-AIR RESPIRATOR WITH A HALF-MASK AND OPERATED IN A PRESSURE-DEMAND OR OTHER POSITIVE PRESSURE MODE.

50 MG/M3- ANY SUPPLIED-AIR RESPIRATOR WITH A FULL FACEPIECE AND OPERATED IN A PRESSURE-DEMAND OR OTHER POSITIVE PRESSURE MODE.

ESCAPE- ANY AIR-PURIFYING FULL FACEPIECE RESPIRATOR WITH A HIGH-EFFICIENCY PARTICULATE FILTER. ANY APPROPRIATE ESCAPE-TYPE SELF-CONTAINED BREATHING APPARATUS.

FOR FIREFIGHTING AND OTHER IMMEDIATELY DANGEROUS TO LIFE OR HEALTH CONDITIONS:

SELF-CONTAINED BREATHING APPARATUS WITH FULL FACEPIECE OPERATED IN PRESSURE-DEMAND OR OTHER POSITIVE PRESSURE MODE.

SUPPLIED-AIR RESPIRATOR WITH FULL FACEPIECE AND OPERATED IN PRESSURE-DEMAND OR OTHER POSITIVE PRESSURE MODE IN COMBINATION WITH AN AUXILIARY SELF-CONTAINED BREATHING APPARATUS OPERATED IN PRESSURE-DEMAND OR OTHER POSITIVE PRESSURE MODE.

CLOTHING: EMPLOYEE MUST WEAR APPROPRIATE PROTECTIVE (IMPERVIOUS) CLOTHING AND EQUIPMENT TO PREVENT ANY POSSIBILITY OF SKIN CONTACT WITH THIS SUBSTANCE.

GLOVES: EMPLOYEE MUST WEAR APPROPRIATE PROTECTIVE GLOVES TO PREVENT CONTACT WITH THIS SUBSTANCE.

EYE PROTECTION: EMPLOYEE MUST WEAR SPLASH-PROOF OR DUST-RESISTANT SAFETY GOGGLES TO PREVENT EYE CONTACT WITH THIS SUBSTANCE.

EMERGENCY EYE WASH: WHERE THERE IS ANY POSSIBILITY THAT AN EMPLOYEE'S EYES MAY BE EXPOSED TO THIS SUBSTANCE, THE EMPLOYER SHOULD PROVIDE AN EYE WASH FOUNTAIN WITHIN THE IMMEDIATE WORK AREA FOR EMERGENCY USE.

AUTHORIZED BY- OCCUPATIONAL HEALTH SERVICES, INC.

CREATION DATE: 10/04/89 ***REVISION DATE:*** 07/13/90

MATERIAL SAFETY DATA SHEET

OCCUPATIONAL HEALTH SERVICES, INC.
AGRICULTURE AND PESTICIDE DIVISION
450 SEVENTH AVENUE, SUITE 2407
NEW YORK, NEW YORK 10123
1-800-445-MSDS OR (212) 967-1100

EMERGENCY CONTACT:
JOHN S. BRANSFORD, JR. (615) 292-1180

SUBSTANCE IDENTIFICATION

CAS-NUMBER 1310-58-3

SUBSTANCE: **POTASSIUM HYDROXIDE, SOLUTION**

TRADE NAMES/SYNONYMS: CAUSTIC POTASH; LYE WATER; POTASSA; POTASSIUM HYDRATE; LYE; CAUSTIC LYE; POTASSIUM HYDROXIDE; STCC 4935230; UN 1814; HKO; PST19430

CHEMICAL FAMILY: INORGANIC BASE

MOLECULAR FORMULA: K-O-H

MOLECULAR WEIGHT: 56.11

CERCLA RATINGS (SCALE 0-3): HEALTH=3 FIRE=0 REACTIVITY=1 PERSISTENCE=0

NFPA RATINGS (SCALE 0-4): HEALTH=3 FIRE=0 REACTIVITY=1

COMPONENTS AND CONTAMINANTS

COMPONENT: POTASSIUM HYDROXIDE ***PERCENT:*** 45.0
CAS# 1310-58-3

COMPONENT: WATER ***PERCENT:*** 55.0

EXPOSURE LIMITS: POTASSIUM HYDROXIDE: 2 MG/M3 OSHA CEILING 2 MG/M3 ACGIH CEILING
1000 POUNDS CERCLA SECTION 103 REPORTABLE QUANTITY

PHYSICAL DATA

DESCRIPTION: ODORLESS, CLEAR TO SLIGHTLY TURBID, COLORLESS TO SLIGHTLY COLORED LIQUID. ***BOILING POINT:*** APPROX. 212 F (100 C)

MELTING POINT: APPROX. 32 F (0 C) ***SPECIFIC GRAVITY:*** APPROX. 1.0

VAPOR PRESSURE: 17.5 MMHG @ 20 C ***PH:*** 13.5 (0.1 M SOLN)

SOLUBILITY IN WATER: COMPLETE ***VAPOR DENSITY:*** APPROX. 0.62

SOLVENT SOLUBILITY: SOLUBLE IN ALCOHOL*, GLYCERINE
*SEE INCOMPATIBILITIES

FIRE AND EXPLOSION DATA

FIRE AND EXPLOSION HAZARD: NEGLIGIBLE FIRE HAZARD WHEN EXPOSED TO HEAT OR FLAME.

FIREFIGHTING MEDIA: DRY CHEMICAL, CARBON DIOXIDE, HALON, WATER SPRAY OR STANDARD FOAM (1987 EMERGENCY RESPONSE GUIDEBOOK, DOT P 5800.4).
FOR LARGER FIRES, USE WATER SPRAY, FOG OR STANDARD FOAM (1987 EMERGENCY RESPONSE GUIDEBOOK, DOT P 5800.4).

FIREFIGHTING: MOVE CONTAINERS FROM FIRE AREA IF POSSIBLE. COOL CONTAINERS EXPOSED TO FLAMES WITH WATER FROM SIDE UNTIL WELL AFTER FIRE IS OUT. STAY AWAY FROM STORAGE TANK ENDS (1987 EMERGENCY RESPONSE GUIDEBOOK, DOT P 5800.4, GUIDE PAGE 60).
USE AGENT SUITABLE FOR TYPE OF FIRE. USE WATER IN FLOODING QUANTITIES AS FOG, APPLY FROM AS FAR A DISTANCE AS POSSIBLE.

TRANSPORTATION DATA

DEPARTMENT OF TRANSPORTATION HAZARD CLASSIFICATION 49 CFR 172.101: CORROSIVE MATERIAL
DEPARTMENT OF TRANSPORTATION LABELING REQUIREMENTS 49 CFR 172.101 AND SUBPART E: CORROSIVE
DEPARTMENT OF TRANSPORTATION PACKAGING REQUIREMENTS: 49 CFR 173.249 EXCEPTIONS: 49 CFR 173.244

TOXICITY

POTASSIUM HYDROXIDE: IRRITATION DATA: 50 MG/24 HOURS SKIN-HUMAN SEVERE; 50 MG/24 HOURS SKIN-RABBIT SEVERE; 50 MG/24 HOURS SKIN-GUINEA PIG SEVERE; 1 MG/24 HOURS RINSED EYE-RABBIT MODERATE. TOXICITY DATA: 273 MG/KG ORAL-RAT LD50; MUTAGENIC DATA (RTECS). CARCINOGEN STATUS: NONE. LOCAL EFFECTS: CORROSIVE- INHALATION, SKIN, AND EYES. ACUTE TOXICITY LEVEL: TOXIC BY INGESTION. TARGET EFFECTS: NO DATA AVAILABLE.

HEALTH EFFECTS AND FIRST AID

INHALATION: POTASSIUM HYDROXIDE: CORROSIVE. **ACUTE EXPOSURE-** INHALATION OF DUST OR MIST MAY CAUSE SYMPTOMS OF RESPIRATORY TRACT IRRITATION POSSIBLY INCLUDING COUGHING, CHOKING, PAIN IN THE NOSE, MOUTH, AND THROAT, LESIONS OF THE NASAL SEPTUM, AND BURNS OF THE MUCOUS MEMBRANES. IF SUFFICIENT QUANTITIES ARE INHALED, PULMONARY EDEMA MAY DEVELOP, OFTEN WITH A LATENT PERIOD OF 5-72 HOURS. THE SYMPTOMS MAY INCLUDE TIGHTNESS IN THE CHEST, DYSPNEA, FROTHY SPUTUM, CYANOSIS, AND DIZZINESS. PHYSICAL FINDINGS MAY INCLUDE WEAK, RAPID PULSE, HYPOTENSION, HEMOCONCENTRATION, AND MOIST RALES. **CHRONIC EXPOSURE-** DEPENDING ON THE CONCENTRATION AND DURATION OF EXPOSURE, REPEATED OR PROLONGED EXPOSURE TO CORROSIVE SUBSTANCES MAY CAUSE INFLAMMATORY AND ULCERATIVE CHANGES IN THE MOUTH AND POSSIBLY BRONCHIAL AND GASTROINTESTINAL DISTURBANCES.

FIRST AID- REMOVE FROM EXPOSURE AREA TO FRESH AIR IMMEDIATELY. IF BREATHING HAS STOPPED, GIVE ARTIFICIAL RESPIRATION. MAINTAIN AIRWAY AND BLOOD PRESSURE AND ADMINISTER OXYGEN IF AVAILABLE. KEEP AFFECTED PERSON WARM AND AT REST. TREAT SYMPTOMATICALLY AND SUPPORTIVELY. ADMINISTRATION OF OXYGEN SHOULD BE PERFORMED BY QUALIFIED PERSONNEL. GET MEDICAL ATTENTION IMMEDIATELY.

SKIN CONTACT: POTASSIUM HYDROXIDE: CORROSIVE. **ACUTE EXPOSURE-** DIRECT CONTACT MAY CAUSE SEVERE PAIN, BURNS, AND POSSIBLY BROWNISH STAINS. THE CORRODED AREAS ARE SOFT, GELATINOUS AND NECROTIC, AND THE TISSUE DESTRUCTION MAY BE DEEP. **CHRONIC EXPOSURE-** REPEATED OR PROLONGED CONTACT MAY CAUSE DERMATITIS OR EFFECTS SIMILAR TO ACUTE EXPOSURE. FREQUENT APPLICATIONS OF AQUEOUS SOLUTIONS (3-6 PERCENT) OF POTASSIUM HYDROXIDE TO THE SKIN OF MICE FOR 46 WEEKS PRODUCED TUMORS IDENTICAL TO THOSE FROM COAL TAR; WARTS OCCURRED FIRST AND THEN SKIN TUMORS DEVELOPED.

FIRST AID- REMOVE CONTAMINATED CLOTHING AND SHOES IMMEDIATELY. WASH AFFECTED AREA WITH SOAP OR MILD DETERGENT AND LARGE AMOUNTS OF WATER UNTIL NO EVIDENCE OF CHEMICAL REMAINS (AT LEAST 15-20 MINUTES). IN CASE OF CHEMICAL BURNS, COVER AREA WITH STERILE, DRY DRESSING. BANDAGE SECURELY, BUT NOT TOO TIGHTLY. GET MEDICAL ATTENTION IMMEDIATELY.

EYE CONTACT: POTASSIUM HYDROXIDE: CORROSIVE. **ACUTE EXPOSURE-** DIRECT CONTACT WITH SOLID OR SOLUTIONS MAY CAUSE PAIN AND BURNS, POSSIBLY SEVERE. THE DEGREE OF INJURY DEPENDS ON THE CONCENTRATION AND DURATION OF CONTACT. THERE MAY BE EDEMA, DESTRUCTION OF EPITHELIUM, CORNEAL OPACIFICATION, AND IRITIS. WHEN DAMAGE IS LESS THAN EXCESSIVE, THESE SYMPTOMS TEND TO AMELIORATE. IN SEVERE BURNS, THE FULL EXTENT OF THE INJURY MAY NOT BE IMMEDIATELY APPARENT. LATE COMPLICATIONS MAY INCLUDE PERSISTENT EDEMA, VASCULARIZATION, AND SCARRING OF THE CORNEA, PERMANENT OPACITY, STAPHYLOMA, CATARACT, AND SYMBLEPHARON. **CHRONIC EXPOSURE-** EFFECTS DEPEND ON CONCENTRATION AND DURATION OF EXPOSURE. REPEATED OR PROLONGED EXPOSURE TO VAPORS AND/OR FUMES MAY RESULT IN CONJUNCTIVITIS OR EFFECTS AS IN ACUTE EXPOSURE.

FIRST AID- WASH EYES IMMEDIATELY WITH LARGE AMOUNTS OF WATER, OCCASIONALLY LIFTING UPPER AND LOWER LIDS, UNTIL NO EVIDENCE OF CHEMICAL REMAINS (AT LEAST 15-20 MINUTES). CONTINUE IRRIGATING WITH NORMAL SALINE UNTIL THE PH HAS RETURNED TO NORMAL (30-60 MINUTES). COVER WITH STERILE BANDAGES. GET MEDICAL ATTENTION IMMEDIATELY.

INGESTION: POTASSIUM HYDROXIDE: CORROSIVE/TOXIC. **ACUTE EXPOSURE-** INGESTION OF 273 MG/KG OF POTASSIUM HYDROXIDE WAS LETHAL TO RATS TESTED. INGESTION OF STRONG ALKALIES MAY BE FOLLOWED BY SEVERE PAIN, VOMITING, DIARRHEA, AND COLLAPSE. THE VOMITUS CONTAINS BLOOD AND DESQUAMATED MUCOSAL LINING. IF DEATH DOES NOT OCCUR IN THE FIRST 24 HOURS, THE PATIENT MAY IMPROVE FOR 2-4 DAYS AND THEN HAVE A SUDDEN ONSET OF SEVERE ABDOMINAL PAIN, BOARDLIKE ABDOMINAL RIGIDITY, AND RAPID FALL OF BLOOD PRESSURE INDICATING DELAYED GASTRIC OR ESOPHAGEAL PERFORATION. DAMAGE TO THE ESOPHAGUS AND STOMACH AFTER INGESTION MAY PROGRESS FOR 2-3 WEEKS. DEATH FROM PERITONITIS MAY OCCUR AS LATE AS 1 MONTH AFTER INGESTION. EVEN THOUGH THE PATIENT RECOVERS FROM THE IMMEDIATE DAMAGE, ESOPHAGEAL STRICTURE MAY OCCUR WEEKS, MONTHS OR EVEN YEARS LATER TO MAKE SWALLOWING DIFFICULT. **CHRONIC EXPOSURE-** THE FOOD AND DRUG ADMINISTRATION LIST POTASSIUM HYDROXIDE AS A DIRECT FOOD SUBSTANCE AFFIRMED AS GENERALLY RECOGNIZED AS SAFE AT LEVELS NOT TO EXCEED CURRENT GOOD MANUFACTURING PRACTICES.

FIRST AID- DILUTE THE ALKALI BY GIVING WATER OR MILK IMMEDIATELY AND ALLOW VOMITING TO OCCUR. AVOID GASTRIC LAVAGE OR EMETICS. ESOPHAGOSCOPY IS THE ONLY WAY TO EXCLUDE THE POSSIBLITY OF CORROSION IN THE UPPER GASTROINTESTINAL TRACT; IF CORROSION IS SUSPECTED, ESOPHAGOSCOPY SHOULD USUALLY BE PERFORMED WITHIN 24 HOURS (DREISBACH, HANDBOOK OF POISONING, 12TH ED.). MAINTAIN AIRWAY AND TREAT SHOCK. IF VOMITING OCCURS, KEEP HEAD BELOW HIPS TO HELP PREVENT ASPIRATION. GET MEDICAL ATTENTION IMMEDIATELY.

ANTIDOTE: NO SPECIFIC ANTIDOTE. TREAT SYMPTOMATICALLY AND SUPPORTIVELY.

REACTIVITY

REACTIVITY: VIGOROUS, EXOTHERMIC REACTION WITH WATER.

INCOMPATIBILITIES: POTASSIUM HYDROXIDE: ACETIC ACID: REACTS VIOLENTLY. ACIDS: VIOLENT REACTION. ACROLEIN: VIOLENT POLYMERIZATION. ACRYLONITRILE: VIOLENT POLYMERIZATION. ALCOHOLS: DISSOLVES EXOTHERMICALLY. ALUMINUM: CORROSIVE IN THE PRESENCE OF MOISTURE. AMMONIUM HEXACHLOROPLATINATE: FORMATION OF EXPLOSIVE PRODUCT. AMMONIUM SALTS: EVOLUTION OF AMMONIA GAS. BENZOYL CHLORIDE + SODIUM AZIDE: VIOLENT EXOTHERMIC REACTION. P-BIS(1,2-DIBROMOETHYL)BENZENE: HIGHLY EXOTHERMIC REACTION. BROMOFORM:

VIOLENT, EXOTHERMIC REACTION. BROMOFORM + CYCLIC POLYETHYLENE OXIDES: POSSIBLE EXPLOSIVE REACTION. CALCIUM CARBIDE + CHLORINE: FORMATION OF EXPLOSIVE DICHLOROACETYLENE. CHLORINE: EXPLOSIVE REACTION. CHLORINE DIOXIDE: EXPLOSION ON CONTACT. CHLORINE + HYDROGEN PEROXIDE: PRODUCES RED LUMINESCENCE DURING REACTION. CHLOROFORM + METHANOL: INTENSE EXOTHERMIC REACTION. CYCLOPENTADIENE: VIGOROUS EXOTHERMIC RESIN FORMATION. 1,2-DICHLOROETHYLENE: FORMATION OF EXPLOSIVE AND SPONTANEOUSLY FLAMMABLE CHLOROACETYLENE. GERMANIUM: INCANDESCENT REACTION. GLASS: SLOWLY ATTACKED. HYDROCARBONS (HALOGENATED): VIOLENT REACTION. HYPONITROUS ACID: IGNITION REACTION. LEAD: CORROSIVE IN THE PRESENCE OF MOISTURE. MALEIC ANHYDRIDE: DECOMPOSES EXOTHERMICALLY OR EXPLOSIVELY. METALS: CORROSIVE REACTION WITH FORMATION OF FLAMMABLE HYDROGEN GAS. N-METHYL-N-NITROSOUREA + METHYLENE CHLORIDE: EXPLOSIVE REACTION. NITRIC TRICHLORIDE: EXPLOSIVE REACTION. NITROALKANES: FORMATION OF EXPLOSIVE SALTS. NITROBENZENE + METHANOL (TRACE): VIOLENT, EXOTHERMIC REACTION. NITROETHANE: FORMATION OF EXPLOSIVE SALT. NITROGEN TRICHLORIDE: EXPLOSIVE REACTION. NITROMETHANE: FORMATION OF EXPLOSIVE SALT. O-NITROPHENOL (MOLTEN): REACTS VIOLENTLY. NITROPROPANE: FORMATION OF EXPLOSIVE SALT. N-NITROSOMETHYLUREA + N-BUTYL ETHER: FORMATION OF EXPLOSIVE COMPOUND. PHOSPHORUS: EVOLUTION OF FLAMMABLE PHOSPHINE. POTASSIUM PEROXODISULFATE: IGNITION REACTION. POTASSIUM PERSULFATE + WATER: EXOTHERMIC REACTION. SUGARS: EVOLVE CARBON MONOXIDE AT OR ABOVE 84 C. TETRACHLOROETHANE: FORMATION OF FLAMMABLE CHLOROACETYLENE GAS. 2,2,3,3-TETRAFLUOROPROPANOL: EXOTHERMIC REACTION. TETRAHYDROFURAN (PEROXIDISED): POSSIBLE EXPLOSIVE REACTION. THORIUM DICARBIDE: INCANDESCENT REACTION ON HEATING. TIN: CORROSIVE IN THE PRESENCE OF MOISTURE. TRICHLOROETHYLENE: FORMATION OF EXPLOSIVE DICHLOROACETYLENE ON HEATING. 2,4,6-TRINITROTOLUENE + METHANOL: FORMATION OF EXPLOSIVE PRODUCT. ZINC: CORROSIVE IN THE PRESENCE OF MOISTURE.

DECOMPOSITION: THERMAL DECOMPOSITION PRODUCTS MAY INCLUDE CORROSIVE FUMES OF POTASSIUM OXIDE.

POLYMERIZATION: HAZARDOUS POLYMERIZATION HAS NOT BEEN REPORTED TO OCCUR UNDER NORMAL TEMPERATURES AND PRESSURES.

STORAGE AND DISPOSAL

OBSERVE ALL FEDERAL, STATE AND LOCAL REGULATIONS WHEN STORING OR DISPOSING OF THIS SUBSTANCE. FOR ASSISTANCE, CONTACT THE DISTRICT DIRECTOR OF THE ENVIRONMENTAL PROTECTION AGENCY.

STORAGE

PROTECT AGAINST PHYSICAL DAMAGE. STORE IN A DRY PLACE; PROTECT AGAINST MOISTURE AND WATER. SEPARATE FROM ACIDS, METALS, EXPLOSIVES, ORGANIC PEROXIDES, AND EASILY IGNITABLE MATERIALS (NFPA 49, HAZARDOUS CHEMICALS DATA, 1975).

STORE AWAY FROM INCOMPATIBLE SUBSTANCES.

DISPOSAL

DISPOSAL MUST BE IN ACCORDANCE WITH STANDARDS APPLICABLE TO GENERATORS OF HAZARDOUS WASTE, 40 CFR 262. EPA HAZARDOUS WASTE NUMBER D002. 100 POUND CERCLA SECTION 103 REPORTABLE QUANTITY.

CONDITIONS TO AVOID

MAY BURN BUT DOES NOT IGNITE READILY. FLAMMABLE, POISONOUS GASES MAY ACCUMULATE IN TANKS AND HOPPER CARS. MAY IGNITE COMBUSTIBLES (WOOD, PAPER, OIL, ETC.).

SPILL AND LEAK PROCEDURES

SOIL SPILL: DIG A PIT, POND, LAGOON OR HOLDING AREA TO CONTAIN LIQUID OR SOLID MATERIAL. DIKE SURFACE FLOW USING SOIL, SANDBAGS, FOAMED POLYURETHANE OR FOAMED CONCRETE. ABSORB BULK LIQUID WITH FLY ASH OR CEMENT POWDER. ADD CAUSTIC SODA.

ADD DILUTE ACID TO NEUTRALIZE.

AIR SPILL: APPLY WATER SPRAY TO KNOCK DOWN VAPORS.

WATER SPILL: NEUTRALIZE WITH DILUTE ACID OR REMOVABLE STRONG ACID.

OCCUPATIONAL SPILL: DO NOT TOUCH SPILLED MATERIAL. STOP LEAK IF YOU CAN DO IT WITHOUT RISK. FOR SMALL SPILLS, TAKE UP WITH SAND OR OTHER ABSORBENT MATERIAL AND PLACE INTO CONTAINERS FOR LATER DISPOSAL. FOR SMALL DRY SPILLS, WITH CLEAN SHOVEL PLACE MATERIAL INTO CLEAN, DRY CONTAINER AND COVER. MOVE CONTAINERS FROM SPILL AREA. FOR LARGER SPILLS, DIKE FAR AHEAD OF SPILL FOR LATER DISPOSAL. KEEP UNNECESSARY PEOPLE AWAY. ISOLATE HAZARD AREA AND DENY ENTRY.

REPORTABLE QUANTITY (RQ): THE SUPERFUND AMENDMENTS AND REAUTHORIZATION ACT (SARA) SECTION 304 REQUIRES THAT A RELEASE EQUAL TO OR GREATER THAN THE REPORTABLE QUANTITY ESTABLISHED FOR THAT SUBSTANCE BE IMMEDIATELY REPORTED TO THE LOCAL EMERGENCY PLANNING COMMITTEE AND THE STATE EMERGENCY RESPONSE COMMISSION (40 CFR 355.40). IF THE RELEASE OF THIS SUBSTANCE IS REPORTABLE UNDER CERCLA SECTION 103, THE NATIONAL RESPONSE CENTER MUST BE NOTIFIED IMMEDIATELY AT (800) 424-8802 OR (202) 426-2675 IN THE METROPOLITAN WASHINGTON, D.C. AREA (40 CFR 302.6).

PROTECTIVE EQUIPMENT

VENTILATION: PROVIDE LOCAL EXHAUST OR PROCESS ENCLOSURE VENTILATION TO MEET PUBLISHED EXPOSURE LIMITS.

RESPIRATOR: THE FOLLOWING RESPIRATORS ARE RECOMMENDED BASED ON INFORMATION FOUND IN THE PHYSICAL DATA, TOXICITY AND HEALTH EFFECTS SECTIONS. THEY ARE RANKED IN ORDER FROM MINIMUM TO MAXIMUM RESPIRATORY PROTECTION. THE SPECIFIC RESPIRATOR SELECTED MUST BE BASED ON CONTAMINATION LEVELS FOUND IN THE WORK PLACE, MUST NOT EXCEED THE WORKING LIMITS OF THE RESPIRATOR AND BE JOINTLY APPROVED BY THE NATIONAL INSTITUTE FOR OCCUPATIONAL SAFETY AND HEALTH AND THE MINE SAFETY AND HEALTH ADMINISTRATION (NIOSH-MSHA).

CHEMICAL CARTRIDGE RESPIRATOR WITH FULL FACEPIECE.

TYPE 'C' SUPPLIED-AIR RESPIRATOR WITH A FULL FACEPIECE OPERATED IN PRESSURE-DEMAND OR OTHER POSITIVE PRESSURE MODE OR WITH A FULL FACEPIECE, HELMET OR HOOD OPERATED IN CONTINUOUS-FLOW MODE.

SELF-CONTAINED BREATHING APPARATUS WITH A FULL FACEPIECE OPERATED IN PRESSURE-DEMAND OR OTHER POSITIVE PRESSURE MODE.

FOR FIREFIGHTING AND OTHER IMMEDIATELY DANGEROUS TO LIFE OR HEALTH CONDITIONS:

SELF-CONTAINED BREATHING APPARATUS WITH FULL FACEPIECE OPERATED IN PRESSURE-DEMAND OR OTHER POSITIVE PRESSURE MODE.

SUPPLIED-AIR RESPIRATOR WITH FULL FACEPIECE AND OPERATED IN PRESSURE-DEMAND OR OTHER POSITIVE PRESSURE MODE IN COMBINATION WITH AN AUXILIARY SELF-CONTAINED BREATHING APPARATUS OPERATED IN PRESSURE-DEMAND OR OTHER POSITIVE PRESSURE MODE.

CLOTHING: EMPLOYEE MUST WEAR APPROPRIATE PROTECTIVE (IMPERVIOUS) CLOTHING AND EQUIPMENT TO PREVENT ANY POSSIBILITY OF SKIN CONTACT WITH THIS SUBSTANCE.

GLOVES: EMPLOYEE MUST WEAR APPROPRIATE PROTECTIVE GLOVES TO PREVENT CONTACT WITH THIS SUBSTANCE.

EYE PROTECTION: EMPLOYEE MUST WEAR SPLASH-PROOF OR DUST-RESISTANT SAFETY GOGGLES AND A FACESHIELD TO PREVENT CONTACT WITH THIS SUBSTANCE.

EMERGENCY WASH FACILITIES: WHERE THERE IS ANY POSSIBILITY THAT AN EMPLOYEE'S EYES AND/OR SKIN MAY BE EXPOSED TO THIS SUBSTANCE, THE EMPLOYER SHOULD PROVIDE AN EYE WASH FOUNTAIN AND QUICK DRENCH SHOWER WITHIN THE IMMEDIATE WORK AREA FOR EMERGENCY USE.

AUTHORIZED BY- OCCUPATIONAL HEALTH SERVICES, INC.

CREATION DATE: 11/17/89 ***REVISION DATE:*** 05/08/90

MATERIAL SAFETY DATA SHEET

OCCUPATIONAL HEALTH SERVICES, INC.
AGRICULTURE AND PESTICIDE DIVISION
450 SEVENTH AVENUE, SUITE 2407
NEW YORK, NEW YORK 10123
1-800-445-MSDS OR (212) 967-1100

EMERGENCY CONTACT:
JOHN S. BRANSFORD, JR. (615) 292-1180

SUBSTANCE IDENTIFICATION

CAS-NUMBER 7681-11-0

SUBSTANCE: POTASSIUM IODIDE

TRADE NAMES/SYNONYMS: POTIDE; KNOLLIDE; KI-N; P-410; P-412; PST19435

CHEMICAL FAMILY: INORGANIC SALT

MOLECULAR FORMULA: K-I

MOLECULAR WEIGHT: 166.0

CERCLA RATINGS (SCALE 0-3): HEALTH=2 FIRE=0 REACTIVITY=0 PERSISTENCE=0

NFPA RATINGS (SCALE 0-4): HEALTH=2 FIRE=0 REACTIVITY=0

COMPONENTS AND CONTAMINANTS

COMPONENT: POTASSIUM IODIDE ***PERCENT:*** 100

CAS# 7681-11-0

OTHER CONTAMINANTS: NONE.

EXPOSURE LIMITS: NO OCCUPATIONAL EXPOSURE LIMITS ESTABLISHED BY OSHA, ACGIH, OR NIOSH.

PHYSICAL DATA

DESCRIPTION: COLORLESS TO WHITE, DELIQUESCENT GRANULES OR POWDER WITH A STRONG, BITTER, SALINE TASTE, WHICH MAY BECOME YELLOW ON EXPOSURE TO AIR.

BOILING POINT: 2426 F (1330 C) ***MELTING POINT:*** 1258 F (681 C)

SPECIFIC GRAVITY: 3.1 ***VAPOR PRESSURE:*** 1 MMHG @ 745 C

PH: 6-9.2 (5% SOLUTION) ***SOLUBILITY IN WATER:*** 127.5%

SOLVENT SOLUBILITY: ALCOHOL, GLYCOL, ACETONE, GLYCEROL, AMMONIA

FIRE AND EXPLOSION DATA

FIRE AND EXPLOSION HAZARD: NEGLIGIBLE FIRE HAZARD WHEN EXPOSED TO HEAT OR FLAME.

FIREFIGHTING MEDIA: DRY CHEMICAL, CARBON DIOXIDE, HALON, WATER SPRAY OR STANDARD FOAM (1987 EMERGENCY RESPONSE GUIDEBOOK, DOT P 5800.4). FOR LARGER FIRES, USE WATER SPRAY, FOG OR STANDARD FOAM (1987 EMERGENCY RESPONSE GUIDEBOOK, DOT P 5800.4).

FIREFIGHTING: NO ACUTE HAZARD. MOVE CONTAINER FROM FIRE AREA IF POSSIBLE. AVOID BREATHING VAPORS OR DUSTS; KEEP UPWIND.

TOXICITY

POTASSIUM IODIDE: TOXICITY DATA: 1862 MG/KG ORAL-MOUSE LDLO; 916 MG/KG ORAL-RABBIT LDLO; 120 MG/KG INTRAVENOUS-RAT LDLO; 1117 MG/KG INTRAPERITONEAL-MOUSE LDLO; MUTAGENIC DATA (RTECS); REPRODUCTIVE EFFECTS DATA (RTECS). CARCINOGEN STATUS: NONE. LOCAL EFFECTS: IRRITANT-EYES. ACUTE TOXICITY LEVEL: INSUFFICIENT DATA. TARGET EFFECTS: POISONING MAY AFFECT THE THYROID GLAND. ADDITIONAL DATA: CONCURRENT USE OF POTASSIUM IODIDE AND LITHIUM MAY CAUSE AN ADDITIVE HYPOTHYROID EFFECT.

HEALTH EFFECTS AND FIRST AID

INHALATION: POTASSIUM IODIDE: **ACUTE EXPOSURE-** INHALATION OF THE DUST MAY BE IRRITATING. **CHRONIC EXPOSURE-** REPEATED OR PROLONGED EXPOSURE MAY RESULT IN "IODISM" AS DETAILED IN CHRONIC INGESTION.

FIRST AID- REMOVE FROM EXPOSURE AREA TO FRESH AIR IMMEDIATELY. IF BREATHING HAS STOPPED, PERFORM ARTIFICIAL RESPIRATION. KEEP PERSON WARM AND AT REST. TREAT SYMPTOMATICALLY AND SUPPORTIVELY. GET MEDICAL ATTENTION IMMEDIATELY.

SKIN CONTACT: POTASSIUM IODIDE: **ACUTE EXPOSURE-** CONTACT WITH THE DUST MAY BE IRRITATING WHILE SOLUTIONS MAY BE CORROSIVE. IODIDES MAY CAUSE SENSITIZATION IN PERSONS PREVIOUSLY EXPOSED. **CHRONIC EXPOSURE-** HYPERSENSITIVITY TO IODIDES MAY DEVELOP CHARACTERIZED BY SKIN RASHES, RHINITIS, ASTHMA, LARYNGEAL EDEMA, SERUM SICKNESS WITH FEVER, JOINT PAIN, AND SWELLING AND LYMPH NODE ENLARGEMENT.

FIRST AID- REMOVE CONTAMINATED CLOTHING AND SHOES IMMEDIATELY. WASH AFFECTED AREA WITH SOAP OR MILD DETERGENT AND LARGE AMOUNTS OF WATER UNTIL NO EVIDENCE OF CHEMICAL REMAINS (AT LEAST 15-20 MINUTES). IN CASE OF CHEMICAL BURNS, COVER AREA WITH STERILE, DRY DRESSING. BANDAGE SECURELY, BUT NOT TOO TIGHTLY. GET MEDICAL ATTENTION IMMEDIATELY.

EYE CONTACT: POTASSIUM IODIDE: IRRITANT. **ACUTE EXPOSURE-** CONTACT WITH THE EYES MAY CAUSE IRRITATION WHILE SOLUTIONS MAY BE CORROSIVE. **CHRONIC EXPOSURE-** REPEATED OR PROLONGED EXPOSURE MAY CAUSE CONJUNCTIVITIS. INGESTION OF IODIDES MAY LEAD TO "IODISM" AND AFFECT THE EYES WITH LACRIMATION, EDEMA OF THE EYELIDS, AND CONJUNCTIVAL HYPEREMIA.

FIRST AID- WASH EYES IMMEDIATELY WITH LARGE AMOUNTS OF WATER, OCCASIONALLY LIFTING UPPER AND LOWER LIDS, UNTIL NO EVIDENCE OF CHEMICAL REMAINS (AT LEAST 15-20 MINUTES). CONTINUE IRRIGATING WITH NORMAL SALINE UNTIL THE PH HAS RETURNED TO NORMAL (30-60 MINUTES). COVER WITH STERILE BANDAGES. GET MEDICAL ATTENTION IMMEDIATELY.

INGESTION: POTASSIUM IODIDE: **ACUTE EXPOSURE-** THE REPORTED LETHAL DOSE FOR POTASSIUM IODIDE IN MICE IS 1862 MG/KG. IODIDE SALTS ACT PRINCIPALLY AS EXPECTORANTS AND DIURETICS. HYPERSENSITIVITY TO IODIDES MAY BE MANIFESTED BY ANGIONEUROTIC EDEMA, CUTANEOUS AND MUCOSAL HEMORRHAGES, AND SYMPTOMS RESEMBLING SERUM SICKNESS, SUCH AS FEVER, ARTHRALGIA, LYMPH NODE ENLARGEMENT AND EOSINOPHILIA. **CHRONIC EXPOSURE-** CHRONIC INGESTION OF POTASSIUM IODIDE MAY RESULT IN THYROID ADENOMA, GOITER, MYXEDEMA, AND THROMBOCYTOPENIA. "IODISM" MAY OCCUR WITH SYMPTOMS OF AN UNPLEASANT BRASSY TASTE IN THE MOUTH, SALIVATION, CORYZA, LACRIMATION, EDEMA OF THE EYELIDS, CONJUNCTIVITIS, SNEEZING, BRONCHITIS, STOMATITIS, PAROTITIS, LARYNGITIS, GLOTTAL EDEMA, HEADACHE, AND FEVER. VARIOUS SKIN RASHES, POSSIBLY WITH ERYTHEMA, ACNE, AND URTICARIA ARE POSSIBLE. ANOREXIA, WEIGHT LOSS, SLEEPLESSNESS, AND NERVOUS SYMPTOMS MAY OCCUR. THE USE OF IODIDES FOR ASTHMA IN PREGNANCY HAS RESULTED IN FETAL DEATH, SEVERE GOITER AND CRETINOID APPEARANCE OF THE NEWBORN. EFFECTS ON THE NEWBORN, FERTILITY, AND THE REPRODUCTIVE SYSTEM OF FEMALES HAVE BEEN REPORTED FROM CHRONIC FEEDING TO ANIMALS.

FIRST AID: GIVE MILK, ABSORB REMAINING IODINE WITH STARCH SOLUTION MADE BY ADDING 15 GRAMS OF CORNSTARCH OR FLOUR TO 500 ML OF WATER. EMESIS AND LAVAGE ARE NOT INDICATED IN THE PRESENCE OF ESOPHAGEAL INJURY. MILK EVERY 15 MINUTES MAY RELIEVED GASTRIC IRRITATION. MAINTAIN AIRWAY AND RESPIRATION. (DREISBACH, HANDBOOK OF POISONING, 11TH EDITION).

ANTIDOTE: NO SPECIFIC ANTIDOTE. TREAT SYMPTOMATICALLY AND SUPPORTIVELY.

REACTIVITY

REACTIVITY: STABLE UNDER NORMAL TEMPERATURES AND PRESSURES.

INCOMPATIBILITIES: POTASSIUM IODIDE: ALKALI METALS: VIOLENT REACTION. BROMINE PENTATRIFLUORIDE: VIOLENT REACTION, OFTEN WITH IGNITION AT AMBIENT OR SLIGHTLY ELEVATED TEMPERATURES. CHLORINE TRIFLUORIDE: VIOLENT REACTION, OFTEN WITH IGNITION AT AMBIENT OR SLIGHTLY ELEVATED TEMPERATURES. DIAZONIUM SALTS: FORMATION OF AN UNSTABLE AND EXPLOSIVE PRODUCT. 2-DIISOPROPYL PEROXYDICARBONATE: INSTANT DECOMPOSITION. FLUORINE PERCHLORATE: EXPLOSION ON CONTACT WITH POTASSIUM IODIDE. METALS: CORROSIVE IN ALL CONCENTRATIONS TO MOST METALS, EXCEPT STAINLESS STEEL, TITANIUM, AND TANTALUM. OXIDANTS (STRONG): VIOLENT REACTION. PERCHLORIC ACID: VIOLENT REACTION. TRIFLUOROACETYL HYPOFLUORITE: MAY REACT EXPLOSIVELY ON CONTACT WITH AQUEOUS POTASSIUM IODIDE ULESS GREATLY DILUTED WITH NITROGEN.

DECOMPOSITION: THERMAL DECOMPOSITION PRODUCTS MAY INCLUDE HIGHLY TOXIC AND HAZARDOUS OXIDES OF POTASSIUM AND HYDROGEN IODIDE.

POLYMERIZATION: HAZARDOUS POLYMERIZATION HAS NOT BEEN REPORTED TO OCCUR UNDER NORMAL TEMPERATURES AND PRESSURES.

STORAGE AND DISPOSAL

OBSERVE ALL FEDERAL, STATE AND LOCAL REGULATIONS WHEN STORING OR DISPOSING OF THIS SUBSTANCE. FOR ASSISTANCE, CONTACT THE DISTRICT DIRECTOR OF THE ENVIRONMENTAL PROTECTION AGENCY.

STORAGE

STORE AWAY FROM INCOMPATIBLE SUBSTANCES.

CONDITIONS TO AVOID

NONE REPORTED.

SPILL AND LEAK PROCEDURES

OCCUPATIONAL SPILL: NO SPECIAL PRECAUTIONS INDICATED.

PROTECTIVE EQUIPMENT

VENTILATION: PROVIDE LOCAL EXHAUST OR GENERAL DILUTION VENTILATION SYSTEM.

RESPIRATOR: THE FOLLOWING RESPIRATORS ARE RECOMMENDED BASED ON INFORMATION FOUND IN THE PHYSICAL DATA, TOXICITY AND HEALTH EFFECTS SECTIONS. THEY ARE RANKED IN ORDER FROM MINIMUM TO MAXIMUM RESPIRATORY PROTECTION. THE SPECIFIC RESPIRATOR SELECTED MUST BE BASED ON CONTAMINATION LEVELS FOUND IN THE WORK PLACE, MUST NOT EXCEED THE WORKING LIMITS OF THE RESPIRATOR AND BE JOINTLY APPROVED BY THE NATIONAL INSTITUTE FOR OCCUPATIONAL SAFETY AND HEALTH AND THE MINE SAFETY AND HEALTH ADMINISTRATION (NIOSH-MSHA).

DUST AND MIST RESPIRATOR WITH A FULL FACEPIECE.

AIR-PURIFYING FULL FACEPIECE RESPIRATOR WITH A HIGH-EFFICIENCY PARTICULATE FILTER.

POWERED AIR-PURIFYING RESPIRATOR WITH A TIGHT-FITTING FACEPIECE AND HIGH-EFFICIENCY PARTICULATE FILTER.

TYPE 'C' SUPPLIED-AIR RESPIRATOR WITH A FULL FACEPIECE OPERATED IN PRESSURE-DEMAND OR OTHER POSITIVE PRESSURE MODE OR WITH A FULL FACEPIECE, HELMET OR HOOD OPERATED IN CONTINUOUS-FLOW MODE.

SELF-CONTAINED BREATHING APPARATUS WITH A FULL FACEPIECE OPERATED IN PRESSURE-DEMAND OR OTHER POSITIVE PRESSURE MODE.

FOR FIREFIGHTING AND OTHER IMMEDIATELY DANGEROUS TO LIFE OR HEALTH CONDITIONS:

SELF-CONTAINED BREATHING APPARATUS WITH FULL FACEPIECE OPERATED IN PRESSURE-DEMAND OR OTHER POSITIVE PRESSURE MODE.

SUPPLIED-AIR RESPIRATOR WITH FULL FACEPIECE AND OPERATED IN PRESSURE-DEMAND OR OTHER POSITIVE PRESSURE MODE IN COMBINATION WITH AN AUXILIARY SELF-CONTAINED BREATHING APPARATUS OPERATED IN PRESSURE-DEMAND OR OTHER POSITIVE PRESSURE MODE.

CLOTHING: EMPLOYEE MUST WEAR APPROPRIATE PROTECTIVE (IMPERVIOUS) CLOTHING AND EQUIPMENT TO PREVENT REPEATED OR PROLONGED SKIN CONTACT WITH THIS SUBSTANCE.
GLOVES: EMPLOYEE MUST WEAR APPROPRIATE PROTECTIVE GLOVES TO PREVENT CONTACT WITH THIS SUBSTANCE.
EYE PROTECTION: EMPLOYEE MUST WEAR SPLASH-PROOF OR DUST-RESISTANT SAFETY GOGGLES TO PREVENT EYE CONTACT WITH THIS SUBSTANCE.
EMERGENCY EYE WASH: WHERE THERE IS ANY POSSIBILITY THAT AN EMPLOYEE'S EYES MAY BE EXPOSED TO THIS SUBSTANCE, THE EMPLOYER SHOULD PROVIDE AN EYE WASH FOUNTAIN WITHIN THE IMMEDIATE WORK AREA FOR EMERGENCY USE.

AUTHORIZED BY- OCCUPATIONAL HEALTH SERVICES, INC.
CREATION DATE: 10/04/89 ***REVISION DATE:*** 05/18/90

MATERIAL SAFETY DATA SHEET

OCCUPATIONAL HEALTH SERVICES, INC.
AGRICULTURE AND PESTICIDE DIVISION
450 SEVENTH AVENUE, SUITE 2407
NEW YORK, NEW YORK 10123
1-800-445-MSDS OR (212) 967-1100

EMERGENCY CONTACT:
JOHN S. BRANSFORD, JR. (615) 292-1180

SUBSTANCE IDENTIFICATION

CAS-NUMBER 7757-79-1
SUBSTANCE: <u>POTASSIUM NITRATE</u>
TRADE NAMES/SYNONYMS: NITRIC ACID POTASSIUM SALT; NITRIC ACID POTASSIUM SALT (1:1); COLLO-BO; NITER; NITRE; SALTPETER; POTASSIUM NITRATE (JT BAKER); STCC 4918737; UN 1486; KNO3; PST19470
CHEMICAL FAMILY: INORGANIC SALT
MOLECULAR FORMULA: K-N-O3
MOLECULAR WEIGHT: 101.11
CERCLA RATINGS (SCALE 0-3): HEALTH=3 FIRE=0 REACTIVITY=0 PERSISTENCE=0
NFPA RATINGS (SCALE 0-4): HEALTH=0 FIRE=0 REACTIVITY=0

COMPONENTS AND CONTAMINANTS

COMPONENT: POTASSIUM NITRATE ***PERCENT:*** 100
CAS# 7757-79-1
OTHER CONTAMINANTS: NONE
EXPOSURE LIMITS: NUISANCE PARTICULATES (NUISANCE DUST): 5 MG/M3 OSHA TWA (RESPIRABLE DUST); 15 MG/M3 OSHA TWA (TOTAL DUST) 10 MG/M3 ACGIH TWA (TOTAL DUST) (NO ASBESTOS AND < 1% CRYSTALLINE SILICA)

PHYSICAL DATA

DESCRIPTION: COLORLESS, TRANSPARENT CRYSTALS OR WHITE POWDER WITH A SALINE TASTE.
BOILING POINT: 752 F (400 C) DEC ***MELTING POINT:*** 633 F (334 C)
SPECIFIC GRAVITY: 2.109 @ 16 C ***PH:*** 7 (APPROX)
SOLUBILITY IN WATER: 13.3% @ 0 C
SOLVENT SOLUBILITY: SOLUBLE IN LIQUID AMMONIA, GLYCEROL; INSOLUBLE IN DILUTE ALCOHOL, ETHER, ABSOLUTE ETHANOL.

FIRE AND EXPLOSION DATA

FIRE AND EXPLOSION HAZARD: NEGLIGIBLE FIRE HAZARD WHEN EXPOSED TO HEAT OR FLAME.
OXIDIZER: OXIDIZERS DECOMPOSE, ESPECIALLY WHEN HEATED, TO YIELD OXYGEN OR OTHER GASES WHICH WILL INCREASE THE BURNING RATE OF COMBUSTIBLE MATTER. CONTACT WITH EASILY OXIDIZABLE, ORGANIC, OR OTHER COMBUSTIBLE MATERIALS MAY RESULT IN IGNITION, VIOLENT COMBUSTION OR EXPLOSION.
FIREFIGHTING MEDIA: DRY CHEMICAL, CARBON DIOXIDE, HALON OR WATER SPRAY (1987 EMERGENCY RESPONSE GUIDEBOOK, DOT P 5800.4).
FOR LARGER FIRES, USE WATER SPRAY OR FOG (1987 EMERGENCY RESPONSE GUIDEBOOK, DOT P 5800.4).
FIREFIGHTING: MOVE CONTAINERS FROM FIRE AREA IF POSSIBLE. COOL CONTAINERS EXPOSED TO FLAMES WITH WATER FROM SIDE UNTIL WELL AFTER FIRE IS OUT. STAY AWAY FROM STORAGE TANK ENDS. FOR MASSIVE FIRE IN STORAGE AREA, USE UNMANNED HOSE HOLDER OR MONITOR NOZZLES; ELSE WITHDRAW FROM AREA AND LET FIRE BURN (1987 EMERGENCY RESPONSE GUIDEBOOK, DOT P 5800.4, GUIDE PAGE 35)
EXTINGUISH USING AGENTS INDICATED. APPLY WATER IN FLOODING QUANTITIES FROM AS FAR A DISTANCE AS POSSIBLE. COOL CONTAINERS WITH WATER. KEEP RUN-OFF AWAY FROM WATER SOURCES AND SEWERS. CONSIDER EVACUATION IF FIRE BECOMES UNCONTROLLABLE.

TRANSPORTATION DATA

DEPARTMENT OF TRANSPORTATION HAZARD CLASSIFICATION 49 CFR 172.101: OXIDIZER
DEPARTMENT OF TRANSPORTATION LABELING REQUIREMENTS 49 CFR 172.101 AND SUBPART E: OXIDIZER
DEPARTMENT OF TRANSPORTATION PACKAGING REQUIREMENTS: 49 CFR 173.182 EXCEPTIONS: 49 CFR 173.153

TOXICITY

POTASSIUM NITRATE: TOXICITY DATA: 3750 MG/KG ORAL-RAT LD50; 1901 MG/KG ORAL-RABBIT LD50; 100 MG/KG INTRAVENOUS-CAT LDLO; MUTAGENIC DATA (RTECS); REPRODUCTIVE EFFECTS DATA (RTECS). CARCINOGEN STATUS: NONE. ACUTE TOXICITY LEVEL: MODERATELY TOXIC BY INGESTION. TARGET EFFECTS: NO DATA AVAILABLE.

HEALTH EFFECTS AND FIRST AID

INHALATION: POTASSIUM NITRATE: **<u>ACUTE EXPOSURE</u>-** MAY CAUSE COUGHING AND SHORTNESS OF BREATH. **<u>CHRONIC EXPOSURE</u>-** NO DATA AVAILABLE.
FIRST AID- REMOVE FROM EXPOSURE AREA TO FRESH AIR IMMEDIATELY. IF BREATHING HAS STOPPED, PERFORM ARTIFICIAL RESPIRATION. KEEP PERSON WARM AND AT REST. TREAT SYMPTOMATICALLY AND SUPPORTIVELY. GET MEDICAL ATTENTION IMMEDIATELY.

SKIN CONTACT: POTASSIUM NITRATE: **<u>ACUTE EXPOSURE</u>-** MAY CAUSE REDNESS. CONTACT WITH A MOLTEN MIXTURE OF SODIUM AND POTASSIUM NITRATE CAUSED THERMAL BURNS AND METHEMOGLOBINEMIA. SYMPTOMS OF METHEMOGLOBINEMIA MAY INCLUDE CYANOSIS, HEADACHE, WEAKNESS, DIZZINESS, LIGHTHEADEDNESS, ATAXIA, SHALLOW RESPIRATION, DROWSINESS, NAUSEA, VOMITING, CONFUSION, LETHARGY, STUPOR, DYSPNEA, TACHYCARDIA, CONVULSIONS, COMA AND POSSIBLY DEATH. **<u>CHRONIC EXPOSURE</u>-** NO DATA AVAILABLE.
FIRST AID- REMOVE CONTAMINATED CLOTHING AND SHOES IMMEDIATELY. WASH AFFECTED AREA WITH SOAP OR MILD DETERGENT AND LARGE AMOUNTS OF WATER UNTIL NO EVIDENCE OF CHEMICAL REMAINS (APPROXIMATELY 15-20 MINUTES). GET MEDICAL ATTENTION IMMEDIATELY.

EYE CONTACT: POTASSIUM NITRATE: **<u>ACUTE EXPOSURE</u>-** DIRECT CONTACT MAY CAUSE REDNESS AND PAIN. **<u>CHRONIC EXPOSURE</u>-** NO DATA AVAILABLE.
FIRST AID- WASH EYES IMMEDIATELY WITH LARGE AMOUNTS OF WATER OR NORMAL SALINE, OCCASIONALLY LIFTING UPPER AND LOWER LIDS, UNTIL NO EVIDENCE OF CHEMICAL REMAINS (APPROXIMATELY 15-20 MINUTES). GET MEDICAL ATTENTION IMMEDIATELY.

INGESTION: POTASSIUM NITRATE: **<u>ACUTE EXPOSURE</u>-** LARGE DOSES MAY CAUSE NAUSEA AND VOMITING WITH TENESMUS, BLOODY DIARRHEA, DIURESIS, GENERALIZED WEAKNESS, CARDIAC IRREGULARITIES, DYSURIA, HEMATURIA, CONVULSIONS, COLLAPSE AND POSSIBLY DEATH. NITRATES MAY ALSO PRODUCE HEMATURIA, CATHARSIS, ALBUMINURIA AND OLIGURIA. RARELY, INORGANIC NITRATES MAY BE CONVERTED TO NITRITES BY NITRATE-REDUCING BACTERIA IN THE UPPER DIGESTIVE TRACT, RESULTING IN METHEMOGLOBINEMIA. **<u>CHRONIC EXPOSURE</u>-** REPRODUCTIVE EFFECTS HAVE BEEN REPORTED IN ANIMALS. REPEATED OR PROLONGED EXPOSURE TO NITRATES MAY CAUSE ANEMIA, NEPHRITIS, AND POSSIBLY METHEMOGLOBINEMIA.
FIRST AID- REMOVE BY GASTRIC LAVAGE OR EMESIS. MAINTAIN BLOOD PRESSURE AND AIRWAY. GIVE OXYGEN IF RESPIRATION IS DEPRESSED. DO NOT PERFORM GASTRIC LAVAGE OR EMESIS IF VICTIM IS UNCONSCIOUS. GET MEDICAL ATTENTION IMMEDIATELY (DREISBACH, HANDBOOK OF POISONING, 11TH ED.). ADMINISTRATION OF GASTRIC LAVAGE OR OXYGEN SHOULD BE PERFORMED BY QUALIFIED MEDICAL PERSONNEL.
ANTIDOTE: THE FOLLOWING ANTIDOTE HAS BEEN RECOMMENDED. HOWEVER, THE DECISION AS TO WHETHER THE SEVERITY OF POISONING REQUIRES ADMINISTRATION OF ANY ANTIDOTE AND ACTUAL DOSE REQUIRED SHOULD BE MADE BY QUALIFIED MEDICAL PERSONNEL.
METHEMOGLOBINEMIA: (WHEN METHEMOGLOBIN CONCENTRATION IS OVER 25-40% OR IN PRESENCE OF SYMPTOMS.) GIVE METHYLENE BLUE, 1% SOLUTION, 0.1 ML/KG INTRAVENOUSLY OVER A 10-MINUTE PERIOD. CYANOSIS MAY DISAPPEAR WITHIN MINUTES OR PERSIST LONGER DEPENDING ON DEGREE OF METHEMOGLOBINEMIA. INTRAVENOUS ADMINISTRATION OF THERAPEUTIC DOSES OF METHYLENE BLUE MAY CAUSE A RISE IN BLOOD PRESSURE, NAUSEA, AND DIZZINESS. LARGER DOSES (>500 MG) CAUSE VOMITING, DIARRHEA, CHEST PAIN, MENTAL CONFUSION, CYANOSIS, AND SWEATING. HEMOLYTIC ANEMIA HAS ALSO OCCURRED SEVERAL DAYS AFTER ADMINISTRATION. THESE EFFECTS ARE

TEMPORARY, AND FATALITIES HAVE NOT BEEN REPORTED. IF METHYLENE BLUE IS NOT AVAILABLE, GIVE ASCORBIC ACID, 1 GRAM SLOWLY INTRAVENOUSLY. WITHOUT TREATMENT, METHEMOGLOBINEMIA LEVELS OF 20-30% REVERT TO NORMAL WITHIN 3 DAYS (DREISBACH, HANDBOOK OF POISONING, 12TH ED.). ANTIDOTE SHOULD BE ADMINISTERED BY QUALIFIED MEDICAL PERSONNEL.

REACTIVITY

REACTIVITY: STABLE UNDER NORMAL TEMPERATURES AND PRESSURES.

INCOMPATIBILITIES: POTASSIUM NITRATE: ACIDS (STRONG): REACT. ALUMINUM, BARIUM NITRATE, POTASSIUM PERCHLORATE, AND WATER: POSSIBLE EXPLOSION. ANTIMONY TRISULFIDE: EXPLOSION ON HEATING. ANTIMONY (POWDERED): EXPLOSION ON HEATING. ARSENIC: MIXTURE MAY EXPLODE WHEN IGNITED. ARSENIC DISULFIDE: MAY FORM EXPLOSIVE MIXTURES. BARIUM SULFIDE: MAY EXPLODE WHEN HEATED. 1,3 BIS(TRICHLOROMETHYL)BENZENE: MAY CAUSE EXPLOSION WHEN HEATED. BORON, LAMINAC, AND TRICHLOROETHYLENE: MIXTURE MAY CAUSE EXPLOSION. BORON (POWDERED): FIRE AND EXPLOSION HAZARD. BORON PHOSPHIDE: MAY CAUSE DEFLAGRATION. CALCIUM HYDROXIDE + CHLORINATED PHENOLS: MAY FORM CHLORINATED BENZODIOXINS. CALCIUM SILICIDE: MAY FORM READILY IGNITABLE PRIMER. CALCIUM SULFIDE: MAY EXPLODE WHEN HEATED. CHARCOAL: MAY FORM A PYROTECHNIC MIXTURE. CHROMIUM NITRIDE: POSSIBLE DEFLAGRATION. COPPER MONOPHOSPHIDE: EXPLODES ON IMPACT. COPPER PHOSPHIDES: EXPLOSION ON HEATING. FLUORINE: ATTACKS POTASSIUM NITRATE TO GIVE EXPLOSIVE FLUORINE NITRATE. GERMANIUM (POWDERED): POSSIBLE EXPLOSION UPON HEATING. GERMANIUM SULFIDE: POSSIBLE EXPLOSION ON HEATING. LACTOSE: EXPLOSION HAZARD. MOLYBDENUM DISULFIDE: MAY FORM DETONABLE MIXTURES. ORGANIC MATERIALS: FIRE AND EXPLOSION HAZARD. PHOSPHIDES: MAY REACT VIOLENTLY. PHOSPHOROUS (RED): REACTS VIGOROUSLY WHEN HEATED. PHOSPHOROUS (WHITE): MAY EXPLODE ON PERCUSSION. REDUCTANTS: MAY REACT VIOLENTLY. SODIUM ACETATE: EXPLOSION HAZARD. SODIUM HYPOPHOSPHITE: FORMS A POWERFUL EXPLOSIVE WHEN MIXED. SODIUM PEROXIDE + DEXTROSE: POSSIBLE EXPLOSION UNDER CONFINEMENT. SODIUM PHOSPHINATE: EXPLOSION HAZARD. SODIUM THIOSULFATE: EXPLOSION HAZARD. SULFIDES: MAY CAUSE VIOLENT INTERACTION IN MOLTEN MIXTURES. SULFUR + ARSENIC TRISULFIDE: MAY FORM EXPLOSIVE COMPOUND. SULFUR + CHARCOAL: FORMS EXPLOSIVE COMPOUND. THORIUM DICARBIDE: MAY CAUSE INCANDESCENCE. TITANIUM (POWDERED): MAY EXPLODE WHEN HEATED. TITANIUM DISULFIDE: MIXTURE MAY DETONATE WHEN HEATED. ZINC (POWDERED): MAY EXPLODE WHEN HEATED. ZIRCONIUM (POWDERED): MIXTURE MAY EXPLODE WHEN HEATED ABOVE MELTING TEMPERATURE.

DECOMPOSITION: THERMAL DECOMPOSITION MAY EMIT TOXIC OXIDES OF NITROGEN AND POTASSIUM.

POLYMERIZATION: HAZARDOUS POLYMERIZATION HAS NOT BEEN REPORTED TO OCCUR UNDER NORMAL TEMPERATURES AND PRESSURES.

STORAGE AND DISPOSAL

OBSERVE ALL FEDERAL, STATE AND LOCAL REGULATIONS WHEN STORING OR DISPOSING OF THIS SUBSTANCE. FOR ASSISTANCE, CONTACT THE DISTRICT DIRECTOR OF THE ENVIRONMENTAL PROTECTION AGENCY.

STORAGE

PROTECT AGAINST PHYSICAL DAMAGE. STORE IN COOL, DRY PLACE. SEPERATE FROM COMBUSTIBLE, ORGANIC, OR OTHER READILY OXIDIZABLE MATERIALS. AVOID STORAGE ON WOOD FLOORS. IMMEDIATELY REMOVE AND DISPOSE OF ANY SPILLED NITRATE (NFPA 49, HAZARDOUS CHEMICALS DATA, 1975). STORE AWAY FROM INCOMPATIBLE SUBSTANCES.

DISPOSAL

DISPOSAL MUST BE IN ACCORDANCE WITH STANDARDS APPLICABLE TO GENERATORS OF HAZARDOUS WASTE, 40 CFR 262. EPA HAZARDOUS WASTE NUMBER D001. 100 POUND CERCLA SECTION 103 REPORTABLE QUANTITY.

CONDITIONS TO AVOID

AVOID CONTACT WITH COMBUSTIBLE MATERIALS (WOOD, PAPER, FUEL, OILS, ETC); IGNITION OR EXPLOSION MAY RESULT. AVOID CONTAMINATION OF WATER SOURCES.

SPILL AND LEAK PROCEDURES

OCCUPATIONAL SPILL: KEEP COMBUSTIBLES (WOOD, PAPER, OIL, ETC) AWAY FROM SPILLED MATERIAL. DO NOT TOUCH SPILLED MATERIAL. FOR SMALL DRY SPILLS, WITH CLEAN SHOVEL PLACE MATERIAL INTO CLEAN, DRY CONTAINER AND COVER; MOVE CONTAINERS FROM SPILL AREA. FOR SMALL LIQUID SPILLS, TAKE UP WITH SAND, EARTH OR OTHER ABSORBENT MATERIAL AND PLACE INTO CONTAINERS FOR LATER DISPOSAL. FOR LARGER SPILLS, DIKE FAR AHEAD OF SPILL FOR LATER DISPOSAL. KEEP UNNECESSARY PEOPLE AWAY. ISOLATE HAZARD AREA AND DENY ENTRY.

PROTECTIVE EQUIPMENT

VENTILATION: PROVIDE LOCAL EXHAUST VENTILATION AND/OR GENERAL DILUTION VENTILATION TO MEET PUBLISHED EXPOSURE LIMITS.

RESPIRATOR: THE FOLLOWING RESPIRATORS ARE RECOMMENDED BASED ON INFORMATION FOUND IN THE PHYSICAL DATA, TOXICITY AND HEALTH EFFECTS SECTIONS. THEY ARE RANKED IN ORDER FROM MINIMUM TO MAXIMUM RESPIRATORY PROTECTION. THE SPECIFIC RESPIRATOR SELECTED MUST BE BASED ON CONTAMINATION LEVELS FOUND IN THE WORK PLACE, MUST NOT EXCEED THE WORKING LIMITS OF THE RESPIRATOR AND BE JOINTLY APPROVED BY THE NATIONAL INSTITUTE FOR OCCUPATIONAL SAFETY AND HEALTH AND THE MINE SAFETY AND HEALTH ADMINISTRATION (NIOSH-MSHA).

DUST AND MIST RESPIRATOR WITH A FULL FACEPIECE.

AIR-PURIFYING FULL FACEPIECE RESPIRATOR WITH A HIGH-EFFICIENCY PARTICULATE FILTER.

POWERED AIR-PURIFYING RESPIRATOR WITH A TIGHT-FITTING FACEPIECE AND HIGH-EFFICIENCY PARTICULATE FILTER.

TYPE 'C' SUPPLIED-AIR RESPIRATOR WITH A FULL FACEPIECE OPERATED IN PRESSURE-DEMAND OR OTHER POSITIVE PRESSURE MODE OR WITH A FULL FACEPIECE, HELMET OR HOOD OPERATED IN CONTINUOUS-FLOW MODE.

SELF-CONTAINED BREATHING APPARATUS WITH A FULL FACEPIECE OPERATED IN PRESSURE-DEMAND OR OTHER POSITIVE PRESSURE MODE.

FOR FIREFIGHTING AND OTHER IMMEDIATELY DANGEROUS TO LIFE OR HEALTH CONDITIONS:

SELF-CONTAINED BREATHING APPARATUS WITH FULL FACEPIECE OPERATED IN PRESSURE-DEMAND OR OTHER POSITIVE PRESSURE MODE.

SUPPLIED-AIR RESPIRATOR WITH FULL FACEPIECE AND OPERATED IN PRESSURE-DEMAND OR OTHER POSITIVE PRESSURE MODE IN COMBINATION WITH AN AUXILIARY SELF-CONTAINED BREATHING APPARATUS OPERATED IN PRESSURE-DEMAND OR OTHER POSITIVE PRESSURE MODE.

CLOTHING: EMPLOYEE MUST WEAR APPROPRIATE PROTECTIVE (IMPERVIOUS) CLOTHING AND EQUIPMENT TO PREVENT REPEATED OR PROLONGED SKIN CONTACT WITH THIS SUBSTANCE.

GLOVES: EMPLOYEE MUST WEAR APPROPRIATE PROTECTIVE GLOVES TO PREVENT CONTACT WITH THIS SUBSTANCE.

EYE PROTECTION: EMPLOYEE MUST WEAR SPLASH-PROOF OR DUST-RESISTANT SAFETY GOGGLES TO PREVENT EYE CONTACT WITH THIS SUBSTANCE. EMERGENCY EYE WASH: WHERE THERE IS ANY POSSIBILITY THAT AN EMPLOYEE'S EYES MAY BE EXPOSED TO THIS SUBSTANCE, THE EMPLOYER SHOULD PROVIDE AN EYE WASH FOUNTAIN WITHIN THE IMMEDIATE WORK AREA FOR EMERGENCY USE.

AUTHORIZED BY- OCCUPATIONAL HEALTH SERVICES, INC.
CREATION DATE: 11/16/89 ***REVISION DATE:*** 03/28/90

MATERIAL SAFETY DATA SHEET

OCCUPATIONAL HEALTH SERVICES, INC.
AGRICULTURE AND PESTICIDE DIVISION
450 SEVENTH AVENUE, SUITE 2407
NEW YORK, NEW YORK 10123
1-800-445-MSDS OR (212) 967-1100

EMERGENCY CONTACT:
JOHN S. BRANSFORD, JR. (615) 292-1180

SUBSTANCE IDENTIFICATION

CAS-NUMBER 7722-64-7

SUBSTANCE: POTASSIUM PERMANGANATE

TRADE NAMES/SYNONYMS: CHAMELEON MINERAL; CONDY'S CRYSTALS; CAIROX; PERMANGANIC ACID POTASSIUM SALT; CAIROX (R) (CARUS CHEMICAL COMPANY); STCC 4918740; UN 1490; PST19520

CHEMICAL FAMILY: INORGANIC SALT

MOLECULAR FORMULA: K-MN-O4

MOLECULAR WEIGHT: 158.03

CERCLA RATINGS (SCALE 0-3): HEALTH=3 FIRE=0 REACTIVITY=0 PERSISTENCE=3

NFPA RATINGS (SCALE 0-4): HEALTH=1 FIRE=0 REACTIVITY=0

COMPONENTS AND CONTAMINANTS

COMPONENT: POTASSIUM PERMANGANATE ***PERCENT:*** 100.0
CAS# 7722-64-7

OTHER CONTAMINANTS: NONE

EXPOSURE LIMITS: POTASSIUM PERMANGANATE: 5 MG(MN)/M3 ACGIH CEILING
100 POUNDS CERCLA SECTION 103 REPORTABLE QUANTITY

PHYSICAL DATA

DESCRIPTION: ODORLESS, DARK PURPLE OR BRONZE-LIKE CRYSTALS WITH A BLUE METALLIC LUSTER AND SWEET, ASTRINGENT TASTE.

MELTING POINT: 464 F (240 C) DECOMPOSES ***SPECIFIC GRAVITY:*** 2.703

SOLUBILITY IN WATER: 6.4% @ 20 C

SOLVENT SOLUBILITY: SOLUBLE IN ACETIC ACID, ACETIC ANHYDRIDE, ACETONE, METHANOL, PYRIDINE, SULFOLANE, SULFURIC ACID, AND TRIFLUOROACETIC ACID.

FIRE AND EXPLOSION DATA

FIRE AND EXPLOSION HAZARD: NEGLIGIBLE FIRE HAZARD WHEN EXPOSED TO HEAT OR FLAME.

OXIDIZER: OXIDIZERS DECOMPOSE, ESPECIALLY WHEN HEATED, TO YIELD OXYGEN OR OTHER GASES WHICH WILL INCREASE THE BURNING RATE OF COMBUSTIBLE MATTER. CONTACT WITH EASILY OXIDIZABLE, ORGANIC, OR OTHER COMBUSTIBLE MATERIALS MAY RESULT IN IGNITION, VIOLENT COMBUSTION OR EXPLOSION.

FIREFIGHTING MEDIA: DRY CHEMICAL, CARBON DIOXIDE, HALON OR WATER SPRAY (1987 EMERGENCY RESPONSE GUIDEBOOK, DOT P 5800.4).

FOR LARGER FIRES, USE WATER SPRAY OR FOG (1987 EMERGENCY RESPONSE GUIDEBOOK, DOT P 5800.4).

FIREFIGHTING: MOVE CONTAINERS FROM FIRE AREA IF POSSIBLE. COOL CONTAINERS EXPOSED TO FLAMES WITH WATER FROM SIDE UNTIL WELL AFTER FIRE IS OUT. STAY AWAY FROM STORAGE TANK ENDS. FOR MASSIVE FIRE IN STORAGE AREA, USE UNMANNED HOSE HOLDER OR MONITOR NOZZLES; ELSE WITHDRAW FROM AREA AND LET FIRE BURN (1987 EMERGENCY RESPONSE GUIDEBOOK, DOT P 5800.4, GUIDE PAGE 35)

USE FLOODING AMOUNTS OF WATER. COOL CONTAINERS WITH FLOODING QUANTITIES OF WATER, APPLY FROM AS FAR A DISTANCE AS POSSIBLE. EVACUATE TO A RADIUS OF 2500 FEET FOR UNCONTROLLABLE FIRES.

TRANSPORTATION DATA

DEPARTMENT OF TRANSPORTATION HAZARD CLASSIFICATION 49 CFR 172.101: OXIDIZER

DEPARTMENT OF TRANSPORTATION LABELING REQUIREMENTS 49 CFR 172.101 AND SUBPART E: OXIDIZER

DEPARTMENT OF TRANSPORTATION PACKAGING REQUIREMENTS: 49 CFR 173.154 AND 49 CFR 173.194 EXCEPTIONS: 49 CFR 173.153

TOXICITY

POTASSIUM PERMANGANATE: TOXICITY DATA: 2400 UG/KG/DAY ORAL-WOMAN TDLO; 143 MG/KG ORAL-HUMAN LDLO; 1090 MG/KG ORAL-RAT LD50; 600 MG/KG ORAL-RABBIT LDLO; 400 MG/KG ORAL-DOG LDLO; 500 MG/KG SUBCUTANEOUS-MOUSE LD50; 70 MG/KG INTRAVENOUS-RABBIT LDLO; MUTAGENIC DATA (RTECS); REPRODUCTIVE EFFECTS DATA (RTECS). CARCINOGEN STATUS: NONE. LOCAL EFFECTS: CORROSIVE- INHALATION, SKIN, AND EYES. ACUTE TOXICITY LEVEL: MODERATELY TOXIC BY INGESTION. TARGET EFFECTS: POISONING MAY AFFECT THE KIDNEYS.

HEALTH EFFECTS AND FIRST AID

INHALATION: POTASSIUM PERMANGANATE: CORROSIVE. **ACUTE EXPOSURE-** MAY CAUSE SEVERE IRRITATION OF THE RESPIRATORY TRACT, LABORED BREATHING, CHOKING, STRIDOR, PERSISTENT, SPASMODIC COUGH, PAIN IN THE NOSE, MOUTH AND THROAT, AND BURNS OF THE MUCOUS MEMBRANES. IF SUFFICIENT QUANTITIES ARE INHALED, PULMONARY EDEMA MAY DEVELOP, OFTEN WITH A LATENT PERIOD OF 5-72 HOURS. THE SYMPTOMS MAY INCLUDE TIGHTNESS IN THE CHEST, FROTHY SPUTUM, CYANOSIS, AND DIZZINESS. PHYSICAL FINDINGS MAY INCLUDE WEAK, RAPID PULSE, HYPOTENSION, MOIST RALES AND HEMOCONCENTRATION. RECOVERY MAY BE PROLONGED AND RELAPSES ARE POSSIBLE. IN SEVERE EXPOSURES, DEATH DUE TO ANOXIA MAY OCCUR WITHIN A FEW HOURS AFTER ONSET OF PULMONARY EDEMA OR FOLLOWING A RELAPSE. **CHRONIC EXPOSURE-** DEPENDING ON THE CONCENTRATION AND DURATION OF EXPOSURE, REPEATED OR PROLONGED EXPOSURE TO ACIDIC SUBSTANCES MAY CAUSE EROSION OF THE TEETH AND INFLAMMATORY AND ULCERATIVE CHANGES IN THE MOUTH. BRONCHIAL AND GASTROINTESTINAL DISTURBANCES ARE ALSO POSSIBLE.

FIRST AID- REMOVE FROM EXPOSURE AREA TO FRESH AIR IMMEDIATELY. IF BREATHING HAS STOPPED, GIVE ARTIFICIAL RESPIRATION. MAINTAIN AIRWAY AND BLOOD PRESSURE AND ADMINISTER OXYGEN IF AVAILABLE. KEEP AFFECTED PERSON WARM AND AT REST. TREAT SYMPTOMATICALLY AND SUPPORTIVELY. ADMINISTRATION OF OXYGEN SHOULD BE PERFORMED BY QUALIFIED PERSONNEL. GET MEDICAL ATTENTION IMMEDIATELY.

SKIN CONTACT: POTASSIUM PERMANGANATE: CORROSIVE. **ACUTE EXPOSURE-** DILUTE AQUEOUS SOLUTIONS MAY BE MILDLY IRRITATING. DIRECT CONTACT WITH THE SOLID MAY CAUSE SEVERE BURNS WITH REDNESS AND PAIN. **CHRONIC EXPOSURE-** EFFECTS DEPEND ON THE CONCENTRATION AND DURATION OF EXPOSURE. REPEATED OR PROLONGED CONTACT WITH CORROSIVE SUBSTANCES MAY RESULT IN DERMATITIS OR EFFECTS SIMILAR TO ACUTE EXPOSURE.

FIRST AID- REMOVE CONTAMINATED CLOTHING AND SHOES IMMEDIATELY. WASH AFFECTED AREA WITH SOAP OR MILD DETERGENT AND LARGE AMOUNTS OF WATER UNTIL NO EVIDENCE OF CHEMICAL REMAINS (AT LEAST 15-20 MINUTES). IN CASE OF CHEMICAL BURNS, COVER AREA WITH STERILE, DRY DRESSING. BANDAGE SECURELY, BUT NOT TOO TIGHTLY. GET MEDICAL ATTENTION IMMEDIATELY.

EYE CONTACT: POTASSIUM PERMANGANATE: CORROSIVE. **ACUTE EXPOSURE-** DILUTE AQUEOUS SOLUTIONS MAY BE ONLY MILDLY IRRITATING, HOWEVER, DIRECT CONTACT WITH THE SOLID MAY CAUSE BURNS WITH REDNESS, PAIN, LACRIMATION AND BLURRED VISION. CONTACT WITH STRONG SOLUTIONS OR CRYSTALS MAY CAUSE A HARDENED, ERODED LESION ACCOMPANIED BY SWELLING OF THE LIDS AND CONJUNCTIVAE AND SUBCONJUNCTIVAL HEMORRHAGE. **CHRONIC EXPOSURE-** EFFECTS DEPEND ON THE CONCENTRATION AND DURATION OF EXPOSURE. REPEATED OR PROLONGED EXPOSURE TO CORROSIVE SUBSTANCES MAY CAUSE CONJUNCTIVITIS OR EFFECTS AS IN ACUTE EXPOSURE. TURBIDITY AND BROWN DISCOLORATION OF THE CORNEA IS POSSIBLE WITH PROLONGED CONTACT.

FIRST AID- WASH EYES IMMEDIATELY WITH LARGE AMOUNTS OF WATER, OCCASIONALLY LIFTING UPPER AND LOWER LIDS, UNTIL NO EVIDENCE OF CHEMICAL REMAINS (AT LEAST 15-20 MINUTES). IN CASE OF BURNS, APPLY STERILE BANDAGES LOOSELY WITHOUT MEDICATION. GET MEDICAL ATTENTION IMMEDIATELY.

VARIOUS AGENTS HAVE BEEN USED AND RECOMMENDED, AIMED AT REDUCING RESIDUAL PERMANGANATE AND SOLUBILIZING AND REMOVING REDUCED MANGANESE COMPOUNDS FROM THE TISSUES, SUCH AS SOLUTIONS OF ASCORBIC ACID, SODIUM THIOSULFATE, HYDROGEN PEROXIDE AND SODIUM EDETATE. ASCORBIC ACID SOLUTION HAS BEEN FOUND TO HASTEN THE REDUCTION OF PERMANGANATE, AND THE EDETATE SOLUTION IS SAID TO HELP IN REMOVING THE REDUCED MANGANESE COMPOUNDS (GRANT, TOXICOLOGY OF THE EYES, 2ND ED.).

INGESTION: POTASSIUM PERMANGANATE: CORROSIVE. **ACUTE EXPOSURE-** MAY CAUSE INFLAMMATION, AND CORROSION OF THE MOUTH, PHARYNX AND LARYNX. DISCOLORATION FROM A PURPLE-BROWN TO COAL BLACK MAY OCCUR. A SLIGHT METALLIC LUSTER MAY ALSO BE APPARENT. ADDITIONAL EFFECTS MAY INCLUDE NAUSEA, VOMITING, DIFFICULTY SPEAKING OR SWALLOWING, BLACK STOOL, EPIGASTRIC PAIN, AND TYMPANIC DISTENTION OF THE ABDOMEN. SHOCK RESULTING IN DEATH MAY ALSO OCCUR. IF DEATH IS NOT IMMEDIATE, JAUNDICE AND OLIGURIA OR ANURIA MAY APPEAR. **CHRONIC EXPOSURE-** DEPENDING ON THE CONCENTRATION, REPEATED INGESTION OF ACIDIC SUBSTANCES MAY RESULT IN INFLAMMATORY AND ULCERATIVE CHANGES IN THE MUCOUS MEMBRANES OF THE MOUTH AND OTHER EFFECTS AS IN ACUTE INGESTION.

FIRST AID- DO NOT USE GASTRIC LAVAGE OR EMESIS. DILUTE THE ACID IMMEDIATELY BY DRINKING LARGE QUANTITIES OF WATER OR MILK. IF VOMITING PERSISTS, ADMINISTER FLUIDS REPEATEDLY. INGESTED ACID MUST BE DILUTED APPROXIMATELY 100 TIMES TO RENDER IT HARMLESS TO TISSUES. IF SYMPTOMS ARE SEVERE AND PERFORATION OF THE STOMACH OR ESOPHAGUS IS SUSPECTED, GIVE NOTHING BY MOUTH UNTIL ENDOSCOPIC EXAMINATION HAS BEEN DONE. (DREISBACH, HANDBOOK OF POISONING, 11TH EDITION) GET MEDICAL ATTENTION IMMEDIATELY. TREATMENT SHOULD BE ADMINISTERED BY QUALIFIED MEDICAL PERSONNEL.

ANTIDOTE: NO SPECIFIC ANTIDOTE. TREAT SYMPTOMATICALLY AND SUPPORTIVELY.

REACTIVITY

REACTIVITY: REACTS VIOLENTLY WITH FINELY DIVIDED, EASILY OXIDIZABLE SUBSTANCES. INCREASES FLAMMABILITY OF COMBUSTIBLE MATERIALS. A POWERFUL OXIDIZER.

INCOMPATIBILITIES: POTASSIUM PERMANGANATE: ACETIC ACID: MAY EXPODE. ACETONE, TERT-BUTYLAMINE: VIOLENT REACTION ACETYLACETONE: MAY IGNITE. ALCOHOLS: METHANOL, ETHANOL, ISOPROPANOL, PENTANOL AND ISOPENTANOL MAY IGNITE. ALCOHOLS, NITRIC ACID: IMMEDIATE IGNITION. ALUMINIUM POWDER + AMMONIUM NITRATE + GLYCERYL NITRATE + NITROCELLULOSE: ALL FIVE COMPONENTS MAY EXPLODE WITH GREAT VIOLENCE. ALUMINIUM CARBIDE: INCANDESCENCE ON WARMING. AMMONIA, SULFURIC ACID: INCANDESCENT REACTION. AMMONIUM NITRATE: SLOW EXOTHERMIC REACTION LEADING TO EXPLOSION. AMMONIUM PERCHLORATE: THE MEDIUM IMPACT-SENSITIVITY OF THIS SOLID IS GREATLY INCREASED. ANTIMONY: IGNITES ON GRINDING. ARSENIC: MAY EXPLODE WITH GRINDING. BENZALDEHYDE: MAY IGNITE. COAL, PEROXOMONOSULFURIC ACID: VIOLENT EXPLOSION WITH HEAT. CARBON: MAY BURN VIGOROUSLY ON HEATING. 3-CHLOROPROPANE-1,2-DIOL: MAY IGNITE. COMBUSTIBLE MATERIALS: MAY INCREASE THE BURNING RATE OR CAUSE IGNITION ON CONTACT; FINELY DIVIDED MATERIALS MAY RESULT IN AN EXPLOSION. DICHLOROMETHYLSILANE: MAY IGNITE. DIMETHYLFORMAMIDE: MAY EXPLODE. DIMETHYLSULFOXIDE: MAY IGNITE. ERYTHRITOL: MAY IGNITE. ESTERS

OF ETHYLENE GLYCOL: MAY IGNITE. ETHANOL, SULFURIC ACID: POSSIBLE VIOLENT EXOTHERMIC REACTION. ETHYLENE GLYCOL: MAY IGNITE. FORMALDEHYDE: FIRE AND EXPLOSION HAZARD. GLYCEROL: MAY CAUSE A VIGOROUS FIRE OR EXPLOSION. HYDROCHLORIC ACID: POSSIBLE EXPLOSION HAZARD. HYDROFLUORIC ACID: MAY CAUSE A VIOLENT EXOTHERM WITH LIGHT EMISSION. HYDROGEN PEROXIDE (STRONG): FIRE AND EXPLOSION HAZARD. HYDROGEN TRISULFIDE: MAY IGNITE. HYDROXYLAMINE: CONTACT IMMEDIATELY PRODUCED A WHITE FLAME. ISOBUTYRALDEHYDE: MAY IGNITE. LACTIC ACID: MAY IGNITE. MANNITOL: MAY IGNITE. NON-METALS: FIRE AND EXPLOSION HAZARD. ORGANIC MATERIALS: MAY INCREASE THE BURNING RATE OR CAUSE IGNITION ON CONTACT; FINELY DIVIDED MATERIALS MAY RESULT IN AN EXPLOSION. ORGANIC NITRO COMPOUNDS: MIXTURES IGNITE EASILY ON HEATING, SHOCK, OR ON CONTACT WITH SULFURIC ACID. OXALIC ACID: MAY IGNITE. OXYGENATED ORGANIC COMPOUNDS: MAY REACT VIOLENTLY OR EXPLOSIVELY. POTASSIUM CHLORIDE + SULFURIC ACID: ADDING CONCENTRATED SULFURIC ACID TO AN INTIMATE MIXTURE OF THE SALTS MAY CAUSE AN EXPLOSION. PROPANE-1,2-DIOL: MAY IGNITE. REDUCING MATERIALS: MAY INCREASE THE BURNING RATE OR CAUSE IGNITION ON CONTACT; FINELY DIVIDED MATERIALS MAY RESULT IN AN EXPLOSION. SLAG WOOL: IGNITES WITH HEAT. SULFUR: EXPLOSION HAZARD. SULFURIC ACID + WATER: ADDITION OF CONCENTRATED SULFURIC ACID TO THE SLIGHTLY DAMP PERMANGANATE CAUSED AN EXPLOSION. TITANIUM: MAY EXPLODE ON HEATING. 3,4,4'-TRIMETHYLDIPHENYL SULFONE: VIGOROUS, EXOTHERMIC REACTION.

DECOMPOSITION: THERMAL DECOMPOSITION PRODUCTS MAY INCLUDE TOXIC AND HAZARDOUS OXIDES OF POTASSIUM AND MANGANESE.

POLYMERIZATION: HAZARDOUS POLYMERIZATION HAS NOT BEEN REPORTED TO OCCUR UNDER NORMAL TEMPERATURES AND PRESSURES.

STORAGE AND DISPOSAL

OBSERVE ALL FEDERAL, STATE AND LOCAL REGULATIONS WHEN STORING OR DISPOSING OF THIS SUBSTANCE. FOR ASSISTANCE, CONTACT THE DISTRICT DIRECTOR OF THE ENVIRONMENTAL PROTECTION AGENCY.

STORAGE

PROTECT AGAINST PHYSICAL DAMAGE. SEPARATE FROM SULFURIC ACID, HYDROGEN PEROXIDE, AND ALL COMBUSTIBLE, ORGANIC OR READILY OXIDIZABLE MATERIALS.(NFPA 49, HAZARDOUS CHEMICALS DATA, 1975).

STORE AWAY FROM INCOMPATIBLE SUBSTANCES.

CONDITIONS TO AVOID

AVOID CONTACT WITH COMBUSTIBLE MATERIALS (WOOD, PAPER, FUEL, OILS, ETC); IGNITION OR EXPLOSION MAY RESULT. AVOID CONTAMINATION OF WATER SOURCES.

SPILL AND LEAK PROCEDURES

SOIL SPILL: DIG A PIT, POND, LAGOON OR HOLDING AREA TO CONTAIN LIQUID OR SOLID MATERIAL. COVER SOLIDS WITH A PLASTIC SHEET TO PREVENT DISSOLVING IN RAIN OR FIREFIGHTING WATER.

USE SODIUM BISULFITE (NA-H-SO3) TO NEUTRALIZE SPILLED MATERIAL.

WATER SPILL: NEUTRALIZE WITH CAUSTIC SODA.

ADD SODIUM BISULFITE.

USE MECHANICAL DREDGES OR LIFTS TO EXTRACT IMMOBILIZED MASSES OF POLLUTION AND PRECIPITATES.

OCCUPATIONAL SPILL: KEEP COMBUSTIBLES (WOOD, PAPER, OIL, ETC) AWAY FROM SPILLED MATERIAL. DO NOT TOUCH SPILLED MATERIAL. FOR SMALL DRY SPILLS, WITH CLEAN SHOVEL PLACE MATERIAL INTO CLEAN, DRY CONTAINER AND COVER; MOVE CONTAINERS FROM SPILL AREA. FOR SMALL LIQUID SPILLS, TAKE UP WITH SAND, EARTH OR OTHER ABSORBENT MATERIAL AND PLACE INTO CONTAINERS FOR LATER DISPOSAL. FOR LARGER SPILLS, DIKE FAR AHEAD OF SPILL FOR LATER DISPOSAL. KEEP UNNECESSARY PEOPLE AWAY. ISOLATE HAZARD AREA AND DENY ENTRY.

REPORTABLE QUANTITY (RQ): 100 POUNDS THE SUPERFUND AMENDMENTS AND REAUTHORIZATION ACT (SARA) SECTION 304 REQUIRES THAT A RELEASE EQUAL TO OR GREATER THAN THE REPORTABLE QUANTITY FOR THIS SUBSTANCE BE IMMEDIATELY REPORTED TO THE LOCAL EMERGENCY PLANNING COMMITTEE AND THE STATE EMERGENCY RESPONSE COMMISSION (40 CFR 355.40). IF THE RELEASE OF THIS SUBSTANCE IS REPORTABLE UNDER CERCLA SECTION 103, THE NATIONAL RESPONSE CENTER MUST BE NOTIFIED IMMEDIATELY AT (800) 424-8802 OR (202) 426-2675 IN THE METROPOLITAN WASHINGTON, D.C. AREA (40 CFR 302.6).

PROTECTIVE EQUIPMENT

VENTILATION: PROVIDE LOCAL EXHAUST VENTILATION AND/OR GENERAL DILUTION VENTILATION TO MEET PUBLISHED EXPOSURE LIMITS.

RESPIRATOR: THE FOLLOWING RESPIRATORS ARE RECOMMENDED BASED ON INFORMATION FOUND IN THE PHYSICAL DATA, TOXICITY AND HEALTH EFFECTS SECTIONS. THEY ARE RANKED IN ORDER FROM MINIMUM TO MAXIMUM RESPIRATORY PROTECTION. THE SPECIFIC RESPIRATOR SELECTED MUST BE BASED ON CONTAMINATION LEVELS FOUND IN THE WORK PLACE, MUST NOT EXCEED THE WORKING LIMITS OF THE RESPIRATOR AND BE JOINTLY APPROVED BY THE NATIONAL INSTITUTE FOR OCCUPATIONAL SAFETY AND HEALTH AND THE MINE SAFETY AND HEALTH ADMINISTRATION (NIOSH-MSHA).

DUST AND MIST RESPIRATOR WITH A FULL FACEPIECE.

AIR-PURIFYING FULL FACEPIECE RESPIRATOR WITH A HIGH-EFFICIENCY PARTICULATE FILTER.

POWERED AIR-PURIFYING RESPIRATOR WITH A TIGHT-FITTING FACEPIECE AND HIGH-EFFICIENCY PARTICULATE FILTER.

TYPE 'C' SUPPLIED-AIR RESPIRATOR WITH A FULL FACEPIECE OPERATED IN PRESSURE-DEMAND OR OTHER POSITIVE PRESSURE MODE OR WITH A FULL FACEPIECE, HELMET OR HOOD OPERATED IN CONTINUOUS-FLOW MODE.

SELF-CONTAINED BREATHING APPARATUS WITH A FULL FACEPIECE OPERATED IN PRESSURE-DEMAND OR OTHER POSITIVE PRESSURE MODE.

FOR FIREFIGHTING AND OTHER IMMEDIATELY DANGEROUS TO LIFE OR HEALTH CONDITIONS:

SELF-CONTAINED BREATHING APPARATUS WITH FULL FACEPIECE OPERATED IN PRESSURE-DEMAND OR OTHER POSITIVE PRESSURE MODE.

SUPPLIED-AIR RESPIRATOR WITH FULL FACEPIECE AND OPERATED IN PRESSURE-DEMAND OR OTHER POSITIVE PRESSURE MODE IN COMBINATION WITH AN AUXILIARY SELF-CONTAINED BREATHING APPARATUS OPERATED IN PRESSURE-DEMAND OR OTHER POSITIVE PRESSURE MODE.

CLOTHING: EMPLOYEE MUST WEAR APPROPRIATE PROTECTIVE (IMPERVIOUS) CLOTHING AND EQUIPMENT TO PREVENT ANY POSSIBILITY OF SKIN CONTACT WITH THIS SUBSTANCE.

GLOVES: EMPLOYEE MUST WEAR APPROPRIATE PROTECTIVE GLOVES TO PREVENT CONTACT WITH THIS SUBSTANCE.

EYE PROTECTION: EMPLOYEE MUST WEAR SPLASH-PROOF OR DUST-RESISTANT SAFETY GOGGLES AND A FACESHIELD TO PREVENT CONTACT WITH THIS SUBSTANCE.

EMERGENCY WASH FACILITIES: WHERE THERE IS ANY POSSIBILITY THAT AN EMPLOYEE'S EYES AND/OR SKIN MAY BE EXPOSED TO THIS SUBSTANCE, THE EMPLOYER SHOULD PROVIDE AN EYE WASH FOUNTAIN AND QUICK DRENCH SHOWER WITHIN THE IMMEDIATE WORK AREA FOR EMERGENCY USE.

AUTHORIZED BY- OCCUPATIONAL HEALTH SERVICES, INC.

CREATION DATE: 10/04/89 ***REVISION DATE:*** 05/25/90

MATERIAL SAFETY DATA SHEET

OCCUPATIONAL HEALTH SERVICES, INC.
AGRICULTURE AND PESTICIDE DIVISION
450 SEVENTH AVENUE, SUITE 2407
NEW YORK, NEW YORK 10123
1-800-445-MSDS OR (212) 967-1100

EMERGENCY CONTACT:
JOHN S. BRANSFORD, JR. (615) 292-1180

SUBSTANCE IDENTIFICATION

CAS-NUMBER 7778-53-2

SUBSTANCE: POTASSIUM PHOSPHATE TRIBASIC

TRADE NAMES/SYNONYMS: POTASSIUM PHOSPHATE, NEUTRAL; TRIPOTASSIUM PHOSPHATE; TRIPOTASSIUM ORTHOPHOSPHATE; POTASSIUM PHOSPHATE, NORMAL; POTASSIUM PHOSPHATE, TERTIARY; PST19544

CHEMICAL FAMILY: INORGANIC SALT

MOLECULAR FORMULA: K3-P-O4

MOLECULAR WEIGHT: 212.27

CERCLA RATINGS (SCALE 0-3): HEALTH=U FIRE=0 REACTIVITY=0 PERSISTENCE=0

NFPA RATINGS (SCALE 0-4): HEALTH=U FIRE=0 REACTIVITY=0

COMPONENTS AND CONTAMINANTS

COMPONENT: POTASSIUM PHOSPHATE TRIBASIC ***PERCENT:*** 100
CAS# 7778-53-2

OTHER CONTAMINANTS: NONE

EXPOSURE LIMITS: NO OCCUPATIONAL EXPOSURE LIMITS ESTABLISHED BY OSHA, ACGIH, OR NIOSH.

PHYSICAL DATA

DESCRIPTION: ODORLESS, WHITE, DELIQUESCENT, ORTHORHOMBIC CRYSTALS OR GRANULAR POWDER. ***MELTING POINT:*** 2444 F (1340 C) ***SPECIFIC GRAVITY:*** 2.6

PH: ALKALINE IN SOLUTION ***SOLUBILITY IN WATER:*** 50.8% AT 25 C

SOLVENT SOLUBILITY: INSOLUBLE IN ALCOHOL

FIRE AND EXPLOSION DATA

FIRE AND EXPLOSION HAZARD: NEGLIGIBLE FIRE HAZARD WHEN EXPOSED TO HEAT OR FLAME.

FIREFIGHTING MEDIA: DRY CHEMICAL, CARBON DIOXIDE, HALON, WATER SPRAY OR STANDARD FOAM (1987 EMERGENCY RESPONSE GUIDEBOOK, DOT P 5800.4). FOR LARGER FIRES, USE WATER SPRAY, FOG OR STANDARD FOAM (1987 EMERGENCY RESPONSE GUIDEBOOK, DOT P 5800.4).

FIREFIGHTING: MOVE CONTAINERS FROM FIRE AREA IF POSSIBLE. COOL CONTAINERS EXPOSED TO FLAMES WITH WATER FROM SIDE UNTIL WELL AFTER FIRE IS OUT. STAY AWAY FROM STORAGE TANK ENDS (1987 EMERGENCY RESPONSE GUIDEBOOK, DOT P 5800.4, GUIDE PAGE 60). EXTINGUISH USING AGENT INDICATED; DO NOT USE WATER DIRECTLY ON MATERIAL. IF LARGE AMOUNTS OF COMBUSTIBLE MATERIALS ARE INVOLVED, USE WATER SPRAY OR FOG IN FLOODING AMOUNTS. AVOID BREATHING CORROSIVE DUSTS AND FUMES FROM BURNING MATERIAL, KEEP UPWIND.

TOXICITY

POTASSIUM PHOSPHATE TRIBASIC: CARCINOGEN STATUS: NONE. LOCAL EFFECTS: IRRITANT- INHALATION, SKIN, AND EYES. ACUTE TOXICITY LEVEL: NO DATA AVAILABLE. TARGET EFFECTS: NO DATA AVAILABLE.

HEALTH EFFECTS AND FIRST AID

INHALATION: POTASSIUM PHOSPHATE TRIBASIC: IRRITANT. **ACUTE EXPOSURE-** THE DUST MAY CAUSE IRRITATION OF THE RESPIRATORY TRACT. SOLUTIONS MAY CAUSE CHEMICAL BURNS. **CHRONIC EXPOSURE-** NO DATA AVAILABLE.

FIRST AID- REMOVE FROM EXPOSURE AREA TO FRESH AIR IMMEDIATELY. IF BREATHING HAS STOPPED, PERFORM ARTIFICIAL RESPIRATION. KEEP PERSON WARM AND AT REST. TREAT SYMPTOMATICALLY AND SUPPORTIVELY. GET MEDICAL ATTENTION IMMEDIATELY.

SKIN CONTACT: POTASSIUM PHOSPHATE TRIBASIC: IRRITANT. **ACUTE EXPOSURE-** DIRECT CONTACT MAY CAUSE IRRITATION AND SOLUTIONS MAY CAUSE CHEMICAL BURNS. **CHRONIC EXPOSURE-** REPEATED AND PROLONGED CONTACT WITH IRRITANTS MAY CAUSE DERMATITIS.

FIRST AID- REMOVE CONTAMINATED CLOTHING AND SHOES IMMEDIATELY. WASH AFFECTED AREA WITH SOAP OR MILD DETERGENT AND LARGE AMOUNTS OF WATER UNTIL NO EVIDENCE OF CHEMICAL REMAINS (APPROXIMATELY 15-20 MINUTES). GET MEDICAL ATTENTION IMMEDIATELY.

EYE CONTACT: POTASSIUM PHOSPHATE TRIBASIC: IRRITANT. **ACUTE EXPOSURE-** DIRECT CONTACT MAY CAUSE IRRITATION AND SOLUTIONS MAY CAUSE CHEMICAL BURNS. **CHRONIC EXPOSURE-** REPEATED AND PROLONGED CONTACT WITH IRRITANTS MAY CAUSE CONJUNCTIVITIS.

FIRST AID- WASH EYES IMMEDIATELY WITH LARGE AMOUNTS OF WATER OR NORMAL SALINE, OCCASIONALLY LIFTING UPPER AND LOWER LIDS, UNTIL NO EVIDENCE OF CHEMICAL REMAINS (APPROXIMATELY 15-20 MINUTES). GET MEDICAL ATTENTION IMMEDIATELY.

INGESTION: POTASSIUM PHOSPHATE TRIBASIC: CORROSIVE. **ACUTE EXPOSURE-** INGESTION MAY CAUSE CORROSIVE EFFECTS DUE TO THE STRONGLY ALKALINE NATURE OF SOLUTIONS. ACUTE INTOXICATION OF POTASSIUM SALTS BY MOUTH IS RARE BECAUSE LARGE SINGLE DOSES USUALLY INDUCE VOMITING AND BECAUSE, IN THE ABSENCE OF PRE-EXISTING KIDNEY DAMAGE, POTASSIUM IS RAPIDLY EXCRETED. INGESTION OF SOME PHOSPHATES MAY CAUSE A SHOCK-LIKE STATE, A FALL IN BLOOD PRESSURE, SLOW PULSE, CYANOSIS, COMA, AND SOMETIMES TETANY AS A RESULT OF REDUCTION IN IONIC CALCIUM. **CHRONIC EXPOSURE-** NO DATA AVAILABLE.

FIRST AID- TREAT SYMPTOMATICALLY AND SUPPORTIVELY. IF PERSON IS CONSCIOUS AND ABLE TO SWALLOW, GIVE LARGE AMOUNTS OF WATER OR MILK TO DILUTE SUBSTANCE. GET MEDICAL ATTENTION IMMEDIATELY. GASTRIC LAVAGE PERFORMED BY QUALIFIED MEDICAL PERSONNEL MIGHT BE ADVISABLE IF THERE ARE NO SIGNS OF PERFORATION FROM THE INGESTION OF A CORROSIVE SUBSTANCE. IF VOMITING OCCURS, KEEP HEAD BELOW HIPS TO HELP PREVENT ASPIRATION.

ANTIDOTE: NO SPECIFIC ANTIDOTE. TREAT SYMPTOMATICALLY AND SUPPORTIVELY.

REACTIVITY

REACTIVITY: STABLE UNDER NORMAL TEMPERATURES AND PRESSURES.

INCOMPATIBILITIES: POTASSIUM PHOSPHATE TRIBASIC: NO DATA AVAILABLE.

DECOMPOSITION: THERMAL DECOMPOSITION MAY RELEASE TOXIC AND/OR HAZARDOUS GASES.

POLYMERIZATION: HAZARDOUS POLYMERIZATION HAS NOT BEEN REPORTED TO OCCUR UNDER NORMAL TEMPERATURES AND PRESSURES.

STORAGE AND DISPOSAL

OBSERVE ALL FEDERAL, STATE AND LOCAL REGULATIONS WHEN STORING OR DISPOSING OF THIS SUBSTANCE. FOR ASSISTANCE, CONTACT THE DISTRICT DIRECTOR OF THE ENVIRONMENTAL PROTECTION AGENCY.

CONDITIONS TO AVOID

NONE REPORTED.

SPILL AND LEAK PROCEDURES

OCCUPATIONAL SPILL: SWEEP UP AND PLACE IN SUITABLE (FIBERBOARD) CONTAINERS FOR RECLAMATION OR LATER DISPOSAL.

PROTECTIVE EQUIPMENT

VENTILATION: PROVIDE LOCAL EXHAUST OR PROCESS ENCLOSURE VENTILATION SYSTEM.

RESPIRATOR: THE FOLLOWING RESPIRATORS ARE RECOMMENDED BASED ON INFORMATION FOUND IN THE PHYSICAL DATA, TOXICITY AND HEALTH EFFECTS SECTIONS. THEY ARE RANKED IN ORDER FROM MINIMUM TO MAXIMUM RESPIRATORY PROTECTION. THE SPECIFIC RESPIRATOR SELECTED MUST BE BASED ON CONTAMINATION LEVELS FOUND IN THE WORK PLACE, MUST NOT EXCEED THE WORKING LIMITS OF THE RESPIRATOR AND BE JOINTLY APPROVED BY THE NATIONAL INSTITUTE FOR OCCUPATIONAL SAFETY AND HEALTH AND THE MINE SAFETY AND HEALTH ADMINISTRATION (NIOSH-MSHA).

DUST AND MIST RESPIRATOR WITH A FULL FACEPIECE.

AIR-PURIFYING FULL FACEPIECE RESPIRATOR WITH A HIGH-EFFICIENCY PARTICULATE FILTER.

POWERED AIR-PURIFYING RESPIRATOR WITH A TIGHT-FITTING FACEPIECE AND HIGH-EFFICIENCY PARTICULATE FILTER.

TYPE 'C' SUPPLIED-AIR RESPIRATOR WITH A FULL FACEPIECE OPERATED IN PRESSURE-DEMAND OR OTHER POSITIVE PRESSURE MODE OR WITH A FULL FACEPIECE, HELMET OR HOOD OPERATED IN CONTINUOUS-FLOW MODE.

SELF-CONTAINED BREATHING APPARATUS WITH A FULL FACEPIECE OPERATED IN PRESSURE-DEMAND OR OTHER POSITIVE PRESSURE MODE.

FOR FIREFIGHTING AND OTHER IMMEDIATELY DANGEROUS TO LIFE OR HEALTH CONDITIONS:

SELF-CONTAINED BREATHING APPARATUS WITH FULL FACEPIECE OPERATED IN PRESSURE-DEMAND OR OTHER POSITIVE PRESSURE MODE.

SUPPLIED-AIR RESPIRATOR WITH FULL FACEPIECE AND OPERATED IN PRESSURE-DEMAND OR OTHER POSITIVE PRESSURE MODE IN COMBINATION WITH AN AUXILIARY SELF-CONTAINED BREATHING APPARATUS OPERATED IN PRESSURE-DEMAND OR OTHER POSITIVE PRESSURE MODE.

CLOTHING: EMPLOYEE MUST WEAR APPROPRIATE PROTECTIVE (IMPERVIOUS) CLOTHING AND EQUIPMENT TO PREVENT REPEATED OR PROLONGED SKIN CONTACT WITH THIS SUBSTANCE.

GLOVES: EMPLOYEE MUST WEAR APPROPRIATE PROTECTIVE GLOVES TO PREVENT CONTACT WITH THIS SUBSTANCE.

EYE PROTECTION: EMPLOYEE MUST WEAR SPLASH-PROOF OR DUST-RESISTANT SAFETY GOGGLES TO PREVENT EYE CONTACT WITH THIS SUBSTANCE. EMERGENCY EYE WASH: WHERE THERE IS ANY POSSIBILITY THAT AN EMPLOYEE'S EYES MAY BE EXPOSED TO THIS SUBSTANCE, THE EMPLOYER SHOULD PROVIDE AN EYE WASH FOUNTAIN WITHIN THE IMMEDIATE WORK AREA FOR EMERGENCY USE.

AUTHORIZED BY- OCCUPATIONAL HEALTH SERVICES, INC.
CREATION DATE: 11/16/89 ***REVISION DATE:*** 05/18/90

MATERIAL SAFETY DATA SHEET

OCCUPATIONAL HEALTH SERVICES, INC.
AGRICULTURE AND PESTICIDE DIVISION
450 SEVENTH AVENUE, SUITE 2407
NEW YORK, NEW YORK 10123
1-800-445-MSDS OR (212) 967-1100

EMERGENCY CONTACT:
JOHN S. BRANSFORD, JR. (615) 292-1180

SUBSTANCE IDENTIFICATION

CAS-NUMBER 7320-34-5

SUBSTANCE: **POTASSIUM PYROPHOSPHATE, ANHYDROUS**

TRADE NAMES/SYNONYMS: TKPP; TETRAPOTASSIUM PYROPHOSPHATE; PHOSPHOSOL; PYROPHOSPHORIC ACID, TETRAPOTASSIUM SALT; DIPHOSPHORIC ACID, TETRAPOTASSIUM SALT; TETRAKALIUM PYROPHOSPHATE; TETRAPOTASSIUM DIPHOSPHATE; POTASSIUM PYROPHOSPHATE, NORMAL; POTASSIUM DIPHOSPHATE(K4P2O7); POTASSIUM PHOSPHATE(K4P2O7); K4O7P2; PST19546

CHEMICAL FAMILY: INORGANIC SALT
MOLECULAR FORMULA: K4.P2-O7
MOLECULAR WEIGHT: 330.34
CERCLA RATINGS (SCALE 0-3): HEALTH=2 FIRE=0 REACTIVITY=0 PERSISTENCE=0
NFPA RATINGS (SCALE 0-4): HEALTH=2 FIRE=0 REACTIVITY=0

COMPONENTS AND CONTAMINANTS

COMPONENT: POTASSIUM PYROPHOSPHATE ***PERCENT:*** 100
CAS# 7320-34-5
OTHER CONTAMINANTS: NONE
EXPOSURE LIMITS: NO OCCUPATIONAL EXPOSURE LIMITS ESTABLISHED BY OSHA, ACGIH, OR NIOSH.
MONSANTO COMPANY RECOMMENDS USING EXPOSURE LIMITS FOR NUISANCE DUST.
NUISANCE PARTICULATES (NUISANCE DUST): 5 MG/M3 OSHA TWA (RESPIRABLE DUST); 15 MG/M3 OSHA TWA (TOTAL DUST) 10 MG/M3 ACGIH TWA (TOTAL DUST) (NO ASBESTOS AND < 1% CRYSTALLINE SILICA)

PHYSICAL DATA

DESCRIPTION: ODORLESS COLORLESS CRYSTALS OR WHITE GRANULAR POWDER.
MELTING POINT: 2028 F (1109 C) ***SPECIFIC GRAVITY:*** 2.33 (+3H2O)
PH: 10.5 @ 1% SOLN ***SOLUBILITY IN WATER:*** 188% @ 25 C
SOLVENT SOLUBILITY: INSOLUBLE IN ALCOHOL

FIRE AND EXPLOSION DATA

FIRE AND EXPLOSION HAZARD: NEGLIGIBLE FIRE HAZARD WHEN EXPOSED TO HEAT OR FLAME.
FIREFIGHTING MEDIA: EXTINGUISH USING AGENT SUITABLE FOR TYPE OF SURROUNDING FIRE.
FIREFIGHTING: NO ACUTE HAZARD. MOVE CONTAINER FROM FIRE AREA IF POSSIBLE. AVOID BREATHING VAPORS OR DUSTS; KEEP UPWIND.

TOXICITY

POTASSIUM PYROPHOSPHATE (TETRAPOTASSIUM PYROPHOSPHATE): TOXICITY DATA: >7940 MG/KG SKIN-RABBIT LD50 (MONSANTO MSDS); 2980 MG/KG ORAL-RAT LD50 (MONSANTO MSDS); CARCINOGEN STATUS: NONE. ACUTE TOXICITY LEVEL: MODERATELY TOXIC BY INGESTION; SLIGHTLY TOXIC BY DERMAL ABSORPTION. TARGET EFFECTS: POISONING BY PHOSPHATE COMPOUNDS MAY AFFECT CALCIUM METABOLISM.

HEALTH EFFECTS AND FIRST AID

INHALATION: POTASSIUM PYROPHOSPHATE (TETRAPOTASSIUM PYROPHOSPHATE):
ACUTE EXPOSURE- NO DATA AVAILABLE. MAY BE IRRITATING. **CHRONIC EXPOSURE-** NO DATA AVAILABLE.
FIRST AID- REMOVE FROM EXPOSURE AREA TO FRESH AIR IMMEDIATELY. IF BREATHING HAS STOPPED, PERFORM ARTIFICIAL RESPIRATION. KEEP PERSON WARM AND AT REST. TREAT SYMPTOMATICALLY AND SUPPORTIVELY. GET MEDICAL ATTENTION IMMEDIATELY.

SKIN CONTACT: POTASSIUM PYROPHOSPHATE (TETRAPOTASSIUM PYROPHOSPHATE):
ACUTE EXPOSURE- ANIMAL STUDIES INDICATE THAT THIS MATERIAL IS ONLY SLIGHTLY IRRITATING RATING 1 ON A SCALE OF 8 WHEN APPLIED TO RABBIT SKIN. ANIMAL STUDIES INDICATE THAT LARGE AMOUNTS WOULD HAVE TO BE ABSORBED THROUGH THE SKIN TO CAUSE DEATH. **CHRONIC EXPOSURE-** NO DATA AVAILABLE.
FIRST AID- REMOVE CONTAMINATED CLOTHING AND SHOES IMMEDIATELY. WASH AFFECTED AREA WITH SOAP OR MILD DETERGENT AND LARGE AMOUNTS OF WATER UNTIL NO EVIDENCE OF CHEMICAL REMAINS (APPROXIMATELY 15-20 MINUTES). GET MEDICAL ATTENTION IMMEDIATELY.

EYE CONTACT: POTASSIUM PYROPHOSPHATE (TETRAPOTASSIUM PYROPHOSPHATE):
ACUTE EXPOSURE- ANIMAL STUDIES INDICATE THAT THE MATERIAL MAY CAUSE MILD IRRITATION. THE MATERIAL RATED 17.3 ON A SCALE OF 110 WHEN APPLIED TO RABBIT EYES. **CHRONIC EXPOSURE-** NO DATA AVAILABLE.
FIRST AID- WASH EYES IMMEDIATELY WITH LARGE AMOUNTS OF WATER OR NORMAL SALINE, OCCASIONALLY LIFTING UPPER AND LOWER LIDS, UNTIL NO EVIDENCE OF CHEMICAL REMAINS (APPROXIMATELY 15-20 MINUTES). GET MEDICAL ATTENTION IMMEDIATELY.

INGESTION: POTASSIUM PYROPHOSPHATE (TETRAPOTASSIUM PYROPHOSPHATE):
ACUTE EXPOSURE- MAY CAUSE GASTROINTESTINAL DISTURBANCES, NAUSEA, VOMITING, AND DIARRHEA. PHOSPHATE COMPOUNDS MAY REDUCE THE IONIC SERUM CALCIUM, WHICH CAN RESULT IN A SHOCK-LIKE STATE, FALL OF BLOOD PRESSURE, SLOW PULSE, CYANOSIS, COMA, AND SOMETIMES TETANY. **CHRONIC EXPOSURE-** NO DATA AVAILABLE.
FIRST AID- TREAT SYMPTOMATICALLY AND SUPPORTIVELY. GET MEDICAL ATTENTION IMMEDIATELY. IF VOMITING OCCURS, KEEP HEAD LOWER THAN HIPS TO PREVENT ASPIRATION.
ANTIDOTE: NO SPECIFIC ANTIDOTE. TREAT SYMPTOMATICALLY AND SUPPORTIVELY.

REACTIVITY

REACTIVITY: STABLE UNDER NORMAL TEMPERATURES AND PRESSURES.
INCOMPATIBILITIES: POTASSIUM PYROPHOSPHATE (TETRAPOTASSIUM PYROPHOSPHATE): NO DATA AVAILABLE.
DECOMPOSITION: THERMAL DECOMPOSITION MAY RELEASE TOXIC AND/OR HAZARDOUS GASES.
POLYMERIZATION: HAZARDOUS POLYMERIZATION HAS NOT BEEN REPORTED TO OCCUR UNDER NORMAL TEMPERATURES AND PRESSURES.

STORAGE AND DISPOSAL

OBSERVE ALL FEDERAL, STATE AND LOCAL REGULATIONS WHEN STORING OR DISPOSING OF THIS SUBSTANCE. FOR ASSISTANCE, CONTACT THE DISTRICT DIRECTOR OF THE ENVIRONMENTAL PROTECTION AGENCY.

STORAGE

STORE IN A COOL, DRY PLACE; KEEP CONTAINER TIGHTLY CLOSED WHEN NOT IN USE.

CONDITIONS TO AVOID

PREVENT DISPERSION OF DUST IN AIR.

SPILL AND LEAK PROCEDURES

OCCUPATIONAL SPILL: FOR LARGE SPILLS, SWEEP UP WITH A MINIMUM OF DUSTING AND PLACE INTO SUITABLE CLEAN, DRY CONTAINERS FOR RECLAMATION OR LATER DISPOSAL.
RESIDUE SHOULD BE CLEANED UP USING A HIGH-EFFICIENCY PARTICULATE FILTER VACUUM.

PROTECTIVE EQUIPMENT

VENTILATION: PROVIDE LOCAL EXHAUST VENTILATION AND/OR GENERAL DILUTION VENTILATION TO MEET PUBLISHED EXPOSURE LIMITS.
RESPIRATOR: THE FOLLOWING RESPIRATORS ARE RECOMMENDED BASED ON INFORMATION FOUND IN THE PHYSICAL DATA, TOXICITY AND HEALTH EFFECTS SECTIONS. THEY ARE RANKED IN ORDER FROM MINIMUM TO MAXIMUM RESPIRATORY PROTECTION. THE SPECIFIC RESPIRATOR SELECTED MUST BE BASED ON CONTAMINATION LEVELS FOUND IN THE WORK PLACE, MUST NOT EXCEED THE WORKING LIMITS OF THE RESPIRATOR AND BE JOINTLY APPROVED BY THE NATIONAL INSTITUTE FOR OCCUPATIONAL SAFETY AND HEALTH AND THE MINE SAFETY AND HEALTH ADMINISTRATION (NIOSH-MSHA).
DUST AND MIST RESPIRATOR.
AIR-PURIFYING RESPIRATOR WITH A HIGH-EFFICIENCY PARTICULATE FILTER.
POWERED AIR-PURIFYING RESPIRATOR WITH A DUST AND MIST FILTER.
POWERED AIR-PURIFYING RESPIRATOR WITH A HIGH-EFFICIENCY PARTICULATE FILTER.
TYPE 'C' SUPPLIED-AIR RESPIRATOR OPERATED IN THE PRESSURE-DEMAND OR OTHER POSITIVE PRESSURE OR CONTINUOUS-FLOW MODE.
SELF-CONTAINED BREATHING APPARATUS.
FOR FIREFIGHTING AND OTHER IMMEDIATELY DANGEROUS TO LIFE OR HEALTH CONDITIONS:
SELF-CONTAINED BREATHING APPARATUS WITH FULL FACEPIECE OPERATED IN PRESSURE-DEMAND OR OTHER POSITIVE PRESSURE MODE.
SUPPLIED-AIR RESPIRATOR WITH FULL FACEPIECE AND OPERATED IN PRESSURE-DEMAND OR OTHER POSITIVE PRESSURE MODE IN COMBINATION WITH AN AUXILIARY SELF-CONTAINED BREATHING APPARATUS OPERATED IN PRESSURE-DEMAND OR OTHER POSITIVE PRESSURE MODE.
CLOTHING: EMPLOYEE MUST WEAR APPROPRIATE PROTECTIVE (IMPERVIOUS) CLOTHING AND EQUIPMENT TO PREVENT REPEATED OR PROLONGED SKIN CONTACT WITH THIS SUBSTANCE.
GLOVES: EMPLOYEE MUST WEAR APPROPRIATE PROTECTIVE GLOVES TO PREVENT CONTACT WITH THIS SUBSTANCE.
EYE PROTECTION: EMPLOYEE MUST WEAR SPLASH-PROOF OR DUST-RESISTANT SAFETY GOGGLES TO PREVENT EYE CONTACT WITH THIS SUBSTANCE.
EMERGENCY EYE WASH: WHERE THERE IS ANY POSSIBILITY THAT AN EMPLOYEE'S EYES MAY BE EXPOSED TO THIS SUBSTANCE, THE EMPLOYER SHOULD PROVIDE AN EYE WASH FOUNTAIN WITHIN THE IMMEDIATE WORK AREA FOR EMERGENCY USE.

AUTHORIZED BY- OCCUPATIONAL HEALTH SERVICES, INC.
CREATION DATE: 11/16/89 ***REVISION DATE:*** 05/18/90

MATERIAL SAFETY DATA SHEET

OCCUPATIONAL HEALTH SERVICES, INC.
AGRICULTURE AND PESTICIDE DIVISION
450 SEVENTH AVENUE, SUITE 2407
NEW YORK, NEW YORK 10123
1-800-445-MSDS OR (212) 967-1100

EMERGENCY CONTACT:
JOHN S. BRANSFORD, JR. (615) 292-1180

SUBSTANCE IDENTIFICATION

CAS-NUMBER 37199-66-9
SUBSTANCE: **POTASSIUM POLYSULFIDE**
TRADE NAMES/SYNONYMS: POTASSIUM SULFIDE; UN 1382; PST19548
CHEMICAL FAMILY: INORGANIC SALT
MOLECULAR FORMULA: K2-SX
MOLECULAR WEIGHT: VARIES
CERCLA RATINGS (SCALE 0-3): HEALTH=U FIRE=3 REACTIVITY=3 PERSISTENCE=0
NFPA RATINGS (SCALE 0-4): HEALTH=U FIRE=3 REACTIVITY=3

COMPONENTS AND CONTAMINANTS

COMPONENT: POTASSIUM POLYSULFIDE ***PERCENT:*** 100.0
CAS# 37199-66-9
OTHER CONTAMINANTS: NONE
EXPOSURE LIMITS: POTASSIUM POLYSULFIDE: NONE ESTABLISHED.

PHYSICAL DATA

DESCRIPTION: CRYSTALS WITH A DISAGREEABLE ODOR. ***MELTING POINT:*** NOT AVAILABLE
SPECIFIC GRAVITY: NOT AVAILABLE ***SOLUBILITY IN WATER:*** SOLUBLE
SOLVENT SOLUBILITY: ALCOHOL

FIRE AND EXPLOSION DATA

FIRE AND EXPLOSION HAZARD: DANGEROUS FIRE HAZARD WHEN EXPOSED TO HEAT OR FLAME.
DUST-AIR MIXTURES MAY IGNITE OR EXPLODE.
FIREFIGHTING MEDIA: DRY CHEMICAL, CARBON DIOXIDE, HALON, WATER SPRAY OR STANDARD FOAM (1987 EMERGENCY RESPONSE GUIDEBOOK, DOT P 5800.4).
FOR LARGER FIRES, USE WATER SPRAY, FOG OR STANDARD FOAM (1987 EMERGENCY RESPONSE GUIDEBOOK, DOT P 5800.4).
FIREFIGHTING: MOVE CONTAINER FROM FIRE AREA IF POSSIBLE. COOL CONTAINERS EXPOSED TO FLAME WITH WATER FROM SIDE UNTIL WELL AFTER FIRE IS OUT. STAY AWAY FROM STORAGE TANK ENDS. FOR MASSIVE FIRE IN CARGO AREA, USE UNMANNED HOSE HOLDER OR MONITOR NOZZLES; ELSE WITHDRAW AND LET FIRE BURN (1987 EMERGENCY RESPONSE GUIDEBOOK, DOT P 5800.4, GUIDE PAGE 32).
USE FLOODING QUANTITIES OF WATER.

TRANSPORTATION DATA

DEPARTMENT OF TRANSPORTATION HAZARD CLASSIFICATION 49 CFR 172.101: FLAMMABLE SOLID
DEPARTMENT OF TRANSPORTATION LABELING REQUIREMENTS 49 CFR 172.101 AND SUBPART E: FLAMMABLE SOLID
DEPARTMENT OF TRANSPORTATION PACKAGING REQUIREMENTS: 49 CFR 173.207 EXCEPTIONS: 49 CFR 173.153

TOXICITY

POTASSIUM POLYSULFIDE: CARCINOGEN STATUS: NONE. ACUTE TOXICITY LEVEL: NO DATA AVAILABLE. TARGET EFFECTS: POISONING MAY AFFECT THE CENTRAL NERVOUS SYSTEM.

HEALTH EFFECTS AND FIRST AID

INHALATION: POTASSIUM POLYSULFIDE: **ACUTE EXPOSURE-** NO DATA SPECIFIC DATA AVAILABLE. A SIMILAR COMPOUND, POTASSIUM SULFIDE, IS CORROSIVE TO MUCOUS MEMBRANES AND WHEN EXPOSED TO MOIST MUCOUS MEMBRANES MAY LIBERATE HYDROGEN SULFIDE GAS. IF HYDROGEN SULFIDE GAS IS RELEASED LOW CONCENTRATIONS MAY CAUSE NAUSEA, VOMITING, DEPRESSED RESPIRATION, SOMNOLENCE, AMNESIA, DELIRIUM, UNCONSCIOUSNESS AND HALLUCINATIONS. EXPOSURE TO HIGH CONCENTRATIONS MAY CAUSE SUDDEN COLLAPSE, CONVULSION, AND DEATH FROM RESPIRATORY PARALYSIS. **CHRONIC EXPOSURE-** NO DATA AVAILABLE.
FIRST AID- REMOVE FROM EXPOSURE AREA TO FRESH AIR IMMEDIATELY. IF BREATHING HAS STOPPED, GIVE ARTIFICIAL RESPIRATION. MAINTAIN AIRWAY AND BLOOD PRESSURE AND ADMINISTER OXYGEN IF AVAILABLE. KEEP AFFECTED PERSON WARM AND AT REST. TREAT SYMPTOMATICALLY AND SUPPORTIVELY. ADMINISTRATION OF OXYGEN SHOULD BE PERFORMED BY QUALIFIED PERSONNEL. GET MEDICAL ATTENTION IMMEDIATELY.

SKIN CONTACT: POTASSIUM POLYSULFIDE: **ACUTE EXPOSURE-** MAY BE IRRITATING TO THE SKIN. A SIMILAR COMPOUND, POTASSIUM SULFIDE IS SEVERELY IRRITATING TO THE SKIN CAUSING REDNESS, PAIN, AND SKIN BURNS. **CHRONIC EXPOSURE-** NO DATA AVAILABLE.
FIRST AID- REMOVE CONTAMINATED CLOTHING AND SHOES IMMEDIATELY. WASH AFFECTED AREA WITH SOAP OR MILD DETERGENT AND LARGE AMOUNTS OF WATER UNTIL NO EVIDENCE OF CHEMICAL REMAINS (AT LEAST 15-20 MINUTES). IN CASE OF CHEMICAL BURNS, COVER AREA WITH STERILE, DRY DRESSING. BANDAGE SECURELY, BUT NOT TOO TIGHTLY. GET MEDICAL ATTENTION IMMEDIATELY.

EYE CONTACT: POTASSIUM POLYSULFIDE: **ACUTE EXPOSURE-** MAY BE IRRITATING TO THE EYES. A SIMILAR COMPOUND, POTASSIUM SULFIDE IS SEVERELY IRRITATING TO THE EYES, CAUSING REDNESS, PAIN, BLURRED VISION AND BURNS. **CHRONIC EXPOSURE-** NO DATA AVAILABLE.
FIRST AID- WASH EYES IMMEDIATELY WITH LARGE AMOUNTS OF WATER, OCCASIONALLY LIFTING UPPER AND LOWER LIDS, UNTIL NO EVIDENCE OF CHEMICAL REMAINS (AT LEAST 15-20 MINUTES). CONTINUE IRRIGATING WITH NORMAL SALINE UNTIL THE PH HAS RETURNED TO NORMAL (30-60 MINUTES). COVER WITH STERILE BANDAGES. GET MEDICAL ATTENTION IMMEDIATELY.

INGESTION: POTASSIUM POLYSULFIDE: **ACUTE EXPOSURE-** NO SPECIFIC DATA AVAILABLE. A SIMILAR COMPOUND, POTASSIUM SULFIDE, MAY CAUSE CORROSION OF THE GASTRIC MUCOSA WITH SORE THROAT, ABDOMINAL PAIN, NAUSEA, VOMITING AND DIARRHEA. UPON CONTACT WITH GASTRIC ACID SIGNIFICANT AMOUNTS OF HYDROGEN GAS AND FREE ALKALI MAY BE PRODUCED. POISONING MAY CAUSE NAUSEA, VOMITING AND DEPRESSED RESPIRATION. SERIOUS POISONING MAY CAUSE SUDDEN COLLAPSE, CONVULSIONS AND DEATH FROM RESPIRATORY PARALYSIS. **CHRONIC EXPOSURE-** NO DATA AVAILABLE.
FIRST AID- TREAT SYMPTOMATICALLY AND SUPPORTIVELY. GET MEDICAL ATTENTION IMMEDIATELY.
ANTIDOTE: NO SPECIFIC ANTIDOTE. TREAT SYMPTOMATICALLY AND SUPPORTIVELY.

REACTIVITY

REACTIVITY: NO DATA AVAILABLE. POTASSIUM SULFIDE, ANHYDROUS MAY EXPLODE UPON FRICTION, CONCUSSION, OR RAPID HEATING. FINELY DIVIDED POTASSIUM MAY FORM EXPLOSIVE MIXTURES IN AIR.
INCOMPATIBILITIES: POTASSIUM POLYSULFIDE: NO DATA AVAILABLE.
DECOMPOSITION: THERMAL DECOMPOSITION MAY RELEASE TOXIC SULFUR DIOXIDE AND HYDROGEN SULFIDE GASES, WHICH INCREASE THE FIRE AND EXPLOSION HAZARD.
POLYMERIZATION: NO DATA AVAILABLE.

CONDITIONS TO AVOID

AVOID CONTACT WITH HEAT, SPARKS, FLAMES OR OTHER SOURCES OF IGNITION. MATERIAL IS EXTREMELY FLAMMABLE AND MAY BURN RAPIDLY WITH FLARE-BURNING EFFECT.

SPILL AND LEAK PROCEDURES

OCCUPATIONAL SPILL: SHUT OFF IGNITION SOURCES. DO NOT TOUCH SPILLED MATERIAL. FOR SMALL SPILLS, WITH CLEAN SHOVEL, PLACE MATERIAL INTO CLEAN, DRY CONTAINER AND COVER; MOVE CONTAINERS FROM SPILL AREA. FOR LARGER SPILLS, WET DOWN WITH WATER AND DIKE FOR LATER DISPOSAL. NO SMOKING, FLAMES OR FLARES IN HAZARD AREA! KEEP UNNECESSARY PEOPLE AWAY. ISOLATE HAZARD AREA AND DENY ENTRY.

PROTECTIVE EQUIPMENT

VENTILATION: PROVIDE LOCAL EXHAUST OR PROCESS ENCLOSURE VENTILATION. VENTILATION EQUIPMENT MUST BE EXPLOSION-PROOF.
RESPIRATOR: THE FOLLOWING RESPIRATORS ARE RECOMMENDED BASED ON INFORMATION FOUND IN THE PHYSICAL DATA, TOXICITY AND HEALTH EFFECTS SECTIONS. THEY ARE RANKED IN ORDER FROM MINIMUM TO MAXIMUM RESPIRATORY PROTECTION. THE SPECIFIC RESPIRATOR SELECTED MUST BE BASED ON CONTAMINATION LEVELS FOUND IN THE WORK PLACE, MUST NOT EXCEED THE WORKING LIMITS OF THE RESPIRATOR AND BE JOINTLY APPROVED BY THE NATIONAL INSTITUTE FOR OCCUPATIONAL SAFETY AND HEALTH AND THE MINE SAFETY AND HEALTH ADMINISTRATION (NIOSH-MSHA).
DUST AND MIST RESPIRATOR WITH A FULL FACEPIECE.
AIR-PURIFYING FULL FACEPIECE RESPIRATOR WITH A HIGH-EFFICIENCY PARTICULATE FILTER.

POWERED AIR-PURIFYING RESPIRATOR WITH A TIGHT-FITTING FACEPIECE AND HIGH-EFFICIENCY PARTICULATE FILTER.
TYPE 'C' SUPPLIED-AIR RESPIRATOR WITH A FULL FACEPIECE OPERATED IN PRESSURE-DEMAND OR OTHER POSITIVE PRESSURE MODE OR WITH A FULL FACEPIECE, HELMET OR HOOD OPERATED IN CONTINUOUS-FLOW MODE.
SELF-CONTAINED BREATHING APPARATUS WITH A FULL FACEPIECE OPERATED IN PRESSURE-DEMAND OR OTHER POSITIVE PRESSURE MODE.
FOR FIREFIGHTING AND OTHER IMMEDIATELY DANGEROUS TO LIFE OR HEALTH CONDITIONS:
SELF-CONTAINED BREATHING APPARATUS WITH FULL FACEPIECE OPERATED IN PRESSURE-DEMAND OR OTHER POSITIVE PRESSURE MODE.
SUPPLIED-AIR RESPIRATOR WITH FULL FACEPIECE AND OPERATED IN PRESSURE-DEMAND OR OTHER POSITIVE PRESSURE MODE IN COMBINATION WITH AN AUXILIARY SELF-CONTAINED BREATHING APPARATUS OPERATED IN PRESSURE-DEMAND OR OTHER POSITIVE PRESSURE MODE.

CLOTHING: EMPLOYEE MUST WEAR APPROPRIATE PROTECTIVE (IMPERVIOUS) CLOTHING AND EQUIPMENT TO PREVENT ANY POSSIBILITY OF SKIN CONTACT WITH THIS SUBSTANCE.

GLOVES: EMPLOYEE MUST WEAR APPROPRIATE PROTECTIVE GLOVES TO PREVENT CONTACT WITH THIS SUBSTANCE.

EYE PROTECTION: EMPLOYEE MUST WEAR SPLASH-PROOF OR DUST-RESISTANT SAFETY GOGGLES AND A FACESHIELD TO PREVENT CONTACT WITH THIS SUBSTANCE.
EMERGENCY WASH FACILITIES: WHERE THERE IS ANY POSSIBILITY THAT AN EMPLOYEE'S EYES AND/OR SKIN MAY BE EXPOSED TO THIS SUBSTANCE, THE EMPLOYER SHOULD PROVIDE AN EYE WASH FOUNTAIN AND QUICK DRENCH SHOWER WITHIN THE IMMEDIATE WORK AREA FOR EMERGENCY USE.

AUTHORIZED BY- OCCUPATIONAL HEALTH SERVICES, INC.
CREATION DATE: 11/16/89 ***REVISION DATE:*** 05/25/90

MATERIAL SAFETY DATA SHEET

OCCUPATIONAL HEALTH SERVICES, INC.
AGRICULTURE AND PESTICIDE DIVISION
450 SEVENTH AVENUE, SUITE 2407
NEW YORK, NEW YORK 10123
1-800-445-MSDS OR (212) 967-1100

EMERGENCY CONTACT:
JOHN S. BRANSFORD, JR. (615) 292-1180

SUBSTANCE IDENTIFICATION

CAS-NUMBER 7778-80-5

SUBSTANCE: POTASSIUM SULFATE

TRADE NAMES/SYNONYMS: NATURAL ARCANITE; SAL POLYCHRESTUM; ARCANUM DUPLICATUM; TARTARUS VITRIOLATUS; POTASSIUM SULPHATE; DIPOTASSIUM SULFATE; SULFURIC ACID DIPOTASSIUM SALT; SULFURIC ACID POTASSIUM SALT; P-304; P-305; POTASSIUM SULFATE (K2(SO4)); POTASSIUM SULFATE (K2SO4); K2O4S; PST19590

CHEMICAL FAMILY: INORGANIC SALT

MOLECULAR FORMULA: K2-S-O4

MOLECULAR WEIGHT: 174.25

CERCLA RATINGS (SCALE 0-3): HEALTH=2 FIRE=0 REACTIVITY=0 PERSISTENCE=0

NFPA RATINGS (SCALE 0-4): HEALTH=U FIRE=0 REACTIVITY=0

COMPONENTS AND CONTAMINANTS

COMPONENT: POTASSIUM SULFATE ***PERCENT:*** 100.0
CAS# 7778-80-5

OTHER CONTAMINANTS: NONE

EXPOSURE LIMITS: NO OCCUPATIONAL EXPOSURE LIMITS ESTABLISHED BY OSHA, ACGIH, OR NIOSH.

PHYSICAL DATA

DESCRIPTION: ODORLESS, COLORLESS TO WHITE CRYSTALS OR POWDER WITH A BITTER, SALINE TASTE. ***BOILING POINT:*** 3072 F (1689 C) ***MELTING POINT:*** 1956 F (1069 C)

SPECIFIC GRAVITY: 2.662 ***PH:*** 5.5-8.5 @ 5% SOLN

SOLUBILITY IN WATER: 12% @ 25 C

SOLVENT SOLUBILITY: SOLUBLE IN GLYCEROL; INSOLUBLE IN ALCOHOL, ACETONE, AND CARBON DISULFIDE.

FIRE AND EXPLOSION DATA

FIRE AND EXPLOSION HAZARD: NEGLIGIBLE FIRE HAZARD WHEN EXPOSED TO HEAT OR FLAME.

FIREFIGHTING MEDIA: EXTINGUISH USING AGENT SUITABLE FOR TYPE OF SURROUNDING FIRE.

FIREFIGHTING: NO ACUTE HAZARD. MOVE CONTAINER FROM FIRE AREA IF POSSIBLE. AVOID BREATHING VAPORS OR DUSTS; KEEP UPWIND.

TOXICITY

POTASSIUM SULFATE: TOXICITY DATA: 800 MG/KG ORAL-WOMAN LDLO; 6600 MG/KG ORAL-RAT LD50; 3000 MG/KG SUBCUTANEOUS-GUINEA PIG LDLO. CARCINOGEN STATUS: NONE. ACUTE TOXICITY LEVEL: SLIGHTLY TOXIC BY INGESTION. TARGET EFFECTS: POISONING MAY AFFECT THE HEART. AT INCREASED RISK FROM EXPOSURE: PERSONS WITH ASTHMA.

HEALTH EFFECTS AND FIRST AID

INHALATION: POTASSIUM SULFATE: **ACUTE EXPOSURE-** NO SPECIFIC DATA AVAILABLE. LEVELS ABOVE 10 UG/M3 OF SUSPENDED SULFATES IN THE AIR MAY CAUSE AN EXCESS RISK OF ASTHMATIC ATTACKS IN SUSCEPTIBLE INDIVIDUALS.
CHRONIC EXPOSURE- NO DATA AVAILABLE.

FIRST AID- REMOVE FROM EXPOSURE AREA TO FRESH AIR IMMEDIATELY. IF BREATHING HAS STOPPED, PERFORM ARTIFICIAL RESPIRATION. KEEP PERSON WARM AND AT REST. TREAT SYMPTOMATICALLY AND SUPPORTIVELY. GET MEDICAL ATTENTION IMMEDIATELY.

SKIN CONTACT: POTASSIUM SULFATE: **ACUTE EXPOSURE-** NO DATA AVAILABLE.
CHRONIC EXPOSURE- NO DATA AVAILABLE.

FIRST AID- REMOVE CONTAMINATED CLOTHING AND SHOES IMMEDIATELY. WASH AFFECTED AREA WITH SOAP OR MILD DETERGENT AND LARGE AMOUNTS OF WATER UNTIL NO EVIDENCE OF CHEMICAL REMAINS (APPROXIMATELY 15-20 MINUTES). GET MEDICAL ATTENTION IMMEDIATELY.

EYE CONTACT: POTASSIUM SULFATE: **ACUTE EXPOSURE-** NO DATA AVAILABLE.
CHRONIC EXPOSURE- NO DATA AVAILABLE.

FIRST AID- WASH EYES IMMEDIATELY WITH LARGE AMOUNTS OF WATER OR NORMAL SALINE, OCCASIONALLY LIFTING UPPER AND LOWER LIDS, UNTIL NO EVIDENCE OF CHEMICAL REMAINS (APPROXIMATELY 15-20 MINUTES). GET MEDICAL ATTENTION IMMEDIATELY.

INGESTION: POTASSIUM SULFATE: **ACUTE EXPOSURE-** ACUTE POTASSIUM INTOXICATION BY MOUTH IS RARE BECAUSE LARGE SINGLE DOSES USUALLY INDUCE VOMITING, SEVERE GASTROINTESTINAL IRRITATION, AND CATHARSIS, AND BECAUSE IN THE ABSENCE OF PRE-EXISTING KIDNEY DAMAGE POTASSIUM IS RAPIDLY EXCRETED. HOWEVER, IF SUFFICIENT AMOUNTS ARE INGESTED AND ABSORBED, POTASSIUM MAY DISTURB THE RHYTHM OF THE HEART CAUSING A SLOW, WEAK PULSE, ARRHYTHMIAS, AND FALL IN BLOOD PRESSURE. RESPIRATIONS ARE INITIALLY ACCELERATED BUT SKELETAL MUSCLE WEAKNESS MAY ADVANCE TO THE STAGE OF PARALYSIS. **CHRONIC EXPOSURE-** NO DATA AVAILABLE.

FIRST AID- TREAT SYMPTOMATICALLY AND SUPPORTIVELY. GET MEDICAL ATTENTION IMMEDIATELY.

ANTIDOTE: NO SPECIFIC ANTIDOTE. TREAT SYMPTOMATICALLY AND SUPPORTIVELY.

REACTIVITY

REACTIVITY: STABLE UNDER NORMAL TEMPERATURES AND PRESSURES.

INCOMPATIBILITIES: POTASSIUM SULFATE: ALUMINUM: VIOLENT EXPLOSION ON MELTING.

DECOMPOSITION: THERMAL DECOMPOSITION MAY RELEASE TOXIC OXIDES OF SULFUR.

POLYMERIZATION: HAZARDOUS POLYMERIZATION HAS NOT BEEN REPORTED TO OCCUR UNDER NORMAL TEMPERATURES AND PRESSURES.

STORAGE AND DISPOSAL

OBSERVE ALL FEDERAL, STATE AND LOCAL REGULATIONS WHEN STORING OR DISPOSING OF THIS SUBSTANCE. FOR ASSISTANCE, CONTACT THE DISTRICT DIRECTOR OF THE ENVIRONMENTAL PROTECTION AGENCY.

STORAGE

STORE AWAY FROM INCOMPATIBLE SUBSTANCES.
STORE IN A TIGHTLY CLOSED CONTAINER.

CONDITIONS TO AVOID

NONE REPORTED.

SPILL AND LEAK PROCEDURES

OCCUPATIONAL SPILL: NO SPECIAL PRECAUTIONS INDICATED.

PROTECTIVE EQUIPMENT

VENTILATION: PROVIDE LOCAL EXHAUST OR GENERAL DILUTION VENTILATION SYSTEM.

RESPIRATOR: THE FOLLOWING RESPIRATORS ARE RECOMMENDED BASED ON INFORMATION FOUND IN THE PHYSICAL DATA, TOXICITY AND HEALTH EFFECTS SECTIONS. THEY ARE RANKED IN ORDER FROM MINIMUM TO MAXIMUM RESPIRATORY PROTECTION. THE SPECIFIC RESPIRATOR SELECTED MUST BE BASED ON CONTAMINATION LEVELS FOUND IN THE WORK PLACE, MUST NOT EXCEED THE WORKING LIMITS OF THE RESPIRATOR AND BE JOINTLY APPROVED BY THE NATIONAL INSTITUTE FOR OCCUPATIONAL SAFETY AND HEALTH AND THE MINE SAFETY AND HEALTH ADMINISTRATION (NIOSH-MSHA).

DUST AND MIST RESPIRATOR WITH A FULL FACEPIECE.

AIR-PURIFYING FULL FACEPIECE RESPIRATOR WITH A HIGH-EFFICIENCY PARTICULATE FILTER.

POWERED AIR-PURIFYING RESPIRATOR WITH A TIGHT-FITTING FACEPIECE AND HIGH-EFFICIENCY PARTICULATE FILTER.

TYPE 'C' SUPPLIED-AIR RESPIRATOR WITH A FULL FACEPIECE OPERATED IN PRESSURE-DEMAND OR OTHER POSITIVE PRESSURE MODE OR WITH A FULL FACEPIECE, HELMET OR HOOD OPERATED IN CONTINUOUS-FLOW MODE.

SELF-CONTAINED BREATHING APPARATUS WITH A FULL FACEPIECE OPERATED IN PRESSURE-DEMAND OR OTHER POSITIVE PRESSURE MODE.

FOR FIREFIGHTING AND OTHER IMMEDIATELY DANGEROUS TO LIFE OR HEALTH CONDITIONS:

SELF-CONTAINED BREATHING APPARATUS WITH FULL FACEPIECE OPERATED IN PRESSURE-DEMAND OR OTHER POSITIVE PRESSURE MODE.

SUPPLIED-AIR RESPIRATOR WITH FULL FACEPIECE AND OPERATED IN PRESSURE-DEMAND OR OTHER POSITIVE PRESSURE MODE IN COMBINATION WITH AN AUXILIARY SELF-CONTAINED BREATHING APPARATUS OPERATED IN PRESSURE-DEMAND OR OTHER POSITIVE PRESSURE MODE.

CLOTHING: EMPLOYEE MUST WEAR APPROPRIATE PROTECTIVE (IMPERVIOUS) CLOTHING AND EQUIPMENT TO PREVENT REPEATED OR PROLONGED SKIN CONTACT WITH THIS SUBSTANCE.

GLOVES: EMPLOYEE MUST WEAR APPROPRIATE PROTECTIVE GLOVES TO PREVENT CONTACT WITH THIS SUBSTANCE.

EYE PROTECTION: EMPLOYEE MUST WEAR SPLASH-PROOF OR DUST-RESISTANT SAFETY GOGGLES TO PREVENT EYE CONTACT WITH THIS SUBSTANCE.

EMERGENCY EYE WASH: WHERE THERE IS ANY POSSIBILITY THAT AN EMPLOYEE'S EYES MAY BE EXPOSED TO THIS SUBSTANCE, THE EMPLOYER SHOULD PROVIDE AN EYE WASH FOUNTAIN WITHIN THE IMMEDIATE WORK AREA FOR EMERGENCY USE.

AUTHORIZED BY- OCCUPATIONAL HEALTH SERVICES, INC.

CREATION DATE: 11/17/89 ***REVISION DATE:*** 11/17/89

MATERIAL SAFETY DATA SHEET

OCCUPATIONAL HEALTH SERVICES, INC.
AGRICULTURE AND PESTICIDE DIVISION
450 SEVENTH AVENUE, SUITE 2407
NEW YORK, NEW YORK 10123
1-800-445-MSDS OR (212) 967-1100

EMERGENCY CONTACT:
JOHN S. BRANSFORD, JR. (615) 292-1180

SUBSTANCE IDENTIFICATION

CAS-NUMBER 333-20-0

SUBSTANCE: POTASSIUM THIOCYANATE

TRADE NAMES/SYNONYMS: POTASSIUM ISOTHIOCYANATE; THIOCARA; PHODA-NIDE; POTASSIUM SULFOCYANATE; POTASSIUM RHODANIDE; POTASSIUM RHODANATE; ATERO-CYN; ARTEROCYN; KYONATE; RHOCYN; RODANCA; P-317; PST19640

CHEMICAL FAMILY: INORGANIC SALT

MOLECULAR FORMULA: C-K-N-S

MOLECULAR WEIGHT: 97.18

CERCLA RATINGS (SCALE 0-3): HEALTH=2 FIRE=0 REACTIVITY=0 PERSISTENCE=0

NFPA RATINGS (SCALE 0-4): HEALTH=2 FIRE=0 REACTIVITY=0

COMPONENTS AND CONTAMINANTS

COMPONENT: POTASSIUM THIOCYANATE ***PERCENT:*** 100
CAS# 333-20-0

OTHER CONTAMINANTS: NONE

EXPOSURE LIMITS: POTASSIUM THIOCYANATE: NONE ESTABLISHED

PHYSICAL DATA

DESCRIPTION: ODORLESS, COLORLESS, DELIQUESCENT CRYSTALS, SALINE TASTE

BOILING POINT: 932 F (500 C) DECOM ***MELTING POINT:*** 344 F (173 C)

SPECIFIC GRAVITY: 1.9 @ 14 C ***PH:*** 7.0 ***SOLUBILITY IN WATER:*** 177.2% @ 0 C

SOLVENT SOLUBILITY: ALCOHOL AND ACETONE

FIRE AND EXPLOSION DATA

FIRE AND EXPLOSION HAZARD: NEGLIGIBLE FIRE HAZARD WHEN EXPOSED TO HEAT OR FLAME.

FLASH POINT: NON-COMBUSTIBLE

FIREFIGHTING MEDIA: DRY CHEMICAL, CARBON DIOXIDE, HALON, WATER SPRAY OR ALCOHOL FOAM (1987 EMERGENCY RESPONSE GUIDEBOOK, DOT P 5800.4).

FOR LARGER FIRES, USE WATER SPRAY, FOG OR ALCOHOL FOAM (1987 EMERGENCY RESPONSE GUIDEBOOK, DOT P 5800.4).

FIREFIGHTING: NO ACUTE HAZARD. MOVE CONTAINER FROM FIRE AREA IF POSSIBLE. AVOID BREATHING VAPORS OR DUSTS; KEEP UPWIND.

TOXICITY

POTASSIUM THIOCYANATE: TOXICITY DATA: 428 MG/KG ORAL-MAN TDLO; 80 MG/KG ORAL-HUMAN LDLO; 854 MG/KG ORAL-RAT LD50; 594 MG/KG ORAL-MOUSE LD50; 500 MG/KG ORAL-RABBIT LDLO; 600 MG/KG ORAL-GUINEA PIG LDLO; 1000 MG/KG SUBCUTANEOUS-RAT LDLO; 550 MG/KG SUBCUTANEOUS-RABBIT LDLO; 150 MG/KG SUBCUTANEOUS-GUINEA PIG LDLO; 88200 UG/KG INTRAVENOUS-MOUSE LD50; 100 MG/KG INTRAVENOUS-DOG LDLO; 150 MG/KG INTRAVENOUS-RABBIT LDLO; 600 MG/KG INTRAPERITONEAL-MOUSE LD50; REPRODUCTIVE EFFECTS DATA (RTECS). CARCINOGEN STATUS: NONE. LOCAL EFFECTS: IRRITANT-INHALATION, SKIN, AND EYES. ACUTE TOXICITY LEVEL: MODERATELY TOXIC BY INGESTION. TARGET EFFECTS: POISONING MAY AFFECT THE BRAIN AND HEART.

HEALTH EFFECTS AND FIRST AID

INHALATION: POTASSIUM THIOCYANATE: **ACUTE EXPOSURE-** LOW DOSES MAY CAUSE HEADACHE, DROWSINESS, DIZZINESS, NARCOSIS, HYPOTENSION, VISUAL HALLUCINATIONS, CONFUSION AND CYANOSIS. LARGE DOSES MAY LEAD TO PSYCHOTIC EPISODES. . **CHRONIC EXPOSURE-** NONE REPORTED IN HUMANS.

FIRST AID- REMOVE FROM EXPOSURE AREA TO FRESH AIR IMMEDIATELY. IF BREATHING HAS STOPPED, PERFORM ARTIFICIAL RESPIRATION. KEEP PERSON WARM AND AT REST. TREAT SYMPTOMATICALLY AND SUPPORTIVELY. GET MEDICAL ATTENTION IMMEDIATELY.

SKIN CONTACT: POTASSIUM THIOCYANATE: IRRITANT. **ACUTE EXPOSURE-** DIRECT CONTACT MAY CAUSE IRRITATION WITH REDNESS AND PAIN. **CHRONIC EXPOSURE-** REPEATED OR PROLONGED CONTACT MAY CAUSE DERMATITIS.

FIRST AID- REMOVE CONTAMINATED CLOTHING AND SHOES IMMEDIATELY. WASH AFFECTED AREA WITH SOAP OR MILD DETERGENT AND LARGE AMOUNTS OF WATER UNTIL NO EVIDENCE OF CHEMICAL REMAINS (APPROXIMATELY 15-20 MINUTES). GET MEDICAL ATTENTION IMMEDIATELY.

EYE CONTACT: POTASSIUM THIOCYANATE: IRRITANT. **ACUTE EXPOSURE-** POTASSIUM THIOCYANATE MAY CAUSE PAIN AND IRRITATION. A 9.7% SOLUTION APPLIED TO CATTLE CORNEA FOR 1 HOUR CAUSED LOOSENING OF THE EPITHELIUM. **CHRONIC EXPOSURE-** PROLONGED OR REPEATED EXPOSURE MAY CAUSE CONJUNCTIVITIS.

FIRST AID- WASH EYES IMMEDIATELY WITH LARGE AMOUNTS OF WATER OR NORMAL SALINE, OCCASIONALLY LIFTING UPPER AND LOWER LIDS, UNTIL NO EVIDENCE OF CHEMICAL REMAINS (APPROXIMATELY 15-20 MINUTES). GET MEDICAL ATTENTION IMMEDIATELY.

INGESTION: POTASSIUM THIOCYANATE: **ACUTE EXPOSURE-** EXCESSIVE DOSES OF THIOCYANATES MAY CAUSE HEADACHE, NAUSEA, VOMITING, DIZZINESS, FATIGUE, DISORIENTATION, HYPOTENSION, CONFUSION, EDEMA OF THE EYELIDS, DELIRIUM, BLURRED VISION, VISUAL HALLUCINATIONS, CEREBRAL EXCITEMENT, PSYCHOTIC BEHAVIOR, EXTENSOR MUSCLE SPASTICITY, CONVULSIONS, CYANOSIS, COLLAPSE AND DEATH. PERSISTENT ALBUMINURIA OR ANURIA HAS BEEN REPORTED IN NON-FATAL ANIMAL POISONING. THE PROBABLE LETHAL DOSE OF THIOCYANATE SALT IS BETWEEN 15-30 GRAMS WHEN INGESTED AT ONE TIME, WITH DEATH IN 10-48 HOURS. THE FATAL SERUM LEVEL OF THIOCYANATE IS 20 MG/DL. PATHOLOGIC FINDINGS INCLUDE MYOCARDIAL DAMAGE, FOCAL BRAIN DAMAGE, THYROID ENLARGEMENT AND THROMBOPHLEBITIS. **CHRONIC EXPOSURE-** PROLONGED ABSORPTION OF THIOCYANATES MAY CAUSE VARIOUS SKIN ERUPTIONS, CORYZA, DIZZINESS, CRAMPS, NAUSEA, VOMITING, ABDOMINAL BLEEDING, ENLARGED THYROID AND MILD OR SEVERE DISTURBANCES OF THE CENTRAL NERVOUS SYSTEM. IN THERAPEUTIC POISONING, AFTER SEVERAL DAYS OF IMPROVEMENT, THE PATIENT MAY RELAPSE AND DIE AS LATE AS 2 WEEKS AFTER THE MEDICATION HAS STOPPED.

FIRST AID- REMOVE BY GASTRIC LAVAGE OR EMESIS. MAINTAIN BLOOD PRESSURE AND AIRWAY. GIVE OXYGEN IF RESPIRATION IS DEPRESSED. DO NOT PERFORM GASTRIC LAVAGE OR EMESIS IF VICTIM IS UNCONSCIOUS. GET MEDICAL

ATTENTION IMMEDIATELY (DREISBACH, HANDBOOK OF POISONING, 11TH ED.). ADMINISTRATION OF GASTRIC LAVAGE OR OXYGEN SHOULD BE PERFORMED BY QUALIFIED MEDICAL PERSONNEL.

ANTIDOTE: NO SPECIFIC ANTIDOTE. TREAT SYMPTOMATICALLY AND SUPPORTIVELY.

REACTIVITY

REACTIVITY: STABLE UNDER NORMAL TEMPERATURES AND PRESSURES.

INCOMPATIBILITIES: POTASSIUM THIOCYANATE: PERCHLORYL FLUORIDE: EXPLOSIVE REACTION AT 100-200 C; UNREACTIVE AT 25 C. CHLORATES: EXPLOSIVE OXIDATION. NITRATES: EXPLOSIVE OXIDATION AT 400 C. CALCIUM CHLORATE: SPONTANEOUS IGNITION. ACIDS: EMITS HIGHLY TOXIC FUMES OF CYANIDES. NITRIC ACID: INCOMPATIBLE. ORGANIC PEROXIDES, PEROXIDES: INCOMPATIBLE.

DECOMPOSITION: THERMAL DECOMPOSITION MAY RELEASE TOXIC FUMES OF CYANIDE AND OXIDES OF SULFUR, NITROGEN, CARBON AND POTASSIUM.

POLYMERIZATION: HAZARDOUS POLYMERIZATION HAS NOT BEEN REPORTED TO OCCUR UNDER NORMAL TEMPERATURES AND PRESSURES.

CONDITIONS TO AVOID

NONE REPORTED.

SPILL AND LEAK PROCEDURES

OCCUPATIONAL SPILL: NO SPECIAL PRECAUTIONS INDICATED.

PROTECTIVE EQUIPMENT

VENTILATION: PROVIDE LOCAL EXHAUST OR GENERAL DILUTION VENTILATION SYSTEM.

RESPIRATOR: THE FOLLOWING RESPIRATORS ARE RECOMMENDED BASED ON INFORMATION FOUND IN THE PHYSICAL DATA, TOXICITY AND HEALTH EFFECTS SECTIONS. THEY ARE RANKED IN ORDER FROM MINIMUM TO MAXIMUM RESPIRATORY PROTECTION. THE SPECIFIC RESPIRATOR SELECTED MUST BE BASED ON CONTAMINATION LEVELS FOUND IN THE WORK PLACE, MUST NOT EXCEED THE WORKING LIMITS OF THE RESPIRATOR AND BE JOINTLY APPROVED BY THE NATIONAL INSTITUTE FOR OCCUPATIONAL SAFETY AND HEALTH AND THE MINE SAFETY AND HEALTH ADMINISTRATION (NIOSH-MSHA).

DUST AND MIST RESPIRATOR WITH A FULL FACEPIECE.

AIR-PURIFYING FULL FACEPIECE RESPIRATOR WITH A HIGH-EFFICIENCY PARTICULATE FILTER.

POWERED AIR-PURIFYING RESPIRATOR WITH A TIGHT-FITTING FACEPIECE AND HIGH-EFFICIENCY PARTICULATE FILTER.

TYPE 'C' SUPPLIED-AIR RESPIRATOR WITH A FULL FACEPIECE OPERATED IN PRESSURE-DEMAND OR OTHER POSITIVE PRESSURE MODE OR WITH A FULL FACEPIECE, HELMET OR HOOD OPERATED IN CONTINUOUS-FLOW MODE.

SELF-CONTAINED BREATHING APPARATUS WITH A FULL FACEPIECE OPERATED IN PRESSURE-DEMAND OR OTHER POSITIVE PRESSURE MODE.

FOR FIREFIGHTING AND OTHER IMMEDIATELY DANGEROUS TO LIFE OR HEALTH CONDITIONS:

SELF-CONTAINED BREATHING APPARATUS WITH FULL FACEPIECE OPERATED IN PRESSURE-DEMAND OR OTHER POSITIVE PRESSURE MODE.

SUPPLIED-AIR RESPIRATOR WITH FULL FACEPIECE AND OPERATED IN PRESSURE-DEMAND OR OTHER POSITIVE PRESSURE MODE IN COMBINATION WITH AN AUXILIARY SELF-CONTAINED BREATHING APPARATUS OPERATED IN PRESSURE-DEMAND OR OTHER POSITIVE PRESSURE MODE.

CLOTHING: EMPLOYEE MUST WEAR APPROPRIATE PROTECTIVE (IMPERVIOUS) CLOTHING AND EQUIPMENT TO PREVENT REPEATED OR PROLONGED SKIN CONTACT WITH THIS SUBSTANCE.

GLOVES: EMPLOYEE MUST WEAR APPROPRIATE PROTECTIVE GLOVES TO PREVENT CONTACT WITH THIS SUBSTANCE.

EYE PROTECTION: EMPLOYEE MUST WEAR SPLASH-PROOF OR DUST-RESISTANT SAFETY GOGGLES AND A FACESHIELD TO PREVENT CONTACT WITH THIS SUBSTANCE.

EMERGENCY WASH FACILITIES: WHERE THERE IS ANY POSSIBILITY THAT AN EMPLOYEE'S EYES AND/OR SKIN MAY BE EXPOSED TO THIS SUBSTANCE, THE EMPLOYER SHOULD PROVIDE AN EYE WASH FOUNTAIN AND QUICK DRENCH SHOWER WITHIN THE IMMEDIATE WORK AREA FOR EMERGENCY USE.

AUTHORIZED BY- OCCUPATIONAL HEALTH SERVICES, INC.

CREATION DATE: 10/04/89 ***REVISION DATE:*** 05/14/90

MATERIAL SAFETY DATA SHEET

OCCUPATIONAL HEALTH SERVICES, INC.
AGRICULTURE AND PESTICIDE DIVISION
450 SEVENTH AVENUE, SUITE 2407
NEW YORK, NEW YORK 10123
1-800-445-MSDS OR (212) 967-1100

EMERGENCY CONTACT:
JOHN S. BRANSFORD, JR. (615) 292-1180

SUBSTANCE IDENTIFICATION

CAS-NUMBER 23950-58-5

SUBSTANCE: **PRONAMIDE**

TRADE NAMES/SYNONYMS: BENZAMIDE, 3,5-DICHLORO-N-(1,1-DIMETHYL-2-PROPYNYL)-; 3,5-DICHLORO-N-(1,1-DIMETHYL-2-PROPYNYL)BENZAMIDE; 3,5-DICHLORO-N-(1,1-DIMETHYLPROPYNYL)BENZAMIDE; N-(1,1-DIMETHYL-2-PROPYNYL) 3,5-DICHLOROBENZAMIDE; KERB; PROPYZAMIDE; RH 315; RCRA U192; C12H11CL2NO; PST19670

CHEMICAL FAMILY: AMIDE, AROMATIC
HALOGEN COMPOUND, AROMATIC

MOLECULAR FORMULA: C12-H11-CL2-N-O

MOLECULAR WEIGHT: 256.14

CERCLA RATINGS (SCALE 0-3): HEALTH=3 FIRE=1 REACTIVITY=0 PERSISTENCE=3

NFPA RATINGS (SCALE 0-4): HEALTH=U FIRE=1 REACTIVITY=0

COMPONENTS AND CONTAMINANTS

COMPONENT: PRONAMIDE ***PERCENT:*** 100.0
CAS# 23950-58-5

OTHER CONTAMINANTS: NONE

EXPOSURE LIMITS: PRONAMIDE: NO OCCUPATIONAL EXPOSURE LIMITS ESTABLISHED BY OSHA, ACGIH, OR NIOSH.
5000 POUNDS CERCLA SECTION 103 REPORTABLE QUANTITY.

PHYSICAL DATA

DESCRIPTION: ODORLESS, WHITE OR OFF-WHITE CRYSTALLINE SOLID.

MELTING POINT: 309-313 F (154-156 C) ***SPECIFIC GRAVITY:*** NOT AVAILABLE

VAPOR PRESSURE: 0.000085 MMHG @ 25 C

SOLUBILITY IN WATER: 0.0015% @ 25C

SOLVENT SOLUBILITY: SOLUBLE IN METHANOL AND ALIPHATIC, AROMATIC, AND POLAR ORGANIC SOLVENTS.

FIRE AND EXPLOSION DATA

FIRE AND EXPLOSION HAZARD: SLIGHT FIRE HAZARD WHEN EXPOSED TO HEAT OR FLAME.

FIREFIGHTING MEDIA: DRY CHEMICAL, CARBON DIOXIDE, HALON, WATER SPRAY OR STANDARD FOAM (1987 EMERGENCY RESPONSE GUIDEBOOK, DOT P 5800.4).
FOR LARGER FIRES, USE WATER SPRAY, FOG OR STANDARD FOAM (1987 EMERGENCY RESPONSE GUIDEBOOK, DOT P 5800.4).

FIREFIGHTING: MOVE CONTAINER FROM FIRE AREA IF POSSIBLE. DO NOT SCATTER SPILLED MATERIAL WITH HIGH PRESSURE WATER STREAMS. DIKE FIRE CONTROL WATER FOR LATER DISPOSAL (1987 EMERGENCY RESPONSE GUIDEBOOK, DOT P 5800.4, GUIDE PAGE 31).
USE AGENTS SUITABLE FOR TYPE OF SURROUNDING FIRE. AVOID BREATHING HAZARDOUS VAPORS, KEEP UPWIND.

TOXICITY

PRONAMIDE: TOXICITY DATA: 5620 MG/KG ORAL-RAT LD50; 10 GM/KG ORAL-DOG LD50; TUMORIGENIC DATA (RTECS). CARCINOGEN STATUS: NONE. ACUTE TOXICITY LEVEL: SLIGHTLY TOXIC BY INGESTION. TARGET EFFECTS: NO DATA AVAILABLE.

HEALTH EFFECTS AND FIRST AID

INHALATION: PRONAMIDE: **ACUTE EXPOSURE-** NO DATA AVAILABLE. **CHRONIC EXPOSURE-** NO DATA AVAILABLE.

FIRST AID- REMOVE FROM EXPOSURE AREA TO FRESH AIR IMMEDIATELY. IF BREATHING HAS STOPPED, PERFORM ARTIFICIAL RESPIRATION. KEEP PERSON WARM AND AT REST. TREAT SYMPTOMATICALLY AND SUPPORTIVELY. GET MEDICAL ATTENTION IMMEDIATELY.

SKIN CONTACT: PRONAMIDE: **ACUTE EXPOSURE-** MAY BE MILDLY IRRITATING TO THE SKIN. A LETHAL DOSE IN RABBITS BY DERMAL ABSORPTION WAS GREATER THAN 3160 MG/KG. **CHRONIC EXPOSURE-** NO DATA AVAILABLE.

FIRST AID- REMOVE CONTAMINATED CLOTHING AND SHOES IMMEDIATELY. WASH AFFECTED AREA WITH SOAP OR MILD DETERGENT AND LARGE AMOUNTS OF WATER UNTIL NO EVIDENCE OF CHEMICAL REMAINS (APPROXIMATELY 15-20 MINUTES). GET MEDICAL ATTENTION IMMEDIATELY.

EYE CONTACT: PRONAMIDE: **ACUTE EXPOSURE-** THIS MATERIAL MAY BE MILDLY IRRITATING TO THE EYES. **CHRONIC EXPOSURE-** NO DATA AVAILABLE.

FIRST AID- WASH EYES IMMEDIATELY WITH LARGE AMOUNTS OF WATER OR NORMAL SALINE, OCCASIONALLY LIFTING UPPER AND LOWER LIDS, UNTIL NO EVIDENCE OF CHEMICAL REMAINS (APPROXIMATELY 15-20 MINUTES). GET MEDICAL ATTENTION IMMEDIATELY.

INGESTION: PRONAMIDE: **ACUTE EXPOSURE-** A LETHAL DOSE IN RATS WAS 5620 MG/KG. **CHRONIC EXPOSURE-** A STATISTICALLY SIGNIFICANT EXCESS OF LIVER CARCINOMAS IN MALES WAS OBSERVED IN MICE FED 1000 AND 2000 PPM OF PRONAMIDE IN THE DIET FOR 78 WEEKS; BLOOD LYMPHOMAS WERE ALSO REPORTED IN THIS STUDY.

FIRST AID- REMOVE BY GASTRIC LAVAGE AND CATHARSIS. MAINTAIN BLOOD PRESSURE AND AIRWAY. GIVE OXYGEN IF RESPIRATION IS DEPRESSED. DO NOT PERFORM GASTRIC LAVAGE IF VICTIM IS UNCONSCIOUS. GET MEDICAL ATTENTION IMMEDIATELY (DREISBACH, HANDBOOK OF POISONING, 12TH ED.). ADMINISTRATION OF LAVAGE OR OXYGEN SHOULD BE PERFORMED BY QUALIFIED MEDICAL PERSONNEL.

ANTIDOTE: NO SPECIFIC ANTIDOTE. TREAT SYMPTOMATICALLY AND SUPPORTIVELY.

REACTIVITY

REACTIVITY: STABLE UNDER NORMAL TEMPERATURES AND PRESSURES.

INCOMPATIBILITIES: PRONAMIDE: OXIDIZERS (STRONG): FIRE AND EXPLOSION HAZARD.

DECOMPOSITION: THERMAL DECOMPOSITION PRODUCTS MAY INCLUDE TOXIC OXIDES OF NITROGEN AND CARBON AND TOXIC AND CORROSIVE FUMES OF CHLORIDES.

POLYMERIZATION: HAZARDOUS POLYMERIZATION HAS NOT BEEN REPORTED TO OCCUR UNDER NORMAL TEMPERATURES AND PRESSURES.

STORAGE AND DISPOSAL

OBSERVE ALL FEDERAL, STATE AND LOCAL REGULATIONS WHEN STORING OR DISPOSING OF THIS SUBSTANCE. FOR ASSISTANCE, CONTACT THE DISTRICT DIRECTOR OF THE ENVIRONMENTAL PROTECTION AGENCY.

****STORAGE****

STORE IN ACCORDANCE WITH 40 CFR 165 RECOMMENDED PROCEDURES FOR THE DISPOSAL AND STORAGE OF PESTICIDES AND PESTICIDE CONTAINERS.
STORE AWAY FROM INCOMPATIBLE SUBSTANCES.
STORE IN A COOL, DRY PLACE; KEEP CONTAINER TIGHTLY CLOSED WHEN NOT IN USE.

****DISPOSAL****

DISPOSAL MUST BE IN ACCORDANCE WITH STANDARDS APPLICABLE TO GENERATORS OF HAZARDOUS WASTE, 40CFR 262. EPA HAZARDOUS WASTE NUMBER U192.

CONDITIONS TO AVOID

MAY BURN BUT DOES NOT IGNITE READILY. AVOID CONTACT WITH STRONG OXIDIZERS, EXCESSIVE HEAT, SPARKS, OR OPEN FLAME.

SPILL AND LEAK PROCEDURES

OCCUPATIONAL SPILL: SWEEP UP AND PLACE IN SUITABLE CLEAN, DRY CONTAINERS FOR RECLAMATION OR LATER DISPOSAL. DO NOT FLUSH SPILLED MATERIAL INTO SEWER. KEEP UNNECESSARY PEOPLE AWAY.

PROTECTIVE EQUIPMENT

VENTILATION: PROVIDE LOCAL EXHAUST OR PROCESS ENCLOSURE VENTILATION SYSTEM.

RESPIRATOR: THE FOLLOWING RESPIRATORS ARE RECOMMENDED BASED ON INFORMATION FOUND IN THE PHYSICAL DATA, TOXICITY AND HEALTH EFFECTS SECTIONS. THEY ARE RANKED IN ORDER FROM MINIMUM TO MAXIMUM RESPIRATORY PROTECTION. THE SPECIFIC RESPIRATOR SELECTED MUST BE BASED ON CONTAMINATION LEVELS FOUND IN THE WORK PLACE, MUST NOT EXCEED THE WORKING LIMITS OF THE RESPIRATOR AND BE JOINTLY APPROVED BY THE NATIONAL INSTITUTE FOR OCCUPATIONAL SAFETY AND HEALTH AND THE MINE SAFETY AND HEALTH ADMINISTRATION (NIOSH-MSHA).
TYPE 'C' SUPPLIED-AIR RESPIRATOR WITH A FULL FACEPIECE OPERATED IN PRESSURE-DEMAND OR OTHER POSITIVE PRESSURE MODE OR WITH A FULL FACEPIECE, HELMET OR HOOD OPERATED IN CONTINOUS-FLOW MODE.
SELF-CONTAINED BREATHING APPARATUS WITH A FULL FACEPIECE OPERATED IN PRESSURE-DEMAND OR OTHER POSITIVE PRESSURE MODE.
FOR FIREFIGHTING AND OTHER IMMEDIATELY DANGEROUS TO LIFE OR HEALTH CONDITIONS:
SELF-CONTAINED BREATHING APPARATUS WITH FULL FACEPIECE OPERATED IN PRESSURE-DEMAND OR OTHER POSITIVE PRESSURE MODE.
SUPPLIED-AIR RESPIRATOR WITH FULL FACEPIECE AND OPERATED IN PRESSURE-DEMAND OR OTHER POSITIVE PRESSURE MODE IN COMBINATION WITH AN AUXILIARY SELF-CONTAINED BREATHING APPARATUS OPERATED IN PRESSURE-DEMAND OR OTHER POSITIVE PRESSURE MODE.

CLOTHING: EMPLOYEE MUST WEAR APPROPRIATE PROTECTIVE (IMPERVIOUS) CLOTHING AND EQUIPMENT TO PREVENT REPEATED OR PROLONGED SKIN CONTACT WITH THIS SUBSTANCE.

GLOVES: EMPLOYEE MUST WEAR APPROPRIATE PROTECTIVE GLOVES TO PREVENT CONTACT WITH THIS SUBSTANCE.

EYE PROTECTION: EMPLOYEE MUST WEAR SPLASH-PROOF OR DUST-RESISTANT SAFETY GOGGLES TO PREVENT EYE CONTACT WITH THIS SUBSTANCE.
EMERGENCY EYE WASH: WHERE THERE IS ANY POSSIBILITY THAT AN EMPLOYEE'S EYES MAY BE EXPOSED TO THIS SUBSTANCE, THE EMPLOYER SHOULD PROVIDE AN EYE WASH FOUNTAIN WITHIN THE IMMEDIATE WORK AREA FOR EMERGENCY USE.

AUTHORIZED BY- OCCUPATIONAL HEALTH SERVICES, INC.
CREATION DATE: 02/08/90 ***REVISION DATE:*** 05/31/90

MATERIAL SAFETY DATA SHEET

OCCUPATIONAL HEALTH SERVICES, INC.
AGRICULTURE AND PESTICIDE DIVISION
450 SEVENTH AVENUE, SUITE 2407
NEW YORK, NEW YORK 10123
1-800-445-MSDS OR (212) 967-1100

EMERGENCY CONTACT:
JOHN S. BRANSFORD, JR. (615) 292-1180

SUBSTANCE IDENTIFICATION

CAS-NUMBER 1918-16-7

SUBSTANCE: **PROPACHLOR**

TRADE NAMES/SYNONYMS: ACETAMIDE, 2-CHLORO-N-(1-METHYLETHYL)-N-PHENYL-; ACETANILIDE, 2-CHLORO-N-ISOPROPYL-; 2-CHLORO-N-(1-METHYLETHYL)-N-PHENYLACETAMIDE; 2-CHLORO-N-ISOPROPYLACETANILIDE; ALPHA-CHLORO-N-ISOPROPYLACETANILIDE; N-ISOPROPYL-ALPHA-CHLOROACETANILIDE; ALBRASS; BEXTON; CP 31393; NITICID; PROPACHLORE; RAMROD; SATECID; C11H14CLNO; PST19686

CHEMICAL FAMILY: NITRILE, AROMATIC HALOGEN

MOLECULAR FORMULA: (CL-C-H2-C-O)-N-(C6-H5)-C-H-(C-H3)2

MOLECULAR WEIGHT: 211.69

CERCLA RATINGS (SCALE 0-3): HEALTH=3 FIRE=1 REACTIVITY=0 PERSISTENCE=2

NFPA RATINGS (SCALE 0-4): HEALTH=3 FIRE=1 REACTIVITY=0

COMPONENTS AND CONTAMINANTS

COMPONENT: PROPACHLOR ***PERCENT:*** 100.0
CAS# 1918-16-7

OTHER CONTAMINANTS: NONE

EXPOSURE LIMITS: NO OCCUPATIONAL EXPOSURE LIMITS ESTABLISHED BY OSHA, ACGIH, OR NIOSH.

PHYSICAL DATA

DESCRIPTION: WHITE TO TAN CRYSTALS OR POWDER.

BOILING POINT: 230 F (110 C) @ 0.03 MMHG ***MELTING POINT:*** 171 F (77 C)

SPECIFIC GRAVITY: 1.242 @ 25 C ***VAPOR PRESSURE:*** 0.00023 MMHG @ 25 C

SOLUBILITY IN WATER: 0.07% @ 20 C

SOLVENT SOLUBILITY: SOLUBLE IN ACETONE, BENZENE, CHLOROFORM, ETHANOL, METHANOL, XYLENE, DICHLOROMETHANE, AND ORGANIC SOLVENTS; INSOLUBLE IN ALIPHATIC HYDROCARBONS. DECOMPOSES @ 338 F (170 C)

FIRE AND EXPLOSION DATA

FIRE AND EXPLOSION HAZARD: SLIGHT FIRE HAZARD WHEN EXPOSED TO HEAT OR FLAME.

FIREFIGHTING MEDIA: DRY CHEMICAL, CARBON DIOXIDE, HALON, WATER SPRAY OR STANDARD FOAM (1987 EMERGENCY RESPONSE GUIDEBOOK, DOT P 5800.4).
FOR LARGER FIRES, USE WATER SPRAY, FOG OR STANDARD FOAM (1987 EMERGENCY RESPONSE GUIDEBOOK, DOT P 5800.4).

FIREFIGHTING: MOVE CONTAINER FROM FIRE AREA IF POSSIBLE. DO NOT SCATTER SPILLED MATERIAL WITH HIGH PRESSURE WATER STREAMS. DIKE FIRE CONTROL WATER FOR LATER DISPOSAL (1987 EMERGENCY RESPONSE GUIDEBOOK, DOT P 5800.4, GUIDE PAGE 31).
USE AGENTS SUITABLE FOR TYPE OF SURROUNDING FIRE. AVOID BREATHING HAZARDOUS VAPORS, KEEP UPWIND.

TOXICITY

PROPACHLOR: TOXICITY DATA: 380 MG/KG SKIN-RABBIT LD50; 710 MG/KG ORAL-RAT LD50; 290 MG/KG ORAL-MOUSE LD50; 700 MG/KG ORAL-RABBIT LD50; 1056 MG/KG UNREPORTED-RAT LD50; 800 MG/KG UNREPORTED-MAMMAL LD50; 306 MG/KG UNREPORTED-MOUSE LD50; MUTAGENIC DATA (RTECS). CARCINOGEN STATUS: NONE. LOCAL EFFECTS: IRRITANT-SKIN, EYE. ACUTE TOXICITY LEVEL: TOXIC BY DERMAL ABSORPTION; MODERATELY TOXIC BY INGESTION. TARGET EFFECTS: SENSITIZER-SKIN.

HEALTH EFFECTS AND FIRST AID

INHALATION: PROPACHLOR: **ACUTE EXPOSURE-** MAY CAUSE IRRITATION OF THE MUCOUS MEMBRANES. SYSTEMIC EFFECTS WERE PRODUCED IN RATS EXPOSED TO 18 MG/M3. **CHRONIC EXPOSURE-** NO DATA AVAILABLE.

FIRST AID- REMOVE FROM EXPOSURE AREA TO FRESH AIR IMMEDIATELY. IF BREATHING HAS STOPPED, PERFORM ARTIFICIAL RESPIRATION. KEEP PERSON WARM AND AT REST. TREAT SYMPTOMATICALLY AND SUPPORTIVELY. GET MEDICAL ATTENTION IMMEDIATELY.

SKIN CONTACT: PROPACHLOR: IRRITANT/SENSITIZER/TOXIC. **ACUTE EXPOSURE-** MAY CAUSE IRRITATION. SENSITIZATION MAY OCCUR IN PERSONS PREVIOUSLY EXPOSED. A LETHAL DOSE IN RABBITS BY DERMAL ABSORPTION WAS 380 MG/KG; SYMPTOMS WERE NOT REPORTED. **CHRONIC EXPOSURE-** ANEMIA AND REDUCED TISSUE CYTOCHROME OXIDASE ACTIVITY WERE OBSERVED IN RATS WITH REPEATED SKIN APPLICATIONS OF 200 MG/KG/DAY FOR 3 WEEKS. DERMAL APPLICATIONS OF 50 MG/KG FOR 90 DAYS INHIBITED BLOOD CATALASE AND SERUM TRANSAMINASE ACTIVITY AND PRODUCED A DECREASE IN SULFHYDRYL CONTENT OF BRAIN.

FIRST AID- REMOVE CONTAMINATED CLOTHING AND SHOES IMMEDIATELY. WASH AFFECTED AREA WITH SOAP OR MILD DETERGENT AND LARGE AMOUNTS OF WATER UNTIL NO EVIDENCE OF CHEMICAL REMAINS (APPROXIMATELY 15-20 MINUTES). GET MEDICAL ATTENTION IMMEDIATELY.

EYE CONTACT: PROPACHLOR: IRRITANT. **ACUTE EXPOSURE-** APPLIED TO RABBIT EYES, THIS MATERIAL PRODUCED CORNEAL OPACITY, ULCERATION, IRIS IRRITATION, CHEMOSIS, AND CONJUNCTIVITIS. **CHRONIC EXPOSURE-** PROLONGED OR REPEATED EXPOSURE MAY CAUSE CONJUNCTIVITIS.

FIRST AID- WASH EYES IMMEDIATELY WITH LARGE AMOUNTS OF WATER OR NORMAL SALINE, OCCASIONALLY LIFTING UPPER AND LOWER LIDS, UNTIL NO EVIDENCE OF CHEMICAL REMAINS (APPROXIMATELY 15-20 MINUTES). GET MEDICAL ATTENTION IMMEDIATELY.

INGESTION: PROPACHLOR: **ACUTE EXPOSURE-** THIS SUBSTANCE PRODUCED MUSCLE WEAKNESS, SALIVATION, TREMORS, COLLAPSE, COMA AND DEATH IN ANIMALS. DYSTROPHIC CHANGES IN VISCERAL ORGANS WERE OBSERVED. **CHRONIC EXPOSURE-** DECREASED BODY WEIGHT GAIN, DECREASED FOOD CONSUMPTION, AND INCREASED LIVER WEIGHT WERE OBSERVED IN A 90-DAY STUDY OF RATS FED 133.3 MG/KG/DAY. EMBRYOTOXICITY AND TERATOGENESIS WERE DESCRIBED IN RATS GIVEN 5 TO 20% OF THE LD50 DURING THE FIRST 20 DAYS OF PREGNANCY.

FIRST AID- REMOVE BY GASTRIC LAVAGE AND CATHARSIS. MAINTAIN BLOOD PRESSURE AND AIRWAY. GIVE OXYGEN IF RESPIRATION IS DEPRESSED. DO NOT PERFORM GASTRIC LAVAGE IF VICTIM IS UNCONSCIOUS. GET MEDICAL ATTENTION IMMEDIATELY (DREISBACH, HANDBOOK OF POISONING, 12TH ED.).
ADMINISTRATION OF LAVAGE OR OXYGEN SHOULD BE PERFORMED BY QUALIFIED MEDICAL PERSONNEL.

ANTIDOTE: NO SPECIFIC ANTIDOTE. TREAT SYMPTOMATICALLY AND SUPPORTIVELY.

REACTIVITY

REACTIVITY: STABLE UNDER NORMAL TEMPERATURES AND PRESSURES.

INCOMPATIBILITIES: PROPACHLOR: OXIDIZERS (STRONG): FIRE AND EXPLOSION HAZARD.

DECOMPOSITION: THERMAL DECOMPOSITION PRODUCTS MAY INCLUDE TOXIC OXIDES OF NITROGEN AND CARBON AND TOXIC AND CORROSIVE FUMES OF CHLORIDES.

POLYMERIZATION: HAZARDOUS POLYMERIZATION HAS NOT BEEN REPORTED TO OCCUR UNDER NORMAL TEMPERATURES AND PRESSURES.

STORAGE AND DISPOSAL

OBSERVE ALL FEDERAL, STATE AND LOCAL REGULATIONS WHEN STORING OR DISPOSING OF THIS SUBSTANCE. FOR ASSISTANCE, CONTACT THE DISTRICT DIRECTOR OF THE ENVIRONMENTAL PROTECTION AGENCY.

****STORAGE****

STORE IN ACCORDANCE WITH 40 CFR 165 RECOMMENDED PROCEDURES FOR THE DISPOSAL AND STORAGE OF PESTICIDES AND PESTICIDE CONTAINERS.
STORE AWAY FROM INCOMPATIBLE SUBSTANCES.

****DISPOSAL****

DISPOSAL MUST BE IN ACCORDANCE WITH 40 CFR 165 RECOMMENDED PROCEDURES FOR THE DISPOSAL AND STORAGE OF PESTICIDES AND PESTICIDE CONTAINERS.

CONDITIONS TO AVOID

MAY BURN BUT DOES NOT IGNITE READILY. AVOID CONTACT WITH STRONG OXIDIZERS, EXCESSIVE HEAT, SPARKS, OR OPEN FLAME.

SPILL AND LEAK PROCEDURES

OCCUPATIONAL SPILL: SWEEP UP AND PLACE IN SUITABLE CLEAN, DRY CONTAINERS FOR RECLAMATION OR LATER DISPOSAL. DO NOT FLUSH SPILLED MATERIAL INTO SEWER. KEEP UNNECESSARY PEOPLE AWAY.

PROTECTIVE EQUIPMENT

VENTILATION: PROVIDE LOCAL EXHAUST OR PROCESS ENCLOSURE VENTILATION SYSTEM.

RESPIRATOR: THE FOLLOWING RESPIRATORS ARE RECOMMENDED BASED ON INFORMATION FOUND IN THE PHYSICAL DATA, TOXICITY AND HEALTH EFFECTS SECTIONS. THEY ARE RANKED IN ORDER FROM MINIMUM TO MAXIMUM RESPIRATORY PROTECTION. THE SPECIFIC RESPIRATOR SELECTED MUST BE BASED ON CONTAMINATION LEVELS FOUND IN THE WORK PLACE, MUST NOT EXCEED THE WORKING LIMITS OF THE RESPIRATOR AND BE JOINTLY APPROVED BY THE NATIONAL INSTITUTE FOR OCCUPATIONAL SAFETY AND HEALTH AND THE MINE SAFETY AND HEALTH ADMINISTRATION (NIOSH-MSHA).
TYPE 'C' SUPPLIED-AIR RESPIRATOR WITH A FULL FACEPIECE OPERATED IN PRESSURE-DEMAND OR OTHER POSITIVE PRESSURE MODE OR WITH A FULL FACEPIECE, HELMET OR HOOD OPERATED IN CONTINOUS-FLOW MODE. SELF-CONTAINED BREATHING APPARATUS WITH A FULL FACEPIECE OPERATED IN PRESSURE-DEMAND OR OTHER POSITIVE PRESSURE MODE.
FOR FIREFIGHTING AND OTHER IMMEDIATELY DANGEROUS TO LIFE OR HEALTH CONDITIONS:
SELF-CONTAINED BREATHING APPARATUS WITH FULL FACEPIECE OPERATED IN PRESSURE-DEMAND OR OTHER POSITIVE PRESSURE MODE.
SUPPLIED-AIR RESPIRATOR WITH FULL FACEPIECE AND OPERATED IN PRESSURE-DEMAND OR OTHER POSITIVE PRESSURE MODE IN COMBINATION WITH AN AUXILIARY SELF-CONTAINED BREATHING APPARATUS OPERATED IN PRESSURE-DEMAND OR OTHER POSITIVE PRESSURE MODE.

CLOTHING: EMPLOYEE MUST WEAR APPROPRIATE PROTECTIVE (IMPERVIOUS) CLOTHING AND EQUIPMENT TO PREVENT ANY POSSIBILITY OF SKIN CONTACT WITH THIS SUBSTANCE.

GLOVES: EMPLOYEE MUST WEAR APPROPRIATE PROTECTIVE GLOVES TO PREVENT CONTACT WITH THIS SUBSTANCE.

EYE PROTECTION: EMPLOYEE MUST WEAR SPLASH-PROOF OR DUST-RESISTANT SAFETY GOGGLES WITH OR WITHOUT A FACESHIELD TO PREVENT CONTACT WITH THIS SUBSTANCE.
EMERGENCY EYE WASH: WHERE THERE IS ANY POSSIBILITY THAT AN EMPLOYEE'S EYES MAY BE EXPOSED TO THIS SUBSTANCE, THE EMPLOYER SHOULD PROVIDE AN EYE WASH FOUNTAIN WITHIN THE IMMEDIATE WORK AREA FOR EMERGENCY USE.

AUTHORIZED BY- OCCUPATIONAL HEALTH SERVICES, INC.
CREATION DATE: 10/04/89 ***REVISION DATE:*** 05/31/90

MATERIAL SAFETY DATA SHEET

OCCUPATIONAL HEALTH SERVICES, INC.
AGRICULTURE AND PESTICIDE DIVISION
450 SEVENTH AVENUE, SUITE 2407
NEW YORK, NEW YORK 10123
1-800-445-MSDS OR (212) 967-1100

EMERGENCY CONTACT:
JOHN S. BRANSFORD, JR. (615) 292-1180

SUBSTANCE IDENTIFICATION

CAS-NUMBER 2312-35-8

SUBSTANCE: PROPARGITE

TRADE NAMES/SYNONYMS: SULFUROUS ACID, 2-(4-(1,1-DIMETHYLETHYL)PHENOXY)CYCLOHEXYL 2-PROPYNYL ESTER; SULFUROUS ACID, 2-(P-TERT-BUTYLPHENOXY)CYCLOHEXYL 2-PROPYNYL ESTER; 2-(P-TERT-BUTYLPHENOXY)CYCLOHEXYL 2-PROPYNYL SULFITE; 2-(4-(1,1-DIMETHYLETHYL)PHENOXYL)CYCLOHEXYL 2-PROPYNYL SULFITE; 2-(4-TERT-BUTYLPHENOXY)CYCLOHEXYL PROP-2-YNYL SULPHITE; 2-(4-TERT-

BUTYLPHENOXY)CYCLOHEXYL PROP-2-YNYL SULFITE; COMITE; D 014; OMITE; PROPARGIL; UNIROYAL D014; ENT 27226; STCC 49611665; C19H26O4S; PST19720

CHEMICAL FAMILY: ESTER

MOLECULAR FORMULA: C19-H26-O4-S

MOLECULAR WEIGHT: 350.51

CERCLA RATINGS (SCALE 0-3): HEALTH=3 FIRE=U REACTIVITY=U PERSISTENCE=2

NFPA RATINGS (SCALE 0-4): HEALTH=3 FIRE=U REACTIVITY=U

COMPONENTS AND CONTAMINANTS

COMPONENT: PROPARGITE ***PERCENT:*** 100.0
CAS# 2312-35-8

EXPOSURE LIMITS: PROPARGITE: NO OCCUPATIONAL EXPOSURE LIMITS ESTABLISHED BY OSHA, ACGIH, OR NIOSH.
10 POUNDS CERCLA SECTION 103 REPORTABLE QUANTITY

PHYSICAL DATA

DESCRIPTION: DARK AMBER VISCOUS LIQUID ***BOILING POINT:*** NOT AVAILABLE

SPECIFIC GRAVITY: 1.085-1.115 ***EVAPORATION RATE:*** NOT AVAILABLE

SOLUBILITY IN WATER: INSOLUBLE

SOLVENT SOLUBILITY: SOLUBLE IN ACETONE, BENZENE, HEPTANE, METHANOL, AND MOST ORGANIC SOLVENTS

FIRE AND EXPLOSION DATA

FIRE AND EXPLOSION HAZARD: UNKNOWN FIRE AND EXPLOSION HAZARD.

FIREFIGHTING MEDIA: DRY CHEMICAL, CARBON DIOXIDE, HALON, WATER SPRAY OR STANDARD FOAM (1987 EMERGENCY RESPONSE GUIDEBOOK, DOT P 5800.4). FOR LARGER FIRES, USE WATER SPRAY, FOG OR STANDARD FOAM (1987 EMERGENCY RESPONSE GUIDEBOOK, DOT P 5800.4).

FIREFIGHTING: MOVE CONTAINERS FROM FIRE AREA IF POSSIBLE. FIGHT FIRE FROM MAXIMUM DISTANCE. STAY AWAY FROM STORAGE TANK ENDS. DIKE FIRE CONTROL WATER FOR LATER DISPOSAL. DO NOT SCATTER MATERIAL (1987 EMERGENCY RESPONSE GUIDEBOOK, DOT P 5800.4, GUIDE PAGE 55).
USE AGENTS SUITABLE FOR TYPE OF FIRE. AVOID BREATHING VAPORS OR DUSTS, KEEP UPWIND.

TRANSPORTATION DATA

DEPARTMENT OF TRANSPORTATION HAZARD CLASSIFICATION 49 CFR 172.101: ORM-E
DEPARTMENT OF TRANSPORTATION LABELING REQUIREMENTS 49 CFR 172.101 AND SUBPART E: NONE
DEPARTMENT OF TRANSPORTATION PACKAGING REQUIREMENTS: 49 CFR 173.510 EXCEPTIONS: NONE

TOXICITY

PROPARGITE: TOXICITY DATA: 250 MG/KG SKIN-RAT LD50; 1480 MG/KG ORAL-RAT LD50; 780 MG/KG UNREPORTED-MOUSE LD50. CARCINOGEN STATUS: NONE. LOCAL EFFECTS: IRRITANT- INHALATION, SKIN, AND EYES. ACUTE TOXICITY LEVEL: TOXIC BY DERMAL ABSORPTION AND MODERATELY TOXIC BY INGESTION. TARGET EFFECTS: NO DATA AVAILABLE.

HEALTH EFFECTS AND FIRST AID

INHALATION: PROPARGITE: IRRITANT. **ACUTE EXPOSURE-** MAY CAUSE IRRITATION. A LETHAL CONCENTRATION IN RATS WAS GREATER THAN 2500 MG/M3. **CHRONIC EXPOSURE-** PROLONGED OR REPEATED EXPOSURE MAY CAUSE IRRITATION.

FIRST AID- REMOVE FROM EXPOSURE AREA TO FRESH AIR IMMEDIATELY. IF BREATHING HAS STOPPED, PERFORM ARTIFICIAL RESPIRATION. KEEP PERSON WARM AND AT REST. TREAT SYMPTOMATICALLY AND SUPPORTIVELY. GET MEDICAL ATTENTION IMMEDIATELY.

SKIN CONTACT: PROPARGITE: IRRITANT/TOXIC. **ACUTE EXPOSURE-** MAY CAUSE IRRITATION. ANIMAL STUDIES INDICATE THAT HARMFUL AMOUNTS MAY BE ABSORBED THROUGH THE SKIN. A LETHAL DOSE IN RATS WAS 250 MG/KG. A LETHAL DOSE IN RABBITS BY DERMAL ABSORPTION WAS GREATER THAN 10,000 MG/KG. **CHRONIC EXPOSURE-** PROLONGED OR REPEATED EXPOSURE MAY CAUSE DERMATITIS.

FIRST AID- REMOVE CONTAMINATED CLOTHING AND SHOES IMMEDIATELY. WASH AFFECTED AREA WITH SOAP OR MILD DETERGENT AND LARGE AMOUNTS OF WATER UNTIL NO EVIDENCE OF CHEMICAL REMAINS (APPROXIMATELY 15-20 MINUTES). GET MEDICAL ATTENTION IMMEDIATELY.

EYE CONTACT: PROPARGITE: IRRITANT. **ACUTE EXPOSURE-** MAY CAUSE IRRITATION. **CHRONIC EXPOSURE-** PROLONGED OR REPEATED EXPOSURE MAY CAUSE CONJUNCTIVITIS.

FIRST AID- WASH EYES IMMEDIATELY WITH LARGE AMOUNTS OF WATER OR NORMAL SALINE, OCCASIONALLY LIFTING UPPER AND LOWER LIDS, UNTIL NO EVIDENCE OF CHEMICAL REMAINS (APPROXIMATELY 15-20 MINUTES). GET MEDICAL ATTENTION IMMEDIATELY.

INGESTION: PROPARGITE: **ACUTE EXPOSURE-** A LETHAL DOSE IN RATS WAS 1480 MG/KG. **CHRONIC EXPOSURE-** REDUCED WEIGHT GAIN AND FOOD CONSUMPTION, LYMPH NODE ABNORMALITIES, INCREASED MORTALITY, AND INCREASED LIVER AND KIDNEY WEIGHTS WERE OBSERVED IN A CHRONIC INGESTION STUDY OF RATS FED 100 MG/KG/DAY. FOUR SARCOMAS WERE REPORTED AMONG THE RATS IN THE STUDY, HOWEVER A DOSE-RELATIONSHIP WAS NOT ESTABLISHED WITH THE OBSERVED FREQUENCY OF TUMORS. NO ADVERSE EFFECTS WERE REPORTED FOR LEVELS OF 45 MG/KG/DAY OR BELOW IN RATS. NO ADVERSE EFFECTS WERE REPORTED IN A TWO YEAR STUDY OF DOGS FED 900 PPM (APPROXIMATELY 22 MG/KG/DAY). A SIGNIFICANT INCREASE IN MISSING RIBS AND RETARDED MOUTH BONE DEVELOPMENT WAS SEEN IN A STUDY OF PREGNANT RATS FED 25 OR 105 MG/KG/DAY.

FIRST AID- REMOVE BY GASTRIC LAVAGE AND CATHARSIS. MAINTAIN BLOOD PRESSURE AND AIRWAY. GIVE OXYGEN IF RESPIRATION IS DEPRESSED. DO NOT PERFORM GASTRIC LAVAGE IF VICTIM IS UNCONSCIOUS. GET MEDICAL ATTENTION IMMEDIATELY (DREISBACH, HANDBOOK OF POISONING, 12TH ED.).
ADMINISTRATION OF LAVAGE OR OXYGEN SHOULD BE PERFORMED BY QUALIFIED MEDICAL PERSONNEL.

ANTIDOTE: NO SPECIFIC ANTIDOTE. TREAT SYMPTOMATICALLY AND SUPPORTIVELY.

REACTIVITY

REACTIVITY: NO DATA AVAILABLE. ***INCOMPATIBILITIES:*** PROPARGITE: NO DATA AVAILABLE.

DECOMPOSITION: THERMAL DECOMPOSITION MAY RELEASE TOXIC OXIDES OF SULFUR.

POLYMERIZATION: NO DATA AVAILABLE.

STORAGE AND DISPOSAL

OBSERVE ALL FEDERAL, STATE AND LOCAL REGULATIONS WHEN STORING OR DISPOSING OF THIS SUBSTANCE. FOR ASSISTANCE, CONTACT THE DISTRICT DIRECTOR OF THE ENVIRONMENTAL PROTECTION AGENCY.

STORAGE

STORE IN ACCORDANCE WITH 40 CFR 165 RECOMMENDED PROCEDURES FOR THE DISPOSAL AND STORAGE OF PESTICIDES AND PESTICIDE CONTAINERS.

DISPOSAL

DISPOSAL MUST BE IN ACCORDANCE WITH 40 CFR 165 RECOMMENDED PROCEDURES FOR THE DISPOSAL AND STORAGE OF PESTICIDES AND PESTICIDE CONTAINERS.

CONDITIONS TO AVOID

NONE REPORTED.

SPILL AND LEAK PROCEDURES

SOIL SPILL: DIG A HOLDING AREA SUCH AS A PIT, POND OR LAGOON TO CONTAIN SPILL AND DIKE SURFACE FLOW USING BARRIER OF SOIL, SANDBAGS, FOAMED POLYURETHANE OR FOAMED CONCRETE. ABSORB LIQUID MASS WITH FLY ASH OR CEMENT POWDER.

WATER SPILL: IF DISSOLVED, AT A CONCENTRATION OF 10 PPM OR GREATER, APPLY ACTIVATED CARBON AT TEN TIMES THE AMOUNT THAT HAS BEEN SPILLED.
USE SUCTION HOSES TO REMOVE TRAPPED SPILL MATERIAL.
USE MECHANICAL DREDGES OR LIFTS TO EXTRACT IMMOBILIZED MASSES OF POLLUTION AND PRECIPITATES.

OCCUPATIONAL SPILL: DO NOT TOUCH SPILLED MATERIAL. STOP LEAK IF YOU CAN DO IT WITHOUT RISK. USE WATER SPRAY TO REDUCE VAPORS. FOR SMALL SPILLS, TAKE UP WITH SAND OR OTHER ABSORBENT MATERIAL AND PLACE INTO CONTAINERS FOR LATER DISPOSAL. FOR SMALL DRY SPILLS, WITH A CLEAN SHOVEL PLACE MATERIAL INTO CLEAN, DRY CONTAINERS AND COVER. MOVE CONTAINERS FROM SPILL AREA. FOR LARGER SPILLS, DIKE FAR AHEAD OF SPILL FOR LATER DISPOSAL. KEEP UNNECESSARY PEOPLE AWAY. ISOLATE HAZARD AREA AND DENY ENTRY. VENTILATE CLOSED SPACES BEFORE ENTERING.
REPORTABLE QUANTITY (RQ): 10 POUNDS THE SUPERFUND AMENDMENTS AND REAUTHORIZATION ACT (SARA) SECTION 304 REQUIRES THAT A RELEASE EQUAL TO OR GREATER THAN THE REPORTABLE QUANTITY FOR THIS SUBSTANCE BE IMMEDIATELY REPORTED TO THE LOCAL EMERGENCY PLANNING COMMITTEE AND THE STATE EMERGENCY RESPONSE COMMISSION (40 CFR 355.40). IF THE RELEASE OF THIS SUBSTANCE IS REPORTABLE UNDER CERCLA SECTION 103, THE NATIONAL RESPONSE CENTER MUST BE NOTIFIED IMMEDIATELY AT (800) 424-8802 OR (202) 426-2675 IN THE METROPOLITAN WASHINGTON, D.C. AREA (40 CFR 302.6).

PROTECTIVE EQUIPMENT

VENTILATION: PROVIDE LOCAL EXHAUST OR PROCESS ENCLOSURE VENTILATION SYSTEM.

RESPIRATOR: THE FOLLOWING RESPIRATORS ARE RECOMMENDED BASED ON INFORMATION FOUND IN THE PHYSICAL DATA, TOXICITY AND HEALTH EFFECTS SECTIONS. THEY ARE RANKED IN ORDER FROM MINIMUM TO MAXIMUM RESPIRATORY PROTECTION. THE SPECIFIC RESPIRATOR SELECTED MUST BE BASED ON CONTAMINATION LEVELS FOUND IN THE WORK PLACE, MUST NOT EXCEED THE WORKING LIMITS OF THE RESPIRATOR AND BE JOINTLY APPROVED BY THE NATIONAL INSTITUTE FOR OCCUPATIONAL SAFETY AND HEALTH AND THE MINE SAFETY AND HEALTH ADMINISTRATION (NIOSH-MSHA).

TYPE 'C' SUPPLIED-AIR RESPIRATOR WITH A FULL FACEPIECE OPERATED IN PRESSURE-DEMAND OR OTHER POSITIVE PRESSURE MODE OR WITH A FULL FACEPIECE, HELMET OR HOOD OPERATED IN CONTINOUS-FLOW MODE.

SELF-CONTAINED BREATHING APPARATUS WITH A FULL FACEPIECE OPERATED IN PRESSURE-DEMAND OR OTHER POSITIVE PRESSURE MODE.

FOR FIREFIGHTING AND OTHER IMMEDIATELY DANGEROUS TO LIFE OR HEALTH CONDITIONS:

SELF-CONTAINED BREATHING APPARATUS WITH FULL FACEPIECE OPERATED IN PRESSURE-DEMAND OR OTHER POSITIVE PRESSURE MODE.

SUPPLIED-AIR RESPIRATOR WITH FULL FACEPIECE AND OPERATED IN PRESSURE-DEMAND OR OTHER POSITIVE PRESSURE MODE IN COMBINATION WITH AN AUXILIARY SELF-CONTAINED BREATHING APPARATUS OPERATED IN PRESSURE-DEMAND OR OTHER POSITIVE PRESSURE MODE.

CLOTHING: EMPLOYEE MUST WEAR APPROPRIATE PROTECTIVE (IMPERVIOUS) CLOTHING AND EQUIPMENT TO PREVENT ANY POSSIBILITY OF SKIN CONTACT WITH THIS SUBSTANCE.

GLOVES: EMPLOYEE MUST WEAR APPROPRIATE PROTECTIVE GLOVES TO PREVENT CONTACT WITH THIS SUBSTANCE.

EYE PROTECTION: EMPLOYEE MUST WEAR SPLASH-PROOF OR DUST-RESISTANT SAFETY GOGGLES AND A FACESHIELD TO PREVENT CONTACT WITH THIS SUBSTANCE.

EMERGENCY WASH FACILITIES: WHERE THERE IS ANY POSSIBILITY THAT AN EMPLOYEE'S EYES AND/OR SKIN MAY BE EXPOSED TO THIS SUBSTANCE, THE EMPLOYER SHOULD PROVIDE AN EYE WASH FOUNTAIN AND QUICK DRENCH SHOWER WITHIN THE IMMEDIATE WORK AREA FOR EMERGENCY USE.

AUTHORIZED BY- OCCUPATIONAL HEALTH SERVICES, INC.

CREATION DATE: 10/04/89 ***REVISION DATE:*** 05/10/90

MATERIAL SAFETY DATA SHEET

OCCUPATIONAL HEALTH SERVICES, INC.
AGRICULTURE AND PESTICIDE DIVISION
450 SEVENTH AVENUE, SUITE 2407
NEW YORK, NEW YORK 10123
1-800-445-MSDS OR (212) 967-1100

EMERGENCY CONTACT:
JOHN S. BRANSFORD, JR. (615) 292-1180

SUBSTANCE IDENTIFICATION

CAS-NUMBER 139-40-2

SUBSTANCE: PROPAZINE

TRADE NAMES/SYNONYMS: 1,3,5-TRIAZINE-2,4-DIAMINE, 6-CHLORO-N,N'-BIS(1-METHYLETHYL)-; S-TRIAZINE, 2-CHLORO-4,6-BIS(ISOPROPYLAMINO)-; 6-CHLORO-N,N'-BIS(1-METHYLETHYL)-1,3,5-TRIAZINE-2,4-DIAMINE; 2-CHLORO-4,6-BIS(ISOPROPYLAMINO)-S-TRIAZINE; 2-CHLORO-4,6-BIS(ISOPROPYLAMINO)-1,3,5-TRIAZINE; 2,4-BIS(ISOPROPYLAMINO)-6-CHLORO-S-TRIAZINE; G 30028; GEIGY 30,028; GESAMIL; MILOGARD; MILO-PRO; PLANTULIN; PROPASIN; PROPAZIN; PRIMATOL P; PROZINEX; C9H16CLN5; PST19736

CHEMICAL FAMILY: S-TRIAZINE

MOLECULAR FORMULA: C9-H16-CL-N5

MOLECULAR WEIGHT: 230.09

CERCLA RATINGS (SCALE 0-3): HEALTH=2 FIRE=1 REACTIVITY=0 PERSISTENCE=3

NFPA RATINGS (SCALE 0-4): HEALTH=2 FIRE=1 REACTIVITY=0

COMPONENTS AND CONTAMINANTS

COMPONENT: PROPAZINE ***PERCENT:*** 100.0
CAS# 139-40-2

OTHER CONTAMINANTS: NONE

EXPOSURE LIMITS: NO OCCUPATIONAL EXPOSURE LIMITS ESTABLISHED BY OSHA, ACGIH, OR NIOSH.

PHYSICAL DATA

DESCRIPTION: COLORLESS CRYSTALLINE SOLID. ***MELTING POINT:*** 413-417 F (212-214 C)

SPECIFIC GRAVITY: 1.162 ***VAPOR PRESSURE:*** NEGLIGIBLE

SOLUBILITY IN WATER: 8.6 PPM @ 20 C

SOLVENT SOLUBILITY: SLIGHTLY SOLUBLE IN BENZENE, TOLUENE, CARBON TETRACHLORIDE, ETHANOL, METHANOL, ACETONE.

FIRE AND EXPLOSION DATA

FIRE AND EXPLOSION HAZARD: SLIGHT FIRE HAZARD WHEN EXPOSED TO HEAT OR FLAME.

FIREFIGHTING MEDIA: DRY CHEMICAL, CARBON DIOXIDE, HALON, WATER SPRAY OR STANDARD FOAM (1987 EMERGENCY RESPONSE GUIDEBOOK, DOT P 5800.4). FOR LARGER FIRES, USE WATER SPRAY, FOG OR STANDARD FOAM (1987 EMERGENCY RESPONSE GUIDEBOOK, DOT P 5800.4).

FIREFIGHTING: MOVE CONTAINERS FROM FIRE AREA IF POSSIBLE (1987 EMERGENCY RESPONSE GUIDEBOOK, DOT P 5800.4, GUIDE PAGE 53).
EXTINGUISH USING AGENTS SUITABLE FOR SURROUNDING FIRE. USE FLOODING QUANTITIES OF WATER AS A FOG. KEEP MATERIAL OUT OF SEWERS AND WATER SOURCES. DO NOT TOUCH SPILLED MATERIAL. AVOID BREATHING HAZARDOUS FUMES; KEEP UPWIND.

TOXICITY

PROPAZINE: IRRITATION DATA: 400 MG OPEN EYE-RABBIT MILD. TOXICITY DATA: 106 GM/M3/4 HOURS INHALATION-RABBIT LC50; 3840 MG/KG ORAL-RAT LD50; 3180 MG/KG ORAL-MOUSE LD50; 1200 MG/KG ORAL-GUINEA PIG LD50; 395 MG/KG SUBCUTANEOUS-RAT LD50; 6 GM/KG UNREPORTED-MAMMAL LD50; TUMORIGENIC DATA (RTECS). CARCINOGEN STATUS: NONE. LOCAL EFFECTS: IRRITANT-INHALATION, SKIN, AND EYES. ACUTE TOXICITY LEVEL: MODERATELY TOXIC BY INGESTION; SLIGHTLY TOXIC BY INHALATION. TARGET EFFECTS: NO DATA AVAILABLE.

HEALTH EFFECTS AND FIRST AID

INHALATION: PROPAZINE: **ACUTE EXPOSURE-** SYSTEMIC EFFECTS WERE OBSERVED IN RATS AND MICE EXPOSED TO CONCENTRATIONS OF 1200-1500 MG/M3/4 HOURS. SOME TRIAZINES ARE MILDLY IRRITATING TO THE UPPER RESPIRATORY TRACT.
CHRONIC EXPOSURE- NO DATA AVAILABLE.

FIRST AID- REMOVE FROM EXPOSURE AREA TO FRESH AIR IMMEDIATELY. IF BREATHING HAS STOPPED, PERFORM ARTIFICIAL RESPIRATION. KEEP PERSON WARM AND AT REST. TREAT SYMPTOMATICALLY AND SUPPORTIVELY. GET MEDICAL ATTENTION IMMEDIATELY.

SKIN CONTACT: PROPAZINE: **ACUTE EXPOSURE-** THIS MATERIAL WAS MILDLY IRRITATING TO RABBIT SKIN. A LETHAL DOSE IN RATS BY DERMAL ABSORPTION WAS GREATER THAN 3100 MG/KG. **CHRONIC EXPOSURE-** DERMATITIS CHARACTERIZED BY ERYTHEMA, EDEMA, AND A VESICULOPAPULAR REACTION WAS REPORTED AMONG WORKERS INVOLVED IN THE PRODUCTION OF PROPAZINE.

FIRST AID- REMOVE CONTAMINATED CLOTHING AND SHOES IMMEDIATELY. WASH AFFECTED AREA WITH SOAP OR MILD DETERGENT AND LARGE AMOUNTS OF WATER UNTIL NO EVIDENCE OF CHEMICAL REMAINS (APPROXIMATELY 15-20 MINUTES). GET MEDICAL ATTENTION IMMEDIATELY.

EYE CONTACT: PROPAZINE: **ACUTE EXPOSURE-** 400 MG APPLIED TO RABBIT EYES WAS MILDLY IRRITATING. **CHRONIC EXPOSURE-** NO DATA AVAILABLE.

FIRST AID- WASH EYES IMMEDIATELY WITH LARGE AMOUNTS OF WATER OR NORMAL SALINE, OCCASIONALLY LIFTING UPPER AND LOWER LIDS, UNTIL NO EVIDENCE OF CHEMICAL REMAINS (APPROXIMATELY 15-20 MINUTES). GET MEDICAL ATTENTION IMMEDIATELY.

INGESTION: PROPAZINE: **ACUTE EXPOSURE-** A LETHAL DOSE IN RAT IS 3840 MG/KG; SYMPTOMS WERE NOT REPORTED. **CHRONIC EXPOSURE-** BLOOD AND LIVER EFFECTS CHARACTERIZED BY HYPOCHROMIC, MACROCYTIC ANEMIA, LEUCOPENIA, SOME ATROPHY OF LYMPH NODES, AND HEPATOMEGALY WITH FOCAL NECROSIS AND FATTY DEGENERATION WERE OBSERVED IN A 4-MONTH STUDY OF RABBITS FED 500 MG/KG/DAY. A SIGNIFICANT DECREASE IN MEAN PUP BODY WEIGHT WAS NOTED IN A MULTI-GENERATION STUDY OF RATS RECEIVING 1000 PPM OF PROPAZINE IN THE DIET. A SIGNIFICANT INCREASE IN MAMMARY ADENOCARCINOMAS WAS REPORTED IN FEMALE RATS FED 1000 PPM IN THE DIET FOR TWO YEARS.

FIRST AID- REMOVE BY GASTRIC LAVAGE AND CATHARSIS. MAINTAIN BLOOD PRESSURE AND AIRWAY. GIVE OXYGEN IF RESPIRATION IS DEPRESSED. DO NOT PERFORM GASTRIC LAVAGE IF VICTIM IS UNCONSCIOUS. GET MEDICAL ATTENTION IMMEDIATELY (DREISBACH, HANDBOOK OF POISONING, 12TH ED.). ADMINISTRATION OF LAVAGE OR OXYGEN SHOULD BE PERFORMED BY QUALIFIED MEDICAL PERSONNEL.

ANTIDOTE: NO SPECIFIC ANTIDOTE. TREAT SYMPTOMATICALLY AND SUPPORTIVELY.

REACTIVITY

REACTIVITY: STABLE UNDER NORMAL TEMPERATURES AND PRESSURES.

INCOMPATIBILITIES: PROPAZINE: ACID (STRONG): HYDROLYZES. ALKALI (STRONG): HYDROLYZES.

DECOMPOSITION: THERMAL DECOMPOSITION PRODUCTS MAY INCLUDE TOXIC OXIDES OF NITROGEN AND CARBON AND TOXIC AND CORROSIVE FUMES OF CHLORIDES.

POLYMERIZATION: HAZARDOUS POLYMERIZATION HAS NOT BEEN REPORTED TO OCCUR UNDER NORMAL TEMPERATURES AND PRESSURES.

STORAGE AND DISPOSAL

OBSERVE ALL FEDERAL, STATE AND LOCAL REGULATIONS WHEN STORING OR DISPOSING OF THIS SUBSTANCE. FOR ASSISTANCE, CONTACT THE DISTRICT DIRECTOR OF THE ENVIRONMENTAL PROTECTION AGENCY.

****STORAGE****

STORE IN ACCORDANCE WITH 40 CFR 165 RECOMMENDED PROCEDURES FOR THE DISPOSAL AND STORAGE OF PESTICIDES AND PESTICIDE CONTAINERS.
STORE AWAY FROM INCOMPATIBLE SUBSTANCES.

****DISPOSAL****

DISPOSAL MUST BE IN ACCORDANCE WITH 40 CFR 165 RECOMMENDED PROCEDURES FOR THE DISPOSAL AND STORAGE OF PESTICIDES AND PESTICIDE CONTAINERS.

CONDITIONS TO AVOID

MAY BURN BUT DOES NOT IGNITE READILY.

SPILL AND LEAK PROCEDURES

OCCUPATIONAL SPILL: DO NOT TOUCH SPILLED MATERIAL. STOP LEAK IF YOU CAN DO IT WITHOUT RISK. FOR SMALL SPILLS, TAKE UP WITH SAND OR OTHER ABSORBENT MATERIAL AND PLACE INTO CONTAINERS FOR LATER DISPOSAL. FOR SMALL DRY SPILLS, WITH A CLEAN SHOVEL PLACE MATERIAL INTO CLEAN, DRY CONTAINER AND COVER. MOVE CONTAINERS FROM SPILL AREA. FOR LARGER SPILLS, DIKE FAR AHEAD OF SPILL FOR LATER DISPOSAL. KEEP UNNECESSARY PEOPLE AWAY. ISOLATE HAZARD AREA AND DENY ENTRY.

PROTECTIVE EQUIPMENT

VENTILATION: PROVIDE LOCAL EXHAUST OR GENERAL DILUTION VENTILATION SYSTEM.

RESPIRATOR: THE FOLLOWING RESPIRATORS ARE RECOMMENDED BASED ON INFORMATION FOUND IN THE PHYSICAL DATA, TOXICITY AND HEALTH EFFECTS SECTIONS. THEY ARE RANKED IN ORDER FROM MINIMUM TO MAXIMUM RESPIRATORY PROTECTION. THE SPECIFIC RESPIRATOR SELECTED MUST BE BASED ON CONTAMINATION LEVELS FOUND IN THE WORK PLACE, MUST NOT EXCEED THE WORKING LIMITS OF THE RESPIRATOR AND BE JOINTLY APPROVED BY THE NATIONAL INSTITUTE FOR OCCUPATIONAL SAFETY AND HEALTH AND THE MINE SAFETY AND HEALTH ADMINISTRATION (NIOSH-MSHA).

CHEMICAL CARTRIDGE RESPIRATOR WITH AN ORGANIC VAPOR CARTRIDGE(S) IN COMBINATION WITH A DUST AND MIST FILTER.

GAS MASK WITH ORGANIC VAPOR CANISTER (CHIN-STYLE OR FRONT- OR BACK-MOUNTED CANISTER) WITH A DUST AND MIST FILTER. GAS MASK WITH ORGANIC VAPOR CANISTER (CHIN-STYLE OR FRONT- OR BACK-MOUNTED CANISTER) WITH A PARTICULATE FILTER.

POWERED AIR-PURIFYING RESPIRATOR WITH A HIGH-EFFICIENCY FILTER.

TYPE 'C' SUPPLIED-AIR RESPIRATOR WITH A FULL FACEPIECE OPERATED IN A PRESSURE-DEMAND OR OTHER POSITIVE PRESSURE MODE.

SELF-CONTAINED BREATHING APPARATUS WITH A FULL FACEPIECE OPERATED IN PRESSURE-DEMAND OR OTHER POSITIVE PRESSURE MODE.

FOR FIREFIGHTING AND OTHER IMMEDIATELY DANGEROUS TO LIFE OR HEALTH CONDITIONS:

SELF-CONTAINED BREATHING APPARATUS WITH FULL FACEPIECE OPERATED IN PRESSURE-DEMAND OR OTHER POSITIVE PRESSURE MODE.

SUPPLIED-AIR RESPIRATOR WITH FULL FACEPIECE AND OPERATED IN PRESSURE-DEMAND OR OTHER POSITIVE PRESSURE MODE IN COMBINATION WITH AN AUXILIARY SELF-CONTAINED BREATHING APPARATUS OPERATED IN PRESSURE-DEMAND OR OTHER POSITIVE PRESSURE MODE.

CLOTHING: EMPLOYEE MUST WEAR APPROPRIATE PROTECTIVE (IMPERVIOUS) CLOTHING AND EQUIPMENT TO PREVENT REPEATED OR PROLONGED SKIN CONTACT WITH THIS SUBSTANCE.

GLOVES: EMPLOYEE MUST WEAR APPROPRIATE PROTECTIVE GLOVES TO PREVENT CONTACT WITH THIS SUBSTANCE.

EYE PROTECTION: EMPLOYEE MUST WEAR SPLASH-PROOF OR DUST-RESISTANT SAFETY GOGGLES TO PREVENT EYE CONTACT WITH THIS SUBSTANCE.

EMERGENCY EYE WASH: WHERE THERE IS ANY POSSIBILITY THAT AN EMPLOYEE'S EYES MAY BE EXPOSED TO THIS SUBSTANCE, THE EMPLOYER SHOULD PROVIDE AN EYE WASH FOUNTAIN WITHIN THE IMMEDIATE WORK AREA FOR EMERGENCY USE.

AUTHORIZED BY- OCCUPATIONAL HEALTH SERVICES, INC.
CREATION DATE: 10/04/89 ***REVISION DATE:*** 05/09/90

MATERIAL SAFETY DATA SHEET

OCCUPATIONAL HEALTH SERVICES, INC.
AGRICULTURE AND PESTICIDE DIVISION
450 SEVENTH AVENUE, SUITE 2407
NEW YORK, NEW YORK 10123
1-800-445-MSDS OR (212) 967-1100

EMERGENCY CONTACT:
JOHN S. BRANSFORD, JR. (615) 292-1180

SUBSTANCE IDENTIFICATION

CAS-NUMBER 79-09-4

SUBSTANCE: **PROPIONIC ACID**

TRADE NAMES/SYNONYMS: CARBOXYETHANE; PROPANOIC ACID; ETHANECARBOXYLIC ACID; ETHYLFORMIC ACID; METHYL ACETIC ACID; METACETONIC ACID; PSEUDOACETIC ACID; LUPRISOL; PROPIONIC ACID GRAIN PRESERVER; PROZOIN; SENTRY GRAIN PRESERVER; TENOX P GRAIN PRESERVATIVE; STCC 4931448; UN 1848; A-258; C3H6O2; PST19750

CHEMICAL FAMILY: CARBOXYLIC ACID, ALIPHATIC

MOLECULAR FORMULA: C3-H6-O2

MOLECULAR WEIGHT: 74.08

CERCLA RATINGS (SCALE 0-3): HEALTH=3 FIRE=2 REACTIVITY=0 PERSISTENCE=0

NFPA RATINGS (SCALE 0-4): HEALTH=2 FIRE=2 REACTIVITY=0

COMPONENTS AND CONTAMINANTS

COMPONENT: PROPIONIC ACID ***PERCENT:*** 100
CAS# 79-09-4

OTHER CONTAMINANTS: NONE

EXPOSURE LIMITS: PROPIONIC ACID: 10 PPM (30 MG/M3) OSHA TWA 10 PPM (30 MG/M3) ACGIH TWA; 15 PPM (45 MG/M3) ACGIH STEL (NOTICE OF INTENDED CHANGES 1988-89)
5000 POUNDS CERCLA SECTION 103 REPORTABLE QUANTITY

PHYSICAL DATA

DESCRIPTION: COLORLESS, OILY LIQUID WITH A PUNGENT, DISAGREEABLE, RANCID ODOR.

BOILING POINT: 286 F (141 C) ***MELTING POINT:*** -6 F (-21 C)

SPECIFIC GRAVITY: 0.9930 ***VISCOSITY:*** 1.020 CP @ 25 C

VAPOR PRESSURE: 10 MMHG @ 39.7 C ***PH:*** ACIDIC IN SOLUTION

SOLUBILITY IN WATER: SOLUBLE ***VAPOR DENSITY:*** 2.5

SOLVENT SOLUBILITY: SOLUBLE IN ALCOHOL, ETHER, CHLOROFORM

FIRE AND EXPLOSION DATA

FIRE AND EXPLOSION HAZARD: MODERATE FIRE HAZARD WHEN EXPOSED TO HEAT OR FLAME.
VAPOR-AIR MIXTURES ARE EXPLOSIVE ABOVE FLASH POINT.
VAPORS ARE HEAVIER THAN AIR AND MAY TRAVEL A CONSIDERABLE DISTANCE TO A SOURCE OF IGNITION AND FLASH BACK.

FLASH POINT: 126 F (52 C) (CC) ***UPPER EXPLOSIVE LIMIT:*** 12.1%

LOWER EXPLOSIVE LIMIT: 2.9% ***AUTOIGNITION TEMP.:*** 870 F (465 C)

FLAMMABILITY CLASS(OSHA): II

FIREFIGHTING MEDIA: DRY CHEMICAL, CARBON DIOXIDE, HALON, WATER SPRAY OR STANDARD FOAM (1987 EMERGENCY RESPONSE GUIDEBOOK, DOT P 5800.4).
FOR LARGER FIRES, USE WATER SPRAY, FOG OR STANDARD FOAM (1987 EMERGENCY RESPONSE GUIDEBOOK, DOT P 5800.4).

FIREFIGHTING: MOVE CONTAINER FROM FIRE AREA IF POSSIBLE. DO NOT GET WATER INSIDE CONTAINER. COOL FIRE-EXPOSED CONTAINERS WITH WATER FROM SIDE UNTIL WELL AFTER FIRE IS OUT. STAY AWAY FROM STORAGE TANK ENDS. WITHDRAW IMMEDIATELY IN CASE OF RISING SOUND FROM VENTING SAFETY DEVICE OR ANY DISCOLORATION OF STORAGE TANK DUE TO FIRE (1987 EMERGENCY RESPONSE GUIDEBOOK, DOT P 5800.4, GUIDE PAGE 29).
USE FLOODING AMOUNTS OF WATER AS FOG, SOLID STREAMS MAY NOT BE EFFECTIVE. COOL CONTAINERS WITH FLOODING QUANTITIES OF WATER, APPLY FROM AS FAR A DISTANCE AS POSSIBLE. USE WATER SPRAY TO ABSORB CORROSIVE VAPORS. AVOID BREATHING CORROSIVE VAPORS, KEEP UPWIND.

TRANSPORTATION DATA

DEPARTMENT OF TRANSPORTATION HAZARD CLASSIFICATION 49 CFR 172.101: CORROSIVE MATERIAL

DEPARTMENT OF TRANSPORTATION LABELING REQUIREMENTS 49 CFR 172.101 AND SUBPART E: CORROSIVE

DEPARTMENT OF TRANSPORTATION PACKAGING REQUIREMENTS: 49 CFR 173.245 EXCEPTIONS: 49 CFR 173.244

TOXICITY

PROPIONIC ACID: IRRITATION DATA: 495 MG OPEN SKIN-RABBIT SEVERE; 990 UG EYE-RABBIT SEVERE. TOXICITY DATA: 500 MG/KG SKIN-RABBIT LD50; 2600 MG/KG ORAL-RAT LD50; 625 MG/KG INTRAVENOUS-MOUSE LD50; 1320 MG/KG INTRAVENOUS-RABBIT LDLO. CARCINOGEN STATUS: NONE. LOCAL EFFECTS: CORROSIVE- INHALATION, SKIN, AND EYES. ACUTE TOXICITY LEVEL: TOXIC BY DERMAL ABSORPTION; MODERATELY TOXIC BY INGESTION. TARGET EFFECTS: NO DATA AVAILABLE.

HEALTH EFFECTS AND FIRST AID

INHALATION: PROPIONIC ACID: CORROSIVE. **ACUTE EXPOSURE-** INHALATION OF VAPORS MAY CAUSE MUCOUS MEMBRANE IRRITATION WITH SORE THROAT AND DYSPNEA. ONE CASE OF MILD COUGH AND AN ASTHMATIC RESPONSE HAS BEEN REPORTED. NO DEATHS OCCURRED IN RATS EXPOSED TO A SATURATED ATMOSPHERE FOR 8 HOURS. **CHRONIC EXPOSURE-** DEPENDING ON THE CONCENTRATION AND DURATION OF EXPOSURE, REPEATED OR PROLONGED EXPOSURE TO CORROSIVE SUBSTANCES MAY CAUSE INFLAMMATORY AND ULCERATIVE CHANGES IN THE MOUTH AND POSSIBLY BRONCHIAL AND GASTROINTESTINAL DISTURBANCES.

FIRST AID- REMOVE FROM EXPOSURE AREA TO FRESH AIR IMMEDIATELY. IF BREATHING HAS STOPPED, GIVE ARTIFICIAL RESPIRATION. MAINTAIN AIRWAY AND BLOOD PRESSURE AND ADMINISTER OXYGEN IF AVAILABLE. KEEP AFFECTED PERSON WARM AND AT REST. TREAT SYMPTOMATICALLY AND SUPPORTIVELY. ADMINISTRATION OF OXYGEN SHOULD BE PERFORMED BY QUALIFIED PERSONNEL. GET MEDICAL ATTENTION IMMEDIATELY.

SKIN CONTACT: PROPIONIC ACID: CORROSIVE/TOXIC. **ACUTE EXPOSURE-** CONTACT MAY CAUSE STRONG IRRITATION WITH REDNESS, PAIN, ERYTHEMA AND BLISTERING. MILD TO MODERATE BURNS HAVE BEEN REPORTED IN WORKERS OCCUPATIONALLY EXPOSED. APPLICATION OF 10 MG FOR 24 HOURS TO RABBIT SKIN PRODUCED TISSUE NECROSIS. PROPIONIC ACID IS RAPIDLY ABSORBED THROUGH THE SKIN AND MAY PRODUCE DEATH. APPLICATION OF 500 MG/KG TO RABBIT SKIN WAS LETHAL TO HALF OF THE ANIMALS TESTED. **CHRONIC EXPOSURE-** EFFECTS ARE DEPENDENT UPON CONCENTRATION AND DURATION OF EXPOSURE. DERMATITIS OR EFFECTS SIMILAR TO THOSE FOR ACUTE EXPOSURE MAY OCCUR.

FIRST AID- REMOVE CONTAMINATED CLOTHING AND SHOES IMMEDIATELY. WASH AFFECTED AREA WITH SOAP OR MILD DETERGENT AND LARGE AMOUNTS OF WATER UNTIL NO EVIDENCE OF CHEMICAL REMAINS (AT LEAST 15-20 MINUTES). IN CASE OF CHEMICAL BURNS, COVER AREA WITH STERILE, DRY DRESSING. BANDAGE SECURELY, BUT NOT TOO TIGHTLY. GET MEDICAL ATTENTION IMMEDIATELY.

EYE CONTACT: PROPIONIC ACID: CORROSIVE. **ACUTE EXPOSURE-** VAPORS MAY CAUSE MILD REDNESS, PAIN AND BLURRED VISION. CONTACT WITH THE LIQUID MAY CAUSE BURNS. APPLICATION OF 990 UG OF PROPIONIC ACID TO RABBIT EYES CAUSED SEVERE INJURY, ESPECIALLY TO THE CORNEA, THAT GRADED 9 ON A SCALE OF 1-10 AFTER 24 HOURS. **CHRONIC EXPOSURE-** EFFECTS ARE DEPENDENT UPON CONCENTRATION AND DURATION OF EXPOSURE. CONJUNCTIVITIS OF EFFECTS SIMILAR TO THOSE FOR ACUTE EXPOSURE MAY OCCUR.

FIRST AID- WASH EYES IMMEDIATELY WITH LARGE AMOUNTS OF WATER, OCCASIONALLY LIFTING UPPER AND LOWER LIDS, UNTIL NO EVIDENCE OF CHEMICAL REMAINS (AT LEAST 15-20 MINUTES). CONTINUE IRRIGATING WITH NORMAL SALINE UNTIL THE PH HAS RETURNED TO NORMAL (30-60 MINUTES). COVER WITH STERILE BANDAGES. GET MEDICAL ATTENTION IMMEDIATELY.

INGESTION: PROPIONIC ACID: CORROSIVE. **ACUTE EXPOSURE-** INGESTION MAY CAUSE SORE THROAT, ABDOMINAL PAIN, VOMITING DESQUAMATION AND BLEEDING OF THE GASTROINTESTINAL TRACT. **CHRONIC EXPOSURE-** RATS FED 750 MG/KG PER DAY OF PROPIONIC ACID AS THE SODIUM SALT SHOWED NO CHANGES IN WEIGHT GAIN AS COMPARED WITH CONTROLS.

FIRST AID- DO NOT USE GASTRIC LAVAGE OR EMESIS. DILUTE IMMEDIATELY BY DRINKING LARGE QUANTITIES OF WATER OR MILK. IF VOMITING PERSISTS, ADMINISTER FLUIDS REPEATEDLY. MAINTAIN AIRWAY AND TREAT SHOCK. IF VOMITING OCCURS, KEEP HEAD BELOW HIPS TO HELP PREVENT ASPIRATION. GET MEDICAL ATTENTION IMMEDIATELY.

ANTIDOTE: NO SPECIFIC ANTIDOTE. TREAT SYMPTOMATICALLY AND SUPPORTIVELY.

REACTIVITY

REACTIVITY: STABLE UNDER NORMAL TEMPERATURES AND PRESSURES.

INCOMPATIBILITIES: PROPIONIC ACID: OXIDIZERS: FIRE AND EXPLOSION HAZARD. LEAD AND MOST OTHER METALS: CORROSIVE ACTION. BASES: VIGOROUS OR VIOLENT REACTION.

DECOMPOSITION: THERMAL DECOMPOSITION MAY RELEASE ACRID SMOKE AND IRRITATING FUMES.

POLYMERIZATION: HAZARDOUS POLYMERIZATION HAS NOT BEEN REPORTED TO OCCUR UNDER NORMAL TEMPERATURES AND PRESSURES.

STORAGE AND DISPOSAL

OBSERVE ALL FEDERAL, STATE AND LOCAL REGULATIONS WHEN STORING OR DISPOSING OF THIS SUBSTANCE. FOR ASSISTANCE, CONTACT THE DISTRICT DIRECTOR OF THE ENVIRONMENTAL PROTECTION AGENCY.

STORAGE

STORAGE: PROTECT AGAINST PHYSICAL DAMAGE. OUTSIDE OR DETACHED STORAGE IS PREFERRED. INSIDE STORAGE SHOULD BE IN A STANDARD FLAMMABLE LIQUIDS STORAGE ROOM OR CABINET. SEPARATE FROM OXIDIZING MATERIALS (NFPA 49, HAZARDOUS CHEMICALS DATA, 1975).
STORE AWAY FROM INCOMPATIBLE SUBSTANCES.

CONDITIONS TO AVOID

AVOID CONTACT WITH HEAT, SPARKS, FLAMES OR OTHER IGNITION SOURCES. VAPORS MAY BE EXPLOSIVE. MATERIAL IS CORROSIVE; AVOID CONTACT WITH SKIN OR EYES. DO NOT ALLOW CONTAMINATION OF WATER SOURCES.

SPILL AND LEAK PROCEDURES

SOIL SPILL: DIG A HOLDING AREA SUCH AS A PIT, POND OR LAGOON TO CONTAIN SPILL AND DIKE SURFACE FLOW USING BARRIER OF SOIL, SANDBAGS, FOAMED POLYURETHANE OR FOAMED CONCRETE. ABSORB LIQUID MASS WITH FLY ASH OR CEMENT POWDER.

AIR SPILL: APPLY WATER SPRAY TO KNOCK DOWN AND REDUCE VAPORS. KNOCK-DOWN WATER IS CORROSIVE AND TOXIC AND SHOULD BE DIKED FOR CONTAINMENT AND LATER DISPOSAL.

WATER SPILL: NEUTRALIZE WITH AGRICULTURAL LIME, SLAKED LIME, CRUSHED LIMESTONE, OR SODIUM BICARBONATE.
IF DISSOLVED, AT A CONCENTRATION OF 10 PPM OR GREATER, APPLY ACTIVATED CARBON AT TEN TIMES THE AMOUNT THAT HAS BEEN SPILLED.
USE MECHANICAL DREDGES OR LIFTS TO EXTRACT IMMOBILIZED MASSES OF POLLUTION AND PRECIPITATES.

OCCUPATIONAL SPILL: SHUT OFF IGNITION SOURCES. DO NOT TOUCH SPILLED MATERIAL. STOP LEAK IF YOU CAN DO IT WITHOUT RISK. USE WATER SPRAY TO REDUCE VAPORS. DO NOT GET WATER INSIDE CONTAINER. FOR SMALL SPILLS, TAKE UP WITH SAND OR OTHER ABSORBENT MATERIAL AND PLACE INTO CONTAINERS FOR LATER DISPOSAL. FOR LARGER SPILLS, DIKE FAR AHEAD OF SPILL FOR LATER DISPOSAL. NO SMOKING, FLAMES OR FLARES IN HAZARD AREA. KEEP UNNECESSARY PEOPLE AWAY; ISOLATE HAZARD AREA AND DENY ENTRY.
REPORTABLE QUANTITY (RQ): 5000 POUNDS THE SUPERFUND AMENDMENTS AND REAUTHORIZATION ACT (SARA) SECTION 304 REQUIRES THAT A RELEASE EQUAL TO OR GREATER THAN THE REPORTABLE QUANTITY FOR THIS SUBSTANCE BE IMMEDIATELY REPORTED TO THE LOCAL EMERGENCY PLANNING COMMITTEE AND THE STATE EMERGENCY RESPONSE COMMISSION (40 CFR 355.40). IF THE RELEASE OF THIS SUBSTANCE IS REPORTABLE UNDER CERCLA SECTION 103, THE NATIONAL RESPONSE CENTER MUST BE NOTIFIED IMMEDIATELY AT (800) 424-8802 OR (202) 426-2675 IN THE METROPOLITAN WASHINGTON, D.C. AREA (40 CFR 302.6).

PROTECTIVE EQUIPMENT

VENTILATION: PROVIDE LOCAL EXHAUST OR PROCESS ENCLOSURE VENTILATION TO MEET THE PUBLISHED EXPOSURE LIMITS. VENTILATION EQUIPMENT MUST BE EXPLOSION-PROOF.

RESPIRATOR: THE FOLLOWING RESPIRATORS ARE RECOMMENDED BASED ON INFORMATION FOUND IN THE PHYSICAL DATA, TOXICITY AND HEALTH EFFECTS SECTIONS. THEY ARE RANKED IN ORDER FROM MINIMUM TO MAXIMUM RESPIRATORY PROTECTION. THE SPECIFIC RESPIRATOR SELECTED MUST BE BASED ON CONTAMINATION LEVELS FOUND IN THE WORK PLACE, MUST NOT EXCEED THE WORKING LIMITS OF THE RESPIRATOR AND BE JOINTLY APPROVED BY THE NATIONAL INSTITUTE FOR OCCUPATIONAL SAFETY AND HEALTH AND THE MINE SAFETY AND HEALTH ADMINISTRATION (NIOSH-MSHA).
CHEMICAL CARTRIDGE RESPIRATOR WITH AN ORGANIC VAPOR CARTRIDGE(S) WITH AN ACID GAS CARTRIDGE(S) AND A FULL FACEPIECE.
GAS MASK WITH ORGANIC VAPOR CANISTER (CHIN-STYLE OR FRONT- OR BACK-MOUNTED CANISTER), WITH A FULL FACEPIECE, PROVIDING PROTECTION AGAINST ACID GASES.
TYPE 'C' SUPPLIED-AIR RESPIRATOR WITH A FULL FACEPIECE OPERATED IN PRESSURE-DEMAND OR OTHER POSITIVE PRESSURE MODE OR WITH A FULL FACEPIECE, HELMET OR HOOD OPERATED IN CONTINUOUS-FLOW MODE.

SELF-CONTAINED BREATHING APPARATUS WITH A FULL FACEPIECE OPERATED IN PRESSURE-DEMAND OR OTHER POSITIVE PRESSURE MODE.
FOR FIREFIGHTING AND OTHER IMMEDIATELY DANGEROUS TO LIFE OR HEALTH CONDITIONS:
SELF-CONTAINED BREATHING APPARATUS WITH FULL FACEPIECE OPERATED IN PRESSURE-DEMAND OR OTHER POSITIVE PRESSURE MODE.
SUPPLIED-AIR RESPIRATOR WITH FULL FACEPIECE AND OPERATED IN PRESSURE-DEMAND OR OTHER POSITIVE PRESSURE MODE IN COMBINATION WITH AN AUXILIARY SELF-CONTAINED BREATHING APPARATUS OPERATED IN PRESSURE-DEMAND OR OTHER POSITIVE PRESSURE MODE.

CLOTHING: EMPLOYEE MUST WEAR APPROPRIATE PROTECTIVE (IMPERVIOUS) CLOTHING AND EQUIPMENT TO PREVENT ANY POSSIBILITY OF SKIN CONTACT WITH THIS SUBSTANCE.

GLOVES: EMPLOYEE MUST WEAR APPROPRIATE PROTECTIVE GLOVES TO PREVENT CONTACT WITH THIS SUBSTANCE.

EYE PROTECTION: EMPLOYEE MUST WEAR SPLASH-PROOF OR DUST-RESISTANT SAFETY GOGGLES AND A FACESHIELD TO PREVENT CONTACT WITH THIS SUBSTANCE.
EMERGENCY WASH FACILITIES: WHERE THERE IS ANY POSSIBILITY THAT AN EMPLOYEE'S EYES AND/OR SKIN MAY BE EXPOSED TO THIS SUBSTANCE, THE EMPLOYER SHOULD PROVIDE AN EYE WASH FOUNTAIN AND QUICK DRENCH SHOWER WITHIN THE IMMEDIATE WORK AREA FOR EMERGENCY USE.

AUTHORIZED BY- OCCUPATIONAL HEALTH SERVICES, INC.
CREATION DATE: 11/17/89 ***REVISION DATE:*** 05/18/90

MATERIAL SAFETY DATA SHEET

OCCUPATIONAL HEALTH SERVICES, INC.
AGRICULTURE AND PESTICIDE DIVISION
450 SEVENTH AVENUE, SUITE 2407
NEW YORK, NEW YORK 10123
1-800-445-MSDS OR (212) 967-1100

EMERGENCY CONTACT:
JOHN S. BRANSFORD, JR. (615) 292-1180

SUBSTANCE IDENTIFICATION

CAS-NUMBER 78-87-5

SUBSTANCE: PROPYLENE DICHLORIDE

TRADE NAMES/SYNONYMS: 1,2-DICHLOROPROPANE; DICHLOROPROPANE; ALPHA,BETA-DICHLOROPROPANE; PROPYLENE CHLORIDE; PROPANE, 1,2-DICHLORO-; ENT 15,406; RCRA U083; STCC 4909269; UN 1279; C3H7C12; PST19860

CHEMICAL FAMILY: HALOGEN COMPOUND, ALIPHATIC

MOLECULAR FORMULA: C-H3-C-H2-CL-C-H2-CL

MOLECULAR WEIGHT: 112.99

CERCLA RATINGS (SCALE 0-3): HEALTH=2 FIRE=3 REACTIVITY=0 PERSISTENCE=1

NFPA RATINGS (SCALE 0-4): HEALTH=2 FIRE=3 REACTIVITY=0

COMPONENTS AND CONTAMINANTS

COMPONENT: PROPYLENE DICHLORIDE ***PERCENT:*** 100.0
CAS# 78-87-5

OTHER CONTAMINANTS: NONE

EXPOSURE LIMITS: PROPYLENE DICHLORIDE: 75 PPM (350 MG/M3) OSHA TWA; 110 PPM (510 MG/M3) OSHA STEL 75 PPM (350 MG/M3) ACGIH TWA; 110 PPM (510 MG/M3) ACGIH STEL
1000 POUNDS CERCLA SECTION 103 REPORTABLE QUANTITY SUBJECT TO SARA SECTION 313 ANNUAL TOXIC CHEMICAL RELEASE REPORTING SUBJECT TO CALIFORNIA PROPOSITION 65 CANCER AND/OR REPRODUCTIVE TOXICITY WARNING AND RELEASE REQUIREMENTS- (JANUARY 1, 1990)

PHYSICAL DATA

DESCRIPTION: COLORLESS LIQUID WITH A CHLOROFORM-LIKE ODOR.

BOILING POINT: 205 F (96 C) ***MELTING POINT:*** -148 F (-100 C)

SPECIFIC GRAVITY: 1.1560 ***VOLATILITY:*** 100%

VAPOR PRESSURE: 39.5 MMHG @ 20 C ***EVAPORATION RATE:*** (BUTYL ACETATE=1) >1

SOLUBILITY IN WATER: 0.26% @ 20 C ***ODOR THRESHOLD:*** 50 PPM

VAPOR DENSITY: 3.9

SOLVENT SOLUBILITY: SOLUBLE IN ALCOHOL, ETHER, BENZENE, CHLOROFORM, CARBON TETRACHLORIDE, MOST ORGANIC SOLVENTS.

FIRE AND EXPLOSION DATA

FIRE AND EXPLOSION HAZARD: DANGEROUS FIRE HAZARD WHEN EXPOSED TO HEAT OR FLAME.
VAPORS ARE HEAVIER THAN AIR AND MAY TRAVEL A CONSIDERABLE DISTANCE TO A SOURCE OF IGNITION AND FLASH BACK.
VAPOR-AIR MIXTURES ARE EXPLOSIVE.

FLASH POINT: 60 F (16 C) (CC) ***UPPER EXPLOSIVE LIMIT:*** 14.5%

LOWER EXPLOSIVE LIMIT: 3.4% ***AUTOIGNITION TEMP.:*** 1035 F (557 C)

FLAMMABILITY CLASS(OSHA): IB

FIREFIGHTING MEDIA: DRY CHEMICAL, CARBON DIOXIDE, HALON, WATER SPRAY OR STANDARD FOAM (1987 EMERGENCY RESPONSE GUIDEBOOK, DOT P 5800.4).
FOR LARGER FIRES, USE WATER SPRAY, FOG OR STANDARD FOAM (1987 EMERGENCY RESPONSE GUIDEBOOK, DOT P 5800.4).

FIREFIGHTING: MOVE CONTAINER FROM FIRE AREA IF POSSIBLE. COOL FIRE-EXPOSED CONTAINERS WITH WATER FROM SIDE UNTIL WELL AFTER FIRE IS OUT. STAY AWAY FROM STORAGE TANK ENDS. FOR MASSIVE FIRE IN STORAGE AREA, USE UNMANNED HOSE HOLDER OR MONITOR NOZZLES, ELSE WITHDRAW FROM AREA AND LET FIRE BURN. WITHDRAW IMMEDIATELY IN CASE OF RISING SOUND FROM VENTING SAFETY DEVICE OR ANY DISCOLORATION OF STORAGE TANK DUE TO FIRE (1987 EMERGENCY RESPONSE GUIDEBOOK, DOT P 5800.4, GUIDE PAGE 27).
EXTINGUISH ONLY IF FLOW CAN BE STOPPED; USE WATER IN FLOODING QUANTITIES AS FOG, SOLID STREAMS MAY SPREAD FIRE. COOL CONTAINERS WITH FLOODING QUANTITIES OF WATER, APPLY FROM AS FAR A DISTANCE AS POSSIBLE. AVOID BREATHING HAZARDOUS VAPORS, KEEP UPWIND.
WATER MAY BE INEFFECTIVE EXCEPT AS A BLANKET (NFPA 325M, FIRE HAZARD PROPERTIES OF FLAMMABLE LIQUIDS, GASES, AND VOLATILE SOLIDS, 1984)

TRANSPORTATION DATA

DEPARTMENT OF TRANSPORTATION HAZARD CLASSIFICATION 49 CFR 172.101: FLAMMABLE LIQUID
DEPARTMENT OF TRANSPORTATION LABELING REQUIREMENTS 49 CFR 172.101 AND SUBPART E: FLAMMABLE LIQUID
DEPARTMENT OF TRANSPORTATION PACKAGING REQUIREMENTS: 49 CFR 173.119 EXCEPTIONS: 49 CFR 173.118

TOXICITY

PROPYLENE DICHLORIDE: IRRITATION DATA: 500 MG EYE-RABBIT MILD. TOXICITY DATA: 14 GM/M3/8 HOURS INHALATION-RAT LC50; 1000 PPM/2 HOURS INHALATION-MOUSE LCLO; 8750 MG/KG SKIN-RABBIT LD50; 1947 MG/KG ORAL-RAT LD50; 860 MG/KG ORAL-MOUSE LD50; 5000 MG/KG ORAL-DOG LDLO; 2 GM/KG ORAL-GUINEA PIG LD50; 960 MG/KG UNREPORTED-MOUSE LD50; MUTAGENIC DATA (RTECS); TUMORIGENIC DATA (RTECS). CARCINOGEN STATUS: ANIMAL LIMITED EVIDENCE (IARC GROUP-3). A DOSE-RELATED INCREASE IN THE INCIDENCE OF HEPATOCELLULAR TUMORS WAS OBSERVED IN MALE AND FEMALE MICE AFTER ORAL ADMINISTRATION OF PROPYLENE DICHLORIDE. LOCAL EFFECTS: IRRITANT- INHALATION, EYE. ACUTE TOXICITY LEVEL: TOXIC BY INHALATION; MODERATELY TOXIC BY INGESTION; SLIGHTLY TOXIC BY DERMAL ABSORPTION. TARGET EFFECTS: CENTRAL NERVOUS SYSTEM DEPRESSANT; HEPATOTOXIN; NEPHROTOXIN. POISONING MAY ALSO AFFECT THE LUNGS AND HEART. AT INCREASED RISK FROM EXPOSURE: PERSONS WITH PRE-EXISTING SKIN, LIVER, OR KIDNEY DISEASE, OR IMPAIRED PULMONARY FUNCTION. ADDITIONAL DATA: ALCOHOL MAY ENHANCE THE TOXIC EFFECTS.

HEALTH EFFECTS AND FIRST AID

INHALATION: PROPYLENE DICHLORIDE:
IRRITANT/NARCOTIC/NEPHROTOXIN/HEPATOTOXIN/TOXIC. 2000 PPM IMMEDIATELY DANGEROUS TO LIFE OR HEALTH. **ACUTE EXPOSURE-** INHALATION MAY CAUSE MUCOUS MEMBRANE IRRITATION WITH SORE THROAT AND COUGHING. ABDOMINAL PAIN, NAUSEA, VOMITING, ANOREXIA, HEMATURIA, AND ECCHYMOSES, POSSIBLY DELAYED UP TO 24 HOURS, MAY OCCUR. HIGH CONCENTRATIONS MAY CAUSE CENTRAL NERVOUS SYSTEM DEPRESSION WITH HEADACHE, DIZZINESS, DROWSINESS, AND INCOORDINATION. ANIMAL STUDIES REPORT SEVERE CENTRILOBULAR LIVER DAMAGE, ACUTE RENAL FAILURE, HEMOLYTIC ANEMIA, ADRENAL INJURY, MARKED VISCERAL CONGESTION, DISSEMINATED INTRAVASCULAR COAGULATION, FATTY DEGENERATION AND NECROSIS OF THE HEART, AND DEATH. IN MICE, DEATH WAS PRIMARILY DUE TO OBSTRUCTIVE RESPIRATORY FAILURE. **CHRONIC EXPOSURE-** REPEATED OR PROLONGED EXPOSURE MAY CAUSE SEVERE LIVER AND KIDNEY INJURY. IN ANIMAL STUDIES, DECREASED WEIGHT GAIN, WEAKNESS, GENERAL DEBILITY, DEGENERATION OF OLFACTORY TISSUES, RESPIRATORY HYPERPLASIA, ANEMIA, AND DELAYED DEATH HAVE BEEN REPORTED. HEPATOMAS WERE NOTED IN SOME SURVIVORS OF ONE STRAIN OF MICE EXPOSED AT 400 PPM.

FIRST AID- REMOVE FROM EXPOSURE AREA TO FRESH AIR IMMEDIATELY. IF BREATHING HAS STOPPED, GIVE ARTIFICIAL RESPIRATION. MAINTAIN AIRWAY AND BLOOD PRESSURE AND ADMINISTER OXYGEN IF AVAILABLE. KEEP AFFECTED PERSON WARM AND AT REST. TREAT SYMPTOMATICALLY AND SUPPORTIVELY.

ADMINISTRATION OF OXYGEN SHOULD BE PERFORMED BY QUALIFIED PERSONNEL. GET MEDICAL ATTENTION IMMEDIATELY.

SKIN CONTACT: PROPYLENE DICHLORIDE: **ACUTE EXPOSURE**- CONTACT WITH THE LIQUID HAS PRODUCED ONLY MILD IRRITATION. HOWEVER, OCCLUDED CONTACT MAY RESULT IN MORE SEVERE IRRITATION. ANIMAL STUDIES INDICATE THAT LETHAL AMOUNTS MAY BE ABSORBED THROUGH INTACT SKIN. **CHRONIC EXPOSURE**- REPEATED CONTACT WITH THE LIQUID MAY CAUSE DERMATITIS DUE TO THE DEFATTING ACTION ON THE SKIN.

FIRST AID- REMOVE CONTAMINATED CLOTHING AND SHOES IMMEDIATELY. WASH AFFECTED AREA WITH SOAP OR MILD DETERGENT AND LARGE AMOUNTS OF WATER UNTIL NO EVIDENCE OF CHEMICAL REMAINS (APPROXIMATELY 15-20 MINUTES). GET MEDICAL ATTENTION IMMEDIATELY.

EYE CONTACT: PROPYLENE DICHLORIDE: IRRITANT. **ACUTE EXPOSURE**- VAPORS MAY CAUSE IRRITATION. HUMAN CONTACT WITH THE LIQUID PRODUCED SMARTING THAT PERSISTED FOR SEVERAL HOURS AND DAMAGE OF THE CORNEAL EPITHELIUM THAT HEALED PROMPTLY. HOWEVER, IN RABBIT EYES, THE LIQUID WAS MODERATELY INJURIOUS PRODUCING SOME PAIN AND IRRITATION, BUT NO SERIOUS OR PERMANENT INJURY. GUINEA PIGS EXPOSED TO 2200 PPM FOR 7 HOURS EXHIBITED LACRIMATION AND SWELLING OF THE EYELIDS AND CONJUNCTIVA, AND DISCOLORATION AND INFECTION OF THE CORNEAS. RABBITS EXPOSED TO THE SAME CONDITIONS SHOWED LITTLE IRRITATION. **CHRONIC EXPOSURE**- REPEATED OR PROLONGED CONTACT WITH IRRITANTS MAY CAUSE CONJUNCTIVITIS.

FIRST AID- WASH EYES IMMEDIATELY WITH LARGE AMOUNTS OF WATER OR NORMAL SALINE, OCCASIONALLY LIFTING UPPER AND LOWER LIDS, UNTIL NO EVIDENCE OF CHEMICAL REMAINS (APPROXIMATELY 15-20 MINUTES). GET MEDICAL ATTENTION IMMEDIATELY.

INGESTION: PROPYLENE DICHLORIDE: NARCOTIC/NEPHROTOXIN/HEPATOTOXIN/LIMITED ANIMAL CARCINOGEN. **ACUTE EXPOSURE**- MAY CAUSE IRRITATION OF THE ORAL MUCOUS MEMBRANES, ABDOMINAL PAIN, NAUSEA, VOMITING, DIARRHEA, CENTRAL NERVOUS SYSTEM DEPRESSION WITH HEADACHE, DROWSINESS, UNCONSCIOUSNESS, AND POSSIBLY LIVER AND KIDNEY DAMAGE. ACCIDENTAL INGESTION OF 50 ML PRODUCED COMA AND HYPERTONIA WITHIN 2 HOURS FOLLOWED BY ACUTE DELIRIUM, HEPATIC FAILURE AND DEATH AT 36 HOURS. OTHER EFFECTS AS DETAILED IN ACUTE INHALATION MAY OCCUR. **CHRONIC EXPOSURE**- REPEATED OR PROLONGED EXPOSURE MAY CAUSE SEVERE LIVER DAMAGE AND DEATH. ANIMAL STUDIES AT HIGH DOSES INDICATE AN INCREASED INCIDENCE OF CLEAR CELL CHANGES. NECROSIS AND ADENOMAS OF THE LIVER, AND DOSE RELATED INCREASES OF ADENOCARCINOMA OF THE MAMMARY GLANDS.

FIRST AID- IF THE PERSON IS CONSCIOUS AND NOT CONVULSING, REMOVE BY GIVING SYRUP OF IPECAC (IF VOMITING OCCURS, KEEP THE HEAD BELOW THE HIPS TO PREVENT ASPIRATION). GIVE ACTIVATED CHARCOAL FOLLOWED BY GASTRIC LAVAGE. FOLLOW WITH A SALINE CATHARTIC. DO NOT GIVE FATS OR OILS. INTESTINAL LAVAGE WITH 20% MANNITOL (200 ML) BY STOMACH TUBE IS ALSO USEFUL. GIVE ARTIFICIAL RESPIRATION WITH OXYGEN IF RESPIRATION IS DEPRESSED (DREISBACH, HANDBOOK OF POISONING, 12TH ED.). TREAT SYMPTOMATICALLY AND SUPPORTIVELY. LAVAGE AND ADMINISTRATION OF OXYGEN SHOULD BE PERFORMED BY QUALIFIED MEDICAL PERSONNEL. GET MEDICAL ATTENTION IMMEDIATELY.

ANTIDOTE: NO SPECIFIC ANTIDOTE. TREAT SYMPTOMATICALLY AND SUPPORTIVELY.

REACTIVITY

REACTIVITY: STABLE UNDER NORMAL TEMPERATURES AND PRESSURES.

INCOMPATIBILITIES: PROPYLENE DICHLORIDE: ACIDS: POSSIBLE VIGOROUS REACTION. ALKALIES: POSSIBLE VIGOROUS REACTION. ALUMINUM: POSSIBLE VIOLENT REACTION, PARTICULARLY IN A CLOSED SYSTEM. METALS: POSSIBLE VIGOROUS REACTION. OXIDIZERS (STRONG): FIRE AND EXPLOSION HAZARD. PLASTICS, RUBBER, AND COATINGS: MAY BE ATTACKED.

DECOMPOSITION: THERMAL DECOMPOSITION PRODUCTS MAY INCLUDE TOXIC AND CORROSIVE FUMES OF CHLORIDES AND PHOSGENE, AND TOXIC OXIDES OF CARBON.

POLYMERIZATION: HAZARDOUS POLYMERIZATION HAS NOT BEEN REPORTED TO OCCUR UNDER NORMAL TEMPERATURES AND PRESSURES.

STORAGE AND DISPOSAL

OBSERVE ALL FEDERAL, STATE AND LOCAL REGULATIONS WHEN STORING OR DISPOSING OF THIS SUBSTANCE. FOR ASSISTANCE, CONTACT THE DISTRICT DIRECTOR OF THE ENVIRONMENTAL PROTECTION AGENCY.

****STORAGE****

STORE IN ACCORDANCE WITH 29 CFR 1910.106.

BONDING AND GROUNDING: SUBSTANCES WITH LOW ELECTROCONDUCTIVITY, WHICH MAY BE IGNITED BY ELECTROSTATIC SPARKS, SHOULD BE STORED IN CONTAINERS WHICH MEET THE BONDING AND GROUNDING GUIDELINES SPECIFIED IN NFPA 77-1983, RECOMMENDED PRACTICE ON STATIC ELECTRICITY.

PROTECT AGAINST PHYSICAL DAMAGE. OUTSIDE OR DETACHED STORAGE IS PREFERRED. INSIDE STORAGE SHOULD BE IN A STANDARD FLAMMABLE LIQUIDS STORAGE ROOM. SEPARATE FROM OXIDIZING MATERIALS (NFPA 49, HAZARDOUS CHEMICALS DATA, 1975).

STORE AWAY FROM INCOMPATIBLE SUBSTANCES.

****DISPOSAL****

DISPOSAL MUST BE IN ACCORDANCE WITH STANDARDS APPLICABLE TO GENERATORS OF HAZARDOUS WASTE, 40CFR 262. EPA HAZARDOUS WASTE NUMBER U083.

CONDITIONS TO AVOID

AVOID CONTACT WITH HEAT, SPARKS, FLAMES, OR OTHER SOURCES OF IGNITION. VAPORS MAY BE EXPLOSIVE. AVOID OVERHEATING OF CONTAINERS; CONTAINERS MAY VIOLENTLY RUPTURE IN HEAT OF FIRE. AVOID CONTAMINATION OF WATER SOURCES.

SPILL AND LEAK PROCEDURES

SOIL SPILL: DIG A HOLDING AREA SUCH AS A PIT, POND OR LAGOON TO CONTAIN SPILL AND DIKE SURFACE FLOW USING BARRIER OF SOIL, SANDBAGS, FOAMED POLYURETHANE OR FOAMED CONCRETE. ABSORB LIQUID MASS WITH FLY ASH OR CEMENT POWDER.

DIMINISH VAPOR AND FIRE HAZARD BY APPLICATION OF APPROPRIATE FOAM.

AIR SPILL: APPLY WATER SPRAY TO KNOCK DOWN AND REDUCE VAPORS. KNOCK-DOWN WATER IS CORROSIVE AND TOXIC AND SHOULD BE DIKED FOR CONTAINMENT.

WATER SPILL: TRAP SPILLED MATERIAL AT BOTTOM IN DEEP WATER POCKETS, EXCAVATED HOLDING AREAS OR WITHIN SAND BAG BARRIERS.

USE SUCTION HOSES TO REMOVE TRAPPED SPILL MATERIAL.

USE MECHANICAL DREDGES OR LIFTS TO EXTRACT IMMOBILIZED MASSES OF POLLUTION AND PRECIPITATES.

THE CALIFORNIA SAFE DRINKING WATER AND TOXIC ENFORCEMENT ACT OF 1986 (PROPOSITION 65) PROHIBITS CONTAMINATING ANY KNOWN SOURCE OF DRINKING WATER WITH SUBSTANCES KNOWN TO CAUSE CANCER AND/OR REPRODUCTIVE TOXICITY.

OCCUPATIONAL SPILL: SHUT OFF IGNITION SOURCES. STOP LEAK IF YOU CAN DO IT WITHOUT RISK. USE WATER SPRAY TO REDUCE VAPORS. FOR SMALL SPILLS, TAKE UP WITH SAND OR OTHER ABSORBENT MATERIAL AND PLACE INTO CONTAINERS FOR LATER DISPOSAL. FOR LARGER SPILLS, DIKE FAR AHEAD OF SPILL FOR LATER DISPOSAL. NO SMOKING, FLAMES OR FLARES IN HAZARD AREA. KEEP UNNECESSARY PEOPLE AWAY; ISOLATE HAZARD AREA AND RESTRICT ENTRY.

REPORTABLE QUANTITY (RQ): 1000 POUNDS THE SUPERFUND AMENDMENTS AND REAUTHORIZATION ACT (SARA) SECTION 304 REQUIRES THAT A RELEASE EQUAL TO OR GREATER THAN THE REPORTABLE QUANTITY FOR THIS SUBSTANCE BE IMMEDIATELY REPORTED TO THE LOCAL EMERGENCY PLANNING COMMITTEE AND THE STATE EMERGENCY RESPONSE COMMISSION (40 CFR 355.40). IF THE RELEASE OF THIS SUBSTANCE IS REPORTABLE UNDER CERCLA SECTION 103, THE NATIONAL RESPONSE CENTER MUST BE NOTIFIED IMMEDIATELY AT (800) 424-8802 OR (202) 426-2675 IN THE METROPOLITAN WASHINGTON, D.C. AREA (40 CFR 302.6).

PROTECTIVE EQUIPMENT

VENTILATION: PROVIDE LOCAL EXHAUST OR GENERAL DILUTION VENTILATION TO MEET PUBLISHED EXPOSURE LIMITS. VENTILATION EQUIPMENT MUST BE EXPLOSION-PROOF.

RESPIRATOR: THE FOLLOWING RESPIRATORS AND MAXIMUM USE CONCENTRATIONS ARE RECOMMENDATIONS BY THE U.S. DEPARTMENT OF HEALTH AND HUMAN SERVICES, NIOSH POCKET GUIDE TO CHEMICAL HAZARDS; NIOSH CRITERIA DOCUMENTS OR BY THE U.S. DEPARTMENT OF LABOR, 29 CFR 1910 SUBPART Z. THE SPECIFIC RESPIRATOR SELECTED MUST BE BASED ON CONTAMINATION LEVELS FOUND IN THE WORK PLACE, MUST NOT EXCEED THE WORKING LIMITS OF THE RESPIRATOR AND BE JOINTLY APPROVED BY THE NATIONAL INSTITUTE FOR OCCUPATIONAL SAFETY AND HEALTH AND THE MINE SAFETY AND HEALTH ADMINISTRATION (NIOSH-MSHA).

PROPYLENE DICHLORIDE:

750 PPM- CHEMICAL CARTRIDGE RESPIRATOR WITH ORGANIC VAPOR CARTRIDGE(S). SUPPLIED-AIR RESPIRATOR. SELF-CONTAINED BREATHING APPARATUS.

1000 PPM- POWERED AIR-PURIFYING RESPIRATOR WITH ORGANIC VAPOR CARTRIDGE(S).

1875 PPM- SUPPLIED-AIR RESPIRATOR OPERATED IN CONTINUOUS FLOW MODE.

2000 PPM- AIR-PURIFYING FULL FACEPIECE RESPIRATOR (GAS MASK) WITH A CHIN-STYLE OR FRONT- OR BACK-MOUNTED ORGANIC VAPOR CANISTER. SELF-CONTAINED BREATHING APPARATUS WITH FULL FACEPIECE. SUPPLIED-AIR RESPIRATOR WITH FULL FACEPIECE.

ESCAPE- AIR-PURIFYING FULL FACEPIECE RESPIRATOR (GAS MASK) WITH A CHIN-

STYLE OR FRONT- OR BACK-MOUNTED ORGANIC VAPOR CANISTER. ESCAPE-TYPE SELF-CONTAINED BREATHING APPARATUS.

FOR FIREFIGHTING AND OTHER IMMEDIATELY DANGEROUS TO LIFE OR HEALTH CONDITIONS:

SELF-CONTAINED BREATHING APPARATUS WITH FULL FACEPIECE OPERATED IN PRESSURE-DEMAND OR OTHER POSITIVE PRESSURE MODE.

SUPPLIED-AIR RESPIRATOR WITH FULL FACEPIECE AND OPERATED IN PRESSURE-DEMAND OR OTHER POSITIVE PRESSURE MODE IN COMBINATION WITH AN AUXILIARY SELF-CONTAINED BREATHING APPARATUS OPERATED IN PRESSURE-DEMAND OR OTHER POSITIVE PRESSURE MODE.

CLOTHING: EMPLOYEE MUST WEAR APPROPRIATE PROTECTIVE (IMPERVIOUS) CLOTHING AND EQUIPMENT TO PREVENT ANY POSSIBILITY OF SKIN CONTACT WITH THIS SUBSTANCE.

GLOVES: EMPLOYEE MUST WEAR APPROPRIATE PROTECTIVE GLOVES TO PREVENT CONTACT WITH THIS SUBSTANCE.

EYE PROTECTION: EMPLOYEE MUST WEAR SPLASH-PROOF OR DUST-RESISTANT SAFETY GOGGLES AND A FACESHIELD TO PREVENT CONTACT WITH THIS SUBSTANCE.

EMERGENCY WASH FACILITIES: WHERE THERE IS ANY POSSIBILITY THAT AN EMPLOYEE'S EYES AND/OR SKIN MAY BE EXPOSED TO THIS SUBSTANCE, THE EMPLOYER SHOULD PROVIDE AN EYE WASH FOUNTAIN AND QUICK DRENCH SHOWER WITHIN THE IMMEDIATE WORK AREA FOR EMERGENCY USE.

AUTHORIZED BY- OCCUPATIONAL HEALTH SERVICES, INC.
CREATION DATE: 10/04/89 ***REVISION DATE:*** 07/13/90

MATERIAL SAFETY DATA SHEET

OCCUPATIONAL HEALTH SERVICES, INC.
AGRICULTURE AND PESTICIDE DIVISION
450 SEVENTH AVENUE, SUITE 2407
NEW YORK, NEW YORK 10123
1-800-445-MSDS OR (212) 967-1100

EMERGENCY CONTACT:
JOHN S. BRANSFORD, JR. (615) 292-1180

SUBSTANCE IDENTIFICATION

CAS-NUMBER 57-55-6

SUBSTANCE: PROPYLENE GLYCOL

TRADE NAMES/SYNONYMS: 1,2-PROPANEDIOL; 1,2-DIHYDROXYPROPANE; DOWFROST; 2-HYDROXYPROPANOL; ISOPROPYLENE GLYCOL; METHYLETHYLENE GLYCOL; METHYLETHYL GLYCOL; MONOPROPYLENE GLYCOL; 2,3-PROPANEDIOL; ALPHA-PROPYLENE GLYCOL; 1,2-PROPYLENE GLYCOL; SIRLENE; C3H8O2; PST19870

CHEMICAL FAMILY: GLYCOL

MOLECULAR FORMULA: C-H3-C-H-(O-H)-C-H2-O-H

MOLECULAR WEIGHT: 76.11

CERCLA RATINGS (SCALE 0-3): HEALTH=3 FIRE=1 REACTIVITY=0 PERSISTENCE=0

NFPA RATINGS (SCALE 0-4): HEALTH=0 FIRE=1 REACTIVITY=0

COMPONENTS AND CONTAMINANTS

COMPONENT: PROPYLENE GLYCOL ***PERCENT:*** 100.0
CAS# 57-55-6

OTHER CONTAMINANTS: NONE

EXPOSURE LIMITS: NO OCCUPATIONAL EXPOSURE LIMITS ESTABLISHED BY OSHA, ACGIH, OR NIOSH.

PHYSICAL DATA

DESCRIPTION: ODORLESS, CLEAR, COLORLESS, HYGROSCOPIC, VISCOUS LIQUID WITH A SLIGHTLY ACRID TASTE. ***BOILING POINT:*** 370-372 F (188-189 C)

MELTING POINT: -75 F (-59 C) ***SPECIFIC GRAVITY:*** 1.0361

VISCOSITY: 58.1 CPS @ 20 C ***VAPOR PRESSURE:*** <0.1 MMHG @ 20 C

EVAPORATION RATE: (BUTYL ACETATE=1) 0.005 ***SOLUBILITY IN WATER:*** COMPLETE

VAPOR DENSITY: 2.62

SOLVENT SOLUBILITY: SOLUBLE IN ALCOHOL, ACETONE, CHLOROFORM, ETHER, BENZENE MANY ORGANIC SOLVENTS; INSOLUBLE IN FIXED OILS.

FIRE AND EXPLOSION DATA

FIRE AND EXPLOSION HAZARD: SLIGHT FIRE HAZARD WHEN EXPOSED TO HEAT OR FLAME.

FLASH POINT: 210 F (99 C) (CC) ***UPPER EXPLOSIVE LIMIT:*** 12.5%

LOWER EXPLOSIVE LIMIT: 2.6% ***AUTOIGNITION TEMP.:*** 700 F (371 C)

FLAMMABILITY CLASS(OSHA): IIIB

FIREFIGHTING MEDIA: DRY CHEMICAL, CARBON DIOXIDE, HALON, WATER SPRAY OR ALCOHOL FOAM (1987 EMERGENCY RESPONSE GUIDEBOOK, DOT P 5800.4).

FOR LARGER FIRES, USE WATER SPRAY, FOG OR ALCOHOL FOAM (1987 EMERGENCY RESPONSE GUIDEBOOK, DOT P 5800.4).

ALCOHOL FOAM (NFPA 325M, FIRE HAZARD PROPERTIES OF FLAMMABLE LIQUIDS, GASES, AND VOLATILE SOLIDS, 1984).

FIREFIGHTING: MOVE CONTAINER FROM FIRE AREA IF POSSIBLE. DO NOT SCATTER SPILLED MATERIAL WITH HIGH PRESSURE WATER STREAMS. DIKE FIRE CONTROL WATER FOR LATER DISPOSAL (1987 EMERGENCY RESPONSE GUIDEBOOK, DOT P 5800.4, GUIDE PAGE 31).

USE AGENTS SUITABLE FOR TYPE OF SURROUNDING FIRE. AVOID BREATHING HAZARDOUS VAPORS, KEEP UPWIND.

TOXICITY

PROPYLENE GLYCOL: IRRITATION DATA: 500 MG/7 DAYS SKIN-HUMAN MILD; 104 MG/3 DAYS INTERMITTENT SKIN-HUMAN MODERATE; 10%/2 DAYS SKIN-MAN; 100 MG EYE-RABBIT MILD; 500 MG/24 HOURS EYE-RABBIT MILD. TOXICITY DATA: 20,800 MG/KG SKIN-RABBIT LD50; 79 GM/KG/56 WEEKS INTERMITTENT ORAL-CHILD TDLO; 20 GM/KG ORAL-RAT LD50; 22 GM/KG ORAL-MOUSE LD50; 18,500 MG/KG ORAL-RABBIT LD50; 22 GM/KG ORAL-DOG LD50; 18,350 MG/KG ORAL-GUINEA PIG LD50; 10 GM/KG/3 DAYS CONTINUOUS PARENTERAL-INFANT TDLO; 22,500 MG/KG SUBCUTANEOUS-RAT LD50; 17,370 MG/KG SUBCUTANEOUS-MOUSE LD50; 15,500 MG/KG SUBCUTANEOUS-GUINEA PIG LDLO; 6423 MG/KG INTRAVENOUS-RAT LD50; 6630 MG/KG INTRAVENOUS-MOUSE LD50; 4200 MG/KG INTRAVENOUS-RABBIT LDLO; 26 GM/KG INTRAVENOUS-DOG LD50; 6660 MG/KG INTRAPERITONEAL-RAT LD50; 9718 INTRAPERITONEAL-MOUSE LD50; 14 GM/KG INTRAMUSCULAR-RAT LD50; MUTAGENIC DATA (RTECS); REPRODUCTIVE EFFECTS DATA (RTECS). CARCINOGEN STATUS: NONE. ACUTE TOXICITY LEVEL: RELATIVELY NON-TOXIC BY DERMAL ABSORPTION AND INGESTION. TARGET EFFECTS: POISONING MAY AFFECT THE CENTRAL NERVOUS SYSTEM AND KIDNEYS. AT INCREASED RISK FROM EXPOSURE: PERSONS WITH IMPAIRED RENAL FUNCTION, OR PREEXISTING SKIN DISORDERS. ADDITIONAL DATA: ALCOHOL MAY ENHANCE THE TOXIC EFFECTS. INTERACTIONS WITH MEDICATIONS HAVE BEEN REPORTED.

HEALTH EFFECTS AND FIRST AID

INHALATION: PROPYLENE GLYCOL: ACUTE EXPOSURE- DUE TO ITS LOW VAPOR PRESSURE, INHALATION IS UNLIKELY AT ROOM TEMPERATURE AND THE LIQUID IS CONSIDERED TO BE A LOW HAZARD FOR USUAL INDUSTRIAL HANDLING. HOWEVER, HIGH CONCENTRATIONS MAY CAUSE HEADACHE, NAUSEA AND DULLNESS. CHRONIC EXPOSURE- REPEATED OR PROLONGED EXPOSURE TO SATURATED AND SUPERSATURATED ATMOSPHERES HAS PRODUCED NO ADVERSE EFFECTS IN HUMANS OR ANIMALS.

FIRST AID- REMOVE FROM EXPOSURE AREA TO FRESH AIR IMMEDIATELY. IF BREATHING HAS STOPPED, PERFORM ARTIFICIAL RESPIRATION. KEEP PERSON WARM AND AT REST. TREAT SYMPTOMATICALLY AND SUPPORTIVELY. GET MEDICAL ATTENTION IMMEDIATELY.

SKIN CONTACT: PROPYLENE GLYCOL: ACUTE EXPOSURE- CONTACT MAY CAUSE IRRITATION WITH REDNESS IN SOME INDIVIDUALS, PARTICULARLY ON DEHYDRATED OR OCCLUDED SKIN. ALLERGIC REACTIONS POSSIBLY INCLUDING DERMATITIS OR ERYTHEMATOUS EDEMATOUS PLAQUES MAY OCCUR IN SENSITIVE PERSONS. SKIN ABSORPTION MAY OCCUR AND PRODUCE CENTRAL NERVOUS SYSTEM DEPRESSION WITH HEADACHE, NAUSEA AND DULLNESS. CHRONIC EXPOSURE- REPEATED OR PROLONGED CONTACT MAY CAUSE MILD TO MODERATE IRRITATION IN HUMANS. ALLERGIC SKIN REACTIONS HAVE BEEN REPORTED. IN EXPERIMENTAL ANIMALS, PROPYLENE GLYCOL MAY POSSESS OTOTOXIC PROPERTIES WHEN INSTILLED IN THE EAR.

FIRST AID- REMOVE CONTAMINATED CLOTHING AND SHOES IMMEDIATELY. WASH AFFECTED AREA WITH SOAP OR MILD DETERGENT AND LARGE AMOUNTS OF WATER UNTIL NO EVIDENCE OF CHEMICAL REMAINS (APPROXIMATELY 15-20 MINUTES). GET MEDICAL ATTENTION IMMEDIATELY.

EYE CONTACT: PROPYLENE GLYCOL: ACUTE EXPOSURE- A DROP APPLIED TO THE HUMAN EYE CAUSED IMMEDIATE STINGING, BLEPHAROSPASM, AND LACRIMATION, FOLLOWED BY MILD TRANSIENT CONJUNCTIVAL HYPEREMIA, BUT NO RESIDUAL DISCOMFORT OR INJURY. CHRONIC EXPOSURE- NO DATA AVAILABLE.

FIRST AID- WASH EYES IMMEDIATELY WITH LARGE AMOUNTS OF WATER OR NORMAL SALINE, OCCASIONALLY LIFTING UPPER AND LOWER LIDS, UNTIL NO EVIDENCE OF CHEMICAL REMAINS (APPROXIMATELY 15-20 MINUTES). GET MEDICAL ATTENTION IMMEDIATELY.

INGESTION: PROPYLENE GLYCOL: ACUTE EXPOSURE- INGESTION OF 60 MILLILITERS HAS PRODUCED REVERSIBLE CENTRAL NERVOUS SYSTEM DEPRESSION WITH STUPOR IN HUMANS. 1-1.5 GM/KG REDUCED INTRAOCULAR PRESSURE IN BOTH

HUMANS AND RABBITS BY RAISING THE OSMOTIC PRESSURE OF THE BLOOD. IN ANIMAL STUDIES, ADDITIONAL SYMPTOMS OF ABDOMINAL SPASMS, VOMITING AND UNCONSICOUSNESS MAY OCCUR. DERMAL ERUPTIONS HAVE BEEN REPORTED FOLLOWING INGESTION IN PERSONS SENSITIVE TO TOPICAL PROPYLENE GLYCOL.

CHRONIC EXPOSURE- REPEATED INGESTION OF VITAMIN PREPARATIONS CONTAINING PROPYLENE GLYCOL HAS RESULTED IN STUPOR, TACHYPNEA, TACHYCARDIA, DIAPHORESIS, SEIZURES AND UNCONSCIOUSNESS IN CHILDREN. FEEDING STUDIES AT VERY HIGH DOSES IN RATS AND RABBITS PRODUCED CENTRAL NERVOUS SYSTEM DEPRESSION, HEMOLYSIS AND MINIMAL KIDNEY CHANGES. VERY SLIGHT LIVER DAMAGE WAS NOTED IN RATS FED 0.9-1.77 ML/KG FOR 24 MONTHS. CHICKS FED 10% IN THE DIET SHOWED DEPRESSED WEIGHT GAIN, REDUCED EFFICIENCY OF FEED UTILIZATION, DIARRHEA AND DEVELOPMENT OF DEFORMED TOES. DEATH OCCURRED IN ANIMALS GIVEN 25-50% IN DRINKING WATER, AND IS USUALLY A RESULT OF RENAL DAMAGE. ADMINISTRATION TO RATS IN THE DIET AT LESS THAN 7.5%, NO ADVERSE EFFECTS ON REPRODUCTION WERE FOUND. HIGHER LEVELS AFFECTED GROWTH, FEEDING, MATING AND WEANING.

FIRST AID- IF THE PERSON IS CONSCIOUS AND NOT CONVULSING, REMOVE BY THOROUGH GASTRIC LAVAGE. IF IMMEDIATE GASTRIC LAVAGE CANNOT BE ACCOMPLISHED, INDUCE EMESIS WITH SYRUP OF IPECAC (DREISBACH, HANDBOOK OF POISONING, 12TH ED.). TREAT SYMPTOMATICALLY AND SUPPORTIVELY. GASTRIC LAVAGE SHOULD BE PERFORMED BY QUALIFIED MEDICAL PERSONNEL. GET MEDICAL ATTENTION IMMEDIATELY.

ANTIDOTE: NO SPECIFIC ANTIDOTE. TREAT SYMPTOMATICALLY AND SUPPORTIVELY.

REACTIVITY

REACTIVITY: STABLE UNDER NORMAL TEMPERATURES AND PRESSURES.

INCOMPATIBILITIES: PROPYLENE GLYCOL: METALS (LIGHT): REACTION FORMS FLAMMABLE HYDROGEN GAS. NITRIC ACID, HYDROFLUORIC ACID AND SILVER NITRATE: MIXTURE FORMS EXPLOSIVE SILVER FULMINATE. OXIDIZERS: FIRE AND EXPLOSION HAZARD. PLASTICS: MAY BE ATTACKED. SEE ALSO: ALCOHOLS. ALCOHOLS: ACETALDEHYDE: VIOLENT CONDENSATION REACTION. BARIUM PERCHLORATE: FORMATION OF HIGHLY EXPLOSIVE PERCHLORIC ESTER ON REFLUXING. CHLORINE: FORMATION OF HIGHLY EXPLOSIVE ALKYL HYPOCHLORITES. DIETHYL ALUMINUM BROMIDE: SPONTANEOUS IGNITION. ETHYLENE OXIDE: POSSIBLE EXPLOSION. HEXAMETHYLENE DIISOCYANATE: POSSIBLE EXPLOSION IN ABSENCE OF SOLVENT. HYDROGEN PEROXIDE + SULFURIC ACID: POSSIBLE EXPLOSION. HYPOCHLOROUS ACID: FORMATION OF HIGHLY EXPLOSIVE ALKYL HYPOCHLORITES. ISOCYANATES: POSSIBLE EXPLOSION IN ABSENCE OF SOLVENT. LITHIUM ALUMINUM HYDRIDE: VIGOROUS REACTION. NITROGEN TETROXIDE: POSSIBLE EXPLOSION. PERCHLORIC ACID (HOT): DANGEROUS INTERACTION. PERMONOSULFURIC ACID: POSSIBLE EXPLOSION ON CONTACT WITH PRIMARY OR SECONDARY ALCOHOLS. TRI-ISO-BUTYL ALUMINUM: VIOLENT REACTION.

DECOMPOSITION: THERMAL DECOMPOSITION PRODUCTS MAY INCLUDE TOXIC OXIDES OF CARBON.

POLYMERIZATION: HAZARDOUS POLYMERIZATION HAS NOT BEEN REPORTED TO OCCUR UNDER NORMAL TEMPERATURES AND PRESSURES.

STORAGE AND DISPOSAL

OBSERVE ALL FEDERAL, STATE AND LOCAL REGULATIONS WHEN STORING OR DISPOSING OF THIS SUBSTANCE. FOR ASSISTANCE, CONTACT THE DISTRICT DIRECTOR OF THE ENVIRONMENTAL PROTECTION AGENCY.

STORAGE

STORE AWAY FROM INCOMPATIBLE SUBSTANCES.

CONDITIONS TO AVOID

MAY BURN BUT DOES NOT IGNITE READILY. AVOID CONTACT WITH STRONG OXIDIZERS, EXCESSIVE HEAT, SPARKS, OR OPEN FLAME.

SPILL AND LEAK PROCEDURES

OCCUPATIONAL SPILL: STOP LEAK IF YOU CAN DO IT WITHOUT RISK. FOR SMALL SPILLS, TAKE UP WITH SAND OR OTHER ABSORBENT MATERIAL AND PLACE INTO CLEAN, DRY CONTAINERS FOR LATER DISPOSAL. KEEP UNNECESSARY PEOPLE AWAY. ISOLATE HAZARD AREA AND DENY ENTRY.

PROTECTIVE EQUIPMENT

VENTILATION: PROVIDE GENERAL DILUTION VENTILATION.

RESPIRATOR: THE FOLLOWING RESPIRATORS ARE RECOMMENDED BASED ON INFORMATION FOUND IN THE PHYSICAL DATA, TOXICITY AND HEALTH EFFECTS SECTIONS. THEY ARE RANKED IN ORDER FROM MINIMUM TO MAXIMUM RESPIRATORY PROTECTION. THE SPECIFIC RESPIRATOR SELECTED MUST BE BASED ON CONTAMINATION LEVELS FOUND IN THE WORK PLACE, MUST NOT EXCEED THE WORKING LIMITS OF THE RESPIRATOR AND BE JOINTLY APPROVED BY THE NATIONAL INSTITUTE FOR OCCUPATIONAL SAFETY AND HEALTH AND THE MINE SAFETY AND HEALTH ADMINISTRATION (NIOSH-MSHA).

CHEMICAL CARTRIDGE RESPIRATOR WITH AN ORGANIC VAPOR CARTRIDGE(S) WITH A FULL FACEPIECE.

GAS MASK WITH ORGANIC VAPOR CANISTER (CHIN-STYLE OR FRONT- OR BACK-MOUNTED CANISTER) WITH A FULL FACEPIECE.

TYPE 'C' SUPPLIED-AIR RESPIRATOR WITH A FULL FACEPIECE OPERATED IN PRESSURE-DEMAND OR OTHER POSITIVE PRESSURE MODE OR WITH A FULL FACEPIECE, HELMET OR HOOD OPERATED IN CONTINUOUS-FLOW MODE.

SELF-CONTAINED BREATHING APPARATUS WITH A FULL FACEPIECE OPERATED IN PRESSURE-DEMAND OR OTHER POSITIVE PRESSURE MODE.

FOR FIREFIGHTING AND OTHER IMMEDIATELY DANGEROUS TO LIFE OR HEALTH CONDITIONS: SELF-CONTAINED BREATHING APPARATUS WITH FULL FACEPIECE OPERATED IN PRESSURE-DEMAND OR OTHER POSITIVE PRESSURE MODE.

SUPPLIED-AIR RESPIRATOR WITH FULL FACEPIECE AND OPERATED IN PRESSURE-DEMAND OR OTHER POSITIVE PRESSURE MODE IN COMBINATION WITH AN AUXILIARY SELF-CONTAINED BREATHING APPARATUS OPERATED IN PRESSURE-DEMAND OR OTHER POSITIVE PRESSURE MODE.

CLOTHING: EMPLOYEE MUST WEAR APPROPRIATE PROTECTIVE (IMPERVIOUS) CLOTHING AND EQUIPMENT TO PREVENT REPEATED OR PROLONGED SKIN CONTACT WITH THIS SUBSTANCE.

GLOVES: EMPLOYEE MUST WEAR APPROPRIATE PROTECTIVE GLOVES TO PREVENT CONTACT WITH THIS SUBSTANCE.

EYE PROTECTION: EMPLOYEE MUST WEAR SPLASH-PROOF OR DUST-RESISTANT SAFETY GOGGLES TO PREVENT EYE CONTACT WITH THIS SUBSTANCE.

EMERGENCY EYE WASH: WHERE THERE IS ANY POSSIBILITY THAT AN EMPLOYEE'S EYES MAY BE EXPOSED TO THIS SUBSTANCE, THE EMPLOYER SHOULD PROVIDE AN EYE WASH FOUNTAIN WITHIN THE IMMEDIATE WORK AREA FOR EMERGENCY USE.

AUTHORIZED BY- OCCUPATIONAL HEALTH SERVICES, INC.

CREATION DATE: 10/04/89 ***REVISION DATE:*** 04/04/90

MATERIAL SAFETY DATA SHEET

OCCUPATIONAL HEALTH SERVICES, INC.	EMERGENCY CONTACT:
AGRICULTURE AND PESTICIDE DIVISION	JOHN S. BRANSFORD, JR. (615) 292-1180
450 SEVENTH AVENUE, SUITE 2407	
NEW YORK, NEW YORK 10123	
1-800-445-MSDS OR (212) 967-1100	

SUBSTANCE IDENTIFICATION

CAS-NUMBER 75-56-9

SUBSTANCE: PROPYLENE OXIDE

TRADE NAMES/SYNONYMS: 1,2-EPOXYPROPANE; METHYL OXIRANE; PROPENE OXIDE; METHYL ETHYLENE OXIDE; 1,2-PROPYLENE OXIDE; PROPYLENE EPOXIDE; EPOXYPROPANE; STCC 4906620; UN 1280; O-4332; PST19910

CHEMICAL FAMILY: EPOXY

MOLECULAR FORMULA: C3-H6-O

MOLECULAR WEIGHT: 58.08

CERCLA RATINGS (SCALE 0-3): HEALTH=3 FIRE=3 REACTIVITY=2 PERSISTENCE=0

NFPA RATINGS (SCALE 0-4): HEALTH=2 FIRE=4 REACTIVITY=2

COMPONENTS AND CONTAMINANTS

COMPONENT: PROPYLENE OXIDE ***PERCENT:*** 100

CAS# 75-56-9

OTHER CONTAMINANTS: NONE

EXPOSURE LIMITS: PROPYLENE OXIDE: 20 PPM (50 MG/M3) OSHA TWA 20 PPM (50 MG/M3) ACGIH TWA LOWEST FEASIBLE LIMIT NIOSH RECOMMENDED EXPOSURE CRITERIA

10,000 POUNDS SARA SECTION 302 THRESHOLD PLANNING QUANTITY 100 POUNDS SARA SECTION 304 REPORTABLE QUANTITY 100 POUNDS CERCLA SECTION 103 REPORTABLE QUANTITY SUBJECT TO SARA SECTION 313 ANNUAL TOXIC CHEMICAL RELEASE REPORTING SUBJECT TO CALIFORNIA PROPOSITION 65 CANCER AND/OR REPRODUCTIVE TOXICITY WARNING AND RELEASE REQUIREMENTS- (OCTOBER 1, 1988)

PHYSICAL DATA

DESCRIPTION: COLORLESS ETHEREAL LIQUID, SWEET ALCOHOL OR ETHER ODOR

BOILING POINT: 94 F (35 C) ***MELTING POINT:*** -170 F (-112 C)

SPECIFIC GRAVITY: 0.9 @ O C ***VAPOR PRESSURE:*** 445 MM @ 68 F

SOLUBILITY IN WATER: SOLUBLE ***ODOR THRESHOLD:*** 200.0 PPM

VAPOR DENSITY: 2.0
SOLVENT SOLUBILITY: ALCOHOL, ETHER, BENZENE, CARBON TETRACHLORIDE, ACETONE, METHANOL

FIRE AND EXPLOSION DATA

FIRE AND EXPLOSION HAZARD: MODERATE FIRE HAZARD WHEN EXPOSED TO HEAT OR FLAME.
VAPORS ARE HEAVIER THAN AIR AND MAY TRAVEL A CONSIDERABLE DISTANCE TO A SOURCE OF IGNITION AND FLASH BACK.
VAPOR-AIR MIXTURES ARE EXPLOSIVE ABOVE FLASH POINT.
FLASH POINT: -35 F (-37 C) (CC) ***UPPER EXPLOSIVE LIMIT:*** 36%
LOWER EXPLOSIVE LIMIT: 2.3% ***AUTOIGNITION TEMP.:*** 840 F (449 C)
FLAMMABILITY CLASS(OSHA): IA
FIREFIGHTING MEDIA: DRY CHEMICAL, CARBON DIOXIDE, HALON, WATER SPRAY OR ALCOHOL FOAM (1987 EMERGENCY RESPONSE GUIDEBOOK, DOT P 5800.4).
FOR LARGER FIRES, USE WATER SPRAY, FOG OR ALCOHOL FOAM (1987 EMERGENCY RESPONSE GUIDEBOOK, DOT P 5800.4).
ALCOHOL FOAM (NFPA 325M, FIRE HAZARD PROPERTIES OF FLAMMABLE LIQUIDS, GASES, AND VOLATILE SOLIDS, 1984).
FIREFIGHTING: MOVE CONTAINER FROM FIRE AREA IF POSSIBLE. COOL FIRE-EXPOSED CONTAINERS WITH WATER FROM SIDE UNTIL WELL AFTER FIRE IS OUT. STAY AWAY FROM STORAGE TANK ENDS. FOR MASSIVE FIRE IN STORAGE AREA, USE UNMANNED HOSE HOLDER OR MONITOR NOZZLES, ELSE WITHDRAW FROM AREA AND LET FIRE BURN. WITHDRAW IMMEDIATELY IN CASE OF RISING SOUND FROM VENTING SAFETY DEVICE OR ANY DISCOLORATION OF STORAGE TANK DUE TO FIRE (1987 EMERGENCY RESPONSE GUIDEBOOK, DOT P 5800.4, GUIDE PAGE 26).
EXTINGUISH ONLY IF FLOW CAN BE STOPPED; USE FLOODING AMOUNTS OF WATER AS FOG, SOLID STREAMS MAY NOT BE EFFECTIVE. COOL CONTAINERS WITH FLOODING QUANTITIES OF WATER, APPLY FROM AS FAR A DISTANCE AS POSSIBLE. EVACUATE TO A RADIUS OF 5000 FEET FOR UNCONTROLLABLE FIRES. CONSIDER EVACUATION OF DOWNWIND AREA IF MATERIAL IS LEAKING.
WATER MAY BE INEFFECTIVE (NFPA 325M, FIRE HAZARD PROPERTIES OF FLAMMABLE LIQUIDS, GASES, AND VOLATILE SOLIDS, 1984)

TRANSPORTATION DATA

DEPARTMENT OF TRANSPORTATION HAZARD CLASSIFICATION 49 CFR 172.101: FLAMMABLE LIQUID DEPARTMENT OF TRANSPORTATION LABELING REQUIREMENTS 49 CFR 172.101 AND SUBPART E: FLAMMABLE LIQUID
DEPARTMENT OF TRANSPORTATION PACKAGING REQUIREMENTS: 49 CFR 173.119 EXCEPTIONS: 49 CFR 173.118

TOXICITY

PROPYLENE OXIDE: IRRITATION DATA: 415 MG OPEN SKIN-RABBIT MODERATE; 50 MG/6 MINUTES SKIN-RABBIT SEVERE; 5 MG EYE-RABBIT SEVERE; 20 MG/24 HOURS EYE-RABBIT MODERATE. TOXICITY DATA: 4000 PPM/4 HOURS INHALATION-RAT LCLO; 1740 PPM/4 HOURS INHALATION-MOUSE LC50; 4000 PPM/4 HOURS INHALATION-GUINEA PIG LCLO; 2005 PPM/4 HOURS INHALATION-DOG LCLO; 1245 MG/KG SKIN-RABBIT LD50; 380 MG/KG ORAL-RAT LD50; 440 MG/KG ORAL-MOUSE LD50; 660 MG/KG ORAL-GUINEA PIG LD50; 150 MG/KG INTRAPERITONEAL-RAT LD50; 175 MG/KG INTRAPERITONEAL-MOUSE LD50; MUTAGENIC DATA (RTECS); REPRODUCTIVE EFFECTS DATA (RTECS); TUMORIGENIC DATA (RTECS).
CARCINOGEN STATUS: ANTICIPATED HUMAN CARCINOGEN (NTP); ANIMAL SUFFICIENT EVIDENCE, HUMAN INADEQUATE EVIDENCE (IARC GROUP-2A).
PROLONGED INHALATION OF PROPYLENE OXIDE PRODUCED HEMANGIOMAS AND HEMANGIOSARCOMAS OF THE NASAL SUBMUCOSA IN MICE AND AN INCREASED INCIDENCE OF ADRENAL PHEOCHROMOCYTOMAS, PERITONEAL MESOTHELIOMAS AND PAPILLARY ADENOMAS OF THE NASAL TURBINATES IN RATS. EXPOSURE BY GAVAGE IN RATS PRODUCED LOCAL TUMORS, MAINLY SQUAMOUS-CELL CARCINOMAS AND PAPILLOMAS OF THE FORESTOMACH. PROPYLENE OXIDE INDUCED LOCAL SARCOMAS, MAINLY FIBROSARCOMAS, AFTER SUBCUTANEOUS ADMINISTRATION TO MICE. LOCAL EFFECTS: CORROSIVE- SKIN, EYE; IRRITANT- INHALATION. ACUTE TOXICITY LEVEL: TOXIC BY INHALATION, INGESTION; MODERATELY TOXIC BY DERMAL ABSORPTION. TARGET EFFECTS: CENTRAL NERVOUS SYSTEM DEPRESSANT. AT INCREASED RISK FROM EXPOSURE: PERSONS WITH A HISTORY OF CHRONIC SKIN OR RESPIRATORY DISEASE.

HEALTH EFFECTS AND FIRST AID

INHALATION: PROPYLENE OXIDE: IRRITANT/NARCOTIC/CARCINOGEN/TOXIC. 2000 PPM IMMEDIATELY DANGEROUS TO LIFE OR HEALTH. **ACUTE EXPOSURE-** VAPORS MAY CAUSE IRRITATION OF THE RESPIRATORY TRACT. HIGH CONCENTRATIONS MAY CAUSE CENTRAL NERVOUS SYSTEM DEPRESSION. A SINGLE CASE OF HUMAN POISONING HAS BEEN REPORTED INVOLVING A WORKER EXPOSED TO 1500 PPM FOR 10 MINUTES. INITIAL SYMPTOMS INCLUDED LUNG IRRITATION, HEADACHE, ASTHENIA AND DIARRHEA. AFTER TWO HOURS, THE PATIENT BECAME CYANOTIC AND COLLAPSED. FOLLOWING TREATMENT HE REGAINED CONSCIOUSNESS AND VOMITED, BUT REMAINED CONFUSED AND WEAK. HOWEVER, AFTER 24 HOURS RECOVERY WAS COMPLETE. EXPOSURE TO 2,000 PPM OR MORE TO ANIMALS CAUSED RESPIRATORY IRRITATION, NARCOSIS WITH DROWSINESS, LACRIMATION, SALIVATION, VOMITING, NASAL DISCHARGE, WEAKNESS, INCOORDINATION, GASPING, LABORED BREATHING, AND SOME DEATHS. SEVERE IRRITATION OF THE LUNGS PERSISTED FOR SEVERAL DAYS. A WEAK ANESTHETIC ACTION HAS BEEN NOTED WITH CONCENTRATIONS OF 4,000 PPM OR MORE. FOLLOWING AN ACUTE EXPOSURE, A POSSIBLY FATAL SECONDARY LUNG INFECTION MAY DEVELOP. **CHRONIC EXPOSURE-** RATS AND GUINEA PIGS EXPOSED TO 457 PPM FOR 79-110 EXPOSURES SHOWED GROWTH DEPRESSION, PULMONARY EDEMA, LUNG AND LIVER INJURY, AND DEATH. ADDITIONAL EFFECTS REPORTED IN ANIMALS INCLUDED DYSPNEA WITH GASPING, HYPOACTIVITY, ATAXIA, RHINITIS, AND DIARRHEA. IN PROLONGED INHALATION STUDIES, PROPYLENE OXIDE CAUSED HEMANGIOMAS AND HEMANGIOSARCOMAS OF THE NASAL SUBMUCOSA IN MICE AND AN INCREASED INCIDENCE OF PAPILLARY ADENOMAS OF THE NASAL TURBINATES IN MICE. IN THE RESPIRATORY EPITHELIUM OF THE NASAL TURBINATES, PROPYLENE OXIDE ALSO CAUSED SUPPURATIVE INFLAMMATION, HYPERPLASIA, AND SQUAMOUS METAPLASIA IN RATS AND INFLAMMATION IN MICE. IN ONE EXPERIMENT, THERE WAS AN INCREASED INCIDENCE OF ADRENAL PHEOCHROMOCYTOMAS AND PERITONEAL MESOTHELIOMAS OBSERVED IN RATS. AN INCREASED INCIDENCE OF MAMMARY TUMORS HAS BEEN REPORTED IN RATS EXPOSED TO 100 OR 300 PPM FOR 123 WEEKS. REPRODUCTIVE EFFECTS HAVE BEEN REPORTED IN ANIMALS.
FIRST AID- REMOVE FROM EXPOSURE AREA TO FRESH AIR IMMEDIATELY. IF BREATHING HAS STOPPED, GIVE ARTIFICIAL RESPIRATION. MAINTAIN AIRWAY AND BLOOD PRESSURE AND ADMINISTER OXYGEN IF AVAILABLE. KEEP AFFECTED PERSON WARM AND AT REST. TREAT SYMPTOMATICALLY AND SUPPORTIVELY. ADMINISTRATION OF OXYGEN SHOULD BE PERFORMED BY QUALIFIED PERSONNEL. GET MEDICAL ATTENTION IMMEDIATELY.

SKIN CONTACT: PROPYLENE OXIDE: CORROSIVE. **ACUTE EXPOSURE-** THE UNDILUTED LIQUID MAY CAUSE SLIGHT IRRITATION IF ALLOWED TO EVAPORATE. HOWEVER, WHEN CONFINED TO THE SKIN, WATER SOLUTIONS AS DILUTE AS 10-20% MAY CAUSE IRRITATION WITH HYPERMIA AND EDEMA, BLISTERING, BURNS, AND SCAR FORMATION. SOLUTIONS AS DILUTE AS 1% MAY ALSO CAUSE ADVERSE EFFECTS. NECROTIC LESIONS AND CONTACT DERMATITIS HAVE ALSO BEEN REPORTED FROM DILUTE SOLUTIONS. APPLICATION TO THE SKIN OF MICE FOR 3.1 MINUTES WAS LETHAL TO 50% OF THE ANIMALS TESTED. **CHRONIC EXPOSURE-** REPEATED OR PROLONGED EXPOSURE MAY CAUSE DELAYED SECONDARY BURNS.
FIRST AID- REMOVE CONTAMINATED CLOTHING AND SHOES IMMEDIATELY. WASH AFFECTED AREA WITH SOAP OR MILD DETERGENT AND LARGE AMOUNTS OF WATER UNTIL NO EVIDENCE OF CHEMICAL REMAINS (AT LEAST 15-20 MINUTES). IN CASE OF CHEMICAL BURNS, COVER AREA WITH STERILE, DRY DRESSING. BANDAGE SECURELY, BUT NOT TOO TIGHTLY. GET MEDICAL ATTENTION IMMEDIATELY.

EYE CONTACT: PROPYLENE OXIDE: CORROSIVE. **ACUTE EXPOSURE-** MAY CAUSE SEVERE IRRITATION, AND CORNEAL BURNS. THE LIQUID APPLIED TO RABBIT EYES CAUSED REVERSIBLE INJURY, AND HAD AN IRRITATION RATING OF 5 ON A SCALE OF 1-10 AFTER 24 HOURS. **CHRONIC EXPOSURE-** NO DATA AVAILABLE.
FIRST AID- WASH EYES IMMEDIATELY WITH LARGE AMOUNTS OF WATER, OCCASIONALLY LIFTING UPPER AND LOWER LIDS, UNTIL NO EVIDENCE OF CHEMICAL REMAINS (AT LEAST 15-20 MINUTES). CONTINUE IRRIGATING WITH NORMAL SALINE UNTIL THE PH HAS RETURNED TO NORMAL (30-60 MINUTES). COVER WITH STERILE BANDAGES. GET MEDICAL ATTENTION IMMEDIATELY.

INGESTION: PROPYLENE OXIDE: CARCINOGEN/TOXIC. **ACUTE EXPOSURE-** THE LETHAL DOSE REPORTED IN RATS WAS 380 MG/KG. THE SYMPTOMS WERE NOT REPORTED. **CHRONIC EXPOSURE-** DOSES OF 0.3 GM/KG/DAY GIVEN TO ANIMALS CAUSED LOSS OF BODY WEIGHT, GASTRIC IRRITATION AND SLIGHT LIVER INJURY. IN FEEDING STUDIES, PROPYLENE OXIDE PRODUCED LOCAL TUMORS, MAINLY SQUAMOUS-CELL CARCINOMAS AND PAPILLOMAS OF THE FORESTOMACH IN RATS.
FIRST AID- IF THE PERSON IS CONSCIOUS AND NOT CONVULSING, INDUCE EMESIS BY GIVING SYRUP OF IPECAC FOLLOWED BY WATER. (IF VOMITING OCCURS KEEP THE HEAD BELOW THE HIPS TO PREVENT ASPIRATION). REPEAT IN 20 MINUTES IF NOT EFFECTIVE INITIALLY. GIVE ACTIVATED CHARCOAL. IN PATIENTS WITH DEPRESSED RESPIRATION OR IF EMESIS IS NOT PRODUCED, PERFORM GASTRIC LAVAGE CAUTIOUSLY (DREISBACH, HANDBOOK OF POISONING, 12TH ED.). TREAT SYMPTOMATICALLY AND SUPPORTIVELY. GASTRIC LAVAGE SHOULD BE PERFORMED BY QUALIFIED MEDICAL PERSONNEL. GET MEDICAL ATTENTION IMMEDIATELY.
ANTIDOTE: NO SPECIFIC ANTIDOTE. TREAT SYMPTOMATICALLY AND SUPPORTIVELY.

REACTIVITY

REACTIVITY: MAY POLYMERIZE ON EXPOSURE TO EXCESSIVE HEAT. IF POLYMERIZATION OCCURS IN A CLOSED CONTAINER, THE INCREASE IN

TEMPERATURE AND PRESSURE MAY RUPTURE THE CONTAINER.

INCOMPATIBILITIES: PROPYLENE OXIDE: ACETYLIDE FORMING METALS: REACTS. ACIDS: MAY INITIATE EXOTHERMIC POLYMERIZATION. ACID ALCOHOLS: MAY INITIATE EXOTHERMIC POLYMERIZATION. ALKALI METAL HYDROXIDES: REACTS. ALKALIS: MAY INITIATE EXOTHERMIC POLYMERIZATION. ALUMINUM CHLORIDE: MAY INITIATE EXOTHERMIC POLYMERIZATION. AMINES: MAY INITIATE EXOTHERMIC POLYMERIZATION. AMMONIA: REACTS. AMMONIUM HYDROXIDE: TEMPERATURE AND PRESSURE INCREASE IN A CLOSED CONTAINER. CHLORIDES: REACTS. CHLORINE: REACTS. CHLOROSULFONIC ACID: TEMPERATURE AND PRESSURE INCREASE IN A CLOSED CONTAINER. COATINGS: ATTACKS. EPOXY RESINS: MAY INITIATE EXOTHERMIC POLYMERIZATION OWING TO AMINE ACCELERATOR IN THE RESIN. HYDROCHLORIC ACID: TEMPERATURE AND PRESSURE INCREASE IN A CLOSED CONTAINER. HYDROFLUORIC ACID: TEMPERATURE AND PRESSURE INCREASE IN A CLOSED CONTAINER. IRON CHLORIDE: MAY INITIATE EXOTHERMIC POLYMERIZATION. METAL CHLORIDES (ANHYDROUS): MAY INITIATE EXOTHERMIC POLYMERIZATION. NITRIC ACID: TEMPERATURE AND PRESSURE INCREASE IN A CLOSED CONTAINER. OLEUM: TEMPERATURE AND PRESSURE INCREASE IN A CLOSED CONTAINER. OXIDES: REACTS. OXIDIZING MATERIALS: REACTS. PEROXIDES: MAY INITIATE EXOTHERMIC POLYMERIZATION. PLASTICS: ATTACKS. RUBBER: ATTACKS. SODIUM HYDROXIDE: INITIATES EXOTHERMIC POLYMERIZATION. SULFURIC ACID: TEMPERATURE AND PRESSURE INCREASE IN A CLOSED CONTAINER.

DECOMPOSITION: THERMAL DECOMPOSITION PRODUCTS MAY INCLUDE TOXIC OXIDES OF CARBON.

POLYMERIZATION: MAY POLYMERIZE ON EXPOSURE TO EXCESSIVE HEAT, PEROXIDES, ACIDS, ALKALIS, OR AMINES. IF POLYMERIZATION OCCURS IN A CLOSED CONTAINER, THE INCREASE IN TEMPERATURE AND PRESSURE MAY RUPTURE THE CONTAINER.

STORAGE AND DISPOSAL

OBSERVE ALL FEDERAL, STATE AND LOCAL REGULATIONS WHEN STORING OR DISPOSING OF THIS SUBSTANCE. FOR ASSISTANCE, CONTACT THE DISTRICT DIRECTOR OF THE ENVIRONMENTAL PROTECTION AGENCY.

****STORAGE****

STORE IN ACCORDANCE WITH 29 CFR 1910.106.

BONDING AND GROUNDING: SUBSTANCES WITH LOW ELECTROCONDUCTIVITY, WHICH MAY BE IGNITED BY ELECTROSTATIC SPARKS, SHOULD BE STORED IN CONTAINERS WHICH MEET THE BONDING AND GROUNDING GUIDELINES SPECIFIED IN NFPA 77-1983, RECOMMENDED PRACTICE ON STATIC ELECTRICITY.

PROTECT AGAINST PHYSICAL DAMAGE. DETACHED OUTSIDE STORAGE IS PREFERRED. INSIDE STORAGE SHOULD BE IN A STANDARD FLAMMABLE LIQUIDS STORAGE ROOM OR CABINET. ISOLATE FROM COMBUSTIBLE MATERIALS AND FROM OXIDIZING MATERIALS (NFPA 49, HAZARDOUS CHEMICALS DATA, 1975). STORE AWAY FROM INCOMPATIBLE SUBSTANCES.

THRESHOLD PLANNING QUANTITY (TPQ): THE SUPERFUND AMENDMENTS AND REAUTHORIZATION ACT (SARA) SECTION 302 REQUIRES THAT EACH FACILITY WHERE ANY EXTREMELY HAZARDOUS SUBSTANCE IS PRESENT IN A QUANTITY EQUAL TO OR GREATER THAN THE TPQ ESTABLISHED FOR THAT SUBSTANCE NOTIFY THE STATE EMERGENCY RESPONSE COMMISSION FOR THE STATE IN WHICH IT IS LOCATED. SECTION 303 OF SARA REQUIRES THESE FACILITIES TO PARTICIPATE IN LOCAL EMERGENCY RESPONSE PLANNING (40 CFR 355.30).

****DISPOSAL****

DISPOSAL MUST BE IN ACCORDANCE WITH STANDARDS APPLICABLE TO GENERATORS OF HAZARDOUS WASTE, 40 CFR 262. EPA HAZARDOUS WASTE NUMBER D001. 100 POUND CERCLA SECTION 103 REPORTABLE QUANTITY.

DISPOSAL MUST BE IN ACCORDANCE WITH STANDARDS APPLICABLE TO GENERATORS OF HAZARDOUS WASTE, 40 CFR 262. EPA HAZARDOUS WASTE NUMBER D003. 100 POUND CERCLA SECTION 103 REPORTABLE QUANTITY.

CONDITIONS TO AVOID

AVOID CONTACT WITH HEAT, SPARKS, FLAMES, OR OTHER SOURCES OF IGNITION. VAPORS MAY BE EXPLOSIVE AND POISONOUS; DO NOT ALLOW UNNECESSARY PERSONNEL IN AREA. DO NOT OVERHEAT CONTAINERS; CONTAINERS MAY VIOLENTLY RUPTURE AND TRAVEL A CONSIDERABLE DISTANCE IN HEAT OF FIRE.

SPILL AND LEAK PROCEDURES

SOIL SPILL: DIG HOLDING AREA SUCH AS LAGOON, POND OR PIT FOR CONTAINMENT. DIKE FLOW OF SPILLED MATERIAL USING SOIL OR SANDBAGS OR FOAMED BARRIERS SUCH AS POLYURETHANE OR CONCRETE.

USE CEMENT POWDER OR FLY ASH TO ABSORB LIQUID MASS.

IMMOBILIZE SPILL WITH UNIVERSAL GELLING AGENT.

AIR SPILL: KNOCK DOWN VAPORS WITH WATER SPRAY. KEEP UPWIND.

WATER SPILL: LIMIT SPILL MOTION AND DISPERSION WITH NATURAL BARRIERS OR OIL SPILL CONTROL BOOMS.

APPLY DETERGENTS, SOAPS, ALCOHOLS OR ANOTHER SURFACE ACTIVE AGENT.

APPLY UNIVERSAL GELLING AGENT TO IMMOBILIZE TRAPPED SPILL AND INCREASE EFFICIENCY OF REMOVAL.

USE ACTIVATED CARBON TO ABSORB SPILLED SUBSTANCE THAT IS DISSOLVED.

USE MECHANICAL DREDGES OR LIFTS TO EXTRACT IMMOBILIZED MASSES OF POLLUTION AND PRECIPITATES.

THE CALIFORNIA SAFE DRINKING WATER AND TOXIC ENFORCEMENT ACT OF 1986 (PROPOSITION 65) PROHIBITS CONTAMINATING ANY KNOWN SOURCE OF DRINKING WATER WITH SUBSTANCES KNOWN TO CAUSE CANCER AND/OR REPRODUCTIVE TOXICITY.

OCCUPATIONAL SPILL: SHUT OFF IGNITION SOURCES. STOP LEAK IF YOU CAN DO IT WITHOUT RISK. USE WATER SPRAY TO REDUCE VAPORS. FOR SMALL SPILLS, TAKE UP WITH SAND OR OTHER ABSORBENT MATERIAL AND PLACE INTO CONTAINERS FOR LATER DISPOSAL. FOR LARGER SPILLS, DIKE FAR AHEAD OF SPILL FOR LATER DISPOSAL. NO SMOKING, FLAMES OR FLARES IN HAZARD AREA. KEEP UNNECESSARY PEOPLE AWAY; ISOLATE HAZARD AREA AND DENY ENTRY.

REPORTABLE QUANTITY (RQ): 100 POUNDS THE SUPERFUND AMENDMENTS AND REAUTHORIZATION ACT (SARA) SECTION 304 REQUIRES THAT A RELEASE EQUAL TO OR GREATER THAN THE REPORTABLE QUANTITY FOR THIS SUBSTANCE BE IMMEDIATELY REPORTED TO THE LOCAL EMERGENCY PLANNING COMMITTEE AND THE STATE EMERGENCY RESPONSE COMMISSION (40 CFR 355.40). IF THE RELEASE OF THIS SUBSTANCE IS REPORTABLE UNDER CERCLA SECTION 103, THE NATIONAL RESPONSE CENTER MUST BE NOTIFIED IMMEDIATELY AT (800) 424-8802 OR (202) 426-2675 IN THE METROPOLITAN WASHINGTON, D.C. AREA (40 CFR 302.6).

PROTECTIVE EQUIPMENT

VENTILATION: PROVIDE LOCAL EXHAUST OR PROCESS ENCLOSURE VENTILATION TO MEET THE PUBLISHED EXPOSURE LIMITS. VENTILATION EQUIPMENT MUST BE EXPLOSION-PROOF.

RESPIRATOR: THE FOLLOWING RESPIRATORS AND MAXIMUM USE CONCENTRATIONS ARE RECOMMENDATIONS BY THE U.S. DEPARTMENT OF HEALTH AND HUMAN SERVICES, NIOSH POCKET GUIDE TO CHEMICAL HAZARDS; NIOSH CRITERIA DOCUMENTS OR BY THE U.S. DEPARTMENT OF LABOR, 29 CFR 1910 SUBPART Z.

THE SPECIFIC RESPIRATOR SELECTED MUST BE BASED ON CONTAMINATION LEVELS FOUND IN THE WORK PLACE, MUST NOT EXCEED THE WORKING LIMITS OF THE RESPIRATOR AND BE JOINTLY APPROVED BY THE NATIONAL INSTITUTE FOR OCCUPATIONAL SAFETY AND HEALTH AND THE MINE SAFETY AND HEALTH ADMINISTRATION (NIOSH-MSHA).

PROPYLENE OXIDE: 200 PPM- ANY SUPPLIED-AIR RESPIRATOR. ANY SELF-CONTAINED BREATHING APPARATUS.

500 PPM- ANY SUPPLIED-AIR RESPIRATOR OPERATED IN A CONTINUOUS FLOW MODE.

1000 PPM- ANY SUPPLIED-AIR RESPIRATOR WITH A FULL FACEPIECE. ANY SELF-CONTAINED BREATHING APPARATUS WITH A FULL FACEPIECE.

2000 PPM- ANY SUPPLIED-AIR RESPIRATOR WITH A FULL FACEPIECE AND OPERATED IN A PRESSURE-DEMAND OR OTHER POSITIVE PRESSURE MODE.

ESCAPE- ANY AIR-PURIFYING FULL FACEPIECE RESPIRATOR (GAS MASK) WITH A CHIN-STYLE OR FRONT- OR BACK-MOUNTED CANISTER PROVIDING PROTECTION AGAINST THE COMPOUND OF CONCERN. ANY APPROPRIATE ESCAPE-TYPE SELF-CONTAINED BREATHING APPARATUS.

FOR FIREFIGHTING AND OTHER IMMEDIATELY DANGEROUS TO LIFE OR HEALTH CONDITIONS:

SELF-CONTAINED BREATHING APPARATUS WITH FULL FACEPIECE OPERATED IN PRESSURE-DEMAND OR OTHER POSITIVE PRESSURE MODE.

SUPPLIED-AIR RESPIRATOR WITH FULL FACEPIECE AND OPERATED IN PRESSURE-DEMAND OR OTHER POSITIVE PRESSURE MODE IN COMBINATION WITH AN AUXILIARY SELF-CONTAINED BREATHING APPARATUS OPERATED IN PRESSURE-DEMAND OR OTHER POSITIVE PRESSURE MODE.

CLOTHING: EMPLOYEE MUST WEAR APPROPRIATE PROTECTIVE (IMPERVIOUS) CLOTHING AND EQUIPMENT TO PREVENT ANY POSSIBILITY OF SKIN CONTACT WITH THIS SUBSTANCE.

GLOVES: EMPLOYEE MUST WEAR APPROPRIATE PROTECTIVE GLOVES TO PREVENT CONTACT WITH THIS SUBSTANCE.

EYE PROTECTION: EMPLOYEE MUST WEAR SPLASH-PROOF OR DUST-RESISTANT SAFETY GOGGLES AND A FACESHIELD TO PREVENT CONTACT WITH THIS SUBSTANCE.

EMERGENCY WASH FACILITIES: WHERE THERE IS ANY POSSIBILITY THAT AN EMPLOYEE'S EYES AND/OR SKIN MAY BE EXPOSED TO THIS SUBSTANCE, THE EMPLOYER SHOULD PROVIDE AN EYE WASH FOUNTAIN AND QUICK DRENCH SHOWER WITHIN THE IMMEDIATE WORK AREA FOR EMERGENCY USE.

AUTHORIZED BY- OCCUPATIONAL HEALTH SERVICES, INC.

CREATION DATE: 10/04/89 ***REVISION DATE:*** 07/12/90

MATERIAL SAFETY DATA SHEET

OCCUPATIONAL HEALTH SERVICES, INC.
AGRICULTURE AND PESTICIDE DIVISION
450 SEVENTH AVENUE, SUITE 2407
NEW YORK, NEW YORK 10123
1-800-445-MSDS OR (212) 967-1100

EMERGENCY CONTACT:
JOHN S. BRANSFORD, JR. (615) 292-1180

SUBSTANCE IDENTIFICATION

CAS-NUMBER 94-13-3

SUBSTANCE: **PROPYL PARABEN**

TRADE NAMES/SYNONYMS: PROPYL P-HYDROXYBENZOATE; NIPASOL; TEGOSEPT P; PROTABEN; 4-HYDROXYBENZOIC ACID, PROPYL ESTER; P-HYDROXYBENZOIC ACID, PROPYL ESTER; PASEPTOL; PARASEPT; ASEPTOFORM P; BETACIDE P; BONOMOLD OP; PROPYL ASEPTOFORM; PROPYL P-OXYBENZOATE; PROPYL CHEMOSEPT; PRESERVAL P; CHEMOCIDE PK; SOLBROL P; PROPYL PARASEPT; C10H12O3; PST19941

CHEMICAL FAMILY: ESTER, CARBOXYLIC, AROMATIC

MOLECULAR FORMULA: H-O-C6-H4-C-O2-C3-H7

MOLECULAR WEIGHT: 180.20

CERCLA RATINGS (SCALE 0-3): HEALTH=3 FIRE=1 REACTIVITY=0 PERSISTENCE=1

NFPA RATINGS (SCALE 0-4): HEALTH=U FIRE=1 REACTIVITY=0

COMPONENTS AND CONTAMINANTS

COMPONENT: PROPYL PARABEN ***PERCENT:*** 100.0
CAS# 94-13-3

OTHER CONTAMINANTS: NONE

EXPOSURE LIMITS: NO OCCUPATIONAL EXPOSURE LIMITS ESTABLISHED BY OSHA, ACGIH, OR NIOSH.

PHYSICAL DATA

DESCRIPTION: ODORLESS, COLORLESS CRYSTALS OR WHITE CRYSTALLINE POWDER.

BOILING POINT: 271 F (133 C) @ 1 MMHG ***MELTING POINT:*** 205-208 F (96-98 C)

SPECIFIC GRAVITY: 1.0630 @ 102C ***VAPOR PRESSURE:*** <0.1 MMHG @ 20 C

SOLUBILITY IN WATER: 0.05%

SOLVENT SOLUBILITY: SOLUBLE IN ALCOHOL, ETHER AND ACETONE.

FIRE AND EXPLOSION DATA

FIRE AND EXPLOSION HAZARD: SLIGHT FIRE HAZARD WHEN EXPOSED TO HEAT OR FLAME.

FIREFIGHTING MEDIA: DRY CHEMICAL, CARBON DIOXIDE, HALON, WATER SPRAY OR STANDARD FOAM (1987 EMERGENCY RESPONSE GUIDEBOOK, DOT P 5800.4).
FOR LARGER FIRES, USE WATER SPRAY, FOG OR STANDARD FOAM (1987 EMERGENCY RESPONSE GUIDEBOOK, DOT P 5800.4).

FIREFIGHTING: MOVE CONTAINER FROM FIRE AREA IF POSSIBLE. DO NOT SCATTER SPILLED MATERIAL WITH HIGH PRESSURE WATER STREAMS. DIKE FIRE CONTROL WATER FOR LATER DISPOSAL (1987 EMERGENCY RESPONSE GUIDEBOOK, DOT P 5800.4, GUIDE PAGE 31).
USE AGENTS SUITABLE FOR TYPE OF SURROUNDING FIRE. AVOID BREATHING HAZARDOUS VAPORS, KEEP UPWIND.

TOXICITY

PROPYL PARABEN: TOXICITY DATA: 6332 MG/KG ORAL-MOUSE LD50; 6 GM/KG ORAL-RABBIT LDLO; 6000 MG/KG ORAL-DOG LD50; 1650 MG/KG SUBCUTANEOUS-MOUSE LD50; 200 MG/KG INTRAPERITONEAL-MOUSE LD50. CARCINOGEN STATUS: NONE. LOCAL EFFECTS: IRRITANT-EYE. ACUTE TOXICITY LEVEL: SLIGHTLY TOXIC BY INGESTION. TARGET EFFECTS: SENSITIZER- DERMAL. ADDITIONAL DATA: CROSS-SENSITIVITY WITH OTHER PARABENS IS POSSIBLE.

HEALTH EFFECTS AND FIRST AID

INHALATION: PROPYL PARABEN: **ACUTE EXPOSURE-** DUST MAY IRRITATE THE NOSE AND THROAT AND CAUSE COUGHING AND CHEST DISCOMFORT. **CHRONIC EXPOSURE-** NO DATA AVAILABLE.

FIRST AID- REMOVE FROM EXPOSURE AREA TO FRESH AIR IMMEDIATELY. IF BREATHING HAS STOPPED, PERFORM ARTIFICIAL RESPIRATION. KEEP PERSON WARM AND AT REST. TREAT SYMPTOMATICALLY AND SUPPORTIVELY. GET MEDICAL ATTENTION IMMEDIATELY.

SKIN CONTACT: PROPYL PARABEN: SENSITIZER. **ACUTE EXPOSURE-** MAY CAUSE ALLERGIC CONTACT URTICARIA OR DERMATITIS IN PREVIOUSLY EXPOSED PERSONS, ESPECIALLY WHEN APPLIED TO A SITE OF PREVIOUS, HEALED DERMATITIS. **CHRONIC EXPOSURE-** REPEATED CONTACT, ESPECIALLY WITH DAMAGED SKIN, MAY LEAD TO SENSITIZATION DERMATITIS, WHICH MAY BE SEVERE.

FIRST AID- REMOVE CONTAMINATED CLOTHING AND SHOES IMMEDIATELY. WASH AFFECTED AREA WITH SOAP OR MILD DETERGENT AND LARGE AMOUNTS OF WATER UNTIL NO EVIDENCE OF CHEMICAL REMAINS (APPROXIMATELY 15-20 MINUTES). GET MEDICAL ATTENTION IMMEDIATELY.

EYE CONTACT: PROPYL PARABEN: IRRITANT. **ACUTE EXPOSURE-** SATURATED AQUEOUS SOLUTIONS MAY CAUSE MODERATE IRRITATION. EYEDROPS CONTAINING 0.04% METHYL PARABEN AND 0.02% PROPYL PARABEN IN 0.9% SODIUM CHLORIDE SOLUTION REPORTEDLY CAUSED SMARTING OF THE EYES IN 75% OF THE PEOPLE TESTED; NO PERSISTENT EFFECTS WERE NOTED. **CHRONIC EXPOSURE-** REPEATED OR PROLONGED EXPOSURE TO IRRITANTS MAY CAUSE CONJUNCTIVITIS. ALLERGIC CONTACT DERMATITIS WITH REDNESS AND SWELLING OF THE EYELIDS HAS OCCASIONALLY OCCURRED FROM APPLICATION OF PRODUCTS CONTAINING PARABENS TO THE AREA AROUND THE EYES.

FIRST AID- WASH EYES IMMEDIATELY WITH LARGE AMOUNTS OF WATER OR NORMAL SALINE, OCCASIONALLY LIFTING UPPER AND LOWER LIDS, UNTIL NO EVIDENCE OF CHEMICAL REMAINS (APPROXIMATELY 15-20 MINUTES). GET MEDICAL ATTENTION IMMEDIATELY.

INGESTION: PROPYL PARABEN: **ACUTE EXPOSURE-** 0.03% AQUEOUS SOLUTIONS MAY CAUSE NUMB AND FELT-LIKE SENSATIONS IN THE MOUTH AND IRRITATION OF THE INTESTINAL MUCOSA. **CHRONIC EXPOSURE-** HAS BEEN USED THERAPEUTICALLY IN HUMANS AT DOSES OF 800 MG/KG FOR 3 DAYS. RATS FED 140 MG/KG/DAY FOR UP TO 18 MONTHS SHOWED NO ADVERSE EFFECTS; 1600 MG/KG/DAY CAUSED GROWTH RETARDATION.

FIRST AID- TREAT SYMPTOMATICALLY AND SUPPORTIVELY. GET MEDICAL ATTENTION IMMEDIATELY. IF VOMITING OCCURS, KEEP HEAD LOWER THAN HIPS TO PREVENT ASPIRATION.

ANTIDOTE: NO SPECIFIC ANTIDOTE. TREAT SYMPTOMATICALLY AND SUPPORTIVELY.

REACTIVITY

REACTIVITY: STABLE UNDER NORMAL TEMPERATURES AND PRESSURES.

INCOMPATIBILITIES: PROPYL PARABEN: OXIDIZERS (STRONG): FIRE AND EXPLOSION HAZARD.

DECOMPOSITION: THERMAL DECOMPOSITION PRODUCTS MAY INCLUDE TOXIC OXIDES OF CARBON.

POLYMERIZATION: HAZARDOUS POLYMERIZATION HAS NOT BEEN REPORTED TO OCCUR UNDER NORMAL TEMPERATURES AND PRESSURES.

STORAGE AND DISPOSAL

OBSERVE ALL FEDERAL, STATE AND LOCAL REGULATIONS WHEN STORING OR DISPOSING OF THIS SUBSTANCE. FOR ASSISTANCE, CONTACT THE DISTRICT DIRECTOR OF THE ENVIRONMENTAL PROTECTION AGENCY.

STORAGE

STORE AWAY FROM INCOMPATIBLE SUBSTANCES.
KEEP IN A TIGHTLY CLOSED CONTAINER. STORE IN A COOL, DRY, VENTILATED AREA.

CONDITIONS TO AVOID

MAY BURN BUT DOES NOT IGNITE READILY. AVOID CONTACT WITH STRONG OXIDIZERS, EXCESSIVE HEAT, SPARKS, OR OPEN FLAME.

SPILL AND LEAK PROCEDURES

OCCUPATIONAL SPILL: SWEEP UP AND PLACE IN SUITABLE CLEAN, DRY CONTAINERS FOR RECLAMATION OR LATER DISPOSAL. DO NOT FLUSH SPILLED MATERIAL INTO SEWER. KEEP UNNECESSARY PEOPLE AWAY.

PROTECTIVE EQUIPMENT

VENTILATION: PROVIDE GENERAL DILUTION VENTILATION.

RESPIRATOR: THE FOLLOWING RESPIRATORS ARE RECOMMENDED BASED ON INFORMATION FOUND IN THE PHYSICAL DATA, TOXICITY AND HEALTH EFFECTS SECTIONS. THEY ARE RANKED IN ORDER FROM MINIMUM TO MAXIMUM RESPIRATORY PROTECTION. THE SPECIFIC RESPIRATOR SELECTED MUST BE BASED ON CONTAMINATION LEVELS FOUND IN THE WORK PLACE, MUST NOT EXCEED THE WORKING LIMITS OF THE RESPIRATOR AND BE JOINTLY APPROVED BY THE NATIONAL INSTITUTE FOR OCCUPATIONAL SAFETY AND HEALTH AND THE MINE SAFETY AND HEALTH ADMINISTRATION (NIOSH-MSHA).
DUST AND MIST RESPIRATOR.
AIR-PURIFYING RESPIRATOR WITH A HIGH-EFFICIENCY PARTICULATE FILTER.
POWERED AIR-PURIFYING RESPIRATOR WITH A DUST AND MIST FILTER.
POWERED AIR-PURIFYING RESPIRATOR WITH A HIGH-EFFICIENCY PARTICULATE FILTER.
TYPE 'C' SUPPLIED-AIR RESPIRATOR OPERATED IN THE PRESSURE-DEMAND OR OTHER POSITIVE PRESSURE OR CONTINUOUS-FLOW MODE.
SELF-CONTAINED BREATHING APPARATUS.
FOR FIREFIGHTING AND OTHER IMMEDIATELY DANGEROUS TO LIFE OR HEALTH CONDITIONS:

SELF-CONTAINED BREATHING APPARATUS WITH FULL FACEPIECE OPERATED IN PRESSURE-DEMAND OR OTHER POSITIVE PRESSURE MODE.
SUPPLIED-AIR RESPIRATOR WITH FULL FACEPIECE AND OPERATED IN PRESSURE-DEMAND OR OTHER POSITIVE PRESSURE MODE IN COMBINATION WITH AN AUXILIARY SELF-CONTAINED BREATHING APPARATUS OPERATED IN PRESSURE-DEMAND OR OTHER POSITIVE PRESSURE MODE.

CLOTHING: EMPLOYEE MUST WEAR APPROPRIATE PROTECTIVE (IMPERVIOUS) CLOTHING AND EQUIPMENT TO PREVENT REPEATED OR PROLONGED SKIN CONTACT WITH THIS SUBSTANCE.

GLOVES: EMPLOYEE MUST WEAR APPROPRIATE PROTECTIVE GLOVES TO PREVENT CONTACT WITH THIS SUBSTANCE.

EYE PROTECTION: EMPLOYEE MUST WEAR SPLASH-PROOF OR DUST-RESISTANT SAFETY GOGGLES TO PREVENT EYE CONTACT WITH THIS SUBSTANCE.
EMERGENCY EYE WASH: WHERE THERE IS ANY POSSIBILITY THAT AN EMPLOYEE'S EYES MAY BE EXPOSED TO THIS SUBSTANCE, THE EMPLOYER SHOULD PROVIDE AN EYE WASH FOUNTAIN WITHIN THE IMMEDIATE WORK AREA FOR EMERGENCY USE.

AUTHORIZED BY- OCCUPATIONAL HEALTH SERVICES, INC.
CREATION DATE: 11/17/89 ***REVISION DATE:*** 05/31/90

MATERIAL SAFETY DATA SHEET

OCCUPATIONAL HEALTH SERVICES, INC.
AGRICULTURE AND PESTICIDE DIVISION
450 SEVENTH AVENUE, SUITE 2407
NEW YORK, NEW YORK 10123
1-800-445-MSDS OR (212) 967-1100

EMERGENCY CONTACT:
JOHN S. BRANSFORD, JR. (615) 292-1180

SUBSTANCE IDENTIFICATION

CAS-NUMBER 2275-18-5

SUBSTANCE: **PROTHOATE**

TRADE NAMES/SYNONYMS: PHOSPHORODITHIOIC ACID, O,O-DIETHYL S-(2-((1-METHYLETHYL)AMINO) -2-OXOETHYL)ESTER; PHOSPHORODITHIOIC ACID, O,O-DIETHYL ESTER, S-ESTER WITH N-ISOPROPYL -2-MERCAPTOACETAMIDE; O,O-DIETHYL S-ISOPROPYLCARBAMOYLMETHYL PHOSPHORODITHIOATE; 2-DIETHOXYPHOSPHINOTHIOYLTHIO-N-ISOPROPYLACETAMIDE; O,O-DIETHYL S-(2((1-METHYLETHYL)AMINO)-2-OXOETHYL) PHOSPHORODITHIOATE; O,O-DIETHYL PHOSPHORODITHIOATE S-ESTER WITH N-ISOPROPYL-2- MERCAPTOACETAMIDE; DIETHYL S-(N-ISOPROPYLCARBAMOYLMETHYL)PHOSPHOROTHIOLOTHIONATE; AMERICAN CYANAMID 18,682; FAC; FAC 20; FAK-40; FOSTION; PROTHOAT; ENT 24 652; PST19943

CHEMICAL FAMILY: ORGANOPHOSPHATE

MOLECULAR FORMULA: C9-H20-N-O3-P-S2

MOLECULAR WEIGHT: 285.39

CERCLA RATINGS (SCALE 0-3): HEALTH=3 FIRE=0 REACTIVITY=0 PERSISTENCE=0

NFPA RATINGS (SCALE 0-4): HEALTH=4 FIRE=0 REACTIVITY=0

COMPONENTS AND CONTAMINANTS

COMPONENT: PROTHOATE ***PERCENT:*** 100
CAS# 2275-18-5

EXPOSURE LIMITS: NO OCCUPATIONAL EXPOSURE LIMITS ESTABLISHED BY OSHA, ACGIH, OR NIOSH.
PROTHOATE: 100/10,000 POUNDS SARA SECTION 302 THRESHOLD PLANNING QUANTITY 1 POUND SARA SECTION 304 REPORTABLE QUANTITY

PHYSICAL DATA

DESCRIPTION: COLORLESS CRYSTALLINE SOLID ***MELTING POINT:*** 84 F (29 C)

SPECIFIC GRAVITY: 1.151 ***VAPOR PRESSURE:*** 0.0001 MMHG @ 40 C

SOLUBILITY IN WATER: 0.25%

SOLVENT SOLUBILITY: SOLUBLE IN MOST ORGANIC SOLVENTS

FIRE AND EXPLOSION DATA

FIRE AND EXPLOSION HAZARD: NEGLIGIBLE FIRE HAZARD WHEN EXPOSED TO HEAT OR FLAME.

FIREFIGHTING MEDIA: DRY CHEMICAL, CARBON DIOXIDE, HALON, WATER SPRAY OR STANDARD FOAM (1987 EMERGENCY RESPONSE GUIDEBOOK, DOT P 5800.4).
FOR LARGER FIRES, USE WATER SPRAY, FOG OR STANDARD FOAM (1987 EMERGENCY RESPONSE GUIDEBOOK, DOT P 5800.4).

FIREFIGHTING: MOVE CONTAINERS FROM FIRE AREA IF POSSIBLE. FIGHT FIRE FROM MAXIMUM DISTANCE. STAY AWAY FROM STORAGE TANK ENDS. DIKE FIRE CONTROL WATER FOR LATER DISPOSAL. DO NOT SCATTER MATERIAL (1987 EMERGENCY RESPONSE GUIDEBOOK, DOT P 5800.4, GUIDE PAGE 55).
EXTINGUISH ONLY IF FLOW CAN BE STOPPED; USE FLOODING AMOUNTS OF WATER AS FOG, SOLID STREAMS MAY BE INEFFECTIVE. COOL CONTAINERS WITH FLOODING AMOUNTS OF WATER FROM AS FAR A DISTANCE AS POSSIBLE. USE WATER SPRAY TO ABSORB TOXIC VAPORS. AVOID BREATHING TOXIC VAPORS; KEEP UPWIND. CONSIDER EVACUATION OF DOWNWIND AREA IF MATERIAL IS LEAKING.

TRANSPORTATION DATA

DEPARTMENT OF TRANSPORTATION HAZARD CLASSIFICATION 49 CFR 172.101: POISON B
DEPARTMENT OF TRANSPORTATION LABELING REQUIREMENTS 49 CFR 172.101 AND SUBPART E: POISON
DEPARTMENT OF TRANSPORTATION PACKAGING REQUIREMENTS: 49 CFR 173.365 EXCEPTIONS: 49 CFR 173.364

TOXICITY

PROTHOATE: TOXICITY DATA: 165 MG/M3/4 HOURS INHALATION-RAT LC50; 14 MG/KG SKIN-RABBIT LD50; 100 MG/KG SKIN-RAT LD50; 8 MG/KG ORAL-RAT LD50; 8 MG/KG ORAL-MOUSE LD50; 15 MG/KG ORAL-DOG LD50; 8500 UG/KG ORAL-RABBIT LD50; 8 MG/KG UNREPORTED-RAT LD50. CARCINOGEN STATUS: NONE. ACUTE TOXICITY LEVEL: HIGHLY TOXIC BY INHALATION, INGESTION, AND DERMAL ABSORPTION. TARGET EFFECTS: CHOLINESTERASE INHIBITOR. POISONING MAY AFFECT THE NERVOUS SYSTEM.* AT INCREASED RISK FROM EXPOSURE: PERSONS WITH RESPIRATORY AILMENTS, RECENT EXPOSURE TO CHOLINESTERASE INHIBITORS OR IMPAIRED CHOLINESTERASE PRODUCTION, OR LIVER MALFUNCTION.* ADDITIONAL DATA: MAY CROSS THE PLACENTA. HIGH ENVIRONMENTAL TEMPERATURES OR EXPOSURE OF THE CHEMICAL TO VISIBLE OR ULTRAVIOLET LIGHT MAY ENHANCE THE TOXICITY. INTERACTIONS WITH MEDICATIONS MAY OCCUR.*
* MAY BE BASED ON GENERAL INFORMATION ON ORGANOPHOSPHATES.

HEALTH EFFECTS AND FIRST AID

INHALATION: PROTHOATE: HIGHLY TOXIC. SEE INFORMATION ON ORGANOPHOSPHATES.
ORGANOPHOSPHATES: CHOLINESTERASE INHIBITOR. **ACUTE EXPOSURE-** WHEN INHALED, THE FIRST EFFECTS OF CHOLINESTERASE INHIBITORS ARE USUALLY RESPIRATORY AND MAY INCLUDE NASAL HYPEREMIA AND WATERY DISCHARGE, COUGH, CHEST DISCOMFORT, DYSPNEA, AND WHEEZING DUE TO INCREASED BRONCHIAL SECRETIONS AND BRONCHOCONSTRICTION. IF SUFFICIENT AMOUNTS ARE ABSORBED, OTHER SYSTEMIC EFFECTS MAY BEGIN WITHIN A FEW MINUTES OR BE DELAYED FOR UP TO 12 HOURS. SYMPTOMS MAY INCLUDE PALLOR, NAUSEA, VOMITING, DIARRHEA, ABDOMINAL CRAMPS, HEADACHE, DIZZINESS, OCULAR PAIN, BLURRED VISION, MIOSIS OR IN SOME CASES, ESPECIALLY INITIALLY, MYDRIASIS, LACRIMATION, SALIVATION, SWEATING, AND CONFUSION. OTHER REPORTED CENTRAL NERVOUS SYSTEM OR NEUROMUSCULAR EFFECTS MAY INCLUDE ATAXIA, SLURRED SPEECH, AREFLEXIA, WEAKNESS, FATIGUE, FASCICULATIONS, TWITCHING, TREMORS POSSIBLY OF THE TONGUE AND EYELIDS, AND EVENTUALLY PARALYSIS OF THE EXTREMITIES AND POSSIBLY OF THE RESPIRATORY MUSCLES. IN SEVERE CASES THERE MAY ALSO BE INVOLUNTARY DEFECATION AND URINATION, CYANOSIS, PSYCHOSIS, HYPERGLYCEMIA, ACUTE PANCREATITIS, CARDIAC IRREGULARITIES, PULMONARY EDEMA, UNCONSCIOUSNESS, CONVULSIONS, AND COMA. DEATH IS PRIMARILY DUE TO RESPIRATORY FAILURE, ALTHOUGH CARDIOVASCULAR EFFECTS INCLUDING CARDIAC ARREST MAY ALSO BE IMPLICATED. LONG TERM SEQUELAE ARE RARE BUT MAY INCLUDE NEUROPSYCHIATRIC DISORDERS AND MYOPATHY WITH MUSCLE TENDERNESS. SOME ORGANOPHOSPHATES MAY CAUSE A DELAYED NEUROPATHY BEGINNING 1-4 WEEKS AFTER AN ACUTE EXPOSURE WHICH MAY OR MAY NOT HAVE CAUSED ACUTE CHOLINERGIC EFFECTS. NUMBNESS, TINGLING, WEAKNESS AND CRAMPING BEGINNING SYMMETRICALLY IN THE LOWER LIMBS MAY PROGRESS TO ATAXIA AND PARALYSIS. IN SEVERE CASES, UPPER LIMB INVOLVEMENT IS POSSIBLE AND FLACCID PARALYSIS MAY PROGRESS TO SPASTIC PARALYSIS WITH EXAGGERATED REFLEXES. IMPROVEMENT MAY OCCUR OVER MONTHS TO YEARS, BUT SOME RESIDUAL IMPAIRMENT USUALLY REMAINS.
CHRONIC EXPOSURE- REPEATED OR PROLONGED EXPOSURE MAY RESULT IN THE EFFECTS OF ACUTE EXPOSURE INCLUDING THE DELAYED NEUROPATHY. OTHER EFFECTS REPORTED IN WORKERS REPEATEDLY EXPOSED INCLUDE IMPAIRED MEMORY AND CONCENTRATION, ACUTE PSYCHOSIS, SEVERE DEPRESSIONS, IRRITABILTY, CONFUSION, APATHY, EMOTIONAL LABILITY, SOCIAL WITHDRAWAL, CONFUSION, HEADACHE, SPEECH DIFFICULTIES, DELAYED REACTION TIMES, SPATIAL DISORIENTATION, NIGHTMARES, SLEEPWALKING, AND DROWSINESS OR INSOMNIA. AN INFLUENZA-LIKE CONDITION WITH HEADACHE, NAUSEA, WEAKNESS, ANOREXIA AND MALAISE HAS ALSO BEEN REPORTED.

FIRST AID- REMOVE FROM EXPOSURE AREA TO FRESH AIR IMMEDIATELY. IF BREATHING HAS STOPPED, GIVE ARTIFICIAL RESPIRATION. MAINTAIN AIRWAY AND BLOOD PRESSURE AND ADMINISTER OXYGEN IF AVAILABLE. KEEP AFFECTED PERSON WARM AND AT REST. TREAT SYMPTOMATICALLY AND SUPPORTIVELY. ADMINISTRATION OF OXYGEN SHOULD BE PERFORMED BY QUALIFIED PERSONNEL. GET MEDICAL ATTENTION IMMEDIATELY.

SKIN CONTACT: PROTHOATE: HIGHLY TOXIC. SEE INFORMATION ON ORGANOPHOSPHATES.
ORGANOPHOSPHATES: CHOLINESTERASE INHIBITOR. **ACUTE EXPOSURE**- LOCALIZED SWEATING AND FASCICULATIONS MAY OCCUR AT THE SITE OF CONTACT. IF SUFFICIENT AMOUNTS ARE ABSORBED, OTHER EFFECTS OF CHOLINESTERASE INHIBITION AS DESCRIBED IN ACUTE INHALATION MAY OCCUR. SYMPTOMS MAY BE DELAYED 2-3 HOURS, BUT USUALLY NO MORE THAN 12 HOURS. THE RATE OF ABSORPTION IS INCREASED BY THE PRESENCE OF DERMATITIS OR HIGH AMBIENT TEMPERATURES. DELAYED NEUROPATHY IS ALSO POSSIBLE. **CHRONIC EXPOSURE**- REPEATED OR PROLONGED EXPOSURE MAY CAUSE EFFECTS AS DESCRIBED IN ACUTE EXPOSURE. SOME ORGANOPHOSPHATES MAY CAUSE SENSITIZATION.

FIRST AID- REMOVE CONTAMINATED CLOTHING IMMEDIATELY. WASH CONTAMINATED AREAS WITH SOAP AND WATER FOLLOWED BY ALCOHOL (ARENA, POISONING, 4TH ED.). EMERGENCY PERSONNEL SHOULD WEAR GLOVES AND AVOID CONTAMINATION. TREAT RESPIRATORY DIFFICULTY WITH ARTIFICIAL RESPIRATION. GET MEDICAL ATTENTION IMMEDIATELY.

EYE CONTACT: PROTHOATE: SEE INFORMATION ON ORGANOPHOSPHATES.
ORGANOPHOSPHATES: CHOLINESTERASE INHIBITOR. **ACUTE EXPOSURE**- DIRECT CONTACT MAY CAUSE PAIN, HYPEREMIA, LACRIMATION, TWITCHING OF THE EYELIDS, MIOSIS, AND CILIARY MUSCLE SPASM WITH LOSS OF ACCOMODATION, BLURRED OR DIMMED VISION AND BROWACHE. SOMETIMES MYDRIASIS MAY OCCUR INSTEAD OF MIOSIS. WITH SUFFICIENT EXPOSURE, OTHER SYMPTOMS OF CHOLINESTERASE INHIBITION AS DESCRIBED IN ACUTE INHALATION MAY OCCUR. **CHRONIC EXPOSURE**- REPEATED OR PROLONGED EXPOSURE MAY CAUSE EFFECTS AS DESCRIBED IN ACUTE EXPOSURE. SOME COMPOUNDS HAVE CAUSED TOXIC EFFECTS ON THE CRYSTALLINE LENS, CONJUNCTIVAL THICKENING AND OBSTRUCTION OF THE NASOLACRIMAL CANALS WHEN USED AS MIOTIC EYEDROPS.

FIRST AID- IRRIGATE EYES WITH WATER OR SALINE SOLUTION. IF SYMPTOMS OF POISONING OCCUR, TREAT RESPIRATORY DIFFICULTY WITH ARTIFICIAL RESPIRATION AND OXYGEN. OBSERVE PATIENT FOR AT LEAST 24-36 HOURS (GOSSELIN, CLINICAL TOXICOLOGY OF COMMERCIAL PRODUCTS, 5TH ED.). GET MEDICAL ATTENTION IMMEDIATELY. OXYGEN SHOULD BE ADMINISTERED BY QUALIFIED MEDICAL PERSONNEL.

INGESTION: PROTHOATE: HIGHLY TOXIC. SEE INFORMATION ON ORGANOPHOSPHATES.
ORGANOPHOSPHATES: CHOLINESTERASE INHIBITOR. **ACUTE EXPOSURE**- WHEN INGESTED, THE FIRST EFFECTS MAY BE NAUSEA, VOMITING, ANOREXIA, ABDOMINAL CRAMPS AND DIARRHEA. GASTROINTESTINAL ABSORPTION MAY CAUSE SYMPTOMS OF CHOLINESTERASE INHIBITION AS DESCRIBED IN ACUTE INHALATION. SYMPTOMS MAY BEGIN WITHIN MINUTES OR BE DELAYED FOR HOURS. DELAYED EFFECTS INCLUDING NEUROPATHY MAY ALSO OCCUR. **CHRONIC EXPOSURE**- REPEATED INGESTION MAY CAUSE EFFECTS AS DESCRIBED IN ACUTE EXPOSURE.

FIRST AID- IF PERSON IS ALERT AND RESPIRATION IS NOT DEPRESSED, GIVE SYRUP OF IPECAC FOLLOWED BY WATER (IF VOMITING OCCURS, KEEP HEAD BELOW HIPS TO PREVENT ASPIRATION). IF CONSCIOUSNESS LEVEL DECLINES OR VOMITING HAS NOT OCCURRED IN 15 MINUTES EMPTY STOMACH BY GASTRIC LAVAGE WITH THE AID OF CUFFED ENDOTRACHEAL TUBE USING ISOTONIC SALINE OR 5% SODIUM BICARBONATE FOLLOW WITH ACTIVATED CHARCOAL. ESTABLISH AND MAINTAIN AIRWAY. TREAT RESPIRATORY DIFFICULTY WITH ARTIFICIAL RESPIRATION AND OXYGEN. DO NOT GIVE MORPHINE, AMINOPHYLLINE, PHENOTHIAZINES, RESERPINE, FUROSEMIDE, OR ETHACRYNIC ACID (MORGAN, RECOGNITION AND MANAGEMENT OF PESTICIDE POISONINGS, 3RD ED.). TREAT SYMPTOMATICALLY AND SUPPORTIVELY. ADMINISTRATION OF OXYGEN AND LAVAGE MUST BE PERFORMED BY QUALIFIED MEDICAL PERSONNEL. GET MEDICAL ATTENTION IMMEDIATELY.

ANTIDOTE: THE FOLLOWING ANTIDOTE(S) HAVE BEEN RECOMMENDED. HOWEVER, THE DECISION AS TO WHETHER THE SEVERITY OF POISONING REQUIRES ADMINISTRATION OF ANY ANTIDOTE AND ACTUAL DOSE REQUIRED SHOULD BE MADE BY QUALIFIED MEDICAL PERSONNEL.
FOR CHOLINESTERASE INHIBITORS: ESTABLISH CLEAR AIRWAY AND TISSUE OXYGENATION BY ASPIRATION OF SECRETIONS, AND IF NECESSARY, BY ASSISTED PULMONARY VENTILATION WITH OXYGEN. IMPROVE TISSUE OXYGENATION AS MUCH AS POSSIBLE BEFORE ADMINISTERING ATROPINE TO MINIMIZE THE RISK OF VENTRICULAR FIBRILLATION. ADMINISTER ATROPINE SULFATE INTRAVENOUSLY, OR INTRAMUSCULARLY IF IV INJECTION IS NOT POSSIBLE. IN MODERATELY SEVERE POISONING ADMINISTER ATROPINE SULFATE, 0.4-2.0 MG REPEATED EVERY 15 MINUTES UNTIL ATROPINIZATION IS ACHIEVED (TACHYCARDIA, FLUSHING, DRY MOUTH, MYDRIASIS). MAINTAIN ATROPINIZATION BY REPEATED DOSES FOR 2-12 HOURS, OR LONGER, DEPENDING ON THE SEVERITY OF POISONING. THE APPEARANCE OF RALES IN THE LUNG BASES, MIOSIS, SALIVATION, NAUSEA, BRADYCARDIA, ARE ALL INDICATIONS OF INADEQUATE ATROPINIZATION.
SEVERELY POISONED INDIVIDUALS MAY EXHIBIT REMARKABLE TOLERANCE TO ATROPINE; TWO OR MORE TIMES THE DOSAGES SUGGESTED ABOVE MAY BE NEEDED. PERSONS NOT POISONED OR ONLY SLIGHTLY POISONED, HOWEVER, MAY DEVELOP SIGNS OF ATROPINE TOXICITY FROM SUCH LARGE DOSAGES: FEVER, MUSCLE FIBRILLATIONS, AND DELIRIUM ARE THE MAIN SIGNS OF ATROPINE TOXICITY. IF THESE SIGNS APPEAR WHILE THE PATIENT IS FULLY ATROPINIZED, ATROPINE ADMINISTRATION SHOULD BE DISCONTINUED, AT LEAST TEMPORARILY. OBSERVE TREATED PATIENTS CLOSELY AT LEAST 24 HOURS TO INSURE THAT SYMPTOMS (POSSIBLY PULMONARY EDEMA) DO NOT RECUR AS ATROPINIZATION WEARS OFF. IN VERY SEVERE POISONINGS, METABOLIC DISPOSITION OF TOXICANT MAY REQUIRE SEVERAL HOURS OR DAYS DURING WHICH ATROPINIZATION MUST BE MAINTAINED. MARKEDLY LOWER LEVELS OF URINARY METABOLITES INDICATE THAT ATROPINE DOSAGE CAN BE TAPERED OFF. AS DOSAGE IS REDUCED, CHECK THE LUNG BASES FREQUENTLY FOR RALES. IF RALES ARE HEARD OR OTHER SYMPTOMS RETURN, RE-ESTABLISH ATROPINIZATION PROMPTLY (MORGAN, RECOGNITION AND MANAGEMENT OF PESTICIDE POISONINGS, 3RD ED.). ADMINISTRATION OF ANTIDOTE MUST BE PERFORMED BY QUALIFIED MEDICAL PERSONNEL.
IN CASES OF SEVERE POISONING BY ORGANOPHOSPHATE PESTICIDES IN WHICH RESPIRATORY DEPRESSION, MUSCLE WEAKNESS AND TWITCHINGS ARE SEVERE, GIVE PRALIDOXIME (PROTOPAM-AYERST, 2-PAM), 1.0 GRAM INTRAVENOUSLY AT NO MORE THAN 0.5 GRAM PER MINUTE. DOSAGE OF PRALIDOXIME MAY BE REPEATED IN 1-2 HOURS, THEN AT 10-12 HOUR INTERVALS IF NEEDED. IN VERY SEVERE POISONINGS, DOSAGE RATES MAY BE DOUBLED. TREATMENT WITH PRALIDOXIME WILL BE MOST EFFECTIVE IF GIVEN WITHIN THIRTY-SIX HOURS AFTER POISONING (MORGAN, RECOGNITION AND MANAGEMENT OF PESTICIDE POISONINGS, 3RD ED.). ANTIDOTE SHOULD BE ADMINISTERED BY QUALIFIED MEDICAL PERSONNEL.

REACTIVITY

REACTIVITY: IS STABLE FROM PH 4 TO PH 8.2, BUT IT IS DECOMPOSED AT 50 C IN 48 HOURS AT PH 9.2.

INCOMPATIBILITIES: PROTHOATE: ALKALINES (STRONG): INCOMPATIBLE. OXIDIZERS (STRONG): FIRE AND EXPLOSION HAZARD.

DECOMPOSITION: THERMAL DECOMPOSITION MAY RELEASE TOXIC AND/OR HAZARDOUS GASES.

POLYMERIZATION: HAZARDOUS POLYMERIZATION HAS NOT BEEN REPORTED TO OCCUR UNDER NORMAL TEMPERATURES AND PRESSURES.

STORAGE AND DISPOSAL

OBSERVE ALL FEDERAL, STATE AND LOCAL REGULATIONS WHEN STORING OR DISPOSING OF THIS SUBSTANCE. FOR ASSISTANCE, CONTACT THE DISTRICT DIRECTOR OF THE ENVIRONMENTAL PROTECTION AGENCY.

STORAGE

STORE IN ACCORDANCE WITH 40 CFR 165 RECOMMENDED PROCEDURES FOR THE DISPOSAL AND STORAGE OF PESTICIDES AND PESTICIDE CONTAINERS.
STORE IN SEALED ORIGINAL CONTAINERS IN A VENTILATED, DRY, SHADED AREA. STORE BELOW 77-86 F (25-30 C). KEEP AWAY FROM HEAT, FLAMES, AND SPARKS.
THRESHOLD PLANNING QUANTITY (TPQ): THE SUPERFUND AMENDMENTS AND REAUTHORIZATION ACT (SARA) SECTION 302 REQUIRES THAT EACH FACILITY WHERE ANY EXTREMELY HAZARDOUS SUBSTANCE IS PRESENT IN A QUANTITY EQUAL TO OR GREATER THAN THE TPQ ESTABLISHED FOR THAT SUBSTANCE NOTIFY THE STATE EMERGENCY RESPONSE COMMISSION FOR THE STATE IN WHICH IT IS LOCATED. SECTION 303 OF SARA REQUIRES THESE FACILITIES TO PARTICIPATE IN LOCAL EMERGENCY RESPONSE PLANNING (40 CFR 355.30).

DISPOSAL

DISPOSAL MUST BE IN ACCORDANCE WITH 40 CFR 165 RECOMMENDED PROCEDURES FOR THE DISPOSAL AND STORAGE OF PESTICIDES AND PESTICIDE CONTAINERS.

CONDITIONS TO AVOID

NONE REPORTED.

SPILL AND LEAK PROCEDURES

OCCUPATIONAL SPILL: DO NOT TOUCH SPILLED MATERIAL. STOP LEAK IF YOU CAN DO IT WITHOUT RISK. USE WATER SPRAY TO REDUCE VAPORS. FOR SMALL SPILLS, TAKE UP WITH SAND OR OTHER ABSORBENT MATERIAL AND PLACE INTO CONTAINERS FOR LATER DISPOSAL. FOR SMALL DRY SPILLS, WITH A CLEAN SHOVEL PLACE MATERIAL INTO CLEAN, DRY CONTAINERS AND COVER. MOVE CONTAINERS FROM SPILL AREA. FOR LARGER SPILLS, DIKE FAR AHEAD OF SPILL

FOR LATER DISPOSAL. KEEP UNNECESSARY PEOPLE AWAY. ISOLATE HAZARD AREA AND DENY ENTRY. VENTILATE CLOSED SPACES BEFORE ENTERING. REPORTABLE QUANTITY (RQ): 1 POUND THE SUPERFUND AMENDMENTS AND REAUTHORIZATION ACT (SARA) SECTION 304 REQUIRES THAT A RELEASE EQUAL TO OR GREATER THAN THE REPORTABLE QUANTITY FOR THIS SUBSTANCE BE IMMEDIATELY REPORTED TO THE LOCAL EMERGENCY PLANNING COMMITTEE AND THE STATE EMERGENCY RESPONSE COMMISSION (40 CFR 355.40). IF THE RELEASE OF THIS SUBSTANCE IS REPORTABLE UNDER CERCLA SECTION 103, THE NATIONAL RESPONSE CENTER MUST BE NOTIFIED IMMEDIATELY AT (800) 424-8802 OR (202) 426-2675 IN THE METROPOLITAN WASHINGTON, D.C. AREA (40 CFR 302.6).

PROTECTIVE EQUIPMENT

VENTILATION: PROCESS ENCLOSURE RECOMMENDED.

RESPIRATOR: THE FOLLOWING RESPIRATORS ARE RECOMMENDED BASED ON INFORMATION FOUND IN THE PHYSICAL DATA, TOXICITY AND HEALTH EFFECTS SECTIONS. THEY ARE RANKED IN ORDER FROM MINIMUM TO MAXIMUM RESPIRATORY PROTECTION. THE SPECIFIC RESPIRATOR SELECTED MUST BE BASED ON CONTAMINATION LEVELS FOUND IN THE WORK PLACE, MUST NOT EXCEED THE WORKING LIMITS OF THE RESPIRATOR AND BE JOINTLY APPROVED BY THE NATIONAL INSTITUTE FOR OCCUPATIONAL SAFETY AND HEALTH AND THE MINE SAFETY AND HEALTH ADMINISTRATION (NIOSH-MSHA).

TYPE 'C' SUPPLIED-AIR RESPIRATOR WITH A FULL FACEPIECE OPERATED IN PRESSURE-DEMAND OR OTHER POSITIVE PRESSURE MODE OR WITH A FULL FACEPIECE, HELMET OR HOOD OPERATED IN CONTINOUS-FLOW MODE.

SELF-CONTAINED BREATHING APPARATUS WITH A FULL FACEPIECE OPERATED IN PRESSURE-DEMAND OR OTHER POSITIVE PRESSURE MODE.

FOR FIREFIGHTING AND OTHER IMMEDIATELY DANGEROUS TO LIFE OR HEALTH CONDITIONS:

SELF-CONTAINED BREATHING APPARATUS WITH FULL FACEPIECE OPERATED IN PRESSURE-DEMAND OR OTHER POSITIVE PRESSURE MODE.

SUPPLIED-AIR RESPIRATOR WITH FULL FACEPIECE AND OPERATED IN PRESSURE-DEMAND OR OTHER POSITIVE PRESSURE MODE IN COMBINATION WITH AN AUXILIARY SELF-CONTAINED BREATHING APPARATUS OPERATED IN PRESSURE-DEMAND OR OTHER POSITIVE PRESSURE MODE.

CLOTHING: EMPLOYEE MUST WEAR APPROPRIATE PROTECTIVE (IMPERVIOUS) CLOTHING AND EQUIPMENT TO PREVENT ANY POSSIBILITY OF SKIN CONTACT WITH THIS SUBSTANCE.

GLOVES: EMPLOYEE MUST WEAR APPROPRIATE PROTECTIVE GLOVES TO PREVENT CONTACT WITH THIS SUBSTANCE.

EYE PROTECTION: EMPLOYEE MUST WEAR SPLASH-PROOF OR DUST-RESISTANT SAFETY GOGGLES AND A FACESHIELD TO PREVENT CONTACT WITH THIS SUBSTANCE.

EMERGENCY WASH FACILITIES: WHERE THERE IS ANY POSSIBILITY THAT AN EMPLOYEE'S EYES AND/OR SKIN MAY BE EXPOSED TO THIS SUBSTANCE, THE EMPLOYER SHOULD PROVIDE AN EYE WASH FOUNTAIN AND QUICK DRENCH SHOWER WITHIN THE IMMEDIATE WORK AREA FOR EMERGENCY USE.

AUTHORIZED BY- OCCUPATIONAL HEALTH SERVICES, INC.
CREATION DATE: 10/04/89 ***REVISION DATE:*** 05/01/90

MATERIAL SAFETY DATA SHEET

OCCUPATIONAL HEALTH SERVICES, INC.
AGRICULTURE AND PESTICIDE DIVISION
450 SEVENTH AVENUE, SUITE 2407
NEW YORK, NEW YORK 10123
1-800-445-MSDS OR (212) 967-1100

EMERGENCY CONTACT:
JOHN S. BRANSFORD, JR. (615) 292-1180

SUBSTANCE IDENTIFICATION

CAS-NUMBER 51630-58-1

SUBSTANCE: FENVALERATE

TRADE NAMES/SYNONYMS: 4-CHLORO-(ALPHA-(1-METHYLETHYL)BENZENEACETIC ACID CYANO (3-PHENOXYPHENYL)METHYL ESTER; CYANO(3-PHENOXYPHENYL)METHYL 4-CHLORO-ALPHA-(1-METHYLETHYL) BENZENEACETATE; ALPHA-CYANO-3-PHENOXYBENZYL ALPHA-(4-CHLOROPHENYL)ISOVALERATE; ALPHA-CYANO-3-PHENOXYBENZYL-2-(4-CHLOROPHENYL)-3-METHYLBUTYRATE; PHENVALERATE; PYDRIN; SUMICIDIN; BELMARK; S 5602; SD 43775; PST19948

CHEMICAL FAMILY: PYRETHROID (SYNTHETIC)

MOLECULAR FORMULA: C25-H22-CL-N-O3

MOLECULAR WEIGHT: 419.93

CERCLA RATINGS (SCALE 0-3): HEALTH=3 FIRE=U REACTIVITY=0 PERSISTENCE=3

NFPA RATINGS (SCALE 0-4): HEALTH=3 FIRE=U REACTIVITY=0

COMPONENTS AND CONTAMINANTS

COMPONENT: FENVALERATE ***PERCENT:*** 100.00
CAS# 51630-58-1

OTHER CONTAMINANTS: NONE

EXPOSURE LIMITS: NO OCCUPATIONAL EXPOSURE LIMITS ESTABLISHED BY OSHA, ACGIH, OR NIOSH.

PHYSICAL DATA

DESCRIPTION: CLEAR YELLOW, VISCOUS LIQUID WITH A MILD CHEMICAL ODOR

BOILING POINT: NOT AVAILABLE ***SPECIFIC GRAVITY:*** 1.17

VAPOR PRESSURE: NEGLIGIBLE ***EVAPORATION RATE:*** NOT AVAILABLE

SOLUBILITY IN WATER: INSOLUBLE

SOLVENT SOLUBILITY: ORGANIC SOLVENTS, ACETONE, ALCOHOL, ETHER, KEROSENE, XYLENE, CHLOROFORM

FIRE AND EXPLOSION DATA

FIRE AND EXPLOSION HAZARD: UNKNOWN FIRE AND EXPLOSION HAZARD.

FIREFIGHTING MEDIA: DRY CHEMICAL, CARBON DIOXIDE, WATER SPRAY OR FOAM FOR LARGER FIRES, USE WATER SPRAY, FOG OR ALCOHOL FOAM

FIREFIGHTING: USE AGENTS SUITABLE FOR TYPE OF SURROUNDING FIRE. AVOID BREATHING HAZARDOUS VAPORS, KEEP UPWIND.

TOXICITY

FENVALERATE: TOXICITY DATA: 2500 MG/KG SKIN-RABBIT LD50; 70200 UG/KG ORAL-RAT LD50; 185 MG/KG ORAL-MOUSE LD50; 50 MG/KG INTRAVENOUS-RAT LDLO; 200 UG/KG INTRACEREBRAL-MOUSE LDLO; 451 MG/KG UNREPORTED-MAMMAL LD50; MUTAGENIC DATA (RTECS); REPRODUCTIVE EFFECTS DATA (RTECS). CARCINOGEN STATUS: NONE. ACUTE TOXICITY LEVEL: TOXIC BY INGESTION AND SLIGHTLY TOXIC BY DERMAL ABSORPTION. TARGET EFFECTS: NO DATA AVAILABLE.

HEALTH EFFECTS AND FIRST AID

INHALATION: FENVALERATE: **ACUTE EXPOSURE-** MAY CAUSE MUCOUS MEMBRANE IRRITATION. FENVALERATE IS A SYNTHETIC PYRETHRIN. SYNTHETIC PYRETHRINS, LIKE THE NATURAL PYRETHRINS, PRODUCE CENTRAL NERVOUS SYSTEM STIMULATION IN ANIMALS WITH SYMPTOMS OF NAUSEA, VOMITING, GASTROENTERITIS WITH DIARRHEA, HYPERSENSITIVITY, INCOORDINATION, TREMORS, MUSCULAR PARALYSIS, CONVULSION, COMA, AND DEATH DUE TO RESPIRATORY FAILURE. UNLIKE NATURAL PYRETHRINS, SYNTHETIC PYRETHRINS NORMALLY DO NOT PRODUCE ALLERGIC REACTIONS IN HUMANS. **CHRONIC EXPOSURE-** PROLONGED OR REPEATED EXPOSURE MAY CAUSE IRRITATION OF THE MUCOUS MEMBRANE.

FIRST AID- REMOVE FROM EXPOSURE AREA TO FRESH AIR IMMEDIATELY. IF BREATHING HAS STOPPED, PERFORM ARTIFICIAL RESPIRATION. KEEP PERSON WARM AND AT REST. TREAT SYMPTOMATICALLY AND SUPPORTIVELY. GET MEDICAL ATTENTION IMMEDIATELY.

SKIN CONTACT: FENVALERATE: **ACUTE EXPOSURE-** MAY CAUSE IRRITATION. EXPOSURE TO THE EMULSIBLE CONCENTRATE FORMULATION OF FENVALERATE MAY CAUSE SEVERE IRRITATION. A MODERATE DOSE WAS LETHAL IN RABBITS BY DERMAL ABSORPTION. FENVALERATE IS A SYNTHETIC PYRETHRIN. SYNTHETIC PYRETHRINS, UNLIKE NATURAL PYRETHRINS, NORMALLY DO NOT PRODUCE ALLERGIC REACTIONS IN HUMANS. HOWEVER, THERE HAVE BEEN SOME REPORTS OF CUTANEOUS PARESTHESIAS AMONG OCCUPATIONALLY EXPOSED INDIVIDUALS. THESE INDIVIDUALS COMPLAINED OF TINGLING, BURNING AND STINGING SENSATIONS ON THE EXPOSED SURFACE OF THE SKIN BEGINNING FROM 30 MINUTES TO 3 HOURS AFTER EXPOSURE. THE DURATION OF SYMPTOMS VARIED FROM 30 MINUTES TO 8 HOURS. **CHRONIC EXPOSURE-** PROLONGED OR REPEATED EXPOSURE MAY CAUSE IRRITATION.

FIRST AID- REMOVE CONTAMINATED CLOTHING AND SHOES IMMEDIATELY. WASH AFFECTED AREA WITH SOAP OR MILD DETERGENT AND LARGE AMOUNTS OF WATER UNTIL NO EVIDENCE OF CHEMICAL REMAINS (APPROXIMATELY 15-20 MINUTES). GET MEDICAL ATTENTION IMMEDIATELY.

EYE CONTACT: FENVALERATE: **ACUTE EXPOSURE-** MAY CAUSE IRRITATION. CONTACT WITH THE EMULSIBLE CONCENTRATE FORMULATION OF FENVALERATE MAY CAUSE SEVERE IRRITATION WITH SUBSTANTIAL BUT TEMPORARY EYE INJURY. **CHRONIC EXPOSURE-** PROLONGED OR REPEATED EXPOSURE MAY CAUSE IRRITATION OR CONJUNCTIVITIS.

FIRST AID- WASH EYES IMMEDIATELY WITH LARGE AMOUNTS OF WATER OR NORMAL SALINE, OCCASIONALLY LIFTING UPPER AND LOWER LIDS, UNTIL NO EVIDENCE OF CHEMICAL REMAINS (APPROXIMATELY 15-20 MINUTES). GET MEDICAL ATTENTION IMMEDIATELY.

INGESTION: FENVALERATE: TOXIC. **ACUTE EXPOSURE-** IN LABORATORY ANIMALS, THIS MATERIAL HAS PRODUCED CENTRAL NERVOUS SYSTEM STIMULATION WITH SYMPTOMS OF NERVOUSNESS, ANXIETY, SALIVATION, TREMORS AND CONVULSIONS. RATS GIVEN HIGH DOSES SUFFERED NERVE DAMAGE. A LOW DOSE OF FENVALERATE MIXED WITH DMSO WAS LETHAL IN RATS; THE DMSO MAY BE RESPONSIBLE FOR AN INCREASE ABSORPTION FROM THE GUT RESULTING IN AN INCREASE IN THE TOXICITY. A MORE MODERATE DOSE OF THE TECHNICAL GRADE OF FENVALERATE SUSPENDED IN WATER WAS LETHAL IN RATS. **CHRONIC EXPOSURE-** RATS FED 1000 PPM IN THE DIET FOR TWO YEARS EXHIBITED SIGNS OF DECREASED BODY WEIGHT WITH SOME INCREASE OF ORGAN/BODY WEIGHT RATIOS. CHRONIC INGESTION OF A CUMULATIVE DOSE OF 1138 MG/KG FOR 26 WEEKS PRODUCED IN DOGS ADVERSE EFFECTS ON THE REPRODUCTIVE SYSTEM OF FEMALES.

FIRST AID- REMOVE BY GASTRIC LAVAGE AND CATHARSIS. MAINTAIN BLOOD PRESSURE AND AIRWAY. GIVE OXYGEN IF RESPIRATION IS DEPRESSED. DO NOT PERFORM GASTRIC LAVAGE IF VICTIM IS UNCONSCIOUS. GET MEDICAL ATTENTION IMMEDIATELY (DREISBACH, HANDBOOK OF POISONING, 12TH ED.).
ADMINISTRATION OF LAVAGE OR OXYGEN SHOULD BE PERFORMED BY QUALIFIED MEDICAL PERSONNEL.

ANTIDOTE: NO SPECIFIC ANTIDOTE. TREAT SYMPTOMATICALLY AND SUPPORTIVELY.

REACTIVITY

REACTIVITY: STABLE UNDER NORMAL TEMPERATURES AND PRESSURES.

INCOMPATIBILITIES: FENVALERATE: ALKALINE MEDIA: UNSTABLE

DECOMPOSITION: THERMAL DECOMPOSITION MAY EMIT TOXIC FUMES OF HYDROGEN CYANIDE, CHLORINE, AND OXIDES OF NITROGEN AND CARBON.

POLYMERIZATION: HAZARDOUS POLYMERIZATION HAS NOT BEEN REPORTED TO OCCUR UNDER NORMAL TEMPERATURES AND PRESSURES.

STORAGE AND DISPOSAL

OBSERVE ALL FEDERAL, STATE AND LOCAL REGULATIONS WHEN STORING OR DISPOSING OF THIS SUBSTANCE. FOR ASSISTANCE, CONTACT THE DISTRICT DIRECTOR OF THE ENVIRONMENTAL PROTECTION AGENCY.

STORAGE

STORE IN ACCORDANCE WITH 40 CFR 165 RECOMMENDED PROCEDURES FOR THE DISPOSAL AND STORAGE OF PESTICIDES AND PESTICIDE CONTAINERS.
STORE AWAY FROM INCOMPATIBLE SUBSTANCES.

DISPOSAL

DISPOSAL MUST BE IN ACCORDANCE WITH 40 CFR 165 RECOMMENDED PROCEDURES FOR THE DISPOSAL AND STORAGE OF PESTICIDES AND PESTICIDE CONTAINERS.

CONDITIONS TO AVOID

NONE REPORTED.

SPILL AND LEAK PROCEDURES

OCCUPATIONAL SPILL: NO SPECIAL PRECAUTIONS INDICATED.

PROTECTIVE EQUIPMENT

VENTILATION: PROVIDE LOCAL EXHAUST OR PROCESS ENCLOSURE VENTILATION. VENTILATION EQUIPMENT MUST BE EXPLOSION-PROOF.

RESPIRATOR: THE FOLLOWING RESPIRATORS ARE RECOMMENDED BASED ON INFORMATION FOUND IN THE PHYSICAL DATA, TOXICITY AND HEALTH EFFECTS SECTIONS. THEY ARE RANKED IN ORDER FROM MINIMUM TO MAXIMUM RESPIRATORY PROTECTION. THE SPECIFIC RESPIRATOR SELECTED MUST BE BASED ON CONTAMINATION LEVELS FOUND IN THE WORK PLACE, MUST NOT EXCEED THE WORKING LIMITS OF THE RESPIRATOR AND BE JOINTLY APPROVED BY THE NATIONAL INSTITUTE FOR OCCUPATIONAL SAFETY AND HEALTH AND THE MINE SAFETY AND HEALTH ADMINISTRATION (NIOSH-MSHA).
CHEMICAL CARTRIDGE RESPIRATOR WITH FULL FACEPIECE AND PESTICIDE CARTRIDGE. TYPE 'C' SUPPLIED-AIR RESPIRATOR WITH A FULL FACEPIECE OPERATED IN PRESSURE-DEMAND OR OTHER POSITIVE PRESSURE MODE OR WITH A FULL FACEPIECE, HELMET OR HOOD OPERATED IN CONTINUOUS-FLOW MODE.
SELF-CONTAINED BREATHING APPARATUS OPERATED IN PRESSURE-DEMAND OR OTHER POSITIVE PRESSURE MODE.
FOR FIREFIGHTING AND OTHER IMMEDIATELY DANGEROUS TO LIFE OR HEALTH CONDITIONS:
SELF-CONTAINED BREATHING APPARATUS WITH FULL FACEPIECE OPERATED IN PRESSURE-DEMAND OR OTHER POSITIVE PRESSURE MODE.
SUPPLIED-AIR RESPIRATOR WITH FULL FACEPIECE AND OPERATED IN PRESSURE-DEMAND OR OTHER POSITIVE PRESSURE MODE IN COMBINATION WITH AN AUXILIARY SELF-CONTAINED BREATHING APPARATUS OPERATED IN PRESSURE-DEMAND OR OTHER POSITIVE PRESSURE MODE.

CLOTHING: EMPLOYEE MUST WEAR APPROPRIATE PROTECTIVE (IMPERVIOUS) CLOTHING AND EQUIPMENT TO PREVENT REPEATED OR PROLONGED SKIN CONTACT WITH THIS SUBSTANCE.

GLOVES: EMPLOYEE MUST WEAR APPROPRIATE PROTECTIVE GLOVES TO PREVENT CONTACT WITH THIS SUBSTANCE.

EYE PROTECTION: EMPLOYEE MUST WEAR SPLASH-PROOF OR DUST-RESISTANT SAFETY GOGGLES TO PREVENT EYE CONTACT WITH THIS SUBSTANCE.
EMERGENCY EYE WASH: WHERE THERE IS ANY POSSIBILITY THAT AN EMPLOYEE'S EYES MAY BE EXPOSED TO THIS SUBSTANCE, THE EMPLOYER SHOULD PROVIDE AN EYE WASH FOUNTAIN WITHIN THE IMMEDIATE WORK AREA FOR EMERGENCY USE.

AUTHORIZED BY- OCCUPATIONAL HEALTH SERVICES, INC.
CREATION DATE: 10/04/89 ***REVISION DATE:*** 05/14/90

MATERIAL SAFETY DATA SHEET

OCCUPATIONAL HEALTH SERVICES, INC.
AGRICULTURE AND PESTICIDE DIVISION
450 SEVENTH AVENUE, SUITE 2407
NEW YORK, NEW YORK 10123
1-800-445-MSDS OR (212) 967-1100

EMERGENCY CONTACT:
JOHN S. BRANSFORD, JR. (615) 292-1180

SUBSTANCE IDENTIFICATION

CAS-NUMBER 97-11-0

SUBSTANCE: **PYPYRETHRIN**

TRADE NAMES/SYNONYMS: 2,2-DIMETHYL-3-(2-METHYL-1-PROPENYL)-CYCLOPROPANECARBOXYLIC ACID, 3- (2-CYCLOPENTEN-1-YL)-2-METHYL-4-OXO-2-CYCLOPENTEN-1-YL ESTER; 2,2-DIMETHYL-3-(2-METHYLPROPENYL)-CYCLOPROPANECARBOXYLIC ACID, ESTER WITH 2-(2-CYCLOPENTEN-1-YL)-4-HYDROXY-3-METHYL-2-CYCLOPENTEN-1-ONE; 3-(2-CYCLOPENTENYL)-2-METHYL-4-OXO-2-CYCLOPENTENYL ESTER OF CHRYSANTHEMUMMONOCARBOXYLIC ACID; CHRYSANTHEMUMMONOCARBOXYLIC ACID ESTER WITH 3-(2-CYCLOPENTEN-1-YL) -2-METHYL-4-OXO-2-CYCLOPENTEN-1-OL; CLCLETHRIN; ENT 22,952; PST19949

CHEMICAL FAMILY: PYRETHROID (SYNTHETIC)

MOLECULAR FORMULA: C21-H28-O3

MOLECULAR WEIGHT: 328.49

CERCLA RATINGS (SCALE 0-3): HEALTH=2 FIRE=U REACTIVITY=0 PERSISTENCE=2

NFPA RATINGS (SCALE 0-4): HEALTH=2 FIRE=U REACTIVITY=0

COMPONENTS AND CONTAMINANTS

COMPONENT: PYPYRETHRIN ***PERCENT:*** 100.0
CAS# 97-11-0

OTHER CONTAMINANTS: NONE

EXPOSURE LIMITS: NO OCCUPATIONAL EXPOSURE LIMITS ESTABLISHED BY OSHA, ACGIH, OR NIOSH.

PHYSICAL DATA

DESCRIPTION: VISCOUS BROWN LIQUID ***BOILING POINT:*** NOT AVAILABLE

SPECIFIC GRAVITY: 1.033 ***EVAPORATION RATE:*** NOT AVAILABLE

SOLUBILITY IN WATER: INSOLUBLE

SOLVENT SOLUBILITY: PETROLEUM SOLVENTS, OTHER COMMON ORGANIC SOLVENTS

FIRE AND EXPLOSION DATA

FIRE AND EXPLOSION HAZARD: UNKNOWN FIRE AND EXPLOSION HAZARD.

FIREFIGHTING MEDIA: DRY CHEMICAL, CARBON DIOXIDE, HALON, WATER SPRAY OR STANDARD FOAM (1987 EMERGENCY RESPONSE GUIDEBOOK, DOT P 5800.4).
FOR LARGER FIRES, USE WATER SPRAY, FOG OR STANDARD FOAM (1987 EMERGENCY RESPONSE GUIDEBOOK, DOT P 5800.4).

FIREFIGHTING: MOVE CONTAINER FROM FIRE AREA IF POSSIBLE. DO NOT SCATTER SPILLED MATERIAL WITH HIGH PRESSURE WATER STREAMS. DIKE FIRE CONTROL WATER FOR LATER DISPOSAL (1987 EMERGENCY RESPONSE GUIDEBOOK, DOT P 5800.4, GUIDE PAGE 31).
USE AGENTS SUITABLE FOR TYPE OF SURROUNDING FIRE. AVOID BREATHING HAZARDOUS VAPORS, KEEP UPWIND.

TOXICITY

PYPYRETHRIN: TOXICITY DATA: 1410 MG/KG ORAL-RAT LD50; 900 MG/KG UNREPORTED-RAT LD50. CARCINOGEN STATUS: NONE. ACUTE TOXICITY LEVEL: MODERATELY TOXIC BY INGESTION. TARGET EFFECTS: POISONING MAY AFFECT THE CENTRAL NERVOUS SYSTEM.

HEALTH EFFECTS AND FIRST AID

INHALATION: PYPYRETHRIN: **ACUTE EXPOSURE-** PYPYRETHRIN IS A SYNTHETIC PYRETHRIN. SYNTHETIC PYRETHRINS, LIKE THE NATURAL PYRETHRINS, PRODUCE CENTRAL NERVOUS SYSTEM STIMULATION IN ANIMALS WITH SYMPTOMS OF NAUSEA, VOMITING, GASTROENTERITIS WITH DIARRHEA, HYPERSENSITIVITY, INCOORDINATION, TREMORS, MUSCULAR PARALYSIS, CONVULSION, COMA, AND DEATH DUE TO RESPIRATORY FAILURE. UNLIKE NATURAL PYRETHRINS, SYNTHETIC PYRETHRINS NORMALLY DO NOT PRODUCE ALLERGIC REACTIONS IN HUMANS. **CHRONIC EXPOSURE-** NO DATA AVAILABLE.

FIRST AID- REMOVE FROM EXPOSURE AREA TO FRESH AIR IMMEDIATELY. IF BREATHING HAS STOPPED, PERFORM ARTIFICIAL RESPIRATION. KEEP PERSON WARM AND AT REST. TREAT SYMPTOMATICALLY AND SUPPORTIVELY. GET MEDICAL ATTENTION IMMEDIATELY.

SKIN CONTACT: PYPYRETHRIN: **ACUTE EXPOSURE-** PYPYRETHRIN IS A SYNTHETIC PYRETHRIN. SYNTHETIC PYRETHRINS ARE NOT IRRITANTS TO RABBIT SKIN AND THE TOXICITY FROM DERMAL ABSORPTION IS USUALLY MODERATE TO LOW. UNLIKE NATURAL PYRETHRINS, SYNTHETIC PYRETHRINS NORMALLY DO NOT PRODUCE ALLERGIC REACTIONS IN HUMANS. HOWEVER, THERE HAVE BEEN SOME REPORTS OF CUTANEOUS PARESTHESIAS AMONG OCCUPATIONALLY EXPOSED INDIVIDUALS. THESE INDIVIDUALS COMPLAINED OF TINGLING, BURNING AND STINGING SENSATIONS ON THE EXPOSED SURFACE OF THE SKIN, BEGINNING FROM 30 MINUTES TO 3 HOURS AFTER EXPOSURE. THE DURATION OF SYMPTOMS VARIED FROM 30 MINUTES TO 8 HOURS. **CHRONIC EXPOSURE-** NO DATA AVAILABLE.

FIRST AID- REMOVE CONTAMINATED CLOTHING AND SHOES IMMEDIATELY. WASH AFFECTED AREA WITH SOAP OR MILD DETERGENT AND LARGE AMOUNTS OF WATER UNTIL NO EVIDENCE OF CHEMICAL REMAINS (APPROXIMATELY 15-20 MINUTES). GET MEDICAL ATTENTION IMMEDIATELY.

EYE CONTACT: PYPYRETHRIN: **ACUTE EXPOSURE-** SYNTHETIC PYRETHRINS ARE NOT IRRITANTS OF RABBIT EYES. **CHRONIC EXPOSURE-** NO DATA AVAILABLE.

FIRST AID- WASH EYES IMMEDIATELY WITH LARGE AMOUNTS OF WATER OR NORMAL SALINE, OCCASIONALLY LIFTING UPPER AND LOWER LIDS, UNTIL NO EVIDENCE OF CHEMICAL REMAINS (APPROXIMATELY 15-20 MINUTES). GET MEDICAL ATTENTION IMMEDIATELY.

INGESTION: PYPYRETHRIN: **ACUTE EXPOSURE-** A MODERATE DOSE WAS LETHAL TO RATS. PYPYRETHRIN IS A SYNTHETIC PYRETHRIN. SYNTHETIC PYRETHRINS, LIKE THE NATURAL PYRETHRINS, PRODUCE CENTRAL NERVOUS SYSTEM STIMULATION IN ANIMALS WITH SYMPTOMS OF NAUSEA, VOMITING, GASTROENTERITIS WITH DIARRHEA, HYPERSENSITIVITY, INCOORDINATION, TREMORS, MUSCULAR PARALYSIS, CONVULSION, COMA, AND DEATH DUE TO RESPIRATORY FAILURE. **CHRONIC EXPOSURE-** NO DATA AVAILABLE.

FIRST AID- TREAT SYMPTOMATICALLY AND SUPPORTIVELY. GET MEDICAL ATTENTION IMMEDIATELY. IF VOMITING OCCURS, KEEP HEAD LOWER THAN HIPS TO PREVENT ASPIRATION.

ANTIDOTE: NO SPECIFIC ANTIDOTE. TREAT SYMPTOMATICALLY AND SUPPORTIVELY.

REACTIVITY

REACTIVITY: MAY DECOMPOSE UPON EXPOSURE TO HEAT OR LIGHT.

INCOMPATIBILITIES: PYPYRETHRIN: NO DATA AVAILABLE.

DECOMPOSITION: THERMAL DECOMPOSITION MAY RELEASE TOXIC AND/OR HAZARDOUS GASES.

POLYMERIZATION: HAZARDOUS POLYMERIZATION HAS NOT BEEN REPORTED TO OCCUR UNDER NORMAL TEMPERATURES AND PRESSURES.

STORAGE AND DISPOSAL

OBSERVE ALL FEDERAL, STATE AND LOCAL REGULATIONS WHEN STORING OR DISPOSING OF THIS SUBSTANCE. FOR ASSISTANCE, CONTACT THE DISTRICT DIRECTOR OF THE ENVIRONMENTAL PROTECTION AGENCY.

****STORAGE****

STORE IN ACCORDANCE WITH 40 CFR 165 RECOMMENDED PROCEDURES FOR THE DISPOSAL AND STORAGE OF PESTICIDES AND PESTICIDE CONTAINERS.

****DISPOSAL****

DISPOSAL MUST BE IN ACCORDANCE WITH 40 CFR 165 RECOMMENDED PROCEDURES FOR THE DISPOSAL AND STORAGE OF PESTICIDES AND PESTICIDE CONTAINERS.

CONDITIONS TO AVOID

MAY BURN BUT DOES NOT IGNITE READILY. AVOID CONTACT WITH STRONG OXIDIZERS, EXCESSIVE HEAT, SPARKS, OR OPEN FLAME.

SPILL AND LEAK PROCEDURES

OCCUPATIONAL SPILL: STOP LEAK IF YOU CAN DO IT WITHOUT RISK. FOR SMALL SPILLS, TAKE UP WITH SAND OR OTHER ABSORBENT MATERIAL AND PLACE INTO CLEAN, DRY CONTAINERS FOR LATER DISPOSAL. KEEP UNNECESSARY PEOPLE AWAY. ISOLATE HAZARD AREA AND DENY ENTRY.

PROTECTIVE EQUIPMENT

VENTILATION: PROVIDE LOCAL EXHAUST OR GENERAL DILUTION VENTILATION SYSTEM.

RESPIRATOR: THE FOLLOWING RESPIRATORS ARE RECOMMENDED BASED ON INFORMATION FOUND IN THE PHYSICAL DATA, TOXICITY AND HEALTH EFFECTS SECTIONS. THEY ARE RANKED IN ORDER FROM MINIMUM TO MAXIMUM RESPIRATORY PROTECTION. THE SPECIFIC RESPIRATOR SELECTED MUST BE BASED ON CONTAMINATION LEVELS FOUND IN THE WORK PLACE, MUST NOT EXCEED THE WORKING LIMITS OF THE RESPIRATOR AND BE JOINTLY APPROVED BY THE NATIONAL INSTITUTE FOR OCCUPATIONAL SAFETY AND HEALTH AND THE MINE SAFETY AND HEALTH ADMINISTRATION (NIOSH-MSHA).

CHEMICAL CARTRIDGE RESPIRATOR WITH PESTICIDE CARTRIDGE.

GAS MASK WITH A PESTICIDE CANISTER (CHIN-STYLE OR FRONT- OR BACK-MOUNTED CANISTER).

TYPE 'C' SUPPLIED-AIR RESPIRATOR OPERATED IN THE PRESSURE-DEMAND OR OTHER POSITIVE PRESSURE OR CONTINUOUS-FLOW MODE.

SELF-CONTAINED BREATHING APPARATUS.

FOR FIREFIGHTING AND OTHER IMMEDIATELY DANGEROUS TO LIFE OR HEALTH CONDITIONS:

SELF-CONTAINED BREATHING APPARATUS WITH FULL FACEPIECE OPERATED IN PRESSURE-DEMAND OR OTHER POSITIVE PRESSURE MODE.

SUPPLIED-AIR RESPIRATOR WITH FULL FACEPIECE AND OPERATED IN PRESSURE-DEMAND OR OTHER POSITIVE PRESSURE MODE IN COMBINATION WITH AN AUXILIARY SELF-CONTAINED BREATHING APPARATUS OPERATED IN PRESSURE-DEMAND OR OTHER POSITIVE PRESSURE MODE.

CLOTHING: EMPLOYEE MUST WEAR APPROPRIATE PROTECTIVE (IMPERVIOUS) CLOTHING AND EQUIPMENT TO PREVENT REPEATED OR PROLONGED SKIN CONTACT WITH THIS SUBSTANCE.

GLOVES: EMPLOYEE MUST WEAR APPROPRIATE PROTECTIVE GLOVES TO PREVENT CONTACT WITH THIS SUBSTANCE.

EYE PROTECTION: EMPLOYEE MUST WEAR SPLASH-PROOF OR DUST-RESISTANT SAFETY GOGGLES TO PREVENT EYE CONTACT WITH THIS SUBSTANCE.

EMERGENCY EYE WASH: WHERE THERE IS ANY POSSIBILITY THAT AN EMPLOYEE'S EYES MAY BE EXPOSED TO THIS SUBSTANCE, THE EMPLOYER SHOULD PROVIDE AN EYE WASH FOUNTAIN WITHIN THE IMMEDIATE WORK AREA FOR EMERGENCY USE.

AUTHORIZED BY- OCCUPATIONAL HEALTH SERVICES, INC.

CREATION DATE: 10/04/89 ***REVISION DATE:*** 05/17/90

MATERIAL SAFETY DATA SHEET

OCCUPATIONAL HEALTH SERVICES, INC.
AGRICULTURE AND PESTICIDE DIVISION
450 SEVENTH AVENUE, SUITE 2407
NEW YORK, NEW YORK 10123
1-800-445-MSDS OR (212) 967-1100

EMERGENCY CONTACT:
JOHN S. BRANSFORD, JR. (615) 292-1180

SUBSTANCE IDENTIFICATION

CAS-NUMBER 121-21-1

SUBSTANCE: **PYRETHRIN I**

TRADE NAMES/SYNONYMS: CYCLOPROPANECARBOXYLIC ACID, 2,2-DIMETHYL-3-(2-METHYL-1-PROPENYL)-, 2-METHYL-4-OXO-3-(2,4-PENTADIENYL)-2-CYCLOPENTEN-1-YL ESTER, (1R-(1ALPHA(S*(Z)),3BETA))-; CYCLOPROPANECARBOXYLIC ACID, 2,2-DIMETHYL-3-(2-METHYLPROPENYL)-, ESTER WITH 4-HYDROXY-3-METHYL-2-(2,4-PENTADIENYL)-2-CYCLOPENTEN-1-ONE; (1R-(1ALPHA(S*(Z)),3BETA))-2,2-DIMETHYL-3-(2-METHYL-1-PROPENYL)- CYCLOPROPANECARBOXYLIC ACID 2-METHYL-4-OXO-3-(2,4-PENTADIENYL)- 2-CYCLOPENTEN-1-YL ESTER; 2,2-DIMETHYL-3-(2-METHYLPROPENYL)CYCLOPROPANECARBOXYLIC ACID ESTER WITH 4-HYDROXY-3-METHYL-2-(2,4-PENTADIENYL)-2-CYCLOPENTEN-1-ONE; PYRETHRIN; C21H28O3; PST19960

CHEMICAL FAMILY: PYRETHRIN (NATURAL)

MOLECULAR FORMULA: C21-H28-O3

MOLECULAR WEIGHT: 328.49

CERCLA RATINGS (SCALE 0-3): HEALTH=3 FIRE=2 REACTIVITY=0 PERSISTENCE=1

NFPA RATINGS (SCALE 0-4): HEALTH=U FIRE=2 REACTIVITY=0

COMPONENTS AND CONTAMINANTS

COMPONENT: PYRETHRIN I ***PERCENT:*** 100.0
CAS# 121-21-1

OTHER CONTAMINANTS: NONE

EXPOSURE LIMITS: PYRETHRUM: 5 MG/M3 OSHA TWA 5 MG/M3 ACGIH TWA
1 POUND CERCLA SECTION 103 REPORTABLE QUANTITY

PHYSICAL DATA

DESCRIPTION: VISCOUS LIQUID. ***BOILING POINT:*** 295-302 F (146-150 C) @ 0.0005 MMHG

SPECIFIC GRAVITY: NOT AVAILABLE ***VAPOR PRESSURE:*** NEGLIGIBLE

SOLUBILITY IN WATER: INSOLUBLE

SOLVENT SOLUBILITY: SOLUBLE IN ETHANOL, PETROLEUM ETHER, KEROSENE, ETHANOL, CARBON TETRACHLORIDE, ETHYLENE DICHLORIDE, NITROMETHANE, CHLORINATED HYDROCARBONS, AND ORGANIC SOLVENTS.

FIRE AND EXPLOSION DATA

FIRE AND EXPLOSION HAZARD: MODERATE FIRE HAZARD WHEN EXPOSED TO HEAT OR FLAME.

FLASH POINT: 180-190 F (82-88 C) (OC) ***FLAMMABILITY CLASS(OSHA):*** IIIA

FIREFIGHTING MEDIA: DRY CHEMICAL, CARBON DIOXIDE, HALON, WATER SPRAY OR STANDARD FOAM (1987 EMERGENCY RESPONSE GUIDEBOOK, DOT P 5800.4). FOR LARGER FIRES, USE WATER SPRAY, FOG OR STANDARD FOAM (1987 EMERGENCY RESPONSE GUIDEBOOK, DOT P 5800.4).

FIREFIGHTING: MOVE CONTAINER FROM FIRE AREA IF POSSIBLE. COOL FIRE-EXPOSED CONTAINERS WITH WATER FROM SIDE UNTIL WELL AFTER FIRE IS OUT. STAY AWAY FROM STORAGE TANK ENDS. FOR MASSIVE FIRE IN STORAGE AREA, USE UNMANNED HOSE HOLDER OR MONITOR NOZZLES, ELSE WITHDRAW FROM AREA AND LET FIRE BURN. WITHDRAW IMMEDIATELY IN CASE OF RISING SOUND FROM VENTING SAFETY DEVICE OR ANY DISCOLORATION OF STORAGE TANK DUE TO FIRE (1987 EMERGENCY RESPONSE GUIDEBOOK, DOT P 5800.4, GUIDE PAGE 27). EXTINGUISH ONLY IF FLOW CAN BE STOPPED; USE FLOODING AMOUNTS OF WATER AS A FOG, SOLID STREAMS MAY BE INEFFECTIVE. COOL CONTAINERS WITH FLOODING AMOUNTS OF WATER, APPLY FROM AS FAR A DISTANCE AS POSSIBLE. AVOID BREATHING VAPORS, KEEP UPWIND.

TRANSPORTATION DATA

DEPARTMENT OF TRANSPORTATION HAZARD CLASSIFICATION 49 CFR 172.101: COMBUSTIBLE LIQUID
DEPARTMENT OF TRANSPORTATION LABELING REQUIREMENTS 49 CFR 172.101 AND SUBPART E: NONE
DEPARTMENT OF TRANSPORTATION PACKAGING REQUIREMENTS: NONE
EXCEPTIONS: 49 CFR 173.118A

TOXICITY

PYRETHRIN I: TOXICITY DATA: 260 MG/KG ORAL-RAT LD50; 5 MG/KG INTRAVENOUS-RAT LDLO; 960 MG/KG UNREPORTED-RAT LD50. CARCINOGEN STATUS: NONE. ACUTE TOXICITY LEVEL: TOXIC BY INGESTION. TARGET EFFECTS: POISONING MAY AFFECT THE RESPIRATORY AND CENTRAL NERVOUS SYSTEMS.* AT INCREASED RISK FROM EXPOSURE: PERSONS WITH ALLERGIES AND CHRONIC RESPIRATORY AND SKIN DISEASES.*
* MAY BE BASED ON GENERAL INFORMATION ON PYRETHRINS.

HEALTH EFFECTS AND FIRST AID

INHALATION: PYRETHRIN I: SEE INFORMATION ON PYRETHRINS.
PYRETHRINS: 5000 MG/M3 IMMEDIATELY DANGEROUS TO LIFE AND HEALTH.
ACUTE EXPOSURE- MAY CAUSE MUCOUS MEMBRANE IRRITATION. NERVOUS IRRITABILITY, TREMORS, AND ATAXIA HAVE RARELY OCCURRED WITH MASSIVE EXPOSURE. SOME PYRETHRINS MAY CAUSE SENSITIZATION REACTIONS IN SUSCEPTIBLE INDIVIDUALS. **CHRONIC EXPOSURE-** PROLONGED OR REPEATED EXPOSURE TO SOME PYRETHRINS MAY RESULT IN SENSITIZATION. EFFECTS MAY INCLUDE SNEEZING, NASAL DISCHARGE AND STUFFINESS, SCRATCHY THROAT, ASTHMA, AND RARELY ANAPHYLACTIC REACTIONS WITH THE POSSIBILITY OF SHOCK AND RESPIRATORY DIFFICULTIES. A CASE OF HYPERSENSITIVITY PNEUMONITIS HAS ALSO BEEN REPORTED.

FIRST AID- REMOVE FROM EXPOSURE AREA TO FRESH AIR IMMEDIATELY. IF BREATHING HAS STOPPED, PERFORM ARTIFICIAL RESPIRATION. KEEP PERSON WARM AND AT REST. TREAT SYMPTOMATICALLY AND SUPPORTIVELY. GET MEDICAL ATTENTION IMMEDIATELY.

SKIN CONTACT: PYRETHRIN I: SEE INFORMATION ON PYRETHRINS.
PYRETHRINS: **ACUTE EXPOSURE-** MAY CAUSE IRRITATION. EXPOSURE TO SOME PYRETHRINS MAY RESULT IN SENSITIZATION REACTIONS IN SUSCEPTIBLE INDIVIDUALS. **CHRONIC EXPOSURE-** PROLONGED OR REPEATED EXPOSURE MAY CAUSE AN ERYTHEMATOUS DERMATITIS WITH VESICLES, PAPULES, ESPECIALLY IN MOIST AREAS, AND INTENSE PRURITIS; TOUGHENING, AND IN SEVERE CASES, EDEMA AND CRACKING OF THE SKIN MAY OCCUR. THE EFFECTS MAY BE ALLERGIC REACTIONS; EOSINOPHILIA MAY ALSO BE PRESENT. EXPOSURE TO THE SUN, WARM WEATHER OR EXCESSIVE PERSPIRATION MAY EXACERBATE THE DERMAL EFFECTS.

FIRST AID- REMOVE CONTAMINATED CLOTHING AND SHOES IMMEDIATELY. WASH AFFECTED AREA WITH SOAP OR MILD DETERGENT AND LARGE AMOUNTS OF WATER UNTIL NO EVIDENCE OF CHEMICAL REMAINS (APPROXIMATELY 15-20 MINUTES). GET MEDICAL ATTENTION IMMEDIATELY.

EYE CONTACT: PYRETHRIN I: SEE INFORMATION ON PYRETHRINS.
PYRETHRINS: **ACUTE EXPOSURE-** MAY CAUSE IRRITATION AND TRANSIENT CONJUNCTIVAL EDEMA AND HYPEREMIA. **CHRONIC EXPOSURE-** NO DATA AVAILABLE.

FIRST AID- WASH EYES IMMEDIATELY WITH LARGE AMOUNTS OF WATER OR NORMAL SALINE, OCCASIONALLY LIFTING UPPER AND LOWER LIDS, UNTIL NO EVIDENCE OF CHEMICAL REMAINS (APPROXIMATELY 15-20 MINUTES). GET MEDICAL ATTENTION IMMEDIATELY.

INGESTION: PYRETHRIN I: TOXIC. SEE INFORMATION ON PYRETHRINS.
PYRETHRINS: **ACUTE EXPOSURE-** LARGE AMOUNTS MAY CAUSE NAUSEA, VOMITING, GASTROENTERITIS WITH DIARRHEA, HYPEREXCITABILITY, INCOORDINATION, TREMORS, MUSCULAR FIBRILLATION, BRADYCARDIA, CONVULSIONS LEADING TO PARALYSIS, AND DEATH DUE TO RESPIRATORY FAILURE. **CHRONIC EXPOSURE-** DOGS FED A DIETARY LEVEL OF 5000 PPM FOR 3 MONTHS EXHIBITED TREMOR, ATAXIA, LABORED RESPIRATION, AND SALIVATION DURING THE FIRST MONTH. SLIGHT LIVER DAMAGE WAS THE ONLY EFFECT REPORTED IN RATS FED DIETARY LEVELS OF 1000 AND 5000 PPM FOR 2 YEARS. AN INCREASED INCIDENCE OF FETAL RESORPTIONS WAS NOTED IN A STUDY OF PREGNANT RATS.

FIRST AID- REMOVE BY GASTRIC LAVAGE AND CATHARSIS. MAINTAIN BLOOD PRESSURE AND AIRWAY. GIVE OXYGEN IF RESPIRATION IS DEPRESSED. DO NOT PERFORM GASTRIC LAVAGE IF VICTIM IS UNCONSCIOUS. GET MEDICAL ATTENTION IMMEDIATELY (DREISBACH, HANDBOOK OF POISONING, 12TH ED.). ADMINISTRATION OF LAVAGE OR OXYGEN SHOULD BE PERFORMED BY QUALIFIED MEDICAL PERSONNEL.

ANTIDOTE: NO SPECIFIC ANTIDOTE. TREAT SYMPTOMATICALLY AND SUPPORTIVELY.

REACTIVITY

REACTIVITY: STABLE UNDER NORMAL TEMPERATURES AND PRESSURES.

INCOMPATIBILITIES: PYRETHRIN I: OXIDIZERS (STRONG): FIRE AND EXPLOSION HAZARD.

DECOMPOSITION: THERMAL DECOMPOSITION PRODUCTS MAY INCLUDE TOXIC OXIDES OF CARBON.

POLYMERIZATION: HAZARDOUS POLYMERIZATION HAS NOT BEEN REPORTED TO OCCUR UNDER NORMAL TEMPERATURES AND PRESSURES.

STORAGE AND DISPOSAL

OBSERVE ALL FEDERAL, STATE AND LOCAL REGULATIONS WHEN STORING OR DISPOSING OF THIS SUBSTANCE. FOR ASSISTANCE, CONTACT THE DISTRICT DIRECTOR OF THE ENVIRONMENTAL PROTECTION AGENCY.

STORAGE

STORE IN ACCORDANCE WITH 29 CFR 1910.106.
STORE IN ACCORDANCE WITH 40 CFR 165 RECOMMENDED PROCEDURES FOR THE DISPOSAL AND STORAGE OF PESTICIDES AND PESTICIDE CONTAINERS. STORE AWAY FROM INCOMPATIBLE SUBSTANCES.
STORE IN A TIGHTLY CLOSED CONTAINER AT TEMPERATURES NOT EXCEEDING 39 F (4 C).

DISPOSAL

DISPOSAL MUST BE IN ACCORDANCE WITH 40 CFR 165 RECOMMENDED PROCEDURES FOR THE DISPOSAL AND STORAGE OF PESTICIDES AND PESTICIDE CONTAINERS.

CONDITIONS TO AVOID

AVOID CONTACT WITH HEAT, SPARKS, FLAMES, OR OTHER SOURCES OF IGNITION. VAPORS MAY BE EXPLOSIVE. AVOID OVERHEATING OF CONTAINERS; CONTAINERS MAY VIOLENTLY RUPTURE IN HEAT OF FIRE. AVOID CONTAMINATION OF WATER SOURCES.

SPILL AND LEAK PROCEDURES

SOIL SPILL: DIG HOLDING AREA SUCH AS LAGOON, POND OR PIT FOR CONTAINMENT. DIKE FLOW OF SPILLED MATERIAL USING SOIL OR SANDBAGS OR FOAMED BARRIERS SUCH AS POLYURETHANE OR CONCRETE.
USE CEMENT POWDER OR FLY ASH TO ABSORB LIQUID MASS.

WATER SPILL: USE ACTIVATED CARBON TO ABSORB SPILLED SUBSTANCE THAT IS DISSOLVED.

USE MECHANICAL DREDGES OR LIFTS TO EXTRACT IMMOBILIZED MASSES OF POLLUTION AND PRECIPITATES.

OCCUPATIONAL SPILL: SHUT OFF IGNITION SOURCES. STOP LEAK IF YOU CAN DO IT WITHOUT RISK. USE WATER SPRAY TO REDUCE VAPORS. FOR SMALL SPILLS, TAKE UP WITH SAND OR OTHER ABSORBENT MATERIAL AND PLACE INTO CONTAINERS FOR LATER DISPOSAL. FOR LARGER SPILLS, DIKE FAR AHEAD OF SPILL FOR LATER DISPOSAL. NO SMOKING, FLAMES OR FLARES IN HAZARD AREA. KEEP UNNECESSARY PEOPLE AWAY; ISOLATE HAZARD AREA AND RESTRICT ENTRY. REPORTABLE QUANTITY (RQ): 1 POUND THE SUPERFUND AMENDMENTS AND REAUTHORIZATION ACT (SARA) SECTION 304 REQUIRES THAT A RELEASE EQUAL TO OR GREATER THAN THE REPORTABLE QUANTITY FOR THIS SUBSTANCE BE IMMEDIATELY REPORTED TO THE LOCAL EMERGENCY PLANNING COMMITTEE AND THE STATE EMERGENCY RESPONSE COMMISSION (40 CFR 355.40). IF THE RELEASE OF THIS SUBSTANCE IS REPORTABLE UNDER CERCLA SECTION 103, THE NATIONAL RESPONSE CENTER MUST BE NOTIFIED IMMEDIATELY AT (800) 424-8802 OR (202) 426-2675 IN THE METROPOLITAN WASHINGTON, D.C. AREA (40 CFR 302.6).

PROTECTIVE EQUIPMENT

VENTILATION: PROVIDE LOCAL EXHAUST VENTILATION AND/OR GENERAL DILUTION VENTILATION TO MEET PUBLISHED EXPOSURE LIMITS.

RESPIRATOR: THE FOLLOWING RESPIRATORS AND MAXIMUM USE CONCENTRATIONS ARE RECOMMENDATIONS BY THE U.S. DEPARTMENT OF HEALTH AND HUMAN SERVICES, NIOSH POCKET GUIDE TO CHEMICAL HAZARDS; NIOSH CRITERIA DOCUMENTS OR BY THE U.S. DEPARTMENT OF LABOR, 29 CFR 1910 SUBPART Z. THE SPECIFIC RESPIRATOR SELECTED MUST BE BASED ON CONTAMINATION LEVELS FOUND IN THE WORK PLACE, MUST NOT EXCEED THE WORKING LIMITS OF THE RESPIRATOR AND BE JOINTLY APPROVED BY THE NATIONAL INSTITUTE FOR OCCUPATIONAL SAFETY AND HEALTH AND THE MINE SAFETY AND HEALTH ADMINISTRATION (NIOSH-MSHA).

PYRETHRUM:

50 MG/M3- ANY CHEMICAL CARTRIDGE RESPIRATOR WITH ORGANIC VAPOR CARTRIDGE(S) IN COMBINATION WITH A DUST, MIST, AND FUME FILTER. ANY SUPPLIED-AIR RESPIRATOR. ANY SELF-CONTAINED BREATHING APPARATUS.

125 MG/M3- ANY SUPPLIED-AIR RESPIRATOR OPERATED IN A CONTINUOUS FLOW MODE. ANY POWERED AIR-PURIFYING RESPIRATOR WITH ORGANIC VAPOR CARTRIDGE(S) IN COMBINATION WITH A DUST, MIST, AND FUME FILTER.

250 MG/M3- ANY CHEMICAL CARTRIDGE RESPIRATOR WITH A FULL FACEPIECE AND ORGANIC VAPOR CARTRIDGE(S) IN COMBINATION WITH A HIGH-EFFICIENCY PARTICULATE FILTER. ANY SUPPLIED-AIR RESPIRATOR WITH A FULL FACEPIECE. ANY SELF-CONTAINED BREATHING APPARATUS WITH A FULL FACEPIECE. ANY POWERED AIR-PURIFYING RESPIRATOR WITH A TIGHT-FITTING FACEPIECE AND ORGANIC VAPOR CARTRIDGE(S) IN COMBINATION WITH A HIGH-EFFICIENCY PARTICULATE FILTER.

5000 MG/M3- ANY SUPPLIED-AIR RESPIRATOR WITH A HALF-MASK AND OPERATED IN A PRESSURE-DEMAND OR OTHER POSITIVE PRESSURE MODE.

ESCAPE- ANY AIR-PURIFYING FULL FACEPIECE RESPIRATOR (GAS MASK) WITH A CHIN STYLE OR FRONT- OR BACK-MOUNTED ORGANIC VAPOR CANISTER HAVING A HIGH-EFFICIENCY PARTICULATE FILTER. ANY APPROPRIATE ESCAPE-TYPE SELF-CONTAINED BREATHING APPARATUS.

FOR FIREFIGHTING AND OTHER IMMEDIATELY DANGEROUS TO LIFE OR HEALTH CONDITIONS:

SELF-CONTAINED BREATHING APPARATUS WITH FULL FACEPIECE OPERATED IN PRESSURE-DEMAND OR OTHER POSITIVE PRESSURE MODE.

SUPPLIED-AIR RESPIRATOR WITH FULL FACEPIECE AND OPERATED IN PRESSURE-DEMAND OR OTHER POSITIVE PRESSURE MODE IN COMBINATION WITH AN AUXILIARY SELF-CONTAINED BREATHING APPARATUS OPERATED IN PRESSURE-DEMAND OR OTHER POSITIVE PRESSURE MODE.

CLOTHING: EMPLOYEE MUST WEAR APPROPRIATE PROTECTIVE (IMPERVIOUS) CLOTHING AND EQUIPMENT TO PREVENT REPEATED OR PROLONGED SKIN CONTACT WITH THIS SUBSTANCE.

GLOVES: EMPLOYEE MUST WEAR APPROPRIATE PROTECTIVE GLOVES TO PREVENT CONTACT WITH THIS SUBSTANCE.

EYE PROTECTION: EMPLOYEE MUST WEAR SPLASH-PROOF OR DUST-RESISTANT SAFETY GOGGLES TO PREVENT EYE CONTACT WITH THIS SUBSTANCE.

EMERGENCY EYE WASH: WHERE THERE IS ANY POSSIBILITY THAT AN EMPLOYEE'S EYES MAY BE EXPOSED TO THIS SUBSTANCE, THE EMPLOYER SHOULD PROVIDE AN EYE WASH FOUNTAIN WITHIN THE IMMEDIATE WORK AREA FOR EMERGENCY USE.

AUTHORIZED BY- OCCUPATIONAL HEALTH SERVICES, INC.

CREATION DATE: 10/04/89 ***REVISION DATE:*** 04/04/90

MATERIAL SAFETY DATA SHEET

OCCUPATIONAL HEALTH SERVICES, INC.
AGRICULTURE AND PESTICIDE DIVISION
450 SEVENTH AVENUE, SUITE 2407
NEW YORK, NEW YORK 10123
1-800-445-MSDS OR (212) 967-1100

EMERGENCY CONTACT:
JOHN S. BRANSFORD, JR. (615) 292-1180

SUBSTANCE IDENTIFICATION

CAS-NUMBER 1610-18-0

***SUBSTANCE:* PROMETON**

TRADE NAMES/SYNONYMS: 1,3,5-TRIAZINE-2,4-DIAMINE, 6-METHOXY-N,N'-BIS(1-METHYLETHYL)-; S-TRIAZINE, 2,4-BIS(ISOPROPYLAMINO)-6-METHOXY-; 6-METHOXY-N,N'-BIS(1-METHYLETHYL)-1,3,5-TRIAZINE-2,4-DIAMINE; 2,4-BIS(ISOPROPYLAMINO)-6-METHOXY-S-TRIAZINE; 2,4-BIS(ISOPROPYLAMINO)-6-METHOXY-1,3,5-TRIAZINE; G 31435; GESAFRAM; GESAGRAM; METHOXYPROPAZINE; PRAMITOL; PROMETONE; C10H19N5O; PST19967

CHEMICAL FAMILY: S-TRIAZINE

MOLECULAR FORMULA: C10-H19-N5-O

MOLECULAR WEIGHT: 225.34

CERCLA RATINGS (SCALE 0-3): HEALTH=2 FIRE=1 REACTIVITY=0 PERSISTENCE=2

NFPA RATINGS (SCALE 0-4): HEALTH=2 FIRE=1 REACTIVITY=0

COMPONENTS AND CONTAMINANTS

COMPONENT: PROMETON ***PERCENT:*** 100.0
CAS# 1610-18-0

OTHER CONTAMINANTS: NONE

EXPOSURE LIMITS: NO OCCUPATIONAL EXPOSURE LIMITS ESTABLISHED BY OSHA, ACGIH, OR NIOSH.

PHYSICAL DATA

DESCRIPTION: COLORLESS OR WHITE CRYSTALLINE SOLID.

MELTING POINT: 196-198 F (91-92 C) ***SPECIFIC GRAVITY:*** 1.088

VAPOR PRESSURE: .0000023 MMHG @ 20 C

SOLUBILITY IN WATER: 750 PPM @ 20C

SOLVENT SOLUBILITY: SOLUBLE IN ACETONE, DICHLOROMETHANE, METHANOL, TOLUENE, OCTAN-1-OL, BENZENE, AND CHLOROFORM

FIRE AND EXPLOSION DATA

FIRE AND EXPLOSION HAZARD: SLIGHT FIRE HAZARD WHEN EXPOSED TO HEAT OR FLAME.

FIREFIGHTING MEDIA: DRY CHEMICAL, CARBON DIOXIDE, HALON, WATER SPRAY OR STANDARD FOAM (1987 EMERGENCY RESPONSE GUIDEBOOK, DOT P 5800.4). FOR LARGER FIRES, USE WATER SPRAY, FOG OR STANDARD FOAM (1987 EMERGENCY RESPONSE GUIDEBOOK, DOT P 5800.4).

FIREFIGHTING: MOVE CONTAINERS FROM FIRE AREA IF POSSIBLE (1987 EMERGENCY RESPONSE GUIDEBOOK, DOT P 5800.4, GUIDE PAGE 53).

EXTINGUISH USING AGENTS SUITABLE FOR SURROUNDING FIRE. USE FLOODING QUANTITIES OF WATER AS A FOG. KEEP MATERIAL OUT OF SEWERS AND WATER SOURCES. DO NOT TOUCH SPILLED MATERIAL. AVOID BREATHING HAZARDOUS FUMES; KEEP UPWIND.

TOXICITY

PROMETON: IRRITATION DATA: 21 MG EYE-RABBIT MODERATE; 105 MG OPEN SKIN-RABBIT MILD. TOXICITY DATA: 36 GM/M3/4 HOURS INHALATION-RAT LC50; 2200 MG/KG SKIN-RABBIT LD50; 503 MG/KG ORAL-RAT LD50; 2160 MG/KG ORAL-MOUSE LD50; 1 GM/KG ORAL-DOMESTIC ANIMAL LD50. CARCINOGEN STATUS: NONE. ACUTE TOXICITY LEVEL: MODERATELY TOXIC BY INHALATION AND INGESTION AND SLIGHTLY TOXIC BY DERMAL ABSORPTION. TARGET EFFECTS: NO DATA AVAILABLE.

HEALTH EFFECTS AND FIRST AID

INHALATION: PROMETON: **ACUTE EXPOSURE-** A LETHAL CONCENTRATION IN RATS WAS GREATER THAN 3260 MG/M3/4 HOURS. SOME TRIAZINES ARE MILDLY IRRITATING TO THE UPPER RESPIRATORY TRACT. **CHRONIC EXPOSURE-** NO DATA AVAILABLE.

FIRST AID- REMOVE FROM EXPOSURE AREA TO FRESH AIR IMMEDIATELY. IF BREATHING HAS STOPPED, PERFORM ARTIFICIAL RESPIRATION. KEEP PERSON WARM AND AT REST. TREAT SYMPTOMATICALLY AND SUPPORTIVELY. GET MEDICAL ATTENTION IMMEDIATELY.

SKIN CONTACT: PROMETON: **ACUTE EXPOSURE-** 105 MG APPLIED TO RABBIT SKIN WAS MILDLY IRRITATING. A LETHAL DOSE IN RABBITS BY DERMAL ABSORPTION WAS GREATER THAN 2200 MG/KG. **CHRONIC EXPOSURE-** NO DATA AVAILABLE.

FIRST AID- REMOVE CONTAMINATED CLOTHING AND SHOES IMMEDIATELY. WASH AFFECTED AREA WITH SOAP OR MILD DETERGENT AND LARGE AMOUNTS OF WATER UNTIL NO EVIDENCE OF CHEMICAL REMAINS (APPROXIMATELY 15-20 MINUTES). GET MEDICAL ATTENTION IMMEDIATELY.

EYE CONTACT: PROMETON: **ACUTE EXPOSURE**- 21 MG APPLIED TO RABBIT EYES WAS MODERATELY IRRITATING. **CHRONIC EXPOSURE**- NO DATA AVAILABLE.
FIRST AID- WASH EYES IMMEDIATELY WITH LARGE AMOUNTS OF WATER OR NORMAL SALINE, OCCASIONALLY LIFTING UPPER AND LOWER LIDS, UNTIL NO EVIDENCE OF CHEMICAL REMAINS (APPROXIMATELY 15-20 MINUTES). GET MEDICAL ATTENTION IMMEDIATELY.

INGESTION: PROMETON: **ACUTE EXPOSURE**- A LETHAL DOSE IN RATS WAS 503 MG/KG; NO SYMPTOMS WERE REPORTED. **CHRONIC EXPOSURE**- NO ADVERSE EFFECTS WERE NOTED IN A 90-DAY STUDY OF RATS FED 5.4 MG/KG/DAY.
FIRST AID- REMOVE BY GASTRIC LAVAGE AND CATHARSIS. MAINTAIN BLOOD PRESSURE AND AIRWAY. GIVE OXYGEN IF RESPIRATION IS DEPRESSED. DO NOT PERFORM GASTRIC LAVAGE IF VICTIM IS UNCONSCIOUS. GET MEDICAL ATTENTION IMMEDIATELY (DREISBACH, HANDBOOK OF POISONING, 12TH ED.).
ADMINISTRATION OF LAVAGE OR OXYGEN SHOULD BE PERFORMED BY QUALIFIED MEDICAL PERSONNEL.
ANTIDOTE: NO SPECIFIC ANTIDOTE. TREAT SYMPTOMATICALLY AND SUPPORTIVELY.

REACTIVITY

REACTIVITY: STABLE UNDER NORMAL TEMPERATURES AND PRESSURES.
INCOMPATIBILITIES: PROMETON: NO DATA AVAILABLE.
DECOMPOSITION: THERMAL DECOMPOSITION PRODUCTS MAY INCLUDE TOXIC OXIDES OF CARBON AND NITROGEN.
POLYMERIZATION: HAZARDOUS POLYMERIZATION HAS NOT BEEN REPORTED TO OCCUR UNDER NORMAL TEMPERATURES AND PRESSURES.

STORAGE AND DISPOSAL

OBSERVE ALL FEDERAL, STATE AND LOCAL REGULATIONS WHEN STORING OR DISPOSING OF THIS SUBSTANCE. FOR ASSISTANCE, CONTACT THE DISTRICT DIRECTOR OF THE ENVIRONMENTAL PROTECTION AGENCY.

****STORAGE****

STORE IN ACCORDANCE WITH 40 CFR 165 RECOMMENDED PROCEDURES FOR THE DISPOSAL AND STORAGE OF PESTICIDES AND PESTICIDE CONTAINERS.

****DISPOSAL****

DISPOSAL MUST BE IN ACCORDANCE WITH 40 CFR 165 RECOMMENDED PROCEDURES FOR THE DISPOSAL AND STORAGE OF PESTICIDES AND PESTICIDE CONTAINERS.

CONDITIONS TO AVOID

MAY BURN BUT DOES NOT IGNITE READILY.

SPILL AND LEAK PROCEDURES

OCCUPATIONAL SPILL: DO NOT TOUCH SPILLED MATERIAL. STOP LEAK IF YOU CAN DO IT WITHOUT RISK. FOR SMALL SPILLS, TAKE UP WITH SAND OR OTHER ABSORBENT MATERIAL AND PLACE INTO CONTAINERS FOR LATER DISPOSAL. FOR SMALL DRY SPILLS, WITH A CLEAN SHOVEL PLACE MATERIAL INTO CLEAN, DRY CONTAINER AND COVER. MOVE CONTAINERS FROM SPILL AREA. FOR LARGER SPILLS, DIKE FAR AHEAD OF SPILL FOR LATER DISPOSAL. KEEP UNNECESSARY PEOPLE AWAY. ISOLATE HAZARD AREA AND DENY ENTRY.

PROTECTIVE EQUIPMENT

VENTILATION: PROVIDE LOCAL EXHAUST OR GENERAL DILUTION VENTILATION SYSTEM.
RESPIRATOR: THE FOLLOWING RESPIRATORS ARE RECOMMENDED BASED ON INFORMATION FOUND IN THE PHYSICAL DATA, TOXICITY AND HEALTH EFFECTS SECTIONS. THEY ARE RANKED IN ORDER FROM MINIMUM TO MAXIMUM RESPIRATORY PROTECTION. THE SPECIFIC RESPIRATOR SELECTED MUST BE BASED ON CONTAMINATION LEVELS FOUND IN THE WORK PLACE, MUST NOT EXCEED THE WORKING LIMITS OF THE RESPIRATOR AND BE JOINTLY APPROVED BY THE NATIONAL INSTITUTE FOR OCCUPATIONAL SAFETY AND HEALTH AND THE MINE SAFETY AND HEALTH ADMINISTRATION (NIOSH-MSHA).
CHEMICAL CARTRIDGE RESPIRATOR WITH AN ORGANIC VAPOR CARTRIDGE(S) IN COMBINATION WITH A DUST AND MIST FILTER.
GAS MASK WITH ORGANIC VAPOR CANISTER (CHIN-STYLE OR FRONT- OR BACK-MOUNTED CANISTER) WITH A DUST AND MIST FILTER.
GAS MASK WITH ORGANIC VAPOR CANISTER (CHIN-STYLE OR FRONT- OR BACK-MOUNTED CANISTER) WITH A PARTICULATE FILTER.
POWERED AIR-PURIFYING RESPIRATOR WITH A HIGH-EFFICIENCY FILTER.
TYPE 'C' SUPPLIED-AIR RESPIRATOR WITH A FULL FACEPIECE OPERATED IN A PRESSURE-DEMAND OR OTHER POSITIVE PRESSURE MODE.
SELF-CONTAINED BREATHING APPARATUS WITH A FULL FACEPIECE OPERATED IN PRESSURE-DEMAND OR OTHER POSITIVE PRESSURE MODE.
FOR FIREFIGHTING AND OTHER IMMEDIATELY DANGEROUS TO LIFE OR HEALTH CONDITIONS:
SELF-CONTAINED BREATHING APPARATUS WITH FULL FACEPIECE OPERATED IN PRESSURE-DEMAND OR OTHER POSITIVE PRESSURE MODE. SUPPLIED-AIR RESPIRATOR WITH FULL FACEPIECE AND OPERATED IN PRESSURE-DEMAND OR OTHER POSITIVE PRESSURE MODE IN COMBINATION WITH AN AUXILIARY SELF-CONTAINED BREATHING APPARATUS OPERATED IN PRESSURE-DEMAND OR OTHER POSITIVE PRESSURE MODE.
CLOTHING: EMPLOYEE MUST WEAR APPROPRIATE PROTECTIVE (IMPERVIOUS) CLOTHING AND EQUIPMENT TO PREVENT REPEATED OR PROLONGED SKIN CONTACT WITH THIS SUBSTANCE.
GLOVES: EMPLOYEE MUST WEAR APPROPRIATE PROTECTIVE GLOVES TO PREVENT CONTACT WITH THIS SUBSTANCE.
EYE PROTECTION: EMPLOYEE MUST WEAR SPLASH-PROOF OR DUST-RESISTANT SAFETY GOGGLES TO PREVENT EYE CONTACT WITH THIS SUBSTANCE.
EMERGENCY EYE WASH: WHERE THERE IS ANY POSSIBILITY THAT AN EMPLOYEE'S EYES MAY BE EXPOSED TO THIS SUBSTANCE, THE EMPLOYER SHOULD PROVIDE AN EYE WASH FOUNTAIN WITHIN THE IMMEDIATE WORK AREA FOR EMERGENCY USE.

AUTHORIZED BY- OCCUPATIONAL HEALTH SERVICES, INC.
CREATION DATE: 10/04/89 ***REVISION DATE:*** 05/09/90

MATERIAL SAFETY DATA SHEET

OCCUPATIONAL HEALTH SERVICES, INC.
AGRICULTURE AND PESTICIDE DIVISION
450 SEVENTH AVENUE, SUITE 2407
NEW YORK, NEW YORK 10123
1-800-445-MSDS OR (212) 967-1100

EMERGENCY CONTACT:
JOHN S. BRANSFORD, JR. (615) 292-1180

SUBSTANCE IDENTIFICATION

CAS-NUMBER 7287-19-6
***SUBSTANCE:* <u>PROMETRYN</u>**
TRADE NAMES/SYNONYMS: 1,3,5-TRIAZINE-2,4-DIAMINE, N,N'-BIS(1-METHYLETHYL)-6-(METHYLTHIO)-; S-TRIZAINE, 2,4-BIS(ISOPROPYLAMINO)-6-(METHYLTHIO)-; N,N'-BIS(1-METHYLETHYL)-6-METHYLTHIO-1,3,5-TRIAZINE-2,4-DIAMINE; 2,4-BIS(ISOPROPYLAMINO)-6-(METHYLTHIO)-S-TRIAZINE; 2-METHYLTHIO-4,6-BIS(ISOPROPYLAMINO)-S-TRIAZINE; N2,N4-DI-ISOPROPYL-6-METHYLTHIO-1,3,5-TRIAZINE-2,4-DIAMINE; 2,4-BIS(ISOPROPYLAMINO)-6-(METHYLTHIO)-1,3,5-TRIAZINE; N,N'-BIS(1-METHYLETHYL)-6-(METHYLTHIO)-1,3-5-TRIAZINE-2,4-DIAMINE; CAPAROL; G34161; GESAGARD; MERCAZIN; MERKAZIN; PRIMATOL Q; PROMETREX; SELECTIN; SELEKTIN; C10H19N5S; PST19968
CHEMICAL FAMILY: S-TRIAZINE
MOLECULAR FORMULA: C10-H19-N5-S
MOLECULAR WEIGHT: 241.37
CERCLA RATINGS (SCALE 0-3): HEALTH=2 FIRE=1 REACTIVITY=0 PERSISTENCE=2
NFPA RATINGS (SCALE 0-4): HEALTH=2 FIRE=1 REACTIVITY=0

COMPONENTS AND CONTAMINANTS

COMPONENT: PROMETRYN ***PERCENT:*** 100.0
CAS# 7287-19-6
OTHER CONTAMINANTS: NONE
EXPOSURE LIMITS: NO OCCUPATIONAL EXPOSURE LIMITS ESTABLISHED BY OSHA, ACGIH, OR NIOSH.

PHYSICAL DATA

DESCRIPTION: COLORLESS TO WHITE CRYSTALS. ***MELTING POINT:*** 244-248 F (118-120 C)
SPECIFIC GRAVITY: 1.157 ***VAPOR PRESSURE:*** 0.000001 MMHG @ 20 C
SOLUBILITY IN WATER: 48 PPM @ 20 C
SOLVENT SOLUBILITY: SOLUBLE IN ETHANOL, METHANOL, ACETONE, DICHLOROMETHANE, TOLUENE, OCTAN-1-OL, AND MOST ORGANIC SOLVENTS; SLIGHTLY SOLUBLE IN HEXANE

FIRE AND EXPLOSION DATA

FIRE AND EXPLOSION HAZARD: SLIGHT FIRE HAZARD WHEN EXPOSED TO HEAT OR FLAME.

FIREFIGHTING MEDIA: DRY CHEMICAL, CARBON DIOXIDE, HALON, WATER SPRAY OR STANDARD FOAM (1987 EMERGENCY RESPONSE GUIDEBOOK, DOT P 5800.4). FOR LARGER FIRES, USE WATER SPRAY, FOG OR STANDARD FOAM (1987 EMERGENCY RESPONSE GUIDEBOOK, DOT P 5800.4).

FIREFIGHTING: MOVE CONTAINERS FROM FIRE AREA IF POSSIBLE (1987 EMERGENCY RESPONSE GUIDEBOOK, DOT P 5800.4, GUIDE PAGE 53).
EXTINGUISH USING AGENTS SUITABLE FOR SURROUNDING FIRE. USE FLOODING QUANTITIES OF WATER AS A FOG. KEEP MATERIAL OUT OF SEWERS AND WATER SOURCES. DO NOT TOUCH SPILLED MATERIAL. AVOID BREATHING HAZARDOUS FUMES; KEEP UPWIND.

TOXICITY

PROMETRYN: IRRITATION DATA: 80 MG EYE-RABBIT MILD. TOXICITY DATA: 1800 MG/KG ORAL-RAT LD50; 2 GM/KG ORAL-MOUSE LD50; 1800 MG/KG UNREPORTED ROUTE-MAMMAL LD50; MUTAGENIC DATA (RTECS); REPRODUCTIVE EFFECTS DATA (RTECS). CARCINOGEN STATUS: NONE. ACUTE TOXICITY LEVEL: MODERATELY TOXIC BY INGESTION. TARGET EFFECTS: NO DATA AVAILABLE.

HEALTH EFFECTS AND FIRST AID

INHALATION: PROMETRYN: **ACUTE EXPOSURE-** SOME TRIAZINES ARE MILDLY IRRITATING TO THE UPPER RESPIRATORY TRACT. NO DEATHS OCCURRED IN RATS EXPOSED TO 4400 MG/M3/4 HOURS OR IN MICE EXPOSED TO 2500 MG/M3/2 HOURS. **CHRONIC EXPOSURE-** NO DATA AVAILABLE.

FIRST AID- REMOVE FROM EXPOSURE AREA TO FRESH AIR IMMEDIATELY. IF BREATHING HAS STOPPED, PERFORM ARTIFICIAL RESPIRATION. KEEP PERSON WARM AND AT REST. TREAT SYMPTOMATICALLY AND SUPPORTIVELY. GET MEDICAL ATTENTION IMMEDIATELY.

SKIN CONTACT: PROMETRYN: **ACUTE EXPOSURE-** THIS MATERIAL WAS NOT IRRITATING TO RABBIT SKIN. A LETHAL DOSE IN RABBITS BY DERMAL ABSORPTION WAS GREATER THAN 3100 MG/KG. **CHRONIC EXPOSURE-** NO DATA AVAILABLE.

FIRST AID- REMOVE CONTAMINATED CLOTHING AND SHOES IMMEDIATELY. WASH AFFECTED AREA WITH SOAP OR MILD DETERGENT AND LARGE AMOUNTS OF WATER UNTIL NO EVIDENCE OF CHEMICAL REMAINS (APPROXIMATELY 15-20 MINUTES). GET MEDICAL ATTENTION IMMEDIATELY.

EYE CONTACT: PROMETRYN: **ACUTE EXPOSURE-** 80 MG APPLIED TO RABBIT EYES WAS MILDLY IRRITATING. **CHRONIC EXPOSURE-** NO DATA AVAILABLE.

FIRST AID- WASH EYES IMMEDIATELY WITH LARGE AMOUNTS OF WATER OR NORMAL SALINE, OCCASIONALLY LIFTING UPPER AND LOWER LIDS, UNTIL NO EVIDENCE OF CHEMICAL REMAINS (APPROXIMATELY 15-20 MINUTES). GET MEDICAL ATTENTION IMMEDIATELY.

INGESTION: PROMETRYN: **ACUTE EXPOSURE-** A LETHAL DOSE IN RATS WAS 1800 MG/KG; SYMPTOMS WERE NOT REPORTED. **CHRONIC EXPOSURE-** IN A 2-YEAR STUDY WITH DOGS FED 1500 PPM, DEGENERATIVE CHANGES IN THE LIVER AND RENAL TUBULES, AND BONE MARROW ATROPHY WERE OBSERVED. IN A 28-DAY STUDY OF RATS FED 500 MG/KG, FATTY LIVER DEGENERATION, CONGESTION AND SEVERE CIRCULATORY DISORDERS, AND WEIGHT LOSS WERE REPORTED.

FIRST AID- REMOVE BY GASTRIC LAVAGE AND CATHARSIS. MAINTAIN BLOOD PRESSURE AND AIRWAY. GIVE OXYGEN IF RESPIRATION IS DEPRESSED. DO NOT PERFORM GASTRIC LAVAGE IF VICTIM IS UNCONSCIOUS. GET MEDICAL ATTENTION IMMEDIATELY (DREISBACH, HANDBOOK OF POISONING, 12TH ED.). ADMINISTRATION OF LAVAGE OR OXYGEN SHOULD BE PERFORMED BY QUALIFIED MEDICAL PERSONNEL.

ANTIDOTE: NO SPECIFIC ANTIDOTE. TREAT SYMPTOMATICALLY AND SUPPORTIVELY.

REACTIVITY

REACTIVITY: STABLE UNDER NORMAL TEMPERATURES AND PRESSURES.

INCOMPATIBILITIES: PROMETRYN: ACIDS (STRONG): HYDROLYZES. BASES (STRONG): HYDROLYZES.

DECOMPOSITION: THERMAL DECOMPOSITION PRODUCTS MAY INCLUDE TOXIC OXIDES OF CARBON, NITROGEN, AND SULFUR.

POLYMERIZATION: HAZARDOUS POLYMERIZATION HAS NOT BEEN REPORTED TO OCCUR UNDER NORMAL TEMPERATURES AND PRESSURES.

STORAGE AND DISPOSAL

OBSERVE ALL FEDERAL, STATE AND LOCAL REGULATIONS WHEN STORING OR DISPOSING OF THIS SUBSTANCE. FOR ASSISTANCE, CONTACT THE DISTRICT DIRECTOR OF THE ENVIRONMENTAL PROTECTION AGENCY.

****STORAGE****

STORE IN ACCORDANCE WITH 40 CFR 165 RECOMMENDED PROCEDURES FOR THE DISPOSAL AND STORAGE OF PESTICIDES AND PESTICIDE CONTAINERS.
STORE AWAY FROM INCOMPATIBLE SUBSTANCES.

****DISPOSAL****

DISPOSAL MUST BE IN ACCORDANCE WITH 40 CFR 165 RECOMMENDED PROCEDURES FOR THE DISPOSAL AND STORAGE OF PESTICIDES AND PESTICIDE CONTAINERS.

CONDITIONS TO AVOID

MAY BURN BUT DOES NOT IGNITE READILY.

SPILL AND LEAK PROCEDURES

OCCUPATIONAL SPILL: DO NOT TOUCH SPILLED MATERIAL. STOP LEAK IF YOU CAN DO IT WITHOUT RISK. FOR SMALL SPILLS, TAKE UP WITH SAND OR OTHER ABSORBENT MATERIAL AND PLACE INTO CONTAINERS FOR LATER DISPOSAL. FOR SMALL DRY SPILLS, WITH A CLEAN SHOVEL PLACE MATERIAL INTO CLEAN, DRY CONTAINER AND COVER. MOVE CONTAINERS FROM SPILL AREA. FOR LARGER SPILLS, DIKE FAR AHEAD OF SPILL FOR LATER DISPOSAL. KEEP UNNECESSARY PEOPLE AWAY. ISOLATE HAZARD AREA AND DENY ENTRY.

PROTECTIVE EQUIPMENT

VENTILATION: PROVIDE LOCAL EXHAUST OR GENERAL DILUTION VENTILATION SYSTEM.

RESPIRATOR: THE FOLLOWING RESPIRATORS ARE RECOMMENDED BASED ON INFORMATION FOUND IN THE PHYSICAL DATA, TOXICITY AND HEALTH EFFECTS SECTIONS. THEY ARE RANKED IN ORDER FROM MINIMUM TO MAXIMUM RESPIRATORY PROTECTION. THE SPECIFIC RESPIRATOR SELECTED MUST BE BASED ON CONTAMINATION LEVELS FOUND IN THE WORK PLACE, MUST NOT EXCEED THE WORKING LIMITS OF THE RESPIRATOR AND BE JOINTLY APPROVED BY THE NATIONAL INSTITUTE FOR OCCUPATIONAL SAFETY AND HEALTH AND THE MINE SAFETY AND HEALTH ADMINISTRATION (NIOSH-MSHA).
CHEMICAL CARTRIDGE RESPIRATOR WITH AN ORGANIC VAPOR CARTRIDGE(S) IN COMBINATION WITH A DUST AND MIST FILTER.
GAS MASK WITH ORGANIC VAPOR CANISTER (CHIN-STYLE OR FRONT- OR BACK-MOUNTED CANISTER) WITH A DUST AND MIST FILTER.
GAS MASK WITH ORGANIC VAPOR CANISTER (CHIN-STYLE OR FRONT- OR BACK-MOUNTED CANISTER) WITH A PARTICULATE FILTER.
POWERED AIR-PURIFYING RESPIRATOR WITH A HIGH-EFFICIENCY FILTER.
TYPE 'C' SUPPLIED-AIR RESPIRATOR WITH A FULL FACEPIECE OPERATED IN A PRESSURE-DEMAND OR OTHER POSITIVE PRESSURE MODE. SELF-CONTAINED BREATHING APPARATUS WITH A FULL FACEPIECE OPERATED IN PRESSURE-DEMAND OR OTHER POSITIVE PRESSURE MODE.
FOR FIREFIGHTING AND OTHER IMMEDIATELY DANGEROUS TO LIFE OR HEALTH CONDITIONS:
SELF-CONTAINED BREATHING APPARATUS WITH FULL FACEPIECE OPERATED IN PRESSURE-DEMAND OR OTHER POSITIVE PRESSURE MODE.
SUPPLIED-AIR RESPIRATOR WITH FULL FACEPIECE AND OPERATED IN PRESSURE-DEMAND OR OTHER POSITIVE PRESSURE MODE IN COMBINATION WITH AN AUXILIARY SELF-CONTAINED BREATHING APPARATUS OPERATED IN PRESSURE-DEMAND OR OTHER POSITIVE PRESSURE MODE.

CLOTHING: EMPLOYEE MUST WEAR APPROPRIATE PROTECTIVE (IMPERVIOUS) CLOTHING AND EQUIPMENT TO PREVENT REPEATED OR PROLONGED SKIN CONTACT WITH THIS SUBSTANCE.

GLOVES: EMPLOYEE MUST WEAR APPROPRIATE PROTECTIVE GLOVES TO PREVENT CONTACT WITH THIS SUBSTANCE.

EYE PROTECTION: EMPLOYEE MUST WEAR SPLASH-PROOF OR DUST-RESISTANT SAFETY GOGGLES TO PREVENT EYE CONTACT WITH THIS SUBSTANCE.
EMERGENCY EYE WASH: WHERE THERE IS ANY POSSIBILITY THAT AN EMPLOYEE'S EYES MAY BE EXPOSED TO THIS SUBSTANCE, THE EMPLOYER SHOULD PROVIDE AN EYE WASH FOUNTAIN WITHIN THE IMMEDIATE WORK AREA FOR EMERGENCY USE.

AUTHORIZED BY- OCCUPATIONAL HEALTH SERVICES, INC.
CREATION DATE: 10/04/89 ***REVISION DATE:*** 05/15/90

MATERIAL SAFETY DATA SHEET

OCCUPATIONAL HEALTH SERVICES, INC.
AGRICULTURE AND PESTICIDE DIVISION
450 SEVENTH AVENUE, SUITE 2407
NEW YORK, NEW YORK 10123
1-800-445-MSDS OR (212) 967-1100

EMERGENCY CONTACT:
JOHN S. BRANSFORD, JR. (615) 292-1180

SUBSTANCE IDENTIFICATION

CAS-NUMBER 121-29-9

SUBSTANCE: **PYRETHRIN II**

TRADE NAMES/SYNONYMS: CYCLOPROPANECARBOXYLIC ACID, 3-(3-METHOXY-2-METHYL-3-OXO-1-PROPENYL)- 2,2-DIMETHYL-, 2-METHYL-4-OXO-3-(2,4-PENTADIENYL)-2-CYCLOPENTEN-1-YL ESTER, (1R-(1ALPHA(S*(Z),3BETA))-; CYCLOPROPANEACRYLIC ACID, 3-CARBOXY-ALPHA,2,2-TRIMETHYL-, 1-METHYL ESTER, ESTER WITH 4-HYDROXY-3-METHYL-2-(2,4-PENTADIENYL)-2- CYCLOPENTEN-1-ONE; (1R-(1ALPHA(S*(Z),3BETA(E))-3-(3-METHOXY-2-METHYL-3-OXO-1-PROPENYL)- 2,2,-DIMETHYLCYCLOPROPANECARBOXYLIC ACID, 2-METHYL-4-OXO-3- (2,4-PENTADIENYL)-2-CYCLOPENTEN-1-YL ESTER; 3-CARBOXY-ALPHA,2-2-TRIMETHYLCYCLOPROPANEACRYLIC ACID, 1-METHYL ESTER, ESTER WITH 4-HYDROXY-3-METHYL-2-(2,4-PENTADIENYL)-2-CYCLOPENTEN-1-ONE; PYRETHRIN 2; PYRETHRIN; C22H28O5; PST19970

CHEMICAL FAMILY: PYRETHRIN (NATURAL)

MOLECULAR FORMULA: C22-H28-O5

MOLECULAR WEIGHT: 372.50

CERCLA RATINGS (SCALE 0-3): HEALTH=3 FIRE=2 REACTIVITY=0 PERSISTENCE=1

NFPA RATINGS (SCALE 0-4): HEALTH=U FIRE=2 REACTIVITY=0

COMPONENTS AND CONTAMINANTS

COMPONENT: PYRETHRIN II ***PERCENT:*** 100.0

CAS# 121-29-9

OTHER CONTAMINANTS: NONE

EXPOSURE LIMITS: PYRETHRUM: 5 MG/M3 OSHA TWA 5 MG/M3 ACGIH TWA
1 POUND CERCLA SECTION 103 REPORTABLE QUANTITY

PHYSICAL DATA

DESCRIPTION: BROWN, VISCOUS LIQUID.

BOILING POINT: 378-379 F (192-193 C) @ 0.007 MMHG

SPECIFIC GRAVITY: NOT AVAILABLE ***VAPOR PRESSURE:*** NEGLIGIBLE

SOLUBILITY IN WATER: INSOLUBLE ***VAPOR DENSITY:*** >1

SOLVENT SOLUBILITY: SOLUBLE IN ETHANOL, ALCOHOL, PETROLEUM ETHER, KEROSENE, CARBON TETRACHLORIDE, ETHYLENE DICHLORIDE, NITROMETHANE, AND ORGANIC SOLVENTS.

FIRE AND EXPLOSION DATA

FIRE AND EXPLOSION HAZARD: MODERATE FIRE HAZARD WHEN EXPOSED TO HEAT OR FLAME.
VAPORS ARE HEAVIER THAN AIR AND MAY TRAVEL A CONSIDERABLE DISTANCE TO A SOURCE OF IGNITION AND FLASH BACK.

FLASH POINT: 180-190 F (82-88 C) ***FLAMMABILITY CLASS(OSHA):*** IIIA

FIREFIGHTING MEDIA: DRY CHEMICAL, CARBON DIOXIDE, HALON, WATER SPRAY OR STANDARD FOAM (1987 EMERGENCY RESPONSE GUIDEBOOK, DOT P 5800.4).
FOR LARGER FIRES, USE WATER SPRAY, FOG OR STANDARD FOAM (1987 EMERGENCY RESPONSE GUIDEBOOK, DOT P 5800.4).

FIREFIGHTING: MOVE CONTAINER FROM FIRE AREA IF POSSIBLE. COOL FIRE-EXPOSED CONTAINERS WITH WATER FROM SIDE UNTIL WELL AFTER FIRE IS OUT. STAY AWAY FROM STORAGE TANK ENDS. FOR MASSIVE FIRE IN STORAGE AREA, USE UNMANNED HOSE HOLDER OR MONITOR NOZZLES, ELSE WITHDRAW FROM AREA AND LET FIRE BURN. WITHDRAW IMMEDIATELY IN CASE OF RISING SOUND FROM VENTING SAFETY DEVICE OR ANY DISCOLORATION OF STORAGE TANK DUE TO FIRE (1987 EMERGENCY RESPONSE GUIDEBOOK, DOT P 5800.4, GUIDE PAGE 27). EXTINGUISH ONLY IF FLOW CAN BE STOPPED; USE FLOODING AMOUNTS OF WATER AS A FOG, SOLID STREAMS MAY BE INEFFECTIVE. COOL CONTAINERS WITH FLOODING AMOUNTS OF WATER, APPLY FROM AS FAR A DISTANCE AS POSSIBLE. AVOID BREATHING VAPORS, KEEP UPWIND.

TRANSPORTATION DATA

DEPARTMENT OF TRANSPORTATION HAZARD CLASSIFICATION 49 CFR 172.101: COMBUSTIBLE LIQUID
DEPARTMENT OF TRANSPORTATION LABELING REQUIREMENTS 49 CFR 172.101 AND SUBPART E: NONE
DEPARTMENT OF TRANSPORTATION PACKAGING REQUIREMENTS: NONE EXCEPTIONS: 49 CFR 173.118A

TOXICITY

PYRETHRIN II: TOXICITY DATA: 200 MG/KG ORAL-RAT LD50; 1 MG/KG INTRAVENOUS-RAT LD50; 1029 MG/KG UNREPORTED-MAN LDLO. CARCINOGEN STATUS: NONE. ACUTE TOXICITY LEVEL: TOXIC BY INGESTION. TARGET EFFECTS: SENSITIZER- PULMONARY, DERMAL. POISONING MAY AFFECT THE RESPIRATORY AND CENTRAL NERVOUS SYSTEMS.* AT INCREASED RISK FROM EXPOSURE: PERSONS WITH ALLERGIES AND CHRONIC RESPIRATORY AND SKIN DISEASES.*

* MAY BE BASED ON GENERAL INFORMATION ON PYRETHRINS.

HEALTH EFFECTS AND FIRST AID

INHALATION: PYRETHRIN II: SENSITIZER. SEE INFORMATION ON PYRETHRINS.
PYRETHRINS: 5000 MG/M3 IMMEDIATELY DANGEROUS TO LIFE AND HEALTH.
ACUTE EXPOSURE- MAY CAUSE MUCOUS MEMBRANE IRRITATION. NERVOUS IRRITABILITY, TREMORS, AND ATAXIA HAVE RARELY OCCURRED WITH MASSIVE EXPOSURE. SOME PYRETHRINS MAY CAUSE SENSITIZATION REACTIONS IN SUSCEPTIBLE INDIVIDUALS. **CHRONIC EXPOSURE**- PROLONGED OR REPEATED EXPOSURE TO SOME PYRETHRINS MAY RESULT IN SENSITIZATION. EFFECTS MAY INCLUDE SNEEZING, NASAL DISCHARGE AND STUFFINESS, SCRATCHY THROAT, ASTHMA, AND RARELY ANAPHYLACTIC REACTIONS WITH THE POSSIBILITY OF SHOCK AND RESPIRATORY DIFFICULTIES. A CASE OF HYPERSENSITIVITY PNEUMONITIS HAS ALSO BEEN REPORTED.

FIRST AID- REMOVE FROM EXPOSURE AREA TO FRESH AIR IMMEDIATELY. IF BREATHING HAS STOPPED, PERFORM ARTIFICIAL RESPIRATION. KEEP PERSON WARM AND AT REST. TREAT SYMPTOMATICALLY AND SUPPORTIVELY. GET MEDICAL ATTENTION IMMEDIATELY.

SKIN CONTACT: PYRETHRIN II: SENSITIZER. SEE INFORMATION ON PYRETHRINS.
PYRETHRINS: **ACUTE EXPOSURE**- MAY CAUSE IRRITATION. EXPOSURE TO SOME PYRETHRINS MAY RESULT IN SENSITIZATION REACTIONS IN SUSCEPTIBLE INDIVIDUALS. **CHRONIC EXPOSURE**- PROLONGED OR REPEATED EXPOSURE MAY CAUSE AN ERYTHEMATOUS DERMATITIS WITH VESICLES, PAPULES, ESPECIALLY IN MOIST AREAS, AND INTENSE PRURITIS; TOUGHENING, AND IN SEVERE CASES, EDEMA AND CRACKING OF THE SKIN MAY OCCUR. THE EFFECTS MAY BE ALLERGIC REACTIONS; EOSINOPHILIA MAY ALSO BE PRESENT. EXPOSURE TO THE SUN, WARM WEATHER OR EXCESSIVE PERSPIRATION MAY EXACERBATE THE DERMAL EFFECTS.

FIRST AID- REMOVE CONTAMINATED CLOTHING AND SHOES IMMEDIATELY. WASH AFFECTED AREA WITH SOAP OR MILD DETERGENT AND LARGE AMOUNTS OF WATER UNTIL NO EVIDENCE OF CHEMICAL REMAINS (APPROXIMATELY 15-20 MINUTES). GET MEDICAL ATTENTION IMMEDIATELY.

EYE CONTACT: PYRETHRIN II: SEE INFORMATION ON PYRETHRINS.
PYRETHRINS: **ACUTE EXPOSURE**- MAY CAUSE IRRITATION AND TRANSIENT CONJUNCTIVAL EDEMA AND HYPEREMIA. **CHRONIC EXPOSURE**- NO DATA AVAILABLE.

FIRST AID- WASH EYES IMMEDIATELY WITH LARGE AMOUNTS OF WATER OR NORMAL SALINE, OCCASIONALLY LIFTING UPPER AND LOWER LIDS, UNTIL NO EVIDENCE OF CHEMICAL REMAINS (APPROXIMATELY 15-20 MINUTES). GET MEDICAL ATTENTION IMMEDIATELY.

INGESTION: PYRETHRIN II: TOXIC. SEE INFORMATION ON PYRETHRINS.
PYRETHRINS: **ACUTE EXPOSURE**- LARGE AMOUNTS MAY CAUSE NAUSEA, VOMITING, GASTROENTERITIS WITH DIARRHEA, HYPEREXCITABILITY, INCOORDINATION, TREMORS, MUSCULAR FIBRILLATION, BRADYCARDIA, CONVULSIONS LEADING TO PARALYSIS, AND DEATH DUE TO RESPIRATORY FAILURE. **CHRONIC EXPOSURE**- DOGS FED A DIETARY LEVEL OF 5000 PPM FOR 3 MONTHS EXHIBITED TREMOR, ATAXIA, LABORED RESPIRATION, AND SALIVATION DURING THE FIRST MONTH. SLIGHT LIVER DAMAGE WAS THE ONLY EFFECT REPORTED IN RATS FED DIETARY LEVELS OF 1000 AND 5000 PPM FOR 2 YEARS. AN INCREASED INCIDENCE OF FETAL RESORPTIONS WAS NOTED IN A STUDY OF PREGNANT RATS.

FIRST AID- REMOVE BY GASTRIC LAVAGE AND CATHARSIS. MAINTAIN BLOOD PRESSURE AND AIRWAY. GIVE OXYGEN IF RESPIRATION IS DEPRESSED. DO NOT PERFORM GASTRIC LAVAGE IF VICTIM IS UNCONSCIOUS. GET MEDICAL ATTENTION IMMEDIATELY (DREISBACH, HANDBOOK OF POISONING, 12TH ED.). ADMINISTRATION OF LAVAGE OR OXYGEN SHOULD BE PERFORMED BY QUALIFIED MEDICAL PERSONNEL.

ANTIDOTE: NO SPECIFIC ANTIDOTE. TREAT SYMPTOMATICALLY AND SUPPORTIVELY.

REACTIVITY

REACTIVITY: STABLE UNDER NORMAL TEMPERATURES AND PRESSURES.

INCOMPATIBILITIES: PYRETHRIN II: OXIDIZERS (STRONG): FIRE AND EXPLOSION HAZARD.

DECOMPOSITION: THERMAL DECOMPOSITION PRODUCTS MAY INCLUDE TOXIC OXIDES OF CARBON.

POLYMERIZATION: HAZARDOUS POLYMERIZATION HAS NOT BEEN REPORTED TO OCCUR UNDER NORMAL TEMPERATURES AND PRESSURES.

STORAGE AND DISPOSAL

OBSERVE ALL FEDERAL, STATE AND LOCAL REGULATIONS WHEN STORING OR DISPOSING OF THIS SUBSTANCE. FOR ASSISTANCE, CONTACT THE DISTRICT DIRECTOR OF THE ENVIRONMENTAL PROTECTION AGENCY.

STORAGE

STORE IN ACCORDANCE WITH 29 CFR 1910.106.
STORE IN ACCORDANCE WITH 40 CFR 165 RECOMMENDED PROCEDURES FOR THE DISPOSAL AND STORAGE OF PESTICIDES AND PESTICIDE CONTAINERS.
STORE AWAY FROM INCOMPATIBLE SUBSTANCES.
STORE IN A COOL, DRY PLACE PROTECTED AGAINST LIGHT.

DISPOSAL

DISPOSAL MUST BE IN ACCORDANCE WITH 40 CFR 165 RECOMMENDED PROCEDURES FOR THE DISPOSAL AND STORAGE OF PESTICIDES AND PESTICIDE CONTAINERS.

CONDITIONS TO AVOID

AVOID CONTACT WITH HEAT, SPARKS, FLAMES, OR OTHER SOURCES OF IGNITION. VAPORS MAY BE EXPLOSIVE. AVOID OVERHEATING OF CONTAINERS; CONTAINERS MAY VIOLENTLY RUPTURE IN HEAT OF FIRE. AVOID CONTAMINATION OF WATER SOURCES.

SPILL AND LEAK PROCEDURES

SOIL SPILL: DIG HOLDING AREA SUCH AS LAGOON, POND OR PIT FOR CONTAINMENT. DIKE FLOW OF SPILLED MATERIAL USING SOIL OR SANDBAGS OR FOAMED BARRIERS SUCH AS POLYURETHANE OR CONCRETE.
USE CEMENT POWDER OR FLY ASH TO ABSORB LIQUID MASS.

WATER SPILL: USE ACTIVATED CARBON TO ABSORB SPILLED SUBSTANCE THAT IS DISSOLVED.
USE MECHANICAL DREDGES OR LIFTS TO EXTRACT IMMOBILIZED MASSES OF POLLUTION AND PRECIPITATES.

OCCUPATIONAL SPILL: SHUT OFF IGNITION SOURCES. STOP LEAK IF YOU CAN DO IT WITHOUT RISK. USE WATER SPRAY TO REDUCE VAPORS. FOR SMALL SPILLS, TAKE UP WITH SAND OR OTHER ABSORBENT MATERIAL AND PLACE INTO CONTAINERS FOR LATER DISPOSAL. FOR LARGER SPILLS, DIKE FAR AHEAD OF SPILL FOR LATER DISPOSAL. NO SMOKING, FLAMES OR FLARES IN HAZARD AREA. KEEP UNNECESSARY PEOPLE AWAY; ISOLATE HAZARD AREA AND RESTRICT ENTRY.
REPORTABLE QUANTITY (RQ): 1 POUND THE SUPERFUND AMENDMENTS AND REAUTHORIZATION ACT (SARA) SECTION 304 REQUIRES THAT A RELEASE EQUAL TO OR GREATER THAN THE REPORTABLE QUANTITY FOR THIS SUBSTANCE BE IMMEDIATELY REPORTED TO THE LOCAL EMERGENCY PLANNING COMMITTEE AND THE STATE EMERGENCY RESPONSE COMMISSION (40 CFR 355.40). IF THE RELEASE OF THIS SUBSTANCE IS REPORTABLE UNDER CERCLA SECTION 103, THE NATIONAL RESPONSE CENTER MUST BE NOTIFIED IMMEDIATELY AT (800) 424-8802 OR (202) 426-2675 IN THE METROPOLITAN WASHINGTON, D.C. AREA (40 CFR 302.6).

PROTECTIVE EQUIPMENT

VENTILATION: PROVIDE LOCAL EXHAUST VENTILATION AND/OR GENERAL DILUTION VENTILATION TO MEET PUBLISHED EXPOSURE LIMITS.

RESPIRATOR: THE FOLLOWING RESPIRATORS AND MAXIMUM USE CONCENTRATIONS ARE RECOMMENDATIONS BY THE U.S. DEPARTMENT OF HEALTH AND HUMAN SERVICES, NIOSH POCKET GUIDE TO CHEMICAL HAZARDS; NIOSH CRITERIA DOCUMENTS OR BY THE U.S. DEPARTMENT OF LABOR, 29 CFR 1910 SUBPART Z. THE SPECIFIC RESPIRATOR SELECTED MUST BE BASED ON CONTAMINATION LEVELS FOUND IN THE WORK PLACE, MUST NOT EXCEED THE WORKING LIMITS OF THE RESPIRATOR AND BE JOINTLY APPROVED BY THE NATIONAL INSTITUTE FOR OCCUPATIONAL SAFETY AND HEALTH AND THE MINE SAFETY AND HEALTH ADMINISTRATION (NIOSH-MSHA).
PYRETHRUM:
50 MG/M3- ANY CHEMICAL CARTRIDGE RESPIRATOR WITH ORGANIC VAPOR CARTRIDGE(S) IN COMBINATION WITH A DUST, MIST, AND FUME FILTER. ANY SUPPLIED-AIR RESPIRATOR. ANY SELF-CONTAINED BREATHING APPARATUS.
125 MG/M3- ANY SUPPLIED-AIR RESPIRATOR OPERATED IN A CONTINUOUS FLOW MODE. ANY POWERED AIR-PURIFYING RESPIRATOR WITH ORGANIC VAPOR CARTRIDGE(S) IN COMBINATION WITH A DUST, MIST, AND FUME FILTER.
250 MG/M3- ANY CHEMICAL CARTRIDGE RESPIRATOR WITH A FULL FACEPIECE AND ORGANIC VAPOR CARTRIDGE(S) IN COMBINATION WITH A HIGH-EFFICIENCY PARTICULATE FILTER. ANY SUPPLIED-AIR RESPIRATOR WITH A FULL FACEPIECE. ANY SELF-CONTAINED BREATHING APPARATUS WITH A FULL FACEPIECE. ANY POWERED AIR-PURIFYING RESPIRATOR WITH A TIGHT-FITTING FACEPIECE AND ORGANIC VAPOR CARTRIDGE(S) IN COMBINATION WITH A HIGH-EFFICIENCY PARTICULATE FILTER.
5000 MG/M3- ANY SUPPLIED-AIR RESPIRATOR WITH A HALF-MASK AND OPERATED IN A PRESSURE-DEMAND OR OTHER POSITIVE PRESSURE MODE.
ESCAPE- ANY AIR-PURIFYING FULL FACEPIECE RESPIRATOR (GAS MASK) WITH A CHIN STYLE OR FRONT- OR BACK-MOUNTED ORGANIC VAPOR CANISTER HAVING A HIGH-EFFICIENCY PARTICULATE FILTER. ANY APPROPRIATE ESCAPE-TYPE SELF-CONTAINED BREATHING APPARATUS.
FOR FIREFIGHTING AND OTHER IMMEDIATELY DANGEROUS TO LIFE OR HEALTH CONDITIONS:
SELF-CONTAINED BREATHING APPARATUS WITH FULL FACEPIECE OPERATED IN PRESSURE-DEMAND OR OTHER POSITIVE PRESSURE MODE.
SUPPLIED-AIR RESPIRATOR WITH FULL FACEPIECE AND OPERATED IN PRESSURE-DEMAND OR OTHER POSITIVE PRESSURE MODE IN COMBINATION WITH AN AUXILIARY SELF-CONTAINED BREATHING APPARATUS OPERATED IN PRESSURE-DEMAND OR OTHER POSITIVE PRESSURE MODE.

CLOTHING: EMPLOYEE MUST WEAR APPROPRIATE PROTECTIVE (IMPERVIOUS) CLOTHING AND EQUIPMENT TO PREVENT REPEATED OR PROLONGED SKIN CONTACT WITH THIS SUBSTANCE.

GLOVES: EMPLOYEE MUST WEAR APPROPRIATE PROTECTIVE GLOVES TO PREVENT CONTACT WITH THIS SUBSTANCE.

EYE PROTECTION: EMPLOYEE MUST WEAR SPLASH-PROOF OR DUST-RESISTANT SAFETY GOGGLES TO PREVENT EYE CONTACT WITH THIS SUBSTANCE.
EMERGENCY EYE WASH: WHERE THERE IS ANY POSSIBILITY THAT AN EMPLOYEE'S EYES MAY BE EXPOSED TO THIS SUBSTANCE, THE EMPLOYER SHOULD PROVIDE AN EYE WASH FOUNTAIN WITHIN THE IMMEDIATE WORK AREA FOR EMERGENCY USE.

AUTHORIZED BY- OCCUPATIONAL HEALTH SERVICES, INC.
CREATION DATE: 10/04/89 ***REVISION DATE:*** 04/04/90

MATERIAL SAFETY DATA SHEET

OCCUPATIONAL HEALTH SERVICES, INC.
AGRICULTURE AND PESTICIDE DIVISION
450 SEVENTH AVENUE, SUITE 2407
NEW YORK, NEW YORK 10123
1-800-445-MSDS OR (212) 967-1100

EMERGENCY CONTACT:
JOHN S. BRANSFORD, JR. (615) 292-1180

SUBSTANCE IDENTIFICATION

CAS-NUMBER 8003-34-7

SUBSTANCE: PYRETHRUM

TRADE NAMES/SYNONYMS: EXTRACT OF CHRYSANTHEMUM CINERARIAEFOLIUM CONTAINING: CINERIN I AND II JASMOLIN I AND II AND PYRETHRIN I AND II; PYRETHRIN; STCC 4963881; PST19980

CHEMICAL FAMILY: PYRETHRIN (NATURAL)

CERCLA RATINGS (SCALE 0-3): HEALTH=3 FIRE=2 REACTIVITY=0 PERSISTENCE=1

NFPA RATINGS (SCALE 0-4): HEALTH=U FIRE=2 REACTIVITY=0

COMPONENTS AND CONTAMINANTS

COMPONENT: PYRETHRUM ***PERCENT:*** 100.0
CAS# 8003-34-7

OTHER CONTAMINANTS: NONE

EXPOSURE LIMITS: PYRETHRUM: 5 MG/M3 OSHA TWA 5 MG/M3 ACGIH TWA
1 POUND CERCLA SECTION 103 REPORTABLE QUANTITY

PHYSICAL DATA

DESCRIPTION: VISCOUS BROWN RESIN OR SOLID. ***MELTING POINT:*** NOT AVAILABLE

SPECIFIC GRAVITY: 1.0 (APPROX) ***VAPOR PRESSURE:*** NEGLIGIBLE

SOLUBILITY IN WATER: INSOLUBLE

SOLVENT SOLUBILITY: SOLUBLE IN ALCOHOL, ACETONE, KEROSENE, NITROMETHANE, CARBON TETRACHLORIDE, ETHYLENE DICHLORIDE, PETROLEUM ETHER, AND MOST ORGANIC SOLVENTS.

FIRE AND EXPLOSION DATA

FIRE AND EXPLOSION HAZARD: MODERATE FIRE HAZARD WHEN EXPOSED TO HEAT OR FLAME.

FLASH POINT: 180-190 F (82-88 C) (OC) ***FLAMMABILITY CLASS(OSHA):*** IIIA

FIREFIGHTING MEDIA: DRY CHEMICAL, CARBON DIOXIDE, HALON, WATER SPRAY OR STANDARD FOAM (1987 EMERGENCY RESPONSE GUIDEBOOK, DOT P 5800.4).
FOR LARGER FIRES, USE WATER SPRAY, FOG OR STANDARD FOAM (1987 EMERGENCY RESPONSE GUIDEBOOK, DOT P 5800.4).

FIREFIGHTING: MOVE CONTAINER FROM FIRE AREA IF POSSIBLE. COOL FIRE-EXPOSED CONTAINERS WITH WATER FROM SIDE UNTIL WELL AFTER FIRE IS OUT. STAY AWAY FROM STORAGE TANK ENDS. FOR MASSIVE FIRE IN STORAGE AREA, USE UNMANNED HOSE HOLDER OR MONITOR NOZZLES, ELSE WITHDRAW FROM AREA

AND LET FIRE BURN. WITHDRAW IMMEDIATELY IN CASE OF RISING SOUND FROM VENTING SAFETY DEVICE OR ANY DISCOLORATION OF STORAGE TANK DUE TO FIRE (1987 EMERGENCY RESPONSE GUIDEBOOK, DOT P 5800.4, GUIDE PAGE 27). EXTINGUISH ONLY IF FLOW CAN BE STOPPED; USE FLOODING AMOUNTS OF WATER AS A FOG, SOLID STREAMS MAY BE INEFFECTIVE. COOL CONTAINERS WITH FLOODING AMOUNTS OF WATER, APPLY FROM AS FAR A DISTANCE AS POSSIBLE. AVOID BREATHING VAPORS, KEEP UPWIND.

TRANSPORTATION DATA

DEPARTMENT OF TRANSPORTATION HAZARD CLASSIFICATION 49 CFR 172.101: COMBUSTIBLE LIQUID
DEPARTMENT OF TRANSPORTATION LABELING REQUIREMENTS 49 CFR 172.101 AND SUBPART E: NONE
DEPARTMENT OF TRANSPORTATION PACKAGING REQUIREMENTS: NONE
EXCEPTIONS: 49 CFR 173.118A

TOXICITY

PYRETHRUM: TOXICITY DATA: 2060 MG/KG SKIN-RABBIT LD50 (PESTICIDES STUDIED IN MAN); 750 MG/KG ORAL-CHILD LDLO; 1 GM/KG ORAL-HUMAN LDLO; 200 MG/KG ORAL-RAT LD50; 370 MG/KG ORAL-MOUSE LD50; 1 GM/KG ORAL-GUINEA PIG LDLO; 250 MG/KG ORAL-MAMMAL LD50; 5 MG/KG INTRAVENOUS-RAT LDLO; 7 MG/KG INTRAVENOUS-DOG LD50; 25 MG/KG INTRAPERITONEAL-MOUSE LDLO; 50 MG/KG INTRAPERITONEAL-GUINEA PIG LDLO; 200 MG/KG INTRAPERITONEAL-RAT LD50; REPRODUCTIVE EFFECTS DATA (RTECS). CARCINOGEN STATUS: NONE. ACUTE TOXICITY LEVEL: TOXIC BY INGESTION; SLIGHTLY TOXIC BY DERMAL ABSORPTION. TARGET EFFECTS: SENSITIZER-PULMONARY, DERMAL. POISONING MAY ALSO AFFECT THE RESPIRATORY AND CENTRAL NERVOUS SYSTEMS. AT INCREASED RISK FROM EXPOSURE: PERSONS WITH ALLERGIES AND CHRONIC RESPIRATORY AND SKIN DISEASES. ADDITIONAL DATA: SENSITIVITY CROSS-REACTIONS MAY OCCUR WITH RAGWEED AND SHASTA DAISIES.

HEALTH EFFECTS AND FIRST AID

INHALATION: PYRETHRUM: SENSITIZER. 5000 MG/M3 IMMEDIATELY DANGEROUS TO LIFE OR HEALTH. **ACUTE EXPOSURE-** MAY CAUSE MUCOUS MEMBRANE IRRITATION. NERVOUS IRRITABILITY, TREMORS AND ATAXIA HAVE RARELY OCCURRED WITH MASSIVE EXPOSURE. SENSITIZATION REACTIONS AS DESCRIBED IN CHRONIC EXPOSURE MAY OCCUR IN SUSCEPTIBLE INDIVIDUALS. **CHRONIC EXPOSURE-** REPEATED OR PROLONGED EXPOSURE MAY CAUSE SENSITIZATION. EFFECTS MAY INCLUDE SNEEZING, NASAL DISCHARGE AND STUFFINESS, AND SCRATCHY THROAT. ASTHMA AND WHEEZING MAY OCCUR IN SOME INDIVIDUALS. ANAPHYLACTIC REACTIONS ARE POSSIBLE AND MAY INCLUDE TACHYCARDIA, PALLOR, SWEATING, FEVER, SWELLING OF THE FACE, EYELIDS, LIPS, AND ORAL AND LARYNGEAL MUCOUS MEMBRANES, REDNESS, ITCHING AND BURNING SENSATION OF THE SKIN, BRONCHOSPASM, SHOCK, AND RESPIRATORY DIFFICULTY. EOSINOPHILIA MAY BE PRESENT. A CASE OF HYPERSENSITIVITY PNEUMONITIS HAS BEEN REPORTED WITH COUGHING, FEVER, DYSPNEA, FATIGUE, CHEST PAINS, AND PATCHY LUNG INFILTRATES ON X-RAY. SLIGHT LUNG IRRITATION WAS OBSERVED IN RATS AND DOGS EXPOSED TO A CONCENTRATION OF 16 MG/M3/30 MINUTES FOR 31 DAYS.

FIRST AID- REMOVE FROM EXPOSURE AREA TO FRESH AIR IMMEDIATELY. IF BREATHING HAS STOPPED, PERFORM ARTIFICIAL RESPIRATION. KEEP PERSON WARM AND AT REST. TREAT SYMPTOMATICALLY AND SUPPORTIVELY. GET MEDICAL ATTENTION IMMEDIATELY.

SKIN CONTACT: PYRETHRUM: SENSITIZER. **ACUTE EXPOSURE-** MAY CAUSE IRRITATION. SENSITIZATION REACTIONS MAY OCCUR IN SUSCEPTIBLE INDIVIDUALS. **CHRONIC EXPOSURE-** REPEATED OR PROLONGED EXPOSURE MAY CAUSE AN ERYTHEMATOUS DERMATITIS WITH VESICLES, PAPULES, ESPECIALLY IN MOIST AREAS, AND INTENSE PRURITIS; TOUGHENING, AND IN SEVERE CASES, EDEMA AND CRACKING OF THE SKIN MAY OCCUR. THE EFFECTS MAY BE ALLERGIC REACTIONS; EOSINOPHILIA MAY ALSO BE PRESENT. EXPOSURE TO THE SUN, WARM WEATHER OR EXCESSIVE PERSPIRATION MAY EXACERBATE THE DERMAL EFFECTS.

FIRST AID- REMOVE CONTAMINATED CLOTHING AND SHOES IMMEDIATELY. WASH AFFECTED AREA WITH SOAP OR MILD DETERGENT AND LARGE AMOUNTS OF WATER UNTIL NO EVIDENCE OF CHEMICAL REMAINS (APPROXIMATELY 15-20 MINUTES). GET MEDICAL ATTENTION IMMEDIATELY.

EYE CONTACT: PYRETHRUM: **ACUTE EXPOSURE-** MAY CAUSE IRRITATION AND TRANSIENT CONJUNCTIVAL EDEMA AND HYPEREMIA. **CHRONIC EXPOSURE-** NO DATA AVAILABLE.

FIRST AID- WASH EYES IMMEDIATELY WITH LARGE AMOUNTS OF WATER OR NORMAL SALINE, OCCASIONALLY LIFTING UPPER AND LOWER LIDS, UNTIL NO EVIDENCE OF CHEMICAL REMAINS (APPROXIMATELY 15-20 MINUTES). GET MEDICAL ATTENTION IMMEDIATELY.

INGESTION: PYRETHRUM: TOXIC. **ACUTE EXPOSURE-** LARGE AMOUNTS MAY CAUSE NAUSEA, VOMITING, GASTROENTERITIS WITH DIARRHEA, HYPEREXCITABILITY, INCOORDINATION, TREMORS, MUSCULAR FIBRILLATION, BRADYCARDIA, CONVULSIONS LEADING TO PARALYSIS, AND DEATH DUE TO RESPIRATORY FAILURE. **CHRONIC EXPOSURE-** DOGS FED PYRETHRINS AT A DIETARY LEVEL OF 5000 PPM FOR 3 MONTHS EXHIBITED TREMOR, ATAXIA, LABORED RESPIRATION, AND SALIVATION DURING THE FIRST MONTH. SLIGHT LIVER DAMAGE WAS THE ONLY EFFECT REPORTED IN RATS FED DIETARY LEVELS OF 1000 AND 5000 PPM FOR 2 YEARS. AN INCREASED INCIDENCE OF FETAL RESORPTIONS WAS NOTED IN A STUDY OF PREGNANT RATS.

FIRST AID- REMOVE BY GASTRIC LAVAGE AND CATHARSIS. MAINTAIN BLOOD PRESSURE AND AIRWAY. GIVE OXYGEN IF RESPIRATION IS DEPRESSED. DO NOT PERFORM GASTRIC LAVAGE IF VICTIM IS UNCONSCIOUS. GET MEDICAL ATTENTION IMMEDIATELY (DREISBACH, HANDBOOK OF POISONING, 12TH ED.). ADMINISTRATION OF LAVAGE OR OXYGEN SHOULD BE PERFORMED BY QUALIFIED MEDICAL PERSONNEL.

ANTIDOTE: NO SPECIFIC ANTIDOTE. TREAT SYMPTOMATICALLY AND SUPPORTIVELY.

REACTIVITY

REACTIVITY: STABLE UNDER NORMAL TEMPERATURES AND PRESSURES.

INCOMPATIBILITIES: PYRETHRUM: OXIDIZERS (STRONG): FIRE AND EXPLOSION HAZARD.

DECOMPOSITION: THERMAL DECOMPOSITION PRODUCTS MAY INCLUDE TOXIC OXIDES OF CARBON.

POLYMERIZATION: HAZARDOUS POLYMERIZATION HAS NOT BEEN REPORTED TO OCCUR UNDER NORMAL TEMPERATURES AND PRESSURES.

STORAGE AND DISPOSAL

OBSERVE ALL FEDERAL, STATE AND LOCAL REGULATIONS WHEN STORING OR DISPOSING OF THIS SUBSTANCE. FOR ASSISTANCE, CONTACT THE DISTRICT DIRECTOR OF THE ENVIRONMENTAL PROTECTION AGENCY.

STORAGE

STORE IN ACCORDANCE WITH 29 CFR 1910.106.
STORE IN ACCORDANCE WITH 40 CFR 165 RECOMMENDED PROCEDURES FOR THE DISPOSAL AND STORAGE OF PESTICIDES AND PESTICIDE CONTAINERS.
STORE AWAY FROM INCOMPATIBLE SUBSTANCES.
STORE IN A TIGHTLY CLOSED CONTAINER AT TEMPERATURES NOT EXCEEDING 39 F (4 C).

DISPOSAL

DISPOSAL MUST BE IN ACCORDANCE WITH 40 CFR 165 RECOMMENDED PROCEDURES FOR THE DISPOSAL AND STORAGE OF PESTICIDES AND PESTICIDE CONTAINERS.

CONDITIONS TO AVOID

AVOID CONTACT WITH HEAT, SPARKS, FLAMES, OR OTHER SOURCES OF IGNITION. VAPORS MAY BE EXPLOSIVE. AVOID OVERHEATING OF CONTAINERS; CONTAINERS MAY VIOLENTLY RUPTURE IN HEAT OF FIRE. AVOID CONTAMINATION OF WATER SOURCES.

SPILL AND LEAK PROCEDURES

SOIL SPILL: DIG HOLDING AREA SUCH AS LAGOON, POND OR PIT FOR CONTAINMENT. DIKE FLOW OF SPILLED MATERIAL USING SOIL OR SANDBAGS OR FOAMED BARRIERS SUCH AS POLYURETHANE OR CONCRETE.
USE CEMENT POWDER OR FLY ASH TO ABSORB LIQUID MASS.

WATER SPILL: USE ACTIVATED CARBON TO ABSORB SPILLED SUBSTANCE THAT IS DISSOLVED.
USE MECHANICAL DREDGES OR LIFTS TO EXTRACT IMMOBILIZED MASSES OF POLLUTION AND PRECIPITATES.

OCCUPATIONAL SPILL: SHUT OFF IGNITION SOURCES. STOP LEAK IF YOU CAN DO IT WITHOUT RISK. USE WATER SPRAY TO REDUCE VAPORS. FOR SMALL SPILLS, TAKE UP WITH SAND OR OTHER ABSORBENT MATERIAL AND PLACE INTO CONTAINERS FOR LATER DISPOSAL. FOR LARGER SPILLS, DIKE FAR AHEAD OF SPILL FOR LATER DISPOSAL. NO SMOKING, FLAMES OR FLARES IN HAZARD AREA. KEEP UNNECESSARY PEOPLE AWAY; ISOLATE HAZARD AREA AND RESTRICT ENTRY.
REPORTABLE QUANTITY (RQ): 1 POUND THE SUPERFUND AMENDMENTS AND REAUTHORIZATION ACT (SARA) SECTION 304 REQUIRES THAT A RELEASE EQUAL TO OR GREATER THAN THE REPORTABLE QUANTITY FOR THIS SUBSTANCE BE IMMEDIATELY REPORTED TO THE LOCAL EMERGENCY PLANNING COMMITTEE AND THE STATE EMERGENCY RESPONSE COMMISSION (40 CFR 355.40). IF THE RELEASE OF THIS SUBSTANCE IS REPORTABLE UNDER CERCLA SECTION 103, THE NATIONAL RESPONSE CENTER MUST BE NOTIFIED IMMEDIATELY AT (800) 424-8802 OR (202) 426-2675 IN THE METROPOLITAN WASHINGTON, D.C. AREA (40 CFR 302.6).

PROTECTIVE EQUIPMENT

VENTILATION: PROVIDE LOCAL EXHAUST VENTILATION AND/OR GENERAL DILUTION VENTILATION TO MEET PUBLISHED EXPOSURE LIMITS.

RESPIRATOR: THE FOLLOWING RESPIRATORS AND MAXIMUM USE CONCENTRATIONS ARE RECOMMENDATIONS BY THE U.S. DEPARTMENT OF HEALTH AND HUMAN SERVICES, NIOSH POCKET GUIDE TO CHEMICAL HAZARDS; NIOSH CRITERIA DOCUMENTS OR BY THE U.S. DEPARTMENT OF LABOR, 29 CFR 1910 SUBPART Z. THE SPECIFIC RESPIRATOR SELECTED MUST BE BASED ON CONTAMINATION LEVELS FOUND IN THE WORK PLACE, MUST NOT EXCEED THE WORKING LIMITS OF THE RESPIRATOR AND BE JOINTLY APPROVED BY THE NATIONAL INSTITUTE FOR OCCUPATIONAL SAFETY AND HEALTH AND THE MINE SAFETY AND HEALTH ADMINISTRATION (NIOSH-MSHA).

PYRETHRUM:

50 MG/M3- ANY CHEMICAL CARTRIDGE RESPIRATOR WITH ORGANIC VAPOR CARTRIDGE(S) IN COMBINATION WITH A DUST, MIST, AND FUME FILTER. ANY SUPPLIED-AIR RESPIRATOR. ANY SELF-CONTAINED BREATHING APPARATUS.

125 MG/M3- ANY SUPPLIED-AIR RESPIRATOR OPERATED IN A CONTINUOUS FLOW MODE. ANY POWERED AIR-PURIFYING RESPIRATOR WITH ORGANIC VAPOR CARTRIDGE(S) IN COMBINATION WITH A DUST, MIST, AND FUME FILTER.

250 MG/M3- ANY CHEMICAL CARTRIDGE RESPIRATOR WITH A FULL FACEPIECE AND ORGANIC VAPOR CARTRIDGE(S) IN COMBINATION WITH A HIGH-EFFICIENCY PARTICULATE FILTER. ANY SUPPLIED-AIR RESPIRATOR WITH A FULL FACEPIECE. ANY SELF-CONTAINED BREATHING APPARATUS WITH A FULL FACEPIECE. ANY POWERED AIR-PURIFYING RESPIRATOR WITH A TIGHT-FITTING FACEPIECE AND ORGANIC VAPOR CARTRIDGE(S) IN COMBINATION WITH A HIGH-EFFICIENCY PARTICULATE FILTER.

5000 MG/M3- ANY SUPPLIED-AIR RESPIRATOR WITH A HALF-MASK AND OPERATED IN A PRESSURE-DEMAND OR OTHER POSITIVE PRESSURE MODE.

ESCAPE- ANY AIR-PURIFYING FULL FACEPIECE RESPIRATOR (GAS MASK) WITH A CHIN STYLE OR FRONT- OR BACK-MOUNTED ORGANIC VAPOR CANISTER HAVING A HIGH-EFFICIENCY PARTICULATE FILTER. ANY APPROPRIATE ESCAPE-TYPE SELF-CONTAINED BREATHING APPARATUS.

FOR FIREFIGHTING AND OTHER IMMEDIATELY DANGEROUS TO LIFE OR HEALTH CONDITIONS:

SELF-CONTAINED BREATHING APPARATUS WITH FULL FACEPIECE OPERATED IN PRESSURE-DEMAND OR OTHER POSITIVE PRESSURE MODE.

SUPPLIED-AIR RESPIRATOR WITH FULL FACEPIECE AND OPERATED IN PRESSURE-DEMAND OR OTHER POSITIVE PRESSURE MODE IN COMBINATION WITH AN AUXILIARY SELF-CONTAINED BREATHING APPARATUS OPERATED IN PRESSURE-DEMAND OR OTHER POSITIVE PRESSURE MODE.

CLOTHING: EMPLOYEE MUST WEAR APPROPRIATE PROTECTIVE (IMPERVIOUS) CLOTHING AND EQUIPMENT TO PREVENT REPEATED OR PROLONGED SKIN CONTACT WITH THIS SUBSTANCE.

GLOVES: EMPLOYEE MUST WEAR APPROPRIATE PROTECTIVE GLOVES TO PREVENT CONTACT WITH THIS SUBSTANCE.

EYE PROTECTION: EMPLOYEE MUST WEAR SPLASH-PROOF OR DUST-RESISTANT SAFETY GOGGLES TO PREVENT EYE CONTACT WITH THIS SUBSTANCE.

EMERGENCY EYE WASH: WHERE THERE IS ANY POSSIBILITY THAT AN EMPLOYEE'S EYES MAY BE EXPOSED TO THIS SUBSTANCE, THE EMPLOYER SHOULD PROVIDE AN EYE WASH FOUNTAIN WITHIN THE IMMEDIATE WORK AREA FOR EMERGENCY USE.

AUTHORIZED BY- OCCUPATIONAL HEALTH SERVICES, INC.

CREATION DATE: 10/04/89 ***REVISION DATE:*** 05/17/90

MATERIAL SAFETY DATA SHEET

OCCUPATIONAL HEALTH SERVICES, INC.
AGRICULTURE AND PESTICIDE DIVISION
450 SEVENTH AVENUE, SUITE 2407
NEW YORK, NEW YORK 10123
1-800-445-MSDS OR (212) 967-1100

EMERGENCY CONTACT:
JOHN S. BRANSFORD, JR. (615) 292-1180

SUBSTANCE IDENTIFICATION

CAS-NUMBER 76578-14-8

SUBSTANCE: **QUIZALOFOP-ETHYL**

TRADE NAMES/SYNONYMS: PROPANOIC ACID, 2-(4-((6-CHLORO-2-QUINOXALINYL)OXY)PHENOXY)-, ETHYL ESTER; ASSURE (FORMULATION); TARGA (FORMULATION); ETHYL-2-(4-((6-CHLORO-2-QUINOXALINYL)OXY)PHENOXY)PROPANOATE; 2-(4-((6-CHLORO-2-QUINOXALINYL)OXY)PHENOXY)PROPANOIC ACID, ETHYL ESTER; C19H17CLN2O4; PST20075

CHEMICAL FAMILY: QUINAZOLINE ESTER, CARBOXYLIC, ALIPHATIC

MOLECULAR FORMULA: C19-H17-CL-N2-O4

MOLECULAR WEIGHT: 372.81

CERCLA RATINGS (SCALE 0-3): HEALTH=U FIRE=1 REACTIVITY=0 PERSISTENCE=2

NFPA RATINGS (SCALE 0-4): HEALTH=U FIRE=1 REACTIVITY=0

COMPONENTS AND CONTAMINANTS

COMPONENT: QUIZALOFOP-ETHYL ***PERCENT:*** 100.0

CAS# 76578-14-8

OTHER CONTAMINANTS: NONE

EXPOSURE LIMITS: NO OCCUPATIONAL EXPOSURE LIMITS ESTABLISHED BY OSHA, ACGIH, OR NIOSH.

QUIZALOFOP ETHYL: 1 MG/M3 8 HOUR TWA DUPONT RECOMMENDED ACCEPTABLE EXPOSURE LIMIT

PHYSICAL DATA

DESCRIPTION: COLORLESS CRYSTALLINE SOLID.

BOILING POINT: 428 F (220 C) @ 0.2 MMHG ***MELTING POINT:*** 196-198 F (91-92 C)

SPECIFIC GRAVITY: NOT AVAILABLE ***VAPOR PRESSURE:*** <0.01 MMHG @ 20 C

SOLUBILITY IN WATER: 0.3 PPM

SOLVENT SOLUBILITY: SOLUBLE IN ACETONE, BENZENE, XYLENE; MODERATELY SOLUBLE IN ALCOHOL, HEXANE.

FIRE AND EXPLOSION DATA

FIRE AND EXPLOSION HAZARD: SLIGHT FIRE HAZARD WHEN EXPOSED TO HEAT OR FLAME.

FIREFIGHTING MEDIA: DRY CHEMICAL, CARBON DIOXIDE, HALON, WATER SPRAY OR STANDARD FOAM (1987 EMERGENCY RESPONSE GUIDEBOOK, DOT P 5800.4).

FOR LARGER FIRES, USE WATER SPRAY, FOG OR STANDARD FOAM (1987 EMERGENCY RESPONSE GUIDEBOOK, DOT P 5800.4).

FIREFIGHTING: MOVE CONTAINER FROM FIRE AREA IF POSSIBLE. DO NOT SCATTER SPILLED MATERIAL WITH HIGH PRESSURE WATER STREAMS. DIKE FIRE CONTROL WATER FOR LATER DISPOSAL (1987 EMERGENCY RESPONSE GUIDEBOOK, DOT P 5800.4, GUIDE PAGE 31).

USE AGENTS SUITABLE FOR TYPE OF SURROUNDING FIRE. AVOID BREATHING HAZARDOUS VAPORS, KEEP UPWIND.

TOXICITY

QUIZALOFOP-ETHYL: TOXICITY DATA: 10 GM/KG SKIN-RAT LD50; 10 GM/KG SKIN-MOUSE LD50; 1480 MG/KG ORAL-RAT LD50; 2350 MG/KG ORAL-MOUSE LD50. CARCINOGEN STATUS: NONE. ACUTE TOXICITY LEVEL: MODERATELY TOXIC BY INGESTION; SLIGHTLY TOXIC BY DERMAL ABSORPTION. TARGET EFFECTS: NO DATA AVAILABLE.

HEALTH EFFECTS AND FIRST AID

INHALATION: QUIZALOFOP-ETHYL: **ACUTE EXPOSURE-** NO DATA AVAILABLE. **CHRONIC EXPOSURE-** NO DATA AVAILABLE.

FIRST AID- REMOVE FROM EXPOSURE AREA TO FRESH AIR IMMEDIATELY. IF BREATHING HAS STOPPED, PERFORM ARTIFICIAL RESPIRATION. KEEP PERSON WARM AND AT REST. TREAT SYMPTOMATICALLY AND SUPPORTIVELY. GET MEDICAL ATTENTION IMMEDIATELY.

SKIN CONTACT: QUIZALOFOP-ETHYL: **ACUTE EXPOSURE-** NON-IRRITATING TO RABBIT SKIN; NON-SENSITIZING TO GUINEA PIGS. **CHRONIC EXPOSURE-** NO DATA AVAILABLE.

FIRST AID- REMOVE CONTAMINATED CLOTHING AND SHOES IMMEDIATELY. WASH AFFECTED AREA WITH SOAP OR MILD DETERGENT AND LARGE AMOUNTS OF WATER UNTIL NO EVIDENCE OF CHEMICAL REMAINS (APPROXIMATELY 15-20 MINUTES). GET MEDICAL ATTENTION IMMEDIATELY.

EYE CONTACT: QUIZALOFOP-ETHYL: **ACUTE EXPOSURE-** NO DATA AVAILABLE. **CHRONIC EXPOSURE-** NO DATA AVAILABLE.

FIRST AID- WASH EYES IMMEDIATELY WITH LARGE AMOUNTS OF WATER OR NORMAL SALINE, OCCASIONALLY LIFTING UPPER AND LOWER LIDS, UNTIL NO EVIDENCE OF CHEMICAL REMAINS (APPROXIMATELY 15-20 MINUTES). GET MEDICAL ATTENTION IMMEDIATELY.

INGESTION: QUIZALOFOP-ETHYL: **ACUTE EXPOSURE-** THE REPORTED LETHAL DOSE IN RATS WAS 1480 MG/KG, THE SYMPTOMS WERE NOT NOTED. **CHRONIC EXPOSURE-** EFFECTS ON THE LIVER AND TESTES HAVE BEEN REPORTED IN ANIMALS. OFFSPRING OF RATS FED 300 MG/KG DURING GESTATION EXHIBITED REDUCED SURVIVAL AND A TRANSIENT INCREASE IN SKELETAL VARIATIONS.

FIRST AID- TREAT SYMPTOMATICALLY AND SUPPORTIVELY. GET MEDICAL ATTENTION IMMEDIATELY. IF VOMITING OCCURS, KEEP HEAD LOWER THAN HIPS TO PREVENT ASPIRATION.

ANTIDOTE: NO SPECIFIC ANTIDOTE. TREAT SYMPTOMATICALLY AND SUPPORTIVELY.

REACTIVITY

REACTIVITY: STABLE UNDER NORMAL TEMPERATURES AND PRESSURES.

INCOMPATIBILITIES: QUIZALOFOP-ETHYL: OXIDIZERS (STRONG): FIRE AND EXPLOSION HAZARD.

DECOMPOSITION: THERMAL DECOMPOSITION PRODUCTS MAY INCLUDE TOXIC OXIDES OF NITROGEN AND CARBON AND TOXIC AND CORROSIVE FUMES OF CHLORIDES.

POLYMERIZATION: HAZARDOUS POLYMERIZATION HAS NOT BEEN REPORTED TO OCCUR UNDER NORMAL TEMPERATURES AND PRESSURES.

STORAGE AND DISPOSAL

OBSERVE ALL FEDERAL, STATE AND LOCAL REGULATIONS WHEN STORING OR DISPOSING OF THIS SUBSTANCE. FOR ASSISTANCE, CONTACT THE DISTRICT DIRECTOR OF THE ENVIRONMENTAL PROTECTION AGENCY.

****STORAGE****

STORE IN ACCORDANCE WITH 40 CFR 165 RECOMMENDED PROCEDURES FOR THE DISPOSAL AND STORAGE OF PESTICIDES AND PESTICIDE CONTAINERS.

STORE AWAY FROM INCOMPATIBLE SUBSTANCES.

KEEP IN A TIGHTLY CLOSED CONTAINER. STORE IN A COOL, DRY, VENTILATED AREA.

****DISPOSAL****

DISPOSAL MUST BE IN ACCORDANCE WITH 40 CFR 165 RECOMMENDED PROCEDURES FOR THE DISPOSAL AND STORAGE OF PESTICIDES AND PESTICIDE CONTAINERS.

CONDITIONS TO AVOID

MAY BURN BUT DOES NOT IGNITE READILY. AVOID CONTACT WITH STRONG OXIDIZERS, EXCESSIVE HEAT, SPARKS, OR OPEN FLAME.

SPILL AND LEAK PROCEDURES

OCCUPATIONAL SPILL: STOP LEAK IF YOU CAN DO IT WITHOUT RISK. FOR SMALL SPILLS, TAKE UP WITH SAND OR OTHER ABSORBENT MATERIAL AND PLACE INTO CLEAN, DRY CONTAINERS FOR LATER DISPOSAL. KEEP UNNECESSARY PEOPLE AWAY. ISOLATE HAZARD AREA AND DENY ENTRY.

PROTECTIVE EQUIPMENT

VENTILATION: PROVIDE LOCAL EXHAUST OR GENERAL DILUTION VENTILATION SYSTEM.

RESPIRATOR: THE FOLLOWING RESPIRATORS ARE RECOMMENDED BASED ON INFORMATION FOUND IN THE PHYSICAL DATA, TOXICITY AND HEALTH EFFECTS SECTIONS. THEY ARE RANKED IN ORDER FROM MINIMUM TO MAXIMUM RESPIRATORY PROTECTION. THE SPECIFIC RESPIRATOR SELECTED MUST BE BASED ON CONTAMINATION LEVELS FOUND IN THE WORK PLACE, MUST NOT EXCEED THE WORKING LIMITS OF THE RESPIRATOR AND BE JOINTLY APPROVED BY THE NATIONAL INSTITUTE FOR OCCUPATIONAL SAFETY AND HEALTH AND THE MINE SAFETY AND HEALTH ADMINISTRATION (NIOSH-MSHA).

CHEMICAL CARTRIDGE RESPIRATOR WITH AN ORGANIC VAPOR CARTRIDGE(S) IN COMBINATION WITH A DUST AND MIST FILTER.

GAS MASK WITH ORGANIC VAPOR CANISTER (CHIN-STYLE OR FRONT- OR BACK-MOUNTED CANISTER) WITH A DUST AND MIST FILTER.

GAS MASK WITH ORGANIC VAPOR CANISTER (CHIN-STYLE OR FRONT- OR BACK-MOUNTED CANISTER) WITH A PARTICULATE FILTER.

POWERED AIR-PURIFYING RESPIRATOR WITH A HIGH-EFFICIENCY FILTER.

TYPE 'C' SUPPLIED-AIR RESPIRATOR WITH A FULL FACEPIECE OPERATED IN A PRESSURE-DEMAND OR OTHER POSITIVE PRESSURE MODE.

SELF-CONTAINED BREATHING APPARATUS WITH A FULL FACEPIECE OPERATED IN PRESSURE-DEMAND OR OTHER POSITIVE PRESSURE MODE.

FOR FIREFIGHTING AND OTHER IMMEDIATELY DANGEROUS TO LIFE OR HEALTH CONDITIONS: SELF-CONTAINED BREATHING APPARATUS WITH FULL FACEPIECE OPERATED IN PRESSURE-DEMAND OR OTHER POSITIVE PRESSURE MODE.

SUPPLIED-AIR RESPIRATOR WITH FULL FACEPIECE AND OPERATED IN PRESSURE-DEMAND OR OTHER POSITIVE PRESSURE MODE IN COMBINATION WITH AN AUXILIARY SELF-CONTAINED BREATHING APPARATUS OPERATED IN PRESSURE-DEMAND OR OTHER POSITIVE PRESSURE MODE.

CLOTHING: EMPLOYEE MUST WEAR APPROPRIATE PROTECTIVE (IMPERVIOUS) CLOTHING AND EQUIPMENT TO PREVENT REPEATED OR PROLONGED SKIN CONTACT WITH THIS SUBSTANCE.

GLOVES: EMPLOYEE MUST WEAR APPROPRIATE PROTECTIVE GLOVES TO PREVENT CONTACT WITH THIS SUBSTANCE.

EYE PROTECTION: EMPLOYEE MUST WEAR SPLASH-PROOF OR DUST-RESISTANT SAFETY GOGGLES TO PREVENT EYE CONTACT WITH THIS SUBSTANCE.

EMERGENCY EYE WASH: WHERE THERE IS ANY POSSIBILITY THAT AN EMPLOYEE'S EYES MAY BE EXPOSED TO THIS SUBSTANCE, THE EMPLOYER SHOULD PROVIDE AN EYE WASH FOUNTAIN WITHIN THE IMMEDIATE WORK AREA FOR EMERGENCY USE.

AUTHORIZED BY- OCCUPATIONAL HEALTH SERVICES, INC.

CREATION DATE: 10/04/89 ***REVISION DATE:*** 06/07/90

MATERIAL SAFETY DATA SHEET

OCCUPATIONAL HEALTH SERVICES, INC.
AGRICULTURE AND PESTICIDE DIVISION
450 SEVENTH AVENUE, SUITE 2407
NEW YORK, NEW YORK 10123
1-800-445-MSDS OR (212) 967-1100

EMERGENCY CONTACT:
JOHN S. BRANSFORD, JR. (615) 292-1180

SUBSTANCE IDENTIFICATION

CAS-NUMBER 28434-01-7

SUBSTANCE: BIORESMETHRIN

TRADE NAMES/SYNONYMS: CYCLOPROPANECARBOXYLIC ACID, 2,2-DIMETHYL-3-(2-METHYL-1-PROPENYL)-, (5-(PHENYLMETHYL)-3-FURANYL)METHYL ESTER, (1R-TRANS)-; CYCLOPROPANECARBOXYLIC ACID, 2,2-DIMETHYL-3-(2-METHYLPROPENYL)-, (5-BENZYL-3-FURYL)METHYL ESTER, TRANS-(+)-; 5-BENZYL-3-FURYLMETHYL (+)-TRANS-CHRYSANTHEMATE; (+)-TRANS-RESMETHRIN; D-TRANS-RESMETHRIN; NRDC 107; PYRETHROID NRDC 107; SBP-1390; NIA-18739; PST20093

CHEMICAL FAMILY: PYRETHROID (SYNTHETIC)

MOLECULAR FORMULA: C22-H26-O3

MOLECULAR WEIGHT: 338.48

CERCLA RATINGS (SCALE 0-3): HEALTH=2 FIRE=U REACTIVITY=0 PERSISTENCE=2

NFPA RATINGS (SCALE 0-4): HEALTH=2 FIRE=U REACTIVITY=0

COMPONENTS AND CONTAMINANTS

COMPONENT: BIORESMETHRIN ***PERCENT:*** 100.0
CAS# 28434-01-7

OTHER CONTAMINANTS: NONE

EXPOSURE LIMITS: NO OCCUPATIONAL EXPOSURE LIMITS ESTABLISHED BY OSHA, ACGIH, OR NIOSH.

PHYSICAL DATA

DESCRIPTION: WAXY OFF-WHITE TO TAN SOLID WITH A CHARACTERISTIC CHRYSANTHEMATE ODOR

BOILING POINT: 345 F (174 C) @ 0.0008 MMHG ***SPECIFIC GRAVITY:*** NOT AVAILABLE

SOLUBILITY IN WATER: INSOLUBLE

SOLVENT SOLUBILITY: KEROSENE, XYLENE, METHYLENE CHLORIDE, ISOPROPYL ALCOHOL, AROMATIC PETROLEUM HYDROCARBONS

FIRE AND EXPLOSION DATA

FIRE AND EXPLOSION HAZARD: UNKNOWN FIRE AND EXPLOSION HAZARD.

FIREFIGHTING MEDIA: DRY CHEMICAL, CARBON DIOXIDE, WATER SPRAY OR FOAM FOR LARGER FIRES, USE WATER SPRAY, FOG OR ALCOHOL FOAM

FIREFIGHTING: MOVE CONTAINER FROM FIRE AREA IF POSSIBLE. DO NOT SCATTER SPILLED MATERIAL WITH HIGH PRESSURE WATER STREAMS. DIKE FIRE CONTROL WATER FOR LATER DISPOSAL (1987 EMERGENCY RESPONSE GUIDEBOOK, DOT P 5800.4, GUIDE PAGE 31).

USE AGENTS SUITABLE FOR TYPE OF SURROUNDING FIRE. AVOID BREATHING HAZARDOUS VAPORS, KEEP UPWIND.

TOXICITY

BIORESMETHRIN: TOXICITY DATA: 7070 MG/KG ORAL-RAT LD50; 590 MG/KG ORAL-MOUSE LD50; 340 MG/KG INTRAVENOUS-RAT LDLO; MUTAGENIC DATA (RTECS). CARCINOGEN STATUS: NONE. ACUTE TOXICITY LEVEL: SLIGHTLY TOXIC BY INGESTION. TARGET EFFECTS: POISONING MAY AFFECT THE CENTRAL NERVOUS SYSTEM.

HEALTH EFFECTS AND FIRST AID

INHALATION: BIORESMETHRIN: <u>ACUTE EXPOSURE</u>- BIORESMETHRIN IS A SYNTHETIC PYRETHRIN. SYNTHETIC PYRETHRINS, LIKE THE NATURAL PYRETHRINS, PRODUCE CENTRAL NERVOUS SYSTEM STIMULATION IN ANIMALS WITH SYMPTOMS OF NAUSEA, VOMITING, GASTROENTERITIS WITH DIARRHEA, HYPERSENSITIVITY,

INCOORDINATION, TREMORS, MUSCULAR PARALYSIS, CONVULSION, COMA AND DEATH DUE TO RESPIRATORY FAILURE. UNLIKE NATURAL PYRETHRINS, SYNTHETIC PYRETHRINS NORMALLY DO NOT PRODUCE ALLERGIC REACTIONS IN HUMANS. **CHRONIC EXPOSURE-** NO DATA AVAILABLE.

FIRST AID- REMOVE FROM EXPOSURE AREA TO FRESH AIR IMMEDIATELY. IF BREATHING HAS STOPPED, PERFORM ARTIFICIAL RESPIRATION. KEEP PERSON WARM AND AT REST. TREAT SYMPTOMATICALLY AND SUPPORTIVELY. GET MEDICAL ATTENTION IMMEDIATELY.

SKIN CONTACT: BIORESMETHRIN: **ACUTE EXPOSURE-** BIORESMETHRIN IS A SYNTHETIC PYRETHRIN. SYNTHETIC PYRETHRINS GENERALLY ARE NOT IRRITANTS TO RABBIT SKIN AND THE TOXICITY FROM DERMAL ABSORPTION IS USUALLY MODERATE TO LOW. UNLIKE NATURAL PYRETHRINS, SYNTHETIC PYRETHRINS NORMALLY DO NOT PRODUCE ALLERGIC REACTIONS IN HUMANS. HOWEVER, THERE HAVE BEEN SOME REPORTS OF CUTANEOUS PARESTHESIAS AMONG INDIVIDUALS OCCUPATIONALLY EXPOSED TO SYNTHETIC PYRETHRINS. THESE INDIVIDUALS COMPLAINED OF TINGLING, BURNING AND STINGING SENSATIONS ON THE EXPOSED SURFACE OF THE SKIN BEGINNING FROM 30 MINUTES TO 3 HOURS AFTER EXPOSURE. THE DURATION OF SYMPTOMS VARIED FROM 30 MINUTES TO 8 HOURS. **CHRONIC EXPOSURE-** NO DATA AVAILABLE.

FIRST AID- REMOVE CONTAMINATED CLOTHING AND SHOES IMMEDIATELY. WASH AFFECTED AREA WITH SOAP OR MILD DETERGENT AND LARGE AMOUNTS OF WATER UNTIL NO EVIDENCE OF CHEMICAL REMAINS (APPROXIMATELY 15-20 MINUTES). GET MEDICAL ATTENTION IMMEDIATELY.

EYE CONTACT: BIORESMETHRIN: **ACUTE EXPOSURE-** SYNTHETIC PYRETHRINS ARE NOT IRRITANTS OF RABBIT EYES. **CHRONIC EXPOSURE-** NO DATA AVAILABLE.

FIRST AID- WASH EYES IMMEDIATELY WITH LARGE AMOUNTS OF WATER OR NORMAL SALINE, OCCASIONALLY LIFTING UPPER AND LOWER LIDS, UNTIL NO EVIDENCE OF CHEMICAL REMAINS (APPROXIMATELY 15-20 MINUTES). GET MEDICAL ATTENTION IMMEDIATELY.

INGESTION: BIORESMETHRIN: **ACUTE EXPOSURE-** A MODERATE DOSE OF BIORESMETHRIN WAS LETHAL IN MICE. BIORESMETHRIN IS A SYNTHETIC PYRETHRIN. SYNTHETIC PYRETHRINS, LIKE THE NATURAL PYRETHRINS, PRODUCE CENTRAL NERVOUS SYSTEM STIMULATION IN ANIMALS WITH SYMPTOMS OF NAUSEA, VOMITING, GASTROENTERITIS WITH DIARRHEA, HYPERSENSITIVITY, INCOORDINATION, TREMORS, MUSCULAR PARALYSIS, CONVULSION, COMA, AND DEATH DUE TO RESPIRATORY FAILURE. **CHRONIC EXPOSURE-** INCREASED LIVER AND KIDNEY WEIGHTS WERE NOTED IN ANIMALS CHRONICALLY FED SYNTHETIC PYRETHRINS.

FIRST AID- TREAT SYMPTOMATICALLY AND SUPPORTIVELY. GET MEDICAL ATTENTION IMMEDIATELY. IF VOMITING OCCURS, KEEP HEAD LOWER THAN HIPS TO PREVENT ASPIRATION.

ANTIDOTE: NO SPECIFIC ANTIDOTE. TREAT SYMPTOMATICALLY AND SUPPORTIVELY.

REACTIVITY

REACTIVITY: MAY DECOMPOSE UPON EXPOSURE TO HEAT OR LIGHT.

INCOMPATIBILITIES: BIORESMETHRIN: NO DATA AVAILABLE.

DECOMPOSITION: THERMAL DECOMPOSITION MAY RELEASE TOXIC AND/OR HAZARDOUS GASES.

POLYMERIZATION: HAZARDOUS POLYMERIZATION HAS NOT BEEN REPORTED TO OCCUR UNDER NORMAL TEMPERATURES AND PRESSURES.

STORAGE AND DISPOSAL

OBSERVE ALL FEDERAL, STATE AND LOCAL REGULATIONS WHEN STORING OR DISPOSING OF THIS SUBSTANCE. FOR ASSISTANCE, CONTACT THE DISTRICT DIRECTOR OF THE ENVIRONMENTAL PROTECTION AGENCY.

STORAGE

STORE IN ACCORDANCE WITH 40 CFR 165 RECOMMENDED PROCEDURES FOR THE DISPOSAL AND STORAGE OF PESTICIDES AND PESTICIDE CONTAINERS.

DISPOSAL

DISPOSAL MUST BE IN ACCORDANCE WITH 40 CFR 165 RECOMMENDED PROCEDURES FOR THE DISPOSAL AND STORAGE OF PESTICIDES AND PESTICIDE CONTAINERS.

CONDITIONS TO AVOID

MAY BURN BUT DOES NOT IGNITE READILY. AVOID CONTACT WITH STRONG OXIDIZERS, EXCESSIVE HEAT, SPARKS, OR OPEN FLAME.

SPILL AND LEAK PROCEDURES

OCCUPATIONAL SPILL: SWEEP UP AND PLACE IN SUITABLE CLEAN, DRY CONTAINERS FOR RECLAMATION OR LATER DISPOSAL. DO NOT FLUSH SPILLED MATERIAL INTO SEWER. KEEP UNNECESSARY PEOPLE AWAY.

PROTECTIVE EQUIPMENT

VENTILATION: PROVIDE LOCAL EXHAUST OR GENERAL DILUTION VENTILATION. VENTILATION EQUIPMENT MUST BE EXPLOSION-PROOF.

RESPIRATOR: THE FOLLOWING RESPIRATORS ARE RECOMMENDED BASED ON INFORMATION FOUND IN THE PHYSICAL DATA, TOXICITY AND HEALTH EFFECTS SECTIONS. THEY ARE RANKED IN ORDER FROM MINIMUM TO MAXIMUM RESPIRATORY PROTECTION. THE SPECIFIC RESPIRATOR SELECTED MUST BE BASED ON CONTAMINATION LEVELS FOUND IN THE WORK PLACE, MUST NOT EXCEED THE WORKING LIMITS OF THE RESPIRATOR AND BE JOINTLY APPROVED BY THE NATIONAL INSTITUTE FOR OCCUPATIONAL SAFETY AND HEALTH AND THE MINE SAFETY AND HEALTH ADMINISTRATION (NIOSH-MSHA).

CHEMICAL CARTRIDGE RESPIRATOR WITH AN ORGANIC VAPOR CARTRIDGE(S) IN COMBINATION WITH A DUST AND MIST FILTER.

GAS MASK WITH ORGANIC VAPOR CANISTER (CHIN-STYLE OR FRONT- OR BACK-MOUNTED CANISTER) WITH A DUST AND MIST FILTER.

GAS MASK WITH ORGANIC VAPOR CANISTER (CHIN-STYLE OR FRONT- OR BACK-MOUNTED CANISTER) WITH A PARTICULATE FILTER. POWERED AIR-PURIFYING RESPIRATOR WITH A HIGH-EFFICIENCY FILTER.

TYPE 'C' SUPPLIED-AIR RESPIRATOR WITH A FULL FACEPIECE OPERATED IN A PRESSURE-DEMAND OR OTHER POSITIVE PRESSURE MODE.

SELF-CONTAINED BREATHING APPARATUS WITH A FULL FACEPIECE OPERATED IN PRESSURE-DEMAND OR OTHER POSITIVE PRESSURE MODE.

FOR FIREFIGHTING AND OTHER IMMEDIATELY DANGEROUS TO LIFE OR HEALTH CONDITIONS:

SELF-CONTAINED BREATHING APPARATUS WITH FULL FACEPIECE OPERATED IN PRESSURE-DEMAND OR OTHER POSITIVE PRESSURE MODE.

SUPPLIED-AIR RESPIRATOR WITH FULL FACEPIECE AND OPERATED IN PRESSURE-DEMAND OR OTHER POSITIVE PRESSURE MODE IN COMBINATION WITH AN AUXILIARY SELF-CONTAINED BREATHING APPARATUS OPERATED IN PRESSURE-DEMAND OR OTHER POSITIVE PRESSURE MODE.

CLOTHING: EMPLOYEE MUST WEAR APPROPRIATE PROTECTIVE (IMPERVIOUS) CLOTHING AND EQUIPMENT TO PREVENT REPEATED OR PROLONGED SKIN CONTACT WITH THIS SUBSTANCE.

GLOVES: EMPLOYEE MUST WEAR APPROPRIATE PROTECTIVE GLOVES TO PREVENT CONTACT WITH THIS SUBSTANCE.

EYE PROTECTION: EMPLOYEE MUST WEAR SPLASH-PROOF OR DUST-RESISTANT SAFETY GOGGLES TO PREVENT EYE CONTACT WITH THIS SUBSTANCE.

EMERGENCY EYE WASH: WHERE THERE IS ANY POSSIBILITY THAT AN EMPLOYEE'S EYES MAY BE EXPOSED TO THIS SUBSTANCE, THE EMPLOYER SHOULD PROVIDE AN EYE WASH FOUNTAIN WITHIN THE IMMEDIATE WORK AREA FOR EMERGENCY USE.

AUTHORIZED BY- OCCUPATIONAL HEALTH SERVICES, INC.

CREATION DATE: 10/04/89 ***REVISION DATE:*** 05/31/90

MATERIAL SAFETY DATA SHEET

OCCUPATIONAL HEALTH SERVICES, INC.
AGRICULTURE AND PESTICIDE DIVISION
450 SEVENTH AVENUE, SUITE 2407
NEW YORK, NEW YORK 10123
1-800-445-MSDS OR (212) 967-1100

EMERGENCY CONTACT:
JOHN S. BRANSFORD, JR. (615) 292-1180

SUBSTANCE IDENTIFICATION

CAS-NUMBER 35764-59-1

SUBSTANCE: CISMETHRIN

TRADE NAMES/SYNONYMS: CYCLOPROPANECARBOXYLIC ACID, 2,2-DIMETHYL-3-(2-METHYL-1-PROPENYL)-, (5-(PHENYLMETHYL)-3-FURANYL)METHYL ESTER, (1R-CIS)-; CYCLOPROPANECARBOXYLIC ACID, 2,2-DIMETHYL-3-(2-METHYLPROPENYL)-, (5-BENZYL-3-FURYL)METHYL ESTER, CIS-(+)-; 5-BENZYL-3-FURYLMETHYL (+)-CIS-CHRYSANTHEMATE; (+)-CIS-RESMETHRIN; D-CIS-RESMETHRIN; 1R, CIS-RESMETHRIN; NRDC 119; PST20094

CHEMICAL FAMILY: PYRETHROID (SYNTHETIC)

MOLECULAR FORMULA: C22-H26-O3

MOLECULAR WEIGHT: 338.48

CERCLA RATINGS (SCALE 0-3): HEALTH=3 FIRE=U REACTIVITY=0 PERSISTENCE=2

NFPA RATINGS (SCALE 0-4): HEALTH=3 FIRE=U REACTIVITY=0

COMPONENTS AND CONTAMINANTS

COMPONENT: CISMETHRIN ***PERCENT:*** 100.0
CAS# 35764-59-1

OTHER CONTAMINANTS: NONE
EXPOSURE LIMITS: NO OCCUPATIONAL EXPOSURE LIMITS ESTABLISHED BY OSHA, ACGIH, OR NIOSH.

PHYSICAL DATA

DESCRIPTION: WAXY OFF-WHITE TO TAN SOLID WITH A CHARACTERISTIC CHRYSANTHEMATE ODOR
SPECIFIC GRAVITY: NOT AVAILABLE ***SOLUBILITY IN WATER:*** INSOLUBLE
SOLVENT SOLUBILITY: KEROSENE, XYLENE, METHYLENE CHLORIDE, ISOPROPYL ALCOHOL, AROMATIC PETROLEUM HYDROCARBONS

FIRE AND EXPLOSION DATA

FIRE AND EXPLOSION HAZARD: UNKNOWN FIRE AND EXPLOSION HAZARD.
FIREFIGHTING MEDIA: DRY CHEMICAL, CARBON DIOXIDE, WATER SPRAY OR FOAM FOR LARGER FIRES, USE WATER SPRAY, FOG OR ALCOHOL FOAM
FIREFIGHTING: MOVE CONTAINER FROM FIRE AREA IF POSSIBLE. DO NOT SCATTER SPILLED MATERIAL WITH HIGH PRESSURE WATER STREAMS. DIKE FIRE CONTROL WATER FOR LATER DISPOSAL (1987 EMERGENCY RESPONSE GUIDEBOOK, DOT P 5800.4, GUIDE PAGE 31).
USE AGENTS SUITABLE FOR TYPE OF SURROUNDING FIRE. AVOID BREATHING HAZARDOUS VAPORS, KEEP UPWIND.

TOXICITY

CISMETHRIN: TOXICITY DATA: 63 MG/KG ORAL-RAT LD50; 152 MG/KG ORAL-MOUSE LD50; 4500 UG/KG INTRAVENOUS-RAT LD50; 320 MG/KG INTRAPERITONEAL-MOUSE LD50; MUTAGENIC DATA (RTECS). CARCINOGEN STATUS: NONE. ACUTE TOXICITY LEVEL: TOXIC BY INGESTION. TARGET EFFECTS: POISONING MAY AFFECT CENTRAL NERVOUS SYSTEM.

HEALTH EFFECTS AND FIRST AID

INHALATION: CISMETHRIN: **ACUTE EXPOSURE-** CISMETHRIN IS A SYNTHETIC PYRETHRIN. SYNTHETIC PYRETHRINS, LIKE THE NATURAL PYRETHRINS, PRODUCE CENTRAL NERVOUS SYSTEM STIMULATION IN ANIMALS WITH SYMPTOMS OF NAUSEA, VOMITING, GASTROENTERITIS WITH DIARRHEA, HYPERSENSITIVITY, INCOORDINATION, TREMORS, MUSCULAR PARALYSIS, CONVULSION, COMA, AND DEATH DUE TO RESPIRATORY FAILURE. UNLIKE NATURAL PYRETHRINS, SYNTHETIC PYRETHRINS NORMALLY DO NOT PRODUCE ALLERGIC REACTIONS IN HUMANS. **CHRONIC EXPOSURE-** NO DATA AVAILABLE.
FIRST AID- REMOVE FROM EXPOSURE AREA TO FRESH AIR IMMEDIATELY. IF BREATHING HAS STOPPED, PERFORM ARTIFICIAL RESPIRATION. KEEP PERSON WARM AND AT REST. TREAT SYMPTOMATICALLY AND SUPPORTIVELY. GET MEDICAL ATTENTION IMMEDIATELY.

SKIN CONTACT: CISMETHRIN: **ACUTE EXPOSURE-** CISMETHRIN IS A SYNTHETIC PYRETHRIN. SYNTHETIC PYRETHRINS GENERALLY ARE NOT IRRITANTS TO RABBIT SKIN AND THE TOXICITY FROM DERMAL ABSORPTION IS USUALLY MODERATE TO LOW. UNLIKE NATURAL PYRETHRINS, SYNTHETIC PYRETHRINS NORMALLY DO NOT PRODUCE ALLERGIC REACTIONS IN HUMANS. HOWEVER, THERE HAVE BEEN SOME REPORTS OF CUTANEOUS PARESTHESIAS AMONG INDIVIDUALS OCCUPATIONALLY EXPOSED TO SYNTHETIC PYRETHRINS. THESE INDIVIDUALS COMPLAINED OF TINGLING, BURNING AND STINGING SENSATIONS ON THE EXPOSED SURFACE OF THE SKIN BEGINNING FROM 30 MINUTES TO 3 HOURS AFTER EXPOSURE. THE DURATION OF SYMPTOMS VARIED FROM 30 MINUTES TO 8 HOURS. **CHRONIC EXPOSURE-** NO DATA AVAILABLE. **FIRST AID-** REMOVE CONTAMINATED CLOTHING AND SHOES IMMEDIATELY. WASH AFFECTED AREA WITH SOAP OR MILD DETERGENT AND LARGE AMOUNTS OF WATER UNTIL NO EVIDENCE OF CHEMICAL REMAINS (APPROXIMATELY 15-20 MINUTES). GET MEDICAL ATTENTION IMMEDIATELY.

EYE CONTACT: CISMETHRIN: **ACUTE EXPOSURE-** SYNTHETIC PYRETHRINS ARE NOT IRRITANTS OF RABBIT EYES. **CHRONIC EXPOSURE-** NO DATA AVAILABLE.
FIRST AID- WASH EYES IMMEDIATELY WITH LARGE AMOUNTS OF WATER OR NORMAL SALINE, OCCASIONALLY LIFTING UPPER AND LOWER LIDS, UNTIL NO EVIDENCE OF CHEMICAL REMAINS (APPROXIMATELY 15-20 MINUTES). GET MEDICAL ATTENTION IMMEDIATELY.

INGESTION: CISMETHRIN: TOXIC. **ACUTE EXPOSURE-** A LOW DOSE OF CISMETHRIN WAS LETHAL IN MICE AND RATS. CISMETHRIN IS A SYNTHETIC PYRETHRIN. SYNTHETIC PYRETHRINS, LIKE THE NATURAL PYRETHRINS, PRODUCE CENTRAL NERVOUS SYSTEM STIMULATION IN ANIMALS WITH SYMPTOMS OF NAUSEA, VOMITING, GASTROENTERITIS WITH DIARRHEA, HYPERSENSITIVITY, INCOORDINATION, TREMORS, MUSCULAR PARALYSIS, CONVULSION, COMA, AND DEATH DUE TO RESPIRATORY FAILURE. **CHRONIC EXPOSURE-** INCREASED LIVER AND KIDNEY WEIGHTS WERE NOTED IN ANIMALS CHRONICALLY FED SYNTHETIC PYRETHRINS.
FIRST AID- TREAT SYMPTOMATICALLY AND SUPPORTIVELY. GET MEDICAL ATTENTION IMMEDIATELY. IF VOMITING OCCURS, KEEP HEAD LOWER THAN HIPS TO PREVENT ASPIRATION.
ANTIDOTE: NO SPECIFIC ANTIDOTE. TREAT SYMPTOMATICALLY AND SUPPORTIVELY.

REACTIVITY

REACTIVITY: MAY DECOMPOSE UPON EXPOSURE TO HEAT OR LIGHT.
INCOMPATIBILITIES: CISMETHRIN: NO DATA AVAILABLE.
DECOMPOSITION: THERMAL DECOMPOSITION MAY RELEASE TOXIC AND/OR HAZARDOUS GASES.
POLYMERIZATION: HAZARDOUS POLYMERIZATION HAS NOT BEEN REPORTED TO OCCUR UNDER NORMAL TEMPERATURES AND PRESSURES.

STORAGE AND DISPOSAL

OBSERVE ALL FEDERAL, STATE AND LOCAL REGULATIONS WHEN STORING OR DISPOSING OF THIS SUBSTANCE. FOR ASSISTANCE, CONTACT THE DISTRICT DIRECTOR OF THE ENVIRONMENTAL PROTECTION AGENCY.

STORAGE

STORE IN ACCORDANCE WITH 40 CFR 165 RECOMMENDED PROCEDURES FOR THE DISPOSAL AND STORAGE OF PESTICIDES AND PESTICIDE CONTAINERS.

DISPOSAL

DISPOSAL MUST BE IN ACCORDANCE WITH 40 CFR 165 RECOMMENDED PROCEDURES FOR THE DISPOSAL AND STORAGE OF PESTICIDES AND PESTICIDE CONTAINERS.

CONDITIONS TO AVOID

MAY BURN BUT DOES NOT IGNITE READILY. AVOID CONTACT WITH STRONG OXIDIZERS, EXCESSIVE HEAT, SPARKS, OR OPEN FLAME.

SPILL AND LEAK PROCEDURES

OCCUPATIONAL SPILL: SWEEP UP AND PLACE IN SUITABLE CLEAN, DRY CONTAINERS FOR RECLAMATION OR LATER DISPOSAL. DO NOT FLUSH SPILLED MATERIAL INTO SEWER. KEEP UNNECESSARY PEOPLE AWAY.

PROTECTIVE EQUIPMENT

VENTILATION: PROCESS ENCLOSURE RECOMMENDED. VENTILATION EQUIPMENT MUST BE EXPLOSION-PROOF.
RESPIRATOR: THE FOLLOWING RESPIRATORS ARE RECOMMENDED BASED ON INFORMATION FOUND IN THE PHYSICAL DATA, TOXICITY AND HEALTH EFFECTS SECTIONS. THEY ARE RANKED IN ORDER FROM MINIMUM TO MAXIMUM RESPIRATORY PROTECTION. THE SPECIFIC RESPIRATOR SELECTED MUST BE BASED ON CONTAMINATION LEVELS FOUND IN THE WORK PLACE, MUST NOT EXCEED THE WORKING LIMITS OF THE RESPIRATOR AND BE JOINTLY APPROVED BY THE NATIONAL INSTITUTE FOR OCCUPATIONAL SAFETY AND HEALTH AND THE MINE SAFETY AND HEALTH ADMINISTRATION (NIOSH-MSHA).
CHEMICAL CARTRIDGE RESPIRATOR WITH AN ORGANIC VAPOR CARTRIDGE(S) IN COMBINATION WITH A DUST AND MIST FILTER.
GAS MASK WITH ORGANIC VAPOR CANISTER (CHIN-STYLE OR FRONT- OR BACK-MOUNTED CANISTER) WITH A DUST AND MIST FILTER.
GAS MASK WITH ORGANIC VAPOR CANISTER (CHIN-STYLE OR FRONT- OR BACK-MOUNTED CANISTER) WITH A PARTICULATE FILTER.
POWERED AIR-PURIFYING RESPIRATOR WITH A HIGH-EFFICIENCY FILTER.
TYPE 'C' SUPPLIED-AIR RESPIRATOR WITH A FULL FACEPIECE OPERATED IN A PRESSURE-DEMAND OR OTHER POSITIVE PRESSURE MODE.
SELF-CONTAINED BREATHING APPARATUS WITH A FULL FACEPIECE OPERATED IN PRESSURE-DEMAND OR OTHER POSITIVE PRESSURE MODE. FOR FIREFIGHTING AND OTHER IMMEDIATELY DANGEROUS TO LIFE OR HEALTH CONDITIONS:
SELF-CONTAINED BREATHING APPARATUS WITH FULL FACEPIECE OPERATED IN PRESSURE-DEMAND OR OTHER POSITIVE PRESSURE MODE.
SUPPLIED-AIR RESPIRATOR WITH FULL FACEPIECE AND OPERATED IN PRESSURE-DEMAND OR OTHER POSITIVE PRESSURE MODE IN COMBINATION WITH AN AUXILIARY SELF-CONTAINED BREATHING APPARATUS OPERATED IN PRESSURE-DEMAND OR OTHER POSITIVE PRESSURE MODE.
CLOTHING: EMPLOYEE MUST WEAR APPROPRIATE PROTECTIVE (IMPERVIOUS) CLOTHING AND EQUIPMENT TO PREVENT REPEATED OR PROLONGED SKIN CONTACT WITH THIS SUBSTANCE.
GLOVES: EMPLOYEE MUST WEAR APPROPRIATE PROTECTIVE GLOVES TO PREVENT CONTACT WITH THIS SUBSTANCE.
EYE PROTECTION: EMPLOYEE MUST WEAR SPLASH-PROOF OR DUST-RESISTANT SAFETY GOGGLES TO PREVENT EYE CONTACT WITH THIS SUBSTANCE.
EMERGENCY EYE WASH: WHERE THERE IS ANY POSSIBILITY THAT AN EMPLOYEE'S EYES MAY BE EXPOSED TO THIS SUBSTANCE, THE EMPLOYER SHOULD PROVIDE AN EYE WASH FOUNTAIN WITHIN THE IMMEDIATE WORK AREA FOR EMERGENCY USE.

AUTHORIZED BY- OCCUPATIONAL HEALTH SERVICES, INC.
CREATION DATE: 10/04/89 ***REVISION DATE:*** 05/31/90

MATERIAL SAFETY DATA SHEET

OCCUPATIONAL HEALTH SERVICES, INC.
AGRICULTURE AND PESTICIDE DIVISION
450 SEVENTH AVENUE, SUITE 2407
NEW YORK, NEW YORK 10123
1-800-445-MSDS OR (212) 967-1100

EMERGENCY CONTACT:
JOHN S. BRANSFORD, JR. (615) 292-1180

SUBSTANCE IDENTIFICATION

CAS-NUMBER 10453-86-8

SUBSTANCE: RESMETHRIN

TRADE NAMES/SYNONYMS: CYCLOPROPANECARBOXYLIC ACID, 2,2-DIMETHYL-3-(2-METHYL-1-PROPENYL)-, (5-(PHENYLMETHYL)-3-FURANYL)METHYL ESTER; CYCLOPROPANECARBOXYLIC ACID, 2,2-DIMETHYL-3-(2-METHYLPROPENYL)-, (5-BENZYL-3-FURYL)METHYL ESTER; 2,2-DIMETHYL-3-(2-METHYL-1-PROPENYL)CYCLOPROPANECARBOXYLIC ACID (5-(PHENYLMETHYL)-3-FURANYL)METHYL ESTER; 2,2-DIMETHYL-3-(2-METHYLPROPENYL)CYCLOPROPANECARBOXYLIC ACID; (5-BENZYL-3-FURYL)METHYL ESTER (5-(PHENYLMETHYL)-3-FURANYL)METHYL 2,2-DIMETHYL-3-(2-METHYL-1- PROPENYL)CYCLOPROPANECARBOXYLATE; (5-BENZYL-3-FURYL)METHYL 2,2-DIMETHYL-3-(2-METHYLPROPENYL) CYCLOPROPANECARBOXYLATE; 5-BENZYL-3-FURYLMETHYL (+-)-CIS-TRANS-CHRYSANTHEMATE; 5-BENZYLFURFURYL CHRYSANTHEMATE; BENZYFURDINE; CHRYSON; SYNTHRIN; OMS 1206; C22H26O3; PST20095

CHEMICAL FAMILY: PYRETHROID (SYNTHETIC)

MOLECULAR FORMULA: C22-H26-O3

MOLECULAR WEIGHT: 338.45

CERCLA RATINGS (SCALE 0-3): HEALTH=3 FIRE=U REACTIVITY=0 PERSISTENCE=1

NFPA RATINGS (SCALE 0-4): HEALTH=U FIRE=U REACTIVITY=0

COMPONENTS AND CONTAMINANTS

COMPONENT: RESMETHRIN ***PERCENT:*** 100.0
CAS# 10453-86-8

OTHER CONTAMINANTS: NONE

EXPOSURE LIMITS: NO OCCUPATIONAL EXPOSURE LIMITS ESTABLISHED BY OSHA, ACGIH, OR NIOSH.
PYRETHROIDS: 1 POUND CERCLA SECTION 103 REPORTABLE QUANTITY

PHYSICAL DATA

DESCRIPTION: WAXY OFF-WHITE TO TAN SOLID WITH A CHARACTERISTIC CHRYSANTHEMATE ODOR.

BOILING POINT: 345 F (174) @ 0.0008 MMHG ***MELTING POINT:*** 109-118 F (43-48 C)

SPECIFIC GRAVITY: NOT AVAILABLE ***VAPOR PRESSURE:*** NEGLIGIBLE

SOLUBILITY IN WATER: <1 PPM @ 30 C

SOLVENT SOLUBILITY: SOLUBLE IN HEXANE, XYLENE, METHYLENE CHLORIDE, KEROSENE, ISOPROPYL ALCOHOL, AROMATIC PETROLEUM HYDROCARBONS; MODERATELY SOLUBLE IN METHANOL.

FIRE AND EXPLOSION DATA

FIRE AND EXPLOSION HAZARD: UNKNOWN FIRE AND EXPLOSION HAZARD.

FIREFIGHTING MEDIA: DRY CHEMICAL, CARBON DIOXIDE, HALON, WATER SPRAY OR STANDARD FOAM (1987 EMERGENCY RESPONSE GUIDEBOOK, DOT P 5800.4).
FOR LARGER FIRES, USE WATER SPRAY, FOG OR STANDARD FOAM (1987 EMERGENCY RESPONSE GUIDEBOOK, DOT P 5800.4).

FIREFIGHTING: MOVE CONTAINER FROM FIRE AREA IF POSSIBLE. COOL FIRE-EXPOSED CONTAINERS WITH WATER FROM SIDE UNTIL WELL AFTER FIRE IS OUT. STAY AWAY FROM STORAGE TANK ENDS. FOR MASSIVE FIRE IN STORAGE AREA, USE UNMANNED HOSE HOLDER OR MONITOR NOZZLES, ELSE WITHDRAW FROM AREA AND LET FIRE BURN. WITHDRAW IMMEDIATELY IN CASE OF RISING SOUND FROM VENTING SAFETY DEVICE OR ANY DISCOLORATION OF STORAGE TANK DUE TO FIRE (1987 EMERGENCY RESPONSE GUIDEBOOK, DOT P 5800.4, GUIDE PAGE 27). EXTINGUISH ONLY IF FLOW CAN BE STOPPED; USE FLOODING AMOUNTS OF WATER AS A FOG, SOLID STREAMS MAY BE INEFFECTIVE. COOL CONTAINERS WITH FLOODING AMOUNTS OF WATER, APPLY FROM AS FAR A DISTANCE AS POSSIBLE. AVOID BREATHING VAPORS, KEEP UPWIND.

TOXICITY

RESMETHRIN: TOXICITY DATA: 99 MG/KG INHALATION-MOUSE LD50; 2500 MG/KG SKIN-RABBIT LD50; 1244 MG/KG ORAL-RAT LD50; 1390 MG/KG ORAL-MOUSE LD50; 160 MG/KG INTRAVENOUS-RAT LDLO. CARCINOGEN STATUS: NONE. ACUTE TOXICITY LEVEL: MODERATELY TOXIC BY INGESTION; SLIGHTLY TOXIC BY DERMAL ABSORPTION. TARGET EFFECTS: POISONING MAY AFFECT THE CENTRAL NERVOUS SYSTEM.*
* MAY BE BASED ON GENERAL INFORMATION OF PYRETHROIDS.

HEALTH EFFECTS AND FIRST AID

INHALATION: RESMETHRIN: SEE INFORMATION ON PYRETHROIDS.
PYRETHROIDS: **ACUTE EXPOSURE-** HEAVY EXPOSURE TO A MIST OF SOME PYRETHROIDS HAS PRODUCED HYPERSENSITIVIITY, ATAXIA, AND URINARY INCONTINENCE. CONVULSIONS MAY ALSO BE POSSIBLE. **CHRONIC EXPOSURE-** ANIMALS EXPOSED TO AEROSOLS OF SOME PYRETHROIDS FOR 3-4 HOURS/DAY FOR UP TO 4 WEEKS DID NOT EXHIBIT ANY SIGNIFICANT COMPOUND RELATED FINDINGS.

FIRST AID- REMOVE FROM EXPOSURE AREA TO FRESH AIR IMMEDIATELY. IF BREATHING HAS STOPPED, PERFORM ARTIFICIAL RESPIRATION. KEEP PERSON WARM AND AT REST. TREAT SYMPTOMATICALLY AND SUPPORTIVELY. GET MEDICAL ATTENTION IMMEDIATELY.

SKIN CONTACT: RESMETHRIN: SEE INFORMATION ON PYRETHROIDS.
PYRETHROIDS: **ACUTE EXPOSURE-** BASED ON ANIMAL AND HUMAN STUDIES AND HUMAN EXPERIENCES WITH SOME PYRETHROIDS, PRIMARY IRRITATION IS UNLIKELY. CUTANEOUS PARESTHESIAS MAY OCCUR INCLUDING NUMBNESS, ITCHING, BURNING, TINGLING AND WARMTH WITHOUT SIGNS OF IRRITATION. THESE EFFECTS MAY BE DELAYED FOR 30 MINUTES OR MORE AND LAST LESS THAN 24 HOURS. **CHRONIC EXPOSURE-** TESTS WITH SOME PYRETHROIDS ON HUMANS AND ANIMALS INDICATE SENSITIZATION IS UNLIKELY.

FIRST AID- REMOVE CONTAMINATED CLOTHING AND SHOES IMMEDIATELY. WASH AFFECTED AREA WITH SOAP OR MILD DETERGENT AND LARGE AMOUNTS OF WATER UNTIL NO EVIDENCE OF CHEMICAL REMAINS (APPROXIMATELY 15-20 MINUTES). GET MEDICAL ATTENTION IMMEDIATELY.

EYE CONTACT: RESMETHRIN: SEE INFORMATION ON PYRETHROIDS.
PYRETHROIDS: **ACUTE EXPOSURE-** MASSIVE INSTILLATION OF SOME PYRETHROIDS INTO RABBIT EYES PRODUCED ONLY A SLIGHT, TRANSIENT CONGESTION OF THE CONJUNCTIVA OR LACRIMATION. **CHRONIC EXPOSURE-** NO DATA AVAILABLE.

FIRST AID- WASH EYES IMMEDIATELY WITH LARGE AMOUNTS OF WATER OR NORMAL SALINE, OCCASIONALLY LIFTING UPPER AND LOWER LIDS, UNTIL NO EVIDENCE OF CHEMICAL REMAINS (APPROXIMATELY 15-20 MINUTES). GET MEDICAL ATTENTION IMMEDIATELY.

INGESTION: RESMETHRIN: SEE INFORMATION ON PYRETHROIDS.
PYRETHROIDS: **ACUTE EXPOSURE-** SOME PYRETHROIDS HAVE PRODUCED HYPERSENSITIVITY, NERVOUS IRRITABILITY, TREMORS, ATAXIA, AND URINARY INCONTINENCE IN ANIMALS. CONVULSIONS MAY ALSO BE POSSIBLE. **CHRONIC EXPOSURE-** INCREASED KIDNEY AND LIVER WEIGHTS AND HEPATIC HISTOPATHOLOGICAL CHANGES WERE NOTED IN ANIMALS CHRONICALLY FED SOME PYRETHROIDS.

FIRST AID- REMOVE BY GASTRIC LAVAGE AND CATHARSIS. MAINTAIN BLOOD PRESSURE AND AIRWAY. GIVE OXYGEN IF RESPIRATION IS DEPRESSED. DO NOT PERFORM GASTRIC LAVAGE IF VICTIM IS UNCONSCIOUS. GET MEDICAL ATTENTION IMMEDIATELY (DREISBACH, HANDBOOK OF POISONING, 12TH ED.). ADMINISTRATION OF LAVAGE OR OXYGEN SHOULD BE PERFORMED BY QUALIFIED MEDICAL PERSONNEL.

ANTIDOTE: NO SPECIFIC ANTIDOTE. TREAT SYMPTOMATICALLY AND SUPPORTIVELY.

REACTIVITY

REACTIVITY: STABLE UNDER NORMAL TEMPERATURES AND PRESSURES.

INCOMPATIBILITIES: RESMETHRIN: ALKALIS: MAY DECOMPOSE. OXIDIZERS (STRONG): FIRE AND EXPLOSION HAZARD.

DECOMPOSITION: THERMAL DECOMPOSITION PRODUCTS MAY INCLUDE TOXIC OXIDES OF CARBON.

POLYMERIZATION: HAZARDOUS POLYMERIZATION HAS NOT BEEN REPORTED TO OCCUR UNDER NORMAL TEMPERATURES AND PRESSURES.

STORAGE AND DISPOSAL

OBSERVE ALL FEDERAL, STATE AND LOCAL REGULATIONS WHEN STORING OR DISPOSING OF THIS SUBSTANCE. FOR ASSISTANCE, CONTACT THE DISTRICT DIRECTOR OF THE ENVIRONMENTAL PROTECTION AGENCY.

****STORAGE****

STORE IN ACCORDANCE WITH 40 CFR 165 RECOMMENDED PROCEDURES FOR THE DISPOSAL AND STORAGE OF PESTICIDES AND PESTICIDE CONTAINERS.
STORE AWAY FROM INCOMPATIBLE SUBSTANCES.

DISPOSAL

DISPOSAL MUST BE IN ACCORDANCE WITH 40 CFR 165 RECOMMENDED PROCEDURES FOR THE DISPOSAL AND STORAGE OF PESTICIDES AND PESTICIDE CONTAINERS.

CONDITIONS TO AVOID

AVOID CONTACT WITH HEAT, SPARKS, FLAMES, OR OTHER SOURCES OF IGNITION. VAPORS MAY BE EXPLOSIVE. AVOID OVERHEATING OF CONTAINERS; CONTAINERS MAY VIOLENTLY RUPTURE IN HEAT OF FIRE. AVOID CONTAMINATION OF WATER SOURCES.

SPILL AND LEAK PROCEDURES

OCCUPATIONAL SPILL: SHUT OFF IGNITION SOURCES. STOP LEAK IF YOU CAN DO IT WITHOUT RISK. USE WATER SPRAY TO REDUCE VAPORS. FOR SMALL SPILLS, TAKE UP WITH SAND OR OTHER ABSORBENT MATERIAL AND PLACE INTO CONTAINERS FOR LATER DISPOSAL. FOR LARGER SPILLS, DIKE FAR AHEAD OF SPILL FOR LATER DISPOSAL. NO SMOKING, FLAMES OR FLARES IN HAZARD AREA. KEEP UNNECESSARY PEOPLE AWAY; ISOLATE HAZARD AREA AND RESTRICT ENTRY.

PROTECTIVE EQUIPMENT

VENTILATION: PROVIDE LOCAL EXHAUST OR GENERAL DILUTION VENTILATION SYSTEM.

RESPIRATOR: THE FOLLOWING RESPIRATORS ARE RECOMMENDED BASED ON INFORMATION FOUND IN THE PHYSICAL DATA, TOXICITY AND HEALTH EFFECTS SECTIONS. THEY ARE RANKED IN ORDER FROM MINIMUM TO MAXIMUM RESPIRATORY PROTECTION. THE SPECIFIC RESPIRATOR SELECTED MUST BE BASED ON CONTAMINATION LEVELS FOUND IN THE WORK PLACE, MUST NOT EXCEED THE WORKING LIMITS OF THE RESPIRATOR AND BE JOINTLY APPROVED BY THE NATIONAL INSTITUTE FOR OCCUPATIONAL SAFETY AND HEALTH AND THE MINE SAFETY AND HEALTH ADMINISTRATION (NIOSH-MSHA).

CHEMICAL CARTRIDGE RESPIRATOR WITH AN ORGANIC VAPOR CARTRIDGE(S) IN COMBINATION WITH A DUST AND MIST FILTER.

GAS MASK WITH ORGANIC VAPOR CANISTER (CHIN-STYLE OR FRONT- OR BACK-MOUNTED CANISTER) WITH A DUST AND MIST FILTER.

GAS MASK WITH ORGANIC VAPOR CANISTER (CHIN-STYLE OR FRONT- OR BACK-MOUNTED CANISTER) WITH A PARTICULATE FILTER.

POWERED AIR-PURIFYING RESPIRATOR WITH A HIGH-EFFICIENCY FILTER.

TYPE 'C' SUPPLIED-AIR RESPIRATOR WITH A FULL FACEPIECE OPERATED IN A PRESSURE-DEMAND OR OTHER POSITIVE PRESSURE MODE.

SELF-CONTAINED BREATHING APPARATUS WITH A FULL FACEPIECE OPERATED IN PRESSURE-DEMAND OR OTHER POSITIVE PRESSURE MODE.

FOR FIREFIGHTING AND OTHER IMMEDIATELY DANGEROUS TO LIFE OR HEALTH CONDITIONS:

SELF-CONTAINED BREATHING APPARATUS WITH FULL FACEPIECE OPERATED IN PRESSURE-DEMAND OR OTHER POSITIVE PRESSURE MODE.

SUPPLIED-AIR RESPIRATOR WITH FULL FACEPIECE AND OPERATED IN PRESSURE-DEMAND OR OTHER POSITIVE PRESSURE MODE IN COMBINATION WITH AN AUXILIARY SELF-CONTAINED BREATHING APPARATUS OPERATED IN PRESSURE-DEMAND OR OTHER POSITIVE PRESSURE MODE.

CLOTHING: EMPLOYEE MUST WEAR APPROPRIATE PROTECTIVE (IMPERVIOUS) CLOTHING AND EQUIPMENT TO PREVENT REPEATED OR PROLONGED SKIN CONTACT WITH THIS SUBSTANCE.

GLOVES: EMPLOYEE MUST WEAR APPROPRIATE PROTECTIVE GLOVES TO PREVENT CONTACT WITH THIS SUBSTANCE.

EYE PROTECTION: EMPLOYEE MUST WEAR SPLASH-PROOF OR DUST-RESISTANT SAFETY GOGGLES TO PREVENT EYE CONTACT WITH THIS SUBSTANCE.

EMERGENCY EYE WASH: WHERE THERE IS ANY POSSIBILITY THAT AN EMPLOYEE'S EYES MAY BE EXPOSED TO THIS SUBSTANCE, THE EMPLOYER SHOULD PROVIDE AN EYE WASH FOUNTAIN WITHIN THE IMMEDIATE WORK AREA FOR EMERGENCY USE.

AUTHORIZED BY- OCCUPATIONAL HEALTH SERVICES, INC.

CREATION DATE: 10/05/89 ***REVISION DATE:*** 05/07/90

MATERIAL SAFETY DATA SHEET

OCCUPATIONAL HEALTH SERVICES, INC.
AGRICULTURE AND PESTICIDE DIVISION
450 SEVENTH AVENUE, SUITE 2407
NEW YORK, NEW YORK 10123
1-800-445-MSDS OR (212) 967-1100

EMERGENCY CONTACT:
JOHN S. BRANSFORD, JR. (615) 292-1180

SUBSTANCE IDENTIFICATION

SUBSTANCE: **(+)-TRANS,CIS-RESMETHRIN**

TRADE NAMES/SYNONYMS: 2,2-DIMETHYL-3-(2-METHYLPROPENYL)-CYCLOPROPANECARBOXYLIC ACID, (5-BENZYL-3-FURYL)METHYL ESTER, (+)-(Z,E)-; PST20096

CHEMICAL FAMILY: PYRETHROID (SYNTHETIC)

MOLECULAR FORMULA: C22-H26-O3

MOLECULAR WEIGHT: 338.48

CERCLA RATINGS (SCALE 0-3): HEALTH=U FIRE=U REACTIVITY=0 PERSISTENCE=2

NFPA RATINGS (SCALE 0-4): HEALTH=U FIRE=U REACTIVITY=0

COMPONENTS AND CONTAMINANTS

COMPONENT: (+)-TRANS,CIS-RESMETHRIN ***PERCENT:*** 100.0

OTHER CONTAMINANTS: NONE

EXPOSURE LIMITS: NO OCCUPATIONAL EXPOSURE LIMITS ESTABLISHED BY OSHA, ACGIH, OR NIOSH.

PHYSICAL DATA

DESCRIPTION: WAXY OFF-WHITE TO TAN SOLID WITH A CHARACTERISTIC CHRYSANTHEMATE ODOR

SPECIFIC GRAVITY: NOT AVAILABLE ***SOLUBILITY IN WATER:*** INSOLUBLE

SOLVENT SOLUBILITY: KEROSENE, XYLENE, METHYLENE CHLORIDE, ISOPROPYL ALCOHOL, AROMATIC PETROLEUM HYDROCARBONS

FIRE AND EXPLOSION DATA

FIRE AND EXPLOSION HAZARD: UNKNOWN FIRE AND EXPLOSION HAZARD.

FIREFIGHTING MEDIA: DRY CHEMICAL, CARBON DIOXIDE, WATER SPRAY OR FOAM FOR LARGER FIRES, USE WATER SPRAY, FOG OR ALCOHOL FOAM

FIREFIGHTING: MOVE CONTAINER FROM FIRE AREA IF POSSIBLE. DO NOT SCATTER SPILLED MATERIAL WITH HIGH PRESSURE WATER STREAMS. DIKE FIRE CONTROL WATER FOR LATER DISPOSAL (1987 EMERGENCY RESPONSE GUIDEBOOK, DOT P 5800.4, GUIDE PAGE 31).

USE AGENTS SUITABLE FOR TYPE OF SURROUNDING FIRE. AVOID BREATHING HAZARDOUS VAPORS, KEEP UPWIND.

TOXICITY

(+)-TRANS, CIS-RESMETHRIN: 400 MG/KG/4 HOURS INHALATION-RAT TCLO; 400 MG/M3/4 HOURS INHALATION-MOUSE TCLO; CARCINOGEN STATUS: NONE. THE TOXICITY HAS NOT BEEN QUANTIFIED. SYNTHETIC PYRETHRINS ARE CENTRAL NERVOUS SYSTEM STIMULANTS IN ANIMALS.

HEALTH EFFECTS AND FIRST AID

INHALATION: (+)-TRANS, CIS-RESMETHRIN: **ACUTE EXPOSURE-** AT A CONCENTRATION OF APPROXIMATELY 1500 MG/M3/4 HOURS, THIS MATERIAL PRODUCED SYMPTOMS OF HYPERSENSITIVITY, MOTOR ATAXIA, AND URINARY INCONTINENCE, BUT NO FATALITIES IN MICE AND RATS. SYSTEMIC EFFECTS WERE FIRST NOTICED AT A CONCENTRATION OF 400 MG/M3. (+)-TRANS, CIS-RESMETHRIN IS A SYNTHETIC PYRETHRIN. SYNTHETIC PYRETHRINS, LIKE THE NATURAL PYRETHRINS, PRODUCE CENTRAL NERVOUS SYSTEM STIMULATION IN ANIMALS WITH SYMPTOMS OF NAUSEA, VOMITING, GASTROENTERITIS WITH DIARRHEA, HYPERSENSITIVITY, INCOORDINATION, TREMORS, MUSCULAR PARALYSIS, CONVULSION, COMA AND DEATH DUE TO RESPIRATORY FAILURE. UNLIKE NATURAL PYRETHRINS, SYNTHETIC PYRETHRINS NORMALLY DO NOT PRODUCE ALLERGIC REACTIONS IN HUMANS. **CHRONIC EXPOSURE-** IN ONE ANIMAL STUDY OF (+)-TRANS, CIS-RESMETHRIN, CHRONIC EXPOSURE TO MIST PREPARATIONS OF 210 MG/M3/4 HOURS 5 DAYS A WEEK FOR 4 WEEKS DID NOT PRODUCED ANY ADVERSE EFFECTS ON THE MAJOR ORGANS AND TISSUES OF MICE AND RATS.

FIRST AID- REMOVE FROM EXPOSURE AREA TO FRESH AIR IMMEDIATELY. IF BREATHING HAS STOPPED, PERFORM ARTIFICIAL RESPIRATION. KEEP PERSON WARM AND AT REST. TREAT SYMPTOMATICALLY AND SUPPORTIVELY. GET MEDICAL ATTENTION IMMEDIATELY.

SKIN CONTACT: (+)-TRANS,CIS-RESMETHRIN: **ACUTE EXPOSURE-** (+)-TRANS,CIS-RESMETHRIN IS A SYNTHETIC PYRETHRIN. SYNTHETIC PYRETHRINS GENERALLY ARE NOT IRRITANTS TO RABBIT SKIN AND THE TOXICITY FROM DERMAL ABSORPTION IS USUALLY MODERATE TO LOW. UNLIKE NATURAL PYRETHRINS, SYNTHETIC PYRETHRINS NORMALLY DO NOT PRODUCE ALLERGIC REACTIONS IN HUMANS. HOWEVER, THERE HAVE BEEN SOME REPORTS OF CUTANEOUS PARESTHESIAS AMONG INDIVIDUALS OCCUPATIONALLY EXPOSED TO SYNTHETIC PYRETHRINS. THESE INDIVIDUALS COMPLAINED OF TINGLING, BURNING AND STINGING SENSATIONS ON THE EXPOSED SURFACE OF THE SKIN BEGINNING FROM 30 MINUTES TO 3 HOURS AFTER EXPOSURE. THE DURATION OF SYMPTOMS VARIED FROM 30 MINUTES TO 8 HOURS. **CHRONIC EXPOSURE-** NO DATA AVAILABLE.

FIRST AID- REMOVE CONTAMINATED CLOTHING AND SHOES IMMEDIATELY. WASH AFFECTED AREA WITH SOAP OR MILD DETERGENT AND LARGE AMOUNTS OF WATER UNTIL NO EVIDENCE OF CHEMICAL REMAINS (APPROXIMATELY 15-20 MINUTES). GET MEDICAL ATTENTION IMMEDIATELY.

EYE CONTACT: (+)-TRANS,CIS-RESMETHRIN: **ACUTE EXPOSURE**- SYNTHETIC PYRETHRINS ARE NOT IRRITANTS OF RABBIT EYES. **CHRONIC EXPOSURE**- NO DATA AVAILABLE.
FIRST AID- WASH EYES IMMEDIATELY WITH LARGE AMOUNTS OF WATER OR NORMAL SALINE, OCCASIONALLY LIFTING UPPER AND LOWER LIDS, UNTIL NO EVIDENCE OF CHEMICAL REMAINS (APPROXIMATELY 15-20 MINUTES). GET MEDICAL ATTENTION IMMEDIATELY.

INGESTION: (+)-TRANS,CIS-RESMETHRIN: **ACUTE EXPOSURE**- (+)-TRANS,CIS-RESMETHRIN IS A SYNTHETIC PYRETHRIN. SYNTHETIC PYRETHRINS, LIKE THE NATURAL PYRETHRINS, PRODUCE CENTRAL NERVOUS SYSTEM STIMULATION IN ANIMALS WITH SYMPTOMS OF NAUSEA, VOMITING, GASTROENTERITIS WITH DIARRHEA, HYPERSENSITIVITY, INCOORDINATION, TREMORS, MUSCULAR PARALYSIS, CONVULSION, COMA, AND DEATH DUE TO RESPIRATORY FAILURE.
CHRONIC EXPOSURE- RATS FED A DIETARY CONCENTRATION OF 5000 PPM FOR 24 WEEKS, EXPERIENCED AN INCREASED IN LIVER WEIGHT.
FIRST AID- TREAT SYMPTOMATICALLY AND SUPPORTIVELY. GET MEDICAL ATTENTION IMMEDIATELY. IF VOMITING OCCURS, KEEP HEAD LOWER THAN HIPS TO PREVENT ASPIRATION.
ANTIDOTE: NO SPECIFIC ANTIDOTE. TREAT SYMPTOMATICALLY AND SUPPORTIVELY.

REACTIVITY

REACTIVITY: MAY DECOMPOSE UPON EXPOSURE TO HEAT OR LIGHT.
INCOMPATIBILITIES: (+)-TRANS,CIS-RESMETHRIN: NO DATA AVAILABLE.
DECOMPOSITION: THERMAL DECOMPOSITION MAY RELEASE TOXIC AND/OR HAZARDOUS GASES.
POLYMERIZATION: HAZARDOUS POLYMERIZATION HAS NOT BEEN REPORTED TO OCCUR UNDER NORMAL TEMPERATURES AND PRESSURES.

STORAGE AND DISPOSAL

OBSERVE ALL FEDERAL, STATE AND LOCAL REGULATIONS WHEN STORING OR DISPOSING OF THIS SUBSTANCE. FOR ASSISTANCE, CONTACT THE DISTRICT DIRECTOR OF THE ENVIRONMENTAL PROTECTION AGENCY.

****STORAGE****

STORE IN ACCORDANCE WITH 40 CFR 165 RECOMMENDED PROCEDURES FOR THE DISPOSAL AND STORAGE OF PESTICIDES AND PESTICIDE CONTAINERS.

****DISPOSAL****

DISPOSAL MUST BE IN ACCORDANCE WITH 40 CFR 165 RECOMMENDED PROCEDURES FOR THE DISPOSAL AND STORAGE OF PESTICIDES AND PESTICIDE CONTAINERS.

CONDITIONS TO AVOID

MAY BURN BUT DOES NOT IGNITE READILY. AVOID CONTACT WITH STRONG OXIDIZERS, EXCESSIVE HEAT, SPARKS, OR OPEN FLAME.

SPILL AND LEAK PROCEDURES

OCCUPATIONAL SPILL: SWEEP UP AND PLACE IN SUITABLE CLEAN, DRY CONTAINERS FOR RECLAMATION OR LATER DISPOSAL. DO NOT FLUSH SPILLED MATERIAL INTO SEWER. KEEP UNNECESSARY PEOPLE AWAY.

PROTECTIVE EQUIPMENT

VENTILATION: PROVIDE LOCAL EXHAUST OR PROCESS ENCLOSURE VENTILATION SYSTEM.
RESPIRATOR: THE FOLLOWING RESPIRATORS ARE RECOMMENDED BASED ON INFORMATION FOUND IN THE PHYSICAL DATA, TOXICITY AND HEALTH EFFECTS SECTIONS. THEY ARE RANKED IN ORDER FROM MINIMUM TO MAXIMUM RESPIRATORY PROTECTION. THE SPECIFIC RESPIRATOR SELECTED MUST BE BASED ON CONTAMINATION LEVELS FOUND IN THE WORK PLACE, MUST NOT EXCEED THE WORKING LIMITS OF THE RESPIRATOR AND BE JOINTLY APPROVED BY THE NATIONAL INSTITUTE FOR OCCUPATIONAL SAFETY AND HEALTH AND THE MINE SAFETY AND HEALTH ADMINISTRATION (NIOSH-MSHA).
CHEMICAL CARTRIDGE RESPIRATOR WITH AN ORGANIC VAPOR CARTRIDGE(S) IN COMBINATION WITH A DUST AND MIST FILTER.
GAS MASK WITH ORGANIC VAPOR CANISTER (CHIN-STYLE OR FRONT- OR BACK-MOUNTED CANISTER) WITH A DUST AND MIST FILTER.
GAS MASK WITH ORGANIC VAPOR CANISTER (CHIN-STYLE OR FRONT- OR BACK-MOUNTED CANISTER) WITH A PARTICULATE FILTER.
POWERED AIR-PURIFYING RESPIRATOR WITH A HIGH-EFFICIENCY FILTER.
TYPE 'C' SUPPLIED-AIR RESPIRATOR WITH A FULL FACEPIECE OPERATED IN A PRESSURE-DEMAND OR OTHER POSITIVE PRESSURE MODE.
SELF-CONTAINED BREATHING APPARATUS WITH A FULL FACEPIECE OPERATED IN PRESSURE-DEMAND OR OTHER POSITIVE PRESSURE MODE.
FOR FIREFIGHTING AND OTHER IMMEDIATELY DANGEROUS TO LIFE OR HEALTH CONDITIONS: SELF-CONTAINED BREATHING APPARATUS WITH FULL FACEPIECE OPERATED IN PRESSURE-DEMAND OR OTHER POSITIVE PRESSURE MODE.
SUPPLIED-AIR RESPIRATOR WITH FULL FACEPIECE AND OPERATED IN PRESSURE-DEMAND OR OTHER POSITIVE PRESSURE MODE IN COMBINATION WITH AN AUXILIARY SELF-CONTAINED BREATHING APPARATUS OPERATED IN PRESSURE-DEMAND OR OTHER POSITIVE PRESSURE MODE.
CLOTHING: EMPLOYEE MUST WEAR APPROPRIATE PROTECTIVE (IMPERVIOUS) CLOTHING AND EQUIPMENT TO PREVENT REPEATED OR PROLONGED SKIN CONTACT WITH THIS SUBSTANCE.
GLOVES: EMPLOYEE MUST WEAR APPROPRIATE PROTECTIVE GLOVES TO PREVENT CONTACT WITH THIS SUBSTANCE.
EYE PROTECTION: EMPLOYEE MUST WEAR SPLASH-PROOF OR DUST-RESISTANT SAFETY GOGGLES TO PREVENT EYE CONTACT WITH THIS SUBSTANCE.
EMERGENCY EYE WASH: WHERE THERE IS ANY POSSIBILITY THAT AN EMPLOYEE'S EYES MAY BE EXPOSED TO THIS SUBSTANCE, THE EMPLOYER SHOULD PROVIDE AN EYE WASH FOUNTAIN WITHIN THE IMMEDIATE WORK AREA FOR EMERGENCY USE.

AUTHORIZED BY- OCCUPATIONAL HEALTH SERVICES, INC.
CREATION DATE: 10/04/89 ***REVISION DATE:*** 05/31/90

MATERIAL SAFETY DATA SHEET

OCCUPATIONAL HEALTH SERVICES, INC.
AGRICULTURE AND PESTICIDE DIVISION
450 SEVENTH AVENUE, SUITE 2407
NEW YORK, NEW YORK 10123
1-800-445-MSDS OR (212) 967-1100

EMERGENCY CONTACT:
JOHN S. BRANSFORD, JR. (615) 292-1180

SUBSTANCE IDENTIFICATION

***SUBSTANCE:* (-)-CIS-RESMETHRIN**
TRADE NAMES/SYNONYMS: 2,2-DIMETHYL-3-(2-METHYLPROPENYL)-CYCLOPROPANECARBOXYLIC ACID, (5-BENZYL-3-FURYL)METHYL ESTER, (+)-(Z)-; PST20097
CHEMICAL FAMILY: PYRETHROID (SYNTHETIC)
MOLECULAR FORMULA: C22-H26-O3
MOLECULAR WEIGHT: 338.48
CERCLA RATINGS (SCALE 0-3): HEALTH=2 FIRE=U REACTIVITY=0 PERSISTENCE=2
NFPA RATINGS (SCALE 0-4): HEALTH=2 FIRE=U REACTIVITY=0

COMPONENTS AND CONTAMINANTS

COMPONENT: (-)-CIS-RESMETHRIN ***PERCENT:*** 100.0
OTHER CONTAMINANTS: NONE
EXPOSURE LIMITS: NO OCCUPATIONAL EXPOSURE LIMITS ESTABLISHED BY OSHA, ACGIH, OR NIOSH.

PHYSICAL DATA

DESCRIPTION: WAXY OFF-WHITE TO TAN SOLID WITH A CHARACTERISTIC CHRYSANTHEMATE ODOR
SPECIFIC GRAVITY: NOT AVAILABLE ***SOLUBILITY IN WATER:*** INSOLUBLE
SOLVENT SOLUBILITY: KEROSENE, XYLENE, METHYLENE CHLORIDE, ISOPROPYL ALCOHOL, AROMATIC PETROLEUM HYDROCARBONS

FIRE AND EXPLOSION DATA

FIRE AND EXPLOSION HAZARD: UNKNOWN FIRE AND EXPLOSION HAZARD.
FIREFIGHTING MEDIA: DRY CHEMICAL, CARBON DIOXIDE, WATER SPRAY OR FOAM FOR LARGER FIRES, USE WATER SPRAY, FOG OR ALCOHOL FOAM
FIREFIGHTING: MOVE CONTAINER FROM FIRE AREA IF POSSIBLE. DO NOT SCATTER SPILLED MATERIAL WITH HIGH PRESSURE WATER STREAMS. DIKE FIRE CONTROL WATER FOR LATER DISPOSAL (1987 EMERGENCY RESPONSE GUIDEBOOK, DOT P 5800.4, GUIDE PAGE 31).
USE AGENTS SUITABLE FOR TYPE OF SURROUNDING FIRE. AVOID BREATHING HAZARDOUS VAPORS, KEEP UPWIND.

TOXICITY

(-)-CIS-RESMETHRIN: 3700 MG/KG ORAL-MOUSE LD50; CARCINOGEN STATUS: NONE. (-)-CIS-RESMETHRIN IS A CENTRAL NERVOUS SYSTEM STIMULANT IN ANIMALS.

HEALTH EFFECTS AND FIRST AID

INHALATION: (-)-CIS-RESMETHRIN: **ACUTE EXPOSURE-** (-)-CIS-RESMETHRIN IS A SYNTHETIC PYRETHRIN. SYNTHETIC PYRETHRINS, LIKE THE NATURAL PYRETHRINS, PRODUCE CENTRAL NERVOUS SYSTEM STIMULATION IN ANIMALS WITH SYMPTOMS OF NAUSEA, VOMITING, GASTROENTERITIS WITH DIARRHEA, HYPERSENSITIVITY, INCOORDINATION, TREMORS, MUSCULAR PARALYSIS, CONVULSION, COMA, AND DEATH DUE TO RESPIRATORY FAILURE. UNLIKE NATURAL PYRETHRINS, SYNTHETIC PYRETHRINS NORMALLY DO NOT PRODUCE ALLERGIC REACTIONS IN HUMANS. **CHRONIC EXPOSURE-** NO DATA AVAILABLE.

FIRST AID- REMOVE FROM EXPOSURE AREA TO FRESH AIR IMMEDIATELY. IF BREATHING HAS STOPPED, PERFORM ARTIFICIAL RESPIRATION. KEEP PERSON WARM AND AT REST. TREAT SYMPTOMATICALLY AND SUPPORTIVELY. GET MEDICAL ATTENTION IMMEDIATELY.

SKIN CONTACT: (-)-CIS-RESMETHRIN: **ACUTE EXPOSURE-** (-)-CIS-RESMETHRIN IS A SYNTHETIC PYRETHRIN. SYNTHETIC PYRETHRINS GENERALLY ARE NOT IRRITANTS TO RABBIT SKIN AND THE TOXICITY FROM DERMAL ABSORPTION IS USUALLY MODERATE TO LOW. UNLIKE NATURAL PYRETHRINS, SYNTHETIC PYRETHRINS NORMALLY DO NOT PRODUCE ALLERGIC REACTIONS IN HUMANS. HOWEVER, THERE HAVE BEEN SOME REPORTS OF CUTANEOUS PARESTHESIAS AMONG INDIVIDUALS OCCUPATIONALLY EXPOSED TO SYNTHETIC PYRETHRINS. THESE INDIVIDUALS COMPLAINED OF TINGLING, BURNING AND STINGING SENSATIONS ON THE EXPOSED SURFACE OF THE SKIN BEGINNING FROM 30 MINUTES TO 3 HOURS AFTER EXPOSURE. THE DURATION OF SYMPTOMS VARIED FROM 30 MINUTES TO 8 HOURS. **CHRONIC EXPOSURE-** NO DATA AVAILABLE.

FIRST AID- REMOVE CONTAMINATED CLOTHING AND SHOES IMMEDIATELY. WASH AFFECTED AREA WITH SOAP OR MILD DETERGENT AND LARGE AMOUNTS OF WATER UNTIL NO EVIDENCE OF CHEMICAL REMAINS (APPROXIMATELY 15-20 MINUTES). GET MEDICAL ATTENTION IMMEDIATELY.

EYE CONTACT: (-)-CIS-RESMETHRIN: **ACUTE EXPOSURE-** SYNTHETIC PYRETHRINS ARE NOT IRRITANTS OF RABBIT EYES. **CHRONIC EXPOSURE-** NO DATA AVAILABLE.

FIRST AID- WASH EYES IMMEDIATELY WITH LARGE AMOUNTS OF WATER OR NORMAL SALINE, OCCASIONALLY LIFTING UPPER AND LOWER LIDS, UNTIL NO EVIDENCE OF CHEMICAL REMAINS (APPROXIMATELY 15-20 MINUTES). GET MEDICAL ATTENTION IMMEDIATELY.

INGESTION: (-)-CIS-RESMETHRIN: **ACUTE EXPOSURE-** IN MICE, A MODERATE DOSE OF (-)-CIS-RESMETHRIN WAS LETHAL. (-)-CIS-RESMETHRIN IS A SYNTHETIC PYRETHRIN. SYNTHETIC PYRETHRINS, LIKE THE NATURAL PYRETHRINS, PRODUCE CENTRAL NERVOUS SYSTEM STIMULATION IN ANIMALS WITH SYMPTOMS OF NAUSEA, VOMITING, GASTROENTERITIS WITH DIARRHEA, HYPERSENSITIVITY, INCOORDINATION, TREMORS, MUSCULAR PARALYSIS, CONVULSION, COMA, AND DEATH DUE TO RESPIRATORY FAILURE. **CHRONIC EXPOSURE-** INCREASED LIVER AND KIDNEY WEIGHTS WERE NOTED IN ANIMALS CHRONICALLY FED SYNTHETIC PYRETHRINS.

FIRST AID- TREAT SYMPTOMATICALLY AND SUPPORTIVELY. GET MEDICAL ATTENTION IMMEDIATELY. IF VOMITING OCCURS, KEEP HEAD LOWER THAN HIPS TO PREVENT ASPIRATION.

ANTIDOTE: NO SPECIFIC ANTIDOTE. TREAT SYMPTOMATICALLY AND SUPPORTIVELY.

REACTIVITY

REACTIVITY: MAY DECOMPOSE UPON EXPOSURE TO HEAT OR LIGHT.

INCOMPATIBILITIES: (-)-CIS-RESMETHRIN: NO DATA AVAILABLE.

DECOMPOSITION: THERMAL DECOMPOSITION MAY RELEASE TOXIC AND/OR HAZARDOUS GASES.

POLYMERIZATION: HAZARDOUS POLYMERIZATION HAS NOT BEEN REPORTED TO OCCUR UNDER NORMAL TEMPERATURES AND PRESSURES.

STORAGE AND DISPOSAL

OBSERVE ALL FEDERAL, STATE AND LOCAL REGULATIONS WHEN STORING OR DISPOSING OF THIS SUBSTANCE. FOR ASSISTANCE, CONTACT THE DISTRICT DIRECTOR OF THE ENVIRONMENTAL PROTECTION AGENCY.

****STORAGE****

STORE IN ACCORDANCE WITH 40 CFR 165 RECOMMENDED PROCEDURES FOR THE DISPOSAL AND STORAGE OF PESTICIDES AND PESTICIDE CONTAINERS.

****DISPOSAL****

DISPOSAL MUST BE IN ACCORDANCE WITH 40 CFR 165 RECOMMENDED PROCEDURES FOR THE DISPOSAL AND STORAGE OF PESTICIDES AND PESTICIDE CONTAINERS.

CONDITIONS TO AVOID

MAY BURN BUT DOES NOT IGNITE READILY. AVOID CONTACT WITH STRONG OXIDIZERS, EXCESSIVE HEAT, SPARKS, OR OPEN FLAME.

SPILL AND LEAK PROCEDURES

OCCUPATIONAL SPILL: SWEEP UP AND PLACE IN SUITABLE CLEAN, DRY CONTAINERS FOR RECLAMATION OR LATER DISPOSAL. DO NOT FLUSH SPILLED MATERIAL INTO SEWER. KEEP UNNECESSARY PEOPLE AWAY.

PROTECTIVE EQUIPMENT

VENTILATION: PROVIDE LOCAL EXHAUST OR PROCESS ENCLOSURE VENTILATION SYSTEM.

RESPIRATOR: THE FOLLOWING RESPIRATORS ARE RECOMMENDED BASED ON INFORMATION FOUND IN THE PHYSICAL DATA, TOXICITY AND HEALTH EFFECTS SECTIONS. THEY ARE RANKED IN ORDER FROM MINIMUM TO MAXIMUM RESPIRATORY PROTECTION. THE SPECIFIC RESPIRATOR SELECTED MUST BE BASED ON CONTAMINATION LEVELS FOUND IN THE WORK PLACE, MUST NOT EXCEED THE WORKING LIMITS OF THE RESPIRATOR AND BE JOINTLY APPROVED BY THE NATIONAL INSTITUTE FOR OCCUPATIONAL SAFETY AND HEALTH AND THE MINE SAFETY AND HEALTH ADMINISTRATION (NIOSH-MSHA).

CHEMICAL CARTRIDGE RESPIRATOR WITH AN ORGANIC VAPOR CARTRIDGE(S) IN COMBINATION WITH A DUST AND MIST FILTER.

GAS MASK WITH ORGANIC VAPOR CANISTER (CHIN-STYLE OR FRONT- OR BACK-MOUNTED CANISTER) WITH A DUST AND MIST FILTER.

GAS MASK WITH ORGANIC VAPOR CANISTER (CHIN-STYLE OR FRONT- OR BACK-MOUNTED CANISTER) WITH A PARTICULATE FILTER.

POWERED AIR-PURIFYING RESPIRATOR WITH A HIGH-EFFICIENCY FILTER.

TYPE 'C' SUPPLIED-AIR RESPIRATOR WITH A FULL FACEPIECE OPERATED IN A PRESSURE-DEMAND OR OTHER POSITIVE PRESSURE MODE.

SELF-CONTAINED BREATHING APPARATUS WITH A FULL FACEPIECE OPERATED IN PRESSURE-DEMAND OR OTHER POSITIVE PRESSURE MODE.

FOR FIREFIGHTING AND OTHER IMMEDIATELY DANGEROUS TO LIFE OR HEALTH CONDITIONS:

SELF-CONTAINED BREATHING APPARATUS WITH FULL FACEPIECE OPERATED IN PRESSURE-DEMAND OR OTHER POSITIVE PRESSURE MODE.

SUPPLIED-AIR RESPIRATOR WITH FULL FACEPIECE AND OPERATED IN PRESSURE-DEMAND OR OTHER POSITIVE PRESSURE MODE IN COMBINATION WITH AN AUXILIARY SELF-CONTAINED BREATHING APPARATUS OPERATED IN PRESSURE-DEMAND OR OTHER POSITIVE PRESSURE MODE.

CLOTHING: EMPLOYEE MUST WEAR APPROPRIATE PROTECTIVE (IMPERVIOUS) CLOTHING AND EQUIPMENT TO PREVENT REPEATED OR PROLONGED SKIN CONTACT WITH THIS SUBSTANCE.

GLOVES: EMPLOYEE MUST WEAR APPROPRIATE PROTECTIVE GLOVES TO PREVENT CONTACT WITH THIS SUBSTANCE.

EYE PROTECTION: EMPLOYEE MUST WEAR SPLASH-PROOF OR DUST-RESISTANT SAFETY GOGGLES TO PREVENT EYE CONTACT WITH THIS SUBSTANCE.

EMERGENCY EYE WASH: WHERE THERE IS ANY POSSIBILITY THAT AN EMPLOYEE'S EYES MAY BE EXPOSED TO THIS SUBSTANCE, THE EMPLOYER SHOULD PROVIDE AN EYE WASH FOUNTAIN WITHIN THE IMMEDIATE WORK AREA FOR EMERGENCY USE.

AUTHORIZED BY- OCCUPATIONAL HEALTH SERVICES, INC.

CREATION DATE: 02/08/90 ***REVISION DATE:*** 05/31/90

MATERIAL SAFETY DATA SHEET

OCCUPATIONAL HEALTH SERVICES, INC.
AGRICULTURE AND PESTICIDE DIVISION
450 SEVENTH AVENUE, SUITE 2407
NEW YORK, NEW YORK 10123
1-800-445-MSDS OR (212) 967-1100

EMERGENCY CONTACT:
JOHN S. BRANSFORD, JR. (615) 292-1180

SUBSTANCE IDENTIFICATION

CAS-NUMBER 33911-28-3

SUBSTANCE: **(-)-TRANS-RESMETHRIN**

TRADE NAMES/SYNONYMS: 2,2-DIMETHYL-3-(2-METHYL-1-PROPENYL)-CYCLOPROPANECARBOXYLIC ACID, (5-(PHENYLMETHYL)-3-FURANYL)METHYL ESTER, TRANS-(-)-; 2,2-DIMETHYL-3-(2-METHYLPROPENYL)-CYCLOPROPANECARBOXYLIC ACID, (5-BENZYL-3-FURYL) METHYL ESTER, TRANS-(-)-; PST20098

CHEMICAL FAMILY: PYRETHROID (SYNTHETIC)

MOLECULAR FORMULA: C22-H26-O3

MOLECULAR WEIGHT: 338.48

CERCLA RATINGS (SCALE 0-3): HEALTH=3 FIRE=U REACTIVITY=0 PERSISTENCE=2

NFPA RATINGS (SCALE 0-4): HEALTH=3 FIRE=U REACTIVITY=0

COMPONENTS AND CONTAMINANTS

COMPONENT: (-)-TRANS-RESMETHRIN ***PERCENT:*** 100.0
CAS# 33911-28-3

OTHER CONTAMINANTS: NONE

EXPOSURE LIMITS: NO OCCUPATIONAL EXPOSURE LIMITS ESTABLISHED BY OSHA, ACGIH, OR NIOSH.

PHYSICAL DATA

DESCRIPTION: WAXY OFF-WHITE TO TAN SOLID WITH A CHARACTERISTIC CHRYSANTHEMATE ODOR

SPECIFIC GRAVITY: NOT AVAILABLE ***SOLUBILITY IN WATER:*** INSOLUBLE

SOLVENT SOLUBILITY: KEROSENE, XYLENE, METHYLENE CHLORIDE, ISOPROPYL ALCOHOL, AROMATIC PETROLEUM HYDROCARBONS

FIRE AND EXPLOSION DATA

FIRE AND EXPLOSION HAZARD: UNKNOWN FIRE AND EXPLOSION HAZARD.

FIREFIGHTING MEDIA: DRY CHEMICAL, CARBON DIOXIDE, WATER SPRAY OR FOAM FOR LARGER FIRES, USE WATER SPRAY, FOG OR ALCOHOL FOAM

FIREFIGHTING: MOVE CONTAINER FROM FIRE AREA IF POSSIBLE. DO NOT SCATTER SPILLED MATERIAL WITH HIGH PRESSURE WATER STREAMS. DIKE FIRE CONTROL WATER FOR LATER DISPOSAL (1987 EMERGENCY RESPONSE GUIDEBOOK, DOT P 5800.4, GUIDE PAGE 31).
USE AGENTS SUITABLE FOR TYPE OF SURROUNDING FIRE. AVOID BREATHING HAZARDOUS VAPORS, KEEP UPWIND.

TOXICITY

(-)-TRANS-RESMETHRIN: TOXICITY DATA: 500 MG/KG ORAL-MOUSE LD50.
CARCINOGEN STATUS: NONE. ACUTE TOXICITY LEVEL: TOXIC BY INGESTION.
TARGET EFFECTS: POISONING MAY AFFECT THE CENTRAL NERVOUS SYSTEM.

HEALTH EFFECTS AND FIRST AID

INHALATION: (-)-TRANS-RESMETHRIN: **ACUTE EXPOSURE-** (-)-TRANS-RESMETHRIN IS A SYNTHETIC PYRETHRIN. SYNTHETIC PYRETHRINS, LIKE THE NATURAL PYRETHRINS, PRODUCE CENTRAL NERVOUS SYSTEM STIMULATION IN ANIMALS WITH SYMPTOMS OF NAUSEA, VOMITING, GASTROENTERITIS WITH DIARRHEA, HYPERSENSITIVITY, INCOORDINATION, TREMORS, MUSCULAR PARALYSIS, CONVULSION, COMA, AND DEATH DUE TO RESPIRATORY FAILURE. UNLIKE NATURAL PYRETHRINS, SYNTHETIC PYRETHRINS NORMALLY DO NOT PRODUCE ALLERGIC REACTIONS IN HUMANS. **CHRONIC EXPOSURE-** NO DATA AVAILABLE.

FIRST AID- REMOVE FROM EXPOSURE AREA TO FRESH AIR IMMEDIATELY. IF BREATHING HAS STOPPED, PERFORM ARTIFICIAL RESPIRATION. KEEP PERSON WARM AND AT REST. TREAT SYMPTOMATICALLY AND SUPPORTIVELY. GET MEDICAL ATTENTION IMMEDIATELY.

SKIN CONTACT: (-)-TRANS-RESMETHRIN: **ACUTE EXPOSURE-** (-)-TRANS-RESMETHRIN IS A SYNTHETIC PYRETHRIN. SYNTHETIC PYRETHRINS GENERALLY ARE NOT IRRITANTS TO RABBIT SKIN AND THE TOXICITY FROM DERMAL ABSORPTION IS USUALLY MODERATE TO LOW. UNLIKE NATURAL PYRETHRINS, SYNTHETIC PYRETHRINS NORMALLY DO NOT PRODUCE ALLERGIC REACTIONS IN HUMANS. HOWEVER, THERE HAVE BEEN SOME REPORTS OF CUTANEOUS PARESTHESIAS AMONG INDIVIDUALS OCCUPATIONALLY EXPOSED TO SYNTHETIC PYRETHRINS. THESE INDIVIDUALS COMPLAINED OF TINGLING, BURNING AND STINGING SENSATIONS ON THE EXPOSED SURFACE OF THE SKIN BEGINNING FROM 30 MINUTES TO 3 HOURS AFTER EXPOSURE. THE DURATION OF SYMPTOMS VARIED FROM 30 MINUTES TO 8 HOURS. **CHRONIC EXPOSURE-** NO DATA AVAILABLE.

FIRST AID- REMOVE CONTAMINATED CLOTHING AND SHOES IMMEDIATELY. WASH AFFECTED AREA WITH SOAP OR MILD DETERGENT AND LARGE AMOUNTS OF WATER UNTIL NO EVIDENCE OF CHEMICAL REMAINS (APPROXIMATELY 15-20 MINUTES). GET MEDICAL ATTENTION IMMEDIATELY.

EYE CONTACT: (-)-TRANS-RESMETHRIN: **ACUTE EXPOSURE-** SYNTHETIC PYRETHRINS ARE NOT IRRITANTS OF RABBIT EYES. **CHRONIC EXPOSURE-** NO DATA AVAILABLE.

FIRST AID- WASH EYES IMMEDIATELY WITH LARGE AMOUNTS OF WATER OR NORMAL SALINE, OCCASIONALLY LIFTING UPPER AND LOWER LIDS, UNTIL NO EVIDENCE OF CHEMICAL REMAINS (APPROXIMATELY 15-20 MINUTES). GET MEDICAL ATTENTION IMMEDIATELY.

INGESTION: (-)-TRANS-RESMETHRIN: TOXIC. **ACUTE EXPOSURE-** A LOW DOSE OF (-)-TRANS-RESMETHRIN WAS LETHAL IN MICE. (-)-TRANS-RESMETHRIN IS A SYNTHETIC PYRETHRIN. SYNTHETIC PYRETHRINS, LIKE THE NATURAL PYRETHRINS, PRODUCE CENTRAL NERVOUS SYSTEM STIMULATION IN ANIMALS WITH SYMPTOMS OF NAUSEA, VOMITING, GASTROENTERITIS WITH DIARRHEA, HYPERSENSITIVITY, INCOORDINATION, TREMORS, MUSCULAR PARALYSIS, CONVULSION, COMA, AND DEATH DUE TO RESPIRATORY FAILURE. **CHRONIC EXPOSURE-** INCREASED LIVER AND KIDNEY WEIGHTS WERE NOTED IN ANIMALS CHRONICALLY FED SYNTHETIC PYRETHRINS.

FIRST AID- IF EXTENSIVE VOMITING HAS NOT OCCURRED, THE SUBSTANCE SHOULD BE REMOVED BY EMESIS OR GASTRIC LAVAGE PROVIDED THAT THE PATIENT IS CONSCIOUS AND CONVULSIONS ARE NOT PRESENT. KEEP HEAD BELOW HIPS DURING VOMITING TO PREVENT ASPIRATION. DO NOT ATTEMPT TO MAKE AN UNCONSCIOUS PERSON VOMIT. TREAT SYMPTOMATICALLY AND SUPPORTIVELY. GET MEDICAL ATTENTION IMMEDIATELY (DREISBACH, HANDBOOK OF POISONING, 12TH ED.). TREATMENT SHOULD BE PERFORMED BY QUALIFIED MEDICAL PERSONNEL.

ANTIDOTE: NO SPECIFIC ANTIDOTE. TREAT SYMPTOMATICALLY AND SUPPORTIVELY.

REACTIVITY

REACTIVITY: MAY DECOMPOSE UPON EXPOSURE TO HEAT OR LIGHT.

INCOMPATIBILITIES: (-)-TRANS-RESMETHRIN: NO DATA AVAILABLE.

DECOMPOSITION: THERMAL DECOMPOSITION MAY RELEASE TOXIC AND/OR HAZARDOUS GASES.

POLYMERIZATION: HAZARDOUS POLYMERIZATION HAS NOT BEEN REPORTED TO OCCUR UNDER NORMAL TEMPERATURES AND PRESSURES.

STORAGE AND DISPOSAL

OBSERVE ALL FEDERAL, STATE AND LOCAL REGULATIONS WHEN STORING OR DISPOSING OF THIS SUBSTANCE. FOR ASSISTANCE, CONTACT THE DISTRICT DIRECTOR OF THE ENVIRONMENTAL PROTECTION AGENCY.

****STORAGE****

STORE IN ACCORDANCE WITH 40 CFR 165 RECOMMENDED PROCEDURES FOR THE DISPOSAL AND STORAGE OF PESTICIDES AND PESTICIDE CONTAINERS.

****DISPOSAL****

DISPOSAL MUST BE IN ACCORDANCE WITH 40 CFR 165 RECOMMENDED PROCEDURES FOR THE DISPOSAL AND STORAGE OF PESTICIDES AND PESTICIDE CONTAINERS.

CONDITIONS TO AVOID

MAY BURN BUT DOES NOT IGNITE READILY. AVOID CONTACT WITH STRONG OXIDIZERS, EXCESSIVE HEAT, SPARKS, OR OPEN FLAME.

SPILL AND LEAK PROCEDURES

OCCUPATIONAL SPILL: SWEEP UP AND PLACE IN SUITABLE CLEAN, DRY CONTAINERS FOR RECLAMATION OR LATER DISPOSAL. DO NOT FLUSH SPILLED MATERIAL INTO SEWER. KEEP UNNECESSARY PEOPLE AWAY.

PROTECTIVE EQUIPMENT

VENTILATION: PROVIDE LOCAL EXHAUST OR PROCESS ENCLOSURE VENTILATION SYSTEM.

RESPIRATOR: THE FOLLOWING RESPIRATORS ARE RECOMMENDED BASED ON INFORMATION FOUND IN THE PHYSICAL DATA, TOXICITY AND HEALTH EFFECTS SECTIONS. THEY ARE RANKED IN ORDER FROM MINIMUM TO MAXIMUM RESPIRATORY PROTECTION. THE SPECIFIC RESPIRATOR SELECTED MUST BE BASED ON CONTAMINATION LEVELS FOUND IN THE WORK PLACE, MUST NOT EXCEED THE WORKING LIMITS OF THE RESPIRATOR AND BE JOINTLY APPROVED BY THE NATIONAL INSTITUTE FOR OCCUPATIONAL SAFETY AND HEALTH AND THE MINE SAFETY AND HEALTH ADMINISTRATION (NIOSH-MSHA).
CHEMICAL CARTRIDGE RESPIRATOR WITH AN ORGANIC VAPOR CARTRIDGE(S) IN COMBINATION WITH A DUST AND MIST FILTER.
GAS MASK WITH ORGANIC VAPOR CANISTER (CHIN-STYLE OR FRONT- OR BACK-MOUNTED CANISTER) WITH A DUST AND MIST FILTER.
GAS MASK WITH ORGANIC VAPOR CANISTER (CHIN-STYLE OR FRONT- OR BACK-MOUNTED CANISTER) WITH A PARTICULATE FILTER.
POWERED AIR-PURIFYING RESPIRATOR WITH A HIGH-EFFICIENCY FILTER.
TYPE 'C' SUPPLIED-AIR RESPIRATOR WITH A FULL FACEPIECE OPERATED IN A PRESSURE-DEMAND OR OTHER POSITIVE PRESSURE MODE.
SELF-CONTAINED BREATHING APPARATUS WITH A FULL FACEPIECE OPERATED IN PRESSURE-DEMAND OR OTHER POSITIVE PRESSURE MODE. FOR FIREFIGHTING AND OTHER IMMEDIATELY DANGEROUS TO LIFE OR HEALTH CONDITIONS:
SELF-CONTAINED BREATHING APPARATUS WITH FULL FACEPIECE OPERATED IN PRESSURE-DEMAND OR OTHER POSITIVE PRESSURE MODE.
SUPPLIED-AIR RESPIRATOR WITH FULL FACEPIECE AND OPERATED IN PRESSURE-DEMAND OR OTHER POSITIVE PRESSURE MODE IN COMBINATION WITH AN AUXILIARY SELF-CONTAINED BREATHING APPARATUS OPERATED IN PRESSURE-DEMAND OR OTHER POSITIVE PRESSURE MODE.

CLOTHING: EMPLOYEE MUST WEAR APPROPRIATE PROTECTIVE (IMPERVIOUS) CLOTHING AND EQUIPMENT TO PREVENT REPEATED OR PROLONGED SKIN CONTACT WITH THIS SUBSTANCE.

GLOVES: EMPLOYEE MUST WEAR APPROPRIATE PROTECTIVE GLOVES TO PREVENT CONTACT WITH THIS SUBSTANCE.

EYE PROTECTION: EMPLOYEE MUST WEAR SPLASH-PROOF OR DUST-RESISTANT SAFETY GOGGLES TO PREVENT EYE CONTACT WITH THIS SUBSTANCE.
EMERGENCY EYE WASH: WHERE THERE IS ANY POSSIBILITY THAT AN EMPLOYEE'S EYES MAY BE EXPOSED TO THIS SUBSTANCE, THE EMPLOYER SHOULD PROVIDE AN EYE WASH FOUNTAIN WITHIN THE IMMEDIATE WORK AREA FOR EMERGENCY USE.

AUTHORIZED BY- OCCUPATIONAL HEALTH SERVICES, INC.
CREATION DATE: 02/08/90 ***REVISION DATE:*** 05/31/90

MATERIAL SAFETY DATA SHEET

OCCUPATIONAL HEALTH SERVICES, INC.
AGRICULTURE AND PESTICIDE DIVISION
450 SEVENTH AVENUE, SUITE 2407
NEW YORK, NEW YORK 10123
1-800-445-MSDS OR (212) 967-1100

EMERGENCY CONTACT:
JOHN S. BRANSFORD, JR. (615) 292-1180

SUBSTANCE IDENTIFICATION

CAS-NUMBER 299-84-3

SUBSTANCE: **RONNEL**

TRADE NAMES/SYNONYMS: PHOSPHOROTHIOIC ACID, O,O-DIMETHYL O-(2,4,5-TRICHLOROPHENYL)ESTER; O,O-DIMETHYL O-2,4,5-TRICHLOROPHENYL PHOSPHOROTHIOATE; O,O-DIMETHYL O-(2,4,5-TRICHLOROPHENYL) PHOSPHOROTHIOATE; DIMETHYL 2,4,5-TRICHLOROPHENYL PHOSPHOROTHIONATE; DIMETHYL TRICHLOROPHENYL THIOPHOSPHATE; ECTORAL; ETROLENE; FENCHLORFOS; FENCHLORPHOS; FENCHLOFOS; KORLAN; NANKOR; TRICHLORMETAPHOS; TRICHLOROMETAPHOS; TROLENE; VIOZENE; OMS 123; ENT 23284; C8H8CL3O3PS; PST20180

CHEMICAL FAMILY: ORGANOPHOSPHATE

MOLECULAR FORMULA: C8-H8-CL3-O3-P-S

MOLECULAR WEIGHT: 321.57

CERCLA RATINGS (SCALE 0-3): HEALTH=3 FIRE=0 REACTIVITY=3 PERSISTENCE=3

NFPA RATINGS (SCALE 0-4): HEALTH=3 FIRE=0 REACTIVITY=3

COMPONENTS AND CONTAMINANTS

COMPONENT: RONNEL ***PERCENT:*** 100
CAS# 299-84-3

OTHER CONTAMINANTS: MAY CONTAIN <0.2-0.5 PPM 2,3,7,8 -TETRACHLORODIBENZODIOXIN

EXPOSURE LIMITS: RONNEL: 10 MG/M3 OSHA TWA 10 MG/M3 ACGIH TWA

PHYSICAL DATA

DESCRIPTION: WHITE CRYSTALLINE POWDER ***BOILING POINT:*** 207 F (97 C) @ 0.01 MMHG

MELTING POINT: 104-108 F (40-42 C) ***SPECIFIC GRAVITY:*** 1.4850

VAPOR PRESSURE: 0.008 MMHG @ 25 C ***SOLUBILITY IN WATER:*** 0.0044% @ 25 C

SOLVENT SOLUBILITY: SOLUBLE IN ACETONE, CARBON TETRACHLORIDE, ETHER, TOLUENE, METHYLENE CHLORIDE, KEROSENE, CHLOROBENZENE, CHLOROFORM, DIETHY ETHER, METHANOL, STODDARD SOLVENT, XYLENE AND MOST ORGANIC SOLVENTS

FIRE AND EXPLOSION DATA

FIRE AND EXPLOSION HAZARD: NEGLIGIBLE FIRE HAZARD WHEN EXPOSED TO HEAT OR FLAME.

FIREFIGHTING MEDIA: DRY CHEMICAL, CARBON DIOXIDE, HALON, WATER SPRAY OR STANDARD FOAM (1987 EMERGENCY RESPONSE GUIDEBOOK, DOT P 5800.4). FOR LARGER FIRES, USE WATER SPRAY, FOG OR STANDARD FOAM (1987 EMERGENCY RESPONSE GUIDEBOOK, DOT P 5800.4).

FIREFIGHTING: MOVE CONTAINERS FROM FIRE AREA IF POSSIBLE. FIGHT FIRE FROM MAXIMUM DISTANCE. STAY AWAY FROM STORAGE TANK ENDS. DIKE FIRE CONTROL WATER FOR LATER DISPOSAL. DO NOT SCATTER MATERIAL (1987 EMERGENCY RESPONSE GUIDEBOOK, DOT P 5800.4, GUIDE PAGE 55).

TOXICITY

RONNEL: TOXICITY DATA: 1 GM/KG SKIN-RABBIT LD50; 2000 MG/KG SKIN-RAT LD50; 2000 MG/KG SKIN-GUINEA PIG LD50; 625 MG/KG ORAL-RAT LD50; 2000 MG/KG ORAL-MOUSE LD50; 1400 MG/KG ORAL-GUINEA PIG LD50; 420 MG/KG ORAL-RABBIT LD50; 500 MG/KG ORAL-DOG LD50; 1 GM/KG ORAL-DOMESTIC ANIMAL LDLO; 1380 MG/KG SUBCUTANEOUS-RAT LD50; 2823 MG/KG INTRAPERITONEAL-RAT LD50; 118 MG/KG INTRAPERITONEAL-MOUSE LD50; 400 MG/KG UNREPORTED-MAMMAL LD50; MUTAGENIC DATA (RTECS); REPRODUCTIVE EFFECTS DATA (RTECS). CARCINOGEN STATUS: NONE. ACUTE TOXICITY LEVEL: TOXIC BY DERMAL ABSORPTION; MODERATELY TOXIC BY INGESTION. TARGET EFFECTS: CHOLINESTERASE INHIBITOR. POISONING MAY AFFECT THE NERVOUS SYSTEM.* AT INCREASED RISK FROM EXPOSURE: PERSONS WITH RESPIRATORY AILMENTS, RECENT EXPOSURE TO CHOLINESTERASE INHIBITORS OR IMPAIRED CHOLINESTERASE PRODUCTION, OR LIVER MALFUNCTION.* ADDITIONAL DATA: MAY CROSS THE PLACENTA. HIGH ENVIRONMENTAL TEMPERATURES OR EXPOSURE OF THE CHEMICAL TO VISIBLE OR ULTRAVIOLET LIGHT MAY ENHANCE THE TOXICITY. INTERACTIONS WITH MEDICATIONS MAY OCCUR.*
* MAY BE BASED ON GENERAL INFORMATION ON ORGANOPHOSPHATES.

HEALTH EFFECTS AND FIRST AID

INHALATION: RONNEL: 5000 MG/M3 IMMEDIATELY DANGEROUS TO LIFE OR DEATH SEE INFORMATION ON ORGANOPHOSPHATES.
ORGANOPHOSPHATES: CHOLINESTERASE INHIBITOR. **ACUTE EXPOSURE-** WHEN INHALED, THE FIRST EFFECTS OF CHOLINESTERASE INHIBITORS ARE USUALLY RESPIRATORY AND MAY INCLUDE NASAL HYPEREMIA AND WATERY DISCHARGE, COUGH, CHEST DISCOMFORT, DYSPNEA, AND WHEEZING DUE TO INCREASED BRONCHIAL SECRETIONS AND BRONCHOCONSTRICTION. IF SUFFICIENT AMOUNTS ARE ABSORBED, OTHER SYSTEMIC EFFECTS MAY BEGIN WITHIN A FEW MINUTES OR BE DELAYED FOR UP TO 12 HOURS. SYMPTOMS MAY INCLUDE PALLOR, NAUSEA, VOMITING, DIARRHEA, ABDOMINAL CRAMPS, HEADACHE, DIZZINESS, OCULAR PAIN, BLURRED VISION, MIOSIS OR IN SOME CASES, ESPECIALLY INITIALLY, MYDRIASIS, LACRIMATION, SALIVATION, SWEATING, AND CONFUSION. OTHER REPORTED CENTRAL NERVOUS SYSTEM OR NEUROMUSCULAR EFFECTS MAY INCLUDE ATAXIA, SLURRED SPEECH, AREFLEXIA, WEAKNESS, FATIGUE, FASCICULATIONS, TWITCHING, TREMORS POSSIBLY OF THE TONGUE AND EYELIDS, AND EVENTUALLY PARALYSIS OF THE EXTREMITIES AND POSSIBLY OF THE RESPIRATORY MUSCLES. IN SEVERE CASES THERE MAY ALSO BE INVOLUNTARY DEFECATION AND URINATION, CYANOSIS, PSYCHOSIS, HYPERGLYCEMIA, ACUTE PANCREATITIS, CARDIAC IRREGULARITIES, PULMONARY EDEMA, UNCONSCIOUSNESS, CONVULSIONS, AND COMA. DEATH IS PRIMARILY DUE TO RESPIRATORY FAILURE, ALTHOUGH CARDIOVASCULAR EFFECTS INCLUDING CARDIAC ARREST MAY ALSO BE IMPLICATED. LONG TERM SEQUELAE ARE RARE BUT MAY INCLUDE NEUROPSYCHIATRIC DISORDERS AND MYOPATHY WITH MUSCLE TENDERNESS. SOME ORGANOPHOSPHATES MAY CAUSE A DELAYED NEUROPATHY BEGINNING 1-4 WEEKS AFTER AN ACUTE EXPOSURE WHICH MAY OR MAY NOT HAVE CAUSED ACUTE CHOLINERGIC EFFECTS. NUMBNESS, TINGLING, WEAKNESS AND CRAMPING BEGINNING SYMMETRICALLY IN THE LOWER LIMBS MAY PROGRESS TO ATAXIA AND PARALYSIS. IN SEVERE CASES, UPPER LIMB INVOLVEMENT IS POSSIBLE AND FLACCID PARALYSIS MAY PROGRESS TO SPASTIC PARALYSIS WITH EXAGGERATED REFLEXES. IMPROVEMENT MAY OCCUR OVER MONTHS TO YEARS, BUT SOME RESIDUAL IMPAIRMENT USUALLY REMAINS.
CHRONIC EXPOSURE- REPEATED OR PROLONGED EXPOSURE MAY RESULT IN THE EFFECTS OF ACUTE EXPOSURE INCLUDING THE DELAYED NEUROPATHY. OTHER EFFECTS REPORTED IN WORKERS REPEATEDLY EXPOSED INCLUDE IMPAIRED MEMORY AND CONCENTRATION, ACUTE PSYCHOSIS, SEVERE DEPRESSIONS, IRRITABILTY, CONFUSION, APATHY, EMOTIONAL LABILITY, SOCIAL WITHDRAWAL, CONFUSION, HEADACHE, SPEECH DIFFICULTIES, DELAYED REACTION TIMES, SPATIAL DISORIENTATION, NIGHTMARES, SLEEPWALKING, AND DROWSINESS OR INSOMNIA. AN INFLUENZA-LIKE CONDITION WITH HEADACHE, NAUSEA, WEAKNESS, ANOREXIA AND MALAISE HAS ALSO BEEN REPORTED.

FIRST AID- REMOVE FROM EXPOSURE AREA TO FRESH AIR IMMEDIATELY. IF BREATHING HAS STOPPED, GIVE ARTIFICIAL RESPIRATION. MAINTAIN AIRWAY AND BLOOD PRESSURE AND ADMINISTER OXYGEN IF AVAILABLE. KEEP AFFECTED PERSON WARM AND AT REST. TREAT SYMPTOMATICALLY AND SUPPORTIVELY. ADMINISTRATION OF OXYGEN SHOULD BE PERFORMED BY QUALIFIED PERSONNEL. GET MEDICAL ATTENTION IMMEDIATELY.

SKIN CONTACT: RONNEL: TOXIC. SEE INFORMATION ON ORGANOPHOSPHATES.
ORGANOPHOSPHATES: CHOLINESTERASE INHIBITOR. **ACUTE EXPOSURE-** LOCALIZED SWEATING AND FASCICULATIONS MAY OCCUR AT THE SITE OF CONTACT. IF SUFFICIENT AMOUNTS ARE ABSORBED, OTHER EFFECTS OF CHOLINESTERASE INHIBITION AS DESCRIBED IN ACUTE INHALATION MAY OCCUR. SYMPTOMS MAY BE DELAYED 2-3 HOURS, BUT USUALLY NO MORE THAN 12 HOURS. THE RATE OF ABSORPTION IS INCREASED BY THE PRESENCE OF DERMATITIS OR HIGH AMBIENT TEMPERATURES. DELAYED NEUROPATHY IS ALSO POSSIBLE. **CHRONIC EXPOSURE-** REPEATED OR PROLONGED EXPOSURE MAY CAUSE EFFECTS AS DESCRIBED IN ACUTE EXPOSURE. SOME ORGANOPHOSPHATES MAY CAUSE SENSITIZATION.

FIRST AID- REMOVE CONTAMINATED CLOTHING IMMEDIATELY. WASH CONTAMINATED AREAS WITH SOAP AND WATER FOLLOWED BY ALCOHOL (ARENA, POISONING, 4TH ED.). EMERGENCY PERSONNEL SHOULD WEAR GLOVES AND

AVOID CONTAMINATION. TREAT RESPIRATORY DIFFICULTY WITH ARTIFICIAL RESPIRATION. GET MEDICAL ATTENTION IMMEDIATELY.

EYE CONTACT: RONNEL: SEE INFORMATION ON ORGANOPHOSPHATES.
ORGANOPHOSPHATES: CHOLINESTERASE INHIBITOR. **ACUTE EXPOSURE-** DIRECT CONTACT MAY CAUSE PAIN, HYPEREMIA, LACRIMATION, TWITCHING OF THE EYELIDS, MIOSIS, AND CILIARY MUSCLE SPASM WITH LOSS OF ACCOMODATION, BLURRED OR DIMMED VISION AND BROWACHE. SOMETIMES MYDRIASIS MAY OCCUR INSTEAD OF MIOSIS. WITH SUFFICIENT EXPOSURE, OTHER SYMPTOMS OF CHOLINESTERASE INHIBITION AS DESCRIBED IN ACUTE INHALATION MAY OCCUR. **CHRONIC EXPOSURE-** REPEATED OR PROLONGED EXPOSURE MAY CAUSE EFFECTS AS DESCRIBED IN ACUTE EXPOSURE. SOME COMPOUNDS HAVE CAUSED TOXIC EFFECTS ON THE CRYSTALLINE LENS, CONJUNCTIVAL THICKENING AND OBSTRUCTION OF THE NASOLACRIMAL CANALS WHEN USED AS MIOTIC EYEDROPS.

FIRST AID- IRRIGATE EYES WITH WATER OR SALINE SOLUTION. IF SYMPTOMS OF POISONING OCCUR, TREAT RESPIRATORY DIFFICULTY WITH ARTIFICIAL RESPIRATION AND OXYGEN. OBSERVE PATIENT FOR AT LEAST 24-36 HOURS (GOSSELIN, CLINICAL TOXICOLOGY OF COMMERCIAL PRODUCTS, 5TH ED.). GET MEDICAL ATTENTION IMMEDIATELY. OXYGEN SHOULD BE ADMINISTERED BY QUALIFIED MEDICAL PERSONNEL.

INGESTION: RONNEL: LIVER DEGENERATION WAS OBSERVED IN A STUDY OF RATS FED 50 MG/KG/DAY. DECREASED FERTILITY, GESTATION, AND VIABILITY OF OFFSPRING INDICES WERE NOTED IN A THREE-GENERATION STUDY OF RATS. SEE INFORMATION ON ORGANOPHOSPHATES.
ORGANOPHOSPHATES: CHOLINESTERASE INHIBITOR. **ACUTE EXPOSURE-** WHEN INGESTED, THE FIRST EFFECTS MAY BE NAUSEA, VOMITING, ANOREXIA, ABDOMINAL CRAMPS AND DIARRHEA. GASTROINTESTINAL ABSORPTION MAY CAUSE SYMPTOMS OF CHOLINESTERASE INHIBITION AS DESCRIBED IN ACUTE INHALATION. SYMPTOMS MAY BEGIN WITHIN MINUTES OR BE DELAYED FOR HOURS. DELAYED EFFECTS INCLUDING NEUROPATHY MAY ALSO OCCUR. **CHRONIC EXPOSURE-** REPEATED INGESTION MAY CAUSE EFFECTS AS DESCRIBED IN ACUTE EXPOSURE.

FIRST AID- IF PERSON IS ALERT AND RESPIRATION IS NOT DEPRESSED, GIVE SYRUP OF IPECAC FOLLOWED BY WATER (IF VOMITING OCCURS, KEEP HEAD BELOW HIPS TO PREVENT ASPIRATION). IF CONSCIOUSNESS LEVEL DECLINES OR VOMITING HAS NOT OCCURRED IN 15 MINUTES EMPTY STOMACH BY GASTRIC LAVAGE WITH THE AID OF CUFFED ENDOTRACHEAL TUBE USING ISOTONIC SALINE OR 5% SODIUM BICARBONATE FOLLOW WITH ACTIVATED CHARCOAL. ESTABLISH AND MAINTAIN AIRWAY. TREAT RESPIRATORY DIFFICULTY WITH ARTIFICIAL RESPIRATION AND OXYGEN. DO NOT GIVE MORPHINE, AMINOPHYLLINE, PHENOTHIAZINES, RESERPINE, FUROSEMIDE, OR ETHACRYNIC ACID (MORGAN, RECOGNITION AND MANAGEMENT OF PESTICIDE POISONINGS, 3RD ED.). TREAT SYMPTOMATICALLY AND SUPPORTIVELY. ADMINISTRATION OF OXYGEN AND LAVAGE MUST BE PERFORMED BY QUALIFIED MEDICAL PERSONNEL. GET MEDICAL ATTENTION IMMEDIATELY.

ANTIDOTE: THE FOLLOWING ANTIDOTE(S) HAVE BEEN RECOMMENDED. HOWEVER, THE DECISION AS TO WHETHER THE SEVERITY OF POISONING REQUIRES ADMINISTRATION OF ANY ANTIDOTE AND ACTUAL DOSE REQUIRED SHOULD BE MADE BY QUALIFIED MEDICAL PERSONNEL.
FOR CHOLINESTERASE INHIBITORS: ESTABLISH CLEAR AIRWAY AND TISSUE OXYGENATION BY ASPIRATION OF SECRETIONS, AND IF NECESSARY, BY ASSISTED PULMONARY VENTILATION WITH OXYGEN. IMPROVE TISSUE OXYGENATION AS MUCH AS POSSIBLE BEFORE ADMINISTERING ATROPINE TO MINIMIZE THE RISK OF VENTRICULAR FIBRILLATION. ADMINISTER ATROPINE SULFATE INTRAVENOUSLY, OR INTRAMUSCULARLY IF IV INJECTION IS NOT POSSIBLE. IN MODERATELY SEVERE POISONING ADMINISTER ATROPINE SULFATE, 0.4-2.0 MG REPEATED EVERY 15 MINUTES UNTIL ATROPINIZATION IS ACHIEVED (TACHYCARDIA, FLUSHING, DRY MOUTH, MYDRIASIS). MAINTAIN ATROPINIZATION BY REPEATED DOSES FOR 2-12 HOURS, OR LONGER, DEPENDING ON THE SEVERITY OF POISONING. THE APPEARANCE OF RALES IN THE LUNG BASES, MIOSIS, SALIVATION, NAUSEA, BRADYCARDIA, ARE ALL INDICATIONS OF INADEQUATE ATROPINIZATION. SEVERELY POISONED INDIVIDUALS MAY EXHIBIT REMARKABLE TOLERANCE TO ATROPINE; TWO OR MORE TIMES THE DOSAGES SUGGESTED ABOVE MAY BE NEEDED. PERSONS NOT POISONED OR ONLY SLIGHTLY POISONED, HOWEVER, MAY DEVELOP SIGNS OF ATROPINE TOXICITY FROM SUCH LARGE DOSAGES: FEVER, MUSCLE FIBRILLATIONS, AND DELIRIUM ARE THE MAIN SIGNS OF ATROPINE TOXICITY. IF THESE SIGNS APPEAR WHILE THE PATIENT IS FULLY ATROPINIZED, ATROPINE ADMINISTRATION SHOULD BE DISCONTINUED, AT LEAST TEMPORARILY. OBSERVE TREATED PATIENTS CLOSELY AT LEAST 24 HOURS TO INSURE THAT SYMPTOMS (POSSIBLY PULMONARY EDEMA) DO NOT RECUR AS ATROPINIZATION WEARS OFF. IN VERY SEVERE POISONINGS, METABOLIC DISPOSITION OF TOXICANT MAY REQUIRE SEVERAL HOURS OR DAYS DURING WHICH ATROPINIZATION MUST BE MAINTAINED. MARKEDLY LOWER LEVELS OF URINARY METABOLITES INDICATE THAT ATROPINE DOSAGE CAN BE TAPERED OFF. AS DOSAGE IS REDUCED, CHECK THE LUNG BASES FREQUENTLY FOR RALES. IF RALES ARE HEARD OR OTHER SYMPTOMS RETURN, RE-ESTABLISH ATROPINIZATION PROMPTLY (MORGAN, RECOGNITION AND MANAGEMENT OF PESTICIDE POISONINGS, 3RD ED.). ADMINISTRATION OF ANTIDOTE MUST BE PERFORMED BY QUALIFIED MEDICAL PERSONNEL.
IN CASES OF SEVERE POISONING BY ORGANOPHOSPHATE PESTICIDES IN WHICH RESPIRATORY DEPRESSION, MUSCLE WEAKNESS AND TWITCHINGS ARE SEVERE, GIVE PRALIDOXIME (PROTOPAM-AYERST, 2-PAM), 1.0 GRAM INTRAVENOUSLY AT NO MORE THAN 0.5 GRAM PER MINUTE. DOSAGE OF PRALIDOXIME MAY BE REPEATED IN 1-2 HOURS, THEN AT 10-12 HOUR INTERVALS IF NEEDED. IN VERY SEVERE POISONINGS, DOSAGE RATES MAY BE DOUBLED. TREATMENT WITH PRALIDOXIME WILL BE MOST EFFECTIVE IF GIVEN WITHIN THIRTY-SIX HOURS AFTER POISONING (MORGAN, RECOGNITION AND MANAGEMENT OF PESTICIDE POISONINGS, 3RD ED.). ANTIDOTE SHOULD BE ADMINISTERED BY QUALIFIED MEDICAL PERSONNEL.

REACTIVITY

REACTIVITY: HEATING ABOVE 300 F (150 C) MAY CAUSE EXPLOSIVE DECOMPOSITION.

INCOMPATIBILITIES: RONNEL: STRONG OXIDIZERS: MAY CAUSE FIRE AND EXPLOSION HAZARD. SOME FORMS OF RUBBER, PLASTICS, AND COATINGS: THE MOLTEN FORM OF RONNEL MAY ATTACK.

DECOMPOSITION: THERMAL DECOMPOSITION PRODUCTS MAY INCLUDE TOXIC AND HAZARDOUS FUMES OF SULFUR, NITROGEN AND PHOSPHORUS.

POLYMERIZATION: HAZARDOUS POLYMERIZATION HAS NOT BEEN REPORTED TO OCCUR UNDER NORMAL TEMPERATURES AND PRESSURES.

STORAGE AND DISPOSAL

OBSERVE ALL FEDERAL, STATE AND LOCAL REGULATIONS WHEN STORING OR DISPOSING OF THIS SUBSTANCE. FOR ASSISTANCE, CONTACT THE DISTRICT DIRECTOR OF THE ENVIRONMENTAL PROTECTION AGENCY.

STORAGE

STORE IN ACCORDANCE WITH 40 CFR 165 RECOMMENDED PROCEDURES FOR THE DISPOSAL AND STORAGE OF PESTICIDES AND PESTICIDE CONTAINERS.
STORE AWAY FROM INCOMPATIBLE SUBSTANCES.

DISPOSAL

DISPOSAL MUST BE IN ACCORDANCE WITH 40 CFR 165 RECOMMENDED PROCEDURES FOR THE DISPOSAL AND STORAGE OF PESTICIDES AND PESTICIDE CONTAINERS.

CONDITIONS TO AVOID

NONE REPORTED.

SPILL AND LEAK PROCEDURES

OCCUPATIONAL SPILL: DO NOT TOUCH SPILLED MATERIAL. STOP LEAK IF YOU CAN DO IT WITHOUT RISK. USE WATER SPRAY TO REDUCE VAPORS. FOR SMALL SPILLS, TAKE UP WITH SAND OR OTHER ABSORBENT MATERIAL AND PLACE INTO CONTAINERS FOR LATER DISPOSAL. FOR SMALL DRY SPILLS, WITH A CLEAN SHOVEL PLACE MATERIAL INTO CLEAN, DRY CONTAINERS AND COVER. MOVE CONTAINERS FROM SPILL AREA. FOR LARGER SPILLS, DIKE FAR AHEAD OF SPILL FOR LATER DISPOSAL. KEEP UNNECESSARY PEOPLE AWAY. ISOLATE HAZARD AREA AND DENY ENTRY. VENTILATE CLOSED SPACES BEFORE ENTERING.

PROTECTIVE EQUIPMENT

VENTILATION: PROVIDE LOCAL EXHAUST OR PROCESS ENCLOSURE VENTILATION TO MEET PUBLISHED EXPOSURE LIMITS.

RESPIRATOR: THE FOLLOWING RESPIRATORS AND MAXIMUM USE CONCENTRATIONS ARE RECOMMENDATIONS BY THE U.S. DEPARTMENT OF HEALTH AND HUMAN SERVICES, NIOSH POCKET GUIDE TO CHEMICAL HAZARDS; NIOSH CRITERIA DOCUMENTS OR BY THE U.S. DEPARTMENT OF LABOR, 29 CFR 1910 SUBPART Z. THE SPECIFIC RESPIRATOR SELECTED MUST BE BASED ON CONTAMINATION LEVELS FOUND IN THE WORK PLACE, MUST NOT EXCEED THE WORKING LIMITS OF THE RESPIRATOR AND BE JOINTLY APPROVED BY THE NATIONAL INSTITUTE FOR OCCUPATIONAL SAFETY AND HEALTH AND THE MINE SAFETY AND HEALTH ADMINISTRATION (NIOSH-MSHA).
RONNEL: 100 MG/M3- ANY CHEMICAL CARTRIDGE RESPIRATOR WITH A ORGANIC VAPOR CARTRIDGE(S) IN COMBINATION WITH A DUST, MIST, AND FUME FILTER. ANY SUPPLIED-AIR RESPIRATOR. ANY SELF-CONTAINED BREATHING APPARATUS.
250 MG/M3- ANY SUPPLIED-AIR RESPIRATOR OPERATED IN A CONTINUOUS FLOW MODE. ANY POWERED AIR-PURIFYING RESPIRATOR WITH ORGANIC VAPOR CARTRIDGE(S) IN COMBINATION WITH A DUST, MIST, AND FUME FILTER.
500 MG/M3- ANY SUPPLIED-AIR RESPIRATOR WITH A FULL FACEPIECE. ANY SELF-CONTAINED BREATHING APPARATUS WITH A FULL FACEPIECE. ANY CHEMICAL CARTRIDGE RESPIRATOR WITH A FULL FACEPIECE AND ORGANIC VAPOR CARTRIDGE(S) IN COMBINATION WITH A HIGH-EFFICIENCY PARTICULATE FILTER. ANY AIR-PURIFYING FULL FACEPIECE RESPIRATOR (GAS MASK) WITH A CHIN-STYLE OR FRONT- OR BACK-MOUNTED ORGANIC VAPOR CANISTER HAVING A HIGH-

EFFICIENCY PARTICULATE FILTER. ANY POWERED AIR-PURIFYING RESPIRATOR WITH A TIGHT-FITTING FACEPIECE AND ORGANIC VAPOR CARTRIDGE(S) IN COMBINATION WITH A HIGH-EFFICIENCY PARTICULATE FILTER.
5000 MG/M3- ANY SUPPLIED-AIR RESPIRATOR WITH A HALF-MASK AND OPERATED IN A PRESSURE-DEMAND OR OTHER POSITIVE PRESSURE MODE.
ESCAPE- ANY AIR-PURIFYING FULL FACEPIECE RESPIRATOR (GAS MASK) WITH A CHIN-STYLE OR FRONT- OR BACK-MOUNTED ORGANIC VAPOR CANISTER HAVING A HIGH-EFFICIENCY PARTICULATE FILTER. ANY APPROPRIATE ESCAPE-TYPE SELF-CONTAINED BREATHING APPARATUS.
FOR FIREFIGHTING AND OTHER IMMEDIATELY DANGEROUS TO LIFE OR HEALTH CONDITIONS:
SELF-CONTAINED BREATHING APPARATUS WITH FULL FACEPIECE OPERATED IN PRESSURE-DEMAND OR OTHER POSITIVE PRESSURE MODE.
SUPPLIED-AIR RESPIRATOR WITH FULL FACEPIECE AND OPERATED IN PRESSURE-DEMAND OR OTHER POSITIVE PRESSURE MODE IN COMBINATION WITH AN AUXILIARY SELF-CONTAINED BREATHING APPARATUS OPERATED IN PRESSURE-DEMAND OR OTHER POSITIVE PRESSURE MODE.

CLOTHING: EMPLOYEE MUST WEAR APPROPRIATE PROTECTIVE (IMPERVIOUS) CLOTHING AND EQUIPMENT TO PREVENT ANY POSSIBILITY OF SKIN CONTACT WITH THIS SUBSTANCE.

GLOVES: EMPLOYEE MUST WEAR APPROPRIATE PROTECTIVE GLOVES TO PREVENT CONTACT WITH THIS SUBSTANCE.

EYE PROTECTION: EMPLOYEE MUST WEAR SPLASH-PROOF OR DUST-RESISTANT SAFETY GOGGLES AND A FACESHIELD TO PREVENT CONTACT WITH THIS SUBSTANCE. EMERGENCY WASH FACILITIES: WHERE THERE IS ANY POSSIBILITY THAT AN EMPLOYEE'S EYES AND/OR SKIN MAY BE EXPOSED TO THIS SUBSTANCE, THE EMPLOYER SHOULD PROVIDE AN EYE WASH FOUNTAIN AND QUICK DRENCH SHOWER WITHIN THE IMMEDIATE WORK AREA FOR EMERGENCY USE.

AUTHORIZED BY- OCCUPATIONAL HEALTH SERVICES, INC.
CREATION DATE: 10/05/89 ***REVISION DATE:*** 06/04/90

MATERIAL SAFETY DATA SHEET

OCCUPATIONAL HEALTH SERVICES, INC.
AGRICULTURE AND PESTICIDE DIVISION
450 SEVENTH AVENUE, SUITE 2407
NEW YORK, NEW YORK 10123
1-800-445-MSDS OR (212) 967-1100

EMERGENCY CONTACT:
JOHN S. BRANSFORD, JR. (615) 292-1180

SUBSTANCE IDENTIFICATION

CAS-NUMBER 83-79-4

SUBSTANCE: **ROTENONE**

TRADE NAMES/SYNONYMS: (1)BENZOPYRANO(3,4-B)FURO(2,3-H)(1)BENZOPYRAN-6(6AH)-ONE, 1,2,12, 12A-TETRAHYDRO-8,9-DIMETHOXY-2-(1-METHYLETHENYL)-, (2R-(2ALPHA, 6(A)ALPHA,12(A)ALPHA))-; (2R-(2ALPHA,6(A)ALPHA,12(A)ALPHA))-1,2,12,12A-TETRAHYDRO-8, 9-DIMETHOXY-2-(1-METHYLETHENYL)(1)BENZOPYRANO(3,4-B)FURO(2,3-H)(1) BENZOPYRAN-6(6AH)-ONE; (1)BENZOPYRANO(3,4-B)FURO(2,3-H)(1)BENZOPYRAN-6(6A ALPHA H)-ONE, 1, 2,12,12A ALPHA-TETRAHYDRO-2ALPHA-ISOPROPENYL-8,9-DIMETHOXY-; 1,2,12,12A ALPHA-TETRAHYDRO-2A ALPHA-ISOPROPENYL-8,9-DIMETHOXY(1) BENZOPYRANOL(3,4-B)FURO(2,3-H(1)BENZOPYRAN-6(6A ALPHA H)-ONE; (2R,6AS,12AS)-1,2,6,6A,12,12A-HEXAHYDRO-2-ISOPROPENYL-8,9-DIMETHOXYCHROMENO(3,4-B)FURO(2,3-H)CHROMEN-6-ONE; 1,2,12,12A-TETRAHYDRO-8,9-DIMETHOXY-2-(1-METHYLETHENYL)-(1) BENZOPYRANO(3,4-B)FURO(2,3-H(1)-BENZOPYRAN-6(6AH)-ONE; DERRIN; DERRIS; NICOULINE; NOXFISH; TUBATOXIN; C23H22O6; PST20200

CHEMICAL FAMILY: HYDROXYL, POLYNUCLEAR

MOLECULAR FORMULA: C23-H22-O6

MOLECULAR WEIGHT: 394.42

CERCLA RATINGS (SCALE 0-3): HEALTH=3 FIRE=1 REACTIVITY=0 PERSISTENCE=1

NFPA RATINGS (SCALE 0-4): HEALTH=U FIRE=1 REACTIVITY=0

COMPONENTS AND CONTAMINANTS

COMPONENT: ROTENONE ***PERCENT:*** 100.0
CAS# 83-79-4

OTHER CONTAMINANTS: NONE

EXPOSURE LIMITS: ROTENONE: 5 MG/M3 OSHA TWA 5 MG/M3 ACGIH TWA

PHYSICAL DATA

DESCRIPTION: ODORLESS WHITE NEEDLES OR LEAFLETS.

BOILING POINT: 410-428 F (210-220 C) @ 0.5 MMHG

MELTING POINT: 329-331 F (165-166 C) ***SPECIFIC GRAVITY:*** 1.27

VAPOR PRESSURE: APPROX 0 @ 20 C ***SOLUBILITY IN WATER:*** 0.00002%

SOLVENT SOLUBILITY: SOLUBLE IN ETHANOL, ACETONE, BENZENE, CHLOROFORM, ABSOLUTE ALCOHOL, ETHER, CARBON TETRACHLORIDE, TRICHLOROETHYLENE, PETROLEUM OILS, POLAR ORGANIC SOLVENTS.
DECOMPOSES ON EXPOSURE TO AIR OR LIGHT.

FIRE AND EXPLOSION DATA

FIRE AND EXPLOSION HAZARD: SLIGHT FIRE HAZARD WHEN EXPOSED TO HEAT OR FLAME.

FIREFIGHTING MEDIA: DRY CHEMICAL, CARBON DIOXIDE, HALON, WATER SPRAY OR STANDARD FOAM (1987 EMERGENCY RESPONSE GUIDEBOOK, DOT P 5800.4).
FOR LARGER FIRES, USE WATER SPRAY, FOG OR STANDARD FOAM (1987 EMERGENCY RESPONSE GUIDEBOOK, DOT P 5800.4).

FIREFIGHTING: MOVE CONTAINERS FROM FIRE AREA IF POSSIBLE (1987 EMERGENCY RESPONSE GUIDEBOOK, DOT P 5800.4, GUIDE PAGE 53).
EXTINGUISH FIRE USING AGENTS SUITABLE FOR TYPE OF SURROUNDING FIRE. USE WATER IN FLOODING AMOUNTS AS A FOG. AVOID BREATHING DUSTS AND FUMES FROM BURNING MATERIAL; KEEP UPWIND.

TOXICITY

ROTENONE: IRRITATION DATA: 1% EYE-RABBIT MILD. TOXICITY DATA: 143 MG/KG ORAL-HUMAN LDLO; 60 MG/KG ORAL-RAT LD50; 350 MG/KG ORAL-MOUSE LD50; 100 MG/KG ORAL-GUINEA PIG LDLO; 300 MG/KG ORAL-DOG LDLO; 1600 MG/KG ORAL-RABBIT LDLO; 20 MG/KG SUBCUTANEOUS-RABBIT LDLO; 350 UG/KG INTRAVENOUS-RABBIT LDLO; 650 UG/KG INTRAVENOUS-CAT LDLO; 650 UG/KG INTRAVENOUS-DOG LDLO; 2650 UG/KG INTRAPERITONEAL-MOUSE LD50; 10 MG/KG INTRAPERITONEAL-GUINEA PIG LDLO; 5 MG/KG INTRAPERITONEAL-RAT LD50; 5 MG/KG INTRAMUSCULAR-RABBIT LDLO; 294 MG/KG UNREPORTED-MAN LDLO; 132 MG/KG UNREPORTED-RAT LD50; MUTAGENIC DATA (RTECS); REPRODUCTIVE EFFECTS DATA (RTECS); TUMORIGENIC DATA (RTECS). CARCINOGEN STATUS: NONE. LOCAL EFFECTS: IRRITANT- EYE. ACUTE TOXICITY LEVEL: TOXIC BY INGESTION. TARGET EFFECTS: POISONING MAY AFFECT THE CENTRAL NERVOUS SYSTEM. ADDITIONAL DATA: FATS AND OILS MAY ENHANCE THE TOXICITY OF ROTENONE.

HEALTH EFFECTS AND FIRST AID

INHALATION: ROTENONE: 5000 MG/M3 IMMEDIATELY DANGEROUS TO LIFE OR HEALTH. **ACUTE EXPOSURE**- DUST MAY CAUSE TRANSIENT NUMBNESS OF THE MUCOSA OF THE NOSE AND THROAT, AND PULMONARY IRRITATION. SYSTEMIC ABSORPTION MAY PRODUCE RESPIRATORY STIMULATION FOLLOWED BY RESPIRATORY DEPRESSION WITH FITS AND CONVULSIONS. DEATH MAY BE DUE TO RESPIRATORY FAILURE. **CHRONIC EXPOSURE**- SEVERE PULMONARY IRRITATION, ULCERATIVE RHINITIS WITH TEMPORARY ANOSMIA, AND PHARYNGITIS WITH PARTIAL DESTRUCTION OF THE SOFT PALATE AND ANTERIOR PILLARS HAVE BEEN DETAILED IN OLDER REPORTS OF PROCESSING OPERATIONS WITH POOR INDUSTRIAL HYGIENE.

FIRST AID- REMOVE FROM EXPOSURE AREA TO FRESH AIR IMMEDIATELY. IF BREATHING HAS STOPPED, PERFORM ARTIFICIAL RESPIRATION. KEEP PERSON WARM AND AT REST. TREAT SYMPTOMATICALLY AND SUPPORTIVELY. GET MEDICAL ATTENTION IMMEDIATELY.

SKIN CONTACT: ROTENONE: **ACUTE EXPOSURE**- MAY CAUSE ERYTHEMA AND IRRITATION. SENSITIZATION REACTIONS MAY OCCUR IN PREVIOUSLY EXPOSED PERSONS. **CHRONIC EXPOSURE**- PROLONGED OR REPEATED EXPOSURE MAY RESULT IN DERMATITIS, WHICH MAY BE ALLERGIC. A SEVERE EXCORIATING DERMATITIS HAS BEEN DETAILED IN OLDER REPORTS OF PROCESSING OPERATIONS WITH POOR INDUSTRIAL HYGIENE.

FIRST AID- REMOVE CONTAMINATED CLOTHING AND SHOES IMMEDIATELY. WASH AFFECTED AREA WITH SOAP OR MILD DETERGENT AND LARGE AMOUNTS OF WATER UNTIL NO EVIDENCE OF CHEMICAL REMAINS (APPROXIMATELY 15-20 MINUTES). GET MEDICAL ATTENTION IMMEDIATELY.

EYE CONTACT: ROTENONE: IRRITANT. **ACUTE EXPOSURE**- MAY CAUSE CONJUNCTIVAL IRRITATION FOLLOWED BY ULCERATIVE KERATITIS. **CHRONIC EXPOSURE**- PROLONGED OR REPEATED EXPOSURE MAY PRODUCE EFFECTS AS DESCRIBED IN ACUTE EXPOSURE.

FIRST AID- WASH EYES IMMEDIATELY WITH LARGE AMOUNTS OF WATER OR NORMAL SALINE, OCCASIONALLY LIFTING UPPER AND LOWER LIDS, UNTIL NO EVIDENCE OF CHEMICAL REMAINS (APPROXIMATELY 15-20 MINUTES). GET MEDICAL ATTENTION IMMEDIATELY.

INGESTION: ROTENONE: TOXIC. **ACUTE EXPOSURE**- MAY CAUSE A METALLIC TASTE WITH NUMBNESS OF THE ORAL MUCOUS MEMBRANES, PROMPT VOMITING,

NAUSEA, ABDOMINAL PAIN WITH GASTROINTESTINAL IRRITATION, LETHARGY, MUSCULAR TREMORS, INCOHERENCE, STUPOR, INCOORDINATION, HYPOGLYCEMIA, RESPIRATORY STIMULATION FOLLOWED BY RESPIRATORY DEPRESSION, AND CONVULSIONS. DEATH MAY BE DUE TO RESPIRATORY DEPRESSION. **CHRONIC EXPOSURE-** REPEATED ADMINISTRATION OF 10 MG/KG WAS LETHAL TO 3 OF 5 DOGS WITH PATHOLOGICAL FINDINGS OF FATTY METAMORPHOSIS OF THE LIVER, KIDNEY AND ADRENAL GLAND. OTHER EFFECTS REPORTED IN ANIMALS INCLUDE INFLAMMATION AND HYPERPLASIA OF THE FORESTOMACH, AND BONE MARROW ATROPHY. SKELETAL ABNORMALITIES, INCREASED INFERTILITY, RESORPTIONS, AND FETAL DEATH WERE REPORTED FROM STUDIES OF PREGNANT RATS; AN INCREASE IN THE NUMBER OF STILLBIRTHS AND A DECREASE IN THE SURVIVAL OF THE OFFSPRING WERE NOTED IN A STUDY OF PREGNANT GUINEA PIGS.

FIRST AID- REMOVE BY GASTRIC LAVAGE OR EMESIS. MAINTAIN BLOOD PRESSURE AND AIRWAY. GIVE OXYGEN IF RESPIRATION IS DEPRESSED. DO NOT PERFORM GASTRIC LAVAGE OR EMESIS IF VICTIM IS UNCONSCIOUS. GET MEDICAL ATTENTION IMMEDIATELY (DREISBACH, HANDBOOK OF POISONING, 11TH ED.). ADMINISTRATION OF GASTRIC LAVAGE OR OXYGEN SHOULD BE PERFORMED BY QUALIFIED MEDICAL PERSONNEL.

ANTIDOTE: NO SPECIFIC ANTIDOTE. TREAT SYMPTOMATICALLY AND SUPPORTIVELY.

REACTIVITY

REACTIVITY: STABLE UNDER NORMAL TEMPERATURES AND PRESSURES.

INCOMPATIBILITIES: ROTENONE: OXIDIZERS (STRONG): FIRE AND EXPLOSION HAZARD.

DECOMPOSITION: THERMAL DECOMPOSITION PRODUCTS MAY INCLUDE TOXIC OXIDES OF CARBON.

POLYMERIZATION: HAZARDOUS POLYMERIZATION HAS NOT BEEN REPORTED TO OCCUR UNDER NORMAL TEMPERATURES AND PRESSURES.

STORAGE AND DISPOSAL

OBSERVE ALL FEDERAL, STATE AND LOCAL REGULATIONS WHEN STORING OR DISPOSING OF THIS SUBSTANCE. FOR ASSISTANCE, CONTACT THE DISTRICT DIRECTOR OF THE ENVIRONMENTAL PROTECTION AGENCY.

STORAGE

STORE IN ACCORDANCE WITH 40 CFR 165 RECOMMENDED PROCEDURES FOR THE DISPOSAL AND STORAGE OF PESTICIDES AND PESTICIDE CONTAINERS.
STORE AWAY FROM INCOMPATIBLE SUBSTANCES.
KEEP CONTAINER TIGHTLY CLOSED. PROTECT FROM EXPOSURE TO AIR OR LIGHT.

DISPOSAL

DISPOSAL MUST BE IN ACCORDANCE WITH 40 CFR 165 RECOMMENDED PROCEDURES FOR THE DISPOSAL AND STORAGE OF PESTICIDES AND PESTICIDE CONTAINERS.

CONDITIONS TO AVOID

MAY BURN BUT DOES NOT IGNITE READILY.

SPILL AND LEAK PROCEDURES

OCCUPATIONAL SPILL: DO NOT TOUCH SPILLED MATERIAL. STOP LEAK IF YOU CAN DO IT WITHOUT RISK. FOR SMALL SPILLS, TAKE UP WITH SAND OR OTHER ABSORBENT MATERIAL AND PLACE INTO CONTAINERS FOR LATER DISPOSAL. FOR SMALL DRY SPILLS, WITH A CLEAN SHOVEL PLACE MATERIAL INTO CLEAN, DRY CONTAINER AND COVER. MOVE CONTAINERS FROM SPILL AREA. FOR LARGER SPILLS, DIKE FAR AHEAD OF SPILL FOR LATER DISPOSAL. KEEP UNNECESSARY PEOPLE AWAY. ISOLATE HAZARD AREA AND DENY ENTRY.

PROTECTIVE EQUIPMENT

VENTILATION: PROVIDE LOCAL EXHAUST VENTILATION AND/OR GENERAL DILUTION VENTILATION TO MEET PUBLISHED EXPOSURE LIMITS.

RESPIRATOR: THE FOLLOWING RESPIRATORS AND MAXIMUM USE CONCENTRATIONS ARE RECOMMENDATIONS BY THE U.S. DEPARTMENT OF HEALTH AND HUMAN SERVICES, NIOSH POCKET GUIDE TO CHEMICAL HAZARDS; NIOSH CRITERIA DOCUMENTS OR BY THE U.S. DEPARTMENT OF LABOR, 29 CFR 1910 SUBPART Z. THE SPECIFIC RESPIRATOR SELECTED MUST BE BASED ON CONTAMINATION LEVELS FOUND IN THE WORK PLACE, MUST NOT EXCEED THE WORKING LIMITS OF THE RESPIRATOR AND BE JOINTLY APPROVED BY THE NATIONAL INSTITUTE FOR OCCUPATIONAL SAFETY AND HEALTH AND THE MINE SAFETY AND HEALTH ADMINISTRATION (NIOSH-MSHA).

ROTENONE: 5 MG/M3- CHEMICAL CARTRIDGE RESPIRATOR WITH ORGANIC VAPOR CARTRIDGE(S) IN COMBINATION WITH A DUST, MIST, AND FUME FILTER. SUPPLIED-AIR RESPIRATOR. SELF-CONTAINED BREATHING APPARATUS.

125 MG/M3- SUPPLIED-AIR RESPIRATOR OPERATED IN CONTINUOUS FLOW MODE. POWERED AIR-PURIFYING RESPIRATOR WITH ORGANIC VAPOR CARTRIDGE(S) IN COMBINATION WITH A DUST, MIST, AND FUME FILTER.

250 MG/M3- SUPPLIED-AIR RESPIRATOR WITH FULL FACEPIECE. SELF-CONTAINED BREATHING APPARATUS WITH FULL FACEPIECE. CHEMICAL CARTRIDGE RESPIRATOR WITH FULL FACEPIECE AND ORGANIC VAPOR CARTRIDGE(S) IN COMBINATION WITH HIGH-EFFICIENCY PARTICULATE FILTER. AIR-PURIFYING FULL FACEPIECE RESPIRATOR (GAS MASK) WITH CHIN-STYLE OR FRONT- OR BACK-MOUNTED ORGANIC VAPOR CANISTER HAVING A HIGH-EFFICIENCY PARTICULATE FILTER. SUPPLIED-AIR RESPIRATOR WITH TIGHT-FITTING FACEPIECE OPERATED IN CONTINUOUS FLOW MODE. POWERED AIR-PURIFYING RESPIRATOR WITH TIGHT-FITTING FACEPIECE AND ORGANIC VAPOR CARTRIDGE(S) IN COMBINATION WITH HIGH-EFFICIENCY PARTICULATE FILTER.

5000 MG/M3- SUPPLIED-AIR RESPIRATOR WITH HALF-MASK OPERATED IN PRESSURE-DEMAND OR OTHER POSITIVE PRESSURE MODE.

ESCAPE- AIR-PURIFYING FULL FACEPIECE RESPIRATOR (GAS MASK) WITH CHIN-STYLE OR FRONT- OR BACK-MOUNTED ORGANIC VAPOR CANISTER HAVING HIGH-EFFICIENCY PARTICULATE FILTER. ESCAPE-TYPE SELF-CONTAINED BREATHING APPARATUS.

FOR FIREFIGHTING AND OTHER IMMEDIATELY DANGEROUS TO LIFE OR HEALTH CONDITIONS:

SELF-CONTAINED BREATHING APPARATUS WITH FULL FACEPIECE OPERATED IN PRESSURE-DEMAND OR OTHER POSITIVE PRESSURE MODE.

SUPPLIED-AIR RESPIRATOR WITH FULL FACEPIECE AND OPERATED IN PRESSURE-DEMAND OR OTHER POSITIVE PRESSURE MODE IN COMBINATION WITH AN AUXILIARY SELF-CONTAINED BREATHING APPARATUS OPERATED IN PRESSURE-DEMAND OR OTHER POSITIVE PRESSURE MODE.

CLOTHING: EMPLOYEE MUST WEAR APPROPRIATE PROTECTIVE (IMPERVIOUS) CLOTHING AND EQUIPMENT TO PREVENT ANY POSSIBILITY OF SKIN CONTACT WITH THIS SUBSTANCE.

GLOVES: EMPLOYEE MUST WEAR APPROPRIATE PROTECTIVE GLOVES TO PREVENT CONTACT WITH THIS SUBSTANCE.

EYE PROTECTION: EMPLOYEE MUST WEAR SPLASH-PROOF OR DUST-RESISTANT SAFETY GOGGLES TO PREVENT EYE CONTACT WITH THIS SUBSTANCE. EMERGENCY EYE WASH: WHERE THERE IS ANY POSSIBILITY THAT AN EMPLOYEE'S EYES MAY BE EXPOSED TO THIS SUBSTANCE, THE EMPLOYER SHOULD PROVIDE AN EYE WASH FOUNTAIN WITHIN THE IMMEDIATE WORK AREA FOR EMERGENCY USE.

AUTHORIZED BY- OCCUPATIONAL HEALTH SERVICES, INC.
CREATION DATE: 10/05/89 ***REVISION DATE:*** 03/16/90

MATERIAL SAFETY DATA SHEET

OCCUPATIONAL HEALTH SERVICES, INC.
AGRICULTURE AND PESTICIDE DIVISION
450 SEVENTH AVENUE, SUITE 2407
NEW YORK, NEW YORK 10123
1-800-445-MSDS OR (212) 967-1100

EMERGENCY CONTACT:
JOHN S. BRANSFORD, JR. (615) 292-1180

SUBSTANCE IDENTIFICATION

CAS-NUMBER 38641-94-0

SUBSTANCE: GLYPHOSATE ISOPROPYLAMINE SALT

TRADE NAMES/SYNONYMS: GLYCINE, N-(PHOSPHONOMETHYL)-, COMPOUNDED WITH 2-PROPANAMINE (1:1); N-(PHOSPHONOMETHYL)GLYCINE COMPOUNDED WITH 2-PROPANAMINE (1:1); GLYPHOSATE MONO(ISOPROPYLAMINE) SALT; GLYPHOSATE ISOPROPYLAMINE; MON 0139; GLYPHOSATE-MONO(ISOPROPYLAMMONIUM); C6H17N2O5P; PST20205

CHEMICAL FAMILY: ORGANOPHOSPHATE

MOLECULAR FORMULA: C3-H9-N.C3-H8-N-O5-P

MOLECULAR WEIGHT: 228.18

CERCLA RATINGS (SCALE 0-3): HEALTH=U FIRE=1 REACTIVITY=0 PERSISTENCE=0

NFPA RATINGS (SCALE 0-4): HEALTH=U FIRE=1 REACTIVITY=0

COMPONENTS AND CONTAMINANTS

COMPONENT: GLYPHOSATE ISOPROPYLAMINE SALT ***PERCENT:*** 100.0
CAS# 38641-94-0

OTHER CONTAMINANTS: NONE

EXPOSURE LIMITS: NO OCCUPATIONAL EXPOSURE LIMITS ESTABLISHED BY OSHA, ACGIH, OR NIOSH.

PHYSICAL DATA

DESCRIPTION: WHITE SOLID. ***MELTING POINT:*** NOT AVAILABLE

SPECIFIC GRAVITY: NOT AVAILABLE ***SOLUBILITY IN WATER:*** VERY SOLUBLE

FIRE AND EXPLOSION DATA

FIRE AND EXPLOSION HAZARD: SLIGHT FIRE HAZARD WHEN EXPOSED TO HEAT OR FLAME.

FIREFIGHTING MEDIA: DRY CHEMICAL, CARBON DIOXIDE, HALON, WATER SPRAY OR STANDARD FOAM (1987 EMERGENCY RESPONSE GUIDEBOOK, DOT P 5800.4). FOR LARGER FIRES, USE WATER SPRAY, FOG OR STANDARD FOAM (1987 EMERGENCY RESPONSE GUIDEBOOK, DOT P 5800.4).

FIREFIGHTING: MOVE CONTAINER FROM FIRE AREA IF POSSIBLE. DO NOT SCATTER SPILLED MATERIAL WITH HIGH PRESSURE WATER STREAMS. DIKE FIRE CONTROL WATER FOR LATER DISPOSAL (1987 EMERGENCY RESPONSE GUIDEBOOK, DOT P 5800.4, GUIDE PAGE 31).

USE AGENTS SUITABLE FOR TYPE OF SURROUNDING FIRE. AVOID BREATHING HAZARDOUS VAPORS, KEEP UPWIND.

TOXICITY

GLYPHOSATE ISOPROPYLAMINE SALT: TOXICITY DATA: 5480 MG/KG ORAL-RAT LD50; 3750 MG/KG SKIN-RABBIT LD50 (PEMNDP); MUTAGENIC DATA (RTECS). CARCINOGEN STATUS: NONE. ACUTE TOXICITY LEVEL: SLIGHTLY TOXIC BY DERMAL ABSORPTION AND INGESTION. TARGET EFFECTS: NO DATA AVAILABLE.

HEALTH EFFECTS AND FIRST AID

INHALATION: GLYPHOSATE ISOPROPYLAMINE SALT: **ACUTE EXPOSURE-** MAY CAUSE IRRITATION OF THE MUCOUS MEMBRANES. **CHRONIC EXPOSURE-** NO DATA AVAILABLE.

FIRST AID- REMOVE FROM EXPOSURE AREA TO FRESH AIR IMMEDIATELY. IF BREATHING HAS STOPPED, PERFORM ARTIFICIAL RESPIRATION. KEEP PERSON WARM AND AT REST. TREAT SYMPTOMATICALLY AND SUPPORTIVELY. GET MEDICAL ATTENTION IMMEDIATELY.

SKIN CONTACT: GLYPHOSATE ISOPROPYLAMINE SALT: **ACUTE EXPOSURE-** MAY CAUSE IRRITATION. ANIMAL STUDIES INDICATE THAT SKIN ABSORPTION MAY OCCUR. **CHRONIC EXPOSURE-** REPEATED APPLICATION OF THE TECHNICAL PRODUCT AT A DOSE OF 2 MG/KG/DAY FOR 3 WEEKS WAS IRRITATING TO RABBIT SKIN. HOWEVER, NO SYSTEMIC EFFECTS WERE OBSERVED.

FIRST AID- REMOVE CONTAMINATED CLOTHING AND SHOES IMMEDIATELY. WASH AFFECTED AREA WITH SOAP OR MILD DETERGENT AND LARGE AMOUNTS OF WATER UNTIL NO EVIDENCE OF CHEMICAL REMAINS (APPROXIMATELY 15-20 MINUTES). GET MEDICAL ATTENTION IMMEDIATELY.

EYE CONTACT: GLYPHOSATE ISOPROPYLAMINE SALT: **ACUTE EXPOSURE-** MAY CAUSE IRRITATION. **CHRONIC EXPOSURE-** NO DATA AVAILABLE.

FIRST AID- WASH EYES IMMEDIATELY WITH LARGE AMOUNTS OF WATER OR NORMAL SALINE, OCCASIONALLY LIFTING UPPER AND LOWER LIDS, UNTIL NO EVIDENCE OF CHEMICAL REMAINS (APPROXIMATELY 15-20 MINUTES). GET MEDICAL ATTENTION IMMEDIATELY.

INGESTION: GLYPHOSATE ISOPROPYLAMINE SALT: **ACUTE EXPOSURE-** THE LETHAL DOSE IN RATS WAS 5480 MG/KG; SYMPTOMS WERE NOT REPORTED. **CHRONIC EXPOSURE-** SLIGHTLY REDUCED BODY WEIGHT GAINS AND INCREASED ALKALINE PHOSPHATASE ACTIVITIES WERE OBSERVED IN A 6-MONTH STUDY OF DOGS RECEIVING 300 MG/KG/DAY OF THE TECHNICAL PRODUCT.

FIRST AID- REMOVE BY GASTRIC LAVAGE AND CATHARSIS. MAINTAIN BLOOD PRESSURE AND AIRWAY. GIVE OXYGEN IF RESPIRATION IS DEPRESSED. DO NOT PERFORM GASTRIC LAVAGE IF VICTIM IS UNCONSCIOUS. GET MEDICAL ATTENTION IMMEDIATELY (DREISBACH, HANDBOOK OF POISONING, 12TH ED.).

ADMINISTRATION OF LAVAGE OR OXYGEN SHOULD BE PERFORMED BY QUALIFIED MEDICAL PERSONNEL.

ANTIDOTE: NO SPECIFIC ANTIDOTE. TREAT SYMPTOMATICALLY AND SUPPORTIVELY.

REACTIVITY

REACTIVITY: STABLE UNDER NORMAL TEMPERATURES AND PRESSURES.

INCOMPATIBILITIES: GLYPHOSATE ISOPROPYLAMINE SALT: GALVANIZED OR UNLINED STEEL: MAY REACT PRODUCING A HIGHLY COMBUSTIBLE GAS. IRON: SOLUTIONS MAY BE CORROSIVE. OXIDIZERS: FIRE AND EXPLOSION HAZARD.

DECOMPOSITION: THERMAL DECOMPOSITION MAY RELEASE TOXIC OXIDES OF NITROGEN, PHOSPHORUS AND CARBON.

POLYMERIZATION: HAZARDOUS POLYMERIZATION HAS NOT BEEN REPORTED TO OCCUR UNDER NORMAL TEMPERATURES AND PRESSURES.

STORAGE AND DISPOSAL

OBSERVE ALL FEDERAL, STATE AND LOCAL REGULATIONS WHEN STORING OR DISPOSING OF THIS SUBSTANCE. FOR ASSISTANCE, CONTACT THE DISTRICT DIRECTOR OF THE ENVIRONMENTAL PROTECTION AGENCY.

STORAGE

STORE IN ACCORDANCE WITH 40 CFR 165 RECOMMENDED PROCEDURES FOR THE DISPOSAL AND STORAGE OF PESTICIDES AND PESTICIDE CONTAINERS.

DO NOT USE OR STORE IN GALVANIZED OR UNLINED STEEL SPRAY EQUIPMENT AS IT WILL REACT WITH THE METAL CAUSING A HIGHLY COMBUSTIBLE GAS.

DISPOSAL

DISPOSAL MUST BE IN ACCORDANCE WITH 40 CFR 165 RECOMMENDED PROCEDURES FOR THE DISPOSAL AND STORAGE OF PESTICIDES AND PESTICIDE CONTAINERS.

CONDITIONS TO AVOID

MAY BURN BUT DOES NOT IGNITE READILY. AVOID CONTACT WITH STRONG OXIDIZERS, EXCESSIVE HEAT, SPARKS, OR OPEN FLAME.

SPILL AND LEAK PROCEDURES

OCCUPATIONAL SPILL: SWEEP UP AND PLACE IN SUITABLE CLEAN, DRY CONTAINERS FOR RECLAMATION OR LATER DISPOSAL. DO NOT FLUSH SPILLED MATERIAL INTO SEWER. KEEP UNNECESSARY PEOPLE AWAY.

PROTECTIVE EQUIPMENT

VENTILATION: PROVIDE LOCAL EXHAUST OR GENERAL DILUTION VENTILATION SYSTEM.

RESPIRATOR: THE FOLLOWING RESPIRATORS ARE RECOMMENDED BASED ON INFORMATION FOUND IN THE PHYSICAL DATA, TOXICITY AND HEALTH EFFECTS SECTIONS. THEY ARE RANKED IN ORDER FROM MINIMUM TO MAXIMUM RESPIRATORY PROTECTION. THE SPECIFIC RESPIRATOR SELECTED MUST BE BASED ON CONTAMINATION LEVELS FOUND IN THE WORK PLACE, MUST NOT EXCEED THE WORKING LIMITS OF THE RESPIRATOR AND BE JOINTLY APPROVED BY THE NATIONAL INSTITUTE FOR OCCUPATIONAL SAFETY AND HEALTH AND THE MINE SAFETY AND HEALTH ADMINISTRATION (NIOSH-MSHA).

CHEMICAL CARTRIDGE RESPIRATOR WITH AN ORGANIC VAPOR CARTRIDGE(S) WITH A FULL FACEPIECE AND ORGANIC VAPOR CARTRIDGE(S) IN COMBINATION WITH A DUST AND MIST FILTER.

POWERED AIR-PURIFYING RESPIRATOR WITH A TIGHT-FITTING FACEPIECE AND ORGANIC VAPOR CARTRIDGE(S) IN COMBINATION WITH A HIGH-EFFICIENCY PARTICULATE FILTER.

TYPE 'C' SUPPLIED-AIR RESPIRATOR WITH A FULL FACEPIECE OPERATED IN A PRESSURE-DEMAND OR OTHER POSITIVE PRESSURE MODE.

SELF-CONTAINED BREATHING APPARATUS WITH A FULL FACEPIECE OPERATED IN PRESSURE-DEMAND OR OTHER POSITIVE PRESSURE MODE.

FOR FIREFIGHTING AND OTHER IMMEDIATELY DANGEROUS TO LIFE OR HEALTH CONDITIONS:

SELF-CONTAINED BREATHING APPARATUS WITH FULL FACEPIECE OPERATED IN PRESSURE-DEMAND OR OTHER POSITIVE PRESSURE MODE.

SUPPLIED-AIR RESPIRATOR WITH FULL FACEPIECE AND OPERATED IN PRESSURE-DEMAND OR OTHER POSITIVE PRESSURE MODE IN COMBINATION WITH AN AUXILIARY SELF-CONTAINED BREATHING APPARATUS OPERATED IN PRESSURE-DEMAND OR OTHER POSITIVE PRESSURE MODE.

CLOTHING: EMPLOYEE MUST WEAR APPROPRIATE PROTECTIVE (IMPERVIOUS) CLOTHING AND EQUIPMENT TO PREVENT REPEATED OR PROLONGED SKIN CONTACT WITH THIS SUBSTANCE.

GLOVES: EMPLOYEE MUST WEAR APPROPRIATE PROTECTIVE GLOVES TO PREVENT CONTACT WITH THIS SUBSTANCE.

EYE PROTECTION: EMPLOYEE MUST WEAR SPLASH-PROOF OR DUST-RESISTANT SAFETY GOGGLES TO PREVENT EYE CONTACT WITH THIS SUBSTANCE.

EMERGENCY EYE WASH: WHERE THERE IS ANY POSSIBILITY THAT AN EMPLOYEE'S EYES MAY BE EXPOSED TO THIS SUBSTANCE, THE EMPLOYER SHOULD PROVIDE AN EYE WASH FOUNTAIN WITHIN THE IMMEDIATE WORK AREA FOR EMERGENCY USE.

AUTHORIZED BY- OCCUPATIONAL HEALTH SERVICES, INC.
CREATION DATE: 10/04/89 ***REVISION DATE:*** 05/31/90

MATERIAL SAFETY DATA SHEET

OCCUPATIONAL HEALTH SERVICES, INC.
AGRICULTURE AND PESTICIDE DIVISION
450 SEVENTH AVENUE, SUITE 2407
NEW YORK, NEW YORK 10123
1-800-445-MSDS OR (212) 967-1100

EMERGENCY CONTACT:
JOHN S. BRANSFORD, JR. (615) 292-1180

SUBSTANCE IDENTIFICATION

SUBSTANCE: **ROUNDUP**

TRADE NAMES/SYNONYMS: ROUNDUP HERBICIDE; PST20207

CHEMICAL FAMILY: MIXTURE, AQUEOUS
CERCLA RATINGS (SCALE 0-3): HEALTH=3 FIRE=1 REACTIVITY=0 PERSISTENCE=0
NFPA RATINGS (SCALE 0-4): HEALTH=3 FIRE=1 REACTIVITY=0

COMPONENTS AND CONTAMINANTS

COMPONENT: GLYPHOSATE ISOPROPYLAMINE SALT ***PERCENT:*** 41.0
CAS# 38641-94-0
COMPONENT: SURFACTANTS ***PERCENT:*** 15.0
COMPONENT: WATER ***PERCENT:*** 44.0
EXPOSURE LIMITS: NO OCCUPATIONAL EXPOSURE LIMITS ESTABLISHED BY OSHA, ACGIH, OR NIOSH.

PHYSICAL DATA

DESCRIPTION: CLEAR, VISCOUS, AMBER-COLORED SOLUTION WITH A SLIGHT AMINE ODOR.
BOILING POINT: NOT AVAILABLE ***SPECIFIC GRAVITY:*** 1.17 ***PH:*** 4.4-4.9
SOLUBILITY IN WATER: COMPLETE

FIRE AND EXPLOSION DATA

FIRE AND EXPLOSION HAZARD: SLIGHT FIRE HAZARD WHEN EXPOSED TO HEAT OR FLAME.
FLASH POINT: >200 F (>93 C) (TCC)
FIREFIGHTING MEDIA: DRY CHEMICAL, CARBON DIOXIDE, HALON, WATER SPRAY OR STANDARD FOAM (1987 EMERGENCY RESPONSE GUIDEBOOK, DOT P 5800.4). FOR LARGER FIRES, USE WATER SPRAY, FOG OR STANDARD FOAM (1987 EMERGENCY RESPONSE GUIDEBOOK, DOT P 5800.4).
FIREFIGHTING: MOVE CONTAINER FROM FIRE AREA IF POSSIBLE. DO NOT SCATTER SPILLED MATERIAL WITH HIGH PRESSURE WATER STREAMS. DIKE FIRE CONTROL WATER FOR LATER DISPOSAL (1987 EMERGENCY RESPONSE GUIDEBOOK, DOT P 5800.4, GUIDE PAGE 31).
USE AGENTS SUITABLE FOR TYPE OF SURROUNDING FIRE. AVOID BREATHING HAZARDOUS VAPORS, KEEP UPWIND.

TOXICITY

ROUNDUP: TOXICITY DATA: 5,400 MG/KG ORAL-RAT LD50 (MONSANTO MSDS); 3.18 MG/L/4 HOURS INHALATION-RAT LC50 (MONSANTO MSDS); >5,400 MG/KG SKIN-RABBIT LD50 (MONSANTO MSDS); 4860 MG/KG ORAL-GOAT LD50 (MONSANTO MSDS). CARCINOGEN STATUS: NONE. ACUTE TOXICITY LEVEL: TOXIC BY INHALATION; SLIGHTLY TOXIC BY INGESTION. TARGET EFFECTS: NO DATA AVAILABLE.

HEALTH EFFECTS AND FIRST AID

INHALATION: ROUNDUP: TOXIC. **ACUTE EXPOSURE-** THE REPORTED LETHAL CONCENTRATION IN RATS WAS 3.18 MG/L. **CHRONIC EXPOSURE-** MINOR NASAL IRRITATION WAS REPORTED IN RATS FOLLOWING EXPOSURE FOR 6 HOURS/DAY FOR A TOTAL OF 22 EXPOSURES.
FIRST AID- REMOVE FROM EXPOSURE AREA TO FRESH AIR IMMEDIATELY. IF BREATHING HAS STOPPED, PERFORM ARTIFICIAL RESPIRATION. KEEP PERSON WARM AND AT REST. TREAT SYMPTOMATICALLY AND SUPPORTIVELY. GET MEDICAL ATTENTION IMMEDIATELY.

SKIN CONTACT: ROUNDUP: IRRITANT. **ACUTE EXPOSURE-** PROLONGED CONTACT MAY CAUSE IRRITATION. **CHRONIC EXPOSURE-** REPEATED APPLICATION TO GUINEA PIG SKIN PRODUCED MILD TO MODERATE ERYTHEMA, EDEMA, AND/OR MILD NECROSIS. APPLICATION TO RABBITS AT 5 TIMES THE USE CONCENTRATION FOR 6 HOURS/DAY FOR 5 DAYS/WEEK FOR 3 WEEKS RESULTED IN SEVERE IRRITATION. REDUCED FOOD CONSUMPTION, BODY WEIGHT LOSS, TESTICULAR EFFECTS, AND DEATH WERE OBSERVED, AND WERE CONSIDERED TO BE A SECONDARY RESPONSE TO THE STRESS OF SEVERE DERMAL IRRITATION. TESTS WITH HUMANS AND ANIMALS INDICATE SENSITIZATION IS UNLIKELY.
FIRST AID- REMOVE CONTAMINATED CLOTHING AND SHOES IMMEDIATELY. WASH AFFECTED AREA WITH SOAP OR MILD DETERGENT AND LARGE AMOUNTS OF WATER UNTIL NO EVIDENCE OF CHEMICAL REMAINS (APPROXIMATELY 15-20 MINUTES). GET MEDICAL ATTENTION IMMEDIATELY.

EYE CONTACT: ROUNDUP: **ACUTE EXPOSURE-** MAY CAUSE IRRITATION AND CONJUNCTIVITIS. **CHRONIC EXPOSURE-** NO DATA AVAILABLE.
FIRST AID- WASH EYES IMMEDIATELY WITH LARGE AMOUNTS OF WATER OR NORMAL SALINE, OCCASIONALLY LIFTING UPPER AND LOWER LIDS, UNTIL NO EVIDENCE OF CHEMICAL REMAINS (APPROXIMATELY 15-20 MINUTES). GET MEDICAL ATTENTION IMMEDIATELY.

INGESTION: ROUNDUP: **ACUTE EXPOSURE-** MAY CAUSE GASTROINTESTINAL DISCOMFORT, VOMITING, AND DIARRHEA. **CHRONIC EXPOSURE-** NO DATA AVAILABLE.
FIRST AID: TREAT SYMPTOMATICALLY AND SUPPORTIVELY. IF PERSON IS CONSCIOUS AND ABLE TO SWALLOW, GIVE LARGE AMOUNTS OF WATER OR MILK TO DILUTE SUBSTANCE. GET MEDICAL ATTENTION IMMEDIATELY. IF VOMITING OCCURS, KEEP HEAD BELOW HIPS TO HELP PREVENT ASPIRATION.

REACTIVITY

REACTIVITY: STABLE UNDER NORMAL TEMPERATURES AND PRESSURES.
INCOMPATIBILITIES: ROUNDUP: BASES: EXOTHERMIC REACTION. GALVANIZED OR UNLINED STEEL: MAY REACT PRODUCING A HIGHLY COMBUSTIBLE GAS. IRON: SOLUTIONS MAY BE CORROSIVE. OXIDIZERS: FIRE AND EXPLOSION HAZARD.
DECOMPOSITION: THERMAL DECOMPOSITION MAY RELEASE TOXIC OXIDES OF NITROGEN, PHOSPHORUS AND CARBON.
POLYMERIZATION: HAZARDOUS POLYMERIZATION HAS NOT BEEN REPORTED TO OCCUR UNDER NORMAL TEMPERATURES AND PRESSURES.

STORAGE AND DISPOSAL

OBSERVE ALL FEDERAL, STATE AND LOCAL REGULATIONS WHEN STORING OR DISPOSING OF THIS SUBSTANCE. FOR ASSISTANCE, CONTACT THE DISTRICT DIRECTOR OF THE ENVIRONMENTAL PROTECTION AGENCY.

****STORAGE****

STORE IN ACCORDANCE WITH 40 CFR 165 RECOMMENDED PROCEDURES FOR THE DISPOSAL AND STORAGE OF PESTICIDES AND PESTICIDE CONTAINERS.
STORE AWAY FROM INCOMPATIBLE SUBSTANCES.

****DISPOSAL****

DISPOSAL MUST BE IN ACCORDANCE WITH 40 CFR 165 RECOMMENDED PROCEDURES FOR THE DISPOSAL AND STORAGE OF PESTICIDES AND PESTICIDE CONTAINERS.

CONDITIONS TO AVOID

MAY BURN BUT DOES NOT IGNITE READILY. AVOID CONTACT WITH STRONG OXIDIZERS, EXCESSIVE HEAT, SPARKS, OR OPEN FLAME.

SPILL AND LEAK PROCEDURES

OCCUPATIONAL SPILL: STOP LEAK IF YOU CAN DO IT WITHOUT RISK. FOR SMALL SPILLS, TAKE UP WITH SAND OR OTHER ABSORBENT MATERIAL AND PLACE INTO CLEAN, DRY CONTAINERS FOR LATER DISPOSAL. KEEP UNNECESSARY PEOPLE AWAY. ISOLATE HAZARD AREA AND DENY ENTRY.

PROTECTIVE EQUIPMENT

VENTILATION: PROVIDE LOCAL EXHAUST OR GENERAL DILUTION VENTILATION SYSTEM.
RESPIRATOR: THE FOLLOWING RESPIRATORS ARE RECOMMENDED BASED ON INFORMATION FOUND IN THE PHYSICAL DATA, TOXICITY AND HEALTH EFFECTS SECTIONS. THEY ARE RANKED IN ORDER FROM MINIMUM TO MAXIMUM RESPIRATORY PROTECTION. THE SPECIFIC RESPIRATOR SELECTED MUST BE BASED ON CONTAMINATION LEVELS FOUND IN THE WORK PLACE, MUST NOT EXCEED THE WORKING LIMITS OF THE RESPIRATOR AND BE JOINTLY APPROVED BY THE NATIONAL INSTITUTE FOR OCCUPATIONAL SAFETY AND HEALTH AND THE MINE SAFETY AND HEALTH ADMINISTRATION (NIOSH-MSHA).
CHEMICAL CARTRIDGE RESPIRATOR WITH FULL FACEPIECE AND PESTICIDE CARTRIDGE.
TYPE 'C' SUPPLIED-AIR RESPIRATOR WITH A FULL FACEPIECE OPERATED IN PRESSURE-DEMAND OR OTHER POSITIVE PRESSURE MODE OR WITH A FULL FACEPIECE, HELMET OR HOOD OPERATED IN CONTINUOUS-FLOW MODE.
SELF-CONTAINED BREATHING APPARATUS OPERATED IN PRESSURE-DEMAND OR OTHER POSITIVE PRESSURE MODE.
FOR FIREFIGHTING AND OTHER IMMEDIATELY DANGEROUS TO LIFE OR HEALTH CONDITIONS:
SELF-CONTAINED BREATHING APPARATUS WITH FULL FACEPIECE OPERATED IN PRESSURE-DEMAND OR OTHER POSITIVE PRESSURE MODE.
SUPPLIED-AIR RESPIRATOR WITH FULL FACEPIECE AND OPERATED IN PRESSURE-DEMAND OR OTHER POSITIVE PRESSURE MODE IN COMBINATION WITH AN AUXILIARY SELF-CONTAINED BREATHING APPARATUS OPERATED IN PRESSURE-DEMAND OR OTHER POSITIVE PRESSURE MODE.
CLOTHING: EMPLOYEE MUST WEAR APPROPRIATE PROTECTIVE (IMPERVIOUS) CLOTHING AND EQUIPMENT TO PREVENT REPEATED OR PROLONGED SKIN CONTACT WITH THIS SUBSTANCE.
GLOVES: EMPLOYEE MUST WEAR APPROPRIATE PROTECTIVE GLOVES TO PREVENT CONTACT WITH THIS SUBSTANCE.
EYE PROTECTION: EMPLOYEE MUST WEAR SPLASH-PROOF OR DUST-RESISTANT SAFETY GOGGLES TO PREVENT EYE CONTACT WITH THIS SUBSTANCE.
EMERGENCY EYE WASH: WHERE THERE IS ANY POSSIBILITY THAT AN EMPLOYEE'S EYES MAY BE EXPOSED TO THIS SUBSTANCE, THE EMPLOYER SHOULD PROVIDE AN EYE WASH FOUNTAIN WITHIN THE IMMEDIATE WORK AREA FOR EMERGENCY USE.

AUTHORIZED BY- OCCUPATIONAL HEALTH SERVICES, INC.
CREATION DATE: 10/05/89 ***REVISION DATE:*** 10/31/89

MATERIAL SAFETY DATA SHEET

OCCUPATIONAL HEALTH SERVICES, INC.
AGRICULTURE AND PESTICIDE DIVISION
450 SEVENTH AVENUE, SUITE 2407
NEW YORK, NEW YORK 10123
1-800-445-MSDS OR (212) 967-1100

EMERGENCY CONTACT:
JOHN S. BRANSFORD, JR. (615) 292-1180

SUBSTANCE IDENTIFICATION

SUBSTANCE: RODEO HERBICIDE
TRADE NAMES/SYNONYMS: RODEO; PST20208
CHEMICAL FAMILY: MIXTURE, AQUEOUS
CERCLA RATINGS (SCALE 0-3): HEALTH=U FIRE=1 REACTIVITY=0 PERSISTENCE=0
NFPA RATINGS (SCALE 0-4): HEALTH=U FIRE=1 REACTIVITY=0

COMPONENTS AND CONTAMINANTS

COMPONENT: GLYPHOSATE ISOPROPYLAMINE SALT ***PERCENT:*** 53.5
CAS# 38641-94-0
COMPONENT: ISOPROPYLAMINE ***PERCENT:*** <3.0
CAS# 75-31-0
COMPONENT: INERT INGREDIENTS (INCLUDING SURFACTANTS AND WATER) ***PERCENT:*** >43.5
EXPOSURE LIMITS: ISOPROPYLAMINE: 5 PPM (12 MG/M3) OSHA TWA; 10 PPM (24 MG/M3) OSHA STEL 5 PPM (12 MG/M3) ACGIH TWA; 10 PPM (24 MG/M3) ACGIH STEL 5 PPM (12 MG/M3) NIOSH RECOMMENDED TWA

PHYSICAL DATA

DESCRIPTION: COLORLESS SOLUTION. ***BOILING POINT:*** NOT AVAILABLE
SPECIFIC GRAVITY: 1.22-1.25 ***PH:*** 4.6-4.8 ***SOLUBILITY IN WATER:*** COMPLETE

FIRE AND EXPLOSION DATA

FIRE AND EXPLOSION HAZARD: SLIGHT FIRE HAZARD WHEN EXPOSED TO HEAT OR FLAME.
FLASH POINT: 200 F (93 C) (TCC)
FIREFIGHTING MEDIA: DRY CHEMICAL, CARBON DIOXIDE, HALON, WATER SPRAY OR STANDARD FOAM (1987 EMERGENCY RESPONSE GUIDEBOOK, DOT P 5800.4). FOR LARGER FIRES, USE WATER SPRAY, FOG OR STANDARD FOAM (1987 EMERGENCY RESPONSE GUIDEBOOK, DOT P 5800.4).
FIREFIGHTING: MOVE CONTAINER FROM FIRE AREA IF POSSIBLE. DO NOT SCATTER SPILLED MATERIAL WITH HIGH PRESSURE WATER STREAMS. DIKE FIRE CONTROL WATER FOR LATER DISPOSAL (1987 EMERGENCY RESPONSE GUIDEBOOK, DOT P 5800.4, GUIDE PAGE 31).
USE AGENTS SUITABLE FOR TYPE OF SURROUNDING FIRE. AVOID BREATHING HAZARDOUS VAPORS, KEEP UPWIND.

TOXICITY

RODEO HERBICIDE: TOXICITY DATA: >5,000 MG/KG ORAL-RAT LD50 (MONSANTO MSDS); >5,000 MG/KG SKIN-RABBIT LD50 (MONSANTO MSDS). CARCINOGEN STATUS: NONE. ACUTE TOXICITY LEVEL: SLIGHTLY TOXIC BY INGESTION AND DERMAL ABSORPTION. TARGET EFFECTS: NO DATA AVAILABLE.

HEALTH EFFECTS AND FIRST AID

INHALATION: RODEO HERBICIDE: **ACUTEEXPOSURE-** OCCUPATIONAL EXPOSURE HAS NOT BEEN REPORTED TO CAUSE SIGNIFICANT ADVERSE HEALTH EFFECTS. **CHRONIC EXPOSURE-** NO DATA AVAILABLE.
FIRST AID- REMOVE FROM EXPOSURE AREA TO FRESH AIR IMMEDIATELY. IF BREATHING HAS STOPPED, PERFORM ARTIFICIAL RESPIRATION. KEEP PERSON WARM AND AT REST. TREAT SYMPTOMATICALLY AND SUPPORTIVELY. GET MEDICAL ATTENTION IMMEDIATELY.

SKIN CONTACT: RODEO HERBICIDE: **ACUTE EXPOSURE-** OCCUPATIONAL EXPOSURE HAS NOT BEEN REPORTED TO CAUSE SIGNIFICANT ADVERSE HEALTH EFFECTS. APPLICATION TO RABBIT SKIN WAS PRACTICALLY NONIRRITATING, SCORING A 0.1 ON A SCALE OF 8.0. **CHRONIC EXPOSURE-** REPEATED APPLICATION ON RABBIT SKIN OF 2 ML OF 0.8% AND 0.4% SOLUTIONS FOR 6 HOURS/DAY, 5 DAYS/WEEK FOR 3 WEEKS PRODUCED IRRITATION BUT NO SYSTEMIC EFFECTS. TESTS WITH GUINEA PIGS INDICATE SENSITIZATION IS UNLIKELY.
FIRST AID- REMOVE CONTAMINATED CLOTHING AND SHOES IMMEDIATELY. WASH AFFECTED AREA WITH SOAP OR MILD DETERGENT AND LARGE AMOUNTS OF WATER UNTIL NO EVIDENCE OF CHEMICAL REMAINS (APPROXIMATELY 15-20 MINUTES). GET MEDICAL ATTENTION IMMEDIATELY.

EYE CONTACT: RODEO HERBICIDE: **ACUTE EXPOSURE-** APPLICATION TO RABBIT EYES WAS PRACTICALLY NONIRRITATING, SCORING A 0.0 ON A SCALE OF 110.0. **CHRONIC EXPOSURE-** NO DATA AVAILABLE.
FIRST AID- WASH EYES IMMEDIATELY WITH LARGE AMOUNTS OF WATER OR NORMAL SALINE, OCCASIONALLY LIFTING UPPER AND LOWER LIDS, UNTIL NO EVIDENCE OF CHEMICAL REMAINS (APPROXIMATELY 15-20 MINUTES). GET MEDICAL ATTENTION IMMEDIATELY.

INGESTION: RODEO HERBICIDE: **ACUTE EXPOSURE-** THE LETHAL DOSE IN RATS IS >5,000 MG/KG. SYMPTOMS WERE NOT REPORTED. **CHRONIC EXPOSURE-** ADMINISTRATION OF 300 MG/KG/DAY FOR 6 MONTHS PRODUCED SLIGHTLY REDUCED BODY WEIGHT GAINS AND INCREASED ALKALINE PHOSPHATASE ACTIVITIES IN DOGS.
FIRST AID- TREAT SYMPTOMATICALLY AND SUPPORTIVELY. GET MEDICAL ATTENTION IMMEDIATELY. IF VOMITING OCCURS, KEEP HEAD LOWER THAN HIPS TO PREVENT ASPIRATION.

REACTIVITY

REACTIVITY: STABLE UNDER NORMAL TEMPERATURES AND PRESSURES.
INCOMPATIBILITIES: RODEO HERBICIDE: BASES: EXOTHERMIC REACTION. GALVANIZED OR UNLINED STEEL: MAY REACT PRODUCING A HIGHLY COMBUSTIBLE GAS. IRON: SOLUTIONS MAY BE CORROSIVE. OXIDIZERS: FIRE AND EXPLOSION HAZARD.
DECOMPOSITION: THERMAL DECOMPOSITION MAY RELEASE TOXIC OXIDES OF NITROGEN, PHOSPHORUS AND CARBON.
POLYMERIZATION: HAZARDOUS POLYMERIZATION HAS NOT BEEN REPORTED TO OCCUR UNDER NORMAL TEMPERATURES AND PRESSURES.

STORAGE AND DISPOSAL

OBSERVE ALL FEDERAL, STATE AND LOCAL REGULATIONS WHEN STORING OR DISPOSING OF THIS SUBSTANCE. FOR ASSISTANCE, CONTACT THE DISTRICT DIRECTOR OF THE ENVIRONMENTAL PROTECTION AGENCY.

STORAGE

STORE IN ACCORDANCE WITH 40 CFR 165 RECOMMENDED PROCEDURES FOR THE DISPOSAL AND STORAGE OF PESTICIDES AND PESTICIDE CONTAINERS.
STORE AWAY FROM INCOMPATIBLE SUBSTANCES.

DISPOSAL

DISPOSAL MUST BE IN ACCORDANCE WITH 40 CFR 165 RECOMMENDED PROCEDURES FOR THE DISPOSAL AND STORAGE OF PESTICIDES AND PESTICIDE CONTAINERS.

CONDITIONS TO AVOID

MAY BURN BUT DOES NOT IGNITE READILY. AVOID CONTACT WITH STRONG OXIDIZERS, EXCESSIVE HEAT, SPARKS, OR OPEN FLAME.

SPILL AND LEAK PROCEDURES

OCCUPATIONAL SPILL: STOP LEAK IF YOU CAN DO IT WITHOUT RISK. FOR SMALL SPILLS, TAKE UP WITH SAND OR OTHER ABSORBENT MATERIAL AND PLACE INTO CLEAN, DRY CONTAINERS FOR LATER DISPOSAL. KEEP UNNECESSARY PEOPLE AWAY. ISOLATE HAZARD AREA AND DENY ENTRY.

PROTECTIVE EQUIPMENT

VENTILATION: PROVIDE GENERAL DILUTION VENTILATION.
RESPIRATOR: THE FOLLOWING RESPIRATORS ARE RECOMMENDED BASED ON INFORMATION FOUND IN THE PHYSICAL DATA, TOXICITY AND HEALTH EFFECTS SECTIONS. THEY ARE RANKED IN ORDER FROM MINIMUM TO MAXIMUM RESPIRATORY PROTECTION. THE SPECIFIC RESPIRATOR SELECTED MUST BE BASED ON CONTAMINATION LEVELS FOUND IN THE WORK PLACE, MUST NOT EXCEED THE WORKING LIMITS OF THE RESPIRATOR AND BE JOINTLY APPROVED BY THE NATIONAL INSTITUTE FOR OCCUPATIONAL SAFETY AND HEALTH AND THE MINE SAFETY AND HEALTH ADMINISTRATION (NIOSH-MSHA).
CHEMICAL CARTRIDGE RESPIRATOR WITH PESTICIDE CARTRIDGE.
GAS MASK WITH A PESTICIDE CANISTER (CHIN-STYLE OR FRONT- OR BACK-MOUNTED CANISTER).
TYPE 'C' SUPPLIED-AIR RESPIRATOR OPERATED IN THE PRESSURE-DEMAND OR OTHER POSITIVE PRESSURE OR CONTINUOUS-FLOW MODE.
SELF-CONTAINED BREATHING APPARATUS.
FOR FIREFIGHTING AND OTHER IMMEDIATELY DANGEROUS TO LIFE OR HEALTH CONDITIONS:
SELF-CONTAINED BREATHING APPARATUS WITH FULL FACEPIECE OPERATED IN PRESSURE-DEMAND OR OTHER POSITIVE PRESSURE MODE.
SUPPLIED-AIR RESPIRATOR WITH FULL FACEPIECE AND OPERATED IN PRESSURE-

DEMAND OR OTHER POSITIVE PRESSURE MODE IN COMBINATION WITH AN AUXILIARY SELF-CONTAINED BREATHING APPARATUS OPERATED IN PRESSURE-DEMAND OR OTHER POSITIVE PRESSURE MODE.

CLOTHING: PROTECTIVE CLOTHING NOT REQUIRED. AVOID REPEATED OR PROLONGED CONTACT WITH THIS SUBSTANCE.

GLOVES: PROTECTIVE GLOVES ARE NOT REQUIRED BUT RECOMMENDED.

EYE PROTECTION: EYE PROTECTION NOT REQUIRED, BUT ADVISABLE.

AUTHORIZED BY- OCCUPATIONAL HEALTH SERVICES, INC.
CREATION DATE: 10/05/89 ***REVISION DATE:*** 10/31/89

MATERIAL SAFETY DATA SHEET

OCCUPATIONAL HEALTH SERVICES, INC.
AGRICULTURE AND PESTICIDE DIVISION
450 SEVENTH AVENUE, SUITE 2407
NEW YORK, NEW YORK 10123
1-800-445-MSDS OR (212) 967-1100

EMERGENCY CONTACT:
JOHN S. BRANSFORD, JR. (615) 292-1180

SUBSTANCE IDENTIFICATION

CAS-NUMBER 69-72-7

SUBSTANCE: <u>SALICYLIC ACID</u>

TRADE NAMES/SYNONYMS: BENZOIC ACID, 2-HYDROXY-; O-CARBOXYPHENOL; 2-CARBOXYPHENOL; 2-HYDROXYBENZENECARBOXYLIC ACID; O-HYDROXYBENZOIC ACID; 2-HYDROXYBENZOIC ACID; PHENOL-2-CARBOXYLIC ACID; C7H6O3; PST20315

CHEMICAL FAMILY: CARBOXYLIC ACID, AROMATIC PHENOL

MOLECULAR FORMULA: H-O-C6-H4-C-O2-H

MOLECULAR WEIGHT: 138.13

CERCLA RATINGS (SCALE 0-3): HEALTH=3 FIRE=1 REACTIVITY=0 PERSISTENCE=1

NFPA RATINGS (SCALE 0-4): HEALTH=0 FIRE=1 REACTIVITY=0

COMPONENTS AND CONTAMINANTS

COMPONENT: SALICYLIC ACID ***PERCENT:*** 100.0
CAS# 69-72-7

EXPOSURE LIMITS: NO OCCUPATIONAL EXPOSURE LIMITS ESTABLISHED BY OSHA, ACGIH, OR NIOSH.

PHYSICAL DATA

DESCRIPTION: WHITE, ACICULAR CRYSTALS OR POWDER WITH AN ACRID TASTE.

BOILING POINT: 412 F (211 C) @ 20 C (SUBLIMES) ***MELTING POINT:*** 318 F (159 C)

SPECIFIC GRAVITY: 1.443 ***VAPOR PRESSURE:*** 1.0 MMHG @ 114C

PH: 2.4 @ SATD SOLUTION ***SOLUBILITY IN WATER:*** 0.22% ***VAPOR DENSITY:*** 4.8

SOLVENT SOLUBILITY: SOLUBLE IN ALCOHOL, ETHER AND ACETONE; SLIGHTLY SOLUBLE IN CHLOROFORM, OIL OF TURPENTINE, GLYCEROL, FATS AND OILS; VERY SLIGHTLY SOLUBLE IN BENZENE.

FIRE AND EXPLOSION DATA

FIRE AND EXPLOSION HAZARD: SLIGHT FIRE HAZARD WHEN EXPOSED TO HEAT OR FLAME.
DUST-AIR MIXTURES MAY IGNITE OR EXPLODE.

FLASH POINT: 315 F (157 C) (CC) ***LOWER EXPLOSIVE LIMIT:*** 1.1% @ 392 F (200 C)

AUTOIGNITION TEMP.: 1004 F (540 C)

FIREFIGHTING MEDIA: DRY CHEMICAL, CARBON DIOXIDE, HALON, WATER SPRAY OR STANDARD FOAM (1987 EMERGENCY RESPONSE GUIDEBOOK, DOT P 5800.4).
FOR LARGER FIRES, USE WATER SPRAY, FOG OR STANDARD FOAM (1987 EMERGENCY RESPONSE GUIDEBOOK, DOT P 5800.4).

FIREFIGHTING: MOVE CONTAINER FROM FIRE AREA IF POSSIBLE. DO NOT SCATTER SPILLED MATERIAL WITH HIGH PRESSURE WATER STREAMS. DIKE FIRE CONTROL WATER FOR LATER DISPOSAL (1987 EMERGENCY RESPONSE GUIDEBOOK, DOT P 5800.4, GUIDE PAGE 31).
USE AGENTS SUITABLE FOR TYPE OF SURROUNDING FIRE. AVOID BREATHING HAZARDOUS VAPORS, KEEP UPWIND.
WATER OR FOAM MAY CAUSE FROTHING (NFPA 325M, FIRE HAZARD PROPERTIES OF FLAMMABLE LIQUIDS, GASES, AND VOLATILE SOLIDS, 1984)

TOXICITY

SALICYLIC ACID: IRRITATION DATA: 500 MG/24 HOURS SKIN-RABBIT MILD; 100 MG EYE-RABBIT SEVERE. TOXICITY DATA: 57 MG/KG SKIN-MAN TDLO; 891 MG/KG ORAL-RAT LD50; 480 MG/KG ORAL-MOUSE LD50; 1300 MG/KG ORAL-RABBIT LD50; 400 MG/KG ORAL-CAT LD50; 520 MG/KG SUBCUTANEOUS-MOUSE LD50; 6 GM/KG SUBCUTANEOUS-RABBIT LDLO; 184 MG/KG INTRAVENOUS-MOUSE LD50; 300 MG/KG INTRAPERITONEAL-MOUSE LD50; MUTAGENIC DATA (RTECS); REPRODUCTIVE EFFECTS DATA (RTECS). CARCINOGEN STATUS: NONE. LOCAL EFFECTS: IRRITANT- INHALATION, EYE. ACUTE TOXICITY LEVEL: MODERATELY TOXIC BY INGESTION. TARGET EFFECTS: POISONING MAY AFFECT THE CENTRAL NERVOUS SYSTEM AND KIDNEYS. AT INCREASED RISK FROM EXPOSURE: PERSONS WITH PRE-EXISTING SKIN AND/OR EYE DISORDERS OR IMPAIRED KIDNEY FUNCTION. ADDITIONAL DATA: SALICYLATES MAY CROSS THE PLACENTA AND BE EXCRETED IN BREAST MILK. INTERACTIONS WITH MEDICATIONS HAVE BEEN REPORTED.

HEALTH EFFECTS AND FIRST AID

INHALATION: SALICYLIC ACID: IRRITANT. **<u>ACUTE EXPOSURE</u>-** INHALATION OF THE DUST MAY CAUSE RESPIRATORY TRACT IRRITATION WITH COUGHING, SNEEZING AND DYSPNEA. SEVERE EXPOSURES MAY CAUSE SYSTEMIC TOXICITY; SYMPTOMS MAY INCLUDE HEADACHE, DIZZINESS, RAPID PULSE, AND TINNITUS. OTHER SYMPTOMS AS DESCRIBED IN ACUTE INGESTION MAY ALSO BE POSSIBLE. EXPOSURE TO 0.9 MG/L OF SALICYLIC ACID CAUSED SALIVATION AND NASAL DISCHARGE IN ANIMALS. **<u>CHRONIC EXPOSURE</u>-** NO DATA AVAILABLE.

FIRST AID- REMOVE FROM EXPOSURE AREA TO FRESH AIR IMMEDIATELY. IF BREATHING HAS STOPPED, PERFORM ARTIFICIAL RESPIRATION. KEEP PERSON WARM AND AT REST. TREAT SYMPTOMATICALLY AND SUPPORTIVELY. GET MEDICAL ATTENTION IMMEDIATELY.

SKIN CONTACT: SALICYLIC ACID: **<u>ACUTE EXPOSURE</u>-** MAY BE MILDLY IRRITATING. INTENSE CONTACT UNDER OCCLUSION, ESPECIALLY WITH DAMAGED SKIN, MAY CAUSE ERYTHEMA, SWELLING, AND SCALING. A SKIN RASH MAY DEVELOP IN SENSITIVE INDIVIDUALS. WHEN APPLIED TO LARGE AREAS OF THE SKIN, ESPECIALLY ABRADED OR DAMAGED SKIN, SUFFICIENT ABSORPTION MAY OCCUR TO PRODUCE TOXIC BLOOD LEVELS WITH SYMPTOMS AS DESCRIBED IN ACUTE INGESTION. THE LETHAL DOSE IN RABBITS BY SKIN ABSORPTION WAS >10,000 MG/KG. **<u>CHRONIC EXPOSURE</u>-** REPEATED OR PROLONGED SKIN CONTACT MAY CAUSE DERMATITIS, MARKED IRRITATION OR MILD BURNS. CHRONIC ABSORPTION MAY CAUSE NAUSEA, VOMITING, DIARRHEA, DIZZINESS, LOSS OF HEARING, TINNITUS, LETHARGY, HYPERNEA, PSYCHIC DISTURBANCES AND OTHER EFFECTS AS DESCRIBED IN INGESTION.

FIRST AID- REMOVE CONTAMINATED CLOTHING AND SHOES IMMEDIATELY. WASH AFFECTED AREA WITH SOAP OR MILD DETERGENT AND LARGE AMOUNTS OF WATER UNTIL NO EVIDENCE OF CHEMICAL REMAINS (APPROXIMATELY 15-20 MINUTES). GET MEDICAL ATTENTION IMMEDIATELY.

EYE CONTACT: SALICYLIC ACID: IRRITANT. **<u>ACUTE EXPOSURE</u>-** IN HUMANS, 3% SOLUTIONS HAVE CAUSED IRRITATION AND MODERATE CONJUNCTIVAL INJURY WITH COMPLETE RECOVERY. APPLICATION TO ANIMAL EYES HAS CAUSED SEVERE IRRITATION. **<u>CHRONIC EXPOSURE</u>-** REPEATED OR PROLONGED EXPOSURE TO IRRITANTS MAY CAUSE CONJUNCTIVITIS.

FIRST AID- WASH EYES IMMEDIATELY WITH LARGE AMOUNTS OF WATER OR NORMAL SALINE, OCCASIONALLY LIFTING UPPER AND LOWER LIDS, UNTIL NO EVIDENCE OF CHEMICAL REMAINS (APPROXIMATELY 15-20 MINUTES). GET MEDICAL ATTENTION IMMEDIATELY.

INGESTION: SALICYLIC ACID: **<u>ACUTE EXPOSURE</u>-** LARGE DOSES OF SALICYLATES MAY INITIALLY CAUSE A BURNING PAIN IN THE MOUTH, THROAT AND GASTROINTESTINAL TRACT, NAUSEA, VOMITING, HEADACHE, DIZZINESS, LETHARGY, TINNITUS, TEMPORARY HEARING LOSS, DIMNESS OF VISION, DEEP, RAPID BREATHING AND OCCASIONALLY, DIARRHEA. IN MORE SERIOUS CASES THERE MAY BE FEVER, SWEATING, THIRST, DEHYDRATION, INCOORDINATION, IRRITABILITY, RESTLESSNESS, CONFUSION, DELIRIUM, TREMOR, DROWSINESS, AND A BLEEDING TENDENCY. IN SEVERE CASES, COMA, CONVULSIONS, OLIGURIA, RENAL FAILURE, PULMONARY EDEMA AND RARELY, CEREBRAL EDEMA MAY OCCUR. OTHER CLINICAL FINDINGS MAY INCLUDE ACID-BASE DISTURBANCES, ALTERED BLOOD GLUCOSE LEVELS AND REVERSIBLE HEPATOTOXICITY. IN FATAL CASES, DEATH IS USUALLY DUE TO RESPIRATORY FAILURE OR CARDIOVASCULAR COLLAPSE. AN ATYPICAL SYNDROME OF ASTHMA, ANGIONEUROTIC EDEMA, AND HIVES HAS BEEN REPORTED AS IDIOSYNCRATIC OR HYPERSENSITIVITY REACTIONS. REPRODUCTIVE EFFECTS HAVE BEEN REPORTED IN ANIMALS. **<u>CHRONIC EXPOSURE</u>-** REPEATED USE OF LARGE AMOUNTS MAY RESULT IN CHRONIC SALYCILISM; EFFECTS MAY INCLUDE SKIN ERUPTIONS, EFFECTS ON THE PANCREAS AND OTHER SYMPTOMS AS DESCRIBED IN ACUTE EXPOSURE. MATERNAL INGESTION OF SALICYLATES LATE IN PREGNANCY HAS BEEN ASSOCIATED WITH LOWER BIRTH WEIGHTS, INCREASED PERINATAL MORTALITY, ANTE- AND POSTPARTUM HEMORRHAGE, PROLONGED GESTATION AND COMPLICATED DELIVERIES. REPRODUCTIVE EFFECTS HAVE BEEN REPORTED IN ANIMALS.

FIRST AID- INDUCE EMESIS WITH SYRUP OF IPECAC UNLESS RESPIRATION IS DEPRESSED, IF SO USE AIRWAY-PROTECTED GASTRIC LAVAGE. GIVE ACTIVATED CHARCOAL. LAVAGE AND CATHARSIS ARE HELPFUL UP TO 12 HOURS AFTER INGESTION. DO NOT USE APOMORPHINE OR OTHER CENTRAL NERVOUS SYSTEM DEPRESSANTS SUCH AS BARBITURATES. MAINTAIN AIRWAY AND BLOOD PRESSURE. GIVE ARTIFICIAL RESPIRATIONWITH OXYGEN IF BREATHING IS STOPPED OR RESPIRATION IS DEPRESSED. (DREISBACH, HANDBOOK OF POISONING, 12TH ED.) GET MEDICAL ATTENTION IMMEDIATELY. ADMINISTRATION OF LAVAGE AND OXYGEN SHOULD BE PERFORMED BY QUALIFIED MEDICAL PERSONNEL.

ANTIDOTE: NO SPECIFIC ANTIDOTE. TREAT SYMPTOMATICALLY AND SUPPORTIVELY.

REACTIVITY

REACTIVITY: STABLE UNDER NORMAL TEMPERATURES AND PRESSURES. GRADUALLY DISCOLORS UPON EXPOSURE TO SUNLIGHT. DECOMPOSES ON HEATING AT ATMOSPHERIC PRESSURE.

INCOMPATIBILITIES: SALICYLIC ACID: OXIDIZERS (STRONG): FIRE AND EXPLOSION HAZARD.

DECOMPOSITION: THERMAL DECOMPOSITION PRODUCTS MAY INCLUDE TOXIC OXIDES OF CARBON.

POLYMERIZATION: HAZARDOUS POLYMERIZATION HAS NOT BEEN REPORTED TO OCCUR UNDER NORMAL TEMPERATURES AND PRESSURES.

STORAGE AND DISPOSAL

OBSERVE ALL FEDERAL, STATE AND LOCAL REGULATIONS WHEN STORING OR DISPOSING OF THIS SUBSTANCE. FOR ASSISTANCE, CONTACT THE DISTRICT DIRECTOR OF THE ENVIRONMENTAL PROTECTION AGENCY.

STORAGE

STORE AWAY FROM INCOMPATIBLE SUBSTANCES.
STORE IN A COOL, DRY PLACE PROTECTED AGAINST LIGHT.

CONDITIONS TO AVOID

PREVENT DISPERSION OF DUST IN AIR.

SPILL AND LEAK PROCEDURES

OCCUPATIONAL SPILL: FOR LARGE SPILLS, SWEEP UP WITH A MINIMUM OF DUSTING AND PLACE INTO SUITABLE CLEAN, DRY CONTAINERS FOR RECLAMATION OR LATER DISPOSAL.
RESIDUE SHOULD BE CLEANED UP USING A HIGH-EFFICIENCY PARTICULATE FILTER VACUUM.

PROTECTIVE EQUIPMENT

VENTILATION: PROVIDE LOCAL EXHAUST OR GENERAL DILUTION VENTILATION SYSTEM.

RESPIRATOR: THE FOLLOWING RESPIRATORS ARE RECOMMENDED BASED ON INFORMATION FOUND IN THE PHYSICAL DATA, TOXICITY AND HEALTH EFFECTS SECTIONS. THEY ARE RANKED IN ORDER FROM MINIMUM TO MAXIMUM RESPIRATORY PROTECTION. THE SPECIFIC RESPIRATOR SELECTED MUST BE BASED ON CONTAMINATION LEVELS FOUND IN THE WORK PLACE, MUST NOT EXCEED THE WORKING LIMITS OF THE RESPIRATOR AND BE JOINTLY APPROVED BY THE NATIONAL INSTITUTE FOR OCCUPATIONAL SAFETY AND HEALTH AND THE MINE SAFETY AND HEALTH ADMINISTRATION (NIOSH-MSHA).
DUST AND MIST RESPIRATOR.
CHEMICAL CARTRIDGE RESPIRATOR WITH ORGANIC VAPOR CARTRIDGE(S) WITH A DUST AND MIST FILTER.
CHEMICAL CARTRIDGE RESPIRATOR WITH ORGANIC VAPOR CARTRIDGE(S) IN COMBINATION WITH A HIGH-EFFICIENCY PARTICULATE FILTER.
GAS MASK WITH ORGANIC VAPOR CANISTER (CHIN STYLE OR FRONT- OR BACK-MOUNTED CANISTER) WITH A DUST AND MIST FILTER.
POWERED AIR-PURIFYING RESPIRATOR WITH HIGH-EFFICIENCY PARTICULATE FILTER.
TYPE 'C' SUPPLIED-AIR RESPIRATOR OPERATED IN THE PRESSURE-DEMAND OR OTHER POSITIVE PRESSURE OR CONTINUOUS-FLOW MODE.
SELF-CONTAINED BREATHING APPARATUS.
FOR FIREFIGHTING AND OTHER IMMEDIATELY DANGEROUS TO LIFE OR HEALTH CONDITIONS:
SELF-CONTAINED BREATHING APPARATUS WITH FULL FACEPIECE OPERATED IN PRESSURE-DEMAND OR OTHER POSITIVE PRESSURE MODE.
SUPPLIED-AIR RESPIRATOR WITH FULL FACEPIECE AND OPERATED IN PRESSURE-DEMAND OR OTHER POSITIVE PRESSURE MODE IN COMBINATION WITH AN AUXILIARY SELF-CONTAINED BREATHING APPARATUS OPERATED IN PRESSURE-DEMAND OR OTHER POSITIVE PRESSURE MODE.

CLOTHING: EMPLOYEE MUST WEAR APPROPRIATE PROTECTIVE (IMPERVIOUS) CLOTHING AND EQUIPMENT TO PREVENT REPEATED OR PROLONGED SKIN CONTACT WITH THIS SUBSTANCE.

GLOVES: EMPLOYEE MUST WEAR APPROPRIATE PROTECTIVE GLOVES TO PREVENT CONTACT WITH THIS SUBSTANCE.

EYE PROTECTION: EMPLOYEE MUST WEAR SPLASH-PROOF OR DUST-RESISTANT SAFETY GOGGLES AND A FACESHIELD TO PREVENT CONTACT WITH THIS SUBSTANCE.
EMERGENCY WASH FACILITIES: WHERE THERE IS ANY POSSIBILITY THAT AN EMPLOYEE'S EYES AND/OR SKIN MAY BE EXPOSED TO THIS SUBSTANCE, THE EMPLOYER SHOULD PROVIDE AN EYE WASH FOUNTAIN AND QUICK DRENCH SHOWER WITHIN THE IMMEDIATE WORK AREA FOR EMERGENCY USE.

AUTHORIZED BY- OCCUPATIONAL HEALTH SERVICES, INC.
CREATION DATE: 11/17/89 ***REVISION DATE:*** 04/13/90

MATERIAL SAFETY DATA SHEET

OCCUPATIONAL HEALTH SERVICES, INC.
AGRICULTURE AND PESTICIDE DIVISION
450 SEVENTH AVENUE, SUITE 2407
NEW YORK, NEW YORK 10123
1-800-445-MSDS OR (212) 967-1100

EMERGENCY CONTACT:
JOHN S. BRANSFORD, JR. (615) 292-1180

SUBSTANCE IDENTIFICATION

CAS-NUMBER 3811-49-2

SUBSTANCE: **SALITHION**

TRADE NAMES/SYNONYMS: 4H-1,3,2-BENZODIOXAPHOSPHORIN, 2-METHOXY-, 2-SULFIDE; 2-METHOXY-4H-1,3,2-BENZODIOXAPHOSPHORIN 2-SULFIDE; PHOSPHOROTHIOIC ACID, CYCLIC O,O-(METHYLENE-O-PHENYLENE) O-METHYL ESTER; CYCLIC O,O-(METHYLENE-O-PHENYLENE) O-METHYLPHOSPHOROTHIOATE; PHOSPHOROTHIOIC ACID, O-METHYL ESTER, CYCLIC O,O-ESTER WITH O-HYDROXYBENZYL ALCOHOL; 2-METHOXY-4H-1,3,2-BENZODIOXAPHOSPHININE 2-SULPHIDE; 2-METHOXY-4H-BENZO-1,3,2-DIOXAPHOSPHORIN 2-SULPHIDE; DIOXABENZOFOS; 2-METHOXY-4H-1,3,2LAMBDA-BENZODIOXAPHOSPHINE 2-SULPHIDE; 2-METHOXY-4H-1,3,2LAMBDA-BENZODIOXAPHOSPHORINE 2-SULFIDE; FENFOSPHORIN; 2-METHOXY-4H-BENZO-1,3,2-DIOXAPHOSPHORINE-2-SULFIDE; C8H9O3PS; PST20325

CHEMICAL FAMILY: ORGANOPHOSPHATE

MOLECULAR FORMULA: C8-H9-O3-P-S

MOLECULAR WEIGHT: 216.20

CERCLA RATINGS (SCALE 0-3): HEALTH=3 FIRE=1 REACTIVITY=0 PERSISTENCE=1

NFPA RATINGS (SCALE 0-4): HEALTH=3 FIRE=1 REACTIVITY=0

COMPONENTS AND CONTAMINANTS

COMPONENT: SALITHION ***PERCENT:*** 100.0
CAS# 3811-49-2

OTHER CONTAMINANTS: NONE

EXPOSURE LIMITS: NO OCCUPATIONAL EXPOSURE LIMITS ESTABLISHED BY OSHA, ACGIH, OR NIOSH.

PHYSICAL DATA

DESCRIPTION: LIGHT YELLOW TO GREY POWDER.

MELTING POINT: 127-129 F (53-54C)

SPECIFIC GRAVITY: NOT AVAILABLE ***VAPOR PRESSURE:*** 0.0032 MMHG @ 20 C

SOLUBILITY IN WATER: 4.3% @ 20 C

SOLVENT SOLUBILITY: SOLUBLE IN BENZENE, ACETONE, ACETONITRILE, CYCLOHEXANONE AND XYLENE; MODERATELY SOLUBLE IN TOLUENE.

FIRE AND EXPLOSION DATA

FIRE AND EXPLOSION HAZARD: SLIGHT FIRE HAZARD WHEN EXPOSED TO HEAT OR FLAME.
DUST-AIR MIXTURES MAY IGNITE OR EXPLODE.

FIREFIGHTING MEDIA: DRY CHEMICAL, CARBON DIOXIDE, HALON, WATER SPRAY OR STANDARD FOAM (1987 EMERGENCY RESPONSE GUIDEBOOK, DOT P 5800.4).
FOR LARGER FIRES, USE WATER SPRAY, FOG OR STANDARD FOAM (1987 EMERGENCY RESPONSE GUIDEBOOK, DOT P 5800.4).

FIREFIGHTING: MOVE CONTAINERS FROM FIRE AREA IF POSSIBLE (1987 EMERGENCY RESPONSE GUIDEBOOK, DOT P 5800.4, GUIDE PAGE 53).
EXTINGUISH USING AGENT SUITABLE FOR TYPE OF SURROUNDING FIRE. AVOID BREATHING VAPORS AND DUSTS. KEEP UPWIND.

TOXICITY

SALITHION: CARCINOGEN STATUS: NONE. ACUTE TOXICITY LEVEL: TOXIC BY DERMAL ABSORPTION, INGESTION. TARGET EFFECTS: CHOLINESTERASE INHIBITOR,

NEUROTOXIN. AT INCREASED RISK FROM EXPOSURE: PERSONS WITH RESPIRATORY AILMENTS, RECENT EXPOSURE TO CHOLINESTERASE INHIBITORS OR IMPAIRED CHOLINESTERASE PRODUCTION, OR LIVER MALFUNCTION.* ADDITIONAL DATA: MAY CROSS THE PLACENTA. HIGH ENVIRONMENTAL TEMPERATURES OR EXPOSURE OF THE CHEMICAL TO VISIBLE OR ULTRAVIOLET LIGHT MAY ENHANCE THE TOXICITY. INTERACTIONS WITH MEDICATIONS MAY OCCUR.*

* MAY BE BASED ON GENERAL INFORMATION ON ORGANOPHOSPHATES.

HEALTH EFFECTS AND FIRST AID

INHALATION: SALITHION: SEE INFORMATION ON ORGANOPHOSPHATES. ORGANOPHOSPHATES: CHOLINESTERASE INHIBITOR. **ACUTE EXPOSURE-** WHEN INHALED, THE FIRST EFFECTS OF CHOLINESTERASE INHIBITORS ARE USUALLY RESPIRATORY AND MAY INCLUDE NASAL HYPEREMIA AND WATERY DISCHARGE, COUGH, CHEST DISCOMFORT, DYSPNEA, AND WHEEZING DUE TO INCREASED BRONCHIAL SECRETIONS AND BRONCHOCONSTRICTION. IF SUFFICIENT AMOUNTS ARE ABSORBED, OTHER SYSTEMIC EFFECTS MAY BEGIN WITHIN A FEW MINUTES OR BE DELAYED FOR UP TO 12 HOURS. SYMPTOMS MAY INCLUDE PALLOR, NAUSEA, VOMITING, DIARRHEA, ABDOMINAL CRAMPS, HEADACHE, DIZZINESS, OCULAR PAIN, BLURRED VISION, MIOSIS OR IN SOME CASES, ESPECIALLY INITIALLY, MYDRIASIS, LACRIMATION, SALIVATION, SWEATING, AND CONFUSION. OTHER REPORTED CENTRAL NERVOUS SYSTEM OR NEUROMUSCULAR EFFECTS MAY INCLUDE ATAXIA, SLURRED SPEECH, AREFLEXIA, WEAKNESS, FATIGUE, FASCICULATIONS, TWITCHING, TREMORS POSSIBLY OF THE TONGUE AND EYELIDS, AND EVENTUALLY PARALYSIS OF THE EXTREMITIES AND POSSIBLY OF THE RESPIRATORY MUSCLES. IN SEVERE CASES THERE MAY ALSO BE INVOLUNTARY DEFECATION AND URINATION, CYANOSIS, PSYCHOSIS, HYPERGLYCEMIA, ACUTE PANCREATITIS, CARDIAC IRREGULARITIES, PULMONARY EDEMA, UNCONSCIOUSNESS, CONVULSIONS, AND COMA. DEATH IS PRIMARILY DUE TO RESPIRATORY FAILURE, ALTHOUGH CARDIOVASCULAR EFFECTS INCLUDING CARDIAC ARREST MAY ALSO BE IMPLICATED. LONG TERM SEQUELAE ARE RARE BUT MAY INCLUDE NEUROPSYCHIATRIC DISORDERS AND MYOPATHY WITH MUSCLE TENDERNESS. SOME ORGANOPHOSPHATES MAY CAUSE A DELAYED NEUROPATHY BEGINNING 1-4 WEEKS AFTER AN ACUTE EXPOSURE WHICH MAY OR MAY NOT HAVE CAUSED ACUTE CHOLINERGIC EFFECTS. NUMBNESS, TINGLING, WEAKNESS AND CRAMPING BEGINNING SYMMETRICALLY IN THE LOWER LIMBS MAY PROGRESS TO ATAXIA AND PARALYSIS. IN SEVERE CASES, UPPER LIMB INVOLVEMENT IS POSSIBLE AND FLACCID PARALYSIS MAY PROGRESS TO SPASTIC PARALYSIS WITH EXAGGERATED REFLEXES. IMPROVEMENT MAY OCCUR OVER MONTHS TO YEARS, BUT SOME RESIDUAL IMPAIRMENT USUALLY REMAINS. **CHRONIC EXPOSURE-** REPEATED OR PROLONGED EXPOSURE MAY RESULT IN THE EFFECTS OF ACUTE EXPOSURE INCLUDING THE DELAYED NEUROPATHY. OTHER EFFECTS REPORTED IN WORKERS REPEATEDLY EXPOSED INCLUDE IMPAIRED MEMORY AND CONCENTRATION, ACUTE PSYCHOSIS, SEVERE DEPRESSIONS, IRRITABILTY, CONFUSION, APATHY, EMOTIONAL LABILITY, SOCIAL WITHDRAWAL, CONFUSION, HEADACHE, SPEECH DIFFICULTIES, DELAYED REACTION TIMES, SPATIAL DISORIENTATION, NIGHTMARES, SLEEPWALKING, AND DROWSINESS OR INSOMNIA. AN INFLUENZA-LIKE CONDITION WITH HEADACHE, NAUSEA, WEAKNESS, ANOREXIA AND MALAISE HAS ALSO BEEN REPORTED.

FIRST AID- REMOVE FROM EXPOSURE AREA TO FRESH AIR IMMEDIATELY. IF BREATHING HAS STOPPED, PERFORM ARTIFICIAL RESPIRATION. KEEP PERSON WARM AND AT REST. TREAT SYMPTOMATICALLY AND SUPPORTIVELY. GET MEDICAL ATTENTION IMMEDIATELY.

SKIN CONTACT: SALITHION: TOXIC. SEE INFORMATION ON ORGANOPHOSPHATES. ORGANOPHOSPHATES: CHOLINESTERASE INHIBITOR. **ACUTE EXPOSURE-** LOCALIZED SWEATING AND FASCICULATIONS MAY OCCUR AT THE SITE OF CONTACT. IF SUFFICIENT AMOUNTS ARE ABSORBED, OTHER EFFECTS OF CHOLINESTERASE INHIBITION AS DESCRIBED IN ACUTE INHALATION MAY OCCUR. SYMPTOMS MAY BE DELAYED 2-3 HOURS, BUT USUALLY NO MORE THAN 12 HOURS. THE RATE OF ABSORPTION IS INCREASED BY THE PRESENCE OF DERMATITIS OR HIGH AMBIENT TEMPERATURES. DELAYED NEUROPATHY IS ALSO POSSIBLE. **CHRONIC EXPOSURE-** REPEATED OR PROLONGED EXPOSURE MAY CAUSE EFFECTS AS DESCRIBED IN ACUTE EXPOSURE. SOME ORGANOPHOSPHATES MAY CAUSE SENSITIZATION.

FIRST AID- REMOVE CONTAMINATED CLOTHING IMMEDIATELY. WASH CONTAMINATED AREAS WITH SOAP AND WATER FOLLOWED BY ALCOHOL (ARENA, POISONING, 4TH ED.). EMERGENCY PERSONNEL SHOULD WEAR GLOVES AND AVOID CONTAMINATION. TREAT RESPIRATORY DIFFICULTY WITH ARTIFICIAL RESPIRATION. GET MEDICAL ATTENTION IMMEDIATELY.

EYE CONTACT: SALITHION: SEE INFORMATION ON ORGANOPHOSPHATES. ORGANOPHOSPHATES: CHOLINESTERASE INHIBITOR. **ACUTE EXPOSURE-** DIRECT CONTACT MAY CAUSE PAIN, HYPEREMIA, LACRIMATION, TWITCHING OF THE EYELIDS, MIOSIS, AND CILIARY MUSCLE SPASM WITH LOSS OF ACCOMODATION, BLURRED OR DIMMED VISION AND BROWACHE. SOMETIMES MYDRIASIS MAY OCCUR INSTEAD OF MIOSIS. WITH SUFFICIENT EXPOSURE, OTHER SYMPTOMS OF CHOLINESTERASE INHIBITION AS DESCRIBED IN ACUTE INHALATION MAY OCCUR. **CHRONIC EXPOSURE-** REPEATED OR PROLONGED EXPOSURE MAY CAUSE EFFECTS AS DESCRIBED IN ACUTE EXPOSURE. SOME COMPOUNDS HAVE CAUSED TOXIC EFFECTS ON THE CRYSTALLINE LENS, CONJUNCTIVAL THICKENING AND OBSTRUCTION OF THE NASOLACRIMAL CANALS WHEN USED AS MIOTIC EYEDROPS.

FIRST AID- IRRIGATE EYES WITH WATER OR SALINE SOLUTION. IF SYMPTOMS OF POISONING OCCUR, TREAT RESPIRATORY DIFFICULTY WITH ARTIFICIAL RESPIRATION AND OXYGEN. OBSERVE PATIENT FOR AT LEAST 24-36 HOURS (GOSSELIN, CLINICAL TOXICOLOGY OF COMMERCIAL PRODUCTS, 5TH ED.). GET MEDICAL ATTENTION IMMEDIATELY. OXYGEN SHOULD BE ADMINISTERED BY QUALIFIED MEDICAL PERSONNEL.

INGESTION: SALITHION: NEUROTOXIN/TOXIC. SEE INFORMATION ON ORGANOPHOSPHATES. A SINGLE DOSE OF 120 MG/KG CAUSED IRREVERSIBLE ATAXIA IN CHICKENS, SHEEP AND MICE. ORGANOPHOSPHATES: CHOLINESTERASE INHIBITOR. **ACUTE EXPOSURE-** WHEN INGESTED, THE FIRST EFFECTS MAY BE NAUSEA, VOMITING, ANOREXIA, ABDOMINAL CRAMPS AND DIARRHEA. GASTROINTESTINAL ABSORPTION MAY CAUSE SYMPTOMS OF CHOLINESTERASE INHIBITION AS DESCRIBED IN ACUTE INHALATION. SYMPTOMS MAY BEGIN WITHIN MINUTES OR BE DELAYED FOR HOURS. DELAYED EFFECTS INCLUDING NEUROPATHY MAY ALSO OCCUR. **CHRONIC EXPOSURE-** REPEATED INGESTION MAY CAUSE EFFECTS AS DESCRIBED IN ACUTE EXPOSURE.

FIRST AID- IF PERSON IS ALERT AND RESPIRATION IS NOT DEPRESSED, GIVE SYRUP OF IPECAC FOLLOWED BY WATER (IF VOMITING OCCURS, KEEP HEAD BELOW HIPS TO PREVENT ASPIRATION). IF CONSCIOUSNESS LEVEL DECLINES OR VOMITING HAS NOT OCCURRED IN 15 MINUTES EMPTY STOMACH BY GASTRIC LAVAGE WITH THE AID OF CUFFED ENDOTRACHEAL TUBE USING ISOTONIC SALINE OR 5% SODIUM BICARBONATE FOLLOW WITH ACTIVATED CHARCOAL. ESTABLISH AND MAINTAIN AIRWAY. TREAT RESPIRATORY DIFFICULTY WITH ARTIFICIAL RESPIRATION AND OXYGEN. DO NOT GIVE MORPHINE, AMINOPHYLLINE, PHENOTHIAZINES, RESERPINE, FUROSEMIDE, OR ETHACRYNIC ACID (MORGAN, RECOGNITION AND MANAGEMENT OF PESTICIDE POISONINGS, 3RD ED.). TREAT SYMPTOMATICALLY AND SUPPORTIVELY. ADMINISTRATION OF OXYGEN AND LAVAGE MUST BE PERFORMED BY QUALIFIED MEDICAL PERSONNEL. GET MEDICAL ATTENTION IMMEDIATELY.

ANTIDOTE: THE FOLLOWING ANTIDOTE(S) HAVE BEEN RECOMMENDED. HOWEVER, THE DECISION AS TO WHETHER THE SEVERITY OF POISONING REQUIRES ADMINISTRATION OF ANY ANTIDOTE AND ACTUAL DOSE REQUIRED SHOULD BE MADE BY QUALIFIED MEDICAL PERSONNEL.

FOR CHOLINESTERASE INHIBITORS: ESTABLISH CLEAR AIRWAY AND TISSUE OXYGENATION BY ASPIRATION OF SECRETIONS, AND IF NECESSARY, BY ASSISTED PULMONARY VENTILATION WITH OXYGEN. IMPROVE TISSUE OXYGENATION AS MUCH AS POSSIBLE BEFORE ADMINISTERING ATROPINE TO MINIMIZE THE RISK OF VENTRICULAR FIBRILLATION. ADMINISTER ATROPINE SULFATE INTRAVENOUSLY, OR INTRAMUSCULARLY IF IV INJECTION IS NOT POSSIBLE. IN MODERATELY SEVERE POISONING ADMINISTER ATROPINE SULFATE, 0.4-2.0 MG REPEATED EVERY 15 MINUTES UNTIL ATROPINIZATION IS ACHIEVED (TACHYCARDIA, FLUSHING, DRY MOUTH, MYDRIASIS). MAINTAIN ATROPINIZATION BY REPEATED DOSES FOR 2-12 HOURS, OR LONGER, DEPENDING ON THE SEVERITY OF POISONING. THE APPEARANCE OF RALES IN THE LUNG BASES, MIOSIS, SALIVATION, NAUSEA, BRADYCARDIA, ARE ALL INDICATIONS OF INADEQUATE ATROPINIZATION. SEVERELY POISONED INDIVIDUALS MAY EXHIBIT REMARKABLE TOLERANCE TO ATROPINE; TWO OR MORE TIMES THE DOSAGES SUGGESTED ABOVE MAY BE NEEDED. PERSONS NOT POISONED OR ONLY SLIGHTLY POISONED, HOWEVER, MAY DEVELOP SIGNS OF ATROPINE TOXICITY FROM SUCH LARGE DOSAGES: FEVER, MUSCLE FIBRILLATIONS, AND DELIRIUM ARE THE MAIN SIGNS OF ATROPINE TOXICITY. IF THESE SIGNS APPEAR WHILE THE PATIENT IS FULLY ATROPINIZED, ATROPINE ADMINISTRATION SHOULD BE DISCONTINUED, AT LEAST TEMPORARILY. OBSERVE TREATED PATIENTS CLOSELY AT LEAST 24 HOURS TO INSURE THAT SYMPTOMS (POSSIBLY PULMONARY EDEMA) DO NOT RECUR AS ATROPINIZATION WEARS OFF. IN VERY SEVERE POISONINGS, METABOLIC DISPOSITION OF TOXICANT MAY REQUIRE SEVERAL HOURS OR DAYS DURING WHICH ATROPINIZATION MUST BE MAINTAINED. MARKEDLY LOWER LEVELS OF URINARY METABOLITES INDICATE THAT ATROPINE DOSAGE CAN BE TAPERED OFF. AS DOSAGE IS REDUCED, CHECK THE LUNG BASES FREQUENTLY FOR RALES. IF RALES ARE HEARD OR OTHER SYMPTOMS RETURN, RE-ESTABLISH ATROPINIZATION PROMPTLY (MORGAN, RECOGNITION AND MANAGEMENT OF PESTICIDE POISONINGS, 3RD ED.). ADMINISTRATION OF ANTIDOTE MUST BE PERFORMED BY QUALIFIED MEDICAL PERSONNEL.

IN CASES OF SEVERE POISONING BY ORGANOPHOSPHATE PESTICIDES IN WHICH RESPIRATORY DEPRESSION, MUSCLE WEAKNESS AND TWITCHINGS ARE SEVERE, GIVE PRALIDOXIME (PROTOPAM-AYERST, 2-PAM), 1.0 GRAM INTRAVENOUSLY AT NO MORE THAN 0.5 GRAM PER MINUTE. DOSAGE OF PRALIDOXIME MAY BE REPEATED IN 1-2 HOURS, THEN AT 10-12 HOUR INTERVALS IF NEEDED. IN VERY SEVERE POISONINGS, DOSAGE RATES MAY BE DOUBLED. TREATMENT WITH

PRALIDOXIME WILL BE MOST EFFECTIVE IF GIVEN WITHIN THIRTY-SIX HOURS AFTER POISONING (MORGAN, RECOGNITION AND MANAGEMENT OF PESTICIDE POISONINGS, 3RD ED.). ANTIDOTE SHOULD BE ADMINISTERED BY QUALIFIED MEDICAL PERSONNEL.

REACTIVITY

REACTIVITY: STABLE UNDER NORMAL TEMPERATURES AND PRESSURES.

INCOMPATIBILITIES: SALITHION: ALKALINE MATERIALS (STRONG): INCOMPATIBLE. OXIDIZERS (STRONG): FIRE AND EXPLOSION HAZARD.

DECOMPOSITION: THERMAL DECOMPOSITION PRODUCTS MAY INCLUDE TOXIC OXIDES OF CARBON, SULFUR, AND PHOSPHORUS.

POLYMERIZATION: HAZARDOUS POLYMERIZATION HAS NOT BEEN REPORTED TO OCCUR UNDER NORMAL TEMPERATURES AND PRESSURES.

STORAGE AND DISPOSAL

OBSERVE ALL FEDERAL, STATE AND LOCAL REGULATIONS WHEN STORING OR DISPOSING OF THIS SUBSTANCE. FOR ASSISTANCE, CONTACT THE DISTRICT DIRECTOR OF THE ENVIRONMENTAL PROTECTION AGENCY.

****STORAGE****

STORE IN ACCORDANCE WITH 40 CFR 165 RECOMMENDED PROCEDURES FOR THE DISPOSAL AND STORAGE OF PESTICIDES AND PESTICIDE CONTAINERS.
STORE AWAY FROM INCOMPATIBLE SUBSTANCES.

****DISPOSAL****

DISPOSAL MUST BE IN ACCORDANCE WITH 40 CFR 165 RECOMMENDED PROCEDURES FOR THE DISPOSAL AND STORAGE OF PESTICIDES AND PESTICIDE CONTAINERS.

CONDITIONS TO AVOID

MAY BURN BUT DOES NOT IGNITE READILY.

SPILL AND LEAK PROCEDURES

OCCUPATIONAL SPILL: DO NOT TOUCH SPILLED MATERIAL. STOP LEAK IF YOU CAN DO IT WITHOUT RISK. FOR SMALL SPILLS, TAKE UP WITH SAND OR OTHER ABSORBENT MATERIAL AND PLACE INTO CONTAINERS FOR LATER DISPOSAL. FOR SMALL DRY SPILLS, WITH A CLEAN SHOVEL PLACE MATERIAL INTO CLEAN, DRY CONTAINER AND COVER. MOVE CONTAINERS FROM SPILL AREA. FOR LARGER SPILLS, DIKE FAR AHEAD OF SPILL FOR LATER DISPOSAL. KEEP UNNECESSARY PEOPLE AWAY. ISOLATE HAZARD AREA AND DENY ENTRY.

PROTECTIVE EQUIPMENT

VENTILATION: PROVIDE LOCAL EXHAUST OR PROCESS ENCLOSURE VENTILATION SYSTEM.

RESPIRATOR: THE FOLLOWING RESPIRATORS ARE RECOMMENDED BASED ON INFORMATION FOUND IN THE PHYSICAL DATA, TOXICITY AND HEALTH EFFECTS SECTIONS. THEY ARE RANKED IN ORDER FROM MINIMUM TO MAXIMUM RESPIRATORY PROTECTION. THE SPECIFIC RESPIRATOR SELECTED MUST BE BASED ON CONTAMINATION LEVELS FOUND IN THE WORK PLACE, MUST NOT EXCEED THE WORKING LIMITS OF THE RESPIRATOR AND BE JOINTLY APPROVED BY THE NATIONAL INSTITUTE FOR OCCUPATIONAL SAFETY AND HEALTH AND THE MINE SAFETY AND HEALTH ADMINISTRATION (NIOSH-MSHA).
CHEMICAL CARTRIDGE RESPIRATOR WITH AN ORGANIC VAPOR CARTRIDGE(S) WITH A FULL FACEPIECE AND ORGANIC VAPOR CARTRIDGE(S) IN COMBINATION WITH A DUST AND MIST FILTER.
POWERED AIR-PURIFYING RESPIRATOR WITH A TIGHT-FITTING FACEPIECE AND ORGANIC VAPOR CARTRIDGE(S) IN COMBINATION WITH A HIGH-EFFICIENCY PARTICULATE FILTER.
TYPE 'C' SUPPLIED-AIR RESPIRATOR WITH A FULL FACEPIECE OPERATED IN A PRESSURE-DEMAND OR OTHER POSITIVE PRESSURE MODE.
SELF-CONTAINED BREATHING APPARATUS WITH A FULL FACEPIECE OPERATED IN PRESSURE-DEMAND OR OTHER POSITIVE PRESSURE MODE.
FOR FIREFIGHTING AND OTHER IMMEDIATELY DANGEROUS TO LIFE OR HEALTH CONDITIONS:
SELF-CONTAINED BREATHING APPARATUS WITH FULL FACEPIECE OPERATED IN PRESSURE-DEMAND OR OTHER POSITIVE PRESSURE MODE.
SUPPLIED-AIR RESPIRATOR WITH FULL FACEPIECE AND OPERATED IN PRESSURE-DEMAND OR OTHER POSITIVE PRESSURE MODE IN COMBINATION WITH AN AUXILIARY SELF-CONTAINED BREATHING APPARATUS OPERATED IN PRESSURE-DEMAND OR OTHER POSITIVE PRESSURE MODE.

CLOTHING: EMPLOYEE MUST WEAR APPROPRIATE PROTECTIVE (IMPERVIOUS) CLOTHING AND EQUIPMENT TO PREVENT ANY POSSIBILITY OF SKIN CONTACT WITH THIS SUBSTANCE.

GLOVES: EMPLOYEE MUST WEAR APPROPRIATE PROTECTIVE GLOVES TO PREVENT CONTACT WITH THIS SUBSTANCE.

EYE PROTECTION: EMPLOYEE MUST WEAR SPLASH-PROOF OR DUST-RESISTANT SAFETY GOGGLES WITH OR WITHOUT A FACESHIELD TO PREVENT CONTACT WITH THIS SUBSTANCE.

EMERGENCY EYE WASH: WHERE THERE IS ANY POSSIBILITY THAT AN EMPLOYEE'S EYES MAY BE EXPOSED TO THIS SUBSTANCE, THE EMPLOYER SHOULD PROVIDE AN EYE WASH FOUNTAIN WITHIN THE IMMEDIATE WORK AREA FOR EMERGENCY USE.

AUTHORIZED BY- OCCUPATIONAL HEALTH SERVICES, INC.
CREATION DATE: 03/30/90 ***REVISION DATE:*** 05/07/90

MATERIAL SAFETY DATA SHEET

OCCUPATIONAL HEALTH SERVICES, INC.
AGRICULTURE AND PESTICIDE DIVISION
450 SEVENTH AVENUE, SUITE 2407
NEW YORK, NEW YORK 10123
1-800-445-MSDS OR (212) 967-1100

EMERGENCY CONTACT:
JOHN S. BRANSFORD, JR. (615) 292-1180

SUBSTANCE IDENTIFICATION

CAS-NUMBER 152-16-9

SUBSTANCE: <u>SCHRADAN</u>

TRADE NAMES/SYNONYMS: DIPHOSPHORAMIDE, OCTAMETHYL-; PYROPHOSPHORAMIDE, OCTAMETHYL-; OCTAMETHYLDIPHOSPHORAMIDE; OCTAMETHYLPYROPHOSPHORAMIDE; OCTAMETHYLPYROPHOSPHORIC TETRA-AMIDE; OCTAMETHYL; OMPA; PESTOX; SCHRADANE; SYTAM; RCRA P085; PST20350

CHEMICAL FAMILY: ORGANOPHOSPHATE

MOLECULAR FORMULA: C8-H24-N4-O3-P2

MOLECULAR WEIGHT: 286.30

CERCLA RATINGS (SCALE 0-3): HEALTH=3 FIRE=0 REACTIVITY=U PERSISTENCE=0

NFPA RATINGS (SCALE 0-4): HEALTH=4 FIRE=0 REACTIVITY=U

COMPONENTS AND CONTAMINANTS

COMPONENT: SCHRADAN ***PERCENT:*** 100
CAS# 152-16-9

EXPOSURE LIMITS: NO OCCUPATIONAL EXPOSURE LIMITS ESTABLISHED BY OSHA, ACGIH, OR NIOSH.
SCHRADAN: 100 POUNDS SARA SECTION 302 THRESHOLD PLANNING QUANTITY 100 POUNDS SARA SECTION 304 REPORTABLE QUANTITY 100 POUNDS CERCLA SECTION 103 REPORTABLE QUANTITY

PHYSICAL DATA

DESCRIPTION: COLORLESS VISCOUS LIQUID

BOILING POINT: 244-257 F (118-125 C) @ 0.3 MMHG

MELTING POINT: 57-68 F (14-20 C) ***SPECIFIC GRAVITY:*** 1.1343

VAPOR PRESSURE: 0.001 @ 25 C ***SOLUBILITY IN WATER:*** MISCIBLE

SOLVENT SOLUBILITY: SOLUBLE IN ETHANOL, ACETONE, CHLOROFORM, BENZENE, AND MOST ORGANIC SOLVENTS; ALMOST INSOLUBLE IN HIGHER ALIPHATIC HYDROCARBONS; INSOLUBLE IN HEPTANE, PETROLEUM ETHER

FIRE AND EXPLOSION DATA

FIRE AND EXPLOSION HAZARD: NEGLIGIBLE FIRE HAZARD WHEN EXPOSED TO HEAT OR FLAME.

FIREFIGHTING MEDIA: DRY CHEMICAL, CARBON DIOXIDE, HALON, WATER SPRAY OR STANDARD FOAM (1987 EMERGENCY RESPONSE GUIDEBOOK, DOT P 5800.4). FOR LARGER FIRES, USE WATER SPRAY, FOG OR STANDARD FOAM (1987 EMERGENCY RESPONSE GUIDEBOOK, DOT P 5800.4).

FIREFIGHTING: MOVE CONTAINERS FROM FIRE AREA IF POSSIBLE. FIGHT FIRE FROM MAXIMUM DISTANCE. STAY AWAY FROM STORAGE TANK ENDS. DIKE FIRE CONTROL WATER FOR LATER DISPOSAL. DO NOT SCATTER MATERIAL (1987 EMERGENCY RESPONSE GUIDEBOOK, DOT P 5800.4, GUIDE PAGE 55). EXTINGUISH ONLY IF FLOW CAN BE STOPPED; USE FLOODING AMOUNTS OF WATER AS FOG, SOLID STREAMS MAY BE INEFFECTIVE. COOL CONTAINERS WITH FLOODING AMOUNTS OF WATER FROM AS FAR A DISTANCE AS POSSIBLE. USE WATER SPRAY TO ABSORB TOXIC VAPORS. AVOID BREATHING TOXIC VAPORS; KEEP UPWIND. CONSIDER EVACUATION OF DOWNWIND AREA IF MATERIAL IS LEAKING.

TRANSPORTATION DATA

DEPARTMENT OF TRANSPORTATION HAZARD CLASSIFICATION 49 CFR 172.101: POISON B

DEPARTMENT OF TRANSPORTATION LABELING REQUIREMENTS 49 CFR 172.101 AND SUBPART E: POISON

TOXICITY

SCHRADAN: TOXICITY DATA: 8 MG/M3/4 HOURS INHALATION-RAT LCLO; 20 MG/KG SKIN-RABBIT LDLO; 15 MG/KG SKIN-RAT LD50; 5 MG/KG OCULAR-RABBIT LDLO; 643 UG/KG/30 DAYS INTERMITTENT ORAL-MAN TDLO; 5 MG/KG ORAL-RAT LD50; 26740 UG/KG ORAL-MOUSE LD50; 25 MG/KG ORAL-RABBIT LD50; 9 MG/KG SUBCUTANEOUS-RAT LD50; 14 MG/KG SUBCUTANEOUS-MOUSE LD50; 6 MG/KG INTRAVENOUS-RABBIT LD50; 9400 UG/KG INTRAVENOUS-MOUSE LD50; 5 MG/KG INTRAVENOUS-DOG LD50; 4900 UG/KG INTRAPERITONEAL-RAT LD50; 10 MG/KG INTRAPERITONEAL-MOUSE LD50; 10 MG/KG INTRAPERITONEAL-GUINEA PIG LD50; 9 MG/KG UNREPORTED-RAT LD50; 28 MG/KG UNREPORTED-MOUSE LD50.
CARCINOGEN STATUS: NONE. ACUTE TOXICITY LEVEL: HIGHLY TOXIC BY DERMAL ABSORPTION AND INGESTION. TARGET EFFECTS: CHOLINESTERASE INHIBITOR. POISONING MAY AFFECT THE NERVOUS SYSTEM.* AT INCREASED RISK FROM EXPOSURE: PERSONS WITH RESPIRATORY AILMENTS, RECENT EXPOSURE TO CHOLINESTERASE INHIBITORS OR IMPAIRED CHOLINESTERASE PRODUCTION, OR LIVER MALFUNCTION.* ADDITIONAL DATA: MAY CROSS THE PLACENTA. HIGH ENVIRONMENTAL TEMPERATURES OR EXPOSURE OF THE CHEMICAL TO VISIBLE OR ULTRAVIOLET LIGHT MAY ENHANCE THE TOXICITY. INTERACTIONS WITH MEDICATIONS MAY OCCUR.*
* MAY BE BASED ON GENERAL INFORMATION ON ORGANOPHOSPHATES.

HEALTH EFFECTS AND FIRST AID

INHALATION: SCHRADAN: SEE INFORMATION ON ORGANOPHOSPHATES.
ORGANOPHOSPHATES: CHOLINESTERASE INHIBITOR. **ACUTE EXPOSURE**- WHEN INHALED, THE FIRST EFFECTS OF CHOLINESTERASE INHIBITORS ARE USUALLY RESPIRATORY AND MAY INCLUDE NASAL HYPEREMIA AND WATERY DISCHARGE, COUGH, CHEST DISCOMFORT, DYSPNEA, AND WHEEZING DUE TO INCREASED BRONCHIAL SECRETIONS AND BRONCHOCONSTRICTION. IF SUFFICIENT AMOUNTS ARE ABSORBED, OTHER SYSTEMIC EFFECTS MAY BEGIN WITHIN A FEW MINUTES OR BE DELAYED FOR UP TO 12 HOURS. SYMPTOMS MAY INCLUDE PALLOR, NAUSEA, VOMITING, DIARRHEA, ABDOMINAL CRAMPS, HEADACHE, DIZZINESS, OCULAR PAIN, BLURRED VISION, MIOSIS OR IN SOME CASES, ESPECIALLY INITIALLY, MYDRIASIS, LACRIMATION, SALIVATION, SWEATING, AND CONFUSION. OTHER REPORTED CENTRAL NERVOUS SYSTEM OR NEUROMUSCULAR EFFECTS MAY INCLUDE ATAXIA, SLURRED SPEECH, AREFLEXIA, WEAKNESS, FATIGUE, FASCICULATIONS, TWITCHING, TREMORS POSSIBLY OF THE TONGUE AND EYELIDS, AND EVENTUALLY PARALYSIS OF THE EXTREMITIES AND POSSIBLY OF THE RESPIRATORY MUSCLES. IN SEVERE CASES THERE MAY ALSO BE INVOLUNTARY DEFECATION AND URINATION, CYANOSIS, PSYCHOSIS, HYPERGLYCEMIA, ACUTE PANCREATITIS, CARDIAC IRREGULARITIES, PULMONARY EDEMA, UNCONSCIOUSNESS, CONVULSIONS, AND COMA. DEATH IS PRIMARILY DUE TO RESPIRATORY FAILURE, ALTHOUGH CARDIOVASCULAR EFFECTS INCLUDING CARDIAC ARREST MAY ALSO BE IMPLICATED. LONG TERM SEQUELAE ARE RARE BUT MAY INCLUDE NEUROPSYCHIATRIC DISORDERS AND MYOPATHY WITH MUSCLE TENDERNESS. SOME ORGANOPHOSPHATES MAY CAUSE A DELAYED NEUROPATHY BEGINNING 1-4 WEEKS AFTER AN ACUTE EXPOSURE WHICH MAY OR MAY NOT HAVE CAUSED ACUTE CHOLINERGIC EFFECTS. NUMBNESS, TINGLING, WEAKNESS AND CRAMPING BEGINNING SYMMETRICALLY IN THE LOWER LIMBS MAY PROGRESS TO ATAXIA AND PARALYSIS. IN SEVERE CASES, UPPER LIMB INVOLVEMENT IS POSSIBLE AND FLACCID PARALYSIS MAY PROGRESS TO SPASTIC PARALYSIS WITH EXAGGERATED REFLEXES. IMPROVEMENT MAY OCCUR OVER MONTHS TO YEARS, BUT SOME RESIDUAL IMPAIRMENT USUALLY REMAINS. **CHRONIC EXPOSURE**- REPEATED OR PROLONGED EXPOSURE MAY RESULT IN THE EFFECTS OF ACUTE EXPOSURE INCLUDING THE DELAYED NEUROPATHY. OTHER EFFECTS REPORTED IN WORKERS REPEATEDLY EXPOSED INCLUDE IMPAIRED MEMORY AND CONCENTRATION, ACUTE PSYCHOSIS, SEVERE DEPRESSIONS, IRRITABILTY, CONFUSION, APATHY, EMOTIONAL LABILITY, SOCIAL WITHDRAWAL, CONFUSION, HEADACHE, SPEECH DIFFICULTIES, DELAYED REACTION TIMES, SPATIAL DISORIENTATION, NIGHTMARES, SLEEPWALKING, AND DROWSINESS OR INSOMNIA. AN INFLUENZA-LIKE CONDITION WITH HEADACHE, NAUSEA, WEAKNESS, ANOREXIA AND MALAISE HAS ALSO BEEN REPORTED.

FIRST AID- REMOVE FROM EXPOSURE AREA TO FRESH AIR IMMEDIATELY. IF BREATHING HAS STOPPED, GIVE ARTIFICIAL RESPIRATION. MAINTAIN AIRWAY AND BLOOD PRESSURE AND ADMINISTER OXYGEN IF AVAILABLE. KEEP AFFECTED PERSON WARM AND AT REST. TREAT SYMPTOMATICALLY AND SUPPORTIVELY. ADMINISTRATION OF OXYGEN SHOULD BE PERFORMED BY QUALIFIED PERSONNEL. GET MEDICAL ATTENTION IMMEDIATELY.

SKIN CONTACT: SCHRADAN: HIGHLY TOXIC. SEE INFORMATION ON ORGANOPHOSPHATES.
ORGANOPHOSPHATES: CHOLINESTERASE INHIBITOR. **ACUTE EXPOSURE**- LOCALIZED SWEATING AND FASCICULATIONS MAY OCCUR AT THE SITE OF CONTACT. IF SUFFICIENT AMOUNTS ARE ABSORBED, OTHER EFFECTS OF CHOLINESTERASE INHIBITION AS DESCRIBED IN ACUTE INHALATION MAY OCCUR. SYMPTOMS MAY BE DELAYED 2-3 HOURS, BUT USUALLY NO MORE THAN 12 HOURS. THE RATE OF ABSORPTION IS INCREASED BY THE PRESENCE OF DERMATITIS OR HIGH AMBIENT TEMPERATURES. DELAYED NEUROPATHY IS ALSO POSSIBLE. **CHRONIC EXPOSURE**- REPEATED OR PROLONGED EXPOSURE MAY CAUSE EFFECTS AS DESCRIBED IN ACUTE EXPOSURE. SOME ORGANOPHOSPHATES MAY CAUSE SENSITIZATION.

FIRST AID- REMOVE CONTAMINATED CLOTHING IMMEDIATELY. WASH CONTAMINATED AREAS WITH SOAP AND WATER FOLLOWED BY ALCOHOL (ARENA, POISONING, 4TH ED.). EMERGENCY PERSONNEL SHOULD WEAR GLOVES AND AVOID CONTAMINATION. TREAT RESPIRATORY DIFFICULTY WITH ARTIFICIAL RESPIRATION. GET MEDICAL ATTENTION IMMEDIATELY.

EYE CONTACT: SCHRADAN: SEE INFORMATION ON ORGANOPHOSPHATES.
ORGANOPHOSPHATES: CHOLINESTERASE INHIBITOR. **ACUTE EXPOSURE**- DIRECT CONTACT MAY CAUSE PAIN, HYPEREMIA, LACRIMATION, TWITCHING OF THE EYELIDS, MIOSIS, AND CILIARY MUSCLE SPASM WITH LOSS OF ACCOMODATION, BLURRED OR DIMMED VISION AND BROWACHE. SOMETIMES MYDRIASIS MAY OCCUR INSTEAD OF MIOSIS. WITH SUFFICIENT EXPOSURE, OTHER SYMPTOMS OF CHOLINESTERASE INHIBITION AS DESCRIBED IN ACUTE INHALATION MAY OCCUR. **CHRONIC EXPOSURE**- REPEATED OR PROLONGED EXPOSURE MAY CAUSE EFFECTS AS DESCRIBED IN ACUTE EXPOSURE. SOME COMPOUNDS HAVE CAUSED TOXIC EFFECTS ON THE CRYSTALLINE LENS, CONJUNCTIVAL THICKENING AND OBSTRUCTION OF THE NASOLACRIMAL CANALS WHEN USED AS MIOTIC EYEDROPS.

FIRST AID- IRRIGATE EYES WITH WATER OR SALINE SOLUTION. IF SYMPTOMS OF POISONING OCCUR, TREAT RESPIRATORY DIFFICULTY WITH ARTIFICIAL RESPIRATION AND OXYGEN. OBSERVE PATIENT FOR AT LEAST 24-36 HOURS (GOSSELIN, CLINICAL TOXICOLOGY OF COMMERCIAL PRODUCTS, 5TH ED.). GET MEDICAL ATTENTION IMMEDIATELY. OXYGEN SHOULD BE ADMINISTERED BY QUALIFIED MEDICAL PERSONNEL.

INGESTION: SCHRADAN: HIGHLY TOXIC. SEE INFORMATION ON ORGANOPHOSPHATES.
ORGANOPHOSPHATES: CHOLINESTERASE INHIBITOR. **ACUTE EXPOSURE**- WHEN INGESTED, THE FIRST EFFECTS MAY BE NAUSEA, VOMITING, ANOREXIA, ABDOMINAL CRAMPS AND DIARRHEA. GASTROINTESTINAL ABSORPTION MAY CAUSE SYMPTOMS OF CHOLINESTERASE INHIBITION AS DESCRIBED IN ACUTE INHALATION. SYMPTOMS MAY BEGIN WITHIN MINUTES OR BE DELAYED FOR HOURS. DELAYED EFFECTS INCLUDING NEUROPATHY MAY ALSO OCCUR. **CHRONIC EXPOSURE**- REPEATED INGESTION MAY CAUSE EFFECTS AS DESCRIBED IN ACUTE EXPOSURE.

FIRST AID- IF PERSON IS ALERT AND RESPIRATION IS NOT DEPRESSED, GIVE SYRUP OF IPECAC FOLLOWED BY WATER (IF VOMITING OCCURS, KEEP HEAD BELOW HIPS TO PREVENT ASPIRATION). IF CONSCIOUSNESS LEVEL DECLINES OR VOMITING HAS NOT OCCURRED IN 15 MINUTES EMPTY STOMACH BY GASTRIC LAVAGE WITH THE AID OF CUFFED ENDOTRACHEAL TUBE USING ISOTONIC SALINE OR 5% SODIUM BICARBONATE FOLLOW WITH ACTIVATED CHARCOAL. ESTABLISH AND MAINTAIN AIRWAY. TREAT RESPIRATORY DIFFICULTY WITH ARTIFICIAL RESPIRATION AND OXYGEN. DO NOT GIVE MORPHINE, AMINOPHYLLINE, PHENOTHIAZINES, RESERPINE, FUROSEMIDE, OR ETHACRYNIC ACID (MORGAN, RECOGNITION AND MANAGEMENT OF PESTICIDE POISONINGS, 3RD ED.). TREAT SYMPTOMATICALLY AND SUPPORTIVELY. ADMINISTRATION OF OXYGEN AND LAVAGE MUST BE PERFORMED BY QUALIFIED MEDICAL PERSONNEL. GET MEDICAL ATTENTION IMMEDIATELY.

ANTIDOTE: THE FOLLOWING ANTIDOTE(S) HAVE BEEN RECOMMENDED. HOWEVER, THE DECISION AS TO WHETHER THE SEVERITY OF POISONING REQUIRES ADMINISTRATION OF ANY ANTIDOTE AND ACTUAL DOSE REQUIRED SHOULD BE MADE BY QUALIFIED MEDICAL PERSONNEL.
FOR CHOLINESTERASE INHIBITORS: ESTABLISH CLEAR AIRWAY AND TISSUE OXYGENATION BY ASPIRATION OF SECRETIONS, AND IF NECESSARY, BY ASSISTED PULMONARY VENTILATION WITH OXYGEN. IMPROVE TISSUE OXYGENATION AS MUCH AS POSSIBLE BEFORE ADMINISTERING ATROPINE TO MINIMIZE THE RISK OF VENTRICULAR FIBRILLATION. ADMINISTER ATROPINE SULFATE INTRAVENOUSLY, OR INTRAMUSCULARLY IF IV INJECTION IS NOT POSSIBLE. IN MODERATELY SEVERE POISONING ADMINISTER ATROPINE SULFATE, 0.4-2.0 MG REPEATED EVERY 15 MINUTES UNTIL ATROPINIZATION IS ACHIEVED (TACHYCARDIA, FLUSHING, DRY MOUTH, MYDRIASIS). MAINTAIN ATROPINIZATION BY REPEATED DOSES FOR 2-12 HOURS, OR LONGER, DEPENDING ON THE SEVERITY OF POISONING. THE APPEARANCE OF RALES IN THE LUNG BASES, MIOSIS, SALIVATION, NAUSEA, BRADYCARDIA, ARE ALL INDICATIONS OF INADEQUATE ATROPINIZATION. SEVERELY POISONED INDIVIDUALS MAY EXHIBIT REMARKABLE TOLERANCE TO ATROPINE; TWO OR MORE TIMES THE DOSAGES SUGGESTED ABOVE MAY BE NEEDED. PERSONS NOT POISONED OR ONLY SLIGHTLY POISONED, HOWEVER, MAY DEVELOP SIGNS OF ATROPINE TOXICITY FROM SUCH LARGE DOSAGES: FEVER, MUSCLE FIBRILLATIONS, AND DELIRIUM ARE THE MAIN SIGNS OF ATROPINE TOXICITY. IF THESE SIGNS APPEAR WHILE THE PATIENT IS FULLY ATROPINIZED,

ATROPINE ADMINISTRATION SHOULD BE DISCONTINUED, AT LEAST TEMPORARILY. OBSERVE TREATED PATIENTS CLOSELY AT LEAST 24 HOURS TO INSURE THAT SYMPTOMS (POSSIBLY PULMONARY EDEMA) DO NOT RECUR AS ATROPINIZATION WEARS OFF. IN VERY SEVERE POISONINGS, METABOLIC DISPOSITION OF TOXICANT MAY REQUIRE SEVERAL HOURS OR DAYS DURING WHICH ATROPINIZATION MUST BE MAINTAINED. MARKEDLY LOWER LEVELS OF URINARY METABOLITES INDICATE THAT ATROPINE DOSAGE CAN BE TAPERED OFF. AS DOSAGE IS REDUCED, CHECK THE LUNG BASES FREQUENTLY FOR RALES. IF RALES ARE HEARD OR OTHER SYMPTOMS RETURN, RE-ESTABLISH ATROPINIZATION PROMPTLY (MORGAN, RECOGNITION AND MANAGEMENT OF PESTICIDE POISONINGS, 3RD ED.). ADMINISTRATION OF ANTIDOTE MUST BE PERFORMED BY QUALIFIED MEDICAL PERSONNEL.

IN CASES OF SEVERE POISONING BY ORGANOPHOSPHATE PESTICIDES IN WHICH RESPIRATORY DEPRESSION, MUSCLE WEAKNESS AND TWITCHINGS ARE SEVERE, GIVE PRALIDOXIME (PROTOPAM-AYERST, 2-PAM), 1.0 GRAM INTRAVENOUSLY AT NO MORE THAN 0.5 GRAM PER MINUTE. DOSAGE OF PRALIDOXIME MAY BE REPEATED IN 1-2 HOURS, THEN AT 10-12 HOUR INTERVALS IF NEEDED. IN VERY SEVERE POISONINGS, DOSAGE RATES MAY BE DOUBLED. TREATMENT WITH PRALIDOXIME WILL BE MOST EFFECTIVE IF GIVEN WITHIN THIRTY-SIX HOURS AFTER POISONING (MORGAN, RECOGNITION AND MANAGEMENT OF PESTICIDE POISONINGS, 3RD ED.). ANTIDOTE SHOULD BE ADMINISTERED BY QUALIFIED MEDICAL PERSONNEL.

REACTIVITY

REACTIVITY: NO SPECIFIC DATA AVAILABLE. HOWEVER, A NUMBER OF PHOSPHATE AND THIOPHOSPHATE ESTERS ARE OF LIMITED THERMAL STABILITY AND UNDERGO HIGHLY EXOTHERMIC SELF-ACCELERATING DECOMPOSITION REACTIONS.

INCOMPATIBILITIES: SCHRADAN: ACIDIC CONDITIONS: MAY CAUSE HYDROLYSIS.

DECOMPOSITION: THERMAL DECOMPOSITION MAY RELEASE TOXIC AND/OR HAZARDOUS GASES.

POLYMERIZATION: HAZARDOUS POLYMERIZATION HAS NOT BEEN REPORTED TO OCCUR UNDER NORMAL TEMPERATURES AND PRESSURES.

STORAGE AND DISPOSAL

OBSERVE ALL FEDERAL, STATE AND LOCAL REGULATIONS WHEN STORING OR DISPOSING OF THIS SUBSTANCE. FOR ASSISTANCE, CONTACT THE DISTRICT DIRECTOR OF THE ENVIRONMENTAL PROTECTION AGENCY.

****STORAGE****

STORE IN ACCORDANCE WITH 40 CFR 165 RECOMMENDED PROCEDURES FOR THE DISPOSAL AND STORAGE OF PESTICIDES AND PESTICIDE CONTAINERS.

STORE AWAY FROM INCOMPATIBLE SUBSTANCES.

THRESHOLD PLANNING QUANTITY (TPQ): THE SUPERFUND AMENDMENTS AND REAUTHORIZATION ACT (SARA) SECTION 302 REQUIRES THAT EACH FACILITY WHERE ANY EXTREMELY HAZARDOUS SUBSTANCE IS PRESENT IN A QUANTITY EQUAL TO OR GREATER THAN THE TPQ ESTABLISHED FOR THAT SUBSTANCE NOTIFY THE STATE EMERGENCY RESPONSE COMMISSION FOR THE STATE IN WHICH IT IS LOCATED. SECTION 303 OF SARA REQUIRES THESE FACILITIES TO PARTICIPATE IN LOCAL EMERGENCY RESPONSE PLANNING (40 CFR 355.30).

****DISPOSAL****

DISPOSAL MUST BE IN ACCORDANCE WITH 40 CFR 165 RECOMMENDED PROCEDURES FOR THE DISPOSAL AND STORAGE OF PESTICIDES AND PESTICIDE CONTAINERS.

CONDITIONS TO AVOID

NONE REPORTED.

SPILL AND LEAK PROCEDURES

OCCUPATIONAL SPILL: DO NOT TOUCH SPILLED MATERIAL. STOP LEAK IF YOU CAN DO IT WITHOUT RISK. USE WATER SPRAY TO REDUCE VAPORS. FOR SMALL SPILLS, TAKE UP WITH SAND OR OTHER ABSORBENT MATERIAL AND PLACE INTO CONTAINERS FOR LATER DISPOSAL. FOR SMALL DRY SPILLS, WITH A CLEAN SHOVEL PLACE MATERIAL INTO CLEAN, DRY CONTAINERS AND COVER. MOVE CONTAINERS FROM SPILL AREA. FOR LARGER SPILLS, DIKE FAR AHEAD OF SPILL FOR LATER DISPOSAL. KEEP UNNECESSARY PEOPLE AWAY. ISOLATE HAZARD AREA AND DENY ENTRY. VENTILATE CLOSED SPACES BEFORE ENTERING.

REPORTABLE QUANTITY (RQ): 100 POUNDS THE SUPERFUND AMENDMENTS AND REAUTHORIZATION ACT (SARA) SECTION 304 REQUIRES THAT A RELEASE EQUAL TO OR GREATER THAN THE REPORTABLE QUANTITY FOR THIS SUBSTANCE BE IMMEDIATELY REPORTED TO THE LOCAL EMERGENCY PLANNING COMMITTEE AND THE STATE EMERGENCY RESPONSE COMMISSION (40 CFR 355.40). IF THE RELEASE OF THIS SUBSTANCE IS REPORTABLE UNDER CERCLA SECTION 103, THE NATIONAL RESPONSE CENTER MUST BE NOTIFIED IMMEDIATELY AT (800) 424-8802 OR (202) 426-2675 IN THE METROPOLITAN WASHINGTON, D.C. AREA (40 CFR 302.6).

PROTECTIVE EQUIPMENT

VENTILATION: PROCESS ENCLOSURE RECOMMENDED.

RESPIRATOR: THE FOLLOWING RESPIRATORS ARE RECOMMENDED BASED ON INFORMATION FOUND IN THE PHYSICAL DATA, TOXICITY AND HEALTH EFFECTS SECTIONS. THEY ARE RANKED IN ORDER FROM MINIMUM TO MAXIMUM RESPIRATORY PROTECTION. THE SPECIFIC RESPIRATOR SELECTED MUST BE BASED ON CONTAMINATION LEVELS FOUND IN THE WORK PLACE, MUST NOT EXCEED THE WORKING LIMITS OF THE RESPIRATOR AND BE JOINTLY APPROVED BY THE NATIONAL INSTITUTE FOR OCCUPATIONAL SAFETY AND HEALTH AND THE MINE SAFETY AND HEALTH ADMINISTRATION (NIOSH-MSHA).

TYPE 'C' SUPPLIED-AIR RESPIRATOR WITH A FULL FACEPIECE OPERATED IN PRESSURE-DEMAND OR OTHER POSITIVE PRESSURE MODE OR WITH A FULL FACEPIECE, HELMET OR HOOD OPERATED IN CONTINOUS-FLOW MODE.

SELF-CONTAINED BREATHING APPARATUS WITH A FULL FACEPIECE OPERATED IN PRESSURE-DEMAND OR OTHER POSITIVE PRESSURE MODE.

FOR FIREFIGHTING AND OTHER IMMEDIATELY DANGEROUS TO LIFE OR HEALTH CONDITIONS:

SELF-CONTAINED BREATHING APPARATUS WITH FULL FACEPIECE OPERATED IN PRESSURE-DEMAND OR OTHER POSITIVE PRESSURE MODE.

SUPPLIED-AIR RESPIRATOR WITH FULL FACEPIECE AND OPERATED IN PRESSURE-DEMAND OR OTHER POSITIVE PRESSURE MODE IN COMBINATION WITH AN AUXILIARY SELF-CONTAINED BREATHING APPARATUS OPERATED IN PRESSURE-DEMAND OR OTHER POSITIVE PRESSURE MODE.

CLOTHING: EMPLOYEE MUST WEAR APPROPRIATE PROTECTIVE (IMPERVIOUS) CLOTHING AND EQUIPMENT TO PREVENT ANY POSSIBILITY OF SKIN CONTACT WITH THIS SUBSTANCE.

GLOVES: EMPLOYEE MUST WEAR APPROPRIATE PROTECTIVE GLOVES TO PREVENT CONTACT WITH THIS SUBSTANCE.

EYE PROTECTION: EMPLOYEE MUST WEAR SPLASH-PROOF OR DUST-RESISTANT SAFETY GOGGLES AND A FACESHIELD TO PREVENT CONTACT WITH THIS SUBSTANCE.

EMERGENCY WASH FACILITIES: WHERE THERE IS ANY POSSIBILITY THAT AN EMPLOYEE'S EYES AND/OR SKIN MAY BE EXPOSED TO THIS SUBSTANCE, THE EMPLOYER SHOULD PROVIDE AN EYE WASH FOUNTAIN AND QUICK DRENCH SHOWER WITHIN THE IMMEDIATE WORK AREA FOR EMERGENCY USE.

AUTHORIZED BY- OCCUPATIONAL HEALTH SERVICES, INC.

CREATION DATE: 10/05/89 ***REVISION DATE:*** 05/01/90

MATERIAL SAFETY DATA SHEET

OCCUPATIONAL HEALTH SERVICES, INC.
AGRICULTURE AND PESTICIDE DIVISION
450 SEVENTH AVENUE, SUITE 2407
NEW YORK, NEW YORK 10123
1-800-445-MSDS OR (212) 967-1100

EMERGENCY CONTACT:
JOHN S. BRANSFORD, JR. (615) 292-1180

SUBSTANCE IDENTIFICATION

CAS-NUMBER 8008-74-0

SUBSTANCE: **SESAME OIL**

TRADE NAMES/SYNONYMS: BENNE OIL; TEEL OIL; GINGILLI OIL; OILS, SESAME; BENI OIL; GINGELLY OIL; TEAL OIL; BENE OIL; SIMSIM OIL; TIL OIL; UFUTA OIL; GINGILI OIL; OIL SESAME 4742; PST20575

CHEMICAL FAMILY: VEGETABLE OIL

CERCLA RATINGS (SCALE 0-3): HEALTH=2 FIRE=1 REACTIVITY=0 PERSISTENCE=0

NFPA RATINGS (SCALE 0-4): HEALTH=0 FIRE=1 REACTIVITY=0

COMPONENTS AND CONTAMINANTS

COMPONENT: SESAME OIL ***PERCENT:*** 100.0
CAS# 8008-74-0

OTHER CONTAMINANTS: NONE

EXPOSURE LIMITS: NO OCCUPATIONAL EXPOSURE LIMITS ESTABLISHED BY OSHA, ACGIH, OR NIOSH.

PHYSICAL DATA

DESCRIPTION: ALMOST ODORLESS, PALE YELLOW OIL WITH A BLAND TASTE.

BOILING POINT: NOT AVAILABLE ***MELTING POINT:*** 21 F (-6 C)

SPECIFIC GRAVITY: 0.916-0.920 ***VAPOR PRESSURE:*** NOT AVAILABLE
SOLUBILITY IN WATER: INSOLUBLE
SOLVENT SOLUBILITY: SOLUBLE IN ETHER, PETROLEUM ETHER, HEXANE, CHLOROFORM, AND CARBON DISULFIDE; SLIGHTLY SOLUBLE IN ALCOHOL.

FIRE AND EXPLOSION DATA

FIRE AND EXPLOSION HAZARD: SLIGHT FIRE HAZARD WHEN EXPOSED TO HEAT OR FLAME.
FLASH POINT: 491 F (255 C) (CC) ***FLAMMABILITY CLASS(OSHA):*** IIIB
FIREFIGHTING MEDIA: DRY CHEMICAL, CARBON DIOXIDE, HALON, WATER SPRAY OR STANDARD FOAM (1987 EMERGENCY RESPONSE GUIDEBOOK, DOT P 5800.4).
FOR LARGER FIRES, USE WATER SPRAY, FOG OR STANDARD FOAM (1987 EMERGENCY RESPONSE GUIDEBOOK, DOT P 5800.4).
FIREFIGHTING: MOVE CONTAINER FROM FIRE AREA IF POSSIBLE. DO NOT SCATTER SPILLED MATERIAL WITH HIGH PRESSURE WATER STREAMS. DIKE FIRE CONTROL WATER FOR LATER DISPOSAL (1987 EMERGENCY RESPONSE GUIDEBOOK, DOT P 5800.4, GUIDE PAGE 31).
USE AGENTS SUITABLE FOR TYPE OF SURROUNDING FIRE. AVOID BREATHING HAZARDOUS VAPORS, KEEP UPWIND.
WATER OR FOAM MAY CAUSE FROTHING (NFPA 325M, FIRE HAZARD PROPERTIES OF FLAMMABLE LIQUIDS, GASES, AND VOLATILE SOLIDS, 1984)

TOXICITY

SESAME OIL: IRRITATION DATA: 300 MG/3 DAYS INTERMITTENT SKIN-HUMAN MILD IRRITATION. TOXICITY DATA: 6[illegible]8 UG/KG INTRAVENOUS-RABBIT LD50; TUMORIGENIC DATA (RTECS). CARCINOGEN STATUS: NONE. ACUTE TOXICITY LEVEL: NO DATA AVAILABLE BY OCCUPATIONAL ROUTE OF EXPOSURE. TARGET EFFECTS: NO DATA AVAILABLE.

HEALTH EFFECTS AND FIRST AID

INHALATION: SESAME OIL: **ACUTE EXPOSURE-** INHALATION MAY RESULT IN CHEMICAL PNEUMONITIS. **CHRONIC EXPOSURE-** NO DATA AVAILABLE.
FIRST AID- REMOVE FROM EXPOSURE AREA TO FRESH AIR IMMEDIATELY. IF BREATHING HAS STOPPED, PERFORM ARTIFICIAL RESPIRATION. KEEP PERSON WARM AND AT REST. TREAT SYMPTOMATICALLY AND SUPPORTIVELY. GET MEDICAL ATTENTION IMMEDIATELY.

SKIN CONTACT: SESAME OIL: **ACUTE EXPOSURE-** CONTACT MAY CAUSE DERMATITIS. IMMEDIATE URTICARIAL REACTIONS HAVE BEEN REPORTED IN SENSITIVE INDIVIDUALS. **CHRONIC EXPOSURE-** PROLONGED INTERMITTENT CONTACT WITH HUMAN SKIN PRODUCED MILD IRRITATION. RARELY, SENSITIZATION MAY OCCUR.
FIRST AID- REMOVE CONTAMINATED CLOTHING AND SHOES IMMEDIATELY. WASH AFFECTED AREA WITH SOAP OR MILD DETERGENT AND LARGE AMOUNTS OF WATER UNTIL NO EVIDENCE OF CHEMICAL REMAINS (APPROXIMATELY 15-20 MINUTES). GET MEDICAL ATTENTION IMMEDIATELY.

EYE CONTACT: SESAME OIL: **ACUTE EXPOSURE-** NO DATA AVAILABLE. **CHRONIC EXPOSURE-** NO DATA AVAILABLE.
FIRST AID- WASH EYES IMMEDIATELY WITH LARGE AMOUNTS OF WATER OR NORMAL SALINE, OCCASIONALLY LIFTING UPPER AND LOWER LIDS, UNTIL NO EVIDENCE OF CHEMICAL REMAINS (APPROXIMATELY 15-20 MINUTES). GET MEDICAL ATTENTION IMMEDIATELY.

INGESTION: SESAME OIL: **ACUTE EXPOSURE-** INGESTION OF LARGE QUANTITIES MAY CAUSE A LAXATIVE EFFECT AND POSSIBLY INTESTINAL OBSTRUCTION. A HEAVY EXPOSURE MAY MAKE AN INDIVIDUAL VULNERABLE TO OTHERWISE TOLERATED TOXIC INSULTS. ASPIRATION MAY RESULT IN CHEMICAL PNEUMONITIS. **CHRONIC EXPOSURE-** NO DATA AVAILABLE.
FIRST AID- TREAT SYMPTOMATICALLY AND SUPPORTIVELY. GET MEDICAL ATTENTION IMMEDIATELY. IF VOMITING OCCURS, KEEP HEAD LOWER THAN HIPS TO PREVENT ASPIRATION.
ANTIDOTE: NO SPECIFIC ANTIDOTE. TREAT SYMPTOMATICALLY AND SUPPORTIVELY.

REACTIVITY

REACTIVITY: STABLE UNDER NORMAL TEMPERATURES AND PRESSURES.
INCOMPATIBILITIES: SESAME OIL: OXIDIZERS (STRONG): FIRE AND EXPLOSION HAZARD.
DECOMPOSITION: THERMAL DECOMPOSITION MAY RELEASE ACRID SMOKE AND IRRITATING FUMES.
POLYMERIZATION: HAZARDOUS POLYMERIZATION HAS NOT BEEN REPORTED TO OCCUR UNDER NORMAL TEMPERATURES AND PRESSURES.

STORAGE AND DISPOSAL

OBSERVE ALL FEDERAL, STATE AND LOCAL REGULATIONS WHEN STORING OR DISPOSING OF THIS SUBSTANCE. FOR ASSISTANCE, CONTACT THE DISTRICT DIRECTOR OF THE ENVIRONMENTAL PROTECTION AGENCY.

****STORAGE****

STORE AWAY FROM INCOMPATIBLE SUBSTANCES.
KEEP CONTAINER TIGHTLY CLOSED. PROTECT FROM EXPOSURE TO AIR OR LIGHT.

CONDITIONS TO AVOID

MAY BURN BUT DOES NOT IGNITE READILY. AVOID CONTACT WITH STRONG OXIDIZERS, EXCESSIVE HEAT, SPARKS, OR OPEN FLAME.

SPILL AND LEAK PROCEDURES

OCCUPATIONAL SPILL: STOP LEAK IF YOU CAN DO IT WITHOUT RISK. FOR SMALL SPILLS, TAKE UP WITH SAND OR OTHER ABSORBENT MATERIAL AND PLACE INTO CLEAN, DRY CONTAINERS FOR LATER DISPOSAL. KEEP UNNECESSARY PEOPLE AWAY. ISOLATE HAZARD AREA AND DENY ENTRY.

PROTECTIVE EQUIPMENT

VENTILATION: PROVIDE LOCAL EXHAUST OR GENERAL DILUTION VENTILATION SYSTEM.
RESPIRATOR: THE FOLLOWING RESPIRATORS ARE RECOMMENDED BASED ON INFORMATION FOUND IN THE PHYSICAL DATA, TOXICITY AND HEALTH EFFECTS SECTIONS. THEY ARE RANKED IN ORDER FROM MINIMUM TO MAXIMUM RESPIRATORY PROTECTION. THE SPECIFIC RESPIRATOR SELECTED MUST BE BASED ON CONTAMINATION LEVELS FOUND IN THE WORK PLACE, MUST NOT EXCEED THE WORKING LIMITS OF THE RESPIRATOR AND BE JOINTLY APPROVED BY THE NATIONAL INSTITUTE FOR OCCUPATIONAL SAFETY AND HEALTH AND THE MINE SAFETY AND HEALTH ADMINISTRATION (NIOSH-MSHA).
CHEMICAL CARTRIDGE RESPIRATOR WITH AN ORGANIC VAPOR CARTRIDGE(S) WITH A FULL FACEPIECE.
GAS MASK WITH ORGANIC VAPOR CANISTER (CHIN-STYLE OR FRONT- OR BACK-MOUNTED CANISTER) WITH A FULL FACEPIECE.
TYPE 'C' SUPPLIED-AIR RESPIRATOR WITH A FULL FACEPIECE OPERATED IN PRESSURE-DEMAND OR OTHER POSITIVE PRESSURE MODE OR WITH A FULL FACEPIECE, HELMET OR HOOD OPERATED IN CONTINUOUS-FLOW MODE.
SELF-CONTAINED BREATHING APPARATUS WITH A FULL FACEPIECE OPERATED IN PRESSURE-DEMAND OR OTHER POSITIVE PRESSURE MODE.
FOR FIREFIGHTING AND OTHER IMMEDIATELY DANGEROUS TO LIFE OR HEALTH CONDITIONS:
SELF-CONTAINED BREATHING APPARATUS WITH FULL FACEPIECE OPERATED IN PRESSURE-DEMAND OR OTHER POSITIVE PRESSURE MODE.
SUPPLIED-AIR RESPIRATOR WITH FULL FACEPIECE AND OPERATED IN PRESSURE-DEMAND OR OTHER POSITIVE PRESSURE MODE IN COMBINATION WITH AN AUXILIARY SELF-CONTAINED BREATHING APPARATUS OPERATED IN PRESSURE-DEMAND OR OTHER POSITIVE PRESSURE MODE.
CLOTHING: EMPLOYEE MUST WEAR APPROPRIATE PROTECTIVE (IMPERVIOUS) CLOTHING AND EQUIPMENT TO PREVENT REPEATED OR PROLONGED SKIN CONTACT WITH THIS SUBSTANCE.
GLOVES: EMPLOYEE MUST WEAR APPROPRIATE PROTECTIVE GLOVES TO PREVENT CONTACT WITH THIS SUBSTANCE.
EYE PROTECTION: EMPLOYEE MUST WEAR SPLASH-PROOF OR DUST-RESISTANT SAFETY GOGGLES TO PREVENT EYE CONTACT WITH THIS SUBSTANCE.
EMERGENCY EYE WASH: WHERE THERE IS ANY POSSIBILITY THAT AN EMPLOYEE'S EYES MAY BE EXPOSED TO THIS SUBSTANCE, THE EMPLOYER SHOULD PROVIDE AN EYE WASH FOUNTAIN WITHIN THE IMMEDIATE WORK AREA FOR EMERGENCY USE.

AUTHORIZED BY- OCCUPATIONAL HEALTH SERVICES, INC.
CREATION DATE: 02/08/90 ***REVISION DATE:*** 03/02/90

MATERIAL SAFETY DATA SHEET

OCCUPATIONAL HEALTH SERVICES, INC.
AGRICULTURE AND PESTICIDE DIVISION
450 SEVENTH AVENUE, SUITE 2407
NEW YORK, NEW YORK 10123
1-800-445-MSDS OR (212) 967-1100

EMERGENCY CONTACT:
JOHN S. BRANSFORD, JR. (615) 292-1180

SUBSTANCE IDENTIFICATION

CAS-NUMBER 74051-80-2
SUBSTANCE: **SETHOXYDIM**
TRADE NAMES/SYNONYMS: 2-CYCLOHEXEN-1-ONE, 2-(1-(ETHOXYIMINO)BUTYL)-5-(2-(ETHYLTHIO)PROPYL) -3-HYDROXY-; 2-(1-(ETHXOYIMINOBUTYL)-5-(2-(ETHYLTHIO)PROPYL)-3-HYDROXY-2- CYCLOHEXENE-1-ONE; (+,-)-(ZE)-2-(1-

ETHOXYIMINOBUTYL)-5-(2-(ETHYLTHIO)PROPYL)-3- HYDROXYCYCLOHEX-2-ENONE; (+,-)-2-(1-(ETHOXYIMINO)BUTYL)-5-(2-(ETHYLTHIO)PROPYL)-3-HYDROXY-2-CYCLOHEXEN-1-ONE; 2-(1-(ETHOXYAMINO)BUTYLIDENE)-5-(2-(ETHYLTHIO)PROPYL)-1,3- CYCLOHEXANEDIONE; ALLOXOL S; ARD 34/02; BASF 9052; BAS 90520H; CYETHOXYDIM; EXPAND; NABU; NP55; POAST; C17H29NO3S; PST20577

CHEMICAL FAMILY: KETONE, ALICYCLIC
MOLECULAR FORMULA: C17-H29-N-O3-S
MOLECULAR WEIGHT: 327.53
CERCLA RATINGS (SCALE 0-3): HEALTH=2 FIRE=U REACTIVITY=0 PERSISTENCE=2
NFPA RATINGS (SCALE 0-4): HEALTH=2 FIRE=U REACTIVITY=0

COMPONENTS AND CONTAMINANTS

COMPONENT: SETHOXYDIM ***PERCENT:*** 100.0
CAS# 74051-80-2
OTHER CONTAMINANTS: NONE
EXPOSURE LIMITS: NO OCCUPATIONAL EXPOSURE LIMITS ESTABLISHED BY OSHA, ACGIH, OR NIOSH.

PHYSICAL DATA

DESCRIPTION: ODORLESS, AMBER OILY LIQUID
MELTING POINT: >194 F (>90 C) @ 0.00003 MMHG ***SPECIFIC GRAVITY:*** 1.043
SOLUBILITY IN WATER: 0.0004% @ PH 7
SOLVENT SOLUBILITY: METHANOL, HEXANE, XYLENE, AND MOST ORGANIC SOLVENTS

FIRE AND EXPLOSION DATA

FIRE AND EXPLOSION HAZARD: UNKNOWN FIRE AND EXPLOSION HAZARD.
FIREFIGHTING MEDIA: DRY CHEMICAL, CARBON DIOXIDE, WATER SPRAY OR FOAM FOR LARGER FIRES, USE WATER SPRAY, FOG OR ALCOHOL FOAM
FIREFIGHTING: MOVE CONTAINER FROM FIRE AREA IF POSSIBLE. DO NOT SCATTER SPILLED MATERIAL WITH MORE WATER THAN NEEDED FOR FIRE CONTROL. DIKE FIRE CONTROL WATER FOR LATER DISPOSAL
USE AGENTS SUITABLE FOR TYPE OF SURROUNDING FIRE. AVOID BREATHING HAZARDOUS VAPORS, KEEP UPWIND.

TOXICITY

SETHOXYDIM: TOXICITY DATA: 3200 MG/KG ORAL-RAT LD50. CARCINOGEN STATUS: NONE. LOCAL EFFECTS: IRRITANT- SKIN AND EYES. ACUTE TOXICITY LEVEL: MODERATELY TOXIC BY INGESTION. TARGET EFFECTS: NO DATA AVAILABLE.

HEALTH EFFECTS AND FIRST AID

INHALATION: SETHOXYDIM: **ACUTE EXPOSURE**- MAY CAUSE IRRITATION OF THE MUCOUS MEMBRANES. **CHRONIC EXPOSURE**- PROLONGED OR REPEATED EXPOSURE MAY CAUSE IRRITATION OF OF THE MUCOUS MEMBRANES.
FIRST AID- REMOVE FROM EXPOSURE AREA TO FRESH AIR IMMEDIATELY. IF BREATHING HAS STOPPED, PERFORM ARTIFICIAL RESPIRATION. KEEP PERSON WARM AND AT REST. TREAT SYMPTOMATICALLY AND SUPPORTIVELY. GET MEDICAL ATTENTION IMMEDIATELY.

SKIN CONTACT: SETHOXYDIM: IRRITANT. **ACUTE EXPOSURE**- MAY CAUSE IRRITATION. ONE STUDY INDICATED THAT AN AVERAGE LETHAL DOSE BY DERMAL ABSORPTION IS GREATER THAN 5,000 MG/KG IN RATS. **CHRONIC EXPOSURE**- PROLONGED OR REPEATED EXPOSURE MAY CAUSE DERMATITIS.
FIRST AID- REMOVE CONTAMINATED CLOTHING AND SHOES IMMEDIATELY. WASH AFFECTED AREA WITH SOAP OR MILD DETERGENT AND LARGE AMOUNTS OF WATER UNTIL NO EVIDENCE OF CHEMICAL REMAINS (APPROXIMATELY 15-20 MINUTES). GET MEDICAL ATTENTION IMMEDIATELY.

EYE CONTACT: SETHOXYDIM: IRRITANT. **ACUTE EXPOSURE**- MAY CAUSE IRRITATION. **CHRONIC EXPOSURE**- PROLONGED OR REPEATED EXPOSURE MAY CAUSE CONJUNCTIVITIS.
FIRST AID- WASH EYES IMMEDIATELY WITH LARGE AMOUNTS OF WATER OR NORMAL SALINE, OCCASIONALLY LIFTING UPPER AND LOWER LIDS, UNTIL NO EVIDENCE OF CHEMICAL REMAINS (APPROXIMATELY 15-20 MINUTES). GET MEDICAL ATTENTION IMMEDIATELY.

INGESTION: SETHOXYDIM: **ACUTE EXPOSURE**- A MODERATE DOSE WAS LETHAL IN RATS; NO SYMPTOMS WERE REPORTED. **CHRONIC EXPOSURE**- NO DATA AVAILABLE.
FIRST AID- REMOVE BY GASTRIC LAVAGE AND CATHARSIS. MAINTAIN BLOOD PRESSURE AND AIRWAY. GIVE OXYGEN IF RESPIRATION IS DEPRESSED. DO NOT PERFORM GASTRIC LAVAGE IF VICTIM IS UNCONSCIOUS. GET MEDICAL ATTENTION IMMEDIATELY (DREISBACH, HANDBOOK OF POISONING, 12TH ED.). ADMINISTRATION OF LAVAGE OR OXYGEN SHOULD BE PERFORMED BY QUALIFIED MEDICAL PERSONNEL.
ANTIDOTE: NO SPECIFIC ANTIDOTE. TREAT SYMPTOMATICALLY AND SUPPORTIVELY.

REACTIVITY

REACTIVITY: STABLE UNDER NORMAL TEMPERATURES AND PRESSURES.
INCOMPATIBILITIES: SETHOXYDIM: NO DATA AVAILABLE.
DECOMPOSITION: THERMAL DECOMPOSITION MAY RELEASE TOXIC AND/OR HAZARDOUS GASES.
POLYMERIZATION: HAZARDOUS POLYMERIZATION HAS NOT BEEN REPORTED TO OCCUR UNDER NORMAL TEMPERATURES AND PRESSURES.

STORAGE AND DISPOSAL

OBSERVE ALL FEDERAL, STATE AND LOCAL REGULATIONS WHEN STORING OR DISPOSING OF THIS SUBSTANCE. FOR ASSISTANCE, CONTACT THE DISTRICT DIRECTOR OF THE ENVIRONMENTAL PROTECTION AGENCY.

STORAGE

STORE IN ACCORDANCE WITH 40 CFR 165 RECOMMENDED PROCEDURES FOR THE DISPOSAL AND STORAGE OF PESTICIDES AND PESTICIDE CONTAINERS.
STORE IN A DRY, COOL, VENTILATED AREA.

DISPOSAL

DISPOSAL MUST BE IN ACCORDANCE WITH 40 CFR 165 RECOMMENDED PROCEDURES FOR THE DISPOSAL AND STORAGE OF PESTICIDES AND PESTICIDE CONTAINERS.

CONDITIONS TO AVOID

NONE REPORTED.

SPILL AND LEAK PROCEDURES

OCCUPATIONAL SPILL: STOP LEAK IF YOU CAN DO IT WITHOUT RISK. FOR SMALL SPILLS, TAKE UP WITH SAND OR OTHER ABSORBENT MATERIAL AND PLACE INTO CLEAN, DRY CONTAINERS FOR LATER DISPOSAL. KEEP UNNECESSARY PEOPLE AWAY. ISOLATE HAZARD AREA AND DENY ENTRY.

PROTECTIVE EQUIPMENT

VENTILATION: PROVIDE LOCAL EXHAUST VENTILATION SYSTEM.
RESPIRATOR: THE FOLLOWING RESPIRATORS ARE RECOMMENDED BASED ON INFORMATION FOUND IN THE PHYSICAL DATA, TOXICITY AND HEALTH EFFECTS SECTIONS. THEY ARE RANKED IN ORDER FROM MINIMUM TO MAXIMUM RESPIRATORY PROTECTION. THE SPECIFIC RESPIRATOR SELECTED MUST BE BASED ON CONTAMINATION LEVELS FOUND IN THE WORK PLACE, MUST NOT EXCEED THE WORKING LIMITS OF THE RESPIRATOR AND BE JOINTLY APPROVED BY THE NATIONAL INSTITUTE FOR OCCUPATIONAL SAFETY AND HEALTH AND THE MINE SAFETY AND HEALTH ADMINISTRATION (NIOSH-MSHA).
CHEMICAL CARTRIDGE RESPIRATOR WITH FULL FACEPIECE AND PESTICIDE CARTRIDGE.
TYPE 'C' SUPPLIED-AIR RESPIRATOR WITH A FULL FACEPIECE OPERATED IN PRESSURE-DEMAND OR OTHER POSITIVE PRESSURE MODE OR WITH A FULL FACEPIECE, HELMET OR HOOD OPERATED IN CONTINUOUS-FLOW MODE.
SELF-CONTAINED BREATHING APPARATUS OPERATED IN PRESSURE-DEMAND OR OTHER POSITIVE PRESSURE MODE.
FOR FIREFIGHTING AND OTHER IMMEDIATELY DANGEROUS TO LIFE OR HEALTH CONDITIONS:
SELF-CONTAINED BREATHING APPARATUS WITH FULL FACEPIECE OPERATED IN PRESSURE-DEMAND OR OTHER POSITIVE PRESSURE MODE.
SUPPLIED-AIR RESPIRATOR WITH FULL FACEPIECE AND OPERATED IN PRESSURE-DEMAND OR OTHER POSITIVE PRESSURE MODE IN COMBINATION WITH AN AUXILIARY SELF-CONTAINED BREATHING APPARATUS OPERATED IN PRESSURE-DEMAND OR OTHER POSITIVE PRESSURE MODE.
CLOTHING: EMPLOYEE MUST WEAR APPROPRIATE PROTECTIVE (IMPERVIOUS) CLOTHING AND EQUIPMENT TO PREVENT REPEATED OR PROLONGED SKIN CONTACT WITH THIS SUBSTANCE.
GLOVES: EMPLOYEE MUST WEAR APPROPRIATE PROTECTIVE GLOVES TO PREVENT CONTACT WITH THIS SUBSTANCE.
EYE PROTECTION: EMPLOYEE MUST WEAR SPLASH-PROOF OR DUST-RESISTANT SAFETY GOGGLES TO PREVENT EYE CONTACT WITH THIS SUBSTANCE.
EMERGENCY EYE WASH: WHERE THERE IS ANY POSSIBILITY THAT AN EMPLOYEE'S EYES MAY BE EXPOSED TO THIS SUBSTANCE, THE EMPLOYER SHOULD PROVIDE AN EYE WASH FOUNTAIN WITHIN THE IMMEDIATE WORK AREA FOR EMERGENCY USE.

AUTHORIZED BY- OCCUPATIONAL HEALTH SERVICES, INC.
CREATION DATE: 10/05/89 ***REVISION DATE:*** 05/15/90

MATERIAL SAFETY DATA SHEET

OCCUPATIONAL HEALTH SERVICES, INC.
AGRICULTURE AND PESTICIDE DIVISION
450 SEVENTH AVENUE, SUITE 2407
NEW YORK, NEW YORK 10123
1-800-445-MSDS OR (212) 967-1100

EMERGENCY CONTACT:
JOHN S. BRANSFORD, JR. (615) 292-1180

SUBSTANCE IDENTIFICATION

CAS-NUMBER 1982-49-6

SUBSTANCE: **SIDURON**

TRADE NAMES/SYNONYMS: UREA, N-(2-METHYLCYCLOHEXYL)-N'-PHENYL-; UREA, 1-(2-METHYLCYCLOHEXYL)-3-PHENYL-; N-(2-METHYLCYCLOHEXYL)-N'-PHENYLUREA; 1-(2-METHYLCYCLOHEXYL)-3-PHENYLUREA; H 1318; TUPERSAN; C14H20N2O; PST20586

CHEMICAL FAMILY: SUBSTITUTED UREA

MOLECULAR FORMULA: C6-H5-N-H-C-O-N-H-C6-H10-(C-H3)

MOLECULAR WEIGHT: 232.32

CERCLA RATINGS (SCALE 0-3): HEALTH=1 FIRE=1 REACTIVITY=0 PERSISTENCE=1

NFPA RATINGS (SCALE 0-4): HEALTH=1 FIRE=1 REACTIVITY=0

COMPONENTS AND CONTAMINANTS

COMPONENT: SIDURON ***PERCENT:*** 100.0
CAS# 1982-49-6

OTHER CONTAMINANTS: NONE

EXPOSURE LIMITS: NO OCCUPATIONAL EXPOSURE LIMITS ESTABLISHED BY OSHA, ACGIH, OR NIOSH.

PHYSICAL DATA

DESCRIPTION: COLORLESS CRYSTALLINE SOLID. ***MELTING POINT:*** 271-280 F (133-138 C)

SPECIFIC GRAVITY: 1.08 ***VAPOR PRESSURE:*** <0.0008 MMHG @ 100 C

SOLUBILITY IN WATER: 0.0018% @ 25 C

SOLVENT SOLUBILITY: SOLUBLE IN ETHANOL, DIMETHYLACETAMIDE, DIMETHYLFORMAMIDE, METHYLENE CHLORIDE AND 3,5,5-TRIMETHYLCYCLOHEX-2-ENONE.

FIRE AND EXPLOSION DATA

FIRE AND EXPLOSION HAZARD: SLIGHT FIRE HAZARD WHEN EXPOSED TO HEAT OR FLAME.

FIREFIGHTING MEDIA: DRY CHEMICAL, CARBON DIOXIDE, HALON, WATER SPRAY OR STANDARD FOAM (1987 EMERGENCY RESPONSE GUIDEBOOK, DOT P 5800.4). FOR LARGER FIRES, USE WATER SPRAY, FOG OR STANDARD FOAM (1987 EMERGENCY RESPONSE GUIDEBOOK, DOT P 5800.4).

FIREFIGHTING: MOVE CONTAINERS FROM FIRE AREA IF POSSIBLE. FIGHT FIRE FROM MAXIMUM DISTANCE. STAY AWAY FROM STORAGE TANK ENDS. DIKE FIRE CONTROL WATER FOR LATER DISPOSAL. DO NOT SCATTER MATERIAL (1987 EMERGENCY RESPONSE GUIDEBOOK, DOT P 5800.4, GUIDE PAGE 55). EXTINGUISH USING AGENT SUITABLE FOR TYPE OF SURROUNDING FIRE. USE WATER IN FLOODING QUANTITIES AS FOG. KEEP SPARKS, FLAMES AND OTHER SOURCES OF IGNITION AWAY. KEEP MATERIAL OUT OF WATER SOURCES AND SEWERS. DO NOT TOUCH MATERIAL AND AVOID BREATHING DUSTS AND FUMES FROM BURNING MATERIAL. KEEP UPWIND.

TOXICITY

SIDURON: TOXICITY DATA: 5000 MG/KG ORAL-RAT LD50. CARCINOGEN STATUS: NONE. ACUTE TOXICITY LEVEL: MODERATELY TOXIC BY INGESTION. TARGET EFFECTS: NO DATA AVAILABLE.

HEALTH EFFECTS AND FIRST AID

INHALATION: SIDURON: **ACUTE EXPOSURE-** MAY CAUSE IRRITATION OF THE NOSE, THROAT, AND MUCOUS MEMBRANES. **CHRONIC EXPOSURE-** NO DATA AVAILABLE.

FIRST AID- REMOVE FROM EXPOSURE AREA TO FRESH AIR IMMEDIATELY. IF BREATHING HAS STOPPED, PERFORM ARTIFICIAL RESPIRATION. KEEP PERSON WARM AND AT REST. TREAT SYMPTOMATICALLY AND SUPPORTIVELY. GET MEDICAL ATTENTION IMMEDIATELY.

SKIN CONTACT: SIDURON: **ACUTE EXPOSURE-** MAY CAUSE IRRITATION. NO SYSTEMIC POISONING WAS PRODUCED FROM APPLICATION OF 5500 MG/KG TO THE ABRADED OR INTACT SKIN OF RABBITS. **CHRONIC EXPOSURE-** NO DATA AVAILABLE.

FIRST AID- REMOVE CONTAMINATED CLOTHING AND SHOES IMMEDIATELY. WASH AFFECTED AREA WITH SOAP OR MILD DETERGENT AND LARGE AMOUNTS OF WATER UNTIL NO EVIDENCE OF CHEMICAL REMAINS (APPROXIMATELY 15-20 MINUTES). GET MEDICAL ATTENTION IMMEDIATELY.

EYE CONTACT: SIDURON: **ACUTE EXPOSURE-** MAY CAUSE EYE IRRITATION. **CHRONIC EXPOSURE-** NO DATA AVAILABLE.

FIRST AID- WASH EYES IMMEDIATELY WITH LARGE AMOUNTS OF WATER OR NORMAL SALINE, OCCASIONALLY LIFTING UPPER AND LOWER LIDS, UNTIL NO EVIDENCE OF CHEMICAL REMAINS (APPROXIMATELY 15-20 MINUTES). GET MEDICAL ATTENTION IMMEDIATELY.

INGESTION: SIDURON: **ACUTE EXPOSURE-** A LETHAL DOSE IN RATS WAS 5000 MG/KG; SYMPTOMS WERE NOT REPORTED. **CHRONIC EXPOSURE-** NO OBSERVABLE EFFECTS WERE REPORTED FROM 2-YEAR STUDIES OF RATS FED 500 MG/KG DIET AND DOGS FED 2500 MG/KG DIET.

FIRST AID- REMOVE BY GASTRIC LAVAGE AND CATHARSIS. MAINTAIN BLOOD PRESSURE AND AIRWAY. GIVE OXYGEN IF RESPIRATION IS DEPRESSED. DO NOT PERFORM GASTRIC LAVAGE IF VICTIM IS UNCONSCIOUS. GET MEDICAL ATTENTION IMMEDIATELY (DREISBACH, HANDBOOK OF POISONING, 12TH ED.). ADMINISTRATION OF LAVAGE OR OXYGEN SHOULD BE PERFORMED BY QUALIFIED MEDICAL PERSONNEL.

ANTIDOTE: NO SPECIFIC ANTIDOTE. TREAT SYMPTOMATICALLY AND SUPPORTIVELY.

REACTIVITY

REACTIVITY: STABLE UNDER NORMAL TEMPERATURES AND PRESSURES.

INCOMPATIBILITIES: SIDURON: ACIDS: SLOWLY DECOMPOSES LIBERATING ANILINE. ALKALI: SLOWLY DECOMPOSES LIBERATING ANILINE. OXIDIZERS (STRONG): FIRE AND EXPLOSION HAZARD.

DECOMPOSITION: THERMAL DECOMPOSITION PRODUCTS MAY INCLUDE TOXIC OXIDES OF CARBON AND NITROGEN.

POLYMERIZATION: HAZARDOUS POLYMERIZATION HAS NOT BEEN REPORTED TO OCCUR UNDER NORMAL TEMPERATURES AND PRESSURES.

STORAGE AND DISPOSAL

OBSERVE ALL FEDERAL, STATE AND LOCAL REGULATIONS WHEN STORING OR DISPOSING OF THIS SUBSTANCE. FOR ASSISTANCE, CONTACT THE DISTRICT DIRECTOR OF THE ENVIRONMENTAL PROTECTION AGENCY.

STORAGE

STORE IN ACCORDANCE WITH 40 CFR 165 RECOMMENDED PROCEDURES FOR THE DISPOSAL AND STORAGE OF PESTICIDES AND PESTICIDE CONTAINERS.
STORE AWAY FROM INCOMPATIBLE SUBSTANCES.

DISPOSAL

DISPOSAL MUST BE IN ACCORDANCE WITH 40 CFR 165 RECOMMENDED PROCEDURES FOR THE DISPOSAL AND STORAGE OF PESTICIDES AND PESTICIDE CONTAINERS.

CONDITIONS TO AVOID

MAY BURN BUT DOES NOT IGNITE READILY. CONTAINERS MAY EXPLODE IN HEAT OF FIRE.

SPILL AND LEAK PROCEDURES

OCCUPATIONAL SPILL: DO NOT TOUCH SPILLED MATERIAL. STOP LEAK IF YOU CAN DO IT WITHOUT RISK. USE WATER SPRAY TO REDUCE VAPORS. FOR SMALL SPILLS, TAKE UP WITH SAND OR OTHER ABSORBENT MATERIAL AND PLACE INTO CONTAINERS FOR LATER DISPOSAL. FOR SMALL DRY SPILLS, WITH A CLEAN SHOVEL PLACE MATERIAL INTO CLEAN, DRY CONTAINERS AND COVER. MOVE CONTAINERS FROM SPILL AREA. FOR LARGER SPILLS, DIKE FAR AHEAD OF SPILL FOR LATER DISPOSAL. KEEP UNNECESSARY PEOPLE AWAY. ISOLATE HAZARD AREA AND DENY ENTRY. VENTILATE CLOSED SPACES BEFORE ENTERING.

PROTECTIVE EQUIPMENT

VENTILATION: PROVIDE GENERAL DILUTION VENTILATION.

RESPIRATOR: THE FOLLOWING RESPIRATORS ARE RECOMMENDED BASED ON INFORMATION FOUND IN THE PHYSICAL DATA, TOXICITY AND HEALTH EFFECTS SECTIONS. THEY ARE RANKED IN ORDER FROM MINIMUM TO MAXIMUM RESPIRATORY PROTECTION. THE SPECIFIC RESPIRATOR SELECTED MUST BE BASED ON CONTAMINATION LEVELS FOUND IN THE WORK PLACE, MUST NOT EXCEED THE WORKING LIMITS OF THE RESPIRATOR AND BE JOINTLY APPROVED BY THE NATIONAL INSTITUTE FOR OCCUPATIONAL SAFETY AND HEALTH AND THE MINE SAFETY AND HEALTH ADMINISTRATION (NIOSH-MSHA).

TYPE 'C' SUPPLIED-AIR RESPIRATOR WITH A FULL FACEPIECE OPERATED IN PRESSURE-DEMAND OR OTHER POSITIVE PRESSURE MODE OR WITH A FULL FACEPIECE, HELMET OR HOOD OPERATED IN CONTINOUS-FLOW MODE.

SELF-CONTAINED BREATHING APPARATUS WITH A FULL FACEPIECE OPERATED IN PRESSURE-DEMAND OR OTHER POSITIVE PRESSURE MODE.

FOR FIREFIGHTING AND OTHER IMMEDIATELY DANGEROUS TO LIFE OR HEALTH CONDITIONS:

SELF-CONTAINED BREATHING APPARATUS WITH FULL FACEPIECE OPERATED IN PRESSURE-DEMAND OR OTHER POSITIVE PRESSURE MODE.

SUPPLIED-AIR RESPIRATOR WITH FULL FACEPIECE AND OPERATED IN PRESSURE-

DEMAND OR OTHER POSITIVE PRESSURE MODE IN COMBINATION WITH AN AUXILIARY SELF-CONTAINED BREATHING APPARATUS OPERATED IN PRESSURE-DEMAND OR OTHER POSITIVE PRESSURE MODE.

CLOTHING: EMPLOYEE MUST WEAR APPROPRIATE PROTECTIVE (IMPERVIOUS) CLOTHING AND EQUIPMENT TO PREVENT REPEATED OR PROLONGED SKIN CONTACT WITH THIS SUBSTANCE.

GLOVES: EMPLOYEE MUST WEAR APPROPRIATE PROTECTIVE GLOVES TO PREVENT CONTACT WITH THIS SUBSTANCE.

EYE PROTECTION: EMPLOYEE MUST WEAR SPLASH-PROOF OR DUST-RESISTANT SAFETY GOGGLES TO PREVENT EYE CONTACT WITH THIS SUBSTANCE. EMERGENCY EYE WASH: WHERE THERE IS ANY POSSIBILITY THAT AN EMPLOYEE'S EYES MAY BE EXPOSED TO THIS SUBSTANCE, THE EMPLOYER SHOULD PROVIDE AN EYE WASH FOUNTAIN WITHIN THE IMMEDIATE WORK AREA FOR EMERGENCY USE.

AUTHORIZED BY- OCCUPATIONAL HEALTH SERVICES, INC.
CREATION DATE: 10/05/89 ***REVISION DATE:*** 05/14/90

MATERIAL SAFETY DATA SHEET

OCCUPATIONAL HEALTH SERVICES, INC.
AGRICULTURE AND PESTICIDE DIVISION
450 SEVENTH AVENUE, SUITE 2407
NEW YORK, NEW YORK 10123
1-800-445-MSDS OR (212) 967-1100

EMERGENCY CONTACT:
JOHN S. BRANSFORD, JR. (615) 292-1180

SUBSTANCE IDENTIFICATION

CAS-NUMBER 7631-86-9

SUBSTANCE: **SILICON DIOXIDE, AMORPHOUS**

TRADE NAMES/SYNONYMS: SILICA, AMORPHOUS FUMED; ARTICEL; AEROSIL; AQUAFIL; AMORPHOUS SILICA DUST; SILICON OXIDE; CATALOID; COLLOIDAL SILICA; COLLOIDAL SILICON DIOXIDE; FOSSIL FLOUR; FUMED SILICA; SANTOCEL; FUMED SILICON DIOXIDE; SILICIC ANHYDRIDE; SILICON(IV) OXIDE; SILICA; SPILL TAMER ABSORBENT (MALLINCKRODT); SILICON DIOXIDE; O2SI; PST20610

CHEMICAL FAMILY: SILICON

MOLECULAR FORMULA: SI-O2

MOLECULAR WEIGHT: 60.09

CERCLA RATINGS (SCALE 0-3): HEALTH=3 FIRE=0 REACTIVITY=0 PERSISTENCE=3

NFPA RATINGS (SCALE 0-4): HEALTH=3 FIRE=0 REACTIVITY=0

COMPONENTS AND CONTAMINANTS

COMPONENT: SILICON DIOXIDE, AMORPHOUS ***PERCENT:*** 100
CAS# 7631-86-9

OTHER CONTAMINANTS: NONE

EXPOSURE LIMITS: SILICON DIOXIDE, AMORPHOUS (SILICA, AMORPHOUS): 6 MG/M3 OSHA TWA (<1% CRYSTALLINE SILICA) 10 MG/M3 ACGIH TWA (TOTAL DUST, CONTAINING <1% QUARTZ) (NOTICE OF INTENDED CHANGES 1989-1990)

PHYSICAL DATA

DESCRIPTION: AN ODORLESS, TASTELESS, SOFT, FINE, CHALKY, COLORLESS, GRAY OR WHITE POWDER. ***BOILING POINT:*** 4046 F (2230 C) ***MELTING POINT:*** 3110 F (1710 C)

SPECIFIC GRAVITY: 2.2 ***VAPOR PRESSURE:*** 10 MMHG @ 1732 C

PH: 2.3-11 (AQ SLURRY) ***SOLUBILITY IN WATER:*** INSOLUBLE

SOLVENT SOLUBILITY: SOLUBLE IN HYDROFLUORIC ACID AND IN MOLTEN ALKALI WHEN FINELY DIVIDED

HARDNESS (MOHS): 5.5-6.5

FIRE AND EXPLOSION DATA

FIRE AND EXPLOSION HAZARD: NEGLIGIBLE FIRE HAZARD WHEN EXPOSED TO HEAT OR FLAME.

FIREFIGHTING MEDIA: DRY CHEMICAL, CARBON DIOXIDE, HALON, WATER SPRAY OR STANDARD FOAM (1987 EMERGENCY RESPONSE GUIDEBOOK, DOT P 5800.4). FOR LARGER FIRES, USE WATER SPRAY, FOG OR STANDARD FOAM (1987 EMERGENCY RESPONSE GUIDEBOOK, DOT P 5800.4).

FIREFIGHTING: NO ACUTE HAZARD. MOVE CONTAINER FROM FIRE AREA IF POSSIBLE. AVOID BREATHING VAPORS OR DUSTS; KEEP UPWIND.

TOXICITY

SILICON DIOXIDE, AMORPHOUS (SILICA, AMORPHOUS): TOXICITY DATA: ANHYDROUS: 3160 MG/KG ORAL-RAT LD50; 10 MG/KG INTRATRACHEAL-RAT LDLO; 15 MG/KG INTRAVENOUS-RAT LD50; 50 MG/KG INTRAPERITONEAL-RAT LDLO; 120 MG/KG INTRAPERITONEAL-GUINEA PIG LDLO; MUTAGENIC DATA (RTECS); TUMORIGENIC DATA (RTECS). HYDRATE: NO DATA AVAILABLE. CARCINOGEN STATUS: HUMAN INADEQUATE EVIDENCE, ANIMAL INADEQUATE EVIDENCE (IARC GROUP-3). ACUTE TOXICITY LEVEL: MODERATELY TOXIC BY INGESTION. TARGET EFFECTS: POISONING MAY AFFECT THE LUNGS. AT INCREASED RISK FROM EXPOSURE: PERSONS WITH IMPAIRED PULMONARY FUNCTION.

HEALTH EFFECTS AND FIRST AID

INHALATION: SILICON DIOXIDE, AMORPHOUS (SILICA, AMORPHOUS): **ACUTE EXPOSURE-** EXPOSURE TO HIGH CONCENTRATIONS MAY CAUSE DRYING OF MUCOUS MEMBRANES, COUGHING AND POSSIBLY NOSEBLEEDS. **CHRONIC EXPOSURE-** PULMONARY EFFECTS OF LONGTERM EXPOSURE MAY VARY WITH THE FORM OF THE NATURAL OR SYNTHETIC AMORPHOUS SILICA AND, MORE IMPORTANTLY, THE DEGREE OF CONTAMINATION WITH A CRYSTALLINE FORM OF SILICA. STUDIES DONE ON A GROUP OF WORKERS EXPOSED TO A PRECIPITATED SILICA DUST FOR AN AVERAGE OF 8.6 YEARS, REVEALED NO ADVERSE EFFECTS ON THEIR PULMONARY FUNCTION TESTS OR CHEST X-RAYS. IT IS POSSIBLE HOWEVER, THAT X-RAY CHANGES IN THE LUNGS, WITH ONLY EXERTIONAL DYSPNEA OR WITHOUT ANY DISABILITY, MAY OCCUR IN SOME WORKERS, IF THE QUANTITY OF DUST TO WHICH THEY ARE EXPOSED IS GREAT ENOUGH. THE PRESENCE OF CRYSTALLINE SILICA MAY GREATLY INCREASE THE POTENTIAL FOR A MORE DISABLING SILICOSIS TO OCCUR WITH THE POSSIBILITY OF ADVANCED FIBROSIS AND DIFFUSE OBSTRUCTIVE EMPHYSEMA LEADING TO SEVERE RESPIRATORY CRIPPLING AND ULTIMATELY, A FATAL CARDIORESPIRATORY FAILURE. IN ADDITION, EPIDEMIOLOGICAL STUDIES INDICATE LUNG CANCER OCCURS MORE FREQUENTLY AMONG PERSONS WITH SILICOSIS THAN IN THE GENERAL POPULATION. STUDIES IN WHICH RATS, GUINEA PIGS AND MONKEYS WERE EXPOSED TO FUMED, GEL AND PRECIPITATED FORMS OF AMORPHOUS SILICA AT CONCENTRATIONS OF 7-10 MG/M3 (RESPIRABLE DUST) FOR 5.5-6 HOURS A DAY FOR UP TO 18 MONTHS, RESULTED IN SOME FIBROGENIC LUNG CHANGES IN MONKEYS ONLY, PARTICULARLY WITH THE FUMED FORM. ALL THREE FORMS CAUSED MACROPHAGE AND MONONUCLEAR CELL AGGREGATES WITH RETICULIN FIBERS AND A RESULTANT REDUCTION IN THE SIZE OF THE BRONCHIOLE LUMINA IN THE LUNGS OF THE MONKEYS.

FIRST AID- REMOVE FROM EXPOSURE AREA TO FRESH AIR IMMEDIATELY. IF BREATHING HAS STOPPED, PERFORM ARTIFICIAL RESPIRATION. KEEP PERSON WARM AND AT REST. TREAT SYMPTOMATICALLY AND SUPPORTIVELY. GET MEDICAL ATTENTION IMMEDIATELY.

SKIN CONTACT: SILICON DIOXIDE, AMORPHOUS (SILICA, AMORPHOUS): **ACUTE EXPOSURE-** NO HUMAN DATA AVAILABLE. ONE FUMED SILICA, PARTICLE SIZE 0.5-10 MICRONS WAS CONSIDERED INERT TO MILDLY IRRITATING WHEN TESTED ON RABBIT SKIN. **CHRONIC EXPOSURE-** REPEATED OR PROLONGED CONTACT MAY HAVE A DRYING AND ABRASIVE EFFECT ON THE SKIN.

FIRST AID- REMOVE CONTAMINATED CLOTHING AND SHOES IMMEDIATELY. WASH AFFECTED AREA WITH SOAP OR MILD DETERGENT AND LARGE AMOUNTS OF WATER UNTIL NO EVIDENCE OF CHEMICAL REMAINS (APPROXIMATELY 15-20 MINUTES). GET MEDICAL ATTENTION IMMEDIATELY.

EYE CONTACT: SILICON DIOXIDE, AMORPHOUS (SILICA, AMORPHOUS): **ACUTE EXPOSURE-** PARTICLES MAY CAUSE IMMEDIATE IRRITATION. ONE FUMED SILICA, PARTICLE SIZE 0.5-10 MICRONS, WAS CONSIDERED INERT TO MILDLY IRRITATING WHEN TESTED IN RABBIT EYES. **CHRONIC EXPOSURE-** NO DATA AVAILABLE.

FIRST AID- WASH EYES IMMEDIATELY WITH LARGE AMOUNTS OF WATER OR NORMAL SALINE, OCCASIONALLY LIFTING UPPER AND LOWER LIDS, UNTIL NO EVIDENCE OF CHEMICAL REMAINS (APPROXIMATELY 15-20 MINUTES). GET MEDICAL ATTENTION IMMEDIATELY.

INGESTION: SILICON DIOXIDE, AMORPHOUS (SILICA, AMORPHOUS): **ACUTE EXPOSURE-** THE EFFECTS OF INGESTION ARE PURELY MECHANICAL AS THE SUBSTANCE IS INERT CHEMICALLY AND BIOLOGICALLY BY THIS ROUTE. **CHRONIC EXPOSURE-** NO ADVERSE EFFECTS HAVE BEEN REPORTED FROM USE IN FOOD.

FIRST AID- GIVE WATER OR FLUIDS. EMESIS IS NOT NECESSARY. TREAT SUPPORTIVELY AND SYMPTOMATICALLY. IF IRRITATION OR DIGESTIVE UPSET OCCURS, GET MEDICAL ATTENTION.

ANTIDOTE: NO SPECIFIC ANTIDOTE. TREAT SYMPTOMATICALLY AND SUPPORTIVELY.

REACTIVITY

REACTIVITY: STABLE UNDER NORMAL TEMPERATURES AND PRESSURES.

INCOMPATIBILITIES: SILICON DIOXIDE, AMORPHOUS (SILICA, AMORPHOUS): CHLORINE TRIFLUORIDE: REACTS EXPLOSIVELY. FLUORINE: INCOMPATIBLE. HYDROCHLORIC ACID, WATER: EXOTHERMIC REACTION WITH GEL FORM. HYDROFLUORIC ACID: DISSOLVES, RELEASING SILICON TETRAFLUORIDE.

MAGNESIUM: MAY REACT EXPLOSIVELY ON HEATING IN THE PRESENCE OF MOISTURE. MANGANESE TRIFLUORIDE: MAY REACT VIOLENTLY ON HEATING, RELEASING SILICON TETRAFLUORIDE. OXYGEN DIFLUORIDE: EXOTHERMIC REACTION WHICH MAY BE EXPLOSIVE UNDER CERTAIN CONDITIONS. OZONE: POTENTIAL EXPLOSION HAZARD AT LOW TEMPERATURES IF ORGANIC MATERIAL IS PRESENT. PHOSPHORIC ACID (CONCENTRATED): SLOWLY ATTACKS ON HEATING. SODIUM (BURNING): REACTS WITH FINELY DIVIDED SILICA. VINYL ACETATE: VAPOR MAY REACT VIGOROUSLY WITH GEL. XENON HEXAFLUORIDE: MAY REACT EXPLOSIVELY BY FORMING XENON TRIOXIDE.

DECOMPOSITION: AT TEMPERATURES ABOVE 800 C, CALCINING MAY OCCUR AND AMORPHOUS SILICA MAY BE CONVERTED TO FIBROGENIC CRYSTALLINE SILICA.

POLYMERIZATION: HAZARDOUS POLYMERIZATION HAS NOT BEEN REPORTED TO OCCUR UNDER NORMAL TEMPERATURES AND PRESSURES.

STORAGE AND DISPOSAL

OBSERVE ALL FEDERAL, STATE AND LOCAL REGULATIONS WHEN STORING OR DISPOSING OF THIS SUBSTANCE. FOR ASSISTANCE, CONTACT THE DISTRICT DIRECTOR OF THE ENVIRONMENTAL PROTECTION AGENCY.

STORAGE

STORE AWAY FROM INCOMPATIBLE SUBSTANCES.

CONDITIONS TO AVOID

NONE REPORTED.

SPILL AND LEAK PROCEDURES

OCCUPATIONAL SPILL: RESIDUE SHOULD BE CLEANED UP USING A HIGH-EFFICIENCY PARTICULATE FILTER VACUUM.

PROTECTIVE EQUIPMENT

VENTILATION: PROVIDE LOCAL EXHAUST OR PROCESS ENCLOSURE VENTILATION TO MEET PUBLISHED EXPOSURE LIMITS.

RESPIRATOR: THE FOLLOWING RESPIRATORS AND MAXIMUM USE CONCENTRATIONS ARE RECOMMENDATIONS BY THE U.S. DEPARTMENT OF HEALTH AND HUMAN SERVICES, NIOSH POCKET GUIDE TO CHEMICAL HAZARDS; NIOSH CRITERIA DOCUMENTS OR BY THE U.S. DEPARTMENT OF LABOR, 29 CFR 1910 SUBPART Z. THE SPECIFIC RESPIRATOR SELECTED MUST BE BASED ON CONTAMINATION LEVELS FOUND IN THE WORK PLACE, MUST NOT EXCEED THE WORKING LIMITS OF THE RESPIRATOR AND BE JOINTLY APPROVED BY THE NATIONAL INSTITUTE FOR OCCUPATIONAL SAFETY AND HEALTH AND THE MINE SAFETY AND HEALTH ADMINISTRATION (NIOSH-MSHA).

SILICON DIOXIDE, AMORPHOUS (SILICA, AMORPHOUS):

100 MPPCF- ANY DUST AND MIST RESPIRATOR.

200 MPPCF- ANY DUST AND MIST RESPIRATOR EXCEPT SINGLE-USE AND QUARTER-MASK RESPIRATORS. ANY SUPPLIED-AIR RESPIRATOR. ANY SELF-CONTAINED BREATHING APPARATUS.

500 MPPCF- ANY POWERED AIR-PURIFYING RESPIRATOR WITH A DUST AND MIST FILTER. ANY SUPPLIED-AIR RESPIRATOR OPERATED IN A CONTINUOUS FLOW MODE.

1000 MPPCF- ANY AIR-PURIFYING FULL FACEPIECE RESPIRATOR WITH A HIGH-EFFICIENCY PARTICULATE FILTER ANY POWERED AIR-PURIFYING RESPIRATOR WITH A TIGHT-FITTING FACEPIECE AND A HIGH-EFFICIENCY PARTICULATE FILTER. ANY SELF-CONTAINED BREATHING APPARATUS WITH A FULL FACEPIECE. ANY SUPPLIED-AIR RESPIRATOR WITH A FULL FACEPIECE. ANY SUPPLIED-AIR RESPIRATOR WITH A TIGHT-FITTING FACEPIECE OPERATED IN A CONTINUOUS FLOW MODE.

10,000 MPPCF- ANY SUPPLIED-AIR RESPIRATOR WITH A HALF-MASK AND OPERATED IN A PRESSURE-DEMAND OR OTHER POSITIVE PRESSURE MODE.

ESCAPE- ANY AIR-PURIFYING FULL FACEPIECE RESPIRATOR WITH A HIGH-EFFICIENCY PARTICULATE FILTER. ANY APPROPRIATE ESCAPE-TYPE SELF-CONTAINED BREATHING APPARATUS.

FOR FIREFIGHTING AND OTHER IMMEDIATELY DANGEROUS TO LIFE OR HEALTH CONDITIONS:

SELF-CONTAINED BREATHING APPARATUS WITH FULL FACEPIECE OPERATED IN PRESSURE-DEMAND OR OTHER POSITIVE PRESSURE MODE.

SUPPLIED-AIR RESPIRATOR WITH FULL FACEPIECE AND OPERATED IN PRESSURE-DEMAND OR OTHER POSITIVE PRESSURE MODE IN COMBINATION WITH AN AUXILIARY SELF-CONTAINED BREATHING APPARATUS OPERATED IN PRESSURE-DEMAND OR OTHER POSITIVE PRESSURE MODE.

CLOTHING: EMPLOYEE MUST WEAR APPROPRIATE PROTECTIVE (IMPERVIOUS) CLOTHING AND EQUIPMENT TO PREVENT REPEATED OR PROLONGED SKIN CONTACT WITH THIS SUBSTANCE.

GLOVES: EMPLOYEE MUST WEAR APPROPRIATE PROTECTIVE GLOVES TO PREVENT CONTACT WITH THIS SUBSTANCE.

EYE PROTECTION: EMPLOYEE MUST WEAR SPLASH-PROOF OR DUST-RESISTANT SAFETY GOGGLES TO PREVENT EYE CONTACT WITH THIS SUBSTANCE.

EMERGENCY EYE WASH: WHERE THERE IS ANY POSSIBILITY THAT AN EMPLOYEE'S EYES MAY BE EXPOSED TO THIS SUBSTANCE, THE EMPLOYER SHOULD PROVIDE AN EYE WASH FOUNTAIN WITHIN THE IMMEDIATE WORK AREA FOR EMERGENCY USE.

AUTHORIZED BY- OCCUPATIONAL HEALTH SERVICES, INC.

CREATION DATE: 11/17/89 ***REVISION DATE:*** 07/12/90

MATERIAL SAFETY DATA SHEET

OCCUPATIONAL HEALTH SERVICES, INC.
AGRICULTURE AND PESTICIDE DIVISION
450 SEVENTH AVENUE, SUITE 2407
NEW YORK, NEW YORK 10123
1-800-445-MSDS OR (212) 967-1100

EMERGENCY CONTACT:
JOHN S. BRANSFORD, JR. (615) 292-1180

SUBSTANCE IDENTIFICATION

CAS-NUMBER 63231-67-4

SUBSTANCE: SILICA GEL

TRADE NAMES/SYNONYMS: HYDROXYLATED SILICON DIOXIDE; HI-SIL; GASIL; BIOSIL; KIESELGEL; HYDRATED AMORPHOUS SILICA; MERCKOSORB M.SI.; PARTISIL; POLYPOR; SYLOID; SORBSIL; SYNTHETIC PRECIPITATED SILICAS; O2SI; PST20670

CHEMICAL FAMILY: NON-METALLIC OXIDE
SILICON

MOLECULAR FORMULA: SI-O2

MOLECULAR WEIGHT: 60.09

CERCLA RATINGS (SCALE 0-3): HEALTH=U FIRE=0 REACTIVITY=0 PERSISTENCE=3

NFPA RATINGS (SCALE 0-4): HEALTH=U FIRE=0 REACTIVITY=0

COMPONENTS AND CONTAMINANTS

COMPONENT: SILICA GEL ***PERCENT:*** 100.0
CAS# 63231-67-4

OTHER CONTAMINANTS: NONE

EXPOSURE LIMITS: SILICON DIOXIDE, AMORPHOUS (SILICA, AMORPHOUS): 6 MG/M3 OSHA TWA (<1% CRYSTALLINE SILICA) 10 MG/M3 ACGIH TWA (TOTAL DUST, CONTAINING <1% QUARTZ) (NOTICE OF INTENDED CHANGES 1989-1990)

PHYSICAL DATA

DESCRIPTION: ODORLESS, COLORLESS TO WHITE, AMORPHOUS HYGROSCOPIC POWDER OR GRANULES.

BOILING POINT: 4046 F (2230 C) ***MELTING POINT:*** 3110 F (1710 C)

SPECIFIC GRAVITY: 2.1 ***VAPOR PRESSURE:*** NIL ***PH:*** 2.3-7.4 (AQ SUSP)

SOLUBILITY IN WATER: INSOLUBLE

SOLVENT SOLUBILITY: SOLUBLE IN HYDROFLUORIC ACID, HOT FIXED ALKALI HYDROXIDE SOLUTIONS.

FIRE AND EXPLOSION DATA

FIRE AND EXPLOSION HAZARD: NEGLIGIBLE FIRE HAZARD WHEN EXPOSED TO HEAT OR FLAME.

FIREFIGHTING MEDIA: EXTINGUISH USING AGENT SUITABLE FOR TYPE OF SURROUNDING FIRE.

FIREFIGHTING: NO ACUTE HAZARD. MOVE CONTAINER FROM FIRE AREA IF POSSIBLE. AVOID BREATHING VAPORS OR DUSTS; KEEP UPWIND.

TOXICITY

SILICA GEL: CARCINOGEN STATUS: HUMAN INADEQUATE EVIDENCE, ANIMAL INADEQUATE EVIDENCE (IARC GROUP-3). ACUTE TOXICITY LEVEL: NO DATA AVAILABLE. TARGET EFFECTS: NO DATA AVAILABLE. AT INCREASED RISK FROM EXPOSURE: PERSONS WITH IMPAIRED PULMONARY FUNCTION.

HEALTH EFFECTS AND FIRST AID

INHALATION: SILICA GEL: **ACUTE EXPOSURE-** EXPOSURE TO HIGH CONCENTRATIONS MAY CAUSE DRYING OF MUCOUS MEMBRANES, COUGHING AND POSSIBLY NOSEBLEEDS. **CHRONIC EXPOSURE-** PULMONARY EFFECTS OF LONGTERM EXPOSURE MAY VARY WITH THE FORM OF THE NATURAL OR SYNTHETIC AMORPHOUS SILICA AND, MORE IMPORTANTLY, THE DEGREE OF CONTAMINATION WITH A CRYSTALLINE FORM OF SILICA. STUDIES DONE ON A GROUP OF WORKERS EXPOSED TO A PRECIPITATED SILICA DUST FOR AN AVERAGE OF 8.6 YEARS, REVEALED NO ADVERSE EFFECTS ON THEIR PULMONARY FUNCTION TESTS OR CHEST X-RAYS. IT IS POSSIBLE HOWEVER, THAT X-RAY CHANGES IN THE LUNGS, WITH ONLY EXERTIONAL DYSPNEA OR WITHOUT ANY DISABILITY, MAY OCCUR IN

SOME WORKERS, IF THE QUANTITY OF DUST TO WHICH THEY ARE EXPOSED IS GREAT ENOUGH. THE PRESENCE OF CRYSTALLINE SILICA MAY GREATLY INCREASE THE POTENTIAL FOR A MORE DISABLING SILICOSIS TO OCCUR WITH THE POSSIBILITY OF ADVANCED FIBROSIS AND DIFFUSE OBSTRUCTIVE EMPHYSEMA LEADING TO SEVERE RESPIRATORY CRIPPLING AND ULTIMATELY, A FATAL CARDIORESPIRATORY FAILURE. IN ADDITION, EPIDEMIOLOGICAL STUDIES INDICATE LUNG CANCER OCCURS MORE FREQUENTLY AMONG PERSONS WITH SILICOSIS THAN IN THE GENERAL POPULATION. STUDIES IN WHICH RATS, GUINEA PIGS AND MONKEYS WERE EXPOSED TO FUMED, GEL AND PRECIPITATED FORMS OF AMORPHOUS SILICA AT CONCENTRATIONS OF 7-10 MG/M3 (RESPIRABLE DUST) FOR 5.5-6 HOURS A DAY FOR UP TO 18 MONTHS, RESULTED IN SOME FIBROGENIC LUNG CHANGES IN MONKEYS ONLY, PARTICULARILY WITH THE FUMED FORM. ALL THREE FORMS CAUSED MACROPHAGE AND MONONUCLEAR CELL AGGREGATES WITH RETICULIN FIBERS AND A RESULTANT REDUCTION IN THE SIZE OF THE BRONCHIOLE LUMINA IN THE LUNGS OF THE MONKEYS.

FIRST AID- REMOVE FROM EXPOSURE AREA TO FRESH AIR IMMEDIATELY. IF BREATHING HAS STOPPED, PERFORM ARTIFICIAL RESPIRATION. KEEP PERSON WARM AND AT REST. TREAT SYMPTOMATICALLY AND SUPPORTIVELY. GET MEDICAL ATTENTION IMMEDIATELY.

SKIN CONTACT: SILICA GEL: **ACUTE EXPOSURE**- NO HUMAN DATA AVAILABLE. ONE FUMED SILICA, PARTICLE SIZE 0.5-10 MICRONS WAS CONSIDERED INERT TO MILDLY IRRITATING WHEN TESTED ON RABBIT SKIN. **CHRONIC EXPOSURE**- REPEATED OR PROLONGED CONTACT MAY HAVE A DRYING AND ABRASIVE EFFECT ON THE SKIN.

FIRST AID- REMOVE CONTAMINATED CLOTHING AND SHOES IMMEDIATELY. WASH AFFECTED AREA WITH SOAP OR MILD DETERGENT AND LARGE AMOUNTS OF WATER UNTIL NO EVIDENCE OF CHEMICAL REMAINS (APPROXIMATELY 15-20 MINUTES). GET MEDICAL ATTENTION IMMEDIATELY.

EYE CONTACT: SILICA GEL: **ACUTE EXPOSURE**- PARTICLES MAY CAUSE IMMEDIATE IRRITATION. ONE FUMED SILICA, PARTICLE SIZE 0.5-10 MICRONS, WAS CONSIDERED INERT TO MILDLY IRRITATING WHEN TESTED IN RABBIT EYES. **CHRONIC EXPOSURE**- NO DATA AVAILABLE.

FIRST AID- WASH EYES IMMEDIATELY WITH LARGE AMOUNTS OF WATER OR NORMAL SALINE, OCCASIONALLY LIFTING UPPER AND LOWER LIDS, UNTIL NO EVIDENCE OF CHEMICAL REMAINS (APPROXIMATELY 15-20 MINUTES). GET MEDICAL ATTENTION IMMEDIATELY.

INGESTION: SILICA GEL: **ACUTE EXPOSURE**- THE EFFECTS OF INGESTION ARE PURELY MECHANICAL AS THE SUBSTANCE IS INERT CHEMICALLY AND BIOLOGICALLY BY THIS ROUTE. **CHRONIC EXPOSURE**- AMORPHOUS SILICA IS PERMITTED IN SOME FORMS AS A FOOD ADDITIVE IN AMOUNTS OF LESS THAN 2% BY WEIGHT.

FIRST AID- GIVE WATER OR FLUIDS. EMESIS IS NOT NECESSARY. TREAT SUPPORTIVELY AND SYMPTOMATICALLY. IF IRRITATION OR DIGESTIVE UPSET OCCURS, GET MEDICAL ATTENTION.

ANTIDOTE: NO SPECIFIC ANTIDOTE. TREAT SYMPTOMATICALLY AND SUPPORTIVELY.

REACTIVITY

REACTIVITY: STABLE UNDER NORMAL TEMPERATURES AND PRESSURES.

INCOMPATIBILITIES: SILICA GEL: FLUORINE: FIRE AND EXPLOSION HAZARD. HYDROCHLORIC ACID: MAY REACT VIOLENTLY DUE TO HEAT OF ADSORPTION. MAGNESIUM: MAY EXPLODE VIOLENTLY. MANGANESE TRIFLUORIDE: MAY CAUSE VIOLENT REACTION IF HEATED WITH RELEASE OF SILICON TRIFLUORIDE. MANGANESE TRIOXIDE: FIRE AND EXPLOSION HAZARD. OXIDIZERS (STRONG): FIRE HAZARD. OXYGEN DIFLUORIDE: EXOTHERMIC REACTION WITH POSSIBLE EXPLOSION. OZONE: POSSIBLE EXPLOSION AT TEMPERATURES BELOW -100 C. VINYL ACETATE: MAY REACT VIGOROUSLY. XENON HEXAFLUORIDE: MAY DETONATE WITH THE FORMATION OF XENON TRIOXIDE.

DECOMPOSITION: AT TEMPERATURES ABOVE 800 C, CALCINING MAY OCCUR AND AMORPHOUS SILICA MAY BE CONVERTED TO FIBROGENIC CRYSTALLINE SILICA.

POLYMERIZATION: HAZARDOUS POLYMERIZATION HAS NOT BEEN REPORTED TO OCCUR UNDER NORMAL TEMPERATURES AND PRESSURES.

STORAGE AND DISPOSAL

OBSERVE ALL FEDERAL, STATE AND LOCAL REGULATIONS WHEN STORING OR DISPOSING OF THIS SUBSTANCE. FOR ASSISTANCE, CONTACT THE DISTRICT DIRECTOR OF THE ENVIRONMENTAL PROTECTION AGENCY.

****STORAGE****

STORE AWAY FROM INCOMPATIBLE SUBSTANCES.

CONDITIONS TO AVOID

PREVENT DISPERSION OF DUST IN AIR.

SPILL AND LEAK PROCEDURES

OCCUPATIONAL SPILL: RESIDUE SHOULD BE CLEANED UP USING A HIGH-EFFICIENCY PARTICULATE FILTER VACUUM.
FOR LARGE SPILLS, SWEEP UP WITH A MINIMUM OF DUSTING AND PLACE INTO SUITABLE CLEAN, DRY CONTAINERS FOR RECLAMATION OR LATER DISPOSAL.

PROTECTIVE EQUIPMENT

VENTILATION: PROVIDE LOCAL EXHAUST OR PROCESS ENCLOSURE VENTILATION TO MEET PUBLISHED EXPOSURE LIMITS.

RESPIRATOR: THE FOLLOWING RESPIRATORS AND MAXIMUM USE CONCENTRATIONS ARE RECOMMENDATIONS BY THE U.S. DEPARTMENT OF HEALTH AND HUMAN SERVICES, NIOSH POCKET GUIDE TO CHEMICAL HAZARDS; NIOSH CRITERIA DOCUMENTS OR BY THE U.S. DEPARTMENT OF LABOR, 29 CFR 1910 SUBPART Z. THE SPECIFIC RESPIRATOR SELECTED MUST BE BASED ON CONTAMINATION LEVELS FOUND IN THE WORK PLACE, MUST NOT EXCEED THE WORKING LIMITS OF THE RESPIRATOR AND BE JOINTLY APPROVED BY THE NATIONAL INSTITUTE FOR OCCUPATIONAL SAFETY AND HEALTH AND THE MINE SAFETY AND HEALTH ADMINISTRATION (NIOSH-MSHA).
SILICON DIOXIDE, AMORPHOUS (SILICA, AMORPHOUS):
100 MPPCF- ANY DUST AND MIST RESPIRATOR.
200 MPPCF- ANY DUST AND MIST RESPIRATOR EXCEPT SINGLE-USE AND QUARTER-MASK RESPIRATORS. ANY SUPPLIED-AIR RESPIRATOR. ANY SELF-CONTAINED BREATHING APPARATUS.
500 MPPCF- ANY POWERED AIR-PURIFYING RESPIRATOR WITH A DUST AND MIST FILTER. ANY SUPPLIED-AIR RESPIRATOR OPERATED IN A CONTINUOUS FLOW MODE.
1000 MPPCF- ANY AIR-PURIFYING FULL FACEPIECE RESPIRATOR WITH A HIGH-EFFICIENCY PARTICULATE FILTER ANY POWERED AIR-PURIFYING RESPIRATOR WITH A TIGHT-FITTING FACEPIECE AND A HIGH-EFFICIENCY PARTICULATE FILTER. ANY SELF-CONTAINED BREATHING APPARATUS WITH A FULL FACEPIECE. ANY SUPPLIED-AIR RESPIRATOR WITH A FULL FACEPIECE. ANY SUPPLIED-AIR RESPIRATOR WITH A TIGHT-FITTING FACEPIECE OPERATED IN A CONTINUOUS FLOW MODE.
10,000 MPPCF- ANY SUPPLIED-AIR RESPIRATOR WITH A HALF-MASK AND OPERATED IN A PRESSURE-DEMAND OR OTHER POSITIVE PRESSURE MODE.
ESCAPE- ANY AIR-PURIFYING FULL FACEPIECE RESPIRATOR WITH A HIGH-EFFICIENCY PARTICULATE FILTER. ANY APPROPRIATE ESCAPE-TYPE SELF-CONTAINED BREATHING APPARATUS.
FOR FIREFIGHTING AND OTHER IMMEDIATELY DANGEROUS TO LIFE OR HEALTH CONDITIONS:
SELF-CONTAINED BREATHING APPARATUS WITH FULL FACEPIECE OPERATED IN PRESSURE-DEMAND OR OTHER POSITIVE PRESSURE MODE.
SUPPLIED-AIR RESPIRATOR WITH FULL FACEPIECE AND OPERATED IN PRESSURE-DEMAND OR OTHER POSITIVE PRESSURE MODE IN COMBINATION WITH AN AUXILIARY SELF-CONTAINED BREATHING APPARATUS OPERATED IN PRESSURE-DEMAND OR OTHER POSITIVE PRESSURE MODE.

CLOTHING: EMPLOYEE MUST WEAR APPROPRIATE PROTECTIVE (IMPERVIOUS) CLOTHING AND EQUIPMENT TO PREVENT REPEATED OR PROLONGED SKIN CONTACT WITH THIS SUBSTANCE.

GLOVES: EMPLOYEE MUST WEAR APPROPRIATE PROTECTIVE GLOVES TO PREVENT CONTACT WITH THIS SUBSTANCE.

EYE PROTECTION: EMPLOYEE MUST WEAR SPLASH-PROOF OR DUST-RESISTANT SAFETY GOGGLES TO PREVENT EYE CONTACT WITH THIS SUBSTANCE.
EMERGENCY EYE WASH: WHERE THERE IS ANY POSSIBILITY THAT AN EMPLOYEE'S EYES MAY BE EXPOSED TO THIS SUBSTANCE, THE EMPLOYER SHOULD PROVIDE AN EYE WASH FOUNTAIN WITHIN THE IMMEDIATE WORK AREA FOR EMERGENCY USE.

AUTHORIZED BY- OCCUPATIONAL HEALTH SERVICES, INC.
CREATION DATE: 11/17/89 ***REVISION DATE:*** 07/12/90

MATERIAL SAFETY DATA SHEET

OCCUPATIONAL HEALTH SERVICES, INC.
AGRICULTURE AND PESTICIDE DIVISION
450 SEVENTH AVENUE, SUITE 2407
NEW YORK, NEW YORK 10123
1-800-445-MSDS OR (212) 967-1100

EMERGENCY CONTACT:
JOHN S. BRANSFORD, JR. (615) 292-1180

SUBSTANCE IDENTIFICATION

CAS-NUMBER 7440-22-4
SUBSTANCE: **SILVER**

TRADE NAMES/SYNONYMS: ALGAEDYN; ARGENTUM; C.I. 77820; E 20; L 3; SHELL SILVER; SILFLAKE 135; SILPOWDER 130; SILVER ATOM; SILVER ELEMENT; SILVER METAL; SILVEST TCG 1; SR 999; TCG 7R; V 9; XA 208; AG; PST20770
CHEMICAL FAMILY: METAL
MOLECULAR FORMULA: AG
MOLECULAR WEIGHT: 107.868
CERCLA RATINGS (SCALE 0-3): HEALTH=3 FIRE=3 REACTIVITY=0 PERSISTENCE=3
NFPA RATINGS (SCALE 0-4): HEALTH=3 FIRE=3 REACTIVITY=0

COMPONENTS AND CONTAMINANTS

COMPONENT: SILVER ***PERCENT:*** 100
CAS# 7440-22-4
OTHER CONTAMINANTS: NONE
EXPOSURE LIMITS: SILVER, METAL (AS AG): 0.01 MG/M3 OSHA TWA 0.1 MG/M3 ACGIH TWA (DUST AND FUME)
1000 POUNDS CERCLA SECTION 103 REPORTABLE QUANTITY SUBJECT TO SARA SECTION 313 ANNUAL TOXIC CHEMICAL RELEASE REPORTING

PHYSICAL DATA

DESCRIPTION: SOFT, DUCTILE, LUSTROUS, WHITE SOLID.
BOILING POINT: 3852 F (2122 C) ***MELTING POINT:*** 1763 F (962 C)
SPECIFIC GRAVITY: 10.5 ***VAPOR PRESSURE:*** 100 MMHG @ 1865 C
SOLUBILITY IN WATER: INSOLUBLE
SOLVENT SOLUBILITY: SOLUBLE IN NITRIC ACID, HOT SULFURIC ACID, POTASSIUM CYANIDE, ALKALI HYDROXIDES, ALKALI CYANIDE SOLUTIONS; INSOLUBLE IN ALKALIES.

FIRE AND EXPLOSION DATA

FIRE AND EXPLOSION HAZARD: NEGLIGIBLE FIRE HAZARD IN METALLIC FORM; HOWEVER, DUST, POWDER, OR FUMES ARE FLAMMABLE OR EXPLOSIVE WHEN EXPOSED TO HEAT OR FLAMES.
FIREFIGHTING MEDIA: USE DRY SAND, DOLOMITE, GRAPHITE, SODIUM CHLORIDE, SODA ASH, OR APPROPRIATE METAL-EXTINGUISHING POWDER. DO NOT APPLY WATER TO BURNING MATERIAL (NFPA FIRE PROTECTION HANDBOOK, 16TH EDITION).
FIREFIGHTING: MOVE CONTAINER FROM FIRE AREA IF POSSIBLE. COOL CONTAINERS EXPOSED TO FLAME WITH WATER FROM SIDE UNTIL WELL AFTER FIRE IS OUT. STAY AWAY FROM STORAGE TANK ENDS. FOR MASSIVE FIRE IN CARGO AREA, USE UNMANNED HOSE HOLDER OR MONITOR NOZZLES; ELSE WITHDRAW AND LET FIRE BURN (1987 EMERGENCY RESPONSE GUIDEBOOK, DOT P 5800.4, GUIDE PAGE 32).
EXTINGUISH USING AGENT FOR TYPE OF FIRE. AVOID BREATHING FUMES FROM BURNING MATERIAL.

TRANSPORTATION DATA

DEPARTMENT OF TRANSPORTATION HAZARD CLASSIFICATION 49 CFR 172.101: *FLAMMABLE SOLID
DEPARTMENT OF TRANSPORTATION LABELING REQUIREMENTS 49 CFR 172.101 AND SUBPART E: *FLAMMABLE SOLID
*HAZARD CLASSIFICATION AND LABEL APPLY TO DUST AND POWDER FORM ONLY.

TOXICITY

SILVER: TOXICITY DATA: TUMORIGENIC DATA (RTECS). CARCINOGEN STATUS: NONE. ACUTE TOXICITY LEVEL: NO DATA AVAILABLE. TARGET EFFECTS: NO DATA AVAILABLE.

HEALTH EFFECTS AND FIRST AID

INHALATION: SILVER: **ACUTE EXPOSURE-** IMPREGNATION OF THE MUCOUS MEMBRANES BY FINE PARTICLES OF METALLIC SILVER MAY CAUSE LOCALIZED ARGYRIA. **CHRONIC EXPOSURE-** REPEATED OR PROLONGED EXPOSURE (2-25 YEARS) TO SILVER DUSTS MAY CAUSE A PERMANENT LOCALIZED BLUE-GREY DISCOLORATION OF THE SKIN, MUCOUS MEMBRANES, AND EYES (ARGYRIA), WITHOUT EVIDENCE OF TISSUE REACTION. DISCOLORATION IS FIRST APPARENT IN THE CONJUNCTIVA, WITH SOME LOCALIZATION IN THE INNER CANTHUS. IN SEVERE CASES, THE SKIN MAY BECOME BLACK WITH A METALLIC LUSTER AND THE EYES MAY BE AFFECTED TO THE POINT THAT THE LENS AND VISION ARE DISTURBED. THE RESPIRATORY TRACT MAY ALSO BE AFFECTED PRODUCING A MILD CHRONIC BRONCHITIS.
FIRST AID- REMOVE FROM EXPOSURE AREA TO FRESH AIR IMMEDIATELY. IF BREATHING HAS STOPPED, PERFORM ARTIFICIAL RESPIRATION. KEEP PERSON WARM AND AT REST. TREAT SYMPTOMATICALLY AND SUPPORTIVELY. GET MEDICAL ATTENTION IMMEDIATELY.

SKIN CONTACT: SILVER: **ACUTE EXPOSURE-** IMPREGNATION OF THE SKIN BY FINE PARTICLES OF METALLIC SILVER MAY CAUSE LOCALIZED ARGYRIA. **CHRONIC EXPOSURE-** REPEATED OR PROLONGED EXPOSURE TO SILVER DUST MAY CAUSE LOCALIZED ARGYRIA.
FIRST AID- REMOVE CONTAMINATED CLOTHING AND SHOES IMMEDIATELY. WASH AFFECTED AREA WITH SOAP OR MILD DETERGENT AND LARGE AMOUNTS OF WATER UNTIL NO EVIDENCE OF CHEMICAL REMAINS (APPROXIMATELY 15-20 MINUTES). GET MEDICAL ATTENTION IMMEDIATELY.

EYE CONTACT: SILVER: **ACUTE EXPOSURE-** CONTACT WITH SILVER DUST MAY CAUSE LOCALIZED ARGYRIA. APPLICATION OF SMALL PARTICLES OF METALLIC SILVER IN THE ANTERIOR CHAMBER OF RABBIT EYES CAUSED LITTLE REACTION; CAUSED ATROPHIC CHANGES IN THE RETINA WHEN PLACED IN THE VITREOUS; AND REACTED WITH SURROUNDING TISSUE WHEN PLACED IN THE CORNEA. **CHRONIC EXPOSURE-** REPEATED OR PROLONGED EXPOSURE TO SILVER DUSTS MAY CAUSE LOCALIZED ARGYRIA.
FIRST AID- WASH EYES IMMEDIATELY WITH LARGE AMOUNTS OF WATER OR NORMAL SALINE, OCCASIONALLY LIFTING UPPER AND LOWER LIDS, UNTIL NO EVIDENCE OF CHEMICAL REMAINS (APPROXIMATELY 15-20 MINUTES). GET MEDICAL ATTENTION IMMEDIATELY.

INGESTION: SILVER: **ACUTE EXPOSURE-** INGESTION OF SILVER BY EXPERIMENTAL ANIMALS WAS RAPIDLY AND ALMOST COMPLETELY ELIMINATED IN THE FECES WITHIN DAYS. **CHRONIC EXPOSURE-** NO DATA AVAILABLE.
FIRST AID- TREAT SYMPTOMATICALLY AND SUPPORTIVELY. GET MEDICAL ATTENTION IMMEDIATELY. IF VOMITING OCCURS, KEEP HEAD LOWER THAN HIPS TO PREVENT ASPIRATION.
ANTIDOTE: NO SPECIFIC ANTIDOTE. TREAT SYMPTOMATICALLY AND SUPPORTIVELY.

REACTIVITY

REACTIVITY: STABLE UNDER NORMAL TEMPERATURES AND PRESSURES.
INCOMPATIBILITIES: SILVER: ACETYLENE (AND COMPOUNDS): FORMS EXPLOSIVE SILVER ACETYLIDE. AMMONIA: FORMS EXPLOSIVE COMPOUNDS. AZIRIDINE: FORMATION OF EXPLOSIVE COMPOUNDS. BROMOAZIDE: PROBABLE EXPLOSION. 1-BROMO-2-PROPYNE: EXPLOSION HAZARD. CARBON: REACTS VIOLENTLY. CHLORINE TRIFLUORIDE: POSSIBLE IGNITION. ETHYLENEIMINE: FORMS EXPLOSIVE COMPOUND. ETHYLENE OXIDE + TRACES OF ACETYLENE: MAY FORM EXPLOSIVE SILVER ACETYLIDE. ETHYL HYDROPEROXIDE: EXPLOSION HAZARD. HYDROGEN PEROXIDE: IGNITION OR VIOLENT DECOMPOSITION. IODOFORM: REACTS WITH INCANDESCENCE. NITRIC ACID + ETHYL ALCOHOL: FORMS EXPLOSIVE COMPOUNDS. OXALIC ACID: FORMS EXPLOSIVE COMPOUND. OZONIDES: DECOMPOSED, POSSIBLY EXPLOSIVELY. PERMONOSULFURIC ACID: EXPLOSIVE DECOMPOSITION. PEROXYFORMIC ACID: REACTS EXPLOSIVELY. SULFURIC ACID: REACTS VIOLENTLY. TARTARIC ACID: FORMATION OF EXPLOSIVE SALT. ZINC + ELECTROLYTES: POSSIBLE SPONTANEOUS IGNITION.
DECOMPOSITION: THERMAL DECOMPOSITION MAY RELEASE TOXIC AND/OR HAZARDOUS GASES.
POLYMERIZATION: HAZARDOUS POLYMERIZATION HAS NOT BEEN REPORTED TO OCCUR UNDER NORMAL TEMPERATURES AND PRESSURES.

STORAGE AND DISPOSAL

OBSERVE ALL FEDERAL, STATE AND LOCAL REGULATIONS WHEN STORING OR DISPOSING OF THIS SUBSTANCE. FOR ASSISTANCE, CONTACT THE DISTRICT DIRECTOR OF THE ENVIRONMENTAL PROTECTION AGENCY.

STORAGE

STORE AWAY FROM INCOMPATIBLE SUBSTANCES.

DISPOSAL

SILVER - REGULATORY LEVEL: 5.0 MG/L MATERIALS WHICH CONTAIN THE ABOVE SUBSTANCE AT OR ABOVE THE REGULATORY LEVEL MEET THE EPA CHARACTERISTIC OF TOXICITY, AND MUST BE DISPOSED OF IN ACCORDANCE WITH 40 CFR PART 262. EPA HAZARDOUS WASTE NUMBER D011.

CONDITIONS TO AVOID

AVOID DISPERSION OF DUST IN AIR. FINELY DIVIDED PARTICLES, DUST, OR FUMES MAY BE FLAMMABLE OR EXPLOSIVE. KEEP AWAY FROM SPARKS OR IGNITION SOURCES.

SPILL AND LEAK PROCEDURES

OCCUPATIONAL SPILL: FOR LARGE SPILLS, SWEEP UP WITH A MINIMUM OF DUSTING AND PLACE INTO SUITABLE CLEAN, DRY CONTAINERS FOR RECLAMATION OR LATER DISPOSAL.
RESIDUE SHOULD BE CLEANED UP USING A HIGH-EFFICIENCY PARTICULATE FILTER VACUUM.
REPORTABLE QUANTITY (RQ): 1000 POUNDS THE SUPERFUND AMENDMENTS AND REAUTHORIZATION ACT (SARA) SECTION 304 REQUIRES THAT A RELEASE EQUAL TO OR GREATER THAN THE REPORTABLE QUANTITY FOR THIS SUBSTANCE BE IMMEDIATELY REPORTED TO THE LOCAL EMERGENCY PLANNING COMMITTEE AND THE STATE EMERGENCY RESPONSE COMMISSION (40 CFR 355.40). IF THE RELEASE

OF THIS SUBSTANCE IS REPORTABLE UNDER CERCLA SECTION 103, THE NATIONAL RESPONSE CENTER MUST BE NOTIFIED IMMEDIATELY AT (800) 424-8802 OR (202) 426-2675 IN THE METROPOLITAN WASHINGTON, D.C. AREA (40 CFR 302.6).

PROTECTIVE EQUIPMENT

VENTILATION: PROVIDE LOCAL EXHAUST OR PROCESS ENCLOSURE VENTILATION TO MEET THE PUBLISHED EXPOSURE LIMITS. VENTILATION EQUIPMENT MUST BE EXPLOSION-PROOF.

RESPIRATOR: THE FOLLOWING RESPIRATORS AND MAXIMUM USE CONCENTRATIONS ARE RECOMMENDATIONS BY THE U.S. DEPARTMENT OF HEALTH AND HUMAN SERVICES, NIOSH POCKET GUIDE TO CHEMICAL HAZARDS; NIOSH CRITERIA DOCUMENTS OR BY THE U.S. DEPARTMENT OF LABOR, 29 CFR 1910 SUBPART Z. THE SPECIFIC RESPIRATOR SELECTED MUST BE BASED ON CONTAMINATION LEVELS FOUND IN THE WORK PLACE, MUST NOT EXCEED THE WORKING LIMITS OF THE RESPIRATOR AND BE JOINTLY APPROVED BY THE NATIONAL INSTITUTE FOR OCCUPATIONAL SAFETY AND HEALTH AND THE MINE SAFETY AND HEALTH ADMINISTRATION (NIOSH-MSHA).

SILVER (METAL AND SOLUBLE COMPOUNDS):

0.25 MG/M3- ANY SUPPLIED-AIR RESPIRATOR OPERATED IN CONTINUOUS FLOW MODE. ANY POWERED AIR-PURIFYING RESPIRATOR WITH A HIGH-EFFICIENCY PARTICULATE FILTER.

0.5 MG/M3- ANY AIR-PURIFYING FULL FACEPIECE RESPIRATOR WITH A HIGH-EFFICIENCY PARTICULATE FILTER. ANY SELF-CONTAINED BREATHING APPARATUS WITH A FULL FACEPIECE. ANY SUPPLIED-AIR RESPIRATOR WITH A FULL FACEPIECE.

20.0 MG/M3- ANY SUPPLIED-AIR RESPIRATOR WITH A FULL FACEPIECE AND OPERATED IN A PRESSURE-DEMAND OR OTHER POSITIVE PRESSURE MODE.

ESCAPE- ANY AIR-PURIFYING FULL FACEPIECE RESPIRATOR WITH A HIGH-EFFICIENCY PARTICULATE FILTER. ANY APPROPRIATE ESCAPE-TYPE SELF-CONTAINED BREATHING APPARATUS.

FOR FIREFIGHTING AND OTHER IMMEDIATELY DANGEROUS TO LIFE OR HEALTH CONDITIONS:

SELF-CONTAINED BREATHING APPARATUS WITH FULL FACEPIECE OPERATED IN PRESSURE-DEMAND OR OTHER POSITIVE PRESSURE MODE.

SUPPLIED-AIR RESPIRATOR WITH FULL FACEPIECE AND OPERATED IN PRESSURE-DEMAND OR OTHER POSITIVE PRESSURE MODE IN COMBINATION WITH AN AUXILIARY SELF-CONTAINED BREATHING APPARATUS OPERATED IN PRESSURE-DEMAND OR OTHER POSITIVE PRESSURE MODE.

CLOTHING: EMPLOYEE MUST WEAR APPROPRIATE PROTECTIVE (IMPERVIOUS) CLOTHING AND EQUIPMENT TO PREVENT REPEATED OR PROLONGED SKIN CONTACT WITH THIS SUBSTANCE.

GLOVES: EMPLOYEE MUST WEAR APPROPRIATE PROTECTIVE GLOVES TO PREVENT CONTACT WITH THIS SUBSTANCE.

EYE PROTECTION: EMPLOYEE MUST WEAR SPLASH-PROOF OR DUST-RESISTANT SAFETY GOGGLES TO PREVENT CONTACT WITH THIS SUBSTANCE.

EMERGENCY WASH FACILITIES: WHERE THERE IS ANY POSSIBILITY THAT AN EMPLOYEE'S EYES AND/OR SKIN MAY BE EXPOSED TO THIS SUBSTANCE, THE EMPLOYER SHOULD PROVIDE AN EYE WASH FOUNTAIN AND QUICK DRENCH SHOWER WITHIN THE IMMEDIATE WORK AREA FOR EMERGENCY USE.

AUTHORIZED BY- OCCUPATIONAL HEALTH SERVICES, INC.

CREATION DATE: 11/17/89 ***REVISION DATE:*** 07/13/90

MATERIAL SAFETY DATA SHEET

OCCUPATIONAL HEALTH SERVICES, INC.
AGRICULTURE AND PESTICIDE DIVISION
450 SEVENTH AVENUE, SUITE 2407
NEW YORK, NEW YORK 10123
1-800-445-MSDS OR (212) 967-1100

EMERGENCY CONTACT:
JOHN S. BRANSFORD, JR. (615) 292-1180

SUBSTANCE IDENTIFICATION

CAS-NUMBER 7783-90-6

SUBSTANCE: **SILVER CHLORIDE**

TRADE NAMES/SYNONYMS: PST20787

CHEMICAL FAMILY: INORGANIC SALT

MOLECULAR FORMULA: AG-CL

MOLECULAR WEIGHT: 143.34

CERCLA RATINGS (SCALE 0-3): HEALTH=U FIRE=0 REACTIVITY=0 PERSISTENCE=3

NFPA RATINGS (SCALE 0-4): HEALTH=U FIRE=0 REACTIVITY=0

COMPONENTS AND CONTAMINANTS

COMPONENT: SILVER CHLORIDE ***PERCENT:*** 100

CAS# 7783-90-6

EXPOSURE LIMITS: SILVER, SOLUBLE COMPOUNDS (AS AG): 0.01 MG/M3 OSHA TWA

0.01 MG/M3 ACGIH TWA

SUBJECT TO SARA SECTION 313 ANNUAL TOXIC CHEMICAL RELEASE REPORTING

PHYSICAL DATA

DESCRIPTION: WHITE, GRANULAR POWDER. DARKENS ON EXPOSURE TO LIGHT AND MAY TURN BLACK

BOILING POINT: 2822 F (1550 C) ***MELTING POINT:*** 851 F (455 C)

SPECIFIC GRAVITY: 5.6 ***SOLUBILITY IN WATER:*** 1.93 MG/L @ 25 C

SOLVENT SOLUBILITY: ALKALIS, THIOSULFATES, CYANIDES, SILVER NITRATE, AMMONIUM HYDROXIDE, CONCENTRATED SULFURIC ACID, POTASSIUM BROMIDE, POTASSIUM CYANIDE

FIRE AND EXPLOSION DATA

FIRE AND EXPLOSION HAZARD: NEGLIGIBLE FIRE HAZARD WHEN EXPOSED TO HEAT OR FLAME.

FIREFIGHTING MEDIA: DRY CHEMICAL, CARBON DIOXIDE, HALON, WATER SPRAY OR STANDARD FOAM (1987 EMERGENCY RESPONSE GUIDEBOOK, DOT P 5800.4). FOR LARGER FIRES, USE WATER SPRAY, FOG OR STANDARD FOAM (1987 EMERGENCY RESPONSE GUIDEBOOK, DOT P 5800.4).

FIREFIGHTING: NO ACUTE HAZARD. MOVE CONTAINER FROM FIRE AREA IF POSSIBLE. AVOID BREATHING VAPORS OR DUSTS; KEEP UPWIND.

TOXICITY

SILVER CHLORIDE: CARCINOGEN STATUS: NONE. ACUTE TOXICITY LEVEL: NO DATA AVAILABLE. TARGET EFFECTS: NO DATA AVAILABLE.

HEALTH EFFECTS AND FIRST AID

INHALATION: SILVER CHLORIDE: **ACUTE EXPOSURE-** NO DATA AVAILABLE. SILVER COMPOUNDS MAY CAUSE ARGYRISM, WHICH IS CHARACTERIZED BY BLUE DISCOLORATION OF THE SKIN, MUCOUS MEMBRANES AND EYES. **CHRONIC EXPOSURE-** NO DATA AVAILABLE. PROLONGED OR REPEATED EXPOSURE TO SILVER COMPOUNDS MAY CAUSE ARGYRISM.

FIRST AID- REMOVE FROM EXPOSURE AREA TO FRESH AIR IMMEDIATELY. IF BREATHING HAS STOPPED, PERFORM ARTIFICIAL RESPIRATION. KEEP PERSON WARM AND AT REST. TREAT SYMPTOMATICALLY AND SUPPORTIVELY. GET MEDICAL ATTENTION IMMEDIATELY.

SKIN CONTACT: SILVER CHLORIDE: **ACUTE EXPOSURE-** NO DATA AVAILABLE. SILVER COMPOUNDS MAY CAUSE ARGYRISM, WHICH IS CHARACTERIZED BY BLUE DISCOLORATION OF THE SKIN, MUCOUS MEMBRANES AND EYES. **CHRONIC EXPOSURE-** NO DATA AVAILABLE. PROLONGED OR REPEATED EXPOSURE TO SILVER COMPOUNDS MAY CAUSE ARGYRISM.

FIRST AID- REMOVE CONTAMINATED CLOTHING AND SHOES IMMEDIATELY. WASH AFFECTED AREA WITH SOAP OR MILD DETERGENT AND LARGE AMOUNTS OF WATER UNTIL NO EVIDENCE OF CHEMICAL REMAINS (APPROXIMATELY 15-20 MINUTES). GET MEDICAL ATTENTION IMMEDIATELY.

EYE CONTACT: SILVER CHLORIDE: **ACUTE EXPOSURE-** NO DATA AVAILABLE. DIRECT APPLICATION MAY CAUSE BLUE DISCOLORATION OF THE CONJUNCTIVA. **CHRONIC EXPOSURE-** NO DATA AVAILABLE. PROLONGED OR REPEATED APPLICATION OF SILVER COMPOUNDS MAY CAUSE ARGYRISM.

FIRST AID- WASH EYES IMMEDIATELY WITH LARGE AMOUNTS OF WATER OR NORMAL SALINE, OCCASIONALLY LIFTING UPPER AND LOWER LIDS, UNTIL NO EVIDENCE OF CHEMICAL REMAINS (APPROXIMATELY 15-20 MINUTES). GET MEDICAL ATTENTION IMMEDIATELY.

INGESTION: SILVER CHLORIDE: **ACUTE EXPOSURE-** NO DATA AVAILABLE. **CHRONIC EXPOSURE-** NO DATA AVAILABLE. PROLONGED OR REPEATED INGESTION OF SILVER COMPOUNDS MAY CAUSE ARGYRISM, WHICH IS CHARACTERIZED BY BLUE DISCOLORATION OF THE SKIN, EYES AND MUCOUS MEMBRANES.

FIRST AID- TREAT SYMPTOMATICALLY AND SUPPORTIVELY. GET MEDICAL ATTENTION IMMEDIATELY. IF VOMITING OCCURS, KEEP HEAD LOWER THAN HIPS TO PREVENT ASPIRATION.

ANTIDOTE: NO SPECIFIC ANTIDOTE. TREAT SYMPTOMATICALLY AND SUPPORTIVELY.

REACTIVITY

REACTIVITY: STABLE UNDER NORMAL TEMPERATURES AND PRESSURES.

INCOMPATIBILITIES: SILVER CHLORIDE: ALKALI METALS: FORMS IMPACT SENSITIVE SYSTEM. ALUMINUM: EXPLOSIVE REACTION UNLESS EXCESS OF ALUMINUM IS PRESENT. AMMONIA: FORMS SHOCK SENSITIVE SYSTEM. BROMINE TRIFLUORIDE: ATTACKS SILVER CHLORIDE. POTASSIUM: FORMS IMPACT SENSITIVE SYSTEM.

SODIUM: FORMS IMPACT SENSITIVE SYSTEM. SODIUM PEROXIDE, CHARCOAL: MIXTURE IGNITES SPONTANEOUSLY.
DECOMPOSITION: THERMAL DECOMPOSITION MAY RELEASE CORROSIVE HYDROGEN CHLORIDE.
POLYMERIZATION: HAZARDOUS POLYMERIZATION HAS NOT BEEN REPORTED TO OCCUR UNDER NORMAL TEMPERATURES AND PRESSURES.

STORAGE AND DISPOSAL

OBSERVE ALL FEDERAL, STATE AND LOCAL REGULATIONS WHEN STORING OR DISPOSING OF THIS SUBSTANCE. FOR ASSISTANCE, CONTACT THE DISTRICT DIRECTOR OF THE ENVIRONMENTAL PROTECTION AGENCY.

DISPOSAL

SILVER - REGULATORY LEVEL: 5.0 MG/L MATERIALS WHICH CONTAIN THE ABOVE SUBSTANCE AT OR ABOVE THE REGULATORY LEVEL MEET THE EPA CHARACTERISTIC OF TOXICITY, AND MUST BE DISPOSED OF IN ACCORDANCE WITH 40 CFR PART 262. EPA HAZARDOUS WASTE NUMBER D011.

CONDITIONS TO AVOID

AVOID HEATING TO DECOMPOSITION AND CONTACT WITH OR STORAGE WITH INCOMPATIBLE SUBSTANCES.

SPILL AND LEAK PROCEDURES

OCCUPATIONAL SPILL: VENTILATE CONFINED SPACES. SWEEP UP, AVOIDING DISPERSION OF DUST, AND COLLECT IN SUITABLE CONTAINER.

PROTECTIVE EQUIPMENT

VENTILATION: PROVIDE LOCAL EXHAUST OR PROCESS ENCLOSURE VENTILATION TO MEET PUBLISHED EXPOSURE LIMITS.
RESPIRATOR: THE FOLLOWING RESPIRATORS ARE RECOMMENDED BASED ON INFORMATION FOUND IN THE PHYSICAL DATA, TOXICITY AND HEALTH EFFECTS SECTIONS. THEY ARE RANKED IN ORDER FROM MINIMUM TO MAXIMUM RESPIRATORY PROTECTION. THE SPECIFIC RESPIRATOR SELECTED MUST BE BASED ON CONTAMINATION LEVELS FOUND IN THE WORK PLACE, MUST NOT EXCEED THE WORKING LIMITS OF THE RESPIRATOR AND BE JOINTLY APPROVED BY THE NATIONAL INSTITUTE FOR OCCUPATIONAL SAFETY AND HEALTH AND THE MINE SAFETY AND HEALTH ADMINISTRATION (NIOSH-MSHA).
DUST AND MIST RESPIRATOR.
AIR-PURIFYING RESPIRATOR WITH A HIGH-EFFICIENCY PARTICULATE FILTER.
POWERED AIR-PURIFYING RESPIRATOR WITH A DUST AND MIST FILTER.
POWERED AIR-PURIFYING RESPIRATOR WITH A HIGH-EFFICIENCY PARTICULATE FILTER.
TYPE 'C' SUPPLIED-AIR RESPIRATOR OPERATED IN THE PRESSURE-DEMAND OR OTHER POSITIVE PRESSURE OR CONTINUOUS-FLOW MODE.
SELF-CONTAINED BREATHING APPARATUS.
FOR FIREFIGHTING AND OTHER IMMEDIATELY DANGEROUS TO LIFE OR HEALTH CONDITIONS:
SELF-CONTAINED BREATHING APPARATUS WITH FULL FACEPIECE OPERATED IN PRESSURE-DEMAND OR OTHER POSITIVE PRESSURE MODE.
SUPPLIED-AIR RESPIRATOR WITH FULL FACEPIECE AND OPERATED IN PRESSURE-DEMAND OR OTHER POSITIVE PRESSURE MODE IN COMBINATION WITH AN AUXILIARY SELF-CONTAINED BREATHING APPARATUS OPERATED IN PRESSURE-DEMAND OR OTHER POSITIVE PRESSURE MODE.
CLOTHING: EMPLOYEE MUST WEAR APPROPRIATE PROTECTIVE (IMPERVIOUS) CLOTHING AND EQUIPMENT TO PREVENT REPEATED OR PROLONGED SKIN CONTACT WITH THIS SUBSTANCE.
GLOVES: EMPLOYEE MUST WEAR APPROPRIATE PROTECTIVE GLOVES TO PREVENT CONTACT WITH THIS SUBSTANCE.
EYE PROTECTION: EMPLOYEE MUST WEAR SPLASH-PROOF OR DUST-RESISTANT SAFETY GOGGLES AND A FACESHIELD TO PREVENT CONTACT WITH THIS SUBSTANCE.
EMERGENCY WASH FACILITIES: WHERE THERE IS ANY POSSIBILITY THAT AN EMPLOYEE'S EYES AND/OR SKIN MAY BE EXPOSED TO THIS SUBSTANCE, THE EMPLOYER SHOULD PROVIDE AN EYE WASH FOUNTAIN AND QUICK DRENCH SHOWER WITHIN THE IMMEDIATE WORK AREA FOR EMERGENCY USE.

AUTHORIZED BY- OCCUPATIONAL HEALTH SERVICES, INC.
CREATION DATE: 11/17/89 ***REVISION DATE:*** 07/13/90

MATERIAL SAFETY DATA SHEET

OCCUPATIONAL HEALTH SERVICES, INC. EMERGENCY CONTACT:
AGRICULTURE AND PESTICIDE DIVISION JOHN S. BRANSFORD, JR. (615) 292-1180
450 SEVENTH AVENUE, SUITE 2407
NEW YORK, NEW YORK 10123
1-800-445-MSDS OR (212) 967-1100

SUBSTANCE IDENTIFICATION

CAS-NUMBER 7761-88-8
SUBSTANCE: SILVER NITRATE
TRADE NAMES/SYNONYMS: LAPIS INFERNALIS; LUNAR CAUSTIC; NITRIC ACID, SILVER(1+) SALT; STCC 4918742; UN 1493; SILVER (1+) NITRATE; SILVER MONONITRATE; ARGENTI NITRAS; ARGEROL; AGNO3; PST20810
CHEMICAL FAMILY: INORGANIC SALT
MOLECULAR FORMULA: AG-N-O3
MOLECULAR WEIGHT: 169.87
CERCLA RATINGS (SCALE 0-3): HEALTH=3 FIRE=0 REACTIVITY=0 PERSISTENCE=3
NFPA RATINGS (SCALE 0-4): HEALTH=0 FIRE=0 REACTIVITY=0

COMPONENTS AND CONTAMINANTS

COMPONENT: SILVER NITRATE ***PERCENT:*** 100.0
CAS# 7761-88-8
OTHER CONTAMINANTS: NONE
EXPOSURE LIMITS: SILVER, SOLUBLE COMPOUNDS (AS AG): 0.01 MG/M3 OSHA TWA 0.01 MG/M3 ACGIH TWA
SUBJECT TO SARA SECTION 313 ANNUAL TOXIC CHEMICAL RELEASE REPORTING
SILVER NITRATE: 1 POUND CERCLA SECTION 103 REPORTABLE QUANTITY

PHYSICAL DATA

DESCRIPTION: ODORLESS, COLORLESS, TRANSPARENT, HYGROSCOPIC CRYSTALS WITH A METALLIC TASTE AND A SLIGHT NITRIC ACID ODOR.
BOILING POINT: 831 F (444 C) (DECOMPOSES) ***MELTING POINT:*** 414 F (212 C)
SPECIFIC GRAVITY: 4.352 @ 19 C ***VAPOR PRESSURE:*** NEGLIGIBLE
PH: 6.0 (AQ SOLN) ***SOLUBILITY IN WATER:*** 122% @ 0 C
SOLVENT SOLUBILITY: SOLUBLE IN ETHER, GLYCEROL; VERY SLIGHTLY SOLUBLE IN ALCOHOL, ACETONE.

FIRE AND EXPLOSION DATA

FIRE AND EXPLOSION HAZARD: NEGLIGIBLE FIRE HAZARD WHEN EXPOSED TO HEAT OR FLAME.
OXIDIZER: OXIDIZERS DECOMPOSE, ESPECIALLY WHEN HEATED, TO YIELD OXYGEN OR OTHER GASES WHICH WILL INCREASE THE BURNING RATE OF COMBUSTIBLE MATTER. CONTACT WITH EASILY OXIDIZABLE, ORGANIC, OR OTHER COMBUSTIBLE MATERIALS MAY RESULT IN IGNITION, VIOLENT COMBUSTION OR EXPLOSION.
FIREFIGHTING MEDIA: WATER ONLY, NO DRY CHEMICAL, CARBON DIOXIDE OR HALON (1987 EMERGENCY RESPONSE GUIDEBOOK, DOT P 5800.4).
FOR LARGER FIRES, FLOOD AREA WITH WATER FROM A DISTANCE (1987 EMERGENCY RESPONSE GUIDEBOOK, DOT P 5800.4).
FIREFIGHTING: MOVE CONTAINERS FROM FIRE AREA IF POSSIBLE. COOL CONTAINERS EXPOSED TO FLAMES WITH WATER FROM SIDE UNTIL WELL AFTER FIRE IS OUT. STAY AWAY FROM STORAGE TANK ENDS. FOR MASSIVE FIRE IN STORAGE AREA, USE UNMANNED HOSE HOLDER OR MONITOR NOZZLES; ELSE WITHDRAW FROM AREA AND LET FIRE BURN (1987 EMERGENCY RESPONSE GUIDEBOOK, DOT P 5800.4 GUIDE PAGE 45).
USE FLOODING AMOUNTS OF WATER. COOL CONTAINERS WITH FLOODING QUANTITIES OF WATER, APPLY FROM AS FAR A DISTANCE AS POSSIBLE.
EVACUATE TO A RADIUS OF 2500 FEET FOR UNCONTROLLABLE FIRES.

TRANSPORTATION DATA

DEPARTMENT OF TRANSPORTATION HAZARD CLASSIFICATION 49 CFR 172.101: OXIDIZER
DEPARTMENT OF TRANSPORTATION LABELING REQUIREMENTS 49 CFR 172.101 AND SUBPART E: OXIDIZER
DEPARTMENT OF TRANSPORTATION PACKAGING REQUIREMENTS: 49 CFR 173.182 EXCEPTIONS: 49 CFR 173.153

TOXICITY

SILVER NITRATE: IRRITATION DATA: 1 MG EYE-RABBIT SEVERE; 10 MG EYE-RABBIT MODERATE. TOXICITY DATA: 50 MG/KG ORAL-MOUSE LD50; 20 MG/KG ORAL-DOG LDLO; 800 MG/KG ORAL-RABBIT LDLO; 62 MG/KG SUBCUTANEOUS-GUINEA PIG LDLO; 8800 UG/KG INTRAVENOUS-RABBIT LDLO; 216 MG/KG INTRAPERITONEAL-GUINEA PIG LDLO; 23,783 UG/KG INTRAPERITONEAL-MOUSE LD50; 29 MG/KG UNREPORTED-MAN LDLO; MUTAGENIC DATA (RTECS); REPRODUCTIVE EFFECTS DATA (RTECS); TUMORIGENIC DATA (RTECS). CARCINOGEN STATUS: NONE. LOCAL EFFECTS: CORROSIVE- INHALATION, SKIN, EYE, INGESTION. ACUTE TOXICITY LEVEL: HIGHLY TOXIC BY INGESTION. TARGET EFFECTS: POISONING MAY DISCOLOR THE SKIN AND EYES (ARGYRIA).

HEALTH EFFECTS AND FIRST AID

INHALATION: SILVER NITRATE: CORROSIVE. **ACUTE EXPOSURE-** MAY CAUSE SEVERE IRRITATION TO MUCOUS MEMBRANES WITH SORE THROAT, COUGHING AND SHORTNESS OF BREATH. **CHRONIC EXPOSURE-** PROLONGED OR REPEATED EXPOSURE, USUALLY FROM 2-25 YEARS, MAY RESULT IN ARGYRIA. GENERALIZED ARGYRIA MAY FIRST BE RECOGNIZED BY A SLATE-GRAY, BLUE TO BLACK DISCOLORATION IN THE CONJUNCTIVA AND SKIN STARTING WITH THE FACE AND SPREADING TO MOST UNCOVERED PARTS OF THE BODY, INCLUDING THE FINGERNAILS WHICH MAY BECOME A DEEP CHOCOLATE BROWN COLOR. THE PERMANENT DISCOLORATION IS UNIFORM IN DISTRIBUTION AND VARIES IN DEPTH DEPENDING ON THE DEGREE OF EXPOSURE. IN THE SEVEREST CASES THE SKIN BECOMES ALMOST BLACK WITH A METALLIC LUSTER. THE BUCCAL MUCOSA, TOENAILS, AND OTHER COVERED PARTS OF THE BODY MAY BE AFFECTED TO A LESSER DEGREE. INVOLVEMENT OF THE CORNEA HAS BEEN RECORDED IN A NUMBER OF SILVER NITRATE WORKERS WITH NO FAILURE OF VISION, BUT SOME DISTURBANCE IN DARK ADAPTATION. LOCALIZED ARGYRIA OF THE RESPIRATORY TRACT HAS BEEN DESCRIBED IN 2 MEN IN THE MANUFACTURE OF SILVER NITRATE. THE ONLY SYMPTOM WAS MILD BRONCHITIS; THE NASAL MUCOSA SHOWED IMPREGNATION IN THE WALLS OF THE MIDDLE AND UPPER REGION AND THERE WAS TRACHEOBRONCHIAL PIGMENTATION. EMPHYSEMA, KIDNEY LESIONS AND THE POSSIBILITY OF ARTERIOSCLEROSIS HAVE BEEN REPORTED IN EXPOSED SILVER WORKERS.

FIRST AID- REMOVE FROM EXPOSURE AREA TO FRESH AIR IMMEDIATELY. IF BREATHING HAS STOPPED, GIVE ARTIFICIAL RESPIRATION. MAINTAIN AIRWAY AND BLOOD PRESSURE AND ADMINISTER OXYGEN IF AVAILABLE. KEEP AFFECTED PERSON WARM AND AT REST. TREAT SYMPTOMATICALLY AND SUPPORTIVELY. ADMINISTRATION OF OXYGEN SHOULD BE PERFORMED BY QUALIFIED PERSONNEL. GET MEDICAL ATTENTION IMMEDIATELY.

SKIN CONTACT: SILVER NITRATE: CORROSIVE. **ACUTE EXPOSURE-** DUST AND SOLUTIONS MAY CAUSE SEVERE IRRITATION, REDNESS, PAIN, ULCERATION, AND DISCOLORATION. RARELY, SENSITIZATION REACTIONS MAY OCCUR FROM TOPICAL APPLICATION OF AGED, BUT NOT FRESH, SILVER NITRATE IN PREVIOUSLY EXPOSED PERSONS. ABSORPTION OF SILVER NITRATE USED TO TREAT BURNED SKIN MAY OCCUR AND CAUSE SERIOUS AND EVEN FATAL METHEMOGLOBINEMIA. **CHRONIC EXPOSURE-** PROLONGED OR REPEATED CONTACT MAY CAUSE ARGYRIA. SIGNS AND SYMPTOMS MAY OCCUR AS DESCRIBED IN CHRONIC INHALATION.

FIRST AID- REMOVE CONTAMINATED CLOTHING AND SHOES IMMEDIATELY. WASH AFFECTED AREA WITH SOAP OR MILD DETERGENT AND LARGE AMOUNTS OF WATER UNTIL NO EVIDENCE OF CHEMICAL REMAINS (AT LEAST 15-20 MINUTES). IN CASE OF CHEMICAL BURNS, COVER AREA WITH STERILE, DRY DRESSING. BANDAGE SECURELY, BUT NOT TOO TIGHTLY. GET MEDICAL ATTENTION IMMEDIATELY.

EYE CONTACT: SILVER NITRATE: CORROSIVE. **ACUTE EXPOSURE-** DUST OR SOLUTIONS MAY CAUSE SEVERE IRRITATION, REDNESS, PAIN, BURNS AND POSSIBLY DISCOLORATION. RAPID APPEARANCE OF EDEMA OF THE CONJUNCTIVA AND LIDS MAY OCCUR WITH BLOODY PURULENT DISCHARGE FROM THE CONJUNCTIVAL SAC. PERMANENT CORNEAL OPACIFICATION, LOSS OF EPITHELIUM AND BLINDNESS MAY RESULT. PARTICLES OF SOLID SILVER NITRATE IN THE CONJUNCTIVAL SAC CAUSED SEVERE INFLAMMATION WITH DEEP INJURY TO SURROUNDING TISSUES, SCARRING, AND SYMBLEPHARON. IN SEVERE CASES, THE SOLID MAY CAUSE THE LENS TO BECOME CATARACTOUS AND THE CORNEA TO BECOME DARK BROWN, POSSIBLY HIDING THE PUPIL. **CHRONIC EXPOSURE-** REPEATED OR PROLONGED CONTACT MAY RESULT IN CONJUNCTIVITIS OR SYMPTOMS SIMILAR TO THOSE IN ACUTE EXPOSURE. PROLONGED EXPOSURE TO DILUTE SOLUTIONS OR FROM INDUSTRIAL EXPOSURE TO DUST HAS CAUSED DISCOLORATION OF THE CORNEA AND CONJUNCTIVA WITHOUT INJURY OR IRRITATION TO THE EYES.

FIRST AID- WASH EYES IMMEDIATELY WITH LARGE AMOUNTS OF WATER, OCCASIONALLY LIFTING UPPER AND LOWER LIDS, UNTIL NO EVIDENCE OF CHEMICAL REMAINS (AT LEAST 15-20 MINUTES). CONTINUE IRRIGATING WITH NORMAL SALINE UNTIL THE PH HAS RETURNED TO NORMAL (30-60 MINUTES). COVER WITH STERILE BANDAGES. GET MEDICAL ATTENTION IMMEDIATELY.

INGESTION: SILVER NITRATE: CORROSIVE/HIGHLY TOXIC. **ACUTE EXPOSURE-** MAY CAUSE PAIN AND BURNING IN THE MOUTH, THROAT AND EPIGASTRIUM, SALIVATION, VIOLENT ABDOMINAL PAIN AND RIGIDITY, BLACK VOMITUS, DIARRHEA, ANURIA, COLLAPSE, SHOCK, VERTIGO, CONVULSIONS, COMA AND DEATH. THE FATAL DOSE IN HUMANS HAS BEEN AS LOW AS 2 GRAMS, AND ALTHOUGH RECOVERY HAS OCCURRED FOLLOWING INGESTION OF LARGER DOSES, 10 GRAMS IS USUALLY FATAL. PATHOLOGICAL FINDINGS INCLUDE LOCAL CORROSIVE DAMAGE TO THE GASTROINTESTINAL TRACT AND POSSIBLY DEGENERATIVE CHANGES IN THE KIDNEYS AND LIVER. APPLICATION TO THE GUMS HAS CAUSED NECROTIZING ULCERATION. RARELY, INORGANIC NITRATES MAY BE CONVERTED TO NITRITES BY NITRATE-REDUCING BACTERIA IN THE DIGESTIVE TRACT, RESULTING IN METHEMOGLOBINEMIA. **CHRONIC EXPOSURE-** REPEATED INGESTION MAY CAUSE ARGYRIA. SIGNS AND SYMPTOMS MAY OCCUR AS DESCRIBED IN CHRONIC INHALATION. REPEATED INGESTION OF NITRATES MAY CAUSE ANEMIA, NEPHRITIS, AND POSSIBLY METHEMOGLOBINEMIA. SILVER SALTS FED TO ANIMALS HAVE PRODUCED RENAL CHANGES AND VASCULAR HYPERTENSION.

FIRST AID- IF VICTIM IS CONSCIOUS, DILUTE INGESTED SILVER NITRATE BY GIVING WATER CONTAINING SODIUM CHLORIDE, 10 G/L, REPEATEDLY TO PRECIPITATE SILVER ION AS SILVER CHLORIDE. FOLLOW WITH CATHARSIS USING 30-60 ML OF FLEET'S PHOSPHO-SODA DILUTED 1:4 IN WATER CONTAINING 5 GRAMS OF SODIUM CHLORIDE TO PRECIPITATE AND REMOVE SILVER FROM THE INTESTINE. TREAT METHEMOGLOBINEMIA. (DREISBACH, HANDBOOK OF POISONING, 11TH ED.)

ANTIDOTE: THE FOLLOWING ANTIDOTE HAS BEEN RECOMMENDED. HOWEVER, THE DECISION AS TO WHETHER THE SEVERITY OF POISONING REQUIRES ADMINISTRATION OF ANY ANTIDOTE AND ACTUAL DOSE REQUIRED SHOULD BE MADE BY QUALIFIED MEDICAL PERSONNEL.

METHEMOGLOBINEMIA: (WHEN METHEMOGLOBIN CONCENTRATION IS OVER 25-40% OR IN PRESENCE OF SYMPTOMS.) GIVE METHYLENE BLUE, 1% SOLUTION, 0.1 ML/KG INTRAVENOUSLY OVER A 10-MINUTE PERIOD. CYANOSIS MAY DISAPPEAR WITHIN MINUTES OR PERSIST LONGER DEPENDING ON DEGREE OF METHEMOGLOBINEMIA. INTRAVENOUS ADMINISTRATION OF THERAPEUTIC DOSES OF METHYLENE BLUE MAY CAUSE A RISE IN BLOOD PRESSURE, NAUSEA, AND DIZZINESS. LARGER DOSES (>500 MG) CAUSE VOMITING, DIARRHEA, CHEST PAIN, MENTAL CONFUSION, CYANOSIS, AND SWEATING. HEMOLYTIC ANEMIA HAS ALSO OCCURRED SEVERAL DAYS AFTER ADMINISTRATION. THESE EFFECTS ARE TEMPORARY, AND FATALITIES HAVE NOT BEEN REPORTED. IF METHYLENE BLUE IS NOT AVAILABLE, GIVE ASCORBIC ACID, 1 GRAM SLOWLY INTRAVENOUSLY. WITHOUT TREATMENT, METHEMOGLOBINEMIA LEVELS OF 20-30% REVERT TO NORMAL WITHIN 3 DAYS (DREISBACH, HANDBOOK OF POISONING, 12TH ED.). ANTIDOTE SHOULD BE ADMINISTERED BY QUALIFIED MEDICAL PERSONNEL.

REACTIVITY

REACTIVITY: STABLE UNDER NORMAL TEMPERATURES AND PRESSURES.

INCOMPATIBILITIES: SILVER NITRATE: ACETALDEHYDE: FORMS EXPLOSIVE SILVER FULMINATE. ACETYLENE + AMMONIA: FORMATION OF EXPLOSIVE SILVER ACETYLIDE. ACETYLIDES (CARBIDES): FORM EXPLOSIVE COMPOUNDS. ACRYLONITRILE: EXPLOSIVE POLYMERIZATION. ALCOHOLS: MAY FORM EXPLOSIVE FULMINATE. ALKYNES: FORM EXPLOSIVE SALT. AMMONIA: MAY EXPLODE ON STANDING. AMMONIA + ALKALIES: MAY EXPLODE. AMMONIUM HYDROXIDE + SODIUM HYDROXIDE: FORMS EXPLOSIVE COMPOUND. AZIRIDINE: FORMATION OF AN EXPLOSIVE COMPOUND. ARSENITES: INCOMPATIBLE. BROMIDES: INCOMPATIBLE. CARBON (POWDER): EXPLOSIVE ON IMPACT. CARBONATES: INCOMPATIBLE. CHARCOAL: MIXTURES IGNITE UNDER IMPACT. CHLORIDES: INCOMPATIBLE. CHLORINE TRIFLUORIDE: POSSIBLE IGNITION AND VIOLENT REACTION. CHLOROSULFONIC ACID: VIOLENT REACTION. COMBUSTIBLE MATERIALS: MAY INCREASE THE RATE OF BURNING MATERIALS OR MAY CAUSE IGNITION OR EXPLOSION ON CONTACT. CREOSOTE: INCOMPATIBLE. DISILVER KETENIDE: FORMS EXPLOSIVE COMPOUND. ETHANOL: MAY FORM EXPLOSIVE FULMINATE. HYDROGEN PEROXIDE: IGNITION OR VIOLENT DECOMPOSITION. HYPOPHOSPHITES: INCOMPATIBLE. IODIDES: INCOMPATIBLE. MAGNESIUM: EXPLOSIVE IGNITION ON CONTACT WITH WATER. METALS AND SALTS: MAY CORRODE IN PRESENCE OF MOISTURE. MORPHINE SALTS: INCOMPATIBLE. OILS: INCOMPATIBLE. ORGANIC MATERIALS: MAY CAUSE IGNITION ON CONTACT, OR MAY INCREASE THE RATE OF BURNING MATERIALS. OXALIC ACID: FORMATION OF AN EXPLOSIVE SALT. PHOSPHATES: INCOMPATIBLE. PHOSPHINE: EXPLOSION MAY OCCUR. PHOSPHONIUM IODIDE: VIGOROUS EXOTHERMIC REACTION. PHOSPHORUS: MIXTURES EXPLODE ON IMPACT. PHOSPHORUS ISOCYANATE: VIOLENT REACTION. PLASTICS, RUBBER, COATINGS: MAY BE ATTACKED. SULFUR: EXPLOSION ON IMPACT. TANNIC ACID: INCOMPATIBLE. TARTARIC ACID: FORMATION OF AN EXPLOSIVE SALT. VEGETABLE DECOCTIONS AND EXTRACTS: INCOMPATIBLE. SEE ALSO METAL NITRATES.

METAL NITRATES: CITRIC ACID: POSSIBLE EXPLOSION HAZARD. ESTERS: POSSIBLE EXPLOSION HAZARD. PHOSPHINATES: MAY EXPLODE WHEN HEATED. PHOSPHOROUS: POSSIBLE EXPLOSIVE REACTION. POTASSIUM HEXANITROCOBALTATE(3-): MAY EXPLODE VIOLENTLY. REDUCTANTS: POSSIBLE EXPLOSION HAZARD. TIN(II) CHLORIDE: POSSIBLE EXPLOSIVE HAZARD.

DECOMPOSITION: THERMAL DECOMPOSITION PRODUCTS MAY INCLUDE TOXIC OXIDES OF NITROGEN.

POLYMERIZATION: HAZARDOUS POLYMERIZATION HAS NOT BEEN REPORTED TO OCCUR UNDER NORMAL TEMPERATURES AND PRESSURES.

STORAGE AND DISPOSAL

OBSERVE ALL FEDERAL, STATE AND LOCAL REGULATIONS WHEN STORING OR DISPOSING OF THIS SUBSTANCE. FOR ASSISTANCE, CONTACT THE DISTRICT DIRECTOR OF THE ENVIRONMENTAL PROTECTION AGENCY.

****STORAGE****

PROTECT AGAINST PHYSICAL DAMAGE. SEPARATE FROM COMBUSTIBLE, ORGANIC, OR OTHER READILY OXIDIZABLE MATERIALS (NFPA 49, HAZARDOUS CHEMICALS DATA, 1975).

CONSULT NFPA PUBLICATION 43A, STORAGE OF LIQUID AND SOLID OXIDIZING MATERIALS, FOR STORAGE REQUIREMENTS.

STORE AWAY FROM INCOMPATIBLE SUBSTANCES.

KEEP CONTAINER TIGHTLY CLOSED. PROTECT FROM EXPOSURE TO AIR OR LIGHT.

****DISPOSAL****

DISPOSAL MUST BE IN ACCORDANCE WITH STANDARDS APPLICABLE TO GENERATORS OF HAZARDOUS WASTE, 40 CFR 262. EPA HAZARDOUS WASTE NUMBER D001. 100 POUND CERCLA SECTION 103 REPORTABLE QUANTITY.

SILVER - REGULATORY LEVEL: 5.0 MG/L MATERIALS WHICH CONTAIN THE ABOVE SUBSTANCE AT OR ABOVE THE REGULATORY LEVEL MEET THE EPA CHARACTERISTIC OF TOXICITY, AND MUST BE DISPOSED OF IN ACCORDANCE WITH 40 CFR PART 262. EPA HAZARDOUS WASTE NUMBER D011.

CONDITIONS TO AVOID

MAY IGNITE OTHER COMBUSTIBLE MATERIALS (WOOD, PAPER, OIL, ETC.). REACTION WITH FUELS MAY BE VIOLENT. FLAMMABLE POISONOUS GASES MAY ACCUMULATE IN TANKS AND HOPPER CARS. RUNOFF TO SEWER MAY CREATE FIRE OR EXPLOSION HAZARD.

SPILL AND LEAK PROCEDURES

SOIL SPILL: DIG A HOLDING AREA SUCH AS PIT, POND OR LAGOON TO CONTAIN SPILLED MATERIAL. USE PROTECTIVE COVER SUCH AS A PLASTIC SHEET TO PREVENT DISSOLVING IN FIREFIGHTING WATER OR RAIN.

WATER SPILL: IF MATERIAL IS DISSOLVED, USE SODIUM SULFIDE SOLUTION TO PRECIPITATE HEAVY METALS.

NEUTRALIZE WITH AGRICULTURAL LIME, SLAKED LIME, CRUSHED LIMESTONE, OR SODIUM BICARBONATE.

USE MECHANICAL DREDGES OR LIFTS TO EXTRACT IMMOBILIZED MASSES OF POLLUTION AND PRECIPITATES.

OCCUPATIONAL SPILL: KEEP COMBUSTIBLES (WOOD, PAPER, OIL, ETC.) AWAY FROM SPILLED MATERIAL. DO NOT TOUCH SPILLED MATERIAL. STOP LEAK IF YOU CAN DO IT WITHOUT RISK. USE WATER SPRAY TO REDUCE VAPORS. DO NOT GET WATER INSIDE CONTAINER. FOR SMALL DRY SPILLS, WITH CLEAN SHOVEL PLACE MATERIAL INTO CLEAN, DRY CONTAINER AND COVER. MOVE CONTAINERS FROM SPILL AREA. FOR SMALL LIQUID SPILLS, FLUSH AREA WITH FLOODING AMOUNTS OF WATER. FOR LARGER SPILLS, DIKE FAR AHEAD OF SPILL FOR LATER DISPOSAL. KEEP UNNECESSARY PEOPLE AWAY. ISOLATE HAZARD AREA AND DENY ENTRY. REPORTABLE QUANTITY (RQ): 1 POUND THE SUPERFUND AMENDMENTS AND REAUTHORIZATION ACT (SARA) SECTION 304 REQUIRES THAT A RELEASE EQUAL TO OR GREATER THAN THE REPORTABLE QUANTITY FOR THIS SUBSTANCE BE IMMEDIATELY REPORTED TO THE LOCAL EMERGENCY PLANNING COMMITTEE AND THE STATE EMERGENCY RESPONSE COMMISSION (40 CFR 355.40). IF THE RELEASE OF THIS SUBSTANCE IS REPORTABLE UNDER CERCLA SECTION 103, THE NATIONAL RESPONSE CENTER MUST BE NOTIFIED IMMEDIATELY AT (800) 424-8802 OR (202) 426-2675 IN THE METROPOLITAN WASHINGTON, D.C. AREA (40 CFR 302.6).

PROTECTIVE EQUIPMENT

VENTILATION: PROVIDE LOCAL EXHAUST OR PROCESS ENCLOSURE VENTILATION TO MEET PUBLISHED EXPOSURE LIMITS.

RESPIRATOR: THE FOLLOWING RESPIRATORS AND MAXIMUM USE CONCENTRATIONS ARE RECOMMENDATIONS BY THE U.S. DEPARTMENT OF HEALTH AND HUMAN SERVICES, NIOSH POCKET GUIDE TO CHEMICAL HAZARDS; NIOSH CRITERIA DOCUMENTS OR BY THE U.S. DEPARTMENT OF LABOR, 29 CFR 1910 SUBPART Z. THE SPECIFIC RESPIRATOR SELECTED MUST BE BASED ON CONTAMINATION LEVELS FOUND IN THE WORK PLACE, MUST NOT EXCEED THE WORKING LIMITS OF THE RESPIRATOR AND BE JOINTLY APPROVED BY THE NATIONAL INSTITUTE FOR OCCUPATIONAL SAFETY AND HEALTH AND THE MINE SAFETY AND HEALTH ADMINISTRATION (NIOSH-MSHA).

SILVER (METAL AND SOLUBLE COMPOUNDS):

0.25 MG/M3- ANY SUPPLIED-AIR RESPIRATOR OPERATED IN CONTINUOUS FLOW MODE. ANY POWERED AIR-PURIFYING RESPIRATOR WITH A HIGH-EFFICIENCY PARTICULATE FILTER.

0.5 MG/M3- ANY AIR-PURIFYING FULL FACEPIECE RESPIRATOR WITH A HIGH-EFFICIENCY PARTICULATE FILTER. ANY SELF-CONTAINED BREATHING APPARATUS WITH A FULL FACEPIECE. ANY SUPPLIED-AIR RESPIRATOR WITH A FULL FACEPIECE.

20.0 MG/M3- ANY SUPPLIED-AIR RESPIRATOR WITH A FULL FACEPIECE AND OPERATED IN A PRESSURE-DEMAND OR OTHER POSITIVE PRESSURE MODE.

ESCAPE- ANY AIR-PURIFYING FULL FACEPIECE RESPIRATOR WITH A HIGH-EFFICIENCY PARTICULATE FILTER. ANY APPROPRIATE ESCAPE-TYPE SELF-CONTAINED BREATHING APPARATUS.

FOR FIREFIGHTING AND OTHER IMMEDIATELY DANGEROUS TO LIFE OR HEALTH CONDITIONS:

SELF-CONTAINED BREATHING APPARATUS WITH FULL FACEPIECE OPERATED IN PRESSURE-DEMAND OR OTHER POSITIVE PRESSURE MODE.

SUPPLIED-AIR RESPIRATOR WITH FULL FACEPIECE AND OPERATED IN PRESSURE-DEMAND OR OTHER POSITIVE PRESSURE MODE IN COMBINATION WITH AN AUXILIARY SELF-CONTAINED BREATHING APPARATUS OPERATED IN PRESSURE-DEMAND OR OTHER POSITIVE PRESSURE MODE.

CLOTHING: EMPLOYEE MUST WEAR APPROPRIATE PROTECTIVE (IMPERVIOUS) CLOTHING AND EQUIPMENT TO PREVENT ANY POSSIBILITY OF SKIN CONTACT WITH THIS SUBSTANCE.

GLOVES: EMPLOYEE MUST WEAR APPROPRIATE PROTECTIVE GLOVES TO PREVENT CONTACT WITH THIS SUBSTANCE.

EYE PROTECTION: EMPLOYEE MUST WEAR SPLASH-PROOF OR DUST-RESISTANT SAFETY GOGGLES AND A FACESHIELD TO PREVENT CONTACT WITH THIS SUBSTANCE.

EMERGENCY WASH FACILITIES: WHERE THERE IS ANY POSSIBILITY THAT AN EMPLOYEE'S EYES AND/OR SKIN MAY BE EXPOSED TO THIS SUBSTANCE, THE EMPLOYER SHOULD PROVIDE AN EYE WASH FOUNTAIN AND QUICK DRENCH SHOWER WITHIN THE IMMEDIATE WORK AREA FOR EMERGENCY USE.

AUTHORIZED BY- OCCUPATIONAL HEALTH SERVICES, INC.

CREATION DATE: 11/17/89 ***REVISION DATE:*** 07/13/90

MATERIAL SAFETY DATA SHEET

OCCUPATIONAL HEALTH SERVICES, INC.
AGRICULTURE AND PESTICIDE DIVISION
450 SEVENTH AVENUE, SUITE 2407
NEW YORK, NEW YORK 10123
1-800-445-MSDS OR (212) 967-1100

EMERGENCY CONTACT:
JOHN S. BRANSFORD, JR. (615) 292-1180

SUBSTANCE IDENTIFICATION

CAS-NUMBER 93-72-1

SUBSTANCE: SILVEX

TRADE NAMES/SYNONYMS: 2-(2,4,5-TRICHLOROPHENOXY)PROPIONIC ACID; 2,4,5-TCPPA; AQUA-VEX; COLOR-SET; DED-WEED; FEROPROP; FRUITORE 1; DOUBLE STRENGTH; FENORMONE; HERBICIDES, SILVEX; KURAN; KURON; 2,4,5-TP SILVEX; KUROSAL G; PROPON; SILVI-RHAP; STA-FAST; WEED-B-GON; RCRA U233; PST20830

MOLECULAR FORMULA: C9-H7-CL3-O3

MOLECULAR WEIGHT: 269.51

CERCLA RATINGS (SCALE 0-3): HEALTH=2 FIRE=1 REACTIVITY=0 PERSISTENCE=3

NFPA RATINGS (SCALE 0-4): HEALTH=2 FIRE=1 REACTIVITY=0

COMPONENTS AND CONTAMINANTS

COMPONENT: SILVEX ***PERCENT:*** 100

CAS# 93-72-1

OTHER CONTAMINANTS: MAY CONTAIN <0.1 PPM OF 2,3,7,8-TETRACHLORODIBENZO-P-DIOXIN

EXPOSURE LIMITS: SILVEX: NO OCCUPATIONAL EXPOSURE LIMIT ESTABLISHED BY OSHA, ACGIH, OR NIOSH.

100 POUNDS CERCLA SECTION 103 REPORTABLE QUANTITY

PHYSICAL DATA

DESCRIPTION: CRYSTALS ***MELTING POINT:*** 360 F (182 C)

SOLUBILITY IN WATER: SLIGHTLY SOLUBLE

SOLVENT SOLUBILITY: ACETONE, METHYL ALCOHOL, ETHER

FIRE AND EXPLOSION DATA

FIRE AND EXPLOSION HAZARD: SLIGHT FIRE HAZARD WHEN EXPOSED TO HEAT OR FLAME.

FIREFIGHTING MEDIA: DRY CHEMICAL, CARBON DIOXIDE, HALON, WATER SPRAY OR STANDARD FOAM (1987 EMERGENCY RESPONSE GUIDEBOOK, DOT P 5800.4). FOR LARGER FIRES, USE WATER SPRAY, FOG OR STANDARD FOAM (1987 EMERGENCY RESPONSE GUIDEBOOK, DOT P 5800.4).

FIREFIGHTING: MOVE CONTAINER FROM FIRE AREA IF POSSIBLE. DO NOT SCATTER SPILLED MATERIAL WITH HIGH PRESSURE WATER STREAMS. DIKE FIRE CONTROL WATER FOR LATER DISPOSAL (1987 EMERGENCY RESPONSE GUIDEBOOK, DOT P 5800.4, GUIDE PAGE 31).

USE AGENTS SUITABLE FOR TYPE OF SURROUNDING FIRE. AVOID BREATHING HAZARDOUS VAPORS, KEEP UPWIND.

TOXICITY

SILVEX: TOXICITY DATA: 650 MG/KG ORAL-RAT LD50; 276 MG/KG ORAL-MOUSE LD50; 650 MG/KG ORAL-MAMMAL LD50; REPRODUCTIVE EFFECTS DATA (RTECS). CARCINOGEN STATUS: HUMAN LIMITED EVIDENCE (IARC GROUP-2B FOR CHLOROPHENOXY HERBICIDES). STUDIES REVEALED A SIGNIFICANT INCREASE IN SOFT-TISSUE SARCOMAS, MALIGNANT LYMPHOMAS AND BRONCHIAL CARCINOMAS IN WORKERS EXPOSED TO CHLOROPHENOXY HERBICIDES. LOCAL EFFECTS: IRRITANT- INHALATION, SKIN, AND EYES. ACUTE TOXICITY DATA: MODERATELY TOXIC BY INGESTION. TARGET EFFECTS: POISONING MAY AFFECT THE GASTROINTESTINAL TRACT AND THE CARDIOVASCULAR SYSTEM.* AT INCREASED RISK FROM EXPOSURE: PERSONS WITH PREEXISTING LIVER, GASTROINTESTINAL TRACT OR SKIN DISORDERS.* ADDITIONAL DATA: STIMULANTS SUCH AS EPINEPHRINE MAY INDUCE VENTRICULAR FIBRILLATION.*
* MAY BE BASED ON GENERAL INFORMATION ON TRICHLOROPHENOXY DERIVATIVES.

HEALTH EFFECTS AND FIRST AID

INHALATION: SILVEX: IRRITANT. SEE 2,4,5-T AND DERIVATIVES.
2,4,5-T AND DERIVATIVES: **ACUTE EXPOSURE-** MAY CAUSE IRRITATION WITH SORE THROAT AND BURNING SENSATIONS IN THE NASOPHARYNX AND CHEST, COUGHING, LACRIMATION, RHINITIS, DULLNESS, DIZZINESS, AND ATAXIA. IF SUFFICIENT AMOUNTS ARE ABSORBED THROUGH THE LUNGS, EFFECTS AS DESCRIBED IN ACUTE INGESTION MAY OCCUR. **CHRONIC EXPOSURE-** OCCUPATIONAL EXPOSURE TO 2,4,5-T AND ITS DERIVATIVES HAS PRODUCED HEADACHE, DECREASED AUDITORY ACUITY, GASTROINTESTINAL SYMPTOMS OF NAUSEA, VOMITING, DIARRHEA, ABDOMINAL PAINS, AND BLOOD IN THE STOOL, CHLORACNE, PORPHYRIA CUTANEA TARDIA, HYPERTRICHOSIS, HYPERPIGMENTATION, INCREASED SKIN FRAGILITY, LIVER DISORDERS, PERSONALITY CHANGES, AND PERIPHERAL NEUROPATHY. MANY OF THESE EFFECTS MAY BE DUE TO DIOXINS, ESPECIALLY TCDD, AS CONTAMINANTS. EPIDEMIOLOGICAL STUDIES HAVE INDICATED AN ASSOCIATION BETWEEN EXPOSURE TO 2,4,5-T COMPOUNDS AND AN INCREASED PREVALENCE OF REPORTED SEXUAL DYSFUNCTION AND DECREASED LIBIDO, ABNORMAL SENSORY FINDINGS, GASTROINTESTINAL TRACT ULCER, AND BIRTH MALFORMATIONS OF THE FEET. AN INCREASED PREVALENCE OF SLOWED NERVE CONDUCTION VELOCITY WITH NO ASSOCIATED SYMPTOMS WAS REPORTED IN A STUDY OF CHEMICAL WORKERS EMPLOYED IN THE PRODUCTION OF 2,4-D AND 2,4,5-T. EPIDEMIOLOGICAL STUDIES REVEALED A SIGNIFICANT INCREASE IN SOFT-TISSUE SARCOMAS, MALIGNANT LYMPHOMAS, AND BRONCHIAL CARCINOMAS IN WORKERS EXPOSED TO CHLOROPHENOXY HERBICIDES INCLUDING 2,4,5-T.
FIRST AID- REMOVE FROM EXPOSURE AREA TO FRESH AIR IMMEDIATELY. IF BREATHING HAS STOPPED, PERFORM ARTIFICIAL RESPIRATION. KEEP PERSON WARM AND AT REST. TREAT SYMPTOMATICALLY AND SUPPORTIVELY. GET MEDICAL ATTENTION IMMEDIATELY.

SKIN CONTACT: SILVEX: IRRITANT. SEE INFORMATION ON 2,4,5-T AND DERIVATIVES.
2,4,5-T AND DERIVATIVES: **ACUTE EXPOSURE-** MAY CAUSE IRRITATION. IF SUFFICIENT AMOUNTS ARE ABSORBED THROUGH THE SKIN, EFFECTS AS DESCRIBED IN ACUTE INGESTION MAY OCCUR. **CHRONIC EXPOSURE-** PROLONGED OR REPEATED EXPOSURE MAY CAUSE DERMATITIS AND EFFECTS AS DESCRIBED IN CHRONIC INHALATION.
FIRST AID- REMOVE CONTAMINATED CLOTHING AND SHOES IMMEDIATELY. WASH AFFECTED AREA WITH SOAP OR MILD DETERGENT AND LARGE AMOUNTS OF WATER UNTIL NO EVIDENCE OF CHEMICAL REMAINS (APPROXIMATELY 15-20 MINUTES). GET MEDICAL ATTENTION IMMEDIATELY.

EYE CONTACT: SILVEX: IRRITANT. **ACUTE EXPOSURE-** MAY CAUSE IRRITATION. **CHRONIC EXPOSURE-** PROLONGED OR REPEATED EXPOSURE TO IRRITANTS MAY CAUSE CONJUNCTIVITIS.
FIRST AID- WASH EYES IMMEDIATELY WITH LARGE AMOUNTS OF WATER OR NORMAL SALINE, OCCASIONALLY LIFTING UPPER AND LOWER LIDS, UNTIL NO EVIDENCE OF CHEMICAL REMAINS (APPROXIMATELY 15-20 MINUTES). GET MEDICAL ATTENTION IMMEDIATELY.

INGESTION: SILVEX: CHRONIC ADMINISTRATION TO PREGNANT MICE AT A DOSAGE OF 400 MG/KG/DAY RESULTED IN REDUCED WEIGHT AND FETAL ABNORMALITY OF CLEFT PALATE. CHRONIC INGESTION OF 2.6-9.9 MG/KG/DAY BY MALE AND FEMALE DOGS PRODUCED A MILD DEGENERATION AND NECROSIS OF HEPATOCYTES. SEE 2,4,5-T AND DERIVATIVES.
2,4,5-T AND DERIVATIVES: **ACUTE EXPOSURE-** MAY CAUSE IRRITATION OF THE MOUTH, THROAT, AND GASTROINTESTINAL TRACT, NAUSEA, VOMITING, CHEST AND ABDOMINAL PAIN, AND DIARRHEA. INGESTION OF VERY LARGE DOSES MAY PRODUCE METABOLIC ACIDOSIS, FEVER OR SUBNORMAL TEMPERATURES, HYPERVENTILATION, HYPOTENSION, VASODILATION, FLUSHING OF THE SKIN, SWEATING, CARDIAC ARRHYTHMIAS, TACHYCARDIA, LETHARGY, WEAKNESS, INTERCOSTAL PARALYSIS, RENAL AND HEPATIC DYSFUNCTION, MYOTONIA, COMA, AND CONVULSIONS. DAMAGE TO SKELETAL MUSCLE MAY BE MANIFEST BY MUSCLE TWITCHING AND ACHING WITH ELEVATED SERUM ENZYMES AND MYOGLOBIN IN THE BLOOD AND URINE. DEATH MAY BE DUE TO CIRCULATORY COLLAPSE. **CHRONIC EXPOSURE-** NO DATA AVAILABLE.
FIRST AID- IF THE PERSON IS CONSCIOUS AND NOT CONVULSING, INDUCE EMESIS BY GIVING SYRUP OF IPECAC (KEEPING THE HEAD BELOW THE HIPS TO PREVENT ASPIRATION) FOLLOWED BY WATER. REPEAT IN 20 MINUTES IF NOT EFFECTIVE INITIALLY. IN PATIENTS WITH DEPRESSED RESPIRATION OR IF EMESIS IS NOT PRODUCED, PERFORM GASTRIC LAVAGE WITH ACTIVATED CHARCOAL. FOLLOW WITH A SALINE CATHARTIC (DREISBACH, HANDBOOK OF POISONING, 12TH ED.). TREAT SYMPTOMATICALLY AND SUPPORTIVELY. GASTRIC LAVAGE SHOULD BE PERFORMED BY QUALIFIED MEDICAL PERSONNEL. GET MEDICAL ATTENTION IMMEDIATELY.
ANTIDOTE: NO SPECIFIC ANTIDOTE. TREAT SYMPTOMATICALLY AND SUPPORTIVELY.

REACTIVITY

REACTIVITY: STABLE UNDER NORMAL TEMPERATURES AND PRESSURES.
INCOMPATIBILITIES: SILVEX: NO DATA AVAILABLE.
DECOMPOSITION: THERMAL DECOMPOSITION MAY RELEASE CORROSIVE FUMES OF HYDROGEN CHLORIDE AND TOXIC OXIDES OF CARBON.
POLYMERIZATION: HAZARDOUS POLYMERIZATION HAS NOT BEEN REPORTED TO OCCUR UNDER NORMAL TEMPERATURES AND PRESSURES.

STORAGE AND DISPOSAL

OBSERVE ALL FEDERAL, STATE AND LOCAL REGULATIONS WHEN STORING OR DISPOSING OF THIS SUBSTANCE. FOR ASSISTANCE, CONTACT THE DISTRICT DIRECTOR OF THE ENVIRONMENTAL PROTECTION AGENCY.

****STORAGE****

STORE IN ACCORDANCE WITH 40 CFR 165 RECOMMENDED PROCEDURES FOR THE DISPOSAL AND STORAGE OF PESTICIDES AND PESTICIDE CONTAINERS.

****DISPOSAL****

DISPOSAL MUST BE IN ACCORDANCE WITH 40 CFR 165 RECOMMENDED PROCEDURES FOR THE DISPOSAL AND STORAGE OF PESTICIDES AND PESTICIDE CONTAINERS.
2,4,5-TP (SILVEX) - REGULATORY LEVEL: 1.0 MG/L MATERIALS WHICH CONTAIN THE ABOVE SUBSTANCE AT OR ABOVE THE REGULATORY LEVEL MEET THE EPA CHARACTERISTIC OF TOXICITY, AND MUST BE DISPOSED OF IN ACCORDANCE WITH 40 CFR PART 262. EPA HAZARDOUS WASTE NUMBER D017.

CONDITIONS TO AVOID

MAY BURN BUT DOES NOT IGNITE READILY. AVOID CONTACT WITH STRONG OXIDIZERS, EXCESSIVE HEAT, SPARKS, OR OPEN FLAME.

SPILL AND LEAK PROCEDURES

SOIL SPILL: DIG A PIT, POND, LAGOON OR HOLDING AREA TO CONTAIN LIQUID OR SOLID MATERIAL. COVER SOLIDS WITH A PLASTIC SHEET TO PREVENT DISSOLVING IN RAIN OR FIREFIGHTING WATER.
WATER SPILL: IF DISSOLVED, AT A CONCENTRATION OF 10 PPM OR GREATER, APPLY ACTIVATED CARBON AT TEN TIMES THE AMOUNT THAT HAS BEEN SPILLED.
USE SUCTION HOSES TO REMOVE TRAPPED SPILL MATERIAL.
USE MECHANICAL DREDGES OR LIFTS TO EXTRACT IMMOBILIZED MASSES OF POLLUTION AND PRECIPITATES.
OCCUPATIONAL SPILL: SWEEP UP AND PLACE IN SUITABLE CLEAN, DRY CONTAINERS FOR RECLAMATION OR LATER DISPOSAL. DO NOT FLUSH SPILLED MATERIAL INTO SEWER. KEEP UNNECESSARY PEOPLE AWAY.
REPORTABLE QUANTITY (RQ): 100 POUNDS THE SUPERFUND AMENDMENTS AND REAUTHORIZATION ACT (SARA) SECTION 304 REQUIRES THAT A RELEASE EQUAL TO OR GREATER THAN THE REPORTABLE QUANTITY FOR THIS SUBSTANCE BE IMMEDIATELY REPORTED TO THE LOCAL EMERGENCY PLANNING COMMITTEE AND THE STATE EMERGENCY RESPONSE COMMISSION (40 CFR 355.40). IF THE RELEASE OF THIS SUBSTANCE IS REPORTABLE UNDER CERCLA SECTION 103, THE NATIONAL RESPONSE CENTER MUST BE NOTIFIED IMMEDIATELY AT (800) 424-8802 OR (202) 426-2675 IN THE METROPOLITAN WASHINGTON, D.C. AREA (40 CFR 302.6).

PROTECTIVE EQUIPMENT

VENTILATION: PROVIDE LOCAL EXHAUST OR GENERAL DILUTION VENTILATION SYSTEM.
RESPIRATOR: THE FOLLOWING RESPIRATORS ARE RECOMMENDED BASED ON INFORMATION FOUND IN THE PHYSICAL DATA, TOXICITY AND HEALTH EFFECTS SECTIONS. THEY ARE RANKED IN ORDER FROM MINIMUM TO MAXIMUM RESPIRATORY PROTECTION. THE SPECIFIC RESPIRATOR SELECTED MUST BE BASED ON CONTAMINATION LEVELS FOUND IN THE WORK PLACE, MUST NOT EXCEED THE WORKING LIMITS OF THE RESPIRATOR AND BE JOINTLY APPROVED BY THE NATIONAL INSTITUTE FOR OCCUPATIONAL SAFETY AND HEALTH AND THE MINE SAFETY AND HEALTH ADMINISTRATION (NIOSH-MSHA).

CHEMICAL CARTRIDGE RESPIRATOR WITH AN ORGANIC VAPOR CARTRIDGE(S) WITH A FULL FACEPIECE AND ORGANIC VAPOR CARTRIDGE(S) IN COMBINATION WITH A DUST AND MIST FILTER.
POWERED AIR-PURIFYING RESPIRATOR WITH A TIGHT-FITTING FACEPIECE AND ORGANIC VAPOR CARTRIDGE(S) IN COMBINATION WITH A HIGH-EFFICIENCY PARTICULATE FILTER.
TYPE 'C' SUPPLIED-AIR RESPIRATOR WITH A FULL FACEPIECE OPERATED IN A PRESSURE-DEMAND OR OTHER POSITIVE PRESSURE MODE.
SELF-CONTAINED BREATHING APPARATUS WITH A FULL FACEPIECE OPERATED IN PRESSURE-DEMAND OR OTHER POSITIVE PRESSURE MODE.
FOR FIREFIGHTING AND OTHER IMMEDIATELY DANGEROUS TO LIFE OR HEALTH CONDITIONS:
SELF-CONTAINED BREATHING APPARATUS WITH FULL FACEPIECE OPERATED IN PRESSURE-DEMAND OR OTHER POSITIVE PRESSURE MODE.
SUPPLIED-AIR RESPIRATOR WITH FULL FACEPIECE AND OPERATED IN PRESSURE-DEMAND OR OTHER POSITIVE PRESSURE MODE IN COMBINATION WITH AN AUXILIARY SELF-CONTAINED BREATHING APPARATUS OPERATED IN PRESSURE-DEMAND OR OTHER POSITIVE PRESSURE MODE.

CLOTHING: EMPLOYEE MUST WEAR APPROPRIATE PROTECTIVE (IMPERVIOUS) CLOTHING AND EQUIPMENT TO PREVENT REPEATED OR PROLONGED SKIN CONTACT WITH THIS SUBSTANCE.

GLOVES: EMPLOYEE MUST WEAR APPROPRIATE PROTECTIVE GLOVES TO PREVENT CONTACT WITH THIS SUBSTANCE.

EYE PROTECTION: EMPLOYEE MUST WEAR SPLASH-PROOF OR DUST-RESISTANT SAFETY GOGGLES TO PREVENT EYE CONTACT WITH THIS SUBSTANCE.
EMERGENCY EYE WASH: WHERE THERE IS ANY POSSIBILITY THAT AN EMPLOYEE'S EYES MAY BE EXPOSED TO THIS SUBSTANCE, THE EMPLOYER SHOULD PROVIDE AN EYE WASH FOUNTAIN WITHIN THE IMMEDIATE WORK AREA FOR EMERGENCY USE.

AUTHORIZED BY- OCCUPATIONAL HEALTH SERVICES, INC.
CREATION DATE: 10/05/89 ***REVISION DATE:*** 07/13/90

MATERIAL SAFETY DATA SHEET

OCCUPATIONAL HEALTH SERVICES, INC.
AGRICULTURE AND PESTICIDE DIVISION
450 SEVENTH AVENUE, SUITE 2407
NEW YORK, NEW YORK 10123
1-800-445-MSDS OR (212) 967-1100

EMERGENCY CONTACT:
JOHN S. BRANSFORD, JR. (615) 292-1180

SUBSTANCE IDENTIFICATION

CAS-NUMBER 4841-20-7

SUBSTANCE: **SILVEX, METHYL ESTER**

TRADE NAMES/SYNONYMS: PROPANOIC ACID, 2-(2,4,5-TRICHLOROPHENOXY)-, METHYL ESTER; 2-(2,4,5-TRICHLOROPHENOXY) METHYL PROPANOATE; PROPIONIC ACID, 2-(2,4,5-TRICHLOROPHENOXY)-, METHYL ESTER; 2-(2,4,5-TRICHLOROPHENOXY) METHYL PROPIONATE; 2-(2,4,5-TP), METHYL ESTER; METHYL-2-(2,4,5-TRICHLOROPHENOXY)PROPIONATE; 2,4,5-TRICHLOROPHENOXYPROPIONIC ACID ESTER; 2-(2,4,5-TRICHLOROPHENOXY)PROPANOIC ACID, METHYL ESTER; 2-(2,4,5-TRICHLOROPHENOXY)PROPIONIC ACID, METHYL ESTER; SILVEX METHYL ESTER; C10H9CL3O3; PST20831

CHEMICAL FAMILY: HALOGEN COMPOUND, AROMATIC ESTER, NON-CARBOXYLIC

MOLECULAR FORMULA: C6-H2-(CL)3-O-C-(C-H3)-H-C-O2-C-H3

MOLECULAR WEIGHT: 283.54

CERCLA RATINGS (SCALE 0-3): HEALTH=3 FIRE=1 REACTIVITY=0 PERSISTENCE=2

NFPA RATINGS (SCALE 0-4): HEALTH=U FIRE=1 REACTIVITY=0

COMPONENTS AND CONTAMINANTS

COMPONENT: SILVEX, METHYL ESTER ***PERCENT:*** 100.0
CAS# 4841-20-7

OTHER CONTAMINANTS: NONE

EXPOSURE LIMITS: NO OCCUPATIONAL EXPOSURE LIMITS ESTABLISHED BY OSHA, ACGIH, OR NIOSH.

PHYSICAL DATA

DESCRIPTION: WHITE POWDER. ***MELTING POINT:*** 192 F (89 C)
SPECIFIC GRAVITY: NOT AVAILABLE ***SOLUBILITY IN WATER:*** SPARINGLY SOLUBLE
SOLVENT SOLUBILITY: SOLUBLE IN MOST ORGANIC SOLVENTS.

FIRE AND EXPLOSION DATA

FIRE AND EXPLOSION HAZARD: SLIGHT FIRE HAZARD WHEN EXPOSED TO HEAT OR FLAME.
DUST-AIR MIXTURES MAY IGNITE OR EXPLODE.

FIREFIGHTING MEDIA: DRY CHEMICAL, CARBON DIOXIDE, HALON, WATER SPRAY OR STANDARD FOAM (1987 EMERGENCY RESPONSE GUIDEBOOK, DOT P 5800.4).
FOR LARGER FIRES, USE WATER SPRAY, FOG OR STANDARD FOAM (1987 EMERGENCY RESPONSE GUIDEBOOK, DOT P 5800.4).

FIREFIGHTING: MOVE CONTAINER FROM FIRE AREA IF POSSIBLE. DO NOT SCATTER SPILLED MATERIAL WITH HIGH PRESSURE WATER STREAMS. DIKE FIRE CONTROL WATER FOR LATER DISPOSAL (1987 EMERGENCY RESPONSE GUIDEBOOK, DOT P 5800.4, GUIDE PAGE 31).
USE AGENTS SUITABLE FOR TYPE OF SURROUNDING FIRE. AVOID BREATHING HAZARDOUS VAPORS, KEEP UPWIND.

TOXICITY

SILVEX, METHYL ESTER: TOXICITY DATA: 650 MG/KG ORAL-RAT LD50 (EPA). CARCINOGEN STATUS: HUMAN LIMITED EVIDENCE (IARC GROUP-2B FOR CHLOROPHENOXY HERBICIDES). STUDIES REVEALED A SIGNIFICANT INCREASE IN SOFT-TISSUE SARCOMAS, MALIGNANT LYMPHOMAS AND BRONCHIAL CARCINOMAS IN WORKERS EXPOSED TO CHLOROPHENOXY HERBICIDES. ACUTE TOXICITY LEVEL: MODERATELY TOXIC BY INGESTION. TARGET EFFECTS: POISONING MAY AFFECT THE GASTROINTESTINAL TRACT AND CARDIOVASCULAR SYSTEM.* AT INCREASED RISK FROM EXPOSURE: PERSONS WITH PREEXISTING LIVER, GASTROINTESTINAL TRACT OR SKIN DISORDERS.* ADDITIONAL DATA: STIMULANTS SUCH AS EPINEPHRINE MAY INDUCE VENTRICULAR FIBRILLATION.*
* MAY BE BASED ON GENERAL INFORMATION ON 2,4,5-T AND DERIVATIVES.

HEALTH EFFECTS AND FIRST AID

INHALATION: SILVEX, METHYL ESTER: SEE INFORMATION ON 2,4,5-T AND DERIVATIVES.
2,4,5-T AND DERIVATIVES: **ACUTE EXPOSURE-** MAY CAUSE IRRITATION WITH SORE THROAT AND BURNING SENSATIONS IN THE NASOPHARYNX AND CHEST, COUGHING, LACRIMATION, RHINITIS, DULLNESS, DIZZINESS, AND ATAXIA. IF SUFFICIENT AMOUNTS ARE ABSORBED THROUGH THE LUNGS, EFFECTS AS DESCRIBED IN ACUTE INGESTION MAY OCCUR. **CHRONIC EXPOSURE-** OCCUPATIONAL EXPOSURE TO 2,4,5-T AND ITS DERIVATIVES HAS PRODUCED HEADACHE, DECREASED AUDITORY ACUITY, GASTROINTESTINAL SYMPTOMS OF NAUSEA, VOMITING, DIARRHEA, ABDOMINAL PAINS, AND BLOOD IN THE STOOL, CHLORACNE, PORPHYRIA CUTANEA TARDIA, HYPERTRICHOSIS, HYPERPIGMENTATION, INCREASED SKIN FRAGILITY, LIVER DISORDERS, PERSONALITY CHANGES, AND PERIPHERAL NEUROPATHY. MANY OF THESE EFFECTS MAY BE DUE TO DIOXINS, ESPECIALLY TCDD, AS CONTAMINANTS. EPIDEMIOLOGICAL STUDIES HAVE INDICATED AN ASSOCIATION BETWEEN EXPOSURE TO 2,4,5-T COMPOUNDS AND AN INCREASED PREVALENCE OF REPORTED SEXUAL DYSFUNCTION AND DECREASED LIBIDO, ABNORMAL SENSORY FINDINGS, GASTROINTESTINAL TRACT ULCER, AND BIRTH MALFORMATIONS OF THE FEET. AN INCREASED PREVALENCE OF SLOWED NERVE CONDUCTION VELOCITY WITH NO ASSOCIATED SYMPTOMS WAS REPORTED IN A STUDY OF CHEMICAL WORKERS EMPLOYED IN THE PRODUCTION OF 2,4-D AND 2,4,5-T. EPIDEMIOLOGICAL STUDIES REVEALED A SIGNIFICANT INCREASE IN SOFT-TISSUE SARCOMAS, MALIGNANT LYMPHOMAS, AND BRONCHIAL CARCINOMAS IN WORKERS EXPOSED TO CHLOROPHENOXY HERBICIDES INCLUDING 2,4,5-T.

FIRST AID- REMOVE FROM EXPOSURE AREA TO FRESH AIR IMMEDIATELY. IF BREATHING HAS STOPPED, PERFORM ARTIFICIAL RESPIRATION. KEEP PERSON WARM AND AT REST. TREAT SYMPTOMATICALLY AND SUPPORTIVELY. GET MEDICAL ATTENTION IMMEDIATELY.

SKIN CONTACT: SILVEX, METHYL ESTER: SEE INFORMATION ON 2,4,5-T AND DERIVATIVES.
2,4,5-T AND DERIVATIVES: **ACUTE EXPOSURE-** MAY CAUSE IRRITATION. IF SUFFICIENT AMOUNTS ARE ABSORBED THROUGH THE SKIN, EFFECTS AS DESCRIBED IN ACUTE INGESTION MAY OCCUR. **CHRONIC EXPOSURE-** PROLONGED OR REPEATED EXPOSURE MAY CAUSE DERMATITIS AND EFFECTS AS DESCRIBED IN CHRONIC INHALATION.

FIRST AID- REMOVE CONTAMINATED CLOTHING AND SHOES IMMEDIATELY. WASH AFFECTED AREA WITH SOAP OR MILD DETERGENT AND LARGE AMOUNTS OF WATER UNTIL NO EVIDENCE OF CHEMICAL REMAINS (APPROXIMATELY 15-20 MINUTES). GET MEDICAL ATTENTION IMMEDIATELY.

EYE CONTACT: SILVEX, METHYL ESTER: SEE INFORMATION ON 2,4,5-T AND DERIVATIVES.
2,4,5-T AND DERIVATIVES: **ACUTE EXPOSURE-** MAY CAUSE IRRITATION. **CHRONIC EXPOSURE-** NO DATA AVAILABLE.

FIRST AID- WASH EYES IMMEDIATELY WITH LARGE AMOUNTS OF WATER OR NORMAL SALINE, OCCASIONALLY LIFTING UPPER AND LOWER LIDS, UNTIL NO EVIDENCE OF CHEMICAL REMAINS (APPROXIMATELY 15-20 MINUTES). GET MEDICAL ATTENTION IMMEDIATELY.

INGESTION: SILVEX, METHYL ESTER: SEE INFORMATION ON 2,4,5-T AND DERIVATIVES.
2,4,5-T AND DERIVATIVES: **ACUTE EXPOSURE**- MAY CAUSE IRRITATION OF THE MOUTH, THROAT, AND GASTROINTESTINAL TRACT, NAUSEA, VOMITING, CHEST AND ABDOMINAL PAIN, AND DIARRHEA. INGESTION OF VERY LARGE DOSES MAY PRODUCE METABOLIC ACIDOSIS, FEVER OR SUBNORMAL TEMPERATURES, HYPERVENTILATION, HYPOTENSION, VASODILATION, FLUSHING OF THE SKIN, SWEATING, CARDIAC ARRHYTHMIAS, TACHYCARDIA, LETHARGY, WEAKNESS, INTERCOSTAL PARALYSIS, RENAL AND HEPATIC DYSFUNCTION, MYOTONIA, COMA, AND CONVULSIONS. DAMAGE TO SKELETAL MUSCLE MAY BE MANIFEST BY MUSCLE TWITCHING AND ACHING WITH ELEVATED SERUM ENZYMES AND MYOGLOBIN IN THE BLOOD AND URINE. DEATH MAY BE DUE TO CIRCULATORY COLLAPSE. **CHRONIC EXPOSURE**- NO DATA AVAILABLE.
FIRST AID- IF THE PERSON IS CONSCIOUS AND NOT CONVULSING, INDUCE EMESIS BY GIVING SYRUP OF IPECAC (KEEPING THE HEAD BELOW THE HIPS TO PREVENT ASPIRATION) FOLLOWED BY WATER. REPEAT IN 20 MINUTES IF NOT EFFECTIVE INITIALLY. IN PATIENTS WITH DEPRESSED RESPIRATION OR IF EMESIS IS NOT PRODUCED, PERFORM GASTRIC LAVAGE WITH ACTIVATED CHARCOAL. FOLLOW WITH A SALINE CATHARTIC (DREISBACH, HANDBOOK OF POISONING, 12TH ED.). TREAT SYMPTOMATICALLY AND SUPPORTIVELY. GASTRIC LAVAGE SHOULD BE PERFORMED BY QUALIFIED MEDICAL PERSONNEL. GET MEDICAL ATTENTION IMMEDIATELY.
ANTIDOTE: NO SPECIFIC ANTIDOTE. TREAT SYMPTOMATICALLY AND SUPPORTIVELY.

REACTIVITY

REACTIVITY: STABLE UNDER NORMAL TEMPERATURES AND PRESSURES.
INCOMPATIBILITIES: SILVEX, METHYL ESTER: OXIDIZERS (STRONG): FIRE AND EXPLOSION HAZARD.
DECOMPOSITION: THERMAL DECOMPOSITION PRODUCTS MAY INCLUDE TOXIC AND CORROSIVE FUMES OF CHLORIDES AND TOXIC OXIDES OF CARBON.
POLYMERIZATION: HAZARDOUS POLYMERIZATION HAS NOT BEEN REPORTED TO OCCUR UNDER NORMAL TEMPERATURES AND PRESSURES.

STORAGE AND DISPOSAL

OBSERVE ALL FEDERAL, STATE AND LOCAL REGULATIONS WHEN STORING OR DISPOSING OF THIS SUBSTANCE. FOR ASSISTANCE, CONTACT THE DISTRICT DIRECTOR OF THE ENVIRONMENTAL PROTECTION AGENCY.

****STORAGE****

STORE IN ACCORDANCE WITH 40 CFR 165 RECOMMENDED PROCEDURES FOR THE DISPOSAL AND STORAGE OF PESTICIDES AND PESTICIDE CONTAINERS.
STORE AWAY FROM INCOMPATIBLE SUBSTANCES.

****DISPOSAL****

DISPOSAL MUST BE IN ACCORDANCE WITH 40 CFR 165 RECOMMENDED PROCEDURES FOR THE DISPOSAL AND STORAGE OF PESTICIDES AND PESTICIDE CONTAINERS.

CONDITIONS TO AVOID

MAY BURN BUT DOES NOT IGNITE READILY. AVOID CONTACT WITH STRONG OXIDIZERS, EXCESSIVE HEAT, SPARKS, OR OPEN FLAME.

SPILL AND LEAK PROCEDURES

OCCUPATIONAL SPILL: SWEEP UP AND PLACE IN SUITABLE CLEAN, DRY CONTAINERS FOR RECLAMATION OR LATER DISPOSAL. DO NOT FLUSH SPILLED MATERIAL INTO SEWER. KEEP UNNECESSARY PEOPLE AWAY.

PROTECTIVE EQUIPMENT

VENTILATION: PROVIDE LOCAL EXHAUST OR PROCESS ENCLOSURE VENTILATION SYSTEM.
RESPIRATOR: THE FOLLOWING RESPIRATORS ARE RECOMMENDED BASED ON INFORMATION FOUND IN THE PHYSICAL DATA, TOXICITY AND HEALTH EFFECTS SECTIONS. THEY ARE RANKED IN ORDER FROM MINIMUM TO MAXIMUM RESPIRATORY PROTECTION. THE SPECIFIC RESPIRATOR SELECTED MUST BE BASED ON CONTAMINATION LEVELS FOUND IN THE WORK PLACE, MUST NOT EXCEED THE WORKING LIMITS OF THE RESPIRATOR AND BE JOINTLY APPROVED BY THE NATIONAL INSTITUTE FOR OCCUPATIONAL SAFETY AND HEALTH AND THE MINE SAFETY AND HEALTH ADMINISTRATION (NIOSH-MSHA).
TYPE 'C' SUPPLIED-AIR RESPIRATOR WITH A FULL FACEPIECE OPERATED IN PRESSURE-DEMAND OR OTHER POSITIVE PRESSURE MODE OR WITH A FULL FACEPIECE, HELMET OR HOOD OPERATED IN CONTINOUS-FLOW MODE.
SELF-CONTAINED BREATHING APPARATUS WITH A FULL FACEPIECE OPERATED IN PRESSURE-DEMAND OR OTHER POSITIVE PRESSURE MODE.
FOR FIREFIGHTING AND OTHER IMMEDIATELY DANGEROUS TO LIFE OR HEALTH CONDITIONS:
SELF-CONTAINED BREATHING APPARATUS WITH FULL FACEPIECE OPERATED IN PRESSURE-DEMAND OR OTHER POSITIVE PRESSURE MODE.
SUPPLIED-AIR RESPIRATOR WITH FULL FACEPIECE AND OPERATED IN PRESSURE-DEMAND OR OTHER POSITIVE PRESSURE MODE IN COMBINATION WITH AN AUXILIARY SELF-CONTAINED BREATHING APPARATUS OPERATED IN PRESSURE-DEMAND OR OTHER POSITIVE PRESSURE MODE.
CLOTHING: EMPLOYEE MUST WEAR APPROPRIATE PROTECTIVE (IMPERVIOUS) CLOTHING AND EQUIPMENT TO PREVENT ANY POSSIBILITY OF SKIN CONTACT WITH THIS SUBSTANCE.
GLOVES: EMPLOYEE MUST WEAR APPROPRIATE PROTECTIVE GLOVES TO PREVENT CONTACT WITH THIS SUBSTANCE.
EYE PROTECTION: EMPLOYEE MUST WEAR SPLASH-PROOF OR DUST-RESISTANT SAFETY GOGGLES AND A FACESHIELD TO PREVENT CONTACT WITH THIS SUBSTANCE.
EMERGENCY WASH FACILITIES: WHERE THERE IS ANY POSSIBILITY THAT AN EMPLOYEE'S EYES AND/OR SKIN MAY BE EXPOSED TO THIS SUBSTANCE, THE EMPLOYER SHOULD PROVIDE AN EYE WASH FOUNTAIN AND QUICK DRENCH SHOWER WITHIN THE IMMEDIATE WORK AREA FOR EMERGENCY USE.

AUTHORIZED BY- OCCUPATIONAL HEALTH SERVICES, INC.
CREATION DATE: 05/02/90 ***REVISION DATE:*** 07/12/90

MATERIAL SAFETY DATA SHEET

OCCUPATIONAL HEALTH SERVICES, INC.
AGRICULTURE AND PESTICIDE DIVISION
450 SEVENTH AVENUE, SUITE 2407
NEW YORK, NEW YORK 10123
1-800-445-MSDS OR (212) 967-1100

EMERGENCY CONTACT:
JOHN S. BRANSFORD, JR. (615) 292-1180

SUBSTANCE IDENTIFICATION

CAS-NUMBER 122-34-9
***SUBSTANCE:* SIMAZINE**
TRADE NAMES/SYNONYMS: 1,3,5-TRIAZINE-2,4-DIAMINE, 6-CHLORO-N,N'-DIETHYL; S-TRIAZINE, 2-CHLORO-4,6-BIS(ETHYLAMINO)-; 6-CHLORO-N,N'-DIETHYL-1,3,5-TRIAZINE-2,4-DIAMINE; 2-CHLORO-4,6-BIS(ETHYLAMINO)-S-TRIAZINE; 2,4-BIS(ETHYLAMINO)-6-CHLORO-S-TRIAZINE; 2-CHLORO-4,6-BIS(ETHYLAMINO)-1,3,5-TRIAZINE; AQUAZINE; CDT; CET; G 27692; GEIGY 27692; GESATOP; HERBAZIN; PRINCEP; PRIMATOL S; SIMADEX; SIMANEX; C7H12CLN5; PST20837
CHEMICAL FAMILY: S-TRIAZINE
MOLECULAR FORMULA: C7-H12-CL-N5
MOLECULAR WEIGHT: 201.67
CERCLA RATINGS (SCALE 0-3): HEALTH=3 FIRE=1 REACTIVITY=0 PERSISTENCE=3
NFPA RATINGS (SCALE 0-4): HEALTH=3 FIRE=1 REACTIVITY=0

COMPONENTS AND CONTAMINANTS

COMPONENT: SIMAZINE ***PERCENT:*** 100.00
CAS# 122-34-9
OTHER CONTAMINANTS: NONE
EXPOSURE LIMITS: NO OCCUPATIONAL EXPOSURE LIMITS ESTABLISHED BY OSHA, ACGIH, OR NIOSH.

PHYSICAL DATA

DESCRIPTION: WHITE CRYSTALLINE SOLID. ***MELTING POINT:*** 439-441 F (226-227 C)
SPECIFIC GRAVITY: 1.302 ***VAPOR PRESSURE:*** NEGLIGIBLE
SOLUBILITY IN WATER: 0.00035%
SOLVENT SOLUBILITY: SLIGHTLY SOLUBLE IN DIOXANE, ETHYL CELLOSOLVE, METHANOL, PETROLEUM ETHER, DIETHYL ETHER, CHLOROFORM AND LIGHT PETROLEUM.

FIRE AND EXPLOSION DATA

FIRE AND EXPLOSION HAZARD: SLIGHT FIRE HAZARD WHEN EXPOSED TO HEAT OR FLAME.
FIREFIGHTING MEDIA: DRY CHEMICAL, CARBON DIOXIDE, HALON, WATER SPRAY OR STANDARD FOAM (1987 EMERGENCY RESPONSE GUIDEBOOK, DOT P 5800.4).
FOR LARGER FIRES, USE WATER SPRAY, FOG OR STANDARD FOAM (1987 EMERGENCY RESPONSE GUIDEBOOK, DOT P 5800.4).

FIREFIGHTING: MOVE CONTAINERS FROM FIRE AREA IF POSSIBLE (1987 EMERGENCY RESPONSE GUIDEBOOK, DOT P 5800.4, GUIDE PAGE 53).
EXTINGUISH USING AGENTS SUITABLE FOR SURROUNDING FIRE. USE FLOODING QUANTITIES OF WATER AS A FOG. KEEP MATERIAL OUT OF SEWERS AND WATER SOURCES. DO NOT TOUCH SPILLED MATERIAL. AVOID BREATHING HAZARDOUS FUMES; KEEP UPWIND.

TOXICITY

SIMAZINE: IRRITATION DATA: 500 MG OPEN SKIN-RABBIT MILD; 80 MG EYE-RABBIT MODERATE. TOXICITY DATA: 580 MG/M3 INHALATION-RAT LCLO; 9800 MG/M3/1 HOUR INHALATION-RAT LC50; 10.2 MG/KG SKIN-RAT LD50 (EPA, PESTICIDE FACT SHEET 1984); 971 MG/KG ORAL-RAT LD50; 2014 MG/KG ORAL-MAMMAL LD50; 100 MG/KG INTRAVENOUS-MOUSE LD50; 1390 MG/KG UNREPORTED-RAT LD50; 1400 MG/KG UNREPORTED-MAMMAL LD50; MUTAGENIC DATA (RTECS); REPRODUCTIVE EFFECTS DATA (RTECS); TUMORIGENIC DATA (RTECS). CARCINOGEN STATUS: NONE. ACUTE TOXICITY LEVEL: HIGHLY TOXIC BY INHALATION; MODERATELY TOXIC BY INGESTION; SLIGHTLY TOXIC BY DERMAL ABSORPTION. TARGET EFFECTS: NO DATA AVAILABLE.

HEALTH EFFECTS AND FIRST AID

INHALATION: SIMAZINE: **ACUTE EXPOSURE-** A CONCENTRATION OF 580 MG/M3 WAS LETHAL TO SOME RATS. SOME TRIAZINES ARE MILDLY IRRITATING TO THE MUCOUS MEMBRANES. **CHRONIC EXPOSURE-** CHRONIC INHALATION OF A CUMULATIVE DOSE OF 17 MG/M3 FOR 2 HOURS FOR 8 DAYS IN PREGNANT RATS RESULTED IN FETOTOXICITY AND FETAL DEVELOPMENTAL ABNORMALITIES.
FIRST AID- REMOVE FROM EXPOSURE AREA TO FRESH AIR IMMEDIATELY. IF BREATHING HAS STOPPED, PERFORM ARTIFICIAL RESPIRATION. KEEP PERSON WARM AND AT REST. TREAT SYMPTOMATICALLY AND SUPPORTIVELY. GET MEDICAL ATTENTION IMMEDIATELY.

SKIN CONTACT: SIMAZINE: **ACUTE EXPOSURE-** 500 MG APPLIED TO OPEN SKIN OF RABBITS WAS MILDLY IRRITATING. AN 80 PERCENT WETTABLE POWDER FORMULATION PRODUCED IRRITATION. MODERATE SKIN SENSITIZATION WAS OBSERVED IN GUINEA PIGS. **CHRONIC EXPOSURE-** DERMATITIS CHARACTERIZED BY ERYTHEMA, EDEMA, AND A VESICULOPAPULAR REACTION WAS REPORTED AMONG WORKER INVOLVED IN THE PRODUCTION OF SIMAZINE AND PROPAZINE. NO SYSTEMIC TOXICITY WAS OBSERVED IN A 21-DAY DERMAL STUDY OF RABBITS AT DOSES UP TO 1 GM/KG.
FIRST AID- REMOVE CONTAMINATED CLOTHING AND SHOES IMMEDIATELY. WASH AFFECTED AREA WITH SOAP OR MILD DETERGENT AND LARGE AMOUNTS OF WATER UNTIL NO EVIDENCE OF CHEMICAL REMAINS (APPROXIMATELY 15-20 MINUTES). GET MEDICAL ATTENTION IMMEDIATELY.

EYE CONTACT: SIMAZINE: **ACUTE EXPOSURE-** 80 MG APPLIED TO RABBIT EYES WAS MODERATELY IRRITATING. A 80 PERCENT WETTABLE POWDER FORMULATION PRODUCED CORNEAL OPACITY IN AN ANIMAL STUDY. **CHRONIC EXPOSURE-** NO DATA AVAILABLE.
FIRST AID- WASH EYES IMMEDIATELY WITH LARGE AMOUNTS OF WATER OR NORMAL SALINE, OCCASIONALLY LIFTING UPPER AND LOWER LIDS, UNTIL NO EVIDENCE OF CHEMICAL REMAINS (APPROXIMATELY 15-20 MINUTES). GET MEDICAL ATTENTION IMMEDIATELY.

INGESTION: SIMAZINE: **ACUTE EXPOSURE-** 500 MG/KG OF THIS MATERIAL WAS FATAL IN SHEEP WITH DEATH DELAYED FOR 5 TO 16 DAYS. THE SHEEP SHOWED SIGNS OF INTAKE OF LESS FOOD BUT MORE WATER THAN USUAL, INCOORDINATION, TREMOR, AND WEAKNESS. CYANOSIS AND CLONIC CONVULSIONS WERE SEEN IN SOME SHEEP. SHEEP APPEARED TO BE MORE SUSCEPTIBLE TO THE TOXICITY OF THIS MATERIAL THAN OTHER ANIMALS. **CHRONIC EXPOSURE-** RATS AND GUINEA PIGS FED 100 MG/KG DAILY FOR 6 MONTHS HAD SUPPRESSED WEIGHT INCREASES, INCREASE IN THE NUMBER OF LEUCOCYTES, DECREASE IN CHOLINESTERASE ACTIVITY IN BLOOD, AND ATROPHIC GASTRITIS. IN A 28-DAY RAT STUDY, INGESTION OF DOSES INCREASED FROM 10 MG/KG/DAY TO 2500 MG/KG/DAY PRODUCED A PROGRESSIVE INCREASE IN THE DEATH OF THE RATS WITH RESULTING EFFECTS OF STOMACH ULCERS AND HYPEREMIA OF THE SMALL INTESTINE. EFFECTS ON THE FETUS AND FERTILITY AND FETAL DEVELOPMENTAL ABNORMALITIES WERE OBSERVED IN A STUDY OF PREGNANT RATS. DECREASED FETAL WEIGHTS AND INCREASED SKELETAL VARIATIONS WERE NOTED IN A STUDY OF PREGNANT RABBITS FED 200 MG/KG/DAY.
FIRST AID- REMOVE BY GASTRIC LAVAGE AND CATHARSIS. MAINTAIN BLOOD PRESSURE AND AIRWAY. GIVE OXYGEN IF RESPIRATION IS DEPRESSED. DO NOT PERFORM GASTRIC LAVAGE IF VICTIM IS UNCONSCIOUS. GET MEDICAL ATTENTION IMMEDIATELY (DREISBACH, HANDBOOK OF POISONING, 12TH ED.).
ADMINISTRATION OF LAVAGE OR OXYGEN SHOULD BE PERFORMED BY QUALIFIED MEDICAL PERSONNEL.
ANTIDOTE: NO SPECIFIC ANTIDOTE. TREAT SYMPTOMATICALLY AND SUPPORTIVELY.

REACTIVITY

REACTIVITY: STABLE UNDER NORMAL TEMPERATURES AND PRESSURES.
INCOMPATIBILITIES: SIMAZINE: ACIDS: HYDROLYSIS MAY OCCUR AT 70 C BASES: HYDROLYSIS MAY OCCUR AT 70 C
DECOMPOSITION: THERMAL DECOMPOSITION PRODUCTS MAY INCLUDE TOXIC OXIDES OF NITROGEN AND CARBON AND TOXIC AND CORROSIVE FUMES OF CHLORIDES.
POLYMERIZATION: HAZARDOUS POLYMERIZATION HAS NOT BEEN REPORTED TO OCCUR UNDER NORMAL TEMPERATURES AND PRESSURES.

STORAGE AND DISPOSAL

OBSERVE ALL FEDERAL, STATE AND LOCAL REGULATIONS WHEN STORING OR DISPOSING OF THIS SUBSTANCE. FOR ASSISTANCE, CONTACT THE DISTRICT DIRECTOR OF THE ENVIRONMENTAL PROTECTION AGENCY.

STORAGE

STORE IN ACCORDANCE WITH 40 CFR 165 RECOMMENDED PROCEDURES FOR THE DISPOSAL AND STORAGE OF PESTICIDES AND PESTICIDE CONTAINERS.
STORE AWAY FROM INCOMPATIBLE SUBSTANCES.

DISPOSAL

DISPOSAL MUST BE IN ACCORDANCE WITH 40 CFR 165 RECOMMENDED PROCEDURES FOR THE DISPOSAL AND STORAGE OF PESTICIDES AND PESTICIDE CONTAINERS.

CONDITIONS TO AVOID

MAY BURN BUT DOES NOT IGNITE READILY.

SPILL AND LEAK PROCEDURES

OCCUPATIONAL SPILL: DO NOT TOUCH SPILLED MATERIAL. STOP LEAK IF YOU CAN DO IT WITHOUT RISK. FOR SMALL SPILLS, TAKE UP WITH SAND OR OTHER ABSORBENT MATERIAL AND PLACE INTO CONTAINERS FOR LATER DISPOSAL. FOR SMALL DRY SPILLS, WITH A CLEAN SHOVEL PLACE MATERIAL INTO CLEAN, DRY CONTAINER AND COVER. MOVE CONTAINERS FROM SPILL AREA. FOR LARGER SPILLS, DIKE FAR AHEAD OF SPILL FOR LATER DISPOSAL. KEEP UNNECESSARY PEOPLE AWAY. ISOLATE HAZARD AREA AND DENY ENTRY.

PROTECTIVE EQUIPMENT

VENTILATION: PROVIDE LOCAL EXHAUST OR GENERAL DILUTION VENTILATION SYSTEM.
RESPIRATOR: THE FOLLOWING RESPIRATORS ARE RECOMMENDED BASED ON INFORMATION FOUND IN THE PHYSICAL DATA, TOXICITY AND HEALTH EFFECTS SECTIONS. THEY ARE RANKED IN ORDER FROM MINIMUM TO MAXIMUM RESPIRATORY PROTECTION. THE SPECIFIC RESPIRATOR SELECTED MUST BE BASED ON CONTAMINATION LEVELS FOUND IN THE WORK PLACE, MUST NOT EXCEED THE WORKING LIMITS OF THE RESPIRATOR AND BE JOINTLY APPROVED BY THE NATIONAL INSTITUTE FOR OCCUPATIONAL SAFETY AND HEALTH AND THE MINE SAFETY AND HEALTH ADMINISTRATION (NIOSH-MSHA).
CHEMICAL CARTRIDGE RESPIRATOR WITH AN ORGANIC VAPOR CARTRIDGE(S) IN COMBINATION WITH A DUST AND MIST FILTER.
GAS MASK WITH ORGANIC VAPOR CANISTER (CHIN-STYLE OR FRONT- OR BACK-MOUNTED CANISTER) WITH A DUST AND MIST FILTER.
GAS MASK WITH ORGANIC VAPOR CANISTER (CHIN-STYLE OR FRONT- OR BACK-MOUNTED CANISTER) WITH A PARTICULATE FILTER.
POWERED AIR-PURIFYING RESPIRATOR WITH A HIGH-EFFICIENCY FILTER.
TYPE 'C' SUPPLIED-AIR RESPIRATOR WITH A FULL FACEPIECE OPERATED IN A PRESSURE-DEMAND OR OTHER POSITIVE PRESSURE MODE.
SELF-CONTAINED BREATHING APPARATUS WITH A FULL FACEPIECE OPERATED IN PRESSURE-DEMAND OR OTHER POSITIVE PRESSURE MODE.
FOR FIREFIGHTING AND OTHER IMMEDIATELY DANGEROUS TO LIFE OR HEALTH CONDITIONS:
SELF-CONTAINED BREATHING APPARATUS WITH FULL FACEPIECE OPERATED IN PRESSURE-DEMAND OR OTHER POSITIVE PRESSURE MODE.
SUPPLIED-AIR RESPIRATOR WITH FULL FACEPIECE AND OPERATED IN PRESSURE-DEMAND OR OTHER POSITIVE PRESSURE MODE IN COMBINATION WITH AN AUXILIARY SELF-CONTAINED BREATHING APPARATUS OPERATED IN PRESSURE-DEMAND OR OTHER POSITIVE PRESSURE MODE.
CLOTHING: EMPLOYEE MUST WEAR APPROPRIATE PROTECTIVE (IMPERVIOUS) CLOTHING AND EQUIPMENT TO PREVENT REPEATED OR PROLONGED SKIN CONTACT WITH THIS SUBSTANCE.
GLOVES: EMPLOYEE MUST WEAR APPROPRIATE PROTECTIVE GLOVES TO PREVENT CONTACT WITH THIS SUBSTANCE.
EYE PROTECTION: EMPLOYEE MUST WEAR SPLASH-PROOF OR DUST-RESISTANT SAFETY GOGGLES TO PREVENT EYE CONTACT WITH THIS SUBSTANCE.
EMERGENCY EYE WASH: WHERE THERE IS ANY POSSIBILITY THAT AN EMPLOYEE'S EYES MAY BE EXPOSED TO THIS SUBSTANCE, THE EMPLOYER SHOULD PROVIDE

AN EYE WASH FOUNTAIN WITHIN THE IMMEDIATE WORK AREA FOR EMERGENCY USE.

AUTHORIZED BY- OCCUPATIONAL HEALTH SERVICES, INC.
CREATION DATE: 10/06/89 ***REVISION DATE:*** 05/07/90

MATERIAL SAFETY DATA SHEET

OCCUPATIONAL HEALTH SERVICES, INC.
AGRICULTURE AND PESTICIDE DIVISION
450 SEVENTH AVENUE, SUITE 2407
NEW YORK, NEW YORK 10123
1-800-445-MSDS OR (212) 967-1100

EMERGENCY CONTACT:
JOHN S. BRANSFORD, JR. (615) 292-1180

SUBSTANCE IDENTIFICATION

CAS-NUMBER 7631-89-2
SUBSTANCE: **SODIUM ARSENATE**
TRADE NAMES/SYNONYMS: ARSENIC ACID, SODIUM SALT; SODIUM METAARSENATE; ORTHOARSENATE; SWEENSY'S ANT-GO; FATSCO ANT POISON; STCC 4923290; UN 1685; PST20940
CHEMICAL FAMILY: INORGANIC SALT
MOLECULAR FORMULA: AS-O4-H.NA2
MOLECULAR WEIGHT: 302.88
CERCLA RATINGS (SCALE 0-3): HEALTH=3 FIRE=0 REACTIVITY=0 PERSISTENCE=3
NFPA RATINGS (SCALE 0-4): HEALTH=3 FIRE=0 REACTIVITY=0

COMPONENTS AND CONTAMINANTS

COMPONENT: SODIUM ARSENATE ***PERCENT:*** 100
CAS# 7631-89-2
OTHER CONTAMINANTS: NONE
EXPOSURE LIMITS: ARSENIC, INORGANIC AND SOLUBLE COMPOUNDS: 10 UG(AS)/M3 OSHA TWA 200 UG(AS)/M3 ACGIH TWA 2 UG(AS)/M3 NIOSH RECOMMENDED 15 MINUTE CEILING
SUBJECT TO SARA SECTION 313 ANNUAL TOXIC CHEMICAL RELEASE REPORTING SUBJECT TO CALIFORNIA PROPOSITION 65 CANCER AND/OR REPRODUCTIVE TOXICITY WARNING AND RELEASE REQUIREMENTS- (FEBRUARY 27, 1987)
SODIUM ARSENATE: 1000/10,000 POUNDS SARA SECTION 302 THRESHOLD PLANNING QUANTITY 1000 POUNDS SARA SECTION 304 REPORTABLE QUANTITY 1 POUND CERCLA SECTION 103 REPORTABLE QUANTITY SUBJECT TO SARA SECTION 313 ANNUAL TOXIC CHEMICAL RELEASE REPORTING SUBJECT TO CALIFORNIA PROPOSITION 65 CANCER AND/OR REPRODUCTIVE TOXICITY WARNING AND RELEASE REQUIREMENTS- (FEBRUARY 27, 1987)

PHYSICAL DATA

DESCRIPTION: CLEAR, COLORLESS, OR WHITE ODORLESS CRYSTALS, WITH AN ALKALINE TASTE.
MELTING POINT: NOT AVAILABLE ***SPECIFIC GRAVITY:*** NOT AVAILABLE
PH: ALKALINE ***SOLUBILITY IN WATER:*** SOLUBLE
SOLVENT SOLUBILITY: ALCOHOL, GLYCEROL, INSOLUBLE IN ETHER

FIRE AND EXPLOSION DATA

FIRE AND EXPLOSION HAZARD: NEGLIGIBLE FIRE HAZARD WHEN EXPOSED TO HEAT OR FLAME.
FIREFIGHTING MEDIA: DRY CHEMICAL, CARBON DIOXIDE, HALON, WATER SPRAY OR STANDARD FOAM (1987 EMERGENCY RESPONSE GUIDEBOOK, DOT P 5800.4).
FOR LARGER FIRES, USE WATER SPRAY, FOG OR STANDARD FOAM (1987 EMERGENCY RESPONSE GUIDEBOOK, DOT P 5800.4).
FIREFIGHTING: MOVE CONTAINERS FROM FIRE AREA IF POSSIBLE (1987 EMERGENCY RESPONSE GUIDEBOOK, DOT P 5800.4, GUIDE PAGE 53).

TOXICITY

SODIUM ARSENATE: TOXICITY DATA: 51 MG/KG ORAL-RABBIT LDLO; 85 MG/KG INTRAVENOUS-RAT LDLO; 188 MG/KG INTRAVENOUS-CAT LD50; 28 MG/KG INTRAVENOUS-RABBIT LDLO; 49 MG/KG INTRAPERITONEAL-RAT LDLO; MUTAGENIC DATA (RTECS); REPRODUCTIVE EFFECTS DATA (RTECS); TUMORIGENIC DATA (RTECS). CARCINOGEN STATUS: OSHA CARCINOGEN; KNOWN HUMAN CARCINOGEN (NTP); HUMAN SUFFICIENT EVIDENCE, ANIMAL LIMITED EVIDENCE (IARC GROUP-1 FOR ARSENIC COMPOUNDS). AN INCREASED INCIDENCE OF SKIN AND LUNG CANCER HAS BEEN ASSOCIATED WITH INORGANIC ARSENIC COMPOUNDS THROUGH MEDICAL TREATMENT, CONTAMINATED DRINKING WATER OR OCCUPATIONAL EXPOSURE. CANCER AT OTHER SITES HAS ALSO BEEN REPORTED, BUT A CLEAR ASSOCIATION HAS NOT BEEN CONFIRMED. LOCAL EFFECTS: IRRITANT- INHALATION, SKIN, AND EYES. ACUTE TOXICITY LEVEL: INSUFFICIENT DATA. TARGET EFFECTS: SENSITIZER- SKIN; NEUROTOXIN. POISONING MAY AFFECT THE LIVER AND KIDNEYS.*
* MAY BE BASED ON GENERAL INFORMATION ON ARSENIC COMPOUNDS.

HEALTH EFFECTS AND FIRST AID

INHALATION: SODIUM ARSENATE: IRRITANT/CARCINOGEN. **ACUTE EXPOSURE-** MAY CAUSE IRRITATION TO THE MUCOUS MEMBRANES. INHALATION OF SOME ARSENIC DUSTS MAY CAUSE ACUTE PULMONARY EDEMA, RESTLESSNESS, DYSPNEA, CYANOSIS, COUGH WITH FOAMY SPUTUM, RALES AND HEMATURIA. **CHRONIC EXPOSURE-** NO DATA AVAILABLE ON THIS SPECIFIC COMPOUND. PROLONGED INHALATION OF SOME ARSENIC COMPOUNDS CAUSE POLYNEURITIS, OPTIC NEURITIS, ANESTHESIAS, PARESTHESIAS, SUCH AS BURNING PAINS IN THE HANDS AND FEET, BRONZING OF THE SKIN, ALOPECIA, LOCALIZED EDEMA, DERMATITIS, CIRRHOSIS OF THE LIVER, NAUSEA, VOMITING, ABDOMINAL CRAMPS, SALIVATION, NASAL SEPTUM PERFORATION, HEMOLYTIC OR APLASTIC ANEMIA, LEUKOPENIA, CHRONIC NEPHRITIS, AND CARDIAC FAILURE. ARSENIC AND INORGANIC ARSENIC COMPOUNDS ARE CONSIDERED TO BE LUNG CARCINOGENS. THREE COHORT STUDIES OF WORKERS MANUFACTURING ARSENICAL PESTICIDES SHOWED AN EXCESS MORTALITY FROM RESPIRATORY CANCER.
FIRST AID- REMOVE FROM EXPOSURE AREA TO FRESH AIR IMMEDIATELY. IF BREATHING HAS STOPPED, PERFORM ARTIFICIAL RESPIRATION. KEEP PERSON WARM AND AT REST. TREAT SYMPTOMATICALLY AND SUPPORTIVELY. GET MEDICAL ATTENTION IMMEDIATELY.

SKIN CONTACT: SODIUM ARSENATE: IRRITANT/SENSITIZER/CARCINOGEN. **ACUTE EXPOSURE-** ARSENIC AND ARSENIC COMPOUNDS MAY IRRITATE THE SKIN. SENSITIZATION DERMATITIS MAY OCCUR IN PREVIOUSLY EXPOSED PERSONS, CHARACTERIZED BY ECZEMA WITH SCALING AND HYPERPIGMENTATION OF THE SKIN AND HYPERKERATOSIS OF THE PALMS OF THE HANDS AND THE SOLES OF THE FEET. INORGANIC ARSENIC COMPOUNDS ARE SLIGHTLY ABSORBED THROUGH THE SKIN WHEN ADMINISTERED IN A LIPID VEHICLE. POISONING HAS CAUSED ALOPECIA, BRONZING OF THE SKIN, AND BRITTLE NAILS. **CHRONIC EXPOSURE-** REPEATED OR PROLONGED EXPOSURE MAY RESULT IN SENSITIZATION DERMATITIS. INORGANIC ARSENIC COMPOUNDS ARE SKIN CARCINOGENS.
FIRST AID- REMOVE CONTAMINATED CLOTHING AND SHOES IMMEDIATELY. WASH AFFECTED AREA WITH SOAP OR MILD DETERGENT AND LARGE AMOUNTS OF WATER UNTIL NO EVIDENCE OF CHEMICAL REMAINS (APPROXIMATELY 15-20 MINUTES). GET MEDICAL ATTENTION IMMEDIATELY.

EYE CONTACT: SODIUM ARSENATE: IRRITANT. **ACUTE EXPOSURE-** MAY CAUSE IRRITATION. **CHRONIC EXPOSURE-** MAY CAUSE CONJUNCTIVITIS AFTER REPEATED OR PROLONGED EXPOSURE. POISONING FROM INHALATION OR INGESTION HAS CAUSED OPTIC NEURITIS.
FIRST AID- WASH EYES IMMEDIATELY WITH LARGE AMOUNTS OF WATER OR NORMAL SALINE, OCCASIONALLY LIFTING UPPER AND LOWER LIDS, UNTIL NO EVIDENCE OF CHEMICAL REMAINS (APPROXIMATELY 15-20 MINUTES). GET MEDICAL ATTENTION IMMEDIATELY.

INGESTION: SODIUM ARSENATE:
ACUTE EXPOSURE- NO DATA AVAILABLE ON THIS SPECIFIC COMPOUND. INGESTION OF NON-FATAL DOSES OF SOME INORGANIC ARSENIC COMPOUNDS CAUSE RESTLESSNESS, NAUSEA, VOMITING, HEADACHE, DIZZINESS, CHILLS, CRAMPS, IRRITABILITY, AND PARALYSIS. JAUNDICE, OLIGURIA, AND ANURIA MAY OCCUR WITHIN 1-3 DAYS. FATAL DOSES MAY CAUSE GASTROINTESTINAL DISTURBANCES, BURNING PAIN IN THE THROAT, VOMITING, WATERY OR BLOODY DIARRHEA WITH MUCOUS, HYPOTENSION, WEAKNESS, CONVULSIONS, COMA AND DEATH FROM CIRCULATORY FAILURE. **CHRONIC EXPOSURE-** MAY AFFECT THE CENTRAL NERVOUS SYSTEM, SKIN, GASTROINTESTINAL TRACT, CARDIOVASCULAR SYSTEM, KIDNEYS, AND LIVER. ARSENIC COMPOUNDS MAY CROSS THE PLACENTAL BARRIER. RATS SHOWED MORTALITIES FOLLOWING ORAL ADMINISTRATION. ARSENIC MAY CAUSE CANCER OF THE LUNGS, LIVER, LARYNX, LYMPHATIC SYSTEM, OR VISCERA. IN ONE EPIDEMIOLOGICAL STUDY, SKIN CANCER WAS POSITIVELY CORRELATED WITH HIGH ARSENIC LEVELS IN DRINKING WATER.
FIRST AID- REMOVE BY GASTRIC LAVAGE OR EMESIS. FOLLOW WITH A SALINE CATHARTIC. MAINTAIN BLOOD PRESSURE, AIRWAY, AND GIVE OXYGEN IF RESPIRATION IS DEPRESSED. DO NOT PERFORM GASTRIC LAVAGE OR EMESIS IF VICTIM IS UNCONSCIOUS. GET MEDICAL ATTENTION IMMEDIATELY. (DREISBACH, HANDBOOK OF POISONING, 12TH ED.) ADMINISTRATION OF GASTRIC LAVAGE OR OXYGEN SHOULD BE PERFORMED BY QUALIFIED MEDICAL PERSONNEL.
ANTIDOTE: THE FOLLOWING ANTIDOTE HAS BEEN RECOMMENDED. HOWEVER, THE DECISION AS TO WHETHER THE SEVERITY OF POISONING REQUIRES ADMINISTRATION OF ANY ANTIDOTE AND ACTUAL DOSE REQUIRED SHOULD BE MADE BY QUALIFIED MEDICAL PERSONNEL.

ARSENIC POISONING: GIVE DIMERCAPROL, 3 MG/KG (OR 0.3 ML/KG) EVERY 4 HOURS FOR 2 DAYS AND THEN 2 MG/KG EVERY 2 HOURS FOR A TOTAL OF 10 DAYS. DIMERCAPROL IS AVAILABLE AS A 10% SOLUTION IN OIL FOR INTRAMUSCULAR ADMINISTRATION. NEXT, GIVE PENICILLAMINE, UP TO 100 MG/KG/DAY (MAXIMUM 1 G/DAY) DIVIDED INTO 4 DOSES FOR NO LONGER THAN 1 WEEK. IF A LONGER ADMINISTRATION PERIOD IS WARRANTED, DOSAGE SHOULD NOT EXCEED 40 MG/KG/DAY. GIVE THE DRUG ORALLY HALF AN HOUR BEFORE MEALS. DISCONTINUE ANTIDOTE WHEN URINE ARSENIC LEVEL FALLS BELOW 50 UG/24 HR. (DREISBACH, HANDBOOK OF POISONING, 12TH ED.). ANITDOTE SHOULD BE ADMINISTERED BY QUALIFIED MEDICAL PERSONNEL.

REACTIVITY

REACTIVITY: STABLE UNDER NORMAL TEMPERATURES AND PRESSURES.

INCOMPATIBILITIES: NO DATA AVAILABLE.

DECOMPOSITION: THERMAL DECOMPOSITION PRODUCTS MAY INCLUDE TOXIC ARSINE GAS.

POLYMERIZATION: NO DATA AVAILABLE.

STORAGE AND DISPOSAL

OBSERVE ALL FEDERAL, STATE AND LOCAL REGULATIONS WHEN STORING OR DISPOSING OF THIS SUBSTANCE. FOR ASSISTANCE, CONTACT THE DISTRICT DIRECTOR OF THE ENVIRONMENTAL PROTECTION AGENCY.

****STORAGE****

THRESHOLD PLANNING QUANTITY (TPQ): THE SUPERFUND AMENDMENTS AND REAUTHORIZATION ACT (SARA) SECTION 302 REQUIRES THAT EACH FACILITY WHERE ANY EXTREMELY HAZARDOUS SUBSTANCE IS PRESENT IN A QUANTITY EQUAL TO OR GREATER THAN THE TPQ ESTABLISHED FOR THAT SUBSTANCE NOTIFY THE STATE EMERGENCY RESPONSE COMMISSION FOR THE STATE IN WHICH IT IS LOCATED. SECTION 303 OF SARA REQUIRES THESE FACILITIES TO PARTICIPATE IN LOCAL EMERGENCY RESPONSE PLANNING (40 CFR 355.30).

****DISPOSAL****

ARSENIC - REGULATORY LEVEL: 5.0 MG/L MATERIALS WHICH CONTAIN THE ABOVE SUBSTANCE AT OR ABOVE THE REGULATORY LEVEL MEET THE EPA CHARACTERISTIC OF TOXICITY, AND MUST BE DISPOSED OF IN ACCORDANCE WITH 40 CFR PART 262. EPA HAZARDOUS WASTE NUMBER D004.

CONDITIONS TO AVOID

MAY BURN BUT DOES NOT IGNITE READILY.

SPILL AND LEAK PROCEDURES

WATER SPILL: THE CALIFORNIA SAFE DRINKING WATER AND TOXIC ENFORCEMENT ACT OF 1986 (PROPOSITION 65) PROHIBITS CONTAMINATING ANY KNOWN SOURCE OF DRINKING WATER WITH SUBSTANCES KNOWN TO CAUSE CANCER AND/OR REPRODUCTIVE TOXICITY.

OCCUPATIONAL SPILL: DO NOT TOUCH SPILLED MATERIAL. STOP LEAK IF YOU CAN DO IT WITHOUT RISK. FOR SMALL SPILLS, TAKE UP WITH SAND OR OTHER ABSORBENT MATERIAL AND PLACE INTO CONTAINERS FOR LATER DISPOSAL. FOR SMALL DRY SPILLS, WITH A CLEAN SHOVEL PLACE MATERIAL INTO CLEAN, DRY CONTAINER AND COVER. MOVE CONTAINERS FROM SPILL AREA. FOR LARGER SPILLS, DIKE FAR AHEAD OF SPILL FOR LATER DISPOSAL. KEEP UNNECESSARY PEOPLE AWAY. ISOLATE HAZARD AREA AND DENY ENTRY.

REPORTABLE QUANTITY (RQ): THE SUPERFUND AMENDMENTS AND REAUTHORIZATION ACT (SARA) SECTION 304 REQUIRES THAT A RELEASE EQUAL TO OR GREATER THAN THE REPORTABLE QUANTITY ESTABLISHED FOR THAT SUBSTANCE BE IMMEDIATELY REPORTED TO THE LOCAL EMERGENCY PLANNING COMMITTEE AND THE STATE EMERGENCY RESPONSE COMMISSION (40 CFR 355.40). IF THE RELEASE OF THIS SUBSTANCE IS REPORTABLE UNDER CERCLA SECTION 103, THE NATIONAL RESPONSE CENTER MUST BE NOTIFIED IMMEDIATELY AT (800) 424-8802 OR (202) 426-2675 IN THE METROPOLITAN WASHINGTON, D.C. AREA (40 CFR 302.6).

PROTECTIVE EQUIPMENT

VENTILATION: PROVIDE LOCAL EXHAUST OR PROCESS ENCLOSURE VENTILATION TO MEET PUBLISHED EXPOSURE LIMITS.

ARSENIC (INORGANIC): VENTILATION SHOULD MEET THE REQUIREMENTS IN 29 CFR 1910.1018(G).

RESPIRATOR: THE FOLLOWING RESPIRATORS ARE THE MINIMUM LEGAL REQUIREMENTS AS SET FORTH BY THE OCCUPATIONAL SAFETY AND HEALTH ADMINISTRATION FOUND IN 29 CFR 1910, SUBPART Z.

RESPIRATORY PROTECTION FOR INORGANIC ARSENIC PARTICULATE EXCEPT THOSE WITH SIGNIFICANT VAPOR PRESSURE

CONCENTRATION OF INORGANIC ARSENIC (AS) REQUIRED RESPIRATOR OR CONDITION OF USE

UNKNOWN OR GREATER OR LESS THAN 20,000 UG/M3 (20 MG/M3) OR FIREFIGHTING ANY FULL FACEPIECE, SELF CONTAINED BREATHING APPARATUS, OPERATED IN POSITIVE PRESSURE MODE.

NOT GREATER THAN 20,000 UG/M3 (20 MG/M3) SUPPLIED-AIR RESPIRATOR WITH FULL FACEPIECE, HOOD OR HELMET OR SUIT AND OPERATED IN POSITIVE PRESSURE MODE.

NOT GREATER THAN 10,000 UG/M3 (10 MG/M3) POWERED-AIR PURIFYING RESPIRATORS IN ALL INLET FACE COVERINGS WITH HIGH EFFICIENCY FILTERS; OR HALF-MASK SUPPLIED-AIR RESPIRATOR OPERATED IN POSITIVE PRESSURE MODE.

NOT GREATER THAN 500 UG/M3 FULL FACEPIECE AIR-PURIFYING RESPIRATOR EQUIPPED WITH HIGH EFFICIENCY FILTERS; OR ANY FULL FACEPIECE SUPPLIED-AIR RESPIRATOR; OR ANY FULL FACEPIECE SELF-CONTAINED BREATHING APPARATUS. NOT GREATER THAN 100 UG/M3 HALF-MASK AIR-PURIFYING RESPIRATOR EQUIPPED WITH HIGH EFFICIENCY FILTERS; OR ANY HALF-MASK SUPPLIED-AIR RESPIRATOR.

(HIGH EFFICIENCY FILTER- 99.97% EFFICIENCY AGAINST 0.3 MICROMETER MONODISPERSE DIETHYL-HEXYL PHTHALATE (DOP) PARTICLES)

RESPIRATORY PROTECTION FOR INORGANIC ARSENICALS (SUCH AS ARSENIC TRICHLORIDE OR ARSENIC PHOSPHIDE) WITH SIGNIFICANT VAPOR PRESSURE.

CONCENTRATION OF INORGANIC ARSENIC (AS) REQUIRED RESPIRATOR OR CONDITION OF USE

UNKNOWN OR GREATER OR LESS THAN 20,000 UG/M3 (20 MG/M3) ANY FULL FACEPIECE SELF-CONTAINED BREATHING APPARATUS OPERATED IN POSITIVE PRESSURE MODE.

NOT GREATER THAN 20,000 UG/M3 (20 MG/M3) SUPPLIED-AIR RESPIRATOR WITH A FULL FACEPIECE, HOOD OR HELMET OR SUIT OPERATED IN POSITIVE PRESSURE MODE.

NOT GREATER THAN 10,000 UG/M3 RESPIRATOR (10 MG/M3) HALF-MASK SUPPLIED AIR OPERATED IN POSITIVE PRESSURE MODE.

NOT GREATER THAN 500 UG/M3 FRONT- OR BACK-MOUNTED GAS MASK EQUIPPED WITH HIGH-EFFICIENCY FILTERS AND ACID GAS CANISTER; OR ANY FULL FACEPIECE SUPPLIED AIR RESPIRATOR; OR ANY FULL FACEPIECE SELF-CONTAINED BREATHING APPARATUS.

NOT GREATER THAN 100 UG/M3 HALF-MASK AIR-PURIFYING RESPIRATOR EQUIPPED WITH HIGH EFFICIENCY FILTER AND ACID GAS CARTRIDGE; OR ANY HALF-MASK SUPPLIED-AIR RESPIRATOR.

(HIGH EFFICIENCY FILTER- 99.97% EFFICIENCY AGAINST 0.3 MICROMETER MONODISPERSE DIETHYL-HEXYL PHTHALATE (DOP) PARTICLES) (HALF-MASK RESPIRATORS SHALL NOT BE USED FOR PROTECTION AGAINST ARSENIC TRICHLORIDE, AS IT IS RAPIDLY ABSORBED THROUGH THE SKIN).

THE FOLLOWING RESPIRATORS AND MAXIMUM USE CONCENTRATIONS ARE RECOMMENDATIONS BY THE U.S. DEPARTMENT OF HEALTH AND HUMAN SERVICES, NIOSH POCKET GUIDE TO CHEMICAL HAZARDS; NIOSH CRITERIA DOCUMENTS OR BY THE U.S. DEPARTMENT OF LABOR, 29 CFR 1910 SUBPART Z.

THE SPECIFIC RESPIRATOR SELECTED MUST BE BASED ON CONTAMINATION LEVELS FOUND IN THE WORK PLACE, MUST NOT EXCEED THE WORKING LIMITS OF THE RESPIRATOR AND BE JOINTLY APPROVED BY THE NATIONAL INSTITUTE FOR OCCUPATIONAL SAFETY AND HEALTH AND THE MINE SAFETY AND HEALTH ADMINISTRATION (NIOSH-MSHA).

AT ANY DETECTABLE CONCENTRATION:

SELF-CONTAINED BREATHING APPARATUS WITH FULL FACEPIECE OPERATED IN PRESSURE-DEMAND OR OTHER POSITIVE PRESSURE MODE. SUPPLIED-AIR RESPIRATOR WITH FULL FACEPIECE OPERATED IN PRESSURE-DEMAND OR OTHER POSITIVE PRESSURE MODE IN COMBINATION WITH AN AUXILIARY SELF-CONTAINED BREATHING APPARATUS OPERATED IN PRESSURE-DEMAND OR OTHER POSITIVE PRESSURE MODE.

ESCAPE- AIR-PURIFYING FULL FACEPIECE RESPIRATOR (GAS MASK) WITH A CHIN-STYLE OR FRONT- OR BACK-MOUNTED ORGANIC VAPOR CANISTER HAVING A HIGH-EFFICIENCY PARTICULATE FILTER. ESCAPE-TYPE SELF-CONTAINED BREATHING APPARATUS.

FOR FIREFIGHTING AND OTHER IMMEDIATELY DANGEROUS TO LIFE OR HEALTH CONDITIONS:

SELF-CONTAINED BREATHING APPARATUS WITH FULL FACEPIECE OPERATED IN PRESSURE-DEMAND OR OTHER POSITIVE PRESSURE MODE.

SUPPLIED-AIR RESPIRATOR WITH FULL FACEPIECE AND OPERATED IN PRESSURE-DEMAND OR OTHER POSITIVE PRESSURE MODE IN COMBINATION WITH AN AUXILIARY SELF-CONTAINED BREATHING APPARATUS OPERATED IN PRESSURE-DEMAND OR OTHER POSITIVE PRESSURE MODE.

CLOTHING: EMPLOYEE MUST WEAR APPROPRIATE PROTECTIVE (IMPERVIOUS) CLOTHING AND EQUIPMENT TO PREVENT ANY POSSIBILITY OF SKIN CONTACT WITH THIS SUBSTANCE. ARSENIC (INORGANIC): PROTECTIVE CLOTHING SHOULD MEET THE REQUIREMENTS FOR PROTECTIVE WORK CLOTHING AND EQUIPMENT IN 29 CFR 1910.1018(J).

GLOVES: EMPLOYEE MUST WEAR APPROPRIATE PROTECTIVE GLOVES TO PREVENT CONTACT WITH THIS SUBSTANCE.

ARSENIC (INORGANIC): PROTECTIVE GLOVES SHOULD MEET THE REQUIREMENTS FOR PROTECTIVE WORK CLOTHING AND EQUIPMENT IN 29 CFR 1910.1018(J).

EYE PROTECTION: EMPLOYEE MUST WEAR SPLASH-PROOF OR DUST-RESISTANT SAFETY GOGGLES WITH OR WITHOUT A FACESHIELD TO PREVENT CONTACT WITH THIS SUBSTANCE.
EMERGENCY EYE WASH: WHERE THERE IS ANY POSSIBILITY THAT AN EMPLOYEE'S EYES MAY BE EXPOSED TO THIS SUBSTANCE, THE EMPLOYER SHOULD PROVIDE AN EYE WASH FOUNTAIN WITHIN THE IMMEDIATE WORK AREA FOR EMERGENCY USE.
ARSENIC (INORGANIC): PROTECTIVE EYE EQUIPMENT SHOULD MEET THE REQUIREMENTS FOR PROTECTIVE WORK CLOTHING AND EQUIPMENT IN 29 CFR 1910.1018(J).

AUTHORIZED BY- OCCUPATIONAL HEALTH SERVICES, INC.
CREATION DATE: 10/05/89 ***REVISION DATE:*** 07/13/90

MATERIAL SAFETY DATA SHEET

OCCUPATIONAL HEALTH SERVICES, INC.
AGRICULTURE AND PESTICIDE DIVISION
450 SEVENTH AVENUE, SUITE 2407
NEW YORK, NEW YORK 10123
1-800-445-MSDS OR (212) 967-1100

EMERGENCY CONTACT:
JOHN S. BRANSFORD, JR. (615) 292-1180

SUBSTANCE IDENTIFICATION

CAS-NUMBER 26628-22-8
SUBSTANCE: **SODIUM AZIDE**
TRADE NAMES/SYNONYMS: AZIUM; AZIDE; KAZOE; RCRA P105; STCC 4923465; UN 1687; HYDRAZOIC ACID, SODIUM SALT; SMITE; SODIUM AZIDE (NA(N3)); N3NA; PST20960
CHEMICAL FAMILY: AZIDE
MOLECULAR FORMULA: NA-N3
MOLECULAR WEIGHT: 65.01
CERCLA RATINGS (SCALE 0-3): HEALTH=3 FIRE=1 REACTIVITY=3 PERSISTENCE=0
NFPA RATINGS (SCALE 0-4): HEALTH=4 FIRE=1 REACTIVITY=3

COMPONENTS AND CONTAMINANTS

COMPONENT: SODIUM AZIDE ***PERCENT:*** 100.0
CAS# 26628-22-8
OTHER CONTAMINANTS: NONE.
EXPOSURE LIMITS: SODIUM AZIDE: 0.1 PPM (HN3) OSHA CEILING (SKIN); 0.3 MG/M3 (NAN3) OSHA CEILING (SKIN) 0.1 PPM (HN3) ACGIH CEILING; 0.3 MG/M3 (NAN3) ACGIH CEILING
500 POUNDS SARA SECTION 302 THRESHOLD PLANNING QUANTITY 1000 POUNDS SARA SECTION 304 REPORTABLE QUANTITY 1000 POUNDS CERCLA SECTION 103 REPORTABLE QUANTITY

PHYSICAL DATA

DESCRIPTION: COLORLESS, CRYSTALLINE SOLID.
MELTING POINT: >527 F (>275 C) (DECOMPOSES) ***SPECIFIC GRAVITY:*** 1.846
SOLUBILITY IN WATER: 41.7% @ 17 C
SOLVENT SOLUBILITY: SOLUBLE IN LIQUID AMMONIA; SLIGHTLY SOLUBLE IN ALCOHOL, BENZENE; INSOLUBLE IN ETHER.

FIRE AND EXPLOSION DATA

FIRE AND EXPLOSION HAZARD: SLIGHT FIRE HAZARD WHEN EXPOSED TO HEAT OR FLAME.
DANGEROUS EXPLOSION HAZARD WHEN EXPOSED TO HEAT OR FLAME.
FIREFIGHTING MEDIA: DRY CHEMICAL, CARBON DIOXIDE, HALON, WATER SPRAY OR STANDARD FOAM (1987 EMERGENCY RESPONSE GUIDEBOOK, DOT P 5800.4).
FOR LARGER FIRES, USE WATER SPRAY, FOG OR STANDARD FOAM (1987 EMERGENCY RESPONSE GUIDEBOOK, DOT P 5800.4).
FIREFIGHTING: MOVE CONTAINERS FROM FIRE AREA IF POSSIBLE. COOL CONTAINERS EXPOSED TO FLAMES WITH WATER FROM SIDE UNTIL WELL AFTER FIRE IS OUT. STAY AWAY FROM STORAGE TANK ENDS. FOR MASSIVE FIRE IN STORAGE AREA, USE UNMANNED HOSE HOLDER OR MONITOR NOZZLES; ELSE WITHDRAW FROM AREA AND LET FIRE BURN (1987 EMERGENCY RESPONSE GUIDEBOOK, DOT P 5800.4, GUIDE PAGE 56).
DO NOT APPLY WATER DIRECTLY TO BURNING MATERIAL. CONTACT MAY RESULT IN A VIOLENT REACTION. USE FLOODING AMOUNTS OF WATER AS A FOG. COOL CONTAINERS WITH FLOODING AMOUNTS OF WATER, APPLIED FROM AS FAR A DISTANCE AS POSSIBLE. AVOID BREATHING POISONOUS VAPORS, KEEP UPWIND. EVACUATE TO A RADIUS OF 2500 FEET FOR UNCONTROLLABLE FIRES.

TRANSPORTATION DATA

DEPARTMENT OF TRANSPORTATION HAZARD CLASSIFICATION 49 CFR 172.101: POISON B
DEPARTMENT OF TRANSPORTATION LABELING REQUIREMENTS 49 CFR 172.101 AND SUBPART E: POISON
DEPARTMENT OF TRANSPORTATION PACKAGING REQUIREMENTS: 49 CFR 173.375 EXCEPTIONS: 49 CFR 173.364

TOXICITY

SODIUM AZIDE: TOXICITY DATA: 20 MG/KG SKIN-RABBIT LD50; 710 UG/KG ORAL-HUMAN TDLO; 143 MG/KG ORAL-MAN LDLO; 3 MG/KG ORAL-WOMAN TDLO; 27 MG/KG ORAL-RAT LD50; 27 MG/KG ORAL-MOUSE LD50; 35 MG/KG SUBCUTANEOUS-RAT LDLO; 17 MG/KG SUBCUTANEOUS-MOUSE LDLO; 17 MG/KG SUBCUTANEOUS-RABBIT LDLO; 19 MG/KG INTRAVENOUS-MOUSE LD50; 12 MG/KG INTRAVENOUS-MONKEY LDLO; 30 MG/KG INTRAPERITONEAL-RAT LDLO; 28 MG/KG INTRAPERITONEAL-MOUSE LD50; 27 MG/KG UNREPORTED-MOUSE LD50; MUTAGENIC DATA (RTECS); TUMORIGENIC DATA (RTECS). CARCINOGEN STATUS: NONE. LOCAL EFFECTS: IRRITANT- INHALATION, SKIN, EYE. ACUTE TOXICITY LEVEL: HIGHLY TOXIC BY DERMAL ABSORPTION AND INGESTION. TARGET EFFECTS: CHEMICAL ASPHYXIANT. MAY ALSO AFFECT THE CENTRAL NERVOUS AND CARDIOVASCULAR SYSTEMS.

HEALTH EFFECTS AND FIRST AID

INHALATION: SODIUM AZIDE: IRRITANT/CHEMICAL ASPHYXIANT. **ACUTE EXPOSURE-** VAPORS OR FUMES MAY CAUSE IRRITATION TO THE MUCOUS MEMBRANES WITH COUGHING AND SORE THROAT. OTHER SYMPTOMS MAY INCLUDE VASODILATION WITH A MODERATE REDUCTION IN BLOOD PRESSURE, VARIABLE PULSE RATE, SLIGHT SHORTNESS OF BREATH, BRONCHITIS, PULMONARY EDEMA, HEADACHE, DIZZINESS, UNSTEADINESS, THROBBING HEADACHES, PALPITATION, FATIGUE, NAUSEA, FAINTNESS, WEAKNESS IN ARMS AND LEGS, BRADYCARDIA, CYANOSIS, AND COLLAPSE. EXPOSURE TO HIGH CONCENTRATIONS MAY RESULT IN CONVULSIONS AND DEATH. **CHRONIC EXPOSURE-** WORKERS EXPOSED TO 0.5 PPM REPORTED HEADACHE AND NASAL STUFFINESS. REPEATED OR PROLONGED EXPOSURE MAY CAUSE NOSE IRRITATION, EPISODES OF FALLING BLOOD PRESSURE, DIZZINESS, AND BRONCHITIS.
FIRST AID- REMOVE FROM EXPOSURE AREA TO FRESH AIR IMMEDIATELY. IF BREATHING HAS STOPPED, PERFORM ARTIFICIAL RESPIRATION. KEEP PERSON WARM AND AT REST. TREAT SYMPTOMATICALLY AND SUPPORTIVELY. GET MEDICAL ATTENTION IMMEDIATELY.

SKIN CONTACT: SODIUM AZIDE: IRRITANT/HIGHLY TOXIC. **ACUTE EXPOSURE-** MAY CAUSE IRRITATION WITH REDNESS AND PAIN. MAY BE ABSORBED THROUGH THE SKIN RESULTING IN SYSTEMIC TOXICITY AS DETAILED IN ACUTE INGESTION. THE LETHAL DOSE REPORTED IN RABBITS WAS 20 MG/KG. **CHRONIC EXPOSURE-** REPEATED OR PROLONGED EXPOSURE TO IRRITANTS MAY CAUSE DERMATITIS.
FIRST AID- REMOVE CONTAMINATED CLOTHING AND SHOES IMMEDIATELY. WASH AFFECTED AREA WITH SOAP OR MILD DETERGENT AND LARGE AMOUNTS OF WATER UNTIL NO EVIDENCE OF CHEMICAL REMAINS (APPROXIMATELY 15-20 MINUTES). GET MEDICAL ATTENTION IMMEDIATELY.

EYE CONTACT: SODIUM AZIDE: IRRITANT. **ACUTE EXPOSURE-** MAY CAUSE IRRITATION WITH REDNESS, PAIN AND BLURRED VISION. SYSTEMIC TOXIC EFFECTS MAY OCCUR. **CHRONIC EXPOSURE-** REPEATED OR PROLONGED EXPOSURE TO IRRITANTS MAY CAUSE CONJUNCTIVITIS.
FIRST AID- WASH EYES IMMEDIATELY WITH LARGE AMOUNTS OF WATER OR NORMAL SALINE, OCCASIONALLY LIFTING UPPER AND LOWER LIDS, UNTIL NO EVIDENCE OF CHEMICAL REMAINS (APPROXIMATELY 15-20 MINUTES). GET MEDICAL ATTENTION IMMEDIATELY.

INGESTION: SODIUM AZIDE: CHEMICAL ASPHYXIANT/HIGHLY TOXIC. **ACUTE EXPOSURE-** VASODILATION WITH A PROMPT FALL IN BLOOD PRESSURE, LASTING 10-15 MINUTES HAS RESULTED FROM HUMAN INGESTION. DIZZINESS, POUNDING OF THE HEART, FAINTNESS AND MYOCARDIAL ISCHEMIA WERE REPORTED FROM 10-20 MG. AN AQUEOUS SOLUTION CONTAINING 150 MG PRODUCED BREATHLESSNESS, RESPIRATORY DISTRESS, RAPID PULSE, AND TACHYCARDIA WITHIN 5 MINUTES; NAUSEA, VOMITING, HEADACHE, RESTLESSNESS, AND DIARRHEA WITHIN 15 MINUTES. LATER POLYDIPSIA, ECG CHANGES, AND LEUKOCYTOSIS OCCURRED. WEAKNESS AND DIZZINESS CONTINUED FOR 10 DAYS. CARDIAC ARRHYTHMIA, DECREASED CARDIAC OUTPUT, ALTERED MENTAL STATUS, PRONOUNCED ACIDOSIS, AND NONCARDIOGENIC PULMONARY EDEMA PRECEDED THE DEATH OF AN INDIVIDUAL WHO INGESTED 10-20 GRAMS OF SODIUM AZIDE. INGESTIONS OF "SEVERAL GRAMS" CAUSED COLLAPSE AND DEATH WITHIN 40 MINUTES. THE PATHOLOGIC FINDINGS INCLUDED SWELLING OF THE BRAIN AND LUNGS, AND MILD FATTY DEGENERATION OF THE LIVER. OTHER

REPORTED SYMPTOMS INCLUDE: ABDOMINAL PAIN AND SPASMS, THROBBING AT BASE OF BRAIN, VIOLENT HEART STIMULATION, GENERAL ANESTHESIA, SWEATING, HYPOTHERMIA, SOMNOLENCE, KIDNEY CHANGES, URINARY INCONTINENCE, LOSS OF VISION, RIGIDITY, INJURY TO THE HEART MUSCLES, LOSS OF CONSCIOUSNESS, CONVULSIONS, COMA, RESPIRATORY ARREST, HEART FAILURE AND DEATH. IN ANIMALS, HEMATURIA AND LESIONS IN OPTIC NERVES AND TRACTS HAVE BEEN REPORTED. **CHRONIC EXPOSURE-** IN HUMANS, THE ADMINISTRATION OF SMALL AMOUNTS AS AN ANTIHYPERTENSIVE AGENT HAS CAUSED HYPOTENSION AND TRANSIENT POUNDING SENSATIONS IN THE HEAD. NO OTHER SIDE EFFECTS WERE NOTED. CHRONIC FEEDING STUDIES ON DOGS WITH DOSES OF 3 AND 10 MG/KG/DAY PRODUCED ATAXIA IN THE 27TH WEEK. PATHOLOGIC FINDINGS REVEALED LESIONS OF THE ANTERIOR AND MIDDLE CEREBRAL SECTIONS. LETHARGY, LABORED BREATHING, LUNG CONGESTION, HEMORRHAGE AND EDEMA, AND NECROSIS OF THE CEREBRUM AND THALAMUS OCCURRED IN RATS CHRONICALLY FED 20 MG/KG OF SODIUM AZIDE IN THE DIET. ORAL ADMINISTRATION OF HALF THE LD50 TO RATS CAUSED DEATH IN 3 DAYS, WITH ACCUMULATION OF THE COMPOUND IN INTERNAL ORGANS, AND HISTOPATHOLOGICAL CHANGES OF THE HEART, LUNGS, KIDNEYS, SPLEEN, ADRENALS, AND BRAIN. HEPATIC EFFECTS WERE ALSO REPORTED. FEMALE RATS FED 100 PPM OF SODIUM AZIDE IN THE DIET FOR 18 MONTHS SHOWED A SIGNIFICANT INCREASE IN THE INCIDENCE OF PITUITARY CHROMOPHOBE ADENOMA.

FIRST AID- TREAT SYMPTOMATICALLY AND SUPPORTIVELY. GET MEDICAL ATTENTION IMMEDIATELY. IF VOMITING OCCURS, KEEP HEAD LOWER THAN HIPS TO PREVENT ASPIRATION.

ANTIDOTE: NO SPECIFIC ANTIDOTE. TREAT SYMPTOMATICALLY AND SUPPORTIVELY.

REACTIVITY

REACTIVITY: MAY UNDERGO EXPLOSIVE DECOMPOSITION AT ELEVATED TEMPERATURES, PARTICULARLY ON RAPID HEATING.

INCOMPATIBILITIES: SODIUM AZIDE: ACIDS: PRODUCES EXPLOSIVE COMPOUND. AMMONIUM CHLORIDE + TRICHLOROACETONITRILE: EXPLOSIVE. BARIUM CARBONATE: EXPLOSIVE @ 630 C. BENZOYL CHLORIDE + POTASSIUM HYDROXIDE: EXOTHERMIC REACTION. BROMINE: EXPLOSIVE. CARBON DISULFIDE: EXPLOSIVE WITH SHOCK AND/OR HEAT. CARBONYL DICHLORIDE (PHOSGENE): DANGEROUS EXPLOSIVE. CHROMYL CHLORIDE: EXPLOSIVE REACTION. COPPER: FORMATION OF AN EXPLOSIVE COMPOUND. CYANURIC ACID: EXPLOSIVE WITH SHOCK. DIBROMOMALONITRILE: FORMS A SHOCK-SENSITIVE COMPOUND. DIMETHYL SULFATE: FORMS EXPLOSIVE COMPOUND AT A PH BELOW 5.0. 2,5-DINITRO-3-METHYLBENZOIC ACID: EXPLOSION HAZARD. LEAD: FORMATION OF AN EXPLOSIVE COMPOUND. METALS (HEAVY): MAY FORM EXTREMELY EXPLOSIVE AZIDES. NITRIC ACID: ENERGETIC REACTION. SULFURIC ACID: FORMS EXPLOSIVE COMPOUND @ 36 C. TRIFLUOROACRYLOYL CHLORIDE: FORMS EXPLOSIVE COMPOUND.

DECOMPOSITION: THERMAL DECOMPOSITION PRODUCTS MAY INCLUDE TOXIC OXIDES OF NITROGEN.

POLYMERIZATION: HAZARDOUS POLYMERIZATION HAS NOT BEEN REPORTED TO OCCUR UNDER NORMAL TEMPERATURES AND PRESSURES.

STORAGE AND DISPOSAL

OBSERVE ALL FEDERAL, STATE AND LOCAL REGULATIONS WHEN STORING OR DISPOSING OF THIS SUBSTANCE. FOR ASSISTANCE, CONTACT THE DISTRICT DIRECTOR OF THE ENVIRONMENTAL PROTECTION AGENCY.

****STORAGE****

STORE AWAY FROM INCOMPATIBLE SUBSTANCES.

THRESHOLD PLANNING QUANTITY (TPQ): THE SUPERFUND AMENDMENTS AND REAUTHORIZATION ACT (SARA) SECTION 302 REQUIRES THAT EACH FACILITY WHERE ANY EXTREMELY HAZARDOUS SUBSTANCE IS PRESENT IN A QUANTITY EQUAL TO OR GREATER THAN THE TPQ ESTABLISHED FOR THAT SUBSTANCE NOTIFY THE STATE EMERGENCY RESPONSE COMMISSION FOR THE STATE IN WHICH IT IS LOCATED. SECTION 303 OF SARA REQUIRES THESE FACILITIES TO PARTICIPATE IN LOCAL EMERGENCY RESPONSE PLANNING (40 CFR 355.30).

****DISPOSAL****

DISPOSAL MUST BE IN ACCORDANCE WITH STANDARDS APPLICABLE TO GENERATORS OF HAZARDOUS WASTE, 40CFR 262. EPA HAZARDOUS WASTE NUMBER P105.

CONDITIONS TO AVOID

MAY BURN BUT DOES NOT IGNITE READILY. MAY EXPLODE FROM FRICTION, HEAT OR CONTAMINATION.

SPILL AND LEAK PROCEDURES

OCCUPATIONAL SPILL: DO NOT TOUCH SPILLED MATERIAL. STOP LEAK IF YOU CAN DO IT WITHOUT RISK. USE WATER SPRAY TO REDUCE VAPORS. FOR SMALL SPILLS, TAKE UP WITH SAND OR OTHER ABSORBENT MATERIAL AND PLACE INTO CONTAINERS FOR LATER DISPOSAL. FOR SMALL DRY SPILLS, WITH CLEAN SHOVEL PLACE MATERIAL INTO CLEAN, DRY CONTAINERS AND COVER. MOVE CONTAINERS FROM SPILL AREA. FOR LARGER SPILLS, DIKE FAR AHEAD OF SPILL FOR LATER DISPOSAL. KEEP UNNECESSARY PEOPLE AWAY. ISOLATE HAZARD AREA AND DENY ENTRY. VENTILATE CLOSED SPACES BEFORE ENTERING.

REPORTABLE QUANTITY (RQ): 1000 POUNDS THE SUPERFUND AMENDMENTS AND REAUTHORIZATION ACT (SARA) SECTION 304 REQUIRES THAT A RELEASE EQUAL TO OR GREATER THAN THE REPORTABLE QUANTITY FOR THIS SUBSTANCE BE IMMEDIATELY REPORTED TO THE LOCAL EMERGENCY PLANNING COMMITTEE AND THE STATE EMERGENCY RESPONSE COMMISSION (40 CFR 355.40). IF THE RELEASE OF THIS SUBSTANCE IS REPORTABLE UNDER CERCLA SECTION 103, THE NATIONAL RESPONSE CENTER MUST BE NOTIFIED IMMEDIATELY AT (800) 424-8802 OR (202) 426-2675 IN THE METROPOLITAN WASHINGTON, D.C. AREA (40 CFR 302.6).

PROTECTIVE EQUIPMENT

VENTILATION: PROCESS ENCLOSURE RECOMMENDED TO MEET PUBLISHED EXPOSURE LIMITS.

RESPIRATOR: THE FOLLOWING RESPIRATORS ARE RECOMMENDED BASED ON INFORMATION FOUND IN THE PHYSICAL DATA, TOXICITY AND HEALTH EFFECTS SECTIONS. THEY ARE RANKED IN ORDER FROM MINIMUM TO MAXIMUM RESPIRATORY PROTECTION. THE SPECIFIC RESPIRATOR SELECTED MUST BE BASED ON CONTAMINATION LEVELS FOUND IN THE WORK PLACE, MUST NOT EXCEED THE WORKING LIMITS OF THE RESPIRATOR AND BE JOINTLY APPROVED BY THE NATIONAL INSTITUTE FOR OCCUPATIONAL SAFETY AND HEALTH AND THE MINE SAFETY AND HEALTH ADMINISTRATION (NIOSH-MSHA).

DUST AND MIST RESPIRATOR WITH A FULL FACEPIECE.

AIR-PURIFYING FULL FACEPIECE RESPIRATOR WITH A HIGH-EFFICIENCY PARTICULATE FILTER.

POWERED AIR-PURIFYING RESPIRATOR WITH A TIGHT-FITTING FACEPIECE AND HIGH-EFFICIENCY PARTICULATE FILTER.

TYPE 'C' SUPPLIED-AIR RESPIRATOR WITH A FULL FACEPIECE OPERATED IN PRESSURE-DEMAND OR OTHER POSITIVE PRESSURE MODE OR WITH A FULL FACEPIECE, HELMET OR HOOD OPERATED IN CONTINUOUS-FLOW MODE.

SELF-CONTAINED BREATHING APPARATUS WITH A FULL FACEPIECE OPERATED IN PRESSURE-DEMAND OR OTHER POSITIVE PRESSURE MODE.

FOR FIREFIGHTING AND OTHER IMMEDIATELY DANGEROUS TO LIFE OR HEALTH CONDITIONS:

SELF-CONTAINED BREATHING APPARATUS WITH FULL FACEPIECE OPERATED IN PRESSURE-DEMAND OR OTHER POSITIVE PRESSURE MODE.

SUPPLIED-AIR RESPIRATOR WITH FULL FACEPIECE AND OPERATED IN PRESSURE-DEMAND OR OTHER POSITIVE PRESSURE MODE IN COMBINATION WITH AN AUXILIARY SELF-CONTAINED BREATHING APPARATUS OPERATED IN PRESSURE-DEMAND OR OTHER POSITIVE PRESSURE MODE.

CLOTHING: EMPLOYEE MUST WEAR APPROPRIATE PROTECTIVE (IMPERVIOUS) CLOTHING AND EQUIPMENT TO PREVENT ANY POSSIBILITY OF SKIN CONTACT WITH THIS SUBSTANCE.

GLOVES: EMPLOYEE MUST WEAR APPROPRIATE PROTECTIVE GLOVES TO PREVENT CONTACT WITH THIS SUBSTANCE.

EYE PROTECTION: EMPLOYEE MUST WEAR SPLASH-PROOF OR DUST-RESISTANT SAFETY GOGGLES AND A FACESHIELD TO PREVENT CONTACT WITH THIS SUBSTANCE.

EMERGENCY WASH FACILITIES: WHERE THERE IS ANY POSSIBILITY THAT AN EMPLOYEE'S EYES AND/OR SKIN MAY BE EXPOSED TO THIS SUBSTANCE, THE EMPLOYER SHOULD PROVIDE AN EYE WASH FOUNTAIN AND QUICK DRENCH SHOWER WITHIN THE IMMEDIATE WORK AREA FOR EMERGENCY USE.

AUTHORIZED BY- OCCUPATIONAL HEALTH SERVICES, INC.

CREATION DATE: 10/05/89 ***REVISION DATE:*** 06/11/90

MATERIAL SAFETY DATA SHEET

OCCUPATIONAL HEALTH SERVICES, INC.
AGRICULTURE AND PESTICIDE DIVISION
450 SEVENTH AVENUE, SUITE 2407
NEW YORK, NEW YORK 10123
1-800-445-MSDS OR (212) 967-1100

EMERGENCY CONTACT:
JOHN S. BRANSFORD, JR. (615) 292-1180

SUBSTANCE IDENTIFICATION

CAS-NUMBER 532-32-1

SUBSTANCE: **SODIUM BENZOATE**

TRADE NAMES/SYNONYMS: BENZOIC ACID, SODIUM SALT; ANTIMOL; BENZOATE OF SODA; BENZOATE SODIUM; SOBENATE; SODIUM BENZOIC ACID; S-224; PST20965

CHEMICAL FAMILY: SALT
MOLECULAR FORMULA: C7-H5-O2.NA
MOLECULAR WEIGHT: 144.11
CERCLA RATINGS (SCALE 0-3): HEALTH=2 FIRE=U REACTIVITY=0 PERSISTENCE=0
NFPA RATINGS (SCALE 0-4): HEALTH=2 FIRE=U REACTIVITY=0

COMPONENTS AND CONTAMINANTS

COMPONENT: SODIUM BENZOATE ***PERCENT:*** 100
CAS# 532-32-1
OTHER CONTAMINANTS: NONE
EXPOSURE LIMITS: NO OCCUPATIONAL EXPOSURE LIMITS ESTABLISHED BY OSHA, ACGIH, OR NIOSH.

PHYSICAL DATA

DESCRIPTION: ODORLESS, COLORLESS TO WHITE HYGROSCOPIC CRYSTALLINE POWDER OR GRANULES WITH A SWEETISH ASTRINGENT TASTE.
MELTING POINT: >572 F (>300 C)
SPECIFIC GRAVITY: NOT AVAILABLE ***PH:*** APPROXIMATELY 8.0
SOLUBILITY IN WATER: 66% @ 20 C
SOLVENT SOLUBILITY: SLIGHTLY SOLUBLE IN ALCOHOL

FIRE AND EXPLOSION DATA

FIRE AND EXPLOSION HAZARD: UNKNOWN FIRE AND EXPLOSION HAZARD.
FIREFIGHTING MEDIA: DRY CHEMICAL, CARBON DIOXIDE, HALON, WATER SPRAY OR STANDARD FOAM (1987 EMERGENCY RESPONSE GUIDEBOOK, DOT P 5800.4). FOR LARGER FIRES, USE WATER SPRAY, FOG OR STANDARD FOAM (1987 EMERGENCY RESPONSE GUIDEBOOK, DOT P 5800.4).
FIREFIGHTING: MOVE CONTAINER FROM FIRE AREA IF POSSIBLE. DO NOT SCATTER SPILLED MATERIAL WITH HIGH PRESSURE WATER STREAMS. DIKE FIRE CONTROL WATER FOR LATER DISPOSAL (1987 EMERGENCY RESPONSE GUIDEBOOK, DOT P 5800.4, GUIDE PAGE 31).
USE AGENTS SUITABLE FOR TYPE OF SURROUNDING FIRE. AVOID BREATHING HAZARDOUS VAPORS, KEEP UPWIND.

TOXICITY

SODIUM BENZOATE: TOXICITY DATA: 4070 MG/KG ORAL-RAT LD50; 1600 MG/KG ORAL-MOUSE LD50; 2 GM/KG ORAL-RABBIT LD50; 2 GM/KG ORAL-DOG LD50; 22 GM/KG SUBCUTANEOUS-RAT LDLO; 2000 MG/KG SUBCUTANEOUS-RABBIT LD50; 1714 MG/KG INTRAVENOUS-RAT LD50; 1440 MG/KG INTRAVENOUS-MOUSE LD50; 1400 MG/KG INTRAPERITONEAL-GUINEA PIG LDLO; 2306 MG/KG INTRAMUSCULAR-MOUSE LD50; MUTAGENIC DATA (RTECS); REPRODUCTIVE EFFECTS DATA (RTECS). CARCINOGEN STATUS: NONE. ACUTE TOXICITY LEVEL: MODERATELY TOXIC BY INGESTION. TARGET EFFECTS: NO DATA AVAILABLE.

HEALTH EFFECTS AND FIRST AID

INHALATION: SODIUM BENZOATE: **ACUTE EXPOSURE-** DUSTS MAY CAUSE MUCOUS MEMBRANE IRRITATION. **CHRONIC EXPOSURE-** NO DATA AVAILABLE.
FIRST AID- REMOVE FROM EXPOSURE AREA TO FRESH AIR IMMEDIATELY. IF BREATHING HAS STOPPED, PERFORM ARTIFICIAL RESPIRATION. KEEP PERSON WARM AND AT REST. TREAT SYMPTOMATICALLY AND SUPPORTIVELY. GET MEDICAL ATTENTION IMMEDIATELY.

SKIN CONTACT: SODIUM BENZOATE: **ACUTE EXPOSURE-** EXCESSIVE CONTACT MAY CAUSE MILD IRRITATION. **CHRONIC EXPOSURE-** NO DATA AVAILABLE.
FIRST AID- REMOVE CONTAMINATED CLOTHING AND SHOES IMMEDIATELY. WASH AFFECTED AREA WITH SOAP OR MILD DETERGENT AND LARGE AMOUNTS OF WATER UNTIL NO EVIDENCE OF CHEMICAL REMAINS (APPROXIMATELY 15-20 MINUTES). GET MEDICAL ATTENTION IMMEDIATELY.

EYE CONTACT: SODIUM BENZOATE: **ACUTE EXPOSURE-** EXCESSIVE CONTACT MAY BE IRRITATING. **CHRONIC EXPOSURE-** NO DATA AVAILABLE.
FIRST AID- WASH EYES IMMEDIATELY WITH LARGE AMOUNTS OF WATER OR NORMAL SALINE, OCCASIONALLY LIFTING UPPER AND LOWER LIDS, UNTIL NO EVIDENCE OF CHEMICAL REMAINS (APPROXIMATELY 15-20 MINUTES). GET MEDICAL ATTENTION IMMEDIATELY.

INGESTION: SODIUM BENZOATE: **ACUTE EXPOSURE-** LARGE DOSES OF 8-10 GRAMS MAY CAUSE NAUSEA AND VOMITING. A RELATIVELY LARGE DOSE WAS REQUIRED TO KILL 50% OF THE RATS TESTED. THE SYMPTOMS WERE NOT REPORTED. SOMEWHAT SMALLER DOSES HAVE CAUSED DEATH IN RABBITS AND DOGS. **CHRONIC EXPOSURE-** THE FOOD AND DRUG ADMINISTRATION LISTS SODIUM BENZOATE AS A DIRECT FOOD SUBSTANCE AFFIRMED AS GENERALLY RECOGNIZED AS SAFE. IN SENSITIVE INDIVIDUALS CHRONIC RELAPSING URTICARIA MAY OCCUR AFTER INGESTION. FETAL DEVELOPMENTAL ABNORMALITIES HAVE BEEN REPORTED FROM INGESTION OF SODIUM BENZOATE IN RATS.
FIRST AID- TREAT SYMPTOMATICALLY AND SUPPORTIVELY. GET MEDICAL ATTENTION IMMEDIATELY. IF VOMITING OCCURS, KEEP HEAD LOWER THAN HIPS TO PREVENT ASPIRATION.
ANTIDOTE: NO SPECIFIC ANTIDOTE. TREAT SYMPTOMATICALLY AND SUPPORTIVELY.

REACTIVITY

REACTIVITY: STABLE UNDER NORMAL TEMPERATURES AND PRESSURES.
INCOMPATIBILITIES: SODIUM BENZOATE: MINERAL ACIDS: INCOMPATIBLE.
DECOMPOSITION: THERMAL DECOMPOSITION MAY RELEASE ACRID FUMES AND SODIUM OXIDE.
POLYMERIZATION: HAZARDOUS POLYMERIZATION HAS NOT BEEN REPORTED TO OCCUR UNDER NORMAL TEMPERATURES AND PRESSURES.

CONDITIONS TO AVOID

NONE REPORTED.

SPILL AND LEAK PROCEDURES

OCCUPATIONAL SPILL: SWEEP UP AND PLACE IN SUITABLE CLEAN, DRY CONTAINERS FOR RECLAMATION OR LATER DISPOSAL. DO NOT FLUSH SPILLED MATERIAL INTO SEWER. KEEP UNNECESSARY PEOPLE AWAY.

PROTECTIVE EQUIPMENT

VENTILATION: PROVIDE LOCAL EXHAUST OR GENERAL DILUTION VENTILATION SYSTEM.
RESPIRATOR: THE FOLLOWING RESPIRATORS ARE RECOMMENDED BASED ON INFORMATION FOUND IN THE PHYSICAL DATA, TOXICITY AND HEALTH EFFECTS SECTIONS. THEY ARE RANKED IN ORDER FROM MINIMUM TO MAXIMUM RESPIRATORY PROTECTION. THE SPECIFIC RESPIRATOR SELECTED MUST BE BASED ON CONTAMINATION LEVELS FOUND IN THE WORK PLACE, MUST NOT EXCEED THE WORKING LIMITS OF THE RESPIRATOR AND BE JOINTLY APPROVED BY THE NATIONAL INSTITUTE FOR OCCUPATIONAL SAFETY AND HEALTH AND THE MINE SAFETY AND HEALTH ADMINISTRATION (NIOSH-MSHA).
DUST AND MIST RESPIRATOR WITH A FULL FACEPIECE.
AIR-PURIFYING FULL FACEPIECE RESPIRATOR WITH A HIGH-EFFICIENCY PARTICULATE FILTER.
POWERED AIR-PURIFYING RESPIRATOR WITH A TIGHT-FITTING FACEPIECE AND HIGH-EFFICIENCY PARTICULATE FILTER.
TYPE 'C' SUPPLIED-AIR RESPIRATOR WITH A FULL FACEPIECE OPERATED IN PRESSURE-DEMAND OR OTHER POSITIVE PRESSURE MODE OR WITH A FULL FACEPIECE, HELMET OR HOOD OPERATED IN CONTINUOUS-FLOW MODE.
SELF-CONTAINED BREATHING APPARATUS WITH A FULL FACEPIECE OPERATED IN PRESSURE-DEMAND OR OTHER POSITIVE PRESSURE MODE.
FOR FIREFIGHTING AND OTHER IMMEDIATELY DANGEROUS TO LIFE OR HEALTH CONDITIONS:
SELF-CONTAINED BREATHING APPARATUS WITH FULL FACEPIECE OPERATED IN PRESSURE-DEMAND OR OTHER POSITIVE PRESSURE MODE.
SUPPLIED-AIR RESPIRATOR WITH FULL FACEPIECE AND OPERATED IN PRESSURE-DEMAND OR OTHER POSITIVE PRESSURE MODE IN COMBINATION WITH AN AUXILIARY SELF-CONTAINED BREATHING APPARATUS OPERATED IN PRESSURE-DEMAND OR OTHER POSITIVE PRESSURE MODE.
CLOTHING: EMPLOYEE MUST WEAR APPROPRIATE PROTECTIVE (IMPERVIOUS) CLOTHING AND EQUIPMENT TO PREVENT REPEATED OR PROLONGED SKIN CONTACT WITH THIS SUBSTANCE.
GLOVES: EMPLOYEE MUST WEAR APPROPRIATE PROTECTIVE GLOVES TO PREVENT CONTACT WITH THIS SUBSTANCE.
EYE PROTECTION: EMPLOYEE MUST WEAR SPLASH-PROOF OR DUST-RESISTANT SAFETY GOGGLES TO PREVENT EYE CONTACT WITH THIS SUBSTANCE.
EMERGENCY EYE WASH: WHERE THERE IS ANY POSSIBILITY THAT AN EMPLOYEE'S EYES MAY BE EXPOSED TO THIS SUBSTANCE, THE EMPLOYER SHOULD PROVIDE AN EYE WASH FOUNTAIN WITHIN THE IMMEDIATE WORK AREA FOR EMERGENCY USE.

AUTHORIZED BY- OCCUPATIONAL HEALTH SERVICES, INC.
CREATION DATE: 11/15/89 ***REVISION DATE:*** 05/31/90

MATERIAL SAFETY DATA SHEET

OCCUPATIONAL HEALTH SERVICES, INC.
AGRICULTURE AND PESTICIDE DIVISION
450 SEVENTH AVENUE, SUITE 2407

EMERGENCY CONTACT:
JOHN S. BRANSFORD, JR. (615) 292-1180

NEW YORK, NEW YORK 10123
1-800-445-MSDS OR (212) 967-1100

SUBSTANCE IDENTIFICATION

CAS-NUMBER 144-55-8

SUBSTANCE: **SODIUM BICARBONATE**

TRADE NAMES/SYNONYMS: CARBONIC ACID MONOSODIUM SALT; CARBONIC ACID SODIUM SALT (1:1); MONOSODIUM CARBONATE; MONOSODIUM HYDROGEN CARBONATE; SODIUM ACID CARBONATE; SODIUM CARBONATE (NA(HCO3); SODIUM HYDROGEN CARBONATE; BAKING SODA; SOLUDAL; CHNAO3; PST20970

CHEMICAL FAMILY: INORGANIC SALT

MOLECULAR FORMULA: NA-H-C-O3

MOLECULAR WEIGHT: 84-01

CERCLA RATINGS (SCALE 0-3): HEALTH=1 FIRE=0 REACTIVITY=0 PERSISTENCE=0

NFPA RATINGS (SCALE 0-4): HEALTH=U FIRE=0 REACTIVITY=0

COMPONENTS AND CONTAMINANTS

COMPONENT: SODIUM BICARBONATE ***PERCENT:*** 100.0
CAS# 144-55-8

OTHER CONTAMINANTS: NONE

EXPOSURE LIMITS: NO OCCUPATIONAL EXPOSURE LIMITS ESTABLISHED BY OSHA, ACGIH, OR NIOSH.

PHYSICAL DATA

DESCRIPTION: ODORLESS, WHITE POWDER OR GRANULES WITH A COOLING, SLIGHTLY ALKALINE TASTE. ***MELTING POINT:*** NOT APPLICABLE ***SPECIFIC GRAVITY:*** 2.159

PH: 8.3 @ 0.84% SOLUTION ***SOLUBILITY IN WATER:*** 10%

SOLVENT SOLUBILITY: SLIGHTLY SOLUBLE IN ALCOHOL.
EVOLVES CO2 @ 212 F (100 C)

FIRE AND EXPLOSION DATA

FIRE AND EXPLOSION HAZARD: NEGLIGIBLE FIRE HAZARD WHEN EXPOSED TO HEAT OR FLAME.

FIREFIGHTING MEDIA: DRY CHEMICAL, CARBON DIOXIDE, WATER SPRAY OR FOAM FOR LARGER FIRES, USE WATER SPRAY, FOG OR ALCOHOL FOAM

FIREFIGHTING: NO ACUTE HAZARD. MOVE CONTAINER FROM FIRE AREA IF POSSIBLE. AVOID BREATHING VAPORS OR DUSTS; KEEP UPWIND.

TOXICITY

SODIUM BICARBONATE: IRRITATION DATA: 30 MG/3 DAYS INTERMITTENT SKIN-HUMAN MILD; 100 MG/30 SECONDS EYE-RABBIT MILD. TOXICITY DATA: 1260 MG/KG ORAL-INFANT TDLO; 4220 MG/KG ORAL-RAT LD50; MUTAGENIC DATA (RTECS); REPRODUCTIVE EFFECTS DATA (RTECS). CARCINOGEN STATUS: NONE. ACUTE TOXICITY LEVEL: MODERATELY TOXIC BY INGESTION. TARGET EFFECTS: NO DATA AVAILABLE. AT INCREASED RISK FROM EXPOSURE: PERSONS WITH RENAL DISORDERS OR HYPERTENSION. ADDITIONAL DATA: INTERACTIONS WITH MEDICATIONS HAVE BEEN REPORTED.

HEALTH EFFECTS AND FIRST AID

INHALATION: SODIUM BICARBONATE: **ACUTE EXPOSURE-** INHALATION MAY CAUSE SORE THROAT AND COUGHING. DUST MAY IRRITATE THE NOSE, THROAT AND LUNGS. **CHRONIC EXPOSURE-** NO DATA AVAILABLE.

FIRST AID- REMOVE FROM EXPOSURE AREA TO FRESH AIR IMMEDIATELY. IF BREATHING HAS STOPPED, PERFORM ARTIFICIAL RESPIRATION. KEEP PERSON WARM AND AT REST. TREAT SYMPTOMATICALLY AND SUPPORTIVELY. GET MEDICAL ATTENTION IMMEDIATELY.

SKIN CONTACT: SODIUM BICARBONATE: **ACUTE EXPOSURE-** PROLONGED CONTACT MAY CAUSE IRRITATION. **CHRONIC EXPOSURE-** HUMANS EXPOSED INTERMITTENTLY FOR 3 DAYS EXPERIENCED ONLY MILD IRRITATION. ALKALOSIS HAS BEEN REPORTED FROM TOPICAL APPLICATION.

FIRST AID- REMOVE CONTAMINATED CLOTHING AND SHOES IMMEDIATELY. WASH AFFECTED AREA WITH SOAP OR MILD DETERGENT AND LARGE AMOUNTS OF WATER UNTIL NO EVIDENCE OF CHEMICAL REMAINS (APPROXIMATELY 15-20 MINUTES). GET MEDICAL ATTENTION IMMEDIATELY.

EYE CONTACT: SODIUM BICARBONATE: **ACUTE EXPOSURE-** DIRECT CONTACT WITH THE EYES MAY CAUSE IRRITATION WITH REDNESS AND PAIN. APPLICATION OF A 0.1 M SOLUTION CONTINUOUSLY FOR 3 HOURS RESULTED IN NO DISTURBANCE OF THE CORNEA IN RABBITS. **CHRONIC EXPOSURE-** NO DATA AVAILABLE.

FIRST AID- WASH EYES IMMEDIATELY WITH LARGE AMOUNTS OF WATER OR NORMAL SALINE, OCCASIONALLY LIFTING UPPER AND LOWER LIDS, UNTIL NO EVIDENCE OF CHEMICAL REMAINS (APPROXIMATELY 15-20 MINUTES). GET MEDICAL ATTENTION IMMEDIATELY.

INGESTION: SODIUM BICARBONATE: **ACUTE EXPOSURE-** MAY CAUSE IRRITATION OF THE MOUTH, ESOPHAGUS, AND STOMACH. IN THE STOMACH, CARBON DIOXIDE GAS MAY BE RELEASED, CAUSING DISTENTION, BELCHING, AND POSSIBLY RUPTURE OF THE STOMACH. DOSES GREATER THAN 5 GM/KG MAY CAUSE ALKALOSIS AND EDEMA. HYPOCALCEMIC TETANY ACCOMPANIED BY HYPOGLYCEMIA, CARPOPEDAL SPASM AND CARDIOPULMONARY ARREST HAVE ALSO BEEN REPORTED. **CHRONIC EXPOSURE-** INGESTION OF UP TO 140 GM/DAY FOR 3 WEEKS CAUSED CONSIDERABLE WEIGHT GAIN DUE TO FLUID RETENTION, ALKALOSIS WITH AN INCREASE IN PLASMA CARBON DIOXIDE AND PH AND 1 CASE OF ALBUMINURIA AND HEMATURIA. INCREASED ACIDITY, SODIUM CONTENT, AND VOLUME OF URINE AND CRYSTALLURIA HAVE BEEN REPORTED IN RATS.

FIRST AID- TREAT SYMPTOMATICALLY AND SUPPORTIVELY. GET MEDICAL ATTENTION IMMEDIATELY. IF VOMITING OCCURS, KEEP HEAD LOWER THAN HIPS TO PREVENT ASPIRATION.

ANTIDOTE: NO SPECIFIC ANTIDOTE. TREAT SYMPTOMATICALLY AND SUPPORTIVELY.

REACTIVITY

REACTIVITY: STABLE UNDER NORMAL TEMPERATURES AND PRESSURES.

INCOMPATIBILITIES: SODIUM BICARBONATE: ACIDS (STRONG): MAY REACT VIOLENTLY AND RELEASE CARBON DIOXIDE. 2-FURALDEHYDE: POSSIBLE IGNITION HAZARD. MONOAMMONIUM PHOSPHATE: SELF-PROPAGATING REACTION WITH RAPID BUILD-UP OF PRESSURE. SODIUM-POTASSIUM ALLOY: VIOLENT REACTION.

DECOMPOSITION: THERMAL DECOMPOSITION PRODUCTS MAY INCLUDE TOXIC OXIDES OF CARBON.

POLYMERIZATION: HAZARDOUS POLYMERIZATION HAS NOT BEEN REPORTED TO OCCUR UNDER NORMAL TEMPERATURES AND PRESSURES.

STORAGE AND DISPOSAL

OBSERVE ALL FEDERAL, STATE AND LOCAL REGULATIONS WHEN STORING OR DISPOSING OF THIS SUBSTANCE. FOR ASSISTANCE, CONTACT THE DISTRICT DIRECTOR OF THE ENVIRONMENTAL PROTECTION AGENCY.

STORAGE

STORE AWAY FROM INCOMPATIBLE SUBSTANCES.
STORE IN TIGHTLY CLOSED CONTAINERS; PREVENT EXPOSURE TO MOISTURE.

CONDITIONS TO AVOID

NO REPORTS FOUND.

SPILL AND LEAK PROCEDURES

OCCUPATIONAL SPILL: SWEEP UP AND PLACE IN SUITABLE CLEAN, DRY CONTAINERS FOR RECLAMATION OR LATER DISPOSAL. DO NOT FLUSH SPILLED MATERIAL INTO SEWER. KEEP UNNECESSARY PEOPLE AWAY.

PROTECTIVE EQUIPMENT

VENTILATION: PROVIDE LOCAL EXHAUST OR GENERAL DILUTION VENTILATION SYSTEM.

RESPIRATOR: THE FOLLOWING RESPIRATORS ARE RECOMMENDED BASED ON INFORMATION FOUND IN THE PHYSICAL DATA, TOXICITY AND HEALTH EFFECTS SECTIONS. THEY ARE RANKED IN ORDER FROM MINIMUM TO MAXIMUM RESPIRATORY PROTECTION. THE SPECIFIC RESPIRATOR SELECTED MUST BE BASED ON CONTAMINATION LEVELS FOUND IN THE WORK PLACE, MUST NOT EXCEED THE WORKING LIMITS OF THE RESPIRATOR AND BE JOINTLY APPROVED BY THE NATIONAL INSTITUTE FOR OCCUPATIONAL SAFETY AND HEALTH AND THE MINE SAFETY AND HEALTH ADMINISTRATION (NIOSH-MSHA).

DUST AND MIST RESPIRATOR WITH A FULL FACEPIECE.

AIR-PURIFYING FULL FACEPIECE RESPIRATOR WITH A HIGH-EFFICIENCY PARTICULATE FILTER.

POWERED AIR-PURIFYING RESPIRATOR WITH A TIGHT-FITTING FACEPIECE AND HIGH-EFFICIENCY PARTICULATE FILTER.

TYPE 'C' SUPPLIED-AIR RESPIRATOR WITH A FULL FACEPIECE OPERATED IN PRESSURE-DEMAND OR OTHER POSITIVE PRESSURE MODE OR WITH A FULL FACEPIECE, HELMET OR HOOD OPERATED IN CONTINUOUS-FLOW MODE.

SELF-CONTAINED BREATHING APPARATUS WITH A FULL FACEPIECE OPERATED IN PRESSURE-DEMAND OR OTHER POSITIVE PRESSURE MODE.

FOR FIREFIGHTING AND OTHER IMMEDIATELY DANGEROUS TO LIFE OR HEALTH CONDITIONS:

SELF-CONTAINED BREATHING APPARATUS WITH FULL FACEPIECE OPERATED IN PRESSURE-DEMAND OR OTHER POSITIVE PRESSURE MODE.

SUPPLIED-AIR RESPIRATOR WITH FULL FACEPIECE AND OPERATED IN PRESSURE-DEMAND OR OTHER POSITIVE PRESSURE MODE IN COMBINATION WITH AN AUXILIARY SELF-CONTAINED BREATHING APPARATUS OPERATED IN PRESSURE-DEMAND OR OTHER POSITIVE PRESSURE MODE.

CLOTHING: PROTECTIVE CLOTHING NOT REQUIRED. AVOID REPEATED OR PROLONGED CONTACT WITH THIS SUBSTANCE.

GLOVES: EMPLOYEE MUST WEAR APPROPRIATE PROTECTIVE GLOVES TO PREVENT CONTACT WITH THIS SUBSTANCE.

EYE PROTECTION: EMPLOYEE MUST WEAR SPLASH-PROOF OR DUST-RESISTANT SAFETY GOGGLES TO PREVENT EYE CONTACT WITH THIS SUBSTANCE.

EMERGENCY EYE WASH: WHERE THERE IS ANY POSSIBILITY THAT AN EMPLOYEE'S EYES MAY BE EXPOSED TO THIS SUBSTANCE, THE EMPLOYER SHOULD PROVIDE AN EYE WASH FOUNTAIN WITHIN THE IMMEDIATE WORK AREA FOR EMERGENCY USE.

AUTHORIZED BY- OCCUPATIONAL HEALTH SERVICES, INC.

CREATION DATE: 11/16/89 ***REVISION DATE:*** 05/31/90

MATERIAL SAFETY DATA SHEET

OCCUPATIONAL HEALTH SERVICES, INC.
AGRICULTURE AND PESTICIDE DIVISION
450 SEVENTH AVENUE, SUITE 2407
NEW YORK, NEW YORK 10123
1-800-445-MSDS OR (212) 967-1100

EMERGENCY CONTACT:
JOHN S. BRANSFORD, JR. (615) 292-1180

SUBSTANCE IDENTIFICATION

CAS-NUMBER 7681-38-1

SUBSTANCE: <u>SODIUM BISULFATE</u>

TRADE NAMES/SYNONYMS: NITRE CAKE; SODIUM ACID SULFATE; SODIUM PYROSULFATE; SODIUM HYDROGEN SULFATE; SUFURIC ACID, SODIUM SALT; NITER CAKE; SODIUM BISULPHATE; SODIUM HYDROSULFATE; BIF; SULFURIC ACID, MONOSODIUM SALT; BISULFATE OF SODA; FANAL; MONOSODIUM SULFATE; MONOSODIUM HYDROGEN SULFATE; SODIUM BISULFATE, ANHYDROUS; WC-PERFECT; WC-SUPER; UN 1821; HNAO4S; PST20990

CHEMICAL FAMILY: INORGANIC SALT

MOLECULAR FORMULA: H-O4-S.NA

MOLECULAR WEIGHT: 120.06

CERCLA RATINGS (SCALE 0-3): HEALTH=U FIRE=0 REACTIVITY=0 PERSISTENCE=0

NFPA RATINGS (SCALE 0-4): HEALTH=U FIRE=0 REACTIVITY=0

COMPONENTS AND CONTAMINANTS

COMPONENT: SODIUM BISULFATE ***PERCENT:*** 100
CAS# 7681-38-1

OTHER CONTAMINANTS: NONE

EXPOSURE LIMITS: NO OCCUPATIONAL EXPOSURE LIMITS ESTABLISHED BY OSHA, ACGIH, OR NIOSH.

PHYSICAL DATA

DESCRIPTION: HYGROSCOPIC COLORLESS CRYSTALS OR WHITE FUSED LUMPS.

BOILING POINT: DECOMPOSES ***MELTING POINT:*** >599 F (>315 C) DECOMPOSES

SPECIFIC GRAVITY: 2.435 @ 13 C ***PH:*** 1.4(0.1M) ***SOLUBILITY IN WATER:*** 28.6%

SOLVENT SOLUBILITY: INSOLUBLE IN ALCOHOL.

FIRE AND EXPLOSION DATA

FIRE AND EXPLOSION HAZARD: NEGLIGIBLE FIRE HAZARD WHEN EXPOSED TO HEAT OR FLAME.

FIREFIGHTING MEDIA: DRY CHEMICAL, CARBON DIOXIDE, HALON, WATER SPRAY OR STANDARD FOAM (1987 EMERGENCY RESPONSE GUIDEBOOK, DOT P 5800.4).
FOR LARGER FIRES, USE WATER SPRAY, FOG OR STANDARD FOAM (1987 EMERGENCY RESPONSE GUIDEBOOK, DOT P 5800.4).

FIREFIGHTING: MOVE CONTAINERS FROM FIRE AREA IF POSSIBLE. COOL CONTAINERS EXPOSED TO FLAMES WITH WATER FROM SIDE UNTIL WELL AFTER FIRE IS OUT. STAY AWAY FROM STORAGE TANK ENDS (1987 EMERGENCY RESPONSE GUIDEBOOK, DOT P 5800.4, GUIDE PAGE 60).
USE AGENTS SUITABLE FOR TYPE OF SURROUNDING FIRE. AVOID BREATHING HAZARDOUS VAPORS, KEEP UPWIND.

TRANSPORTATION DATA

DEPARTMENT OF TRANSPORTATION HAZARD CLASSIFICATION 49 CFR 172.101: ORM-B

DEPARTMENT OF TRANSPORTATION LABELING REQUIREMENTS 49 CFR 172.101 AND SUBPART E: NONE

DEPARTMENT OF TRANSPORTATION PACKAGING REQUIREMENTS: 49 CFR 173.800 EXCEPTIONS: 49 CFR 173.505

TOXICITY

SODIUM BISULFATE: TOXICITY DATA: ANHYDROUS: MUTAGENIC DATA (RTECS). MONOHYDRATE: 193 MG/KG INTRAPERITONEAL-MOUSE LD50. CARCINOGEN STATUS: NONE. LOCAL EFFECTS: CORROSIVE- INHALATION, SKIN, AND EYES. ACUTE TOXICITY LEVEL: INSUFFICIENT DATA. TARGET EFFECTS: NO DATA AVAILABLE.

HEALTH EFFECTS AND FIRST AID

INHALATION: SODIUM BISULFATE: CORROSIVE. **<u>ACUTE EXPOSURE-</u>** ON CONTACT WITH MOISTURE, SODIUM BISULFATE RELEASES SULFURIC ACID WHICH IS AN ACID CORROSIVE. INHALATION OF ACIDIC SUBSTANCES MAY CAUSE SEVERE RESPIRATORY IRRITATION WITH COUGHING, CHOKING, AND POSSIBLY BURNS OF THE MUCOUS MEMBRANES. OTHER INITIAL SYMPTOMS MAY INCLUDE DIZZINESS, HEADACHE, NAUSEA AND WEAKNESS. PULMONARY EDEMA MAY BE IMMEDIATE IN THE MOST SEVERE EXPOSURES, BUT MORE LIKELY WILL OCCUR AFTER A LATENT PERIOD OF 5-72 HOURS, AS A SLOWLY PROGRESSIVE, BUT MARKED INFLAMMATORY REACTION TAKES PLACE, THE SYMPTOMS MAY INCLUDE TIGHTNESS IN THE CHEST, DYSPNEA, DIZZINESS, FROTHY SPUTUM, AND CYANOSIS. PHYSICAL FINDINGS MAY INCLUDE HYPOTENSION, WEAK, RAPID PULSE, MOIST RALES, AND HEMOCONCENTRATION. IN NON-FATAL CASES, COMPLETE RECOVERY MAY OCCUR WITHIN A FEW DAYS OR WEEKS OR, CONVALESCENCE MAY BE PROLONGED WITH FREQUENT RELAPSES AND CONTINUED DYSPNEA AND OTHER SIGNS AND SYMPTOMS OF PULMONARY INSUFFICIENCY. IN SEVERE EXPOSURES, DEATH DUE TO ANOXIA MAY OCCUR WITHIN A FEW HOURS AFTER ONSET OF THE SYMPTOMS OF PULMONARY EDEMA OR FOLLOWING A RELAPSE. **<u>CHRONIC EXPOSURE-</u>** DEPENDING ON THE CONCENTRATION AND DURATION OF EXPOSURE, REPEATED OR PROLONGED EXPOSURE TO AN ACIDIC SUBSTANCE MAY CAUSE EROSION OF THE TEETH, INFLAMMATORY AND ULCERATIVE CHANGES IN THE MOUTH, AND POSSIBLY JAW NECROSIS. BRONCHIAL IRRITATION WITH COUGH AND FREQUENT ATTACKS OF BRONCHIAL PNEUMONIA MAY OCCUR. GASTROINTESTINAL DISTURBANCES ARE ALSO POSSIBLE.

FIRST AID- REMOVE FROM EXPOSURE AREA TO FRESH AIR IMMEDIATELY. IF BREATHING HAS STOPPED, GIVE ARTIFICIAL RESPIRATION. MAINTAIN AIRWAY AND BLOOD PRESSURE AND ADMINISTER OXYGEN IF AVAILABLE. KEEP AFFECTED PERSON WARM AND AT REST. TREAT SYMPTOMATICALLY AND SUPPORTIVELY. ADMINISTRATION OF OXYGEN SHOULD BE PERFORMED BY QUALIFIED PERSONNEL. GET MEDICAL ATTENTION IMMEDIATELY.

SKIN CONTACT: SODIUM BISULFATE: CORROSIVE. **<u>ACUTE EXPOSURE-</u>** DIRECT CONTACT WITH ACIDIC SUBSTANCES MAY CAUSE SEVERE PAIN, BURNS AND POSSIBLY BROWNISH OR YELLOWISH STAINS. BURNS MAY BE DEEP WITH SHARP EDGES AND HEAL SLOWLY WITH SCAR TISSUE FORMATION. **<u>CHRONIC EXPOSURE-</u>** EFFECTS DEPEND ON THE CONCENTRATION AND DURATION OF EXPOSURE. REPEATED RO PROLONGED CONTACT WITH ACIDIC SUBSTANCES MAY RESULT IN DERMATITIS OR EFFECTS SIMILAR TO ACUTE EXPOSURE.

FIRST AID- REMOVE CONTAMINATED CLOTHING AND SHOES IMMEDIATELY. WASH AFFECTED AREA WITH SOAP OR MILD DETERGENT AND LARGE AMOUNTS OF WATER UNTIL NO EVIDENCE OF CHEMICAL REMAINS (AT LEAST 15-20 MINUTES). IN CASE OF CHEMICAL BURNS, COVER AREA WITH STERILE, DRY DRESSING. BANDAGE SECURELY, BUT NOT TOO TIGHTLY. GET MEDICAL ATTENTION IMMEDIATELY.

EYE CONTACT: SODIUM BISULFATE: CORROSIVE. **<u>ACUTE EXPOSURE-</u>** DIRECT CONTACT WITH ACIDIC SUBSTANCES MAY CAUSE PAIN, LACRIMATION, PHOTOPHOBIA, AND BURNS, POSSIBLY SEVERE. THE DEGREE OF INJURY DEPENDS ON THE CONCENTRATION AND DURATION OF CONTACT. IN MILD BURNS, THE EPITHELIUM REGENERATES RAPIDLY AND THE EYE RECOVERS COMPLETELY. IN SEVERE CASES, THE EXTENT OF INJURY MAY NOT BE FULLY APPARENT FOR SEVERAL WEEKS. ULTIMATELY, THE WHOLE CORNEA MAY BECOME DEEPLY VASCULARIZED AND OPAQUE RESULTING IN BLINDNESS. IN THE WORST CASES, THE EYE MAY BE TOTALLY DESTROYED. **<u>CHRONIC EXPOSURE-</u>** EFFECTS DEPEND ON THE CONCENTRATION AND DURATION OF EXPOSURE. REPEATED OR PROLONGED EXPOSURE TO ACIDIC SUBSTANCES MAY CAUSE CONJUNCTIVITIS OR EFFECTS AS IN ACUTE EXPOSURE.

FIRST AID- WASH EYES IMMEDIATELY WITH LARGE AMOUNTS OF WATER, OCCASIONALLY LIFTING UPPER AND LOWER LIDS, UNTIL NO EVIDENCE OF CHEMICAL REMAINS (AT LEAST 15-20 MINUTES). CONTINUE IRRIGATING WITH NORMAL SALINE UNTIL THE PH HAS RETURNED TO NORMAL (30-60 MINUTES). COVER WITH STERILE BANDAGES. GET MEDICAL ATTENTION IMMEDIATELY.

INGESTION: SODIUM BISULFATE: CORROSIVE. **<u>ACUTE EXPOSURE-</u>** ACIDIC SUBSTANCES MAY CAUSE CIRCUMORAL BURNS WITH DISCOLORATION AND CORROSION OF THE MUCOUS MEMBRANES OF THE MOUTH, THROAT AND ESOPHAGUS. THERE MAY BE IMMEDIATE PAIN AND DIFFICULTY OR INABILITY TO SWALLOW OR SPEAK. EPIGLOTTAL EDEMA MAY RESULT IN RESPIRATORY

DISTRESS AND POSSIBLY ASPHYXIA. MARKED THIRST, EPIGASTRIC PAIN, NAUSEA, VOMITING AND DIARRHEA MAY OCCUR. DEPENDING ON THE DEGREE OF ESOPHAGEAL AND GASTRIC CORROSION, THE VOMITUS MAY CONTAIN FRESH OR DARK PRECIPITATED BLOOD AND LARGE SHREDS OF MUCOSA. SHOCK WITH MARKED HYPOTENSION, WEAK, RAPID PULSE, SHALLOW RESPIRATION, AND CLAMMY SKIN MAY OCCUR. CIRCULATORY COLLAPSE MAY ENSUE IF UNCORRECTED, LEAD TO RENAL FAILURE. IN SEVERE CASES, GASTRIC, AND TO A LESSER DEGREE, ESOPHAGEAL PERFORATION AND SUBSEQUENT PERITONITIS MAY OCCUR AND BE ACCOMPANIED BY FEVER AND ABDOMINAL RIGIDITY. ESOPHAGEAL, GASTRIC AND PYLORIC STRICTURE MAY OCCUR WITHIN A FEW WEEKS, BUT MAY BE DELAYED FOR MONTHS OR EVEN YEARS. DEATH MAY RESULT WITHIN A SHORT TIME LATER DEATH MAY BE DUE TO PERITONITIS, SEVERE NEPHRITIS OR PNEUMONIA. COMA AND CONVULSIONS SOMETIMES OCCUR TERMINALLY. **CHRONIC EXPOSURE**- DEPENDING ON THE CONCENTRATION, REPEATED INGESTION OF ACIDIC SUBSTANCES MAY RESULT IN INFLAMMATORY AND ULCERATIVE CHANGES IN THE MUCOUS MEMBRANES OF THE MOUTH AND OTHER EFFECTS AS IN ACUTE INGESTION.

FIRST AID- DO NOT USE GASTRIC LAVAGE OR EMESIS. DILUTE THE ACID IMMEDIATELY BY DRINKING LARGE QUANTITIES OF WATER OR MILK. IF VOMITING PERSISTS, ADMINISTER FLUIDS REPEATEDLY. INGESTED ACID MUST BE DILUTED APPROXIMATELY 100 FOLD TO RENDER IT HARMLESS TO TISSUES. MAINTAIN AIRWAY AND TREAT SHOCK (DREISBACH, HANDBOOK OF POISONING, 12TH ED.). GET MEDICAL ATTENTION IMMEDIATELY. IF VOMITING OCCURS, KEEP HEAD BELOW HIPS TO HELP PREVENT ASPIRATION.

ANTIDOTE: NO SPECIFIC ANTIDOTE. TREAT SYMPTOMATICALLY AND SUPPORTIVELY.

REACTIVITY

REACTIVITY: STABLE UNDER NORMAL CONDITIONS IN ENCLOSED CONTAINERS. IT IS HYGROSCOPIC ON CONTACT WITH AIR.

INCOMPATIBILITIES: SODIUM BISULFATE: CALCIUM HYPOCHLORITE: INCOMPATIBLE. ALCOHOL: DECOMPOSES.

DECOMPOSITION: THERMAL DECOMPOSITION RELEASES TOXIC FUMES OF SODIUM OXIDE AND OXIDES OF SULFUR.

POLYMERIZATION: HAZARDOUS POLYMERIZATION HAS NOT BEEN REPORTED TO OCCUR UNDER NORMAL TEMPERATURES AND PRESSURES.

STORAGE AND DISPOSAL

OBSERVE ALL FEDERAL, STATE AND LOCAL REGULATIONS WHEN STORING OR DISPOSING OF THIS SUBSTANCE. FOR ASSISTANCE, CONTACT THE DISTRICT DIRECTOR OF THE ENVIRONMENTAL PROTECTION AGENCY.

****STORAGE****

STORE AWAY FROM INCOMPATIBLE SUBSTANCES.

****DISPOSAL****

DISPOSAL MUST BE IN ACCORDANCE WITH STANDARDS APPLICABLE TO GENERATORS OF HAZARDOUS WASTE, 40 CFR 262. EPA HAZARDOUS WASTE NUMBER D002. 100 POUND CERCLA SECTION 103 REPORTABLE QUANTITY.

CONDITIONS TO AVOID

MAY BURN BUT DOES NOT IGNITE READILY. FLAMMABLE, POISONOUS GASES MAY ACCUMULATE IN TANKS AND HOPPER CARS. MAY IGNITE COMBUSTIBLES (WOOD, PAPER, OIL, ETC.).

SPILL AND LEAK PROCEDURES

OCCUPATIONAL SPILL: DO NOT TOUCH SPILLED MATERIAL. STOP LEAK IF YOU CAN DO IT WITHOUT RISK. FOR SMALL SPILLS, TAKE UP WITH SAND OR OTHER ABSORBENT MATERIAL AND PLACE INTO CONTAINERS FOR LATER DISPOSAL. FOR SMALL DRY SPILLS, WITH CLEAN SHOVEL PLACE MATERIAL INTO CLEAN, DRY CONTAINER AND COVER. MOVE CONTAINERS FROM SPILL AREA. FOR LARGER SPILLS, DIKE FAR AHEAD OF SPILL FOR LATER DISPOSAL. KEEP UNNECESSARY PEOPLE AWAY. ISOLATE HAZARD AREA AND DENY ENTRY.

PROTECTIVE EQUIPMENT

VENTILATION: PROVIDE LOCAL EXHAUST OR PROCESS ENCLOSURE VENTILATION SYSTEM.

RESPIRATOR: THE FOLLOWING RESPIRATORS ARE RECOMMENDED BASED ON INFORMATION FOUND IN THE PHYSICAL DATA, TOXICITY AND HEALTH EFFECTS SECTIONS. THEY ARE RANKED IN ORDER FROM MINIMUM TO MAXIMUM RESPIRATORY PROTECTION. THE SPECIFIC RESPIRATOR SELECTED MUST BE BASED ON CONTAMINATION LEVELS FOUND IN THE WORK PLACE, MUST NOT EXCEED THE WORKING LIMITS OF THE RESPIRATOR AND BE JOINTLY APPROVED BY THE NATIONAL INSTITUTE FOR OCCUPATIONAL SAFETY AND HEALTH AND THE MINE SAFETY AND HEALTH ADMINISTRATION (NIOSH-MSHA).

DUST AND MIST RESPIRATOR WITH A FULL FACEPIECE.

AIR-PURIFYING FULL FACEPIECE RESPIRATOR WITH A HIGH-EFFICIENCY PARTICULATE FILTER.

POWERED AIR-PURIFYING RESPIRATOR WITH A TIGHT-FITTING FACEPIECE AND HIGH-EFFICIENCY PARTICULATE FILTER.

TYPE 'C' SUPPLIED-AIR RESPIRATOR WITH A FULL FACEPIECE OPERATED IN PRESSURE-DEMAND OR OTHER POSITIVE PRESSURE MODE OR WITH A FULL FACEPIECE, HELMET OR HOOD OPERATED IN CONTINUOUS-FLOW MODE.

SELF-CONTAINED BREATHING APPARATUS WITH A FULL FACEPIECE OPERATED IN PRESSURE-DEMAND OR OTHER POSITIVE PRESSURE MODE.

FOR FIREFIGHTING AND OTHER IMMEDIATELY DANGEROUS TO LIFE OR HEALTH CONDITIONS:

SELF-CONTAINED BREATHING APPARATUS WITH FULL FACEPIECE OPERATED IN PRESSURE-DEMAND OR OTHER POSITIVE PRESSURE MODE.

SUPPLIED-AIR RESPIRATOR WITH FULL FACEPIECE AND OPERATED IN PRESSURE-DEMAND OR OTHER POSITIVE PRESSURE MODE IN COMBINATION WITH AN AUXILIARY SELF-CONTAINED BREATHING APPARATUS OPERATED IN PRESSURE-DEMAND OR OTHER POSITIVE PRESSURE MODE.

CLOTHING: EMPLOYEE MUST WEAR APPROPRIATE PROTECTIVE (IMPERVIOUS) CLOTHING AND EQUIPMENT TO PREVENT ANY POSSIBILITY OF SKIN CONTACT WITH THIS SUBSTANCE.

GLOVES: EMPLOYEE MUST WEAR APPROPRIATE PROTECTIVE GLOVES TO PREVENT CONTACT WITH THIS SUBSTANCE.

EYE PROTECTION: EMPLOYEE MUST WEAR SPLASH-PROOF OR DUST-RESISTANT SAFETY GOGGLES AND A FACESHIELD TO PREVENT CONTACT WITH THIS SUBSTANCE.

EMERGENCY WASH FACILITIES: WHERE THERE IS ANY POSSIBILITY THAT AN EMPLOYEE'S EYES AND/OR SKIN MAY BE EXPOSED TO THIS SUBSTANCE, THE EMPLOYER SHOULD PROVIDE AN EYE WASH FOUNTAIN AND QUICK DRENCH SHOWER WITHIN THE IMMEDIATE WORK AREA FOR EMERGENCY USE.

AUTHORIZED BY- OCCUPATIONAL HEALTH SERVICES, INC.

CREATION DATE: 11/17/89 ***REVISION DATE:*** 05/18/90

MATERIAL SAFETY DATA SHEET

OCCUPATIONAL HEALTH SERVICES, INC.
AGRICULTURE AND PESTICIDE DIVISION
450 SEVENTH AVENUE, SUITE 2407
NEW YORK, NEW YORK 10123
1-800-445-MSDS OR (212) 967-1100

EMERGENCY CONTACT:
JOHN S. BRANSFORD, JR. (615) 292-1180

SUBSTANCE IDENTIFICATION

CAS-NUMBER 7631-90-5

SUBSTANCE: **SODIUM BISULFITE**

TRADE NAMES/SYNONYMS: SULFUROUS ACID, MONOSODIUM SALT; HYDROGEN SODIUM SULFATE; HYDROGEN SULFITE SODIUM; MONOSODIUM SULFITE; SODIUM ACID SULFITE; SODIUM BISULPHITE; SODIUM HYDROGEN SULFITE; SODIUM SULFITE; KODAK SODIUM BISULFITE,ANHYDROUS (KODAK); STCC 4944155; PST21000

CHEMICAL FAMILY: INORGANIC SALT

MOLECULAR FORMULA: NA-H-S-O3

MOLECULAR WEIGHT: 104.06

CERCLA RATINGS (SCALE 0-3): HEALTH=3 FIRE=0 REACTIVITY=0 PERSISTENCE=0

NFPA RATINGS (SCALE 0-4): HEALTH=3 FIRE=0 REACTIVITY=0

COMPONENTS AND CONTAMINANTS

COMPONENT: SODIUM BISULFITE ***PERCENT:*** 100
CAS# 7631-90-5

OTHER CONTAMINANTS: NONE

EXPOSURE LIMITS: SODIUM BISULFITE: 5 MG/M3 OSHA TWA 5 MG/M3 ACGIH TWA 5000 POUNDS CERCLA SECTION 103 REPORTABLE QUANTITY

PHYSICAL DATA

DESCRIPTION: WHITE CRYSTALS OR CRYSTALLINE POWDER WITH A SLIGHT SULFUROUS ODOR AND TASTE. ***BOILING POINT:*** DECOMPOSES ***MELTING POINT:*** DECOMPOSES

SPECIFIC GRAVITY: 1.48 ***PH:*** ACIDIC IN SOLUTION

SOLUBILITY IN WATER: SOLUBLE

SOLVENT SOLUBILITY: SLIGHTLY SOLUBLE IN ALCOHOL

FIRE AND EXPLOSION DATA

FIRE AND EXPLOSION HAZARD: NEGLIGIBLE FIRE HAZARD WHEN EXPOSED TO HEAT OR FLAME.

FIREFIGHTING MEDIA: DRY CHEMICAL, CARBON DIOXIDE, HALON, WATER SPRAY OR STANDARD FOAM (1987 EMERGENCY RESPONSE GUIDEBOOK, DOT P 5800.4).
FOR LARGER FIRES, USE WATER SPRAY, FOG OR STANDARD FOAM (1987 EMERGENCY RESPONSE GUIDEBOOK, DOT P 5800.4).

FIREFIGHTING: MOVE CONTAINERS FROM FIRE AREA IF POSSIBLE. COOL CONTAINERS EXPOSED TO FLAMES WITH WATER FROM SIDE UNTIL WELL AFTER FIRE IS OUT. STAY AWAY FROM STORAGE TANK ENDS (1987 EMERGENCY RESPONSE GUIDEBOOK, DOT P 5800.4, GUIDE PAGE 60).
USE AGENTS SUITABLE FOR TYPE OF FIRE. USE WATER IN FLOODING AMOUNTS AS FOG. COOL CONTAINERS WITH FLOODING AMOUNTS OF WATER, APPLY FROM AS FAR A DISTANCE AS POSSIBLE. AVOID BREATHING CORROSIVE VAPORS, KEEP UPWIND.

TRANSPORTATION DATA

DEPARTMENT OF TRANSPORTATION HAZARD CLASSIFICATION 49 CFR 172.101: FORM-B
DEPARTMENT OF TRANSPORTATION LABELING REQUIREMENTS 49 CFR 172.101 AND SUBPART E: NONE
DEPARTMENT OF TRANSPORTATION PACKAGING REQUIREMENTS: 49 CFR 173.800 EXCEPTIONS: 49 CFR 173.505

TOXICITY

SODIUM BISULFITE: TOXICITY DATA: 2 GM/KG ORAL-RAT LD50; 115 MG/KG INTRAVENOUS-RAT LD50; 130 MG/KG INTRAVENOUS-MOUSE LD50; 65 MG/KG INTRAVENOUSE-RABBIT LD50; 95 MG/KG INTRAVENOUS-HAMSTER LD50; 475 MG/KG INTRAPERITONEAL-RAT LD50; 675 MG/KG INTRAPERITONEAL-MOUSE LD50; 300 MG/KG INTRAPERITONEAL-RABBIT LD50; 244 MG/KG INTRAPERITONEAL-DOG LD50; 779 MG/KG INTRAPERITONEAL-GUINEA PIG LD50; 487 MG/KG INTRAPERITONEAL-HAMSTER LD50; MUTAGENIC DATA (RTECS). CARCINOGEN STATUS: NONE. LOCAL EFFECTS: IRRITANT- INHALATION, SKIN, AND EYES. ACUTE TOXICITY LEVEL: MODERATELY TOXIC BY INGESTION. TARGET EFFECTS: SENSITIZER- PULMONARY, SKIN, AND INGESTION. AT INCREASED RISK FROM EXPOSURE: ASTHMATICS.

HEALTH EFFECTS AND FIRST AID

INHALATION: SODIUM BISULFITE: IRRITANT/SENSITIZER. **ACUTE EXPOSURE-** MAY CAUSE IRRITATION WITH SORE THROAT, COUGHING, AND SHORTNESS OF BREATH. AQUEOUS SOLUTIONS MAY CAUSE SEVERE IRRITATION. SULFITES MAY CAUSE SENSITIZATION REACTIONS IN PREVIOUSLY EXPOSED PERSONS, ESPECIALLY ASTHMATICS. SYMPTOMS MAY INCLUDE FLUSHING, SEVERE WHEEZING, SWELLING OF THE THROAT, AND GENERALIZED ITCHING. **CHRONIC EXPOSURE-** REPEATED OR PROLONGED EXPOSURE MAY CAUSE SENSITIZATION.

FIRST AID- REMOVE FROM EXPOSURE AREA TO FRESH AIR IMMEDIATELY. IF BREATHING HAS STOPPED, PERFORM ARTIFICIAL RESPIRATION. KEEP PERSON WARM AND AT REST. TREAT SYMPTOMATICALLY AND SUPPORTIVELY. GET MEDICAL ATTENTION IMMEDIATELY.

SKIN CONTACT: SODIUM BISULFITE: IRRITANT/SENSITIZER. **ACUTE EXPOSURE-** CONTACT WITH THE SKIN MAY CAUSE IRRITATION. AQUEOUS SOLUTIONS MAY CAUSE SEVERE IRRITATION WITH POSSIBLE CORROSION. SENSITIZATION DERMATITIS MAY OCCUR IN PREVIOUSLY EXPOSED PERSONS. **CHRONIC EXPOSURE-** REPEATED OR PROLONGED EXPOSURE MAY CAUSE CONTACT DERMATITIS. SENSITIZATION REACTIONS HAVE BEEN REPORTED ALSO.

FIRST AID- REMOVE CONTAMINATED CLOTHING AND SHOES IMMEDIATELY. WASH AFFECTED AREA WITH SOAP OR MILD DETERGENT AND LARGE AMOUNTS OF WATER UNTIL NO EVIDENCE OF CHEMICAL REMAINS (APPROXIMATELY 15-20 MINUTES). GET MEDICAL ATTENTION IMMEDIATELY.

EYE CONTACT: SODIUM BISULFITE: IRRITANT. **ACUTE EXPOSURE-** CONTACT WITH THE EYES MAY CAUSE IRRITATION. AQUEOUS SOLUTIONS MAY CAUSE SEVERE IRRITATION WITH POSSIBLE CORROSION. **CHRONIC EXPOSURE-** REPEATED OR PROLONGED EXPOSURE MAY CAUSE CONJUNCTIVITIS.

FIRST AID- WASH EYES IMMEDIATELY WITH LARGE AMOUNTS OF WATER OR NORMAL SALINE, OCCASIONALLY LIFTING UPPER AND LOWER LIDS, UNTIL NO EVIDENCE OF CHEMICAL REMAINS (APPROXIMATELY 15-20 MINUTES). GET MEDICAL ATTENTION IMMEDIATELY.

INGESTION: SODIUM BISULFITE: SENSITIZER. **ACUTE EXPOSURE-** MAY CAUSE IRRITATION OF THE STOMACH WITH ABDOMINAL PAIN AND NAUSEA. THE ESTIMATED LETHAL DOSE IN HUMANS IS 10 GRAMS. IN SUSCEPTIBLE INDIVIDUALS, PARTICULARLY ASTHMATICS, SULFITES MAY CAUSE GENERALIZED FLUSHING, FAINTNESS, BRONCHOSPASMS WITH WHEEZING AND SHORTNESS OF BREATH, ANGIOEDEMA, HIVES, GENERALIZED ITCHING, LARYNGEAL EDEMA, HYPOTENSION, CYANOSIS, RAPID PULSE, COLD, CLAMMY SKIN, ANAPHYLAXIS, RESPIRATORY ARREST, AND UNCONSCIOUSNESS. INGESTION OF VERY LARGE DOSES OF SULFITES CAUSED VIOLENT COLIC AND DIARRHEA, CIRCULATORY DISTURBANCES, CENTRAL NERVOUS SYSTEM DEPRESSION, AND DEATH IN RATS. **CHRONIC EXPOSURE-** REPEATED OR PROLONGED INGESTION OF FOODS CONTAINING SULFITES MAY CAUSE SENSITIZATION.

FIRST AID- DO NOT USE GASTRIC LAVAGE OR EMESIS. DILUTE THE ACID IMMEDIATELY BY DRINKING LARGE QUANTITIES OF WATER OR MILK. IF VOMITING PERSISTS, ADMINISTER FLUIDS REPEATEDLY. INGESTED ACID MUST BE DILUTED APPROXIMATELY 100 FOLD TO RENDER IT HARMLESS TO TISSUES. MAINTAIN AIRWAY AND TREAT SHOCK (DREISBACH, HANDBOOK OF POISONING, 12TH ED.). GET MEDICAL ATTENTION IMMEDIATELY. IF VOMITING OCCURS, KEEP HEAD BELOW HIPS TO HELP PREVENT ASPIRATION.

ANTIDOTE: NO SPECIFIC ANTIDOTE. TREAT SYMPTOMATICALLY AND SUPPORTIVELY.

REACTIVITY

REACTIVITY: STABLE UNDER NORMAL TEMPERATURES AND PRESSURES IN AN ENCLOSED CONTAINER. SLOWLY OXIDIZED TO THE SULFATE IN AIR.

INCOMPATIBILITIES: SODIUM BISULFITE: ACIDS (STRONG): RELEASES SULFUR DIOXIDE. ALUMINUM: CORROSIVE. OXIDIZERS: REACTS.

DECOMPOSITION: THERMAL DECOMPOSITION MAY RELEASE TOXIC OXIDES OF SULFUR AND TOXIC SODIUM OXIDE.

POLYMERIZATION: HAZARDOUS POLYMERIZATION HAS NOT BEEN REPORTED TO OCCUR UNDER NORMAL TEMPERATURES AND PRESSURES.

STORAGE AND DISPOSAL

OBSERVE ALL FEDERAL, STATE AND LOCAL REGULATIONS WHEN STORING OR DISPOSING OF THIS SUBSTANCE. FOR ASSISTANCE, CONTACT THE DISTRICT DIRECTOR OF THE ENVIRONMENTAL PROTECTION AGENCY.

STORAGE

STORE AWAY FROM INCOMPATIBLE SUBSTANCES.

CONDITIONS TO AVOID

NONE REPORTED.

SPILL AND LEAK PROCEDURES

SOIL SPILL: DIG A PIT, POND, LAGOON OR HOLDING AREA TO CONTAIN LIQUID OR SOLID MATERIAL. COVER SOLIDS WITH A PLASTIC SHEET TO PREVENT DISSOLVING IN RAIN OR FIREFIGHTING WATER.

WATER SPILL: NEUTRALIZE WITH CAUSTIC SODA.
ADD CALCIUM HYPOCHLORITE TO SPILL.
ADD SUITABLE AGENT TO NEUTRALIZE SPILLED MATERIAL TO PH-7.

OCCUPATIONAL SPILL: SWEEP UP AND PLACE IN SUITABLE CLEAN, DRY CONTAINERS FOR RECLAMATION OR LATER DISPOSAL. DO NOT FLUSH SPILLED MATERIAL INTO SEWER. KEEP UNNECESSARY PEOPLE AWAY.
REPORTABLE QUANTITY (RQ): 5000 POUNDS THE SUPERFUND AMENDMENTS AND REAUTHORIZATION ACT (SARA) SECTION 304 REQUIRES THAT A RELEASE EQUAL TO OR GREATER THAN THE REPORTABLE QUANTITY FOR THIS SUBSTANCE BE IMMEDIATELY REPORTED TO THE LOCAL EMERGENCY PLANNING COMMITTEE AND THE STATE EMERGENCY RESPONSE COMMISSION (40 CFR 355.40). IF THE RELEASE OF THIS SUBSTANCE IS REPORTABLE UNDER CERCLA SECTION 103, THE NATIONAL RESPONSE CENTER MUST BE NOTIFIED IMMEDIATELY AT (800) 424-8802 OR (202) 426-2675 IN THE METROPOLITAN WASHINGTON, D.C. AREA (40 CFR 302.6).

PROTECTIVE EQUIPMENT

VENTILATION: PROVIDE LOCAL EXHAUST VENTILATION AND/OR GENERAL DILUTION VENTILATION TO MEET PUBLISHED EXPOSURE LIMITS.

RESPIRATOR: THE FOLLOWING RESPIRATORS ARE RECOMMENDED BASED ON INFORMATION FOUND IN THE PHYSICAL DATA, TOXICITY AND HEALTH EFFECTS SECTIONS. THEY ARE RANKED IN ORDER FROM MINIMUM TO MAXIMUM RESPIRATORY PROTECTION. THE SPECIFIC RESPIRATOR SELECTED MUST BE BASED ON CONTAMINATION LEVELS FOUND IN THE WORK PLACE, MUST NOT EXCEED THE WORKING LIMITS OF THE RESPIRATOR AND BE JOINTLY APPROVED BY THE NATIONAL INSTITUTE FOR OCCUPATIONAL SAFETY AND HEALTH AND THE MINE SAFETY AND HEALTH ADMINISTRATION (NIOSH-MSHA).
DUST AND MIST RESPIRATOR WITH A FULL FACEPIECE.
AIR-PURIFYING FULL FACEPIECE RESPIRATOR WITH A HIGH-EFFICIENCY PARTICULATE FILTER.
POWERED AIR-PURIFYING RESPIRATOR WITH A TIGHT-FITTING FACEPIECE AND HIGH-EFFICIENCY PARTICULATE FILTER.
TYPE 'C' SUPPLIED-AIR RESPIRATOR WITH A FULL FACEPIECE OPERATED IN PRESSURE-DEMAND OR OTHER POSITIVE PRESSURE MODE OR WITH A FULL FACEPIECE, HELMET OR HOOD OPERATED IN CONTINUOUS-FLOW MODE.
SELF-CONTAINED BREATHING APPARATUS WITH A FULL FACEPIECE OPERATED IN PRESSURE-DEMAND OR OTHER POSITIVE PRESSURE MODE.

FOR FIREFIGHTING AND OTHER IMMEDIATELY DANGEROUS TO LIFE OR HEALTH CONDITIONS:
SELF-CONTAINED BREATHING APPARATUS WITH FULL FACEPIECE OPERATED IN PRESSURE-DEMAND OR OTHER POSITIVE PRESSURE MODE.
SUPPLIED-AIR RESPIRATOR WITH FULL FACEPIECE AND OPERATED IN PRESSURE-DEMAND OR OTHER POSITIVE PRESSURE MODE IN COMBINATION WITH AN AUXILIARY SELF-CONTAINED BREATHING APPARATUS OPERATED IN PRESSURE-DEMAND OR OTHER POSITIVE PRESSURE MODE.

CLOTHING: EMPLOYEE MUST WEAR APPROPRIATE PROTECTIVE (IMPERVIOUS) CLOTHING AND EQUIPMENT TO PREVENT REPEATED OR PROLONGED SKIN CONTACT WITH THIS SUBSTANCE.

GLOVES: EMPLOYEE MUST WEAR APPROPRIATE PROTECTIVE GLOVES TO PREVENT CONTACT WITH THIS SUBSTANCE.

EYE PROTECTION: EMPLOYEE MUST WEAR SPLASH-PROOF OR DUST-RESISTANT SAFETY GOGGLES TO PREVENT EYE CONTACT WITH THIS SUBSTANCE.
EMERGENCY EYE WASH: WHERE THERE IS ANY POSSIBILITY THAT AN EMPLOYEE'S EYES MAY BE EXPOSED TO THIS SUBSTANCE, THE EMPLOYER SHOULD PROVIDE AN EYE WASH FOUNTAIN WITHIN THE IMMEDIATE WORK AREA FOR EMERGENCY USE.

AUTHORIZED BY- OCCUPATIONAL HEALTH SERVICES, INC.
CREATION DATE: 11/17/89 ***REVISION DATE:*** 05/31/90

MATERIAL SAFETY DATA SHEET

OCCUPATIONAL HEALTH SERVICES, INC.
AGRICULTURE AND PESTICIDE DIVISION
450 SEVENTH AVENUE, SUITE 2407
NEW YORK, NEW YORK 10123
1-800-445-MSDS OR (212) 967-1100

EMERGENCY CONTACT:
JOHN S. BRANSFORD, JR. (615) 292-1180

SUBSTANCE IDENTIFICATION

CAS-NUMBER 1303-96-4

SUBSTANCE: **SODIUM BORATE DECAHYDRATE**

TRADE NAMES/SYNONYMS: BORAX (B4NA2O7.10H2O); BORAX; BORAX DECAHYDRATE; DISODIUM TETRABORATE DECAHYDRATE; SODIUM BIBORATE DECAHYDRATE; SODIUM PYROBORATE DECAHYDRATE; SODIUM TETRABORATE DECAHYDRATE; BORIC ACID, DISODIUM SALT, DECAHYDRATE; SODIUM BORATE; B4H20NA2O17; PST21010

CHEMICAL FAMILY: INORGANIC SALT

MOLECULAR FORMULA: NA2.B4-O7.10(H2-O)

MOLECULAR WEIGHT: 381.37

CERCLA RATINGS (SCALE 0-3): HEALTH=2 FIRE=0 REACTIVITY=0 PERSISTENCE=0

NFPA RATINGS (SCALE 0-4): HEALTH=2 FIRE=0 REACTIVITY=0

COMPONENTS AND CONTAMINANTS

COMPONENT: SODIUM BORATE DECAHYDRATE ***PERCENT:*** 100.0
CAS# 1303-96-4

OTHER CONTAMINANTS: NONE

EXPOSURE LIMITS: SODIUM BORATE, DECAHYDRATE (BORAX): 10 MG/M3 OSHA TWA
5 MG/M3 ACGIH TWA

PHYSICAL DATA

DESCRIPTION: ODORLESS, HARD CRYSTALS, GRANULES OR CRYSTALLINE POWDER WITH A WHITE COATING; EFFLORESCENT IN DRY AIR.

BOILING POINT: 608 F (320 C)

MELTING POINT: 167 F (75 C) (RAPID HEATING) ***SPECIFIC GRAVITY:*** 1.73

PH: 9.5 (AQUEOUS SOLN) ***SOLUBILITY IN WATER:*** 6.25%

SOLVENT SOLUBILITY: SOLUBLE IN GLYCEROL; VERY SLIGHTLY SOLUBLE IN ALCOHOL; INSOLUBLE IN ACIDS.
LOSSES 5 WATERS OF HYDRATION @ 212 F (100 C) LOSSES 9 WATERS OF HYDRATION @ 302 F (150 C) LOSSES 10 WATERS OF HYDRATION @ 608 F (320 C)

FIRE AND EXPLOSION DATA

FIRE AND EXPLOSION HAZARD: NEGLIGIBLE FIRE HAZARD WHEN EXPOSED TO HEAT OR FLAME.

FIREFIGHTING MEDIA: EXTINGUISH USING AGENT SUITABLE FOR TYPE OF SURROUNDING FIRE.

FIREFIGHTING: NO ACUTE HAZARD. MOVE CONTAINER FROM FIRE AREA IF POSSIBLE. AVOID BREATHING VAPORS OR DUSTS; KEEP UPWIND.

TOXICITY

SODIUM BORATE: TOXICITY DATA: ANHYDROUS: REPRODUCTIVE EFFECTS DATA (RTECS). TETRAHYDRATE: 2330 MG/KG ORAL-RAT LD50. PENTAHYDRATE: NO DATA AVAILABLE. HEPTAHYDRATE: 450 MG/KG INTRAPERITONEAL-MOUSE LD50. DECAHYDRATE: 1000 MG/KG ORAL-INFANT LDLO; 709 MG/KG ORAL-MAN LDLO; 2660 MG/KG ORAL-RAT LD50; 2000 MG/KG ORAL-MOUSE LD50; 5330 MG/KG ORAL-GUINEA PIG LD50; 3 GM/KG ORAL-DOG LDLO; 2711 MG/KG INTRAPERITONEAL-MOUSE LD50; 1320 MG/KG INTRAVENOUS-MOUSE LD50; MUTAGENIC DATA (RTECS); REPRODUCTIVE EFFECTS DATA (RTECS). CARCINOGEN STATUS: NONE. LOCAL EFFECTS: IRRITANT- INHALATION, SKIN, EYE. ACUTE TOXICITY LEVEL: MODERATELY TOXIC BY INGESTION (TETRAHYDRATE, DECAHYDRATE). TARGET EFFECTS: CENTRAL NERVOUS SYSTEM DEPRESSANT; NEPHROTOXIN. POISONING MAY ALSO AFFECT THE LIVER AND GASTROINTESTINAL SYSTEM.

HEALTH EFFECTS AND FIRST AID

INHALATION: SODIUM BORATE: IRRITANT/NARCOTIC/NEPHROTOXIN. **ACUTE EXPOSURE-** BORATES MAY CAUSE MUCOUS MEMBRANE IRRITATION WITH COUGHING AND MAY BE ABSORBED CAUSING SYSTEMIC EFFECTS AS DETAILED IN ACUTE INGESTION. **CHRONIC EXPOSURE-** REPEATED OR PROLONGED ABSORPTION OF BORATES MAY CAUSE BRONCHITIS, LARYNGITIS, AND OTHER EFFECTS AS DETAILED IN CHRONIC INGESTION.

FIRST AID- REMOVE FROM EXPOSURE AREA TO FRESH AIR IMMEDIATELY. IF BREATHING HAS STOPPED, PERFORM ARTIFICIAL RESPIRATION. KEEP PERSON WARM AND AT REST. TREAT SYMPTOMATICALLY AND SUPPORTIVELY. GET MEDICAL ATTENTION IMMEDIATELY.

SKIN CONTACT: SODIUM BORATE: IRRITANT/NARCOTIC/NEPHROTOXIN. **ACUTE EXPOSURE-** BORATES MAY BE IRRITATING TO THE SKIN AND MAY BE ABSORBED THROUGH INTACT OR DAMAGED SKIN. SYSTEMIC EFFECTS AS DETAILED IN ACUTE INGESTION MAY OCCUR. **CHRONIC EXPOSURE-** REPEATED OR PROLONGED CONTACT MAY CAUSE DERMATITIS. IF SUFFICIENT QUANTITIES ARE ABSORBED, SYSTEMIC POISONING AS DETAILED IN CHRONIC INGESTION MAY OCCUR.

FIRST AID- REMOVE CONTAMINATED CLOTHING AND SHOES IMMEDIATELY. WASH AFFECTED AREA WITH SOAP OR MILD DETERGENT AND LARGE AMOUNTS OF WATER UNTIL NO EVIDENCE OF CHEMICAL REMAINS (APPROXIMATELY 15-20 MINUTES). GET MEDICAL ATTENTION IMMEDIATELY.

EYE CONTACT: SODIUM BORATE: IRRITANT. **ACUTE EXPOSURE-** MAY CAUSE IRRITATION WITH REDNESS AND PAIN. **CHRONIC EXPOSURE-** REPEATED OR PROLONGED EXPOSURE TO BORAX DUST MAY CAUSE CONJUNCTIVITIS.

FIRST AID- WASH EYES IMMEDIATELY WITH LARGE AMOUNTS OF WATER OR NORMAL SALINE, OCCASIONALLY LIFTING UPPER AND LOWER LIDS, UNTIL NO EVIDENCE OF CHEMICAL REMAINS (APPROXIMATELY 15-20 MINUTES). GET MEDICAL ATTENTION IMMEDIATELY.

INGESTION: SODIUM BORATE: NARCOTIC/NEPHROTOXIN. **ACUTE EXPOSURE-** BORATES MAY CAUSE DELAYED SYMPTOMS INCLUDING MALAISE, NAUSEA, SEVERE EPIGASTRIC PAIN, HEMORRHAGIC GASTROENTERITIS WITH BLOODY VOMITUS AND DIARRHEA, WEAKNESS, LETHARGY, FEVER AND HEADACHE. TACHYPNEA, TACHYCARDIA, RESTLESSNESS, DELIRIUM, TREMORS AND TWITCHING OF FACIAL MUSCLES AND EXTREMITIES, INTERMITTENT CONVULSIONS, AND SUBSEQUENT CENTRAL NERVOUS SYSTEM DEPRESSION, HYPOTHERMIA AND CHEYNE-STOKES RESPIRATION FOLLOWED BY RESPIRATORY ARREST MAY OCCUR. SHOCK MAY BE SEEN WITH COLD CLAMMY SKIN, CYANOSIS, THREADY PULSE, HYPOTENSION AND COMA. ERYTHRODERMA MAY OCCUR, FOLLOWED BY DESQUAMATION, EXCORIATION, BLISTERING AND BULLAE, TYPICALLY LOCATED ON THE PALMS, SOLES, BUTTOCKS AND SCROTUM AND LATER BECOMING GENERALIZED OVER THE BODY. THE PHARYNX AND TYMPANIC MEMBRANES MAY ALSO BE AFFECTED. KIDNEY DAMAGE, PRIMARILY RENAL TUBULAR NECROSIS, IS INDICATED BY OLIGURIA, ALBUMINURIA, AND ANURIA. LIVER DAMAGE WITH JAUNDICE AND HEPATOMEGALY IS RARE. OTHER SYMPTOMS OF POISONING MAY INCLUDE METABOLIC ACIDOSIS AND INTRAVASCULAR COAGULATION. EARLY DEATHS, GENERALLY OCCURRING WITHIN SEVERAL HOURS, MAY BE DUE TO CARDIOVASCULAR COLLAPSE WHEREAS LATER ONES, USUALLY DELAYED SEVERAL DAYS, MAY BE DUE TO CENTRAL NERVOUS SYSTEM DEPRESSION OR RENAL FAILURE. PATHOLOGIC FINDINGS MAY INCLUDE FATTY DEGENERATION OF THE LIVER AND KIDNEYS, CEREBRAL EDEMA AND CONGESTION OF ALL ORGANS. **CHRONIC EXPOSURE-** REPEATED INGESTION MAY RESULT IN ANOREXIA, WEIGHT LOSS, MILD GASTROINTESTINAL IRRITATION WITH DISTURBED DIGESTION, NAUSEA, VOMITING, MILD DIARRHEA AND GASTROENTERITIS. ERYTHEMATOUS SKIN RASHES, DRY SKIN AND MUCOUS MEMBRANES WITH CRACKED LIPS, RED TONGUE, CONJUNCTIVITIS, ANEMIA, IRRITABILITY, PATCHY ALOPECIA, PERIORBITAL EDEMA, KIDNEY INJURY AND CONVULSIONS MAY ALSO OCCUR. REPEATED DOSES MAY HAVE A CUMMULATIVE EFFECT. 1% BORAX IN THE DIET OF

DOGS AND RATS IN A 2-YEAR FEEDING STUDY CAUSED GROWTH SUPPRESSION, DECREASED FOOD UTILIZATION EFFICIENCY, DEGENERATION OF GONADS, AND SKIN DESQUAMATION ON PAWS AND TAILS. TESTICULAR ATROPHY ALSO OCCURRED AT THIS LEVEL IN BOTH DOGS AND RATS. OTHER REPRODUCTIVE EFFECTS HAVE BEEN REPORTED IN ANIMALS.

FIRST AID- MAINTAIN RESPIRATION. REMOVE BY IPECAC EMESIS FOLLOWED BY ACTIVATED CHARCOAL. GASTRIC LAVAGE MAY BE USEFUL. (DREISBACH, HANDBOOK OF POISONING, 11TH EDITION) GET MEDICAL ATTENTION IMMEDIATELY. LAVAGE MUST BE PERFORMED BY QUALIFIED MEDICAL PERSONNEL.

ANTIDOTE: NO SPECIFIC ANTIDOTE. TREAT SYMPTOMATICALLY AND SUPPORTIVELY.

REACTIVITY

REACTIVITY: STABLE UNDER NORMAL TEMPERATURES AND PRESSURES.

INCOMPATIBILITIES: SODIUM BORATE: ZIRCONIUM: EXPLOSIVE REACTION WHEN HEATED.

DECOMPOSITION: THERMAL DECOMPOSITION PRODUCTS MAY INCLUDE TOXIC SODIUM OXIDE.

POLYMERIZATION: HAZARDOUS POLYMERIZATION HAS NOT BEEN REPORTED TO OCCUR UNDER NORMAL TEMPERATURES AND PRESSURES.

STORAGE AND DISPOSAL

OBSERVE ALL FEDERAL, STATE AND LOCAL REGULATIONS WHEN STORING OR DISPOSING OF THIS SUBSTANCE. FOR ASSISTANCE, CONTACT THE DISTRICT DIRECTOR OF THE ENVIRONMENTAL PROTECTION AGENCY.

STORAGE

STORE AWAY FROM INCOMPATIBLE SUBSTANCES.

STORE IN A COOL, DRY PLACE; KEEP CONTAINER TIGHTLY CLOSED WHEN NOT IN USE.

CONDITIONS TO AVOID

IF MATERIAL IS INVOLVED IN A FIRE, IT MAY MELT TO A GLASSY MATERIAL WHICH CAN FLOW IN LARGE QUANTITIES AND IGNITE SURROUNDING COMBUSTIBLE MATERIALS.

SPILL AND LEAK PROCEDURES

OCCUPATIONAL SPILL: SWEEP UP AND PLACE IN SUITABLE CLEAN, DRY CONTAINERS FOR RECLAMATION OR LATER DISPOSAL. DO NOT FLUSH SPILLED MATERIAL INTO SEWER. KEEP UNNECESSARY PEOPLE AWAY.

PROTECTIVE EQUIPMENT

VENTILATION: PROVIDE LOCAL EXHAUST VENTILATION AND/OR GENERAL DILUTION VENTILATION TO MEET PUBLISHED EXPOSURE LIMITS.

RESPIRATOR: THE FOLLOWING RESPIRATORS ARE RECOMMENDED BASED ON INFORMATION FOUND IN THE PHYSICAL DATA, TOXICITY AND HEALTH EFFECTS SECTIONS. THEY ARE RANKED IN ORDER FROM MINIMUM TO MAXIMUM RESPIRATORY PROTECTION. THE SPECIFIC RESPIRATOR SELECTED MUST BE BASED ON CONTAMINATION LEVELS FOUND IN THE WORK PLACE, MUST NOT EXCEED THE WORKING LIMITS OF THE RESPIRATOR AND BE JOINTLY APPROVED BY THE NATIONAL INSTITUTE FOR OCCUPATIONAL SAFETY AND HEALTH AND THE MINE SAFETY AND HEALTH ADMINISTRATION (NIOSH-MSHA).

DUST AND MIST RESPIRATOR WITH A FULL FACEPIECE.

AIR-PURIFYING FULL FACEPIECE RESPIRATOR WITH A HIGH-EFFICIENCY PARTICULATE FILTER.

POWERED AIR-PURIFYING RESPIRATOR WITH A TIGHT-FITTING FACEPIECE AND HIGH-EFFICIENCY PARTICULATE FILTER.

TYPE 'C' SUPPLIED-AIR RESPIRATOR WITH A FULL FACEPIECE OPERATED IN PRESSURE-DEMAND OR OTHER POSITIVE PRESSURE MODE OR WITH A FULL FACEPIECE, HELMET OR HOOD OPERATED IN CONTINUOUS-FLOW MODE.

SELF-CONTAINED BREATHING APPARATUS WITH A FULL FACEPIECE OPERATED IN PRESSURE-DEMAND OR OTHER POSITIVE PRESSURE MODE.

FOR FIREFIGHTING AND OTHER IMMEDIATELY DANGEROUS TO LIFE OR HEALTH CONDITIONS:

SELF-CONTAINED BREATHING APPARATUS WITH FULL FACEPIECE OPERATED IN PRESSURE-DEMAND OR OTHER POSITIVE PRESSURE MODE.

SUPPLIED-AIR RESPIRATOR WITH FULL FACEPIECE AND OPERATED IN PRESSURE-DEMAND OR OTHER POSITIVE PRESSURE MODE IN COMBINATION WITH AN AUXILIARY SELF-CONTAINED BREATHING APPARATUS OPERATED IN PRESSURE-DEMAND OR OTHER POSITIVE PRESSURE MODE.

CLOTHING: EMPLOYEE MUST WEAR APPROPRIATE PROTECTIVE (IMPERVIOUS) CLOTHING AND EQUIPMENT TO PREVENT REPEATED OR PROLONGED SKIN CONTACT WITH THIS SUBSTANCE.

GLOVES: EMPLOYEE MUST WEAR APPROPRIATE PROTECTIVE GLOVES TO PREVENT CONTACT WITH THIS SUBSTANCE.

EYE PROTECTION: EMPLOYEE MUST WEAR SPLASH-PROOF OR DUST-RESISTANT SAFETY GOGGLES AND A FACESHIELD TO PREVENT CONTACT WITH THIS SUBSTANCE.

EMERGENCY WASH FACILITIES: WHERE THERE IS ANY POSSIBILITY THAT AN EMPLOYEE'S EYES AND/OR SKIN MAY BE EXPOSED TO THIS SUBSTANCE, THE EMPLOYER SHOULD PROVIDE AN EYE WASH FOUNTAIN AND QUICK DRENCH SHOWER WITHIN THE IMMEDIATE WORK AREA FOR EMERGENCY USE.

AUTHORIZED BY- OCCUPATIONAL HEALTH SERVICES, INC.

CREATION DATE: 10/05/89 ***REVISION DATE:*** 05/31/90

MATERIAL SAFETY DATA SHEET

OCCUPATIONAL HEALTH SERVICES, INC.
AGRICULTURE AND PESTICIDE DIVISION
450 SEVENTH AVENUE, SUITE 2407
NEW YORK, NEW YORK 10123
1-800-445-MSDS OR (212) 967-1100

EMERGENCY CONTACT:
JOHN S. BRANSFORD, JR. (615) 292-1180

SUBSTANCE IDENTIFICATION

CAS-NUMBER 7647-15-6

SUBSTANCE: **SODIUM BROMIDE**

TRADE NAMES/SYNONYMS: BROMIDE SALT OF SODIUM; SEDONEURAL; BROMNATRIUM; SODIUM BROMIDE (NABR); S-255; NABR; PST21060

CHEMICAL FAMILY: INORGANIC SALT

MOLECULAR FORMULA: BR-NA

MOLECULAR WEIGHT: 102.90

CERCLA RATINGS (SCALE 0-3): HEALTH=2 FIRE=0 REACTIVITY=0 PERSISTENCE=0

NFPA RATINGS (SCALE 0-4): HEALTH=U FIRE=0 REACTIVITY=0

COMPONENTS AND CONTAMINANTS

COMPONENT: SODIUM BROMIDE ***PERCENT:*** 100

CAS# 7647-15-6

OTHER CONTAMINANTS: NONE

EXPOSURE LIMITS: NO OCCUPATIONAL EXPOSURE LIMITS ESTABLISHED BY OSHA, ACGIH, OR NIOSH.

PHYSICAL DATA

DESCRIPTION: WHITE CUBIC, HYGROSCOPIC CRYSTALS OR POWDER WITH A SALINE, BITTER TASTE. ***BOILING POINT:*** 2534 F (1390 C)

MELTING POINT: 1377 F (747C)

SPECIFIC GRAVITY: 3.203 @ 25 C ***PH:*** 6.5-8.0 (SOLN)

SOLUBILITY IN WATER: 116 % @ 50 C

SOLVENT SOLUBILITY: SLIGHTLY SOLUBLE IN ALCOHOL.

FIRE AND EXPLOSION DATA

FIRE AND EXPLOSION HAZARD: NEGLIGIBLE FIRE HAZARD WHEN EXPOSED TO HEAT OR FLAME.

FLASH POINT: NONFLAMMABLE

FIREFIGHTING MEDIA: DRY CHEMICAL, CARBON DIOXIDE, WATER SPRAY OR FOAM FOR LARGER FIRES, USE WATER SPRAY, FOG OR ALCOHOL FOAM

FIREFIGHTING: NO ACUTE HAZARD. MOVE CONTAINER FROM FIRE AREA IF POSSIBLE. AVOID BREATHING VAPORS OR DUSTS; KEEP UPWIND.

TOXICITY

SODIUM BROMIDE: TOXICITY DATA: 3500 MG/KG ORAL-RAT LD50; 7000 MG/KG ORAL-MOUSE LD50; 580 MG/KG ORAL-RABBIT LDLO; 5020 MG/KG SUBCUTANEOUS-MOUSE LD50; 2900 MG/KG SUBCUTANEOUS-RAT LD50; REPRODUCTIVE EFFECTS DATA (RTECS). CARCINOGEN STATUS: NONE. ACUTE TOXICITY LEVEL: MODERATELY TOXIC BY INGESTION. TARGET EFFECTS: POISONING MAY AFFECT THE SKIN AND THE GASTROINTESTINAL AND CENTRAL NERVOUS SYSTEMS. AT INCREASED RISK FROM EXPOSURE: PERSONS WITH IMPAIRED LIVER FUNCTION.

HEALTH EFFECTS AND FIRST AID

INHALATION: SODIUM BROMIDE: **ACUTE EXPOSURE**- DUSTS MAY CAUSE MUCOUS MEMBRANE IRRITATION. **CHRONIC EXPOSURE**- SYSTEMIC EFFECTS DUE TO INGESTION AND THE SUBSEQUENT EXCRETION OF THE BROMIDE ION THROUGH THE RESPIRATORY TRACT MAY CAUSE RHINITIS AND BRONCHIAL IRRITATION.

FIRST AID- REMOVE FROM EXPOSURE AREA TO FRESH AIR IMMEDIATELY. IF BREATHING HAS STOPPED, PERFORM ARTIFICIAL RESPIRATION. KEEP PERSON WARM AND AT REST. TREAT SYMPTOMATICALLY AND SUPPORTIVELY. GET MEDICAL ATTENTION IMMEDIATELY.

SKIN CONTACT: SODIUM BROMIDE: **ACUTE EXPOSURE-** NO DATA AVAILABLE. **CHRONIC EXPOSURE-** NO DATA AVAILABLE.

FIRST AID- REMOVE CONTAMINATED CLOTHING AND SHOES IMMEDIATELY. WASH AFFECTED AREA WITH SOAP OR MILD DETERGENT AND LARGE AMOUNTS OF WATER UNTIL NO EVIDENCE OF CHEMICAL REMAINS (APPROXIMATELY 15-20 MINUTES). GET MEDICAL ATTENTION IMMEDIATELY.

EYE CONTACT: SODIUM BROMIDE: **ACUTE EXPOSURE-** NO DATA AVAILABLE. **CHRONIC EXPOSURE-** NO DATA AVAILABLE.

FIRST AID- WASH EYES IMMEDIATELY WITH LARGE AMOUNTS OF WATER OR NORMAL SALINE, OCCASIONALLY LIFTING UPPER AND LOWER LIDS, UNTIL NO EVIDENCE OF CHEMICAL REMAINS (APPROXIMATELY 15-20 MINUTES). GET MEDICAL ATTENTION IMMEDIATELY.

INGESTION: SODIUM BROMIDE: **ACUTE EXPOSURE-** POISONING BY ACUTE EXPOSURE IS RARE BECAUSE BROMIDES IRRITATE THE GASTRIC MUCOSA WHEN INGESTED IN LARGE AMOUNTS AS A SINGLE DOSE AND CAUSE IMMEDIATE ABDOMINAL PAIN, NAUSEA AND VOMITING. HOWEVER, IN THE EVENT OF KIDNEY DAMAGE SYSTEMIC POISONING MAY OCCUR BY A SINGLE DOSE AND POSSIBLY CAUSE PARALYSIS AND COMA. **CHRONIC EXPOSURE-** REPEATED OR PROLONGED INGESTION OF BROMIDES MAY CAUSE "BROMISM" WHICH MOST FREQUENTLY AFFECTS THE GASTROINTESTINAL SYSTEM, THE CENTRAL NERVOUS SYSTEM, AND THE SKIN. GASTROINTESTINAL DISTURBANCES MAY INCLUDE NAUSEA AND VOMITING FROM GASTRIC IRRITATION, FOUL BREATH, ANOREXIA, WEIGHT LOSS, DEHYDRATION AND CONSTIPATION. NEUROLOGICAL MANIFESTATIONS MAY INCLUDE HEADACHE, APATHY, SLURRED SPEECH, DECREASED MEMORY, DROWSINESS, IMPAIRED INTELLECTUAL CAPACITY AND EMOTIONAL CONTROL, TREMULOUSNESS, AND ATAXIA. DELUSIONS AND HALLUCINATIONS MAY OCCUR. HYPERACTIVITY, SLUGGISH OR ABSENT DEEP TENDON REFLEXES, GENERALIZED WEAKNESS, ABSENCE OF SEXUAL DESIRE AND TRANSITORY SCHIZOPHRENIA HAVE ALSO BEEN REPORTED. OTHER EFFECTS MAY INCLUDE INCREASED INTRACRANIAL PRESSURE, PAPILLEDEMA AND HYPERTENSION. CONTINUED EXPOSURE MAY RESULT IN STUPOR AND COMA. SKIN MANIFESTATIONS MAY INCLUDE AN ACNEIFORM, NODULAR, OR ERYTHEMATOUS RASH. EARLY LESIONS MAY INCLUDE PAPULES, PUSTULES, EDEMATOUS PLAQUES, AND ULCERS. THE CLASSIC CUTANEOUS SIGN OF BROMISM IS A PUSTULE-STUDDED, ECTHYMA-LIKE PLAQUE ON THE LEGS. OTHER SYSTEMIC EFFECTS MAY INCLUDE RHINITIS, BRONCHIAL IRRITATION, LACRIMATION, CONJUNCTIVITIS, BLEPHARITIS, INCREASE IN PUPIL SIZE, SUBNORMAL REACTIONS TO LIGHT OR ACCOMODATION, DISTURBANCES OF COLOR VISION, AND VISUAL HALLUCINATIONS. DISCONTINUATION OF EXPOSURE WILL NORMALLY RESULT IN REVERSAL OF SYMPTOMS. MATERNAL EXPOSURE MAY RESULT IN HYPOTONIA IN NEONATES.

FIRST AID- TREAT SYMPTOMATICALLY AND SUPPORTIVELY. GET MEDICAL ATTENTION IMMEDIATELY. IF VOMITING OCCURS, KEEP HEAD LOWER THAN HIPS TO PREVENT ASPIRATION.

ANTIDOTE: THE FOLLOWING ANTIDOTE HAS BEEN RECOMMENDED. HOWEVER, THE DECISION AS TO WHETHER THE SEVERITY OF POISONING REQUIRES ADMINISTRATION OF ANY ANTIDOTE AND ACTUAL DOSE REQUIRED SHOULD BE MADE BY QUALIFIED MEDICAL PERSONNEL.
BROMIDE POISONING: GIVE SODIUM CHLORIDE, 1 GRAM ORALLY EVERY HOUR IN WATER OR AS SALT TABLETS; FOR MORE SEVERE INVOLVEMENT IN WHICH ORAL MEDICATION IS IMPOSSIBLE, GIVE NORMAL SALINE, 1 LITER EVERY 8 HOURS INTRAVENOUSLY TO A MAXIMUM OF 2 LITERS DAILY. SODIUM CHLORIDE THERAPY MUST BE CONTINUED UNTIL THE BLOOD BROMIDE LEVEL DROPS BELOW 50 MG/DL. SIMULTANEOUS ADMINISTRATION OF DIURETICS IS ALSO USEFUL (DREISBACH, HANDBOOK OF POISONING, 11TH ED.). ANTIDOTE SHOULD BE ADMINISTERED BY QUALIFIED MEDICAL PERSONNEL.

REACTIVITY

REACTIVITY: STABLE UNDER NORMAL TEMPERATURES AND PRESSURES.

INCOMPATIBILITIES: SODIUM BROMIDE: ACIDS: INCOMPATIBLE. ALKALOIDAL SALTS: INCOMPATIBLE. BROMINE TRIFLUORIDE: RAPIDLY ATTACKED. HEAVY METAL SALTS: INCOMPATIBLE.

DECOMPOSITION: THERMAL DECOMPOSITION MAY RELEASE HAZARDOUS FUMES OF HYDROGEN BROMIDE AND SODIUM OXIDE.

POLYMERIZATION: HAZARDOUS POLYMERIZATION HAS NOT BEEN REPORTED TO OCCUR UNDER NORMAL TEMPERATURES AND PRESSURES.

STORAGE AND DISPOSAL

STORAGE

OBSERVE ALL FEDERAL, STATE AND LOCAL REGULATIONS WHEN STORING OR DISPOSING OF THIS SUBSTANCE. FOR ASSISTANCE, CONTACT THE DISTRICT DIRECTOR OF THE ENVIRONMENTAL PROTECTION AGENCY.
STORE AWAY FROM INCOMPATIBLE SUBSTANCES.

CONDITIONS TO AVOID

NONE REPORTED.

SPILL AND LEAK PROCEDURES

OCCUPATIONAL SPILL: SWEEP UP AND PLACE IN SUITABLE CLEAN, DRY CONTAINERS FOR RECLAMATION OR LATER DISPOSAL. DO NOT FLUSH SPILLED MATERIAL INTO SEWER. KEEP UNNECESSARY PEOPLE AWAY.

PROTECTIVE EQUIPMENT

VENTILATION: PROVIDE LOCAL EXHAUST OR GENERAL DILUTION VENTILATION SYSTEM.

RESPIRATOR: THE FOLLOWING RESPIRATORS ARE RECOMMENDED BASED ON INFORMATION FOUND IN THE PHYSICAL DATA, TOXICITY AND HEALTH EFFECTS SECTIONS. THEY ARE RANKED IN ORDER FROM MINIMUM TO MAXIMUM RESPIRATORY PROTECTION. THE SPECIFIC RESPIRATOR SELECTED MUST BE BASED ON CONTAMINATION LEVELS FOUND IN THE WORK PLACE, MUST NOT EXCEED THE WORKING LIMITS OF THE RESPIRATOR AND BE JOINTLY APPROVED BY THE NATIONAL INSTITUTE FOR OCCUPATIONAL SAFETY AND HEALTH AND THE MINE SAFETY AND HEALTH ADMINISTRATION (NIOSH-MSHA).
DUST AND MIST RESPIRATOR WITH A FULL FACEPIECE.
AIR-PURIFYING FULL FACEPIECE RESPIRATOR WITH A HIGH-EFFICIENCY PARTICULATE FILTER.
POWERED AIR-PURIFYING RESPIRATOR WITH A TIGHT-FITTING FACEPIECE AND HIGH-EFFICIENCY PARTICULATE FILTER.
TYPE 'C' SUPPLIED-AIR RESPIRATOR WITH A FULL FACEPIECE OPERATED IN PRESSURE-DEMAND OR OTHER POSITIVE PRESSURE MODE OR WITH A FULL FACEPIECE, HELMET OR HOOD OPERATED IN CONTINUOUS-FLOW MODE.
SELF-CONTAINED BREATHING APPARATUS WITH A FULL FACEPIECE OPERATED IN PRESSURE-DEMAND OR OTHER POSITIVE PRESSURE MODE.
FOR FIREFIGHTING AND OTHER IMMEDIATELY DANGEROUS TO LIFE OR HEALTH CONDITIONS:
SELF-CONTAINED BREATHING APPARATUS WITH FULL FACEPIECE OPERATED IN PRESSURE-DEMAND OR OTHER POSITIVE PRESSURE MODE.
SUPPLIED-AIR RESPIRATOR WITH FULL FACEPIECE AND OPERATED IN PRESSURE-DEMAND OR OTHER POSITIVE PRESSURE MODE IN COMBINATION WITH AN AUXILIARY SELF-CONTAINED BREATHING APPARATUS OPERATED IN PRESSURE-DEMAND OR OTHER POSITIVE PRESSURE MODE.

CLOTHING: EMPLOYEE MUST WEAR APPROPRIATE PROTECTIVE (IMPERVIOUS) CLOTHING AND EQUIPMENT TO PREVENT REPEATED OR PROLONGED SKIN CONTACT WITH THIS SUBSTANCE.

GLOVES: EMPLOYEE MUST WEAR APPROPRIATE PROTECTIVE GLOVES TO PREVENT CONTACT WITH THIS SUBSTANCE.

EYE PROTECTION: EMPLOYEE MUST WEAR SPLASH-PROOF OR DUST-RESISTANT SAFETY GOGGLES TO PREVENT EYE CONTACT WITH THIS SUBSTANCE.
EMERGENCY EYE WASH: WHERE THERE IS ANY POSSIBILITY THAT AN EMPLOYEE'S EYES MAY BE EXPOSED TO THIS SUBSTANCE, THE EMPLOYER SHOULD PROVIDE AN EYE WASH FOUNTAIN WITHIN THE IMMEDIATE WORK AREA FOR EMERGENCY USE.

AUTHORIZED BY- OCCUPATIONAL HEALTH SERVICES, INC.
CREATION DATE: 11/16/89 ***REVISION DATE:*** 05/31/90

MATERIAL SAFETY DATA SHEET

OCCUPATIONAL HEALTH SERVICES, INC.
AGRICULTURE AND PESTICIDE DIVISION
450 SEVENTH AVENUE, SUITE 2407
NEW YORK, NEW YORK 10123
1-800-445-MSDS OR (212) 967-1100

EMERGENCY CONTACT:
JOHN S. BRANSFORD, JR. (615) 292-1180

SUBSTANCE IDENTIFICATION

CAS-NUMBER 124-65-2

SUBSTANCE: **SODIUM CACODYLATE**

TRADE NAMES/SYNONYMS: HYDROXYDIMETHYLARSINE OXIDE, SODIUM SALT; DIMETHYLARSINIC ACID, SODIUM SALT; SODIUM SALT OF CACODYLAC ACID; ((DIMETHYLARSINO)OXY)SODIUM, AS-OXIDE; ALKARSODYL; ARSECODILE; ARSICODILE; ARSYCODILE; CHEMAID; SODIUM DIMETHYLARSINATE; UN 1688; BP-325; PST21070

CHEMICAL FAMILY: ORGANIC ARSENIC

MOLECULAR FORMULA: C5-H7-AS-O2.NA

MOLECULAR WEIGHT: 159.99

CERCLA RATINGS (SCALE 0-3): HEALTH=2 FIRE=0 REACTIVITY=0 PERSISTENCE=3
NFPA RATINGS (SCALE 0-4): HEALTH=2 FIRE=0 REACTIVITY=0

COMPONENTS AND CONTAMINANTS

COMPONENT: SODIUM CACODYLATE ***PERCENT:*** 100%
CAS# 124-65-2
OTHER CONTAMINANTS: NONE
EXPOSURE LIMITS: SODIUM CACODYLATE: 0.5 MG(AS)/M3 OSHA TWA 0.2 MG(AS)/M3 ACGIH TWA
100/10,000 POUNDS SARA SECTION 302 THRESHOLD PLANNING QUANTITY 1 POUND SARA SECTION 304 REPORTABLE QUANTITY

PHYSICAL DATA

DESCRIPTION: WHITE CRYSTALINE SOLID WITH A SLIGHT ODOR.
BOILING POINT: DECOMPOSES ***MELTING POINT:*** 140 F (60 C)
SPECIFIC GRAVITY: >1 @ 20 C ***PH:*** 8-9 ***SOLUBILITY IN WATER:*** SOLUBLE
VAPOR DENSITY: 7.4
SOLVENT SOLUBILITY: ALCOHOL

FIRE AND EXPLOSION DATA

FIRE AND EXPLOSION HAZARD: NEGLIGIBLE FIRE HAZARD WHEN EXPOSED TO HEAT OR FLAME.
FIREFIGHTING MEDIA: DRY CHEMICAL, CARBON DIOXIDE, HALON, WATER SPRAY OR STANDARD FOAM (1987 EMERGENCY RESPONSE GUIDEBOOK, DOT P 5800.4). FOR LARGER FIRES, USE WATER SPRAY, FOG OR STANDARD FOAM (1987 EMERGENCY RESPONSE GUIDEBOOK, DOT P 5800.4).
FIREFIGHTING: MOVE CONTAINERS FROM FIRE AREA IF POSSIBLE (1987 EMERGENCY RESPONSE GUIDEBOOK, DOT P 5800.4, GUIDE PAGE 53).
EXTINGUISH ONLY IF FLOW CAN BE STOPPED. EXTINGUISH USING AGENT INDICATED. USE FLOODING AMOUNTS OF WATER AS A FOG. COOL CONTAINERS WITH FLOODING AMOUNTS OF WATER FROM AS FAR A DISTANCE AS POSSIBLE. AVOID BREATHING POISONOUS VAPORS, KEEP UPWIND. CONSIDER EVACUATION OF DOWNWIND AREA IF MATERIAL IS LEAKING.

TOXICITY

SODIUM CACODYLATE: TOXICITY DATA: 2600 MG/KG ORAL-RAT LD50; 4 MG/KG ORAL-MOUSE LD50; 1250 MG/KG SUBCUTANEOUS-MOUSE LD50; 500 MG/KG SUBCUTANEOUS-RABBIT LDLO; REPRODUCTIVE EFFECTS DATA (RTECS). CARCINOGEN STATUS: NONE. NO ADEQUATE DATA ON ORGANIC ARSENICALS WERE AVAILABLE FOR EVALUATION. LOCAL EFFECTS: IRRITANT- INHALATION, SKIN, AND EYES. ACUTE TOXICITY LEVEL: MODERATELY TOXIC BY INGESTION. TARGET EFFECTS: POISONING MAY AFFECT THE HEART, KIDNEYS, DIGESTIVE TRACT, AND SKIN.

HEALTH EFFECTS AND FIRST AID

INHALATION: SODIUM CACODYLATE: IRRITANT. **ACUTE EXPOSURE-** FORESTRY WORKERS EXPOSED TO DIMETHYLARSENIC ACID HERBICIDES HAD ELEVATED URINARY LEVELS OF ARSENIC, BUT NO CLINICAL SIGNS OF TOXICITY WERE REPORTED. IN RATS, CACODYLIC ACID IS ABSORBED MORE READILY BY INHALATION THAN INGESTION, AND MODERATE DOSES ARE LETHAL. IN PERSONS EXPOSED TO SUFFICIENT ARSENICAL DUST, THE ONSET OF ILLNESS IS USUALLY CHARACTERIZED BY DYSPNEA WITH OPPRESSION AND PAIN IN THE CHEST, FOLLOWED BY NAUSEA AND DIARRHEA. SEVERE ARSENIC POISONING CAUSES VOMITING, PROFUSE AND WATERY DIARRHEA FOLLOWED BY DEHYDRATION, ELECTROLYTE IMBALANCE, GRADUAL FALL IN BLOOD PRESSURE AND POSSIBLE DEATH WITHIN 3 TO 14 DAYS. OTHER PERSISTENT SEQUELLAE OF ARSENIC POISONING INCLUDE: GARLIC ODOR IMPARTED TO BREATH, URINE AND SWEAT, CIRRHOSIS, HYPOPLASTIC BONE MARROW, RENAL INSUFFICIENCY AND LOSS OF SENSORY AND MOTOR FUNCTIONS. **CHRONIC EXPOSURE-** EXCESSIVE INHALATION OF ARSENICAL DUSTS MAY CAUSE COUGHING, RHINITIS, PULMONARY IRRITATION, BRONCHITIS OR PNEUMONIA.
FIRST AID- REMOVE FROM EXPOSURE AREA TO FRESH AIR IMMEDIATELY. IF BREATHING HAS STOPPED, PERFORM ARTIFICIAL RESPIRATION. KEEP PERSON WARM AND AT REST. TREAT SYMPTOMATICALLY AND SUPPORTIVELY. GET MEDICAL ATTENTION IMMEDIATELY.

SKIN CONTACT: SODIUM CACODYLATE: IRRITANT. **ACUTE EXPOSURE-** DIRECT CONTACT MAY CAUSE IRRITATION, WHICH MAY BE GREATER IN THE PRESENCE OF IMPURITIES. EXCESSIVE EXPOSURE MAY RESULT IN ABSORPTION OF TOXIC AMOUNTS AND MAY PRODUCE DERMATITIS OR SKIN ERUPTIONS. **CHRONIC EXPOSURE-** REPEATED OR PROLONGED EXPOSURE TO ARSENICALS MAY PRODUCE ERYTHEMATOUS, PUSTULAR OR ULCERATIVE DERMATITIS, PERHAPS DUE TO LOCAL ACTION ON CAPILLARIES.
FIRST AID- REMOVE CONTAMINATED CLOTHING AND SHOES IMMEDIATELY. WASH AFFECTED AREA WITH SOAP OR MILD DETERGENT AND LARGE AMOUNTS OF WATER UNTIL NO EVIDENCE OF CHEMICAL REMAINS (APPROXIMATELY 15-20 MINUTES). GET MEDICAL ATTENTION IMMEDIATELY.

EYE CONTACT: SODIUM CACODYLATE: IRRITANT. **ACUTE EXPOSURE-** DUST MAY CAUSE IRRITATION. **CHRONIC EXPOSURE-** MAY CAUSE CONJUNCTIVITIS. PROLONGED EXPOSURE TO ARSENICALS HAS CAUSED ERUPTIONS OF EYELIDS, CONJUNCTIVA AND EVEN THE CORNEA.
FIRST AID- WASH EYES IMMEDIATELY WITH LARGE AMOUNTS OF WATER OR NORMAL SALINE, OCCASIONALLY LIFTING UPPER AND LOWER LIDS, UNTIL NO EVIDENCE OF CHEMICAL REMAINS (APPROXIMATELY 15-20 MINUTES). GET MEDICAL ATTENTION IMMEDIATELY.

INGESTION: SODIUM CACODYLATE: **ACUTE EXPOSURE-** METHYLATED PENTAVALENT ARSENICALS ARE CONSIDERABLY LESS TOXIC THAN TRIVALENT INORGANIC ARSENICALS. IN FACT, METHYLATION IS THE PRINCIPLE MECHANISM OF DETOXIFICATION AND ELIMINATION OF INORGANIC ARSENICAL IN MAMMALS. HOWEVER, ARSENIC MAY BE RELEASED SLOWLY, PERHAPS DUE TO GASTRIC PH OF INTESTINAL BACTERIAL ACTION, TO PRODUCE DELAYED ARSENIC POISONING. ARSENIC POISONING CAUSES DILATION AND INCREASED PERMEABILITY OF CAPILLARIES, ESPECIALLY IN THE INTESTINAL TRACT REGARDLESS OF THE ROUTE OF EXPOSURE. LOCAL ACTION ON CAPILLARIES CAN CAUSE CONGESTION AND STASIS, THROMBOSIS, ISCHEMIA AND NECROSIS. SEVERE ARSENIC POISONING MAY CAUSE VOMITING, PROFUSE AND WATERY DIARRHEA FOLLOWED BY DEHYDRATION, ELECTROLYTE IMBALANCE, GRADUALLY FALLING BLOOD PRESSURE AND POSSIBLE DEATH WITHIN 3 TO 14 DAYS. IF THE ACUTE PHASE IS SURVIVED, SKIN ERUPTIONS MAY OCCUR AND PROGRESS TO EXFOLIATIVE DERMATITIS. DERMATITIS MAY BE PROMINENT ON THE PALMS AND SOLES. WHITE TRANSVERSE BANDS IN THE NAILS FREQUENTLY APPEAR IN ABOUT 6 WEEKS AND ACCOMPANY POLYNEUROPATHY, WHICH OFTEN APPEARS IN 1 TO 3 WEEKS AFTER EXPOSURE. POLYNEUROPATHY INVOLVES PARATHESIS, PAIN, BURNING AND TENDERNESS OF AFFECTED LIMBS. PERIPHERAL CIRCULATORY DIFFICULTY CHARACTERIZED BY BLANCHING OR FLUSHING SKIN MAY OCCUR, ESPECIALLY IN THE FINGERS. OTHER PERSISTENT SEQUELLAE OF ARSENIC POISONING INCLUDE: A GARLIC ODOR IMPARTED TO BREATH, URINE, AND SWEAT, CIRRHOSIS, HYPOPLASTIC BONE MARROW, RENAL INSUFFICIENCY AND LOSS OF SENSORY AND MOTOR FUNCTIONS. IN RATS, THE AVERAGE LETHAL DOSE WAS MODERATE, HOWEVER IM MICE THE AVERAGE LETHAL DOSE WAS MUCH SMALLER. **CHRONIC EXPOSURE-** REPEATED EXPOSURE TO LOW LEVELS OF ARSENIC MAY PRODUCE INCREASED TOLERANCE FOR ARSENIC. ARSENIC COMPOUNDS ACCUMULATE IN THE SKIN, HAIR AND NAILS. SIGNS OF CHRONIC ARSENIC POISONING INCLUDE LOSS OF APPETITE, WEIGHT LOSS, WEAKNESS, NAUSEA, ALTERNATING DIARRHEA AND CONSTIPATION, COLIC, PERIPHERAL NEUROPATHY, DERMATITIS, DYSCHROMIA, HYPERKERATOSIS OF PLANTAR SURFACES, ALOPECIA, GIDDINESS AND HEADACHE PROLONGED EXPOSURE MAY CAUSE GRADUAL MENTAL AND PHYSICAL DETERIORATION AND A STATE OF CACHEXIA. POLYNEUROPATHY, SIMILAR TO ACUTE EXPOSURE, MAY OCCUR, AS WELL AS DISTURBANCES OF SIGHT, TASTE, SMELL AND BLADDER FUNCTION. EXPOSURE TO ARSENIC COMPOUNDS HAS BEEN ASSOCIATED WITH INCREASED INCIDENCE OF SKIN AND OTHER CANCERS.
FIRST AID- REMOVE BY GASTRIC LAVAGE OR EMESIS. FOLLOW WITH A SALINE CATHARTIC. MAINTAIN BLOOD PRESSURE, AIRWAY, AND GIVE OXYGEN IF RESPIRATION IS DEPRESSED. DO NOT PERFORM GASTRIC LAVAGE OR EMESIS IF VICTIM IS UNCONSCIOUS. GET MEDICAL ATTENTION IMMEDIATELY. (DREISBACH, HANDBOOK OF POISONING, 12TH ED.) ADMINISTRATION OF GASTRIC LAVAGE OR OXYGEN SHOULD BE PERFORMED BY QUALIFIED MEDICAL PERSONNEL.
ANTIDOTE: THE FOLLOWING ANTIDOTE HAS BEEN RECOMMENDED. HOWEVER, THE DECISION AS TO WHETHER THE SEVERITY OF POISONING REQUIRES ADMINISTRATION OF ANY ANTIDOTE AND ACTUAL DOSE REQUIRED SHOULD BE MADE BY QUALIFIED MEDICAL PERSONNEL.
ARSENIC POISONING: GIVE DIMERCAPROL, 3 MG/KG (OR 0.3 ML/KG) EVERY 4 HOURS FOR 2 DAYS AND THEN 2 MG/KG EVERY 2 HOURS FOR A TOTAL OF 10 DAYS. DIMERCAPROL IS AVAILABLE AS A 10% SOLUTION IN OIL FOR INTRAMUSCULAR ADMINISTRATION. NEXT, GIVE PENICILLAMINE, UP TO 100 MG/KG/DAY (MAXIMUM 1 G/DAY) DIVIDED INTO 4 DOSES FOR NO LONGER THAN 1 WEEK. IF A LONGER ADMINISTRATION PERIOD IS WARRANTED, DOSAGE SHOULD NOT EXCEED 40 MG/KG/DAY. GIVE THE DRUG ORALLY HALF AN HOUR BEFORE MEALS. DISCONTINUE ANTIDOTE WHEN URINE ARSENIC LEVEL FALLS BELOW 50 UG/24 HR. (DREISBACH, HANDBOOK OF POISONING, 12TH ED.). ANITDOTE SHOULD BE ADMINISTERED BY QUALIFIED MEDICAL PERSONNEL.

REACTIVITY

REACTIVITY: STABLE UNDER NORMAL TEMPERATURES AND PRESSURES.
INCOMPATIBILITIES: SODIUM CACODYLATE: ACIDS: REACTS TO RELEASE EXTREMELY TOXIC DIMETHYL ARSINE. ACTIVE METALS (FE, AL, ZN): WHEN IN AQUEOUS SOLUTION REACTS TO RELEASE TOXIC ARSENIC FUMES. STRONG OXIDIZERS: REACTS.

DECOMPOSITION: THERMAL DECOMPOSITION PRODUCTS MAY INCLUDE TOXIC OXIDES OF ARSENIC AND CARBON.
POLYMERIZATION: HAZARDOUS POLYMERIZATION HAS NOT BEEN REPORTED TO OCCUR UNDER NORMAL TEMPERATURES AND PRESSURES.

STORAGE AND DISPOSAL

OBSERVE ALL FEDERAL, STATE AND LOCAL REGULATIONS WHEN STORING OR DISPOSING OF THIS SUBSTANCE. FOR ASSISTANCE, CONTACT THE DISTRICT DIRECTOR OF THE ENVIRONMENTAL PROTECTION AGENCY.

****STORAGE****

THRESHOLD PLANNING QUANTITY (TPQ): THE SUPERFUND AMENDMENTS AND REAUTHORIZATION ACT (SARA) SECTION 302 REQUIRES THAT EACH FACILITY WHERE ANY EXTREMELY HAZARDOUS SUBSTANCE IS PRESENT IN A QUANTITY EQUAL TO OR GREATER THAN THE TPQ ESTABLISHED FOR THAT SUBSTANCE NOTIFY THE STATE EMERGENCY RESPONSE COMMISSION FOR THE STATE IN WHICH IT IS LOCATED. SECTION 303 OF SARA REQUIRES THESE FACILITIES TO PARTICIPATE IN LOCAL EMERGENCY RESPONSE PLANNING (40 CFR 355.30).

CONDITIONS TO AVOID

MAY BURN BUT DOES NOT IGNITE READILY.

SPILL AND LEAK PROCEDURES

OCCUPATIONAL SPILL: DO NOT TOUCH SPILLED MATERIAL. STOP LEAK IF YOU CAN DO IT WITHOUT RISK. FOR SMALL SPILLS, TAKE UP WITH SAND OR OTHER ABSORBENT MATERIAL AND PLACE INTO CONTAINERS FOR LATER DISPOSAL. FOR SMALL DRY SPILLS, WITH A CLEAN SHOVEL PLACE MATERIAL INTO CLEAN, DRY CONTAINER AND COVER. MOVE CONTAINERS FROM SPILL AREA. FOR LARGER SPILLS, DIKE FAR AHEAD OF SPILL FOR LATER DISPOSAL. KEEP UNNECESSARY PEOPLE AWAY. ISOLATE HAZARD AREA AND DENY ENTRY.
REPORTABLE QUANTITY (RQ): 1 POUND THE SUPERFUND AMENDMENTS AND REAUTHORIZATION ACT (SARA) SECTION 304 REQUIRES THAT A RELEASE EQUAL TO OR GREATER THAN THE REPORTABLE QUANTITY FOR THIS SUBSTANCE BE IMMEDIATELY REPORTED TO THE LOCAL EMERGENCY PLANNING COMMITTEE AND THE STATE EMERGENCY RESPONSE COMMISSION (40 CFR 355.40). IF THE RELEASE OF THIS SUBSTANCE IS REPORTABLE UNDER CERCLA SECTION 103, THE NATIONAL RESPONSE CENTER MUST BE NOTIFIED IMMEDIATELY AT (800) 424-8802 OR (202) 426-2675 IN THE METROPOLITAN WASHINGTON, D.C. AREA (40 CFR 302.6).

PROTECTIVE EQUIPMENT

VENTILATION: PROVIDE LOCAL EXHAUST VENTILATION AND/OR GENERAL DILUTION VENTILATION TO MEET PUBLISHED EXPOSURE LIMITS.
RESPIRATOR: THE FOLLOWING RESPIRATORS ARE RECOMMENDED BASED ON INFORMATION FOUND IN THE PHYSICAL DATA, TOXICITY AND HEALTH EFFECTS SECTIONS. THEY ARE RANKED IN ORDER FROM MINIMUM TO MAXIMUM RESPIRATORY PROTECTION. THE SPECIFIC RESPIRATOR SELECTED MUST BE BASED ON CONTAMINATION LEVELS FOUND IN THE WORK PLACE, MUST NOT EXCEED THE WORKING LIMITS OF THE RESPIRATOR AND BE JOINTLY APPROVED BY THE NATIONAL INSTITUTE FOR OCCUPATIONAL SAFETY AND HEALTH AND THE MINE SAFETY AND HEALTH ADMINISTRATION (NIOSH-MSHA). AT ANY DETECTABLE CONCENTRATION:
SELF-CONTAINED BREATHING APPARATUS WITH FULL FACEPIECE OPERATED IN PRESSURE-DEMAND OR OTHER POSITIVE PRESSURE MODE. SUPPLIED-AIR RESPIRATOR WITH FULL FACEPIECE OPERATED IN PRESSURE-DEMAND OR OTHER POSITIVE PRESSURE MODE IN COMBINATION WITH AN AUXILIARY SELF-CONTAINED BREATHING APPARATUS OPERATED IN PRESSURE-DEMAND OR OTHER POSITIVE PRESSURE MODE.
ESCAPE- AIR-PURIFYING FULL FACEPIECE RESPIRATOR (GAS MASK) WITH A CHIN-STYLE OR FRONT- OR BACK-MOUNTED ACID GAS CANISTER HAVING A HIGH-EFFICIENCY PARTICULATE FILTER. ESCAPE-TYPE SELF-CONTAINED BREATHING APPARATUS.
FOR FIREFIGHTING AND OTHER IMMEDIATELY DANGEROUS TO LIFE OR HEALTH CONDITIONS:
SELF-CONTAINED BREATHING APPARATUS WITH FULL FACEPIECE OPERATED IN PRESSURE-DEMAND OR OTHER POSITIVE PRESSURE MODE.
SUPPLIED-AIR RESPIRATOR WITH FULL FACEPIECE AND OPERATED IN PRESSURE-DEMAND OR OTHER POSITIVE PRESSURE MODE IN COMBINATION WITH AN AUXILIARY SELF-CONTAINED BREATHING APPARATUS OPERATED IN PRESSURE-DEMAND OR OTHER POSITIVE PRESSURE MODE.
CLOTHING: EMPLOYEE MUST WEAR APPROPRIATE PROTECTIVE (IMPERVIOUS) CLOTHING AND EQUIPMENT TO PREVENT REPEATED OR PROLONGED SKIN CONTACT WITH THIS SUBSTANCE.
GLOVES: EMPLOYEE MUST WEAR APPROPRIATE PROTECTIVE GLOVES TO PREVENT CONTACT WITH THIS SUBSTANCE.
EYE PROTECTION: EMPLOYEE MUST WEAR SPLASH-PROOF OR DUST-RESISTANT SAFETY GOGGLES TO PREVENT EYE CONTACT WITH THIS SUBSTANCE.
EMERGENCY EYE WASH: WHERE THERE IS ANY POSSIBILITY THAT AN EMPLOYEE'S EYES MAY BE EXPOSED TO THIS SUBSTANCE, THE EMPLOYER SHOULD PROVIDE AN EYE WASH FOUNTAIN WITHIN THE IMMEDIATE WORK AREA FOR EMERGENCY USE.

AUTHORIZED BY- OCCUPATIONAL HEALTH SERVICES, INC.
CREATION DATE: 10/05/89 ***REVISION DATE:*** 05/04/90

MATERIAL SAFETY DATA SHEET

OCCUPATIONAL HEALTH SERVICES, INC.
AGRICULTURE AND PESTICIDE DIVISION
450 SEVENTH AVENUE, SUITE 2407
NEW YORK, NEW YORK 10123
1-800-445-MSDS OR (212) 967-1100

EMERGENCY CONTACT:
JOHN S. BRANSFORD, JR. (615) 292-1180

SUBSTANCE IDENTIFICATION

CAS-NUMBER 497-19-8
SUBSTANCE: **SODIUM CARBONATE**
TRADE NAMES/SYNONYMS: CARBONIC ACID, DISODIUM SALT; BISODIUM CARBONATE; CALCINED SODA; CARBONIC ACID SODIUM SALT; CARBONIC ACID SODIUM SALT (1:2); DISODIUM CARBONATE; NA-X; SODA; SODA ASH; PST21080
CHEMICAL FAMILY: INORGANIC SALT
MOLECULAR FORMULA: C-O3.2NA
MOLECULAR WEIGHT: 105.99
CERCLA RATINGS (SCALE 0-3): HEALTH=2 FIRE=0 REACTIVITY=1 PERSISTENCE=0
NFPA RATINGS (SCALE 0-4): HEALTH=2 FIRE=0 REACTIVITY=1

COMPONENTS AND CONTAMINANTS

COMPONENT: SODIUM CARBONATE ***PERCENT:*** 100
CAS# 497-19-8
OTHER CONTAMINANTS: NONE
EXPOSURE LIMITS: NO OCCUPATIONAL EXPOSURE LIMITS ESTABLISHED BY OSHA, ACGIH, OR NIOSH.

PHYSICAL DATA

DESCRIPTION: ODORLESS, COLORLESS TO WHITE, HYGROSCOPIC CRYSTALLINE POWDER, SMALL CRYSTALS, OR GRANULES WITH AN ALKALINE TASTE.
BOILINGPOINT: DECOMPOSES
MELTING POINT: 1564 F (851 C) ***SPECIFIC GRAVITY:*** 2.536
PH: 11.5 @ 1% AQ SOLN ***SOLUBILITY IN WATER:*** 7.1% @ 0 C
SOLVENT SOLUBILITY: SOLUBLE IN GLYCEROL; INSOLUBLE IN ALCOHOL, ACETONE

FIRE AND EXPLOSION DATA

FIRE AND EXPLOSION HAZARD: NEGLIGIBLE FIRE HAZARD WHEN EXPOSED TO HEAT OR FLAME.
FIREFIGHTING MEDIA: DRY CHEMICAL, CARBON DIOXIDE, HALON, WATER SPRAY OR STANDARD FOAM (1987 EMERGENCY RESPONSE GUIDEBOOK, DOT P 5800.4). FOR LARGER FIRES, USE WATER SPRAY, FOG OR STANDARD FOAM (1987 EMERGENCY RESPONSE GUIDEBOOK, DOT P 5800.4).
FIREFIGHTING: NO ACUTE HAZARD. MOVE CONTAINER FROM FIRE AREA IF POSSIBLE. AVOID BREATHING VAPORS OR DUSTS; KEEP UPWIND.

TOXICITY

SODIUM CARBONATE: IRRITATION DATA: ANHYDROUS: 500 MG/24 HOURS SKIN-RABBIT MILD; 100 MG/24 HOURS EYE-RABBIT MODERATE; 100 MG/30 SECONDS RINSED EYE-RABBIT MILD. TOXICITY DATA: ANHYDROUS: 2300 MG/M3/2 HOURS INHALATION-RAT LC50; 1200 MG/M3/2 HOURS INHALATION-MOUSE LC50; 800 MG/M3/2 HOURS INHALATION-GUINEA PIG LC50; 4090 MG/KG ORAL-RAT LD50; 2210 MG/KG SUBCUTANEOUS-MOUSE LD50; 117 MG/KG INTRAPERITONEAL-MOUSE LD50; REPRODUCTIVE EFFECTS DATA (RTECS). MONOHYDRATE: NO DATA AVAILABLE. DECAHYDRATE: NO DATA AVAILABLE. CARCINOGEN STATUS: NONE. LOCAL EFFECTS: CORROSIVE- INGESTION; IRRITANT- INHALATION, SKIN, EYE. ACUTE TOXICITY LEVEL: TOXIC BY INHALATION; MODERATELY TOXIC BY INGESTION. TARGET EFFECTS: NO DATA AVAILABLE.

HEALTH EFFECTS AND FIRST AID

INHALATION: SODIUM CARBONATE: IRRITANT/TOXIC. **ACUTE EXPOSURE**- DUSTS OR VAPORS MAY CAUSE MUCOUS MEMBRANE IRRITATION WITH COUGHING, SHORTNESS OF BREATH, AND GASTROINTESTINAL CHANGES. EXPOSURE TO 1200

MG/M3/2 HOURS WAS THE LETHAL CONCENTRATION IN MICE TESTED. **CHRONIC EXPOSURE-** REPEATED OR PROLONGED EXPOSURE MAY CAUSE PERFORATION OF THE NASAL SEPTUM. EXPOSURE TO A CONCENTRATION OF 10 TO 20 MG/M3 OF A 2% AQUEOUS SOLUTION OF SODIUM CARBONATE FOR 4 HOURS/DAY, 5 DAYS/WEEK, FOR 3 AND A HALF MONTHS CAUSED NO PRONOUNCED EFFECTS IN MALE MICE. HOWEVER, AT HIGHER CONCENTRATIONS, A DECREASE IN WEIGHT GAIN WAS RECORDED. HISTOLOGICAL EXAMINATIONS SHOWED THICKENING OF THE INTRA-ALVEOLAR WALLS, HYPEREMIA, LYMPHOID INFILTRATION, AND DESQUAMATION OF THE LUNGS.

FIRST AID- REMOVE FROM EXPOSURE AREA TO FRESH AIR IMMEDIATELY. IF BREATHING HAS STOPPED, PERFORM ARTIFICIAL RESPIRATION. KEEP PERSON WARM AND AT REST. TREAT SYMPTOMATICALLY AND SUPPORTIVELY. GET MEDICAL ATTENTION IMMEDIATELY.

SKIN CONTACT: SODIUM CARBONATE: IRRITANT. **ACUTE EXPOSURE-** CONTACT MAY CAUSE IRRITATION AND REDNESS. CONCENTRATED SOLUTIONS MAY CAUSE ERYTHEMA, BLISTERING AND SKIN NECROSIS. 500 MG APPLIED TO RABBIT SKIN FOR 24 HOURS PRODUCED MILD IRRITATION. A SINGLE APPLICATION OF A 50% WEIGHT BY VOLUME AQUEOUS SOLUTION OF SODIUM CARBONATE TO INTACT SKIN OF RABBITS, GUINEA PIGS, AND HUMANS SHOWED NO ERYTHEMA, EDEMA, OR CORROSION. HOWEVER, WHEN APPLIED TO ABRADED SKIN, MODERATE ERYTHEMA AND EDEMA RESULTED IN RABBITS AND HUMANS, WITH NEGLIGIBLE EFFECTS IN GUINEA PIGS. IN ONE-THIRD OF THE HUMAN VOLUNTEERS, TISSUE DESTRUCTION WAS SEEN AT THE ABRADED SITES. **CHRONIC EXPOSURE-** REPEATED OR PROLONGED EXPOSURE MAY CAUSE DERMATITIS AND POSSIBLE "SODA ULCERS" OF THE HANDS AND WRISTS. SENSITIVITY REACTIONS MAY OCCUR FROM REPEATED EXPOSURES.

FIRST AID- REMOVE CONTAMINATED CLOTHING AND SHOES IMMEDIATELY. WASH AFFECTED AREA WITH SOAP OR MILD DETERGENT AND LARGE AMOUNTS OF WATER UNTIL NO EVIDENCE OF CHEMICAL REMAINS (APPROXIMATELY 15-20 MINUTES). GET MEDICAL ATTENTION IMMEDIATELY.

EYE CONTACT: SODIUM CARBONATE: IRRITANT. **ACUTE EXPOSURE-** CONTACT WITH DUSTS MAY CAUSE SEVERE IRRITATION WITH REDNESS, PAIN, AND BLURRED VISION. APPLICATION OF 100 MG TO RABBIT EYES AND THEN RINSED CAUSED ONLY MILD IRRITATION. IN SOLUTION, SODIUM CARBONATE IS SUFFICIENTLY ALKALINE TO DAMAGE THE CORNEAL EPITHELIUM, BUT IF PROMPTLY WASHED FROM THE EYES WITH WATER IT IS UNLIKELY TO CAUSE PERMANENT DAMAGE TO THE CORNEAL STROMA. AN APPLICATION OF SEVERAL DROPS OF A 10% SOLUTION (PH 10.7) TO A RABBIT'S EYE FOLLOWED BY IRRIGATION WITH WATER FOR 30 SECONDS CAUSED NO DETECTABLE INJURY. CONCENTRATED SOLUTIONS MAY CAUSE NECROSIS OF THE EYE. **CHRONIC EXPOSURE-** DEPENDING UPON CONCENTRATION AND DURATION, SYMPTOMS MAY BE THOSE AS FOR ACUTE EXPOSURE.

FIRST AID- WASH EYES IMMEDIATELY WITH LARGE AMOUNTS OF WATER, OCCASIONALLY LIFTING UPPER AND LOWER LIDS, UNTIL NO EVIDENCE OF CHEMICAL REMAINS (AT LEAST 15-20 MINUTES). CONTINUE IRRIGATING WITH NORMAL SALINE UNTIL THE PH HAS RETURNED TO NORMAL (30-60 MINUTES). COVER WITH STERILE BANDAGES. GET MEDICAL ATTENTION IMMEDIATELY.

INGESTION: SODIUM CARBONATE: CORROSIVE. **ACUTE EXPOSURE-** INGESTION MAY CAUSE CORROSION OF THE GASTRIC MUCOSA WITH SORE THROAT AND PAIN. IT MAY CAUSE GASTROINTESTINAL DISTURBANCES SUCH AS NAUSEA, VOMITING, ABDOMINAL PAIN, AND DIARRHEA. DEATH IS GENERALLY DUE TO CIRCULATORY COLLAPSE. THE ESTIMATED LETHAL HUMAN DOSE IS APPROXIMATELY 30 GRAMS. **CHRONIC EXPOSURE-** SODIUM CARBONATE IS USED AS A GENERAL PURPOSE FOOD ADDITIVE. NO ADVERSE EFFECTS HAVE BEEN REPORTED FROM EXPOSURE TO SMALL AMOUNTS.

FIRST AID- DILUTE THE ALKALI BY GIVING WATER OR MILK IMMEDIATELY AND ALLOW VOMITING TO OCCUR. AVOID GASTRIC LAVAGE OR EMETICS. ESOPHAGOSCOPY IS THE ONLY WAY TO EXCLUDE THE POSSIBLITY OF CORROSION IN THE UPPER GASTROINTESTINAL TRACT; IF CORROSION IS SUSPECTED, ESOPHAGOSCOPY SHOULD USUALLY BE PERFORMED WITHIN 24 HOURS (DREISBACH, HANDBOOK OF POISONING, 12TH ED.). MAINTAIN AIRWAY AND TREAT SHOCK. IF VOMITING OCCURS, KEEP HEAD BELOW HIPS TO HELP PREVENT ASPIRATION. GET MEDICAL ATTENTION IMMEDIATELY.

ANTIDOTE: NO SPECIFIC ANTIDOTE. TREAT SYMPTOMATICALLY AND SUPPORTIVELY.

REACTIVITY

REACTIVITY: REACTS WITH WATER WITH THE EVOLUTION OF HEAT.

INCOMPATIBILITIES: SODIUM CARBONATE: ACIDS (STRONG): MAY REACT VIOLENTLY. ALUMINUM (HOT): EXPLOSIVE REACTION. AMMONIA + SILVER NITRATE: EXPLOSIVE REACTION UPON HEATING. AN AROMATIC AMINE + A CHLORONITRO COMPOUND: EXOTHERMIC REACTION. 2,4-DINITROTOLUENE: INCREASES EXPLOSIVENESS. FLUORINE: VIOLENT IGNITION. LITHIUM (BURNING): RELEASES REACTIVE SODIUM. PHOSPHORUS PENTOXIDE: HIGHLY EXOTHERMIC REACTION. SODIUM SULFIDE (HOT): EXPLOSIVE REACTION ON CONTACT WITH WATER. SULFURIC ACID: VIOLENT ERUPTION. 2,4,6-TRINITROTOLUENE: REDUCED EXPLOSION TEMPERATURE. ZINC: CORROSIVE.

DECOMPOSITION: THERMAL DECOMPOSITION PRODUCTS MAY INCLUDE TOXIC SODIUM OXIDE AND TOXIC OXIDES OF CARBON.

POLYMERIZATION: HAZARDOUS POLYMERIZATION HAS NOT BEEN REPORTED TO OCCUR UNDER NORMAL TEMPERATURES AND PRESSURES.

STORAGE AND DISPOSAL

OBSERVE ALL FEDERAL, STATE AND LOCAL REGULATIONS WHEN STORING OR DISPOSING OF THIS SUBSTANCE.

****STORAGE****

STORE AWAY FROM INCOMPATIBLE SUBSTANCES.

CONDITIONS TO AVOID

NONE REPORTED.

SPILL AND LEAK PROCEDURES

OCCUPATIONAL SPILL: SWEEP UP AND PLACE IN SUITABLE (FIBERBOARD) CONTAINERS FOR RECLAMATION OR LATER DISPOSAL.

PROTECTIVE EQUIPMENT

VENTILATION: PROVIDE LOCAL EXHAUST OR GENERAL DILUTION VENTILATION SYSTEM.

RESPIRATOR: THE FOLLOWING RESPIRATORS ARE RECOMMENDED BASED ON INFORMATION FOUND IN THE PHYSICAL DATA, TOXICITY AND HEALTH EFFECTS SECTIONS. THEY ARE RANKED IN ORDER FROM MINIMUM TO MAXIMUM RESPIRATORY PROTECTION. THE SPECIFIC RESPIRATOR SELECTED MUST BE BASED ON CONTAMINATION LEVELS FOUND IN THE WORK PLACE, MUST NOT EXCEED THE WORKING LIMITS OF THE RESPIRATOR AND BE JOINTLY APPROVED BY THE NATIONAL INSTITUTE FOR OCCUPATIONAL SAFETY AND HEALTH AND THE MINE SAFETY AND HEALTH ADMINISTRATION (NIOSH-MSHA).

DUST AND MIST RESPIRATOR WITH A FULL FACEPIECE.

AIR-PURIFYING FULL FACEPIECE RESPIRATOR WITH A HIGH-EFFICIENCY PARTICULATE FILTER.

POWERED AIR-PURIFYING RESPIRATOR WITH A TIGHT-FITTING FACEPIECE AND HIGH-EFFICIENCY PARTICULATE FILTER.

TYPE 'C' SUPPLIED-AIR RESPIRATOR WITH A FULL FACEPIECE OPERATED IN PRESSURE-DEMAND OR OTHER POSITIVE PRESSURE MODE OR WITH A FULL FACEPIECE, HELMET OR HOOD OPERATED IN CONTINUOUS-FLOW MODE.

SELF-CONTAINED BREATHING APPARATUS WITH A FULL FACEPIECE OPERATED IN PRESSURE-DEMAND OR OTHER POSITIVE PRESSURE MODE.

FOR FIREFIGHTING AND OTHER IMMEDIATELY DANGEROUS TO LIFE OR HEALTH CONDITIONS:

SELF-CONTAINED BREATHING APPARATUS WITH FULL FACEPIECE OPERATED IN PRESSURE-DEMAND OR OTHER POSITIVE PRESSURE MODE.

SUPPLIED-AIR RESPIRATOR WITH FULL FACEPIECE AND OPERATED IN PRESSURE-DEMAND OR OTHER POSITIVE PRESSURE MODE IN COMBINATION WITH AN AUXILIARY SELF-CONTAINED BREATHING APPARATUS OPERATED IN PRESSURE-DEMAND OR OTHER POSITIVE PRESSURE MODE.

CLOTHING: EMPLOYEE MUST WEAR APPROPRIATE PROTECTIVE (IMPERVIOUS) CLOTHING AND EQUIPMENT TO PREVENT REPEATED OR PROLONGED SKIN CONTACT WITH THIS SUBSTANCE.

GLOVES: EMPLOYEE MUST WEAR APPROPRIATE PROTECTIVE GLOVES TO PREVENT CONTACT WITH THIS SUBSTANCE.

EYE PROTECTION: EMPLOYEE MUST WEAR SPLASH-PROOF OR DUST-RESISTANT SAFETY GOGGLES TO PREVENT CONTACT WITH THIS SUBSTANCE.

EMERGENCY WASH FACILITIES: WHERE THERE IS ANY POSSIBILITY THAT AN EMPLOYEE'S EYES AND/OR SKIN MAY BE EXPOSED TO THIS SUBSTANCE, THE EMPLOYER SHOULD PROVIDE AN EYE WASH FOUNTAIN AND QUICK DRENCH SHOWER WITHIN THE IMMEDIATE WORK AREA FOR EMERGENCY USE.

AUTHORIZED BY- OCCUPATIONAL HEALTH SERVICES, INC.
CREATION DATE: 11/17/89 ***REVISION DATE:*** 05/30/90

MATERIAL SAFETY DATA SHEET

OCCUPATIONAL HEALTH SERVICES, INC.
AGRICULTURE AND PESTICIDE DIVISION
450 SEVENTH AVENUE, SUITE 2407

EMERGENCY CONTACT:
JOHN S. BRANSFORD, JR. (615) 292-1180

NEW YORK, NEW YORK 10123
1-800-445-MSDS OR (212) 967-1100

SUBSTANCE IDENTIFICATION

CAS-NUMBER 7775-09-9

***SUBSTANCE:* SODIUM CHLORATE**

TRADE NAMES/SYNONYMS: CHLORATE OF SODA; SODIUM CHLORATE (NACLO3); CHLORIC ACID, SODIUM SALT; ATLACIDE; SHED-A-LEAF; ASEX; OXYCIL; TRAVEX; SODA CHLORATE; CHLORATE SALT OF SODIUM; UN 1495; S-268; STCC 4918723; CLNAO3; PST21100

CHEMICAL FAMILY: INORGANIC SALT

MOLECULAR FORMULA: NA-CL-O3

MOLECULAR WEIGHT: 106.44

CERCLA RATINGS (SCALE 0-3): HEALTH=3 FIRE=0 REACTIVITY=2 PERSISTENCE=0

NFPA RATINGS (SCALE 0-4): HEALTH=0 FIRE=0 REACTIVITY=2

COMPONENTS AND CONTAMINANTS

COMPONENT: SODIUM CHLORATE ***PERCENT:*** 100.0
CAS# 7775-09-9

OTHER CONTAMINANTS: NONE

EXPOSURE LIMITS: NO OCCUPATIONAL EXPOSURE LIMITS ESTABLISHED BY OSHA, ACGIH, OR NIOSH.

PHYSICAL DATA

DESCRIPTION: ODORLESS, COLORLESS, DELIQUESCENT CRYSTALS OR WHITE GRANULES WITH A COOLING SALINE TASTE. ***MELTING POINT:*** 478-502 F (248-261 C)

SPECIFIC GRAVITY: 2.490 @ 15 C ***PH:*** 5.0-7.0 @ 5% SOLN.

SOLUBILITY IN WATER: 79% @ 0 C

SOLVENT SOLUBILITY: SOLUBLE IN ALCOHOLS, LIQUID AMMONIA, GLYCEROL.

FIRE AND EXPLOSION DATA

FIRE AND EXPLOSION HAZARD: NEGLIGIBLE FIRE HAZARD WHEN EXPOSED TO HEAT OR FLAME.
OXIDIZER: OXIDIZERS DECOMPOSE, ESPECIALLY WHEN HEATED, TO YIELD OXYGEN OR OTHER GASES WHICH WILL INCREASE THE BURNING RATE OF COMBUSTIBLE MATTER. CONTACT WITH EASILY OXIDIZABLE, ORGANIC, OR OTHER COMBUSTIBLE MATERIALS MAY RESULT IN IGNITION, VIOLENT COMBUSTION OR EXPLOSION.

FIREFIGHTING MEDIA: DRY CHEMICAL, CARBON DIOXIDE, HALON OR WATER SPRAY (1987 EMERGENCY RESPONSE GUIDEBOOK, DOT P 5800.4).
FOR LARGER FIRES, USE WATER SPRAY OR FOG (1987 EMERGENCY RESPONSE GUIDEBOOK, DOT P 5800.4).

FIREFIGHTING: MOVE CONTAINERS FROM FIRE AREA IF POSSIBLE. COOL CONTAINERS EXPOSED TO FLAMES WITH WATER FROM SIDE UNTIL WELL AFTER FIRE IS OUT. STAY AWAY FROM STORAGE TANK ENDS. FOR MASSIVE FIRE IN STORAGE AREA, USE UNMANNED HOSE HOLDER OR MONITOR NOZZLES; ELSE WITHDRAW FROM AREA AND LET FIRE BURN (1987 EMERGENCY RESPONSE GUIDEBOOK, DOT P 5800.4, GUIDE PAGE 35)
FLOOD WITH WATER. COOL CONTAINERS WITH FLOODING QUANTITIES OF WATER, APPLY FROM AS FAR A DISTANCE AS POSSIBLE. EVACUATE TO A RADIUS OF 1500 FEET FOR UNCONTROLLABLE FIRES.

TRANSPORTATION DATA

DEPARTMENT OF TRANSPORTATION HAZARD CLASSIFICATION 49 CFR 172.101: OXIDIZER
DEPARTMENT OF TRANSPORTATION LABELING REQUIREMENTS 49 CFR 172.101 AND SUBPART E: OXIDIZER
DEPARTMENT OF TRANSPORTATION PACKAGING REQUIREMENTS: 49 CFR 173.163 EXCEPTIONS: 49 CFR 173.153

TOXICITY

SODIUM CHLORATE: IRRITATION DATA: 500 MG/24 HOURS SKIN-RABBIT MILD; 10 MG EYE-RABBIT MILD. TOXICITY DATA: 1200 MG/KG ORAL-RAT LD50; 700 MG/KG ORAL-DOG LDLO; 800 MG/KG ORAL-WOMAN TDLO; 1350 MG/KG ORAL-CAT LDLO; 7200 MG/KG ORAL-RABBIT LD50; 8350 MG/KG ORAL-MOUSE LD50; 596 MG/KG INTRAPERITONEAL-MOUSE LD50; 214 MG/KG UNREPORTED-HUMAN LDLO; 185 MG/KG UNREPORTED-CHILD LD50; MUTAGENIC DATA (RTECS). CARCINOGEN STATUS: NONE. ACUTE TOXICITY LEVEL: MODERATELY TOXIC BY INGESTION. TARGET EFFECTS: METHEMOGLOBIN FORMER; NEPHROTOXIN. POISONING MAY AFFECT THE CENTRAL NERVOUS SYSTEM.

HEALTH EFFECTS AND FIRST AID

INHALATION: SODIUM CHLORATE: METHEMOGLOBIN FORMER/NEPHROTOXIN. **ACUTE EXPOSURE-** INHALATION MAY CAUSE MUCOUS MEMBRANE IRRITATION WITH SORE THROAT, COUGHING, HEADACHE, DIZZINESS, FAINTNESS AND BLUISH SKIN. SYSTEMIC POISONING MAY OCCUR AS DETAILED IN ACUTE INGESTION. **CHRONIC EXPOSURE-** PROLONGED EXPOSURE MAY CAUSE MUCOUS MEMBRANE IRRITATION.

FIRST AID- REMOVE FROM EXPOSURE AREA TO FRESH AIR IMMEDIATELY. IF BREATHING HAS STOPPED, PERFORM ARTIFICIAL RESPIRATION. KEEP PERSON WARM AND AT REST. TREAT SYMPTOMATICALLY AND SUPPORTIVELY. GET MEDICAL ATTENTION IMMEDIATELY.

SKIN CONTACT: SODIUM CHLORATE: **ACUTE EXPOSURE-** CONTACT MAY CAUSE IRRITATION. APPLICATION TO RABBIT SKIN PRODUCED MILD IRRITATION. **CHRONIC EXPOSURE-** REPEATED OR PROLONGED CONTACT MAY CAUSE IRRITATION.

FIRST AID- REMOVE CONTAMINATED CLOTHING AND SHOES IMMEDIATELY. WASH AFFECTED AREA WITH SOAP OR MILD DETERGENT AND LARGE AMOUNTS OF WATER UNTIL NO EVIDENCE OF CHEMICAL REMAINS (APPROXIMATELY 15-20 MINUTES). GET MEDICAL ATTENTION IMMEDIATELY.

EYE CONTACT: SODIUM CHLORATE: **ACUTE EXPOSURE-** CONTACT MAY CAUSE IRRITATION. APPLICATION TO RABBIT EYES PRODUCED MILD IRRITATION. **CHRONIC EXPOSURE-** REPEATED OR PROLONGED CONTACT MAY CAUSE IRRITATION AND CONJUNCTIVITIS.

FIRST AID- WASH EYES IMMEDIATELY WITH LARGE AMOUNTS OF WATER OR NORMAL SALINE, OCCASIONALLY LIFTING UPPER AND LOWER LIDS, UNTIL NO EVIDENCE OF CHEMICAL REMAINS (APPROXIMATELY 15-20 MINUTES). GET MEDICAL ATTENTION IMMEDIATELY.

INGESTION: SODIUM CHLORATE: METHEMOGLOBIN FORMER/NEPHROTOXIN. **ACUTE EXPOSURE-** INGESTION MAY CAUSE IRRITATION OF THE GASTROINTESTINAL MUCOSA WITH SWELLING OF THE PHARYNGEAL MEMBRANES, ABDOMINAL PAIN, NAUSEA, VOMITING, DIARRHEA, INTRAVASCULAR HEMOLYSIS, ANEMIA, METHEMOGLOBINEMIA WITH CYANOSIS, HYPERNATREMIA, HYPERKALEMIA, TISSUE HYPOXIA, HYPOTENSION, RESTLESSNESS FOLLOWED BY APATHY, AND CENTRAL NERVOUS SYSTEM DEPRESSION WITH CONFUSION AND UNCONSCIOUSNESS. KIDNEY INJURY WITH ACUTE TUBULAR NECROSIS, HEMOGLOBINURIA, ALBUMINURIA, HEMATURIA OR ANURIA WITH AZOTEMIA, LATE TOXIC NEPHRITIS, AND RENAL FAILURE MAY OCCUR. IN ADDITION, IRREGULAR HEART BEAT, POSSIBLY RESPIRATORY DIFFICULTY AND FAILURE, ENLARGED AND TENDER LIVER WITH JAUNDICE, ENLARGED SPLEEN, CONVULSIONS AND COMA MAY OCCUR. DEATH IS GENERALLY DUE TO MASSIVE INTRAVASCULAR HEMOLYSIS, RENAL FAILURE OR TISSUE ANOXIA AND OCCURS ON THE 4TH OR 5TH DAY AFTER POISONING. THE ESTIMATED LETHAL DOSE IN MAN IS 15 GRAMS. PATHOLOGIC FINDINGS MAY INCLUDE CHOCOLATE DISCOLORATION OF THE BLOOD AND VISCERA, NORMOCYTIC NORMOCHROMIC ANEMIA, THROMBOCYTOPENIA, FREE PLASMA HAPTOGLOBIN, POLYMORPHONUCLEAR LEUKOCYTOSIS, HEINZ BODIES, GHOST CELLS, ENLARGED KIDNEYS WITH DILATED TUBULES POSSIBLY BLOCKED BY DEBRIS, LIVER DAMAGE AND GASTROINTESTINAL CONGESTION AND CORRROSION. **CHRONIC EXPOSURE-** REPEATED INGESTION OF SMALL DOSES MAY CAUSE ANOREXIA AND WEIGHT LOSS. THE KIDNEY TUBULES MAY BE SEVERELY DAMAGED WITHOUT PRODUCING DETECTABLE METHEMOGLOBINEMIA.

FIRST AID- REMOVE INGESTED POISON BY IPECAC EMESIS FOLLOWED BY ACTIVATED CHARCOAL. AIRWAY-PROTECTED GASTRIC LAVAGE IS NECESSARY IN PATIENTS WITH DEPRESSED RESPIRATION. GET MEDICAL ATTENTION IMMEDIATELY. (DREISBACH, HANDBOOK OF POISONING, 11TH ED.). TREATMENT SHOULD BE ADMINISTERED BY QUALIFIED MEDICAL PERSONNEL.

ANTIDOTE: THE FOLLOWING ANTIDOTE HAS BEEN RECOMMENDED. HOWEVER, THE DECISION AS TO WHETHER THE SEVERITY OF POISONING REQUIRES ADMINISTRATION OF ANY ANTIDOTE AND ACTUAL DOSE REQUIRED SHOULD BE MADE BY QUALIFIED MEDICAL PERSONNEL.
CHLORATE POISONING: GIVE SODIUM THIOSULFATE, 2-5 GRAMS IN 200 ML OF 5% SODIUM BICARBONATE, ORALLY, TO DECOMPOSE CHLORATES. METHYLENE BLUE IS NOT USEFUL FOR REVERSING CHLORATE METHEMOGLOBINEMIA AND MAY BE HAZARDOUS. ASCORBIC ACID ACTS SLOWLY (DREISBACH, HANDBOOK OF POISONING, 11TH ED.). ANTIDOTE SHOULD BE ADMINISTERED BY QUALIFIED MEDICAL PERSONNEL.

REACTIVITY

REACTIVITY: AT TEMPERATURES ABOVE THE MELTING POINT, MAY UNDERGO VIOLENT, SELF-ACCELERATING DECOMPOSITION WITH THE EVOLUTION OF OXYGEN. THE INCREASE IN OXYGEN, ALONG WITH THE INCREASE IN PRESSURE, MAY RESULT IN AN EXPLOSION.

INCOMPATIBILITIES: SODIUM CHLORATE: AMINES: FORMS SHOCK-SENSITIVE MIXTURE. AMMONIUM SALTS: POSSIBLE IGNITION AND EXPLOSION. AMMONIUM THOISULFATE: VIOLENT DECOMPOSITION. ANTIMONY SULFIDE: FORMS SHOCK-SENSITIVE MIXTURE. ARSENIC (POWDERED): FORMS SHOCK-SENSITIVE MIXTURE. ARSENIC TRIOXIDE: IGNITION ON CONTACT. 1,3-BIS(TRICHLOROMETHYL)BENZENE: MAY EXPLODE VIOLENTLY AT ELEVATED TEMPERATURES. CARBON (FINELY DIVIDED): MAY EXPLODE WITH HEAT, PERCUSSION, AND SOMETIMES LIGHT

FRICTION. CARBON DISULFIDE: FORMS SHOCK-SENSITIVE MIXTURE. COPPER: MAY EXPLODE WITH HEAT, PERCUSSION, AND SOMETIMES LIGHT FRICTION. CYANOBORANE OLIGOMER: FORMS SHOCK-SENSITIVE MIXTURE. DIOLS: POSSIBLE EXPLOSIVE REACTION. HYDRAZINE: FORMS EXTREMELY SHOCK-SENSITIVE MIXTURE. HYDROXYLAMINE: INCOMPATIBLE. MANGANESE DIOXIDE: FORMS SHOCK-SENSITIVE MIXTURE. METALS (POWDERED): POSSIBLE IGNITION AND EXPLOSION. NITRIC ACID (CONCENTRATED): MAY IGNITE ON CONTACT. NITROBENZENE: FORMS EXPLOSIVE MIXTURE. ORGANIC MATERIALS: MAY IGNITE OR EXPLODE. OSMIUM: POSSIBLE VIOLENT REACTION. PHOSPHORUS: POSSIBLE IGNITION AND EXPLOSION. POTASSIUM CYANIDE: EXPLOSIVE REACTION. SILICON: IGNITION AND POSSIBLE EXPLOSION. SULFURIC ACID: EXPLOSIVE REACTION. SULFUR OR SULFIDES: POSSIBLE IGNITION AND EXPLOSION. SODIUM HYPOCHLORITE: FORMS SHOCK-SENSITIVE MIXTURE. SODIUM PHOSPHINATE: POSSIBLE EXPLOSION. THIOCYANATES: FORMS EXPLOSIVE MIXTURE. ZINC: FORMS SHOCK-SENSITIVE MIXTURE. SEE ALSO METAL CHLORATES.

METAL CHLORATES: ACIDS (STRONG): LIBERATES EXPLOSIVE CHLORINE DIOXIDE GAS. ANTIMONY SULFIDE: EXPLOSIVE REACTION. CALCIUM HYDRIDE: EXPLODES ON FRICTION. COMBUSTIBLE MATERIALS: MAY INCREASE THE BURNING RATE OR CAUSE IGNITION ON CONTACT; FINELY DIVIDED MATERIALS MAY RESULT IN AN EXPLOSION. CYANIDES: EXPLOSIVE REACTION. MANGANESE DIOXIDE: POSSIBLE EXPLOSION. MERCURY TETRATRIPHOSPHIDE: EXPLODES WITH PERCUSSION. METALS (POWDERED): POSSIBLE EXPLOSION. METAL SULFIDES: POSSIBLE EXPLOSION. ORGANIC ACIDS (DIBASIC): LIBERATES EXPLOSIVE CHLORINE DIOXIDE WHEN HEATED. ORGANIC MATERIALS: AMY INCREASE THE BURNING RATE OR CAUSE IGNITION ON CONTACT; FINELY DIVIDED MATERIALS MAY RESULT IN AN EXPLOSION. PHOSPHONIUM IODIDE: POSSIBLE EXPLOSION. PHOSPHORUS: POSSIBLE EXPLOSION. REDUCING MATERIALS: FIRE OR EXPLOSION HAZARD. SELENIUM: INCANDESCENT REACTION. SODIUM HYPOPHOSPHITE: POSSIBLE EXPLOSION. STRONTIUM HYDRIDE: EXPLODES ON FRICTION. SULFUR: POSSIBLE EXPLOSION. SULFUR DIOXIDE: LIBERATES EXPLOSIVE CHLORINE PEROXIDE. THIOCYANATES: EXPLODES ABOVE 750 F OR WHEN EXPOSED TO SPARKS OR FLAME.

DECOMPOSITION: THERMAL DECOMPOSITION MAY RELEASE HAZARDOUS FUMES OF SODIUM OXIDES AND HYDROGEN CHLORIDE.

POLYMERIZATION: HAZARDOUS POLYMERIZATION HAS NOT BEEN REPORTED TO OCCUR UNDER NORMAL TEMPERATURES AND PRESSURES.

STORAGE AND DISPOSAL

OBSERVE ALL FEDERAL, STATE AND LOCAL REGULATIONS WHEN STORING OR DISPOSING OF THIS SUBSTANCE. FOR ASSISTANCE, CONTACT THE DISTRICT DIRECTOR OF THE ENVIRONMENTAL PROTECTION AGENCY.

STORAGE

PROTECT AGAINST PHYSICAL DAMAGE. SEPARATE FROM COMBUSTIBLE, ORGANIC OR OTHER READILY OXIDIZABLE MATERIALS, ACIDS, AMMONIUM SALTS, SULFUR AND FLAMMABLE VAPORS. AVOID STORAGE ON WOODEN FLOORS. IMMEDIATELY REMOVE AND DISPOSE OF ANY SPILLED CHLORATE (NFPA 49, HAZARDOUS CHEMICALS DATA, 1975).

STORE AWAY FROM INCOMPATIBLE SUBSTANCES.

CONSULT NFPA PUBLICATION 43A, STORAGE OF LIQUID AND SOLID OXIDIZING MATERIALS, FOR STORAGE REQUIREMENTS.

KEEP IN A TIGHTLY CLOSED CONTAINER. STORE IN A COOL, DRY, VENTILATED AREA.

CONDITIONS TO AVOID

AVOID CONTACT WITH COMBUSTIBLE MATERIALS (WOOD, PAPER, FUEL, OILS, ETC); IGNITION OR EXPLOSION MAY RESULT. AVOID CONTAMINATION OF WATER SOURCES.

SPILL AND LEAK PROCEDURES

OCCUPATIONAL SPILL: KEEP COMBUSTIBLES (WOOD, PAPER, OIL, ETC) AWAY FROM SPILLED MATERIAL. DO NOT TOUCH SPILLED MATERIAL. FOR SMALL DRY SPILLS, WITH CLEAN SHOVEL PLACE MATERIAL INTO CLEAN, DRY CONTAINER AND COVER; MOVE CONTAINERS FROM SPILL AREA. FOR SMALL LIQUID SPILLS, TAKE UP WITH SAND, EARTH OR OTHER ABSORBENT MATERIAL AND PLACE INTO CONTAINERS FOR LATER DISPOSAL. FOR LARGER SPILLS, DIKE FAR AHEAD OF SPILL FOR LATER DISPOSAL. KEEP UNNECESSARY PEOPLE AWAY. ISOLATE HAZARD AREA AND DENY ENTRY.

PROTECTIVE EQUIPMENT

VENTILATION: PROVIDE LOCAL EXHAUST OR PROCESS ENCLOSURE VENTILATION SYSTEM.

RESPIRATOR: THE FOLLOWING RESPIRATORS ARE RECOMMENDED BASED ON INFORMATION FOUND IN THE PHYSICAL DATA, TOXICITY AND HEALTH EFFECTS SECTIONS. THEY ARE RANKED IN ORDER FROM MINIMUM TO MAXIMUM RESPIRATORY PROTECTION. THE SPECIFIC RESPIRATOR SELECTED MUST BE BASED ON CONTAMINATION LEVELS FOUND IN THE WORK PLACE, MUST NOT EXCEED THE WORKING LIMITS OF THE RESPIRATOR AND BE JOINTLY APPROVED BY THE NATIONAL INSTITUTE FOR OCCUPATIONAL SAFETY AND HEALTH AND THE MINE SAFETY AND HEALTH ADMINISTRATION (NIOSH-MSHA).

DUST AND MIST RESPIRATOR WITH A FULL FACEPIECE.

AIR-PURIFYING FULL FACEPIECE RESPIRATOR WITH A HIGH-EFFICIENCY PARTICULATE FILTER.

POWERED AIR-PURIFYING RESPIRATOR WITH A TIGHT-FITTING FACEPIECE AND HIGH-EFFICIENCY PARTICULATE FILTER.

TYPE 'C' SUPPLIED-AIR RESPIRATOR WITH A FULL FACEPIECE OPERATED IN PRESSURE-DEMAND OR OTHER POSITIVE PRESSURE MODE OR WITH A FULL FACEPIECE, HELMET OR HOOD OPERATED IN CONTINUOUS-FLOW MODE.

SELF-CONTAINED BREATHING APPARATUS WITH A FULL FACEPIECE OPERATED IN PRESSURE-DEMAND OR OTHER POSITIVE PRESSURE MODE.

FOR FIREFIGHTING AND OTHER IMMEDIATELY DANGEROUS TO LIFE OR HEALTH CONDITIONS:

SELF-CONTAINED BREATHING APPARATUS WITH FULL FACEPIECE OPERATED IN PRESSURE-DEMAND OR OTHER POSITIVE PRESSURE MODE.

SUPPLIED-AIR RESPIRATOR WITH FULL FACEPIECE AND OPERATED IN PRESSURE-DEMAND OR OTHER POSITIVE PRESSURE MODE IN COMBINATION WITH AN AUXILIARY SELF-CONTAINED BREATHING APPARATUS OPERATED IN PRESSURE-DEMAND OR OTHER POSITIVE PRESSURE MODE.

CLOTHING: EMPLOYEE MUST WEAR APPROPRIATE PROTECTIVE (IMPERVIOUS) CLOTHING AND EQUIPMENT TO PREVENT REPEATED OR PROLONGED SKIN CONTACT WITH THIS SUBSTANCE.

GLOVES: EMPLOYEE MUST WEAR APPROPRIATE PROTECTIVE GLOVES TO PREVENT CONTACT WITH THIS SUBSTANCE.

EYE PROTECTION: EMPLOYEE MUST WEAR SPLASH-PROOF OR DUST-RESISTANT SAFETY GOGGLES TO PREVENT EYE CONTACT WITH THIS SUBSTANCE.

EMERGENCY EYE WASH: WHERE THERE IS ANY POSSIBILITY THAT AN EMPLOYEE'S EYES MAY BE EXPOSED TO THIS SUBSTANCE, THE EMPLOYER SHOULD PROVIDE AN EYE WASH FOUNTAIN WITHIN THE IMMEDIATE WORK AREA FOR EMERGENCY USE.

AUTHORIZED BY- OCCUPATIONAL HEALTH SERVICES, INC.

CREATION DATE: 11/16/89 ***REVISION DATE:*** 05/16/90

MATERIAL SAFETY DATA SHEET

OCCUPATIONAL HEALTH SERVICES, INC.
AGRICULTURE AND PESTICIDE DIVISION
450 SEVENTH AVENUE, SUITE 2407
NEW YORK, NEW YORK 10123
1-800-445-MSDS OR (212) 967-1100

EMERGENCY CONTACT:
JOHN S. BRANSFORD, JR. (615) 292-1180

SUBSTANCE IDENTIFICATION

CAS-NUMBER 7647-14-5

SUBSTANCE: **SODIUM CHLORIDE**

TRADE NAMES/SYNONYMS: COMMON SALT; HALITE; ROCK SALT; SODIUM MONOCHLORIDE; SALT; SEA SALT; TABLE SALT; SODIUM CHLORIDE (NACL); MORTON SOLAR SALT (MORTON THIOKOL); CLNA; PST21105

CHEMICAL FAMILY: INORGANIC SALT

MOLECULAR FORMULA: NA-CL

MOLECULAR WEIGHT: 58.44

CERCLA RATINGS (SCALE 0-3): HEALTH=2 FIRE=0 REACTIVITY=0 PERSISTENCE=0

NFPA RATINGS (SCALE 0-4): HEALTH=U FIRE=0 REACTIVITY=0

COMPONENTS AND CONTAMINANTS

COMPONENT: SODIUM CHLORIDE ***PERCENT:*** 100.0
CAS# 7647-14-5

OTHER CONTAMINANTS: NONE

EXPOSURE LIMITS: NO OCCUPATIONAL EXPOSURE LIMITS ESTABLISHED BY OSHA, ACGIH, OR NIOSH.

PHYSICAL DATA

DESCRIPTION: ODORLESS, COLORLESS TO WHITE, SLIGHTLY HYGROSCOPIC, CRYSTALLINE POWDER. ***BOILING POINT:*** 2575 F (1413 C)

MELTING POINT: 1474F (801 C)

SPECIFIC GRAVITY: 2.165 @ 25 C ***VAPOR PRESSURE:*** 1 MM @ 865 C

PH: 5.5-8.5 @ 5% SOLN ***SOLUBILITY IN WATER:*** 35.7% @ 0 C

SOLVENT SOLUBILITY: SOLUBLE IN GLYCEROL; SLIGHTLY SOLUBLE IN ALCOHOL, LIQUID AMMONIA; INSOLUBLE IN HYDROCHLORIC ACID.

FIRE AND EXPLOSION DATA

FIRE AND EXPLOSION HAZARD: NEGLIGIBLE FIRE HAZARD WHEN EXPOSED TO HEAT OR FLAME.

FIREFIGHTING MEDIA: EXTINGUISH USING AGENT SUITABLE FOR TYPE OF SURROUNDING FIRE.

FIREFIGHTING: NO ACUTE HAZARD. MOVE CONTAINER FROM FIRE AREA IF POSSIBLE. AVOID BREATHING VAPORS OR DUSTS; KEEP UPWIND.

TOXICITY

SODIUM CHLORIDE: IRRITATION DATA: 50 MG/24 HOURS SKIN-RABBIT MILD; 500 MG/24 HOURS SKIN-RABBIT MILD; 100 MG EYE-RABBIT MILD; 100 MG/24 HOURS EYE-RABBIT MODERATE; 10 MG EYE-RABBIT MODERATE. TOXICITY DATA: 12,357 MG/KG/23 DAYS CONTINUOUS ORAL-HUMAN TDLO; 3000 MG/KG ORAL-RAT LD50; 4000 MG/KG ORAL-MOUSE LD50; 8 GM/KG ORAL-RABBIT LDLO; 3500 MG/KG SUBCUTANEOUS-RAT LDLO; 3 GM/KG SUBCUTANEOUS-MOUSE LD50; 2160 MG/KG SUBCUTANEOUS-GUINEA PIG LDLO; 645 MG/KG INTRAVENOUS-MOUSE LD50; 2 GM/KG INTRAVENOUS-DOG LDLO; 1100 MG/KG INTRAVENOUS-RABBIT LDLO; 300 MG/KG INTRAVENOUS-GUINEA PIG LDLO; 6614 MG/KG INTRAPERITONEAL-MOUSE LD50; 364 MG/KG INTRAPERITONEAL-DOG LDLO; 131 MG/KG INTRACERVICAL-MOUSE LD50; 300 MG/KG INTRAARTERIAL-GUINEA PIG LDLO; MUTAGENIC DATA (RTECS); REPRODUCTIVE EFFECTS DATA (RTECS). CARCINOGEN STATUS: NONE. LOCAL EFFECTS: IRRITANT- EYE. ACUTE TOXICITY LEVEL: MODERATELY TOXIC BY INGESTION. TARGET EFFECTS: POISONING MAY AFFECT THE CENTRAL NERVOUS SYSTEM.

HEALTH EFFECTS AND FIRST AID

INHALATION: SODIUM CHLORIDE: **ACUTE EXPOSURE-** INHALATION OF DUST MAY LEAVE A SALTY TASTE AND CAUSE IRRITATION TO THE NOSE AND THROAT. SYMPTOMS MAY INCLUDE COUGHING, DRYNESS, AND SORE THROAT. **CHRONIC EXPOSURE-** NO DATA AVAILABLE.

FIRST AID- REMOVE FROM EXPOSURE AREA TO FRESH AIR IMMEDIATELY. IF BREATHING HAS STOPPED, PERFORM ARTIFICIAL RESPIRATION. KEEP PERSON WARM AND AT REST. TREAT SYMPTOMATICALLY AND SUPPORTIVELY. GET MEDICAL ATTENTION IMMEDIATELY.

SKIN CONTACT: SODIUM CHLORIDE: **ACUTE EXPOSURE-** MAY CAUSE MILD IRRITATION UNLESS THE CONTACT IS INTENSIVE WHICH MAY RESULT IN DERMATITIS. **CHRONIC EXPOSURE-** PRIMARY IRRITANT DERMATITIS MAY RESULT FROM SODIUM CHLORIDE BEING TRAPPED BETWEEN THE SKIN AND JEWELRY SINCE SOME METAL ALLOYS MAY BE CORRODED AND DISCOLORED BY SUCH CONTACT.

FIRST AID- REMOVE CONTAMINATED CLOTHING AND SHOES IMMEDIATELY. WASH AFFECTED AREA WITH SOAP OR MILD DETERGENT AND LARGE AMOUNTS OF WATER UNTIL NO EVIDENCE OF CHEMICAL REMAINS (APPROXIMATELY 15-20 MINUTES). GET MEDICAL ATTENTION IMMEDIATELY.

EYE CONTACT: SODIUM CHLORIDE: IRRITANT. **ACUTE EXPOSURE-** SOLID PARTICLES OR HYPERTONIC SOLUTIONS MAY CAUSE REDNESS, PAIN, IRRITATION AND A STINGING SENSATION ON CONTACT. SOLUTIONS MORE DILUTE THAN 0.9% SODIUM CHLORIDE CAUSE INCREASED PERMEABILITY OF THE CORNEAL EPITHELIUM. **CHRONIC EXPOSURE-** REPEATED AND PROLONGED CONTACT WITH IRRITANTS MAY CAUSE CONJUNCTIVITIS.

FIRST AID- WASH EYES IMMEDIATELY WITH LARGE AMOUNTS OF WATER OR NORMAL SALINE, OCCASIONALLY LIFTING UPPER AND LOWER LIDS, UNTIL NO EVIDENCE OF CHEMICAL REMAINS (APPROXIMATELY 15-20 MINUTES). GET MEDICAL ATTENTION IMMEDIATELY.

INGESTION: SODIUM CHLORIDE: **ACUTE EXPOSURE-** INGESTION OF VERY LARGE DOSES OF HYPERTONIC SOLUTIONS MAY CAUSE DRYNESS OF MUCOUS MEMBRANES AND A VIOLENT INFLAMMATORY REACTION IN THE GASTROINTESTINAL TRACT; ULCERATION MAY OCCUR. SYMPTOMS MAY INCLUDE NAUSEA, VOMITING, DIARRHEA, ANOREXIA, THIRST, FEVER, MUSCULAR TWITCHING, RIGIDITY, CONVULSIONS, HYPERNEA AND PROSTRATION. DEHYDRATION AND CONGESTION MAY OCCUR IN MOST INTERNAL ORGANS, PARTICULARLY THE MENINGES AND BRAIN. CENTRAL NERVOUS SYSTEM DISTURBANCES SUCH AS CONFUSION AND COMA MAY RESULT. GENERALIZED AND PULMONARY EDEMA ARE POSSIBLE. DEATH MAY OCCUR FROM RESPIRATORY FAILURE SECONDARY TO AN ACUTE ENCEPHALOPATHY. **CHRONIC EXPOSURE-** DIETS HIGH IN SODIUM CHLORIDE MAY CAUSE ELEVATED BLOOD PRESSURE, ESPECIALLY IN PREDISPOSED INDIVIDUALS. REPRODUCTIVE EFFECTS HAVE BEEN REPORTED IN ANIMALS.

FIRST AID- IF PERSON IS CONSCIOUS, GIVE LARGE AMOUNTS OF WATER. TREAT SYMPTOMATICALLY AND SUPPORTIVELY. IF VOMITING OCCURS, KEEP HEAD BELOW HIPS TO PREVENT ASPIRATION. GET MEDICAL ATTENTION.

ANTIDOTE: NO SPECIFIC ANTIDOTE. TREAT SYMPTOMATICALLY AND SUPPORTIVELY.

REACTIVITY

REACTIVITY: STABLE UNDER NORMAL TEMPERATURES AND PRESSURES.

INCOMPATIBILITIES: SODIUM CHLORIDE: BROMINE TRIFLUORIDE: POSSIBLE VIOLENT REACTION. BUILDING MATERIALS: MAY BE ATTACKED. DICHLOROMALEIC ANHYDRIDE + UREA: EXPLOSIVE REACTION ABOVE 118 C. LITHIUM (BURNING): RELEASES VIOLENTLY FLAMMABLE SODIUM. METALS: MAY BE ATTACKED. NITROGEN COMPOUNDS: MAY FORM EXPLOSIVE COMPOUNDS UNDER ELECTROLYSIS CONDITIONS.

DECOMPOSITION: THERMAL DECOMPOSITION PRODUCTS MAY INCLUDE TOXIC FUMES OF CHLORIDE AND SODIUM OXIDE.

POLYMERIZATION: HAZARDOUS POLYMERIZATION HAS NOT BEEN REPORTED TO OCCUR UNDER NORMAL TEMPERATURES AND PRESSURES.

STORAGE AND DISPOSAL

OBSERVE ALL FEDERAL, STATE AND LOCAL REGULATIONS WHEN STORING OR DISPOSING OF THIS SUBSTANCE. FOR ASSISTANCE, CONTACT THE DISTRICT DIRECTOR OF THE ENVIRONMENTAL PROTECTION AGENCY.

****STORAGE****

STORE AWAY FROM INCOMPATIBLE SUBSTANCES.
STORE IN A TIGHTLY CLOSED CONTAINER.

CONDITIONS TO AVOID

NO REPORTS FOUND.

SPILL AND LEAK PROCEDURES

OCCUPATIONAL SPILL: SWEEP UP AND PLACE IN SUITABLE CLEAN, DRY CONTAINERS FOR RECLAMATION OR LATER DISPOSAL. DO NOT FLUSH SPILLED MATERIAL INTO SEWER. KEEP UNNECESSARY PEOPLE AWAY.

PROTECTIVE EQUIPMENT

VENTILATION: PROVIDE LOCAL EXHAUST OR GENERAL DILUTION VENTILATION SYSTEM.

RESPIRATOR: THE FOLLOWING RESPIRATORS ARE RECOMMENDED BASED ON INFORMATION FOUND IN THE PHYSICAL DATA, TOXICITY AND HEALTH EFFECTS SECTIONS. THEY ARE RANKED IN ORDER FROM MINIMUM TO MAXIMUM RESPIRATORY PROTECTION. THE SPECIFIC RESPIRATOR SELECTED MUST BE BASED ON CONTAMINATION LEVELS FOUND IN THE WORK PLACE, MUST NOT EXCEED THE WORKING LIMITS OF THE RESPIRATOR AND BE JOINTLY APPROVED BY THE NATIONAL INSTITUTE FOR OCCUPATIONAL SAFETY AND HEALTH AND THE MINE SAFETY AND HEALTH ADMINISTRATION (NIOSH-MSHA).

DUST AND MIST RESPIRATOR WITH A FULL FACEPIECE.

AIR-PURIFYING FULL FACEPIECE RESPIRATOR WITH A HIGH-EFFICIENCY PARTICULATE FILTER.

POWERED AIR-PURIFYING RESPIRATOR WITH A TIGHT-FITTING FACEPIECE AND HIGH-EFFICIENCY PARTICULATE FILTER.

TYPE 'C' SUPPLIED-AIR RESPIRATOR WITH A FULL FACEPIECE OPERATED IN PRESSURE-DEMAND OR OTHER POSITIVE PRESSURE MODE OR WITH A FULL FACEPIECE, HELMET OR HOOD OPERATED IN CONTINUOUS-FLOW MODE. SELF-CONTAINED BREATHING APPARATUS WITH A FULL FACEPIECE OPERATED IN PRESSURE-DEMAND OR OTHER POSITIVE PRESSURE MODE.

FOR FIREFIGHTING AND OTHER IMMEDIATELY DANGEROUS TO LIFE OR HEALTH CONDITIONS:

SELF-CONTAINED BREATHING APPARATUS WITH FULL FACEPIECE OPERATED IN PRESSURE-DEMAND OR OTHER POSITIVE PRESSURE MODE.

SUPPLIED-AIR RESPIRATOR WITH FULL FACEPIECE AND OPERATED IN PRESSURE-DEMAND OR OTHER POSITIVE PRESSURE MODE IN COMBINATION WITH AN AUXILIARY SELF-CONTAINED BREATHING APPARATUS OPERATED IN PRESSURE-DEMAND OR OTHER POSITIVE PRESSURE MODE.

CLOTHING: PROTECTIVE CLOTHING NOT REQUIRED. AVOID REPEATED OR PROLONGED CONTACT WITH THIS SUBSTANCE.

GLOVES: PROTECTIVE GLOVES ARE NOT REQUIRED BUT RECOMMENDED.

EYE PROTECTION: EMPLOYEE MUST WEAR SPLASH-PROOF OR DUST-RESISTANT SAFETY GOGGLES TO PREVENT EYE CONTACT WITH THIS SUBSTANCE. EMERGENCY EYE WASH: WHERE THERE IS ANY POSSIBILITY THAT AN EMPLOYEE'S EYES MAY BE EXPOSED TO THIS SUBSTANCE, THE EMPLOYER SHOULD PROVIDE AN EYE WASH FOUNTAIN WITHIN THE IMMEDIATE WORK AREA FOR EMERGENCY USE.

AUTHORIZED BY- OCCUPATIONAL HEALTH SERVICES, INC.
CREATION DATE: 11/16/89 ***REVISION DATE:*** 05/31/90

MATERIAL SAFETY DATA SHEET

OCCUPATIONAL HEALTH SERVICES, INC.
AGRICULTURE AND PESTICIDE DIVISION
450 SEVENTH AVENUE, SUITE 2407
NEW YORK, NEW YORK 10123
1-800-445-MSDS OR (212) 967-1100

EMERGENCY CONTACT:
JOHN S. BRANSFORD, JR. (615) 292-1180

SUBSTANCE IDENTIFICATION

CAS-NUMBER 7758-19-2
SUBSTANCE: **SODIUM CHLORITE**
TRADE NAMES/SYNONYMS: CHLOROUS ACID, SODIUM SALT; STCC 4918360; UN 1496; PST21110
CHEMICAL FAMILY: INORGANIC SALT
MOLECULAR FORMULA: CL-NA-O2
MOLECULAR WEIGHT: 90.44
CERCLA RATINGS (SCALE 0-3): HEALTH = 3 FIRE = 1 REACTIVITY = 3 PERSISTENCE = 0
NFPA RATINGS (SCALE 0-4): HEALTH = 3 FIRE = 1 REACTIVITY = 2

COMPONENTS AND CONTAMINANTS

COMPONENT: SODIUM CHLORITE ***PERCENT:*** 100
CAS# 7758-19-2
OTHER CONTAMINANTS: NONE
EXPOSURE LIMITS: NO OCCUPATIONAL EXPOSURE LIMITS ESTABLISHED BY OSHA, ACGIH, OR NIOSH.

PHYSICAL DATA

DESCRIPTION: WHITE CRYSTALS OR CRYSTALLINE POWDER, HYGROSCOPIC.
MELTING POINT: 356 F (180 C) DECOMPOSES ***SPECIFIC GRAVITY:*** NOT AVAILABLE
SOLUBILITY IN WATER: 74%

FIRE AND EXPLOSION DATA

FIRE AND EXPLOSION HAZARD: SLIGHT FIRE HAZARD WHEN EXPOSED TO HEAT OR FLAME.
MODERATE EXPLOSION HAZARD WHEN EXPOSED TO HEAT OR FLAME.
FIREFIGHTING MEDIA: DRY CHEMICAL, CARBON DIOXIDE, HALON, WATER SPRAY OR STANDARD FOAM (1987 EMERGENCY RESPONSE GUIDEBOOK, DOT P 5800.4).
FOR LARGER FIRES, USE WATER SPRAY, FOG OR STANDARD FOAM (1987 EMERGENCY RESPONSE GUIDEBOOK, DOT P 5800.4).
FIREFIGHTING: DO NOT MOVE CONTAINERS IF EXPOSURE TO HEAT HAS OCCURRED. COOL CONTAINERS EXPOSED TO FLAMES WITH WATER FROM SIDE UNTIL WELL AFTER FIRE IS OUT. STAY AWAY FROM STORAGE TANK ENDS. FOR MASSIVE FIRE IN STORAGE AREA, USE UNMANNED HOSE HOLDER OR MONITOR NOZZLES; ELSE WITHDRAW FROM AREA AND LET FIRE BURN (1987 EMERGENCY RESPONSE GUIDEBOOK, DOT P 5800.4, GUIDE PAGE 43).
FLOOD WITH WATER. COOL CONTAINERS WITH FLOODING AMOUNTS OF WATER, APPLY FROM AS FAR A DISTANCE AS POSSIBLE. EVACUATE TO A RADIUS OF 1500 FEET FOR UNCONTROLLABLE FIRES.

TRANSPORTATION DATA

DEPARTMENT OF TRANSPORTATION HAZARD CLASSIFICATION 49 CFR 172.101: OXIDIZER
DEPARTMENT OF TRANSPORTATION LABELING REQUIREMENTS 49 CFR 172.101 AND SUBPART E: OXIDIZER
DEPARTMENT OF TRANSPORTATION PACKAGING REQUIREMENTS: 49 CFR 173.160 EXCEPTIONS: NONE

TOXICITY

SODIUM CHLORITE: TOXICITY DATA: 165 MG/KG ORAL-RAT LD50; 350 MG/KG ORAL-MOUSE LD50; 300 MG/KG ORAL-GUINEA PIG LD50; MUTAGENIC DATA (RTECS); REPRODUCTIVE EFFECTS DATA (RTECS); TUMORIGENIC DATA (RTECS). CARCINOGEN STATUS: NONE. LOCAL EFFECTS: CORROSIVE- INHALATION, SKIN, EYE, INGESTION. ACUTE TOXICITY LEVEL: TOXIC BY INGESTION. TARGET EFFECTS: METHEMOGLOBIN FORMER.

HEALTH EFFECTS AND FIRST AID

INHALATION: SODIUM CHLORITE: CORROSIVE. **ACUTE EXPOSURE-** MAY CAUSE SORE THROAT, COUGHING, LABORED BREATHING, AND SHORTNESS OF BREATH. DELAYED PULMONARY EDEMA MAY OCCUR. CHLORITE HAS BEEN SHOWN TO PRODUCE METHEMOGLOBIN IN RATS AND CATS, AND INSOLATED BLOOD SPECIMENS OF RAT, CAT AND MAN. **CHRONIC EXPOSURE-** PULMONARY EDEMA MAY OCCUR.
FIRST AID- REMOVE FROM EXPOSURE AREA TO FRESH AIR IMMEDIATELY. IF BREATHING HAS STOPPED, GIVE ARTIFICIAL RESPIRATION. MAINTAIN AIRWAY AND BLOOD PRESSURE AND ADMINISTER OXYGEN IF AVAILABLE. KEEP AFFECTED PERSON WARM AND AT REST. TREAT SYMPTOMATICALLY AND SUPPORTIVELY. ADMINISTRATION OF OXYGEN SHOULD BE PERFORMED BY QUALIFIED PERSONNEL. GET MEDICAL ATTENTION IMMEDIATELY.

SKIN CONTACT: SODIUM CHLORITE: CORROSIVE **ACUTE EXPOSURE-** MAY CAUSE SEVERE IRRITATION WITH REDNESS, PAIN, AND BURNS. **CHRONIC EXPOSURE-** REPEATED OR PROLONGED EXPOSURE MAY RESULT IN DERMATITIS.
FIRST AID- REMOVE CONTAMINATED CLOTHING AND SHOES IMMEDIATELY. WASH AFFECTED AREA WITH SOAP OR MILD DETERGENT AND LARGE AMOUNTS OF WATER UNTIL NO EVIDENCE OF CHEMICAL REMAINS (AT LEAST 15-20 MINUTES). IN CASE OF CHEMICAL BURNS, COVER AREA WITH STERILE, DRY DRESSING. BANDAGE SECURELY, BUT NOT TOO TIGHTLY. GET MEDICAL ATTENTION IMMEDIATELY.

EYE CONTACT: SODIUM CHLORITE: CORROSIVE. **ACUTE EXPOSURE-** DIRECT CONTACT MAY CAUSE REDNESS, PAIN, BLURRED VISION AND BURNS. **CHRONIC EXPOSURE-** REPEATED OR PROLONGED EXPOSURE MAY CAUSE CONJUNCTIVITIS.
FIRST AID- WASH EYES IMMEDIATELY WITH LARGE AMOUNTS OF WATER, OCCASIONALLY LIFTING UPPER AND LOWER LIDS, UNTIL NO EVIDENCE OF CHEMICAL REMAINS (AT LEAST 15-20 MINUTES). CONTINUE IRRIGATING WITH NORMAL SALINE UNTIL THE PH HAS RETURNED TO NORMAL (30-60 MINUTES). COVER WITH STERILE BANDAGES. GET MEDICAL ATTENTION IMMEDIATELY.

INGESTION: SODIUM CHLORITE: CORROSIVE/TOXIC. **ACUTE EXPOSURE-** MAY CAUSE ABDOMINAL SPASMS AND PAIN, VOMITING, DIARRHEA, SEVERE GASTROINTESTINAL IRRITATION AND INTESTINAL DAMAGE. CHLORITE HAS BEEN SHOWN TO PRODUCE METHEMOGLOBIN IN RATS AND CATS, AND IN ISOLATED BLOOD SPECIMENS OF RATS, CATS, AND MAN. **CHRONIC EXPOSURE-** FEMALE RATS CHRONICALLY FED DURING PREGNANCY EXHIBITED POST-IMPLANTATION MORTALITY AND FETOTOXICITY. FEMALE MICE FED DURING PREGNANCY AND FOR 28 DAYS AFTER HAD REDUCED WEIGHT GAIN OF THE NEWBORN. MALE RATS FED BEFORE MATING EXHIBITED SPERMATOGENESIS.
FIRST AID- IF PERSON IS CONSCIOUS, IMMEDIATELY GIVE LARGE AMOUNTS OF WATER OR MILK. DO NOT INDUCE VOMITING. DO NOT USE GASTRIC LAVAGE OR EMESIS. IF VOMITING PERSISTS, ADMINISTER FLUIDS REPEATEDLY. GET MEDICAL ATTENTION IMMEDIATELY. (DRIESBACH, HANDBOOK OF POISONING, 11TH ED.)
ANTIDOTE: NO SPECIFIC ANTIDOTE. TREAT SYMPTOMATICALLY AND SUPPORTIVELY.

REACTIVITY

REACTIVITY: THIS SUBSTANCE IS A VERY STRONG OXIDIZER. IT IS SELF-REACTIVE AND SENSITIVE TO SHOCK.
INCOMPATIBILITIES: SODIUM CHLORITE: STRONG ACIDS: EXPLOSION HAZARD AND FORMATION OF EXTREMELY POISONOUS CHLORINE DIOXIDE. ORGANIC MATTER MIXTURES: SENSITIVE TO HEAT, IMPACT, OR FRICTION. AMMONIUM COMPOUNDS: FORMATION OF EXPLOSIVE MIXTURES. CYANIDES: FORMATION OF EXPLOSIVE MIXTURES. FINELY POWDERED METALS: FORMATION OF EXPLOSIVE MIXTURES. OXALIC ACID: REACTS EXPLOSIVELY WHEN WATER IS ADDED AND EMITS TOXIC CHLORINE DIOXIDE. RED PHOSPHORUS: EXOTHERMIC REACTION AND EXPLOSION HAZARD IN AQUEOUS SOLUTION SULFUR: IGNITES WHEN MOISTENED. SULFURIC ACID: IGNITION OR EXPLOSION HAZARD. NITRIC ACID: IGNITION OR EXPLOSION HAZARD. SODIUM DITHIONITE: IGNITION OR EXPLOSION HAZARD. CARBON DISULFIDE: IGNITION OR EXPLOSION HAZARD. ORGANIC SULFIDES: IGNITION OR EXPLOSION HAZARD. REDUCING MATERIALS: VIGOROUS REACTIONS.
DECOMPOSITION: DECOMPOSES EXOTHERMICALLY AT 347 F; EVOLVES OXYGEN, WHICH MAY ACT AS A COMBUSTION ACCELERATOR. THERMAL DECOMPOSITION EMITS TOXIC FUMES OF HYDROCHLORIC ACID AND SODIUM OXIDE; MAY BE EXPLOSIVE.
POLYMERIZATION: HAZARDOUS POLYMERIZATION HAS NOT BEEN REPORTED TO OCCUR UNDER NORMAL TEMPERATURES AND PRESSURES.

STORAGE AND DISPOSAL

OBSERVE ALL FEDERAL, STATE AND LOCAL REGULATIONS WHEN STORING OR DISPOSING OF THIS SUBSTANCE. FOR ASSISTANCE, CONTACT THE DISTRICT DIRECTOR OF THE ENVIRONMENTAL PROTECTION AGENCY.

STORAGE

STORAGE: PROTECT AGAINST PHYSICAL DAMAGE. STORE IN A COOL, DRY PLACE, PREFERABLY IN A DETACHED FIRE-RESISTIVE BUILDING. SEPARATE FROM COMBUSTIBLE, ORGANIC OR OTHER READILY OXIDIZABLE MATERIALS, ACIDS, SULFUR AND FLAMMABLE VAPORS. IMMEDIATELY REMOVE AND DISPOSE OF ANY SPILLED CHLORATE (NFPA 49, HAZARDOUS CHEMICALS DATA, 1975).

CONDITIONS TO AVOID

MAY IGNITE OTHER COMBUSTIBLE MATERIALS (WOOD, PAPER, OIL, ETC.). MAY EXPLODE WITH MIXTURE OF FUELS, FROM FRICTION, HEAT OR CONTAMINATION. CONTAINER MAY EXPLODE IN HEAT OF FIRE. RUNOFF TO SEWER MAY CREATE FIRE OR EXPLOSION HAZARD.

SPILL AND LEAK PROCEDURES

OCCUPATIONAL SPILL: KEEP COMBUSTIBLES (WOOD, PAPER, OIL, ETC.) AWAY FROM SPILLED MATERIAL. DO NOT TOUCH SPILLED MATERIAL. STOP LEAK IF YOU CAN DO IT WITHOUT RISK. USE WATER SPRAY TO REDUCE VAPORS. FOR SMALL SPILLS, TAKE UP ABSORBENT MATERIAL AND PLACE INTO CONTAINERS FOR LATER DISPOSAL. FOR LARGER SPILLS, DIKE SPILL FOR LATER DISPOSAL. KEEP UNNECESSARY PEOPLE AWAY. ISOLATE HAZARD AREA AND DENY ENTRY.

PROTECTIVE EQUIPMENT

VENTILATION: PROVIDE GENERAL DILUTION VENTILATION.

RESPIRATOR: THE FOLLOWING RESPIRATORS ARE RECOMMENDED BASED ON INFORMATION FOUND IN THE PHYSICAL DATA, TOXICITY AND HEALTH EFFECTS SECTIONS. THEY ARE RANKED IN ORDER FROM MINIMUM TO MAXIMUM RESPIRATORY PROTECTION. THE SPECIFIC RESPIRATOR SELECTED MUST BE BASED ON CONTAMINATION LEVELS FOUND IN THE WORK PLACE, MUST NOT EXCEED THE WORKING LIMITS OF THE RESPIRATOR AND BE JOINTLY APPROVED BY THE NATIONAL INSTITUTE FOR OCCUPATIONAL SAFETY AND HEALTH AND THE MINE SAFETY AND HEALTH ADMINISTRATION (NIOSH-MSHA).

DUST AND MIST RESPIRATOR WITH A FULL FACEPIECE.

AIR-PURIFYING FULL FACEPIECE RESPIRATOR WITH A HIGH-EFFICIENCY PARTICULATE FILTER.

POWERED AIR-PURIFYING RESPIRATOR WITH A TIGHT-FITTING FACEPIECE AND HIGH-EFFICIENCY PARTICULATE FILTER.

TYPE 'C' SUPPLIED-AIR RESPIRATOR WITH A FULL FACEPIECE OPERATED IN PRESSURE-DEMAND OR OTHER POSITIVE PRESSURE MODE OR WITH A FULL FACEPIECE, HELMET OR HOOD OPERATED IN CONTINUOUS-FLOW MODE.

SELF-CONTAINED BREATHING APPARATUS WITH A FULL FACEPIECE OPERATED IN PRESSURE-DEMAND OR OTHER POSITIVE PRESSURE MODE.

FOR FIREFIGHTING AND OTHER IMMEDIATELY DANGEROUS TO LIFE OR HEALTH CONDITIONS:

SELF-CONTAINED BREATHING APPARATUS WITH FULL FACEPIECE OPERATED IN PRESSURE-DEMAND OR OTHER POSITIVE PRESSURE MODE.

SUPPLIED-AIR RESPIRATOR WITH FULL FACEPIECE AND OPERATED IN PRESSURE-DEMAND OR OTHER POSITIVE PRESSURE MODE IN COMBINATION WITH AN AUXILIARY SELF-CONTAINED BREATHING APPARATUS OPERATED IN PRESSURE-DEMAND OR OTHER POSITIVE PRESSURE MODE.

CLOTHING: EMPLOYEE MUST WEAR APPROPRIATE PROTECTIVE (IMPERVIOUS) CLOTHING AND EQUIPMENT TO PREVENT ANY POSSIBILITY OF SKIN CONTACT WITH THIS SUBSTANCE.

GLOVES: EMPLOYEE MUST WEAR APPROPRIATE PROTECTIVE GLOVES TO PREVENT CONTACT WITH THIS SUBSTANCE.

EYE PROTECTION: EMPLOYEE MUST WEAR SPLASH-PROOF OR DUST-RESISTANT SAFETY GOGGLES AND A FACESHIELD TO PREVENT CONTACT WITH THIS SUBSTANCE.

EMERGENCY WASH FACILITIES: WHERE THERE IS ANY POSSIBILITY THAT AN EMPLOYEE'S EYES AND/OR SKIN MAY BE EXPOSED TO THIS SUBSTANCE, THE EMPLOYER SHOULD PROVIDE AN EYE WASH FOUNTAIN AND QUICK DRENCH SHOWER WITHIN THE IMMEDIATE WORK AREA FOR EMERGENCY USE.

AUTHORIZED BY- OCCUPATIONAL HEALTH SERVICES, INC.

CREATION DATE: 11/15/89 ***REVISION DATE:*** 03/28/90

MATERIAL SAFETY DATA SHEET

OCCUPATIONAL HEALTH SERVICES, INC.	EMERGENCY CONTACT:
AGRICULTURE AND PESTICIDE DIVISION	JOHN S. BRANSFORD, JR. (615) 292-1180
450 SEVENTH AVENUE, SUITE 2407	
NEW YORK, NEW YORK 10123	
1-800-445-MSDS OR (212) 967-1100	

SUBSTANCE IDENTIFICATION

CAS-NUMBER 143-33-9

***SUBSTANCE:* <u>SODIUM CYANIDE, SOLID</u>**

TRADE NAMES/SYNONYMS: SODIUM CYANIDE (NA(CN)); WHITE CYANIDE; SODIUM CYANIDE; CYANOBRIK (R)/CYANOGRAM (R) (E.I. DU PONT DE NEMOURS AND CO.); S-283; S-284; RCRA P106; STCC 4923228; UN 1689; CNNA; PST21160

CHEMICAL FAMILY: INORGANIC SALT

MOLECULAR FORMULA: NA-C-N

MOLECULAR WEIGHT: 49.01

CERCLA RATINGS (SCALE 0-3): HEALTH=3 FIRE=0 REACTIVITY=0 PERSISTENCE=0

NFPA RATINGS (SCALE 0-4): HEALTH=3 FIRE=0 REACTIVITY=0

COMPONENTS AND CONTAMINANTS

COMPONENT: SODIUM CYANIDE ***PERCENT:*** 100

CAS# 143-33-9

OTHER CONTAMINANTS: NONE

EXPOSURE LIMITS: CYANIDES (AS CN): 5 MG(CN)/M3 OSHA TWA (SKIN)

10 POUNDS CERCLA SECTION 103 REPORTABLE QUANTITY (SOLUBLE CYANIDE SALTS)

FOR HYDROGEN CYANIDE GAS: 4.7 PPM (5 MG/M3) OSHA STEL (SKIN) 10 PPM (11 MG/M3) ACGIH CEILING (SKIN) 4.7 PPM (5 MG/M3) NIOSH RECOMMENDED 10 MINUTE CEILING

SODIUM CYANIDE: 5 MG(CN)/M3 OSHA TWA (SKIN) 5 MG(CN)/M3 ACGIH TWA (SKIN) 5 MG(CN)/M3/10 MINUTES NIOSH RECOMMENDED CEILING 100 POUNDS SARA SECTION 302 THRESHOLD PLANNING QUANTITY 10 POUNDS SARA SECTION 304 REPORTABLE QUANTITY 10 POUNDS CERCLA SECTION 103 REPORTABLE QUANTITY SUBJECT TO SARA SECTION 313 ANNUAL TOXIC CHEMICAL RELEASE REPORTING

PHYSICAL DATA

DESCRIPTION: COLORLESS TO WHITE DELIQUESCENT GRANULES, FLAKES, OR CRYSTALLINE POWDER, WITH AN ODOR OF BITTER ALMONDS WHEN MOIST.

BOILING POINT:2725 F (1496 C)

MELTING POINT: 1047 F (564 C) ***SPECIFIC GRAVITY:*** 1.61

VAPOR PRESSURE: 1 MMHG @ 817 C ***PH:*** BASIC IN SOLUTION

SOLUBILITY IN WATER: 58% @ 20 C

SOLVENT SOLUBILITY: SOLUBLE IN AMMONIA; SLIGHTLY SOLUBLE IN ALCOHOL.

FIRE AND EXPLOSION DATA

FIRE AND EXPLOSION HAZARD: NEGLIGIBLE FIRE HAZARD WHEN EXPOSED TO HEAT OR FLAME.

FIREFIGHTING MEDIA: DRY CHEMICAL, CARBON DIOXIDE, HALON, WATER SPRAY OR STANDARD FOAM (1987 EMERGENCY RESPONSE GUIDEBOOK, DOT P 5800.4).

FOR LARGER FIRES, USE WATER SPRAY, FOG OR STANDARD FOAM (1987 EMERGENCY RESPONSE GUIDEBOOK, DOT P 5800.4).

FIREFIGHTING: MOVE CONTAINERS FROM FIRE AREA IF POSSIBLE. FIGHT FIRE FROM MAXIMUM DISTANCE. STAY AWAY FROM STORAGE TANK ENDS. DIKE FIRE CONTROL WATER FOR LATER DISPOSAL. DO NOT SCATTER MATERIAL (1987 EMERGENCY RESPONSE GUIDEBOOK, DOT P 5800.4, GUIDE PAGE 55).

USE AGENT SUITABLE FOR TYPE OF FIRE; USE WATER IN FLOODING QUANTITIES AS FOG. COOL CONTAINERS WITH FLOODING AMOUNTS OF WATER, APPLY FROM AS FAR A DISTANCE AS POSSIBLE. AVOID BREATHING POISONOUS VAPORS, KEEP UPWIND.

TRANSPORTATION DATA

DEPARTMENT OF TRANSPORTATION HAZARD CLASSIFICATION 49 CFR 172.101: POISON B

DEPARTMENT OF TRANSPORTATION LABELING REQUIREMENTS 49 CFR 172.101 AND SUBPART E: POISON

DEPARTMENT OF TRANSPORTATION PACKAGING REQUIREMENTS: 49 CFR 173.370 EXCEPTIONS: 49 CFR 173.370

TOXICITY

SODIUM CYANIDE: TOXICITY DATA: 5048 UG/KG OCULAR-RABBIT LD50; 714 UG/KG ORAL-MAN TDLO; 6557 UG/KG ORAL-MAN LDLO; 2857 UG/KG ORAL-HUMAN LDLO; 6440 UG/KG ORAL-RAT LD50; 4 MG/KG ORAL-DOMESTIC ANIMAL LD50; 2200 UG/KG SUBCUTANEOUS-RABBIT LDLO; 3600 UG/KG SUBCUTANEOUS-MOUSE LD50; 5800 UG/KG SUBCUTANEOUS-GUINEA PIG LD50; 1300 UG/KG INTRAVENOUS-DOG LDLO; 4300 UG/KG INTRAPERITONEAL-RAT LD50; 5881 UG/KG INTRAPERITONEAL-MOUSE LD50; 1666 UG/KG INTRAMUSCULAR-RABBIT LD50; 2206 UG/KG UNREPORTED-MAN LDLO; REPRODUCTIVE EFFECTS DATA (RTECS). CARCINOGEN STATUS: NONE. LOCAL EFFECTS: CORROSIVE- INHALATION, SKIN, AND EYES. ACUTE TOXICITY LEVEL: HIGHLY TOXIC BY INGESTION. TARGET EFFECTS: CHEMICAL ASPHYXIANT. POISONING MAY AFFECT THE RESPIRATORY, CARDIOVASCULAR AND CENTRAL NERVOUS SYSTEMS. AT INCREASED RISK FROM EXPOSURE: PERSONS WITH HISTORY OF FAINTING SPELLS (SYMPTOMS OF VARIOUS TYPES OF CARDIOVASCULAR AND NERVOUS DISORDERS), UNUSUAL SUSCEPTIBILITY TO EFFECTS OF ANOXIA OR WITH ANEMIA, PRE-EXISTING SKIN DISORDERS AND/OR IMPAIRED PULMONARY FUNCTION.

HEALTH EFFECTS AND FIRST AID

INHALATION: SODIUM CYANIDE: IRRITANT/CHEMICAL ASPHYXIANT. 50 MG/M3 IS IMMEDIATELY DANGEROUS TO LIFE OR HEALTH. **<u>ACUTE EXPOSURE</u>-** MAY CAUSE IRRITATION TO THE NOSE AND MUCOUS MEMBRANES. MISTS OF ALKALI CYANIDES, IN CONCENTRATIONS SLIGHTLY MORE THAN 5 MG/M3, HAVE BEEN

REPORTED TO CAUSE NOSEBLEED AND NASAL ULCERATION. IF SUFFICIENT AMOUNTS ARE ABSORBED, SYSTEMIC EFFECTS MAY OCCUR, AS IN ACUTE INGESTION. **CHRONIC EXPOSURE-** EXPOSURE TO LOW LEVELS OF CYANIDE COMPOUNDS OVER LONG PERIODS OF TIME, IS REPORTED TO CAUSE LOSS OF APPETITE, HEADACHE, WEAKNESS, NAUSEA, DIZZINESS AND SYMPTOMS OF UPPER RESPIRATORY TRACT IRRITATION.

FIRST AID- REMOVE FROM EXPOSURE. IF BREATHING HAS STOPPED OR IS DEPRESSED, GIVE ARTIFICIAL RESPIRATION. MAINTAIN AIRWAY AND ADMINISTER OXYGEN TO MAINTAIN HIGH BLOOD/OXYGEN TENSION. GET MEDICAL ATTENTION IMMEDIATELY. (DREISBACH, HANDBOOK OF POISONING, 11TH ED.).

SKIN CONTACT: SODIUM CYANIDE: CORROSIVE/CHEMICAL ASPHYXIANT. **ACUTE EXPOSURE-** DIRECT CONTACT WITH AQUEOUS SOLUTIONS OR SOLID ON MOIST SKIN MAY CAUSE REDNESS, PAIN, BURNS, CONTACT DERMATITIS AND ULCERS WHICH ARE SLOW TO HEAL. SODIUM CYANIDE MAY BE ABSORBED THROUGH THE SKIN, ESPECIALLY IF OPEN WOUNDS ARE PRESENT. IF SUFFICIENT AMOUNTS ARE ABSORBED, SYSTEMIC EFFECTS MAY OCCUR, AS IN ACUTE INGESTION. **CHRONIC EXPOSURE-** PROLONGED AND REPEATED EXPOSURE MAY CAUSE DERMATITIS AND "CYANIDE RASH", CHARACTERIZED BY ITCHING, MACULAR, PAPULAR AND VESICULAR ERUPTIONS. EXPOSURE TO LOW LEVELS OF CYANIDE COMPOUNDS OVER LONG PERIODS OF TIME IS REPORTED TO CAUSE LOSS OF APPETITE, HEADACHE, WEAKNESS, NAUSEA, AND DIZZINESS.

FIRST AID- REMOVE CONTAMINATED CLOTHING AND SHOES AND WASH AFFECTED AREAS WITH SOAP OR MILD DETERGENT AND LARGE AMOUNTS OF WATER, TAKING CARE NOT TO CONTACT THE CHEMICAL. GET MEDICAL ATTENTION IMMEDIATELY. (CAIN, EMERGENCY TREATMENT AND MANAGEMENT, 7TH ED.).

EYE CONTACT: SODIUM CYANIDE: CORROSIVE/CHEMICAL ASPHYXIANT/HIGHLY TOXIC. **ACUTE EXPOSURE-** THE LETHAL DOSE FOR RABBITS IS 5048 UG/KG. DUST MAY CAUSE IRRITATION. SOLUTIONS ARE CORROSIVE AND MAY CAUSE REDNESS, PAIN, BLURRED VISION, AND SERIOUS CORNEAL BURNS. IN THE PRESENCE OF TEARS, SYSTEMIC INTOXICATION MAY OCCUR, DEMONSTRATING SYMPTOMS SIMILAR TO THOSE DESCRIBED IN ACUTE INGESTION SECTION. **CHRONIC EXPOSURE-** EFFECTS DEPEND ON CONCENTRATION AND DURATION OF EXPOSURE. REPEATED OR PROLONGED CONTACT WITH CORROSIVE SUBSTANCES MAY RESULT IN CONJUNCTIVITIS OR EFFECTS AS IN ACUTE EXPOSURE.

FIRST AID- WASH EYES IMMEDIATELY WITH LARGE AMOUNTS OF WATER, OCCASIONALLY LIFTING UPPER AND LOWER LIDS, UNTIL NO EVIDENCE OF CHEMICAL REMAINS (AT LEAST 15-20 MINUTES). CONTINUE IRRIGATING WITH NORMAL SALINE UNTIL THE PH HAS RETURNED TO NORMAL (30-60 MINUTES). COVER WITH STERILE BANDAGES. GET MEDICAL ATTENTION IMMEDIATELY.

INGESTION: SODIUM CYANIDE: CORROSIVE/CHEMICAL ASPHYXIANT/HIGHLY TOXIC. **ACUTE EXPOSURE-** MASSIVE DOSES MAY RESULT IN IMMEDIATE UNCONSCIOUSNESS, OFTEN WITH CONVULIONS AND DEATH, USUALLY WITHIN 1-15 MINUTES. LOWER LEVELS MAY RESULT IN CORROSION OF THE GASTRIC MUCOSA, A BITTER ALMOND ODOR ON THE BREATH, A BURNING TASTE, FEELING OF CONSTRICTION OF THE THROAT, BLOTCHY SKIN ERUPTIONS ON THE FACE, SALIVATION, NAUSEA WITH OR WITHOUT VOMITING, ANXIETY, CONFUSION, VERTIGO, GIDDINESS, WEAKNESS, HEADACHE, RAPID PULSE, PALPITATIONS, LOWER JAW STIFFNESS, AND OPISTHOTONOS. RESPIRATORY RATE AND DEPTH USUALLY INCREASE INITIALLY, BECOMING SLOW AND GASPING. CYANOSIS, COMA, CONVULSIONS, AND BRADYCARDIA OCCUR IN SOME CASES. INVOLUNTARY MICTURITION AND DEFECATION MAY OCCUR. PARALYSIS MAY FOLLOW THE CONVULSIVE STAGE. THE EYEBALLS MAY PROTRUDE AND THE PUPILS MAY BE UNREACTIVE. DAMAGE TO THE OPTIC NERVES AND RETINA AND BLINDNESS ARE POSSIBLE. THE MOUTH MAY BE COVERED WITH FOAM, WHICH IS SOMETIMES BLOOD-STAINED, INDICATIVE OF PULMONARY EDEMA. IF DEATH OCCURS IT IS USUALLY WITHIN 4 HOURS AND MAY BE DUE TO RESPIRATORY ARREST OR TISSUE ANOXIA. OTHER SYMPTOMS MAY INCLUDE CHEST PAIN, CHERRY-RED COLORING, IRREGULAR SPEECH, AND A TRANSIENT STAGE OF CENTRAL NERVOUS SYSTEM STIMULATION WITH HYPERNEA AND HEADACHE. THE LETHAL DOSE IN RATS IS 6440 UG/KG. **CHRONIC EXPOSURE-** EXPOSURE TO LOW LEVELS OF CYANIDE COMPOUNDS OVER LONG PERIODS OF TIME, IS REPORTED TO CAUSE LOSS OF APPETITE, HEADACHE, WEAKNESS, NAUSEA, AND DIZZINESS.

FIRST AID- IF PATIENT IS ASYMPTOMATIC ADMINISTER SYRUP OF IPECAC AND/OR PERFORM GASTRIC LAVAGE, USING TAP WATER, DILUTE SODIUM BICARBONATE SOLUTION OR PREFERABLY, IF AVAILABLE, DILUTE POTASSIUM PERMANGANATE SOLUTION (1:5000). ACTIVATED CHARCOAL IS INEFFECTIVE. IF BREATHING HAS STOPPED, GIVE ARTIFICIAL RESPIRATION. MAINTAIN AIRWAY. OXYGEN THERAPY MAY BE OF VALUE IN COMBINATION WITH THE ANTIDOTE (GOSSELIN, CLINICAL TOXICOLOGY OF COMMERCIAL PRODUCTS, 5TH ED.). TREATMENT SHOULD BE PERFORMED BY QUALIFIED MEDICAL PERSONNEL. GET MEDICAL ATTENTION IMMEDIATELY.

ANTIDOTE: THE FOLLOWING ANTIDOTE HAS BEEN RECOMMENDED. HOWEVER, THE DECISION AS TO WHETHER THE SEVERITY OF POISONING REQUIRES ADMINISTRATION OF ANY ANTIDOTE AND ACTUAL DOSE REQUIRED SHOULD BE MADE BY QUALIFIED MEDICAL PERSONNEL.
FOR CYANIDE POISONING: IF SYMPTOMS OF CYANIDE POISONING ARE EVIDENT, ADMINISTER IMMEDIATELY BEFORE ANY OTHER FIRST AID MEASURES.
ADMINISTER AMYL NITRITE (AMYL NITRITE PERLES) BY INHALATION FOR 15 TO 30 SECONDS OF EVERY MINUTE, WHILE SODIUM NITRITE SOLUTION IS BEING PREPARED. DISCONTINUE AMYL NITRITE AND IMMEDIATELY INJECT 10 ML OF A 3% SOLUTION OF SODIUM NITRITE INTRAVENOUSLY OVER A PERIOD OF 2 TO 4 MINUTES. IF NECESSARY, INJECT A NON-STERILE SOLUTION. DO NOT REMOVE THE NEEDLE. CAUTION: APPROPRIATE ADJUSTMENTS IN THE DOSE SHOULD BE MADE ON A BODY WEIGHT BASIS. THROUGH THE SAME NEEDLE, INFUSE INTRAVENOUSLY 50 ML OF A 25% AQUEOUS SOLUTION OF SODIUM THIOSULFATE. THE INJECTION SHOULD TAKE ABOUT 10 MINUTES. OTHER CONCENTRATIONS (5 TO 50%) ARE PERMISSIBLE IF THE TOTAL DOSE IS HELD AT APPROXIMATELY 12 GRAMS.
OXYGEN THERAPY MAY BE OF VALUE IN COMBINATION WITH NITRITE AND SODIUM THIOSULFATE THERAPY. IF SYMPTOMS RECUR, THE INJECTIONS OF NITRITE AND THIOSULFATE MAY BE REPEATED AT HALF THE ABOVE DOSES. IN VERY SEVERE POISONINGS IT IS SAFER AND PERHAPS MORE EFFICIENT TO KEEP REPEATING THE THIOSULFATE INJECTIONS INSTEAD OF THE NITRITE (GOSSELIN, SMITH, HODGE, CLINICAL TOXICOLOGY OF COMMERCIAL PRODUCTS, 5TH ED.).
ANTIDOTE SHOULD BE ADMINISTERED BY QUALIFIED MEDICAL PERSONNEL.

REACTIVITY

REACTIVITY: STABLE UNDER NORMAL TEMPERATURES AND PRESSURES.

INCOMPATIBILITIES: SODIUM CYANIDE: ACIDS, ACID SALTS: FORM TOXIC AND FLAMMABLE HYDROGEN CYANIDE GAS. CHLORATES: EXPLODE ABOVE 450 C. ETHYL CHLOROACETATE: POSSIBLE VIOLENT REACTION. NITRATES (MOLTEN): EXPLODE. NITRIC ACID: EXPLOSIVE REACTION. NITRITES (MOLTEN): EXLPODE. OXIDIZERS (STRONG): EXPLOSION HAZARD. PEROXIDES: VIOLENT REACTION. SEE ALSO CYANIDE SALTS.
CYANIDE SALTS: ACIDS, ACID SALTS: FORM TOXIC AND FLAMMABLE HYDROGEN GAS. CHLORATES: POSSIBLE EXPLOSION ON HEATING. FLUORINE: VIGOROUS REACTION. MAGNESIUM: POSSIBLE INCANDESCENT REACTION. NITRATES (MOLTEN): POSSIBLE EXPLOSIVE REACTION. NITRIC ACID: POSSIBLE EXPLOSIVE REACTION. NITRITES: POSSIBLE EXPLOSION ON HEATING. OXIDIZERS (STRONG): FIRE AND EXPLOSION HAZARD.

DECOMPOSITION: THERMAL DECOMPOSITION PRODUCTS MAY INCLUDE HIGHLY TOXIC FUMES OF HYDROGEN CYANIDE.

POLYMERIZATION: HAZARDOUS POLYMERIZATION HAS NOT BEEN REPORTED TO OCCUR UNDER NORMAL TEMPERATURES AND PRESSURES.

STORAGE AND DISPOSAL

OBSERVE ALL FEDERAL, STATE AND LOCAL REGULATIONS WHEN STORING OR DISPOSING OF THIS SUBSTANCE. FOR ASSISTANCE, CONTACT THE DISTRICT DIRECTOR OF THE ENVIRONMENTAL PROTECTION AGENCY.

****STORAGE****

PROTECT AGAINST PHYSICAL DAMAGE. STORE IN A COOL, DRY PLACE. SEPARATE FROM OTHER STORAGE AND PROTECT FROM ACIDS AND OXIDIZING MATERIALS (NFPA 49, HAZARDOUS CHEMICALS DATA, 1975).
STORE AWAY FROM INCOMPATIBLE SUBSTANCES.
THRESHOLD PLANNING QUANTITY (TPQ): THE SUPERFUND AMENDMENTS AND REAUTHORIZATION ACT (SARA) SECTION 302 REQUIRES THAT EACH FACILITY WHERE ANY EXTREMELY HAZARDOUS SUBSTANCE IS PRESENT IN A QUANTITY EQUAL TO OR GREATER THAN THE TPQ ESTABLISHED FOR THAT SUBSTANCE NOTIFY THE STATE EMERGENCY RESPONSE COMMISSION FOR THE STATE IN WHICH IT IS LOCATED. SECTION 303 OF SARA REQUIRES THESE FACILITIES TO PARTICIPATE IN LOCAL EMERGENCY RESPONSE PLANNING (40 CFR 355.30).

****DISPOSAL****

DISPOSAL MUST BE IN ACCORDANCE WITH STANDARDS APPLICABLE TO GENERATORS OF HAZARDOUS WASTE, 40CFR 262. EPA HAZARDOUS WASTE NUMBER P106.

CONDITIONS TO AVOID

MAY BURN BUT DOES NOT IGNITE READILY. CONTAINERS MAY EXPLODE IN HEAT OF FIRE.

SPILL AND LEAK PROCEDURES

SOIL SPILL: DIG A HOLDING AREA SUCH AS PIT, POND OR LAGOON TO CONTAIN SPILLED MATERIAL. USE PROTECTIVE COVER SUCH AS A PLASTIC SHEET TO PREVENT DISSOLVING IN FIREFIGHTING WATER OR RAIN.

AIR SPILL: APPLY WATER SPRAY TO KNOCK DOWN AND REDUCE VAPORS. KNOCK-DOWN WATER IS CORROSIVE AND TOXIC AND SHOULD BE DIKED FOR CONTAINMENT.

WATER SPILL: NEUTRALIZE WITH CAUSTIC SODA.
ADD CALCIUM HYPOCHLORITE TO SPILL.

OCCUPATIONAL SPILL: DO NOT TOUCH SPILLED MATERIAL. STOP LEAK IF YOU CAN DO IT WITHOUT RISK. USE WATER SPRAY TO REDUCE VAPORS. FOR SMALL SPILLS, TAKE UP WITH SAND OR OTHER ABSORBENT MATERIAL AND PLACE INTO CONTAINERS FOR LATER DISPOSAL. FOR SMALL DRY SPILLS, WITH A CLEAN SHOVEL PLACE MATERIAL INTO CLEAN, DRY CONTAINERS AND COVER. MOVE CONTAINERS FROM SPILL AREA. FOR LARGER SPILLS, DIKE FAR AHEAD OF SPILL FOR LATER DISPOSAL. KEEP UNNECESSARY PEOPLE AWAY. ISOLATE HAZARD AREA AND DENY ENTRY. VENTILATE CLOSED SPACES BEFORE ENTERING. REPORTABLE QUANTITY (RQ): 10 POUNDS THE SUPERFUND AMENDMENTS AND REAUTHORIZATION ACT (SARA) SECTION 304 REQUIRES THAT A RELEASE EQUAL TO OR GREATER THAN THE REPORTABLE QUANTITY FOR THIS SUBSTANCE BE IMMEDIATELY REPORTED TO THE LOCAL EMERGENCY PLANNING COMMITTEE AND THE STATE EMERGENCY RESPONSE COMMISSION (40 CFR 355.40). IF THE RELEASE OF THIS SUBSTANCE IS REPORTABLE UNDER CERCLA SECTION 103, THE NATIONAL RESPONSE CENTER MUST BE NOTIFIED IMMEDIATELY AT (800) 424-8802 OR (202) 426-2675 IN THE METROPOLITAN WASHINGTON, D.C. AREA (40 CFR 302.6).

PROTECTIVE EQUIPMENT

VENTILATION: PROVIDE LOCAL EXHAUST OR PROCESS ENCLOSURE VENTILATION TO MEET PUBLISHED EXPOSURE LIMITS.

RESPIRATOR: THE FOLLOWING RESPIRATORS AND MAXIMUM USE CONCENTRATIONS ARE RECOMMENDATIONS BY THE U.S. DEPARTMENT OF HEALTH AND HUMAN SERVICES, NIOSH POCKET GUIDE TO CHEMICAL HAZARDS; NIOSH CRITERIA DOCUMENTS OR BY THE U.S. DEPARTMENT OF LABOR, 29 CFR 1910 SUBPART Z. THE SPECIFIC RESPIRATOR SELECTED MUST BE BASED ON CONTAMINATION LEVELS FOUND IN THE WORK PLACE, MUST NOT EXCEED THE WORKING LIMITS OF THE RESPIRATOR AND BE JOINTLY APPROVED BY THE NATIONAL INSTITUTE FOR OCCUPATIONAL SAFETY AND HEALTH AND THE MINE SAFETY AND HEALTH ADMINISTRATION (NIOSH-MSHA).

CYANIDES (AS CN):

50 MG(CN)/M3- SUPPLIED-AIR RESPIRATOR. SELF-CONTAINED BREATHING APPARATUS.

ESCAPE- AIR-PURIFYING FULL FACEPIECE RESPIRATOR (GAS MASK) WITH CHIN-STYLE OR FRONT- OR BACK-MOUNTED CANISTER PROVIDING PROTECTION AGAINST CYANIDE AND HAVING A HIGH-EFFICIENCY PARTICULATE FILTER. APPROPRIATE ESCAPE-TYPE SELF-CONTAINED BREATHING APPARATUS.

FOR FIREFIGHTING AND OTHER IMMEDIATELY DANGEROUS TO LIFE OR HEALTH CONDITIONS:

SELF-CONTAINED BREATHING APPARATUS WITH FULL FACEPIECE OPERATED IN PRESSURE-DEMAND OR OTHER POSITIVE PRESSURE MODE.

SUPPLIED-AIR RESPIRATOR WITH FULL FACEPIECE AND OPERATED IN PRESSURE-DEMAND OR OTHER POSITIVE PRESSURE MODE IN COMBINATION WITH AN AUXILIARY SELF-CONTAINED BREATHING APPARATUS OPERATED IN PRESSURE-DEMAND OR OTHER POSITIVE PRESSURE MODE.

CLOTHING: EMPLOYEE MUST WEAR APPROPRIATE PROTECTIVE (IMPERVIOUS) CLOTHING AND EQUIPMENT TO PREVENT ANY POSSIBILITY OF SKIN CONTACT WITH THIS SUBSTANCE.

GLOVES: EMPLOYEE MUST WEAR APPROPRIATE PROTECTIVE GLOVES TO PREVENT CONTACT WITH THIS SUBSTANCE.

EYE PROTECTION: EMPLOYEE MUST WEAR SPLASH-PROOF OR DUST-RESISTANT SAFETY GOGGLES AND A FACESHIELD TO PREVENT CONTACT WITH THIS SUBSTANCE.

EMERGENCY WASH FACILITIES: WHERE THERE IS ANY POSSIBILITY THAT AN EMPLOYEE'S EYES AND/OR SKIN MAY BE EXPOSED TO THIS SUBSTANCE, THE EMPLOYER SHOULD PROVIDE AN EYE WASH FOUNTAIN AND QUICK DRENCH SHOWER WITHIN THE IMMEDIATE WORK AREA FOR EMERGENCY USE.

AUTHORIZED BY- OCCUPATIONAL HEALTH SERVICES, INC.

CREATION DATE: 10/05/89 ***REVISION DATE:*** 05/16/90

MATERIAL SAFETY DATA SHEET

OCCUPATIONAL HEALTH SERVICES, INC.
AGRICULTURE AND PESTICIDE DIVISION
450 SEVENTH AVENUE, SUITE 2407
NEW YORK, NEW YORK 10123
1-800-445-MSDS OR (212) 967-1100

EMERGENCY CONTACT:
JOHN S. BRANSFORD, JR. (615) 292-1180

SUBSTANCE IDENTIFICATION

CAS-NUMBER 2893-78-9

SUBSTANCE: **SODIUM DICHLOROISOCYANURATE**

TRADE NAMES/SYNONYMS: SODIUM DICHLORO-S-TRIAZINETRIONE; SIMPLA; ACL 60; SODIUM DICHLORISOCYANURATE; DICHLOROISOCYANURIC ACID, SODIUM SALT; DIKONITE; SODIUM DICYLOROCYANURATE; S-TARIAZINE-2,4,6(1H,3H,5H)-TRIONE, DICHLORO, SODIUM SALT; DIMANINC; SDIC; 1-SODIUM-3,5-DICHLORO-S-TRIAZINE-2,4,6-TRIONE; STCC 4918435; UN 2465; PST21180

CHEMICAL FAMILY: HETEROCYCLIC NITROGEN HALOGEN

MOLECULAR FORMULA: C3-H-CL2-N3-O3.NA

MOLECULAR WEIGHT: 220.96

CERCLA RATINGS (SCALE 0-3): HEALTH=2 FIRE=0 REACTIVITY=2 PERSISTENCE=0

NFPA RATINGS (SCALE 0-4): HEALTH=2 FIRE=0 REACTIVITY=2

COMPONENTS AND CONTAMINANTS

COMPONENT: SODIUM DICHLOROISOCYANURATE ***PERCENT:*** 100%
CAS# 2893-78-9

OTHER CONTAMINANTS: NONE

EXPOSURE LIMITS: NO OCCUPATIONAL EXPOSURE LIMITS ESTABLISHED BY OSHA, ACGIH, OR NIOSH.

PHYSICAL DATA

DESCRIPTION: WHITE CRYSTALS WITH A CHLORINE ODOR AND SLIGHLTY HYGROSCOPIC. ***MELTING POINT:*** 446 F (230 C)

SPECIFIC GRAVITY: 0.96 ***SOLUBILITY IN WATER:*** SOLUBLE

FIRE AND EXPLOSION DATA

FIRE AND EXPLOSION HAZARD: NEGLIGIBLE FIRE HAZARD WHEN EXPOSED TO HEAT OR FLAME. OXIDIZER: OXIDIZERS DECOMPOSE, ESPECIALLY WHEN HEATED, TO YIELD OXYGEN OR OTHER GASES WHICH WILL INCREASE THE BURNING RATE OF COMBUSTIBLE MATTER. CONTACT WITH EASILY OXIDIZABLE, ORGANIC, OR OTHER COMBUSTIBLE MATERIALS MAY RESULT IN IGNITION, VIOLENT COMBUSTION OR EXPLOSION.

FIREFIGHTING MEDIA: DRY CHEMICAL, CARBON DIOXIDE, HALON OR WATER SPRAY (1987 EMERGENCY RESPONSE GUIDEBOOK, DOT P 5800.4).

FOR LARGER FIRES, USE WATER SPRAY OR FOG (1987 EMERGENCY RESPONSE GUIDEBOOK, DOT P 5800.4).

FIREFIGHTING: MOVE CONTAINERS FROM FIRE AREA IF POSSIBLE. COOL CONTAINERS EXPOSED TO FLAME WITH WATER FROM SIDE UNTIL WELL AFTER FIRE IS OUT. KEEP AWAY FROM STORAGE TANK ENDS. FOR MASSIVE FIRE IN STORAGE AREA, USE UNMANNED HOSE HOLDER OR MONITOR NOZZLES (1987 EMERGENCY RESPONSE GUIDEBOOK, DOT 5800.4, GUIDE PAGE 42).

FLOOD WITH WATER. COOL CONTAINERS WITH FLOODING AMOUNTS OF WATER,APPLY FROM AS FAR A DISTANCE AS POSSIBLE. AVOID BREATHING TOXIC VAPORS, KEEP UPWIND. EVACUATE TO A RADIUS OF 2500 FEET FOR UNCONTROLLABLE FIRES.

TRANSPORTATION DATA

DEPARTMENT OF TRANSPORTATION HAZARD CLASSIFICATION 49 CFR 172.101: OXIDIZER

DEPARTMENT OF TRANSPORTATION LABELING REQUIREMENTS 49 CFR 172.101 AND SUBPART E: OXIDIZER

DEPARTMENT OF TRANSPORTATION PACKAGING REQUIREMENTS: 49 CFR 173.217 EXCEPTIONS: 49 CFR 173.153

TOXICITY

SODIUM DICHLOROISOCYANURATE: IRRITATION DATA: 500 MG/24 HOURS SKIN-RABBIT MILD; 500 MG SKIN-RABBIT SEVERE; 10 MG/24 HOURS EYE-RABBIT MODERATE. TOXICITY DATA: 3570 MG/KG ORAL-HUMAN LDLO; REPRODUCTIVE EFFECTS DATA (RTECS). CARCINOGEN STATUS: NONE. LOCAL EFFECTS: IRRITANT-INHALATION, SKIN, AND EYES. ACUTE TOXICITY LEVEL: INSUFFICIENT DATA. TARGET EFFECTS: NO DATA AVAILABLE.

HEALTH EFFECTS AND FIRST AID

INHALATION: SODIUM DICHLOROISOCYANURATE: IRRITANT. **ACUTE EXPOSURE-** MAY CAUSE RESPIRATORY TRACT IRRITATION, COUGHING AND CHOKING. BRONCHOSPASMS MAY OCCUR IN SOME PERSONS. **CHRONIC EXPOSURE-** NO DATA AVAILABLE.

FIRST AID- REMOVE FROM EXPOSURE AREA TO FRESH AIR IMMEDIATELY. IF BREATHING HAS STOPPED, GIVE ARTIFICIAL RESPIRATION. MAINTAIN AIRWAY AND BLOOD PRESSURE AND ADMINISTER OXYGEN IF AVAILABLE. KEEP AFFECTED PERSON WARM AND AT REST. TREAT SYMPTOMATICALLY AND SUPPORTIVELY. ADMINISTRATION OF OXYGEN SHOULD BE PERFORMED BY QUALIFIED PERSONNEL. GET MEDICAL ATTENTION IMMEDIATELY.

SKIN CONTACT: SODIUM DICHLOROISOCYANURATE: IRRITANT. **ACUTE EXPOSURE-** DIRECT CONTACT WITH CRYSTALS MAY CAUSE MILD IRRITATION ON DRY SKIN.

THE PRESENCE OF MOISTURE MAY CAUSE INCREASED IRRITATION. **CHRONIC EXPOSURE-** PROLONGED OR REPEATED CONTACT MAY CAUSE DERMATITIS. ANIMAL STUDIES INDICATE THAT DAILY APPLICATIONS OF DILUTE SOLUTIONS CAUSED LITTLE OR NO IRRITATION.

FIRST AID- REMOVE CONTAMINATED CLOTHING AND SHOES IMMEDIATELY. WASH AFFECTED AREA WITH SOAP OR MILD DETERGENT AND LARGE AMOUNTS OF WATER UNTIL NO EVIDENCE OF CHEMICAL REMAINS (AT LEAST 15-20 MINUTES). IN CASE OF CHEMICAL BURNS, COVER AREA WITH STERILE, DRY DRESSING. BANDAGE SECURELY, BUT NOT TOO TIGHTLY. GET MEDICAL ATTENTION IMMEDIATELY.

EYE CONTACT: SODIUM DICHLOROISOCYANURATE: IRRITANT. **ACUTE EXPOSURE-** CRYSTALS MAY CAUSE LACRIMATION AND MODERATE IRRITATION. 10 MG PRODUCED SEVERE IRRITATION IN RABBIT EYES. **CHRONIC EXPOSURE-** PROLONGED OR REPEATED EXPOSURE MAY CAUSE CONJUNCTIVITIS. ANIMAL STUDIES INDICATE THAT REPEATED APPLICATION OF DILUTE AQUEOUS SOLUTIONS CAUSED LITTLE OR NO IRRITATION.

FIRST AID- WASH EYES IMMEDIATELY WITH LARGE AMOUNTS OF WATER, OCCASIONALLY LIFTING UPPER AND LOWER LIDS, UNTIL NO EVIDENCE OF CHEMICAL REMAINS (AT LEAST 15-20 MINUTES). CONTINUE IRRIGATING WITH NORMAL SALINE UNTIL THE PH HAS RETURNED TO NORMAL (30-60 MINUTES). COVER WITH STERILE BANDAGES. GET MEDICAL ATTENTION IMMEDIATELY.

INGESTION: SODIUM DICHLOROISOCYANURATE: **ACUTE EXPOSURE-** MAY CAUSE GASTROINTESTINAL IRRITATION, SALIVATION, DYSPNEA, LACRIMATION, WEAKNESS, EMACIATION, LETHARGY, DIARRHEA, AND COMA. INGESTION OF LARGE DOSES MAY RESULT IN DEATH WHICH MAY BE DELAYED 1-8 DAYS. PATHOLOGICAL FINDINGS INCLUDE IRRITATION OF THE STOMACH AND GASTROINTESTINAL TRACT, LIVER DYSFUNCTION AND LUNG CONGESTION. **CHRONIC EXPOSURE-** NO HUMAN DATA AVAILABLE. ANIMAL STUDIES INDICATE THAT REPEATED ADMINISTRATION OF DILUTE AQUEOUS SOLUTIONS DID NOT PRODUCE ANY LOCAL OR SYSTEMIC EFFECTS. ADMINISTRATION OF A TOTAL DOSE OF 4 GM/KG TO PREGNANT MICE FOR 10 DAYS EARLY IN GESTATION RESULTED IN MUSCULOSKELETAL DEVELOPMENTAL ABNORMALITIES, REDUCED WEIGHT GAIN IN NEWBORNS, AND OTHER UNSPECIFIED PHYSICAL EFFECTS.

FIRST AID- CAUTIOUSLY PERFORM GASTRIC LAVAGE, FOLLOWED BY MILK OR OTHER DEMULCENT. AVOID CARBONATES AND BICARBONATES BECAUSE OF GAS FORMATION. (ARENA, POISONING, 4TH ED.). GASTRIC LAVAGE SHOULD BE PERFORMED BY QUALIFIED MEDICAL PERSONNEL ONLY.

ANTIDOTE: NO SPECIFIC ANTIDOTE. TREAT SYMPTOMATICALLY AND SUPPORTIVELY.

REACTIVITY

REACTIVITY: MAY VIGOROUSLY REACT WITH SMALL QUANITIES OF WATER RELEASING CHLORINE GAS. MOISTURE SENSITIVE.

INCOMPATIBILITIES: UREA: REACTS AND MAY FORM HIGHLY EXPLOSIVE NITROGEN TRICHLORIDE. NITROGEN CONTAINING COMPOUNDS: REACTS AND MAY FORM HIGHLY EXPLOSIVE NITROGEN TRICHLORIDE. DIMETHYLSULFOXIDE: REACTS AND GIVES OFF FUMES. ORGANIC COMPOUNDS: POSSIBLE OXIDIZING REACTION.

DECOMPOSITION: THERMAL DECOMPOSITION MAY EMIT TOXIC FUMES OF CHLORINE, OXIDES OF CARBON AND NITROGEN.

POLYMERIZATION: HAZARDOUS POLYMERIZATION HAS NOT BEEN REPORTED TO OCCUR UNDER NORMAL TEMPERATURES AND PRESSURES.

STORAGE AND DISPOSAL

OBSERVE ALL FEDERAL, STATE AND LOCAL REGULATIONS WHEN STORING OR DISPOSING OF THIS SUBSTANCE. FOR ASSISTANCE, CONTACT THE DISTRICT DIRECTOR OF THE ENVIRONMENTAL PROTECTION AGENCY.

****STORAGE****

STORAGE: PROTECT AGAINST PHYSICAL DAMAGE. STORE IN A COOL, DRY, WELL VENTILATED PLACE AWAY FROM FLAMMABLE LIQUIDS, COMBUSTIBLE MATERIALS, AND OXIDIZABLE MATERIALS. DRUMS MAY RUPTURE IF THE CONTENTS ARE EXPOSED TO HEAT OR BECOME CONTAMINATED OR WET. DRUMS SHOULD BE PALLETIZED TO PREVENT WETTING FROM FLOOR WASHINGS OR DRAINAGE. AVOID PROLONGED STORAGE IN UNVENTILATED AREAS AT SUMMER TEMPERATURES (NFPA 49, HAZARDOUS CHEMICALS DATA, 1975).

CONDITIONS TO AVOID

AVOID CONTACT WITH OTHER COMBUSTIBLE MATERIALS (WOOD, PAPER, OIL, ETC.). AVOID CONTACT WITH EYES AND SKIN; MATERIAL MAY BE POISONOUS OR CORROSIVE.

SPILL AND LEAK PROCEDURES

OCCUPATIONAL SPILL: KEEP COMBUSTIBLES (WOOD, PAPER, OIL, ETC.) AWAY FROM SPILLED MATERIAL. DO NOT TOUCH SPILLED MATERIAL. FOR SMALL DRY SPILLS, WITH CLEAN SHOVEL PLACE MATERIAL INTO CLEAN, DRY CONTAINER AND COVER; MOVE CONTAINERS FROM SPILL AREA. FOR LARGER SPILLS, DIKE FAR AHEAD OF SPILL FOR LATER DISPOSAL. KEEP UNNECESSARY PEOPLE AWAY. ISOLATE HAZARD AREA AND DENY ENTRY.

PROTECTIVE EQUIPMENT

VENTILATION: PROVIDE LOCAL EXHAUST VENTILATION SYSTEM.

RESPIRATOR: THE FOLLOWING RESPIRATORS ARE RECOMMENDED BASED ON INFORMATION FOUND IN THE PHYSICAL DATA, TOXICITY AND HEALTH EFFECTS SECTIONS. THEY ARE RANKED IN ORDER FROM MINIMUM TO MAXIMUM RESPIRATORY PROTECTION. THE SPECIFIC RESPIRATOR SELECTED MUST BE BASED ON CONTAMINATION LEVELS FOUND IN THE WORK PLACE, MUST NOT EXCEED THE WORKING LIMITS OF THE RESPIRATOR AND BE JOINTLY APPROVED BY THE NATIONAL INSTITUTE FOR OCCUPATIONAL SAFETY AND HEALTH AND THE MINE SAFETY AND HEALTH ADMINISTRATION (NIOSH-MSHA).

DUST AND MIST RESPIRATOR WITH A FULL FACEPIECE.

AIR-PURIFYING FULL FACEPIECE RESPIRATOR WITH A HIGH-EFFICIENCY PARTICULATE FILTER.

POWERED AIR-PURIFYING RESPIRATOR WITH A TIGHT-FITTING FACEPIECE AND HIGH-EFFICIENCY PARTICULATE FILTER.

TYPE 'C' SUPPLIED-AIR RESPIRATOR WITH A FULL FACEPIECE OPERATED IN PRESSURE-DEMAND OR OTHER POSITIVE PRESSURE MODE OR WITH A FULL FACEPIECE, HELMET OR HOOD OPERATED IN CONTINUOUS-FLOW MODE.

SELF-CONTAINED BREATHING APPARATUS WITH A FULL FACEPIECE OPERATED IN PRESSURE-DEMAND OR OTHER POSITIVE PRESSURE MODE.

FOR FIREFIGHTING AND OTHER IMMEDIATELY DANGEROUS TO LIFE OR HEALTH CONDITIONS:

SELF-CONTAINED BREATHING APPARATUS WITH FULL FACEPIECE OPERATED IN PRESSURE-DEMAND OR OTHER POSITIVE PRESSURE MODE.

SUPPLIED-AIR RESPIRATOR WITH FULL FACEPIECE AND OPERATED IN PRESSURE-DEMAND OR OTHER POSITIVE PRESSURE MODE IN COMBINATION WITH AN AUXILIARY SELF-CONTAINED BREATHING APPARATUS OPERATED IN PRESSURE-DEMAND OR OTHER POSITIVE PRESSURE MODE.

CLOTHING: EMPLOYEE MUST WEAR APPROPRIATE PROTECTIVE (IMPERVIOUS) CLOTHING AND EQUIPMENT TO PREVENT REPEATED OR PROLONGED SKIN CONTACT WITH THIS SUBSTANCE.

GLOVES: EMPLOYEE MUST WEAR APPROPRIATE PROTECTIVE GLOVES TO PREVENT CONTACT WITH THIS SUBSTANCE.

EYE PROTECTION: EMPLOYEE MUST WEAR SPLASH-PROOF OR DUST-RESISTANT SAFETY GOGGLES TO PREVENT EYE CONTACT WITH THIS SUBSTANCE.

EMERGENCY EYE WASH: WHERE THERE IS ANY POSSIBILITY THAT AN EMPLOYEE'S EYES MAY BE EXPOSED TO THIS SUBSTANCE, THE EMPLOYER SHOULD PROVIDE AN EYE WASH FOUNTAIN WITHIN THE IMMEDIATE WORK AREA FOR EMERGENCY USE.

AUTHORIZED BY- OCCUPATIONAL HEALTH SERVICES, INC.

CREATION DATE: 10/05/89 ***REVISION DATE:*** 05/25/90

MATERIAL SAFETY DATA SHEET

OCCUPATIONAL HEALTH SERVICES, INC.
AGRICULTURE AND PESTICIDE DIVISION
450 SEVENTH AVENUE, SUITE 2407
NEW YORK, NEW YORK 10123
1-800-445-MSDS OR (212) 967-1100

EMERGENCY CONTACT:
JOHN S. BRANSFORD, JR. (615) 292-1180

SUBSTANCE IDENTIFICATION

CAS-NUMBER 10588-01-9

SUBSTANCE: **SODIUM DICHROMATE**

TRADE NAMES/SYNONYMS: CHROMIC ACID (H2CR2O7), DISODIUM SALT; DICHROMIC ACID (H2CR2O7), DISODIUM SALT; CHROMIUM SODIUM OXIDE (CR3NA2O7); DISODIUM DICHROMATE; SODIUM CHROMATE (NA2CR2O7); SODIUM DICHROMATE (NA2CR2O7); SODIUM DICHROMATE (VI); SODIUM CHROMATE; SODIUM BICHROMATE; STCC 4941170; NA 1479; CR2NA2O7; PST21190

CHEMICAL FAMILY: INORGANIC SALT

MOLECULAR FORMULA: NA2-(O-CR-O2-O-CR-O2-O)

MOLECULAR WEIGHT: 261.90

CERCLA RATINGS (SCALE 0-3): HEALTH=3 FIRE=0 REACTIVITY=0 PERSISTENCE=3

NFPA RATINGS (SCALE 0-4): HEALTH=1 FIRE=0 REACTIVITY=0

COMPONENTS AND CONTAMINANTS

COMPONENT: SODIUM DICHROMATE ***PERCENT:*** 100.0
CAS# 10588-01-9

OTHER CONTAMINANTS: NONE

EXPOSURE LIMITS: CHROMIC ACID AND CHROMATES: 0.1 MG(CRO3)/M3 OSHA CEILING 0.05 MG(CR)/M3 ACGIH TWA ACGIH A1-CONFIRMED HUMAN CARCINOGEN. 1 UG(CR(VI))/M3 NIOSH RECOMMENDED 10 HOUR TWA (CARCINOGENIC COMPOUNDS)
SUBJECT TO SARA SECTION 313 ANNUAL TOXIC CHEMICAL RELEASE REPORTING
SUBJECT TO CALIFORNIA PROPOSITION 65 CANCER AND/OR REPRODUCTIVE TOXICITY WARNING AND RELEASE REQUIREMENTS (HEXAVALENT CHROMIUM COMPOUNDS) (FEBRUARY 27, 1987)
SODIUM DICHROMATE: 10 POUNDS CERCLA SECTION 103 REPORTABLE QUANTITY

PHYSICAL DATA

DESCRIPTION: ODORLESS, RED TO ORANGE SOLID.

BOILING POINT: 752 F (400 C) (DECOMPOSES) ***MELTING POINT:*** 667 F (357 C)

SPECIFIC GRAVITY: 2.348 @ 25 C ***PH:*** 4.0 @ 1% SOLUTION

SOLUBILITY IN WATER: 270% @ 20 C

FIRE AND EXPLOSION DATA

FIRE AND EXPLOSION HAZARD: NEGLIGIBLE FIRE HAZARD WHEN EXPOSED TO HEAT OR FLAME.
OXIDIZER: OXIDIZERS DECOMPOSE, ESPECIALLY WHEN HEATED, TO YIELD OXYGEN OR OTHER GASES WHICH WILL INCREASE THE BURNING RATE OF COMBUSTIBLE MATTER. CONTACT WITH EASILY OXIDIZABLE, ORGANIC, OR OTHER COMBUSTIBLE MATERIALS MAY RESULT IN IGNITION, VIOLENT COMBUSTION OR EXPLOSION.

FIREFIGHTING MEDIA: DRY CHEMICAL, CARBON DIOXIDE, HALON OR WATER SPRAY (1987 EMERGENCY RESPONSE GUIDEBOOK, DOT P 5800.4).
FOR LARGER FIRES, USE WATER SPRAY OR FOG (1987 EMERGENCY RESPONSE GUIDEBOOK, DOT P 5800.4).

FIREFIGHTING: MOVE CONTAINERS FROM FIRE AREA IF POSSIBLE. COOL CONTAINERS EXPOSED TO FLAMES WITH WATER FROM SIDE UNTIL WELL AFTER FIRE IS OUT. STAY AWAY FROM STORAGE TANK ENDS. FOR MASSIVE FIRE IN STORAGE AREA, USE UNMANNED HOSE HOLDER OR MONITOR NOZZLES; ELSE WITHDRAW FROM AREA AND LET FIRE BURN (1987 EMERGENCY RESPONSE GUIDEBOOK, DOT P 5800.4, GUIDE PAGE 35)
FLOOD WITH WATER. COOL CONTAINERS WITH FLOODING AMOUNTS OF WATER FROM AS FAR A DISTANCE AS POSSIBLE. AVOID BREATHING VAPORS OR DUSTS. EVACUATE TO A RADIUS OF 2500 FEET FOR UNCONTROLLABLE FIRES.

TRANSPORTATION DATA

DEPARTMENT OF TRANSPORTATION HAZARD CLASSIFICATION 49 CFR 172.101: ORM-A
DEPARTMENT OF TRANSPORTATION LABELING REQUIREMENTS 49 CFR 172.101 AND SUBPART E: NONE
DEPARTMENT OF TRANSPORTATION PACKAGING REQUIREMENTS: 49 CFR 173.510 EXCEPTIONS: 49 CFR 173.505

TOXICITY

SODIUM DICHROMATE: TOXICITY DATA: ANHYDROUS: 335 MG/KG SKIN-GUINEA PIG LDLO; 338 MG/KG SKIN-GUINEA PIG LD50 (DOW MSDS); 50 MG/KG ORAL-CHILD LDLO; 250 MG/KG ORAL-CHILD TDLO; 50 MG/KG ORAL-RAT LD50; 80 MG/KG SUBCUTANEOUS-RAT LDLO; 23 MG/KG SUBCUTANEOUS-GUINEA PIG LDLO; 26200 UG/KG INTRAVENOUS-MOUSE LDLO; 18400 UG/KG INTRAVENOUS-RABBIT LDLO; 335 MG/KG INTRAPERITONEAL-GUINEA PIG LDLO; MUTAGENIC DATA (RTECS); TUMORIGENIC DATA (RTECS). DIHYDRATE: MUTAGENIC DATA (RTECS); TUMORIGENIC DATA (RTECS). CARCINOGEN STATUS: KNOWN HUMAN CARCINOGEN (NTP); ANIMAL INADEQUATE EVIDENCE (FOR SODIUM DICHROMATE), HUMAN SUFFICIENT EVIDENCE, ANIMAL SUFFICIENT EVIDENCE (IARC GROUP-1 FOR HEXAVALENT CHROMIUM COMPOUNDS). AN INCREASED INCIDENCE OF LUNG CANCER HAS BEEN OBSERVED AMONG WORKERS OCCUPATIONALLY EXPOSED DURING CHROMATE PRODUCTION, PIGMENT MANUFACTURING AND PLATING AND ALLOYING PROCESSES. INCIDENCES OF CANCERS AT OTHER SITES MAY ALSO BE INCREASED IN SUCH PERSONS. HOWEVER, A CLEAR DISTINCTION BETWEEN THE RELATIVE CARCINOGENICITY OF CHROMIUM COMPOUNDS OF DIFFERENT OXIDATION STATES OR SOLUBILITIES HAS BEEN DIFFICULT TO ACHIEVE. LOCAL EFFECTS: CORROSIVE- INHALATION, SKIN, EYE, INGESTION. ACUTE TOXICITY LEVEL: HIGHLY TOXIC BY INGESTION, TOXIC BY DERMAL ABSORPTION. TARGET EFFECTS: SENSITIZER- PULMONARY, SKIN. POISONING MAY ALSO AFFECT THE KIDNEYS, LIVER, AND GASTROINTESTINAL TRACT. AT INCREASED RISK FROM EXPOSURE: PERSONS WITH PREEXISTING SKIN OR EYE DISORDERS OR IMPAIRED KIDNEY, LIVER, OR RESPIRATORY FUNCTION.

HEALTH EFFECTS AND FIRST AID

INHALATION: SODIUM DICHROMATE: CORROSIVE/SENSITIZER/CARCINOGEN. **ACUTE EXPOSURE-** MAY CAUSE SEVERE NASAL IRRITATION, SNEEZING, LIGHTHEADEDNESS, LOSS OF THE SENSES OF TASTE AND SMELL, INFLAMED, SORE THROAT, LOSS OF APPETITE, FEVER, ACUTE TRACHEOBRONCHITIS, AND EPIGASTRIC PAIN. DEATH MAY RESULT FROM DELAYED PULMONARY EDEMA OR KIDNEY FAILURE. LIVER DAMAGE MAY ALSO OCCUR. SENSITIZATION MAY OCCUR IN PREVIOUSLY EXPOSED INDIVIDUALS. **CHRONIC EXPOSURE-** REPEATED OR PROLONGED EXPOSURE MAY CAUSE ULCERATION OF THE NASAL MUCOSA WITH NOSEBLEEDS, FOUL DISCHARGE, AND EVENTUAL PERFORATION OF THE NASAL SEPTUM, KERATOSIS OF THE LIPS, GINGIVA, AND PALATE, PERIODONTITIS AND YELLOWING OF THE TEETH AND TONGUE, AND EAR DISORDERS INCLUDING DISCHARGE, TINNITUS, AND PERFORATION OF THE EARDRUM. OTHER SYMPTOMS MAY INCLUDE LARYNGITIS, COUGHING, CHEST PAIN, HEADACHE, DYSPNEA, FATIGUE, LASSITUDE, RHEUMATIC PAIN, BRONCHITIS, AND BRONCHIAL ASTHMA. GASTROINTESTINAL SPASMS, GASTRITIS, AND ULCERS, BLOOD CHANGES INCLUDING LEUCOCYTOSIS, LEUCOPENIA, MONOCYTOSIS, AND EOSINOPHILIA, AND KIDNEY AND LIVER DAMAGE HAVE ALSO BEEN REPORTED. WORKERS EXPOSED TO CHROMATES HAVE INCREASED INCIDENCES OF LUNG CANCERS. REPEATED OR PROLONGED EXPOSURE MAY ALSO CAUSE SENSITIZATION.

FIRST AID- REMOVE FROM EXPOSURE AREA TO FRESH AIR IMMEDIATELY. IF BREATHING HAS STOPPED, GIVE ARTIFICIAL RESPIRATION. MAINTAIN AIRWAY AND BLOOD PRESSURE AND ADMINISTER OXYGEN IF AVAILABLE. KEEP AFFECTED PERSON WARM AND AT REST. TREAT SYMPTOMATICALLY AND SUPPORTIVELY. ADMINISTRATION OF OXYGEN SHOULD BE PERFORMED BY QUALIFIED PERSONNEL. GET MEDICAL ATTENTION IMMEDIATELY.

SKIN CONTACT: SODIUM DICHROMATE: CORROSIVE/SENSITIZER/TOXIC. **ACUTE EXPOSURE-** MAY CAUSE PRIMARY IRRITANT DERMATITIS WITH REDNESS AND PAIN. A 0.005% SOLUTION CAUSED LESIONS ON ABRADED SKIN. ABSORPTION MAY OCCUR, ESPECIALLY ON WET SKIN, AND MAY CAUSE KIDNEY DAMAGE. THE LETHAL DOSE REPORTED IN GUINEA PIGS IS 338 MG/KG. THE SYMPTOMS WERE NOT REPORTED. ECZEMATOUS AND NONECZEMATOUS ALLERGIC DERMATITIS MAY OCCUR IN PREVIOUSLY EXPOSED INDIVIDUALS. **CHRONIC EXPOSURE-** REPEATED OR PROLONGED EXPOSURE MAY CAUSE DERMATITIS, AND PAINLESS, PENETRATING ULCERS THAT HEAL SLOWLY AND LEAVE A SCAR. A 0.005% SOLUTION IN CONTACT WITH THE SKIN FOR 8 HOURS/DAY PRODUCED LESIONS IN 3 DAYS. REPEATED OR PROLONGED EXPOSURE MAY ALSO CAUSE SENSITIZATION.

FIRST AID- REMOVE CONTAMINATED CLOTHING AND SHOES IMMEDIATELY. WASH AFFECTED AREA WITH SOAP OR MILD DETERGENT AND LARGE AMOUNTS OF WATER UNTIL NO EVIDENCE OF CHEMICAL REMAINS (AT LEAST 15-20 MINUTES). IN CASE OF CHEMICAL BURNS, COVER AREA WITH STERILE, DRY DRESSING. BANDAGE SECURELY, BUT NOT TOO TIGHTLY. GET MEDICAL ATTENTION IMMEDIATELY.

EYE CONTACT: SODIUM DICHROMATE: CORROSIVE. **ACUTE EXPOSURE-** CONTACT MAY CAUSE SEVERE IRRITATION, LACRIMATION, INFLAMMATION OF THE CONJUNCTIVA, CORNEAL BURNS, AND PERMANENT INJURY, POSSIBLY RESULTING IN BLINDNESS. **CHRONIC EXPOSURE-** EFFECTS DEPEND ON THE CONCENTRATION AND DURATION OF EXPOSURE. REPEATED OR PROLONGED CONTACT WITH CORROSIVE SUBSTANCES MAY RESULT IN CONJUNCTIVITIS OR IN EFFECTS AS IN ACUTE EXPOSURE.

FIRST AID- WASH EYES IMMEDIATELY WITH LARGE AMOUNTS OF WATER, OCCASIONALLY LIFTING UPPER AND LOWER LIDS, UNTIL NO EVIDENCE OF CHEMICAL REMAINS (AT LEAST 15-20 MINUTES). CONTINUE IRRIGATING WITH NORMAL SALINE UNTIL THE PH HAS RETURNED TO NORMAL (30-60 MINUTES). COVER WITH STERILE BANDAGES. GET MEDICAL ATTENTION IMMEDIATELY.

INGESTION: SODIUM DICHROMATE: CORROSIVE/HIGHLY TOXIC. **ACUTE EXPOSURE-** INGESTION MAY CAUSE GASTROINTESTINAL TRACT IRRITATION, NAUSEA, VOMITING OF YELLOWISH OR GREENISH MATERIAL, WATERY, BLOODY DIARRHEA, INTENSE THIRST, COLD, CLAMMY SKIN, DIZZINESS, AND MUSCLE CRAMPS. FULMINANT GASTROENTERITIS, HEMORRHAGE INTO THE GASTROINTESTINAL TRACT, PERIPHERAL VASCULAR COLLAPSE, AND CARDIOVASCULAR SHOCK MAY OCCUR. DEATH MAY FOLLOW KIDNEY FAILURE WITH OLIGURIA AND ANURIA OR HEPATIC COMA WITH CONVULSIONS. **CHRONIC EXPOSURE-** REPEATED INGESTION MAY CAUSE KIDNEY DAMAGE.
FIRST AID: TREAT SYMPTOMATICALLY AND SUPPORTIVELY. IF PERSON IS CONSCIOUS AND ABLE TO SWALLOW, GIVE LARGE AMOUNTS OF WATER OR MILK TO DILUTE SUBSTANCE. GET MEDICAL ATTENTION IMMEDIATELY. GASTRIC LAVAGE PERFORMED BY QUALIFIED MEDICAL PERSONNEL MIGHT BE ADVISABLE IF THERE ARE NO SIGNS OF PERFORATION FROM THE INGESTION OF A CORROSIVE SUBSTANCE. IF VOMITING OCCURS, KEEP HEAD BELOW HIPS TO HELP PREVENT ASPIRATION.

ANTIDOTE: THE FOLLOWING ANTIDOTE HAS BEEN RECOMMENDED. HOWEVER, THE DECISION AS TO WHETHER THE SEVERITY OF POISONING REQUIRES ADMINISTRATION OF ANY ANTIDOTE AND ACTUAL DOSE REQUIRED SHOULD BE MADE BY QUALIFIED MEDICAL PERSONNEL.

CHROMIUM POISONING: USE OF DIMERCAPROL HAS BEEN SUGGESTED ON THE BASIS OF FINDINGS IN ANIMALS. GIVE 3 MG/KG (OR 0.3 ML/10 KG) EVERY 4 HOURS, INTRAMUSCULARLY FOR THE FIRST 2 DAYS AND THEN 2 MG/KG EVERY 12 HOURS FOR A TOTAL OF 10 DAYS (DREISBACH, HANDBOOK OF POISONING, 11TH ED.). ANTIDOTE SHOULD BE ADMINISTERED BY QUALIFIED MEDICAL PERSONNEL.

REACTIVITY

REACTIVITY: STABLE UNDER NORMAL TEMPERATURES AND PRESSURES.

INCOMPATIBILITIES: SODIUM DICHROMATE: ACETIC ANHYDRIDE: VIOLENT EXOTHERMIC REACTION. BORON: FORMS A FLAMMABLE MIXTURE. COMBUSTIBLE MATERIALS: MAY INCREASE THE BURNING RATE OR CAUSE IGNITION ON CONTACT; FINELY DIVIDED MATERIALS MAY RESULT IN AN EXPLOSION. ETHANOL + SULFURIC ACID: POSSIBLE EXPLOSION. HYDRAZINE: EXPLOSIVE REACTION. HYDROXYLAMINE: INCOMPATIBLE. 2-PROPANOL: POSSIBLE EXOTHERMIC REACTION. REDUCING MATERIALS: MAY CAUSE IGNITION OR EXPLOSION OF FINELY DIVIDED MATERIALS. MAY INCREASE THE RATE OF BURNING MATERIALS. SULFURIC ACID + ORGANIC MATERIALS: VIOLENT REACTION. SULFURIC ACID + TRINITROTOLUENE: MAY IGNITE IF NOT STIRRED.

DECOMPOSITION: THERMAL DECOMPOSITION PRODUCTS INCLUDE TOXIC FUMES OF CHROMIUM.

POLYMERIZATION: HAZARDOUS POLYMERIZATION HAS NOT BEEN REPORTED TO OCCUR UNDER NORMAL TEMPERATURES AND PRESSURES.

STORAGE AND DISPOSAL

OBSERVE ALL FEDERAL, STATE AND LOCAL REGULATIONS WHEN STORING OR DISPOSING OF THIS SUBSTANCE. FOR ASSISTANCE, CONTACT THE DISTRICT DIRECTOR OF THE ENVIRONMENTAL PROTECTION AGENCY.

STORAGE

CONSULT NFPA PUBLICATION 43A, STORAGE OF LIQUID AND SOLID OXIDIZING MATERIALS, FOR STORAGE REQUIREMENTS.

PROTECT AGAINST PHYSICAL DAMAGE. STORE IN A DRY LOCATION SEPARATE FROM COMBUSTIBLE, ORGANIC OR OTHER READILY OXIDIZABLE MATERIALS. AVOID STORAGE ON WOOD FLOORS. REMOVE AND DISPOSE OF ANY SPILLED DICHROMATES; DO NOT RETURN TO ORIGINAL CONTAINERS. (NFPA 49, HAZARDOUS CHEMICALS DATA, 1979)

STORE AWAY FROM INCOMPATIBLE SUBSTANCES.

DISPOSAL

CHROMIUM - REGULATORY LEVEL: 5.0 MG/L MATERIALS WHICH CONTAIN THE ABOVE SUBSTANCE AT OR ABOVE THE REGULATORY LEVEL MEET THE EPA CHARACTERISTIC OF TOXICITY, AND MUST BE DISPOSED OF IN ACCORDANCE WITH 40 CFR PART 262. EPA HAZARDOUS WASTE NUMBER D007.

CONDITIONS TO AVOID

AVOID CONTACT WITH COMBUSTIBLE MATERIALS (WOOD, PAPER, FUEL, OILS, ETC); IGNITION OR EXPLOSION MAY RESULT. AVOID CONTAMINATION OF WATER SOURCES.

SPILL AND LEAK PROCEDURES

WATER SPILL: THE CALIFORNIA SAFE DRINKING WATER AND TOXIC ENFORCEMENT ACT OF 1986 (PROPOSITION 65) PROHIBITS CONTAMINATING ANY KNOWN SOURCE OF DRINKING WATER WITH SUBSTANCES KNOWN TO CAUSE CANCER AND/OR REPRODUCTIVE TOXICITY.

OCCUPATIONAL SPILL: KEEP COMBUSTIBLES (WOOD, PAPER, OIL, ETC) AWAY FROM SPILLED MATERIAL. DO NOT TOUCH SPILLED MATERIAL. FOR SMALL DRY SPILLS, WITH CLEAN SHOVEL PLACE MATERIAL INTO CLEAN, DRY CONTAINER AND COVER; MOVE CONTAINERS FROM SPILL AREA. FOR SMALL LIQUID SPILLS, TAKE UP WITH SAND, EARTH OR OTHER ABSORBENT MATERIAL AND PLACE INTO CONTAINERS FOR LATER DISPOSAL. FOR LARGER SPILLS, DIKE FAR AHEAD OF SPILL FOR LATER DISPOSAL. KEEP UNNECESSARY PEOPLE AWAY. ISOLATE HAZARD AREA AND DENY ENTRY.

REPORTABLE QUANTITY (RQ): 10 POUNDS THE SUPERFUND AMENDMENTS AND REAUTHORIZATION ACT (SARA) SECTION 304 REQUIRES THAT A RELEASE EQUAL TO OR GREATER THAN THE REPORTABLE QUANTITY FOR THIS SUBSTANCE BE IMMEDIATELY REPORTED TO THE LOCAL EMERGENCY PLANNING COMMITTEE AND THE STATE EMERGENCY RESPONSE COMMISSION (40 CFR 355.40). IF THE RELEASE OF THIS SUBSTANCE IS REPORTABLE UNDER CERCLA SECTION 103, THE NATIONAL RESPONSE CENTER MUST BE NOTIFIED IMMEDIATELY AT (800) 424-8802 OR (202) 426-2675 IN THE METROPOLITAN WASHINGTON, D.C. AREA (40 CFR 302.6).

PROTECTIVE EQUIPMENT

VENTILATION: PROVIDE LOCAL EXHAUST OR PROCESS ENCLOSURE VENTILATION TO MEET PUBLISHED EXPOSURE LIMITS.

RESPIRATOR: THE FOLLOWING RESPIRATORS AND MAXIMUM USE CONCENTRATIONS ARE RECOMMENDATIONS BY THE U.S. DEPARTMENT OF HEALTH AND HUMAN SERVICES, NIOSH POCKET GUIDE TO CHEMICAL HAZARDS; NIOSH CRITERIA DOCUMENTS OR BY THE U.S. DEPARTMENT OF LABOR, 29 CFR 1910 SUBPART Z. THE SPECIFIC RESPIRATOR SELECTED MUST BE BASED ON CONTAMINATION LEVELS FOUND IN THE WORK PLACE, MUST NOT EXCEED THE WORKING LIMITS OF THE RESPIRATOR AND BE JOINTLY APPROVED BY THE NATIONAL INSTITUTE FOR OCCUPATIONAL SAFETY AND HEALTH AND THE MINE SAFETY AND HEALTH ADMINISTRATION (NIOSH-MSHA).

CARCINOGENIC HEXAVALENT CHROMIUM COMPOUNDS: AT ANY DETECTABLE CONCENTRATION:

SELF-CONTAINED BREATHING APPARATUS WITH FULL FACEPIECE OPERATED IN PRESSURE-DEMAND OR OTHER POSITIVE PRESSURE MODE. SUPPLIED-AIR RESPIRATOR WITH FULL FACEPIECE OPERATED IN PRESSURE-DEMAND OR OTHER POSITIVE PRESSURE MODE IN COMBINATION WITH AN AUXILIARY SELF-CONTAINED BREATHING APPARATUS OPERATED IN PRESSURE-DEMAND OR OTHER POSITIVE PRESSURE MODE.

ESCAPE- AIR-PURIFYING FULL FACEPIECE RESPIRATOR WITH A HIGH-EFFICIENCY PARTICULATE FILTER. ESCAPE-TYPE SELF-CONTAINED BREATHING APPARATUS.

FOR FIREFIGHTING AND OTHER IMMEDIATELY DANGEROUS TO LIFE OR HEALTH CONDITIONS:

SELF-CONTAINED BREATHING APPARATUS WITH FULL FACEPIECE OPERATED IN PRESSURE-DEMAND OR OTHER POSITIVE PRESSURE MODE.

SUPPLIED-AIR RESPIRATOR WITH FULL FACEPIECE AND OPERATED IN PRESSURE-DEMAND OR OTHER POSITIVE PRESSURE MODE IN COMBINATION WITH AN AUXILIARY SELF-CONTAINED BREATHING APPARATUS OPERATED IN PRESSURE-DEMAND OR OTHER POSITIVE PRESSURE MODE.

CLOTHING: EMPLOYEE MUST WEAR APPROPRIATE PROTECTIVE (IMPERVIOUS) CLOTHING AND EQUIPMENT TO PREVENT ANY POSSIBILITY OF SKIN CONTACT WITH THIS SUBSTANCE.

GLOVES: EMPLOYEE MUST WEAR APPROPRIATE PROTECTIVE GLOVES TO PREVENT CONTACT WITH THIS SUBSTANCE.

EYE PROTECTION: EMPLOYEE MUST WEAR SPLASH-PROOF OR DUST-RESISTANT SAFETY GOGGLES AND A FACESHIELD TO PREVENT CONTACT WITH THIS SUBSTANCE.

EMERGENCY WASH FACILITIES: WHERE THERE IS ANY POSSIBILITY THAT AN EMPLOYEE'S EYES AND/OR SKIN MAY BE EXPOSED TO THIS SUBSTANCE, THE EMPLOYER SHOULD PROVIDE AN EYE WASH FOUNTAIN AND QUICK DRENCH SHOWER WITHIN THE IMMEDIATE WORK AREA FOR EMERGENCY USE.

AUTHORIZED BY- OCCUPATIONAL HEALTH SERVICES, INC.
CREATION DATE: 10/05/89 ***REVISION DATE:*** 07/13/90

MATERIAL SAFETY DATA SHEET

OCCUPATIONAL HEALTH SERVICES, INC.
AGRICULTURE AND PESTICIDE DIVISION
450 SEVENTH AVENUE, SUITE 2407
NEW YORK, NEW YORK 10123
1-800-445-MSDS OR (212) 967-1100

EMERGENCY CONTACT:
JOHN S. BRANSFORD, JR. (615) 292-1180

SUBSTANCE IDENTIFICATION

CAS-NUMBER 25155-30-0

SUBSTANCE: **SODIUM DODECYLBENZENESULFONATE**

TRADE NAMES/SYNONYMS: SODIUM ALKYLARYLSULFONATE; SODIUM DODECYLPHENYLSULFONATE; ABS (DETERGENT); DODECYLBENZENESULFONIC ACID, SODIUM SALT; DODECYLBENZENE SODIUM SULFONATE; BENZENESULFONIC ACID, DODECYL-, SODIUM SALT; NACCONAL 90F; DODECYLBENZENESULPHONATE, SODIUM SALT; DODECYL BENZENE SODIUM SULPHONATE; SODIUM LAURYLBENZENESULFONATE; SODIUM DODECYLBENZENESULPHONATE; STCC 4963374; C18HS9NAO3S; PST21220

CHEMICAL FAMILY: SULFONATE

MOLECULAR FORMULA: C12-H25-C6-H4-S-O3.NA

MOLECULAR WEIGHT: 348.52

CERCLA RATINGS (SCALE 0-3): HEALTH=3 FIRE=1 REACTIVITY=0 PERSISTENCE=2

NFPA RATINGS (SCALE 0-4): HEALTH=3 FIRE=1 REACTIVITY=0

COMPONENTS AND CONTAMINANTS

COMPONENT: SODIUM DODECYLBENZENESULFONATE ***PERCENT:*** 100.0
CAS# 25155-30-0

OTHER CONTAMINANTS: NONE

EXPOSURE LIMITS: NO OCCUPATIONAL EXPOSURE LIMITS ESTABLISHED BY OSHA, ACGIH, OR NIOSH.

SODIUM DODECYLBENZENESULFONATE: 1000 LBS CERCLA SECTION 103 REPORTABLE QUANTITY

PHYSICAL DATA

DESCRIPTION: WHITE TO LIGHT YELLOW FLAKES, GRANULES, OR POWDER.
MELTING POINT: >572 F (300 C) ***SPECIFIC GRAVITY:*** NOT AVAILABLE
SOLUBILITY IN WATER: SOLUBLE

FIRE AND EXPLOSION DATA

FIRE AND EXPLOSION HAZARD: SLIGHT FIRE HAZARD WHEN EXPOSED TO HEAT OR FLAME.
DUST-AIR MIXTURES MAY IGNITE OR EXPLODE.
FLASH POINT: 210 F (99 C) (OC)
FIREFIGHTING MEDIA: DRY CHEMICAL, CARBON DIOXIDE, HALON, WATER SPRAY OR STANDARD FOAM (1987 EMERGENCY RESPONSE GUIDEBOOK, DOT P 5800.4).
FOR LARGER FIRES, USE WATER SPRAY, FOG OR STANDARD FOAM (1987 EMERGENCY RESPONSE GUIDEBOOK, DOT P 5800.4).
FIREFIGHTING: MOVE CONTAINER FROM FIRE AREA IF POSSIBLE. DO NOT SCATTER SPILLED MATERIAL WITH HIGH PRESSURE WATER STREAMS. DIKE FIRE CONTROL WATER FOR LATER DISPOSAL (1987 EMERGENCY RESPONSE GUIDEBOOK, DOT P 5800.4, GUIDE PAGE 31).
USE AGENTS SUITABLE FOR TYPE OF SURROUNDING FIRE. AVOID BREATHING HAZARDOUS VAPORS, KEEP UPWIND.

TOXICITY

SODIUM DODECYLBENZENESULFONATE: IRRITATION DATA: 20 MG/24 HOURS SKIN-RABBIT MODERATE; 250 UG/24 HOURS EYE-RABBIT SEVERE; 1% EYE-RABBIT SEVERE. TOXICITY DATA: 438 MG/KG ORAL-RAT LD50; 1330 MG/KG ORAL-MOUSE LD50; 105 MG/KG INTRAVENOUS-MOUSE LD50. CARCINOGEN STATUS: NONE. LOCAL EFFECTS: IRRITANT- INHALATION, SKIN, EYE. ACUTE TOXICITY LEVEL: TOXIC BY INGESTION. TARGET EFFECTS: NO DATA AVAILABLE.

HEALTH EFFECTS AND FIRST AID

INHALATION: SODIUM DODECYLBENZENESULFONATE: IRRITANT. **ACUTE EXPOSURE-** MAY CAUSE IRRITATION OF THE UPPER RESPIRATORY TRACT WITH COUGHING AND SHORTNESS OF BREATH. AIRBORNE SULFONATES MAY BE THE SOURCE FOR RESPIRATORY ALLERGIES. **CHRONIC EXPOSURE-** REPEATED EXPOSURE TO SULFONATES MAY CAUSE RESPIRATORY ALLERGIES IN SOME INDIVIDUALS.
FIRST AID- REMOVE FROM EXPOSURE AREA TO FRESH AIR IMMEDIATELY. IF BREATHING HAS STOPPED, PERFORM ARTIFICIAL RESPIRATION. KEEP PERSON WARM AND AT REST. TREAT SYMPTOMATICALLY AND SUPPORTIVELY. GET MEDICAL ATTENTION IMMEDIATELY.

SKIN CONTACT: SODIUM DODECYLBENZENESULFONATE: IRRITANT. **ACUTE EXPOSURE-** MAY CAUSE IRRITATION WITH REDNESS. SULFONATES MAY BE DERMAL ALLERGENS. **CHRONIC EXPOSURE-** REPEATED OR PROLONGED CONTACT WITH IRRITANTS MAY CAUSE DERMATITIS. IN PREVIOUSLY EXPOSED PERSONS, ANIONIC DETERGENTS MAY CAUSE THICKENING OF THE SKIN WITH WEEPING, CRACKING, SCALING AND BLISTERING.
FIRST AID- REMOVE CONTAMINATED CLOTHING AND SHOES IMMEDIATELY. WASH AFFECTED AREA WITH SOAP OR MILD DETERGENT AND LARGE AMOUNTS OF WATER UNTIL NO EVIDENCE OF CHEMICAL REMAINS (APPROXIMATELY 15-20 MINUTES). GET MEDICAL ATTENTION IMMEDIATELY.

EYE CONTACT: SODIUM DODECYLBENZENESULFONATE: IRRITANT. **ACUTE EXPOSURE-** MAY CAUSE MODERATE IRRITATION WITH REDNESS. ALKYL BENZENE SULFONATE DETERGENTS MAY CAUSE CORNEAL INJURY. **CHRONIC EXPOSURE-** REPEATED AND PROLONGED CONTACT WITH IRRITANTS MAY CAUSE CONJUNCTIVITIS. ALKYL BENZENE SULFONATE DETERGENTS HAVE BEEN REPORTED TO CAUSE DELICATE PUNCTATE SPECKLING OF THE CORNEAL EPITHELIUM IN THE PALPEBRAL FISSURES IN SOME WORKERS.
FIRST AID- WASH EYES IMMEDIATELY WITH LARGE AMOUNTS OF WATER OR NORMAL SALINE, OCCASIONALLY LIFTING UPPER AND LOWER LIDS, UNTIL NO EVIDENCE OF CHEMICAL REMAINS (APPROXIMATELY 15-20 MINUTES). GET MEDICAL ATTENTION IMMEDIATELY.

INGESTION: SODIUM DODECYLBENZENESULFONATE: TOXIC. **ACUTE EXPOSURE-** THE LETHAL DOSE REPORTED IN RATS WAS 438 MG/KG. INGESTION OF ANIONIC DETERGENTS MAY CAUSE ABDOMINAL PAIN, NAUSEA, DIARRHEA, INTESTINAL DISTENTION AND OCCASIONALLY VOMITING. **CHRONIC EXPOSURE-** NO DATA AVAILABLE.
FIRST AID- IF EXTENSIVE VOMITING HAS NOT OCCURRED, THE SUBSTANCE SHOULD BE REMOVED BY EMESIS OR GASTRIC LAVAGE PROVIDED THAT THE PATIENT IS CONSCIOUS AND CONVULSIONS ARE NOT PRESENT. KEEP HEAD BELOW HIPS DURING VOMITING TO PREVENT ASPIRATION. DO NOT ATTEMPT TO MAKE AN UNCONSCIOUS PERSON VOMIT. TREAT SYMPTOMATICALLY AND SUPPORTIVELY. GET MEDICAL ATTENTION IMMEDIATELY (DREISBACH, HANDBOOK OF POISONING, 12TH ED.). TREATMENT SHOULD BE PERFORMED BY QUALIFIED MEDICAL PERSONNEL.
ANTIDOTE: NO SPECIFIC ANTIDOTE. TREAT SYMPTOMATICALLY AND SUPPORTIVELY.

REACTIVITY

REACTIVITY: STABLE UNDER NORMAL TEMPERATURES AND PRESSURES.
INCOMPATIBILITIES: SODIUM DODECYLBENZENESULFONATE: OXIDIZERS (STRONG): FIRE AND EXPLOSION HAZARD.
DECOMPOSITION: THERMAL DECOMPOSITION PRODUCTS MAY INCLUDE HIGHLY TOXIC FUMES OF HYDROGEN SULFIDE AND TOXIC OXIDES OF SULFUR AND CARBON.
POLYMERIZATION: HAZARDOUS POLYMERIZATION HAS NOT BEEN REPORTED TO OCCUR UNDER NORMAL TEMPERATURES AND PRESSURES.

STORAGE AND DISPOSAL

OBSERVE ALL FEDERAL, STATE AND LOCAL REGULATIONS WHEN STORING OR DISPOSING OF THIS SUBSTANCE. FOR ASSISTANCE, CONTACT THE DISTRICT DIRECTOR OF THE ENVIRONMENTAL PROTECTION AGENCY.

STORAGE

STORE AWAY FROM INCOMPATIBLE SUBSTANCES.

CONDITIONS TO AVOID

MAY BURN BUT DOES NOT IGNITE READILY. AVOID CONTACT WITH STRONG OXIDIZERS, EXCESSIVE HEAT, SPARKS, OR OPEN FLAME.

SPILL AND LEAK PROCEDURES

SOIL SPILL: DIG HOLDING AREA SUCH AS LAGOON, POND OR PIT FOR CONTAINMENT.
USE PROTECTIVE COVER SUCH AS A PLASTIC SHEET TO PREVENT MATERIAL FROM DISSOLVING IN FIRE EXTINGUISHING WATER OR RAIN.
WATER SPILL: USE ACTIVATED CARBON TO ABSORB SPILLED SUBSTANCE THAT IS DISSOLVED.
USE MECHANICAL DREDGES OR LIFTS TO EXTRACT IMMOBILIZED MASSES OF POLLUTION AND PRECIPITATES.
OCCUPATIONAL SPILL: SWEEP UP AND PLACE IN SUITABLE CLEAN, DRY CONTAINERS FOR RECLAMATION OR LATER DISPOSAL. DO NOT FLUSH SPILLED MATERIAL INTO SEWER. KEEP UNNECESSARY PEOPLE AWAY.
REPORTABLE QUANTITY (RQ): 1000 POUNDS THE SUPERFUND AMENDMENTS AND REAUTHORIZATION ACT (SARA) SECTION 304 REQUIRES THAT A RELEASE EQUAL TO OR GREATER THAN THE REPORTABLE QUANTITY FOR THIS SUBSTANCE BE IMMEDIATELY REPORTED TO THE LOCAL EMERGENCY PLANNING COMMITTEE AND THE STATE EMERGENCY RESPONSE COMMISSION (40 CFR 355.40). IF THE RELEASE OF THIS SUBSTANCE IS REPORTABLE UNDER CERCLA SECTION 103, THE NATIONAL RESPONSE CENTER MUST BE NOTIFIED IMMEDIATELY AT (800) 424-8802 OR (202) 426-2675 IN THE METROPOLITAN WASHINGTON, D.C. AREA (40 CFR 302.6).

PROTECTIVE EQUIPMENT

VENTILATION: PROVIDE LOCAL EXHAUST OR PROCESS ENCLOSURE VENTILATION SYSTEM.
RESPIRATOR: THE FOLLOWING RESPIRATORS AND MAXIMUM USE CONCENTRATIONS ARE RECOMMENDATIONS BY THE U.S. DEPARTMENT OF HEALTH AND HUMAN SERVICES, NIOSH POCKET GUIDE TO CHEMICAL HAZARDS; NIOSH CRITERIA DOCUMENTS OR BY THE U.S. DEPARTMENT OF LABOR, 29 CFR 1910 SUBPART Z.
THE SPECIFIC RESPIRATOR SELECTED MUST BE BASED ON CONTAMINATION LEVELS FOUND IN THE WORK PLACE, MUST NOT EXCEED THE WORKING LIMITS OF THE RESPIRATOR AND BE JOINTLY APPROVED BY THE NATIONAL INSTITUTE FOR OCCUPATIONAL SAFETY AND HEALTH AND THE MINE SAFETY AND HEALTH ADMINISTRATION (NIOSH-MSHA).
TYPE 'C' SUPPLIED-AIR RESPIRATOR WITH A FULL FACEPIECE OPERATED IN PRESSURE-DEMAND OR OTHER POSITIVE PRESSURE MODE OR WITH A FULL FACEPIECE, HELMET OR HOOD OPERATED IN CONTINOUS-FLOW MODE.
SELF-CONTAINED BREATHING APPARATUS WITH A FULL FACEPIECE OPERATED IN PRESSURE-DEMAND OR OTHER POSITIVE PRESSURE MODE.
FOR FIREFIGHTING AND OTHER IMMEDIATELY DANGEROUS TO LIFE OR HEALTH CONDITIONS:
SELF-CONTAINED BREATHING APPARATUS WITH FULL FACEPIECE OPERATED IN PRESSURE-DEMAND OR OTHER POSITIVE PRESSURE MODE.
SUPPLIED-AIR RESPIRATOR WITH FULL FACEPIECE AND OPERATED IN PRESSURE-DEMAND OR OTHER POSITIVE PRESSURE MODE IN COMBINATION WITH AN AUXILIARY SELF-CONTAINED BREATHING APPARATUS OPERATED IN PRESSURE-DEMAND OR OTHER POSITIVE PRESSURE MODE.
CLOTHING: EMPLOYEE MUST WEAR APPROPRIATE PROTECTIVE (IMPERVIOUS) CLOTHING AND EQUIPMENT TO PREVENT ANY POSSIBILITY OF SKIN CONTACT WITH THIS SUBSTANCE.
GLOVES: EMPLOYEE MUST WEAR APPROPRIATE PROTECTIVE GLOVES TO PREVENT CONTACT WITH THIS SUBSTANCE.

EYE PROTECTION: EMPLOYEE MUST WEAR SPLASH-PROOF OR DUST-RESISTANT SAFETY GOGGLES AND A FACESHIELD TO PREVENT CONTACT WITH THIS SUBSTANCE.

EMERGENCY WASH FACILITIES: WHERE THERE IS ANY POSSIBILITY THAT AN EMPLOYEE'S EYES AND/OR SKIN MAY BE EXPOSED TO THIS SUBSTANCE, THE EMPLOYER SHOULD PROVIDE AN EYE WASH FOUNTAIN AND QUICK DRENCH SHOWER WITHIN THE IMMEDIATE WORK AREA FOR EMERGENCY USE.

AUTHORIZED BY- OCCUPATIONAL HEALTH SERVICES, INC.
CREATION DATE: 11/15/89 ***REVISION DATE:*** 05/31/90

MATERIAL SAFETY DATA SHEET

OCCUPATIONAL HEALTH SERVICES, INC.
AGRICULTURE AND PESTICIDE DIVISION
450 SEVENTH AVENUE, SUITE 2407
NEW YORK, NEW YORK 10123
1-800-445-MSDS OR (212) 967-1100

EMERGENCY CONTACT:
JOHN S. BRANSFORD, JR. (615) 292-1180

SUBSTANCE IDENTIFICATION

CAS-NUMBER 7681-49-4

SUBSTANCE: **SODIUM FLUORIDE, SOLID**

TRADE NAMES/SYNONYMS: FDA 0101; FLUOROCID; FLURSOL; SODIUM MONOFLUORIDE; SODIUM FLUORIDE; T-FLUORIDE; FUNGOL B; ZYMAFLUOR; FLUORIGARD; STCC 4944150; UN 1690; S-299; ACT; ANTIBULIT; KARIDIUM; FLUORODAY; OSSIN; SODIUM FLUORIDE(NAF); NATURAL VILLIAUMITE; FNA; PST21230

CHEMICAL FAMILY: INORGANIC SALT

MOLECULAR FORMULA: NA-F

MOLECULAR WEIGHT: 41.99

CERCLA RATINGS (SCALE 0-3): HEALTH=3 FIRE=0 REACTIVITY=0 PERSISTENCE=0

NFPA RATINGS (SCALE 0-4): HEALTH=3 FIRE=0 REACTIVITY=0

COMPONENTS AND CONTAMINANTS

COMPONENT: SODIUM FLUORIDE ***PERCENT:*** 100
CAS# 7681-49-4

OTHER CONTAMINANTS: NONE

EXPOSURE LIMITS: SODIUM FLUORIDE, SOLID: 2.5 MG(F)/M3 OSHA TWA 2.5 MG(F)/M3 ACGIH TWA 2.5 MG(F)/M3 NIOSH RECOMMENDED TWA
1000 POUNDS CERCLA SECTION 103 REPORTABLE QUANTITY

PHYSICAL DATA

DESCRIPTION: COLORLESS CRYSTALLINE SOLID OR WHITE POWDER.

BOILING POINT: 3083 F (1695 C) ***MELTING POINT:*** 1819 F (993 C)

SPECIFIC GRAVITY: 2.558 @ 41 C ***VAPOR PRESSURE:*** 1 MMHG @ 1077 C

PH: 7.4 SATURATED SOLN. ***SOLUBILITY IN WATER:*** 4.3% @ 25 C

SOLVENT SOLUBILITY: SOLUBLE IN HYDROGEN FLUORIDE AND VERY SLIGHTLY SOLUBLE IN ALCOHOL.

FIRE AND EXPLOSION DATA

FIRE AND EXPLOSION HAZARD: NEGLIGIBLE FIRE HAZARD WHEN EXPOSED TO HEAT OR FLAME.

FIREFIGHTING MEDIA: DRY CHEMICAL, CARBON DIOXIDE, HALON, WATER SPRAY OR STANDARD FOAM (1987 EMERGENCY RESPONSE GUIDEBOOK, DOT P 5800.4).
FOR LARGER FIRES, USE WATER SPRAY, FOG OR STANDARD FOAM (1987 EMERGENCY RESPONSE GUIDEBOOK, DOT P 5800.4).

FIREFIGHTING: MOVE CONTAINERS FROM FIRE AREA IF POSSIBLE (1987 EMERGENCY RESPONSE GUIDEBOOK, DOT P 5800.4, GUIDE PAGE 54).
USE AGENTS SUITABLE FOR TYPE OF FIRE. AVOID BREATHING CORROSIVE VAPORS, KEEP UPWIND.

TRANSPORTATION DATA

DEPARTMENT OF TRANSPORTATION HAZARD CLASSIFICATION 49 CFR 172.101: ORM-B
DEPARTMENT OF TRANSPORTATION LABELING REQUIREMENTS 49 CFR 172.101 AND SUBPART E: NONE
DEPARTMENT OF TRANSPORTATION PACKAGING REQUIREMENTS: 49 CFR 173.510 EXCEPTIONS: 49 CFR 173.505

TOXICITY

SODIUM FLUORIDE: IRRITATION DATA: 20 MG/24 HOURS EYE-RABBIT MODERATE. TOXICITY DATA: 300 MG/KG SKIN-MOUSE LDLO; 214 UG/KG ORAL-HUMAN TDLO; 71 MG/KG ORAL-HUMAN LDLO; 75 MG/KG ORAL-HUMAN LDLO; 1662 MG/KG ORAL-MAN TDLO; 90 MG/KG ORAL-WOMAN LDLO; 360 MG/KG ORAL-WOMAN LDLO; 7 MG/KG ORAL-WOMAN TDLO; 52 MG/KG ORAL-RAT LD50; 57 MG/KG ORAL-MOUSE LD50; 200 MG/KG ORAL-RABBIT LD50; 75 MG/KG ORAL-DOG LDLO; 100 MG/KG ORAL-DOMESTIC ANIMAL LD50; 175 MG/KG SUBCUTANEOUS-RAT LD50; 70 MG/KG SUBCUTANEOUS-MOUSE LD50; 14 MG/KG SUBCUTANEOUS-CAT LDLO; 155 MG/KG SUBCUTANEOUS-DOG LDLO; 100 MG/KG SUBCUTANEOUS-RABBIT LDLO; 100 MG/KG SUBCUTANEOUS-GUINEA PIG LDLO; 26 MG/KG INTRAVENOUS-RAT LD50; 26,600 UG/KG INTRAVENOUS-MONKEY LD50; 50,830 UG/KG INTRAVENOUS-MOUSE LD50; 80 MG/KG INTRAVENOUS-DOG LDLO; 14 UG/KG INTRADERMAL-HUMAN TDLO; 40 MG/KG INTRAMUSCULAR-DOG LDLO; 22 MG/KG INTRAPERITONEAL-RAT LD50; 38 MG/KG INTRAPERITONEAL-MOUSE LD50; 50 MG/KG INTRAPERITONEAL-DOG LDLO; 250 MG/KG INTRAPERITONEAL-RABBIT LDLO; 75 MG/KG UNREPORTED-MAN LDLO; MUTAGENIC DATA (RTECS); REPRODUCTIVE EFFECTS DATA (RTECS); TUMORIGENIC DATA (RTECS). CARCINOGEN STATUS: HUMAN INADEQUATE EVIDENCE, ANIMAL INADEQUATE EVIDENCE (IARC GROUP-3). UNDER THE CONDITIONS OF TWO YEAR DOSED WATER STUDIES, THERE WAS EQUIVOCAL EVIDENCE OF CARCINOGENIC ACTIVITY OF SODIUM FLUORIDE IN RATS BASED ON THE OCCURRENCE OF A SMALL NUMBER OF OSTEOSARCOMAS IN DOSED ANIMALS. (NTP TR-393 DRAFT). LOCAL EFFECTS: CORROSIVE- INHALATION, SKIN, EYES, INGESTION. ACUTE TOXICITY LEVEL: TOXIC BY INGESTION. TARGET EFFECTS: POISONING MAY AFFECT THE BONES.

HEALTH EFFECTS AND FIRST AID

INHALATION: SODIUM FLUORIDE: CORROSIVE. 500 MG(F)/M3 IMMEDIATELY DANGEROUS TO LIFE AND HEALTH. **ACUTE EXPOSURE-** MAY CAUSE SEVERE MUCOUS MEMBRANE IRRITATION WITH COUGHING, SORE THROAT, SHORTNESS OF BREATH AND LABORED BREATHING. HEADACHE, CYANOSIS, PNEUMOCONIOSIS, RESPIRATORY DEPRESSION, AND DELAYED LUNG EDEMA MAY ALSO OCCUR. SERIOUS POISONING MAY RESULT IN THE ONSET OF RESPIRATORY DISEASE OR HEART DISEASE WHICH MAY BE FATAL. **CHRONIC EXPOSURE-**
REPEATED EXPOSURE TO EXCESSIVE CONCENTRATIONS OF FLUORIDE OVER A PERIOD OF YEARS RESULTS IN INCREASED RADIOGRAPHIC DENSITY OF BONE AND EVENTUALLY MAY CAUSE CRIPPLING FLUOROSIS (OSTEOSCLEROSIS DUE TO FLUORIDE DEPOSITION), NOW AN EXCEEDINGLY RARE PHENOMENON. THE GROSS CHANGES IN THE SKELETON ARE QUITE DISTINCTIVE AND CHARACTERISTIC; AS THE AMOUNT OF FLUORIDE IN THE BONE INCREASES, EXOSTOSES MAY DEVELOP, ESPECIALLY ON THE LONG BONES; THE SACROTUBEROUS AND SACROSCIATIC LIGAMENTS BEGIN TO CALCIFY, VERTEBRAE OCCASIONALLY FUSE TOGETHER, AND TYPICAL STIFFNESS OF THE SPINAL COLUMN DEVELOPS.

FIRST AID- REMOVE FROM EXPOSURE AREA TO FRESH AIR IMMEDIATELY. IF BREATHING HAS STOPPED, GIVE ARTIFICIAL RESPIRATION. MAINTAIN AIRWAY AND BLOOD PRESSURE AND ADMINISTER OXYGEN IF AVAILABLE. KEEP AFFECTED PERSON WARM AND AT REST. TREAT SYMPTOMATICALLY AND SUPPORTIVELY. ADMINISTRATION OF OXYGEN SHOULD BE PERFORMED BY QUALIFIED PERSONNEL. GET MEDICAL ATTENTION IMMEDIATELY.

SKIN CONTACT: SODIUM FLUORIDE: CORROSIVE. **ACUTE EXPOSURE-** DUSTS MAY CAUSE IRRITATION WITH REDNESS AND PAIN. SODIUM FLUORIDE IS CORROSIVE WHEN IN AN AQUEOUS SOLUTIONS AND MAY CAUSE CORROSION WITH SKIN BURNS ON MOIST SKIN. **CHRONIC EXPOSURE-** REPEATED OR PROLONGED CONTACT WITH DUSTS MAY CAUSE DERMATITIS.

FIRST AID- REMOVE CONTAMINATED CLOTHING AND SHOES IMMEDIATELY. WASH AFFECTED AREA WITH SOAP OR MILD DETERGENT AND LARGE AMOUNTS OF WATER UNTIL NO EVIDENCE OF CHEMICAL REMAINS (AT LEAST 15-20 MINUTES). IN CASE OF CHEMICAL BURNS, COVER AREA WITH STERILE, DRY DRESSING. BANDAGE SECURELY, BUT NOT TOO TIGHTLY. GET MEDICAL ATTENTION IMMEDIATELY.

EYE CONTACT: SODIUM FLUORIDE: CORROSIVE. **ACUTE EXPOSURE-** CONTACT MAY CAUSE SEVERE IRRITATION, REDNESS, PAIN AND BLURRED VISION. APPLICATION OF A 2% AQUEOUS SOLUTION TO RABBIT EYES HAS CAUSED CORNEAL EPITHELIAL DEFECTS AND NECROTIC AREAS IN THE CONJUNCTIVAE. **CHRONIC EXPOSURE-** REPEATED OR PROLONGED EXPOSURE MAY CAUSE CONJUNCTIVITIS. 20 MG APPLIED TO RABBIT EYES FOR 24 HOURS CAUSED MODERATE IRRITATION.

FIRST AID- WASH EYES IMMEDIATELY WITH LARGE AMOUNTS OF WATER, OCCASIONALLY LIFTING UPPER AND LOWER LIDS, UNTIL NO EVIDENCE OF CHEMICAL REMAINS (AT LEAST 15-20 MINUTES). CONTINUE IRRIGATING WITH NORMAL SALINE UNTIL THE PH HAS RETURNED TO NORMAL (30-60 MINUTES). COVER WITH STERILE BANDAGES. GET MEDICAL ATTENTION IMMEDIATELY.

INGESTION: SODIUM FLUORIDE: CORROSIVE/TOXIC. **ACUTE EXPOSURE-** MAY CAUSE DAMAGE TO THE GASTRIC MUCOSA WITH PETECHIAE OR EROSIONS, NAUSEA, VOMITING, DIARRHEA, SALIVATION, THIRST, ABDOMINAL PAIN, PERSPIRATION

AND DYSPNEA. PARESIS OF CERTAIN MUSCLE GROUPS, HICCUPS AND CONTRACTIONS OF THE PUPILS MAY OCCUR. SERIOUS POISONING MAY INCLUDE WEAKNESS, TREMORS, CONVULSIONS, COLLAPSE, LOW BLOOD CALCIUM LEVELS AND COMA. DEATH IS DUE TO CARDIOVASCULAR COLLAPSE, RESPIRATORY FAILURE OR VENTRICULAR FIBRILLATION. **CHRONIC EXPOSURE**- REPEATED OR PROLONGED EXPOSURE TO SODIUM FLUORIDE MAY CAUSE FLUOROSIS. SYMPTOMS ARE WEIGHT LOSS, BRITTLENESS OF BONES, ANEMIA, WEAKNESS, STIFFNESS OF JOINTS, AND MOTTLING OF TOOTH ENAMEL AND OSTEOSCLEROSIS. AFTER CHRONIC EXPOSURE THE BONE STRUCTURE SHOWS THICKENING WITH CALCIFICATION IN THE LIGAMENTOUS ATTACHMENTS OF THE RIBS AND PELVIS. IN A CHRONIC DRINKING WATER STUDY, A SMALL NUMBER OF OSTEOSARCOMAS OCCURRED IN MID- AND HIGH-DOSE MALE RATS. THE RESULTS ARE WEAKLY SUPPORTIVE OF AN ASSOCIATION BETWEEN SODIUM FLUORIDE ADMINISTRATION AND THE OCCURRENCE OF OSTEOSARCOMAS IN MALE RATS. REPRODUCTIVE EFFECTS HAVE BEEN REPORTED IN ANIMALS.

FIRST AID- IF VICTIM IS CONSCIOUS, GIVE SOLUBLE CALCIUM IN ANY FORM: MILK, CALCIUM GLUCONATE SOLUTION, OR CALCIUM LACTATE SOLUTION. THE CONCENTRATION FOR CALCIUM SALTS SHOULD BE 10 GRAMS IN 250 ML OF WATER. GIVE CALCIUM GLUCONATE, 10 GRAMS AND MAGNESIUM SULFATE, 30 GRAMS, IN 200 ML OF WATER ORALLY TO PRECIPITATE AND REMOVE FLUORIDE FROM THE INTESTINE. (DREISBACH, HANDBOOK OF POISONING, 12TH ED.). TREATMENT SHOULD BE ADMINISTERED BY QUALIFIED MEDICAL PERSONNEL. GET MEDICAL ATTENTION IMMEDIATELY.

ANTIDOTE: THE FOLLOWING ANTIDOTE HAS BEEN RECOMMENDED. HOWEVER, THE DECISION AS TO WHETHER THE SEVERITY OF POISONING REQUIRES ADMINISTRATION OF ANY ANTIDOTE AND ACTUAL DOSE REQUIRED SHOULD BE MADE BY QUALIFIED MEDICAL PERSONNEL.
POISONING FROM SOLUBLE FLUORIDE SALTS: GIVE CALCIUM GLUCONATE, 10 ML OF 10% SOLUTION INTRAVENOUSLY SLOWLY; REPEAT UNTIL SYMPTOMS DISAPPEAR. IF SERUM MAGNESIUM IS REDUCED, GIVE MILK OF MAGNESIA, 10 ML EVERY HOUR (DREISBACH, HANDBOOK OF POISONING, 11TH ED.). ANTIDOTE SHOULD BE ADMINISTERED BY QUALIFIED MEDICAL PERSONNEL.

REACTIVITY

REACTIVITY: STABLE UNDER NORMAL TEMPERATURES AND PRESSURES.

INCOMPATIBILITIES: SODIUM FLUORIDE: ACIDS: REACTS TO EVOLVE TOXIC AND CORROSIVE FUMES OF HYDROGEN FLUORIDE. ALUMINUM: ATTACKED BY AQUEOUS SOLUTIONS. GLASS: ATTACKED BY AQUEOUS SOLUTIONS.

DECOMPOSITION: THERMAL DECOMPOSITION MAY YIELD TOXIC FLUORIDES AND SODIUM OXIDE.

POLYMERIZATION: HAZARDOUS POLYMERIZATION HAS NOT BEEN REPORTED TO OCCUR UNDER NORMAL TEMPERATURES AND PRESSURES.

STORAGE AND DISPOSAL

OBSERVE ALL FEDERAL, STATE AND LOCAL REGULATIONS WHEN STORING OR DISPOSING OF THIS SUBSTANCE. FOR ASSISTANCE, CONTACT THE DISTRICT DIRECTOR OF THE ENVIRONMENTAL PROTECTION AGENCY.

STORAGE

STORE AWAY FROM INCOMPATIBLE SUBSTANCES.
STORAGE: PROTECT FROM PHYSICAL DAMAGE. STORE IN A DRY LOCATION. DO NOT STORE ADJACENT TO ACIDS OR ALKALIS (NFPA 49, HAZARDOUS CHEMICALS DATA, 1975)

CONDITIONS TO AVOID

MAY BURN BUT DOES NOT IGNITE READILY. AVOID CONTACT WITH STRONG OXIDIZERS, EXCESSIVE HEAT, SPARKS, OR OPEN FLAME.

SPILL AND LEAK PROCEDURES

SOIL SPILL: DIG HOLDING AREA SUCH AS LAGOON, POND OR PIT FOR CONTAINMENT. USE PROTECTIVE COVER SUCH AS A PLASTIC SHEET TO PREVENT MATERIAL FROM DISSOLVING IN FIRE EXTINGUISHING WATER OR RAIN.

WATER SPILL: NEUTRALIZE WITH AGRICULTURAL LIME, SLAKED LIME, CRUSHED LIMESTONE, OR SODIUM BICARBONATE.
ADD SUITABLE AGENT TO NEUTRALIZE SPILLED MATERIAL TO PH-7.

OCCUPATIONAL SPILL: DO NOT TOUCH SPILLED MATERIAL. STOP LEAK IF YOU CAN DO IT WITHOUT RISK. FOR SMALL SPILLS, TAKE UP WITH SAND OR OTHER ABSORBENT MATERIAL AND PLACE INTO CONTAINERS FOR LATER DISPOSAL. FOR SMALL DRY SPILLS, PLACE MATERIAL INTO A CLEAN, DRY CONTAINER WITH A CLEAN SHOVEL AND COVER. MOVE CONTAINERS FROM SPILL AREA. FOR LARGER SPILLS, DIKE FAR AHEAD OF SPILL FOR LATER DISPOSAL. KEEP UNNECESSARY PEOPLE AWAY. ISOLATE HAZARD AREA AND DENY ENTRY.
REPORTABLE QUANTITY (RQ): 1000 POUNDS THE SUPERFUND AMENDMENTS AND REAUTHORIZATION ACT (SARA) SECTION 304 REQUIRES THAT A RELEASE EQUAL TO OR GREATER THAN THE REPORTABLE QUANTITY FOR THIS SUBSTANCE BE IMMEDIATELY REPORTED TO THE LOCAL EMERGENCY PLANNING COMMITTEE AND THE STATE EMERGENCY RESPONSE COMMISSION (40 CFR 355.40). IF THE RELEASE OF THIS SUBSTANCE IS REPORTABLE UNDER CERCLA SECTION 103, THE NATIONAL RESPONSE CENTER MUST BE NOTIFIED IMMEDIATELY AT (800) 424-8802 OR (202) 426-2675 IN THE METROPOLITAN WASHINGTON, D.C. AREA (40 CFR 302.6).

PROTECTIVE EQUIPMENT

VENTILATION: PROVIDE LOCAL EXHAUST OR PROCESS ENCLOSURE VENTILATION TO MEET PUBLISHED EXPOSURE LIMITS.

RESPIRATOR: THE FOLLOWING RESPIRATORS AND MAXIMUM USE CONCENTRATIONS ARE RECOMMENDATIONS BY THE U.S. DEPARTMENT OF HEALTH AND HUMAN SERVICES, NIOSH POCKET GUIDE TO CHEMICAL HAZARDS; NIOSH CRITERIA DOCUMENTS OR BY THE U.S. DEPARTMENT OF LABOR, 29 CFR 1910 SUBPART Z. THE SPECIFIC RESPIRATOR SELECTED MUST BE BASED ON CONTAMINATION LEVELS FOUND IN THE WORK PLACE, MUST NOT EXCEED THE WORKING LIMITS OF THE RESPIRATOR AND BE JOINTLY APPROVED BY THE NATIONAL INSTITUTE FOR OCCUPATIONAL SAFETY AND HEALTH AND THE MINE SAFETY AND HEALTH ADMINISTRATION (NIOSH-MSHA).
SODIUM FLUORIDE, SOLID: 12.5 MG(F)/M3- ANY DUST AND MIST RESPIRATOR EXCEPT SINGLE-USE RESPIRATORS.
25 MG(F)/M3- ANY DUST AND MIST RESPIRATOR EXCEPT SINGLE-USE AND QUARTER-MASK RESPIRATORS. ANY SUPPLIED-AIR RESPIRATOR. ANY SELF-CONTAINED BREATHING APPARATUS.
62.5 MG(F)/M3- ANY POWERED AIR-PURIFYING RESPIRATOR WITH A DUST, MIST AND FUME FILTER. ANY SUPPLIED-AIR RESPIRATOR OPERATED IN A CONTINUOUS FLOW MODE.
125 MG(F)/M3- ANY SELF-CONTAINED BREATHING APPARATUS WITH A FULL FACEPIECE. ANY AIR-PURIFYING FULL FACEPIECE RESPIRATOR WITH A HIGH-EFFICIENCY PARTICULATE FILTER. ANY SUPPLIED-AIR RESPIRATOR WITH A FULL FACEPIECE.
500 MG(F)/M3- ANY SUPPLIED-AIR RESPIRATOR WITH A FULL FACEPIECE AND OPERATED IN A PRESSURE-DEMAND OR OTHER POSITIVE PRESSURE MODE.
ESCAPE- ANY AIR-PURIFYING FULL FACEPIECE RESPIRATOR (GAS MASK) WITH A CHIN-STYLE OR FRONT- OR BACK-MOUNTED ACID GAS CANISTER HAVING A HIGH-EFFICIENCY PARTICULATE FILTER. ANY APPROPRIATE ESCAPE-TYPE SELF-CONTAINED BREATHING APPARATUS.
NOTE: MAY NEED ACID GAS SORBENT.
FOR FIREFIGHTING AND OTHER IMMEDIATELY DANGEROUS TO LIFE OR HEALTH CONDITIONS:
SELF-CONTAINED BREATHING APPARATUS WITH FULL FACEPIECE OPERATED IN PRESSURE-DEMAND OR OTHER POSITIVE PRESSURE MODE.
SUPPLIED-AIR RESPIRATOR WITH FULL FACEPIECE AND OPERATED IN PRESSURE-DEMAND OR OTHER POSITIVE PRESSURE MODE IN COMBINATION WITH AN AUXILIARY SELF-CONTAINED BREATHING APPARATUS OPERATED IN PRESSURE-DEMAND OR OTHER POSITIVE PRESSURE MODE.

CLOTHING: EMPLOYEE MUST WEAR APPROPRIATE PROTECTIVE (IMPERVIOUS) CLOTHING AND EQUIPMENT TO PREVENT ANY POSSIBILITY OF SKIN CONTACT WITH THIS SUBSTANCE.

GLOVES: EMPLOYEE MUST WEAR APPROPRIATE PROTECTIVE GLOVES TO PREVENT CONTACT WITH THIS SUBSTANCE.

EYE PROTECTION: EMPLOYEE MUST WEAR SPLASH-PROOF OR DUST-RESISTANT SAFETY GOGGLES AND A FACESHIELD TO PREVENT CONTACT WITH THIS SUBSTANCE.
EMERGENCY WASH FACILITIES: WHERE THERE IS ANY POSSIBILITY THAT AN EMPLOYEE'S EYES AND/OR SKIN MAY BE EXPOSED TO THIS SUBSTANCE, THE EMPLOYER SHOULD PROVIDE AN EYE WASH FOUNTAIN AND QUICK DRENCH SHOWER WITHIN THE IMMEDIATE WORK AREA FOR EMERGENCY USE.

AUTHORIZED BY- OCCUPATIONAL HEALTH SERVICES, INC.
CREATION DATE: 10/05/89 ***REVISION DATE:*** 07/12/90

MATERIAL SAFETY DATA SHEET

OCCUPATIONAL HEALTH SERVICES, INC.
AGRICULTURE AND PESTICIDE DIVISION
450 SEVENTH AVENUE, SUITE 2407
NEW YORK, NEW YORK 10123
1-800-445-MSDS OR (212) 967-1100

EMERGENCY CONTACT:
JOHN S. BRANSFORD, JR. (615) 292-1180

SUBSTANCE IDENTIFICATION

CAS-NUMBER 62-74-8
SUBSTANCE: **SODIUM FLUOROACETATE**

TRADE NAMES/SYNONYMS: 1080; SFA; FLUOROACETIC ACID, SODIUM SALT; RCRA P058; COMPOUND NO. 1080; SODIUM FLUORACETATE; FRATOL; FURATOL; RATBANE 1080; SODIUM FLUOACETATE; SODIUM MONOFLUOROACETATE; SODIUM FLUOACETIC ACID; UN 2629; PST21240

CHEMICAL FAMILY: ESTER, CARBOXYLIC, ALIPHATIC HALOGEN COMPOUND, ALIPHATIC

MOLECULAR FORMULA: C2-H2-F-O2.NA MOL WT: 100.03

CERCLA RATINGS (SCALE 0-3): HEALTH=3 FIRE=0 REACTIVITY=0 PERSISTENCE=0

NFPA RATINGS (SCALE 0-4): HEALTH=4 FIRE=0 REACTIVITY=0

COMPONENTS AND CONTAMINANTS

COMPONENT: SODIUM FLUOROACETATE ***PERCENT:*** 100 CAS# 62-74-8

OTHER CONTAMINANTS: NONE

EXPOSURE LIMITS: SODIUM FLUOROACETATE: 0.05 MG/M3 OSHA TWA (SKIN); 0.15 MG/M3 OSHA STEL 0.05 MG/M3 ACGIH TWA (SKIN); 0.15 MG/M3 ACGIH STEL 10/10,000 POUNDS SARA SECTION 302 THRESHOLD PLANNING QUANTITY 10 POUNDS SARA SECTION 304 REPORTABLE QUANTITY 10 POUNDS CERCLA SECTION 103 REPORTABLE QUANTITY

PHYSICAL DATA

DESCRIPTION: ODORLESS, FINE WHITE CRYSTALLINE POWDER WITH A TART SOUR TASTE. ***MELTING POINT:*** 392 F (200 C) DECOMP

SOLUBILITY IN WATER: SOLUBLE

SOLVENT SOLUBILITY: MOST ORGANIC SOLVENTS

FIRE AND EXPLOSION DATA

FIRE AND EXPLOSION HAZARD: NEGLIGIBLE FIRE HAZARD WHEN EXPOSED TO HEAT OR FLAME.

FIREFIGHTING MEDIA: DRY CHEMICAL, CARBON DIOXIDE, HALON, WATER SPRAY OR STANDARD FOAM (1987 EMERGENCY RESPONSE GUIDEBOOK, DOT P 5800.4). FOR LARGER FIRES, USE WATER SPRAY, FOG OR STANDARD FOAM (1987 EMERGENCY RESPONSE GUIDEBOOK, DOT P 5800.4).

FIREFIGHTING: MOVE CONTAINERS FROM FIRE AREA IF POSSIBLE (1987 EMERGENCY RESPONSE GUIDEBOOK, DOT P 5800.4, GUIDE PAGE 53). EXTINGUISH USING AGENT SUITABLE FOR TYPE OF SURROUNDING FIRE. AVOID BREATHING VAPORS AND DUSTS. KEEP UPWIND.

TRANSPORTATION DATA

DEPARTMENT OF TRANSPORTATION HAZARD CLASSIFICATION 49 CFR 172.101: POISON B

DEPARTMENT OF TRANSPORTATION LABELING REQUIREMENTS 49 CFR 172.101 AND SUBPART E: POISON

DEPARTMENT OF TRANSPORTATION PACKAGING REQUIREMENTS: 49 CFR 173.365 EXCEPTIONS: 49 CFR 173.364

TOXICITY

SODIUM FLUOROACETATE: TOXICITY DATA: 48 MG/KG SKIN-RAT LD50; 25300 UG/KG SKIN-MOUSE LD50; 1600 UG/KG SKIN-GUINEA PIG LD50; 714 UG/KG ORAL-HUMAN LDLO; 100 UG/KG ORAL-RAT LD50; 100 UG/KG ORAL-MOUSE LD50; 340 UG/KG ORAL-RABBIT LD50; 66 UG/KG ORAL-DOG LD50; 300 UG/KG ORAL-GUINEA PIG LD50; 110 UG/KG ORAL-MAMMAL LD50; 500 UG/KG ORAL-DOMESTIC ANIMAL LD50; 300 MG/KG ORAL-MONKEY LD50; 350 UG/KG ORAL-CAT LD50; 300 UG/KG ORAL-SQUIRREL LD50; 281 UG/KG SUBCUTANEOUS-RABBIT LD50; 250 UG/KG SUBCUTANEOUS-GUINEA PIG LD50; 7200 UG/KG SUBCUTANEOUS-MOUSE LD50; 5 MG/KG INTRAVENOUS-MONKEY LD50; 60 UG/KG INTRAVENOUS-DOG LD50; 300 UG/KG INTRAVENOUS-RABBIT LD50; 3 MG/KG INTRAPERITONEAL-RAT LDLO; 300 UG/KG INTRAPERITONEAL-CAT LD50; 200 UG/KG INTRAPERITONEAL-DOMESTIC ANIMAL LD50; 378 UG/KG INTRAPERITONEAL-GUINEA PIG LD50; 100 UG/KG INTRAPERITONEAL-MAMMAL LD50; 7 MG/KG INTRAPERITONEAL-MOUSE LD50; 300 UG/KG INTRAPERITONEAL-PIG LD50; 400 UG/KG INTRAPERITONEAL-SQUIRREL LD50; 700 UG/KG INTRAMUSCULAR-DOMESTIC ANIMAL LD50; 5 MG/KG UNREPORTED-MAN LDLO; 15 MG/KG UNREPORTED-RAT LD50; 10 MG/KG UNREPORTED-MOUSE LD50; 1 MG/KG UNREPORTED-HORSE LD50; REPRODUCTIVE EFFECTS DATA (RTECS). ACUTE TOXICITY LEVEL: HIGHLY TOXIC BY DERMAL ABSORPTION AND INGESTION. TARGET EFFECTS: CONVULSANT. POISONING MAY AFFECT THE LUNGS, KIDNEYS, SKELETAL MUSCLES, AND THE CARDIOVASCULAR AND NERVOUS SYSTEMS.

HEALTH EFFECTS AND FIRST AID

INHALATION: CONVULSANT/HIGHLY TOXIC. 5 MG/M3 IMMEDIATELY DANGEROUS TO LIFE OR HEALTH. **ACUTE EXPOSURE**- SYMPTOMS MAY BEGIN WITHIN MINUTES TO 4-5 HOURS AND MAY INCLUDE VOMITING, NAUSEA, APPREHENSION, EXCITABILITY, AUDITORY HALLUCINATIONS, NYSTAGMUS, TINGLING SENSATION OF NOSE, NUMBNESS OF FACE, FACIAL TWITCHING, EPILEPTIFORM CONVULSIONS, EXHAUSTION, COMA AND AND RESPIRATORY DEPRESSION. AFTER SEVERAL HOURS THERE MAY BE ALTERNATING PULSEBEATS FROM STRONGER TO WEAKER, LONG SEQUENCES OF ECTOPIC HEARTBEATS, TACHYCARDIA, AND VENTRICULAR FIBRILLATION. DEATH MAY OCCUR FROM RESPIRATORY FAILURE ASSOCIATED WITH PULMONARY EDEMA AND BRONCHIAL PNEUMONIA. COMPLETE RECOVERY MAY FOLLOW REPEATED CONVULSIONS. RAPID PROGRESSION OF SYMPTOMS WITHIN 1-2 HOURS AFTER POISONING IS LIKELY TO RESULT IN DEATH. SURVIVAL FOR MORE THAN 24 HOURS INDICATES A FAVORABLE OUTCOME. IN ONE CASE, A MAN WORKING WITH SODIUM ACETATE, A GUST OF WIND BLEW THE POWDER INTO HIS FACE, AND SOME OF IT WAS INHALED. THIS CAUSED AN ALMOST IMMEDIATE TINGLING SENSATION AROUND THE CORNERS OF THE MOUTH AND IN THE NASAL PASSAGES, AND SOON THE ENTIRE FACE BECAME NUMB. THIS WAS ACCOMPANIED BY SALIVATION AND LOSS OF SPEECH. VISION WAS BLURRED FROM THE ONSET, WITH AN INABILITY TO FOCUS ON OBJECTS. ALTHOUGH PARESTHESIAS SPREAD TO THE ARMS AND LEGS, AND VIOLENT CONVULSIONS AND COMA FOLLOWED, THE PATIENT ULTIMATELY RECOVERED COMPLETELY. **CHRONIC EXPOSURE**- NO DATA AVAILABLE.

FIRST AID- REMOVE FROM EXPOSURE AREA TO FRESH AIR IMMEDIATELY. IF BREATHING HAS STOPPED, PERFORM ARTIFICIAL RESPIRATION. KEEP PERSON WARM AND AT REST. TREAT SYMPTOMATICALLY AND SUPPORTIVELY. GET MEDICAL ATTENTION IMMEDIATELY.

SKIN CONTACT: IRRITANT/CONVULSANT. **ACUTE EXPOSURE**- MAY CAUSE IRRITATION. THE AGENT IS SLOWLY ABSORBED VIA THE SKIN, UNLESS THE SKIN IS CUT OR ABRADED AND THEN ABSORPTION MAY OCCUR QUICKLY. MAY CAUSE EXCITABILITY, EPILEPTIFORM CONVULSIONS, EXHAUSTION, COMA, RESPIRATORY DEPRESSION, AND CARDIAC IRREGULARITIES. **CHRONIC EXPOSURE**- NO DATA AVAILABLE.

FIRST AID- REMOVE CONTAMINATED CLOTHING AND SHOES IMMEDIATELY. WASH AFFECTED AREA WITH SOAP OR MILD DETERGENT AND LARGE AMOUNTS OF WATER UNTIL NO EVIDENCE OF CHEMICAL REMAINS (APPROXIMATELY 15-20 MINUTES). GET MEDICAL ATTENTION IMMEDIATELY.

EYE CONTACT: **ACUTE EXPOSURE**- POISONING MAY CAUSE TRANSIENT DISTURBANCE OF VISION AND BLURRED VISION. A HUMAN WHO WAS WORKING WITH SODIUM FLUOROACETATE ACCIDENTALLY INHALED SOME DUST WHICH CAUSED BLURRED VISION WITH AN INABILITY TO FOCUS ON OBJECTS. SEVERELY POISONED CATTLE HAVE BEEN REPORTED TO HAVE IMPAIRED VISION CAUSING THE ANIMALS NOT TO AVOID OBJECTS, BUT TO WALK INTO THEM. **CHRONIC EXPOSURE**- NO DATA AVAILABLE.

FIRST AID- WASH EYES IMMEDIATELY WITH LARGE AMOUNTS OF WATER OR NORMAL SALINE, OCCASIONALLY LIFTING UPPER AND LOWER LIDS, UNTIL NO EVIDENCE OF CHEMICAL REMAINS (APPROXIMATELY 15-20 MINUTES). GET MEDICAL ATTENTION IMMEDIATELY.

INGESTION: CONVULSANT/HIGHLY TOXIC. **ACUTE EXPOSURE**- SYMPTOMS MAY BEGIN WITHIN MINUTES TO 4-5 HOURS AND MAY INCLUDE VOMITING, NAUSEA, APPREHENSION, EXCITABILITY, AUDITORY HALLUCINATIONS, NYSTAGMUS, TINGLING SENSATION OF NOSE, NUMBNESS OF FACE, FACIAL TWITCHING, EPILEPTIFORM CONVULSIONS, EXHAUSTION, COMA AND RESPIRATORY DEPRESSION. AFTER SEVERAL HOURS THERE MAY BE ALTERNATING PULSEBEATS FROM STRONGER TO WEAKER, LONG SEQUENCES OF ECTOPIC HEARTBEATS, TACHYCARDIA, AND VENTRICULAR FIBRILLATION. DEATH MAY BE CAUSED BY HEMORRHAGIC PULMONARY EDEMA AND DEGENERATION OF RENAL TUBULES. COMPLETE RECOVERY MAY FOLLOW REPEATED CONVULSIONS. RAPID PROGRESSION OF SYMPTOMS WITHIN 1-2 HOURS AFTER POISONING IS LIKELY TO RESULT IN DEATH. SURVIVAL FOR MORE THAN 24 HOURS INDICATES A FAVORABLE OUTCOME. A DOSEAGE OF 0.5 TO 2.0 GM/KG MUST BE CONSIDERED HIGHLY DANGEROUS. **CHRONIC EXPOSURE**- REPRODUCTIVE EFFECTS IN RATS EXPOSED 3 TO 11 DAYS INCLUDE EFFECTS ON THE TESTES, EPIDIDYMUS, AND SPERM DUCT. RATS ACQUIRED A TOLERANCE TO SODIUM FLUOROACETATE BY INGESTING SUBLETHAL DOSES OVER OVER A PERIOD OF 5 TO 14 DAYS. HOWEVER THE TOLERANCE IS LOST IF INTAKE OF THE COMPOUND IS INTERRUPTED FOR AS LITTLE AS 7 DAYS.

FIRST AID- REMOVE BY EMESIS OR GASTRIC LAVAGE WITH TAP WATER. FOLLOW WITH A SALINE CATHARTIC. DO NOT PERFORM GASTRIC LAVAGE OR EMESIS IF VICTIM IS UNCONSCIUS. GET MEDICAL ATTENTION IMMEDIATELY. (DREISBACH, HANDBOOK OF POISONING, 11TH EDITION, 1983). GASTRIC LAVAGE SHOULD BE PERFORMED BY QUALIFIED MEDICAL PERSONNEL.

ANTIDOTE: THE FOLLOWING ANTIDOTE HAS BEEN RECOMMENDED. HOWEVER, THE DECISION AS TO WHETHER THE SEVERITY OF POISONING REQUIRES ADMINISTRATION OF ANY ANTIDOTE AND ACTUAL DOSE REQUIRED SHOULD BE MADE BY QUALIFIED MEDICAL PERSONNEL.

FOR FLUOROACETATE AND FLUOROACETAMIDE POISONING: ADMINISTRATION OF CERTAIN COMPOUNDS CAPABLE OF SUPPLYING ACETATE IONS HAS SHOWN ANTIDOTAL EFFECTS IN ANIMALS, INCLUDING MONKEYS. THE CHOICE DRUGS ARE

MONOACETIN (GLYCERYL MONOACETATE 0.24 GM/KG) AND A COMBINATION OF SODIUM ACETATE AND ETHANOL (0.12 GM/KG OF EACH), BUT REPORTS OF THEIR USE IN HUMANS HAVE RARELY APPEARED IN LITERATURE. IF PARENTERAL ADMINISTRATION IS NOT FEASIBLE, A MIXTURE OF 100 ML OF UNDILUTED MONOACETIN IN 500 ML OF WATER CAN BE GIVEN ORALLY AND REPEATED IN AN HOUR. A SINGLE DOSE OF MAGNESIUM SULFATE (800 MG/KG) GIVEN INTRAMUSCULARLY AS A 50% SOLUTION HAS PROVED SUCCESSFUL IN ANIMALS DOSED WITH LETHAL AMOUNTS OF SODIUM FLUOROACETATE (ARENA, POISONING, 4TH ED.). ANTIDOTE SHOULD BE ADMINISTERED BY QUALIFIED MEDICAL PERSONNEL.

REACTIVITY

REACTIVITY: STABLE UNDER NORMAL TEMPERATURES AND PRESSURES.

INCOMPATIBILITIES: CARBON DISULFIDES: INCOMPATIBLE ALKALINE METALS: INCOMPATIBLE

DECOMPOSITION: THERMAL DECOMPOSITION MAY RELEASE TOXIC OXIDES OF CARBON, CORROSIVE SODIUM FUMES AND CORROSIVE HYDROGEN FLOURIDE.

POLYMERIZATION: HAZARDOUS POLYMERIZATION HAS NOT BEEN REPORTED TO OCCUR UNDER NORMAL TEMPERATURES AND PRESSURES.

STORAGE AND DISPOSAL

OBSERVE ALL FEDERAL, STATE AND LOCAL REGULATIONS WHEN STORING OR DISPOSING OF THIS SUBSTANCE. FOR ASSISTANCE, CONTACT THE DISTRICT DIRECTOR OF THE ENVIRONMENTAL PROTECTION AGENCY.

STORAGE

THRESHOLD PLANNING QUANTITY (TPQ): THE SUPERFUND AMENDMENTS AND REAUTHORIZATION ACT (SARA) SECTION 302 REQUIRES THAT EACH FACILITY WHERE ANY EXTREMELY HAZARDOUS SUBSTANCE IS PRESENT IN A QUANTITY EQUAL TO OR GREATER THAN THE TPQ ESTABLISHED FOR THAT SUBSTANCE NOTIFY THE STATE EMERGENCY RESPONSE COMMISSION FOR THE STATE IN WHICH IT IS LOCATED. SECTION 303 OF SARA REQUIRES THESE FACILITIES TO PARTICIPATE IN LOCAL EMERGENCY RESPONSE PLANNING (40 CFR 355.30).

CONDITIONS TO AVOID

MAY BURN BUT DOES NOT IGNITE READILY.

SPILL AND LEAK PROCEDURES

OCCUPATIONAL SPILL: DO NOT TOUCH SPILLED MATERIAL. STOP LEAK IF YOU CAN DO IT WITHOUT RISK. FOR SMALL SPILLS, TAKE UP WITH SAND OR OTHER ABSORBENT MATERIAL AND PLACE INTO CONTAINERS FOR LATER DISPOSAL. FOR SMALL DRY SPILLS, WITH A CLEAN SHOVEL PLACE MATERIAL INTO CLEAN, DRY CONTAINER AND COVER. MOVE CONTAINERS FROM SPILL AREA. FOR LARGER SPILLS, DIKE FAR AHEAD OF SPILL FOR LATER DISPOSAL. KEEP UNNECESSARY PEOPLE AWAY. ISOLATE HAZARD AREA AND DENY ENTRY.

REPORTABLE QUANTITY (RQ): 10 POUNDS THE SUPERFUND AMENDMENTS AND REAUTHORIZATION ACT (SARA) SECTION 304 REQUIRES THAT A RELEASE EQUAL TO OR GREATER THAN THE REPORTABLE QUANTITY FOR THIS SUBSTANCE BE IMMEDIATELY REPORTED TO THE LOCAL EMERGENCY PLANNING COMMITTEE AND THE STATE EMERGENCY RESPONSE COMMISSION (40 CFR 355.40). IF THE RELEASE OF THIS SUBSTANCE IS REPORTABLE UNDER CERCLA SECTION 103, THE NATIONAL RESPONSE CENTER MUST BE NOTIFIED IMMEDIATELY AT (800) 424-8802 OR (202) 426-2675 IN THE METROPOLITAN WASHINGTON, D.C. AREA (40 CFR 302.6).

PROTECTIVE EQUIPMENT

VENTILATION: PROCESS ENCLOSURE RECOMMENDED.

RESPIRATOR: THE FOLLOWING RESPIRATORS AND MAXIMUM USE CONCENTRATIONS ARE RECOMMENDATIONS BY THE U.S. DEPARTMENT OF HEALTH AND HUMAN SERVICES, NIOSH POCKET GUIDE TO CHEMICAL HAZARDS; NIOSH CRITERIA DOCUMENTS OR BY THE U.S. DEPARTMENT OF LABOR, 29 CFR 1910 SUBPART Z. THE SPECIFIC RESPIRATOR SELECTED MUST BE BASED ON CONTAMINATION LEVELS FOUND IN THE WORK PLACE, MUST NOT EXCEED THE WORKING LIMITS OF THE RESPIRATOR AND BE JOINTLY APPROVED BY THE NATIONAL INSTITUTE FOR OCCUPATIONAL SAFETY AND HEALTH AND THE MINE SAFETY AND HEALTH ADMINISTRATION (NIOSH-MSHA).

0.25 MG/M3- DUST AND MIST, EXCEPT SINGLE USE RESPIRATOR.

0.5 MG/M3- DUST AND MIST, EXCEPT SINGLE USE AND QUARTER-MASK RESPIRATOR. HIGH-EFFICIENCY PARTICULATE RESPIRATOR. SUPPLIED-AIR RESPIRATOR. SELF-CONTAINED BREATHING APPARATUS.

2.5 MG/M3- HIGH-EFFICIENCY PARTICULATE RESPIRATOR WITH FULL FACEPIECE. SUPPLIED-AIR WITH FULL FACEPIECE, HELMET, OR HOOD. SELF-CONTAINED BREATHING APPARATUS WITH A FULL FACEPIECE.

5 MG/M3- POWERED AIR-PURIFYING RESPIRATOR WITH A HIGH-EFFICIENCY FILTER. TYPE C SUPPLIED-AIR RESPIRATOR OPERATED IN PRESSURE-DEMAND OR OTHER POSITIVE PRESSURE OR CONTINUOUS-FLOW MODE.

ESCAPE- DUST MASK, EXCEPT SINGLE USE. SELF-CONTAINED BREATHING APPARATUS.

FOR FIREFIGHTING AND OTHER IMMEDIATELY DANGEROUS TO LIFE OR HEALTH CONDITIONS:

SELF-CONTAINED BREATHING APPARATUS WITH FULL FACEPIECE OPERATED IN PRESSURE-DEMAND OR OTHER POSITIVE PRESSURE MODE.

SUPPLIED-AIR RESPIRATOR WITH FULL FACEPIECE AND OPERATED IN PRESSURE-DEMAND OR OTHER POSITIVE PRESSURE MODE IN COMBINATION WITH AN AUXILIARY SELF-CONTAINED BREATHING APPARATUS OPERATED IN PRESSURE-DEMAND OR OTHER POSITIVE PRESSURE MODE.

CLOTHING: EMPLOYEE MUST WEAR APPROPRIATE PROTECTIVE (IMPERVIOUS) CLOTHING AND EQUIPMENT TO PREVENT ANY POSSIBILITY OF SKIN CONTACT WITH THIS SUBSTANCE.

GLOVES: EMPLOYEE MUST WEAR APPROPRIATE PROTECTIVE GLOVES TO PREVENT CONTACT WITH THIS SUBSTANCE.

EYE PROTECTION: EMPLOYEE MUST WEAR SPLASH-PROOF OR DUST-RESISTANT SAFETY GOGGLES AND A FACESHIELD TO PREVENT CONTACT WITH THIS SUBSTANCE.

EMERGENCY WASH FACILITIES: WHERE THERE IS ANY POSSIBILITY THAT AN EMPLOYEE'S EYES AND/OR SKIN MAY BE EXPOSED TO THIS SUBSTANCE, THE EMPLOYER SHOULD PROVIDE AN EYE WASH FOUNTAIN AND QUICK DRENCH SHOWER WITHIN THE IMMEDIATE WORK AREA FOR EMERGENCY USE.

AUTHORIZED BY- OCCUPATIONAL HEALTH SERVICES, INC.
CREATION DATE: 10/05/89 ***REVISION DATE:*** 05/25/90

MATERIAL SAFETY DATA SHEET

OCCUPATIONAL HEALTH SERVICES, INC.
AGRICULTURE AND PESTICIDE DIVISION
450 SEVENTH AVENUE, SUITE 2407
NEW YORK, NEW YORK 10123
1-800-445-MSDS OR (212) 967-1100

EMERGENCY CONTACT:
JOHN S. BRANSFORD, JR. (615) 292-1180

SUBSTANCE IDENTIFICATION

CAS-NUMBER 1310-73-2

SUBSTANCE: SODIUM HYDROXIDE

TRADE NAMES/SYNONYMS: CAUSTIC SODA; SODA LYE; LYE; WHITE CAUSTIC; CAUSTIC SODA, BEAD; CAUSTIC SODA, DRY; CAUSTIC SODA, FLAKE; CAUSTIC SODA, GRANULAR; CAUSTIC SODA, SOLID; SODIUM HYDRATE; SODIUM HYDROXIDE (NA(OH)); SODIUM HYDROXIDE, FLAKE; SODIUM HYDROXIDE, DRY; SODIUM HYDROXIDE, SOLID; ASCARITE; SODIUM HYDROXIDE, DRY SOLID, FLAKE, BEAD, OR GRANULAR; STCC 4935235; UN 1823; NAOH; PST21300

CHEMICAL FAMILY: INORGANIC BASE

MOLECULAR FORMULA: NA-O-H

MOLECULAR WEIGHT: 40.00

CERCLA RATINGS (SCALE 0-3): HEALTH=3 FIRE=0 REACTIVITY=1 PERSISTENCE=0

NFPA RATINGS (SCALE 0-4): HEALTH=3 FIRE=0 REACTIVITY=1

COMPONENTS AND CONTAMINANTS

COMPONENT: SODIUM HYDROXIDE ***PERCENT:*** 100
CAS# 1310-73-2

OTHER CONTAMINANTS: NONE

EXPOSURE LIMITS: SODIUM HYDROXIDE: 2 MG/M3 OSHA CEILING 2 MG/M3 ACGIH CEILING 2 MG/M3 NIOSH RECOMMENDED 15 MINUTE CEILING
1000 POUNDS CERCLA SECTION 103 REPORTABLE QUANTITY

PHYSICAL DATA

DESCRIPTION: ODORLESS, WHITE OR OFF-WHITE HYGROSCOPIC SOLID.

BOILING POINT: 2534 F (1390 C) ***MELTING POINT:*** 604 F (318 C)

SPECIFIC GRAVITY: 2.130 ***VAPOR PRESSURE:*** 100 MMHG @ 1111 C

PH: 14 @ 5% SOLUTION ***SOLUBILITY IN WATER:*** 111 %

SOLVENT SOLUBILITY: SOLUBLE IN ALCOHOL, GLYCEROL; INSOLUBLE ACETONE, ETHER.

FIRE AND EXPLOSION DATA

FIRE AND EXPLOSION HAZARD: NEGLIGIBLE FIRE HAZARD WHEN EXPOSED TO HEAT OR FLAME.

FIREFIGHTING MEDIA: DRY CHEMICAL, CARBON DIOXIDE, HALON, WATER SPRAY OR STANDARD FOAM (1987 EMERGENCY RESPONSE GUIDEBOOK, DOT P 5800.4). FOR LARGER FIRES, USE WATER SPRAY, FOG OR STANDARD FOAM (1987 EMERGENCY RESPONSE GUIDEBOOK, DOT P 5800.4).

FIREFIGHTING: MOVE CONTAINERS FROM FIRE AREA IF POSSIBLE. COOL CONTAINERS EXPOSED TO FLAMES WITH WATER FROM SIDE UNTIL WELL AFTER FIRE IS OUT. STAY AWAY FROM STORAGE TANK ENDS (1987 EMERGENCY RESPONSE GUIDEBOOK, DOT P 5800.4, GUIDE PAGE 60).
USE AGENT SUITABLE FOR TYPE OF FIRE. USE WATER IN FLOODING QUANTITIES AS FOG. APPLY WATER FROM AS FAR A DISTANCE AS POSSIBLE.

TRANSPORTATION DATA

DEPARTMENT OF TRANSPORTATION HAZARD CLASSIFICATION 49 CFR 172.101: CORROSIVE MATERIAL
DEPARTMENT OF TRANSPORTATION LABELING REQUIREMENTS 49 CFR 172.101 AND SUBPART E: CORROSIVE
DEPARTMENT OF TRANSPORTATION PACKAGING REQUIREMENTS: 49 CFR 173.245B EXCEPTIONS: 49 CFR 173.244

TOXICITY

SODIUM HYDROXIDE: IRRITATION DATA: 500 MG/24 HOURS SKIN-RABBIT SEVERE; 1% EYE-RABBIT SEVERE; 50 UG/24 HOURS EYE-RABBIT SEVERE; 1 MG/24 HOURS EYE-RABBIT SEVERE; 400 UG EYE-RABBIT MILD; 1 MG/30 SECONDS RINSED EYE-RABBIT SEVERE; 1%/24 HOURS EYE-MONKEY SEVERE. TOXICITY DATA: 140-340 MG/KG ORAL-RAT LD50 (VAN WATERS & ROGERS INC. MSDS); 500 MG/KG ORAL-RABBIT LDLO; 1350 MG/KG SKIN-RABBIT LD50 (VAN WATERS & ROGERS INC. MSDS); 40 MG/KG INTRAPERITONEAL-MOUSE LD50; MUTAGENIC DATA (RTECS). CARCINOGEN STATUS: NONE. LOCAL EFFECTS: CORROSIVE- EYE, SKIN, MUCOUS MEMBRANES. ACUTE TOXICITY LEVEL: TOXIC BY INGESTION; MODERATELY TOXIC BY DERMAL ABSORPTION. TARGET EFFECTS: NO DATA AVAILABLE.

HEALTH EFFECTS AND FIRST AID

INHALATION: SODIUM HYDROXIDE: CORROSIVE. 250 MG/M3 IMMEDIATELY DANGEROUS TO LIFE OR HEALTH. **ACUTE EXPOSURE-** EFFECTS DUE TO INHALATION OF DUSTS OR MIST MAY VARY FROM MILD IRRITATION OF THE NOSE AT 2 MG/M3 TO SEVERE PNEUMONITIS DEPENDING ON THE SEVERITY OF EXPOSURE. LOW CONCENTRATIONS MAY CAUSE MUCOUS MEMBRANE IRRITATION WITH SORE THROAT, COUGHING, AND DYSPNEA. INTENSE EXPOSURES MAY RESULT IN DESTRUCTION OF MUCOUS MEMBRANES AND DELAYED PULMONARY EDEMA OR PNEUMONITIS. SHOCK MAY OCCUR. **CHRONIC EXPOSURE-** REPEATED EXPOSURES OF 5000 MG/L WERE HARMLESS TO RATS, BUT 10,000 MG/L LED TO NERVOUSNESS, SORE EYES, DIARRHEA AND RETARDED GROWTH. PROLONGED EXPOSURE TO HIGH CONCENTRATIONS OF DUSTS OR MISTS MAY CAUSE DISCOMFORT AND ULCERATION OF NASAL PASSAGES. RATS EXPOSED 30 MINUTES/DAY TO UNMEASURED CONCENTRATIONS OF SODIUM HYDROXIDE AEROSOLS SUFFERED PULMONARY DAMAGE AFTER 2-3 MONTHS. DEATH OCCURRED IN 2 OF 10 RATS EXPOSED TO AN AEROSOL OF 40% AQUEOUS SODIUM HYDROXIDE FOR 30 MINUTES, TWICE A WEEK FOR 3 WEEKS. HISTOPATHOLOGICAL EXAMINATION SHOWED MOSTLY NORMAL LUNG TISSUE WITH FOCI OF ENLARGED ALVEOLAR SEPTAE, EMPHYSEMA, BRONCHIAL ULCERATION, AND ENLARGED LYMPH ADENOIDAL TISSUES. AN EPIDEMIOLOGIC STUDY OF 291 WORKERS CHRONICALLY EXPOSED TO CAUSTIC DUSTS FOR 30 YEARS OR MORE FOUND NO SIGNIFICANT INCREASE IN MORTALITY IN RELATION TO DURATION OR INTENSITY OF SUCH EXPOSURES.

FIRST AID- REMOVE FROM EXPOSURE AREA TO FRESH AIR IMMEDIATELY. IF BREATHING HAS STOPPED, GIVE ARTIFICIAL RESPIRATION. MAINTAIN AIRWAY AND BLOOD PRESSURE AND ADMINISTER OXYGEN IF AVAILABLE. KEEP AFFECTED PERSON WARM AND AT REST. TREAT SYMPTOMATICALLY AND SUPPORTIVELY. ADMINISTRATION OF OXYGEN SHOULD BE PERFORMED BY QUALIFIED PERSONNEL. GET MEDICAL ATTENTION IMMEDIATELY.

SKIN CONTACT: SODIUM HYDROXIDE: CORROSIVE. **ACUTE EXPOSURE-** UPON CONTACT WITH THE SKIN, DAMAGE INCLUDING REDNESS, CUTANEOUS BURNS, SKIN FISSURES AND WHITE ESCHARS MAY OCCUR WITHOUT IMMEDIATE PAIN. EXPOSURE TO SOLUTIONS AS WEAK AS 0.03 N (0.12%) FOR 1 HOUR HAS CAUSED INJURY TO HEALTHY SKIN. SOLUTIONS OF 25-50% CAUSED NO SENSATION OF IRRITATION WITHIN 3 MINUTES IN HUMAN SUBJECTS. WITH SOLUTIONS OF 0.4-4%, IRRITATION DOES NOT OCCUR UNTIL AFTER SEVERAL HOURS. SKIN BIOPSIES FROM HUMAN SUBJECTS HAVING 1 N SODIUM HYDROXIDE APPLIED TO THEIR ARMS FOR 15 TO 180 MINUTES SHOWED PROGRESSIVE CHANGES BEGINNING WITH DISSOLUTION OF THE CELLS IN THE HORNY LAYER AND PROGRESSING THROUGH EDEMA TO TOTAL DESTRUCTION OF THE EPIDERMIS IN 60 MINUTES. A 5% AQUEOUS SOLUTION CAUSED SEVERE NECROSIS TO THE SKIN OF RABBITS WHEN APPLIED FOR 4 HOURS. ALKALIES PENETRATE THE SKIN SLOWLY. THE EXTENT OF INJURY DEPENDS ON THE DURATION OF CONTACT. IF SODIUM HYDROXIDE IS NOT REMOVED FROM THE SKIN, SEVERE BURNS WITH DEEP ULCERATION MAY OCCUR. EXPOSURE TO THE DUST OR MIST MAY CAUSE MULTIPLE SMALL BURNS AND TEMPORARY LOSS OF HAIR. PATHOLOGIC FINDINGS DUE TO ALKALIES MAY INCLUDE GELATINOUS, NECROTIC AREAS AT THE SITE OF CONTACT. **CHRONIC EXPOSURE-** EFFECTS ARE DEPENDENT UPON CONCENTRATION AND DURATION OF EXPOSURE. DERMATITIS OR EFFECTS SIMILAR TO THOSE FOR ACUTE EXPOSURE MAY OCCUR.

FIRST AID- REMOVE CONTAMINATED CLOTHING AND SHOES IMMEDIATELY. WASH AFFECTED AREA WITH SOAP OR MILD DETERGENT AND LARGE AMOUNTS OF WATER UNTIL NO EVIDENCE OF CHEMICAL REMAINS (AT LEAST 15-20 MINUTES). IN CASE OF CHEMICAL BURNS, COVER AREA WITH STERILE, DRY DRESSING. BANDAGE SECURELY, BUT NOT TOO TIGHTLY. GET MEDICAL ATTENTION IMMEDIATELY.

EYE CONTACT: SODIUM HYDROXIDE: CORROSIVE. **ACUTE EXPOSURE-** CONTACT MAY CAUSE DISINTEGRATION AND SLOUGHING OF CONJUNCTIVAL AND CORNEAL EPITHELIUM, CORNEAL OPACIFICATION, MARKED EDEMA AND ULCERATION. AFTER 7 TO 13 DAYS EITHER GRADUAL RECOVERY BEGINS OR THERE IS PROGRESSION OF ULCERATION AND CORNEAL OPACIFICATION. COMPLICATIONS OF SEVERE EYE BURNS ARE SYMBLEPHARON WITH OVERGROWTH OF THE CORNEA BY A VASCULARIZED MEMBRANE, PROGRESSIVE OR RECURRENT CORNEAL ULCERATION AND PERMANENT CORNEAL OPACIFICATION. BLINDNESS MAY OCCUR. **CHRONIC EXPOSURE-** EFFECTS ARE DEPENDENT UPON CONCENTRATION AND DURATION OF EXPOSURE. CONJUNCTIVITIS OR EFFECTS SIMILAR TO THOSE FOR ACUTE EXPOSURE MAY OCCUR.

FIRST AID- WASH EYES IMMEDIATELY WITH LARGE AMOUNTS OF WATER, OCCASIONALLY LIFTING UPPER AND LOWER LIDS, UNTIL NO EVIDENCE OF CHEMICAL REMAINS (AT LEAST 15-20 MINUTES). CONTINUE IRRIGATING WITH NORMAL SALINE UNTIL THE PH HAS RETURNED TO NORMAL (30-60 MINUTES). COVER WITH STERILE BANDAGES. GET MEDICAL ATTENTION IMMEDIATELY.

INGESTION: SODIUM HYDROXIDE: CORROSIVE/TOXIC. **ACUTE EXPOSURE-** THE REPORTED LETHAL DOSE IN RATS IS 140-340 MG/KG. INGESTION MAY CAUSE A BURNING SENSATION IN THE MOUTH, CORROSION OF THE LIPS, MOUTH, TONGUE AND PHARYNX, AND SEVERE ESOPHAGEAL AND ABDOMINAL PAIN, VOMITING OF BLOOD AND LARGE PIECES OF MUCOSA, AND BLOODY DIARRHEA. ASPHYXIA CAN OCCUR FROM SWELLING OF THE THROAT. MEDIASTINITIS, ALKALEMIA, PALLOR, WEAK, SLOW PULSE, CARDIOVASCULAR COLLAPSE, SHOCK, COMA AND DEATH MAY OCCUR. PERFORATION OF THE ALIMENTARY TRACT AND CONSTRICTIVE SCARRING MAY RESULT. ESOPHAGEAL STRICTURE MAY OCCUR WEEKS, MONTHS, OR EVEN YEARS LATER TO MAKE SWALLOWING DIFFICULT. THE ESTIMATED FATAL DOSE IN MAN IS 5 GRAMS. CASES OF SQUAMOUS CELL CARCINOMA OF THE ESOPHAGUS HAVE OCCURRED WITH LATENT PERIODS OF 12 TO 42 YEARS AFTER INGESTION. THESE CANCERS WERE BELIEVED TO BE SEQUELA OF TISSUE DESTRUCTION AND POSSIBLY SCAR FORMATION RATHER THAN THE RESULT OF DIRECT CARCINOGENIC ACTION OF SODIUM HYDROXIDE. **CHRONIC EXPOSURE-** DEPENDING ON THE CONCENTRATION, REPEATED INGESTION OF ALKALINE SUBSTANCES MAY RESULT IN INFLAMMATORY AND ULCERATIVE EFFECTS ON THE ORAL MUCOUS MEMBRANES AND OTHER EFFECTS AS WITH ACUTE INGESTION.

FIRST AID- DO NOT USE GASTRIC LAVAGE OR EMESIS. DILUTE THE ALKALI BY GIVING WATER OR MILK TO DRINK IMMEDIATELY AND ALLOWING VOMITING TO OCCUR. AS SOON AS POSSIBLE, HAVE QUALIFIED MEDICAL PERSONNEL DO ESOPHAGOSCOPY AND IRRIGATE INJURED AREAS WITH 1% ACETIC ACID UNTIL THE ALKALI IS COMPLETELY NEUTRALIZED. (DREISBACH, HANDBOOK OF POISONING, 11TH EDITION). GET MEDICAL ATTENTION IMMEDIATELY.

ANTIDOTE: NO SPECIFIC ANTIDOTE. TREAT SYMPTOMATICALLY AND SUPPORTIVELY.

REACTIVITY

REACTIVITY: REACTS EXOTHERMICALLY WITH WATER.

INCOMPATIBILITIES: SODIUM HYDROXIDE: ACETALDEHYDE: MAY RESULT IN VIOLENT POLYMERIZATION. ACETIC ACID: MIXING IN CLOSED CONTAINER INCREASES TEMPERATURE AND PRESSURE. ACETIC ANHYDRIDE: MIXING IN A CLOSED CONTAINER INCREASES TEMPERATURE AND PRESSURE. ACIDS: MAY REACT VIOLENTLY. ACROLEIN: MAY RESULT IN AN EXTREMELY VIOLENT POLYMERIZATION. ACRYLONITRILE: MAY CAUSE VIOLENT POLYMERIZATION. ALLYL ALCOHOL + BENZENE SULFONYL CHLORIDE: POSSIBLE EXPLOSION HAZARD. ALLYL CHLORIDE: HYDROLYZES. ALUMINUM: VIGOROUS REACTION. ALUMINUM, ARSENIC TRIOXIDE, SODIUM ARSENATE: MAY GENERATE FLAMMABLE HYDROGEN GAS. AMMONIA AND SILVER NITRATE: PRECIPITATION OF EXPLOSIVE SIVLER NITRIDE MAY OCCUR. AMMONIUM SALTS: MAY REACT VIOLENTLY EVOLVING AMMONIA GAS. BENZENE-1,4-DIOL: EXOTHERMIC REACTION. N,N'-BIS(TRINITROETHYL)UREA: FORMATION OF EXPLOSIVE COMPOUND. BROMINE: POSSIBLE EXPLOSION IF NOT STIRRED CONTINOUSLY. CHLORINE TRIFLUORIDE: MAY CAUSE VIOLENT REACTION. CHLOROFORM AND METHYL ALCOHOL: EXOTHERMIC REACTION. CHLOROHYDRIN: MIXING IN A CLOSED CONTAINER CAUSES AN INCREASE IN TEMPERATURE AND PRESSURE. 4-CHLORO-2-METHYLPHENOL: POSSIBLE IGNITION. CHLORONITROTOLUENES: POSSIBLE EXPLOSION. CHLOROPICRIN: MAY CAUSE VIOLENT REACTION. CHLOROSULFONIC ACID: MIXING IN A CLOSED CONTAINER CAUSES AN INCREASE IN TEMPERATURE AND PRESSURE. CINNAMALDEHYDE: EXOTHERMIC REACTION. COATINGS: MAY BE ATTACKED. CYANOGEN AZIDE: MAY FORM SODIUM 5-AZIDOTETRAZOLIDE, WHICH IS EXPLOSIVE IF ISOLATED. 2,2-

DICHLORO-3,3-DIMETHYLBUTANE: HAZARDOUS REACTION. 1,2-DICHLOROETHYLENE: MAY FORM SPONTANEOUSLY FLAMMABLE MONOCHLOROACETYLENE. DIBORANE AND OCTANAL OXIME: EXOTHERMIC REACTION. ETHYLENE CYANOHYDRIN: MIXING IN A CLOSED CONTAINER CAUSES AN INCREASE IN TEMPERATURE AND PRESSURE. FLAMMABLE LIQUIDS: FIRE AND EXPLOSION HAZARD. GLYCOLS: MAY CAUSE EXOTHERMIC DECOMPOSITION WITH EVOLUTION OF HYDROGEN GAS. GLYOXAL: MIXING IN A CLOSED CONTAINER INCREASES TEMPERATURE AND PRESSURE. HALOGENATED HYDROCARBONS: VIOLENT REACTION. HYDROCHLORIC ACID: MIXING IN A CLOSED CONTAINER CAUSES AN INCREASE IN TEMPERATURE AND PRESSURE. HYDROFLUORIC ACID: MIXING IN A CLOSED CONTAINER CAUSES AN INCREASE IN TEMPERATURE AND PRESSURE. HYDROQUINONE: RAPID DECOMPOSITION OF HYDROQUINONE WITH EVOLUTION OF HEAT. LEAD: MAY BE ATTACKED; FLAMMABLE HYDROGEN GAS MAY BE LIBERATED. LEATHER: MAY BE ATTACKED. MALEIC ANHYDRIDE: EXPLOSIVE DECOMPOSITION. METALS: CORRODES METALS, REACTING TO FORM FLAMMABLE HYDROGEN GAS. 4-METHYL-2-NITROPHENOL: EXOTHERMIC REACTION. NITRIC ACID: MIXING IN CLOSED CONTAINER INCREASES TEMPERATURE AND PRESSURE. NITROBENZENE: POSSIBLY EXPLOSIVE REACTION UPON HEATING IN PRESENCE OF WATER. NITROETHANE: FORMS AN EXPLOSIVE SALT. NITROMETHANE: FORMS AN EXPLOSIVE SALT. NITROPARAFFINS: THE NITROPARAFFINS, IN THE PRESENCE OF WATER, FORM DRY SALTS WITH ORGANIC BASES. THE DRY SALTS ARE EXPLOSIVE. NITROPROPANE: FORMS AN EXPLOSIVE SALT. O-NITROTOLUENE: POSSIBLE EXPLOSION. OLEUM: MIXING IN A CLOSED CONTAINER CAUSES AN INCREASE IN TEMPERATURE AND PRESSURE. ORGANIC PEROXIDES: INCOMPATIBLE. PENTOL (3-METHYL-2-PENTENE-4-YN-1-OL): POSSIBLE EXPLOSION. PHOSPHORUS: MAY FORM MIXED PHOSPHINES WHICH MAY IGNITE SPONTANEOUSLY IN AIR. PHOSPHORUS PENTOXIDE: MAY REACT VIOLENTLY WHEN HEATED. PLASTICS: MAY BE ATTACKED. B-PROPIOLACTONE: MIXING IN A CLOSED CONTAINER CAUSES AN INCREASE IN TEMPERATURE AND PRESSURE. PROPYLENE OXIDE: IGNITION OR EXPLOSION MAY OCCUR. RUBBER: MAY BE ATTACKED. SODIUM TETRAHYDROBORATE: DRY MIXTURES WITH SODIUM HYDROXIDE CONTAINING 15-40% OF TETRAHYDROBORATE LIBERATE HYDROGEN EXPLOSIVELY AT 230-270 C. SULFURIC ACID: MIXING IN A CLOSED CONTAINER CAUSES AN INCREASE IN TEMPERAURE AND PRESSURE. 1,2,4,5-TETRACHLOROBENZENE: VIOLENT REACTION. TETRACHLOROBENZENE + METHYL ALCOHOL: POSSIBLE EXPLOSION. TETRACHLOROETHYLENE: POSSIBLE EXPLOSION. TETRAHYDROFURAN: SERIOUS EXPLOSIONS CAN OCCUR. TIN: EVOLUTION OF HYDROGEN GAS WHICH MAY FORM AN EXPLOSIVE MIXTURE. 1,1,1-TRICHLOROETHANOL: EXPLOSION MAY OCCUR. TRICHLOROETHYLENE: FORMATION OF EXPLOSIVE MIXTURES OF DICHLOROACETYLENE. TRICHLORONITROMETHANE + METHANOL: MAY CAUSE VIOLENT REACTION. WOOL: MAY BE ATTACKED. ZINC (DUST): FIRE AND EXPLOSION HAZARD. ZIRCONIUM: MAY CAUSE EXPLOSIVE REACTION UPON HEATING.

DECOMPOSITION: THERMAL DECOMPOSITION MAY RELEASE TOXIC FUMES OF SODIUM OXIDE.

POLYMERIZATION: HAZARDOUS POLYMERIZATION HAS NOT BEEN REPORTED TO OCCUR UNDER NORMAL TEMPERATURES AND PRESSURES.

STORAGE AND DISPOSAL

OBSERVE ALL FEDERAL, STATE AND LOCAL REGULATIONS WHEN STORING OR DISPOSING OF THIS SUBSTANCE. FOR ASSISTANCE, CONTACT THE DISTRICT DIRECTOR OF THE ENVIRONMENTAL PROTECTION AGENCY.

STORAGE

PROTECT AGAINST PHYSICAL DAMAGE. STORE IN A DRY PLACE; PROTECT AGAINST MOISTURE AND WATER. SEPARATE FROM ACIDS, METALS, EXPLOSIVES, ORGANIC PEROXIDES, AND EASILY IGNITABLE MATERIALS (NFPA 49, HAZARDOUS CHEMICALS DATA, 1975).

STORE AWAY FROM INCOMPATIBLE SUBSTANCES.

DISPOSAL

DISPOSAL MUST BE IN ACCORDANCE WITH STANDARDS APPLICABLE TO GENERATORS OF HAZARDOUS WASTE, 40 CFR 262. EPA HAZARDOUS WASTE NUMBER D002. 100 POUND CERCLA SECTION 103 REPORTABLE QUANTITY.

CONDITIONS TO AVOID

MAY BURN BUT DOES NOT IGNITE READILY. FLAMMABLE, POISONOUS GASES MAY ACCUMULATE IN TANKS AND HOPPER CARS. MAY IGNITE COMBUSTIBLES (WOOD, PAPER, OIL, ETC.).

SPILL AND LEAK PROCEDURES

SOIL SPILL: DIG HOLDING AREA SUCH AS LAGOON, POND OR PIT FOR CONTAINMENT. USE PROTECTIVE COVER SUCH AS A PLASTIC SHEET TO PREVENT MATERIAL FROM DISSOLVING IN FIRE EXTINGUISHING WATER OR RAIN.

WATER SPILL: ADD SUITABLE AGENT TO NEUTRALIZE SPILLED MATERIAL TO PH-7.

OCCUPATIONAL SPILL: DO NOT TOUCH SPILLED MATERIAL. STOP LEAK IF YOU CAN DO IT WITHOUT RISK. FOR SMALL SPILLS, TAKE UP WITH SAND OR OTHER ABSORBENT MATERIAL AND PLACE INTO CONTAINERS FOR LATER DISPOSAL. FOR SMALL DRY SPILLS, WITH CLEAN SHOVEL PLACE MATERIAL INTO CLEAN, DRY CONTAINER AND COVER. MOVE CONTAINERS FROM SPILL AREA. FOR LARGER SPILLS, DIKE FAR AHEAD OF SPILL FOR LATER DISPOSAL. KEEP UNNECESSARY PEOPLE AWAY. ISOLATE HAZARD AREA AND DENY ENTRY.

REPORTABLE QUANTITY (RQ): 1000 POUNDS THE SUPERFUND AMENDMENTS AND REAUTHORIZATION ACT (SARA) SECTION 304 REQUIRES THAT A RELEASE EQUAL TO OR GREATER THAN THE REPORTABLE QUANTITY FOR THIS SUBSTANCE BE IMMEDIATELY REPORTED TO THE LOCAL EMERGENCY PLANNING COMMITTEE AND THE STATE EMERGENCY RESPONSE COMMISSION (40 CFR 355.40). IF THE RELEASE OF THIS SUBSTANCE IS REPORTABLE UNDER CERCLA SECTION 103, THE NATIONAL RESPONSE CENTER MUST BE NOTIFIED IMMEDIATELY AT (800) 424-8802 OR (202) 426-2675 IN THE METROPOLITAN WASHINGTON, D.C. AREA (40 CFR 302.6).

PROTECTIVE EQUIPMENT

VENTILATION: PROVIDE LOCAL EXHAUST OR PROCESS ENCLOSURE VENTILATION TO MEET PUBLISHED EXPOSURE LIMITS.

RESPIRATOR: THE FOLLOWING RESPIRATORS AND MAXIMUM USE CONCENTRATIONS ARE RECOMMENDATIONS BY THE U.S. DEPARTMENT OF HEALTH AND HUMAN SERVICES, NIOSH POCKET GUIDE TO CHEMICAL HAZARDS; NIOSH CRITERIA DOCUMENTS OR BY THE U.S. DEPARTMENT OF LABOR, 29 CFR 1910 SUBPART Z. THE SPECIFIC RESPIRATOR SELECTED MUST BE BASED ON CONTAMINATION LEVELS FOUND IN THE WORK PLACE, MUST NOT EXCEED THE WORKING LIMITS OF THE RESPIRATOR AND BE JOINTLY APPROVED BY THE NATIONAL INSTITUTE FOR OCCUPATIONAL SAFETY AND HEALTH AND THE MINE SAFETY AND HEALTH ADMINISTRATION (NIOSH-MSHA).

SODIUM HYDROXIDE:

50 MG/M3- ANY POWERED AIR-PURIFYING RESPIRATOR WITH A DUST AND MIST FILTER. ANY SUPPLIED-AIR RESPIRATOR OPERATED IN A CONTINUOUS FLOW MODE.

100 MG/M3- ANY SELF-CONTAINED BREATHING APPARATUS WITH A FULL FACEPIECE. ANY SUPPLIED-AIR RESPIRATOR WITH A FULL FACEPIECE. ANY AIR-PURIFYING FULL FACEPIECE RESPIRATOR WITH A HIGH EFFICIENCY PARTICULATE FILTER.

250 MG/M3- ANY SUPPLIED-AIR RESPIRATOR WITH A FULL FACEPIECE AND OPERATED IN A PRESSURE-DEMAND OR OTHER POSITIVE PRESSURE MODE.

ESCAPE- ANY AIR-PURIFYING FULL FACEPIECE RESPIRATOR WITH A HIGH EFFICIENCY PARTICULATE FILTER. ANY APPROPRIATE ESCAPE-TYPE SELF-CONTAINED BREATHING APPARATUS.

FOR FIREFIGHTING AND OTHER IMMEDIATELY DANGEROUS TO LIFE OR HEALTH CONDITIONS:

SELF-CONTAINED BREATHING APPARATUS WITH FULL FACEPIECE OPERATED IN PRESSURE-DEMAND OR OTHER POSITIVE PRESSURE MODE.

SUPPLIED-AIR RESPIRATOR WITH FULL FACEPIECE AND OPERATED IN PRESSURE-DEMAND OR OTHER POSITIVE PRESSURE MODE IN COMBINATION WITH AN AUXILIARY SELF-CONTAINED BREATHING APPARATUS OPERATED IN PRESSURE-DEMAND OR OTHER POSITIVE PRESSURE MODE.

CLOTHING: EMPLOYEE MUST WEAR APPROPRIATE PROTECTIVE (IMPERVIOUS) CLOTHING AND EQUIPMENT TO PREVENT ANY POSSIBILITY OF SKIN CONTACT WITH THIS SUBSTANCE.

GLOVES: EMPLOYEE MUST WEAR APPROPRIATE PROTECTIVE GLOVES TO PREVENT CONTACT WITH THIS SUBSTANCE.

EYE PROTECTION: EMPLOYEE MUST WEAR SPLASH-PROOF OR DUST-RESISTANT SAFETY GOGGLES AND A FACESHIELD TO PREVENT CONTACT WITH THIS SUBSTANCE.

EMERGENCY WASH FACILITIES: WHERE THERE IS ANY POSSIBILITY THAT AN EMPLOYEE'S EYES AND/OR SKIN MAY BE EXPOSED TO THIS SUBSTANCE, THE EMPLOYER SHOULD PROVIDE AN EYE WASH FOUNTAIN AND QUICK DRENCH SHOWER WITHIN THE IMMEDIATE WORK AREA FOR EMERGENCY USE.

AUTHORIZED BY- OCCUPATIONAL HEALTH SERVICES, INC.

CREATION DATE: 11/17/89 ***REVISION DATE:*** 05/09/90

MATERIAL SAFETY DATA SHEET

OCCUPATIONAL HEALTH SERVICES, INC.
AGRICULTURE AND PESTICIDE DIVISION
450 SEVENTH AVENUE, SUITE 2407
NEW YORK, NEW YORK 10123
1-800-445-MSDS OR (212) 967-1100

EMERGENCY CONTACT:
JOHN S. BRANSFORD, JR. (615) 292-1180

SUBSTANCE IDENTIFICATION

CAS-NUMBER 7681-52-9
SUBSTANCE: **SODIUM HYPOCHLORITE**
TRADE NAMES/SYNONYMS: HYPOCHLOROUS ACID, SODIUM SALT; SODIUM HYPOCHLORITE (NACLO); SODIUM HYPOCHLORITE (NAOCL); CLOROX; BLEACH LIQUOR; SODIUM HYPOCHLORITE SOLUTION; UN 1791; CLHONA1; PST21310
CHEMICAL FAMILY: INORGANIC SALT
MOLECULAR FORMULA: NA-O-CL
MOLECULAR WEIGHT: 74.44
CERCLA RATINGS (SCALE 0-3): HEALTH=U FIRE=0 REACTIVITY=0 PERSISTENCE=0
NFPA RATINGS (SCALE 0-4): HEALTH=U FIRE=0 REACTIVITY=0

COMPONENTS AND CONTAMINANTS

COMPONENT: SODIUM HYPOCHLORITE ***PERCENT:*** <50
CAS# 7681-52-9
COMPONENT: WATER ***PERCENT:*** >50
OTHER CONTAMINANTS: NONE
EXPOSURE LIMITS: NO OCCUPATIONAL EXPOSURE LIMITS ESTABLISHED BY OSHA, ACGIH, OR NIOSH.
SODIUM HYPOCHLORITE: 100 POUNDS CERCLA SECTION 103 REPORTABLE QUANTITY

PHYSICAL DATA

DESCRIPTION: CLEAR, PALE GREENISH YELLOW LIQUID WITH A SLIGHT ODOR OF CHLORINE.
BOILING POINT: DECOMPOSES ***SPECIFIC GRAVITY:*** >1
VAPOR PRESSURE: NOT AVAILABLE ***EVAPORATION RATE:*** (ETHER=1) >1
PH: 11 (APPROX.) ***SOLUBILITY IN WATER:*** COMPLETE

FIRE AND EXPLOSION DATA

FIRE AND EXPLOSION HAZARD: UNKNOWN FIRE AND EXPLOSION HAZARD.
OXIDIZER: OXIDIZERS DECOMPOSE, ESPECIALLY WHEN HEATED, TO YIELD OXYGEN OR OTHER GASES WHICH WILL INCREASE THE BURNING RATE OF COMBUSTIBLE MATTER. CONTACT WITH EASILY OXIDIZABLE, ORGANIC, OR OTHER COMBUSTIBLE MATERIALS MAY RESULT IN IGNITION, VIOLENT COMBUSTION OR EXPLOSION.
FIREFIGHTING MEDIA: DRY CHEMICAL, CARBON DIOXIDE, HALON, WATER SPRAY OR STANDARD FOAM (1987 EMERGENCY RESPONSE GUIDEBOOK, DOT P 5800.4).
FOR LARGER FIRES, USE WATER SPRAY, FOG OR STANDARD FOAM (1987 EMERGENCY RESPONSE GUIDEBOOK, DOT P 5800.4).
FIREFIGHTING: MOVE CONTAINERS FROM FIRE AREA IF POSSIBLE. COOL CONTAINERS EXPOSED TO FLAMES WITH WATER FROM SIDE UNTIL WELL AFTER FIRE IS OUT. STAY AWAY FROM STORAGE TANK ENDS (1987 EMERGENCY RESPONSE GUIDEBOOK, DOT P 5800.4, GUIDE PAGE 60).
EXTINGUISH USING AGENTS INDICATED; DO NOT USE WATER DIRECTLY ON MATERIAL. IF LARGE AMOUNTS OF COMBUSTIBLE MATERIALS ARE INVOLVED, USE WATER SPRAY OR FOG IN FLOODING AMOUNTS. USE WATER SPRAY TO ABSORB CORROSIVE VAPORS. COOL CONTAINERS WITH FLOODING AMOUNTS OF WATER FROM AS FAR A DISTANCE AS POSSIBLE. AVOID BREATHING CORROSIVE VAPORS; KEEP UPWIND.

TRANSPORTATION DATA

DEPARTMENT OF TRANSPORTATION HAZARD CLASSIFICATION 49 CFR 172.101: CORROSIVE MATERIAL
DEPARTMENT OF TRANSPORTATION LABELING REQUIREMENTS 49 CFR 172.101 AND SUBPART E: CORROSIVE
DEPARTMENT OF TRANSPORTATION PACKAGING REQUIREMENTS: 49 CFR 173.277 EXCEPTIONS: 49 CFR 173.244

TOXICITY

SODIUM HYPOCHLORITE: IRRITATION DATA: SODIUM HYPOCHLORITE: 10 MG/KG EYE-RABBIT MODERATE. PENTAHYDRATE: 500 MG/24 HOURS SKIN-RABBIT MODERATE; 100 MG EYE-RABBIT MODERATE. TOXICITY DATA: SODIUM HYPOCHLORITE: 8910 MG/KG ORAL-RAT LD50 (BIOFX*); 1 GM/KG ORAL-WOMAN TCLO; >10.5 MG/L INHALATION-RAT LCLO; >10,000 MG/KG SKIN-RABBIT LDLO; MUTAGENIC DATA (RTECS). PENTAHYDRATE: 8910 MG/KG ORAL-RAT LD50. CARCINOGEN STATUS: NONE. LOCAL EFFECTS: CORROSIVE- INHALATION, SKIN, EYE. ACUTE TOXICITY LEVEL: SLIGHTLY TOXIC BY INGESTION. TARGET EFFECTS: SENSITIZER- DERMAL.

HEALTH EFFECTS AND FIRST AID

INHALATION: SODIUM HYPOCHLORITE: CORROSIVE. **ACUTE EXPOSURE-** MAY CAUSE SEVERE BRONCHIAL IRRITATION, SORE THROAT WITH POSSIBLE BLISTERING, COUGHING, STOMATITIS, NAUSEA, LABORED BREATHING, SHORTNESS OF BREATH AND PULMONARY EDEMA. 10-20 MG/M3 CAUSES BURNING OF THE NOSE AND THROAT; 40-60 MG/M3 MAY BE FATAL. IF SUFFICIENT AMOUNTS ARE ABSORBED, MAY CAUSE EFFECTS AS DETAILED IN ACUTE INGESTION. **CHRONIC EXPOSURE-** NO DATA AVAILABLE.
FIRST AID- REMOVE FROM EXPOSURE AREA TO FRESH AIR IMMEDIATELY. IF BREATHING HAS STOPPED, GIVE ARTIFICIAL RESPIRATION. MAINTAIN AIRWAY AND BLOOD PRESSURE AND ADMINISTER OXYGEN IF AVAILABLE. KEEP AFFECTED PERSON WARM AND AT REST. TREAT SYMPTOMATICALLY AND SUPPORTIVELY. ADMINISTRATION OF OXYGEN SHOULD BE PERFORMED BY QUALIFIED PERSONNEL. GET MEDICAL ATTENTION IMMEDIATELY.

SKIN CONTACT: SODIUM HYPOCHLORITE: CORROSIVE. **ACUTE EXPOSURE-** EXTENT OF DAMAGE DEPENDS ON CONCENTRATION, PH, VOLUME OF SOLUTION AND DURATION OF CONTACT. MAY CAUSE REDNESS, PAIN, BLISTERING, ITCHY ECZEMA AND CHEMICAL BURNS. SENSITIZATION REACTIONS ARE POSSIBLE IN PREVIOUSLY EXPOSED PERSONS. **CHRONIC EXPOSURE-** EFFECTS DEPEND ON CONCENTRATION AND DURATION OF EXPOSURE. REPEATED OR PROLONGED CONTACT WITH CORROSIVE SUBSTANCES MAY RESULT IN DERMATITIS OR EFFECTS SIMILAR TO ACUTE EXPOSURE.
FIRST AID- REMOVE CONTAMINATED CLOTHING AND SHOES IMMEDIATELY. WASH AFFECTED AREA WITH SOAP OR MILD DETERGENT AND LARGE AMOUNTS OF WATER UNTIL NO EVIDENCE OF CHEMICAL REMAINS (AT LEAST 15-20 MINUTES). IN CASE OF CHEMICAL BURNS, COVER AREA WITH STERILE, DRY DRESSING. BANDAGE SECURELY, BUT NOT TOO TIGHTLY. GET MEDICAL ATTENTION IMMEDIATELY.

EYE CONTACT: SODIUM HYPOCHLORITE: CORROSIVE. **ACUTE EXPOSURE-** MAY CAUSE REDNESS, PAIN, AND BLURRED VISION. SOLUTIONS OF 5% SPLASHED IN HUMAN EYES HAVE CAUSED A BURNING SENSATION AND LATER ONLY SLIGHT SUPERFICIAL DISTURBANCE OF THE CORNEAL EPITHELIUM WHICH CLEARED COMPLETELY IN THE NEXT DAY OR TWO WITHOUT SPECIAL TREATMENT. HOWEVER, ONE ANIMAL STUDY REPORTS A 5% SOLUTION CAUSING ONLY MODERATE IRRITATION WITH CLEARING WITHIN 7 DAYS. A HIGHER CONCENTRATION OF 15% TESTED ON RABBIT EYES CAUSED IMMEDIATE SEVERE PAIN, HEMORRHAGES, RAPID ONSET OF GROUND-GLASS APPEARANCE OF THE CORNEAL EPITHELIUM, MODERATE BLUISH EDEMA OF THE WHOLE CORNEA, CHEMOSIS AND DISCHARGE FOR SEVERAL DAYS. SUCH EYES HAVE SOMETIMES HEALED IN 2-3 WEEKS WITH SLIGHT OR NO RESIDUAL CORNEAL DAMAGE BUT THEY HAD NEOVASCULARIZATION OF THE CONJUNCTIVA AND DISTORTION OF THE NICTITATING MEMBRANE BY SCARRING. **CHRONIC EXPOSURE-** DEPENDING ON CONCENTRATION AND DURATION OF EXPOSURE, SYMPTOMS MAY BE AS THOSE OF ACUTE EXPOSURE.
FIRST AID- WASH EYES IMMEDIATELY WITH LARGE AMOUNTS OF WATER, OCCASIONALLY LIFTING UPPER AND LOWER LIDS, UNTIL NO EVIDENCE OF CHEMICAL REMAINS (AT LEAST 15-20 MINUTES). CONTINUE IRRIGATING WITH NORMAL SALINE UNTIL THE PH HAS RETURNED TO NORMAL (30-60 MINUTES). COVER WITH STERILE BANDAGES. GET MEDICAL ATTENTION IMMEDIATELY.

INGESTION: SODIUM HYPOCHLORITE: CORROSIVE. **ACUTE EXPOSURE-** MAY CAUSE IRRITATION AND EROSION OF THE MUCOUS MEMBRANES, VOMITING (POSSIBLY BLOODY) AND ABDOMINAL PAIN AND SPASMS. A DROP IN BLOOD PRESSURE, SHALLOW RESPIRATION, EDEMA (POSSIBLY SEVERE) OF PHARYNX, LARYNX, AND GLOTTIS, CONFUSION, CONVULSIONS, DELIRIUM AND COMA MAY OCCUR. CYANOSIS AND CIRCULATORY COLLAPSE ARE POSSIBLE. ESOPHAGEAL OR GASTRIC PERFORATION AND STRICTURES ARE RARE. DEATH MAY OCCUR, USUALLY DUE TO COMPLICATIONS OF SEVERE LOCAL INJURY SUCH AS: TOXEMIA, SHOCK, PERFORATIONS, HEMORRHAGE, INFECTION AND OBSTRUCTION. MASSIVE INGESTIONS MAY PRODUCE FATAL HYPERCHLOREMIC METABOLIC ACIDOSIS OR ASPIRATION PNEUMONITIS. **CHRONIC EXPOSURE-** SENSITIZATION REACTIONS ARE REPORTED IN INDIVIDUALS WHO ARE EXPOSED IN SMALL AMOUNTS THROUGH THEIR WATER SUPPLY. HIGH DOSES HAVE CAUSED SPERM ABNORMALITY IN MICE.
FIRST AID- IF CONSCIOUS, GIVE MILK, MELTED ICE CREAM, OR BEATEN EGGS. DO NOT USE EMESIS OR GASTRIC LAVAGE OR ACID ANTIDOTES. ANTACIDS SUCH AS MILK OF MAGNESIA OR ALUMINUM HYDROXIDE GEL ARE ALSO USEFUL. MAINTAIN AIRWAY, RESPIRATION, AND BLOOD PRESSURE. GET MEDICAL ATTENTION IMMEDIATELY. (DREISBACH, HANDBOOK OF POISONING, 12TH. ED.) AVOID USE OF SODIUM BICARBONATE.
ANTIDOTE: NO SPECIFIC ANTIDOTE. TREAT SYMPTOMATICALLY AND SUPPORTIVELY.

REACTIVITY

REACTIVITY: STABLE UNDER NORMAL TEMPERATURES AND PRESSURES.
INCOMPATIBILITIES: SODIUM HYPOCHLORITE: ACIDS: VIOLENT REACTION. ALUMINUM: CORROSIVE ACTION. AMINES: FORM EXPLOSIVE CHLOROAMINES. AMMONIUM SALTS: MAY FORM EXPLOSIVE PRODUCT. BENZYL CYANIDE (ACIDIFIED): EXPLOSIVE REACTION. CELLULOSE: VIOLENT REACTION. ETHYLENEIMINE: FORMS EXPLOSIVE 1-CHLOROETHYLENEIMINE. FORMIC ACID: EXPLOSIVE MIXTURE. METHANOL: MAY FORM EXPLOSIVE COMPOUND. NITROGEN COMPOUNDS: FORMS EXPLOSIVE N-CHLORO COMPOUNDS. ORGANIC AND

COMBUSTIBLE MATERIALS: FIRE AND EXPLOSION HAZARD. OXALIC ACID: INTENSE REACTION. REDUCING AGENTS: FIRE AND EXPLOSION HAZARD. ZINC: CORROSIVE.

DECOMPOSITION: THERMAL DECOMPOSITION PRODUCTS MAY INCLUDE TOXIC AND CORROSIVE FUMES OF CHLORINE.

POLYMERIZATION: HAZARDOUS POLYMERIZATION HAS NOT BEEN REPORTED TO OCCUR UNDER NORMAL TEMPERATURES AND PRESSURES.

STORAGE AND DISPOSAL

OBSERVE ALL FEDERAL, STATE AND LOCAL REGULATIONS WHEN STORING OR DISPOSING OF THIS SUBSTANCE. FOR ASSISTANCE, CONTACT THE DISTRICT DIRECTOR OF THE ENVIRONMENTAL PROTECTION AGENCY.

****STORAGE****

STORE AWAY FROM INCOMPATIBLE SUBSTANCES.

CONSULT NFPA PUBLICATION 43A, STORAGE OF LIQUID AND SOLID OXIDIZING MATERIALS, FOR STORAGE REQUIREMENTS.

STORE IN A COOL, DRY PLACE PROTECTED AGAINST LIGHT.

****DISPOSAL****

DISPOSAL MUST BE IN ACCORDANCE WITH STANDARDS APPLICABLE TO GENERATORS OF HAZARDOUS WASTE, 40 CFR 262. EPA HAZARDOUS WASTE NUMBER D001. 100 POUND CERCLA SECTION 103 REPORTABLE QUANTITY.

CONDITIONS TO AVOID

MAY BURN BUT DOES NOT IGNITE READILY. FLAMMABLE, POISONOUS GASES MAY ACCUMULATE IN TANKS AND HOPPER CARS. MAY IGNITE COMBUSTIBLES (WOOD, PAPER, OIL, ETC.).

SPILL AND LEAK PROCEDURES

OCCUPATIONAL SPILL: DO NOT TOUCH SPILLED MATERIAL. STOP LEAK IF YOU CAN DO IT WITHOUT RISK. FOR SMALL SPILLS, TAKE UP WITH SAND OR OTHER ABSORBENT MATERIAL AND PLACE INTO CONTAINERS FOR LATER DISPOSAL. FOR SMALL DRY SPILLS, WITH CLEAN SHOVEL PLACE MATERIAL INTO CLEAN, DRY CONTAINER AND COVER. MOVE CONTAINERS FROM SPILL AREA. FOR LARGER SPILLS, DIKE FAR AHEAD OF SPILL FOR LATER DISPOSAL. KEEP UNNECESSARY PEOPLE AWAY. ISOLATE HAZARD AREA AND DENY ENTRY.

REPORTABLE QUANTITY (RQ): 100 POUNDS THE SUPERFUND AMENDMENTS AND REAUTHORIZATION ACT (SARA) SECTION 304 REQUIRES THAT A RELEASE EQUAL TO OR GREATER THAN THE REPORTABLE QUANTITY FOR THIS SUBSTANCE BE IMMEDIATELY REPORTED TO THE LOCAL EMERGENCY PLANNING COMMITTEE AND THE STATE EMERGENCY RESPONSE COMMISSION (40 CFR 355.40). IF THE RELEASE OF THIS SUBSTANCE IS REPORTABLE UNDER CERCLA SECTION 103, THE NATIONAL RESPONSE CENTER MUST BE NOTIFIED IMMEDIATELY AT (800) 424-8802 OR (202) 426-2675 IN THE METROPOLITAN WASHINGTON, D.C. AREA (40 CFR 302.6).

PROTECTIVE EQUIPMENT

VENTILATION: PROVIDE LOCAL EXHAUST OR PROCESS ENCLOSURE VENTILATION SYSTEM.

RESPIRATOR: THE FOLLOWING RESPIRATORS ARE RECOMMENDED BASED ON INFORMATION FOUND IN THE PHYSICAL DATA, TOXICITY AND HEALTH EFFECTS SECTIONS. THEY ARE RANKED IN ORDER FROM MINIMUM TO MAXIMUM RESPIRATORY PROTECTION. THE SPECIFIC RESPIRATOR SELECTED MUST BE BASED ON CONTAMINATION LEVELS FOUND IN THE WORK PLACE, MUST NOT EXCEED THE WORKING LIMITS OF THE RESPIRATOR AND BE JOINTLY APPROVED BY THE NATIONAL INSTITUTE FOR OCCUPATIONAL SAFETY AND HEALTH AND THE MINE SAFETY AND HEALTH ADMINISTRATION (NIOSH-MSHA).

CHEMICAL CARTRIDGE RESPIRATOR WITH FULL FACEPIECE.

TYPE 'C' SUPPLIED-AIR RESPIRATOR WITH A FULL FACEPIECE OPERATED IN PRESSURE-DEMAND OR OTHER POSITIVE PRESSURE MODE OR WITH A FULL FACEPIECE, HELMET OR HOOD OPERATED IN CONTINUOUS-FLOW MODE.

SELF-CONTAINED BREATHING APPARATUS WITH A FULL FACEPIECE OPERATED IN PRESSURE-DEMAND OR OTHER POSITIVE PRESSURE MODE.

FOR FIREFIGHTING AND OTHER IMMEDIATELY DANGEROUS TO LIFE OR HEALTH CONDITIONS:

SELF-CONTAINED BREATHING APPARATUS WITH FULL FACEPIECE OPERATED IN PRESSURE-DEMAND OR OTHER POSITIVE PRESSURE MODE.

SUPPLIED-AIR RESPIRATOR WITH FULL FACEPIECE AND OPERATED IN PRESSURE-DEMAND OR OTHER POSITIVE PRESSURE MODE IN COMBINATION WITH AN AUXILIARY SELF-CONTAINED BREATHING APPARATUS OPERATED IN PRESSURE-DEMAND OR OTHER POSITIVE PRESSURE MODE.

CLOTHING: EMPLOYEE MUST WEAR APPROPRIATE PROTECTIVE (IMPERVIOUS) CLOTHING AND EQUIPMENT TO PREVENT ANY POSSIBILITY OF SKIN CONTACT WITH THIS SUBSTANCE.

GLOVES: EMPLOYEE MUST WEAR APPROPRIATE PROTECTIVE GLOVES TO PREVENT CONTACT WITH THIS SUBSTANCE.

EYE PROTECTION: EMPLOYEE MUST WEAR SPLASH-PROOF OR DUST-RESISTANT SAFETY GOGGLES AND A FACESHIELD TO PREVENT CONTACT WITH THIS SUBSTANCE.

EMERGENCY WASH FACILITIES: WHERE THERE IS ANY POSSIBILITY THAT AN EMPLOYEE'S EYES AND/OR SKIN MAY BE EXPOSED TO THIS SUBSTANCE, THE EMPLOYER SHOULD PROVIDE AN EYE WASH FOUNTAIN AND QUICK DRENCH SHOWER WITHIN THE IMMEDIATE WORK AREA FOR EMERGENCY USE.

AUTHORIZED BY- OCCUPATIONAL HEALTH SERVICES, INC.

CREATION DATE: 10/05/89 ***REVISION DATE:*** 04/17/90

MATERIAL SAFETY DATA SHEET

OCCUPATIONAL HEALTH SERVICES, INC.
AGRICULTURE AND PESTICIDE DIVISION
450 SEVENTH AVENUE, SUITE 2407
NEW YORK, NEW YORK 10123
1-800-445-MSDS OR (212) 967-1100

EMERGENCY CONTACT:
JOHN S. BRANSFORD, JR. (615) 292-1180

SUBSTANCE IDENTIFICATION

CAS-NUMBER 6834-92-0

SUBSTANCE: **SODIUM METASILICATE, ANHYDROUS**

TRADE NAMES/SYNONYMS: SILICIC ACID, DISODIUM SALT; DISODIUM METASILICATE; DISODIUM MONOSILICATE; DISODIUM SILICATE; SODIUM METASILICATE; SODIUM SILICATE; METSO BEADS, DRYMET; WATER GLASS; SILICIC ACID (H2SIO3), DISODIUM SALT; SODIUM METASILICATE (NA2SIO3); SODIUM SILICATE (NA2SIO3); METSIL; METSO 200; NA2SIO3; PST21373

CHEMICAL FAMILY: SILICATE

MOLECULAR FORMULA: NA2-SI-O3

MOLECULAR WEIGHT: 122.06

CERCLA RATINGS (SCALE 0-3): HEALTH=2 FIRE=0 REACTIVITY=0 PERSISTENCE=3

NFPA RATINGS (SCALE 0-4): HEALTH=2 FIRE=0 REACTIVITY=0

COMPONENTS AND CONTAMINANTS

COMPONENT: SODIUM METASILICATE, ANHYDROUS ***PERCENT:*** 100
CAS# 6834-92-0

OTHER CONTAMINANTS: NONE

EXPOSURE LIMITS: NO OCCUPATIONAL EXPOSURE LIMITS ESTABLISHED BY OSHA, ACGIH, OR NIOSH.

PHYSICAL DATA

DESCRIPTION: COLORLESS MONOCLINIC CRYSTALS OR AMORPHOUS BEADS.

MELTING POINT: 1990 F (1088 C) ***SPECIFIC GRAVITY:*** 2.4

PH: 12.6 @ 1% SOLUTION ***SOLUBILITY IN WATER:*** SOLUBLE

SOLVENT SOLUBILITY: INSOLUBLE IN ALCOHOL, ACIDS, POTASSIUM AND SODIUM SALTS

FIRE AND EXPLOSION DATA

FIRE AND EXPLOSION HAZARD: NEGLIGIBLE FIRE HAZARD WHEN EXPOSED TO HEAT OR FLAME.

FIREFIGHTING MEDIA: EXTINGUISH USING AGENT SUITABLE FOR TYPE OF SURROUNDING FIRE.

FIREFIGHTING: NO ACUTE HAZARD. MOVE CONTAINER FROM FIRE AREA IF POSSIBLE. AVOID BREATHING VAPORS OR DUSTS; KEEP UPWIND.

TOXICITY

SODIUM METASILICATE: IRRITATION DATA: ANHYDROUS: 250 MG/24 HOURS SKIN-HUMAN SEVERE; 250 MG/24 HOURS SKIN-RABBIT SEVERE; 250 MG/24 HOURS SKIN-GUINEA PIG MODERATE. PENTAHYDRATE: NO DATA AVAILABLE. NONAHYDRATE: NO DATA AVAILABLE. TOXICITY DATA: ANHYDROUS; 1153 MG/KG ORAL-RAT LD50; 770 MG/KG ORAL-MOUSE LD50; 250 MG/KG ORAL-DOG LDLO; 250 MG/KG ORAL-PIG LDLO; 200 MG/KG INTRAPERITONEAL-GUINEA PIG LDLO; REPRODUCTIVE EFFECTS DATA (RTECS). PENTAHYDRATE: NO DATA AVAILABLE. NONAHYDRATE: NO DATA AVAILABLE. CARCINOGEN STATUS: NONE. LOCAL EFFECTS: CORROSIVE- EYE, SKIN AND MUCOUS MEMBRANES. ACUTE TOXICITY LEVEL: MODERATELY TOXIC BY INGESTION. TARGET EFFECTS: POISONING MAY AFFECT THE KIDNEYS.

MATERIAL SAFETY DATA SHEET

OCCUPATIONAL HEALTH SERVICES, INC.
AGRICULTURE AND PESTICIDE DIVISION
450 SEVENTH AVENUE, SUITE 2407
NEW YORK, NEW YORK 10123
1-800-445-MSDS OR (212) 967-1100

EMERGENCY CONTACT:
JOHN S. BRANSFORD, JR. (615) 292-1180

SUBSTANCE IDENTIFICATION

CAS-NUMBER 7631-99-4
SUBSTANCE: SODIUM NITRATE

HEALTH EFFECTS AND FIRST AID

INHALATION: SODIUM METASILICATE: CORROSIVE. **ACUTE EXPOSURE-** INHALATION OF DUSTS MAY CAUSE IRRITATION OF THE UPPER RESPIRATORY TRACT WITH SORE THROAT, COUGHING AND SHORTNESS OF BREATH. UPON CONTACT WITH MOIST MUCOUS MEMBRANES, SODIUM METASILICATE IS HIGHLY ALKALINE AND MAY CAUSE CORROSIVE DAMAGE. **CHRONIC EXPOSURE-** DEPENDING ON CONCENTRATION AND DURATION OF EXPOSURE, REPEATED OR PROLONGED EXPOSURE TO CORROSIVE SUBSTANCES MAY CAUSE INFLAMMATORY AND ULCERATIVE CHANGES IN THE MOUTH AND POSSIBLY BRONCHIAL AND GASTROINTESTINAL DISTURBANCES.

FIRST AID- REMOVE FROM EXPOSURE AREA TO FRESH AIR IMMEDIATELY. IF BREATHING HAS STOPPED, GIVE ARTIFICIAL RESPIRATION. MAINTAIN AIRWAY AND BLOOD PRESSURE AND ADMINISTER OXYGEN IF AVAILABLE. KEEP AFFECTED PERSON WARM AND AT REST. TREAT SYMPTOMATICALLY AND SUPPORTIVELY. ADMINISTRATION OF OXYGEN SHOULD BE PERFORMED BY QUALIFIED PERSONNEL. GET MEDICAL ATTENTION IMMEDIATELY.

SKIN CONTACT: SODIUM METASILICATE: CORROSIVE. **ACUTE EXPOSURE-** DUSTS MAY CAUSE SKIN IRRITATION. UPON CONTACT WITH MOIST SKIN, SODIUM METASILICATE MAY CAUSE STRONG IRRITATION WITH ERYTHEMA, PAIN AND BLISTERING. 250 MG APPLIED TO HUMAN SKIN FOR 24 HOURS RESULTED IN SEVERE IRRITATION. **CHRONIC EXPOSURE-** EFFECTS ARE DEPENDENT UPON CONCENTRATION AND DURATION OF EXPOSURE. DERMATITIS OR EFFECTS SIMILAR TO THOSE FOR ACUTE EXPOSURE MAY OCCUR.

FIRST AID- REMOVE CONTAMINATED CLOTHING AND SHOES IMMEDIATELY. WASH AFFECTED AREA WITH SOAP OR MILD DETERGENT AND LARGE AMOUNTS OF WATER UNTIL NO EVIDENCE OF CHEMICAL REMAINS (AT LEAST 15-20 MINUTES). IN CASE OF CHEMICAL BURNS, COVER AREA WITH STERILE, DRY DRESSING. BANDAGE SECURELY, BUT NOT TOO TIGHTLY. GET MEDICAL ATTENTION IMMEDIATELY.

EYE CONTACT: SODIUM METASILICATE: CORROSIVE. **ACUTE EXPOSURE-** DUSTS MAY CAUSE REDNESS, PAIN AND POSSIBLY CORNEAL BURNS. ACCIDENTAL SPLASHES IN THE EYE OF SODIUM SILICATE FOLLOWED PROMPTLY BY WASHING WITH WATER HAVE BEEN OBSERVED TO DAMAGE THE CORNEAL EPITHELIUM. **CHRONIC EXPOSURE-** EFFECTS DEPEND ON CONCENTRATION AND DURATION OF EXPOSURE. REPEATED OR PROLONGED CONTACT WITH ALKALINE SUBSTANCES MAY RESULT IN CONJUNCTIVITIS OR EFFECTS AS IN ACUTE EXPOSURE.

FIRST AID- WASH EYES IMMEDIATELY WITH LARGE AMOUNTS OF WATER, OCCASIONALLY LIFTING UPPER AND LOWER LIDS, UNTIL NO EVIDENCE OF CHEMICAL REMAINS (AT LEAST 15-20 MINUTES). CONTINUE IRRIGATING WITH NORMAL SALINE UNTIL THE PH HAS RETURNED TO NORMAL (30-60 MINUTES). COVER WITH STERILE BANDAGES. GET MEDICAL ATTENTION IMMEDIATELY.

INGESTION: SODIUM METASILICATE: CORROSIVE. **ACUTE EXPOSURE-** INGESTION MAY CAUSE GASTROINTESTINAL UPSET WITH PAINFUL SWALLOWING, ABDOMINAL PAIN, VOMITING, NAUSEA AND BURNS IN THE ORAL AND ALIMENTARY CANAL. IN A STUDY 11 DOGS WERE GIVEN SODIUM SILICATE BY GASTRIC INTUBATION AND IT WAS FOUND THAT 8 MG/KG AS A 10.5% AQUEOUS SOLUTION PRODUCED EMESIS IN 6 MINUTES WHICH CONTINUED FOR UP TO 33 MINUTES. **CHRONIC EXPOSURE-** IN A STUDY, DOGS FED SODIUM SILICATE IN THEIR DIET AT A DOSE OF 2.4 G/KG PER DAY FOR 4 WEEKS EXHIBITED POLYDIPSIA AND POLYURIA. DAMAGE TO RENAL TUBULES WAS OBSERVED IN 15 OF 16 DOGS TESTED. PROLONGED ORAL ADMINISTRATION TO MALE AND FEMALE RATS BEFORE MATING RESULTED IN EFFECTS ON THE NEWBORN.

FIRST AID- DILUTE THE ALKALI BY GIVING WATER OR MILK IMMEDIATELY AND ALLOW VOMITING TO OCCUR. AVOID GASTRIC LAVAGE OR EMETICS. ESOPHAGOSCOPY IS THE ONLY WAY TO EXCLUDE THE POSSIBLITY OF CORROSION IN THE UPPER GASTROINTESTINAL TRACT; IF CORROSION IS SUSPECTED, ESOPHAGOSCOPY SHOULD USUALLY BE PERFORMED WITHIN 24 HOURS (DREISBACH, HANDBOOK OF POISONING, 12TH ED.). MAINTAIN AIRWAY AND TREAT SHOCK. IF VOMITING OCCURS, KEEP HEAD BELOW HIPS TO HELP PREVENT ASPIRATION. GET MEDICAL ATTENTION IMMEDIATELY.

ANTIDOTE: NO SPECIFIC ANTIDOTE. TREAT SYMPTOMATICALLY AND SUPPORTIVELY.

REACTIVITY

REACTIVITY: STABLE UNDER NORMAL TEMPERATURES AND PRESSURES.

INCOMPATIBILITIES: SODIUM METASILICATE: ACIDS: VIOLENT REACTION. ALUMINUM: CORROSIVE ACTION. FLUORINE: IGNITES ON CONTACT. ZINC: CORROSIVE ACTION.

DECOMPOSITION: THERMAL DECOMPOSITION MAY RELEASE TOXIC AND/OR HAZARDOUS GASES.

POLYMERIZATION: HAZARDOUS POLYMERIZATION HAS NOT BEEN REPORTED TO OCCUR UNDER NORMAL TEMPERATURES AND PRESSURES.

STORAGE AND DISPOSAL

OBSERVE ALL FEDERAL, STATE AND LOCAL REGULATIONS WHEN STORING OR DISPOSING OF THIS SUBSTANCE. FOR ASSISTANCE, CONTACT THE DISTRICT DIRECTOR OF THE ENVIRONMENTAL PROTECTION AGENCY.

STORAGE

STORE AWAY FROM INCOMPATIBLE SUBSTANCES.

CONDITIONS TO AVOID

PREVENT DISPERSION OF DUST IN AIR.

SPILL AND LEAK PROCEDURES

OCCUPATIONAL SPILL: FOR LARGE SPILLS, SWEEP UP WITH A MINIMUM OF DUSTING AND PLACE INTO SUITABLE CLEAN, DRY CONTAINERS FOR RECLAMATION OR LATER DISPOSAL.
RESIDUE SHOULD BE CLEANED UP USING A HIGH-EFFICIENCY PARTICULATE FILTER VACUUM.

PROTECTIVE EQUIPMENT

VENTILATION: PROVIDE LOCAL EXHAUST OR GENERAL DILUTION VENTILATION SYSTEM.

RESPIRATOR: THE FOLLOWING RESPIRATORS ARE RECOMMENDED BASED ON INFORMATION FOUND IN THE PHYSICAL DATA, TOXICITY AND HEALTH EFFECTS SECTIONS. THEY ARE RANKED IN ORDER FROM MINIMUM TO MAXIMUM RESPIRATORY PROTECTION. THE SPECIFIC RESPIRATOR SELECTED MUST BE BASED ON CONTAMINATION LEVELS FOUND IN THE WORK PLACE, MUST NOT EXCEED THE WORKING LIMITS OF THE RESPIRATOR AND BE JOINTLY APPROVED BY THE NATIONAL INSTITUTE FOR OCCUPATIONAL SAFETY AND HEALTH AND THE MINE SAFETY AND HEALTH ADMINISTRATION (NIOSH-MSHA).
DUST AND MIST RESPIRATOR WITH A FULL FACEPIECE. AIR-PURIFYING FULL FACEPIECE RESPIRATOR WITH A HIGH-EFFICIENCY PARTICULATE FILTER.
POWERED AIR-PURIFYING RESPIRATOR WITH A TIGHT-FITTING FACEPIECE AND HIGH-EFFICIENCY PARTICULATE FILTER.
TYPE 'C' SUPPLIED-AIR RESPIRATOR WITH A FULL FACEPIECE OPERATED IN PRESSURE-DEMAND OR OTHER POSITIVE PRESSURE MODE OR WITH A FULL FACEPIECE, HELMET OR HOOD OPERATED IN CONTINUOUS-FLOW MODE.
SELF-CONTAINED BREATHING APPARATUS WITH A FULL FACEPIECE OPERATED IN PRESSURE-DEMAND OR OTHER POSITIVE PRESSURE MODE.
FOR FIREFIGHTING AND OTHER IMMEDIATELY DANGEROUS TO LIFE OR HEALTH CONDITIONS:
SELF-CONTAINED BREATHING APPARATUS WITH FULL FACEPIECE OPERATED IN PRESSURE-DEMAND OR OTHER POSITIVE PRESSURE MODE.
SUPPLIED-AIR RESPIRATOR WITH FULL FACEPIECE AND OPERATED IN PRESSURE-DEMAND OR OTHER POSITIVE PRESSURE MODE IN COMBINATION WITH AN AUXILIARY SELF-CONTAINED BREATHING APPARATUS OPERATED IN PRESSURE-DEMAND OR OTHER POSITIVE PRESSURE MODE.

CLOTHING: EMPLOYEE MUST WEAR APPROPRIATE PROTECTIVE (IMPERVIOUS) CLOTHING AND EQUIPMENT TO PREVENT ANY POSSIBILITY OF SKIN CONTACT WITH THIS SUBSTANCE.

GLOVES: EMPLOYEE MUST WEAR APPROPRIATE PROTECTIVE GLOVES TO PREVENT CONTACT WITH THIS SUBSTANCE.

EYE PROTECTION: EMPLOYEE MUST WEAR SPLASH-PROOF OR DUST-RESISTANT SAFETY GOGGLES AND A FACESHIELD TO PREVENT CONTACT WITH THIS SUBSTANCE.
EMERGENCY WASH FACILITIES: WHERE THERE IS ANY POSSIBILITY THAT AN EMPLOYEE'S EYES AND/OR SKIN MAY BE EXPOSED TO THIS SUBSTANCE, THE EMPLOYER SHOULD PROVIDE AN EYE WASH FOUNTAIN AND QUICK DRENCH SHOWER WITHIN THE IMMEDIATE WORK AREA FOR EMERGENCY USE.

AUTHORIZED BY- OCCUPATIONAL HEALTH SERVICES, INC.
CREATION DATE: 11/17/89 ***REVISION DATE:*** 05/31/90

TRADE NAMES/SYNONYMS: NITRATINE; SODIUM NITER; CHILE SALTPETER; CUBIC NITER; SODIUM(I) NITRATE; SODIUM(+1) NITRATE; NITRIC ACID, SODIUM SALT; NITER; NITRIC ACID, SODIUM SALT(1:1); SALTPETER(CHILE); SODA NITER; STCC 4918746; UN 1498; S-343,S-342; NNAO3; PST21400

CHEMICAL FAMILY: INORGANIC SALT

MOLECULAR FORMULA: NA-N-O3

MOLECULAR WEIGHT: 84.99

CERCLA RATINGS (SCALE 0-3): HEALTH=3 FIRE=0 REACTIVITY=0 PERSISTENCE=0

NFPA RATINGS (SCALE 0-4): HEALTH=0 FIRE=0 REACTIVITY=0

COMPONENTS AND CONTAMINANTS

COMPONENT: SODIUM NITRATE ***PERCENT:*** 100
CAS# 7631-99-4

OTHER CONTAMINANTS: NONE

EXPOSURE LIMITS: NO OCCUPATIONAL EXPOSURE LIMITS ESTABLISHED BY OSHA, ACGIH, OR NIOSH.

PHYSICAL DATA

DESCRIPTION: ODORLESS, TRANSPARENT, COLORLESS DELIQUESCENT CRYSTALS WITH A SLIGHTLY BITTER SALINE TASTE.

BOILING POINT: 716 F (380 C) DECOMPOSES

MELTING POINT: 585 F (307 C) ***SPECIFIC GRAVITY:*** 2.261

PH: NEUTRAL IN SOLUTION ***SOLUBILITY IN WATER:*** 92.1% @ 25 C

SOLVENT SOLUBILITY: SOLUBLE IN ALCOHOL, METHANOL, AMMONIA; SLIGHTLY SOLUBLE IN GLYCERINE; VERY SLIGHTLY SOLUBLE IN ACETONE.

FIRE AND EXPLOSION DATA

FIRE AND EXPLOSION HAZARD: NEGLIGIBLE FIRE HAZARD WHEN EXPOSED TO HEAT OR FLAME.

OXIDIZER: OXIDIZERS DECOMPOSE, ESPECIALLY WHEN HEATED, TO YIELD OXYGEN OR OTHER GASES WHICH WILL INCREASE THE BURNING RATE OF COMBUSTIBLE MATTER. CONTACT WITH EASILY OXIDIZABLE, ORGANIC, OR OTHER COMBUSTIBLE MATERIALS MAY RESULT IN IGNITION, VIOLENT COMBUSTION OR EXPLOSION.

FIREFIGHTING MEDIA: DRY CHEMICAL, CARBON DIOXIDE, HALON OR WATER SPRAY (1987 EMERGENCY RESPONSE GUIDEBOOK, DOT P 5800.4).

FOR LARGER FIRES, USE WATER SPRAY OR FOG (1987 EMERGENCY RESPONSE GUIDEBOOK, DOT P 5800.4).

FIREFIGHTING: MOVE CONTAINERS FROM FIRE AREA IF POSSIBLE. COOL CONTAINERS EXPOSED TO FLAMES WITH WATER FROM SIDE UNTIL WELL AFTER FIRE IS OUT. STAY AWAY FROM STORAGE TANK ENDS. FOR MASSIVE FIRE IN STORAGE AREA, USE UNMANNED HOSE HOLDER OR MONITOR NOZZLES; ELSE WITHDRAW FROM AREA AND LET FIRE BURN (1987 EMERGENCY RESPONSE GUIDEBOOK, DOT P 5800.4, GUIDE PAGE 35)

FLOOD WITH WATER. COOL CONTAINERS WITH FLOODING QUANTITIES OF WATER, APPLY FROM AS FAR A DISTANCE AS POSSIBLE. EVACUATE TO A RADIUS OF 2500 FEET FOR UNCONTROLLABLE FIRES.

TRANSPORTATION DATA

DEPARTMENT OF TRANSPORTATION HAZARD CLASSIFICATION 49 CFR 172.101: OXIDIZER

DEPARTMENT OF TRANSPORTATION LABELING REQUIREMENTS 49 CFR 172.101 AND SUBPART E: OXIDIZER

DEPARTMENT OF TRANSPORTATION PACKAGING REQUIREMENTS: 49 CFR 173.182 EXCEPTIONS: 49 CFR 173.153

TOXICITY

SODIUM NITRATE: TOXICITY DATA: 114 MG/KG ORAL-MAN LDLO; 3236 MG/KG ORAL-RAT LD50; 2680 MG/KG ORAL-RABBIT LD50; 175 MG/KG INTRAVENOUS-MOUSE LD50; MUTAGENIC DATA (RTECS); REPRODUCTIVE EFFECTS DATA (RTECS); TUMORIGENIC DATA (RTECS). CARCINOGEN STATUS: NONE. ACUTE TOXICITY LEVEL: MODERATELY TOXIC BY INGESTION. TARGET EFFECTS: NO DATA AVAILABLE.

HEALTH EFFECTS AND FIRST AID

INHALATION: SODIUM NITRATE: ACUTE EXPOSURE- MAY CAUSE COUGHING AND SHORTNESS OF BREATH. CHRONIC EXPOSURE- NO DATA AVAILABLE.

FIRST AID- REMOVE FROM EXPOSURE AREA TO FRESH AIR IMMEDIATELY. IF BREATHING HAS STOPPED, PERFORM ARTIFICIAL RESPIRATION. KEEP PERSON WARM AND AT REST. TREAT SYMPTOMATICALLY AND SUPPORTIVELY. GET MEDICAL ATTENTION IMMEDIATELY.

SKIN CONTACT: SODIUM NITRATE: ACUTE EXPOSURE- MAY CAUSE REDNESS. CONTACT WITH A MOLTEN MIXTURE OF SODIUM AND POTASSIUM NITRATE CAUSED THERMAL BURNS AND METHEMOGLOBINEMIA. SYMPTOMS MAY INCLUDE CYANOSIS, HEADACHE, WEAKNESS, DIZZINESS, LIGHTHEADEDNESS, ATAXIA, SHALLOW RESPIRATION, DROWSINESS, NAUSEA, VOMITING, CONFUSION, LETHARGY, STUPOR, DYSPNEA, TACHYCARDIA, CONVULSIONS, COMA AND POSSIBLY DEATH. CHRONIC EXPOSURE- NO DATA AVAILABLE.

FIRST AID- REMOVE CONTAMINATED CLOTHING AND SHOES IMMEDIATELY. WASH AFFECTED AREA WITH SOAP OR MILD DETERGENT AND LARGE AMOUNTS OF WATER UNTIL NO EVIDENCE OF CHEMICAL REMAINS (APPROXIMATELY 15-20 MINUTES). GET MEDICAL ATTENTION IMMEDIATELY.

EYE CONTACT: SODIUM NITRATE: ACUTE EXPOSURE- MAY CAUSE REDNESS AND PAIN. IN TESTS ON RABBIT EYES, A 10% AQUEOUS SOLUTION APPLIED CONTINUOUSLY FOR 5 MINUTES WAS PRACTICALLY INNOCUOUS TO THE SURFACE OF THE EYES. THE CONJUNCTIVA BECAME MILDLY HYPEREMIC, BUT THE CORNEAS REMAINED CLEAR AND RECOVERY WAS RAPID. CONTINUOUS APPLICATION FOR 3 HOURS OF A 0.1 MOLAR SOLUTION AT PH OF 7.0 OR 7.5, ALSO, PRODUCED NO CORNEAL DISTURBANCES. CHRONIC EXPOSURE- NO DATA AVAILABLE.

FIRST AID- WASH EYES IMMEDIATELY WITH LARGE AMOUNTS OF WATER OR NORMAL SALINE, OCCASIONALLY LIFTING UPPER AND LOWER LIDS, UNTIL NO EVIDENCE OF CHEMICAL REMAINS (APPROXIMATELY 15-20 MINUTES). GET MEDICAL ATTENTION IMMEDIATELY.

INGESTION: SODIUM NITRATE: ACUTE EXPOSURE- MAY CAUSE ABDOMINAL SPASMS, FAINTNESS, AND MUSCULAR SPASMS. A GIRL WHO INGESTED 16 GRAMS EXPERIENCED TRANSITORY BLINDNESS, DEAFNESS SPEECHLESSNESS AND TETANIC CONVULSIONS, BUT GRADUALLY RECOVERED. NITRATES MAY ALSO PRODUCE GASTROINTESTINAL IRRITATION, BLOODY DIARRHEA, HEMATURIA, CATHARSIS, DIURESIS, ALBUMINURIA AND OLIGURIA. RARELY, INORGANIC NITRATES MAY BE CONVERTED TO NITRITES BY NITRATE-REDUCING BACTERIA IN THE UPPER GASTROINTESTINAL TRACT, RESULTING IN METHEMOGLOBINEMIA. CHRONIC EXPOSURE- REPEATED OR PROLONGED EXPOSURE TO NITRATES MAY LEAD TO WEAKNESS, GENERAL DEPRESSION, HEADACHE, MENTAL IMPAIRMENT, ANEMIA, NEPHRITIS, AND POSSIBLY METHEMOGLOBINEMIA.

FIRST AID- REMOVE BY GASTRIC LAVAGE OR EMESIS. MAINTAIN BLOOD PRESSURE AND AIRWAY. GIVE OXYGEN IF RESPIRATION IS DEPRESSED. DO NOT PERFORM GASTRIC LAVAGE OR EMESIS IF VICTIM IS UNCONSCIOUS. GET MEDICAL ATTENTION IMMEDIATELY (DREISBACH, HANDBOOK OF POISONING, 11TH ED.). ADMINISTRATION OF GASTRIC LAVAGE OR OXYGEN SHOULD BE PERFORMED BY QUALIFIED MEDICAL PERSONNEL.

ANTIDOTE: THE FOLLOWING ANTIDOTE HAS BEEN RECOMMENDED. HOWEVER, THE DECISION AS TO WHETHER THE SEVERITY OF POISONING REQUIRES ADMINISTRATION OF ANY ANTIDOTE AND ACTUAL DOSE REQUIRED SHOULD BE MADE BY QUALIFIED MEDICAL PERSONNEL.

METHEMOGLOBINEMIA: (WHEN METHEMOGLOBIN CONCENTRATION IS OVER 25-40% OR IN PRESENCE OF SYMPTOMS.) GIVE METHYLENE BLUE, 1% SOLUTION, 0.1 ML/KG INTRAVENOUSLY OVER A 10-MINUTE PERIOD. CYANOSIS MAY DISAPPEAR WITHIN MINUTES OR PERSIST LONGER DEPENDING ON DEGREE OF METHEMOGLOBINEMIA. INTRAVENOUS ADMINISTRATION OF THERAPEUTIC DOSES OF METHYLENE BLUE MAY CAUSE A RISE IN BLOOD PRESSURE, NAUSEA, AND DIZZINESS. LARGER DOSES (>500 MG) CAUSE VOMITING, DIARRHEA, CHEST PAIN, MENTAL CONFUSION, CYANOSIS, AND SWEATING. HEMOLYTIC ANEMIA HAS ALSO OCCURRED SEVERAL DAYS AFTER ADMINISTRATION. THESE EFFECTS ARE TEMPORARY, AND FATALITIES HAVE NOT BEEN REPORTED. IF METHYLENE BLUE IS NOT AVAILABLE, GIVE ASCORBIC ACID, 1 GRAM SLOWLY INTRAVENOUSLY. WITHOUT TREATMENT, METHEMOGLOBINEMIA LEVELS OF 20-30% REVERT TO NORMAL WITHIN 3 DAYS (DREISBACH, HANDBOOK OF POISONING, 12TH ED.). ANTIDOTE SHOULD BE ADMINISTERED BY QUALIFIED MEDICAL PERSONNEL.

REACTIVITY

REACTIVITY: STABLE UNDER NORMAL TEMPERATURES AND PRESSURES.

INCOMPATIBILITIES: SODIUM NITRATE: ACETIC ANHYDRIDE: POSSIBLE VIOLENT REACTION. ALUMINUM OR ALUMINUM OXIDE: POSSIBLE EXPLOSION. ALUMINUM + WATER: EXOTHERMIC REACTION ABOVE 704 C. ANTIMONY (POWDERED): EXPLOSION HAZARD ON HEATING. ARSENIC TRIOXIDE + IRON SULFATE: MAY IGNITE SPONTANEOUSLY. BARIUM RHODANIDE: EXPLOSION HAZARD. BARIUM THIOCYANATE: POSSIBLE EXPLOSION. BITUMEN: EXOTHERMIC REACTION AT ELEVATED TEMPERATURES. BORON PHOSPHIDE: DEFLAGRATION ON CONTACT WITH THE MOLTEN MIXTURE. CALCIUM-SILICON ALLOY: MAY FORM COMBUSTIBLE MIXTURE. CARBON (POWDER): POSSIBLE IGNITION. CYANIDES: EXPLOSION HAZARD. FIBROUS MATERIAL (WOOD, ETC.): POSSIBLE IGNITION. IRON (II) SULFATE: MAY IGNITE SPONTANEOUSLY. MAGNESIUM: MAY IGNITE. METAL AMIDOSULFATE: POSSIBLE EXPLOSION ON HEATING. ORGANIC MATTER: FIRE AND EXPLOSION HAZARD. PEROXYFORMIC ACID: POSSIBLE EXPLOSIVE DECOMPOSITION. PHENOL + TRIFLUOROACETIC ACID: RAPID EXOTHERMIC REACTION. SODIUM: MAY FORM AN EXPLOSIVE COMPOUND. SODIUM HYPOPHOSPHITE: EXPLOSION HAZARD. SODIUM THIOSULFATE: POSSIBLE EXPLOSION UPON HEATING. SULFUR + CHARCOAL: EXPLOSION HAZARD.

DECOMPOSITION: THERMAL DECOMPOSITION MAY YIELD TOXIC OXIDES OF NITROGEN AND TOXIC SODIUM OXIDE.
POLYMERIZATION: HAZARDOUS POLYMERIZATION HAS NOT BEEN REPORTED TO OCCUR UNDER NORMAL TEMPERATURES AND PRESSURES.

STORAGE AND DISPOSAL

OBSERVE ALL FEDERAL, STATE AND LOCAL REGULATIONS WHEN STORING OR DISPOSING OF THIS SUBSTANCE. FOR ASSISTANCE, CONTACT THE DISTRICT DIRECTOR OF THE ENVIRONMENTAL PROTECTION AGENCY.

STORAGE

PROTECT AGAINST PHYSICAL DAMAGE. STORE IN A DRY, COOL PLACE. SEPERATE FROM COMBUSTIBLE, ORGANIC OR OTHER READILY OXIDIZABLE MATERIALS. AVOID STORAGE ON ON WOOD FLOORS. IMMEDIATELY REMOVE AND DISPOSE OF ANY SPILLED NITRATE (NFPA 49, HAZARDOUS CHEMICALS DATA, 1975).

DISPOSAL

DISPOSAL MUST BE IN ACCORDANCE WITH STANDARDS APPLICABLE TO GENERATORS OF HAZARDOUS WASTE, 40 CFR 262. EPA HAZARDOUS WASTE NUMBER D001. 100 POUND CERCLA SECTION 103 REPORTABLE QUANTITY.

CONDITIONS TO AVOID

AVOID CONTACT WITH COMBUSTIBLE MATERIALS (WOOD, PAPER, FUEL, OILS, ETC); IGNITION OR EXPLOSION MAY RESULT. AVOID CONTAMINATION OF WATER SOURCES.

SPILL AND LEAK PROCEDURES

OCCUPATIONAL SPILL: KEEP COMBUSTIBLES (WOOD, PAPER, OIL, ETC) AWAY FROM SPILLED MATERIAL. DO NOT TOUCH SPILLED MATERIAL. FOR SMALL DRY SPILLS, WITH CLEAN SHOVEL PLACE MATERIAL INTO CLEAN, DRY CONTAINER AND COVER; MOVE CONTAINERS FROM SPILL AREA. FOR SMALL LIQUID SPILLS, TAKE UP WITH SAND, EARTH OR OTHER ABSORBENT MATERIAL AND PLACE INTO CONTAINERS FOR LATER DISPOSAL. FOR LARGER SPILLS, DIKE FAR AHEAD OF SPILL FOR LATER DISPOSAL. KEEP UNNECESSARY PEOPLE AWAY. ISOLATE HAZARD AREA AND DENY ENTRY.

PROTECTIVE EQUIPMENT

VENTILATION: PROVIDE LOCAL EXHAUST OR PROCESS ENCLOSURE VENTILATION SYSTEM.
RESPIRATOR: THE FOLLOWING RESPIRATORS ARE RECOMMENDED BASED ON INFORMATION FOUND IN THE PHYSICAL DATA, TOXICITY AND HEALTH EFFECTS SECTIONS. THEY ARE RANKED IN ORDER FROM MINIMUM TO MAXIMUM RESPIRATORY PROTECTION. THE SPECIFIC RESPIRATOR SELECTED MUST BE BASED ON CONTAMINATION LEVELS FOUND IN THE WORK PLACE, MUST NOT EXCEED THE WORKING LIMITS OF THE RESPIRATOR AND BE JOINTLY APPROVED BY THE NATIONAL INSTITUTE FOR OCCUPATIONAL SAFETY AND HEALTH AND THE MINE SAFETY AND HEALTH ADMINISTRATION (NIOSH-MSHA).
DUST AND MIST RESPIRATOR WITH A FULL FACEPIECE.
AIR-PURIFYING FULL FACEPIECE RESPIRATOR WITH A HIGH-EFFICIENCY PARTICULATE FILTER. POWERED AIR-PURIFYING RESPIRATOR WITH A TIGHT-FITTING FACEPIECE AND HIGH-EFFICIENCY PARTICULATE FILTER.
TYPE 'C' SUPPLIED-AIR RESPIRATOR WITH A FULL FACEPIECE OPERATED IN PRESSURE-DEMAND OR OTHER POSITIVE PRESSURE MODE OR WITH A FULL FACEPIECE, HELMET OR HOOD OPERATED IN CONTINUOUS-FLOW MODE.
SELF-CONTAINED BREATHING APPARATUS WITH A FULL FACEPIECE OPERATED IN PRESSURE-DEMAND OR OTHER POSITIVE PRESSURE MODE.
FOR FIREFIGHTING AND OTHER IMMEDIATELY DANGEROUS TO LIFE OR HEALTH CONDITIONS:
SELF-CONTAINED BREATHING APPARATUS WITH FULL FACEPIECE OPERATED IN PRESSURE-DEMAND OR OTHER POSITIVE PRESSURE MODE.
SUPPLIED-AIR RESPIRATOR WITH FULL FACEPIECE AND OPERATED IN PRESSURE-DEMAND OR OTHER POSITIVE PRESSURE MODE IN COMBINATION WITH AN AUXILIARY SELF-CONTAINED BREATHING APPARATUS OPERATED IN PRESSURE-DEMAND OR OTHER POSITIVE PRESSURE MODE.
CLOTHING: EMPLOYEE MUST WEAR APPROPRIATE PROTECTIVE (IMPERVIOUS) CLOTHING AND EQUIPMENT TO PREVENT REPEATED OR PROLONGED SKIN CONTACT WITH THIS SUBSTANCE.
GLOVES: EMPLOYEE MUST WEAR APPROPRIATE PROTECTIVE GLOVES TO PREVENT CONTACT WITH THIS SUBSTANCE.
EYE PROTECTION: EMPLOYEE MUST WEAR SPLASH-PROOF OR DUST-RESISTANT SAFETY GOGGLES TO PREVENT EYE CONTACT WITH THIS SUBSTANCE.
EMERGENCY EYE WASH: WHERE THERE IS ANY POSSIBILITY THAT AN EMPLOYEE'S EYES MAY BE EXPOSED TO THIS SUBSTANCE, THE EMPLOYER SHOULD PROVIDE AN EYE WASH FOUNTAIN WITHIN THE IMMEDIATE WORK AREA FOR EMERGENCY USE.

AUTHORIZED BY- OCCUPATIONAL HEALTH SERVICES, INC.
CREATION DATE: 11/16/89 ***REVISION DATE:*** 05/16/90

MATERIAL SAFETY DATA SHEET

OCCUPATIONAL HEALTH SERVICES, INC.
AGRICULTURE AND PESTICIDE DIVISION
450 SEVENTH AVENUE, SUITE 2407
NEW YORK, NEW YORK 10123
1-800-445-MSDS OR (212) 967-1100

EMERGENCY CONTACT:
JOHN S. BRANSFORD, JR. (615) 292-1180

SUBSTANCE IDENTIFICATION

CAS-NUMBER 7632-00-0
SUBSTANCE: **SODIUM NITRITE**
TRADE NAMES/SYNONYMS: NITROUS ACID, SODIUM SALT; NITROUS ACID SODIUM SALT(1:1); STCC 4918747; UN 1500; NNAO2; PST21410
CHEMICAL FAMILY: INORGANIC SALT
MOLECULAR FORMULA: NA-N-O2
MOLECULAR WEIGHT: 69.00
CERCLA RATINGS (SCALE 0-3): HEALTH=3 FIRE=1 REACTIVITY=0 PERSISTENCE=1
NFPA RATINGS (SCALE 0-4): HEALTH=3 FIRE=1 REACTIVITY=0

COMPONENTS AND CONTAMINANTS

COMPONENT: SODIUM NITRITE ***PERCENT:*** 100.0
CAS# 7632-00-0
OTHER CONTAMINANTS: NONE
EXPOSURE LIMITS: NO OCCUPATIONAL EXPOSURE LIMITS ESTABLISHED BY OSHA, ACGIH, OR NIOSH.
SODIUM NITRITE: 100 POUNDS CERCLA SECTION 103 REPORTABLE QUANTITY

PHYSICAL DATA

DESCRIPTION: ODORLESS, WHITE OR SLIGHTLY YELLOW, HYGROSCOPIC GRANULES, RODS OR POWDER.
BOILING POINT: 608 F (320 C) (DECOMPOSES)
MELTING POINT: 520 F (271 C) ***SPECIFIC GRAVITY:*** 2.168 @ 0 C
SOLUBILITY IN WATER: 82% @ 15 C
SOLVENT SOLUBILITY: SOLUBLE IN AMMONIA AND ABSOLUTE ALCOHOL; MODERATELY SOLUBLE IN METHANOL; VERY SLIGHTLY SOLUBLE IN ETHER.

FIRE AND EXPLOSION DATA

FIRE AND EXPLOSION HAZARD: SLIGHT FIRE HAZARD WHEN EXPOSED TO HEAT OR FLAME.
OXIDIZER: OXIDIZERS DECOMPOSE, ESPECIALLY WHEN HEATED, TO YIELD OXYGEN OR OTHER GASES WHICH WILL INCREASE THE BURNING RATE OF COMBUSTIBLE MATTER. CONTACT WITH EASILY OXIDIZABLE, ORGANIC, OR OTHER COMBUSTIBLE MATERIALS MAY RESULT IN IGNITION, VIOLENT COMBUSTION OR EXPLOSION.
AUTOIGNITION TEMP.: 1000 F (538 C)
FIREFIGHTING MEDIA: DRY CHEMICAL, CARBON DIOXIDE, HALON OR WATER SPRAY (1987 EMERGENCY RESPONSE GUIDEBOOK, DOT P 5800.4).
FOR LARGER FIRES, USE WATER SPRAY OR FOG (1987 EMERGENCY RESPONSE GUIDEBOOK, DOT P 5800.4).
FIREFIGHTING: MOVE CONTAINERS FROM FIRE AREA IF POSSIBLE. COOL CONTAINERS EXPOSED TO FLAMES WITH WATER FROM SIDE UNTIL WELL AFTER FIRE IS OUT. STAY AWAY FROM STORAGE TANK ENDS. FOR MASSIVE FIRE IN STORAGE AREA, USE UNMANNED HOSE HOLDER OR MONITOR NOZZLES; ELSE WITHDRAW FROM AREA AND LET FIRE BURN (1987 EMERGENCY RESPONSE GUIDEBOOK, DOT P 5800.4, GUIDE PAGE 35)
FLOODING WITH WATER. COOL CONTAINERS WITH FLOODING QUANTITIES OF WATER, APPLY FROM AS FAR A DISTANCE AS POSSIBLE. AVOID BREATHING HAZARDOUS VAPORS,KEEP UPWIND. EVACUATE TO A RADIUS OF 2500 FEET FOR UNCONTROLLABLE FIRES.

TRANSPORTATION DATA

DEPARTMENT OF TRANSPORTATION HAZARD CLASSIFICATION 49 CFR 172.101: OXIDIZER
DEPARTMENT OF TRANSPORTATION LABELING REQUIREMENTS 49 CFR 172.101 AND SUBPART E: OXIDIZER
DEPARTMENT OF TRANSPORTATION PACKAGING REQUIREMENTS: 49 CFR 173.234 EXCEPTIONS: 49 CFR 173.153

TOXICITY

SODIUM NITRITE: IRRITATION DATA: 500 MG/24 HOURS EYE-RABBIT MILD. TOXICITY DATA: 5500 UG/M3 INHALATION-RAT LC50; 1714 UG/KG/70 MINUTES ORAL-MAN TDLO; 71 MG/KG ORAL-HUMAN LDLO; 14 MG/KG ORAL-HUMAN TDLO; 22 MG/KG ORAL-CHILD LDLO; 85 MG/KG ORAL-RAT LD50; 175 MG/KG ORAL-MOUSE LD50; 1500 MG/KG ORAL-CAT LDLO; 330 MG/KG ORAL-DOG LDLO; 186 MG/KG ORAL-RABBIT LD50; 10 MG/KG SUBCUTANEOUS-RAT LDLO; 150 MG/KG SUBCUTANEOUS-MOUSE LDLO; 60 MG/KG SUBCUTANEOUS-RABBIT LDLO; 60 MG/KG SUBCUTANEOUS-DOG LDLO; 35 MG/KG SUBCUTANEOUS-CAT LDLO; 65 MG/KG INTRAVENOUS-RAT LD50; 80 MG/KG INTRAVENOUS-RABBIT LDLO; 15 MG/KG INTRAVENOUS-DOG LDLO; 158 MG/KG INTRAPERITONEAL-MOUSE LD50; MUTAGENIC DATA (RTECS); REPRODUCTIVE EFFECTS DATA (RTECS); TUMORIGENIC DATA (RTECS). CARCINOGEN STATUS: NONE. LOCAL EFFECTS: IRRITANT-INHALATION, SKIN, EYE. ACUTE TOXICITY LEVEL: HIGHLY TOXIC BY INHALATION; TOXIC BY INGESTION. TARGET EFFECTS: METHEMOGLOBIN FORMER.

HEALTH EFFECTS AND FIRST AID

INHALATION: SODIUM NITRITE: IRRITANT/HIGHLY TOXIC. **ACUTE EXPOSURE-** THE LETHAL DOSE REPORTED IN RATS WAS 5500 UG/M3. THE SYMPTOMS WERE NOT REPORTED. HIGH CONCENTRATIONS OF DUST OR MIST MAY IRRITATE THE NOSE, THROAT AND RESPIRATORY TRACT WITH SORE THROAT AND SHORTNESS OF BREATH. IT IS UNCLEAR IF LARGE QUANTITIES CAN BE ABSORBED, BUT IF SO, HYPOTENSION AND METHEMOGLOBIN FORMATION WITH CYANOSIS, HEADACHE, DIZZINESS, WEAKNESS, AND DYSPNEA MAY OCCUR. **CHRONIC EXPOSURE-** NO DATA AVAILABLE.

FIRST AID- REMOVE FROM EXPOSURE AREA TO FRESH AIR IMMEDIATELY. IF BREATHING HAS STOPPED, PERFORM ARTIFICIAL RESPIRATION. KEEP PERSON WARM AND AT REST. TREAT SYMPTOMATICALLY AND SUPPORTIVELY. GET MEDICAL ATTENTION IMMEDIATELY.

SKIN CONTACT: SODIUM NITRITE: IRRITANT. **ACUTE EXPOSURE-** MAY CAUSE REDNESS AND IRRITATION. IT IS UNCLEAR WHETHER AMOUNTS SUFFICIENT TO CAUSE SYSTEMIC EFFECTS MAY BE ABSORBED THROUGH INTACT SKIN. ONE INDUSTRIAL ACCIDENT INVOLVING THREE MEN WHO WERE BURNED OVER 30-70% OF THEIR BODIES WITH A MOLTEN MIXTURE OF SODIUM AND POTASSIUM NITRATES RESULTED IN METHEMOGLOBINEMIA IN ALL THREE. DUE TO THE HIGH TEMPERATURE OF THE MIXTURE, THERE IS A POSSIBILITY THAT THE NITRATES WERE CONVERTED TO NITRITES, THUS IT IS NOT CERTAIN WHICH WAS RESPONSIBLE FOR THE METHEMOGLOBINEMIA. **CHRONIC EXPOSURE-** REPEATED OR PROLONGED CONTACT MAY CAUSE DERMATITIS.

FIRST AID- REMOVE CONTAMINATED CLOTHING AND SHOES IMMEDIATELY. WASH AFFECTED AREA WITH SOAP OR MILD DETERGENT AND LARGE AMOUNTS OF WATER UNTIL NO EVIDENCE OF CHEMICAL REMAINS (APPROXIMATELY 15-20 MINUTES). GET MEDICAL ATTENTION IMMEDIATELY.

EYE CONTACT: SODIUM NITRITE: IRRITANT. **ACUTE EXPOSURE-** MAY CAUSE IRRITATION OF THE EYES. IN ONE STUDY SODIUM NITRITE WAS FOUND TO BE SEVERELY IRRITATING TO RABBITS' EYES, HOWEVER OTHER DATA INDICATED THAT TESTING DONE ON RABBIT EYES CAUSED NO DISTURBANCES OF THE CORNEA OR LOCAL INJURY. **CHRONIC EXPOSURE-** PROLONGED EXPOSURE MAY CAUSE CONJUNCTIVITIS.

FIRST AID- WASH EYES IMMEDIATELY WITH LARGE AMOUNTS OF WATER OR NORMAL SALINE, OCCASIONALLY LIFTING UPPER AND LOWER LIDS, UNTIL NO EVIDENCE OF CHEMICAL REMAINS (APPROXIMATELY 15-20 MINUTES). GET MEDICAL ATTENTION IMMEDIATELY.

INGESTION: SODIUM NITRITE: METHEMOGLOBIN FORMER/TOXIC. **ACUTE EXPOSURE-** MAY CAUSE GASTROINTESTINAL IRRITATION WITH NAUSEA, VOMITING, DIARRHEA, AND ABDOMINAL PAINS, DILATION OF PUPILS, VERTIGO, TACHYCARDIA, ROARING SOUND IN THE EARS, GENERALIZED TINGLING SENSATION, VISUAL DISTURBANCES, PROMPT HYPOTENSION, AND PERIPHERAL CIRCULATORY FAILURE. METHEMOGLOBINEMIA MAY OCCUR. THE FIRST SYMPTOMS, WHICH MAY BE DELAYED FOR SEVERAL HOURS, ARE CYANOSIS AND PERSISTENT, INCREASINGLY SEVERE, THROBBING HEADACHE. AS THE CONCENTRATION OF METHEMOGLOBIN INCREASES, SHALLOW RESPIRATION AND DIZZINESS MAY APPEAR FOLLOWED BY CONFUSION, LETHARGY AND STUPOR. AT CONCENTRATIONS OF 70% OR HIGHER, CONVULSIONS OR COMA MAY OCCUR WITH THE POSSIBILITY OF DEATH DUE TO CIRCULATORY COLLAPSE. **CHRONIC EXPOSURE-** AS EVALUATED BY RTECS, ADMINISTRATION TO RATS AND MICE BY INGESTION RESULTED IN A STATISTICALLY SIGNIFICANT INCREASE IN THE INCIDENCE OF NEOPLASTIC AND CARCINOGENIC TUMORS OF THE GASTROINTESTINAL TRACT, LIVER AND LUNGS. RATS GIVEN 2-3 GRAMS IN DRINKING WATER THROUGH GESTATION AND LACTATION WERE ANEMIC AND HAD SOME IRON DEFICIENCY AND HAD NEONATES THAT SUFFERED SEVERE MICROCYTIC ANEMIA, OTHER EFFECTS CHARACTERISTIC OF IRON DEFIENCY SYNDROME, GROWTH RETARDATION AND HIGH MORTALITY. REPRODUCTIVE EFFECTS HAVE ALSO BEEN REPORTED IN ANIMAL STUDIES.

FIRST AID- REMOVE BY GASTRIC LAVAGE OR EMESIS. MAINTAIN BLOOD PRESSURE AND AIRWAY. GIVE OXYGEN IF RESPIRATION IS DEPRESSED. DO NOT PERFORM GASTRIC LAVAGE OR EMESIS IF VICTIM IS UNCONSCIOUS. GET MEDICAL ATTENTION IMMEDIATELY (DREISBACH, HANDBOOK OF POISONING, 11TH ED.). ADMINISTRATION OF GASTRIC LAVAGE OR OXYGEN SHOULD BE PERFORMED BY QUALIFIED MEDICAL PERSONNEL.

ANTIDOTE: THE FOLLOWING ANTIDOTE HAS BEEN RECOMMENDED. HOWEVER, THE DECISION AS TO WHETHER THE SEVERITY OF POISONING REQUIRES ADMINISTRATION OF ANY ANTIDOTE AND ACTUAL DOSE REQUIRED SHOULD BE MADE BY QUALIFIED MEDICAL PERSONNEL.

METHEMOGLOBINEMIA: (WHEN METHEMOGLOBIN CONCENTRATION IS OVER 25-40% OR IN PRESENCE OF SYMPTOMS.) GIVE METHYLENE BLUE, 1% SOLUTION, 0.1 ML/KG INTRAVENOUSLY OVER A 10-MINUTE PERIOD. CYANOSIS MAY DISAPPEAR WITHIN MINUTES OR PERSIST LONGER DEPENDING ON DEGREE OF METHEMOGLOBINEMIA. INTRAVENOUS ADMINISTRATION OF THERAPEUTIC DOSES OF METHYLENE BLUE MAY CAUSE A RISE IN BLOOD PRESSURE, NAUSEA, AND DIZZINESS. LARGER DOSES (>500 MG) CAUSE VOMITING, DIARRHEA, CHEST PAIN, MENTAL CONFUSION, CYANOSIS, AND SWEATING. HEMOLYTIC ANEMIA HAS ALSO OCCURRED SEVERAL DAYS AFTER ADMINISTRATION. THESE EFFECTS ARE TEMPORARY, AND FATALITIES HAVE NOT BEEN REPORTED. IF METHYLENE BLUE IS NOT AVAILABLE, GIVE ASCORBIC ACID, 1 GRAM SLOWLY INTRAVENOUSLY. WITHOUT TREATMENT, METHEMOGLOBINEMIA LEVELS OF 20-30% REVERT TO NORMAL WITHIN 3 DAYS (DREISBACH, HANDBOOK OF POISONING, 12TH ED.). ANTIDOTE SHOULD BE ADMINISTERED BY QUALIFIED MEDICAL PERSONNEL.

REACTIVITY

REACTIVITY: STABLE UNDER NORMAL TEMPERATURES AND PRESSURES.

INCOMPATIBILITIES: SODIUM NITRITE: AMINOGUANIDINE: FORMS EXPLOSIVE COMPOUND. AMMONIUM SALTS: REACT VIOLENTLY ON MELTING. 1,3-BUTADIENE: IGNITABLE BLACK SLUDGE MAY FORM. CELLULOSE: DECOMPOSES VIOLENTLY. CYANIDE + CHLORATES: REACT VIOLENTLY ON MELTING. LITHIUM: FORMS EXPLOSIVE COMPOUNDS. METAL AMIDOSULFATES: VIOLENTLY EXPLOSIVE. METAL CYANIDE: EXPLODES ON HEATING. PHENOL: VIOLENTLY EXPLOSIVE ON HEATING. PHTHALIC ACID: EXPLODES VIOLENTLY. PHTHALIC ANHYDRIDE: REACTS EXPLOSIVELY. POTASSIUM + AMMONIA: REACTS VIOLENTLY ON MELTING FORMING EXPLOSIVE COMPOUND. REDUCING AGENTS: FIRE AND EXPLOSION HAZARD. SODIUM AMIDE: VIOLENTLY EXPLOSIVE. SODIUM DISULPHITE: EXOTHERMIC REACTION. SODIUM THIOCYANATE: REACTS EXPLOSIVELY ON HEATING. SODIUM THIOSULFATE: RESIDUE EXPLODES ON HEATING. UREA: REACTS EXPLOSIVELY ON HEATING.

DECOMPOSITION: THERMAL DECOMPOSITION MAY YIELD TOXIC OXIDES OF NITROGEN AND TOXIC SODIUM OXIDE.

POLYMERIZATION: HAZARDOUS POLYMERIZATION HAS NOT BEEN REPORTED TO OCCUR UNDER NORMAL TEMPERATURES AND PRESSURES.

STORAGE AND DISPOSAL

OBSERVE ALL FEDERAL, STATE AND LOCAL REGULATIONS WHEN STORING OR DISPOSING OF THIS SUBSTANCE. FOR ASSISTANCE, CONTACT THE DISTRICT DIRECTOR OF THE ENVIRONMENTAL PROTECTION AGENCY.

STORAGE

STORE AWAY FROM INCOMPATIBLE SUBSTANCES.

CONSULT NFPA PUBLICATION 43A, STORAGE OF LIQUID AND SOLID OXIDIZING MATERIALS, FOR STORAGE REQUIREMENTS.

STORE IN TIGHTLY CLOSED CONTAINERS; PREVENT EXPOSURE TO MOISTURE.

DISPOSAL

DISPOSAL MUST BE IN ACCORDANCE WITH STANDARDS APPLICABLE TO GENERATORS OF HAZARDOUS WASTE, 40 CFR 262. EPA HAZARDOUS WASTE NUMBER D001. 100 POUND CERCLA SECTION 103 REPORTABLE QUANTITY.

CONDITIONS TO AVOID

AVOID CONTACT WITH COMBUSTIBLE MATERIALS (WOOD, PAPER, FUEL, OILS, ETC); IGNITION OR EXPLOSION MAY RESULT. AVOID CONTAMINATION OF WATER SOURCES.

SPILL AND LEAK PROCEDURES

SOIL SPILL: DIG A HOLDING AREA SUCH AS PIT, POND OR LAGOON TO CONTAIN SPILLED MATERIAL. USE PROTECTIVE COVER SUCH AS A PLASTIC SHEET TO PREVENT DISSOLVING IN FIREFIGHTING WATER OR RAIN.

WATER SPILL: ADD SODA ASH.

ADD CALCIUM HYPOCHLORITE TO SPILL.

ADD SUITABLE AGENT TO NEUTRALIZE SPILLED MATERIAL TO PH-7.

OCCUPATIONAL SPILL: KEEP COMBUSTIBLES (WOOD, PAPER, OIL, ETC) AWAY FROM SPILLED MATERIAL. DO NOT TOUCH SPILLED MATERIAL. FOR SMALL DRY SPILLS, WITH CLEAN SHOVEL PLACE MATERIAL INTO CLEAN, DRY CONTAINER AND COVER; MOVE CONTAINERS FROM SPILL AREA. FOR SMALL LIQUID SPILLS, TAKE UP WITH

SAND, EARTH OR OTHER ABSORBENT MATERIAL AND PLACE INTO CONTAINERS FOR LATER DISPOSAL. FOR LARGER SPILLS, DIKE FAR AHEAD OF SPILL FOR LATER DISPOSAL. KEEP UNNECESSARY PEOPLE AWAY. ISOLATE HAZARD AREA AND DENY ENTRY.

REPORTABLE QUANTITY (RQ): 100 POUNDS THE SUPERFUND AMENDMENTS AND REAUTHORIZATION ACT (SARA) SECTION 304 REQUIRES THAT A RELEASE EQUAL TO OR GREATER THAN THE REPORTABLE QUANTITY FOR THIS SUBSTANCE BE IMMEDIATELY REPORTED TO THE LOCAL EMERGENCY PLANNING COMMITTEE AND THE STATE EMERGENCY RESPONSE COMMISSION (40 CFR 355.40). IF THE RELEASE OF THIS SUBSTANCE IS REPORTABLE UNDER CERCLA SECTION 103, THE NATIONAL RESPONSE CENTER MUST BE NOTIFIED IMMEDIATELY AT (800) 424-8802 OR (202) 426-2675 IN THE METROPOLITAN WASHINGTON, D.C. AREA (40 CFR 302.6).

PROTECTIVE EQUIPMENT

VENTILATION: PROVIDE LOCAL EXHAUST OR PROCESS ENCLOSURE VENTILATION SYSTEM.

RESPIRATOR: THE FOLLOWING RESPIRATORS ARE RECOMMENDED BASED ON INFORMATION FOUND IN THE PHYSICAL DATA, TOXICITY AND HEALTH EFFECTS SECTIONS. THEY ARE RANKED IN ORDER FROM MINIMUM TO MAXIMUM RESPIRATORY PROTECTION. THE SPECIFIC RESPIRATOR SELECTED MUST BE BASED ON CONTAMINATION LEVELS FOUND IN THE WORK PLACE, MUST NOT EXCEED THE WORKING LIMITS OF THE RESPIRATOR AND BE JOINTLY APPROVED BY THE NATIONAL INSTITUTE FOR OCCUPATIONAL SAFETY AND HEALTH AND THE MINE SAFETY AND HEALTH ADMINISTRATION (NIOSH-MSHA).

DUST AND MIST RESPIRATOR WITH A FULL FACEPIECE.

AIR-PURIFYING FULL FACEPIECE RESPIRATOR WITH A HIGH-EFFICIENCY PARTICULATE FILTER.

POWERED AIR-PURIFYING RESPIRATOR WITH A TIGHT-FITTING FACEPIECE AND HIGH-EFFICIENCY PARTICULATE FILTER.

TYPE 'C' SUPPLIED-AIR RESPIRATOR WITH A FULL FACEPIECE OPERATED IN PRESSURE-DEMAND OR OTHER POSITIVE PRESSURE MODE OR WITH A FULL FACEPIECE, HELMET OR HOOD OPERATED IN CONTINUOUS-FLOW MODE.

SELF-CONTAINED BREATHING APPARATUS WITH A FULL FACEPIECE OPERATED IN PRESSURE-DEMAND OR OTHER POSITIVE PRESSURE MODE.

FOR FIREFIGHTING AND OTHER IMMEDIATELY DANGEROUS TO LIFE OR HEALTH CONDITIONS:

SELF-CONTAINED BREATHING APPARATUS WITH FULL FACEPIECE OPERATED IN PRESSURE-DEMAND OR OTHER POSITIVE PRESSURE MODE.

SUPPLIED-AIR RESPIRATOR WITH FULL FACEPIECE AND OPERATED IN PRESSURE-DEMAND OR OTHER POSITIVE PRESSURE MODE IN COMBINATION WITH AN AUXILIARY SELF-CONTAINED BREATHING APPARATUS OPERATED IN PRESSURE-DEMAND OR OTHER POSITIVE PRESSURE MODE.

CLOTHING: EMPLOYEE MUST WEAR APPROPRIATE PROTECTIVE (IMPERVIOUS) CLOTHING AND EQUIPMENT TO PREVENT REPEATED OR PROLONGED SKIN CONTACT WITH THIS SUBSTANCE.

GLOVES: EMPLOYEE MUST WEAR APPROPRIATE PROTECTIVE GLOVES TO PREVENT CONTACT WITH THIS SUBSTANCE.

EYE PROTECTION: EMPLOYEE MUST WEAR SPLASH-PROOF OR DUST-RESISTANT SAFETY GOGGLES TO PREVENT EYE CONTACT WITH THIS SUBSTANCE.

EMERGENCY EYE WASH: WHERE THERE IS ANY POSSIBILITY THAT AN EMPLOYEE'S EYES MAY BE EXPOSED TO THIS SUBSTANCE, THE EMPLOYER SHOULD PROVIDE AN EYE WASH FOUNTAIN WITHIN THE IMMEDIATE WORK AREA FOR EMERGENCY USE.

AUTHORIZED BY- OCCUPATIONAL HEALTH SERVICES, INC.

CREATION DATE: 11/16/89 ***REVISION DATE:*** 03/28/90

MATERIAL SAFETY DATA SHEET

OCCUPATIONAL HEALTH SERVICES, INC.
AGRICULTURE AND PESTICIDE DIVISION
450 SEVENTH AVENUE, SUITE 2407
NEW YORK, NEW YORK 10123
1-800-445-MSDS OR (212) 967-1100

EMERGENCY CONTACT:
JOHN S. BRANSFORD, JR. (615) 292-1180

SUBSTANCE IDENTIFICATION

CAS-NUMBER 143-19-1

SUBSTANCE: **SODIUM OLEATE**

TRADE NAMES/SYNONYMS: (Z)-9-OCTADECENOIC ACID, SODIUM SALT; OLEIC ACID, SODIUM SALT; EUNATROL; PST21418

CHEMICAL FAMILY: SALT

MOLECULAR FORMULA: C18-H33-O2.NA

MOLECULAR WEIGHT: 304.50

CERCLA RATINGS (SCALE 0-3): HEALTH = 3 FIRE = U REACTIVITY = 0 PERSISTENCE = 0

NFPA RATINGS (SCALE 0-4): HEALTH = 3 FIRE = U REACTIVITY = 0

COMPONENTS AND CONTAMINANTS

COMPONENT: SODIUM OLEATE ***PERCENT:*** 100
CAS# 143-19-1

OTHER CONTAMINANTS: NONE

EXPOSURE LIMITS: NO OCCUPATIONAL EXPOSURE LIMITS ESTABLISHED BY OSHA, ACGIH, OR NIOSH.

PHYSICAL DATA

DESCRIPTION: WHITE POWDER OR YELLOW AMORPHOUS GRANULES WITH A SLIGHT TALLOW-LIKE ODOR

MELTING POINT: 450-455 F (232-235 C)

SPECIFIC GRAVITY: NOT AVAILABLE ***SOLUBILITY IN WATER:*** SOLUBLE

SOLVENT SOLUBILITY: SOLUBLE IN ALCOHOL; SLIGHTLY SOLUBLE IN ETHER

FIRE AND EXPLOSION DATA

FIRE AND EXPLOSION HAZARD: UNKNOWN FIRE AND EXPLOSION HAZARD.

FIREFIGHTING MEDIA: DRY CHEMICAL, CARBON DIOXIDE, WATER SPRAY OR FOAM FOR LARGER FIRES, USE WATER SPRAY, FOG OR ALCOHOL FOAM

FIREFIGHTING: MOVE CONTAINER FROM FIRE AREA IF POSSIBLE. DO NOT SCATTER SPILLED MATERIAL WITH HIGH PRESSURE WATER STREAMS. DIKE FIRE CONTROL WATER FOR LATER DISPOSAL (1987 EMERGENCY RESPONSE GUIDEBOOK, DOT P 5800.4, GUIDE PAGE 31).

USE AGENTS SUITABLE FOR TYPE OF SURROUNDING FIRE. AVOID BREATHING HAZARDOUS VAPORS, KEEP UPWIND.

TOXICITY

SODIUM OLEATE: TOXICITY DATA: 152 MG/KG INTRAVENOUS-MOUSE LD50; 150 MG/KG INTRAVENOUS-RABBIT LDLO. CARCINOGEN STATUS: NONE. ACUTE TOXICITY DATA: NO DATA AVAILABLE. TARGET EFFECTS: NO DATA AVAILABLE.

HEALTH EFFECTS AND FIRST AID

INHALATION: SODIUM OLEATE: **ACUTE EXPOSURE-** NO DATA AVAILABLE. **CHRONIC EXPOSURE-** NO DATA AVAILABLE.

FIRST AID- REMOVE FROM EXPOSURE AREA TO FRESH AIR IMMEDIATELY. IF BREATHING HAS STOPPED, PERFORM ARTIFICIAL RESPIRATION. KEEP PERSON WARM AND AT REST. TREAT SYMPTOMATICALLY AND SUPPORTIVELY. GET MEDICAL ATTENTION IMMEDIATELY.

SKIN CONTACT: SODIUM OLEATE: **ACUTE EXPOSURE-** NO SPECIFIC DATA AVAILABLE.SOME SOAPS MAY CAUSE IRRITATION DUE TO THEIR DEFATTING ACTION ON THE SKIN. **CHRONIC EXPOSURE-** NO DATA AVAILABLE.

FIRST AID- REMOVE CONTAMINATED CLOTHING AND SHOES IMMEDIATELY. WASH AFFECTED AREA WITH SOAP OR MILD DETERGENT AND LARGE AMOUNTS OF WATER UNTIL NO EVIDENCE OF CHEMICAL REMAINS (APPROXIMATELY 15-20 MINUTES). GET MEDICAL ATTENTION IMMEDIATELY.

EYE CONTACT: SODIUM OLEATE: **ACUTE EXPOSURE-** NO SPECIFIC DATA AVAILABLE. MANY SOAPS ARE COMPOSED OF SODIUM OLEATE AND THERE ARE A FEW REPORTS OF TRANSIENT INJURIES TO HUMAN EYES BY SOAPS. **CHRONIC EXPOSURE-** NO DATA AVAILABLE.

FIRST AID- WASH EYES IMMEDIATELY WITH LARGE AMOUNTS OF WATER OR NORMAL SALINE, OCCASIONALLY LIFTING UPPER AND LOWER LIDS, UNTIL NO EVIDENCE OF CHEMICAL REMAINS (APPROXIMATELY 15-20 MINUTES). GET MEDICAL ATTENTION IMMEDIATELY.

INGESTION: SODIUM OLEATE: **ACUTE EXPOSURE-** INGESTION OF SOAPS MAY CAUSE DIARRHEA, INTESTINAL DISTENTION AND OCCASIONALLY VOMITING. **CHRONIC EXPOSURE-** NO DATA AVAILABLE.

FIRST AID- TREAT SYMPTOMATICALLY AND SUPPORTIVELY. GET MEDICAL ATTENTION IMMEDIATELY. IF VOMITING OCCURS, KEEP HEAD LOWER THAN HIPS TO PREVENT ASPIRATION.

ANTIDOTE: NO SPECIFIC ANTIDOTE. TREAT SYMPTOMATICALLY AND SUPPORTIVELY.

REACTIVITY

REACTIVITY: STABLE UNDER NORMAL TEMPERATURES AND PRESSURES.

INCOMPATIBILITIES: SODIUM OLEATE: NO DATA AVAILABLE.

DECOMPOSITION: THERMAL DECOMPOSITION MAY YIELD TOXIC SODIUM OXIDE.

POLYMERIZATION: HAZARDOUS POLYMERIZATION HAS NOT BEEN REPORTED TO OCCUR UNDER NORMAL TEMPERATURES AND PRESSURES.

CONDITIONS TO AVOID

NONE REPORTED.

SPILL AND LEAK PROCEDURES

OCCUPATIONAL SPILL: SWEEP UP AND PLACE IN SUITABLE CLEAN, DRY CONTAINERS FOR RECLAMATION OR LATER DISPOSAL. DO NOT FLUSH SPILLED MATERIAL INTO SEWER. KEEP UNNECESSARY PEOPLE AWAY.

PROTECTIVE EQUIPMENT

VENTILATION: PROVIDE LOCAL EXHAUST VENTILATION SYSTEM.

RESPIRATOR: THE FOLLOWING RESPIRATORS ARE RECOMMENDED BASED ON INFORMATION FOUND IN THE PHYSICAL DATA, TOXICITY AND HEALTH EFFECTS SECTIONS. THEY ARE RANKED IN ORDER FROM MINIMUM TO MAXIMUM RESPIRATORY PROTECTION. THE SPECIFIC RESPIRATOR SELECTED MUST BE BASED ON CONTAMINATION LEVELS FOUND IN THE WORK PLACE, MUST NOT EXCEED THE WORKING LIMITS OF THE RESPIRATOR AND BE JOINTLY APPROVED BY THE NATIONAL INSTITUTE FOR OCCUPATIONAL SAFETY AND HEALTH AND THE MINE SAFETY AND HEALTH ADMINISTRATION (NIOSH-MSHA).

DUST AND MIST RESPIRATOR WITH A FULL FACEPIECE.

AIR-PURIFYING FULL FACEPIECE RESPIRATOR WITH A HIGH-EFFICIENCY PARTICULATE FILTER.

POWERED AIR-PURIFYING RESPIRATOR WITH A TIGHT-FITTING FACEPIECE AND HIGH-EFFICIENCY PARTICULATE FILTER.

TYPE 'C' SUPPLIED-AIR RESPIRATOR WITH A FULL FACEPIECE OPERATED IN PRESSURE-DEMAND OR OTHER POSITIVE PRESSURE MODE OR WITH A FULL FACEPIECE, HELMET OR HOOD OPERATED IN CONTINUOUS-FLOW MODE.

SELF-CONTAINED BREATHING APPARATUS WITH A FULL FACEPIECE OPERATED IN PRESSURE-DEMAND OR OTHER POSITIVE PRESSURE MODE.

FOR FIREFIGHTING AND OTHER IMMEDIATELY DANGEROUS TO LIFE OR HEALTH CONDITIONS:

SELF-CONTAINED BREATHING APPARATUS WITH FULL FACEPIECE OPERATED IN PRESSURE-DEMAND OR OTHER POSITIVE PRESSURE MODE.

SUPPLIED-AIR RESPIRATOR WITH FULL FACEPIECE AND OPERATED IN PRESSURE-DEMAND OR OTHER POSITIVE PRESSURE MODE IN COMBINATION WITH AN AUXILIARY SELF-CONTAINED BREATHING APPARATUS OPERATED IN PRESSURE-DEMAND OR OTHER POSITIVE PRESSURE MODE.

CLOTHING: EMPLOYEE MUST WEAR APPROPRIATE PROTECTIVE (IMPERVIOUS) CLOTHING AND EQUIPMENT TO PREVENT REPEATED OR PROLONGED SKIN CONTACT WITH THIS SUBSTANCE.

GLOVES: EMPLOYEE MUST WEAR APPROPRIATE PROTECTIVE GLOVES TO PREVENT CONTACT WITH THIS SUBSTANCE.

EYE PROTECTION: EMPLOYEE MUST WEAR SPLASH-PROOF OR DUST-RESISTANT SAFETY GOGGLES TO PREVENT EYE CONTACT WITH THIS SUBSTANCE.

EMERGENCY EYE WASH: WHERE THERE IS ANY POSSIBILITY THAT AN EMPLOYEE'S EYES MAY BE EXPOSED TO THIS SUBSTANCE, THE EMPLOYER SHOULD PROVIDE AN EYE WASH FOUNTAIN WITHIN THE IMMEDIATE WORK AREA FOR EMERGENCY USE.

AUTHORIZED BY- OCCUPATIONAL HEALTH SERVICES, INC.
CREATION DATE: 02/08/90 ***REVISION DATE:*** 05/31/90

MATERIAL SAFETY DATA SHEET

OCCUPATIONAL HEALTH SERVICES, INC.
AGRICULTURE AND PESTICIDE DIVISION
450 SEVENTH AVENUE, SUITE 2407
NEW YORK, NEW YORK 10123
1-800-445-MSDS OR (212) 967-1100

EMERGENCY CONTACT:
JOHN S. BRANSFORD, JR. (615) 292-1180

SUBSTANCE IDENTIFICATION

CAS-NUMBER 15922-78-8

SUBSTANCE: **SODIUM PYRIDINETHIONE**

TRADE NAMES/SYNONYMS: 1-HYDROXY-2-(IH)-PYRIDINETHIONE, SODIUM SALT; OMACIDE 24; OMADINE SODIUM; OMADINE SODIUM SALT; SODIUM OMADINE; SODIUM PYRITHIONE; PST21420

CHEMICAL FAMILY: PYRIDINE

MOLECULAR FORMULA: C5-H5-N-O-S.NA

MOLECULAR WEIGHT: 150.16

CERCLA RATINGS (SCALE 0-3): HEALTH=2 FIRE=U REACTIVITY=0 PERSISTENCE=1

NFPA RATINGS (SCALE 0-4): HEALTH=2 FIRE=U REACTIVITY=0

COMPONENTS AND CONTAMINANTS

COMPONENT: SODIUM PYRIDINOTHIONE ***PERCENT:*** 100
CAS# 15922-78-8

OTHER CONTAMINANTS: NONE

EXPOSURE LIMITS: NO OCCUPATIONAL EXPOSURE LIMITS ESTABLISHED BY OSHA, ACGIH, OR NIOSH.

PHYSICAL DATA

DESCRIPTION: OFF-WHITE POWDER WITH A MILD ODOR

MELTING POINT: 482 F (250 C) DECOMPOSES ***SPECIFIC GRAVITY:*** 1.167

SOLUBILITY IN WATER: SOLUBLE

SOLVENT SOLUBILITY: METHANOL, ETHANOL, GLYCOLS, DIMETHYL SULFOXIDE, DIMETHYL FORMAMIDE

FIRE AND EXPLOSION DATA

FIRE AND EXPLOSION HAZARD: UNKNOWN FIRE AND EXPLOSION HAZARD.

FIREFIGHTING MEDIA: DRY CHEMICAL, CARBON DIOXIDE, HALON, WATER SPRAY OR STANDARD FOAM (1987 EMERGENCY RESPONSE GUIDEBOOK, DOT P 5800.4).

FOR LARGER FIRES, USE WATER SPRAY, FOG OR STANDARD FOAM (1987 EMERGENCY RESPONSE GUIDEBOOK, DOT P 5800.4).

FIREFIGHTING: MOVE CONTAINER FROM FIRE AREA IF POSSIBLE. DO NOT SCATTER SPILLED MATERIAL WITH HIGH PRESSURE WATER STREAMS. DIKE FIRE CONTROL WATER FOR LATER DISPOSAL (1987 EMERGENCY RESPONSE GUIDEBOOK, DOT P 5800.4, GUIDE PAGE 31).

USE AGENTS SUITABLE FOR TYPE OF SURROUNDING FIRE. AVOID BREATHING HAZARDOUS VAPORS, KEEP UPWIND.

TOXICITY

SODIUM PYRIDINETHIONE: TOXICITY DATA: 745 MG/KG ORAL-RAT LDLO; 870 MG/KG ORAL-MOUSE LD50; 428 MG/KG SUBCUTANEOUS-MOUSE LD50; 200 MG/KG INTRAVENOUS-RABBIT LDLO; 335 MG/KG INTRAVENOUS-MOUSE LD50; 265 MG/KG INTRAPERITONEAL-MOUSE LD50; 385 MG/KG INTRAPERITONEAL-RAT LDLO. CARCINOGEN STATUS: NONE. ACUTE TOXICITY LEVEL: MODERATELY TOXIC BY INGESTION. TARGET EFFECTS: NO DATA AVAILABLE.

HEALTH EFFECTS AND FIRST AID

INHALATION: SODIUM PYRITHIONE: **ACUTE EXPOSURE-** NO DATA AVAILABLE. **CHRONIC EXPOSURE-** NO DATA AVAILABLE.

FIRST AID- REMOVE FROM EXPOSURE AREA TO FRESH AIR IMMEDIATELY. IF BREATHING HAS STOPPED, PERFORM ARTIFICIAL RESPIRATION. KEEP PERSON WARM AND AT REST. TREAT SYMPTOMATICALLY AND SUPPORTIVELY. GET MEDICAL ATTENTION IMMEDIATELY.

SKIN CONTACT: SODIUM PYRIDINOTHIONE: **ACUTE EXPOSURE-** MAY CAUSE IRRITATION. THIS SUBSTANCE WAS MILDLY IRRITATING TO RABBITS, GUINEA PIGS, AND RATS SKINS. A MODERATE DOSE WAS LETHAL IN RABBITS BY DERMAL ABSORPTION. DERMAL ABSORPTION PRODUCED TRANSIENT OCULAR EFFECTS CHARACTERIZED BY PHOTOPHOBIA, CONJUNCTIVITIS, LACRIMATION, AND SLUGGISH PUPILLARY RESPONSE. **CHRONIC EXPOSURE-** REPEATED SKIN EXPOSURE CAUSED OCULAR CHANGES AND HIND-LEG WEAKNESS IN RABBITS.

FIRST AID- REMOVE CONTAMINATED CLOTHING AND SHOES IMMEDIATELY. WASH AFFECTED AREA WITH SOAP OR MILD DETERGENT AND LARGE AMOUNTS OF WATER UNTIL NO EVIDENCE OF CHEMICAL REMAINS (APPROXIMATELY 15-20 MINUTES). GET MEDICAL ATTENTION IMMEDIATELY.

EYE CONTACT: SODIUM PYRIDINOTHIONE: **ACUTE EXPOSURE-** THIS MATERIAL, IN VARIOUS CONCENTRATIONS, WAS NOT SIGNIFICANTLY IRRITATING TO RABBIT EYES. **CHRONIC EXPOSURE-** NO DATA AVAILABLE.

FIRST AID- WASH EYES IMMEDIATELY WITH LARGE AMOUNTS OF WATER OR NORMAL SALINE, OCCASIONALLY LIFTING UPPER AND LOWER LIDS, UNTIL NO EVIDENCE OF CHEMICAL REMAINS (APPROXIMATELY 15-20 MINUTES). GET MEDICAL ATTENTION IMMEDIATELY.

INGESTION: SODIUM PYRIDINOTHIONE: **ACUTE EXPOSURE-** A MODERATE DOSE WAS LETHAL IN RATS AND MICE. IN RATS, A 40% SOLUTION PRODUCED SALIVATION, LACRIMATION, AND INCREASED MOTOR ACTIVITY FOLLOWED BY SEVERE RESPIRATORY DEPRESSION AND INCREASED MUSCLE TONE. RESPIRATORY FAILURE, PRECEDED BY CONVULSIONS, APPEARED TO BE THE CAUSE OF DEATH. **CHRONIC EXPOSURE-** THIS SUBSTANCE REDUCED FERTILITY AND WAS EMBRYOTOXIC WHEN GIVEN TO MALE AND FEMALE RATS ORALLY PRIOR TO MATING. IT ALSO CAUSED MINOR FETAL SKELETAL ABNORMALITIES WHEN GIVEN ORALLY TO PREGNANT RATS FROM DAY 6 TO 15 GESTATION.

FIRST AID- TREAT SYMPTOMATICALLY AND SUPPORTIVELY. GET MEDICAL ATTENTION IMMEDIATELY. IF VOMITING OCCURS, KEEP HEAD LOWER THAN HIPS TO PREVENT ASPIRATION.

ANTIDOTE: NO SPECIFIC ANTIDOTE. TREAT SYMPTOMATICALLY AND SUPPORTIVELY.

REACTIVITY

REACTIVITY: STABLE UNDER NORMAL TEMPERATURES AND PRESSURES.
INCOMPATIBILITIES: SODIUM PYRIDINOTHIONE: NO DATA AVAILABLE.
DECOMPOSITION: THERMAL DECOMPOSITION MAY RELEASE TOXIC OXIDES OF NITROGEN AND SULFUR.
POLYMERIZATION: HAZARDOUS POLYMERIZATION HAS NOT BEEN REPORTED TO OCCUR UNDER NORMAL TEMPERATURES AND PRESSURES.

CONDITIONS TO AVOID

NONE REPORTED.

SPILL AND LEAK PROCEDURES

OCCUPATIONAL SPILL: SWEEP UP AND PLACE IN SUITABLE CLEAN, DRY CONTAINERS FOR RECLAMATION OR LATER DISPOSAL. DO NOT FLUSH SPILLED MATERIAL INTO SEWER. KEEP UNNECESSARY PEOPLE AWAY.

PROTECTIVE EQUIPMENT

VENTILATION: PROVIDE LOCAL EXHAUST VENTILATION SYSTEM.
RESPIRATOR: THE FOLLOWING RESPIRATORS ARE RECOMMENDED BASED ON INFORMATION FOUND IN THE PHYSICAL DATA, TOXICITY AND HEALTH EFFECTS SECTIONS. THEY ARE RANKED IN ORDER FROM MINIMUM TO MAXIMUM RESPIRATORY PROTECTION. THE SPECIFIC RESPIRATOR SELECTED MUST BE BASED ON CONTAMINATION LEVELS FOUND IN THE WORK PLACE, MUST NOT EXCEED THE WORKING LIMITS OF THE RESPIRATOR AND BE JOINTLY APPROVED BY THE NATIONAL INSTITUTE FOR OCCUPATIONAL SAFETY AND HEALTH AND THE MINE SAFETY AND HEALTH ADMINISTRATION (NIOSH-MSHA).
DUST AND MIST RESPIRATOR WITH A FULL FACEPIECE.
AIR-PURIFYING FULL FACEPIECE RESPIRATOR WITH A HIGH-EFFICIENCY PARTICULATE FILTER.
POWERED AIR-PURIFYING RESPIRATOR WITH A TIGHT-FITTING FACEPIECE AND HIGH-EFFICIENCY PARTICULATE FILTER.
TYPE 'C' SUPPLIED-AIR RESPIRATOR WITH A FULL FACEPIECE OPERATED IN PRESSURE-DEMAND OR OTHER POSITIVE PRESSURE MODE OR WITH A FULL FACEPIECE, HELMET OR HOOD OPERATED IN CONTINUOUS-FLOW MODE.
SELF-CONTAINED BREATHING APPARATUS WITH A FULL FACEPIECE OPERATED IN PRESSURE-DEMAND OR OTHER POSITIVE PRESSURE MODE.
FOR FIREFIGHTING AND OTHER IMMEDIATELY DANGEROUS TO LIFE OR HEALTH CONDITIONS:
SELF-CONTAINED BREATHING APPARATUS WITH FULL FACEPIECE OPERATED IN PRESSURE-DEMAND OR OTHER POSITIVE PRESSURE MODE.
SUPPLIED-AIR RESPIRATOR WITH FULL FACEPIECE AND OPERATED IN PRESSURE-DEMAND OR OTHER POSITIVE PRESSURE MODE IN COMBINATION WITH AN AUXILIARY SELF-CONTAINED BREATHING APPARATUS OPERATED IN PRESSURE-DEMAND OR OTHER POSITIVE PRESSURE MODE.
CLOTHING: EMPLOYEE MUST WEAR APPROPRIATE PROTECTIVE (IMPERVIOUS) CLOTHING AND EQUIPMENT TO PREVENT REPEATED OR PROLONGED SKIN CONTACT WITH THIS SUBSTANCE.
GLOVES: EMPLOYEE MUST WEAR APPROPRIATE PROTECTIVE GLOVES TO PREVENT CONTACT WITH THIS SUBSTANCE.
EYE PROTECTION: EMPLOYEE MUST WEAR SPLASH-PROOF OR DUST-RESISTANT SAFETY GOGGLES TO PREVENT EYE CONTACT WITH THIS SUBSTANCE.
EMERGENCY EYE WASH: WHERE THERE IS ANY POSSIBILITY THAT AN EMPLOYEE'S EYES MAY BE EXPOSED TO THIS SUBSTANCE, THE EMPLOYER SHOULD PROVIDE AN EYE WASH FOUNTAIN WITHIN THE IMMEDIATE WORK AREA FOR EMERGENCY USE.

AUTHORIZED BY- OCCUPATIONAL HEALTH SERVICES, INC.
CREATION DATE: 10/05/89 ***REVISION DATE:*** 05/31/90

MATERIAL SAFETY DATA SHEET

OCCUPATIONAL HEALTH SERVICES, INC.
AGRICULTURE AND PESTICIDE DIVISION
450 SEVENTH AVENUE, SUITE 2407
NEW YORK, NEW YORK 10123
1-800-445-MSDS OR (212) 967-1100

EMERGENCY CONTACT:
JOHN S. BRANSFORD, JR. (615) 292-1180

SUBSTANCE IDENTIFICATION

CAS-NUMBER 139-02-6

SUBSTANCE: **SODIUM PHENOLATE**
TRADE NAMES/SYNONYMS: PHENOL, SODIUM SALT, (SOLID); PHENOL SODIUM; SODIUM PHENOXIDE; SODIUM CARBOLATE; SODIUM PHENATE; SODIUM PHENYLATE; STCC 4935270; UN 2497; PST21530
CHEMICAL FAMILY: PHENOL
MOLECULAR FORMULA: C6-H5-O.NA
MOLECULAR WEIGHT: 116.10
CERCLA RATINGS (SCALE 0-3): HEALTH=3 FIRE=0 REACTIVITY=U PERSISTENCE=2
NFPA RATINGS (SCALE 0-4): HEALTH=3 FIRE=0 REACTIVITY=U

COMPONENTS AND CONTAMINANTS

COMPONENT: SODIUM PHENOLATE ***PERCENT:*** 100
CAS# 139-02-6
OTHER CONTAMINANTS: NONE
EXPOSURE LIMITS: NO OCCUPATIONAL EXPOSURE LIMITS ESTABLISHED BY OSHA, ACGIH, OR NIOSH.

PHYSICAL DATA

DESCRIPTION: WHITE TO REDDISH, DELIQUESCENT RODS OR GRANULES OR NEEDLES WHICH IS DECOMPOSED BY CARBON DIOXIDE IN THE AIR. ***MELTING POINT:*** NOT AVAILABLE
SPECIFIC GRAVITY: 1.318 @ 15.5 C ***SOLUBILITY IN WATER:*** VERY SOLUBLE
SOLVENT SOLUBILITY: SOLUBLE IN ALCOHOL, ACETONE; DECOMPOSES IN ACID

FIRE AND EXPLOSION DATA

FIRE AND EXPLOSION HAZARD: NEGLIGIBLE FIRE HAZARD WHEN EXPOSED TO HEAT OR FLAME.
FIREFIGHTING MEDIA: DRY CHEMICAL, CARBON DIOXIDE, HALON, WATER SPRAY OR STANDARD FOAM (1987 EMERGENCY RESPONSE GUIDEBOOK, DOT P 5800.4).
FOR LARGER FIRES, USE WATER SPRAY, FOG OR STANDARD FOAM (1987 EMERGENCY RESPONSE GUIDEBOOK, DOT P 5800.4).
FIREFIGHTING: MOVE CONTAINERS FROM FIRE AREA IF POSSIBLE. COOL CONTAINERS EXPOSED TO FLAMES WITH WATER FROM SIDE UNTIL WELL AFTER FIRE IS OUT. STAY AWAY FROM STORAGE TANK ENDS (1987 EMERGENCY RESPONSE GUIDEBOOK, DOT P 5800.4, GUIDE PAGE 60).
USE AGENTS SUITABLE FOR TYPE OF FIRE. USE WATER IN FLOODING AMOUNTS AS FOG APPLY FROM AS FAR A DISTANCE AS POSSIBLE. AVOID BREATHING CORROSIVE VAPORS, KEEP UPWIND.

TRANSPORTATION DATA

DEPARTMENT OF TRANSPORTATION HAZARD CLASSIFICATION 49 CFR 172.101: CORROSIVE MATERIAL
DEPARTMENT OF TRANSPORTATION LABELING REQUIREMENTS 49 CFR 172.101 AND SUBPART E: CORROSIVE
DEPARTMENT OF TRANSPORTATION PACKAGING REQUIREMENTS: 49 CFR 173.245B EXCEPTIONS: 49 CFR 173.244

TOXICITY

SODIUM PHENOLATE: TOXICITY DATA: 350 MG/KG SUBCUTANEOUS-MOUSE LDLO. CARCINOGEN STATUS: NONE. LOCAL EFFECTS: CORROSIVE- INHALATION, SKIN, EYES, AND INGESTION. ACUTE TOXICITY LEVEL: INSUFFICIENT DATA. TARGET EFFECTS: POISONING MAY AFFECT THE CENTRAL NERVOUS SYSTEM, LIVER, AND KIDNEYS.

HEALTH EFFECTS AND FIRST AID

INHALATION: SODIUM PHENOLATE: CORROSIVE. **ACUTE EXPOSURE-** EFFECTS MAY VARY FROM MILD IRRITATION OF THE MUCOUS MEMBRANES TO A SEVERE PNEUMONITIS. INHALATION OF CORROSIVE SUBSTANCES MAY CAUSE SYMPTOMS OF RESPIRATORY TRACT IRRITATION POSSIBLY INCLUDING COUGHING, CHOKING, PAIN IN THE NOSE, MOUTH AND THROAT AND BURNS OF THE MUCOUS MEMBRANES. IF SUFFICIENT QUANTITIES ARE INHALED, PULMONARY EDEMA MAY DEVELOP, OFTEN WITH A LATENT PERIOD OF 5-72 HOURS. THE SYMPTOMS MAY INCLUDE TIGHTNESS IN THE CHEST, DYSPNEA, FROTHY SPUTUM, CYANOSIS, AND DIZZINESS. PHYSICAL FINDINGS MAY INCLUDE WEAK, RAPID PULSE, HYPOTENSION, HEMOCONCENTRATION AND MOIST RALES. **CHRONIC EXPOSURE-** DEPENDING ON THE CONCENTRATION AND DURATION OF EXPOSURE, REPEATED OR PROLONGED EXPOSURE TO CORROSIVE SUBSTANCES MAY CAUSE INFLAMMATORY AND ULCERATIVE CHANGES IN THE MOUTH AND POSSIBLY BRONCHIAL AND GASTROINTESTINAL DISTURBANCES.
FIRST AID- REMOVE FROM EXPOSURE AREA TO FRESH AIR IMMEDIATELY. IF BREATHING HAS STOPPED, GIVE ARTIFICIAL RESPIRATION. MAINTAIN AIRWAY AND BLOOD PRESSURE AND ADMINISTER OXYGEN IF AVAILABLE. KEEP AFFECTED PERSON WARM AND AT REST. TREAT SYMPTOMATICALLY AND SUPPORTIVELY. ADMINISTRATION OF OXYGEN SHOULD BE PERFORMED BY QUALIFIED PERSONNEL. GET MEDICAL ATTENTION IMMEDIATELY.

SKIN CONTACT: SODIUM PHENOLATE: CORROSIVE. **ACUTE EXPOSURE-** DIRECT CONTACT WITH ALKALINE SUBSTANCES MAY CAUSE SEVERE PAIN, BURNS, AND POSSIBLY BROWNISH STAINS. THE CORRODED AREAS ARE SOFT, GELATINOUS, AND NECROTIC AND THE TISSUE DESTRUCTION MAY BE DEEP. **CHRONIC EXPOSURE-** EFFECTS DEPEND ON THE CONCENTRATION AND DURATION OF EXPOSURE. REPEATED OR PROLONGED CONTACT WITH ALKALINE SUBSTANCES MAY CAUSE DERMATITIS OR EFFECTS SIMILAR TO ACUTE EXPOSURE.

FIRST AID- REMOVE CONTAMINATED CLOTHING AND SHOES IMMEDIATELY. WASH AFFECTED AREA WITH SOAP OR MILD DETERGENT AND LARGE AMOUNTS OF WATER UNTIL NO EVIDENCE OF CHEMICAL REMAINS (AT LEAST 15-20 MINUTES). IN CASE OF CHEMICAL BURNS, COVER AREA WITH STERILE, DRY DRESSING. BANDAGE SECURELY, BUT NOT TOO TIGHTLY. GET MEDICAL ATTENTION IMMEDIATELY.

EYE CONTACT: SODIUM PHENOLATE: CORROSIVE. **ACUTE EXPOSURE-** DIRECT CONTACT WITH ALKALINE SUBSTANCES MAY CAUSE PAIN AND BURNS, POSSIBLY SEVERE. THE DEGREE OF INJURY DEPENDS ON THE CONCENTRATION AND DURATION OF CONTACT. THERE MAY BE EDEMA, DESTRUCTION OF EPITHELIUM, CORNEAL OPACIFICATION, AND IRITIS. WHEN DAMAGE IS LESS THAN EXCESSIVE, THESE SYMPTOMS TEND TO AMELIORATE. IN SEVERE BURNS, THE FULL EXTENT OF THE INJURY MAY NOT BE IMMEDIATELY APPARENT. LATE COMPLICATIONS MAY INCLUDE PERSISTENT EDEMA, VASCULARIZATION AND SCARRING OF THE CORNEA, PERMANENT OPACITY, STAPHYLOMA, CATARACT, AND SYMBLEPHARON. **CHRONIC EXPOSURE-** EFFECTS DEPEND ON CONCENTRATION AND DURATION OF EXPOSURE. REPEATED OR PROLONGED CONTACT WITH ALKALINE SUBSTANCES MAY RESULT IN CONJUNCTIVITIS OR EFFECTS AS IN ACUTE EXPOSURE.

FIRST AID- WASH EYES IMMEDIATELY WITH LARGE AMOUNTS OF WATER, OCCASIONALLY LIFTING UPPER AND LOWER LIDS, UNTIL NO EVIDENCE OF CHEMICAL REMAINS (AT LEAST 15-20 MINUTES). CONTINUE IRRIGATING WITH NORMAL SALINE UNTIL THE PH HAS RETURNED TO NORMAL (30-60 MINUTES). COVER WITH STERILE BANDAGES. GET MEDICAL ATTENTION IMMEDIATELY.

INGESTION: SODIUM PHENOLATE: CORROSIVE. **ACUTE EXPOSURE-** ALKALINE SUBSTANCES MAY CAUSE IMMEDIATE PAIN AND CIRCUMORAL BURNS AND CORROSION OF THE MUCOUS MEMBRANES WHICH AT FIRST TURN WHITE AND SOAPY AND THEN BECOME BROWN, EDEMATOUS AND ULCERATED. THERE MAY BE PROFUSE SALIVATION. SWALLOWING AND SPEECH MAY BE DIFFICULT AT FIRST AND THEN ALMOST IMPOSSIBLE. EVEN WHEN THERE IS NO EVIDENCE OF ORAL BURNS, THE ESOPHAGUS AND STOMACH MAY BE INVOLVED WITH BURNING PAIN, VOMITING, AND DIARRHEA. THE VOMITUS MAY BE THICK AND SLIMY WITH MUCUS, AND LATER CONTAIN BLOOD AND SHREDS OF MUCOUS MEMBRANE. EPIGLOTTAL EDEMA MAY RESULT IN RESPIRATORY DISTRESS AND POSSIBLY ASPHYXIA. SHOCK WITH MARKED HYPOTENSION, WEAK AND RAPID PULSE, SHALLOW RESPIRATION, AND CLAMMY SKIN MAY OCCUR. CIRCULATORY COLLAPSE MAY ENSUE AND IF UNCORRECTED, LEAD TO RENAL FAILURE. IN SEVERE CASES, ESOPHAGEAL OR GASTRIC PERFORATION ARE POSSIBLE AND MAY BE ACCOMPANIED BY MEDIASTINITIS, SUBSTERNAL PAIN, PERITONITIS, ABDOMINAL RIGIDITY, AND FEVER. ESOPHAGEAL, AND POSSIBLY GASTRIC OR PYLORIC STRICTURE MAY OCCUR WITHIN A FEW WEEKS, BUT MAY BE DELAYED FOR MONTHS OR EVEN YEARS. DEATH MAY RESULT WITHIN A SHORT TIME FROM ASPHYXIA, CIRCULATORY COLLAPSE, OR ASPIRATION OF EVEN MINUTE AMOUNTS. LATER DEATH MAY BE DUE TO THE COMPLICATIONS OF PERFORATION, PNEUMONIA, OR THE EFFECTS OF STRICTURE FORMATION. **CHRONIC EXPOSURE-** DEPENDING ON THE CONCENTRATION, REPEATED INGESTION OF ALKALINE SUBSTANCES MAY RESULT IN INFLAMMATORY AND ULCERATIVE EFFECTS ON THE ORAL MUCOUS MEMBRANES AND OTHER EFFECTS AS WITH ACUTE INGESTION.

FIRST AID- DILUTE THE ALKALI BY GIVING WATER OR MILK IMMEDIATELY AND ALLOW VOMITING TO OCCUR. AVOID GASTRIC LAVAGE OR EMETICS. ESOPHAGOSCOPY IS THE ONLY WAY TO EXCLUDE THE POSSIBLITY OF CORROSION IN THE UPPER GASTROINTESTINAL TRACT; IF CORROSION IS SUSPECTED, ESOPHAGOSCOPY SHOULD USUALLY BE PERFORMED WITHIN 24 HOURS (DREISBACH, HANDBOOK OF POISONING, 12TH ED.). MAINTAIN AIRWAY AND TREAT SHOCK. IF VOMITING OCCURS, KEEP HEAD BELOW HIPS TO HELP PREVENT ASPIRATION. GET MEDICAL ATTENTION IMMEDIATELY.

ANTIDOTE: NO SPECIFIC ANTIDOTE. TREAT SYMPTOMATICALLY AND SUPPORTIVELY.

REACTIVITY

REACTIVITY: NO DATA AVAILABLE.

INCOMPATIBILITIES: SODIUM PHENOLATE: METALS: CORRODES.

DECOMPOSITION: THERMAL DECOMPOSITION MAY RELEASE ACRID SMOKE AND IRRITATING FUMES.

POLYMERIZATION: HAZARDOUS POLYMERIZATION HAS NOT BEEN REPORTED TO OCCUR UNDER NORMAL TEMPERATURES AND PRESSURES.

STORAGE AND DISPOSAL

OBSERVE ALL FEDERAL, STATE AND LOCAL REGULATIONS WHEN STORING OR DISPOSING OF THIS SUBSTANCE. FOR ASSISTANCE, CONTACT THE DISTRICT DIRECTOR OF THE ENVIRONMENTAL PROTECTION AGENCY.

CONDITIONS TO AVOID

MAY BURN BUT DOES NOT IGNITE READILY. FLAMMABLE, POISONOUS GASES MAY ACCUMULATE IN TANKS AND HOPPER CARS. MAY IGNITE COMBUSTIBLES (WOOD, PAPER, OIL, ETC.).

SPILL AND LEAK PROCEDURES

OCCUPATIONAL SPILL: DO NOT TOUCH SPILLED MATERIAL. STOP LEAK IF YOU CAN DO IT WITHOUT RISK. FOR SMALL SPILLS, TAKE UP WITH SAND OR OTHER ABSORBENT MATERIAL AND PLACE INTO CONTAINERS FOR LATER DISPOSAL. FOR SMALL DRY SPILLS, WITH CLEAN SHOVEL PLACE MATERIAL INTO CLEAN, DRY CONTAINER AND COVER. MOVE CONTAINERS FROM SPILL AREA. FOR LARGER SPILLS, DIKE FAR AHEAD OF SPILL FOR LATER DISPOSAL. KEEP UNNECESSARY PEOPLE AWAY. ISOLATE HAZARD AREA AND DENY ENTRY.

PROTECTIVE EQUIPMENT

VENTILATION: PROVIDE LOCAL EXHAUST OR PROCESS ENCLOSURE VENTILATION SYSTEM.

RESPIRATOR: THE FOLLOWING RESPIRATORS ARE RECOMMENDED BASED ON INFORMATION FOUND IN THE PHYSICAL DATA, TOXICITY AND HEALTH EFFECTS SECTIONS. THEY ARE RANKED IN ORDER FROM MINIMUM TO MAXIMUM RESPIRATORY PROTECTION. THE SPECIFIC RESPIRATOR SELECTED MUST BE BASED ON CONTAMINATION LEVELS FOUND IN THE WORK PLACE, MUST NOT EXCEED THE WORKING LIMITS OF THE RESPIRATOR AND BE JOINTLY APPROVED BY THE NATIONAL INSTITUTE FOR OCCUPATIONAL SAFETY AND HEALTH AND THE MINE SAFETY AND HEALTH ADMINISTRATION (NIOSH-MSHA).

TYPE 'C' SUPPLIED-AIR RESPIRATOR WITH A FULL FACEPIECE OPERATED IN PRESSURE-DEMAND OR OTHER POSITIVE PRESSURE MODE OR WITH A FULL FACEPIECE, HELMET OR HOOD OPERATED IN CONTINOUS-FLOW MODE.

SELF-CONTAINED BREATHING APPARATUS WITH A FULL FACEPIECE OPERATED IN PRESSURE-DEMAND OR OTHER POSITIVE PRESSURE MODE.

FOR FIREFIGHTING AND OTHER IMMEDIATELY DANGEROUS TO LIFE OR HEALTH CONDITIONS:

SELF-CONTAINED BREATHING APPARATUS WITH FULL FACEPIECE OPERATED IN PRESSURE-DEMAND OR OTHER POSITIVE PRESSURE MODE.

SUPPLIED-AIR RESPIRATOR WITH FULL FACEPIECE AND OPERATED IN PRESSURE-DEMAND OR OTHER POSITIVE PRESSURE MODE IN COMBINATION WITH AN AUXILIARY SELF-CONTAINED BREATHING APPARATUS OPERATED IN PRESSURE-DEMAND OR OTHER POSITIVE PRESSURE MODE.

CLOTHING: EMPLOYEE MUST WEAR APPROPRIATE PROTECTIVE (IMPERVIOUS) CLOTHING AND EQUIPMENT TO PREVENT ANY POSSIBILITY OF SKIN CONTACT WITH THIS SUBSTANCE.

GLOVES: EMPLOYEE MUST WEAR APPROPRIATE PROTECTIVE GLOVES TO PREVENT CONTACT WITH THIS SUBSTANCE.

EYE PROTECTION: EMPLOYEE MUST WEAR SPLASH-PROOF OR DUST-RESISTANT SAFETY GOGGLES AND A FACESHIELD TO PREVENT CONTACT WITH THIS SUBSTANCE.

EMERGENCY WASH FACILITIES: WHERE THERE IS ANY POSSIBILITY THAT AN EMPLOYEE'S EYES AND/OR SKIN MAY BE EXPOSED TO THIS SUBSTANCE, THE EMPLOYER SHOULD PROVIDE AN EYE WASH FOUNTAIN AND QUICK DRENCH SHOWER WITHIN THE IMMEDIATE WORK AREA FOR EMERGENCY USE.

AUTHORIZED BY- OCCUPATIONAL HEALTH SERVICES, INC.

CREATION DATE: 11/17/89 ***REVISION DATE:*** 05/09/90

MATERIAL SAFETY DATA SHEET

OCCUPATIONAL HEALTH SERVICES, INC.
AGRICULTURE AND PESTICIDE DIVISION
450 SEVENTH AVENUE, SUITE 2407
NEW YORK, NEW YORK 10123
1-800-445-MSDS OR (212) 967-1100

EMERGENCY CONTACT:
JOHN S. BRANSFORD, JR. (615) 292-1180

SUBSTANCE IDENTIFICATION

CAS-NUMBER 137-40-6

SUBSTANCE: **SODIUM PROPIONATE**

TRADE NAMES/SYNONYMS: PROPRIONIC ACID SODIUM SALT; MYCOBAN; BIOBAN-S; DEKETON; IMPEDEX; KEENATE; NAPROPION; OCUSEPTINE; PROPIOFAR; PROPION;

PROPISOL; SODIUM PROPANOATE; WHI-PRO; SODIUM PROPIONATE, ANHYDROUS; PROPANOIC ACID, SODIUM SALT; C3H5O2NA; PST21575

CHEMICAL FAMILY: ESTER, CARBOXYLIC, ALIPHATIC

MOLECULAR FORMULA: C3-H5-O2.NA

MOLECULAR WEIGHT: 96.06

CERCLA RATINGS (SCALE 0-3): HEALTH=2 FIRE=1 REACTIVITY=0 PERSISTENCE=0

NFPA RATINGS (SCALE 0-4): HEALTH=U FIRE=1 REACTIVITY=0

COMPONENTS AND CONTAMINANTS

COMPONENT: SODIUM PROPIONATE ***PERCENT:*** 100.0
CAS# 137-40-6

OTHER CONTAMINANTS: NONE

EXPOSURE LIMITS: NO OCCUPATIONAL EXPOSURE LIMITS ESTABLISHED BY OSHA, ACGIH, OR NIOSH.

PHYSICAL DATA

DESCRIPTION: ODORLESS, TRANSPARENT, FINE POWDER OR CRYSTALS

MELTING POINT: 545-547 F (285-286 C) ***SPECIFIC GRAVITY:*** NOT AVAILABLE

PH: 8.0-10.5 (10% SOLN) ***SOLUBILITY IN WATER:*** SOLUBLE

SOLVENT SOLUBILITY: SOLUBLE IN ALCOHOL

FIRE AND EXPLOSION DATA

FIRE AND EXPLOSION HAZARD: SLIGHT FIRE HAZARD WHEN EXPOSED TO HEAT OR FLAME.

FIREFIGHTING MEDIA: DRY CHEMICAL, CARBON DIOXIDE, HALON, WATER SPRAY OR STANDARD FOAM (1987 EMERGENCY RESPONSE GUIDEBOOK, DOT P 5800.4). FOR LARGER FIRES, USE WATER SPRAY, FOG OR STANDARD FOAM (1987 EMERGENCY RESPONSE GUIDEBOOK, DOT P 5800.4).

FIREFIGHTING: MOVE CONTAINER FROM FIRE AREA IF POSSIBLE. DO NOT SCATTER SPILLED MATERIAL WITH HIGH PRESSURE WATER STREAMS. DIKE FIRE CONTROL WATER FOR LATER DISPOSAL (1987 EMERGENCY RESPONSE GUIDEBOOK, DOT P 5800.4, GUIDE PAGE 31).
USE AGENTS SUITABLE FOR TYPE OF SURROUNDING FIRE. AVOID BREATHING HAZARDOUS VAPORS, KEEP UPWIND.

TOXICITY

SODIUM PROPIONATE: TOXICITY DATA: 1640 MG/KG SKIN-RABBIT LD50; 6332 MG/KG ORAL-MOUSE LD50; 2100 MG/KG SUBCUTANEOUS-MOUSE LD50; 6750 MG/KG UNREPORTED-RABBIT LDLO. CARCINOGEN STATUS: NONE. ACUTE TOXICITY LEVEL: MODERATELY TOXIC BY DERMAL ABSORPTION; SLIGHTLY TOXIC BY INGESTION. TARGET EFFECTS: NO DATA AVAILABLE.

HEALTH EFFECTS AND FIRST AID

INHALATION: SODIUM PROPIONATE: **ACUTE EXPOSURE-** NO DATA AVAILABLE. **CHRONIC EXPOSURE-** NO DATA AVAILABLE.

FIRST AID- REMOVE FROM EXPOSURE AREA TO FRESH AIR IMMEDIATELY. IF BREATHING HAS STOPPED, PERFORM ARTIFICIAL RESPIRATION. KEEP PERSON WARM AND AT REST. TREAT SYMPTOMATICALLY AND SUPPORTIVELY. GET MEDICAL ATTENTION IMMEDIATELY.

SKIN CONTACT: SODIUM PROPIONATE: **ACUTE EXPOSURE-** CONTACT MAY CAUSE IRRITATION. SKIN ABSORPTION MAY OCCUR. **CHRONIC EXPOSURE-** REPEATED APPLICATIONS MAY ELICIT ALLERGIC SKIN REACTIONS.

FIRST AID- REMOVE CONTAMINATED CLOTHING AND SHOES IMMEDIATELY. WASH AFFECTED AREA WITH SOAP OR MILD DETERGENT AND LARGE AMOUNTS OF WATER UNTIL NO EVIDENCE OF CHEMICAL REMAINS (APPROXIMATELY 15-20 MINUTES). GET MEDICAL ATTENTION IMMEDIATELY.

EYE CONTACT: SODIUM PROPIONATE: **ACUTE EXPOSURE-** SOLUTIONS OF SODIUM PROPIONATE AT CONCENTRATIONS UP TO 15% IN HUMAN EYES AND 20% IN RABBIT EYES CAUSED ONLY TRANSITORY BURNING AND REDNESS. **CHRONIC EXPOSURE-** NO DATA AVAILABLE.

FIRST AID- WASH EYES IMMEDIATELY WITH LARGE AMOUNTS OF WATER OR NORMAL SALINE, OCCASIONALLY LIFTING UPPER AND LOWER LIDS, UNTIL NO EVIDENCE OF CHEMICAL REMAINS (APPROXIMATELY 15-20 MINUTES). GET MEDICAL ATTENTION IMMEDIATELY.

INGESTION: SODIUM PROPIONATE: **ACUTE EXPOSURE-** INGESTED SODIUM PROPIONATE MAY BE CONVERTED TO PROPIONIC ACID WHICH PENETRATES THE GASTRIC MUCOSA READILY AND MAY CAUSE DESQUAMATION AND BLEEDING. **CHRONIC EXPOSURE-** AN ADULT MALE RECEIVING 6000 MG DAILY WAS FOUND TO HAVE FAINTLY ALKALINE URINE BUT SHOWED NO OTHER EFFECTS. PROLONGED FEEDING STUDIES IN ANIMALS RESULTED IN NO ADVERSE EFFECTS.

FIRST AID- TREAT SYMPTOMATICALLY AND SUPPORTIVELY. GET MEDICAL ATTENTION IMMEDIATELY. IF VOMITING OCCURS, KEEP HEAD LOWER THAN HIPS TO PREVENT ASPIRATION.

ANTIDOTE: NO SPECIFIC ANTIDOTE. TREAT SYMPTOMATICALLY AND SUPPORTIVELY.

REACTIVITY

REACTIVITY: STABLE UNDER NORMAL TEMPERATURES AND PRESSURES.

INCOMPATIBILITIES: SODIUM PROPIONATE: NO DATA AVAILABLE.

DECOMPOSITION: THERMAL DECOMPOSITION EMITS ACRID SMOKE AND SODIUM MONOXIDE FUMES.

POLYMERIZATION: HAZARDOUS POLYMERIZATION HAS NOT BEEN REPORTED TO OCCUR UNDER NORMAL TEMPERATURES AND PRESSURES.

STORAGE AND DISPOSAL

OBSERVE ALL FEDERAL, STATE AND LOCAL REGULATIONS WHEN STORING OR DISPOSING OF THIS SUBSTANCE. FOR ASSISTANCE, CONTACT THE DISTRICT DIRECTOR OF THE ENVIRONMENTAL PROTECTION AGENCY.

CONDITIONS TO AVOID

MAY BURN BUT DOES NOT IGNITE READILY. AVOID CONTACT WITH STRONG OXIDIZERS, EXCESSIVE HEAT, SPARKS, OR OPEN FLAME.

SPILL AND LEAK PROCEDURES

OCCUPATIONAL SPILL: SWEEP UP AND PLACE IN SUITABLE CLEAN, DRY CONTAINERS FOR RECLAMATION OR LATER DISPOSAL. DO NOT FLUSH SPILLED MATERIAL INTO SEWER. KEEP UNNECESSARY PEOPLE AWAY.

PROTECTIVE EQUIPMENT

VENTILATION: PROVIDE LOCAL EXHAUST OR GENERAL DILUTION VENTILATION SYSTEM.

RESPIRATOR: THE FOLLOWING RESPIRATORS ARE RECOMMENDED BASED ON INFORMATION FOUND IN THE PHYSICAL DATA, TOXICITY AND HEALTH EFFECTS SECTIONS. THEY ARE RANKED IN ORDER FROM MINIMUM TO MAXIMUM RESPIRATORY PROTECTION. THE SPECIFIC RESPIRATOR SELECTED MUST BE BASED ON CONTAMINATION LEVELS FOUND IN THE WORK PLACE, MUST NOT EXCEED THE WORKING LIMITS OF THE RESPIRATOR AND BE JOINTLY APPROVED BY THE NATIONAL INSTITUTE FOR OCCUPATIONAL SAFETY AND HEALTH AND THE MINE SAFETY AND HEALTH ADMINISTRATION (NIOSH-MSHA).
DUST AND MIST RESPIRATOR.
AIR-PURIFYING RESPIRATOR WITH A HIGH-EFFICIENCY PARTICULATE FILTER.
POWERED AIR-PURIFYING RESPIRATOR WITH A DUST AND MIST FILTER.
POWERED AIR-PURIFYING RESPIRATOR WITH A HIGH-EFFICIENCY PARTICULATE FILTER.
TYPE 'C' SUPPLIED-AIR RESPIRATOR OPERATED IN THE PRESSURE-DEMAND OR OTHER POSITIVE PRESSURE OR CONTINUOUS-FLOW MODE.
SELF-CONTAINED BREATHING APPARATUS.
FOR FIREFIGHTING AND OTHER IMMEDIATELY DANGEROUS TO LIFE OR HEALTH CONDITIONS:
SELF-CONTAINED BREATHING APPARATUS WITH FULL FACEPIECE OPERATED IN PRESSURE-DEMAND OR OTHER POSITIVE PRESSURE MODE.
SUPPLIED-AIR RESPIRATOR WITH FULL FACEPIECE AND OPERATED IN PRESSURE-DEMAND OR OTHER POSITIVE PRESSURE MODE IN COMBINATION WITH AN AUXILIARY SELF-CONTAINED BREATHING APPARATUS OPERATED IN PRESSURE-DEMAND OR OTHER POSITIVE PRESSURE MODE.

CLOTHING: EMPLOYEE MUST WEAR APPROPRIATE PROTECTIVE (IMPERVIOUS) CLOTHING AND EQUIPMENT TO PREVENT REPEATED OR PROLONGED SKIN CONTACT WITH THIS SUBSTANCE.

GLOVES: EMPLOYEE MUST WEAR APPROPRIATE PROTECTIVE GLOVES TO PREVENT CONTACT WITH THIS SUBSTANCE.

EYE PROTECTION: EMPLOYEE MUST WEAR SPLASH-PROOF OR DUST-RESISTANT SAFETY GOGGLES TO PREVENT EYE CONTACT WITH THIS SUBSTANCE.
EMERGENCY EYE WASH: WHERE THERE IS ANY POSSIBILITY THAT AN EMPLOYEE'S EYES MAY BE EXPOSED TO THIS SUBSTANCE, THE EMPLOYER SHOULD PROVIDE AN EYE WASH FOUNTAIN WITHIN THE IMMEDIATE WORK AREA FOR EMERGENCY USE.

AUTHORIZED BY- OCCUPATIONAL HEALTH SERVICES, INC.
CREATION DATE: 11/17/89 ***REVISION DATE:*** 05/31/90

MATERIAL SAFETY DATA SHEET

OCCUPATIONAL HEALTH SERVICES, INC. AGRICULTURE AND PESTICIDE DIVISION
EMERGENCY CONTACT: JOHN S. BRANSFORD, JR. (615) 292-1180

450 SEVENTH AVENUE, SUITE 2407
NEW YORK, NEW YORK 10123
1-800-445-MSDS OR (212) 967-1100

SUBSTANCE IDENTIFICATION

CAS-NUMBER 16893-85-9

***SUBSTANCE:* SODIUM SILICOFLUORIDE**

TRADE NAMES/SYNONYMS: SODIUM FLUOSILICATE; SODIUM HEXAFLUOROSILICATE; DISODIUM HEXAFLUOROSILICATE; SILICON SODIUM FLUORIDE; SODIUM SILICON FLUORIDE; SODIUM FLUOROSILICATE; SATSAN; DESTRUXOL APPLEX; PRODAN; SALUFER; SODIUM HEXAFLUOSILICATE; UN 2674; PST21620

CHEMICAL FAMILY: INORGANIC SALT

MOLECULAR FORMULA: F6-SI.2NA

MOLECULAR WEIGHT: 188.07

CERCLA RATINGS (SCALE 0-3): HEALTH=3 FIRE=0 REACTIVITY=0 PERSISTENCE=0

NFPA RATINGS (SCALE 0-4): HEALTH=3 FIRE=0 REACTIVITY=0

COMPONENTS AND CONTAMINANTS

COMPONENT: SODIUM SILICOFLUORIDE ***PERCENT:*** 100
CAS# 16893-85-9

OTHER CONTAMINANTS: NONE

EXPOSURE LIMITS: SODIUM SILICOFLUORIDE: 2.5 MG(F)/M3 OSHA TWA; 2.5 MG(F)/M3 ACGIH TWA; 2.5 MG(F)/M3 NIOSH RECOMMENDED TWA;

PHYSICAL DATA

DESCRIPTION: ODORLESS, TASTELESS, WHITE, HEXAGONAL CRYSTALLINE SOLID OR FREE-FLOWING GRANULAR POWDER.

MELTING POINT: DECOMP @ RED HEAT

SPECIFIC GRAVITY: 2.755 ***PH:*** NEUTRAL ***SOLUBILITY IN WATER:*** 0.0652% @ 17 C

SOLVENT SOLUBILITY: INSOLUBLE IN ALCOHOL

FIRE AND EXPLOSION DATA

FIRE AND EXPLOSION HAZARD: NEGLIGIBLE FIRE HAZARD WHEN EXPOSED TO HEAT OR FLAME.

FIREFIGHTING MEDIA: DRY CHEMICAL, CARBON DIOXIDE, HALON, WATER SPRAY OR STANDARD FOAM (1987 EMERGENCY RESPONSE GUIDEBOOK, DOT P 5800.4). FOR LARGER FIRES, USE WATER SPRAY, FOG OR STANDARD FOAM (1987 EMERGENCY RESPONSE GUIDEBOOK, DOT P 5800.4).

FIREFIGHTING: MOVE CONTAINERS FROM FIRE AREA IF POSSIBLE (1987 EMERGENCY RESPONSE GUIDEBOOK, DOT P 5800.4, GUIDE PAGE 53).
EXTINGUISH USING AGENT SUITABLE FOR TYPE OF SURROUNDING FIRE. AVOID BREATHING VAPORS AND DUSTS. KEEP UPWIND.

TOXICITY

SODIUM SILICOFLUORIDE: IRRITATION DATA: 500 MG SKIN-RABBIT MILD; 100 MG EYE-RABBIT SEVERE; 100 MG/4 SECONDS EYE-RABBIT SEVERE. TOXICITY DATA: 125 MG/KG ORAL-RAT LD50; 125 MG/KG ORAL-RABBIT LD50; 220 MG/KG ORAL-MOUSE LD50; 70 MG/KG SUBCUTANEOUS-RAT LDLO. CARCINOGEN STATUS: HUMAN INADEQUATE EVIDENCE, ANIMAL INADEQUATE EVIDENCE (IARC GROUP-3). LOCAL EFFECTS: CORROSIVE- EYES. IRRITANT- INHALATION AND SKIN. ACUTE TOXICITY LEVEL: TOXIC BY INGESTION. TARGET EFFECTS: NO DATA AVAILABLE.

HEALTH EFFECTS AND FIRST AID

INHALATION: SODIUM SILICOFLUORIDE: IRRITANT. 500 MG(F)/M3 IMMEDIATELY DANGEROUS TO LIFE OR HEALTH. **ACUTE EXPOSURE-** DUSTS MAY CAUSE IRRITATION OF THE NOSE, THROAT AND LUNGS. COUGHING AND DIFFICULT BREATHING MAY OCCUR. GUINEA PIGS EXPOSED TO SODIUM SILICOFLUORIDE DUST IN CONCENTRATIONS RANGING FROM 13 TO 55 MG/M3 SHOWED SIGNS OF PULMONARY EDEMA. LABORATORY TESTS HAVE SHOWN THAT THE LEAST CONCENTRATION THAT CAUSED DEATH IN LABORATORY ANIMALS FOR 6 HOURS WAS 33 MG/M3. NO SYMPTOMS WERE REPORTED. **CHRONIC EXPOSURE-** NO DATA AVAILABLE. HOWEVER, REPEATED OR PROLONGED EXPOSURE TO EXCESSIVE CONCENTRATIONS OF FLUORIDE COMPOUNDS MAY CAUSE FLUOROSIS WITH INCREASED RADIOGRAPHIC DENSITY OF BONE. THE GROSS CHANGES IN THE SKELETON ARE QUITE DISTINCTIVE AND CHARACTERISTIC; AS THE AMOUNT OF FLUORIDE IN THE BONE INCREASES, EXOSTOSES MAY DEVELOP, ESPECIALLY ON THE LONG BONES; THE SACROTUBEROUS AND SACROSCIATIC LIGAMENTS BEGIN TO CALCIFY, VERTEBRAE OCCASIONALLY FUSE TOGETHER, AND TYPICAL STIFFNESS OF THE SPINAL COLLUMN DEVELOPS.

FIRST AID- REMOVE FROM EXPOSURE AREA TO FRESH AIR IMMEDIATELY. IF BREATHING HAS STOPPED, PERFORM ARTIFICIAL RESPIRATION. KEEP PERSON WARM AND AT REST. TREAT SYMPTOMATICALLY AND SUPPORTIVELY. GET MEDICAL ATTENTION IMMEDIATELY.

SKIN CONTACT: SODIUM SILICOFLUORIDE: IRRITANT. **ACUTE EXPOSURE-** CONTACT MAY CAUSE IRRITATION AND A BURNING SENSATION. 500 MG APPLIED TO RABBIT SKIN CAUSED MILD IRRITATION. **CHRONIC EXPOSURE-** AFTER REPEATED OR PROLONGED CONTACT, DERMATITIS, A PUSTULAR RASH AND POSSIBLE ULCERATION MAY OCCUR IN SOME INDIVIDUALS.

FIRST AID- REMOVE CONTAMINATED CLOTHING AND SHOES IMMEDIATELY. WASH AFFECTED AREA WITH SOAP OR MILD DETERGENT AND LARGE AMOUNTS OF WATER UNTIL NO EVIDENCE OF CHEMICAL REMAINS (APPROXIMATELY 15-20 MINUTES). GET MEDICAL ATTENTION IMMEDIATELY.

EYE CONTACT: SODIUM SILICOFLUORIDE: CORROSIVE. **ACUTE EXPOSURE-** MAY CAUSE SEVERE IRRITATION WITH REDNESS AND PAIN. 100 MG APPLIED TO RABBIT EYES PRODUCED SEVERE IRRITATION. 100 MG APPLIED TO RABBIT EYES FOR 4 SECONDS AND THEN RINSED PRODUCED SEVERE IRRITATION ALSO. **CHRONIC EXPOSURE-** REPEATED OR PROLONGED CONTACT MAY CAUSE CONJUNCTIVITIS AND POSSIBLE CORNEAL DAMAGE.

FIRST AID- WASH EYES IMMEDIATELY WITH LARGE AMOUNTS OF WATER, OCCASIONALLY LIFTING UPPER AND LOWER LIDS, UNTIL NO EVIDENCE OF CHEMICAL REMAINS (AT LEAST 15-20 MINUTES). CONTINUE IRRIGATING WITH NORMAL SALINE UNTIL THE PH HAS RETURNED TO NORMAL (30-60 MINUTES). COVER WITH STERILE BANDAGES. GET MEDICAL ATTENTION IMMEDIATELY.

INGESTION: SODIUM SILICOFLUORIDE: TOXIC. **ACUTE EXPOSURE-** MAY CAUSE GASTROINTESTINAL IRRITATION WITH NAUSEA AND VOMITING. LOSS OF CONSCIOUSNESS MAY OCCUR. SERIOUS POISONING DUE TO FLUORIDE COMPOUNDS MAY INCLUDE WEAKNESS, TREMORS, CONVULSIONS, COLLAPSE, LOW BLOOD CALCIUM LEVELS AND COMA. DEATH IS DUE TO CARDIOVASCULAR COLLAPSE, RESPIRATORY FAILURE OR VENTRICULAR FIBRILLATION. **CHRONIC EXPOSURE-** REPEATED OR PROLONGED EXPOSURE TO SODIUM SILICOFLUORIDE MAY CAUSE FLUOROSIS. SYMPTOMS ARE WEIGHT LOSS, BRITTLENESS OF BONES, ANEMIA, WEAKNESS, STIFFNESS OF JOINTS AND MOTTLING OF TOOTH ENAMEL AND OSTEOSCLEROSIS. THE BONE STRUCTURE SHOWS THICKENING WITH CALCIFICATION IN THE LIGAMENTOUS ATTACHMENTS OF THE RIBS AND PELVIS.

FIRST AID- PERFORM GASTRIC LAVAGE WITH CALCIUM HYDROXIDE AND ADMINISTER ALUMINUM HYDROXIDE ANTACID PREPARATION TO TRAP FLUORIDES. GET MEDICAL ATTENTION IMMEDIATELY. (GOSSELIN, SMITH AND HODGE, CLINICAL TOXICOLOGY OF COMMERCIAL PRODUCTS, 5TH EDITION)

ANTIDOTE: NO SPECIFIC ANTIDOTE. TREAT SYMPTOMATICALLY AND SUPPORTIVELY.

REACTIVITY

REACTIVITY: STABLE UNDER NORMAL TEMPERATURES AND PRESSURES.

INCOMPATIBILITIES: NO DATA AVAILABLE.

DECOMPOSITION: THERMAL DECOMPOSITION MAY RELEASE HAZARDOUS HYDROGEN FLUORIDE AND SODIUM OXIDE GAS.

POLYMERIZATION: HAZARDOUS POLYMERIZATION HAS NOT BEEN REPORTED TO OCCUR UNDER NORMAL TEMPERATURES AND PRESSURES.

CONDITIONS TO AVOID

MAY BURN BUT DOES NOT IGNITE READILY.

SPILL AND LEAK PROCEDURES

OCCUPATIONAL SPILL: DO NOT TOUCH SPILLED MATERIAL. STOP LEAK IF YOU CAN DO IT WITHOUT RISK. FOR SMALL SPILLS, TAKE UP WITH SAND OR OTHER ABSORBENT MATERIAL AND PLACE INTO CONTAINERS FOR LATER DISPOSAL. FOR SMALL DRY SPILLS, WITH A CLEAN SHOVEL PLACE MATERIAL INTO CLEAN, DRY CONTAINER AND COVER. MOVE CONTAINERS FROM SPILL AREA. FOR LARGER SPILLS, DIKE FAR AHEAD OF SPILL FOR LATER DISPOSAL. KEEP UNNECESSARY PEOPLE AWAY. ISOLATE HAZARD AREA AND DENY ENTRY.

PROTECTIVE EQUIPMENT

VENTILATION: PROVIDE LOCAL EXHAUST OR PROCESS ENCLOSURE VENTILATION TO MEET PUBLISHED EXPOSURE LIMITS.

RESPIRATOR: THE FOLLOWING RESPIRATORS AND MAXIMUM USE CONCENTRATIONS ARE RECOMMENDATIONS BY THE U.S. DEPARTMENT OF HEALTH AND HUMAN SERVICES, NIOSH POCKET GUIDE TO CHEMICAL HAZARDS; NIOSH CRITERIA DOCUMENTS OR BY THE U.S. DEPARTMENT OF LABOR, 29 CFR 1910 SUBPART Z. THE SPECIFIC RESPIRATOR SELECTED MUST BE BASED ON CONTAMINATION LEVELS FOUND IN THE WORK PLACE, MUST NOT EXCEED THE WORKING LIMITS OF THE RESPIRATOR AND BE JOINTLY APPROVED BY THE NATIONAL INSTITUTE FOR OCCUPATIONAL SAFETY AND HEALTH AND THE MINE SAFETY AND HEALTH ADMINISTRATION (NIOSH-MSHA).

12.5 MG(F)/M3- ANY DUST AND MIST RESPIRATOR EXCEPT SINGLE-USE RESPIRATORS.

25 MG(F)/M3- ANY DUST AND MIST RESPIRATOR EXCEPT SINGLE-USE AND QUARTER-MASK RESPIRATORS. ANY SUPPLIED AIR RESPIRATOR. ANY SELF-CONTAINED BREATHING APPARATUS.

62.5 MG(F)/M3- ANY POWERED AIR-PURIFYING RESPIRATOR WITH A DUST AND

MIST FILTER. (MAY NEED ACID GAS SORBENT) ANY SUPPLIED-AIR RESPIRATOR OPERATED IN A CONTINUOUS FLOW MODE.
125 MG(F)/M3- ANY SELF-CONTAINED BREATHING APPARATUS WITH A FULL FACEPIECE. ANY AIR-PURIFYING FULL FACEPIECE RESPIRATOR WITH A HIGH-EFFICIENCY PARTICULATE FILTER. (MAY NEED ACID GAS SORBENT) ANY SUPPLIED-AIR RESPIRATOR WITH A FULL FACEPIECE.
500 MG(F)/M3- ANY SUPPLIED-AIR RESPIRATOR WITH A FULL FACEPIECE AND OPERATED IN A PRESSURE-DEMAND OR OTHER POSITIVE PRESSURE MODE.
ESCAPE- ANY AIR-PURIFYING FULL FACEPIECE RESPIRATOR (GAS MASK) WITH A CHIN-STYLE OR FRONT- OR BACK-MOUNTED ACID GAS CANISTER HAVING A HIGH-EFFICIENCY PARTICULATE FILTER. ANY APPROPRIATE ESCAPE-TYPE SELF-CONTAINED BREATHING APPARATUS.
FOR FIREFIGHTING AND OTHER IMMEDIATELY DANGEROUS TO LIFE OR HEALTH CONDITIONS:
SELF-CONTAINED BREATHING APPARATUS WITH FULL FACEPIECE OPERATED IN PRESSURE-DEMAND OR OTHER POSITIVE PRESSURE MODE.
SUPPLIED-AIR RESPIRATOR WITH FULL FACEPIECE AND OPERATED IN PRESSURE-DEMAND OR OTHER POSITIVE PRESSURE MODE IN COMBINATION WITH AN AUXILIARY SELF-CONTAINED BREATHING APPARATUS OPERATED IN PRESSURE-DEMAND OR OTHER POSITIVE PRESSURE MODE.

CLOTHING: EMPLOYEE MUST WEAR APPROPRIATE PROTECTIVE (IMPERVIOUS) CLOTHING AND EQUIPMENT TO PREVENT REPEATED OR PROLONGED SKIN CONTACT WITH THIS SUBSTANCE.

GLOVES: EMPLOYEE MUST WEAR APPROPRIATE PROTECTIVE GLOVES TO PREVENT CONTACT WITH THIS SUBSTANCE.

EYE PROTECTION: EMPLOYEE MUST WEAR SPLASH-PROOF OR DUST-RESISTANT SAFETY GOGGLES AND A FACESHIELD TO PREVENT CONTACT WITH THIS SUBSTANCE.
EMERGENCY WASH FACILITIES: WHERE THERE IS ANY POSSIBILITY THAT AN EMPLOYEE'S EYES AND/OR SKIN MAY BE EXPOSED TO THIS SUBSTANCE, THE EMPLOYER SHOULD PROVIDE AN EYE WASH FOUNTAIN AND QUICK DRENCH SHOWER WITHIN THE IMMEDIATE WORK AREA FOR EMERGENCY USE.

AUTHORIZED BY- OCCUPATIONAL HEALTH SERVICES, INC.
CREATION DATE: 11/16/89 ***REVISION DATE:*** 07/12/90

MATERIAL SAFETY DATA SHEET

OCCUPATIONAL HEALTH SERVICES, INC.
AGRICULTURE AND PESTICIDE DIVISION
450 SEVENTH AVENUE, SUITE 2407
NEW YORK, NEW YORK 10123
1-800-445-MSDS OR (212) 967-1100

EMERGENCY CONTACT:
JOHN S. BRANSFORD, JR. (615) 292-1180

SUBSTANCE IDENTIFICATION

CAS-NUMBER 7757-83-7

SUBSTANCE: **SODIUM SULFITE**

TRADE NAMES/SYNONYMS: ANHYDROUS SODIUM SULFITE; DISODIUM SULFITE; SODIUM SULPHITE; SODIUM SULFITE, ANHYDROUS; SULFUROUS ACID, SODIUM SALT (1:2); SULFUROUS ACID, DISODIUM SALT; EXSICCATED SODIUM SULFITE; PST21660

CHEMICAL FAMILY: INORGANIC SALT

MOLECULAR FORMULA: NA2-S-O3

MOLECULAR WEIGHT: 126.04

CERCLA RATINGS (SCALE 0-3): HEALTH=3 FIRE=0 REACTIVITY=0 PERSISTENCE=0

NFPA RATINGS (SCALE 0-4): HEALTH=3 FIRE=0 REACTIVITY=0

COMPONENTS AND CONTAMINANTS

COMPONENT: SODIUM SULFITE ***PERCENT:*** 100
CAS# 7757-83-7

OTHER CONTAMINANTS: NONE

EXPOSURE LIMITS: NO OCCUPATIONAL EXPOSURE LIMITS ESTABLISHED BY OSHA, ACGIH, OR NIOSH.

PHYSICAL DATA

DESCRIPTION: ODORLESS, WHITE CRYSTALS OR POWDER WITH A SALINE, SULFUROUS TASTE.

BOILING POINT: DECOMPOSES ***MELTING POINT:*** DECOMPOSES @ RED HEAT

SPECIFIC GRAVITY: 2.633 ***PH:*** APPROXIMATELY 9.0

SOLUBILITY IN WATER: 12.5% @ 0 C

SOLVENT SOLUBILITY: SOLUBLE IN GLYCEROL; SLIGHTLY SOLUBLE IN ALCOHOL; INSOLUBLE IN LIQUID CHLORINE, AMMONIA

FIRE AND EXPLOSION DATA

FIRE AND EXPLOSION HAZARD: NEGLIGIBLE FIRE HAZARD WHEN EXPOSED TO HEAT OR FLAME.

FIREFIGHTING MEDIA: DRY CHEMICAL, CARBON DIOXIDE, WATER SPRAY OR FOAM FOR LARGER FIRES, USE WATER SPRAY, FOG OR ALCOHOL FOAM

FIREFIGHTING: MOVE CONTAINER FROM FIRE AREA IF POSSIBLE. DO NOT SCATTER SPILLED MATERIAL WITH MORE WATER THAN NEEDED FOR FIRE CONTROL. DIKE FIRE CONTROL WATER FOR LATER DISPOSAL
USE AGENTS SUITABLE FOR TYPE OF SURROUNDING FIRE. AVOID BREATHING HAZARDOUS VAPORS, KEEP UPWIND.

TOXICITY

SODIUM SULFITE: TOXICITY DATA: ANHYDROUS: 115 MG/KG INTRAVENOUS-RAT LD50; 950 MG/KG INTRAPERITONEAL-MOUSE LD50; 130 MG/KG INTRAVENOUS-MOUSE LD50; 1300 MG/KG SUBCUTANEOUS-DOG LDLO; 1300 MG/KG SUBCUTANEOUS-CAT LDLO; 200 MG/KG INTRAVENOUS-CAT LDLO; 2825 MG/KG ORAL-RABBIT LDLO; 65 MG/KG INTRAVENOUS-RABBIT LD50; 600 MG/KG SUBCUTANEOUS-GUINEA PIG LDLO; 200 MG/KG INTRAVENOUS-GUINEA PIG LDLO; 95 MG/KG INTRAVENOUS-HAMSTER LD50; 7 MG/KG ORAL-HUMAN TDLO (THIDD6); 300 MG/KG SUBCUTANEOUS-RABBIT LDLO; MUTAGENIC DATA (RTECS). HEPTAHYDRATE: 277 MG/KG INTRAPERITONEAL-MOUSE LD50; 743 MG/KG INTRAVENOUS-MAN LDLO. CARCINOGEN STATUS: NONE. ACUTE TOXICITY LEVEL: INSUFFICIENT DATA. TARGET EFFECTS: SENSITIZER. AT INCREASED RISK FROM EXPOSURE: ASTHMATICS.

HEALTH EFFECTS AND FIRST AID

INHALATION: SODIUM SULFITE: SENSITIZER. **ACUTE EXPOSURE-** MAY CAUSE MUCOUS MEMBRANE IRRITATION. INHALATION OF THIS MATERIAL MAY CAUSE ADVERSE REACTIONS INCLUDING BRONCHOSPASMS IN SUSCEPTIBLE INDIVIDUALS, ESPECIALLY ASTHMATICS. SYMPTOMS MAY INCLUDE FLUSHING, SEVERE WHEEZING, SWELLING OF THE THROAT, AND PALATAL AND GENERALIZED ITCHING. **CHRONIC EXPOSURE-** REPEATED OR PROLONGED EXPOSURE MAY CAUSE SENSITIZATION.

FIRST AID- REMOVE FROM EXPOSURE AREA TO FRESH AIR IMMEDIATELY. IF BREATHING HAS STOPPED, PERFORM ARTIFICIAL RESPIRATION. KEEP PERSON WARM AND AT REST. TREAT SYMPTOMATICALLY AND SUPPORTIVELY. GET MEDICAL ATTENTION IMMEDIATELY.

SKIN CONTACT: SODIUM SULFITE: **ACUTE EXPOSURE-** DIRECT CONTACT MAY CAUSE IRRITATION AND CONTACT DERMATITIS. SOME SULFITES MAY CAUSE SENSITIZATION DERMATITIS IN PREVIOUSLY EXPOSED INDIVIDUALS. **CHRONIC EXPOSURE-** REPEATED OR PROLONGED EXPOSURE MAY CAUSE CONTACT DERMATITIS. REPEATED EXPOSURE TO SULFITES MAY RESULT IN SENSITIZATION.

FIRST AID- REMOVE CONTAMINATED CLOTHING AND SHOES IMMEDIATELY. WASH AFFECTED AREA WITH SOAP OR MILD DETERGENT AND LARGE AMOUNTS OF WATER UNTIL NO EVIDENCE OF CHEMICAL REMAINS (APPROXIMATELY 15-20 MINUTES). GET MEDICAL ATTENTION IMMEDIATELY.

EYE CONTACT: SODIUM SULFITE: **ACUTE EXPOSURE-** DIRECT CONTACT MAY CAUSE IRRITATION AND REDNESS. **CHRONIC EXPOSURE-** NO DATA AVAILABLE.

FIRST AID- WASH EYES IMMEDIATELY WITH LARGE AMOUNTS OF WATER OR NORMAL SALINE, OCCASIONALLY LIFTING UPPER AND LOWER LIDS, UNTIL NO EVIDENCE OF CHEMICAL REMAINS (APPROXIMATELY 15-20 MINUTES). GET MEDICAL ATTENTION IMMEDIATELY.

INGESTION: SODIUM SULFITE: SENSITIZER. **ACUTE EXPOSURE-** MAY CAUSE GASTROINTESTINAL IRRITATION WITH ABDOMINAL PAIN, NAUSEA, VOMITING AND DIARRHEA. IN SUSCEPTIBLE INDIVIDUALS, PARTICULARLY ASTHMATICS, SULFITES MAY CAUSE WHEEZING, SHORTNESS OF BREATH, UNCONSCIOUSNESS AND ANAPHYLAXIS. SIGNS AND SYMPTOMS MAY INCLUDE GENERALIZED FLUSHING AND ITCHING AND RESPIRATORY ARREST. THE ESTIMATED HUMAN LETHAL DOSE IS 10 GRAMS. IN ANIMALS, LARGE DOSES HAVE CAUSED VIOLENT COLIC AND DIARRHEA, CIRCULATORY DISTURBANCES, CENTRAL NERVOUS SYSTEM DEPRESSION AND DEATH. **CHRONIC EXPOSURE-** REPEATED INGESTION OF FOOD CONTAINING SULFITES MAY CAUSE SENSITIZATION.

FIRST AID- TREAT SYMPTOMATICALLY AND SUPPORTIVELY. GET MEDICAL ATTENTION IMMEDIATELY. IF VOMITING OCCURS, KEEP HEAD LOWER THAN HIPS TO PREVENT ASPIRATION.

ANTIDOTE: NO SPECIFIC ANTIDOTE. TREAT SYMPTOMATICALLY AND SUPPORTIVELY.

REACTIVITY

REACTIVITY: STABLE UNDER NORMAL TEMPERATURES AND PRESSURES.

INCOMPATIBILITIES: SODIUM SULFITE: MINERAL ACIDS (STRONG): REACTS TO FORM SULFUR DIOXIDE.
DECOMPOSITION: THERMAL DECOMPOSITION MAY RELEASE TOXIC OXIDES OF SULFUR AND TOXIC SODIUM OXIDE.
POLYMERIZATION: HAZARDOUS POLYMERIZATION HAS NOT BEEN REPORTED TO OCCUR UNDER NORMAL TEMPERATURES AND PRESSURES.

STORAGE AND DISPOSAL

OBSERVE ALL FEDERAL, STATE AND LOCAL REGULATIONS WHEN STORING OR DISPOSING OF THIS SUBSTANCE. FOR ASSISTANCE, CONTACT THE DISTRICT DIRECTOR OF THE ENVIRONMENTAL PROTECTION AGENCY.

STORAGE

STORE AWAY FROM INCOMPATIBLE SUBSTANCES.

CONDITIONS TO AVOID

NONE REPORTED.

SPILL AND LEAK PROCEDURES

OCCUPATIONAL SPILL: SWEEP UP AND PLACE IN SUITABLE CLEAN, DRY CONTAINERS FOR RECLAMATION OR LATER DISPOSAL. DO NOT FLUSH SPILLED MATERIAL INTO SEWER. KEEP UNNECESSARY PEOPLE AWAY.

PROTECTIVE EQUIPMENT

VENTILATION: PROVIDE LOCAL EXHAUST OR GENERAL DILUTION VENTILATION SYSTEM.
RESPIRATOR: THE FOLLOWING RESPIRATORS ARE RECOMMENDED BASED ON INFORMATION FOUND IN THE PHYSICAL DATA, TOXICITY AND HEALTH EFFECTS SECTIONS. THEY ARE RANKED IN ORDER FROM MINIMUM TO MAXIMUM RESPIRATORY PROTECTION. THE SPECIFIC RESPIRATOR SELECTED MUST BE BASED ON CONTAMINATION LEVELS FOUND IN THE WORK PLACE, MUST NOT EXCEED THE WORKING LIMITS OF THE RESPIRATOR AND BE JOINTLY APPROVED BY THE NATIONAL INSTITUTE FOR OCCUPATIONAL SAFETY AND HEALTH AND THE MINE SAFETY AND HEALTH ADMINISTRATION (NIOSH-MSHA).
DUST AND MIST RESPIRATOR WITH A FULL FACEPIECE.
AIR-PURIFYING FULL FACEPIECE RESPIRATOR WITH A HIGH-EFFICIENCY PARTICULATE FILTER.
POWERED AIR-PURIFYING RESPIRATOR WITH A TIGHT-FITTING FACEPIECE AND HIGH-EFFICIENCY PARTICULATE FILTER.
TYPE 'C' SUPPLIED-AIR RESPIRATOR WITH A FULL FACEPIECE OPERATED IN PRESSURE-DEMAND OR OTHER POSITIVE PRESSURE MODE OR WITH A FULL FACEPIECE, HELMET OR HOOD OPERATED IN CONTINUOUS-FLOW MODE.
SELF-CONTAINED BREATHING APPARATUS WITH A FULL FACEPIECE OPERATED IN PRESSURE-DEMAND OR OTHER POSITIVE PRESSURE MODE.
FOR FIREFIGHTING AND OTHER IMMEDIATELY DANGEROUS TO LIFE OR HEALTH CONDITIONS:
SELF-CONTAINED BREATHING APPARATUS WITH FULL FACEPIECE OPERATED IN PRESSURE-DEMAND OR OTHER POSITIVE PRESSURE MODE.
SUPPLIED-AIR RESPIRATOR WITH FULL FACEPIECE AND OPERATED IN PRESSURE-DEMAND OR OTHER POSITIVE PRESSURE MODE IN COMBINATION WITH AN AUXILIARY SELF-CONTAINED BREATHING APPARATUS OPERATED IN PRESSURE-DEMAND OR OTHER POSITIVE PRESSURE MODE.
CLOTHING: EMPLOYEE MUST WEAR APPROPRIATE PROTECTIVE (IMPERVIOUS) CLOTHING AND EQUIPMENT TO PREVENT REPEATED OR PROLONGED SKIN CONTACT WITH THIS SUBSTANCE.
GLOVES: EMPLOYEE MUST WEAR APPROPRIATE PROTECTIVE GLOVES TO PREVENT CONTACT WITH THIS SUBSTANCE.
EYE PROTECTION: EMPLOYEE MUST WEAR SPLASH-PROOF OR DUST-RESISTANT SAFETY GOGGLES TO PREVENT EYE CONTACT WITH THIS SUBSTANCE.
EMERGENCY EYE WASH: WHERE THERE IS ANY POSSIBILITY THAT AN EMPLOYEE'S EYES MAY BE EXPOSED TO THIS SUBSTANCE, THE EMPLOYER SHOULD PROVIDE AN EYE WASH FOUNTAIN WITHIN THE IMMEDIATE WORK AREA FOR EMERGENCY USE.

AUTHORIZED BY- OCCUPATIONAL HEALTH SERVICES, INC.
CREATION DATE: 11/17/89 ***REVISION DATE:*** 07/13/90

MATERIAL SAFETY DATA SHEET

OCCUPATIONAL HEALTH SERVICES, INC.
AGRICULTURE AND PESTICIDE DIVISION
450 SEVENTH AVENUE, SUITE 2407
NEW YORK, NEW YORK 10123
1-800-445-MSDS OR (212) 967-1100

EMERGENCY CONTACT:
JOHN S. BRANSFORD, JR. (615) 292-1180

SUBSTANCE IDENTIFICATION

CAS-NUMBER 136-32-3
SUBSTANCE: **2,4,5-SODIUM TRICHLOROPHENATE**
TRADE NAMES/SYNONYMS: 2,4,5-TRICHLOROPHENOL, SODIUM SALT; (2,4,5-TRICHLOROPHENOXY)-SODIUM; DOWICIDE B; SODIUM 2,4,5-TRICHLOROPHENATE; SODIUM 2,4,5- TRICHLOROPHENOLATE; SODIUM 2,4,5-TRICHLOROPHENOXIDE; PST21713
CHEMICAL FAMILY: HALOGEN COMPOUND, AROMATIC
MOLECULAR FORMULA: C6-H2-CL3-O.NA
MOLECULAR WEIGHT: 219.42
CERCLA RATINGS (SCALE 0-3): HEALTH=3 FIRE=0 REACTIVITY=0 PERSISTENCE=3
NFPA RATINGS (SCALE 0-4): HEALTH=2 FIRE=0 REACTIVITY=0

COMPONENTS AND CONTAMINANTS

COMPONENT: 2,4,5-SODIUM TRICHLOROPHENATE ***PERCENT:*** 100
CAS# 136-32-3
EXPOSURE LIMITS: 2,4,5-SODIUM TRICHLOROPHENATE: NO OCCUPATIONAL EXPOSURE LIMITS ESTABLISHED BY OSHA, ACGIH, OR NIOSH. 1 PPM DOW CHEMICAL RECOMMENDED TWA

PHYSICAL DATA

DESCRIPTION: FLAKES WITH A PHENOLIC ODOR.
BOILING POINT: 536 F (280 C) DECOMPOSES ***MELTING POINT:*** NOT AVAILABLE
SPECIFIC GRAVITY: NOT AVAILABLE ***PH:*** 11-13 @ SATD SOLN
SOLUBILITY IN WATER: VERY SOLUBLE
SOLVENT SOLUBILITY: ACETONE, DENATURED ALCOHOL, ETHYLENE GLYCOL

FIRE AND EXPLOSION DATA

FIRE AND EXPLOSION HAZARD: NEGLIGIBLE FIRE HAZARD WHEN EXPOSED TO HEAT OR FLAME.

FIREFIGHTING MEDIA: DRY CHEMICAL, CARBON DIOXIDE, HALON, WATER SPRAY OR STANDARD FOAM (1987 EMERGENCY RESPONSE GUIDEBOOK, DOT P 5800.4).
FOR LARGER FIRES, USE WATER SPRAY, FOG OR STANDARD FOAM (1987 EMERGENCY RESPONSE GUIDEBOOK, DOT P 5800.4).
FIREFIGHTING: MOVE CONTAINERS FROM FIRE AREA IF POSSIBLE. COOL CONTAINERS EXPOSED TO FLAMES WITH WATER FROM SIDE UNTIL WELL AFTER FIRE IS OUT. STAY AWAY FROM STORAGE TANK ENDS (1987 EMERGENCY RESPONSE GUIDEBOOK, DOT P 5800.4, GUIDE PAGE 60).
EXTINGUISH USING AGENT INDICATED; DO NOT USE WATER DIRECTLY ON MATERIAL. IF LARGE AMOUNTS OF COMBUSTIBLE MATERIALS ARE INVOLVED, USE WATER SPRAY OR FOG IN FLOODING AMOUNTS. AVOID BREATHING CORROSIVE DUSTS AND FUMES FROM BURNING MATERIAL, KEEP UPWIND.

TRANSPORTATION DATA

DEPARTMENT OF TRANSPORTATION HAZARD CLASSIFICATION 49 CFR 172.101: CORROSIVE MATERIAL
DEPARTMENT OF TRANSPORTATION LABELING REQUIREMENTS 49 CFR 172.101 AND SUBPART E: CORROSIVE
DEPARTMENT OF TRANSPORTATION PACKAGING REQUIREMENTS: 49 CFR 173.245B EXCEPTIONS: 49 CFR 173.244

TOXICITY

2,4,5-SODIUM TRICHLOROPHENATE: TOXICITY DATA: 2000-4000 MG/KG SKIN-RABBIT LD50 (DOW CHEMICAL CO. MSDS); 1620 MG/KG ORAL-RAT LD50. CARCINOGEN STATUS: HUMAN LIMITED EVIDENCE (IARC GROUP-2B FOR CHLOROPHENOLS). A SIGNIFICANT ASSOCIATION BETWEEN SOFT-TISSUE SARCOMA AND EXPOSURE TO CHLOROPHENOLS AND A SIGNIFICANT ASSOCIATION BETWEEN NASAL AND NASOPHARYNGEAL CANCERS AND EXPOSURE TO CHLOROPHENOLS HAVE BEEN REPORTED FROM CASE-CONTROL STUDIES. LOCAL EFFECTS: CORROSIVE- INHALATION, SKIN AND EYES. ACUTE TOXICITY LEVEL: MODERATELY TOXIC BY INGESTION; SLIGHTLY TOXIC BY DERMAL ABSORPTION. TARGET EFFECTS: NO DATA AVAILABLE.

HEALTH EFFECTS AND FIRST AID

INHALATION: 2,4,5-SODIUM TRICHLOROPHENATE: CORROSIVE. **ACUTE EXPOSURE-** INHALATION OF DUSTS MAY CAUSE IRRITATION TO THE NOSE AND THROAT. AQUEOUS SOLUTIONS ARE CORROSIVE AND MAY PRODUCE SEVERE IRRITATION TO THE RESPIRATORY TRACT. THE DUSTS HAVE A STRONG ODOR WARNING PROPERTY, POSSIBLY REDUCING POTENTIAL HAZARD. **CHRONIC EXPOSURE-** NO DATA AVAILABLE.

FIRST AID- REMOVE FROM EXPOSURE AREA TO FRESH AIR IMMEDIATELY. IF BREATHING HAS STOPPED, GIVE ARTIFICIAL RESPIRATION. MAINTAIN AIRWAY AND BLOOD PRESSURE AND ADMINISTER OXYGEN IF AVAILABLE. KEEP AFFECTED PERSON WARM AND AT REST. TREAT SYMPTOMATICALLY AND SUPPORTIVELY. ADMINISTRATION OF OXYGEN SHOULD BE PERFORMED BY QUALIFIED PERSONNEL. GET MEDICAL ATTENTION IMMEDIATELY.

SKIN CONTACT: 2,4,5-SODIUM TRICHLOROPHENATE: CORROSIVE. **ACUTE EXPOSURE**- CONTACT OF THE DUST WITH DRY SKIN MAY CAUSE IRRITATION. HOWEVER, CONTACT WITH MOIST SKIN OR AQUEOUS SOLUTIONS MAY CAUSE SEVERE IRRITATION WITH BURNS. ANIMAL STUDIES INDICATE MODERATE DOSES WERE ABSORBED THROUGH INTACT SKIN TO CAUSE DEATH. SYSTEMIC EFFECTS WERE REPORTED. **CHRONIC EXPOSURE**- DEPENDING ON CONCENTRATION AND DURATION OF EXPOSURE, SYMPTOMS MAY BE AS THOSE OF ACUTE EXPOSURE.

FIRST AID- REMOVE CONTAMINATED CLOTHING AND SHOES IMMEDIATELY. WASH AFFECTED AREA WITH SOAP OR MILD DETERGENT AND LARGE AMOUNTS OF WATER UNTIL NO EVIDENCE OF CHEMICAL REMAINS (AT LEAST 15-20 MINUTES). IN CASE OF CHEMICAL BURNS, COVER AREA WITH STERILE, DRY DRESSING. BANDAGE SECURELY, BUT NOT TOO TIGHTLY. GET MEDICAL ATTENTION IMMEDIATELY.

EYE CONTACT: 2,4,5-SODIUM TRICHLOROPHENATE: CORROSIVE. **ACUTE EXPOSURE**- CONTACT WITH THE EYE MAY CAUSE SEVERE IRRITATION AND CORNEAL INJURY, WHICH MAY BE SLOW IN HEALING, POSSIBLY CAUSING PERMANENT DAMAGE. **CHRONIC EXPOSURE**- DEPENDING ON CONCENTRATION AND DURATION OF EXPOSURE, EFFECTS MAY BE AS THOSE OF ACUTE EXPOSURE.

FIRST AID- WASH EYES IMMEDIATELY WITH LARGE AMOUNTS OF WATER, OCCASIONALLY LIFTING UPPER AND LOWER LIDS, UNTIL NO EVIDENCE OF CHEMICAL REMAINS (AT LEAST 15-20 MINUTES). CONTINUE IRRIGATING WITH NORMAL SALINE UNTIL THE PH HAS RETURNED TO NORMAL (30-60 MINUTES). COVER WITH STERILE BANDAGES. GET MEDICAL ATTENTION IMMEDIATELY.

INGESTION: 2,4,5-SODIUM TRICHLOROPHENATE: CORROSIVE. **ACUTE EXPOSURE**- INGESTION MAY CAUSE SEVERE IRRITATION OF THE GASTROINTESTINAL TRACT. A MODERATE DOSE WAS LETHAL TO RATS BUT SYSTEMIC EFFECTS WERE NOT REPORTED. **CHRONIC EXPOSURE**- NO DATA AVAILABLE.

FIRST AID: TREAT SYMPTOMATICALLY AND SUPPORTIVELY. IF PERSON IS CONSCIOUS AND ABLE TO SWALLOW, GIVE LARGE AMOUNTS OF WATER OR MILK TO DILUTE SUBSTANCE. GET MEDICAL ATTENTION IMMEDIATELY. GASTRIC LAVAGE PERFORMED BY QUALIFIED MEDICAL PERSONNEL MIGHT BE ADVISABLE IF THERE ARE NO SIGNS OF PERFORATION FROM THE INGESTION OF A CORROSIVE SUBSTANCE. IF VOMITING OCCURS, KEEP HEAD BELOW HIPS TO HELP PREVENT ASPIRATION.

ANTIDOTE: NO SPECIFIC ANTIDOTE. TREAT SYMPTOMATICALLY AND SUPPORTIVELY.

REACTIVITY

REACTIVITY: STABLE UNDER NORMAL TEMPERATURES AND PRESSURES.

INCOMPATIBILITIES: 2,4,5-SODIUM TRICHLOROPHENATE: OXIDIZERS: INCOMPATIBLE.

DECOMPOSITION: EXOTHERMIC DECOMPOSITION BEGINS BETWEEN 220 AND 245 C WITH THE FORMATION OF THE HIGHLY TOXIC 2,3,7,8-TETRACHLORODIBENZO-P-DIOXIN AND HYDROGEN CHLORIDE.

POLYMERIZATION: HAZARDOUS POLYMERIZATION HAS NOT BEEN REPORTED TO OCCUR UNDER NORMAL TEMPERATURES AND PRESSURES.

CONDITIONS TO AVOID

MAY BURN BUT DOES NOT IGNITE READILY.

SPILL AND LEAK PROCEDURES

OCCUPATIONAL SPILL: DO NOT TOUCH SPILLED MATERIAL. STOP LEAK IF YOU CAN DO IT WITHOUT RISK. FOR SMALL SPILLS, TAKE UP WITH SAND OR OTHER ABSORBENT MATERIAL AND PLACE INTO CONTAINERS FOR LATER DISPOSAL. FOR SMALL DRY SPILLS, WITH A CLEAN SHOVEL PLACE MATERIAL INTO CLEAN, DRY CONTAINER AND COVER. MOVE CONTAINERS FROM SPILL AREA. FOR LARGER SPILLS, DIKE FAR AHEAD OF SPILL FOR LATER DISPOSAL. KEEP UNNECESSARY PEOPLE AWAY. ISOLATE HAZARD AREA AND DENY ENTRY.

PROTECTIVE EQUIPMENT

VENTILATION: PROVIDE LOCAL EXHAUST OR GENERAL DILUTION VENTILATION SYSTEM.

RESPIRATOR: THE FOLLOWING RESPIRATORS ARE RECOMMENDED BASED ON INFORMATION FOUND IN THE PHYSICAL DATA, TOXICITY AND HEALTH EFFECTS SECTIONS. THEY ARE RANKED IN ORDER FROM MINIMUM TO MAXIMUM RESPIRATORY PROTECTION. THE SPECIFIC RESPIRATOR SELECTED MUST BE BASED ON CONTAMINATION LEVELS FOUND IN THE WORK PLACE, MUST NOT EXCEED THE WORKING LIMITS OF THE RESPIRATOR AND BE JOINTLY APPROVED BY THE NATIONAL INSTITUTE FOR OCCUPATIONAL SAFETY AND HEALTH AND THE MINE SAFETY AND HEALTH ADMINISTRATION (NIOSH-MSHA).

DUST AND MIST RESPIRATOR WITH A FULL FACEPIECE.

AIR-PURIFYING FULL FACEPIECE RESPIRATOR WITH A HIGH-EFFICIENCY PARTICULATE FILTER.

POWERED AIR-PURIFYING RESPIRATOR WITH A TIGHT-FITTING FACEPIECE AND HIGH-EFFICIENCY PARTICULATE FILTER. TYPE 'C' SUPPLIED-AIR RESPIRATOR WITH A FULL FACEPIECE OPERATED IN PRESSURE-DEMAND OR OTHER POSITIVE PRESSURE MODE OR WITH A FULL FACEPIECE, HELMET OR HOOD OPERATED IN CONTINUOUS-FLOW MODE.

SELF-CONTAINED BREATHING APPARATUS WITH A FULL FACEPIECE OPERATED IN PRESSURE-DEMAND OR OTHER POSITIVE PRESSURE MODE.

FOR FIREFIGHTING AND OTHER IMMEDIATELY DANGEROUS TO LIFE OR HEALTH CONDITIONS:

SELF-CONTAINED BREATHING APPARATUS WITH FULL FACEPIECE OPERATED IN PRESSURE-DEMAND OR OTHER POSITIVE PRESSURE MODE.

SUPPLIED-AIR RESPIRATOR WITH FULL FACEPIECE AND OPERATED IN PRESSURE-DEMAND OR OTHER POSITIVE PRESSURE MODE IN COMBINATION WITH AN AUXILIARY SELF-CONTAINED BREATHING APPARATUS OPERATED IN PRESSURE-DEMAND OR OTHER POSITIVE PRESSURE MODE.

CLOTHING: EMPLOYEE MUST WEAR APPROPRIATE PROTECTIVE (IMPERVIOUS) CLOTHING AND EQUIPMENT TO PREVENT ANY POSSIBILITY OF SKIN CONTACT WITH THIS SUBSTANCE.

GLOVES: EMPLOYEE MUST WEAR APPROPRIATE PROTECTIVE GLOVES TO PREVENT CONTACT WITH THIS SUBSTANCE.

EYE PROTECTION: EMPLOYEE MUST WEAR SPLASH-PROOF OR DUST-RESISTANT SAFETY GOGGLES AND A FACESHIELD TO PREVENT CONTACT WITH THIS SUBSTANCE.

EMERGENCY WASH FACILITIES: WHERE THERE IS ANY POSSIBILITY THAT AN EMPLOYEE'S EYES AND/OR SKIN MAY BE EXPOSED TO THIS SUBSTANCE, THE EMPLOYER SHOULD PROVIDE AN EYE WASH FOUNTAIN AND QUICK DRENCH SHOWER WITHIN THE IMMEDIATE WORK AREA FOR EMERGENCY USE.

AUTHORIZED BY- OCCUPATIONAL HEALTH SERVICES, INC.
CREATION DATE: 10/05/89 ***REVISION DATE:*** 07/12/90

MATERIAL SAFETY DATA SHEET

OCCUPATIONAL HEALTH SERVICES, INC.
AGRICULTURE AND PESTICIDE DIVISION
450 SEVENTH AVENUE, SUITE 2407
NEW YORK, NEW YORK 10123
1-800-445-MSDS OR (212) 967-1100

EMERGENCY CONTACT:
JOHN S. BRANSFORD, JR. (615) 292-1180

SUBSTANCE IDENTIFICATION

CAS-NUMBER 7758-29-4

SUBSTANCE: **SODIUM TRIPOLYPHOSPHATE**

TRADE NAMES/SYNONYMS: TRIPHOSPHORIC ACID, PENTASODIUM SALT; PENTASODIUM TRIPHOSPHATE; PENTASODIUM TRIPOLYPHOSPHATE; SODIUM PHOSPHATE (NA5P3O10); SODIUM POLYPHOSPHATE (NA5P3O10); SODIUM TRIPHOSPHATE; SODIUM TRIPHOSPHATE (NA5P3O10); SODIUM POLYPHOSPHATE; SODIUM TRIPOLYPHOSPHATE (NA5P3O10); SODIUM PHOSPHATE; STPP; NA5O10P3; PST21730

CHEMICAL FAMILY: INORGANIC SALT

MOLECULAR FORMULA: NA5-P3-O10

MOLECULAR WEIGHT: 367.58

CERCLA RATINGS (SCALE 0-3): HEALTH=3 FIRE=0 REACTIVITY=0 PERSISTENCE=0

NFPA RATINGS (SCALE 0-4): HEALTH=U FIRE=0 REACTIVITY=0

COMPONENTS AND CONTAMINANTS

COMPONENT: SODIUM TRIPOLYPHOSPHATE ***PERCENT:*** 100.0
CAS# 7758-29-4

OTHER CONTAMINANTS: NONE

EXPOSURE LIMITS: NO OCCUPATIONAL EXPOSURE LIMITS ESTABLISHED BY OSHA, ACGIH, OR NIOSH.

SODIUM TRIPOLYPHOSPHATE: 5000 POUNDS CERCLA SECTION 103 REPORTABLE QUANTITY

PHYSICAL DATA

DESCRIPTION: ODORLESS, WHITE, SLIGHTLY HYGROSCOPIC GRANULES OR POWDER.

MELTING POINT: 1152 F (622 C) DECOMPOSES ***SPECIFIC GRAVITY:*** >1.5

PH: 9.7-9.8 @ 1% SOLN. *SOLUBILITY IN WATER:* 20% @ 25 C

FIRE AND EXPLOSION DATA

FIRE AND EXPLOSION HAZARD: NEGLIGIBLE FIRE HAZARD WHEN EXPOSED TO HEAT OR FLAME.

FIREFIGHTING MEDIA: EXTINGUISH USING AGENT SUITABLE FOR TYPE OF SURROUNDING FIRE.

FIREFIGHTING: NO ACUTE HAZARD. MOVE CONTAINER FROM FIRE AREA IF POSSIBLE. AVOID BREATHING VAPORS OR DUSTS; KEEP UPWIND.

TOXICITY

SODIUM TRIPOLYPHOSPHATE: TOXICITY DATA: >7940 MG/KG SKIN-RABBIT LD50 (MONSANTO MSDS); 4100 MG/KG ORAL-RAT LD50; 3210 MG/KG ORAL-MOUSE LD50; 2060 MG/KG SUBCUTANEOUS-RAT LD50; 900 MG/KG SUBCUTANEOUS-MOUSE LD50; 750 MG/KG SUBCUTANEOUS-GUINEA PIG LD50; 71 MG/KG INTRAVENOUS-MOUSE LD50; 525 MG/KG INTRAPERITONEAL-RAT LD50; 700 MG/KG INTRAPERITONEAL-MOUSE LD50. CARCINOGEN STATUS: NONE. ACUTE TOXICITY LEVEL: MODERATELY TOXIC BY INGESTION; SLIGHTLY TOXIC BY DERMAL ABSORPTION. TARGET EFFECTS: POISONING MAY AFFECT THE BLOOD CALCIUM LEVEL.

HEALTH EFFECTS AND FIRST AID

INHALATION: SODIUM TRIPOLYPHOSPHATE: **ACUTE EXPOSURE-** INHALATION OF DUST MAY CAUSE IRRITATION WITH SORE THROAT, COUGHING, AND SHORTNESS OF BREATH. **CHRONIC EXPOSURE-** NO DATA AVAILABLE.

FIRST AID- REMOVE FROM EXPOSURE AREA TO FRESH AIR IMMEDIATELY. IF BREATHING HAS STOPPED, PERFORM ARTIFICIAL RESPIRATION. KEEP PERSON WARM AND AT REST. TREAT SYMPTOMATICALLY AND SUPPORTIVELY. GET MEDICAL ATTENTION IMMEDIATELY.

SKIN CONTACT: SODIUM TRIPOLYPHOSPHATE: **ACUTE EXPOSURE-** CONTACT MAY CAUSE IRRITATION WITH REDNESS AND PAIN. **CHRONIC EXPOSURE-** NO DATA AVAILABLE.

FIRST AID- REMOVE CONTAMINATED CLOTHING AND SHOES IMMEDIATELY. WASH AFFECTED AREA WITH SOAP OR MILD DETERGENT AND LARGE AMOUNTS OF WATER UNTIL NO EVIDENCE OF CHEMICAL REMAINS (APPROXIMATELY 15-20 MINUTES). GET MEDICAL ATTENTION IMMEDIATELY.

EYE CONTACT: SODIUM TRIPOLYPHOSPHATE: **ACUTE EXPOSURE-** DIRECT CONTACT MAY CAUSE IRRITATION WITH REDNESS AND PAIN. **CHRONIC EXPOSURE-** NO DATA AVAILABLE.

FIRST AID- WASH EYES IMMEDIATELY WITH LARGE AMOUNTS OF WATER OR NORMAL SALINE, OCCASIONALLY LIFTING UPPER AND LOWER LIDS, UNTIL NO EVIDENCE OF CHEMICAL REMAINS (APPROXIMATELY 15-20 MINUTES). GET MEDICAL ATTENTION IMMEDIATELY.

INGESTION: SODIUM TRIPOLYPHOSPHATE: **ACUTE EXPOSURE-** MAY CAUSE SORE THROAT, ABDOMINAL PAIN, VOMITING, DIARRHEA, AND POSSIBLY GASTROINTESTINAL HEMORRHAGE. IF INGESTED IN DETERGENT FORM, SODIUM TRIPOLYPHOSPHATE MAY CAUSE A SHOCKLIKE STATE, FALL OF BLOOD PRESSURE, SLOW PULSE, CYANOSIS, AND COMA. THE IONIC SERUM CALCIUM LEVEL MAY BE REDUCED AND RESULT IN TETANY. HYDROLYSIS OF POLYMERIC PHOSPHATES CAN CAUSE ACIDOSIS. **CHRONIC EXPOSURE-** A 5% SODIUM TRIPOLYPHOSPHATE DIET FED TO RATS FOR 24 MONTHS CAUSED GROWTH RETARDATION, ELEVATED KIDNEY/BODY WEIGHT RATIOS, AND TUBULAR NEPHROPATHY.

FIRST AID- DILUTE THE ALKALI BY GIVING WATER OR MILK IMMEDIATELY AND ALLOW VOMITING TO OCCUR. AVOID GASTRIC LAVAGE OR EMETICS. ESOPHAGOSCOPY IS THE ONLY WAY TO EXCLUDE THE POSSIBLITY OF CORROSION IN THE UPPER GASTROINTESTINAL TRACT; IF CORROSION IS SUSPECTED, ESOPHAGOSCOPY SHOULD USUALLY BE PERFORMED WITHIN 24 HOURS (DREISBACH, HANDBOOK OF POISONING, 12TH ED.). MAINTAIN AIRWAY AND TREAT SHOCK. IF VOMITING OCCURS, KEEP HEAD BELOW HIPS TO HELP PREVENT ASPIRATION. GET MEDICAL ATTENTION IMMEDIATELY.

ANTIDOTE: THE FOLLOWING ANTIDOTE HAS BEEN RECOMMENDED. HOWEVER, THE DECISION AS TO WHETHER THE SEVERITY OF POISONING REQUIRES ADMINISTRATION OF ANY ANTIDOTE AND ACTUAL DOSE REQUIRED SHOULD BE MADE BY QUALIFIED MEDICAL PERSONNEL.
PHOSPHATES: FOR HYPOCALCEMIA, AFTER PHOSPHATE INGESTION, GIVE CALCIUM GLUCONATE, 5 ML OF 10% SOLUTION SLOWLY INTRAVENOUSLY, TO RESTORE IONIC CALCIUM TO NORMAL LEVEL (DREISBACH, HANDBOOK OF POISONING, 12TH ED.). ANTIDOTE SHOULD BE ADMINISTERED BY QUALIFIED MEDICAL PERSONNEL.

REACTIVITY

REACTIVITY: STABLE UNDER NORMAL TEMPERATURES AND PRESSURES.

INCOMPATIBILITIES: SODIUM TRIPOLYPHOSPHATE: NO DATA AVAILABLE.

DECOMPOSITION: THERMAL DECOMPOSITION PRODUCTS MAY INCLUDE TOXIC AND HAZARDOUS SODIUM OXIDE AND OXIDES OF PHOSPHORUS.

POLYMERIZATION: HAZARDOUS POLYMERIZATION HAS NOT BEEN REPORTED TO OCCUR UNDER NORMAL TEMPERATURES AND PRESSURES.

STORAGE AND DISPOSAL

OBSERVE ALL FEDERAL, STATE AND LOCAL REGULATIONS WHEN STORING OR DISPOSING OF THIS SUBSTANCE. FOR ASSISTANCE, CONTACT THE DISTRICT DIRECTOR OF THE ENVIRONMENTAL PROTECTION AGENCY.

STORAGE

STORE IN TIGHTLY CLOSED CONTAINERS; PREVENT EXPOSURE TO MOISTURE.

CONDITIONS TO AVOID

PREVENT DISPERSION OF DUST IN AIR.

SPILL AND LEAK PROCEDURES

OCCUPATIONAL SPILL: FOR LARGE SPILLS, SWEEP UP WITH A MINIMUM OF DUSTING AND PLACE INTO SUITABLE CLEAN, DRY CONTAINERS FOR RECLAMATION OR LATER DISPOSAL.
RESIDUE SHOULD BE CLEANED UP USING A HIGH-EFFICIENCY PARTICULATE FILTER VACUUM.
REPORTABLE QUANTITY (RQ): 5000 POUNDS THE SUPERFUND AMENDMENTS AND REAUTHORIZATION ACT (SARA) SECTION 304 REQUIRES THAT A RELEASE EQUAL TO OR GREATER THAN THE REPORTABLE QUANTITY FOR THIS SUBSTANCE BE IMMEDIATELY REPORTED TO THE LOCAL EMERGENCY PLANNING COMMITTEE AND THE STATE EMERGENCY RESPONSE COMMISSION (40 CFR 355.40). IF THE RELEASE OF THIS SUBSTANCE IS REPORTABLE UNDER CERCLA SECTION 103, THE NATIONAL RESPONSE CENTER MUST BE NOTIFIED IMMEDIATELY AT (800) 424-8802 OR (202) 426-2675 IN THE METROPOLITAN WASHINGTON, D.C. AREA (40 CFR 302.6).

PROTECTIVE EQUIPMENT

VENTILATION: PROVIDE LOCAL EXHAUST VENTILATION SYSTEM.

RESPIRATOR: THE FOLLOWING RESPIRATORS ARE RECOMMENDED BASED ON INFORMATION FOUND IN THE PHYSICAL DATA, TOXICITY AND HEALTH EFFECTS SECTIONS. THEY ARE RANKED IN ORDER FROM MINIMUM TO MAXIMUM RESPIRATORY PROTECTION. THE SPECIFIC RESPIRATOR SELECTED MUST BE BASED ON CONTAMINATION LEVELS FOUND IN THE WORK PLACE, MUST NOT EXCEED THE WORKING LIMITS OF THE RESPIRATOR AND BE JOINTLY APPROVED BY THE NATIONAL INSTITUTE FOR OCCUPATIONAL SAFETY AND HEALTH AND THE MINE SAFETY AND HEALTH ADMINISTRATION (NIOSH-MSHA).
DUST AND MIST RESPIRATOR WITH A FULL FACEPIECE.
AIR-PURIFYING FULL FACEPIECE RESPIRATOR WITH A HIGH-EFFICIENCY PARTICULATE FILTER.
POWERED AIR-PURIFYING RESPIRATOR WITH A TIGHT-FITTING FACEPIECE AND HIGH-EFFICIENCY PARTICULATE FILTER.
TYPE 'C' SUPPLIED-AIR RESPIRATOR WITH A FULL FACEPIECE OPERATED IN PRESSURE-DEMAND OR OTHER POSITIVE PRESSURE MODE OR WITH A FULL FACEPIECE, HELMET OR HOOD OPERATED IN CONTINUOUS-FLOW MODE.
SELF-CONTAINED BREATHING APPARATUS WITH A FULL FACEPIECE OPERATED IN PRESSURE-DEMAND OR OTHER POSITIVE PRESSURE MODE. FOR FIREFIGHTING AND OTHER IMMEDIATELY DANGEROUS TO LIFE OR HEALTH CONDITIONS:
SELF-CONTAINED BREATHING APPARATUS WITH FULL FACEPIECE OPERATED IN PRESSURE-DEMAND OR OTHER POSITIVE PRESSURE MODE.
SUPPLIED-AIR RESPIRATOR WITH FULL FACEPIECE AND OPERATED IN PRESSURE-DEMAND OR OTHER POSITIVE PRESSURE MODE IN COMBINATION WITH AN AUXILIARY SELF-CONTAINED BREATHING APPARATUS OPERATED IN PRESSURE-DEMAND OR OTHER POSITIVE PRESSURE MODE.

CLOTHING: EMPLOYEE MUST WEAR APPROPRIATE PROTECTIVE (IMPERVIOUS) CLOTHING AND EQUIPMENT TO PREVENT REPEATED OR PROLONGED SKIN CONTACT WITH THIS SUBSTANCE.

GLOVES: EMPLOYEE MUST WEAR APPROPRIATE PROTECTIVE GLOVES TO PREVENT CONTACT WITH THIS SUBSTANCE.

EYE PROTECTION: EMPLOYEE MUST WEAR SPLASH-PROOF OR DUST-RESISTANT SAFETY GOGGLES TO PREVENT EYE CONTACT WITH THIS SUBSTANCE.
EMERGENCY EYE WASH: WHERE THERE IS ANY POSSIBILITY THAT AN EMPLOYEE'S EYES MAY BE EXPOSED TO THIS SUBSTANCE, THE EMPLOYER SHOULD PROVIDE AN EYE WASH FOUNTAIN WITHIN THE IMMEDIATE WORK AREA FOR EMERGENCY USE.

AUTHORIZED BY- OCCUPATIONAL HEALTH SERVICES, INC.
CREATION DATE: 11/16/89 *REVISION DATE:* 05/16/90

MATERIAL SAFETY DATA SHEET

OCCUPATIONAL HEALTH SERVICES, INC.
AGRICULTURE AND PESTICIDE DIVISION
450 SEVENTH AVENUE, SUITE 2407
NEW YORK, NEW YORK 10123
1-800-445-MSDS OR (212) 967-1100

EMERGENCY CONTACT:
JOHN S. BRANSFORD, JR. (615) 292-1180

SUBSTANCE IDENTIFICATION

CAS-NUMBER 8001-22-7

***SUBSTANCE:* SOYBEAN OIL**

TRADE NAMES/SYNONYMS: DEGUMMED SOYBEAN OIL; SOYA BEAN OIL; CHINESE BEAN OIL; SOY OIL; SOY BEAN OIL; PST21765

CHEMICAL FAMILY: VEGETABLE OIL

CERCLA RATINGS (SCALE 0-3): HEALTH=1 FIRE=1 REACTIVITY=0 PERSISTENCE=0

NFPA RATINGS (SCALE 0-4): HEALTH=0 FIRE=1 REACTIVITY=0

COMPONENTS AND CONTAMINANTS

COMPONENT: SOYBEAN OIL ***PERCENT:*** 100.0
CAS# 8001-22-7

OTHER CONTAMINANTS: NONE

EXPOSURE LIMITS: NO OCCUPATIONAL EXPOSURE LIMITS ESTABLISHED BY OSHA, ACGIH, OR NIOSH.

PHYSICAL DATA

DESCRIPTION: PALE YELLOW TO BROWNISH-YELLOW OIL WITH A SLIGHT CHARACTERISTIC ODOR AND TASTE.

MELTING POINT: 3-14 F (-16 - -10 C)

SPECIFIC GRAVITY: 0.916-0.922 ***VISCOSITY:*** 50.09 CPS @ 25 C

VAPOR PRESSURE: NOT AVAILABLE ***SOLUBILITY IN WATER:*** INSOLUBLE

SOLVENT SOLUBILITY: SOLUBLE IN ALCOHOL, ETHER, CHLOROFORM, CARBON DISULFIDE, AND PETROLEUM ETHER.

FIRE AND EXPLOSION DATA

FIRE AND EXPLOSION HAZARD: SLIGHT FIRE HAZARD WHEN EXPOSED TO HEAT OR FLAME.

FLASH POINT: 540 F (282 C) ***AUTOIGNITION TEMP.:*** 833 F (445 C)

FLAMMABILITY CLASS(OSHA): IIIB

FIREFIGHTING MEDIA: DRY CHEMICAL, CARBON DIOXIDE, HALON, WATER SPRAY OR STANDARD FOAM (1987 EMERGENCY RESPONSE GUIDEBOOK, DOT P 5800.4).
FOR LARGER FIRES, USE WATER SPRAY, FOG OR STANDARD FOAM (1987 EMERGENCY RESPONSE GUIDEBOOK, DOT P 5800.4).

FIREFIGHTING: MOVE CONTAINER FROM FIRE AREA IF POSSIBLE. DO NOT SCATTER SPILLED MATERIAL WITH HIGH PRESSURE WATER STREAMS. DIKE FIRE CONTROL WATER FOR LATER DISPOSAL (1987 EMERGENCY RESPONSE GUIDEBOOK, DOT P 5800.4, GUIDE PAGE 31).
USE AGENTS SUITABLE FOR TYPE OF SURROUNDING FIRE. AVOID BREATHING HAZARDOUS VAPORS, KEEP UPWIND.
WATER OR FOAM MAY CAUSE FROTHING (NFPA 325M, FIRE HAZARD PROPERTIES OF FLAMMABLE LIQUIDS, GASES, AND VOLATILE SOLIDS, 1984)

TOXICITY

SOYBEAN OIL: TOXICITY DATA: 16,500 MG/KG INTRAVENOUS-RAT LD50; 22,100 MG/KG INTRAVENOUS-MOUSE LD50. CARCINOGEN STATUS: NONE. ACUTE TOXICITY LEVEL: NO DATA AVAILABLE BY OCCUPATIONAL ROUTE OF EXPOSURE. TARGET EFFECTS: NO DATA AVAILABLE.

HEALTH EFFECTS AND FIRST AID

INHALATION: SOYBEAN OIL: **ACUTE EXPOSURE-** INHALATION MAY CAUSE AN ALLERGIC ASTHMATIC REACTION IN PREVIOUSLY EXPOSED INDIVIDUALS. **CHRONIC EXPOSURE-** REPEATED OR PROLONGED EXPOSURE MAY RESULT IN SENSITIZATION.

FIRST AID- REMOVE FROM EXPOSURE AREA TO FRESH AIR IMMEDIATELY. IF BREATHING HAS STOPPED, PERFORM ARTIFICIAL RESPIRATION. KEEP PERSON WARM AND AT REST. TREAT SYMPTOMATICALLY AND SUPPORTIVELY. GET MEDICAL ATTENTION IMMEDIATELY.

SKIN CONTACT: SOYBEAN OIL: **ACUTE EXPOSURE-** NO DATA AVAILABLE. **CHRONIC EXPOSURE-** NO DATA AVAILABLE.

FIRST AID- REMOVE CONTAMINATED CLOTHING AND SHOES IMMEDIATELY. WASH AFFECTED AREA WITH SOAP OR MILD DETERGENT AND LARGE AMOUNTS OF WATER UNTIL NO EVIDENCE OF CHEMICAL REMAINS (APPROXIMATELY 15-20 MINUTES). GET MEDICAL ATTENTION IMMEDIATELY.

EYE CONTACT: SOYBEAN OIL: **ACUTE EXPOSURE-** NO DATA AVAILABLE. **CHRONIC EXPOSURE-** NO DATA AVAILABLE.

FIRST AID- WASH EYES IMMEDIATELY WITH LARGE AMOUNTS OF WATER OR NORMAL SALINE, OCCASIONALLY LIFTING UPPER AND LOWER LIDS, UNTIL NO EVIDENCE OF CHEMICAL REMAINS (APPROXIMATELY 15-20 MINUTES). GET MEDICAL ATTENTION IMMEDIATELY.

INGESTION: SOYBEAN OIL: **ACUTE EXPOSURE-** ASPIRATION OF VEGETABLE OILS MAY RESULT IN LIPOID PNEUMONIA. **CHRONIC EXPOSURE-** NO DATA AVAILABLE.

FIRST AID- TREAT SYMPTOMATICALLY AND SUPPORTIVELY. GET MEDICAL ATTENTION IMMEDIATELY. IF VOMITING OCCURS, KEEP HEAD LOWER THAN HIPS TO PREVENT ASPIRATION.

ANTIDOTE: NO SPECIFIC ANTIDOTE. TREAT SYMPTOMATICALLY AND SUPPORTIVELY.

REACTIVITY

REACTIVITY: STABLE UNDER NORMAL TEMPERATURES AND PRESSURES.

INCOMPATIBILITIES: SOYBEAN OIL: OXIDIZERS (STRONG): FIRE AND EXPLOSION HAZARD.

DECOMPOSITION: THERMAL DECOMPOSITION MAY RELEASE ACRID SMOKE AND IRRITATING FUMES.

POLYMERIZATION: HAZARDOUS POLYMERIZATION HAS NOT BEEN REPORTED TO OCCUR UNDER NORMAL TEMPERATURES AND PRESSURES.

STORAGE AND DISPOSAL

OBSERVE ALL FEDERAL, STATE AND LOCAL REGULATIONS WHEN STORING OR DISPOSING OF THIS SUBSTANCE. FOR ASSISTANCE, CONTACT THE DISTRICT DIRECTOR OF THE ENVIRONMENTAL PROTECTION AGENCY.

STORAGE

STORE AWAY FROM INCOMPATIBLE SUBSTANCES.
KEEP CONTAINER TIGHTLY CLOSED. PROTECT FROM EXPOSURE TO AIR OR LIGHT.

CONDITIONS TO AVOID

MAY BURN BUT DOES NOT IGNITE READILY. AVOID CONTACT WITH STRONG OXIDIZERS, EXCESSIVE HEAT, SPARKS, OR OPEN FLAME.

SPILL AND LEAK PROCEDURES

OCCUPATIONAL SPILL: STOP LEAK IF YOU CAN DO IT WITHOUT RISK. FOR SMALL SPILLS, TAKE UP WITH SAND OR OTHER ABSORBENT MATERIAL AND PLACE INTO CLEAN, DRY CONTAINERS FOR LATER DISPOSAL. KEEP UNNECESSARY PEOPLE AWAY. ISOLATE HAZARD AREA AND DENY ENTRY.

PROTECTIVE EQUIPMENT

VENTILATION: PROVIDE GENERAL DILUTION VENTILATION TO MEET PUBLISHED EXPOSURE LIMITS.

RESPIRATOR: THE FOLLOWING RESPIRATORS ARE RECOMMENDED BASED ON INFORMATION FOUND IN THE PHYSICAL DATA, TOXICITY AND HEALTH EFFECTS SECTIONS. THEY ARE RANKED IN ORDER FROM MINIMUM TO MAXIMUM RESPIRATORY PROTECTION. THE SPECIFIC RESPIRATOR SELECTED MUST BE BASED ON CONTAMINATION LEVELS FOUND IN THE WORK PLACE, MUST NOT EXCEED THE WORKING LIMITS OF THE RESPIRATOR AND BE JOINTLY APPROVED BY THE NATIONAL INSTITUTE FOR OCCUPATIONAL SAFETY AND HEALTH AND THE MINE SAFETY AND HEALTH ADMINISTRATION (NIOSH-MSHA).
CHEMICAL CARTRIDGE RESPIRATOR WITH AN ORGANIC VAPOR CARTRIDGE(S) WITH A FULL FACEPIECE.
GAS MASK WITH ORGANIC VAPOR CANISTER (CHIN-STYLE OR FRONT- OR BACK-MOUNTED CANISTER) WITH A FULL FACEPIECE.
TYPE 'C' SUPPLIED-AIR RESPIRATOR WITH A FULL FACEPIECE OPERATED IN PRESSURE-DEMAND OR OTHER POSITIVE PRESSURE MODE OR WITH A FULL FACEPIECE, HELMET OR HOOD OPERATED IN CONTINUOUS-FLOW MODE.
SELF-CONTAINED BREATHING APPARATUS WITH A FULL FACEPIECE OPERATED IN PRESSURE-DEMAND OR OTHER POSITIVE PRESSURE MODE.
FOR FIREFIGHTING AND OTHER IMMEDIATELY DANGEROUS TO LIFE OR HEALTH CONDITIONS:
SELF-CONTAINED BREATHING APPARATUS WITH FULL FACEPIECE OPERATED IN PRESSURE-DEMAND OR OTHER POSITIVE PRESSURE MODE.
SUPPLIED-AIR RESPIRATOR WITH FULL FACEPIECE AND OPERATED IN PRESSURE-DEMAND OR OTHER POSITIVE PRESSURE MODE IN COMBINATION WITH AN AUXILIARY SELF-CONTAINED BREATHING APPARATUS OPERATED IN PRESSURE-DEMAND OR OTHER POSITIVE PRESSURE MODE.

CLOTHING: EMPLOYEE MUST WEAR APPROPRIATE PROTECTIVE (IMPERVIOUS) CLOTHING AND EQUIPMENT TO PREVENT REPEATED OR PROLONGED SKIN CONTACT WITH THIS SUBSTANCE.

GLOVES: EMPLOYEE MUST WEAR APPROPRIATE PROTECTIVE GLOVES TO PREVENT CONTACT WITH THIS SUBSTANCE.

EYE PROTECTION: EMPLOYEE MUST WEAR SPLASH-PROOF OR DUST-RESISTANT SAFETY GOGGLES TO PREVENT EYE CONTACT WITH THIS SUBSTANCE.
EMERGENCY EYE WASH: WHERE THERE IS ANY POSSIBILITY THAT AN EMPLOYEE'S EYES MAY BE EXPOSED TO THIS SUBSTANCE, THE EMPLOYER SHOULD PROVIDE

AN EYE WASH FOUNTAIN WITHIN THE IMMEDIATE WORK AREA FOR EMERGENCY USE.

AUTHORIZED BY- OCCUPATIONAL HEALTH SERVICES, INC.
CREATION DATE: 02/08/90 ***REVISION DATE:*** 04/16/90

MATERIAL SAFETY DATA SHEET

OCCUPATIONAL HEALTH SERVICES, INC.
AGRICULTURE AND PESTICIDE DIVISION
450 SEVENTH AVENUE, SUITE 2407
NEW YORK, NEW YORK 10123
1-800-445-MSDS OR (212) 967-1100

EMERGENCY CONTACT:
JOHN S. BRANSFORD, JR. (615) 292-1180

SUBSTANCE IDENTIFICATION

CAS-NUMBER 57-92-1
SUBSTANCE: **STREPTOMYCIN**
TRADE NAMES/SYNONYMS: AGREPT; AGRIMYCIN; NEODIESTROPTOPAB; STREPTOMYCIN A; O-2-DEOXY-2-(METHYLAMINO)-ALPHA-L-GLUCOPYRANOSYL-(1-2)-O-5-DEOXY- 3-C-FORMYL-ALPHA-L-LYXOFURANOSYL-(1-4)-N,N'-BIS(AMINOIMINOMETHYL)- D-STREPTAMINE; CHEMFORM; GEROX; HOKKO-MYCIN; NSC 14083; STREPCEN; STREPTOMICINA; AGRIMYCIN 17; STREPTOMYCINE; STREPTOMYCINUM; PST21917
CHEMICAL FAMILY: ANTIBIOTIC
MOLECULAR FORMULA: C21-H39-N7-O12
MOLECULAR WEIGHT: 581.58
CERCLA RATINGS (SCALE 0-3): HEALTH=1 FIRE=U REACTIVITY=0 PERSISTENCE=2
NFPA RATINGS (SCALE 0-4): HEALTH=1 FIRE=U REACTIVITY=0

COMPONENTS AND CONTAMINANTS

COMPONENT: STREPTOMYCIN ***PERCENT:*** 100
CAS# 57-92-1
OTHER CONTAMINANTS: NONE
EXPOSURE LIMITS: NO OCCUPATIONAL EXPOSURE LIMITS ESTABLISHED BY OSHA, ACGIH, OR NIOSH.

PHYSICAL DATA

DESCRIPTION: VERY HYGROSCOPIC ODORLESS SOLID WITH A SLIGHTLY BITTER TASTE.
MELTING POINT: NOT AVAILABLE ***SPECIFIC GRAVITY:*** NOT AVAILABLE
SOLUBILITY IN WATER: NOT AVAILABLE

FIRE AND EXPLOSION DATA

FIRE AND EXPLOSION HAZARD: UNKNOWN FIRE AND EXPLOSION HAZARD.
FIREFIGHTING MEDIA: DRY CHEMICAL, CARBON DIOXIDE, WATER SPRAY OR FOAM FOR LARGER FIRES, USE WATER SPRAY, FOG OR ALCOHOL FOAM
FIREFIGHTING: MOVE CONTAINER FROM FIRE AREA IF POSSIBLE. DO NOT SCATTER SPILLED MATERIAL WITH MORE WATER THAN NEEDED FOR FIRE CONTROL. DIKE FIRE CONTROL WATER FOR LATER DISPOSAL
USE AGENTS SUITABLE FOR TYPE OF SURROUNDING FIRE. AVOID BREATHING HAZARDOUS VAPORS, KEEP UPWIND.

TOXICITY

STREPTOMYCIN: 400 MG/KG/28 DAYS-INTERMITTENT ORAL-HUMAN TDLO; 9 GM/KG ORAL-RAT LD50; 143 MG/KG INTRAPERITONEAL-HUMAN TDLO; 28 MG/KG/DAY PARENTERAL-HUMAN TDLO; 600 MG/KG SUBCUTANEOUS-RAT LDLO; 175 MG/KG INTRAVENOUS-RAT LDLO; 9000 MG/KG ORAL-MOUSE LD50; 1250 MG/KG INTRAPERITONEAL-MOUSE LD50; 520 MG/KG SUBCUTANEOUS-MOUSE LD50; 90,200 UG/KG INTRAVENOUS-MOUSE LD50; 300 MG/KG SUBCUTANEOUS-DOG LDLO; 400 MG/KG SUBCUTANEOUS-MONKEY LDLO; 2000 MG/KG ORAL-CAT LDLO; 600 MG/KG SUBCUTANEOUS-CAT LDLO; 150 MG/KG INTRAVENOUS-CAT LDLO; 600 MG/KG SUBCUTANEOUS-RABBIT LDLO; 225 MG/KG INTRAVENOUS-RABBIT LDLO; 600 MG/KG SUBCUTANEOUS-GUINEA PIG LDLO; MUTAGENIC DATA (RTEC); REPRODUCTIVE EFFECTS DATA (RTEC); CARCINOGEN STATUS: NONE. STREPTOMYCIN IS A SKIN AND PULMONARY SENSITIZER. PARENTERALLY, STREPTOMYCIN MAY AFFECT THE BLOOD, KIDNEYS AND NERVOUS SYSTEM, ESPECIALLY THE VESTIBULAR BRANCH OF THE AUDITORY NERVE. RECOVERY IS GENERALLY COMPLETE FOLLOWING DISCONTINUANCE OF THE DRUG; HOWEVER, LONG TERM THERAPY HAS RESULTED IN LOSS OF HEARING. STREPTOMYCIN IS REPORTED TO HAVE INDUCED APLASTIC ANEMIA, PANCYTOPENIA AND HEMOLYSIS OF RED BLOOD CELLS IN SENSITIZED AND NONSENSITIZED INDIVIDUALS. PERSONS OF ADVANCED AGE OR THOSE WITH IMPAIRED KIDNEY FUNCTION OR PRERENAL AZOTEMIA MAY BE AT INCREASED RISK FROM EXPOSURE. STREPTOMYCIN READILY CROSSES THE PLACENTAL BARRIER; THEREFORE, UNBORN CHILDREN MAY BE AT RISK. STREPTOMYCIN IS AN AMINOGLYCOSIDE. AMINOGLYCOSIDES ARE USED TO TREAT INFECTIONS CAUSED BY GRAM-NEGATIVE BACTERIA. THEY ACT TO INTERFERE WITH PROTEIN SYNTHESIS IN SUSCEPTIBLE MICROORGANISMS. INTERACTIONS WITH MEDICATIONS HAVE BEEN REPORTED.

HEALTH EFFECTS AND FIRST AID

INHALATION: STREPTOMYCIN: SENSITIZER. **ACUTE EXPOSURE-** DUSTS MAY CAUSE IRRITATION OF THE MUCOUS MEMBRANES. ALLERGIC REACTIONS MAY OCCUR IN PREVIOUSLY SENSITIZED INDIVIDUALS. ABSORPTION THROUGH THE LUNGS MAY OCCUR. PALLOR, CYANOSIS, WHEEZING, COLLAPSE, FROTHY SPUTUM, PULMONARY EDEMA, AND DEATH IN RESPIRATORY FAILURE MAY OCCUR WITHIN SECONDS TO MINUTES AFTER THE APPLICATION OF STREPTOMYCIN TO THE MUCOUS MEMBRANES. DELAYED REACTIONS MAY CONSIST OF FEVER, SKIN ERUPTIONS AND PHARYNGEAL OR LARYNGEAL EDEMA. **CHRONIC EXPOSURE-** REPEATED OR PROLONGED EXPOSURE MAY RESULT IN SENSITIZATION.
FIRST AID- REMOVE FROM EXPOSURE AREA TO FRESH AIR IMMEDIATELY. IF BREATHING HAS STOPPED, PERFORM ARTIFICIAL RESPIRATION. KEEP PERSON WARM AND AT REST. TREAT SYMPTOMATICALLY AND SUPPORTIVELY. GET MEDICAL ATTENTION IMMEDIATELY.

SKIN CONTACT: STREPTOMYCIN: SENSITIZER. **ACUTE EXPOSURE-** EXCESSIVE AMOUNTS OF DUST MAY BE IRRITATING AND MAY CAUSE CONTACT DERMATITIS, SKIN RASH, URTICARIA, AND EXFOLIATIVE DERMATITIS IN SENSITIZED INDIVIDUALS HANDLING STREPTOMYCIN WITHOUT GLOVES. ANAPHYLAXIS HAS OCCURRED AFTER ADMINISTRATION OF TOPICAL STREPTOMYCIN. A NURSE DEVELOPED CONTACT URTICARIA WHEN SEVERAL DROPS OF STREPTOMYCIN WERE PLACED ON HER FOREARM. AFTER 2 MINUTES HAD ELAPSED, A LARGE WHEAL APPEARED AND A FEW MINUTES LATER, RHINITIS AND LACRIMATION DEVELOPED. INTOXICATION MAY OCCUR WHEN AMINOGLYCOSIDES ARE APPLIED TOPICALLY TO LARGE WOUNDS, BURNS, OR CUTANEOUS ULCERS, PARTICULARLY IF THERE IS RENAL INSUFFICIENCY. **CHRONIC EXPOSURE-** TOPICALLY, STREPTOMYCIN HAS CAUSED A HIGH INCIDENCE OF SENSITIZATION. PROLONGED CONTACT MAY PRODUCE DEEP FISSURES AND HYPERKERATOSIS WITH SUPERIMPOSED ECZEMATIZATION IN SENSITIZED INDIVIDUALS.
FIRST AID- REMOVE CONTAMINATED CLOTHING AND SHOES IMMEDIATELY. WASH AFFECTED AREA WITH SOAP OR MILD DETERGENT AND LARGE AMOUNTS OF WATER UNTIL NO EVIDENCE OF CHEMICAL REMAINS (APPROXIMATELY 15-20 MINUTES). GET MEDICAL ATTENTION IMMEDIATELY.

EYE CONTACT: STRETOMYCIN: **ACUTE EXPOSURE-** DUSTS MAY BE IRRITATING. STREPTOMYCIN MAY CAUSE CONTACT DERMATITIS OF THE EYELID. THIS PRESUMABLY IS CAUSED FROM RUBBING THE EYES WITH CONTAMINATED FINGERS. **CHRONIC EXPOSURE-** GREEN COLOR BLINDNESS MAY OCCUR AS A SYSTEMIC EFFECT DUE TO PARENTERAL ADMINISTRATION.
FIRST AID- WASH EYES IMMEDIATELY WITH LARGE AMOUNTS OF WATER OR NORMAL SALINE, OCCASIONALLY LIFTING UPPER AND LOWER LIDS, UNTIL NO EVIDENCE OF CHEMICAL REMAINS (APPROXIMATELY 15-20 MINUTES). GET MEDICAL ATTENTION IMMEDIATELY.

INGESTION: STREPTOMYCIN: **ACUTE EXPOSURE-** STREPTOMYCIN MAY BE ADMINISTERED ORALLY. HOWEVER THIS ROUTE IS INEFFECTIVE AGAINST SYSTEMIC INFECTIONS. THE AMINOGLYCOSIDES ARE HIGHLY POLAR CATIONS; THEY ARE THUS VERY POORLY ABSORBED FROM THE INTESTINAL TRACT. LESS THAN 1% OF A DOSE IS ABSORBED FOLLOWING ORAL ADMINISTRATION. AMINOGLYCOSIDES ARE NOT INACTIVATED IN THE INTESTINE, AND ARE ELIMINATED QUANTITATIVELY IN THE FECES. ORAL ADMINISTRATION OF STREPTOMYCIN CAN CAUSE ANAPHYLACTOID REACTIONS CHARACTERIZED BY NAUSEA AND VOMITING, ABDOMINAL PAIN AND CRAMPING, LOCALIZED EDEMA, CYANOSIS, RESPIRATORY DISTRESS, CONVULSIONS, SEVERE CHEST PAIN AND DEATH IN RESPIRATORY FAILURE. **CHRONIC EXPOSURE-** REPEATED ORAL ADMINISTRATION MAY RESULT IN HYPOVITAMINOSIS AND STREPTOMYCIN ACCUMULATION TO TOXIC CONCENTRATIONS IN PATIENTS WITH RENAL IMPAIRMENT. THE MOST COMMON UNTOWARD REACTION TO THE ADMINISTRATION OF ANTIBIOTICS IS THE OVERGROWTH OF ORGANISMS NOT AFFECTED BY THE ANTIBIOTIC AGENT. IN SOME CASES THESE ORGANISMS PRODUCE TOXINS THAT CAN CAUSE VOMITING, DIARRHEA AND CARDIOVASCULAR COLLAPSE.
FIRST AID- IF ANAPHYLAXIS OCCURS, THE ANTIDOTE SHOULD BE ADMINISTERED BY QUALIFIED MEDICAL PERSONNEL. IF STREPTOMYCIN IS BEING GIVEN FOR THERAPEUTIC PURPOSES, DISCONTINUE USE OF THE DRUG. GET MEDICAL ATTENTION IMMEDIATELY. (DREISBACH HANDBOOK OF POISONING, 11TH ED.)

ANTIDOTE: NO SPECIFIC ANTIDOTE. TREAT SYMPTOMATICALLY AND SUPPORTIVELY.

REACTIVITY

REACTIVITY: STABLE UNDER NORMAL TEMPERATURES AND PRESSURES.
INCOMPATIBILITIES: STREPTOMYCIN: NO DATA AVAILABLE.
DECOMPOSITION: THERMAL DECOMPOSITION PRODUCTS MAY INCLUDE TOXIC OXIDES OF NITROGEN.
POLYMERIZATION: HAZARDOUS POLYMERIZATION HAS NOT BEEN REPORTED TO OCCUR UNDER NORMAL TEMPERATURES AND PRESSURES.

CONDITIONS TO AVOID

NONE REPORTED.

SPILL AND LEAK PROCEDURES

OCCUPATIONAL SPILL: SWEEP UP AND PLACE IN SUITABLE CLEAN, DRY CONTAINERS FOR RECLAMATION OR LATER DISPOSAL. DO NOT FLUSH SPILLED MATERIAL INTO SEWER. KEEP UNNECESSARY PEOPLE AWAY.

PROTECTIVE EQUIPMENT

VENTILATION: PROVIDE LOCAL EXHAUST OR GENERAL DILUTION VENTILATION SYSTEM.
RESPIRATOR: THE FOLLOWING RESPIRATORS ARE RECOMMENDED BASED ON INFORMATION FOUND IN THE PHYSICAL DATA, TOXICITY AND HEALTH EFFECTS SECTIONS. THEY ARE RANKED IN ORDER FROM MINIMUM TO MAXIMUM RESPIRATORY PROTECTION. THE SPECIFIC RESPIRATOR SELECTED MUST BE BASED ON CONTAMINATION LEVELS FOUND IN THE WORK PLACE, MUST NOT EXCEED THE WORKING LIMITS OF THE RESPIRATOR AND BE JOINTLY APPROVED BY THE NATIONAL INSTITUTE FOR OCCUPATIONAL SAFETY AND HEALTH AND THE MINE SAFETY AND HEALTH ADMINISTRATION (NIOSH-MSHA).
TYPE 'C' SUPPLIED-AIR RESPIRATOR WITH A FULL FACEPIECE OPERATED IN PRESSURE-DEMAND OR OTHER POSITIVE PRESSURE MODE OR WITH A FULL FACEPIECE, HELMET OR HOOD OPERATED IN CONTINOUS-FLOW MODE.
SELF-CONTAINED BREATHING APPARATUS WITH A FULL FACEPIECE OPERATED IN PRESSURE-DEMAND OR OTHER POSITIVE PRESSURE MODE.
FOR FIREFIGHTING AND OTHER IMMEDIATELY DANGEROUS TO LIFE OR HEALTH CONDITIONS:
SELF-CONTAINED BREATHING APPARATUS WITH FULL FACEPIECE OPERATED IN PRESSURE-DEMAND OR OTHER POSITIVE PRESSURE MODE.
SUPPLIED-AIR RESPIRATOR WITH FULL FACEPIECE AND OPERATED IN PRESSURE-DEMAND OR OTHER POSITIVE PRESSURE MODE IN COMBINATION WITH AN AUXILIARY SELF-CONTAINED BREATHING APPARATUS OPERATED IN PRESSURE-DEMAND OR OTHER POSITIVE PRESSURE MODE.
CLOTHING: EMPLOYEE MUST WEAR APPROPRIATE PROTECTIVE (IMPERVIOUS) CLOTHING AND EQUIPMENT TO PREVENT REPEATED OR PROLONGED SKIN CONTACT WITH THIS SUBSTANCE.
GLOVES: EMPLOYEE MUST WEAR APPROPRIATE PROTECTIVE GLOVES TO PREVENT CONTACT WITH THIS SUBSTANCE.
EYE PROTECTION: EMPLOYEE MUST WEAR SPLASH-PROOF OR DUST-RESISTANT SAFETY GOGGLES TO PREVENT EYE CONTACT WITH THIS SUBSTANCE.
EMERGENCY EYE WASH: WHERE THERE IS ANY POSSIBILITY THAT AN EMPLOYEE'S EYES MAY BE EXPOSED TO THIS SUBSTANCE, THE EMPLOYER SHOULD PROVIDE AN EYE WASH FOUNTAIN WITHIN THE IMMEDIATE WORK AREA FOR EMERGENCY USE.

AUTHORIZED BY- OCCUPATIONAL HEALTH SERVICES, INC.
CREATION DATE: 10/05/89 ***REVISION DATE:*** 05/31/90

MATERIAL SAFETY DATA SHEET

OCCUPATIONAL HEALTH SERVICES, INC.
AGRICULTURE AND PESTICIDE DIVISION
450 SEVENTH AVENUE, SUITE 2407
NEW YORK, NEW YORK 10123
1-800-445-MSDS OR (212) 967-1100

EMERGENCY CONTACT:
JOHN S. BRANSFORD, JR. (615) 292-1180

SUBSTANCE IDENTIFICATION

CAS-NUMBER 57-24-9
SUBSTANCE: **STRYCHNINE**
TRADE NAMES/SYNONYMS: STRYCHNIDIN-10-ONE; STRYCHNIN; (-)-STRYCHNINE; CERTOX; KWIK-KIL; MOUSE-RID; MOUSE TOX; RO-DEX; NUX VOMICA; RCRA P108; STCC 4921477; UN 1692; C21H22N2O2; PST22080
CHEMICAL FAMILY: HETEROCYCLIC NITROGEN ALKALOID
MOLECULAR FORMULA: C21-H22-N2-O2
MOLECULAR WEIGHT: 334.42
CERCLA RATINGS (SCALE 0-3): HEALTH=3 FIRE=1 REACTIVITY=0 PERSISTENCE=0
NFPA RATINGS (SCALE 0-4): HEALTH=3 FIRE=1 REACTIVITY=0

COMPONENTS AND CONTAMINANTS

COMPONENT: STRYCHNINE ***PERCENT:*** 100.0
CAS# 57-24-9
OTHER CONTAMINANTS: NONE
EXPOSURE LIMITS: STRYCHNINE: 0.15 MG/M3 OSHA TWA 0.15 MG/M3 ACGIH TWA 100/10,000 POUNDS SARA SECTION 302 THRESHOLD PLANNING QUANTITY 10 POUNDS SARA SECTION 304 REPORTABLE QUANTITY 10 POUNDS CERCLA SECTION 103 REPORTABLE QUANTITY

PHYSICAL DATA

DESCRIPTION: ODORLESS, WHITE ORTHORHOMBIC PRISMS WITH A VERY BITTER TASTE.
BOILING POINT: 518 F (270 C) @ 5 MMHG (DECOMPOSES)
MELTING POINT: 547-550 F (286-288 C) ***SPECIFIC GRAVITY:*** 1.36
VAPOR PRESSURE: APPROX 0 MMHG @ 20 C ***PH:*** ALKALINE IN SOLUTION
SOLUBILITY IN WATER: 0.0156%
SOLVENT SOLUBILITY: SOLUBLE IN CHLOROFORM; VERY SLIGHTLY SOLUBLE IN ALCOHOL, BENZENE, ETHER, TOLUENE, METHANOL, GLYCEROL, AMYL ALCOHOL, PETROLEUM ETHER.

FIRE AND EXPLOSION DATA

FIRE AND EXPLOSION HAZARD: SLIGHT FIRE HAZARD WHEN EXPOSED TO HEAT OR FLAME.
FIREFIGHTING MEDIA: DRY CHEMICAL, CARBON DIOXIDE, HALON, WATER SPRAY OR STANDARD FOAM (1987 EMERGENCY RESPONSE GUIDEBOOK, DOT P 5800.4).
FOR LARGER FIRES, USE WATER SPRAY, FOG OR STANDARD FOAM (1987 EMERGENCY RESPONSE GUIDEBOOK, DOT P 5800.4).
FIREFIGHTING: MOVE CONTAINERS FROM FIRE AREA IF POSSIBLE (1987 EMERGENCY RESPONSE GUIDEBOOK, DOT P 5800.4, GUIDE PAGE 53).
USE AGENTS SUITABLE FOR TYPE OF FIRE. USE WATER IN FLOODING AMOUNTS AS FOG AVOID BREATHING POISONOUS VAPORS, KEEP UPWIND.

TRANSPORTATION DATA

DEPARTMENT OF TRANSPORTATION HAZARD CLASSIFICATION 49 CFR 172.101: POISON B
DEPARTMENT OF TRANSPORTATION LABELING REQUIREMENTS 49 CFR 172.101 AND SUBPART E: POISON
DEPARTMENT OF TRANSPORTATION PACKAGING REQUIREMENTS: 49 CFR 173.365 EXCEPTIONS: 49 CFR 173.364

TOXICITY

STRYCHNINE: TOXICITY DATA: 30 MG/KG ORAL-MAN LDLO; 30 MG/KG ORAL-HUMAN LDLO; 2350 UG/KG ORAL-RAT LD50; 2 MG/KG ORAL-MOUSE LD50; 600 UG/KG ORAL-RABBIT LDLO; 500 UG/KG ORAL-DOG LD50; 500 UG/KG ORAL-CAT LD50; 1400 UG/KG INTRAMUSCULAR-RAT LD50; 628 UG/KG INTRAMUSCULAR-MOUSE LD50; 1100 UG/KG INTRAPERITONEAL-RAT LD50; 980 UG/KG INTRAPERITONEAL-MOUSE LD50; 582 UG/KG INTRAVENOUS-RAT LD50; 410 UG/KG INTRAVENOUS-MOUSE LD50; 330 UG/KG INTRAVENOUS-CAT LDLO; 800 UG/KG INTRAVENOUS-DOG LD50; 400 UG/KG INTRAVENOUS-RABBIT LD50; 1200 UG/KG SUBCUTANEOUS-RAT LD50; 474 UG/KG SUBCUTANEOUS-MOUSE LD50; 3200 UG/KG SUBCUTANEOUS-GUINEA PIG LDLO; 1103 UG/KG UNREPORTED-MAN LDLO; REPRODUCTIVE EFFECTS DATA (RTECS). CARCINOGEN STATUS: NONE. ACUTE TOXICITY LEVEL: HIGHLY TOXIC BY INGESTION. TARGET EFFECTS: CONVULSANT. AT INCREASED RISK FROM EXPOSURE: PERSONS WITH A HISTORY OF CONVULSANT DISORDERS. ADDITIONAL DATA: WORKING IN A COLD ENVIRONMENT MAY ENHANCE THE TOXIC EFFECTS.

HEALTH EFFECTS AND FIRST AID

INHALATION: STRYCHNINE: CONVULSANT. 3 MG/KG IMMEDIATELY DANGEROUS TO LIFE OR HEALTH. **ACUTE EXPOSURE-** INHALATION MAY CAUSE EFFECTS AS DETAILED IN ACUTE INGESTION. **CHRONIC EXPOSURE-** REPEATED OR PROLONGED EXPOSURE MAY CAUSE EFFECTS AS DETAILED IN CHRONIC INGESTION.
FIRST AID- REMOVE FROM EXPOSURE AREA TO FRESH AIR IMMEDIATELY. IF BREATHING HAS STOPPED, GIVE ARTIFICIAL RESPIRATION. MAINTAIN AIRWAY AND BLOOD PRESSURE AND ADMINISTER OXYGEN IF AVAILABLE. KEEP AFFECTED PERSON WARM AND AT REST. TREAT SYMPTOMATICALLY AND SUPPORTIVELY. ADMINISTRATION OF OXYGEN SHOULD BE PERFORMED BY QUALIFIED PERSONNEL. GET MEDICAL ATTENTION IMMEDIATELY.

SKIN CONTACT: STRYCHNINE: **ACUTE EXPOSURE-** SYSTEMIC ABSORPTION HAS NOT BEEN REPORTED. **CHRONIC EXPOSURE-** NO DATA AVAILABLE.

FIRST AID- REMOVE CONTAMINATED CLOTHING AND SHOES IMMEDIATELY. WASH AFFECTED AREA WITH SOAP OR MILD DETERGENT AND LARGE AMOUNTS OF WATER UNTIL NO EVIDENCE OF CHEMICAL REMAINS (APPROXIMATELY 15-20 MINUTES). GET MEDICAL ATTENTION IMMEDIATELY.

EYE CONTACT: STRYCHNINE: **ACUTE EXPOSURE-** APPLICATION OF 5 MG TO THE EYE HAS BEEN REPORTED TO RESULT IN TOXIC EFFECTS WITHIN 3-4 MINUTES. **CHRONIC EXPOSURE-** NO DATA AVAILABLE.

FIRST AID- WASH EYES IMMEDIATELY WITH LARGE AMOUNTS OF WATER OR NORMAL SALINE, OCCASIONALLY LIFTING UPPER AND LOWER LIDS, UNTIL NO EVIDENCE OF CHEMICAL REMAINS (APPROXIMATELY 15-20 MINUTES). GET MEDICAL ATTENTION IMMEDIATELY.

INGESTION: STRYCHNINE: CONVULSANT/HIGHLY TOXIC. **ACUTE EXPOSURE-** 10-60 MINUTES AFTER INGESTION NAUSEA, PRODROMAL RESTLESSNESS, APPREHENSION, FEELINGS OF DEPERSONLIZATION, MUSCLE TWITCHING AND HYPERREFLEXIA MAY DEVELOP. ENHANCED SENSATIONS INCLUDING HYPERACUITY OF HEARING, VISION, ECT. HAVE BEEN REPORTED. VOMITING IS UNLIKELY EXCEPT WITH DOSES >12 MG/KG. EXTENSOR MUSCLE SPASMS, CLONIC THEN TONIC CONVULSIONS LASTING BETWEEN 30 SECONDS AND 2 MINUTES WITH RIGIDITY OF THE MUSCLES, TRISMUS, RISUS SARCONICUS AND OPISTHOTONOS MAY OCCUR. DYSPNEA, CYANOSIS, BULGING EYES, MYDRIASIS, AND CONJUGATE OR DISSOCIATED DEVIATIONS OF THE EYE AND SENSORY DISORDERS INCLUDING GREEN-COLORED VISION MAY OCCUR DURING THE CONVULSION. IN THE ABSENCE OF ANOXIA, THE VICTIM MAY BE CONSCIOUS DURING THE PAINFUL CONVULSIONS AND MAY EXPERIENCE OVERWHELMING FEAR, A SENSATION OF BEING HURLED THROUGH SPACE OR A FEELING OF SUFFOCATION. COMPLETE MUSCLE RELAXATION AND NORMAL BREATHING OCCURS, GENERALLY LASTING 5-15 MINUTES, IN THE PERIOD BETWEEN EPISODES. THE PERSON MAY BE DEPRESSED OR ANXIOUS WITH A FEELING OF IMPENDING DOOM OR MAY SLEEP FROM EXHAUSTION. PROFUSE PERSPIRATION AND THIRST MAY BE PRESENT. MINOR SENSORY STIMULI MAY TRIGGER A VIOLENT MOTOR RESPONSE CAUSING THE CONVULSIONS TO RESUME. COMA MAY FOLLOW REPEATED CONVULSIONS. EFFECTS DUE TO THE SPASMS AND HYPOXEMIA MAY INCLUDE HYPERTHERMIA, PROFOUND LACTIC ACIDOSIS, MYOGLOBINURIA, RHABDOMYOLYSIS, HYPOTENSIVE SHOCK AND RENAL DAMAGE OR FAILURE. DEATH MAY OCCUR FROM ASPHYXIA DUE TO SPASM OF THE DIAPHRAGM AND MEDULLARY PARALYSIS DURING A SEIZURE, FROM EXHAUSTION FOLLOWING THE FINAL TETANUS, OR RARELY FOLLOWING SUDDEN COLLAPSE BEFORE CONVULSIONS DEVELOP. THE REPORTED MEDIAN LETHAL DOSE IN HUMANS RANGES FROM 15-120 MG. IN NON-FATAL POISONING, MOST REACTIONS SUBSIDE WITHIN 6 HOURS, BUT, FEVER, HYPERREFLEXIA, STIFFNESS AND MUSCLE SORENESS MAY PERSIST UP TO 7 DAYS. **CHRONIC EXPOSURE-** CONTINUED USE IN MEDICATION HAS LEAD TO PHOTOPHOBIA, MUSCULAR RIGIDITY, STIFFNESS IN THE JOINTS, MYALGIA, LASSITUDE AND HEADACHE.

FIRST AID- GIVE LARGE QUANITIES OF WATER IMMEDIATELY. AFTER WATER HAS BEEN SWALLOWED, TRY TO INDUCE VOMITING BY TOUCHING THE BACK OF THROAT WITH A FINGER. DO NOT MAKE AN UNCONSCIOUS PERSON VOMIT. GET MEDICAL ATTENTION IMMEDIATELY (OSHA GUIDELINES, SEPT. 1978). IF SYMPTOMS HAVE BEGUN, AVOID ANY MANIPULATION SUCH AS GASTRIC LAVAGE OR EMESIS. ENFORCE ABSOLUTE QUIET AND ABSENCE OF STIMULI. CONTROL CONVULSIONS BY ADMINISTRATION OF ANTIDOTES AFTER CONVULSIONS AND HYPERACTIVITY ARE CONTROLED; REMOVE STRYCHNINE BY GASTRIC LAVAGE USING ACTIVATED CHARCOAL (DRIESBACH, HANDBOOK OF POISONING, 11TH ED.). ACTIVATED CHARCOAL IS AN EFFECTIVE METHOD OF REDUCING ABSORPTION WHEN USED AS A SLURRY IN GASTRIC LAVAGE. IODINE TINCTURE DILUTED WITH WATER (1:250), TANNIC ACID SOLUTION (2.0%, OR IN THE FORM OF STRONG TEA), OR POTASSIUM PERMANGANATE (1:5000) MAY ALSO BE USED (GOODMAN AND GILMAN, THE PHARMACOLOGICAL BASIS OF THERAPEUTICS, 6TH ED.). GASTRIC LAVAGE AND ANTIDOTE SHOULD BE ADMINISTERED BY QUALIFIED MEDICAL PERSONNEL ONLY.

ANTIDOTE: NO SPECIFIC ANTIDOTE. TREAT SYMPTOMATICALLY AND SUPPORTIVELY.

REACTIVITY

REACTIVITY: STABLE UNDER NORMAL TEMPERATURES AND PRESSURES.

INCOMPATIBILITIES: STRYCHNINE: OXIDIZERS (STRONG): FIRE AND EXPLOSION HAZARD.

DECOMPOSITION: THERMAL DECOMPOSITION PRODUCTS MAY INCLUDE TOXIC OXIDES OF CARBON AND NITROGEN.

POLYMERIZATION: HAZARDOUS POLYMERIZATION HAS NOT BEEN REPORTED TO OCCUR UNDER NORMAL TEMPERATURES AND PRESSURES.

STORAGE AND DISPOSAL

OBSERVE ALL FEDERAL, STATE AND LOCAL REGULATIONS WHEN STORING OR DISPOSING OF THIS SUBSTANCE. FOR ASSISTANCE, CONTACT THE DISTRICT DIRECTOR OF THE ENVIRONMENTAL PROTECTION AGENCY.

****STORAGE****

STORE AWAY FROM INCOMPATIBLE SUBSTANCES.

THRESHOLD PLANNING QUANTITY (TPQ): THE SUPERFUND AMENDMENTS AND REAUTHORIZATION ACT (SARA) SECTION 302 REQUIRES THAT EACH FACILITY WHERE ANY EXTREMELY HAZARDOUS SUBSTANCE IS PRESENT IN A QUANTITY EQUAL TO OR GREATER THAN THE TPQ ESTABLISHED FOR THAT SUBSTANCE NOTIFY THE STATE EMERGENCY RESPONSE COMMISSION FOR THE STATE IN WHICH IT IS LOCATED. SECTION 303 OF SARA REQUIRES THESE FACILITIES TO PARTICIPATE IN LOCAL EMERGENCY RESPONSE PLANNING (40 CFR 355.30).

CONDITIONS TO AVOID

MAY BURN BUT DOES NOT IGNITE READILY.

SPILL AND LEAK PROCEDURES

OCCUPATIONAL SPILL: DO NOT TOUCH SPILLED MATERIAL. STOP LEAK IF YOU CAN DO IT WITHOUT RISK. FOR SMALL SPILLS, TAKE UP WITH SAND OR OTHER ABSORBENT MATERIAL AND PLACE INTO CONTAINERS FOR LATER DISPOSAL. FOR SMALL DRY SPILLS, WITH A CLEAN SHOVEL PLACE MATERIAL INTO CLEAN, DRY CONTAINER AND COVER. MOVE CONTAINERS FROM SPILL AREA. FOR LARGER SPILLS, DIKE FAR AHEAD OF SPILL FOR LATER DISPOSAL. KEEP UNNECESSARY PEOPLE AWAY. ISOLATE HAZARD AREA AND DENY ENTRY.

REPORTABLE QUANTITY (RQ): 10 POUNDS THE SUPERFUND AMENDMENTS AND REAUTHORIZATION ACT (SARA) SECTION 304 REQUIRES THAT A RELEASE EQUAL TO OR GREATER THAN THE REPORTABLE QUANTITY FOR THIS SUBSTANCE BE IMMEDIATELY REPORTED TO THE LOCAL EMERGENCY PLANNING COMMITTEE AND THE STATE EMERGENCY RESPONSE COMMISSION (40 CFR 355.40). IF THE RELEASE OF THIS SUBSTANCE IS REPORTABLE UNDER CERCLA SECTION 103, THE NATIONAL RESPONSE CENTER MUST BE NOTIFIED IMMEDIATELY AT (800) 424-8802 OR (202) 426-2675 IN THE METROPOLITAN WASHINGTON, D.C. AREA (40 CFR 302.6).

PROTECTIVE EQUIPMENT

VENTILATION: PROVIDE LOCAL EXHAUST OR PROCESS ENCLOSURE VENTILATION TO MEET PUBLISHED EXPOSURE LIMITS.

RESPIRATOR: THE FOLLOWING RESPIRATORS AND MAXIMUM USE CONCENTRATIONS ARE RECOMMENDATIONS BY THE U.S. DEPARTMENT OF HEALTH AND HUMAN SERVICES, NIOSH POCKET GUIDE TO CHEMICAL HAZARDS; NIOSH CRITERIA DOCUMENTS OR BY THE U.S. DEPARTMENT OF LABOR, 29 CFR 1910 SUBPART Z. THE SPECIFIC RESPIRATOR SELECTED MUST BE BASED ON CONTAMINATION LEVELS FOUND IN THE WORK PLACE, MUST NOT EXCEED THE WORKING LIMITS OF THE RESPIRATOR AND BE JOINTLY APPROVED BY THE NATIONAL INSTITUTE FOR OCCUPATIONAL SAFETY AND HEALTH AND THE MINE SAFETY AND HEALTH ADMINISTRATION (NIOSH-MSHA).

STRYCHNINE:

0.75 MG/M3- ANY DUST AND MIST RESPIRATOR EXCEPT SINGLE-USE RESPIRATOR.

1.5 MG/M3- ANY DUST AND MIST RESPIRATOR EXCEPT SINGLE-USE AND QUARTER MASK RESPIRATORS. ANY SUPPLIED-AIR RESPIRATOR. ANY SELF-CONTAINED BREATHING APPARATUS.

3 MG/M3- ANY POWERED AIR-PURIFYING RESPIRATOR WITH A DUST AND MIST FILTER. ANY SUPPLIED-AIR RESPIRATOR OPERATED IN A CONTINUOUS FLOW MODE. ANY AIR-PURIFYING FULL FACEPIECE RESPIRATOR WITH A HIGH-EFFICIENCY PARTICULATE FILTER. ANY SUPPLIED-AIR RESPIRATOR WITH A FULL FACEPIECE. ANY SELF-CONTAINED BREATHING APPARATUS WITH A FULL FACEPIECE.

ESCAPE- ANY AIR-PURIFYING FULL FACEPIECE RESPIRATOR WITH A HIGH-EFFICIENCY PARTICULATE FILTER. ANY APPROPRIATE ESCAPE-TYPE SELF-CONTAINED BREATHING APPARATUS.

FOR FIREFIGHTING AND OTHER IMMEDIATELY DANGEROUS TO LIFE OR HEALTH CONDITIONS:

SELF-CONTAINED BREATHING APPARATUS WITH FULL FACEPIECE OPERATED IN PRESSURE-DEMAND OR OTHER POSITIVE PRESSURE MODE.

SUPPLIED-AIR RESPIRATOR WITH FULL FACEPIECE AND OPERATED IN PRESSURE-DEMAND OR OTHER POSITIVE PRESSURE MODE IN COMBINATION WITH AN AUXILIARY SELF-CONTAINED BREATHING APPARATUS OPERATED IN PRESSURE-DEMAND OR OTHER POSITIVE PRESSURE MODE.

CLOTHING: EMPLOYEE MUST WEAR APPROPRIATE PROTECTIVE (IMPERVIOUS) CLOTHING AND EQUIPMENT TO PREVENT REPEATED OR PROLONGED SKIN CONTACT WITH THIS SUBSTANCE.

GLOVES: EMPLOYEE MUST WEAR APPROPRIATE PROTECTIVE GLOVES TO PREVENT CONTACT WITH THIS SUBSTANCE.

EYE PROTECTION: EMPLOYEE MUST WEAR SPLASH-PROOF OR DUST-RESISTANT SAFETY GOGGLES TO PREVENT EYE CONTACT WITH THIS SUBSTANCE.

EMERGENCY EYE WASH: WHERE THERE IS ANY POSSIBILITY THAT AN EMPLOYEE'S EYES MAY BE EXPOSED TO THIS SUBSTANCE, THE EMPLOYER SHOULD PROVIDE AN EYE WASH FOUNTAIN WITHIN THE IMMEDIATE WORK AREA FOR EMERGENCY USE.

AUTHORIZED BY- OCCUPATIONAL HEALTH SERVICES, INC.
CREATION DATE: 10/05/89 ***REVISION DATE:*** 03/28/90

MATERIAL SAFETY DATA SHEET

OCCUPATIONAL HEALTH SERVICES, INC.
AGRICULTURE AND PESTICIDE DIVISION
450 SEVENTH AVENUE, SUITE 2407
NEW YORK, NEW YORK 10123
1-800-445-MSDS OR (212) 967-1100

EMERGENCY CONTACT:
JOHN S. BRANSFORD, JR. (615) 292-1180

SUBSTANCE IDENTIFICATION

CAS-NUMBER 60-41-3
SUBSTANCE: **STRYCHNINE SULFATE**
TRADE NAMES/SYNONYMS: STRYCHNIDIN-10-ONE, SULFATE; ANTIVAMPIRE; STRYCHNINIUM SULFATE; VAMPIROL; PST22090
CHEMICAL FAMILY: STRYCHNINE
MOLECULAR FORMULA: C42-H46-N4-O8-S
MOLECULAR WEIGHT: 766.92
CERCLA RATINGS (SCALE 0-3): HEALTH=3 FIRE=U REACTIVITY=U PERSISTENCE=2
NFPA RATINGS (SCALE 0-4): HEALTH=3 FIRE=U REACTIVITY=U

COMPONENTS AND CONTAMINANTS

COMPONENT: STRYCHNINE SULFATE ***PERCENT:*** 100
CAS# 60-41-3
OTHER CONTAMINANTS: NONE
EXPOSURE LIMITS: STRYCHNINE SULFATE: NO OCCUPATIONAL EXPOSURE LIMITS ESTABLISHED BY OSHA, ACGIH, OR NIOSH.
100/10,000 POUNDS SARA SECTION 302 THRESHOLD PLANNING QUANTITY; 1 POUND SARA SECTION 304 REPORTABLE QUANTITY.

PHYSICAL DATA

DESCRIPTION: COLORLESS, ODORLESS, BITTER TASTING CRYSTALS.
MELTING POINT: 392 F (200 C) ***SPECIFIC GRAVITY:*** NOT AVAILABLE
SOLUBILITY IN WATER: 2.86 % W/V.

FIRE AND EXPLOSION DATA

FIRE AND EXPLOSION HAZARD: UNKNOWN FIRE AND EXPLOSION HAZARD.
FIREFIGHTING MEDIA: DRY CHEMICAL, CARBON DIOXIDE, HALON, WATER SPRAY OR STANDARD FOAM (1987 EMERGENCY RESPONSE GUIDEBOOK, DOT P 5800.4).
FOR LARGER FIRES, USE WATER SPRAY, FOG OR STANDARD FOAM (1987 EMERGENCY RESPONSE GUIDEBOOK, DOT P 5800.4).
FIREFIGHTING: MOVE CONTAINERS FROM FIRE AREA IF POSSIBLE (1987 EMERGENCY RESPONSE GUIDEBOOK, DOT P 5800.4, GUIDE PAGE 53).
EXTINGUISH USING AGENT SUITABLE FOR TYPE OF SURROUNDING FIRE. AVOID BREATHING VAPORS AND DUSTS. KEEP UPWIND.

TRANSPORTATION DATA

DEPARTMENT OF TRANSPORTATION HAZARD CLASSIFICATION 49 CFR 172.101: POISON B
DEPARTMENT OF TRANSPORTATION LABELING REQUIREMENTS 49 CFR 172.101 AND SUBPART E: POISON
DEPARTMENT OF TRANSPORTATION PACKAGING REQUIREMENTS: 49 CFR 173.365 EXCEPTIONS: 49 CFR 173.364

TOXICITY

STRYCHNINE SULFATE: TOXICITY DATA: 2600 UG/KG ORAL-RAT LD50; 8 MG/KG ORAL-MOUSE LDLO; 1700 UG/KG SUBCUTANEOUS-RAT LD50; 1250 UG/KG SUBCUTANEOUS-MOUSE LD50; 4800 UG/KG SUBCUTANEOUS-GUINEA PIG LD50; 570 UG/KG INTRAVENOUS-RAT LD50; 475 UG/KG INTRAVENOUS-MOUSE LD50; 2500 UG/KG INTRAVENOUS-CAT LD50; 390 UG/KG INTRAVENOUS-GUINEA PIG LD50; 1 MG/KG INTRAPERITONEAL-RAT LD50; 900 UG/KG INTRAPERITONEAL-MOUSE LD50; 10900 UG/KG INTRAPERITONEAL-GUINEA PIG LD50; CARCINOGEN STATUS: NONE. ACUTE TOXICITY LEVEL: HIGHLY TOXIC BY INGESTION. TARGET EFFECTS: POISONING MAY AFFECT THE CENTRAL NERVOUS SYSTEM. AT INCREASED RISK FROM EXPOSURE: PERSONS WITH A HISTORY OF CONVULSIVE DISORDERS. ADDITIONAL DATA: IN THE CASE OF STRYCHNINE POISONING, EMETICS, CAFFEINE, BROMIDES, OPIATES, CATHARTICS, PURGATIVES OR DIURETICS SHOULD BE AVOIDED.

HEALTH EFFECTS AND FIRST AID

INHALATION: STRYCHNINE SULFATE: 3 MG/M3 STRYCHNINE IMMEDIATELY DANGEROUS TO LIFE AND HEALTH. **ACUTE EXPOSURE-** NO DATA AVAILABLE. **CHRONIC EXPOSURE-** NO DATA AVAILABLE.
FIRST AID- REMOVE FROM EXPOSURE AREA TO FRESH AIR IMMEDIATELY. IF BREATHING HAS STOPPED, GIVE ARTIFICIAL RESPIRATION. MAINTAIN AIRWAY AND BLOOD PRESSURE AND ADMINISTER OXYGEN IF AVAILABLE. KEEP AFFECTED PERSON WARM AND AT REST. TREAT SYMPTOMATICALLY AND SUPPORTIVELY. ADMINISTRATION OF OXYGEN SHOULD BE PERFORMED BY QUALIFIED PERSONNEL. GET MEDICAL ATTENTION IMMEDIATELY.

SKIN CONTACT: STRYCHNINE SULFATE: **ACUTE EXPOSURE-** NO DATA AVAILABLE. **CHRONIC EXPOSURE-** NO DATA AVAILABLE.
FIRST AID- REMOVE CONTAMINATED CLOTHING AND SHOES IMMEDIATELY. WASH AFFECTED AREA WITH SOAP OR MILD DETERGENT AND LARGE AMOUNTS OF WATER UNTIL NO EVIDENCE OF CHEMICAL REMAINS (APPROXIMATELY 15-20 MINUTES). GET MEDICAL ATTENTION IMMEDIATELY.

EYE CONTACT: STRYCHNINE SULFATE: **ACUTE EXPOSURE-** UNSPECIFIED TOXIC EFFECTS WERE OBSERVED WITHIN 3 TO 4 MINUTES AFTER APPLICATION OF 5 MG TO AN EYE. NOT KNOWN TO BE AN IRRITANT. **CHRONIC EXPOSURE-** NO DATA AVAILABLE.
FIRST AID- WASH EYES IMMEDIATELY WITH LARGE AMOUNTS OF WATER OR NORMAL SALINE, OCCASIONALLY LIFTING UPPER AND LOWER LIDS, UNTIL NO EVIDENCE OF CHEMICAL REMAINS (APPROXIMATELY 15-20 MINUTES). GET MEDICAL ATTENTION IMMEDIATELY.

INGESTION: STRYCHNINE SULFATE: NEUROTOXIN/HIGHLY TOXIC. **ACUTE EXPOSURE-** THE LETHAL AMOUNT OF STRYCHNINE SULFATE WAS 5 MG/KG IN RATS; 5600 UG/KG WAS THE LETHAL DOSE IN WILD BIRDS. STRYCHNINE IS A POISONOUS ALKALOID WHOSE EFFECTS UPON INGESTION DEPEND PARTLY ON THE AMOUNT OF FOOD IN THE STOMACH. IT IS RAPIDLY ABSORBED FROM THE STOMACH; THE FIRST EFFECTS MAY BE NOTED 15 TO 30 MINUTES AFTER INGESTION. THE FIRST SYMPTOMS MAY BE A FEELING OF UNEASINESS, WITH A HEIGHTENED REFLEX OF IRRITABILITY. THIS MAY BE FOLLOWED BY A SERIES OF SEVERE CONVULSIONS, PERHAPS BECOMING SO SEVERE THAT THE VICTIM IS COMPLETELY RIGID, WITH ONLY THE HEELS OF THE FEET AND CROWN OF THE HEAD TOUCHING THE FLOOR. ANY STIMULUS, SUCH AS A SOUND OR MOVEMENT, MAY TRIGGER THESE INTENSELY PAINFUL AND FRIGHTENING SPASMS. DEATH MAY RESULT FROM RESPIRATORY FAILURE, EITHER DURING ONE OF THESE SPASMS, AS THE DIAPHRAGM IS PARALYZED, OR BETWEEN CONVULSIONS, WHEN THE PATIENT IS EXHAUSTED AND DEPRESSED. THE LONGER THE PERSON SURVIVES, THE BETTER THE PROGNOSIS. **CHRONIC EXPOSURE-** CONTINUED MEDICATION WITH STRYCHNINE MAY LEAD TO PHOTOPHOBIA, MUSCULAR RIGIDITY, STIFFNESS IN THE JOINTS, MYALGIA, LASSITUDE AND HEADACHE.
FIRST AID- GIVE LARGE QUANITIES OF WATER IMMEDIATELY. AFTER WATER HAS BEEN SWALLOWED, TRY TO INDUCE VOMITING BY TOUCHING THE BACK OF THROAT WITH A FINGER. DO NOT MAKE AN UNCONSCIOUS PERSON VOMIT. GET MEDICAL ATTENTION IMMEDIATELY (OSHA GUIDELINES, SEPT. 1978). IF SYMPTOMS HAVE BEGUN, AVOID ANY MANIPULATION SUCH AS GASTRIC LAVAGE OR EMESIS. ENFORCE ABSOLUTE QUIET AND ABSENCE OF STIMULI. CONTROL CONVULSIONS BY ADMINISTRATION OF ANTIDOTES AFTER CONVULSIONS AND HYPERACTIVITY ARE CONTROLED; REMOVE STRYCHNINE BY GASTRIC LAVAGE USING ACTIVATED CHARCOAL (DRIESBACH, HANDBOOK OF POISONING, 11TH ED.). ACTIVATED CHARCOAL IS AN EFFECTIVE METHOD OF REDUCING ABSORPTION WHEN USED AS A SLURRY IN GASTRIC LAVAGE. IODINE TINCTURE DILUTED WITH WATER (1:250), TANNIC ACID SOLUTION (2.0%, OR IN THE FORM OF STRONG TEA), OR POTASSIUM PERMANGANATE (1:5000) MAY ALSO BE USED (GOODMAN AND GILMAN, THE PHARMACOLOGICAL BASIS OF THERAPEUTICS, 6TH ED.). GASTRIC LAVAGE AND ANTIDOTE SHOULD BE ADMINISTERED BY QUALIFIED MEDICAL PERSONNEL ONLY.
ANTIDOTE: NO SPECIFIC ANTIDOTE. TREAT SYMPTOMATICALLY AND SUPPORTIVELY.

REACTIVITY

REACTIVITY: NO DATA AVAILABLE.
INCOMPATIBILITIES: STRYCHNINE SULFATE: THESE COMPOUNDS ARE INCOMPATIBLE WITH ALL STRYCHNINE SALTS: ALKALIES ALKALI CARBONATES BENZOATES BICARBONATES BORAX BROMIDES DICHROMATE GOLD CHLORIDE IODIDES PICRIC ACID PIPERAZINE POTASSIUM-MERCURIC IODIDE SALICYLATES TANNIC ACIDS.
DECOMPOSITION: THERMAL DECOMPOSITION MAY RELEASE TOXIC OXIDES OF NITROGEN AND SULFUR.
POLYMERIZATION: HAZARDOUS POLYMERIZATION HAS NOT BEEN REPORTED TO OCCUR UNDER NORMAL TEMPERATURES AND PRESSURES.

STORAGE AND DISPOSAL

OBSERVE ALL FEDERAL, STATE AND LOCAL REGULATIONS WHEN STORING OR DISPOSING OF THIS SUBSTANCE. FOR ASSISTANCE, CONTACT THE DISTRICT DIRECTOR OF THE ENVIRONMENTAL PROTECTION AGENCY.

STORAGE

THRESHOLD PLANNING QUANTITY (TPQ): THE SUPERFUND AMENDMENTS AND REAUTHORIZATION ACT (SARA) SECTION 302 REQUIRES THAT EACH FACILITY WHERE ANY EXTREMELY HAZARDOUS SUBSTANCE IS PRESENT IN A QUANTITY EQUAL TO OR GREATER THAN THE TPQ ESTABLISHED FOR THAT SUBSTANCE NOTIFY THE STATE EMERGENCY RESPONSE COMMISSION FOR THE STATE IN WHICH IT IS LOCATED. SECTION 303 OF SARA REQUIRES THESE FACILITIES TO PARTICIPATE IN LOCAL EMERGENCY RESPONSE PLANNING (40 CFR 355.30).

CONDITIONS TO AVOID

AVOID EXPOSURE TO LIGHT

SPILL AND LEAK PROCEDURES

OCCUPATIONAL SPILL: DO NOT TOUCH SPILLED MATERIAL. STOP LEAK IF YOU CAN DO IT WITHOUT RISK. FOR SMALL SPILLS, TAKE UP WITH SAND OR OTHER ABSORBENT MATERIAL AND PLACE INTO CONTAINERS FOR LATER DISPOSAL. FOR SMALL DRY SPILLS, WITH A CLEAN SHOVEL PLACE MATERIAL INTO CLEAN, DRY CONTAINER AND COVER. MOVE CONTAINERS FROM SPILL AREA. FOR LARGER SPILLS, DIKE FAR AHEAD OF SPILL FOR LATER DISPOSAL. KEEP UNNECESSARY PEOPLE AWAY. ISOLATE HAZARD AREA AND DENY ENTRY.

REPORTABLE QUANTITY (RQ): 1 POUND THE SUPERFUND AMENDMENTS AND REAUTHORIZATION ACT (SARA) SECTION 304 REQUIRES THAT A RELEASE EQUAL TO OR GREATER THAN THE REPORTABLE QUANTITY FOR THIS SUBSTANCE BE IMMEDIATELY REPORTED TO THE LOCAL EMERGENCY PLANNING COMMITTEE AND THE STATE EMERGENCY RESPONSE COMMISSION (40 CFR 355.40). IF THE RELEASE OF THIS SUBSTANCE IS REPORTABLE UNDER CERCLA SECTION 103, THE NATIONAL RESPONSE CENTER MUST BE NOTIFIED IMMEDIATELY AT (800) 424-8802 OR (202) 426-2675 IN THE METROPOLITAN WASHINGTON, D.C. AREA (40 CFR 302.6).

PROTECTIVE EQUIPMENT

VENTILATION: PROCESS ENCLOSURE VENTILATION RECOMMENDED TO MEET PUBLISHED EXPOSURE LIMITS. VENTILATION EQUIPMENT MUST BE EXPLOSION-PROOF.

RESPIRATOR: THE FOLLOWING RESPIRATORS AND MAXIMUM USE CONCENTRATIONS ARE RECOMMENDATIONS BY THE U.S. DEPARTMENT OF HEALTH AND HUMAN SERVICES, NIOSH POCKET GUIDE TO CHEMICAL HAZARDS; NIOSH CRITERIA DOCUMENTS OR BY THE U.S. DEPARTMENT OF LABOR, 29 CFR 1910 SUBPART Z. THE SPECIFIC RESPIRATOR SELECTED MUST BE BASED ON CONTAMINATION LEVELS FOUND IN THE WORK PLACE, MUST NOT EXCEED THE WORKING LIMITS OF THE RESPIRATOR AND BE JOINTLY APPROVED BY THE NATIONAL INSTITUTE FOR OCCUPATIONAL SAFETY AND HEALTH AND THE MINE SAFETY AND HEALTH ADMINISTRATION (NIOSH-MSHA).

STRYCHNINE:

0.75 MG/M3- ANY DUST AND MIST RESPIRATOR EXCEPT SINGLE-USE RESPIRATOR.

1.5 MG/M3- ANY DUST AND MIST RESPIRATOR EXCEPT SINGLE-USE AND QUARTER MASK RESPIRATORS. ANY SUPPLIED-AIR RESPIRATOR. ANY SELF-CONTAINED BREATHING APPARATUS.

3 MG/M3- ANY POWERED AIR-PURIFYING RESPIRATOR WITH A DUST AND MIST FILTER. ANY SUPPLIED-AIR RESPIRATOR OPERATED IN A CONTINUOUS FLOW MODE. ANY AIR-PURIFYING FULL FACEPIECE RESPIRATOR WITH A HIGH-EFFICIENCY PARTICULATE FILTER. ANY SUPPLIED-AIR RESPIRATOR WITH A FULL FACEPIECE. ANY SELF-CONTAINED BREATHING APPARATUS WITH A FULL FACEPIECE.

ESCAPE- ANY AIR-PURIFYING FULL FACEPIECE RESPIRATOR WITH A HIGH-EFFICIENCY PARTICULATE FILTER. ANY APPROPRIATE ESCAPE-TYPE SELF-CONTAINED BREATHING APPARATUS.

FOR FIREFIGHTING AND OTHER IMMEDIATELY DANGEROUS TO LIFE OR HEALTH CONDITIONS:

SELF-CONTAINED BREATHING APPARATUS WITH FULL FACEPIECE OPERATED IN PRESSURE-DEMAND OR OTHER POSITIVE PRESSURE MODE.

SUPPLIED-AIR RESPIRATOR WITH FULL FACEPIECE AND OPERATED IN PRESSURE-DEMAND OR OTHER POSITIVE PRESSURE MODE IN COMBINATION WITH AN AUXILIARY SELF-CONTAINED BREATHING APPARATUS OPERATED IN PRESSURE-DEMAND OR OTHER POSITIVE PRESSURE MODE.

CLOTHING: EMPLOYEE MUST WEAR APPROPRIATE PROTECTIVE (IMPERVIOUS) CLOTHING AND EQUIPMENT TO PREVENT ANY POSSIBILITY OF SKIN CONTACT WITH THIS SUBSTANCE.

GLOVES: EMPLOYEE MUST WEAR APPROPRIATE PROTECTIVE GLOVES TO PREVENT CONTACT WITH THIS SUBSTANCE.

EYE PROTECTION: EMPLOYEE MUST WEAR SPLASH-PROOF OR DUST-RESISTANT SAFETY GOGGLES AND A FACESHIELD TO PREVENT CONTACT WITH THIS SUBSTANCE.

EMERGENCY WASH FACILITIES: WHERE THERE IS ANY POSSIBILITY THAT AN EMPLOYEE'S EYES AND/OR SKIN MAY BE EXPOSED TO THIS SUBSTANCE, THE EMPLOYER SHOULD PROVIDE AN EYE WASH FOUNTAIN AND QUICK DRENCH SHOWER WITHIN THE IMMEDIATE WORK AREA FOR EMERGENCY USE.

AUTHORIZED BY- OCCUPATIONAL HEALTH SERVICES, INC.
CREATION DATE: 10/05/89 ***REVISION DATE:*** 05/18/90

MATERIAL SAFETY DATA SHEET

OCCUPATIONAL HEALTH SERVICES, INC.
AGRICULTURE AND PESTICIDE DIVISION
450 SEVENTH AVENUE, SUITE 2407
NEW YORK, NEW YORK 10123
1-800-445-MSDS OR (212) 967-1100

EMERGENCY CONTACT:
JOHN S. BRANSFORD, JR. (615) 292-1180

SUBSTANCE IDENTIFICATION

CAS-NUMBER 95-06-7

SUBSTANCE: **SULFALLATE**

TRADE NAMES/SYNONYMS: CARBAMODITHIOIC ACID, DIETHYL,2-CHLORO-2-PROPENYL ESTER; CARBAMIC ACID, DIETHYLDITHIO, 2-CHLOROALLYL ESTER; CHLORALLYL DIETHYLDITHIOCARBAMATE; 2-CHLOROALLYL DIETHYLDITHIOCARBAMATE; 2-CHLOROALLYL N,N-DIETHYLDITHIOCARBAMATE; 2-CHLORO-2-PROPENE-1-THIOL DIETHYLDITHIOCARBAMATE; DIETHYLADITHIOCARBSMIC ACID 2-CHLOROALLYL ESTER; DIETHYLCARBAMODITHIOIC ACID 2-CHLORO-2-PROPENYL ESTER; 2-PROPENE-1-THIOL,2-CHLORO-, DIETHYLDITHIOCARBAMATE; 2-CHLORO-2-PROPENYL DIETHYLCARBAMODITHIOATE; CDEC; CP 4,742; VEGADEX SUPER; THIOALLATE; VEGADEX; NCI-C00453; PST22190

CHEMICAL FAMILY: THIOCARBAMATE

MOLECULAR FORMULA: C8-H14-CL-N-S2

MOLECULAR WEIGHT: 223.80

CERCLA RATINGS (SCALE 0-3): HEALTH=3 FIRE=0 REACTIVITY=0 PERSISTENCE=1

NFPA RATINGS (SCALE 0-4): HEALTH=3 FIRE=0 REACTIVITY=0

COMPONENTS AND CONTAMINANTS

COMPONENT: SULFALLATE ***PERCENT:*** 100
CAS# 95-06-7

EXPOSURE LIMITS: NO OCCUPATIONAL EXPOSURE LIMITS ESTABLISHED BY OSHA, ACGIH, OR NIOSH.

PHYSICAL DATA

DESCRIPTION: AMBER, OILY LIQUID ***BOILING POINT:*** 262-266 F (128-130 C) @ 1 MMHG

SPECIFIC GRAVITY: 1.088 ***VAPOR PRESSURE:*** 0.0022 MMHG @ 20 C

EVAPORATION RATE: NOT AVAILABLE ***SOLUBILITY IN WATER:*** 100 PPM

SOLVENT SOLUBILITY: SOLUBLE IN ETHER, ACETONE, BENZENE, CHLOROFORM, ETHANOL, ETHYL ACETATE, HEPTANE, KEROSENE, ISOPROPYL ALCOHOL, MOST ORGANIC SOLVENTS

FIRE AND EXPLOSION DATA

FIRE AND EXPLOSION HAZARD: NEGLIGIBLE FIRE HAZARD WHEN EXPOSED TO HEAT OR FLAME.

FIREFIGHTING MEDIA: DRY CHEMICAL, CARBON DIOXIDE, HALON, WATER SPRAY OR STANDARD FOAM (1987 EMERGENCY RESPONSE GUIDEBOOK, DOT P 5800.4).
FOR LARGER FIRES, USE WATER SPRAY, FOG OR STANDARD FOAM (1987 EMERGENCY RESPONSE GUIDEBOOK, DOT P 5800.4).

FIREFIGHTING: MOVE CONTAINER FROM FIRE AREA IF POSSIBLE. DO NOT SCATTER SPILLED MATERIAL WITH HIGH PRESSURE WATER STREAMS. DIKE FIRE CONTROL WATER FOR LATER DISPOSAL (1987 EMERGENCY RESPONSE GUIDEBOOK, DOT P 5800.4, GUIDE PAGE 31).
USE AGENTS SUITABLE FOR TYPE OF SURROUNDING FIRE. AVOID BREATHING HAZARDOUS VAPORS, KEEP UPWIND.

TOXICITY

SULFALLATE: TOXICITY DATA: 2200 MG/KG SKIN-RABBIT LD50; 850 MG/KG ORAL-RAT LD50; MUTAGENIC DATA (RTECS); TUMORIGENIC DATA (RTECS). CARCINOGEN STATUS: ANIMAL SUFFICIENT EVIDENCE (IARC GROUP-2B); ANTICIPATED HUMAN CARCINOGEN (NTP). INGESTION BY RATS AND MICE PRODUCED MAMMARY GLAND TUMORS IN FEMALES OF BOTH SPECIES, TUMORS OF THE FORESTOMACH IN MALE RATS, AND LUNG TUMORS IN MALE MICE. ACUTE TOXICITY LEVEL: MODERATELY

TOXIC BY INGESTION; SLIGHTLY TOXIC BY DERMAL ABSORPTION. TARGET EFFECTS: INTERACTIONS WITH ALCOHOL MAY OCCUR.

HEALTH EFFECTS AND FIRST AID

INHALATION: SULFALLATE: **ACUTE EXPOSURE-** MAY CAUSE IRRITATION. SULFALLATE IS A DITHIOCARBAMATE. INHALATION OF DITHIOCARBAMATES HAVE PRODUCED IRRITATION OF THE RESPIRATORY TRACT WITH SYMPTOMS OF NASAL STUFFINESS, HOARSENESS, COUGH, AND RARELY, PNEUMONITIS. **CHRONIC EXPOSURE-** NO DATA AVAILABLE.

FIRST AID- REMOVE FROM EXPOSURE AREA TO FRESH AIR IMMEDIATELY. IF BREATHING HAS STOPPED, PERFORM ARTIFICIAL RESPIRATION. KEEP PERSON WARM AND AT REST. TREAT SYMPTOMATICALLY AND SUPPORTIVELY. GET MEDICAL ATTENTION IMMEDIATELY.

SKIN CONTACT: SULFALLATE: **ACUTE EXPOSURE-** MAY CAUSE IRRITATION. ANIMAL STUDIES INDICATE THAT HARMFUL AMOUNTS MAY BE ABSORBED THROUGH THE SKIN. A LETHAL DOSE IN RABBITS WAS 2200 MG/KG. DITHIOCARBAMATES MAY CAUSE ITCHING, REDNESS, AND ECZEMATOID DERMATITIS IN PREDISPOSED INDIVIDUALS. **CHRONIC EXPOSURE-** PROLONGED CONTACT MAY CAUSE IRRITATION. PROLONGED OR REPEATED EXPOSURE TO DITHIOCARBAMATES MAY CAUSE SENSITIZATION IN SOME INDIVIDUALS.

FIRST AID- REMOVE CONTAMINATED CLOTHING AND SHOES IMMEDIATELY. WASH AFFECTED AREA WITH SOAP OR MILD DETERGENT AND LARGE AMOUNTS OF WATER UNTIL NO EVIDENCE OF CHEMICAL REMAINS (APPROXIMATELY 15-20 MINUTES). GET MEDICAL ATTENTION IMMEDIATELY.

EYE CONTACT: SULFALLATE: **ACUTE EXPOSURE-** MAY CAUSE IRRITATION. **CHRONIC EXPOSURE-** PROLONGED CONTACT MAY CAUSE IRRITATION.

FIRST AID- WASH EYES IMMEDIATELY WITH LARGE AMOUNTS OF WATER OR NORMAL SALINE, OCCASIONALLY LIFTING UPPER AND LOWER LIDS, UNTIL NO EVIDENCE OF CHEMICAL REMAINS (APPROXIMATELY 15-20 MINUTES). GET MEDICAL ATTENTION IMMEDIATELY.

INGESTION: SULFALLATE: CARCINOGEN. **ACUTE EXPOSURE-** INGESTION OF DITHIOCARBAMATES MAY CAUSE NAUSEA, VOMITING, DIARRHEA, ANOREXIA, HEADACHE, LETHAGRY, DIZZINESS, ATAXIA, CONFUSION, DROWSINESS, EMOTIONAL LABILITY, AND COMA. IN ANIMAL STUDIES, MUSCLE WEAKNESS AND ASCENDING PARALYSIS PROGRESSED TO RESPIRATORY PARALYSIS AND DEATH. **CHRONIC EXPOSURE-** IN CHRONIC FEEDING EXPERIMENTS, RATS DEVELOPED EYE IRRITATION, TOXIC TUBULAR NEPHROPATHY, AND ACANTHOSIS AND HYPERKERATOSIS OF THE FORESTOMACH. INCREASED INCIDENCE OF MAMMARY ADENOCARCINOMA AND OF SQUAMOUS CELL CARCINOMAS OF SKIN, ESOPHAGUS AND STOMACH WAS ALSO OBSERVED. CHRONIC ADMINISTRATION OF THIS PRODUCT IN MICE PRODUCED HEPATOCELLULAR CARCINOMAS AND LUNG TUMORS.

FIRST AID- IF VIGOROUS EMESIS HAS NOT ALREADY OCCURRED AND VICTIM IS FULLY ALERT, GIVE SYRUP OF IPECAC, FOLLOWED BY 1-2 GLASSES OF WATER TO INDUCE VOMITING (ADULTS, 12 YEARS AND OLDER: 30 ML; CHILDREN UNDER 12: 15 ML). IF CONSCIOUSNESS LEVEL DECLINES OR VOMITING HAS NOT OCCURRED IN 15 MINUTES, EMPTY THE STOMACH BY INTUBATION, ASPIRATION, AND LAVAGE, USING ALL AVAILABLE MEANS TO AVOID ASPIRATION OF VOMITUS. AFTER ASPIRATION OF THE STOMACH AND WASHING WITH ISOTONIC SALINE OR SODIUM BICARBONATE, INSTILL 30-50 GM OF ACTIVATED CHARCOAL IN 3-4 OUNCES OF WATER THROUGH THE STOMACH TUBE TO LIMIT ABSORPTION OF REMAINING TOXICANT. IF THE IRRITANT PROPERTIES OF THE TOXICANT FAIL TO PRODUCE A BOWEL MOVEMENT IN 4 HOURS, ADMINISTER SODIUM OR MAGNESIUM SULFATE AS A CATHARTIC: 0.25 GM/KG BODY WEIGHT IN 1-6 OUNCES OF WATER. ADMINISTER GLUCOSE-CONTAINING FLUIDS INTRAVENOUSLY TO ACCELERATE EXCRETION OF TOXICANT. (MORGAN, RECOGNITION AND MANAGEMENT OF PESTICIDE POISONINGS, THIRD EDITION) GET MEDICAL ATTENTION. TREATMENT SHOULD BE BE ADMINISTERED BY QUALIFIED MEDICAL PERSONNEL.

ANTIDOTE: NO SPECIFIC ANTIDOTE. TREAT SYMPTOMATICALLY AND SUPPORTIVELY.

REACTIVITY

REACTIVITY: STABLE UNDER NORMAL TEMPERATURES AND PRESSURES.

INCOMPATIBILITIES: SULFALLATE: WEAK ACID: MAY CAUSE HYDROLYSIS. WEAK BASE: MAY CAUSE HYDROLYSIS. STRONG OXIDIZING AGENTS: MAY CAUSE DECOMPOSITION.

DECOMPOSITION: THERMAL DECOMPOSITION MAY RELEASE TOXIC AND/OR HAZARDOUS GASES.

POLYMERIZATION: HAZARDOUS POLYMERIZATION HAS NOT BEEN REPORTED TO OCCUR UNDER NORMAL TEMPERATURES AND PRESSURES.

STORAGE AND DISPOSAL

OBSERVE ALL FEDERAL, STATE AND LOCAL REGULATIONS WHEN STORING OR DISPOSING OF THIS SUBSTANCE. FOR ASSISTANCE, CONTACT THE DISTRICT DIRECTOR OF THE ENVIRONMENTAL PROTECTION AGENCY.

****STORAGE****

STORE IN ACCORDANCE WITH 40 CFR 165 RECOMMENDED PROCEDURES FOR THE DISPOSAL AND STORAGE OF PESTICIDES AND PESTICIDE CONTAINERS.
STORE AWAY FROM INCOMPATIBLE SUBSTANCES.

****DISPOSAL****

DISPOSAL MUST BE IN ACCORDANCE WITH 40 CFR 165 RECOMMENDED PROCEDURES FOR THE DISPOSAL AND STORAGE OF PESTICIDES AND PESTICIDE CONTAINERS.

CONDITIONS TO AVOID

MAY BURN BUT DOES NOT IGNITE READILY. AVOID CONTACT WITH STRONG OXIDIZERS, EXCESSIVE HEAT, SPARKS, OR OPEN FLAME.

SPILL AND LEAK PROCEDURES

OCCUPATIONAL SPILL: STOP LEAK IF YOU CAN DO IT WITHOUT RISK. FOR SMALL SPILLS, TAKE UP WITH SAND OR OTHER ABSORBENT MATERIAL AND PLACE INTO CLEAN, DRY CONTAINERS FOR LATER DISPOSAL. KEEP UNNECESSARY PEOPLE AWAY. ISOLATE HAZARD AREA AND DENY ENTRY.

PROTECTIVE EQUIPMENT

VENTILATION: PROVIDE LOCAL EXHAUST OR PROCESS ENCLOSURE VENTILATION SYSTEM.

RESPIRATOR: THE FOLLOWING RESPIRATORS ARE RECOMMENDED BASED ON INFORMATION FOUND IN THE PHYSICAL DATA, TOXICITY AND HEALTH EFFECTS SECTIONS. THEY ARE RANKED IN ORDER FROM MINIMUM TO MAXIMUM RESPIRATORY PROTECTION. THE SPECIFIC RESPIRATOR SELECTED MUST BE BASED ON CONTAMINATION LEVELS FOUND IN THE WORK PLACE, MUST NOT EXCEED THE WORKING LIMITS OF THE RESPIRATOR AND BE JOINTLY APPROVED BY THE NATIONAL INSTITUTE FOR OCCUPATIONAL SAFETY AND HEALTH AND THE MINE SAFETY AND HEALTH ADMINISTRATION (NIOSH-MSHA).
TYPE 'C' SUPPLIED-AIR RESPIRATOR WITH A FULL FACEPIECE OPERATED IN PRESSURE-DEMAND OR OTHER POSITIVE PRESSURE MODE OR WITH A FULL FACEPIECE, HELMET OR HOOD OPERATED IN CONTINOUS-FLOW MODE.
SELF-CONTAINED BREATHING APPARATUS WITH A FULL FACEPIECE OPERATED IN PRESSURE-DEMAND OR OTHER POSITIVE PRESSURE MODE.
FOR FIREFIGHTING AND OTHER IMMEDIATELY DANGEROUS TO LIFE OR HEALTH CONDITIONS:
SELF-CONTAINED BREATHING APPARATUS WITH FULL FACEPIECE OPERATED IN PRESSURE-DEMAND OR OTHER POSITIVE PRESSURE MODE.
SUPPLIED-AIR RESPIRATOR WITH FULL FACEPIECE AND OPERATED IN PRESSURE-DEMAND OR OTHER POSITIVE PRESSURE MODE IN COMBINATION WITH AN AUXILIARY SELF-CONTAINED BREATHING APPARATUS OPERATED IN PRESSURE-DEMAND OR OTHER POSITIVE PRESSURE MODE.

CLOTHING: EMPLOYEE MUST WEAR APPROPRIATE PROTECTIVE (IMPERVIOUS) CLOTHING AND EQUIPMENT TO PREVENT REPEATED OR PROLONGED SKIN CONTACT WITH THIS SUBSTANCE.

GLOVES: EMPLOYEE MUST WEAR APPROPRIATE PROTECTIVE GLOVES TO PREVENT CONTACT WITH THIS SUBSTANCE.

EYE PROTECTION: EMPLOYEE MUST WEAR SPLASH-PROOF OR DUST-RESISTANT SAFETY GOGGLES TO PREVENT EYE CONTACT WITH THIS SUBSTANCE.
EMERGENCY EYE WASH: WHERE THERE IS ANY POSSIBILITY THAT AN EMPLOYEE'S EYES MAY BE EXPOSED TO THIS SUBSTANCE, THE EMPLOYER SHOULD PROVIDE AN EYE WASH FOUNTAIN WITHIN THE IMMEDIATE WORK AREA FOR EMERGENCY USE.

AUTHORIZED BY- OCCUPATIONAL HEALTH SERVICES, INC.
CREATION DATE: 10/05/89 ***REVISION DATE:*** 07/12/90

MATERIAL SAFETY DATA SHEET

OCCUPATIONAL HEALTH SERVICES, INC.
AGRICULTURE AND PESTICIDE DIVISION
450 SEVENTH AVENUE, SUITE 2407
NEW YORK, NEW YORK 10123
1-800-445-MSDS OR (212) 967-1100

EMERGENCY CONTACT:
JOHN S. BRANSFORD, JR. (615) 292-1180

SUBSTANCE IDENTIFICATION

CAS-NUMBER 5329-14-6

SUBSTANCE: **SULFAMIC ACID**

TRADE NAMES/SYNONYMS: AMIDOSULFONIC ACID; AMIDOSULFURIC ACID; AMINESULFONIC ACID; AMINOSULFONIC ACID; AMINOSULFURIC ACID; JUMBO; SULFAMIDIC ACID; SULPHAMIC ACID; SEL-REX PLATINEX III REPLENISHER B (OXY METAL INDUSTRIES CORP.); SEL-REX PLATINEX III MAKE UP SALT B (OXY METAL INDUSTRIES CORP.); UN 2967; PST22200

CHEMICAL FAMILY: INORGANIC ACID

MOLECULAR FORMULA: H3-N-O3-S

MOLECULAR WEIGHT: 97.10

CERCLA RATINGS (SCALE 0-3): HEALTH=2 FIRE=1 REACTIVITY=1 PERSISTENCE=0

NFPA RATINGS (SCALE 0-4): HEALTH=2 FIRE=1 REACTIVITY=1

COMPONENTS AND CONTAMINANTS

COMPONENT: SULFAMIC ACID ***PERCENT:*** >99
CAS# 5329-14-6

OTHER CONTAMINANTS: NONE.

EXPOSURE LIMITS: NO OCCUPATIONAL EXPOSURE LIMITS ESTABLISHED BY OSHA, ACGIH, OR NIOSH.

PHYSICAL DATA

DESCRIPTION: COLORLESS, ODORLESS, NON-VOLATILE, NON-HYGROSCOPIC CRYSTALS

BOILING POINT: DECOMPOSES ***MELTING POINT:*** 392 F (200 C) DEC.

SPECIFIC GRAVITY: 2.15 ***VOLATILITY:*** NIL ***EVAPORATION RATE:*** NOT AVAILABLE

PH: 1.18 @ 1% SOLUTION ***SOLUBILITY IN WATER:*** 14.7% @ 0 C

SOLVENT SOLUBILITY: SOLUBLE IN LIQUID AMMONIA, DIMETHYLFORMAMIDE, PYRIDINE, FORMAMIDE, NITROGEN CONTAINING ORGANIC SOLVENTS; SPARINGLY SOLUBLE IN ALCOHOL, METHANOL; SLIGHTY SOLUBLE IN ACETONE; INSOLUBLE IN ETHER

FIRE AND EXPLOSION DATA

FIRE AND EXPLOSION HAZARD: SLIGHT FIRE HAZARD WHEN EXPOSED TO HEAT OR FLAME.

FIREFIGHTING MEDIA: DRY CHEMICAL, CARBON DIOXIDE, HALON, WATER SPRAY OR STANDARD FOAM (1987 EMERGENCY RESPONSE GUIDEBOOK, DOT P 5800.4).
FOR LARGER FIRES, USE WATER SPRAY, FOG OR STANDARD FOAM (1987 EMERGENCY RESPONSE GUIDEBOOK, DOT P 5800.4).

FIREFIGHTING: MOVE CONTAINERS FROM FIRE AREA IF POSSIBLE. COOL CONTAINERS EXPOSED TO FLAMES WITH WATER FROM SIDE UNTIL WELL AFTER FIRE IS OUT. STAY AWAY FROM STORAGE TANK ENDS (1987 EMERGENCY RESPONSE GUIDEBOOK, DOT P 5800.4, GUIDE PAGE 60).
EXTINGUISH USING AGENT INDICATED; DO NOT USE WATER DIRECTLY ON MATERIAL. IF LARGE AMOUNTS OF COMBUSTIBLE MATERIALS ARE INVOLVED, USE WATER SPRAY OR FOG IN FLOODING AMOUNTS. AVOID BREATHING CORROSIVE DUSTS AND FUMES FROM BURNING MATERIAL, KEEP UPWIND.

TOXICITY

SULFAMIC ACID: IRRITATION DATA: 4% SOLUTION/5 DAYS-INTERMITTENT SKIN-HUMAN MILD; 500 MG/24 HOURS SKIN-RABBIT SEVERE; 250 UG/24 HOURS EYE-RABBIT SEVERE; 20 MG EYE-RABBIT MODERATE. TOXICITY DATA: 3160 MG/KG ORAL-RAT LD50; 1312 MG/KG ORAL-MOUSE LD50; 1050 MG/KG ORAL-GUINEA PIG LD50; 100 MG/KG INTRAPERITONEAL-RAT LDLO. CARCINOGEN STATUS: NONE. LOCAL EFFECTS: CORROSIVE- INHALATION, SKIN, AND EYES. ACUTE TOXICITY LEVEL: MODERATELY TOXIC BY INGESTION. TARGET EFFECTS: NO DATA AVAILABLE.

HEALTH EFFECTS AND FIRST AID

INHALATION: SULFAMIC ACID: CORROSIVE. **ACUTE EXPOSURE-** INHALATION OF FUMES OR MIST FROM ACIDS MAY CAUSE COUGHING, CHOKING, HEADACHE, DIZZINESS, WEAKNESS, HYPOTENSION, AND DELAYED PULMONARY EDEMA WITH CHEST TIGHTNESS, APNEA, FROTHY SPUTUM, AND CYANOSIS. DYSPNEA AND HEMOPTYSIS ARE POSSIBLE FOR SEVERAL WEEKS AFTER EXPOSURE. AFTER INHALATION OF CORROSIVE ATMOSPHERES, CONVALESCENCE MAY BE PROLONGED AND FREQUENT RELAPSES MAY OCCUR. **CHRONIC EXPOSURE-** REPEATED OR PROLONGED EXPOSURE TO ACIDIC FUMES MAY CAUSE EROSION OF TEETH FOLLOWED BY JAW NECROSIS. BRONCHIAL IRRITATION WITH COUGH AND FREQUENT ATTACKS OF BRONCHIAL PNEUMONIA MAY OCCUR. GASTROINTESTINAL DISTURBANCES ARE ALSO POSSIBLE.

FIRST AID- REMOVE FROM EXPOSURE AREA TO FRESH AIR IMMEDIATELY. IF BREATHING HAS STOPPED, GIVE ARTIFICIAL RESPIRATION. MAINTAIN AIRWAY AND BLOOD PRESSURE AND ADMINISTER OXYGEN IF AVAILABLE. KEEP AFFECTED PERSON WARM AND AT REST. TREAT SYMPTOMATICALLY AND SUPPORTIVELY. ADMINISTRATION OF OXYGEN SHOULD BE PERFORMED BY QUALIFIED PERSONNEL. GET MEDICAL ATTENTION IMMEDIATELY.

SKIN CONTACT: SULFAMIC ACID: CORROSIVE. **ACUTE EXPOSURE-** DIRECT CONTACT WITH ACIDS MAY CAUSE SEVERE PAIN, BURNS AND STAINS. EXTENSIVE SCARRING MAY OCCUR FROM THE BURNS PENETRATING DEEP INTO THE SKIN LAYERS REQUIRING A LONG PERIOD TO HEAL. CONCENTRATIONS OF GREATER THAN 20% OF SULFAMIC ACID MAY INJURE THE SKIN. **CHRONIC EXPOSURE-** REPEATED APPLICATION OF A 4% SOLUTION OF SULFAMIC ACID SEVERAL TIMES A DAY FOR 5 DAYS ON THE SKIN OF 5 HUMAN SUBJECTS PRODUCED MILD IRRITATION.

FIRST AID- REMOVE CONTAMINATED CLOTHING AND SHOES IMMEDIATELY. WASH AFFECTED AREA WITH SOAP OR MILD DETERGENT AND LARGE AMOUNTS OF WATER UNTIL NO EVIDENCE OF CHEMICAL REMAINS (AT LEAST 15-20 MINUTES). IN CASE OF CHEMICAL BURNS, COVER AREA WITH STERILE, DRY DRESSING. BANDAGE SECURELY, BUT NOT TOO TIGHTLY. GET MEDICAL ATTENTION IMMEDIATELY.

EYE CONTACT: SULFAMIC ACID: CORROSIVE. **ACUTE EXPOSURE-** CONTACT WITH DILUTE ACIDS WILL CAUSE IMMEDIATE PAIN, CONJUNCTIVAL HYPEREMIA AND SOMETIMES INJURY OF THE CORNEAL EPITHELIUM WITH SYMPTOMS OF PAIN, TEARING, AND PHOTOPHOBIA. USUALLY THE CORNEAL EPITHELIUM WILL REGENERATE PROMPTLY AND WITHOUT ANY CORNEAL OPACITIES. CONTACT WITH CONCENTRATED ACIDS MAY CAUSE EXTENSIVE NECROSIS OF THE CONJUNCTIVA AND CORNEAL EPITHELIUM WITH POSSIBLE PENETRATION AND DAMAGE TO THE STROMA OF THE CORNEA. CORNEAL DAMAGE FREQUENTLY RESULTS IN BLINDNESS. THE INSTILLATION OF 0.5 CC OF A 4 PER CENT SOLUTION WITH A PH OF 0.82 INTO THE CONJUNCTIVAL SAC OF 5 RABBITS PRODUCED A MODERATE DEGREE OF CONJUNCTIVITIS AND EDEMA. SUBSTANCES WITH A PH OF LESS THAN 2.0 ARE CONSIDERED CORROSIVE TO THE EYES. **CHRONIC EXPOSURE-** PROLONGED OR REPEATED EXPOSURE TO THE DUST OR MISTS MAY CAUSE EFFECTS AS DESCRIBED IN ACUTE EXPOSURE.

FIRST AID- WASH EYES IMMEDIATELY WITH LARGE AMOUNTS OF WATER, OCCASIONALLY LIFTING UPPER AND LOWER LIDS, UNTIL NO EVIDENCE OF CHEMICAL REMAINS (AT LEAST 15-20 MINUTES). CONTINUE IRRIGATING WITH NORMAL SALINE UNTIL THE PH HAS RETURNED TO NORMAL (30-60 MINUTES). COVER WITH STERILE BANDAGES. GET MEDICAL ATTENTION IMMEDIATELY.

INGESTION: SULFAMIC ACID: CORROSIVE. **ACUTE EXPOSURE-** INGESTION OF ACIDS MAY CAUSE SEVERE BURNING PAIN IN THE MOUTH, PHARYNX, AND ABDOMEN, FOLLOWED BY VOMITING, DIARRHEA OF DARK PRECIPITATED BLOOD AND A DROP IN THE BLOOD PRESSURE. DISCOLORATION MAY BE FOUND AROUND THE MOUTH AND THROAT. ASPHYXIA MAY OCCUR FROM EDEMA OF THE GLOTTIS. AFTER INITIAL RECOVERY, ONSET OF FEVER INDICATES MEDIASTINITIS OR PERITONITIS FROM PERFORATION OF THE ESOPHAGUS OR STOMACH. THE PATIENT MAY HAVE A RIGID ABDOMEN WITHOUT PERFORATION. IF THE PATIENT RECOVERS, SCAR FORMATION IS MORE APT TO PRODUCE STRICTURE OF THE PYLORUS THAN STRICTURE OF THE ESOPHAGUS. INGESTION OF GREATER THAN 10% OF SULFAMIC ACID SOLUTIONS WILL CAUSE LESIONS OF THE STOMACH. **CHRONIC EXPOSURE-** CHRONIC INGESTION OF A 2% CONCENTRATION IN THE DIET OF RATS FOR 105 DAYS PRODUCED A DECLINE IN THE GROWTH RATE; A 1% CONCENTRATION IN THE DIET DID NOT PRODUCED ANY ADVERSE EFFECTS.

FIRST AID- DO NOT USE GASTRIC LAVAGE OR EMESIS. DILUTE THE ACID IMMEDIATELY BY DRINKING LARGE QUANTITIES OF WATER OR MILK. IF VOMITING PERSISTS, ADMINISTER FLUIDS REPEATEDLY. INGESTED ACID MUST BE DILUTED APPROXIMATELY 100 TIMES TO RENDER IT HARMLESS TO TISSUES. IF SYMPTOMS ARE SEVERE AND PERFORATION OF THE STOMACH OR ESOPHAGUS IS SUSPECTED, GIVE NOTHING BY MOUTH UNTIL ENDOSCOPIC EXAMINATION HAS BEEN DONE. (DREISBACH, HANDBOOK OF POISONING, 11TH EDITION) GET MEDICAL ATTENTION IMMEDIATELY. TREATMENT SHOULD BE ADMINISTERED BY QUALIFIED MEDICAL PERSONNEL.

REACTIVITY

REACTIVITY: THE SUBSTANCE IS HIGHLY STABLE AS A DRY, CRYSTALLINE SOLID, BUT IN WATER SOLUTION IT SLOWLY HYDROLYZES TO FORM AMMONIUM SULFATE AND BISULFATE. WHEN DISSOLVED IN WATER, IT IS A STRONG ACID.

INCOMPATIBILITIES: SULFAMIC ACID: CHLORINE: FORMATION OF A VERY SENSITIVE, EXPLOSIVE NITROGEN TRICHLORIDE. POTASSIUM CHLORATE: OXIDIZES TO SULFURIC ACID AND NITROGEN GAS. NITRIC ACID: FUMING NITRIC ACID COMBINED WITH SULFAMIC ACID CAUSES VIOLENT RELEASE OF NITROUS OXIDE. METAL NITRATES AND NITRITES: HEATING MAY RESULT IN A VIOLENT REACTION. WATER: SLOWLY HYDROLYZES SULFAMIC ACID TO AMMONIUM SULFATE AND BISULFATE. BASES: VIOLENT REACTION. BROMINE GAS: OXIDIZES TO SULFURIC ACID AND NITROGEN GAS.

DECOMPOSITION: THERMAL DECOMPOSITION PRODUCTS MAY INCLUDE TOXIC AND CORROSIVE FUMES OF AMMONIA, AND TOXIC OXIDES OF NITROGEN AND SULFUR.

POLYMERIZATION: HAZARDOUS POLYMERIZATION HAS NOT BEEN REPORTED TO OCCUR UNDER NORMAL TEMPERATURES AND PRESSURES.

CONDITIONS TO AVOID

MAY BURN BUT DOES NOT IGNITE READILY. FLAMMABLE, POISONOUS GASES MAY ACCUMULATE IN TANKS AND HOPPER CARS. MAY IGNITE COMBUSTIBLES (WOOD, PAPER, OIL, ETC.).

SPILL AND LEAK PROCEDURES

OCCUPATIONAL SPILL: DO NOT TOUCH SPILLED MATERIAL. STOP LEAK IF YOU CAN DO IT WITHOUT RISK. FOR SMALL SPILLS, TAKE UP WITH SAND OR OTHER ABSORBENT MATERIAL AND PLACE INTO CONTAINERS FOR LATER DISPOSAL. FOR SMALL DRY SPILLS, WITH CLEAN SHOVEL PLACE MATERIAL INTO CLEAN, DRY CONTAINER AND COVER. MOVE CONTAINERS FROM SPILL AREA. FOR LARGER SPILLS, DIKE FAR AHEAD OF SPILL FOR LATER DISPOSAL. KEEP UNNECESSARY PEOPLE AWAY. ISOLATE HAZARD AREA AND DENY ENTRY.

PROTECTIVE EQUIPMENT

VENTILATION: PROVIDE LOCAL EXHAUST OR GENERAL DILUTION VENTILATION SYSTEM.

RESPIRATOR: THE FOLLOWING RESPIRATORS ARE RECOMMENDED BASED ON INFORMATION FOUND IN THE PHYSICAL DATA, TOXICITY AND HEALTH EFFECTS SECTIONS. THEY ARE RANKED IN ORDER FROM MINIMUM TO MAXIMUM RESPIRATORY PROTECTION. THE SPECIFIC RESPIRATOR SELECTED MUST BE BASED ON CONTAMINATION LEVELS FOUND IN THE WORK PLACE, MUST NOT EXCEED THE WORKING LIMITS OF THE RESPIRATOR AND BE JOINTLY APPROVED BY THE NATIONAL INSTITUTE FOR OCCUPATIONAL SAFETY AND HEALTH AND THE MINE SAFETY AND HEALTH ADMINISTRATION (NIOSH-MSHA).

DUST AND MIST RESPIRATOR WITH A FULL FACEPIECE.

AIR-PURIFYING FULL FACEPIECE RESPIRATOR WITH A HIGH-EFFICIENCY PARTICULATE FILTER.

POWERED AIR-PURIFYING RESPIRATOR WITH A TIGHT-FITTING FACEPIECE AND HIGH-EFFICIENCY PARTICULATE FILTER.

TYPE 'C' SUPPLIED-AIR RESPIRATOR WITH A FULL FACEPIECE OPERATED IN PRESSURE-DEMAND OR OTHER POSITIVE PRESSURE MODE OR WITH A FULL FACEPIECE, HELMET OR HOOD OPERATED IN CONTINUOUS-FLOW MODE.

SELF-CONTAINED BREATHING APPARATUS WITH A FULL FACEPIECE OPERATED IN PRESSURE-DEMAND OR OTHER POSITIVE PRESSURE MODE.

FOR FIREFIGHTING AND OTHER IMMEDIATELY DANGEROUS TO LIFE OR HEALTH CONDITIONS:

SELF-CONTAINED BREATHING APPARATUS WITH FULL FACEPIECE OPERATED IN PRESSURE-DEMAND OR OTHER POSITIVE PRESSURE MODE.

SUPPLIED-AIR RESPIRATOR WITH FULL FACEPIECE AND OPERATED IN PRESSURE-DEMAND OR OTHER POSITIVE PRESSURE MODE IN COMBINATION WITH AN AUXILIARY SELF-CONTAINED BREATHING APPARATUS OPERATED IN PRESSURE-DEMAND OR OTHER POSITIVE PRESSURE MODE.

CLOTHING: EMPLOYEE MUST WEAR APPROPRIATE PROTECTIVE (IMPERVIOUS) CLOTHING AND EQUIPMENT TO PREVENT ANY POSSIBILITY OF SKIN CONTACT WITH THIS SUBSTANCE.

GLOVES: EMPLOYEE MUST WEAR APPROPRIATE PROTECTIVE GLOVES TO PREVENT CONTACT WITH THIS SUBSTANCE.

EYE PROTECTION: EMPLOYEE MUST WEAR SPLASH-PROOF OR DUST-RESISTANT SAFETY GOGGLES AND A FACESHIELD TO PREVENT CONTACT WITH THIS SUBSTANCE.

EMERGENCY WASH FACILITIES: WHERE THERE IS ANY POSSIBILITY THAT AN EMPLOYEE'S EYES AND/OR SKIN MAY BE EXPOSED TO THIS SUBSTANCE, THE EMPLOYER SHOULD PROVIDE AN EYE WASH FOUNTAIN AND QUICK DRENCH SHOWER WITHIN THE IMMEDIATE WORK AREA FOR EMERGENCY USE.

AUTHORIZED BY- OCCUPATIONAL HEALTH SERVICES, INC.

CREATION DATE: 02/08/90 ***REVISION DATE:*** 05/14/90

MATERIAL SAFETY DATA SHEET

OCCUPATIONAL HEALTH SERVICES, INC.
AGRICULTURE AND PESTICIDE DIVISION
450 SEVENTH AVENUE, SUITE 2407
NEW YORK, NEW YORK 10123
1-800-445-MSDS OR (212) 967-1100

EMERGENCY CONTACT:
JOHN S. BRANSFORD, JR. (615) 292-1180

SUBSTANCE IDENTIFICATION

CAS-NUMBER 7704-34-9

SUBSTANCE: SULFUR

TRADE NAMES/SYNONYMS: AGRI-SUL; BENSULFOID; COSAN; CRYSTEX; ELOSAL; HEXASUL; KOLO 100; KUMULUS; SOLFRIL; SUFRAN; SULFEX; SULPHUR; SVOVL; THIOVIT; BRIMSTONE; FLOWERS OF SULFUR; SULFUR FLOUR; UN 1350; SUBLIMED SULFUR; S8; PST22280

CHEMICAL FAMILY: NON-METALLIC ELEMENT

MOLECULAR FORMULA: S8

MOLECULAR WEIGHT: 256.48

CERCLA RATINGS (SCALE 0-3): HEALTH = 1 FIRE = 1 REACTIVITY = 0 PERSISTENCE = 0

NFPA RATINGS (SCALE 0-4): HEALTH = 1 FIRE = 1 REACTIVITY = 0

COMPONENTS AND CONTAMINANTS

COMPONENT: SULFUR ***PERCENT:*** 100.0
CAS# 7704-34-9

OTHER CONTAMINANTS: NONE

EXPOSURE LIMITS: NO OCCUPATIONAL EXPOSURE LIMITS ESTABLISHED BY OSHA, ACGIH, OR NIOSH.

PHYSICAL DATA

DESCRIPTION: ODORLESS, TASTELESS, PALE YELLOW SOLID.

BOILING POINT: 832 F (445 C) ***MELTING POINT:*** 235 F (113 C)

SPECIFIC GRAVITY: 2.07 ***VAPOR PRESSURE:*** 1 MMHG @ 184 C

SOLUBILITY IN WATER: INSOLUBLE

SOLVENT SOLUBILITY: SOLUBLE IN CARBON DISULFIDE, CARBON TETRACHLORIDE, BENZENE, LIQUID AMMONIA, METHYLENE IODIDE. SLIGHTLY SOLUBLE IN TOLUENE, ACETONE, CHLOROFORM, ALCOHOL, ETHER.

HARDNESS (MOHS): 1.5-2.5

FIRE AND EXPLOSION DATA

FIRE AND EXPLOSION HAZARD: SLIGHT FIRE HAZARD WHEN EXPOSED TO HEAT OR FLAME.

DUST-AIR MIXTURES MAY IGNITE OR EXPLODE.

MAY BE IGNITED BY STATIC ELECTRICITY.

FLASH POINT: 405 F (207 C) (CC) ***UPPER EXPLOSIVE LIMIT:*** 1400 G/M3

LOWER EXPLOSIVE LIMIT: 35 G/M3 ***AUTOIGNITION TEMP.:*** 450 F (232 C)

FIREFIGHTING MEDIA: DRY CHEMICAL, SAND, WATER SPRAY OR FOAM (1987 EMERGENCY RESPONSE GUIDEBOOK, DOT P 5800.4).

FOR LARGER FIRES, USE WATER SPRAY, FOG OR STANDARD FOAM (1987 EMERGENCY RESPONSE GUIDEBOOK, DOT P 5800.4).

FIREFIGHTING: MOVE CONTAINER FROM FIRE AREA IF POSSIBLE. COOL CONTAINERS EXPOSED TO FLAME WITH WATER FROM SIDE UNTIL WELL AFTER FIRE IS OUT. STAY AWAY FROM STORAGE TANK ENDS. FOR MASSIVE FIRE IN CARGO AREA, USE UNMANNED HOSE HOLDER OR MONITOR NOZZLES; ELSE WITHDRAW AND LET FIRE BURN (1987 EMERGENCY RESPONSE GUIDEBOOK, DOT P 5800.4, GUIDE PAGE 32).

APPLY WATER IN FLOODING QUANTITIES AS A FOG. COOL FIRE-EXPOSED CONTAINERS WITH FLOODING AMOUNTS OF WATER APPLIED FROM AS FAR A DISTANCE AS POSSIBLE. AVOID BREATHING VAPORS OR DUST; KEEP UPWIND.

TRANSPORTATION DATA

DEPARTMENT OF TRANSPORTATION HAZARD CLASSIFICATION 49 CFR 172.101: ORM-C

DEPARTMENT OF TRANSPORTATION LABELING REQUIREMENTS 49 CFR 172.101 AND SUBPART E: NONE

DEPARTMENT OF TRANSPORTATION PACKAGING REQUIREMENTS: 49 CFR 173.1080 EXCEPTIONS: 49 CFR 173.505

TOXICITY

SULFUR: IRRITATION DATA: 8 PPM EYE-HUMAN. TOXICITY DATA: 175 MG/KG ORAL-RABBIT LDLO; 8 MG/KG INTRAVENOUS-RAT LDLO; 10 MG/KG INTRAVENOUS-DOG LDLO; 5 MG/KG INTRAVENOUS-RABBIT LDLO; 55 MG/KG INTRAPERITONEAL-GUINEA PIG LDLO. CARCINOGEN STATUS: NONE. LOCAL EFFECTS: IRRITANT-INHALATION, SKIN, AND EYE. ACUTE TOXICITY LEVEL: INSUFFICIENT DATA. TARGET EFFECTS: POISONING MAY AFFECT THE RESPIRATORY SYSTEM.

HEALTH EFFECTS AND FIRST AID

INHALATION: SULFUR: IRRITANT. **ACUTE EXPOSURE**- INHALATION OF LARGE AMOUNTS OF THE DUST MAY CAUSE CATARRHAL INFLAMMATION OF THE NASAL MUCOSA WHICH MAY LEAD TO HYPERPLASIA WITH ABUNDANT NASAL SECRETIONS. TRACHIOBRONCHITIS IS A FREQUENT OCCURRENCE, WITH DYSPNEA, PERSISTENT COUGH AND EXPECTORATION WHICH MAY SOMETIMES BE STREAKED WITH BLOOD. **CHRONIC EXPOSURE**- REPEATED OR PROLONGED EXPOSURE TO DUST MAY CAUSE IRRITATION TO THE MUCOUS MEMBRANES.

BRONCHOPULMONARY DISEASE MAY OCCUR WHICH, AFTER SEVERAL YEARS, MAY BE COMPLICATED BY EMPHYSEMA AND BRONCHIECTASIS. EARLY SYMPTOMS IN SULFUR MINERS OFTEN INCLUDE UPPER RESPIRATORY TRACT CATARRH, WITH COUGH AND EXPECTORATION WHICH IS MUCOID AND MAY EVEN CONTAIN GRANULES OF SULFUR. ASTHMA IS A FREQUENT COMPLICATION. THE MAXILLARY AND FRONTAL SINUSES MAY BE AFFECTED; INVOLVEMENT IS USUALLY BILATERAL AND PANSINUITIS MAY OCCUR. PULMONARY FUNCTION MAY BE REDUCED. RADIOLOGICAL EXAMINATIONS HAVE REVEALED IRREGULAR OPACITIES IN THE LUNGS AND OCCASIONALLY NODULATION HAS BEEN REPORTED, BUT NOT TRUE NODULAR FIBROSIS.

FIRST AID- REMOVE FROM EXPOSURE AREA TO FRESH AIR IMMEDIATELY. IF BREATHING HAS STOPPED, PERFORM ARTIFICIAL RESPIRATION. KEEP PERSON WARM AND AT REST. TREAT SYMPTOMATICALLY AND SUPPORTIVELY. GET MEDICAL ATTENTION IMMEDIATELY.

SKIN CONTACT: SULFUR: IRRITANT. **ACUTE EXPOSURE**- MAY CAUSE IRRITATION, REDNESS, AND PAIN. SENSITIVITY TO SULFUR, PARTICULARLY WHEN USED AS A TOPICAL AGENT, IS RARE. TWO CASES OF ALLERGIC HYPERSENSITIVITY TO SULFUR HAVE BEEN REPORTED. ABSORPTION OF SULFUR USED TO TREAT SCABIES AND OTHER SKIN DISORDERS MAY OCCUR AND CAUSE POISONING WITH SHOCK, SYNCOPE, FEVER AND POSSIBLY DEATH. ABSORPTION DEPENDS ON THE DEGREE OF INJURY TO THE SKIN; INTACT SKIN IS ALMOST IMPERVIOUS. **CHRONIC EXPOSURE**- REPEATED OR PROLONGED CONTACT MAY CAUSE DERMATITIS, POSSIBLY WITH ERYTHEMATOUS AND ECZEMATOUS LESIONS AND SIGNS OF ULCERATION.

FIRST AID- REMOVE CONTAMINATED CLOTHING AND SHOES IMMEDIATELY. WASH AFFECTED AREA WITH SOAP OR MILD DETERGENT AND LARGE AMOUNTS OF WATER UNTIL NO EVIDENCE OF CHEMICAL REMAINS (APPROXIMATELY 15-20 MINUTES). GET MEDICAL ATTENTION IMMEDIATELY.

EYE CONTACT: SULFUR: IRRITANT. **ACUTE EXPOSURE**- 8 PPM HAS CAUSED IRRITATION OF HUMAN EYES. DUST MAY CAUSE IRRITATION, REDNESS AND PAIN WITH LACRIMATION, PHOTOPHOBIA, CONJUNCTIVITIS AND BLEPHAROCONJUNCTIVITIS. CASES OF DAMAGE TO THE CRYSTALLINE LENS HAVE BEEN REPORTED WITH THE FORMATION OF OPACITIES AND EVEN CATARACT AND FOCAL CHORIORETINITIS. **CHRONIC EXPOSURE**- REPEATED OR PROLONGED EXPOSURE MAY CAUSE CONJUNCTIVITIS.

FIRST AID- WASH EYES IMMEDIATELY WITH LARGE AMOUNTS OF WATER OR NORMAL SALINE, OCCASIONALLY LIFTING UPPER AND LOWER LIDS, UNTIL NO EVIDENCE OF CHEMICAL REMAINS (APPROXIMATELY 15-20 MINUTES). GET MEDICAL ATTENTION IMMEDIATELY.

INGESTION: SULFUR: **ACUTE EXPOSURE**- A MAN HAS SURVIVED INGESTION OF 60 GRAMS OF SULFUR OVER A PERIOD OF 24 HOURS. LARGE DOSES (15 GRAMS) BY MOUTH MAY LEAD TO HYDROGEN SULFIDE PRODUCTION CHIEFLY DUE TO BACTERIAL ACTION WITHIN THE COLON. WITH LESSER AMOUNTS THIS IS RARE AND UNLIKELY IN THE ABSENCE OF MECHANICAL OBSTRUCTION. SMALL PARTICLES ARE GENERALLY MORE TOXIC THAN LARGE ONES. IN RABBITS A DOSE OF 175 MG/KG CAUSED CONVULSIONS, UNCONSCIOUSNESS, A HYDROGEN SULFIDE ODOR OF THE BREATH, FALL IN BLOOD PRESSURE, BRADYCARDIA, STIMULATION OF RESPIRATION FOLLOWED BY RESPIRATORY ARREST, AND DEATH. PATHOLOGIC FINDINGS INCLUDED PULONARY EDEMA AND HEMORRHAGE. **CHRONIC EXPOSURE**- VOLUNTEERS WHO INGESTED DAILY DOSES OF 500 OR 750 MG OF COLLOIDAL SULFUR ABSORBED IT COMPLETELY, TOLERATED IT EASILY, AND EXCRETED MOST OF IT WITHIN 24 HOURS.

FIRST AID- TREAT SYMPTOMATICALLY AND SUPPORTIVELY. GET MEDICAL ATTENTION IMMEDIATELY. IF VOMITING OCCURS, KEEP HEAD LOWER THAN HIPS TO PREVENT ASPIRATION.

ANTIDOTE: NO SPECIFIC ANTIDOTE. TREAT SYMPTOMATICALLY AND SUPPORTIVELY.

REACTIVITY

REACTIVITY: STABLE UNDER NORMAL TEMPERATURES AND PRESSURES.

INCOMPATIBILITIES: SULFUR: ALKALI METAL NITRIDES: FORMS HIGHLY FLAMMABLE MIXTURE WHICH EVOLVES AMMONIA AND HYDROGEN SULFIDE ON CONTACT WITH WATER. ALUMINUM (POWDER): POSSIBLE EXPLOSION. AMMONIA: MAY FORM EXPLOSIVE SULFUR NITRIDE. AMMONIUM NITRATE: FORMS SHOCK-SENSITIVE MIXTURE. BORON: INCANDESCENT REACTION ABOVE 600 C. BROMATES: CONTACT MAY RESULT IN IGNITION OR AN EXPLOSION. CADMIUM: EXPLOSIVE REACTION. CALCIUM: EXPLODES ON IGNITION. CALCIUM HYPOCHLORITE: EXPLOSIVE REACTION ON HEATING IN A CLOSED CONTAINER. CALCIUM PHOSPHIDE: INCANDESCES AT 300 C. CARBON (ACTIVATED): MAY IGNITE SPONTANEOUSLY. CHLORATES: CONTACT MAY RESULT IN IGNITION OR AN EXPLOSION. CHLORINE DIOXIDE: IGNITION WITH POSSIBLE EXPLOSION. CHLORINE MONOXIDE: VIOLENT EXPLOSION. CHLORINE TRIOXIDE: VIOLENT REACTION. CHROMIC ANHYDRIDE: IGNITION ON HEATING, POSSIBLE EXPLOSION. CHROMYL CHLORIDE: IGNITES. COPPER (POWDER): IGNITION ON WARMING. FLUORINE: IGNITION AT AMBIENT TEMPERATURES. GADOLINIUM: POSSIBLE EXPLOSION. HEPTASILVER NITRATE OCTAOXIDE: EXPLOSION ON IMPACT. HYDROCARBONS: MAY FORM EXPLOSIVE CONCENTRATIONS OF HYDROGEN SULFIDE AND CARBON DISULFIDE. INDIUM: IGNITION AND INCANDESCENCE ON HEATING. INTERHALOGENS: IGNITION WITH POSSIBLE INCANDESCENCE. IODATES: CONTACT MAY RESULT IN IGNITION OR AN EXPLOSION. IODINE PENTOXIDE: EXPLOSIVE REACTION ON WARMING. IRON: INCANDESCENT REACTION ON HEATING. LEAD CHLORITE: EXPLODES. LEAD CHROMATE: FORMS PYROPHORIC MIXTURE. LEAD DIOXIDE: EXPLODES. LITHIUM: VIOLENT, POSSIBLY EXPLOSIVE REACTION. MAGNESIUM: EXOTHERMIC REACTION. MERCURIC NITRATE: EXPLOSIVE REACTION. MERCURIC OXIDE: VIOLENT EXPLOSION. MERCUROUS OXIDE: IGNITION ON LIGHT IMPACT. MERCURY: EXOTHERMIC REACTION. METAL ACETYLIDES: CONTACT MAY RESULT IN IGNITION AND POSSIBLE INCANDESCENCE. METAL CARBIDES: CONTACT MAY RESULT IN IGNITION AND POSSIBLE INCANDESCENCE. METAL OXIDES: POSSIBLE IGNITION OR EXPLOSION. METALS: POSSIBLE IGNITION OR EXPLOSION. NICKEL (POWDER): IGNITES WITH INCANDESCENCE WITH BOILING SULFUR. NITROGEN DIOXIDE: BURNS VIGOROUSLY. OSMIUM (POWDER): IGNITES WITH INCANDESCENCE IN BOILING SULFUR. OXIDIZERS (STRONG): FIRE AND EXPLOSION HAZARD. PALLADIUM: IGNITES WITH INCANDESCENCE ON HEATING. PERCHLORATES: FORMS SHOCK SENSITIVE MIXTURES. PHOSPHORUS: IGNITION OR EXPLOSION WHEM WARMED. PHOSPHORUS TRIOXIDE: VIOLENT REACTION. POTASSIUM: VIOLENT REACTION ON WARMING. POTASSIUM + STANNIC IODIDE: EXPLOSIVE MIXTURE. POTASSIUM CHLORITE: VIOLENT REACTION. POTASSIUM NITRATE + ARSENIC TRISULFIDE: FORMS EXPLOSIVE MIXTURE. POTASSIUM PERMANGANATE: POSSIBLE EXPLOSION WITH FRICTION OR HEATING. RHODIUM: IGNITION AND INCANDESCENCE ON HEATING. RUBIDIUM (MOLTEN): IGNITES IN THE VAPOR. SELENIUM: IGNITION WITH INCANDESCENCE. SILVER CHLORITE: EXPLODES WITH FRICTION. SILVER NITRATE: VIOLENT EXPLOSION ON IMPACT. SILVER OXIDE: IGNITES ON FRICTION. SODIUM: VIOLENT OR EXPLOSIVE REACTION WITH HEAT OR FRICTION. SODIUM + STANNIC IODIDE: IMPACT SENSITIVE MIXTURE. SODIUM CHLORITE: IGNITES WITH MOISTURE. SODIUM HYDRIDE: VIGOROUS REACTION WITH SULFUR VAPOR. SODIUM NITRATE + CHARCOAL: EXPLOSIVE REACTION. SODIUM PEROXIDE: FORMS EXPLOSIVE MIXTURE. TANTALUM: POSSIBLE EXPLOSION. TETRAPHENYLLEAD: POSSIBLE EXPLOSION. TETRAPHOSPHORUS HEXOXIDE: VIOLENT REACTION @ 160 C. THALLIC OXIDE: EXPLODES WITH FRICTION. THORIUM: IGNITION AND INCANDESCENCE WITH HEATING. TIN: VIGOROUS REACTION WITH INCANDESCENCE AND IGNITION ON HEATING. URANIUM: INCANDESCENCE AND IGNITION WITH BOILING SULFUR. VANADIUM (V) OXIDE, WATER: IGNITION. ZINC (POWDER): EXPLOSIVE REACTION WHEN WARMED.

DECOMPOSITION: THERMAL DECOMPOSITION PRODUCTS MAY INCLUDE TOXIC OXIDES OF SULFUR.

POLYMERIZATION: HAZARDOUS POLYMERIZATION HAS NOT BEEN REPORTED TO OCCUR UNDER NORMAL TEMPERATURES AND PRESSURES.

STORAGE AND DISPOSAL

OBSERVE ALL FEDERAL, STATE AND LOCAL REGULATIONS WHEN STORING OR DISPOSING OF THIS SUBSTANCE. FOR ASSISTANCE, CONTACT THE DISTRICT DIRECTOR OF THE ENVIRONMENTAL PROTECTION AGENCY.

****STORAGE****

STORE AWAY FROM INCOMPATIBLE SUBSTANCES.

CONDITIONS TO AVOID

AVOID CONTACT WITH HEAT, SPARKS, FLAMES OR OTHER SOURCES OF IGNITION. MATERIAL IS EXTREMELY FLAMMABLE AND MAY BURN RAPIDLY WITH FLARE-BURNING EFFECT.

SPILL AND LEAK PROCEDURES

OCCUPATIONAL SPILL: SHUT OFF IGNITION SOURCES. DO NOT TOUCH SPILLED MATERIAL. FOR SMALL SPILLS, WITH CLEAN SHOVEL, PLACE MATERIAL INTO CLEAN, DRY CONTAINER AND COVER; MOVE CONTAINERS FROM SPILL AREA. FOR LARGER SPILLS, WET DOWN WITH WATER AND DIKE FOR LATER DISPOSAL. NO SMOKING, FLAMES OR FLARES IN HAZARD AREA! KEEP UNNECESSARY PEOPLE AWAY. ISOLATE HAZARD AREA AND DENY ENTRY.

PROTECTIVE EQUIPMENT

VENTILATION: PROVIDE GENERAL DILUTION VENTILATION.

RESPIRATOR: THE FOLLOWING RESPIRATORS ARE RECOMMENDED BASED ON INFORMATION FOUND IN THE PHYSICAL DATA, TOXICITY AND HEALTH EFFECTS SECTIONS. THEY ARE RANKED IN ORDER FROM MINIMUM TO MAXIMUM RESPIRATORY PROTECTION. THE SPECIFIC RESPIRATOR SELECTED MUST BE BASED ON CONTAMINATION LEVELS FOUND IN THE WORK PLACE, MUST NOT EXCEED THE WORKING LIMITS OF THE RESPIRATOR AND BE JOINTLY APPROVED BY THE NATIONAL INSTITUTE FOR OCCUPATIONAL SAFETY AND HEALTH AND THE MINE SAFETY AND HEALTH ADMINISTRATION (NIOSH-MSHA).

DUST AND MIST RESPIRATOR WITH A FULL FACEPIECE.

AIR-PURIFYING FULL FACEPIECE RESPIRATOR WITH A HIGH-EFFICIENCY

PARTICULATE FILTER.
POWERED AIR-PURIFYING RESPIRATOR WITH A TIGHT-FITTING FACEPIECE AND HIGH-EFFICIENCY PARTICULATE FILTER.
TYPE 'C' SUPPLIED-AIR RESPIRATOR WITH A FULL FACEPIECE OPERATED IN PRESSURE-DEMAND OR OTHER POSITIVE PRESSURE MODE OR WITH A FULL FACEPIECE, HELMET OR HOOD OPERATED IN CONTINUOUS-FLOW MODE.
SELF-CONTAINED BREATHING APPARATUS WITH A FULL FACEPIECE OPERATED IN PRESSURE-DEMAND OR OTHER POSITIVE PRESSURE MODE.
FOR FIREFIGHTING AND OTHER IMMEDIATELY DANGEROUS TO LIFE OR HEALTH CONDITIONS:
SELF-CONTAINED BREATHING APPARATUS WITH FULL FACEPIECE OPERATED IN PRESSURE-DEMAND OR OTHER POSITIVE PRESSURE MODE.
SUPPLIED-AIR RESPIRATOR WITH FULL FACEPIECE AND OPERATED IN PRESSURE-DEMAND OR OTHER POSITIVE PRESSURE MODE IN COMBINATION WITH AN AUXILIARY SELF-CONTAINED BREATHING APPARATUS OPERATED IN PRESSURE-DEMAND OR OTHER POSITIVE PRESSURE MODE.

CLOTHING: EMPLOYEE MUST WEAR APPROPRIATE PROTECTIVE (IMPERVIOUS) CLOTHING AND EQUIPMENT TO PREVENT REPEATED OR PROLONGED SKIN CONTACT WITH THIS SUBSTANCE.

GLOVES: EMPLOYEE MUST WEAR APPROPRIATE PROTECTIVE GLOVES TO PREVENT CONTACT WITH THIS SUBSTANCE.

EYE PROTECTION: EMPLOYEE MUST WEAR SPLASH-PROOF OR DUST-RESISTANT SAFETY GOGGLES TO PREVENT EYE CONTACT WITH THIS SUBSTANCE.
EMERGENCY EYE WASH: WHERE THERE IS ANY POSSIBILITY THAT AN EMPLOYEE'S EYES MAY BE EXPOSED TO THIS SUBSTANCE, THE EMPLOYER SHOULD PROVIDE AN EYE WASH FOUNTAIN WITHIN THE IMMEDIATE WORK AREA FOR EMERGENCY USE.

AUTHORIZED BY- OCCUPATIONAL HEALTH SERVICES, INC.
CREATION DATE: 10/05/89 ***REVISION DATE:*** 04/17/90

MATERIAL SAFETY DATA SHEET

OCCUPATIONAL HEALTH SERVICES, INC.
AGRICULTURE AND PESTICIDE DIVISION
450 SEVENTH AVENUE, SUITE 2407
NEW YORK, NEW YORK 10123
1-800-445-MSDS OR (212) 967-1100

EMERGENCY CONTACT:
JOHN S. BRANSFORD, JR. (615) 292-1180

SUBSTANCE IDENTIFICATION

CAS-NUMBER 7446-09-5
SUBSTANCE: SULFUR DIOXIDE
TRADE NAMES/SYNONYMS: SULFUROUS ACID ANHYDRIDE; SULFUROUS OXIDE; SULPHUR DIOXIDE; SULFUROUS ANHYDRIDE; FERMENTICIDE LIQUID; SULFUR DIOXIDE(SO2); SULFUR OXIDE; SULFUR OXIDE(SO2); STCC 4904290; UN 1079; O2S; PST22290
CHEMICAL FAMILY: INORGANIC GAS
MOLECULAR FORMULA: S-O2
MOLECULAR WEIGHT: 64.06
CERCLA RATINGS (SCALE 0-3): HEALTH=3 FIRE=0 REACTIVITY=0 PERSISTENCE=0
NFPA RATINGS (SCALE 0-4): HEALTH=2 FIRE=0 REACTIVITY=0

COMPONENTS AND CONTAMINANTS

COMPONENT: SULFUR DIOXIDE ***PERCENT:*** 100
CAS# 7446-09-5
OTHER CONTAMINANTS: NONE
EXPOSURE LIMITS: SULFUR DIOXIDE: 2 PPM (5 MG/M3) OSHA TWA; 5 PPM (10 MG/M3) OSHA STEL 2 PPM (5 MG/M3) ACGIH TWA; 5 PPM (10 MG/M3) ACGIH STEL 0.5 PPM NIOSH RECOMMENDED 10 HOUR TWA
500 POUNDS SARA SECTION 302 THRESHOLD PLANNING QUANTITY 1 POUND SARA SECTION 304 REPORTABLE QUANTITY

PHYSICAL DATA

DESCRIPTION: COLORLESS GAS OR LIQUID WITH A SUFFOCATING ODOR.
BOILING POINT: 14 F (-10 C) ***MELTING POINT:*** -99 F (-73 C)
SPECIFIC GRAVITY: 1.462 @ -10 C ***VAPOR PRESSURE:*** 2432 MMHG @ 20 C
EVAPORATION RATE: (BUTYL ACETATE=1) >1 ***PH:*** ACIDIC IN SOLUTION
SOLUBILITY IN WATER: 22.8% @ 0 C ***ODOR THRESHOLD:*** 3-5 PPM
VAPOR DENSITY: 2.26
SOLVENT SOLUBILITY: SOLUBLE IN ALCOHOL, ACETIC ACID, SULFURIC ACID, ETHER, CHLOROFORM, BENZENE, SULFURYL CHLORIDE, NITROBENZENE, TOLUENE, ACETONE.

FIRE AND EXPLOSION DATA

FIRE AND EXPLOSION HAZARD: NEGLIGIBLE FIRE HAZARD WHEN EXPOSED TO HEAT OR FLAME.
FIREFIGHTING MEDIA: DRY CHEMICAL, CARBON DIOXIDE OR HALON (1987 EMERGENCY RESPONSE GUIDEBOOK, DOT P 5800.4).
FOR LARGER FIRES, USE WATER SPRAY, FOG OR STANDARD FOAM (1987 EMERGENCY RESPONSE GUIDEBOOK, DOT P 5800.4).
FIREFIGHTING: MOVE CONTAINER FROM FIRE AREA IF POSSIBLE. STAY AWAY FROM STORAGE TANK ENDS. COOL FIRE-EXPOSED CONTAINERS WITH WATER FROM SIDE UNTIL WELL AFTER FIRE IS OUT. ISOLATE AREA UNTIL GAS HAS DISPERSED (1987 EMERGENCY RESPONSE GUIDEBOOK, DOT P 5800.4, GUIDE PAGE 16).
USE AGENTS SUITABLE FOR TYPE OF FIRE. COOL CONTAINERS WITH FLOODING AMOUNTS OF WATER, APPLY FROM AS FAR A DISTANCE AS POSSIBLE. AVOID BREATHING CORROSIVE VAPORS, KEEP UPWIND. CONSIDER EVACUATION OF DOWNWIND AREA IF MATERIAL IS LEAKING.

TRANSPORTATION DATA

DEPARTMENT OF TRANSPORTATION HAZARD CLASSIFICATION 49 CFR 172.101: NONFLAMMABLE GAS
DEPARTMENT OF TRANSPORTATION LABELING REQUIREMENTS 49 CFR 172.101 AND SUBPART E: NONFLAMMABLE GAS
DEPARTMENT OF TRANSPORTATION PACKAGING REQUIREMENTS: 49 CFR 173.304; 49 CFR 173.314 AND 49 CFR 173.315 EXCEPTIONS: 49 CFR 173.306

TOXICITY

SULFUR DIOXIDE: IRRITATION DATA: 6 PPM/4 HOURS/32 DAYS EYE-RABBIT MILD IRRITATION. TOXICITY DATA: 1000 PPM/10 MINUTES INHALATION-HUMAN LCLO; 3 PPM/5 DAYS INHALATION-HUMAN TCLO; 12 PPM/1 HOUR INHALATION-HUMAN TCLO; 3000 PPM/5 MINUTES INHALATION-HUMAN LCLO; 2520 PPM/1 HOUR INHALATION-RAT LC50; 3000 PPM/30 MINUTES INHALATION-MOUSE LC50; 3000 PPM/5 MINUTES INHALATION-MAMMAL LCLO; 1039 PPM/24 HOURS INHALATION-GUINEA PIG LCLO; MUTAGENIC DATA (RTECS); REPRODUCTIVE EFFECTS DATA (RTECS); TUMORIGENIC DATA (RTECS). CARCINOGEN STATUS: NONE. ANIMAL EXPERIMENTATION HAS INDICATED THAT SULFUR DIOXIDE MAY BE A POSSIBLE COCARCINOGENIC AGENT. LOCAL EFFECTS: CORROSIVE- EYE, SKIN AND MUCOUS MEMBRANES. ACUTE TOXICITY LEVEL: MODERATELY TOXIC BY INHALATION. TARGET EFFECTS: SENSITIZER- RESPIRATORY. AT INCREASED RISK FROM EXPOSURE: PERSONS WITH ASTHMA OR PRE-EXISTING RESPIRATORY DISORDERS. EXPERIMENTATION HAS INDICATED THAT SULFUR DIOXIDE MAY BE A COCARCINOGENIC AGENT.

HEALTH EFFECTS AND FIRST AID

INHALATION: SULFUR DIOXIDE: CORROSIVE/SENSITIZER. 100 PPM IMMEDIATELY DANGEROUS TO LIFE OR HEALTH. ACUTE EXPOSURE- RESPIRATORY EFFECTS MAY OCCUR AT 5 PPM AND HIGHER LEVELS MAY CAUSE INTENSE IRRITATION OF THE MUCOUS MEMBRANES, SEVERE CHOKING, VIOLENT COUGH, HOARSENESS, SNEEZING, NASOPHARYNGITIS, RHINORRHEA, CHEST PAIN OR TIGHTNESS, REFLEX BRONCHOCONSTRICTION WITH INCREASED PULMONARY RESISTANCE, DYSPNEA, CYANOSIS, NAUSEA, VOMITING, ABDOMINAL PAIN, SYSTEMIC ACIDOSIS, AND UNCONSCIOUSNESS. IN SEVERE EXPOSURES SYMPTOMS, POSSIBLY DELAYED, MAY INCLUDE PULMONARY AND GLOTTAL EDEMA, CHEMICAL PNEUMONITIS OR BRONCHOPNEUMONIA WITH BRONCHIOLITIS OBLITERANS AND RALES. DEATH MAY BE CAUSED BY RESPIRATORY PARALYSIS, PULMONARY EDEMA OR SYSTEMIC ACIDOSIS. CONVULSIONS MAY OCCUR TERMINALLY. THE EFFECTS ON PULMONARY FUNCTION ARE INCREASED IN THE PRESENCE OF RESPIRABLE PARTICLES AND SOME INDIVIDUALS ARE MORE SENSITIVE THAN OTHERS.
CHRONIC EXPOSURE- REPEATED OR PROLONGED EXPOSURE MAY CAUSE IRRITATION AND INFLAMMATION OF THE RESPIRATORY TRACT, A SENSATION OF BURNING, DRYNESS, AND PAIN IN THE NOSE AND THROAT, COUGH, POSSIBLY WITH BLOODY SPUTUM, NOSEBLEEDS, ULCERATION OF THE NASAL SEPTUM, INCREASED MUCUS SECRETION, ALTERATION OF THE SENSE OF TASTE AND SMELL, DYSPNEA, INCREASED AIRWAY RESISTANCE AND EMPHYSEMA. THERE MAY ALSO BE POLYCYTHEMIA, FATIGUE, GASTRIC DISTURBANCES, NERVOUS SYSTEM DISORDERS, GINGIVAL DISORDERS, DENTAL CARIES AND RAPID, PAINLESS DENTAL DESTRUCTION. STUDIES INDICATE THERE MAY BE A RELATIONSHIP BETWEEN CHRONIC RESPIRATORY ILLNESS AND THE FREQUENCY OF EXPOSURE TO SULFUR DIOXIDE. INCREASED SENSITIVITY HAS BEEN REPORTED IN SOME PERSONS. SLIGHT TOLERANCE TO THE ODOR THRESHOLD AND GENERAL ACCLIMATIZATION ARE COMMON IN EXPERIENCED WORKERS. IN A 32 YEAR EPIDEMIOLOGICAL STUDY ON 14,562 WHITE MALE WORKERS FROM THE COPPER AND ZINC SMELTING INDUSTRIES, A STATISTICALLY SIGNIFICANT ASSOCIATION WAS NOTED FOR EMPHYSEMA MORTALITY WITH INCREASING DURATION OF EXPOSURE TO SULFUR DIOXIDE AT PEAK VALUES EXCEEDING 24 PPM. STUDIES

WITH EXPERIMENTAL ANIMALS INDICATE THAT REPEATED EXPOSURE BEFORE OR DURING PREGNANCY MAY CAUSE FEMALE REPRODUCTIVE SYSTEM EFFECTS, MALE REPRODUCTIVE SYSTEM EFFECTS, EFFECTS ON THE NEWBORN, AND SPECIFIC DEVELOPMENTAL ABNORMALITIES.

FIRST AID- REMOVE FROM EXPOSURE AREA TO FRESH AIR IMMEDIATELY. IF BREATHING HAS STOPPED, GIVE ARTIFICIAL RESPIRATION. MAINTAIN AIRWAY AND BLOOD PRESSURE AND ADMINISTER OXYGEN IF AVAILABLE. KEEP AFFECTED PERSON WARM AND AT REST. TREAT SYMPTOMATICALLY AND SUPPORTIVELY. ADMINISTRATION OF OXYGEN SHOULD BE PERFORMED BY QUALIFIED PERSONNEL. GET MEDICAL ATTENTION IMMEDIATELY.

SKIN CONTACT: SULFUR DIOXIDE: CORROSIVE. **ACUTE EXPOSURE**- HIGH CONCENTRATIONS OF GAS IN CONTACT WITH MOIST SKIN MAY CAUSE IRRITATION, POSSIBLY SEVERE. CONTACT WITH LIQUIFIED GAS MAY CAUSE FROSTBITE, REDNESS, PAIN AND BURNS. **CHRONIC EXPOSURE**- REPEATED OR PROLONGED CONTACT MAY RESULT IN DERMATITIS.

FIRST AID- REMOVE CONTAMINATED CLOTHING AND SHOES IMMEDIATELY. WASH AFFECTED AREA WITH SOAP OR MILD DETERGENT AND LARGE AMOUNTS OF WATER UNTIL NO EVIDENCE OF CHEMICAL REMAINS (AT LEAST 15-20 MINUTES). IN CASE OF CHEMICAL BURNS, COVER AREA WITH STERILE, DRY DRESSING. BANDAGE SECURELY, BUT NOT TOO TIGHTLY. GET MEDICAL ATTENTION IMMEDIATELY.

EYE CONTACT: SULFUR DIOXIDE: CORROSIVE. **ACUTE EXPOSURE**- IRRITATION MAY BEGIN AROUND 10-20 PPM WITH SMARTING AND LACRIMATION. HIGHER CONCENTRATIONS MAY CAUSE INTENSE IRRITATION AND INFLAMMATION OF THE CONJUNCTIVA. MILD CASES OF DIRECT LIQUID CONTACT HAVE RESULTED IN SUPERFICIAL INJURY TO THE CORNEA AND CONJUNCTIVA WITH RECOVERY. SEVERE CASES HAVE TYPICALLY RESULTED IN LITTLE DISCOMFORT, IMMEDIATE BLURRING AND PROGRESSIVE WORSENING OF VISION AND, IN THE WORST CASES, PERMANENT OPACITY OF THE CORNEA, SOMETIMES ACCOMPANIED BY EXTENSIVE SYMBLEPHARON AND LOSS OF VISION. **CHRONIC EXPOSURE**- REPEATED OR PROLONGED EXPOSURE MAY CAUSE CONJUNCTIVITIS WITH DISCOMFORT AND LACRIMATION.

FIRST AID- WASH EYES IMMEDIATELY WITH LARGE AMOUNTS OF WATER, OCCASIONALLY LIFTING UPPER AND LOWER LIDS, UNTIL NO EVIDENCE OF CHEMICAL REMAINS (AT LEAST 15-20 MINUTES). CONTINUE IRRIGATING WITH NORMAL SALINE UNTIL THE PH HAS RETURNED TO NORMAL (30-60 MINUTES). COVER WITH STERILE BANDAGES. GET MEDICAL ATTENTION IMMEDIATELY.

INGESTION: SULFUR DIOXIDE: **ACUTE EXPOSURE**- INGESTION OF A GAS IS UNLIKELY, ALTHOUGH SMALL AMOUNTS MAY BE DISSOLVED AND SWALLOWED IN THE SALIVA. **CHRONIC EXPOSURE**- NO DATA AVAILABLE.

FIRST AID- IT IS UNLIKELY THAT EMERGENCY TREATMENT WILL BE REQUIRED. IF ADVERSE EFFECTS OCCUR, TREAT SYMPTOMATICALLY AND SUPPORTIVELY AND GET MEDICAL ATTENTION.

ANTIDOTE: NO SPECIFIC ANTIDOTE. TREAT SYMPTOMATICALLY AND SUPPORTIVELY.

REACTIVITY

REACTIVITY: STABLE UNDER NORMAL TEMPERATURES AND PRESSURES.

INCOMPATIBILITIES: SULFUR DIOXIDE: ACROLEIN: EXOTHERMIC POLYMERIZATION ON CONTACT. ALUMINUM: IGNITES. AMMONIA: VIOLENT REACTION. BARIUM PEROXIDE: INCANDESCES WHEN HEATED. BROMINE PENTAFLUORIDE: VIOLENT REACTION AND POSSIBLE IGNITION. CESIUM ACETYLIDE: INCANDESCENT REACTION. CESIUM AZIDE: IGNITES ON CONTACT. CESIUM MONOXIDE: INCANDESCENT REACTION WHEN HEATED. CHLORATES: FORMS EXPLOSIVE CHLORINE PEROXIDE. CHLORINE TRIFLUORIDE: VIOLENT OR EXPLOSIVE REACTION. CHROMIUM: INCANDESCENT REACTION. DIETHYLZINC: VIOLENT EXPLOSIVE REACTION @ -15 C. FERROUS OXIDE: INCANDESCENT REACTION. FLUORINE: EXPLODES ON CONTACT. HALOGENS: IGNITION OR VIOLENT REACTION. INTERHALOGENS: IGNITION OR VIOLENT REACTION. LEAD OXIDE: IGNITES ON HEATING. LITHIUM ACETYLIDE: IGNITES ON CONTACT. LITHIUM NITRATE AND PROPYLENE: EXPLOSIVE POLYMERIZATION REACTION. MANGANESE: IGNITES WHEN HEATED. METAL ACETYLIDES: POSSIBLE INCANDESCENT REACTION. METAL OXIDES: IGNITION OR VIOLENT REACTION. METALS: MAY CORRODE IN THE PRESENCE OF MOISTURE. METALS (POWDERED): FIRE AND EXPLOSION HAZARD. NITRIC ACID: EXPLOSIVE REACTION. POTASSIUM: IGNITION @ 60 C. POTASSIUM ACETYLIDE: IGNITION REACTION. POTASSIUM CHLORATE: MAY IGNITE ABOVE 60 C. POTASSIUM CHLORATE + ETHANOL: EXPLODES ON CONTACT. POTASSIUM CHLORATE + ETHER: EXPLODES ON CONTACT. RUBIDIUM CARBIDE: IGNITES WHEN WARMED. SILVER AZIDE: EXPLOSIVE @ ELEVATED TEMPERATURES. SODIUM: VIOLENT REACTION. SODIUM ACETYLIDE: EXPLOSIVE REACTION. SODIUM HYDRIDE: EXPLOSIVE REACTION. STANNOUS OXIDE: IGNITION REACTION.

DECOMPOSITION: THERMAL DECOMPOSITION PRODUCTS MAY INCLUDE TOXIC OXIDES OF SULFUR.

POLYMERIZATION: HAZARDOUS POLYMERIZATION HAS NOT BEEN REPORTED TO OCCUR UNDER NORMAL TEMPERATURES AND PRESSURES.

STORAGE AND DISPOSAL

OBSERVE ALL FEDERAL, STATE AND LOCAL REGULATIONS WHEN STORING OR DISPOSING OF THIS SUBSTANCE. FOR ASSISTANCE, CONTACT THE DISTRICT DIRECTOR OF THE ENVIRONMENTAL PROTECTION AGENCY.

****STORAGE****

PROTECT AGAINST PHYSICAL DAMAGE; STORE OUTDOORS OR IN A WELL VENTILATED AREA OF NONCOMBUSTIBLE CONSTRUCTION (NFPA 49, HAZARDOUS CHEMICALS DATA, 1975).

STORE AWAY FROM INCOMPATIBLE SUBSTANCES.

THRESHOLD PLANNING QUANTITY (TPQ): THE SUPERFUND AMENDMENTS AND REAUTHORIZATION ACT (SARA) SECTION 302 REQUIRES THAT EACH FACILITY WHERE ANY EXTREMELY HAZARDOUS SUBSTANCE IS PRESENT IN A QUANTITY EQUAL TO OR GREATER THAN THE TPQ ESTABLISHED FOR THAT SUBSTANCE NOTIFY THE STATE EMERGENCY RESPONSE COMMISSION FOR THE STATE IN WHICH IT IS LOCATED. SECTION 303 OF SARA REQUIRES THESE FACILITIES TO PARTICIPATE IN LOCAL EMERGENCY RESPONSE PLANNING (40 CFR 355.30).

CONDITIONS TO AVOID

AVOID CONTACT WITH SKIN OR INHALATION OF VAPORS. CONTAINERS MAY PRESENT AN EXPLOSION HAZARD IN FIRE CONDITIONS.

SPILL AND LEAK PROCEDURES

OCCUPATIONAL SPILL: STOP LEAK IF YOU CAN DO IT WITHOUT RISK. USE WATER SPRAY TO REDUCE VAPORS BUT DO NOT PUT WATER ON LEAK OR SPILL AREA. ISOLATE AREA UNTIL GAS HAS DISPERSED. KEEP UNNECESSARY PEOPLE AWAY; ISOLATE HAZARD AREA AND DENY ENTRY. VENTILATE CLOSED SPACES BEFORE ENTERING.

REPORTABLE QUANTITY (RQ): 1 POUND THE SUPERFUND AMENDMENTS AND REAUTHORIZATION ACT (SARA) SECTION 304 REQUIRES THAT A RELEASE EQUAL TO OR GREATER THAN THE REPORTABLE QUANTITY FOR THIS SUBSTANCE BE IMMEDIATELY REPORTED TO THE LOCAL EMERGENCY PLANNING COMMITTEE AND THE STATE EMERGENCY RESPONSE COMMISSION (40 CFR 355.40). IF THE RELEASE OF THIS SUBSTANCE IS REPORTABLE UNDER CERCLA SECTION 103, THE NATIONAL RESPONSE CENTER MUST BE NOTIFIED IMMEDIATELY AT (800) 424-8802 OR (202) 426-2675 IN THE METROPOLITAN WASHINGTON, D.C. AREA (40 CFR 302.6).

PROTECTIVE EQUIPMENT

VENTILATION: PROVIDE LOCAL EXHAUST OR PROCESS ENCLOSURE VENTILATION TO MEET PUBLISHED EXPOSURE LIMITS.

RESPIRATOR: THE FOLLOWING RESPIRATORS AND MAXIMUM USE CONCENTRATIONS ARE RECOMMENDATIONS BY THE U.S. DEPARTMENT OF HEALTH AND HUMAN SERVICES, NIOSH POCKET GUIDE TO CHEMICAL HAZARDS; NIOSH CRITERIA DOCUMENTS OR BY THE U.S. DEPARTMENT OF LABOR, 29 CFR 1910 SUBPART Z. THE SPECIFIC RESPIRATOR SELECTED MUST BE BASED ON CONTAMINATION LEVELS FOUND IN THE WORK PLACE, MUST NOT EXCEED THE WORKING LIMITS OF THE RESPIRATOR AND BE JOINTLY APPROVED BY THE NATIONAL INSTITUTE FOR OCCUPATIONAL SAFETY AND HEALTH AND THE MINE SAFETY AND HEALTH ADMINISTRATION (NIOSH-MSHA).

SULFUR DIOXIDE: 5 PPM- ANY SUPPLIED-AIR RESPIRATOR. ANY SELF-CONTAINED BREATHING APPARATUS. ANY CHEMICAL CARTRIDGE RESPIRATOR WITH CARTRIDGE(S) PROVIDING PROTECTION AGAINST SULFUR DIOXIDE.

12.5 PPM- ANY SUPPLIED-AIR RESPIRATOR OPERATED IN A CONTINUOUS FLOW MODE. ANY POWERED AIR-PURIFYING RESPIRATOR WITH CARTRIDGE(S) PROVIDING PROTECTION AGAINST SULFUR DIOXIDE.

25 PPM- ANY SUPPLIED-AIR RESPIRATOR WITH A FULL FACEPIECE. ANY SELF-CONTAINED BREATHING APPARATUS WITH A FULL FACEPIECE. ANY CHEMICAL CARTRIDGE RESPIRATOR WITH A FULL FACEPIECE AND CARTRIDGE(S) PROVIDING PROTECTION AGAINST SULFUR DIOXIDE. ANY AIR-PURIFYING FULL FACEPIECE RESPIRATOR (GAS MASK) WITH CHIN-STYLE OR FRONT- OR BACK-MOUNTED CANISTER PROVIDING PROTECTION AGAINST SULFUR DIOXIDE.

100 PPM- ANY SUPPLIED-AIR RESPIRATOR WITH FULL FACEPIECE OPERATED IN PRESSURE-DEMAND OR OTHER POSITIVE PRESSURE MODE.

ESCAPE- ANY AIR-PURIFYING FULL FACEPIECE RESPIRATOR (GAS MASK) WITH CHIN-STYLE OR FRONT- OR BACK-MOUNTED CANISTER PROVIDING PROTECTION AGAINST SULFUR DIOXIDE. ANY ESCAPE-TYPE SELF-CONTAINED BREATHING APPARATUS.

FOR FIREFIGHTING AND OTHER IMMEDIATELY DANGEROUS TO LIFE OR HEALTH CONDITIONS:

SELF-CONTAINED BREATHING APPARATUS WITH FULL FACEPIECE OPERATED IN PRESSURE-DEMAND OR OTHER POSITIVE PRESSURE MODE.

SUPPLIED-AIR RESPIRATOR WITH FULL FACEPIECE AND OPERATED IN PRESSURE-DEMAND OR OTHER POSITIVE PRESSURE MODE IN COMBINATION WITH AN AUXILIARY SELF-CONTAINED BREATHING APPARATUS OPERATED IN PRESSURE-DEMAND OR OTHER POSITIVE PRESSURE MODE.

CLOTHING: WEAR IMPERVIOUS CLOTHING TO PREVENT CONTACT WITH THE GAS FORM. IF CONTACT WITH THE LIQUIFIED GAS IS POSSIBLE, EMPLOYEE MUST WEAR APPROPRIATE PROTECTIVE CLOTHING AND EQUIPMENT TO PREVENT SKIN FROM FREEZING.

GLOVES: WEAR FULL PROTECTIVE, COLD INSULATING GLOVES.

EYE PROTECTION: EMPLOYEE MUST WEAR SPLASH-PROOF OR DUST-RESISTANT SAFETY GOGGLES AND A FACESHIELD TO PREVENT CONTACT WITH THIS SUBSTANCE.

EMERGENCY WASH FACILITIES: WHERE THERE IS ANY POSSIBILITY THAT AN EMPLOYEE'S EYES AND/OR SKIN MAY BE EXPOSED TO THIS SUBSTANCE, THE EMPLOYER SHOULD PROVIDE AN EYE WASH FOUNTAIN AND QUICK DRENCH SHOWER WITHIN THE IMMEDIATE WORK AREA FOR EMERGENCY USE.

AUTHORIZED BY- OCCUPATIONAL HEALTH SERVICES, INC.
CREATION DATE: 02/08/90 ***REVISION DATE:*** 05/16/90

MATERIAL SAFETY DATA SHEET

OCCUPATIONAL HEALTH SERVICES, INC.
AGRICULTURE AND PESTICIDE DIVISION
450 SEVENTH AVENUE, SUITE 2407
NEW YORK, NEW YORK 10123
1-800-445-MSDS OR (212) 967-1100

EMERGENCY CONTACT:
JOHN S. BRANSFORD, JR. (615) 292-1180

SUBSTANCE IDENTIFICATION

CAS-NUMBER 7664-93-9

SUBSTANCE: **SULFURIC ACID**

TRADE NAMES/SYNONYMS: OIL OF VITRIOL; BOV; DIPPING ACID; VITRIOL BROWN OIL; HYDROGEN SULFATE; NORDHADSEN ACID; DIHYDROGEN SULFATE; SULPHURIC ACID; MATTING ACID; DITHIONIC ACID; STCC 4930040; UN 1830; SULFURIC ACID 66 BAUME (COLLIER CARBON & CHEMICAL CORP.); H2O4S; OIL OF VITRIOL BATTERY ACID (SPECTRUM CHEMICAL MFG.CORP.); PST22350

CHEMICAL FAMILY: INORGANIC ACID

MOLECULAR FORMULA: H2-S-O4

MOLECULAR WEIGHT: 98.07

CERCLA RATINGS (SCALE 0-3): HEALTH=3 FIRE=0 REACTIVITY=2 PERSISTENCE=0

NFPA RATINGS (SCALE 0-4): HEALTH=3 FIRE=0 REACTIVITY=2

COMPONENTS AND CONTAMINANTS

COMPONENT: SULFURIC ACID ***PERCENT:*** 98

COMPONENT: WATER ***PERCENT:*** 2

OTHER CONTAMINANTS: NONE

EXPOSURE LIMITS: SULFURIC ACID: 1 MG/M3 OSHA TWA 1 MG/M3 ACGIH TWA; 3 MG/M3 ACGIH STEL 1 MG/M3 NIOSH RECOMMENDED 10 HOUR TWA
1000 POUNDS SARA SECTION 302 THRESHOLD PLANNING QUANTITY 1000 POUNDS SARA SECTION 304 REPORTABLE QUANTITY 1000 POUNDS CERCLA SECTION 103 REPORTABLE QUANTITY SUBJECT TO SARA SECTION 313 ANNUAL TOXIC CHEMICAL RELEASE REPORTING

PHYSICAL DATA

DESCRIPTION: ODORLESS, CLEAR, COLORLESS, DENSE HYGROSCOPIC OILY LIQUID WITH A MARKED ACID TASTE WHEN PURE.

BOILING POINT: 559 F (290 C)

MELTING POINT: 50 F (10 C) ***SPECIFIC GRAVITY:*** 1.84

VAPOR PRESSURE: <0.001 @ 20 C ***PH:*** <3 ***SOLUBILITY IN WATER:*** SOLUBLE

ODOR THRESHOLD: >1 MG/M3 (MIST) ***VAPOR DENSITY:*** 3.4

SOLVENT SOLUBILITY: DECOMPOSES IN ETHYL ALCOHOL
@ 340 C IT DECOMPOSES INTO SULFUR TRIOXIDE AND WATER

FIRE AND EXPLOSION DATA

FIRE AND EXPLOSION HAZARD: NEGLIGIBLE FIRE HAZARD WHEN EXPOSED TO HEAT OR FLAME.

OXIDIZER: OXIDIZERS DECOMPOSE, ESPECIALLY WHEN HEATED, TO YIELD OXYGEN OR OTHER GASES WHICH WILL INCREASE THE BURNING RATE OF COMBUSTIBLE MATTER. CONTACT WITH EASILY OXIDIZABLE, ORGANIC, OR OTHER COMBUSTIBLE MATERIALS MAY RESULT IN IGNITION, VIOLENT COMBUSTION OR EXPLOSION.

FIREFIGHTING MEDIA: DRY CHEMICAL, CARBON DIOXIDE OR HALON (1987 EMERGENCY RESPONSE GUIDEBOOK, DOT P 5800.4).

FOR LARGER FIRES, FLOOD AREA WITH WATER FROM A DISTANCE (1987 EMERGENCY RESPONSE GUIDEBOOK, DOT P 5800.4).

FIREFIGHTING: DO NOT GET SOLID STREAM OF WATER ON SPILLED MATERIAL. MOVE CONTAINERS FROM FIRE AREA IF POSSIBLE. COOL CONTAINERS EXPOSED TO FLAMES WITH WATER FROM SIDE UNTIL WELL AFTER FIRE IS OUT. KEEP AWAY FROM STORAGE TANK ENDS (1987 EMERGENCY RESPONSE GUIDEBOOK, DOT P 5800.4 GUIDE PAGE 39).

USE AGENT SUITABLE FOR TYPE OF FIRE; USE FLOODING AMOUNTS OF WATER AS A FOG. COOL CONTAINERS WITH FLOODING AMOUNTS OF WATER, APPLY FROM AS FAR A DISTANCE AS POSSIBLE. AVOID BREATHING CORROSIVE VAPORS, KEEP UPWIND.

TRANSPORTATION DATA

DEPARTMENT OF TRANSPORTATION HAZARD CLASSIFICATION 49 CFR 172.101: CORROSIVE MATERIAL

DEPARTMENT OF TRANSPORTATION LABELING REQUIREMENTS 49 CFR 172.101 AND SUBPART E: CORROSIVE

DEPARTMENT OF TRANSPORTATION PACKAGING REQUIREMENTS: 49 CFR 173.272 EXCEPTIONS: 49 CFR 173.244

TOXICITY

SULFURIC ACID: IRRITATION DATA: 1380 UG EYE-RABBIT SEVERE; 5 MG/30 SECONDS RINSED EYE-RABBIT SEVERE. TOXICITY DATA: 3 MG/M3/24 WEEKS INHALATION-HUMAN TCLO; 510 MG/M3/2 HOURS INHALATION-RAT LC50; 320 MG/M3/2 HOURS INHALATION-MOUSE LC50; 18 MG/M3 INHALATION-GUINEA PIG LC50; 2140 MG/KG ORAL-RAT LD50; 135 MG/KG UNREPORTED-MAN LDLO; REPRODUCTIVE EFFECTS DATA (RTECS); TUMORIGENIC DATA (AJEPAS 120(3), 358, 84). CARCINOGEN STATUS: NONE. LOCAL EFFECTS: CORROSIVE- INHALATION, SKIN, AND EYES. ACUTE TOXICITY LEVEL: HIGHLY TOXIC BY INHALATION; MODERATELY TOXIC BY INGESTION. TARGET EFFECTS: POISONING MAY AFFECT THE BODY'S PH BALANCE AND IN TURN AFFECT THE NERVOUS SYSTEM.

HEALTH EFFECTS AND FIRST AID

INHALATION: SULFURIC ACID: CORROSIVE/HIGHLY TOXIC. 80 MG/M3 IMMEDIATELY DANGEROUS TO LIFE OR HEALTH. **ACUTE EXPOSURE-** INHALATION OF MISTS MAY CAUSE MUCOUS MEMBRANE IRRITATION PRINCIPALLY AFFECTING THE RESPIRATORY TRACT EPITHELIUM. LOW CONCENTRATIONS, 0.35-5 MG/M3, MAY CAUSE INCREASED PULMONARY AIR FLOW RESISTANCE AND SUBSEQUENT SHALLOWER AND MORE RAPID BREATHING. HOT CONCENTRATED MISTS MAY CAUSE RAPID LOSS OF CONSCIOUSNESS WITH POSSIBLE DAMAGE TO LUNG TISSUE. VAPORS MAY CAUSE NASAL SECRETIONS, SNEEZING, A BURNING OR TICKLING SENSATION IN THE NOSE AND THROAT AND RETROSTERNAL REGION, FOLLOWED BY COUGH, RESPIRATORY DISTRESS, TRACHEOBRONCHITIS, CHEMICAL PNEUMONITIS AND POSSIBLE SPASM OF THE VOCAL CORDS. HIGH CONCENTRATIONS MAY PRODUCE BLOODY NASAL SECRETIONS AND SPUTUM, HEMATEMESIS GASTRITIS, AND PULMONARY EDEMA. A SINGLE OVEREXPOSURE MAY LEAD TO LARYNGEAL, TRACHEOBRONCHIAL AND PULMONARY EDEMA. ONE INDIVIDUAL SPRAYED IN THE FACE WITH SULFURIC ACID LIQUID EXPERIENCED DELAYED SYMPTOMS OF PULMONARY FIBROSIS, RESIDUAL BRONCHITIS, AND PULMONARY EMPHYSEMA. VAPORS FROM DILUTE SOLUTIONS MAY IRRITATE MUCOUS MEMBRANES. **CHRONIC EXPOSURE-** REPEATED EXPOSURE TO THE MIST MAY CAUSE INFLAMMATION OF THE UPPER RESPIRATORY TRACT, CHRONIC BRONCHITIS AND ETCHING OF THE DENTAL ENAMEL. THE CENTRAL AND LATERAL INCISORS ARE PRIMARILY AFFECTED. REPEATED EXCESSIVE EXPOSURE OVER LONG PERIODS OF TIME HAVE RESULTED IN BRONCHITIC SYMPTOMS, RHINORRHEA, FREQUENT RESPIRATORY TRACT INFECTIONS, EMPHYSEMA, STOMATITIS AND DIGESTIVE DISTURBANCES. CHRONIC INHALATION MAY CAUSE ALKALINE DEPLETION OF THE BODY PRODUCING AN ACIDOSIS WHICH AFFECTS THE NERVOUS SYSTEM AND PRODUCES AGITATION, HESITANT GAIT AND GENERALIZED WEAKNESS. AN EPIDEMIOLOGICAL STUDY OF WORKERS AT A REFINERY AND CHEMICAL PLANT SUGGESTS AN INCREASED RISK OF LARYNGEAL CANCER FROM EXPOSURE TO HIGH CONCENTRATIONS OF SULFURIC ACID. REPRODUCTIVE EFFECTS HAVE BEEN REPORTED IN ANIMALS.

FIRST AID- REMOVE FROM EXPOSURE AREA TO FRESH AIR IMMEDIATELY. IF BREATHING HAS STOPPED, GIVE ARTIFICIAL RESPIRATION. MAINTAIN AIRWAY AND BLOOD PRESSURE AND ADMINISTER OXYGEN IF AVAILABLE. KEEP AFFECTED PERSON WARM AND AT REST. TREAT SYMPTOMATICALLY AND SUPPORTIVELY. ADMINISTRATION OF OXYGEN SHOULD BE PERFORMED BY QUALIFIED PERSONNEL. GET MEDICAL ATTENTION IMMEDIATELY.

SKIN CONTACT: SULFURIC ACID: CORROSIVE. **ACUTE EXPOSURE-** CONTACT WITH CONCENTRATED SULFURIC ACID MAY CAUSE SEVERE SECOND AND THIRD DEGREE SKIN BURNS WITH NECROSIS DUE TO ITS AFFINITY FOR WATER AND SUBSEQUENT SEVERE DEHYDRATING ACTION, AND ITS EXOTHERMIC REACTION WITH MOISTURE. POSSIBLE CHARRING MAY OCCUR LEADING TO SHOCK AND COLLAPSE DEPENDING ON THE AMOUNT OF TISSUE INVOLVED. THE RESULTING WOUNDS MAY BE LONG IN HEALING AND MAY CAUSE EXTENSIVE SCARRING THAT MAY RESULT IN FUNCTIONAL INHIBITION. CONTACT WITH DILUTE SOLUTIONS MAY CAUSE SKIN

IRRITATION. **CHRONIC EXPOSURE-** REPEATED CONTACT WITH LOW CONCENTRATIONS MAY CAUSE SKIN DESICCATION AND ULCERATION OF THE HANDS, AND PANARIS OR CHRONIC PURULENT INFLAMMATION AROUND THE NAILS. REPEATED CONTACT WITH DILUTE SOLUTIONS MAY CAUSE DERMATITIS.
FIRST AID- REMOVE CONTAMINATED CLOTHING AND SHOES IMMEDIATELY. WASH AFFECTED AREA WITH SOAP OR MILD DETERGENT AND LARGE AMOUNTS OF WATER UNTIL NO EVIDENCE OF CHEMICAL REMAINS (AT LEAST 15-20 MINUTES). IN CASE OF CHEMICAL BURNS, COVER AREA WITH STERILE, DRY DRESSING. BANDAGE SECURELY, BUT NOT TOO TIGHTLY. GET MEDICAL ATTENTION IMMEDIATELY.

EYE CONTACT: SULFURIC ACID: CORROSIVE. **ACUTE EXPOSURE-** EXPOSURE TO THE VAPORS MAY CAUSE A BURNING OR STINGING SENSATION IN THE EYES WITH LACRIMATION, BLURRED VISION AND CONJUNCTIVAL CONGESTION. SPLASHES OF ACID IN THE EYES MAY PRODUCE DEEP CORNEAL ULCERATION, KERATO-CONJUNCTIVITIS AND PALPEBRAL LESIONS WITH SEVERE SEQUELAE. IRREPARABLE CORNEAL DAMAGE AND BLINDNESS AS WELL AS SCARRING OF THE EYELIDS MAY OCCUR. SEVERE SULFURIC ACID EYE BURNS HAVE INCLUDED GLAUCOMA AND CATARACT AS COMPLICATIONS IN THE MOST SEVERE CASES. CONTACT WITH DILUTED ACID MAY PRODUCE MORE TRANSIENT EFFECTS FROM WHICH RECOVERY MAY BE COMPLETE. **CHRONIC EXPOSURE-** REPEATED EXPOSURE MAY RESULT IN LACRIMATION AND CHRONIC CONJUNCTIVITIS.
FIRST AID- WASH EYES IMMEDIATELY WITH LARGE AMOUNTS OF WATER, OCCASIONALLY LIFTING UPPER AND LOWER LIDS, UNTIL NO EVIDENCE OF CHEMICAL REMAINS (AT LEAST 15-20 MINUTES). CONTINUE IRRIGATING WITH NORMAL SALINE UNTIL THE PH HAS RETURNED TO NORMAL (30-60 MINUTES). COVER WITH STERILE BANDAGES. GET MEDICAL ATTENTION IMMEDIATELY.

INGESTION: SULFURIC ACID: CORROSIVE: **ACUTE EXPOSURE-** INGESTION MAY CAUSE BURNING PAIN IN THE MOUTH, THROAT, ESOPHAGUS AND ABDOMEN, A SOUR TASTE AND NAUSEA FOLLOWED BY VOMITING AND DIARRHEA OF CHARRED BLACK STOMACH CONTENTS. DEHYDRATION AND CARBONIZATION OF TISSUE MAY OCCUR WITH ESCHARS ON THE LIPS AND MOUTH. BROWNISH OR YELLOWISH STAINS MAY BE FOUND AROUND THE MOUTH, INTENSE THIRST, DIFFICULT SWALLOWING, ACIDEMIA, STOMATITIS, RAPID AND WEAK PULSE, SHALLOW BREATHING, SHOCK AND POSSIBLE CONVULSIONS MAY OCCUR. ALBUMIN, BLOOD AND CASTS IN URINE, ANURIA, ESOPHAGEAL AND DELAYED GASTRIC STENOSIS HAS BEEN REPORTED. POSSIBLE PERFORATION OF THE GASTROINTESTINAL TRACT MAY RESULT IN PERITONITIS. **CHRONIC EXPOSURE-** NO DATA AVAILABLE.
FIRST AID- DO NOT USE GASTRIC LAVAGE OR EMESIS. DILUTE THE ACID IMMEDIATELY BY DRINKING LARGE QUANTITIES OF WATER OR MILK. IF VOMITING PERSISTS, ADMINISTER FLUIDS REPEATEDLY. INGESTED ACID MUST BE DILUTED APPROXIMATELY 100 FOLD TO RENDER IT HARMLESS TO TISSUES. MAINTAIN AIRWAY AND TREAT SHOCK (DREISBACH, HANDBOOK OF POISONING, 12TH ED.). GET MEDICAL ATTENTION IMMEDIATELY. IF VOMITING OCCURS, KEEP HEAD BELOW HIPS TO HELP PREVENT ASPIRATION.
ANTIDOTE: NO SPECIFIC ANTIDOTE. TREAT SYMPTOMATICALLY AND SUPPORTIVELY.

REACTIVITY

REACTIVITY: SULFURIC ACID: VIOLENT EXOTHERMIC REACTION WITH WATER.
INCOMPATIBILITIES: SULFURIC ACID: ACETALDEHYDE: VIOLENTLY POLYMERIZED BY CONCENTRATED ACID. ACETIC ANHYDRIDE: TEMPERATURE AND PRESSURE INCREASE IN CLOSED CONTAINER. ACETONE + NITRIC ACID: VIOLENT DECOMPOSITION. ACETONE + POTASSIUM DICHROMATE: IGNITION. ACETONE CYANHYDRIN: PRESSURE INCREASE WITH POSSIBLE EXPLOSIVE RUPTURE OF VESSEL. ACETONITRILE: VIOLENT EXOTHERM ON HEATING; SULFUR TRIOXIDE REDUCES INITIATION TEMPERATURE. ACROLEIN: TEMPERATURE AND PRESSURE INCREASE IN CLOSED CONTAINER. ACRYLONITRILE: VIGOROUS EXOTHERMIC POLYMERIZATION. ALCOHOL: EXOTHERMIC REACTION AND CONTRACTION OF VOLUME. ALCOHOLS AND HYDROGEN PEROXIDE: POSSIBLE EXPLOSION. ALLYL ALCOHOL: TEMPERATURE AND PRESSURE INCREASE IN CLOSED CONTAINER. ALLYL CHLORIDE: VIOLENT POLYMERIZATION. ALKYL NITRATES: MAY CAUSE VIOLENT REACTION. 2-AMINOETHANOL: TEMPERATURE AND PRESSURE INCREASE IN CLOSED CONTAINER. AMMONIUM HYDROXIDE: TEMPERATURE AND PRESSURE INCREASE IN CLOSED CONTAINER. AMMONIUM IRON(III) SULFATE DODECAHYDRATE: VIOLENT, EXOTHERMIC REACTION ON HEATING. AMMONIUM TRIPERCHROMATE: FIRE OR EXPLOSION HAZARD. ANILINE: TEMPERATURE AND PRESSURE INCREASE IN CLOSED CONTAINER. BASES: VIOLENT REACTION. BENZYL ALCOHOL: MAY DECOMPOSES EXPLOSIVELY AT ABOUT 180 C. BROMATES + METALS: POSSIBLE IGNITION. BROMINE PENTAFLUORIDE: VIOLENT REACTION WITH POSSIBLE IGNITION. TERT-BUTYL-M-XYLENE: VIOLENT EXOTHERMIC REACTION WITHOUT AGITATION. N-BUTYRALDEHYDE: TEMPERATURE AND PRESSURE INCREASE IN CLOSED CONTAINER. CARBIDES: HAZARDOUS MIXTURE. CESIUM ACETYLIDE: IGNITION ON CONTACT. 4-CHLORONITROBENZENE AND SULFUR TRIOXIDE: POSSIBLE EXPLOSIVE REACTION. CHLORATES: ALL CHLORATES, WHEN BROUGHT IN CONTACT WITH SULFURIC ACID MAY GIVE OFF EXPLOSIVE CHLORINE DIOXIDE GAS. A VIOLENT EXPLOSION IS USUAL. CHLORATES + METALS: POSSIBLE IGNITION. CHLORINE TRIFLUORIDE: VIOLENT REACTION. CHLOROSULFONIC ACID: TEMPERATURE AND PRESSURE INCREASE IN CLOSED CONTAINER. CHROMATES: FIRE AND EXPLOSION HAZARD. COATINGS: ATTACKED. COMBUSTIBLE MATERIALS (FINELY DIVIDED): MAY IGNITE. COPPER: EVOLUTION OF SULFUR DIOXIDE. CUPROUS NITRIDE: VIOLENT REACTION. 2-CYANO-4-NITROBENZENEDIAZONIUM HYDROGEN SULFATE: EXOTHERMIC REACTION. 2-CYANO-2-PROPANOL: VIOLENT REACTION WITH INCREASE IN PRESSURE. CYCLOPENTADIENE: VIOLENT OR EXPLOSIVE REACTION. CYCLOPENTANONE OXIME: VIOLENT REACTION. 1,3-DIAZIDOBENZENE: IGNITION FOLLOWED BY EXPLOSIVE REACTION. DIETHYLAMINE: EXOTHERMIC REACTION. DIISOBUTYLENE: TEMPERATURE AND PRESSURE INCREASE IN CLOSED CONTAINER. DIMETHYLBENZYLCARBINOL + HYDROGEN PEROXIDE: EXPLODES. DIMETHOXYANTHRAQUINONE: EXOTHERMIC REACTION ABOVE 150 C. 2,5-DINITRO-3-METHYLBENZOIC ACID + SODIUM AZIDE: EXPLOSIVE REACTION. 1,5-DINITRONAPHTHALENE + SULFUR: EXOTHERMIC REACTION. EPICHLOROHYDRIN: VIOLENT REACTION. ETHOXYLATED NONYLPHENOL: POSSIBLE IGNITION. ETHANOL + HYDROGEN PEROXIDE: POSSIBLE EXPLOSION. ETHYLENE CYANOHYDRIN: VIOLENT REACTION. ETHYLENE DIAMINE: TEMPERATURE AND PRESSURE INCREASE IN CLOSED CONTAINER. ETHYLENE GLYCOL: TEMPERATURE AND PRESSURE INCREASE IN CLOSED CONTAINER. ETHYLENIMINE: TEMPERATURE AND PRESSURE INCREASE IN CLOSED CONTAINER. FULMINATES: EXTREMELY HAZARDOUS MIXTURE. HEXALITHIUM DISILICIDE: INCANDESCENT REACTION. HYDROCHLORIC ACID: TEMPERATURE AND PRESSURE INCREASE IN CLOSED CONTAINER. HYDROGEN PEROXIDE (>50%): EXPLOSIVE REACTION AFTER EVAPORATION. HYDROFLUORIC ACID: TEMPERATURE AND PRESSURE INCREASE IN CLOSED CONTAINER. INDANE + NITRIC ACID: POSSIBLE EXPLOSION. IODINE HEPTAFLUORIDE: THE ACID BECOMES EFFERVESCENT. IRON: POSSIBLE EXPLOSION DUE TO HYDROGEN GAS FROM THE ACID-METAL REACTION. ISOPRENE: TEMPERATURE AND PRESSURE INCREASE IN CLOSED CONTAINER. LITHIUM SILICIDE: INCANDESCENT REACTION. MERCURY NITRIDE: EXPLOSION ON CONTACT. MESITYL OXIDE: TEMPERATURE AND PRESSURE INCREASE IN CLOSED CONTAINER. METALS: MAY LIBERATE FLAMMABLE HYDROGEN GAS. METALS (POWDERED): EXTREMELY HAZARDOUS MIXTURE. METAL ACETYLIDES: IGNITION REACTION. METAL CHLORATES: VIOLENT EXPLOSION UNLESS PROPERLY COOLED. METAL PERCHLORATES: FORMATION OF EXPLOSIVE PERCHLORIC ACID. 4-METHYLPYRIDINE: EXOTHERMIC REACTION. NITRAMIDE: MAY DECOMPOSE EXPLOSIVELY ON CONTACT. NITRATES: INCOMPATIBLE. NITRIC ACID + GLYCERIDES: EXPLOSION. NITRIC ACID + ORGANIC MATERIAL: MAY CAUSE VIOLENT REACTION. NITRIC ACID + TOLUENE: POSSIBLE VIOLENT REACTION OR EXPLOSION. NITROARYL BASES AND DERIVATIVES: MAY CAUSE VIOLENT REACTION OR EXPLOSION. NITROBENZENE: EXOTHERMIC REACTION AT ELEVATED TEMPERATURES. 3-NITROBENZENESULFONIC ACID: EXOTHERMIC REACTION. NITROMETHANE: FORMATION OF EXPLOSIVE MIXTURE. N-NITROMETHYLAMINE: EXPLOSIVE DECOMPOSITION. 4-NITROTOLUENE: EXPLOSIVE AT 80 C. ORGANICS: VIOLENT EXOTHERMIC REACTION. PENTASILVER TRIHYDROXYDIAMIDOPHOSPHATE: EXPLOSION ON CONTACT. PERCHLORATES: POSSIBLE EXPLOSION. PERCHLORIC ACID: FORMATION OF DANGEROUS ANHYDROUS PERCHLORIC ACID. PERMANGANATES: FORMATION OF PERMANGANIC ACID. PERMANGANATES + BENZENE: POSSIBLE EXPLOSION. 1-PHENYL-2-METHYL-PROPYL ALCOHOL + HYDROGEN PEROXIDE: POSSIBLE EXPLOSION. PHOSPHORUS (WHITE OR YELLOW): IGNITION IN CONTACT WITH BOILING ACID. PHOSPHORUS ISOCYANATE: VIOLENT REACTION. PHOSPHORUS TRIOXIDE: VIOLENT OXIDATION WITH POSSIBLE IGNITION. PICRATES: EXTREMELY HAZARDOUS MIXTURE. PLASTICS: ATTACKED. POLYSILYLENE: EXPLOSION ON CONTACT. POTASSIUM: EXPLOSIVE INTERACTION. POTASSIUM TERT-BUTOXIDE: IGNITION. POTASSIUM CHLORATE: POSSIBLE FIRE AND EXPLOSION. POTASSIUM PERMANGANATE: POSSIBLE EXPLOSION IN THE PRESENCE OF MOISTURE. POTASSIUM PERMANGANATE + POTASSIUM CHLORIDE: VIOLENT EXPLOSION. PROPIOLACTONE (BETA): TEMPERATURE AND PRESSURE INCREASE IN CLOSED CONTAINER. PROPYLENE OXIDE: TEMPERATURE AND PRESSURE INCREASE IN CLOSED CONTAINER. 3-PROPYNOL: POSSIBLE EXPLOSION UNLESS ADEQUATELY COOLED. PYRIDINE: TEMPERATURE AND PRESSURE INCREASE IN CLOSED CONTAINER. REDUCING AGENTS: REACTS. RUBBER: ATTACKED. RUBIDIUM ACETYLIDE: IGNITION ON CONTACT. SILVER PERMANGANATE (MOIST): EXPLOSIVE REACTION. SILVER PEROXOCHROMATE: EXPLOSIVE REACTION. SODIUM: EXPLOSIVE REACTION WITH AQUEOUS ACID. SODIUM CARBONATE: VIOLENT REACTION. SODIUM CHLORATE: POSSIBLE FIRE OR EXPLOSION. SODIUM HYDROXIDE: TEMPERATURE AND PRESSURE INCREASE IN CLOSED CONTAINER. SODIUM TETRAHYDROBORATE: VIOLENT, EXOTHERMIC REACTION. SODIUM THIOCYANATE: VIOLENT EXOTHERMIC WITH EVOLUTION OF CARBONYL SULFIDE. STEEL: POSSIBLE EXPLOSION DUE TO HYDROGEN GAS FROM THE ACID-METAL REACTION. STYRENE MONOMER: TEMPERATURE AND PRESSURE INCREASE IN CLOSED CONTAINER. TETRAMETHYLBENZENES: VIOLENT REACTION IN CLOSED CONTAINERS. 1,2,4,5-TETRAZINE: VIOLENT DECOMPOSITION ON CONTACT. THALLIUM(I) AZIDIDITHIOCARBONATE: MAY EXPLODE ON CONTACT. 1,3,5-TRINITROSOHEXAHYDRO-1,3,5-TRIAZINE: EXPLOSIVE DECOMPOSITION ON

CONTACT. VINYL ACETATE: TEMPERATURE AND PRESSURE INCREASE IN CLOSED CONTAINER. ZINC CHLORATE: LIKELY TO CAUSE FIRES AND EXPLOSIONS. ZINC IODIDE: VIOLENT INTERACTION.

DECOMPOSITION: THERMAL DECOMPOSITION MAY RELEASE TOXIC OXIDES OF SULFUR.

POLYMERIZATION: HAZARDOUS POLYMERIZATION HAS NOT BEEN REPORTED TO OCCUR UNDER NORMAL TEMPERATURES AND PRESSURES.

STORAGE AND DISPOSAL

OBSERVE ALL FEDERAL, STATE AND LOCAL REGULATIONS WHEN STORING OR DISPOSING OF THIS SUBSTANCE. FOR ASSISTANCE, CONTACT THE DISTRICT DIRECTOR OF THE ENVIRONMENTAL PROTECTION AGENCY.

STORAGE

PROTECT AGAINST PHYSICAL DAMAGE AND WATER. SEPARATE FROM CARBIDES, CHLORATES, FULMINATES, NITRATES, PICRATES, POWDERED METALS, AND COMBUSTIBLE MATERIALS (NFPA 49, HAZARDOUS CHEMICALS DATA, 1975). STORE AWAY FROM INCOMPATIBLE SUBSTANCES.

THRESHOLD PLANNING QUANTITY (TPQ): THE SUPERFUND AMENDMENTS AND REAUTHORIZATION ACT (SARA) SECTION 302 REQUIRES THAT EACH FACILITY WHERE ANY EXTREMELY HAZARDOUS SUBSTANCE IS PRESENT IN A QUANTITY EQUAL TO OR GREATER THAN THE TPQ ESTABLISHED FOR THAT SUBSTANCE NOTIFY THE STATE EMERGENCY RESPONSE COMMISSION FOR THE STATE IN WHICH IT IS LOCATED. SECTION 303 OF SARA REQUIRES THESE FACILITIES TO PARTICIPATE IN LOCAL EMERGENCY RESPONSE PLANNING (40 CFR 355.30).

DISPOSAL

DISPOSAL MUST BE IN ACCORDANCE WITH STANDARDS APPLICABLE TO GENERATORS OF HAZARDOUS WASTE, 40 CFR 262. EPA HAZARDOUS WASTE NUMBER D002. 100 POUND CERCLA SECTION 103 REPORTABLE QUANTITY.

CONDITIONS TO AVOID

MAY IGNITE OTHER COMBUSTIBLE MATERIALS (WOOD, PAPER, OIL, ETC.). VIOLENT REACTION WITH WATER. FLAMMABLE, POISONOUS GASES MAY ACCUMULATE IN CONFINED SPACES. RUNOFF TO SEWER MAY CREATE FIRE OR EXPLOSION HAZARD.

SPILL AND LEAK PROCEDURES

SOIL SPILL: DIG HOLDING AREA SUCH AS LAGOON, POND OR PIT FOR CONTAINMENT. DIKE FLOW OF SPILLED MATERIAL USING SOIL OR SANDBAGS OR FOAMED BARRIERS SUCH AS POLYURETHANE OR CONCRETE.
USE CEMENT POWDER OR FLY ASH TO ABSORB LIQUID MASS.
NEUTRALIZE SPILL WITH SLAKED LIME, SODIUM BICARBONATE OR CRUSHED LIMESTONE.

AIR SPILL: APPLY WATER SPRAY TO KNOCK DOWN AND REDUCE VAPORS. KNOCK-DOWN WATER IS CORROSIVE AND TOXIC AND SHOULD BE DIKED FOR CONTAINMENT AND LATER DISPOSAL.

WATER SPILL: NEUTRALIZE WITH AGRICULTURAL LIME, SLAKED LIME, CRUSHED LIMESTONE, OR SODIUM BICARBONATE.

OCCUPATIONAL SPILL: KEEP COMBUSTIBLES (WOOD, PAPER, OIL, ETC.) AWAY FROM SPILLED MATERIAL. DO NOT TOUCH SPILLED MATERIAL. DO NOT GET WATER INSIDE CONTAINER. STOP LEAK IF YOU CAN DO IT WITHOUT RISK. USE WATER SPRAY TO REDUCE VAPORS. DO NOT PUT WATER ON LEAK OR SPILL AREA. CLEAN UP ONLY UNDER THE SUPERVISION OF AN EXPERT. DIKE SPILL FOR LATER DISPOSAL. DO NOT APPLY WATER UNLESS DIRECTED TO DO SO. KEEP UNNECESSARY PEOPLE AWAY. ISOLATE HAZARD AREA AND DENY ENTRY. VENTILATE CLOSED SPACES BEFORE ENTERING.
REPORTABLE QUANTITY (RQ): 1000 POUNDS THE SUPERFUND AMENDMENTS AND REAUTHORIZATION ACT (SARA) SECTION 304 REQUIRES THAT A RELEASE EQUAL TO OR GREATER THAN THE REPORTABLE QUANTITY FOR THIS SUBSTANCE BE IMMEDIATELY REPORTED TO THE LOCAL EMERGENCY PLANNING COMMITTEE AND THE STATE EMERGENCY RESPONSE COMMISSION (40 CFR 355.40). IF THE RELEASE OF THIS SUBSTANCE IS REPORTABLE UNDER CERCLA SECTION 103, THE NATIONAL RESPONSE CENTER MUST BE NOTIFIED IMMEDIATELY AT (800) 424-8802 OR (202) 426-2675 IN THE METROPOLITAN WASHINGTON, D.C. AREA (40 CFR 302.6).

PROTECTIVE EQUIPMENT

VENTILATION: PROCESS ENCLOSURE RECOMMENDED TO MEET PUBLISHED EXPOSURE LIMITS.

RESPIRATOR: THE FOLLOWING RESPIRATORS AND MAXIMUM USE CONCENTRATIONS ARE RECOMMENDATIONS BY THE U.S. DEPARTMENT OF HEALTH AND HUMAN SERVICES, NIOSH POCKET GUIDE TO CHEMICAL HAZARDS; NIOSH CRITERIA DOCUMENTS OR BY THE U.S. DEPARTMENT OF LABOR, 29 CFR 1910 SUBPART Z. THE SPECIFIC RESPIRATOR SELECTED MUST BE BASED ON CONTAMINATION LEVELS FOUND IN THE WORK PLACE, MUST NOT EXCEED THE WORKING LIMITS OF THE RESPIRATOR AND BE JOINTLY APPROVED BY THE NATIONAL INSTITUTE FOR OCCUPATIONAL SAFETY AND HEALTH AND THE MINE SAFETY AND HEALTH ADMINISTRATION (NIOSH-MSHA).
SULFURIC ACID:
25 MG/M3- ANY POWERED AIR-PURIFYING RESPIRATOR WITH AN ACID GAS CARTRIDGE(S) AND HAVING A HIGH-EFFICIENCY PARTICULATE FILTER. ANY SUPPLIED-AIR RESPIRATOR OPERATED IN A CONTINUOUS FLOW MODE.
50 MG/M3- ANY CHEMICAL CARTRIDGE RESPIRATOR WITH A FULL FACEPIECE AND ACID GAS CARTRIDGE(S) IN COMBINATION WITH A HIGH-EFFICIENCY PARTICULATE FILTER. ANY SELF-CONTAINED BREATHING APPARATUS WITH A FULL FACEPIECE. ANY SUPPLIED-AIR RESPIRATOR WITH A FULL FACEPIECE. ANY AIR-PURIFYING FULL FACEPIECE RESPIRATOR (GAS MASK) WITH A CHIN-STYLE OR FRONT- OR BACK-MOUNTED ACID GAS CANISTER HAVING A HIGH-EFFICIENCY PARTICULATE FILTER.
80 MG/M3- ANY SUPPLIED-AIR RESPIRATOR WITH A FULL FACEPIECE AND OPERATED IN A PRESSURE-DEMAND OR OTHER POSITIVE PRESSURE MODE.
ESCAPE- ANY AIR-PURIFYING FULL FACEPIECE RESPIRATOR (GAS MASK) WITH A CHIN-STYLE OR FRONT- OR BACK-MOUNTED ACID GAS CANISTER HAVING A HIGH-EFFICIENCY PARTICULATE FILTER. ANY APPROPRIATE ESCAPE-TYPE SELF-CONTAINED BREATHING APPARATUS.
FOR FIREFIGHTING AND OTHER IMMEDIATELY DANGEROUS TO LIFE OR HEALTH CONDITIONS:
SELF-CONTAINED BREATHING APPARATUS WITH FULL FACEPIECE OPERATED IN PRESSURE-DEMAND OR OTHER POSITIVE PRESSURE MODE.
SUPPLIED-AIR RESPIRATOR WITH FULL FACEPIECE AND OPERATED IN PRESSURE-DEMAND OR OTHER POSITIVE PRESSURE MODE IN COMBINATION WITH AN AUXILIARY SELF-CONTAINED BREATHING APPARATUS OPERATED IN PRESSURE-DEMAND OR OTHER POSITIVE PRESSURE MODE.

CLOTHING: WEAR APPROPRIATE PROTECTIVE CLOTHING TO AVOID ANY POSSIBILITY OF SKIN CONTACT WITH LIQUIDS CONTAINING MORE THAN 1% SULFURIC ACID. AVOID REPEATED OR PROLONGED SKIN CONTACT WITH LIQUIDS CONTAINING 1% OR LESS SULFURIC ACID.

GLOVES: EMPLOYEE MUST WEAR APPROPRIATE PROTECTIVE GLOVES TO PREVENT CONTACT WITH THIS SUBSTANCE.

EYE PROTECTION: EMPLOYEE MUST WEAR SPLASH-PROOF OR DUST-RESISTANT SAFETY GOGGLES AND A FACESHIELD TO PREVENT CONTACT WITH THIS SUBSTANCE.
EMERGENCY WASH FACILITIES: WHERE THERE IS ANY POSSIBILITY THAT AN EMPLOYEE'S EYES AND/OR SKIN MAY BE EXPOSED TO THIS SUBSTANCE, THE EMPLOYER SHOULD PROVIDE AN EYE WASH FOUNTAIN AND QUICK DRENCH SHOWER WITHIN THE IMMEDIATE WORK AREA FOR EMERGENCY USE.

AUTHORIZED BY- OCCUPATIONAL HEALTH SERVICES, INC.
CREATION DATE: 11/17/89 ***REVISION DATE:*** 05/18/90

MATERIAL SAFETY DATA SHEET

OCCUPATIONAL HEALTH SERVICES, INC.
AGRICULTURE AND PESTICIDE DIVISION
450 SEVENTH AVENUE, SUITE 2407
NEW YORK, NEW YORK 10123
1-800-445-MSDS OR (212) 967-1100

EMERGENCY CONTACT:
JOHN S. BRANSFORD, JR. (615) 292-1180

SUBSTANCE IDENTIFICATION

CAS-NUMBER 2699-79-8

SUBSTANCE: **SULFURYL FLUORIDE**

TRADE NAMES/SYNONYMS: SULFURIC OXYFLUORIDE; VIKANE; VIKANE FUMIGANT; STCC 4904578; UN 2191; PST22380

CHEMICAL FAMILY: INORGANIC GAS

MOLECULAR FORMULA: F2-O2-S MOL WT: 102.06

CERCLA RATINGS (SCALE 0-3): HEALTH=3 FIRE=0 REACTIVITY=0 PERSISTENCE=0

NFPA RATINGS (SCALE 0-4): HEALTH=3 FIRE=0 REACTIVITY=0

COMPONENTS AND CONTAMINANTS

COMPONENT: SULFURYL FLUORIDE ***PERCENT:*** >99
CAS# 2699-79-8

EXPOSURE LIMITS: SULFURYL FLUORIDE: 5 PPM (20 MG/M3) OSHA TWA; 10 PPM (40 MG/M3) OSHA STEL 5 PPM (20 MG/M3) ACGIH TWA; 10 PPM (40 MG/M3) ACGIH STEL

PHYSICAL DATA

DESCRIPTION: COLORLESS, ODORLESS GAS

BOILING POINT: -68 F (-55 C)

MELTING POINT: -214 F (-137 C) ***SPECIFIC GRAVITY:*** 1.8 (-80 C)

VAPOR PRESSURE: >760 MMHG @ 20 C ***SOLUBILITY IN WATER:*** 10% @ 9 C
VAPOR DENSITY: 3.7
SOLVENT SOLUBILITY: ALCOHOL, TOLUENE, CARBON TETRACHLORIDE

FIRE AND EXPLOSION DATA

FIRE AND EXPLOSION HAZARD: NEGLIGIBLE FIRE HAZARD WHEN EXPOSED TO HEAT OR FLAME.
FLASH POINT: NON-COMBUSTIBLE
FIREFIGHTING MEDIA: DRY CHEMICAL, CARBON DIOXIDE OR HALON (1987 EMERGENCY RESPONSE GUIDEBOOK, DOT P 5800.4).
FOR LARGER FIRES, USE WATER SPRAY, FOG OR STANDARD FOAM (1987 EMERGENCY RESPONSE GUIDEBOOK, DOT P 5800.4).
FIREFIGHTING: DO NOT GET WATER INSIDE CONTAINER. MOVE CONTAINER FROM FIRE AREA IF POSSIBLE. STAY AWAY FROM STORAGE TANK ENDS. COOL FIRE-EXPOSED CONTAINERS WITH WATER FROM SIDE UNTIL WELL AFTER FIRE IS OUT. ISOLATE AREA UNTIL GAS HAS DISPERSED (1987 EMERGENCY RESPONSE GUIDEBOOK, DOT P 5800.4, GUIDE PAGE 15).
USE AGENTS SUITABLE FOR TYPE OF FIRE. COOL CONTAINERS WITH FLOODING AMOUNTS OF WATER, APPLY FROM AS FAR A DISTANCE AS POSSIBLE. AVOID BREATHING POISONOUS VAPORS, KEEP UPWIND.

TRANSPORTATION DATA

DEPARTMENT OF TRANSPORTATION HAZARD CLASSIFICATION 49 CFR 172.101: NONFLAMMABLE GAS
DEPARTMENT OF TRANSPORTATION LABELING REQUIREMENTS 49 CFR 172.101 AND SUBPART E: NONFLAMMABLE GAS
DEPARTMENT OF TRANSPORTATION PACKAGING REQUIREMENTS: 49 CFR 173.304 AND 49 CFR 173.314 EXCEPTIONS: 49 CFR 173.306

TOXICITY

SULFURYL FLUORIDE: TOXICITY DATA: 100 MG/KG ORAL-RAT LD50; 100 MG/KG ORAL-GUINEA PIG LD50; 991 PPM/4 HOUR INHALATION-RAT LC50; 1200 PPM/1 HOUR INHALATION-MOUSE LCLO; 5000 PPM/1 HOUR INHALATION-RABBIT LCLO. CARCINOGEN STATUS: NONE. LOCAL EFFECTS: IRRITANT- INHALATION AND EYES. ACUTE TOXICITY LEVEL: TOXIC BY INGESTION. TARGET EFFECTS: CENTRAL NERVOUS SYSTEM DEPRESSANT. AT INCREASED RISK FROM EXPOSURE: PERSONS WITH A HISTORY OF CHRONIC RESPIRATORY DISEASE.

HEALTH EFFECTS AND FIRST AID

INHALATION: SULFURYL FLUORIDE: IRRITANT/TOXIC. 1000 PPM IS IMMEDIATELY DANGEROUS TO LIFE AND HEALTH. **ACUTE EXPOSURE-** MAY CAUSE IRRITATION OF UPPER RESPIRATORY TRACT, NAUSEA, VOMITING, CRAMPY ABDOMINAL PAIN, PRURITIS, DIFFUSE RHONCI, AND PARESTHESIA. HIGH CONCENTRATIONS MAY CAUSE A "CONFUSED" STATE, NARCOSIS, AND POSSIBLY TREMOR, CONVULSIONS, AND DELAYED PULMONARY EDEMA. **CHRONIC EXPOSURE-** REPEATED OR PROLONGED EXPOSURE MAY CAUSE LUNG AND KIDNEY INJURY. CHRONIC FLUORIDE EXPOSURE MAY RESULT IN WEAKNESS, WEIGHT LOSS, ANEMIA, BONE BRITTLENESS, JOINT STIFFNESS, AND GENERAL ILL HEALTH.
FIRST AID- REMOVE FROM EXPOSURE AREA TO FRESH AIR IMMEDIATELY. IF BREATHING HAS STOPPED, PERFORM ARTIFICIAL RESPIRATION. KEEP PERSON WARM AND AT REST. TREAT SYMPTOMATICALLY AND SUPPORTIVELY. GET MEDICAL ATTENTION IMMEDIATELY.

SKIN CONTACT: SULFURYL FLUORIDE: **ACUTE EXPOSURE-** DIRECT CONTACT WITH LIQUID MAY CAUSE PAIN AND FROSTBITE DUE TO RAPID VAPORIZATION. **CHRONIC EXPOSURE-** NO DATA AVAILABLE.
FIRST AID- IT IS UNLIKELY THAT EMERGENCY TREATMENT WILL BE REQUIRED. IF ADVERSE EFFECTS OCCUR, GET MEDICAL ATTENTION. IN CASE OF FROSTBITE, WARM AFFECTED SKIN IN WARM WATER AT A TEMPERATURE OF 107 F. IF WARM WATER IS NOT AVAILABLE OR IMPRACTICAL TO USE, GENTLY WRAP AFFECTED PART IN BLANKETS. ENCOURAGE VICTIM TO EXERCISE AFFECTED PART WHILE IT IS BEING WARMED. ALLOW CIRCULATION TO RETURN NATURALLY (MATHESON GAS, 6TH ED.). GET MEDICAL ATTENTION IMMEDIATELY.
EYE CONTACT: SULFURYL FLUORIDE: IRRITANT. **ACUTE EXPOSURE-** VAPOR MAY CAUSE REDNESS. LIQUID MAY CAUSE PAIN, BLURRED VISION AND FROST BITE (DUE TO RAPID VAPORIZATION). **CHRONIC EXPOSURE-** NO KNOWN EFFECTS IN HUMANS.
FIRST AID- WASH EYES IMMEDIATELY WITH LARGE AMOUNTS OF WATER OR NORMAL SALINE, OCCASIONALLY LIFTING UPPER AND LOWER LIDS, UNTIL NO EVIDENCE OF CHEMICAL REMAINS (APPROXIMATELY 15-20 MINUTES). GET MEDICAL ATTENTION IMMEDIATELY.

INGESTION: SULFURYL FLUORIDE: **ACUTE EXPOSURE-** INGESTION OF A GAS IN UNLIKELY. **CHRONIC EXPOSURE-** NO DATA AVAILABLE.
FIRST AID- IT IS UNLIKELY THAT EMERGENCY TREATMENT WILL BE REQUIRED. IF ADVERSE EFFECTS OCCUR, TREAT SYMPTOMATICALLY AND SUPPORTIVELY AND GET MEDICAL ATTENTION.
ANTIDOTE: NO SPECIFIC ANTIDOTE. TREAT SYMPTOMATICALLY AND SUPPORTIVELY.

REACTIVITY

REACTIVITY: STABLE UNDER NORMAL TEMPERATURES AND PRESSURES.
INCOMPATIBILITIES: NONE KNOWN.
DECOMPOSITION: THERMAL DECOMPOSITION OR REACTION WITH WATER RELEASES CORROSIVE HYDROGEN FLUORIDE AND OXIDES OF SULFUR. ***POLYMERIZATION:*** HAZARDOUS POLYMERIZATION HAS NOT BEEN REPORTED TO OCCUR UNDER NORMAL TEMPERATURES AND PRESSURES.

CONDITIONS TO AVOID

MATERIAL IS EXTREMELY POISONOUS; AVOID INHALATION OF VAPORS OR CONTACT WITH SKIN. CONTENTS MAY BE UNDER PRESSURE; CONTAINERS MAY RUPTURE VIOLENTLY AND TRAVEL A CONSIDERABLE DISTANCE.

SPILL AND LEAK PROCEDURES

OCCUPATIONAL SPILL: STOP LEAK IF YOU CAN DO IT WITHOUT RISK. USE WATER SPRAY TO REDUCE VAPORS BUT DO NOT PUT WATER ON LEAK OR SPILL AREA. DO NOT GET WATER INSIDE CONTAINER. ISOLATE AREA UNTIL GAS HAS DISPERSED. FOR SMALL SPILLS, FLUSH AREA WITH FLOODING AMOUNTS OF WATER. FOR LARGER SPILLS, DIKE FAR AHEAD OF SPILL FOR LATER DISPOSAL. KEEP UNNECESSARY PEOPLE AWAY; ISOLATE HAZARD AREA AND DENY ENTRY. VENTILATE CLOSED SPACES BEFORE ENTERING. EVACUATE AREA ENDANGERED BY GAS.

PROTECTIVE EQUIPMENT

VENTILATION: PROVIDE LOCAL EXHAUST VENTILATION AND/OR GENERAL DILUTION VENTILATION TO MEET PUBLISHED EXPOSURE LIMITS.
RESPIRATOR: 50 PPM- SUPPLIED-AIR RESPIRATOR. SELF-CONTAINED BREATHING APPARATUS.
250 PPM- SUPPLIED-AIR RESPIRATOR WITH A FULL FACEPIECE, HELMET, OR HOOD. SELF-CONTAINED BREATHING APPARATUS WITH A FULL FACEPIECE.
1000 PPM- TYPE C SUPPLIED-AIR RESPIRATOR WITH A FULL FACEPIECE OPERATED IN PRESSURE-DEMAND OR OTHER POSITIVE PRESSURE MODE OR WITH A FULL FACEPIECE, HELMET, OR HOOD OPERATED IN CONTINOUS-FLOW.
ESCAPE- GAS MASK WITH A CANISTER PROVIDING PROTECTION AGAINST SULFURYL CHLORIDE (CHIN-STYLE OR FRONT- OR BACK-MOUNTED CANISTER). SELF-CONTAINED BREATHING APPARATUS.
FIREFIGHTING- SELF-CONTAINED BREATHING APPARATUS WITH A FULL FACEPIECE OPERATED IN PRESSURE-DEMAND OR OTHER POSITIVE PRESSURE MODE.
CLOTHING: FOR THE GAS FORM, PROTECTIVE CLOTHING NOT REQUIRED. IF CONTACT WITH THE LIQUID FORM IS POSSIBLE, EMPLOYEE MUST WEAR APPROPRIATE PROTECTIVE CLOTHING AND EQUIPMENT TO PREVENT SKIN FROM FREEZING.
GLOVES: WEAR FULL PROTECTIVE, COLD INSULATING GLOVES.
EYE PROTECTION: EMPLOYEE MUST WEAR SPLASH-PROOF OR DUST-RESISTANT SAFETY GOGGLES AND A FACESHIELD TO PREVENT CONTACT WITH THIS SUBSTANCE.
EMERGENCY WASH FACILITIES: WHERE THERE IS ANY POSSIBILITY THAT AN EMPLOYEE'S EYES AND/OR SKIN MAY BE EXPOSED TO THIS SUBSTANCE, THE EMPLOYER SHOULD PROVIDE AN EYE WASH FOUNTAIN AND QUICK DRENCH SHOWER WITHIN THE IMMEDIATE WORK AREA FOR EMERGENCY USE.

AUTHORIZED BY- OCCUPATIONAL HEALTH SERVICES, INC.
CREATION DATE: 10/05/89 ***REVISION DATE:*** 05/11/90

MATERIAL SAFETY DATA SHEET

OCCUPATIONAL HEALTH SERVICES, INC.
AGRICULTURE AND PESTICIDE DIVISION
450 SEVENTH AVENUE, SUITE 2407
NEW YORK, NEW YORK 10123
1-800-445-MSDS OR (212) 967-1100

EMERGENCY CONTACT:
JOHN S. BRANSFORD, JR. (615) 292-1180

SUBSTANCE IDENTIFICATION

CAS-NUMBER 35400-43-2
SUBSTANCE: **SULPROFOS**
TRADE NAMES/SYNONYMS: O-ETHYL O-(4-(METHYLMERCAPTO)PHENYL)-S-N-PROPYLPHOSPHOROTHIONOTHIOLATE; PHOSPHORODITHIOIC ACID, O-ETHYL O-(4-(METHYLTHIO)PHENYL)S-PROPYL ESTER; O-ETHYL O-4-(METHYLTHIO)PHENYL S-

PROPYL PHOSPHORODITHIOATE; BOLSTAR; BAYER NTN 9306; HELOTHION; MERCAPROFOS; MERCAPROPHOS; MERPAFOS; PST22387

CHEMICAL FAMILY: AROMATIC ESTER

MOLECULAR FORMULA: C12-H19-O2-P-S3

MOLECULAR WEIGHT: 322.46

CERCLA RATINGS (SCALE 0-3): HEALTH=3 FIRE=U REACTIVITY=0 PERSISTENCE=1

NFPA RATINGS (SCALE 0-4): HEALTH=3 FIRE=U REACTIVITY=0

COMPONENTS AND CONTAMINANTS

COMPONENT: SULPROFOS ***PERCENT:*** 100.00
CAS# 35400-43-2

EXPOSURE LIMITS: SULPROFOS: 1 MG/M3 OSHA TWA 1 MG/M3 ACGIH TWA

PHYSICAL DATA

DESCRIPTION: TAN LIQUID WITH PHOSPHORUS ODOR

BOILING POINT: 311-316 F (155-158 C) ***MELTING POINT:*** <-58 F (-50 C)

SPECIFIC GRAVITY: 1.20 @ 20 C ***VAPOR PRESSURE:*** <0.05 MMHG @ 20 C

SOLUBILITY IN WATER: 0.3 PPM @ 20 C

SOLVENT SOLUBILITY: MOST ORGANIC SOLVENTS

FIRE AND EXPLOSION DATA

FIRE AND EXPLOSION HAZARD: UNKNOWN FIRE AND EXPLOSION HAZARD.

FIREFIGHTING MEDIA: DRY CHEMICAL, CARBON DIOXIDE, HALON, WATER SPRAY OR STANDARD FOAM (1987 EMERGENCY RESPONSE GUIDEBOOK, DOT P 5800.4). FOR LARGER FIRES, USE WATER SPRAY, FOG OR STANDARD FOAM (1987 EMERGENCY RESPONSE GUIDEBOOK, DOT P 5800.4).

FIREFIGHTING: MOVE CONTAINERS FROM FIRE AREA IF POSSIBLE. FIGHT FIRE FROM MAXIMUM DISTANCE. STAY AWAY FROM STORAGE TANK ENDS. DIKE FIRE CONTROL WATER FOR LATER DISPOSAL. DO NOT SCATTER MATERIAL (1987 EMERGENCY RESPONSE GUIDEBOOK, DOT P 5800.4, GUIDE PAGE 55). EXTINGUISH ONLY IF FLOW CAN BE STOPPED; USE FLOODING AMOUNTS OF WATER AS FOG, SOLID STREAMS MAY BE INEFFECTIVE. COOL CONTAINERS WITH FLOODING AMOUNTS OF WATER FROM AS FAR A DISTANCE AS POSSIBLE. USE WATER SPRAY TO ABSORB TOXIC VAPORS. AVOID BREATHING TOXIC VAPORS; KEEP UPWIND. CONSIDER EVACUATION OF DOWNWIND AREA IF MATERIAL IS LEAKING.

TOXICITY

SULPROFOS: TOXICITY DATA: 820 MG/KG SKIN-RABBIT LD50; 65 MG/KG ORAL-RAT LD50; 1600 MG/KG ORAL-MOUSE LD50. CARCINOGEN STATUS: NONE. ACUTE TOXICITY LEVEL: TOXIC BY DERMAL ABSORPTION AND INGESTION. TARGET EFFECTS: CHOLINESTERASE INHIBITOR. POISONING MAY AFFECT THE NERVOUS SYSTEM.* AT INCREASED RISK FROM EXPOSURE: PERSONS WITH RESPIRATORY AILMENTS, RECENT EXPOSURE TO CHOLINESTERASE INHIBITORS OR IMPAIRED CHOLINESTERASE PRODUCTION, OR LIVER MALFUNCTION.* ADDITIONAL DATA: MAY CROSS THE PLACENTA. HIGH ENVIRONMENTAL TEMPERATURES OR EXPOSURE OF THE CHEMICAL TO VISIBLE OR ULTRAVIOLET LIGHT MAY ENHANCE THE TOXICITY. INTERACTIONS WITH MEDICATIONS MAY OCCUR.*

* MAY BE BASED ON GENERAL INFORMATION ON ORGANOPHOSPHATES.

HEALTH EFFECTS AND FIRST AID

INHALATION: SULPROFOS: SEE INFORMATION ON ORGANOPHOSPHATES. ORGANOPHOSPHATES: CHOLINESTERASE INHIBITOR. **ACUTE EXPOSURE-** WHEN INHALED, THE FIRST EFFECTS OF CHOLINESTERASE INHIBITORS ARE USUALLY RESPIRATORY AND MAY INCLUDE NASAL HYPEREMIA AND WATERY DISCHARGE, COUGH, CHEST DISCOMFORT, DYSPNEA, AND WHEEZING DUE TO INCREASED BRONCHIAL SECRETIONS AND BRONCHOCONSTRICTION. IF SUFFICIENT AMOUNTS ARE ABSORBED, OTHER SYSTEMIC EFFECTS MAY BEGIN WITHIN A FEW MINUTES OR BE DELAYED FOR UP TO 12 HOURS. SYMPTOMS MAY INCLUDE PALLOR, NAUSEA, VOMITING, DIARRHEA, ABDOMINAL CRAMPS, HEADACHE, DIZZINESS, OCULAR PAIN, BLURRED VISION, MIOSIS OR IN SOME CASES, ESPECIALLY INITIALLY, MYDRIASIS, LACRIMATION, SALIVATION, SWEATING, AND CONFUSION. OTHER REPORTED CENTRAL NERVOUS SYSTEM OR NEUROMUSCULAR EFFECTS MAY INCLUDE ATAXIA, SLURRED SPEECH, AREFLEXIA, WEAKNESS, FATIGUE, FASCICULATIONS, TWITCHING, TREMORS POSSIBLY OF THE TONGUE AND EYELIDS, AND EVENTUALLY PARALYSIS OF THE EXTREMITIES AND POSSIBLY OF THE RESPIRATORY MUSCLES. IN SEVERE CASES THERE MAY ALSO BE INVOLUNTARY DEFECATION AND URINATION, CYANOSIS, PSYCHOSIS, HYPERGLYCEMIA, ACUTE PANCREATITIS, CARDIAC IRREGULARITIES, PULMONARY EDEMA, UNCONSCIOUSNESS, CONVULSIONS, AND COMA. DEATH IS PRIMARILY DUE TO RESPIRATORY FAILURE, ALTHOUGH CARDIOVASCULAR EFFECTS INCLUDING CARDIAC ARREST MAY ALSO BE IMPLICATED. LONG TERM SEQUELAE ARE RARE BUT MAY INCLUDE NEUROPSYCHIATRIC DISORDERS AND MYOPATHY WITH MUSCLE TENDERNESS. SOME ORGANOPHOSPHATES MAY CAUSE A DELAYED NEUROPATHY BEGINNING 1-4 WEEKS AFTER AN ACUTE EXPOSURE WHICH MAY OR MAY NOT HAVE CAUSED ACUTE CHOLINERGIC EFFECTS. NUMBNESS, TINGLING, WEAKNESS AND CRAMPING BEGINNING SYMMETRICALLY IN THE LOWER LIMBS MAY PROGRESS TO ATAXIA AND PARALYSIS. IN SEVERE CASES, UPPER LIMB INVOLVEMENT IS POSSIBLE AND FLACCID PARALYSIS MAY PROGRESS TO SPASTIC PARALYSIS WITH EXAGGERATED REFLEXES. IMPROVEMENT MAY OCCUR OVER MONTHS TO YEARS, BUT SOME RESIDUAL IMPAIRMENT USUALLY REMAINS. **CHRONIC EXPOSURE-** REPEATED OR PROLONGED EXPOSURE MAY RESULT IN THE EFFECTS OF ACUTE EXPOSURE INCLUDING THE DELAYED NEUROPATHY. OTHER EFFECTS REPORTED IN WORKERS REPEATEDLY EXPOSED INCLUDE IMPAIRED MEMORY AND CONCENTRATION, ACUTE PSYCHOSIS, SEVERE DEPRESSIONS, IRRITABILTY, CONFUSION, APATHY, EMOTIONAL LABILITY, SOCIAL WITHDRAWAL, CONFUSION, HEADACHE, SPEECH DIFFICULTIES, DELAYED REACTION TIMES, SPATIAL DISORIENTATION, NIGHTMARES, SLEEPWALKING, AND DROWSINESS OR INSOMNIA. AN INFLUENZA-LIKE CONDITION WITH HEADACHE, NAUSEA, WEAKNESS, ANOREXIA AND MALAISE HAS ALSO BEEN REPORTED.

FIRST AID- REMOVE FROM EXPOSURE AREA TO FRESH AIR IMMEDIATELY. IF BREATHING HAS STOPPED, GIVE ARTIFICIAL RESPIRATION. MAINTAIN AIRWAY AND BLOOD PRESSURE AND ADMINISTER OXYGEN IF AVAILABLE. KEEP AFFECTED PERSON WARM AND AT REST. TREAT SYMPTOMATICALLY AND SUPPORTIVELY. ADMINISTRATION OF OXYGEN SHOULD BE PERFORMED BY QUALIFIED PERSONNEL. GET MEDICAL ATTENTION IMMEDIATELY.

SKIN CONTACT: SULPROFOS: TOXIC. SEE INFORMATION ON ORGANOPHOSPHATES. ORGANOPHOSPHATES: CHOLINESTERASE INHIBITOR. **ACUTE EXPOSURE-** LOCALIZED SWEATING AND FASCICULATIONS MAY OCCUR AT THE SITE OF CONTACT. IF SUFFICIENT AMOUNTS ARE ABSORBED, OTHER EFFECTS OF CHOLINESTERASE INHIBITION AS DESCRIBED IN ACUTE INHALATION MAY OCCUR. SYMPTOMS MAY BE DELAYED 2-3 HOURS, BUT USUALLY NO MORE THAN 12 HOURS. THE RATE OF ABSORPTION IS INCREASED BY THE PRESENCE OF DERMATITIS OR HIGH AMBIENT TEMPERATURES. DELAYED NEUROPATHY IS ALSO POSSIBLE. **CHRONIC EXPOSURE-** REPEATED OR PROLONGED EXPOSURE MAY CAUSE EFFECTS AS DESCRIBED IN ACUTE EXPOSURE. SOME ORGANOPHOSPHATES MAY CAUSE SENSITIZATION.

FIRST AID- REMOVE CONTAMINATED CLOTHING IMMEDIATELY. WASH CONTAMINATED AREAS WITH SOAP AND WATER FOLLOWED BY ALCOHOL (ARENA, POISONING, 4TH ED.). EMERGENCY PERSONNEL SHOULD WEAR GLOVES AND AVOID CONTAMINATION. TREAT RESPIRATORY DIFFICULTY WITH ARTIFICIAL RESPIRATION. GET MEDICAL ATTENTION IMMEDIATELY.

EYE CONTACT: SULPROFOS: SEE INFORMATION ON ORGANOPHOSPHATES. ORGANOPHOSPHATES: CHOLINESTERASE INHIBITOR. **ACUTE EXPOSURE-** DIRECT CONTACT MAY CAUSE PAIN, HYPEREMIA, LACRIMATION, TWITCHING OF THE EYELIDS, MIOSIS, AND CILIARY MUSCLE SPASM WITH LOSS OF ACCOMODATION, BLURRED OR DIMMED VISION AND BROWACHE. SOMETIMES MYDRIASIS MAY OCCUR INSTEAD OF MIOSIS. WITH SUFFICIENT EXPOSURE, OTHER SYMPTOMS OF CHOLINESTERASE INHIBITION AS DESCRIBED IN ACUTE INHALATION MAY OCCUR. **CHRONIC EXPOSURE-** REPEATED OR PROLONGED EXPOSURE MAY CAUSE EFFECTS AS DESCRIBED IN ACUTE EXPOSURE. SOME COMPOUNDS HAVE CAUSED TOXIC EFFECTS ON THE CRYSTALLINE LENS, CONJUNCTIVAL THICKENING AND OBSTRUCTION OF THE NASOLACRIMAL CANALS WHEN USED AS MIOTIC EYEDROPS.

FIRST AID- IRRIGATE EYES WITH WATER OR SALINE SOLUTION. IF SYMPTOMS OF POISONING OCCUR, TREAT RESPIRATORY DIFFICULTY WITH ARTIFICIAL RESPIRATION AND OXYGEN. OBSERVE PATIENT FOR AT LEAST 24-36 HOURS (GOSSELIN, CLINICAL TOXICOLOGY OF COMMERCIAL PRODUCTS, 5TH ED.). GET MEDICAL ATTENTION IMMEDIATELY. OXYGEN SHOULD BE ADMINISTERED BY QUALIFIED MEDICAL PERSONNEL.

INGESTION: SULPROFOS: TOXIC. SEE INFORMATION ON ORGANOPHOSPHATES. ORGANOPHOSPHATES: CHOLINESTERASE INHIBITOR. **ACUTE EXPOSURE-** WHEN INGESTED, THE FIRST EFFECTS MAY BE NAUSEA, VOMITING, ANOREXIA, ABDOMINAL CRAMPS AND DIARRHEA. GASTROINTESTINAL ABSORPTION MAY CAUSE SYMPTOMS OF CHOLINESTERASE INHIBITION AS DESCRIBED IN ACUTE INHALATION. SYMPTOMS MAY BEGIN WITHIN MINUTES OR BE DELAYED FOR HOURS. DELAYED EFFECTS INCLUDING NEUROPATHY MAY ALSO OCCUR. **CHRONIC EXPOSURE-** REPEATED INGESTION MAY CAUSE EFFECTS AS DESCRIBED IN ACUTE EXPOSURE.

FIRST AID- IF PERSON IS ALERT AND RESPIRATION IS NOT DEPRESSED, GIVE SYRUP OF IPECAC FOLLOWED BY WATER (IF VOMITING OCCURS, KEEP HEAD BELOW HIPS TO PREVENT ASPIRATION). IF CONSCIOUSNESS LEVEL DECLINES OR VOMITING HAS NOT OCCURRED IN 15 MINUTES EMPTY STOMACH BY GASTRIC LAVAGE WITH THE AID OF CUFFED ENDOTRACHEAL TUBE USING ISOTONIC SALINE OR 5% SODIUM BICARBONATE FOLLOW WITH ACTIVATED CHARCOAL. ESTABLISH AND MAINTAIN AIRWAY. TREAT RESPIRATORY DIFFICULTY WITH ARTIFICIAL RESPIRATION AND OXYGEN. DO NOT GIVE MORPHINE, AMINOPHYLLINE, PHENOTHIAZINES, RESERPINE,

FUROSEMIDE, OR ETHACRYNIC ACID (MORGAN, RECOGNITION AND MANAGEMENT OF PESTICIDE POISONINGS, 3RD ED.). TREAT SYMPTOMATICALLY AND SUPPORTIVELY. ADMINISTRATION OF OXYGEN AND LAVAGE MUST BE PERFORMED BY QUALIFIED MEDICAL PERSONNEL. GET MEDICAL ATTENTION IMMEDIATELY.

ANTIDOTE: THE FOLLOWING ANTIDOTE(S) HAVE BEEN RECOMMENDED. HOWEVER, THE DECISION AS TO WHETHER THE SEVERITY OF POISONING REQUIRES ADMINISTRATION OF ANY ANTIDOTE AND ACTUAL DOSE REQUIRED SHOULD BE MADE BY QUALIFIED MEDICAL PERSONNEL.

FOR CHOLINESTERASE INHIBITORS: ESTABLISH CLEAR AIRWAY AND TISSUE OXYGENATION BY ASPIRATION OF SECRETIONS, AND IF NECESSARY, BY ASSISTED PULMONARY VENTILATION WITH OXYGEN. IMPROVE TISSUE OXYGENATION AS MUCH AS POSSIBLE BEFORE ADMINISTERING ATROPINE TO MINIMIZE THE RISK OF VENTRICULAR FIBRILLATION. ADMINISTER ATROPINE SULFATE INTRAVENOUSLY, OR INTRAMUSCULARLY IF IV INJECTION IS NOT POSSIBLE. IN MODERATELY SEVERE POISONING ADMINISTER ATROPINE SULFATE, 0.4-2.0 MG REPEATED EVERY 15 MINUTES UNTIL ATROPINIZATION IS ACHIEVED (TACHYCARDIA, FLUSHING, DRY MOUTH, MYDRIASIS). MAINTAIN ATROPINIZATION BY REPEATED DOSES FOR 2-12 HOURS, OR LONGER, DEPENDING ON THE SEVERITY OF POISONING. THE APPEARANCE OF RALES IN THE LUNG BASES, MIOSIS, SALIVATION, NAUSEA, BRADYCARDIA, ARE ALL INDICATIONS OF INADEQUATE ATROPINIZATION. SEVERELY POISONED INDIVIDUALS MAY EXHIBIT REMARKABLE TOLERANCE TO ATROPINE; TWO OR MORE TIMES THE DOSAGES SUGGESTED ABOVE MAY BE NEEDED. PERSONS NOT POISONED OR ONLY SLIGHTLY POISONED, HOWEVER, MAY DEVELOP SIGNS OF ATROPINE TOXICITY FROM SUCH LARGE DOSAGES: FEVER, MUSCLE FIBRILLATIONS, AND DELIRIUM ARE THE MAIN SIGNS OF ATROPINE TOXICITY. IF THESE SIGNS APPEAR WHILE THE PATIENT IS FULLY ATROPINIZED, ATROPINE ADMINISTRATION SHOULD BE DISCONTINUED, AT LEAST TEMPORARILY. OBSERVE TREATED PATIENTS CLOSELY AT LEAST 24 HOURS TO INSURE THAT SYMPTOMS (POSSIBLY PULMONARY EDEMA) DO NOT RECUR AS ATROPINIZATION WEARS OFF. IN VERY SEVERE POISONINGS, METABOLIC DISPOSITION OF TOXICANT MAY REQUIRE SEVERAL HOURS OR DAYS DURING WHICH ATROPINIZATION MUST BE MAINTAINED. MARKEDLY LOWER LEVELS OF URINARY METABOLITES INDICATE THAT ATROPINE DOSAGE CAN BE TAPERED OFF. AS DOSAGE IS REDUCED, CHECK THE LUNG BASES FREQUENTLY FOR RALES. IF RALES ARE HEARD OR OTHER SYMPTOMS RETURN, RE-ESTABLISH ATROPINIZATION PROMPTLY (MORGAN, RECOGNITION AND MANAGEMENT OF PESTICIDE POISONINGS, 3RD ED.). ADMINISTRATION OF ANTIDOTE MUST BE PERFORMED BY QUALIFIED MEDICAL PERSONNEL.

IN CASES OF SEVERE POISONING BY ORGANOPHOSPHATE PESTICIDES IN WHICH RESPIRATORY DEPRESSION, MUSCLE WEAKNESS AND TWITCHINGS ARE SEVERE, GIVE PRALIDOXIME (PROTOPAM-AYERST, 2-PAM), 1.0 GRAM INTRAVENOUSLY AT NO MORE THAN 0.5 GRAM PER MINUTE. DOSAGE OF PRALIDOXIME MAY BE REPEATED IN 1-2 HOURS, THEN AT 10-12 HOUR INTERVALS IF NEEDED. IN VERY SEVERE POISONINGS, DOSAGE RATES MAY BE DOUBLED. TREATMENT WITH PRALIDOXIME WILL BE MOST EFFECTIVE IF GIVEN WITHIN THIRTY-SIX HOURS AFTER POISONING (MORGAN, RECOGNITION AND MANAGEMENT OF PESTICIDE POISONINGS, 3RD ED.). ANTIDOTE SHOULD BE ADMINISTERED BY QUALIFIED MEDICAL PERSONNEL.

REACTIVITY

REACTIVITY: STABLE UNDER NORMAL TEMPERATURES AND PRESSURES.

INCOMPATIBILITIES: SULPROFOS: STRONG OXIDIZERS: FIRE AND EXPLOSION HAZARD. STRONG ALKALINE: MAY CAUSE HYDROLYSIS.

DECOMPOSITION: THERMAL DECOMPOSITION MAY RELEASE TOXIC OXIDES OF CARBON, PHOSPHOROUS AND SULFUR.

POLYMERIZATION: HAZARDOUS POLYMERIZATION HAS NOT BEEN REPORTED TO OCCUR UNDER NORMAL TEMPERATURES AND PRESSURES.

STORAGE AND DISPOSAL

OBSERVE ALL FEDERAL, STATE AND LOCAL REGULATIONS WHEN STORING OR DISPOSING OF THIS SUBSTANCE. FOR ASSISTANCE, CONTACT THE DISTRICT DIRECTOR OF THE ENVIRONMENTAL PROTECTION AGENCY.

****STORAGE****

STORE IN ACCORDANCE WITH 40 CFR 165 RECOMMENDED PROCEDURES FOR THE DISPOSAL AND STORAGE OF PESTICIDES AND PESTICIDE CONTAINERS. STORE AWAY FROM INCOMPATIBLE SUBSTANCES.

****DISPOSAL****

DISPOSAL MUST BE IN ACCORDANCE WITH 40 CFR 165 RECOMMENDED PROCEDURES FOR THE DISPOSAL AND STORAGE OF PESTICIDES AND PESTICIDE CONTAINERS.

CONDITIONS TO AVOID

NONE REPORTED.

SPILL AND LEAK PROCEDURES

OCCUPATIONAL SPILL: DO NOT TOUCH SPILLED MATERIAL. STOP LEAK IF YOU CAN DO IT WITHOUT RISK. USE WATER SPRAY TO REDUCE VAPORS. FOR SMALL SPILLS, TAKE UP WITH SAND OR OTHER ABSORBENT MATERIAL AND PLACE INTO CONTAINERS FOR LATER DISPOSAL. FOR SMALL DRY SPILLS, WITH A CLEAN SHOVEL PLACE MATERIAL INTO CLEAN, DRY CONTAINERS AND COVER. MOVE CONTAINERS FROM SPILL AREA. FOR LARGER SPILLS, DIKE FAR AHEAD OF SPILL FOR LATER DISPOSAL. KEEP UNNECESSARY PEOPLE AWAY. ISOLATE HAZARD AREA AND DENY ENTRY. VENTILATE CLOSED SPACES BEFORE ENTERING.

PROTECTIVE EQUIPMENT

VENTILATION: PROVIDE LOCAL EXHAUST OR PROCESS ENCLOSURE VENTILATION TO MEET THE PUBLISHED EXPOSURE LIMITS. VENTILATION EQUIPMENT MUST BE EXPLOSION-PROOF.

RESPIRATOR: THE FOLLOWING RESPIRATORS ARE RECOMMENDED BASED ON INFORMATION FOUND IN THE PHYSICAL DATA, TOXICITY AND HEALTH EFFECTS SECTIONS. THEY ARE RANKED IN ORDER FROM MINIMUM TO MAXIMUM RESPIRATORY PROTECTION. THE SPECIFIC RESPIRATOR SELECTED MUST BE BASED ON CONTAMINATION LEVELS FOUND IN THE WORK PLACE, MUST NOT EXCEED THE WORKING LIMITS OF THE RESPIRATOR AND BE JOINTLY APPROVED BY THE NATIONAL INSTITUTE FOR OCCUPATIONAL SAFETY AND HEALTH AND THE MINE SAFETY AND HEALTH ADMINISTRATION (NIOSH-MSHA).

TYPE 'C' SUPPLIED-AIR RESPIRATOR WITH A FULL FACEPIECE OPERATED IN PRESSURE-DEMAND OR OTHER POSITIVE PRESSURE MODE OR WITH A FULL FACEPIECE, HELMET OR HOOD OPERATED IN CONTINOUS-FLOW MODE.

SELF-CONTAINED BREATHING APPARATUS WITH A FULL FACEPIECE OPERATED IN PRESSURE-DEMAND OR OTHER POSITIVE PRESSURE MODE.

FOR FIREFIGHTING AND OTHER IMMEDIATELY DANGEROUS TO LIFE OR HEALTH CONDITIONS:

SELF-CONTAINED BREATHING APPARATUS WITH FULL FACEPIECE OPERATED IN PRESSURE-DEMAND OR OTHER POSITIVE PRESSURE MODE.

SUPPLIED-AIR RESPIRATOR WITH FULL FACEPIECE AND OPERATED IN PRESSURE-DEMAND OR OTHER POSITIVE PRESSURE MODE IN COMBINATION WITH AN AUXILIARY SELF-CONTAINED BREATHING APPARATUS OPERATED IN PRESSURE-DEMAND OR OTHER POSITIVE PRESSURE MODE.

CLOTHING: EMPLOYEE MUST WEAR APPROPRIATE PROTECTIVE (IMPERVIOUS) CLOTHING AND EQUIPMENT TO PREVENT ANY POSSIBILITY OF SKIN CONTACT WITH THIS SUBSTANCE.

GLOVES: EMPLOYEE MUST WEAR APPROPRIATE PROTECTIVE GLOVES TO PREVENT CONTACT WITH THIS SUBSTANCE.

EYE PROTECTION: EMPLOYEE MUST WEAR SPLASH-PROOF OR DUST-RESISTANT SAFETY GOGGLES AND A FACESHIELD TO PREVENT CONTACT WITH THIS SUBSTANCE.

EMERGENCY WASH FACILITIES: WHERE THERE IS ANY POSSIBILITY THAT AN EMPLOYEE'S EYES AND/OR SKIN MAY BE EXPOSED TO THIS SUBSTANCE, THE EMPLOYER SHOULD PROVIDE AN EYE WASH FOUNTAIN AND QUICK DRENCH SHOWER WITHIN THE IMMEDIATE WORK AREA FOR EMERGENCY USE.

AUTHORIZED BY- OCCUPATIONAL HEALTH SERVICES, INC.

CREATION DATE: 10/05/89 ***REVISION DATE:*** 05/02/90

MATERIAL SAFETY DATA SHEET

OCCUPATIONAL HEALTH SERVICES, INC.
AGRICULTURE AND PESTICIDE DIVISION
450 SEVENTH AVENUE, SUITE 2407
NEW YORK, NEW YORK 10123
1-800-445-MSDS OR (212) 967-1100

EMERGENCY CONTACT:
JOHN S. BRANSFORD, JR. (615) 292-1180

SUBSTANCE IDENTIFICATION

CAS-NUMBER 1928-37-6

SUBSTANCE: **2,4,5-T METHYL ESTER**

TRADE NAMES/SYNONYMS: ACETIC ACID, (2,4,5-TRICHLOROPHENOXY)-, METHYL ESTER; (2,4,5-TRICHLOROPHENOXY) METHYL ACETATE; METHYL(2,4,5-TRICHLOROPHENOXY) ACETATE; (2,4,5-TRICHLOROPHENOXY)-ACETIC ACID, METHYL ESTER; C9H7CL3O3; PST22392

CHEMICAL FAMILY: HALOGEN COMPOUND, AROMATIC ESTER, NON-CARBOXYLIC

MOLECULAR FORMULA: C6-H2-(CL)3-O-C-H2-C-O2-C-H3

MOLECULAR WEIGHT: 269.52

CERCLA RATINGS (SCALE 0-3): HEALTH=3 FIRE=1 REACTIVITY=0 PERSISTENCE=2

NFPA RATINGS (SCALE 0-4): HEALTH=U FIRE=1 REACTIVITY=0

COMPONENTS AND CONTAMINANTS

COMPONENT: 2,4,5-T METHYL ESTER ***PERCENT:*** 100.0
CAS# 1928-37-6

OTHER CONTAMINANTS: NONE

EXPOSURE LIMITS: NO OCCUPATIONAL EXPOSURE LIMITS ESTABLISHED BY OSHA, ACGIH, OR NIOSH.
2,4,5-T; SALTS AND ESTERS: 1000 POUNDS CERCLA SECTION 103 REPORTABLE QUANTITY

PHYSICAL DATA

DESCRIPTION: WHITE POWDER. ***MELTING POINT:*** 194 F (90 C)

SPECIFIC GRAVITY: NOT AVAILABLE ***SOLUBILITY IN WATER:*** PRACTICALLY INSOLUBLE

SOLVENT SOLUBILITY: SOLUBLE IN PETROLEUM OILS.

FIRE AND EXPLOSION DATA

FIRE AND EXPLOSION HAZARD: SLIGHT FIRE HAZARD WHEN EXPOSED TO HEAT OR FLAME.
DUST-AIR MIXTURES MAY IGNITE OR EXPLODE.

FIREFIGHTING MEDIA: DRY CHEMICAL, CARBON DIOXIDE, HALON, WATER SPRAY OR STANDARD FOAM (1987 EMERGENCY RESPONSE GUIDEBOOK, DOT P 5800.4).
FOR LARGER FIRES, USE WATER SPRAY, FOG OR STANDARD FOAM (1987 EMERGENCY RESPONSE GUIDEBOOK, DOT P 5800.4).

FIREFIGHTING: MOVE CONTAINER FROM FIRE AREA IF POSSIBLE. DO NOT SCATTER SPILLED MATERIAL WITH HIGH PRESSURE WATER STREAMS. DIKE FIRE CONTROL WATER FOR LATER DISPOSAL (1987 EMERGENCY RESPONSE GUIDEBOOK, DOT P 5800.4, GUIDE PAGE 31).
USE AGENTS SUITABLE FOR TYPE OF SURROUNDING FIRE. AVOID BREATHING HAZARDOUS VAPORS, KEEP UPWIND.

TOXICITY

2,4,5-T METHYL ESTER: TOXICITY DATA: 100 MG/KG ORAL-DOG LD50 (EPA). CARCINOGEN STATUS: HUMAN LIMITED EVIDENCE (IARC GROUP-2B FOR CHLOROPHENOXY HERBICIDES). STUDIES REVEALED A SIGNIFICANT INCREASE IN SOFT-TISSUE SARCOMAS, MALIGNANT LYMPHOMAS AND BRONCHIAL CARCINOMAS IN WORKERS EXPOSED TO CHLOROPHENOXY HERBICIDES. ACUTE TOXICITY LEVEL: TOXIC BY INGESTION. TARGET EFFECTS: POISONING MAY AFFECT THE GASTROINTESTINAL TRACT AND CARDIOVASCULAR SYSTEM.* AT INCREASED RISK FROM EXPOSURE: PERSONS WITH PREEXISTING LIVER, GASTROINTESTINAL TRACT OR SKIN DISORDERS.* ADDITIONAL DATA: STIMULANTS SUCH AS EPINEPHRINE MAY INDUCE VENTRICULAR FIBRILLATION.*
* MAY BE BASED ON GENERAL INFORMATION ON 2,4,5-T AND DERIVATIVES.

HEALTH EFFECTS AND FIRST AID

INHALATION: 2,4,5-T METHYL ESTER: SEE INFORMATION ON 2,4,5-T AND DERIVATIVES.
2,4,5-T AND DERIVATIVES: **ACUTE EXPOSURE-** MAY CAUSE IRRITATION WITH SORE THROAT AND BURNING SENSATIONS IN THE NASOPHARYNX AND CHEST, COUGHING, LACRIMATION, RHINITIS, DULLNESS, DIZZINESS, AND ATAXIA. IF SUFFICIENT AMOUNTS ARE ABSORBED THROUGH THE LUNGS, EFFECTS AS DESCRIBED IN ACUTE INGESTION MAY OCCUR. **CHRONIC EXPOSURE-** OCCUPATIONAL EXPOSURE TO 2,4,5-T AND ITS DERIVATIVES HAS PRODUCED HEADACHE, DECREASED AUDITORY ACUITY, GASTROINTESTINAL SYMPTOMS OF NAUSEA, VOMITING, DIARRHEA, ABDOMINAL PAINS, AND BLOOD IN THE STOOL, CHLORACNE, PORPHYRIA CUTANEA TARDIA, HYPERTRICHOSIS, HYPERPIGMENTATION, INCREASED SKIN FRAGILITY, LIVER DISORDERS, PERSONALITY CHANGES, AND PERIPHERAL NEUROPATHY. MANY OF THESE EFFECTS MAY BE DUE TO DIOXINS, ESPECIALLY TCDD, AS CONTAMINANTS. EPIDEMIOLOGICAL STUDIES HAVE INDICATED AN ASSOCIATION BETWEEN EXPOSURE TO 2,4,5-T COMPOUNDS AND AN INCREASED PREVALENCE OF REPORTED SEXUAL DYSFUNCTION AND DECREASED LIBIDO, ABNORMAL SENSORY FINDINGS, GASTROINTESTINAL TRACT ULCER, AND BIRTH MALFORMATIONS OF THE FEET. AN INCREASED PREVALENCE OF SLOWED NERVE CONDUCTION VELOCITY WITH NO ASSOCIATED SYMPTOMS WAS REPORTED IN A STUDY OF CHEMICAL WORKERS EMPLOYED IN THE PRODUCTION OF 2,4-D AND 2,4,5-T. EPIDEMIOLOGICAL STUDIES REVEALED A SIGNIFICANT INCREASE IN SOFT-TISSUE SARCOMAS, MALIGNANT LYMPHOMAS, AND BRONCHIAL CARCINOMAS IN WORKERS EXPOSED TO CHLOROPHENOXY HERBICIDES INCLUDING 2,4,5-T.

FIRST AID- REMOVE FROM EXPOSURE AREA TO FRESH AIR IMMEDIATELY. IF BREATHING HAS STOPPED, PERFORM ARTIFICIAL RESPIRATION. KEEP PERSON WARM AND AT REST. TREAT SYMPTOMATICALLY AND SUPPORTIVELY. GET MEDICAL ATTENTION IMMEDIATELY.

SKIN CONTACT: 2,4,5-T METHYL ESTER: SEE INFORMATION ON 2,4,5-T AND DERIVATIVES.
2,4,5-T AND DERIVATIVES: **ACUTE EXPOSURE-** MAY CAUSE IRRITATION. IF SUFFICIENT AMOUNTS ARE ABSORBED THROUGH THE SKIN, EFFECTS AS DESCRIBED IN ACUTE INGESTION MAY OCCUR. **CHRONIC EXPOSURE-** PROLONGED OR REPEATED EXPOSURE MAY CAUSE DERMATITIS AND EFFECTS AS DESCRIBED IN CHRONIC INHALATION.

FIRST AID- REMOVE CONTAMINATED CLOTHING AND SHOES IMMEDIATELY. WASH AFFECTED AREA WITH SOAP OR MILD DETERGENT AND LARGE AMOUNTS OF WATER UNTIL NO EVIDENCE OF CHEMICAL REMAINS (APPROXIMATELY 15-20 MINUTES). GET MEDICAL ATTENTION IMMEDIATELY.

EYE CONTACT: 2,4,5-T METHYL ESTER: SEE INFORMATION ON 2,4,5-T AND DERIVATIVES.
2,4,5-T AND DERIVATIVES: **ACUTE EXPOSURE-** MAY CAUSE IRRITATION. **CHRONIC EXPOSURE-** NO DATA AVAILABLE.

FIRST AID- WASH EYES IMMEDIATELY WITH LARGE AMOUNTS OF WATER OR NORMAL SALINE, OCCASIONALLY LIFTING UPPER AND LOWER LIDS, UNTIL NO EVIDENCE OF CHEMICAL REMAINS (APPROXIMATELY 15-20 MINUTES). GET MEDICAL ATTENTION IMMEDIATELY.

INGESTION: 2,4,5-T METHYL ESTER: TOXIC. SEE INFORMATION ON 2,4,5-T AND DERIVATIVES.
2,4,5-T AND DERIVATIVES: **ACUTE EXPOSURE-** MAY CAUSE IRRITATION OF THE MOUTH, THROAT, AND GASTROINTESTINAL TRACT, NAUSEA, VOMITING, CHEST AND ABDOMINAL PAIN, AND DIARRHEA. INGESTION OF VERY LARGE DOSES MAY PRODUCE METABOLIC ACIDOSIS, FEVER OR SUBNORMAL TEMPERATURES, HYPERVENTILATION, HYPOTENSION, VASODILATION, FLUSHING OF THE SKIN, SWEATING, CARDIAC ARRHYTHMIAS, TACHYCARDIA, LETHARGY, WEAKNESS, INTERCOSTAL PARALYSIS, RENAL AND HEPATIC DYSFUNCTION, MYOTONIA, COMA, AND CONVULSIONS. DAMAGE TO SKELETAL MUSCLE MAY BE MANIFEST BY MUSCLE TWITCHING AND ACHING WITH ELEVATED SERUM ENZYMES AND MYOGLOBIN IN THE BLOOD AND URINE. DEATH MAY BE DUE TO CIRCULATORY COLLAPSE. **CHRONIC EXPOSURE-** NO DATA AVAILABLE.

FIRST AID- IF THE PERSON IS CONSCIOUS AND NOT CONVULSING, INDUCE EMESIS BY GIVING SYRUP OF IPECAC (KEEPING THE HEAD BELOW THE HIPS TO PREVENT ASPIRATION) FOLLOWED BY WATER. REPEAT IN 20 MINUTES IF NOT EFFECTIVE INITIALLY. IN PATIENTS WITH DEPRESSED RESPIRATION OR IF EMESIS IS NOT PRODUCED, PERFORM GASTRIC LAVAGE WITH ACTIVATED CHARCOAL. FOLLOW WITH A SALINE CATHARTIC (DREISBACH, HANDBOOK OF POISONING, 12TH ED.). TREAT SYMPTOMATICALLY AND SUPPORTIVELY. GASTRIC LAVAGE SHOULD BE PERFORMED BY QUALIFIED MEDICAL PERSONNEL. GET MEDICAL ATTENTION IMMEDIATELY.

ANTIDOTE: NO SPECIFIC ANTIDOTE. TREAT SYMPTOMATICALLY AND SUPPORTIVELY.

REACTIVITY

REACTIVITY: STABLE UNDER NORMAL TEMPERATURES AND PRESSURES.

INCOMPATIBILITIES: 2,4,5-T METHYL ESTER: OXIDIZERS (STRONG): FIRE AND EXPLOSION HAZARD.

DECOMPOSITION: THERMAL DECOMPOSITION PRODUCTS MAY INCLUDE TOXIC AND CORROSIVE FUMES OF CHLORIDES AND TOXIC OXIDES OF CARBON.

POLYMERIZATION: HAZARDOUS POLYMERIZATION HAS NOT BEEN REPORTED TO OCCUR UNDER NORMAL TEMPERATURES AND PRESSURES.

STORAGE AND DISPOSAL

OBSERVE ALL FEDERAL, STATE AND LOCAL REGULATIONS WHEN STORING OR DISPOSING OF THIS SUBSTANCE. FOR ASSISTANCE, CONTACT THE DISTRICT DIRECTOR OF THE ENVIRONMENTAL PROTECTION AGENCY.

****STORAGE****

STORE IN ACCORDANCE WITH 40 CFR 165 RECOMMENDED PROCEDURES FOR THE DISPOSAL AND STORAGE OF PESTICIDES AND PESTICIDE CONTAINERS.
STORE AWAY FROM INCOMPATIBLE SUBSTANCES.

****DISPOSAL****

DISPOSAL MUST BE IN ACCORDANCE WITH 40 CFR 165 RECOMMENDED PROCEDURES FOR THE DISPOSAL AND STORAGE OF PESTICIDES AND PESTICIDE CONTAINERS.

CONDITIONS TO AVOID

MAY BURN BUT DOES NOT IGNITE READILY. AVOID CONTACT WITH STRONG OXIDIZERS, EXCESSIVE HEAT, SPARKS, OR OPEN FLAME.

SPILL AND LEAK PROCEDURES

SOIL SPILL: DIG HOLDING AREA SUCH AS LAGOON, POND OR PIT FOR CONTAINMENT.
USE PROTECTIVE COVER SUCH AS A PLASTIC SHEET TO PREVENT MATERIAL FROM DISSOLVING IN FIRE EXTINGUISHING WATER OR RAIN.

WATER SPILL: USE ACTIVATED CARBON TO ABSORB SPILLED SUBSTANCE THAT IS DISSOLVED.
USE SUCTION HOSES TO REMOVE TRAPPED SPILL MATERIAL.

USE MECHANICAL DREDGES OR LIFTS TO EXTRACT IMMOBILIZED MASSES OF POLLUTION AND PRECIPITATES.

OCCUPATIONAL SPILL: SWEEP UP AND PLACE IN SUITABLE CLEAN, DRY CONTAINERS FOR RECLAMATION OR LATER DISPOSAL. DO NOT FLUSH SPILLED MATERIAL INTO SEWER. KEEP UNNECESSARY PEOPLE AWAY.

REPORTABLE QUANTITY (RQ): 1000 POUNDS THE SUPERFUND AMENDMENTS AND REAUTHORIZATION ACT (SARA) SECTION 304 REQUIRES THAT A RELEASE EQUAL TO OR GREATER THAN THE REPORTABLE QUANTITY FOR THIS SUBSTANCE BE IMMEDIATELY REPORTED TO THE LOCAL EMERGENCY PLANNING COMMITTEE AND THE STATE EMERGENCY RESPONSE COMMISSION (40 CFR 355.40). IF THE RELEASE OF THIS SUBSTANCE IS REPORTABLE UNDER CERCLA SECTION 103, THE NATIONAL RESPONSE CENTER MUST BE NOTIFIED IMMEDIATELY AT (800) 424-8802 OR (202) 426-2675 IN THE METROPOLITAN WASHINGTON, D.C. AREA (40 CFR 302.6).

PROTECTIVE EQUIPMENT

VENTILATION: PROVIDE LOCAL EXHAUST OR PROCESS ENCLOSURE VENTILATION SYSTEM.

RESPIRATOR: THE FOLLOWING RESPIRATORS ARE RECOMMENDED BASED ON INFORMATION FOUND IN THE PHYSICAL DATA, TOXICITY AND HEALTH EFFECTS SECTIONS. THEY ARE RANKED IN ORDER FROM MINIMUM TO MAXIMUM RESPIRATORY PROTECTION. THE SPECIFIC RESPIRATOR SELECTED MUST BE BASED ON CONTAMINATION LEVELS FOUND IN THE WORK PLACE, MUST NOT EXCEED THE WORKING LIMITS OF THE RESPIRATOR AND BE JOINTLY APPROVED BY THE NATIONAL INSTITUTE FOR OCCUPATIONAL SAFETY AND HEALTH AND THE MINE SAFETY AND HEALTH ADMINISTRATION (NIOSH-MSHA).

TYPE 'C' SUPPLIED-AIR RESPIRATOR WITH A FULL FACEPIECE OPERATED IN PRESSURE-DEMAND OR OTHER POSITIVE PRESSURE MODE OR WITH A FULL FACEPIECE, HELMET OR HOOD OPERATED IN CONTINOUS-FLOW MODE.

SELF-CONTAINED BREATHING APPARATUS WITH A FULL FACEPIECE OPERATED IN PRESSURE-DEMAND OR OTHER POSITIVE PRESSURE MODE.

FOR FIREFIGHTING AND OTHER IMMEDIATELY DANGEROUS TO LIFE OR HEALTH CONDITIONS:

SELF-CONTAINED BREATHING APPARATUS WITH FULL FACEPIECE OPERATED IN PRESSURE-DEMAND OR OTHER POSITIVE PRESSURE MODE.

SUPPLIED-AIR RESPIRATOR WITH FULL FACEPIECE AND OPERATED IN PRESSURE-DEMAND OR OTHER POSITIVE PRESSURE MODE IN COMBINATION WITH AN AUXILIARY SELF-CONTAINED BREATHING APPARATUS OPERATED IN PRESSURE-DEMAND OR OTHER POSITIVE PRESSURE MODE.

CLOTHING: EMPLOYEE MUST WEAR APPROPRIATE PROTECTIVE (IMPERVIOUS) CLOTHING AND EQUIPMENT TO PREVENT ANY POSSIBILITY OF SKIN CONTACT WITH THIS SUBSTANCE.

GLOVES: EMPLOYEE MUST WEAR APPROPRIATE PROTECTIVE GLOVES TO PREVENT CONTACT WITH THIS SUBSTANCE.

EYE PROTECTION: EMPLOYEE MUST WEAR SPLASH-PROOF OR DUST-RESISTANT SAFETY GOGGLES AND A FACESHIELD TO PREVENT CONTACT WITH THIS SUBSTANCE.

EMERGENCY WASH FACILITIES: WHERE THERE IS ANY POSSIBILITY THAT AN EMPLOYEE'S EYES AND/OR SKIN MAY BE EXPOSED TO THIS SUBSTANCE, THE EMPLOYER SHOULD PROVIDE AN EYE WASH FOUNTAIN AND QUICK DRENCH SHOWER WITHIN THE IMMEDIATE WORK AREA FOR EMERGENCY USE.

AUTHORIZED BY- OCCUPATIONAL HEALTH SERVICES, INC.
CREATION DATE: 05/02/90 ***REVISION DATE:*** 07/12/90

MATERIAL SAFETY DATA SHEET

OCCUPATIONAL HEALTH SERVICES, INC.
AGRICULTURE AND PESTICIDE DIVISION
450 SEVENTH AVENUE, SUITE 2407
NEW YORK, NEW YORK 10123
1-800-445-MSDS OR (212) 967-1100

EMERGENCY CONTACT:
JOHN S. BRANSFORD, JR. (615) 292-1180

SUBSTANCE IDENTIFICATION

CAS-NUMBER 3084-62-6

SUBSTANCE: **2,4,5-T, PROPYLENE GLYCOL BUTYL ETHER ESTER**

TRADE NAMES/SYNONYMS: 2,4,5-TRICHLOROPHENOXY-, 2-BUTOXYPROPYL ESTER; 2,4,5-TRICHLOROPHENOXY ACETIC ACID, PROPYLENE GLYCOL BUTYL ETHER ESTER; C15H19CL3O4; PST22393

CHEMICAL FAMILY: HALOGEN COMPOUND, AROMATIC
ESTER
ETHER

MOLECULAR FORMULA: C15-H19-CL3-O4

MOLECULAR WEIGHT: 369.67

CERCLA RATINGS (SCALE 0-3): HEALTH=3 FIRE=1 REACTIVITY=0 PERSISTENCE=1

NFPA RATINGS (SCALE 0-4): HEALTH=U FIRE=1 REACTIVITY=0

COMPONENTS AND CONTAMINANTS

COMPONENT: 2,4,5-T, PROPYLENE GLYCOL BUTYL ETHER ESTER ***PERCENT:*** 100.0
CAS# 3084-62-6

OTHER CONTAMINANTS: NONE

EXPOSURE LIMITS: NO OCCUPATIONAL EXPOSURE LIMITS ESTABLISHED BY OSHA, ACGIH, OR NIOSH.

2,4,5-T; SALTS AND ESTERS: 1000 POUNDS CERCLA SECTION 103 REPORTABLE QUANTITY

PHYSICAL DATA

DESCRIPTION: AMBER LIQUID. ***BOILING POINT:*** 651 F (344 C)

SPECIFIC GRAVITY: NOT AVAILABLE ***VAPOR PRESSURE:*** NOT AVAILABLE

EVAPORATION RATE: NOT AVAILABLE ***SOLUBILITY IN WATER:*** PRACTICALLY INSOLUBLE

SOLVENT SOLUBILITY: SOLUBLE IN PETROLEUM OILS.

FIRE AND EXPLOSION DATA

FIRE AND EXPLOSION HAZARD: SLIGHT FIRE HAZARD WHEN EXPOSED TO HEAT OR FLAME.

FLASH POINT: >265 F (>129 C) (OC)

FIREFIGHTING MEDIA: DRY CHEMICAL, CARBON DIOXIDE, HALON, WATER SPRAY OR STANDARD FOAM (1987 EMERGENCY RESPONSE GUIDEBOOK, DOT P 5800.4).
FOR LARGER FIRES, USE WATER SPRAY, FOG OR STANDARD FOAM (1987 EMERGENCY RESPONSE GUIDEBOOK, DOT P 5800.4).

FIREFIGHTING: MOVE CONTAINERS FROM FIRE AREA IF POSSIBLE. FIGHT FIRE FROM MAXIMUM DISTANCE. STAY AWAY FROM STORAGE TANK ENDS. DIKE FIRE CONTROL WATER FOR LATER DISPOSAL. DO NOT SCATTER MATERIAL (1987 EMERGENCY RESPONSE GUIDEBOOK, DOT P 5800.4, GUIDE PAGE 55).
EXTINGUISH ONLY IF FLOW CAN BE STOPPED. EXTINGUISH USING AGENT INDICATED. USE FLOODING AMOUNTS OF WATER AS A FOG. COOL CONTAINERS WITH FLOODING AMOUNTS OF WATER FROM AS FAR A DISTANCE AS POSSIBLE. AVOID BREATHING POISONOUS VAPORS, KEEP UPWIND. CONSIDER EVACUATION OF DOWNWIND AREA IF MATERIAL IS LEAKING.

TOXICITY

2,4,5-T, PROPYLENE GLYCOL BUTYL ETHER ESTER: TOXICITY DATA: 500 MG/KG ORAL-RAT LD50. CARCINOGEN STATUS: HUMAN LIMITED EVIDENCE (IARC GROUP-2B FOR CHLOROPHENOXY HERBICIDES). STUDIES REVEALED A SIGNIFICANT INCREASE IN SOFT-TISSUE SARCOMAS, MALIGNANT LYMPHOMAS AND BRONCHIAL CARCINOMAS IN WORKERS EXPOSED TO CHLOROPHENOXY HERBICIDES. ACUTE TOXICITY LEVEL: TOXIC BY INGESTION. TARGET EFFECTS: POISONING MAY AFFECT THE GASTROINTESTINAL TRACT AND CARDIOVASCULAR SYSTEM.* AT INCREASED RISK FROM EXPOSURE: PERSONS WITH PREEXISTING LIVER, GASTROINTESTINAL TRACT OR SKIN DISORDERS.* ADDITIONAL DATA: STIMULANTS SUCH AS EPINEPHRINE MAY INDUCE VENTRICULAR FIBRILLATION.*

* MAY BE BASED ON GENERAL INFORMATION ON 2,4,5-T AND DERIVATIVES.

HEALTH EFFECTS AND FIRST AID

INHALATION: 2,4,5-T, PROPYLENE GLYCOL BUTYL ETHER ESTER: SEE INFORMATION ON 2,4,5-T AND DERIVATIVES.

2,4,5-T AND DERIVATIVES: **ACUTE EXPOSURE-** MAY CAUSE IRRITATION WITH SORE THROAT AND BURNING SENSATIONS IN THE NASOPHARYNX AND CHEST, COUGHING, LACRIMATION, RHINITIS, DULLNESS, DIZZINESS, AND ATAXIA. IF SUFFICIENT AMOUNTS ARE ABSORBED THROUGH THE LUNGS, EFFECTS AS DESCRIBED IN ACUTE INGESTION MAY OCCUR. **CHRONIC EXPOSURE-** OCCUPATIONAL EXPOSURE TO 2,4,5-T AND ITS DERIVATIVES HAS PRODUCED HEADACHE, DECREASED AUDITORY ACUITY, GASTROINTESTINAL SYMPTOMS OF NAUSEA, VOMITING, DIARRHEA, ABDOMINAL PAINS, AND BLOOD IN THE STOOL, CHLORACNE, PORPHYRIA CUTANEA TARDIA, HYPERTRICHOSIS, HYPERPIGMENTATION, INCREASED SKIN FRAGILITY, LIVER DISORDERS, PERSONALITY CHANGES, AND PERIPHERAL NEUROPATHY. MANY OF THESE EFFECTS MAY BE DUE TO DIOXINS, ESPECIALLY TCDD, AS CONTAMINANTS. EPIDEMIOLOGICAL STUDIES HAVE INDICATED AN ASSOCIATION BETWEEN EXPOSURE TO 2,4,5-T COMPOUNDS AND AN INCREASED PREVALENCE OF REPORTED SEXUAL DYSFUNCTION AND DECREASED LIBIDO, ABNORMAL SENSORY FINDINGS, GASTROINTESTINAL TRACT ULCER, AND BIRTH MALFORMATIONS OF THE FEET. AN INCREASED PREVALENCE OF SLOWED NERVE CONDUCTION VELOCITY WITH NO ASSOCIATED SYMPTOMS WAS REPORTED IN A STUDY OF CHEMICAL WORKERS EMPLOYED IN THE PRODUCTION OF 2,4-D AND 2,4,5-T. EPIDEMIOLOGICAL STUDIES REVEALED A SIGNIFICANT INCREASE IN SOFT-TISSUE

SARCOMAS, MALIGNANT LYMPHOMAS, AND BRONCHIAL CARCINOMAS IN WORKERS EXPOSED TO CHLOROPHENOXY HERBICIDES INCLUDING 2,4,5-T.
FIRST AID- REMOVE FROM EXPOSURE AREA TO FRESH AIR IMMEDIATELY. IF BREATHING HAS STOPPED, PERFORM ARTIFICIAL RESPIRATION. KEEP PERSON WARM AND AT REST. TREAT SYMPTOMATICALLY AND SUPPORTIVELY. GET MEDICAL ATTENTION IMMEDIATELY.

SKIN CONTACT: 2,4,5-T, PROPYLENE GLYCOL BUTYL ETHER ESTER: SEE INFORMATION ON 2,4,5-T AND DERIVATIVES.
2,4,5-T AND DERIVATIVES: **ACUTE EXPOSURE**- MAY CAUSE IRRITATION. IF SUFFICIENT AMOUNTS ARE ABSORBED THROUGH THE SKIN, EFFECTS AS DESCRIBED IN ACUTE INGESTION MAY OCCUR. **CHRONIC EXPOSURE**- PROLONGED OR REPEATED EXPOSURE MAY CAUSE DERMATITIS AND EFFECTS AS DESCRIBED IN CHRONIC INHALATION.
FIRST AID- REMOVE CONTAMINATED CLOTHING AND SHOES IMMEDIATELY. WASH AFFECTED AREA WITH SOAP OR MILD DETERGENT AND LARGE AMOUNTS OF WATER UNTIL NO EVIDENCE OF CHEMICAL REMAINS (APPROXIMATELY 15-20 MINUTES). GET MEDICAL ATTENTION IMMEDIATELY.

EYE CONTACT: 2,4,5-T, PROPYLENE GLYCOL BUTYL ETHER ESTER: SEE INFORMATION ON 2,4,5-T AND DERIVATIVES.
2,4,5-T AND DERIVATIVES: **ACUTE EXPOSURE**- MAY CAUSE IRRITATION. **CHRONIC EXPOSURE**- NO DATA AVAILABLE.
FIRST AID- WASH EYES IMMEDIATELY WITH LARGE AMOUNTS OF WATER OR NORMAL SALINE, OCCASIONALLY LIFTING UPPER AND LOWER LIDS, UNTIL NO EVIDENCE OF CHEMICAL REMAINS (APPROXIMATELY 15-20 MINUTES). GET MEDICAL ATTENTION IMMEDIATELY.

INGESTION: 2,4,5-T, PROPYLENE GLYCOL BUTYL ETHER ESTER: TOXIC. REPRODUCTIVE EFFECTS WERE REPORTED IN ANIMALS. SEE INFORMATION ON 2,4,5-T AND DERIVATIVES.
2,4,5-T AND DERIVATIVES: **ACUTE EXPOSURE**- MAY CAUSE IRRITATION OF THE MOUTH, THROAT, AND GASTROINTESTINAL TRACT, NAUSEA, VOMITING, CHEST AND ABDOMINAL PAIN, AND DIARRHEA. INGESTION OF VERY LARGE DOSES MAY PRODUCE METABOLIC ACIDOSIS, FEVER OR SUBNORMAL TEMPERATURES, HYPERVENTILATION, HYPOTENSION, VASODILATION, FLUSHING OF THE SKIN, SWEATING, CARDIAC ARRHYTHMIAS, TACHYCARDIA, LETHARGY, WEAKNESS, INTERCOSTAL PARALYSIS, RENAL AND HEPATIC DYSFUNCTION, MYOTONIA, COMA, AND CONVULSIONS. DAMAGE TO SKELETAL MUSCLE MAY BE MANIFEST BY MUSCLE TWITCHING AND ACHING WITH ELEVATED SERUM ENZYMES AND MYOGLOBIN IN THE BLOOD AND URINE. DEATH MAY BE DUE TO CIRCULATORY COLLAPSE. **CHRONIC EXPOSURE**- NO DATA AVAILABLE.
FIRST AID- IF THE PERSON IS CONSCIOUS AND NOT CONVULSING, INDUCE EMESIS BY GIVING SYRUP OF IPECAC (KEEPING THE HEAD BELOW THE HIPS TO PREVENT ASPIRATION) FOLLOWED BY WATER. REPEAT IN 20 MINUTES IF NOT EFFECTIVE INITIALLY. IN PATIENTS WITH DEPRESSED RESPIRATION OR IF EMESIS IS NOT PRODUCED, PERFORM GASTRIC LAVAGE WITH ACTIVATED CHARCOAL. FOLLOW WITH A SALINE CATHARTIC (DREISBACH, HANDBOOK OF POISONING, 12TH ED.). TREAT SYMPTOMATICALLY AND SUPPORTIVELY. GASTRIC LAVAGE SHOULD BE PERFORMED BY QUALIFIED MEDICAL PERSONNEL. GET MEDICAL ATTENTION IMMEDIATELY.
ANTIDOTE: NO SPECIFIC ANTIDOTE. TREAT SYMPTOMATICALLY AND SUPPORTIVELY.

REACTIVITY

REACTIVITY: STABLE UNDER NORMAL TEMPERATURES AND PRESSURES.
INCOMPATIBILITIES: 2,4,5-T, PROPYLENE GLYCOL BUTYL ETHER ESTER: OXIDIZERS (STRONG): FIRE AND EXPLOSION HAZARD.
DECOMPOSITION: THERMAL DECOMPOSITION PRODUCTS MAY INCLUDE TOXIC AND CORROSIVE FUMES OF CHLORIDES AND TOXIC OXIDES OF CARBON.
POLYMERIZATION: HAZARDOUS POLYMERIZATION HAS NOT BEEN REPORTED TO OCCUR UNDER NORMAL TEMPERATURES AND PRESSURES.

STORAGE AND DISPOSAL

OBSERVE ALL FEDERAL, STATE AND LOCAL REGULATIONS WHEN STORING OR DISPOSING OF THIS SUBSTANCE. FOR ASSISTANCE, CONTACT THE DISTRICT DIRECTOR OF THE ENVIRONMENTAL PROTECTION AGENCY.

STORAGE

STORE IN ACCORDANCE WITH 40 CFR 165 RECOMMENDED PROCEDURES FOR THE DISPOSAL AND STORAGE OF PESTICIDES AND PESTICIDE CONTAINERS.
STORE AWAY FROM INCOMPATIBLE SUBSTANCES.

DISPOSAL

DISPOSAL MUST BE IN ACCORDANCE WITH 40 CFR 165 RECOMMENDED PROCEDURES FOR THE DISPOSAL AND STORAGE OF PESTICIDES AND PESTICIDE CONTAINERS.

CONDITIONS TO AVOID

MAY BURN BUT DOES NOT IGNITE READILY. CONTAINERS MAY EXPLODE IN HEAT OF FIRE.

SPILL AND LEAK PROCEDURES

OCCUPATIONAL SPILL: DO NOT TOUCH SPILLED MATERIAL. STOP LEAK IF YOU CAN DO IT WITHOUT RISK. USE WATER SPRAY TO REDUCE VAPORS. FOR SMALL SPILLS, TAKE UP WITH SAND OR OTHER ABSORBENT MATERIAL AND PLACE INTO CONTAINERS FOR LATER DISPOSAL. FOR SMALL DRY SPILLS, WITH A CLEAN SHOVEL PLACE MATERIAL INTO CLEAN, DRY CONTAINERS AND COVER. MOVE CONTAINERS FROM SPILL AREA. FOR LARGER SPILLS, DIKE FAR AHEAD OF SPILL FOR LATER DISPOSAL. KEEP UNNECESSARY PEOPLE AWAY. ISOLATE HAZARD AREA AND DENY ENTRY. VENTILATE CLOSED SPACES BEFORE ENTERING.
REPORTABLE QUANTITY (RQ): 1000 POUNDS THE SUPERFUND AMENDMENTS AND REAUTHORIZATION ACT (SARA) SECTION 304 REQUIRES THAT A RELEASE EQUAL TO OR GREATER THAN THE REPORTABLE QUANTITY FOR THIS SUBSTANCE BE IMMEDIATELY REPORTED TO THE LOCAL EMERGENCY PLANNING COMMITTEE AND THE STATE EMERGENCY RESPONSE COMMISSION (40 CFR 355.40). IF THE RELEASE OF THIS SUBSTANCE IS REPORTABLE UNDER CERCLA SECTION 103, THE NATIONAL RESPONSE CENTER MUST BE NOTIFIED IMMEDIATELY AT (800) 424-8802 OR (202) 426-2675 IN THE METROPOLITAN WASHINGTON, D.C. AREA (40 CFR 302.6).

PROTECTIVE EQUIPMENT

VENTILATION: PROVIDE LOCAL EXHAUST OR PROCESS ENCLOSURE VENTILATION SYSTEM.
RESPIRATOR: THE FOLLOWING RESPIRATORS ARE RECOMMENDED BASED ON INFORMATION FOUND IN THE PHYSICAL DATA, TOXICITY AND HEALTH EFFECTS SECTIONS. THEY ARE RANKED IN ORDER FROM MINIMUM TO MAXIMUM RESPIRATORY PROTECTION. THE SPECIFIC RESPIRATOR SELECTED MUST BE BASED ON CONTAMINATION LEVELS FOUND IN THE WORK PLACE, MUST NOT EXCEED THE WORKING LIMITS OF THE RESPIRATOR AND BE JOINTLY APPROVED BY THE NATIONAL INSTITUTE FOR OCCUPATIONAL SAFETY AND HEALTH AND THE MINE SAFETY AND HEALTH ADMINISTRATION (NIOSH-MSHA).
TYPE 'C' SUPPLIED-AIR RESPIRATOR WITH A FULL FACEPIECE OPERATED IN PRESSURE-DEMAND OR OTHER POSITIVE PRESSURE MODE OR WITH A FULL FACEPIECE, HELMET OR HOOD OPERATED IN CONTINOUS-FLOW MODE.
SELF-CONTAINED BREATHING APPARATUS WITH A FULL FACEPIECE OPERATED IN PRESSURE-DEMAND OR OTHER POSITIVE PRESSURE MODE.
FOR FIREFIGHTING AND OTHER IMMEDIATELY DANGEROUS TO LIFE OR HEALTH CONDITIONS:
SELF-CONTAINED BREATHING APPARATUS WITH FULL FACEPIECE OPERATED IN PRESSURE-DEMAND OR OTHER POSITIVE PRESSURE MODE.
SUPPLIED-AIR RESPIRATOR WITH FULL FACEPIECE AND OPERATED IN PRESSURE-DEMAND OR OTHER POSITIVE PRESSURE MODE IN COMBINATION WITH AN AUXILIARY SELF-CONTAINED BREATHING APPARATUS OPERATED IN PRESSURE-DEMAND OR OTHER POSITIVE PRESSURE MODE.
CLOTHING: EMPLOYEE MUST WEAR APPROPRIATE PROTECTIVE (IMPERVIOUS) CLOTHING AND EQUIPMENT TO PREVENT ANY POSSIBILITY OF SKIN CONTACT WITH THIS SUBSTANCE.
GLOVES: EMPLOYEE MUST WEAR APPROPRIATE PROTECTIVE GLOVES TO PREVENT CONTACT WITH THIS SUBSTANCE.
EYE PROTECTION: EMPLOYEE MUST WEAR SPLASH-PROOF OR DUST-RESISTANT SAFETY GOGGLES AND A FACESHIELD TO PREVENT CONTACT WITH THIS SUBSTANCE.
EMERGENCY WASH FACILITIES: WHERE THERE IS ANY POSSIBILITY THAT AN EMPLOYEE'S EYES AND/OR SKIN MAY BE EXPOSED TO THIS SUBSTANCE, THE EMPLOYER SHOULD PROVIDE AN EYE WASH FOUNTAIN AND QUICK DRENCH SHOWER WITHIN THE IMMEDIATE WORK AREA FOR EMERGENCY USE.

AUTHORIZED BY- OCCUPATIONAL HEALTH SERVICES, INC.
CREATION DATE: 03/23/90 ***REVISION DATE:*** 07/12/90

MATERIAL SAFETY DATA SHEET

OCCUPATIONAL HEALTH SERVICES, INC.
AGRICULTURE AND PESTICIDE DIVISION
450 SEVENTH AVENUE, SUITE 2407
NEW YORK, NEW YORK 10123
1-800-445-MSDS OR (212) 967-1100

EMERGENCY CONTACT:
JOHN S. BRANSFORD, JR. (615) 292-1180

SUBSTANCE IDENTIFICATION

CAS-NUMBER 10004-44-1

SUBSTANCE: **HYMEXAZOL**

TRADE NAMES/SYNONYMS: 3(2H)-ISOXAZOLONE, 5-METHYL-; 5-METHYL-3(2H)-ISOXAZOLONE; 3-ISOXAZOLOL, 5-METHYL-; 3-HYDROXY-5-METHYLISOXAZOLE; 5-METHYL-3-ISOOXAZOLOL; 5-METHYLISOXAZOL-3-OL; HYDROXYISOXAZOLE (PESTICIDE); HYDROXYISOXAZOLE; HYMEXAZOLE; TACHIGAREN; F-319; SF-6505; C4H5NO2; PST22404

CHEMICAL FAMILY: OXAZOLE

MOLECULAR FORMULA: (C-H3)-C3-O-N-H-(O-H)

MOLECULAR WEIGHT: 99.09

CERCLA RATINGS (SCALE 0-3): HEALTH=2 FIRE=1 REACTIVITY=0 PERSISTENCE=1

NFPA RATINGS (SCALE 0-4): HEALTH=U FIRE=1 REACTIVITY=0

COMPONENTS AND CONTAMINANTS

COMPONENT: HYMEXAZOL ***PERCENT:*** 100.0

CAS# 10004-44-1

OTHER CONTAMINANTS: NONE

EXPOSURE LIMITS: NO OCCUPATIONAL EXPOSURE LIMITS ESTABLISHED BY OSHA, ACGIH, OR NIOSH.

PHYSICAL DATA

DESCRIPTION: COLORLESS CRYSTALS. ***MELTING POINT:*** 187-189 F (86-87 C)

SPECIFIC GRAVITY: NOT AVAILABLE ***VAPOR PRESSURE:*** 0.001 MMHG @ 25 C

SOLUBILITY IN WATER: 8.5%

SOLVENT SOLUBILITY: SOLUBLE IN ACETONE, ALCOHOL, METHYL ISOBUTYL KETONE, TETRAHYDROFURAN, DIOXANE, DIMETHYLFORMAMIDE, ETHYLENE GLYCOL, CHLOROFORM, ETHER, BENZENE, XYLENE, TRICHLOROMETHYLENE, AND MOST ORGANIC SOLVENTS.

FIRE AND EXPLOSION DATA

FIRE AND EXPLOSION HAZARD: SLIGHT FIRE HAZARD WHEN EXPOSED TO HEAT OR FLAME.

FIREFIGHTING MEDIA: DRY CHEMICAL, CARBON DIOXIDE, HALON, WATER SPRAY OR STANDARD FOAM (1987 EMERGENCY RESPONSE GUIDEBOOK, DOT P 5800.4).
FOR LARGER FIRES, USE WATER SPRAY, FOG OR STANDARD FOAM (1987 EMERGENCY RESPONSE GUIDEBOOK, DOT P 5800.4).

FIREFIGHTING: MOVE CONTAINER FROM FIRE AREA IF POSSIBLE. DO NOT SCATTER SPILLED MATERIAL WITH HIGH PRESSURE WATER STREAMS. DIKE FIRE CONTROL WATER FOR LATER DISPOSAL (1987 EMERGENCY RESPONSE GUIDEBOOK, DOT P 5800.4, GUIDE PAGE 31).
USE AGENTS SUITABLE FOR TYPE OF SURROUNDING FIRE. AVOID BREATHING HAZARDOUS VAPORS, KEEP UPWIND.

TOXICITY

HYMEXAZOL: TOXICITY DATA: 3112 MG/KG ORAL-RAT LD50; 1968 MG/KG ORAL-MOUSE LD50; 1884 MG/KG SUBCUTANEOUS-RAT LD50; 1167 MG/KG SUBCUTANEOUS-MOUSE LD50; 445 MG/KG INTRAVENOUS-MOUSE LD50; >2000 MG/KG SKIN-RABBIT LD50 (85JFAN); >10000 MG/KG SKIN-RAT LD50 (85JFAN); MUTAGENIC DATA (RTECS). CARCINOGEN STATUS: NONE. ACUTE TOXICITY LEVEL: MODERATELY TOXIC BY INGESTION; SLIGHTLY TOXIC BY DERMAL ABSORPTION. TARGET EFFECTS: NO DATA AVAILABLE.

HEALTH EFFECTS AND FIRST AID

INHALATION: HYMEXAZOL: **ACUTE EXPOSURE**- NO DATA AVAILABLE. **CHRONIC EXPOSURE**- NO DATA AVAILABLE.

FIRST AID- REMOVE FROM EXPOSURE AREA TO FRESH AIR IMMEDIATELY. IF BREATHING HAS STOPPED, PERFORM ARTIFICIAL RESPIRATION. KEEP PERSON WARM AND AT REST. TREAT SYMPTOMATICALLY AND SUPPORTIVELY. GET MEDICAL ATTENTION IMMEDIATELY.

SKIN CONTACT: HYMEXAZOL: **ACUTE EXPOSURE**- THE LD50 IN RABBITS WAS GREATER THAN 2000 MG/KG; SYMPTOMS WERE NOT REPORTED. **CHRONIC EXPOSURE**- NO DATA AVAILABLE.

FIRST AID- REMOVE CONTAMINATED CLOTHING AND SHOES IMMEDIATELY. WASH AFFECTED AREA WITH SOAP OR MILD DETERGENT AND LARGE AMOUNTS OF WATER UNTIL NO EVIDENCE OF CHEMICAL REMAINS (APPROXIMATELY 15-20 MINUTES). GET MEDICAL ATTENTION IMMEDIATELY.

EYE CONTACT: HYMEXAZOL: **ACUTE EXPOSURE**- NO DATA AVAILABLE. **CHRONIC EXPOSURE**- NO DATA AVAILABLE.

FIRST AID- WASH EYES IMMEDIATELY WITH LARGE AMOUNTS OF WATER OR NORMAL SALINE, OCCASIONALLY LIFTING UPPER AND LOWER LIDS, UNTIL NO EVIDENCE OF CHEMICAL REMAINS (APPROXIMATELY 15-20 MINUTES). GET MEDICAL ATTENTION IMMEDIATELY.

INGESTION: HYMEXAZOL: **ACUTE EXPOSURE**- A LETHAL DOSE REPORTED IN RATS WAS 3212 MG/KG; SYMPTOMS WERE NOT REPORTED. **CHRONIC EXPOSURE**- NO OBSERVABLE EFFECTS WERE REPORTED IN 2-YEAR STUDIES OF RATS RECEIVING 19-20 MG/KG/DAY AND DOGS RECEIVING 15 MG/KG/DAY.

FIRST AID- IF THE PERSON IS CONSCIOUS AND NOT CONVULSING, REMOVE BY GASTRIC LAVAGE AND FOLLOW WITH A CATHARTIC (DREISBACH, HANDBOOK OF POISONING, 12TH ED.). TREAT SYMPTOMATICALLY AND SUPPORTIVELY. GASTRIC LAVAGE SHOULD BE PERFORMED BY QUALIFIED MEDICAL PERSONNEL. GET MEDICAL ATTENTION IMMEDIATELY.

ANTIDOTE: NO SPECIFIC ANTIDOTE. TREAT SYMPTOMATICALLY AND SUPPORTIVELY.

REACTIVITY

REACTIVITY: STABLE UNDER NORMAL TEMPERATURES AND PRESSURES.

INCOMPATIBILITIES: HYMEXAZOL: OXIDIZERS (STRONG): FIRE AND EXPLOSION HAZARD.

DECOMPOSITION: THERMAL DECOMPOSITION PRODUCTS MAY INCLUDE TOXIC OXIDES OF CARBON AND NITROGEN.

POLYMERIZATION: HAZARDOUS POLYMERIZATION HAS NOT BEEN REPORTED TO OCCUR UNDER NORMAL TEMPERATURES AND PRESSURES.

STORAGE AND DISPOSAL

OBSERVE ALL FEDERAL, STATE AND LOCAL REGULATIONS WHEN STORING OR DISPOSING OF THIS SUBSTANCE. FOR ASSISTANCE, CONTACT THE DISTRICT DIRECTOR OF THE ENVIRONMENTAL PROTECTION AGENCY.

STORAGE

STORE IN ACCORDANCE WITH 40 CFR 165 RECOMMENDED PROCEDURES FOR THE DISPOSAL AND STORAGE OF PESTICIDES AND PESTICIDE CONTAINERS.
STORE AWAY FROM INCOMPATIBLE SUBSTANCES.

DISPOSAL

DISPOSAL MUST BE IN ACCORDANCE WITH 40 CFR 165 RECOMMENDED PROCEDURES FOR THE DISPOSAL AND STORAGE OF PESTICIDES AND PESTICIDE CONTAINERS.

CONDITIONS TO AVOID

MAY BURN BUT DOES NOT IGNITE READILY. AVOID CONTACT WITH STRONG OXIDIZERS, EXCESSIVE HEAT, SPARKS, OR OPEN FLAME.

SPILL AND LEAK PROCEDURES

OCCUPATIONAL SPILL: SWEEP UP AND PLACE IN SUITABLE CLEAN, DRY CONTAINERS FOR RECLAMATION OR LATER DISPOSAL. DO NOT FLUSH SPILLED MATERIAL INTO SEWER. KEEP UNNECESSARY PEOPLE AWAY.

PROTECTIVE EQUIPMENT

VENTILATION: PROVIDE LOCAL EXHAUST OR GENERAL DILUTION VENTILATION SYSTEM.

RESPIRATOR: THE FOLLOWING RESPIRATORS ARE RECOMMENDED BASED ON INFORMATION FOUND IN THE PHYSICAL DATA, TOXICITY AND HEALTH EFFECTS SECTIONS. THEY ARE RANKED IN ORDER FROM MINIMUM TO MAXIMUM RESPIRATORY PROTECTION. THE SPECIFIC RESPIRATOR SELECTED MUST BE BASED ON CONTAMINATION LEVELS FOUND IN THE WORK PLACE, MUST NOT EXCEED THE WORKING LIMITS OF THE RESPIRATOR AND BE JOINTLY APPROVED BY THE NATIONAL INSTITUTE FOR OCCUPATIONAL SAFETY AND HEALTH AND THE MINE SAFETY AND HEALTH ADMINISTRATION (NIOSH-MSHA).

CHEMICAL CARTRIDGE RESPIRATOR WITH AN ORGANIC VAPOR CARTRIDGE(S) WITH A FULL FACEPIECE AND ORGANIC VAPOR CARTRIDGE(S) IN COMBINATION WITH A DUST AND MIST FILTER.

POWERED AIR-PURIFYING RESPIRATOR WITH A TIGHT-FITTING FACEPIECE AND ORGANIC VAPOR CARTRIDGE(S) IN COMBINATION WITH A HIGH-EFFICIENCY PARTICULATE FILTER.

TYPE 'C' SUPPLIED-AIR RESPIRATOR WITH A FULL FACEPIECE OPERATED IN A PRESSURE-DEMAND OR OTHER POSITIVE PRESSURE MODE.

SELF-CONTAINED BREATHING APPARATUS WITH A FULL FACEPIECE OPERATED IN PRESSURE-DEMAND OR OTHER POSITIVE PRESSURE MODE.

FOR FIREFIGHTING AND OTHER IMMEDIATELY DANGEROUS TO LIFE OR HEALTH CONDITIONS:

SELF-CONTAINED BREATHING APPARATUS WITH FULL FACEPIECE OPERATED IN PRESSURE-DEMAND OR OTHER POSITIVE PRESSURE MODE.

SUPPLIED-AIR RESPIRATOR WITH FULL FACEPIECE AND OPERATED IN PRESSURE-DEMAND OR OTHER POSITIVE PRESSURE MODE IN COMBINATION WITH AN AUXILIARY SELF-CONTAINED BREATHING APPARATUS OPERATED IN PRESSURE-DEMAND OR OTHER POSITIVE PRESSURE MODE.

CLOTHING: EMPLOYEE MUST WEAR APPROPRIATE PROTECTIVE (IMPERVIOUS) CLOTHING AND EQUIPMENT TO PREVENT REPEATED OR PROLONGED SKIN CONTACT WITH THIS SUBSTANCE.

GLOVES: EMPLOYEE MUST WEAR APPROPRIATE PROTECTIVE GLOVES TO PREVENT CONTACT WITH THIS SUBSTANCE.
EYE PROTECTION: EMPLOYEE MUST WEAR SPLASH-PROOF OR DUST-RESISTANT SAFETY GOGGLES TO PREVENT EYE CONTACT WITH THIS SUBSTANCE. EMERGENCY EYE WASH: WHERE THERE IS ANY POSSIBILITY THAT AN EMPLOYEE'S EYES MAY BE EXPOSED TO THIS SUBSTANCE, THE EMPLOYER SHOULD PROVIDE AN EYE WASH FOUNTAIN WITHIN THE IMMEDIATE WORK AREA FOR EMERGENCY USE.

AUTHORIZED BY- OCCUPATIONAL HEALTH SERVICES, INC.
CREATION DATE: 12/14/89 ***REVISION DATE:*** 05/31/90

MATERIAL SAFETY DATA SHEET

OCCUPATIONAL HEALTH SERVICES, INC.
AGRICULTURE AND PESTICIDE DIVISION
450 SEVENTH AVENUE, SUITE 2407
NEW YORK, NEW YORK 10123
1-800-445-MSDS OR (212) 967-1100

EMERGENCY CONTACT:
JOHN S. BRANSFORD, JR. (615) 292-1180

SUBSTANCE IDENTIFICATION

CAS-NUMBER 1934-21-0
SUBSTANCE: **TARTRAZINE YELLOW DYE**
TRADE NAMES/SYNONYMS: FD(C YELLOW NO.5; 4,5-DIHYDRO-5-OXO-1-(4-SULFOPHENYL)-4-((4-SULFOPHENYL)AZO)-1H- PYRAZOLE-3-CARBOXYLIC ACID, TRISODIUM SALT; C.I.ACID YELLOW 23, TRISODIUM SALT; C.I. ACID YELLOW 23; B 3014; C.I. 19140; C.I. FOOD YELLOW 4; ELOZ; EGG YELLOW A; HEXACOL TARTRAZINE; HYDRAZINE YELLOW; LAKE YELLOW; LEMON YELOW A; TARTRAN YELLOW; TARTRAZIN; WOOL YELLOW; 1310 YELLOW; 1409 YELLOW; YELLOW LAKE 69; PST22465
CHEMICAL FAMILY: AROMATIC
PYRAZOLE
SALT
MOLECULAR FORMULA: C16-H9-N4-O9-S2.3NA
MOLECULAR WEIGHT: 534.38
CERCLA RATINGS (SCALE 0-3): HEALTH=1 FIRE=0 REACTIVITY=0 PERSISTENCE=3
NFPA RATINGS (SCALE 0-4): HEALTH=1 FIRE=0 REACTIVITY=0

COMPONENTS AND CONTAMINANTS

COMPONENT: TARTRAZINE YELLOW DYE ***PERCENT:*** 100
CAS# 1934-21-0
EXPOSURE LIMITS: NO OCCUPATIONAL EXPOSURE LIMITS ESTABLISHED BY OSHA, ACGIH, OR NIOSH.

PHYSICAL DATA

DESCRIPTION: BRIGHT ORANGE TO YELLOW POWDER. ***MELTING POINT:*** NOT AVAILABLE
SPECIFIC GRAVITY: NOT AVAILABLE ***SOLUBILITY IN WATER:*** SOLUBLE

FIRE AND EXPLOSION DATA

FIRE AND EXPLOSION HAZARD: NEGLIGIBLE FIRE HAZARD WHEN EXPOSED TO HEAT OR FLAME.

FIREFIGHTING MEDIA: DRY CHEMICAL, CARBON DIOXIDE, WATER SPRAY OR FOAM FOR LARGER FIRES, USE WATER SPRAY, FOG OR ALCOHOL FOAM
FIREFIGHTING: NO ACUTE HAZARD. MOVE CONTAINER FROM FIRE AREA IF POSSIBLE. AVOID BREATHING VAPORS OR DUSTS; KEEP UPWIND.

TOXICITY

TARTRAZINE YELLOW DYE: TOXICITY DATA: 14 UG/KG ORAL-HUMAN TDLO; 12750 MG/KG ORAL-MOUSE LD50; MUTAGENIC DATA (RTECS); REPRODUCTIVE EFFECTS DATA (RTECS). CARCINOGEN STATUS: NONE. ACUTE TOXICITY LEVEL: SLIGHTLY TOXIC BY INGESTION. TARGET EFFECTS: ALLERGIC REACTIONS MAY OCCUR IN SENSITIZED INDIVIDUALS.

HEALTH EFFECTS AND FIRST AID

INHALATION: TARTRAZINE YELLOW DYE: **ACUTE EXPOSURE-** NO DATA AVAILABLE. **CHRONIC EXPOSURE-** SUSCEPTIBLE PERSONS MAY DEVELOP ALLERGIC-TYPE REACTIONS (INCLUDING BRONCHIAL ASTHMA) AFTER PROLONGED OR REPEATED INHALATION OF A PRODUCT WHICH CONTAINS THE COLOR ADDITIVE TARTRAZINE YELLOW DYE. THIS DYE HAS BEEN APPROVED BY THE FOOD AND DRUG ADMINISTRATION AS AN ADDITIVE IN FOOD, DRUGS, AND COSMETICS, HOWEVER THE PRODUCT MUST BE LABELED IN ORDER TO WARN SUSCEPTIBLE PERSONS.
FIRST AID- REMOVE FROM EXPOSURE AREA TO FRESH AIR IMMEDIATELY. IF BREATHING HAS STOPPED, PERFORM ARTIFICIAL RESPIRATION. KEEP PERSON WARM AND AT REST. TREAT SYMPTOMATICALLY AND SUPPORTIVELY. GET MEDICAL ATTENTION IMMEDIATELY.

SKIN CONTACT: TARTRAZINE YELLOW DYE: **ACUTE EXPOSURE-** NO DATA AVAILABLE. MAY BE IRRITATING. **CHRONIC EXPOSURE-** SUSCEPTIBLE PERSONS MAY EXPERIENCE ALLERGIC-TYPE REACTIONS INCLUDING ALLERGIC URTICARIA AFTER PROLONGED OR REPEATED USE OF PRODUCTS CONTAINING THE COLOR ADDITIVE TARTRAZINE YELLOW DYE. ALLERGIC URTICARIA IS CHARACTERIZED BY THE SUDDEN ERUPTION OF PAPULES OR WHEALS WITH INTENSE ITCHING AND MAY OCCUR AS A RESULT OF EXTERNAL CONTACT WITH THE IRRITANT OR FROM REPEATED OR PROLONGED INGESTION.
FIRST AID- REMOVE CONTAMINATED CLOTHING AND SHOES IMMEDIATELY. WASH AFFECTED AREA WITH SOAP OR MILD DETERGENT AND LARGE AMOUNTS OF WATER UNTIL NO EVIDENCE OF CHEMICAL REMAINS (APPROXIMATELY 15-20 MINUTES). GET MEDICAL ATTENTION IMMEDIATELY.

EYE CONTACT: TARTRAZINE YELLOW DYE: **ACUTE EXPOSURE-** NO DATA AVAILABLE. MAY BE IRRITATING. **CHRONIC EXPOSURE-** NO DATA AVAILABLE.
FIRST AID- WASH EYES IMMEDIATELY WITH LARGE AMOUNTS OF WATER OR NORMAL SALINE, OCCASIONALLY LIFTING UPPER AND LOWER LIDS, UNTIL NO EVIDENCE OF CHEMICAL REMAINS (APPROXIMATELY 15-20 MINUTES). GET MEDICAL ATTENTION IMMEDIATELY.

INGESTION: TARTRAZINE YELLOW DYE: **ACUTE EXPOSURE-** NO DATA AVAILABLE. **CHRONIC EXPOSURE-** CERTAIN SUSCEPTIBLE INDIVIDUALS MAY DEVELOP LIGE-THREATENING ALLERGIC REACTIONS INCLUDING ALLERGIC URTICARIA AND NOTHROMBOCYTOPENIC VASCULAR PURPURA AFTER REPEATED OR PROLONGED INGESTION OF A PRODUCT CONTAINING TARTRAZINE YELLOW DYE. SENSITIZED PERSONS SHOULD LIMIT THEIR FOOD TO FRESH RED MEATS, GREEN VEGETABLES AND WHEN TAKING MEDICATION, WHITE TABLETS. ALTHOUGH THE OVERALL INCIDENCE OF SENSITIVITY IS LOW, IT IS FREQUENTLY SEEN IN PATIENTS WHO HAVE ASPIRIN HYPERSENSITIVITY. THIS DYE HAS BEEN APPROVED BY THE FOOD AND DRUG ADMINISTRATION AS A COLOR ADDITIVE IN FOODS, DRUGS, AND COSMETICS, HOWEVER THE PRODUCT MUST BE LABELED IN ORDER TO WARN SUSCEPTIBLE INDIVIDUALS.
FIRST AID- TREAT SYMPTOMATICALLY AND SUPPORTIVELY. GET MEDICAL ATTENTION IMMEDIATELY. IF VOMITING OCCURS, KEEP HEAD LOWER THAN HIPS TO PREVENT ASPIRATION.
ANTIDOTE: NO SPECIFIC ANTIDOTE. TREAT SYMPTOMATICALLY AND SUPPORTIVELY.

REACTIVITY

REACTIVITY: STABLE UNDER NORMAL TEMPERATURES AND PRESSURES.
INCOMPATIBILITIES: TARTRAZINE YELLOW DYE: NO DATA AVAILABLE.
DECOMPOSITION: THERMAL DECOMPOSITION PRODUCTS MAY INCLUDE TOXIC OXIDES OF CARBON.
POLYMERIZATION: HAZARDOUS POLYMERIZATION HAS NOT BEEN REPORTED TO OCCUR UNDER NORMAL TEMPERATURES AND PRESSURES.

CONDITIONS TO AVOID

NONE REPORTED.

SPILL AND LEAK PROCEDURES

OCCUPATIONAL SPILL: NO SPECIAL PRECAUTIONS INDICATED.

PROTECTIVE EQUIPMENT

VENTILATION: PROVIDE LOCAL EXHAUST OR GENERAL DILUTION VENTILATION SYSTEM.
RESPIRATOR: THE FOLLOWING RESPIRATORS ARE RECOMMENDED BASED ON INFORMATION FOUND IN THE PHYSICAL DATA, TOXICITY AND HEALTH EFFECTS SECTIONS. THEY ARE RANKED IN ORDER FROM MINIMUM TO MAXIMUM RESPIRATORY PROTECTION. THE SPECIFIC RESPIRATOR SELECTED MUST BE BASED ON CONTAMINATION LEVELS FOUND IN THE WORK PLACE, MUST NOT EXCEED THE WORKING LIMITS OF THE RESPIRATOR AND BE JOINTLY APPROVED BY THE NATIONAL INSTITUTE FOR OCCUPATIONAL SAFETY AND HEALTH AND THE MINE SAFETY AND HEALTH ADMINISTRATION (NIOSH-MSHA).
DUST AND MIST RESPIRATOR WITH A FULL FACEPIECE.
AIR-PURIFYING FULL FACEPIECE RESPIRATOR WITH A HIGH-EFFICIENCY PARTICULATE FILTER.
POWERED AIR-PURIFYING RESPIRATOR WITH A TIGHT-FITTING FACEPIECE AND HIGH-EFFICIENCY PARTICULATE FILTER.
TYPE 'C' SUPPLIED-AIR RESPIRATOR WITH A FULL FACEPIECE OPERATED IN

PRESSURE-DEMAND OR OTHER POSITIVE PRESSURE MODE OR WITH A FULL FACEPIECE, HELMET OR HOOD OPERATED IN CONTINUOUS-FLOW MODE.
SELF-CONTAINED BREATHING APPARATUS WITH A FULL FACEPIECE OPERATED IN PRESSURE-DEMAND OR OTHER POSITIVE PRESSURE MODE.
FOR FIREFIGHTING AND OTHER IMMEDIATELY DANGEROUS TO LIFE OR HEALTH CONDITIONS:
SELF-CONTAINED BREATHING APPARATUS WITH FULL FACEPIECE OPERATED IN PRESSURE-DEMAND OR OTHER POSITIVE PRESSURE MODE.
SUPPLIED-AIR RESPIRATOR WITH FULL FACEPIECE AND OPERATED IN PRESSURE-DEMAND OR OTHER POSITIVE PRESSURE MODE IN COMBINATION WITH AN AUXILIARY SELF-CONTAINED BREATHING APPARATUS OPERATED IN PRESSURE-DEMAND OR OTHER POSITIVE PRESSURE MODE.

CLOTHING: EMPLOYEE MUST WEAR APPROPRIATE PROTECTIVE (IMPERVIOUS) CLOTHING AND EQUIPMENT TO PREVENT REPEATED OR PROLONGED SKIN CONTACT WITH THIS SUBSTANCE.

GLOVES: EMPLOYEE MUST WEAR APPROPRIATE PROTECTIVE GLOVES TO PREVENT CONTACT WITH THIS SUBSTANCE.

EYE PROTECTION: EMPLOYEE MUST WEAR SPLASH-PROOF OR DUST-RESISTANT SAFETY GOGGLES TO PREVENT EYE CONTACT WITH THIS SUBSTANCE.
EMERGENCY EYE WASH: WHERE THERE IS ANY POSSIBILITY THAT AN EMPLOYEE'S EYES MAY BE EXPOSED TO THIS SUBSTANCE, THE EMPLOYER SHOULD PROVIDE AN EYE WASH FOUNTAIN WITHIN THE IMMEDIATE WORK AREA FOR EMERGENCY USE.

AUTHORIZED BY- OCCUPATIONAL HEALTH SERVICES, INC.
CREATION DATE: 11/15/89 ***REVISION DATE:*** 05/29/90

MATERIAL SAFETY DATA SHEET

OCCUPATIONAL HEALTH SERVICES, INC.
AGRICULTURE AND PESTICIDE DIVISION
450 SEVENTH AVENUE, SUITE 2407
NEW YORK, NEW YORK 10123
1-800-445-MSDS OR (212) 967-1100

EMERGENCY CONTACT:
JOHN S. BRANSFORD, JR. (615) 292-1180

SUBSTANCE IDENTIFICATION

CAS-NUMBER 3689-24-5
SUBSTANCE: **SULFOTEP**
TRADE NAMES/SYNONYMS: THIODIPHOSPHORIC ACID(HO)2P(S))2O), TETRAETHYL ESTER; THIOPYROPHOSPHORIC ACID (((HO)2PS)2O), TETRAETHYL ESTER; ETHYL THIOPYROPHOSPHATE; O,O,O',O'-TETRAETHYL DITHIOPYROPHOSPHATE; TETRAETHYL THIODIPHOSPHATE; THIODIPHOSPHORIC ACID (((HO)2-(S))2O) TETRAETHYL ESTER; TETRAETHYL THIOPYROPHOSPHATE; THIOPYROPHOSPHORIC ACID, TETRAETHYL ESTER; THIODIPHOSPHORIC ACID, TETRAETHYL ESTER; TETRAETHYL DITHIOPYROPHOSPHATE; BLADAFUM; DITHIONE; TEDP; SULFOTEPP; THIOTEPP; ENT 16273; RCRA P109; STCC 4921480; UN 1704; C8H22O5P2S2; PST22470
CHEMICAL FAMILY: ORGANOPHOSPHATE
MOLECULAR FORMULA: C8-H22-O5-P2-S2
MOLECULAR WEIGHT: 322.34
CERCLA RATINGS (SCALE 0-3): HEALTH=3 FIRE=0 REACTIVITY=0 PERSISTENCE=0
NFPA RATINGS (SCALE 0-4): HEALTH=4 FIRE=0 REACTIVITY=0

COMPONENTS AND CONTAMINANTS

COMPONENT: SULFOTEP ***PERCENT:*** 100
CAS# 3689-24-5
EXPOSURE LIMITS: SULFOTEP (TEDP): 0.2 MG/M3 OSHA TWA (SKIN) 0.2 MG/M3 ACGIH TWA (SKIN)
500 POUNDS SARA SECTION 302 THRESHOLD PLANNING QUANTITY 100 POUNDS SARA SECTION 304 REPORTABLE QUANTITY 100 POUNDS CERCLA SECTION 103 REPORTABLE QUANTITY

PHYSICAL DATA

DESCRIPTION: PALE YELLOW MOBILE LIQUID WITH A GARLIC ODOR
BOILING POINT: 280 F (138 C) 2 MMHG ***SPECIFIC GRAVITY:*** 1.196
VAPOR PRESSURE: 0.00017 MMHG @ 20 C ***EVAPORATION RATE:*** NOT AVAILABLE
SOLUBILITY IN WATER: 25 PPM
SOLVENT SOLUBILITY: SOLUBLE IN ALCOHOL, CHLOROMETHANE AND MOST ORGANIC SOLVENTS

FIRE AND EXPLOSION DATA

FIRE AND EXPLOSION HAZARD: NEGLIGIBLE FIRE HAZARD WHEN EXPOSED TO HEAT OR FLAME.
FIREFIGHTING MEDIA: DRY CHEMICAL, CARBON DIOXIDE, HALON, WATER SPRAY OR STANDARD FOAM (1987 EMERGENCY RESPONSE GUIDEBOOK, DOT P 5800.4).
FOR LARGER FIRES, USE WATER SPRAY, FOG OR STANDARD FOAM (1987 EMERGENCY RESPONSE GUIDEBOOK, DOT P 5800.4).
FIREFIGHTING: MOVE CONTAINERS FROM FIRE AREA IF POSSIBLE. FIGHT FIRE FROM MAXIMUM DISTANCE. STAY AWAY FROM STORAGE TANK ENDS. DIKE FIRE CONTROL WATER FOR LATER DISPOSAL. DO NOT SCATTER MATERIAL (1987 EMERGENCY RESPONSE GUIDEBOOK, DOT P 5800.4, GUIDE PAGE 55).
EXTINGUISH ONLY IF FLOW CAN BE STOPPED; USE FLOODING AMOUNTS OF WATER AS FOG, SOLID STREAMS MAY BE INEFFECTIVE. COOL CONTAINERS WITH FLOODING AMOUNTS OF WATER FROM AS FAR A DISTANCE AS POSSIBLE. USE WATER SPRAY TO ABSORB TOXIC VAPORS. AVOID BREATHING TOXIC VAPORS; KEEP UPWIND. CONSIDER EVACUATION OF DOWNWIND AREA IF MATERIAL IS LEAKING.

TRANSPORTATION DATA

DEPARTMENT OF TRANSPORTATION HAZARD CLASSIFICATION 49 CFR 172.101: POISON B
DEPARTMENT OF TRANSPORTATION LABELING REQUIREMENTS 49 CFR 172.101 AND SUBPART E: POISON
DEPARTMENT OF TRANSPORTATION PACKAGING REQUIREMENTS: 49 CFR 173.358 EXCEPTIONS: NONE

TOXICITY

SULFOTEP (TEDP): TOXICITY DATA: 38 MG/M3/4 HOURS INHALATION-RAT LC50; 40 MG/M3/4 HOURS INHALATION-MOUSE LC50; 20 MG/KG SKIN-RABBIT LD50; 65 MG/KG SKIN-RAT LD50; 5 MG/KG ORAL-RAT LD50; 22 MG/KG ORAL-MOUSE LD50; 25 MG/KG ORAL-RABBIT LD50; 5 MG/KG ORAL-DOG LD50; 3 MG/KG ORAL-CAT LD50, 8 MG/KG SUBCUTANEOUS-MOUSE LD50; 300 UG/KG INTRAVENOUS-MOUSE LD50; 6600 UG/KG INTRAPERITONEAL-RAT LD50; 940 UG/KG INTRAPERITONEAL-MOUSE LD50; 55 UG/KG INTRAMUSCULAR-RAT LD50; 500 UG/KG INTRAMUSCULAR-MOUSE LD50; MUTAGENIC DATA (RTECS). CARCINOGEN STATUS: NONE. ACUTE TOXICITY LEVEL: HIGHLY TOXIC BY INHALATION, DERMAL ABSORPTION, OR INGESTION. TARGET EFFECTS: CHOLINESTERASE INHIBITOR. POISONING MAY AFFECT THE NERVOUS SYSTEM.* AT INCREASED RISK FROM EXPOSURE: PERSONS WITH RESPIRATORY AILMENTS, RECENT EXPOSURE TO CHOLINESTERASE INHIBITORS OR IMPAIRED CHOLINESTERASE PRODUCTION, OR LIVER MALFUNCTION.* ADDITIONAL DATA: MAY CROSS THE PLACENTA. HIGH ENVIRONMENTAL TEMPERATURES OR EXPOSURE OF THE CHEMICAL TO VISIBLE OR ULTRAVIOLET LIGHT MAY ENHANCE THE TOXICITY. INTERACTIONS WITH MEDICATIONS MAY OCCUR.*
* MAY BE BASED ON GENERAL INFORMATION ON ORGANOPHOSPHATES.

HEALTH EFFECTS AND FIRST AID

INHALATION: SULFOTEP (TEDP): HIGHLY TOXIC. 35 MG/M3 IMMEDIATELY DANGEROUS TO LIFE OR HEALTH. SEE INFORMATION ON ORGANOPHOSPHATES.
ORGANOPHOSPHATES: CHOLINESTERASE INHIBITOR. **ACUTE EXPOSURE-** WHEN INHALED, THE FIRST EFFECTS OF CHOLINESTERASE INHIBITORS ARE USUALLY RESPIRATORY AND MAY INCLUDE NASAL HYPEREMIA AND WATERY DISCHARGE, COUGH, CHEST DISCOMFORT, DYSPNEA, AND WHEEZING DUE TO INCREASED BRONCHIAL SECRETIONS AND BRONCHOCONSTRICTION. IF SUFFICIENT AMOUNTS ARE ABSORBED, OTHER SYSTEMIC EFFECTS MAY BEGIN WITHIN A FEW MINUTES OR BE DELAYED FOR UP TO 12 HOURS. SYMPTOMS MAY INCLUDE PALLOR, NAUSEA, VOMITING, DIARRHEA, ABDOMINAL CRAMPS, HEADACHE, DIZZINESS, OCULAR PAIN, BLURRED VISION, MIOSIS OR IN SOME CASES, ESPECIALLY INITIALLY, MYDRIASIS, LACRIMATION, SALIVATION, SWEATING, AND CONFUSION. OTHER REPORTED CENTRAL NERVOUS SYSTEM OR NEUROMUSCULAR EFFECTS MAY INCLUDE ATAXIA, SLURRED SPEECH, AREFLEXIA, WEAKNESS, FATIGUE, FASCICULATIONS, TWITCHING, TREMORS POSSIBLY OF THE TONGUE AND EYELIDS, AND EVENTUALLY PARALYSIS OF THE EXTREMITIES AND POSSIBLY OF THE RESPIRATORY MUSCLES. IN SEVERE CASES THERE MAY ALSO BE INVOLUNTARY DEFECATION AND URINATION, CYANOSIS, PSYCHOSIS, HYPERGLYCEMIA, ACUTE PANCREATITIS, CARDIAC IRREGULARITIES, PULMONARY EDEMA, UNCONSCIOUSNESS, CONVULSIONS, AND COMA. DEATH IS PRIMARILY DUE TO RESPIRATORY FAILURE, ALTHOUGH CARDIOVASCULAR EFFECTS INCLUDING CARDIAC ARREST MAY ALSO BE IMPLICATED. LONG TERM SEQUELAE ARE RARE BUT MAY INCLUDE NEUROPSYCHIATRIC DISORDERS AND MYOPATHY WITH MUSCLE TENDERNESS. SOME ORGANOPHOSPHATES MAY CAUSE A DELAYED NEUROPATHY BEGINNING 1-4 WEEKS AFTER AN ACUTE EXPOSURE WHICH MAY OR MAY NOT HAVE CAUSED ACUTE CHOLINERGIC EFFECTS. NUMBNESS, TINGLING, WEAKNESS AND CRAMPING BEGINNING SYMMETRICALLY IN THE LOWER LIMBS MAY PROGRESS TO ATAXIA AND PARALYSIS. IN SEVERE CASES, UPPER LIMB INVOLVEMENT IS POSSIBLE AND FLACCID PARALYSIS MAY PROGRESS TO SPASTIC

PARALYSIS WITH EXAGGERATED REFLEXES. IMPROVEMENT MAY OCCUR OVER MONTHS TO YEARS, BUT SOME RESIDUAL IMPAIRMENT USUALLY REMAINS. **CHRONIC EXPOSURE-** REPEATED OR PROLONGED EXPOSURE MAY RESULT IN THE EFFECTS OF ACUTE EXPOSURE INCLUDING THE DELAYED NEUROPATHY. OTHER EFFECTS REPORTED IN WORKERS REPEATEDLY EXPOSED INCLUDE IMPAIRED MEMORY AND CONCENTRATION, ACUTE PSYCHOSIS, SEVERE DEPRESSIONS, IRRITABILTY, CONFUSION, APATHY, EMOTIONAL LABILITY, SOCIAL WITHDRAWAL, CONFUSION, HEADACHE, SPEECH DIFFICULTIES, DELAYED REACTION TIMES, SPATIAL DISORIENTATION, NIGHTMARES, SLEEPWALKING, AND DROWSINESS OR INSOMNIA. AN INFLUENZA-LIKE CONDITION WITH HEADACHE, NAUSEA, WEAKNESS, ANOREXIA AND MALAISE HAS ALSO BEEN REPORTED.

FIRST AID- REMOVE FROM EXPOSURE AREA TO FRESH AIR IMMEDIATELY. IF BREATHING HAS STOPPED, GIVE ARTIFICIAL RESPIRATION. MAINTAIN AIRWAY AND BLOOD PRESSURE AND ADMINISTER OXYGEN IF AVAILABLE. KEEP AFFECTED PERSON WARM AND AT REST. TREAT SYMPTOMATICALLY AND SUPPORTIVELY. ADMINISTRATION OF OXYGEN SHOULD BE PERFORMED BY QUALIFIED PERSONNEL. GET MEDICAL ATTENTION IMMEDIATELY.

SKIN CONTACT: SULFOTEP (TEDP): HIGHLY TOXIC. SEE INFORMATION ON ORGANOPHOSPHATES.

ORGANOPHOSPHATES: CHOLINESTERASE INHIBITOR. **ACUTE EXPOSURE-** LOCALIZED SWEATING AND FASCICULATIONS MAY OCCUR AT THE SITE OF CONTACT. IF SUFFICIENT AMOUNTS ARE ABSORBED, OTHER EFFECTS OF CHOLINESTERASE INHIBITION AS DESCRIBED IN ACUTE INHALATION MAY OCCUR. SYMPTOMS MAY BE DELAYED 2-3 HOURS, BUT USUALLY NO MORE THAN 12 HOURS. THE RATE OF ABSORPTION IS INCREASED BY THE PRESENCE OF DERMATITIS OR HIGH AMBIENT TEMPERATURES. DELAYED NEUROPATHY IS ALSO POSSIBLE. **CHRONIC EXPOSURE-** REPEATED OR PROLONGED EXPOSURE MAY CAUSE EFFECTS AS DESCRIBED IN ACUTE EXPOSURE. SOME ORGANOPHOSPHATES MAY CAUSE SENSITIZATION.

FIRST AID- REMOVE CONTAMINATED CLOTHING IMMEDIATELY. WASH CONTAMINATED AREAS WITH SOAP AND WATER FOLLOWED BY ALCOHOL (ARENA, POISONING, 4TH ED.). EMERGENCY PERSONNEL SHOULD WEAR GLOVES AND AVOID CONTAMINATION. TREAT RESPIRATORY DIFFICULTY WITH ARTIFICIAL RESPIRATION. GET MEDICAL ATTENTION IMMEDIATELY.

EYE CONTACT: SULFOTEP (TEDP): SEE INFORMATION ON ORGANOPHOSPHATES.

ORGANOPHOSPHATES: CHOLINESTERASE INHIBITOR. **ACUTE EXPOSURE-** DIRECT CONTACT MAY CAUSE PAIN, HYPEREMIA, LACRIMATION, TWITCHING OF THE EYELIDS, MIOSIS, AND CILIARY MUSCLE SPASM WITH LOSS OF ACCOMODATION, BLURRED OR DIMMED VISION AND BROWACHE. SOMETIMES MYDRIASIS MAY OCCUR INSTEAD OF MIOSIS. WITH SUFFICIENT EXPOSURE, OTHER SYMPTOMS OF CHOLINESTERASE INHIBITION AS DESCRIBED IN ACUTE INHALATION MAY OCCUR. **CHRONIC EXPOSURE-** REPEATED OR PROLONGED EXPOSURE MAY CAUSE EFFECTS AS DESCRIBED IN ACUTE EXPOSURE. SOME COMPOUNDS HAVE CAUSED TOXIC EFFECTS ON THE CRYSTALLINE LENS, CONJUNCTIVAL THICKENING AND OBSTRUCTION OF THE NASOLACRIMAL CANALS WHEN USED AS MIOTIC EYEDROPS.

FIRST AID- IRRIGATE EYES WITH WATER OR SALINE SOLUTION. IF SYMPTOMS OF POISONING OCCUR, TREAT RESPIRATORY DIFFICULTY WITH ARTIFICIAL RESPIRATION AND OXYGEN. OBSERVE PATIENT FOR AT LEAST 24-36 HOURS (GOSSELIN, CLINICAL TOXICOLOGY OF COMMERCIAL PRODUCTS, 5TH ED.). GET MEDICAL ATTENTION IMMEDIATELY. OXYGEN SHOULD BE ADMINISTERED BY QUALIFIED MEDICAL PERSONNEL.

INGESTION: SULFOTEP (TEDP): HIGHLY TOXIC. SEE INFORMATION ON ORGANOPHOSPHATES.

ORGANOPHOSPHATES: CHOLINESTERASE INHIBITOR. **ACUTE EXPOSURE-** WHEN INGESTED, THE FIRST EFFECTS MAY BE NAUSEA, VOMITING, ANOREXIA, ABDOMINAL CRAMPS AND DIARRHEA. GASTROINTESTINAL ABSORPTION MAY CAUSE SYMPTOMS OF CHOLINESTERASE INHIBITION AS DESCRIBED IN ACUTE INHALATION. SYMPTOMS MAY BEGIN WITHIN MINUTES OR BE DELAYED FOR HOURS. DELAYED EFFECTS INCLUDING NEUROPATHY MAY ALSO OCCUR. **CHRONIC EXPOSURE-** REPEATED INGESTION MAY CAUSE EFFECTS AS DESCRIBED IN ACUTE EXPOSURE.

FIRST AID- IF PERSON IS ALERT AND RESPIRATION IS NOT DEPRESSED, GIVE SYRUP OF IPECAC FOLLOWED BY WATER (IF VOMITING OCCURS, KEEP HEAD BELOW HIPS TO PREVENT ASPIRATION). IF CONSCIOUSNESS LEVEL DECLINES OR VOMITING HAS NOT OCCURRED IN 15 MINUTES EMPTY STOMACH BY GASTRIC LAVAGE WITH THE AID OF CUFFED ENDOTRACHEAL TUBE USING ISOTONIC SALINE OR 5% SODIUM BICARBONATE FOLLOW WITH ACTIVATED CHARCOAL. ESTABLISH AND MAINTAIN AIRWAY. TREAT RESPIRATORY DIFFICULTY WITH ARTIFICIAL RESPIRATION AND OXYGEN. DO NOT GIVE MORPHINE, AMINOPHYLLINE, PHENOTHIAZINES, RESERPINE, FUROSEMIDE, OR ETHACRYNIC ACID (MORGAN, RECOGNITION AND MANAGEMENT OF PESTICIDE POISONINGS, 3RD ED.). TREAT SYMPTOMATICALLY AND SUPPORTIVELY. ADMINISTRATION OF OXYGEN AND LAVAGE MUST BE PERFORMED BY QUALIFIED MEDICAL PERSONNEL. GET MEDICAL ATTENTION IMMEDIATELY.

ANTIDOTE: THE FOLLOWING ANTIDOTE(S) HAVE BEEN RECOMMENDED. HOWEVER, THE DECISION AS TO WHETHER THE SEVERITY OF POISONING REQUIRES ADMINISTRATION OF ANY ANTIDOTE AND ACTUAL DOSE REQUIRED SHOULD BE MADE BY QUALIFIED MEDICAL PERSONNEL.

FOR CHOLINESTERASE INHIBITORS: ESTABLISH CLEAR AIRWAY AND TISSUE OXYGENATION BY ASPIRATION OF SECRETIONS, AND IF NECESSARY, BY ASSISTED PULMONARY VENTILATION WITH OXYGEN. IMPROVE TISSUE OXYGENATION AS MUCH AS POSSIBLE BEFORE ADMINISTERING ATROPINE TO MINIMIZE THE RISK OF VENTRICULAR FIBRILLATION. ADMINISTER ATROPINE SULFATE INTRAVENOUSLY, OR INTRAMUSCULARLY IF IV INJECTION IS NOT POSSIBLE. IN MODERATELY SEVERE POISONING ADMINISTER ATROPINE SULFATE, 0.4-2.0 MG REPEATED EVERY 15 MINUTES UNTIL ATROPINIZATION IS ACHIEVED (TACHYCARDIA, FLUSHING, DRY MOUTH, MYDRIASIS). MAINTAIN ATROPINIZATION BY REPEATED DOSES FOR 2-12 HOURS, OR LONGER, DEPENDING ON THE SEVERITY OF POISONING. THE APPEARANCE OF RALES IN THE LUNG BASES, MIOSIS, SALIVATION, NAUSEA, BRADYCARDIA, ARE ALL INDICATIONS OF INADEQUATE ATROPINIZATION. SEVERELY POISONED INDIVIDUALS MAY EXHIBIT REMARKABLE TOLERANCE TO ATROPINE; TWO OR MORE TIMES THE DOSAGES SUGGESTED ABOVE MAY BE NEEDED. PERSONS NOT POISONED OR ONLY SLIGHTLY POISONED, HOWEVER, MAY DEVELOP SIGNS OF ATROPINE TOXICITY FROM SUCH LARGE DOSAGES: FEVER, MUSCLE FIBRILLATIONS, AND DELIRIUM ARE THE MAIN SIGNS OF ATROPINE TOXICITY. IF THESE SIGNS APPEAR WHILE THE PATIENT IS FULLY ATROPINIZED, ATROPINE ADMINISTRATION SHOULD BE DISCONTINUED, AT LEAST TEMPORARILY. OBSERVE TREATED PATIENTS CLOSELY AT LEAST 24 HOURS TO INSURE THAT SYMPTOMS (POSSIBLY PULMONARY EDEMA) DO NOT RECUR AS ATROPINIZATION WEARS OFF. IN VERY SEVERE POISONINGS, METABOLIC DISPOSITION OF TOXICANT MAY REQUIRE SEVERAL HOURS OR DAYS DURING WHICH ATROPINIZATION MUST BE MAINTAINED. MARKEDLY LOWER LEVELS OF URINARY METABOLITES INDICATE THAT ATROPINE DOSAGE CAN BE TAPERED OFF. AS DOSAGE IS REDUCED, CHECK THE LUNG BASES FREQUENTLY FOR RALES. IF RALES ARE HEARD OR OTHER SYMPTOMS RETURN, RE-ESTABLISH ATROPINIZATION PROMPTLY (MORGAN, RECOGNITION AND MANAGEMENT OF PESTICIDE POISONINGS, 3RD ED.). ADMINISTRATION OF ANTIDOTE MUST BE PERFORMED BY QUALIFIED MEDICAL PERSONNEL.

IN CASES OF SEVERE POISONING BY ORGANOPHOSPHATE PESTICIDES IN WHICH RESPIRATORY DEPRESSION, MUSCLE WEAKNESS AND TWITCHINGS ARE SEVERE, GIVE PRALIDOXIME (PROTOPAM-AYERST, 2-PAM), 1.0 GRAM INTRAVENOUSLY AT NO MORE THAN 0.5 GRAM PER MINUTE. DOSAGE OF PRALIDOXIME MAY BE REPEATED IN 1-2 HOURS, THEN AT 10-12 HOUR INTERVALS IF NEEDED. IN VERY SEVERE POISONINGS, DOSAGE RATES MAY BE DOUBLED. TREATMENT WITH PRALIDOXIME WILL BE MOST EFFECTIVE IF GIVEN WITHIN THIRTY-SIX HOURS AFTER POISONING (MORGAN, RECOGNITION AND MANAGEMENT OF PESTICIDE POISONINGS, 3RD ED.). ANTIDOTE SHOULD BE ADMINISTERED BY QUALIFIED MEDICAL PERSONNEL.

REACTIVITY

REACTIVITY: STABLE UNDER NORMAL TEMPERATURES AND PRESSURES.

INCOMPATIBILITIES: SULFOTEP (TEDP): IRON: MAY BE CORRODED. RUBBER, PLASTICS AND COATINGS: SOME FORMS MAY BE ATTACKED. STRONG OXIDIZERS: MAY CAUSE FIRE AND EXPLOSION HAZARD.

DECOMPOSITION: THERMAL DECOMPOSITION MAY RELEASE TOXIC OXIDES OF PHOSPHORUS AND SULFUR.

POLYMERIZATION: HAZARDOUS POLYMERIZATION HAS NOT BEEN REPORTED TO OCCUR UNDER NORMAL TEMPERATURES AND PRESSURES.

STORAGE AND DISPOSAL

OBSERVE ALL FEDERAL, STATE AND LOCAL REGULATIONS WHEN STORING OR DISPOSING OF THIS SUBSTANCE. FOR ASSISTANCE, CONTACT THE DISTRICT DIRECTOR OF THE ENVIRONMENTAL PROTECTION AGENCY.

****STORAGE****

STORE IN ACCORDANCE WITH 40 CFR 165 RECOMMENDED PROCEDURES FOR THE DISPOSAL AND STORAGE OF PESTICIDES AND PESTICIDE CONTAINERS.

STORE AWAY FROM INCOMPATIBLE SUBSTANCES.

THRESHOLD PLANNING QUANTITY (TPQ): THE SUPERFUND AMENDMENTS AND REAUTHORIZATION ACT (SARA) SECTION 302 REQUIRES THAT EACH FACILITY WHERE ANY EXTREMELY HAZARDOUS SUBSTANCE IS PRESENT IN A QUANTITY EQUAL TO OR GREATER THAN THE TPQ ESTABLISHED FOR THAT SUBSTANCE NOTIFY THE STATE EMERGENCY RESPONSE COMMISSION FOR THE STATE IN WHICH IT IS LOCATED. SECTION 303 OF SARA REQUIRES THESE FACILITIES TO PARTICIPATE IN LOCAL EMERGENCY RESPONSE PLANNING (40 CFR 355.30).

****DISPOSAL****

DISPOSAL MUST BE IN ACCORDANCE WITH STANDARDS APPLICABLE TO GENERATORS OF HAZARDOUS WASTE, 40CFR 262. EPA HAZARDOUS WASTE NUMBER P109.

CONDITIONS TO AVOID

MAY BURN BUT DOES NOT IGNITE READILY. CONTAINERS MAY EXPLODE IN HEAT OF FIRE.

SPILL AND LEAK PROCEDURES

OCCUPATIONAL SPILL: DO NOT TOUCH SPILLED MATERIAL. STOP LEAK IF YOU CAN DO IT WITHOUT RISK. USE WATER SPRAY TO REDUCE VAPORS. FOR SMALL SPILLS, TAKE UP WITH SAND OR OTHER ABSORBENT MATERIAL AND PLACE INTO CONTAINERS FOR LATER DISPOSAL. FOR SMALL DRY SPILLS, WITH A CLEAN SHOVEL PLACE MATERIAL INTO CLEAN, DRY CONTAINERS AND COVER. MOVE CONTAINERS FROM SPILL AREA. FOR LARGER SPILLS, DIKE FAR AHEAD OF SPILL FOR LATER DISPOSAL. KEEP UNNECESSARY PEOPLE AWAY. ISOLATE HAZARD AREA AND DENY ENTRY. VENTILATE CLOSED SPACES BEFORE ENTERING. REPORTABLE QUANTITY (RQ): 100 POUNDS THE SUPERFUND AMENDMENTS AND REAUTHORIZATION ACT (SARA) SECTION 304 REQUIRES THAT A RELEASE EQUAL TO OR GREATER THAN THE REPORTABLE QUANTITY FOR THIS SUBSTANCE BE IMMEDIATELY REPORTED TO THE LOCAL EMERGENCY PLANNING COMMITTEE AND THE STATE EMERGENCY RESPONSE COMMISSION (40 CFR 355.40). IF THE RELEASE OF THIS SUBSTANCE IS REPORTABLE UNDER CERCLA SECTION 103, THE NATIONAL RESPONSE CENTER MUST BE NOTIFIED IMMEDIATELY AT (800) 424-8802 OR (202) 426-2675 IN THE METROPOLITAN WASHINGTON, D.C. AREA (40 CFR 302.6).

PROTECTIVE EQUIPMENT

VENTILATION: PROCESS ENCLOSURE RECOMMENDED TO MEET PUBLISHED EXPOSURE LIMITS.

RESPIRATOR: THE FOLLOWING RESPIRATORS AND MAXIMUM USE CONCENTRATIONS ARE RECOMMENDATIONS BY THE U.S. DEPARTMENT OF HEALTH AND HUMAN SERVICES, NIOSH POCKET GUIDE TO CHEMICAL HAZARDS; NIOSH CRITERIA DOCUMENTS OR BY THE U.S. DEPARTMENT OF LABOR, 29 CFR 1910 SUBPART Z. THE SPECIFIC RESPIRATOR SELECTED MUST BE BASED ON CONTAMINATION LEVELS FOUND IN THE WORK PLACE, MUST NOT EXCEED THE WORKING LIMITS OF THE RESPIRATOR AND BE JOINTLY APPROVED BY THE NATIONAL INSTITUTE FOR OCCUPATIONAL SAFETY AND HEALTH AND THE MINE SAFETY AND HEALTH ADMINISTRATION (NIOSH-MSHA).

2 MG/M3- ANY SUPPLIED-AIR RESPIRATOR. ANY SELF-CONTAINED BREATHING APPARATUS.

5 MG/M3- ANY SUPPLIED-AIR RESPIRATOR OPERATED IN A CONTINUOUS FLOW MODE.

10 MG/M3- ANY SELF-CONTAINED BREATHING APPARATUS WITH A FULL FACEPIECE. ANY SUPPLIED-AIR RESPIRATOR WITH A FULL FACEPIECE.

35 MG/M3- ANY SUPPLIED-AIR RESPIRATOR WITH A HALF-MASK AND OPERATED IN A PRESSURE-DEMAND OR OTHER POSITIVE PRESSURE MODE.

ESCAPE- ANY AIR-PURIFYING FULL FACEPIECE RESPIRATOR (GAS MASK) WITH A CHIN-STYLE OR FRONT- OR BACK-MOUNTED ORGANIC VAPOR CANISTER HAVING A HIGH-EFFICIENCY PARTICULATE FILTER. ANY APPROPRIATE ESCAPE-TYPE SELF-CONTAINED BREATHING APPARATUS.

FOR FIREFIGHTING AND OTHER IMMEDIATELY DANGEROUS TO LIFE OR HEALTH CONDITIONS:

SELF-CONTAINED BREATHING APPARATUS WITH FULL FACEPIECE OPERATED IN PRESSURE-DEMAND OR OTHER POSITIVE PRESSURE MODE.

SUPPLIED-AIR RESPIRATOR WITH FULL FACEPIECE AND OPERATED IN PRESSURE-DEMAND OR OTHER POSITIVE PRESSURE MODE IN COMBINATION WITH AN AUXILIARY SELF-CONTAINED BREATHING APPARATUS OPERATED IN PRESSURE-DEMAND OR OTHER POSITIVE PRESSURE MODE.

CLOTHING: EMPLOYEE MUST WEAR APPROPRIATE PROTECTIVE (IMPERVIOUS) CLOTHING AND EQUIPMENT TO PREVENT ANY POSSIBILITY OF SKIN CONTACT WITH THIS SUBSTANCE.

GLOVES: EMPLOYEE MUST WEAR APPROPRIATE PROTECTIVE GLOVES TO PREVENT CONTACT WITH THIS SUBSTANCE.

EYE PROTECTION: EMPLOYEE MUST WEAR SPLASH-PROOF OR DUST-RESISTANT SAFETY GOGGLES AND A FACESHIELD TO PREVENT CONTACT WITH THIS SUBSTANCE.

EMERGENCY WASH FACILITIES: WHERE THERE IS ANY POSSIBILITY THAT AN EMPLOYEE'S EYES AND/OR SKIN MAY BE EXPOSED TO THIS SUBSTANCE, THE EMPLOYER SHOULD PROVIDE AN EYE WASH FOUNTAIN AND QUICK DRENCH SHOWER WITHIN THE IMMEDIATE WORK AREA FOR EMERGENCY USE.

AUTHORIZED BY- OCCUPATIONAL HEALTH SERVICES, INC.
CREATION DATE: 10/05/89 ***REVISION DATE:*** 04/26/90

MATERIAL SAFETY DATA SHEET

OCCUPATIONAL HEALTH SERVICES, INC.
AGRICULTURE AND PESTICIDE DIVISION
450 SEVENTH AVENUE, SUITE 2407
NEW YORK, NEW YORK 10123
1-800-445-MSDS OR (212) 967-1100

EMERGENCY CONTACT:
JOHN S. BRANSFORD, JR. (615) 292-1180

SUBSTANCE IDENTIFICATION

CAS-NUMBER 545-55-1

SUBSTANCE: TEPA

TRADE NAMES/SYNONYMS: TRIAZIRIDINOPHOSPHINE OXIDE; 1-AZIRIDINYL PHOSPHINE OXIDE (TRIS); TRIETHYLENEPHOSPHOROTRIAMIDE; TRIS(N-ETHYLENE)PHOSPHOROTRIAMIDATE; INPERON FIXER T; APHOXIDE; APO; 1,1',1"-PHOSPHINYLIDYNETRIS-AZIRIDINE; N,N',N"-TRIETHYLENEPHOSPHORAMIDE; TRIETHYLENEPHOSPHORIC TRIAMIDE; N,N',N"-TRIETHYLENEPHOSPHORIC TRIAMIDE; TRIS(AZIRIDINYL)PHOSPHINE OXIDE; TRIS(1-AZIRIDINYL)PHOSPHINE OXIDE; N,N',N"-TRI-1,2-ETHANEDIYLPHOSPHORIC TRIAMIDE; TRIAETHYLENPHOSPHORSAEUREAMID; PHOSPHORIC ACID TRIETHYLENEIMINE; STCC 4935520; UN 2501; PST22510

CHEMICAL FAMILY: PHOSPHINE AZIRIDINE

MOLECULAR FORMULA: C6-H12-N3-O-P

MOLECULAR WEIGHT: 173.18

CERCLA RATINGS (SCALE 0-3): HEALTH=3 FIRE=0 REACTIVITY=0 PERSISTENCE=0

NFPA RATINGS (SCALE 0-4): HEALTH=4 FIRE=0 REACTIVITY=0

COMPONENTS AND CONTAMINANTS

COMPONENT: TEPA ***PERCENT:*** 100
CAS# 545-55-1

OTHER CONTAMINANTS: NONE

EXPOSURE LIMITS: NO OCCUPATIONAL EXPOSURE LIMITS ESTABLISHED BY OSHA, ACGIH, OR NIOSH.

PHYSICAL DATA

DESCRIPTION: COLORLESS HYGROSCOPIC CRYSTALS

BOILING POINT: 196 F (91 C) @ 23 MMHG ***MELTING POINT:*** 106 F (41 C)

SPECIFIC GRAVITY: NOT AVAILABLE ***SOLUBILITY IN WATER:*** COMPLETE

SOLVENT SOLUBILITY: SOLUBLE IN ALCOHOL, ETHER, ACETONE

FIRE AND EXPLOSION DATA

FIRE AND EXPLOSION HAZARD: NEGLIGIBLE FIRE HAZARD WHEN EXPOSED TO HEAT OR FLAME.

FIREFIGHTING MEDIA: DRY CHEMICAL, CARBON DIOXIDE, HALON, WATER SPRAY OR STANDARD FOAM (1987 EMERGENCY RESPONSE GUIDEBOOK, DOT P 5800.4). FOR LARGER FIRES, USE WATER SPRAY, FOG OR STANDARD FOAM (1987 EMERGENCY RESPONSE GUIDEBOOK, DOT P 5800.4).

FIREFIGHTING: MOVE CONTAINERS FROM FIRE AREA IF POSSIBLE. FIGHT FIRE FROM MAXIMUM DISTANCE. STAY AWAY FROM STORAGE TANK ENDS. DIKE FIRE CONTROL WATER FOR LATER DISPOSAL. DO NOT SCATTER MATERIAL (1987 EMERGENCY RESPONSE GUIDEBOOK, DOT P 5800.4, GUIDE PAGE 55). EXTINGUISH ONLY IF FLOW CAN BE STOPPED; USE WATER IN FLOODING AMOUNTS AS FOG, SOLID STREAMS MAY NOT BE EFFECTIVE. COOL CONTAINERS WITH FLOODING QUANTITIES OF WATER, APPLY FROM AS FAR A DISTANCE AS POSSIBLE. AVOID BREATHING CORROSIVE VAPORS, KEEP UPWIND.

TRANSPORTATION DATA

DEPARTMENT OF TRANSPORTATION HAZARD CLASSIFICATION 49 CFR 172.101: CORROSIVE MATERIAL

DEPARTMENT OF TRANSPORTATION LABELING REQUIREMENTS 49 CFR 172.101 AND SUBPART E: CORROSIVE

DEPARTMENT OF TRANSPORTATION PACKAGING REQUIREMENTS: 49 CFR 173.299A EXCEPTIONS: 49 CFR 173.244

TOXICITY

TEPA: 37 MG/KG ORAL-RAT LD50; 87 MG/KG SKIN-RAT LD50; 420 MG/KG ORAL-MOUSE LD50; 156 UG/KG INTRAPERITONEAL-MOUSE LDLO; 178 MG/KG INTRAVENOUS-MOUSE LD50; 870 UG/KG INTRAVENOUS-MONKEY LDLO; 15 MG/KG UNREPORTED ROUTE-MAMMAL LD50; 50 MG/KG ORAL-DOMESTIC ANIMAL LDLO; 430 UG/KG INTRAVENOUS-DOG LDLO; MUTAGENIC DATA (RTECS); REPRODUCTIVE EFFECTS DATA (RTECS); TUMORIGENIC DATA (RTECS). CARCINOGEN STATUS: ANIMAL INADEQUATE EVIDENCE (IARC GROUP-3). TEPA IS HIGHLY TOXIC, AND A SKIN, EYE, AND MUCOUS MEMBRANE IRRITANT.

HEALTH EFFECTS AND FIRST AID

INHALATION: TEPA: IRRITANT. **ACUTE EXPOSURE-** EXPOSURE TO DUSTS MAY CAUSE MUCOUS MEMBRANE IRRITATION. **CHRONIC EXPOSURE-** NO DATA AVAILABLE.

FIRST AID- REMOVE FROM EXPOSURE AREA TO FRESH AIR IMMEDIATELY. IF BREATHING HAS STOPPED, PERFORM ARTIFICIAL RESPIRATION. KEEP PERSON WARM AND AT REST. TREAT SYMPTOMATICALLY AND SUPPORTIVELY. GET MEDICAL ATTENTION IMMEDIATELY.

SKIN CONTACT: TEPA: IRRITANT/HIGHLY TOXIC. **ACUTE EXPOSURE-** CONTACT MAY CAUSE SKIN IRRITATION. 87 MG/KG WAS LETHAL TO 50% OF THE RATS TESTED. MAY BE ABSORBED THROUGH THE SKIN AND CAUSE SYSTEMIC POISONING. **CHRONIC EXPOSURE-** MAY CAUSE DERMATITIS AFTER REPEATED OR PROLONGED EXPOSURE.

FIRST AID- REMOVE CONTAMINATED CLOTHING AND SHOES IMMEDIATELY. WASH AFFECTED AREA WITH SOAP OR MILD DETERGENT AND LARGE AMOUNTS OF WATER UNTIL NO EVIDENCE OF CHEMICAL REMAINS (APPROXIMATELY 15-20 MINUTES). GET MEDICAL ATTENTION IMMEDIATELY.

EYE CONTACT: TEPA: IRRITANT. **ACUTE EXPOSURE-** CONTACT MAY CAUSE EYE IRRITATION. **CHRONIC EXPOSURE-** MAY CAUSE CONJUNCTIVITIS AFTER REPEATED OR PROLONGED EXPOSURE.

FIRST AID- WASH EYES IMMEDIATELY WITH LARGE AMOUNTS OF WATER OR NORMAL SALINE, OCCASIONALLY LIFTING UPPER AND LOWER LIDS, UNTIL NO EVIDENCE OF CHEMICAL REMAINS (APPROXIMATELY 15-20 MINUTES). GET MEDICAL ATTENTION IMMEDIATELY.

INGESTION: TEPA: HIGHLY TOXIC. **ACUTE EXPOSURE-** MAY CAUSE DEPRESSION, ANOREXIA AND DIARRHEA APPEARING 2-3 DAYS BEFORE DEATH, FOLLOWED BY TERMINAL DYSPNEA, INCOORDINATION, EPISTAXIS, SALIVATION, PROSTRATION AND CYANOSIS. LIVER DAMAGE WITH CONGESTION OF HEPATIC SINUSOIDS, CLOUDY SWELLING, FATTY DEGENERATION AND NECROSIS RESULTING IN HEPATITIS MAY OCCUR. **CHRONIC EXPOSURE-** NO DATA AVAILABLE.

FIRST AID- TREAT SYMPTOMATICALLY AND SUPPORTIVELY. GET MEDICAL ATTENTION IMMEDIATELY. IF VOMITING OCCURS, KEEP HEAD LOWER THAN HIPS TO PREVENT ASPIRATION.

ANTIDOTE: NO SPECIFIC ANTIDOTE. TREAT SYMPTOMATICALLY AND SUPPORTIVELY.

REACTIVITY

REACTIVITY: STABLE UNDER NORMAL TEMPERATURES AND PRESSURES.

INCOMPATIBILITIES: NO DATA AVAILABLE.

DECOMPOSITION: THERMAL DECOMPOSITION MAY RELEASE TOXIC OXIDES OF NITROGEN, PHOSPHORUS AND CARBON.

POLYMERIZATION: HAZARDOUS POLYMERIZATION HAS NOT BEEN REPORTED TO OCCUR UNDER NORMAL TEMPERATURES AND PRESSURES.

CONDITIONS TO AVOID

AVOID CONTACT WITH COMBUSTIBLE MATERIALS (WOOD, PAPER, FUEL, OILS, ETC); IGNITION OR EXPLOSION MAY RESULT. AVOID CONTAMINATION OF WATER SOURCES.

SPILL AND LEAK PROCEDURES

OCCUPATIONAL SPILL: KEEP COMBUSTIBLES (WOOD, PAPER, OIL, ETC) AWAY FROM SPILLED MATERIAL. DO NOT TOUCH SPILLED MATERIAL. FOR SMALL DRY SPILLS, WITH CLEAN SHOVEL PLACE MATERIAL INTO CLEAN, DRY CONTAINER AND COVER; MOVE CONTAINERS FROM SPILL AREA. FOR SMALL LIQUID SPILLS, TAKE UP WITH SAND, EARTH OR OTHER ABSORBENT MATERIAL AND PLACE INTO CONTAINERS FOR LATER DISPOSAL. FOR LARGER SPILLS, DIKE FAR AHEAD OF SPILL FOR LATER DISPOSAL. KEEP UNNECESSARY PEOPLE AWAY. ISOLATE HAZARD AREA AND DENY ENTRY.

PROTECTIVE EQUIPMENT

VENTILATION: PROCESS ENCLOSURE RECOMMENDED.

RESPIRATOR: THE FOLLOWING RESPIRATORS ARE RECOMMENDED BASED ON INFORMATION FOUND IN THE PHYSICAL DATA, TOXICITY AND HEALTH EFFECTS SECTIONS. THEY ARE RANKED IN ORDER FROM MINIMUM TO MAXIMUM RESPIRATORY PROTECTION. THE SPECIFIC RESPIRATOR SELECTED MUST BE BASED ON CONTAMINATION LEVELS FOUND IN THE WORK PLACE, MUST NOT EXCEED THE WORKING LIMITS OF THE RESPIRATOR AND BE JOINTLY APPROVED BY THE NATIONAL INSTITUTE FOR OCCUPATIONAL SAFETY AND HEALTH AND THE MINE SAFETY AND HEALTH ADMINISTRATION (NIOSH-MSHA).

DUST AND MIST RESPIRATOR WITH A FULL FACEPIECE.

AIR-PURIFYING FULL FACEPIECE RESPIRATOR WITH A HIGH-EFFICIENCY PARTICULATE FILTER.

POWERED AIR-PURIFYING RESPIRATOR WITH A TIGHT-FITTING FACEPIECE AND HIGH-EFFICIENCY PARTICULATE FILTER.

TYPE 'C' SUPPLIED-AIR RESPIRATOR WITH A FULL FACEPIECE OPERATED IN PRESSURE-DEMAND OR OTHER POSITIVE PRESSURE MODE OR WITH A FULL FACEPIECE, HELMET OR HOOD OPERATED IN CONTINUOUS-FLOW MODE.

SELF-CONTAINED BREATHING APPARATUS WITH A FULL FACEPIECE OPERATED IN PRESSURE-DEMAND OR OTHER POSITIVE PRESSURE MODE.

FOR FIREFIGHTING AND OTHER IMMEDIATELY DANGEROUS TO LIFE OR HEALTH CONDITIONS:

SELF-CONTAINED BREATHING APPARATUS WITH FULL FACEPIECE OPERATED IN PRESSURE-DEMAND OR OTHER POSITIVE PRESSURE MODE.

SUPPLIED-AIR RESPIRATOR WITH FULL FACEPIECE AND OPERATED IN PRESSURE-DEMAND OR OTHER POSITIVE PRESSURE MODE IN COMBINATION WITH AN AUXILIARY SELF-CONTAINED BREATHING APPARATUS OPERATED IN PRESSURE-DEMAND OR OTHER POSITIVE PRESSURE MODE.

CLOTHING: EMPLOYEE MUST WEAR APPROPRIATE PROTECTIVE (IMPERVIOUS) CLOTHING AND EQUIPMENT TO PREVENT REPEATED OR PROLONGED SKIN CONTACT WITH THIS SUBSTANCE.

GLOVES: EMPLOYEE MUST WEAR APPROPRIATE PROTECTIVE GLOVES TO PREVENT CONTACT WITH THIS SUBSTANCE.

EYE PROTECTION: EMPLOYEE MUST WEAR SPLASH-PROOF OR DUST-RESISTANT SAFETY GOGGLES TO PREVENT EYE CONTACT WITH THIS SUBSTANCE.

EMERGENCY EYE WASH: WHERE THERE IS ANY POSSIBILITY THAT AN EMPLOYEE'S EYES MAY BE EXPOSED TO THIS SUBSTANCE, THE EMPLOYER SHOULD PROVIDE AN EYE WASH FOUNTAIN WITHIN THE IMMEDIATE WORK AREA FOR EMERGENCY USE.

AUTHORIZED BY- OCCUPATIONAL HEALTH SERVICES, INC.

CREATION DATE: 10/05/89 ***REVISION DATE:*** 07/12/90

MATERIAL SAFETY DATA SHEET

OCCUPATIONAL HEALTH SERVICES, INC.
AGRICULTURE AND PESTICIDE DIVISION
450 SEVENTH AVENUE, SUITE 2407
NEW YORK, NEW YORK 10123
1-800-445-MSDS OR (212) 967-1100

EMERGENCY CONTACT:
JOHN S. BRANSFORD, JR. (615) 292-1180

SUBSTANCE IDENTIFICATION

CAS-NUMBER 107-49-3

SUBSTANCE: **TETRAETHYL PYROPHOSPHATE**

TRADE NAMES/SYNONYMS: DIPHOSPHORIC ACID TETRAETHYL ESTER; PYROPHOSPHORIC ACID TETRAETHYL ESTER; TETRAETHYL DIPHOSPHATE; BIS-O,O-DIETHYLPHOSPHORIC ANHYDRIDE; TEPP; VAPOTONE; TETRON; ENT 18,771; RCRA P111; STCC 4921486; C8H20O7P2; PST22520

CHEMICAL FAMILY: ORGANOPHOSPHATE

MOLECULAR FORMULA: C8-H20-O7-P2

MOLECULAR WEIGHT: 290.22

CERCLA RATINGS (SCALE 0-3): HEALTH=3 FIRE=0 REACTIVITY=0 PERSISTENCE=0

NFPA RATINGS (SCALE 0-4): HEALTH=4 FIRE=0 REACTIVITY=0

COMPONENTS AND CONTAMINANTS

COMPONENT: TETRAETHYL PYROPHOSPHATE ***PERCENT:*** 100
CAS# 107-49-3

EXPOSURE LIMITS: TETRAETHYL PYROPHOSPHATE: 0.05 MG/M3 OSHA TWA (SKIN)
0.004 PPM (0.05 MG/M3) ACGIH TWA (SKIN)
100 POUNDS SARA SECTION 302 THRESHOLD PLANNING QUANTITY 10 POUNDS SARA SECTION 304 REPORTABLE QUANTITY 10 POUNDS CERCLA SECTION 103 REPORTABLE QUANTITY

PHYSICAL DATA

DESCRIPTION: COLORLESS, ODORLESS, HYGROSCOPIC LIQUID

BOILING POINT: 255 F (124 C) @ 1 MMHG ***SPECIFIC GRAVITY:*** 1.185

VAPOR PRESSURE: 0.00047 MMHG @ 30 C ***SOLUBILITY IN WATER:*** SOLUBLE

SOLVENT SOLUBILITY: SOLUBLE IN ALCOHOL, BENZENE, ACETONE, BENZENE, CHLOROFORM, CARBON TETRACHLORIDE, GLYCEROL, ETHYLENE GLYCOL, PROPYLENE GLYCOL, TOLUENE, XYLENE, MOST ORGANIC SOLVENTS; INSOLUBLE IN PETROLEUM OILS

FIRE AND EXPLOSION DATA

FIRE AND EXPLOSION HAZARD: NEGLIGIBLE FIRE HAZARD WHEN EXPOSED TO HEAT OR FLAME.

FIREFIGHTING MEDIA: DRY CHEMICAL, CARBON DIOXIDE, HALON, WATER SPRAY OR STANDARD FOAM (1987 EMERGENCY RESPONSE GUIDEBOOK, DOT P 5800.4). FOR LARGER FIRES, USE WATER SPRAY, FOG OR STANDARD FOAM (1987 EMERGENCY RESPONSE GUIDEBOOK, DOT P 5800.4).

FIREFIGHTING: MOVE CONTAINERS FROM FIRE AREA IF POSSIBLE. FIGHT FIRE FROM MAXIMUM DISTANCE. STAY AWAY FROM STORAGE TANK ENDS. DIKE FIRE CONTROL WATER FOR LATER DISPOSAL. DO NOT SCATTER MATERIAL (1987 EMERGENCY RESPONSE GUIDEBOOK, DOT P 5800.4, GUIDE PAGE 55). EXTINGUISH ONLY IF FLOW CAN BE STOPPED; USE FLOODING AMOUNTS OF WATER AS FOG, SOLID STREAMS MAY BE INEFFECTIVE. COOL CONTAINERS WITH FLOODING AMOUNTS OF WATER FROM AS FAR A DISTANCE AS POSSIBLE. USE WATER SPRAY TO ABSORB TOXIC VAPORS. AVOID BREATHING TOXIC VAPORS; KEEP UPWIND. CONSIDER EVACUATION OF DOWNWIND AREA IF MATERIAL IS LEAKING.

TRANSPORTATION DATA

DEPARTMENT OF TRANSPORTATION HAZARD CLASSIFICATION 49 CFR 172.101: POISON B

DEPARTMENT OF TRANSPORTATION LABELING REQUIREMENTS 49 CFR 172.101 AND SUBPART E: POISON

DEPARTMENT OF TRANSPORTATION PACKAGING REQUIREMENTS: 49 CFR 173.358 EXCEPTIONS: NONE

TOXICITY

TETRAETHYL PYROPHOSPHATE: TOXICITY DATA: 2400 UG/KG SKIN-RAT LD50; 8 MG/KG SKIN-MOUSE LD50; 309 UG/KG ORAL-HUMAN TDLO; 1429 UG/KG ORAL-HUMAN LDLO; 500 UG/KG ORAL-RAT LD50; 3 MG/KG ORAL-MOUSE LD50; 2300 UG/KG ORAL-GUINEA PIG LD50; 2 MG/KG SUBCUTANEOUS-RABBIT LD50; 279 UG/KG SUBCUTANEOUS-RAT LD50; 500 UG/KG SUBCUTANEOUS-MOUSE LD50; 300 UG/KG INTRAVENOUS-RAT LD50; 200 UG/KG INTRAVENOUS-MOUSE LD50; 650 UG/KG INTRAPERITONEAL-RAT LD50; 830 UG/KG INTRAPERITONEAL-MOUSE LD50; 71 UG/KG PARENTERAL-HUMAN TDLO; 286 UG/KG INTRAMUSCULAR-HUMAN LDLO; 1800 UG/KG INTRAMUSCULAR-RAT LD50. CARCINOGEN STATUS: NONE. ACUTE TOXICITY LEVEL: HIGHLY TOXIC BY DERMAL ABSORPTION AND INGESTION. TARGET EFFECTS: CHOLINESTERASE INHIBITOR. POISONING MAY AFFECT THE NERVOUS SYSTEM.* AT INCREASED RISK FROM EXPOSURE: PERSONS WITH REDUCED PULMONARY FUNCTION, CONVULSIVE DISORDERS, OR RECENT EXPOSURE TO ANTICHLOINESTERASE AGENTS. ADDITIONAL DATA: MAY CROSS THE PLACENTA. HIGH ENVIRONMENTAL TEMPERATURES OR EXPOSURE OF THE CHEMICAL TO VISIBLE OR ULTRAVIOLET LIGHT MAY ENHANCE THE TOXICITY. INTERACTIONS WITH MEDICATIONS MAY OCCUR.*

* MAY BE BASED ON GENERAL INFORMATION ON ORGANOPHOSPHATES.

HEALTH EFFECTS AND FIRST AID

INHALATION: TETRAETHYL PYROPHOSPHATE: 10 MG/M3 IMMEDIATELY DANGEROUS TO LIFE OR HEALTH. SOME INDIVIDUALS EXPERIENCED SHORTNESS OF BREATH AND OTHER SYMPTOMS AS A RESULT OF EXPOSURE TO A DUST OF 1 PER CENT TETRAETHYL PYROPHOSPHATE. THE SYMPTOMS SUBSIDED ONCE EXPOSURE WAS TERMINATED. SEE INFORMATION ON ORGANOPHOSPHATES.

ORGANOPHOSPHATES: CHOLINESTERASE INHIBITOR. **ACUTE EXPOSURE-** WHEN INHALED, THE FIRST EFFECTS OF CHOLINESTERASE INHIBITORS ARE USUALLY RESPIRATORY AND MAY INCLUDE NASAL HYPEREMIA AND WATERY DISCHARGE, COUGH, CHEST DISCOMFORT, DYSPNEA, AND WHEEZING DUE TO INCREASED BRONCHIAL SECRETIONS AND BRONCHOCONSTRICTION. IF SUFFICIENT AMOUNTS ARE ABSORBED, OTHER SYSTEMIC EFFECTS MAY BEGIN WITHIN A FEW MINUTES OR BE DELAYED FOR UP TO 12 HOURS. SYMPTOMS MAY INCLUDE PALLOR, NAUSEA, VOMITING, DIARRHEA, ABDOMINAL CRAMPS, HEADACHE, DIZZINESS, OCULAR PAIN, BLURRED VISION, MIOSIS OR IN SOME CASES, ESPECIALLY INITIALLY, MYDRIASIS, LACRIMATION, SALIVATION, SWEATING, AND CONFUSION. OTHER REPORTED CENTRAL NERVOUS SYSTEM OR NEUROMUSCULAR EFFECTS MAY INCLUDE ATAXIA, SLURRED SPEECH, AREFLEXIA, WEAKNESS, FATIGUE, FASCICULATIONS, TWITCHING, TREMORS POSSIBLY OF THE TONGUE AND EYELIDS, AND EVENTUALLY PARALYSIS OF THE EXTREMITIES AND POSSIBLY OF THE RESPIRATORY MUSCLES. IN SEVERE CASES THERE MAY ALSO BE INVOLUNTARY DEFECATION AND URINATION, CYANOSIS, PSYCHOSIS, HYPERGLYCEMIA, ACUTE PANCREATITIS, CARDIAC IRREGULARITIES, PULMONARY EDEMA, UNCONSCIOUSNESS, CONVULSIONS, AND COMA. DEATH IS PRIMARILY DUE TO RESPIRATORY FAILURE, ALTHOUGH CARDIOVASCULAR EFFECTS INCLUDING CARDIAC ARREST MAY ALSO BE IMPLICATED. LONG TERM SEQUELAE ARE RARE BUT MAY INCLUDE NEUROPSYCHIATRIC DISORDERS AND MYOPATHY WITH MUSCLE TENDERNESS. SOME ORGANOPHOSPHATES MAY CAUSE A DELAYED NEUROPATHY BEGINNING 1-4 WEEKS AFTER AN ACUTE EXPOSURE WHICH MAY OR MAY NOT HAVE CAUSED ACUTE CHOLINERGIC EFFECTS. NUMBNESS, TINGLING, WEAKNESS AND CRAMPING BEGINNING SYMMETRICALLY IN THE LOWER LIMBS MAY PROGRESS TO ATAXIA AND PARALYSIS. IN SEVERE CASES, UPPER LIMB INVOLVEMENT IS POSSIBLE AND FLACCID PARALYSIS MAY PROGRESS TO SPASTIC PARALYSIS WITH EXAGGERATED REFLEXES. IMPROVEMENT MAY OCCUR OVER MONTHS TO YEARS, BUT SOME RESIDUAL IMPAIRMENT USUALLY REMAINS. **CHRONIC EXPOSURE-** REPEATED OR PROLONGED EXPOSURE MAY RESULT IN THE EFFECTS OF ACUTE EXPOSURE INCLUDING THE DELAYED NEUROPATHY. OTHER EFFECTS REPORTED IN WORKERS REPEATEDLY EXPOSED INCLUDE IMPAIRED MEMORY AND CONCENTRATION, ACUTE PSYCHOSIS, SEVERE DEPRESSIONS, IRRITABILTY, CONFUSION, APATHY, EMOTIONAL LABILITY, SOCIAL WITHDRAWAL, CONFUSION, HEADACHE, SPEECH DIFFICULTIES, DELAYED REACTION TIMES, SPATIAL DISORIENTATION, NIGHTMARES, SLEEPWALKING, AND DROWSINESS OR INSOMNIA. AN INFLUENZA-LIKE CONDITION WITH HEADACHE, NAUSEA, WEAKNESS, ANOREXIA AND MALAISE HAS ALSO BEEN REPORTED.

FIRST AID- REMOVE FROM EXPOSURE AREA TO FRESH AIR IMMEDIATELY. IF BREATHING HAS STOPPED, GIVE ARTIFICIAL RESPIRATION. MAINTAIN AIRWAY AND BLOOD PRESSURE AND ADMINISTER OXYGEN IF AVAILABLE. KEEP AFFECTED PERSON WARM AND AT REST. TREAT SYMPTOMATICALLY AND SUPPORTIVELY. ADMINISTRATION OF OXYGEN SHOULD BE PERFORMED BY QUALIFIED PERSONNEL. GET MEDICAL ATTENTION IMMEDIATELY.

SKIN CONTACT: TETRAETHYL PYROPHOSPHATE: HIGHLY TOXIC. SEE INFORMATION ON ORGANOPHOSPHATES.

ORGANOPHOSPHATES: CHOLINESTERASE INHIBITOR. **ACUTE EXPOSURE-** LOCALIZED SWEATING AND FASCICULATIONS MAY OCCUR AT THE SITE OF CONTACT. IF SUFFICIENT AMOUNTS ARE ABSORBED, OTHER EFFECTS OF CHOLINESTERASE INHIBITION AS DESCRIBED IN ACUTE INHALATION MAY OCCUR. SYMPTOMS MAY BE DELAYED 2-3 HOURS, BUT USUALLY NO MORE THAN 12 HOURS. THE RATE OF ABSORPTION IS INCREASED BY THE PRESENCE OF DERMATITIS OR HIGH AMBIENT TEMPERATURES. DELAYED NEUROPATHY IS ALSO POSSIBLE. **CHRONIC EXPOSURE-** REPEATED OR PROLONGED EXPOSURE MAY CAUSE EFFECTS AS DESCRIBED IN ACUTE EXPOSURE. SOME ORGANOPHOSPHATES MAY CAUSE SENSITIZATION.

FIRST AID- REMOVE CONTAMINATED CLOTHING IMMEDIATELY. WASH CONTAMINATED AREAS WITH SOAP AND WATER FOLLOWED BY ALCOHOL (ARENA, POISONING, 4TH ED.). EMERGENCY PERSONNEL SHOULD WEAR GLOVES AND AVOID CONTAMINATION. TREAT RESPIRATORY DIFFICULTY WITH ARTIFICIAL RESPIRATION. GET MEDICAL ATTENTION IMMEDIATELY.

EYE CONTACT: TETRAETHYL PYROPHOSPHATE: SEE INFORMATION ON ORGANOPHOSPHATES.

ORGANOPHOSPHATES: CHOLINESTERASE INHIBITOR. **ACUTE EXPOSURE-** DIRECT CONTACT MAY CAUSE PAIN, HYPEREMIA, LACRIMATION, TWITCHING OF THE EYELIDS, MIOSIS, AND CILIARY MUSCLE SPASM WITH LOSS OF ACCOMODATION, BLURRED OR DIMMED VISION AND BROWACHE. SOMETIMES MYDRIASIS MAY OCCUR INSTEAD OF MIOSIS. WITH SUFFICIENT EXPOSURE, OTHER SYMPTOMS OF CHOLINESTERASE INHIBITION AS DESCRIBED IN ACUTE INHALATION MAY OCCUR. **CHRONIC EXPOSURE-** REPEATED OR PROLONGED EXPOSURE MAY CAUSE EFFECTS AS DESCRIBED IN ACUTE EXPOSURE. SOME COMPOUNDS HAVE CAUSED TOXIC EFFECTS ON THE CRYSTALLINE LENS, CONJUNCTIVAL THICKENING AND OBSTRUCTION OF THE NASOLACRIMAL CANALS WHEN USED AS MIOTIC EYEDROPS.

FIRST AID- IRRIGATE EYES WITH WATER OR SALINE SOLUTION. IF SYMPTOMS OF POISONING OCCUR, TREAT RESPIRATORY DIFFICULTY WITH ARTIFICIAL RESPIRATION AND OXYGEN. OBSERVE PATIENT FOR AT LEAST 24-36 HOURS (GOSSELIN, CLINICAL TOXICOLOGY OF COMMERCIAL PRODUCTS, 5TH ED.). GET MEDICAL ATTENTION IMMEDIATELY. OXYGEN SHOULD BE ADMINISTERED BY QUALIFIED MEDICAL PERSONNEL.

INGESTION: TETRAETHYL PYROPHOSPHATE: HIGHLY TOXIC. SEE INFORMATION ON ORGANOPHOSPHATES.

ORGANOPHOSPHATES: CHOLINESTERASE INHIBITOR. **ACUTE EXPOSURE-** WHEN INGESTED, THE FIRST EFFECTS MAY BE NAUSEA, VOMITING, ANOREXIA, ABDOMINAL CRAMPS AND DIARRHEA. GASTROINTESTINAL ABSORPTION MAY CAUSE SYMPTOMS OF CHOLINESTERASE INHIBITION AS DESCRIBED IN ACUTE INHALATION. SYMPTOMS MAY BEGIN WITHIN MINUTES OR BE DELAYED FOR HOURS. DELAYED EFFECTS INCLUDING NEUROPATHY MAY ALSO OCCUR. **CHRONIC EXPOSURE-** REPEATED INGESTION MAY CAUSE EFFECTS AS DESCRIBED IN ACUTE EXPOSURE.

FIRST AID- IF PERSON IS ALERT AND RESPIRATION IS NOT DEPRESSED, GIVE SYRUP OF IPECAC FOLLOWED BY WATER (IF VOMITING OCCURS, KEEP HEAD BELOW HIPS TO PREVENT ASPIRATION). IF CONSCIOUSNESS LEVEL DECLINES OR VOMITING HAS NOT OCCURRED IN 15 MINUTES EMPTY STOMACH BY GASTRIC LAVAGE WITH THE AID OF CUFFED ENDOTRACHEAL TUBE USING ISOTONIC SALINE OR 5% SODIUM BICARBONATE FOLLOW WITH ACTIVATED CHARCOAL. ESTABLISH AND MAINTAIN AIRWAY. TREAT RESPIRATORY DIFFICULTY WITH ARTIFICIAL RESPIRATION AND OXYGEN. DO NOT GIVE MORPHINE, AMINOPHYLLINE, PHENOTHIAZINES, RESERPINE, FUROSEMIDE, OR ETHACRYNIC ACID (MORGAN, RECOGNITION AND MANAGEMENT OF PESTICIDE POISONINGS, 3RD ED.). TREAT SYMPTOMATICALLY AND

SUPPORTIVELY. ADMINISTRATION OF OXYGEN AND LAVAGE MUST BE PERFORMED BY QUALIFIED MEDICAL PERSONNEL. GET MEDICAL ATTENTION IMMEDIATELY.

ANTIDOTE: THE FOLLOWING ANTIDOTE(S) HAVE BEEN RECOMMENDED. HOWEVER, THE DECISION AS TO WHETHER THE SEVERITY OF POISONING REQUIRES ADMINISTRATION OF ANY ANTIDOTE AND ACTUAL DOSE REQUIRED SHOULD BE MADE BY QUALIFIED MEDICAL PERSONNEL.

FOR CHOLINESTERASE INHIBITORS: ESTABLISH CLEAR AIRWAY AND TISSUE OXYGENATION BY ASPIRATION OF SECRETIONS, AND IF NECESSARY, BY ASSISTED PULMONARY VENTILATION WITH OXYGEN. IMPROVE TISSUE OXYGENATION AS MUCH AS POSSIBLE BEFORE ADMINISTERING ATROPINE TO MINIMIZE THE RISK OF VENTRICULAR FIBRILLATION. ADMINISTER ATROPINE SULFATE INTRAVENOUSLY, OR INTRAMUSCULARLY IF IV INJECTION IS NOT POSSIBLE. IN MODERATELY SEVERE POISONING ADMINISTER ATROPINE SULFATE, 0.4-2.0 MG REPEATED EVERY 15 MINUTES UNTIL ATROPINIZATION IS ACHIEVED (TACHYCARDIA, FLUSHING, DRY MOUTH, MYDRIASIS). MAINTAIN ATROPINIZATION BY REPEATED DOSES FOR 2-12 HOURS, OR LONGER, DEPENDING ON THE SEVERITY OF POISONING. THE APPEARANCE OF RALES IN THE LUNG BASES, MIOSIS, SALIVATION, NAUSEA, BRADYCARDIA, ARE ALL INDICATIONS OF INADEQUATE ATROPINIZATION. SEVERELY POISONED INDIVIDUALS MAY EXHIBIT REMARKABLE TOLERANCE TO ATROPINE; TWO OR MORE TIMES THE DOSAGES SUGGESTED ABOVE MAY BE NEEDED. PERSONS NOT POISONED OR ONLY SLIGHTLY POISONED, HOWEVER, MAY DEVELOP SIGNS OF ATROPINE TOXICITY FROM SUCH LARGE DOSAGES: FEVER, MUSCLE FIBRILLATIONS, AND DELIRIUM ARE THE MAIN SIGNS OF ATROPINE TOXICITY. IF THESE SIGNS APPEAR WHILE THE PATIENT IS FULLY ATROPINIZED, ATROPINE ADMINISTRATION SHOULD BE DISCONTINUED, AT LEAST TEMPORARILY. OBSERVE TREATED PATIENTS CLOSELY AT LEAST 24 HOURS TO INSURE THAT SYMPTOMS (POSSIBLY PULMONARY EDEMA) DO NOT RECUR AS ATROPINIZATION WEARS OFF. IN VERY SEVERE POISONINGS, METABOLIC DISPOSITION OF TOXICANT MAY REQUIRE SEVERAL HOURS OR DAYS DURING WHICH ATROPINIZATION MUST BE MAINTAINED. MARKEDLY LOWER LEVELS OF URINARY METABOLITES INDICATE THAT ATROPINE DOSAGE CAN BE TAPERED OFF. AS DOSAGE IS REDUCED, CHECK THE LUNG BASES FREQUENTLY FOR RALES. IF RALES ARE HEARD OR OTHER SYMPTOMS RETURN, RE-ESTABLISH ATROPINIZATION PROMPTLY (MORGAN, RECOGNITION AND MANAGEMENT OF PESTICIDE POISONINGS, 3RD ED.). ADMINISTRATION OF ANTIDOTE MUST BE PERFORMED BY QUALIFIED MEDICAL PERSONNEL.

IN CASES OF SEVERE POISONING BY ORGANOPHOSPHATE PESTICIDES IN WHICH RESPIRATORY DEPRESSION, MUSCLE WEAKNESS AND TWITCHINGS ARE SEVERE, GIVE PRALIDOXIME (PROTOPAM-AYERST, 2-PAM), 1.0 GRAM INTRAVENOUSLY AT NO MORE THAN 0.5 GRAM PER MINUTE. DOSAGE OF PRALIDOXIME MAY BE REPEATED IN 1-2 HOURS, THEN AT 10-12 HOUR INTERVALS IF NEEDED. IN VERY SEVERE POISONINGS, DOSAGE RATES MAY BE DOUBLED. TREATMENT WITH PRALIDOXIME WILL BE MOST EFFECTIVE IF GIVEN WITHIN THIRTY-SIX HOURS AFTER POISONING (MORGAN, RECOGNITION AND MANAGEMENT OF PESTICIDE POISONINGS, 3RD ED.). ANTIDOTE SHOULD BE ADMINISTERED BY QUALIFIED MEDICAL PERSONNEL.

REACTIVITY

REACTIVITY: TETRAETHYL PYROPHOSPHATE: DECOMPOSES AT 338 F (170 C) WITH THE FORMATION OF FLAMMABLE ETHYLENE.

INCOMPATIBILITIES: TETRAETHYL PYROPHOSPHATE: ALKALINE MATERIALS: INCOMPATIBLE. ALUMINUM CONTAINERS: MAY BE CORRODED. BRASS: MAY BE CORRODED. COPPER: MAY BE CORRODED. METALS: MAY BE CORRODED. PLASTICS, RUBBER AND COATINGS: SOME FORMS MAY BE ATTACKED. OXIDIZERS (STRONG): MAY CAUSE FIRE AND EXPLOSION HAZARD. TIN: MAY BE CORRODED. ZINC: MAY BE CORRODED.

DECOMPOSITION: THERMAL DECOMPOSITION MAY RELEASE TOXIC OXIDES OF PHOSPHORUS.

POLYMERIZATION: HAZARDOUS POLYMERIZATION HAS NOT BEEN REPORTED TO OCCUR UNDER NORMAL TEMPERATURES AND PRESSURES.

STORAGE AND DISPOSAL

OBSERVE ALL FEDERAL, STATE AND LOCAL REGULATIONS WHEN STORING OR DISPOSING OF THIS SUBSTANCE. FOR ASSISTANCE, CONTACT THE DISTRICT DIRECTOR OF THE ENVIRONMENTAL PROTECTION AGENCY.

STORAGE

STORE IN ACCORDANCE WITH 40 CFR 165 RECOMMENDED PROCEDURES FOR THE DISPOSAL AND STORAGE OF PESTICIDES AND PESTICIDE CONTAINERS.

STORE AWAY FROM INCOMPATIBLE SUBSTANCES.

THRESHOLD PLANNING QUANTITY (TPQ): THE SUPERFUND AMENDMENTS AND REAUTHORIZATION ACT (SARA) SECTION 302 REQUIRES THAT EACH FACILITY WHERE ANY EXTREMELY HAZARDOUS SUBSTANCE IS PRESENT IN A QUANTITY EQUAL TO OR GREATER THAN THE TPQ ESTABLISHED FOR THAT SUBSTANCE NOTIFY THE STATE EMERGENCY RESPONSE COMMISSION FOR THE STATE IN WHICH IT IS LOCATED. SECTION 303 OF SARA REQUIRES THESE FACILITIES TO PARTICIPATE IN LOCAL EMERGENCY RESPONSE PLANNING (40 CFR 355.30).

DISPOSAL

DISPOSAL MUST BE IN ACCORDANCE WITH STANDARDS APPLICABLE TO GENERATORS OF HAZARDOUS WASTE, 40CFR 262. EPA HAZARDOUS WASTE NUMBER P111.

CONDITIONS TO AVOID

NONE REPORTED.

SPILL AND LEAK PROCEDURES

SOIL SPILL: DIG HOLDING AREA SUCH AS LAGOON, POND OR PIT FOR CONTAINMENT. DIKE FLOW OF SPILLED MATERIAL USING SOIL OR SANDBAGS OR FOAMED BARRIERS SUCH AS POLYURETHANE OR CONCRETE.

USE CEMENT POWDER OR FLY ASH TO ABSORB LIQUID MASS.

AIR SPILL: KNOCK DOWN VAPORS WITH WATER SPRAY. KEEP UPWIND.

WATER SPILL: NEUTRALIZE WITH AGRICULTURAL LIME, SLAKED LIME, CRUSHED LIMESTONE, OR SODIUM BICARBONATE.

ADD SUITABLE AGENT TO NEUTRALIZE SPILLED MATERIAL TO PH-7.

USE MECHANICAL DREDGES OR LIFTS TO EXTRACT IMMOBILIZED MASSES OF POLLUTION AND PRECIPITATES.

OCCUPATIONAL SPILL: DO NOT TOUCH SPILLED MATERIAL. STOP LEAK IF YOU CAN DO IT WITHOUT RISK. USE WATER SPRAY TO REDUCE VAPORS. FOR SMALL SPILLS, TAKE UP WITH SAND OR OTHER ABSORBENT MATERIAL AND PLACE INTO CONTAINERS FOR LATER DISPOSAL. FOR SMALL DRY SPILLS, WITH A CLEAN SHOVEL PLACE MATERIAL INTO CLEAN, DRY CONTAINERS AND COVER. MOVE CONTAINERS FROM SPILL AREA. FOR LARGER SPILLS, DIKE FAR AHEAD OF SPILL FOR LATER DISPOSAL. KEEP UNNECESSARY PEOPLE AWAY. ISOLATE HAZARD AREA AND DENY ENTRY. VENTILATE CLOSED SPACES BEFORE ENTERING.

REPORTABLE QUANTITY (RQ): 10 POUNDS THE SUPERFUND AMENDMENTS AND REAUTHORIZATION ACT (SARA) SECTION 304 REQUIRES THAT A RELEASE EQUAL TO OR GREATER THAN THE REPORTABLE QUANTITY FOR THIS SUBSTANCE BE IMMEDIATELY REPORTED TO THE LOCAL EMERGENCY PLANNING COMMITTEE AND THE STATE EMERGENCY RESPONSE COMMISSION (40 CFR 355.40). IF THE RELEASE OF THIS SUBSTANCE IS REPORTABLE UNDER CERCLA SECTION 103, THE NATIONAL RESPONSE CENTER MUST BE NOTIFIED IMMEDIATELY AT (800) 424-8802 OR (202) 426-2675 IN THE METROPOLITAN WASHINGTON, D.C. AREA (40 CFR 302.6).

PROTECTIVE EQUIPMENT

VENTILATION: PROCESS ENCLOSURE RECOMMENDED TO MEET PUBLISHED EXPOSURE LIMITS.

RESPIRATOR: THE FOLLOWING RESPIRATORS AND MAXIMUM USE CONCENTRATIONS ARE RECOMMENDATIONS BY THE U.S. DEPARTMENT OF HEALTH AND HUMAN SERVICES, NIOSH POCKET GUIDE TO CHEMICAL HAZARDS; NIOSH CRITERIA DOCUMENTS OR BY THE U.S. DEPARTMENT OF LABOR, 29 CFR 1910 SUBPART Z. THE SPECIFIC RESPIRATOR SELECTED MUST BE BASED ON CONTAMINATION LEVELS FOUND IN THE WORK PLACE, MUST NOT EXCEED THE WORKING LIMITS OF THE RESPIRATOR AND BE JOINTLY APPROVED BY THE NATIONAL INSTITUTE FOR OCCUPATIONAL SAFETY AND HEALTH AND THE MINE SAFETY AND HEALTH ADMINISTRATION (NIOSH-MSHA).

0.05 MG/M3- ANY SUPPLIED-AIR RESPIRATOR. ANY SELF-CONTAINED BREATHING APPARATUS.

1.25 MG/M3- ANY SUPPLIED-AIR RESPIRATOR OPERATED IN A CONTINUOUS FLOW MODE.

2.5 MG/M3- ANY SUPPLIED-AIR RESPIRATOR WITH A FULL FACEPIECE. ANY SELF-CONTAINED BREATHING APPARATUS WITH A FULL FACEPIECE. ANY SUPPLIED-AIR RESPIRATOR WITH A TIGHT-FITTING FACEPIECE OPERATED IN A CONTINUOUS FLOW MODE.

10 MG/M3- ANY SUPPLIED-AIR RESPIRATOR WITH A HALF-MASK AND OPERATED IN A PRESSURE-DEMAND OR OTHER POSITIVE PRESSURE MODE.

ESCAPE- ANY AIR-PURIFYING FULL FACEPIECE RESPIRATOR (GAS MASK) WITH A CHIN-STYLE OR FRONT- OR BACK-MOUNTED ORGANIC VAPOR CANISTER HAVING A HIGH-EFFICIENCY PARTICULATE FILTER. ANY APPROPRIATE ESCAPE-TYPE SELF-CONTAINED BREATHING APPARATUS.

FOR FIREFIGHTING AND OTHER IMMEDIATELY DANGEROUS TO LIFE OR HEALTH CONDITIONS:

SELF-CONTAINED BREATHING APPARATUS WITH FULL FACEPIECE OPERATED IN PRESSURE-DEMAND OR OTHER POSITIVE PRESSURE MODE.

SUPPLIED-AIR RESPIRATOR WITH FULL FACEPIECE AND OPERATED IN PRESSURE-DEMAND OR OTHER POSITIVE PRESSURE MODE IN COMBINATION WITH AN AUXILIARY SELF-CONTAINED BREATHING APPARATUS OPERATED IN PRESSURE-DEMAND OR OTHER POSITIVE PRESSURE MODE.

CLOTHING: EMPLOYEE MUST WEAR APPROPRIATE PROTECTIVE (IMPERVIOUS) CLOTHING AND EQUIPMENT TO PREVENT ANY POSSIBILITY OF SKIN CONTACT WITH THIS SUBSTANCE.

GLOVES: EMPLOYEE MUST WEAR APPROPRIATE PROTECTIVE GLOVES TO PREVENT CONTACT WITH THIS SUBSTANCE.

EYE PROTECTION: EMPLOYEE MUST WEAR SPLASH-PROOF OR DUST-RESISTANT SAFETY GOGGLES AND A FACESHIELD TO PREVENT CONTACT WITH THIS SUBSTANCE.
EMERGENCY WASH FACILITIES: WHERE THERE IS ANY POSSIBILITY THAT AN EMPLOYEE'S EYES AND/OR SKIN MAY BE EXPOSED TO THIS SUBSTANCE, THE EMPLOYER SHOULD PROVIDE AN EYE WASH FOUNTAIN AND QUICK DRENCH SHOWER WITHIN THE IMMEDIATE WORK AREA FOR EMERGENCY USE.

AUTHORIZED BY- OCCUPATIONAL HEALTH SERVICES, INC.
CREATION DATE: 05/18/90 ***REVISION DATE:*** 05/18/90

MATERIAL SAFETY DATA SHEET

OCCUPATIONAL HEALTH SERVICES, INC.
AGRICULTURE AND PESTICIDE DIVISION
450 SEVENTH AVENUE, SUITE 2407
NEW YORK, NEW YORK 10123
1-800-445-MSDS OR (212) 967-1100

EMERGENCY CONTACT:
JOHN S. BRANSFORD, JR. (615) 292-1180

SUBSTANCE IDENTIFICATION

CAS-NUMBER 5915-41-3
SUBSTANCE: **TERBUTHYLAZINE**
TRADE NAMES/SYNONYMS: 1,3,5-TRIAZINE-2,4-DIAMINE, 6-CHLORO-N-(1,1-DIMETHYLETHYL)-N'-ETHYL-; S-TRIAZINE, 2-(TERT-BUTYLAMINO)-4-CHLORO-6-(ETHYLAMINO)-; 6-CHLORO-N-(1,1-DIMETHYLETHYL)-N'-ETHYL-1,3,5-TRIAZINE-2,4-DIAMINE; 2-(TERT-BUTYLAMINO)-4-CHLORO-6-(ETHYLAMINO)-S-TRIAZINE; 2-TERT-BUTYLAMINO-4-CHLORO-6-ETHYLAMINO-1,3,5-TRIAZINE; 4-TERT-BUTYLAMINO-2-CHLORO-6-ETHYLAMINO-S-TRIAZINE; CHLORCARAGARD; G 13529; GARDOPRIM; GS 13529; PRIMATOL M; TERBUTAZINE; TERBUTYLAZINE; TERBUTYLETHYLAZINE; C9H16CLN5; PST22536
CHEMICAL FAMILY: S-TRIAZINE
MOLECULAR FORMULA: C9-H16-CL-N5
MOLECULAR WEIGHT: 229.75
CERCLA RATINGS (SCALE 0-3): HEALTH=2 FIRE=1 REACTIVITY=0 PERSISTENCE=3
NFPA RATINGS (SCALE 0-4): HEALTH=2 FIRE=1 REACTIVITY=0

COMPONENTS AND CONTAMINANTS

COMPONENT: TERBUTHYLAZINE ***PERCENT:*** 100.0
CAS# 5915-41-3
OTHER CONTAMINANTS: NONE
EXPOSURE LIMITS: NO OCCUPATIONAL EXPOSURE LIMITS ESTABLISHED BY OSHA, ACGIH, OR NIOSH.

PHYSICAL DATA

DESCRIPTION: COLORLESS TO WHITE POWDER.
MELTING POINT: 351-354 F (177-179 C)
SPECIFIC GRAVITY: 1.188 ***VAPOR PRESSURE:*** .00000113 MMHG @ 20
SOLUBILITY IN WATER: 8.5 PPM @ 20 C
SOLVENT SOLUBILITY: SOLUBLE IN DIMETHYLFORMAMIDE; SLIGHTLY SOLUBLE IN ETHYLACETATE, OCTAN-1-OL, AND ISOPROPANOL

FIRE AND EXPLOSION DATA

FIRE AND EXPLOSION HAZARD: SLIGHT FIRE HAZARD WHEN EXPOSED TO HEAT OR FLAME.
FIREFIGHTING MEDIA: DRY CHEMICAL, CARBON DIOXIDE, HALON, WATER SPRAY OR STANDARD FOAM (1987 EMERGENCY RESPONSE GUIDEBOOK, DOT P 5800.4).
FOR LARGER FIRES, USE WATER SPRAY, FOG OR STANDARD FOAM (1987 EMERGENCY RESPONSE GUIDEBOOK, DOT P 5800.4).
FIREFIGHTING: MOVE CONTAINERS FROM FIRE AREA IF POSSIBLE (1987 EMERGENCY RESPONSE GUIDEBOOK, DOT P 5800.4, GUIDE PAGE 53).
EXTINGUISH USING AGENTS SUITABLE FOR SURROUNDING FIRE. USE FLOODING QUANTITIES OF WATER AS A FOG. KEEP MATERIAL OUT OF SEWERS AND WATER SOURCES. DO NOT TOUCH SPILLED MATERIAL. AVOID BREATHING HAZARDOUS FUMES; KEEP UPWIND.

TOXICITY

TERBUTHYLAZINE: TOXICITY DATA: 1845 MG/KG ORAL-RAT LD50; 2500 MG/KG UNREPORTED-RAT LD50. CARCINOGEN STATUS: NONE. ACUTE TOXICITY LEVEL: MODERATELY TOXIC BY INGESTION. TARGET EFFECTS: NO DATA AVAILABLE.

HEALTH EFFECTS AND FIRST AID

INHALATION: TERBUTHYLAZINE: **ACUTE EXPOSURE-** A LETHAL CONCENTRATION IN RATS WAS GREATER THAN 3510 MG/M3. **CHRONIC EXPOSURE-** NO DATA AVAILABLE.
FIRST AID- REMOVE FROM EXPOSURE AREA TO FRESH AIR IMMEDIATELY. IF BREATHING HAS STOPPED, PERFORM ARTIFICIAL RESPIRATION. KEEP PERSON WARM AND AT REST. TREAT SYMPTOMATICALLY AND SUPPORTIVELY. GET MEDICAL ATTENTION IMMEDIATELY.

SKIN CONTACT: TERBUTHYLAZINE: **ACUTE EXPOSURE-** THIS MATERIAL WAS SLIGHTLY IRRITATING TO RABBIT SKIN. A LETHAL DOSE IN RATS BY DERMAL ABSORPTION WAS GREATER THAN 3000 MG/KG. **CHRONIC EXPOSURE-** NO DATA AVAILABLE.
FIRST AID- REMOVE CONTAMINATED CLOTHING AND SHOES IMMEDIATELY. WASH AFFECTED AREA WITH SOAP OR MILD DETERGENT AND LARGE AMOUNTS OF WATER UNTIL NO EVIDENCE OF CHEMICAL REMAINS (APPROXIMATELY 15-20 MINUTES). GET MEDICAL ATTENTION IMMEDIATELY.

EYE CONTACT: TERBUTHYLAZINE: **ACUTE EXPOSURE-** TERBUTHYLAZINE WAS NOT AN IRRITANT OF RABBIT EYES. **CHRONIC EXPOSURE-** NO DATA AVAILABLE.
FIRST AID- WASH EYES IMMEDIATELY WITH LARGE AMOUNTS OF WATER OR NORMAL SALINE, OCCASIONALLY LIFTING UPPER AND LOWER LIDS, UNTIL NO EVIDENCE OF CHEMICAL REMAINS (APPROXIMATELY 15-20 MINUTES). GET MEDICAL ATTENTION IMMEDIATELY.

INGESTION: TERBUTHYLAZINE: **ACUTE EXPOSURE-** A LETHAL DOSE IN RATS WAS 1845 MG/KG; SYMPTOMS WERE NOT REPORTED. **CHRONIC EXPOSURE-** NO ADVERSE EFFECTS WERE NOTED IN A 90-DAY STUDY OF DOGS FED 3.5 MG/KG/DAY.
FIRST AID- REMOVE BY GASTRIC LAVAGE AND CATHARSIS. MAINTAIN BLOOD PRESSURE AND AIRWAY. GIVE OXYGEN IF RESPIRATION IS DEPRESSED. DO NOT PERFORM GASTRIC LAVAGE IF VICTIM IS UNCONSCIOUS. GET MEDICAL ATTENTION IMMEDIATELY (DREISBACH, HANDBOOK OF POISONING, 12TH ED.).
ADMINISTRATION OF LAVAGE OR OXYGEN SHOULD BE PERFORMED BY QUALIFIED MEDICAL PERSONNEL.
ANTIDOTE: NO SPECIFIC ANTIDOTE. TREAT SYMPTOMATICALLY AND SUPPORTIVELY.

REACTIVITY

REACTIVITY: STABLE UNDER NORMAL TEMPERATURES AND PRESSURES.
INCOMPATIBILITIES: TERBUTHYLAZINE: NO DATA AVAILABLE.
DECOMPOSITION: THERMAL DECOMPOSITION PRODUCTS MAY INCLUDE TOXIC OXIDES OF NITROGEN AND CARBON AND TOXIC AND CORROSIVE FUMES OF CHLORIDES.
POLYMERIZATION: HAZARDOUS POLYMERIZATION HAS NOT BEEN REPORTED TO OCCUR UNDER NORMAL TEMPERATURES AND PRESSURES.

STORAGE AND DISPOSAL

OBSERVE ALL FEDERAL, STATE AND LOCAL REGULATIONS WHEN STORING OR DISPOSING OF THIS SUBSTANCE. FOR ASSISTANCE, CONTACT THE DISTRICT DIRECTOR OF THE ENVIRONMENTAL PROTECTION AGENCY.

STORAGE

STORE IN ACCORDANCE WITH 40 CFR 165 RECOMMENDED PROCEDURES FOR THE DISPOSAL AND STORAGE OF PESTICIDES AND PESTICIDE CONTAINERS.

DISPOSAL

DISPOSAL MUST BE IN ACCORDANCE WITH 40 CFR 165 RECOMMENDED PROCEDURES FOR THE DISPOSAL AND STORAGE OF PESTICIDES AND PESTICIDE CONTAINERS.

CONDITIONS TO AVOID

MAY BURN BUT DOES NOT IGNITE READILY.

SPILL AND LEAK PROCEDURES

OCCUPATIONAL SPILL: DO NOT TOUCH SPILLED MATERIAL. STOP LEAK IF YOU CAN DO IT WITHOUT RISK. FOR SMALL SPILLS, TAKE UP WITH SAND OR OTHER ABSORBENT MATERIAL AND PLACE INTO CONTAINERS FOR LATER DISPOSAL. FOR SMALL DRY SPILLS, WITH A CLEAN SHOVEL PLACE MATERIAL INTO CLEAN, DRY CONTAINER AND COVER. MOVE CONTAINERS FROM SPILL AREA. FOR LARGER SPILLS, DIKE FAR AHEAD OF SPILL FOR LATER DISPOSAL. KEEP UNNECESSARY PEOPLE AWAY. ISOLATE HAZARD AREA AND DENY ENTRY.

PROTECTIVE EQUIPMENT

VENTILATION: PROVIDE LOCAL EXHAUST OR GENERAL DILUTION VENTILATION SYSTEM.
RESPIRATOR: THE FOLLOWING RESPIRATORS ARE RECOMMENDED BASED ON INFORMATION FOUND IN THE PHYSICAL DATA, TOXICITY AND HEALTH EFFECTS SECTIONS. THEY ARE RANKED IN ORDER FROM MINIMUM TO MAXIMUM

RESPIRATORY PROTECTION. THE SPECIFIC RESPIRATOR SELECTED MUST BE BASED ON CONTAMINATION LEVELS FOUND IN THE WORK PLACE, MUST NOT EXCEED THE WORKING LIMITS OF THE RESPIRATOR AND BE JOINTLY APPROVED BY THE NATIONAL INSTITUTE FOR OCCUPATIONAL SAFETY AND HEALTH AND THE MINE SAFETY AND HEALTH ADMINISTRATION (NIOSH-MSHA).
CHEMICAL CARTRIDGE RESPIRATOR WITH AN ORGANIC VAPOR CARTRIDGE(S) IN COMBINATION WITH A DUST AND MIST FILTER.
GAS MASK WITH ORGANIC VAPOR CANISTER (CHIN-STYLE OR FRONT- OR BACK-MOUNTED CANISTER) WITH A DUST AND MIST FILTER.
GAS MASK WITH ORGANIC VAPOR CANISTER (CHIN-STYLE OR FRONT- OR BACK-MOUNTED CANISTER) WITH A PARTICULATE FILTER.
POWERED AIR-PURIFYING RESPIRATOR WITH A HIGH-EFFICIENCY FILTER.
TYPE 'C' SUPPLIED-AIR RESPIRATOR WITH A FULL FACEPIECE OPERATED IN A PRESSURE-DEMAND OR OTHER POSITIVE PRESSURE MODE.
SELF-CONTAINED BREATHING APPARATUS WITH A FULL FACEPIECE OPERATED IN PRESSURE-DEMAND OR OTHER POSITIVE PRESSURE MODE.
FOR FIREFIGHTING AND OTHER IMMEDIATELY DANGEROUS TO LIFE OR HEALTH CONDITIONS:
SELF-CONTAINED BREATHING APPARATUS WITH FULL FACEPIECE OPERATED IN PRESSURE-DEMAND OR OTHER POSITIVE PRESSURE MODE.
SUPPLIED-AIR RESPIRATOR WITH FULL FACEPIECE AND OPERATED IN PRESSURE-DEMAND OR OTHER POSITIVE PRESSURE MODE IN COMBINATION WITH AN AUXILIARY SELF-CONTAINED BREATHING APPARATUS OPERATED IN PRESSURE-DEMAND OR OTHER POSITIVE PRESSURE MODE.

CLOTHING: EMPLOYEE MUST WEAR APPROPRIATE PROTECTIVE (IMPERVIOUS) CLOTHING AND EQUIPMENT TO PREVENT REPEATED OR PROLONGED SKIN CONTACT WITH THIS SUBSTANCE.

GLOVES: EMPLOYEE MUST WEAR APPROPRIATE PROTECTIVE GLOVES TO PREVENT CONTACT WITH THIS SUBSTANCE.

EYE PROTECTION: EMPLOYEE MUST WEAR SPLASH-PROOF OR DUST-RESISTANT SAFETY GOGGLES TO PREVENT EYE CONTACT WITH THIS SUBSTANCE.
EMERGENCY EYE WASH: WHERE THERE IS ANY POSSIBILITY THAT AN EMPLOYEE'S EYES MAY BE EXPOSED TO THIS SUBSTANCE, THE EMPLOYER SHOULD PROVIDE AN EYE WASH FOUNTAIN WITHIN THE IMMEDIATE WORK AREA FOR EMERGENCY USE.

AUTHORIZED BY- OCCUPATIONAL HEALTH SERVICES, INC.
CREATION DATE: 10/05/89 ***REVISION DATE:*** 05/15/90

MATERIAL SAFETY DATA SHEET

OCCUPATIONAL HEALTH SERVICES, INC.
AGRICULTURE AND PESTICIDE DIVISION
450 SEVENTH AVENUE, SUITE 2407
NEW YORK, NEW YORK 10123
1-800-445-MSDS OR (212) 967-1100

EMERGENCY CONTACT:
JOHN S. BRANSFORD, JR. (615) 292-1180

SUBSTANCE IDENTIFICATION

CAS-NUMBER 56070-15-6
SUBSTANCE: **TERBUFOS OXYGEN ANALOG SULFONE**
TRADE NAMES/SYNONYMS: PHOSPHOROTHIOIC ACID, S-(((1,1-DIMETHYLETHYL)SULFONYL)METHYL) O,O- DIETHYL ESTER; O,O-DIETHYL S-(((1,1-DIMETHYLETHYL)SULFONYL)METHYL)PHOSPHOROTHIOATE; TERBUFOS OXON SULFONE; TERBUFOXON SULFONE; COUNTER OXYGEN ANALOG SULFONE; C9H21O5PS2; PST22537
CHEMICAL FAMILY: ORGANOPHOSPHATE
MOLECULAR FORMULA: (C2-H5-O)2-P-(O)-S-C-H2-S-(O2)-C-(C-H3)3
MOLECULAR WEIGHT: 288.0
CERCLA RATINGS (SCALE 0-3): HEALTH=U FIRE=U REACTIVITY=0 PERSISTENCE=0
NFPA RATINGS (SCALE 0-4): HEALTH=U FIRE=U REACTIVITY=0

COMPONENTS AND CONTAMINANTS

COMPONENT: TERBUFOS OXYGEN ANALOG SULFONE ***PERCENT:*** 100.0
CAS# 56070-15-6
OTHER CONTAMINANTS: NONE
EXPOSURE LIMITS: NO OCCUPATIONAL EXPOSURE LIMITS ESTABLISHED BY OSHA, ACGIH, OR NIOSH.

PHYSICAL DATA

DESCRIPTION: CLEAR LIQUID. ***BOILING POINT:*** NOT AVAILABLE
SPECIFIC GRAVITY: NOT AVAILABLE ***VAPOR PRESSURE:*** NOT AVAILABLE
SOLUBILITY IN WATER: NOT AVAILABLE

FIRE AND EXPLOSION DATA

FIRE AND EXPLOSION HAZARD: UNKNOWN FIRE AND EXPLOSION HAZARD.
FIREFIGHTING MEDIA: DRY CHEMICAL, CARBON DIOXIDE, HALON, WATER SPRAY OR STANDARD FOAM (1987 EMERGENCY RESPONSE GUIDEBOOK, DOT P 5800.4).
FOR LARGER FIRES, USE WATER SPRAY, FOG OR STANDARD FOAM (1987 EMERGENCY RESPONSE GUIDEBOOK, DOT P 5800.4).
FIREFIGHTING: MOVE CONTAINER FROM FIRE AREA IF POSSIBLE. DIKE FIRE CONTROL WATER FOR LATER DISPOSAL; DO NOT SCATTER THE MATERIAL. COOL FIRE-EXPOSED CONTAINERS WITH WATER FROM SIDE UNTIL WELL AFTER FIRE IS OUT. STAY AWAY FROM STORAGE TANK ENDS. WITHDRAW IMMEDIATELY IN CASE OF RISING SOUND FROM VENTING SAFETY DEVICE OR ANY DISCOLORATION OF STORAGE TANK DUE TO FIRE (1987 EMERGENCY RESPONSE GUIDEBOOK, DOT P 5800.4, GUIDE PAGE 28).
EXTINGUISH ONLY IF FLOW CAN BE STOPPED. USE FLOODING AMOUNTS OF WATER AS A FOG; SOLID STREAMS MAY BE INEFFECTIVE. COOL CONTAINERS WITH FLOODING AMOUNTS OF WATER FROM AS FAR A DISTANCE AS POSSIBLE. AVOID BREATHING POISONOUS VAPORS, KEEP UPWIND.

TOXICITY

TERBUFOS OXYGEN ANALOG SULFONE: CARCINOGEN STATUS: NONE. ACUTE TOXICITY LEVEL: NO DATA AVAILABLE. TARGET EFFECTS: CHOLINESTERASE INHIBITOR. POISONING MAY AFFECT THE NERVOUS SYSTEM.* AT INCREASED RISK FROM EXPOSURE: PERSONS WITH RESPIRATORY AILMENTS, RECENT EXPOSURE TO CHOLINESTERASE INHIBITORS OR IMPAIRED CHOLINESTERASE PRODUCTION, OR LIVER MALFUNCTION.* ADDITIONAL DATA: MAY CROSS THE PLACENTA. HIGH ENVIRONMENTAL TEMPERATURES OR EXPOSURE OF THE CHEMICAL TO VISIBLE OR ULTRAVIOLET LIGHT MAY ENHANCE THE TOXICITY. INTERACTIONS WITH MEDICATIONS MAY OCCUR.*
* MAY BE BASED ON GENERAL INFORMATION ON ORGANOPHOSPHATES.

HEALTH EFFECTS AND FIRST AID

INHALATION: TERBUFOS OXYGEN ANALOG SULFONE: SEE INFORMATION ON ORGANOPHOSPHATES.
ORGANOPHOSPHATES: CHOLINESTERASE INHIBITOR. **ACUTE EXPOSURE**- WHEN INHALED, THE FIRST EFFECTS OF CHOLINESTERASE INHIBITORS ARE USUALLY RESPIRATORY AND MAY INCLUDE NASAL HYPEREMIA AND WATERY DISCHARGE, COUGH, CHEST DISCOMFORT, DYSPNEA, AND WHEEZING DUE TO INCREASED BRONCHIAL SECRETIONS AND BRONCHOCONSTRICTION. IF SUFFICIENT AMOUNTS ARE ABSORBED, OTHER SYSTEMIC EFFECTS MAY BEGIN WITHIN A FEW MINUTES OR BE DELAYED FOR UP TO 12 HOURS. SYMPTOMS MAY INCLUDE PALLOR, NAUSEA, VOMITING, DIARRHEA, ABDOMINAL CRAMPS, HEADACHE, DIZZINESS, OCULAR PAIN, BLURRED VISION, MIOSIS OR IN SOME CASES, ESPECIALLY INITIALLY, MYDRIASIS, LACRIMATION, SALIVATION, SWEATING, AND CONFUSION. OTHER REPORTED CENTRAL NERVOUS SYSTEM OR NEUROMUSCULAR EFFECTS MAY INCLUDE ATAXIA, SLURRED SPEECH, AREFLEXIA, WEAKNESS, FATIGUE, FASCICULATIONS, TWITCHING, TREMORS POSSIBLY OF THE TONGUE AND EYELIDS, AND EVENTUALLY PARALYSIS OF THE EXTREMITIES AND POSSIBLY OF THE RESPIRATORY MUSCLES. IN SEVERE CASES THERE MAY ALSO BE INVOLUNTARY DEFECATION AND URINATION, CYANOSIS, PSYCHOSIS, HYPERGLYCEMIA, ACUTE PANCREATITIS, CARDIAC IRREGULARITIES, PULMONARY EDEMA, UNCONSCIOUSNESS, CONVULSIONS, AND COMA. DEATH IS PRIMARILY DUE TO RESPIRATORY FAILURE, ALTHOUGH CARDIOVASCULAR EFFECTS INCLUDING CARDIAC ARREST MAY ALSO BE IMPLICATED. LONG TERM SEQUELAE ARE RARE BUT MAY INCLUDE NEUROPSYCHIATRIC DISORDERS AND MYOPATHY WITH MUSCLE TENDERNESS. SOME ORGANOPHOSPHATES MAY CAUSE A DELAYED NEUROPATHY BEGINNING 1-4 WEEKS AFTER AN ACUTE EXPOSURE WHICH MAY OR MAY NOT HAVE CAUSED ACUTE CHOLINERGIC EFFECTS. NUMBNESS, TINGLING, WEAKNESS AND CRAMPING BEGINNING SYMMETRICALLY IN THE LOWER LIMBS MAY PROGRESS TO ATAXIA AND PARALYSIS. IN SEVERE CASES, UPPER LIMB INVOLVEMENT IS POSSIBLE AND FLACCID PARALYSIS MAY PROGRESS TO SPASTIC PARALYSIS WITH EXAGGERATED REFLEXES. IMPROVEMENT MAY OCCUR OVER MONTHS TO YEARS, BUT SOME RESIDUAL IMPAIRMENT USUALLY REMAINS.
CHRONIC EXPOSURE- REPEATED OR PROLONGED EXPOSURE MAY RESULT IN THE EFFECTS OF ACUTE EXPOSURE INCLUDING THE DELAYED NEUROPATHY. OTHER EFFECTS REPORTED IN WORKERS REPEATEDLY EXPOSED INCLUDE IMPAIRED MEMORY AND CONCENTRATION, ACUTE PSYCHOSIS, SEVERE DEPRESSIONS, IRRITABILTY, CONFUSION, APATHY, EMOTIONAL LABILITY, SOCIAL WITHDRAWAL, CONFUSION, HEADACHE, SPEECH DIFFICULTIES, DELAYED REACTION TIMES, SPATIAL DISORIENTATION, NIGHTMARES, SLEEPWALKING, AND DROWSINESS OR INSOMNIA. AN INFLUENZA-LIKE CONDITION WITH HEADACHE, NAUSEA, WEAKNESS, ANOREXIA AND MALAISE HAS ALSO BEEN REPORTED.

FIRST AID- REMOVE FROM EXPOSURE AREA TO FRESH AIR IMMEDIATELY. IF BREATHING HAS STOPPED, GIVE ARTIFICIAL RESPIRATION. MAINTAIN AIRWAY AND

BLOOD PRESSURE AND ADMINISTER OXYGEN IF AVAILABLE. KEEP AFFECTED PERSON WARM AND AT REST. TREAT SYMPTOMATICALLY AND SUPPORTIVELY. ADMINISTRATION OF OXYGEN SHOULD BE PERFORMED BY QUALIFIED PERSONNEL. GET MEDICAL ATTENTION IMMEDIATELY.

SKIN CONTACT: TERBUFOS OXYGEN ANALOG SULFONE: SEE INFORMATION ON ORGANOPHOSPHATES.
ORGANOPHOSPHATES: CHOLINESTERASE INHIBITOR. **ACUTE EXPOSURE-** LOCALIZED SWEATING AND FASCICULATIONS MAY OCCUR AT THE SITE OF CONTACT. IF SUFFICIENT AMOUNTS ARE ABSORBED, OTHER EFFECTS OF CHOLINESTERASE INHIBITION AS DESCRIBED IN ACUTE INHALATION MAY OCCUR. SYMPTOMS MAY BE DELAYED 2-3 HOURS, BUT USUALLY NO MORE THAN 12 HOURS. THE RATE OF ABSORPTION IS INCREASED BY THE PRESENCE OF DERMATITIS OR HIGH AMBIENT TEMPERATURES. DELAYED NEUROPATHY IS ALSO POSSIBLE. **CHRONIC EXPOSURE-** REPEATED OR PROLONGED EXPOSURE MAY CAUSE EFFECTS AS DESCRIBED IN ACUTE EXPOSURE. SOME ORGANOPHOSPHATES MAY CAUSE SENSITIZATION.
FIRST AID- REMOVE CONTAMINATED CLOTHING IMMEDIATELY. WASH CONTAMINATED AREAS WITH SOAP AND WATER FOLLOWED BY ALCOHOL (ARENA, POISONING, 4TH ED.). EMERGENCY PERSONNEL SHOULD WEAR GLOVES AND AVOID CONTAMINATION. TREAT RESPIRATORY DIFFICULTY WITH ARTIFICIAL RESPIRATION. GET MEDICAL ATTENTION IMMEDIATELY.

EYE CONTACT: TERBUFOS OXYGEN ANALOG SULFONE: SEE INFORMATION ON ORGANOPHOSPHATES. ORGANOPHOSPHATES: CHOLINESTERASE INHIBITOR. **ACUTE EXPOSURE-** DIRECT CONTACT MAY CAUSE PAIN, HYPEREMIA, LACRIMATION, TWITCHING OF THE EYELIDS, MIOSIS, AND CILIARY MUSCLE SPASM WITH LOSS OF ACCOMODATION, BLURRED OR DIMMED VISION AND BROWACHE. SOMETIMES MYDRIASIS MAY OCCUR INSTEAD OF MIOSIS. WITH SUFFICIENT EXPOSURE, OTHER SYMPTOMS OF CHOLINESTERASE INHIBITION AS DESCRIBED IN ACUTE INHALATION MAY OCCUR. **CHRONIC EXPOSURE-** REPEATED OR PROLONGED EXPOSURE MAY CAUSE EFFECTS AS DESCRIBED IN ACUTE EXPOSURE. SOME COMPOUNDS HAVE CAUSED TOXIC EFFECTS ON THE CRYSTALLINE LENS, CONJUNCTIVAL THICKENING AND OBSTRUCTION OF THE NASOLACRIMAL CANALS WHEN USED AS MIOTIC EYEDROPS.
FIRST AID- IRRIGATE EYES WITH WATER OR SALINE SOLUTION. IF SYMPTOMS OF POISONING OCCUR, TREAT RESPIRATORY DIFFICULTY WITH ARTIFICIAL RESPIRATION AND OXYGEN. OBSERVE PATIENT FOR AT LEAST 24-36 HOURS (GOSSELIN, CLINICAL TOXICOLOGY OF COMMERCIAL PRODUCTS, 5TH ED.). GET MEDICAL ATTENTION IMMEDIATELY. OXYGEN SHOULD BE ADMINISTERED BY QUALIFIED MEDICAL PERSONNEL.

INGESTION: TERBUFOS OXYGEN ANALOG SULFONE: SEE INFORMATION ON ORGANOPHOSPHATES.
ORGANOPHOSPHATES: CHOLINESTERASE INHIBITOR. **ACUTE EXPOSURE-** WHEN INGESTED, THE FIRST EFFECTS MAY BE NAUSEA, VOMITING, ANOREXIA, ABDOMINAL CRAMPS AND DIARRHEA. GASTROINTESTINAL ABSORPTION MAY CAUSE SYMPTOMS OF CHOLINESTERASE INHIBITION AS DESCRIBED IN ACUTE INHALATION. SYMPTOMS MAY BEGIN WITHIN MINUTES OR BE DELAYED FOR HOURS. DELAYED EFFECTS INCLUDING NEUROPATHY MAY ALSO OCCUR. **CHRONIC EXPOSURE-** REPEATED INGESTION MAY CAUSE EFFECTS AS DESCRIBED IN ACUTE EXPOSURE.
FIRST AID- IF PERSON IS ALERT AND RESPIRATION IS NOT DEPRESSED, GIVE SYRUP OF IPECAC FOLLOWED BY WATER (IF VOMITING OCCURS, KEEP HEAD BELOW HIPS TO PREVENT ASPIRATION). IF CONSCIOUSNESS LEVEL DECLINES OR VOMITING HAS NOT OCCURRED IN 15 MINUTES EMPTY STOMACH BY GASTRIC LAVAGE WITH THE AID OF CUFFED ENDOTRACHEAL TUBE USING ISOTONIC SALINE OR 5% SODIUM BICARBONATE FOLLOW WITH ACTIVATED CHARCOAL. ESTABLISH AND MAINTAIN AIRWAY. TREAT RESPIRATORY DIFFICULTY WITH ARTIFICIAL RESPIRATION AND OXYGEN. DO NOT GIVE MORPHINE, AMINOPHYLLINE, PHENOTHIAZINES, RESERPINE, FUROSEMIDE, OR ETHACRYNIC ACID (MORGAN, RECOGNITION AND MANAGEMENT OF PESTICIDE POISONINGS, 3RD ED.). TREAT SYMPTOMATICALLY AND SUPPORTIVELY. ADMINISTRATION OF OXYGEN AND LAVAGE MUST BE PERFORMED BY QUALIFIED MEDICAL PERSONNEL. GET MEDICAL ATTENTION IMMEDIATELY.
ANTIDOTE: THE FOLLOWING ANTIDOTE(S) HAVE BEEN RECOMMENDED. HOWEVER, THE DECISION AS TO WHETHER THE SEVERITY OF POISONING REQUIRES ADMINISTRATION OF ANY ANTIDOTE AND ACTUAL DOSE REQUIRED SHOULD BE MADE BY QUALIFIED MEDICAL PERSONNEL.
FOR CHOLINESTERASE INHIBITORS: ESTABLISH CLEAR AIRWAY AND TISSUE OXYGENATION BY ASPIRATION OF SECRETIONS, AND IF NECESSARY, BY ASSISTED PULMONARY VENTILATION WITH OXYGEN. IMPROVE TISSUE OXYGENATION AS MUCH AS POSSIBLE BEFORE ADMINISTERING ATROPINE TO MINIMIZE THE RISK OF VENTRICULAR FIBRILLATION. ADMINISTER ATROPINE SULFATE INTRAVENOUSLY, OR INTRAMUSCULARLY IF IV INJECTION IS NOT POSSIBLE. IN MODERATELY SEVERE POISONING ADMINISTER ATROPINE SULFATE, 0.4-2.0 MG REPEATED EVERY 15 MINUTES UNTIL ATROPINIZATION IS ACHIEVED (TACHYCARDIA, FLUSHING, DRY MOUTH, MYDRIASIS). MAINTAIN ATROPINIZATION BY REPEATED DOSES FOR 2-12 HOURS, OR LONGER, DEPENDING ON THE SEVERITY OF POISONING. THE APPEARANCE OF RALES IN THE LUNG BASES, MIOSIS, SALIVATION, NAUSEA, BRADYCARDIA, ARE ALL INDICATIONS OF INADEQUATE ATROPINIZATION. SEVERELY POISONED INDIVIDUALS MAY EXHIBIT REMARKABLE TOLERANCE TO ATROPINE; TWO OR MORE TIMES THE DOSAGES SUGGESTED ABOVE MAY BE NEEDED. PERSONS NOT POISONED OR ONLY SLIGHTLY POISONED, HOWEVER, MAY DEVELOP SIGNS OF ATROPINE TOXICITY FROM SUCH LARGE DOSAGES: FEVER, MUSCLE FIBRILLATIONS, AND DELIRIUM ARE THE MAIN SIGNS OF ATROPINE TOXICITY. IF THESE SIGNS APPEAR WHILE THE PATIENT IS FULLY ATROPINIZED, ATROPINE ADMINISTRATION SHOULD BE DISCONTINUED, AT LEAST TEMPORARILY. OBSERVE TREATED PATIENTS CLOSELY AT LEAST 24 HOURS TO INSURE THAT SYMPTOMS (POSSIBLY PULMONARY EDEMA) DO NOT RECUR AS ATROPINIZATION WEARS OFF. IN VERY SEVERE POISONINGS, METABOLIC DISPOSITION OF TOXICANT MAY REQUIRE SEVERAL HOURS OR DAYS DURING WHICH ATROPINIZATION MUST BE MAINTAINED. MARKEDLY LOWER LEVELS OF URINARY METABOLITES INDICATE THAT ATROPINE DOSAGE CAN BE TAPERED OFF. AS DOSAGE IS REDUCED, CHECK THE LUNG BASES FREQUENTLY FOR RALES. IF RALES ARE HEARD OR OTHER SYMPTOMS RETURN, RE-ESTABLISH ATROPINIZATION PROMPTLY (MORGAN, RECOGNITION AND MANAGEMENT OF PESTICIDE POISONINGS, 3RD ED.). ADMINISTRATION OF ANTIDOTE MUST BE PERFORMED BY QUALIFIED MEDICAL PERSONNEL.
IN CASES OF SEVERE POISONING BY ORGANOPHOSPHATE PESTICIDES IN WHICH RESPIRATORY DEPRESSION, MUSCLE WEAKNESS AND TWITCHINGS ARE SEVERE, GIVE PRALIDOXIME (PROTOPAM-AYERST, 2-PAM), 1.0 GRAM INTRAVENOUSLY AT NO MORE THAN 0.5 GRAM PER MINUTE. DOSAGE OF PRALIDOXIME MAY BE REPEATED IN 1-2 HOURS, THEN AT 10-12 HOUR INTERVALS IF NEEDED. IN VERY SEVERE POISONINGS, DOSAGE RATES MAY BE DOUBLED. TREATMENT WITH PRALIDOXIME WILL BE MOST EFFECTIVE IF GIVEN WITHIN THIRTY-SIX HOURS AFTER POISONING (MORGAN, RECOGNITION AND MANAGEMENT OF PESTICIDE POISONINGS, 3RD ED.). ANTIDOTE SHOULD BE ADMINISTERED BY QUALIFIED MEDICAL PERSONNEL.

REACTIVITY

REACTIVITY: STABLE UNDER NORMAL TEMPERATURES AND PRESSURES.
INCOMPATIBILITIES: TERBUFOS OXYGEN ANALOG SULFONE: OXIDIZERS (STRONG): FIRE AND EXPLOSION HAZARD.
DECOMPOSITION: THERMAL DECOMPOSITION PRODUCTS MAY INCLUDE TOXIC OXIDES OF CARBON, SULFUR, AND PHOSPHORUS.
POLYMERIZATION: HAZARDOUS POLYMERIZATION HAS NOT BEEN REPORTED TO OCCUR UNDER NORMAL TEMPERATURES AND PRESSURES.

STORAGE AND DISPOSAL

OBSERVE ALL FEDERAL, STATE AND LOCAL REGULATIONS WHEN STORING OR DISPOSING OF THIS SUBSTANCE. FOR ASSISTANCE, CONTACT THE DISTRICT DIRECTOR OF THE ENVIRONMENTAL PROTECTION AGENCY.

STORAGE

STORE IN ACCORDANCE WITH 40 CFR 165 RECOMMENDED PROCEDURES FOR THE DISPOSAL AND STORAGE OF PESTICIDES AND PESTICIDE CONTAINERS.
STORE AWAY FROM INCOMPATIBLE SUBSTANCES.

DISPOSAL

DISPOSAL MUST BE IN ACCORDANCE WITH 40 CFR 165 RECOMMENDED PROCEDURES FOR THE DISPOSAL AND STORAGE OF PESTICIDES AND PESTICIDE CONTAINERS.

CONDITIONS TO AVOID

AVOID CONTACT WITH HEAT, SPARKS, FLAMES OR OTHER IGNITION SOURCES. VAPORS MAY BE EXPLOSIVE. MATERIAL IS POISONOUS; AVOID INHALATION OF VAPORS OR CONTACT WITH SKIN. DO NOT ALLOW MATERIAL TO CONTAMINATE WATER SOURCES.

SPILL AND LEAK PROCEDURES

OCCUPATIONAL SPILL: STOP LEAK IF YOU CAN DO IT WITHOUT RISK. FOR SMALL SPILLS, TAKE UP WITH SAND OR OTHER ABSORBENT MATERIAL AND PLACE INTO CLEAN, DRY CONTAINERS FOR LATER DISPOSAL. KEEP UNNECESSARY PEOPLE AWAY. ISOLATE HAZARD AREA AND DENY ENTRY.

PROTECTIVE EQUIPMENT

VENTILATION: PROCESS ENCLOSURE RECOMMENDED.
RESPIRATOR: THE FOLLOWING RESPIRATORS ARE RECOMMENDED BASED ON INFORMATION FOUND IN THE PHYSICAL DATA, TOXICITY AND HEALTH EFFECTS SECTIONS. THEY ARE RANKED IN ORDER FROM MINIMUM TO MAXIMUM RESPIRATORY PROTECTION. THE SPECIFIC RESPIRATOR SELECTED MUST BE BASED ON CONTAMINATION LEVELS FOUND IN THE WORK PLACE, MUST NOT EXCEED THE WORKING LIMITS OF THE RESPIRATOR AND BE JOINTLY APPROVED BY THE NATIONAL INSTITUTE FOR OCCUPATIONAL SAFETY AND HEALTH AND THE MINE

SAFETY AND HEALTH ADMINISTRATION (NIOSH-MSHA).
TYPE 'C' SUPPLIED-AIR RESPIRATOR WITH A FULL FACEPIECE OPERATED IN PRESSURE-DEMAND OR OTHER POSITIVE PRESSURE MODE OR WITH A FULL FACEPIECE, HELMET OR HOOD OPERATED IN CONTINOUS-FLOW MODE.
SELF-CONTAINED BREATHING APPARATUS WITH A FULL FACEPIECE OPERATED IN PRESSURE-DEMAND OR OTHER POSITIVE PRESSURE MODE.
FOR FIREFIGHTING AND OTHER IMMEDIATELY DANGEROUS TO LIFE OR HEALTH CONDITIONS:
SELF-CONTAINED BREATHING APPARATUS WITH FULL FACEPIECE OPERATED IN PRESSURE-DEMAND OR OTHER POSITIVE PRESSURE MODE.
SUPPLIED-AIR RESPIRATOR WITH FULL FACEPIECE AND OPERATED IN PRESSURE-DEMAND OR OTHER POSITIVE PRESSURE MODE IN COMBINATION WITH AN AUXILIARY SELF-CONTAINED BREATHING APPARATUS OPERATED IN PRESSURE-DEMAND OR OTHER POSITIVE PRESSURE MODE.

CLOTHING: EMPLOYEE MUST WEAR APPROPRIATE PROTECTIVE (IMPERVIOUS) CLOTHING AND EQUIPMENT TO PREVENT ANY POSSIBILITY OF SKIN CONTACT WITH THIS SUBSTANCE.

GLOVES: EMPLOYEE MUST WEAR APPROPRIATE PROTECTIVE GLOVES TO PREVENT CONTACT WITH THIS SUBSTANCE.

EYE PROTECTION: EMPLOYEE MUST WEAR SPLASH-PROOF OR DUST-RESISTANT SAFETY GOGGLES AND A FACESHIELD TO PREVENT CONTACT WITH THIS SUBSTANCE.
EMERGENCY WASH FACILITIES: WHERE THERE IS ANY POSSIBILITY THAT AN EMPLOYEE'S EYES AND/OR SKIN MAY BE EXPOSED TO THIS SUBSTANCE, THE EMPLOYER SHOULD PROVIDE AN EYE WASH FOUNTAIN AND QUICK DRENCH SHOWER WITHIN THE IMMEDIATE WORK AREA FOR EMERGENCY USE.

AUTHORIZED BY- OCCUPATIONAL HEALTH SERVICES, INC.
CREATION DATE: 10/27/89 ***REVISION DATE:*** 05/01/90

MATERIAL SAFETY DATA SHEET

OCCUPATIONAL HEALTH SERVICES, INC.
AGRICULTURE AND PESTICIDE DIVISION
450 SEVENTH AVENUE, SUITE 2407
NEW YORK, NEW YORK 10123
1-800-445-MSDS OR (212) 967-1100

EMERGENCY CONTACT:
JOHN S. BRANSFORD, JR. (615) 292-1180

SUBSTANCE IDENTIFICATION

CAS-NUMBER 886-50-0

SUBSTANCE: **TERBUTRYN**

TRADE NAMES/SYNONYMS: 1,3,5-TRIAZINE-2,4-DIAMINE, N-(1,1-DIMETHYLETHYL)-N'-ETHYL-6 -(METHYLTHIO)-; N-(1,1-DIMETHYLETHYL)-N'-ETHYL-6-(METHYLTHIO)-1,3,5-TRIAZINE -2,4-DIAMINE; S-TRIAZINE, 2-(TERT-BUTYLAMINO)-4-(ETHYLAMINO)-6-(METHYLTHIO)-; 2-(TERT-BUTYLAMINO)-4-(ETHYLAMINO)-6-(METHYLTHIO)-S-TRIAZINE; 2-TERT-BUTYLAMINO-4-ETHYLAMINO-6-METHYLTHIO-1,3,5-TRIAZINE; A 1866; CLAROSAN; GS 14260; IGRAN; PREBAN; TERBUTRYNE; TERBUTREX; C10H19N5S; PST22538

CHEMICAL FAMILY: S-TRIAZINE

MOLECULAR FORMULA: C10-H19-N5-S

MOLECULAR WEIGHT: 241.40

CERCLA RATINGS (SCALE 0-3): HEALTH=2 FIRE=1 REACTIVITY=0 PERSISTENCE=2

NFPA RATINGS (SCALE 0-4): HEALTH=2 FIRE=1 REACTIVITY=0

COMPONENTS AND CONTAMINANTS

COMPONENT: TERBUTRYN ***PERCENT:*** 100.0
CAS# 886-50-0

OTHER CONTAMINANTS: NONE

EXPOSURE LIMITS: NO OCCUPATIONAL EXPOSURE LIMITS ESTABLISHED BY OSHA, ACGIH, OR NIOSH.

PHYSICAL DATA

DESCRIPTION: WHITE CRYSTALLINE SOLID. ***MELTING POINT:*** 219-221 F (104-105 C)

SPECIFIC GRAVITY: 1.115 ***VAPOR PRESSURE:*** NEGLIGIBLE

SOLUBILITY IN WATER: 25 PPM

SOLVENT SOLUBILITY: SOLUBLE IN ACETONE, DICHLOROMETHANE, METHANOL, XYLENE, ISOPROPANOL, OCTAN-1-OL, AND MOST ORGANIC SOLVENTS; SLIGHTLY SOLUBLE IN TOLUENE, HEXANE

FIRE AND EXPLOSION DATA

FIRE AND EXPLOSION HAZARD: SLIGHT FIRE HAZARD WHEN EXPOSED TO HEAT OR FLAME.
SLIGHT EXPLOSION HAZARD WHEN EXPOSED TO HEAT OR FLAME.

FIREFIGHTING MEDIA: DRY CHEMICAL, CARBON DIOXIDE, HALON, WATER SPRAY OR STANDARD FOAM (1987 EMERGENCY RESPONSE GUIDEBOOK, DOT P 5800.4).
FOR LARGER FIRES, USE WATER SPRAY, FOG OR STANDARD FOAM (1987 EMERGENCY RESPONSE GUIDEBOOK, DOT P 5800.4).

FIREFIGHTING: MOVE CONTAINERS FROM FIRE AREA IF POSSIBLE (1987 EMERGENCY RESPONSE GUIDEBOOK, DOT P 5800.4, GUIDE PAGE 53).
EXTINGUISH USING AGENTS SUITABLE FOR SURROUNDING FIRE. USE FLOODING QUANTITIES OF WATER AS A FOG. KEEP MATERIAL OUT OF SEWERS AND WATER SOURCES. DO NOT TOUCH SPILLED MATERIAL. AVOID BREATHING HAZARDOUS FUMES; KEEP UPWIND.

TOXICITY

TERBUTRYN: IRRITATION DATA: 380 MG SKIN-RABBIT MILD; 76 MG EYE-RABBIT MODERATE. TOXICITY DATA: 2045 MG/KG ORAL-RAT LD50; 3884 MG/KG ORAL-MOUSE LD50; 699 MG/KG INTRAPERITONEAL-RAT LD50; 554 MG/KG INTRAPERITONEAL-MOUSE LD50; 2900 MG/KG UNREPORTED-MAMMAL LD50. CARCINOGEN STATUS: NONE. ACUTE TOXICITY LEVEL: MODERATELY TOXIC BY INGESTION. TARGET EFFECTS: NO DATA AVAILABLE.

HEALTH EFFECTS AND FIRST AID

INHALATION: TERBUTRYN: **ACUTE EXPOSURE**- A LETHAL CONCENTRATION IN RATS IS GREATER THAN 8000 MG/M3/4 HOURS. SOME TRIAZINES ARE MILDLY IRRITATING TO THE UPPER RESPIRATORY TRACT. **CHRONIC EXPOSURE**- NO DATA AVAILABLE.

FIRST AID- REMOVE FROM EXPOSURE AREA TO FRESH AIR IMMEDIATELY. IF BREATHING HAS STOPPED, PERFORM ARTIFICIAL RESPIRATION. KEEP PERSON WARM AND AT REST. TREAT SYMPTOMATICALLY AND SUPPORTIVELY. GET MEDICAL ATTENTION IMMEDIATELY.

SKIN CONTACT: TERBUTRYN: **ACUTE EXPOSURE**- 380 MG APPLIED TO RABBIT-SKIN WAS MILDLY IRRITATING. A LETHAL CONCENTRATION IN RABBITS BY DERMAL ABSORPTION WAS GREATER THAN 10,200 PPM **CHRONIC EXPOSURE**- NO DATA AVAILABLE. **FIRST AID**- REMOVE CONTAMINATED CLOTHING AND SHOES IMMEDIATELY. WASH AFFECTED AREA WITH SOAP OR MILD DETERGENT AND LARGE AMOUNTS OF WATER UNTIL NO EVIDENCE OF CHEMICAL REMAINS (APPROXIMATELY 15-20 MINUTES). GET MEDICAL ATTENTION IMMEDIATELY.

EYE CONTACT: TERBUTRYN: **ACUTE EXPOSURE**- 76 MG APPLIED TO RABBIT EYES WAS MODERATELY IRRITATING. **CHRONIC EXPOSURE**- NO DATA AVAILABLE.

FIRST AID- WASH EYES IMMEDIATELY WITH LARGE AMOUNTS OF WATER OR NORMAL SALINE, OCCASIONALLY LIFTING UPPER AND LOWER LIDS, UNTIL NO EVIDENCE OF CHEMICAL REMAINS (APPROXIMATELY 15-20 MINUTES). GET MEDICAL ATTENTION IMMEDIATELY.

INGESTION: TERBUTRYN: **ACUTE EXPOSURE**- A LETHAL DOSE IN RATS WAS 2045 MG/KG; NO SYMPTOMS WERE REPORTED. **CHRONIC EXPOSURE**- NO ADVERSE EFFECTS WERE NOTED IN A 90-DAY STUDY OF RATS FED 50 MG/KG/DAY. GROWTH RETARDATION, SLIGHT LEUKOPENIA AND HEPATOTOXICITY WERE OBSERVED IN RATS FED HIGH CHRONIC DOSES OF TERBUTRYN OVER A SIX-MONTH PERIOD.

FIRST AID- REMOVE BY GASTRIC LAVAGE AND CATHARSIS. MAINTAIN BLOOD PRESSURE AND AIRWAY. GIVE OXYGEN IF RESPIRATION IS DEPRESSED. DO NOT PERFORM GASTRIC LAVAGE IF VICTIM IS UNCONSCIOUS. GET MEDICAL ATTENTION IMMEDIATELY (DREISBACH, HANDBOOK OF POISONING, 12TH ED.).
ADMINISTRATION OF LAVAGE OR OXYGEN SHOULD BE PERFORMED BY QUALIFIED MEDICAL PERSONNEL.

ANTIDOTE: NO SPECIFIC ANTIDOTE. TREAT SYMPTOMATICALLY AND SUPPORTIVELY.

REACTIVITY

REACTIVITY: STABLE UNDER NORMAL TEMPERATURES AND PRESSURES.

INCOMPATIBILITIES: TERBUTRYN: NO DATA AVAILABLE.

DECOMPOSITION: THERMAL DECOMPOSITION PRODUCTS MAY INCLUDE TOXIC OXIDES OF CARBON, NITROGEN, AND SULFUR.

POLYMERIZATION: HAZARDOUS POLYMERIZATION HAS NOT BEEN REPORTED TO OCCUR UNDER NORMAL TEMPERATURES AND PRESSURES.

STORAGE AND DISPOSAL

OBSERVE ALL FEDERAL, STATE AND LOCAL REGULATIONS WHEN STORING OR DISPOSING OF THIS SUBSTANCE. FOR ASSISTANCE, CONTACT THE DISTRICT DIRECTOR OF THE ENVIRONMENTAL PROTECTION AGENCY.

STORAGE

STORE IN ACCORDANCE WITH 40 CFR 165 RECOMMENDED PROCEDURES FOR THE DISPOSAL AND STORAGE OF PESTICIDES AND PESTICIDE CONTAINERS.

DISPOSAL

DISPOSAL MUST BE IN ACCORDANCE WITH 40 CFR 165 RECOMMENDED PROCEDURES FOR THE DISPOSAL AND STORAGE OF PESTICIDES AND PESTICIDE CONTAINERS.

CONDITIONS TO AVOID

MAY BURN BUT DOES NOT IGNITE READILY.

SPILL AND LEAK PROCEDURES

OCCUPATIONAL SPILL: DO NOT TOUCH SPILLED MATERIAL. STOP LEAK IF YOU CAN DO IT WITHOUT RISK. FOR SMALL SPILLS, TAKE UP WITH SAND OR OTHER ABSORBENT MATERIAL AND PLACE INTO CONTAINERS FOR LATER DISPOSAL. FOR SMALL DRY SPILLS, WITH A CLEAN SHOVEL PLACE MATERIAL INTO CLEAN, DRY CONTAINER AND COVER. MOVE CONTAINERS FROM SPILL AREA. FOR LARGER SPILLS, DIKE FAR AHEAD OF SPILL FOR LATER DISPOSAL. KEEP UNNECESSARY PEOPLE AWAY. ISOLATE HAZARD AREA AND DENY ENTRY.

PROTECTIVE EQUIPMENT

VENTILATION: PROVIDE LOCAL EXHAUST OR GENERAL DILUTION VENTILATION SYSTEM.

RESPIRATOR: THE FOLLOWING RESPIRATORS ARE RECOMMENDED BASED ON INFORMATION FOUND IN THE PHYSICAL DATA, TOXICITY AND HEALTH EFFECTS SECTIONS. THEY ARE RANKED IN ORDER FROM MINIMUM TO MAXIMUM RESPIRATORY PROTECTION. THE SPECIFIC RESPIRATOR SELECTED MUST BE BASED ON CONTAMINATION LEVELS FOUND IN THE WORK PLACE, MUST NOT EXCEED THE WORKING LIMITS OF THE RESPIRATOR AND BE JOINTLY APPROVED BY THE NATIONAL INSTITUTE FOR OCCUPATIONAL SAFETY AND HEALTH AND THE MINE SAFETY AND HEALTH ADMINISTRATION (NIOSH-MSHA).

CHEMICAL CARTRIDGE RESPIRATOR WITH AN ORGANIC VAPOR CARTRIDGE(S) IN COMBINATION WITH A DUST AND MIST FILTER.

GAS MASK WITH ORGANIC VAPOR CANISTER (CHIN-STYLE OR FRONT- OR BACK-MOUNTED CANISTER) WITH A DUST AND MIST FILTER.

GAS MASK WITH ORGANIC VAPOR CANISTER (CHIN-STYLE OR FRONT- OR BACK-MOUNTED CANISTER) WITH A PARTICULATE FILTER.

POWERED AIR-PURIFYING RESPIRATOR WITH A HIGH-EFFICIENCY FILTER.

TYPE 'C' SUPPLIED-AIR RESPIRATOR WITH A FULL FACEPIECE OPERATED IN A PRESSURE-DEMAND OR OTHER POSITIVE PRESSURE MODE.

SELF-CONTAINED BREATHING APPARATUS WITH A FULL FACEPIECE OPERATED IN PRESSURE-DEMAND OR OTHER POSITIVE PRESSURE MODE.

FOR FIREFIGHTING AND OTHER IMMEDIATELY DANGEROUS TO LIFE OR HEALTH CONDITIONS:

SELF-CONTAINED BREATHING APPARATUS WITH FULL FACEPIECE OPERATED IN PRESSURE-DEMAND OR OTHER POSITIVE PRESSURE MODE.

SUPPLIED-AIR RESPIRATOR WITH FULL FACEPIECE AND OPERATED IN PRESSURE-DEMAND OR OTHER POSITIVE PRESSURE MODE IN COMBINATION WITH AN AUXILIARY SELF-CONTAINED BREATHING APPARATUS OPERATED IN PRESSURE-DEMAND OR OTHER POSITIVE PRESSURE MODE.

CLOTHING: EMPLOYEE MUST WEAR APPROPRIATE PROTECTIVE (IMPERVIOUS) CLOTHING AND EQUIPMENT TO PREVENT REPEATED OR PROLONGED SKIN CONTACT WITH THIS SUBSTANCE.

GLOVES: EMPLOYEE MUST WEAR APPROPRIATE PROTECTIVE GLOVES TO PREVENT CONTACT WITH THIS SUBSTANCE.

EYE PROTECTION: EMPLOYEE MUST WEAR SPLASH-PROOF OR DUST-RESISTANT SAFETY GOGGLES TO PREVENT EYE CONTACT WITH THIS SUBSTANCE.

EMERGENCY EYE WASH: WHERE THERE IS ANY POSSIBILITY THAT AN EMPLOYEE'S EYES MAY BE EXPOSED TO THIS SUBSTANCE, THE EMPLOYER SHOULD PROVIDE AN EYE WASH FOUNTAIN WITHIN THE IMMEDIATE WORK AREA FOR EMERGENCY USE.

AUTHORIZED BY- OCCUPATIONAL HEALTH SERVICES, INC.

CREATION DATE: 10/05/89 ***REVISION DATE:*** 05/17/90

MATERIAL SAFETY DATA SHEET

OCCUPATIONAL HEALTH SERVICES, INC.
AGRICULTURE AND PESTICIDE DIVISION
450 SEVENTH AVENUE, SUITE 2407
NEW YORK, NEW YORK 10123

EMERGENCY CONTACT:
JOHN S. BRANSFORD, JR. (615) 292-1180

1-800-445-MSDS OR (212) 967-1100

SUBSTANCE IDENTIFICATION

CAS-NUMBER 13071-79-9

SUBSTANCE: TERBUFOS

TRADE NAMES/SYNONYMS: PHOSPHORODITHIOIC ACID, S-(((1,1-DIMETHYLETHYL)THIO)METHYL) O,O-DIETHYL ESTER; S-(((1,1-DIMETHYLETHYL)THIO)METHYL) O,O-DIETHYL PHOSOHORODITHIOATER; PHOSPHORODITHIOIC ACID, S-((TERT-BUTYLTHIO)METHYL) O,O-DIETHYL ESTER; S-(TERT-BUTYLTHIO)METHYL O,O-DIETHYL PHOSPHORODITHIOATE; COUNTER; AC 92100; C9H21O2PS3; PST22545

CHEMICAL FAMILY: ORGANOPHOSPHATE

THIO

MOLECULAR FORMULA: (C-H3)3-C-S-C-H2-S-P-(S)-(O-C-H2-C-H3)2

MOLECULAR WEIGHT: 288.41

CERCLA RATINGS (SCALE 0-3): HEALTH=3 FIRE=2 REACTIVITY=0 PERSISTENCE=0

NFPA RATINGS (SCALE 0-4): HEALTH=4 FIRE=2 REACTIVITY=0

COMPONENTS AND CONTAMINANTS

COMPONENT: TERBUFOS ***PERCENT:*** 100.0

CAS# 13071-79-9

OTHER CONTAMINANTS: NONE

EXPOSURE LIMITS: NO OCCUPATIONAL EXPOSURE LIMITS ESTABLISHED BY OSHA, ACGIH, OR NIOSH.

TERBUFOS: 100 POUNDS SARA SECTION 302 THRESHOLD PLANNING QUANTITY 1 POUND SARA SECTION 304 REPORTABLE QUANTITY

PHYSICAL DATA

DESCRIPTION: CLEAR, COLORLESS TO PALE YELLOW LIQUID WITH A MERCAPTAN-LIKE ODOR.

BOILING POINT: 156 F (69 C) 0.01 MMHG ***MELTING POINT:*** -21 F (-29 C)

SPECIFIC GRAVITY: 1.105 @ 24 C ***VAPOR PRESSURE:*** 0.0003 MMHG

SOLUBILITY IN WATER: 10-15 PPM

SOLVENT SOLUBILITY: SOLUBLE IN ACETONE, ALCOHOLS, AROMATIC AND CHLORINATED HYDROCARBONS AND DIMETHYLSULFOXIDE.

FIRE AND EXPLOSION DATA

FIRE AND EXPLOSION HAZARD: MODERATE FIRE HAZARD WHEN EXPOSED TO HEAT OR FLAME.

VAPOR-AIR MIXTURES ARE EXPLOSIVE ABOVE FLASH POINT.

FLASH POINT: 190 F (88 C) (OC) ***FLAMMABILITY CLASS(OSHA):*** IIIA

FIREFIGHTING MEDIA: DRY CHEMICAL, CARBON DIOXIDE, HALON, WATER SPRAY OR STANDARD FOAM (1987 EMERGENCY RESPONSE GUIDEBOOK, DOT P 5800.4).

FOR LARGER FIRES, USE WATER SPRAY, FOG OR STANDARD FOAM (1987 EMERGENCY RESPONSE GUIDEBOOK, DOT P 5800.4).

FIREFIGHTING: MOVE CONTAINERS FROM FIRE AREA IF POSSIBLE. COOL CONTAINERS EXPOSED TO FLAMES WITH WATER FROM SIDE UNTIL WELL AFTER FIRE IS OUT. FIGHT FIRE FROM MAXIMUM DISTANCE. STAY AWAY FROM STORAGE TANK ENDS. DIKE FIRE CONTROL WATER FOR LATER DISPOSAL. DO NOT SCATTER MATERIAL. (1987 EMERGENCY RESPONSE GUIDEBOOK, DOT P 5800.4, GUIDE PAGE 57).

EXTINGUISH ONLY IF FLOW CAN BE STOPPED. USE FLOODING AMOUNTS OF WATER AS A FOG; SOLID STREAMS MAY BE INEFFECTIVE. COOL CONTAINERS WITH FLOODING AMOUNTS OF WATER FROM AS FAR A DISTANCE AS POSSIBLE. AVOID BREATHING POISONOUS VAPORS, KEEP UPWIND.

TRANSPORTATION DATA

DEPARTMENT OF TRANSPORTATION HAZARD CLASSIFICATION 49 CFR 172.101: POISON B

DEPARTMENT OF TRANSPORTATION LABELING REQUIREMENTS 49 CFR 172.101 AND SUBPART E: POISON

DEPARTMENT OF TRANSPORTATION PACKAGING REQUIREMENTS: 49 CFR 173.365 EXCEPTIONS: 49 CFR 173.364

TOXICITY

TERBUFOS: TOXICITY DATA: 1100 UG/KG/24 HOURS SKIN-RABBIT LD50; 7400 UG/KG SKIN-RAT LD50; 1600 UG/KG ORAL-RAT LD50; 3500 UG/KG ORAL-MOUSE LD50. CARCINOGEN STATUS: NONE. ACUTE TOXICITY LEVEL: HIGHLY TOXIC BY INGESTION AND DERMAL ABSORPTION. TARGET EFFECTS: CHOLINESTERASE INHIBITOR. POISONING MAY AFFECT THE NERVOUS SYSTEM.* AT INCREASED RISK FROM EXPOSURE: PERSONS WITH RESPIRATORY AILMENTS, RECENT EXPOSURE TO CHOLINESTERASE INHIBITORS OR IMPAIRED CHOLINESTERASE PRODUCTION, OR LIVER MALFUNCTION.* ADDITIONAL DATA: MAY CROSS THE PLACENTA. HIGH ENVIRONMENTAL TEMPERATURES OR EXPOSURE OF THE CHEMICAL TO VISIBLE OR ULTRAVIOLET LIGHT MAY ENHANCE THE TOXICITY. INTERACTIONS WITH

MEDICATIONS MAY OCCUR.*
* MAY BE BASED ON GENERAL INFORMATION ON ORGANOPHOSPHATES.

HEALTH EFFECTS AND FIRST AID

INHALATION: TERBUFOS: SEE INFORMATION ON ORGANOPHOSPHATES.
ORGANOPHOSPHATES: CHOLINESTERASE INHIBITOR. **ACUTE EXPOSURE**- WHEN INHALED, THE FIRST EFFECTS OF CHOLINESTERASE INHIBITORS ARE USUALLY RESPIRATORY AND MAY INCLUDE NASAL HYPEREMIA AND WATERY DISCHARGE, COUGH, CHEST DISCOMFORT, DYSPNEA, AND WHEEZING DUE TO INCREASED BRONCHIAL SECRETIONS AND BRONCHOCONSTRICTION. IF SUFFICIENT AMOUNTS ARE ABSORBED, OTHER SYSTEMIC EFFECTS MAY BEGIN WITHIN A FEW MINUTES OR BE DELAYED FOR UP TO 12 HOURS. SYMPTOMS MAY INCLUDE PALLOR, NAUSEA, VOMITING, DIARRHEA, ABDOMINAL CRAMPS, HEADACHE, DIZZINESS, OCULAR PAIN, BLURRED VISION, MIOSIS OR IN SOME CASES, ESPECIALLY INITIALLY, MYDRIASIS, LACRIMATION, SALIVATION, SWEATING, AND CONFUSION. OTHER REPORTED CENTRAL NERVOUS SYSTEM OR NEUROMUSCULAR EFFECTS MAY INCLUDE ATAXIA, SLURRED SPEECH, AREFLEXIA, WEAKNESS, FATIGUE, FASCICULATIONS, TWITCHING, TREMORS POSSIBLY OF THE TONGUE AND EYELIDS, AND EVENTUALLY PARALYSIS OF THE EXTREMITIES AND POSSIBLY OF THE RESPIRATORY MUSCLES. IN SEVERE CASES THERE MAY ALSO BE INVOLUNTARY DEFECATION AND URINATION, CYANOSIS, PSYCHOSIS, HYPERGLYCEMIA, ACUTE PANCREATITIS, CARDIAC IRREGULARITIES, PULMONARY EDEMA, UNCONSCIOUSNESS, CONVULSIONS, AND COMA. DEATH IS PRIMARILY DUE TO RESPIRATORY FAILURE, ALTHOUGH CARDIOVASCULAR EFFECTS INCLUDING CARDIAC ARREST MAY ALSO BE IMPLICATED. LONG TERM SEQUELAE ARE RARE BUT MAY INCLUDE NEUROPSYCHIATRIC DISORDERS AND MYOPATHY WITH MUSCLE TENDERNESS. SOME ORGANOPHOSPHATES MAY CAUSE A DELAYED NEUROPATHY BEGINNING 1-4 WEEKS AFTER AN ACUTE EXPOSURE WHICH MAY OR MAY NOT HAVE CAUSED ACUTE CHOLINERGIC EFFECTS. NUMBNESS, TINGLING, WEAKNESS AND CRAMPING BEGINNING SYMMETRICALLY IN THE LOWER LIMBS MAY PROGRESS TO ATAXIA AND PARALYSIS. IN SEVERE CASES, UPPER LIMB INVOLVEMENT IS POSSIBLE AND FLACCID PARALYSIS MAY PROGRESS TO SPASTIC PARALYSIS WITH EXAGGERATED REFLEXES. IMPROVEMENT MAY OCCUR OVER MONTHS TO YEARS, BUT SOME RESIDUAL IMPAIRMENT USUALLY REMAINS.
CHRONIC EXPOSURE- REPEATED OR PROLONGED EXPOSURE MAY RESULT IN THE EFFECTS OF ACUTE EXPOSURE INCLUDING THE DELAYED NEUROPATHY. OTHER EFFECTS REPORTED IN WORKERS REPEATEDLY EXPOSED INCLUDE IMPAIRED MEMORY AND CONCENTRATION, ACUTE PSYCHOSIS, SEVERE DEPRESSIONS, IRRITABILTY, CONFUSION, APATHY, EMOTIONAL LABILITY, SOCIAL WITHDRAWAL, CONFUSION, HEADACHE, SPEECH DIFFICULTIES, DELAYED REACTION TIMES, SPATIAL DISORIENTATION, NIGHTMARES, SLEEPWALKING, AND DROWSINESS OR INSOMNIA. AN INFLUENZA-LIKE CONDITION WITH HEADACHE, NAUSEA, WEAKNESS, ANOREXIA AND MALAISE HAS ALSO BEEN REPORTED.
FIRST AID- REMOVE FROM EXPOSURE AREA TO FRESH AIR IMMEDIATELY. IF BREATHING HAS STOPPED, GIVE ARTIFICIAL RESPIRATION. MAINTAIN AIRWAY AND BLOOD PRESSURE AND ADMINISTER OXYGEN IF AVAILABLE. KEEP AFFECTED PERSON WARM AND AT REST. TREAT SYMPTOMATICALLY AND SUPPORTIVELY. ADMINISTRATION OF OXYGEN SHOULD BE PERFORMED BY QUALIFIED PERSONNEL. GET MEDICAL ATTENTION IMMEDIATELY.

SKIN CONTACT: TERBUFOS: HIGHLY TOXIC. SEE INFORMATION ON ORGANOPHOSPHATES.
ORGANOPHOSPHATES: CHOLINESTERASE INHIBITOR. **ACUTE EXPOSURE**- LOCALIZED SWEATING AND FASCICULATIONS MAY OCCUR AT THE SITE OF CONTACT. IF SUFFICIENT AMOUNTS ARE ABSORBED, OTHER EFFECTS OF CHOLINESTERASE INHIBITION AS DESCRIBED IN ACUTE INHALATION MAY OCCUR. SYMPTOMS MAY BE DELAYED 2-3 HOURS, BUT USUALLY NO MORE THAN 12 HOURS. THE RATE OF ABSORPTION IS INCREASED BY THE PRESENCE OF DERMATITIS OR HIGH AMBIENT TEMPERATURES. DELAYED NEUROPATHY IS ALSO POSSIBLE. **CHRONIC EXPOSURE**- REPEATED OR PROLONGED EXPOSURE MAY CAUSE EFFECTS AS DESCRIBED IN ACUTE EXPOSURE. SOME ORGANOPHOSPHATES MAY CAUSE SENSITIZATION.
FIRST AID- REMOVE CONTAMINATED CLOTHING IMMEDIATELY. WASH CONTAMINATED AREAS WITH SOAP AND WATER FOLLOWED BY ALCOHOL (ARENA, POISONING, 4TH ED.). EMERGENCY PERSONNEL SHOULD WEAR GLOVES AND AVOID CONTAMINATION. TREAT RESPIRATORY DIFFICULTY WITH ARTIFICIAL RESPIRATION. GET MEDICAL ATTENTION IMMEDIATELY.

EYE CONTACT: TERBUFOS: SEE INFORMATION ON ORGANOPHOSPHATES.
ORGANOPHOSPHATES: CHOLINESTERASE INHIBITOR. **ACUTE EXPOSURE**- DIRECT CONTACT MAY CAUSE PAIN, HYPEREMIA, LACRIMATION, TWITCHING OF THE EYELIDS, MIOSIS, AND CILIARY MUSCLE SPASM WITH LOSS OF ACCOMODATION, BLURRED OR DIMMED VISION AND BROWACHE. SOMETIMES MYDRIASIS MAY OCCUR INSTEAD OF MIOSIS. WITH SUFFICIENT EXPOSURE, OTHER SYMPTOMS OF CHOLINESTERASE INHIBITION AS DESCRIBED IN ACUTE INHALATION MAY OCCUR.
CHRONIC EXPOSURE- REPEATED OR PROLONGED EXPOSURE MAY CAUSE EFFECTS AS DESCRIBED IN ACUTE EXPOSURE. SOME COMPOUNDS HAVE CAUSED TOXIC EFFECTS ON THE CRYSTALLINE LENS, CONJUNCTIVAL THICKENING AND OBSTRUCTION OF THE NASOLACRIMAL CANALS WHEN USED AS MIOTIC EYEDROPS.
FIRST AID- IRRIGATE EYES WITH WATER OR SALINE SOLUTION. IF SYMPTOMS OF POISONING OCCUR, TREAT RESPIRATORY DIFFICULTY WITH ARTIFICIAL RESPIRATION AND OXYGEN. OBSERVE PATIENT FOR AT LEAST 24-36 HOURS (GOSSELIN, CLINICAL TOXICOLOGY OF COMMERCIAL PRODUCTS, 5TH ED.). GET MEDICAL ATTENTION IMMEDIATELY. OXYGEN SHOULD BE ADMINISTERED BY QUALIFIED MEDICAL PERSONNEL.

INGESTION: TERBUFOS: HIGHLY TOXIC. SEE INFORMATION ON ORGANOPHOSPHATES.
ORGANOPHOSPHATES: CHOLINESTERASE INHIBITOR. **ACUTE EXPOSURE**- WHEN INGESTED, THE FIRST EFFECTS MAY BE NAUSEA, VOMITING, ANOREXIA, ABDOMINAL CRAMPS AND DIARRHEA. GASTROINTESTINAL ABSORPTION MAY CAUSE SYMPTOMS OF CHOLINESTERASE INHIBITION AS DESCRIBED IN ACUTE INHALATION. SYMPTOMS MAY BEGIN WITHIN MINUTES OR BE DELAYED FOR HOURS. DELAYED EFFECTS INCLUDING NEUROPATHY MAY ALSO OCCUR.
CHRONIC EXPOSURE- REPEATED INGESTION MAY CAUSE EFFECTS AS DESCRIBED IN ACUTE EXPOSURE.
FIRST AID- IF PERSON IS ALERT AND RESPIRATION IS NOT DEPRESSED, GIVE SYRUP OF IPECAC FOLLOWED BY WATER (IF VOMITING OCCURS, KEEP HEAD BELOW HIPS TO PREVENT ASPIRATION). IF CONSCIOUSNESS LEVEL DECLINES OR VOMITING HAS NOT OCCURRED IN 15 MINUTES EMPTY STOMACH BY GASTRIC LAVAGE WITH THE AID OF CUFFED ENDOTRACHEAL TUBE USING ISOTONIC SALINE OR 5% SODIUM BICARBONATE FOLLOW WITH ACTIVATED CHARCOAL. ESTABLISH AND MAINTAIN AIRWAY. TREAT RESPIRATORY DIFFICULTY WITH ARTIFICIAL RESPIRATION AND OXYGEN. DO NOT GIVE MORPHINE, AMINOPHYLLINE, PHENOTHIAZINES, RESERPINE, FUROSEMIDE, OR ETHACRYNIC ACID (MORGAN, RECOGNITION AND MANAGEMENT OF PESTICIDE POISONINGS, 3RD ED.). TREAT SYMPTOMATICALLY AND SUPPORTIVELY. ADMINISTRATION OF OXYGEN AND LAVAGE MUST BE PERFORMED BY QUALIFIED MEDICAL PERSONNEL. GET MEDICAL ATTENTION IMMEDIATELY.

ANTIDOTE: THE FOLLOWING ANTIDOTE(S) HAVE BEEN RECOMMENDED. HOWEVER, THE DECISION AS TO WHETHER THE SEVERITY OF POISONING REQUIRES ADMINISTRATION OF ANY ANTIDOTE AND ACTUAL DOSE REQUIRED SHOULD BE MADE BY QUALIFIED MEDICAL PERSONNEL.
FOR CHOLINESTERASE INHIBITORS: ESTABLISH CLEAR AIRWAY AND TISSUE OXYGENATION BY ASPIRATION OF SECRETIONS, AND IF NECESSARY, BY ASSISTED PULMONARY VENTILATION WITH OXYGEN. IMPROVE TISSUE OXYGENATION AS MUCH AS POSSIBLE BEFORE ADMINISTERING ATROPINE TO MINIMIZE THE RISK OF VENTRICULAR FIBRILLATION. ADMINISTER ATROPINE SULFATE INTRAVENOUSLY, OR INTRAMUSCULARLY IF IV INJECTION IS NOT POSSIBLE. IN MODERATELY SEVERE POISONING ADMINISTER ATROPINE SULFATE, 0.4-2.0 MG REPEATED EVERY 15 MINUTES UNTIL ATROPINIZATION IS ACHIEVED (TACHYCARDIA, FLUSHING, DRY MOUTH, MYDRIASIS). MAINTAIN ATROPINIZATION BY REPEATED DOSES FOR 2-12 HOURS, OR LONGER, DEPENDING ON THE SEVERITY OF POISONING. THE APPEARANCE OF RALES IN THE LUNG BASES, MIOSIS, SALIVATION, NAUSEA, BRADYCARDIA, ARE ALL INDICATIONS OF INADEQUATE ATROPINIZATION. SEVERELY POISONED INDIVIDUALS MAY EXHIBIT REMARKABLE TOLERANCE TO ATROPINE; TWO OR MORE TIMES THE DOSAGES SUGGESTED ABOVE MAY BE NEEDED. PERSONS NOT POISONED OR ONLY SLIGHTLY POISONED, HOWEVER, MAY DEVELOP SIGNS OF ATROPINE TOXICITY FROM SUCH LARGE DOSAGES: FEVER, MUSCLE FIBRILLATIONS, AND DELIRIUM ARE THE MAIN SIGNS OF ATROPINE TOXICITY. IF THESE SIGNS APPEAR WHILE THE PATIENT IS FULLY ATROPINIZED, ATROPINE ADMINISTRATION SHOULD BE DISCONTINUED, AT LEAST TEMPORARILY. OBSERVE TREATED PATIENTS CLOSELY AT LEAST 24 HOURS TO INSURE THAT SYMPTOMS (POSSIBLY PULMONARY EDEMA) DO NOT RECUR AS ATROPINIZATION WEARS OFF. IN VERY SEVERE POISONINGS, METABOLIC DISPOSITION OF TOXICANT MAY REQUIRE SEVERAL HOURS OR DAYS DURING WHICH ATROPINIZATION MUST BE MAINTAINED. MARKEDLY LOWER LEVELS OF URINARY METABOLITES INDICATE THAT ATROPINE DOSAGE CAN BE TAPERED OFF. AS DOSAGE IS REDUCED, CHECK THE LUNG BASES FREQUENTLY FOR RALES. IF RALES ARE HEARD OR OTHER SYMPTOMS RETURN, RE-ESTABLISH ATROPINIZATION PROMPTLY (MORGAN, RECOGNITION AND MANAGEMENT OF PESTICIDE POISONINGS, 3RD ED.). ADMINISTRATION OF ANTIDOTE MUST BE PERFORMED BY QUALIFIED MEDICAL PERSONNEL.
IN CASES OF SEVERE POISONING BY ORGANOPHOSPHATE PESTICIDES IN WHICH RESPIRATORY DEPRESSION, MUSCLE WEAKNESS AND TWITCHINGS ARE SEVERE, GIVE PRALIDOXIME (PROTOPAM-AYERST, 2-PAM), 1.0 GRAM INTRAVENOUSLY AT NO MORE THAN 0.5 GRAM PER MINUTE. DOSAGE OF PRALIDOXIME MAY BE REPEATED IN 1-2 HOURS, THEN AT 10-12 HOUR INTERVALS IF NEEDED. IN VERY SEVERE POISONINGS, DOSAGE RATES MAY BE DOUBLED. TREATMENT WITH PRALIDOXIME WILL BE MOST EFFECTIVE IF GIVEN WITHIN THIRTY-SIX HOURS AFTER POISONING (MORGAN, RECOGNITION AND MANAGEMENT OF PESTICIDE POISONINGS, 3RD ED.). ANTIDOTE SHOULD BE ADMINISTERED BY QUALIFIED MEDICAL PERSONNEL.

REACTIVITY

REACTIVITY: STABLE UNDER NORMAL TEMPERATURES AND PRESSURES.
INCOMPATIBILITIES: TERBUFOS: OXIDIZERS (STRONG): FIRE AND EXPLOSION HAZARD.
DECOMPOSITION: THERMAL DECOMPOSITION PRODUCTS MAY INCLUDE TOXIC OXIDES OF CARBON, SULFUR, AND PHOSPHORUS.
POLYMERIZATION: HAZARDOUS POLYMERIZATION HAS NOT BEEN REPORTED TO OCCUR UNDER NORMAL TEMPERATURES AND PRESSURES.

STORAGE AND DISPOSAL

OBSERVE ALL FEDERAL, STATE AND LOCAL REGULATIONS WHEN STORING OR DISPOSING OF THIS SUBSTANCE. FOR ASSISTANCE, CONTACT THE DISTRICT DIRECTOR OF THE ENVIRONMENTAL PROTECTION AGENCY.

****STORAGE****

STORE IN ACCORDANCE WITH 29 CFR 1910.106.
BONDING AND GROUNDING: SUBSTANCES WITH LOW ELECTROCONDUCTIVITY, WHICH MAY BE IGNITED BY ELECTROSTATIC SPARKS, SHOULD BE STORED IN CONTAINERS WHICH MEET THE BONDING AND GROUNDING GUIDELINES SPECIFIED IN NFPA 77-1983, RECOMMENDED PRACTICE ON STATIC ELECTRICITY.
STORE IN ACCORDANCE WITH 40 CFR 165 RECOMMENDED PROCEDURES FOR THE DISPOSAL AND STORAGE OF PESTICIDES AND PESTICIDE CONTAINERS.
STORE AWAY FROM INCOMPATIBLE SUBSTANCES.
THRESHOLD PLANNING QUANTITY (TPQ): THE SUPERFUND AMENDMENTS AND REAUTHORIZATION ACT (SARA) SECTION 302 REQUIRES THAT EACH FACILITY WHERE ANY EXTREMELY HAZARDOUS SUBSTANCE IS PRESENT IN A QUANTITY EQUAL TO OR GREATER THAN THE TPQ ESTABLISHED FOR THAT SUBSTANCE NOTIFY THE STATE EMERGENCY RESPONSE COMMISSION FOR THE STATE IN WHICH IT IS LOCATED. SECTION 303 OF SARA REQUIRES THESE FACILITIES TO PARTICIPATE IN LOCAL EMERGENCY RESPONSE PLANNING (40 CFR 355.30).

****DISPOSAL****

DISPOSAL MUST BE IN ACCORDANCE WITH 40 CFR 165 RECOMMENDED PROCEDURES FOR THE DISPOSAL AND STORAGE OF PESTICIDES AND PESTICIDE CONTAINERS.

CONDITIONS TO AVOID

MAY BE IGNITED BY HEAT, SPARKS OR FLAMES. CONTAINER MAY EXPLODE IN HEAT OF FIRE. VAPOR EXPLOSION AND POISON HAZARD INDOORS, OUTDOORS OR IN SEWERS.

SPILL AND LEAK PROCEDURES

OCCUPATIONAL SPILL: SHUT OFF IGNITION SOURCES. DO NOT TOUCH SPILLED MATERIAL. STOP LEAK IF YOU CAN DO IT WITHOUT RISK. USE WATER SPRAY TO REDUCE VAPORS. FOR SMALL SPILLS, TAKE UP WITH SAND OR OTHER ABSORBENT MATERIAL AND PLACE INTO CONTAINERS FOR LATER DISPOSAL. FOR SMALL DRY SPILLS, WITH CLEAN SHOVEL PLACE MATERIAL INTO CLEAN, DRY CONTAINERS AND COVER. MOVE CONTAINERS FROM SPILL AREA. FOR LARGER SPILLS, DIKE FAR AHEAD OF SPILL FOR LATER DISPOSAL. NO SMOKING, FLAMES OR FLARES IN HAZARD AREA! KEEP UNNECESSARY PEOPLE AWAY. ISOLATE HAZARD AREA AND DENY ENTRY. VENTILATE CLOSED SPACES BEFORE ENTERING.
REPORTABLE QUANTITY (RQ): 1 POUND THE SUPERFUND AMENDMENTS AND REAUTHORIZATION ACT (SARA) SECTION 304 REQUIRES THAT A RELEASE EQUAL TO OR GREATER THAN THE REPORTABLE QUANTITY FOR THIS SUBSTANCE BE IMMEDIATELY REPORTED TO THE LOCAL EMERGENCY PLANNING COMMITTEE AND THE STATE EMERGENCY RESPONSE COMMISSION (40 CFR 355.40). IF THE RELEASE OF THIS SUBSTANCE IS REPORTABLE UNDER CERCLA SECTION 103, THE NATIONAL RESPONSE CENTER MUST BE NOTIFIED IMMEDIATELY AT (800) 424-8802 OR (202) 426-2675 IN THE METROPOLITAN WASHINGTON, D.C. AREA (40 CFR 302.6).

PROTECTIVE EQUIPMENT

VENTILATION: PROCESS ENCLOSURE RECOMMENDED.
RESPIRATOR: THE FOLLOWING RESPIRATORS ARE RECOMMENDED BASED ON INFORMATION FOUND IN THE PHYSICAL DATA, TOXICITY AND HEALTH EFFECTS SECTIONS. THEY ARE RANKED IN ORDER FROM MINIMUM TO MAXIMUM RESPIRATORY PROTECTION. THE SPECIFIC RESPIRATOR SELECTED MUST BE BASED ON CONTAMINATION LEVELS FOUND IN THE WORK PLACE, MUST NOT EXCEED THE WORKING LIMITS OF THE RESPIRATOR AND BE JOINTLY APPROVED BY THE NATIONAL INSTITUTE FOR OCCUPATIONAL SAFETY AND HEALTH AND THE MINE SAFETY AND HEALTH ADMINISTRATION (NIOSH-MSHA).
TYPE 'C' SUPPLIED-AIR RESPIRATOR WITH A FULL FACEPIECE OPERATED IN PRESSURE-DEMAND OR OTHER POSITIVE PRESSURE MODE OR WITH A FULL FACEPIECE, HELMET OR HOOD OPERATED IN CONTINOUS-FLOW MODE.
SELF-CONTAINED BREATHING APPARATUS WITH A FULL FACEPIECE OPERATED IN PRESSURE-DEMAND OR OTHER POSITIVE PRESSURE MODE.
FOR FIREFIGHTING AND OTHER IMMEDIATELY DANGEROUS TO LIFE OR HEALTH CONDITIONS:
SELF-CONTAINED BREATHING APPARATUS WITH FULL FACEPIECE OPERATED IN PRESSURE-DEMAND OR OTHER POSITIVE PRESSURE MODE.
SUPPLIED-AIR RESPIRATOR WITH FULL FACEPIECE AND OPERATED IN PRESSURE-DEMAND OR OTHER POSITIVE PRESSURE MODE IN COMBINATION WITH AN AUXILIARY SELF-CONTAINED BREATHING APPARATUS OPERATED IN PRESSURE-DEMAND OR OTHER POSITIVE PRESSURE MODE.
CLOTHING: EMPLOYEE MUST WEAR APPROPRIATE PROTECTIVE (IMPERVIOUS) CLOTHING AND EQUIPMENT TO PREVENT ANY POSSIBILITY OF SKIN CONTACT WITH THIS SUBSTANCE.
GLOVES: EMPLOYEE MUST WEAR APPROPRIATE PROTECTIVE GLOVES TO PREVENT CONTACT WITH THIS SUBSTANCE.
EYE PROTECTION: EMPLOYEE MUST WEAR SPLASH-PROOF OR DUST-RESISTANT SAFETY GOGGLES WITH OR WITHOUT A FACESHIELD TO PREVENT CONTACT WITH THIS SUBSTANCE.
EMERGENCY EYE WASH: WHERE THERE IS ANY POSSIBILITY THAT AN EMPLOYEE'S EYES MAY BE EXPOSED TO THIS SUBSTANCE, THE EMPLOYER SHOULD PROVIDE AN EYE WASH FOUNTAIN WITHIN THE IMMEDIATE WORK AREA FOR EMERGENCY USE.

AUTHORIZED BY- OCCUPATIONAL HEALTH SERVICES, INC.
CREATION DATE: 10/05/89 ***REVISION DATE:*** 07/10/90

MATERIAL SAFETY DATA SHEET

OCCUPATIONAL HEALTH SERVICES, INC.
AGRICULTURE AND PESTICIDE DIVISION
450 SEVENTH AVENUE, SUITE 2407
NEW YORK, NEW YORK 10123
1-800-445-MSDS OR (212) 967-1100

EMERGENCY CONTACT:
JOHN S. BRANSFORD, JR. (615) 292-1180

SUBSTANCE IDENTIFICATION

CAS-NUMBER 75-65-0
SUBSTANCE: **TERT-BUTYL ALCOHOL**
TRADE NAMES/SYNONYMS: 2-PROPANOL, 2-METHYL-; T-BUTANOL; TERT-BUTANOL; 1,1-DIMETHYLETHANOL; TRIMETHYLCARBINOL; TRIMETHYLMETHANOL; TRIMETHYL METHANOL; BUTYL ALCOHOL; 2-METHYL-2-PROPANOL; STCC 4909130; NA 1120; UN 1120; C4H10O; PST22630
CHEMICAL FAMILY: ALCOHOL, ALIPHATIC
MOLECULAR FORMULA: (C-H3)3-C-O-H
MOLECULAR WEIGHT: 74.12
CERCLA RATINGS (SCALE 0-3): HEALTH=2 FIRE=3 REACTIVITY=0 PERSISTENCE=0
NFPA RATINGS (SCALE 0-4): HEALTH=1 FIRE=3 REACTIVITY=0

COMPONENTS AND CONTAMINANTS

COMPONENT: TERT-BUTYL ALCOHOL ***PERCENT:*** 100.0
CAS# 75-65-0
OTHER CONTAMINANTS: NONE
EXPOSURE LIMITS: TERT-BUTYL ALCOHOL: 100 PPM (300 MG/M3) OSHA TWA; 150 PPM (450 MG/M3) OSHA STEL 100 PPM (300 MG/M3) ACGIH TWA; 150 PPM (450 MG/M3) ACGIH STEL
SUBJECT TO SARA SECTION 313 ANNUAL TOXIC CHEMICAL RELEASE REPORTING

PHYSICAL DATA

DESCRIPTION: COLORLESS LIQUID OR HYGROSCOPIC CRYSTALS WITH A CAMPHOR-LIKE ODOR.
BOILING POINT: 180 F (82 C) ***MELTING POINT:*** 79 F (26 C)
SPECIFIC GRAVITY: 0.7887 ***VISCOSITY:*** 3.3 CPS @ 30 C
VAPOR PRESSURE: 31 MMHG @ 20 C ***EVAPORATION RATE:*** (BUTYL ACETATE=1) 1.05
SOLUBILITY IN WATER: SOLUBLE ***ODOR THRESHOLD:*** 73 PPM ***VAPOR DENSITY:*** 2.6
SOLVENT SOLUBILITY: SOLUBLE IN ALCOHOL, ETHER, ACETONE, BENZENE.

FIRE AND EXPLOSION DATA

FIRE AND EXPLOSION HAZARD: DANGEROUS FIRE HAZARD WHEN EXPOSED TO HEAT OR FLAME.
VAPORS ARE HEAVIER THAN AIR AND MAY TRAVEL A CONSIDERABLE DISTANCE TO A SOURCE OF IGNITION AND FLASH BACK.
VAPOR-AIR MIXTURES ARE EXPLOSIVE.
FLASH POINT: 52 F (11 C) (CC) ***UPPER EXPLOSIVE LIMIT:*** 8.0%
LOWER EXPLOSIVE LIMIT: 2.4% ***AUTOIGNITION TEMP.:*** 892 F (478 C)
FLAMMABILITY CLASS(OSHA): IB

FIREFIGHTING MEDIA: DRY CHEMICAL, CARBON DIOXIDE, HALON, WATER SPRAY OR ALCOHOL FOAM (1987 EMERGENCY RESPONSE GUIDEBOOK, DOT P 5800.4).
FOR LARGER FIRES, USE WATER SPRAY, FOG OR ALCOHOL FOAM (1987 EMERGENCY RESPONSE GUIDEBOOK, DOT P 5800.4).
ALCOHOL FOAM (NFPA 325M, FIRE HAZARD PROPERTIES OF FLAMMABLE LIQUIDS, GASES, AND VOLATILE SOLIDS, 1984).

FIREFIGHTING: MOVE CONTAINER FROM FIRE AREA IF POSSIBLE. COOL FIRE-EXPOSED CONTAINERS WITH WATER FROM SIDE UNTIL WELL AFTER FIRE IS OUT. STAY AWAY FROM STORAGE TANK ENDS. FOR MASSIVE FIRE IN STORAGE AREA, USE UNMANNED HOSE HOLDER OR MONITOR NOZZLES, ELSE WITHDRAW FROM AREA AND LET FIRE BURN. WITHDRAW IMMEDIATELY IN CASE OF RISING SOUND FROM VENTING SAFETY DEVICE OR ANY DISCOLORATION OF STORAGE TANK DUE TO FIRE (1987 EMERGENCY RESPONSE GUIDEBOOK, DOT P 5800.4, GUIDE PAGE 26). EXTINGUISH ONLY IF FLOW CAN BE STOPPED. USE WATER IN FLOODING AMOUNTS AS A FOG, SOLID STREAMS MAY NOT BE EFFECTIVE. COOL CONTAINERS WITH FLOODING AMOUNTS OF WATER; APPLY FROM AS FAR A DISTANCE AS POSSIBLE. AVOID BREATHING TOXIC VAPORS, KEEP UPWIND.
WATER MAY BE INEFFECTIVE (NFPA 325M, FIRE HAZARD PROPERTIES OF FLAMMABLE LIQUIDS, GASES, AND VOLATILE SOLIDS, 1984)

TRANSPORTATION DATA

DEPARTMENT OF TRANSPORTATION HAZARD CLASSIFICATION 49 CFR 172.101: FLAMMABLE LIQUID
DEPARTMENT OF TRANSPORTATION LABELING REQUIREMENTS 49 CFR 172.101 AND SUBPART E: FLAMMABLE LIQUID
DEPARTMENT OF TRANSPORTATION PACKAGING REQUIREMENTS: 49 CFR 173.125 EXCEPTIONS: 49 CFR 173.118

TOXICITY

TERT-BUTYL ALCOHOL (TERT-BUTANOL): TOXICITY DATA: 3500 MG/KG ORAL-RAT LD50; 3559 MG/KG ORAL-RABBIT LD50; 1538 MG/KG INTRAVENOUS-MOUSE LD50; 933 MG/KG INTRAPERITONEAL-MOUSE LD50; 12 GM/KG PARENTERAL-FROG LDLO; REPRODUCTIVE EFFECTS DATA (RTECS). CARCINOGEN STATUS: NONE. LOCAL EFFECTS: IRRITANT- EYE, INHALATION. ACUTE TOXICITY LEVEL: MODERATELY TOXIC BY INGESTION. TARGET EFFECTS: CENTRAL NERVOUS SYSTEM DEPRESSANT. POISONING MAY ALSO AFFECT THE LIVER, AND KIDNEYS. AT INCREASED RISK FROM EXPOSURE: PERSONS WITH PREEXISTING SKIN DISORDERS OR LIVER DISEASE, KIDNEY DISEASE, OR CHRONIC RESPIRATORY DISEASE. ADDITIONAL DATA: ALCOHOL MAY ENHANCE THE TOXIC EFFECTS.

HEALTH EFFECTS AND FIRST AID

INHALATION: TERT-BUTYL ALCOHOL (TERT-BUTANOL): IRRITANT/NARCOTIC. 8000 PPM IMMEDIATELY DANGEROUS TO LIFE OR HEALTH. **ACUTE EXPOSURE-** GREATER THAN 100 PPM MAY CAUSE NOSE AND THROAT IRRITATION. MAY ALSO CAUSE COUGHING, SHORTNESS OF BREATH, AND CENTRAL NERVOUS SYSTEM DEPRESSION WITH HEADACHE, DIZZINESS, DROWSINESS, VERTIGO, NAUSEA, VOMITING, FATIGUE, DULLNESS, BLURRED VISION, ATAXIA AND UNCONSCIOUSNESS. THERE WAS LIVER DAMAGE IN RATS AFTER A SINGLE DOSE. **CHRONIC EXPOSURE-** IN MICE THERE WAS MODERATE, REVERSIBLE FATTY INFILTRATION OF THE LIVER, KIDNEYS AND HEART. 18 REPEATED, DAILY NARCOTIC DOSES WERE NOT FATAL TO RATS AND NO HARMFUL EFFECTS RESULTED FROM A LONG CONTINUED, EASILY TOLERATED DOSE. REPRODUCTIVE EFFECTS HAVE BEEN REPORTED IN ANIMALS.

FIRST AID- REMOVE FROM EXPOSURE AREA TO FRESH AIR IMMEDIATELY. IF BREATHING HAS STOPPED, PERFORM ARTIFICIAL RESPIRATION. KEEP PERSON WARM AND AT REST. TREAT SYMPTOMATICALLY AND SUPPORTIVELY. GET MEDICAL ATTENTION IMMEDIATELY.

SKIN CONTACT: TERT-BUTYL ALCOHOL (TERT-BUTANOL): **ACUTE EXPOSURE-** CONTACT WITH THE LIQUID MAY CAUSE SLIGHT IRRITATION WITH ERYTHEMA AND HYPEREMIA. **CHRONIC EXPOSURE-** PROLONGED EXPOSURE MAY CAUSE DERMATITIS WITH DRYING AND CRACKING OF THE SKIN. PATCH TESTS ON FOUR WOMEN FOR 48 HOURS WERE NEGATIVE.

FIRST AID- REMOVE CONTAMINATED CLOTHING AND SHOES IMMEDIATELY. WASH AFFECTED AREA WITH SOAP OR MILD DETERGENT AND LARGE AMOUNTS OF WATER UNTIL NO EVIDENCE OF CHEMICAL REMAINS (APPROXIMATELY 15-20 MINUTES). GET MEDICAL ATTENTION IMMEDIATELY.

EYE CONTACT: TERT-BUTYL ALCOHOL (TERT-BUTANOL): IRRITANT. **ACUTE EXPOSURE-** CONTACT WITH THE LIQUID OR HIGH VAPOR CONCENTRATIONS MAY CAUSE MILD TO SEVERE IRRITATION WITH STINGING SENSATION, REDNESS, PAIN, BLURRED VISION, KERATITIS, AND CORNEAL INFLAMMATION. **CHRONIC EXPOSURE-** REPEATED OR PROLONGED EXPOSURE TO IRRITANTS MAY CAUSE CONJUNCTIVITIS.

FIRST AID- WASH EYES IMMEDIATELY WITH LARGE AMOUNTS OF WATER OR NORMAL SALINE, OCCASIONALLY LIFTING UPPER AND LOWER LIDS, UNTIL NO EVIDENCE OF CHEMICAL REMAINS (APPROXIMATELY 15-20 MINUTES). GET MEDICAL ATTENTION IMMEDIATELY.

INGESTION: TERT-BUTYL ALCOHOL (TERT-BUTANOL): NARCOTIC. **ACUTE EXPOSURE-** INGESTION MAY CAUSE ABDOMINAL PAIN, NAUSEA, VOMITING, AND DIARRHEA. MAY ALSO CAUSE CENTRAL NERVOUS SYSTEM DEPRESSION WITH DROWSINESS, HEADACHE, DIZZINESS, DULLNESS, FATIGUE, ATAXIA, AND UNCONSCIOUNESS. ALCOHOLS MAY BE ASPIRATED AND CONCENTRATIONS THAT WOULD BE TOLERATED BY INGESTION MAY CAUSE RESPIRATORY FAILURE AND DEATH. DEATH MAY ALSO OCCUR FROM CARDIAC ARRYTHMIAS. **CHRONIC EXPOSURE-** REPRODUCTIVE EFFECTS HAVE BEEN REPORTED IN ANIMALS.

FIRST AID- REMOVE INGESTED MATERIAL BY GASTRIC LAVAGE OR EMESIS. GIVE ARTIFICIAL RESPIRATION WITH OXYGEN IF RESPIRATION IS DEPRESSED. (DREISBACH HANDBOOK OF POISONING, 11TH ED.). GET MEDICAL ATTENTION IMMEDIATELY. ADMINISTRATION OF GASTRIC LAVAGE SHOULD BE PERFORMED BY QUALIFIED MEDICAL PERSONNEL.

ANTIDOTE: NO SPECIFIC ANTIDOTE. TREAT SYMPTOMATICALLY AND SUPPORTIVELY.

REACTIVITY

REACTIVITY: STABLE UNDER NORMAL TEMPERATURES AND PRESSURES.

INCOMPATIBILITIES: TERT-BUTYL ALCOHOL (TERT-BUTANOL): ALKALI METALS: VIOLENT REACTION AND FORMATION OF FLAMMABLE HYDROGEN GAS. ALUMINUM: MAY REACT AT ELEVATED TEMPERATURES. HYDROCHLORIC ACID: FORMS VOLATILE TERT-BUTYL CHLORIDE. HYDROGEN PEROXIDE + SULFURIC ACID (2:1): SEVERE EXPLOSIVE REACTION. MINERAL ACIDS (STRONG): FORMS FLAMMABLE ISOBUTYLENE GAS. NITRATES: FIRE AND EXPLOSION HAZARD. OXIDIZERS (STRONG): FIRE AND EXPLOSION HAZARD. PERCHLORATES: FIRE AND EXPLOSION HAZARD. PLASTICS, RUBBER, COATINGS: MAY BE ATTACKED. POTASSIUM-SODIUM ALLOY: IGNITION ON CONTACT. SEE ALSO: ALCOHOLS.

DECOMPOSITION: THERMAL DECOMPOSITION PRODUCTS MAY INCLUDE TOXIC OXIDES OF CARBON.

POLYMERIZATION: HAZARDOUS POLYMERIZATION HAS NOT BEEN REPORTED TO OCCUR UNDER NORMAL TEMPERATURES AND PRESSURES.

STORAGE AND DISPOSAL

OBSERVE ALL FEDERAL, STATE AND LOCAL REGULATIONS WHEN STORING OR DISPOSING OF THIS SUBSTANCE. FOR ASSISTANCE, CONTACT THE DISTRICT DIRECTOR OF THE ENVIRONMENTAL PROTECTION AGENCY.

STORAGE

STORE IN ACCORDANCE WITH 29 CFR 1910.106.
BONDING AND GROUNDING: SUBSTANCES WITH LOW ELECTROCONDUCTIVITY, WHICH MAY BE IGNITED BY ELECTROSTATIC SPARKS, SHOULD BE STORED IN CONTAINERS WHICH MEET THE BONDING AND GROUNDING GUIDELINES SPECIFIED IN NFPA 77-1983, RECOMMENDED PRACTICE ON STATIC ELECTRICITY.
STORE AWAY FROM INCOMPATIBLE SUBSTANCES.

DISPOSAL

DISPOSAL MUST BE IN ACCORDANCE WITH STANDARDS APPLICABLE TO GENERATORS OF HAZARDOUS WASTE, 40 CFR 262. EPA HAZARDOUS WASTE NUMBER D001. 100 POUND CERCLA SECTION 103 REPORTABLE QUANTITY.

CONDITIONS TO AVOID

AVOID CONTACT WITH HEAT, SPARKS, FLAMES, OR OTHER SOURCES OF IGNITION. VAPORS MAY BE EXPLOSIVE AND POISONOUS; DO NOT ALLOW UNNECESSARY PERSONNEL IN AREA. DO NOT OVERHEAT CONTAINERS; CONTAINERS MAY VIOLENTLY RUPTURE AND TRAVEL A CONSIDERABLE DISTANCE IN HEAT OF FIRE.

SPILL AND LEAK PROCEDURES

OCCUPATIONAL SPILL: SHUT OFF IGNITION SOURCES. STOP LEAK IF YOU CAN DO IT WITHOUT RISK. USE WATER SPRAY TO REDUCE VAPORS. FOR SMALL SPILLS, TAKE UP WITH SAND OR OTHER ABSORBENT MATERIAL AND PLACE INTO CONTAINERS FOR LATER DISPOSAL. FOR LARGER SPILLS, DIKE FAR AHEAD OF SPILL FOR LATER DISPOSAL. NO SMOKING, FLAMES OR FLARES IN HAZARD AREA. KEEP UNNECESSARY PEOPLE AWAY; ISOLATE HAZARD AREA AND DENY ENTRY.

PROTECTIVE EQUIPMENT

VENTILATION: PROVIDE LOCAL EXHAUST OR GENERAL DILUTION VENTILATION TO MEET PUBLISHED EXPOSURE LIMITS. VENTILATION EQUIPMENT MUST BE EXPLOSION-PROOF.

RESPIRATOR: THE FOLLOWING RESPIRATORS AND MAXIMUM USE CONCENTRATIONS ARE RECOMMENDATIONS BY THE U.S. DEPARTMENT OF HEALTH AND HUMAN SERVICES, NIOSH POCKET GUIDE TO CHEMICAL HAZARDS; NIOSH CRITERIA DOCUMENTS OR BY THE U.S. DEPARTMENT OF LABOR, 29 CFR 1910 SUBPART Z. THE SPECIFIC RESPIRATOR SELECTED MUST BE BASED ON CONTAMINATION LEVELS FOUND IN THE WORK PLACE, MUST NOT EXCEED THE WORKING LIMITS OF THE RESPIRATOR AND BE JOINTLY APPROVED BY THE NATIONAL INSTITUTE FOR

OCCUPATIONAL SAFETY AND HEALTH AND THE MINE SAFETY AND HEALTH ADMINISTRATION (NIOSH-MSHA).
TERT-BUTYL ALCOHOL:
1000 PPM- ANY POWERED AIR-PURIFYING RESPIRATOR WITH ORGANIC VAPOR CARTRIDGE(S). ANY CHEMICAL CARTRIDGE RESPIRATOR WITH A FULL FACEPIECE AND ORGANIC VAPOR CARTRIDGE(S).
2500 PPM- ANY SUPPLIED-AIR RESPIRATOR OPERATED IN A CONTINUOUS FLOW MODE.
5000 PPM- ANY AIR-PURIFYING FULL FACEPIECE RESPIRATOR (GAS MASK) WITH A CHIN-STYLE OR FRONT- OR BACK-MOUNTED ORGANIC VAPOR CANISTER. ANY SELF-CONTAINED BREATHING APPARATUS WITH A FULL FACEPIECE. ANY SUPPLIED-AIR RESPIRATOR WITH A FULL FACEPIECE.
8000 PPM- ANY SUPPLIED-AIR RESPIRATOR WITH A FULL FACEPIECE AND OPERATED IN A PRESSURE-DEMAND OR OTHER POSITIVE PRESSURE MODE.
ESCAPE- ANY AIR-PURIFYING FULL FACEPIECE RESPIRATOR (GAS MASK) WITH A CHIN-STYLE OR FRONT- OR BACK-MOUNTED ORGANIC VAPOR CANISTER. ANY APPROPRIATE ESCAPE-TYPE SELF-CONTAINED BREATHING APPARATUS.
FOR FIREFIGHTING AND OTHER IMMEDIATELY DANGEROUS TO LIFE OR HEALTH CONDITIONS:
SELF-CONTAINED BREATHING APPARATUS WITH FULL FACEPIECE OPERATED IN PRESSURE-DEMAND OR OTHER POSITIVE PRESSURE MODE.
SUPPLIED-AIR RESPIRATOR WITH FULL FACEPIECE AND OPERATED IN PRESSURE-DEMAND OR OTHER POSITIVE PRESSURE MODE IN COMBINATION WITH AN AUXILIARY SELF-CONTAINED BREATHING APPARATUS OPERATED IN PRESSURE-DEMAND OR OTHER POSITIVE PRESSURE MODE.

CLOTHING: EMPLOYEE MUST WEAR APPROPRIATE PROTECTIVE (IMPERVIOUS) CLOTHING AND EQUIPMENT TO PREVENT REPEATED OR PROLONGED SKIN CONTACT WITH THIS SUBSTANCE.

GLOVES: EMPLOYEE MUST WEAR APPROPRIATE PROTECTIVE GLOVES TO PREVENT CONTACT WITH THIS SUBSTANCE.

EYE PROTECTION: EMPLOYEE MUST WEAR SPLASH-PROOF OR DUST-RESISTANT SAFETY GOGGLES TO PREVENT EYE CONTACT WITH THIS SUBSTANCE.
EMERGENCY EYE WASH: WHERE THERE IS ANY POSSIBILITY THAT AN EMPLOYEE'S EYES MAY BE EXPOSED TO THIS SUBSTANCE, THE EMPLOYER SHOULD PROVIDE AN EYE WASH FOUNTAIN WITHIN THE IMMEDIATE WORK AREA FOR EMERGENCY USE.

AUTHORIZED BY- OCCUPATIONAL HEALTH SERVICES, INC.
CREATION DATE: 11/15/89 ***REVISION DATE:*** 05/16/90

MATERIAL SAFETY DATA SHEET

OCCUPATIONAL HEALTH SERVICES, INC.
AGRICULTURE AND PESTICIDE DIVISION
450 SEVENTH AVENUE, SUITE 2407
NEW YORK, NEW YORK 10123
1-800-445-MSDS OR (212) 967-1100

EMERGENCY CONTACT:
JOHN S. BRANSFORD, JR. (615) 292-1180

SUBSTANCE IDENTIFICATION

CAS-NUMBER 127-18-4

SUBSTANCE: **TETRACHLOROETHYLENE**

TRADE NAMES/SYNONYMS: ETHENE, TETRACHLORO-; ETHYLENE, TETRACHLORO-; ANKILOSTIN; DIDAKEN; NEMA; ETHYLENE TETRACHLORIDE; PERCHLOROETHYLENE; PERC; PERCHLOROETHENE; PERCLENE; 1,1,2,2-TETRACHLOROETHYLENE; TETRACAP; TETRACHLOROETHENE; LASER GUARD (DYNATEX CORPORATION); RCRA U210; NCI-C04580; ENT 1,860; STCC 4940355; UN 1897; C2CL4; PST22900

CHEMICAL FAMILY: HALOGEN COMPOUND, ALIPHATIC

MOLECULAR FORMULA: CL2-C-C-CL2

MOLECULAR WEIGHT: 165.83

CERCLA RATINGS (SCALE 0-3): HEALTH=3 FIRE=0 REACTIVITY=0 PERSISTENCE=2

NFPA RATINGS (SCALE 0-4): HEALTH=2 FIRE=0 REACTIVITY=0

COMPONENTS AND CONTAMINANTS

COMPONENT: TETRACHLOROETHYLENE ***PERCENT:*** 100.0
CAS# 127-18-4

OTHER CONTAMINANTS: NONE

EXPOSURE LIMITS: TETRACHLOROETHYLENE (PERCHLOROETHYLENE): 25 PPM (170 MG/M3) OSHA TWA 50 PPM (335 MG/M3) ACGIH TWA; 200 PPM (1340 MG/M3) ACGIH STEL LOWEST FEASIBLE LIMIT NIOSH RECOMMENDED EXPOSURE CRITERIA 100 POUND CERCLA SECTION 103 REPORTABLE QUANTITY SUBJECT TO SARA SECTION 313 ANNUAL TOXIC CHEMICAL RELEASE REPORTING SUBJECT TO CALIFORNIA PROPOSITION 65 CANCER AND/OR REPRODUCTIVE TOXICITY WARNING AND RELEASE REQUIREMENTS- (APRIL 1, 1988)

PHYSICAL DATA

DESCRIPTION: CLEAR, COLORLESS, VOLATILE LIQUID WITH A MILD ETHER-LIKE ODOR.

BOILING POINT: 250 F (121 C) ***MELTING POINT:*** -2 F (-19 C)

SPECIFIC GRAVITY: 1.6227 ***VOLATILITY:*** 100%

VAPOR PRESSURE: 14 MMHG @ 20C

EVAPORATION RATE: (BUTYL ACETATE=1) 2.8 ***SOLUBILITY IN WATER:*** 0.015%

ODOR THRESHOLD: 50 PPM ***VAPOR DENSITY:*** 5.83

SOLVENT SOLUBILITY: SOLUBLE IN ALCOHOL, ETHER, BENZENE, CHLOROFORM, OILS, HEXANE.

FIRE AND EXPLOSION DATA

FIRE AND EXPLOSION HAZARD: NEGLIGIBLE FIRE HAZARD WHEN EXPOSED TO HEAT OR FLAME.

FIREFIGHTING MEDIA: DRY CHEMICAL, CARBON DIOXIDE OR HALON (1987 EMERGENCY RESPONSE GUIDEBOOK, DOT P 5800.4).
FOR LARGER FIRES, USE WATER SPRAY, FOG OR STANDARD FOAM (1987 EMERGENCY RESPONSE GUIDEBOOK, DOT P 5800.4).

FIREFIGHTING: STAY AWAY FROM STORAGE TANK ENDS. COOL CONTAINERS EXPOSED TO FLAMES WITH WATER FROM SIDE UNTIL WELL AFTER FIRE IS OUT (1987 EMERGENCY RESPONSE GUIDEBOOK, DOT P 5800.4, GUIDE PAGE 74).
EXTINGUISH USING AGENT(S) SUITABLE FOR TYPE OF SURROUNDING FIRE. AVOID CONTAMINATION OF WATER SOURCES AND SEWERS. BUILD DIKES TO CONTAIN FLOW. AVOID BREATHING VAPORS; KEEP UPWIND.

TRANSPORTATION DATA

DEPARTMENT OF TRANSPORTATION HAZARD CLASSIFICATION 49 CFR 172.101: ORM-A
DEPARTMENT OF TRANSPORTATION LABELING REQUIREMENTS 49 CFR 172.101 AND SUBPART E: NONE
DEPARTMENT OF TRANSPORTATION PACKAGING REQUIREMENTS: 49 CFR 173.605 EXCEPTIONS: 49 CFR 173.505

TOXICITY

TETRACHLOROETHYLENE (PERCHLOROETHYLENE): IRRITATION DATA: 810 MG/24 HOURS SKIN-RABBIT SEVERE; 500 MG/24 HOURS SKIN-RABBIT MILD; 162 MG EYE-RABBIT MILD; 500 MG/24 HOURS EYE-RABBIT MILD. TOXICITY DATA: 96 PPM/7 HOURS INHALATION-HUMAN TCLO; 280 PPM/2 HOURS INHALATION-MAN TCLO; 600 PPM/10 MINUTES INHALATION-MAN TCLO; 34,200 MG/M3/8 HOURS INHALATION-RAT LC50; 5200 PPM/4 HOURS INHALATION-MOUSE LC50; >10,000 MG/KG SKIN-RABBIT LD50 (DOW MSDS); 2629 MG/KG ORAL-RAT LD50; 8100 MG/KG ORAL-MOUSE LD50; 5000 MG/KG ORAL-RABBIT LDLO; 4000 MG/KG ORAL-CAT LDLO; 4000 MG/KG ORAL-DOG LDLO; 2200 MG/KG SUBCUTANEOUS-RABBIT LDLO; 85 MG/KG INTRAVENOUS-DOG LDLO; 4678 MG/KG INTRAPERITONEAL-RAT LD50; 2100 MG/KG INTRAPERITONEAL-DOG LD50; MUTAGENIC DATA (RTECS); REPRODUCTIVE EFFECTS DATA (RTECS); TUMORIGENIC DATA (RTECS).
CARCINOGEN STATUS: ANTICIPATED HUMAN CARCINOGEN (NTP); HUMAN INADEQUATE EVIDENCE, ANIMAL SUFFICIENT EVIDENCE (IARC GROUP-2B). IN MICE, ORAL ADMINISTRATION AND INHALATION PRODUCED HEPATOCELLULAR CARCINOMAS IN BOTH SEXES. EXPOSURE OF RATS BY INHALATION PRODUCED AN INCREASED INCIDENCE OF MONONUCLEAR CELL LEUKEMIA IN BOTH SEXES.
LOCAL EFFECTS: IRRITANT- INHALATION, SKIN, EYES. ACUTE TOXICITY LEVEL: MODERATELY TOXIC BY INHALATION, INGESTION; SLIGHTLY TOXIC BY SKIN ABSORPTION. TARGET EFFECTS: CENTRAL NERVOUS SYSTEM DEPRESSANT. POISONING MAY ALSO AFFECT THE LIVER AND KIDNEYS. AT INCREASED RISK FROM EXPOSURE: PERSONS WITH PRE-EXISTING SKIN, EYE, LIVER, KIDNEY, CARDIOVASCULAR OR NEUROLOGICAL DISORDERS. ADDITIONAL DATA: ALCOHOL MAY ENHANCE THE TOXIC EFFECTS. STIMULANTS SUCH AS EPINEPHRINE MAY INDUCE VENTRICULAR FIBRILLATION. MAY BE EXCRETED IN BREAST MILK. ONE STUDY SHOWS AN INCREASED RISK OF LEUKEMIA FOR CHILDREN WHOSE FATHERS HAD OCCUPATIONAL EXPOSURE TO CHLORINATED SOLVENTS AFTER THE BIRTH OF THE CHILD.

HEALTH EFFECTS AND FIRST AID

INHALATION: TETRACHLOROETHYLENE (PERCHLOROETHYLENE): IRRITANT/NARCOTIC/CARCINOGEN. **ACUTE EXPOSURE-** VAPOR CONCENTRATIONS FROM 100-400 PPM MAY CAUSE IRRITATION OF THE NOSE, THROAT AND MUCOUS MEMBRANES, FLUSHED FACE AND NECK, SINUS CONGESTION, NASAL DISCHARGE, HEADACHE, DIZZINESS, LIGHTHEADEDNESS, DROWSINESS, THICK TONGUE, TIGHTNESS AROUND THE MOUTH, SLURRED SPEECH, CONFUSION, INCOORDINATION, NAUSEA, AND REVERSIBLE LIVER AND KIDNEY CHANGES; 400-600 PPM MAY CAUSE SALIVATION, METALLIC TASTE, PERSPIRATION OF THE HANDS, AND LOSS OF INHIBITIONS; 1000-2000 PPM MAY CAUSE MARKED UPPER

RESPIRATORY IRRITATION, ANESTHESIA OF THE LIPS AND NOSE, CONGESTED EUSTACHIAN TUBES, ACHING FACIAL MUSCLES, INEBRIATION, EXHILARATION, MENTAL SLUGGISHNESS, LASSITUDE, GAGGING, FAINTNESS, TINNITUS, DYSPNEA UPON EXERTION, NARCOSIS, AND LIVER AND KIDNEY DAMAGE. OTHER REPORTED SYMPTOMS INCLUDE WEAKNESS, ATAXIA, COUGHING, CHEST PAINS, RAPID, WEAK PULSE, BLURRED VISION, IRRITABILITY, ANOREXIA, VOMITING, HALLUCINATIONS, DISTORTED PERCEPTIONS, ACIDOSIS, LATENT JAUNDICE AND ABNORMAL LIVER FUNCTION TESTS, ALBUMINURIA, HEMATURIA, ANURIA, AND PREMATURE VENTRICULAR BEATS. MASSIVE EXPOSURES MAY CAUSE PULMONARY EDEMA, UNCONSCIOUSNESS, COMA AND DEATH FROM ANESTHESIA OR RESPIRATORY ARREST. IN ONE FATAL CASE, PATHOLOGIC FINDINGS INCLUDED CENTRAL FATTY NECROSIS AND FATTY INFILTRATION OF THE LIVER AND MODERATE CLOUDY SWELLING OF THE RENAL TUBULAR EPITHELIUM. EPINEPHRINE-INDUCED CARDIAC ARRHYTHMIAS HAVE OCCURRED WITH SOME HYDROCARBONS, BUT TESTING OF TETRACHLOROETHYLENE IN DOGS HAS BEEN NEGATIVE. **CHRONIC EXPOSURE-** WORKERS EXPOSED TO 1-40 PPM OVER 7.5 YEARS SHOWED ALTERED ELECTRODIAGNOSTIC AND NEUROLOGICAL RATING SCORES; 4 OF 16 EXPOSED TO 60-450 PPM FOR 2-20 YEARS HAD ABNORMAL EEG'S. REPEATED EXPOSURE MAY ALSO CAUSE RESPIRATORY TRACT IRRITATION, CENTRAL NERVOUS SYSTEM DEPRESSION WITHOUT NARCOSIS, CONFUSION, HEADACHE, FATIGUE, DIZZINESS, INEBRIATION, INSOMNIA, NAUSEA, ANOREXIA, ABDOMINAL PAIN, CONSTIPATION, BLURRED VISION, MULTIPLE PREMATURE VENTRICULAR BEATS, AND PERIPHERAL NEUROPATHY WITH NUMBNESS IN THE FINGERS, TREMBLING, NEURITIS, AND MEMORY DEFECTS. HEPATIC DAMAGE MAY OCCUR AND BE PERSISTENT. EXPOSURE TO LEVELS AROUND 250 PPM FOR 4 MONTHS HAS BEEN REPORTED TO HAVE CAUSED HEMOPTYSIS, COUGHING, SWEATING ATTACKS, JAUNDICE, OLIGURIA, HEMATEMESIS, CARDIOVASCULAR FAILURE AND DEATH. OCCASIONAL IDIOSYNCRATIC REACTIONS HAVE BEEN REPORTED INCLUDING PULMONARY EDEMA, BRONCHIAL ASTHMA, DEPENDENCY, AND HYPERSENSITIVITY. CHRONIC STUDIES IN RATS HAVE PRODUCED LIVER AND KIDNEY DAMAGE. ONE STUDY OF WOMEN WITH EXPOSURE TO TETRACHLOROETHYLENE EARLY IN THEIR PREGNANCY FROM WORKING IN THE DRY CLEANING INDUSTRY INDICATED AN ASSOCIATION WITH A SIGNIFICANTLY INCREASED INCIDENCE OF SPONTANEOUS ABORTIONS. REPRODUCTIVE EFFECTS HAVE BEEN REPORTED IN ANIMALS. INHALATION STUDIES INDICATE AN INCREASED INCIDENCE OF LIVER CARCINOMAS IN MICE AND MONONUCLEAR CELL LEUKEMIA IN RATS.

FIRST AID- REMOVE FROM EXPOSURE AREA TO FRESH AIR IMMEDIATELY. IF BREATHING HAS STOPPED, GIVE ARTIFICIAL RESPIRATION. MAINTAIN AIRWAY AND BLOOD PRESSURE AND ADMINISTER OXYGEN IF AVAILABLE. KEEP AFFECTED PERSON WARM AND AT REST. TREAT SYMPTOMATICALLY AND SUPPORTIVELY. ADMINISTRATION OF OXYGEN SHOULD BE PERFORMED BY QUALIFIED PERSONNEL. GET MEDICAL ATTENTION IMMEDIATELY.

SKIN CONTACT: TETRACHLOROETHYLENE (PERCHLOROETHYLENE): IRRITANT. **ACUTE EXPOSURE-** BRIEF IMMERSION OF THE HANDS IN THE LIQUID USUALLY CAUSES ONLY MILD IRRITATION. HOWEVER, THE LIQUID ON THE SKIN FOR 40 MINUTES RESULTED IN A PROGRESSIVELY SEVERE BURNING SENSATION, BEGINNING WITHIN 5-10 MINUTES, AND MARKED ERYTHEMA, WHICH SUBSIDED AFTER 1-2 HOURS. SEVERE EXPOSURES MAY RESULT IN VESICULATION AND POSSIBLY BURNS. ABSORPTION MAY OCCUR BUT IS PROBABLY NOT A SIGNIFICANT ROUTE OF EXPOSURE. **CHRONIC EXPOSURE-** REPEATED OR PROLONGED SKIN CONTACT MAY PRODUCE DERMATITIS WITH DRY, SCALY, FISSURED SKIN.

FIRST AID- REMOVE CONTAMINATED CLOTHING AND SHOES IMMEDIATELY. WASH AFFECTED AREA WITH SOAP OR MILD DETERGENT AND LARGE AMOUNTS OF WATER UNTIL NO EVIDENCE OF CHEMICAL REMAINS (APPROXIMATELY 15-20 MINUTES). GET MEDICAL ATTENTION IMMEDIATELY.

EYE CONTACT: TETRACHLOROETHYLENE (PERCHLOROETHYLENE): IRRITANT. **ACUTE EXPOSURE-** VAPOR CONCENTRATIONS FROM 100-200 MAY CAUSE MILD IRRITATION. HIGHER LEVELS OR DIRECT CONTACT MAY CAUSE PAIN, LACRIMATION, AND BURNING, BUT SERIOUS INJURY IS UNLIKELY. AT 1500 PMM, THE IRRITATION IS ALMOST INTOLERABLE. TWO STUDIES OF DIRECT APPLICATION TO RABBIT EYES RESULTED IN CONJUNCTIVITIS AND EFFECTS ON THE CORNEAL EPITHELIUM; RECOVERY WAS COMPLETE IN 2 DAYS TO 2 WEEKS. **CHRONIC EXPOSURE-** REPEATED OR PROLONGED EXPOSURE MAY CAUSE CONJUNCTIVITIS. ONE STUDY HAS REPORTED AN INCREASED INCIDENCE OF LACRIMAL DUCT DISEASE IN EXPOSED WORKERS.

FIRST AID- WASH EYES IMMEDIATELY WITH LARGE AMOUNTS OF WATER OR NORMAL SALINE, OCCASIONALLY LIFTING UPPER AND LOWER LIDS, UNTIL NO EVIDENCE OF CHEMICAL REMAINS (APPROXIMATELY 15-20 MINUTES). GET MEDICAL ATTENTION IMMEDIATELY.

INGESTION: TETRACHLOROETHYLENE (PERCHLOROETHYLENE): NARCOTIC/CARCINOGEN. **ACUTE EXPOSURE-** MAY CAUSE SEVERE GASTROINTESTINAL IRRITATION WITH NAUSEA, VOMITING, ABDOMINAL CRAMPS AND DIARRHEA, POSSIBLY WITH BLOODY STOOLS. NARCOTIC EFFECTS MAY INCLUDE HEADACHE, DIZZINESS, EXHILARATION, INEBRIATION AND OTHER EFFECTS AS IN ACUTE INHALATION. A DOSE OF 500 MG/KG HAS BEEN INGESTED AND SURVIVED. DOGS GIVEN LETHAL DOSES EXHIBITED CARDIAC AND RESPIRATORY DEPRESSION; AUTOPSY REVEALED FATTY INFILTRATION OF THE HEART AND LIVER AND MARKED INFLAMMATION AND SHRIVELING OF THE SMALL INTESTINE. **CHRONIC EXPOSURE-** LONGTERM INGESTION OF 50 MG/KG PRODUCED LIVER AND KIDNEY DAMAGE IN MICE. CHRONIC INGESTION HAS PRODUCED HEPATOCELLULAR CARCINOMAS IN MICE.

FIRST AID- REMOVE BY GASTRIC LAVAGE OR EMESIS. MAINTAIN BLOOD PRESSURE AND AIRWAY. GIVE OXYGEN IF RESPIRATION IS DEPRESSED. DO NOT PERFORM GASTRIC LAVAGE OR EMESIS IF VICTIM IS UNCONSCIOUS. GET MEDICAL ATTENTION IMMEDIATELY (DREISBACH, HANDBOOK OF POISONING, 11TH ED.). ADMINISTRATION OF GASTRIC LAVAGE OR OXYGEN SHOULD BE PERFORMED BY QUALIFIED MEDICAL PERSONNEL.

ANTIDOTE: NO SPECIFIC ANTIDOTE. TREAT SYMPTOMATICALLY AND SUPPORTIVELY.

REACTIVITY

REACTIVITY: STABLE UNDER NORMAL TEMPERATURES AND PRESSURES.

INCOMPATIBILITIES: TETRACHLOROETHYLENE (PERCHLOROETHYLENE): ALUMINUM: MAY FORM EXPLOSIVE MIXTURE. BARIUM: FORMS A DETONABLE MIXTURE. BASES: MAY FORM EXPLOSIVE MIXTURE. BERYLLIUM: POSSIBLE EXPLOSIVE MIXTURE. DINITROGEN TETRAOXIDE: EXPLOSIVE WHEN SUBJECTED TO EXTREME SHOCK. METALS (LIGHT): VIOLENT REACTION. OXYGEN (LIQUID): INCOMPATIBLE. PLASTICS, RUBBER, AND COATINGS: MAY BE ATTACKED. POTASSIUM HYDROXIDE: MAY FORM EXPLOSIVE MIXTURE. SODIUM HYDROXIDE: MAY FORM EXPLOSIVE MIXTURE.

DECOMPOSITION: THERMAL DECOMPOSITION PRODUCTS MAY INCLUDE HIGHLY TOXIC FUMES OF PHOSGENE, TOXIC AND CORROSIVE FUMES OF CHLORIDES, AND OXIDES OF CARBON.

POLYMERIZATION: HAZARDOUS POLYMERIZATION HAS NOT BEEN REPORTED TO OCCUR UNDER NORMAL TEMPERATURES AND PRESSURES.

STORAGE AND DISPOSAL

OBSERVE ALL FEDERAL, STATE AND LOCAL REGULATIONS WHEN STORING OR DISPOSING OF THIS SUBSTANCE. FOR ASSISTANCE, CONTACT THE DISTRICT DIRECTOR OF THE ENVIRONMENTAL PROTECTION AGENCY.

****STORAGE****

STORE IN A COOL, DRY, WELL-VENTILATED LOCATION, AWAY FROM ANY AREA WHERE THE FIRE HAZARD MAY BE ACUTE (NFPA 49, HAZARDOUS CHEMICALS DATA, 1975).

STORE AWAY FROM INCOMPATIBLE SUBSTANCES.

****DISPOSAL****

DISPOSAL MUST BE IN ACCORDANCE WITH STANDARDS APPLICABLE TO GENERATORS OF HAZARDOUS WASTE, 40CFR 262. EPA HAZARDOUS WASTE NUMBER U210.

TETRACHLOROETHYLENE - REGULATORY LEVEL: 0.7 MG/L MATERIALS WHICH CONTAIN THE ABOVE SUBSTANCE AT OR ABOVE THE REGULATORY LEVEL MEET THE EPA CHARACTERISTIC OF TOXICITY, AND MUST BE DISPOSED OF IN ACCORDANCE WITH 40 CFR PART 262. EPA HAZARDOUS WASTE NUMBER D039.

CONDITIONS TO AVOID

MAY BURN BUT DOES NOT IGNITE READILY. CONTAINER MAY EXPLODE IN HEAT OF FIRE.

SPILL AND LEAK PROCEDURES

SOIL SPILL: DIG A HOLDING AREA SUCH AS A PIT, POND OR LAGOON TO CONTAIN SPILL AND DIKE SURFACE FLOW USING BARRIER OF SOIL, SANDBAGS, FOAMED POLYURETHANE OR FOAMED CONCRETE. ABSORB LIQUID MASS WITH FLY ASH OR CEMENT POWDER.

AIR SPILL: APPLY WATER SPRAY TO KNOCK DOWN AND REDUCE VAPORS. KNOCK-DOWN WATER IS CORROSIVE AND TOXIC AND SHOULD BE DIKED FOR CONTAINMENT AND LATER DISPOSAL.

WATER SPILL: USE ACTIVATED CARBON TO ABSORB SPILLED SUBSTANCE THAT IS DISSOLVED.

USE SUCTION HOSES TO REMOVE TRAPPED SPILL MATERIAL.

THE CALIFORNIA SAFE DRINKING WATER AND TOXIC ENFORCEMENT ACT OF 1986 (PROPOSITION 65) PROHIBITS CONTAMINATING ANY KNOWN SOURCE OF DRINKING WATER WITH SUBSTANCES KNOWN TO CAUSE CANCER AND/OR REPRODUCTIVE TOXICITY.

OCCUPATIONAL SPILL: SHUT OFF IGNITION SOURCES. STOP LEAK IF YOU CAN DO IT WITHOUT RISK. FOR SMALL LIQUID SPILLS, TAKE UP WITH SAND, EARTH OR OTHER ABSORBENT MATERIAL. FOR LARGER SPILLS, DIKE FAR AHEAD OF SPILL FOR LATER DISPOSAL. NO SMOKING, FLAMES OR FLARES IN HAZARD AREA! KEEP UNNECESSARY PEOPLE AWAY.

REPORTABLE QUANTITY (RQ): 1 POUND THE SUPERFUND AMENDMENTS AND REAUTHORIZATION ACT (SARA) SECTION 304 REQUIRES THAT A RELEASE EQUAL

TO OR GREATER THAN THE REPORTABLE QUANTITY FOR THIS SUBSTANCE BE IMMEDIATELY REPORTED TO THE LOCAL EMERGENCY PLANNING COMMITTEE AND THE STATE EMERGENCY RESPONSE COMMISSION (40 CFR 355.40). IF THE RELEASE OF THIS SUBSTANCE IS REPORTABLE UNDER CERCLA SECTION 103, THE NATIONAL RESPONSE CENTER MUST BE NOTIFIED IMMEDIATELY AT (800) 424-8802 OR (202) 426-2675 IN THE METROPOLITAN WASHINGTON, D.C. AREA (40 CFR 302.6).

PROTECTIVE EQUIPMENT

VENTILATION: PROVIDE LOCAL EXHAUST OR PROCESS ENCLOSURE VENTILATION TO MEET PUBLISHED EXPOSURE LIMITS.

RESPIRATOR: THE FOLLOWING RESPIRATORS AND MAXIMUM USE CONCENTRATIONS ARE RECOMMENDATIONS BY THE U.S. DEPARTMENT OF HEALTH AND HUMAN SERVICES, NIOSH POCKET GUIDE TO CHEMICAL HAZARDS; NIOSH CRITERIA DOCUMENTS OR BY THE U.S. DEPARTMENT OF LABOR, 29 CFR 1910 SUBPART Z. THE SPECIFIC RESPIRATOR SELECTED MUST BE BASED ON CONTAMINATION LEVELS FOUND IN THE WORK PLACE, MUST NOT EXCEED THE WORKING LIMITS OF THE RESPIRATOR AND BE JOINTLY APPROVED BY THE NATIONAL INSTITUTE FOR OCCUPATIONAL SAFETY AND HEALTH AND THE MINE SAFETY AND HEALTH ADMINISTRATION (NIOSH-MSHA).

TETRACHLOROETHYLENE:

AT ANY DETECTABLE CONCENTRATION:

AIR-PURIFYING FULL FACEPIECE RESPIRATOR (GAS MASK) WITH A CHIN-STYLE OR FRONT- OR BACK-MOUNTED ORGANIC VAPOR CANISTER. SELF-CONTAINED BREATHING APPARATUS WITH FULL FACEPIECE OPERATED IN PRESSURE-DEMAND OR OTHER POSITIVE PRESSURE MODE. SUPPLIED-AIR RESPIRATOR WITH FULL FACEPIECE OPERATED IN PRESSURE-DEMAND OR OTHER POSITIVE PRESSURE MODE IN COMBINATION WITH AN AUXILIARY SELF-CONTAINED BREATHING APPARATUS OPERATED IN PRESSURE-DEMAND OR OTHER POSITIVE PRESSURE MODE.

ESCAPE- AIR-PURIFYING FULL FACEPIECE RESPIRATOR (GAS MASK) WITH A CHIN-STYLE OR FRONT- OR BACK-MOUNTED ORGANIC VAPOR CANISTER. ESCAPE-TYPE SELF-CONTAINED BREATHING APPARATUS.

FOR FIREFIGHTING AND OTHER IMMEDIATELY DANGEROUS TO LIFE OR HEALTH CONDITIONS:

SELF-CONTAINED BREATHING APPARATUS WITH FULL FACEPIECE OPERATED IN PRESSURE-DEMAND OR OTHER POSITIVE PRESSURE MODE.

SUPPLIED-AIR RESPIRATOR WITH FULL FACEPIECE AND OPERATED IN PRESSURE-DEMAND OR OTHER POSITIVE PRESSURE MODE IN COMBINATION WITH AN AUXILIARY SELF-CONTAINED BREATHING APPARATUS OPERATED IN PRESSURE-DEMAND OR OTHER POSITIVE PRESSURE MODE.

CLOTHING: EMPLOYEE MUST WEAR APPROPRIATE PROTECTIVE (IMPERVIOUS) CLOTHING AND EQUIPMENT TO PREVENT REPEATED OR PROLONGED SKIN CONTACT WITH THIS SUBSTANCE.

GLOVES: EMPLOYEE MUST WEAR APPROPRIATE PROTECTIVE GLOVES TO PREVENT CONTACT WITH THIS SUBSTANCE.

EYE PROTECTION: EMPLOYEE MUST WEAR SPLASH-PROOF OR DUST-RESISTANT SAFETY GOGGLES TO PREVENT EYE CONTACT WITH THIS SUBSTANCE.

EMERGENCY EYE WASH: WHERE THERE IS ANY POSSIBILITY THAT AN EMPLOYEE'S EYES MAY BE EXPOSED TO THIS SUBSTANCE, THE EMPLOYER SHOULD PROVIDE AN EYE WASH FOUNTAIN WITHIN THE IMMEDIATE WORK AREA FOR EMERGENCY USE.

AUTHORIZED BY- OCCUPATIONAL HEALTH SERVICES, INC.

CREATION DATE: 10/05/89 ***REVISION DATE:*** 07/13/90

MATERIAL SAFETY DATA SHEET

OCCUPATIONAL HEALTH SERVICES, INC.
AGRICULTURE AND PESTICIDE DIVISION
450 SEVENTH AVENUE, SUITE 2407
NEW YORK, NEW YORK 10123
1-800-445-MSDS OR (212) 967-1100

EMERGENCY CONTACT:
JOHN S. BRANSFORD, JR. (615) 292-1180

SUBSTANCE IDENTIFICATION

CAS-NUMBER 27954-37-6

SUBSTANCE: **TETRAFLUORON**

TRADE NAMES/SYNONYMS: UREA, N,N-DIMETHYL-N'-(3-(1,1,2,2-TETRAFLUOROETHOXY)PHENYL)-; UREA, 1,1-DIMETHYL-3-(M-(1,1,2,2-TETRAFLUOROETHOXY)PHENYL)-; N,N-DIMETHYL-N'-(3-(1,1,2,2-TETRAFLUOROETHOXY)PHENYL)UREA; 1,1-DIMETHYL-3-(M-(1,1,2,2-TETRAFLUOROETHOXY)PHENYL)UREA; FLUORETOXURON; HOE 2991; TOMILON; C11F4H12N2O2; PST23002

CHEMICAL FAMILY: SUBSTITUTED UREA
HALOGEN COMPOUND, AROMATIC

MOLECULAR FORMULA: C11-H12-F4-N2-O2

MOLECULAR WEIGHT: 280.25

CERCLA RATINGS (SCALE 0-3): HEALTH=1 FIRE=1 REACTIVITY=0 PERSISTENCE=3

NFPA RATINGS (SCALE 0-4): HEALTH=1 FIRE=1 REACTIVITY=0

COMPONENTS AND CONTAMINANTS

COMPONENT: TETRAFLUORON ***PERCENT:*** 100.0
CAS# 27954-37-6

OTHER CONTAMINANTS: NONE

EXPOSURE LIMITS: NO OCCUPATIONAL EXPOSURE LIMITS ESTABLISHED BY OSHA, ACGIH, OR NIOSH.

PHYSICAL DATA

DESCRIPTION: WHITE CRYSTALLINE SOLID. ***MELTING POINT:*** 239-243 F (115-117 C)

SPECIFIC GRAVITY: NOT AVAILABLE ***SOLUBILITY IN WATER:*** 225 PPM @ 23 C

FIRE AND EXPLOSION DATA

FIRE AND EXPLOSION HAZARD: SLIGHT FIRE HAZARD WHEN EXPOSED TO HEAT OR FLAME.

FIREFIGHTING MEDIA: DRY CHEMICAL, CARBON DIOXIDE, HALON, WATER SPRAY OR STANDARD FOAM (1987 EMERGENCY RESPONSE GUIDEBOOK, DOT P 5800.4). FOR LARGER FIRES, USE WATER SPRAY, FOG OR STANDARD FOAM (1987 EMERGENCY RESPONSE GUIDEBOOK, DOT P 5800.4).

FIREFIGHTING: MOVE CONTAINERS FROM FIRE AREA IF POSSIBLE. FIGHT FIRE FROM MAXIMUM DISTANCE. STAY AWAY FROM STORAGE TANK ENDS. DIKE FIRE CONTROL WATER FOR LATER DISPOSAL. DO NOT SCATTER MATERIAL (1987 EMERGENCY RESPONSE GUIDEBOOK, DOT P 5800.4, GUIDE PAGE 55). EXTINGUISH USING AGENT SUITABLE FOR TYPE OF SURROUNDING FIRE. USE WATER IN FLOODING QUANTITIES AS FOG. KEEP SPARKS, FLAMES AND OTHER SOURCES OF IGNITION AWAY. KEEP MATERIAL OUT OF WATER SOURCES AND SEWERS. DO NOT TOUCH MATERIAL AND AVOID BREATHING DUSTS AND FUMES FROM BURNING MATERIAL. KEEP UPWIND.

TOXICITY

TETRAFLUORON: TOXICITY DATA: 1265 MG/KG ORAL-RAT LD50. CARCINOGEN STATUS: NONE. ACUTE TOXICITY LEVEL: MODERATELY TOXIC BY INGESTION. TARGET EFFECTS: NO DATA AVAILABLE.

HEALTH EFFECTS AND FIRST AID

INHALATION: TETRAFLUORON: **ACUTE EXPOSURE**- MANY SUBSTITUTED UREA HERBICIDES ARE MODERATELY IRRITATING TO THE MUCOUS MEMBRANES. **CHRONIC EXPOSURE**- NO DATA AVAILABLE.

FIRST AID- REMOVE FROM EXPOSURE AREA TO FRESH AIR IMMEDIATELY. IF BREATHING HAS STOPPED, PERFORM ARTIFICIAL RESPIRATION. KEEP PERSON WARM AND AT REST. TREAT SYMPTOMATICALLY AND SUPPORTIVELY. GET MEDICAL ATTENTION IMMEDIATELY.

SKIN CONTACT: TETRAFLUORON: **ACUTE EXPOSURE**- MANY SUBSTITUTED UREA HERBICIDES ARE MODERATELY IRRITATING TO THE SKIN. A LETHAL DOSE BY DERMAL ABSORPTION IN RATS IS GREATER THAN 2000 MG/KG. **CHRONIC EXPOSURE**- NO DATA AVAILABLE.

FIRST AID- REMOVE CONTAMINATED CLOTHING AND SHOES IMMEDIATELY. WASH AFFECTED AREA WITH SOAP OR MILD DETERGENT AND LARGE AMOUNTS OF WATER UNTIL NO EVIDENCE OF CHEMICAL REMAINS (APPROXIMATELY 15-20 MINUTES). GET MEDICAL ATTENTION IMMEDIATELY.

EYE CONTACT: TETRAFLUORON: **ACUTE EXPOSURE**- MANY SUBSTITUTED UREA HERBICIDES ARE MODERATELY IRRITATING TO THE EYES. **CHRONIC EXPOSURE**- NO DATA AVAILABLE. **FIRST AID**- WASH EYES IMMEDIATELY WITH LARGE AMOUNTS OF WATER OR NORMAL SALINE, OCCASIONALLY LIFTING UPPER AND LOWER LIDS, UNTIL NO EVIDENCE OF CHEMICAL REMAINS (APPROXIMATELY 15-20 MINUTES). GET MEDICAL ATTENTION IMMEDIATELY.

INGESTION: TETRAFLUORON: **ACUTE EXPOSURE**- A LETHAL DOSE IN RATS WAS 1265 MG/KG. **CHRONIC EXPOSURE**- NO DATA AVAILABLE.

FIRST AID- REMOVE BY GASTRIC LAVAGE AND CATHARSIS. MAINTAIN BLOOD PRESSURE AND AIRWAY. GIVE OXYGEN IF RESPIRATION IS DEPRESSED. DO NOT PERFORM GASTRIC LAVAGE IF VICTIM IS UNCONSCIOUS. GET MEDICAL ATTENTION IMMEDIATELY (DREISBACH, HANDBOOK OF POISONING, 12TH ED.). ADMINISTRATION OF LAVAGE OR OXYGEN SHOULD BE PERFORMED BY QUALIFIED MEDICAL PERSONNEL.

ANTIDOTE: NO SPECIFIC ANTIDOTE. TREAT SYMPTOMATICALLY AND SUPPORTIVELY.

REACTIVITY

REACTIVITY: STABLE UNDER NORMAL TEMPERATURES AND PRESSURES.
INCOMPATIBILITIES: TETRAFLUORON: OXIDIZERS (STRONG): FIRE AND EXPLOSION HAZARD.
DECOMPOSITION: THERMAL DECOMPOSITION PRODUCTS MAY INCLUDE TOXIC AND CORROSIVE FUMES OF FLUORIDES AND TOXIC OXIDES OF CARBON.
POLYMERIZATION: HAZARDOUS POLYMERIZATION HAS NOT BEEN REPORTED TO OCCUR UNDER NORMAL TEMPERATURES AND PRESSURES.

STORAGE AND DISPOSAL

OBSERVE ALL FEDERAL, STATE AND LOCAL REGULATIONS WHEN STORING OR DISPOSING OF THIS SUBSTANCE. FOR ASSISTANCE, CONTACT THE DISTRICT DIRECTOR OF THE ENVIRONMENTAL PROTECTION AGENCY.

STORAGE

STORE IN ACCORDANCE WITH 40 CFR 165 RECOMMENDED PROCEDURES FOR THE DISPOSAL AND STORAGE OF PESTICIDES AND PESTICIDE CONTAINERS.
STORE AWAY FROM INCOMPATIBLE SUBSTANCES.

DISPOSAL

DISPOSAL MUST BE IN ACCORDANCE WITH 40 CFR 165 RECOMMENDED PROCEDURES FOR THE DISPOSAL AND STORAGE OF PESTICIDES AND PESTICIDE CONTAINERS.

CONDITIONS TO AVOID

MAY BURN BUT DOES NOT IGNITE READILY. CONTAINERS MAY EXPLODE IN HEAT OF FIRE.

SPILL AND LEAK PROCEDURES

OCCUPATIONAL SPILL: DO NOT TOUCH SPILLED MATERIAL. STOP LEAK IF YOU CAN DO IT WITHOUT RISK. USE WATER SPRAY TO REDUCE VAPORS. FOR SMALL SPILLS, TAKE UP WITH SAND OR OTHER ABSORBENT MATERIAL AND PLACE INTO CONTAINERS FOR LATER DISPOSAL. FOR SMALL DRY SPILLS, WITH A CLEAN SHOVEL PLACE MATERIAL INTO CLEAN, DRY CONTAINERS AND COVER. MOVE CONTAINERS FROM SPILL AREA. FOR LARGER SPILLS, DIKE FAR AHEAD OF SPILL FOR LATER DISPOSAL. KEEP UNNECESSARY PEOPLE AWAY. ISOLATE HAZARD AREA AND DENY ENTRY. VENTILATE CLOSED SPACES BEFORE ENTERING.

PROTECTIVE EQUIPMENT

VENTILATION: PROVIDE LOCAL EXHAUST OR GENERAL DILUTION VENTILATION SYSTEM.
RESPIRATOR: THE FOLLOWING RESPIRATORS ARE RECOMMENDED BASED ON INFORMATION FOUND IN THE PHYSICAL DATA, TOXICITY AND HEALTH EFFECTS SECTIONS. THEY ARE RANKED IN ORDER FROM MINIMUM TO MAXIMUM RESPIRATORY PROTECTION. THE SPECIFIC RESPIRATOR SELECTED MUST BE BASED ON CONTAMINATION LEVELS FOUND IN THE WORK PLACE, MUST NOT EXCEED THE WORKING LIMITS OF THE RESPIRATOR AND BE JOINTLY APPROVED BY THE NATIONAL INSTITUTE FOR OCCUPATIONAL SAFETY AND HEALTH AND THE MINE SAFETY AND HEALTH ADMINISTRATION (NIOSH-MSHA).
CHEMICAL CARTRIDGE RESPIRATOR WITH AN ORGANIC VAPOR CARTRIDGE(S) WITH A FULL FACEPIECE AND ORGANIC VAPOR CARTRIDGE(S) IN COMBINATION WITH A DUST AND MIST FILTER.
POWERED AIR-PURIFYING RESPIRATOR WITH A TIGHT-FITTING FACEPIECE AND ORGANIC VAPOR CARTRIDGE(S) IN COMBINATION WITH A HIGH-EFFICIENCY PARTICULATE FILTER.
TYPE 'C' SUPPLIED-AIR RESPIRATOR WITH A FULL FACEPIECE OPERATED IN A PRESSURE-DEMAND OR OTHER POSITIVE PRESSURE MODE.
SELF-CONTAINED BREATHING APPARATUS WITH A FULL FACEPIECE OPERATED IN PRESSURE-DEMAND OR OTHER POSITIVE PRESSURE MODE.
FOR FIREFIGHTING AND OTHER IMMEDIATELY DANGEROUS TO LIFE OR HEALTH CONDITIONS:
SELF-CONTAINED BREATHING APPARATUS WITH FULL FACEPIECE OPERATED IN PRESSURE-DEMAND OR OTHER POSITIVE PRESSURE MODE.
SUPPLIED-AIR RESPIRATOR WITH FULL FACEPIECE AND OPERATED IN PRESSURE-DEMAND OR OTHER POSITIVE PRESSURE MODE IN COMBINATION WITH AN AUXILIARY SELF-CONTAINED BREATHING APPARATUS OPERATED IN PRESSURE-DEMAND OR OTHER POSITIVE PRESSURE MODE.
CLOTHING: EMPLOYEE MUST WEAR APPROPRIATE PROTECTIVE (IMPERVIOUS) CLOTHING AND EQUIPMENT TO PREVENT REPEATED OR PROLONGED SKIN CONTACT WITH THIS SUBSTANCE.
GLOVES: EMPLOYEE MUST WEAR APPROPRIATE PROTECTIVE GLOVES TO PREVENT CONTACT WITH THIS SUBSTANCE.
EYE PROTECTION: EMPLOYEE MUST WEAR SPLASH-PROOF OR DUST-RESISTANT SAFETY GOGGLES TO PREVENT EYE CONTACT WITH THIS SUBSTANCE.
EMERGENCY EYE WASH: WHERE THERE IS ANY POSSIBILITY THAT AN EMPLOYEE'S EYES MAY BE EXPOSED TO THIS SUBSTANCE, THE EMPLOYER SHOULD PROVIDE AN EYE WASH FOUNTAIN WITHIN THE IMMEDIATE WORK AREA FOR EMERGENCY USE.

AUTHORIZED BY- OCCUPATIONAL HEALTH SERVICES, INC.
CREATION DATE: 10/05/89 ***REVISION DATE:*** 05/10/90

MATERIAL SAFETY DATA SHEET

OCCUPATIONAL HEALTH SERVICES, INC.
AGRICULTURE AND PESTICIDE DIVISION
450 SEVENTH AVENUE, SUITE 2407
NEW YORK, NEW YORK 10123
1-800-445-MSDS OR (212) 967-1100

EMERGENCY CONTACT:
JOHN S. BRANSFORD, JR. (615) 292-1180

SUBSTANCE IDENTIFICATION

CAS-NUMBER 7696-12-0
SUBSTANCE: TETRAMETHRIN
TRADE NAMES/SYNONYMS: 2,2-DIMETHYL-3-(2-METHYL-1-PROPENYL)-CYCLOPROPANECARBOXYLIC ACID, (1,3,4,5,6,7,-HEXAHYDRO-1,3-DIOXO-2H-ISOINDOL-2-YL)METHYL ESTER; 2,2-DIMETHYL-3-(2-METHYLPROPENYL)-CYCLOPROPANECARBOXYLIC ACID, ESTER WITH N-(HYDROXYMETHYL)-1-CYCLOHEXENE-1,2-DICARBOXIMIDE; 3,4,5,6-TETRAHYDROPHTHALIMIDOMETHYL(1RS)-CIS,TRANS-CHRYSANTHEMATE; (1,3,4,5,6,7-HEXAHYDRO-1,3-DIOXO-2H-ISOINDOL-2-YL)METHYL 2,2-DIMETHYL -3-(2-METHYL-1-PROPENYL)CYCLOPROPANECARBOXYLATE; 1-CYCLOHEXENE-1,2-DICARBOXIMIDOMETHYL 2,2-DIMETHYL-3-(2 -METHYLPROPENYL)CYCLOPROPANECARBOXYLATE; BIONEOPYNAMIN; INSECTOL; NEOPYNAMIN; PHTHALTHRIN; ENT 27339; PST23061
CHEMICAL FAMILY: PYRETHROID (SYNTHETIC)
MOLECULAR FORMULA: C19-H25-N-O4
MOLECULAR WEIGHT: 331.45
CERCLA RATINGS (SCALE 0-3): HEALTH=1 FIRE=U REACTIVITY=0 PERSISTENCE=2
NFPA RATINGS (SCALE 0-4): HEALTH=1 FIRE=U REACTIVITY=0

COMPONENTS AND CONTAMINANTS

COMPONENT: TETRAMETHRIN ***PERCENT:*** 100.0
CAS# 7696-12-0
OTHER CONTAMINANTS: NONE
EXPOSURE LIMITS: NO OCCUPATIONAL EXPOSURE LIMITS ESTABLISHED BY OSHA, ACGIH, OR NIOSH.

PHYSICAL DATA

DESCRIPTION: WHITE CRYSTALLINE SOLID WITH A SLIGHT PYRETHRUM-LIKE ODOR
BOILING POINT: 365-374 F (185-190 C) @ 0.13 MBAR
MELTING POINT: 149-176 F (65-80 C) ***SPECIFIC GRAVITY:*** 1.108 @ 20 C
VAPOR PRESSURE: .000000047 @ 20 C ***SOLUBILITY IN WATER:*** INSOLUBLE
SOLVENT SOLUBILITY: AROMATIC HYDROCARBONS, ALIPHATIC HYDROCARBONS

FIRE AND EXPLOSION DATA

FIRE AND EXPLOSION HAZARD: UNKNOWN FIRE AND EXPLOSION HAZARD.
FIREFIGHTING MEDIA: DRY CHEMICAL, CARBON DIOXIDE, HALON, WATER SPRAY OR STANDARD FOAM (1987 EMERGENCY RESPONSE GUIDEBOOK, DOT P 5800.4).
FOR LARGER FIRES, USE WATER SPRAY, FOG OR STANDARD FOAM (1987 EMERGENCY RESPONSE GUIDEBOOK, DOT P 5800.4).
FIREFIGHTING: MOVE CONTAINER FROM FIRE AREA IF POSSIBLE. DO NOT SCATTER SPILLED MATERIAL WITH HIGH PRESSURE WATER STREAMS. DIKE FIRE CONTROL WATER FOR LATER DISPOSAL (1987 EMERGENCY RESPONSE GUIDEBOOK, DOT P 5800.4, GUIDE PAGE 31).
USE AGENTS SUITABLE FOR TYPE OF SURROUNDING FIRE. AVOID BREATHING HAZARDOUS VAPORS, KEEP UPWIND.

TOXICITY

TETRAMETHRIN: IRRITATION DATA: 100 MG/1 HOUR EYE-RABBIT MILD. TOXICITY DATA: 4640 MG/KG ORAL-RAT LD50; 1000 MG/KG ORAL-MOUSE LD50; 5700 MG/KG SUBCUTANEOUS-RAT LD50; 1950 MG/KG SUBCUTANEOUS-MOUSE LD50; 3500 UG/KG INTRAVENOUS-RAT LD50; 548 MG/KG INTRAPERITONEAL-RAT LD50; 527 MG/KG INTRAPERITONEAL-MOUSE LD50; MUTAGENIC DATA (RTECS). CARCINOGEN STATUS: NONE. ACUTE TOXICITY LEVEL: MODERATELY TOXIC BY INGESTION. TARGET EFFECTS: POISONING MAY AFFECT THE CENTRAL NERVOUS SYSTEM.

HEALTH EFFECTS AND FIRST AID

INHALATION: TETRAMETHRIN: **ACUTE EXPOSURE-** AT A CONCENTRATION OF APPROXIMATELY 2000 MG/M3, THIS MATERIAL PRODUCED SYMPTOMS OF HYPERSENSITIVITY, MOTOR ATAXIA, AND URINARY INCONTINENCE, BUT NO FATALITIES IN MICE AND RATS. TETRAMETHRIN IS A SYNTHETIC PYRETHRIN. SYNTHETIC PYRETHRINS, LIKE THE NATURAL PYRETHRINS, PRODUCE CENTRAL NERVOUS SYSTEM STIMULATION IN ANIMALS WITH SYMPTOMS OF NAUSEA, VOMITING, GASTROENTERITIS WITH DIARRHEA, HYPERSENSITIVITY, INCOORDINATION, TREMORS, MUSCULAR PARALYSIS, CONVULSION, COMA, AND DEATH DUE TO RESPIRATORY FAILURE. UNLIKE NATURAL PYRETHRINS, SYNTHETIC PYRETHRINS NORMALLY DO NOT PRODUCE ALLERGIC REACTIONS IN HUMANS. **CHRONIC EXPOSURE-** IN ONE STUDY OF TETRAMETHRIN, CHRONIC EXPOSURE OF RATS AND MICE TO MIST PREPARATIONS OF 210 MG/M3/4 HOURS 5 DAYS A WEEK FOR 4 WEEKS DID NOT PRODUCED ANY ADVERSE EFFECTS ON THE MAJOR ORGANS AND TISSUES.

FIRST AID- REMOVE FROM EXPOSURE AREA TO FRESH AIR IMMEDIATELY. IF BREATHING HAS STOPPED, PERFORM ARTIFICIAL RESPIRATION. KEEP PERSON WARM AND AT REST. TREAT SYMPTOMATICALLY AND SUPPORTIVELY. GET MEDICAL ATTENTION IMMEDIATELY.

SKIN CONTACT: TETRAMETHRIN: **ACUTE EXPOSURE-** THE RESULT OF A PATCH TEST INVOLVING 200 HUMAN VOLUNTEERS, INDICATED THAT TETRAMETHRIN WAS NOT AN IRRITANT OR A SENSITIZER TO HUMAN SKIN. TETRAMETHRIN IS A SYNTHETIC PYRETHRIN. SYNTHETIC PYRETHRINS GENERALLY ARE NOT IRRITANTS TO RABBIT SKIN AND THE TOXICITY FROM DERMAL ABSORPTION IS USUALLY MODERATE TO LOW. **CHRONIC EXPOSURE-** NO DATA AVAILABLE.

FIRST AID- REMOVE CONTAMINATED CLOTHING AND SHOES IMMEDIATELY. WASH AFFECTED AREA WITH SOAP OR MILD DETERGENT AND LARGE AMOUNTS OF WATER UNTIL NO EVIDENCE OF CHEMICAL REMAINS (APPROXIMATELY 15-20 MINUTES). GET MEDICAL ATTENTION IMMEDIATELY.

EYE CONTACT: TETRAMETHRIN: **ACUTE EXPOSURE-** 100 MG APPLIED TO RABBIT EYES FOR 1 HOUR PRODUCED MILD IRRITATION. IN ANOTHER STUDY, MASSIVE INSTILLATION OF TETRAMETHRIN INTO RABBIT EYES PRODUCED A SLIGHT, TRANSIENT CONGESTION OF CONJUNCTIVA OR LACRIMATION BUT THE EFFECT WAS NOT SEVERE ENOUGH TO BE CONSIDERED AN IRRITANT. **CHRONIC EXPOSURE-** NO DATA AVAILABLE.

FIRST AID- WASH EYES IMMEDIATELY WITH LARGE AMOUNTS OF WATER OR NORMAL SALINE, OCCASIONALLY LIFTING UPPER AND LOWER LIDS, UNTIL NO EVIDENCE OF CHEMICAL REMAINS (APPROXIMATELY 15-20 MINUTES). GET MEDICAL ATTENTION IMMEDIATELY.

INGESTION: TETRAMETHRIN: **ACUTE EXPOSURE-** A HIGH DOSE WAS LETHAL TO RATS. TETRAMETHRIN IS A SYNTHETIC PYRETHRIN. SYNTHETIC PYRETHRINS, LIKE THE NATURAL PYRETHRINS, PRODUCE CENTRAL NERVOUS SYSTEM STIMULATION IN ANIMALS WITH SYMPTOMS OF NAUSEA, VOMITING, GASTROENTERITIS WITH DIARRHEA, HYPERSENSITIVITY, INCOORDINATION, TREMORS, MUSCULAR PARALYSIS, CONVULSION, COMA, AND DEATH DUE TO RESPIRATORY FAILURE. **CHRONIC EXPOSURE-** RATS FED A DIETARY CONCENTRATION OF 2000 PPM FOR 3 MONTHS, EXPERIENCED NO ADVERSE EFFECTS.

FIRST AID- TREAT SYMPTOMATICALLY AND SUPPORTIVELY. GET MEDICAL ATTENTION IMMEDIATELY. IF VOMITING OCCURS, KEEP HEAD LOWER THAN HIPS TO PREVENT ASPIRATION.

ANTIDOTE: NO SPECIFIC ANTIDOTE. TREAT SYMPTOMATICALLY AND SUPPORTIVELY.

REACTIVITY

REACTIVITY: STABLE UNDER NORMAL TEMPERATURES AND PRESSURES.

INCOMPATIBILITIES: TETRAMETHRIN: ALKALIES: INCOMPATIBLE. STRONG ACIDS: INCOMPATIBLE. ALCOHOLIC SOLUTION: UNSTABLE.

DECOMPOSITION: THERMAL DECOMPOSITION PRODUCTS MAY INCLUDE TOXIC OXIDES OF NITROGEN.

POLYMERIZATION: HAZARDOUS POLYMERIZATION HAS NOT BEEN REPORTED TO OCCUR UNDER NORMAL TEMPERATURES AND PRESSURES.

STORAGE AND DISPOSAL

OBSERVE ALL FEDERAL, STATE AND LOCAL REGULATIONS WHEN STORING OR DISPOSING OF THIS SUBSTANCE. FOR ASSISTANCE, CONTACT THE DISTRICT DIRECTOR OF THE ENVIRONMENTAL PROTECTION AGENCY.

****STORAGE****

STORE IN ACCORDANCE WITH 40 CFR 165 RECOMMENDED PROCEDURES FOR THE DISPOSAL AND STORAGE OF PESTICIDES AND PESTICIDE CONTAINERS.

STORE AWAY FROM INCOMPATIBLE SUBSTANCES.

****DISPOSAL****

DISPOSAL MUST BE IN ACCORDANCE WITH 40 CFR 165 RECOMMENDED PROCEDURES FOR THE DISPOSAL AND STORAGE OF PESTICIDES AND PESTICIDE CONTAINERS.

CONDITIONS TO AVOID

NONE REPORTED.

SPILL AND LEAK PROCEDURES

OCCUPATIONAL SPILL: SWEEP UP AND PLACE IN SUITABLE (FIBERBOARD) CONTAINERS FOR RECLAMATION OR LATER DISPOSAL.

PROTECTIVE EQUIPMENT

VENTILATION: PROVIDE LOCAL EXHAUST OR GENERAL DILUTION VENTILATION SYSTEM.

RESPIRATOR: THE FOLLOWING RESPIRATORS ARE RECOMMENDED BASED ON INFORMATION FOUND IN THE PHYSICAL DATA, TOXICITY AND HEALTH EFFECTS SECTIONS. THEY ARE RANKED IN ORDER FROM MINIMUM TO MAXIMUM RESPIRATORY PROTECTION. THE SPECIFIC RESPIRATOR SELECTED MUST BE BASED ON CONTAMINATION LEVELS FOUND IN THE WORK PLACE, MUST NOT EXCEED THE WORKING LIMITS OF THE RESPIRATOR AND BE JOINTLY APPROVED BY THE NATIONAL INSTITUTE FOR OCCUPATIONAL SAFETY AND HEALTH AND THE MINE SAFETY AND HEALTH ADMINISTRATION (NIOSH-MSHA).

CHEMICAL CARTRIDGE RESPIRATOR WITH AN ORGANIC VAPOR CARTRIDGE(S) IN COMBINATION WITH A DUST AND MIST FILTER.

GAS MASK WITH ORGANIC VAPOR CANISTER (CHIN-STYLE OR FRONT- OR BACK-MOUNTED CANISTER) WITH A DUST AND MIST FILTER.

GAS MASK WITH ORGANIC VAPOR CANISTER (CHIN-STYLE OR FRONT- OR BACK-MOUNTED CANISTER) WITH A PARTICULATE FILTER.

POWERED AIR-PURIFYING RESPIRATOR WITH A HIGH-EFFICIENCY FILTER.

TYPE 'C' SUPPLIED-AIR RESPIRATOR WITH A FULL FACEPIECE OPERATED IN A PRESSURE-DEMAND OR OTHER POSITIVE PRESSURE MODE.

SELF-CONTAINED BREATHING APPARATUS WITH A FULL FACEPIECE OPERATED IN PRESSURE-DEMAND OR OTHER POSITIVE PRESSURE MODE.

FOR FIREFIGHTING AND OTHER IMMEDIATELY DANGEROUS TO LIFE OR HEALTH CONDITIONS:

SELF-CONTAINED BREATHING APPARATUS WITH FULL FACEPIECE OPERATED IN PRESSURE-DEMAND OR OTHER POSITIVE PRESSURE MODE.

SUPPLIED-AIR RESPIRATOR WITH FULL FACEPIECE AND OPERATED IN PRESSURE-DEMAND OR OTHER POSITIVE PRESSURE MODE IN COMBINATION WITH AN AUXILIARY SELF-CONTAINED BREATHING APPARATUS OPERATED IN PRESSURE-DEMAND OR OTHER POSITIVE PRESSURE MODE.

CLOTHING: EMPLOYEE MUST WEAR APPROPRIATE PROTECTIVE (IMPERVIOUS) CLOTHING AND EQUIPMENT TO PREVENT REPEATED OR PROLONGED SKIN CONTACT WITH THIS SUBSTANCE.

GLOVES: EMPLOYEE MUST WEAR APPROPRIATE PROTECTIVE GLOVES TO PREVENT CONTACT WITH THIS SUBSTANCE.

EYE PROTECTION: EMPLOYEE MUST WEAR SPLASH-PROOF OR DUST-RESISTANT SAFETY GOGGLES TO PREVENT EYE CONTACT WITH THIS SUBSTANCE.

EMERGENCY EYE WASH: WHERE THERE IS ANY POSSIBILITY THAT AN EMPLOYEE'S EYES MAY BE EXPOSED TO THIS SUBSTANCE, THE EMPLOYER SHOULD PROVIDE AN EYE WASH FOUNTAIN WITHIN THE IMMEDIATE WORK AREA FOR EMERGENCY USE.

AUTHORIZED BY- OCCUPATIONAL HEALTH SERVICES, INC.

CREATION DATE: 10/05/89 ***REVISION DATE:*** 05/17/90

MATERIAL SAFETY DATA SHEET

OCCUPATIONAL HEALTH SERVICES, INC.
AGRICULTURE AND PESTICIDE DIVISION
450 SEVENTH AVENUE, SUITE 2407
NEW YORK, NEW YORK 10123
1-800-445-MSDS OR (212) 967-1100

EMERGENCY CONTACT:
JOHN S. BRANSFORD, JR. (615) 292-1180

SUBSTANCE IDENTIFICATION

CAS-NUMBER 51348-90-4

SUBSTANCE: **(+)-CIS-TETRAMETHRIN**

TRADE NAMES/SYNONYMS: 2,2-DIMETHYL-3-(2-METHYL-1-PROPENYL)-CYCLOPROPANECARBOXYLIC ACID, (1,3,4,5,6,7,-HEXAHYDRO-1,3-DIOXO-2H-ISOINDOL-2-YL)METHYL ESTER, (1R-CIS)-; (1R)-CIS-TETRAMETHRIN; PST23062

CHEMICAL FAMILY: PYRETHROID (SYNTHETIC)

MOLECULAR FORMULA: C19-H25-N-O4

MOLECULAR WEIGHT: 331.45

CERCLA RATINGS (SCALE 0-3): HEALTH=3 FIRE=U REACTIVITY=0 PERSISTENCE=2
NFPA RATINGS (SCALE 0-4): HEALTH=3 FIRE=U REACTIVITY=0

COMPONENTS AND CONTAMINANTS

COMPONENT: (+)-CIS-TETRAMETHRIN ***PERCENT:*** 100.0
CAS# 51348-90-4
OTHER CONTAMINANTS: NONE
EXPOSURE LIMITS: NO OCCUPATIONAL EXPOSURE LIMITS ESTABLISHED BY OSHA, ACGIH, OR NIOSH.

PHYSICAL DATA

DESCRIPTION: WHITE CRYSTALLINE SOLID WITH A SLIGHT PYRETHRUM-LIKE ODOR
SPECIFIC GRAVITY: NOT AVAILABLE ***SOLUBILITY IN WATER:*** NOT AVAILABLE
SOLVENT SOLUBILITY: AROMATIC HYDROCARBONS, ALIPHATIC HYDROCARBONS

FIRE AND EXPLOSION DATA

FIRE AND EXPLOSION HAZARD: UNKNOWN FIRE AND EXPLOSION HAZARD.
FIREFIGHTING MEDIA: DRY CHEMICAL, CARBON DIOXIDE, HALON, WATER SPRAY OR STANDARD FOAM (1987 EMERGENCY RESPONSE GUIDEBOOK, DOT P 5800.4). FOR LARGER FIRES, USE WATER SPRAY, FOG OR STANDARD FOAM (1987 EMERGENCY RESPONSE GUIDEBOOK, DOT P 5800.4).
FIREFIGHTING: MOVE CONTAINER FROM FIRE AREA IF POSSIBLE. DO NOT SCATTER SPILLED MATERIAL WITH HIGH PRESSURE WATER STREAMS. DIKE FIRE CONTROL WATER FOR LATER DISPOSAL (1987 EMERGENCY RESPONSE GUIDEBOOK, DOT P 5800.4, GUIDE PAGE 31).
USE AGENTS SUITABLE FOR TYPE OF SURROUNDING FIRE. AVOID BREATHING HAZARDOUS VAPORS, KEEP UPWIND.

TOXICITY

(+)-CIS-TETRAMETHRIN: TOXICITY DATA: 20 MG/KG INTRAPERITONEAL-MOUSE LD50. CARCINOGEN STATUS: NONE. ACUTE TOXICITY LEVEL: INSUFFICIENT DATA. TARGET EFFECTS: POISONING MAY AFFECT THE CENTRAL NERVOUS SYSTEM.

HEALTH EFFECTS AND FIRST AID

INHALATION: (+)-CIS-TETRAMETHRIN: **ACUTE EXPOSURE-** AT A CONCENTRATION OF APPROXIMATELY 2000 MG/M3, TETRAMETHRIN PRODUCED SYMPTOMS OF HYPERSENSITIVITY, MOTOR ATAXIA, AND URINARY INCONTINENCE, BUT NO FATALITIES IN MICE AND RATS. (+)-CIS-TETRAMETHRIN IS A SYNTHETIC PYRETHRIN. SYNTHETIC PYRETHRINS, LIKE THE NATURAL PYRETHRINS, PRODUCE CENTRAL NERVOUS SYSTEM STIMULATION IN ANIMALS WITH SYMPTOMS OF NAUSEA, VOMITING, GASTROENTERITIS WITH DIARRHEA, HYPERSENSITIVITY, INCOORDINATION, TREMORS, MUSCULAR PARALYSIS, CONVULSION, COMA, AND DEATH DUE TO RESPIRATORY FAILURE. UNLIKE NATURAL PYRETHRINS, SYNTHETIC PYRETHRINS NORMALLY DO NOT PRODUCE ALLERGIC REACTIONS IN HUMANS. **CHRONIC EXPOSURE-** IN ONE STUDY OF TETRAMETHRIN, CHRONIC EXPOSURE OF RATS AND MICE TO MIST PREPARATIONS OF 210 MG/M3/4 HOURS 5 DAYS A WEEK FOR 4 WEEKS DID NOT PRODUCED ANY ADVERSE EFFECTS ON THE MAJOR ORGANS AND TISSUES.
FIRST AID- REMOVE FROM EXPOSURE AREA TO FRESH AIR IMMEDIATELY. IF BREATHING HAS STOPPED, PERFORM ARTIFICIAL RESPIRATION. KEEP PERSON WARM AND AT REST. TREAT SYMPTOMATICALLY AND SUPPORTIVELY. GET MEDICAL ATTENTION IMMEDIATELY.

SKIN CONTACT: (+)-CIS-TETRAMETHRIN: **ACUTE EXPOSURE-** THE RESULT OF A PATCH TEST INVOLVING 200 HUMAN VOLUNTEERS, INDICATED THAT TETRAMETHRIN WAS NOT AN IRRITANT OR A SENSITIZER TO HUMAN SKIN. (+)-CIS-TETRAMETHRIN IS A SYNTHETIC PYRETHRIN. SYNTHETIC PYRETHRINS GENERALLY ARE NOT IRRITANTS TO RABBIT SKIN AND THE TOXICITY FROM DERMAL ABSORPTION IS USUALLY MODERATE TO LOW. **CHRONIC EXPOSURE-** NO DATA AVAILABLE.
FIRST AID- REMOVE CONTAMINATED CLOTHING AND SHOES IMMEDIATELY. WASH AFFECTED AREA WITH SOAP OR MILD DETERGENT AND LARGE AMOUNTS OF WATER UNTIL NO EVIDENCE OF CHEMICAL REMAINS (APPROXIMATELY 15-20 MINUTES). GET MEDICAL ATTENTION IMMEDIATELY.

EYE CONTACT: (+)-CIS-TETRAMETHRIN: **ACUTE EXPOSURE-** MASSIVE INSTILLATION OF TETRAMETHRIN INTO RABBIT EYES PRODUCED A SLIGHT, TRANSIENT CONGESTION OF CONJUNCTIVA OR LACRIMATION BUT THE EFFECT WAS NOT SEVERE ENOUGH TO BE CONSIDERED AN IRRITANT. **CHRONIC EXPOSURE-** NO DATA AVAILABLE.
FIRST AID- WASH EYES IMMEDIATELY WITH LARGE AMOUNTS OF WATER OR NORMAL SALINE, OCCASIONALLY LIFTING UPPER AND LOWER LIDS, UNTIL NO EVIDENCE OF CHEMICAL REMAINS (APPROXIMATELY 15-20 MINUTES). GET MEDICAL ATTENTION IMMEDIATELY.

INGESTION: (+)-CIS-TETRAMETHRIN: **ACUTE EXPOSURE-** AN ACUTE DOSE OF 1000 MG/KG WAS NOT LETHAL IN MICE. (+)-CIS-TETRAMETHRIN IS A SYNTHETIC PYRETHRIN. SYNTHETIC PYRETHRINS, LIKE THE NATURAL PYRETHRINS, PRODUCE CENTRAL NERVOUS SYSTEM STIMULATION IN ANIMALS WITH SYMPTOMS OF NAUSEA, VOMITING, GASTROENTERITIS WITH DIARRHEA, HYPERSENSITIVITY, INCOORDINATION, TREMORS, MUSCULAR PARALYSIS, CONVULSION, COMA, AND DEATH DUE TO RESPIRATORY FAILURE. **CHRONIC EXPOSURE-** RATS FED A DIETARY CONCENTRATION OF 2000 PPM OF TETRAMETHRIN FOR 3 MONTHS EXPERIENCED NO ADVERSE EFFECTS.
FIRST AID- TREAT SYMPTOMATICALLY AND SUPPORTIVELY. GET MEDICAL ATTENTION IMMEDIATELY. IF VOMITING OCCURS, KEEP HEAD LOWER THAN HIPS TO PREVENT ASPIRATION.
ANTIDOTE: NO SPECIFIC ANTIDOTE. TREAT SYMPTOMATICALLY AND SUPPORTIVELY.

REACTIVITY

REACTIVITY: STABLE UNDER NORMAL TEMPERATURES AND PRESSURES.
INCOMPATIBILITIES: (+)-CIS-TETRAMETHRIN: ALKALIES: INCOMPATIBLE. STRONG ACIDS: INCOMPATIBLE. ALCOHOLIC SOLUTION: UNSTABLE.
DECOMPOSITION: THERMAL DECOMPOSITION PRODUCTS MAY INCLUDE TOXIC OXIDES OF NITROGEN.
POLYMERIZATION: HAZARDOUS POLYMERIZATION HAS NOT BEEN REPORTED TO OCCUR UNDER NORMAL TEMPERATURES AND PRESSURES.

STORAGE AND DISPOSAL

OBSERVE ALL FEDERAL, STATE AND LOCAL REGULATIONS WHEN STORING OR DISPOSING OF THIS SUBSTANCE. FOR ASSISTANCE, CONTACT THE DISTRICT DIRECTOR OF THE ENVIRONMENTAL PROTECTION AGENCY.

STORAGE

STORE IN ACCORDANCE WITH 40 CFR 165 RECOMMENDED PROCEDURES FOR THE DISPOSAL AND STORAGE OF PESTICIDES AND PESTICIDE CONTAINERS.
STORE AWAY FROM INCOMPATIBLE SUBSTANCES.

DISPOSAL

DISPOSAL MUST BE IN ACCORDANCE WITH 40 CFR 165 RECOMMENDED PROCEDURES FOR THE DISPOSAL AND STORAGE OF PESTICIDES AND PESTICIDE CONTAINERS.

CONDITIONS TO AVOID

NONE REPORTED.

SPILL AND LEAK PROCEDURES

OCCUPATIONAL SPILL: SWEEP UP AND PLACE IN SUITABLE (FIBERBOARD) CONTAINERS FOR RECLAMATION OR LATER DISPOSAL.

PROTECTIVE EQUIPMENT

VENTILATION: PROVIDE LOCAL EXHAUST OR GENERAL DILUTION VENTILATION SYSTEM.
RESPIRATOR: THE FOLLOWING RESPIRATORS ARE RECOMMENDED BASED ON INFORMATION FOUND IN THE PHYSICAL DATA, TOXICITY AND HEALTH EFFECTS SECTIONS. THEY ARE RANKED IN ORDER FROM MINIMUM TO MAXIMUM RESPIRATORY PROTECTION. THE SPECIFIC RESPIRATOR SELECTED MUST BE BASED ON CONTAMINATION LEVELS FOUND IN THE WORK PLACE, MUST NOT EXCEED THE WORKING LIMITS OF THE RESPIRATOR AND BE JOINTLY APPROVED BY THE NATIONAL INSTITUTE FOR OCCUPATIONAL SAFETY AND HEALTH AND THE MINE SAFETY AND HEALTH ADMINISTRATION (NIOSH-MSHA).
CHEMICAL CARTRIDGE RESPIRATOR WITH AN ORGANIC VAPOR CARTRIDGE(S) IN COMBINATION WITH A DUST AND MIST FILTER.
GAS MASK WITH ORGANIC VAPOR CANISTER (CHIN-STYLE OR FRONT- OR BACK-MOUNTED CANISTER) WITH A DUST AND MIST FILTER.
GAS MASK WITH ORGANIC VAPOR CANISTER (CHIN-STYLE OR FRONT- OR BACK-MOUNTED CANISTER) WITH A PARTICULATE FILTER.
POWERED AIR-PURIFYING RESPIRATOR WITH A HIGH-EFFICIENCY FILTER.
TYPE 'C' SUPPLIED-AIR RESPIRATOR WITH A FULL FACEPIECE OPERATED IN A PRESSURE-DEMAND OR OTHER POSITIVE PRESSURE MODE.
SELF-CONTAINED BREATHING APPARATUS WITH A FULL FACEPIECE OPERATED IN PRESSURE-DEMAND OR OTHER POSITIVE PRESSURE MODE. FOR FIREFIGHTING AND OTHER IMMEDIATELY DANGEROUS TO LIFE OR HEALTH CONDITIONS:
SELF-CONTAINED BREATHING APPARATUS WITH FULL FACEPIECE OPERATED IN PRESSURE-DEMAND OR OTHER POSITIVE PRESSURE MODE.
SUPPLIED-AIR RESPIRATOR WITH FULL FACEPIECE AND OPERATED IN PRESSURE-DEMAND OR OTHER POSITIVE PRESSURE MODE IN COMBINATION WITH AN AUXILIARY SELF-CONTAINED BREATHING APPARATUS OPERATED IN PRESSURE-DEMAND OR OTHER POSITIVE PRESSURE MODE.
CLOTHING: EMPLOYEE MUST WEAR APPROPRIATE PROTECTIVE (IMPERVIOUS) CLOTHING AND EQUIPMENT TO PREVENT REPEATED OR PROLONGED SKIN CONTACT WITH THIS SUBSTANCE.

GLOVES: EMPLOYEE MUST WEAR APPROPRIATE PROTECTIVE GLOVES TO PREVENT CONTACT WITH THIS SUBSTANCE.

EYE PROTECTION: EMPLOYEE MUST WEAR SPLASH-PROOF OR DUST-RESISTANT SAFETY GOGGLES TO PREVENT EYE CONTACT WITH THIS SUBSTANCE.
EMERGENCY EYE WASH: WHERE THERE IS ANY POSSIBILITY THAT AN EMPLOYEE'S EYES MAY BE EXPOSED TO THIS SUBSTANCE, THE EMPLOYER SHOULD PROVIDE AN EYE WASH FOUNTAIN WITHIN THE IMMEDIATE WORK AREA FOR EMERGENCY USE.

AUTHORIZED BY- OCCUPATIONAL HEALTH SERVICES, INC.
CREATION DATE: 10/04/89 ***REVISION DATE:*** 05/14/90

MATERIAL SAFETY DATA SHEET

OCCUPATIONAL HEALTH SERVICES, INC.
AGRICULTURE AND PESTICIDE DIVISION
450 SEVENTH AVENUE, SUITE 2407
NEW YORK, NEW YORK 10123
1-800-445-MSDS OR (212) 967-1100

EMERGENCY CONTACT:
JOHN S. BRANSFORD, JR. (615) 292-1180

SUBSTANCE IDENTIFICATION

CAS-NUMBER 1166-46-7

SUBSTANCE: **(+)-TRANS-TETRAMETHRIN**

TRADE NAMES/SYNONYMS: 2,2-DIMETHYL-3-(2-METHYL-1-PROPENYL)-CYCLOPROPANECARBOXYLIC ACID, (1,3,4,5,6,7,-HEXAHYDRO-1,3-DIOXO-2H-ISOINDOL-2-YL)METHYL ESTER, (1R-TRANS); 2,2-DIMETHYL-3-(2-METHYLPROPENYL)-CYCLOPROPANECARBOXYLIC ACID,ESTER WITH N-(HYDROXYMETHYL)-1-CYCLOHEXENE-1,2-DICARBOXIMIDE, TRANS-(+)-; BIOTETRAMETHRIN; (+)-TRANS-PHTHALTHRIN; PST23063

CHEMICAL FAMILY: PYRETHROID (SYNTHETIC)

MOLECULAR FORMULA: C19-H25-N-O4

MOLECULAR WEIGHT: 331.45

CERCLA RATINGS (SCALE 0-3): HEALTH=2 FIRE=U REACTIVITY=0 PERSISTENCE=2

NFPA RATINGS (SCALE 0-4): HEALTH=2 FIRE=U REACTIVITY=0

COMPONENTS AND CONTAMINANTS

COMPONENT: (+)-TRANS-TETRAMETHRIN ***PERCENT:*** 100.0
CAS# 1166-46-7

OTHER CONTAMINANTS: NONE

EXPOSURE LIMITS: NO OCCUPATIONAL EXPOSURE LIMITS ESTABLISHED BY OSHA, ACGIH, OR NIOSH.

PHYSICAL DATA

DESCRIPTION: WHITE CRYSTALLINE SOLID WITH A SLIGHT PYRETHRUM-LIKE ODOR

SPECIFIC GRAVITY: NOT AVAILABLE ***SOLUBILITY IN WATER:*** NOT AVAILABLE

SOLVENT SOLUBILITY: AROMATIC HYDROCARBONS, ALIPHATIC HYDROCARBONS

FIRE AND EXPLOSION DATA

FIRE AND EXPLOSION HAZARD: UNKNOWN FIRE AND EXPLOSION HAZARD.

FIREFIGHTING MEDIA: DRY CHEMICAL, CARBON DIOXIDE, HALON, WATER SPRAY OR STANDARD FOAM (1987 EMERGENCY RESPONSE GUIDEBOOK, DOT P 5800.4).
FOR LARGER FIRES, USE WATER SPRAY, FOG OR STANDARD FOAM (1987 EMERGENCY RESPONSE GUIDEBOOK, DOT P 5800.4).

FIREFIGHTING: MOVE CONTAINER FROM FIRE AREA IF POSSIBLE. DO NOT SCATTER SPILLED MATERIAL WITH HIGH PRESSURE WATER STREAMS. DIKE FIRE CONTROL WATER FOR LATER DISPOSAL (1987 EMERGENCY RESPONSE GUIDEBOOK, DOT P 5800.4, GUIDE PAGE 31).
USE AGENTS SUITABLE FOR TYPE OF SURROUNDING FIRE. AVOID BREATHING HAZARDOUS VAPORS, KEEP UPWIND.

TOXICITY

(+)-TRANS-TETRAMETHRIN: TOXICITY DATA: 910 MG/KG ORAL-MOUSE LD50; 42 MG/KG INTRAPERITONEAL-MOUSE LD50. CARCINOGEN STATUS: NONE. ACUTE TOXICITY LEVEL: MODERATELY TOXIC BY INGESTION. TARGET EFFECTS: POISONING MAY AFFECT THE NERVOUS SYSTEM.

HEALTH EFFECTS AND FIRST AID

INHALATION: (+)-TRANS-TETRAMETHRIN: **ACUTE EXPOSURE-** AT A CONCENTRATION OF APPROXIMATELY 2000 MG/M3, TETRAMETHRIN PRODUCED SYMPTOMS OF HYPERSENSITIVITY, MOTOR ATAXIA, AND URINARY INCONTINENCE, BUT NO FATALITIES IN MICE AND RATS. (+)-TRANS-TETRAMETHRIN IS A SYNTHETIC PYRETHRIN. SYNTHETIC PYRETHRINS, LIKE THE NATURAL PYRETHRINS, PRODUCE CENTRAL NERVOUS SYSTEM STIMULATION IN ANIMALS WITH SYMPTOMS OF NAUSEA, VOMITING, GASTROENTERITIS WITH DIARRHEA, HYPERSENSITIVITY, INCOORDINATION, TREMORS, MUSCULAR PARALYSIS, CONVULSION, COMA, AND DEATH DUE TO RESPIRATORY FAILURE. UNLIKE NATURAL PYRETHRINS, SYNTHETIC PYRETHRINS NORMALLY DO NOT PRODUCE ALLERGIC REACTIONS IN HUMANS. **CHRONIC EXPOSURE-** IN ONE STUDY OF TETRAMETHRIN, CHRONIC EXPOSURE OF RATS AND MICE TO MIST PREPARATIONS OF 210 MG/M3/4 HOURS 5 DAYS A WEEK FOR 4 WEEKS DID NOT PRODUCED ANY ADVERSE EFFECTS ON THE MAJOR ORGANS AND TISSUES.

FIRST AID- REMOVE FROM EXPOSURE AREA TO FRESH AIR IMMEDIATELY. IF BREATHING HAS STOPPED, PERFORM ARTIFICIAL RESPIRATION. KEEP PERSON WARM AND AT REST. TREAT SYMPTOMATICALLY AND SUPPORTIVELY. GET MEDICAL ATTENTION IMMEDIATELY.

SKIN CONTACT: (+)-TRANS-TETRAMETHRIN: **ACUTE EXPOSURE-** THE RESULT OF A PATCH TEST INVOLVING 200 HUMAN VOLUNTEERS, INDICATED THAT TETRAMETHRIN WAS NOT AN IRRITANT OR A SENSITIZER TO HUMAN SKIN. (+)-TRANS-TETRAMETHRIN IS A SYNTHETIC PYRETHRIN. SYNTHETIC PYRETHRINS GENERALLY ARE NOT IRRITANTS TO RABBIT SKIN AND THE TOXICITY FROM DERMAL ABSORPTION IS USUALLY MODERATE TO LOW. **CHRONIC EXPOSURE-** NO DATA AVAILABLE.

FIRST AID- REMOVE CONTAMINATED CLOTHING AND SHOES IMMEDIATELY. WASH AFFECTED AREA WITH SOAP OR MILD DETERGENT AND LARGE AMOUNTS OF WATER UNTIL NO EVIDENCE OF CHEMICAL REMAINS (APPROXIMATELY 15-20 MINUTES). GET MEDICAL ATTENTION IMMEDIATELY.

EYE CONTACT: (+)-TRANS-TETRAMETHRIN: **ACUTE EXPOSURE-** MASSIVE INSTILLATION OF TETRAMETHRIN INTO RABBIT EYES PRODUCED A SLIGHT, TRANSIENT CONGESTION OF CONJUNCTIVA OR LACRIMATION BUT THE EFFECT WAS NOT SEVERE ENOUGH TO BE CONSIDERED AN IRRITANT. **CHRONIC EXPOSURE-** NO DATA AVAILABLE.

FIRST AID- WASH EYES IMMEDIATELY WITH LARGE AMOUNTS OF WATER OR NORMAL SALINE, OCCASIONALLY LIFTING UPPER AND LOWER LIDS, UNTIL NO EVIDENCE OF CHEMICAL REMAINS (APPROXIMATELY 15-20 MINUTES). GET MEDICAL ATTENTION IMMEDIATELY.

INGESTION: (+)-TRANS-TETRAMETHRIN: **ACUTE EXPOSURE-** A MODERATE DOSE WAS LETHAL TO MICE. (+)-TRANS-TETRAMETHRIN IS A SYNTHETIC PYRETHRIN. SYNTHETIC PYRETHRINS, LIKE THE NATURAL PYRETHRINS, PRODUCE CENTRAL NERVOUS SYSTEM STIMULATION IN ANIMALS WITH SYMPTOMS OF NAUSEA, VOMITING, GASTROENTERITIS WITH DIARRHEA, HYPERSENSITIVITY, INCOORDINATION, TREMORS, MUSCULAR PARALYSIS, CONVULSIONS, COMA, AND DEATH DUE TO RESPIRATORY FAILURE. **CHRONIC EXPOSURE-** RATS FED A DIETARY CONCENTRATION OF 2000 PPM OF TETRAMETHRIN FOR 3 MONTHS EXPERIENCED NO ADVERSE EFFECTS.

FIRST AID- TREAT SYMPTOMATICALLY AND SUPPORTIVELY. GET MEDICAL ATTENTION IMMEDIATELY. IF VOMITING OCCURS, KEEP HEAD LOWER THAN HIPS TO PREVENT ASPIRATION.

ANTIDOTE: NO SPECIFIC ANTIDOTE. TREAT SYMPTOMATICALLY AND SUPPORTIVELY.

REACTIVITY

REACTIVITY: STABLE UNDER NORMAL TEMPERATURES AND PRESSURES.

INCOMPATIBILITIES: (+)-TRANS-TETRAMETHRIN: ALKALIES: INCOMPATIBLE. STRONG ACIDS: INCOMPATIBLE. ALCOHOLIC SOLUTION: UNSTABLE.

DECOMPOSITION: THERMAL DECOMPOSITION PRODUCTS MAY INCLUDE TOXIC OXIDES OF NITROGEN.

POLYMERIZATION: HAZARDOUS POLYMERIZATION HAS NOT BEEN REPORTED TO OCCUR UNDER NORMAL TEMPERATURES AND PRESSURES.

STORAGE AND DISPOSAL

OBSERVE ALL FEDERAL, STATE AND LOCAL REGULATIONS WHEN STORING OR DISPOSING OF THIS SUBSTANCE. FOR ASSISTANCE, CONTACT THE DISTRICT DIRECTOR OF THE ENVIRONMENTAL PROTECTION AGENCY.

STORAGE

STORE IN ACCORDANCE WITH 40 CFR 165 RECOMMENDED PROCEDURES FOR THE DISPOSAL AND STORAGE OF PESTICIDES AND PESTICIDE CONTAINERS.
STORE AWAY FROM INCOMPATIBLE SUBSTANCES.

DISPOSAL

DISPOSAL MUST BE IN ACCORDANCE WITH 40 CFR 165 RECOMMENDED PROCEDURES FOR THE DISPOSAL AND STORAGE OF PESTICIDES AND PESTICIDE CONTAINERS.

CONDITIONS TO AVOID

NONE REPORTED.

SPILL AND LEAK PROCEDURES

OCCUPATIONAL SPILL: SWEEP UP AND PLACE IN SUITABLE (FIBERBOARD) CONTAINERS FOR RECLAMATION OR LATER DISPOSAL.

PROTECTIVE EQUIPMENT

VENTILATION: PROVIDE LOCAL EXHAUST OR GENERAL DILUTION VENTILATION SYSTEM.

RESPIRATOR: THE FOLLOWING RESPIRATORS ARE RECOMMENDED BASED ON INFORMATION FOUND IN THE PHYSICAL DATA, TOXICITY AND HEALTH EFFECTS SECTIONS. THEY ARE RANKED IN ORDER FROM MINIMUM TO MAXIMUM RESPIRATORY PROTECTION. THE SPECIFIC RESPIRATOR SELECTED MUST BE BASED ON CONTAMINATION LEVELS FOUND IN THE WORK PLACE, MUST NOT EXCEED THE WORKING LIMITS OF THE RESPIRATOR AND BE JOINTLY APPROVED BY THE NATIONAL INSTITUTE FOR OCCUPATIONAL SAFETY AND HEALTH AND THE MINE SAFETY AND HEALTH ADMINISTRATION (NIOSH-MSHA).

CHEMICAL CARTRIDGE RESPIRATOR WITH AN ORGANIC VAPOR CARTRIDGE(S) IN COMBINATION WITH A DUST AND MIST FILTER.

GAS MASK WITH ORGANIC VAPOR CANISTER (CHIN-STYLE OR FRONT- OR BACK-MOUNTED CANISTER) WITH A DUST AND MIST FILTER.

GAS MASK WITH ORGANIC VAPOR CANISTER (CHIN-STYLE OR FRONT- OR BACK-MOUNTED CANISTER) WITH A PARTICULATE FILTER.

POWERED AIR-PURIFYING RESPIRATOR WITH A HIGH-EFFICIENCY FILTER.

TYPE 'C' SUPPLIED-AIR RESPIRATOR WITH A FULL FACEPIECE OPERATED IN A PRESSURE-DEMAND OR OTHER POSITIVE PRESSURE MODE.

SELF-CONTAINED BREATHING APPARATUS WITH A FULL FACEPIECE OPERATED IN PRESSURE-DEMAND OR OTHER POSITIVE PRESSURE MODE. FOR FIREFIGHTING AND OTHER IMMEDIATELY DANGEROUS TO LIFE OR HEALTH CONDITIONS:

SELF-CONTAINED BREATHING APPARATUS WITH FULL FACEPIECE OPERATED IN PRESSURE-DEMAND OR OTHER POSITIVE PRESSURE MODE.

SUPPLIED-AIR RESPIRATOR WITH FULL FACEPIECE AND OPERATED IN PRESSURE-DEMAND OR OTHER POSITIVE PRESSURE MODE IN COMBINATION WITH AN AUXILIARY SELF-CONTAINED BREATHING APPARATUS OPERATED IN PRESSURE-DEMAND OR OTHER POSITIVE PRESSURE MODE.

CLOTHING: EMPLOYEE MUST WEAR APPROPRIATE PROTECTIVE (IMPERVIOUS) CLOTHING AND EQUIPMENT TO PREVENT REPEATED OR PROLONGED SKIN CONTACT WITH THIS SUBSTANCE.

GLOVES: EMPLOYEE MUST WEAR APPROPRIATE PROTECTIVE GLOVES TO PREVENT CONTACT WITH THIS SUBSTANCE.

EYE PROTECTION: EMPLOYEE MUST WEAR SPLASH-PROOF OR DUST-RESISTANT SAFETY GOGGLES TO PREVENT EYE CONTACT WITH THIS SUBSTANCE.

EMERGENCY EYE WASH: WHERE THERE IS ANY POSSIBILITY THAT AN EMPLOYEE'S EYES MAY BE EXPOSED TO THIS SUBSTANCE, THE EMPLOYER SHOULD PROVIDE AN EYE WASH FOUNTAIN WITHIN THE IMMEDIATE WORK AREA FOR EMERGENCY USE.

AUTHORIZED BY- OCCUPATIONAL HEALTH SERVICES, INC.

CREATION DATE: 10/04/89 ***REVISION DATE:*** 05/07/90

MATERIAL SAFETY DATA SHEET

OCCUPATIONAL HEALTH SERVICES, INC.
AGRICULTURE AND PESTICIDE DIVISION
450 SEVENTH AVENUE, SUITE 2407
NEW YORK, NEW YORK 10123
1-800-445-MSDS OR (212) 967-1100

EMERGENCY CONTACT:
JOHN S. BRANSFORD, JR. (615) 292-1180

SUBSTANCE IDENTIFICATION

CAS-NUMBER 39765-80-5

SUBSTANCE: **TRANS-NONACHLOR**

TRADE NAMES/SYNONYMS: 4,7-METHANO-1H-INDENE, 1,2,3,4,5,6,7,8,8-NONACHLORO-2,3,3A,4,7, 7A-HEXAHYDRO-, (1ALPHA,2BETA,3ALPHA,3A ALPHA,4BETA,7BETA,7A ALPHA)-; (1ALPHA,2BETA,3ALPHA,3A ALPHA,4BETA,7BETA,7A ALPHA)-1,2,3,4,5,6,7,8, 8-NONACHLORO-2,3,3A,4,7,7A-HEXAHYDRO-4,7-METHANO-1H-INDENE; T-NONACHLOR; NONACHLOR; C10H5CL9; PST23079

CHEMICAL FAMILY: HALOGEN COMPOUND, ALICYCLIC

MOLECULAR FORMULA: C10-H5-CL9

MOLECULAR WEIGHT: 444.20

CERCLA RATINGS (SCALE 0-3): HEALTH=3 FIRE=0 REACTIVITY=0 PERSISTENCE=3

NFPA RATINGS (SCALE 0-4): HEALTH=U FIRE=0 REACTIVITY=0

COMPONENTS AND CONTAMINANTS

COMPONENT: TRANS-NONACHLOR ***PERCENT:*** 100.0

CAS# 39765-80-5

OTHER CONTAMINANTS: NONE

EXPOSURE LIMITS: NO OCCUPATIONAL EXPOSURE LIMITS ESTABLISHED BY OSHA, ACGIH, OR NIOSH.

PHYSICAL DATA

DESCRIPTION: WHITE SOLID. ***MELTING POINT:*** 261 F (127 C)

SPECIFIC GRAVITY: NOT AVAILABLE ***SOLUBILITY IN WATER:*** NOT AVAILABLE

FIRE AND EXPLOSION DATA

FIRE AND EXPLOSION HAZARD: NEGLIGIBLE FIRE HAZARD WHEN EXPOSED TO HEAT OR FLAME.

FIREFIGHTING MEDIA: DRY CHEMICAL, CARBON DIOXIDE, HALON, WATER SPRAY OR STANDARD FOAM (1987 EMERGENCY RESPONSE GUIDEBOOK, DOT P 5800.4). FOR LARGER FIRES, USE WATER SPRAY, FOG OR STANDARD FOAM (1987 EMERGENCY RESPONSE GUIDEBOOK, DOT P 5800.4).

FIREFIGHTING: MOVE CONTAINERS FROM FIRE AREA IF POSSIBLE (1987 EMERGENCY RESPONSE GUIDEBOOK, DOT P 5800.4, GUIDE PAGE 53).

EXTINGUISH USING AGENT SUITABLE FOR TYPE OF SURROUNDING FIRE. AVOID BREATHING VAPORS AND DUSTS. KEEP UPWIND.

TOXICITY

TRANS-NONACHLOR: TOXICITY DATA: 500 MG/KG ORAL-RAT LD50. CARCINOGEN STATUS: NONE. ACUTE TOXICITY LEVEL: TOXIC BY INGESTION. TARGET EFFECTS: POISONING MAY AFFECT THE LIVER, KIDNEYS, BLOOD, AND CARDIOVASCULAR SYSTEM.* AT INCREASED RISK FROM EXPOSURE: PERSONS WITH CONVULSIVE DISORDERS.* ADDITIONAL DATA: MAY BE STORED IN ADIPOSE TISSUE; MAY CROSS THE PLACENTA AND BE EXCRETED IN HUMAN MILK. STIMULANTS SUCH AS EPINEPHRINE MAY INDUCE VENTRICULAR FIBRILLATIONS.*

* MAY BE BASED ON GENERAL INFORMATION ON CHLORINATED CYCLODIENE DERIVATIVES.

HEALTH EFFECTS AND FIRST AID

INHALATION: TRANS-NONACHLOR: **ACUTE EXPOSURE-** CHLORINATED CYCLODIENE DERIVATIVES MAY PRODUCE HEADACHE, NAUSEA, VOMITING, MALAISE, DIZZINESS, APPREHENSION, PARESTHESIA, HYPERIRRITABILITY, ATAXIA, MUSCLE TWITCHING, MYOCLONIC JERKING, AND CONVULSIVE SEIZURES. IN SEVERE CASES, CONVULSIONS MAY OCCUR WITHOUT ANY ANY PRIOR SYMPTOMS. THE CONVULSIONS MAY BE CONTINUOUS WITH ELEVATED BODY TEMPERATURE, UNCONSCIOUSNESS, LABORED BREATHING WITH VIGOROUS, RAPID HEART BEAT, AND DEATH FROM RESPIRATORY DEPRESSION. **CHRONIC EXPOSURE-** CHRONIC INTOXICATION FROM CHLORINATED CYCLODIENE DERIVATIVES MAY BE CHARACTERIZED BY NERVOUS SYSTEM, LIVER, AND KIDNEY DAMAGE, CARDIOVASCULAR DISTURBANCES, AND BLOOD AND CAPILLARY DISTURBANCES. IN ADDITION TO THE SYMPTOMS DETAILED IN ACUTE EXPOSURE, ANOREXIA, BLURRED VISION, AND DROWSINESS MAY ALSO OCCUR.

FIRST AID- REMOVE FROM EXPOSURE AREA TO FRESH AIR IMMEDIATELY. IF BREATHING HAS STOPPED, PERFORM ARTIFICIAL RESPIRATION. KEEP PERSON WARM AND AT REST. TREAT SYMPTOMATICALLY AND SUPPORTIVELY. GET MEDICAL ATTENTION IMMEDIATELY.

SKIN CONTACT: TRANS-NONACHLOR: **ACUTE EXPOSURE-** CHLORINATED CYCLODIENE DERIVATIVES MAY PRODUCE HEADACHE, NAUSEA, VOMITING, MALAISE, DIZZINESS, APPREHENSION, PARESTHESIA, HYPERIRRITABILITY, ATAXIA, MUSCLE TWITCHING, MYOCLONIC JERKING, AND CONVULSIVE SEIZURES. IN SEVERE CASES, CONVULSIONS MAY OCCUR WITHOUT ANY PRIOR SYMPTOMS. THE CONVULSIONS MAY BE CONTINUOUS WITH ELEVATED BODY TEMPERATURES, UNCONSCIOUSNESS, LABORED BREATHING WITH VIGOROUS, RAPID HEART BEAT, AND DEATH FROM RESPIRATORY DEPRESSION. **CHRONIC EXPOSURE-** CHRONIC INTOXICATION FROM CHLORINATED CYCLODIENE DERIVATIVES MAY BE CHARACTERIZED BY NERVOUS SYSTEM, LIVER, AND KIDNEY DAMAGE, CARDIOVASCULAR DISTURBANCES, AND BLOOD AND CAPILLARY DISTURBANCES. IN ADDITION TO THE SYMPTOMS DETAILED IN ACUTE EXPOSURE, SKIN IRRITATION, ANOREXIA, BLURRED VISION, AND DROWSINESS MAY ALSO OCCUR.

FIRST AID- REMOVE CONTAMINATED CLOTHING AND SHOES IMMEDIATELY. WASH AFFECTED AREA WITH SOAP OR MILD DETERGENT AND LARGE AMOUNTS OF WATER UNTIL NO EVIDENCE OF CHEMICAL REMAINS (APPROXIMATELY 15-20 MINUTES). GET MEDICAL ATTENTION IMMEDIATELY.

EYE CONTACT: TRANS-NONACHLOR: **ACUTE EXPOSURE-** NO DATA AVAILABLE. **CHRONIC EXPOSURE-** NO DATA AVAILABLE.

FIRST AID- WASH EYES IMMEDIATELY WITH LARGE AMOUNTS OF WATER OR NORMAL SALINE, OCCASIONALLY LIFTING UPPER AND LOWER LIDS, UNTIL NO EVIDENCE OF CHEMICAL REMAINS (APPROXIMATELY 15-20 MINUTES). GET MEDICAL ATTENTION IMMEDIATELY.

INGESTION: TRANS-NONACHLOR: TOXIC. **ACUTE EXPOSURE-** CHLORINATED CYCLODIENE DERIVATIVES MAY PRODUCE HEADACHE, NAUSEA, VOMITING, MALAISE, DIZZINESS, APPREHENSION, PARESTHESIA, HYPERIRRITABILITY, ATAXIA, MUSCLE TWITCHING, MYOCLONIC JERKING, AND CONVULSIVE SEIZURES. IN SEVERE CASES, CONVULSIONS MAY OCCUR WITHOUT ANY PRIOR SYMPTOMS. THE CONVULSIONS MAY BE CONTINUOUS WITH ELEVATED BODY TEMPERATURE, UNCONSCIOUSNESS, LABORED BREATHING WITH VIGOROUS, RAPID HEART BEAT, AND DEATH FROM RESPIRATORY DEPRESSION. **CHRONIC EXPOSURE-** CHRONIC INTOXICATION FROM CHLORINATED CYCLODIENE DERIVATIVES MAY BE CHARACTERIZED BY NERVOUS SYSTEM, LIVER, AND KIDNEY DAMAGE, CARDIOVASCULAR DISTURBANCES, AND BLOOD AND CAPILLARY DISTURBANCES. IN ADDITION TO THE SYMPTOMS DETAILED IN ACUTE EXPOSURE, ANOREXIA, BLURRED VISION, AND DROWSINESS MAY ALSO OCCUR.

FIRST AID- IF THE PERSON IS CONSCIOUS AND NOT CONVULSING, REMOVE BY GIVING SYRUP OF IPECAC (IF VOMITING OCCURS, KEEP THE HEAD BELOW THE HIPS TO PREVENT ASPIRATION). GIVE ACTIVATED CHARCOAL FOLLOWED BY GASTRIC LAVAGE. FOLLOW WITH A SALINE CATHARTIC. DO NOT GIVE FATS OR OILS. INTESTINAL LAVAGE WITH 20% MANNITOL (200 ML) BY STOMACH TUBE IS ALSO USEFUL. GIVE ARTIFICIAL RESPIRATION WITH OXYGEN IF RESPIRATION IS DEPRESSED (DREISBACH, HANDBOOK OF POISONING, 12TH ED.). TREAT SYMPTOMATICALLY AND SUPPORTIVELY. LAVAGE AND ADMINISTRATION OF OXYGEN SHOULD BE PERFORMED BY QUALIFIED MEDICAL PERSONNEL. GET MEDICAL ATTENTION IMMEDIATELY.

ANTIDOTE: NO SPECIFIC ANTIDOTE. TREAT SYMPTOMATICALLY AND SUPPORTIVELY.

REACTIVITY

REACTIVITY: STABLE UNDER NORMAL TEMPERATURES AND PRESSURES.

INCOMPATIBILITIES: TRANS-NONACHLOR: OXIDIZERS (STRONG): FIRE AND EXPLOSION HAZARD.

DECOMPOSITION: THERMAL DECOMPOSITION PRODUCTS MAY INCLUDE TOXIC AND CORROSIVE FUMES OF CHLORINE.

POLYMERIZATION: HAZARDOUS POLYMERIZATION HAS NOT BEEN REPORTED TO OCCUR UNDER NORMAL TEMPERATURES AND PRESSURES.

STORAGE AND DISPOSAL

OBSERVE ALL FEDERAL, STATE AND LOCAL REGULATIONS WHEN STORING OR DISPOSING OF THIS SUBSTANCE. FOR ASSISTANCE, CONTACT THE DISTRICT DIRECTOR OF THE ENVIRONMENTAL PROTECTION AGENCY.

STORAGE

STORE IN ACCORDANCE WITH 40 CFR 165 RECOMMENDED PROCEDURES FOR THE DISPOSAL AND STORAGE OF PESTICIDES AND PESTICIDE CONTAINERS.
STORE AWAY FROM INCOMPATIBLE SUBSTANCES.

DISPOSAL

DISPOSAL MUST BE IN ACCORDANCE WITH 40 CFR 165 RECOMMENDED PROCEDURES FOR THE DISPOSAL AND STORAGE OF PESTICIDES AND PESTICIDE CONTAINERS.

CONDITIONS TO AVOID

MAY BURN BUT DOES NOT IGNITE READILY.

SPILL AND LEAK PROCEDURES

OCCUPATIONAL SPILL: DO NOT TOUCH SPILLED MATERIAL. STOP LEAK IF YOU CAN DO IT WITHOUT RISK. FOR SMALL SPILLS, TAKE UP WITH SAND OR OTHER ABSORBENT MATERIAL AND PLACE INTO CONTAINERS FOR LATER DISPOSAL. FOR SMALL DRY SPILLS, WITH A CLEAN SHOVEL PLACE MATERIAL INTO CLEAN, DRY CONTAINER AND COVER. MOVE CONTAINERS FROM SPILL AREA. FOR LARGER SPILLS, DIKE FAR AHEAD OF SPILL FOR LATER DISPOSAL. KEEP UNNECESSARY PEOPLE AWAY. ISOLATE HAZARD AREA AND DENY ENTRY.

PROTECTIVE EQUIPMENT

VENTILATION: PROVIDE LOCAL EXHAUST OR GENERAL DILUTION VENTILATION SYSTEM.

RESPIRATOR: THE FOLLOWING RESPIRATORS ARE RECOMMENDED BASED ON INFORMATION FOUND IN THE PHYSICAL DATA, TOXICITY AND HEALTH EFFECTS SECTIONS. THEY ARE RANKED IN ORDER FROM MINIMUM TO MAXIMUM RESPIRATORY PROTECTION. THE SPECIFIC RESPIRATOR SELECTED MUST BE BASED ON CONTAMINATION LEVELS FOUND IN THE WORK PLACE, MUST NOT EXCEED THE WORKING LIMITS OF THE RESPIRATOR AND BE JOINTLY APPROVED BY THE NATIONAL INSTITUTE FOR OCCUPATIONAL SAFETY AND HEALTH AND THE MINE SAFETY AND HEALTH ADMINISTRATION (NIOSH-MSHA).

TYPE 'C' SUPPLIED-AIR RESPIRATOR WITH A FULL FACEPIECE OPERATED IN PRESSURE-DEMAND OR OTHER POSITIVE PRESSURE MODE OR WITH A FULL FACEPIECE, HELMET OR HOOD OPERATED IN CONTINOUS-FLOW MODE.

SELF-CONTAINED BREATHING APPARATUS WITH A FULL FACEPIECE OPERATED IN PRESSURE-DEMAND OR OTHER POSITIVE PRESSURE MODE.

FOR FIREFIGHTING AND OTHER IMMEDIATELY DANGEROUS TO LIFE OR HEALTH CONDITIONS:

SELF-CONTAINED BREATHING APPARATUS WITH FULL FACEPIECE OPERATED IN PRESSURE-DEMAND OR OTHER POSITIVE PRESSURE MODE.

SUPPLIED-AIR RESPIRATOR WITH FULL FACEPIECE AND OPERATED IN PRESSURE-DEMAND OR OTHER POSITIVE PRESSURE MODE IN COMBINATION WITH AN AUXILIARY SELF-CONTAINED BREATHING APPARATUS OPERATED IN PRESSURE-DEMAND OR OTHER POSITIVE PRESSURE MODE.

CLOTHING: EMPLOYEE MUST WEAR APPROPRIATE PROTECTIVE (IMPERVIOUS) CLOTHING AND EQUIPMENT TO PREVENT ANY POSSIBILITY OF SKIN CONTACT WITH THIS SUBSTANCE.

GLOVES: EMPLOYEE MUST WEAR APPROPRIATE PROTECTIVE GLOVES TO PREVENT CONTACT WITH THIS SUBSTANCE.

EYE PROTECTION: EMPLOYEE MUST WEAR SPLASH-PROOF OR DUST-RESISTANT SAFETY GOGGLES AND A FACESHIELD TO PREVENT CONTACT WITH THIS SUBSTANCE.

EMERGENCY WASH FACILITIES: WHERE THERE IS ANY POSSIBILITY THAT AN EMPLOYEE'S EYES AND/OR SKIN MAY BE EXPOSED TO THIS SUBSTANCE, THE EMPLOYER SHOULD PROVIDE AN EYE WASH FOUNTAIN AND QUICK DRENCH SHOWER WITHIN THE IMMEDIATE WORK AREA FOR EMERGENCY USE.

AUTHORIZED BY- OCCUPATIONAL HEALTH SERVICES, INC.
CREATION DATE: 02/08/90 ***REVISION DATE:*** 02/08/90

MATERIAL SAFETY DATA SHEET

OCCUPATIONAL HEALTH SERVICES, INC.
AGRICULTURE AND PESTICIDE DIVISION
450 SEVENTH AVENUE, SUITE 2407
NEW YORK, NEW YORK 10123
1-800-445-MSDS OR (212) 967-1100

EMERGENCY CONTACT:
JOHN S. BRANSFORD, JR. (615) 292-1180

SUBSTANCE IDENTIFICATION

CAS-NUMBER 64-02-8

SUBSTANCE: **ETHYLENEDIAMINETETRAACETIC ACID, TETRASODIUM SALT**

TRADE NAMES/SYNONYMS: CALSOL; CELON E; CHEELOX BF-12; WARKEELATE PS-42; N,N-ETHYLENEDIAMINEDIACETIC ACID TETRASODIUM SALT; EDTA TETRASODIUM SALT; (ETHYLENEDINITRILOENDACETIC ACID; SNYTRON B; QUESTEX; GLYCINE, N,N'-1,2-ETHANEDIYLBIS(N-(CARBOXYMETHYL)-, TETRASODIUM SALT; N,N'-1,2-ETHANEDIYLBIS(N-(CARBOXYMETHYL)GLYCINE, TETRASODIUM SALT; EDETATE TETRASODIUM; CHEMCOLOX 200; TETRASODIUM EDTA; SODIUM (TETRA) ETHYLENEDIAMINE TETRAACETATE; VERSENE 220; TETRACEMATE TETRASODIUM; SYNTES; S-657; S-660; C10H12N2NA4O8; PST23137

CHEMICAL FAMILY: EDETATE

MOLECULAR FORMULA: C10-H12-N2-O8.NA4

MOLECULAR WEIGHT: 380.20

CERCLA RATINGS (SCALE 0-3): HEALTH=3 FIRE=1 REACTIVITY=0 PERSISTENCE=1

NFPA RATINGS (SCALE 0-4): HEALTH=U FIRE=1 REACTIVITY=0

COMPONENTS AND CONTAMINANTS

COMPONENT: ETHYLENEDIAMINETETRAACETIC ACID TETRASODIUM SALT ***PERCENT:*** 100.0
CAS# 64-02-8

OTHER CONTAMINANTS: NONE

EXPOSURE LIMITS: NO OCCUPATIONAL EXPOSURE LIMITS ESTABLISHED BY OSHA, ACGIH, OR NIOSH.

PHYSICAL DATA

DESCRIPTION: HYGROSCOPIC, WHITE SOLID. ***MELTING POINT:*** >572 F (>300 C)

SPECIFIC GRAVITY: NOT AVAILABLE ***PH:*** 11.3 @ 1% SOLN

SOLUBILITY IN WATER: 103%

SOLVENT SOLUBILITY: SLIGHTLY SOLUBLE IN ALCOHOL.

FIRE AND EXPLOSION DATA

FIRE AND EXPLOSION HAZARD: SLIGHT FIRE HAZARD WHEN EXPOSED TO HEAT OR FLAME.
DUST-AIR MIXTURES MAY IGNITE OR EXPLODE.

FIREFIGHTING MEDIA: DRY CHEMICAL, CARBON DIOXIDE, HALON, WATER SPRAY OR STANDARD FOAM (1987 EMERGENCY RESPONSE GUIDEBOOK, DOT P 5800.4).
FOR LARGER FIRES, USE WATER SPRAY, FOG OR STANDARD FOAM (1987 EMERGENCY RESPONSE GUIDEBOOK, DOT P 5800.4).

FIREFIGHTING: MOVE CONTAINER FROM FIRE AREA IF POSSIBLE. DO NOT SCATTER SPILLED MATERIAL WITH HIGH PRESSURE WATER STREAMS. DIKE FIRE CONTROL WATER FOR LATER DISPOSAL (1987 EMERGENCY RESPONSE GUIDEBOOK, DOT P 5800.4, GUIDE PAGE 31).
USE AGENTS SUITABLE FOR TYPE OF SURROUNDING FIRE. AVOID BREATHING CORROSIVE DUSTS OR VAPORS, KEEP UPWIND.

TOXICITY

ETHYLENEDIAMINETETRAACETIC ACID, TETRASODIUM SALT: IRRITATION DATA: 500 MG/24 HOURS SKIN-RABBIT MODERATE; 1900 UG EYE-RABBIT; 100 MG/24 HOURS EYE-RABBIT MODERATE. TOXICITY DATA: 330 MG/KG INTRAPERITONEAL-MOUSE LD50. CARCINOGEN STATUS: NONE. LOCAL EFFECTS: IRRITANT- SKIN, EYE. ACUTE TOXICITY LEVEL: INSUFFICIENT DATA. TARGET EFFECTS: POISONING MAY AFFECT THE KIDNEY. AT INCREASED RISK FROM EXPOSURE: PERSONS WITH RENAL OR HEART DISEASE; A HISTORY OF SEIZURES OR INTRACRANIAL LESIONS; POTASSIUM DEFICIENCY; OR INSULIN-DEPENDENT DIABETES. ADDITIONAL DATA: PARENTERAL ADMINISTRATION OF EDTA OR ITS SALTS IN HIGH DOSES MAY CAUSE SEVERE RENAL LESIONS AND TUBULAR NECROSIS, INTERNAL HEMORRHAGE, LIFE-THREATENING HYPOCALCEMIA, AND DEATH. PROLONGED PARENTERAL ADMINISTRATION MAY LEAD TO ELECTROLYTE IMBALANCE AND CARDIAC ARRHYTHMIAS.

HEALTH EFFECTS AND FIRST AID

INHALATION: ETHYLENEDIAMINETETRAACETIC ACID, TETRASODIUM SALT: **ACUTE EXPOSURE-** NO SPECIFIC DATA AVAILABLE. INHALATION OF DUSTS OR MISTS OF EDTA SALTS MAY CAUSE MUCOUS MEMBRANE IRRITATION WITH SORE THROAT AND COUGHING. **CHRONIC EXPOSURE-** NO DATA AVAILABLE.

FIRST AID- REMOVE FROM EXPOSURE AREA TO FRESH AIR IMMEDIATELY. IF BREATHING HAS STOPPED, PERFORM ARTIFICIAL RESPIRATION. KEEP PERSON WARM AND AT REST. TREAT SYMPTOMATICALLY AND SUPPORTIVELY. GET MEDICAL ATTENTION IMMEDIATELY.

SKIN CONTACT: ETHYLENEDIAMINETETRAACETIC ACID, TETRASODIUM SALT: IRRITANT. **ACUTE EXPOSURE-** CONTACT MAY CAUSE IRRITATION WITH REDNESS AND PAIN. APPLICATION OF 500 MG TO RABBIT SKIN FOR 24 HOURS RESULTED IN MODERATE IRRITATION. **CHRONIC EXPOSURE-** REPEATED OR PROLONGED CONTACT WITH SKIN MAY CAUSE MODERATE IRRITATION AND POSSIBLY A MILD BURN.

FIRST AID- REMOVE CONTAMINATED CLOTHING AND SHOES IMMEDIATELY. WASH AFFECTED AREA WITH SOAP OR MILD DETERGENT AND LARGE AMOUNTS OF WATER UNTIL NO EVIDENCE OF CHEMICAL REMAINS (APPROXIMATELY 15-20 MINUTES). GET MEDICAL ATTENTION IMMEDIATELY.

EYE CONTACT: ETHYLENEDIAMINETETRAACETIC ACID, TETRASODIUM SALT: IRRITANT. **ACUTE EXPOSURE-** CONTACT MAY CAUSE IRRITATION WITH REDNESS AND PAIN. MAY CAUSE TRANSIENT CORNEAL INJURY. SOLUTIONS OF EDTA TETRASODIUM SALT ARE SUFFICIENTLY ALKALINE TO BE INJURIOUS TO THE EYE. APPLICATION OF 1900 UG TO RABBIT EYES CAUSED IRRITATION. APPLICATION OF 100 MG TO RABBIT EYES FOR 24 HOURS CAUSED MODERATE IRRITATION. **CHRONIC EXPOSURE-** REPEATED OR PROLONGED CONTACT WITH IRRITANTS MAY CAUSE CONJUNCTIVITIS.

FIRST AID- WASH EYES IMMEDIATELY WITH LARGE AMOUNTS OF WATER OR NORMAL SALINE, OCCASIONALLY LIFTING UPPER AND LOWER LIDS, UNTIL NO EVIDENCE OF CHEMICAL REMAINS (APPROXIMATELY 15-20 MINUTES). GET MEDICAL ATTENTION IMMEDIATELY.

INGESTION: ETHYLENEDIAMINETETRAACETIC ACID, TETRASODIUM SALT: **ACUTE EXPOSURE-** SOLUTIONS OF THE SALTS OF EDTA ARE EXTREMELY IRRITATING TO THE GASTROINTESTINAL SYSTEM. ALTHOUGH POORLY ABSORBED, IF SUFFICIENT AMOUNTS ARE INGESTED SYSTEMIC TOXICITY MAY RESULT. EDTA AND ITS SALTS MAY CHELATE LEAD, MAGNESIUM, ZINC, AND TRACE METALS IF THEY ARE PRESENT IN THE INTESTINE, POSSIBLY CAUSING THEIR INCREASED ABSORPTION AND THEREBY INCREASING TOTAL BODY STORES OF THESE METALS. **CHRONIC EXPOSURE-** NO DATA AVAILABLE.

FIRST AID- TREAT SYMPTOMATICALLY AND SUPPORTIVELY. GET MEDICAL ATTENTION IMMEDIATELY. IF VOMITING OCCURS, KEEP HEAD LOWER THAN HIPS TO PREVENT ASPIRATION.

ANTIDOTE: NO SPECIFIC ANTIDOTE. TREAT SYMPTOMATICALLY AND SUPPORTIVELY.

REACTIVITY

REACTIVITY: STABLE UNDER NORMAL TEMPERATURES AND PRESSURES.

INCOMPATIBILITIES: ETHYLENEDIAMINETETRAACETIC ACID, TETRASODIUM SALT: ACIDS: INCOMPATIBLE. ALUMINUM: MAY FORM FLAMMABLE HYDROGEN GAS. METALS: MAY FORM FLAMMABLE HYDROGEN GAS. OXIDIZERS (STRONG): FIRE AND EXPLOSION HAZARD.

DECOMPOSITION: THERMAL DECOMPOSITION PRODUCTS MAY INCLUDE TOXIC AND HAZARDOUS OXIDES OF CARBON, NITROGEN, AND SODIUM.

POLYMERIZATION: HAZARDOUS POLYMERIZATION HAS NOT BEEN REPORTED TO OCCUR UNDER NORMAL TEMPERATURES AND PRESSURES.

STORAGE AND DISPOSAL

OBSERVE ALL FEDERAL, STATE AND LOCAL REGULATIONS WHEN STORING OR DISPOSING OF THIS SUBSTANCE. FOR ASSISTANCE, CONTACT THE DISTRICT DIRECTOR OF THE ENVIRONMENTAL PROTECTION AGENCY.

STORAGE

STORE AWAY FROM INCOMPATIBLE SUBSTANCES.
KEEP IN A TIGHTLY CLOSED CONTAINER. STORE IN A COOL, DRY, VENTILATED AREA.

CONDITIONS TO AVOID

MAY BURN BUT DOES NOT IGNITE READILY. AVOID CONTACT WITH STRONG OXIDIZERS, EXCESSIVE HEAT, SPARKS, OR OPEN FLAME.
PREVENT DISPERSION OF DUST IN AIR.

SPILL AND LEAK PROCEDURES

OCCUPATIONAL SPILL: SWEEP UP AND PLACE IN SUITABLE CLEAN, DRY CONTAINERS FOR RECLAMATION OR LATER DISPOSAL. DO NOT FLUSH SPILLED MATERIAL INTO SEWER. KEEP UNNECESSARY PEOPLE AWAY.

PROTECTIVE EQUIPMENT

VENTILATION: PROVIDE LOCAL EXHAUST OR PROCESS ENCLOSURE VENTILATION SYSTEM.

RESPIRATOR: THE FOLLOWING RESPIRATORS ARE RECOMMENDED BASED ON INFORMATION FOUND IN THE PHYSICAL DATA, TOXICITY AND HEALTH EFFECTS SECTIONS. THEY ARE RANKED IN ORDER FROM MINIMUM TO MAXIMUM RESPIRATORY PROTECTION. THE SPECIFIC RESPIRATOR SELECTED MUST BE BASED ON CONTAMINATION LEVELS FOUND IN THE WORK PLACE, MUST NOT EXCEED THE WORKING LIMITS OF THE RESPIRATOR AND BE JOINTLY APPROVED BY THE NATIONAL INSTITUTE FOR OCCUPATIONAL SAFETY AND HEALTH AND THE MINE SAFETY AND HEALTH ADMINISTRATION (NIOSH-MSHA).
DUST AND MIST RESPIRATOR WITH A FULL FACEPIECE.
AIR-PURIFYING FULL FACEPIECE RESPIRATOR WITH A HIGH-EFFICIENCY PARTICULATE FILTER.
POWERED AIR-PURIFYING RESPIRATOR WITH A TIGHT-FITTING FACEPIECE AND HIGH-EFFICIENCY PARTICULATE FILTER.
TYPE 'C' SUPPLIED-AIR RESPIRATOR WITH A FULL FACEPIECE OPERATED IN PRESSURE-DEMAND OR OTHER POSITIVE PRESSURE MODE OR WITH A FULL FACEPIECE, HELMET OR HOOD OPERATED IN CONTINUOUS-FLOW MODE.
SELF-CONTAINED BREATHING APPARATUS WITH A FULL FACEPIECE OPERATED IN PRESSURE-DEMAND OR OTHER POSITIVE PRESSURE MODE.
FOR FIREFIGHTING AND OTHER IMMEDIATELY DANGEROUS TO LIFE OR HEALTH CONDITIONS:
SELF-CONTAINED BREATHING APPARATUS WITH FULL FACEPIECE OPERATED IN PRESSURE-DEMAND OR OTHER POSITIVE PRESSURE MODE.
SUPPLIED-AIR RESPIRATOR WITH FULL FACEPIECE AND OPERATED IN PRESSURE-DEMAND OR OTHER POSITIVE PRESSURE MODE IN COMBINATION WITH AN AUXILIARY SELF-CONTAINED BREATHING APPARATUS OPERATED IN PRESSURE-DEMAND OR OTHER POSITIVE PRESSURE MODE.

CLOTHING: EMPLOYEE MUST WEAR APPROPRIATE PROTECTIVE (IMPERVIOUS) CLOTHING AND EQUIPMENT TO PREVENT REPEATED OR PROLONGED SKIN CONTACT WITH THIS SUBSTANCE.

GLOVES: EMPLOYEE MUST WEAR APPROPRIATE PROTECTIVE GLOVES TO PREVENT CONTACT WITH THIS SUBSTANCE.

EYE PROTECTION: EMPLOYEE MUST WEAR SPLASH-PROOF OR DUST-RESISTANT SAFETY GOGGLES TO PREVENT EYE CONTACT WITH THIS SUBSTANCE.
EMERGENCY EYE WASH: WHERE THERE IS ANY POSSIBILITY THAT AN EMPLOYEE'S EYES MAY BE EXPOSED TO THIS SUBSTANCE, THE EMPLOYER SHOULD PROVIDE AN EYE WASH FOUNTAIN WITHIN THE IMMEDIATE WORK AREA FOR EMERGENCY USE.

AUTHORIZED BY- OCCUPATIONAL HEALTH SERVICES, INC.
CREATION DATE: 11/16/89 ***REVISION DATE:*** 05/31/90

MATERIAL SAFETY DATA SHEET

OCCUPATIONAL HEALTH SERVICES, INC.
AGRICULTURE AND PESTICIDE DIVISION
450 SEVENTH AVENUE, SUITE 2407
NEW YORK, NEW YORK 10123
1-800-445-MSDS OR (212) 967-1100

EMERGENCY CONTACT:
JOHN S. BRANSFORD, JR. (615) 292-1180

SUBSTANCE IDENTIFICATION

CAS-NUMBER 7722-88-5

SUBSTANCE: **TETRASODIUM PYROPHOSPHATE, ANHYDROUS**

TRADE NAMES/SYNONYMS: SODIUM PYROPHOSPHATE; TETRASODIUM DIPHOSPHATE; DIPHOSPHORIC ACID, TETRASODIUM SALT; PYRO; TSPP; PYROPHOSPHORIC ACID, TETRASODIUM SALT; PHOSPHOTEX; SODIUM DIPHOSPHATE; SODIUM PHOSPHATTE; TETRON; TETRON (DISPERSANT); VICTOR TSPP; SODIUM DIPHOSPHATE (NA4P2O7); SODIUM PHOSPHATE (NA4P2O7); SODIUM PYROPHOSPHATE (NA4P2O7); TETRASODIUM DIPHOSPHATE (NA4P2O7); TETRASODIUM PYROPHOSPHATE (HUGHES); NA4O7P2; PST23140

CHEMICAL FAMILY: INORGANIC SALT

MOLECULAR FORMULA: NA4-P2-O7

MOLECULAR WEIGHT: 265.90

CERCLA RATINGS (SCALE 0-3): HEALTH=2 FIRE=0 REACTIVITY=0 PERSISTENCE=0

NFPA RATINGS (SCALE 0-4): HEALTH=2 FIRE=0 REACTIVITY=0

COMPONENTS AND CONTAMINANTS

COMPONENT: TETRASODIUM PYROPHOSPHATE, ANHYDROUS ***PERCENT:*** 100
CAS# 7722-88-5

OTHER CONTAMINANTS: NONE

EXPOSURE LIMITS: TETRASODIUM PYROPHOSPHATE: 5 MG/M3 OSHA TWA 5 MG/M3 ACGIH TWA

PHYSICAL DATA

DESCRIPTION: ODORLESS WHITE POWDER. ***MELTING POINT:*** 1616 F (880 C)

SPECIFIC GRAVITY: 2.534 ***PH:*** 10.2 @ 1% SOLN

SOLUBILITY IN WATER: 6.7% @ 20 C

SOLVENT SOLUBILITY: DECOMPOSES IN ALCOHOL.

FIRE AND EXPLOSION DATA

FIRE AND EXPLOSION HAZARD: NEGLIGIBLE FIRE HAZARD WHEN EXPOSED TO HEAT OR FLAME.

FIREFIGHTING MEDIA: EXTINGUISH USING AGENT SUITABLE FOR TYPE OF SURROUNDING FIRE.

FIREFIGHTING: NO ACUTE HAZARD. MOVE CONTAINER FROM FIRE AREA IF POSSIBLE. AVOID BREATHING VAPORS OR DUSTS; KEEP UPWIND.

TOXICITY

TETRASODIUM PYROPHOSPHATE, ANHYDROUS: TOXICITY DATA: 4000 MG/KG ORAL-RAT LD50; 2980 MG/KG ORAL-MOUSE LD50; 400 MG/KG SUBCUTANEOUS-MOUSE LD50; 100 MG/KG INTRAVENOUS-RAT LD50; 69 MG/KG INTRAVENOUS-MOUSE LD50; 50 MG/KG INTRAVENOUS-RABBIT LDLO; 59 MG/KG INTRAPERITONEAL-RAT LD50; 380 MG/KG INTRAPERITONEAL-MOUSE LD50. CARCINOGEN STATUS: NONE. LOCAL EFFECTS: IRRITANT- INHALAITON, SKIN, AND EYES. ACUTE TOXICITY LEVEL: MODERATELY TOXIC BY INGESTION. TARGET EFFECTS: NO DATA AVAILABLE. ADDITIONAL DATA: SOME PHOSPHATES MAY CAUSE HYPOCALCEMIA.

HEALTH EFFECTS AND FIRST AID

INHALATION: TETRASODIUM PYROPHOSPHATE, ANHYDROUS: IRRITANT. **ACUTE EXPOSURE-** MAY CAUSE MUCOUS MEMBRANE IRRITATION WITH SORE THROAT, COUGHING, AND SHORTNESS OF BREATH. **CHRONIC EXPOSURE-** NO DATA AVAILABLE.

FIRST AID- REMOVE FROM EXPOSURE AREA TO FRESH AIR IMMEDIATELY. IF BREATHING HAS STOPPED, PERFORM ARTIFICIAL RESPIRATION. KEEP PERSON WARM AND AT REST. TREAT SYMPTOMATICALLY AND SUPPORTIVELY. GET MEDICAL ATTENTION IMMEDIATELY.

SKIN CONTACT: TETRASODIUM PYROPHOSPHATE, ANHYDROUS: IRRITANT. **ACUTE EXPOSURE-** CONTACT MAY PRODUCE STRONG IRRITATION, ERYTHEMA, PAIN AND BLISTERING. **CHRONIC EXPOSURE-** REPEATED OR PROLONGED CONTACT MAY RESULT IN DERMATITIS.

FIRST AID- REMOVE CONTAMINATED CLOTHING AND SHOES IMMEDIATELY. WASH AFFECTED AREA WITH SOAP OR MILD DETERGENT AND LARGE AMOUNTS OF WATER UNTIL NO EVIDENCE OF CHEMICAL REMAINS (APPROXIMATELY 15-20 MINUTES). GET MEDICAL ATTENTION IMMEDIATELY.

EYE CONTACT: TETRASODIUM PYROPHOSPHATE, ANHYDROUS: IRRITANT. **ACUTE EXPOSURE-** DIRECT CONTACT MAY CAUSE IRRITATION, PAIN, AND BLURRED VISION. **CHRONIC EXPOSURE-** REPEATED OR PROLONGED CONTACT WITH THE DUST MAY RESULT IN CONJUNCTIVITIS.

FIRST AID- WASH EYES IMMEDIATELY WITH LARGE AMOUNTS OF WATER OR NORMAL SALINE, OCCASIONALLY LIFTING UPPER AND LOWER LIDS, UNTIL NO EVIDENCE OF CHEMICAL REMAINS (APPROXIMATELY 15-20 MINUTES). GET MEDICAL ATTENTION IMMEDIATELY.

INGESTION: TETRASODIUM PYROPHOSPHATE, ANHYDROUS: **ACUTE EXPOSURE-** INGESTION MAY CAUSE ABDOMINAL PAIN, NAUSEA, VOMITING, AND DIARRHEA. THE ESTIMATED FATAL DOSE FOR HUMANS IS 50 GRAMS. INGESTION OF SOME PHOSPHATES IN THE FORM OF DETERGENTS MAY CAUSE A SHOCK-LIKE STATE, FALL OF BLOOD PRESSURE, SLOW PULSE, CYANOSIS, AND COMA. THE IONIC SERUM CALCIUM LEVEL MAY BE REDUCED AND RESULT IN TETANY. **CHRONIC EXPOSURE-** NO DATA AVAILABLE.

FIRST AID- DILUTE THE ALKALI BY GIVING WATER OR MILK IMMEDIATELY AND ALLOW VOMITING TO OCCUR. AVOID GASTRIC LAVAGE OR EMETICS. ESOPHAGOSCOPY IS THE ONLY WAY TO EXCLUDE THE POSSIBLITY OF CORROSION IN THE UPPER GASTROINTESTINAL TRACT; IF CORROSION IS SUSPECTED, ESOPHAGOSCOPY SHOULD USUALLY BE PERFORMED WITHIN 24 HOURS (DREISBACH, HANDBOOK OF POISONING, 12TH ED.). MAINTAIN AIRWAY AND TREAT SHOCK. IF VOMITING OCCURS, KEEP HEAD BELOW HIPS TO HELP PREVENT ASPIRATION. GET MEDICAL ATTENTION IMMEDIATELY.

ANTIDOTE: THE FOLLOWING ANTIDOTE HAS BEEN RECOMMENDED. HOWEVER, THE DECISION AS TO WHETHER THE SEVERITY OF POISONING REQUIRES ADMINISTRATION OF ANY ANTIDOTE AND ACTUAL DOSE REQUIRED SHOULD BE MADE BY QUALIFIED MEDICAL PERSONNEL.
PHOSPHATES: FOR HYPOCALCEMIA, AFTER PHOSPHATE INGESTION, GIVE CALCIUM GLUCONATE, 5 ML OF 10% SOLUTION SLOWLY INTRAVENOUSLY, TO RESTORE IONIC CALCIUM TO NORMAL LEVEL (DREISBACH, HANDBOOK OF POISONING, 12TH ED.). ANTIDOTE SHOULD BE ADMINISTERED BY QUALIFIED MEDICAL PERSONNEL.

REACTIVITY

REACTIVITY: STABLE UNDER NORMAL TEMPERATURES AND PRESSURES.

INCOMPATIBILITIES: TETRASODIUM PYROPHOSPHATE: NO DATA AVAILABLE.

DECOMPOSITION: THERMAL DECOMPOSITION PRODUCTS MAY INCLUDE TOXIC AND HAZARDOUS SODIUM OXIDE AND OXIDES OF PHOSPHORUS.

POLYMERIZATION: HAZARDOUS POLYMERIZATION HAS NOT BEEN REPORTED TO OCCUR UNDER NORMAL TEMPERATURES AND PRESSURES.

STORAGE AND DISPOSAL

OBSERVE ALL FEDERAL, STATE AND LOCAL REGULATIONS WHEN STORING OR DISPOSING OF THIS SUBSTANCE. FOR ASSISTANCE, CONTACT THE DISTRICT DIRECTOR OF THE ENVIRONMENTAL PROTECTION AGENCY.

CONDITIONS TO AVOID

PREVENT DISPERSION OF DUST IN AIR.

SPILL AND LEAK PROCEDURES

OCCUPATIONAL SPILL: FOR LARGE SPILLS, SWEEP UP WITH A MINIMUM OF DUSTING AND PLACE INTO SUITABLE CLEAN, DRY CONTAINERS FOR RECLAMATION OR LATER DISPOSAL.
RESIDUE SHOULD BE CLEANED UP USING A HIGH-EFFICIENCY PARTICULATE FILTER VACUUM.

PROTECTIVE EQUIPMENT

VENTILATION: PROVIDE LOCAL EXHAUST VENTILATION AND/OR GENERAL DILUTION VENTILATION TO MEET PUBLISHED EXPOSURE LIMITS.

RESPIRATOR: THE FOLLOWING RESPIRATORS ARE RECOMMENDED BASED ON INFORMATION FOUND IN THE PHYSICAL DATA, TOXICITY AND HEALTH EFFECTS SECTIONS. THEY ARE RANKED IN ORDER FROM MINIMUM TO MAXIMUM RESPIRATORY PROTECTION. THE SPECIFIC RESPIRATOR SELECTED MUST BE BASED ON CONTAMINATION LEVELS FOUND IN THE WORK PLACE, MUST NOT EXCEED THE WORKING LIMITS OF THE RESPIRATOR AND BE JOINTLY APPROVED BY THE NATIONAL INSTITUTE FOR OCCUPATIONAL SAFETY AND HEALTH AND THE MINE SAFETY AND HEALTH ADMINISTRATION (NIOSH-MSHA).
DUST AND MIST RESPIRATOR WITH A FULL FACEPIECE.
AIR-PURIFYING FULL FACEPIECE RESPIRATOR WITH A HIGH-EFFICIENCY PARTICULATE FILTER.
POWERED AIR-PURIFYING RESPIRATOR WITH A TIGHT-FITTING FACEPIECE AND

HIGH-EFFICIENCY PARTICULATE FILTER.
TYPE 'C' SUPPLIED-AIR RESPIRATOR WITH A FULL FACEPIECE OPERATED IN PRESSURE-DEMAND OR OTHER POSITIVE PRESSURE MODE OR WITH A FULL FACEPIECE, HELMET OR HOOD OPERATED IN CONTINUOUS-FLOW MODE.
SELF-CONTAINED BREATHING APPARATUS WITH A FULL FACEPIECE OPERATED IN PRESSURE-DEMAND OR OTHER POSITIVE PRESSURE MODE.
FOR FIREFIGHTING AND OTHER IMMEDIATELY DANGEROUS TO LIFE OR HEALTH CONDITIONS:
SELF-CONTAINED BREATHING APPARATUS WITH FULL FACEPIECE OPERATED IN PRESSURE-DEMAND OR OTHER POSITIVE PRESSURE MODE. SUPPLIED-AIR RESPIRATOR WITH FULL FACEPIECE AND OPERATED IN PRESSURE-DEMAND OR OTHER POSITIVE PRESSURE MODE IN COMBINATION WITH AN AUXILIARY SELF-CONTAINED BREATHING APPARATUS OPERATED IN PRESSURE-DEMAND OR OTHER POSITIVE PRESSURE MODE.

CLOTHING: EMPLOYEE MUST WEAR APPROPRIATE PROTECTIVE (IMPERVIOUS) CLOTHING AND EQUIPMENT TO PREVENT REPEATED OR PROLONGED SKIN CONTACT WITH THIS SUBSTANCE.

GLOVES: EMPLOYEE MUST WEAR APPROPRIATE PROTECTIVE GLOVES TO PREVENT CONTACT WITH THIS SUBSTANCE.

EYE PROTECTION: EMPLOYEE MUST WEAR SPLASH-PROOF OR DUST-RESISTANT SAFETY GOGGLES TO PREVENT EYE CONTACT WITH THIS SUBSTANCE.
EMERGENCY EYE WASH: WHERE THERE IS ANY POSSIBILITY THAT AN EMPLOYEE'S EYES MAY BE EXPOSED TO THIS SUBSTANCE, THE EMPLOYER SHOULD PROVIDE AN EYE WASH FOUNTAIN WITHIN THE IMMEDIATE WORK AREA FOR EMERGENCY USE.

AUTHORIZED BY- OCCUPATIONAL HEALTH SERVICES, INC.
CREATION DATE: 11/16/89 ***REVISION DATE:*** 05/16/90

MATERIAL SAFETY DATA SHEET

OCCUPATIONAL HEALTH SERVICES, INC.
AGRICULTURE AND PESTICIDE DIVISION
450 SEVENTH AVENUE, SUITE 2407
NEW YORK, NEW YORK 10123
1-800-445-MSDS OR (212) 967-1100

EMERGENCY CONTACT:
JOHN S. BRANSFORD, JR. (615) 292-1180

SUBSTANCE IDENTIFICATION

CAS-NUMBER 51707-55-2

SUBSTANCE: **THIDIAZURON**

TRADE NAMES/SYNONYMS: UREA, N-PHENYL-N'-1,2,3-THIADIAZOL-5-YL-; N-PHENYL-N'-1,2,3-THIADIAZOL-5-YL-UREA; 1-PHENYL-3-(1,2,3-THIADIAZOL-5-YL)UREA; N-PHENYL-N'-1,2,3-THIADIAZOL-5-YL UREA; DROPP; SN49537; THIADIAZURON; C9H8N4OS; PST23299

CHEMICAL FAMILY: SUBSTITUTED UREA

MOLECULAR FORMULA: C9-H8-N4-O-S

MOLECULAR WEIGHT: 220.27

CERCLA RATINGS (SCALE 0-3): HEALTH=1 FIRE=1 REACTIVITY=0 PERSISTENCE=1

NFPA RATINGS (SCALE 0-4): HEALTH=1 FIRE=1 REACTIVITY=0

COMPONENTS AND CONTAMINANTS

COMPONENT: THIDIAZURON ***PERCENT:*** 100.0
CAS# 51707-55-2

OTHER CONTAMINANTS: NONE

EXPOSURE LIMITS: NO OCCUPATIONAL EXPOSURE LIMITS ESTABLISHED BY OSHA, ACGIH, OR NIOSH.

PHYSICAL DATA

DESCRIPTION: COLORLESS CRYSTALLINE SOLID.

MELTING POINT: 415 F (213 C) (DECOMPOSES) ***VAPOR PRESSURE:*** NEGLIGIBLE

SOLUBILITY IN WATER: 0.002% @ 23 C

SOLVENT SOLUBILITY: VERY SOLUBLE IN DIMETHYLFORMAMIDE AND DIMETHYL SULFOXIDE; SLIGHTLY SOLUBLE IN ACETONE, CYLCOHEXANONE, ETHYL ACETATE AND METHANOL.

FIRE AND EXPLOSION DATA

FIRE AND EXPLOSION HAZARD: SLIGHT FIRE HAZARD WHEN EXPOSED TO HEAT OR FLAME.

FIREFIGHTING MEDIA: DRY CHEMICAL, CARBON DIOXIDE, HALON, WATER SPRAY OR STANDARD FOAM (1987 EMERGENCY RESPONSE GUIDEBOOK, DOT P 5800.4).
FOR LARGER FIRES, USE WATER SPRAY, FOG OR STANDARD FOAM (1987 EMERGENCY RESPONSE GUIDEBOOK, DOT P 5800.4).

FIREFIGHTING: MOVE CONTAINERS FROM FIRE AREA IF POSSIBLE. FIGHT FIRE FROM MAXIMUM DISTANCE. STAY AWAY FROM STORAGE TANK ENDS. DIKE FIRE CONTROL WATER FOR LATER DISPOSAL. DO NOT SCATTER MATERIAL (1987 EMERGENCY RESPONSE GUIDEBOOK, DOT P 5800.4, GUIDE PAGE 55).
EXTINGUISH USING AGENT SUITABLE FOR TYPE OF SURROUNDING FIRE. USE WATER IN FLOODING QUANTITIES AS FOG. KEEP SPARKS, FLAMES AND OTHER SOURCES OF IGNITION AWAY. KEEP MATERIAL OUT OF WATER SOURCES AND SEWERS. DO NOT TOUCH MATERIAL AND AVOID BREATHING DUSTS AND FUMES FROM BURNING MATERIAL. KEEP UPWIND.

TOXICITY

THIDIAZURON: TOXICITY DATA: 5350 MG/KG ORAL-RAT LD50; 3740 MG/KG ORAL-MOUSE LD50; 7100 MG/KG ORAL-RABBIT LD50; 2813 MG/KG ORAL-GUINEA PIG LD50; 4200 MG/KG INTRAPERITONEAL-RAT LD50; REPRODUCTIVE EFFECTS DATA (RTECS). CARCINOGEN STATUS: NONE. ACUTE TOXICITY DATA: SLIGHTLY TOXIC BY INGESTION. TARGET EFFECTS: NO DATA AVAILABLE.

HEALTH EFFECTS AND FIRST AID

INHALATION: THIDIAZURON: **ACUTE EXPOSURE-** MANY SUBSTITUTED UREA HERBICIDES ARE MODERATELY IRRITATING TO THE MUCOUS MEMBRANES. **CHRONIC EXPOSURE-** NO DATA AVAILABLE.

FIRST AID- REMOVE FROM EXPOSURE AREA TO FRESH AIR IMMEDIATELY. IF BREATHING HAS STOPPED, PERFORM ARTIFICIAL RESPIRATION. KEEP PERSON WARM AND AT REST. TREAT SYMPTOMATICALLY AND SUPPORTIVELY. GET MEDICAL ATTENTION IMMEDIATELY.

SKIN CONTACT: THIDIAZURON: **ACUTE EXPOSURE-** MANY SUBSTITUTED UREA HERBICIDES ARE MODERATELY IRRITATING TO THE SKIN. A LETHAL DOSE IN RATS AND RABBITS BY DERMAL ABSORPTION IS GREATER THAN 1000 MG/KG. **CHRONIC EXPOSURE-** NO DATA AVAILABLE.

FIRST AID- REMOVE CONTAMINATED CLOTHING AND SHOES IMMEDIATELY. WASH AFFECTED AREA WITH SOAP OR MILD DETERGENT AND LARGE AMOUNTS OF WATER UNTIL NO EVIDENCE OF CHEMICAL REMAINS (APPROXIMATELY 15-20 MINUTES). GET MEDICAL ATTENTION IMMEDIATELY.

EYE CONTACT: THIDIAZURON: **ACUTE EXPOSURE-** MANY SUBSTITUTED UREA HERBICIDES ARE MODERATELY IRRITATING TO THE EYES. **CHRONIC EXPOSURE-** NO DATA AVAILABLE.

FIRST AID- WASH EYES IMMEDIATELY WITH LARGE AMOUNTS OF WATER OR NORMAL SALINE, OCCASIONALLY LIFTING UPPER AND LOWER LIDS, UNTIL NO EVIDENCE OF CHEMICAL REMAINS (APPROXIMATELY 15-20 MINUTES). GET MEDICAL ATTENTION IMMEDIATELY.

INGESTION: THIDIAZURON: **ACUTE EXPOSURE-** A LETHAL DOSE IN RATS WAS 5350 MG/KG; SYMPTOMS WERE NOT REPORTED. **CHRONIC EXPOSURE-** EFFECTS ON THE REPRODUCTIVE SYSTEM WERE OBSERVED IN MALE RATS FED THIDIAZURON PRIOR TO MATING.

FIRST AID- TREAT SYMPTOMATICALLY AND SUPPORTIVELY. GET MEDICAL ATTENTION IMMEDIATELY. IF VOMITING OCCURS, KEEP HEAD LOWER THAN HIPS TO PREVENT ASPIRATION.

ANTIDOTE: NO SPECIFIC ANTIDOTE. TREAT SYMPTOMATICALLY AND SUPPORTIVELY.

REACTIVITY

REACTIVITY: STABLE UNDER NORMAL TEMPERATURES AND PRESSURES.

INCOMPATIBILITIES: THIDIAZURON: OXIDIZERS (STRONG): FIRE AND EXPLOSION HAZARD.

DECOMPOSITION: THERMAL DECOMPOSITION PRODUCTS MAY INCLUDE TOXIC OXIDES OF CARBON, NITROGEN, AND SULFUR.

POLYMERIZATION: HAZARDOUS POLYMERIZATION HAS NOT BEEN REPORTED TO OCCUR UNDER NORMAL TEMPERATURES AND PRESSURES.

STORAGE AND DISPOSAL

OBSERVE ALL FEDERAL, STATE AND LOCAL REGULATIONS WHEN STORING OR DISPOSING OF THIS SUBSTANCE. FOR ASSISTANCE, CONTACT THE DISTRICT DIRECTOR OF THE ENVIRONMENTAL PROTECTION AGENCY.

STORAGE

STORE IN ACCORDANCE WITH 40 CFR 165 RECOMMENDED PROCEDURES FOR THE DISPOSAL AND STORAGE OF PESTICIDES AND PESTICIDE CONTAINERS.
STORE AWAY FROM INCOMPATIBLE SUBSTANCES.

DISPOSAL

DISPOSAL MUST BE IN ACCORDANCE WITH 40 CFR 165 RECOMMENDED PROCEDURES FOR THE DISPOSAL AND STORAGE OF PESTICIDES AND PESTICIDE CONTAINERS.

CONDITIONS TO AVOID

MAY BURN BUT DOES NOT IGNITE READILY. CONTAINERS MAY EXPLODE IN HEAT OF FIRE.

SPILL AND LEAK PROCEDURES

OCCUPATIONAL SPILL: DO NOT TOUCH SPILLED MATERIAL. STOP LEAK IF YOU CAN DO IT WITHOUT RISK. USE WATER SPRAY TO REDUCE VAPORS. FOR SMALL SPILLS, TAKE UP WITH SAND OR OTHER ABSORBENT MATERIAL AND PLACE INTO CONTAINERS FOR LATER DISPOSAL. FOR SMALL DRY SPILLS, WITH A CLEAN SHOVEL PLACE MATERIAL INTO CLEAN, DRY CONTAINERS AND COVER. MOVE CONTAINERS FROM SPILL AREA. FOR LARGER SPILLS, DIKE FAR AHEAD OF SPILL FOR LATER DISPOSAL. KEEP UNNECESSARY PEOPLE AWAY. ISOLATE HAZARD AREA AND DENY ENTRY. VENTILATE CLOSED SPACES BEFORE ENTERING.

PROTECTIVE EQUIPMENT

VENTILATION: PROVIDE GENERAL DILUTION VENTILATION.

RESPIRATOR: THE FOLLOWING RESPIRATORS ARE RECOMMENDED BASED ON INFORMATION FOUND IN THE PHYSICAL DATA, TOXICITY AND HEALTH EFFECTS SECTIONS. THEY ARE RANKED IN ORDER FROM MINIMUM TO MAXIMUM RESPIRATORY PROTECTION. THE SPECIFIC RESPIRATOR SELECTED MUST BE BASED ON CONTAMINATION LEVELS FOUND IN THE WORK PLACE, MUST NOT EXCEED THE WORKING LIMITS OF THE RESPIRATOR AND BE JOINTLY APPROVED BY THE NATIONAL INSTITUTE FOR OCCUPATIONAL SAFETY AND HEALTH AND THE MINE SAFETY AND HEALTH ADMINISTRATION (NIOSH-MSHA).

CHEMICAL CARTRIDGE RESPIRATOR WITH AN ORGANIC VAPOR CARTRIDGE(S) WITH A FULL FACEPIECE AND ORGANIC VAPOR CARTRIDGE(S) IN COMBINATION WITH A DUST AND MIST FILTER.

POWERED AIR-PURIFYING RESPIRATOR WITH A TIGHT-FITTING FACEPIECE AND ORGANIC VAPOR CARTRIDGE(S) IN COMBINATION WITH A HIGH-EFFICIENCY PARTICULATE FILTER.

TYPE 'C' SUPPLIED-AIR RESPIRATOR WITH A FULL FACEPIECE OPERATED IN A PRESSURE-DEMAND OR OTHER POSITIVE PRESSURE MODE.

SELF-CONTAINED BREATHING APPARATUS WITH A FULL FACEPIECE OPERATED IN PRESSURE-DEMAND OR OTHER POSITIVE PRESSURE MODE.

FOR FIREFIGHTING AND OTHER IMMEDIATELY DANGEROUS TO LIFE OR HEALTH CONDITIONS:

SELF-CONTAINED BREATHING APPARATUS WITH FULL FACEPIECE OPERATED IN PRESSURE-DEMAND OR OTHER POSITIVE PRESSURE MODE. SUPPLIED-AIR RESPIRATOR WITH FULL FACEPIECE AND OPERATED IN PRESSURE-DEMAND OR OTHER POSITIVE PRESSURE MODE IN COMBINATION WITH AN AUXILIARY SELF-CONTAINED BREATHING APPARATUS OPERATED IN PRESSURE-DEMAND OR OTHER POSITIVE PRESSURE MODE.

CLOTHING: EMPLOYEE MUST WEAR APPROPRIATE PROTECTIVE (IMPERVIOUS) CLOTHING AND EQUIPMENT TO PREVENT REPEATED OR PROLONGED SKIN CONTACT WITH THIS SUBSTANCE.

GLOVES: EMPLOYEE MUST WEAR APPROPRIATE PROTECTIVE GLOVES TO PREVENT CONTACT WITH THIS SUBSTANCE.

EYE PROTECTION: EMPLOYEE MUST WEAR SPLASH-PROOF OR DUST-RESISTANT SAFETY GOGGLES TO PREVENT EYE CONTACT WITH THIS SUBSTANCE.

EMERGENCY EYE WASH: WHERE THERE IS ANY POSSIBILITY THAT AN EMPLOYEE'S EYES MAY BE EXPOSED TO THIS SUBSTANCE, THE EMPLOYER SHOULD PROVIDE AN EYE WASH FOUNTAIN WITHIN THE IMMEDIATE WORK AREA FOR EMERGENCY USE.

AUTHORIZED BY- OCCUPATIONAL HEALTH SERVICES, INC.
CREATION DATE: 10/05/89 ***REVISION DATE:*** 05/14/90

MATERIAL SAFETY DATA SHEET

OCCUPATIONAL HEALTH SERVICES, INC.
AGRICULTURE AND PESTICIDE DIVISION
450 SEVENTH AVENUE, SUITE 2407
NEW YORK, NEW YORK 10123
1-800-445-MSDS OR (212) 967-1100

EMERGENCY CONTACT:
JOHN S. BRANSFORD, JR. (615) 292-1180

SUBSTANCE IDENTIFICATION

CAS-NUMBER 39196-18-4

SUBSTANCE: THIOFANOX

TRADE NAMES/SYNONYMS: 3,3-DIMETHYL-1-(METHYLTHIO)-2-BUTANONE O-((METHYLAMINO)CARBONYL) OXIME; 1-(2,2-DIMETHYL-1-METHYLTHIOMETHYLPROPYLIDENEAMINO-OXY)-N- METHYLFORMAMIDE; 2-BUTANONE, 3,3-DIMETHYL-1-(METHYLTHIO)-, O-((METHYLAMINO)CARBONYL); OXIME; BENELUX; DACAMOX; DS 15647; ENT 27851; RCRA P045; C9H18N2O2S; PST23330

CHEMICAL FAMILY: CARBAMATE

MOLECULAR FORMULA: C9-H18-N2-O2-S

MOLECULAR WEIGHT: 218.35

CERCLA RATINGS (SCALE 0-3): HEALTH=3 FIRE=U REACTIVITY=0 PERSISTENCE=U

NFPA RATINGS (SCALE 0-4): HEALTH=3 FIRE=U REACTIVITY=0

COMPONENTS AND CONTAMINANTS

COMPONENT: THIOFANOX ***PERCENT:*** 100.0
CAS# 39196-18-4

EXPOSURE LIMITS: NO OCCUPATIONAL EXPOSURE LIMITS ESTABLISHED BY OSHA, ACGIH, OR NIOSH.

THIOFANOX: 100/10,000 POUNDS SARA SECTION 302 THRESHOLD PLANNING QUANTITY 100 POUNDS SARA SECTION 304 REPORTABLE QUANTITY 100 POUNDS CERCLA SECTION REPORTABLE QUANTITY

PHYSICAL DATA

DESCRIPTION: COLORLESS SOLID WITH A PUNGENT ODOR

MELTING POINT: 134-136 F (57-58 C) ***SPECIFIC GRAVITY:*** NOT AVAILABLE

VAPOR PRESSURE: NEGLIGIBLE ***SOLUBILITY IN WATER:*** 0.5%

SOLVENT SOLUBILITY: SOLUBLE IN CHLORINATED AND AROMATIC HYDROCARBONS, KETONES; SPARINGLY SOLUBLE IN ALIPHATIC HYDROCARBONS

FIRE AND EXPLOSION DATA

FIRE AND EXPLOSION HAZARD: UNKNOWN FIRE AND EXPLOSION HAZARD.

FIREFIGHTING MEDIA: DRY CHEMICAL, CARBON DIOXIDE, WATER SPRAY OR FOAM FOR LARGER FIRES, USE WATER SPRAY, FOG OR ALCOHOL FOAM

FIREFIGHTING: MOVE CONTAINERS FROM FIRE AREA IF POSSIBLE. FIGHT FIRE FROM MAXIMUM DISTANCE. STAY AWAY FROM STORAGE TANK ENDS. DIKE FIRE CONTROL WATER FOR LATER DISPOSAL. DO NOT SCATTER MATERIAL (1987 EMERGENCY RESPONSE GUIDEBOOK, DOT P 5800.4, GUIDE PAGE 55).

TRANSPORTATION DATA

DEPARTMENT OF TRANSPORTATION HAZARD CLASSIFICATION 49 CFR 172.101: POISON B

DEPARTMENT OF TRANSPORTATION LABELING REQUIREMENTS 49 CFR 172.101 AND SUBPART E: POISON

DEPARTMENT OF TRANSPORTATION PACKAGING REQUIREMENTS: 49 CFR 173.365 EXCEPTIONS: 49 CFR 173.364

TOXICITY

THIOFANOX: TOXICITY DATA: 39 MG/KG SKIN-RABBIT LD50; 8500 UG/KG ORAL-RAT LD50. CARCINOGEN STATUS: NONE. ACUTE TOXICITY LEVEL: HIGHLY TOXIC BY DERMAL ABSORPTION AND INGESTION. TARGET EFFECTS: CHOLINESTERASE INHIBITOR. AT INCREASED RISK FROM EXPOSURE: PERSONS WITH ASTHMA, DIABETES, CARDIOVASCULAR DISEASE, MECHANICAL OBSTRUCTION OF THE GASTROINTESTINAL OR UROGENITAL TRACT, AND THOSE IN VAGOTONIC STATES.*

* MAY BE BASED ON GENERAL INFORMATION ON CARBAMATES.

HEALTH EFFECTS AND FIRST AID

INHALATION: THIOFANOX: SEE INFORMATION ON CARBAMATES.

CARBAMATES: CHOLINESTERASE INHIBITOR. <u>ACUTE EXPOSURE</u>- WHEN INHALED, THE FIRST EFFECTS OF CHOLINESTERASE INHIBITION ARE USUALLY RESPIRATORY AND MAY INCLUDE NASAL HYPEREMIA AND WATERY DISCHARGE, CHEST DISCOMFORT, DYSPNEA, AND WHEEZING DUE TO INCREASED BRONCHIAL SECRETIONS AND BRONCHOCONSTRICTION. OTHER SYSTEMIC EFFECTS MAY BEGIN WITHIN A FEW MINUTES OR SEVERAL HOURS OF EXPOSURE. SYMPTOMS MAY INCLUDE NAUSEA, VOMITING, DIARRHEA, ABDOMINAL CRAMPS, HEADACHE, VERTIGO, OCULAR PAIN, CILIARY MUSCLE SPASM, BLURRING OR DIMNESS OF VISION, MIOSIS, OR IN SOME CASES MYDRIASIS, LACRIMATION, SALIVATION, SWEATING, AND CONFUSION. OTHER REPORTED CENTRAL NERVOUS SYSTEM OR NEUROMUSCULAR EFFECTS INCLUDE ATAXIA, SLURRED SPEECH, AREFLEXIA, WEAKNESS, FATIGUE, TWITCHING, FASCICULATION, TREMOR, AND EVENTUALLY PARALYSIS OF THE EXTREMITIES AND POSSIBLY OF THE RESPIRATORY MUSCLES. IN SEVERE CASES, THERE MAY ALSO BE INVOLUNTARY DEFECATION AND URINATION, BRADYCARDIA, HYPOTENSION, PULMONARY EDEMA, CONVULSIONS, COMA, AND DEATH FROM RESPIRATORY FAILURE OR CARDIAC ARREST. CARBAMATES GENERALLY DO NOT ACCUMULATE IN MAMMALIAN TISSUE AND THE CHOLINESTERASE INHIBITION REVERSES RATHER RAPIDLY. IN NON-FATAL CASES, THE ILLNESS GENERALLY LASTS LESS THAN 24 HOURS. <u>CHRONIC EXPOSURE</u>- PROLONGED OR REPEATED EXPOSURE MAY CAUSE EFFECTS AS DESCRIBED IN ACUTE EXPOSURE.

FIRST AID- REMOVE FROM EXPOSURE AREA TO FRESH AIR IMMEDIATELY. IF BREATHING HAS STOPPED, GIVE ARTIFICIAL RESPIRATION. MAINTAIN AIRWAY AND BLOOD PRESSURE AND ADMINISTER OXYGEN IF AVAILABLE. KEEP AFFECTED PERSON WARM AND AT REST. TREAT SYMPTOMATICALLY AND SUPPORTIVELY. ADMINISTRATION OF OXYGEN SHOULD BE PERFORMED BY QUALIFIED PERSONNEL. GET MEDICAL ATTENTION IMMEDIATELY.

SKIN CONTACT: THIOFANOX: HIGHLY TOXIC. SEE INFORMATION ON CARBAMATES. CARBAMATES: CHOLINESTERASE INHIBITOR. **ACUTE EXPOSURE**- SOME COMPOUNDS MAY CAUSE IRRITATION. LOCALIZED SWEATING AND FASCICULATIONS MAY OCCUR AT THE SITE OF CONTACT. IF SUFFICIENT AMOUNTS ARE ABSORBED THROUGH THE SKIN, OTHER EFFECTS OF CHOLINESTERASE INHIBITION MAY OCCUR AS DESCRIBED IN ACUTE INHALATION; SYMPTOMS MAY BE DELAYED FOR 2-3 HOURS, USUALLY NO MORE THAN 8 HOURS. **CHRONIC EXPOSURE**- REPEATED OR PROLONGED EXPOSURE MAY CAUSE EFFECTS AS DESCRIBED IN ACUTE EXPOSURE.

FIRST AID- REMOVE CONTAMINATED CLOTHING IMMEDIATELY. WASH CONTAMINATED AREAS WITH SOAP AND WATER FOLLOWED BY ALCOHOL (ARENA, POISONING, 4TH ED.). EMERGENCY PERSONNEL SHOULD WEAR GLOVES AND AVOID CONTAMINATION. TREAT RESPIRATORY DIFFICULTY WITH ARTIFICIAL RESPIRATION. GET MEDICAL ATTENTION IMMEDIATELY.

EYE CONTACT: THIOFANOX: SEE INFORMATION ON CARBAMATES. CARBAMATES: CHOLINESTERASE INHIBITOR. **ACUTE EXPOSURE**- DIRECT CONTACT MAY CAUSE PAIN, HYPEREMIA, LACRIMATION, TWITCHING OF THE EYELIDS, MIOSIS, AND CILIARY MUSCLE SPASM WITH LOSS OF ACCOMODATION, BLURRED OR DIMMED VISION AND BROWACHE. SOMETIMES MYDRIASIS MAY OCCUR INSTEAD OF MIOSIS. WITH SUFFICIENT EXPOSURE, OTHER SYMPTOMS OF CHOLINESTERASE INHIBITION MAY OCCUR AS DESCRIBED IN ACUTE INHALATION. **CHRONIC EXPOSURE**- PROLONGED EXPOSURE MAY CAUSE EFFECTS AS DESCRIBED IN ACUTE EXPOSURE. SOME COMPOUNDS HAVE CAUSED TOXIC EFFECTS ON THE CRYSTALLINE LENS, CONJUNCTIVAL THICKENING AND OBSTRUCTION OF NASOLACRIMAL CANALS WHEN USED AS MIOTIC EYE DROPS.

FIRST AID- IRRIGATE EYES WITH WATER OR SALINE SOLUTION. IF SYMPTOMS OF POISONING OCCUR, TREAT RESPIRATORY DIFFICULTY WITH ARTIFICIAL RESPIRATION AND OXYGEN. OBSERVE PATIENT FOR AT LEAST 24-36 HOURS (GOSSELIN, CLINICAL TOXICOLOGY OF COMMERCIAL PRODUCTS, 5TH ED.). GET MEDICAL ATTENTION IMMEDIATELY. OXYGEN SHOULD BE ADMINISTERED BY QUALIFIED MEDICAL PERSONNEL.

INGESTION: THIOFANOX: HIGHLY TOXIC. SEE INFORMATION ON CARBAMATES. CARBAMATES: CHOLINESTERASE INHIBITOR. **ACUTE EXPOSURE**- WHEN INGESTED, THE FIRST EFFECTS MAY BE NAUSEA, VOMITING, ANOREXIA, ABDOMINAL CRAMPS, AND DIARRHEA. WITH ABSORPTION FROM THE GASTROINTESTINAL TRACT, THE OTHER EFFECTS OF CHOLINESTERASE INHIBITION AS DESCRIBED IN ACUTE INHALATION MAY OCCUR; SYMPTOMS MAY BEGIN WITHIN MINUTES OR BE DELAYED SEVERAL HOURS. **CHRONIC EXPOSURE**- REPEATED INGESTION MAY CAUSE EFFECTS AS DESCRIBED IN ACUTE EXPOSURE.

FIRST AID- IF PERSON IS ALERT AND RESPIRATION IS NOT DEPRESSED, GIVE SYRUP OF IPECAC FOLLOWED BY WATER (IF VOMITING OCCURS, KEEP HEAD BELOW HIPS TO PREVENT ASPIRATION). IF CONSCIOUSNESS LEVEL DECLINES OR VOMITING HAS NOT OCCURRED IN 15 MINUTES EMPTY STOMACH BY GASTRIC LAVAGE WITH THE AID OF CUFFED ENDOTRACHEAL TUBE USING ISOTONIC SALINE OR 5% SODIUM BICARBONATE FOLLOW WITH ACTIVATED CHARCOAL. ESTABLISH AND MAINTAIN AIRWAY. TREAT RESPIRATORY DIFFICULTY WITH ARTIFICIAL RESPIRATION AND OXYGEN. DO NOT GIVE MORPHINE, AMINOPHYLLINE, PHENOTHIAZINES, RESERPINE, FUROSEMIDE, OR ETHACRYNIC ACID (MORGAN, RECOGNITION AND MANAGEMENT OF PESTICIDE POISONINGS, 3RD ED.). TREAT SYMPTOMATICALLY AND SUPPORTIVELY. ADMINISTRATION OF OXYGEN AND LAVAGE MUST BE PERFORMED BY QUALIFIED MEDICAL PERSONNEL. GET MEDICAL ATTENTION IMMEDIATELY.

ANTIDOTE: THE FOLLOWING ANTIDOTE HAS BEEN RECOMMENDED. HOWEVER, THE DECISION AS TO WHETHER THE SEVERITY OF POISONING REQUIRES ADMINISTRATION OF ANY ANTIDOTE AND ACTUAL DOSE REQUIRED SHOULD BE MADE BY QUALIFIED MEDICAL PERSONNEL.

FOR CHOLINESTERASE INHIBITORS: ESTABLISH CLEAR AIRWAY AND TISSUE OXYGENATION BY ASPIRATION OF SECRETIONS, AND IF NECESSARY, BY ASSISTED PULMONARY VENTILATION WITH OXYGEN. IMPROVE TISSUE OXYGENATION AS MUCH AS POSSIBLE BEFORE ADMINISTERING ATROPINE TO MINIMIZE THE RISK OF VENTRICULAR FIBRILLATION. ADMINISTER ATROPINE SULFATE INTRAVENOUSLY, OR INTRAMUSCULARLY IF IV INJECTION IS NOT POSSIBLE. IN MODERATELY SEVERE POISONING ADMINISTER ATROPINE SULFATE, 0.4-2.0 MG REPEATED EVERY 15 MINUTES UNTIL ATROPINIZATION IS ACHIEVED (TACHYCARDIA, FLUSHING, DRY MOUTH, MYDRIASIS). MAINTAIN ATROPINIZATION BY REPEATED DOSES FOR 2-12 HOURS, OR LONGER, DEPENDING ON THE SEVERITY OF POISONING. THE APPEARANCE OF RALES IN THE LUNG BASES, MIOSIS, SALIVATION, NAUSEA, BRADYCARDIA, ARE ALL INDICATIONS OF INADEQUATE ATROPINIZATION. SEVERELY POISONED INDIVIDUALS MAY EXHIBIT REMARKABLE TOLERANCE TO ATROPINE; TWO OR MORE TIMES THE DOSAGES SUGGESTED ABOVE MAY BE NEEDED. PERSONS NOT POISONED OR ONLY SLIGHTLY POISONED, HOWEVER, MAY DEVELOP SIGNS OF ATROPINE TOXICITY FROM SUCH LARGE DOSAGES: FEVER, MUSCLE FIBRILLATIONS, AND DELIRIUM ARE THE MAIN SIGNS OF ATROPINE TOXICITY. IF THESE SIGNS APPEAR WHILE THE PATIENT IS FULLY ATROPINIZED, ATROPINE ADMINISTRATION SHOULD BE DISCONTINUED, AT LEAST TEMPORARILY. OBSERVE TREATED PATIENTS CLOSELY AT LEAST 24 HOURS TO INSURE THAT SYMPTOMS (POSSIBLY PULMONARY EDEMA) DO NOT RECUR AS ATROPINIZATION WEARS OFF. IN VERY SEVERE POISONINGS, METABOLIC DISPOSITION OF TOXICANT MAY REQUIRE SEVERAL HOURS OR DAYS DURING WHICH ATROPINIZATION MUST BE MAINTAINED. MARKEDLY LOWER LEVELS OF URINARY METABOLITES INDICATE THAT ATROPINE DOSAGE CAN BE TAPERED OFF. AS DOSAGE IS REDUCED, CHECK THE LUNG BASES FREQUENTLY FOR RALES. IF RALES ARE HEARD OR OTHER SYMPTOMS RETURN, RE-ESTABLISH ATROPINIZATION PROMPTLY (MORGAN, RECOGNITION AND MANAGEMENT OF PESTICIDE POISONINGS, 3RD ED.). ADMINISTRATION OF ANTIDOTE MUST BE PERFORMED BY QUALIFIED MEDICAL PERSONNEL.

REACTIVITY

REACTIVITY: STABLE UNDER NORMAL TEMPERATURES AND PRESSURES.

INCOMPATIBILITIES: THIOFANOX: OXIDIZERS: FIRE AND EXPLOSION HAZARD.

DECOMPOSITION: THERMAL DECOMPOSITION MAY RELEASE TOXIC AND/OR HAZARDOUS GASES.

POLYMERIZATION: HAZARDOUS POLYMERIZATION HAS NOT BEEN REPORTED TO OCCUR UNDER NORMAL TEMPERATURES AND PRESSURES.

STORAGE AND DISPOSAL

OBSERVE ALL FEDERAL, STATE AND LOCAL REGULATIONS WHEN STORING OR DISPOSING OF THIS SUBSTANCE. FOR ASSISTANCE, CONTACT THE DISTRICT DIRECTOR OF THE ENVIRONMENTAL PROTECTION AGENCY.

STORAGE

STORE IN ACCORDANCE WITH 40 CFR 165 RECOMMENDED PROCEDURES FOR THE DISPOSAL AND STORAGE OF PESTICIDES AND PESTICIDE CONTAINERS.

THRESHOLD PLANNING QUANTITY (TPQ): THE SUPERFUND AMENDMENTS AND REAUTHORIZATION ACT (SARA) SECTION 302 REQUIRES THAT EACH FACILITY WHERE ANY EXTREMELY HAZARDOUS SUBSTANCE IS PRESENT IN A QUANTITY EQUAL TO OR GREATER THAN THE TPQ ESTABLISHED FOR THAT SUBSTANCE NOTIFY THE STATE EMERGENCY RESPONSE COMMISSION FOR THE STATE IN WHICH IT IS LOCATED. SECTION 303 OF SARA REQUIRES THESE FACILITIES TO PARTICIPATE IN LOCAL EMERGENCY RESPONSE PLANNING (40 CFR 355.30).

DISPOSAL

DISPOSAL MUST BE IN ACCORDANCE WITH STANDARDS APPLICABLE TO GENERATORS OF HAZARDOUS WASTE, 40CFR 262. EPA HAZARDOUS WASTE NUMBER P045.

CONDITIONS TO AVOID

NONE REPORTED.

SPILL AND LEAK PROCEDURES

OCCUPATIONAL SPILL: DO NOT TOUCH SPILLED MATERIAL. STOP LEAK IF YOU CAN DO IT WITHOUT RISK. USE WATER SPRAY TO REDUCE VAPORS. FOR SMALL SPILLS, TAKE UP WITH SAND OR OTHER ABSORBENT MATERIAL AND PLACE INTO CONTAINERS FOR LATER DISPOSAL. FOR SMALL DRY SPILLS, WITH A CLEAN SHOVEL PLACE MATERIAL INTO CLEAN, DRY CONTAINERS AND COVER. MOVE CONTAINERS FROM SPILL AREA. FOR LARGER SPILLS, DIKE FAR AHEAD OF SPILL FOR LATER DISPOSAL. KEEP UNNECESSARY PEOPLE AWAY. ISOLATE HAZARD AREA AND DENY ENTRY. VENTILATE CLOSED SPACES BEFORE ENTERING.

REPORTABLE QUANTITY (RQ): 100 POUNDS THE SUPERFUND AMENDMENTS AND REAUTHORIZATION ACT (SARA) SECTION 304 REQUIRES THAT A RELEASE EQUAL TO OR GREATER THAN THE REPORTABLE QUANTITY FOR THIS SUBSTANCE BE IMMEDIATELY REPORTED TO THE LOCAL EMERGENCY PLANNING COMMITTEE AND THE STATE EMERGENCY RESPONSE COMMISSION (40 CFR 355.40). IF THE RELEASE OF THIS SUBSTANCE IS REPORTABLE UNDER CERCLA SECTION 103, THE NATIONAL RESPONSE CENTER MUST BE NOTIFIED IMMEDIATELY AT (800) 424-8802 OR (202) 426-2675 IN THE METROPOLITAN WASHINGTON, D.C. AREA (40 CFR 302.6).

PROTECTIVE EQUIPMENT

VENTILATION: PROCESS ENCLOSURE RECOMMENDED.

RESPIRATOR: THE FOLLOWING RESPIRATORS ARE RECOMMENDED BASED ON INFORMATION FOUND IN THE PHYSICAL DATA, TOXICITY AND HEALTH EFFECTS SECTIONS. THEY ARE RANKED IN ORDER FROM MINIMUM TO MAXIMUM RESPIRATORY PROTECTION. THE SPECIFIC RESPIRATOR SELECTED MUST BE BASED ON CONTAMINATION LEVELS FOUND IN THE WORK PLACE, MUST NOT EXCEED THE WORKING LIMITS OF THE RESPIRATOR AND BE JOINTLY APPROVED BY THE NATIONAL INSTITUTE FOR OCCUPATIONAL SAFETY AND HEALTH AND THE MINE

SAFETY AND HEALTH ADMINISTRATION (NIOSH-MSHA).
TYPE 'C' SUPPLIED-AIR RESPIRATOR WITH A FULL FACEPIECE OPERATED IN PRESSURE-DEMAND OR OTHER POSITIVE PRESSURE MODE OR WITH A FULL FACEPIECE, HELMET OR HOOD OPERATED IN CONTINOUS-FLOW MODE.
SELF-CONTAINED BREATHING APPARATUS WITH A FULL FACEPIECE OPERATED IN PRESSURE-DEMAND OR OTHER POSITIVE PRESSURE MODE.
FOR FIREFIGHTING AND OTHER IMMEDIATELY DANGEROUS TO LIFE OR HEALTH CONDITIONS:
SELF-CONTAINED BREATHING APPARATUS WITH FULL FACEPIECE OPERATED IN PRESSURE-DEMAND OR OTHER POSITIVE PRESSURE MODE.
SUPPLIED-AIR RESPIRATOR WITH FULL FACEPIECE AND OPERATED IN PRESSURE-DEMAND OR OTHER POSITIVE PRESSURE MODE IN COMBINATION WITH AN AUXILIARY SELF-CONTAINED BREATHING APPARATUS OPERATED IN PRESSURE-DEMAND OR OTHER POSITIVE PRESSURE MODE.

CLOTHING: EMPLOYEE MUST WEAR APPROPRIATE PROTECTIVE (IMPERVIOUS) CLOTHING AND EQUIPMENT TO PREVENT ANY POSSIBILITY OF SKIN CONTACT WITH THIS SUBSTANCE.

GLOVES: EMPLOYEE MUST WEAR APPROPRIATE PROTECTIVE GLOVES TO PREVENT CONTACT WITH THIS SUBSTANCE.

EYE PROTECTION: EMPLOYEE MUST WEAR SPLASH-PROOF OR DUST-RESISTANT SAFETY GOGGLES WITH OR WITHOUT A FACESHIELD TO PREVENT CONTACT WITH THIS SUBSTANCE.
EMERGENCY EYE WASH: WHERE THERE IS ANY POSSIBILITY THAT AN EMPLOYEE'S EYES MAY BE EXPOSED TO THIS SUBSTANCE, THE EMPLOYER SHOULD PROVIDE AN EYE WASH FOUNTAIN WITHIN THE IMMEDIATE WORK AREA FOR EMERGENCY USE.

AUTHORIZED BY- OCCUPATIONAL HEALTH SERVICES, INC.
CREATION DATE: 10/05/89 ***REVISION DATE:*** 06/12/90

MATERIAL SAFETY DATA SHEET

OCCUPATIONAL HEALTH SERVICES, INC.
AGRICULTURE AND PESTICIDE DIVISION
450 SEVENTH AVENUE, SUITE 2407
NEW YORK, NEW YORK 10123
1-800-445-MSDS OR (212) 967-1100

EMERGENCY CONTACT:
JOHN S. BRANSFORD, JR. (615) 292-1180

SUBSTANCE IDENTIFICATION

CAS-NUMBER 137-26-8

SUBSTANCE: THIRAM

TRADE NAMES/SYNONYMS: THIOPEROXYDICARBONIC DIAMIDE (((H2N)C'S))2S2), TETRAMETHYL-; DISULFIDE, BIS(DIMETHYLTHIOCARBAMOYL); TETRAMETHYLTHIURAM DISULPHIDE; TETRAMETHYLTHIURAM DISULFIDE; BIS(DIMETHYLTHIOCARBAMOYL)DISULPHIDE; TETRAMETHYLTHIOPEROXYDICARBONIC DIAMIDE (((ME2N)C(S))2S2); BIS(DIMETHYLTHIOCARBAMOYL) DISULFIDE; TETRAMETHYLTHIURAM BISULFIDE; ARASAN; FERNASAN; NORMERSAN; POMARSOL; TERSAN; THIOSAN; THIOTOX; TMTD; ENT 987; RCRA U244; STCC 4941187; C6H12N2S4; PST23430

CHEMICAL FAMILY: THIOCARBAMATE

MOLECULAR FORMULA: ((C-H3)2-N-C-S)2-S2

MOLECULAR WEIGHT: 240.41

CERCLA RATINGS (SCALE 0-3): HEALTH=3 FIRE=1 REACTIVITY=0 PERSISTENCE=1

NFPA RATINGS (SCALE 0-4): HEALTH=U FIRE=1 REACTIVITY=0

COMPONENTS AND CONTAMINANTS

COMPONENT: THIRAM ***PERCENT:*** 100.0
CAS# 137-26-8

EXPOSURE LIMITS: THIRAM: 5 MG/M3 OSHA TWA 5 MG/M3 ACGIH TWA (NOTICE OF INTENDED CHANGE 1987-1988)
10 POUNDS CERCLA SECTION 103 REPORTABLE QUANTITY

PHYSICAL DATA

DESCRIPTION: WHITE TO YELLOW CRYSTALLINE POWDER WITH CHARACTERISTIC ODOR.

BOILING POINT: 264 F (129 C) @ 20 MMHG ***MELTING POINT:*** 311-313 F (155-156 C)

SPECIFIC GRAVITY: 1.29 @ 20 C ***VAPOR PRESSURE:*** NEGLIGIBLE @ 20 C

SOLUBILITY IN WATER: 30 PPM

SOLVENT SOLUBILITY: SOLUBLE IN CHLOROFORM AND MOST ORGANIC SOLVENTS; MODERATELY SOLUBLE IN ACETONE AND BENZENE; SLIGHTLY SOLUBLE IN ETHANOL, ETHER, CARBON DISULFIDE; INSOLUBLE IN DILUTE ALKALI, GASOLINE, ALIPHATIC HYDROCARBONS

FIRE AND EXPLOSION DATA

FIRE AND EXPLOSION HAZARD: SLIGHT FIRE HAZARD WHEN EXPOSED TO HEAT OR FLAME.
DUST-AIR MIXTURES MAY IGNITE OR EXPLODE.

FLASH POINT: 280 F (138 C) (CC) ***FLAMMABILITY CLASS(OSHA):*** IIIB

FIREFIGHTING MEDIA: DRY CHEMICAL, CARBON DIOXIDE, HALON, WATER SPRAY OR STANDARD FOAM (1987 EMERGENCY RESPONSE GUIDEBOOK, DOT P 5800.4).
FOR LARGER FIRES, USE WATER SPRAY, FOG OR STANDARD FOAM (1987 EMERGENCY RESPONSE GUIDEBOOK, DOT P 5800.4).

FIREFIGHTING: MOVE CONTAINERS FROM FIRE AREA IF POSSIBLE. FIGHT FIRE FROM MAXIMUM DISTANCE. STAY AWAY FROM STORAGE TANK ENDS. DIKE FIRE CONTROL WATER FOR LATER DISPOSAL. DO NOT SCATTER MATERIAL (1987 EMERGENCY RESPONSE GUIDEBOOK, DOT P 5800.4, GUIDE PAGE 55).
EXTINGUISH FIRE USING AGENTS SUITABLE FOR TYPE OF SURROUNDING FIRE. USE WATER IN FLOODING AMOUNTS AS FOG. USE ALCOHOL FOAM, CARBON DIOXIDE OR DRY CHEMICAL. AVOID BREATHING TOXIC VAPORS, KEEP UPWIND.

TRANSPORTATION DATA

DEPARTMENT OF TRANSPORTATION HAZARD CLASSIFICATION 49 CFR 172.101: ORM-A
DEPARTMENT OF TRANSPORTATION LABELING REQUIREMENTS 49 CFR 172.101 AND SUBPART E: NONE
DEPARTMENT OF TRANSPORTATION PACKAGING REQUIREMENTS: 49 CFR 173.510 EXCEPTIONS: 49 CFR 173.505

TOXICITY

THIRAM: IRRITATION DATA: 100 MG/24 HOURS EYE-RABBIT MODERATE. TOXICITY DATA: 30 UG/M3/5 YEARS INTERMITTENT INHALATION-HUMAN TCLO; 500 MG/M3/4 HOURS INHALATION-RAT LC50; 1 GM/KG SKIN-RABBIT LDLO; 560 MG/KG ORAL-RAT LD50; 1350 MG/KG ORAL-MOUSE LD50; 210 MG/KG ORAL-RABBIT LD50; 230 MG/KG ORAL-CAT LDLO; 1150 MG/KG SUBCUTANEOUS-MOUSE LD50; 138 MG/KG INTRAPERITONEAL-RAT LD50; 70 MG/KG INTRAPERITONEAL-MOUSE LD50; 740 MG/KG UNREPORTED-RAT LD50; 1150 MG/KG UNREPORTED-MOUSE LD50; 210 MG/KG UNREPORTED-RABBIT LD50; 225 MG/KG UNREPORTED-DOMESTIC ANIMAL LD50; 400 MG/KG UNREPORTED-MAMMAL LD50; MUTAGENIC DATA (RTECS); REPRODUCTIVE EFFECTS DATA (RTECS); TUMORIGENIC DATA (RTECS).
CARCINOGEN STATUS: ANIMAL INADEQUATE EVIDENCE (IARC GROUP-3). THIRAM CAN REACT WITH NITRITE UNDER MILDLY ACID CONDITIONS, SIMULATING THOSE IN THE HUMAN STOMACH, TO FORM N-NITROSODIMETHYLAMINE, WHICH HAS BEEN SHOWN TO BE CARCINOGENIC IN ANIMAL STUDIES. LOCAL EFFECTS: IRRITANT- INHALATION, SKIN, AND EYE. ACUTE TOXICITY LEVEL: HIGHLY TOXIC BY INHALATION; MODERATELY TOXIC BY INGESTION. LOCAL EFFECTS: SENSITIZER-SKIN. POISONING MAY AFFECT THE NERVOUS SYSTEM, BLOOD, LIVER, AND KIDNEY. AT INCREASED RISK FROM EXPOSURE: PERSONS WITH CHRONIC RESPIRATORY OR SKIN DISEASE. ADDITIONAL DATA: TOXICITY IS GREATER IN THE PRESENCE OF FATS, OILS, AND FAT SOLVENTS. THE USE OF ALCOHOLIC BEVERAGES MAY ENHANCE THE TOXIC EFFECTS.

HEALTH EFFECTS AND FIRST AID

INHALATION: THIRAM: IRRITANT/HIGHLY TOXIC. 1500 MG/M3 IMMEDIATELY DANGEROUS TO LIFE OR HEALTH. **ACUTE EXPOSURE-** EXCESSIVE EXPOSURE MAY CAUSE IRRITATION OF THE RESPIRATORY TRACT, NASAL STUFFINESS, HOARSENESS, COUGHING, RHINITIS, SNEEZING, HEADACHES, DIZZINESS, FATIGUE, NAUSEA, DIARRHEA, AND OTHER GASTROINTESTINAL COMPLAINTS. ONE REPORTED CASE OF DEATH HAS OCCURRED FROM OVEREXPOSURE. SENSITIZATION WAS OBSERVED IN GUINEA PIGS FOLLOWING INTRATRACHEAL ADMINISTRATION. **CHRONIC EXPOSURE-** IN ONE EPIDEMIOLOGICAL STUDY OF WORKERS EXPOSED TO THIRAM FOR MORE THAN 3 YEARS, THERE WERE INCREASED COMPLAINTS OF COUGHING, THORACIC PAIN, TACHYCARDIA, EPISTAXIS, DERMAL LESIONS, MYOCARDIODYSTROPHIA, LIVER DYSFUNCTION, AND ASTHENIA AS COMPARED TO THE GROUP USED AS CONTROLS. ENLARGEMENT OF THE THYROID GLAND, THYROID ABNORMALITIES, AND ONE CASE OF ADENOCARCINOMA WERE ALSO REPORTED. ONE REPORTED CASE OF HENOCH SCHONLEIN PURPURA WAS THOUGHT TO HAVE BEEN INDUCED BY REPEATED EXPOSURE TO THIRAM. WORKERS USING THIRAM AS A PESTICIDE DEVELOPED SIGNIFICANT DEVIATION FROM CONTROL VALUES IN CORNEAL SENSITIVITY AND BLOOD PRESSURE IN THE CENTRAL RETINAL ARTERY. DELAYED ESTROUS CYCLE, DECREASED FERTILITY, AND DECREASED WEIGHT OF OFFSPRING WERE OBSERVED IN A STUDY OF RATS EXPOSED TO A CONCENTRATION OF 3.8 MG/M3/6 HOURS A DAY, 5 DAYS A WEEK FOR 4.5 MONTHS.

FIRST AID- REMOVE FROM EXPOSURE AREA TO FRESH AIR IMMEDIATELY. IF BREATHING HAS STOPPED, GIVE ARTIFICIAL RESPIRATION. MAINTAIN AIRWAY AND BLOOD PRESSURE AND ADMINISTER OXYGEN IF AVAILABLE. KEEP AFFECTED

PERSON WARM AND AT REST. TREAT SYMPTOMATICALLY AND SUPPORTIVELY. ADMINISTRATION OF OXYGEN SHOULD BE PERFORMED BY QUALIFIED PERSONNEL. GET MEDICAL ATTENTION IMMEDIATELY.

SKIN CONTACT: THIRAM: IRRITANT/SENSITIZER. **ACUTE EXPOSURE-** MAY CAUSE IRRITATION. A SENSITIZATION REACTION WITH ECZEMA ON THE HANDS, FOREARMS, AND FEET MAY OCCUR IN PERSONS PREVIOUSLY EXPOSED. **CHRONIC EXPOSURE-** PROLONGED OR REPEATED EXPOSURE MAY PRODUCE SENSITIZATION DERMATITIS AND OTHER EFFECTS AS LISTED IN CHRONIC INHALATION.

FIRST AID- REMOVE CONTAMINATED CLOTHING AND SHOES IMMEDIATELY. WASH AFFECTED AREA WITH SOAP OR MILD DETERGENT AND LARGE AMOUNTS OF WATER UNTIL NO EVIDENCE OF CHEMICAL REMAINS (APPROXIMATELY 15-20 MINUTES). GET MEDICAL ATTENTION IMMEDIATELY.

EYE CONTACT: THIRAM: IRRITANT. **ACUTE EXPOSURE-** MAY CAUSE IRRITATION. **CHRONIC EXPOSURE-** PROLONGED OR REPEATED EXPOSURE MAY CAUSE LACRIMATION, PHOTOPHOBIA, AND CHRONIC CONJUNCTIVITIS; THESE EFFECTS MAY BE SLOWLY REVERSED UPON CESSATION OF EXPOSURE.

FIRST AID- WASH EYES IMMEDIATELY WITH LARGE AMOUNTS OF WATER OR NORMAL SALINE, OCCASIONALLY LIFTING UPPER AND LOWER LIDS, UNTIL NO EVIDENCE OF CHEMICAL REMAINS (APPROXIMATELY 15-20 MINUTES). GET MEDICAL ATTENTION IMMEDIATELY.

INGESTION: THIRAM: **ACUTE EXPOSURE-** MAY CAUSE HEADACHES, DIZZINESS, FATIGUE, NAUSEA, DIARRHEA, AND OTHER GASTROINTESTINAL COMPLAINTS. IN RATS AND MICE, THIRAM PRODUCED ATAXIA AND HYPERACTIVITY FOLLOWED BY INACTIVITY, LOSS OF MUSCULAR TONE, LABORED BREATHING, AND CLONIC CONVULSIONS. SKELETAL MALFORMATIONS WERE OBSERVED IN A STUDY OF HAMSTERS GIVEN A SINGLE DOSE DURING THE PERIOD OF ORGANOGENESIS. **CHRONIC EXPOSURE-** IN ADDITION TO THE SYMPTOMS LISTED IN ACUTE EXPOSURE, REPEATED INGESTION MAY RESULT IN BEHAVIORAL ABNORMALITIES OF DROWSINESS, CONFUSION, LOSS OF LIBIDO, AND NEUROLOGICAL DISORDERS INCLUDING ATAXIA, SLURRED SPEECH, AND WEAKNESS. INCREASED MORTALITY, THYROID HYPERPLASIA, EFFECTS ON THE HEMATOPOIETIC SYSTEM, FATTY INFILTRATION OF THE PANCREAS, AND CALCIFICATION OF THE CEREBELLUM, HYPOTHALAMUS AND MEDULLA OBLONGATA WERE OBSERVED IN ANIMALS. INCREASED RESORPTION OF EMBRYOS, RETARDED FETAL DEVELOPMENT, AND SKELETAL MALFORMATIONS WERE OBSERVED IN PREGNANT MICE RECEIVING THIRAM AS LEVELS THAT WERE NONTOXIC TO ADULTS. DELAYED ESTROUS CYCLE, INFERTILITY IN MALE RATS, DECREASED LITTER SIZE, INCREASED NUMBER OF FETAL RESORPTIONS, AND AN INCREASED NUMBER OF FETUSES WITH SUBCUTANEOUS HEMATOMA WERE OBSERVED IN RATS RECEIVING THIRAM AT LEVELS THAT PRODUCED TOXICITY IN ADULTS. A HIGH INCIDENCE OF NASAL CAVITY TUMORS AND AN INCREASE IN FORESTOMACH CARCINOMAS VERSUS NO TUMORS IN CONTROLS OR IN ANIMALS GIVEN ONLY ONE COMPOUND WERE NOTED IN A STUDY OF RATS FED 500 PPM THIRAM PLUS 2000 PPM SODIUM NITRITE FOR 2 YEARS.

FIRST AID- IF VIGOROUS EMESIS HAS NOT ALREADY OCCURRED AND VICTIM IS FULLY ALERT, GIVE SYRUP OF IPECAC, FOLLOWED BY 1-2 GLASSES OF WATER TO INDUCE VOMITING (ADULTS, 12 YEARS AND OLDER: 30 ML; CHILDREN UNDER 12: 15 ML). IF CONSCIOUSNESS LEVEL DECLINES OR VOMITING HAS NOT OCCURRED IN 15 MINUTES, EMPTY THE STOMACH BY INTUBATION, ASPIRATION, AND LAVAGE, USING ALL AVAILABLE MEANS TO AVOID ASPIRATION OF VOMITUS. AFTER ASPIRATION OF THE STOMACH AND WASHING WITH ISOTONIC SALINE OR SODIUM BICARBONATE, INSTILL 30-50 GM OF ACTIVATED CHARCOAL IN 3-4 OUNCES OF WATER THROUGH THE STOMACH TUBE TO LIMIT ABSORPTION OF REMAINING TOXICANT. IF THE IRRITANT PROPERTIES OF THE TOXICANT FAIL TO PRODUCE A BOWEL MOVEMENT IN 4 HOURS, ADMINISTER SODIUM OR MAGNESIUM SULFATE AS A CATHARTIC: 0.25 GM/KG BODY WEIGHT IN 1-6 OUNCES OF WATER. ADMINISTER GLUCOSE-CONTAINING FLUIDS INTRAVENOUSLY TO ACCELERATE EXCRETION OF TOXICANT. (MORGAN, RECOGNITION AND MANAGEMENT OF PESTICIDE POISONINGS, THIRD EDITION) GET MEDICAL ATTENTION. TREATMENT SHOULD BE BE ADMINISTERED BY QUALIFIED MEDICAL PERSONNEL.

ANTIDOTE: NO SPECIFIC ANTIDOTE. TREAT SYMPTOMATICALLY AND SUPPORTIVELY.

REACTIVITY

REACTIVITY: STABLE UNDER NORMAL TEMPERATURES AND PRESSURES.

INCOMPATIBILITIES: THIRAM: ACIDS: MAY CAUSE FORMATION OF HYDROGEN SULFIDE OR CARBON DISULFIDE. OXIDIZERS (STRONG): FIRE AND EXPLOSION HAZARD. REDUCING AGENTS: MAY CAUSE FORMATION OF HYDROGEN SULFIDE OR CARBON DISULFIDE.

DECOMPOSITION: THERMAL DECOMPOSITION PRODUCTS MAY INCLUDE TOXIC OXIDES OF CARBON, NITROGEN, AND SULFUR.

POLYMERIZATION: HAZARDOUS POLYMERIZATION HAS NOT BEEN REPORTED TO OCCUR UNDER NORMAL TEMPERATURES AND PRESSURES.

STORAGE AND DISPOSAL

OBSERVE ALL FEDERAL, STATE AND LOCAL REGULATIONS WHEN STORING OR DISPOSING OF THIS SUBSTANCE. FOR ASSISTANCE, CONTACT THE DISTRICT DIRECTOR OF THE ENVIRONMENTAL PROTECTION AGENCY.

****STORAGE****

STORE AWAY FROM INCOMPATIBLE SUBSTANCES.

STORE IN A COOL, DRY PLACE; KEEP CONTAINER TIGHTLY CLOSED WHEN NOT IN USE.

****DISPOSAL****

DISPOSAL MUST BE IN ACCORDANCE WITH STANDARDS APPLICABLE TO GENERATORS OF HAZARDOUS WASTE, 40CFR 262. EPA HAZARDOUS WASTE NUMBER U244.

CONDITIONS TO AVOID

MAY BURN BUT DOES NOT IGNITE READILY. CONTAINERS MAY EXPLODE IN HEAT OF FIRE.

SPILL AND LEAK PROCEDURES

OCCUPATIONAL SPILL: DO NOT TOUCH SPILLED MATERIAL. STOP LEAK IF YOU CAN DO IT WITHOUT RISK. USE WATER SPRAY TO REDUCE VAPORS. FOR SMALL SPILLS, TAKE UP WITH SAND OR OTHER ABSORBENT MATERIAL AND PLACE INTO CONTAINERS FOR LATER DISPOSAL. FOR SMALL DRY SPILLS, WITH A CLEAN SHOVEL PLACE MATERIAL INTO CLEAN, DRY CONTAINERS AND COVER. MOVE CONTAINERS FROM SPILL AREA. FOR LARGER SPILLS, DIKE FAR AHEAD OF SPILL FOR LATER DISPOSAL. KEEP UNNECESSARY PEOPLE AWAY. ISOLATE HAZARD AREA AND DENY ENTRY. VENTILATE CLOSED SPACES BEFORE ENTERING. REPORTABLE QUANTITY (RQ): 10 POUNDS THE SUPERFUND AMENDMENTS AND REAUTHORIZATION ACT (SARA) SECTION 304 REQUIRES THAT A RELEASE EQUAL TO OR GREATER THAN THE REPORTABLE QUANTITY FOR THIS SUBSTANCE BE IMMEDIATELY REPORTED TO THE LOCAL EMERGENCY PLANNING COMMITTEE AND THE STATE EMERGENCY RESPONSE COMMISSION (40 CFR 355.40). IF THE RELEASE OF THIS SUBSTANCE IS REPORTABLE UNDER CERCLA SECTION 103, THE NATIONAL RESPONSE CENTER MUST BE NOTIFIED IMMEDIATELY AT (800) 424-8802 OR (202) 426-2675 IN THE METROPOLITAN WASHINGTON, D.C. AREA (40 CFR 302.6).

PROTECTIVE EQUIPMENT

VENTILATION: PROVIDE LOCAL EXHAUST VENTILATION AND/OR GENERAL DILUTION VENTILATION TO MEET PUBLISHED EXPOSURE LIMITS.

RESPIRATOR: THE FOLLOWING RESPIRATORS AND MAXIMUM USE CONCENTRATIONS ARE RECOMMENDATIONS BY THE U.S. DEPARTMENT OF HEALTH AND HUMAN SERVICES, NIOSH POCKET GUIDE TO CHEMICAL HAZARDS; NIOSH CRITERIA DOCUMENTS OR BY THE U.S. DEPARTMENT OF LABOR, 29 CFR 1910 SUBPART Z. THE SPECIFIC RESPIRATOR SELECTED MUST BE BASED ON CONTAMINATION LEVELS FOUND IN THE WORK PLACE, MUST NOT EXCEED THE WORKING LIMITS OF THE RESPIRATOR AND BE JOINTLY APPROVED BY THE NATIONAL INSTITUTE FOR OCCUPATIONAL SAFETY AND HEALTH AND THE MINE SAFETY AND HEALTH ADMINISTRATION (NIOSH-MSHA).

THIRAM: 50 MG/M3- ANY CHEMICAL CARTRIDGE RESPIRATOR WITH ORGANIC VAPOR CARTRIDGE(S) IN COMBINATION WITH A DUST, MIST, AND FUME FILTER. ANY SUPPLIED-AIR RESPIRATOR. ANY SELF-CONTAINED BREATHING APPARATUS.

125 MG/M3- ANY POWERED AIR-PURIFYING RESPIRATOR WITH ORGANIC VAPOR CARTRIDGE(S) IN COMBINATION WITH A DUST, MIST, AND FUME FILTER. ANY SUPPLIED-AIR RESPIRATOR OPERATED IN A CONTINUOUS FLOW MODE.

250 MG/M3- ANY SELF-CONTAINED BREATHING APPARATUS WITH A FULL FACEPIECE. ANY CHEMICAL CARTRIDGE RESPIRATOR WITH A FULL FACEPIECE AND ORGANIC VAPOR CARTRIDGE(S) IN COMBINATION WITH A HIGH-EFFICIENCY PARTICULATE FILTER. ANY SUPPLIED-AIR RESPIRATOR WITH A FULL FACEPIECE. ANY POWERED AIR-PURIFYING RESPIRATOR WITH A TIGHT-FITTING FACEPIECE AND ORGANIC VAPOR CARTRIDGE(S) IN COMBINATION WITH A HIGH-EFFICIENCY PARTICULATE FILTER. ANY AIR-PURIFYING FULL FACEPIECE RESPIRATOR (GAS MASK) WITH A CHIN-STYLE OR FRONT- OR BACK-MOUNTED ORGANIC VAPOR CANISTER HAVING A HIGH-EFFICIENCY PARTICULATE FILTER.

1500 MG/M3- ANY SUPPLIED-AIR RESPIRATOR WITH A FULL FACEPIECE AND OPERATED IN A PRESSURE-DEMAND OR OTHER POSITIVE PRESSURE MODE.

ESCAPE- ANY AIR-PURIFYING FULL FACEPIECE RESPIRATOR (GAS MASK) WITH A CHIN-STYLE OR FRONT- OR BACK-MOUNTED ORGANIC VAPOR CANISTER HAVING A HIGH-EFFICIENCY PARTICULATE FILTER. ANY APPROPRIATE ESCAPE-TYPE SELF-CONTAINED BREATHING APPARATUS.

FOR FIREFIGHTING AND OTHER IMMEDIATELY DANGEROUS TO LIFE OR HEALTH CONDITIONS:

SELF-CONTAINED BREATHING APPARATUS WITH FULL FACEPIECE OPERATED IN PRESSURE-DEMAND OR OTHER POSITIVE PRESSURE MODE.

SUPPLIED-AIR RESPIRATOR WITH FULL FACEPIECE AND OPERATED IN PRESSURE-DEMAND OR OTHER POSITIVE PRESSURE MODE IN COMBINATION WITH AN AUXILIARY SELF-CONTAINED BREATHING APPARATUS OPERATED IN PRESSURE-DEMAND OR OTHER POSITIVE PRESSURE MODE.

CLOTHING: EMPLOYEE MUST WEAR APPROPRIATE PROTECTIVE (IMPERVIOUS) CLOTHING AND EQUIPMENT TO PREVENT REPEATED OR PROLONGED SKIN CONTACT WITH THIS SUBSTANCE.
GLOVES: EMPLOYEE MUST WEAR APPROPRIATE PROTECTIVE GLOVES TO PREVENT CONTACT WITH THIS SUBSTANCE.
EYE PROTECTION: EMPLOYEE MUST WEAR SPLASH-PROOF OR DUST-RESISTANT SAFETY GOGGLES TO PREVENT EYE CONTACT WITH THIS SUBSTANCE.
EMERGENCY EYE WASH: WHERE THERE IS ANY POSSIBILITY THAT AN EMPLOYEE'S EYES MAY BE EXPOSED TO THIS SUBSTANCE, THE EMPLOYER SHOULD PROVIDE AN EYE WASH FOUNTAIN WITHIN THE IMMEDIATE WORK AREA FOR EMERGENCY USE.

AUTHORIZED BY- OCCUPATIONAL HEALTH SERVICES, INC.
CREATION DATE: 10/05/89 ***REVISION DATE:*** 07/12/90

MATERIAL SAFETY DATA SHEET

OCCUPATIONAL HEALTH SERVICES, INC.
AGRICULTURE AND PESTICIDE DIVISION
450 SEVENTH AVENUE, SUITE 2407
NEW YORK, NEW YORK 10123
1-800-445-MSDS OR (212) 967-1100

EMERGENCY CONTACT:
JOHN S. BRANSFORD, JR. (615) 292-1180

SUBSTANCE IDENTIFICATION

CAS-NUMBER 89-83-8
SUBSTANCE: **THYMOL**
TRADE NAMES/SYNONYMS: THYME CAMPHOR; 5-METHYL-2-(1-METHYLETHYL) PHENOL; 5-METHYL-2-ISOPROPYL-1-PHENOL; 1-METHYL-3-HYDROXY-4-ISOPROPYLBENZENE; 3-P-CY-MENOL; M-THYMOL; THYMIC ACID; ISOPROPYL-META-CRESOL; 2-ISOPROPYL-5-METHYL-PHENOL; P-CYMEN-3-OL; 3-HYDROXY-P-CYMENE; ISOPROPYL-CRESOL; META-CRESOL,6 ISO-PROPYL; O-4744; T-185; PST23475
CHEMICAL FAMILY: HYDROXYL, AROMATIC
MOLECULAR FORMULA: C10-H14-O MOL WT: 150.24
CERCLA RATINGS (SCALE 0-3): HEALTH=2 FIRE=0 REACTIVITY=0 PERSISTENCE=0
NFPA RATINGS (SCALE 0-4): HEALTH=2 FIRE=0 REACTIVITY=0

COMPONENTS AND CONTAMINANTS

COMPONENT: THYMOL ***PERCENT:*** 100
CAS# 89-83-8
OTHER CONTAMINANTS: NONE
EXPOSURE LIMITS: NO OCCUPATIONAL EXPOSURE LIMITS ESTABLISHED BY OSHA, ACGIH, OR NIOSH.

PHYSICAL DATA

DESCRIPTION: COLORLESS-WHITE CRYSTALS WITH AN AROMATIC ODOR AND TASTE
BOILING POINT: 451 F (233 C) ***MELTING POINT:*** 126 F (52 F)
SPECIFIC GRAVITY: 0.97 ***VAPOR PRESSURE:*** 1MMHG @ 64.3 C
SOLUBILITY IN WATER: SLIGHTLY SOLUBLE
SOLVENT SOLUBILITY: OILS, GLACIAL ACETIC ACID, CS2, CHCL3, AL, ETHER

FIRE AND EXPLOSION DATA

FIRE AND EXPLOSION HAZARD: NEGLIGIBLE FIRE HAZARD WHEN EXPOSED TO HEAT OR FLAME.
FLASH POINT: COMBUSTIBLE
FIREFIGHTING MEDIA: DRY CHEMICAL, CARBON DIOXIDE, HALON, WATER SPRAY OR STANDARD FOAM (1987 EMERGENCY RESPONSE GUIDEBOOK, DOT P 5800.4).
FOR LARGER FIRES, USE WATER SPRAY, FOG OR STANDARD FOAM (1987 EMERGENCY RESPONSE GUIDEBOOK, DOT P 5800.4).
FIREFIGHTING: MOVE CONTAINERS FROM FIRE AREA IF POSSIBLE (1987 EMERGENCY RESPONSE GUIDEBOOK, DOT P 5800.4, GUIDE PAGE 53).
EXTINGUISH USING AGENT SUITABLE FOR TYPE OF SURROUNDING FIRE. AVOID BREATHING VAPORS AND DUSTS. KEEP UPWIND.

TOXICITY

THYMOL: TOXICITY DATA: 980 MG/KG ORAL-RAT LD50; 640 MG/KG ORAL-MOUSE LD50; 750 MG/KG ORAL-RABBIT LDLO; 250 MG/KG ORAL-CAT LDLO; 880 MG/KG ORAL-GUINEA PIG LD50; 1600 MG/KG SUBCUTANEOUS-RAT LDLO; 243 MG/KG SUBCUTANEOUS-MOUSE LD50; 1100 MG/KG SUBCUTANEOUS-GUINEA PIG LDLO; 100 MG/KG INTRAVENOUS-MOUSE LD50; 150 MG/KG INTRAVENOUS-DOG LDLO; 60 MG/KG INTRAVENOUS-RABBIT LDLO; 110 MG/KG INTRAPERITONEAL-MOUSE LD50; 300 MG/KG INTRAPERITONEAL-GUINEA PIG LDLO; MUTAGENIC DATA (RTECS); REPRODUCTIVE EFFECTS DATA (RTECS). CARCINOGEN STATUS: NONE. LOCAL EFFECTS: CORROSIVE- INHALATION, SKIN, EYES, AND INGESTION. ACUTE TOXICITY LEVEL: MODERATELY TOXIC BY INGESTION. TARGET EFFECTS: NO DATA AVAILABLE. ADDITIONAL DATA: OILS AND ALCOHOL MAY PROMOTE SKIN ABSORPTION.

HEALTH EFFECTS AND FIRST AID

INHALATION: THYMOL: CORROSIVE. **ACUTE EXPOSURE-** MAY CAUSE SORE THROAT, COUGHING, LABORED BREATHING, FATIGUE, PHARYNGITIS, RESPIRATORY IRRITATION AND PULMONARY EDEMA. **CHRONIC EXPOSURE-** PROLONGED EXPOSURE TO VAPORS AND/OR FUMES MAY CAUSE PULMONARY EDEMA WITH FROTHY SPUTUM AND DYSPNEA.
FIRST AID- REMOVE FROM EXPOSURE AREA TO FRESH AIR IMMEDIATELY. IF BREATHING HAS STOPPED, GIVE ARTIFICIAL RESPIRATION. MAINTAIN AIRWAY AND BLOOD PRESSURE AND ADMINISTER OXYGEN IF AVAILABLE. KEEP AFFECTED PERSON WARM AND AT REST. TREAT SYMPTOMATICALLY AND SUPPORTIVELY. ADMINISTRATION OF OXYGEN SHOULD BE PERFORMED BY QUALIFIED PERSONNEL. GET MEDICAL ATTENTION IMMEDIATELY.

SKIN CONTACT: THYMOL: CORROSIVE. **ACUTE EXPOSURE-** CONTACT WITH THIS SUBSTANCE MAY CAUSE IRRITATION AND PAIN. ALLERGIC SKIN REACTIONS MAY ALSO OCCUR. BURNS MAY OCCUR IF EXPOSURE TIME IS PROLONGED. **CHRONIC EXPOSURE-** PROLONGED OR REPEATED EXPOSURE MAY RESULT IN BURNS OF THE SKIN.
FIRST AID- REMOVE CONTAMINATED CLOTHING AND SHOES IMMEDIATELY. WASH AFFECTED AREA WITH SOAP OR MILD DETERGENT AND LARGE AMOUNTS OF WATER UNTIL NO EVIDENCE OF CHEMICAL REMAINS (AT LEAST 15-20 MINUTES). IN CASE OF CHEMICAL BURNS, COVER AREA WITH STERILE, DRY DRESSING. BANDAGE SECURELY, BUT NOT TOO TIGHTLY. GET MEDICAL ATTENTION IMMEDIATELY.

EYE CONTACT: THYMOL: CORROSIVE. **ACUTE EXPOSURE-** DIRECT CONTACT WITH SUBSTANCE MAY CAUSE IRRITATION, PAIN, REDNESS, CONJUNCTIVITIS AND CORNEAL BURNS MAY OCCUR. **CHRONIC EXPOSURE-** PROLONGED EXPOSURE TO THE SUBSTANCE MAY CAUSE BURNS.
FIRST AID- WASH EYES IMMEDIATELY WITH LARGE AMOUNTS OF WATER, OCCASIONALLY LIFTING UPPER AND LOWER LIDS, UNTIL NO EVIDENCE OF CHEMICAL REMAINS (AT LEAST 15-20 MINUTES). CONTINUE IRRIGATING WITH NORMAL SALINE UNTIL THE PH HAS RETURNED TO NORMAL (30-60 MINUTES). COVER WITH STERILE BANDAGES. GET MEDICAL ATTENTION IMMEDIATELY.

INGESTION: THYMOL: CORROSIVE. **ACUTE EXPOSURE-** EPIGASTRIC BURNING, NAUSEA, VOMITING, DIZZINESS, DROWSINESS, HYPERACTIVITY, OCCASIONALLY CONVULSIONS, CARDIAC AND RESPIRATORY COLLAPSE, AND COMA. IN ANIMAL STUDIES, DEPRESSION, ATAXIA, TREMORS, RESPIRATORY FAILURE, GASTROINTESTINAL TRACT IRRITATION, AND COMA WERE REPORTED. **CHRONIC EXPOSURE-** NONE REPORTED IN HUMANS.
FIRST AID- IF THE PERSON IS CONSCIOUS AND NOT CONVULSING, INDUCE EMESIS BY GIVING SYRUP OF IPECAC FOLLOWED BY WATER. (IF VOMITING OCCURS KEEP THE HEAD BELOW THE HIPS TO PREVENT ASPIRATION). REPEAT IN 20 MINUTES IF NOT EFFECTIVE INITIALLY. GIVE ACTIVATED CHARCOAL. IN PATIENTS WITH DEPRESSED RESPIRATION OR IF EMESIS IS NOT PRODUCED, PERFORM GASTRIC LAVAGE CAUTIOUSLY (DREISBACH, HANDBOOK OF POISONING, 12TH ED.). TREAT SYMPTOMATICALLY AND SUPPORTIVELY. GASTRIC LAVAGE SHOULD BE PERFORMED BY QUALIFIED MEDICAL PERSONNEL. GET MEDICAL ATTENTION IMMEDIATELY.
ANTIDOTE: NO SPECIFIC ANTIDOTE. TREAT SYMPTOMATICALLY AND SUPPORTIVELY.

REACTIVITY

REACTIVITY: STABLE UNDER NORMAL TEMPERATURES AND PRESSURES.
INCOMPATIBILITIES: REACTS WITH ACETANILIDE, ANTIPYRINE, CAMPHOR, MONOBROMATED CAMPHOR, CHLOROHYDRATE, MENTHOL, QUININE SULFATE, SULOL, URETHANE, SPIRIT NITROUS ETHER;INTRITURATIONS BECAUSE OF LIQUEFICATION. VOLATILIZES IN WATER VAPORS; APPRECIABLY VOLATILE AT 100 C.
DECOMPOSITION: THERMAL DECOMPOSITION MAY RELEASE ACRID SMOKE AND IRRITATING FUMES.
POLYMERIZATION: HAZARDOUS POLYMERIZATION HAS NOT BEEN REPORTED TO OCCUR UNDER NORMAL TEMPERATURES AND PRESSURES.

SPILL AND LEAK PROCEDURES

OCCUPATIONAL SPILL: NO SPECIAL PRECAUTIONS INDICATED.

PROTECTIVE EQUIPMENT

VENTILATION: PROVIDE LOCAL EXHAUST OR GENERAL DILUTION VENTILATION SYSTEM.

RESPIRATOR: ROOM TEMPERATURE- DUST MASK. ELEVATED TEMPERATURES- CHEMICAL CARTRIDGE RESPIRATOR WITH AN ORGANIC VAPOR CARTRIDGE WITH A FULL FACEPIECE.
FIREFIGHTING- SELF-CONTAINED BREATHING APPARATUS WITH A FULL FACEPIECE OPERATED IN PRESSURE-DEMAND OR OTHER POSITIVE PRESSURE MODE.

CLOTHING: EMPLOYEE MUST WEAR APPROPRIATE PROTECTIVE (IMPERVIOUS) CLOTHING AND EQUIPMENT TO PREVENT ANY POSSIBILITY OF SKIN CONTACT WITH THIS SUBSTANCE.

GLOVES: EMPLOYEE MUST WEAR APPROPRIATE PROTECTIVE GLOVES TO PREVENT CONTACT WITH THIS SUBSTANCE.

EYE PROTECTION: EMPLOYEE MUST WEAR SPLASH-PROOF OR DUST-RESISTANT SAFETY GOGGLES TO PREVENT EYE CONTACT WITH THIS SUBSTANCE.
EMERGENCY EYE WASH: WHERE THERE IS ANY POSSIBILITY THAT AN EMPLOYEE'S EYES MAY BE EXPOSED TO THIS SUBSTANCE, THE EMPLOYER SHOULD PROVIDE AN EYE WASH FOUNTAIN WITHIN THE IMMEDIATE WORK AREA FOR EMERGENCY USE.

AUTHORIZED BY- OCCUPATIONAL HEALTH SERVICES, INC.
CREATION DATE: 10/05/89 ***REVISION DATE:*** 05/17/90

MATERIAL SAFETY DATA SHEET

OCCUPATIONAL HEALTH SERVICES, INC.
AGRICULTURE AND PESTICIDE DIVISION
450 SEVENTH AVENUE, SUITE 2407
NEW YORK, NEW YORK 10123
1-800-445-MSDS OR (212) 967-1100

EMERGENCY CONTACT:
JOHN S. BRANSFORD, JR. (615) 292-1180

SUBSTANCE IDENTIFICATION

CAS-NUMBER 1836-75-5

SUBSTANCE: **NITROFEN**

TRADE NAMES/SYNONYMS: BENZENE, 2,4-DICHLORO-1-(4-NITROPHENOXY)-; ETHER, 2,4-DICHLOROPHENYL P-NITROPHENYL; 2,4-DICHLORO-1-(4-NITROPHENOXY)BENZENE; 2,4-DICHLOROPHENYL P-NITROPHENYL ETHER; 2,4-DICHLOROPHENYL 4-NITROPHENYL ETHER; FW 925; MEZOTOX; NICLOFEN; NIP; NITROCHLOR; NITROFENE; NITROPHEN; NITROPHENE; TOK; TRIZILIN; C12H7CL2NO3; PST23580

CHEMICAL FAMILY: ETHER, AROMATIC
HALOGEN
NITRO

MOLECULAR FORMULA: C12-H7-CL2-N-O3

MOLECULAR WEIGHT: 284.10

CERCLA RATINGS (SCALE 0-3): HEALTH=3 FIRE=2 REACTIVITY=0 PERSISTENCE=2

NFPA RATINGS (SCALE 0-4): HEALTH=U FIRE=2 REACTIVITY=0

COMPONENTS AND CONTAMINANTS

COMPONENT: NITROFEN ***PERCENT:*** 100.0
CAS# 1836-75-5

OTHER CONTAMINANTS: MAY CONTAIN 2,7-DICHLORODIBENZODIOXIN AND OTHER DIOXINS

EXPOSURE LIMITS: NO OCCUPATIONAL EXPOSURE LIMITS ESTABLISHED BY OSHA, ACGIH, OR NIOSH.
NITROFEN: 0.01 MG/M3 ROHM AND HAAS RECOMMENDED TWA FOR FEMALES (SKIN) 1.0 MG/M3 ROHM AND HAAS RECOMMENDED TWA FOR MALES (SKIN)
SUBJECT TO SARA SECTION 313 ANNUAL TOXIC CHEMICAL RELEASE REPORTING
SUBJECT TO CALIFORNIA PROPOSITION 65 CANCER AND/OR REPRODUCTIVE TOXICITY WARNING AND RELEASE REQUIREMENTS- (JANUARY 1, 1988)

PHYSICAL DATA

DESCRIPTION: COLORLESS TO DARK-BROWN CRYSTALLINE SOLID WITH A MILD INOFFENSIVE ODOR; MAY DARKEN ON EXPOSURE TO UV LIGHT

BOILING POINT: 356-374 F (180-190 C) @ 0.25 MMHG

MELTING POINT: 158-160 F (70-71 C) ***SPECIFIC GRAVITY:*** 1.33 @ 90 C

VOLATILITY: <1% ***VAPOR PRESSURE:*** NEGLIGIBLE

EVAPORATION RATE: (BUTYL ACETATE=1) <1 ***SOLUBILITY IN WATER:*** 0.7-1.2 PPM

VAPOR DENSITY: >1

SOLVENT SOLUBILITY: SOLUBLE IN N-HEXANE, BENZENE, XYLENE, ACETONE, METHANOL; MODERATELY SOLUBLE IN ETHANOL.

FIRE AND EXPLOSION DATA

FIRE AND EXPLOSION HAZARD: MODERATE FIRE HAZARD WHEN EXPOSED TO HEAT OR FLAME.

FLASH POINT: 175 F (79 C) (CC)

FIREFIGHTING MEDIA: DRY CHEMICAL, CARBON DIOXIDE, HALON, WATER SPRAY OR STANDARD FOAM (1987 EMERGENCY RESPONSE GUIDEBOOK, DOT P 5800.4).
FOR LARGER FIRES, USE WATER SPRAY, FOG OR STANDARD FOAM (1987 EMERGENCY RESPONSE GUIDEBOOK, DOT P 5800.4).

FIREFIGHTING: MOVE CONTAINERS FROM FIRE AREA IF POSSIBLE (1987 EMERGENCY RESPONSE GUIDEBOOK, DOT P 5800.4, GUIDE PAGE 53).
EXTINGUISH USING AGENT SUITABLE FOR TYPE OF SURROUNDING FIRE. AVOID BREATHING VAPORS AND DUSTS. KEEP UPWIND.

TOXICITY

NITROFEN: TOXICITY DATA: 620 MG/M3/4 HOURS INHALATION-CAT LCLO; 205 MG/L/1 HOUR INHALATION-RAT LD50 (TXCYAC); 5000 MG/KG SKIN-RAT LD50; 1620 MG/KG SKIN-RABBIT LD50 (85JFAN); 740 MG/KG ORAL-RAT LD50; 450 MG/KG ORAL-MOUSE LD50; 1620 MG/KG ORAL-RABBIT LD50; 300 MG/KG ORAL-CAT LDLO; 3000 MG/KG UNREPORTED-RAT LD50; MUTAGENIC DATA (RTECS); REPRODUCTIVE EFFECTS DATA (RTECS); TUMORIGENIC DATA (RTECS). CARCINOGEN STATUS: ANTICIPATED HUMAN CARCINOGEN (NTP); ANIMAL SUFFICIENT EVIDENCE (IARC GROUP 2B). NITROFEN (TECHNICAL GRADE) INDUCED HEPATOCELLULAR CARCINOMAS AND HEMANGIOSARCOMAS AT VARIOUS ANATOMICAL SITES IN MICE AND ADENOCARCINOMAS OF THE PANCREAS IN RATS FOLLOWING ORAL ADMINISTRATION. ACUTE TOXICITY LEVEL: MODERATELY TOXIC BY DERMAL ABSORPTION AND INGESTION; SLIGHTLY TOXIC BY INHALATION. TARGET EFFECTS: TERATOGEN. POISONING MAY AFFECT THE LIVER AND PANCREAS. ADDITIONAL DATA: MAY BE EXCRETED IN BREAST MILK.

HEALTH EFFECTS AND FIRST AID

INHALATION: NITROFEN: **ACUTE EXPOSURE-** DUST MAY CAUSE IRRITATION OF THE NOSE AND THROAT, WEAKNESS, DIZZINESS, HEADACHE, NAUSEA, SNEEZING, AND ABDOMINAL PAIN. ACUTE INTOXICATION IN LABORATORY ANIMALS PRODUCED DECREASED HEMOGLOBIN COUNTS AND PEROXIDASE ACTIVITY, AN INCREASE OF BLOOD SUGAR LEVEL, NEUROLOGICAL EFFECTS, RESPIRATORY DISTRESS, PULMONARY EDEMA, HEMORRHAGE AND DEATH. **CHRONIC EXPOSURE-** OCCUPATIONAL EXPOSURE HAS RESULTED IN CENTRAL NERVOUS SYSTEM DISTURBANCES, ANEMIA, RAISED TEMPERATURE, DECREASED BODY WEIGHT, AND FATIGUE.

FIRST AID- REMOVE FROM EXPOSURE AREA TO FRESH AIR IMMEDIATELY. IF BREATHING HAS STOPPED, PERFORM ARTIFICIAL RESPIRATION. KEEP PERSON WARM AND AT REST. TREAT SYMPTOMATICALLY AND SUPPORTIVELY. GET MEDICAL ATTENTION IMMEDIATELY.

SKIN CONTACT: NITROFEN: TERATOGEN. **ACUTE EXPOSURE-** MAY CAUSE IRRITATION. ACUTE INTOXICATION IN LABORATORY ANIMALS PRODUCED MAINLY NEUROLOGICAL AND RESPIRATORY EFFECTS. APPLICATION OF 160 MG/KG OF NITROFEN TO THE SKIN OF PREGNANT MICE RESULTED IN DECREASED POSTNATAL SURVIVAL. **CHRONIC EXPOSURE-** PROLONGED OR REPEATED EXPOSURE MAY CAUSE DERMATITIS. OCCUPATIONAL EXPOSURE HAS RESULTED IN EFFECTS OF CENTRAL NERVOUS SYSTEM DISTURBANCES, ANEMIA, RAISED TEMPERATURE, DECREASED BODY WEIGHT, AND FATIGUE. REPEATED APPLICATIONS TO THE SKIN OF PREGNANT RATS PRODUCED DECREASED PUP WEIGHT, DIAPHRAGMATIC HERNIAS, AND ABNORMAL DEVELOPMENT OF THE LUNGS, TESTES, AND HARDERIAN GLANDS AT DOSE LEVELS AS LITTLE AS 12 MG/KG/DAY; NEONATAL DEATHS APPEAR AFTER REPEATED MATERNAL DOSES OF 3 MG/KG/DAY.

FIRST AID- REMOVE CONTAMINATED CLOTHING AND SHOES IMMEDIATELY. WASH AFFECTED AREA WITH SOAP OR MILD DETERGENT AND LARGE AMOUNTS OF WATER UNTIL NO EVIDENCE OF CHEMICAL REMAINS (APPROXIMATELY 15-20 MINUTES). GET MEDICAL ATTENTION IMMEDIATELY.

EYE CONTACT: NITROFEN: **ACUTE EXPOSURE-** MAY CAUSE EYE IRRITATION. **CHRONIC EXPOSURE-** NO DATA AVAILABLE.

FIRST AID- WASH EYES IMMEDIATELY WITH LARGE AMOUNTS OF WATER, OCCASIONALLY LIFTING UPPER AND LOWER LIDS, UNTIL NO EVIDENCE OF CHEMICAL REMAINS (AT LEAST 15-20 MINUTES). CONTINUE IRRIGATING WITH NORMAL SALINE UNTIL THE PH HAS RETURNED TO NORMAL (30-60 MINUTES). COVER WITH STERILE BANDAGES. GET MEDICAL ATTENTION IMMEDIATELY.

INGESTION: NITROFEN: TERATOGEN/CARCINOGEN. **ACUTE EXPOSURE-** ACUTE INTOXICATION IN RATS PRODUCED DECREASED LEVELS OF ACTIVITY, PROGRESSIVE DEPRESSION, DIFFICULTY IN BREATHING, TREMORS, AND CONVULSIONS. DEATH FROM ACUTE EXPOSURE GENERALLY OCCURRED WITHIN 2-8 DAYS. AN ACUTE DOSE FED TO PREGNANT RATS PRODUCED FETAL

MALFORMATIONS OF THE HEART, DIAPHRAGM AND KIDNEY. **CHRONIC EXPOSURE-** CHRONIC ADMINISTRATION AT DOSE LEVELS OF 20 MG/KG/DAY AND HIGHER PRODUCED LIVER TOXICITY IN MICE, RATS, AND DOGS. PANCREATIC TUMORS WERE OBSERVED IN FEMALE RATS AT LEVELS AT AND ABOVE 65 MG/KG/DAY. AN INCREASED INCIDENCE OF HEPATOCELLULAR CARCINOMAS IN MICE OF BOTH SEXES AND HEMANGIOSARCOMAS OF THE LIVER IN MALE MICE DEVELOPED AT DOSE LEVELS OF 470 MG/KG/DAY. REPEATED DOSES GIVEN DURING PREGNANCEY TO RATS MICE, AND HAMSTERS PRODUCED NEONATAL LETHALITY, STILLBIRTHS, REDUCED BIRTH WEIGHT, HYDROCEPHALY, MICROPHTHALMIA, AND ABNORMAL FETAL DEVELOPMENT OF LUNG, KIDNEY, HEART, HARDERIAN GLAND, DIAPHRAGM, AND REPRODUCTIVE ORGANS; SKELETAL DEFORMITIES OBSERVED IN MICE INCLUDED CLEFT PALATE AND DELAYED SKULL DEVELOPMENT.

FIRST AID- IF THE PERSON IS CONSCIOUS AND NOT CONVULSING, REMOVE BY GASTRIC LAVAGE AND FOLLOW WITH A CATHARTIC (DREISBACH, HANDBOOK OF POISONING, 12TH ED.). TREAT SYMPTOMATICALLY AND SUPPORTIVELY. GASTRIC LAVAGE SHOULD BE PERFORMED BY QUALIFIED MEDICAL PERSONNEL. GET MEDICAL ATTENTION IMMEDIATELY.

ANTIDOTE: NO SPECIFIC ANTIDOTE. TREAT SYMPTOMATICALLY AND SUPPORTIVELY.

REACTIVITY

REACTIVITY: STABLE UNDER NORMAL TEMPERATURES AND PRESSURES.

INCOMPATIBILITIES: NITROFEN: OXIDIZERS (STRONG): FIRE AND EXPLOSION HAZARD.

DECOMPOSITION: THERMAL DECOMPOSITION PRODUCTS MAY INCLUDE TOXIC OXIDES OF NITROGEN AND CARBON AND TOXIC AND CORROSIVE FUMES OF CHLORIDES.

POLYMERIZATION: HAZARDOUS POLYMERIZATION HAS NOT BEEN REPORTED TO OCCUR UNDER NORMAL TEMPERATURES AND PRESSURES.

STORAGE AND DISPOSAL

OBSERVE ALL FEDERAL, STATE AND LOCAL REGULATIONS WHEN STORING OR DISPOSING OF THIS SUBSTANCE. FOR ASSISTANCE, CONTACT THE DISTRICT DIRECTOR OF THE ENVIRONMENTAL PROTECTION AGENCY.

****STORAGE****

STORE IN ACCORDANCE WITH 40 CFR 165 RECOMMENDED PROCEDURES FOR THE DISPOSAL AND STORAGE OF PESTICIDES AND PESTICIDE CONTAINERS.
STORE AWAY FROM INCOMPATIBLE SUBSTANCES.

****DISPOSAL****

DISPOSAL MUST BE IN ACCORDANCE WITH 40 CFR 165 RECOMMENDED PROCEDURES FOR THE DISPOSAL AND STORAGE OF PESTICIDES AND PESTICIDE CONTAINERS.

CONDITIONS TO AVOID

MAY BURN BUT DOES NOT IGNITE READILY.

SPILL AND LEAK PROCEDURES

WATER SPILL: THE CALIFORNIA SAFE DRINKING WATER AND TOXIC ENFORCEMENT ACT OF 1986 (PROPOSITION 65) PROHIBITS CONTAMINATING ANY KNOWN SOURCE OF DRINKING WATER WITH SUBSTANCES KNOWN TO CAUSE CANCER AND/OR REPRODUCTIVE TOXICITY.

OCCUPATIONAL SPILL: DO NOT TOUCH SPILLED MATERIAL. STOP LEAK IF YOU CAN DO IT WITHOUT RISK. FOR SMALL SPILLS, TAKE UP WITH SAND OR OTHER ABSORBENT MATERIAL AND PLACE INTO CONTAINERS FOR LATER DISPOSAL. FOR SMALL DRY SPILLS, WITH A CLEAN SHOVEL PLACE MATERIAL INTO CLEAN, DRY CONTAINER AND COVER. MOVE CONTAINERS FROM SPILL AREA. FOR LARGER SPILLS, DIKE FAR AHEAD OF SPILL FOR LATER DISPOSAL. KEEP UNNECESSARY PEOPLE AWAY. ISOLATE HAZARD AREA AND DENY ENTRY.

PROTECTIVE EQUIPMENT

VENTILATION: PROVIDE LOCAL EXHAUST OR PROCESS ENCLOSURE VENTILATION SYSTEM.

RESPIRATOR: THE FOLLOWING RESPIRATORS ARE RECOMMENDED BASED ON INFORMATION FOUND IN THE PHYSICAL DATA, TOXICITY AND HEALTH EFFECTS SECTIONS. THEY ARE RANKED IN ORDER FROM MINIMUM TO MAXIMUM RESPIRATORY PROTECTION. THE SPECIFIC RESPIRATOR SELECTED MUST BE BASED ON CONTAMINATION LEVELS FOUND IN THE WORK PLACE, MUST NOT EXCEED THE WORKING LIMITS OF THE RESPIRATOR AND BE JOINTLY APPROVED BY THE NATIONAL INSTITUTE FOR OCCUPATIONAL SAFETY AND HEALTH AND THE MINE SAFETY AND HEALTH ADMINISTRATION (NIOSH-MSHA).

TYPE 'C' SUPPLIED-AIR RESPIRATOR WITH A FULL FACEPIECE OPERATED IN PRESSURE-DEMAND OR OTHER POSITIVE PRESSURE MODE OR WITH A FULL FACEPIECE, HELMET OR HOOD OPERATED IN CONTINOUS-FLOW MODE.

SELF-CONTAINED BREATHING APPARATUS WITH A FULL FACEPIECE OPERATED IN PRESSURE-DEMAND OR OTHER POSITIVE PRESSURE MODE.

FOR FIREFIGHTING AND OTHER IMMEDIATELY DANGEROUS TO LIFE OR HEALTH CONDITIONS:

SELF-CONTAINED BREATHING APPARATUS WITH FULL FACEPIECE OPERATED IN PRESSURE-DEMAND OR OTHER POSITIVE PRESSURE MODE.

SUPPLIED-AIR RESPIRATOR WITH FULL FACEPIECE AND OPERATED IN PRESSURE-DEMAND OR OTHER POSITIVE PRESSURE MODE IN COMBINATION WITH AN AUXILIARY SELF-CONTAINED BREATHING APPARATUS OPERATED IN PRESSURE-DEMAND OR OTHER POSITIVE PRESSURE MODE.

CLOTHING: EMPLOYEE MUST WEAR APPROPRIATE PROTECTIVE (IMPERVIOUS) CLOTHING AND EQUIPMENT TO PREVENT ANY POSSIBILITY OF SKIN CONTACT WITH THIS SUBSTANCE.

GLOVES: EMPLOYEE MUST WEAR APPROPRIATE PROTECTIVE GLOVES TO PREVENT CONTACT WITH THIS SUBSTANCE.

EYE PROTECTION: EMPLOYEE MUST WEAR SPLASH-PROOF OR DUST-RESISTANT SAFETY GOGGLES AND A FACESHIELD TO PREVENT CONTACT WITH THIS SUBSTANCE.

EMERGENCY WASH FACILITIES: WHERE THERE IS ANY POSSIBILITY THAT AN EMPLOYEE'S EYES AND/OR SKIN MAY BE EXPOSED TO THIS SUBSTANCE, THE EMPLOYER SHOULD PROVIDE AN EYE WASH FOUNTAIN AND QUICK DRENCH SHOWER WITHIN THE IMMEDIATE WORK AREA FOR EMERGENCY USE.

AUTHORIZED BY- OCCUPATIONAL HEALTH SERVICES, INC.

CREATION DATE: 10/04/89 ***REVISION DATE:*** 07/12/90

MATERIAL SAFETY DATA SHEET

OCCUPATIONAL HEALTH SERVICES, INC.
AGRICULTURE AND PESTICIDE DIVISION
450 SEVENTH AVENUE, SUITE 2407
NEW YORK, NEW YORK 10123
1-800-445-MSDS OR (212) 967-1100

EMERGENCY CONTACT:
JOHN S. BRANSFORD, JR. (615) 292-1180

SUBSTANCE IDENTIFICATION

CAS-NUMBER 10311-84-9

SUBSTANCE: **DIALIFOR**

TRADE NAMES/SYNONYMS: PHOSPHORODITHIOIC ACID, S-(2-CHLORO-1-(1,3-DIHYDRO-1,3-DIOXO-2H -ISOINDOL-2-YL)ETHYL) O,O-DIETHYL ESTER; PHOSPHORODITHIOIC ACID O,O-DIETHYL ESTER S-ESTER WITH N-(2-CHLORO -1-MERCAPTOETHYL)PHTHALIMIDE; S-2-CHLORO-1-PHTHALIMIDOETHYL O,O-DIETHYL PHOSPHORODITHIOATE; N-(2-CHLORO-1-(DIETHOXYPHOSPHINOTHIOYLTHIO)ETHYL)PHTHALIMIDE; S-(2-CHLORO-1-(1,3-DIHYDRO-1,3-DIOXO-2H-ISOINDOL-2-YL)ETHYL) O,O -DIETHYL PHOSPHORODITHIOATE; O,O-DIETHYL PHOSPHORODITHIOATE S-ESTER WITH N-(2-CHLORO-1 -MERCAPTOETHYL)PHTHALIMIDE; HERCULES 14 503; TORAK; ENT 27320; C14H17CLNO4PS2; PST23630

CHEMICAL FAMILY: ORGANOPHOSPHATE

MOLECULAR FORMULA: C14-H17-CL-N-O4-P-S2

MOLECULAR WEIGHT: 393.84

CERCLA RATINGS (SCALE 0-3): HEALTH=3 FIRE=0 REACTIVITY=0 PERSISTENCE=1

NFPA RATINGS (SCALE 0-4): HEALTH=4 FIRE=0 REACTIVITY=0

COMPONENTS AND CONTAMINANTS

COMPONENT: DIALIFOR ***PERCENT:*** 100
CAS# 10311-84-9

OTHER CONTAMINANTS: NORCHLORO-DIALIFOR

EXPOSURE LIMITS: DIALIFOR: NO OCCUPATIONAL EXPOSURE LIMITS ESTABLISHED BY OSHA, ACGIH, OR NIOSH.

100/10,000 POUNDS SARA SECTION 302 THRESHOLD PLANNING QUANTITY 1 POUND SARA SECTION 304 REPORTABLE QUANTITY

PHYSICAL DATA

DESCRIPTION: COLORLESS CRYSTALLINE SOLID ***MELTING POINT:*** 153 F (67 C)

SPECIFIC GRAVITY: NOT AVAILABLE ***SOLUBILITY IN WATER:*** INSOLUBLE

SOLVENT SOLUBILITY: SOLUBLE IN ACETONE, CHLOROFORM, XYLENE, ETHER, CYCLOHEXANE, ISOPHORONE AND AROMATIC HYDROCARBONS; SLIGHTLY SOLUBLE IN ALIPHATIC HYDROCARBONS AND ALCOHOLS

FIRE AND EXPLOSION DATA

FIRE AND EXPLOSION HAZARD: NEGLIGIBLE FIRE HAZARD WHEN EXPOSED TO HEAT OR FLAME.

FIREFIGHTING MEDIA: DRY CHEMICAL, CARBON DIOXIDE, HALON, WATER SPRAY OR STANDARD FOAM (1987 EMERGENCY RESPONSE GUIDEBOOK, DOT P 5800.4).

FOR LARGER FIRES, USE WATER SPRAY, FOG OR STANDARD FOAM (1987 EMERGENCY RESPONSE GUIDEBOOK, DOT P 5800.4).

FIREFIGHTING: MOVE CONTAINERS FROM FIRE AREA IF POSSIBLE. FIGHT FIRE FROM MAXIMUM DISTANCE. STAY AWAY FROM STORAGE TANK ENDS. DIKE FIRE CONTROL WATER FOR LATER DISPOSAL. DO NOT SCATTER MATERIAL (1987 EMERGENCY RESPONSE GUIDEBOOK, DOT P 5800.4, GUIDE PAGE 55). EXTINGUISH ONLY IF FLOW CAN BE STOPPED; USE FLOODING AMOUNTS OF WATER AS FOG, SOLID STREAMS MAY BE INEFFECTIVE. COOL CONTAINERS WITH FLOODING AMOUNTS OF WATER FROM AS FAR A DISTANCE AS POSSIBLE. USE WATER SPRAY TO ABSORB TOXIC VAPORS. AVOID BREATHING TOXIC VAPORS; KEEP UPWIND. CONSIDER EVACUATION OF DOWNWIND AREA IF MATERIAL IS LEAKING.

TRANSPORTATION DATA

DEPARTMENT OF TRANSPORTATION HAZARD CLASSIFICATION 49 CFR 172.101: POISON B

DEPARTMENT OF TRANSPORTATION LABELING REQUIREMENTS 49 CFR 172.101 AND SUBPART E: POISON

DEPARTMENT OF TRANSPORTATION PACKAGING REQUIREMENTS: 49 CFR 173.365 EXCEPTIONS: 49 CFR 173.364

TOXICITY

DIALIFOR: TOXICITY DATA: 145 MG/KG SKIN-RABBIT LD50; 28 MG/KG SKIN-RAT LD50; 5 MG/KG ORAL-RAT LD50; 39 MG/KG ORAL-MOUSE LD50; 94 MG/KG ORAL-DOG LD50; 35 MG/KG ORAL-RABBIT LD50; REPRODUCTIVE EFFECTS DATA (RTECS). CARCINOGEN STATUS: NONE. ACUTE TOXICITY LEVEL: HIGHLY TOXIC BY INGESTION AND DERMAL ABSORPTION. TARGET EFFECTS: CHOLINESTERASE INHIBITOR. POISONING MAY AFFECT THE NERVOUS SYSTEM.* AT INCREASED RISK FROM EXPOSURE: PERSONS WITH RESPIRATORY AILMENTS, RECENT EXPOSURE TO CHOLINESTERASE INHIBITORS OR IMPAIRED CHOLINESTERASE PRODUCTION, OR LIVER MALFUNCTION.* ADDITIONAL DATA: MAY CROSS THE PLACENTA. HIGH ENVIRONMENTAL TEMPERATURES OR EXPOSURE OF THE CHEMICAL TO VISIBLE OR ULTRAVIOLET LIGHT MAY ENHANCE THE TOXICITY. INTERACTIONS WITH MEDICATIONS MAY OCCUR.*

* MAY BE BASED ON GENERAL INFORMATION ON ORGANOPHOSPHATES.

HEALTH EFFECTS AND FIRST AID

INHALATION: DIALIFOR: SEE INFORMATION ON ORGANOPHOSPHATES.
ORGANOPHOSPHATES: CHOLINESTERASE INHIBITOR. **ACUTE EXPOSURE-** WHEN INHALED, THE FIRST EFFECTS OF CHOLINESTERASE INHIBITORS ARE USUALLY RESPIRATORY AND MAY INCLUDE NASAL HYPEREMIA AND WATERY DISCHARGE, COUGH, CHEST DISCOMFORT, DYSPNEA, AND WHEEZING DUE TO INCREASED BRONCHIAL SECRETIONS AND BRONCHOCONSTRICTION. IF SUFFICIENT AMOUNTS ARE ABSORBED, OTHER SYSTEMIC EFFECTS MAY BEGIN WITHIN A FEW MINUTES OR BE DELAYED FOR UP TO 12 HOURS. SYMPTOMS MAY INCLUDE PALLOR, NAUSEA, VOMITING, DIARRHEA, ABDOMINAL CRAMPS, HEADACHE, DIZZINESS, OCULAR PAIN, BLURRED VISION, MIOSIS OR IN SOME CASES, ESPECIALLY INITIALLY, MYDRIASIS, LACRIMATION, SALIVATION, SWEATING, AND CONFUSION. OTHER REPORTED CENTRAL NERVOUS SYSTEM OR NEUROMUSCULAR EFFECTS MAY INCLUDE ATAXIA, SLURRED SPEECH, AREFLEXIA, WEAKNESS, FATIGUE, FASCICULATIONS, TWITCHING, TREMORS POSSIBLY OF THE TONGUE AND EYELIDS, AND EVENTUALLY PARALYSIS OF THE EXTREMITIES AND POSSIBLY OF THE RESPIRATORY MUSCLES. IN SEVERE CASES THERE MAY ALSO BE INVOLUNTARY DEFECATION AND URINATION, CYANOSIS, PSYCHOSIS, HYPERGLYCEMIA, ACUTE PANCREATITIS, CARDIAC IRREGULARITIES, PULMONARY EDEMA, UNCONSCIOUSNESS, CONVULSIONS, AND COMA. DEATH IS PRIMARILY DUE TO RESPIRATORY FAILURE, ALTHOUGH CARDIOVASCULAR EFFECTS INCLUDING CARDIAC ARREST MAY ALSO BE IMPLICATED. LONG TERM SEQUELAE ARE RARE BUT MAY INCLUDE NEUROPSYCHIATRIC DISORDERS AND MYOPATHY WITH MUSCLE TENDERNESS. SOME ORGANOPHOSPHATES MAY CAUSE A DELAYED NEUROPATHY BEGINNING 1-4 WEEKS AFTER AN ACUTE EXPOSURE WHICH MAY OR MAY NOT HAVE CAUSED ACUTE CHOLINERGIC EFFECTS. NUMBNESS, TINGLING, WEAKNESS AND CRAMPING BEGINNING SYMMETRICALLY IN THE LOWER LIMBS MAY PROGRESS TO ATAXIA AND PARALYSIS. IN SEVERE CASES, UPPER LIMB INVOLVEMENT IS POSSIBLE AND FLACCID PARALYSIS MAY PROGRESS TO SPASTIC PARALYSIS WITH EXAGGERATED REFLEXES. IMPROVEMENT MAY OCCUR OVER MONTHS TO YEARS, BUT SOME RESIDUAL IMPAIRMENT USUALLY REMAINS. **CHRONIC EXPOSURE-** REPEATED OR PROLONGED EXPOSURE MAY RESULT IN THE EFFECTS OF ACUTE EXPOSURE INCLUDING THE DELAYED NEUROPATHY. OTHER EFFECTS REPORTED IN WORKERS REPEATEDLY EXPOSED INCLUDE IMPAIRED MEMORY AND CONCENTRATION, ACUTE PSYCHOSIS, SEVERE DEPRESSIONS, IRRITABILTY, CONFUSION, APATHY, EMOTIONAL LABILITY, SOCIAL WITHDRAWAL, CONFUSION, HEADACHE, SPEECH DIFFICULTIES, DELAYED REACTION TIMES, SPATIAL DISORIENTATION, NIGHTMARES, SLEEPWALKING, AND DROWSINESS OR INSOMNIA. AN INFLUENZA-LIKE CONDITION WITH HEADACHE, NAUSEA, WEAKNESS, ANOREXIA AND MALAISE HAS ALSO BEEN REPORTED.

FIRST AID- REMOVE FROM EXPOSURE AREA TO FRESH AIR IMMEDIATELY. IF BREATHING HAS STOPPED, GIVE ARTIFICIAL RESPIRATION. MAINTAIN AIRWAY AND BLOOD PRESSURE AND ADMINISTER OXYGEN IF AVAILABLE. KEEP AFFECTED PERSON WARM AND AT REST. TREAT SYMPTOMATICALLY AND SUPPORTIVELY. ADMINISTRATION OF OXYGEN SHOULD BE PERFORMED BY QUALIFIED PERSONNEL. GET MEDICAL ATTENTION IMMEDIATELY.

SKIN CONTACT: DIALIFOR: HIGHLY TOXIC. SEE INFORMATION ON ORGANOPHOSPHATES.
ORGANOPHOSPHATES: CHOLINESTERASE INHIBITOR. **ACUTE EXPOSURE-** LOCALIZED SWEATING AND FASCICULATIONS MAY OCCUR AT THE SITE OF CONTACT. IF SUFFICIENT AMOUNTS ARE ABSORBED, OTHER EFFECTS OF CHOLINESTERASE INHIBITION AS DESCRIBED IN ACUTE INHALATION MAY OCCUR. SYMPTOMS MAY BE DELAYED 2-3 HOURS, BUT USUALLY NO MORE THAN 12 HOURS. THE RATE OF ABSORPTION IS INCREASED BY THE PRESENCE OF DERMATITIS OR HIGH AMBIENT TEMPERATURES. DELAYED NEUROPATHY IS ALSO POSSIBLE. **CHRONIC EXPOSURE-** REPEATED OR PROLONGED EXPOSURE MAY CAUSE EFFECTS AS DESCRIBED IN ACUTE EXPOSURE. SOME ORGANOPHOSPHATES MAY CAUSE SENSITIZATION.

FIRST AID- REMOVE CONTAMINATED CLOTHING IMMEDIATELY. WASH CONTAMINATED AREAS WITH SOAP AND WATER FOLLOWED BY ALCOHOL (ARENA, POISONING, 4TH ED.). EMERGENCY PERSONNEL SHOULD WEAR GLOVES AND AVOID CONTAMINATION. TREAT RESPIRATORY DIFFICULTY WITH ARTIFICIAL RESPIRATION. GET MEDICAL ATTENTION IMMEDIATELY.

EYE CONTACT: DIALIFOR: SEE INFORMATION ON ORGANOPHOSPHATES.
ORGANOPHOSPHATES: CHOLINESTERASE INHIBITOR. **ACUTE EXPOSURE-** DIRECT CONTACT MAY CAUSE PAIN, HYPEREMIA, LACRIMATION, TWITCHING OF THE EYELIDS, MIOSIS, AND CILIARY MUSCLE SPASM WITH LOSS OF ACCOMODATION, BLURRED OR DIMMED VISION AND BROWACHE. SOMETIMES MYDRIASIS MAY OCCUR INSTEAD OF MIOSIS. WITH SUFFICIENT EXPOSURE, OTHER SYMPTOMS OF CHOLINESTERASE INHIBITION AS DESCRIBED IN ACUTE INHALATION MAY OCCUR. **CHRONIC EXPOSURE-** REPEATED OR PROLONGED EXPOSURE MAY CAUSE EFFECTS AS DESCRIBED IN ACUTE EXPOSURE. SOME COMPOUNDS HAVE CAUSED TOXIC EFFECTS ON THE CRYSTALLINE LENS, CONJUNCTIVAL THICKENING AND OBSTRUCTION OF THE NASOLACRIMAL CANALS WHEN USED AS MIOTIC EYEDROPS.

FIRST AID- IRRIGATE EYES WITH WATER OR SALINE SOLUTION. IF SYMPTOMS OF POISONING OCCUR, TREAT RESPIRATORY DIFFICULTY WITH ARTIFICIAL RESPIRATION AND OXYGEN. OBSERVE PATIENT FOR AT LEAST 24-36 HOURS (GOSSELIN, CLINICAL TOXICOLOGY OF COMMERCIAL PRODUCTS, 5TH ED.). GET MEDICAL ATTENTION IMMEDIATELY. OXYGEN SHOULD BE ADMINISTERED BY QUALIFIED MEDICAL PERSONNEL.

INGESTION: DIALIFOR: HIGHLY TOXIC. FETAL DEATH AND FETAL DEVELOPMENTAL ABNORMALITIES WERE OBSERVED IN A STUDY OF PREGNANT HAMSTERS FED DIALIFOR AT LEVELS THAT PRODUCED ADVERSE EFFECTS IN THE DAMS. SEE INFORMATION ON ORGANOPHOSPHATES.
ORGANOPHOSPHATES: CHOLINESTERASE INHIBITOR. **ACUTE EXPOSURE-** WHEN INGESTED, THE FIRST EFFECTS MAY BE NAUSEA, VOMITING, ANOREXIA, ABDOMINAL CRAMPS AND DIARRHEA. GASTROINTESTINAL ABSORPTION MAY CAUSE SYMPTOMS OF CHOLINESTERASE INHIBITION AS DESCRIBED IN ACUTE INHALATION. SYMPTOMS MAY BEGIN WITHIN MINUTES OR BE DELAYED FOR HOURS. DELAYED EFFECTS INCLUDING NEUROPATHY MAY ALSO OCCUR. **CHRONIC EXPOSURE-** REPEATED INGESTION MAY CAUSE EFFECTS AS DESCRIBED IN ACUTE EXPOSURE.

FIRST AID- IF PERSON IS ALERT AND RESPIRATION IS NOT DEPRESSED, GIVE SYRUP OF IPECAC FOLLOWED BY WATER (IF VOMITING OCCURS, KEEP HEAD BELOW HIPS TO PREVENT ASPIRATION). IF CONSCIOUSNESS LEVEL DECLINES OR VOMITING HAS NOT OCCURRED IN 15 MINUTES EMPTY STOMACH BY GASTRIC LAVAGE WITH THE AID OF CUFFED ENDOTRACHEAL TUBE USING ISOTONIC SALINE OR 5% SODIUM BICARBONATE FOLLOW WITH ACTIVATED CHARCOAL. ESTABLISH AND MAINTAIN AIRWAY. TREAT RESPIRATORY DIFFICULTY WITH ARTIFICIAL RESPIRATION AND OXYGEN. DO NOT GIVE MORPHINE, AMINOPHYLLINE, PHENOTHIAZINES, RESERPINE, FUROSEMIDE, OR ETHACRYNIC ACID (MORGAN, RECOGNITION AND MANAGEMENT OF PESTICIDE POISONINGS, 3RD ED.). TREAT SYMPTOMATICALLY AND SUPPORTIVELY. ADMINISTRATION OF OXYGEN AND LAVAGE MUST BE PERFORMED BY QUALIFIED MEDICAL PERSONNEL. GET MEDICAL ATTENTION IMMEDIATELY.

ANTIDOTE: THE FOLLOWING ANTIDOTE(S) HAVE BEEN RECOMMENDED. HOWEVER, THE DECISION AS TO WHETHER THE SEVERITY OF POISONING REQUIRES ADMINISTRATION OF ANY ANTIDOTE AND ACTUAL DOSE REQUIRED SHOULD BE MADE BY QUALIFIED MEDICAL PERSONNEL.
FOR CHOLINESTERASE INHIBITORS: ESTABLISH CLEAR AIRWAY AND TISSUE OXYGENATION BY ASPIRATION OF SECRETIONS, AND IF NECESSARY, BY ASSISTED PULMONARY VENTILATION WITH OXYGEN. IMPROVE TISSUE OXYGENATION AS MUCH AS POSSIBLE BEFORE ADMINISTERING ATROPINE TO MINIMIZE THE RISK OF

VENTRICULAR FIBRILLATION. ADMINISTER ATROPINE SULFATE INTRAVENOUSLY, OR INTRAMUSCULARLY IF IV INJECTION IS NOT POSSIBLE. IN MODERATELY SEVERE POISONING ADMINISTER ATROPINE SULFATE, 0.4-2.0 MG REPEATED EVERY 15 MINUTES UNTIL ATROPINIZATION IS ACHIEVED (TACHYCARDIA, FLUSHING, DRY MOUTH, MYDRIASIS). MAINTAIN ATROPINIZATION BY REPEATED DOSES FOR 2-12 HOURS, OR LONGER, DEPENDING ON THE SEVERITY OF POISONING. THE APPEARANCE OF RALES IN THE LUNG BASES, MIOSIS, SALIVATION, NAUSEA, BRADYCARDIA, ARE ALL INDICATIONS OF INADEQUATE ATROPINIZATION. SEVERELY POISONED INDIVIDUALS MAY EXHIBIT REMARKABLE TOLERANCE TO ATROPINE; TWO OR MORE TIMES THE DOSAGES SUGGESTED ABOVE MAY BE NEEDED. PERSONS NOT POISONED OR ONLY SLIGHTLY POISONED, HOWEVER, MAY DEVELOP SIGNS OF ATROPINE TOXICITY FROM SUCH LARGE DOSAGES: FEVER, MUSCLE FIBRILLATIONS, AND DELIRIUM ARE THE MAIN SIGNS OF ATROPINE TOXICITY. IF THESE SIGNS APPEAR WHILE THE PATIENT IS FULLY ATROPINIZED, ATROPINE ADMINISTRATION SHOULD BE DISCONTINUED, AT LEAST TEMPORARILY. OBSERVE TREATED PATIENTS CLOSELY AT LEAST 24 HOURS TO INSURE THAT SYMPTOMS (POSSIBLY PULMONARY EDEMA) DO NOT RECUR AS ATROPINIZATION WEARS OFF. IN VERY SEVERE POISONINGS, METABOLIC DISPOSITION OF TOXICANT MAY REQUIRE SEVERAL HOURS OR DAYS DURING WHICH ATROPINIZATION MUST BE MAINTAINED. MARKEDLY LOWER LEVELS OF URINARY METABOLITES INDICATE THAT ATROPINE DOSAGE CAN BE TAPERED OFF. AS DOSAGE IS REDUCED, CHECK THE LUNG BASES FREQUENTLY FOR RALES. IF RALES ARE HEARD OR OTHER SYMPTOMS RETURN, RE-ESTABLISH ATROPINIZATION PROMPTLY (MORGAN, RECOGNITION AND MANAGEMENT OF PESTICIDE POISONINGS, 3RD ED.). ADMINISTRATION OF ANTIDOTE MUST BE PERFORMED BY QUALIFIED MEDICAL PERSONNEL.

IN CASES OF SEVERE POISONING BY ORGANOPHOSPHATE PESTICIDES IN WHICH RESPIRATORY DEPRESSION, MUSCLE WEAKNESS AND TWITCHINGS ARE SEVERE, GIVE PRALIDOXIME (PROTOPAM-AYERST, 2-PAM), 1.0 GRAM INTRAVENOUSLY AT NO MORE THAN 0.5 GRAM PER MINUTE. DOSAGE OF PRALIDOXIME MAY BE REPEATED IN 1-2 HOURS, THEN AT 10-12 HOUR INTERVALS IF NEEDED. IN VERY SEVERE POISONINGS, DOSAGE RATES MAY BE DOUBLED. TREATMENT WITH PRALIDOXIME WILL BE MOST EFFECTIVE IF GIVEN WITHIN THIRTY-SIX HOURS AFTER POISONING (MORGAN, RECOGNITION AND MANAGEMENT OF PESTICIDE POISONINGS, 3RD ED.). ANTIDOTE SHOULD BE ADMINISTERED BY QUALIFIED MEDICAL PERSONNEL.

REACTIVITY

REACTIVITY: STABLE UNDER NORMAL TEMPERATURES AND PRESSURES.

INCOMPATIBILITIES: DIALIFOR: STRONG ALKALI: MAY CAUSE HYDROLYSIS.

DECOMPOSITION: THERMAL DECOMPOSITION PRODUCTS MAY INCLUDE TOXIC AND HAZARDOUS FUMES OF SULFUR, NITROGEN AND PHOSPHORUS.

POLYMERIZATION: HAZARDOUS POLYMERIZATION HAS NOT BEEN REPORTED TO OCCUR UNDER NORMAL TEMPERATURES AND PRESSURES.

STORAGE AND DISPOSAL

OBSERVE ALL FEDERAL, STATE AND LOCAL REGULATIONS WHEN STORING OR DISPOSING OF THIS SUBSTANCE. FOR ASSISTANCE, CONTACT THE DISTRICT DIRECTOR OF THE ENVIRONMENTAL PROTECTION AGENCY.

STORAGE

STORE IN ACCORDANCE WITH 40 CFR 165 RECOMMENDED PROCEDURES FOR THE DISPOSAL AND STORAGE OF PESTICIDES AND PESTICIDE CONTAINERS.

STORE AWAY FROM INCOMPATIBLE SUBSTANCES.

THRESHOLD PLANNING QUANTITY (TPQ): THE SUPERFUND AMENDMENTS AND REAUTHORIZATION ACT (SARA) SECTION 302 REQUIRES THAT EACH FACILITY WHERE ANY EXTREMELY HAZARDOUS SUBSTANCE IS PRESENT IN A QUANTITY EQUAL TO OR GREATER THAN THE TPQ ESTABLISHED FOR THAT SUBSTANCE NOTIFY THE STATE EMERGENCY RESPONSE COMMISSION FOR THE STATE IN WHICH IT IS LOCATED. SECTION 303 OF SARA REQUIRES THESE FACILITIES TO PARTICIPATE IN LOCAL EMERGENCY RESPONSE PLANNING (40 CFR 355.30).

DISPOSAL

DISPOSAL MUST BE IN ACCORDANCE WITH 40 CFR 165 RECOMMENDED PROCEDURES FOR THE DISPOSAL AND STORAGE OF PESTICIDES AND PESTICIDE CONTAINERS.

CONDITIONS TO AVOID

NONE REPORTED.

SPILL AND LEAK PROCEDURES

OCCUPATIONAL SPILL: DO NOT TOUCH SPILLED MATERIAL. STOP LEAK IF YOU CAN DO IT WITHOUT RISK. USE WATER SPRAY TO REDUCE VAPORS. FOR SMALL SPILLS, TAKE UP WITH SAND OR OTHER ABSORBENT MATERIAL AND PLACE INTO CONTAINERS FOR LATER DISPOSAL. FOR SMALL DRY SPILLS, WITH A CLEAN SHOVEL PLACE MATERIAL INTO CLEAN, DRY CONTAINERS AND COVER. MOVE CONTAINERS FROM SPILL AREA. FOR LARGER SPILLS, DIKE FAR AHEAD OF SPILL FOR LATER DISPOSAL. KEEP UNNECESSARY PEOPLE AWAY. ISOLATE HAZARD AREA AND DENY ENTRY. VENTILATE CLOSED SPACES BEFORE ENTERING.

REPORTABLE QUANTITY (RQ): 1 POUND THE SUPERFUND AMENDMENTS AND REAUTHORIZATION ACT (SARA) SECTION 304 REQUIRES THAT A RELEASE EQUAL TO OR GREATER THAN THE REPORTABLE QUANTITY FOR THIS SUBSTANCE BE IMMEDIATELY REPORTED TO THE LOCAL EMERGENCY PLANNING COMMITTEE AND THE STATE EMERGENCY RESPONSE COMMISSION (40 CFR 355.40). IF THE RELEASE OF THIS SUBSTANCE IS REPORTABLE UNDER CERCLA SECTION 103, THE NATIONAL RESPONSE CENTER MUST BE NOTIFIED IMMEDIATELY AT (800) 424-8802 OR (202) 426-2675 IN THE METROPOLITAN WASHINGTON, D.C. AREA (40 CFR 302.6).

PROTECTIVE EQUIPMENT

VENTILATION: PROCESS ENCLOSURE RECOMMENDED.

RESPIRATOR: THE FOLLOWING RESPIRATORS ARE RECOMMENDED BASED ON INFORMATION FOUND IN THE PHYSICAL DATA, TOXICITY AND HEALTH EFFECTS SECTIONS. THEY ARE RANKED IN ORDER FROM MINIMUM TO MAXIMUM RESPIRATORY PROTECTION. THE SPECIFIC RESPIRATOR SELECTED MUST BE BASED ON CONTAMINATION LEVELS FOUND IN THE WORK PLACE, MUST NOT EXCEED THE WORKING LIMITS OF THE RESPIRATOR AND BE JOINTLY APPROVED BY THE NATIONAL INSTITUTE FOR OCCUPATIONAL SAFETY AND HEALTH AND THE MINE SAFETY AND HEALTH ADMINISTRATION (NIOSH-MSHA).

TYPE 'C' SUPPLIED-AIR RESPIRATOR WITH A FULL FACEPIECE OPERATED IN PRESSURE-DEMAND OR OTHER POSITIVE PRESSURE MODE OR WITH A FULL FACEPIECE, HELMET OR HOOD OPERATED IN CONTINOUS-FLOW MODE.

SELF-CONTAINED BREATHING APPARATUS WITH A FULL FACEPIECE OPERATED IN PRESSURE-DEMAND OR OTHER POSITIVE PRESSURE MODE.

FOR FIREFIGHTING AND OTHER IMMEDIATELY DANGEROUS TO LIFE OR HEALTH CONDITIONS:

SELF-CONTAINED BREATHING APPARATUS WITH FULL FACEPIECE OPERATED IN PRESSURE-DEMAND OR OTHER POSITIVE PRESSURE MODE.

SUPPLIED-AIR RESPIRATOR WITH FULL FACEPIECE AND OPERATED IN PRESSURE-DEMAND OR OTHER POSITIVE PRESSURE MODE IN COMBINATION WITH AN AUXILIARY SELF-CONTAINED BREATHING APPARATUS OPERATED IN PRESSURE-DEMAND OR OTHER POSITIVE PRESSURE MODE.

CLOTHING: EMPLOYEE MUST WEAR APPROPRIATE PROTECTIVE (IMPERVIOUS) CLOTHING AND EQUIPMENT TO PREVENT ANY POSSIBILITY OF SKIN CONTACT WITH THIS SUBSTANCE.

GLOVES: EMPLOYEE MUST WEAR APPROPRIATE PROTECTIVE GLOVES TO PREVENT CONTACT WITH THIS SUBSTANCE.

EYE PROTECTION: EMPLOYEE MUST WEAR SPLASH-PROOF OR DUST-RESISTANT SAFETY GOGGLES AND A FACESHIELD TO PREVENT CONTACT WITH THIS SUBSTANCE.

EMERGENCY WASH FACILITIES: WHERE THERE IS ANY POSSIBILITY THAT AN EMPLOYEE'S EYES AND/OR SKIN MAY BE EXPOSED TO THIS SUBSTANCE, THE EMPLOYER SHOULD PROVIDE AN EYE WASH FOUNTAIN AND QUICK DRENCH SHOWER WITHIN THE IMMEDIATE WORK AREA FOR EMERGENCY USE.

AUTHORIZED BY- OCCUPATIONAL HEALTH SERVICES, INC.

CREATION DATE: 10/04/89 ***REVISION DATE:*** 04/27/90

MATERIAL SAFETY DATA SHEET

OCCUPATIONAL HEALTH SERVICES, INC.
AGRICULTURE AND PESTICIDE DIVISION
450 SEVENTH AVENUE, SUITE 2407
NEW YORK, NEW YORK 10123
1-800-445-MSDS OR (212) 967-1100

EMERGENCY CONTACT:
JOHN S. BRANSFORD, JR. (615) 292-1180

SUBSTANCE IDENTIFICATION

CAS-NUMBER 8001-35-2

SUBSTANCE: <u>TOXAPHENE</u>

TRADE NAMES/SYNONYMS: ALLTOX; ANATOX; CAMPHECHLOR; CAMPHOCHLOR; CHLORINATED CAMPHENE; ESTONOX; GENIPHENE; M 5055; MELIPAX; OCTACHLOROCAMPHENE; PHENACIDE; PHENATOX; POLYCHLOROCAMPHENE; STROBANE T; TOXAKIL; TOXAPHEN; RCRA P123; STCC 4941189; PST23640

CHEMICAL FAMILY: TERPENE

MOLECULAR FORMULA: C10-H10-CL8 (APPROXIMATE)

MOLECULAR WEIGHT: 413.80 (APPROXIMATE)

CERCLA RATINGS (SCALE 0-3): HEALTH = 3 FIRE = 1 REACTIVITY = 0 PERSISTENCE = 3
NFPA RATINGS (SCALE 0-4): HEALTH = 3 FIRE = 1 REACTIVITY = 0

COMPONENTS AND CONTAMINANTS

COMPONENT: TOXAPHENE ***PERCENT:*** 100.0
CAS# 8001-35-2
OTHER CONTAMINANTS: NONE
EXPOSURE LIMITS: TOXAPHENE: 0.5 MG/M3 OSHA TWA (SKIN); 1 MG/M3 OSHA STEL 0.5 MG/M3 ACGIH TWA (SKIN); 1 MG/M3 ACGIH STEL
500/10,000 POUNDS SARA SECTION 302 THRESHOLD PLANNING QUANTITY 1 POUND SARA SECTION 304 REPORTABLE QUANTITY 1 POUND CERCLA SECTION 103 REPORTABLE QUANTITY SUBJECT TO SARA SECTION 313 ANNUAL TOXIC CHEMICAL RELEASE REPORTING SUBJECT TO CALIFORNIA PROPOSITION 65 CANCER AND/OR REPRODUCTIVE TOXICITY WARNING AND RELEASE REQUIREMENTS- (JANUARY 1, 1988)

PHYSICAL DATA

DESCRIPTION: YELLOW OR AMBER WAXY SOLID WITH A PLEASANT, PINEY ODOR.
BOILING POINT: 311 F (155 C) (DECOMPOSES) ***MELTING POINT:*** 149-194 F (65-90 C)
SPECIFIC GRAVITY: 1.66 @ 27 C ***VAPOR PRESSURE:*** 0.2-0.4 MMHG @ 25 C
SOLUBILITY IN WATER: 0.0003% @ 20 C
SOLVENT SOLUBILITY: SOLUBLE IN ACETONE, BENZENE, CARBON TETRACHLORIDE, TOLUENE, XYLENE, HEXANE, DEODORIZED KEROSENE, MINERAL OIL, ETHANOL, ISOPROPYL ALCOHOL, PETROLEUM OILS, AND MOST AROMATIC HYDROCARBONS.

FIRE AND EXPLOSION DATA

FIRE AND EXPLOSION HAZARD: SLIGHT FIRE HAZARD WHEN EXPOSED TO HEAT OR FLAME.
FLASH POINT: 275 F (135 C) (CC) ***FLAMMABILITY CLASS(OSHA):*** IIIB
FIREFIGHTING MEDIA: DRY CHEMICAL, CARBON DIOXIDE, HALON, WATER SPRAY OR ALCOHOL FOAM (1987 EMERGENCY RESPONSE GUIDEBOOK, DOT P 5800.4).
FOR LARGER FIRES, USE WATER SPRAY, FOG OR ALCOHOL FOAM (1987 EMERGENCY RESPONSE GUIDEBOOK, DOT P 5800.4).
FIREFIGHTING: MOVE CONTAINER FROM FIRE AREA IF POSSIBLE. COOL FIRE-EXPOSED CONTAINERS WITH WATER FROM SIDE UNTIL WELL AFTER FIRE IS OUT. STAY AWAY FROM STORAGE TANK ENDS. FOR MASSIVE FIRE IN STORAGE AREA, USE UNMANNED HOSE HOLDER OR MONITOR NOZZLES, ELSE WITHDRAW FROM AREA AND LET FIRE BURN. WITHDRAW IMMEDIATELY IN CASE OF RISING SOUND FROM VENTING SAFETY DEVICE OR ANY DISCOLORATION OF STORAGE TANK DUE TO FIRE (1987 EMERGENCY RESPONSE GUIDEBOOK, DOT P 5800.4, GUIDE PAGE 26). USE AGENTS SUITABLE FOR TYPE OF FIRE. COOL CONTAINERS WITH FLOODING AMOUNTS OF WATER. AVOID BREATHING VAPORS OR DUSTS, KEEP UPWIND.

TRANSPORTATION DATA

DEPARTMENT OF TRANSPORTATION HAZARD CLASSIFICATION 49 CFR 172.101: ORM-A
DEPARTMENT OF TRANSPORTATION LABELING REQUIREMENTS 49 CFR 172.101 AND SUBPART E: NONE
DEPARTMENT OF TRANSPORTATION PACKAGING REQUIREMENTS: 49 CFR 173.510 EXCEPTIONS: 49 CFR 173.505

TOXICITY

TOXAPHENE: IRRITATION DATA: 500 MG SKIN-MAMMAL MODERATE. TOXICITY DATA: 2000 MG/M3/2 HOURS INHALATION-MOUSE LCLO; 657 MG/KG SKIN-HUMAN TDLO; 1025 MG/KG SKIN-RABBIT LD50; 600 MG/KG SKIN-RAT LD50; 28 MG/KG ORAL-HUMAN LDLO; 29 MG/KG ORAL-MAN LDLO; 50 MG/KG ORAL-RAT LD50; 112 MG/KG ORAL-MOUSE LD50; 15 MG/KG ORAL-DOG LD50; 75 MG/KG ORAL-RABBIT LD50; 250 MG/KG ORAL-GUINEA PIG LD50; 200 MG/KG ORAL-HAMSTER LD50; 42 MG/KG INTRAPERITONEAL-MOUSE LD50; 70 MG/KG INTRAPERITONEAL-RAT LDLO; 44 MG/KG UNREPORTED-MAN LDLO; 46 MG/KG UNREPORTED-MOUSE LD50; 240 MG/KG UNREPORTED-RAT LD50; MUTAGENIC DATA (RTECS); REPRODUCTIVE EFFECTS DATA (RTECS); TUMORIGENIC DATA (RTECS). CARCINOGEN STATUS: ANTICIPATED HUMAN CARCINOGEN (NTP); ANIMAL SUFFICIENT EVIDENCE (IARC GROUP-2B). PROLONGED ORAL ADMINISTRATION RESULTED IN AN INCREASE IN THE INCIDENCE OF HEPATOCELLULAR CARCINOMAS IN MICE AND THYROID TUMORS IN RATS. ACUTE TOXICITY LEVEL: HIGHLY TOXIC BY INGESTION; MODERATELY TOXIC BY DERMAL ABSORPTION. TARGET EFFECTS: POISONING MAY AFFECT THE LIVER, KIDNEYS, AND NERVOUS SYSTEM.

HEALTH EFFECTS AND FIRST AID

INHALATION: TOXAPHENE: **ACUTE EXPOSURE-** MAY BE IRRITATING TO THE MUCOUS MEMBRANES. CASES OF ACUTE INTOXICATION BY INHALATION HAVE NOT BEEN REPORTED, HOWEVER IF POISONING DOES OCCUR SYMPTOMS MAY INCLUDE NAUSEA, VOMITING, DIARRHEA, STOMACH PAINS, HEADACHE, DIZZINESS, ATAXIA, MENTAL CONFUSION, JERKING OF THE ARMS AND LEGS, AND CONVULSIONS. GRADUAL TREMORS MAY SET IN STARTING FROM THE EYELIDS AND THE FACE MUSCLES, DESCENDING TOWARDS THE WHOLE BODY AND IN THE LIMBS. ALLERGIC BRONCHOPNEUMONIA WAS OBSERVED IN 2 WORKERS USING A TOXAPHENE SPRAY. **CHRONIC EXPOSURE-** TWENTY-FIVE VOLUNTEERS WERE EXPOSED IN A CLOSED CHAMBER TO AN AEROSOL OF TOXAPHENE FOR 30 MINUTES A DAY FOR 10 CONSECUTIVE DAYS AT A MAXIMAL, NOMINAL CONCENTRATION OF 500 MG/M3. AFTER THREE WEEKS THE SAME EXPOSURE WAS REPEATED FOR 3 DAYS. PHYSICAL EXAMINATION AND STUDY OF THE BLOOD AND URINE FAILED TO REVEAL ANY TOXIC EFFECT. OCCUPATIONAL EXPOSURE TO SOME ORGANOCHLORINE PESTICIDES HAS BEEN REPORTED TO CAUSE POLYNEURITIS, ENCEPHALOPOLYNEURITIS, AND NEUROVEGETATIVE SYNDROMES. OTHER EFFECTS MAY INCLUDE LIVER AND KIDNEY DAMAGE, CARDIOVASCULAR DISTURBANCES WITH DYSPNEA, HIGH HEART RATE, OPPRESSION AND PAIN IN THE REGION OF THE HEART. BLOOD AND CAPILLARY DISTURBANCES MAY OCCUR AND APPEARS AS THROMBOPENIA, ANEMIA, PANCYTOPENIA, AGRANULOCYTOSIS, HEMOLYSIS AND CAPILLARY DISORDERS.
FIRST AID- REMOVE FROM EXPOSURE AREA TO FRESH AIR IMMEDIATELY. IF BREATHING HAS STOPPED, PERFORM ARTIFICIAL RESPIRATION. KEEP PERSON WARM AND AT REST. TREAT SYMPTOMATICALLY AND SUPPORTIVELY. GET MEDICAL ATTENTION IMMEDIATELY.

SKIN CONTACT: TOXAPHENE: **ACUTE EXPOSURE-** MAY CAUSE IRRITATION AND BE ABSORBED THROUGH THE SKIN. SYMPTOMS MAY INCLUDE CONVULSIONS PRECEDED BY NAUSEA AND VOMITING. IN NONFATAL POISONING CESSATION OF CONVULSIONS MAY BE FOLLOWED BY A PERIOD OF WEAKNESS, LASSITUDE AND AMNESIA. IN FATAL POISONING, CONVULSIONS OCCUR AT DECREASING INTERVALS UNTIL REPIRATORY FAILURE SUPERVENES USUALLY WITHIN 4-24 HOURS. **CHRONIC EXPOSURE-** MAY CAUSE DERMATITIS AFTER REPEATED OR PROLONGED EXPOSURE.
FIRST AID- REMOVE CONTAMINATED CLOTHING AND SHOES IMMEDIATELY. WASH AFFECTED AREA WITH SOAP OR MILD DETERGENT AND LARGE AMOUNTS OF WATER UNTIL NO EVIDENCE OF CHEMICAL REMAINS (APPROXIMATELY 15-20 MINUTES). GET MEDICAL ATTENTION IMMEDIATELY.

EYE CONTACT: TOXAPHENE: **ACUTE EXPOSURE-** MAY CAUSE IRRITATION. **CHRONIC EXPOSURE-** NO DATA AVAILABLE.
FIRST AID- WASH EYES IMMEDIATELY WITH LARGE AMOUNTS OF WATER OR NORMAL SALINE, OCCASIONALLY LIFTING UPPER AND LOWER LIDS, UNTIL NO EVIDENCE OF CHEMICAL REMAINS (APPROXIMATELY 15-20 MINUTES). GET MEDICAL ATTENTION IMMEDIATELY.

INGESTION: TOXAPHENE: CONVULSANT/CARCINOGEN/TOXIC. **ACUTE EXPOSURE-** THE SUSPECTED LETHAL DOSE FOR HUMANS IS 2-7 GRAMS. SYMPTOMS USUALLY APPEAR WITHIN 1 HOUR, AND DEATH WITHIN 4 TO 8 HOURS. SYMPTOMS MAY INCLUDE NAUSEA, VOMITING, DIARRHEA, STOMACH PAINS, HEADACHE, DIZZINESS, ATAXIA, MENTAL CONFUSION, JERKING OF THE ARMS AND LEGS, AND CONVULSIONS. GRADUAL TREMORS MAY OCCUR STARTING FROM THE EYELIDS AND THE FACE MUSCLES, DESCENDING TOWARDS THE WHOLE BODY AND IN THE LIMBS. IN FATAL CASES, SYMPTOMS BEGIN AS EARLY AS HALF AN HOUR AFTER EXPOSURE AND INCLUDE FREQUENT VIOLENT CONVULSIONS AND CYANOSIS. CONVULSIONS MAY BE ACCOMPANIED WITH ELEVATED TEMPERATURE, UNCONSCIOUSNESS, AND GENERALIZED DEPRESSION AND MAY RESULT IN DEATH DUE TO ANOXIA AND RESPIRATORY FAILURE. IN NONFATAL CASES, PATIENTS MAY DEVELOP SIGNS OF TOXIC HEPATITIS, TOXIC NEPHROPATHY, PROLONGED TOXIC POLYNEURITIS, ANEMIA AND HEMORRHAGIC DIATHESIS. ALLERGIC BRONCHOPNEUMONIA IS TYPICAL OF TOXAPHENE POISONING. **CHRONIC EXPOSURE-** ANIMAL STUDIES INDICATE REPEATED OR PROLONGED INGESTION MAY CAUSE CONVULSIONS, DAMAGE TO THE KIDNEYS, AND DEGENERATIVE CHANGES TO THE LIVER. AN INCREASE IN THE INCIDENCE OF HEPATOCELLULAR CARCINOMA AND THYROID TUMORS WAS OBSERVED IN MICE AND RATS RESPECTIVELY AFTER CHRONIC ORAL ADMINISTRATION.
FIRST AID- GIVE SYRUP OF IPECAC. GIVE ACTIVATED CHARCOAL FOLLOWED BY GASTRIC LAVAGE WITH 2-4 LITERS OF WATER. FOLLOW WITH SALINE CATHARTIC. DO NOT GIVE FATS OR OILS. INTESTINAL LAVAGE WITH 20% MANNITOL (200 ML) BY STOMACH TUBE IS ALSO USEFUL. MAINTAIN RESPIRATION, GIVE OXYGEN IF RESPIRATION IS DEPRESSED. (DREISBACH, HANDBOOK OF POISONING, 11TH ED.) GET MEDICAL ATTENTION IMMEDIATELY. LAVAGE AND OXYGEN MUST BE ADMINISTERED BY QUALIFIED MEDICAL PERSONNEL.
ANTIDOTE: NO SPECIFIC ANTIDOTE. TREAT SYMPTOMATICALLY AND SUPPORTIVELY.

REACTIVITY

REACTIVITY: STABLE UNDER NORMAL TEMPERATURES AND PRESSURES.
INCOMPATIBILITIES: TOXAPHENE: ALKALIS: DEHYDROCHLORINATES WITH HEAT. IRON: CORRODES WITH MOISTURE. OXIDIZERS (STRONG): FIRE AND EXPLOSION HAZARD.

DECOMPOSITION: THERMAL DECOMPOSITION PRODUCTS MAY INCLUDE TOXIC AND CORROSIVE FUMES OF CHLORIDES AND TOXIC OXIDES OF CARBON.
POLYMERIZATION: HAZARDOUS POLYMERIZATION HAS NOT BEEN REPORTED TO OCCUR UNDER NORMAL TEMPERATURES AND PRESSURES.

STORAGE AND DISPOSAL

OBSERVE ALL FEDERAL, STATE AND LOCAL REGULATIONS WHEN STORING OR DISPOSING OF THIS SUBSTANCE. FOR ASSISTANCE, CONTACT THE DISTRICT DIRECTOR OF THE ENVIRONMENTAL PROTECTION AGENCY.

STORAGE

STORE IN ACCORDANCE WITH 40 CFR 165 RECOMMENDED PROCEDURES FOR THE DISPOSAL AND STORAGE OF PESTICIDES AND PESTICIDE CONTAINERS.
STORE IN A COOL, DRY PLACE PROTECTED AGAINST LIGHT.
STORE AWAY FROM INCOMPATIBLE SUBSTANCES.
THRESHOLD PLANNING QUANTITY (TPQ): THE SUPERFUND AMENDMENTS AND REAUTHORIZATION ACT (SARA) SECTION 302 REQUIRES THAT EACH FACILITY WHERE ANY EXTREMELY HAZARDOUS SUBSTANCE IS PRESENT IN A QUANTITY EQUAL TO OR GREATER THAN THE TPQ ESTABLISHED FOR THAT SUBSTANCE NOTIFY THE STATE EMERGENCY RESPONSE COMMISSION FOR THE STATE IN WHICH IT IS LOCATED. SECTION 303 OF SARA REQUIRES THESE FACILITIES TO PARTICIPATE IN LOCAL EMERGENCY RESPONSE PLANNING (40 CFR 355.30).

DISPOSAL

DISPOSAL MUST BE IN ACCORDANCE WITH STANDARDS APPLICABLE TO GENERATORS OF HAZARDOUS WASTE, 40CFR 262. EPA HAZARDOUS WASTE NUMBER P123.
TOXAPHENE - REGULATORY LEVEL: 0.5 MG/L MATERIALS WHICH CONTAIN THE ABOVE SUBSTANCE AT OR ABOVE THE REGULATORY LEVEL MEET THE EPA CHARACTERISTIC OF TOXICITY, AND MUST BE DISPOSED OF IN ACCORDANCE WITH 40 CFR PART 262. EPA HAZARDOUS WASTE NUMBER D015.

CONDITIONS TO AVOID

AVOID CONTACT WITH HEAT, SPARKS, FLAMES, OR OTHER SOURCES OF IGNITION. VAPORS MAY BE EXPLOSIVE AND POISONOUS; DO NOT ALLOW UNNECESSARY PERSONNEL IN AREA. DO NOT OVERHEAT CONTAINERS; CONTAINERS MAY VIOLENTLY RUPTURE AND TRAVEL A CONSIDERABLE DISTANCE IN HEAT OF FIRE.

SPILL AND LEAK PROCEDURES

SOIL SPILL: DIG A PIT, POND, LAGOON OR HOLDING AREA TO CONTAIN LIQUID OR SOLID MATERIAL. COVER SOLIDS WITH A PLASTIC SHEET TO PREVENT DISSOLVING IN RAIN OR FIREFIGHTING WATER.
WATER SPILL: USE NATURAL DEEP WATER POCKETS, EXCAVATED LAGOONS, OR SAND BAG BARRIERS TO TRAP MATERIAL AT BOTTOM. USE ACTIVATED CARBON AT 10 TIMES THE SPILLED AMOUNT IF IT IS DISSOLVED AT 10 PPM OR GREATER CONCENTRATION. REMOVE TRAPPED MATERIAL WITH SUCTION HOSES. USE MECHANICAL DREDGES OR LIFTS TO REMOVE IMMOBILIZED MASSES OF POLLUTION AND PRECIPITATES.
THE CALIFORNIA SAFE DRINKING WATER AND TOXIC ENFORCEMENT ACT OF 1986 (PROPOSITION 65) PROHIBITS CONTAMINATING ANY KNOWN SOURCE OF DRINKING WATER WITH SUBSTANCES KNOWN TO CAUSE CANCER AND/OR REPRODUCTIVE TOXICITY.
OCCUPATIONAL SPILL: DO NOT TOUCH SPILLED MATERIAL. STOP LEAK IF YOU CAN DO IT WITHOUT RISK. FOR SMALL SPILLS, TAKE UP WITH SAND OR OTHER ABSORBENT MATERIAL AND PLACE INTO CONTAINERS FOR LATER DISPOSAL. FOR SMALL DRY SPILLS, WITH A CLEAN SHOVEL PLACE MATERIAL INTO CLEAN, DRY CONTAINER AND COVER. MOVE CONTAINERS FROM SPILL AREA. FOR LARGER SPILLS, DIKE FAR AHEAD OF SPILL FOR LATER DISPOSAL. KEEP UNNECESSARY PEOPLE AWAY. ISOLATE HAZARD AREA AND DENY ENTRY.
REPORTABLE QUANTITY (RQ): 1 POUND THE SUPERFUND AMENDMENTS AND REAUTHORIZATION ACT (SARA) SECTION 304 REQUIRES THAT A RELEASE EQUAL TO OR GREATER THAN THE REPORTABLE QUANTITY FOR THIS SUBSTANCE BE IMMEDIATELY REPORTED TO THE LOCAL EMERGENCY PLANNING COMMITTEE AND THE STATE EMERGENCY RESPONSE COMMISSION (40 CFR 355.40). IF THE RELEASE OF THIS SUBSTANCE IS REPORTABLE UNDER CERCLA SECTION 103, THE NATIONAL RESPONSE CENTER MUST BE NOTIFIED IMMEDIATELY AT (800) 424-8802 OR (202) 426-2675 IN THE METROPOLITAN WASHINGTON, D.C. AREA (40 CFR 302.6).

PROTECTIVE EQUIPMENT

VENTILATION: PROVIDE LOCAL EXHAUST OR PROCESS ENCLOSURE VENTILATION TO MEET PUBLISHED EXPOSURE LIMITS.
RESPIRATOR: THE FOLLOWING RESPIRATORS ARE RECOMMENDED BASED ON INFORMATION FOUND IN THE PHYSICAL DATA, TOXICITY AND HEALTH EFFECTS SECTIONS. THEY ARE RANKED IN ORDER FROM MINIMUM TO MAXIMUM RESPIRATORY PROTECTION. THE SPECIFIC RESPIRATOR SELECTED MUST BE BASED ON CONTAMINATION LEVELS FOUND IN THE WORK PLACE, MUST NOT EXCEED THE WORKING LIMITS OF THE RESPIRATOR AND BE JOINTLY APPROVED BY THE NATIONAL INSTITUTE FOR OCCUPATIONAL SAFETY AND HEALTH AND THE MINE SAFETY AND HEALTH ADMINISTRATION (NIOSH-MSHA).
TYPE 'C' SUPPLIED-AIR RESPIRATOR WITH A FULL FACEPIECE OPERATED IN PRESSURE-DEMAND OR OTHER POSITIVE PRESSURE MODE OR WITH A FULL FACEPIECE, HELMET OR HOOD OPERATED IN CONTINOUS-FLOW MODE.
SELF-CONTAINED BREATHING APPARATUS WITH A FULL FACEPIECE OPERATED IN PRESSURE-DEMAND OR OTHER POSITIVE PRESSURE MODE.
FOR FIREFIGHTING AND OTHER IMMEDIATELY DANGEROUS TO LIFE OR HEALTH CONDITIONS:
SELF-CONTAINED BREATHING APPARATUS WITH FULL FACEPIECE OPERATED IN PRESSURE-DEMAND OR OTHER POSITIVE PRESSURE MODE.
SUPPLIED-AIR RESPIRATOR WITH FULL FACEPIECE AND OPERATED IN PRESSURE-DEMAND OR OTHER POSITIVE PRESSURE MODE IN COMBINATION WITH AN AUXILIARY SELF-CONTAINED BREATHING APPARATUS OPERATED IN PRESSURE-DEMAND OR OTHER POSITIVE PRESSURE MODE.
CLOTHING: EMPLOYEE MUST WEAR APPROPRIATE PROTECTIVE (IMPERVIOUS) CLOTHING AND EQUIPMENT TO PREVENT REPEATED OR PROLONGED SKIN CONTACT WITH THIS SUBSTANCE.
GLOVES: EMPLOYEE MUST WEAR APPROPRIATE PROTECTIVE GLOVES TO PREVENT CONTACT WITH THIS SUBSTANCE.
EYE PROTECTION: EMPLOYEE MUST WEAR SPLASH-PROOF OR DUST-RESISTANT SAFETY GOGGLES TO PREVENT EYE CONTACT WITH THIS SUBSTANCE.
EMERGENCY EYE WASH: WHERE THERE IS ANY POSSIBILITY THAT AN EMPLOYEE'S EYES MAY BE EXPOSED TO THIS SUBSTANCE, THE EMPLOYER SHOULD PROVIDE AN EYE WASH FOUNTAIN WITHIN THE IMMEDIATE WORK AREA FOR EMERGENCY USE.

AUTHORIZED BY- OCCUPATIONAL HEALTH SERVICES, INC.
CREATION DATE: 10/05/89 ***REVISION DATE:*** 07/13/90

MATERIAL SAFETY DATA SHEET

OCCUPATIONAL HEALTH SERVICES, INC.
AGRICULTURE AND PESTICIDE DIVISION
450 SEVENTH AVENUE, SUITE 2407
NEW YORK, NEW YORK 10123
1-800-445-MSDS OR (212) 967-1100

EMERGENCY CONTACT:
JOHN S. BRANSFORD, JR. (615) 292-1180

SUBSTANCE IDENTIFICATION

CAS-NUMBER 51877-74-8
SUBSTANCE: **TRANS-PERMETHRIN**
TRADE NAMES/SYNONYMS: CYCLOPROPANECARBOXYLIC ACID, 3-(2,2-DICHLOROETHENYL)-2,2-DIMETHYL-, (3-PHENOXYPHENYL)METHYL ESTER, (1R-TRANS)-; (1R-TRANS)-3-(2,2-DICHLOROETHENYL)-2,2-DIMETHYL-CYCLOPROPANECARBOXYLIC ACID, (3-PHENOXYPHENYL)METHYL ESTER; BIOPERMETHRIN; 1R,TRANS-PERMETHRIN; PERMETHRIN; 3-(PHENOXYPHENYL)METHYL-TRANS-3-(2,2-DICHLOROETHENYL)-2,2-DIMETHYLCYCLOPROPANECARBOXYLATE; 3-(PHENOXYPHENYL)METHYL-TRANS-3-(2,2-DICHLOROVINYL)-2,2- DIMETHYLCYCLOPROPANECARBOXYLATE; C21H20CL2O3; PST23708
CHEMICAL FAMILY: PYRETHROID (SYNTHETIC)
MOLECULAR FORMULA: C21-H20-CL2-O3
MOLECULAR WEIGHT: 391.29
CERCLA RATINGS (SCALE 0-3): HEALTH=U FIRE=1 REACTIVITY=0 PERSISTENCE=2
NFPA RATINGS (SCALE 0-4): HEALTH=U FIRE=1 REACTIVITY=0

COMPONENTS AND CONTAMINANTS

COMPONENT: TRANS-PERMETHRIN ***PERCENT:*** 100.0
CAS# 51877-74-8
OTHER CONTAMINANTS: NONE
EXPOSURE LIMITS: NO OCCUPATIONAL EXPOSURE LIMITS ESTABLISHED BY OSHA, ACGIH, OR NIOSH.
PYRETHROIDS: 1 POUND CERCLA SECTION 103 REPORTABLE QUANTITY

PHYSICAL DATA

DESCRIPTION: COLORLESS OR YELLOW-BROWN TO BROWN CRYSTALLINE SOLID.
MELTING POINT: 111-117 F (44-47 C) ***SPECIFIC GRAVITY:*** 1.190-1.272
VAPOR PRESSURE: NIL ***SOLUBILITY IN WATER:*** <1 PPM
SOLVENT SOLUBILITY: SOLUBLE IN MOST ORGANIC SOLVENTS; INSOLUBLE IN ETHYLENE GLYCOL.

FIRE AND EXPLOSION DATA

FIRE AND EXPLOSION HAZARD: SLIGHT FIRE HAZARD WHEN EXPOSED TO HEAT OR FLAME.

FIREFIGHTING MEDIA: DRY CHEMICAL, CARBON DIOXIDE, HALON, WATER SPRAY OR STANDARD FOAM (1987 EMERGENCY RESPONSE GUIDEBOOK, DOT P 5800.4). FOR LARGER FIRES, USE WATER SPRAY, FOG OR STANDARD FOAM (1987 EMERGENCY RESPONSE GUIDEBOOK, DOT P 5800.4).

FIREFIGHTING: MOVE CONTAINER FROM FIRE AREA IF POSSIBLE. DO NOT SCATTER SPILLED MATERIAL WITH HIGH PRESSURE WATER STREAMS. DIKE FIRE CONTROL WATER FOR LATER DISPOSAL (1987 EMERGENCY RESPONSE GUIDEBOOK, DOT P 5800.4, GUIDE PAGE 31).
USE AGENTS SUITABLE FOR TYPE OF SURROUNDING FIRE. AVOID BREATHING HAZARDOUS VAPORS, KEEP UPWIND.

TOXICITY

TRANS-PERMETHRIN: TOXICITY DATA: 3100 MG/KG ORAL-MOUSE LD50; 7500 UG/KG SUBCUTANEOUS-FROG LD50. CARCINOGEN STATUS: NONE. ACUTE TOXICITY LEVEL: MODERATELY TOXIC BY INGESTION. TARGET EFFECTS: POISONING MAY AFFECT THE CENTRAL NERVOUS SYSTEM.*
* MAY BE BASED ON GROUP INFORMATION ON PYRETHROIDS.

HEALTH EFFECTS AND FIRST AID

INHALATION: TRANS-PERMETHRIN: SEE INFORMATION ON PYRETHROIDS.
PYRETHROIDS: **ACUTE EXPOSURE**- HEAVY EXPOSURE TO A MIST OF SOME PYRETHROIDS HAS PRODUCED HYPERSENSITIVIITY, ATAXIA, AND URINARY INCONTINENCE. CONVULSIONS MAY ALSO BE POSSIBLE. **CHRONIC EXPOSURE**- ANIMALS EXPOSED TO AEROSOLS OF SOME PYRETHROIDS FOR 3-4 HOURS/DAY FOR UP TO 4 WEEKS DID NOT EXHIBIT ANY SIGNIFICANT COMPOUND RELATED FINDINGS.

FIRST AID- REMOVE FROM EXPOSURE AREA TO FRESH AIR IMMEDIATELY. IF BREATHING HAS STOPPED, PERFORM ARTIFICIAL RESPIRATION. KEEP PERSON WARM AND AT REST. TREAT SYMPTOMATICALLY AND SUPPORTIVELY. GET MEDICAL ATTENTION IMMEDIATELY.

SKIN CONTACT: TRANS-PERMETHRIN: SEE INFORMATION ON PYRETHROIDS.
PYRETHROIDS: **ACUTE EXPOSURE**- BASED ON ANIMAL AND HUMAN STUDIES AND HUMAN EXPERIENCES WITH SOME PYRETHROIDS, PRIMARY IRRITATION IS UNLIKELY. CUTANEOUS PARESTHESIAS MAY OCCUR INCLUDING NUMBNESS, ITCHING, BURNING, TINGLING AND WARMTH WITHOUT SIGNS OF IRRITATION. THESE EFFECTS MAY BE DELAYED FOR 30 MINUTES OR MORE AND LAST LESS THAN 24 HOURS. **CHRONIC EXPOSURE**- TESTS WITH SOME PYRETHROIDS ON HUMANS AND ANIMALS INDICATE SENSITIZATION IS UNLIKELY.

FIRST AID- REMOVE CONTAMINATED CLOTHING AND SHOES IMMEDIATELY. WASH AFFECTED AREA WITH SOAP OR MILD DETERGENT AND LARGE AMOUNTS OF WATER UNTIL NO EVIDENCE OF CHEMICAL REMAINS (APPROXIMATELY 15-20 MINUTES). GET MEDICAL ATTENTION IMMEDIATELY.

EYE CONTACT: TRANS-PERMETHRIN: SEE INFORMATION ON PYRETHROIDS.
PYRETHROIDS: **ACUTE EXPOSURE**- MASSIVE INSTILLATION OF SOME PYRETHROIDS INTO RABBIT EYES PRODUCED ONLY A SLIGHT, TRANSIENT CONGESTION OF THE CONJUNCTIVA OR LACRIMATION. **CHRONIC EXPOSURE**- NO DATA AVAILABLE.

FIRST AID- WASH EYES IMMEDIATELY WITH LARGE AMOUNTS OF WATER OR NORMAL SALINE, OCCASIONALLY LIFTING UPPER AND LOWER LIDS, UNTIL NO EVIDENCE OF CHEMICAL REMAINS (APPROXIMATELY 15-20 MINUTES). GET MEDICAL ATTENTION IMMEDIATELY.

INGESTION: TRANS-PERMETHRIN: SEE INFORMATION ON PYRETHROIDS.
PYRETHROIDS: **ACUTE EXPOSURE**- SOME PYRETHROIDS HAVE PRODUCED HYPERSENSITIVITY, NERVOUS IRRITABILITY, TREMORS, ATAXIA, AND URINARY INCONTINENCE IN ANIMALS. CONVULSIONS MAY ALSO BE POSSIBLE. **CHRONIC EXPOSURE**- INCREASED KIDNEY AND LIVER WEIGHTS AND HEPATIC HISTOPATHOLOGICAL CHANGES WERE NOTED IN ANIMALS CHRONICALLY FED SOME PYRETHROIDS.

FIRST AID- REMOVE BY GASTRIC LAVAGE AND CATHARSIS. MAINTAIN BLOOD PRESSURE AND AIRWAY. GIVE OXYGEN IF RESPIRATION IS DEPRESSED. DO NOT PERFORM GASTRIC LAVAGE IF VICTIM IS UNCONSCIOUS. GET MEDICAL ATTENTION IMMEDIATELY (DREISBACH, HANDBOOK OF POISONING, 12TH ED.).
ADMINISTRATION OF LAVAGE OR OXYGEN SHOULD BE PERFORMED BY QUALIFIED MEDICAL PERSONNEL.

ANTIDOTE: NO SPECIFIC ANTIDOTE. TREAT SYMPTOMATICALLY AND SUPPORTIVELY.

REACTIVITY

REACTIVITY: STABLE UNDER NORMAL TEMPERATURES AND PRESSURES.

INCOMPATIBILITIES: TRANS-PERMETHRIN: OXIDIZERS (STRONG): FIRE AND EXPLOSION HAZARD.

DECOMPOSITION: THERMAL DECOMPOSITION PRODUCTS MAY INCLUDE TOXIC OXIDES OF CARBON.

POLYMERIZATION: HAZARDOUS POLYMERIZATION HAS NOT BEEN REPORTED TO OCCUR UNDER NORMAL TEMPERATURES AND PRESSURES.

STORAGE AND DISPOSAL

OBSERVE ALL FEDERAL, STATE AND LOCAL REGULATIONS WHEN STORING OR DISPOSING OF THIS SUBSTANCE. FOR ASSISTANCE, CONTACT THE DISTRICT DIRECTOR OF THE ENVIRONMENTAL PROTECTION AGENCY.

STORAGE

STORE IN ACCORDANCE WITH 40 CFR 165 RECOMMENDED PROCEDURES FOR THE DISPOSAL AND STORAGE OF PESTICIDES AND PESTICIDE CONTAINERS.
STORE AWAY FROM INCOMPATIBLE SUBSTANCES.

DISPOSAL

DISPOSAL MUST BE IN ACCORDANCE WITH 40 CFR 165 RECOMMENDED PROCEDURES FOR THE DISPOSAL AND STORAGE OF PESTICIDES AND PESTICIDE CONTAINERS.

CONDITIONS TO AVOID

MAY BURN BUT DOES NOT IGNITE READILY. AVOID CONTACT WITH STRONG OXIDIZERS, EXCESSIVE HEAT, SPARKS, OR OPEN FLAME.

SPILL AND LEAK PROCEDURES

OCCUPATIONAL SPILL: STOP LEAK IF YOU CAN DO IT WITHOUT RISK. FOR SMALL SPILLS, TAKE UP WITH SAND OR OTHER ABSORBENT MATERIAL AND PLACE INTO CLEAN, DRY CONTAINERS FOR LATER DISPOSAL. KEEP UNNECESSARY PEOPLE AWAY. ISOLATE HAZARD AREA AND DENY ENTRY.
REPORTABLE QUANTITY (RQ): 1 POUND THE SUPERFUND AMENDMENTS AND REAUTHORIZATION ACT (SARA) SECTION 304 REQUIRES THAT A RELEASE EQUAL TO OR GREATER THAN THE REPORTABLE QUANTITY FOR THIS SUBSTANCE BE IMMEDIATELY REPORTED TO THE LOCAL EMERGENCY PLANNING COMMITTEE AND THE STATE EMERGENCY RESPONSE COMMISSION (40 CFR 355.40). IF THE RELEASE OF THIS SUBSTANCE IS REPORTABLE UNDER CERCLA SECTION 103, THE NATIONAL RESPONSE CENTER MUST BE NOTIFIED IMMEDIATELY AT (800) 424-8802 OR (202) 426-2675 IN THE METROPOLITAN WASHINGTON, D.C. AREA (40 CFR 302.6).

PROTECTIVE EQUIPMENT

VENTILATION: PROVIDE LOCAL EXHAUST OR GENERAL DILUTION VENTILATION SYSTEM.

RESPIRATOR: THE FOLLOWING RESPIRATORS ARE RECOMMENDED BASED ON INFORMATION FOUND IN THE PHYSICAL DATA, TOXICITY AND HEALTH EFFECTS SECTIONS. THEY ARE RANKED IN ORDER FROM MINIMUM TO MAXIMUM RESPIRATORY PROTECTION. THE SPECIFIC RESPIRATOR SELECTED MUST BE BASED ON CONTAMINATION LEVELS FOUND IN THE WORK PLACE, MUST NOT EXCEED THE WORKING LIMITS OF THE RESPIRATOR AND BE JOINTLY APPROVED BY THE NATIONAL INSTITUTE FOR OCCUPATIONAL SAFETY AND HEALTH AND THE MINE SAFETY AND HEALTH ADMINISTRATION (NIOSH-MSHA).
CHEMICAL CARTRIDGE RESPIRATOR WITH AN ORGANIC VAPOR CARTRIDGE(S) WITH A FULL FACEPIECE AND ORGANIC VAPOR CARTRIDGE(S) IN COMBINATION WITH A DUST AND MIST FILTER.
POWERED AIR-PURIFYING RESPIRATOR WITH A TIGHT-FITTING FACEPIECE AND ORGANIC VAPOR CARTRIDGE(S) IN COMBINATION WITH A HIGH-EFFICIENCY PARTICULATE FILTER.
TYPE 'C' SUPPLIED-AIR RESPIRATOR WITH A FULL FACEPIECE OPERATED IN A PRESSURE-DEMAND OR OTHER POSITIVE PRESSURE MODE.
SELF-CONTAINED BREATHING APPARATUS WITH A FULL FACEPIECE OPERATED IN PRESSURE-DEMAND OR OTHER POSITIVE PRESSURE MODE.
FOR FIREFIGHTING AND OTHER IMMEDIATELY DANGEROUS TO LIFE OR HEALTH CONDITIONS:
SELF-CONTAINED BREATHING APPARATUS WITH FULL FACEPIECE OPERATED IN PRESSURE-DEMAND OR OTHER POSITIVE PRESSURE MODE.
SUPPLIED-AIR RESPIRATOR WITH FULL FACEPIECE AND OPERATED IN PRESSURE-DEMAND OR OTHER POSITIVE PRESSURE MODE IN COMBINATION WITH AN AUXILIARY SELF-CONTAINED BREATHING APPARATUS OPERATED IN PRESSURE-DEMAND OR OTHER POSITIVE PRESSURE MODE.

CLOTHING: EMPLOYEE MUST WEAR APPROPRIATE PROTECTIVE (IMPERVIOUS) CLOTHING AND EQUIPMENT TO PREVENT REPEATED OR PROLONGED SKIN CONTACT WITH THIS SUBSTANCE.

GLOVES: EMPLOYEE MUST WEAR APPROPRIATE PROTECTIVE GLOVES TO PREVENT CONTACT WITH THIS SUBSTANCE.

EYE PROTECTION: EMPLOYEE MUST WEAR SPLASH-PROOF OR DUST-RESISTANT SAFETY GOGGLES TO PREVENT EYE CONTACT WITH THIS SUBSTANCE.
EMERGENCY EYE WASH: WHERE THERE IS ANY POSSIBILITY THAT AN EMPLOYEE'S EYES MAY BE EXPOSED TO THIS SUBSTANCE, THE EMPLOYER SHOULD PROVIDE AN EYE WASH FOUNTAIN WITHIN THE IMMEDIATE WORK AREA FOR EMERGENCY USE.

AUTHORIZED BY- OCCUPATIONAL HEALTH SERVICES, INC.
CREATION DATE: 10/05/89 ***REVISION DATE:*** 05/14/90

MATERIAL SAFETY DATA SHEET

OCCUPATIONAL HEALTH SERVICES, INC.
AGRICULTURE AND PESTICIDE DIVISION
450 SEVENTH AVENUE, SUITE 2407
NEW YORK, NEW YORK 10123
1-800-445-MSDS OR (212) 967-1100

EMERGENCY CONTACT:
JOHN S. BRANSFORD, JR. (615) 292-1180

SUBSTANCE IDENTIFICATION

CAS-NUMBER 52-68-6
SUBSTANCE: **TRICHLORFON**
TRADE NAMES/SYNONYMS: PHOSPHONIC ACID, (2,2,2-TRICHLORO-1-HYDROXYETHYL)-, DIMETHYL ESTER; 2,2,2-TRICHLORO-1-HYDROXYETHYL)-PHOSPHONIC ACID DIMETHYL ESTER; DIMETHYL 2,2,2-TRICHLORO-1-HYDROXYETHYLPHOSPHONATE; DIMETHYL (2,2,2-TRICHLORO-1-HYDROXYETHYL)PHOSPHONATE; O,O-DIMETHYL(2,2,2-TRICHLORO-1-HYDROXYETHYL)PHOSPHONATE; O,O-DIMETHYL 2,2,2-TRICHLORO-1-HYDROXYETHYLPHOSPHONATE; O,O-DIMETHYL-1-HYDROXY-2,2,2-TRICHLOROETHYLPHOSPHONATE; METRIFONATE; METRIPHONATE; ANTHON; DIPTEREX; DYLOX; DYREX; FOSCHLOR; NEGUVON; TRICHLORPHON; STCC 4940377; NCI-C54831; ENT 19,763; PST23790
CHEMICAL FAMILY: ORGANOPHOSPHATE
HALOGEN
MOLECULAR FORMULA: C4-H8-CL3-O4-P
MOLECULAR WEIGHT: 257.44
CERCLA RATINGS (SCALE 0-3): HEALTH=3 FIRE=0 REACTIVITY=0
PERSISTENCE=2
NFPA RATINGS (SCALE 0-4): HEALTH=4 FIRE=0 REACTIVITY=0

COMPONENTS AND CONTAMINANTS

COMPONENT: TRICHLORFON ***PERCENT:*** 100.00
CAS# 52-68-6
EXPOSURE LIMITS: NO OCCUPATIONAL EXPOSURE LIMITS ESTABLISHED BY OSHA, ACGIH, OR NIOSH.

PHYSICAL DATA

DESCRIPTION: WHITE CRYSTALLINE POWDER WITH ETHYL ETHER ODOR
BOILING POINT: 212 F (100 C) @ 0.1 MMHG ***MELTING POINT:*** 181-183 F (83-84 C)
SPECIFIC GRAVITY: 1.73 ***VAPOR PRESSURE:*** .0000078 @ 20 C
SOLUBILITY IN WATER: 15.4 GM/100 ML
SOLVENT SOLUBILITY: SOLUBLE IN ALCOHOLS, KETONES, CHLOROFORM, ETHER, BENZENE, MOST CHLORINATED HYDROCARBONS; SLIGHTLY SOLUBLE IN HEXANE, PENTANE, CARBON TETRACHLORIDE, DIETHYL ETHER, PETROLEUM ETHER

FIRE AND EXPLOSION DATA

FIRE AND EXPLOSION HAZARD: NEGLIGIBLE FIRE HAZARD WHEN EXPOSED TO HEAT OR FLAME.
FIREFIGHTING MEDIA: DRY CHEMICAL, CARBON DIOXIDE, HALON, WATER SPRAY OR STANDARD FOAM (1987 EMERGENCY RESPONSE GUIDEBOOK, DOT P 5800.4). FOR LARGER FIRES, USE WATER SPRAY, FOG OR STANDARD FOAM (1987 EMERGENCY RESPONSE GUIDEBOOK, DOT P 5800.4).
FIREFIGHTING: MOVE CONTAINERS FROM FIRE AREA IF POSSIBLE. FIGHT FIRE FROM MAXIMUM DISTANCE. STAY AWAY FROM STORAGE TANK ENDS. DIKE FIRE CONTROL WATER FOR LATER DISPOSAL. DO NOT SCATTER MATERIAL (1987 EMERGENCY RESPONSE GUIDEBOOK, DOT P 5800.4, GUIDE PAGE 55). EXTINGUISH ONLY IF FLOW CAN BE STOPPED; USE FLOODING AMOUNTS OF WATER AS FOG, SOLID STREAMS MAY BE INEFFECTIVE. COOL CONTAINERS WITH FLOODING AMOUNTS OF WATER FROM AS FAR A DISTANCE AS POSSIBLE. USE WATER SPRAY TO ABSORB TOXIC VAPORS. AVOID BREATHING TOXIC VAPORS; KEEP UPWIND. CONSIDER EVACUATION OF DOWNWIND AREA IF MATERIAL IS LEAKING.

TRANSPORTATION DATA

DEPARTMENT OF TRANSPORTATION HAZARD CLASSIFICATION 49 CFR 172.101: ORM-A
DEPARTMENT OF TRANSPORTATION LABELING REQUIREMENTS 49 CFR 172.101 AND SUBPART E: NONE
DEPARTMENT OF TRANSPORTATION PACKAGING REQUIREMENTS: 49 CFR 173.510 EXCEPTIONS: 49 CFR 173.505

TOXICITY

TRICHLORFON: IRRITATION DATA: 120 MG/6 DAYS INTERMITTENT EYE-RABBIT MILD. TOXICITY DATA: 1710 UG/M3/90 DAYS INTERMITTENT INHALATION-HUMAN TCLO; 1300 MG/M3 INHALATION-RAT LC50; 1500 MG/KG SKIN-RABBIT LD50; 2000 MG/KG SKIN-RAT LD50; 250 MG/KG ORAL-RAT LD50; 300 MG/KG ORAL-MOUSE LD50; 160 MG/KG ORAL-RABBIT LD50; 97 MG/KG ORAL-CAT LD50; 400 MG/KG ORAL-DOG LD50; 420 MG/KG ORAL-GUINEA PIG LDLO; 400 MG/KG SUBCUTANEOUS-RAT LD50; 267 MG/KG SUBCUTANEOUS-MOUSE LD50; 269 MG/KG SUBCUTANEOUS-DOG LD50; 150 MG/KG INTRAVENOUS-DOG LD50; 290 MG/KG INTRAVENOUS-MOUSE LD50; 160 MG/KG INTRAPERITONEAL-RAT LD50; 60 MG/KG INTRAPERITONEAL-RABBIT LD50; 196 MG/KG INTRAPERITONEAL-MOUSE LD50; 300 MG/KG INTRAPERITONEAL-GUINEA PIG LD50; 395 MG/KG INTRAMUSCULAR-RAT LD50; MUTAGENIC DATA (RTECS); REPRODUCTIVE EFFECTS DATA (RTECS); TUMORIGENIC DATA (RTECS). CARCINOGEN STATUS: ANIMAL INADEQUATE EVIDENCE (IARC GROUP-3). ACUTE TOXICITY LEVEL: HIGHLY TOXIC BY INHALATION; TOXIC BY INGESTION; MODERATELY TOXIC BY DERMAL ABSORPTION. TARGET EFFECTS: CHOLINESTERASE INHIBITOR; NEUROTOXIN. AT INCREASED RISK FROM EXPOSURE: PERSONS WITH RESPIRATORY AILMENTS, RECENT EXPOSURE TO CHOLINESTERASE INHIBITORS OR IMPAIRED CHOLINESTERASE PRODUCTION, OR LIVER MALFUNCTION.* ADDITIONAL DATA: TRICHLORFON POTENTIATES THE TOXICITY OF MALATION, EPN, AND AZINPHOS-METHYL. MAY CROSS THE PLACENTA. HIGH ENVIRONMENTAL TEMPERATURES OR EXPOSURE OF THE CHEMICAL TO VISIBLE OR ULTRAVIOLET LIGHT MAY ENHANCE THE TOXICITY. INTERACTIONS WITH MEDICATIONS MAY OCCUR.*
* MAY BE BASED ON GENERAL INFORMATION ON ORGANOPHOSPHATES.

HEALTH EFFECTS AND FIRST AID

INHALATION: TRICHLORFON: HIGHLY TOXIC. SEE INFORMATION ON ORGANOPHOSPHATES.
ORGANOPHOSPHATES: CHOLINESTERASE INHIBITOR. **ACUTE EXPOSURE-** WHEN INHALED, THE FIRST EFFECTS OF CHOLINESTERASE INHIBITORS ARE USUALLY RESPIRATORY AND MAY INCLUDE NASAL HYPEREMIA AND WATERY DISCHARGE, COUGH, CHEST DISCOMFORT, DYSPNEA, AND WHEEZING DUE TO INCREASED BRONCHIAL SECRETIONS AND BRONCHOCONSTRICTION. IF SUFFICIENT AMOUNTS ARE ABSORBED, OTHER SYSTEMIC EFFECTS MAY BEGIN WITHIN A FEW MINUTES OR BE DELAYED FOR UP TO 12 HOURS. SYMPTOMS MAY INCLUDE PALLOR, NAUSEA, VOMITING, DIARRHEA, ABDOMINAL CRAMPS, HEADACHE, DIZZINESS, OCULAR PAIN, BLURRED VISION, MIOSIS OR IN SOME CASES, ESPECIALLY INITIALLY, MYDRIASIS, LACRIMATION, SALIVATION, SWEATING, AND CONFUSION. OTHER REPORTED CENTRAL NERVOUS SYSTEM OR NEUROMUSCULAR EFFECTS MAY INCLUDE ATAXIA, SLURRED SPEECH, AREFLEXIA, WEAKNESS, FATIGUE, FASCICULATIONS, TWITCHING, TREMORS POSSIBLY OF THE TONGUE AND EYELIDS, AND EVENTUALLY PARALYSIS OF THE EXTREMITIES AND POSSIBLY OF THE RESPIRATORY MUSCLES. IN SEVERE CASES THERE MAY ALSO BE INVOLUNTARY DEFECATION AND URINATION, CYANOSIS, PSYCHOSIS, HYPERGLYCEMIA, ACUTE PANCREATITIS, CARDIAC IRREGULARITIES, PULMONARY EDEMA, UNCONSCIOUSNESS, CONVULSIONS, AND COMA. DEATH IS PRIMARILY DUE TO RESPIRATORY FAILURE, ALTHOUGH CARDIOVASCULAR EFFECTS INCLUDING CARDIAC ARREST MAY ALSO BE IMPLICATED. LONG TERM SEQUELAE ARE RARE BUT MAY INCLUDE NEUROPSYCHIATRIC DISORDERS AND MYOPATHY WITH MUSCLE TENDERNESS. SOME ORGANOPHOSPHATES MAY CAUSE A DELAYED NEUROPATHY BEGINNING 1-4 WEEKS AFTER AN ACUTE EXPOSURE WHICH MAY OR MAY NOT HAVE CAUSED ACUTE CHOLINERGIC EFFECTS. NUMBNESS, TINGLING, WEAKNESS AND CRAMPING BEGINNING SYMMETRICALLY IN THE LOWER LIMBS MAY PROGRESS TO ATAXIA AND PARALYSIS. IN SEVERE CASES, UPPER LIMB INVOLVEMENT IS POSSIBLE AND FLACCID PARALYSIS MAY PROGRESS TO SPASTIC PARALYSIS WITH EXAGGERATED REFLEXES. IMPROVEMENT MAY OCCUR OVER MONTHS TO YEARS, BUT SOME RESIDUAL IMPAIRMENT USUALLY REMAINS.
CHRONIC EXPOSURE- REPEATED OR PROLONGED EXPOSURE MAY RESULT IN THE EFFECTS OF ACUTE EXPOSURE INCLUDING THE DELAYED NEUROPATHY. OTHER EFFECTS REPORTED IN WORKERS REPEATEDLY EXPOSED INCLUDE IMPAIRED MEMORY AND CONCENTRATION, ACUTE PSYCHOSIS, SEVERE DEPRESSIONS, IRRITABILTY, CONFUSION, APATHY, EMOTIONAL LABILITY, SOCIAL WITHDRAWAL, CONFUSION, HEADACHE, SPEECH DIFFICULTIES, DELAYED REACTION TIMES, SPATIAL DISORIENTATION, NIGHTMARES, SLEEPWALKING, AND DROWSINESS OR INSOMNIA. AN INFLUENZA-LIKE CONDITION WITH HEADACHE, NAUSEA, WEAKNESS, ANOREXIA AND MALAISE HAS ALSO BEEN REPORTED.
FIRST AID- REMOVE FROM EXPOSURE AREA TO FRESH AIR IMMEDIATELY. IF BREATHING HAS STOPPED, GIVE ARTIFICIAL RESPIRATION. MAINTAIN AIRWAY AND BLOOD PRESSURE AND ADMINISTER OXYGEN IF AVAILABLE. KEEP AFFECTED PERSON WARM AND AT REST. TREAT SYMPTOMATICALLY AND SUPPORTIVELY. ADMINISTRATION OF OXYGEN SHOULD BE PERFORMED BY QUALIFIED PERSONNEL. GET MEDICAL ATTENTION IMMEDIATELY.

SKIN CONTACT: TRICHLORFON: SEE INFORMATION ON ORGANOPHOSPHATES. ORGANOPHOSPHATES: CHOLINESTERASE INHIBITOR. **ACUTE EXPOSURE-** LOCALIZED SWEATING AND FASCICULATIONS MAY OCCUR AT THE SITE OF CONTACT. IF SUFFICIENT AMOUNTS ARE ABSORBED, OTHER EFFECTS OF CHOLINESTERASE INHIBITION AS DESCRIBED IN ACUTE INHALATION MAY OCCUR. SYMPTOMS MAY BE DELAYED 2-3 HOURS, BUT USUALLY NO MORE THAN 12 HOURS. THE RATE OF ABSORPTION IS INCREASED BY THE PRESENCE OF DERMATITIS OR HIGH AMBIENT TEMPERATURES. DELAYED NEUROPATHY IS ALSO POSSIBLE. **CHRONIC EXPOSURE-** REPEATED OR PROLONGED EXPOSURE MAY CAUSE EFFECTS AS DESCRIBED IN ACUTE EXPOSURE. SOME ORGANOPHOSPHATES MAY CAUSE SENSITIZATION.

FIRST AID- REMOVE CONTAMINATED CLOTHING IMMEDIATELY. WASH CONTAMINATED AREAS WITH SOAP AND WATER FOLLOWED BY ALCOHOL (ARENA, POISONING, 4TH ED.). EMERGENCY PERSONNEL SHOULD WEAR GLOVES AND AVOID CONTAMINATION. TREAT RESPIRATORY DIFFICULTY WITH ARTIFICIAL RESPIRATION. GET MEDICAL ATTENTION IMMEDIATELY.

EYE CONTACT: TRICHLORFON: SEE INFORMATION ON ORGANOPHOSPHATES. ORGANOPHOSPHATES: CHOLINESTERASE INHIBITOR. **ACUTE EXPOSURE-** DIRECT CONTACT MAY CAUSE PAIN, HYPEREMIA, LACRIMATION, TWITCHING OF THE EYELIDS, MIOSIS, AND CILIARY MUSCLE SPASM WITH LOSS OF ACCOMODATION, BLURRED OR DIMMED VISION AND BROWACHE. SOMETIMES MYDRIASIS MAY OCCUR INSTEAD OF MIOSIS. WITH SUFFICIENT EXPOSURE, OTHER SYMPTOMS OF CHOLINESTERASE INHIBITION AS DESCRIBED IN ACUTE INHALATION MAY OCCUR. **CHRONIC EXPOSURE-** REPEATED OR PROLONGED EXPOSURE MAY CAUSE EFFECTS AS DESCRIBED IN ACUTE EXPOSURE. SOME COMPOUNDS HAVE CAUSED TOXIC EFFECTS ON THE CRYSTALLINE LENS, CONJUNCTIVAL THICKENING AND OBSTRUCTION OF THE NASOLACRIMAL CANALS WHEN USED AS MIOTIC EYEDROPS.

FIRST AID- IRRIGATE EYES WITH WATER OR SALINE SOLUTION. IF SYMPTOMS OF POISONING OCCUR, TREAT RESPIRATORY DIFFICULTY WITH ARTIFICIAL RESPIRATION AND OXYGEN. OBSERVE PATIENT FOR AT LEAST 24-36 HOURS (GOSSELIN, CLINICAL TOXICOLOGY OF COMMERCIAL PRODUCTS, 5TH ED.). GET MEDICAL ATTENTION IMMEDIATELY. OXYGEN SHOULD BE ADMINISTERED BY QUALIFIED MEDICAL PERSONNEL.

INGESTION: TRICHLORFON: NEUROTOXIN/TOXIC. COMPLICATIONS OF DELAYED POLYNEUROPATHY HAVE OCCURRED AFTER SOME CASES OF ACUTE POISONING FROM TRICHLORFON. 80 MG/KG FED TO RATS ON DAY 13 OF PREGNANCY PRODUCED A DECREASED NUMBER OF LIVE FETUSES AND AN INCREASED NUMBER OF EMBRYONIC DEATHS AND FETAL ABNORMALITIES. CHRONIC INGESTION BY PREGNANT MICE, RATS AND HAMSTERS RESULTED IN FETAL DEVELOPMENTAL ABNORMALITIES AND ADVERSE EFFECTS ON THE FETUS. SEE INFORMATION ON ORGANOPHOSPHATES.

ORGANOPHOSPHATES: CHOLINESTERASE INHIBITOR. **ACUTE EXPOSURE-** WHEN INGESTED, THE FIRST EFFECTS MAY BE NAUSEA, VOMITING, ANOREXIA, ABDOMINAL CRAMPS AND DIARRHEA. GASTROINTESTINAL ABSORPTION MAY CAUSE SYMPTOMS OF CHOLINESTERASE INHIBITION AS DESCRIBED IN ACUTE INHALATION. SYMPTOMS MAY BEGIN WITHIN MINUTES OR BE DELAYED FOR HOURS. DELAYED EFFECTS INCLUDING NEUROPATHY MAY ALSO OCCUR. **CHRONIC EXPOSURE-** REPEATED INGESTION MAY CAUSE EFFECTS AS DESCRIBED IN ACUTE EXPOSURE.

FIRST AID- IF PERSON IS ALERT AND RESPIRATION IS NOT DEPRESSED, GIVE SYRUP OF IPECAC FOLLOWED BY WATER (IF VOMITING OCCURS, KEEP HEAD BELOW HIPS TO PREVENT ASPIRATION). IF CONSCIOUSNESS LEVEL DECLINES OR VOMITING HAS NOT OCCURRED IN 15 MINUTES EMPTY STOMACH BY GASTRIC LAVAGE WITH THE AID OF CUFFED ENDOTRACHEAL TUBE USING ISOTONIC SALINE OR 5% SODIUM BICARBONATE FOLLOW WITH ACTIVATED CHARCOAL. ESTABLISH AND MAINTAIN AIRWAY. TREAT RESPIRATORY DIFFICULTY WITH ARTIFICIAL RESPIRATION AND OXYGEN. DO NOT GIVE MORPHINE, AMINOPHYLLINE, PHENOTHIAZINES, RESERPINE, FUROSEMIDE, OR ETHACRYNIC ACID (MORGAN, RECOGNITION AND MANAGEMENT OF PESTICIDE POISONINGS, 3RD ED.). TREAT SYMPTOMATICALLY AND SUPPORTIVELY. ADMINISTRATION OF OXYGEN AND LAVAGE MUST BE PERFORMED BY QUALIFIED MEDICAL PERSONNEL. GET MEDICAL ATTENTION IMMEDIATELY.

ANTIDOTE: THE FOLLOWING ANTIDOTE(S) HAVE BEEN RECOMMENDED. HOWEVER, THE DECISION AS TO WHETHER THE SEVERITY OF POISONING REQUIRES ADMINISTRATION OF ANY ANTIDOTE AND ACTUAL DOSE REQUIRED SHOULD BE MADE BY QUALIFIED MEDICAL PERSONNEL.

FOR CHOLINESTERASE INHIBITORS: ESTABLISH CLEAR AIRWAY AND TISSUE OXYGENATION BY ASPIRATION OF SECRETIONS, AND IF NECESSARY, BY ASSISTED PULMONARY VENTILATION WITH OXYGEN. IMPROVE TISSUE OXYGENATION AS MUCH AS POSSIBLE BEFORE ADMINISTERING ATROPINE TO MINIMIZE THE RISK OF VENTRICULAR FIBRILLATION. ADMINISTER ATROPINE SULFATE INTRAVENOUSLY, OR INTRAMUSCULARLY IF IV INJECTION IS NOT POSSIBLE. IN MODERATELY SEVERE POISONING ADMINISTER ATROPINE SULFATE, 0.4-2.0 MG REPEATED EVERY 15 MINUTES UNTIL ATROPINIZATION IS ACHIEVED (TACHYCARDIA, FLUSHING, DRY MOUTH, MYDRIASIS). MAINTAIN ATROPINIZATION BY REPEATED DOSES FOR 2-12 HOURS, OR LONGER, DEPENDING ON THE SEVERITY OF POISONING. THE APPEARANCE OF RALES IN THE LUNG BASES, MIOSIS, SALIVATION, NAUSEA, BRADYCARDIA, ARE ALL INDICATIONS OF INADEQUATE ATROPINIZATION. SEVERELY POISONED INDIVIDUALS MAY EXHIBIT REMARKABLE TOLERANCE TO ATROPINE; TWO OR MORE TIMES THE DOSAGES SUGGESTED ABOVE MAY BE NEEDED. PERSONS NOT POISONED OR ONLY SLIGHTLY POISONED, HOWEVER, MAY DEVELOP SIGNS OF ATROPINE TOXICITY FROM SUCH LARGE DOSAGES: FEVER, MUSCLE FIBRILLATIONS, AND DELIRIUM ARE THE MAIN SIGNS OF ATROPINE TOXICITY. IF THESE SIGNS APPEAR WHILE THE PATIENT IS FULLY ATROPINIZED, ATROPINE ADMINISTRATION SHOULD BE DISCONTINUED, AT LEAST TEMPORARILY. OBSERVE TREATED PATIENTS CLOSELY AT LEAST 24 HOURS TO INSURE THAT SYMPTOMS (POSSIBLY PULMONARY EDEMA) DO NOT RECUR AS ATROPINIZATION WEARS OFF. IN VERY SEVERE POISONINGS, METABOLIC DISPOSITION OF TOXICANT MAY REQUIRE SEVERAL HOURS OR DAYS DURING WHICH ATROPINIZATION MUST BE MAINTAINED. MARKEDLY LOWER LEVELS OF URINARY METABOLITES INDICATE THAT ATROPINE DOSAGE CAN BE TAPERED OFF. AS DOSAGE IS REDUCED, CHECK THE LUNG BASES FREQUENTLY FOR RALES. IF RALES ARE HEARD OR OTHER SYMPTOMS RETURN, RE-ESTABLISH ATROPINIZATION PROMPTLY (MORGAN, RECOGNITION AND MANAGEMENT OF PESTICIDE POISONINGS, 3RD ED.). ADMINISTRATION OF ANTIDOTE MUST BE PERFORMED BY QUALIFIED MEDICAL PERSONNEL.

IN CASES OF SEVERE POISONING BY ORGANOPHOSPHATE PESTICIDES IN WHICH RESPIRATORY DEPRESSION, MUSCLE WEAKNESS AND TWITCHINGS ARE SEVERE, GIVE PRALIDOXIME (PROTOPAM-AYERST, 2-PAM), 1.0 GRAM INTRAVENOUSLY AT NO MORE THAN 0.5 GRAM PER MINUTE. DOSAGE OF PRALIDOXIME MAY BE REPEATED IN 1-2 HOURS, THEN AT 10-12 HOUR INTERVALS IF NEEDED. IN VERY SEVERE POISONINGS, DOSAGE RATES MAY BE DOUBLED. TREATMENT WITH PRALIDOXIME WILL BE MOST EFFECTIVE IF GIVEN WITHIN THIRTY-SIX HOURS AFTER POISONING (MORGAN, RECOGNITION AND MANAGEMENT OF PESTICIDE POISONINGS, 3RD ED.). ANTIDOTE SHOULD BE ADMINISTERED BY QUALIFIED MEDICAL PERSONNEL.

REACTIVITY

REACTIVITY: STABLE AT NORMAL TEMPERATURES AND PRESSURES BUT DECOMPOSES AT HIGHER TEMPERATURES.

INCOMPATIBILITIES: TRICHLORFON: ACIDS: DECOMPOSE TO FORM DICHLORVOS. ALKALI: DECOMPOSE. STRONG OXIDIZING AGENTS: INCOMPATIBLE.

DECOMPOSITION: THERMAL DECOMPOSITION MAY PRODUCE DICHLORVOS, HYDROGEN CHLORIDE, AND OXIDES OF PHOSPHORUS.

POLYMERIZATION: HAZARDOUS POLYMERIZATION HAS NOT BEEN REPORTED TO OCCUR UNDER NORMAL TEMPERATURES AND PRESSURES.

STORAGE AND DISPOSAL

OBSERVE ALL FEDERAL, STATE AND LOCAL REGULATIONS WHEN STORING OR DISPOSING OF THIS SUBSTANCE. FOR ASSISTANCE, CONTACT THE DISTRICT DIRECTOR OF THE ENVIRONMENTAL PROTECTION AGENCY.

STORAGE

STORE IN ACCORDANCE WITH 40 CFR 165 RECOMMENDED PROCEDURES FOR THE DISPOSAL AND STORAGE OF PESTICIDES AND PESTICIDE CONTAINERS.

STORE AWAY FROM INCOMPATIBLE SUBSTANCES.

THRESHOLD PLANNING QUANTITY (TPQ): THE SUPERFUND AMENDMENTS AND REAUTHORIZATION ACT (SARA) SECTION 302 REQUIRES THAT EACH FACILITY WHERE ANY EXTREMELY HAZARDOUS SUBSTANCE IS PRESENT IN A QUANTITY EQUAL TO OR GREATER THAN THE TPQ ESTABLISHED FOR THAT SUBSTANCE NOTIFY THE STATE EMERGENCY RESPONSE COMMISSION FOR THE STATE IN WHICH IT IS LOCATED. SECTION 303 OF SARA REQUIRES THESE FACILITIES TO PARTICIPATE IN LOCAL EMERGENCY RESPONSE PLANNING (40 CFR 355.30).

DISPOSAL

DISPOSAL MUST BE IN ACCORDANCE WITH 40 CFR 165 RECOMMENDED PROCEDURES FOR THE DISPOSAL AND STORAGE OF PESTICIDES AND PESTICIDE CONTAINERS.

CONDITIONS TO AVOID

NONE REPORTED.

SPILL AND LEAK PROCEDURES

SOIL SPILL: DIG A PIT, POND, OR LAGOON TO HOLD MATERIAL. COVER WITH OIL. DIKE FLOW OF SPILLED MATERIAL USING SOIL OR SANDBAGS OR FOAMED BARRIERS SUCH AS POLYURETHANE OR CONCRETE.

ABSORB BULK LIQUID WITH FLY ASH, CEMENT POWDER, SAWDUST, OR COMMERCIAL SORBENTS.

IMMOBILIZE SPILL WITH UNIVERSAL GELLING AGENT.

WATER SPILL: IF DISSOLVED, AT A CONCENTRATION OF 10 PPM OR GREATER, APPLY ACTIVATED CARBON AT TEN TIMES THE AMOUNT THAT HAS BEEN SPILLED.

USE MECHANICAL DREDGES OR LIFTS TO EXTRACT IMMOBILIZED MASSES OF POLLUTION AND PRECIPITATES.

OCCUPATIONAL SPILL: DO NOT TOUCH SPILLED MATERIAL. STOP LEAK IF YOU CAN DO IT WITHOUT RISK. USE WATER SPRAY TO REDUCE VAPORS. FOR SMALL SPILLS, TAKE UP WITH SAND OR OTHER ABSORBENT MATERIAL AND PLACE INTO CONTAINERS FOR LATER DISPOSAL. FOR SMALL DRY SPILLS, WITH A CLEAN SHOVEL PLACE MATERIAL INTO CLEAN, DRY CONTAINERS AND COVER. MOVE CONTAINERS FROM SPILL AREA. FOR LARGER SPILLS, DIKE FAR AHEAD OF SPILL FOR LATER DISPOSAL. KEEP UNNECESSARY PEOPLE AWAY. ISOLATE HAZARD AREA AND DENY ENTRY. VENTILATE CLOSED SPACES BEFORE ENTERING.

PROTECTIVE EQUIPMENT

VENTILATION: PROCESS ENCLOSURE RECOMMENDED.

RESPIRATOR: THE FOLLOWING RESPIRATORS ARE RECOMMENDED BASED ON INFORMATION FOUND IN THE PHYSICAL DATA, TOXICITY AND HEALTH EFFECTS SECTIONS. THEY ARE RANKED IN ORDER FROM MINIMUM TO MAXIMUM RESPIRATORY PROTECTION. THE SPECIFIC RESPIRATOR SELECTED MUST BE BASED ON CONTAMINATION LEVELS FOUND IN THE WORK PLACE, MUST NOT EXCEED THE WORKING LIMITS OF THE RESPIRATOR AND BE JOINTLY APPROVED BY THE NATIONAL INSTITUTE FOR OCCUPATIONAL SAFETY AND HEALTH AND THE MINE SAFETY AND HEALTH ADMINISTRATION (NIOSH-MSHA).

TYPE 'C' SUPPLIED-AIR RESPIRATOR WITH A FULL FACEPIECE OPERATED IN PRESSURE-DEMAND OR OTHER POSITIVE PRESSURE MODE OR WITH A FULL FACEPIECE, HELMET OR HOOD OPERATED IN CONTINOUS-FLOW MODE.

SELF-CONTAINED BREATHING APPARATUS WITH A FULL FACEPIECE OPERATED IN PRESSURE-DEMAND OR OTHER POSITIVE PRESSURE MODE.

FOR FIREFIGHTING AND OTHER IMMEDIATELY DANGEROUS TO LIFE OR HEALTH CONDITIONS:

SELF-CONTAINED BREATHING APPARATUS WITH FULL FACEPIECE OPERATED IN PRESSURE-DEMAND OR OTHER POSITIVE PRESSURE MODE.

SUPPLIED-AIR RESPIRATOR WITH FULL FACEPIECE AND OPERATED IN PRESSURE-DEMAND OR OTHER POSITIVE PRESSURE MODE IN COMBINATION WITH AN AUXILIARY SELF-CONTAINED BREATHING APPARATUS OPERATED IN PRESSURE-DEMAND OR OTHER POSITIVE PRESSURE MODE.

CLOTHING: EMPLOYEE MUST WEAR APPROPRIATE PROTECTIVE (IMPERVIOUS) CLOTHING AND EQUIPMENT TO PREVENT ANY POSSIBILITY OF SKIN CONTACT WITH THIS SUBSTANCE.

GLOVES: EMPLOYEE MUST WEAR APPROPRIATE PROTECTIVE GLOVES TO PREVENT CONTACT WITH THIS SUBSTANCE.

EYE PROTECTION: EMPLOYEE MUST WEAR SPLASH-PROOF OR DUST-RESISTANT SAFETY GOGGLES AND A FACESHIELD TO PREVENT CONTACT WITH THIS SUBSTANCE.

EMERGENCY WASH FACILITIES: WHERE THERE IS ANY POSSIBILITY THAT AN EMPLOYEE'S EYES AND/OR SKIN MAY BE EXPOSED TO THIS SUBSTANCE, THE EMPLOYER SHOULD PROVIDE AN EYE WASH FOUNTAIN AND QUICK DRENCH SHOWER WITHIN THE IMMEDIATE WORK AREA FOR EMERGENCY USE.

AUTHORIZED BY- OCCUPATIONAL HEALTH SERVICES, INC.

CREATION DATE: 10/05/89 ***REVISION DATE:*** 07/12/90

MATERIAL SAFETY DATA SHEET

OCCUPATIONAL HEALTH SERVICES, INC.
AGRICULTURE AND PESTICIDE DIVISION
450 SEVENTH AVENUE, SUITE 2407
NEW YORK, NEW YORK 10123
1-800-445-MSDS OR (212) 967-1100

EMERGENCY CONTACT:
JOHN S. BRANSFORD, JR. (615) 292-1180

SUBSTANCE IDENTIFICATION

CAS-NUMBER 76-03-9

SUBSTANCE: TRICHLOROACETIC ACID, SOLID

TRADE NAMES/SYNONYMS: ACETO-CAUSTIN; TRICHLOROETHANOIC ACID; AMCHEM; TCA; ACETIC ACID, TRICHLORO-; TRICHLORACETIC ACID; STCC 4931470; UN 1839; C2HCL3O2; PST23810

CHEMICAL FAMILY: CARBOXYLIC ACID, ALIPHATIC HALOGEN

MOLECULAR FORMULA: CL3-C-C-O2-H

MOLECULAR WEIGHT: 163.39

CERCLA RATINGS (SCALE 0-3): HEALTH=2 FIRE=0 REACTIVITY=0 PERSISTENCE=1

NFPA RATINGS (SCALE 0-4): HEALTH=U FIRE=0 REACTIVITY=0

COMPONENTS AND CONTAMINANTS

COMPONENT: TRICHLOROACETIC ACID ***PERCENT:*** 100.0
CAS# 76-03-9

OTHER CONTAMINANTS: NONE

EXPOSURE LIMITS: TRICHLOROACETIC ACID: 1 PPM (7 MG/M3) OSHA TWA 1 PPM (7 MG/M3) ACGIH TWA

PHYSICAL DATA

DESCRIPTION: COLORLESS, DELIQUESCENT CRYSTALS WITH A SHARP, PUNGENT ODOR.

BOILING POINT: 388 F (198 C) ***MELTING POINT:*** 136 F (58 C)

SPECIFIC GRAVITY: 1.62 @ 25 C ***VOLATILITY:*** 100%

VAPOR PRESSURE: 1.3 MMHG @ 51 C ***PH:*** 1.2 @ 0.1 M SOLUTION

SOLUBILITY IN WATER: 120% ***VAPOR DENSITY:*** 5.6

SOLVENT SOLUBILITY: SOLUBLE IN ALCOHOL, ETHER.

FIRE AND EXPLOSION DATA

FIRE AND EXPLOSION HAZARD: NEGLIGIBLE FIRE HAZARD WHEN EXPOSED TO HEAT OR FLAME.

FIREFIGHTING MEDIA: DRY CHEMICAL, CARBON DIOXIDE, HALON, WATER SPRAY OR ALCOHOL FOAM (1987 EMERGENCY RESPONSE GUIDEBOOK, DOT P 5800.4).

FOR LARGER FIRES, USE WATER SPRAY, FOG OR STANDARD FOAM (1987 EMERGENCY RESPONSE GUIDEBOOK, DOT P 5800.4).

FIREFIGHTING: MOVE CONTAINERS FROM FIRE AREA IF POSSIBLE. COOL CONTAINERS EXPOSED TO FLAMES WITH WATER FROM SIDE UNTIL WELL AFTER FIRE IS OUT. STAY AWAY FROM STORAGE TANK ENDS (1987 EMERGENCY RESPONSE GUIDEBOOK, DOT P 5800.4, GUIDE PAGE 59).

USE AGENTS SUITABLE FOR TYPE OF FIRE. USE WATER IN FLOODING AMOUNTS AS FOG. COOL CONTAINERS WITH FLOODING QUANTITIES OF WATER, APPLY FROM AS FAR A DISTANCE AS POSSIBLE. AVOID BREATHING CORROSIVE VAPORS, KEEP UPWIND.

TRANSPORTATION DATA

DEPARTMENT OF TRANSPORTATION HAZARD CLASSIFICATION 49 CFR 172.101: CORROSIVE MATERIAL

DEPARTMENT OF TRANSPORTATION LABELING REQUIREMENTS 49 CFR 172.101 AND SUBPART E: CORROSIVE

DEPARTMENT OF TRANSPORTATION PACKAGING REQUIREMENTS: 49 CFR 173.245B EXCEPTIONS: 49 CFR 173.244

TOXICITY

TRICHLOROACETIC ACID: IRRITATION DATA: 210 UG SKIN-RABBIT MILD; 3500 UG/5 SECONDS EYE-RABBIT SEVERE. TOXICITY DATA: 400 MG/KG ORAL-RAT LD50; 270 MG/KG SUBCUTANEOUS-MOUSE LD50; 500 MG/KG INTRAPERITONEAL-MOUSE LDLO; MUTAGENIC DATA (RTECS); REPRODUCTIVE EFFECTS DATA (RTECS); TUMORIGENIC DATA (RTECS). CARCINOGEN STATUS: NONE. LOCAL EFFECTS: CORROSIVE- INHALATION, SKIN, EYE, INGESTION. ACUTE TOXICITY LEVEL: TOXIC BY INGESTION. TARGET EFFECTS: NO DATA AVAILABLE. AT INCREASED RISK FROM EXPOSURE: PERSONS WITH SKIN, EYE, OR RESPIRATORY DISORDERS.

HEALTH EFFECTS AND FIRST AID

INHALATION: TRICHLOROACETIC ACID: CORROSIVE. SEE INFORMATION ON ACIDIC CORROSIVES.

ACIDIC CORROSIVES: **ACUTE EXPOSURE-** MAY CAUSE RESPIRATORY TRACT IRRITATION WITH COUGHING, CHOKING, AND POSSIBLY BURNS OF THE MUCOUS MEMBRANES. OTHER INITIAL SYMPTOMS MAY INCLUDE DIZZINESS, HEADACHE, NAUSEA AND WEAKNESS. IN SOME CASES PULMONARY EDEMA MAY DEVELOP, EITHER IMMEDIATELY IN SEVERE CASES, OR MORE LIKELY AFTER A LATENT PERIOD OF 5-72 HOURS. THE SYMPTOMS MAY INCLUDE TIGHTNESS IN THE CHEST, DYSPNEA, FROTHY SPUTUM, AND CYANOSIS. PHYSICAL FINDINGS MAY INCLUDE HYPOTENSION, WEAK, RAPID PULSE AND MOIST RALES. RECOVERY MAY BE PROLONGED AND RELAPSES ARE POSSIBLE. IN SEVERE EXPOSURES, DEATH DUE TO ANOXIA MAY OCCUR WITHIN A FEW HOURS AFTER ONSET OF PULMONARY EDEMA SYMPTOMS OR FOLLOWING A RELAPSE. **CHRONIC EXPOSURE-** DEPENDING ON THE CONCENTRATION AND DURATION OF EXPOSURE, REPEATED OR PROLONGED EXPOSURE MAY CAUSE EROSION OF THE TEETH, INFLAMMATORY AND ULCERATIVE CHANGES IN THE MOUTH, AND POSSIBLY JAW NECROSIS. BRONCHIAL IRRITATION WITH COUGH AND FREQUENT ATTACKS OF BRONCHIAL PNEUMONIA MAY OCCUR. GASTROINTESTINAL DISTURBANCES ARE ALSO POSSIBLE.

FIRST AID- REMOVE FROM EXPOSURE AREA TO FRESH AIR IMMEDIATELY. IF BREATHING HAS STOPPED, GIVE ARTIFICIAL RESPIRATION. MAINTAIN AIRWAY AND BLOOD PRESSURE AND ADMINISTER OXYGEN IF AVAILABLE. KEEP AFFECTED PERSON WARM AND AT REST. TREAT SYMPTOMATICALLY AND SUPPORTIVELY.

ADMINISTRATION OF OXYGEN SHOULD BE PERFORMED BY QUALIFIED PERSONNEL. GET MEDICAL ATTENTION IMMEDIATELY.

SKIN CONTACT: TRICHLOROACETIC ACID: CORROSIVE. SEE INFORMATION ON ACIDIC CORROSIVES.
ACIDIC CORROSIVES: **ACUTE EXPOSURE-** DIRECT CONTACT MAY CAUSE SEVERE PAIN, BURNS AND POSSIBLY BROWNISH OR YELLOWISH STAINS. BURNS MAY BE DEEP WITH SHARP EDGES AND HEAL SLOWLY WITH SCAR TISSUE FORMATION. **CHRONIC EXPOSURE-** EFFECTS DEPEND ON THE CONCENTRATION AND DURATION OF EXPOSURE. REPEATED OR PROLONGED CONTACT MAY RESULT IN DERMATITIS OR EFFECTS SIMILAR TO ACUTE EXPOSURE.
FIRST AID- REMOVE CONTAMINATED CLOTHING AND SHOES IMMEDIATELY. WASH AFFECTED AREA WITH SOAP OR MILD DETERGENT AND LARGE AMOUNTS OF WATER UNTIL NO EVIDENCE OF CHEMICAL REMAINS (AT LEAST 15-20 MINUTES). IN CASE OF CHEMICAL BURNS, COVER AREA WITH STERILE, DRY DRESSING. BANDAGE SECURELY, BUT NOT TOO TIGHTLY. GET MEDICAL ATTENTION IMMEDIATELY.

EYE CONTACT: TRICHLOROACETIC ACID: CORROSIVE. SEE INFORMATION ON ACIDIC CORROSIVES.
ACIDIC CORROSIVES: **ACUTE EXPOSURE-** DIRECT CONTACT MAY CAUSE PAIN, LACRIMATION, PHOTOPHOBIA AND AND BURNS. IN MILD BURNS, THE EPITHELIUM REGENERATES RAPIDLY AND THE EYE RECOVERS COMPLETELY. IN SEVERE CASES, THE EXTENT OF INJURY MAY NOT BE FULLY APPARENT FOR SEVERAL WEEKS. ULTIMATELY, THE WHOLE CORNEA MAY BECOME DEEPLY VASCULARIZED AND OPAQUE RESULTING IN BLINDNESS. IN THE WORST CASES, THE EYE MAY BE TOTALLY DESTROYED. **CHRONIC EXPOSURE-** EFFECTS DEPEND ON THE CONCENTRATION AND DURATION OF EXPOSURE. REPEATED OR PROLONGED CONTACT MAY CAUSE CONJUNCTIVITIS OR EFFECTS AS IN ACUTE EXPOSURE.
FIRST AID- WASH EYES IMMEDIATELY WITH LARGE AMOUNTS OF WATER, OCCASIONALLY LIFTING UPPER AND LOWER LIDS, UNTIL NO EVIDENCE OF CHEMICAL REMAINS (AT LEAST 15-20 MINUTES). CONTINUE IRRIGATING WITH NORMAL SALINE UNTIL THE PH HAS RETURNED TO NORMAL (30-60 MINUTES). COVER WITH STERILE BANDAGES. GET MEDICAL ATTENTION IMMEDIATELY.

INGESTION: TRICHLOROACETIC ACID: CORROSIVE/TOXIC. THE LETHAL DOSE REPORTED IN RATS WAS 400 MG/KG. THE SYMPTOMS WERE NOT REPORTED. POISONED ANIMALS MAY EXHIBIT NARCOSIS AND WITHIN 36 HOURS, EITHER RECOVER COMPLETELY OR DIE. AS EVALUATED BY RTECS, ADMINISTRATION TO MICE BY INGESTION RESULTED IN A STATISTICALLY SIGNIFICANT INCREASE IN THE INCIDENCE OF CARCINOGENIC TUMORS IN THE LIVER. SEE INFORMATION ON ACIDIC CORROSIVES.
ACIDIC CORROSIVES: **ACUTE EXPOSURE-** MAY CAUSE CIRCUMORAL BURNS WITH DISCOLORATION AND CORROSION OF THE MUCOUS MEMBRANES OF THE MOUTH, THROAT AND ESOPHAGUS. THERE MAY BE IMMEDIATE PAIN AND DIFFICULTY OR INABILITY TO SWALLOW OR SPEAK. EPIGLOTTAL EDEMA MAY RESULT IN RESPIRATORY DISTRESS AND POSSIBLY ASPHYXIA. MARKED THIRST, NAUSEA, VOMITING AND DIARRHEA MAY OCCUR. DEPENDING ON THE AREA AND DEGREE OF CORROSION, THE VOMITUS MAY CONTAIN FRESH OR DARK BLOOD AND LARGE SHREDS OF MUCOSA. SHOCK MAY OCCUR WITH MARKED HYPOTENSION, WEAK AND RAPID PULSE, SHALLOW RESPIRATION, AND CLAMMY SKIN. CIRCULATORY COLLAPSE MAY DEVELOP AND IF UNCORRECTED, LEAD TO RENAL FAILURE. IN SEVERE CASES, GASTRIC AND, TO A LESSER DEGREE, ESOPHAGEAL PERFORATION MAY OCCUR WITH PERITONITIS ACCOMPANIED BY FEVER AND ABDOMINAL RIGIDITY. ESOPHAGEAL, GASTRIC OR PYLORIC STRICTURE MAY OCCUR WITHIN A FEW WEEKS, OR MAY BE DELAYED FOR MONTHS OR EVEN YEARS. DEATH MAY RESULT WITHIN A SHORT TIME FROM ASPHYXIA, CIRCULATORY COLLAPSE OR ASPIRATION OF EVEN MINUTE AMOUNTS. IF DEATH IS DELAYED, IT MAY BE DUE TO PERITONITIS, SEVERE NEPHRITIS OR PNEUMONIA. COMA AND CONVULSIONS SOMETIMES OCCUR TERMINALLY. **CHRONIC EXPOSURE-** DEPENDING ON THE CONCENTRATION, REPEATED INGESTION MAY RESULT IN INFLAMMATORY AND ULCERATIVE CHANGES IN THE MUCOUS MEMBRANES OF THE MOUTH AND OTHER EFFECTS AS IN ACUTE INGESTION.
FIRST AID- DO NOT USE GASTRIC LAVAGE OR EMESIS. DILUTE THE ACID IMMEDIATELY BY DRINKING LARGE QUANTITIES OF WATER OR MILK. IF VOMITING PERSISTS, ADMINISTER FLUIDS REPEATEDLY. INGESTED ACID MUST BE DILUTED APPROXIMATELY 100 FOLD TO RENDER IT HARMLESS TO TISSUES. MAINTAIN AIRWAY AND TREAT SHOCK (DREISBACH, HANDBOOK OF POISONING, 12TH ED.). GET MEDICAL ATTENTION IMMEDIATELY. IF VOMITING OCCURS, KEEP HEAD BELOW HIPS TO HELP PREVENT ASPIRATION.
ANTIDOTE: NO SPECIFIC ANTIDOTE. TREAT SYMPTOMATICALLY AND SUPPORTIVELY.

REACTIVITY

REACTIVITY: STABLE UNDER NORMAL TEMPERATURES AND PRESSURES.
INCOMPATIBILITIES: TRICHLOROACETIC ACID: BASES: POSSIBLE VIOLENT REACTION. COPPER + DIMETHYLSULFOXIDE: INTENSE EXOTHERMIC REACTION. METALS: CORROSIVE IN THE PRESENCE OF MOISTURE.
DECOMPOSITION: THERMAL DECOMPOSITION PRODUCTS MAY INCLUDE TOXIC FUMES OF PHOSGENE, TOXIC AND CORROSIVE FUMES OF HYDROGEN CHLORIDE, TOXIC OXIDES OF CARBON, AND CHLOROFORM.
POLYMERIZATION: HAZARDOUS POLYMERIZATION HAS NOT BEEN REPORTED TO OCCUR UNDER NORMAL TEMPERATURES AND PRESSURES.

STORAGE AND DISPOSAL

OBSERVE ALL FEDERAL, STATE AND LOCAL REGULATIONS WHEN STORING OR DISPOSING OF THIS SUBSTANCE. FOR ASSISTANCE, CONTACT THE DISTRICT DIRECTOR OF THE ENVIRONMENTAL PROTECTION AGENCY.

STORAGE

STORE IN A COOL, DRY PLACE; KEEP CONTAINER TIGHTLY CLOSED WHEN NOT IN USE.
STORE AWAY FROM INCOMPATIBLE SUBSTANCES.

CONDITIONS TO AVOID

MAY BURN BUT DOES NOT IGNITE READILY. MAY IGNITE COMBUSTIBLES (WOOD, PAPER, OIL, ETC.).

SPILL AND LEAK PROCEDURES

OCCUPATIONAL SPILL: DO NOT TOUCH SPILLED MATERIAL. STOP LEAK IF YOU CAN DO IT WITHOUT RISK. USE WATER SPRAY TO REDUCE VAPORS. FOR SMALL SPILLS, TAKE UP WITH SAND OR OTHER ABSORBENT MATERIAL AND PLACE INTO CONTAINERS FOR LATER DISPOSAL. FOR LARGER SPILLS, DIKE SPILL FOR LATER DISPOSAL. KEEP UNNECESSARY PEOPLE AWAY. ISOLATE HAZARD AREA AND DENY ENTRY.

PROTECTIVE EQUIPMENT

VENTILATION: PROVIDE LOCAL EXHAUST VENTILATION AND/OR GENERAL DILUTION VENTILATION TO MEET PUBLISHED EXPOSURE LIMITS.
RESPIRATOR: THE FOLLOWING RESPIRATORS ARE RECOMMENDED BASED ON INFORMATION FOUND IN THE PHYSICAL DATA, TOXICITY AND HEALTH EFFECTS SECTIONS. THEY ARE RANKED IN ORDER FROM MINIMUM TO MAXIMUM RESPIRATORY PROTECTION. THE SPECIFIC RESPIRATOR SELECTED MUST BE BASED ON CONTAMINATION LEVELS FOUND IN THE WORK PLACE, MUST NOT EXCEED THE WORKING LIMITS OF THE RESPIRATOR AND BE JOINTLY APPROVED BY THE NATIONAL INSTITUTE FOR OCCUPATIONAL SAFETY AND HEALTH AND THE MINE SAFETY AND HEALTH ADMINISTRATION (NIOSH-MSHA).
CHEMICAL CARTRIDGE RESPIRATOR WITH FULL FACEPIECE AND ORGANIC VAPOR CARTRIDGE(S) IN COMBINATION WITH A DUST AND MIST FILTER.
CHEMICAL CARTRIDGE RESPIRATOR WITH FULL FACEPIECE AND ORGANIC VAPOR CARTRIDGE(S) IN COMBINATION WITH A HIGH-EFFICIENCY PARTICULATE FILTER.
GAS MASK WITH ORGANIC VAPOR CANISTER (CHIN-STYLE OR FRONT- OR BACK-MOUNTED CANISTER) WITH A FULL FACEPIECE AND A HIGH-EFFICIENCY PARTICULATE FILTER.
POWERED AIR-PURIFYING RESPIRATOR WITH TIGHT-FITTING FACEPIECE AND ORGANIC VAPOR CARTRIDGE(S) IN COMBINATION WITH A HIGH-EFFICIENCY PARTICULATE FILTER.
TYPE 'C' SUPPLIED-AIR RESPIRATOR WITH A FULL FACEPIECE OPERATED IN PRESSURE-DEMAND OR OTHER POSITIVE PRESSURE MODE OR WITH A FULL FACEPIECE, HELMET OR HOOD OPERATED IN CONTINUOUS-FLOW MODE.
SELF-CONTAINED BREATHING APPARATUS WITH A FULL FACEPIECE OPERATED IN PRESSURE-DEMAND OR OTHER POSITIVE PRESSURE MODE.
FOR FIREFIGHTING AND OTHER IMMEDIATELY DANGEROUS TO LIFE OR HEALTH CONDITIONS:
SELF-CONTAINED BREATHING APPARATUS WITH FULL FACEPIECE OPERATED IN PRESSURE-DEMAND OR OTHER POSITIVE PRESSURE MODE.
SUPPLIED-AIR RESPIRATOR WITH FULL FACEPIECE AND OPERATED IN PRESSURE-DEMAND OR OTHER POSITIVE PRESSURE MODE IN COMBINATION WITH AN AUXILIARY SELF-CONTAINED BREATHING APPARATUS OPERATED IN PRESSURE-DEMAND OR OTHER POSITIVE PRESSURE MODE.
CLOTHING: EMPLOYEE MUST WEAR APPROPRIATE PROTECTIVE (IMPERVIOUS) CLOTHING AND EQUIPMENT TO PREVENT ANY POSSIBILITY OF SKIN CONTACT WITH THIS SUBSTANCE.
GLOVES: EMPLOYEE MUST WEAR APPROPRIATE PROTECTIVE GLOVES TO PREVENT CONTACT WITH THIS SUBSTANCE.
EYE PROTECTION: EMPLOYEE MUST WEAR SPLASH-PROOF OR DUST-RESISTANT SAFETY GOGGLES AND A FACESHIELD TO PREVENT CONTACT WITH THIS SUBSTANCE.
EMERGENCY WASH FACILITIES: WHERE THERE IS ANY POSSIBILITY THAT AN EMPLOYEE'S EYES AND/OR SKIN MAY BE EXPOSED TO THIS SUBSTANCE, THE EMPLOYER SHOULD PROVIDE AN EYE WASH FOUNTAIN AND QUICK DRENCH SHOWER WITHIN THE IMMEDIATE WORK AREA FOR EMERGENCY USE.

AUTHORIZED BY- OCCUPATIONAL HEALTH SERVICES, INC.
CREATION DATE: 02/08/90 ***REVISION DATE:*** 05/16/90

MATERIAL SAFETY DATA SHEET

OCCUPATIONAL HEALTH SERVICES, INC.
AGRICULTURE AND PESTICIDE DIVISION
450 SEVENTH AVENUE, SUITE 2407
NEW YORK, NEW YORK 10123
1-800-445-MSDS OR (212) 967-1100

EMERGENCY CONTACT:
JOHN S. BRANSFORD, JR. (615) 292-1180

SUBSTANCE IDENTIFICATION

CAS-NUMBER 87-90-1

SUBSTANCE: **TRICHLOROISOCYANURIC ACID**

TRADE NAMES/SYNONYMS: 1,3,5-TRIAZINE-2,4,6(1H,3H,5H)-TRIONE, 1,3,5-TRICHLORO; S-TRIAZINE-2,4,6(1H,3H,5H)-TRIONE, 1,3,5-TRICHLORO-; 1,3,5-TRICHLORO-1,3,5-TRIAZINE-2,4,6-(1H,3H,5H,)-TRIONE; 1,3,5-TRICHLORO-S-TRIAZINE-2,4,6(1H,3H,5H)-TRIONE; S-TRIAZINE-2,4,6(1H,3H,5H)-TRIONE, TRICHLORO-; TRICHLORO-S-TRIAZINE-2,4,6(1H,3H,5H)-TRIONE; ISOCYANURIC CHLORIDE; TRICHLOROCYANURIC ACID; N,N'N"-TRICHLOROISOCYANURIC ACID; 1,3,5-TRICHLOROISOCYANURIC ACID; TRICHLORO-S-TRIAZINETRIONE; 1,3,5-TRICHLORO-S-TRIAZINE-2,4,6-TRIONE; ACL 85; CDB 90; CHLOREAL; FICHLOR 91; SYMCLOSEN; SYMCLOSENE; STCC 4918448; UN 2468; PST23860

CHEMICAL FAMILY: HETEROCYCLIC NITROGEN HALOGEN

MOLECULAR FORMULA: C3-CL3-N3-O3

MOLECULAR WEIGHT: 232.41

CERCLA RATINGS (SCALE 0-3): HEALTH=3 FIRE=0 REACTIVITY=2 PERSISTENCE=1

NFPA RATINGS (SCALE 0-4): HEALTH=3 FIRE=0 REACTIVITY=2

COMPONENTS AND CONTAMINANTS

COMPONENT: TRICHLOROISOCYANURIC ACID ***PERCENT:*** 100
CAS# 87-90-1

OTHER CONTAMINANTS: NONE

EXPOSURE LIMITS: NO OCCUPATIONAL EXPOSURE LIMITS ESTABLISHED BY OSHA, ACGIH, OR NIOSH.

PHYSICAL DATA

DESCRIPTION: WHITE, SLIGHTLY HYGROSCOPIC, CRYSTALLINE SOLID WITH A STRONG CHLORINE ODOR

MELTING POINT: 437 F (225 C) DECOMPOSES ***SPECIFIC GRAVITY:*** 1.2

PH: 4.4 (AQUEOUS SOLN) ***SOLUBILITY IN WATER:*** 0.2%

SOLVENT SOLUBILITY: SOLUBLE IN CHLORINATED AND HIGHLY POLAR SOLVENTS

FIRE AND EXPLOSION DATA

FIRE AND EXPLOSION HAZARD: NEGLIGIBLE FIRE HAZARD WHEN EXPOSED TO HEAT OR FLAME.

OXIDIZER: OXIDIZERS DECOMPOSE, ESPECIALLY WHEN HEATED, TO YIELD OXYGEN OR OTHER GASES WHICH WILL INCREASE THE BURNING RATE OF COMBUSTIBLE MATTER. CONTACT WITH EASILY OXIDIZABLE, ORGANIC, OR OTHER COMBUSTIBLE MATERIALS MAY RESULT IN IGNITION, VIOLENT COMBUSTION OR EXPLOSION.

FIREFIGHTING MEDIA: DRY CHEMICAL, CARBON DIOXIDE, HALON, WATER SPRAY OR STANDARD FOAM (1987 EMERGENCY RESPONSE GUIDEBOOK, DOT P 5800.4).
FOR LARGER FIRES, USE WATER SPRAY, FOG OR STANDARD FOAM (1987 EMERGENCY RESPONSE GUIDEBOOK, DOT P 5800.4).

FIREFIGHTING: MOVE CONTAINERS FROM FIRE AREA IF POSSIBLE. COOL CONTAINERS EXPOSED TO FLAME WITH WATER FROM SIDE UNTIL WELL AFTER FIRE IS OUT. KEEP AWAY FROM STORAGE TANK ENDS. FOR MASSIVE FIRE IN STORAGE AREA, USE UNMANNED HOSE HOLDER OR MONITOR NOZZLES (1987 EMERGENCY RESPONSE GUIDEBOOK, DOT 5800.4, GUIDE PAGE 42).
FLOOD WITH WATER. COOL CONTAINERS WITH FLOODING AMOUNTS OF WATER, APPLY FROM AS FAR A DISTANCE AS POSSIBLE. AVOID BREATHING DUSTS. EVACUATE TO 2500 FEET FOR UNCONTROLLABLE FIRES.

TRANSPORTATION DATA

DEPARTMENT OF TRANSPORTATION HAZARD CLASSIFICATION 49 CFR 172.101: OXIDIZER
DEPARTMENT OF TRANSPORTATION LABELING REQUIREMENTS 49 CFR 172.101 AND SUBPART E: OXIDIZER
DEPARTMENT OF TRANSPORTATION PACKAGING REQUIREMENTS: 49 CFR 173.217
EXCEPTIONS: 49 CFR 173.153

TOXICITY

TRICHLOROISOCYANURIC ACID: IRRITATION DATA: 500 MG/24 HOURS SKIN-RABBIT MODERATE; 50 UG/24 HOURS EYE-RABBIT SEVERE. TOXICITY DATA: 3570 MG/KG ORAL-HUMAN LDLO; 406 MG/KG ORAL-RAT LD50. CARCINOGEN STATUS: NONE. LOCAL EFFECTS: IRRITANT- INHALATION, SKIN, AND EYES. ACUTE TOXICITY LEVEL: TOXIC BY INGESTION. TARGET EFFECTS: NO DATA AVAILABLE.

HEALTH EFFECTS AND FIRST AID

INHALATION: TRICHLOROISOCYANURIC ACID: IRRITANT. **ACUTE EXPOSURE-** MAY CAUSE MILD INFLAMMATION OF THE UPPER RESPIRATORY TRACT WITH SORE THROAT, COUGHING OR DIFFICULT BREATHING. BRONCHOSPASM MAY OCCUR IN INDIVIDUALS SENSITIVE TO CHLORINE. **CHRONIC EXPOSURE-** NO DATA AVAILABLE.

FIRST AID- REMOVE FROM EXPOSURE AREA TO FRESH AIR IMMEDIATELY. IF BREATHING HAS STOPPED, PERFORM ARTIFICIAL RESPIRATION. KEEP PERSON WARM AND AT REST. TREAT SYMPTOMATICALLY AND SUPPORTIVELY. GET MEDICAL ATTENTION IMMEDIATELY.

SKIN CONTACT: TRICHLOROISOCYANURIC ACID: IRRITANT. **ACUTE EXPOSURE-** A CONCENTRATED SOLUTION WAS MODERATELY IRRITATING TO THE INTACT SKIN OF RABBITS. IN THE DRY FORM, THIS MATERIAL WAS NOT IRRITATING TO THE INTACT SKIN OF RABBITS; HOWEVER, ON ABRADED RABBIT SKIN, THIS MATERIAL PRODUCED IRRITATION. **CHRONIC EXPOSURE-** PROLONGED OR REPEATED EXPOSURE TO IRRITANTS MAY CAUSE DERMATITIS. A NEUTRALIZED SOLUTION OF TRICHLOROISOCYANURIC ACID DID NOT PRODUCED IRRITATION OR SENSITIZATION ON THE FOREARMS OF 10 INDIVIDUALS AFTER REPEATED APPLICATIONS.

FIRST AID- REMOVE CONTAMINATED CLOTHING AND SHOES IMMEDIATELY. WASH AFFECTED AREA WITH SOAP OR MILD DETERGENT AND LARGE AMOUNTS OF WATER UNTIL NO EVIDENCE OF CHEMICAL REMAINS (APPROXIMATELY 15-20 MINUTES). GET MEDICAL ATTENTION IMMEDIATELY.

EYE CONTACT: TRICHLOROISOCYANURIC ACID: IRRITANT. **ACUTE EXPOSURE-** MAY CAUSE MILD INFLAMMATION AND EDEMA OF THE EYES. THIS MATERIAL WAS IRRITATING TO RABBIT EYES. IT MAY DECOMPOSE TO NITROGEN TRICHLORIDE WHICH IS A STRONG LACRIMATOR. **CHRONIC EXPOSURE-** PROLONGED OR REPEATED EXPOSURE TO IRRITANTS MAY CAUSE CONJUNCTIVITIS.

FIRST AID- WASH EYES IMMEDIATELY WITH LARGE AMOUNTS OF WATER OR NORMAL SALINE, OCCASIONALLY LIFTING UPPER AND LOWER LIDS, UNTIL NO EVIDENCE OF CHEMICAL REMAINS (APPROXIMATELY 15-20 MINUTES). GET MEDICAL ATTENTION IMMEDIATELY.

INGESTION: TRICHLOROISOCYANURIC ACID: CORROSIVE/TOXIC. **ACUTE EXPOSURE-** MAY CAUSE INJURY TO THE LINING OF THE STOMACH; LARGE INGESTED DOSES MAY CAUSE WEAKNESS, LETHARGY, TREMORS, SALIVATION, LACRIMATION, DYSPNEA, AND COMA. **CHRONIC EXPOSURE-** NO DATA AVAILABLE.

FIRST AID- REMOVE BY GASTRIC LAVAGE OR EMESIS. MAINTAIN BLOOD PRESSURE AND AIRWAY. GIVE OXYGEN IF RESPIRATION IS DEPRESSED. DO NOT PERFORM GASTRIC LAVAGE OR EMESIS IF VICTIM IS UNCONSCIOUS. GET MEDICAL ATTENTION IMMEDIATELY (DREISBACH, HANDBOOK OF POISONING, 11TH ED.).
ADMINISTRATION OF GASTRIC LAVAGE OR OXYGEN SHOULD BE PERFORMED BY QUALIFIED MEDICAL PERSONNEL.

ANTIDOTE: NO SPECIFIC ANTIDOTE. TREAT SYMPTOMATICALLY AND SUPPORTIVELY.

REACTIVITY

REACTIVITY: HIGHLY REACTIVE OXIDIZING AND CHLORINATING AGENT THAT MAY CAUSE IGNITION BY CONTACT WITH MOST FOREIGN MATERIAL, ORGANIC MATTER OR EASILY CHLORINATED OR OXIDIZED MATERIALS. REACTS WITH WATER TO RELEASE TOXIC CHLORINE GAS AND NITROGEN TRICHLORIDE; IF THE AMOUNT OF WATER IS SMALL THE NITROGEN TRICHLORIDE MAY EXPLODE.

INCOMPATIBILITIES: TRICHLOROISOCYANURIC ACID: AMINE: MAY FORM EXPLOSIVE NITROGEN TRICHLORIDE. AMMONIA: MAY FORM EXPLOSIVE NITROGEN TRICHLORIDE. AMMONIA SALTS: MAY FORM EXPLOSIVE NITROGEN TRICHLORIDE. COMBUSTIBLE MATERIALS: MAY CAUSE IGNITION ON CONTACT. FLOOR SWEEPINGS: MAY CAUSE IGNITION ON CONTACT. GREASE: MAY CAUSE IGNITION ON CONTACT. NITROGEN CONTAINING COMPOUNDS: MAY FORM EXPLOSIVE NITROGEN TRICHLORIDE VAPORS. OIL: MAY CAUSE IGNITION ON CONTACT. OXIDIZED ORGANIC COMPOUNDS: MAY CREATE A FIRE HAZARD. REDUCING MATERIALS: MAY REACT VIOLENTLY OR CAUSE IGNITION ON CONTACT. UREA: MAY FORM EXPLOSIVE NITROGEN TRICHLORIDE.

DECOMPOSITION: THERMAL DECOMPOSITION MAY EMIT TOXIC FUMES OF HYDROGEN CYANIDE, CHLORINE, AND OXIDES OF NITROGEN AND CARBON.

POLYMERIZATION: HAZARDOUS POLYMERIZATION HAS NOT BEEN REPORTED TO OCCUR UNDER NORMAL TEMPERATURES AND PRESSURES.

STORAGE AND DISPOSAL

OBSERVE ALL FEDERAL, STATE AND LOCAL REGULATIONS WHEN STORING OR DISPOSING OF THIS SUBSTANCE. FOR ASSISTANCE, CONTACT THE DISTRICT DIRECTOR OF THE ENVIRONMENTAL PROTECTION AGENCY.

STORAGE

PROTECT AGAINST PHYSICAL DAMAGE. STORE IN A COOL, DRY, WELL VENTILATED LOCATION AWAY FROM FLAMMABLE LIQUIDS, COMBUSTIBLE MATERIALS AND OXIDIZABLE MATERIALS. DRUMS MAY RUPTURE IF THE CONTENTS ARE EXPOSED TO HEAT OR BECOME CONTAMINATED OR WET. DRUMS SHOULD BE PALLETIZED TO PREVENT WETTING FROM FLOOR WASHINGS OR DRAINAGE. AVOID PROLONGED STORAGE IN UNVENTILATED AREAS AT SUMMER TEMPERATURES (NFPA 49, HAZARDOUS CHEMICALS DATA, 1975).

STORE AWAY FROM INCOMPATIBLE SUBSTANCES.

CONDITIONS TO AVOID

AVOID CONTACT WITH OTHER COMBUSTIBLE MATERIALS (WOOD, PAPER, OIL, ETC.). AVOID CONTACT WITH EYES AND SKIN; MATERIAL MAY BE POISONOUS OR CORROSIVE.

SPILL AND LEAK PROCEDURES

OCCUPATIONAL SPILL: KEEP COMBUSTIBLES (WOOD, PAPER, OIL, ETC.) AWAY FROM SPILLED MATERIAL. DO NOT TOUCH SPILLED MATERIAL. FOR SMALL DRY SPILLS, WITH CLEAN SHOVEL PLACE MATERIAL INTO CLEAN, DRY CONTAINER AND COVER; MOVE CONTAINERS FROM SPILL AREA. FOR LARGER SPILLS, DIKE FAR AHEAD OF SPILL FOR LATER DISPOSAL. KEEP UNNECESSARY PEOPLE AWAY. ISOLATE HAZARD AREA AND DENY ENTRY.

PROTECTIVE EQUIPMENT

VENTILATION: PROVIDE GENERAL DILUTION VENTILATION.

RESPIRATOR: THE FOLLOWING RESPIRATORS ARE RECOMMENDED BASED ON INFORMATION FOUND IN THE PHYSICAL DATA, TOXICITY AND HEALTH EFFECTS SECTIONS. THEY ARE RANKED IN ORDER FROM MINIMUM TO MAXIMUM RESPIRATORY PROTECTION. THE SPECIFIC RESPIRATOR SELECTED MUST BE BASED ON CONTAMINATION LEVELS FOUND IN THE WORK PLACE, MUST NOT EXCEED THE WORKING LIMITS OF THE RESPIRATOR AND BE JOINTLY APPROVED BY THE NATIONAL INSTITUTE FOR OCCUPATIONAL SAFETY AND HEALTH AND THE MINE SAFETY AND HEALTH ADMINISTRATION (NIOSH-MSHA).

DUST AND MIST RESPIRATOR WITH A FULL FACEPIECE.

AIR-PURIFYING FULL FACEPIECE RESPIRATOR WITH A HIGH-EFFICIENCY PARTICULATE FILTER.

POWERED AIR-PURIFYING RESPIRATOR WITH A TIGHT-FITTING FACEPIECE AND HIGH-EFFICIENCY PARTICULATE FILTER.

TYPE 'C' SUPPLIED-AIR RESPIRATOR WITH A FULL FACEPIECE OPERATED IN PRESSURE-DEMAND OR OTHER POSITIVE PRESSURE MODE OR WITH A FULL FACEPIECE, HELMET OR HOOD OPERATED IN CONTINUOUS-FLOW MODE.

SELF-CONTAINED BREATHING APPARATUS WITH A FULL FACEPIECE OPERATED IN PRESSURE-DEMAND OR OTHER POSITIVE PRESSURE MODE.

FOR FIREFIGHTING AND OTHER IMMEDIATELY DANGEROUS TO LIFE OR HEALTH CONDITIONS:

SELF-CONTAINED BREATHING APPARATUS WITH FULL FACEPIECE OPERATED IN PRESSURE-DEMAND OR OTHER POSITIVE PRESSURE MODE.

SUPPLIED-AIR RESPIRATOR WITH FULL FACEPIECE AND OPERATED IN PRESSURE-DEMAND OR OTHER POSITIVE PRESSURE MODE IN COMBINATION WITH AN AUXILIARY SELF-CONTAINED BREATHING APPARATUS OPERATED IN PRESSURE-DEMAND OR OTHER POSITIVE PRESSURE MODE.

CLOTHING: EMPLOYEE MUST WEAR APPROPRIATE PROTECTIVE (IMPERVIOUS) CLOTHING AND EQUIPMENT TO PREVENT REPEATED OR PROLONGED SKIN CONTACT WITH THIS SUBSTANCE.

GLOVES: EMPLOYEE MUST WEAR APPROPRIATE PROTECTIVE GLOVES TO PREVENT CONTACT WITH THIS SUBSTANCE.

EYE PROTECTION: EMPLOYEE MUST WEAR SPLASH-PROOF OR DUST-RESISTANT SAFETY GOGGLES TO PREVENT EYE CONTACT WITH THIS SUBSTANCE.

EMERGENCY EYE WASH: WHERE THERE IS ANY POSSIBILITY THAT AN EMPLOYEE'S EYES MAY BE EXPOSED TO THIS SUBSTANCE, THE EMPLOYER SHOULD PROVIDE AN EYE WASH FOUNTAIN WITHIN THE IMMEDIATE WORK AREA FOR EMERGENCY USE.

AUTHORIZED BY- OCCUPATIONAL HEALTH SERVICES, INC.

CREATION DATE: 10/05/89 ***REVISION DATE:*** 05/25/90

MATERIAL SAFETY DATA SHEET

OCCUPATIONAL HEALTH SERVICES, INC.
AGRICULTURE AND PESTICIDE DIVISION
450 SEVENTH AVENUE, SUITE 2407
NEW YORK, NEW YORK 10123
1-800-445-MSDS OR (212) 967-1100

EMERGENCY CONTACT:
JOHN S. BRANSFORD, JR. (615) 292-1180

SUBSTANCE IDENTIFICATION

CAS-NUMBER 1836-77-7

SUBSTANCE: **CHLORNITROFEN**

TRADE NAMES/SYNONYMS: ETHER, P-NITROPHENYL 2,4,6-TRICHLOROPHENYL; 2,4,6-TRICHLOROPHENYL-4-NITROPHENYL ETHER; BENZENE, 1,3,5-TRICHLORO-2-(4-NITROPHENOXY)-; P-NITROPHENYL 2,4,6-TRICHLOROPHENYL ETHER; 1,3,5-TRICHLORO-2-(4-NITROPHENOXY)BENZENE; CNP; MO; C12H6CL3NO3; PST23865

CHEMICAL FAMILY: ETHER, AROMATIC
NITRO
HALOGEN

MOLECULAR FORMULA: CL3-C6-H2-O-C6-H4-N-O2

MOLECULAR WEIGHT: 318.54

CERCLA RATINGS (SCALE 0-3): HEALTH=1 FIRE=1 REACTIVITY=0 PERSISTENCE=3

NFPA RATINGS (SCALE 0-4): HEALTH=U FIRE=1 REACTIVITY=0

COMPONENTS AND CONTAMINANTS

COMPONENT: CHLORNITROFEN ***PERCENT:*** 100.0
CAS# 1836-77-7

OTHER CONTAMINANTS: NONE

EXPOSURE LIMITS: NO OCCUPATIONAL EXPOSURE LIMITS ESTABLISHED BY OSHA, ACGIH, OR NIOSH.

PHYSICAL DATA

DESCRIPTION: CLEAR CRYSTALS. ***MELTING POINT:*** 225 F (107 C)

SPECIFIC GRAVITY: NOT AVAILABLE ***SOLUBILITY IN WATER:*** NOT AVAILABLE

FIRE AND EXPLOSION DATA

FIRE AND EXPLOSION HAZARD: SLIGHT FIRE HAZARD WHEN EXPOSED TO HEAT OR FLAME.

FIREFIGHTING MEDIA: DRY CHEMICAL, CARBON DIOXIDE, HALON, WATER SPRAY OR STANDARD FOAM (1987 EMERGENCY RESPONSE GUIDEBOOK, DOT P 5800.4).
FOR LARGER FIRES, USE WATER SPRAY, FOG OR STANDARD FOAM (1987 EMERGENCY RESPONSE GUIDEBOOK, DOT P 5800.4).

FIREFIGHTING: MOVE CONTAINER FROM FIRE AREA IF POSSIBLE. DO NOT SCATTER SPILLED MATERIAL WITH HIGH PRESSURE WATER STREAMS. DIKE FIRE CONTROL WATER FOR LATER DISPOSAL (1987 EMERGENCY RESPONSE GUIDEBOOK, DOT P 5800.4, GUIDE PAGE 31).
USE AGENTS SUITABLE FOR TYPE OF SURROUNDING FIRE. AVOID BREATHING HAZARDOUS VAPORS, KEEP UPWIND.

TOXICITY

CHLORNITROFEN: TOXICITY DATA: 10800 MG/KG ORAL-RAT LD50; 11800 MG/KG ORAL-MOUSE LD50; MUTAGENIC DATA (RTECS). CARCINOGEN STATUS: NONE. ACUTE TOXICITY LEVEL: SLIGHTLY TOXIC BY INGESTION. TARGET EFFECTS: NO DATA AVAILABLE.

HEALTH EFFECTS AND FIRST AID

INHALATION: CHLORNITROFEN: **ACUTE EXPOSURE-** NO DATA AVAILABLE. **CHRONIC EXPOSURE-** NO DATA AVAILABLE.

FIRST AID- REMOVE FROM EXPOSURE AREA TO FRESH AIR IMMEDIATELY. IF BREATHING HAS STOPPED, PERFORM ARTIFICIAL RESPIRATION. KEEP PERSON WARM AND AT REST. TREAT SYMPTOMATICALLY AND SUPPORTIVELY. GET MEDICAL ATTENTION IMMEDIATELY.

SKIN CONTACT: CHLORNITROFEN: **ACUTE EXPOSURE-** NO DATA AVAILABLE. **CHRONIC EXPOSURE-** NO DATA AVAILABLE.

FIRST AID- REMOVE CONTAMINATED CLOTHING AND SHOES IMMEDIATELY. WASH AFFECTED AREA WITH SOAP OR MILD DETERGENT AND LARGE AMOUNTS OF WATER UNTIL NO EVIDENCE OF CHEMICAL REMAINS (APPROXIMATELY 15-20 MINUTES). GET MEDICAL ATTENTION IMMEDIATELY.

EYE CONTACT: CHLORNITROFEN: **ACUTE EXPOSURE-** NO DATA AVAILABLE. **CHRONIC EXPOSURE-** NO DATA AVAILABLE.

FIRST AID- WASH EYES IMMEDIATELY WITH LARGE AMOUNTS OF WATER OR NORMAL SALINE, OCCASIONALLY LIFTING UPPER AND LOWER LIDS, UNTIL NO EVIDENCE OF CHEMICAL REMAINS (APPROXIMATELY 15-20 MINUTES). GET MEDICAL ATTENTION IMMEDIATELY.

INGESTION: CHLORNITROFEN: **ACUTE EXPOSURE-** A LETHAL DOSE IN RATS WAS 10800 MG/KG. THE SYMPTOMS WERE NOT REPORTED. **CHRONIC EXPOSURE-** SOME EFFECTS ON THE RED BLOOD CELLS WERE OBSERVED IN RABBITS REPEATEDLY FED THIS MATERIAL.

FIRST AID- TREAT SYMPTOMATICALLY AND SUPPORTIVELY. GET MEDICAL ATTENTION IMMEDIATELY. IF VOMITING OCCURS, KEEP HEAD LOWER THAN HIPS TO PREVENT ASPIRATION.

ANTIDOTE: NO SPECIFIC ANTIDOTE. TREAT SYMPTOMATICALLY AND SUPPORTIVELY.

REACTIVITY

REACTIVITY: STABLE UNDER NORMAL TEMPERATURES AND PRESSURES.

INCOMPATIBILITIES: CHLORNITROFEN: OXIDIZERS (STRONG): FIRE AND EXPLOSION HAZARD.

DECOMPOSITION: THERMAL DECOMPOSITION PRODUCTS MAY INCLUDE TOXIC OXIDES OF NITROGEN AND CARBON AND TOXIC AND CORROSIVE FUMES OF CHLORIDES.

POLYMERIZATION: HAZARDOUS POLYMERIZATION HAS NOT BEEN REPORTED TO OCCUR UNDER NORMAL TEMPERATURES AND PRESSURES.

STORAGE AND DISPOSAL

OBSERVE ALL FEDERAL, STATE AND LOCAL REGULATIONS WHEN STORING OR DISPOSING OF THIS SUBSTANCE. FOR ASSISTANCE, CONTACT THE DISTRICT DIRECTOR OF THE ENVIRONMENTAL PROTECTION AGENCY.

****STORAGE****

STORE IN ACCORDANCE WITH 40 CFR 165 RECOMMENDED PROCEDURES FOR THE DISPOSAL AND STORAGE OF PESTICIDES AND PESTICIDE CONTAINERS.

STORE AWAY FROM INCOMPATIBLE SUBSTANCES.

****DISPOSAL****

DISPOSAL MUST BE IN ACCORDANCE WITH 40 CFR 165 RECOMMENDED PROCEDURES FOR THE DISPOSAL AND STORAGE OF PESTICIDES AND PESTICIDE CONTAINERS.

CONDITIONS TO AVOID

MAY BURN BUT DOES NOT IGNITE READILY. AVOID CONTACT WITH STRONG OXIDIZERS, EXCESSIVE HEAT, SPARKS, OR OPEN FLAME.

SPILL AND LEAK PROCEDURES

OCCUPATIONAL SPILL: SWEEP UP AND PLACE IN SUITABLE CLEAN, DRY CONTAINERS FOR RECLAMATION OR LATER DISPOSAL. DO NOT FLUSH SPILLED MATERIAL INTO SEWER. KEEP UNNECESSARY PEOPLE AWAY.

PROTECTIVE EQUIPMENT

VENTILATION: PROVIDE GENERAL DILUTION VENTILATION.

RESPIRATOR: THE FOLLOWING RESPIRATORS ARE RECOMMENDED BASED ON INFORMATION FOUND IN THE PHYSICAL DATA, TOXICITY AND HEALTH EFFECTS SECTIONS. THEY ARE RANKED IN ORDER FROM MINIMUM TO MAXIMUM RESPIRATORY PROTECTION. THE SPECIFIC RESPIRATOR SELECTED MUST BE BASED ON CONTAMINATION LEVELS FOUND IN THE WORK PLACE, MUST NOT EXCEED THE WORKING LIMITS OF THE RESPIRATOR AND BE JOINTLY APPROVED BY THE NATIONAL INSTITUTE FOR OCCUPATIONAL SAFETY AND HEALTH AND THE MINE SAFETY AND HEALTH ADMINISTRATION (NIOSH-MSHA).

CHEMICAL CARTRIDGE RESPIRATOR WITH AN ORGANIC VAPOR CARTRIDGE(S) WITH A FULL FACEPIECE AND ORGANIC VAPOR CARTRIDGE(S) IN COMBINATION WITH A DUST AND MIST FILTER.

POWERED AIR-PURIFYING RESPIRATOR WITH A TIGHT-FITTING FACEPIECE AND ORGANIC VAPOR CARTRIDGE(S) IN COMBINATION WITH A HIGH-EFFICIENCY PARTICULATE FILTER.

TYPE 'C' SUPPLIED-AIR RESPIRATOR WITH A FULL FACEPIECE OPERATED IN A PRESSURE-DEMAND OR OTHER POSITIVE PRESSURE MODE.

SELF-CONTAINED BREATHING APPARATUS WITH A FULL FACEPIECE OPERATED IN PRESSURE-DEMAND OR OTHER POSITIVE PRESSURE MODE.

FOR FIREFIGHTING AND OTHER IMMEDIATELY DANGEROUS TO LIFE OR HEALTH CONDITIONS:

SELF-CONTAINED BREATHING APPARATUS WITH FULL FACEPIECE OPERATED IN PRESSURE-DEMAND OR OTHER POSITIVE PRESSURE MODE.

SUPPLIED-AIR RESPIRATOR WITH FULL FACEPIECE AND OPERATED IN PRESSURE-DEMAND OR OTHER POSITIVE PRESSURE MODE IN COMBINATION WITH AN AUXILIARY SELF-CONTAINED BREATHING APPARATUS OPERATED IN PRESSURE-DEMAND OR OTHER POSITIVE PRESSURE MODE.

CLOTHING: EMPLOYEE MUST WEAR APPROPRIATE PROTECTIVE (IMPERVIOUS) CLOTHING AND EQUIPMENT TO PREVENT REPEATED OR PROLONGED SKIN CONTACT WITH THIS SUBSTANCE.

GLOVES: EMPLOYEE MUST WEAR APPROPRIATE PROTECTIVE GLOVES TO PREVENT CONTACT WITH THIS SUBSTANCE.

EYE PROTECTION: EMPLOYEE MUST WEAR SPLASH-PROOF OR DUST-RESISTANT SAFETY GOGGLES TO PREVENT EYE CONTACT WITH THIS SUBSTANCE.

EMERGENCY EYE WASH: WHERE THERE IS ANY POSSIBILITY THAT AN EMPLOYEE'S EYES MAY BE EXPOSED TO THIS SUBSTANCE, THE EMPLOYER SHOULD PROVIDE AN EYE WASH FOUNTAIN WITHIN THE IMMEDIATE WORK AREA FOR EMERGENCY USE.

AUTHORIZED BY- OCCUPATIONAL HEALTH SERVICES, INC.
CREATION DATE: 10/18/89 ***REVISION DATE:*** 05/31/90

MATERIAL SAFETY DATA SHEET

OCCUPATIONAL HEALTH SERVICES, INC.
AGRICULTURE AND PESTICIDE DIVISION
450 SEVENTH AVENUE, SUITE 2407
NEW YORK, NEW YORK 10123
1-800-445-MSDS OR (212) 967-1100

EMERGENCY CONTACT:
JOHN S. BRANSFORD, JR. (615) 292-1180

SUBSTANCE IDENTIFICATION

CAS-NUMBER 6492-18-8

SUBSTANCE: **TRICHLORONATE OXYGEN ANALOG**

TRADE NAMES/SYNONYMS: PHOSPHONIC ACID, ETHYL-, ETHYL 2,4,5-TRICHLOROPHENYL ESTER; ETHYL 2,4,5-TRICHLOROPHENYL ETHYL-PHOSPHONATE; TRICHLORONATE OXON; TRICHLORONATOXON; AGRITOX OXON; BAY 37289 OXYGEN ANALOG; C10H12CL3O3P; PST23871

CHEMICAL FAMILY: ORGANOPHOSPHATE
HALOGEN COMPOUND, AROMATIC

MOLECULAR FORMULA: (C-H3-C-H2)2-C6-H2-CL3-O3-P

MOLECULAR WEIGHT: 317.54

CERCLA RATINGS (SCALE 0-3): HEALTH=U FIRE=U REACTIVITY=0 PERSISTENCE=2

NFPA RATINGS (SCALE 0-4): HEALTH=U FIRE=U REACTIVITY=0

COMPONENTS AND CONTAMINANTS

COMPONENT: TRICHLORONATE OXYGEN ANALOG ***PERCENT:*** 100.0
CAS# 6492-18-8

OTHER CONTAMINANTS: NONE

EXPOSURE LIMITS: NO OCCUPATIONAL EXPOSURE LIMITS ESTABLISHED BY OSHA, ACGIH, OR NIOSH.

PHYSICAL DATA

DESCRIPTION: CLEAR LIQUID. ***BOILING POINT:*** NOT AVAILABLE

SPECIFIC GRAVITY: NOT AVAILABLE ***VAPOR PRESSURE:*** NOT AVAILABLE

SOLUBILITY IN WATER: NOT AVAILABLE

FIRE AND EXPLOSION DATA

FIRE AND EXPLOSION HAZARD: UNKNOWN FIRE AND EXPLOSION HAZARD.

FIREFIGHTING MEDIA: DRY CHEMICAL, CARBON DIOXIDE, HALON, WATER SPRAY OR STANDARD FOAM (1987 EMERGENCY RESPONSE GUIDEBOOK, DOT P 5800.4). FOR LARGER FIRES, USE WATER SPRAY, FOG OR STANDARD FOAM (1987 EMERGENCY RESPONSE GUIDEBOOK, DOT P 5800.4).

FIREFIGHTING: MOVE CONTAINER FROM FIRE AREA IF POSSIBLE. DIKE FIRE CONTROL WATER FOR LATER DISPOSAL; DO NOT SCATTER THE MATERIAL. COOL FIRE-EXPOSED CONTAINERS WITH WATER FROM SIDE UNTIL WELL AFTER FIRE IS OUT. STAY AWAY FROM STORAGE TANK ENDS. WITHDRAW IMMEDIATELY IN CASE OF RISING SOUND FROM VENTING SAFETY DEVICE OR ANY DISCOLORATION OF STORAGE TANK DUE TO FIRE (1987 EMERGENCY RESPONSE GUIDEBOOK, DOT P 5800.4, GUIDE PAGE 28).

EXTINGUISH ONLY IF FLOW CAN BE STOPPED. USE FLOODING AMOUNTS OF WATER AS A FOG; SOLID STREAMS MAY BE INEFFECTIVE. COOL CONTAINERS WITH FLOODING AMOUNTS OF WATER FROM AS FAR A DISTANCE AS POSSIBLE. AVOID BREATHING POISONOUS VAPORS, KEEP UPWIND.

TOXICITY

TRICHLORONATE OXYGEN ANALOG: CARCINOGEN STATUS: NONE. ACUTE TOXICITY LEVEL: NO DATA AVAILABLE. TARGET EFFECTS: CHOLINESTERASE INHIBITOR. POISONING MAY AFFECT THE NERVOUS SYSTEM.* AT INCREASED RISK FROM EXPOSURE: PERSONS WITH RESPIRATORY AILMENTS, RECENT EXPOSURE TO CHOLINESTERASE INHIBITORS OR IMPAIRED CHOLINESTERASE PRODUCTION, OR LIVER MALFUNCTION.* ADDITIONAL DATA: MAY CROSS THE PLACENTA. HIGH ENVIRONMENTAL TEMPERATURES OR EXPOSURE OF THE CHEMICAL TO VISIBLE OR ULTRAVIOLET LIGHT MAY ENHANCE THE TOXICITY. INTERACTIONS WITH

MEDICATIONS MAY OCCUR.*
* MAY BE BASED ON GENERAL INFORMATION ON ORGANOPHOSPHATES.

HEALTH EFFECTS AND FIRST AID

INHALATION: TRICHLORONATE OXYGEN ANALOG: SEE INFORMATION ON ORGANOPHOSPHATES.
ORGANOPHOSPHATES: CHOLINESTERASE INHIBITOR. **ACUTE EXPOSURE-** WHEN INHALED, THE FIRST EFFECTS OF CHOLINESTERASE INHIBITORS ARE USUALLY RESPIRATORY AND MAY INCLUDE NASAL HYPEREMIA AND WATERY DISCHARGE, COUGH, CHEST DISCOMFORT, DYSPNEA, AND WHEEZING DUE TO INCREASED BRONCHIAL SECRETIONS AND BRONCHOCONSTRICTION. IF SUFFICIENT AMOUNTS ARE ABSORBED, OTHER SYSTEMIC EFFECTS MAY BEGIN WITHIN A FEW MINUTES OR BE DELAYED FOR UP TO 12 HOURS. SYMPTOMS MAY INCLUDE PALLOR, NAUSEA, VOMITING, DIARRHEA, ABDOMINAL CRAMPS, HEADACHE, DIZZINESS, OCULAR PAIN, BLURRED VISION, MIOSIS OR IN SOME CASES, ESPECIALLY INITIALLY, MYDRIASIS, LACRIMATION, SALIVATION, SWEATING, AND CONFUSION. OTHER REPORTED CENTRAL NERVOUS SYSTEM OR NEUROMUSCULAR EFFECTS MAY INCLUDE ATAXIA, SLURRED SPEECH, AREFLEXIA, WEAKNESS, FATIGUE, FASCICULATIONS, TWITCHING, TREMORS POSSIBLY OF THE TONGUE AND EYELIDS, AND EVENTUALLY PARALYSIS OF THE EXTREMITIES AND POSSIBLY OF THE RESPIRATORY MUSCLES. IN SEVERE CASES THERE MAY ALSO BE INVOLUNTARY DEFECATION AND URINATION, CYANOSIS, PSYCHOSIS, HYPERGLYCEMIA, ACUTE PANCREATITIS, CARDIAC IRREGULARITIES, PULMONARY EDEMA, UNCONSCIOUSNESS, CONVULSIONS, AND COMA. DEATH IS PRIMARILY DUE TO RESPIRATORY FAILURE, ALTHOUGH CARDIOVASCULAR EFFECTS INCLUDING CARDIAC ARREST MAY ALSO BE IMPLICATED. LONG TERM SEQUELAE ARE RARE BUT MAY INCLUDE NEUROPSYCHIATRIC DISORDERS AND MYOPATHY WITH MUSCLE TENDERNESS. SOME ORGANOPHOSPHATES MAY CAUSE A DELAYED NEUROPATHY BEGINNING 1-4 WEEKS AFTER AN ACUTE EXPOSURE WHICH MAY OR MAY NOT HAVE CAUSED ACUTE CHOLINERGIC EFFECTS. NUMBNESS, TINGLING, WEAKNESS AND CRAMPING BEGINNING SYMMETRICALLY IN THE LOWER LIMBS MAY PROGRESS TO ATAXIA AND PARALYSIS. IN SEVERE CASES, UPPER LIMB INVOLVEMENT IS POSSIBLE AND FLACCID PARALYSIS MAY PROGRESS TO SPASTIC PARALYSIS WITH EXAGGERATED REFLEXES. IMPROVEMENT MAY OCCUR OVER MONTHS TO YEARS, BUT SOME RESIDUAL IMPAIRMENT USUALLY REMAINS.
CHRONIC EXPOSURE- REPEATED OR PROLONGED EXPOSURE MAY RESULT IN THE EFFECTS OF ACUTE EXPOSURE INCLUDING THE DELAYED NEUROPATHY. OTHER EFFECTS REPORTED IN WORKERS REPEATEDLY EXPOSED INCLUDE IMPAIRED MEMORY AND CONCENTRATION, ACUTE PSYCHOSIS, SEVERE DEPRESSIONS, IRRITABILTY, CONFUSION, APATHY, EMOTIONAL LABILITY, SOCIAL WITHDRAWAL, CONFUSION, HEADACHE, SPEECH DIFFICULTIES, DELAYED REACTION TIMES, SPATIAL DISORIENTATION, NIGHTMARES, SLEEPWALKING, AND DROWSINESS OR INSOMNIA. AN INFLUENZA-LIKE CONDITION WITH HEADACHE, NAUSEA, WEAKNESS, ANOREXIA AND MALAISE HAS ALSO BEEN REPORTED.

FIRST AID- REMOVE FROM EXPOSURE AREA TO FRESH AIR IMMEDIATELY. IF BREATHING HAS STOPPED, GIVE ARTIFICIAL RESPIRATION. MAINTAIN AIRWAY AND BLOOD PRESSURE AND ADMINISTER OXYGEN IF AVAILABLE. KEEP AFFECTED PERSON WARM AND AT REST. TREAT SYMPTOMATICALLY AND SUPPORTIVELY. ADMINISTRATION OF OXYGEN SHOULD BE PERFORMED BY QUALIFIED PERSONNEL. GET MEDICAL ATTENTION IMMEDIATELY.

SKIN CONTACT: TRICHLORONATE OXYGEN ANALOG: SEE INFORMATION ON ORGANOPHOSPHATES.
ORGANOPHOSPHATES: CHOLINESTERASE INHIBITOR. **ACUTE EXPOSURE-** LOCALIZED SWEATING AND FASCICULATIONS MAY OCCUR AT THE SITE OF CONTACT. IF SUFFICIENT AMOUNTS ARE ABSORBED, OTHER EFFECTS OF CHOLINESTERASE INHIBITION AS DESCRIBED IN ACUTE INHALATION MAY OCCUR. SYMPTOMS MAY BE DELAYED 2-3 HOURS, BUT USUALLY NO MORE THAN 12 HOURS. THE RATE OF ABSORPTION IS INCREASED BY THE PRESENCE OF DERMATITIS OR HIGH AMBIENT TEMPERATURES. DELAYED NEUROPATHY IS ALSO POSSIBLE. **CHRONIC EXPOSURE-** REPEATED OR PROLONGED EXPOSURE MAY CAUSE EFFECTS AS DESCRIBED IN ACUTE EXPOSURE. SOME ORGANOPHOSPHATES MAY CAUSE SENSITIZATION.

FIRST AID- REMOVE CONTAMINATED CLOTHING IMMEDIATELY. WASH CONTAMINATED AREAS WITH SOAP AND WATER FOLLOWED BY ALCOHOL (ARENA, POISONING, 4TH ED.). EMERGENCY PERSONNEL SHOULD WEAR GLOVES AND AVOID CONTAMINATION. TREAT RESPIRATORY DIFFICULTY WITH ARTIFICIAL RESPIRATION. GET MEDICAL ATTENTION IMMEDIATELY.

EYE CONTACT: TRICHLORONATE OXYGEN ANALOG: SEE INFORMATION ON ORGANOPHOSPHATES.
ORGANOPHOSPHATES: CHOLINESTERASE INHIBITOR. **ACUTE EXPOSURE-** DIRECT CONTACT MAY CAUSE PAIN, HYPEREMIA, LACRIMATION, TWITCHING OF THE EYELIDS, MIOSIS, AND CILIARY MUSCLE SPASM WITH LOSS OF ACCOMODATION, BLURRED OR DIMMED VISION AND BROWACHE. SOMETIMES MYDRIASIS MAY OCCUR INSTEAD OF MIOSIS. WITH SUFFICIENT EXPOSURE, OTHER SYMPTOMS OF CHOLINESTERASE INHIBITION AS DESCRIBED IN ACUTE INHALATION MAY OCCUR. **CHRONIC EXPOSURE-** REPEATED OR PROLONGED EXPOSURE MAY CAUSE EFFECTS AS DESCRIBED IN ACUTE EXPOSURE. SOME COMPOUNDS HAVE CAUSED TOXIC EFFECTS ON THE CRYSTALLINE LENS, CONJUNCTIVAL THICKENING AND OBSTRUCTION OF THE NASOLACRIMAL CANALS WHEN USED AS MIOTIC EYEDROPS.

FIRST AID- IRRIGATE EYES WITH WATER OR SALINE SOLUTION. IF SYMPTOMS OF POISONING OCCUR, TREAT RESPIRATORY DIFFICULTY WITH ARTIFICIAL RESPIRATION AND OXYGEN. OBSERVE PATIENT FOR AT LEAST 24-36 HOURS (GOSSELIN, CLINICAL TOXICOLOGY OF COMMERCIAL PRODUCTS, 5TH ED.). GET MEDICAL ATTENTION IMMEDIATELY. OXYGEN SHOULD BE ADMINISTERED BY QUALIFIED MEDICAL PERSONNEL.

INGESTION: TRICHLORONATE OXYGEN ANALOG: SEE INFORMATION ON ORGANOPHOSPHATES.
ORGANOPHOSPHATES: CHOLINESTERASE INHIBITOR. **ACUTE EXPOSURE-** WHEN INGESTED, THE FIRST EFFECTS MAY BE NAUSEA, VOMITING, ANOREXIA, ABDOMINAL CRAMPS AND DIARRHEA. GASTROINTESTINAL ABSORPTION MAY CAUSE SYMPTOMS OF CHOLINESTERASE INHIBITION AS DESCRIBED IN ACUTE INHALATION. SYMPTOMS MAY BEGIN WITHIN MINUTES OR BE DELAYED FOR HOURS. DELAYED EFFECTS INCLUDING NEUROPATHY MAY ALSO OCCUR. **CHRONIC EXPOSURE-** REPEATED INGESTION MAY CAUSE EFFECTS AS DESCRIBED IN ACUTE EXPOSURE.

FIRST AID- IF PERSON IS ALERT AND RESPIRATION IS NOT DEPRESSED, GIVE SYRUP OF IPECAC FOLLOWED BY WATER (IF VOMITING OCCURS, KEEP HEAD BELOW HIPS TO PREVENT ASPIRATION). IF CONSCIOUSNESS LEVEL DECLINES OR VOMITING HAS NOT OCCURRED IN 15 MINUTES EMPTY STOMACH BY GASTRIC LAVAGE WITH THE AID OF CUFFED ENDOTRACHEAL TUBE USING ISOTONIC SALINE OR 5% SODIUM BICARBONATE FOLLOW WITH ACTIVATED CHARCOAL. ESTABLISH AND MAINTAIN AIRWAY. TREAT RESPIRATORY DIFFICULTY WITH ARTIFICIAL RESPIRATION AND OXYGEN. DO NOT GIVE MORPHINE, AMINOPHYLLINE, PHENOTHIAZINES, RESERPINE, FUROSEMIDE, OR ETHACRYNIC ACID (MORGAN, RECOGNITION AND MANAGEMENT OF PESTICIDE POISONINGS, 3RD ED.). TREAT SYMPTOMATICALLY AND SUPPORTIVELY. ADMINISTRATION OF OXYGEN AND LAVAGE MUST BE PERFORMED BY QUALIFIED MEDICAL PERSONNEL. GET MEDICAL ATTENTION IMMEDIATELY.

ANTIDOTE: THE FOLLOWING ANTIDOTE(S) HAVE BEEN RECOMMENDED. HOWEVER, THE DECISION AS TO WHETHER THE SEVERITY OF POISONING REQUIRES ADMINISTRATION OF ANY ANTIDOTE AND ACTUAL DOSE REQUIRED SHOULD BE MADE BY QUALIFIED MEDICAL PERSONNEL.
FOR CHOLINESTERASE INHIBITORS: ESTABLISH CLEAR AIRWAY AND TISSUE OXYGENATION BY ASPIRATION OF SECRETIONS, AND IF NECESSARY, BY ASSISTED PULMONARY VENTILATION WITH OXYGEN. IMPROVE TISSUE OXYGENATION AS MUCH AS POSSIBLE BEFORE ADMINISTERING ATROPINE TO MINIMIZE THE RISK OF VENTRICULAR FIBRILLATION. ADMINISTER ATROPINE SULFATE INTRAVENOUSLY, OR INTRAMUSCULARLY IF IV INJECTION IS NOT POSSIBLE. IN MODERATELY SEVERE POISONING ADMINISTER ATROPINE SULFATE, 0.4-2.0 MG REPEATED EVERY 15 MINUTES UNTIL ATROPINIZATION IS ACHIEVED (TACHYCARDIA, FLUSHING, DRY MOUTH, MYDRIASIS). MAINTAIN ATROPINIZATION BY REPEATED DOSES FOR 2-12 HOURS, OR LONGER, DEPENDING ON THE SEVERITY OF POISONING. THE APPEARANCE OF RALES IN THE LUNG BASES, MIOSIS, SALIVATION, NAUSEA, BRADYCARDIA, ARE ALL INDICATIONS OF INADEQUATE ATROPINIZATION. SEVERELY POISONED INDIVIDUALS MAY EXHIBIT REMARKABLE TOLERANCE TO ATROPINE; TWO OR MORE TIMES THE DOSAGES SUGGESTED ABOVE MAY BE NEEDED. PERSONS NOT POISONED OR ONLY SLIGHTLY POISONED, HOWEVER, MAY DEVELOP SIGNS OF ATROPINE TOXICITY FROM SUCH LARGE DOSAGES: FEVER, MUSCLE FIBRILLATIONS, AND DELIRIUM ARE THE MAIN SIGNS OF ATROPINE TOXICITY. IF THESE SIGNS APPEAR WHILE THE PATIENT IS FULLY ATROPINIZED, ATROPINE ADMINISTRATION SHOULD BE DISCONTINUED, AT LEAST TEMPORARILY. OBSERVE TREATED PATIENTS CLOSELY AT LEAST 24 HOURS TO INSURE THAT SYMPTOMS (POSSIBLY PULMONARY EDEMA) DO NOT RECUR AS ATROPINIZATION WEARS OFF. IN VERY SEVERE POISONINGS, METABOLIC DISPOSITION OF TOXICANT MAY REQUIRE SEVERAL HOURS OR DAYS DURING WHICH ATROPINIZATION MUST BE MAINTAINED. MARKEDLY LOWER LEVELS OF URINARY METABOLITES INDICATE THAT ATROPINE DOSAGE CAN BE TAPERED OFF. AS DOSAGE IS REDUCED, CHECK THE LUNG BASES FREQUENTLY FOR RALES. IF RALES ARE HEARD OR OTHER SYMPTOMS RETURN, RE-ESTABLISH ATROPINIZATION PROMPTLY (MORGAN, RECOGNITION AND MANAGEMENT OF PESTICIDE POISONINGS, 3RD ED.). ADMINISTRATION OF ANTIDOTE MUST BE PERFORMED BY QUALIFIED MEDICAL PERSONNEL.
IN CASES OF SEVERE POISONING BY ORGANOPHOSPHATE PESTICIDES IN WHICH RESPIRATORY DEPRESSION, MUSCLE WEAKNESS AND TWITCHINGS ARE SEVERE, GIVE PRALIDOXIME (PROTOPAM-AYERST, 2-PAM), 1.0 GRAM INTRAVENOUSLY AT NO MORE THAN 0.5 GRAM PER MINUTE. DOSAGE OF PRALIDOXIME MAY BE REPEATED IN 1-2 HOURS, THEN AT 10-12 HOUR INTERVALS IF NEEDED. IN VERY SEVERE POISONINGS, DOSAGE RATES MAY BE DOUBLED. TREATMENT WITH PRALIDOXIME WILL BE MOST EFFECTIVE IF GIVEN WITHIN THIRTY-SIX HOURS

AFTER POISONING (MORGAN, RECOGNITION AND MANAGEMENT OF PESTICIDE POISONINGS, 3RD ED.). ANTIDOTE SHOULD BE ADMINISTERED BY QUALIFIED MEDICAL PERSONNEL.

REACTIVITY

REACTIVITY: STABLE UNDER NORMAL TEMPERATURES AND PRESSURES.
INCOMPATIBILITIES: TRICHLORONATE OXYGEN ANALOG: OXIDIZERS (STRONG): FIRE AND EXPLOSION HAZARD.
DECOMPOSITION: THERMAL DECOMPOSITION PRODUCTS MAY INCLUDE TOXIC OXIDES OF CARBON AND PHOSPHOROUS AND TOXIC AND CORROSIVE FUMES OF CHLORIDES.
POLYMERIZATION: HAZARDOUS POLYMERIZATION HAS NOT BEEN REPORTED TO OCCUR UNDER NORMAL TEMPERATURES AND PRESSURES.

STORAGE AND DISPOSAL

OBSERVE ALL FEDERAL, STATE AND LOCAL REGULATIONS WHEN STORING OR DISPOSING OF THIS SUBSTANCE. FOR ASSISTANCE, CONTACT THE DISTRICT DIRECTOR OF THE ENVIRONMENTAL PROTECTION AGENCY.

STORAGE

STORE AWAY FROM INCOMPATIBLE SUBSTANCES.

CONDITIONS TO AVOID

AVOID CONTACT WITH HEAT, SPARKS, FLAMES OR OTHER IGNITION SOURCES. VAPORS MAY BE EXPLOSIVE. MATERIAL IS POISONOUS; AVOID INHALATION OF VAPORS OR CONTACT WITH SKIN. DO NOT ALLOW MATERIAL TO CONTAMINATE WATER SOURCES.

SPILL AND LEAK PROCEDURES

OCCUPATIONAL SPILL: SHUT OFF IGNITION SOURCES. DO NOT TOUCH SPILLED MATERIAL. STOP LEAK IF YOU CAN DO IT WITHOUT RISK. USE WATER SPRAY TO REDUCE VAPORS. FOR SMALL SPILLS, TAKE UP WITH SAND OR OTHER ABSORBENT MATERIAL AND PLACE INTO CONTAINERS FOR LATER DISPOSAL. FOR LARGER SPILLS, DIKE FAR AHEAD OF SPILL FOR LATER DISPOSAL. NO SMOKING, FLAMES OR FLARES IN HAZARD AREA! KEEP UNNECESSARY PEOPLE AWAY; ISOLATE HAZARD AREA AND DENY ENTRY.

PROTECTIVE EQUIPMENT

VENTILATION: PROCESS ENCLOSURE VENTILATION RECOMMENDED TO MEET PUBLISHED EXPOSURE LIMITS. VENTILATION EQUIPMENT MUST BE EXPLOSION-PROOF.
RESPIRATOR: THE FOLLOWING RESPIRATORS ARE RECOMMENDED BASED ON INFORMATION FOUND IN THE PHYSICAL DATA, TOXICITY AND HEALTH EFFECTS SECTIONS. THEY ARE RANKED IN ORDER FROM MINIMUM TO MAXIMUM RESPIRATORY PROTECTION. THE SPECIFIC RESPIRATOR SELECTED MUST BE BASED ON CONTAMINATION LEVELS FOUND IN THE WORK PLACE, MUST NOT EXCEED THE WORKING LIMITS OF THE RESPIRATOR AND BE JOINTLY APPROVED BY THE NATIONAL INSTITUTE FOR OCCUPATIONAL SAFETY AND HEALTH AND THE MINE SAFETY AND HEALTH ADMINISTRATION (NIOSH-MSHA).
CHEMICAL CARTRIDGE RESPIRATOR WITH FULL FACEPIECE AND PESTICIDE CARTRIDGE.
TYPE 'C' SUPPLIED-AIR RESPIRATOR WITH A FULL FACEPIECE OPERATED IN PRESSURE-DEMAND OR OTHER POSITIVE PRESSURE MODE OR WITH A FULL FACEPIECE, HELMET OR HOOD OPERATED IN CONTINUOUS-FLOW MODE.
SELF-CONTAINED BREATHING APPARATUS OPERATED IN PRESSURE-DEMAND OR OTHER POSITIVE PRESSURE MODE.
FOR FIREFIGHTING AND OTHER IMMEDIATELY DANGEROUS TO LIFE OR HEALTH CONDITIONS:
SELF-CONTAINED BREATHING APPARATUS WITH FULL FACEPIECE OPERATED IN PRESSURE-DEMAND OR OTHER POSITIVE PRESSURE MODE.
SUPPLIED-AIR RESPIRATOR WITH FULL FACEPIECE AND OPERATED IN PRESSURE-DEMAND OR OTHER POSITIVE PRESSURE MODE IN COMBINATION WITH AN AUXILIARY SELF-CONTAINED BREATHING APPARATUS OPERATED IN PRESSURE-DEMAND OR OTHER POSITIVE PRESSURE MODE.
CLOTHING: EMPLOYEE MUST WEAR APPROPRIATE PROTECTIVE (IMPERVIOUS) CLOTHING AND EQUIPMENT TO PREVENT REPEATED OR PROLONGED SKIN CONTACT WITH THIS SUBSTANCE.
GLOVES: EMPLOYEE MUST WEAR APPROPRIATE PROTECTIVE GLOVES TO PREVENT CONTACT WITH THIS SUBSTANCE.
EYE PROTECTION: EMPLOYEE MUST WEAR SPLASH-PROOF OR DUST-RESISTANT SAFETY GOGGLES TO PREVENT EYE CONTACT WITH THIS SUBSTANCE.
EMERGENCY EYE WASH: WHERE THERE IS ANY POSSIBILITY THAT AN EMPLOYEE'S EYES MAY BE EXPOSED TO THIS SUBSTANCE, THE EMPLOYER SHOULD PROVIDE AN EYE WASH FOUNTAIN WITHIN THE IMMEDIATE WORK AREA FOR EMERGENCY USE.

AUTHORIZED BY- OCCUPATIONAL HEALTH SERVICES, INC.

CREATION DATE: 02/02/90 ***REVISION DATE:*** 04/26/90

MATERIAL SAFETY DATA SHEET

OCCUPATIONAL HEALTH SERVICES, INC.
AGRICULTURE AND PESTICIDE DIVISION
450 SEVENTH AVENUE, SUITE 2407
NEW YORK, NEW YORK 10123
1-800-445-MSDS OR (212) 967-1100

EMERGENCY CONTACT:
JOHN S. BRANSFORD, JR. (615) 292-1180

SUBSTANCE IDENTIFICATION

CAS-NUMBER 1912-26-1
SUBSTANCE: **TRIETAZINE**
TRADE NAMES/SYNONYMS: 1,3,5-TRIAZINE-2,4-DIAMINE, 6-CHLORO-N,N,N'-TRIETHYL-; S-TRIAZINE, 2-CHLORO-4-(DIETHYLAMINO)-6-(ETHYLAMINO)-; 6-CHLORO-N,N,N'-TRIETHYL-1,3,5-TRIAZINE-2,4-DIAMINE; 2-CHLORO-4-(DIETHYLAMINO)-6-(ETHYLAMINO)-S-TRIAZINE; 2-ETHYLAMINO-4-DIETHYLAMINO-6-CHLORO-S-TRIAZINE; 2-CHLORO-4-DIETHYLAMINO-6-ETHYLAMINO-1,3,5-TRIAZINE; G 27901; GESAFLOC; NC 1667; TRIETHAZINE; TERBUTONE; C9H16CLN5; PST23927
CHEMICAL FAMILY: S-TRIAZINE
MOLECULAR FORMULA: CL-C3-N3-(N-(C2-H5)2)-N-H-C2-H5
MOLECULAR WEIGHT: 229.73
CERCLA RATINGS (SCALE 0-3): HEALTH=2 FIRE=1 REACTIVITY=0 PERSISTENCE=3
NFPA RATINGS (SCALE 0-4): HEALTH=2 FIRE=1 REACTIVITY=0

COMPONENTS AND CONTAMINANTS

COMPONENT: TRIETAZINE ***PERCENT:*** 100.0
CAS# 1912-26-1
OTHER CONTAMINANTS: NONE
EXPOSURE LIMITS: NO OCCUPATIONAL EXPOSURE LIMITS ESTABLISHED BY OSHA, ACGIH, OR NIOSH.

PHYSICAL DATA

DESCRIPTION: CRYSTALLINE SOLID ***MELTING POINT:*** 212-216 F (100-102 C)
SPECIFIC GRAVITY: NOT AVAILABLE ***SOLUBILITY IN WATER:*** 20 PPM @ 25 C
SOLVENT SOLUBILITY: PARTIALLY SOLUBLE IN ACETONE, BENZENE, CHLOROFORM, DIOXANE, SLIGHTLY SOLUBLE IN ETHANOL.

FIRE AND EXPLOSION DATA

FIRE AND EXPLOSION HAZARD: SLIGHT FIRE HAZARD WHEN EXPOSED TO HEAT OR FLAME.
FIREFIGHTING MEDIA: DRY CHEMICAL, CARBON DIOXIDE, HALON, WATER SPRAY OR STANDARD FOAM (1987 EMERGENCY RESPONSE GUIDEBOOK, DOT P 5800.4).
FOR LARGER FIRES, USE WATER SPRAY, FOG OR STANDARD FOAM (1987 EMERGENCY RESPONSE GUIDEBOOK, DOT P 5800.4).
FIREFIGHTING: MOVE CONTAINERS FROM FIRE AREA IF POSSIBLE (1987 EMERGENCY RESPONSE GUIDEBOOK, DOT P 5800.4, GUIDE PAGE 53).
EXTINGUISH USING AGENTS SUITABLE FOR SURROUNDING FIRE. USE FLOODING QUANTITIES OF WATER AS A FOG. KEEP MATERIAL OUT OF SEWERS AND WATER SOURCES. DO NOT TOUCH SPILLED MATERIAL. AVOID BREATHING HAZARDOUS FUMES; KEEP UPWIND.

TOXICITY

TRIETAZINE: TOXICITY DATA: 594 MG/KG ORAL-RAT LD50. CARCINOGEN STATUS: NONE. ACUTE TOXICITY LEVEL: MODERATELY TOXIC BY INGESTION. TARGET EFFECTS: NO DATA AVAILABLE.

HEALTH EFFECTS AND FIRST AID

INHALATION: TRIETAZINE: **ACUTE EXPOSURE-** SOME TRIAZINES ARE MILDLY IRRITATING TO THE UPPER RESPIRATORY TRACT. **CHRONIC EXPOSURE-** NO DATA AVAILABLE.
FIRST AID- REMOVE FROM EXPOSURE AREA TO FRESH AIR IMMEDIATELY. IF BREATHING HAS STOPPED, PERFORM ARTIFICIAL RESPIRATION. KEEP PERSON WARM AND AT REST. TREAT SYMPTOMATICALLY AND SUPPORTIVELY. GET MEDICAL ATTENTION IMMEDIATELY.

SKIN CONTACT: TRIETAZINE: **ACUTE EXPOSURE-** APPLICATION OF 1000 MG/KG TO THE SKIN OF RATS FOR A 24 HOUR PERIOD DID NOT PRODUCED ANY ILL EFFECTS. SOME TRIAZINES ARE MILDLY IRRITATING TO THE SKIN. **CHRONIC EXPOSURE-** NO DATA AVAILABLE.

FIRST AID- REMOVE CONTAMINATED CLOTHING AND SHOES IMMEDIATELY. WASH AFFECTED AREA WITH SOAP OR MILD DETERGENT AND LARGE AMOUNTS OF WATER UNTIL NO EVIDENCE OF CHEMICAL REMAINS (APPROXIMATELY 15-20 MINUTES). GET MEDICAL ATTENTION IMMEDIATELY.

EYE CONTACT: TRIETAZINE: **ACUTE EXPOSURE**- SOME TRIAZINES ARE MILDLY IRRITATING TO THE EYES. **CHRONIC EXPOSURE**- NO DATA AVAILABLE.
FIRST AID- WASH EYES IMMEDIATELY WITH LARGE AMOUNTS OF WATER OR NORMAL SALINE, OCCASIONALLY LIFTING UPPER AND LOWER LIDS, UNTIL NO EVIDENCE OF CHEMICAL REMAINS (APPROXIMATELY 15-20 MINUTES). GET MEDICAL ATTENTION IMMEDIATELY.

INGESTION: TRIETAZINE: **ACUTE EXPOSURE**- A LETHAL DOSE IN RATS WAS 594 MG/KG; SYMPTOMS WERE NOT REPORTED. **CHRONIC EXPOSURE**- NO ADVERSE EFFECTS WERE NOTED IN A 90-DAY STUDY OF RATS FED A 16 MG/KG DIET.
FIRST AID- REMOVE BY GASTRIC LAVAGE AND CATHARSIS. MAINTAIN BLOOD PRESSURE AND AIRWAY. GIVE OXYGEN IF RESPIRATION IS DEPRESSED. DO NOT PERFORM GASTRIC LAVAGE IF VICTIM IS UNCONSCIOUS. GET MEDICAL ATTENTION IMMEDIATELY (DREISBACH, HANDBOOK OF POISONING, 12TH ED.).
ADMINISTRATION OF LAVAGE OR OXYGEN SHOULD BE PERFORMED BY QUALIFIED MEDICAL PERSONNEL.
ANTIDOTE: NO SPECIFIC ANTIDOTE. TREAT SYMPTOMATICALLY AND SUPPORTIVELY.

REACTIVITY

REACTIVITY: STABLE UNDER NORMAL TEMPERATURES AND PRESSURES.
INCOMPATIBILITIES: TRIETAZINE: NO DATA AVAILABLE.
DECOMPOSITION: THERMAL DECOMPOSITION PRODUCTS MAY INCLUDE TOXIC OXIDES OF CARBON AND NITROGEN.
POLYMERIZATION: HAZARDOUS POLYMERIZATION HAS NOT BEEN REPORTED TO OCCUR UNDER NORMAL TEMPERATURES AND PRESSURES.

STORAGE AND DISPOSAL

OBSERVE ALL FEDERAL, STATE AND LOCAL REGULATIONS WHEN STORING OR DISPOSING OF THIS SUBSTANCE. FOR ASSISTANCE, CONTACT THE DISTRICT DIRECTOR OF THE ENVIRONMENTAL PROTECTION AGENCY.

****STORAGE****

STORE IN ACCORDANCE WITH 40 CFR 165 RECOMMENDED PROCEDURES FOR THE DISPOSAL AND STORAGE OF PESTICIDES AND PESTICIDE CONTAINERS.

****DISPOSAL****

DISPOSAL MUST BE IN ACCORDANCE WITH 40 CFR 165 RECOMMENDED PROCEDURES FOR THE DISPOSAL AND STORAGE OF PESTICIDES AND PESTICIDE CONTAINERS.

CONDITIONS TO AVOID

MAY BURN BUT DOES NOT IGNITE READILY.

SPILL AND LEAK PROCEDURES

OCCUPATIONAL SPILL: DO NOT TOUCH SPILLED MATERIAL. STOP LEAK IF YOU CAN DO IT WITHOUT RISK. FOR SMALL SPILLS, TAKE UP WITH SAND OR OTHER ABSORBENT MATERIAL AND PLACE INTO CONTAINERS FOR LATER DISPOSAL. FOR SMALL DRY SPILLS, WITH A CLEAN SHOVEL PLACE MATERIAL INTO CLEAN, DRY CONTAINER AND COVER. MOVE CONTAINERS FROM SPILL AREA. FOR LARGER SPILLS, DIKE FAR AHEAD OF SPILL FOR LATER DISPOSAL. KEEP UNNECESSARY PEOPLE AWAY. ISOLATE HAZARD AREA AND DENY ENTRY.

PROTECTIVE EQUIPMENT

VENTILATION: PROVIDE LOCAL EXHAUST OR GENERAL DILUTION VENTILATION SYSTEM.
RESPIRATOR: THE FOLLOWING RESPIRATORS ARE RECOMMENDED BASED ON INFORMATION FOUND IN THE PHYSICAL DATA, TOXICITY AND HEALTH EFFECTS SECTIONS. THEY ARE RANKED IN ORDER FROM MINIMUM TO MAXIMUM RESPIRATORY PROTECTION. THE SPECIFIC RESPIRATOR SELECTED MUST BE BASED ON CONTAMINATION LEVELS FOUND IN THE WORK PLACE, MUST NOT EXCEED THE WORKING LIMITS OF THE RESPIRATOR AND BE JOINTLY APPROVED BY THE NATIONAL INSTITUTE FOR OCCUPATIONAL SAFETY AND HEALTH AND THE MINE SAFETY AND HEALTH ADMINISTRATION (NIOSH-MSHA).
CHEMICAL CARTRIDGE RESPIRATOR WITH AN ORGANIC VAPOR CARTRIDGE(S) IN COMBINATION WITH A DUST AND MIST FILTER.
GAS MASK WITH ORGANIC VAPOR CANISTER (CHIN-STYLE OR FRONT- OR BACK-MOUNTED CANISTER) WITH A DUST AND MIST FILTER.
GAS MASK WITH ORGANIC VAPOR CANISTER (CHIN-STYLE OR FRONT- OR BACK-MOUNTED CANISTER) WITH A PARTICULATE FILTER.
POWERED AIR-PURIFYING RESPIRATOR WITH A HIGH-EFFICIENCY FILTER.
TYPE 'C' SUPPLIED-AIR RESPIRATOR WITH A FULL FACEPIECE OPERATED IN A PRESSURE-DEMAND OR OTHER POSITIVE PRESSURE MODE.
SELF-CONTAINED BREATHING APPARATUS WITH A FULL FACEPIECE OPERATED IN PRESSURE-DEMAND OR OTHER POSITIVE PRESSURE MODE.
FOR FIREFIGHTING AND OTHER IMMEDIATELY DANGEROUS TO LIFE OR HEALTH CONDITIONS:
SELF-CONTAINED BREATHING APPARATUS WITH FULL FACEPIECE OPERATED IN PRESSURE-DEMAND OR OTHER POSITIVE PRESSURE MODE.
SUPPLIED-AIR RESPIRATOR WITH FULL FACEPIECE AND OPERATED IN PRESSURE-DEMAND OR OTHER POSITIVE PRESSURE MODE IN COMBINATION WITH AN AUXILIARY SELF-CONTAINED BREATHING APPARATUS OPERATED IN PRESSURE-DEMAND OR OTHER POSITIVE PRESSURE MODE. ***CLOTHING:*** EMPLOYEE MUST WEAR APPROPRIATE PROTECTIVE (IMPERVIOUS) CLOTHING AND EQUIPMENT TO PREVENT REPEATED OR PROLONGED SKIN CONTACT WITH THIS SUBSTANCE.
GLOVES: EMPLOYEE MUST WEAR APPROPRIATE PROTECTIVE GLOVES TO PREVENT CONTACT WITH THIS SUBSTANCE.
EYE PROTECTION: EMPLOYEE MUST WEAR SPLASH-PROOF OR DUST-RESISTANT SAFETY GOGGLES TO PREVENT EYE CONTACT WITH THIS SUBSTANCE.
EMERGENCY EYE WASH: WHERE THERE IS ANY POSSIBILITY THAT AN EMPLOYEE'S EYES MAY BE EXPOSED TO THIS SUBSTANCE, THE EMPLOYER SHOULD PROVIDE AN EYE WASH FOUNTAIN WITHIN THE IMMEDIATE WORK AREA FOR EMERGENCY USE.

AUTHORIZED BY- OCCUPATIONAL HEALTH SERVICES, INC.
CREATION DATE: 10/05/89 ***REVISION DATE:*** 05/09/90

MATERIAL SAFETY DATA SHEET

OCCUPATIONAL HEALTH SERVICES, INC.
AGRICULTURE AND PESTICIDE DIVISION
450 SEVENTH AVENUE, SUITE 2407
NEW YORK, NEW YORK 10123
1-800-445-MSDS OR (212) 967-1100

EMERGENCY CONTACT:
JOHN S. BRANSFORD, JR. (615) 292-1180

SUBSTANCE IDENTIFICATION

CAS-NUMBER 102-71-6
***SUBSTANCE:* TRIETHANOLAMINE**
TRADE NAMES/SYNONYMS: 2,2',2''-NITRILOTRIETHANOL; 2,2,2-TRIHYDROXYTRIETHYLAMINE; TRI(HYDROXYETHYL)AMINE; TRIHYDROXYETHYL AMINE; TRIS(2-HYDROXYETHYL)AMINE; TROLAMINE; DALTOGEN; STEROLAMIDE; TRIETHANOLAMIN; NITRILOTRIETHANOL; STING-KILL; TRIHYDROXYTRIETHYLAMINE; TEA; 2,2',2''-NITRILOTRIS(ETHANOL); ETHANOL, 2,2',2''-NITRILOTRIS-; ETHANOL, 2,2',2''-NITRILOTRI-; TRIS(BETA-HYDROXYETHYL)AMINE; C6H15NO3; PST23932
CHEMICAL FAMILY: AMINE, ALIPHATIC
HYDROXYL, ALIPHATIC
MOLECULAR FORMULA: (H-O-C-H2-C-H2)3-N
MOLECULAR WEIGHT: 149.19
CERCLA RATINGS (SCALE 0-3): HEALTH=3 FIRE=1 REACTIVITY=1 PERSISTENCE=0
NFPA RATINGS (SCALE 0-4): HEALTH=1 FIRE=1 REACTIVITY=1

COMPONENTS AND CONTAMINANTS

COMPONENT: TRIETHANOLAMINE ***PERCENT:*** 100
CAS# 102-71-6
OTHER CONTAMINANTS: NONE
EXPOSURE LIMITS: NO OCCUPATIONAL EXPOSURE LIMITS ESTABLISHED BY OSHA, ACGIH, OR NIOSH.

PHYSICAL DATA

DESCRIPTION: COLORLESS TO PALE YELLOW, VISCOUS, HYGROSCOPIC LIQUID OR CRYSTALS WITH A SLIGHT AMMONIACAL ODOR; BECOMES BROWN ON EXPOSURE TO AIR AND LIGHT.
BOILING POINT: 635 F (335 C) ***MELTING POINT:*** 70-72 F (21-22 C)
SPECIFIC GRAVITY: 1.1242 @ 20 C ***VISCOSITY:*** 590.5 CPS @ 25 C
VOLATILITY: 100% ***VAPOR PRESSURE:*** <0.01 MMHG @ 20 C
EVAPORATION RATE: (BUTYL ACETATE=1) <0.01 ***PH:*** 10.5 @ 0.1 N SOLN
SOLUBILITY IN WATER: SOLUBLE ***VAPOR DENSITY:*** 5.1
SOLVENT SOLUBILITY: SOLUBLE IN METHANOL, ACETONE, CHLOROFORM, ALCOHOL; SLIGHTLY SOLUBLE IN BENZENE, ETHER, PETROLEUM ETHER, CARBON TETRACHLORIDE; ALMOST INSOLUBLE IN N-HEPTANE

FIRE AND EXPLOSION DATA

FIRE AND EXPLOSION HAZARD: SLIGHT FIRE HAZARD WHEN EXPOSED TO HEAT OR FLAME.

FLASH POINT: 365 F (185 C) (CC) ***LOWER EXPLOSIVE LIMIT:*** 1.3%
AUTOIGNITION TEMP.: 615 F (324 C) ***FLAMMABILITY CLASS(OSHA):*** IIIB
FIREFIGHTING MEDIA: DRY CHEMICAL, CARBON DIOXIDE, HALON, WATER SPRAY OR ALCOHOL FOAM (1987 EMERGENCY RESPONSE GUIDEBOOK, DOT P 5800.4).
FOR LARGER FIRES, USE WATER SPRAY, FOG OR ALCOHOL FOAM (1987 EMERGENCY RESPONSE GUIDEBOOK, DOT P 5800.4).
ALCOHOL FOAM (NFPA 325M, FIRE HAZARD PROPERTIES OF FLAMMABLE LIQUIDS, GASES, AND VOLATILE SOLIDS, 1984).
FIREFIGHTING: MOVE CONTAINER FROM FIRE AREA IF POSSIBLE. DO NOT SCATTER SPILLED MATERIAL WITH HIGH PRESSURE WATER STREAMS. DIKE FIRE CONTROL WATER FOR LATER DISPOSAL (1987 EMERGENCY RESPONSE GUIDEBOOK, DOT P 5800.4, GUIDE PAGE 31).
USE AGENTS SUITABLE FOR TYPE OF SURROUNDING FIRE. AVOID BREATHING HAZARDOUS VAPORS, KEEP UPWIND.
WATER OR FOAM MAY CAUSE FROTHING (NFPA 325M, FIRE HAZARD PROPERTIES OF FLAMMABLE LIQUIDS, GASES, AND VOLATILE SOLIDS, 1984)

TOXICITY

TRIETHANOLAMINE: IRRITATION DATA: 15 MG/3 DAYS INTERMITTENT SKIN-HUMAN MILD; 560 MG/24 HOURS SKIN-RABBIT MILD; 5620 UG EYE-RABBIT SEVERE; 10 MG EYE-RABBIT MILD. TOXICITY DATA: 8 GM/KG ORAL-RAT LD50; 7400 MG/KG ORAL-MOUSE LD50; 2200 MG/KG ORAL-GUINEA PIG LD50; 2200 MG/KG ORAL-RABBIT LD50; 1450 MG/KG INTRAPERITONEAL-MOUSE LD50; MUTAGENIC DATA (RTECS); TUMORIGENIC DATA (RTECS). CARCINOGEN STATUS: NONE. LOCAL EFFECTS: IRRITANT- EYE, SKIN. ACUTE TOXICITY LEVEL: SLIGHTLY TOXIC BY INGESTION. TARGET ORGAN EFFECTS: POISONING MAY AFFECT THE KIDNEYS AND LIVER. AT INCREASED RISK FROM EXPOSURE: PERSONS WITH LIVER AND KIDNEY DISEASES. ADDITIONAL DATA: CROSS SENSITIZATION REACTIONS HAVE BEEN REPORTED BETWEEN TRIETHANOLAMINE AND OTHER TERTIARY AMINES.

HEALTH EFFECTS AND FIRST AID

INHALATION: TRIETHANOLAMINE: **ACUTE EXPOSURE-** DUE TO LOW VAPOR PRESSURE, INHALATION OF TOXIC AMOUNTS IS UNLIKELY. HOWEVER, IF SUFFICIENT QUANTITIES ARE INHALED, IRRITATION OF MUCOUS MEMBRANES, COUGHING, SORE THROAT, AND SHORTNESS OF BREATH MAY OCCUR. ANIMAL EXPERIMENTS INDICATE THAT ACUTE HIGH LEVEL EXPOSURES TO ETHANOLAMINES MAY CAUSE CENTRAL NERVOUS SYSTEM DEPRESSION, PULMONARY DAMAGE AND NON-SPECIFIC HEPATIC AND RENAL LESIONS IN ANIMALS. **CHRONIC EXPOSURE-** NO DATA AVAILABLE.
FIRST AID- REMOVE FROM EXPOSURE AREA TO FRESH AIR IMMEDIATELY. IF BREATHING HAS STOPPED, PERFORM ARTIFICIAL RESPIRATION. KEEP PERSON WARM AND AT REST. TREAT SYMPTOMATICALLY AND SUPPORTIVELY. GET MEDICAL ATTENTION IMMEDIATELY.

SKIN CONTACT: TRIETHANOLAMINE: IRRITANT. **ACUTE EXPOSURE-** CONTACT MAY CAUSE IRRITATION WITH REDNESS AND PAIN, AND POSSIBLY BLISTERING. SYSTEMIC POISONING MAY OCCUR DUE TO SKIN ABSORPTION. **CHRONIC EXPOSURE-** REPEATED EXPOSURE MAY CAUSE ALLERGIC CONTACT DERMATITIS OR ECZEMA IN PREVIOUSLY SENSITIZED INDIVIDUALS. REPEATED APPLICATION TO THE SKIN OF GUINEA PIGS RESULTED IN INFLAMMATION AND SKIN ABSORPTION AFFECTING THE LUNGS, LIVER, AND KIDNEYS.
FIRST AID- REMOVE CONTAMINATED CLOTHING AND SHOES IMMEDIATELY. WASH AFFECTED AREA WITH SOAP OR MILD DETERGENT AND LARGE AMOUNTS OF WATER UNTIL NO EVIDENCE OF CHEMICAL REMAINS (APPROXIMATELY 15-20 MINUTES). GET MEDICAL ATTENTION IMMEDIATELY.

EYE CONTACT: TRIETHANOLAMINE: IRRITANT. **ACUTE EXPOSURE-** CONTACT MAY CAUSE IRRITATION, POSSIBLY SEVERE. APPLICATION OF A DROP TO RABBIT EYES CAUSED MODERATE, TRANSIENT INJURY GRADED 5 ON A SCALE OF 1-10 AFTER 24 HOURS. CONTINUOUS APPLICATION OF A 0.023 MOLAR SOLUTION ADJUSTED TO PH 11 TESTED ON RABBIT EYES CAUSED TRANSIENT IRRITATION WITH MODERATE CORNEAL SWELLING, AND HYPEREMIA OF THE IRIS AND CONJUNCTIVA. **CHRONIC EXPOSURE-** REPEATED OR PROLONGED EXPOSURE TO IRRITANTS MAY CAUSE CONJUNCTIVITIS.
FIRST AID- WASH EYES IMMEDIATELY WITH LARGE AMOUNTS OF WATER OR NORMAL SALINE, OCCASIONALLY LIFTING UPPER AND LOWER LIDS, UNTIL NO EVIDENCE OF CHEMICAL REMAINS (APPROXIMATELY 15-20 MINUTES). GET MEDICAL ATTENTION IMMEDIATELY.

INGESTION: TRIETHANOLAMINE: **ACUTE EXPOSURE-** INGESTION OF SEVERAL OUNCES OF UNNEUTRALIZED SOLUTION MAY CAUSE ALKALI BURNS OF THE MOUTH, PHARYNX, AND ESOPHAGUS, GASTROINTESTINAL IRRITATION, ABDOMINAL PAIN, VOMITING, AND DIARRHEA. SYSTEMIC ALKALOSIS AND LIVER AND KIDNEY EFFECTS HAVE BEEN REPORTED IN ANIMALS. **CHRONIC EXPOSURE-** ANIMAL STUDIES INDICATE THAT PROLONGED OR REPEATED FEEDING OF TRIETHANOLAMINE HAS CAUSED ALTERATIONS IN LIVER AND KIDNEY WEIGHT, NEPHROTOXICITY, MICROSCOPIC LESIONS, AND DEATH. AS EVALUATED BY RTECS, REPEATED ORAL ADMINISTRATION TO MICE RESULTED IN A STATISTICALLY SIGNIFICANT INCREASE IN THE INCIDENCE OF CARCINOGENIC TUMORS OF THE BLOOD, SKIN AND APPENDAGES.
FIRST AID- DILUTE THE ALKALI BY GIVING WATER OR MILK IMMEDIATELY AND ALLOW VOMITING TO OCCUR. AVOID GASTRIC LAVAGE OR EMETICS. ESOPHAGOSCOPY IS THE ONLY WAY TO EXCLUDE THE POSSIBLITY OF CORROSION IN THE UPPER GASTROINTESTINAL TRACT; IF CORROSION IS SUSPECTED, ESOPHAGOSCOPY SHOULD USUALLY BE PERFORMED WITHIN 24 HOURS (DREISBACH, HANDBOOK OF POISONING, 12TH ED.). MAINTAIN AIRWAY AND TREAT SHOCK. IF VOMITING OCCURS, KEEP HEAD BELOW HIPS TO HELP PREVENT ASPIRATION. GET MEDICAL ATTENTION IMMEDIATELY.
ANTIDOTE: NO SPECIFIC ANTIDOTE. TREAT SYMPTOMATICALLY AND SUPPORTIVELY.

REACTIVITY

REACTIVITY: NORMALLY STABLE BUT MAY BECOME UNSTABLE AT ELEVATED TEMPERATURES AND PRESSURE.
INCOMPATIBILITIES: TRIETHANOLAMINE: ACIDS (STRONG): VIOLENT REACTION. COPPER (AND ALLOYS): CORRODES. OXIDIZERS: FIRE AND EXPLOSION HAZARD.
DECOMPOSITION: THERMAL DECOMPOSITION PRODUCTS MAY INCLUDE TOXIC OXIDES OF CARBON AND NITROGEN.
POLYMERIZATION: HAZARDOUS POLYMERIZATION HAS NOT BEEN REPORTED TO OCCUR UNDER NORMAL TEMPERATURES AND PRESSURES.

STORAGE AND DISPOSAL

OBSERVE ALL FEDERAL, STATE AND LOCAL REGULATIONS WHEN STORING OR DISPOSING OF THIS SUBSTANCE. FOR ASSISTANCE, CONTACT THE DISTRICT DIRECTOR OF THE ENVIRONMENTAL PROTECTION AGENCY.

STORAGE

PROTECT AGAINST PHYSICAL DAMAGE. STORE IN A COOL, DRY, WELL VENTILATED LOCATION, AWAY FROM ANY AREA WHERE THE FIRE HAZARD MAY BE ACUTE. AVOID CONTACT WITH COPPER OR COPPER ALLOYS. OUTSIDE OR DETACHED STORAGE IS PREFERRED. ISOLATE FROM ACIDIC MATERIALS (NFPA 49, HAZARDOUS CHEMICALS DATA, 1975).
STORE AWAY FROM INCOMPATIBLE SUBSTANCES.

CONDITIONS TO AVOID

MAY BURN BUT DOES NOT IGNITE READILY. AVOID CONTACT WITH STRONG OXIDIZERS, EXCESSIVE HEAT, SPARKS, OR OPEN FLAME.

SPILL AND LEAK PROCEDURES

OCCUPATIONAL SPILL: STOP LEAK IF YOU CAN DO IT WITHOUT RISK. FOR SMALL SPILLS, TAKE UP WITH SAND OR OTHER ABSORBENT MATERIAL AND PLACE INTO CLEAN, DRY CONTAINERS FOR LATER DISPOSAL. KEEP UNNECESSARY PEOPLE AWAY. ISOLATE HAZARD AREA AND DENY ENTRY.

PROTECTIVE EQUIPMENT

VENTILATION: PROVIDE LOCAL EXHAUST OR GENERAL DILUTION VENTILATION SYSTEM.
RESPIRATOR: THE FOLLOWING RESPIRATORS ARE RECOMMENDED BASED ON INFORMATION FOUND IN THE PHYSICAL DATA, TOXICITY AND HEALTH EFFECTS SECTIONS. THEY ARE RANKED IN ORDER FROM MINIMUM TO MAXIMUM RESPIRATORY PROTECTION. THE SPECIFIC RESPIRATOR SELECTED MUST BE BASED ON CONTAMINATION LEVELS FOUND IN THE WORK PLACE, MUST NOT EXCEED THE WORKING LIMITS OF THE RESPIRATOR AND BE JOINTLY APPROVED BY THE NATIONAL INSTITUTE FOR OCCUPATIONAL SAFETY AND HEALTH AND THE MINE SAFETY AND HEALTH ADMINISTRATION (NIOSH-MSHA).
CHEMICAL CARTRIDGE RESPIRATOR WITH AN ORGANIC VAPOR CARTRIDGE(S) WITH A FULL FACEPIECE.
GAS MASK WITH ORGANIC VAPOR CANISTER (CHIN-STYLE OR FRONT- OR BACK-MOUNTED CANISTER) WITH A FULL FACEPIECE.
TYPE 'C' SUPPLIED-AIR RESPIRATOR WITH A FULL FACEPIECE OPERATED IN PRESSURE-DEMAND OR OTHER POSITIVE PRESSURE MODE OR WITH A FULL FACEPIECE, HELMET OR HOOD OPERATED IN CONTINUOUS-FLOW MODE.
SELF-CONTAINED BREATHING APPARATUS WITH A FULL FACEPIECE OPERATED IN PRESSURE-DEMAND OR OTHER POSITIVE PRESSURE MODE.
FOR FIREFIGHTING AND OTHER IMMEDIATELY DANGEROUS TO LIFE OR HEALTH CONDITIONS:
SELF-CONTAINED BREATHING APPARATUS WITH FULL FACEPIECE OPERATED IN PRESSURE-DEMAND OR OTHER POSITIVE PRESSURE MODE.
SUPPLIED-AIR RESPIRATOR WITH FULL FACEPIECE AND OPERATED IN PRESSURE-DEMAND OR OTHER POSITIVE PRESSURE MODE IN COMBINATION WITH AN AUXILIARY SELF-CONTAINED BREATHING APPARATUS OPERATED IN PRESSURE-DEMAND OR OTHER POSITIVE PRESSURE MODE.

CLOTHING: EMPLOYEE MUST WEAR APPROPRIATE PROTECTIVE (IMPERVIOUS) CLOTHING AND EQUIPMENT TO PREVENT REPEATED OR PROLONGED SKIN CONTACT WITH THIS SUBSTANCE.
GLOVES: EMPLOYEE MUST WEAR APPROPRIATE PROTECTIVE GLOVES TO PREVENT CONTACT WITH THIS SUBSTANCE.
EYE PROTECTION: EMPLOYEE MUST WEAR SPLASH-PROOF OR DUST-RESISTANT SAFETY GOGGLES TO PREVENT EYE CONTACT WITH THIS SUBSTANCE.
EMERGENCY EYE WASH: WHERE THERE IS ANY POSSIBILITY THAT AN EMPLOYEE'S EYES MAY BE EXPOSED TO THIS SUBSTANCE, THE EMPLOYER SHOULD PROVIDE AN EYE WASH FOUNTAIN WITHIN THE IMMEDIATE WORK AREA FOR EMERGENCY USE.

AUTHORIZED BY- OCCUPATIONAL HEALTH SERVICES, INC.
CREATION DATE: 10/05/89 ***REVISION DATE:*** 04/11/90

MATERIAL SAFETY DATA SHEET

OCCUPATIONAL HEALTH SERVICES, INC.
AGRICULTURE AND PESTICIDE DIVISION
450 SEVENTH AVENUE, SUITE 2407
NEW YORK, NEW YORK 10123
1-800-445-MSDS OR (212) 967-1100

EMERGENCY CONTACT:
JOHN S. BRANSFORD, JR. (615) 292-1180

SUBSTANCE IDENTIFICATION

CAS-NUMBER 112-27-6
SUBSTANCE: <u>TRIETHYLENE GLYCOL</u>
TRADE NAMES/SYNONYMS: DI-BETA-HYDROXYETHOXYETHANE; ETHANOL,2,2'-(1,2-ETHANEDIYLBIS(OXY))BIS-,; 2,2'-ETHYLENEDIOXYDIETHANOL; 2,2'-(1,2-ETHANDIYLBISLOXY))BISETHANOL; ETHYLENE GLYCOL DI-HYDROXYDIETHYL ETHER; GLYCOL BIS(HYDROXYETHYL) ETHER; TEG; TRIGEN; DICAPROATE; T-346; TRIGLYCOL; C6H14O4; PST24000
CHEMICAL FAMILY: HYDROXYL, ALIPHATIC ETHER, ALIPHATIC
MOLECULAR FORMULA: H-O-(C-H2-C-H2-O)2-C-H2-C-H2-O-H
MOLECULAR WEIGHT: 150.20
CERCLA RATINGS (SCALE 0-3): HEALTH=1 FIRE=1 REACTIVITY=0 PERSISTENCE=0
NFPA RATINGS (SCALE 0-4): HEALTH=1 FIRE=1 REACTIVITY=0

COMPONENTS AND CONTAMINANTS

COMPONENT: TRIETHYLENE GLYCOL ***PERCENT:*** 100.0
CAS# 112-27-6
OTHER CONTAMINANTS: NONE
EXPOSURE LIMITS: TRIETHYLENE GLYCOL: NO OCCUPATIONAL EXPOSURE LIMITS ESTABLISHED BY OSHA, ACGIH, OR NIOSH.
SUBJECT TO SARA SECTION 313 ANNUAL TOXIC CHEMICAL RELEASE REPORTING

PHYSICAL DATA

DESCRIPTION: ODORLESS, COLORLESS, HYGROSCOPIC LIQUID.
BOILING POINT: 533 F (278 C) ***MELTING POINT:*** 23 F (-5 C)
SPECIFIC GRAVITY: 1.1274 @ 15/4 C ***VISCOSITY:*** 47.8 CPS @ 20 C
VAPOR PRESSURE: 1.0 MMHG @ 114 C ***SOLUBILITY IN WATER:*** SOLUBLE
VAPOR DENSITY: 5.2
SOLVENT SOLUBILITY: SOLUBLE IN ALCOHOL, BENZENE, TOLUENE, GASOLINE; SPARINGLY SOLUBLE IN ETHER; PRACTICALLY INSOLUBLE IN PETROLEUM ETHER, ALIPHATIC HYDROCARBONS, AND FATS.

FIRE AND EXPLOSION DATA

FIRE AND EXPLOSION HAZARD: SLIGHT FIRE HAZARD WHEN EXPOSED TO HEAT OR FLAME.
FLASH POINT: 350 F (177 C) (CC) ***UPPER EXPLOSIVE LIMIT:*** 9.2%
LOWER EXPLOSIVE LIMIT: 0.9% ***AUTOIGNITION TEMP.:*** 700 F (371 C)
FLAMMABILITY CLASS(OSHA): IIIB
FIREFIGHTING MEDIA: DRY CHEMICAL, CARBON DIOXIDE, HALON, WATER SPRAY OR ALCOHOL FOAM (1987 EMERGENCY RESPONSE GUIDEBOOK, DOT P 5800.4).
FOR LARGER FIRES, USE WATER SPRAY, FOG OR ALCOHOL FOAM (1987 EMERGENCY RESPONSE GUIDEBOOK, DOT P 5800.4).
ALCOHOL FOAM (NFPA 325M, FIRE HAZARD PROPERTIES OF FLAMMABLE LIQUIDS, GASES, AND VOLATILE SOLIDS, 1984).
FIREFIGHTING: MOVE CONTAINER FROM FIRE AREA IF POSSIBLE. COOL FIRE-EXPOSED CONTAINERS WITH WATER FROM SIDE UNTIL WELL AFTER FIRE IS OUT. STAY AWAY FROM STORAGE TANK ENDS. FOR MASSIVE FIRE IN STORAGE AREA, USE UNMANNED HOSE HOLDER OR MONITOR NOZZLES, ELSE WITHDRAW FROM AREA AND LET FIRE BURN. WITHDRAW IMMEDIATELY IN CASE OF RISING SOUND FROM VENTING SAFETY DEVICE OR ANY DISCOLORATION OF STORAGE TANK DUE TO FIRE (1987 EMERGENCY RESPONSE GUIDEBOOK, DOT P 5800.4, GUIDE PAGE 26). EXTINGUISH ONLY IF FLOW CAN BE STOPPED; USE FLOODING AMOUNTS OF WATER AS A FOG, SOLID STREAMS MAY BE INEFFECTIVE. COOL CONTAINERS WITH FLOODING AMOUNTS OF WATER, APPLY FROM AS FAR A DISTANCE AS POSSIBLE. AVOID BREATHING VAPORS, KEEP UPWIND.
WATER OR FOAM MAY CAUSE FROTHING (NFPA 325M, FIRE HAZARD PROPERTIES OF FLAMMABLE LIQUIDS, GASES, AND VOLATILE SOLIDS, 1984)

TOXICITY

TRIETHYLENE GLYCOL: IRRITATION DATA: 500 MG/24 HOURS SKIN-RABBIT MILD. TOXICITY DATA: 5000 MG/KG ORAL-HUMAN LDLO; 17 GM/KG ORAL-RAT LD50; 18,500 MG/KG ORAL-MOUSE LDLO; 8400 MG/KG ORAL-RABBIT LD50; 7900 MG/KG ORAL-GUINEA PIG LD50; 8750 MG/KG SUBCUTANEOUS-MOUSE LD50; 11,700 MG/KG INTRAVENOUS-RAT LD50; 6500 MG/KG INTRAVENOUS-MOUSE LD50; 10,600 MG/KG INTRAVENOUS-GUINEA PIG LD50; 1900 MG/KG INTRAVENOUS-RABBIT LD50; 8141 MG/KG INTRAPERITONEAL-MOUSE LD50; 8400 MG/KG INTRAMUSCULAR-RAT LDLO; REPRODUCTIVE EFFECTS DATA (RTECS). CARCINOGEN STATUS: NONE. ACUTE TOXICITY LEVEL: RELATIVELY NON-TOXIC BY INGESTION. TARGET EFFECTS: NARCOTIC. POISONING MAY AFFECT THE KIDNEYS.

HEALTH EFFECTS AND FIRST AID

INHALATION: TRIETHYLENE GLYCOL: **<u>ACUTE EXPOSURE</u>-** DUE TO LOW VAPOR PRESSURE, INHALATION HAZARD IS UNLIKELY AT ROOM TEMPERATURE. **<u>CHRONIC EXPOSURE</u>-** PROLONGED INHALATION OF SATURATED VAPORS (APPROXIMATELY 1 PPM) WAS REPORTED TO BE WITHOUT ANY PHYSIOLOGICAL EFFECT ON MONKEYS AND RATS.
FIRST AID- REMOVE FROM EXPOSURE AREA TO FRESH AIR IMMEDIATELY. IF BREATHING HAS STOPPED, PERFORM ARTIFICIAL RESPIRATION. KEEP PERSON WARM AND AT REST. TREAT SYMPTOMATICALLY AND SUPPORTIVELY. GET MEDICAL ATTENTION IMMEDIATELY.

SKIN CONTACT: TRIETHYLENE GLYCOL: **<u>ACUTE EXPOSURE</u>-** APPLICATION OF 500 MG FOR 24 HOURS TO RABBIT SKIN UNDER OCCLUSION PRODUCED SLIGHT IRRITATION. HOWEVER, WHEN TESTED AT 20%, TRIETHYLENE GLYCOL PRODUCED NO IRRITATION AFTER A 48 HOUR CLOSED PATCH TEST IN HUMANS. NO SENSITIZATION REACTIONS WERE PRODUCED WHEN TESTED ON THE SKIN AT A 20% CONCENTRATION. **<u>CHRONIC EXPOSURE</u>-** PROLONGED CONTACT MAY RESULT IN A MACERATING ACTION ON THE SKIN.
FIRST AID- REMOVE CONTAMINATED CLOTHING AND SHOES IMMEDIATELY. WASH AFFECTED AREA WITH SOAP OR MILD DETERGENT AND LARGE AMOUNTS OF WATER UNTIL NO EVIDENCE OF CHEMICAL REMAINS (APPROXIMATELY 15-20 MINUTES). GET MEDICAL ATTENTION IMMEDIATELY.

EYE CONTACT: TRIETHYLENE GLYCOL: **<u>ACUTE EXPOSURE</u>-** A SPLASH IN HUMAN EYES CAUSES ACUTE SMARTING AND MAY BE FOLLOWED BY TRANSITORY DISTURBANCE OF CORNEAL EPITHELIUM WITH A GRADUALLY DIMINISHING SENSATION AND SIGNS OF IRRITATION. A DROP APPLIED TO RABBIT EYES CAUSED IMMEDIATE PAIN WITH NO INJURY DETECTABLE 24 HOURS LATER. APPLICATION OF 0.5 ML OF UNDILUTED TRIETHYLENE GLYCOL FAILED TO CAUSE APPRECIABLE IRRITATION IN RABBIT EYES. **<u>CHRONIC EXPOSURE</u>-** REPEATED OR PROLONGED CONTACT WITH IRRITANTS MAY CAUSE CONJUNCTIVITIS.
FIRST AID- WASH EYES IMMEDIATELY WITH LARGE AMOUNTS OF WATER OR NORMAL SALINE, OCCASIONALLY LIFTING UPPER AND LOWER LIDS, UNTIL NO EVIDENCE OF CHEMICAL REMAINS (APPROXIMATELY 15-20 MINUTES). GET MEDICAL ATTENTION IMMEDIATELY.

INGESTION: TRIETHYLENE GLYCOL: NARCOTIC. **<u>ACUTE EXPOSURE</u>-** INGESTION MAY CAUSE TRANSIENT CENTRAL NERVOUS SYSTEM STIMULATION FOLLOWED BY DEPRESSION, HEADACHE, NAUSEA, VOMITING, DROWSINESS, COMA, RESPIRATORY FAILURE, CONVULSIONS, BRAIN DAMAGE AND RENAL DAMAGE WHICH CAN ULTIMATELY CAUSE DEATH. **<u>CHRONIC EXPOSURE</u>-** RATS FED TRIETHYLENE GLYCOL AT CONCENTRATIONS OF 1.0, 2.0 AND 4.0% IN THEIR DIET FOR 2 YEARS SHOWED NO ADVERSE EFFECTS. IN ANOTHER STUDY, RATS TOLERATED 3% IN THEIR DRINKING WATER FOR 30 DAYS WITHOUT EFFECTS, BUT 5% PRODUCED ILL EFFECTS. EFFECTS ON THE NEWBORN HAVE BEEN REPORTED FROM INGESTION ON DAYS 7-14 OF PREGNANCY IN MICE.
FIRST AID- REMOVE INGESTED MATERIAL BY GASTRIC LAVAGE OR EMESIS. GIVE ARTIFICIAL RESPIRATION WITH OXYGEN IF RESPIRATION IS DEPRESSED. (DREISBACH HANDBOOK OF POISONING, 11TH ED.). GET MEDICAL ATTENTION IMMEDIATELY. ADMINISTRATION OF GASTRIC LAVAGE SHOULD BE PERFORMED BY QUALIFIED MEDICAL PERSONNEL.
ANTIDOTE: NO SPECIFIC ANTIDOTE. TREAT SYMPTOMATICALLY AND SUPPORTIVELY.

MATERIAL SAFETY DATA SHEET

OCCUPATIONAL HEALTH SERVICES, INC.
AGRICULTURE AND PESTICIDE DIVISION
450 SEVENTH AVENUE, SUITE 2407
NEW YORK, NEW YORK 10123
1-800-445-MSDS OR (212) 967-1100

EMERGENCY CONTACT:
JOHN S. BRANSFORD, JR. (615) 292-1180

SUBSTANCE IDENTIFICATION

CAS-NUMBER 1582-09-8
SUBSTANCE: **TRIFLURALIN**
TRADE NAMES/SYNONYMS: 2,6-DINITRO-N,N-DIPROPYL-4-(TRIFLUOROMETHYL)BENZENAMINE; ALPHA, ALPHA, ALPHA-TRIFLUORO-2,6-DINITRO-N,N-DIPROPYL-P-TOLUIDINE; BENZENAMINE, 2,6-DINITRO-N,N-DIPROPYL-4-(TRIFLUOROMETHYL)-; P-TOLUIDINE, ALPHA,ALPHA,ALPHA-TRIFLUORO-2,6-DINITRO-N,N-DIPROPYL; 2,6-DINITRO-N,N-DIPROPYL-ALPHA,ALPHA,ALPHA-TRIFLUORO-P-TOLUIDINE; 2,6-DINITRO-N,N-DIPROPYL-4-TRIFLUOROMETHYLANILINE; N,N-DIPROPYL-2,6-DINITRO-4-TRIFLUOROMETHYLANILINE; AGREFLAN; ELANCOLAN; L 36352; NITRAN; OLITREF; SYNFLORAN; TREFANOCIDE; TREFLAN; TRIFLORAN; TRIFLURALILNE; TRIKEPIN; C13H16F3N3O4; PST24085
CHEMICAL FAMILY: NITRO AMINE, AROMATIC
MOLECULAR FORMULA: C13-H16-F3-N3-O4
MOLECULAR WEIGHT: 335.29
CERCLA RATINGS (SCALE 0-3): HEALTH=3 FIRE=0 REACTIVITY=0 PERSISTENCE=2
NFPA RATINGS (SCALE 0-4): HEALTH=U FIRE=0 REACTIVITY=0

COMPONENTS AND CONTAMINANTS

COMPONENT: TRIFLURALIN ***PERCENT:*** 100.0
CAS# 1582-09-8
OTHER CONTAMINANTS: MAY CONTAIN 0.5 PPM N-NITROSAMINE COMPOUNDS
EXPOSURE LIMITS: TRIFLURALIN: NO OCCUPATIONAL EXPOSURE LIMITS ESTABLISHED BY OSHA, ACGIH, OR NIOSH.
SUBJECT TO SARA SECTION 313 ANNUAL TOXIC CHEMICAL RELEASE REPORTING

PHYSICAL DATA

DESCRIPTION: YELLOW-ORANGE CRYSTALLINE SOLID.
BOILING POINT: 282-284 F (139-140 C) @ 4.2 MMHG
MELTING POINT: 115-117 F (46-47 C) ***SPECIFIC GRAVITY:*** 1.294 @ 25 C
VAPOR PRESSURE: 0.0002 MMHG @ 29.5 C ***PH:*** 7.0 (50% SUSPENSION)
SOLUBILITY IN WATER: 0.0024% @ 27 C
SOLVENT SOLUBILITY: SOLUBLE IN ACETONE, ETHANOL, STODDARD SOLVENT, XYLENE, AROMATIC NAPHTHA, ORGANIC SOLVENTS

FIRE AND EXPLOSION DATA

FIRE AND EXPLOSION HAZARD: NEGLIGIBLE FIRE HAZARD WHEN EXPOSED TO HEAT OR FLAME.
FIREFIGHTING MEDIA: DRY CHEMICAL, CARBON DIOXIDE, HALON, WATER SPRAY OR STANDARD FOAM (1987 EMERGENCY RESPONSE GUIDEBOOK, DOT P 5800.4).
FOR LARGER FIRES, USE WATER SPRAY, FOG OR STANDARD FOAM (1987 EMERGENCY RESPONSE GUIDEBOOK, DOT P 5800.4).
FIREFIGHTING: NO ACUTE HAZARD. MOVE CONTAINER FROM FIRE AREA IF POSSIBLE. AVOID BREATHING VAPORS OR DUSTS; KEEP UPWIND.

TOXICITY

TRIFLURALIN: TOXICITY DATA: 5000 MG/KG ORAL-MOUSE LD50; 3700 MG/KG ORAL-MAMMAL LD50; 1500 MG/KG INTRAPERITONEAL-MOUSE LDLO; 5 GM/KG UNREPORTED-MAMMAL LDLO; MUTAGENIC DATA (RTECS); REPRODUCTIVE EFFECTS DATA (RTECS); TUMORIGENIC DATA (RTECS). CARCINOGEN STATUS: NONE. ACUTE TOXICITY LEVEL: MODERATELY TOXIC BY INGESTION. TARGET EFFECTS: SENSITIZER-SKIN.

HEALTH EFFECTS AND FIRST AID

INHALATION: TRIFLURALIN: **ACUTE EXPOSURE-** MAY CAUSE IRRITATION OF THE MUCOUS MEMBRANES. EXPOSURE OF RATS TO A MIST OF TRIFLURALIN CONTAINING 2.8 MG/LITER CAUSED NO ADVERSE EFFECTS. **CHRONIC EXPOSURE-** PROLONGED OR REPEATED EXPOSURE MAY CAUSE IRRITATION OF THE MUCOUS MEMBRANE.
FIRST AID- REMOVE FROM EXPOSURE AREA TO FRESH AIR IMMEDIATELY. IF BREATHING HAS STOPPED, PERFORM ARTIFICIAL RESPIRATION. KEEP PERSON WARM AND AT REST. TREAT SYMPTOMATICALLY AND SUPPORTIVELY. GET MEDICAL ATTENTION IMMEDIATELY.

REACTIVITY

REACTIVITY: STABLE UNDER NORMAL TEMPERATURES AND PRESSURES.
INCOMPATIBILITIES: TRIETHYLENE GLYCOL: OXIDIZERS (STRONG): FIRE AND EXPLOSION HAZARD.
DECOMPOSITION: THERMAL DECOMPOSITION MAY YIELD ACRID SMOKE AND IRRITATING FUMES.
POLYMERIZATION: HAZARDOUS POLYMERIZATION HAS NOT BEEN REPORTED TO OCCUR UNDER NORMAL TEMPERATURES AND PRESSURES.

STORAGE AND DISPOSAL

OBSERVE ALL FEDERAL, STATE AND LOCAL REGULATIONS WHEN STORING OR DISPOSING OF THIS SUBSTANCE. FOR ASSISTANCE, CONTACT THE DISTRICT DIRECTOR OF THE ENVIRONMENTAL PROTECTION AGENCY.

****STORAGE****

STORE AWAY FROM INCOMPATIBLE SUBSTANCES.

CONDITIONS TO AVOID

AVOID CONTACT WITH HEAT, SPARKS, FLAMES, OR OTHER SOURCES OF IGNITION. VAPORS MAY BE EXPLOSIVE AND POISONOUS; DO NOT ALLOW UNNECESSARY PERSONNEL IN AREA. DO NOT OVERHEAT CONTAINERS; CONTAINERS MAY VIOLENTLY RUPTURE AND TRAVEL A CONSIDERABLE DISTANCE IN HEAT OF FIRE.

SPILL AND LEAK PROCEDURES

OCCUPATIONAL SPILL: SHUT OFF IGNITION SOURCES. STOP LEAK IF YOU CAN DO IT WITHOUT RISK. USE WATER SPRAY TO REDUCE VAPORS. FOR SMALL SPILLS, TAKE UP WITH SAND OR OTHER ABSORBENT MATERIAL AND PLACE INTO CONTAINERS FOR LATER DISPOSAL. FOR LARGER SPILLS, DIKE FAR AHEAD OF SPILL FOR LATER DISPOSAL. NO SMOKING, FLAMES OR FLARES IN HAZARD AREA. KEEP UNNECESSARY PEOPLE AWAY; ISOLATE HAZARD AREA AND DENY ENTRY.

PROTECTIVE EQUIPMENT

VENTILATION: PROVIDE GENERAL DILUTION VENTILATION.
RESPIRATOR: THE FOLLOWING RESPIRATORS ARE RECOMMENDED BASED ON INFORMATION FOUND IN THE PHYSICAL DATA, TOXICITY AND HEALTH EFFECTS SECTIONS. THEY ARE RANKED IN ORDER FROM MINIMUM TO MAXIMUM RESPIRATORY PROTECTION. THE SPECIFIC RESPIRATOR SELECTED MUST BE BASED ON CONTAMINATION LEVELS FOUND IN THE WORK PLACE, MUST NOT EXCEED THE WORKING LIMITS OF THE RESPIRATOR AND BE JOINTLY APPROVED BY THE NATIONAL INSTITUTE FOR OCCUPATIONAL SAFETY AND HEALTH AND THE MINE SAFETY AND HEALTH ADMINISTRATION (NIOSH-MSHA).
CHEMICAL CARTRIDGE RESPIRATOR WITH AN ORGANIC VAPOR CARTRIDGE(S) WITH A FULL FACEPIECE.
GAS MASK WITH ORGANIC VAPOR CANISTER (CHIN-STYLE OR FRONT- OR BACK-MOUNTED CANISTER) WITH A FULL FACEPIECE.
TYPE 'C' SUPPLIED-AIR RESPIRATOR WITH A FULL FACEPIECE OPERATED IN PRESSURE-DEMAND OR OTHER POSITIVE PRESSURE MODE OR WITH A FULL FACEPIECE, HELMET OR HOOD OPERATED IN CONTINUOUS-FLOW MODE.
SELF-CONTAINED BREATHING APPARATUS WITH A FULL FACEPIECE OPERATED IN PRESSURE-DEMAND OR OTHER POSITIVE PRESSURE MODE.
FOR FIREFIGHTING AND OTHER IMMEDIATELY DANGEROUS TO LIFE OR HEALTH CONDITIONS:
SELF-CONTAINED BREATHING APPARATUS WITH FULL FACEPIECE OPERATED IN PRESSURE-DEMAND OR OTHER POSITIVE PRESSURE MODE.
SUPPLIED-AIR RESPIRATOR WITH FULL FACEPIECE AND OPERATED IN PRESSURE-DEMAND OR OTHER POSITIVE PRESSURE MODE IN COMBINATION WITH AN AUXILIARY SELF-CONTAINED BREATHING APPARATUS OPERATED IN PRESSURE-DEMAND OR OTHER POSITIVE PRESSURE MODE.
CLOTHING: EMPLOYEE MUST WEAR APPROPRIATE PROTECTIVE (IMPERVIOUS) CLOTHING AND EQUIPMENT TO PREVENT REPEATED OR PROLONGED SKIN CONTACT WITH THIS SUBSTANCE.
GLOVES: EMPLOYEE MUST WEAR APPROPRIATE PROTECTIVE GLOVES TO PREVENT CONTACT WITH THIS SUBSTANCE.
EYE PROTECTION: EMPLOYEE MUST WEAR SPLASH-PROOF OR DUST-RESISTANT SAFETY GOGGLES TO PREVENT EYE CONTACT WITH THIS SUBSTANCE.
EMERGENCY EYE WASH: WHERE THERE IS ANY POSSIBILITY THAT AN EMPLOYEE'S EYES MAY BE EXPOSED TO THIS SUBSTANCE, THE EMPLOYER SHOULD PROVIDE AN EYE WASH FOUNTAIN WITHIN THE IMMEDIATE WORK AREA FOR EMERGENCY USE.

AUTHORIZED BY- OCCUPATIONAL HEALTH SERVICES, INC.
CREATION DATE: 10/05/89 ***REVISION DATE:*** 05/11/90

SKIN CONTACT: TRIFLURALIN: SENSITIZER. **ACUTE EXPOSURE**- SENSITIZATION DERMATITIS MAY OCCUR IN PERSONS PREVIOUSLY EXPOSED. NO SKIN IRRITATION OR TOXICITY TO RABBITS WAS OBSERVED WHEN TRIFLURALIN WAS PAINTED ON THE SKIN AT A LEVEL OF 2.5 GM/KG **CHRONIC EXPOSURE**- PROLONGED OR REPEATED EXPOSURE MAY CAUSE SENSITIZATION DERMATITIS IN SOME INDIVIDUALS. EXTENSIVELY EXPOSED WORKERS HAVE DEVELOPED CONTACT DERMATITIS AND PHOTODERMATITIS.

FIRST AID- REMOVE CONTAMINATED CLOTHING AND SHOES IMMEDIATELY. WASH AFFECTED AREA WITH SOAP OR MILD DETERGENT AND LARGE AMOUNTS OF WATER UNTIL NO EVIDENCE OF CHEMICAL REMAINS (APPROXIMATELY 15-20 MINUTES). GET MEDICAL ATTENTION IMMEDIATELY.

EYE CONTACT: TRIFLURALIN: **ACUTE EXPOSURE**- APPLIED TO THE EYES OF RABBITS, THIS MATERIAL PRODUCED SLIGHT IRRITATION WHICH CLEARED WITHIN 7 DAYS. **CHRONIC EXPOSURE**- NO DATA AVAILABLE.

FIRST AID- WASH EYES IMMEDIATELY WITH LARGE AMOUNTS OF WATER OR NORMAL SALINE, OCCASIONALLY LIFTING UPPER AND LOWER LIDS, UNTIL NO EVIDENCE OF CHEMICAL REMAINS (APPROXIMATELY 15-20 MINUTES). GET MEDICAL ATTENTION IMMEDIATELY.

INGESTION: TRIFLURALIN: **ACUTE EXPOSURE**- A LETHAL DOSE IN MICE WAS 5000 MG/KG. IN 1-2 DAY OLD RATS, A LETHAL DOSE WAS 500 MG/KG. HOWEVER, THIS MATERIAL WAS RELATIVELY NONTOXIC IN RATS AGED 49-56 DAYS WITH A LETHAL DOSE GREATER THAN 36,500 MG/KG. THIS SUBSTANCE IS POORLY ABSORBED FROM THE GASTROINTESTINAL TRACT, AND 80% OF AN ORAL DOSE IN RATS AND DOGS WAS EXCRETED IN THE FECES. **CHRONIC EXPOSURE**- REPEATED GAVAGE TO PREGNANT MICE RESULTED IN AN INCREASED FREQUENCY OF STILLBIRTHS AND ATYPICAL PUPS INCLUDING INCIDENCES OF SKELETAL VARIATION. ANOREXIA AND CACHEXIA WITH RESULTING ABORTION WERE OBSERVED IN A STUDY OF PREGNANT RABBITS FED AT DOSAGES OF 224 OR 500 MG/KG/DAY. DEPRESSED FETAL WEIGHT AND AN INCREASED NUMBER OF FETAL RUNTS WERE ALSO OBSERVED AT THE 500 MG/KG/DAY DOSAGE. IN A TWO-YEAR STUDY OF RATS, STATISTICALLY SIGNIFICANT INCIDENCES OF MALIGNANT NEOPLASMS OF THE KIDNEY, COMBINED BENIGN AND MALIGNANT NEOPLASMS OF THE BLADDER, AND FOLLICULAR CELL ADENOMAS AND CARCINOMAS OF THE THYROID WERE REPORTED AT A DIETARY LEVEL OF 6500 PPM. OTHER EFFECTS OBSERVED IN THIS STUDY INCLUDED THE FORMATION OF RENAL CALCULI, SIGNIFICANT INCREASES IN HYPERPLASIA OF THE PELVIC EPITHELIA, SIGNIFICANT INCREASES IN CHRONIC PROGRESSIVE NEPHROSIS; AND INCREASED BLOOD UREA NITROGEN.

FIRST AID- REMOVE BY GASTRIC LAVAGE AND CATHARSIS. MAINTAIN BLOOD PRESSURE AND AIRWAY. GIVE OXYGEN IF RESPIRATION IS DEPRESSED. DO NOT PERFORM GASTRIC LAVAGE IF VICTIM IS UNCONSCIOUS. GET MEDICAL ATTENTION IMMEDIATELY (DREISBACH, HANDBOOK OF POISONING, 12TH ED.).
ADMINISTRATION OF LAVAGE OR OXYGEN SHOULD BE PERFORMED BY QUALIFIED MEDICAL PERSONNEL.

ANTIDOTE: NO SPECIFIC ANTIDOTE. TREAT SYMPTOMATICALLY AND SUPPORTIVELY.

REACTIVITY

REACTIVITY: STABLE UNDER NORMAL CONDITIONS IN AN ENCLOSED CONTAINER. TRIFLURALIN IS UNSTABLE TO BOTH SUNLIGHT AND ARTIFICIAL LIGHT.

INCOMPATIBILITIES: TRIFLURALIN: OXIDIZERS: FIRE AND EXPLOSION HAZARD.

DECOMPOSITION: THERMAL DECOMPOSITION MAY PRODUCE CORROSIVE FUMES OF HYDROGEN FLUORIDE AND TOXIC OXIDES OF NITROGEN.

POLYMERIZATION: HAZARDOUS POLYMERIZATION HAS NOT BEEN REPORTED TO OCCUR UNDER NORMAL TEMPERATURES AND PRESSURES.

STORAGE AND DISPOSAL

OBSERVE ALL FEDERAL, STATE AND LOCAL REGULATIONS WHEN STORING OR DISPOSING OF THIS SUBSTANCE. FOR ASSISTANCE, CONTACT THE DISTRICT DIRECTOR OF THE ENVIRONMENTAL PROTECTION AGENCY.

****STORAGE****

STORE IN ACCORDANCE WITH 40 CFR 165 RECOMMENDED PROCEDURES FOR THE DISPOSAL AND STORAGE OF PESTICIDES AND PESTICIDE CONTAINERS.
STORE AWAY FROM INCOMPATIBLE SUBSTANCES.

****DISPOSAL****

DISPOSAL MUST BE IN ACCORDANCE WITH 40 CFR 165 RECOMMENDED PROCEDURES FOR THE DISPOSAL AND STORAGE OF PESTICIDES AND PESTICIDE CONTAINERS.

CONDITIONS TO AVOID

NONE REPORTED.

SPILL AND LEAK PROCEDURES

OCCUPATIONAL SPILL: NO SPECIAL PRECAUTIONS INDICATED.

PROTECTIVE EQUIPMENT

VENTILATION: PROVIDE LOCAL EXHAUST VENTILATION SYSTEM.

RESPIRATOR: THE FOLLOWING RESPIRATORS ARE RECOMMENDED BASED ON INFORMATION FOUND IN THE PHYSICAL DATA, TOXICITY AND HEALTH EFFECTS SECTIONS. THEY ARE RANKED IN ORDER FROM MINIMUM TO MAXIMUM RESPIRATORY PROTECTION. THE SPECIFIC RESPIRATOR SELECTED MUST BE BASED ON CONTAMINATION LEVELS FOUND IN THE WORK PLACE, MUST NOT EXCEED THE WORKING LIMITS OF THE RESPIRATOR AND BE JOINTLY APPROVED BY THE NATIONAL INSTITUTE FOR OCCUPATIONAL SAFETY AND HEALTH AND THE MINE SAFETY AND HEALTH ADMINISTRATION (NIOSH-MSHA).
CHEMICAL CARTRIDGE RESPIRATOR WITH AN ORGANIC VAPOR CARTRIDGE(S) WITH A FULL FACEPIECE AND ORGANIC VAPOR CARTRIDGE(S) IN COMBINATION WITH A DUST AND MIST FILTER.
POWERED AIR-PURIFYING RESPIRATOR WITH A TIGHT-FITTING FACEPIECE AND ORGANIC VAPOR CARTRIDGE(S) IN COMBINATION WITH A HIGH-EFFICIENCY PARTICULATE FILTER.
TYPE 'C' SUPPLIED-AIR RESPIRATOR WITH A FULL FACEPIECE OPERATED IN A PRESSURE-DEMAND OR OTHER POSITIVE PRESSURE MODE.
SELF-CONTAINED BREATHING APPARATUS WITH A FULL FACEPIECE OPERATED IN PRESSURE-DEMAND OR OTHER POSITIVE PRESSURE MODE.
FOR FIREFIGHTING AND OTHER IMMEDIATELY DANGEROUS TO LIFE OR HEALTH CONDITIONS:
SELF-CONTAINED BREATHING APPARATUS WITH FULL FACEPIECE OPERATED IN PRESSURE-DEMAND OR OTHER POSITIVE PRESSURE MODE.
SUPPLIED-AIR RESPIRATOR WITH FULL FACEPIECE AND OPERATED IN PRESSURE-DEMAND OR OTHER POSITIVE PRESSURE MODE IN COMBINATION WITH AN AUXILIARY SELF-CONTAINED BREATHING APPARATUS OPERATED IN PRESSURE-DEMAND OR OTHER POSITIVE PRESSURE MODE.

CLOTHING: EMPLOYEE MUST WEAR APPROPRIATE PROTECTIVE (IMPERVIOUS) CLOTHING AND EQUIPMENT TO PREVENT REPEATED OR PROLONGED SKIN CONTACT WITH THIS SUBSTANCE.

GLOVES: EMPLOYEE MUST WEAR APPROPRIATE PROTECTIVE GLOVES TO PREVENT CONTACT WITH THIS SUBSTANCE.

EYE PROTECTION: EMPLOYEE MUST WEAR SPLASH-PROOF OR DUST-RESISTANT SAFETY GOGGLES TO PREVENT EYE CONTACT WITH THIS SUBSTANCE.
EMERGENCY EYE WASH: WHERE THERE IS ANY POSSIBILITY THAT AN EMPLOYEE'S EYES MAY BE EXPOSED TO THIS SUBSTANCE, THE EMPLOYER SHOULD PROVIDE AN EYE WASH FOUNTAIN WITHIN THE IMMEDIATE WORK AREA FOR EMERGENCY USE.

AUTHORIZED BY- OCCUPATIONAL HEALTH SERVICES, INC.
CREATION DATE: 10/05/89 ***REVISION DATE:*** 05/07/90

MATERIAL SAFETY DATA SHEET

OCCUPATIONAL HEALTH SERVICES, INC.
AGRICULTURE AND PESTICIDE DIVISION
450 SEVENTH AVENUE, SUITE 2407
NEW YORK, NEW YORK 10123
1-800-445-MSDS OR (212) 967-1100

EMERGENCY CONTACT:
JOHN S. BRANSFORD, JR. (615) 292-1180

SUBSTANCE IDENTIFICATION

CAS-NUMBER 26644-46-2

SUBSTANCE: **TRIFORINE**

TRADE NAMES/SYNONYMS: FORMAMIDE, N,N'-(1,4-PIPERAZINEDIYLBIS(2,2,2-TRICHLOROETHYLIDENE)BIS-; N,N'-(1,4-PIPERAZINEDIYLBIS(2,2,2-TRICHLOROETHYLIDENE))BISFORMAMIDE; 1,4-DI(2,2,2-TRICHLORO-1-FORMAMIDOETHYL)PIPERAZINE; 1,4-BIS(1-FORMAMIDO-2,2,2-TRICHLOROETHYL)PIPERAZINE; N,N'-(PIPERAZINE-1,4-DIYLBIS((TRICHLOROMETHYL)METHYLENE))DIFORMAMIDE; 1,1'-PIPERAZINE-1,4-DIYLDI-(N-(2,2,2-TRICHLOROETHYL)FORMAMIDE; 1,4-BIS(2,2,2-TRICHLORO-1-FORMAMIDOETHYL)PIPERAZINE; N,N'-(1,4-PIPERAZINEDIYLBIS(2,2,2-TRICHLOROETHYLIDENE)BIS(FORMAMIDE); ASEPTA FUNGINEX; BIFORMYLCHLORAZIN; CA 70203; CELA W 524; FUNGINEX; SAPROL; TRIFORIN; C10H14CL6N4O2; PST24086

CHEMICAL FAMILY: PIPERAZINE

MOLECULAR FORMULA: C10-H14-CL6-N4-O2

MOLECULAR WEIGHT: 434.98

CERCLA RATINGS (SCALE 0-3): HEALTH = 1 FIRE = U REACTIVITY = U PERSISTENCE = 3

NFPA RATINGS (SCALE 0-4): HEALTH = 1 FIRE = U REACTIVITY = U

COMPONENTS AND CONTAMINANTS

COMPONENT: TRIFORINE ***PERCENT:*** 100.0
CAS# 26644-46-2
OTHER CONTAMINANTS: NONE
EXPOSURE LIMITS: NO OCCUPATIONAL EXPOSURE LIMITS ESTABLISHED BY OSHA, ACGIH, OR NIOSH.

PHYSICAL DATA

DESCRIPTION: WHITE CRYSTALS ***MELTING POINT:*** 311 F (155 C)
SPECIFIC GRAVITY: NOT AVAILABLE ***VAPOR PRESSURE:*** .0000002 MMHG @ 25C
SOLUBILITY IN WATER: 0.003% @ 20 C
SOLVENT SOLUBILITY: SOLUBLE IN TETRAHYDROFURAN, DIMETHYLFORMAMIDE, DIMETHYL SULFOXIDE, 1-METHYLPYRROLID-2-ONE; SLIGHTLY SOLUBLE IN DIOXANE, CYCLOHEXANONE; LOW SOLUBILITY IN ACETONE, BENZENE, CHLOROFORM, DICHLOROMETHANE

FIRE AND EXPLOSION DATA

FIRE AND EXPLOSION HAZARD: UNKNOWN FIRE AND EXPLOSION HAZARD.
FIREFIGHTING MEDIA: DRY CHEMICAL, CARBON DIOXIDE, WATER SPRAY OR FOAM FOR LARGER FIRES, USE WATER SPRAY, FOG OR ALCOHOL FOAM
FIREFIGHTING: MOVE CONTAINER FROM FIRE AREA IF POSSIBLE. DO NOT SCATTER SPILLED MATERIAL WITH HIGH PRESSURE WATER STREAMS. DIKE FIRE CONTROL WATER FOR LATER DISPOSAL (1987 EMERGENCY RESPONSE GUIDEBOOK, DOT P 5800.4, GUIDE PAGE 31).
USE AGENTS SUITABLE FOR TYPE OF SURROUNDING FIRE. AVOID BREATHING HAZARDOUS VAPORS, KEEP UPWIND.

TOXICITY

TRIFORINE: TOXICITY DATA: 6 GM/KG ORAL-RAT LD50. CARCINOGEN STATUS: NONE. ACUTE TOXICITY LEVEL: SLIGHTLY TOXIC BY INGESTION. TARGET EFFECTS: NO DATA AVAILABLE.

HEALTH EFFECTS AND FIRST AID

INHALATION: TRIFORINE: **ACUTE EXPOSURE-** A LETHAL CONCENTRATION IN RATS WAS GREATER THAN 4500 MG/M3/1 HOUR. **CHRONIC EXPOSURE-** NO DATA AVAILABLE.
FIRST AID- REMOVE FROM EXPOSURE AREA TO FRESH AIR IMMEDIATELY. IF BREATHING HAS STOPPED, PERFORM ARTIFICIAL RESPIRATION. KEEP PERSON WARM AND AT REST. TREAT SYMPTOMATICALLY AND SUPPORTIVELY. GET MEDICAL ATTENTION IMMEDIATELY.

SKIN CONTACT: TRIFORINE: **ACUTE EXPOSURE-** A LETHAL DOSE BY DERMAL ABSORPTION IN RABBITS WAS GREATER THAN 10,000 MG/KG. **CHRONIC EXPOSURE-** NO DATA AVAILABLE.
FIRST AID- REMOVE CONTAMINATED CLOTHING AND SHOES IMMEDIATELY. WASH AFFECTED AREA WITH SOAP OR MILD DETERGENT AND LARGE AMOUNTS OF WATER UNTIL NO EVIDENCE OF CHEMICAL REMAINS (APPROXIMATELY 15-20 MINUTES). GET MEDICAL ATTENTION IMMEDIATELY.

EYE CONTACT: TRIFORINE: **ACUTE EXPOSURE-** NO DATA AVAILABLE. **CHRONIC EXPOSURE-** NO DATA AVAILABLE.
FIRST AID- WASH EYES IMMEDIATELY WITH LARGE AMOUNTS OF WATER OR NORMAL SALINE, OCCASIONALLY LIFTING UPPER AND LOWER LIDS, UNTIL NO EVIDENCE OF CHEMICAL REMAINS (APPROXIMATELY 15-20 MINUTES). GET MEDICAL ATTENTION IMMEDIATELY.

INGESTION: TRIFORINE: **ACUTE EXPOSURE-** A LETHAL DOSE IN RATS WAS 6 GM/KG. THIS COMPOUND IS RAPIDLY ABSORBED AND METABOLIZED BY THE RAT. **CHRONIC EXPOSURE-** A DECREASED NUMBER OF FETUSES AND AN INCREASED NUMBER OF OF RESORPTIONS WERE OBSERVED IN A STUDY OF PREGNANT RATS FED TRIFORINE AT A DIETARY LEVEL OF 1600 MG/KG. HIGH DOSAGES IN SUBCHRONIC ANIMAL STUDIES DEMONSTRATED ADVERSE EFFECTS ON RED BLOOD CELLS AND DEPOSITION OF IRON IN SEVERAL ORGANS.
FIRST AID- REMOVE BY GASTRIC LAVAGE AND CATHARSIS. MAINTAIN BLOOD PRESSURE AND AIRWAY. GIVE OXYGEN IF RESPIRATION IS DEPRESSED. DO NOT PERFORM GASTRIC LAVAGE IF VICTIM IS UNCONSCIOUS. GET MEDICAL ATTENTION IMMEDIATELY (DREISBACH, HANDBOOK OF POISONING, 12TH ED.).
ADMINISTRATION OF LAVAGE OR OXYGEN SHOULD BE PERFORMED BY QUALIFIED MEDICAL PERSONNEL.
ANTIDOTE: NO SPECIFIC ANTIDOTE. TREAT SYMPTOMATICALLY AND SUPPORTIVELY.

REACTIVITY

REACTIVITY: NO DATA AVAILABLE.
INCOMPATIBILITIES: TRIFORINE: CONCENTRATED SULFURIC ACID: DECOMPOSES. CONCENTRATED HYDROCHLORIC ACID: DECOMPOSES. CONCENTRATED ALKALI: DECOMPOSES.
DECOMPOSITION: THERMAL DECOMPOSITION MAY RELEASE TOXIC AND/OR HAZARDOUS GASES.
POLYMERIZATION: HAZARDOUS POLYMERIZATION HAS NOT BEEN REPORTED TO OCCUR UNDER NORMAL TEMPERATURES AND PRESSURES.

STORAGE AND DISPOSAL

OBSERVE ALL FEDERAL, STATE AND LOCAL REGULATIONS WHEN STORING OR DISPOSING OF THIS SUBSTANCE. FOR ASSISTANCE, CONTACT THE DISTRICT DIRECTOR OF THE ENVIRONMENTAL PROTECTION AGENCY.

****STORAGE****

STORE IN ACCORDANCE WITH 40 CFR 165 RECOMMENDED PROCEDURES FOR THE DISPOSAL AND STORAGE OF PESTICIDES AND PESTICIDE CONTAINERS.
STORE AWAY FROM INCOMPATIBLE SUBSTANCES.

****DISPOSAL****

DISPOSAL MUST BE IN ACCORDANCE WITH 40 CFR 165 RECOMMENDED PROCEDURES FOR THE DISPOSAL AND STORAGE OF PESTICIDES AND PESTICIDE CONTAINERS.

CONDITIONS TO AVOID

NONE REPORTED.

SPILL AND LEAK PROCEDURES

OCCUPATIONAL SPILL: SWEEP UP AND PLACE IN SUITABLE CLEAN, DRY CONTAINERS FOR RECLAMATION OR LATER DISPOSAL. DO NOT FLUSH SPILLED MATERIAL INTO SEWER. KEEP UNNECESSARY PEOPLE AWAY.

PROTECTIVE EQUIPMENT

VENTILATION: PROVIDE LOCAL EXHAUST OR GENERAL DILUTION VENTILATION SYSTEM.
RESPIRATOR: THE FOLLOWING RESPIRATORS ARE RECOMMENDED BASED ON INFORMATION FOUND IN THE PHYSICAL DATA, TOXICITY AND HEALTH EFFECTS SECTIONS. THEY ARE RANKED IN ORDER FROM MINIMUM TO MAXIMUM RESPIRATORY PROTECTION. THE SPECIFIC RESPIRATOR SELECTED MUST BE BASED ON CONTAMINATION LEVELS FOUND IN THE WORK PLACE, MUST NOT EXCEED THE WORKING LIMITS OF THE RESPIRATOR AND BE JOINTLY APPROVED BY THE NATIONAL INSTITUTE FOR OCCUPATIONAL SAFETY AND HEALTH AND THE MINE SAFETY AND HEALTH ADMINISTRATION (NIOSH-MSHA).
CHEMICAL CARTRIDGE RESPIRATOR WITH AN ORGANIC VAPOR CARTRIDGE(S) WITH A FULL FACEPIECE AND ORGANIC VAPOR CARTRIDGE(S) IN COMBINATION WITH A DUST AND MIST FILTER.
POWERED AIR-PURIFYING RESPIRATOR WITH A TIGHT-FITTING FACEPIECE AND ORGANIC VAPOR CARTRIDGE(S) IN COMBINATION WITH A HIGH-EFFICIENCY PARTICULATE FILTER.
TYPE 'C' SUPPLIED-AIR RESPIRATOR WITH A FULL FACEPIECE OPERATED IN A PRESSURE-DEMAND OR OTHER POSITIVE PRESSURE MODE.
SELF-CONTAINED BREATHING APPARATUS WITH A FULL FACEPIECE OPERATED IN PRESSURE-DEMAND OR OTHER POSITIVE PRESSURE MODE.
FOR FIREFIGHTING AND OTHER IMMEDIATELY DANGEROUS TO LIFE OR HEALTH CONDITIONS:
SELF-CONTAINED BREATHING APPARATUS WITH FULL FACEPIECE OPERATED IN PRESSURE-DEMAND OR OTHER POSITIVE PRESSURE MODE.
SUPPLIED-AIR RESPIRATOR WITH FULL FACEPIECE AND OPERATED IN PRESSURE-DEMAND OR OTHER POSITIVE PRESSURE MODE IN COMBINATION WITH AN AUXILIARY SELF-CONTAINED BREATHING APPARATUS OPERATED IN PRESSURE-DEMAND OR OTHER POSITIVE PRESSURE MODE.
CLOTHING: EMPLOYEE MUST WEAR APPROPRIATE PROTECTIVE (IMPERVIOUS) CLOTHING AND EQUIPMENT TO PREVENT REPEATED OR PROLONGED SKIN CONTACT WITH THIS SUBSTANCE.
GLOVES: EMPLOYEE MUST WEAR APPROPRIATE PROTECTIVE GLOVES TO PREVENT CONTACT WITH THIS SUBSTANCE.
EYE PROTECTION: EMPLOYEE MUST WEAR SPLASH-PROOF OR DUST-RESISTANT SAFETY GOGGLES TO PREVENT EYE CONTACT WITH THIS SUBSTANCE.
EMERGENCY EYE WASH: WHERE THERE IS ANY POSSIBILITY THAT AN EMPLOYEE'S EYES MAY BE EXPOSED TO THIS SUBSTANCE, THE EMPLOYER SHOULD PROVIDE AN EYE WASH FOUNTAIN WITHIN THE IMMEDIATE WORK AREA FOR EMERGENCY USE.

AUTHORIZED BY- OCCUPATIONAL HEALTH SERVICES, INC.
CREATION DATE: 10/05/89 ***REVISION DATE:*** 05/31/90

MATERIAL SAFETY DATA SHEET

OCCUPATIONAL HEALTH SERVICES, INC.
AGRICULTURE AND PESTICIDE DIVISION
450 SEVENTH AVENUE, SUITE 2407
NEW YORK, NEW YORK 10123
1-800-445-MSDS OR (212) 967-1100

EMERGENCY CONTACT:
JOHN S. BRANSFORD, JR. (615) 292-1180

SUBSTANCE IDENTIFICATION

CAS-NUMBER 900-95-8

SUBSTANCE: **TRIPHENYLTIN ACETATE**

TRADE NAMES/SYNONYMS: ACETOXYTRIPHENYLSTANNANE; (ACETOXY)TRIPHENYLSTANNANE; BATASAN; BRESTAN; FENTIN ACETATE; GC 6936; LIROMATIN; LIROSTANOL; PHENTIN ACETATE; SUZU; TINESTAN; TIN TRIPHENYL ACETATE; TPTA; TRIPHENYLACETO STANNANE; VP 19-40; PST24378

CHEMICAL FAMILY: HYDROCARBON, AROMATIC

MOLECULAR FORMULA: C20-H18-02-SN

MOLECULAR WEIGHT: 409.07

CERCLA RATINGS (SCALE 0-3): HEALTH=3 FIRE=U REACTIVITY=0 PERSISTENCE=3

NFPA RATINGS (SCALE 0-4): HEALTH=3 FIRE=U REACTIVITY=3

COMPONENTS AND CONTAMINANTS

COMPONENT: TRIPHENYLTIN ACETATE ***PERCENT:*** 100.0
CAS# 900-95-8

OTHER CONTAMINANTS: NONE

EXPOSURE LIMITS: TRIPHENYLTIN ACETATE: 0.1 MG(SN)/M3 OSHA TWA 0.1 MG(SN)/M3 ACGIH TWA (SKIN) 0.1 MG(SN)/M3 NIOSH RECOMMENDED 10 HOUR TWA
500/10,000 POUNDS SARA SECTION 302 THRESHOLD PLANNING QUANTITY 1 POUND SARA SECTION 304 REPORTABLE QUANTITY

PHYSICAL DATA

DESCRIPTION: WHITE CRYSTALLINE SOLID ***MELTING POINT:*** 250-255 F (121-124 C)

SPECIFIC GRAVITY: NOT AVAILABLE ***VAPOR PRESSURE:*** .014 MMHG @ 60 C

SOLUBILITY IN WATER: SLIGHTLY SOLUBLE

SOLVENT SOLUBILITY: SOLUBLE IN ETHER; SLIGHTLY SOL IN ALCOHOL, BENZENE; POORLY SOLUBLE IN MOST ORGANIC SOLVENTS

FIRE AND EXPLOSION DATA

FIRE AND EXPLOSION HAZARD: UNKNOWN FIRE AND EXPLOSION HAZARD.

FIREFIGHTING MEDIA: DRY CHEMICAL, CARBON DIOXIDE, HALON, WATER SPRAY OR STANDARD FOAM (1987 EMERGENCY RESPONSE GUIDEBOOK, DOT P 5800.4).
FOR LARGER FIRES, USE WATER SPRAY, FOG OR STANDARD FOAM (1987 EMERGENCY RESPONSE GUIDEBOOK, DOT P 5800.4).

FIREFIGHTING: MOVE CONTAINERS FROM FIRE AREA IF POSSIBLE (1987 EMERGENCY RESPONSE GUIDEBOOK, DOT P 5800.4, GUIDE PAGE 53).
EXTINGUISH USING AGENT SUITABLE FOR TYPE OF SURROUNDING FIRE. AVOID BREATHING VAPORS AND DUSTS. KEEP UPWIND.

TOXICITY

TRIPHENYLTIN ACETATE: TOXICITY DATA: 450 MG/KG SKIN-RAT LD50; 180 MG/KG SKIN-GUINEA PIG LDLO; 125 MG/KG ORAL-RAT LD50; 81 MG/KG ORAL-MOUSE LD50; 30 MG/KG ORAL-RABBIT LD50; 21 MG/KG ORAL-GUINEA PIG LD50; 44 MG/KG SUBCUTANEOUS-MOUSE LD50; 18 MG/KG INTRAVENOUS-RAT LD50; 18 MG/KG INTRAVENOUS-MOUSE LD50; 8500 UG/KG INTRAPERITONEAL-RAT LD50; 719 MG/KG INTRAPERITONEAL-MOUSE LD50; 10 MG/KG INTRAPERITONEAL-RABBIT LD50; 374 UG/KG INTRAPERITONEAL-GUINEA PIG LD50; REPRODUCTIVE EFFECTS DATA (RTECS); TUMORIGENIC DATA (RTECS). CARCINOGEN STATUS: NONE. LOCAL EFFECTS: IRRITANT- INHALATION, SKIN, AND EYES. ACUTE TOXICITY LEVEL: TOXIC BY DERMAL ABSORPTION AND INGESTION. TARGET EFFECTS: POISONING MAY AFFECT THE LUNGS, LIVER, KIDNEYS, AND CENTRAL NERVOUS SYSTEM. AT INCREASED RISK FROM EXPOSURE: PERSONS WITH LUNG, SKIN, LIVER, AND KIDNEY DISEASES.

HEALTH EFFECTS AND FIRST AID

INHALATION: TRIPHENYLTIN ACETATE: 100 MG(SN)/M3 IMMEDIATELY DANGEROUS TO LIFE OR DEATH. IRRITANT. **ACUTE EXPOSURE-** IN MAN, OCCUPATIONAL EXPOSURES HAVE CAUSED IRRITATION OF THE RESPIRATORY TRACT WITH SYMPTOMS OF HEADACHE, FATIGUE, SORE THROAT, AND COUGHING, AND GASTROINTESTINAL DISTURBANCES OF NAUSEA, VOMITING, AND EPIGASTRIC PAIN. DIZZINESS, GLYCOSURIA, HYPERGLYCEMIA AND TRANSIENT LOSS OF CONSCIOUSNESS HAVE ALSO OCCURRED AMONG INDIVIDUALS AFTER EXPOSURE. **CHRONIC EXPOSURE-** IN MAN, LIVER DAMAGE HAS OCCURRED AFTER REPEATED EXPOSURE. CHRONIC EXPOSURE TO ORGANOTIN COMPOUNDS PRODUCED IN ANIMALS PULMONARY EDEMA, PNEUMONIA, AND DAMAGE TO THE LIVER AND KIDNEYS.

FIRST AID- REMOVE FROM EXPOSURE AREA TO FRESH AIR IMMEDIATELY. IF BREATHING HAS STOPPED, GIVE ARTIFICIAL RESPIRATION. MAINTAIN AIRWAY AND BLOOD PRESSURE AND ADMINISTER OXYGEN IF AVAILABLE. KEEP AFFECTED PERSON WARM AND AT REST. TREAT SYMPTOMATICALLY AND SUPPORTIVELY. ADMINISTRATION OF OXYGEN SHOULD BE PERFORMED BY QUALIFIED PERSONNEL. GET MEDICAL ATTENTION IMMEDIATELY.

SKIN CONTACT: TRIPHENYLTIN ACETATE: IRRITANT/TOXIC. **ACUTE EXPOSURE-** A LOW DOSE WAS LETHAL IN RATS; NO SYMPTOMS WERE REPORTED. TRIPHENYLTIN ACETATE IS AN ORGANOTIN COMPOUND. ORGANOTIN COMPOUNDS ARE IN GENERAL STRONG IRRITANTS CAUSING REDNESS, ITCHING, PAIN, AND BLISTERS OR LESIONS. CHEMICAL BURNS MAY RESULT FROM ONLY BRIEF CONTACT WITH THE SKIN. IRRITATION HAS OCCURRED FROM CONTACT WITH CLOTHES CONTAMINATED WITH ORGANOTIN COMPOUNDS. **CHRONIC EXPOSURE-** PROLONGED CONTACT OF THE SKIN WITH CLOTHES CONTAMINATED WITH ORGANOTIN COMPOUNDS HAVE BEEN RESPONSIBLE FOR ACUTE LOCAL BURNS, SUBACUTE DIFFUSE ERYTHEMATOID DERMATITIS WITH PRURITUS AND SOME PUSTULAR ERUPTION IN THE HAIR-COVERED AREAS.

FIRST AID- REMOVE CONTAMINATED CLOTHING AND SHOES IMMEDIATELY. WASH AFFECTED AREA WITH SOAP OR MILD DETERGENT AND LARGE AMOUNTS OF WATER UNTIL NO EVIDENCE OF CHEMICAL REMAINS (AT LEAST 15-20 MINUTES). IN CASE OF CHEMICAL BURNS, COVER AREA WITH STERILE, DRY DRESSING. BANDAGE SECURELY, BUT NOT TOO TIGHTLY. GET MEDICAL ATTENTION IMMEDIATELY.

EYE CONTACT: TRIPHENYLTIN ACETATE: IRRITANT. **ACUTE EXPOSURE-** TRIPHENYLTIN ACETATE IS AN ORGANOTIN COMPOUND. ORGANOTIN COMPOUNDS ARE IN GENERAL STRONG IRRITANTS, AND ACUTE CONJUNCTIVITIS HAS BEEN OBSERVED AS A RESULT OF EYE SPLASHES, EVEN WHEN FOLLOWED BY IMMEDIATE LAVAGE; CORNEAL OPACITIES HAVE ALSO BEEN REPORTED. EXPOSURE TO THE VAPOR OF ORGANOTIN COMPOUNDS HAVE ALSO CAUSED IRRITATION. NO PERMANENT EYE DAMAGE FROM ORGANOTIN COMPOUNDS WERE REPORTED. **CHRONIC EXPOSURE-** PROLONGED OR REPEATED EXPOSURE MAY CAUSE EFFECTS AS DESCRIBED IN ACUTE EXPOSURE.

FIRST AID- WASH EYES IMMEDIATELY WITH LARGE AMOUNTS OF WATER, OCCASIONALLY LIFTING UPPER AND LOWER LIDS, UNTIL NO EVIDENCE OF CHEMICAL REMAINS (AT LEAST 15-20 MINUTES). CONTINUE IRRIGATING WITH NORMAL SALINE UNTIL THE PH HAS RETURNED TO NORMAL (30-60 MINUTES). COVER WITH STERILE BANDAGES. GET MEDICAL ATTENTION IMMEDIATELY.

INGESTION: TRIPHENYTIN ACETATE: TOXIC. **ACUTE EXPOSURE-** IN RATS, THIS MATERIAL PRODUCED SLUGGISHNESS, UNSTEADINESS, MODERATE DIARRHEA, ANOREXIA, BLOODY STAIN AROUND THE NOSE AND EYES, AND WHEEZING. A LOW DOSE WAS LETHAL IN RATS. **CHRONIC EXPOSURE-** MARKED TESTICULAR ATROPHY WAS OBSERVED IN RATS AFTER CHRONICALLY INGESTING 20 MG/KG/DAY FOR 20 DAYS. AS EVALUATED BY RTECS, ADMINISTRATION TO MICE RESULTED IN A STATISTICALLY SIGNIFICANT INCREASE IN THE INCIDENCE OF NEOPLASTIC TUMORS OF THE LIVER.

FIRST AID- IF EXTENSIVE VOMITING HAS NOT OCCURRED, THE SUBSTANCE SHOULD BE REMOVED BY EMESIS OR GASTRIC LAVAGE PROVIDED THAT THE PATIENT IS CONSCIOUS AND CONVULSIONS ARE NOT PRESENT. KEEP HEAD BELOW HIPS DURING VOMITING TO PREVENT ASPIRATION. DO NOT ATTEMPT TO MAKE AN UNCONSCIOUS PERSON VOMIT. TREAT SYMPTOMATICALLY AND SUPPORTIVELY. GET MEDICAL ATTENTION IMMEDIATELY (DREISBACH, HANDBOOK OF POISONING, 12TH ED.). TREATMENT SHOULD BE PERFORMED BY QUALIFIED MEDICAL PERSONNEL.

ANTIDOTE: NO SPECIFIC ANTIDOTE. TREAT SYMPTOMATICALLY AND SUPPORTIVELY.

REACTIVITY

REACTIVITY: STABLE UNDER NORMAL TEMPERATURES AND PRESSURES.

INCOMPATIBILITIES: TRIPHENYLTIN ACETATE: STRONG OXIDIZERS: INCOMPATIBLE.

DECOMPOSITION: THERMAL DECOMPOSITION MAY RELEASE TOXIC AND/OR HAZARDOUS GASES.

POLYMERIZATION: HAZARDOUS POLYMERIZATION HAS NOT BEEN REPORTED TO OCCUR UNDER NORMAL TEMPERATURES AND PRESSURES.

STORAGE AND DISPOSAL

OBSERVE ALL FEDERAL, STATE AND LOCAL REGULATIONS WHEN STORING OR DISPOSING OF THIS SUBSTANCE. FOR ASSISTANCE, CONTACT THE DISTRICT DIRECTOR OF THE ENVIRONMENTAL PROTECTION AGENCY.

STORAGE

STORE IN ACCORDANCE WITH 40 CFR 165 RECOMMENDED PROCEDURES FOR THE DISPOSAL AND STORAGE OF PESTICIDES AND PESTICIDE CONTAINERS.
STORE AWAY FROM INCOMPATIBLE SUBSTANCES.
THRESHOLD PLANNING QUANTITY (TPQ): THE SUPERFUND AMENDMENTS AND

REAUTHORIZATION ACT (SARA) SECTION 302 REQUIRES THAT EACH FACILITY WHERE ANY EXTREMELY HAZARDOUS SUBSTANCE IS PRESENT IN A QUANTITY EQUAL TO OR GREATER THAN THE TPQ ESTABLISHED FOR THAT SUBSTANCE NOTIFY THE STATE EMERGENCY RESPONSE COMMISSION FOR THE STATE IN WHICH IT IS LOCATED. SECTION 303 OF SARA REQUIRES THESE FACILITIES TO PARTICIPATE IN LOCAL EMERGENCY RESPONSE PLANNING (40 CFR 355.30).

DISPOSAL

DISPOSAL MUST BE IN ACCORDANCE WITH 40 CFR 165 RECOMMENDED PROCEDURES FOR THE DISPOSAL AND STORAGE OF PESTICIDES AND PESTICIDE CONTAINERS.

CONDITIONS TO AVOID

NONE REPORTED.

SPILL AND LEAK PROCEDURES

OCCUPATIONAL SPILL: DO NOT TOUCH SPILLED MATERIAL. STOP LEAK IF YOU CAN DO IT WITHOUT RISK. FOR SMALL SPILLS, TAKE UP WITH SAND OR OTHER ABSORBENT MATERIAL AND PLACE INTO CONTAINERS FOR LATER DISPOSAL. FOR SMALL DRY SPILLS, WITH A CLEAN SHOVEL PLACE MATERIAL INTO CLEAN, DRY CONTAINER AND COVER. MOVE CONTAINERS FROM SPILL AREA. FOR LARGER SPILLS, DIKE FAR AHEAD OF SPILL FOR LATER DISPOSAL. KEEP UNNECESSARY PEOPLE AWAY. ISOLATE HAZARD AREA AND DENY ENTRY.

REPORTABLE QUANTITY (RQ): 1 POUND THE SUPERFUND AMENDMENTS AND REAUTHORIZATION ACT (SARA) SECTION 304 REQUIRES THAT A RELEASE EQUAL TO OR GREATER THAN THE REPORTABLE QUANTITY FOR THIS SUBSTANCE BE IMMEDIATELY REPORTED TO THE LOCAL EMERGENCY PLANNING COMMITTEE AND THE STATE EMERGENCY RESPONSE COMMISSION (40 CFR 355.40). IF THE RELEASE OF THIS SUBSTANCE IS REPORTABLE UNDER CERCLA SECTION 103, THE NATIONAL RESPONSE CENTER MUST BE NOTIFIED IMMEDIATELY AT (800) 424-8802 OR (202) 426-2675 IN THE METROPOLITAN WASHINGTON, D.C. AREA (40 CFR 302.6).

PROTECTIVE EQUIPMENT

VENTILATION: PROVIDE LOCAL EXHAUST OR PROCESS ENCLOSURE VENTILATION TO MEET PUBLISHED EXPOSURE LIMITS.

RESPIRATOR: THE FOLLOWING RESPIRATORS AND MAXIMUM USE CONCENTRATIONS ARE RECOMMENDATIONS BY THE U.S. DEPARTMENT OF HEALTH AND HUMAN SERVICES, NIOSH POCKET GUIDE TO CHEMICAL HAZARDS; NIOSH CRITERIA DOCUMENTS OR BY THE U.S. DEPARTMENT OF LABOR, 29 CFR 1910 SUBPART Z. THE SPECIFIC RESPIRATOR SELECTED MUST BE BASED ON CONTAMINATION LEVELS FOUND IN THE WORK PLACE, MUST NOT EXCEED THE WORKING LIMITS OF THE RESPIRATOR AND BE JOINTLY APPROVED BY THE NATIONAL INSTITUTE FOR OCCUPATIONAL SAFETY AND HEALTH AND THE MINE SAFETY AND HEALTH ADMINISTRATION (NIOSH-MSHA).

TIN, ORGANIC COMPOUNDS, (AS SN):

1 MG/M3- ANY CHEMICAL CARTRIDGE RESPIRATOR WITH ORGANIC VAPOR CARTRIDGE IN COMBINATION WITH A DUST AND MIST FILTER. ANY SUPPLIED-AIR RESPIRATOR. ANY SELF-CONTAINED BREATHING APPARATUS.

2.5 MG/M3- ANY SUPPLIED-AIR RESPIRATOR OPERATED IN CONTINOUS FLOW MODE. ANY POWERED AIR-PURIFYING RESPIRATOR WITH ORGANIC VAPOR CARTRIDGE IN COMBINATION WITH A DUST AND MIST FILTER.

5 MG/M3- ANY CHEMICAL CARTRIDGE RESPIRATOR WITH A FULL FACEPIECE AND ORGANIC VAPOR CARTRIDGE IN COMBINATION WITH A HIGH-EFFICIENCY PARTICULATE FILTER. ANY SUPPLIED-AIR RESPIRATOR WITH A FULL FACEPIECE. ANY SELF-CONTAINED BREATHING APPARATUS WITH A FULL FACEPIECE. ANY AIR-PURIFYING FULL FACEPIECE RESPIRATOR (GAS MASK) WITH A CHIN STYLE OR BACK-MOUNTED ORGANIC CANISTER HAVING A HIGH-EFFICIENCY PARTICULATE FILTER. ANY POWERED AIR-PURIFYING RESPIRATOR WITH A TIGHT-FITTING FACEPIECE AND ORGANIC VAPOR CARTRIDGE IN COMBINATION WITH A HIGH-EFFICIENCY PARTICULATE FILTER. ANY SUPPLIED-AIR RESPIRATOR WITH A TIGHT-FITTING FACEPIECE OPERATED IN CONTINOUS FLOW MODE.

200 MG/M3- ANY SUPPLIED-AIR RESPIRATOR WITH A FULL-FACEPIECE AND OPERATED IN PRESSURE-DEMAND OR OTHER POSITIVE PRESSURE MODE.

ESCAPE- ANY AIR-PURIFYING FULL FACEPIECE RESPIRATOR (GAS MASK) WITH A CHIN STYLE OR BACK-MOUNTED ORGANIC CANISTER HAVING A HIGH-EFFICIENCY PARTICULATE FILTER. ANY APPROPRIATE ESCAPE-TYPE SELF-CONTAINED BREATHING APPARATUS.

FOR FIREFIGHTING AND OTHER IMMEDIATELY DANGEROUS TO LIFE OR HEALTH CONDITIONS:

SELF-CONTAINED BREATHING APPARATUS WITH FULL FACEPIECE OPERATED IN PRESSURE-DEMAND OR OTHER POSITIVE PRESSURE MODE.

SUPPLIED-AIR RESPIRATOR WITH FULL FACEPIECE AND OPERATED IN PRESSURE-DEMAND OR OTHER POSITIVE PRESSURE MODE IN COMBINATION WITH AN AUXILIARY SELF-CONTAINED BREATHING APPARATUS OPERATED IN PRESSURE-DEMAND OR OTHER POSITIVE PRESSURE MODE.

CLOTHING: EMPLOYEE MUST WEAR APPROPRIATE PROTECTIVE (IMPERVIOUS) CLOTHING AND EQUIPMENT TO PREVENT ANY POSSIBILITY OF SKIN CONTACT WITH THIS SUBSTANCE.

GLOVES: EMPLOYEE MUST WEAR APPROPRIATE PROTECTIVE GLOVES TO PREVENT CONTACT WITH THIS SUBSTANCE.

EYE PROTECTION: EMPLOYEE MUST WEAR SPLASH-PROOF OR DUST-RESISTANT SAFETY GOGGLES AND A FACESHIELD TO PREVENT CONTACT WITH THIS SUBSTANCE.

EMERGENCY WASH FACILITIES: WHERE THERE IS ANY POSSIBILITY THAT AN EMPLOYEE'S EYES AND/OR SKIN MAY BE EXPOSED TO THIS SUBSTANCE, THE EMPLOYER SHOULD PROVIDE AN EYE WASH FOUNTAIN AND QUICK DRENCH SHOWER WITHIN THE IMMEDIATE WORK AREA FOR EMERGENCY USE.

AUTHORIZED BY- OCCUPATIONAL HEALTH SERVICES, INC.
CREATION DATE: 10/05/89 ***REVISION DATE:*** 05/18/90

MATERIAL SAFETY DATA SHEET

OCCUPATIONAL HEALTH SERVICES, INC.
AGRICULTURE AND PESTICIDE DIVISION
450 SEVENTH AVENUE, SUITE 2407
NEW YORK, NEW YORK 10123
1-800-445-MSDS OR (212) 967-1100

EMERGENCY CONTACT:
JOHN S. BRANSFORD, JR. (615) 292-1180

SUBSTANCE IDENTIFICATION

CAS-NUMBER 639-58-7

SUBSTANCE: TRIPHENYLTIN CHLORIDE

TRADE NAMES/SYNONYMS: CHLOROTRIPHENYL-STANNANE; CHLOROTRIPHENYLSTANNANE; CHLOROTRIPHENYLTIN; TPTC; FENTIN CHLORIDE; TRIPHENYLCHLOROSTANNANE; TRIPHENLYCHLOROTIN; BRESTANOL; GC 8993; GENERAL CHEMICALS 8993; HOE 2872; LS 4442; PST24380

CHEMICAL FAMILY: AROMATIC HALOGEN

MOLECULAR FORMULA: C18-H15-CL-SN

MOLECULAR WEIGHT: 385.47

CERCLA RATINGS (SCALE 0-3): HEALTH=3 FIRE=U REACTIVITY=0 PERSISTENCE=3

NFPA RATINGS (SCALE 0-4): HEALTH=3 FIRE=U REACTIVITY=3

COMPONENTS AND CONTAMINANTS

COMPONENT: TRIPHENYLTIN CHLORIDE ***PERCENT:*** 100.0
CAS# 639-58-7

OTHER CONTAMINANTS: NONE

EXPOSURE LIMITS: TRIPHENYLTIN CHLORIDE: 0.1 MG(SN)/M3 OSHA TWA 0.1 MG(SN)/M3 ACGIH TWA (SKIN) 0.1 MG(SN)/M3 NIOSH RECOMMENDED 10 HOUR TWA

500/10,000 POUNDS SARA SECTION 302 THRESHOLD PLANNING QUANTITY 1 POUND SARA SECTION 304 REPORTABLE QUANTITY

PHYSICAL DATA

DESCRIPTION: WHITE CRYSTALLINE SOLID ***BOILING POINT:*** 464 F (240 C)

MELTING POINT: 223 F (106 C) ***SPECIFIC GRAVITY:*** >1

VAPOR PRESSURE: < 1 MMHG @ 20 C ***SOLUBILITY IN WATER:*** INSOLUBLE

SOLVENT SOLUBILITY: ORGANIC SOLVENTS

FIRE AND EXPLOSION DATA

FIRE AND EXPLOSION HAZARD: UNKNOWN FIRE AND EXPLOSION HAZARD.

FIREFIGHTING MEDIA: DRY CHEMICAL, CARBON DIOXIDE, WATER SPRAY OR FOAM FOR LARGER FIRES, USE WATER SPRAY, FOG OR ALCOHOL FOAM

FIREFIGHTING: MOVE CONTAINER FROM FIRE AREA IF POSSIBLE. DO NOT SCATTER SPILLED MATERIAL WITH MORE WATER THAN NEEDED FOR FIRE CONTROL. DIKE FIRE CONTROL WATER FOR LATER DISPOSAL

USE AGENTS SUITABLE FOR TYPE OF SURROUNDING FIRE. AVOID BREATHING HAZARDOUS VAPORS, KEEP UPWIND.

TOXICITY

TRIPHENYLTIN CHLORIDE: TOXICITY DATA: 135 MG/KG ORAL-RAT LD50; 18 MG/KG ORAL-MOUSE LD50; 18 MG/KG INTRAVENOUS-MOUSE LD50; REPRODUCTIVE EFFECTS DATA (RTECS). CARCINOGEN STATUS: NONE. ACUTE TOXICITY LEVEL: TOXIC BY INGESTION. TARGET EFFECTS: POISONING MAY AFFECT THE LUNGS, LIVER, KIDNEYS, AND CENTRAL NERVOUS SYSTEM.* AT INCREASED RISK FROM EXPOSURE: PERSONS WITH LUNG, SKIN, LIVER, AND KIDNEY DISEASES.*

* MAY BE BASED ON GENERAL INFORMATION ON ORGANOTIN COMPOUNDS.

HEALTH EFFECTS AND FIRST AID

INHALATION: TRIPHENYLTIN CHLORIDE: 200 MG(SN)/M3 IMMEDIATELY DANGEROUS TO LIFE OR DEATH. **ACUTE EXPOSURE-** TRIPHENYLTIN CHLORIDE IS AN ORGANOTIN COMPOUND. IN MAN, ORGANOTIN COMPOUNDS HAVE PRODUCED IRRITATION OF THE RESPIRATORY TRACT WITH SYMPTOMS OF HEADACHE, FATIGUE, SORE THROAT, AND COUGHING, AND GASTROINTESTINAL DISTURBANCES OF NAUSEA, VOMITING, AND EPIGASTRIC PAIN. IN ONE STUDY OF SEVERAL ORGANOTIN COMPOUNDS, PULMONARY EDEMA AND FATTY CHANGES OF THE LIVER AND KIDNEYS WERE OBSERVED IN MICE. **CHRONIC EXPOSURE-** THERE IS ONE REPORT OF LIVER DAMAGE OCCURRING FROM OCCUPATIONAL EXPOSURE TO ONE ORGANOTIN COMPOUND, TRIPHENYLTIN ACETATE. CHRONIC EXPOSURE TO ORGANOTIN COMPOUNDS PRODUCED IN ANIMALS PULMONARY EDEMA, PNEUMONIA, AND DAMAGE TO THE LIVER AND KIDNEYS.

FIRST AID- REMOVE FROM EXPOSURE AREA TO FRESH AIR IMMEDIATELY. IF BREATHING HAS STOPPED, PERFORM ARTIFICIAL RESPIRATION. KEEP PERSON WARM AND AT REST. TREAT SYMPTOMATICALLY AND SUPPORTIVELY. GET MEDICAL ATTENTION IMMEDIATELY.

SKIN CONTACT: TRIPHENYLTIN CHLORIDE: **ACUTE EXPOSURE-** TRIPHENYLTIN CHLORIDE IS AN ORGANOTIN COMPOUND. ORGANOTIN COMPOUNDS ARE IN GENERAL STRONG IRRITANTS CAUSING REDNESS, ITCHING, PAIN AND BLISTERS OR LESIONS. CHEMICAL BURNS MAY RESULT FROM ONLY BRIEF CONTACT WITH THE SKIN. IRRITATION HAS OCCURRED FROM CONTACT WITH CLOTHES CONTAMINATED WITH ORGANOTIN COMPOUNDS. **CHRONIC EXPOSURE-** PROLONGED CONTACT WITH CLOTHES CONTAMINATED WITH ORGANOTIN COMPOUNDS HAS BEEN RESPONSIBLE FOR ACUTE LOCAL BURNS, SUBACUTE DIFFUSE ERYTHEMATOID DERMATITIS WITH PRURITUS AND SOME PUSTULAR ERUPTION IN THE HAIR-COVERED AREAS.

FIRST AID- REMOVE CONTAMINATED CLOTHING AND SHOES IMMEDIATELY. WASH AFFECTED AREA WITH SOAP OR MILD DETERGENT AND LARGE AMOUNTS OF WATER UNTIL NO EVIDENCE OF CHEMICAL REMAINS (APPROXIMATELY 15-20 MINUTES). GET MEDICAL ATTENTION IMMEDIATELY.

EYE CONTACT: TRIPHENYLTIN CHLORIDE: **ACUTE EXPOSURE-** TRIPHENYLTIN CHLORIDE IS AN ORGANOTIN COMPOUND. ORGANOTIN COMPOUNDS ARE IN GENERAL STRONG IRRITANTS, AND ACUTE CONJUNCTIVITIS HAS BEEN OBSERVED AS A RESULT OF EYE SPLASHES, EVEN WHEN FOLLOWED BY IMMEDIATE LAVAGE; CORNEAL OPACITIES HAVE ALSO BEEN REPORTED. EXPOSURE TO THE VAPOR OF ORGANOTIN COMPOUNDS HAVE ALSO CAUSED IRRITATION. NO PERMANENT EYE DAMAGE FROM ORGANOTIN COMPOUNDS WERE REPORTED. **CHRONIC EXPOSURE-** PROLONGED OR REPEATED EXPOSURE MAY CAUSE EFFECTS AS DESCRIBED IN ACUTE EXPOSURE.

FIRST AID- WASH EYES IMMEDIATELY WITH LARGE AMOUNTS OF WATER OR NORMAL SALINE, OCCASIONALLY LIFTING UPPER AND LOWER LIDS, UNTIL NO EVIDENCE OF CHEMICAL REMAINS (APPROXIMATELY 15-20 MINUTES). GET MEDICAL ATTENTION IMMEDIATELY.

INGESTION: TRIPHENYLTIN CHLORIDE: TOXIC. **ACUTE EXPOSURE-** A LOW DOSE WAS LETHAL IN RATS; NO SYMPTOMS OF POISONING WERE REPORTED. TRIPHENYLTIN CHLORIDE IS AN ORGANOTIN COMPOUND. IN RATS, THESE COMPOUNDS PRODUCED PARESIS, TREMORS, CONVULSIONS, AND INTERSTITIAL EDEMA OF THE WHITE MATTER OF THE BRAIN AND SPINAL CORD. **CHRONIC EXPOSURE-** TRIPHENYLTIN CHLORIDE ADMINISTERED IN THE DIET FOR 18 DAYS AT 20 MG/KG ADVERSELY AFFECTED THE REPRODUCTIVE ORGANS OF MALE AND FEMALE RATS. HUMANS GIVEN ORGANIC TIN AS MEDICATION EXPERIENCED PARALYSIS, WEIGHT LOSS, AND ENCEPHALOPATHY. CHRONIC INGESTION PRODUCED SIMILAR RESULTS IN ANIMALS. IN RATS, REPEATED DOSES PRODUCED NECROSIS OF THE LIVER.

FIRST AID- IF EXTENSIVE VOMITING HAS NOT OCCURRED, THE SUBSTANCE SHOULD BE REMOVED BY EMESIS OR GASTRIC LAVAGE PROVIDED THAT THE PATIENT IS CONSCIOUS AND CONVULSIONS ARE NOT PRESENT. KEEP HEAD BELOW HIPS DURING VOMITING TO PREVENT ASPIRATION. DO NOT ATTEMPT TO MAKE AN UNCONSCIOUS PERSON VOMIT. TREAT SYMPTOMATICALLY AND SUPPORTIVELY. GET MEDICAL ATTENTION IMMEDIATELY (DREISBACH, HANDBOOK OF POISONING, 12TH ED.). TREATMENT SHOULD BE PERFORMED BY QUALIFIED MEDICAL PERSONNEL.

ANTIDOTE: NO SPECIFIC ANTIDOTE. TREAT SYMPTOMATICALLY AND SUPPORTIVELY.

REACTIVITY

REACTIVITY: STABLE UNDER NORMAL TEMPERATURES AND PRESSURES.

INCOMPATIBILITIES: TRIPHENYLTIN CHLORIDE: STRONG OXIDIZERS: INCOMPATIBLE.

DECOMPOSITION: THERMAL DECOMPOSITION PRODUCTS MAY INCLUDE TOXIC AND CORROSIVE FUMES OF CHLORIDES.

POLYMERIZATION: HAZARDOUS POLYMERIZATION HAS NOT BEEN REPORTED TO OCCUR UNDER NORMAL TEMPERATURES AND PRESSURES.

STORAGE AND DISPOSAL

OBSERVE ALL FEDERAL, STATE AND LOCAL REGULATIONS WHEN STORING OR DISPOSING OF THIS SUBSTANCE. FOR ASSISTANCE, CONTACT THE DISTRICT DIRECTOR OF THE ENVIRONMENTAL PROTECTION AGENCY.

****STORAGE****

STORE IN ACCORDANCE WITH 40 CFR 165 RECOMMENDED PROCEDURES FOR THE DISPOSAL AND STORAGE OF PESTICIDES AND PESTICIDE CONTAINERS.
STORE AWAY FROM INCOMPATIBLE SUBSTANCES.
THRESHOLD PLANNING QUANTITY (TPQ): THE SUPERFUND AMENDMENTS AND REAUTHORIZATION ACT (SARA) SECTION 302 REQUIRES THAT EACH FACILITY WHERE ANY EXTREMELY HAZARDOUS SUBSTANCE IS PRESENT IN A QUANTITY EQUAL TO OR GREATER THAN THE TPQ ESTABLISHED FOR THAT SUBSTANCE NOTIFY THE STATE EMERGENCY RESPONSE COMMISSION FOR THE STATE IN WHICH IT IS LOCATED. SECTION 303 OF SARA REQUIRES THESE FACILITIES TO PARTICIPATE IN LOCAL EMERGENCY RESPONSE PLANNING (40 CFR 355.30).

****DISPOSAL****

DISPOSAL MUST BE IN ACCORDANCE WITH 40 CFR 165 RECOMMENDED PROCEDURES FOR THE DISPOSAL AND STORAGE OF PESTICIDES AND PESTICIDE CONTAINERS.

CONDITIONS TO AVOID

NONE REPORTED.

SPILL AND LEAK PROCEDURES

OCCUPATIONAL SPILL: DO NOT TOUCH SPILLED MATERIAL. STOP LEAK IF YOU CAN DO IT WITHOUT RISK. USE WATER SPRAY TO REDUCE VAPORS. FOR SMALL SPILLS, TAKE UP WITH SAND OR OTHER ABSORBENT MATERIAL AND PLACE INTO CONTAINERS FOR LATER DISPOSAL. FOR SMALL DRY SPILLS, WITH A CLEAN SHOVEL PLACE MATERIAL INTO CLEAN, DRY CONTAINERS AND COVER. MOVE CONTAINERS FROM SPILL AREA. FOR LARGER SPILLS, DIKE FAR AHEAD OF SPILL FOR LATER DISPOSAL. KEEP UNNECESSARY PEOPLE AWAY. ISOLATE HAZARD AREA AND DENY ENTRY. VENTILATE CLOSED SPACES BEFORE ENTERING.
REPORTABLE QUANTITY (RQ): 1 POUND THE SUPERFUND AMENDMENTS AND REAUTHORIZATION ACT (SARA) SECTION 304 REQUIRES THAT A RELEASE EQUAL TO OR GREATER THAN THE REPORTABLE QUANTITY FOR THIS SUBSTANCE BE IMMEDIATELY REPORTED TO THE LOCAL EMERGENCY PLANNING COMMITTEE AND THE STATE EMERGENCY RESPONSE COMMISSION (40 CFR 355.40). IF THE RELEASE OF THIS SUBSTANCE IS REPORTABLE UNDER CERCLA SECTION 103, THE NATIONAL RESPONSE CENTER MUST BE NOTIFIED IMMEDIATELY AT (800) 424-8802 OR (202) 426-2675 IN THE METROPOLITAN WASHINGTON, D.C. AREA (40 CFR 302.6).

PROTECTIVE EQUIPMENT

VENTILATION: PROVIDE LOCAL EXHAUST OR PROCESS ENCLOSURE VENTILATION TO MEET PUBLISHED EXPOSURE LIMITS.

RESPIRATOR: THE FOLLOWING RESPIRATORS AND MAXIMUM USE CONCENTRATIONS ARE RECOMMENDATIONS BY THE U.S. DEPARTMENT OF HEALTH AND HUMAN SERVICES, NIOSH POCKET GUIDE TO CHEMICAL HAZARDS; NIOSH CRITERIA DOCUMENTS OR BY THE U.S. DEPARTMENT OF LABOR, 29 CFR 1910 SUBPART Z. THE SPECIFIC RESPIRATOR SELECTED MUST BE BASED ON CONTAMINATION LEVELS FOUND IN THE WORK PLACE, MUST NOT EXCEED THE WORKING LIMITS OF THE RESPIRATOR AND BE JOINTLY APPROVED BY THE NATIONAL INSTITUTE FOR OCCUPATIONAL SAFETY AND HEALTH AND THE MINE SAFETY AND HEALTH ADMINISTRATION (NIOSH-MSHA).
TIN, ORGANIC COMPOUNDS, (AS SN):
1 MG/M3- ANY CHEMICAL CARTRIDGE RESPIRATOR WITH ORGANIC VAPOR CARTRIDGE IN COMBINATION WITH A DUST AND MIST FILTER. ANY SUPPLIED-AIR RESPIRATOR. ANY SELF-CONTAINED BREATHING APPARATUS.
2.5 MG/M3- ANY SUPPLIED-AIR RESPIRATOR OPERATED IN CONTINOUS FLOW MODE. ANY POWERED AIR-PURIFYING RESPIRATOR WITH ORGANIC VAPOR CARTRIDGE IN COMBINATION WITH A DUST AND MIST FILTER.
5 MG/M3- ANY CHEMICAL CARTRIDGE RESPIRATOR WITH A FULL FACEPIECE AND ORGANIC VAPOR CARTRIDGE IN COMBINATION WITH A HIGH-EFFICIENCY PARTICULATE FILTER. ANY SUPPLIED-AIR RESPIRATOR WITH A FULL FACEPIECE. ANY SELF-CONTAINED BREATHING APPARATUS WITH A FULL FACEPIECE. ANY AIR-PURIFYING FULL FACEPIECE RESPIRATOR (GAS MASK) WITH A CHIN STYLE OR BACK-MOUNTED ORGANIC CANISTER HAVING A HIGH-EFFICIENCY PARTICULATE FILTER. ANY POWERED AIR-PURIFYING RESPIRATOR WITH A TIGHT-FITTING FACEPIECE AND ORGANIC VAPOR CARTRIDGE IN COMBINATION WITH A HIGH-EFFICIENCY PARTICULATE FILTER. ANY SUPPLIED-AIR RESPIRATOR WITH A TIGHT-FITTING FACEPIECE OPERATED IN CONTINOUS FLOW MODE.
200 MG/M3- ANY SUPPLIED-AIR RESPIRATOR WITH A FULL-FACEPIECE AND OPERATED IN PRESSURE-DEMAND OR OTHER POSITIVE PRESSURE MODE.
ESCAPE- ANY AIR-PURIFYING FULL FACEPIECE RESPIRATOR (GAS MASK) WITH A CHIN STYLE OR BACK-MOUNTED ORGANIC CANISTER HAVING A HIGH-EFFICIENCY PARTICULATE FILTER. ANY APPROPRIATE ESCAPE-TYPE SELF-CONTAINED BREATHING APPARATUS.

FOR FIREFIGHTING AND OTHER IMMEDIATELY DANGEROUS TO LIFE OR HEALTH CONDITIONS:
SELF-CONTAINED BREATHING APPARATUS WITH FULL FACEPIECE OPERATED IN PRESSURE-DEMAND OR OTHER POSITIVE PRESSURE MODE.
SUPPLIED-AIR RESPIRATOR WITH FULL FACEPIECE AND OPERATED IN PRESSURE-DEMAND OR OTHER POSITIVE PRESSURE MODE IN COMBINATION WITH AN AUXILIARY SELF-CONTAINED BREATHING APPARATUS OPERATED IN PRESSURE-DEMAND OR OTHER POSITIVE PRESSURE MODE.

CLOTHING: EMPLOYEE MUST WEAR APPROPRIATE PROTECTIVE (IMPERVIOUS) CLOTHING AND EQUIPMENT TO PREVENT REPEATED OR PROLONGED SKIN CONTACT WITH THIS SUBSTANCE.

GLOVES: EMPLOYEE MUST WEAR APPROPRIATE PROTECTIVE GLOVES TO PREVENT CONTACT WITH THIS SUBSTANCE.

EYE PROTECTION: EMPLOYEE MUST WEAR SPLASH-PROOF OR DUST-RESISTANT SAFETY GOGGLES TO PREVENT EYE CONTACT WITH THIS SUBSTANCE.
EMERGENCY EYE WASH: WHERE THERE IS ANY POSSIBILITY THAT AN EMPLOYEE'S EYES MAY BE EXPOSED TO THIS SUBSTANCE, THE EMPLOYER SHOULD PROVIDE AN EYE WASH FOUNTAIN WITHIN THE IMMEDIATE WORK AREA FOR EMERGENCY USE.

AUTHORIZED BY- OCCUPATIONAL HEALTH SERVICES, INC.
CREATION DATE: 10/05/89 ***REVISION DATE:*** 05/17/90

MATERIAL SAFETY DATA SHEET

OCCUPATIONAL HEALTH SERVICES, INC.
AGRICULTURE AND PESTICIDE DIVISION
450 SEVENTH AVENUE, SUITE 2407
NEW YORK, NEW YORK 10123
1-800-445-MSDS OR (212) 967-1100

EMERGENCY CONTACT:
JOHN S. BRANSFORD, JR. (615) 292-1180

SUBSTANCE IDENTIFICATION

CAS-NUMBER 126-11-4

SUBSTANCE: **2-(HYDROXYMETHYL)-2-NITRO-1,3-PROPANEDIOL**

TRADE NAMES/SYNONYMS: 1,3-PROPANEDIOL, 2-(HYDROXYMETHYL)-2-NITRO-; NITROISOBUTYLGLYCEROL; NITROTRIMETHYLOLMETHANE; NITROTRIS(HYDROXYMETHYL)METHANE; TRIHYDROXYMETHYLNITROMETHANE; TRIMETHYLOLNITROMETHANE; TRIS(HYDROXYMETHYL)NITROMETHANE; TRIS NITRO; C4H9NO5; PST24430

CHEMICAL FAMILY: NITRO ALCOHOL, ALIPHATIC

MOLECULAR FORMULA: (H-O-C-H2)3-C-N-O2

MOLECULAR WEIGHT: 151.12

CERCLA RATINGS (SCALE 0-3): HEALTH=2 FIRE=1 REACTIVITY=0 PERSISTENCE=0

NFPA RATINGS (SCALE 0-4): HEALTH=U FIRE=1 REACTIVITY=0

COMPONENTS AND CONTAMINANTS

COMPONENT: 2-(HYDROXYMETHYL)-2-NITRO-1,3-PROPANEDIOL ***PERCENT:*** 100.0
CAS# 126-11-4

OTHER CONTAMINANTS: NONE

EXPOSURE LIMITS: NO OCCUPATIONAL EXPOSURE LIMITS ESTABLISHED BY OSHA, ACGIH, OR NIOSH.

PHYSICAL DATA

DESCRIPTION: WHITE CRYSTALS OR AMORPHOUS SOLID. ***BOILING POINT:*** DECOMPOSES

MELTING POINT: 329 F (165 C) ***SPECIFIC GRAVITY:*** NOT AVAILABLE

PH: 4.5 @ 0.1 M SOLN ***SOLUBILITY IN WATER:*** 220% @ 20 C

SOLVENT SOLUBILITY: SOLUBLE IN ALCOHOL, ETHER; SLIGHTLY SOLUBLE IN BENZENE, HYDROCARBONS.

FIRE AND EXPLOSION DATA

FIRE AND EXPLOSION HAZARD: SLIGHT FIRE HAZARD WHEN EXPOSED TO HEAT OR FLAME.

FIREFIGHTING MEDIA: DRY CHEMICAL, CARBON DIOXIDE, HALON, WATER SPRAY OR STANDARD FOAM (1987 EMERGENCY RESPONSE GUIDEBOOK, DOT P 5800.4).
FOR LARGER FIRES, USE WATER SPRAY, FOG OR STANDARD FOAM (1987 EMERGENCY RESPONSE GUIDEBOOK, DOT P 5800.4).

FIREFIGHTING: MOVE CONTAINER FROM FIRE AREA IF POSSIBLE. DO NOT SCATTER SPILLED MATERIAL WITH HIGH PRESSURE WATER STREAMS. DIKE FIRE CONTROL WATER FOR LATER DISPOSAL (1987 EMERGENCY RESPONSE GUIDEBOOK, DOT P 5800.4, GUIDE PAGE 31).
USE AGENTS SUITABLE FOR TYPE OF SURROUNDING FIRE. AVOID BREATHING HAZARDOUS VAPORS, KEEP UPWIND.

TOXICITY

2-(HYDROXYMETHYL)-2-NITRO-1,3-PROPANEDIOL: TOXICITY DATA: 1900 MG/KG ORAL-RAT LD50; 1900 MG/KG ORAL-MOUSE LD50; 250 MG/KG ORAL-RABBIT LDLO; 4000 MG/KG INTRAPERITONEAL-MOUSE LD50. CARCINOGEN STATUS: NONE. LOCAL EFFECTS: IRRITANT- SKIN, MUCOUS MEMBRANES. ACUTE TOXICITY LEVEL: MODERATELY TOXIC BY INGESTION. TARGET EFFECTS: NO DATA AVAILABLE.

HEALTH EFFECTS AND FIRST AID

INHALATION: 2-(HYDROXYMETHYL)-2-NITRO-1,3-PROPANEDIOL: IRRITANT. **ACUTE EXPOSURE-** MAY BE IRRITATING TO THE MUCOUS MEMBRANES. **CHRONIC EXPOSURE-** NO DATA AVAILABLE.

FIRST AID- REMOVE FROM EXPOSURE AREA TO FRESH AIR IMMEDIATELY. IF BREATHING HAS STOPPED, PERFORM ARTIFICIAL RESPIRATION. KEEP PERSON WARM AND AT REST. TREAT SYMPTOMATICALLY AND SUPPORTIVELY. GET MEDICAL ATTENTION IMMEDIATELY.

SKIN CONTACT: 2-(HYDROXYMETHYL)-2-NITRO-1,3-PROPANEDIOL: IRRITANT. **ACUTE EXPOSURE-** MAY CAUSE MILD IRRITATION AND REDDENING. HOWEVER, ONE SOURCE INDICATED THAT THIS CHEMICAL IS NON-IRRITATING. **CHRONIC EXPOSURE-** NO IRRITATION OR SENSITIVITY HAS BEEN REPORTED IN WORKERS WHO MAKE THIS CHEMICAL. ALSO NO IRRITATION WAS REPORTED TO HUMANS SUBJECTED TO EXAGGERATED CUTANEOUS EXPOSURE.

FIRST AID- REMOVE CONTAMINATED CLOTHING AND SHOES IMMEDIATELY. WASH AFFECTED AREA WITH SOAP OR MILD DETERGENT AND LARGE AMOUNTS OF WATER UNTIL NO EVIDENCE OF CHEMICAL REMAINS (APPROXIMATELY 15-20 MINUTES). GET MEDICAL ATTENTION IMMEDIATELY.

EYE CONTACT: 2-(HYDROXYMETHYL)-2-NITRO-1,3-PROPANEDIOL: **ACUTE EXPOSURE-** THIS CHEMICAL HAS BEEN USED FOR THE TREATMENT OF ACID BURNS OF THE EYE. NO ADVERSE EFFECT ON THE EYES HAS BEEN REPORTED. **CHRONIC EXPOSURE-** NO DATA AVAILABLE.

FIRST AID- WASH EYES IMMEDIATELY WITH LARGE AMOUNTS OF WATER OR NORMAL SALINE, OCCASIONALLY LIFTING UPPER AND LOWER LIDS, UNTIL NO EVIDENCE OF CHEMICAL REMAINS (APPROXIMATELY 15-20 MINUTES). GET MEDICAL ATTENTION IMMEDIATELY.

INGESTION: 2-(HYDROXYMETHYL)-2-NITRO-1,3-PROPANEDIOL: **ACUTE EXPOSURE-** THE LETHAL DOSE IN RATS IS REPORTED TO BE 1900 MG/KG. SYMPTOMS OF POISONING WERE NOT REPORTED. ORAL ADMINISTRATION TO DOGS CAUSED SEVERE DIARRHEA. **CHRONIC EXPOSURE-** NO DATA AVAILABLE.

FIRST AID- TREAT SYMPTOMATICALLY AND SUPPORTIVELY. GET MEDICAL ATTENTION IMMEDIATELY. IF VOMITING OCCURS, KEEP HEAD LOWER THAN HIPS TO PREVENT ASPIRATION.

REACTIVITY

REACTIVITY: STABLE UNDER NORMAL TEMPERATURES AND PRESSURES.

INCOMPATIBILITIES: 2-(HYDROXYMETHYL)-2-NITRO-1,3-PROPANEDIOL: HYDROGEN + NICKEL(CATALYST): POSSIBLE VIOLENT REACTION. OXIDIZERS (STRONG): FIRE AND EXPLOSION HAZARD.

DECOMPOSITION: THERMAL DECOMPOSITION PRODUCTS MAY INCLUDE TOXIC OXIDES OF CARBON AND NITROGEN.

POLYMERIZATION: HAZARDOUS POLYMERIZATION HAS NOT BEEN REPORTED TO OCCUR UNDER NORMAL TEMPERATURES AND PRESSURES.

STORAGE AND DISPOSAL

OBSERVE ALL FEDERAL, STATE AND LOCAL REGULATIONS WHEN STORING OR DISPOSING OF THIS SUBSTANCE. FOR ASSISTANCE, CONTACT THE DISTRICT DIRECTOR OF THE ENVIRONMENTAL PROTECTION AGENCY.

STORAGE

STORE AWAY FROM INCOMPATIBLE SUBSTANCES.

CONDITIONS TO AVOID

MAY BURN BUT DOES NOT IGNITE READILY. AVOID CONTACT WITH STRONG OXIDIZERS, EXCESSIVE HEAT, SPARKS, OR OPEN FLAME.

SPILL AND LEAK PROCEDURES

OCCUPATIONAL SPILL: SWEEP UP AND PLACE IN SUITABLE CLEAN, DRY CONTAINERS FOR RECLAMATION OR LATER DISPOSAL. DO NOT FLUSH SPILLED MATERIAL INTO SEWER. KEEP UNNECESSARY PEOPLE AWAY.

PROTECTIVE EQUIPMENT

VENTILATION: PROVIDE LOCAL EXHAUST OR GENERAL DILUTION VENTILATION SYSTEM.

RESPIRATOR: THE FOLLOWING RESPIRATORS ARE RECOMMENDED BASED ON INFORMATION FOUND IN THE PHYSICAL DATA, TOXICITY AND HEALTH EFFECTS SECTIONS. THEY ARE RANKED IN ORDER FROM MINIMUM TO MAXIMUM RESPIRATORY PROTECTION. THE SPECIFIC RESPIRATOR SELECTED MUST BE BASED ON CONTAMINATION LEVELS FOUND IN THE WORK PLACE, MUST NOT EXCEED THE WORKING LIMITS OF THE RESPIRATOR AND BE JOINTLY APPROVED BY THE NATIONAL INSTITUTE FOR OCCUPATIONAL SAFETY AND HEALTH AND THE MINE SAFETY AND HEALTH ADMINISTRATION (NIOSH-MSHA).

CHEMICAL CARTRIDGE RESPIRATOR WITH FULL FACEPIECE AND ORGANIC VAPOR CARTRIDGE(S) IN COMBINATION WITH A DUST AND MIST FILTER.

CHEMICAL CARTRIDGE RESPIRATOR WITH FULL FACEPIECE AND ORGANIC VAPOR CARTRIDGE(S) IN COMBINATION WITH A HIGH-EFFICIENCY PARTICULATE FILTER.

GAS MASK WITH ORGANIC VAPOR CANISTER (CHIN-STYLE OR FRONT- OR BACK-MOUNTED CANISTER) WITH A FULL FACEPIECE AND A HIGH-EFFICIENCY PARTICULATE FILTER.

POWERED AIR-PURIFYING RESPIRATOR WITH TIGHT-FITTING FACEPIECE AND ORGANIC VAPOR CARTRIDGE(S) IN COMBINATION WITH A HIGH-EFFICIENCY PARTICULATE FILTER.

TYPE 'C' SUPPLIED-AIR RESPIRATOR WITH A FULL FACEPIECE OPERATED IN PRESSURE-DEMAND OR OTHER POSITIVE PRESSURE MODE OR WITH A FULL FACEPIECE, HELMET OR HOOD OPERATED IN CONTINUOUS-FLOW MODE.

SELF-CONTAINED BREATHING APPARATUS WITH A FULL FACEPIECE OPERATED IN PRESSURE-DEMAND OR OTHER POSITIVE PRESSURE MODE.

FOR FIREFIGHTING AND OTHER IMMEDIATELY DANGEROUS TO LIFE OR HEALTH CONDITIONS:

SELF-CONTAINED BREATHING APPARATUS WITH FULL FACEPIECE OPERATED IN PRESSURE-DEMAND OR OTHER POSITIVE PRESSURE MODE.

SUPPLIED AIR RESPIRATOR WITH FULL FACEPIECE AND OPERATED IN PRESSURE-DEMAND OR OTHER POSITIVE PRESSURE MODE IN COMBINATION WITH AN AUXILIARY SELF-CONTAINED BREATHING APPARATUS OPERATED IN PRESSURE-DEMAND OR OTHER POSITIVE PRESSURE MODE.

CLOTHING: EMPLOYEE MUST WEAR APPROPRIATE PROTECTIVE (IMPERVIOUS) CLOTHING AND EQUIPMENT TO PREVENT REPEATED OR PROLONGED SKIN CONTACT WITH THIS SUBSTANCE.

GLOVES: EMPLOYEE MUST WEAR APPROPRIATE PROTECTIVE GLOVES TO PREVENT CONTACT WITH THIS SUBSTANCE.

EYE PROTECTION: EMPLOYEE MUST WEAR SPLASH-PROOF OR DUST-RESISTANT SAFETY GOGGLES TO PREVENT EYE CONTACT WITH THIS SUBSTANCE.

EMERGENCY EYE WASH: WHERE THERE IS ANY POSSIBILITY THAT AN EMPLOYEE'S EYES MAY BE EXPOSED TO THIS SUBSTANCE, THE EMPLOYER SHOULD PROVIDE AN EYE WASH FOUNTAIN WITHIN THE IMMEDIATE WORK AREA FOR EMERGENCY USE.

AUTHORIZED BY- OCCUPATIONAL HEALTH SERVICES, INC.

CREATION DATE: 10/05/89 ***REVISION DATE:*** 05/31/90

MATERIAL SAFETY DATA SHEET

OCCUPATIONAL HEALTH SERVICES, INC.
AGRICULTURE AND PESTICIDE DIVISION
450 SEVENTH AVENUE, SUITE 2407
NEW YORK, NEW YORK 10123
1-800-445-MSDS OR (212) 967-1100

EMERGENCY CONTACT:
JOHN S. BRANSFORD, JR. (615) 292-1180

SUBSTANCE IDENTIFICATION

CAS-NUMBER 5064-31-3

SUBSTANCE: **TRISODIUM NITRILOTRIACETATE**

TRADE NAMES/SYNONYMS: N,N-BIS(CARBOXYMETHYL)GLYCINE, TRISODIUM SALT; NITRILOTRIACETIC ACID, TRISODIUM SALT; NTA TRISODIUM SALT; PST24475

CHEMICAL FAMILY: SALT

MOLECULAR FORMULA: C6-H9-N-O6.3NA

MOLECULAR WEIGHT: 257.10

CERCLA RATINGS (SCALE 0-3): HEALTH=3 FIRE=U REACTIVITY=0 PERSISTENCE=0

NFPA RATINGS (SCALE 0-4): HEALTH=3 FIRE=U REACTIVITY=0

COMPONENTS AND CONTAMINANTS

COMPONENT: TRISODIUM NITRILOTRIACETATE ***PERCENT:*** 100.0

CAS# 5064-31-3

OTHER CONTAMINANTS: NONE

EXPOSURE LIMITS: NO OCCUPATIONAL EXPOSURE LIMITS ESTABLISHED BY OSHA, ACGIH, OR NIOSH.

PHYSICAL DATA

DESCRIPTION: WHITE CRYSTALLINE POWDER WITH TYPICAL AMINOACETATE ODOR

BOILING POINT: DECOMPOSES ***MELTING POINT:*** >608 F (>320 C)

SPECIFIC GRAVITY: >1.0 ***PH:*** 10.5-11.7 @ 1% SOLN

SOLUBILITY IN WATER: 48.4 @ 25 C

FIRE AND EXPLOSION DATA

FIRE AND EXPLOSION HAZARD: UNKNOWN FIRE AND EXPLOSION HAZARD.

FIREFIGHTING MEDIA: DRY CHEMICAL, CARBON DIOXIDE, WATER SPRAY OR FOAM FOR LARGER FIRES, USE WATER SPRAY, FOG OR ALCOHOL FOAM

FIREFIGHTING: MOVE CONTAINER FROM FIRE AREA IF POSSIBLE. DO NOT SCATTER SPILLED MATERIAL WITH MORE WATER THAN NEEDED FOR FIRE CONTROL. DIKE FIRE CONTROL WATER FOR LATER DISPOSAL

TOXICITY

TRISODIUM NITRILOTRIACETATE: TOXICITY DATA: 1100 MG/KG ORAL-RAT LD50; 681 MG/KG ORAL-MOUSE LD50; 750 MG/KG ORAL-MONKEY LD50; 254 MG/KG INTRAPERITONEAL-RAT LD50; MUTAGENIC DATA (RTECS); REPRODUCTIVE EFFECTS DATA (RTECS); TUMORIGENIC DATA (RTECS). CARCINOGEN STATUS: ANTICIPATED HUMAN CARCINOGEN (NTP). TRISODIUM NITRILOTRIACETATE ADMINISTERED IN THE DIET INDUCED KIDNEY TRANSITIONAL CELL CARCINOMAS, TUBULAR CELL ADENOMAS, AND URETER TRANSITIONAL CELL CARCINOMAS IN MALE RATS AND KIDNEY TUBULAR CELL ADENOCARCINOMAS AND TRANSITIONAL CELL CARCINOMAS OF THE URETER, URINARY BLADDER, AND LUNG WITH SOME METASTASES IN FEMALE RATS. ADMINISTRATION IN DRINKING WATER INDUCED RENAL ADENOMAS AND ADENOCARCINOMAS IN MALE RATS. LOCAL EFFECTS: IRRITANT- INHALATION, SKIN, AND EYES. ACUTE TOXICITY LEVEL: MODERATELY TOXIC BY INGESTION. TARGET EFFECTS: POISONING MAY AFFECT THE KIDNEYS.

HEALTH EFFECTS AND FIRST AID

INHALATION: SODIUM NITRILOTRIACETATE: IRRITANT. **ACUTE EXPOSURE-** MAY CAUSE IRRITATION. **CHRONIC EXPOSURE-** PROLONGED OR REPEATED EXPOSURE MAY CAUSE IRRITATION OF THE MUCOUS MEMBRANES.

FIRST AID- REMOVE FROM EXPOSURE AREA TO FRESH AIR IMMEDIATELY. IF BREATHING HAS STOPPED, PERFORM ARTIFICIAL RESPIRATION. KEEP PERSON WARM AND AT REST. TREAT SYMPTOMATICALLY AND SUPPORTIVELY. GET MEDICAL ATTENTION IMMEDIATELY.

SKIN CONTACT: TRISODIUM NITRILOTRIACETATE: IRRITANT. **ACUTE EXPOSURE-** MAY CAUSE IRRITATION. THIS MATERIAL WAS SLIGHTLY IRRITATING TO RABBIT SKIN. HOWEVER, INDUSTRIAL EXPERIENCE INDICATES THAT MAN IS MORE SENSITIVE TO THE EFFECTS OF THIS PRODUCT THAN LABORATORY ANIMALS, AND THE IRRITATION EFFECTS ARE MORE SEVERE. 2,000 MG/KG WAS NOT LETHAL BY DERMAL ABSORPTION IN RABBITS. **CHRONIC EXPOSURE-** PROLONGED OR REPEATED EXPOSURE MAY CAUSE DERMATITIS.

FIRST AID- REMOVE CONTAMINATED CLOTHING AND SHOES IMMEDIATELY. WASH AFFECTED AREA WITH SOAP OR MILD DETERGENT AND LARGE AMOUNTS OF WATER UNTIL NO EVIDENCE OF CHEMICAL REMAINS (APPROXIMATELY 15-20 MINUTES). GET MEDICAL ATTENTION IMMEDIATELY.

EYE CONTACT: TRISODIUM NITRILOTRIACETATE: IRRITANT. **ACUTE EXPOSURE-** MAY CAUSE IRRITATION. THIS MATERIAL WAS MODERATELY IRRITATING TO RABBITS EYES. HOWEVER, THE IRRITATION MAY BE GREATER IN THE EYES OF MAN DUE TO MAN BEING MORE SENSITIVE TO THIS MATERIAL THAN LABORATORY ANIMALS. **CHRONIC EXPOSURE-** PROLONGED OR REPEATED EXPOSURE MAY CAUSE CONJUNCTIVITIS.

FIRST AID- WASH EYES IMMEDIATELY WITH LARGE AMOUNTS OF WATER OR NORMAL SALINE, OCCASIONALLY LIFTING UPPER AND LOWER LIDS, UNTIL NO EVIDENCE OF CHEMICAL REMAINS (APPROXIMATELY 15-20 MINUTES). GET MEDICAL ATTENTION IMMEDIATELY.

INGESTION: TRISODIUM NITRILOTRIACETATE: CARCINOGEN. **ACUTE EXPOSURE-** A MODERATE DOSE WAS LETHAL IN RATS; SYMPTOMS WERE NOT REPORTED. **CHRONIC EXPOSURE-** EPA ESTIMATES THE AVERAGE DAILY ADULT EXPOSURE TO BE LOW (1 UG/KG) WHICH PROBABLY RESULTS FROM TRACE RESIDUES IN PROCESS FOODS AND DRINKING WATER. PROLONGED INGESTION BY MICE AND RATS PRODUCED LESIONS OF THE URINARY TRACT, CHARACTERIZED BY HYDRONEPHROSIS AND NEPHRITIS. TUMORS OF THE URINARY TRACT WERE ALSO OBSERVED IN RATS FED 20,000 PPM FOR 2 YEARS. PROLONGED INGESTION BY MALE AND FEMALE RATS PRIOR TO MATING THROUGH 3 WEEKS LACTATION RESULTED IN ADVERSE EFFECTS ON FERTILITY AND THE OFFSPRING. TRISODIUM

NITRILOTRIACETATE ADMINISTERED IN THE DIET INDUCED KIDNEY TRANSITIONAL CELL CARCINOMAS, TUBULAR CELL ADENOMAS, AND URETER TRANSITIONAL CELL CARCINOMAS IN MALE RATS AND KIDNEY TUBULAR CELL ADENOCARCINOMAS AND TRANSITIONAL CELL CARCINOMAS OF THE URETER, URINARY BLADDER, AND LUNG WITH SOME METASTASES IN FEMALE RATS. ADMINISTRATION IN DRINKING WATER INDUCED RENAL ADENOMAS AND ADENOCARCINOMAS IN MALE RATS.

FIRST AID- TREAT SYMPTOMATICALLY AND SUPPORTIVELY. GET MEDICAL ATTENTION IMMEDIATELY. IF VOMITING OCCURS, KEEP HEAD LOWER THAN HIPS TO PREVENT ASPIRATION.

ANTIDOTE: NO SPECIFIC ANTIDOTE. TREAT SYMPTOMATICALLY AND SUPPORTIVELY.

REACTIVITY

REACTIVITY: STABLE UNDER NORMAL TEMPERATURES AND PRESSURES.

INCOMPATIBILITIES: TRISODIUM NITRILOTRIACTATE: OXIDIZING MATERIAL: INCOMPATIBLE. ALUMINUM: MAY REACT FORMING HYDROGEN GAS.

DECOMPOSITION: THERMAL DECOMPOSITION MAY RELEASE CAUSTIC SODIUM MONOXIDE FUMES AND TOXIC OXIDES OF CARBON AND NITROGEN.

POLYMERIZATION: HAZARDOUS POLYMERIZATION HAS NOT BEEN REPORTED TO OCCUR UNDER NORMAL TEMPERATURES AND PRESSURES.

CONDITIONS TO AVOID

NONE REPORTED.

SPILL AND LEAK PROCEDURES

OCCUPATIONAL SPILL: SWEEP UP AND PLACE IN SUITABLE CLEAN, DRY CONTAINERS FOR RECLAMATION OR LATER DISPOSAL. DO NOT FLUSH SPILLED MATERIAL INTO SEWER. KEEP UNNECESSARY PEOPLE AWAY.

PROTECTIVE EQUIPMENT

VENTILATION: PROVIDE LOCAL EXHAUST VENTILATION SYSTEM.

RESPIRATOR: THE FOLLOWING RESPIRATORS ARE RECOMMENDED BASED ON INFORMATION FOUND IN THE PHYSICAL DATA, TOXICITY AND HEALTH EFFECTS SECTIONS. THEY ARE RANKED IN ORDER FROM MINIMUM TO MAXIMUM RESPIRATORY PROTECTION. THE SPECIFIC RESPIRATOR SELECTED MUST BE BASED ON CONTAMINATION LEVELS FOUND IN THE WORK PLACE, MUST NOT EXCEED THE WORKING LIMITS OF THE RESPIRATOR AND BE JOINTLY APPROVED BY THE NATIONAL INSTITUTE FOR OCCUPATIONAL SAFETY AND HEALTH AND THE MINE SAFETY AND HEALTH ADMINISTRATION (NIOSH-MSHA).

DUST AND MIST RESPIRATOR WITH A FULL FACEPIECE.

AIR-PURIFYING FULL FACEPIECE RESPIRATOR WITH A HIGH-EFFICIENCY PARTICULATE FILTER.

POWERED AIR-PURIFYING RESPIRATOR WITH A TIGHT-FITTING FACEPIECE AND HIGH-EFFICIENCY PARTICULATE FILTER.

TYPE 'C' SUPPLIED-AIR RESPIRATOR WITH A FULL FACEPIECE OPERATED IN PRESSURE-DEMAND OR OTHER POSITIVE PRESSURE MODE OR WITH A FULL FACEPIECE, HELMET OR HOOD OPERATED IN CONTINUOUS-FLOW MODE.

SELF-CONTAINED BREATHING APPARATUS WITH A FULL FACEPIECE OPERATED IN PRESSURE-DEMAND OR OTHER POSITIVE PRESSURE MODE.

FOR FIREFIGHTING AND OTHER IMMEDIATELY DANGEROUS TO LIFE OR HEALTH CONDITIONS:

SELF-CONTAINED BREATHING APPARATUS WITH FULL FACEPIECE OPERATED IN PRESSURE-DEMAND OR OTHER POSITIVE PRESSURE MODE.

SUPPLIED-AIR RESPIRATOR WITH FULL FACEPIECE AND OPERATED IN PRESSURE-DEMAND OR OTHER POSITIVE PRESSURE MODE IN COMBINATION WITH AN AUXILIARY SELF-CONTAINED BREATHING APPARATUS OPERATED IN PRESSURE-DEMAND OR OTHER POSITIVE PRESSURE MODE.

CLOTHING: EMPLOYEE MUST WEAR APPROPRIATE PROTECTIVE (IMPERVIOUS) CLOTHING AND EQUIPMENT TO PREVENT REPEATED OR PROLONGED SKIN CONTACT WITH THIS SUBSTANCE.

GLOVES: EMPLOYEE MUST WEAR APPROPRIATE PROTECTIVE GLOVES TO PREVENT CONTACT WITH THIS SUBSTANCE.

EYE PROTECTION: EMPLOYEE MUST WEAR SPLASH-PROOF OR DUST-RESISTANT SAFETY GOGGLES TO PREVENT EYE CONTACT WITH THIS SUBSTANCE.

EMERGENCY EYE WASH: WHERE THERE IS ANY POSSIBILITY THAT AN EMPLOYEE'S EYES MAY BE EXPOSED TO THIS SUBSTANCE, THE EMPLOYER SHOULD PROVIDE AN EYE WASH FOUNTAIN WITHIN THE IMMEDIATE WORK AREA FOR EMERGENCY USE.

AUTHORIZED BY- OCCUPATIONAL HEALTH SERVICES, INC.

CREATION DATE: 11/15/89 ***REVISION DATE:*** 05/31/90

MATERIAL SAFETY DATA SHEET

OCCUPATIONAL HEALTH SERVICES, INC.
AGRICULTURE AND PESTICIDE DIVISION
450 SEVENTH AVENUE, SUITE 2407
NEW YORK, NEW YORK 10123
1-800-445-MSDS OR (212) 967-1100

EMERGENCY CONTACT:
JOHN S. BRANSFORD, JR. (615) 292-1180

SUBSTANCE IDENTIFICATION

CAS-NUMBER 7601-54-9

SUBSTANCE: **TRISODIUM PHOSPHATE**

TRADE NAMES/SYNONYMS: PHOSPHORIC ACID, TRISODIUM SALT; PHOSPHORIC ACID SODIUM SALT (1:3); SODIUM PHOSPHATE; SODIUM PHOSPHATE (NA3PO4); SODIUM PHOSPHATE, TRIBASIC; SODDIUM TERTIARY PHOSPHATE; TRIBASIC SODIUM ORTHOPHOSPHATE; TRIBASIC SODIUM PHOSPHATE; TRISODIUM ORTHOPHOSPHATE; TROMETE; TSP; NA 9148; STCC 4966383; NA3O4P; PST24480

CHEMICAL FAMILY: INORGANIC SALT

MOLECULAR FORMULA: NA3-P-O4

MOLECULAR WEIGHT: 163.94

CERCLA RATINGS (SCALE 0-3): HEALTH = 1 FIRE = 0 REACTIVITY = 0 PERSISTENCE = 0

NFPA RATINGS (SCALE 0-4): HEALTH = 1 FIRE = 0 REACTIVITY = 0

COMPONENTS AND CONTAMINANTS

COMPONENT: TRISODIUM PHOSPHATE ***PERCENT:*** 100.0
CAS# 7601-54-9

OTHER CONTAMINANTS: NONE

EXPOSURE LIMITS: NO OCCUPATIONAL EXPOSURE LIMITS ESTABLISHED BY OSHA, ACGIH, OR NIOSH.

TRISODIUM PHOSPHATE: AMERICAN INDUSTRIAL HYGIENE ASSOCIATION RECOMMENDS 5 MG/M3 FOR WORKPLACE ENVIRONMENTAL EXPLOSURE LEVEL.

5000 LBS. CERCLA SECTION 103 REPORTABLE QUANTITY.

PHYSICAL DATA

DESCRIPTION: ODORLESS, COLORLESS OR WHITE CRYSTALS.

MELTING POINT: >63 F (>73 C) (DECOMPOSES) ***SPECIFIC GRAVITY:*** 1.62

PH: 11.9 @ 1.0% SOLUTION ***SOLUBILITY IN WATER:*** 28.3% @ 15 C

SOLVENT SOLUBILITY: INSOLUBLE IN ALCOHOL AND CARBON DISULFIDE.

FIRE AND EXPLOSION DATA

FIRE AND EXPLOSION HAZARD: UNKNOWN FIRE AND EXPLOSION HAZARD.

FIREFIGHTING MEDIA: DRY CHEMICAL, CARBON DIOXIDE, HALON, WATER SPRAY OR STANDARD FOAM (1987 EMERGENCY RESPONSE GUIDEBOOK, DOT P 5800.4).

FOR LARGER FIRES, USE WATER SPRAY, FOG OR STANDARD FOAM (1987 EMERGENCY RESPONSE GUIDEBOOK, DOT P 5800.4).

FIREFIGHTING: MOVE CONTAINER FROM FIRE AREA IF POSSIBLE. DO NOT SCATTER SPILLED MATERIAL WITH HIGH PRESSURE WATER STREAMS. DIKE FIRE CONTROL WATER FOR LATER DISPOSAL (1987 EMERGENCY RESPONSE GUIDEBOOK, DOT P 5800.4, GUIDE PAGE 31).

USE AGENTS SUITABLE FOR TYPE OF SURROUNDING FIRE. AVOID BREATHING HAZARDOUS VAPORS, KEEP UPWIND.

TRANSPORTATION DATA

DEPARTMENT OF TRANSPORTATION HAZARD CLASSIFICATION 49 CFR 172.101: ORM-E

DEPARTMENT OF TRANSPORTATION LABELING REQUIREMENTS 49 CFR 172.101 AND SUBPART E: NONE

DEPARTMENT OF TRANSPORTATION PACKAGING REQUIREMENTS: 49 CFR 173.1300 EXCEPTIONS: NONE

TOXICITY

TRISODIUM PHOSPHATE (SODIUM PHOSPHATE, TRIBASIC): TOXICITY DATA: ANHYDROUS: 1580 MG/KG INTRAVENOUS-RABBIT LDLO; MUTAGENIC DATA (RTEC). DODECAHYDRATE: 430 MG/KG INTRAPERITONEAL-MOUSE LD50; 7400 MG/KG ORAL-RAT LD50. CARCINOGEN STATUS: NONE. LOCAL EFFECTS: CORROSIVE: INHALATION, SKIN, AND EYES. ACUTE TOXICITY LEVEL: SLIGHTLY TOXIC BY INGESTION. TARGET EFFECTS: POISONING MAY AFFECT THE SERUM CALCIUM LEVEL.

HEALTH EFFECTS AND FIRST AID

INHALATION: TRISODIUM PHOSPHATE (SODIUM PHOSPHATE, TRIBASIC): CORROSIVE.

ACUTE EXPOSURE- MAY CAUSE SEVERE IRRITATION AND POSSIBLY CORROSIVE EFFECTS. IF SUFFICIENT QUANTITIES OF A CORROSIVE SUBSTANCE ARE INHALED,

PULMONARY EDEMA MAY DEVELOP, OFTEN WITH A LATENCY PERIOD OF 48-72 HOURS. **CHRONIC EXPOSURE-** DEPENDING ON CONCENTRATION AND DURATION OF CONTACT, EFFECTS AS IN ACUTE EXPOSURE MAY OCCUR WITH REPEATED OR PROLONGED EXPOSURE.

FIRST AID- REMOVE FROM EXPOSURE AREA TO FRESH AIR IMMEDIATELY. IF BREATHING HAS STOPPED, GIVE ARTIFICIAL RESPIRATION. MAINTAIN AIRWAY AND BLOOD PRESSURE AND ADMINISTER OXYGEN IF AVAILABLE. KEEP AFFECTED PERSON WARM AND AT REST. TREAT SYMPTOMATICALLY AND SUPPORTIVELY. ADMINISTRATION OF OXYGEN SHOULD BE PERFORMED BY QUALIFIED PERSONNEL. GET MEDICAL ATTENTION IMMEDIATELY.

SKIN CONTACT: TRISODIUM PHOSPHATE (SODIUM PHOSPHATE, TRIBASIC): CORROSIVE. **ACUTE EXPOSURE-** CONTACT MAY PRODUCE STRONG IRRITATION, ERYTHEMA, PAIN AND BLISTERING. SOLUTIONS MAY CAUSE CAUSTIC BURNS. **CHRONIC EXPOSURE-** DEPENDING ON CONCENTRATION AND DURATION OF CONTACT, EFFECTS AS IN ACUTE EXPOSURE MAY OCCUR WITH REPEATED OR PROLONGED EXPOSURE.

FIRST AID- REMOVE CONTAMINATED CLOTHING AND SHOES IMMEDIATELY. WASH AFFECTED AREA WITH SOAP OR MILD DETERGENT AND LARGE AMOUNTS OF WATER UNTIL NO EVIDENCE OF CHEMICAL REMAINS (AT LEAST 15-20 MINUTES). IN CASE OF CHEMICAL BURNS, COVER AREA WITH STERILE, DRY DRESSING. BANDAGE SECURELY, BUT NOT TOO TIGHTLY. GET MEDICAL ATTENTION IMMEDIATELY.

EYE CONTACT: TRISODIUM PHOSPHATE (SODIUM PHOSPHATE, TRIBASIC): CORROSIVE. **ACUTE EXPOSURE-** DIRECT CONTACT MAY CAUSE IRRITATION, PAIN, AND POSSIBLY CORNEAL INJURY. SOLUTIONS MAY CAUSE CORNEAL DAMAGE. A SPLASH OF AQUEOUS SOLUTION IN HUMAN EYES HAS CAUSED SLIGHT TRANSIENT INJURY IN ONE CASE AND MODERATE PERMANENT CORNEAL OPACIFICATION AND VASCULARIZATION IN TWO CASES. **CHRONIC EXPOSURE-** DEPENDING ON CONCENTRATION AND DURATION OF CONTACT, EFFECTS AS IN ACUTE EXPOSURE MAY OCCUR WITH REPEATED OR PROLONGED EXPOSURE.

FIRST AID- WASH EYES IMMEDIATELY WITH LARGE AMOUNTS OF WATER, OCCASIONALLY LIFTING UPPER AND LOWER LIDS, UNTIL NO EVIDENCE OF CHEMICAL REMAINS (AT LEAST 15-20 MINUTES). CONTINUE IRRIGATING WITH NORMAL SALINE UNTIL THE PH HAS RETURNED TO NORMAL (30-60 MINUTES). COVER WITH STERILE BANDAGES. GET MEDICAL ATTENTION IMMEDIATELY.

INGESTION: TRISODIUM PHOSPHATE (SODIUM PHOSPHATE, TRIBASIC): CORROSIVE. **ACUTE EXPOSURE-** A VERY LARGE DOSE OF TRISODIUM PHOSPHATE, DODECAHYDRATE WAS LETHAL IN RATS. INGESTION OF STRONG ALKALIES MAY CAUSE SEVERE PAIN, VOMITING, DIARRHEA, AND COLLAPSE. GASTRIC OR ESOPAGEAL PERFORATION MAY BE DELAYED FOR 2-4 DAYS, AND MAY BE INDICATED BY SUDDEN ONSET OF SEVERE ABDOMINAL PAIN, BOARDLIKE ABDOMINAL RIGIDITY AND RAPID HYPOTENSION. ESOPHAGEAL STRICTURE MAY BE DELAYED SEVERAL WEEKS, MONTHS, OR YEARS AFTER INITIAL RECOVERY. **CHRONIC EXPOSURE-** TRISODIUM PHOSPHATE IS USED AS A FOOD ADDITIVE, NUTRIENT, SEQUESTRANT, AND DIETARY SUPPLEMENT.

FIRST AID- TREAT SYMPTOMATICALLY AND SUPPORTIVELY. IF PERSON IS CONSCIOUS AND ABLE TO SWALLOW, GIVE LARGE AMOUNTS OF WATER OR MILK TO DILUTE SUBSTANCE. GET MEDICAL ATTENTION AND ADVICE ON WHETHER OR NOT TO USE GASTRIC LAVAGE. CARE MUST BE TAKEN TO PREVENT ASPIRATION. A CUFFED ENDOTRACHEAL TUBE USED BY QUALIFIED MEDICAL PERSONNEL MIGHT BE ADVISABLE IF THERE ARE NO SIGNS OF PERFORATION FROM THE INGESTION OF A CORROSIVE SUBSTANCE. KEEP HEAD LOWER THAN HIPS TO PREVENT ASPIRATION IF VOMITING SHOULD OCCUR.

ANTIDOTE: THE FOLLOWING ANTIDOTE HAS BEEN RECOMMENDED. HOWEVER, THE DECISION AS TO WHETHER THE SEVERITY OF POISONING REQUIRES ADMINISTRATION OF ANY ANTIDOTE AND ACTUAL DOSE REQUIRED SHOULD BE MADE BY QUALIFIED MEDICAL PERSONNEL.

PHOSPHATES: FOR HYPOCALCEMIA, AFTER PHOSPHATE INGESTION, GIVE CALCIUM GLUCONATE, 5 ML OF 10% SOLUTION SLOWLY INTRAVENOUSLY, TO RESTORE IONIC CALCIUM TO NORMAL LEVEL (DREISBACH, HANDBOOK OF POISONING, 12TH ED.). ANTIDOTE SHOULD BE ADMINISTERED BY QUALIFIED MEDICAL PERSONNEL.

REACTIVITY

REACTIVITY: STABLE UNDER NORMAL TEMPERATURES AND PRESSURES.

INCOMPATIBILITIES: TRISODIUM PHOSPHATE (SODIUM PHOSPHATE, TRIBASIC): ACIDS (STRONG): VIOLENT REACTION. MAGNESIUM: VIOLENT REACTION. METALS: CORROSIVE WITH RELEASE OF HYDDROGEN GAS. OXIDIZERS (STRONG): FIRE AND EXPLOSION HAZARD.

DECOMPOSITION: THERMAL DECOMPOSITION PRODUCTS MAY INCLUDE TOXIC AND HAZARDOUS SODIUM OXIDE AND OXIDES OF PHOSPHORUS.

POLYMERIZATION: HAZARDOUS POLYMERIZATION HAS NOT BEEN REPORTED TO OCCUR UNDER NORMAL TEMPERATURES AND PRESSURES.

STORAGE AND DISPOSAL

OBSERVE ALL FEDERAL, STATE AND LOCAL REGULATIONS WHEN STORING OR DISPOSING OF THIS SUBSTANCE. FOR ASSISTANCE, CONTACT THE DISTRICT DIRECTOR OF THE ENVIRONMENTAL PROTECTION AGENCY.

****STORAGE****

STORE AWAY FROM INCOMPATIBLE SUBSTANCES.

CONDITIONS TO AVOID

NO REPORTS FOUND.

SPILL AND LEAK PROCEDURES

SOIL SPILL: DIG A PIT, POND, LAGOON OR HOLDING AREA TO CONTAIN LIQUID OR SOLID MATERIAL. COVER SOLIDS WITH A PLASTIC SHEET TO PREVENT DISSOLVING IN RAIN OR FIREFIGHTING WATER.

WATER SPILL: NEUTRALIZE WITH AGRICULTURAL LIME, SLAKED LIME, CRUSHED LIMESTONE, OR SODIUM BICARBONATE.

ADD SUITABLE AGENT TO NEUTRALIZE SPILLED MATERIAL TO PH-7.

USE MECHANICAL DREDGES OR LIFTS TO EXTRACT IMMOBILIZED MASSES OF POLLUTION AND PRECIPITATES.

OCCUPATIONAL SPILL: SWEEP UP AND PLACE IN SUITABLE CLEAN, DRY CONTAINERS FOR RECLAMATION OR LATER DISPOSAL. DO NOT FLUSH SPILLED MATERIAL INTO SEWER. KEEP UNNECESSARY PEOPLE AWAY.

REPORTABLE QUANTITY (RQ): 5000 POUNDS THE SUPERFUND AMENDMENTS AND REAUTHORIZATION ACT (SARA) SECTION 304 REQUIRES THAT A RELEASE EQUAL TO OR GREATER THAN THE REPORTABLE QUANTITY FOR THIS SUBSTANCE BE IMMEDIATELY REPORTED TO THE LOCAL EMERGENCY PLANNING COMMITTEE AND THE STATE EMERGENCY RESPONSE COMMISSION (40 CFR 355.40). IF THE RELEASE OF THIS SUBSTANCE IS REPORTABLE UNDER CERCLA SECTION 103, THE NATIONAL RESPONSE CENTER MUST BE NOTIFIED IMMEDIATELY AT (800) 424-8802 OR (202) 426-2675 IN THE METROPOLITAN WASHINGTON, D.C. AREA (40 CFR 302.6).

PROTECTIVE EQUIPMENT

VENTILATION: PROVIDE LOCAL EXHAUST OR GENERAL DILUTION VENTILATION SYSTEM.

RESPIRATOR: THE FOLLOWING RESPIRATORS ARE RECOMMENDED BASED ON INFORMATION FOUND IN THE PHYSICAL DATA, TOXICITY AND HEALTH EFFECTS SECTIONS. THEY ARE RANKED IN ORDER FROM MINIMUM TO MAXIMUM RESPIRATORY PROTECTION. THE SPECIFIC RESPIRATOR SELECTED MUST BE BASED ON CONTAMINATION LEVELS FOUND IN THE WORK PLACE, MUST NOT EXCEED THE WORKING LIMITS OF THE RESPIRATOR AND BE JOINTLY APPROVED BY THE NATIONAL INSTITUTE FOR OCCUPATIONAL SAFETY AND HEALTH AND THE MINE SAFETY AND HEALTH ADMINISTRATION (NIOSH-MSHA).

DUST AND MIST RESPIRATOR WITH A FULL FACEPIECE.

AIR-PURIFYING FULL FACEPIECE RESPIRATOR WITH A HIGH-EFFICIENCY PARTICULATE FILTER.

POWERED AIR-PURIFYING RESPIRATOR WITH A TIGHT-FITTING FACEPIECE AND HIGH-EFFICIENCY PARTICULATE FILTER.

TYPE 'C' SUPPLIED-AIR RESPIRATOR WITH A FULL FACEPIECE OPERATED IN PRESSURE-DEMAND OR OTHER POSITIVE PRESSURE MODE OR WITH A FULL FACEPIECE, HELMET OR HOOD OPERATED IN CONTINUOUS-FLOW MODE. SELF-CONTAINED BREATHING APPARATUS WITH A FULL FACEPIECE OPERATED IN PRESSURE-DEMAND OR OTHER POSITIVE PRESSURE MODE.

FOR FIREFIGHTING AND OTHER IMMEDIATELY DANGEROUS TO LIFE OR HEALTH CONDITIONS:

SELF-CONTAINED BREATHING APPARATUS WITH FULL FACEPIECE OPERATED IN PRESSURE-DEMAND OR OTHER POSITIVE PRESSURE MODE.

SUPPLIED-AIR RESPIRATOR WITH FULL FACEPIECE AND OPERATED IN PRESSURE-DEMAND OR OTHER POSITIVE PRESSURE MODE IN COMBINATION WITH AN AUXILIARY SELF-CONTAINED BREATHING APPARATUS OPERATED IN PRESSURE-DEMAND OR OTHER POSITIVE PRESSURE MODE.

CLOTHING: EMPLOYEE MUST WEAR APPROPRIATE PROTECTIVE (IMPERVIOUS) CLOTHING AND EQUIPMENT TO PREVENT ANY POSSIBILITY OF SKIN CONTACT WITH THIS SUBSTANCE.

GLOVES: EMPLOYEE MUST WEAR APPROPRIATE PROTECTIVE GLOVES TO PREVENT CONTACT WITH THIS SUBSTANCE.

EYE PROTECTION: EMPLOYEE MUST WEAR SPLASH-PROOF OR DUST-RESISTANT SAFETY GOGGLES AND A FACESHIELD TO PREVENT CONTACT WITH THIS SUBSTANCE.

EMERGENCY WASH FACILITIES: WHERE THERE IS ANY POSSIBILITY THAT AN EMPLOYEE'S EYES AND/OR SKIN MAY BE EXPOSED TO THIS SUBSTANCE, THE EMPLOYER SHOULD PROVIDE AN EYE WASH FOUNTAIN AND QUICK DRENCH SHOWER WITHIN THE IMMEDIATE WORK AREA FOR EMERGENCY USE.

AUTHORIZED BY- OCCUPATIONAL HEALTH SERVICES, INC.

CREATION DATE: 11/16/89 ***REVISION DATE:*** 05/31/90

MATERIAL SAFETY DATA SHEET

OCCUPATIONAL HEALTH SERVICES, INC.
AGRICULTURE AND PESTICIDE DIVISION
450 SEVENTH AVENUE, SUITE 2407
NEW YORK, NEW YORK 10123
1-800-445-MSDS OR (212) 967-1100

EMERGENCY CONTACT:
JOHN S. BRANSFORD, JR. (615) 292-1180

SUBSTANCE IDENTIFICATION

CAS-NUMBER 8002-33-3
SUBSTANCE: **TURKEY RED OIL**
TRADE NAMES/SYNONYMS: CASTOR OIL, SULFATED; AQUASOL; AVIROL 130; MONOPOLE OIL MDD; RED OIL, DISTILLED; SULFATED CASTOR OIL; PST24575
CHEMICAL FAMILY: FATTY ACID
SULFONIC ACID
CERCLA RATINGS (SCALE 0-3): HEALTH=0 FIRE=1 REACTIVITY=0 PERSISTENCE=0
NFPA RATINGS (SCALE 0-4): HEALTH=0 FIRE=1 REACTIVITY=0

COMPONENTS AND CONTAMINANTS

COMPONENT: TURKEY RED OIL ***PERCENT:*** 100
CAS# 8002-33-3
OTHER CONTAMINANTS: NONE
EXPOSURE LIMITS: NO OCCUPATIONAL EXPOSURE LIMITS ESTABLISHED BY OSHA, ACGIH, OR NIOSH.

PHYSICAL DATA

DESCRIPTION: REDDISH VISCOUS LIQUID, CHARACTERISTIC ODOR.
BOILING POINT: NOT AVAILABLE ***SPECIFIC GRAVITY:*** 1.0
SOLUBILITY IN WATER: SOLUBLE

FIRE AND EXPLOSION DATA

FIRE AND EXPLOSION HAZARD: NEGLIGIBLE FIRE HAZARD WHEN EXPOSED TO HEAT OR FLAME.
FLASH POINT: 476F (247 C) (CC) ***AUTOIGNITION TEMP.:*** 833 F (445 C)
FIREFIGHTING MEDIA: DRY CHEMICAL, CARBON DIOXIDE, HALON, WATER SPRAY OR STANDARD FOAM (1987 EMERGENCY RESPONSE GUIDEBOOK, DOT P 5800.4).
FOR LARGER FIRES, USE WATER SPRAY, FOG OR STANDARD FOAM (1987 EMERGENCY RESPONSE GUIDEBOOK, DOT P 5800.4).
ALCOHOL FOAM (NFPA 325M, FIRE HAZARD PROPERTIES OF FLAMMABLE LIQUIDS, GASES, AND VOLATILE SOLIDS, 1984).
FIREFIGHTING: MOVE CONTAINER FROM FIRE AREA IF POSSIBLE. DO NOT SCATTER SPILLED MATERIAL WITH HIGH PRESSURE WATER STREAMS. DIKE FIRE CONTROL WATER FOR LATER DISPOSAL (1987 EMERGENCY RESPONSE GUIDEBOOK, DOT P 5800.4, GUIDE PAGE 31).
USE AGENTS SUITABLE FOR TYPE OF SURROUNDING FIRE. AVOID BREATHING HAZARDOUS VAPORS, KEEP UPWIND.
WATER OR FOAM MAY CAUSE FROTHING (NFPA 325M, FIRE HAZARD PROPERTIES OF FLAMMABLE LIQUIDS, GASES, AND VOLATILE SOLIDS, 1984)

TOXICITY

CARCINOGEN STATUS: NONE. TURKEY RED OIL MAY CAUSE SKIN, EYE AND MUCOUS MEMBRANE IRRITATION.

HEALTH EFFECTS AND FIRST AID

INHALATION: **ACUTE EXPOSURE**- NO DATA AVAILABLE, ALTHOUGH THE LOW VAPOR PRESSURE IS UNLIKELY TO CAUSE INHALATION PROBLEMS. **CHRONIC EXPOSURE**- NO DATA AVAILABLE.
FIRST AID- REMOVE FROM EXPOSURE AREA TO FRESH AIR IMMEDIATELY. IF BREATHING HAS STOPPED, PERFORM ARTIFICIAL RESPIRATION. KEEP PERSON WARM AND AT REST. TREAT SYMPTOMATICALLY AND SUPPORTIVELY. GET MEDICAL ATTENTION IMMEDIATELY.

SKIN CONTACT: **ACUTE EXPOSURE**- NO DATA IS AVAILABLE ON THIS SPECIFIC SUBSTANCE, BUT ANIONIC DETERGENTS MAY CAUSE REDNESS, SORENESS AND PAPULAR DERMATITIS. SENSITIVE PERSONS MAY EXPERIENCE SKIN THICHENING WITH WEEPING, CRACKING, SCALING AND BLISTERING. **CHRONIC EXPOSURE**- PROLONGED OR REPEATED EXPOSURE MAY CAUSE DERMATITIS.
FIRST AID- REMOVE CONTAMINATED CLOTHING AND SHOES IMMEDIATELY. WASH AFFECTED AREA WITH SOAP OR MILD DETERGENT AND LARGE AMOUNTS OF WATER UNTIL NO EVIDENCE OF CHEMICAL REMAINS (APPROXIMATELY 15-20 MINUTES). GET MEDICAL ATTENTION IMMEDIATELY.

EYE CONTACT: **ACUTE EXPOSURE**- MAY CAUSE REDNESS AND IRRITATION. **CHRONIC EXPOSURE**- PROLONGED OR REPEATED EXPOSURE MAY CAUSE CONJUNCTIVITIS.
FIRST AID- WASH THE AREA WITH LARGE AMOUNTS OF WATER OCCASIONALLY LIFTING THE UPPER AND LOWER EYELIDS UNTIL ALL TRACES OF THE CHEMICAL ARE GONE.

INGESTION: **ACUTE EXPOSURE**- MAY CAUSE NAUSEA, VOMITING, ABDOMINAL PAIN, BURNING PAIN IN THE MOUTH, BLOODY DIARRHEA, COLLAPSE, AND COMA. **CHRONIC EXPOSURE**- NO DATA AVAILABLE.
FIRST AID- GIVE FLUIDS AND ALLOW VOMITING. GET MEDICAL ATTENTION. DO NOT INDUCE VOMITING IF UNCONSCIOUS.
ANTIDOTE: NO SPECIFIC ANTIDOTE. TREAT SYMPTOMATICALLY AND SUPPORTIVELY.

REACTIVITY

REACTIVITY: STABLE UNDER NORMAL TEMPERATURES AND PRESSURES.
INCOMPATIBILITIES: NONE KNOWN.
DECOMPOSITION: THERMAL DECOMPOSITION PRODUCTS MAY INCLUDE TOXIC OXIDES OF SULFUR AND CARBON.
POLYMERIZATION: HAZARDOUS POLYMERIZATION HAS NOT BEEN REPORTED TO OCCUR UNDER NORMAL TEMPERATURES AND PRESSURES.

CONDITIONS TO AVOID

NONE REPORTED.

SPILL AND LEAK PROCEDURES

OCCUPATIONAL SPILL: NO SPECIAL PRECAUTIONS INDICATED.

PROTECTIVE EQUIPMENT

VENTILATION: PROVIDE GENERAL DILUTION VENTILATION.
RESPIRATOR: HIGH LEVELS- CHEMICAL CARTRIDGE RESPIRATOR WITH AN ORGANIC VAPOR CARTRIDGE.
FIREFIGHTING- SELF-CONTAINED BREATHING APPARATUS WITH A FULL FACEPIECE OPERATED IN PRESSURE-DEMAND OR OTHER POSITIVE-PRESSURE MODE.
CLOTHING: PROTECTIVE CLOTHING NOT REQUIRED. AVOID REPEATED OR PROLONGED CONTACT WITH THIS SUBSTANCE.
GLOVES: PROTECTIVE GLOVES ARE NOT REQUIRED BUT RECOMMENDED.
EYE PROTECTION: EYE PROTECTION NOT REQUIRED, BUT ADVISABLE.

AUTHORIZED BY- OCCUPATIONAL HEALTH SERVICES, INC.
CREATION DATE: 02/08/90 ***REVISION DATE:*** 03/02/90

MATERIAL SAFETY DATA SHEET

OCCUPATIONAL HEALTH SERVICES, INC.
AGRICULTURE AND PESTICIDE DIVISION
450 SEVENTH AVENUE, SUITE 2407
NEW YORK, NEW YORK 10123
1-800-445-MSDS OR (212) 967-1100

EMERGENCY CONTACT:
JOHN S. BRANSFORD, JR. (615) 292-1180

SUBSTANCE IDENTIFICATION

CAS-NUMBER 8006-64-2
SUBSTANCE: **TURPENTINE**
TRADE NAMES/SYNONYMS: TURPENTINE, OIL; OIL OF TURPENTINE, RECTIFIED; OIL OF TURPENTINE; SPIRITS OF TURPENTINE; TURPENTINE OIL; TURPENTINE OIL, RECTIFIED; GUM SPIRITS OF TURPENTINE (GRUMBACHER); GUM TURPENTINE (PARKS CORP.); STCC 4910313; UN 1299; PST24580
CHEMICAL FAMILY: TERPENE
MOLECULAR FORMULA: C10-H16 (APPROX)
MOLECULAR WEIGHT: 136 (APPROX)
CERCLA RATINGS (SCALE 0-3): HEALTH=1 FIRE=3 REACTIVITY=0 PERSISTENCE=1
NFPA RATINGS (SCALE 0-4): HEALTH=1 FIRE=3 REACTIVITY=0

COMPONENTS AND CONTAMINANTS

COMPONENT: TURPENTINE ***PERCENT:*** 100.0
CAS# 8006-64-2
OTHER CONTAMINANTS: NONE
EXPOSURE LIMITS: TURPENTINE: 100 PPM (560 MG/M3) OSHA TWA 100 PPM (560 MG/M3) ACGIH TWA

PHYSICAL DATA

DESCRIPTION: COLORLESS LIQUID WITH A CHARACTERISTIC ODOR AND TASTE.
BOILING POINT: 309-338 F (154-170 C) ***MELTING POINT:*** -67 F (-55 C)
SPECIFIC GRAVITY: 0.854-0.868 @ 25 C ***VOLATILITY:*** 100%
VAPOR PRESSURE: 4 MMHG @ 20 C ***EVAPORATION RATE:*** (BUTYL ACETATE=1) 0.86
SOLUBILITY IN WATER: INSOLUBLE ***ODOR THRESHOLD:*** 200 PPM
VAPOR DENSITY: 4.84
SOLVENT SOLUBILITY: SOLUBLE IN BENZENE, CHLOROFORM, ETHER, CARBON DISULFIDE, OILS, ALCOHOL, PETROLEUM ETHER AND GLACIAL ACETIC ACID.

FIRE AND EXPLOSION DATA

FIRE AND EXPLOSION HAZARD: DANGEROUS FIRE HAZARD WHEN EXPOSED TO HEAT OR FLAME.
VAPORS ARE HEAVIER THAN AIR AND MAY TRAVEL A CONSIDERABLE DISTANCE TO A SOURCE OF IGNITION AND FLASH BACK.
VAPOR-AIR MIXTURES ARE EXPLOSIVE ABOVE FLASH POINT.
FLASH POINT: 95 F (35 C) (CC) ***LOWER EXPLOSIVE LIMIT:*** 0.8%
AUTOIGNITION TEMP.: 488 F (253 C) ***FLAMMABILITY CLASS(OSHA):*** IC
FIREFIGHTING MEDIA: DRY CHEMICAL, CARBON DIOXIDE, HALON, WATER SPRAY OR STANDARD FOAM (1987 EMERGENCY RESPONSE GUIDEBOOK, DOT P 5800.4).
FOR LARGER FIRES, USE WATER SPRAY, FOG OR STANDARD FOAM (1987 EMERGENCY RESPONSE GUIDEBOOK, DOT P 5800.4).
FIREFIGHTING: MOVE CONTAINER FROM FIRE AREA IF POSSIBLE. COOL FIRE-EXPOSED CONTAINERS WITH WATER FROM SIDE UNTIL WELL AFTER FIRE IS OUT. STAY AWAY FROM STORAGE TANK ENDS. FOR MASSIVE FIRE IN STORAGE AREA, USE UNMANNED HOSE HOLDER OR MONITOR NOZZLES, ELSE WITHDRAW FROM AREA AND LET FIRE BURN. WITHDRAW IMMEDIATELY IN CASE OF RISING SOUND FROM VENTING SAFETY DEVICE OR ANY DISCOLORATION OF STORAGE TANK DUE TO FIRE (1987 EMERGENCY RESPONSE GUIDEBOOK, DOT P 5800.4, GUIDE PAGE 27).
EXTINGUISH ONLY IF FLOW CAN BE STOPPED; USE WATER IN FLOODING AMOUNTS AS FOG, SOLID STREAMS MAY SPREAD FIRE. COOL CONTAINERS WITH FLOODING AMOUNTS OF WATER, APPLY FROM AS FAR A DISTANCE AS POSSIBLE. AVOID BREATHING TOXIC VAPORS, KEEP UPWIND.
WATER MAY BE INEFFECTIVE (NFPA 325M, FIRE HAZARD PROPERTIES OF FLAMMABLE LIQUIDS, GASES, AND VOLATILE SOLIDS, 1984)

TRANSPORTATION DATA

DEPARTMENT OF TRANSPORTATION HAZARD CLASSIFICATION 49 CFR 172.101: FLAMMABLE LIQUID
DEPARTMENT OF TRANSPORTATION LABELING REQUIREMENTS 49 CFR 172.101 AND SUBPART E: FLAMMABLE LIQUID
DEPARTMENT OF TRANSPORTATION PACKAGING REQUIREMENTS: 49 CFR 173.119 EXCEPTIONS: 49 CFR 173.118

TOXICITY

TURPENTINE: IRRITATION DATA: 175 PPM EYE-HUMAN. TOXICITY DATA: 175 PPM INHALATION-HUMAN TCLO; 6 GM/M3/3 HOURS INHALATION-HUMAN TCLO; 12 GM/M3/6 HOURS INHALATION-RAT LC50; 29 GM/M3/2 HOURS INHALATION-MOUSE LC50; 16 GM/M3/1 HOUR INHALATION-GUINEA PIG LCLO; 560 MG/KG ORAL-WOMAN TDLO; 1748 MG/KG ORAL-INFANT LDLO; 874 MG/KG ORAL-INFANT TDLO; 5760 MG/KG ORAL-RAT LD50; 1180 UG/KG INTRAVENOUS-MOUSE LD50; 441 MG/KG UNREPORTED-MAN LDLO; TUMORIGENIC DATA (RTECS). CARCINOGEN STATUS: NONE. LOCAL EFFECTS: IRRITANT- INHALATION, SKIN, EYE. ACUTE TOXICITY LEVEL: TOXIC BY INHALATION; SLIGHTLY TOXIC BY INGESTION. TARGET EFFECTS: SENSITIZER- SKIN; CENTRAL NERVOUS SYSTEM DEPRESSANT; POISONING MAY ALSO AFFECT THE BLADDER AND KIDNEYS. AT INCREASED RISK FROM EXPOSURE: PERSONS WITH PRE-EXISTING PULMONARY, KIDNEY, OR SKIN DISORDERS. ADDITIONAL DATA: ALCOHOL MAY ENHANCE THE TOXIC EFFECTS. CROSS SENSITIZATION MAY OCCUR WITH BALSAM OF PERU, BENZOIN, RAGWEED OIL, CHRYSANTHEMUM, AND PYRETHRUM.

HEALTH EFFECTS AND FIRST AID

INHALATION: IRRITANT. 1900 PPM IMMEDIATELY DANGEROUS TO LIFE OR HEALTH. **ACUTE EXPOSURE-** MAY CAUSE IRRITATION, HEADACHE, CONFUSION, VERTIGO, NAUSEA, COUGH, RESPIRATORY AND GASTROENTERIC DISTRESS, CYANOSIS, LOSS OF APPETITE, NARCOSIS, AND PULMONARY EDEMA. **CHRONIC EXPOSURE-** REPEATED OR PROLONGED EXPOSURE MAY CAUSE MUCOUS MEMBRANE IRRITATION AND BRONCHITIS.
FIRST AID- REMOVE FROM EXPOSURE AREA TO FRESH AIR IMMEDIATELY. IF BREATHING HAS STOPPED, PERFORM ARTIFICIAL RESPIRATION. KEEP PERSON WARM AND AT REST. TREAT SYMPTOMATICALLY AND SUPPORTIVELY. GET MEDICAL ATTENTION IMMEDIATELY.

SKIN CONTACT: IRRITANT. **ACUTE EXPOSURE-** MAY CAUSE IRRITATION, ERYTHEMA, AND ITCHING. SENSITIZATION DERMATITIS MAY OCCUR IN PREVIOUSLY EXPOSED PEOPLE. **CHRONIC EXPOSURE-** REPEATED OR PROLONGED CONTACT MAY CAUSE SENSITIZATION DERMATITIS.
FIRST AID- REMOVE CONTAMINATED CLOTHING AND SHOES IMMEDIATELY. WASH AFFECTED AREA WITH SOAP OR MILD DETERGENT AND LARGE AMOUNTS OF WATER UNTIL NO EVIDENCE OF CHEMICAL REMAINS (APPROXIMATELY 15-20 MINUTES). GET MEDICAL ATTENTION IMMEDIATELY.

EYE CONTACT: IRRITANT. **ACUTE EXPOSURE-** MAY CAUSE IRRITATION AND PAIN AT 175 PPM. DIRECT LIQUID CONTACT MAY CAUSE SEVERE BLEPHAROSPASM, CONJUNCTIVAL HYPEREMIA, SLIGHT INJURY TO THE CORNEAL EPITHELIUM, CORNEAL BURNS, AND TEMPERARY EROSION OF THE EPITHELIUM. **CHRONIC EXPOSURE-** REPEATED OR PROLONGED CONTACT MAY CAUSE CONJUNCTIVITIS.
FIRST AID- WASH EYES IMMEDIATELY WITH LARGE AMOUNTS OF WATER OR NORMAL SALINE, OCCASIONALLY LIFTING UPPER AND LOWER LIDS, UNTIL NO EVIDENCE OF CHEMICAL REMAINS (APPROXIMATELY 15-20 MINUTES). GET MEDICAL ATTENTION IMMEDIATELY.

INGESTION: IRRITANT. **ACUTE EXPOSURE-** MAY CAUSE NAUSEA, VOMITING, COUGHING, CHOKING, CHEST PAIN, DIZZINESS, ASPIRATION INTO THE LUNGS, PULMONARY EDEMA, CHEMICAL PNEUMONITIS, DYSPNEA, CYANOSIS, GASTROENTERITIS, FEVER, LOSS OF APPETITE, OLIGURIA, HEMATURIA, ALBUMINURIA, AND CASTS IN THE URINE. MAY ALSO CAUSE KIDNEY DAMAGE. **CHRONIC EXPOSURE-** NONE KNOWN IN HUMANS.
FIRST AID- GIVE 120-240 ML OF MILK; THEN REMOVE BY GASTRIC LAVAGE OR EMESIS, TAKING CARE TO PREVENT ASPIRATION. FOLLOW THESE PROCEDURES BY ADMINISTERING 30-60 ML OF FLEET'S PHOSPHO-SODA DILUTED 1:4 IN WATER. PERFORM ARTIFICIAL RESPIRATION IF NECESSARY. GET MEDICAL ATTENTION (DREISBACH, HANDBOOK OF POISONING, 12TH ED.). FIRST AID SHOULD BE PERFORMED BY QUALIFIED MEDICAL PERSONNEL.
ANTIDOTE: NO SPECIFIC ANTIDOTE. TREAT SYMPTOMATICALLY AND SUPPORTIVELY.

REACTIVITY

REACTIVITY: STABLE UNDER NORMAL TEMPERATURES AND PRESSURES.
INCOMPATIBILITIES: TURPENTINE: CALCIUM HYPOCHLORITE: POSSIBLE EXPLOSION. CHLORINE: VIGOROUS REACTION WITH POSSIBLE IGNITION. CHROMIC ANHYDRIDE: VIOLENT REACTION. CHROMYL CHLORIDE: IGNITES. HEXACHLOROMELAMINE: POSSIBLE EXPLOSION. OXIDIZERS (STRONG): FIRE AND EXPLOSION HAZARD. PLASTICS, RUBBERS AND COATING: MAY BE ATTACKED. STANNIC CHLORIDE: HEAT BUILD-UP WITH POSSIBLE FLAMING. TRICHLOROMELAMINE: POSSIBLE EXPLOSION HAZARD.
DECOMPOSITION: THERMAL DECOMPOSITION PRODUCTS MAY INCLUDE TOXIC OXIDES OF CARBON.
POLYMERIZATION: HAZARDOUS POLYMERIZATION HAS NOT BEEN REPORTED TO OCCUR UNDER NORMAL TEMPERATURES AND PRESSURES.

STORAGE AND DISPOSAL

OBSERVE ALL FEDERAL, STATE AND LOCAL REGULATIONS WHEN STORING OR DISPOSING OF THIS SUBSTANCE. FOR ASSISTANCE, CONTACT THE DISTRICT DIRECTOR OF THE ENVIRONMENTAL PROTECTION AGENCY.

STORAGE

STORE IN ACCORDANCE WITH 29 CFR 1910.106.
BONDING AND GROUNDING: SUBSTANCES WITH LOW ELECTROCONDUCTIVITY, WHICH MAY BE IGNITED BY ELECTROSTATIC SPARKS, SHOULD BE STORED IN CONTAINERS WHICH MEET THE BONDING AND GROUNDING GUIDELINES SPECIFIED IN NFPA 77-1983, RECOMMENDED PRACTICE ON STATIC ELECTRICITY.
STORE AWAY FROM INCOMPATIBLE SUBSTANCES.

DISPOSAL

DISPOSAL MUST BE IN ACCORDANCE WITH STANDARDS APPLICABLE TO GENERATORS OF HAZARDOUS WASTE, 40 CFR 262. EPA HAZARDOUS WASTE NUMBER D001. 100 POUND CERCLA SECTION 103 REPORTABLE QUANTITY.

CONDITIONS TO AVOID

AVOID CONTACT WITH HEAT, SPARKS, FLAMES, OR OTHER SOURCES OF IGNITION. VAPORS MAY BE EXPLOSIVE. AVOID OVERHEATING OF CONTAINERS; CONTAINERS MAY VIOLENTLY RUPTURE IN HEAT OF FIRE. AVOID CONTAMINATION OF WATER SOURCES.

SPILL AND LEAK PROCEDURES

OCCUPATIONAL SPILL: SHUT OFF IGNITION SOURCES. STOP LEAK IF YOU CAN DO IT WITHOUT RISK. USE WATER SPRAY TO REDUCE VAPORS. FOR SMALL SPILLS, TAKE UP WITH SAND OR OTHER ABSORBENT MATERIAL AND PLACE INTO CONTAINERS FOR LATER DISPOSAL. FOR LARGER SPILLS, DIKE FAR AHEAD OF SPILL FOR LATER DISPOSAL. NO SMOKING, FLAMES OR FLARES IN HAZARD AREA. KEEP UNNECESSARY PEOPLE AWAY; ISOLATE HAZARD AREA AND RESTRICT ENTRY.

PROTECTIVE EQUIPMENT

VENTILATION: PROVIDE LOCAL EXHAUST VENTILATION SYSTEM TO MEET PUBLISHED EXPOSURE LIMITS.

RESPIRATOR: THE FOLLOWING RESPIRATORS AND MAXIMUM USE CONCENTRATIONS ARE RECOMMENDATIONS BY THE U.S. DEPARTMENT OF HEALTH AND HUMAN SERVICES, NIOSH POCKET GUIDE TO CHEMICAL HAZARDS; NIOSH CRITERIA DOCUMENTS OR BY THE U.S. DEPARTMENT OF LABOR, 29 CFR 1910 SUBPART Z. THE SPECIFIC RESPIRATOR SELECTED MUST BE BASED ON CONTAMINATION LEVELS FOUND IN THE WORK PLACE, MUST NOT EXCEED THE WORKING LIMITS OF THE RESPIRATOR AND BE JOINTLY APPROVED BY THE NATIONAL INSTITUTE FOR OCCUPATIONAL SAFETY AND HEALTH AND THE MINE SAFETY AND HEALTH ADMINISTRATION (NIOSH-MSHA).

TURPENTINE:

1000 PPM- ANY CHEMICAL CARTRIDGE RESPIRATOR WITH FULL FACEPIECE AND ORGANIC VAPOR CARTRIDGES. ANY POWERED AIR-PURIFYING RESPIRATOR WITH ORGANIC VAPOR CARTRIDGE(S).

1900 PPM- ANY SUPPLIED-AIR RESPIRATOR OPERATED IN A CONTINUOUS FLOW MODE. ANY AIR-PURIFYING FULL FACEPIECE RESPIRATOR (GAS MASK) WITH A CHIN-STYLE OR FRONT- OR BACK-MOUNTED ORGANIC VAPOR CANISTER. ANY SUPPLIED-AIR RESPIRATOR WITH A FULL FACEPIECE. ANY SELF-CONTAINED BREATHING APPARATUS WITH A FULL FACEPIECE.

ESCAPE- ANY AIR-PURIFYING FULL FACEPIECE RESPIRATOR (GAS MASK) WITH A CHIN-STYLE OR FRONT- OR BACK-MOUNTED ORGANIC VAPOR CANISTER. ANY APPROPRIATE ESCAPE-TYPE SELF-CONTAINED BREATHING APPARATUS.

FOR FIREFIGHTING AND OTHER IMMEDIATELY DANGEROUS TO LIFE OR HEALTH CONDITIONS:

SELF-CONTAINED BREATHING APPARATUS WITH FULL FACEPIECE OPERATED IN PRESSURE-DEMAND OR OTHER POSITIVE PRESSURE MODE.

SUPPLIED-AIR RESPIRATOR WITH FULL FACEPIECE AND OPERATED IN PRESSURE-DEMAND OR OTHER POSITIVE PRESSURE MODE IN COMBINATION WITH AN AUXILIARY SELF-CONTAINED BREATHING APPARATUS OPERATED IN PRESSURE-DEMAND OR OTHER POSITIVE PRESSURE MODE.

CLOTHING: PROTECTIVE CLOTHING NOT REQUIRED. AVOID REPEATED OR PROLONGED CONTACT WITH THIS SUBSTANCE.

GLOVES: PROTECTIVE GLOVES ARE NOT REQUIRED BUT RECOMMENDED.

EYE PROTECTION: EMPLOYEE MUST WEAR SPLASH-PROOF OR DUST-RESISTANT SAFETY GOGGLES AND A FACESHIELD TO PREVENT CONTACT WITH THIS SUBSTANCE.

EMERGENCY WASH FACILITIES: WHERE THERE IS ANY POSSIBILITY THAT AN EMPLOYEE'S EYES AND/OR SKIN MAY BE EXPOSED TO THIS SUBSTANCE, THE EMPLOYER SHOULD PROVIDE AN EYE WASH FOUNTAIN AND QUICK DRENCH SHOWER WITHIN THE IMMEDIATE WORK AREA FOR EMERGENCY USE.

AUTHORIZED BY- OCCUPATIONAL HEALTH SERVICES, INC.
CREATION DATE: 10/05/89 ***REVISION DATE:*** 03/28/90

MATERIAL SAFETY DATA SHEET

OCCUPATIONAL HEALTH SERVICES, INC.
AGRICULTURE AND PESTICIDE DIVISION
450 SEVENTH AVENUE, SUITE 2407
NEW YORK, NEW YORK 10123
1-800-445-MSDS OR (212) 967-1100

EMERGENCY CONTACT:
JOHN S. BRANSFORD, JR. (615) 292-1180

SUBSTANCE IDENTIFICATION

CAS-NUMBER 83-28-3

SUBSTANCE: **VALONE**

TRADE NAMES/SYNONYMS: 1H-INDENE-1,3(2H)-DIONE, 2-(3-METHYL-1-OXOBUTYL)-; 1,3-INDANDIONE, 2-ISOVALERYL-; 2-(3-METHYL-1-OXOBUTYL)-1H-INDENE -1,3(2H)-DIONE; 2-ISOVALERYL-1,3-INDANDIONE; 1,3-INDANDIONE, 2-(3-METHYLBUTOXY)-; 2-(3-METHYLBUTOXY)-1,3-INDANDIONE; C14H14O3; PST24738

CHEMICAL FAMILY: INDANDIONE

MOLECULAR FORMULA: C14-H14-O3

MOLECULAR WEIGHT: 230.28

CERCLA RATINGS (SCALE 0-3): HEALTH=U FIRE=1 REACTIVITY=0 PERSISTENCE=2

NFPA RATINGS (SCALE 0-4): HEALTH=U FIRE=1 REACTIVITY=0

COMPONENTS AND CONTAMINANTS

COMPONENT: VALONE ***PERCENT:*** 100.0
CAS# 83-28-3

OTHER CONTAMINANTS: NONE

EXPOSURE LIMITS: NO OCCUPATIONAL EXPOSURE LIMITS ESTABLISHED BY OSHA, ACGIH, OR NIOSH.

PHYSICAL DATA

DESCRIPTION: YELLOW CRYSTALLINE SOLID. ***MELTING POINT:*** (153-154 F) (67-68 C)

SPECIFIC GRAVITY: NOT AVAILABLE ***SOLUBILITY IN WATER:*** INSOLUBLE

SOLVENT SOLUBILITY: SOLUBLE IN ALCOHOL, ETHER, ACETONE, AND COMMON ORGANIC SOLVENTS.

FIRE AND EXPLOSION DATA

FIRE AND EXPLOSION HAZARD: SLIGHT FIRE HAZARD WHEN EXPOSED TO HEAT OR FLAME.

FIREFIGHTING MEDIA: DRY CHEMICAL, CARBON DIOXIDE, HALON, WATER SPRAY OR STANDARD FOAM (1987 EMERGENCY RESPONSE GUIDEBOOK, DOT P 5800.4). FOR LARGER FIRES, USE WATER SPRAY, FOG OR STANDARD FOAM (1987 EMERGENCY RESPONSE GUIDEBOOK, DOT P 5800.4).

FIREFIGHTING: MOVE CONTAINERS FROM FIRE AREA IF POSSIBLE (1987 EMERGENCY RESPONSE GUIDEBOOK, DOT P 5800.4, GUIDE PAGE 53).

EXTINGUISH FIRE USING AGENTS SUITABLE FOR TYPE OF SURROUNDING FIRE. USE WATER IN FLOODING AMOUNTS AS A FOG. AVOID BREATHING DUSTS AND FUMES FROM BURNING MATERIAL; KEEP UPWIND.

TOXICITY

VALONE: TOXICITY DATA: 100 MG/KG ORAL-RAT LDLO; 150 MG/KG ORAL-RABBIT LDLO. CARCINOGEN STATUS: NONE. ACUTE TOXICITY LEVEL: INSUFFICIENT DATA. TARGET EFFECTS: HEMORRHAGIC AGENT.* AT INCREASED RISK FROM EXPOSURE: PERSONS WITH BLOOD DYSCRASIAS, BLEEDING TENDENCIES, LIVER OR KIDNEY DISEASE, ULCERS OF THE GASTROINTESTINAL TRACT, OR HYPERTENSION.*

* MAY BE BASED ON GENERAL INFORMATION ON INDANDIONE DERIVATIVES.

HEALTH EFFECTS AND FIRST AID

INHALATION: VALONE: SEE INFORMATION ON INDANDIONE DERIVATIVES.
INDANDIONE DERIVATIVES: HEMORRHAGIC AGENT. **ACUTE EXPOSURE**- ABSORPTION BY THE LUNGS MAY RESULT IN HEMORRHAGIC EFFECTS AS DESCRIBED IN CHRONIC EXPOSURE. SEVERE CASES MAY BE FATAL. **CHRONIC EXPOSURE**- REPEATED ABSORPTION MAY CAUSE THE INHIBITION OF PROTHROMBIN SYNTHESIS AND DAMAGE TO CAPILLARY PERMEABILITY RESULTING IN WIDESPREAD INTERNAL HEMORRHAGE WITH ASSOCIATED EFFECTS OF NOSEBLEED, HEMATOMA, HEMATURIA, WIDESPREAD BRUISING, AND ANEMIA.

FIRST AID- REMOVE FROM EXPOSURE AREA TO FRESH AIR IMMEDIATELY. IF BREATHING HAS STOPPED, PERFORM ARTIFICIAL RESPIRATION. KEEP PERSON WARM AND AT REST. TREAT SYMPTOMATICALLY AND SUPPORTIVELY. GET MEDICAL ATTENTION IMMEDIATELY.

SKIN CONTACT: VALONE: SEE INFORMATION ON INDANDIONE DERIVATIVES.
INDANDIONE DERIVATIVES: HEMORRHAGIC AGENT. **ACUTE EXPOSURE**- ABSORPTION THROUGH THE SKIN MAY RESULT IN HEMORRHAGIC EFFECTS AS DESCRIBED IN CHRONIC EXPOSURE. SEVERE CASES MAY BE FATAL. **CHRONIC EXPOSURE**- REPEATED ABSORPTION MAY CAUSE THE INHIBITION OF PROTHROMBIN SYNTHESIS AND DAMAGE TO CAPILLARY PERMEABILITY RESULTING IN WIDESPREAD INTERNAL HEMORRHAGE WITH ASSOCIATED EFFECTS OF NOSEBLEED, HEMATOMA, HEMATURIA, WIDESPREAD BRUISING, AND ANEMIA.

FIRST AID- REMOVE CONTAMINATED CLOTHING AND SHOES IMMEDIATELY. WASH AFFECTED AREA WITH SOAP OR MILD DETERGENT AND LARGE AMOUNTS OF WATER UNTIL NO EVIDENCE OF CHEMICAL REMAINS (APPROXIMATELY 15-20 MINUTES). GET MEDICAL ATTENTION IMMEDIATELY.

EYE CONTACT: VALONE: **ACUTE EXPOSURE**- NO DATA AVAILABLE. **CHRONIC EXPOSURE**- NO DATA AVAILABLE.

FIRST AID- WASH EYES IMMEDIATELY WITH LARGE AMOUNTS OF WATER OR NORMAL SALINE, OCCASIONALLY LIFTING UPPER AND LOWER LIDS, UNTIL NO EVIDENCE OF CHEMICAL REMAINS (APPROXIMATELY 15-20 MINUTES). GET MEDICAL ATTENTION IMMEDIATELY.

INGESTION: VALONE: SEE INFORMATION ON INDANDIONE DERIVATIVES.
INDANDIONE DERIVATIVES: HEMORRHAGIC AGENT. **ACUTE EXPOSURE**- LETHAL DOSES IN ANIMALS HAVE PRODUCED LABORED BREATHING, PROGRESSIVE MUSCULAR WEAKNESS, HYPEREXCITABILITY, PULMONARY CONGESTION, VENOUS ENGORGEMENT, AND CARDIAC STANDSTILL. **CHRONIC EXPOSURE**- MAY BE READILY ABSORBED FROM THE GASTROINTESTINAL TRACT AND CAUSE THE INHIBITION OF PROTHROMBIN SYNTHESIS AND DAMAGE TO CAPILLARY PERMEABILITY. HEMORRHAGIC EFFECTS FROM SYSTEMIC ABSORPTION MAY INCLUDE NOSEBLEED, BLEEDING GUMS AND PHARYNX, PETECHIAL RASH, WIDESPREAD BRUISING, HEMATOMA, HEMOPTYSIS, HEMATEMESIS, HEMATURIA, BLOODY STOOLS, BLEEDING INTO THE ORGANS, GASTROINTESTINAL TRACT,

JOINTS, ABDOMINAL OR RETROPERITONEAL AREA WITH ABDOMINAL, BACK, JOINT AND LIMB PAIN AND CEREBROVASCULAR ACCIDENT. ANEMIA ACCOMPANIED BY WEAKNESS, PALLOR, AND SHOCK MAY OCCUR. SEVERE HEMORRHAGING MAY CAUSE DEATH. THERAPEUTIC USE OF SOME INDANDIONE DERIVATIVES HAS PRODUCED SIDE EFFECTS OF AGRANULOCYTOSIS, THROMBOCYTOPENIA, PYREXIA, DIARRHEA, STEATORRHEA, HEPATITIS, RENAL TUBULAR NECROSIS, EXFOLIATIVE DERMATITIS AND PARALYSIS OF ACCOMMODATION.

FIRST AID- IF ONLY A FEW GRAINS OF ANTICOAGULANT BAIT HAVE BEEN INGESTED BY AN ADULT OR CHILD HAVING NO ANTECEDENT LIVER OR BLOOD CLOTTING DISEASE, TREATMENT IS PROBABLY UNNECESSARY. IF LARGE AMOUNTS OF ANTICOAGULANT WERE INGESTED IN THE PRECEDING 2-3 HOURS, INDUCE VOMITING WITH SYRUP OF IPECAC, FOLLOWED BY 1-2 GLASSES OF WATER. FOLLOWING EMESIS, GIVE ACTIVATED CHARCOAL IN 4-6 OUNCES OF WATER TO LIMIT ABSORPTION OF ANTICOAGULANT REMAINING IN THE GUT. OBSERVE PATIENT 4-5 DAYS AFTER INGESTION. (MORGAN, RECOGNITION AND MANAGEMENT OF PESTICIDE POISONINGS, THIRD EDITION). GET MEDICAL ATTENTION.

ANTIDOTE: THE FOLLOWING ANTIDOTE HAS BEEN RECOMMENDED. HOWEVER, THE DECISION AS TO WHETHER THE SEVERITY OF POISONING REQUIRES ADMINISTRATION OF ANY ANTIDOTE AND ACTUAL DOSE REQUIRED SHOULD BE MADE BY QUALIFIED MEDICAL PERSONNEL.
OVERDOSE OF ANTICOAGULANTS: VITAMIN K IS A SPECIFIC ANTIDOTE. VITAMIN K1 EMULSION IS THE PREFERRED FORM. THE INITIAL SUBCUTANEOUS OR INTRAMUSCULAR DOSE IN ADULTS IS 5 TO 10 MG (UP TO 25 MG), REPEATED ONCE IF NECESSARY. ONLY IN VICTIMS WHO ARE BLEEDING SEVERLY OR OTHERWISE IN SERIOUS DISTRESS SHOULD THE DRUG BE GIVEN INTRAVENOUSLY AND THEN AT A RATE NO FASTER THAN 1 MG/MINUTE. IF NECESSARY, ON SUBSEQUENT DAYS, VITAMIN K1 SHOULD BE CONTINUED AT A REDUCED LEVEL UNTIL THE PROTHROMBIN TIME RETURNS TO NORMAL. VITAMIN K1 IS PREFERABLE TO K1 OXIDE (DOSE 0.5-2.5) AND CERTAINLY PREFERABLE TO MENADIONE OR MENADIONE SODIUM BISULFITE (GOSSELIN, CLINICAL TOXICOLOGY OF COMMERCIAL PRODUCTS, 5TH ED.). ANTIDOTE SHOULD BE ADMINISTERED BY QUALIFIED MEDICAL PERSONNEL.

REACTIVITY

REACTIVITY: STABLE UNDER NORMAL TEMPERATURES AND PRESSURES.
INCOMPATIBILITIES: VALONE: OXIDIZERS (STRONG): FIRE AND EXPLOSION HAZARD.
DECOMPOSITION: THERMAL DECOMPOSITION PRODUCTS MAY INCLUDE TOXIC OXIDES OF CARBON.
POLYMERIZATION: HAZARDOUS POLYMERIZATION HAS NOT BEEN REPORTED TO OCCUR UNDER NORMAL TEMPERATURES AND PRESSURES.

STORAGE AND DISPOSAL

OBSERVE ALL FEDERAL, STATE AND LOCAL REGULATIONS WHEN STORING OR DISPOSING OF THIS SUBSTANCE. FOR ASSISTANCE, CONTACT THE DISTRICT DIRECTOR OF THE ENVIRONMENTAL PROTECTION AGENCY.

****STORAGE****

STORE IN ACCORDANCE WITH 40 CFR 165 RECOMMENDED PROCEDURES FOR THE DISPOSAL AND STORAGE OF PESTICIDES AND PESTICIDE CONTAINERS.
STORE AWAY FROM INCOMPATIBLE SUBSTANCES.

****DISPOSAL****

DISPOSAL MUST BE IN ACCORDANCE WITH 40 CFR 165 RECOMMENDED PROCEDURES FOR THE DISPOSAL AND STORAGE OF PESTICIDES AND PESTICIDE CONTAINERS.

CONDITIONS TO AVOID

MAY BURN BUT DOES NOT IGNITE READILY.

SPILL AND LEAK PROCEDURES

OCCUPATIONAL SPILL: DO NOT TOUCH SPILLED MATERIAL. STOP LEAK IF YOU CAN DO IT WITHOUT RISK. FOR SMALL SPILLS, TAKE UP WITH SAND OR OTHER ABSORBENT MATERIAL AND PLACE INTO CONTAINERS FOR LATER DISPOSAL. FOR SMALL DRY SPILLS, WITH A CLEAN SHOVEL PLACE MATERIAL INTO CLEAN, DRY CONTAINER AND COVER. MOVE CONTAINERS FROM SPILL AREA. FOR LARGER SPILLS, DIKE FAR AHEAD OF SPILL FOR LATER DISPOSAL. KEEP UNNECESSARY PEOPLE AWAY. ISOLATE HAZARD AREA AND DENY ENTRY.

PROTECTIVE EQUIPMENT

VENTILATION: PROVIDE LOCAL EXHAUST OR PROCESS ENCLOSURE VENTILATION SYSTEM.
RESPIRATOR: THE FOLLOWING RESPIRATORS ARE RECOMMENDED BASED ON INFORMATION FOUND IN THE PHYSICAL DATA, TOXICITY AND HEALTH EFFECTS SECTIONS. THEY ARE RANKED IN ORDER FROM MINIMUM TO MAXIMUM RESPIRATORY PROTECTION. THE SPECIFIC RESPIRATOR SELECTED MUST BE BASED ON CONTAMINATION LEVELS FOUND IN THE WORK PLACE, MUST NOT EXCEED THE WORKING LIMITS OF THE RESPIRATOR AND BE JOINTLY APPROVED BY THE NATIONAL INSTITUTE FOR OCCUPATIONAL SAFETY AND HEALTH AND THE MINE SAFETY AND HEALTH ADMINISTRATION (NIOSH-MSHA).
TYPE 'C' SUPPLIED-AIR RESPIRATOR WITH A FULL FACEPIECE OPERATED IN PRESSURE-DEMAND OR OTHER POSITIVE PRESSURE MODE OR WITH A FULL FACEPIECE, HELMET OR HOOD OPERATED IN CONTINOUS-FLOW MODE.
SELF-CONTAINED BREATHING APPARATUS WITH A FULL FACEPIECE OPERATED IN PRESSURE-DEMAND OR OTHER POSITIVE PRESSURE MODE.
FOR FIREFIGHTING AND OTHER IMMEDIATELY DANGEROUS TO LIFE OR HEALTH CONDITIONS:
SELF-CONTAINED BREATHING APPARATUS WITH FULL FACEPIECE OPERATED IN PRESSURE-DEMAND OR OTHER POSITIVE PRESSURE MODE.
SUPPLIED-AIR RESPIRATOR WITH FULL FACEPIECE AND OPERATED IN PRESSURE-DEMAND OR OTHER POSITIVE PRESSURE MODE IN COMBINATION WITH AN AUXILIARY SELF-CONTAINED BREATHING APPARATUS OPERATED IN PRESSURE-DEMAND OR OTHER POSITIVE PRESSURE MODE.
CLOTHING: EMPLOYEE MUST WEAR APPROPRIATE PROTECTIVE (IMPERVIOUS) CLOTHING AND EQUIPMENT TO PREVENT ANY POSSIBILITY OF SKIN CONTACT WITH THIS SUBSTANCE.
GLOVES: EMPLOYEE MUST WEAR APPROPRIATE PROTECTIVE GLOVES TO PREVENT CONTACT WITH THIS SUBSTANCE.
EYE PROTECTION: EMPLOYEE MUST WEAR SPLASH-PROOF OR DUST-RESISTANT SAFETY GOGGLES WITH OR WITHOUT A FACESHIELD TO PREVENT CONTACT WITH THIS SUBSTANCE.
EMERGENCY EYE WASH: WHERE THERE IS ANY POSSIBILITY THAT AN EMPLOYEE'S EYES MAY BE EXPOSED TO THIS SUBSTANCE, THE EMPLOYER SHOULD PROVIDE AN EYE WASH FOUNTAIN WITHIN THE IMMEDIATE WORK AREA FOR EMERGENCY USE.

AUTHORIZED BY- OCCUPATIONAL HEALTH SERVICES, INC.
CREATION DATE: 02/08/90 ***REVISION DATE:*** 02/08/90

MATERIAL SAFETY DATA SHEET

OCCUPATIONAL HEALTH SERVICES, INC.
AGRICULTURE AND PESTICIDE DIVISION
450 SEVENTH AVENUE, SUITE 2407
NEW YORK, NEW YORK 10123
1-800-445-MSDS OR (212) 967-1100

EMERGENCY CONTACT:
JOHN S. BRANSFORD, JR. (615) 292-1180

SUBSTANCE IDENTIFICATION

CAS-NUMBER 13356-08-6
SUBSTANCE: VENDEX
TRADE NAMES/SYNONYMS: HEXAKIS(2-METHYL-2-PHENYLPROPYL)-DISTANNOXANE; HEXAKIS(B,B-DIMETHYLPHENETHYL)-DISTANNOXANE; FENBUTATIN OXIDE; NEOXTANOX; SD 14114; TORQUE; TRINEOPHYLTIN OXIDE; PST24866
CHEMICAL FAMILY: AROMATIC ORGANOMETALLIC
MOLECULAR FORMULA: C60-H78-O-SN2
MOLECULAR WEIGHT: 1052.76
CERCLA RATINGS (SCALE 0-3): HEALTH=3 FIRE=U REACTIVITY=0 PERSISTENCE=3
NFPA RATINGS (SCALE 0-4): HEALTH=3 FIRE=U REACTIVITY=3

COMPONENTS AND CONTAMINANTS

COMPONENT: VENDEX ***PERCENT:*** 100.0
CAS# 13356-08-6
OTHER CONTAMINANTS: NONE
EXPOSURE LIMITS: TIN, ORGANIC COMPOUNDS (AS SN): 0.1 MG/M3 OSHA TWA 0.1 MG/M3 ACGIH TWA (SKIN) (NOTICE OF INTENDED CHANGE 1988-89) 0.1 MG/M3 NIOSH RECOMMENDED 10 HOUR TWA

PHYSICAL DATA

DESCRIPTION: WHITE CRYSTALLINE SOLID ***MELTING POINT:*** 280-282 F (138-139 C)
SPECIFIC GRAVITY: NOT AVAILABLE ***SOLUBILITY IN WATER:*** INSOLUBLE
SOLVENT SOLUBILITY: BENZENE, AROMATIC SOLVENTS, ACETONE, METHYLENE CHLORIDE

FIRE AND EXPLOSION DATA

FIRE AND EXPLOSION HAZARD: UNKNOWN FIRE AND EXPLOSION HAZARD.
FIREFIGHTING MEDIA: DRY CHEMICAL, CARBON DIOXIDE, WATER SPRAY OR FOAM FOR LARGER FIRES, USE WATER SPRAY, FOG OR ALCOHOL FOAM

FIREFIGHTING: MOVE CONTAINER FROM FIRE AREA IF POSSIBLE. DO NOT SCATTER SPILLED MATERIAL WITH MORE WATER THAN NEEDED FOR FIRE CONTROL. DIKE FIRE CONTROL WATER FOR LATER DISPOSAL
USE AGENTS SUITABLE FOR TYPE OF SURROUNDING FIRE. AVOID BREATHING HAZARDOUS VAPORS, KEEP UPWIND.

TOXICITY

VENDEX: TOXICITY DATA: 1000 MG/KG SKIN-RAT LD50; 2630 MG/KG ORAL-RAT LD50; 1450 MG/KG ORAL-MOUSE LD50. CARCINOGEN STATUS: NONE. LOCAL EFFECTS: CORROSIVE-INHALATION, SKIN, AND EYES. ACUTE TOXICITY LEVEL: TOXIC BY DERMAL ABSORPTION AND MODERATELY TOXIC BY INGESTION. TARGET EFFECTS: POISONING MAY AFFECT THE LUNGS, LIVER, KIDNEYS, AND CENTRAL NERVOUS SYSTEM. AT INCREASED RISK FROM EXPOSURE: PERSONS WITH LUNG, SKIN, LIVER, AND KIDNEY DISEASES.

HEALTH EFFECTS AND FIRST AID

INHALATION: VENDEX: CORROSIVE. 200 MG/M3 IMMEDIATELY DANGEROUS TO LIFE OR DEATH. **ACUTE EXPOSURE-** MAY CAUSE SEVERE IRRITATION AND POSSIBLY CORROSIVE EFFECTS. IF SUFFICIENT QUANTITIES OF VENDEX IS INHALED, PULMONARY EDEMA MAY DEVELOP, OFTEN WITH A LATENCY PERIOD OF 48-72 HOURS. VENDEX IS AN ORGANOTIN COMPOUND. IN MAN, ORGANOTIN COMPOUNDS HAVE PRODUCED IRRITATION OF THE RESPIRATORY TRACT WITH SYMPTOMS OF HEADACHE, FATIGUE, SORETHROAT, AND COUGHING, AND GASTROINTESTINAL DISTURBANCES OF NAUSEA, VOMITING, AND EPIGASTRIC PAIN. IN ONE STUDY OF SEVERAL ORGANOTIN COMPOUNDS, PULMONARY EDEMA AND FATTY CHANGES OF THE LIVER AND KIDNEYS WERE OBSERVED IN MICE. **CHRONIC EXPOSURE-** THERE IS ONE REPORT OF LIVER DAMAGE OCCURRING FROM OCCUPATIONAL EXPOSURE TO ONE ORGANOTIN COMPOUND, TRIPHENYLTIN ACETATE. CHRONIC EXPOSURE TO ORGANOTIN COMPOUNDS PRODUCED IN ANIMALS PULMONARY EDEMA, PNEUMONIA, AND DAMAGE TO THE LIVER AND KIDNEYS.
FIRST AID- REMOVE FROM EXPOSURE AREA TO FRESH AIR IMMEDIATELY. IF BREATHING HAS STOPPED, GIVE ARTIFICIAL RESPIRATION. MAINTAIN AIRWAY AND BLOOD PRESSURE AND ADMINISTER OXYGEN IF AVAILABLE. KEEP AFFECTED PERSON WARM AND AT REST. TREAT SYMPTOMATICALLY AND SUPPORTIVELY. ADMINISTRATION OF OXYGEN SHOULD BE PERFORMED BY QUALIFIED PERSONNEL. GET MEDICAL ATTENTION IMMEDIATELY.

SKIN CONTACT: VENDEX: CORROSIVE/TOXIC. **ACUTE EXPOSURE-** MAY CAUSE SEVERE IRRITATION AND CORROSIVE EFFECTS. A HIGH DOSE WAS TOXIC IN RATS; NO SYMPTOMS WERE REPORTED. VENDEX IS AN ORGANOTIN COMPOUND. ORGANOTIN COMPOUNDS ARE IN GENERAL STRONG IRRITANTS CAUSING REDNESS, ITCHING, PAIN, AND BLISTERS OR LESIONS. CHEMICAL BURNS MAY RESULT FROM ONLY BRIEF CONTACT WITH THE SKIN. IRRITATION HAS OCCURRED FROM CONTACT WITH CLOTHES CONTAMINATED WITH ORGANOTIN COMPOUNDS. **CHRONIC EXPOSURE-** PROLONGED CONTACT OF THE SKIN WITH CLOTHES CONTAMINATED WITH ORGANOTIN COMPOUNDS HAVE BEEN RESPONSIBLE FOR ACUTE LOCAL BURNS, SUBACUTE DIFFUSE ERYTHEMATOID DERMATITIS WITH PRURITUS AND SOME PUSTULAR ERUPTION IN THE HAIR-COVERED AREAS.
FIRST AID- REMOVE CONTAMINATED CLOTHING AND SHOES IMMEDIATELY. WASH AFFECTED AREA WITH SOAP OR MILD DETERGENT AND LARGE AMOUNTS OF WATER UNTIL NO EVIDENCE OF CHEMICAL REMAINS (AT LEAST 15-20 MINUTES). IN CASE OF CHEMICAL BURNS, COVER AREA WITH STERILE, DRY DRESSING. BANDAGE SECURELY, BUT NOT TOO TIGHTLY. GET MEDICAL ATTENTION IMMEDIATELY.

EYE CONTACT: VENDEX: CORROSIVE. **ACUTE EXPOSURE-** MAY CAUSE IRRITATION AND POSSIBLY CORROSIVE EFFECTS. VENDEX IS AN ORGANOTIN COMPOUND. ORGANOTIN COMPOUNDS ARE IN GENERAL STRONG IRRITANTS, AND ACUTE CONJUNCTIVITIS HAS BEEN OBSERVED AS A RESULT OF EYE SPLASHES, EVEN WHEN FOLLOWED BY IMMEDIATE LAVAGE; CORNEAL OPACITIES HAVE ALSO BEEN REPORTED. EXPOSURE TO THE VAPOR OF ORGANOTIN COMPOUNDS HAVE ALSO CAUSED IRRITATION. **CHRONIC EXPOSURE-** DEPENDING ON CONCENTRATION AND DURATION OF CONTACT, EFFECTS AS IN ACUTE EXPOSURE MAY OCCUR WITH REPEATED OR PROLONGED EXPOSURE.
FIRST AID- WASH EYES IMMEDIATELY WITH LARGE AMOUNTS OF WATER, OCCASIONALLY LIFTING UPPER AND LOWER LIDS, UNTIL NO EVIDENCE OF CHEMICAL REMAINS (AT LEAST 15-20 MINUTES). CONTINUE IRRIGATING WITH NORMAL SALINE UNTIL THE PH HAS RETURNED TO NORMAL (30-60 MINUTES). COVER WITH STERILE BANDAGES. GET MEDICAL ATTENTION IMMEDIATELY.

INGESTION: VENDEX: CORROSIVE. **ACUTE EXPOSURE-** MAY CAUSE SEVERE IRRITATION AND POSSIBLY CORROSIVE EFFECTS. A MODERATE DOSE WAS LETHAL IN RATS; NO SYMPTOMS WERE REPORTED. VENDEX IS AN ORGANOTIN COMPOUND. IN RATS, THESE COMPOUNDS PRODUCED PARESIS, TREMORS, CONVULSIONS, AND INTERSTITIAL EDEMA OF THE WHITE MATTER OF THE BRAIN AND SPINAL CORD. **CHRONIC EXPOSURE-** DEPENDING ON THE CONCENTRATION, REPEATED INGESTION MAY RESULT IN EFFECTS AS IN ACUTE INGESTION. HUMANS GIVEN ORGANIC TIN AS MEDICATION EXPERIENCED PARALYSIS, WEIGHT LOSS, AND ENCEPHALOPATHY. CHRONIC INGESTION PRODUCED SIMILAR RESULTS IN ANIMALS.
FIRST AID- TREAT SYMPTOMATICALLY AND SUPPORTIVELY. GET MEDICAL ATTENTION IMMEDIATELY. IF VOMITING OCCURS, KEEP HEAD LOWER THAN HIPS TO PREVENT ASPIRATION.
ANTIDOTE: NO SPECIFIC ANTIDOTE. TREAT SYMPTOMATICALLY AND SUPPORTIVELY.

REACTIVITY

REACTIVITY: STABLE UNDER NORMAL TEMPERATURES AND PRESSURES.
INCOMPATIBILITIES: VENDEX: STRONG OXIDIZERS: INCOMPATIBLE.
DECOMPOSITION: THERMAL DECOMPOSITION MAY RELEASE TOXIC AND/OR HAZARDOUS GASES.
POLYMERIZATION: HAZARDOUS POLYMERIZATION HAS NOT BEEN REPORTED TO OCCUR UNDER NORMAL TEMPERATURES AND PRESSURES.

CONDITIONS TO AVOID

NONE REPORTED.

SPILL AND LEAK PROCEDURES

OCCUPATIONAL SPILL: SWEEP UP AND PLACE IN SUITABLE CLEAN, DRY CONTAINERS FOR RECLAMATION OR LATER DISPOSAL. DO NOT FLUSH SPILLED MATERIAL INTO SEWER. KEEP UNNECESSARY PEOPLE AWAY.

PROTECTIVE EQUIPMENT

VENTILATION: PROVIDE LOCAL EXHAUST OR PROCESS ENCLOSURE VENTILATION TO MEET PUBLISHED EXPOSURE LIMITS.
RESPIRATOR: THE FOLLOWING RESPIRATORS AND MAXIMUM USE CONCENTRATIONS ARE RECOMMENDATIONS BY THE U.S. DEPARTMENT OF HEALTH AND HUMAN SERVICES, NIOSH POCKET GUIDE TO CHEMICAL HAZARDS; NIOSH CRITERIA DOCUMENTS OR BY THE U.S. DEPARTMENT OF LABOR, 29 CFR 1910 SUBPART Z. THE SPECIFIC RESPIRATOR SELECTED MUST BE BASED ON CONTAMINATION LEVELS FOUND IN THE WORK PLACE, MUST NOT EXCEED THE WORKING LIMITS OF THE RESPIRATOR AND BE JOINTLY APPROVED BY THE NATIONAL INSTITUTE FOR OCCUPATIONAL SAFETY AND HEALTH AND THE MINE SAFETY AND HEALTH ADMINISTRATION (NIOSH-MSHA).
TIN, ORGANIC COMPOUNDS, (AS SN):
1 MG/M3- ANY CHEMICAL CARTRIDGE RESPIRATOR WITH ORGANIC VAPOR CARTRIDGE IN COMBINATION WITH A DUST AND MIST FILTER. ANY SUPPLIED-AIR RESPIRATOR. ANY SELF-CONTAINED BREATHING APPARATUS.
2.5 MG/M3- ANY SUPPLIED-AIR RESPIRATOR OPERATED IN CONTINOUS FLOW MODE. ANY POWERED AIR-PURIFYING RESPIRATOR WITH ORGANIC VAPOR CARTRIDGE IN COMBINATION WITH A DUST AND MIST FILTER.
5 MG/M3- ANY CHEMICAL CARTRIDGE RESPIRATOR WITH A FULL FACEPIECE AND ORGANIC VAPOR CARTRIDGE IN COMBINATION WITH A HIGH-EFFICIENCY PARTICULATE FILTER. ANY SUPPLIED-AIR RESPIRATOR WITH A FULL FACEPIECE. ANY SELF-CONTAINED BREATHING APPARATUS WITH A FULL FACEPIECE. ANY AIR-PURIFYING FULL FACEPIECE RESPIRATOR (GAS MASK) WITH A CHIN STYLE OR BACK-MOUNTED ORGANIC CANISTER HAVING A HIGH-EFFICIENCY PARTICULATE FILTER. ANY POWERED AIR-PURIFYING RESPIRATOR WITH A TIGHT-FITTING FACEPIECE AND ORGANIC VAPOR CARTRIDGE IN COMBINATION WITH A HIGH-EFFICIENCY PARTICULATE FILTER. ANY SUPPLIED-AIR RESPIRATOR WITH A TIGHT-FITTING FACEPIECE OPERATED IN CONTINOUS FLOW MODE.
200 MG/M3- ANY SUPPLIED-AIR RESPIRATOR WITH A FULL-FACEPIECE AND OPERATED IN PRESSURE-DEMAND OR OTHER POSITIVE PRESSURE MODE.
ESCAPE- ANY AIR-PURIFYING FULL FACEPIECE RESPIRATOR (GAS MASK) WITH A CHIN STYLE OR BACK-MOUNTED ORGANIC CANISTER HAVING A HIGH-EFFICIENCY PARTICULATE FILTER. ANY APPROPRIATE ESCAPE-TYPE SELF-CONTAINED BREATHING APPARATUS.
FOR FIREFIGHTING AND OTHER IMMEDIATELY DANGEROUS TO LIFE OR HEALTH CONDITIONS:
SELF-CONTAINED BREATHING APPARATUS WITH FULL FACEPIECE OPERATED IN PRESSURE-DEMAND OR OTHER POSITIVE PRESSURE MODE.
SUPPLIED-AIR RESPIRATOR WITH FULL FACEPIECE AND OPERATED IN PRESSURE-DEMAND OR OTHER POSITIVE PRESSURE MODE IN COMBINATION WITH AN AUXILIARY SELF-CONTAINED BREATHING APPARATUS OPERATED IN PRESSURE-DEMAND OR OTHER POSITIVE PRESSURE MODE.
CLOTHING: EMPLOYEE MUST WEAR APPROPRIATE PROTECTIVE (IMPERVIOUS) CLOTHING AND EQUIPMENT TO PREVENT ANY POSSIBILITY OF SKIN CONTACT WITH THIS SUBSTANCE.
GLOVES: EMPLOYEE MUST WEAR APPROPRIATE PROTECTIVE GLOVES TO PREVENT CONTACT WITH THIS SUBSTANCE.

EYE PROTECTION: EMPLOYEE MUST WEAR SPLASH-PROOF OR DUST-RESISTANT SAFETY GOGGLES AND A FACESHIELD TO PREVENT CONTACT WITH THIS SUBSTANCE.
EMERGENCY WASH FACILITIES: WHERE THERE IS ANY POSSIBILITY THAT AN EMPLOYEE'S EYES AND/OR SKIN MAY BE EXPOSED TO THIS SUBSTANCE, THE EMPLOYER SHOULD PROVIDE AN EYE WASH FOUNTAIN AND QUICK DRENCH SHOWER WITHIN THE IMMEDIATE WORK AREA FOR EMERGENCY USE.

AUTHORIZED BY- OCCUPATIONAL HEALTH SERVICES, INC.
CREATION DATE: 10/05/89 ***REVISION DATE:*** 05/31/90

MATERIAL SAFETY DATA SHEET

OCCUPATIONAL HEALTH SERVICES, INC.
AGRICULTURE AND PESTICIDE DIVISION
450 SEVENTH AVENUE, SUITE 2407
NEW YORK, NEW YORK 10123
1-800-445-MSDS OR (212) 967-1100

EMERGENCY CONTACT:
JOHN S. BRANSFORD, JR. (615) 292-1180

SUBSTANCE IDENTIFICATION

CAS-NUMBER 3983-45-7
SUBSTANCE: **VIOZENE OXON**
TRADE NAMES/SYNONYMS: PHOSPHORIC ACID, DIMETHYL 2,4,5-TRICHLOROPHENYL ESTER; FENCHLORPHOS-OXON; RONNEL OXON; RONNEL OXYGEN ANALOG; RONNOXON; RONOXON; DIMETHYL 2,4,5-TRICHLOROPHENYLPHOSPHATE; C8H8CL3O4P; PST25082
CHEMICAL FAMILY: ESTER
PHOSPHORIC ACID
HALOGEN
MOLECULAR FORMULA: C8-H8-CL3-04-P
MOLECULAR WEIGHT: 305.48
CERCLA RATINGS (SCALE 0-3): HEALTH=U FIRE=U REACTIVITY=0 PERSISTENCE=1
NFPA RATINGS (SCALE 0-4): HEALTH=U FIRE=U REACTIVITY=0

COMPONENTS AND CONTAMINANTS

COMPONENT: VIOZENE OXON ***PERCENT:*** 100.0
CAS# 3983-45-7
OTHER CONTAMINANTS: NONE
EXPOSURE LIMITS: NO OCCUPATIONAL EXPOSURE LIMITS ESTABLISHED BY OSHA, ACGIH, OR NIOSH.

PHYSICAL DATA

DESCRIPTION: LIQUID. ***BOILING POINT:*** 304-309 F (151-154 C) @ 0.4 MMHG
SPECIFIC GRAVITY: 1.44 @ 32 C ***VAPOR PRESSURE:*** NOT AVAILABLE
SOLUBILITY IN WATER: NOT AVAILABLE

FIRE AND EXPLOSION DATA

FIRE AND EXPLOSION HAZARD: UNKNOWN FIRE AND EXPLOSION HAZARD.
FIREFIGHTING MEDIA: DRY CHEMICAL, CARBON DIOXIDE, HALON, WATER SPRAY OR STANDARD FOAM (1987 EMERGENCY RESPONSE GUIDEBOOK, DOT P 5800.4).
FOR LARGER FIRES, USE WATER SPRAY, FOG OR STANDARD FOAM (1987 EMERGENCY RESPONSE GUIDEBOOK, DOT P 5800.4).
FIREFIGHTING: MOVE CONTAINER FROM FIRE AREA IF POSSIBLE. DIKE FIRE CONTROL WATER FOR LATER DISPOSAL; DO NOT SCATTER THE MATERIAL. COOL FIRE-EXPOSED CONTAINERS WITH WATER FROM SIDE UNTIL WELL AFTER FIRE IS OUT. STAY AWAY FROM STORAGE TANK ENDS. WITHDRAW IMMEDIATELY IN CASE OF RISING SOUND FROM VENTING SAFETY DEVICE OR ANY DISCOLORATION OF STORAGE TANK DUE TO FIRE (1987 EMERGENCY RESPONSE GUIDEBOOK, DOT P 5800.4, GUIDE PAGE 28).
EXTINGUISH ONLY IF FLOW CAN BE STOPPED. USE FLOODING AMOUNTS OF WATER AS A FOG; SOLID STREAMS MAY BE INEFFECTIVE. COOL CONTAINERS WITH FLOODING AMOUNTS OF WATER FROM AS FAR A DISTANCE AS POSSIBLE. AVOID BREATHING POISONOUS VAPORS, KEEP UPWIND.

TOXICITY

VIOZENE OXON: TOXICITY DATA: 18 MG/KG ORAL-BIRD LD50. CARCINOGEN STATUS: NONE. ACUTE TOXICITY: INSUFFICIENT DATA. TARGET EFFECTS: CHOLINESTERASE INHIBITOR. POISONING MAY AFFECT THE NERVOUS SYSTEM.* AT INCREASED RISK FROM EXPOSURE: PERSONS WITH RESPIRATORY AILMENTS, RECENT EXPOSURE TO CHOLINESTERASE INHIBITORS OR IMPAIRED CHOLINESTERASE PRODUCTION, OR LIVER MALFUNCTION.* ADDITIONAL DATA: MAY CROSS THE PLACENTA. HIGH ENVIRONMENTAL TEMPERATURES OR EXPOSURE OF THE CHEMICAL TO VISIBLE OR ULTRAVIOLET LIGHT MAY ENHANCE THE TOXICITY. INTERACTIONS WITH MEDICATIONS MAY OCCUR.*
* MAY BE BASED ON GENERAL INFORMATION ON ORGANOPHOSPHATES.

HEALTH EFFECTS AND FIRST AID

INHALATION: VIOZENE OXON: SEE INFORMATION ON ORGANOPHOSPHATES.
ORGANOPHOSPHATES: CHOLINESTERASE INHIBITOR. **ACUTE EXPOSURE-** WHEN INHALED, THE FIRST EFFECTS OF CHOLINESTERASE INHIBITORS ARE USUALLY RESPIRATORY AND MAY INCLUDE NASAL HYPEREMIA AND WATERY DISCHARGE, COUGH, CHEST DISCOMFORT, DYSPNEA, AND WHEEZING DUE TO INCREASED BRONCHIAL SECRETIONS AND BRONCHOCONSTRICTION. IF SUFFICIENT AMOUNTS ARE ABSORBED, OTHER SYSTEMIC EFFECTS MAY BEGIN WITHIN A FEW MINUTES OR BE DELAYED FOR UP TO 12 HOURS. SYMPTOMS MAY INCLUDE PALLOR, NAUSEA, VOMITING, DIARRHEA, ABDOMINAL CRAMPS, HEADACHE, DIZZINESS, OCULAR PAIN, BLURRED VISION, MIOSIS OR IN SOME CASES, ESPECIALLY INITIALLY, MYDRIASIS, LACRIMATION, SALIVATION, SWEATING, AND CONFUSION. OTHER REPORTED CENTRAL NERVOUS SYSTEM OR NEUROMUSCULAR EFFECTS MAY INCLUDE ATAXIA, SLURRED SPEECH, AREFLEXIA, WEAKNESS, FATIGUE, FASCICULATIONS, TWITCHING, TREMORS POSSIBLY OF THE TONGUE AND EYELIDS, AND EVENTUALLY PARALYSIS OF THE EXTREMITIES AND POSSIBLY OF THE RESPIRATORY MUSCLES. IN SEVERE CASES THERE MAY ALSO BE INVOLUNTARY DEFECATION AND URINATION, CYANOSIS, PSYCHOSIS, HYPERGLYCEMIA, ACUTE PANCREATITIS, CARDIAC IRREGULARITIES, PULMONARY EDEMA, UNCONSCIOUSNESS, CONVULSIONS, AND COMA. DEATH IS PRIMARILY DUE TO RESPIRATORY FAILURE, ALTHOUGH CARDIOVASCULAR EFFECTS INCLUDING CARDIAC ARREST MAY ALSO BE IMPLICATED. LONG TERM SEQUELAE ARE RARE BUT MAY INCLUDE NEUROPSYCHIATRIC DISORDERS AND MYOPATHY WITH MUSCLE TENDERNESS. SOME ORGANOPHOSPHATES MAY CAUSE A DELAYED NEUROPATHY BEGINNING 1-4 WEEKS AFTER AN ACUTE EXPOSURE WHICH MAY OR MAY NOT HAVE CAUSED ACUTE CHOLINERGIC EFFECTS. NUMBNESS, TINGLING, WEAKNESS AND CRAMPING BEGINNING SYMMETRICALLY IN THE LOWER LIMBS MAY PROGRESS TO ATAXIA AND PARALYSIS. IN SEVERE CASES, UPPER LIMB INVOLVEMENT IS POSSIBLE AND FLACCID PARALYSIS MAY PROGRESS TO SPASTIC PARALYSIS WITH EXAGGERATED REFLEXES. IMPROVEMENT MAY OCCUR OVER MONTHS TO YEARS, BUT SOME RESIDUAL IMPAIRMENT USUALLY REMAINS.
CHRONIC EXPOSURE- REPEATED OR PROLONGED EXPOSURE MAY RESULT IN THE EFFECTS OF ACUTE EXPOSURE INCLUDING THE DELAYED NEUROPATHY. OTHER EFFECTS REPORTED IN WORKERS REPEATEDLY EXPOSED INCLUDE IMPAIRED MEMORY AND CONCENTRATION, ACUTE PSYCHOSIS, SEVERE DEPRESSIONS, IRRITABILTY, CONFUSION, APATHY, EMOTIONAL LABILITY, SOCIAL WITHDRAWAL, CONFUSION, HEADACHE, SPEECH DIFFICULTIES, DELAYED REACTION TIMES, SPATIAL DISORIENTATION, NIGHTMARES, SLEEPWALKING, AND DROWSINESS OR INSOMNIA. AN INFLUENZA-LIKE CONDITION WITH HEADACHE, NAUSEA, WEAKNESS, ANOREXIA AND MALAISE HAS ALSO BEEN REPORTED.
FIRST AID- REMOVE FROM EXPOSURE AREA TO FRESH AIR IMMEDIATELY. IF BREATHING HAS STOPPED, GIVE ARTIFICIAL RESPIRATION. MAINTAIN AIRWAY AND BLOOD PRESSURE AND ADMINISTER OXYGEN IF AVAILABLE. KEEP AFFECTED PERSON WARM AND AT REST. TREAT SYMPTOMATICALLY AND SUPPORTIVELY. ADMINISTRATION OF OXYGEN SHOULD BE PERFORMED BY QUALIFIED PERSONNEL. GET MEDICAL ATTENTION IMMEDIATELY.

SKIN CONTACT: VIOZENE OXON: SEE INFORMATION ON ORGANOPHOSPHATES.
ORGANOPHOSPHATES: CHOLINESTERASE INHIBITOR. **ACUTE EXPOSURE-** LOCALIZED SWEATING AND FASCICULATIONS MAY OCCUR AT THE SITE OF CONTACT. IF SUFFICIENT AMOUNTS ARE ABSORBED, OTHER EFFECTS OF CHOLINESTERASE INHIBITION AS DESCRIBED IN ACUTE INHALATION MAY OCCUR. SYMPTOMS MAY BE DELAYED 2-3 HOURS, BUT USUALLY NO MORE THAN 12 HOURS. THE RATE OF ABSORPTION IS INCREASED BY THE PRESENCE OF DERMATITIS OR HIGH AMBIENT TEMPERATURES. DELAYED NEUROPATHY IS ALSO POSSIBLE. **CHRONIC EXPOSURE-** REPEATED OR PROLONGED EXPOSURE MAY CAUSE EFFECTS AS DESCRIBED IN ACUTE EXPOSURE. SOME ORGANOPHOSPHATES MAY CAUSE SENSITIZATION.
FIRST AID- REMOVE CONTAMINATED CLOTHING IMMEDIATELY. WASH CONTAMINATED AREAS WITH SOAP AND WATER FOLLOWED BY ALCOHOL (ARENA, POISONING, 4TH ED.). EMERGENCY PERSONNEL SHOULD WEAR GLOVES AND AVOID CONTAMINATION. TREAT RESPIRATORY DIFFICULTY WITH ARTIFICIAL RESPIRATION. GET MEDICAL ATTENTION IMMEDIATELY.

EYE CONTACT: VIOZENE OXON: SEE INFORMATION ON ORGANOPHOSPHATES.
ORGANOPHOSPHATES: CHOLINESTERASE INHIBITOR. **ACUTE EXPOSURE-** DIRECT CONTACT MAY CAUSE PAIN, HYPEREMIA, LACRIMATION, TWITCHING OF THE EYELIDS, MIOSIS, AND CILIARY MUSCLE SPASM WITH LOSS OF ACCOMODATION, BLURRED OR DIMMED VISION AND BROWACHE. SOMETIMES MYDRIASIS MAY OCCUR INSTEAD OF MIOSIS. WITH SUFFICIENT EXPOSURE, OTHER SYMPTOMS OF

CHOLINESTERASE INHIBITION AS DESCRIBED IN ACUTE INHALATION MAY OCCUR. **CHRONIC EXPOSURE**- REPEATED OR PROLONGED EXPOSURE MAY CAUSE EFFECTS AS DESCRIBED IN ACUTE EXPOSURE. SOME COMPOUNDS HAVE CAUSED TOXIC EFFECTS ON THE CRYSTALLINE LENS, CONJUNCTIVAL THICKENING AND OBSTRUCTION OF THE NASOLACRIMAL CANALS WHEN USED AS MIOTIC EYEDROPS.

FIRST AID- IRRIGATE EYES WITH WATER OR SALINE SOLUTION. IF SYMPTOMS OF POISONING OCCUR, TREAT RESPIRATORY DIFFICULTY WITH ARTIFICIAL RESPIRATION AND OXYGEN. OBSERVE PATIENT FOR AT LEAST 24-36 HOURS (GOSSELIN, CLINICAL TOXICOLOGY OF COMMERCIAL PRODUCTS, 5TH ED.). GET MEDICAL ATTENTION IMMEDIATELY. OXYGEN SHOULD BE ADMINISTERED BY QUALIFIED MEDICAL PERSONNEL.

INGESTION: VIOZENE OXON: SEE INFORMATION ON ORGANOPHOSPHATES. ORGANOPHOSPHATES: CHOLINESTERASE INHIBITOR. **ACUTE EXPOSURE**- WHEN INGESTED, THE FIRST EFFECTS MAY BE NAUSEA, VOMITING, ANOREXIA, ABDOMINAL CRAMPS AND DIARRHEA. GASTROINTESTINAL ABSORPTION MAY CAUSE SYMPTOMS OF CHOLINESTERASE INHIBITION AS DESCRIBED IN ACUTE INHALATION. SYMPTOMS MAY BEGIN WITHIN MINUTES OR BE DELAYED FOR HOURS. DELAYED EFFECTS INCLUDING NEUROPATHY MAY ALSO OCCUR. **CHRONIC EXPOSURE**- REPEATED INGESTION MAY CAUSE EFFECTS AS DESCRIBED IN ACUTE EXPOSURE.

FIRST AID- IF PERSON IS ALERT AND RESPIRATION IS NOT DEPRESSED, GIVE SYRUP OF IPECAC FOLLOWED BY WATER (IF VOMITING OCCURS, KEEP HEAD BELOW HIPS TO PREVENT ASPIRATION). IF CONSCIOUSNESS LEVEL DECLINES OR VOMITING HAS NOT OCCURRED IN 15 MINUTES EMPTY STOMACH BY GASTRIC LAVAGE WITH THE AID OF CUFFED ENDOTRACHEAL TUBE USING ISOTONIC SALINE OR 5% SODIUM BICARBONATE FOLLOW WITH ACTIVATED CHARCOAL. ESTABLISH AND MAINTAIN AIRWAY. TREAT RESPIRATORY DIFFICULTY WITH ARTIFICIAL RESPIRATION AND OXYGEN. DO NOT GIVE MORPHINE, AMINOPHYLLINE, PHENOTHIAZINES, RESERPINE, FUROSEMIDE, OR ETHACRYNIC ACID (MORGAN, RECOGNITION AND MANAGEMENT OF PESTICIDE POISONINGS, 3RD ED.). TREAT SYMPTOMATICALLY AND SUPPORTIVELY. ADMINISTRATION OF OXYGEN AND LAVAGE MUST BE PERFORMED BY QUALIFIED MEDICAL PERSONNEL. GET MEDICAL ATTENTION IMMEDIATELY.

ANTIDOTE: THE FOLLOWING ANTIDOTE(S) HAVE BEEN RECOMMENDED. HOWEVER, THE DECISION AS TO WHETHER THE SEVERITY OF POISONING REQUIRES ADMINISTRATION OF ANY ANTIDOTE AND ACTUAL DOSE REQUIRED SHOULD BE MADE BY QUALIFIED MEDICAL PERSONNEL.

FOR CHOLINESTERASE INHIBITORS: ESTABLISH CLEAR AIRWAY AND TISSUE OXYGENATION BY ASPIRATION OF SECRETIONS, AND IF NECESSARY, BY ASSISTED PULMONARY VENTILATION WITH OXYGEN. IMPROVE TISSUE OXYGENATION AS MUCH AS POSSIBLE BEFORE ADMINISTERING ATROPINE TO MINIMIZE THE RISK OF VENTRICULAR FIBRILLATION. ADMINISTER ATROPINE SULFATE INTRAVENOUSLY, OR INTRAMUSCULARLY IF IV INJECTION IS NOT POSSIBLE. IN MODERATELY SEVERE POISONING ADMINISTER ATROPINE SULFATE, 0.4-2.0 MG REPEATED EVERY 15 MINUTES UNTIL ATROPINIZATION IS ACHIEVED (TACHYCARDIA, FLUSHING, DRY MOUTH, MYDRIASIS). MAINTAIN ATROPINIZATION BY REPEATED DOSES FOR 2-12 HOURS, OR LONGER, DEPENDING ON THE SEVERITY OF POISONING. THE APPEARANCE OF RALES IN THE LUNG BASES, MIOSIS, SALIVATION, NAUSEA, BRADYCARDIA, ARE ALL INDICATIONS OF INADEQUATE ATROPINIZATION. SEVERELY POISONED INDIVIDUALS MAY EXHIBIT REMARKABLE TOLERANCE TO ATROPINE; TWO OR MORE TIMES THE DOSAGES SUGGESTED ABOVE MAY BE NEEDED. PERSONS NOT POISONED OR ONLY SLIGHTLY POISONED, HOWEVER, MAY DEVELOP SIGNS OF ATROPINE TOXICITY FROM SUCH LARGE DOSAGES: FEVER, MUSCLE FIBRILLATIONS, AND DELIRIUM ARE THE MAIN SIGNS OF ATROPINE TOXICITY. IF THESE SIGNS APPEAR WHILE THE PATIENT IS FULLY ATROPINIZED, ATROPINE ADMINISTRATION SHOULD BE DISCONTINUED, AT LEAST TEMPORARILY. OBSERVE TREATED PATIENTS CLOSELY AT LEAST 24 HOURS TO INSURE THAT SYMPTOMS (POSSIBLY PULMONARY EDEMA) DO NOT RECUR AS ATROPINIZATION WEARS OFF. IN VERY SEVERE POISONINGS, METABOLIC DISPOSITION OF TOXICANT MAY REQUIRE SEVERAL HOURS OR DAYS DURING WHICH ATROPINIZATION MUST BE MAINTAINED. MARKEDLY LOWER LEVELS OF URINARY METABOLITES INDICATE THAT ATROPINE DOSAGE CAN BE TAPERED OFF. AS DOSAGE IS REDUCED, CHECK THE LUNG BASES FREQUENTLY FOR RALES. IF RALES ARE HEARD OR OTHER SYMPTOMS RETURN, RE-ESTABLISH ATROPINIZATION PROMPTLY (MORGAN, RECOGNITION AND MANAGEMENT OF PESTICIDE POISONINGS, 3RD ED.). ADMINISTRATION OF ANTIDOTE MUST BE PERFORMED BY QUALIFIED MEDICAL PERSONNEL.

IN CASES OF SEVERE POISONING BY ORGANOPHOSPHATE PESTICIDES IN WHICH RESPIRATORY DEPRESSION, MUSCLE WEAKNESS AND TWITCHINGS ARE SEVERE, GIVE PRALIDOXIME (PROTOPAM-AYERST, 2-PAM), 1.0 GRAM INTRAVENOUSLY AT NO MORE THAN 0.5 GRAM PER MINUTE. DOSAGE OF PRALIDOXIME MAY BE REPEATED IN 1-2 HOURS, THEN AT 10-12 HOUR INTERVALS IF NEEDED. IN VERY SEVERE POISONINGS, DOSAGE RATES MAY BE DOUBLED. TREATMENT WITH PRALIDOXIME WILL BE MOST EFFECTIVE IF GIVEN WITHIN THIRTY-SIX HOURS AFTER POISONING (MORGAN, RECOGNITION AND MANAGEMENT OF PESTICIDE POISONINGS, 3RD ED.). ANTIDOTE SHOULD BE ADMINISTERED BY QUALIFIED MEDICAL PERSONNEL.

REACTIVITY

REACTIVITY: STABLE UNDER NORMAL TEMPERATURES AND PRESSURES.

INCOMPATIBILITIES: VIOZENE OXON: OXIDIZERS (STRONG): MAY CAUSE FIRE AND EXPLOSION HAZARD.

DECOMPOSITION: THERMAL DECOMPOSITION PRODUCTS MAY INCLUDE TOXIC OXIDES OF CARBON AND PHOSPHOROUS AND TOXIC AND CORROSIVE FUMES OF CHLORIDES.

POLYMERIZATION: HAZARDOUS POLYMERIZATION HAS NOT BEEN REPORTED TO OCCUR UNDER NORMAL TEMPERATURES AND PRESSURES.

STORAGE AND DISPOSAL

OBSERVE ALL FEDERAL, STATE AND LOCAL REGULATIONS WHEN STORING OR DISPOSING OF THIS SUBSTANCE. FOR ASSISTANCE, CONTACT THE DISTRICT DIRECTOR OF THE ENVIRONMENTAL PROTECTION AGENCY.

STORAGE

STORE AWAY FROM INCOMPATIBLE SUBSTANCES.

CONDITIONS TO AVOID

AVOID CONTACT WITH HEAT, SPARKS, FLAMES OR OTHER IGNITION SOURCES. VAPORS MAY BE EXPLOSIVE. MATERIAL IS POISONOUS; AVOID INHALATION OF VAPORS OR CONTACT WITH SKIN. DO NOT ALLOW MATERIAL TO CONTAMINATE WATER SOURCES.

SPILL AND LEAK PROCEDURES

OCCUPATIONAL SPILL: SHUT OFF IGNITION SOURCES. DO NOT TOUCH SPILLED MATERIAL. STOP LEAK IF YOU CAN DO IT WITHOUT RISK. USE WATER SPRAY TO REDUCE VAPORS. FOR SMALL SPILLS, TAKE UP WITH SAND OR OTHER ABSORBENT MATERIAL AND PLACE INTO CONTAINERS FOR LATER DISPOSAL. FOR LARGER SPILLS, DIKE FAR AHEAD OF SPILL FOR LATER DISPOSAL. NO SMOKING, FLAMES OR FLARES IN HAZARD AREA! KEEP UNNECESSARY PEOPLE AWAY; ISOLATE HAZARD AREA AND DENY ENTRY.

PROTECTIVE EQUIPMENT

VENTILATION: PROVIDE LOCAL EXHAUST OR PROCESS ENCLOSURE VENTILATION SYSTEM.

RESPIRATOR: THE FOLLOWING RESPIRATORS ARE RECOMMENDED BASED ON INFORMATION FOUND IN THE PHYSICAL DATA, TOXICITY AND HEALTH EFFECTS SECTIONS. THEY ARE RANKED IN ORDER FROM MINIMUM TO MAXIMUM RESPIRATORY PROTECTION. THE SPECIFIC RESPIRATOR SELECTED MUST BE BASED ON CONTAMINATION LEVELS FOUND IN THE WORK PLACE, MUST NOT EXCEED THE WORKING LIMITS OF THE RESPIRATOR AND BE JOINTLY APPROVED BY THE NATIONAL INSTITUTE FOR OCCUPATIONAL SAFETY AND HEALTH AND THE MINE SAFETY AND HEALTH ADMINISTRATION (NIOSH-MSHA).

TYPE 'C' SUPPLIED-AIR RESPIRATOR WITH A FULL FACEPIECE OPERATED IN PRESSURE-DEMAND OR OTHER POSITIVE PRESSURE MODE OR WITH A FULL FACEPIECE, HELMET OR HOOD OPERATED IN CONTINOUS-FLOW MODE.

SELF-CONTAINED BREATHING APPARATUS WITH A FULL FACEPIECE OPERATED IN PRESSURE-DEMAND OR OTHER POSITIVE PRESSURE MODE.

FOR FIREFIGHTING AND OTHER IMMEDIATELY DANGEROUS TO LIFE OR HEALTH CONDITIONS:

SELF-CONTAINED BREATHING APPARATUS WITH FULL FACEPIECE OPERATED IN PRESSURE-DEMAND OR OTHER POSITIVE PRESSURE MODE.

SUPPLIED-AIR RESPIRATOR WITH FULL FACEPIECE AND OPERATED IN PRESSURE-DEMAND OR OTHER POSITIVE PRESSURE MODE IN COMBINATION WITH AN AUXILIARY SELF-CONTAINED BREATHING APPARATUS OPERATED IN PRESSURE-DEMAND OR OTHER POSITIVE PRESSURE MODE.

CLOTHING: EMPLOYEE MUST WEAR APPROPRIATE PROTECTIVE (IMPERVIOUS) CLOTHING AND EQUIPMENT TO PREVENT REPEATED OR PROLONGED SKIN CONTACT WITH THIS SUBSTANCE.

GLOVES: EMPLOYEE MUST WEAR APPROPRIATE PROTECTIVE GLOVES TO PREVENT CONTACT WITH THIS SUBSTANCE.

EYE PROTECTION: EMPLOYEE MUST WEAR SPLASH-PROOF OR DUST-RESISTANT SAFETY GOGGLES TO PREVENT EYE CONTACT WITH THIS SUBSTANCE.

EMERGENCY EYE WASH: WHERE THERE IS ANY POSSIBILITY THAT AN EMPLOYEE'S EYES MAY BE EXPOSED TO THIS SUBSTANCE, THE EMPLOYER SHOULD PROVIDE AN EYE WASH FOUNTAIN WITHIN THE IMMEDIATE WORK AREA FOR EMERGENCY USE.

AUTHORIZED BY- OCCUPATIONAL HEALTH SERVICES, INC.

CREATION DATE: 10/05/89 ***REVISION DATE:*** 04/27/90

MATERIAL SAFETY DATA SHEET

OCCUPATIONAL HEALTH SERVICES, INC.
AGRICULTURE AND PESTICIDE DIVISION
450 SEVENTH AVENUE, SUITE 2407
NEW YORK, NEW YORK 10123
1-800-445-MSDS OR (212) 967-1100

EMERGENCY CONTACT:
JOHN S. BRANSFORD, JR. (615) 292-1180

SUBSTANCE IDENTIFICATION

CAS-NUMBER 81-81-2

SUBSTANCE: **WARFARIN**

TRADE NAMES/SYNONYMS: 2H-1-BENZOPYRAN-2-ONE, 4-HYDROXY-3-(3-OXO-1-PHENYLBUTYL)-; COUMARIN, 3-(ALPHA-ACETONYLBENZYL)-4-HYDROXY-; 4-HYDROXY-3-(3-OXO-1-PHENYLBUTYL)-2H-1-BENZOPYRAN-2-ONE; 3-(ALPHA-ACETONYLBENZYL)-4-HYDROXYCOUMARIN; 4-HYDROXY-3-(3-OXO-1-PHENYLBUTYL)COUMARIN; 1-(4'-HYDROXY-3'-COUMARINYL)-1-PHENYL-3-BUTANONE; 3-ALPHA-PHENYL-BETA-ACETYLETHYL-4-HYDROXYCOUMARIN; ATHROMBINE-K; COMPOUND 42; COUMAFENE; COUMAPHEN; DETHMOR; KYPFARIN; RAX; W.A.R.F. 42; WARF COMPOUND 42; ZOOCOUMARIN; RCRA P001; C19H16O4; PST25090

CHEMICAL FAMILY: COUMARIN

MOLECULAR FORMULA: C19-H16-O4

MOLECULAR WEIGHT: 308.33

CERCLA RATINGS (SCALE 0-3): HEALTH=3 FIRE=1 REACTIVITY=0 PERSISTENCE=2

NFPA RATINGS (SCALE 0-4): HEALTH=4 FIRE=1 REACTIVITY=0

COMPONENTS AND CONTAMINANTS

COMPONENT: WARFARIN ***PERCENT:*** 100.0
CAS# 81-81-2

OTHER CONTAMINANTS: NONE

EXPOSURE LIMITS: WARFARIN: 0.1 MG/M3 OSHA TWA 0.1 MG/M3 ACGIH TWA 500/10,000 POUNDS SARA SECTION 302 THRESHOLD PLANNING QUANTITY 100 POUNDS SARA SECTION 304 REPORTABLE QUANTITY 100 POUNDS CERCLA SECTION 103 REPORTABLE QUANTITY SUBJECT TO CALIFORNIA PROPOSITION 65 CANCER AND/OR REPRODUCTIVE TOXICITY WARNING AND RELEASE REQUIREMENTS- (JULY 1, 1987)

PHYSICAL DATA

DESCRIPTION: TASTELESS, ODORLESS, COLORLESS, CRYSTALLINE POWDER.

MELTING POINT: 318-322 F (159-161 C) DECOMPOSES ***SPECIFIC GRAVITY:*** >1

SOLUBILITY IN WATER: 17 PPM @ 20 C

SOLVENT SOLUBILITY: SOLUBLE IN ACETONE, DIOXANE, ALKALINE SOLUTIONS, ETHER, ORGANIC SOLVENTS; MODERATELY SOLUBLE IN METHANOL, ETHANOL, ISOPROPANOL, SOME OILS; PRACTICALLY INSOLUBLE IN BENZENE, CYCLOHEXANE.

FIRE AND EXPLOSION DATA

FIRE AND EXPLOSION HAZARD: SLIGHT FIRE HAZARD WHEN EXPOSED TO HEAT OR FLAME.

FIREFIGHTING MEDIA: DRY CHEMICAL, CARBON DIOXIDE, HALON, WATER SPRAY OR STANDARD FOAM (1987 EMERGENCY RESPONSE GUIDEBOOK, DOT P 5800.4). FOR LARGER FIRES, USE WATER SPRAY, FOG OR STANDARD FOAM (1987 EMERGENCY RESPONSE GUIDEBOOK, DOT P 5800.4).

FIREFIGHTING: MOVE CONTAINERS FROM FIRE AREA IF POSSIBLE. FIGHT FIRE FROM MAXIMUM DISTANCE. STAY AWAY FROM STORAGE TANK ENDS. DIKE FIRE CONTROL WATER FOR LATER DISPOSAL. DO NOT SCATTER MATERIAL (1987 EMERGENCY RESPONSE GUIDEBOOK, DOT P 5800.4, GUIDE PAGE 55). EXTINGUISH USING AGENT SUITABLE FOR TYPE OF SURROUNDING FIRE. AVOID BREATHING VAPORS AND DUSTS. KEEP UPWIND.

TRANSPORTATION DATA

DEPARTMENT OF TRANSPORTATION HAZARD CLASSIFICATION 49 CFR 172.101: POISON B

DEPARTMENT OF TRANSPORTATION LABELING REQUIREMENTS 49 CFR 172.101 AND SUBPART E: POISON

DEPARTMENT OF TRANSPORTATION PACKAGING REQUIREMENTS: 49 CFR 173.365 EXCEPTIONS: 49 CFR 173.364

TOXICITY

WARFARIN: TOXICITY DATA: 320 MG/M3 INHALATION-RAT LC50; 1400 MG/KG SKIN-RAT LD50; 15 MG/KG/21 WEEKS INTERMITTENT ORAL-WOMAN TDLO; 10200 UG/KG ORAL-MAN TDLO; 6667 MG/KG ORAL-HUMAN LDLO; 1600 UG/KG ORAL-RAT LD50; 60 MG/KG ORAL-MOUSE LD50; 12 MG/KG ORAL-CAT LDLO; 1200 UG/KG ORAL-PIG LDLO; 800 MG/KG SUBCUTANEOUS-MOUSE LDLO; 165 MG/KG INTRAVENOUS-MOUSE LD50; 420 MG/KG INTRAPERITONEAL-RAT LDLO; 50 MG/KG UNREPORTED-RAT LD50; 60 MG/KG UNREPORTED-MOUSE LD50; REPRODUCTIVE EFFECTS DATA (RTECS). CARCINOGEN STATUS: NONE. ACUTE TOXICITY LEVEL: HIGHLY TOXIC BY INHALATION AND INGESTION; MODERATELY TOXIC BY DERMAL ABSORPTION. TARGET EFFECTS: TERATOGEN; HEMORRHAGIC AGENT. AT INCREASED RISK FROM EXPOSURE: PERSONS WITH BLOOD DYSCRASIAS, BLEEDING TENDENCIES, LIVER OR KIDNEY DISEASE, ULCERS OF THE GASTROINTESTINAL TRACT, OR HYPERTENSION. ADDITIONAL DATA: INTERACTIONS WITH MEDICATIONS HAVE BEEN REPORTED.

HEALTH EFFECTS AND FIRST AID

INHALATION: WARFARIN: HIGHLY TOXIC. 200 MG/M3 IMMEDIATELY DANGEROUS TO LIFE OR HEALTH. SEE INFORMATION ON COUMARIN DERIVATIVES.
COUMARIN DERIVATIVES: HEMORRHAGIC AGENT. **ACUTE EXPOSURE-** ABSORPTION BY THE LUNGS MAY RESULT IN HEMORRHAGIC EFFECTS AS DESCRIBED IN CHRONIC EXPOSURE. SEVERE CASES MAY BE FATAL. **CHRONIC EXPOSURE-** REPEATED ABSORPTION MAY CAUSE THE INHIBITION OF PROTHROMBIN SYNTHESIS AND DAMAGE TO CAPILLARY PERMEABILITY RESULTING IN WIDESPREAD INTERNAL HEMORRHAGE WITH ASSOCIATED EFFECTS OF NOSEBLEED, HEMATOMA, HEMATURIA, WIDESPREAD BRUISING, AND ANEMIA.

FIRST AID- REMOVE FROM EXPOSURE AREA TO FRESH AIR IMMEDIATELY. IF BREATHING HAS STOPPED, PERFORM ARTIFICIAL RESPIRATION. KEEP PERSON WARM AND AT REST. TREAT SYMPTOMATICALLY AND SUPPORTIVELY. GET MEDICAL ATTENTION IMMEDIATELY.

SKIN CONTACT: WARFARIN: SEE INFORMATION ON COUMARIN DERIVATIVES.
COUMARIN DERIVATIVES: HEMORRHAGIC AGENT. **ACUTE EXPOSURE-** ABSORPTION THROUGH THE SKIN MAY RESULT IN HEMORRHAGIC EFFECTS AS DESCRIBED IN CHRONIC EXPOSURE. SEVERE CASES MAY BE FATAL. **CHRONIC EXPOSURE-** REPEATED ABSORPTION MAY CAUSE THE INHIBITION OF PROTHROMBIN SYNTHESIS AND DAMAGE TO CAPILLARY PERMEABILITY RESULTING IN WIDESPREAD INTERNAL HEMORRHAGE WITH ASSOCIATED EFFECTS OF NOSEBLEED, HEMATOMA, HEMATURIA, WIDESPREAD BRUISING, AND ANEMIA.

FIRST AID- REMOVE CONTAMINATED CLOTHING AND SHOES IMMEDIATELY. WASH AFFECTED AREA WITH SOAP OR MILD DETERGENT AND LARGE AMOUNTS OF WATER UNTIL NO EVIDENCE OF CHEMICAL REMAINS (APPROXIMATELY 15-20 MINUTES). GET MEDICAL ATTENTION IMMEDIATELY.

EYE CONTACT: WARFARIN: **ACUTE EXPOSURE-** TECHNICAL WARFARIN PRODUCED MILD CONJUNCTIVAL IRRITATION IN RABBIT EYES. **CHRONIC EXPOSURE-** NO DATA AVAILABLE.

FIRST AID- WASH EYES IMMEDIATELY WITH LARGE AMOUNTS OF WATER OR NORMAL SALINE, OCCASIONALLY LIFTING UPPER AND LOWER LIDS, UNTIL NO EVIDENCE OF CHEMICAL REMAINS (APPROXIMATELY 15-20 MINUTES). GET MEDICAL ATTENTION IMMEDIATELY.

INGESTION: WARFARIN: TERATOGEN/HIGHLY TOXIC. SEE INFORMATION ON COUMARIN DERIVATIVES. THERAPEUTIC USE BY PREGNANT WOMEN HAS RESULTED IN FATAL HEMORRHAGING OF THE FETUS, AND MALFORMATIONS AND MENTAL RETARDATION IN INFANTS.
COUMARIN DERIVATIVES: HEMORRHAGIC AGENT. **ACUTE EXPOSURE-** MAY BE READILY ABSORBED FROM THE GASTROINTESTINAL TRACT AND CAUSE THE INHIBITION OF PROTHROMBIN SYNTHESIS AND DAMAGE TO CAPILLARY PERMEABILITY RESULTING IN WIDESPREAD INTERNAL HEMORRHAGE ACCOMPANIED BY THE HEMORRHAGIC SYMPTOMS AS DESCRIBED IN CHRONIC EXPOSURE. SEVERE CASES MAY BE FATAL. **CHRONIC EXPOSURE-** REPEATED INGESTION MAY CAUSE NOSEBLEED, BLEEDING GUMS AND PHARYNX, PETECHIAL RASH, WIDESPREAD BRUISING, HEMATOMA, HEMOPTYSIS, HEMATEMESIS, HEMATURIA, BLOODY STOOLS, BLEEDING INTO THE ORGANS, GASTROINTESTINAL TRACT, JOINTS, ABDOMINAL OR RETROPERITONEAL AREA WITH ABDOMINAL, BACK, JOINT AND LIMB PAIN AND CEREBROVASCULAR ACCIDENT. ANEMIA ACCOMPANIED BY WEAKNESS, PALLOR, AND SHOCK MAY OCCUR. SEVERE HEMORRHAGING MAY CAUSE DEATH. THERAPEUTIC USE OF SOME COUMARIN DERIVATIVES HAS INFREQUENTLY PRODUCED GASTROINTESTINAL DISTURBANCES, ELEVATED TRANSAMINASE, URTICARIA, DERMATITIS, LEUKOPENIA, ALOPECIA, FEVER, HYPERSENSITIVITY REACTIONS, AND RARELY SKIN NECROSIS.

FIRST AID- IF ONLY A FEW GRAINS OF ANTICOAGULANT BAIT HAVE BEEN INGESTED BY AN ADULT OR CHILD HAVING NO ANTECEDENT LIVER OR BLOOD CLOTTING DISEASE, TREATMENT IS PROBABLY UNNECESSARY. IF LARGE AMOUNTS OF ANTICOAGULANT WERE INGESTED IN THE PRECEDING 2-3 HOURS, INDUCE VOMITING WITH SYRUP OF IPECAC, FOLLOWED BY 1-2 GLASSES OF WATER. FOLLOWING EMESIS, GIVE ACTIVATED CHARCOAL IN 4-6 OUNCES OF WATER TO LIMIT ABSORPTION OF ANTICOAGULANT REMAINING IN THE GUT. OBSERVE PATIENT 4-5 DAYS AFTER INGESTION. (MORGAN, RECOGNITION AND

MANAGEMENT OF PESTICIDE POISONINGS, THIRD EDITION). GET MEDICAL ATTENTION.

ANTIDOTE: THE FOLLOWING ANTIDOTE HAS BEEN RECOMMENDED. HOWEVER, THE DECISION AS TO WHETHER THE SEVERITY OF POISONING REQUIRES ADMINISTRATION OF ANY ANTIDOTE AND ACTUAL DOSE REQUIRED SHOULD BE MADE BY QUALIFIED MEDICAL PERSONNEL.

OVERDOSE OF ANTICOAGULANTS: VITAMIN K IS A SPECIFIC ANTIDOTE. VITAMIN K1 EMULSION IS THE PREFERRED FORM. THE INITIAL SUBCUTANEOUS OR INTRAMUSCULAR DOSE IN ADULTS IS 5 TO 10 MG (UP TO 25 MG), REPEATED ONCE IF NECESSARY. ONLY IN VICTIMS WHO ARE BLEEDING SEVERLY OR OTHERWISE IN SERIOUS DISTRESS SHOULD THE DRUG BE GIVEN INTRAVENOUSLY AND THEN AT A RATE NO FASTER THAN 1 MG/MINUTE. IF NECESSARY, ON SUBSEQUENT DAYS, VITAMIN K1 SHOULD BE CONTINUED AT A REDUCED LEVEL UNTIL THE PROTHROMBIN TIME RETURNS TO NORMAL. VITAMIN K1 IS PREFERABLE TO K1 OXIDE (DOSE 0.5-2.5) AND CERTAINLY PREFERABLE TO MENADIONE OR MENADIONE SODIUM BISULFITE (GOSSELIN, CLINICAL TOXICOLOGY OF COMMERCIAL PRODUCTS, 5TH ED.). ANTIDOTE SHOULD BE ADMINISTERED BY QUALIFIED MEDICAL PERSONNEL.

REACTIVITY

REACTIVITY: STABLE UNDER NORMAL TEMPERATURES AND PRESSURES.

INCOMPATIBILITIES: WARFARIN: OXIDIZERS (STRONG): FIRE AND EXPLOSION HAZARD.

DECOMPOSITION: THERMAL DECOMPOSITION PRODUCTS MAY INCLUDE TOXIC OXIDES OF CARBON.

POLYMERIZATION: HAZARDOUS POLYMERIZATION HAS NOT BEEN REPORTED TO OCCUR UNDER NORMAL TEMPERATURES AND PRESSURES.

STORAGE AND DISPOSAL

OBSERVE ALL FEDERAL, STATE AND LOCAL REGULATIONS WHEN STORING OR DISPOSING OF THIS SUBSTANCE. FOR ASSISTANCE, CONTACT THE DISTRICT DIRECTOR OF THE ENVIRONMENTAL PROTECTION AGENCY.

STORAGE

STORE IN ACCORDANCE WITH 40 CFR 165 RECOMMENDED PROCEDURES FOR THE DISPOSAL AND STORAGE OF PESTICIDES AND PESTICIDE CONTAINERS.

STORE AWAY FROM INCOMPATIBLE SUBSTANCES.

THRESHOLD PLANNING QUANTITY (TPQ): THE SUPERFUND AMENDMENTS AND REAUTHORIZATION ACT (SARA) SECTION 302 REQUIRES THAT EACH FACILITY WHERE ANY EXTREMELY HAZARDOUS SUBSTANCE IS PRESENT IN A QUANTITY EQUAL TO OR GREATER THAN THE TPQ ESTABLISHED FOR THAT SUBSTANCE NOTIFY THE STATE EMERGENCY RESPONSE COMMISSION FOR THE STATE IN WHICH IT IS LOCATED. SECTION 303 OF SARA REQUIRES THESE FACILITIES TO PARTICIPATE IN LOCAL EMERGENCY RESPONSE PLANNING (40 CFR 355.30).

DISPOSAL

DISPOSAL MUST BE IN ACCORDANCE WITH STANDARDS APPLICABLE TO GENERATORS OF HAZARDOUS WASTE, 40CFR 262. EPA HAZARDOUS WASTE NUMBER P001.

CONDITIONS TO AVOID

MAY BURN BUT DOES NOT IGNITE READILY. CONTAINERS MAY EXPLODE IN HEAT OF FIRE.

SPILL AND LEAK PROCEDURES

WATER SPILL: THE CALIFORNIA SAFE DRINKING WATER AND TOXIC ENFORCEMENT ACT OF 1986 (PROPOSITION 65) PROHIBITS CONTAMINATING ANY KNOWN SOURCE OF DRINKING WATER WITH SUBSTANCES KNOWN TO CAUSE CANCER AND/OR REPRODUCTIVE TOXICITY.

OCCUPATIONAL SPILL: DO NOT TOUCH SPILLED MATERIAL. STOP LEAK IF YOU CAN DO IT WITHOUT RISK. USE WATER SPRAY TO REDUCE VAPORS. FOR SMALL SPILLS, TAKE UP WITH SAND OR OTHER ABSORBENT MATERIAL AND PLACE INTO CONTAINERS FOR LATER DISPOSAL. FOR SMALL DRY SPILLS, WITH A CLEAN SHOVEL PLACE MATERIAL INTO CLEAN, DRY CONTAINERS AND COVER. MOVE CONTAINERS FROM SPILL AREA. FOR LARGER SPILLS, DIKE FAR AHEAD OF SPILL FOR LATER DISPOSAL. KEEP UNNECESSARY PEOPLE AWAY. ISOLATE HAZARD AREA AND DENY ENTRY. VENTILATE CLOSED SPACES BEFORE ENTERING.

REPORTABLE QUANTITY (RQ): 100 POUNDS THE SUPERFUND AMENDMENTS AND REAUTHORIZATION ACT (SARA) SECTION 304 REQUIRES THAT A RELEASE EQUAL TO OR GREATER THAN THE REPORTABLE QUANTITY FOR THIS SUBSTANCE BE IMMEDIATELY REPORTED TO THE LOCAL EMERGENCY PLANNING COMMITTEE AND THE STATE EMERGENCY RESPONSE COMMISSION (40 CFR 355.40). IF THE RELEASE OF THIS SUBSTANCE IS REPORTABLE UNDER CERCLA SECTION 103, THE NATIONAL RESPONSE CENTER MUST BE NOTIFIED IMMEDIATELY AT (800) 424-8802 OR (202) 426-2675 IN THE METROPOLITAN WASHINGTON, D.C. AREA (40 CFR 302.6).

PROTECTIVE EQUIPMENT

VENTILATION: PROCESS ENCLOSURE RECOMMENDED TO MEET PUBLISHED EXPOSURE LIMITS.

RESPIRATOR: THE FOLLOWING RESPIRATORS AND MAXIMUM USE CONCENTRATIONS ARE RECOMMENDATIONS BY THE U.S. DEPARTMENT OF HEALTH AND HUMAN SERVICES, NIOSH POCKET GUIDE TO CHEMICAL HAZARDS; NIOSH CRITERIA DOCUMENTS OR BY THE U.S. DEPARTMENT OF LABOR, 29 CFR 1910 SUBPART Z. THE SPECIFIC RESPIRATOR SELECTED MUST BE BASED ON CONTAMINATION LEVELS FOUND IN THE WORK PLACE, MUST NOT EXCEED THE WORKING LIMITS OF THE RESPIRATOR AND BE JOINTLY APPROVED BY THE NATIONAL INSTITUTE FOR OCCUPATIONAL SAFETY AND HEALTH AND THE MINE SAFETY AND HEALTH ADMINISTRATION (NIOSH-MSHA).

WARFARIN: 0.5 MG/M3- ANY DUST AND MIST RESPIRATOR EXCEPT SINGLE-USE RESPIRATORS.

1.0 MG/M3- ANY DUST AND MIST RESPIRATOR, EXCEPT SINGLE-USE AND QUARTER-MASK RESPIRATORS. ANY SUPPLIED-AIR RESPIRATOR. ANY SELF-CONTAINED BREATHING APPARATUS.

2.5 MG/M3- ANY POWERED AIR-PURIFYING RESPIRATOR WITH A DUST AND MIST FILTER. ANY SUPPLIED-AIR RESPIRATOR OPERATED IN A CONTINUOUS FLOW MODE.

5.0 MG/M3- ANY AIR-PURIFYING FULL FACEPIECE RESPIRATOR WITH A HIGH-EFFICIENCY PARTICULATE FILTER. ANY POWERED AIR-PURIFYING RESPIRATOR WITH A TIGHT-FITTING FACEPIECE AND A HIGH-EFFICIENCY PARTICULATE FILTER. ANY SELF-CONTAINED BREATHING APPARATUS WITH A FULL FACEPIECE. ANY SUPPLIED-AIR RESPIRATOR WITH A FULL FACEPIECE. ANY SUPPLIED-AIR RESPIRATOR WITH A TIGHT-FITTING FACEPIECE OPERATED IN A CONTINUOUS FLOW MODE.

100 MG/M3- ANY SUPPLIED-AIR RESPIRATOR WITH A HALF-MASK AND OPERATED IN A PRESSURE-DEMAND OR OTHER POSITIVE PRESSURE MODE.

200 MG/M3- ANY SUPPLIED-AIR RESPIRATOR WITH A FULL FACEPIECE AND OPERATED IN A PRESSURE-DEMAND OR OTHER POSITIVE PRESSURE MODE.

ESCAPE- ANY AIR-PURIFYING FULL FACEPIECE RESPIRATOR WITH A HIGH-EFFICIENCY PARTICULATE FILTER. ANY APPROPRIATE ESCAPE-TYPE SELF-CONTAINED BREATHING APPARATUS. FOR FIREFIGHTING AND OTHER IMMEDIATELY DANGEROUS TO LIFE OR HEALTH CONDITIONS:

SELF-CONTAINED BREATHING APPARATUS WITH FULL FACEPIECE OPERATED IN PRESSURE-DEMAND OR OTHER POSITIVE PRESSURE MODE.

SUPPLIED-AIR RESPIRATOR WITH FULL FACEPIECE AND OPERATED IN PRESSURE-DEMAND OR OTHER POSITIVE PRESSURE MODE IN COMBINATION WITH AN AUXILIARY SELF-CONTAINED BREATHING APPARATUS OPERATED IN PRESSURE-DEMAND OR OTHER POSITIVE PRESSURE MODE.

CLOTHING: EMPLOYEE MUST WEAR APPROPRIATE PROTECTIVE (IMPERVIOUS) CLOTHING AND EQUIPMENT TO PREVENT ANY POSSIBILITY OF SKIN CONTACT WITH THIS SUBSTANCE.

GLOVES: EMPLOYEE MUST WEAR APPROPRIATE PROTECTIVE GLOVES TO PREVENT CONTACT WITH THIS SUBSTANCE.

EYE PROTECTION: EMPLOYEE MUST WEAR SPLASH-PROOF OR DUST-RESISTANT SAFETY GOGGLES WITH OR WITHOUT A FACESHIELD TO PREVENT CONTACT WITH THIS SUBSTANCE.

EMERGENCY EYE WASH: WHERE THERE IS ANY POSSIBILITY THAT AN EMPLOYEE'S EYES MAY BE EXPOSED TO THIS SUBSTANCE, THE EMPLOYER SHOULD PROVIDE AN EYE WASH FOUNTAIN WITHIN THE IMMEDIATE WORK AREA FOR EMERGENCY USE.

AUTHORIZED BY- OCCUPATIONAL HEALTH SERVICES, INC.

CREATION DATE: 10/05/89 ***REVISION DATE:*** 05/17/90

MATERIAL SAFETY DATA SHEET

OCCUPATIONAL HEALTH SERVICES, INC.
AGRICULTURE AND PESTICIDE DIVISION
450 SEVENTH AVENUE, SUITE 2407
NEW YORK, NEW YORK 10123
1-800-445-MSDS OR (212) 967-1100

EMERGENCY CONTACT:
JOHN S. BRANSFORD, JR. (615) 292-1180

SUBSTANCE IDENTIFICATION

SUBSTANCE: WHITMIRE PT 250

TRADE NAMES/SYNONYMS: EPA REG. NO. 499-157; PST25105

CERCLA RATINGS (SCALE 0-3): HEALTH=3 FIRE=1 REACTIVITY=0 PERSISTENCE=3

NFPA RATINGS (SCALE 0-4): HEALTH=4 FIRE=1 REACTIVITY=0

COMPONENTS AND CONTAMINANTS

COMPONENT: METHYLENE CHLORIDE ***PERCENT:*** >1.0
CAS# 75-09-2
COMPONENT: 1,1,1-TRICHLORETHANE ***PERCENT:*** >1.0
CAS# 71-55-6
COMPONENT: CARBON DIOXIDE ***PERCENT:*** >1.0
CAS# 124-38-9
COMPONENT: O-ISOPROPOXYPHENYL METHYLCARBAMATE (BAYGON) ***PERCENT:*** 1.0
CAS# 114-26-1

EXPOSURE LIMITS: DICHLOROMETHANE (METHYLENE CHLORIDE): 500 PPM OSHA TWA; 1000 PPM OSHA CEILING; 2000 PPM/5 MIN IN 2 HOURS OSHA PEAK 50 PPM (174 MG/M3) ACGIH TWA ACGIH A2- SUSPECTED HUMAN CARCINOGEN. LOWEST FEASIBLE LIMIT NIOSH RECOMMENDED EXPOSURE CRITERIA

1000 POUNDS CERCLA SECTION 103 REPORTABLE QUANTITY SUBJECT TO SARA SECTION 313 ANNUAL TOXIC CHEMICAL RELEASE REPORTING SUBJECT TO CALIFORNIA PROPOSITION 65 CANCER AND/OR REPRODUCTIVE TOXICITY WARNING AND RELEASE REQUIREMENTS- (APRIL 1, 1988)

METHYL CHLOROFORM (1,1,1-TRICHLOROETHANE): 350 PPM (1900 MG/M3) OSHA TWA; 450 PPM (2450 MG/M3) OSHA STEL 350 PPM (1900 MG/M3) ACGIH TWA; 450 PPM (2450 MG/M3) ACGIH STEL 350 PPM NIOSH RECOMMENDED 15 MINUTE CEILING

1000 POUNDS CERCLA SECTION 103 REPORTABLE QUANTITY SUBJECT TO SARA SECTION 313 ANNUAL TOXIC CHEMICAL RELEASE REPORTING

CARBON DIOXIDE: 10,000 PPM (18,000 MG/M3) OSHA TWA; 30,000 PPM (54,000 MG/M3) OSHA STEL 5000 PPM (9000 MG/M3) ACGIH TWA; 30,000 PPM (54,000 MG/M3) ACGIH STEL 10,000 PPM NIOSH RECOMMENDED 10 HOUR TWA; 30,000 PPM NIOSH RECOMMENDED 10 MINUTE CEILING O-ISOPROPOXYPHENYL METHYLCARBAMATE: 0.5 MG/M3 OSHA TWA 0.5 MG/M3 ACGIH TWA SUBJECT TO SARA SECTION 313 ANNUAL TOXIC CHEMICAL RELEASE REPORTING

PHYSICAL DATA

DESCRIPTION: AEROSOL SPRAY WITH A CHARACTERISTIC PROPOXUR ODOR
BOILING POINT: NOT AVAILABLE ***SPECIFIC GRAVITY:*** 1.335 ***VOLATILITY:*** >99%
EVAPORATION RATE: NOT AVAILABLE ***SOLUBILITY IN WATER:*** INSOLUBLE
VAPOR PRESSURE: 3620 MMHG (CONTAINER)

FIRE AND EXPLOSION DATA

FIRE AND EXPLOSION HAZARD: SLIGHT FIRE HAZARD WHEN EXPOSED TO HEAT OR FLAME.
CYLINDER MAY EXPLODE IN HEAT OF FIRE.
FLASH POINT: NONE
FIREFIGHTING MEDIA: DRY CHEMICAL, CARBON DIOXIDE OR HALON (1987 EMERGENCY RESPONSE GUIDEBOOK, DOT P 5800.4).
FOR LARGER FIRES, USE WATER SPRAY, FOG OR STANDARD FOAM (1987 EMERGENCY RESPONSE GUIDEBOOK, DOT P 5800.4).
FIREFIGHTING: MOVE CONTAINER FROM FIRE AREA IF POSSIBLE. STAY AWAY FROM STORAGE TANK ENDS. COOL FIRE-EXPOSED CONTAINERS WITH WATER FROM THE SIDE UNTIL WELL AFTER THE FIRE IS OUT. WITHDRAW IMMEDIATELY IF RISING SOUND FROM VENTING SAFETY DEVICE OR ANY DISCOLORATION OF STORAGE TANKS DUE TO FIRE (1987 EMERGENCY RESPONSE GUIDEBOOK, DOT P 5800.4, GUIDE PAGE 12).
EXTINGUISH USING AGENT INDICATED. COOL CYLINDERS WITH FLOODING AMOUNTS OF WATER FROM AS FAR A DISTANCE AS POSSIBLE. DO NOT USE WATER DIRECTLY ON MATERIAL. USE WATER SPRAY TO ABSORB VAPORS. AVOID BREATHING VAPORS; KEEP UPWIND. CONSIDER EVACUATION OF DOWNWIND AREA IF MATERIAL IS LEAKING.

TRANSPORTATION DATA

DEPARTMENT OF TRANSPORTATION HAZARD CLASSIFICATION 49 CFR 172.101: NONFLAMMABLE GAS
DEPARTMENT OF TRANSPORTATION LABELING REQUIREMENTS 49 CFR 172.101 AND SUBPART E: NONFLAMMABLE GAS
DEPARTMENT OF TRANSPORTATION PACKAGING REQUIREMENTS: 49 CFR 173.302; 49 CFR 173.304 AND 49 CFR 173.305 EXCEPTIONS: 49 CFR 173.306 AND 49 CFR 173.307

TOXICITY

DICHLOROMETHANE (METHYLENE CHLORIDE): IRRITATION DATA: 162 MG EYE-RABBIT MODERATE; 10 MG EYE-RABBIT MILD; 500 MG/24 HOURS EYE-RABBIT MILD; 810 MG/24 HOURS SKIN-RABBIT SEVERE; 100 MG/24 HOURS SKIN-RABBIT MODERATE. TOXICITY DATA: 500 PPM/1 YEAR-INTERMITTENT INHALATION-HUMAN TCLO; 500 PPM/8 HOURS INHALATION-HUMAN TCLO; 88000 MG/M3/30 MINUTES INHALATION-RAT LC50; 14400 PPM/7 HOURS INHALATION-MOUSE LC50; 10000 PPM/7 HOURS INHALATION-RABBIT LCLO; 5000 PPM/2 HOURS INHALATION-GUINEA PIG LCLO; 14108 PPM/7 HOURS INHALATION-DOG LCLO; 43400 MG/M3/4.5 HOURS INHALATION-CAT LCLO; 357 MG/KG ORAL-HUMAN LDLO; 1600 MG/KG ORAL-RAT LD50; 1900 MG/KG ORAL-RABBIT LDLO; 3 GM/KG ORAL-DOG LDLO; 6460 MG/KG SUBCUTANEOUS-MOUSE LD50; 2700 MG/KG SUBCUTANEOUS-RABBIT LDLO; 2700 MG/KG SUBCUTANEOUS-DOG LDLO; 200 MG/KG INTRAVENOUS-DOG LDLO; 916 MG/KG INTRAPERITONEAL-RAT LD50; 950 MG/KG INTRAPERITONEAL-DOG LDLO; 437 MG/KG INTRAPERITONEAL-MOUSE LD50; 4770 MG/KG UNREPORTED-MOUSE LD50; MUTAGENIC DATA (RTECS); REPRODUCTIVE EFFECTS DATA (RTECS); TUMORIGENIC DATA (RTECS). CARCINOGEN STATUS: ANTICIPATED HUMAN CARCINOGEN (NTP); HUMAN INADEQUATE EVIDENCE, ANIMAL SUFFICIENT EVIDENCE (IARC GROUP-2B). EXPOSURE BY INHALATION INCREASED THE INCIDENCE OF BENIGN AND MALIGNANT LUNG AND LIVER TUMORS IN MICE OF EACH SEX AND THE INCIDENCE OR MULTIPLICITY OF BENIGN MAMMARY TUMORS IN RATS OF EACH SEX; IN MALE RATS, AN INCREASED INCIDENCE OF SARCOMAS LOCATED IN THE NECK WAS ALSO OBSERVED. LOCAL EFFECTS: IRRITANT-INHALATION, SKIN, EYE. ACUTE TOXICITY LEVEL: MODERATELY TOXIC BY INHALATION AND INGESTION. TARGET EFFECTS: CENTRAL NERVOUS SYSTEM DEPRESSANT; CHEMICAL ASPHYXIANT. POISONING MAY AFFECT THE BLOOD, LIVER AND KIDNEYS. AT INCREASED RISK FROM EXPOSURE: PERSONS WITH SKIN, LIVER, KIDNEY, CARDIOVASCULAR DISEASE OR ANEMIA. ADDITIONAL DATA: CONCURRENT EXPOSURE TO OTHER SOURCES OF CARBON MONOXIDE, SMOKING, OR PHYSICAL ACTIVITY MAY INCREASE THE LEVEL OF CARBOXYHEMOGLOBIN IN THE BLOOD RESULTING IN ADDITIVE EFFECTS. ALCOHOLIC BEVERAGES MAY ENHANCE THE TOXIC EFFECTS. STIMULANTS SUCH AS EPINEPHRINE MAY INDUCE CARDIAC ARRHYTHMIAS. ONE STUDY INDICATED THAT CHRONIC EXPOSURE MAY BE ASSOCIATED WITH AN INCREASED RISK OF SPONTANEOUS ABORTION. DICHLOROMETHANE CROSSES THE PLACENTAL BARRIER AND IS EXCRETED IN HUMAN MILK.

METHYL CHLOROFORM (1,1,1-TRICHLOROETHANE): IRRITATION DATA: 450 PPM/8 HOURS EYE-MAN; 5 GM/12 DAYS INTERMITTENT SKIN-RABBIT MILD; 20 MG/24 HOURS SKIN-RABBIT MODERATE; 100 MG EYE-RABBIT MILD; 2 MG/24 HOURS EYE-RABBIT SEVERE. TOXICITY DATA: 27 GM/M3/10 MINUTES INHALATION-MAN LCLO; 350 PPM INHALATION-MAN TCLO; 200 PPM/4 HOURS INHALATION-MAN TCLO; 920 PPM/70 MINUTES INHALATION-HUMAN TCLO; 18000 PPM/4 HOURS INHALATION-RAT LC50; 3911 PPM/2 HOURS INHALATION-MOUSE LC50; 24400 MG/M3 INHALATION-CAT LC50; 15800 MG/KG SKIN-RABBIT LD50 (EPA-600/8-82-003F, 1984); 1 GM/KG SKIN-RABBIT LDLO; 670 MG/KG ORAL-HUMAN TDLO; 10300 MG/KG ORAL-RAT LD50; 11240 MG/KG ORAL-MOUSE LD50; 5660 MG/KG ORAL-RABBIT LD50; 9470 MG/KG ORAL-GUINEA PIG LD50; 750 MG/KG ORAL-DOG LD50; 16 GM/KG SUBCUTANEOUS-MOUSE LD50; 500 MG/KG SUBCUTANEOUS-RABBIT LDLO; 95 MG/KG INTRAVENOUS-DOG LDLO; 3593 MG/KG INTRAPERITONEAL-RAT LD50; 3636 MG/KG INTRAPERITONEAL-MOUSE LD50; 3100 MG/KG INTRAPERITONEAL-DOG LD50; MUTAGENIC DATA (RTECS); REPRODUCTIVE EFFECTS DATA (RTECS). CARCINOGEN STATUS: ANIMAL INADEQUATE EVIDENCE (IARC GROUP-3). LOCAL EFFECTS: IRRITANT- INHALATION, SKIN, EYE. ACUTE TOXICITY LEVEL: SLIGHTLY TOXIC BY INHALATION, DERMAL ABSORPTION AND INGESTION. TARGET EFFECTS: CENTRAL NERVOUS SYSTEM DEPRESSANT. POISONING MAY ALSO AFFECT THE HEART AND POSSIBLY LIVER AND KIDNEYS. AT INCREASED RISK FROM EXPOSURE: PERSONS WITH PRE-EXISTING SKIN DISORDERS, LIVER DISEASE OR CARDIOVASCULAR DISEASE. ADDITIONAL DATA: ALCOHOL MAY POTENTIATE BOTH CARDIAC AND HEPATIC TOXICITY. EPINEPHRINE OR OTHER STIMULANTS MAY INDUCE VENTRICULAR ARRHYTHMIAS.

CARBON DIOXIDE: TOXICITY DATA: 9 PPH/5 MINUTES INHALATION-HUMAN LCLO; 90000 PPM/5 MINUTES INHALATION-MAMMAL LCLO; REPRODUCTIVE EFFECTS DATA (RTECS). CARCINOGEN STATUS: NONE. ACUTE TOXICITY LEVEL: INSUFFICIENT DATA. TARGET EFFECTS: SIMPLE ASPHYXIANT. POISONING MAY AFFECT THE RESPIRATORY AND NERVOUS SYSTEMS AND HEART. AT INCREASED RISK FROM EXPOSURE: PERSONS WITH A HISTORY OF CARDIOVASCULAR OR PULMONARY IMPAIRMENT.

O-ISOPROPOXYPHENYL METHYLCARBAMATE: TOXICITY DATA: 1440 MG/M3/1 HOUR INHALATION-RAT LC50; 800 MG/KG SKIN-RAT LD50; 24 MG/KG ORAL-WOMAN LDLO; 70 MG/KG ORAL-RAT LD50; 23500 UG/KG ORAL-MOUSE LD50; 40 MG/KG ORAL-GUINEA PIG LD50; 11400 UG/KG SUBCUTANEOUS-MOUSE LD50; 56 MG/KG SUBCUTANEOUS-RAT LD50; 11 MG/KG INTRAVENOUS-RAT LD50; 30 MG/KG INTRAPERITONEAL-RAT LD50; 12 MG/KG INTRAPERITONEAL-MOUSE LD50; 500 MG/KG INTRAPERITONEAL-HAMSTER LD50; 53 MG/KG INTRAMUSCULAR-RAT LD50; 100 MG/KG UNREPORTED-RAT LD50; 100 MG/KG UNREPORTED-MAMMAL LD50; MUTAGENIC DATA (RTECS); REPRODUCTIVE EFFECTS DATA (RTECS). CARCINOGEN STATUS: NONE. ACUTE TOXICITY LEVEL: HIGHLY TOXIC BY INHALATION; TOXIC BY DERMAL ABSORPTION AND INGESTION. TARGET EFFECTS: CHOLINESTERASE INHIBITOR. AT INCREASED RISK FROM EXPOSURE: PERSONS WITH ASTHMA, DIABETES, CARDIOVASCULAR DISEASE, MECHANICAL OBSTRUCTION OF THE GASTROINTESTINAL OR UROGENITAL TRACT, AND THOSE IN VAGOTONIC STATES.*

* MAY BE BASED ON GENERAL INFORMATION ON CARBAMATES.

HEALTH EFFECTS AND FIRST AID

INHALATION: DICHLOROMETHANE (METHYLENE CHLORIDE): IRRITANT/NARCOTIC/CHEMICAL ASPHYXIANT/CARCINOGEN. **ACUTE EXPOSURE-** HUMAN EXPOSURE TO 100 PPM HAS RESULTED IN UPPER RESPIRATORY TRACT IRRITATION; CONCENTRATIONS AS LOW AS 200 PPM HAVE PRODUCED TEMPORARY NEUROBEHAVIOURAL EFFECTS; 500-1000 PPM FOR 1-2 HOURS HAS CAUSED LIGHTHEADEDNESS AND ELEVATED CARBOXYHEMOGLOBIN LEVEL; 2300 PPM FOR 30 MINUTES HAS CAUSED NAUSEA AND NARCOSIS; 5000 PPM HAS CAUSED HEADACHE, FATIGUE, NEURASTHENIC DISORDERS AND DIGESTIVE DISTURBANCES. OTHER SYMPTOMS MAY INCLUDE DIZZINESS, TINGLING, NUMBNESS OF THE EXTREMITIES, A SENSATION OF HEAT, A SENSATION OF FULLNESS IN THE HEAD, DRUNKENNESS, STUPOR, DULLNESS AND MENTAL CONFUSION. MASSIVE EXPOSURE MAY CAUSE PHARYNGEAL EROSION, PULMONARY EDEMA, STAGGERING, HEMOLYSIS WITH GROSS HEMATURIA, RAPID UNCONSCIOUSNESS AND DEATH. RECOVERY IS GENERALLY COMPLETE IF EXPOSURE IS TERMINATED BEFORE ANESTHETIC DEATH. EXPOSURE TO HIGH LEVELS MAY ALSO CAUSE CARDIAC ARRHYTHMIAS. **CHRONIC EXPOSURE-** MORE THAN 100 WORKERS EXPOSED TO LEVELS BELOW 500 PPM HAVE DEVELOPED HEALTH PROBLEMS INCLUDING SIGNIFICANT UPPER RESPIRATORY IRRITATION, EXACERBATION OF CORONARY ARTERY DISEASE, AND A HIGH INCIDENCE OF NEUROTOXICITY; INCREASED COMPLAINTS OF CHEST PAINS WERE REPORTED AT CONCENTRATIONS OF 10 TO 35 PPM. REPEATED HUMAN EXPOSURE TO 500-3600 PPM HAS CAUSED SIGNS OF TOXIC ENCEPHALOPATHY WITH ACOUSTICAL AND OPTICAL DELUSIONS AND HALLUCINATIONS. A CASE OF SERIOUS CEREBRAL DETERIORATION WAS OBSERVED IN AN INDIVIDUAL EXPOSED FOR SEVERAL YEARS TO DICHLOROMETHANE. IN A MORTALITY STUDY OF TWO GROUPS OF WORKERS, ONE EXPOSED TO ACETONE AND THE OTHER TO DICHLOROMETHANE AND ACETONE, A STATISTICALLY SIGNIFICANT DIFFERENCE IN DEATHS FROM DISEASES OF THE CIRCULATORY SYSTEM AND FROM ISCHEMIC HEART DISEASE WERE REPORTED FROM THE DICHLOROMETHANE AND ACETONE GROUP. IN ANOTHER MORTALITY STUDY OF WORKERS EXPOSED TO DICHLOROMETHANE, A SIGNIFICANT INCREASE IN HYPERTENSIVE DISEASE AND A "SUGGESTIVE EXCESS" OF PANCREATIC CANCER WERE REPORTED. LIVER DISEASE HAS BEEN REPORTED IN WORKERS. IN ONE STUDY, AN INCREASE IN SERUM BILIRUBIN WAS OBSERVED IN EXPOSED WORKERS, BUT NO OTHER SIGN OF LIVER INJURY OR HEMOLYSIS WAS REPORTED. ADVERSE LIVER EFFECTS WERE OBSERVED IN SEVERAL ANIMAL SPECIES CHEMICALLY EXPOSED. TESTICULAR ATROPHY WAS REPORTED IN MICE EXPOSED TO 4000 PPM OVER 2 YEARS. REPEATED INHALATION BY RODENTS PRIOR TO AND/OR DURING GESTATION CAUSED FETAL SKELETAL ABNORMALITIES AND BEHAVIORAL EFFECTS IN NEWBORN OFFSPRING. REPEATED INHALATION INCREASED THE INCIDENCE OF BENIGN AND MALIGNANT LUNG AND LIVER TUMORS IN MICE OF EACH SEX AND THE INCIDENCE OR MULTIPLICITY OF BENIGN MAMMARY TUMORS IN RATS OF EACH SEX; IN MALE RATS, AN INCREASED INCIDENCE OF SARCOMAS LOCATED IN THE NECK WAS ALSO OBSERVED.

METHYL CHLOROFORM (1,1,1-TRICHLOROETHANE): IRRITANT/NARCOTIC. 1000 PPM IMMEDIATELY DANGEROUS TO LIFE OR HEALTH. **ACUTE EXPOSURE-** EXPOSURE TO 500 PPM FOR 60 MINUTES SHOULD CAUSE NO EFFECT EXCEPT FOR A DISTINCTIVE ODOR WHILE 900-1000 PPM FOR 20 MINUTES MAY CAUSE MILD RESPIRATORY TRACT IRRITATION AND PROMPT BUT MINIMAL IMPAIRMENT OF EQUILIBRIUM WHICH MAY BE ACCOMPANIED BY HEADACHE, LASSITUDE AND ATAXIA. IMPAIRED PERFORMANCE OF BEHAVIORAL TESTS WAS ALSO REPORTED AT 1000 PPM. HIGHER LEVELS OF 2000-5000 PPM MAY CAUSE INCOORDINATION, ANESTHESIA, LOSS OF CONSCIOUSNESS, COMA AND DEATH. EXCESSIVE CONCENTRATIONS OF 10,000 PPM MAY CAUSE DEATH DUE TO RESPIRATORY OR CARDIAC FAILURE. CARDIAC SENSITIZATION MAY BE A CONTRIBUTING FACTOR. OTHER EFFECTS MAY INCLUDE NAUSEA, VOMITING, DROWSINESS, CONVULSIONS, FALL OF BLOOD PRESSURE LIVER AND KIDNEY DAMAGE, BRADYCARDIA AND BLOOD CLOTTING CHANGES. **CHRONIC EXPOSURE-** NO ADVERSE EFFECTS RELATED TO EXPOSURE WERE REPORTED IN VOLUNTEERS EXPOSED TO 500 PPM FOR 7 HOURS A DAY FOR 5 DAYS, OR IN WORKERS EXPOSED TO 200 PPM FOR SEVERAL MONTHS TO 6 YEARS. EXPOSURE OF ANIMALS FOR 3 MONTHS AT CONCENTRATIONS FROM 1000 TO 10,000 PPM CAUSED SYMPTOMS OF CENTRAL NERVOUS SYSTEM DEPRESSION AND SOME PATHOLOGICAL CHANGES IN THE LIVERS AND LUNGS OF SOME SPECIES. REPRODUCTIVE EFFECTS HAVE BEEN REPORTED IN ANIMALS.

CARBON DIOXIDE: SIMPLE ASPHYXIANT. 50,000 PPM IMMEDIATELY DANGEROUS TO LIFE OR HEALTH. **ACUTE EXPOSURE-** IN THE SOLID OR LIQUID FORM CARBON DIOXIDE IS VERY VOLATILE, READILY RELEASING THE GAS. AT CONCENTRATIONS FROM 2-10% IT MAY CAUSE ACIDIC TASTE, DYSPNEA, HEADACHE, VERTIGO, NAUSEA, LABORED BREATHING, WEAKNESS, DROWSINESS, MENTAL CONFUSION, AND INCREASE IN BLOOD PRESSURE, PULSE, AND RESPIRATORY RATE. EXPOSURE TO 10% FOR A FEW MINUTES HAS BEEN REPORTED TO CAUSE VISUAL DISTURBANCES, TINNITUS, TREMORS, PROFUSE PERSPIRATION, RESTLESSNESS, PARESTHESIAS, GENERAL FEELING OF DISCOMFORT, LOSS OF CONSCIOUSNESS, AND COMA. CONCENTRATIONS OF 25-30% MAY CAUSE COMA AND CONVULSIONS WITHIN ONE MINUTE. TACHYCARDIA AND ARRHYTHMIAS ARE POSSIBLE. CONCENTRATIONS OF 50% MAY CAUSE SYMPTOMS OF HYPOCALCEMIA INCLUDING CARPOPEDAL SPASMS. EXCESSIVE CARBON DIOXIDE FOR A TIME PERIOD OF NOT MORE THAN 5 MINUTES WAS REPORTED TO CAUSE EFFECTS ON VISION WITH CONSTRICTION OF VISUAL FIELDS, ENLARGEMENT OF BLIND SPOTS, PHOTOPHOBIA, LOSS OF CONVERGENCE AND ACCOMMODATION, AND DEFICIENT DARK ADAPTATION AS WELL AS HEADACHE, INSOMNIA, AND PERSONALITY CHANGES, LARGELY DEPRESSION AND IRRITABILITY. EVEN WHEN THERE IS SUFFICIENT OXYGEN PRESENT TO PREVENT SIMPLE ASPHYXIATION BY CARBON DIOXIDE, HIGH CONCENTRATIONS MAY CAUSE ADVERSE EFFECTS BY INTERFERING WITH ITS NORMAL ELIMINATION FROM THE BODY. INITIALLY, EXPOSURE TO INCREASED CARBON DIOXIDE CONCENTRATIONS RESULTS IN A COMPENSATORY INCREASE IN BOTH RATE AND DEPTH OF VENTILATION. BEYOND A CERTAIN POINT, HOWEVER, THIS MAY REVERSE TO HYPOVENTILATION RESULTING IN RESPIRATORY ACIDOSIS. DEATH FROM ASPHYXIA MAY OCCUR IF THE CONCENTRATION AND DURATION OF EXPOSURE ARE SUFFICIENT. REPRODUCTIVE EFFECTS HAVE BEEN REPORTED IN ANIMALS. **CHRONIC EXPOSURE-** IT HAS BEEN REPORTED THAT PERSONS MAY TOLERATE 1.5% IN INHALED AIR FOR PROLONGED PERIODS WITHOUT ADVERSE EFFECTS, BUT CALCIUM/ PHOSPHORUS METABOLISM MAY BE AFFECTED WITH SERUM LEVELS OF CALCIUM AND URINARY PHOSPHORUS PROGRESSIVELY FALLING. AT 2% CONCENTRATION, DEEPENED RESPIRATION MAY OCCUR. AT 3% IMPAIRMENT OF PERFORMANCE HAS BEEN NOTED. IT HAS, HOWEVER, BEEN DEMONSTRATED THAT THE DEVELOPMENT OF TOLERANCE MAY OCCUR DURING PROLONGED EXPOSURE TO LOW LEVELS. REPRODUCTIVE EFFECTS HAVE BEEN REPORTED IN ANIMALS.

O-ISOPROPOXYPHENYL METHYLCARBAMATE: HIGHLY TOXIC. SEE INFORMATION ON CARBAMATES.

CARBAMATES: CHOLINESTERASE INHIBITOR. **ACUTE EXPOSURE-** WHEN INHALED, THE FIRST EFFECTS OF CHOLINESTERASE INHIBITION ARE USUALLY RESPIRATORY AND MAY INCLUDE NASAL HYPEREMIA AND WATERY DISCHARGE, CHEST DISCOMFORT, DYSPNEA, AND WHEEZING DUE TO INCREASED BRONCHIAL SECRETIONS AND BRONCHOCONSTRICTION. OTHER SYSTEMIC EFFECTS MAY BEGIN WITHIN A FEW MINUTES OR SEVERAL HOURS OF EXPOSURE. SYMPTOMS MAY INCLUDE NAUSEA, VOMITING, DIARRHEA, ABDOMINAL CRAMPS, HEADACHE, VERTIGO, OCULAR PAIN, CILIARY MUSCLE SPASM, BLURRING OR DIMNESS OF VISION, MIOSIS, OR IN SOME CASES MYDRIASIS, LACRIMATION, SALIVATION, SWEATING, AND CONFUSION. OTHER REPORTED CENTRAL NERVOUS SYSTEM OR NEUROMUSCULAR EFFECTS INCLUDE ATAXIA, SLURRED SPEECH, AREFLEXIA, WEAKNESS, FATIGUE, TWITCHING, FASCICULATION, TREMOR, AND EVENTUALLY PARALYSIS OF THE EXTREMITIES AND POSSIBLY OF THE RESPIRATORY MUSCLES. IN SEVERE CASES, THERE MAY ALSO BE INVOLUNTARY DEFECATION AND URINATION, BRADYCARDIA, HYPOTENSION, PULMONARY EDEMA, CONVULSIONS, COMA, AND DEATH FROM RESPIRATORY FAILURE OR CARDIAC ARREST. CARBAMATES GENERALLY DO NOT ACCUMULATE IN MAMMALIAN TISSUE AND THE CHOLINESTERASE INHIBITION REVERSES RATHER RAPIDLY. IN NON-FATAL CASES, THE ILLNESS GENERALLY LASTS LESS THAN 24 HOURS. **CHRONIC EXPOSURE-** PROLONGED OR REPEATED EXPOSURE MAY CAUSE EFFECTS AS DESCRIBED IN ACUTE EXPOSURE.

FIRST AID- REMOVE FROM EXPOSURE AREA TO FRESH AIR IMMEDIATELY. IF BREATHING HAS STOPPED, GIVE ARTIFICIAL RESPIRATION. MAINTAIN AIRWAY AND BLOOD PRESSURE AND ADMINISTER OXYGEN IF AVAILABLE. KEEP AFFECTED PERSON WARM AND AT REST. TREAT SYMPTOMATICALLY AND SUPPORTIVELY. ADMINISTRATION OF OXYGEN SHOULD BE PERFORMED BY QUALIFIED PERSONNEL. GET MEDICAL ATTENTION IMMEDIATELY.

SKIN CONTACT: DICHLOROMETHANE (METHYLENE CHLORIDE): IRRITANT. **ACUTE EXPOSURE-** MAY CAUSE EFFECTS RANGING FROM MILD IRRITATION TO SEVERE PAIN, PARESTHESIAS, AND POSSIBLY BURNS, DEPENDING ON THE INTENSITY OF CONTACT. **CHRONIC EXPOSURE-** PROLONGED OR REPEATED CONTACT MAY CAUSE A DRY, SCALY AND FISSURED DERMATITIS DUE TO DEFATTING ACTION OF LIQUID ON SKIN.

METHYL CHLOROFORM (1,1,1-TRICHLOROETHANE): IRRITANT. **ACUTE EXPOSURE-** DIRECT CONTACT MAY CAUSE IRRITATION AND REDNESS. VAPORS ARE POORLY ABSORBED, BUT THE LIQUID, ESPECIALLY IF CONFINED UNDER AN IMPERMEABLE BARRIER MAY BE ABSORBED TO SOME EXTENT. THIS ALONE IS UNLIKELY TO RESULT IN TOXIC EFFECTS, BUT MAY ADD TO THE EFFECTS OF INHALATION EXPOSURE. **CHRONIC EXPOSURE-** REPEATED SKIN CONTACT MAY PRODUCE A DRY, SCALY, FISSURED DERMATITIS DUE TO THE DEFATTING PROPERTIES OF THE LIQUID, AND POSSIBLY BURNS.

CARBON DIOXIDE: **ACUTE EXPOSURE-** NO ADVERSE EFFECTS HAVE BEEN REPORTED FROM EXPOSURE TO THE GAS. DUE TO RAPID EVAPORATION, THE LIQUID OR SOLID MAY CAUSE FROSTBITE WITH REDNESS, TINGLING AND PAIN OR NUMBNESS. IN MORE SEVERE CASES, THE SKIN MAY BECOME HARD AND WHITE AND DEVELOP BLISTERS. **CHRONIC EXPOSURE-** NO ADVERSE EFFECTS ARE EXPECTED FROM EXPOSURE AT LOW LEVELS.

O-ISOPROPOXYPHENYL METHYLCARBAMATE: TOXIC. SEE INFORMATION ON CARBAMATES.

CARBAMATES: CHOLINESTERASE INHIBITOR. **ACUTE EXPOSURE-** SOME COMPOUNDS MAY CAUSE IRRITATION. LOCALIZED SWEATING AND FASCICULATIONS MAY OCCUR AT THE SITE OF CONTACT. IF SUFFICIENT AMOUNTS ARE ABSORBED THROUGH THE SKIN, OTHER EFFECTS OF CHOLINESTERASE INHIBITION MAY OCCUR AS DESCRIBED IN ACUTE INHALATION; SYMPTOMS MAY BE DELAYED FOR 2-3 HOURS, USUALLY NO MORE THAN 8 HOURS. **CHRONIC EXPOSURE-** REPEATED OR PROLONGED EXPOSURE MAY CAUSE EFFECTS AS DESCRIBED IN ACUTE EXPOSURE.

FIRST AID- REMOVE CONTAMINATED CLOTHING IMMEDIATELY. WASH CONTAMINATED AREAS WITH SOAP AND WATER FOLLOWED BY ALCOHOL (ARENA, POISONING, 4TH ED.). EMERGENCY PERSONNEL SHOULD WEAR GLOVES AND AVOID CONTAMINATION. TREAT RESPIRATORY DIFFICULTY WITH ARTIFICIAL RESPIRATION. GET MEDICAL ATTENTION IMMEDIATELY.

EYE CONTACT: DICHLOROMETHANE (METHYLENE CHLORIDE): IRRITANT. **ACUTE EXPOSURE-** VAPOR CONCENTRATIONS ABOVE 2000 PPM MAY CAUSE IRRITATION. DIRECT CONTACT MAY CAUSE PAIN AND EXTREME IRRITATION, BUT IT IS NOT LIKELY TO CAUSE SERIOUS INJURY. 10 MG APPLIED TO RABBIT EYES PRODUCED KERATITIS, IRITIS, INCREASED CORNEAL THICKNESS, AND INFLAMMATION OF THE CONJUNCTIVA AND EYELIDS WITH SOME EFFECTS LASTING UP TO TWO WEEKS. **CHRONIC EXPOSURE-** REPEATED OR PROLONGED EXPOSURE TO IRRITANTS MAY CAUSE CONJUNCTIVITIS.

METHYL CHLOROFORM (1,1,1-TRICHLOROETHANE): IRRITANT. **ACUTE EXPOSURE-** EXPOSURE TO 500 PPM MAY CAUSE IRRITATION AND REDNESS. DIRECT CONTACT WITH THE LIQUID MAY CAUSE TEMPORARY INJURY WITH COMPLETE RECOVERY EXPECTED IN 48 HOURS. DIRECT APPLICATION TO THE EYES OF RABBITS HAS CAUSED CONJUNCTIVAL IRRITATION, BUT NO CORNEAL DAMAGE. **CHRONIC EXPOSURE-** REPEATED OR PROLONGED CONTACT MAY CAUSE CONJUNCTIVITIS.

CARBON DIOXIDE: **ACUTE EXPOSURE-** AT HIGH CONCENTRATIONS IN AIR, CARBON DIOXIDE MAY CAUSE A STINGING SENSATION OF THE EYES. 200,000 PPM OF THE GAS MAY CAUSE IRRITATION. DUE TO RAPID EVAPORATION, THE LIQUID OR SOLID MAY CAUSE FROSTBITE WITH REDNESS, PAIN, AND BLURRED VISION. **CHRONIC EXPOSURE-** NO ADVERSE EFFECTS ARE EXPECTED FROM EXPOSURE TO LOW LEVELS.

O-ISOPROPOXYPHENYL METHYLCARBAMATE: SEE INFORMATION ON CARBAMATES.

CARBAMATES: CHOLINESTERASE INHIBITOR. **ACUTE EXPOSURE-** DIRECT CONTACT MAY CAUSE PAIN, HYPEREMIA, LACRIMATION, TWITCHING OF THE EYELIDS, MIOSIS, AND CILIARY MUSCLE SPASM WITH LOSS OF ACCOMODATION, BLURRED OR DIMMED VISION AND BROWACHE. SOMETIMES MYDRIASIS MAY OCCUR INSTEAD OF MIOSIS. WITH SUFFICIENT EXPOSURE, OTHER SYMPTOMS OF CHOLINESTERASE INHIBITION MAY OCCUR AS DESCRIBED IN ACUTE INHALATION. **CHRONIC EXPOSURE-** PROLONGED EXPOSURE MAY CAUSE EFFECTS AS DESCRIBED IN ACUTE EXPOSURE. SOME COMPOUNDS HAVE CAUSED TOXIC EFFECTS ON THE CRYSTALLINE LENS, CONJUNCTIVAL THICKENING AND OBSTRUCTION OF NASOLACRIMAL CANALS WHEN USED AS MIOTIC EYE DROPS.

FIRST AID- IRRIGATE EYES WITH WATER OR SALINE SOLUTION. IF SYMPTOMS OF POISONING OCCUR, TREAT RESPIRATORY DIFFICULTY WITH ARTIFICIAL RESPIRATION AND OXYGEN. OBSERVE PATIENT FOR AT LEAST 24-36 HOURS (GOSSELIN, CLINICAL TOXICOLOGY OF COMMERCIAL PRODUCTS, 5TH ED.). GET MEDICAL ATTENTION IMMEDIATELY. OXYGEN SHOULD BE ADMINISTERED BY QUALIFIED MEDICAL PERSONNEL.

INGESTION: DICHLOROMETHANE (METHYLENE CHLORIDE): NARCOTIC/CHEMICAL ASPHYXIANT. **ACUTE EXPOSURE-** MAY CAUSE RAPID, THEN SLOWED RESPIRATION, GLOTTAL AND PHARYNGEAL EDEMA, INTRAVASCULAR HEMOLYSIS WITH GROSS HEMATURIA, GASTROINTESTINAL ULCERATION AND HEMORRHAGE, AND CARBOXYHEMOGLOBINEMIA. THESE SYMPTOMS MAY PROGRESS RAPIDLY TO UNCONSCIOUSNESS AND LACK OF RESPONSE TO PAINFUL STIMULI. PHARYNGEAL EROSIONS MAY DISTURB THE SWALLOWING MECHANISM RESULTING IN ASPIRATION PNEUMONIA. IN ADDITION, SYMPTOMS OF CENTRAL NERVOUS SYSTEM DEPRESSION MAY OCCUR FOLLOWED BY CONVULSIONS AND PARESTHESIA OF THE EXTREMITIES. LARGE DOSES MAY CAUSE LIVER AND KIDNEY DAMAGE. THE ESTIMATED LETHAL DOSE FOR AN ADULT IS 25 GRAMS. **CHRONIC EXPOSURE-** REPEATED INGESTION BY RATS AND MICE RESULTED IN HISTOMORPHOLOGICAL CHANGES IN THE LIVER.

METHYL CHLOROFORM (1,1,1-TRICHLOROETHANE): NARCOTIC. **ACUTE EXPOSURE-** MAY CAUSE NAUSEA, VOMITING, DIARRHEA, GASTROINTESTINAL DISTURBANCES AND ABDOMINAL PAIN FOLLOWED BY CENTRAL NERVOUS SYSTEM DEPRESSION WITH HEADACHE, DIZZINESS, WEAKNESS, INCOORDINATION, MENTAL CONFUSION AND UNCONSCIOUSNESS. DEATH MAY OCCUR FROM CHRONIC RESPIRATORY FAILURE. OTHER SYMPTOMS AS DESCRIBED IN ACUTE INHALATION MAY ALSO OCCUR. MYOCARDIAL SENSITIZATION TO EPINEPHRINE AND SUBSEQUENT DEATH DUE TO CARDIAC ARREST MAY OCCUR. ASPIRATION MAY RESULT IN PULMONARY EDEMA OR CHEMICAL PNEUMONITIS. **CHRONIC EXPOSURE-** REPRODUCTIVE EFFECTS HAVE BEEN REPORTED IN ANIMALS.

CARBON DIOXIDE: **ACUTE EXPOSURE-** INGESTION OF A GAS IS UNLIKELY. IF THE LIQUID OR SOLID IS SWALLOWED, FROSTBITE DAMAGE OF THE LIPS, MOUTH AND MUCOUS MEMBRANES MAY OCCUR. **CHRONIC EXPOSURE-** NO DATA AVAILABLE.

O-ISOPROPOXYPHENYL METHYLCARBAMATE: TOXIC. CHRONIC INGESTION OF A DIETARY LEVEL OF 1,000 PPM FROM DAY 6 OF GESTATION TO DAY 15 OF LACTATION PRODUCED SLIGHTLY REDUCED WEIGHT GAIN OF THE DAMS AND TH BIRTH WEIGHT OF THE YOUNG. THE YOUNG ALSO SHOWED A SIGNIFICANT DELAY IN DEVELOPING, THE STARTLE REFLEX AND SHOWED SOME DIFFERENCES IN THE EEG. SOME HISTOLOGICAL CHANGES IN THE LIVER AND DEPRESSED CHOLINESTERASE ACTIVITY OF THE BRAIN AND BLOOD WERE OBSERVED IN A STUDY OF RATS FED A DIETARY LEVEL OF 1,000 AND 2,000 PPM. SEE INFORMATION ON CARBAMATES.

CARBAMATES: CHOLINESTERASE INHIBITOR. **ACUTE EXPOSURE-** WHEN INGESTED, THE FIRST EFFECTS MAY BE NAUSEA, VOMITING, ANOREXIA, ABDOMINAL CRAMPS, AND DIARRHEA. WITH ABSORPTION FROM THE GASTROINTESTINAL TRACT, THE OTHER EFFECTS OF CHOLINESTERASE INHIBITION AS DESCRIBED IN ACUTE INHALATION MAY OCCUR; SYMPTOMS MAY BEGIN WITHIN MINUTES OR BE DELAYED SEVERAL HOURS. **CHRONIC EXPOSURE-** REPEATED INGESTION MAY CAUSE EFFECTS AS DESCRIBED IN ACUTE EXPOSURE.

FIRST AID- IF PERSON IS ALERT AND RESPIRATION IS NOT DEPRESSED, GIVE SYRUP OF IPECAC FOLLOWED BY WATER (IF VOMITING OCCURS, KEEP HEAD BELOW HIPS TO PREVENT ASPIRATION). IF CONSCIOUSNESS LEVEL DECLINES OR VOMITING HAS NOT OCCURRED IN 15 MINUTES EMPTY STOMACH BY GASTRIC LAVAGE WITH THE AID OF CUFFED ENDOTRACHEAL TUBE USING ISOTONIC SALINE OR 5% SODIUM BICARBONATE FOLLOW WITH ACTIVATED CHARCOAL. ESTABLISH AND MAINTAIN AIRWAY. TREAT RESPIRATORY DIFFICULTY WITH ARTIFICIAL RESPIRATION AND OXYGEN. DO NOT GIVE MORPHINE, AMINOPHYLLINE, PHENOTHIAZINES, RESERPINE, FUROSEMIDE, OR ETHACRYNIC ACID (MORGAN, RECOGNITION AND MANAGEMENT OF PESTICIDE POISONINGS, 3RD ED.). TREAT SYMPTOMATICALLY AND SUPPORTIVELY. ADMINISTRATION OF OXYGEN AND LAVAGE MUST BE PERFORMED BY QUALIFIED MEDICAL PERSONNEL. GET MEDICAL ATTENTION IMMEDIATELY.

ANTIDOTE: BECAUSE IT IS DIFFICULT TO DETERMINE HOW CHEMICALS WILL INTERACT ONCE COMBINED IN A MIXTURE, AN ANTIDOTE IS NOT NORMALLY LISTED. HOWEVER DUE TO THE SEVERE POISONING POTENTIAL OF O-ISOPROPOXYPHENYL METHYLCARBAMATE, THE ANTIDOTE IS MENTIONED MERELY AS A POSSIBLE AID TO A QUALIFIED MEDICAL PERSON TO DETERMINE IF THE SYMPTOMS DISPLAYED BY THE POISONED VICTIM MERIT THE USE OF THE ANTIDOTE.

FOR CHOLINESTERASE INHIBITORS: ESTABLISH CLEAR AIRWAY AND TISSUE OXYGENATION BY ASPIRATION OF SECRETIONS, AND IF NECESSARY, BY ASSISTED PULMONARY VENTILATION WITH OXYGEN. IMPROVE TISSUE OXYGENATION AS MUCH AS POSSIBLE BEFORE ADMINISTERING ATROPINE TO MINIMIZE THE RISK OF VENTRICULAR FIBRILLATION. ADMINISTER ATROPINE SULFATE INTRAVENOUSLY, OR INTRAMUSCULARLY IF IV INJECTION IS NOT POSSIBLE. IN MODERATELY SEVERE POISONING ADMINISTER ATROPINE SULFATE, 0.4-2.0 MG REPEATED EVERY 15 MINUTES UNTIL ATROPINIZATION IS ACHIEVED (TACHYCARDIA, FLUSHING, DRY MOUTH, MYDRIASIS). MAINTAIN ATROPINIZATION BY REPEATED DOSES FOR 2-12 HOURS, OR LONGER, DEPENDING ON THE SEVERITY OF POISONING. THE APPEARANCE OF RALES IN THE LUNG BASES, MIOSIS, SALIVATION, NAUSEA, BRADYCARDIA, ARE ALL INDICATIONS OF INADEQUATE ATROPINIZATION. SEVERELY POISONED INDIVIDUALS MAY EXHIBIT REMARKABLE TOLERANCE TO ATROPINE; TWO OR MORE TIMES THE DOSAGES SUGGESTED ABOVE MAY BE NEEDED. PERSONS NOT POISONED OR ONLY SLIGHTLY POISONED, HOWEVER, MAY DEVELOP SIGNS OF ATROPINE TOXICITY FROM SUCH LARGE DOSAGES: FEVER, MUSCLE FIBRILLATIONS, AND DELIRIUM ARE THE MAIN SIGNS OF ATROPINE TOXICITY. IF THESE SIGNS APPEAR WHILE THE PATIENT IS FULLY ATROPINIZED, ATROPINE ADMINISTRATION SHOULD BE DISCONTINUED, AT LEAST TEMPORARILY. OBSERVE TREATED PATIENTS CLOSELY AT LEAST 24 HOURS TO INSURE THAT SYMPTOMS (POSSIBLY PULMONARY EDEMA) DO NOT RECUR AS ATROPINIZATION WEARS OFF. IN VERY SEVERE POISONINGS, METABOLIC DISPOSITION OF TOXICANT MAY REQUIRE SEVERAL HOURS OR DAYS DURING WHICH ATROPINIZATION MUST BE MAINTAINED. MARKEDLY LOWER LEVELS OF URINARY METABOLITES INDICATE THAT ATROPINE DOSAGE CAN BE TAPERED OFF. AS DOSAGE IS REDUCED, CHECK THE LUNG BASES FREQUENTLY FOR RALES. IF RALES ARE HEARD OR OTHER SYMPTOMS RETURN, RE-ESTABLISH ATROPINIZATION PROMPTLY (MORGAN, RECOGNITION AND MANAGEMENT OF PESTICIDE POISONINGS, 3RD ED.). ADMINISTRATION OF ANTIDOTE MUST BE PERFORMED BY QUALIFIED MEDICAL PERSONNEL.

REACTIVITY

REACTIVITY: STABLE UNDER NORMAL TEMPERATURES AND PRESSURES.

INCOMPATIBILITIES: DICHLOROMETHANE (METHYLENE CHLORIDE): ALKALI METALS: POSSIBLE EXPLOSIVE REACTION. ALUMINUM: VIOLENT, UNCONTROLLABLE REACTION ABOVE 95 C. CAUSTICS (STRONG): VIGOROUS, POSSIBLY VIOLENT REACTION. COPPER: MAY CORRODE AT ELEVATED TEMPERATURES IN THE PRESENCE OF MOISTURE. DINITROGEN PENTOXIDE: POSSIBLE EXPLOSION.

DINITROGEN TETROXIDE: FORMS SHOCK-SENSITIVE MIXTURE. IRON: MAY CORRODE AT ELEVATED TEMPERATURES IN THE PRESENCE OF MOISTURE. LITHIUM: FORMS SHOCK-SENSITIVE MIXTURE. MAGNESIUM: POSSIBLE EXPLOSION. NICKEL: MAY CORRODE AT ELEVATED TEMPERATURES IN THE PRESENCE OF MOISTURE. NITRIC ACID: EXOTHERMIC REACTION YIELDING DETONABLE SOLUTION. OXIDIZERS (STRONG): FIRE AND EXPLOSION HAZARD. OXYGEN (LIQUID): EXPLOSIVE REACTION ON IGNITION. PLASTICS, RUBBER, AND COATINGS: MAY BE ATTACKED. POTASSIUM: EXPLOSIVE REACTION. POTASSIUM HYDROXIDE + N-METHYL-N-NITROSO UREA: POSSIBLE EXPLOSION. POTASSIUM TERT-BUTOXIDE: IGNITION REACTION. SODIUM: FORMS SHOCK-SENSITIVE MIXTURE. SODIUM-POTASSIUM ALLOY: FORMS SHOCK-SENSITIVE MIXTURE. STAINLESS STEEL: MAY CORRODE AT ELEVATED TEMPERATURES IN THE PRESENCE OF MOISTURE. TITANIUM: POSSIBLE VIOLENT REACTION. ZINC: POSSIBLE VIOLENT REACTION.

METHYL CHLOROFORM (1,1,1-TRICHLOROETHANE): ACETONE: EXOTHERMIC REACTION. ALKALI (STRONG): POSSIBLE VIOLENT REACTION. ALUMINUM AND ALLOYS: MAY DECOMPOSE VIOLENTLY. BARIUM: FIRE AND EXPLOSION HAZARD. MAGNESIUM: VIOLENT DECOMPOSITION WITH EVOLUTION OF HYDROGEN CHLORIDE. METALS (POWDERED): FIRE AND EXPLOSION HAZARD. NITROGEN TETROXIDE: FORMS EXPLOSIVE MIXTURE. OXIDIZERS (STRONG): POSSIBLE VIOLENT REACTION. OXYGEN (GAS): POSSIBLE EXPLOSION WHEN HEATED @ 100 C. OXYGEN (LIQUID): POSSIBLE VIOLENT EXPLOSION. POTASH: FORMS FLAMMABLE OR EXPLOSIVE PRODUCT. POTASSIUM AND ALLOYS: FORMS SHOCK-SENSITIVE MIXTURE. POTASSIUM HYDROXIDE: FORMATION OF SPONTANEOUSLY FLAMMABLE PRODUCT. RUBBER, PLASTICS, COATINGS: MAY BE ATTACKED. SODIUM AND ALLOYS: FIRE AND EXPLOSION HAZARD. SODIUM HYDROXIDE: FORMS SPONTANEOUSLY FLAMMABLE PRODUCT. SODIUM-POTASSIUM ALLOY: POSSIBLE EXPLOSION. TIN AND ALLOYS: INCOMPATIBLE. ZINC AND ALLOYS: INCOMPATIBLE.

CARBON DIOXIDE: ACRYLALDEHYDE: EXOTHERMIC POLYMERIZATION. BARIUM PEROXIDE: INCANDESCENT REACTION. CESIUM OXIDE: IGNITION. DIETHYL MAGNESIUM: IGNITION. ETHYLENEIMINE: EXPLOSIVE POLYMERIZATION. HYDRAZINE: DECOMPOSITION. METAL ACETYLIDES: IGNITION OR INCANDESCENCE. METAL HYDRIDES: REDUCTION REACTION. METALS: DUSTS OF MANY METALS SUSPENDED IN CARBON DIOXIDE ATMOSPHERES ARE IGNITABLE AND EXPLOSIVE; SOME BULK METALS WILL BURN IN THE GAS AT ELEVATED TEMPERATURES. POTASSIUM: MIXTURES OF THE SOLIDS ARE IMPACT-SENSITIVE. POTASSIUM-SODIUM ALLOY: MIXTURES OF THE SOLIDS ARE IMPACT-SENSITIVE. SODIUM: MIXTURES OF THE SOLIDS ARE IMPACT-SENSITIVE. SODIUM PEROXIDE: HIGHLY EXOTHERMIC REACTION; MAY BE EXPLOSIVE IN THE PRESENCE OF METALS. O-ISOPROPOXYPHENYL METHYLCARBAMATE: ALKALINE CONDITIONS: IS UNSTABLE.

DECOMPOSITION: THERMAL DECOMPOSITION PRODUCTS MAY INCLUDE TOXIC AND CORROSIVE FUMES OF CHLORIDES AND PHOSGENE, AND TOXIC OXIDES OF CARBON.

POLYMERIZATION: HAZARDOUS POLYMERIZATION HAS NOT BEEN REPORTED TO OCCUR UNDER NORMAL TEMPERATURES AND PRESSURES.

STORAGE AND DISPOSAL

OBSERVE ALL FEDERAL, STATE AND LOCAL REGULATIONS WHEN STORING OR DISPOSING OF THIS SUBSTANCE. FOR ASSISTANCE, CONTACT THE DISTRICT DIRECTOR OF THE ENVIRONMENTAL PROTECTION AGENCY.

****STORAGE****

STORE AWAY FROM INCOMPATIBLE SUBSTANCES.
DO NOT STORE AT TEMPERATURES ABOVE 120 F.

CONDITIONS TO AVOID

DO NOT PERMIT PHYSICAL DAMAGE OR OVERHEATING OF CONTAINERS. CONTENTS ARE UNDER PRESSURE; CONTAINERS MAY VIOLENTLY RUPTURE AND TRAVEL A CONSIDERABLE DISTANCE.
DO NOT PUNCTURE OR INCINERATE AEROSOL CONTAINER.

SPILL AND LEAK PROCEDURES

OCCUPATIONAL SPILL: STOP LEAK IF YOU CAN DO IT WITHOUT RISK. KEEP UNNECESSARY PEOPLE AWAY; ISOLATE HAZARD AREA AND DENY ENTRY.
REPORTABLE QUANTITY (RQ): THE SUPERFUND AMENDMENTS AND REAUTHORIZATION ACT (SARA) SECTION 304 REQUIRES THAT A RELEASE EQUAL TO OR GREATER THAN THE REPORTABLE QUANTITY ESTABLISHED FOR THAT SUBSTANCE BE IMMEDIATELY REPORTED TO THE LOCAL EMERGENCY PLANNING COMMITTEE AND THE STATE EMERGENCY RESPONSE COMMISSION (40 CFR 355.40). IF THE RELEASE OF THIS SUBSTANCE IS REPORTABLE UNDER CERCLA SECTION 103, THE NATIONAL RESPONSE CENTER MUST BE NOTIFIED IMMEDIATELY AT (800) 424-8802 OR (202) 426-2675 IN THE METROPOLITAN WASHINGTON, D.C. AREA (40 CFR 302.6).

PROTECTIVE EQUIPMENT

VENTILATION: PROVIDE LOCAL EXHAUST OR PROCESS ENCLOSURE VENTILATION TO MEET PUBLISHED EXPOSURE LIMITS.

RESPIRATOR: THE FOLLOWING RESPIRATORS ARE RECOMMENDED BASED ON INFORMATION FOUND IN THE PHYSICAL DATA, TOXICITY AND HEALTH EFFECTS SECTIONS. THEY ARE RANKED IN ORDER FROM MINIMUM TO MAXIMUM RESPIRATORY PROTECTION. THE SPECIFIC RESPIRATOR SELECTED MUST BE BASED ON CONTAMINATION LEVELS FOUND IN THE WORK PLACE, MUST NOT EXCEED THE WORKING LIMITS OF THE RESPIRATOR AND BE JOINTLY APPROVED BY THE NATIONAL INSTITUTE FOR OCCUPATIONAL SAFETY AND HEALTH AND THE MINE SAFETY AND HEALTH ADMINISTRATION (NIOSH-MSHA).
TYPE 'C' SUPPLIED-AIR RESPIRATOR WITH A FULL FACEPIECE OPERATED IN PRESSURE-DEMAND OR OTHER POSITIVE PRESSURE MODE OR WITH A FULL FACEPIECE, HELMET OR HOOD OPERATED IN CONTINOUS-FLOW MODE.
SELF-CONTAINED BREATHING APPARATUS WITH A FULL FACEPIECE OPERATED IN PRESSURE-DEMAND OR OTHER POSITIVE PRESSURE MODE.
FOR FIREFIGHTING AND OTHER IMMEDIATELY DANGEROUS TO LIFE OR HEALTH CONDITIONS:
SELF-CONTAINED BREATHING APPARATUS WITH FULL FACEPIECE OPERATED IN PRESSURE-DEMAND OR OTHER POSITIVE PRESSURE MODE.
SUPPLIED-AIR RESPIRATOR WITH FULL FACEPIECE AND OPERATED IN PRESSURE-DEMAND OR OTHER POSITIVE PRESSURE MODE IN COMBINATION WITH AN AUXILIARY SELF-CONTAINED BREATHING APPARATUS OPERATED IN PRESSURE-DEMAND OR OTHER POSITIVE PRESSURE MODE.

CLOTHING: EMPLOYEE MUST WEAR APPROPRIATE PROTECTIVE (IMPERVIOUS) CLOTHING AND EQUIPMENT TO PREVENT ANY POSSIBILITY OF SKIN CONTACT WITH THIS SUBSTANCE.

GLOVES: EMPLOYEE MUST WEAR APPROPRIATE PROTECTIVE GLOVES TO PREVENT CONTACT WITH THIS SUBSTANCE.

EYE PROTECTION: EMPLOYEE MUST WEAR SPLASH-PROOF OR DUST-RESISTANT SAFETY GOGGLES AND A FACESHIELD TO PREVENT CONTACT WITH THIS SUBSTANCE.
EMERGENCY WASH FACILITIES: WHERE THERE IS ANY POSSIBILITY THAT AN EMPLOYEE'S EYES AND/OR SKIN MAY BE EXPOSED TO THIS SUBSTANCE, THE EMPLOYER SHOULD PROVIDE AN EYE WASH FOUNTAIN AND QUICK DRENCH SHOWER WITHIN THE IMMEDIATE WORK AREA FOR EMERGENCY USE.

AUTHORIZED BY- OCCUPATIONAL HEALTH SERVICES, INC.
CREATION DATE: 10/05/89 ***REVISION DATE:*** 07/12/90

MATERIAL SAFETY DATA SHEET

OCCUPATIONAL HEALTH SERVICES, INC.
AGRICULTURE AND PESTICIDE DIVISION
450 SEVENTH AVENUE, SUITE 2407
NEW YORK, NEW YORK 10123
1-800-445-MSDS OR (212) 967-1100

EMERGENCY CONTACT:
JOHN S. BRANSFORD, JR. (615) 292-1180

SUBSTANCE IDENTIFICATION

CAS-NUMBER 1330-20-7

SUBSTANCE: XYLENE

TRADE NAMES/SYNONYMS: BENZENE, DIMETHYL-; DILAN; DIMETHYLBENZENE; XYLOL; HUMISEAL THINNER NO.33 (HUMISEAL DIV.); HUMISEAL THINNER NO.SP 420 (HUMISEAL DIV.); SOLVESSO XYLENE (HUMBLE OIL AND REFINING COMPANY); TT-X-9166 REDUCER (ADVANCED COATINGS AND CHEMICALS); DYNACHEM (R) DEVELOPER DCR (THIOKOL/DYNACHEM CORPORATION); THINNER 2000 (KOP-COAT); SOL 9050 XYLENE (CHEMTECH INDUSTRIES, INC.); HUMISEAL THINNER NO. 521 (M.W. RIEDEL AND COMPANY); RCRA U239; STCC 4904350; UN 1307; C8H10; PST25150

CHEMICAL FAMILY: HYDROCARBON, AROMATIC

MOLECULAR FORMULA: C6-H4-(C-H3)2

MOLECULAR WEIGHT: 106.16

CERCLA RATINGS (SCALE 0-3): HEALTH=2 FIRE=3 REACTIVITY=0 PERSISTENCE=1

NFPA RATINGS (SCALE 0-4): HEALTH=2 FIRE=3 REACTIVITY=0

COMPONENTS AND CONTAMINANTS

COMPONENT: XYLENE (O-, M-, P-ISOMERS) ***PERCENT:*** 100
CAS# 1330-20-7

OTHER CONTAMINANTS: NONE

EXPOSURE LIMITS: XYLENE: 100 PPM (435 MG/M3) OSHA TWA; 150 PPM (655 MG/M3) OSHA STEL 100 PPM (435 MG/M3) ACGIH TWA; 150 PPM (655 MG/M3) ACGIH STEL 100 PPM (435 MG/M3) NIOSH RECOMMENDED 10 HOUR TWA; 200

PPM (870 MG/M3) NIOSH RECOMMENDED 10 MINUTE CEILING
1000 POUNDS CERCLA SECTION 103 REPORTABLE QUANTITY SUBJECT TO SARA SECTION 313 ANNUAL TOXIC CHEMICAL RELEASE REPORTING

PHYSICAL DATA

DESCRIPTION: LIGHT COLORED OR COLORLESS MOBILE LIQUID WITH AN AROMATIC ODOR.
BOILING POINT: 280-291 F (138-144 C) ***MELTING POINT:*** -54-55 F (-48-13 C)
SPECIFIC GRAVITY: 0.8611-0.8802 ***VOLATILITY:*** 100%
VAPOR PRESSURE: 7-9 MMHG @ 20 C ***EVAPORATION RATE:*** (BUTYL ACETATE = 1) 0.6
SOLUBILITY IN WATER: 0.00003% ***ODOR THRESHOLD:*** 0.3 PPM ***VAPOR DENSITY:*** 3.7
SOLVENT SOLUBILITY: SOLUBLE IN ALCOHOL, ETHER, ACETONE, PETROLEUM ETHER, BENZENE, CARBON TETRACHLORIDE, ORGANIC SOLVENTS.

FIRE AND EXPLOSION DATA

FIRE AND EXPLOSION HAZARD: DANGEROUS FIRE HAZARD WHEN EXPOSED TO HEAT OR FLAME.
DUE TO LOW ELECTROCONDUCTIVITY OF THE SUBSTANCE, FLOW OR AGITATION MAY GENERATE ELECTROSTATIC CHARGES RESULTING IN SPARKS WITH POSSIBLE IGNITION.
VAPORS ARE HEAVIER THAN AIR AND MAY TRAVEL A CONSIDERABLE DISTANCE TO A SOURCE OF IGNITION AND FLASH BACK.
VAPOR-AIR MIXTURES ARE EXPLOSIVE.
FLASH POINT: 81-90 F (27-32 C) (CC) ***UPPER EXPLOSIVE LIMIT:*** 7.0%
LOWER EXPLOSIVE LIMIT: 1.0% ***AUTOIGNITION TEMP.:*** 867-984 F (464-529 C)
FLAMMABILITY CLASS(OSHA): IC
FIREFIGHTING MEDIA: DRY CHEMICAL, CARBON DIOXIDE, HALON, WATER SPRAY OR STANDARD FOAM (1987 EMERGENCY RESPONSE GUIDEBOOK, DOT P 5800.4).
FOR LARGER FIRES, USE WATER SPRAY, FOG OR STANDARD FOAM (1987 EMERGENCY RESPONSE GUIDEBOOK, DOT P 5800.4).
FIREFIGHTING: MOVE CONTAINER FROM FIRE AREA IF POSSIBLE. COOL FIRE-EXPOSED CONTAINERS WITH WATER FROM SIDE UNTIL WELL AFTER FIRE IS OUT. STAY AWAY FROM STORAGE TANK ENDS. FOR MASSIVE FIRE IN STORAGE AREA, USE UNMANNED HOSE HOLDER OR MONITOR NOZZLES, ELSE WITHDRAW FROM AREA AND LET FIRE BURN. WITHDRAW IMMEDIATELY IN CASE OF RISING SOUND FROM VENTING SAFETY DEVICE OR ANY DISCOLORATION OF STORAGE TANK DUE TO FIRE (1987 EMERGENCY RESPONSE GUIDEBOOK, DOT P 5800.4, GUIDE PAGE 27).
EXTINGUISH ONLY IF FLOW CAN BE STOPPED; USE WATER IN FLOODING AMOUNTS AS FOG, SOLID STREAMS MAY SPREAD FIRE. COOL CONTAINERS WITH FLOODING QUANTITIES OF WATER, APPLY FROM AS FAR A DISTANCE AS POSSIBLE. AVOID BREATHING TOXIC VAPORS, KEEP UPWIND.
WATER MAY BE INEFFECTIVE (NFPA 325M, FIRE HAZARD PROPERTIES OF FLAMMABLE LIQUIDS, GASES, AND VOLATILE SOLIDS, 1984)

TRANSPORTATION DATA

DEPARTMENT OF TRANSPORTATION HAZARD CLASSIFICATION 49 CFR 172.101: FLAMMABLE LIQUID
DEPARTMENT OF TRANSPORTATION LABELING REQUIREMENTS 49 CFR 172.101 AND SUBPART E: FLAMMABLE LIQUID
DEPARTMENT OF TRANSPORTATION PACKAGING REQUIREMENTS: 49 CFR 173.119 EXCEPTIONS: 49 CFR 173.118

TOXICITY

XYLENE: IRRITATION DATA: 200 PPM EYE-HUMAN; 87 MG EYE-RABBIT MILD; 5 MG/24 HOURS EYE-RABBIT SEVERE; 100% SKIN-RABBIT MODERATE; 500 MG/24 HOURS SKIN-RABBIT MODERATE. TOXICITY DATA: 10000 PPM/6 HOURS INHALATION-MAN LCLO; 200 PPM INHALATION-HUMAN TCLO; 5000 PPM/4 HOURS INHALATION-RAT LC50; 450 PPM INHALATION-GUINEA PIG LCLO; 50 MG/KG ORAL-HUMAN LDLO; 4300 MG/KG ORAL-RAT LD50; 1700 MG/KG SUBCUTANEOUS-RAT LD50; 129 MG/KG INTRAVENOUS-RABBIT LDLO; 2 GM/KG INTRAPERITONEAL-MAMMAL LDLO; 2459 MG/KG INTRAPERITONEAL-RAT LD50; 1548 MG/KG INTRAPERITONEAL-MOUSE LD50; 2000 MG/KG INTRAPERITONEAL-GUINEA PIG LDLO; REPRODUCTIVE EFFECTS DATA (RTECS). CARCINOGEN STATUS: NONE. LOCAL EFFECTS: IRRITANT- INHALATION, SKIN, EYE. ACUTE TOXICITY LEVEL: MODERATELY TOXIC BY INHALATION, INGESTION. TARGET EFFECTS: CENTRAL NERVOUS SYSTEM DEPRESSANT. POISONING MAY ALSO AFFECT THE NERVOUS SYSTEM, LIVER AND KIDNEYS. AT INCREASED RISK FROM EXPOSURE: PREGNANT WOMEN. ADDITIONAL INFORMATION: CONSUMPTION OF ALCOHOLIC BEVERAGES MAY ENHANCE THE TOXIC EFFECTS. STIMULANTS SUCH AS EPINEPHRINE OR EPHEDRINE MAY INDUCE VENTRICULAR FIBRILLATION.

HEALTH EFFECTS AND FIRST AID

INHALATION: XYLENE: IRRITANT/NARCOTIC. 1000 PPM IMMEDIATELY DANGEROUS TO LIFE OR HEALTH. **ACUTE EXPOSURE-** IRRITATION OF THE UPPER RESPIRATORY TRACT MAY OCCUR AT 200 PPM. EXPOSURE TO HIGHER CONCENTRATIONS MAY CAUSE MORE SEVERE IRRITATION AND INITIAL CENTRAL NERVOUS SYSTEM EXCITATION FOLLOWED BY DEPRESSION. SIGNS AND SYMPTOMS MAY INCLUDE RESPIRATORY DIFFICULTY AND SUBSTERNAL PAIN, TRANSIENT EUPHORIA AND EMOTIONAL LABILITY, HEADACHE, NAUSEA, VOMITING, ANOREXIA, ABDOMINAL PAIN, DIZZINESS, DROWSINESS, ATAXIA, AND STAGGERING. THERE MAY BE SALIVATION, SLURRED SPEECH, BLURRED VISION, NYSTAGMUS, TINNITUS, TREMORS, CONFUSION, AND FLUSHING OF THE FACE AND A FEELING OF INCREASED BODY HEAT. IN SEVERE EXPOSURES, THERE MAY BE STUPOR, ANESTHESIA, UNCONSCIOUSNESS, AND COMA WHICH MAY BE PUNCTUATED BY EPISODES OF NEUROIRRITABILITY, BUT RARELY FRANK CONVULSIONS, EXCEPT IN TERMINAL ASPHYXIA. LIVER AND KIDNEY DAMAGE MAY OCCUR, BUT ARE USUALLY MILD AND TRANSIENT. A GROUP OF SUBJECTS WHO INHALED 12.3 UMOL/L OF XYLENE WHILE EXERCISING BECAME SIGNIFICANTLY IMPAIRED ON 3 NEUROPSYCHOLOGICAL TESTS. EXPOSURE OF 3 PAINTERS TO APPROXIMATELY 10,000 PPM FOR 18.5 HOURS RESULTED IN 1 DEATH FROM PULMONARY EDEMA AND PETECHIAL BRAIN HEMORRHAGE. BOTH SURVIVORS WERE UNCONSCIOUS FOR 19-24 HOURS AND EXPERIENCED RETROGRADE AMNESIA, HYPOTHERMIA, AND LUNG CONGESTION. RENAL AND HEPATIC IMPAIRMENT ALSO DEVELOPED. COMPLETE RECOVERY TOOK 15 DAYS. HIGH CONCENTRATIONS MAY CAUSE DEATH FROM SUDDEN VENTRICULAR FIBRILLATION, BUT MORE FREQUENTLY DEATH OCCURS FROM RESPIRATORY ARREST. **CHRONIC EXPOSURE-** REPEATED OR PROLONGED INHALATION OF VAPORS ABOVE 200 PPM MAY CAUSE NAUSEA, VOMITING, ABDOMINAL PAIN, AND ANOREXIA. OTHER COMMON COMPLAINTS INCLUDE HEADACHE, FATIGUE, LASSITUDE, IRRITABILITY, BREATHING DIFFICULTIES, AND FLATULENCE. EFFECTS ON THE NERVOUS SYSTEM MAY RESULT IN EXCITATION, FOLLOWED BY DEPRESSION, PARESTHESIAS, TREMORS, APPREHENSION, IMPAIRED MEMORY, INSOMNIA, VERTIGO, AND TINNITUS. EFFECTS ON REACTION TIME, MANUAL COORDINATION, BODY BALANCE AND EEG OCCURRED WITH REPEATED EXPOSURE TO 90 PPM OF M-XYLENE. SWEETISH TASTE IN THE MOUTH, DRY NOSE AND THROAT, STRONG THIRST, MUCOSAL HEMORRHAGE, AND ANEMIA HAVE BEEN REPORTED. EFFECTS ON THE LIVER, KIDNEY, CARDIOVASCULAR SYSTEM, AND THE BONE MARROW HAVE ALSO BEEN REPORTED, ALTHOUGH THE LATTER HAS BEEN QUESTIONED. EXPOSURE OF RABBITS TO 1150 PPM FOR 40-55 DAYS RESULTED IN A REVERSIBLE DECREASE IN THE RED AND WHITE CELL COUNTS AND AN INCREASE IN THE PLATELETS. ONE CASE OF AN APPARENT EPILEPTIFORM SEIZURE FOLLOWING A RELATIVELY BRIEF EXPOSURE HAS OCCURRED. WOMEN MAY DEVELOP MENSTRUAL DISORDERS, SUCH AS MENORRHAGIA OR METRORRHAGIA, INFERTILITY, AND PATHOLOGICAL PREGNANCY CONDITIONS INCLUDING TOXICOSIS, DANGER OF MISCARRIAGE, AND HEMORRHAGING DURING DELIVERY. REPEATED EXPOSURE OF PREGNANT MICE, RATS AND RABBITS TO THE INDIVIDUAL OR THE MIXED ISOMERS HAS RESULTED IN MATERNAL EFFECTS AND EFFECTS ON FERTILITY, ON THE EMBRYO OR FETUS, AND SPECIFIC DEVELOPMENTAL ABNORMALITIES. INCLUDED AMONG THESE EFFECTS ARE FETAL DEATH, FETOTOXICITY, PRE- AND POST-IMPLANTATION MORTALITY, ABORTION, CRANIOFACIAL AND MUSCULOSKELETAL ABNORMALITIES, AND EXTRA EMBRYONIC STRUCTURES.
FIRST AID- REMOVE FROM EXPOSURE AREA TO FRESH AIR IMMEDIATELY. IF BREATHING HAS STOPPED, PERFORM ARTIFICIAL RESPIRATION. KEEP PERSON WARM AND AT REST. TREAT SYMPTOMATICALLY AND SUPPORTIVELY. GET MEDICAL ATTENTION IMMEDIATELY.

SKIN CONTACT: XYLENE: IRRITANT. **ACUTE EXPOSURE-** LIQUID XYLENE IS A DEFATTING AGENT AND MAY CAUSE A BURNING SENSATION, DRYING, VASODILATION, ERYTHEMA, AND POSSIBLY BLISTERING. THE LIQUID IS READILY ABSORBED THROUGH INTACT OR BROKEN SKIN AT A RATE OF APPROXIMATELY 4-10 MG/CM2/HOUR, BUT SYSTEMIC EFFECTS HAVE NOT BEEN REPORTED. **CHRONIC EXPOSURE-** REPEATED OR PROLONGED CONTACT MAY CAUSE DEFATTING OF THE SKIN WITH DRYING, ERYTHEMA, CRACKING, THICKENING AND BLISTERING. REPEATED APPLICATION OF 95% XYLENE TO RABBIT SKIN CAUSED MODERATE TO MARKED IRRITATION WITH ERYTHEMA AND MODERATE NECROSIS. ONE CASE OF ALLERGIC CONTACT URTICARIA HAS BEEN REPORTED.
FIRST AID- REMOVE CONTAMINATED CLOTHING AND SHOES IMMEDIATELY. WASH AFFECTED AREA WITH SOAP OR MILD DETERGENT AND LARGE AMOUNTS OF WATER UNTIL NO EVIDENCE OF CHEMICAL REMAINS (APPROXIMATELY 15-20 MINUTES). GET MEDICAL ATTENTION IMMEDIATELY.

EYE CONTACT: XYLENE: IRRITANT. **ACUTE EXPOSURE-** 200 PPM HAS CAUSED CONJUNCTIVAL IRRITATION IN HUMANS; AT HIGHER CONCENTRATIONS, IRRITATION MAY BE SEVERE. VAPOR EXPOSURE HAS ALSO CAUSED TEARING AND PHOTOPHOBIA. AN ACCIDENTAL SPLASH IN THE HUMAN EYE CAUSED TRANSIENT SUPERFICIAL DAMAGE WITH RAPID RECOVERY, ALTHOUGH REVERSIBLE CORNEAL BURNS HAVE ALSO BEEN REPORTED. **CHRONIC EXPOSURE-** REPEATED OR PROLONGED EXPOSURE TO HIGH VAPOR CONCENTRATIONS MAY CAUSE A BURNING SENSATION, CONJUNCTIVITIS AND BLURRED VISION; REVERSIBLE VACUOLAR, EPITHELIAL KERATOPATHY HAS BEEN REPORTED IN SOME WORKERS.

FIRST AID- WASH EYES IMMEDIATELY WITH LARGE AMOUNTS OF WATER OR NORMAL SALINE, OCCASIONALLY LIFTING UPPER AND LOWER LIDS, UNTIL NO EVIDENCE OF CHEMICAL REMAINS (APPROXIMATELY 15-20 MINUTES). GET MEDICAL ATTENTION IMMEDIATELY.

INGESTION: XYLENE: NARCOTIC. **ACUTE EXPOSURE**- MAY CAUSE A BURNING SENSATION IN THE MOUTH AND STOMACH, SALIVATION, SEVERE GASTROINTESTINAL DISTRESS WITH NAUSEA AND VOMITING, POSSIBLY HEMATEMESIS, AND TOXIC EFFECTS INCLUDING SIGNS OF CENTRAL NERVOUS SYSTEM DEPRESSION AND OTHER SYMPTOMS AS IN ACUTE INHALATION, INCLUDING VENTRICULAR FIBRILLATION AND LIVER AND KIDNEY INJURY. INGESTION OF SMALL QUANTITIES OF 90% XYLENE PLUS TOLUENE PRODUCED URINARY DEXTROSE AND UROBILINOGEN EXCRETION WITH TOXIC HEPATITIS, WHICH WAS REVERSIBLE IN 20 DAYS. A DOSE OF 15-30 MILLILITERS (ABOUT 1/2-1 OUNCE) IS THE EXPECTED HUMAN LETHAL DOSE. WITH ASPIRATION OF EVEN A FEW MILLILITERS INTO THE LUNGS, SEVERE COUGHING, DISTRESS, CHEMICAL PNEUMONITIS, RAPIDLY DEVELOPING PULMONARY EDEMA, AND HEMORRHAGE MAY OCCUR. **CHRONIC EXPOSURE**- NO DATA AVAILABLE ON THE ORTHO-ISOMER. REPEATED INGESTION OF THE MIXED, META-, OR PARA-ISOMERS BY PREGNANT MICE RESULTED IN EFFECTS ON FERTILITY, ON THE EMBRYO OR FETUS, OR SPECIFIC DEVELOPMENTAL ABNORMALITIES. INCLUDED AMONG THESE EFFECTS WERE FETOTOXICITY, LITTER SIZE, CRANIOFACIAL AND MUSCULOSKELETAL SYSTEM ABNORMALITIES, AND POST-IMPLANTATION MORTALITY.

FIRST AID- EXTREME CARE MUST BE USED TO PREVENT ASPIRATION. GASTRIC LAVAGE WITH A CUFFED ENDOTRACHEAL TUBE IN PLACE TO PREVENT FURTHER ASPIRATION SHOULD BE DONE WITHIN 15 MINUTES. IN THE ABSENCE OF DEPRESSION OR CONVULSIONS OR IMPAIRED GAG REFLEX, EMESIS CAN ALSO BE INDUCED USING SYRUP OF IPECAC WITHOUT INCREASING THE HAZARD OF ASPIRATION (DREISBACH, HANDBOOK OF POISONING, 12TH ED.). TREAT SYMPTOMATICALLY AND SUPPORTIVELY. GASTRIC LAVAGE SHOULD BE PERFORMED BY QUALIFIED MEDICAL PERSONNEL. GET MEDICAL ATTENTION IMMEDIATELY.

ANTIDOTE: NO SPECIFIC ANTIDOTE. TREAT SYMPTOMATICALLY AND SUPPORTIVELY.

REACTIVITY

REACTIVITY: STABLE UNDER NORMAL TEMPERATURES AND PRESSURES.

INCOMPATIBILITIES: XYLENE: NITRIC ACID: EXOTHERMIC REACTION. OXIDIZERS (STRONG): FIRE AND EXPLOSION HAZARD. PLASTICS, RUBBER, COATINGS: MAY BE ATTACKED. SULFURIC ACID: EXOTHERMIC REACTION.

DECOMPOSITION: THERMAL DECOMPOSITION PRODUCTS MAY INCLUDE TOXIC OXIDES OF CARBON.

POLYMERIZATION: HAZARDOUS POLYMERIZATION HAS NOT BEEN REPORTED TO OCCUR UNDER NORMAL TEMPERATURES AND PRESSURES.

STORAGE AND DISPOSAL

OBSERVE ALL FEDERAL, STATE AND LOCAL REGULATIONS WHEN STORING OR DISPOSING OF THIS SUBSTANCE. FOR ASSISTANCE, CONTACT THE DISTRICT DIRECTOR OF THE ENVIRONMENTAL PROTECTION AGENCY.

****STORAGE****

STORE IN ACCORDANCE WITH 29 CFR 1910.106.

BONDING AND GROUNDING: SUBSTANCES WITH LOW ELECTROCONDUCTIVITY, WHICH MAY BE IGNITED BY ELECTROSTATIC SPARKS, SHOULD BE STORED IN CONTAINERS WHICH MEET THE BONDING AND GROUNDING GUIDELINES SPECIFIED IN NFPA 77-1983, RECOMMENDED PRACTICE ON STATIC ELECTRICITY.

PROTECT AGAINST PHYSICAL DAMAGE. OUTSIDE OR DETACHED STORAGE IS PREFERABLE. INSIDE STORAGE SHOULD BE IN A STANDARD FLAMMABLE LIQUIDS STORAGE ROOM OR CABINET. SEPARATE FROM OXIDIZING MATERIALS (NFPA 49, HAZARDOUS CHEMICALS DATA, 1975).

STORE AWAY FROM INCOMPATIBLE SUBSTANCES.

****DISPOSAL****

DISPOSAL MUST BE IN ACCORDANCE WITH STANDARDS APPLICABLE TO GENERATORS OF HAZARDOUS WASTE, 40CFR 262. EPA HAZARDOUS WASTE NUMBER U239.

CONDITIONS TO AVOID

AVOID CONTACT WITH HEAT, SPARKS, FLAMES, OR OTHER SOURCES OF IGNITION. VAPORS MAY BE EXPLOSIVE. AVOID OVERHEATING OF CONTAINERS; CONTAINERS MAY VIOLENTLY RUPTURE IN HEAT OF FIRE. AVOID CONTAMINATION OF WATER SOURCES.

SPILL AND LEAK PROCEDURES

SOIL SPILL: DIG A HOLDING AREA SUCH AS A PIT, POND OR LAGOON TO CONTAIN SPILL AND DIKE SURFACE FLOW USING BARRIER OF SOIL, SANDBAGS, FOAMED POLYURETHANE OR FOAMED CONCRETE. ABSORB LIQUID MASS WITH FLY ASH OR CEMENT POWDER.

IMMOBILIZE SPILL WITH UNIVERSAL GELLING AGENT.

REDUCE VAPOR AND FIRE HAZARD WITH APPROPRIATE FOAM.

AIR SPILL: KNOCK DOWN VAPORS WITH WATER SPRAY. KEEP UPWIND.

WATER SPILL: LIMIT SPILL MOTION AND DISPERSION WITH NATURAL BARRIERS OR OIL SPILL CONTROL BOOMS.

APPLY DETERGENTS, SOAPS, ALCOHOLS OR ANOTHER SURFACE ACTIVE AGENT.

APPLY UNIVERSAL GELLING AGENT TO IMMOBILIZE TRAPPED SPILL AND INCREASE EFFICIENCY OF REMOVAL.

IF DISSOLVED, AT A CONCENTRATION OF 10 PPM OR GREATER, APPLY ACTIVATED CARBON AT TEN TIMES THE AMOUNT THAT HAS BEEN SPILLED.

USE SUCTION HOSES TO REMOVE TRAPPED SPILL MATERIAL.

USE MECHANICAL DREDGES OR LIFTS TO EXTRACT IMMOBILIZED MASSES OF POLLUTION AND PRECIPITATES.

OCCUPATIONAL SPILL: SHUT OFF IGNITION SOURCES. STOP LEAK IF YOU CAN DO IT WITHOUT RISK. USE WATER SPRAY TO REDUCE VAPORS. FOR SMALL SPILLS, TAKE UP WITH SAND OR OTHER ABSORBENT MATERIAL AND PLACE INTO CONTAINERS FOR LATER DISPOSAL. FOR LARGER SPILLS, DIKE FAR AHEAD OF SPILL FOR LATER DISPOSAL. NO SMOKING, FLAMES OR FLARES IN HAZARD AREA. KEEP UNNECESSARY PEOPLE AWAY; ISOLATE HAZARD AREA AND RESTRICT ENTRY.

REPORTABLE QUANTITY (RQ): 1000 POUNDS THE SUPERFUND AMENDMENTS AND REAUTHORIZATION ACT (SARA) SECTION 304 REQUIRES THAT A RELEASE EQUAL TO OR GREATER THAN THE REPORTABLE QUANTITY FOR THIS SUBSTANCE BE IMMEDIATELY REPORTED TO THE LOCAL EMERGENCY PLANNING COMMITTEE AND THE STATE EMERGENCY RESPONSE COMMISSION (40 CFR 355.40). IF THE RELEASE OF THIS SUBSTANCE IS REPORTABLE UNDER CERCLA SECTION 103, THE NATIONAL RESPONSE CENTER MUST BE NOTIFIED IMMEDIATELY AT (800) 424-8802 OR (202) 426-2675 IN THE METROPOLITAN WASHINGTON, D.C. AREA (40 CFR 302.6).

PROTECTIVE EQUIPMENT

VENTILATION: PROVIDE LOCAL EXHAUST OR GENERAL DILUTION VENTILATION TO MEET PUBLISHED EXPOSURE LIMITS. VENTILATION EQUIPMENT MUST BE EXPLOSION-PROOF.

RESPIRATOR: THE FOLLOWING RESPIRATORS AND MAXIMUM USE CONCENTRATIONS ARE RECOMMENDATIONS BY THE U.S. DEPARTMENT OF HEALTH AND HUMAN SERVICES, NIOSH POCKET GUIDE TO CHEMICAL HAZARDS; NIOSH CRITERIA DOCUMENTS OR BY THE U.S. DEPARTMENT OF LABOR, 29 CFR 1910 SUBPART Z. THE SPECIFIC RESPIRATOR SELECTED MUST BE BASED ON CONTAMINATION LEVELS FOUND IN THE WORK PLACE, MUST NOT EXCEED THE WORKING LIMITS OF THE RESPIRATOR AND BE JOINTLY APPROVED BY THE NATIONAL INSTITUTE FOR OCCUPATIONAL SAFETY AND HEALTH AND THE MINE SAFETY AND HEALTH ADMINISTRATION (NIOSH-MSHA).

XYLENE (O-, M-, AND P-ISOMERS): 1000 PPM- ANY CHEMICAL CARTRIDGE RESPIRATOR WITH ORGANIC VAPOR CARTRIDGE(S). ANY POWERED AIR-PURIFYING RESPIRATOR WITH ORGANIC VAPOR CARTRIDGE(S). ANY SUPPLIED-AIR RESPIRATOR. ANY SELF-CONTAINED BREATHING APPARATUS.

ESCAPE- ANY AIR-PURIFYING FULL FACEPIECE RESPIRATOR (GAS MASK) WITH A CHIN-STYLE OR FRONT- OR BACK-MOUNTED ORGANIC VAPOR CANISTER. ANY APPROPRIATE ESCAPE-TYPE SELF-CONTAINED BREATHING APPARATUS.

FOR FIREFIGHTING AND OTHER IMMEDIATELY DANGEROUS TO LIFE OR HEALTH CONDITIONS:

SELF-CONTAINED BREATHING APPARATUS WITH FULL FACEPIECE OPERATED IN PRESSURE-DEMAND OR OTHER POSITIVE PRESSURE MODE.

SUPPLIED-AIR RESPIRATOR WITH FULL FACEPIECE AND OPERATED IN PRESSURE-DEMAND OR OTHER POSITIVE PRESSURE MODE IN COMBINATION WITH AN AUXILIARY SELF-CONTAINED BREATHING APPARATUS OPERATED IN PRESSURE-DEMAND OR OTHER POSITIVE PRESSURE MODE.

CLOTHING: EMPLOYEE MUST WEAR APPROPRIATE PROTECTIVE (IMPERVIOUS) CLOTHING AND EQUIPMENT TO PREVENT REPEATED OR PROLONGED SKIN CONTACT WITH THIS SUBSTANCE.

GLOVES: EMPLOYEE MUST WEAR APPROPRIATE PROTECTIVE GLOVES TO PREVENT CONTACT WITH THIS SUBSTANCE.

EYE PROTECTION: EMPLOYEE MUST WEAR SPLASH-PROOF OR DUST-RESISTANT SAFETY GOGGLES TO PREVENT EYE CONTACT WITH THIS SUBSTANCE.

EMERGENCY EYE WASH: WHERE THERE IS ANY POSSIBILITY THAT AN EMPLOYEE'S EYES MAY BE EXPOSED TO THIS SUBSTANCE, THE EMPLOYER SHOULD PROVIDE AN EYE WASH FOUNTAIN WITHIN THE IMMEDIATE WORK AREA FOR EMERGENCY USE.

AUTHORIZED BY- OCCUPATIONAL HEALTH SERVICES, INC.

CREATION DATE: 10/05/89 ***REVISION DATE:*** 05/09/90

MATERIAL SAFETY DATA SHEET

OCCUPATIONAL HEALTH SERVICES, INC.
AGRICULTURE AND PESTICIDE DIVISION
450 SEVENTH AVENUE, SUITE 2407
NEW YORK, NEW YORK 10123
1-800-445-MSDS OR (212) 967-1100

EMERGENCY CONTACT:
JOHN S. BRANSFORD, JR. (615) 292-1180

SUBSTANCE IDENTIFICATION

CAS-NUMBER 1300-71-6

SUBSTANCE: **XYLENOL (MIXED ISOMERS)**

TRADE NAMES/SYNONYMS: DIMETHYL PHENOL; DIMETHYLPHENOL; XYLENOL; PHENOL, DIMETHYL; HYDROXYDIMETHYLBENZENE; STCC 4941193; UN 2261; C8H10O; PST25160

CHEMICAL FAMILY: HYDROXYL, AROMATIC

MOLECULAR FORMULA: (C-H3)2-C6-H3-O-H

MOLECULAR WEIGHT: 122.17

CERCLA RATINGS (SCALE 0-3): HEALTH=3 FIRE=1 REACTIVITY=0 PERSISTENCE=1

NFPA RATINGS (SCALE 0-4): HEALTH=3 FIRE=1 REACTIVITY=0

COMPONENTS AND CONTAMINANTS

COMPONENT: 2,3-DIMETHYL PHENOL ***PERCENT:*** >1.0
CAS# 526-75-0

COMPONENT: 2,4-DIMETHYL PHENOL ***PERCENT:*** >1.0
CAS# 105-67-9

COMPONENT: 2,5-DIMETHYL PHENOL ***PERCENT:*** >1.0
CAS# 95-87-4

COMPONENT: 2,6-DIMETHYL PHENOL ***PERCENT:*** >1.0
CAS# 576-26-1

COMPONENT: 3,4-DIMETHYL PHENOL ***PERCENT:*** >1.0
CAS# 95-65-8

COMPONENT: 3,5-DIMETHYL PHENOL ***PERCENT:*** >1.0
CAS# 108-68-9

OTHER CONTAMINANTS: NONE

EXPOSURE LIMITS: NO OCCUPATIONAL EXPOSURE LIMITS ESTABLISHED BY OSHA, ACGIH, OR NIOSH.
XYLENOL: 1000 POUNDS CERCLA SECTION 103 REPORTABLE QUANTITY
2,4-XYLENOL: 100 POUNDS CERCLA SECTION 103 REPORTABLE QUANTITY
SUBJECT TO SARA SECTION 313 ANNUAL TOXIC CHEMICAL RELEASE REPORTING

PHYSICAL DATA

DESCRIPTION: WHITE CRYSTALLINE SOLID. ***BOILING POINT:*** 397-437 F (203-225 C)

MELTING POINT: 68-169 F (20-76 C) ***SPECIFIC GRAVITY:*** 1.02-1.03

SOLUBILITY IN WATER: SLIGHTLY SOLUBLE

SOLVENT SOLUBILITY: SOLUBLE IN ALCOHOL, CHLOROFORM, BENZENE, ETHER, OTHER ORGANIC SOLVENTS, SODIUM HYDROXIDE SOLUTIONS.

FIRE AND EXPLOSION DATA

FIRE AND EXPLOSION HAZARD: SLIGHT FIRE HAZARD WHEN EXPOSED TO HEAT OR FLAME.

FIREFIGHTING MEDIA: DRY CHEMICAL, CARBON DIOXIDE, HALON, WATER SPRAY OR STANDARD FOAM (1987 EMERGENCY RESPONSE GUIDEBOOK, DOT P 5800.4).
FOR LARGER FIRES, USE WATER SPRAY, FOG OR STANDARD FOAM (1987 EMERGENCY RESPONSE GUIDEBOOK, DOT P 5800.4).

FIREFIGHTING: MOVE CONTAINERS FROM FIRE AREA IF POSSIBLE. FIGHT FIRE FROM MAXIMUM DISTANCE. STAY AWAY FROM STORAGE TANK ENDS. DIKE FIRE CONTROL WATER FOR LATER DISPOSAL. DO NOT SCATTER MATERIAL (1987 EMERGENCY RESPONSE GUIDEBOOK, DOT P 5800.4, GUIDE PAGE 55).
EXTINGUISH ONLY IF FLOW CAN BE STOPPED; USE WATER IN FLOODING AMOUNTS AS FOG, COOL CONTAINERS WITH FLOODING QUANTITIES OF WATER, APPLY FROM AS FAR A DISTANCE AS POSSIBLE. AVOID BREATHING TOXIC VAPORS, KEEP UPWIND.

TRANSPORTATION DATA

DEPARTMENT OF TRANSPORTATION HAZARD CLASSIFICATION 49 CFR 172.101: ORM-A
DEPARTMENT OF TRANSPORTATION LABELING REQUIREMENTS 49 CFR 172.101 AND SUBPART E: NONE
DEPARTMENT OF TRANSPORTATION PACKAGING REQUIREMENTS: 49 CFR 173.510 EXCEPTIONS: 49 CFR 173.505

TOXICITY

XYLENOL: TOXICITY DATA: 5 GM/KG ORAL-MAN LDLO. CARCINOGEN STATUS: NONE. ACUTE TOXICITY LEVEL: INSUFFICIENT DATA. TARGET EFFECTS: NO DATA AVAILABLE.
2,3-XYLENOL: TOXICITY DATA: 56 MG/KG INTRAVENOUS-MOUSE LD50. CARCINOGEN STATUS: NONE. LOCAL EFFECTS: CORROSIVE- SKIN, EYE. ACUTE TOXICITY LEVEL: INSUFFICIENT DATA. TARGET EFFECTS: NO DATA AVAILABLE.
2,4-XYLENOL (2,4-DIMETHYLPHENOL): TOXICITY DATA: 1040 MG/KG SKIN-RAT LD50; 3200 MG/KG ORAL-RAT LD50; 809 MG/KG ORAL-MOUSE LD50; 183 MG/KG INTRAPERITONEAL-MOUSE LD50; 100 MG/KG INTRAVENOUS-MOUSE LD50; TUMORIGENIC DATA (RTECS). CARCINOGEN STATUS: NONE. LOCAL EFFECTS: CORROSIVE- SKIN, EYE; IRRITANT- INHALATION. ACUTE TOXICITY LEVEL: MODERATELY TOXIC BY DERMAL ABSORPTION AND INGESTION. TARGET EFFECTS: NO DATA AVAILABLE.
2,5-XYLENOL: TOXICITY DATA: 444 MG/KG ORAL-RAT LD50; 383 MG/KG ORAL-MOUSE LD50; 938 MG/KG ORAL-RABBIT LD50; 730 MG/KG UNREPORTED-RAT LD50; TUMORIGENIC DATA (RTECS). CARCINOGEN STATUS: NONE. ACUTE TOXICITY LEVEL: TOXIC BY INGESTION. TARGET EFFECTS: NO DATA AVAILABLE.
2,6-XYLENOL: IRRITATION DATA: 100 MG EYE-RABBIT. TOXICITY DATA: 1000 MG/KG SKIN-RABBIT LD50; 920 MG/KG SKIN-MOUSE LD50; 296 MG/KG ORAL-RAT LD50; 479 MG/KG ORAL-MOUSE LD50; 700 MG/KG ORAL-RABBIT LD50; 150 MG/KG INTRAPERITONEAL-MOUSE LD50; 80 MG/KG INTRAVENOUS-MOUSE LD50; TUMORIGENIC DATA (RTECS). CARCINOGEN STATUS: NONE. LOCAL EFFECTS: CORROSIVE- SKIN, EYE. ACUTE TOXICITY LEVEL: TOXIC BY INGESTION, DERMAL ABSORPTION. TARGET EFFECTS: NO DATA AVAILABLE.
3,4-XYLENOL: TOXICITY DATA: 727 MG/KG ORAL-RAT LD50; 400 MG/KG ORAL-MOUSE LD50; 800 MG/KG ORAL-RABBIT LD50; TUMORIGENIC DATA (RTECS). CARCINOGEN STATUS: NONE. LOCAL EFFECTS: CORROSIVE- SKIN, EYE. ACUTE TOXICITY LEVEL: MODERATELY TOXIC BY INGESTION. TARGET EFFECTS: NO DATA AVAILBLE.
3,5-XYLENOL: IRRITATION DATA: 726 UG EYE-RABBIT SEVERE. TOXICITY DATA: 608 MG/KG ORAL-RAT LD50; 477 MG/KG ORAL-MOUSE LD50; 1313 MG/KG ORAL-RABBIT LD50; 156 MG/KG INTRAPERITONEAL-MOUSE LD50; TUMORIGENIC DATA (RTECS). CARCINOGEN STATUS: NONE. LOCAL EFFECTS: CORROSIVE- SKIN, EYE. ACUTE TOXICITY LEVEL: MODERATELY TOXIC BY INGESTION. TARGET EFFECTS: NO DATA AVAILABLE.

HEALTH EFFECTS AND FIRST AID

INHALATION: XYLENOL: **ACUTE EXPOSURE-** MAY BE IRRITATING. SOME PHENOL DERIVATIVES AFFECT THE BLOOD AND THE RESPIRATORY, CIRCULATORY, AND CARDIOVASCULAR SYSTEMS. **CHRONIC EXPOSURE-** NO DATA AVAILABLE.

FIRST AID- REMOVE FROM EXPOSURE AREA TO FRESH AIR IMMEDIATELY. IF BREATHING HAS STOPPED, PERFORM ARTIFICIAL RESPIRATION. KEEP PERSON WARM AND AT REST. TREAT SYMPTOMATICALLY AND SUPPORTIVELY. GET MEDICAL ATTENTION IMMEDIATELY.

SKIN CONTACT: XYLENOL: CORROSIVE/TOXIC. **ACUTE EXPOSURE-** MAY CAUSE SEVERE IRRITATION AND BURNS. SOME PHENOL DERIVATIVES MAY BE ABSORBED THROUGH THE SKIN AND AFFECT THE BLOOD AND THE RESPIRATORY, CIRCULATORY, AND CARDIOVASCULAR SYSTEMS. 1000 MG/KG OF 2,6-XYLENOL CAUSED DEATH IN RABBITS. **CHRONIC EXPOSURE-** EFFECTS DEPEND ON CONCENTRATION AND DURATION OF EXPOSURE. REPEATED OR PROLONGED CONTACT WITH CORROSIVE SUBSTANCES MAY RESULT IN DERMATITIS OR EFFECTS SIMILAR TO ACUTE EXPOSURE.

FIRST AID- REMOVE CONTAMINATED CLOTHING AND SHOES IMMEDIATELY. WASH AFFECTED AREA WITH SOAP OR MILD DETERGENT AND LARGE AMOUNTS OF WATER UNTIL NO EVIDENCE OF CHEMICAL REMAINS (AT LEAST 15-20 MINUTES). IN CASE OF CHEMICAL BURNS, COVER AREA WITH STERILE, DRY DRESSING. BANDAGE SECURELY, BUT NOT TOO TIGHTLY. GET MEDICAL ATTENTION IMMEDIATELY.

EYE CONTACT: XYLENOL: CORROSIVE. **ACUTE EXPOSURE-** MAY CAUSE SEVERE IRRITATION AND BURNS. THE 3,5-XYLENOL ISOMER IS GRADED A 9 ON A SCALE OF 1 TO 10, HAVING CAUSED SEVERE AND PRESUMABLY PERMANENT INJURY TO RABBIT EYES. **CHRONIC EXPOSURE-** EFFECTS DEPEND ON CONCENTRATION AND DURATION OF EXPOSURE. REPEATED OR PROLONGED CONTACT WITH CORROSIVE SUBSTANCES MAY RESULT IN CONJUNCTIVITIS OR EFFECTS SIMILAR TO ACUTE EXPOSURE.

FIRST AID- WASH EYES IMMEDIATELY WITH LARGE AMOUNTS OF WATER, OCCASIONALLY LIFTING UPPER AND LOWER LIDS, UNTIL NO EVIDENCE OF CHEMICAL REMAINS (AT LEAST 15-20 MINUTES). CONTINUE IRRIGATING WITH NORMAL SALINE UNTIL THE PH HAS RETURNED TO NORMAL (30-60 MINUTES). COVER WITH STERILE BANDAGES. GET MEDICAL ATTENTION IMMEDIATELY.

INGESTION: XYLENOL: CORROSIVE/TOXIC. **ACUTE EXPOSURE-** SOME PHENOL DERIVATIVES AFFECT THE BLOOD AND THE RESPIRATORY, CIRCULATORY, AND CARDIOVASCULAR SYSTEMS. LOW LEVELS OF 2,5-XYLENOL AND 2,6-XYLENOL CAUSED DEATH IN LABORATORY ANIMALS. **CHRONIC EXPOSURE-** NO DATA AVAILABLE.

FIRST AID- IF EXTENSIVE VOMITING HAS NOT OCCURRED, THE SUBSTANCE SHOULD BE REMOVED BY EMESIS OR GASTRIC LAVAGE PROVIDED THAT THE PATIENT IS CONSCIOUS AND CONVULSIONS ARE NOT PRESENT. KEEP HEAD BELOW HIPS DURING VOMITING TO PREVENT ASPIRATION. DO NOT ATTEMPT TO MAKE AN UNCONSCIOUS PERSON VOMIT. TREAT SYMPTOMATICALLY AND SUPPORTIVELY. GET MEDICAL ATTENTION IMMEDIATELY (DREISBACH, HANDBOOK OF POISONING, 12TH ED.). TREATMENT SHOULD BE PERFORMED BY QUALIFIED MEDICAL PERSONNEL.

ANTIDOTE: NO SPECIFIC ANTIDOTE. TREAT SYMPTOMATICALLY AND SUPPORTIVELY.

REACTIVITY

REACTIVITY: STABLE UNDER NORMAL TEMPERATURES AND PRESSURES.

INCOMPATIBILITIES: XYLENOL: OXIDIZERS (STRONG): FIRE AND EXPLOSION HAZARD.

DECOMPOSITION: THERMAL DECOMPOSITION PRODUCTS MAY INCLUDE TOXIC OXIDES OF CARBON.

POLYMERIZATION: HAZARDOUS POLYMERIZATION HAS NOT BEEN REPORTED TO OCCUR UNDER NORMAL TEMPERATURES AND PRESSURES.

STORAGE AND DISPOSAL

OBSERVE ALL FEDERAL, STATE AND LOCAL REGULATIONS WHEN STORING OR DISPOSING OF THIS SUBSTANCE. FOR ASSISTANCE, CONTACT THE DISTRICT DIRECTOR OF THE ENVIRONMENTAL PROTECTION AGENCY.

STORAGE

STORE AWAY FROM INCOMPATIBLE SUBSTANCES.

CONDITIONS TO AVOID

MAY BURN BUT DOES NOT IGNITE READILY. CONTAINERS MAY EXPLODE IN HEAT OF FIRE.

SPILL AND LEAK PROCEDURES

SOIL SPILL: DIG HOLDING AREA SUCH AS LAGOON, POND OR PIT FOR CONTAINMENT. USE PROTECTIVE COVER SUCH AS A PLASTIC SHEET TO PREVENT MATERIAL FROM DISSOLVING IN FIRE EXTINGUISHING WATER OR RAIN.

AIR SPILL: APPLY WATER SPRAY TO KNOCK DOWN VAPORS.

WATER SPILL: LIMIT SPILL MOTION AND DISPERSION WITH NATURAL BARRIERS OR OIL SPILL CONTROL BOOMS.
USE ACTIVATED CARBON TO ABSORB SPILLED SUBSTANCE THAT IS DISSOLVED.
USE SUCTION HOSES TO REMOVE TRAPPED SPILL MATERIAL.
USE MECHANICAL DREDGES OR LIFTS TO EXTRACT IMMOBILIZED MASSES OF POLLUTION AND PRECIPITATES.

OCCUPATIONAL SPILL: DO NOT TOUCH SPILLED MATERIAL. STOP LEAK IF YOU CAN DO IT WITHOUT RISK. USE WATER SPRAY TO REDUCE VAPORS. FOR SMALL SPILLS, TAKE UP WITH SAND OR OTHER ABSORBENT MATERIAL AND PLACE INTO CONTAINERS FOR LATER DISPOSAL. FOR SMALL DRY SPILLS, WITH A CLEAN SHOVEL PLACE MATERIAL INTO CLEAN, DRY CONTAINERS AND COVER. MOVE CONTAINERS FROM SPILL AREA. FOR LARGER SPILLS, DIKE FAR AHEAD OF SPILL FOR LATER DISPOSAL. KEEP UNNECESSARY PEOPLE AWAY. ISOLATE HAZARD AREA AND DENY ENTRY. VENTILATE CLOSED SPACES BEFORE ENTERING.
REPORTABLE QUANTITY (RQ): 1000 POUNDS THE SUPERFUND AMENDMENTS AND REAUTHORIZATION ACT (SARA) SECTION 304 REQUIRES THAT A RELEASE EQUAL TO OR GREATER THAN THE REPORTABLE QUANTITY FOR THIS SUBSTANCE BE IMMEDIATELY REPORTED TO THE LOCAL EMERGENCY PLANNING COMMITTEE AND THE STATE EMERGENCY RESPONSE COMMISSION (40 CFR 355.40). IF THE RELEASE OF THIS SUBSTANCE IS REPORTABLE UNDER CERCLA SECTION 103, THE NATIONAL RESPONSE CENTER MUST BE NOTIFIED IMMEDIATELY AT (800) 424-8802 OR (202) 426-2675 IN THE METROPOLITAN WASHINGTON, D.C. AREA (40 CFR 302.6).

PROTECTIVE EQUIPMENT

VENTILATION: PROVIDE LOCAL EXHAUST OR PROCESS ENCLOSURE VENTILATION SYSTEM.

RESPIRATOR: THE FOLLOWING RESPIRATORS ARE RECOMMENDED BASED ON INFORMATION FOUND IN THE PHYSICAL DATA, TOXICITY AND HEALTH EFFECTS SECTIONS. THEY ARE RANKED IN ORDER FROM MINIMUM TO MAXIMUM RESPIRATORY PROTECTION. THE SPECIFIC RESPIRATOR SELECTED MUST BE BASED ON CONTAMINATION LEVELS FOUND IN THE WORK PLACE, MUST NOT EXCEED THE WORKING LIMITS OF THE RESPIRATOR AND BE JOINTLY APPROVED BY THE NATIONAL INSTITUTE FOR OCCUPATIONAL SAFETY AND HEALTH AND THE MINE SAFETY AND HEALTH ADMINISTRATION (NIOSH-MSHA).
TYPE 'C' SUPPLIED-AIR RESPIRATOR WITH A FULL FACEPIECE OPERATED IN PRESSURE-DEMAND OR OTHER POSITIVE PRESSURE MODE OR WITH A FULL FACEPIECE, HELMET OR HOOD OPERATED IN CONTINOUS-FLOW MODE.
SELF-CONTAINED BREATHING APPARATUS WITH A FULL FACEPIECE OPERATED IN PRESSURE-DEMAND OR OTHER POSITIVE PRESSURE MODE.
FOR FIREFIGHTING AND OTHER IMMEDIATELY DANGEROUS TO LIFE OR HEALTH CONDITIONS:
SELF-CONTAINED BREATHING APPARATUS WITH FULL FACEPIECE OPERATED IN PRESSURE-DEMAND OR OTHER POSITIVE PRESSURE MODE.
SUPPLIED-AIR RESPIRATOR WITH FULL FACEPIECE AND OPERATED IN PRESSURE-DEMAND OR OTHER POSITIVE PRESSURE MODE IN COMBINATION WITH AN AUXILIARY SELF-CONTAINED BREATHING APPARATUS OPERATED IN PRESSURE-DEMAND OR OTHER POSITIVE PRESSURE MODE.

CLOTHING: EMPLOYEE MUST WEAR APPROPRIATE PROTECTIVE (IMPERVIOUS) CLOTHING AND EQUIPMENT TO PREVENT ANY POSSIBILITY OF SKIN CONTACT WITH THIS SUBSTANCE.

GLOVES: EMPLOYEE MUST WEAR APPROPRIATE PROTECTIVE GLOVES TO PREVENT CONTACT WITH THIS SUBSTANCE.

EYE PROTECTION: EMPLOYEE MUST WEAR SPLASH-PROOF OR DUST-RESISTANT SAFETY GOGGLES AND A FACESHIELD TO PREVENT CONTACT WITH THIS SUBSTANCE.
EMERGENCY WASH FACILITIES: WHERE THERE IS ANY POSSIBILITY THAT AN EMPLOYEE'S EYES AND/OR SKIN MAY BE EXPOSED TO THIS SUBSTANCE, THE EMPLOYER SHOULD PROVIDE AN EYE WASH FOUNTAIN AND QUICK DRENCH SHOWER WITHIN THE IMMEDIATE WORK AREA FOR EMERGENCY USE.

AUTHORIZED BY- OCCUPATIONAL HEALTH SERVICES, INC.
CREATION DATE: 02/08/90 ***REVISION DATE:*** 05/07/90

MATERIAL SAFETY DATA SHEET

OCCUPATIONAL HEALTH SERVICES, INC.
AGRICULTURE AND PESTICIDE DIVISION
450 SEVENTH AVENUE, SUITE 2407
NEW YORK, NEW YORK 10123
1-800-445-MSDS OR (212) 967-1100

EMERGENCY CONTACT:
JOHN S. BRANSFORD, JR. (615) 292-1180

SUBSTANCE IDENTIFICATION

CAS-NUMBER 2655-14-3

SUBSTANCE: **3,5-XYLYL METHYLCARBAMATE**

TRADE NAMES/SYNONYMS: PHENOL, 3,5-DIMETHYL-, METHYLCARBAMATE; 3,5-DIMETHYLPHENOL METHYLCARBAMATE; CARBAMIC ACID, METHYL-, 3, 5-XYLYL ESTER; METHYLCARBAMIC ACID 3,5-XYLYL ESTER; 3,5-DIMETHYLPHENYL METHYLCARBAMATE; 3,5-XYLYL N-METHYL CARBAMATE; MACBAL; COSBAN; 3,5-XMC; XMC; XMC (PESTICIDE); C10H13NO2; PST25171

CHEMICAL FAMILY: CARBAMATE
AROMATIC

MOLECULAR FORMULA: C-H3-N-(H)-C-O2-C6-H3-(C-H3)2

MOLECULAR WEIGHT: 179.24

CERCLA RATINGS (SCALE 0-3): HEALTH=3 FIRE=1 REACTIVITY=0 PERSISTENCE=0

NFPA RATINGS (SCALE 0-4): HEALTH=U FIRE=1 REACTIVITY=0

COMPONENTS AND CONTAMINANTS

COMPONENT: 3,5-XYLYL METHYLCARBAMATE ***PERCENT:*** 100.0
CAS# 2655-14-3

OTHER CONTAMINANTS: NONE

EXPOSURE LIMITS: NO OCCUPATIONAL EXPOSURE LIMITS ESTABLISHED BY OSHA, ACGIH, OR NIOSH.

PHYSICAL DATA

DESCRIPTION: COLORLESS OR WHITE CRYSTALLINE SOLID. ***MELTING POINT:*** 210 F (99 C)

SPECIFIC GRAVITY: 0.54 ***SOLUBILITY IN WATER:*** 0.047%

SOLVENT SOLUBILITY: SOLUBLE IN 3,5,5-TRIMETHYLCYCLOHEX-2-ENONE AND CYCLOHEXANONE; SLIGHTLY SOLUBLE IN ACETONE, BENZENE, ALCOHOL, ETHYL ACETATE.

FIRE AND EXPLOSION DATA

FIRE AND EXPLOSION HAZARD: SLIGHT FIRE HAZARD WHEN EXPOSED TO HEAT OR FLAME.

FIREFIGHTING MEDIA: DRY CHEMICAL, CARBON DIOXIDE, HALON, WATER SPRAY OR STANDARD FOAM (1987 EMERGENCY RESPONSE GUIDEBOOK, DOT P 5800.4). FOR LARGER FIRES, USE WATER SPRAY, FOG OR STANDARD FOAM (1987 EMERGENCY RESPONSE GUIDEBOOK, DOT P 5800.4).

FIREFIGHTING: MOVE CONTAINER FROM FIRE AREA IF POSSIBLE. DO NOT SCATTER SPILLED MATERIAL WITH HIGH PRESSURE WATER STREAMS. DIKE FIRE CONTROL WATER FOR LATER DISPOSAL (1987 EMERGENCY RESPONSE GUIDEBOOK, DOT P 5800.4, GUIDE PAGE 31).

USE AGENTS SUITABLE FOR TYPE OF SURROUNDING FIRE. AVOID BREATHING HAZARDOUS VAPORS, KEEP UPWIND.

TOXICITY

3,5-XYLYL METHYLCARBAMATE: TOXICITY DATA: 542 MG/KG ORAL-RAT LD50; 280 MG/KG ORAL-MOUSE LD50; 374 MG/KG ORAL-RABBIT LD50; 245 MG/KG UNREPORTED-RAT LD50. CARCINOGEN STATUS: NONE. ACUTE TOXICITY LEVEL: MODERATELY TOXIC BY INGESTION. TARGET EFFECTS: CHOLINESTERASE INHIBITOR. AT INCREASED RISK FROM EXPOSURE: PERSONS WITH ASTHMA, DIABETES, CARDIOVASCULAR DISEASE, MECHANICAL OBSTRUCTION OF THE GASTROINTESTINAL OR UROGENITAL TRACT, AND THOSE IN VAGOTONIC STATES.*

* MAY BE BASED ON GENERAL INFORMATION ON CARBAMATES.

HEALTH EFFECTS AND FIRST AID

INHALATION: 3,5-XYLYL METHYLCARBAMATE: SEE INFORMATION ON CARBAMATES. CARBAMATES: CHOLINESTERASE INHIBITOR. **ACUTE EXPOSURE**- WHEN INHALED, THE FIRST EFFECTS OF CHOLINESTERASE INHIBITION ARE USUALLY RESPIRATORY AND MAY INCLUDE NASAL HYPEREMIA AND WATERY DISCHARGE, CHEST DISCOMFORT, DYSPNEA, AND WHEEZING DUE TO INCREASED BRONCHIAL SECRETIONS AND BRONCHOCONSTRICTION. OTHER SYSTEMIC EFFECTS MAY BEGIN WITHIN A FEW MINUTES OR SEVERAL HOURS OF EXPOSURE. SYMPTOMS MAY INCLUDE NAUSEA, VOMITING, DIARRHEA, ABDOMINAL CRAMPS, HEADACHE, VERTIGO, OCULAR PAIN, CILIARY MUSCLE SPASM, BLURRING OR DIMNESS OF VISION, MIOSIS, OR IN SOME CASES MYDRIASIS, LACRIMATION, SALIVATION, SWEATING, AND CONFUSION. OTHER REPORTED CENTRAL NERVOUS SYSTEM OR NEUROMUSCULAR EFFECTS INCLUDE ATAXIA, SLURRED SPEECH, AREFLEXIA, WEAKNESS, FATIGUE, TWITCHING, FASCICULATION, TREMOR, AND EVENTUALLY PARALYSIS OF THE EXTREMITIES AND POSSIBLY OF THE RESPIRATORY MUSCLES. IN SEVERE CASES, THERE MAY ALSO BE INVOLUNTARY DEFECATION AND URINATION, BRADYCARDIA, HYPOTENSION, PULMONARY EDEMA, CONVULSIONS, COMA, AND DEATH FROM RESPIRATORY FAILURE OR CARDIAC ARREST. CARBAMATES GENERALLY DO NOT ACCUMULATE IN MAMMALIAN TISSUE AND THE CHOLINESTERASE INHIBITION REVERSES RATHER RAPIDLY. IN NON-FATAL CASES, THE ILLNESS GENERALLY LASTS LESS THAN 24 HOURS. **CHRONIC EXPOSURE**- PROLONGED OR REPEATED EXPOSURE MAY CAUSE EFFECTS AS DESCRIBED IN ACUTE EXPOSURE.

FIRST AID- REMOVE FROM EXPOSURE AREA TO FRESH AIR IMMEDIATELY. IF BREATHING HAS STOPPED, GIVE ARTIFICIAL RESPIRATION. MAINTAIN AIRWAY AND BLOOD PRESSURE AND ADMINISTER OXYGEN IF AVAILABLE. KEEP AFFECTED PERSON WARM AND AT REST. TREAT SYMPTOMATICALLY AND SUPPORTIVELY. ADMINISTRATION OF OXYGEN SHOULD BE PERFORMED BY QUALIFIED PERSONNEL. GET MEDICAL ATTENTION IMMEDIATELY.

SKIN CONTACT: 3,5-XYLYL METHYLCARBAMATE: SEE INFORMATION ON CARBAMATES.

CARBAMATES: CHOLINESTERASE INHIBITOR. **ACUTE EXPOSURE**- SOME COMPOUNDS MAY CAUSE IRRITATION. LOCALIZED SWEATING AND FASCICULATIONS MAY OCCUR AT THE SITE OF CONTACT. IF SUFFICIENT AMOUNTS ARE ABSORBED THROUGH THE SKIN, OTHER EFFECTS OF CHOLINESTERASE INHIBITION MAY OCCUR AS DESCRIBED IN ACUTE INHALATION; SYMPTOMS MAY BE DELAYED FOR 2-3 HOURS, USUALLY NO MORE THAN 8 HOURS. **CHRONIC EXPOSURE**- REPEATED OR PROLONGED EXPOSURE MAY CAUSE EFFECTS AS DESCRIBED IN ACUTE EXPOSURE.

FIRST AID- REMOVE CONTAMINATED CLOTHING IMMEDIATELY. WASH CONTAMINATED AREAS WITH SOAP AND WATER FOLLOWED BY ALCOHOL (ARENA, POISONING, 4TH ED.). EMERGENCY PERSONNEL SHOULD WEAR GLOVES AND AVOID CONTAMINATION. TREAT RESPIRATORY DIFFICULTY WITH ARTIFICIAL RESPIRATION. GET MEDICAL ATTENTION IMMEDIATELY.

EYE CONTACT: 3,5-XYLYL METHYLCARBAMATE: SEE INFORMATION ON CARBAMATES.

CARBAMATES: CHOLINESTERASE INHIBITOR. **ACUTE EXPOSURE**- DIRECT CONTACT MAY CAUSE PAIN, HYPEREMIA, LACRIMATION, TWITCHING OF THE EYELIDS, MIOSIS, AND CILIARY MUSCLE SPASM WITH LOSS OF ACCOMODATION, BLURRED OR DIMMED VISION AND BROWACHE. SOMETIMES MYDRIASIS MAY OCCUR INSTEAD OF MIOSIS. WITH SUFFICIENT EXPOSURE, OTHER SYMPTOMS OF CHOLINESTERASE INHIBITION MAY OCCUR AS DESCRIBED IN ACUTE INHALATION. **CHRONIC EXPOSURE**- PROLONGED EXPOSURE MAY CAUSE EFFECTS AS DESCRIBED IN ACUTE EXPOSURE. SOME COMPOUNDS HAVE CAUSED TOXIC EFFECTS ON THE CRYSTALLINE LENS, CONJUNCTIVAL THICKENING AND OBSTRUCTION OF NASOLACRIMAL CANALS WHEN USED AS MIOTIC EYE DROPS.

FIRST AID- IRRIGATE EYES WITH WATER OR SALINE SOLUTION. IF SYMPTOMS OF POISONING OCCUR, TREAT RESPIRATORY DIFFICULTY WITH ARTIFICIAL RESPIRATION AND OXYGEN. OBSERVE PATIENT FOR AT LEAST 24-36 HOURS (GOSSELIN, CLINICAL TOXICOLOGY OF COMMERCIAL PRODUCTS, 5TH ED.). GET MEDICAL ATTENTION IMMEDIATELY. OXYGEN SHOULD BE ADMINISTERED BY QUALIFIED MEDICAL PERSONNEL.

INGESTION: 3,5-XYLYL METHYLCARBAMATE: SEE INFORMATION ON CARBAMATES. CARBAMATES: CHOLINESTERASE INHIBITOR. **ACUTE EXPOSURE**- WHEN INGESTED, THE FIRST EFFECTS MAY BE NAUSEA, VOMITING, ANOREXIA, ABDOMINAL CRAMPS, AND DIARRHEA. WITH ABSORPTION FROM THE GASTROINTESTINAL TRACT, THE OTHER EFFECTS OF CHOLINESTERASE INHIBITION AS DESCRIBED IN ACUTE INHALATION MAY OCCUR; SYMPTOMS MAY BEGIN WITHIN MINUTES OR BE DELAYED SEVERAL HOURS. **CHRONIC EXPOSURE**- REPEATED INGESTION MAY CAUSE EFFECTS AS DESCRIBED IN ACUTE EXPOSURE.

FIRST AID- IF PERSON IS ALERT AND RESPIRATION IS NOT DEPRESSED, GIVE SYRUP OF IPECAC FOLLOWED BY WATER (IF VOMITING OCCURS, KEEP HEAD BELOW HIPS TO PREVENT ASPIRATION). IF CONSCIOUSNESS LEVEL DECLINES OR VOMITING HAS NOT OCCURRED IN 15 MINUTES EMPTY STOMACH BY GASTRIC LAVAGE WITH THE AID OF CUFFED ENDOTRACHEAL TUBE USING ISOTONIC SALINE OR 5% SODIUM BICARBONATE FOLLOW WITH ACTIVATED CHARCOAL. ESTABLISH AND MAINTAIN AIRWAY. TREAT RESPIRATORY DIFFICULTY WITH ARTIFICIAL RESPIRATION AND OXYGEN. DO NOT GIVE MORPHINE, AMINOPHYLLINE, PHENOTHIAZINES, RESERPINE, FUROSEMIDE, OR ETHACRYNIC ACID (MORGAN, RECOGNITION AND MANAGEMENT OF PESTICIDE POISONINGS, 3RD ED.). TREAT SYMPTOMATICALLY AND SUPPORTIVELY. ADMINISTRATION OF OXYGEN AND LAVAGE MUST BE PERFORMED BY QUALIFIED MEDICAL PERSONNEL. GET MEDICAL ATTENTION IMMEDIATELY.

ANTIDOTE: THE FOLLOWING ANTIDOTE HAS BEEN RECOMMENDED. HOWEVER, THE DECISION AS TO WHETHER THE SEVERITY OF POISONING REQUIRES ADMINISTRATION OF ANY ANTIDOTE AND ACTUAL DOSE REQUIRED SHOULD BE MADE BY QUALIFIED MEDICAL PERSONNEL.

FOR CHOLINESTERASE INHIBITORS: ESTABLISH CLEAR AIRWAY AND TISSUE OXYGENATION BY ASPIRATION OF SECRETIONS, AND IF NECESSARY, BY ASSISTED PULMONARY VENTILATION WITH OXYGEN. IMPROVE TISSUE OXYGENATION AS MUCH AS POSSIBLE BEFORE ADMINISTERING ATROPINE TO MINIMIZE THE RISK OF VENTRICULAR FIBRILLATION. ADMINISTER ATROPINE SULFATE INTRAVENOUSLY, OR INTRAMUSCULARLY IF IV INJECTION IS NOT POSSIBLE. IN MODERATELY SEVERE POISONING ADMINISTER ATROPINE SULFATE, 0.4-2.0 MG REPEATED EVERY 15 MINUTES UNTIL ATROPINIZATION IS ACHIEVED (TACHYCARDIA, FLUSHING, DRY MOUTH, MYDRIASIS). MAINTAIN ATROPINIZATION BY REPEATED DOSES FOR 2-12 HOURS, OR LONGER, DEPENDING ON THE SEVERITY OF POISONING. THE APPEARANCE OF RALES IN THE LUNG BASES, MIOSIS, SALIVATION, NAUSEA, BRADYCARDIA, ARE ALL INDICATIONS OF INADEQUATE ATROPINIZATION. SEVERELY POISONED INDIVIDUALS MAY EXHIBIT REMARKABLE TOLERANCE TO ATROPINE; TWO OR MORE TIMES THE DOSAGES SUGGESTED ABOVE MAY BE NEEDED. PERSONS NOT POISONED OR ONLY SLIGHTLY POISONED, HOWEVER, MAY DEVELOP SIGNS OF ATROPINE TOXICITY FROM SUCH LARGE DOSAGES: FEVER, MUSCLE FIBRILLATIONS, AND DELIRIUM ARE THE MAIN SIGNS OF ATROPINE TOXICITY. IF THESE SIGNS APPEAR WHILE THE PATIENT IS FULLY ATROPINIZED, ATROPINE ADMINISTRATION SHOULD BE DISCONTINUED, AT LEAST TEMPORARILY. OBSERVE TREATED PATIENTS CLOSELY AT LEAST 24 HOURS TO INSURE THAT SYMPTOMS (POSSIBLY PULMONARY EDEMA) DO NOT RECUR AS ATROPINIZATION WEARS OFF. IN VERY SEVERE POISONINGS, METABOLIC DISPOSITION OF TOXICANT MAY REQUIRE SEVERAL HOURS OR DAYS DURING WHICH ATROPINIZATION MUST BE MAINTAINED. MARKEDLY LOWER LEVELS OF URINARY METABOLITES INDICATE THAT ATROPINE DOSAGE CAN BE TAPERED OFF. AS DOSAGE IS REDUCED, CHECK THE LUNG BASES FREQUENTLY FOR RALES. IF RALES ARE HEARD OR OTHER SYMPTOMS RETURN, RE-ESTABLISH ATROPINIZATION PROMPTLY (MORGAN, RECOGNITION AND MANAGEMENT OF PESTICIDE POISONINGS, 3RD ED.). ADMINISTRATION OF ANTIDOTE MUST BE PERFORMED BY QUALIFIED MEDICAL PERSONNEL.

REACTIVITY

REACTIVITY: STABLE UNDER NORMAL TEMPERATURES AND PRESSURES.

INCOMPATIBILITIES: 3,5-XYLYL METHYLCARBAMATE: OXIDIZERS (STRONG): FIRE AND EXPLOSION HAZARD.

DECOMPOSITION: THERMAL DECOMPOSITION PRODUCTS MAY INCLUDE TOXIC OXIDES OF CARBON AND NITROGEN.

POLYMERIZATION: HAZARDOUS POLYMERIZATION HAS NOT BEEN REPORTED TO OCCUR UNDER NORMAL TEMPERATURES AND PRESSURES.

STORAGE AND DISPOSAL

OBSERVE ALL FEDERAL, STATE AND LOCAL REGULATIONS WHEN STORING OR DISPOSING OF THIS SUBSTANCE. FOR ASSISTANCE, CONTACT THE DISTRICT DIRECTOR OF THE ENVIRONMENTAL PROTECTION AGENCY.

STORAGE

STORE IN ACCORDANCE WITH 40 CFR 165 RECOMMENDED PROCEDURES FOR THE DISPOSAL AND STORAGE OF PESTICIDES AND PESTICIDE CONTAINERS. STORE AWAY FROM INCOMPATIBLE SUBSTANCES.

****DISPOSAL****

DISPOSAL MUST BE IN ACCORDANCE WITH 40 CFR 165 RECOMMENDED PROCEDURES FOR THE DISPOSAL AND STORAGE OF PESTICIDES AND PESTICIDE CONTAINERS.

CONDITIONS TO AVOID

MAY BURN BUT DOES NOT IGNITE READILY. AVOID CONTACT WITH STRONG OXIDIZERS, EXCESSIVE HEAT, SPARKS, OR OPEN FLAME.

SPILL AND LEAK PROCEDURES

OCCUPATIONAL SPILL: SWEEP UP AND PLACE IN SUITABLE CLEAN, DRY CONTAINERS FOR RECLAMATION OR LATER DISPOSAL. DO NOT FLUSH SPILLED MATERIAL INTO SEWER. KEEP UNNECESSARY PEOPLE AWAY.

PROTECTIVE EQUIPMENT

VENTILATION: PROVIDE LOCAL EXHAUST OR GENERAL DILUTION VENTILATION SYSTEM.

RESPIRATOR: THE FOLLOWING RESPIRATORS ARE RECOMMENDED BASED ON INFORMATION FOUND IN THE PHYSICAL DATA, TOXICITY AND HEALTH EFFECTS SECTIONS. THEY ARE RANKED IN ORDER FROM MINIMUM TO MAXIMUM RESPIRATORY PROTECTION. THE SPECIFIC RESPIRATOR SELECTED MUST BE BASED ON CONTAMINATION LEVELS FOUND IN THE WORK PLACE, MUST NOT EXCEED THE WORKING LIMITS OF THE RESPIRATOR AND BE JOINTLY APPROVED BY THE NATIONAL INSTITUTE FOR OCCUPATIONAL SAFETY AND HEALTH AND THE MINE SAFETY AND HEALTH ADMINISTRATION (NIOSH-MSHA).

CHEMICAL CARTRIDGE RESPIRATOR WITH AN ORGANIC VAPOR CARTRIDGE(S) IN COMBINATION WITH A DUST AND MIST FILTER.

GAS MASK WITH ORGANIC VAPOR CANISTER (CHIN-STYLE OR FRONT- OR BACK-MOUNTED CANISTER) WITH A DUST AND MIST FILTER.

GAS MASK WITH ORGANIC VAPOR CANISTER (CHIN-STYLE OR FRONT- OR BACK-MOUNTED CANISTER) WITH A PARTICULATE FILTER.

POWERED AIR-PURIFYING RESPIRATOR WITH A HIGH-EFFICIENCY FILTER.

TYPE 'C' SUPPLIED-AIR RESPIRATOR WITH A FULL FACEPIECE OPERATED IN A PRESSURE-DEMAND OR OTHER POSITIVE PRESSURE MODE.

SELF-CONTAINED BREATHING APPARATUS WITH A FULL FACEPIECE OPERATED IN PRESSURE-DEMAND OR OTHER POSITIVE PRESSURE MODE.

CHEMICAL CARTRIDGE RESPIRATOR WITH AN ORGANIC VAPOR CARTRIDGE(S) WITH A FULL FACEPIECE AND ORGANIC VAPOR CARTRIDGE(S) IN COMBINATION WITH A DUST AND MIST FILTER.

POWERED AIR-PURIFYING RESPIRATOR WITH A TIGHT-FITTING FACEPIECE AND ORGANIC VAPOR CARTRIDGE(S) IN COMBINATION WITH A HIG H-EFFICIENCY PARTICULATE FILTER.

TYPE 'C' SUPPLIED-AIR RESPIRATOR WITH A FULL FACEPIECE OPERATED IN A PRESSURE-DEMAND OR OTHER POSITIVE PRESSURE MODE.

SELF-CONTAINED BREATHING APPARATUS WITH A FULL FACEPIECE OPERATED IN PRESSURE-DEMAND OR OTHER POSITIVE PRESSURE MODE.

CLOTHING: EMPLOYEE MUST WEAR APPROPRIATE PROTECTIVE (IMPERVIOUS) CLOTHING AND EQUIPMENT TO PREVENT REPEATED OR PROLONGED SKIN CONTACT WITH THIS SUBSTANCE.

GLOVES: EMPLOYEE MUST WEAR APPROPRIATE PROTECTIVE GLOVES TO PREVENT CONTACT WITH THIS SUBSTANCE.

EYE PROTECTION: EMPLOYEE MUST WEAR SPLASH-PROOF OR DUST-RESISTANT SAFETY GOGGLES TO PREVENT EYE CONTACT WITH THIS SUBSTANCE.

EMERGENCY EYE WASH: WHERE THERE IS ANY POSSIBILITY THAT AN EMPLOYEE'S EYES MAY BE EXPOSED TO THIS SUBSTANCE, THE EMPLOYER SHOULD PROVIDE AN EYE WASH FOUNTAIN WITHIN THE IMMEDIATE WORK AREA FOR EMERGENCY USE.

AUTHORIZED BY- OCCUPATIONAL HEALTH SERVICES, INC.

CREATION DATE: 12/20/89 ***REVISION DATE:*** 06/12/90

MATERIAL SAFETY DATA SHEET

OCCUPATIONAL HEALTH SERVICES, INC.
AGRICULTURE AND PESTICIDE DIVISION
450 SEVENTH AVENUE, SUITE 2407
NEW YORK, NEW YORK 10123
1-800-445-MSDS OR (212) 967-1100

EMERGENCY CONTACT:
JOHN S. BRANSFORD, JR. (615) 292-1180

SUBSTANCE IDENTIFICATION

CAS-NUMBER 7646-85-7

SUBSTANCE: **ZINC CHLORIDE, SOLID**

TRADE NAMES/SYNONYMS: ZINC DICHLORIDE; ZINC BUTTER; BUTTER OF ZINC; STCC 4966790; UN 2331; Z-31; Z-33; ZINC CHLORIDE; CL2ZN; PST25350

CHEMICAL FAMILY: INORGANIC SALT

MOLECULAR FORMULA: ZN-CL2

MOLECULAR WEIGHT: 136.29

CERCLA RATINGS (SCALE 0-3): HEALTH=3 FIRE=0 REACTIVITY=0 PERSISTENCE=3

NFPA RATINGS (SCALE 0-4): HEALTH=U FIRE=0 REACTIVITY=0

COMPONENTS AND CONTAMINANTS

COMPONENT: ZINC CHLORIDE ***PERCENT:*** 100.0

CAS# 7646-85-7

OTHER CONTAMINANTS: NONE

EXPOSURE LIMITS: ZINC CHLORIDE, FUME: 1 MG/M3 OSHA TWA; 2 MG/M3 OSHA STEL 1 MG/M3 ACGIH TWA; 2 MG/M3 ACGIH STEL

ZINC COMPOUNDS: SUBJECT TO SARA SECTION 313 ANNUAL TOXIC CHEMICAL RELEASE REPORTING

PHYSICAL DATA

DESCRIPTION: ODORLESS, WHITE, HEXAGONAL, DELIQUESCENT CRYSTALS.

BOILING POINT: 1350 F (732 C) ***MELTING POINT:*** 541 F (283 C)

SPECIFIC GRAVITY: 2.91 @ 25 C ***PH:*** 1 @ 17% SOLN.

SOLUBILITY IN WATER: 432% @ 25 C

SOLVENT SOLUBILITY: SOLUBLE IN ALCOHOL, ETHER, HYDROCHLORIC ACID, GLYCEROL, ACETONE; INSOLUBLE IN AMMONIA.

FIRE AND EXPLOSION DATA

FIRE AND EXPLOSION HAZARD: NEGLIGIBLE FIRE HAZARD WHEN EXPOSED TO HEAT OR FLAME.

FIREFIGHTING MEDIA: DRY CHEMICAL, CARBON DIOXIDE, HALON, WATER SPRAY OR STANDARD FOAM (1987 EMERGENCY RESPONSE GUIDEBOOK, DOT P 5800.4).

FOR LARGER FIRES, USE WATER SPRAY, FOG OR STANDARD FOAM (1987 EMERGENCY RESPONSE GUIDEBOOK, DOT P 5800.4).

FIREFIGHTING: MOVE CONTAINERS FROM FIRE AREA IF POSSIBLE. COOL CONTAINERS EXPOSED TO FLAMES WITH WATER FROM SIDE UNTIL WELL AFTER FIRE IS OUT. STAY AWAY FROM STORAGE TANK ENDS (1987 EMERGENCY RESPONSE GUIDEBOOK, DOT P 5800.4, GUIDE PAGE 60).

USE AGENTS SUITABLE FOR TYPE OF FIRE. AVOID BREATHING CORROSIVE VAPORS, KEEP UPWIND.

TOXICITY

ZINC CHLORIDE: TOXICITY DATA: 4800 MG/M3/3 HOURS INHALATION-HUMAN TCLO; 4800 MG/M3/30 MINUTES INHALATION-MAN TCLO; 1960 MG/M3/10 MINUTES INHALATION-RAT LCLO; 350 MG/KG ORAL-RAT LD50; 350 MG/KG ORAL-MOUSE LD50; 200 MG/KG ORAL-GUINEA PIG LD50; 330 MG/KG SUBCUTANEOUS-MOUSE LD50; 30 MG/KG INTRAVENOUS-RAT LDLO; 11 MG/KG INTRAVENOUS-RABBIT LDLO; 24 MG/KG INTRAPERITONEAL-MOUSE LD50; 58 MG/KG INTRAPERITONEAL-RAT LD50; 173 MG/KG INTRAPERITONEAL-GUINEA PIG LDLO; MUTAGENIC DATA (RTECS); REPRODUCTIVE EFFECTS DATA (RTECS); TUMORIGENIC DATA (RTECS). CARCINOGEN STATUS: NONE. LOCAL EFFECTS: CORROSIVE- SKIN, EYE, AND MUCOUS MEMBRANES. ACUTE TOXICITY LEVEL: TOXIC BY INGESTION. TARGET EFFECTS: SENSITIZER- DERMAL. POISONING MAY ALSO AFFECT THE KIDNEYS, AND THE RESPIRATORY AND DIGESTIVE SYSTEMS.

HEALTH EFFECTS AND FIRST AID

INHALATION: ZINC CHLORIDE: CORROSIVE. 2000 MG/M3 IMMEDIATELY DANGEROUS TO LIFE OR HEALTH. **ACUTE EXPOSURE-** FUMES MAY BE SEVERELY IRRITATING TO THE UPPER RESPIRATORY TRACT AND MAY CAUSE A METALLIC TASTE, LACRIMATION, SORE THROAT, LOSS OF VOICE, HOARSENESS, COUGHING WITH COPIOUS SPUTUM, A CONSTRICTIVE SENSATION IN THE CHEST, STRIDER, CHEST PAIN AND SORENESS. GASTROINTESTINAL DISTURBANCES INCLUDING NAUSEA, ABDOMINAL PAIN AND SEVERE GASTRITIS WITH VOMITING MAY OCCUR. FEVER, DYSPNEA AND TACHYPNEA, SHORTNESS OR BREATH, LISTLESSNESS, PALE, GRAY CYANOSIS, RAPID PULSE, TACHYCARDIA AND COMA HAVE ALSO BEEN REPORTED. RESPIRATORY EFFECTS MAY INCLUDE SEVERE INFLAMMATION OF THE UPPER RESPIRATORY TRACT, RHINITIS, HEMORRHAGIC ALVEOLITIS, SEVERE PNEUMONITIS, TRACHEOBRONCHITIS, DIFFUSE PULMONARY INFILTRATIONS, ACUTE INTERSTITIAL AND ADVANCED PULMONARY FIBROSIS, PULMONARY EDEMA AND BRONCHOPNEUMONIA. DEATH MAY BE DUE TO PULMONARY EDEMA, RESPIRATORY FAILURE AND BRONCHOPNEUMONIA. AUTOPSY REVEALED RED AND EDEMATOUS MUCOUS MEMBRANE AND PULMONARY NECROSIS, ACTIVE FIBROBLASTIC PROLIFERATION AND COR PULMONALE. **CHRONIC EXPOSURE-** PROLONGED INHALATION MAY RESULT IN ULCERATION OF THE NASAL SEPTUM.

FIRST AID- REMOVE FROM EXPOSURE AREA TO FRESH AIR IMMEDIATELY. IF BREATHING HAS STOPPED, GIVE ARTIFICIAL RESPIRATION. MAINTAIN AIRWAY AND

BLOOD PRESSURE AND ADMINISTER OXYGEN IF AVAILABLE. KEEP AFFECTED PERSON WARM AND AT REST. TREAT SYMPTOMATICALLY AND SUPPORTIVELY. ADMINISTRATION OF OXYGEN SHOULD BE PERFORMED BY QUALIFIED PERSONNEL. GET MEDICAL ATTENTION IMMEDIATELY.

SKIN CONTACT: ZINC CHLORIDE: CORROSIVE/SENSITIZER. **ACUTE EXPOSURE-** DUST, FUMES OR SOLUTIONS MAY CAUSE SEVERE IRRITATION, REDNESS, PAIN, PAPULAR AND PRIMARY DERMATITIS, CHEMICAL BURNS, OF THE SKIN, BOILS, AND ULCERATION OF THE FINGERS, HANDS AND FOREARMS. SENSITIZATION REACTIONS IN THE FORM OF ECZEMATOID DERMATITIS HAVE BEEN REPORTED. **CHRONIC EXPOSURE-** REPEATED OR PROLONGED CONTACT MAY CAUSE BOILS, DERMATITIS OR SENSITIZATION DERMATITIS IN PREVIOUSLY EXPOSED PERSONS. REPEATED CONTACT HAS PRODUCED FATIGABILITY, POOR APPETITE, CONSTIPATION AND PAINS IN THE LONG BONES OF THE LEGS.

FIRST AID- REMOVE CONTAMINATED CLOTHING AND SHOES IMMEDIATELY. WASH AFFECTED AREA WITH SOAP OR MILD DETERGENT AND LARGE AMOUNTS OF WATER UNTIL NO EVIDENCE OF CHEMICAL REMAINS (AT LEAST 15-20 MINUTES). IN CASE OF CHEMICAL BURNS, COVER AREA WITH STERILE, DRY DRESSING. BANDAGE SECURELY, BUT NOT TOO TIGHTLY. GET MEDICAL ATTENTION IMMEDIATELY.

EYE CONTACT: ZINC CHLORIDE: CORROSIVE. **ACUTE EXPOSURE-** CONTACT MAY CAUSE SEVERE IRRITATION AND PAIN, REDNESS, BLURRED VISION AND INJURIES INCLUDING CORNEAL BURNS, ULCERATION AND VASCULARIZATION, CONJUNCTIVITIS, DERMATITIS, AND IRITIS. A SPLASH IN THE EYE CAUSED, INITIALLY, SOME REDNESS AND PERSISTENT DISCOMFORT, BUT WITHIN 6 DAYS IT LEAD TO A DISCRETE STROMAL OPACITY IN THE LOWER PART OF THE CORNEA WITH IRREGULARITIES OF THE OVERLYING EPITHELIUM. FROM AN ACCIDENTAL INSTILLATION OF A DROP OF 50% ZINC CHLORIDE SOLUTION, THE CORNEAL EPITHELIUM BECAME ERODED, THE LIDS RED AND SWOLLEN, AND A MUCOPURULENT DISCHARGE DEVELOPED. LARGE FOLDS DEVELOPED IN THE DESCEMET'S MEMBRANE, AND THE CORNEAL STROMA BECAME TURBID. THIS WAS ACCOMPANIED BY SEVERE IRITIS WITH SMALL HEMORRHAGES IN THE IRIS. DEEP AND SUPERFICIAL VASCULARIZATION OF THE CORNEA FOLLOWED. **CHRONIC EXPOSURE-** REPEATED AND PROLONGED CONTACT TO DUST OR VAPOR MAY CAUSE CONJUNCTIVITIS.

FIRST AID- WASH EYES IMMEDIATELY WITH LARGE AMOUNTS OF WATER, OCCASIONALLY LIFTING UPPER AND LOWER LIDS, UNTIL NO EVIDENCE OF CHEMICAL REMAINS (AT LEAST 15-20 MINUTES). CONTINUE IRRIGATING WITH NORMAL SALINE UNTIL THE PH HAS RETURNED TO NORMAL (30-60 MINUTES). COVER WITH STERILE BANDAGES. GET MEDICAL ATTENTION IMMEDIATELY.

INGESTION: ZINC CHLORIDE: TOXIC. **ACUTE EXPOSURE-** INGESTION MAY CAUSE SEVERE IRRITATION OF MUCOUS MEMBRANES WITH CORROSION, SWOLLEN LIPS, EDEMA OF THE GLOTTIS, SORE THROAT, CHEST PAIN AND GASTROINTESTINAL DISTURBANCES INCLUDING NAUSEA, VOMITING, BLOODY DIARRHEA, AND ABDOMINAL PAIN. PERFORATION OF THE VISCUS MAY OCCUR. LETHARGY, BLOODY URINE, ALBUMINURIA, GASTRITIS AND PYLORIC STENOSIS HAVE BEEN REPORTED. OTHER EFFECTS MAY INCLUDE COLD SKIN, LOW BLOOD PRESSURE, DYSPNEA AND COLLAPSE WITH SHOCK AND HYPOCALCEMIA. DEATH HAS BEEN REPORTED. DELAYED DEATHS HAVE BEEN ASCRIBED TO INANITION FOLLOWING SEVERE STRICTURES OF THE ESOPHAGUS AND PYLORIS. SURVIVORS OF ZINC SALT INGESTION MAY HAVE RESIDUAL NEPHRITIS. **CHRONIC EXPOSURE-** NO DATA AVAILABLE.

FIRST AID- TREAT SYMPTOMATICALLY AND SUPPORTIVELY. IF PERSON IS CONSCIOUS AND ABLE TO SWALLOW, GIVE LARGE AMOUNTS OF WATER OR MILK TO DILUTE SUBSTANCE. GET MEDICAL ATTENTION IMMEDIATELY. GASTRIC LAVAGE PERFORMED BY QUALIFIED MEDICAL PERSONNEL MIGHT BE ADVISABLE IF THERE ARE NO SIGNS OF PERFORATION FROM THE INGESTION OF A CORROSIVE SUBSTANCE. IF VOMITING OCCURS, KEEP HEAD BELOW HIPS TO HELP PREVENT ASPIRATION.

ANTIDOTE: THE FOLLOWING ANTIDOTE HAS BEEN RECOMMENDED. HOWEVER, THE DECISION AS TO WHETHER THE SEVERITY OF POISONING REQUIRES ADMINISTRATION OF ANY ANTIDOTE AND ACTUAL DOSE REQUIRED SHOULD BE MADE BY QUALIFIED MEDICAL PERSONNEL.
POISONING FROM ZINC SALTS: GIVE CALCIUM DISODIUM EDETATE 15-25 MG/KG (0.08-0.125 ML OF 20% SOLUTION PER KILOGRAM OF BODY WEIGHT) IN 250-500 ML OF 5% DEXTROSE INTRAVENOUSLY OVER A 1 TO 2 HOUR PERIOD TWICE DAILY. THE MAXIMUM DOSE SHOULD NOT EXCEED 50 MG/KG/DAY. THE DRUG SHOULD BE GIVEN IN 5-DAY COURSES WITH A REST PERIOD OF AT LEAST 2 DAYS BETWEEN COURSES. AFTER THE FIRST COURSE, SUBSEQUENT COURSES SHOULD NOT EXCEED 50 MG/KG/DAY. DAILY URINALYSES SHOULD BE DONE DURING THE TREATMENT PERIOD. THE DOSAGE SHOULD BE REDUCED IF ANY UNUSUAL URINARY FINDINGS APPEAR. FOR INTRAMUSCULAR ADMINISTRATION, GIVE 12.5 MG/KG BODY WEIGHT EVERY 4-6 HOURS. DILUTE EACH DOSE WITH AN EQUAL VOLUME OF 1% PROCAINE. DOSE LIMITATION IS THE SAME AS THAT GIVEN ABOVE. (DREISBACH, HANDBOOK OF POISONING, 12TH ED.). ANTIDOTE SHOULD BE ADMINISTERED BY QUALIFIED MEDICAL PERSONNEL.

REACTIVITY

REACTIVITY: STABLE UNDER NORMAL TEMPERATURES AND PRESSURES.

INCOMPATIBILITIES: ZINC CHLORIDE: BASES: POSSIBLE VIOLENT REACTION. POTASSIUM: FORMS IMPACT-SENSITIVE MIXTURE. ZINC: FORMS FLAMMABLE MIXTURE.

DECOMPOSITION: THERMAL DECOMPOSITION PRODUCTS MAY INCLUDE TOXIC AND CORROSIVE FUMES OF CHLORIDES AND TOXIC OXIDES OF ZINC.

POLYMERIZATION: HAZARDOUS POLYMERIZATION HAS NOT BEEN REPORTED TO OCCUR UNDER NORMAL TEMPERATURES AND PRESSURES.

STORAGE AND DISPOSAL

OBSERVE ALL FEDERAL, STATE AND LOCAL REGULATIONS WHEN STORING OR DISPOSING OF THIS SUBSTANCE. FOR ASSISTANCE, CONTACT THE DISTRICT DIRECTOR OF THE ENVIRONMENTAL PROTECTION AGENCY.

STORAGE

STORE AWAY FROM INCOMPATIBLE SUBSTANCES.
KEEP IN A TIGHTLY CLOSED CONTAINER. STORE IN A COOL, DRY, VENTILATED AREA.

CONDITIONS TO AVOID

MAY BURN BUT DOES NOT IGNITE READILY. FLAMMABLE, POISONOUS GASES MAY ACCUMULATE IN TANKS AND HOPPER CARS. MAY IGNITE COMBUSTIBLES (WOOD, PAPER, OIL, ETC.).

SPILL AND LEAK PROCEDURES

SOIL SPILL: DIG HOLDING AREA SUCH AS LAGOON, POND OR PIT FOR CONTAINMENT. USE PROTECTIVE COVER SUCH AS A PLASTIC SHEET TO PREVENT MATERIAL FROM DISSOLVING IN FIRE EXTINGUISHING WATER OR RAIN.

WATER SPILL: NEUTRALIZE WITH AGRICULTURAL LIME, SLAKED LIME, CRUSHED LIMESTONE, OR SODIUM BICARBONATE.
ADD SUITABLE AGENT TO NEUTRALIZE SPILLED MATERIAL TO PH-7.
USE MECHANICAL DREDGES OR LIFTS TO EXTRACT IMMOBILIZED MASSES OF POLLUTION AND PRECIPITATES.

OCCUPATIONAL SPILL: DO NOT TOUCH SPILLED MATERIAL. STOP LEAK IF YOU CAN DO IT WITHOUT RISK. FOR SMALL SPILLS, TAKE UP WITH SAND OR OTHER ABSORBENT MATERIAL AND PLACE INTO CONTAINERS FOR LATER DISPOSAL. FOR SMALL DRY SPILLS, WITH CLEAN SHOVEL PLACE MATERIAL INTO CLEAN, DRY CONTAINER AND COVER. MOVE CONTAINERS FROM SPILL AREA. FOR LARGER SPILLS, DIKE FAR AHEAD OF SPILL FOR LATER DISPOSAL. KEEP UNNECESSARY PEOPLE AWAY. ISOLATE HAZARD AREA AND DENY ENTRY.
REPORTABLE QUANTITY (RQ): 1000 POUNDS THE SUPERFUND AMENDMENTS AND REAUTHORIZATION ACT (SARA) SECTION 304 REQUIRES THAT A RELEASE EQUAL TO OR GREATER THAN THE REPORTABLE QUANTITY FOR THIS SUBSTANCE BE IMMEDIATELY REPORTED TO THE LOCAL EMERGENCY PLANNING COMMITTEE AND THE STATE EMERGENCY RESPONSE COMMISSION (40 CFR 355.40). IF THE RELEASE OF THIS SUBSTANCE IS REPORTABLE UNDER CERCLA SECTION 103, THE NATIONAL RESPONSE CENTER MUST BE NOTIFIED IMMEDIATELY AT (800) 424-8802 OR (202) 426-2675 IN THE METROPOLITAN WASHINGTON, D.C. AREA (40 CFR 302.6).

PROTECTIVE EQUIPMENT

VENTILATION: PROVIDE LOCAL EXHAUST OR PROCESS ENCLOSURE VENTILATION TO MEET PUBLISHED EXPOSURE LIMITS.

RESPIRATOR: THE FOLLOWING RESPIRATORS AND MAXIMUM USE CONCENTRATIONS ARE RECOMMENDATIONS BY THE U.S. DEPARTMENT OF HEALTH AND HUMAN SERVICES, NIOSH POCKET GUIDE TO CHEMICAL HAZARDS; NIOSH CRITERIA DOCUMENTS OR BY THE U.S. DEPARTMENT OF LABOR, 29 CFR 1910 SUBPART Z. THE SPECIFIC RESPIRATOR SELECTED MUST BE BASED ON CONTAMINATION LEVELS FOUND IN THE WORK PLACE, MUST NOT EXCEED THE WORKING LIMITS OF THE RESPIRATOR AND BE JOINTLY APPROVED BY THE NATIONAL INSTITUTE FOR OCCUPATIONAL SAFETY AND HEALTH AND THE MINE SAFETY AND HEALTH ADMINISTRATION (NIOSH-MSHA).
FOR ZINC CHLORIDE FUMES:
10 MG/M3- ANY DUST, MIST AND FUME RESPIRATOR WITH A FULL FACEPIECE. ANY SUPPLIED-AIR RESPIRATOR. ANY SELF-CONTAINED BREATHING APPARATUS.
25 MG/M3- ANY POWERED AIR-PURIFYING RESPIRATOR WITH A DUST, MIST, AND FUME FILTER. ANY SUPPLIED-AIR RESPIRATOR OPERATED IN A CONTINUOUS-FLOW MODE.
50 MG/M3- ANY AIR-PURIFYING FULL FACEPIECE RESPIRTOR WITH A HIGH-EFFICIENCY PARTICULATE FILTER. ANY POWERED AIR-PURIFYING RESPIRATOR WITH A TIGHT-FITTING FACEPIECE AND A HIGH-EFFICIENCY PARTICULATE FILTER. ANY SELF-CONTAINED BREATHING APPARATUS WITH A FULL FACEPIECE. ANY SUPPLIED-AIR RESPIRATOR WITH A FULL FACEPIECE.
2000 MG/M3- ANY SUPPLIED-AIR RESPIRATOR WITH A FULL FACEPIECE AND

OPERATED IN A PRESSURE-DEMAND OR OTHER POSTIVE PRESSURE MODE.
ESCAPE- ANY AIR-PURIFYING FULL FACEPIECE RESPIRATOR WITH A HIGH-EFFICIENCY PARTICULATE FILTER. ANY APPROPRIATE ESCAPE-TYPE SELF-CONTAINED BREATHING APPARATUS.
FOR FIREFIGHTING AND OTHER IMMEDIATELY DANGEROUS TO LIFE OR HEALTH CONDITIONS:
SELF-CONTAINED BREATHING APPARATUS WITH FULL FACEPIECE OPERATED IN PRESSURE-DEMAND OR OTHER POSITIVE PRESSURE MODE.
SUPPLIED-AIR RESPIRATOR WITH FULL FACEPIECE AND OPERATED IN PRESSURE-DEMAND OR OTHER POSITIVE PRESSURE MODE IN COMBINATION WITH AN AUXILIARY SELF-CONTAINED BREATHING APPARATUS OPERATED IN PRESSURE-DEMAND OR OTHER POSITIVE PRESSURE MODE.

CLOTHING: EMPLOYEE MUST WEAR APPROPRIATE PROTECTIVE (IMPERVIOUS) CLOTHING AND EQUIPMENT TO PREVENT ANY POSSIBILITY OF SKIN CONTACT WITH THIS SUBSTANCE.

GLOVES: EMPLOYEE MUST WEAR APPROPRIATE PROTECTIVE GLOVES TO PREVENT CONTACT WITH THIS SUBSTANCE.

EYE PROTECTION: EMPLOYEE MUST WEAR SPLASH-PROOF OR DUST-RESISTANT SAFETY GOGGLES AND A FACESHIELD TO PREVENT CONTACT WITH THIS SUBSTANCE.
EMERGENCY WASH FACILITIES: WHERE THERE IS ANY POSSIBILITY THAT AN EMPLOYEE'S EYES AND/OR SKIN MAY BE EXPOSED TO THIS SUBSTANCE, THE EMPLOYER SHOULD PROVIDE AN EYE WASH FOUNTAIN AND QUICK DRENCH SHOWER WITHIN THE IMMEDIATE WORK AREA FOR EMERGENCY USE.

AUTHORIZED BY- OCCUPATIONAL HEALTH SERVICES, INC.
CREATION DATE: 02/08/90 ***REVISION DATE:*** 05/15/90

MATERIAL SAFETY DATA SHEET

OCCUPATIONAL HEALTH SERVICES, INC.
AGRICULTURE AND PESTICIDE DIVISION
450 SEVENTH AVENUE, SUITE 2407
NEW YORK, NEW YORK 10123
1-800-445-MSDS OR (212) 967-1100

EMERGENCY CONTACT:
JOHN S. BRANSFORD, JR. (615) 292-1180

SUBSTANCE IDENTIFICATION

CAS-NUMBER 137-30-4
SUBSTANCE: **ZINC DIMETHYLDITHIOCARBAMATE**
TRADE NAMES/SYNONYMS: ZINC, BIS(DIMETHYLCARBAMODITHIOATO-S,S')-,(T-4); ZINC, BIS(DIMETHYLDITHIOCARBAMATO)-; ZINC BIS(DIMETHYLDITHIOCARBAMATE); BIS(DIMETHYLDITHIOCARBAMATO)ZINC; (T-4)-BIS(DIMETHYLDITHIOCARBAMATO-S,S')ZINC; AAPROTECT; CARBAZINC; COROZATE; CUMAN; FUCLASIN; FUKLASIN; HEXAZIR; KARBAM WHITE; METHASAN; MEZENE; ZERLATE; ZIMATE; ZIRAM; ZIRBERK; PST25397
CHEMICAL FAMILY: THIOCARBAMATE
ORGANOMETALLIC
MOLECULAR FORMULA: C6-H12-N2-S4.ZN
MOLECULAR WEIGHT: 305.81
CERCLA RATINGS (SCALE 0-3): HEALTH=2 FIRE=U REACTIVITY=0 PERSISTENCE=3
NFPA RATINGS (SCALE 0-4): HEALTH=2 FIRE=U REACTIVITY=0

COMPONENTS AND CONTAMINANTS

COMPONENT: ZINC DIMETHYLDITHIOCARBAMATE ***PERCENT:*** 100
CAS# 137-30-4
OTHER CONTAMINANTS: NONE

PHYSICAL DATA

DESCRIPTION: ODORLESS, COLORLESS CRYSTALS OR CREAMY-WHITE POWDER.
MELTING POINT: 482 F (250 C) ***SPECIFIC GRAVITY:*** 1.66
VAPOR PRESSURE: NEGLIGIBLE @ 20 C ***SOLUBILITY IN WATER:*** 65 PPM @ 25 C
SOLVENT SOLUBILITY: SOLUBLE IN DILUTE ALKALI, CARBON DISULPHIDE, CHLOROFORM; CONCENTRATED HYDROCHLORIC ACID; MODERATELY SOLUBLE IN ACETONE, BENZENE, NAPHTHA; SLIGHTLY SOLUBLE IN DIETHYL ETHER, ETHANOL

FIRE AND EXPLOSION DATA

FIRE AND EXPLOSION HAZARD: UNKNOWN FIRE AND EXPLOSION HAZARD. DUST-AIR MIXTURES MAY IGNITE OR EXPLODE.
FIREFIGHTING MEDIA: DRY CHEMICAL, CARBON DIOXIDE OR HALON (1987 EMERGENCY RESPONSE GUIDEBOOK, DOT P 5800.4).
FOR LARGER FIRES, USE WATER SPRAY, FOG OR STANDARD FOAM (1987 EMERGENCY RESPONSE GUIDEBOOK, DOT P 5800.4).
FIREFIGHTING: DO NOT TOUCH SPILLED MATERIAL (1987 EMERGENCY RESPONSE GUIDEBOOK, DOT P 5800.4, GUIDE PAGE 58).
EXTINGUISH USING AGENTS INDICATED. USE FLOODING AMOUNTS OF WATER AS A FOG. COOL CONTAINERS WITH FLOODING AMOUNTS OF WATER. USE WATER TO ABSORB VAPORS. AVOID BREATHING IRRITATING VAPORS; KEEP UPWIND.

TOXICITY

ZINC DIMETHYLDITHIOCARBAMATE: TOXICITY DATA: 1400 MG/KG ORAL-RAT LD50; 480 MG/KG ORAL-MOUSE LD50; 400 MG/KG ORAL-RABBIT LD50; 200 MG/KG ORAL-GUINEA PIG LD50; 1340 MG/KG SUBCUTANEOUS-RAT LD50; 800 MG/KG SUBCUTANEOUS-MOUSE LD50; 400 MG/KG SUBCUTANEOUS-RABBIT LD50; 18 MG/KG INTRAVENOUS-MOUSE LD50; 23 MG/KG INTRAPERITONEAL-RAT LD50; 73 MG/KG INTRAPERITONEAL-MOUSE LD50; 50 MG/KG INTRAPERITONEAL-RABBIT LDLO; 30 MG/KG INTRAPERITONEAL-GUINEA PIG LDLO; 1230 MG/KG UNREPORTED-RAT LD50; MUTAGENIC DATA (RTECS); REPRODUCTIVE EFFECTS DATA (RTECS); TUMORIGENIC DATA (RTECS). CARCINOGEN STATUS: ANIMAL INADEQUATE EVIDENCE (IARC GROUP-3). LOCAL EFFECTS: IRRITANT- INHALATION, SKIN, AND EYES. ACUTE TOXICITY LEVEL: MODERATELY TOXIC BY INGESTION. TARGET EFFECTS: POSIONING MAY AFFECT THE NERVOUS SYSTEM AND BLOOD. ADDITIONAL DATA: MAY REACT WITH NITRITE UNDER MILDLY ACIDIC CONDITONS SUCH AS THOSE IN THE HUMAN STOMACH, TO FORM N-NITROSODIMETHYLAMINE, WHICH HAS BEEN SHOWN TO BE CARCINOGENIC IN SEVEN ANIMAL SPECIES. INTERACTIONS WITH ALCOHOL MAY OCCUR.

HEALTH EFFECTS AND FIRST AID

INHALATION: ZINC DIMETHYLDITHIOCARBAMATE: IRRITANT. **ACUTE EXPOSURE-** EXPOSURE TO THE AEROSOL HAS CAUSED IRRITATION OF THE NOSE AND THROAT, GASTRITIS, ANEMIA, AND VEGETODYSTONIA. THE DUST MAY CAUSE BURNING SENSATION IN THE EYES, NOSE, AND THROAT, EPISTAXIS AND DIFFICULTY IN BREATHING. **CHRONIC EXPOSURE-** PROLONGED OR REPEATED EXPOSURE MAY CAUSE EFFECTS AS DESCRIBED IN ACUTE EXPOSURE. NEURAL AND VISUAL DISTURBANCES WERE ALSO REPORTED FROM PROLONGED EXPOSURE. A HIGHER FREQUENCY OF ABNORMAL CHROMOSOMES OR CHROMATIDS WAS REPORTED IN CULTURED LYMPHOCYTES OF WORKERS EXPOSED TO ZINC DIMETHYLDITHIOCARBAMATE.
FIRST AID- REMOVE FROM EXPOSURE AREA TO FRESH AIR IMMEDIATELY. IF BREATHING HAS STOPPED, PERFORM ARTIFICIAL RESPIRATION. KEEP PERSON WARM AND AT REST. TREAT SYMPTOMATICALLY AND SUPPORTIVELY. GET MEDICAL ATTENTION IMMEDIATELY.

SKIN CONTACT: ZINC DIMETHYLDITHIOCARBAMATE: IRRITANT. **ACUTE EXPOSURE-** MAY CAUSE IRRITATION. IT MAY BE ABSORBED THROUGH INTACT SKIN. DITHIOCARBAMATES MAY CAUSE ITCHING, REDNESS, AND ECZEMATOID DERMATITIS IN PREDISPOSED INDIVIDUALS. **CHRONIC EXPOSURE-** MAY CAUSE DERMATITIS UPON HEAVY EXPOSURE. REPEATED CONTACT WITH DITHIOCARBAMATES MAY CAUSE SENSITIZATION IN SOME INDIVIDUALS.
FIRST AID- REMOVE CONTAMINATED CLOTHING AND SHOES IMMEDIATELY. WASH AFFECTED AREA WITH SOAP OR MILD DETERGENT AND LARGE AMOUNTS OF WATER UNTIL NO EVIDENCE OF CHEMICAL REMAINS (APPROXIMATELY 15-20 MINUTES). GET MEDICAL ATTENTION IMMEDIATELY.

EYE CONTACT: ZINC DIMETHYLDITHIOCARBAMATE: IRRITANT. **ACUTE EXPOSURE-** MAY CAUSE IRRITATION, A BURNING SENSATION AND MILD CONJUNCTIVITIS. **CHRONIC EXPOSURE-** REPEATED OR PROLONGED CONTACT MAY CAUSE CONJUNCTIVITIS.
FIRST AID- WASH EYES IMMEDIATELY WITH LARGE AMOUNTS OF WATER OR NORMAL SALINE, OCCASIONALLY LIFTING UPPER AND LOWER LIDS, UNTIL NO EVIDENCE OF CHEMICAL REMAINS (APPROXIMATELY 15-20 MINUTES). GET MEDICAL ATTENTION IMMEDIATELY.

INGESTION: ZINC DIMETHYLDITHIOCARBAMATE: **ACUTE EXPOSURE-** EMPHYSEMA, HEMOLYSIS, BRAIN EDEMA AND HEMORRHAGE, DYSTROPHY OF THE MUSCLE, LIVER AND KIDNEY, AND LOCAL NECROSIS OF THE INTESTINE WERE REPORTED IN A FATAL CASE OF HUMAN POISONING. INGESTION OF DITHIOCARBAMATES MAY CAUSE NAUSEA, VOMITING, DIARRHEA, ANOREXIA, HEADACHE, LETHARGY, DIZZINESS, ATAXIA, CONFUSION, DROWSINESS, EMOTIONAL LABILITY AND COMA. IN ANIMAL STUDIES, MUSCLE WEAKNESS AND ASCENDING PARALYSIS PROGRESSED TO RESPIRATORY PARALYSIS AND DEATH. **CHRONIC EXPOSURE-** RATS GIVEN DIETS CONTAINING 2500 PPM FOR 2 YEARS EXPERIENCED SOME WEIGHT REDUCTION, BUT NO MORTALITIES WERE REPORTED. ADVERSE EFFECTS ON FERTILITY, THE FETUS, AND FETAL DEVELOPMENTAL ABNORMALITIES WERE REPORTED FROM CHRONIC FEEDING STUDIES OF PREGNANT RATS. IN A NTP STUDY, INCREASE INCIDENCES OF C-CELL CARCINOMAS OF THE THYROID GLAND WAS OBSERVED IN MALE RATS AND INCREASE INCIDENCES OF

ALVEOLAR/BRONCHIOLAR ADENOMAS AND OF COMBINED ALVEOLAR/BRONCHIOLAR ADENOMAS OR CARCINOMAS OCCURRED IN FEMALE MICE. NO EVIDENCE OF CARCINOGENIC ACTIVITY WAS OBSERVED IN THE OPPOSITE SEX OF EACH SPECIES.

FIRST AID- IF VIGOROUS EMESIS HAS NOT ALREADY OCCURRED AND VICTIM IS FULLY ALERT, GIVE SYRUP OF IPECAC, FOLLOWED BY 1-2 GLASSES OF WATER TO INDUCE VOMITING (ADULTS, 12 YEARS AND OLDER: 30 ML; CHILDREN UNDER 12: 15 ML). IF CONSCIOUSNESS LEVEL DECLINES OR VOMITING HAS NOT OCCURRED IN 15 MINUTES, EMPTY THE STOMACH BY INTUBATION, ASPIRATION, AND LAVAGE, USING ALL AVAILABLE MEANS TO AVOID ASPIRATION OF VOMITUS. AFTER ASPIRATION OF THE STOMACH AND WASHING WITH ISOTONIC SALINE OR SODIUM BICARBONATE, INSTILL 30-50 GM OF ACTIVATED CHARCOAL IN 3-4 OUNCES OF WATER THROUGH THE STOMACH TUBE TO LIMIT ABSORPTION OF REMAINING TOXICANT. IF THE IRRITANT PROPERTIES OF THE TOXICANT FAIL TO PRODUCE A BOWEL MOVEMENT IN 4 HOURS, ADMINISTER SODIUM OR MAGNESIUM SULFATE AS A CATHARTIC: 0.25 GM/KG BODY WEIGHT IN 1-8 OUNCES OF WATER. ADMINISTER GLUCOSE-CONTAINING FLUIDS INTRAVENOUSLY TO ACCELERATE EXCRETION OF TOXICANT. (MORGAN, RECOGNITION AND MANAGEMENT OF PESTICIDE POISONINGS, THIRD EDITION) GET MEDICAL ATTENTION. TREATMENT SHOULD BE BE ADMINISTERED BY QUALIFIED MEDICAL PERSONNEL.

ANTIDOTE: NO SPECIFIC ANTIDOTE. TREAT SYMPTOMATICALLY AND SUPPORTIVELY.

REACTIVITY

REACTIVITY: STABLE UNDER NORMAL TEMPERATURES AND PRESSURES.

INCOMPATIBILITIES: ZINC DIMETHYLDITHIOCARBAMATE: ACIDS: DECOMPOSITION WITH EVOLUTION OF CARBON DISULPHIDE. COPPER: INCOMPATIBLE. MERCURY: INCOMPATIBLE.

DECOMPOSITION: THERMAL DECOMPOSITION PRODUCTS MAY INCLUDE TOXIC OXIDES OF CARBON, NITROGEN, AND SULFUR.

POLYMERIZATION: HAZARDOUS POLYMERIZATION HAS NOT BEEN REPORTED TO OCCUR UNDER NORMAL TEMPERATURES AND PRESSURES.

STORAGE AND DISPOSAL

OBSERVE ALL FEDERAL, STATE AND LOCAL REGULATIONS WHEN STORING OR DISPOSING OF THIS SUBSTANCE. FOR ASSISTANCE, CONTACT THE DISTRICT DIRECTOR OF THE ENVIRONMENTAL PROTECTION AGENCY.

STORAGE

STORE IN ACCORDANCE WITH 40 CFR 165 RECOMMENDED PROCEDURES FOR THE DISPOSAL AND STORAGE OF PESTICIDES AND PESTICIDE CONTAINERS.
STORE AWAY FROM INCOMPATIBLE SUBSTANCES.

DISPOSAL

DISPOSAL MUST BE IN ACCORDANCE WITH 40 CFR 165 RECOMMENDED PROCEDURES FOR THE DISPOSAL AND STORAGE OF PESTICIDES AND PESTICIDE CONTAINERS.

CONDITIONS TO AVOID

MAY BURN BUT DOES NOT IGNITE READILY. AVOID CONTACT WITH STRONG OXIDIZERS, EXCESSIVE HEAT, SPARKS, OR OPEN FLAME.

SPILL AND LEAK PROCEDURES

OCCUPATIONAL SPILL: SWEEP UP AND PLACE IN SUITABLE CLEAN, DRY CONTAINERS FOR RECLAMATION OR LATER DISPOSAL. DO NOT FLUSH SPILLED MATERIAL INTO SEWER. KEEP UNNECESSARY PEOPLE AWAY.

PROTECTIVE EQUIPMENT

VENTILATION: PROVIDE LOCAL EXHAUST OR GENERAL DILUTION VENTILATION SYSTEM.

RESPIRATOR: THE FOLLOWING RESPIRATORS ARE RECOMMENDED BASED ON INFORMATION FOUND IN THE PHYSICAL DATA, TOXICITY AND HEALTH EFFECTS SECTIONS. THEY ARE RANKED IN ORDER FROM MINIMUM TO MAXIMUM RESPIRATORY PROTECTION. THE SPECIFIC RESPIRATOR SELECTED MUST BE BASED ON CONTAMINATION LEVELS FOUND IN THE WORK PLACE, MUST NOT EXCEED THE WORKING LIMITS OF THE RESPIRATOR AND BE JOINTLY APPROVED BY THE NATIONAL INSTITUTE FOR OCCUPATIONAL SAFETY AND HEALTH AND THE MINE SAFETY AND HEALTH ADMINISTRATION (NIOSH-MSHA).
CHEMICAL CARTRIDGE RESPIRATOR WITH AN ORGANIC VAPOR CARTRIDGE(S) WITH A FULL FACEPIECE AND ORGANIC VAPOR CARTRIDGE(S) IN COMBINATION WITH A DUST AND MIST FILTER.
POWERED AIR-PURIFYING RESPIRATOR WITH A TIGHT-FITTING FACEPIECE AND ORGANIC VAPOR CARTRIDGE(S) IN COMBINATION WITH A HIGH-EFFICIENCY PARTICULATE FILTER.
TYPE 'C' SUPPLIED-AIR RESPIRATOR WITH A FULL FACEPIECE OPERATED IN A PRESSURE-DEMAND OR OTHER POSITIVE PRESSURE MODE.
SELF-CONTAINED BREATHING APPARATUS WITH A FULL FACEPIECE OPERATED IN PRESSURE-DEMAND OR OTHER POSITIVE PRESSURE MODE.
FOR FIREFIGHTING AND OTHER IMMEDIATELY DANGEROUS TO LIFE OR HEALTH CONDITIONS:
SELF-CONTAINED BREATHING APPARATUS WITH FULL FACEPIECE OPERATED IN PRESSURE-DEMAND OR OTHER POSITIVE PRESSURE MODE.
SUPPLIED-AIR RESPIRATOR WITH FULL FACEPIECE AND OPERATED IN PRESSURE-DEMAND OR OTHER POSITIVE PRESSURE MODE IN COMBINATION WITH AN AUXILIARY SELF-CONTAINED BREATHING APPARATUS OPERATED IN PRESSURE-DEMAND OR OTHER POSITIVE PRESSURE MODE.

CLOTHING: EMPLOYEE MUST WEAR APPROPRIATE PROTECTIVE (IMPERVIOUS) CLOTHING AND EQUIPMENT TO PREVENT REPEATED OR PROLONGED SKIN CONTACT WITH THIS SUBSTANCE.

GLOVES: EMPLOYEE MUST WEAR APPROPRIATE PROTECTIVE GLOVES TO PREVENT CONTACT WITH THIS SUBSTANCE.

EYE PROTECTION: EMPLOYEE MUST WEAR SPLASH-PROOF OR DUST-RESISTANT SAFETY GOGGLES TO PREVENT EYE CONTACT WITH THIS SUBSTANCE.
EMERGENCY EYE WASH: WHERE THERE IS ANY POSSIBILITY THAT AN EMPLOYEE'S EYES MAY BE EXPOSED TO THIS SUBSTANCE, THE EMPLOYER SHOULD PROVIDE AN EYE WASH FOUNTAIN WITHIN THE IMMEDIATE WORK AREA FOR EMERGENCY USE.

AUTHORIZED BY- OCCUPATIONAL HEALTH SERVICES, INC.
CREATION DATE: 10/05/89 ***REVISION DATE:*** 07/12/90

MATERIAL SAFETY DATA SHEET

OCCUPATIONAL HEALTH SERVICES, INC.
AGRICULTURE AND PESTICIDE DIVISION
450 SEVENTH AVENUE, SUITE 2407
NEW YORK, NEW YORK 10123
1-800-445-MSDS OR (212) 967-1100

EMERGENCY CONTACT:
JOHN S. BRANSFORD, JR. (615) 292-1180

SUBSTANCE IDENTIFICATION

CAS-NUMBER 16871-71-9

SUBSTANCE: **ZINC SILICOFLUORIDE**

TRADE NAMES/SYNONYMS: ZINC FLUOROSILICATE; ZINC HEXAFLUOROSILICATE; ZINC FLUOSILICATE; STCC 4966392; UN 2855; SILICATE(2-), HEXAFLUORO-, ZINC; SILICON ZINC FLUORIDE; ZINC HEXAFLUOROSILICATE(2-); PST25410

CHEMICAL FAMILY: INORGANIC SALT

MOLECULAR FORMULA: ZN.SI-F6

MOLECULAR WEIGHT: 207.46

CERCLA RATINGS (SCALE 0-3): HEALTH=3 FIRE=0 REACTIVITY=0 PERSISTENCE=3

NFPA RATINGS (SCALE 0-4): HEALTH=3 FIRE=0 REACTIVITY=0

COMPONENTS AND CONTAMINANTS

COMPONENT: ZINC SILICOFLUORIDE ***PERCENT:*** 100
CAS# 16871-71-9

EXPOSURE LIMITS: ZINC SILICOFLUORIDE: 2.5 MG(F)/M3 OSHA TWA 2.5 MG(F)/M3 ACGIH TWA 2.5 MG(F)/M3 NIOSH RECOMMENDED 10 HOUR TWA
5000 POUNDS CERCLA SECTION 103 REPORTABLE QUANTITY SUBJECT TO SARA SECTION 313 ANNUAL TOXIC CHEMICAL RELEASE REPORTING

PHYSICAL DATA

DESCRIPTION: ODORLESS, COLORLESS TO WHITE, TRANSPARENT, HEXAGONAL PRISMS.

MELTING POINT: NOT AVAILABLE ***SPECIFIC GRAVITY:*** 2.104 (HEXAHYDRATE)

PH: 3.2 (1% AQ SOLN) ***SOLUBILITY IN WATER:*** 77% @ 10 C

FIRE AND EXPLOSION DATA

FIRE AND EXPLOSION HAZARD: NEGLIGIBLE FIRE HAZARD WHEN EXPOSED TO HEAT OR FLAME.

FIREFIGHTING MEDIA: DRY CHEMICAL, CARBON DIOXIDE, HALON, WATER SPRAY OR STANDARD FOAM (1987 EMERGENCY RESPONSE GUIDEBOOK, DOT P 5800.4).
FOR LARGER FIRES, USE WATER SPRAY, FOG OR STANDARD FOAM (1987 EMERGENCY RESPONSE GUIDEBOOK, DOT P 5800.4).

FIREFIGHTING: MOVE CONTAINERS FROM FIRE AREA IF POSSIBLE (1987 EMERGENCY RESPONSE GUIDEBOOK, DOT P 5800.4, GUIDE PAGE 53).
USE AGENTS SUITABLE FOR TYPE OF SURROUNDING FIRE. AVOID BREATHING VAPORS OR DUSTS, KEEP UPWIND.

TRANSPORTATION DATA

DEPARTMENT OF TRANSPORTATION HAZARD CLASSIFICATION 49 CFR 172.101: ORM-E
DEPARTMENT OF TRANSPORTATION LABELING REQUIREMENTS 49 CFR 172.101 AND SUBPART E: NONE
DEPARTMENT OF TRANSPORTATION PACKAGING REQUIREMENTS: 49 CFR 173.510 EXCEPTIONS: NONE

TOXICITY

ZINC SILICOFLUORIDE: TOXICITY DATA: 100 MG/KG ORAL-RAT LDLO. CARCINOGEN STATUS: NONE. LOCAL EFFECTS: IRRITANT- INHALATION, SKIN, AND EYES. ACUTE TOXICITY LEVEL: TOXIC BY INGESTION. TARGET EFFECTS: INSUFFICIENT DATA.

HEALTH EFFECTS AND FIRST AID

INHALATION: ZINC SILICOFLUORIDE: CORROSIVE. 500 MG(F)/M3 IMMEDIATELY DANGEROUS TO LIFE AND HEALTH. **ACUTE EXPOSURE-** SALIVATION, COUGHING, CHOKING, AND CHILLS MAY OCCUR UP TO 2 HOURS AFTER EXPOSURE. IN 1-2 DAYS, SYMPTOMS MAY PROGRESS TO FEVER, FEVER, COUGH, ANGINA, PULMONARY RALES, PULMONARY EDEMA WITH CYANOSIS. KIDNEY AND LIVER DAMAGE MAY OCCUR. **CHRONIC EXPOSURE-** CHRONIC FLUORIDE INHALATION MAY CAUSE WEIGHT LOSS, BRITTLE BONES, ANEMIA, WEAKNESS, AND STIFFNESS OF JOINTS.

FIRST AID- REMOVE FROM EXPOSURE AREA TO FRESH AIR IMMEDIATELY. IF BREATHING HAS STOPPED, GIVE ARTIFICIAL RESPIRATION. MAINTAIN AIRWAY AND BLOOD PRESSURE AND ADMINISTER OXYGEN IF AVAILABLE. KEEP AFFECTED PERSON WARM AND AT REST. TREAT SYMPTOMATICALLY AND SUPPORTIVELY. ADMINISTRATION OF OXYGEN SHOULD BE PERFORMED BY QUALIFIED PERSONNEL. GET MEDICAL ATTENTION IMMEDIATELY.

SKIN CONTACT: ZINC SILICOFLUORIDE: CORROSIVE. **ACUTE EXPOSURE-** VAPORS ARE IRRITATING TO THE SKIN. DIRECT CONTACT MAY CAUSE SERIOUS BURNS AND ULCERATION. **CHRONIC EXPOSURE-** PROLONGED VAPOR CONTACT MAY PRODUCE DERMATITIS.

FIRST AID- REMOVE CONTAMINATED CLOTHING AND SHOES IMMEDIATELY. WASH AFFECTED AREA WITH SOAP OR MILD DETERGENT AND LARGE AMOUNTS OF WATER UNTIL NO EVIDENCE OF CHEMICAL REMAINS (AT LEAST 15-20 MINUTES). IN CASE OF CHEMICAL BURNS, COVER AREA WITH STERILE, DRY DRESSING. BANDAGE SECURELY, BUT NOT TOO TIGHTLY. GET MEDICAL ATTENTION IMMEDIATELY.

EYE CONTACT: ZINC SILICOFLUORIDE: CORROSIVE. **ACUTE EXPOSURE-** VAPOR CONTACT MAY RESULT IN IRRITATION, LACRIMATION, SWELLING OF THE EYELIDS, AND CORNEAL OPACITY. DIRECT CONTACTMAY PRODUCE SERIOUS BURNS. **CHRONIC EXPOSURE-** REPEATED OR PROLONGED VAPOR CONTACT MAY CAUSE CONJUNCTIVITIS.

FIRST AID- WASH EYES IMMEDIATELY WITH LARGE AMOUNTS OF WATER, OCCASIONALLY LIFTING UPPER AND LOWER LIDS, UNTIL NO EVIDENCE OF CHEMICAL REMAINS (AT LEAST 15-20 MINUTES). CONTINUE IRRIGATING WITH NORMAL SALINE UNTIL THE PH HAS RETURNED TO NORMAL (30-60 MINUTES). COVER WITH STERILE BANDAGES. GET MEDICAL ATTENTION IMMEDIATELY.

INGESTION: ZINA SILICOFLUORIDE: CORROSIVE. **ACUTE EXPOSURE-** GASTROINTESTINAL CORROSION FOLLOWED BY NAUSEA, VOMITING, AND DIARRHEA. **CHRONIC EXPOSURE-** MAY LEAD TO FLUOROSIS, WITH BRITTLE BONES, STIFFNESS OF JOINTS, ANEMIA, AND WEIGHT LOSS.

FIRST AID- DILUTE THE INGESTED CHEMICAL IMMEDIATELY BY DRINKING LARGE QUANTITIES OF MILK OR WATER. IF VOMITING IS PERSISTENT, ADMINISTER FLUIDS REPEATEDLY. INGESTED CORROSIVE MATERIAL SHOULD BE DILUTED APPROXIMATELY 100 TIMES TO RENDER IT HARMLESS TO TISSUES.GIVE MORPHINE SULFATE TO RELEIVE PAIN. TREAT SHOCK. ADMINISTRATION OF MORPHINE MUST BE PERFORMED BY QUALIFIED MEDICAL PERSONNEL. (DREISBACH, HANDBOOK OF POISONING, 11TH ED.) GET MEDICAL ATTENTION IMMEDIATELY.

ANTIDOTE: NO SPECIFIC ANTIDOTE. TREAT SYMPTOMATICALLY AND SUPPORTIVELY.

REACTIVITY

REACTIVITY: STABLE UNDER NORMAL TEMPERATURES AND PRESSURES.
INCOMPATIBILITIES: CONTACT WITH ACIDS MAY RELEASE TOXIC AND CORROSIVE DECOMPOSITION PRODUCTS.
DECOMPOSITION: DECOMPOSITION FROM HEAT OR ACIDS RELEASES TOXIC FUMES OF ZINC OXIDE AND CORROSIVE HYDROGEN FLUORIDE AND SILICON TETRAFLUORIDE.
POLYMERIZATION: HAZARDOUS POLYMERIZATION HAS NOT BEEN REPORTED TO OCCUR UNDER NORMAL TEMPERATURES AND PRESSURES.

STORAGE AND DISPOSAL

OBSERVE ALL FEDERAL, STATE AND LOCAL REGULATIONS WHEN STORING OR DISPOSING OF THIS SUBSTANCE.

****STORAGE****

STORE AWAY FROM INCOMPATIBLE SUBSTANCES.

CONDITIONS TO AVOID

MAY BURN BUT DOES NOT IGNITE READILY.

SPILL AND LEAK PROCEDURES

SOIL SPILL: DIG HOLDING AREA SUCH AS LAGOON, POND OR PIT FOR CONTAINMENT. USE PROTECTIVE COVER SUCH AS A PLASTIC SHEET TO PREVENT MATERIAL FROM DISSOLVING IN FIRE EXTINGUISHING WATER OR RAIN.
WATER SPILL: ADD SUITABLE AGENT TO NEUTRALIZE SPILLED MATERIAL TO PH-7. USE MECHANICAL DREDGES OR LIFTS TO EXTRACT IMMOBILIZED MASSES OF POLLUTION AND PRECIPITATES.
OCCUPATIONAL SPILL: DO NOT TOUCH SPILLED MATERIAL. STOP LEAK IF YOU CAN DO IT WITHOUT RISK. FOR SMALL SPILLS, TAKE UP WITH SAND OR OTHER ABSORBENT MATERIAL AND PLACE INTO CONTAINERS FOR LATER DISPOSAL. FOR SMALL DRY SPILLS, WITH A CLEAN SHOVEL PLACE MATERIAL INTO CLEAN, DRY CONTAINER AND COVER. MOVE CONTAINERS FROM SPILL AREA. FOR LARGER SPILLS, DIKE FAR AHEAD OF SPILL FOR LATER DISPOSAL. KEEP UNNECESSARY PEOPLE AWAY. ISOLATE HAZARD AREA AND DENY ENTRY.
REPORTABLE QUANTITY (RQ): 5000 POUNDS THE SUPERFUND AMENDMENTS AND REAUTHORIZATION ACT (SARA) SECTION 304 REQUIRES THAT A RELEASE EQUAL TO OR GREATER THAN THE REPORTABLE QUANTITY FOR THIS SUBSTANCE BE IMMEDIATELY REPORTED TO THE LOCAL EMERGENCY PLANNING COMMITTEE AND THE STATE EMERGENCY RESPONSE COMMISSION (40 CFR 355.40). IF THE RELEASE OF THIS SUBSTANCE IS REPORTABLE UNDER CERCLA SECTION 103, THE NATIONAL RESPONSE CENTER MUST BE NOTIFIED IMMEDIATELY AT (800) 424-8802 OR (202) 426-2675 IN THE METROPOLITAN WASHINGTON, D.C. AREA (40 CFR 302.6).

PROTECTIVE EQUIPMENT

VENTILATION: PROVIDE LOCAL EXHAUST VENTILATION SYSTEM TO MEET PUBLISHED EXPOSURE LIMITS.
RESPIRATOR: 12.5 MG(F)/M3- DUST MASK.
25 MG(F)/M3- DUST MASK, EXCEPT SINGLE-USE AND QUARTER-MASK RESPIRATORS WITH WITH AN ACID GAS SORBENT. SUPPLIED-AIR RESPIRATOR. SELF-CONTAINED BREATHING APPARATUS.
125 MG(F)/M3- HIGH-EFFICIENCY PARTICULATE RESPIRATOR WITH A FULL FACEPIECE. SUPPLIED-AIR RESPIRATOR WITH A FULL FACEPIECE, HELMET, OR HOOD. SELF-CONTAINED BREATHING APPARATUS WITH A FULL FACEPIECE.
250 MG(F)/M3- POWERED AIR-PURIFYING RESPIRATOR WITH A HIGH-EFFICIENCY FILTER AND A FULL FACEPIECE. TYPE "C" SUPPLIED AIR RESPIRATOR WITH FULL FACEPIECE OPERATED IN PRESSURE-DEMAND OR OTHER POSITIVE PRESSURE MODE OR WITH FULL FACEPIECE, HELMET OR HOOD OPERATED IN CONTINUOUS FLOW MODE.
ESCAPE- GAS MASK WITH ORGANIC VAPOR CANNISTER (CHIN-STYLE OR FRONT-OR BACK-MOUNTED CANNISTER). SELF-CONTAINED BREATHING APPARATUS.
CLOTHING: EMPLOYEE MUST WEAR APPROPRIATE PROTECTIVE (IMPERVIOUS) CLOTHING AND EQUIPMENT TO PREVENT ANY POSSIBILITY OF SKIN CONTACT WITH THIS SUBSTANCE.
GLOVES: EMPLOYEE MUST WEAR APPROPRIATE PROTECTIVE GLOVES TO PREVENT CONTACT WITH THIS SUBSTANCE.
EYE PROTECTION: EMPLOYEE MUST WEAR SPLASH-PROOF OR DUST-RESISTANT SAFETY GOGGLES AND A FACESHIELD TO PREVENT CONTACT WITH THIS SUBSTANCE.
EMERGENCY WASH FACILITIES: WHERE THERE IS ANY POSSIBILITY THAT AN EMPLOYEE'S EYES AND/OR SKIN MAY BE EXPOSED TO THIS SUBSTANCE, THE EMPLOYER SHOULD PROVIDE AN EYE WASH FOUNTAIN AND QUICK DRENCH SHOWER WITHIN THE IMMEDIATE WORK AREA FOR EMERGENCY USE.

AUTHORIZED BY- OCCUPATIONAL HEALTH SERVICES, INC.
CREATION DATE: 11/16/89 ***REVISION DATE:*** 05/09/90

MATERIAL SAFETY DATA SHEET

OCCUPATIONAL HEALTH SERVICES, INC.
AGRICULTURE AND PESTICIDE DIVISION
450 SEVENTH AVENUE, SUITE 2407
NEW YORK, NEW YORK 10123
1-800-445-MSDS OR (212) 967-1100

EMERGENCY CONTACT:
JOHN S. BRANSFORD, JR. (615) 292-1180

SUBSTANCE IDENTIFICATION

CAS-NUMBER 1314-13-2

SUBSTANCE: **ZINC OXIDE**

TRADE NAMES/SYNONYMS: ZINC WHITE; CHINESE WHITE; FLOWERS OF ZINC; ZINC MONOXIDE; ZINC GELATIN; WHITE ZINC; OZIDE; AMALOX; PERMANENT WHITE; C.I. 77947; C.I. PIGMENT WHITE 4; HUBBUCK'S WHITE; AZODOX; EMAR; PHILOSOPHER'S WOOL; ZINCOID; SNOW WHITE; POLY-F-POWDER; 0-5023; ZNO; PST25490

CHEMICAL FAMILY: INORGANIC SALT

MOLECULAR FORMULA: ZN-O

MOLECULAR WEIGHT: 81.37

CERCLA RATINGS (SCALE 0-3): HEALTH=3 FIRE=0 REACTIVITY=0 PERSISTENCE=3

NFPA RATINGS (SCALE 0-4): HEALTH=3 FIRE=0 REACTIVITY=0

COMPONENTS AND CONTAMINANTS

COMPONENT: ZINC OXIDE ***PERCENT:*** 100

CAS# 1314-13-2

OTHER CONTAMINANTS: NONE

EXPOSURE LIMITS: ZINC OXIDE: 5 MG/M3 OSHA TWA (RESPIRABLE FRACTION); 10 MG/M3 OSHA TWA (TOTAL DUST) 5 MG/M3 OSHA TWA (FUME); 10 MG/M3 OSHA STEL (FUME) 10 MG/M3 ACGIH TWA (DUST); 5 MG/M3 ACGIH TWA (FUME); 10 MG/M3 ACGIH STEL (FUME) 5 MG/M3 NIOSH RECOMMENDED 10-HOUR TWA; 15 MG/M3 NIOSH RECOMMENDED 15 MINUTE CEILING

ZINC COMPOUNDS: SUBJECT TO SARA SECTION 313 ANNUAL TOXIC CHEMICAL RELEASE REPORTING

PHYSICAL DATA

DESCRIPTION: ODORLESS, WHITE, YELLOWISH-WHITE, OR GRAYISH FINE OR COARSE AMORPHOUS POWDER OR HEXAGONAL CRYSTALS, WITH A BITTER TASTE WHICH GRADUALLY

ABSORBS CARBON DIOXIDE FROM THE AIR. ***MELTING POINT:*** 3587 F (1975 C)

SPECIFIC GRAVITY: 5.6 ***PH:*** 6.95-7.37 ***SOLUBILITY IN WATER:*** 1.6 MG/L @ 29 C

SOLVENT SOLUBILITY: SOLUBLE IN DILUTE ACETIC OR MINERAL ACIDS, AMMONIA, AMMONIUM CHLORIDE, AMMONIUM SALT SOLUTIONS, FIXED ALKALI HYDROXIDES, STRONG BASES; INSOLUBLE IN ALCOHOL, ETHER, DILUTE SULFURIC ACID

FIRE AND EXPLOSION DATA

FIRE AND EXPLOSION HAZARD: NEGLIGIBLE FIRE HAZARD WHEN EXPOSED TO HEAT OR FLAME.

FIREFIGHTING MEDIA: DRY CHEMICAL, CARBON DIOXIDE, HALON, WATER SPRAY OR STANDARD FOAM (1987 EMERGENCY RESPONSE GUIDEBOOK, DOT P 5800.4). FOR LARGER FIRES, USE WATER SPRAY, FOG OR STANDARD FOAM (1987 EMERGENCY RESPONSE GUIDEBOOK, DOT P 5800.4).

FIREFIGHTING: NO ACUTE HAZARD. MOVE CONTAINER FROM FIRE AREA IF POSSIBLE. AVOID BREATHING VAPORS OR DUSTS; KEEP UPWIND.

TOXICITY

ZINC OXIDE: IRRITATION DATA: 500 MG/24 HOURS SKIN-RABBIT MILD; 500 MG/24 HOURS EYE-RABBIT MILD. TOXICITY DATA: 600 MG/M3 INHALATION-HUMAN TCLO; 2500 MG/M3 INHALATION-MOUSE LC50; 500 MG/KG ORAL-HUMAN LDLO; 7950 MG/KG ORAL-MOUSE LD50; 240 MG/KG INTRAPERITONEAL-RAT LD50; MUTAGENIC DATA (RTECS); REPRODUCTIVE EFFECTS DATA (RTECS). CARCINOGEN STATUS: NONE. LOCAL EFFECTS: IRRITANT- INHALATION, SKIN, AND EYES. ACUTE TOXICITY LEVEL: TOXIC BY INHALATION AND SLIGHTLY TOXIC BY INGESTION. TARGET EFFECTS: NO DATA AVAILABLE. AT INCREASED RISK FROM EXPOSURE: PERSONS WITH A HISTORY OF CHRONIC RESPIRATORY DISEASE.

HEALTH EFFECTS AND FIRST AID

INHALATION: ZINC OXIDE: IRRITANT. **ACUTE EXPOSURE-** INHALATION OF ZINC OXIDE MAY CAUSE IRRITATION OF THE RESPIRATORY TRACT AND CHEMICAL PNEUMONITIS. INHALATION OF HIGH LEVELS OF FRESHLY FORMED ZINC OXIDE FUMES MAY CAUSE ZINC FUME FEVER, AN INFLUENZA-LIKE ILLNESS, CHARACTERIZED BY IMMEDIATE DRYNESS AND IRRITATION OF THE THROAT, METALLIC OR SWEET TASTE IN THE MOUTH, TIGHTNESS IN THE CHEST, DYSPNEA, RALES, AND DRY COUGH. OTHER SYMPTOMS, INCLUDING FEVER, CHILLS, LASSITUDE, MALAISE, FATIGUE, HEADACHE, BLURRED VISION, NAUSEA, VOMITING, MUSCLE ACHES, AND LEUKOCYTOSIS, MAY BE DELAYED FOR 4-12 HOURS. THE ATTACK MAY LAST 6-24 HOURS. TOLERANCE TO ZINC FUME FEVER MAY DEVELOP RAPIDLY, BUT IS LOST QUICKLY. PRELIMINARY EXPOSURE TO ACETIC ACID VAPORS MAY INCREASE SUSCEPTIBILITY TO ZINC FUME FEVER. **CHRONIC EXPOSURE-** LATENT LIVER DYSFUNCTION AND GASTROINTESTINAL DISTURBANCES WITH PRESSURE IN THE STOMACH REGION, NAUSEA, AND WEAKNESS HAVE BEEN REPORTED FROM REPEATED EXPOSURE TO ZINC OXIDE.

FIRST AID- REMOVE FROM EXPOSURE AREA TO FRESH AIR IMMEDIATELY. IF BREATHING HAS STOPPED, PERFORM ARTIFICIAL RESPIRATION. KEEP PERSON WARM AND AT REST. TREAT SYMPTOMATICALLY AND SUPPORTIVELY. GET MEDICAL ATTENTION IMMEDIATELY.

SKIN CONTACT: ZINC OXIDE: IRRITANT. **ACUTE EXPOSURE-** ZINC OXIDE IS A CONSTITUENT OF MANY TOPICAL DERMATOLOGICAL PREPARATIONS AND HAS DEMONSTRATED A LOW POTENTIAL FOR SKIN IRRITATION, ALTHOUGH IT CAN ALTER SKIN PIGMENTATION. **CHRONIC EXPOSURE-** REPEATED OR PROLONGED EXPOSURE TO ZINC OXIDE, COUPLED WITH POOR PERSONAL HYGIENE, MAY RESULT IN "OXIDE POX" DUE TO CLOGGING OF SEBACEOUS GLANDS. "OXIDE POX", ESPECIALLY LOCALIZED TO MOIST AREAS, IS CHARACTERIZED BY SMALL RED, HARD PROJECTING PAPULES WITH A CENTRAL WHITE PLUG, WHICH DEVELOPS INTO A PUSTULE WITH INTENSE ITCHING. THE LESIONS USUALLY CLEAR WITHIN 7-10 DAYS. EXPOSURE TO 500 MG/KG OF ZINC OXIDE PRODUCED MILD IRRITATION TO RABBIT SKIN AFTER 24 HOURS.

FIRST AID- REMOVE CONTAMINATED CLOTHING AND SHOES IMMEDIATELY. WASH AFFECTED AREA WITH SOAP OR MILD DETERGENT AND LARGE AMOUNTS OF WATER UNTIL NO EVIDENCE OF CHEMICAL REMAINS (APPROXIMATELY 15-20 MINUTES). GET MEDICAL ATTENTION IMMEDIATELY.

EYE CONTACT: ZINC OXIDE: IRRITANT. **ACUTE EXPOSURE-** CONTACT WITH THE FUME MAY CAUSE IRRITATION, REDNESS, AND PAIN. **CHRONIC EXPOSURE-** REPEATED OR PROLONGED CONTACT WITH ZINC OXIDE FUME MAY PRODUCE CONJUNCTIVITIS. EXPOSURE TO 500 MG/KG FOR 24 HOURS CAUSED MILD IRRITATION TO THE EYES OF RABBITS.

FIRST AID- WASH EYES IMMEDIATELY WITH LARGE AMOUNTS OF WATER OR NORMAL SALINE, OCCASIONALLY LIFTING UPPER AND LOWER LIDS, UNTIL NO EVIDENCE OF CHEMICAL REMAINS (APPROXIMATELY 15-20 MINUTES). GET MEDICAL ATTENTION IMMEDIATELY.

INGESTION: ZINC OXIDE: **ACUTE EXPOSURE-** THE TOXIC DOSE OF ZINC OXIDE IS ESTIMATED TO BE 2 GM/KG. THE GREATEST DANGER FROM INGESTION MAY BE INTENSE GASTROENTERITIS, WITH NAUSEA, DIARRHEA, OR CONSTIPATION. **CHRONIC EXPOSURE-** REPEATED OR PROLONGED ADMINISTRATION OF 0.5-34.4 MG OF ZINC OXIDE PER DAY FOR PERIODS OF 1 MONTH TO 1 YEAR RESULTED IN NO INJURIES IN RATS. REPEATED OR PROLONGED ADMINISTRATION TO PREGNANT RATS HAVE RESULTED IN ADVERSE EFFECTS ON THE NEWBORN.

FIRST AID- TREAT SYMPTOMATICALLY AND SUPPORTIVELY. GET MEDICAL ATTENTION IMMEDIATELY. IF VOMITING OCCURS, KEEP HEAD LOWER THAN HIPS TO PREVENT ASPIRATION. ***ANTIDOTE:*** NO SPECIFIC ANTIDOTE. TREAT SYMPTOMATICALLY AND SUPPORTIVELY.

REACTIVITY

REACTIVITY: STABLE UNDER NORMAL TEMPERATURES AND PRESSURES.

INCOMPATIBILITIES: ZINC OXIDE: CHLORINATED RUBBER: VIOLENT OR EXPLOSIVE REACTION WHEN HEATED ABOVE 216 C. LINSEED OIL: EXOTHERMIC REACTION WITH POSSIBLE IGNITION. MAGNESIUM: EXPLOSIVE REACTION ON HEATING.

DECOMPOSITION: WHEN HEATED AT ELEVATED TEMPERATURES, ZINC OXIDE SUBLIMES TO PRODUCE TOXIC FUMES.

POLYMERIZATION: HAZARDOUS POLYMERIZATION HAS NOT BEEN REPORTED TO OCCUR UNDER NORMAL TEMPERATURES AND PRESSURES.

STORAGE AND DISPOSAL

OBSERVE ALL FEDERAL, STATE AND LOCAL REGULATIONS WHEN STORING OR DISPOSING OF THIS SUBSTANCE. FOR ASSISTANCE, CONTACT THE DISTRICT DIRECTOR OF THE ENVIRONMENTAL PROTECTION AGENCY.

****STORAGE****

STORE AWAY FROM INCOMPATIBLE SUBSTANCES.

CONDITIONS TO AVOID

NONE REPORTED.

SPILL AND LEAK PROCEDURES

OCCUPATIONAL SPILL: SWEEP UP AND PLACE IN SUITABLE (FIBERBOARD) CONTAINERS FOR RECLAMATION OR LATER DISPOSAL.

PROTECTIVE EQUIPMENT

VENTILATION: PROVIDE LOCAL EXHAUST OR PROCESS ENCLOSURE VENTILATION TO MEET PUBLISHED EXPOSURE LIMITS.

RESPIRATOR: THE FOLLOWING RESPIRATORS AND MAXIMUM USE CONCENTRATIONS ARE RECOMMENDATIONS BY THE U.S. DEPARTMENT OF HEALTH AND HUMAN SERVICES, NIOSH POCKET GUIDE TO CHEMICAL HAZARDS; NIOSH CRITERIA DOCUMENTS OR BY THE U.S. DEPARTMENT OF LABOR, 29 CFR 1910 SUBPART Z. THE SPECIFIC RESPIRATOR SELECTED MUST BE BASED ON CONTAMINATION LEVELS FOUND IN THE WORK PLACE, MUST NOT EXCEED THE WORKING LIMITS OF

THE RESPIRATOR AND BE JOINTLY APPROVED BY THE NATIONAL INSTITUTE FOR OCCUPATIONAL SAFETY AND HEALTH AND THE MINE SAFETY AND HEALTH ADMINISTRATION (NIOSH-MSHA).
FOR ZINC OXIDE FUME:
50 MG/M3- ANY DUST, MIST AND FUME RESPIRATOR WITH A FULL FACEPIECE. ANY SUPPLIED-AIR RESPIRATOR. ANY SELF-CONTAINED BREATHING APPARATUS.
125 MG/M3- ANY POWERED AIR-PURIFYING RESPIRATOR WITH A DUST, MIST AND FUME FILTER. ANY SUPPLIED-AIR RESPIRATOR OPERATED IN A CONTINUOUS FLOW MODE.
250 MG/M3- ANY AIR-PURIFYING FULL FACEPIECE RESPIRATOR WITH A HIGH-EFFICIENCY PARTICULATE FILTER. ANY POWERED AIR-PURIFYING RESPIRATOR WITH A TIGHT-FITTING FACEPIECE AND A HIGH-EFFICIENCY PARTICULATE FILTER. ANY SELF-CONTAINED BREATHING APPARATUS WITH A FULL FACEPIECE. ANY SUPPLIED-AIR RESPIRATOR WITH A FULL FACEPIECE. ANY SUPPLIED-AIR RESPIRATOR WITH A TIGHT-FITTING FACEPIECE OPERATED IN A CONTINUOUS FLOW MODE.
2500 MG/M3- ANY SUPPLIED-AIR RESPIRATOR WITH A HALF-MASK AND OPERATED IN A PRESSURE-DEMAND OR OTHER POSITIVE PRESSURE MODE.
ESCAPE- ANY AIR-PURIFYING FULL FACEPIECE RESPIRATOR WITH A HIGH-EFFICIENCY PARTICULATE FILTER. ANY APPROPRIATE ESCAPE-TYPE SELF-CONTAINED BREATHING APPARATUS.
FOR FIREFIGHTING AND OTHER IMMEDIATELY DANGEROUS TO LIFE OR HEALTH CONDITIONS:
SELF-CONTAINED BREATHING APPARATUS WITH FULL FACEPIECE OPERATED IN PRESSURE-DEMAND OR OTHER POSITIVE PRESSURE MODE.
SUPPLIED-AIR RESPIRATOR WITH FULL FACEPIECE AND OPERATED IN PRESSURE-DEMAND OR OTHER POSITIVE PRESSURE MODE IN COMBINATION WITH AN AUXILIARY SELF-CONTAINED BREATHING APPARATUS OPERATED IN PRESSURE-DEMAND OR OTHER POSITIVE PRESSURE MODE.

CLOTHING: EMPLOYEE MUST WEAR APPROPRIATE PROTECTIVE (IMPERVIOUS) CLOTHING AND EQUIPMENT TO PREVENT REPEATED OR PROLONGED SKIN CONTACT WITH THIS SUBSTANCE.

GLOVES: EMPLOYEE MUST WEAR APPROPRIATE PROTECTIVE GLOVES TO PREVENT CONTACT WITH THIS SUBSTANCE.

EYE PROTECTION: EMPLOYEE MUST WEAR SPLASH-PROOF OR DUST-RESISTANT SAFETY GOGGLES TO PREVENT EYE CONTACT WITH THIS SUBSTANCE.
EMERGENCY EYE WASH: WHERE THERE IS ANY POSSIBILITY THAT AN EMPLOYEE'S EYES MAY BE EXPOSED TO THIS SUBSTANCE, THE EMPLOYER SHOULD PROVIDE AN EYE WASH FOUNTAIN WITHIN THE IMMEDIATE WORK AREA FOR EMERGENCY USE.

AUTHORIZED BY- OCCUPATIONAL HEALTH SERVICES, INC.
CREATION DATE: 02/08/90 ***REVISION DATE:*** 05/11/90

MATERIAL SAFETY DATA SHEET

OCCUPATIONAL HEALTH SERVICES, INC.
AGRICULTURE AND PESTICIDE DIVISION
450 SEVENTH AVENUE, SUITE 2407
NEW YORK, NEW YORK 10123
1-800-445-MSDS OR (212) 967-1100

EMERGENCY CONTACT:
JOHN S. BRANSFORD, JR. (615) 292-1180

SUBSTANCE IDENTIFICATION

CAS-NUMBER 1314-84-7

***SUBSTANCE:* ZINC PHOSPHIDE**

TRADE NAMES/SYNONYMS: TRIZINC DIPHOSPHIDE; PHOSPHURE DE ZINC; KILRAT; GOPHA-RID (FORMULATION); MOUSE-CON; PHOSVIN; RUMETAN; RATOL; ZINC-TOX; RCRA P122; STCC 4923496; UN 1714; P2ZN3; PST25540

CHEMICAL FAMILY: METAL PHOSPHIDE

MOLECULAR FORMULA: ZN3-P2

MOLECULAR WEIGHT: 258.09

CERCLA RATINGS (SCALE 0-3): HEALTH=3 FIRE=3 REACTIVITY=2 PERSISTENCE=3

NFPA RATINGS (SCALE 0-4): HEALTH=3 FIRE=3 REACTIVITY=2

COMPONENTS AND CONTAMINANTS

COMPONENT: ZINC PHOSPHIDE ***PERCENT:*** 100.0
CAS# 1314-84-7

EXPOSURE LIMITS: NO OCCUPATIONAL EXPOSURE LIMITS ESTABLISHED BY OSHA, ACGIH, OR NIOSH.
ZINC PHOSPHIDE: 500 POUNDS SARA SECTION 302 THRESHOLD PLANNING QUANTITY 100 POUNDS SARA SECTION 304 REPORTABLE QUANTITY 100 POUNDS CERCLA SECTION 103 REPORTABLE QUANTITY
ZINC COMPOUNDS: SUBJECT TO SARA SECTION 313 ANNUAL TOXIC CHEMICAL RELEASE REPORTING

PHYSICAL DATA

DESCRIPTION: AMORPHOUS GREY-BLACK POWDER WITH A FAINT GARLIC-LIKE ODOR AND TASTE.
BOILING POINT: 2012 F (1110 C) ***MELTING POINT:*** >788 F (>420 C)
SPECIFIC GRAVITY: 4.55 @ 13 C ***VAPOR PRESSURE:*** NEGLIGIBLE
SOLUBILITY IN WATER: PRACTICALLY INSOLUBLE
SOLVENT SOLUBILITY: SOLUBLE IN BENZENE, CARBON DISULFIDE, AND ACIDS; INSOLUBLE IN ALCOHOL.

FIRE AND EXPLOSION DATA

FIRE AND EXPLOSION HAZARD: DANGEROUS WHEN WET! DANGEROUS FIRE HAZARD AND SLIGHT EXPLOSION HAZARD WHEN EXPOSED TO WATER.
DUST-AIR MIXTURES MAY IGNITE OR EXPLODE.

FIREFIGHTING MEDIA: DRY CHEMICAL, SODA ASH, LIME OR SAND (1987 EMERGENCY RESPONSE GUIDEBOOK, DOT P 5800.4).
FOR LARGER FIRES, WITHDRAW FROM AREA AND LET FIRE BURN (1987 EMERGENCY RESPONSE GUIDEBOOK, DOT P 5800.4).

FIREFIGHTING: MOVE CONTAINER FROM FIRE AREA IF POSSIBLE. DO NOT USE WATER OR FOAM! (1987 EMERGENCY RESPONSE GUIDEBOOK, DOT P 5800.4, GUIDE PAGE 41).
EXTINGUISH USING AGENT INDICATED. AVOID BREATHING POISONOUS DUSTS AND FUMES FROM MATERIAL.

TRANSPORTATION DATA

DEPARTMENT OF TRANSPORTATION HAZARD CLASSIFICATION 49 CFR 172.101: POISON B
DEPARTMENT OF TRANSPORTATION LABELING REQUIREMENTS 49 CFR 172.101 AND SUBPART E: POISON
DEPARTMENT OF TRANSPORTATION PACKAGING REQUIREMENTS: 49 CFR 173.365 EXCEPTIONS: 49 CFR 173.364

TOXICITY

ZINC PHOSPHIDE: TOXICITY DATA: 2 GM/KG SKIN-RABBIT LD50; 80 MG/KG ORAL-WOMAN LDLO; 12 MG/KG ORAL-RAT LD50; 40 MG/KG ORAL-MOUSE LD50; 40 MG/KG ORAL-CAT LDLO; 40 MG/KG ORAL-DOG LDLO; 40 MG/KG ORAL-RABBIT LDLO; 450 MG/KG INTRAPERITONEAL-RAT LD50; 263 MG/KG INTRAPERITONEAL-MOUSE LD50; 40 MG/KG UNREPORTED-MAN LDLO; 45 MG/KG UNREPORTED-RAT LD50. CARCINOGEN STATUS: NONE. ACUTE TOXICITY LEVEL: HIGHLY TOXIC BY INGESTION; MODERATELY TOXIC BY DERMAL ABSORPTION. TARGET EFFECTS: HEPATOTOXIN; NEPHROTOXIN. POISONING MAY AFFECT THE CENTRAL NERVOUS SYSTEM AND HEART.

HEALTH EFFECTS AND FIRST AID

INHALATION: ZINC PHOSPHIDE: **ACUTE EXPOSURE-** MAY CAUSE DIZZINESS, COUGH, FATIGUE, NAUSEA, VOMITING, DIARRHEA, JAUNDICE, METEORISM, FEVER, DIPLOPIA, IRRITABILITY, CYANOSIS, RAPID PULSE, PARESTHESIAS, ATAXIA, TREMOR, HYPOTENSION, DYSPNEA, PULMONARY EDEMA, COLLAPSE, CARDIAC ARRHYTHMIAS, CONVULSIONS, AND COMA. RENAL DAMAGE, ALBUMINURIA, AND LEUKOPENIA MAY DEVELOP. DEATH MAY OCCUR WITHIN 4 DAYS OR BE DELAYED 1-2 WEEKS. **CHRONIC EXPOSURE-** PROLONGED INHALATION BY EXPERIMENTAL ANIMALS AT CONCENTRATIONS OF 1 MG/M3 PRODUCED ABNORMALITIES IN LIPID AND CARBOHYDRATE METABOLISM AND DISTURBANCES OF THE BLOOD, NERVOUS, CARDIOVASCULAR AND ENDOCRINE SYSTEMS. CHRONIC POISONING FROM PHOSPHIDES MAY CAUSE TOOTHACHE, FOLLOWED BY SWELLING OF THE JAW, AND LATER NECROSIS OF THE JAW. OTHER SYMPTOMS MAY INCLUDE WEAKNESS, WEIGHT LOSS, LOSS OF APPETITE, ANEMIA, SPONTANEOUS BONE FRACTURES, BRONCHITIS, AND GASTROINTESTINAL, VISUAL, SPEECH, AND MOTOR DISTURBANCES.

FIRST AID- REMOVE FROM EXPOSURE AREA TO FRESH AIR IMMEDIATELY. IF BREATHING HAS STOPPED, PERFORM ARTIFICIAL RESPIRATION. KEEP PERSON WARM AND AT REST. TREAT SYMPTOMATICALLY AND SUPPORTIVELY. GET MEDICAL ATTENTION IMMEDIATELY.

SKIN CONTACT: ZINC PHOSPHIDE: **ACUTE EXPOSURE-** THIS MATERIAL WAS NOT IRRITATING TO RABBIT SKIN. THIS MATERIAL IS NOT ABSORBED THROUGH INTACT SKIN BUT CAN ENTER THE BLOOD STREAM THROUGH CUTS. **CHRONIC EXPOSURE-** NO DATA AVAILABLE.

FIRST AID- REMOVE CONTAMINATED CLOTHING AND SHOES IMMEDIATELY. WASH AFFECTED AREA WITH SOAP OR MILD DETERGENT AND LARGE AMOUNTS OF

WATER UNTIL NO EVIDENCE OF CHEMICAL REMAINS (APPROXIMATELY 15-20 MINUTES). GET MEDICAL ATTENTION IMMEDIATELY.

EYE CONTACT: ZINC PHOSPHIDE: **ACUTE EXPOSURE-** THIS MATERIAL DOES NOT PRODUCED IRRITATION OF RABBIT'S EYES. **CHRONIC EXPOSURE-** NO DATA AVAILABLE.

FIRST AID- WASH EYES IMMEDIATELY WITH LARGE AMOUNTS OF WATER OR NORMAL SALINE, OCCASIONALLY LIFTING UPPER AND LOWER LIDS, UNTIL NO EVIDENCE OF CHEMICAL REMAINS (APPROXIMATELY 15-20 MINUTES). GET MEDICAL ATTENTION IMMEDIATELY.

INGESTION: ZINC PHOSPHIDE: HEPATOTOXIN/NEPHROTOXIN/HIGHLY TOXIC. **ACUTE EXPOSURE-** MAY CAUSE NAUSEA, VOMITING, ABDOMINAL PAIN, CHILLS, HEADACHE, EXCITEMENT, AGITATION, AND DIZZINESS. TIGHTNESS IN THE CHEST, COUGH, DYSPNEA, AND CYANOSIS INDICATE THE DEVELOPMENT OF PULMONARY EDEMA. OTHER EFFECTS INCLUDE HYPERTENSION, DYSRHYTHMIAS, METABOLIC ACIDOSIS, SHOCK, CONVULSION, AND COMA. OTHER COMPLICATIONS MAY INVOLVE JAUNDICE AND LIVER TENDERNESS AND ENLARGEMENT FROM LIVER NECROSIS AND ANURIA FROM RENAL TUBULAR INJURY. DEATH IS DUE TO SEVERE HEPATIC, RENAL, AND CARDIAC DAMAGE AND MAY OCCUR UP TO A WEEK AFTER POISONING. HYPOCALCEMIC TETANY AND PURPURA HAVE OCCURRED IN SOME POISONINGS. **CHRONIC EXPOSURE-** REPEATED INGESTION MAY CAUSE EFFECTS AS DESCRIBED IN CHRONIC INHALATION. CROUGHING, HEAVY BREATHING, ATAXIA, HIND LIMB PARALYSIS, EFFECTS ON THE BLOOD, COMA, CONVULSIONS, AND DEATH WERE REPORTED IN RATS RECEIVING A DIETARY LEVEL OF 500 PPM. HISTOPATHOLOGICAL EXAMINATIONS REVEALED SLIGHT PATHOLOGICAL CHANGES IN THE LIVER AND KIDNEY, BILE DUCT PROLIFERATION, AND FOCAL NECROSIS OF HEART TISSUE.

FIRST AID- TREAT SYMPTOMATICALLY AND SUPPORTIVELY. GET MEDICAL ATTENTION IMMEDIATELY. IF VOMITING OCCURS, KEEP HEAD LOWER THAN HIPS TO PREVENT ASPIRATION.

ANTIDOTE: NO SPECIFIC ANTIDOTE. TREAT SYMPTOMATICALLY AND SUPPORTIVELY.

REACTIVITY

REACTIVITY: ZINC PHOSPHIDE: STABLE WHEN DRY. CONTACT WITH WATER MAY RELEASE FLAMMABLE AND EXPLOSIVE PHOSPHINE GAS.

INCOMPATIBILITIES: ZINC PHOSPHIDE: ACIDS: MAY REACT TO PRODUCE FLAMMABLE AND EXPLOSIVE PHOSPHINE GAS. HYDROCHLORIC ACID: MAY REACT TO PRODUCE FLAMMABLE AND EXPLOSIVE PHOSPHINE GAS. METALS: MAY CORRODE. NITRIC ACID: MAY REACT TO PRODUCE FLAMMABLE AND EXPLOSIVE PHOSPHINE GAS. OXIDIZING AGENTS: MAY REACT VIOLENTLY. PERCHLORIC ACID: MAY REACT TO PRODUCE FLAMMABLE AND EXPLOSIVE PHOSPHINE GAS. SULFURIC ACID: MAY REACT TO PRODUCE FLAMMABLE AND EXPLOSIVE PHOSPHINE GAS.

DECOMPOSITION: THERMAL DECOMPOSITION PRODUCTS MAY INCLUDE TOXIC AND HAZARDOUS OXIDES OF PHOSPHORUS AND ZINC AND FLAMMABLE AND EXPLOSIVE PHOSPHINE GAS.

POLYMERIZATION: HAZARDOUS POLYMERIZATION HAS NOT BEEN REPORTED TO OCCUR UNDER NORMAL TEMPERATURES AND PRESSURES.

STORAGE AND DISPOSAL

OBSERVE ALL FEDERAL, STATE AND LOCAL REGULATIONS WHEN STORING OR DISPOSING OF THIS SUBSTANCE. FOR ASSISTANCE, CONTACT THE DISTRICT DIRECTOR OF THE ENVIRONMENTAL PROTECTION AGENCY.

****STORAGE****

STORE IN ACCORDANCE WITH 40 CFR 165 RECOMMENDED PROCEDURES FOR THE DISPOSAL AND STORAGE OF PESTICIDES AND PESTICIDE CONTAINERS.

STORE AWAY FROM INCOMPATIBLE SUBSTANCES.

THRESHOLD PLANNING QUANTITY (TPQ): THE SUPERFUND AMENDMENTS AND REAUTHORIZATION ACT (SARA) SECTION 302 REQUIRES THAT EACH FACILITY WHERE ANY EXTREMELY HAZARDOUS SUBSTANCE IS PRESENT IN A QUANTITY EQUAL TO OR GREATER THAN THE TPQ ESTABLISHED FOR THAT SUBSTANCE NOTIFY THE STATE EMERGENCY RESPONSE COMMISSION FOR THE STATE IN WHICH IT IS LOCATED. SECTION 303 OF SARA REQUIRES THESE FACILITIES TO PARTICIPATE IN LOCAL EMERGENCY RESPONSE PLANNING (40 CFR 355.30).

****DISPOSAL****

DISPOSAL MUST BE IN ACCORDANCE WITH STANDARDS APPLICABLE TO GENERATORS OF HAZARDOUS WASTE, 40CFR 262. EPA HAZARDOUS WASTE NUMBER P122.

DISPOSAL MUST BE IN ACCORDANCE WITH 40 CFR 165 RECOMMENDED PROCEDURES FOR THE DISPOSAL AND STORAGE OF PESTICIDES AND PESTICIDE CONTAINERS.

CONDITIONS TO AVOID

MAY IGNITE IN PRESENCE OF MOISTURE AND CONTACT WITH WATER PRODUCES FLAMMABLE GAS. RUNOFF TO SEWER MAY CREATE FIRE OR EXPLOSION HAZARD.

SPILL AND LEAK PROCEDURES

SOIL SPILL: DIG HOLDING AREA SUCH AS LAGOON, POND OR PIT FOR CONTAINMENT. USE PROTECTIVE COVER SUCH AS A PLASTIC SHEET TO PREVENT MATERIAL FROM DISSOLVING IN FIRE EXTINGUISHING WATER OR RAIN.

WATER SPILL: NEUTRALIZE WITH AGRICULTURAL LIME, SLAKED LIME, CRUSHED LIMESTONE, OR SODIUM BICARBONATE.

USE MECHANICAL DREDGES OR LIFTS TO EXTRACT IMMOBILIZED MASSES OF POLLUTION AND PRECIPITATES.

OCCUPATIONAL SPILL: SHUT OFF IGNITION SOUCES. DO NOT TOUCH SPILLED MATERIAL. DO NOT GET WATER ON SPILLED MATERIAL OR INSIDE CONTAINER. FOR SMALL SPILL, WITH CLEAN SHOVEL PLACE MATERIAL INTO CLEAN, DRY CONTAINER AND COVER; MOVE CONTAINERS FROM SPILL AREA. FOR LARGER SPILLS, DIKE SPILL FOR LATER DISPOSAL. COVER POWDER SPILLS WITH PLASTIC SHEET OR TARP TO MINIMIZE SPREADING. CLEAN UP ONLY UNDER SUPERVISION OF AN EXPERT. KEEP UNNECESSARY PEOPLE AWAY. ISOLATE HAZARD AREA AND DENY ENTRY.

REPORTABLE QUANTITY (RQ): 100 POUNDS THE SUPERFUND AMENDMENTS AND REAUTHORIZATION ACT (SARA) SECTION 304 REQUIRES THAT A RELEASE EQUAL TO OR GREATER THAN THE REPORTABLE QUANTITY FOR THIS SUBSTANCE BE IMMEDIATELY REPORTED TO THE LOCAL EMERGENCY PLANNING COMMITTEE AND THE STATE EMERGENCY RESPONSE COMMISSION (40 CFR 355.40). IF THE RELEASE OF THIS SUBSTANCE IS REPORTABLE UNDER CERCLA SECTION 103, THE NATIONAL RESPONSE CENTER MUST BE NOTIFIED IMMEDIATELY AT (800) 424-8802 OR (202) 426-2675 IN THE METROPOLITAN WASHINGTON, D.C. AREA (40 CFR 302.6).

PROTECTIVE EQUIPMENT

VENTILATION: PROVIDE LOCAL EXHAUST OR PROCESS ENCLOSURE VENTILATION. VENTILATION EQUIPMENT MUST BE EXPLOSION-PROOF.

RESPIRATOR: THE FOLLOWING RESPIRATORS ARE RECOMMENDED BASED ON INFORMATION FOUND IN THE PHYSICAL DATA, TOXICITY AND HEALTH EFFECTS SECTIONS. THEY ARE RANKED IN ORDER FROM MINIMUM TO MAXIMUM RESPIRATORY PROTECTION. THE SPECIFIC RESPIRATOR SELECTED MUST BE BASED ON CONTAMINATION LEVELS FOUND IN THE WORK PLACE, MUST NOT EXCEED THE WORKING LIMITS OF THE RESPIRATOR AND BE JOINTLY APPROVED BY THE NATIONAL INSTITUTE FOR OCCUPATIONAL SAFETY AND HEALTH AND THE MINE SAFETY AND HEALTH ADMINISTRATION (NIOSH-MSHA).

TYPE 'C' SUPPLIED-AIR RESPIRATOR WITH A FULL FACEPIECE OPERATED IN PRESSURE-DEMAND OR OTHER POSITIVE PRESSURE MODE OR WITH A FULL FACEPIECE, HELMET OR HOOD OPERATED IN CONTINOUS-FLOW MODE.

SELF-CONTAINED BREATHING APPARATUS WITH A FULL FACEPIECE OPERATED IN PRESSURE-DEMAND OR OTHER POSITIVE PRESSURE MODE.

FOR FIREFIGHTING AND OTHER IMMEDIATELY DANGEROUS TO LIFE OR HEALTH CONDITIONS:

SELF-CONTAINED BREATHING APPARATUS WITH FULL FACEPIECE OPERATED IN PRESSURE-DEMAND OR OTHER POSITIVE PRESSURE MODE.

SUPPLIED-AIR RESPIRATOR WITH FULL FACEPIECE AND OPERATED IN PRESSURE-DEMAND OR OTHER POSITIVE PRESSURE MODE IN COMBINATION WITH AN AUXILIARY SELF-CONTAINED BREATHING APPARATUS OPERATED IN PRESSURE-DEMAND OR OTHER POSITIVE PRESSURE MODE.

CLOTHING: EMPLOYEE MUST WEAR APPROPRIATE PROTECTIVE (IMPERVIOUS) CLOTHING AND EQUIPMENT TO PREVENT REPEATED OR PROLONGED SKIN CONTACT WITH THIS SUBSTANCE.

GLOVES: EMPLOYEE MUST WEAR APPROPRIATE PROTECTIVE GLOVES TO PREVENT CONTACT WITH THIS SUBSTANCE.

EYE PROTECTION: EMPLOYEE MUST WEAR SPLASH-PROOF OR DUST-RESISTANT SAFETY GOGGLES TO PREVENT EYE CONTACT WITH THIS SUBSTANCE.

EMERGENCY EYE WASH: WHERE THERE IS ANY POSSIBILITY THAT AN EMPLOYEE'S EYES MAY BE EXPOSED TO THIS SUBSTANCE, THE EMPLOYER SHOULD PROVIDE AN EYE WASH FOUNTAIN WITHIN THE IMMEDIATE WORK AREA FOR EMERGENCY USE.

AUTHORIZED BY- OCCUPATIONAL HEALTH SERVICES, INC.

CREATION DATE: 10/05/89 ***REVISION DATE:*** 03/28/90

MATERIAL SAFETY DATA SHEET

OCCUPATIONAL HEALTH SERVICES, INC.
AGRICULTURE AND PESTICIDE DIVISION

EMERGENCY CONTACT:
JOHN S. BRANSFORD, JR. (615) 292-1180

450 SEVENTH AVENUE, SUITE 2407
NEW YORK, NEW YORK 10123
1-800-445-MSDS OR (212) 967-1100

SUBSTANCE IDENTIFICATION

CAS-NUMBER 7733-02-0
SUBSTANCE: **ZINC SULFATE**
TRADE NAMES/SYNONYMS: ZINC SULPHATE; SULFURIC ACID, ZINC SALT; WHITE VITRIOL; ZINC VITRIOL; SULFURIC ACID, ZINC SALT (1:1); BONAZEN; BUFOPTO ZINC SULFATE; ZINC SULFATE (1:1); VERAZINC; ZINKOSITE; ZINC SULFATE (ZNSO4); ZINCOMED; SULFURIC ACID ZINC SALT; STCC 4963786; O4SZN; PST25570
CHEMICAL FAMILY: INORGANIC SALT
MOLECULAR FORMULA: ZN-S-O4
MOLECULAR WEIGHT: 161.44
CERCLA RATINGS (SCALE 0-3): HEALTH=3 FIRE=0 REACTIVITY=0 PERSISTENCE=3
NFPA RATINGS (SCALE 0-4): HEALTH=3 FIRE=0 REACTIVITY=0

COMPONENTS AND CONTAMINANTS

COMPONENT: ZINC SULFATE (1:1) ***PERCENT:*** 100
CAS# 7733-02-0
OTHER CONTAMINANTS: NONE
EXPOSURE LIMITS: ZINC SULFATE: NO OCCUPATIONAL EXPOSURE LIMITS ESTABLISHED BY OSHA, ACGIH, OR NIOSH.
1000 POUNDS CERCLA SECTION 103 REPORTABLE QUANTITY SUBJECT TO SARA SECTION 313 ANNUAL TOXIC CHEMICAL RELEASE REPORTING

PHYSICAL DATA

DESCRIPTION: ODORLESS, COLORLESS CRYSTALS OR WHITE POWDER.
MELTING POINT: 1112 F (600 C) DECOMPOSES ***SPECIFIC GRAVITY:*** 3.54 @ 25 C
VAPOR PRESSURE: 60 MMHG @ 700 C ***PH:*** ACIDIC IN SOLUTION
SOLUBILITY IN WATER: SOLUBLE
SOLVENT SOLUBILITY: SOLUBLE IN METHANOL, GLYCEROL; SLIGHTLY SOLUBLE IN ALCOHOL

FIRE AND EXPLOSION DATA

FIRE AND EXPLOSION HAZARD: NEGLIGIBLE FIRE HAZARD WHEN EXPOSED TO HEAT OR FLAME.
FIREFIGHTING MEDIA: DRY CHEMICAL, CARBON DIOXIDE, HALON, WATER SPRAY OR STANDARD FOAM (1987 EMERGENCY RESPONSE GUIDEBOOK, DOT P 5800.4).
FOR LARGER FIRES, USE WATER SPRAY, FOG OR STANDARD FOAM (1987 EMERGENCY RESPONSE GUIDEBOOK, DOT P 5800.4).
FIREFIGHTING: MOVE CONTAINER FROM FIRE AREA IF POSSIBLE. DO NOT SCATTER SPILLED MATERIAL WITH HIGH PRESSURE WATER STREAMS. DIKE FIRE CONTROL WATER FOR LATER DISPOSAL (1987 EMERGENCY RESPONSE GUIDEBOOK, DOT P 5800.4, GUIDE PAGE 31).
EXTINGUISH USING AGENTS SUITABLE FOR TYPE OF SURROUNDING FIRE. AVOID BREATHING VAPORS OR DUSTS, KEEP UPWIND.

TOXICITY

ZINC SULFATE: IRRITATION DATA: ANHYDROUS: 420 UG EYE-RABBIT MODERATE. TOXICITY DATA: ANHYDROUS: 45 MG/KG/7 DAYS CONTINUOUS ORAL-HUMAN TDLO; 106 MG/KG ORAL-HUMAN TDLO; 180 MG/KG/6 WEEKS INTERMITTENT ORAL-MAN TDLO; 3120 MG/KG/43 WEEKS INTERMITTENT ORAL-WOMAN TDLO; 2949 MG/KG ORAL-RAT LD50; 2000 MG/KG ORAL-RABBIT LDLO; 330 MG/KG SUBCUTANEOUS-RAT LDLO; 1500 UG/KG SUBCUTANEOUS-MOUSE LDLO; 300 MG/KG SUBCUTANEOUS-RABBIT LDLO; 78 MG/KG SUBCUTANEOUS-DOG LDLO; 50 MG/KG INTRAVENOUS-RAT LDLO; 66 MG/KG INTRAVENOUS-DOG LDLO; 23 MG/KG INTRAVENOUS-RABBIT LDLO; 71750 UG/KG INTRAPERITONEAL-MOUSE LD50; MUTAGENIC DATA (RTECS); REPRODUCTIVE EFFECTS DATA (RTECS); TUMORIGENIC DATA (RTECS). HEPTAHYDRATE: 2150 MG/KG ORAL-RAT LD50; 2200 MG/KG ORAL-MOUSE LD50; 1914 MG/KG ORAL-RABBIT LDLO; 330 MG/KG SUBCUTANEOUS-RAT LDLO; 78 MG/KG SUBCUTANEOUS-DOG LDLO; 590 MG/KG SUBCUTANEOUS-GUINEA PIG LDLO; 49 MG/KG INTRAVENOUS-RAT LDLO; 66 MG/KG INTRAVENOUS-DOG LDLO; 44 MG/KG INTRAVENOUS-RABBIT LDLO; 200 MG/KG INTRAPERITONEAL-RAT LD50; 260 MG/KG INTRAPERITONEAL-MOUSE LD50; 221 MG/KG UNREPORTED-MAN LDLO; MUTAGENIC DATA (RTECS); REPRODUCTIVE EFFECTS DATA (RTECS). CARCINOGEN STATUS: NONE. LOCAL EFFECTS: CORROSIVE- INHALATION, SKIN, EYE, INGESTION. ACUTE TOXICITY LEVEL: MODERATELY TOXIC BY INGESTION. TARGET EFFECTS: POISONING MAY RESULT IN LIVER AND KIDNEY DAMAGE.

HEALTH EFFECTS AND FIRST AID

INHALATION: ZINC SULFATE: CORROSIVE. **ACUTE EXPOSURE-** INHALATION OF DUST OR SOLUTION MIST MAY CAUSE IRRITATION OF THE RESPIRATORY TRACT WITH SORE THROAT, COUGHING, SHORTNESS OF BREATH, LABORED BREATHING, PAIN IN THE NOSE, MOUTH, AND THROAT, AND BURNS OF THE MUCOUS MEMBRANES. IF SUFFICIENT QUANTITIES ARE INHALED, PULMONARY EDEMA MAY DEVELOP, OFTEN WITH A LATENT PERIOD OF 5-72 HOURS. THE SYMPTOMS MAY INCLUDE TIGHTNESS IN THE CHEST, DYSPNEA, FROTHY SPUTUM, CYANOSIS, AND DIZZINESS. PHYSICAL FINDINGS MAY INCLUDE WEAK, RAPID PULSE, HYPOTENSION, HEMOCONCENTRATION, AND MOIST RALES. **CHRONIC EXPOSURE-** DEPENDING ON THE CONCENTRATION AND DURATION OF EXPOSURE, REPEATED OR PROLONGED EXPOSURE TO CORROSIVE SUBSTANCES MAY CAUSE INFLAMMATORY AND ULCERATIVE CHANGES IN THE MOUTH AND POSSIBLY BRONCHIAL AND GASTROINTESTINAL DISTURBANCES.
FIRST AID- REMOVE FROM EXPOSURE AREA TO FRESH AIR IMMEDIATELY. IF BREATHING HAS STOPPED, GIVE ARTIFICIAL RESPIRATION. MAINTAIN AIRWAY AND BLOOD PRESSURE AND ADMINISTER OXYGEN IF AVAILABLE. KEEP AFFECTED PERSON WARM AND AT REST. TREAT SYMPTOMATICALLY AND SUPPORTIVELY. ADMINISTRATION OF OXYGEN SHOULD BE PERFORMED BY QUALIFIED PERSONNEL. GET MEDICAL ATTENTION IMMEDIATELY.

SKIN CONTACT: ZINC SULFATE: CORROSIVE. **ACUTE EXPOSURE-** DIRECT CONTACT WITH CORROSIVE SUBSTANCES MAY CAUSE SEVERE IRRITATION, REDNESS, PAIN, AND POSSIBLY BURNS. **CHRONIC EXPOSURE-** EFFECTS DEPEND ON CONCENTRATION AND DURATION OF EXPOSURE. REPEATED OR PROLONGED CONTACT WITH METAL SALTS MAY RESULT IN DERMATITIS WITH ERYTHEMATOUS, PAPULAR, AND GRANULOMATOUS REACTIONS IN SUSCEPTIBLE INDIVIDUALS OR EFFECTS SIMILAR TO ACUTE EXPOSURE.
FIRST AID- REMOVE CONTAMINATED CLOTHING AND SHOES IMMEDIATELY. WASH AFFECTED AREA WITH SOAP OR MILD DETERGENT AND LARGE AMOUNTS OF WATER UNTIL NO EVIDENCE OF CHEMICAL REMAINS (AT LEAST 15-20 MINUTES). IN CASE OF CHEMICAL BURNS, COVER AREA WITH STERILE, DRY DRESSING. BANDAGE SECURELY, BUT NOT TOO TIGHTLY. GET MEDICAL ATTENTION IMMEDIATELY.

EYE CONTACT: ZINC SULFATE: CORROSIVE. **ACUTE EXPOSURE-** DIRECT CONTACT MAY CAUSE SEVERE IRRITATION, REDNESS, PAIN, BLURRED VISION, AND BURNS, POSSIBLY SEVERE. THE DEGREE OF INJURY DEPENDS ON THE CONCENTRATION AND DURATION OF CONTACT. THE FULL EXTENT OF THE INJURY MAY NOT BE IMMEDIATELY APPARENT. APPLICATION OF A 20% ZINC SULFATE SOLUTION TO CORNEAS INFECTED WITH HERPETIC KERATITIS ULCERS RESULTED IN EDEMA AND RESIDUAL SCARRING UPON HEALING. **CHRONIC EXPOSURE-** EFFECTS DEPEND ON CONCENTRATION AND DURATION OF EXPOSURE. REPEATED OR PROLONGED CONTACT WITH CORROSIVE SUBSTANCES MAY RESULT IN CONJUNCTIVITIS OR EFFECTS AS IN ACUTE EXPOSURE.
FIRST AID- WASH EYES IMMEDIATELY WITH LARGE AMOUNTS OF WATER, OCCASIONALLY LIFTING UPPER AND LOWER LIDS, UNTIL NO EVIDENCE OF CHEMICAL REMAINS (AT LEAST 15-20 MINUTES). CONTINUE IRRIGATING WITH NORMAL SALINE UNTIL THE PH HAS RETURNED TO NORMAL (30-60 MINUTES). COVER WITH STERILE BANDAGES. GET MEDICAL ATTENTION IMMEDIATELY.

INGESTION: ZINC SULFATE: CORROSIVE. **ACUTE EXPOSURE-** INGESTION MAY CAUSE A BURNING PAIN IN THE MOUTH AND THROAT, FEVER, NAUSEA, VIOLENT VOMITING WITH SEVERE ABDOMINAL PAIN, WATERY OR BLOODY DIARRHEA, PROSTRATION, TENESMUS, RETCHING, HYPERGLYCEMIA, ANURIA, LIVER DAMAGE, KIDNEY DAMAGE WITH ALBUMINURIA, ACETONURIA, AND GLYCOSURIA, HYPOTENSION, SUDDEN COLLAPSE, AND CONVULSIONS. **CHRONIC EXPOSURE-** DEPENDING ON THE CONCENTRATION, REPEATED INGESTION OF CORROSIVE SUBSTANCES MAY RESULT IN EFFECTS AS WITH ACUTE INGESTION. PROLONGED INGESTION OF 33,000 MG/KG IN DRINKING WATER RESULTED IN SEVERE ANEMIA IN MICE. EFFECTS ON FERTILITY AND ON THE NEWBORN HAVE BEEN REPORTED FROM PROLONGED EXPOSURE IN EXPERIMENTAL ANIMALS TO ZINC SULFATE. EFFECTS ON THE REPRODUCTIVE SYSTEMS OF MALES AND FEMALES HAVE BEEN REPORTED FROM PROLONGED EXPOSURE IN EXPERIMENTAL ANIMALS TO ZINC SULFATE, HEPTAHYDRATE.
FIRST AID- DILUTE THE POISON IMMEDIATELY WITH LARGE AMOUNTS OF WATER OR MILK AND REMOVE BY GASTRIC LAVAGE UNLESS THE VICTIM IS ALREADY VOMITING. (DREISBACH, HANDBOOK OF POISONING, 12TH ED.) GET MEDICAL ATTENTION IMMEDIATELY. ADMINISTRATION OF GASTRIC LAVAGE SHOULD BE PERFORMED BY QUALIFIED MEDICAL PERSONNEL.
ANTIDOTE: THE FOLLOWING ANTIDOTE HAS BEEN RECOMMENDED. HOWEVER, THE DECISION AS TO WHETHER THE SEVERITY OF POISONING REQUIRES ADMINISTRATION OF ANY ANTIDOTE AND ACTUAL DOSE REQUIRED SHOULD BE MADE BY QUALIFIED MEDICAL PERSONNEL.
POISONING FROM ZINC SALTS: GIVE CALCIUM DISODIUM EDETATE 15-25 MG/KG (0.08-0.125 ML OF 20% SOLUTION PER KILOGRAM OF BODY WEIGHT) IN 250-500 ML OF 5% DEXTROSE INTRAVENOUSLY OVER A 1 TO 2 HOUR PERIOD TWICE DAILY. THE MAXIMUM DOSE SHOULD NOT EXCEED 50 MG/KG/DAY. THE DRUG SHOULD BE GIVEN IN 5-DAY COURSES WITH A REST PERIOD OF AT LEAST 2 DAYS BETWEEN COURSES. AFTER THE FIRST COURSE, SUBSEQUENT COURSES SHOULD NOT EXCEED 50 MG/KG/DAY. DAILY URINALYSES SHOULD BE DONE DURING THE

TREATMENT PERIOD. THE DOSAGE SHOULD BE REDUCED IF ANY UNUSUAL URINARY FINDINGS APPEAR. FOR INTRAMUSCULAR ADMINISTRATION, GIVE 12.5 MG/KG BODY WEIGHT EVERY 4-6 HOURS. DILUTE EACH DOSE WITH AN EQUAL VOLUME OF 1% PROCAINE. DOSE LIMITATION IS THE SAME AS THAT GIVEN ABOVE. (DREISBACH, HANDBOOK OF POISONING, 12TH ED.). ANTIDOTE SHOULD BE ADMINISTERED BY QUALIFIED MEDICAL PERSONNEL.

REACTIVITY

REACTIVITY: STABLE UNDER NORMAL TEMPERATURES AND PRESSURES.

INCOMPATIBILITIES: ZINC SULFATE: NO DATA AVAILABLE. SEE METAL SULFATES. METAL SULFATES: ALUMINUM: POSSIBLE EXPLOSION ON MELTING. MAGNESIUM: POSSIBLE EXPLOSION.

DECOMPOSITION: THERMAL DECOMPOSITION MAY RELEASE TOXIC OXIDES OF SULFUR AND ZINC OXIDE FUMES.

POLYMERIZATION: HAZARDOUS POLYMERIZATION HAS NOT BEEN REPORTED TO OCCUR UNDER NORMAL TEMPERATURES AND PRESSURES.

STORAGE AND DISPOSAL

OBSERVE ALL FEDERAL, STATE AND LOCAL REGULATIONS WHEN STORING OR DISPOSING OF THIS SUBSTANCE. FOR ASSISTANCE, CONTACT THE DISTRICT DIRECTOR OF THE ENVIRONMENTAL PROTECTION AGENCY.

****STORAGE****

STORE AWAY FROM INCOMPATIBLE SUBSTANCES.

****DISPOSAL****

NEUTRALIZE WITH SODA ASH OR SODIUM BICARBONATE FOR DISPOSAL. BURY IN APPROVED LANDFILL (G.E. MSDS).

CONDITIONS TO AVOID

MAY BURN BUT DOES NOT IGNITE READILY. AVOID CONTACT WITH STRONG OXIDIZERS, EXCESSIVE HEAT, SPARKS, OR OPEN FLAME.

SPILL AND LEAK PROCEDURES

SOIL SPILL: DIG HOLDING AREA SUCH AS LAGOON, POND OR PIT FOR CONTAINMENT. USE PROTECTIVE COVER SUCH AS A PLASTIC SHEET TO PREVENT MATERIAL FROM DISSOLVING IN FIRE EXTINGUISHING WATER OR RAIN.

WATER SPILL: NEUTRALIZE WITH AGRICULTURAL LIME, SLAKED LIME, CRUSHED LIMESTONE, OR SODIUM BICARBONATE.
ADD SUITABLE AGENT TO NEUTRALIZE SPILLED MATERIAL TO PH-7.
USE MECHANICAL DREDGES OR LIFTS TO EXTRACT IMMOBILIZED MASSES OF POLLUTION AND PRECIPITATES.

OCCUPATIONAL SPILL: SWEEP UP AND PLACE IN SUITABLE CLEAN, DRY CONTAINERS FOR RECLAMATION OR LATER DISPOSAL. DO NOT FLUSH SPILLED MATERIAL INTO SEWER. KEEP UNNECESSARY PEOPLE AWAY.
REPORTABLE QUANTITY (RQ): 1000 POUNDS THE SUPERFUND AMENDMENTS AND REAUTHORIZATION ACT (SARA) SECTION 304 REQUIRES THAT A RELEASE EQUAL TO OR GREATER THAN THE REPORTABLE QUANTITY FOR THIS SUBSTANCE BE IMMEDIATELY REPORTED TO THE LOCAL EMERGENCY PLANNING COMMITTEE AND THE STATE EMERGENCY RESPONSE COMMISSION (40 CFR 355.40). IF THE RELEASE OF THIS SUBSTANCE IS REPORTABLE UNDER CERCLA SECTION 103, THE NATIONAL RESPONSE CENTER MUST BE NOTIFIED IMMEDIATELY AT (800) 424-8802 OR (202) 426-2675 IN THE METROPOLITAN WASHINGTON, D.C. AREA (40 CFR 302.6).

PROTECTIVE EQUIPMENT

VENTILATION: PROVIDE LOCAL EXHAUST OR PROCESS ENCLOSURE VENTILATION TO MEET PUBLISHED EXPOSURE LIMITS.

RESPIRATOR: THE FOLLOWING RESPIRATORS ARE RECOMMENDED BASED ON INFORMATION FOUND IN THE PHYSICAL DATA, TOXICITY AND HEALTH EFFECTS SECTIONS. THEY ARE RANKED IN ORDER FROM MINIMUM TO MAXIMUM RESPIRATORY PROTECTION. THE SPECIFIC RESPIRATOR SELECTED MUST BE BASED ON CONTAMINATION LEVELS FOUND IN THE WORK PLACE, MUST NOT EXCEED THE WORKING LIMITS OF THE RESPIRATOR AND BE JOINTLY APPROVED BY THE NATIONAL INSTITUTE FOR OCCUPATIONAL SAFETY AND HEALTH AND THE MINE SAFETY AND HEALTH ADMINISTRATION (NIOSH-MSHA).
DUST AND MIST RESPIRATOR WITH A FULL FACEPIECE.
AIR-PURIFYING FULL FACEPIECE RESPIRATOR WITH A HIGH-EFFICIENCY PARTICULATE FILTER.
POWERED AIR-PURIFYING RESPIRATOR WITH A TIGHT-FITTING FACEPIECE AND HIGH-EFFICIENCY PARTICULATE FILTER.
TYPE 'C' SUPPLIED-AIR RESPIRATOR WITH A FULL FACEPIECE OPERATED IN PRESSURE-DEMAND OR OTHER POSITIVE PRESSURE MODE OR WITH A FULL FACEPIECE, HELMET OR HOOD OPERATED IN CONTINUOUS-FLOW MODE.
SELF-CONTAINED BREATHING APPARATUS WITH A FULL FACEPIECE OPERATED IN PRESSURE-DEMAND OR OTHER POSITIVE PRESSURE MODE.
FOR FIREFIGHTING AND OTHER IMMEDIATELY DANGEROUS TO LIFE OR HEALTH CONDITIONS:
SELF-CONTAINED BREATHING APPARATUS WITH FULL FACEPIECE OPERATED IN PRESSURE-DEMAND OR OTHER POSITIVE PRESSURE MODE.
SUPPLIED-AIR RESPIRATOR WITH FULL FACEPIECE AND OPERATED IN PRESSURE-DEMAND OR OTHER POSITIVE PRESSURE MODE IN COMBINATION WITH AN AUXILIARY SELF-CONTAINED BREATHING APPARATUS OPERATED IN PRESSURE-DEMAND OR OTHER POSITIVE PRESSURE MODE.

CLOTHING: EMPLOYEE MUST WEAR APPROPRIATE PROTECTIVE (IMPERVIOUS) CLOTHING AND EQUIPMENT TO PREVENT ANY POSSIBILITY OF SKIN CONTACT WITH THIS SUBSTANCE.

GLOVES: EMPLOYEE MUST WEAR APPROPRIATE PROTECTIVE GLOVES TO PREVENT CONTACT WITH THIS SUBSTANCE.

EYE PROTECTION: EMPLOYEE MUST WEAR SPLASH-PROOF OR DUST-RESISTANT SAFETY GOGGLES AND A FACESHIELD TO PREVENT CONTACT WITH THIS SUBSTANCE.
EMERGENCY WASH FACILITIES: WHERE THERE IS ANY POSSIBILITY THAT AN EMPLOYEE'S EYES AND/OR SKIN MAY BE EXPOSED TO THIS SUBSTANCE, THE EMPLOYER SHOULD PROVIDE AN EYE WASH FOUNTAIN AND QUICK DRENCH SHOWER WITHIN THE IMMEDIATE WORK AREA FOR EMERGENCY USE.

AUTHORIZED BY- OCCUPATIONAL HEALTH SERVICES, INC.
CREATION DATE: 02/08/90 ***REVISION DATE:*** 05/31/90

MATERIAL SAFETY DATA SHEET

OCCUPATIONAL HEALTH SERVICES, INC.
AGRICULTURE AND PESTICIDE DIVISION
450 SEVENTH AVENUE, SUITE 2407
NEW YORK, NEW YORK 10123
1-800-445-MSDS OR (212) 967-1100

EMERGENCY CONTACT:
JOHN S. BRANSFORD, JR. (615) 292-1180

SUBSTANCE IDENTIFICATION

CAS-NUMBER 297-97-2

SUBSTANCE: **THIONAZIN**

TRADE NAMES/SYNONYMS: O,O-DIETHYL O-PYRAZINYL ESTER PHOSPHOROTHIOIC ACID; ETHYL PYRAZINYL PHOSPHOROTHIOATE; O,O-DIETHYL O,2-PYRAZINYL PHOSPHOROTHIOATE; DIETHYL O-2-PYRAZINYL PHOSPHOROTHIONATE; O,O-DIETHYL O-PYRAZINYL THIOPHOSPHATE; AMERICAN CYANAMID 18133; CYNEM; CYNOPHOS; NEMAFOS; NEMAPHOS; NEMATOCIDE GR; THIONAZINE; ZINOPHOS; ZYNOPHOS; ENT 25,580; RCRA P040; Z-68; Z-70; Z-76; C8H13N2O3PS; PST25590

CHEMICAL FAMILY: THIOPHOSPHATE
PYRAZINE

MOLECULAR FORMULA: C8-H13-N2-O3-P-S

MOLECULAR WEIGHT: 248.26

CERCLA RATINGS (SCALE 0-3): HEALTH=3 FIRE=U REACTIVITY=U PERSISTENCE=2

NFPA RATINGS (SCALE 0-4): HEALTH=4 FIRE=U REACTIVITY=U

COMPONENTS AND CONTAMINANTS

COMPONENT: THIONAZIN ***PERCENT:*** 100.0
CAS# 297-97-2

OTHER CONTAMINANTS: NONE

EXPOSURE LIMITS: NO OCCUPATIONAL EXPOSURE LIMITS ESTABLISHED BY OSHA, ACGIH, OR NIOSH.
THIONAZIN: 500 POUNDS SARA SECTION 302 THRESHOLD PLANNING QUANTITY 100 POUNDS SARA SECTION 304 REPORTABLE QUANTITY 100 POUNDS CERLCA SECTION 103 REPORTABLE QUANTITY

PHYSICAL DATA

DESCRIPTION: CLEAR TO PALE YELLOW LIQUID ***BOILING POINT:*** 176 F (80 C)
MELTING POINT: 29 F (-1.7 C) ***SPECIFIC GRAVITY:*** NOT AVAILABLE
VAPOR PRESSURE: 0.003 @ 30 C ***SOLUBILITY IN WATER:*** 0.1% @ 25 C
SOLVENT SOLUBILITY: MOST ORGANIC SOLVENTS

FIRE AND EXPLOSION DATA

FIRE AND EXPLOSION HAZARD: UNKNOWN FIRE AND EXPLOSION HAZARD.

FIREFIGHTING MEDIA: DRY CHEMICAL, CARBON DIOXIDE, HALON, WATER SPRAY OR STANDARD FOAM (1987 EMERGENCY RESPONSE GUIDEBOOK, DOT P 5800.4).
FOR LARGER FIRES, USE WATER SPRAY, FOG OR STANDARD FOAM (1987 EMERGENCY RESPONSE GUIDEBOOK, DOT P 5800.4).

FIREFIGHTING: MOVE CONTAINERS FROM FIRE AREA IF POSSIBLE. FIGHT FIRE FROM MAXIMUM DISTANCE. STAY AWAY FROM STORAGE TANK ENDS. DIKE FIRE CONTROL WATER FOR LATER DISPOSAL. DO NOT SCATTER MATERIAL (1987

EMERGENCY RESPONSE GUIDEBOOK, DOT P 5800.4, GUIDE PAGE 55). EXTINGUISH ONLY IF FLOW CAN BE STOPPED; USE FLOODING AMOUNTS OF WATER AS FOG, SOLID STREAMS MAY BE INEFFECTIVE. COOL CONTAINERS WITH FLOODING AMOUNTS OF WATER FROM AS FAR A DISTANCE AS POSSIBLE. USE WATER SPRAY TO ABSORB TOXIC VAPORS. AVOID BREATHING TOXIC VAPORS; KEEP UPWIND. CONSIDER EVACUATION OF DOWNWIND AREA IF MATERIAL IS LEAKING.

TRANSPORTATION DATA

DEPARTMENT OF TRANSPORTATION HAZARD CLASSIFICATION 49 CFR 172.101: POISON B

DEPARTMENT OF TRANSPORTATION LABELING REQUIREMENTS 49 CFR 172.101 AND SUBPART E: POISON

DEPARTMENT OF TRANSPORTATION PACKAGING REQUIREMENTS: 49 CFR 173.346 EXCEPTIONS: 49 CFR 173.345

TOXICITY

THIONAZIN: TOXICITY DATA: 8 MG/KG SKIN-RAT LD50; 10 MG/KG SKIN-GUINEA PIG LD50; 50 MG/KG OCULAR-RABBIT LDLO; 3500 UG/KG ORAL-RAT LD50; 5 MG/KG ORAL-MOUSE LD50. CARCINOGEN STATUS: NONE. ACUTE TOXICITY LEVEL: HIGHLY TOXIC BY INGESTION AND DERMAL ABSORPTION. TARGET EFFECTS: CHOLINESTERASE INHIBITOR. POISONING MAY AFFECT THE NERVOUS SYSTEM.* AT INCREASED RISK FROM EXPOSURE: PERSONS WITH RESPIRATORY AILMENTS, RECENT EXPOSURE TO CHOLINESTERASE INHIBITORS OR IMPAIRED CHOLINESTERASE PRODUCTION, OR LIVER MALFUNCTION.* ADDITIONAL DATA: MAY CROSS THE PLACENTA. HIGH ENVIRONMENTAL TEMPERATURES OR EXPOSURE OF THE CHEMICAL TO VISIBLE OR ULTRAVIOLET LIGHT MAY ENHANCE THE TOXICITY. INTERACTIONS WITH MEDICATIONS MAY OCCUR.* * MAY BE BASED ON GENERAL INFORMATION ON ORGANOPHOSPHATES.

HEALTH EFFECTS AND FIRST AID

INHALATION: THIONAZIN: SEE INFORMATION ON ORGANOPHOSPHATES.
ORGANOPHOSPHATES: CHOLINESTERASE INHIBITOR. **ACUTE EXPOSURE-** WHEN INHALED, THE FIRST EFFECTS OF CHOLINESTERASE INHIBITORS ARE USUALLY RESPIRATORY AND MAY INCLUDE NASAL HYPEREMIA AND WATERY DISCHARGE, COUGH, CHEST DISCOMFORT, DYSPNEA, AND WHEEZING DUE TO INCREASED BRONCHIAL SECRETIONS AND BRONCHOCONSTRICTION. IF SUFFICIENT AMOUNTS ARE ABSORBED, OTHER SYSTEMIC EFFECTS MAY BEGIN WITHIN A FEW MINUTES OR BE DELAYED FOR UP TO 12 HOURS. SYMPTOMS MAY INCLUDE PALLOR, NAUSEA, VOMITING, DIARRHEA, ABDOMINAL CRAMPS, HEADACHE, DIZZINESS, OCULAR PAIN, BLURRED VISION, MIOSIS OR IN SOME CASES, ESPECIALLY INITIALLY, MYDRIASIS, LACRIMATION, SALIVATION, SWEATING, AND CONFUSION. OTHER REPORTED CENTRAL NERVOUS SYSTEM OR NEUROMUSCULAR EFFECTS MAY INCLUDE ATAXIA, SLURRED SPEECH, AREFLEXIA, WEAKNESS, FATIGUE, FASCICULATIONS, TWITCHING, TREMORS POSSIBLY OF THE TONGUE AND EYELIDS, AND EVENTUALLY PARALYSIS OF THE EXTREMITIES AND POSSIBLY OF THE RESPIRATORY MUSCLES. IN SEVERE CASES THERE MAY ALSO BE INVOLUNTARY DEFECATION AND URINATION, CYANOSIS, PSYCHOSIS, HYPERGLYCEMIA, ACUTE PANCREATITIS, CARDIAC IRREGULARITIES, PULMONARY EDEMA, UNCONSCIOUSNESS, CONVULSIONS, AND COMA. DEATH IS PRIMARILY DUE TO RESPIRATORY FAILURE, ALTHOUGH CARDIOVASCULAR EFFECTS INCLUDING CARDIAC ARREST MAY ALSO BE IMPLICATED. LONG TERM SEQUELAE ARE RARE BUT MAY INCLUDE NEUROPSYCHIATRIC DISORDERS AND MYOPATHY WITH MUSCLE TENDERNESS. SOME ORGANOPHOSPHATES MAY CAUSE A DELAYED NEUROPATHY BEGINNING 1-4 WEEKS AFTER AN ACUTE EXPOSURE WHICH MAY OR MAY NOT HAVE CAUSED ACUTE CHOLINERGIC EFFECTS. NUMBNESS, TINGLING, WEAKNESS AND CRAMPING BEGINNING SYMMETRICALLY IN THE LOWER LIMBS MAY PROGRESS TO ATAXIA AND PARALYSIS. IN SEVERE CASES, UPPER LIMB INVOLVEMENT IS POSSIBLE AND FLACCID PARALYSIS MAY PROGRESS TO SPASTIC' PARALYSIS WITH EXAGGERATED REFLEXES. IMPROVEMENT MAY OCCUR OVER MONTHS TO YEARS, BUT SOME RESIDUAL IMPAIRMENT USUALLY REMAINS. **CHRONIC EXPOSURE-** REPEATED OR PROLONGED EXPOSURE MAY RESULT IN THE EFFECTS OF ACUTE EXPOSURE INCLUDING THE DELAYED NEUROPATHY. OTHER EFFECTS REPORTED IN WORKERS REPEATEDLY EXPOSED INCLUDE IMPAIRED MEMORY AND CONCENTRATION, ACUTE PSYCHOSIS, SEVERE DEPRESSIONS, IRRITABILTY, CONFUSION, APATHY, EMOTIONAL LABILITY, SOCIAL WITHDRAWAL, CONFUSION, HEADACHE, SPEECH DIFFICULTIES, DELAYED REACTION TIMES, SPATIAL DISORIENTATION, NIGHTMARES, SLEEPWALKING, AND DROWSINESS OR INSOMNIA. AN INFLUENZA-LIKE CONDITION WITH HEADACHE, NAUSEA, WEAKNESS, ANOREXIA AND MALAISE HAS ALSO BEEN REPORTED.

FIRST AID- REMOVE FROM EXPOSURE AREA TO FRESH AIR IMMEDIATELY. IF BREATHING HAS STOPPED, GIVE ARTIFICIAL RESPIRATION. MAINTAIN AIRWAY AND BLOOD PRESSURE AND ADMINISTER OXYGEN IF AVAILABLE. KEEP AFFECTED PERSON WARM AND AT REST. TREAT SYMPTOMATICALLY AND SUPPORTIVELY. ADMINISTRATION OF OXYGEN SHOULD BE PERFORMED BY QUALIFIED PERSONNEL. GET MEDICAL ATTENTION IMMEDIATELY.

SKIN CONTACT: THIONAZIN: HIGHLY TOXIC. SEE INFORMATION ON ORGANOPHOSPHATES.
ORGANOPHOSPHATES: CHOLINESTERASE INHIBITOR. **ACUTE EXPOSURE-** LOCALIZED SWEATING AND FASCICULATIONS MAY OCCUR AT THE SITE OF CONTACT. IF SUFFICIENT AMOUNTS ARE ABSORBED, OTHER EFFECTS OF CHOLINESTERASE INHIBITION AS DESCRIBED IN ACUTE INHALATION MAY OCCUR. SYMPTOMS MAY BE DELAYED 2-3 HOURS, BUT USUALLY NO MORE THAN 12 HOURS. THE RATE OF ABSORPTION IS INCREASED BY THE PRESENCE OF DERMATITIS OR HIGH AMBIENT TEMPERATURES. DELAYED NEUROPATHY IS ALSO POSSIBLE. **CHRONIC EXPOSURE-** REPEATED OR PROLONGED EXPOSURE MAY CAUSE EFFECTS AS DESCRIBED IN ACUTE EXPOSURE. SOME ORGANOPHOSPHATES MAY CAUSE SENSITIZATION.

FIRST AID- REMOVE CONTAMINATED CLOTHING IMMEDIATELY. WASH CONTAMINATED AREAS WITH SOAP AND WATER FOLLOWED BY ALCOHOL (ARENA, POISONING, 4TH ED.). EMERGENCY PERSONNEL SHOULD WEAR GLOVES AND AVOID CONTAMINATION. TREAT RESPIRATORY DIFFICULTY WITH ARTIFICIAL RESPIRATION. GET MEDICAL ATTENTION IMMEDIATELY.

EYE CONTACT: THIONAZIN: SEE INFORMATION ON ORGANOPHOSPHATES.
ORGANOPHOSPHATES: CHOLINESTERASE INHIBITOR. **ACUTE EXPOSURE-** DIRECT CONTACT MAY CAUSE PAIN, HYPEREMIA, LACRIMATION, TWITCHING OF THE EYELIDS, MIOSIS, AND CILIARY MUSCLE SPASM WITH LOSS OF ACCOMODATION, BLURRED OR DIMMED VISION AND BROWACHE. SOMETIMES MYDRIASIS MAY OCCUR INSTEAD OF MIOSIS. WITH SUFFICIENT EXPOSURE, OTHER SYMPTOMS OF CHOLINESTERASE INHIBITION AS DESCRIBED IN ACUTE INHALATION MAY OCCUR. **CHRONIC EXPOSURE-** REPEATED OR PROLONGED EXPOSURE MAY CAUSE EFFECTS AS DESCRIBED IN ACUTE EXPOSURE. SOME COMPOUNDS HAVE CAUSED TOXIC EFFECTS ON THE CRYSTALLINE LENS, CONJUNCTIVAL THICKENING AND OBSTRUCTION OF THE NASOLACRIMAL CANALS WHEN USED AS MIOTIC EYEDROPS.

FIRST AID- IRRIGATE EYES WITH WATER OR SALINE SOLUTION. IF SYMPTOMS OF POISONING OCCUR, TREAT RESPIRATORY DIFFICULTY WITH ARTIFICIAL RESPIRATION AND OXYGEN. OBSERVE PATIENT FOR AT LEAST 24-36 HOURS (GOSSELIN, CLINICAL TOXICOLOGY OF COMMERCIAL PRODUCTS, 5TH ED.). GET MEDICAL ATTENTION IMMEDIATELY. OXYGEN SHOULD BE ADMINISTERED BY QUALIFIED MEDICAL PERSONNEL.

INGESTION: THIONAZIN: HIGHLY TOXIC. SEE INFORMATION ON ORGANOPHOSPHATES.
ORGANOPHOSPHATES: CHOLINESTERASE INHIBITOR. **ACUTE EXPOSURE-** WHEN INGESTED, THE FIRST EFFECTS MAY BE NAUSEA, VOMITING, ANOREXIA, ABDOMINAL CRAMPS AND DIARRHEA. GASTROINTESTINAL ABSORPTION MAY CAUSE SYMPTOMS OF CHOLINESTERASE INHIBITION AS DESCRIBED IN ACUTE INHALATION. SYMPTOMS MAY BEGIN WITHIN MINUTES OR BE DELAYED FOR HOURS. DELAYED EFFECTS INCLUDING NEUROPATHY MAY ALSO OCCUR. **CHRONIC EXPOSURE-** REPEATED INGESTION MAY CAUSE EFFECTS AS DESCRIBED IN ACUTE EXPOSURE.

FIRST AID- IF PERSON IS ALERT AND RESPIRATION IS NOT DEPRESSED, GIVE SYRUP OF IPECAC FOLLOWED BY WATER (IF VOMITING OCCURS, KEEP HEAD BELOW HIPS TO PREVENT ASPIRATION). IF CONSCIOUSNESS LEVEL DECLINES OR VOMITING HAS NOT OCCURRED IN 15 MINUTES EMPTY STOMACH BY GASTRIC LAVAGE WITH THE AID OF CUFFED ENDOTRACHEAL TUBE USING ISOTONIC SALINE OR 5% SODIUM BICARBONATE FOLLOW WITH ACTIVATED CHARCOAL. ESTABLISH AND MAINTAIN AIRWAY. TREAT RESPIRATORY DIFFICULTY WITH ARTIFICIAL RESPIRATION AND OXYGEN. DO NOT GIVE MORPHINE, AMINOPHYLLINE, PHENOTHIAZINES, RESERPINE, FUROSEMIDE, OR ETHACRYNIC ACID (MORGAN, RECOGNITION AND MANAGEMENT OF PESTICIDE POISONINGS, 3RD ED.). TREAT SYMPTOMATICALLY AND SUPPORTIVELY. ADMINISTRATION OF OXYGEN AND LAVAGE MUST BE PERFORMED BY QUALIFIED MEDICAL PERSONNEL. GET MEDICAL ATTENTION IMMEDIATELY.

ANTIDOTE: THE FOLLOWING ANTIDOTE(S) HAVE BEEN RECOMMENDED. HOWEVER, THE DECISION AS TO WHETHER THE SEVERITY OF POISONING REQUIRES ADMINISTRATION OF ANY ANTIDOTE AND ACTUAL DOSE REQUIRED SHOULD BE MADE BY QUALIFIED MEDICAL PERSONNEL.
FOR CHOLINESTERASE INHIBITORS: ESTABLISH CLEAR AIRWAY AND TISSUE OXYGENATION BY ASPIRATION OF SECRETIONS, AND IF NECESSARY, BY ASSISTED PULMONARY VENTILATION WITH OXYGEN. IMPROVE TISSUE OXYGENATION AS MUCH AS POSSIBLE BEFORE ADMINISTERING ATROPINE TO MINIMIZE THE RISK OF VENTRICULAR FIBRILLATION. ADMINISTER ATROPINE SULFATE INTRAVENOUSLY, OR INTRAMUSCULARLY IF IV INJECTION IS NOT POSSIBLE. IN MODERATELY SEVERE POISONING ADMINISTER ATROPINE SULFATE, 0.4-2.0 MG REPEATED EVERY 15 MINUTES UNTIL ATROPINIZATION IS ACHIEVED (TACHYCARDIA, FLUSHING, DRY MOUTH, MYDRIASIS). MAINTAIN ATROPINIZATION BY REPEATED DOSES FOR 2-12 HOURS, OR LONGER, DEPENDING ON THE SEVERITY OF POISONING. THE APPEARANCE OF RALES IN THE LUNG BASES, MIOSIS, SALIVATION, NAUSEA, BRADYCARDIA, ARE ALL INDICATIONS OF INADEQUATE ATROPINIZATION. SEVERELY POISONED INDIVIDUALS MAY EXHIBIT REMARKABLE TOLERANCE TO

ATROPINE; TWO OR MORE TIMES THE DOSAGES SUGGESTED ABOVE MAY BE NEEDED. PERSONS NOT POISONED OR ONLY SLIGHTLY POISONED, HOWEVER, MAY DEVELOP SIGNS OF ATROPINE TOXICITY FROM SUCH LARGE DOSAGES: FEVER, MUSCLE FIBRILLATIONS, AND DELIRIUM ARE THE MAIN SIGNS OF ATROPINE TOXICITY. IF THESE SIGNS APPEAR WHILE THE PATIENT IS FULLY ATROPINIZED, ATROPINE ADMINISTRATION SHOULD BE DISCONTINUED, AT LEAST TEMPORARILY. OBSERVE TREATED PATIENTS CLOSELY AT LEAST 24 HOURS TO INSURE THAT SYMPTOMS (POSSIBLY PULMONARY EDEMA) DO NOT RECUR AS ATROPINIZATION WEARS OFF. IN VERY SEVERE POISONINGS, METABOLIC DISPOSITION OF TOXICANT MAY REQUIRE SEVERAL HOURS OR DAYS DURING WHICH ATROPINIZATION MUST BE MAINTAINED. MARKEDLY LOWER LEVELS OF URINARY METABOLITES INDICATE THAT ATROPINE DOSAGE CAN BE TAPERED OFF. AS DOSAGE IS REDUCED, CHECK THE LUNG BASES FREQUENTLY FOR RALES. IF RALES ARE HEARD OR OTHER SYMPTOMS RETURN, RE-ESTABLISH ATROPINIZATION PROMPTLY (MORGAN, RECOGNITION AND MANAGEMENT OF PESTICIDE POISONINGS, 3RD ED.). ADMINISTRATION OF ANTIDOTE MUST BE PERFORMED BY QUALIFIED MEDICAL PERSONNEL.

IN CASES OF SEVERE POISONING BY ORGANOPHOSPHATE PESTICIDES IN WHICH RESPIRATORY DEPRESSION, MUSCLE WEAKNESS AND TWITCHINGS ARE SEVERE, GIVE PRALIDOXIME (PROTOPAM-AYERST, 2-PAM), 1.0 GRAM INTRAVENOUSLY AT NO MORE THAN 0.5 GRAM PER MINUTE. DOSAGE OF PRALIDOXIME MAY BE REPEATED IN 1-2 HOURS, THEN AT 10-12 HOUR INTERVALS IF NEEDED. IN VERY SEVERE POISONINGS, DOSAGE RATES MAY BE DOUBLED. TREATMENT WITH PRALIDOXIME WILL BE MOST EFFECTIVE IF GIVEN WITHIN THIRTY-SIX HOURS AFTER POISONING (MORGAN, RECOGNITION AND MANAGEMENT OF PESTICIDE POISONINGS, 3RD ED.). ANTIDOTE SHOULD BE ADMINISTERED BY QUALIFIED MEDICAL PERSONNEL.

REACTIVITY

REACTIVITY: DECOMPOSES OVER A PERIOD OF WEEKS TO MONTHS IN STORAGE.

INCOMPATIBILITIES: THIONAZIN. OXIDIZERS (STRONG): FIRE AND EXPLOSION HAZARD.

DECOMPOSITION: THERMAL DECOMPOSITION MAY RELEASE TOXIC AND/OR HAZARDOUS GASES.

POLYMERIZATION: HAZARDOUS POLYMERIZATION HAS NOT BEEN REPORTED TO OCCUR UNDER NORMAL TEMPERATURES AND PRESSURES.

STORAGE AND DISPOSAL

OBSERVE ALL FEDERAL, STATE AND LOCAL REGULATIONS WHEN STORING OR DISPOSING OF THIS SUBSTANCE. FOR ASSISTANCE, CONTACT THE DISTRICT DIRECTOR OF THE ENVIRONMENTAL PROTECTION AGENCY.

****STORAGE****

STORE IN ACCORDANCE WITH 40 CFR 165 RECOMMENDED PROCEDURES FOR THE DISPOSAL AND STORAGE OF PESTICIDES AND PESTICIDE CONTAINERS.

DECOMPOSES IN A PERIOD OF WEEKS OR MONTHS IN STORAGE; THUS THE SHELF LIFE FOR UNUSED STOCKS IS LIMITED.

THRESHOLD PLANNING QUANTITY (TPQ): THE SUPERFUND AMENDMENTS AND REAUTHORIZATION ACT (SARA) SECTION 302 REQUIRES THAT EACH FACILITY WHERE ANY EXTREMELY HAZARDOUS SUBSTANCE IS PRESENT IN A QUANTITY EQUAL TO OR GREATER THAN THE TPQ ESTABLISHED FOR THAT SUBSTANCE NOTIFY THE STATE EMERGENCY RESPONSE COMMISSION FOR THE STATE IN WHICH IT IS LOCATED. SECTION 303 OF SARA REQUIRES THESE FACILITIES TO PARTICIPATE IN LOCAL EMERGENCY RESPONSE PLANNING (40 CFR 355.30).

****DISPOSAL****

DISPOSAL MUST BE IN ACCORDANCE WITH STANDARDS APPLICABLE TO GENERATORS OF HAZARDOUS WASTE, 40CFR 262. EPA HAZARDOUS WASTE NUMBER P040.

CONDITIONS TO AVOID

NONE REPORTED.

SPILL AND LEAK PROCEDURES

OCCUPATIONAL SPILL: DO NOT TOUCH SPILLED MATERIAL. STOP LEAK IF YOU CAN DO IT WITHOUT RISK. USE WATER SPRAY TO REDUCE VAPORS. FOR SMALL SPILLS, TAKE UP WITH SAND OR OTHER ABSORBENT MATERIAL AND PLACE INTO CONTAINERS FOR LATER DISPOSAL. FOR SMALL DRY SPILLS, WITH A CLEAN SHOVEL PLACE MATERIAL INTO CLEAN, DRY CONTAINERS AND COVER. MOVE CONTAINERS FROM SPILL AREA. FOR LARGER SPILLS, DIKE FAR AHEAD OF SPILL FOR LATER DISPOSAL. KEEP UNNECESSARY PEOPLE AWAY. ISOLATE HAZARD AREA AND DENY ENTRY. VENTILATE CLOSED SPACES BEFORE ENTERING.

REPORTABLE QUANTITY (RQ): 100 POUNDS THE SUPERFUND AMENDMENTS AND REAUTHORIZATION ACT (SARA) SECTION 304 REQUIRES THAT A RELEASE EQUAL TO OR GREATER THAN THE REPORTABLE QUANTITY FOR THIS SUBSTANCE BE IMMEDIATELY REPORTED TO THE LOCAL EMERGENCY PLANNING COMMITTEE AND THE STATE EMERGENCY RESPONSE COMMISSION (40 CFR 355.40). IF THE RELEASE OF THIS SUBSTANCE IS REPORTABLE UNDER CERCLA SECTION 103, THE NATIONAL RESPONSE CENTER MUST BE NOTIFIED IMMEDIATELY AT (800) 424-8802 OR (202) 426-2675 IN THE METROPOLITAN WASHINGTON, D.C. AREA (40 CFR 302.6).

PROTECTIVE EQUIPMENT

VENTILATION: PROCESS ENCLOSURE RECOMMENDED.

RESPIRATOR: THE FOLLOWING RESPIRATORS ARE RECOMMENDED BASED ON INFORMATION FOUND IN THE PHYSICAL DATA, TOXICITY AND HEALTH EFFECTS SECTIONS. THEY ARE RANKED IN ORDER FROM MINIMUM TO MAXIMUM RESPIRATORY PROTECTION. THE SPECIFIC RESPIRATOR SELECTED MUST BE BASED ON CONTAMINATION LEVELS FOUND IN THE WORK PLACE, MUST NOT EXCEED THE WORKING LIMITS OF THE RESPIRATOR AND BE JOINTLY APPROVED BY THE NATIONAL INSTITUTE FOR OCCUPATIONAL SAFETY AND HEALTH AND THE MINE SAFETY AND HEALTH ADMINISTRATION (NIOSH-MSHA).

TYPE 'C' SUPPLIED-AIR RESPIRATOR WITH A FULL FACEPIECE OPERATED IN PRESSURE-DEMAND OR OTHER POSITIVE PRESSURE MODE OR WITH A FULL FACEPIECE, HELMET OR HOOD OPERATED IN CONTINOUS-FLOW MODE.

SELF-CONTAINED BREATHING APPARATUS WITH A FULL FACEPIECE OPERATED IN PRESSURE-DEMAND OR OTHER POSITIVE PRESSURE MODE.

FOR FIREFIGHTING AND OTHER IMMEDIATELY DANGEROUS TO LIFE OR HEALTH CONDITIONS:

SELF-CONTAINED BREATHING APPARATUS WITH FULL FACEPIECE OPERATED IN PRESSURE-DEMAND OR OTHER POSITIVE PRESSURE MODE.

SUPPLIED-AIR RESPIRATOR WITH FULL FACEPIECE AND OPERATED IN PRESSURE-DEMAND OR OTHER POSITIVE PRESSURE MODE IN COMBINATION WITH AN AUXILIARY SELF-CONTAINED BREATHING APPARATUS OPERATED IN PRESSURE-DEMAND OR OTHER POSITIVE PRESSURE MODE.

CLOTHING: EMPLOYEE MUST WEAR APPROPRIATE PROTECTIVE (IMPERVIOUS) CLOTHING AND EQUIPMENT TO PREVENT ANY POSSIBILITY OF SKIN CONTACT WITH THIS SUBSTANCE.

GLOVES: EMPLOYEE MUST WEAR APPROPRIATE PROTECTIVE GLOVES TO PREVENT CONTACT WITH THIS SUBSTANCE.

EYE PROTECTION: EMPLOYEE MUST WEAR SPLASH-PROOF OR DUST-RESISTANT SAFETY GOGGLES AND A FACESHIELD TO PREVENT CONTACT WITH THIS SUBSTANCE.

EMERGENCY WASH FACILITIES: WHERE THERE IS ANY POSSIBILITY THAT AN EMPLOYEE'S EYES AND/OR SKIN MAY BE EXPOSED TO THIS SUBSTANCE, THE EMPLOYER SHOULD PROVIDE AN EYE WASH FOUNTAIN AND QUICK DRENCH SHOWER WITHIN THE IMMEDIATE WORK AREA FOR EMERGENCY USE.

AUTHORIZED BY- OCCUPATIONAL HEALTH SERVICES, INC.

CREATION DATE: 10/05/89 ***REVISION DATE:*** 05/09/90

MATERIAL SAFETY DATA SHEET

OCCUPATIONAL HEALTH SERVICES, INC.
AGRICULTURE AND PESTICIDE DIVISION
450 SEVENTH AVENUE, SUITE 2407
NEW YORK, NEW YORK 10123
1-800-445-MSDS OR (212) 967-1100

EMERGENCY CONTACT:
JOHN S. BRANSFORD, JR. (615) 292-1180

SUBSTANCE IDENTIFICATION

CAS-NUMBER 1314-23-4

SUBSTANCE: **ZIRCONIUM OXIDE**

TRADE NAMES/SYNONYMS: ZIRCONIUM DIOXIDE; ZIRCONIC ANHYDRIDE; ZIRCONIA; ZIRCONIUM(IV) OXIDE; BADDELEYITE; Z-83; C.I. 77990; C.I. PIGMENT WHITE 12; ZIRBEADS; ZIRCONIUM WHITE; ZIRCONOTRAST; O2ZR; PST25635

CHEMICAL FAMILY: METAL

MOLECULAR FORMULA: ZR-O2

MOLECULAR WEIGHT: 123.22

CERCLA RATINGS (SCALE 0-3): HEALTH=U FIRE=0 REACTIVITY=0 PERSISTENCE=3

NFPA RATINGS (SCALE 0-4): HEALTH=U FIRE=0 REACTIVITY=0

COMPONENTS AND CONTAMINANTS

COMPONENT: ZIRCONIUM OXIDE ***PERCENT:*** 100
CAS# 1314-23-4

OTHER CONTAMINANTS: NONE

EXPOSURE LIMITS: ZIRCONIUM COMPOUNDS (AS ZR): 5 MG/M3 OSHA TWA; 10 MG/M3 OSHA STEL 5 MG/M3 ACGIH TWA; 10 MG/M3 ACGIH STEL

PHYSICAL DATA

DESCRIPTION: ODORLESS, TASTELESS, WHITE TO YELLOW-BROWN, HEAVY, MONOCLINIC CRYSTALS OR AMORPHOUS POWDER.

BOILING POINT: 9032 F (5000 C)

MELTING POINT: 4892 F (2700 C) ***SPECIFIC GRAVITY:*** 5.6-6.2

SOLUBILITY IN WATER: INSOLUBLE

SOLVENT SOLUBILITY: INSOLUBLE IN ALKALIES; SLIGHTLY SOLUBLE IN CONCENTRATED HYDROCHLORIC ACID (HOT), NITRIC ACID; SLOWLY SOLUBLE IN HYDROGEN FLUORIDE; SOLUBLE IN SULFURIC ACID

HARDNESS (MOHS): 6.5

FIRE AND EXPLOSION DATA

FIRE AND EXPLOSION HAZARD: NEGLIGIBLE FIRE HAZARD WHEN EXPOSED TO HEAT OR FLAME.

FIREFIGHTING MEDIA: EXTINGUISH USING AGENT SUITABLE FOR TYPE OF SURROUNDING FIRE.

FOR LARGER FIRES, USE WATER SPRAY, FOG OR STANDARD FOAM (1987 EMERGENCY RESPONSE GUIDEBOOK, DOT P 5800.4).

FIREFIGHTING: NO ACUTE HAZARD. MOVE CONTAINER FROM FIRE AREA IF POSSIBLE. AVOID BREATHING VAPORS OR DUSTS; KEEP UPWIND.

TOXICITY

ZIRCONIUM OXIDE: CARCINOGEN STATUS: NONE. ACUTE TOXICITY LEVEL: NO DATA AVAILABLE. TARGET EFFECTS: SENSITIZER- SKIN. AT INCREASED RISK FROM EXPOSURE: PERSONS WHO HAVE EXPERIENCED GRANULOMAS FROM ZIRCONIUM.

HEALTH EFFECTS AND FIRST AID

INHALATION: ZIRCONIUM OXIDE: 500 MG(ZR)/M3 IMMEDIATELY DANGEROUS TO LIFE OR HEALTH. **ACUTE EXPOSURE**- INHALATION OF DUST OR FUMES MAY CAUSE IRRITATION. EXPOSURE TO FRESHLY FORMED METAL OXIDE FUMES MAY CAUSE "METAL FUME FEVER" WHICH IS CHARACTERIZED BY CHILLS, FEVER, MUSCULAR PAINS, NAUSEA, VOMITING, AND WEAKNESS. **CHRONIC EXPOSURE**- INHALATION EXPOSURE STUDIES TO ZIRCONIUM OXIDE FOR 30 DAYS, 60 DAYS, AND 1 YEAR AT 75 MG, 11 MG, AND 3.5 MG ZR/M3, RESPECTIVELY, RESULTED IN NO DETECTABLE EFFECTS IN ANIMALS. REPEATED OR PROLONGED INDUSTRIAL EXPOSURE TO ZIRCONIUM COMPOUNDS HAS REVEALED NO RESPIRATORY OR OTHER PATHOLOGICAL PROBLEMS; HOWEVER, PNEUMONITIS AND PULMONARY GRANULOMA MAY DEVELOP.

FIRST AID- REMOVE FROM EXPOSURE AREA TO FRESH AIR IMMEDIATELY. IF BREATHING HAS STOPPED, PERFORM ARTIFICIAL RESPIRATION. KEEP PERSON WARM AND AT REST. TREAT SYMPTOMATICALLY AND SUPPORTIVELY. GET MEDICAL ATTENTION IMMEDIATELY.

SKIN CONTACT: ZIRCONIUM OXIDE: IRRITANT/SENSITIZER. **ACUTE EXPOSURE**- DIRECT CONTACT MAY CAUSE IRRITATION. APPLICATION TO ABRADED SKIN MAY CAUSE SENSITIZATION AND ALLERGIC GRANULOMA FORMATION IN PREVIOUSLY EXPOSED PERSONS. THE PAPULES GENERALLY DISAPPEAR SPONTANEOUSLY, BUT SLOWLY, PERSISTING FOR MONTHS OR YEARS. **CHRONIC EXPOSURE**- REPEATED OR PROLONGED CONTACT TO ABRADED SKIN MAY CAUSE DERMATITIS, SENSITIZATION REACTIONS, AND ALLERGIC GRANULOMA, CHARACTERIZED BY RED-BROWN PAPULES. REPEATED APPLICATION TO POISON IVY AFFECTED SKIN RESULTED IN NUMEROUS 2-6 MM, FIRM, SHINY, ERYTHEMATOUS, NONTENDER PAPULES 6 MONTHS LATER ON A 15-YEAR OLD BOY.

FIRST AID- REMOVE CONTAMINATED CLOTHING AND SHOES IMMEDIATELY. WASH AFFECTED AREA WITH SOAP OR MILD DETERGENT AND LARGE AMOUNTS OF WATER UNTIL NO EVIDENCE OF CHEMICAL REMAINS (APPROXIMATELY 15-20 MINUTES). GET MEDICAL ATTENTION IMMEDIATELY.

EYE CONTACT: ZIRCONIUM OXIDE: **ACUTE EXPOSURE**- NO AVAILABLE DATA. MAY CAUSE IRRITATION. **CHRONIC EXPOSURE**- NO AVAILABLE DATA.

FIRST AID- WASH EYES IMMEDIATELY WITH LARGE AMOUNTS OF WATER OR NORMAL SALINE, OCCASIONALLY LIFTING UPPER AND LOWER LIDS, UNTIL NO EVIDENCE OF CHEMICAL REMAINS (APPROXIMATELY 15-20 MINUTES). GET MEDICAL ATTENTION IMMEDIATELY.

INGESTION: ZIRCONIUM OXIDE: **ACUTE EXPOSURE**- INGESTION OF DOSES EQUIVALENT TO 2, 4, 8, OR 10 MG/KG RESULTED IN NO DEATHS IN RATS. **CHRONIC EXPOSURE**- REPEATED OR PROLONGED INGESTION OF A DIET CONTAINING 20% BY WEIGHT OF A MOIST PASTE CONTAINING 20.9% OF ZIRCONIUM OXIDE HAS PRODUCED NO HARMFUL EFFECTS IN RATS, OR IN KITTENS INGESTING FOOD CONTAINING 5% OF THE COMPOUND.

FIRST AID- TREAT SYMPTOMATICALLY AND SUPPORTIVELY. GET MEDICAL ATTENTION IMMEDIATELY. IF VOMITING OCCURS, KEEP HEAD LOWER THAN HIPS TO PREVENT ASPIRATION.

ANTIDOTE: NO SPECIFIC ANTIDOTE. TREAT SYMPTOMATICALLY AND SUPPORTIVELY.

REACTIVITY

REACTIVITY: STABLE UNDER NORMAL TEMPERATURES AND PRESSURES.

INCOMPATIBILITIES: ZIRCONIUM OXIDE: NO DATA AVAILABLE.

DECOMPOSITION: THERMAL DECOMPOSITION MAY RELEASE TOXIC AND/OR HAZARDOUS GASES.

POLYMERIZATION: HAZARDOUS POLYMERIZATION HAS NOT BEEN REPORTED TO OCCUR UNDER NORMAL TEMPERATURES AND PRESSURES.

STORAGE AND DISPOSAL

OBSERVE ALL FEDERAL, STATE AND LOCAL REGULATIONS WHEN STORING OR DISPOSING OF THIS SUBSTANCE. FOR ASSISTANCE, CONTACT THE DISTRICT DIRECTOR OF THE ENVIRONMENTAL PROTECTION AGENCY.

CONDITIONS TO AVOID

NONE REPORTED.

SPILL AND LEAK PROCEDURES

OCCUPATIONAL SPILL: SWEEP UP AND PLACE IN SUITABLE (FIBERBOARD) CONTAINERS FOR RECLAMATION OR LATER DISPOSAL.

PROTECTIVE EQUIPMENT

VENTILATION: PROVIDE LOCAL EXHAUST OR PROCESS ENCLOSURE VENTILATION TO MEET PUBLISHED EXPOSURE LIMITS.

RESPIRATOR: THE FOLLOWING RESPIRATORS AND MAXIMUM USE CONCENTRATIONS ARE RECOMMENDATIONS BY THE U.S. DEPARTMENT OF HEALTH AND HUMAN SERVICES, NIOSH POCKET GUIDE TO CHEMICAL HAZARDS; NIOSH CRITERIA DOCUMENTS OR BY THE U.S. DEPARTMENT OF LABOR, 29 CFR 1910 SUBPART Z. THE SPECIFIC RESPIRATOR SELECTED MUST BE BASED ON CONTAMINATION LEVELS FOUND IN THE WORK PLACE, MUST NOT EXCEED THE WORKING LIMITS OF THE RESPIRATOR AND BE JOINTLY APPROVED BY THE NATIONAL INSTITUTE FOR OCCUPATIONAL SAFETY AND HEALTH AND THE MINE SAFETY AND HEALTH ADMINISTRATION (NIOSH-MSHA).

ZIRCONIUM COMPOUNDS AS ZR:

25 MG/M3- ANY DUST AND MIST RESPIRATOR EXCEPT SINGLE-USE RESPIRATORS.

50 MG/M3- ANY DUST AND MIST RESPIRATOR EXCEPT SINGLE-USE AND QUARTER-MASK RESPIRATORS. ANY SUPPLIED-AIR RESPIRATOR. ANY SELF-CONTAINED BREATHING APPARATUS.

125 MG/M3- ANY POWERED AIR-PURIFYING RESPIRATOR WITH A DUST AND MIST FILTER. ANY SUPPLIED-AIR RESPIRATOR OPERATED IN A CONTINUOUS FLOW MODE.

250 MG/M3- ANY AIR-PURIFYING FULL FACEPIECE RESPIRATOR WITH A HIGH-EFFICIENCY PARTICULATE FILTER. ANY POWERED AIR-PURIFYING RESPIRATOR WITH A TIGHT-FITTING FACEPIECE AND A HIGH-EFFICIENCY PARTICULATE FILTER. ANY SELF-CONTAINED BREATHING APPARATUS WITH A FULL FACEPIECE. ANY SUPPLIED-AIR RESPIRATOR WITH A FULL FACEPIECE. ANY SUPPLIED-AIR RESPIRATOR WITH A TIGHT-FITTING FACEPIECE OPERATED IN A CONTINUOUS FLOW MODE.

500 MG/M3- ANY SUPPLIED-AIR RESPIRATOR WITH A HALF-MASK AND OPERATED IN A PRESSURE-DEMAND OR OTHER POSITIVE PRESSURE MODE.

ESCAPE- ANY AIR-PURIFYING FULL FACEPIECE RESPIRATOR WITH A HIGH-EFFICIENCY PARTICULATE FILTER. ANY APPROPRIATE ESCAPE-TYPE SELF-CONTAINED BREATHING APPARATUS. FOR FIREFIGHTING AND OTHER IMMEDIATELY DANGEROUS TO LIFE OR HEALTH CONDITIONS:

SELF-CONTAINED BREATHING APPARATUS WITH FULL FACEPIECE OPERATED IN PRESSURE-DEMAND OR OTHER POSITIVE PRESSURE MODE.

SUPPLIED-AIR RESPIRATOR WITH FULL FACEPIECE AND OPERATED IN PRESSURE-DEMAND OR OTHER POSITIVE PRESSURE MODE IN COMBINATION WITH AN AUXILIARY SELF-CONTAINED BREATHING APPARATUS OPERATED IN PRESSURE-DEMAND OR OTHER POSITIVE PRESSURE MODE.

CLOTHING: EMPLOYEE MUST WEAR APPROPRIATE PROTECTIVE (IMPERVIOUS) CLOTHING AND EQUIPMENT TO PREVENT REPEATED OR PROLONGED SKIN CONTACT WITH THIS SUBSTANCE.

GLOVES: EMPLOYEE MUST WEAR APPROPRIATE PROTECTIVE GLOVES TO PREVENT CONTACT WITH THIS SUBSTANCE.

EYE PROTECTION: EMPLOYEE MUST WEAR SPLASH-PROOF OR DUST-RESISTANT SAFETY GOGGLES TO PREVENT EYE CONTACT WITH THIS SUBSTANCE.

EMERGENCY EYE WASH: WHERE THERE IS ANY POSSIBILITY THAT AN EMPLOYEE'S EYES MAY BE EXPOSED TO THIS SUBSTANCE, THE EMPLOYER SHOULD PROVIDE AN EYE WASH FOUNTAIN WITHIN THE IMMEDIATE WORK AREA FOR EMERGENCY USE.

AUTHORIZED BY- OCCUPATIONAL HEALTH SERVICES, INC.

CREATION DATE: 02/08/90 ***REVISION DATE:*** 05/18/90

MATERIAL SAFETY DATA SHEET

OCCUPATIONAL HEALTH SERVICES, INC.
AGRICULTURE AND PESTICIDE DIVISION
450 SEVENTH AVENUE, SUITE 2407
NEW YORK, NEW YORK 10123
1-800-445-MSDS OR (212) 967-1100

EMERGENCY CONTACT:
JOHN S. BRANSFORD, JR. (615) 292-1180

SUBSTANCE IDENTIFICATION

CAS-NUMBER 2310-17-0

SUBSTANCE: **PHOSALONE**

TRADE NAMES/SYNONYMS: PHOSPHORODITHIOIC ACID, S-((6-CHLORO-2-OXO-3(2H)-BENZOXAZOYL)METHYL) O,O-DIETHYL ESTER; PHOSPHORODITHIOIC ACID, O,O-DIETHYL ESTER, S-ESTER WITH 6-CHLORO -3-(MERCAPTOMETHYL)-2-BENZOXAZOLINONE; S-((6-CHLORO-2-OXO-3(2H)-BENZOXAZOYL)METHYL) O,O-DIETHYL PHOSPHORODITHIOATE; S-6-CHLORO-2,3-DIHYDRO-2-OXO-1,3-BENZOXAZOL-3-YLMETHYL O,O-DIETHYL PHOSPHORODITHIOATE; S-6-CHLORO-2,3-DIHYDRO-2-OXOBENZOXAZOL-3-YLMETHYL O,O-DIETHYL PHOSPHORODITHIOATE; 6-CHLORO-3-DIETHOXYPHOSPHINOTHIOYLTHIOMETHYL-1,3-BENZOXAZOL-2(3H)-ONE; O,O-DIETHYL PHOSPHORODITHIOATE S-ESTER WITH 6-CHLORO-3- MERCAPTOMETHYL)-2-BENZOXAZOLINONE; PHOSALON; RP11974; RUBITOX; ZOLONE; ENT 27163; C12H15CLNO4PS2; PST25720

CHEMICAL FAMILY: PHOSPHOROTHIOATE

MOLECULAR FORMULA: C12-H15-CL-N-O4-P-S2

MOLECULAR WEIGHT: 367.80

CERCLA RATINGS (SCALE 0-3): HEALTH=3 FIRE=1 REACTIVITY=0 PERSISTENCE=3

NFPA RATINGS (SCALE 0-4): HEALTH=3 FIRE=1 REACTIVITY=0

COMPONENTS AND CONTAMINANTS

COMPONENT: PHOSALONE ***PERCENT:*** 100.0
CAS# 2310-17-0

OTHER CONTAMINANTS: NONE

EXPOSURE LIMITS: NO OCCUPATIONAL EXPOSURE LIMITS ESTABLISHED BY OSHA, ACGIH, OR NIOSH.

PHYSICAL DATA

DESCRIPTION: COLORLESS OR WHITE CRYSTALLINE SOLID WITH A SLIGHT GARLIC ODOR.

MELTING POINT: 117-118 F (47-48 C) ***SPECIFIC GRAVITY:*** NOT AVAILABLE

VAPOR PRESSURE: NEGLIGIBLE ***SOLUBILITY IN WATER:*** 0.0010% @ 20 C

SOLVENT SOLUBILITY: SOLUBLE IN ACETONE, ACETONITRILE, BENZENE, CHLOROFORM, DIOXANE, ETHANOL, METHANOL, TOLUENE, XYLENE, KETONES, ALCOHOLS, AND AROMATIC SOLVENTS; SPARINGLY SOLUBLE IN CYCLOHEXANE AND LIGHT PETROLEUM.

FIRE AND EXPLOSION DATA

FIRE AND EXPLOSION HAZARD: SLIGHT FIRE HAZARD WHEN EXPOSED TO HEAT OR FLAME.

FIREFIGHTING MEDIA: DRY CHEMICAL, CARBON DIOXIDE, HALON, WATER SPRAY OR STANDARD FOAM (1987 EMERGENCY RESPONSE GUIDEBOOK, DOT P 5800.4). FOR LARGER FIRES, USE WATER SPRAY, FOG OR STANDARD FOAM (1987 EMERGENCY RESPONSE GUIDEBOOK, DOT P 5800.4).

FIREFIGHTING: MOVE CONTAINERS FROM FIRE AREA IF POSSIBLE. FIGHT FIRE FROM MAXIMUM DISTANCE. STAY AWAY FROM STORAGE TANK ENDS. DIKE FIRE CONTROL WATER FOR LATER DISPOSAL. DO NOT SCATTER MATERIAL (1987 EMERGENCY RESPONSE GUIDEBOOK, DOT P 5800.4, GUIDE PAGE 55). EXTINGUISH ONLY IF FLOW CAN BE STOPPED; USE FLOODING AMOUNTS OF WATER AS FOG, SOLID STREAMS MAY BE INEFFECTIVE. COOL CONTAINERS WITH FLOODING AMOUNTS OF WATER FROM AS FAR A DISTANCE AS POSSIBLE. USE WATER SPRAY TO ABSORB TOXIC VAPORS. AVOID BREATHING TOXIC VAPORS; KEEP UPWIND. CONSIDER EVACUATION OF DOWNWIND AREA IF MATERIAL IS LEAKING.

TOXICITY

PHOSALONE: TOXICITY DATA: 1000 MG/KG SKIN-RABBIT LD50; 390 MG/KG SKIN-RAT LD50; 85 MG/KG ORAL-RAT LD50; 73 MG/KG ORAL-MOUSE LD50; 150 MG/KG ORAL-GUINEA PIG LD50; 112 MG/KG ORAL-CAT LD50; 135 MG/KG UNREPORTED-RAT LD50. CARCINOGEN STATUS: NONE. ACUTE TOXICITY LEVEL: TOXIC BY DERMAL ABSORPTION AND INGESTION. TARGET EFFECTS: CHOLINESTERASE INHIBITOR. AT INCREASED RISK FROM EXPOSURE: PERSONS WITH RESPIRATORY AILMENTS, RECENT EXPOSURE TO CHOLINESTERASE INHIBITORS OR IMPAIRED CHOLINESTERASE PRODUCTION, OR LIVER MALFUNCTION.* ADDITIONAL DATA: MAY CROSS THE PLACENTA. HIGH ENVIRONMENTAL TEMPERATURES OR EXPOSURE OF THE CHEMICAL TO VISIBLE OR ULTRAVIOLET LIGHT MAY ENHANCE THE TOXICITY. INTERACTIONS WITH MEDICATIONS MAY OCCUR.*

* MAY BE BASED ON GENERAL INFORMATION ON ORGANOPHOSPHATES.

HEALTH EFFECTS AND FIRST AID

INHALATION: PHOSALONE: SEE INFORMATION ON ORGANOPHOSPHATES.
ORGANOPHOSPHATES: CHOLINESTERASE INHIBITOR. **ACUTE EXPOSURE-** WHEN INHALED, THE FIRST EFFECTS OF CHOLINESTERASE INHIBITORS ARE USUALLY RESPIRATORY AND MAY INCLUDE NASAL HYPEREMIA AND WATERY DISCHARGE, COUGH, CHEST DISCOMFORT, DYSPNEA, AND WHEEZING DUE TO INCREASED BRONCHIAL SECRETIONS AND BRONCHOCONSTRICTION. IF SUFFICIENT AMOUNTS ARE ABSORBED, OTHER SYSTEMIC EFFECTS MAY BEGIN WITHIN A FEW MINUTES OR BE DELAYED FOR UP TO 12 HOURS. SYMPTOMS MAY INCLUDE PALLOR, NAUSEA, VOMITING, DIARRHEA, ABDOMINAL CRAMPS, HEADACHE, DIZZINESS, OCULAR PAIN, BLURRED VISION, MIOSIS OR IN SOME CASES, ESPECIALLY INITIALLY, MYDRIASIS, LACRIMATION, SALIVATION, SWEATING, AND CONFUSION. OTHER REPORTED CENTRAL NERVOUS SYSTEM OR NEUROMUSCULAR EFFECTS MAY INCLUDE ATAXIA, SLURRED SPEECH, AREFLEXIA, WEAKNESS, FATIGUE, FASCICULATIONS, TWITCHING, TREMORS POSSIBLY OF THE TONGUE AND EYELIDS, AND EVENTUALLY PARALYSIS OF THE EXTREMITIES AND POSSIBLY OF THE RESPIRATORY MUSCLES. IN SEVERE CASES THERE MAY ALSO BE INVOLUNTARY DEFECATION AND URINATION, CYANOSIS, PSYCHOSIS, HYPERGLYCEMIA, ACUTE PANCREATITIS, CARDIAC IRREGULARITIES, PULMONARY EDEMA, UNCONSCIOUSNESS, CONVULSIONS, AND COMA. DEATH IS PRIMARILY DUE TO RESPIRATORY FAILURE, ALTHOUGH CARDIOVASCULAR EFFECTS INCLUDING CARDIAC ARREST MAY ALSO BE IMPLICATED. LONG TERM SEQUELAE ARE RARE BUT MAY INCLUDE NEUROPSYCHIATRIC DISORDERS AND MYOPATHY WITH MUSCLE TENDERNESS. **CHRONIC EXPOSURE-** REPEATED OR PROLONGED EXPOSURE MAY RESULT IN THE EFFECTS OF ACUTE EXPOSURE. OTHER EFFECTS REPORTED IN WORKERS REPEATEDLY EXPOSED INCLUDE IMPAIRED MEMORY AND CONCENTRATION, ACUTE PSYCHOSIS, SEVERE DEPRESSIONS, IRRITABILTY, CONFUSION, APATHY, EMOTIONAL LABILITY, SOCIAL WITHDRAWAL, CONFUSION, HEADACHE, SPEECH DIFFICULTIES, DELAYED REACTION TIMES, SPATIAL DISORIENTATION, NIGHTMARES, SLEEPWALKING, AND DROWSINESS OR INSOMNIA. AN INFLUENZA-LIKE CONDITION WITH HEADACHE, NAUSEA, WEAKNESS, ANOREXIA AND MALAISE HAS ALSO BEEN REPORTED.

FIRST AID- REMOVE FROM EXPOSURE AREA TO FRESH AIR IMMEDIATELY. IF BREATHING HAS STOPPED, GIVE ARTIFICIAL RESPIRATION. MAINTAIN AIRWAY AND BLOOD PRESSURE AND ADMINISTER OXYGEN IF AVAILABLE. KEEP AFFECTED PERSON WARM AND AT REST. TREAT SYMPTOMATICALLY AND SUPPORTIVELY. ADMINISTRATION OF OXYGEN SHOULD BE PERFORMED BY QUALIFIED PERSONNEL. GET MEDICAL ATTENTION IMMEDIATELY.

SKIN CONTACT: PHOSALONE: TOXIC. MAY CAUSE IRRITATION. SEE INFORMATION ON ORGANOPHOSPHATES.
ORGANOPHOSPHATES: CHOLINESTERASE INHIBITOR. **ACUTE EXPOSURE-** LOCALIZED SWEATING AND FASCICULATIONS MAY OCCUR AT THE SITE OF CONTACT. IF SUFFICIENT AMOUNTS ARE ABSORBED, OTHER EFFECTS OF CHOLINESTERASE INHIBITION AS DESCRIBED IN ACUTE INHALATION MAY OCCUR. SYMPTOMS MAY BE DELAYED 2-3 HOURS, BUT USUALLY NO MORE THAN 12 HOURS. THE RATE OF ABSORPTION IS INCREASED BY THE PRESENCE OF DERMATITIS OR HIGH AMBIENT TEMPERATURES. **CHRONIC EXPOSURE-** REPEATED OR PROLONGED EXPOSURE MAY CAUSE EFFECTS AS DESCRIBED IN ACUTE EXPOSURE. SOME ORGANOPHOSPHATES MAY CAUSE SENSITIZATION.

FIRST AID- REMOVE CONTAMINATED CLOTHING IMMEDIATELY. WASH CONTAMINATED AREAS WITH SOAP AND WATER FOLLOWED BY ALCOHOL (ARENA, POISONING, 4TH ED.). EMERGENCY PERSONNEL SHOULD WEAR GLOVES AND AVOID CONTAMINATION. TREAT RESPIRATORY DIFFICULTY WITH ARTIFICIAL RESPIRATION. GET MEDICAL ATTENTION IMMEDIATELY.

EYE CONTACT: PHOSALONE: EMULSIFIABLE CONCENTRATE FORMULATIONS OF THIS MATERIAL PRODUCED SEVERE IRRITATION WITH CORNEAL OPACITY WHEN APPLIED TO RABBIT EYES. SEE INFORMATION ON ORGANOPHOSPHATES.
ORGANOPHOSPHATES: CHOLINESTERASE INHIBITOR. **ACUTE EXPOSURE-** DIRECT CONTACT MAY CAUSE PAIN, HYPEREMIA, LACRIMATION, TWITCHING OF THE EYELIDS, MIOSIS, AND CILIARY MUSCLE SPASM WITH LOSS OF ACCOMODATION, BLURRED OR DIMMED VISION AND BROWACHE. SOMETIMES MYDRIASIS MAY OCCUR INSTEAD OF MIOSIS. WITH SUFFICIENT EXPOSURE, OTHER SYMPTOMS OF CHOLINESTERASE INHIBITION AS DESCRIBED IN ACUTE INHALATION MAY OCCUR. **CHRONIC EXPOSURE-** REPEATED OR PROLONGED EXPOSURE MAY CAUSE EFFECTS AS DESCRIBED IN ACUTE EXPOSURE. SOME COMPOUNDS HAVE CAUSED TOXIC EFFECTS ON THE CRYSTALLINE LENS, CONJUNCTIVAL THICKENING AND OBSTRUCTION OF THE NASOLACRIMAL CANALS WHEN USED AS MIOTIC EYEDROPS.

FIRST AID- IRRIGATE EYES WITH WATER OR SALINE SOLUTION. IF SYMPTOMS OF POISONING OCCUR, TREAT RESPIRATORY DIFFICULTY WITH ARTIFICIAL RESPIRATION AND OXYGEN. OBSERVE PATIENT FOR AT LEAST 24-36 HOURS (GOSSELIN, CLINICAL TOXICOLOGY OF COMMERCIAL PRODUCTS, 5TH ED.). GET MEDICAL ATTENTION IMMEDIATELY. OXYGEN SHOULD BE ADMINISTERED BY QUALIFIED MEDICAL PERSONNEL.

INGESTION: PHOSALONE: TOXIC. NO DEMYELINATION WAS OBSERVED IN A NEUROTOXICITY STUDY OF CHICKENS RECEIVING DIETARY LEVELS UP TO 500 PPM FOR 45 DAYS. SEE INFORMATION ON ORGANOPHOSPHATES.
ORGANOPHOSPHATES: CHOLINESTERASE INHIBITOR. **ACUTE EXPOSURE**- WHEN INGESTED, THE FIRST EFFECTS MAY BE NAUSEA, VOMITING, ANOREXIA, ABDOMINAL CRAMPS AND DIARRHEA. GASTROINTESTINAL ABSORPTION MAY CAUSE THE SYMPTOMS OF CHOLINESTERASE INHIBITION AS DESCRIBED IN ACUTE INHALATION. SYMPTOMS MAY BEGIN WITHIN MINUTES OR BE DELAYED. **CHRONIC EXPOSURE**- REPEATED INGESTION MAY CAUSE EFFECTS AS DESCRIBED IN ACUTE EXPOSURE.

FIRST AID- IF PERSON IS ALERT AND RESPIRATION IS NOT DEPRESSED, GIVE SYRUP OF IPECAC FOLLOWED BY WATER (IF VOMITING OCCURS, KEEP HEAD BELOW HIPS TO PREVENT ASPIRATION). IF CONSCIOUSNESS LEVEL DECLINES OR VOMITING HAS NOT OCCURRED IN 15 MINUTES EMPTY STOMACH BY GASTRIC LAVAGE WITH THE AID OF CUFFED ENDOTRACHEAL TUBE USING ISOTONIC SALINE OR 5% SODIUM BICARBONATE FOLLOW WITH ACTIVATED CHARCOAL. ESTABLISH AND MAINTAIN AIRWAY. TREAT RESPIRATORY DIFFICULTY WITH ARTIFICIAL RESPIRATION AND OXYGEN. DO NOT GIVE MORPHINE, AMINOPHYLLINE, PHENOTHIAZINES, RESERPINE, FUROSEMIDE, OR ETHACRYNIC ACID (MORGAN, RECOGNITION AND MANAGEMENT OF PESTICIDE POISONINGS, 3RD ED.). TREAT SYMPTOMATICALLY AND SUPPORTIVELY. ADMINISTRATION OF OXYGEN AND LAVAGE MUST BE PERFORMED BY QUALIFIED MEDICAL PERSONNEL. GET MEDICAL ATTENTION IMMEDIATELY.

ANTIDOTE: THE FOLLOWING ANTIDOTE(S) HAVE BEEN RECOMMENDED. HOWEVER, THE DECISION AS TO WHETHER THE SEVERITY OF POISONING REQUIRES ADMINISTRATION OF ANY ANTIDOTE AND ACTUAL DOSE REQUIRED SHOULD BE MADE BY QUALIFIED MEDICAL PERSONNEL.
FOR CHOLINESTERASE INHIBITORS: ESTABLISH CLEAR AIRWAY AND TISSUE OXYGENATION BY ASPIRATION OF SECRETIONS, AND IF NECESSARY, BY ASSISTED PULMONARY VENTILATION WITH OXYGEN. IMPROVE TISSUE OXYGENATION AS MUCH AS POSSIBLE BEFORE ADMINISTERING ATROPINE TO MINIMIZE THE RISK OF VENTRICULAR FIBRILLATION. ADMINISTER ATROPINE SULFATE INTRAVENOUSLY, OR INTRAMUSCULARLY IF IV INJECTION IS NOT POSSIBLE. IN MODERATELY SEVERE POISONING ADMINISTER ATROPINE SULFATE, 0.4-2.0 MG REPEATED EVERY 15 MINUTES UNTIL ATROPINIZATION IS ACHIEVED (TACHYCARDIA, FLUSHING, DRY MOUTH, MYDRIASIS). MAINTAIN ATROPINIZATION BY REPEATED DOSES FOR 2-12 HOURS, OR LONGER, DEPENDING ON THE SEVERITY OF POISONING. THE APPEARANCE OF RALES IN THE LUNG BASES, MIOSIS, SALIVATION, NAUSEA, BRADYCARDIA, ARE ALL INDICATIONS OF INADEQUATE ATROPINIZATION. SEVERELY POISONED INDIVIDUALS MAY EXHIBIT REMARKABLE TOLERANCE TO ATROPINE; TWO OR MORE TIMES THE DOSAGES SUGGESTED ABOVE MAY BE NEEDED. PERSONS NOT POISONED OR ONLY SLIGHTLY POISONED, HOWEVER, MAY DEVELOP SIGNS OF ATROPINE TOXICITY FROM SUCH LARGE DOSAGES: FEVER, MUSCLE FIBRILLATIONS, AND DELIRIUM ARE THE MAIN SIGNS OF ATROPINE TOXICITY. IF THESE SIGNS APPEAR WHILE THE PATIENT IS FULLY ATROPINIZED, ATROPINE ADMINISTRATION SHOULD BE DISCONTINUED, AT LEAST TEMPORARILY. OBSERVE TREATED PATIENTS CLOSELY AT LEAST 24 HOURS TO INSURE THAT SYMPTOMS (POSSIBLY PULMONARY EDEMA) DO NOT RECUR AS ATROPINIZATION WEARS OFF. IN VERY SEVERE POISONINGS, METABOLIC DISPOSITION OF TOXICANT MAY REQUIRE SEVERAL HOURS OR DAYS DURING WHICH ATROPINIZATION MUST BE MAINTAINED. MARKEDLY LOWER LEVELS OF URINARY METABOLITES INDICATE THAT ATROPINE DOSAGE CAN BE TAPERED OFF. AS DOSAGE IS REDUCED, CHECK THE LUNG BASES FREQUENTLY FOR RALES. IF RALES ARE HEARD OR OTHER SYMPTOMS RETURN, RE-ESTABLISH ATROPINIZATION PROMPTLY (MORGAN, RECOGNITION AND MANAGEMENT OF PESTICIDE POISONINGS, 3RD ED.). ADMINISTRATION OF ANTIDOTE MUST BE PERFORMED BY QUALIFIED MEDICAL PERSONNEL.
IN CASES OF SEVERE POISONING BY ORGANOPHOSPHATE PESTICIDES IN WHICH RESPIRATORY DEPRESSION, MUSCLE WEAKNESS AND TWITCHINGS ARE SEVERE, GIVE PRALIDOXIME (PROTOPAM-AYERST, 2-PAM), 1.0 GRAM INTRAVENOUSLY AT NO MORE THAN 0.5 GRAM PER MINUTE. DOSAGE OF PRALIDOXIME MAY BE REPEATED IN 1-2 HOURS, THEN AT 10-12 HOUR INTERVALS IF NEEDED. IN VERY SEVERE POISONINGS, DOSAGE RATES MAY BE DOUBLED. TREATMENT WITH PRALIDOXIME WILL BE MOST EFFECTIVE IF GIVEN WITHIN THIRTY-SIX HOURS AFTER POISONING (MORGAN, RECOGNITION AND MANAGEMENT OF PESTICIDE POISONINGS, 3RD ED.). ANTIDOTE SHOULD BE ADMINISTERED BY QUALIFIED MEDICAL PERSONNEL.

REACTIVITY

REACTIVITY: STABLE UNDER NORMAL TEMPERATURES AND PRESSURES.

INCOMPATIBILITIES: PHOSALONE: ALKALIES: HYDROLYZES. OXIDIZERS (STRONG): FIRE AND EXPLOSION HAZARD.

DECOMPOSITION: THERMAL DECOMPOSITION PRODUCTS MAY INCLUDE TOXIC AND CORROSIVE FUMES OF CHLORIDES, AND TOXIC OXIDES OF PHOSPHORUS, NITROGEN AND SULFUR.

POLYMERIZATION: HAZARDOUS POLYMERIZATION HAS NOT BEEN REPORTED TO OCCUR UNDER NORMAL TEMPERATURES AND PRESSURES.

STORAGE AND DISPOSAL

OBSERVE ALL FEDERAL, STATE AND LOCAL REGULATIONS WHEN STORING OR DISPOSING OF THIS SUBSTANCE. FOR ASSISTANCE, CONTACT THE DISTRICT DIRECTOR OF THE ENVIRONMENTAL PROTECTION AGENCY.

****STORAGE****

STORE IN ACCORDANCE WITH 40 CFR 165 RECOMMENDED PROCEDURES FOR THE DISPOSAL AND STORAGE OF PESTICIDES AND PESTICIDE CONTAINERS.
STORE AWAY FROM INCOMPATIBLE SUBSTANCES.
DO NOT STORE BELOW 32 F (0 C).

****DISPOSAL****

DISPOSAL MUST BE IN ACCORDANCE WITH 40 CFR 165 RECOMMENDED PROCEDURES FOR THE DISPOSAL AND STORAGE OF PESTICIDES AND PESTICIDE CONTAINERS.

CONDITIONS TO AVOID

MAY BURN BUT DOES NOT IGNITE READILY. CONTAINERS MAY EXPLODE IN HEAT OF FIRE.

SPILL AND LEAK PROCEDURES

OCCUPATIONAL SPILL: DO NOT TOUCH SPILLED MATERIAL. STOP LEAK IF YOU CAN DO IT WITHOUT RISK. USE WATER SPRAY TO REDUCE VAPORS. FOR SMALL SPILLS, TAKE UP WITH SAND OR OTHER ABSORBENT MATERIAL AND PLACE INTO CONTAINERS FOR LATER DISPOSAL. FOR SMALL DRY SPILLS, WITH A CLEAN SHOVEL PLACE MATERIAL INTO CLEAN, DRY CONTAINERS AND COVER. MOVE CONTAINERS FROM SPILL AREA. FOR LARGER SPILLS, DIKE FAR AHEAD OF SPILL FOR LATER DISPOSAL. KEEP UNNECESSARY PEOPLE AWAY. ISOLATE HAZARD AREA AND DENY ENTRY. VENTILATE CLOSED SPACES BEFORE ENTERING.

PROTECTIVE EQUIPMENT

VENTILATION: PROVIDE LOCAL EXHAUST OR PROCESS ENCLOSURE VENTILATION SYSTEM.

RESPIRATOR: THE FOLLOWING RESPIRATORS ARE RECOMMENDED BASED ON INFORMATION FOUND IN THE PHYSICAL DATA, TOXICITY AND HEALTH EFFECTS SECTIONS. THEY ARE RANKED IN ORDER FROM MINIMUM TO MAXIMUM RESPIRATORY PROTECTION. THE SPECIFIC RESPIRATOR SELECTED MUST BE BASED ON CONTAMINATION LEVELS FOUND IN THE WORK PLACE, MUST NOT EXCEED THE WORKING LIMITS OF THE RESPIRATOR AND BE JOINTLY APPROVED BY THE NATIONAL INSTITUTE FOR OCCUPATIONAL SAFETY AND HEALTH AND THE MINE SAFETY AND HEALTH ADMINISTRATION (NIOSH-MSHA).
TYPE 'C' SUPPLIED-AIR RESPIRATOR WITH A FULL FACEPIECE OPERATED IN PRESSURE-DEMAND OR OTHER POSITIVE PRESSURE MODE OR WITH A FULL FACEPIECE, HELMET OR HOOD OPERATED IN CONTINOUS-FLOW MODE.
SELF-CONTAINED BREATHING APPARATUS WITH A FULL FACEPIECE OPERATED IN PRESSURE-DEMAND OR OTHER POSITIVE PRESSURE MODE.
FOR FIREFIGHTING AND OTHER IMMEDIATELY DANGEROUS TO LIFE OR HEALTH CONDITIONS:
SELF-CONTAINED BREATHING APPARATUS WITH FULL FACEPIECE OPERATED IN PRESSURE-DEMAND OR OTHER POSITIVE PRESSURE MODE.
SUPPLIED-AIR RESPIRATOR WITH FULL FACEPIECE AND OPERATED IN PRESSURE-DEMAND OR OTHER POSITIVE PRESSURE MODE IN COMBINATION WITH AN AUXILIARY SELF-CONTAINED BREATHING APPARATUS OPERATED IN PRESSURE-DEMAND OR OTHER POSITIVE PRESSURE MODE.

CLOTHING: EMPLOYEE MUST WEAR APPROPRIATE PROTECTIVE (IMPERVIOUS) CLOTHING AND EQUIPMENT TO PREVENT ANY POSSIBILITY OF SKIN CONTACT WITH THIS SUBSTANCE.

GLOVES: EMPLOYEE MUST WEAR APPROPRIATE PROTECTIVE GLOVES TO PREVENT CONTACT WITH THIS SUBSTANCE.

EYE PROTECTION: EMPLOYEE MUST WEAR SPLASH-PROOF OR DUST-RESISTANT SAFETY GOGGLES WITH OR WITHOUT A FACESHIELD TO PREVENT CONTACT WITH THIS SUBSTANCE.
EMERGENCY EYE WASH: WHERE THERE IS ANY POSSIBILITY THAT AN EMPLOYEE'S EYES MAY BE EXPOSED TO THIS SUBSTANCE, THE EMPLOYER SHOULD PROVIDE AN EYE WASH FOUNTAIN WITHIN THE IMMEDIATE WORK AREA FOR EMERGENCY USE.

AUTHORIZED BY- OCCUPATIONAL HEALTH SERVICES, INC.
CREATION DATE: 10/04/89 ***REVISION DATE:*** 06/20/90

MATERIAL SAFETY DATA SHEET

OCCUPATIONAL HEALTH SERVICES, INC.
AGRICULTURE AND PESTICIDE DIVISION
450 SEVENTH AVENUE, SUITE 2407
NEW YORK, NEW YORK 10123
1-800-445-MSDS OR (212) 967-1100

EMERGENCY CONTACT:
JOHN S. BRANSFORD, JR. (615) 292-1180

SUBSTANCE IDENTIFICATION

CAS-NUMBER 86-87-3

SUBSTANCE: **1-NAPHTHALENEACETIC ACID**

TRADE NAMES/SYNONYMS: CELMONE; FRUITOFIX; FRUITONE N; NAA; ALPHA-NAA; 1-NAA; NAFUSAKU; NAPHTHALENEACETIC ACID; ALPHA-NAPHTHALENEACETIC ACID; ALPHA-NAPHTHYLACETIC ACID; 2-(1-NAPHTHYL)ACETIC ACID; PLANOFIX; 1-NAPHTHYLACETIC ACID; C12H10O2; PST26130

CHEMICAL FAMILY: NAPHTHALENE

MOLECULAR FORMULA: C10-H7-C-H2-C-O2-H

MOLECULAR WEIGHT: 186.21

CERCLA RATINGS (SCALE 0-3): HEALTH=2 FIRE=1 REACTIVITY=0 PERSISTENCE=2

NFPA RATINGS (SCALE 0-4): HEALTH=2 FIRE=1 REACTIVITY=0

COMPONENTS AND CONTAMINANTS

COMPONENT: 1-NAPHTHALENEACETIC ACID ***PERCENT:*** 100
CAS# 86-87-3

OTHER CONTAMINANTS: NONE

EXPOSURE LIMITS: NO OCCUPATIONAL EXPOSURE LIMITS ESTABLISHED BY OSHA, ACGIH, OR NIOSH.

PHYSICAL DATA

DESCRIPTION: ODORLESS WHITE NEEDLES OR CRYSTALS ***MELTING POINT:*** 271 F (133 C)

SPECIFIC GRAVITY: NOT AVAILABLE ***VAPOR PRESSURE:*** NEGLIGIBLE

EVAPORATION RATE: NEGLIGIBLE ***SOLUBILITY IN WATER:*** 0.04%

SOLVENT SOLUBILITY: SOLUBLE IN ETHER, ACETONE, BENZENE, CHLOROFORM, ABSOLUTE ALCOHOL, CARBON TETRACHLORIDE, XYLENE, ISOPROPANOL, 2% SODIUM BICARBONATE, 0.1N AMMONIUM HYDROXIDE

FIRE AND EXPLOSION DATA

FIRE AND EXPLOSION HAZARD: SLIGHT FIRE HAZARD WHEN EXPOSED TO HEAT OR FLAME.

FIREFIGHTING MEDIA: DRY CHEMICAL, CARBON DIOXIDE, HALON, WATER SPRAY OR STANDARD FOAM (1987 EMERGENCY RESPONSE GUIDEBOOK, DOT P 5800.4). FOR LARGER FIRES, USE WATER SPRAY, FOG OR STANDARD FOAM (1987 EMERGENCY RESPONSE GUIDEBOOK, DOT P 5800.4).

FIREFIGHTING: MOVE CONTAINER FROM FIRE AREA IF POSSIBLE. DO NOT SCATTER SPILLED MATERIAL WITH HIGH PRESSURE WATER STREAMS. DIKE FIRE CONTROL WATER FOR LATER DISPOSAL (1987 EMERGENCY RESPONSE GUIDEBOOK, DOT P 5800.4, GUIDE PAGE 31).
USE AGENTS SUITABLE FOR TYPE OF SURROUNDING FIRE. AVOID BREATHING HAZARDOUS VAPORS, KEEP UPWIND.

TOXICITY

1-NAPHTHALENEACETIC ACID: IRRITATION DATA: 100 MG EYE-RABBIT SEVERE. TOXICITY DATA: 1000 MG/KG ORAL-RAT LD50; 743 MG/KG ORAL-MOUSE LD50; 733 MG/KG SUBCUTANEOUS-MOUSE LD50; 100 MG/KG INTRAPERITONEAL-RAT LD50; 609 MG/KG INTRAPERITONEAL-MOUSE LD50; MUTAGENIC DATA (RTECS); REPRODUCTIVE EFFECTS DATA (RTECS). CARCINOGEN STATUS: NONE. LOCAL EFFECTS: CORROSIVE- EYES; IRRITANT- INHALATION AND DERMAL ABSORPTION. ACUTE TOXICITY LEVEL: MODERATELY TOXIC BY INGESTION. TARGET EFFECTS: NO DATA AVAILABLE.

HEALTH EFFECTS AND FIRST AID

INHALATION: 1-NAPHTHALENEACETIC ACID: IRRITANT. **ACUTE EXPOSURE-** MAY CAUSE IRRITATION OF THE MUCOUS MEMBRANES. **CHRONIC EXPOSURE-** PROLONGED OR REPEATED EXPOSURE MAY CAUSE IRRITATION OF THE MUCOUS MEMBRANES.

FIRST AID- REMOVE FROM EXPOSURE AREA TO FRESH AIR IMMEDIATELY. IF BREATHING HAS STOPPED, PERFORM ARTIFICIAL RESPIRATION. KEEP PERSON WARM AND AT REST. TREAT SYMPTOMATICALLY AND SUPPORTIVELY. GET MEDICAL ATTENTION IMMEDIATELY.

SKIN CONTACT: 1-NAPHTHALENEACETIC ACID: IRRITANT. **ACUTE EXPOSURE-** MAY CAUSE IRRITATION. A LETHAL DOSE IN RABBITS BY DERMAL ABSORPTION WAS GREATER THAN 5000 MG/KG. **CHRONIC EXPOSURE-** THIS MATERIAL REPEATEDLY APPLIED TO RABBIT SKIN WAS MILDLY TO MODERATELY IRRITATING.

FIRST AID- REMOVE CONTAMINATED CLOTHING AND SHOES IMMEDIATELY. WASH AFFECTED AREA WITH SOAP OR MILD DETERGENT AND LARGE AMOUNTS OF WATER UNTIL NO EVIDENCE OF CHEMICAL REMAINS (APPROXIMATELY 15-20 MINUTES). GET MEDICAL ATTENTION IMMEDIATELY.

EYE CONTACT: 1-NAPHTHALENEACETIC ACID: CORROSIVE. **ACUTE EXPOSURE-** 100 MG APPLIED TO RABBIT EYES WAS SEVERELY IRRITATING. **CHRONIC EXPOSURE-** NO DATA AVAILABLE.

FIRST AID- WASH EYES IMMEDIATELY WITH LARGE AMOUNTS OF WATER, OCCASIONALLY LIFTING UPPER AND LOWER LIDS, UNTIL NO EVIDENCE OF CHEMICAL REMAINS (AT LEAST 15-20 MINUTES). CONTINUE IRRIGATING WITH NORMAL SALINE UNTIL THE PH HAS RETURNED TO NORMAL (30-60 MINUTES). COVER WITH STERILE BANDAGES. GET MEDICAL ATTENTION IMMEDIATELY.

INGESTION: 1-NAPHTHALENEACETIC ACID: **ACUTE EXPOSURE-** A LETHAL DOSE IN RATS WAS 1000 MG/KG. **CHRONIC EXPOSURE-** GLYCOGEN DEPLETION AND DEGENERATIVE CHANGES IN THE LIVER WERE OBSERVED IN A SIX-MONTH STUDY OF DOGS FED 150 MG/KG/DAY. REPEATED DOSES OF 4000 MG/KG WERE LETHAL IN RATS AFTER TWO TO THREE DAYS; REPORTED SIGNS OF TOXICITY INCLUDED DYSPNEA, ATAXIA, LETHARGY AND PROSTRATION. LIVER GLYCOGEN DEPLETION AND AN INCREASE IN KIDNEY WEIGHT WERE REPORTED IN A STUDY OF RATS FED A DIETARY LEVEL OF 1500 PPM; AT 7500 PPM, A SLIGHT INCREASE IN LIVER WEIGHT WAS ALSO OBSERVED. EFFECTS ON THE MALE REPRODUCTIVE SYSTEM WERE OBSERVED IN A STUDY OF RATS.

FIRST AID- REMOVE BY GASTRIC LAVAGE AND CATHARSIS. MAINTAIN BLOOD PRESSURE AND AIRWAY. GIVE OXYGEN IF RESPIRATION IS DEPRESSED. DO NOT PERFORM GASTRIC LAVAGE IF VICTIM IS UNCONSCIOUS. GET MEDICAL ATTENTION IMMEDIATELY (DREISBACH, HANDBOOK OF POISONING, 12TH ED.).
ADMINISTRATION OF LAVAGE OR OXYGEN SHOULD BE PERFORMED BY QUALIFIED MEDICAL PERSONNEL.

ANTIDOTE: NO SPECIFIC ANTIDOTE. TREAT SYMPTOMATICALLY AND SUPPORTIVELY.

REACTIVITY

REACTIVITY: STABLE UNDER NORMAL TEMPERATURES AND PRESSURES.

INCOMPATIBILITIES: 1-NAPHTHALENEACETIC ACID: OXIDIZERS (STRONG): INCOMPATIBLE.

DECOMPOSITION: THERMAL DECOMPOSITION PRODUCTS MAY INCLUDE TOXIC OXIDES OF CARBON.

POLYMERIZATION: HAZARDOUS POLYMERIZATION HAS NOT BEEN REPORTED TO OCCUR UNDER NORMAL TEMPERATURES AND PRESSURES.

STORAGE AND DISPOSAL

OBSERVE ALL FEDERAL, STATE AND LOCAL REGULATIONS WHEN STORING OR DISPOSING OF THIS SUBSTANCE. FOR ASSISTANCE, CONTACT THE DISTRICT DIRECTOR OF THE ENVIRONMENTAL PROTECTION AGENCY.

****STORAGE****

STORE IN ACCORDANCE WITH 40 CFR 165 RECOMMENDED PROCEDURES FOR THE DISPOSAL AND STORAGE OF PESTICIDES AND PESTICIDE CONTAINERS.
STORE AWAY FROM INCOMPATIBLE SUBSTANCES.

****DISPOSAL****

DISPOSAL MUST BE IN ACCORDANCE WITH 40 CFR 165 RECOMMENDED PROCEDURES FOR THE DISPOSAL AND STORAGE OF PESTICIDES AND PESTICIDE CONTAINERS.

CONDITIONS TO AVOID

MAY BURN BUT DOES NOT IGNITE READILY. AVOID CONTACT WITH STRONG OXIDIZERS, EXCESSIVE HEAT, SPARKS, OR OPEN FLAME.

SPILL AND LEAK PROCEDURES

OCCUPATIONAL SPILL: STOP LEAK IF YOU CAN DO IT WITHOUT RISK. FOR SMALL SPILLS, TAKE UP WITH SAND OR OTHER ABSORBENT MATERIAL AND PLACE INTO CLEAN, DRY CONTAINERS FOR LATER DISPOSAL. KEEP UNNECESSARY PEOPLE AWAY. ISOLATE HAZARD AREA AND DENY ENTRY.

PROTECTIVE EQUIPMENT

VENTILATION: PROVIDE LOCAL EXHAUST OR GENERAL DILUTION VENTILATION SYSTEM.

RESPIRATOR: THE FOLLOWING RESPIRATORS ARE RECOMMENDED BASED ON INFORMATION FOUND IN THE PHYSICAL DATA, TOXICITY AND HEALTH EFFECTS SECTIONS. THEY ARE RANKED IN ORDER FROM MINIMUM TO MAXIMUM RESPIRATORY PROTECTION. THE SPECIFIC RESPIRATOR SELECTED MUST BE BASED ON CONTAMINATION LEVELS FOUND IN THE WORK PLACE, MUST NOT EXCEED THE

WORKING LIMITS OF THE RESPIRATOR AND BE JOINTLY APPROVED BY THE NATIONAL INSTITUTE FOR OCCUPATIONAL SAFETY AND HEALTH AND THE MINE SAFETY AND HEALTH ADMINISTRATION (NIOSH-MSHA).
CHEMICAL CARTRIDGE RESPIRATOR WITH AN ORGANIC VAPOR CARTRIDGE(S) WITH A FULL FACEPIECE AND ORGANIC VAPOR CARTRIDGE(S) IN COMBINATION WITH A DUST AND MIST FILTER.
POWERED AIR-PURIFYING RESPIRATOR WITH A TIGHT-FITTING FACEPIECE AND ORGANIC VAPOR CARTRIDGE(S) IN COMBINATION WITH A HIGH-EFFICIENCY PARTICULATE FILTER.
TYPE 'C' SUPPLIED-AIR RESPIRATOR WITH A FULL FACEPIECE OPERATED IN A PRESSURE-DEMAND OR OTHER POSITIVE PRESSURE MODE.
SELF-CONTAINED BREATHING APPARATUS WITH A FULL FACEPIECE OPERATED IN PRESSURE-DEMAND OR OTHER POSITIVE PRESSURE MODE. FOR FIREFIGHTING AND OTHER IMMEDIATELY DANGEROUS TO LIFE OR HEALTH CONDITIONS:
SELF-CONTAINED BREATHING APPARATUS WITH FULL FACEPIECE OPERATED IN PRESSURE-DEMAND OR OTHER POSITIVE PRESSURE MODE.
SUPPLIED-AIR RESPIRATOR WITH FULL FACEPIECE AND OPERATED IN PRESSURE-DEMAND OR OTHER POSITIVE PRESSURE MODE IN COMBINATION WITH AN AUXILIARY SELF-CONTAINED BREATHING APPARATUS OPERATED IN PRESSURE-DEMAND OR OTHER POSITIVE PRESSURE MODE.

CLOTHING: EMPLOYEE MUST WEAR APPROPRIATE PROTECTIVE (IMPERVIOUS) CLOTHING AND EQUIPMENT TO PREVENT REPEATED OR PROLONGED SKIN CONTACT WITH THIS SUBSTANCE.

GLOVES: EMPLOYEE MUST WEAR APPROPRIATE PROTECTIVE GLOVES TO PREVENT CONTACT WITH THIS SUBSTANCE.

EYE PROTECTION: EMPLOYEE MUST WEAR SPLASH-PROOF OR DUST-RESISTANT SAFETY GOGGLES AND A FACESHIELD TO PREVENT CONTACT WITH THIS SUBSTANCE.
EMERGENCY WASH FACILITIES: WHERE THERE IS ANY POSSIBILITY THAT AN EMPLOYEE'S EYES AND/OR SKIN MAY BE EXPOSED TO THIS SUBSTANCE, THE EMPLOYER SHOULD PROVIDE AN EYE WASH FOUNTAIN AND QUICK DRENCH SHOWER WITHIN THE IMMEDIATE WORK AREA FOR EMERGENCY USE.

AUTHORIZED BY- OCCUPATIONAL HEALTH SERVICES, INC.
CREATION DATE: 10/05/89 ***REVISION DATE:*** 05/16/90

MATERIAL SAFETY DATA SHEET

OCCUPATIONAL HEALTH SERVICES, INC.
AGRICULTURE AND PESTICIDE DIVISION
450 SEVENTH AVENUE, SUITE 2407
NEW YORK, NEW YORK 10123
1-800-445-MSDS OR (212) 967-1100

EMERGENCY CONTACT:
JOHN S. BRANSFORD, JR. (615) 292-1180

SUBSTANCE IDENTIFICATION

CAS-NUMBER 35691-65-7

SUBSTANCE: 1,2-DIBROMO-2,4-DICYANOBUTANE

TRADE NAMES/SYNONYMS: TEKTAMER 38; 2-BROMO-2-BROMOMETHYLGLURATONITRILE; PST26487

CHEMICAL FAMILY: NITRILE, ALIPHATIC HALOGEN

MOLECULAR FORMULA: C6-H6-BR2-N2 MOL WT: 266

CERCLA RATINGS (SCALE 0-3): HEALTH=3 FIRE=0 REACTIVITY=0 PERSISTENCE=1

NFPA RATINGS (SCALE 0-4): HEALTH=3 FIRE=0 REACTIVITY=0

COMPONENTS AND CONTAMINANTS

COMPONENT: 1,2-DIBROMO-2,4-DICYANOBUTANE ***PERCENT:*** 100%
CAS# 35691-65-7

OTHER CONTAMINANTS: NONE

EXPOSURE LIMITS: NO OCCUPATIONAL EXPOSURE LIMITS ESTABLISHED BY OSHA, ACGIH, OR NIOSH.

PHYSICAL DATA

DESCRIPTION: OFF-WHITE TO TAN CRYSTALLINE POWDER, WITH A MILDLY PUNGENT ODOR.

MELTING POINT: 124 F (51 C)

SPECIFIC GRAVITY: 2.02 @ 25 C

FIRE AND EXPLOSION DATA

FIRE AND EXPLOSION HAZARD: NEGLIGIBLE FIRE HAZARD WHEN EXPOSED TO HEAT OR FLAME.

FIREFIGHTING MEDIA: DRY CHEMICAL, CARBON DIOXIDE, HALON, WATER SPRAY OR STANDARD FOAM (1987 EMERGENCY RESPONSE GUIDEBOOK, DOT P 5800.4).
FOR LARGER FIRES, USE WATER SPRAY, FOG OR STANDARD FOAM (1987 EMERGENCY RESPONSE GUIDEBOOK, DOT P 5800.4).

FIREFIGHTING: MOVE CONTAINER FROM FIRE AREA IF POSSIBLE. DO NOT SCATTER SPILLED MATERIAL WITH HIGH PRESSURE WATER STREAMS. DIKE FIRE CONTROL WATER FOR LATER DISPOSAL (1987 EMERGENCY RESPONSE GUIDEBOOK, DOT P 5800.4, GUIDE PAGE 31).
USE AGENTS SUITABLE FOR TYPE OF SURROUNDING FIRE. AVOID BREATHING HAZARDOUS VAPORS, KEEP UPWIND.

TOXICITY

1,2-DIBROMO-2,4-DICYANOBUTANE: TOXICITY DATA: >200 PPM/1 HOUR INHALATION-RAT LC50 (MERCK TECHNICAL SERVICE); >5 GM/KG SKIN-RABBIT LD50 (MERCK TECHNICAL SERVICE); 541 MG/KG ORAL-RAT LD50 (MERCK TECHNICAL SERVICE); REPRODUCTIVE EFFECTS DATA (RTECS). CARCINOGEN STATUS: NONE. LOCAL EFFECTS: IRRITANT: INHALATION, SKIN, AND EYES. ACUTE TOXICITY LEVEL: MODERATELY TOXIC BY INGESTION; SLIGHTLY TOXIC BY DERMAL ABSORPTION. TARGET EFFECTS: NO DATA AVAILABLE.

HEALTH EFFECTS AND FIRST AID

INHALATION: IRRITANT/TOXIC. **ACUTE EXPOSURE-** MAY BE IRRITATING. GREATER THAN 200 PPM FOR 1 HOUR AS A POWDER ADMINISTERED AT AN AIR FLOW RATE OF 5 LITERS/MINUTE KILLED 50% OF THE RATS TESTED. THE MECHANISM OF THE TOXICITY HAS NOT BEEN DESCRIBED, HOWEVER, CYANIDE AND/OR BROMIDE COULD BE RELEASED. CYANIDES MAY CAUSE DIZZINESS, RAPID RESPIRATION, VOMITING, FLUSHING, HEADACHE, DROWSINESS, DROP IN BLOOD PRESSURE, RAPID PULSE, UNCONSIOUSNESS AND POSSIBLE DEATH IN CONVULSIONS. LARGE DOSES OF BROMIDE MAY CAUSE NAUSEA, VOMITING, ABDOMINAL PAIN, COMA, AND PARALYSIS. **CHRONIC EXPOSURE-** NO DATA AVAILABLE. HOWEVER, REPEATED INHALATION OF SMALL AMOUNTS OF CYANIDES MAY CAUSE DIZZINESS, WEAKNESS, CONGESTION OF LUNGS, HOARSENESS, LOSS OF APPETITE, WEIGHT LOSS, AND MENTAL DETERIORATION. BROMIDES MAY CAUSE CONFUSION, IRRITABILITY, TREMOR, MEMORY LOSS, ANOREXIA, EMACIATION, HEADACHE, SLURRED SPEECH, DELUSIONS, PSYCHOTIC BEHAVIOR, ATAXIA, STUPOR, AND COMA.

FIRST AID- REMOVE FROM EXPOSURE AREA TO FRESH AIR IMMEDIATELY. IF BREATHING HAS STOPPED, PERFORM ARTIFICIAL RESPIRATION. KEEP PERSON WARM AND AT REST. TREAT SYMPTOMATICALLY AND SUPPORTIVELY. GET MEDICAL ATTENTION IMMEDIATELY.

SKIN CONTACT: IRRITANT. **ACUTE EXPOSURE-** MAY BE IRRITATING. REPORTED TO BE MODERATELY IRRITATING TO RABBIT'S SKIN. GREATER THAN 5 GRAMS/KG WAS REQUIRED TO KILL 50% OF THE RABBITS TESTED BY SKIN APPLICATION. **CHRONIC EXPOSURE-** REPEATED OR PROLONGED CONTACT MAY CAUSE DERMATITIS.

FIRST AID- REMOVE CONTAMINATED CLOTHING AND SHOES IMMEDIATELY. WASH AFFECTED AREA WITH SOAP OR MILD DETERGENT AND LARGE AMOUNTS OF WATER UNTIL NO EVIDENCE OF CHEMICAL REMAINS (APPROXIMATELY 15-20 MINUTES). GET MEDICAL ATTENTION IMMEDIATELY.

EYE CONTACT: IRRITANT. **ACUTE EXPOSURE-** MAY BE SEVERELY IRRITATING AND CAUSE REDNESS, PAIN, AND POSSIBLE EYE BURNS. REPORTED TO BE SEVERELY IRRITATING TO RABBIT'S EYES. **CHRONIC EXPOSURE-** MAY CAUSE CONJUNCTIVITIS.

FIRST AID- WASH EYES IMMEDIATELY WITH LARGE AMOUNTS OF WATER OR NORMAL SALINE, OCCASIONALLY LIFTING UPPER AND LOWER LIDS, UNTIL NO EVIDENCE OF CHEMICAL REMAINS (APPROXIMATELY 15-20 MINUTES). GET MEDICAL ATTENTION IMMEDIATELY.

INGESTION:

ACUTE EXPOSURE- ORAL FEEDING OF 541 MG/KG KILLED 50% OF THE RATS TESTED. 1064 MG/KG KILLED 50% OF THE DUCKS TESTED. THE MECHANISM OF TOXICITY HAS NOT BEEN DESCRIBED, HOWEVER, THE COMPOUND COULD RELEASE CYANIDE AND/OR BROMIDE. CYANIDES MAY CAUSE DIZZINESS, RAPID RESPIRATION, VOMITING, FLUSHING, HEADACHE, DROWSINESS, DROP IN BLOOD PRESSURE, RAPID PULSE, UNCONSCIOUSNESS, AND POSSIBLE DEATH IN CONVULSIONS. BROMIDES MAY CAUSE VOMITING, ABDOMINAL PAIN, COMA, AND PARALYSIS. **CHRONIC EXPOSURE-** A DIET CONTAINING GREATER THAN 10,000 PPM FOR 8 DAYS WAS THE REPORTED LETHAL CONCENTRATION, FOR 50% OF THE DUCKS TESTED; 4042 PPM FOR 8 DAYS WAS THE LETHAL CONCENTRATION FOR 50% OF THE QUAILS TESTED. THE SYSTEMIC EFFECTS WERE NOT DESCRIBED.

FIRST AID- TREAT SYMTOMATICALLY AND SUPPORTIVELY. GET MEDICAL ATTENTION.

ANTIDOTE: NO SPECIFIC ANTIDOTE. TREAT SYMPTOMATICALLY AND SUPPORTIVELY.

REACTIVITY

REACTIVITY: STABLE UNDER NORMAL TEMPERATURES AND PRESSURES.
INCOMPATIBILITIES: NONE KNOWN.
DECOMPOSITION: THERMAL DECOMPOSITION PRODUCTS MAY INCLUDE VERY TOXIC FUMES OF HYDROGEN CYANIDE AND TOXIC OXIDES OF CARBON AND NITROGEN. THERMAL DECOMPOSITION MAY RELEASE TOXIC AND CORROSIVE BROMIDES.
POLYMERIZATION: HAZARDOUS POLYMERIZATION HAS NOT BEEN REPORTED TO OCCUR UNDER NORMAL TEMPERATURES AND PRESSURES.

CONDITIONS TO AVOID

MAY BURN BUT DOES NOT IGNITE READILY. AVOID CONTACT WITH STRONG OXIDIZERS, EXCESSIVE HEAT, SPARKS, OR OPEN FLAME.

SPILL AND LEAK PROCEDURES

OCCUPATIONAL SPILL: STOP LEAK IF YOU CAN DO IT WITHOUT RISK. FOR SMALL SPILLS, TAKE UP WITH SAND OR OTHER ABSORBENT MATERIAL AND PLACE INTO CLEAN, DRY CONTAINERS FOR LATER DISPOSAL. KEEP UNNECESSARY PEOPLE AWAY. ISOLATE HAZARD AREA AND DENY ENTRY.

PROTECTIVE EQUIPMENT

VENTILATION: PROVIDE LOCAL EXHAUST OR PROCESS ENCLOSURE VENTILATION SYSTEM.
RESPIRATOR: THE FOLLOWING RESPIRATORS ARE RECOMMENDED BASED ON INFORMATION FOUND IN THE PHYSICAL DATA, TOXICITY AND HEALTH EFFECTS SECTIONS. THEY ARE RANKED IN ORDER FROM MINIMUM TO MAXIMUM RESPIRATORY PROTECTION. THE SPECIFIC RESPIRATOR SELECTED MUST BE BASED ON CONTAMINATION LEVELS FOUND IN THE WORK PLACE, MUST NOT EXCEED THE WORKING LIMITS OF THE RESPIRATOR AND BE JOINTLY APPROVED BY THE NATIONAL INSTITUTE FOR OCCUPATIONAL SAFETY AND HEALTH AND THE MINE SAFETY AND HEALTH ADMINISTRATION (NIOSH-MSHA).
DUST AND MIST RESPIRATOR WITH A FULL FACEPIECE.
AIR-PURIFYING FULL FACEPIECE RESPIRATOR WITH A HIGH-EFFICIENCY PARTICULATE FILTER.
POWERED AIR-PURIFYING RESPIRATOR WITH A TIGHT-FITTING FACEPIECE AND HIGH-EFFICIENCY PARTICULATE FILTER.
TYPE 'C' SUPPLIED-AIR RESPIRATOR WITH A FULL FACEPIECE OPERATED IN PRESSURE-DEMAND OR OTHER POSITIVE PRESSURE MODE OR WITH A FULL FACEPIECE, HELMET OR HOOD OPERATED IN CONTINUOUS-FLOW MODE.
SELF-CONTAINED BREATHING APPARATUS WITH A FULL FACEPIECE OPERATED IN PRESSURE-DEMAND OR OTHER POSITIVE PRESSURE MODE.
FOR FIREFIGHTING AND OTHER IMMEDIATELY DANGEROUS TO LIFE OR HEALTH CONDITIONS:
SELF-CONTAINED BREATHING APPARATUS WITH FULL FACEPIECE OPERATED IN PRESSURE-DEMAND OR OTHER POSITIVE PRESSURE MODE.
SUPPLIED-AIR RESPIRATOR WITH FULL FACEPIECE AND OPERATED IN PRESSURE-DEMAND OR OTHER POSITIVE PRESSURE MODE IN COMBINATION WITH AN AUXILIARY SELF-CONTAINED BREATHING APPARATUS OPERATED IN PRESSURE-DEMAND OR OTHER POSITIVE PRESSURE MODE.
CLOTHING: EMPLOYEE MUST WEAR APPROPRIATE PROTECTIVE (IMPERVIOUS) CLOTHING AND EQUIPMENT TO PREVENT REPEATED OR PROLONGED SKIN CONTACT WITH THIS SUBSTANCE.
GLOVES: EMPLOYEE MUST WEAR APPROPRIATE PROTECTIVE GLOVES TO PREVENT CONTACT WITH THIS SUBSTANCE.
EYE PROTECTION: EMPLOYEE MUST WEAR SPLASH-PROOF OR DUST-RESISTANT SAFETY GOGGLES TO PREVENT EYE CONTACT WITH THIS SUBSTANCE.
EMERGENCY EYE WASH: WHERE THERE IS ANY POSSIBILITY THAT AN EMPLOYEE'S EYES MAY BE EXPOSED TO THIS SUBSTANCE, THE EMPLOYER SHOULD PROVIDE AN EYE WASH FOUNTAIN WITHIN THE IMMEDIATE WORK AREA FOR EMERGENCY USE.

AUTHORIZED BY- OCCUPATIONAL HEALTH SERVICES, INC.
CREATION DATE: 10/05/89 ***REVISION DATE:*** 05/25/90

MATERIAL SAFETY DATA SHEET

OCCUPATIONAL HEALTH SERVICES, INC.
AGRICULTURE AND PESTICIDE DIVISION
450 SEVENTH AVENUE, SUITE 2407
NEW YORK, NEW YORK 10123
1-800-445-MSDS OR (212) 967-1100

EMERGENCY CONTACT:
JOHN S. BRANSFORD, JR. (615) 292-1180

SUBSTANCE IDENTIFICATION

CAS-NUMBER 96-12-8
SUBSTANCE: **1,2-DIBROMO-3-CHLOROPROPANE**
TRADE NAMES/SYNONYMS: 1-CHLORO-2,3-DIBROMOPROPANE; 3-CHLORO-1,2-DIBROMOPROPANE; DIBROMOCHLOROPROPANE; 2-DIBROMO-3-CHLOROPROPANE; DBCP; FUMAZONE; NEMAGON; NEMAFUME; NEMAGON SOIL FUMIGANT; NEMAPAZ; NEMAZON; NCI-C00500; OS 1897; RCRA U066; SD1897; UN 2872; C3H5BR2CL; PST26490
CHEMICAL FAMILY: HALOGEN COMPOUND, ALIPHATIC
MOLECULAR FORMULA: C3-H5-BR2-CL
MOLECULAR WEIGHT: 236.36
CERCLA RATINGS (SCALE 0-3): HEALTH=3 FIRE=2 REACTIVITY=0 PERSISTENCE=3
NFPA RATINGS (SCALE 0-4): HEALTH=3 FIRE=2 REACTIVITY=0

COMPONENTS AND CONTAMINANTS

COMPONENT: 1,2-DIBROMO-3-CHLOROPROPANE ***PERCENT:*** 100.0
CAS# 96-12-8
EXPOSURE LIMITS: 1,2-DIBROMO-3-CHLOROPROPANE: 1 PPB OSHA TWA 10 PPB (0.1 MG/M3) NIOSH RECOMMENDED 10 HOUR TWA
1 POUND CERCLA SECTION 103 REPORTABLE QUANTITY SUBJECT TO SARA SECTION 313 ANNUAL TOXIC CHEMICAL RELEASE REPORTING SUBJECT TO CALIFORNIA PROPOSITION 65 CANCER AND/OR REPRODUCTIVE TOXICITY WARNING AND RELEASE REQUIRMENTS- (FEBRUARY 27, 1987)

PHYSICAL DATA

DESCRIPTION: DENSE, COLORLESS TO YELLOW OR AMBER LIQUID WITH A PUNGENT ODOR AT HIGH CONCENTRATIONS ***BOILING POINT:*** 383.9 F (195.5 C)
MELTING POINT: 44.1 F (6.7 C) ***SPECIFIC GRAVITY:*** 2.093
VAPOR PRESSURE: 0.8 MMHG @ 21 C
EVAPORATION RATE: (BUTYL ACETATE =1) <1
SOLUBILITY IN WATER: 1000 PPM ***VAPOR DENSITY:*** 8.2
SOLVENT SOLUBILITY: SOLUBLE IN HALOGENATED HYDROCARBONS, ACETONE, METHANOL, DICHLOROPROPANE, DIMETHYL SULFOXIDE, ETHANOL, ETHER, BENZENE, HEPTANE, OILS, ISOPROPYL ALCOHOL, ALILPHATIC AND AROMATIC HYDROCARBONS,

FIRE AND EXPLOSION DATA

FIRE AND EXPLOSION HAZARD: MODERATE FIRE HAZARD WHEN EXPOSED TO HEAT OR FLAME.
VAPOR-AIR MIXTURES ARE EXPLOSIVE ABOVE FLASH POINT.
VAPORS ARE HEAVIER THAN AIR AND MAY TRAVEL A CONSIDERABLE DISTANCE TO A SOURCE OF IGNITION AND FLASH BACK.
FLASH POINT: 170 F (76.6 C) (CC) ***FLAMMABILITY CLASS(OSHA):*** IIIA
FIREFIGHTING MEDIA: DRY CHEMICAL, CARBON DIOXIDE, HALON, WATER SPRAY OR STANDARD FOAM (1987 EMERGENCY RESPONSE GUIDEBOOK, DOT P 5800.4).
FOR LARGER FIRES, USE WATER SPRAY, FOG OR STANDARD FOAM (1987 EMERGENCY RESPONSE GUIDEBOOK, DOT P 5800.4).
FIREFIGHTING: MOVE CONTAINER FROM FIRE AREA IF POSSIBLE. COOL FIRE-EXPOSED CONTAINERS WITH WATER FROM SIDE UNTIL WELL AFTER FIRE IS OUT. STAY AWAY FROM STORAGE TANK ENDS. FOR MASSIVE FIRE IN STORAGE AREA, USE UNMANNED HOSE HOLDER OR MONITOR NOZZLES, ELSE WITHDRAW FROM AREA AND LET FIRE BURN. WITHDRAW IMMEDIATELY IN CASE OF RISING SOUND FROM VENTING SAFETY DEVICE OR ANY DISCOLORATION OF STORAGE TANK DUE TO FIRE (1987 EMERGENCY RESPONSE GUIDEBOOK, DOT P 5800.4, GUIDE PAGE 27).
EXTINGUISH ONLY IF FLOW CAN BE STOPPED; USE FLOODING AMOUNTS OF WATER AS A FOG, SOLID STREAMS MAY BE INEFFECTIVE. COOL CONTAINERS WITH FLOODING AMOUNTS OF WATER, APPLY FROM AS FAR A DISTANCE AS POSSIBLE. AVOID BREATHING VAPORS, KEEP UPWIND.

TRANSPORTATION DATA

DEPARTMENT OF TRANSPORTATION HAZARD CLASSIFICATION 49 CFR 172.101: COMBUSTIBLE LIQUID
DEPARTMENT OF TRANSPORTATION LABELING REQUIREMENTS 49 CFR 172.101 AND SUBPART E: NONE
DEPARTMENT OF TRANSPORTATION PACKAGING REQUIREMENTS: NONE
EXCEPTIONS: 49 CFR 173.118A

TOXICITY

1,2-DIBROMO-3-CHLOROPROPANE: IRRITATION DATA: 10 GM SKIN-RABBIT SEVERE; 1% SOLUTION EYE-RABBIT MILD. TOXICITY DATA: 103 PPM/8 HOURS INHALATION-RAT LC50; 1400 MG/KG SKIN-RABBIT LD50; 170 MG/KG ORAL-RAT LD50; 257 MG/KG ORAL-MOUSE LD50; 180 MG/KG ORAL-RABBIT LD50; 150 MG/KG ORAL-GUINEA PIG LD50; 100 MG/KG SUBCUTANEOUS-RAT LD50; 123 MG/KG INTRAPERITONEAL-MOUSE LD50; MUTAGENIC DATA (RTECS); REPRODUCTIVE EFFECTS DATA (RTECS); TUMORIGENIC DATA (RTECS). CARCINOGEN STATUS:

OSHA CARCINOGEN; ANTICIPATED HUMAN CARCINOGEN (NTP); HUMAN INADEQUATE EVIDENCE, ANIMAL SUFFICIENT EVIDENCE (IARC GROUP-2B). 1,2-DIBROMO-3-CHLOROPROPANE PRODUCED SQUAMOUS-CELL CARCINOMAS OF THE FORESTOMACH IN RATS AND MICE AND CARCINOMAS OF THE MAMMARY GLAND IN FEMALE RATS BY CHRONIC ORAL INGESTION. CHRONIC INHALATION STUDIES IN RATS AND MICE REPORTED AN INCREASED INCIDENCE OF LUNG AND NASAL CAVITY TUMORS IN MICE, TUMORS OF THE NASAL CAVITY AND TONGUE IN BOTH SEXES OF RATS, AND CORTICAL ADENOMAS IN THE ADRENAL GLAND OF FEMALE RATS. LOCAL EFFECTS: IRRITANT- INHALATION, SKIN, AND EYE. ACUTE TOXICITY LEVEL: HIGHLY TOXIC BY INHALATION; TOXIC BY INGESTION; MODERATELY TOXIC BY DERMAL ABSORPTION. TARGET EFFECTS: CENTRAL NERVOUS SYSTEM DEPRESSANT. POISONING MAY AFFECT THE LUNGS, LIVER, AND KIDNEYS. AT INCREASED RISK FROM EXPOSURE: PERSONS WITH LIVER, RENAL, AND SKIN DISEASES OR BLOOD AND REPRODUCTIVE DISORDERS. ADDITIONAL DATA: THIS CHEMICAL WAS REPORTED TO HAVE INDUCED STERILITY AMONG EXPOSED MALE WORKERS. STIMULANTS SUCH AS EPINEPHRINE MAY INDUCE VENTRICULAR FIBRILLATION.

HEALTH EFFECTS AND FIRST AID

INHALATION: 1,2-DIBROMO-3-CHLOROPROPANE: IRRITANT/NARCOTIC/CARCINOGEN/TOXIC. **ACUTE EXPOSURE-** MAY CAUSE RESPIRATORY IRRITATION, NAUSEA, PULMONARY CONGESTION OR EDEMA AND CENTRAL NERVOUS SYSTEM DEPRESSION WITH APATHY, SLUGGISHNESS, AND ATAXIA. VAPOR CONCENTRATIONS OF 60 PPM PRODUCED IRRITATION OF THE RESPIRATORY TRACT, NAUSEA, CHILLS, CENTRAL NERVOUS DEPRESSION WITH APATHY AND ATAXIA, AND KIDNEY DAMAGE IN RATS. **CHRONIC EXPOSURE-** MALE WORKERS EMPLOYED IN THE PRODUCTION AND FORMULATION OF 1,2 DIBROMO-3-CHLOROPROPANE HAVE EXPERIENCED A DECREASED SPERMATOGENSIS, DECREASED TESTICULAR SIZE AND INCREASED FOLLICLE STIMULATING HORMONE (FSH) LEVELS. IT IS NOT CLEARLY ESTABLISHED WHETHER THIS CONDITION IS COMPLETELY REVERSIBLE IN ALL CASES ONCE EXPOSURE IS DISCONTINUED. HOWEVER SOME INDIVIDUALS HAVE FATHERED NORMAL CHILDREN AFTER RECOVERY OF THE SPERM COUNT. REPEATED EXPOSURES OF RATS TO 12 PPM PRODUCED SEVERE ATROPHY AND DEGENERATION OF TESTES, DEGENERATIVE CHANGES OF THE SEMINIFEROUS TUBULES, REDUCTION IN SPERM COUNT, AND ABNORMAL DEVELOPMENT OS SPERM CELLS; MILD DAMAGE TO THE LIVER AND KIDNEYS WAS ALSO REPORTED. RABBITS EXPOSED TO 1 PPM FOR 14 WEEKS HAD A 50% REDUCTION IN TESTICULAR SIZE AND DECREASED SPERMATOGENESIS IN THE REMAINING TUBULES; 10 PPM PRODUCED ALMOST COMPLETE ATROPHY OF THE TESTES IN RABBITS BY THE 8TH WEEK OF EXPOSURE. TWO FEMALE MONKEYS REPEATED EXPOSED TO 12 PPM DEVELOPED SEVERE LEUKOPENIAS AND ANEMIAS. CHRONIC INHALATION STUDIES OF RATS AND MICE REPORTED AN INCREASED INCIDENCE OF LUNG AND NASAL CAVITY TUMORS IN MICE, NASAL CAVITY TUMORS AND TUMORS OF THE TONGUE IN BOTH SEXES OF RATS, AND CORTICAL ADENOMAS IN THE ADRENAL GLAND OF FEMALE RATS.

FIRST AID- REMOVE FROM EXPOSURE AREA TO FRESH AIR IMMEDIATELY. IF BREATHING HAS STOPPED, PERFORM ARTIFICIAL RESPIRATION. KEEP PERSON WARM AND AT REST. TREAT SYMPTOMATICALLY AND SUPPORTIVELY. GET MEDICAL ATTENTION IMMEDIATELY.

SKIN CONTACT: 1,2-DIBROMO-3-CHLOROPROPANE: IRRITANT. **ACUTE EXPOSURE-** MAY CAUSE IRRITATION. APPLICATION OF 0.5 ML TO THE SHAVEN BACKS OF 4 RABBITS PRODUCED SLIGHT ERYTHEMA IN ABRADED AREAS OF SKIN AND NO SIGNS OF IRRITATION IN INTACT SKIN. A LETHAL DOSE IN RABBITS BY DERMAL ABSORPTION WAS 1400 MG/KG. **CHRONIC EXPOSURE-** REPEATED EXPOSURE MAY CAUSE ERYTHEMA OR INFLAMMATION AND DERMATITIS. REPEATED APPLICATION TO THE SKIN OF A RABBIT RESULTED IN A SLIGHT CRUSTINESS OF THE EPIDERMIS AND EXTENSIVE NECROSIS OF THE DERMIS AND SUBCUTANOUS TISSUE. AS EVALUATED BY RTECS, REPEATED APPLICATION TO THE SKINS OF MICE RESULTED IN A STATISTICALLY SIGNIFICANT INCREASE IN THE INCIDENCE OF CARCINOGENIC TUMORS OF SKIN AND APPENDAGES AND THE RESPIRATORY SYSTEM.

FIRST AID- REMOVE CONTAMINATED CLOTHING AND SHOES IMMEDIATELY. WASH AFFECTED AREA WITH SOAP OR MILD DETERGENT AND LARGE AMOUNTS OF WATER UNTIL NO EVIDENCE OF CHEMICAL REMAINS (APPROXIMATELY 15-20 MINUTES). GET MEDICAL ATTENTION IMMEDIATELY.

EYE CONTACT: 1,2-DIBROMO-3-CHLOROPROPANE: IRRITANT: **ACUTE EXPOSURE-** THE LIQUID APPLIED TO RABBIT EYES IN UNDILUTED FORM OR AS A 1% SOLUTION IN PROPYLENE GLYCOL CAUSED SLIGHT IRRITATION AND PAIN OF THE CONJUNCTIVAE AND IRIS THAT DISAPPEARED AFTER 1-2 DAYS. EXPOSURE TO CONCENTRATION AS HIGH AS 400 PPM PRODUCED CLOUDING OF THE CORNEA OR LENS IN RATS. **CHRONIC EXPOSURE-** CHRONIC EXPOSURE TO VAPORS MAY LEAD TO PERMANENT EYE DAMAGE. REPEATED EXPOSURES TO 12 PPM IN LABORATORY ANIMALS CAUSED CORNEAL DAMAGE.

FIRST AID- WASH EYES IMMEDIATELY WITH LARGE AMOUNTS OF WATER OR NORMAL SALINE, OCCASIONALLY LIFTING UPPER AND LOWER LIDS, UNTIL NO EVIDENCE OF CHEMICAL REMAINS (APPROXIMATELY 15-20 MINUTES). GET MEDICAL ATTENTION IMMEDIATELY.

INGESTION: 1,2-DIBROMO-3-CHLOROPROPANE: NARCOTIC/CARCINOGEN/TOXIC. **ACUTE EXPOSURE-** A LETHAL DOSE IN RATS WAS 170 MG/KG. A DOSE OF 100 MG/KG PRODUCED INHIBITION OF THE CENTRAL NERVOUS SYSTEM, PROLONGED WEIGHT LOSS, AND DECREASED SPERMATOGENSIS IN RATS. IN FEMALE RATS, A DOSE OF 100 MG/KG PROLONGED THE ESTRUS CYCLE. A SINGLE DOSE OF 126 MG/KG GIVEN TO MALE RATS RESULTED IN KIDNEY DEGENERATION AND DEPRESSED BODY WEIGHT, WHICH TOOK A LONG TIME FOR RECOVERY. **CHRONIC EXPOSURE-** REPEATED INGESTION BY RATS OF DAILY DOSES OF 0.5 MG/KG RESULTED IN PRONOUNCED NECROTIC ACTION ON THE PARENCHYMATOUS ORGANS (I.E., LIVER, KIDNEY, SPLEEN) AND ON THE TESTICLES OF RATS. DAILY DOSES OF 10 MG/KG ADMINISTERED TO RATS FOR 4 TO 5 MONTHS DECREASED THE CONCENTRATION OF SPERMATOZOA IN THE SEMEN AND THE DURATION OF MOTILITY OF THE SPERMATOZOA IN MALE RATS; IN FEMALE RATS, THE ESTRUS CYCLE WAS PROLONGED WITH BOTH ESTRUS AND DIESTRUS BECOMING LONGER. REPEATED ORAL DOSES OF THIS MATERIAL IN MICE AND RATS PRODUCED SQUAMOUS-CELL CARCINOMAS OF THE FORESTOMACH IN ANIMALS OF BOTH SPECIES AND ADENOCARCINOMAS OF THE MAMMARY GLAND IN FEMALE RATS.

FIRST AID- REMOVE BY GASTRIC LAVAGE OR EMESIS. MAINTAIN BLOOD PRESSURE AND AIRWAY. GIVE OXYGEN IF RESPIRATION IS DEPRESSED. DO NOT PERFORM GASTRIC LAVAGE OR EMESIS IF VICTIM IS UNCONSCIOUS. GET MEDICAL ATTENTION IMMEDIATELY (DREISBACH, HANDBOOK OF POISONING, 11TH ED.). ADMINISTRATION OF GASTRIC LAVAGE OR OXYGEN SHOULD BE PERFORMED BY QUALIFIED MEDICAL PERSONNEL.

ANTIDOTE: NO SPECIFIC ANTIDOTE. TREAT SYMPTOMATICALLY AND SUPPORTIVELY.

REACTIVITY

REACTIVITY: STABLE UNDER NORMAL TEMPERATURES AND PRESSURES.

INCOMPATIBILITIES: 1,2-DIBROMO-3-CHLOROPROPANE: ALKALI: MAY CAUSE HYDROLYSIS TO 2-BROMOALLYL ALCOHOL. ALUMINIUM AND ITS ALLOYS: MAY BE CORRODED. COPPER ALLOYS + WATER: MAY BE CORRODED. MAGNESIUM AND ITS ALLOYS: MAY BE CORRODED. RUBBER AND COATINGS: SOME FORMS MAY BE ATTACKED. STEEL ALLOYS + WATER: MAY BE CORRODED. TIN AND ITS ALLOYS: MAY BE CORRODED.

DECOMPOSITION: THERMAL DECOMPOSITION MAY PRODUCE TOXIC GASES OF BROMIDE AND CHLORIDE.

POLYMERIZATION: HAZARDOUS POLYMERIZATION HAS NOT BEEN REPORTED TO OCCUR UNDER NORMAL TEMPERATURES AND PRESSURES.

STORAGE AND DISPOSAL

OBSERVE ALL FEDERAL, STATE AND LOCAL REGULATIONS WHEN STORING OR DISPOSING OF THIS SUBSTANCE. FOR ASSISTANCE, CONTACT THE DISTRICT DIRECTOR OF THE ENVIRONMENTAL PROTECTION AGENCY.

****STORAGE****

STORE IN ACCORDANCE WITH 29 CFR 1910.106.

STORE AWAY FROM INCOMPATIBLE SUBSTANCES.

STORE IN TIGHTLY CLOSED CONTAINER IN A COOL, WELL VENTILATED AREA.

****DISPOSAL****

DISPOSAL MUST BE IN ACCORDANCE WITH STANDARDS APPLICABLE TO GENERATORS OF HAZARDOUS WASTE, 40CFR 262. EPA HAZARDOUS WASTE NUMBER U066.

CONDITIONS TO AVOID

AVOID CONTACT WITH HEAT, SPARKS, FLAMES, OR OTHER SOURCES OF IGNITION. VAPORS MAY BE EXPLOSIVE. AVOID OVERHEATING OF CONTAINERS; CONTAINERS MAY VIOLENTLY RUPTURE IN HEAT OF FIRE. AVOID CONTAMINATION OF WATER SOURCES.

SPILL AND LEAK PROCEDURES

WATER SPILL: THE CALIFORNIA SAFE DRINKING WATER AND TOXIC ENFORCEMENT ACT OF 1986 (PROPOSITION 65) PROHIBITS CONTAMINATING ANY KNOWN SOURCE OF DRINKING WATER WITH SUBSTANCES KNOWN TO CAUSE CANCER AND/OR REPRODUCTIVE TOXICITY.

OCCUPATIONAL SPILL: SHUT OFF IGNITION SOURCES. STOP LEAK IF YOU CAN DO IT WITHOUT RISK. USE WATER SPRAY TO REDUCE VAPORS. FOR SMALL SPILLS, TAKE UP WITH SAND OR OTHER ABSORBENT MATERIAL AND PLACE INTO CONTAINERS FOR LATER DISPOSAL. FOR LARGER SPILLS, DIKE FAR AHEAD OF SPILL FOR LATER DISPOSAL. NO SMOKING, FLAMES OR FLARES IN HAZARD AREA. KEEP UNNECESSARY PEOPLE AWAY; ISOLATE HAZARD AREA AND RESTRICT ENTRY. REPORTABLE QUANTITY (RQ): 1 POUND THE SUPERFUND AMENDMENTS AND REAUTHORIZATION ACT (SARA) SECTION 304 REQUIRES THAT A RELEASE EQUAL TO OR GREATER THAN THE REPORTABLE QUANTITY FOR THIS SUBSTANCE BE IMMEDIATELY REPORTED TO THE LOCAL EMERGENCY PLANNING COMMITTEE AND THE STATE EMERGENCY RESPONSE COMMISSION (40 CFR 355.40). IF THE RELEASE

OF THIS SUBSTANCE IS REPORTABLE UNDER CERCLA SECTION 103, THE NATIONAL RESPONSE CENTER MUST BE NOTIFIED IMMEDIATELY AT (800) 424-8802 OR (202) 426-2675 IN THE METROPOLITAN WASHINGTON, D.C. AREA (40 CFR 302.6).

PROTECTIVE EQUIPMENT

VENTILATION: PROVIDE LOCAL EXHAUST OR PROCESS ENCLOSURE VENTILATION TO MEET PUBLISHED EXPOSURE LIMITS.

RESPIRATOR: THE FOLLOWING RESPIRATORS ARE RECOMMENDED BASED ON INFORMATION FOUND IN THE PHYSICAL DATA, TOXICITY AND HEALTH EFFECTS SECTIONS. THEY ARE RANKED IN ORDER FROM MINIMUM TO MAXIMUM RESPIRATORY PROTECTION. THE SPECIFIC RESPIRATOR SELECTED MUST BE BASED ON CONTAMINATION LEVELS FOUND IN THE WORK PLACE, MUST NOT EXCEED THE WORKING LIMITS OF THE RESPIRATOR AND BE JOINTLY APPROVED BY THE NATIONAL INSTITUTE FOR OCCUPATIONAL SAFETY AND HEALTH AND THE MINE SAFETY AND HEALTH ADMINISTRATION (NIOSH-MSHA).

TYPE 'C' SUPPLIED-AIR RESPIRATOR WITH A FULL FACEPIECE OPERATED IN PRESSURE-DEMAND OR OTHER POSITIVE PRESSURE MODE OR WITH A FULL FACEPIECE, HELMET OR HOOD OPERATED IN CONTINOUS-FLOW MODE.

SELF-CONTAINED BREATHING APPARATUS WITH A FULL FACEPIECE OPERATED IN PRESSURE-DEMAND OR OTHER POSITIVE PRESSURE MODE.

FOR FIREFIGHTING AND OTHER IMMEDIATELY DANGEROUS TO LIFE OR HEALTH CONDITIONS:

SELF-CONTAINED BREATHING APPARATUS WITH FULL FACEPIECE OPERATED IN PRESSURE-DEMAND OR OTHER POSITIVE PRESSURE MODE.

SUPPLIED-AIR RESPIRATOR WITH FULL FACEPIECE AND OPERATED IN PRESSURE-DEMAND OR OTHER POSITIVE PRESSURE MODE IN COMBINATION WITH AN AUXILIARY SELF-CONTAINED BREATHING APPARATUS OPERATED IN PRESSURE-DEMAND OR OTHER POSITIVE PRESSURE MODE.

CLOTHING: EMPLOYEE MUST WEAR APPROPRIATE PROTECTIVE (IMPERVIOUS) CLOTHING AND EQUIPMENT TO PREVENT ANY POSSIBILITY OF SKIN CONTACT WITH THIS SUBSTANCE.

1,2-DIBROMO-3-CHLOROPROPANE: PROTECTIVE CLOTHING SHOULD MEET THE REQUIREMENTS FOR PROTECTIVE CLOTHING AND EQUIPMENT IN 29 CFR 1910.1044(J).

GLOVES: EMPLOYEE MUST WEAR APPROPRIATE PROTECTIVE GLOVES TO PREVENT CONTACT WITH THIS SUBSTANCE.

1,2-DIBROMO-3-CHLOROPROPANE: PROTECTIVE GLOVES SHOULD MEET THE REQUIREMENTS FOR PROTECTIVE CLOTHING AND EQUIPMENT IN 29 CFR 1910.1044(J).

EYE PROTECTION: EMPLOYEE MUST WEAR SPLASH-PROOF OR DUST-RESISTANT SAFETY GOGGLES AND A FACESHIELD TO PREVENT CONTACT WITH THIS SUBSTANCE.

EMERGENCY WASH FACILITIES: WHERE THERE IS ANY POSSIBILITY THAT AN EMPLOYEE'S EYES AND/OR SKIN MAY BE EXPOSED TO THIS SUBSTANCE, THE EMPLOYER SHOULD PROVIDE AN EYE WASH FOUNTAIN AND QUICK DRENCH SHOWER WITHIN THE IMMEDIATE WORK AREA FOR EMERGENCY USE.

1,2-DIBROMO-3-CHLOROPROPANE: PROTECTIVE EYE EQUIPMENT SHOULD MEET THE REQUIREMENTS FOR PROTECTIVE CLOTHING AND EQUIPMENT IN 29 CFR 1910.1044(J).

AUTHORIZED BY- OCCUPATIONAL HEALTH SERVICES, INC.
CREATION DATE: 10/05/89 ***REVISION DATE:*** 07/12/90

MATERIAL SAFETY DATA SHEET

OCCUPATIONAL HEALTH SERVICES, INC.
AGRICULTURE AND PESTICIDE DIVISION
450 SEVENTH AVENUE, SUITE 2407
NEW YORK, NEW YORK 10123
1-800-445-MSDS OR (212) 967-1100

EMERGENCY CONTACT:
JOHN S. BRANSFORD, JR. (615) 292-1180

SUBSTANCE IDENTIFICATION

CAS-NUMBER 107-88-0

SUBSTANCE: **1,3-BUTANEDIOL**

TRADE NAMES/SYNONYMS: 1,3-BUTYLENE GLYCOL; 1,3-DIHYDROXYBUTANE; GLYCOL; BUTANE -1,3-DIOL; METHYLTRIMETHYLENE GLYCOL; 1-METHYL-1,3-PROPANEDIOL; BETA BUTYLENE GLYCOL; LB-BUTYLENE GLYCOL; O-1637; PST26730

CHEMICAL FAMILY: HYDROXYL, ALIPHATIC

MOLECULAR FORMULA: C4-H10-O2 MOL WT: 90.14

CERCLA RATINGS (SCALE 0-3): HEALTH=1 FIRE=1 REACTIVITY=0 PERSISTENCE=0

NFPA RATINGS (SCALE 0-4): HEALTH=1 FIRE=1 REACTIVITY=0

COMPONENTS AND CONTAMINANTS

COMPONENT: 1,3-BUTANEDIOL ***PERCENT:*** 100
CAS# 107-88-0

OTHER CONTAMINANTS: NONE

EXPOSURE LIMITS: NONE ESTABLISHED

PHYSICAL DATA

DESCRIPTION: VISCOUS, PRACTICALLY COLORLESS LIQUID, VERY HYGROSCOPIC

BOILING POINT: 406 F (207.5 C) ***MELTING POINT:*** -58 F (<-50 C)

SPECIFIC GRAVITY: 1.0+ ***VAPOR PRESSURE:*** 0.06 MM HG @ 20 C

SOLUBILITY IN WATER: SOLUBLE ***VAPOR DENSITY:*** 3.1

SOLVENT SOLUBILITY: ALCOHOL, ACETONE

FIRE AND EXPLOSION DATA

FIRE AND EXPLOSION HAZARD: SLIGHT FIRE HAZARD WHEN EXPOSED TO HEAT OR FLAME.

VAPORS ARE HEAVIER THAN AIR AND MAY TRAVEL A CONSIDERABLE DISTANCE TO A SOURCE OF IGNITION AND FLASH BACK.

FLASH POINT: 250 F (121 C) (CC) ***AUTOIGNITION TEMP.:*** 741 F (393.9 C)

FLAMMABILITY CLASS(OSHA): IIIB

FIREFIGHTING MEDIA: DRY CHEMICAL, CARBON DIOXIDE, HALON, WATER SPRAY OR STANDARD FOAM (1987 EMERGENCY RESPONSE GUIDEBOOK, DOT P 5800.4).

FOR LARGER FIRES, USE WATER SPRAY, FOG OR STANDARD FOAM (1987 EMERGENCY RESPONSE GUIDEBOOK, DOT P 5800.4).

FIREFIGHTING: MOVE CONTAINER FROM FIRE AREA IF POSSIBLE. DO NOT SCATTER SPILLED MATERIAL WITH HIGH PRESSURE WATER STREAMS. DIKE FIRE CONTROL WATER FOR LATER DISPOSAL (1987 EMERGENCY RESPONSE GUIDEBOOK, DOT P 5800.4, GUIDE PAGE 31).

USE AGENTS SUITABLE FOR TYPE OF SURROUNDING FIRE. AVOID BREATHING HAZARDOUS VAPORS, KEEP UPWIND.

TOXICITY

1,3-BUTANEDIOL (1,3-BUTYLENE GLYCOL): IRRITATION DATA: 500 MG/24 HOURS SKIN-RABBIT MILD; 505 MG EYE-RABBIT; 500 MG/24 HOURS EYE-RABBIT MILD. TOXICITY DATA: 18610 MG/KG ORAL-RAT LD50; 12,980 MG/KG ORAL-MOUSE LD50; 11 GM/KG ORAL-GUINEA PIG; 20 GM/KG SUBCUTANEOUS-RAT LD50; REPRODUCTIVE EFFECTS DATA (RTECS). CARCINOGEN STATUS: NONE. LOCAL EFFECTS: IRRITANT- EYES. ACUTE TOXICITY LEVEL: RELATIVELY NON-TOXIC BY INGESTION. TARGET EFFECTS: NO DATA AVAILABLE.

HEALTH EFFECTS AND FIRST AID

INHALATION: 1,3-BUTANEDIOL (1,3-BUTYLENE GLYCOL): **ACUTE EXPOSURE-** VERY HIGH CONCENTRATIONS MAY PRODUCE COUGHING, HEADACHE, PHARYNGITIS, DIZZINESS, NAUSEA, AND DYSPNEA. **CHRONIC EXPOSURE-** NO EFFECTS REPORTED.

FIRST AID- REMOVE FROM EXPOSURE AREA TO FRESH AIR IMMEDIATELY. IF BREATHING HAS STOPPED, PERFORM ARTIFICIAL RESPIRATION. KEEP PERSON WARM AND AT REST. TREAT SYMPTOMATICALLY AND SUPPORTIVELY. GET MEDICAL ATTENTION IMMEDIATELY.

SKIN CONTACT: 1,3-BUTANEDIOL (1,3-BUTYLENE GLYCOL): IRRITANT. **ACUTE EXPOSURE-** MAY CAUSE SLIGHT IRRITATION AND DERMATITIS. **CHRONIC EXPOSURE-** NO EFFECTS REPORTED.

FIRST AID- REMOVE CONTAMINATED CLOTHING AND SHOES IMMEDIATELY. WASH AFFECTED AREA WITH SOAP OR MILD DETERGENT AND LARGE AMOUNTS OF WATER UNTIL NO EVIDENCE OF CHEMICAL REMAINS (APPROXIMATELY 15-20 MINUTES). GET MEDICAL ATTENTION IMMEDIATELY.

EYE CONTACT: 1,3-BUTANEDIOL (1,3-BUTYLENE GLYCOL): IRRITANT. **ACUTE EXPOSURE-** MAY CAUSE EDEMA, AND SEVERE STINGING. **CHRONIC EXPOSURE-** MAY CAUSE CONJUNCTIVITIS.

FIRST AID- WASH EYES IMMEDIATELY WITH LARGE AMOUNTS OF WATER OR NORMAL SALINE, OCCASIONALLY LIFTING UPPER AND LOWER LIDS, UNTIL NO EVIDENCE OF CHEMICAL REMAINS (APPROXIMATELY 15-20 MINUTES). GET MEDICAL ATTENTION IMMEDIATELY.

INGESTION: 1,3-BUTANEDIOL (1,3-BURYLENE GLYCOL): **ACUTE EXPOSURE-** VERY HIGH CONCENTRATIONS MAY PRODUCE GASTROINTESTINAL IRRITATION, ABDOMINAL PAIN, NAUSEA, AND DIARRHEA. **CHRONIC EXPOSURE-** MAY CAUSE SLIGHT DECREASE IN BLOOD GLUCOSE LEVELS. NO OTHER EFFECTS REPORTED.

FIRST AID- IF VICTIM IS CONSCIOUS, IMMEDIATELY GIVE 2 TO 4 GLASSES OF WATER, AND INDUCE VOMITING BY TOUCHING FINGER TO BACK OF THROAT. GET MEDICAL ATTENTION IMMEDIATELY.

ANTIDOTE: NO SPECIFIC ANTIDOTE. TREAT SYMPTOMATICALLY AND SUPPORTIVELY.

REACTIVITY

REACTIVITY: STABLE UNDER NORMAL TEMPERATURES AND PRESSURES.

INCOMPATIBILITIES: 1,3-BUTANEDIOL (1,3-BUTYLENE GLYCOL): OXIDIZING AGENTS: MAY REACT VIGOROUSLY ON CONTACT. EPOXIDES: MAY REACT VIGOROUSLY ON CONTACT.

DECOMPOSITION: THERMAL DECOMPOSITION MAY RELEASE ACRID SMOKE AND IRRITATING FUMES.

POLYMERIZATION: HAZARDOUS POLYMERIZATION HAS NOT BEEN REPORTED TO OCCUR UNDER NORMAL TEMPERATURES AND PRESSURES.

CONDITIONS TO AVOID

AVOID HEAT, OXIDIZING AGENTS, AND EPOXIDES.

SPILL AND LEAK PROCEDURES

WATER SPILL: IF WATER POLLUTION OCCURS, NOTIFY APPROPRIATE AUTHORITIES.

OCCUPATIONAL SPILL: SHUT OFF IGNITION SOURCES. STOP LEAK IF YOU CAN DO IT WITHOUT RISK. USE WATER SPRAY TO REDUCE VAPORS. FOR SMALL SPILLS, TAKE UP WITH SAND OR OTHER ABSORBENT MATERIAL AND PLACE INTO CONTAINERS FOR LATER DISPOSAL. FOR LARGER SPILLS, DIKE FAR AHEAD OF SPILL FOR LATER DISPOSAL. NO SMOKING, FLAMES OR FLARES IN HAZARD AREA. KEEP UNNECESSARY PEOPLE AWAY; ISOLATE HAZARD AREA AND RESTRICT ENTRY.

PROTECTIVE EQUIPMENT

VENTILATION: PROVIDE GENERAL DILUTION VENTILATION.

RESPIRATOR: THE FOLLOWING RESPIRATORS ARE RECOMMENDED BASED ON INFORMATION FOUND IN THE PHYSICAL DATA, TOXICITY AND HEALTH EFFECTS SECTIONS. THEY ARE RANKED IN ORDER FROM MINIMUM TO MAXIMUM RESPIRATORY PROTECTION. THE SPECIFIC RESPIRATOR SELECTED MUST BE BASED ON CONTAMINATION LEVELS FOUND IN THE WORK PLACE, MUST NOT EXCEED THE WORKING LIMITS OF THE RESPIRATOR AND BE JOINTLY APPROVED BY THE NATIONAL INSTITUTE FOR OCCUPATIONAL SAFETY AND HEALTH AND THE MINE SAFETY AND HEALTH ADMINISTRATION (NIOSH-MSHA).

CHEMICAL CARTRIDGE RESPIRATOR WITH AN ORGANIC VAPOR CARTRIDGE(S) WITH A FULL FACEPIECE.

GAS MASK WITH ORGANIC VAPOR CANISTER (CHIN-STYLE OR FRONT- OR BACK-MOUNTED CANISTER) WITH A FULL FACEPIECE.

TYPE 'C' SUPPLIED-AIR RESPIRATOR WITH A FULL FACEPIECE OPERATED IN PRESSURE-DEMAND OR OTHER POSITIVE PRESSURE MODE OR WITH A FULL FACEPIECE, HELMET OR HOOD OPERATED IN CONTINUOUS-FLOW MODE.

SELF-CONTAINED BREATHING APPARATUS WITH A FULL FACEPIECE OPERATED IN PRESSURE-DEMAND OR OTHER POSITIVE PRESSURE MODE.

FOR FIREFIGHTING AND OTHER IMMEDIATELY DANGEROUS TO LIFE OR HEALTH CONDITIONS:

SELF-CONTAINED BREATHING APPARATUS WITH FULL FACEPIECE OPERATED IN PRESSURE-DEMAND OR OTHER POSITIVE PRESSURE MODE.

SUPPLIED-AIR RESPIRATOR WITH FULL FACEPIECE AND OPERATED IN PRESSURE-DEMAND OR OTHER POSITIVE PRESSURE MODE IN COMBINATION WITH AN AUXILIARY SELF-CONTAINED BREATHING APPARATUS OPERATED IN PRESSURE-DEMAND OR OTHER POSITIVE PRESSURE MODE.

CLOTHING: EMPLOYEE MUST WEAR APPROPRIATE PROTECTIVE (IMPERVIOUS) CLOTHING AND EQUIPMENT TO PREVENT REPEATED OR PROLONGED SKIN CONTACT WITH THIS SUBSTANCE.

GLOVES: EMPLOYEE MUST WEAR APPROPRIATE PROTECTIVE GLOVES TO PREVENT CONTACT WITH THIS SUBSTANCE.

EYE PROTECTION: EMPLOYEE MUST WEAR SPLASH-PROOF OR DUST-RESISTANT SAFETY GOGGLES AND A FACESHIELD TO PREVENT CONTACT WITH THIS SUBSTANCE.

EMERGENCY WASH FACILITIES: WHERE THERE IS ANY POSSIBILITY THAT AN EMPLOYEE'S EYES AND/OR SKIN MAY BE EXPOSED TO THIS SUBSTANCE, THE EMPLOYER SHOULD PROVIDE AN EYE WASH FOUNTAIN AND QUICK DRENCH SHOWER WITHIN THE IMMEDIATE WORK AREA FOR EMERGENCY USE.

AUTHORIZED BY- OCCUPATIONAL HEALTH SERVICES, INC.

CREATION DATE: 11/15/89 ***REVISION DATE:*** 05/11/90

MATERIAL SAFETY DATA SHEET

OCCUPATIONAL HEALTH SERVICES, INC.
AGRICULTURE AND PESTICIDE DIVISION
450 SEVENTH AVENUE, SUITE 2407
NEW YORK, NEW YORK 10123

EMERGENCY CONTACT:
JOHN S. BRANSFORD, JR. (615) 292-1180
1-800-445-MSDS OR (212) 967-1100

SUBSTANCE IDENTIFICATION

CAS-NUMBER 118-52-5

SUBSTANCE: **1,3-DICHLORO-5,5-DIMETHYLHYDANTOIN**

TRADE NAMES/SYNONYMS: HALANE; DACTIN; DCA; OMCHLOR; DDH; DANTOIN; DCDMH; DICHLORODIMETHYLHYDANTOIN; 1,3-DICHLORO-5,5-METHYLHYDANTOIN; DICHLORANTIN; 1,3-DICHLORO-5,5-DIMETHYL-2-IMIDAZOLIDINEDIONE; PST26800

CHEMICAL FAMILY: IMIDE, CARBOXYLIC

MOLECULAR FORMULA: C5-H6-CL2-N2-O2 MOL WT: 197.03

CERCLA RATINGS (SCALE 0-3): HEALTH=2 FIRE=0 REACTIVITY=1 PERSISTENCE=1

NFPA RATINGS (SCALE 0-4): HEALTH=2 FIRE=0 REACTIVITY=1

COMPONENTS AND CONTAMINANTS

COMPONENT: 1,3-DICHLORO-5,5-DIMETHYLHYDANTOIN ***PERCENT:*** 100
CAS# 118-52-5

OTHER CONTAMINANTS: NONE

EXPOSURE LIMITS: 1,3-DICHLORO-5,5-DIMETHYL HYDANTOIN: 0.2 MG/M3 OSHA TWA; 0.4 MG/M3 OSHA STEL 0.2 MG/M3 ACGIH TWA; 0.4 MG/M3 ACGIH STEL

PHYSICAL DATA

DESCRIPTION: WHITE POWDER WITH A MILD CHLORINE ODOR.

BOILING POINT: SUBLIMES @ 100 C ***MELTING POINT:*** 270 F (132 C)

SPECIFIC GRAVITY: 1.5 ***PH:*** 4.4 @ AQ SOLUTION ***SOLUBILITY IN WATER:*** 0.2%

VAPOR DENSITY: 6.8

SOLVENT SOLUBILITY: CHLOROFORM, METHYLENE CHLORIDE, BENZENE, CCL4

FIRE AND EXPLOSION DATA

FIRE AND EXPLOSION HAZARD: NEGLIGIBLE FIRE HAZARD WHEN EXPOSED TO HEAT OR FLAME.

FIREFIGHTING MEDIA: DRY CHEMICAL, CARBON DIOXIDE, HALON, WATER SPRAY OR STANDARD FOAM (1987 EMERGENCY RESPONSE GUIDEBOOK, DOT P 5800.4). FOR LARGER FIRES, USE WATER SPRAY, FOG OR STANDARD FOAM (1987 EMERGENCY RESPONSE GUIDEBOOK, DOT P 5800.4).

FIREFIGHTING: MOVE CONTAINER FROM FIRE AREA IF POSSIBLE. DO NOT SCATTER SPILLED MATERIAL WITH HIGH PRESSURE WATER STREAMS. DIKE FIRE CONTROL WATER FOR LATER DISPOSAL (1987 EMERGENCY RESPONSE GUIDEBOOK, DOT P 5800.4, GUIDE PAGE 31).

USE AGENTS SUITABLE FOR TYPE OF SURROUNDING FIRE. AVOID BREATHING HAZARDOUS VAPORS, KEEP UPWIND.

TOXICITY

1,3-DICHLORO-5,5-DIMETHYLHYDANTOIN: IRRITATION DATA: 500 MG/24 HOURS SKIN-RABBIT SEVERE; 100 MG/24 HOURS SKIN-RABBIT SEVERE. TOXICITY DATA: 20 GM/M3/1 HOUR INHALATION-RAT LCLO; 542 MG/KG ORAL-RAT LD50; 1520 MG/KG ORAL-RABBIT LD50; 1350 MG/KG ORAL-GUINEA PIG LD50; 500 MG/KG UNREPORTED-MAMMAL LD50; 550 MG/KG UNREPORTED-RAT LD50; MUTAGENIC DATA. CARCINOGEN STATUS: NONE. LOCAL EFFECTS: IRRITANT- INHALATION, SKIN, AND EYES. ACUTE TOXICITY LEVEL: TOXIC BY INHALATION AND MODERATELY TOXIC BY INGESTION. TARGET EFFECTS: POISONING MAY AFFECT THE GASTROINTESTINAL TRACT. AT INCREASED RISK FROM EXPOSURE: INDIVIDUALS WITH A HISTORY OF CHRONIC RESPIRATORY DISEASE.

HEALTH EFFECTS AND FIRST AID

INHALATION: IRRITANT. 5 MG/M3 IMMEDIATELY DANGEROUS TO LIFE OR HEALTH.
ACUTE EXPOSURE- WORKMEN EXPOSED TO A CONCENTRATION OF 1.97 MG/M3 OF THIS COMPOUND WERE REPORTED TO HAVE EXPERIENCED EXTREME RESPIRATORY IRRITATION. EXPOSURE MAY CAUSE INFLAMMATION AND EDEMA OF THE UPPER RESPIRATORY TRACT, AND BRONCHOSPASMS. THE LOSS OF CHLORINE IN DRY CRYSTALS OVER 14 DAYS AT 60 C IS ONLY 1.5%. ON CONTACT WITH WATER, ESPECIALLY HOT WATER, HYPOCHLOROUS ACID IS FORMED, AND CHLORINE GAS RELEASED. HOWEVER, THE LOW SOLUBILITY IN WATER AT NORMAL TEMPERATURES MAKES THE DANGER OF ACUTE EXPOSURE TO CHLORINE GAS UNLIKELY. **CHRONIC EXPOSURE-** NO DATA AVAILABLE, HOWEVER, MILD IRRITATION MAY RESULT FROM PROLONGED EXPOSURE TO THE LOW LEVELS OF CHLORINE GAS RELEASED.

FIRST AID- REMOVE FROM EXPOSURE AREA TO FRESH AIR IMMEDIATELY. IF BREATHING HAS STOPPED, PERFORM ARTIFICIAL RESPIRATION. KEEP PERSON WARM AND AT REST. TREAT SYMPTOMATICALLY AND SUPPORTIVELY. GET MEDICAL ATTENTION IMMEDIATELY.

SKIN CONTACT: IRRITANT. **ACUTE EXPOSURE-** NO DATA AVAILABLE, HOWEVER, 3,3'-DICHLORO-5, 5-DIMETHYLHYDANTOIN, ON CONTACT WITH MOISTURE, SLOWLY

RELEASES CHLORINE WHICH MAY CAUSE IRRITATION. **CHRONIC EXPOSURE**- NO DATA AVAILABLE, HOWEVER, BASED ON THE POSSIBILITY OF THE SLOW RELEASE OF CHLORINE IT MAY CAUSE DERMATITIS AND CHLORACNE.

FIRST AID- REMOVE CONTAMINATED CLOTHING AND SHOES IMMEDIATELY. WASH AFFECTED AREA WITH SOAP OR MILD DETERGENT AND LARGE AMOUNTS OF WATER UNTIL NO EVIDENCE OF CHEMICAL REMAINS (APPROXIMATELY 15-20 MINUTES). GET MEDICAL ATTENTION IMMEDIATELY.

EYE CONTACT: IRRITANT. **ACUTE EXPOSURE**- MAY CAUSE INFLAMMATION AND EDEMA. **CHRONIC EXPOSURE**- NO DATA AVAILABLE.

FIRST AID- WASH EYES IMMEDIATELY WITH LARGE AMOUNTS OF WATER OR NORMAL SALINE, OCCASIONALLY LIFTING UPPER AND LOWER LIDS, UNTIL NO EVIDENCE OF CHEMICAL REMAINS (APPROXIMATELY 15-20 MINUTES). GET MEDICAL ATTENTION IMMEDIATELY.

INGESTION: **ACUTE EXPOSURE**- 2,3-DICHLORO-5,5-DIMETHYLHYDANTOIN IS A SANITIZING AGENT IN SWIMMING POOLS. A MAXIMAL LEVEL OF 10 PPM HAS BEEN RECOMMENDED FOR THIS USE BASED ON ACCIDENTAL SWALLOWING OF 100 TO 200 ML OF POOL WATER. RELATIVELY LARGE INGESTED AMOUNTS OF THIS SUBSTANCE MAY CAUSE WEAKNESS, LETHARGY, TREMORS, SALIVATION, COMA, AND IRRITATION OR CORROSIVE DAMAGE TO THE STOMACH. A DOSE OF 542 MG/KG ADMINISTERED ORALLY TO RATS IN THE FORM OF AN AQUEOUS SUSPENSION RESULTED IN DEATH OF 50% OF THE ANIMALS. HEMORRHAGES OF THE GASTROINTESTINAL TRACT WERE FOUND AT NECROPSY OF THE RATS WHICH DIED WITHIN 48 HOURS OF TREATMENT. **CHRONIC EXPOSURE**- NO DATA AVAILABLE.

FIRST AID- REMOVE BY GASTRIC LAVAGE OF EMESIS. MAINTAIN BLOOD PRESSURE AND AIRWAY. DO NOT PERFORM GASTRIC LAVAGE OR EMESIS IF VICTIM IS UNCONSCIOUS. GET MEDICAL ATTENTION IMMEDIATELY. (DREISBACH, HANDBOOK OF POISONING, 11TH ED.) ADMINISTRATION OF GASTRIC LAVAGE SHOULD BE PERFORMED BY QUALIFIED MEDICAL PERSONNEL.

REACTIVITY

REACTIVITY: REACTS WITH WATER OR MOISTURE FORMING CORROSIVE CHLORINE GAS.

INCOMPATIBILITIES: XYLENE: VIOLENT EXPLOSION. WATER: FORMATION OF TOXIC FUMES. STRONG ACIDS: POSSIBLE EXPLOSION AND FORMATION OF TOXIC FUMES. REDUCING AGENTS: POSSIBLE EXPLOSION AND FORMATION OF TOXIC FUMES. PLASTICS: ATTACKS. RUBBER: ATTACKS. COATINGS: ATTACKS.

DECOMPOSITION: IT DECOMPOSES AND CONFLAGERATES WITH FORMATION OF TOXIC GASES AT 212 C. IF THE MATERIAL IS WET IT MAY DECOMPOSE AT LOWER TEMPERATURES. IT DECOMPOSES COMPLETELY AT PH 9 FORMING TOXIC FUMES OF CHLORINE AND NITROGEN TRICHLORIDE. THERMAL DECOMPOSITION MAY RELEASE TOXIC GASES WHICH INCLUDE CHLORINE, HYDROGEN CHLORIDE, PHOSGENE, AND CARBON DIOXIDE.

POLYMERIZATION: POLYMERIZATION CATALYST.

CONDITIONS TO AVOID

MAY BURN BUT DOES NOT IGNITE READILY. AVOID CONTACT WITH STRONG OXIDIZERS, EXCESSIVE HEAT, SPARKS, OR OPEN FLAME.

SPILL AND LEAK PROCEDURES

OCCUPATIONAL SPILL: SWEEP UP AND PLACE IN SUITABLE CLEAN, DRY CONTAINERS FOR RECLAMATION OR LATER DISPOSAL. DO NOT FLUSH SPILLED MATERIAL INTO SEWER. KEEP UNNECESSARY PEOPLE AWAY.

PROTECTIVE EQUIPMENT

VENTILATION: PROVIDE LOCAL EXHAUST VENTILATION SYSTEM TO MEET PUBLISHED EXPOSURE LIMITS.

RESPIRATOR: THE FOLLOWING RESPIRATORS AND MAXIMUM USE CONCENTRATIONS ARE RECOMMENDATIONS BY THE U.S. DEPARTMENT OF HEALTH AND HUMAN SERVICES, NIOSH POCKET GUIDE TO CHEMICAL HAZARDS; NIOSH CRITERIA DOCUMENTS OR BY THE U.S. DEPARTMENT OF LABOR, 29 CFR 1910 SUBPART Z. THE SPECIFIC RESPIRATOR SELECTED MUST BE BASED ON CONTAMINATION LEVELS FOUND IN THE WORK PLACE, MUST NOT EXCEED THE WORKING LIMITS OF THE RESPIRATOR AND BE JOINTLY APPROVED BY THE NATIONAL INSTITUTE FOR OCCUPATIONAL SAFETY AND HEALTH AND THE MINE SAFETY AND HEALTH ADMINISTRATION (NIOSH-MSHA).

1,3-DICHLORO-5,5-DIMETHYLHYDANTOIN:

2 MG/M3- ANY SUPPLIED-AIR RESPIRATOR. ANY SELF-CONTAINED BREATHING APPARATUS.

5 MG/M3- ANY SUUPLIED-AIR RESPIRATOR OPERATED IN A CONTINUOUS FLOW MODE. ANY SUPPLIED-AIR RESPIRATOR WITH A FULL FACEPIECE. ANY SELF-CONTIANED BREATHING APPARATUS WITH A FULL FACEPIECE.

ESCAPE- ANY AIR-PURIFYING FULL FACEPIECE RESPIRATOR (GAS MASK) WITH A CHIN-STYLE OR FRONT- OR BACK-MOUNTED ORGANIC VAPOR CANISTER. ANY APPROPRIATE ESCAPE-TYPE SELF-CONTAINED BREATHING APPARATUS.

FOR FIREFIGHTING AND OTHER IMMEDIATELY DANGEROUS TO LIFE OR HEALTH CONDITIONS:

SELF-CONTAINED BREATHING APPARATUS WITH FULL FACEPIECE OPERATED IN PRESSURE-DEMAND OR OTHER POSITIVE PRESSURE MODE. SUPPLIED-AIR RESPIRATOR WITH FULL FACEPIECE AND OPERATED IN PRESSURE-DEMAND OR OTHER POSITIVE PRESSURE MODE IN COMBINATION WITH AN AUXILIARY SELF-CONTAINED BREATHING APPARATUS OPERATED IN PRESSURE-DEMAND OR OTHER POSITIVE PRESSURE MODE.

CLOTHING: EMPLOYEE MUST WEAR APPROPRIATE PROTECTIVE (IMPERVIOUS) CLOTHING AND EQUIPMENT TO PREVENT REPEATED OR PROLONGED SKIN CONTACT WITH THIS SUBSTANCE.

GLOVES: EMPLOYEE MUST WEAR APPROPRIATE PROTECTIVE GLOVES TO PREVENT CONTACT WITH THIS SUBSTANCE.

EYE PROTECTION: EMPLOYEE MUST WEAR SPLASH-PROOF OR DUST-RESISTANT SAFETY GOGGLES TO PREVENT EYE CONTACT WITH THIS SUBSTANCE.

EMERGENCY EYE WASH: WHERE THERE IS ANY POSSIBILITY THAT AN EMPLOYEE'S EYES MAY BE EXPOSED TO THIS SUBSTANCE, THE EMPLOYER SHOULD PROVIDE AN EYE WASH FOUNTAIN WITHIN THE IMMEDIATE WORK AREA FOR EMERGENCY USE.

AUTHORIZED BY- OCCUPATIONAL HEALTH SERVICES, INC.

CREATION DATE: 10/05/89 ***REVISION DATE:*** 05/31/90

MATERIAL SAFETY DATA SHEET

OCCUPATIONAL HEALTH SERVICES, INC.
AGRICULTURE AND PESTICIDE DIVISION
450 SEVENTH AVENUE, SUITE 2407
NEW YORK, NEW YORK 10123
1-800-445-MSDS OR (212) 967-1100

EMERGENCY CONTACT:
JOHN S. BRANSFORD, JR. (615) 292-1180

SUBSTANCE IDENTIFICATION

CAS-NUMBER 542-75-6

SUBSTANCE: **1,3-DICHLOROPROPENE**

TRADE NAMES/SYNONYMS: 1,3-DICHLORO-1-PROPENE; 3-CHLOROALLYL CHLORIDE; 3-CHLOROPROPENYL CHLORIDE; DICHLOROPROPYLENE; GAMMA-CHLOROALLYL CHLORIDE; ALPHA,GAMMA-DICHLOROPROPYLENE; 1,3-DICHLOROPROPYLENE; DICHLOROPROPENE; 1-PROPENE, 1,3-DICHLORO-; PROPENE, 1,3-DICHLORO-; 1,3-D; RCRA U084; STCC 4909255; UN 2047; C3H4CL2; PST26820

CHEMICAL FAMILY: HALOGEN COMPOUND, ALIPHATIC

MOLECULAR FORMULA: CL-C-H2-C-H-C-H-CL

MOLECULAR WEIGHT: 110.97

CERCLA RATINGS (SCALE 0-3): HEALTH=3 FIRE=3 REACTIVITY=0 PERSISTENCE=3

NFPA RATINGS (SCALE 0-4): HEALTH=2 FIRE=3 REACTIVITY=0

COMPONENTS AND CONTAMINANTS

COMPONENT: 1,3-DICHLOROPROPENE ***PERCENT:*** >99.0
CAS# 542-75-6

OTHER CONTAMINANTS: TRACES OF A STABILIZER; SOME FORMULATIONS MAY CONTAIN EPICHLOROHYDRIN.

EXPOSURE LIMITS: 1,3-DICHLOROPROPENE: 1 PPM (5 MG/M3) OSHA TWA (SKIN) 1 PPM (5 MG/M3) ACGIH TWA (SKIN)

100 POUNDS CERCLA SECTION 103 REPORTABLE QUANTITY SUBJECT TO SARA SECTION 313 ANNUAL TOXIC CHEMICAL RELEASE REPORTING SUBJECT TO CALIFORNIA PROPOSITION 65 CANCER AND/OR REPRODUCTIVE TOXICITY WARNING AND RELEASE REQUIREMENTS- (JANUARY 1, 1989)

EPICHLOROHYDRIN: 2 PPM (8 MG/M3) OSHA TWA (SKIN) 2 PPM (8 MG/M3) ACGIH TWA (SKIN) LOWEST FEASIBLE LIMIT NIOSH RECOMMENDED EXPOSURE CRITERIA 1,000 POUNDS SARA SECTION 302 THRESHOLD PLANNING QUANTITY 1,000 POUNDS SARA SECTION 304 REPORTABLE QUANTITY 100 POUNDS CERCLA SECTION 103 REPORTABLE QUANTITY SUBJECT TO SARA SECTION 313 ANNUAL TOXIC CHEMICAL RELEASE REPORTING SUBJECT TO CALIFORNIA PROPOSITION 65 CANCER AND/OR REPRODUCTIVE TOXICITY WARNING AND RELEASE REQUIREMENTS- (OCTOBER 1, 1987)

PHYSICAL DATA

DESCRIPTION: CLEAR TO YELLOW LIQUID WITH A CHLOROFORM-LIKE ODOR.

BOILING POINT: 226 F (108 C) ***SPECIFIC GRAVITY:*** 1.220

VAPOR PRESSURE: 24 MMHG @ 20 C ***SOLUBILITY IN WATER:*** 0.1%

VAPOR DENSITY: 3.8

SOLVENT SOLUBILITY: SOLUBLE IN ETHER, BENZENE, CHLOROFORM, ACETONE, TOLUENE, OCTANE.

FIRE AND EXPLOSION DATA

FIRE AND EXPLOSION HAZARD: DANGEROUS FIRE HAZARD WHEN EXPOSED TO HEAT OR FLAME.

VAPOR-AIR MIXTURES ARE EXPLOSIVE ABOVE FLASH POINT.

VAPORS ARE HEAVIER THAN AIR AND MAY TRAVEL A CONSIDERABLE DISTANCE TO A SOURCE OF IGNITION AND FLASH BACK.

DUE TO LOW ELECTROCONDUCTIVITY OF THE SUBSTANCE, FLOW OR AGITATION MAY GENERATE ELECTROSTATIC CHARGES RESULTING IN SPARKS WITH POSSIBLE IGNITION.

FLASH POINT: 83 F (28 C) (CC) ***UPPER EXPLOSIVE LIMIT:*** 14.5%

LOWER EXPLOSIVE LIMIT: 5.3% ***FLAMMABILITY CLASS(OSHA):*** IC

FIREFIGHTING MEDIA: DRY CHEMICAL, CARBON DIOXIDE, HALON, WATER SPRAY OR STANDARD FOAM (1987 EMERGENCY RESPONSE GUIDEBOOK, DOT P 5800.4).

FOR LARGER FIRES, USE WATER SPRAY, FOG OR STANDARD FOAM (1987 EMERGENCY RESPONSE GUIDEBOOK, DOT P 5800.4).

FIREFIGHTING: MOVE CONTAINER FROM FIRE AREA IF POSSIBLE. DO NOT GET WATER INSIDE CONTAINER. COOL FIRE-EXPOSED CONTAINERS WITH WATER FROM SIDE UNTIL WELL AFTER FIRE IS OUT. STAY AWAY FROM STORAGE TANK ENDS. WITHDRAW IMMEDIATELY IN CASE OF RISING SOUND FROM VENTING SAFETY DEVICE OR ANY DISCOLORATION OF STORAGE TANK DUE TO FIRE (1987 EMERGENCY RESPONSE GUIDEBOOK, DOT P 5800.4, GUIDE PAGE 29).

EXTINGUISH ONLY IF FLOW CAN BE STOPPED; USE WATER IN FLOODING AMOUNTS AS FOG, SOLID STREAMS MAY SPREAD FIRE. COOL CONTAINERS WITH FLOODING QUANTITIES OF WATER, APPLY FROM AS FAR A DISTANCE AS POSSIBLE. AVOID BREATHING TOXIC VAPORS, KEEP UPWIND.

TRANSPORTATION DATA

DEPARTMENT OF TRANSPORTATION HAZARD CLASSIFICATION 49 CFR 172.101: FLAMMABLE LIQUID

DEPARTMENT OF TRANSPORTATION LABELING REQUIREMENTS 49 CFR 172.101 AND SUBPART E: FLAMMABLE LIQUID

DEPARTMENT OF TRANSPORTATION PACKAGING REQUIREMENTS: 49 CFR 173.119 EXCEPTIONS: 49 CFR 173.118

TOXICITY

1,3-DICHLOROPROPENE: TOXICITY DATA: 500 PPM INHALATION-RAT LC50; 4650 MG/M3/2 HOURS INHALATION-MOUSE LC50; 504 MG/KG SKIN-RABBIT LD50; 775 MG/KG SKIN-RAT LD50; 470 MG/KG ORAL-RAT LD50; 640 MG/KG ORAL-MOUSE LD50; 175 MG/KG INTRAPERITONEAL-RAT LD50; MUTAGENIC DATA (RTECS); TUMORIGENIC DATA (RTECS). CARCINOGEN STATUS: HUMAN INADEQUATE EVIDENCE, ANIMAL SUFFICIENT EVIDENCE (IARC GROUP-2B). TECHNICAL-GRADE 1,3-DICHLOROPROPENE (CONTAINING 1.0% EPICHLOROHYDRIN) ADMINISTERED BY GAVAGE, PRODUCED MALIGNANT TUMORS OF THE URINARY BLADDER, LUNG AND FORESTOMACH IN MICE AND OF THE FORESTOMACH IN RATS. AFTER SUBCUTANEOUS ADMINISTRATION TO MICE, THE PURIFIED CIS-ISOMER PRODUCED MALIGNANT TUMORS AT THE SITE OF INJECTION. LOCAL EFFECTS: IRRITANT- INHALATION, SKIN, EYE. ACUTE TOXICITY LEVEL: TOXIC BY INHALATION, DERMAL ABSORPTION, AND INGESTION. TARGET EFFECTS: CENTRAL NERVOUS SYSTEM DEPRESSANT. POISONING MAY ALSO AFFECT THE LUNGS, LIVER, AND KIDNEYS. ADDITIONAL DATA: THE HUMAN AND ANIMAL DATA REPORTED IN THE HEALTH EFFECTS SECTIONS BELOW HAVE BEEN REPORTED FROM EXPOSURES TO TECHNICAL GRADE MIXTURES WHICH MAY CONTAIN FROM 88-98% DICHLOROPROPENE AND VARIOUS OTHER ISOMERS, RELATED COMPOUNDS, AND STABILIZERS. USE OF ALCOHOLIC BEVERAGES MAY ENHANCE THE TOXIC EFFECTS.

EPICHLOROHYDRIN: IRRITATION DATA: 10 MG/24 HOURS OPEN SKIN-RABBIT; 23 MG EYE-RABBIT; 100 MG/24 HOURS EYE-RABBIT MODERATE. TOXICITY DATA: 40 PPM/2 HOURS INHALATION-HUMAN TCLO; 20 PPM INHALATION-HUMAN TCLO; 250 PPM/8 HOURS INHALATION-RAT LC50; 515 MG/KG SKIN-RABBIT LD50; 1000 MG/KG SKIN-RAT LDLO; 250 MG/KG SKIN-MOUSE LD50; 90 MG/KG ORAL-RAT LD50; 345 MG/KG ORAL-RABBIT LD50; 236 MG/KG ORAL-MOUSE LD50; 280 MG/KG ORAL-GUINEA PIG LD50; 150 MG/KG SUBCUTANEOUS-RAT LD50; 154 MG/KG INTRAVENOUS-RAT LD50; 118 MG/KG INTRAPERITONEAL-GUINEA PIG LD50; 133 MG/KG INTRAPERITONEAL-RAT LD50; 118 MG/KG INTRAPERITONEAL-RABBIT LD50; 250 MG/KG PARENTERAL-MOUSE LDLO; MUTAGENIC DATA (RTECS); REPRODUCTIVE EFFECTS DATA (RTECS); TUMORIGENIC DATA (RTECS). CARCINOGEN STATUS: ANTICIPATED HUMAN CARCINOGEN (NTP); HUMAN INADEQUATE EVIDENCE, ANIMAL SUFFICIENT EVIDENCE (IARC GROUP-2A). IN RATS, ORAL ADMINISTRATION INDUCED PAPILLOMAS AND CARCINOMAS OF THE FORESTOMACH, AND INHALATION INDUCED PAPILLOMAS AND CARCINOMAS OF THE NASAL CAVITY. IN MICE, IT WAS ACTIVE AS AN INITIATOR ON SKIN, PRODUCED LOCAL SARCOMAS AFTER SUBCUTANEOUS INJECTION AND WAS ACTIVE IN A LUNG TUMOR BIOASSY BY INTRAPERITONEAL INJECTION. LOCAL EFFECTS: CORROSIVE- SKIN; IRRITANT- INHALATION, EYE. ACUTE TOXICITY LEVEL: TOXIC BY INHALATION, DERMAL ABSORPTION, INGESTION. TARGET EFFECTS: SENSITIZER- DERMAL; CENTRAL NERVOUS SYSTEM DEPRESSANT; NEPHROTOXIN. POISONING MAY ALSO AFFECT THE RESPIRATORY SYSTEM, LIVER, AND HEART. AT INCREASED RISK FROM EXPOSURE: PERSONS WITH PREEXISTING EYE OR SKIN PROBLEMS OR LIVER, KIDNEY, OR RESPIRATORY DISORDERS.

HEALTH EFFECTS AND FIRST AID

INHALATION: 1,3-DICHLOROPROPENE: IRRITANT/NARCOTIC/TOXIC. **ACUTE EXPOSURE-** VAPOR CONCENTRATIONS LOWER THAN 1500 PPM MAY CAUSE MODERATE RESPIRATORY TRACT IRRITATION AND CENTRAL NERVOUS SYSTEM DEPRESSION. AT HIGHER LEVELS EFFECTS MAY INCLUDE DIZZINESS, DULLNESS, NAUSEA, VOMITING, GASPING, COUGHING, CHEST PAIN, RESPIRATORY DISTRESS, AND UNCONSCIOUSNESS. SOME ELEVATION OF HEPATIC ENZYMES HAS BEEN REPORTED. HEAVY EXPOSURE MAY RESULT IN PERSISTENT HEADACHE, FATIGUE, IRRITABILITY, AND CHEST OR ABDOMINAL DISCOMFORT. IN RATS, 2,700 PPM CAUSED IRRITATION OF THE NOSE AND SEVERE LUNG, LIVER, AND KIDNEY INJURY. A 2 HOUR EXPOSURE TO 1000 PPM WAS LETHAL. **CHRONIC EXPOSURE-** IN ANIMALS, REPEATED OR PROLONGED EXPOSURE TO VAPORS HAS CAUSED EFFECTS ON WEIGHT GAIN, NASAL EPITHELIUM, AND THE LIVER AND KIDNEY.

FIRST AID- REMOVE FROM EXPOSURE AREA TO FRESH AIR IMMEDIATELY. IF BREATHING HAS STOPPED, GIVE ARTIFICIAL RESPIRATION. MAINTAIN AIRWAY AND BLOOD PRESSURE AND ADMINISTER OXYGEN IF AVAILABLE. KEEP AFFECTED PERSON WARM AND AT REST. TREAT SYMPTOMATICALLY AND SUPPORTIVELY. ADMINISTRATION OF OXYGEN SHOULD BE PERFORMED BY QUALIFIED PERSONNEL. GET MEDICAL ATTENTION IMMEDIATELY.

SKIN CONTACT: 1,3-DICHLOROPROPENE: IRRITANT/TOXIC. **ACUTE EXPOSURE-** INTENSE CONTACT WITH THE LIQUID MAY CAUSE SEVERE IRRITATION AND POSSIBLY BLISTERS OR BURNS. CONFINEMENT TO RABBIT SKIN RESULTED IN ERYTHEMA, EDEMA AND NECROSIS. THE LETHAL DOSE IN RABBITS WAS 504 MG/KG. **CHRONIC EXPOSURE-** REPEATED OR PROLONGED EXPOSURE TO THE LIQUID MAY CAUSE DERMATITIS, SEVERE IRRITATION, AND POSSIBLY BURNS. ANIMAL STUDIES INDICATE IT IS A POTENTIAL SKIN SENSITIZER.

FIRST AID- REMOVE CONTAMINATED CLOTHING AND SHOES IMMEDIATELY. WASH AFFECTED AREA WITH SOAP OR MILD DETERGENT AND LARGE AMOUNTS OF WATER UNTIL NO EVIDENCE OF CHEMICAL REMAINS (AT LEAST 15-20 MINUTES). IN CASE OF CHEMICAL BURNS, COVER AREA WITH STERILE, DRY DRESSING. BANDAGE SECURELY, BUT NOT TOO TIGHTLY. GET MEDICAL ATTENTION IMMEDIATELY.

EYE CONTACT: 1,3-DICHLOROPROPENE: IRRITANT. **ACUTE EXPOSURE-** VAPORS AT 1000 PPM HAVE CAUSED LACRIMATION AND IRRITATION IN ANIMALS. APPLICATION TO RABBIT EYES PRODUCED SEVERE CONJUNCTIVITIS AND MODERATE TO SEVERE CORNEAL INJURY WHICH HEALED IN 8 DAYS. **CHRONIC EXPOSURE-** REPEATED OR PROLONGED EXPOSURE TO IRRITANTS MAY CAUSE CONJUNCTIVITIS.

FIRST AID- WASH EYES IMMEDIATELY WITH LARGE AMOUNTS OF WATER OR NORMAL SALINE, OCCASIONALLY LIFTING UPPER AND LOWER LIDS, UNTIL NO EVIDENCE OF CHEMICAL REMAINS (APPROXIMATELY 15-20 MINUTES). GET MEDICAL ATTENTION IMMEDIATELY.

INGESTION: 1,3-DICHLOROPROPENE: NARCOTIC/CARCINOGEN/TOXIC. **ACUTE EXPOSURE-** MAY CAUSE ACUTE GASTROINTESTINAL DISTRESS, NAUSEA, ABDOMINAL PAIN, DIARRHEA, PULMONARY CONGESTION AND EDEMA, CENTRAL NERVOUS SYSTEM DEPRESSION, AND DEATH. ANIMAL STUDIES INDICATE LIVER, KIDNEY, AND LUNG DAMAGE MAY RESULT FROM A SINGLE EXPOSURE. **CHRONIC EXPOSURE-** REPEATED GAVAGE ADMINISTRATION PRODUCED PAPILLOMAS AND CARCINOMAS OF THE FORESTOMACH, AND NEOPLASTIC LIVER NODULES IN RATS; AND BLADDER CARCINOMAS AND ALVEOLAR/BRONCHIOLAR ADENOMAS OF THE LUNGS, AND PAPILLOMAS OR CARCINOMAS OF THE FORESTOMACH IN MICE.

FIRST AID- REMOVE BY GASTRIC LAVAGE OR EMESIS. MAINTAIN BLOOD PRESSURE AND AIRWAY. GIVE OXYGEN IF RESPIRATION IS DEPRESSED. DO NOT PERFORM GASTRIC LAVAGE OR EMESIS IF VICTIM IS UNCONSCIOUS. GET MEDICAL ATTENTION IMMEDIATELY (DREISBACH, HANDBOOK OF POISONING, 11TH ED.). ADMINISTRATION OF GASTRIC LAVAGE OR OXYGEN SHOULD BE PERFORMED BY QUALIFIED MEDICAL PERSONNEL.

ANTIDOTE: NO SPECIFIC ANTIDOTE. TREAT SYMPTOMATICALLY AND SUPPORTIVELY.

REACTIVITY

REACTIVITY: STABLE UNDER NORMAL TEMPERATURES AND PRESSURES.

INCOMPATIBILITIES: 1,3-DICHLOROPROPENE: ALUMINUM AND ALLOYS: POSSIBLE VIGOROUS EXOTHERMIC REACTION. BASES: POSSIBLE VIGOROUS REACTION. CADMIUM AND ALLOYS: POSSIBLE VIGOROUS EXOTHERMIC REACTION. HALOGENS: POSSIBLE EXOTHERMIC REACTION. MAGNESIUM AND ALLOYS: POSSIBLE VIGOROUS EXOTHERMIC REACTION. METALS AND SALTS: MAY REACT

VIGOROUSLY. OXIDIZERS (STRONG): FIRE AND EXPLOSION HAZARD. ZINC AND ALLOYS: POSSIBLE VIGOROUS EXOTHERMIC REACTION. SEE ALSO ALKENES. ALKENES: FLUORINE: SPONTANEOUS IGNITION. NITROGEN OXIDES: IGNITION. PEROXYFORMIC ACID: VIOLENT REACTION.

DECOMPOSITION: THERMAL DECOMPOSITION PRODUCTS MAY INCLUDE HIGHLY TOXIC FUMES OF PHOSGENE, TOXIC AND CORROSIVE FUMES OF CHLORIDES, AND OXIDES OF CARBON.

POLYMERIZATION: HAZARDOUS POLYMERIZATION HAS NOT BEEN REPORTED TO OCCUR UNDER NORMAL TEMPERATURES AND PRESSURES.

STORAGE AND DISPOSAL

OBSERVE ALL FEDERAL, STATE AND LOCAL REGULATIONS WHEN STORING OR DISPOSING OF THIS SUBSTANCE. FOR ASSISTANCE, CONTACT THE DISTRICT DIRECTOR OF THE ENVIRONMENTAL PROTECTION AGENCY.

STORAGE

STORE IN ACCORDANCE WITH 29 CFR 1910.106.

BONDING AND GROUNDING: SUBSTANCES WITH LOW ELECTROCONDUCTIVITY, WHICH MAY BE IGNITED BY ELECTROSTATIC SPARKS, SHOULD BE STORED IN CONTAINERS WHICH MEET THE BONDING AND GROUNDING GUIDELINES SPECIFIED IN NFPA 77-1983, RECOMMENDED PRACTICE ON STATIC ELECTRICITY.

PROTECT AGAINST PHYSICAL DAMAGE. SEPARATE FROM OTHER STORAGE. OUTSIDE OR DETACHED STORAGE IS PREFERRED. INSIDE STORAGE SHOULD BE IN A STANDARD FLAMMABLE LIQUIDS STORAGE ROOM (NFPA 49, HAZARDOUS CHEMICALS DATA, 1975).

STORE AWAY FROM INCOMPATIBLE SUBSTANCES.

DISPOSAL

DISPOSAL MUST BE IN ACCORDANCE WITH STANDARDS APPLICABLE TO GENERATORS OF HAZARDOUS WASTE, 40CFR 262. EPA HAZARDOUS WASTE NUMBER U084.

CONDITIONS TO AVOID

AVOID CONTACT WITH HEAT, SPARKS, FLAMES OR OTHER IGNITION SOURCES. VAPORS MAY BE EXPLOSIVE. MATERIAL IS CORROSIVE; AVOID CONTACT WITH SKIN OR EYES. DO NOT ALLOW CONTAMINATION OF WATER SOURCES.

SPILL AND LEAK PROCEDURES

SOIL SPILL: DIG HOLDING AREA SUCH AS LAGOON, POND OR PIT FOR CONTAINMENT. DIKE FLOW OF SPILLED MATERIAL USING SOIL OR SANDBAGS OR FOAMED BARRIERS SUCH AS POLYURETHANE OR CONCRETE.
USE CEMENT POWDER OR FLY ASH TO ABSORB LIQUID MASS.
REDUCE VAPOR AND FIRE HAZARD WITH APPROPRIATE FOAM.

AIR SPILL: APPLY WATER SPRAY TO KNOCK DOWN VAPORS.
COMBUSTION PRODUCTS INCLUDE CORROSIVE OR TOXIC VAPORS.

WATER SPILL: TRAP SPILLED MATERIAL AT BOTTOM IN DEEP WATER POCKETS, EXCAVATED HOLDING AREAS OR WITHIN SAND BAG BARRIERS.
USE SUCTION HOSES TO REMOVE TRAPPED SPILL MATERIAL.
USE MECHANICAL DREDGES OR LIFTS TO EXTRACT IMMOBILIZED MASSES OF POLLUTION AND PRECIPITATES.
THE CALIFORNIA SAFE DRINKING WATER AND TOXIC ENFORCEMENT ACT OF 1986 (PROPOSITION 65) PROHIBITS CONTAMINATING ANY KNOWN SOURCE OF DRINKING WATER WITH SUBSTANCES KNOWN TO CAUSE CANCER AND/OR REPRODUCTIVE TOXICITY.

OCCUPATIONAL SPILL: SHUT OFF IGNITION SOURCES. DO NOT TOUCH SPILLED MATERIAL. STOP LEAK IF YOU CAN DO IT WITHOUT RISK. USE WATER SPRAY TO REDUCE VAPORS. DO NOT GET WATER INSIDE CONTAINER. FOR SMALL SPILLS, TAKE UP WITH SAND OR OTHER ABSORBENT MATERIAL AND PLACE INTO CONTAINERS FOR LATER DISPOSAL. FOR LARGER SPILLS, DIKE FAR AHEAD OF SPILL FOR LATER DISPOSAL. NO SMOKING, FLAMES OR FLARES IN HAZARD AREA. KEEP UNNECESSARY PEOPLE AWAY; ISOLATE HAZARD AREA AND DENY ENTRY.
REPORTABLE QUANTITY (RQ): 100 POUNDS THE SUPERFUND AMENDMENTS AND REAUTHORIZATION ACT (SARA) SECTION 304 REQUIRES THAT A RELEASE EQUAL TO OR GREATER THAN THE REPORTABLE QUANTITY FOR THIS SUBSTANCE BE IMMEDIATELY REPORTED TO THE LOCAL EMERGENCY PLANNING COMMITTEE AND THE STATE EMERGENCY RESPONSE COMMISSION (40 CFR 355.40). IF THE RELEASE OF THIS SUBSTANCE IS REPORTABLE UNDER CERCLA SECTION 103, THE NATIONAL RESPONSE CENTER MUST BE NOTIFIED IMMEDIATELY AT (800) 424-8802 OR (202) 426-2675 IN THE METROPOLITAN WASHINGTON, D.C. AREA (40 CFR 302.6).

PROTECTIVE EQUIPMENT

VENTILATION: PROVIDE LOCAL EXHAUST OR PROCESS ENCLOSURE VENTILATION TO MEET THE PUBLISHED EXPOSURE LIMITS. VENTILATION EQUIPMENT MUST BE EXPLOSION-PROOF.

RESPIRATOR: THE FOLLOWING RESPIRATORS ARE RECOMMENDED BASED ON INFORMATION FOUND IN THE PHYSICAL DATA, TOXICITY AND HEALTH EFFECTS SECTIONS. THEY ARE RANKED IN ORDER FROM MINIMUM TO MAXIMUM RESPIRATORY PROTECTION. THE SPECIFIC RESPIRATOR SELECTED MUST BE BASED ON CONTAMINATION LEVELS FOUND IN THE WORK PLACE, MUST NOT EXCEED THE WORKING LIMITS OF THE RESPIRATOR AND BE JOINTLY APPROVED BY THE NATIONAL INSTITUTE FOR OCCUPATIONAL SAFETY AND HEALTH AND THE MINE SAFETY AND HEALTH ADMINISTRATION (NIOSH-MSHA).
TYPE 'C' SUPPLIED-AIR RESPIRATOR WITH A FULL FACEPIECE OPERATED IN PRESSURE-DEMAND OR OTHER POSITIVE PRESSURE MODE OR WITH A FULL FACEPIECE, HELMET OR HOOD OPERATED IN CONTINOUS-FLOW MODE.
SELF-CONTAINED BREATHING APPARATUS WITH A FULL FACEPIECE OPERATED IN PRESSURE-DEMAND OR OTHER POSITIVE PRESSURE MODE.
FOR FIREFIGHTING AND OTHER IMMEDIATELY DANGEROUS TO LIFE OR HEALTH CONDITIONS:
SELF-CONTAINED BREATHING APPARATUS WITH FULL FACEPIECE OPERATED IN PRESSURE-DEMAND OR OTHER POSITIVE PRESSURE MODE.
SUPPLIED-AIR RESPIRATOR WITH FULL FACEPIECE AND OPERATED IN PRESSURE-DEMAND OR OTHER POSITIVE PRESSURE MODE IN COMBINATION WITH AN AUXILIARY SELF-CONTAINED BREATHING APPARATUS OPERATED IN PRESSURE-DEMAND OR OTHER POSITIVE PRESSURE MODE.

CLOTHING: EMPLOYEE MUST WEAR APPROPRIATE PROTECTIVE (IMPERVIOUS) CLOTHING AND EQUIPMENT TO PREVENT ANY POSSIBILITY OF SKIN CONTACT WITH THIS SUBSTANCE.

GLOVES: EMPLOYEE MUST WEAR APPROPRIATE PROTECTIVE GLOVES TO PREVENT CONTACT WITH THIS SUBSTANCE.

EYE PROTECTION: EMPLOYEE MUST WEAR SPLASH-PROOF OR DUST-RESISTANT SAFETY GOGGLES AND A FACESHIELD TO PREVENT CONTACT WITH THIS SUBSTANCE.
EMERGENCY WASH FACILITIES: WHERE THERE IS ANY POSSIBILITY THAT AN EMPLOYEE'S EYES AND/OR SKIN MAY BE EXPOSED TO THIS SUBSTANCE, THE EMPLOYER SHOULD PROVIDE AN EYE WASH FOUNTAIN AND QUICK DRENCH SHOWER WITHIN THE IMMEDIATE WORK AREA FOR EMERGENCY USE.

AUTHORIZED BY- OCCUPATIONAL HEALTH SERVICES, INC.
CREATION DATE: 10/05/89 ***REVISION DATE:*** 07/12/90

MATERIAL SAFETY DATA SHEET

OCCUPATIONAL HEALTH SERVICES, INC.
AGRICULTURE AND PESTICIDE DIVISION
450 SEVENTH AVENUE, SUITE 2407
NEW YORK, NEW YORK 10123
1-800-445-MSDS OR (212) 967-1100

EMERGENCY CONTACT:
JOHN S. BRANSFORD, JR. (615) 292-1180

SUBSTANCE IDENTIFICATION

CAS-NUMBER 155-04-4

SUBSTANCE: **2-MERCAPTOBENZOTHIAZOLE, ZINC SALT**

TRADE NAMES/SYNONYMS: 2-BENZOTHIAZOLETHIOL, ZINC SALT; BANTEX; BIS(2-BENZOTHIAZOLYTHIO)ZINC; BIS(MERCAPTOBENZOTHIAZOLATO)ZINC; ZMBT; ZNBT; OXAF; PENNAC ZT; ZETAX; ZINC BENZOTHIAZOL-2-YLTHIOLATE; VULKACIT; PST27776

CHEMICAL FAMILY: THIAZOLE
ORGANOMETALLIC

MOLECULAR FORMULA: C14-H8-N2-S4-ZN

MOLECULAR WEIGHT: 397.85

CERCLA RATINGS (SCALE 0-3): HEALTH=2 FIRE=0 REACTIVITY=0 PERSISTENCE=3

NFPA RATINGS (SCALE 0-4): HEALTH=2 FIRE=0 REACTIVITY=0

COMPONENTS AND CONTAMINANTS

COMPONENT: 2-MERCAPTOBENZOTHIAZOLE, ZINC SALT ***PERCENT:*** 100
CAS# 155-04-4

OTHER CONTAMINANTS: NONE.

EXPOSURE LIMITS: 2-MERCAPTOBENZOTHIAZOLE, ZINC SALT: NO OCCUPATIONAL EXPOSURE LIMITS ESTABLISHED BY OSHA, ACGIH, OR NIOSH.
SUBJECT TO SARA SECTION 313 ANNUAL TOXIC CHEMICAL RELEASE REPORTING

PHYSICAL DATA

DESCRIPTION: ODORLESS, LIGHT YELLOW TO CREAM-COLORED POWDER.

MELTING POINT: DECOMPOSES ***SPECIFIC GRAVITY:*** 1.70 @ 25 C

SOLUBILITY IN WATER: INSOLUBLE

FIRE AND EXPLOSION DATA

FIRE AND EXPLOSION HAZARD: NEGLIGIBLE FIRE HAZARD WHEN EXPOSED TO HEAT OR FLAME. DUST-AIR MIXTURES MAY IGNITE OR EXPLODE.

FIREFIGHTING MEDIA: DRY CHEMICAL, CARBON DIOXIDE, HALON, WATER SPRAY OR STANDARD FOAM (1987 EMERGENCY RESPONSE GUIDEBOOK, DOT P 5800.4). FOR LARGER FIRES, USE WATER SPRAY, FOG OR STANDARD FOAM (1987 EMERGENCY RESPONSE GUIDEBOOK, DOT P 5800.4).

FIREFIGHTING: MOVE CONTAINER FROM FIRE AREA IF POSSIBLE. DO NOT SCATTER SPILLED MATERIAL WITH HIGH PRESSURE WATER STREAMS. DIKE FIRE CONTROL WATER FOR LATER DISPOSAL (1987 EMERGENCY RESPONSE GUIDEBOOK, DOT P 5800.4, GUIDE PAGE 31).
USE AGENTS SUITABLE FOR TYPE OF SURROUNDING FIRE. AVOID BREATHING HAZARDOUS VAPORS, KEEP UPWIND.

TOXICITY

2-MERCAPTOBENZOTHIAZOLE, ZINC SALT: TOXICITY DATA: 540 MG/KG ORAL-RAT LD50; 200 MG/KG INTRAPERITONEAL-MOUSE LD50; TUMORIGENIC DATA (RTECS). CARCINOGEN STATUS: NONE. ACUTE TOXICITY LEVEL: MODERATELY TOXIC BY INGESTION. TARGET EFFECTS: SENSITIZER- SKIN.

HEALTH EFFECTS AND FIRST AID

INHALATION: 2-MERCAPTOBENZOTHIAZOLE, ZINC SALT: **ACUTE EXPOSURE-** NO DATA AVAILABLE. DUST MAY BE IRRITATING. **CHRONIC EXPOSURE-** NO DATA AVAILABLE.

FIRST AID- REMOVE FROM EXPOSURE AREA TO FRESH AIR IMMEDIATELY. IF BREATHING HAS STOPPED, PERFORM ARTIFICIAL RESPIRATION. KEEP PERSON WARM AND AT REST. TREAT SYMPTOMATICALLY AND SUPPORTIVELY. GET MEDICAL ATTENTION IMMEDIATELY.

SKIN CONTACT: 2-MERCAPTOBENZOTHIAZOLE, ZINC SALT: SENSITIZER. **ACUTE EXPOSURE-** MAY BE IRRITATING. SENSITIZATION DERMATITIS MAY OCCUR IN PERSONS PREVIOUSLY EXPOSED. **CHRONIC EXPOSURE-** REPEATED CONTACT MAY LEAD TO SENSITIZATION DERMATITIS.

FIRST AID- REMOVE CONTAMINATED CLOTHING AND SHOES IMMEDIATELY. WASH AFFECTED AREA WITH SOAP OR MILD DETERGENT AND LARGE AMOUNTS OF WATER UNTIL NO EVIDENCE OF CHEMICAL REMAINS (APPROXIMATELY 15-20 MINUTES). GET MEDICAL ATTENTION IMMEDIATELY.

EYE CONTACT: 2-MERCAPTOBENZOTHIAZOLE, ZINC SALT: **ACUTE EXPOSURE-** NO DATA AVAILABLE FOR THIS SALT. HOWEVER, MERCAPTOBENZOTHIAZOLE IS VERY IRRITATING. **CHRONIC EXPOSURE-** NO DATA AVAILABLE.

FIRST AID- WASH EYES IMMEDIATELY WITH LARGE AMOUNTS OF WATER OR NORMAL SALINE, OCCASIONALLY LIFTING UPPER AND LOWER LIDS, UNTIL NO EVIDENCE OF CHEMICAL REMAINS (APPROXIMATELY 15-20 MINUTES). GET MEDICAL ATTENTION IMMEDIATELY.

INGESTION: 2-MERCAPTOBENZOTHIAZOLE, ZINC SALT: **ACUTE EXPOSURE-** MAY CAUSE NAUSEA AND VOMITING. 540 MG/KG WAS LETHAL TO 50% OF RATS TESTED. **CHRONIC EXPOSURE-** NO DATA AVAILABLE.

FIRST AID- IF VICTIM IS CONSCIOUS, IMMEDIATELY GIVE 2 TO 4 GLASSES OF WATER, AND INDUCE VOMITING BY TOUCHING FINGER TO BACK OF THROAT. GET MEDICAL ATTENTION IMMEDIATELY.

REACTIVITY

REACTIVITY: STABLE UNDER NORMAL TEMPERATURES AND PRESSURES.

INCOMPATIBILITIES: NONE KNOWN.

DECOMPOSITION: THERMAL DECOMPOSITION PRODUCTS MAY INCLUDE ZINC FUMES AND TOXIC OXIDES OF SULFUR AND NITROGEN.

POLYMERIZATION: HAZARDOUS POLYMERIZATION HAS NOT BEEN REPORTED TO OCCUR UNDER NORMAL TEMPERATURES AND PRESSURES.

CONDITIONS TO AVOID

MAY BURN BUT DOES NOT IGNITE READILY. AVOID CONTACT WITH STRONG OXIDIZERS, EXCESSIVE HEAT, SPARKS, OR OPEN FLAME.

SPILL AND LEAK PROCEDURES

OCCUPATIONAL SPILL: SWEEP UP AND PLACE IN SUITABLE CLEAN, DRY CONTAINERS FOR RECLAMATION OR LATER DISPOSAL. DO NOT FLUSH SPILLED MATERIAL INTO SEWER. KEEP UNNECESSARY PEOPLE AWAY.

PROTECTIVE EQUIPMENT

VENTILATION: PROVIDE LOCAL EXHAUST VENTILATION AND/OR GENERAL DILUTION VENTILATION TO MEET PUBLISHED EXPOSURE LIMITS.

RESPIRATOR: HIGH LEVELS- HIGH-EFFICIENCY PARTICULATE RESPIRATOR. SUPPLIED-AIR RESPIRATOR. SELF-CONTAINED BREATHING APPARATUS.
FIRE FIGHTING- SELF-CONTAINED BREATHING APPARATUS WITH A FULL FACEPIECE, OPERATED IN PRESSURE-DEMAND OR OTHER POSITIVE PRESSURE MODE.

CLOTHING: EMPLOYEE MUST WEAR APPROPRIATE PROTECTIVE (IMPERVIOUS) CLOTHING AND EQUIPMENT TO PREVENT REPEATED OR PROLONGED SKIN CONTACT WITH THIS SUBSTANCE.

GLOVES: EMPLOYEE MUST WEAR APPROPRIATE PROTECTIVE GLOVES TO PREVENT CONTACT WITH THIS SUBSTANCE.

EYE PROTECTION: EMPLOYEE MUST WEAR SPLASH-PROOF OR DUST-RESISTANT SAFETY GOGGLES TO PREVENT EYE CONTACT WITH THIS SUBSTANCE.
EMERGENCY EYE WASH: WHERE THERE IS ANY POSSIBILITY THAT AN EMPLOYEE'S EYES MAY BE EXPOSED TO THIS SUBSTANCE, THE EMPLOYER SHOULD PROVIDE AN EYE WASH FOUNTAIN WITHIN THE IMMEDIATE WORK AREA FOR EMERGENCY USE.

AUTHORIZED BY- OCCUPATIONAL HEALTH SERVICES, INC.
CREATION DATE: 10/05/89 *REVISION DATE:* 05/31/90

MATERIAL SAFETY DATA SHEET

OCCUPATIONAL HEALTH SERVICES, INC.
AGRICULTURE AND PESTICIDE DIVISION
450 SEVENTH AVENUE, SUITE 2407
NEW YORK, NEW YORK 10123
1-800-445-MSDS OR (212) 967-1100

EMERGENCY CONTACT:
JOHN S. BRANSFORD, JR. (615) 292-1180

SUBSTANCE IDENTIFICATION

CAS-NUMBER 94-74-6

SUBSTANCE: **MCPA**

TRADE NAMES/SYNONYMS: (4-CHLORO-2-METHYLPHENOXY)ACETIC ACID; ((4-CHLORO-ORTHO-TOLYL)OXY)ACETIC ACID; 2-METHYL-4-CHLOROPHENOXYACETIC ACID; AGROXON; AGROXONE; ANICON KOMBI; ANICON M; BETA-SELEKTONON M; CHWASTOX 30; CHWASTOX F; DICOPUR M; EMCEPAN; HEDAPUR M 52; 2M-4CH; MCP; MEPHANAC; METAXON; METHOXONE; NETAZOL; OKULTIN M; PST27880

CHEMICAL FAMILY: HALOGEN COMPOUND, AROMATIC CARBOXYLIC ACID, AROMATIC

MOLECULAR FORMULA: C9-H9-CL-O3

MOLECULAR WEIGHT: 200.63

CERCLA RATINGS (SCALE 0-3): HEALTH=2 FIRE=0 REACTIVITY=0 PERSISTENCE=3

NFPA RATINGS (SCALE 0-4): HEALTH=2 FIRE=0 REACTIVITY=0

COMPONENTS AND CONTAMINANTS

COMPONENT: MCPA *PERCENT:* 100.0
CAS# 94-74-6

OTHER CONTAMINANTS: NONE

EXPOSURE LIMITS: NO OCCUPATIONAL EXPOSURE LIMITS ESTABLISHED BY OSHA, ACGIH, OR NIOSH.

PHYSICAL DATA

DESCRIPTION: WHITE CRYSTALLINE POWDER OR FLAKES

MELTING POINT: 244-246 F (118-119 C) *SPECIFIC GRAVITY:* 1.56

SOLUBILITY IN WATER: .08%

SOLVENT SOLUBILITY: SOLUBLE IN ETHANOL, ETHYL ETHER, TOLUENE, AND XYLENE; SLIGHTLY SOLUBLE IN HEPTANE; INSOLUBLE IN CARBON DISULPHIDE

FIRE AND EXPLOSION DATA

FIRE AND EXPLOSION HAZARD: NEGLIGIBLE FIRE HAZARD WHEN EXPOSED TO HEAT OR FLAME.

FIREFIGHTING MEDIA: DRY CHEMICAL, CARBON DIOXIDE, HALON, WATER SPRAY OR STANDARD FOAM (1987 EMERGENCY RESPONSE GUIDEBOOK, DOT P 5800.4). FOR LARGER FIRES, USE WATER SPRAY, FOG OR STANDARD FOAM (1987 EMERGENCY RESPONSE GUIDEBOOK, DOT P 5800.4).

FIREFIGHTING: NO ACUTE HAZARD. MOVE CONTAINER FROM FIRE AREA IF POSSIBLE. AVOID BREATHING VAPORS OR DUSTS; KEEP UPWIND.

TOXICITY

MCPA: TOXICITY DATA: 814 MG/KG ORAL-MAN LDLO; 700 MG/KG ORAL-RAT LD50; 439 MG/KG ORAL-MOUSE LD50; 700 MG/KG ORAL-GUINEA PIG LD50; 28 MG/KG SUBCUTANEOUS-MOUSE LDLO; 28 MG/KG INTRAVENOUS-MOUSE LD50; MUTAGENIC DATA (RTECS); REPRODUCTIVE EFFECTS DATA (RTECS). CARCINOGEN STATUS: HUMAN LIMITED EVIDENCE (IARC GROUP-2B FOR CHLOROPHENOXY

HERBICIDES). STUDIES REVEALED A SIGNIFICANT INCREASE IN SOFT-TISSUE SARCOMAS, MALIGNANT LYMPHOMAS AND BRONCHIAL CARCINOMAS IN WORKERS EXPOSED TO CHLOROPHENOXY HERBICIDES. LOCAL EFFECTS: IRRITANT- EYES. ACUTE TOXICITY LEVEL: MODERATELY TOXIC BY INGESTION. TARGET EFFECTS: NO DATA AVAILABLE. ADDITIONAL DATA: MAY CROSS THE PLACENTA.

HEALTH EFFECTS AND FIRST AID

INHALATION: MCPA: A FEW WEEKS AFTER USING THIS MATERIAL, ONE INDIVIDUAL DEVELOPED APLASTIC ANEMIA WITH SYMPTOMS OF MUSCULAR WEAKNESS, HEMORRHAGIC GASTRITIS AND PANCYTOPENIA ASSOCIATED WITH SLIGHTLY IMPAIRED LIVER FUNCTION. TWELVE MONTHS AFTER EXPOSURE, HE DEVELOPED ACUTE MYELOMONOCYTIC LEUKEMIA FROM WHICH HE LATER DIED. SEE INFORMATION ON CHLOROPHENOXY COMPOUNDS.

CHLOROPHENOXY COMPOUNDS: **ACUTE EXPOSURE-** MAY CAUSE IRRITATION WITH SORE THROAT AND BURNING SENSATIONS IN THE NASOPHARYNX AND CHEST, COUGHING, LACRIMATION, RHINITIS, DULLNESS, DIZZINESS, AND ATAXIA. IF SUFFICIENT AMOUNTS ARE ABSORBED THROUGH THE LUNGS, EFFECTS AS DESCRIBED IN ACUTE INGESTION MAY OCCUR. **CHRONIC EXPOSURE-** EPIDEMIOLOGICAL STUDIES REVEALED A SIGNIFICANT INCREASE IN SOFT-TISSUE SARCOMAS, MALIGNANT LYMPHOMAS AND BRONCHIAL CARCINOMAS IN WORKERS EXPOSED TO CHLOROPHENOXY HERBICIDES.

FIRST AID- REMOVE FROM EXPOSURE AREA TO FRESH AIR IMMEDIATELY. IF BREATHING HAS STOPPED, PERFORM ARTIFICIAL RESPIRATION. KEEP PERSON WARM AND AT REST. TREAT SYMPTOMATICALLY AND SUPPORTIVELY. GET MEDICAL ATTENTION IMMEDIATELY.

SKIN CONTACT: MCPA: DAILY APPLICATION OF RATES OF 2,000 AND 1,000 MG/KG TO THE SKINS OF RABBITS PRODUCED MODERATE ERYTHEMA, LOSS OF ELASTICITY OF THE SKIN, HIGH MORTALITY, WEIGHT LOSS, AND HISTOLOGICAL CHANGES IN THE LIVER, KIDNEYS, SPLEEN AND THYMUS. SEE INFORMATION ON CHLOROPHENOXY COMPOUNDS.

CHLOROPHENOXY COMPOUNDS: **ACUTE EXPOSURE-** MAY CAUSE IRRITATION. IF SUFFICIENT AMOUNTS ARE ABSORBED THROUGH THE SKIN, EFFECTS AS DESCRIBED IN ACUTE INGESTION MAY OCCUR. **CHRONIC EXPOSURE-** PROLONGED OR REPEATED CONTACT MAY CAUSED DERMATITIS. EPIDEMIOLOGICAL STUDIES REVEALED A SIGNIFICANT INCREASE IN SOFT-TISSUE SARCOMAS, MALIGNANT LYMPHOMAS AND BRONCHIAL CARCINOMAS IN WORKERS EXPOSED TO CHLOROPHENOXY HERBICIDES.

FIRST AID- REMOVE CONTAMINATED CLOTHING AND SHOES IMMEDIATELY. WASH AFFECTED AREA WITH SOAP OR MILD DETERGENT AND LARGE AMOUNTS OF WATER UNTIL NO EVIDENCE OF CHEMICAL REMAINS (APPROXIMATELY 15-20 MINUTES). GET MEDICAL ATTENTION IMMEDIATELY.

EYE CONTACT: MCPA: IRRITANT: **ACUTE EXPOSURE-** MAY CAUSE IRRITATION AND POSSIBLY SERIOUS INJURY TO THE EYES. **CHRONIC EXPOSURE-** PROLONGED OR REPEATED EXPOSURE TO IRRITANTS MAY CAUSE CONJUNCTIVITIS.

FIRST AID- WASH EYES IMMEDIATELY WITH LARGE AMOUNTS OF WATER OR NORMAL SALINE, OCCASIONALLY LIFTING UPPER AND LOWER LIDS, UNTIL NO EVIDENCE OF CHEMICAL REMAINS (APPROXIMATELY 15-20 MINUTES). GET MEDICAL ATTENTION IMMEDIATELY.

INGESTION: MCPA: THIS MATERIAL PRODUCED REDUCED SPERMATOGENESIS AND TUBULAR ATROPHY IN THE TESTES IN MALE RATS AND DOGS. CHRONIC INGESTION BY PREGNANT MICE RESULTED IN FETOTOXICITY, FETAL DEVELOPMENTAL ABNORMALITIES, AND ADVERSE EFFECTS ON FERTILITY. SEE INFORMATION ON CHLOROPHENOXY COMPOUNDS.

CHLOROPHENOXY COMPOUNDS: **ACUTE EXPOSURE-** MAY CAUSE IRRITATION OF THE MOUTH, THROAT, AND GASTROINTESTINAL TRACT, NAUSEA, VOMITING, CHEST AND ABDOMINAL PAIN, AND DIARRHEA. INGESTION OF VERY LARGE DOSES MAY PRODUCE METABOLIC ACIDOSIS, FEVER OR SUBNORMAL TEMPERATURES, HYPERVENTILATION, HYPOTENSION, VASODILATION, FLUSHING OF THE SKIN, SWEATING, CARDIAC ARRHYTHMIAS, TACHYCARDIA, LETHARGY, WEAKNESS, INTERCOSTAL PARALYSIS, RENAL AND HEPATIC DYSFUNCTION, MYOTONIA, COMA, AND CONVULSIONS. DAMAGE TO SKELETAL MUSCLE MAY BE MANIFEST BY MUSCLE TWITCHING AND ACHING WITH ELEVATED SERUM ENZYMES AND MYOGLOBIN IN THE BLOOD AND URINE. DEATH MAY BE DUE TO CIRCULATORY COLLAPSE. **CHRONIC EXPOSURE-** NO DATA AVAILABLE.

FIRST AID- IF THE PERSON IS CONSCIOUS AND NOT CONVULSING, INDUCE EMESIS BY GIVING SYRUP OF IPECAC (KEEPING THE HEAD BELOW THE HIPS TO PREVENT ASPIRATION) FOLLOWED BY WATER. REPEAT IN 20 MINUTES IF NOT EFFECTIVE INITIALLY. IN PATIENTS WITH DEPRESSED RESPIRATION OR IF EMESIS IS NOT PRODUCED, PERFORM GASTRIC LAVAGE WITH ACTIVATED CHARCOAL. FOLLOW WITH A SALINE CATHARTIC (DREISBACH, HANDBOOK OF POISONING, 12TH ED.). TREAT SYMPTOMATICALLY AND SUPPORTIVELY. GASTRIC LAVAGE SHOULD BE PERFORMED BY QUALIFIED MEDICAL PERSONNEL. GET MEDICAL ATTENTION IMMEDIATELY.

ANTIDOTE: NO SPECIFIC ANTIDOTE. TREAT SYMPTOMATICALLY AND SUPPORTIVELY.

REACTIVITY

REACTIVITY: STABLE UNDER NORMAL TEMPERATURES AND PRESSURES.

INCOMPATIBILITIES: MCPA: NO DATA AVAILABLE.

DECOMPOSITION: THERMAL DECOMPOSITION MAY RELEASE CORROSIVE FUMES OF HYDROGEN CHLORIDE AND TOXIC OXIDES OF CARBON.

POLYMERIZATION: HAZARDOUS POLYMERIZATION HAS NOT BEEN REPORTED TO OCCUR UNDER NORMAL TEMPERATURES AND PRESSURES.

STORAGE AND DISPOSAL

OBSERVE ALL FEDERAL, STATE AND LOCAL REGULATIONS WHEN STORING OR DISPOSING OF THIS SUBSTANCE. FOR ASSISTANCE, CONTACT THE DISTRICT DIRECTOR OF THE ENVIRONMENTAL PROTECTION AGENCY.

STORAGE

STORE IN ACCORDANCE WITH 40 CFR 165 RECOMMENDED PROCEDURES FOR THE DISPOSAL AND STORAGE OF PESTICIDES AND PESTICIDE CONTAINERS.

DISPOSAL

DISPOSAL MUST BE IN ACCORDANCE WITH 40 CFR 165 RECOMMENDED PROCEDURES FOR THE DISPOSAL AND STORAGE OF PESTICIDES AND PESTICIDE CONTAINERS.

CONDITIONS TO AVOID

NONE REPORTED.

SPILL AND LEAK PROCEDURES

OCCUPATIONAL SPILL: SWEEP UP AND PLACE IN SUITABLE (FIBERBOARD) CONTAINERS FOR RECLAMATION OR LATER DISPOSAL.

PROTECTIVE EQUIPMENT

VENTILATION: PROVIDE LOCAL EXHAUST OR GENERAL DILUTION VENTILATION SYSTEM.

RESPIRATOR: THE FOLLOWING RESPIRATORS ARE RECOMMENDED BASED ON INFORMATION FOUND IN THE PHYSICAL DATA, TOXICITY AND HEALTH EFFECTS SECTIONS. THEY ARE RANKED IN ORDER FROM MINIMUM TO MAXIMUM RESPIRATORY PROTECTION. THE SPECIFIC RESPIRATOR SELECTED MUST BE BASED ON CONTAMINATION LEVELS FOUND IN THE WORK PLACE, MUST NOT EXCEED THE WORKING LIMITS OF THE RESPIRATOR AND BE JOINTLY APPROVED BY THE NATIONAL INSTITUTE FOR OCCUPATIONAL SAFETY AND HEALTH AND THE MINE SAFETY AND HEALTH ADMINISTRATION (NIOSH-MSHA).

CHEMICAL CARTRIDGE RESPIRATOR WITH AN ORGANIC VAPOR CARTRIDGE(S) WITH A FULL FACEPIECE AND ORGANIC VAPOR CARTRIDGE(S) IN COMBINATION WITH A DUST AND MIST FILTER.

POWERED AIR-PURIFYING RESPIRATOR WITH A TIGHT-FITTING FACEPIECE AND ORGANIC VAPOR CARTRIDGE(S) IN COMBINATION WITH A HIGH-EFFICIENCY PARTICULATE FILTER.

TYPE 'C' SUPPLIED-AIR RESPIRATOR WITH A FULL FACEPIECE OPERATED IN A PRESSURE-DEMAND OR OTHER POSITIVE PRESSURE MODE.

SELF-CONTAINED BREATHING APPARATUS WITH A FULL FACEPIECE OPERATED IN PRESSURE-DEMAND OR OTHER POSITIVE PRESSURE MODE.

FOR FIREFIGHTING AND OTHER IMMEDIATELY DANGEROUS TO LIFE OR HEALTH CONDITIONS:

SELF-CONTAINED BREATHING APPARATUS WITH FULL FACEPIECE OPERATED IN PRESSURE-DEMAND OR OTHER POSITIVE PRESSURE MODE.

SUPPLIED-AIR RESPIRATOR WITH FULL FACEPIECE AND OPERATED IN PRESSURE-DEMAND OR OTHER POSITIVE PRESSURE MODE IN COMBINATION WITH AN AUXILIARY SELF-CONTAINED BREATHING APPARATUS OPERATED IN PRESSURE-DEMAND OR OTHER POSITIVE PRESSURE MODE.

CLOTHING: EMPLOYEE MUST WEAR APPROPRIATE PROTECTIVE (IMPERVIOUS) CLOTHING AND EQUIPMENT TO PREVENT REPEATED OR PROLONGED SKIN CONTACT WITH THIS SUBSTANCE.

GLOVES: EMPLOYEE MUST WEAR APPROPRIATE PROTECTIVE GLOVES TO PREVENT CONTACT WITH THIS SUBSTANCE.

EYE PROTECTION: EMPLOYEE MUST WEAR SPLASH-PROOF OR DUST-RESISTANT SAFETY GOGGLES TO PREVENT EYE CONTACT WITH THIS SUBSTANCE.

EMERGENCY EYE WASH: WHERE THERE IS ANY POSSIBILITY THAT AN EMPLOYEE'S EYES MAY BE EXPOSED TO THIS SUBSTANCE, THE EMPLOYER SHOULD PROVIDE AN EYE WASH FOUNTAIN WITHIN THE IMMEDIATE WORK AREA FOR EMERGENCY USE.

AUTHORIZED BY- OCCUPATIONAL HEALTH SERVICES, INC.

CREATION DATE: 10/04/89 ***REVISION DATE:*** 07/12/90

MATERIAL SAFETY DATA SHEET

OCCUPATIONAL HEALTH SERVICES, INC.
AGRICULTURE AND PESTICIDE DIVISION
450 SEVENTH AVENUE, SUITE 2407
NEW YORK, NEW YORK 10123
1-800-445-MSDS OR (212) 967-1100

EMERGENCY CONTACT:
JOHN S. BRANSFORD, JR. (615) 292-1180

SUBSTANCE IDENTIFICATION

CAS-NUMBER 2436-73-9

SUBSTANCE: **MCPA METHYL ESTER**

TRADE NAMES/SYNONYMS: ACETIC ACID, (4-CHLORO-2-METHYLPHENOXY)-, METHYL ESTER; (4-CHLORO-2-METHYLPHENOXY)METHYL ACETATE; ACETIC ACID, ((4-CHLORO-O-TOLYL)OXY)-, METHYL ESTER; ((4-CHLORO-O-TOLYL)OXY)METHYL ACETATE; MCP METHYL ESTER; METHYL 4-CHLORO-2-METHYLPHENOXY ACETATE; (4-CHLORO-2-METHYLPHENOXY) ACETIC ACID, METHYL ESTER; ((4-CHLORO-O-TOLY)OXY) ACETIC ACID, METHYL ESTER; C10H11CLO3; PST27881

CHEMICAL FAMILY: HALOGEN COMPOUND, AROMATIC ESTER, NON-CARBOXYLIC

MOLECULAR FORMULA: C6-H3-(CL)-(C-H3)-(O-C-H2-C-O-O-C-H3)

MOLECULAR WEIGHT: 214.65

CERCLA RATINGS (SCALE 0-3): HEALTH=3 FIRE=1 REACTIVITY=0 PERSISTENCE=2

NFPA RATINGS (SCALE 0-4): HEALTH=U FIRE=1 REACTIVITY=0

COMPONENTS AND CONTAMINANTS

COMPONENT: MCPA METHYL ESTER ***PERCENT:*** 100.0
CAS# 2436-73-9

OTHER CONTAMINANTS: NONE

EXPOSURE LIMITS: NO OCCUPATIONAL EXPOSURE LIMITS ESTABLISHED BY OSHA, ACGIH, OR NIOSH.

PHYSICAL DATA

DESCRIPTION: WHITE CRYSTALS. ***MELTING POINT:*** 64 F (18 C) (APPROX.)

SPECIFIC GRAVITY: NOT AVAILABLE ***SOLUBILITY IN WATER:*** NOT AVAILABLE

SOLVENT SOLUBILITY: SOLUBLE IN METHANOL, ACETONE AND CHLOROFORM.

FIRE AND EXPLOSION DATA

FIRE AND EXPLOSION HAZARD: SLIGHT FIRE HAZARD WHEN EXPOSED TO HEAT OR FLAME.
DUST-AIR MIXTURES MAY IGNITE OR EXPLODE.

FIREFIGHTING MEDIA: DRY CHEMICAL, CARBON DIOXIDE, HALON, WATER SPRAY OR STANDARD FOAM (1987 EMERGENCY RESPONSE GUIDEBOOK, DOT P 5800.4).
FOR LARGER FIRES, USE WATER SPRAY, FOG OR STANDARD FOAM (1987 EMERGENCY RESPONSE GUIDEBOOK, DOT P 5800.4).

FIREFIGHTING: MOVE CONTAINER FROM FIRE AREA IF POSSIBLE. DO NOT SCATTER SPILLED MATERIAL WITH HIGH PRESSURE WATER STREAMS. DIKE FIRE CONTROL WATER FOR LATER DISPOSAL (1987 EMERGENCY RESPONSE GUIDEBOOK, DOT P 5800.4, GUIDE PAGE 31).
USE AGENTS SUITABLE FOR TYPE OF SURROUNDING FIRE. AVOID BREATHING HAZARDOUS VAPORS, KEEP UPWIND.

TOXICITY

MCPA METHYL ESTER: TOXICITY DATA: 700 MG/KG ORAL-RAT LD50 (EPA). CARCINOGEN STATUS: HUMAN LIMITED EVIDENCE (IARC GROUP-2B FOR CHLOROPHENOXY HERBICIDES). STUDIES REVEALED A SIGNIFICANT INCREASE IN SOFT-TISSUE SARCOMAS, MALIGNANT LYMPHOMAS AND BRONCHIAL CARCINOMAS IN WORKERS EXPOSED TO CHLOROPHENOXY HERBICIDES. ACUTE TOXICITY LEVEL: MODERATELY TOXIC BY INGESTION. TARGET EFFECTS: POISONING MAY AFFECT THE CARDIOVASCULAR SYSTEM. ADDITIONAL DATA: MAY CROSS THE PLACENTA.

HEALTH EFFECTS AND FIRST AID

INHALATION: MCPA METHYL ESTER SEE INFORMATION ON CHLOROPHENOXY COMPOUNDS.
CHLOROPHENOXY COMPOUNDS: **ACUTE EXPOSURE-** MAY CAUSE IRRITATION WITH SORE THROAT AND BURNING SENSATIONS IN THE NASOPHARYNX AND CHEST, COUGHING, LACRIMATION, RHINITIS, DULLNESS, DIZZINESS, AND ATAXIA. IF SUFFICIENT AMOUNTS ARE ABSORBED THROUGH THE LUNGS, EFFECTS AS DESCRIBED IN ACUTE INGESTION MAY OCCUR. **CHRONIC EXPOSURE-** EPIDEMIOLOGICAL STUDIES REVEALED A SIGNIFICANT INCREASE IN SOFT-TISSUE SARCOMAS, MALIGNANT LYMPHOMAS AND BRONCHIAL CARCINOMAS IN WORKERS EXPOSED TO CHLOROPHENOXY HERBICIDES.

FIRST AID- REMOVE FROM EXPOSURE AREA TO FRESH AIR IMMEDIATELY. IF BREATHING HAS STOPPED, PERFORM ARTIFICIAL RESPIRATION. KEEP PERSON WARM AND AT REST. TREAT SYMPTOMATICALLY AND SUPPORTIVELY. GET MEDICAL ATTENTION IMMEDIATELY.

SKIN CONTACT: MCPA METHYL ESTER: SEE INFORMATION ON CHLOROPHENOXY COMPOUNDS.
CHLOROPHENOXY COMPOUNDS: **ACUTE EXPOSURE-** MAY CAUSE IRRITATION. IF SUFFICIENT AMOUNTS ARE ABSORBED THROUGH THE SKIN, EFFECTS AS DESCRIBED IN ACUTE INGESTION MAY OCCUR. **CHRONIC EXPOSURE-** PROLONGED OR REPEATED CONTACT MAY CAUSED DERMATITIS. EPIDEMIOLOGICAL STUDIES REVEALED A SIGNIFICANT INCREASE IN SOFT-TISSUE SARCOMAS, MALIGNANT LYMPHOMAS AND BRONCHIAL CARCINOMAS IN WORKERS EXPOSED TO CHLOROPHENOXY HERBICIDES.

FIRST AID- REMOVE CONTAMINATED CLOTHING AND SHOES IMMEDIATELY. WASH AFFECTED AREA WITH SOAP OR MILD DETERGENT AND LARGE AMOUNTS OF WATER UNTIL NO EVIDENCE OF CHEMICAL REMAINS (APPROXIMATELY 15-20 MINUTES). GET MEDICAL ATTENTION IMMEDIATELY.

EYE CONTACT: MCPA METHYL ESTER: SEE INFORMATION ON CHLOROPHENOXY COMPOUNDS.
CHLOROPHENOXY COMPOUNDS: **ACUTE EXPOSURE-** MAY CAUSE IRRITATION. **CHRONIC EXPOSURE-** NO DATA AVAILABLE.

FIRST AID- WASH EYES IMMEDIATELY WITH LARGE AMOUNTS OF WATER OR NORMAL SALINE, OCCASIONALLY LIFTING UPPER AND LOWER LIDS, UNTIL NO EVIDENCE OF CHEMICAL REMAINS (APPROXIMATELY 15-20 MINUTES). GET MEDICAL ATTENTION IMMEDIATELY.

INGESTION: MCPA METHYL ESTER: SEE INFORMATION ON CHLOROPHENOXY COMPOUNDS.
CHLOROPHENOXY COMPOUNDS: **ACUTE EXPOSURE-** MAY CAUSE IRRITATION OF THE MOUTH, THROAT, AND GASTROINTESTINAL TRACT, NAUSEA, VOMITING, CHEST AND ABDOMINAL PAIN, AND DIARRHEA. INGESTION OF VERY LARGE DOSES MAY PRODUCE METABOLIC ACIDOSIS, FEVER OR SUBNORMAL TEMPERATURES, HYPERVENTILATION, HYPOTENSION, VASODILATION, FLUSHING OF THE SKIN, SWEATING, CARDIAC ARRHYTHMIAS, TACHYCARDIA, LETHARGY, WEAKNESS, INTERCOSTAL PARALYSIS, RENAL AND HEPATIC DYSFUNCTION, MYOTONIA, COMA, AND CONVULSIONS. DAMAGE TO SKELETAL MUSCLE MAY BE MANIFEST BY MUSCLE TWITCHING AND ACHING WITH ELEVATED SERUM ENZYMES AND MYOGLOBIN IN THE BLOOD AND URINE. DEATH MAY BE DUE TO CIRCULATORY COLLAPSE. **CHRONIC EXPOSURE-** NO DATA AVAILABLE.

FIRST AID- IF THE PERSON IS CONSCIOUS AND NOT CONVULSING, INDUCE EMESIS BY GIVING SYRUP OF IPECAC (KEEPING THE HEAD BELOW THE HIPS TO PREVENT ASPIRATION) FOLLOWED BY WATER. REPEAT IN 20 MINUTES IF NOT EFFECTIVE INITIALLY. IN PATIENTS WITH DEPRESSED RESPIRATION OR IF EMESIS IS NOT PRODUCED, PERFORM GASTRIC LAVAGE WITH ACTIVATED CHARCOAL. FOLLOW WITH A SALINE CATHARTIC (DREISBACH, HANDBOOK OF POISONING, 12TH ED.). TREAT SYMPTOMATICALLY AND SUPPORTIVELY. GASTRIC LAVAGE SHOULD BE PERFORMED BY QUALIFIED MEDICAL PERSONNEL. GET MEDICAL ATTENTION IMMEDIATELY.

ANTIDOTE: NO SPECIFIC ANTIDOTE. TREAT SYMPTOMATICALLY AND SUPPORTIVELY.

REACTIVITY

REACTIVITY: STABLE UNDER NORMAL TEMPERATURES AND PRESSURES.

INCOMPATIBILITIES: MCPA METHYL ESTER: OXIDIZERS (STRONG): FIRE AND EXPLOSION HAZARD.

DECOMPOSITION: THERMAL DECOMPOSITION PRODUCTS MAY INCLUDE TOXIC AND CORROSIVE FUMES OF CHLORIDES AND TOXIC OXIDES OF CARBON.

POLYMERIZATION: HAZARDOUS POLYMERIZATION HAS NOT BEEN REPORTED TO OCCUR UNDER NORMAL TEMPERATURES AND PRESSURES.

STORAGE AND DISPOSAL

OBSERVE ALL FEDERAL, STATE AND LOCAL REGULATIONS WHEN STORING OR DISPOSING OF THIS SUBSTANCE. FOR ASSISTANCE, CONTACT THE DISTRICT DIRECTOR OF THE ENVIRONMENTAL PROTECTION AGENCY.

****STORAGE****

STORE IN ACCORDANCE WITH 40 CFR 165 RECOMMENDED PROCEDURES FOR THE DISPOSAL AND STORAGE OF PESTICIDES AND PESTICIDE CONTAINERS.
STORE AWAY FROM INCOMPATIBLE SUBSTANCES.

****DISPOSAL****

DISPOSAL MUST BE IN ACCORDANCE WITH 40 CFR 165 RECOMMENDED PROCEDURES FOR THE DISPOSAL AND STORAGE OF PESTICIDES AND PESTICIDE CONTAINERS.

CONDITIONS TO AVOID

MAY BURN BUT DOES NOT IGNITE READILY. AVOID CONTACT WITH STRONG OXIDIZERS, EXCESSIVE HEAT, SPARKS, OR OPEN FLAME.

SPILL AND LEAK PROCEDURES

OCCUPATIONAL SPILL: SWEEP UP AND PLACE IN SUITABLE CLEAN, DRY CONTAINERS FOR RECLAMATION OR LATER DISPOSAL. DO NOT FLUSH SPILLED MATERIAL INTO SEWER. KEEP UNNECESSARY PEOPLE AWAY.

PROTECTIVE EQUIPMENT

VENTILATION: PROVIDE LOCAL EXHAUST OR PROCESS ENCLOSURE VENTILATION SYSTEM.

RESPIRATOR: THE FOLLOWING RESPIRATORS ARE RECOMMENDED BASED ON INFORMATION FOUND IN THE PHYSICAL DATA, TOXICITY AND HEALTH EFFECTS SECTIONS. THEY ARE RANKED IN ORDER FROM MINIMUM TO MAXIMUM RESPIRATORY PROTECTION. THE SPECIFIC RESPIRATOR SELECTED MUST BE BASED ON CONTAMINATION LEVELS FOUND IN THE WORK PLACE, MUST NOT EXCEED THE WORKING LIMITS OF THE RESPIRATOR AND BE JOINTLY APPROVED BY THE NATIONAL INSTITUTE FOR OCCUPATIONAL SAFETY AND HEALTH AND THE MINE SAFETY AND HEALTH ADMINISTRATION (NIOSH-MSHA).

TYPE 'C' SUPPLIED-AIR RESPIRATOR WITH A FULL FACEPIECE OPERATED IN PRESSURE-DEMAND OR OTHER POSITIVE PRESSURE MODE OR WITH A FULL FACEPIECE, HELMET OR HOOD OPERATED IN CONTINOUS-FLOW MODE.

SELF-CONTAINED BREATHING APPARATUS WITH A FULL FACEPIECE OPERATED IN PRESSURE-DEMAND OR OTHER POSITIVE PRESSURE MODE.

FOR FIREFIGHTING AND OTHER IMMEDIATELY DANGEROUS TO LIFE OR HEALTH CONDITIONS:

SELF-CONTAINED BREATHING APPARATUS WITH FULL FACEPIECE OPERATED IN PRESSURE-DEMAND OR OTHER POSITIVE PRESSURE MODE.

SUPPLIED-AIR RESPIRATOR WITH FULL FACEPIECE AND OPERATED IN PRESSURE-DEMAND OR OTHER POSITIVE PRESSURE MODE IN COMBINATION WITH AN AUXILIARY SELF-CONTAINED BREATHING APPARATUS OPERATED IN PRESSURE-DEMAND OR OTHER POSITIVE PRESSURE MODE.

CLOTHING: EMPLOYEE MUST WEAR APPROPRIATE PROTECTIVE (IMPERVIOUS) CLOTHING AND EQUIPMENT TO PREVENT REPEATED OR PROLONGED SKIN CONTACT WITH THIS SUBSTANCE.

GLOVES: EMPLOYEE MUST WEAR APPROPRIATE PROTECTIVE GLOVES TO PREVENT CONTACT WITH THIS SUBSTANCE.

EYE PROTECTION: EMPLOYEE MUST WEAR SPLASH-PROOF OR DUST-RESISTANT SAFETY GOGGLES TO PREVENT EYE CONTACT WITH THIS SUBSTANCE.

EMERGENCY EYE WASH: WHERE THERE IS ANY POSSIBILITY THAT AN EMPLOYEE'S EYES MAY BE EXPOSED TO THIS SUBSTANCE, THE EMPLOYER SHOULD PROVIDE AN EYE WASH FOUNTAIN WITHIN THE IMMEDIATE WORK AREA FOR EMERGENCY USE.

AUTHORIZED BY- OCCUPATIONAL HEALTH SERVICES, INC.

CREATION DATE: 05/04/90 ***REVISION DATE:*** 07/12/90

MATERIAL SAFETY DATA SHEET

OCCUPATIONAL HEALTH SERVICES, INC.
AGRICULTURE AND PESTICIDE DIVISION
450 SEVENTH AVENUE, SUITE 2407
NEW YORK, NEW YORK 10123
1-800-445-MSDS OR (212) 967-1100

EMERGENCY CONTACT:
JOHN S. BRANSFORD, JR. (615) 292-1180

SUBSTANCE IDENTIFICATION

CAS-NUMBER 828-00-2

SUBSTANCE: **DIMETHOXANE**

TRADE NAMES/SYNONYMS: 1,3-DIOXAN-4-OL, 2,6-DIMETHYL-, ACETATE; 2,6-DIMETHYL-1,3-DIOXAN-4-OL ACETATE; M-DIOXAN-4-OL, 2,6-DIMETHYL-, ACETATE; 2,6-DIMETHYL-M-DIOXAN-4-OL ACETATE; ACETIC ACID, 2,6-DIMETHYL-M-DIOXAN-4-OL ESTER; G1V-GARD DXN; 6-ACETOXY-2,4-DIMETHYL-M-DIOXAN-4-YL ESTER; ACETOMETHOXANE; C8H14O4; PST28395

CHEMICAL FAMILY: ESTER

MOLECULAR FORMULA: C-H3-C-O-O-(C4-H6-O2)-(C-H3)2

MOLECULAR WEIGHT: 174.19

CERCLA RATINGS (SCALE 0-3): HEALTH=3 FIRE=2 REACTIVITY=0 PERSISTENCE=2

NFPA RATINGS (SCALE 0-4): HEALTH=3 FIRE=2 REACTIVITY=0

COMPONENTS AND CONTAMINANTS

COMPONENT: DIMETHOXANE ***PERCENT:*** 100.0
CAS# 828-00-2

OTHER CONTAMINANTS: NONE

EXPOSURE LIMITS: NO OCCUPATIONAL EXPOSURE LIMITS ESTABLISHED BY OSHA, ACGIH, OR NIOSH.

PHYSICAL DATA

DESCRIPTION: CLEAR YELLOW TO LIGHT AMBER LIQUID WITH A MUSTARD-LIKE ODOR.

BOILING POINT: 165-167 F (74-75 C) @ 6 MMHG ***MELTING POINT:*** <-13 F (<-25 C)

SPECIFIC GRAVITY: 1.069-1.076 @ 25 C ***VAPOR PRESSURE:*** NOT AVAILABLE

EVAPORATION RATE: NOT AVAILABLE ***SOLUBILITY IN WATER:*** SOLUBLE

SOLVENT SOLUBILITY: SOLUBLE IN ORGANIC SOLVENTS AND ALCOHOL.

FIRE AND EXPLOSION DATA

FIRE AND EXPLOSION HAZARD: MODERATE FIRE HAZARD WHEN EXPOSED TO HEAT OR FLAME.

FLASH POINT: 142 F (61 C) ***FLAMMABILITY CLASS(OSHA):*** IIIA

FIREFIGHTING MEDIA: DRY CHEMICAL, CARBON DIOXIDE, HALON, WATER SPRAY OR STANDARD FOAM (1987 EMERGENCY RESPONSE GUIDEBOOK, DOT P 5800.4). FOR LARGER FIRES, USE WATER SPRAY, FOG OR STANDARD FOAM (1987 EMERGENCY RESPONSE GUIDEBOOK, DOT P 5800.4).

FIREFIGHTING: MOVE CONTAINER FROM FIRE AREA IF POSSIBLE. COOL FIRE-EXPOSED CONTAINERS WITH WATER FROM SIDE UNTIL WELL AFTER FIRE IS OUT. STAY AWAY FROM STORAGE TANK ENDS. FOR MASSIVE FIRE IN STORAGE AREA, USE UNMANNED HOSE HOLDER OR MONITOR NOZZLES, ELSE WITHDRAW FROM AREA AND LET FIRE BURN. WITHDRAW IMMEDIATELY IN CASE OF RISING SOUND FROM VENTING SAFETY DEVICE OR ANY DISCOLORATION OF STORAGE TANK DUE TO FIRE (1987 EMERGENCY RESPONSE GUIDEBOOK, DOT P 5800.4, GUIDE PAGE 27). EXTINGUISH ONLY IF FLOW CAN BE STOPPED; USE FLOODING AMOUNTS OF WATER AS A FOG, SOLID STREAMS MAY BE INEFFECTIVE. COOL CONTAINERS WITH FLOODING AMOUNTS OF WATER, APPLY FROM AS FAR A DISTANCE AS POSSIBLE. AVOID BREATHING VAPORS, KEEP UPWIND.

TRANSPORTATION DATA

DEPARTMENT OF TRANSPORTATION HAZARD CLASSIFICATION 49 CFR 172.101: COMBUSTIBLE LIQUID

DEPARTMENT OF TRANSPORTATION LABELING REQUIREMENTS 49 CFR 172.101 AND SUBPART E: NONE

DEPARTMENT OF TRANSPORTATION PACKAGING REQUIREMENTS: NONE EXCEPTIONS: 49 CFR 173.118A

TOXICITY

DIMETHOXANE: TOXICITY DATA: 1930 MG/KG ORAL-RAT LD50; MUTAGENIC DATA (RTECS); TUMORIGENIC DATA (RTECS). CARCINOGEN STATUS: ANIMAL LIMITED EVIDENCE (IARC GROUP-3). DIMETHOXANE IS CARCINOGENIC IN MALE RATS AFTER ITS ORAL ADMINISTRATION, THE ONLY SPECIES, SEX AND ROUTE TESTED; IT PRODUCED MALIGNANT TUMORS PREDOMINATELY IN THE LIVER. ACUTE TOXICITY LEVEL: MODERATELY TOXIC BY INGESTION. TARGET EFFECTS: NO DATA AVAILABLE.

HEALTH EFFECTS AND FIRST AID

INHALATION: DIMETHOXANE: **ACUTE EXPOSURE-** NO DATA AVAILABLE. **CHRONIC EXPOSURE-** NO DATA AVAILABLE.

FIRST AID- REMOVE FROM EXPOSURE AREA TO FRESH AIR IMMEDIATELY. IF BREATHING HAS STOPPED, PERFORM ARTIFICIAL RESPIRATION. KEEP PERSON WARM AND AT REST. TREAT SYMPTOMATICALLY AND SUPPORTIVELY. GET MEDICAL ATTENTION IMMEDIATELY.

SKIN CONTACT: DIMETHOXANE: **ACUTE EXPOSURE-** CONTACT MAY CAUSE IRRITATION. **CHRONIC EXPOSURE-** ALLERGIC SENSITIZATION HAS BEEN REPORTED WITH COMMERCIAL DIMETHOXANE. HOWEVER, PATCH TEST RESULTS SUGGEST THAT THIS MAY BE DUE TO CONTAMINANTS.

FIRST AID- REMOVE CONTAMINATED CLOTHING AND SHOES IMMEDIATELY. WASH AFFECTED AREA WITH SOAP OR MILD DETERGENT AND LARGE AMOUNTS OF WATER UNTIL NO EVIDENCE OF CHEMICAL REMAINS (APPROXIMATELY 15-20 MINUTES). GET MEDICAL ATTENTION IMMEDIATELY.

EYE CONTACT: DIMETHOXANE: **ACUTE EXPOSURE-** CONTACT MAY CAUSE IRRITATION. **CHRONIC EXPOSURE-** NO DATA AVAILABLE.

FIRST AID- WASH EYES IMMEDIATELY WITH LARGE AMOUNTS OF WATER OR NORMAL SALINE, OCCASIONALLY LIFTING UPPER AND LOWER LIDS, UNTIL NO EVIDENCE OF CHEMICAL REMAINS (APPROXIMATELY 15-20 MINUTES). GET MEDICAL ATTENTION IMMEDIATELY.

INGESTION: DIMETHOXANE: LIMITED ANIMAL CARCINOGEN. **ACUTE EXPOSURE-** INGESTION OF 1930 MG/KG WAS LETHAL TO HALF OF THE RATS TESTED. **CHRONIC EXPOSURE-** GAVAGE STUDIES RANGING FROM 16 DAYS TO TWO YEARS IN RATS AND MICE REPORTED THE FOLLOWING DOSE RELATED EFFECTS. IN RATS, DECREASED BODY WEIGHT, LESIONS OF THE FORESTOMACH INCLUDING

INFLAMMATION, HYPERPLASIA, ULCERATION AND ACANTHOSIS WITH HYPERKERATOSIS WERE REPORTED. HEMORRHAGE AND NECROSIS OF THE STOMACH WERE SEEN PATHOLOGICALLY. LESIONS OF THE FORESTOMACH INCLUDING EROSION, ULCERATION, HYPERPLASIA AND HYPERKERATOSIS, MINIMAL TO MILD ACANTHOSIS AND INFLAMMATION WERE REPORTED IN MICE. THERE WAS AN INCREASED INCIDENCE OF SQUAMOUS CELL PAPILLOMAS OF THE FORESTOMACH AND HARDARIAN GLAND ADENOMAS AND ADENOCARCINOMAS IN HIGH DOSE MICE. RATS GIVEN A 1% SOLUTION OF DIMETHOXANE IN DRINKING WATER FOR 613 DAYS (TOTAL DOSE 237 GM/ANIMAL) DEVELOPED MALIGNANT TUMORS, PREDOMINATELY IN THE LIVER.

FIRST AID- TREAT SYMPTOMATICALLY AND SUPPORTIVELY. GET MEDICAL ATTENTION IMMEDIATELY. IF VOMITING OCCURS, KEEP HEAD LOWER THAN HIPS TO PREVENT ASPIRATION.

ANTIDOTE: NO SPECIFIC ANTIDOTE. TREAT SYMPTOMATICALLY AND SUPPORTIVELY.

REACTIVITY

REACTIVITY: STABLE UNDER NORMAL TEMPERATURES AND PRESSURES.

INCOMPATIBILITIES: DIMETHOXANE: OXIDIZERS (STRONG): FIRE AND EXPLOSION HAZARD. SEE ALSO ESTERS.
ESTERS: NITRATES: POSSIBLE EXPLOSIVE REACTION.

DECOMPOSITION: THERMAL DECOMPOSITION PRODUCTS MAY INCLUDE TOXIC OXIDES OF CARBON.

POLYMERIZATION: HAZARDOUS POLYMERIZATION HAS NOT BEEN REPORTED TO OCCUR UNDER NORMAL TEMPERATURES AND PRESSURES.

STORAGE AND DISPOSAL

OBSERVE ALL FEDERAL, STATE AND LOCAL REGULATIONS WHEN STORING OR DISPOSING OF THIS SUBSTANCE. FOR ASSISTANCE, CONTACT THE DISTRICT DIRECTOR OF THE ENVIRONMENTAL PROTECTION AGENCY.

****STORAGE****

STORE IN ACCORDANCE WITH 29 CFR 1910.106.

BONDING AND GROUNDING: SUBSTANCES WITH LOW ELECTROCONDUCTIVITY, WHICH MAY BE IGNITED BY ELECTROSTATIC SPARKS, SHOULD BE STORED IN CONTAINERS WHICH MEET THE BONDING AND GROUNDING GUIDELINES SPECIFIED IN NFPA 77-1983, RECOMMENDED PRACTICE ON STATIC ELECTRICITY.

STORE AWAY FROM INCOMPATIBLE SUBSTANCES.

CONDITIONS TO AVOID

AVOID CONTACT WITH HEAT, SPARKS, FLAMES, OR OTHER SOURCES OF IGNITION. VAPORS MAY BE EXPLOSIVE. AVOID OVERHEATING OF CONTAINERS; CONTAINERS MAY VIOLENTLY RUPTURE IN HEAT OF FIRE. AVOID CONTAMINATION OF WATER SOURCES.

SPILL AND LEAK PROCEDURES

OCCUPATIONAL SPILL: SHUT OFF IGNITION SOURCES. STOP LEAK IF YOU CAN DO IT WITHOUT RISK. USE WATER SPRAY TO REDUCE VAPORS. FOR SMALL SPILLS, TAKE UP WITH SAND OR OTHER ABSORBENT MATERIAL AND PLACE INTO CONTAINERS FOR LATER DISPOSAL. FOR LARGER SPILLS, DIKE FAR AHEAD OF SPILL FOR LATER DISPOSAL. NO SMOKING, FLAMES OR FLARES IN HAZARD AREA. KEEP UNNECESSARY PEOPLE AWAY; ISOLATE HAZARD AREA AND RESTRICT ENTRY.

PROTECTIVE EQUIPMENT

VENTILATION: PROVIDE LOCAL EXHAUST OR PROCESS ENCLOSURE VENTILATION SYSTEM.

RESPIRATOR: THE FOLLOWING RESPIRATORS ARE RECOMMENDED BASED ON INFORMATION FOUND IN THE PHYSICAL DATA, TOXICITY AND HEALTH EFFECTS SECTIONS. THEY ARE RANKED IN ORDER FROM MINIMUM TO MAXIMUM RESPIRATORY PROTECTION. THE SPECIFIC RESPIRATOR SELECTED MUST BE BASED ON CONTAMINATION LEVELS FOUND IN THE WORK PLACE, MUST NOT EXCEED THE WORKING LIMITS OF THE RESPIRATOR AND BE JOINTLY APPROVED BY THE NATIONAL INSTITUTE FOR OCCUPATIONAL SAFETY AND HEALTH AND THE MINE SAFETY AND HEALTH ADMINISTRATION (NIOSH-MSHA).

CHEMICAL CARTRIDGE RESPIRATOR WITH AN ORGANIC VAPOR CARTRIDGE(S) WITH A FULL FACEPIECE.

GAS MASK WITH ORGANIC VAPOR CANISTER (CHIN-STYLE OR FRONT- OR BACK-MOUNTED CANISTER) WITH A FULL FACEPIECE.

TYPE 'C' SUPPLIED-AIR RESPIRATOR WITH A FULL FACEPIECE OPERATED IN PRESSURE-DEMAND OR OTHER POSITIVE PRESSURE MODE OR WITH A FULL FACEPIECE, HELMET OR HOOD OPERATED IN CONTINUOUS-FLOW MODE.

SELF-CONTAINED BREATHING APPARATUS WITH A FULL FACEPIECE OPERATED IN PRESSURE-DEMAND OR OTHER POSITIVE PRESSURE MODE.

FOR FIREFIGHTING AND OTHER IMMEDIATELY DANGEROUS TO LIFE OR HEALTH CONDITIONS:

SELF-CONTAINED BREATHING APPARATUS WITH FULL FACEPIECE OPERATED IN PRESSURE-DEMAND OR OTHER POSITIVE PRESSURE MODE.

SUPPLIED-AIR RESPIRATOR WITH FULL FACEPIECE AND OPERATED IN PRESSURE-DEMAND OR OTHER POSITIVE PRESSURE MODE IN COMBINATION WITH AN AUXILIARY SELF-CONTAINED BREATHING APPARATUS OPERATED IN PRESSURE-DEMAND OR OTHER POSITIVE PRESSURE MODE.

CLOTHING: EMPLOYEE MUST WEAR APPROPRIATE PROTECTIVE (IMPERVIOUS) CLOTHING AND EQUIPMENT TO PREVENT REPEATED OR PROLONGED SKIN CONTACT WITH THIS SUBSTANCE.

GLOVES: EMPLOYEE MUST WEAR APPROPRIATE PROTECTIVE GLOVES TO PREVENT CONTACT WITH THIS SUBSTANCE.

EYE PROTECTION: EMPLOYEE MUST WEAR SPLASH-PROOF OR DUST-RESISTANT SAFETY GOGGLES TO PREVENT EYE CONTACT WITH THIS SUBSTANCE.
EMERGENCY EYE WASH: WHERE THERE IS ANY POSSIBILITY THAT AN EMPLOYEE'S EYES MAY BE EXPOSED TO THIS SUBSTANCE, THE EMPLOYER SHOULD PROVIDE AN EYE WASH FOUNTAIN WITHIN THE IMMEDIATE WORK AREA FOR EMERGENCY USE.

AUTHORIZED BY- OCCUPATIONAL HEALTH SERVICES, INC.
CREATION DATE: 10/04/89 ***REVISION DATE:*** 07/13/90

MATERIAL SAFETY DATA SHEET

OCCUPATIONAL HEALTH SERVICES, INC.
AGRICULTURE AND PESTICIDE DIVISION
450 SEVENTH AVENUE, SUITE 2407
NEW YORK, NEW YORK 10123
1-800-445-MSDS OR (212) 967-1100

EMERGENCY CONTACT:
JOHN S. BRANSFORD, JR. (615) 292-1180

SUBSTANCE IDENTIFICATION

CAS-NUMBER 94-75-7

SUBSTANCE: 2,4-DICHLOROPHENOXYACETIC ACID

TRADE NAMES/SYNONYMS: ACETIC ACID, (2,4-DICHLOROPHENOXY)-; 2,4-DICHLOROPHENOXYETHANOIC ACID; (2,4-DICHLOROPHENOXY)ACETIC ACID; DICHLOROPHENOXYACETIC ACID; 2,4-D; 2,4-D ACID; FERNIMINE; HEDONAL; ENT 8,538; NSC-423; STCC 4941126; RCRA U240; C8H6CL2O3; PST28510

CHEMICAL FAMILY: CARBOXYLIC ACID, AROMATIC HALOGEN

MOLECULAR FORMULA: (CL2-C6-H3-O)-C-H2-C-O2-H

MOLECULAR WEIGHT: 221.04

CERCLA RATINGS (SCALE 0-3): HEALTH=3 FIRE=1 REACTIVITY=0 PERSISTENCE=1

NFPA RATINGS (SCALE 0-4): HEALTH=U FIRE=1 REACTIVITY=0

COMPONENTS AND CONTAMINANTS

COMPONENT: 2,4-DICHLOROPHENOXYACETIC ACID ***PERCENT:*** 100.0
CAS# 94-75-7

EXPOSURE LIMITS: 2,4-DICHLOROPHENOXYACETIC ACID: 10 MG/M3 OSHA TWA 10 MG/M3 ACGIH TWA
100 POUNDS CERCLA SECTION 103 REPORTABLE QUANTITY SUBJECT TO SARA SECTION 313 ANNUAL TOXIC CHEMICAL RELEASE REPORTING

PHYSICAL DATA

DESCRIPTION: WHITE TO YELLOW CRYSTALLINE POWDER WITH A SLIGHT PHENOLIC ODOR.

BOILING POINT: 320 F (160 C) @ 0.4 MMHG ***MELTING POINT:*** 248-246 F (140-141 C)

SPECIFIC GRAVITY: 1.565 @ 30 C ***VAPOR PRESSURE:*** 0.4 MMHG @ 160 C

SOLUBILITY IN WATER: 0.06% @ 20 C ***VAPOR DENSITY:*** 7.63

SOLVENT SOLUBILITY: SOLUBLE IN ETHER, ACETONE, ALCOHOL, AND AQUEOUS ALKALI; SLIGHTLY SOLUBLE IN N-HEPTANE, TOLUENE AND XYLENE; INSOLUBLE IN PETROLEUM OILS.

FIRE AND EXPLOSION DATA

FIRE AND EXPLOSION HAZARD: SLIGHT FIRE HAZARD WHEN EXPOSED TO HEAT OR FLAME.
DUST-AIR MIXTURES MAY IGNITE OR EXPLODE.

FIREFIGHTING MEDIA: DRY CHEMICAL, CARBON DIOXIDE, HALON, WATER SPRAY OR STANDARD FOAM (1987 EMERGENCY RESPONSE GUIDEBOOK, DOT P 5800.4).
FOR LARGER FIRES, USE WATER SPRAY, FOG OR STANDARD FOAM (1987 EMERGENCY RESPONSE GUIDEBOOK, DOT P 5800.4).

FIREFIGHTING: MOVE CONTAINERS FROM FIRE AREA IF POSSIBLE. FIGHT FIRE FROM MAXIMUM DISTANCE. STAY AWAY FROM STORAGE TANK ENDS. DIKE FIRE CONTROL WATER FOR LATER DISPOSAL. DO NOT SCATTER MATERIAL (1987 EMERGENCY RESPONSE GUIDEBOOK, DOT P 5800.4, GUIDE PAGE 55).

USE AGENTS SUITABLE FOR TYPE OF FIRE. AVOID BREATHING VAPORS OR DUSTS, KEEP UPWIND.

TRANSPORTATION DATA

DEPARTMENT OF TRANSPORTATION HAZARD CLASSIFICATION 49 CFR 172.101: ORM-A

DEPARTMENT OF TRANSPORTATION LABELING REQUIREMENTS 49 CFR 172.101 AND SUBPART E: NONE

DEPARTMENT OF TRANSPORTATION PACKAGING REQUIREMENTS: 49 CFR 173.510 EXCEPTIONS: 49 CFR 173.505

TOXICITY

2,4-DICHLOROPHENOXYACETIC ACID: IRRITATION DATA: 500 MG/24 HOURS SKIN-RABBIT MILD; 750 UG/24 HOURS EYE-RABBIT SEVERE. TOXICITY DATA: 1400 MG/KG SKIN-RABBIT LD50; 1500 MG/KG SKIN-RAT LD50; 93 MG/KG ORAL-MAN LDLO; 80 MG/KG ORAL-HUMAN LDLO; 375 MG/KG ORAL-RAT LD50; 347 MG/KG ORAL-MOUSE LD50; 500 MG/KG ORAL-HAMSTER LD50; 100 MG/KG ORAL-DOG LD50; 800 MG/KG ORAL-RAT LDLO; 375 MG/KG ORAL-MAMMAL LD50; 400 MG/KG INTRAVENOUS-RABBIT LDLO; 666 MG/KG INTRAPERITONEAL-RAT LDLO; 125 MG/KG INTRAPERITONEAL-MOUSE LDLO; 400 MG/KG INTRAPERITONEAL-RABBIT LDLO; 666 MG/KG INTRAPERITONEAL-GUINEA PIG LDLO; MUTAGENIC DATA (RTECS); REPRODUCTIVE EFFECTS DATA (RTECS). CARCINOGEN STATUS: HUMAN LIMITED EVIDENCE*, ANIMAL INADEQUATE EVIDENCE (IARC GROUP-2B*) * FOR CHLOROPHENOXY HERBICIDES. STUDIES REVEALED A SIGNIFICANT INCREASE IN SOFT-TISSUE SARCOMAS, MALIGNANT LYMPHOMAS AND BRONCHIAL CARCINOMAS IN WORKERS EXPOSED TO CHLOROPHENOXY HERBICIDES. LOCAL EFFECTS: IRRITANT- INHALATION, SKIN, AND EYES. ACUTE TOXICITY LEVEL: TOXIC BY INGESTION; MODERATELY TOXIC BY DERMAL ABSORPTION. TARGET EFFECTS: POISONING MAY AFFECT THE GASTROINTESTINAL TRACT AND THE CARDIOVASCULAR AND NERVOUS SYSTEMS. AT INCREASED RISK FROM EXPOSURE: PERSONS WITH LIVER, KIDNEY, CARDIOVASCULAR, OR SKIN DISEASES, AND CONVULSIVE DISORDERS OR NEUROPATHY. ADDITIONAL DATA: STIMULANTS SUCH AS EPINEPHRINE MAY INDUCE VENTRICULAR FIBRILLATIONS.

HEALTH EFFECTS AND FIRST AID

INHALATION: 2,4-DICHLOROPHENOXYACETIC ACID: IRRITANT. 500 MG/M3 IMMEDIATELY DANGEROUS TO LIFE OR HEALTH. **ACUTE EXPOSURE-** EXPOSURE TO 2,4-D AND ITS DERIVATIVES MAY CAUSE IRRITATION WITH SORE THROAT AND BURNING SENSATIONS IN THE NASOPHARYNX AND CHEST, COUGHING, LACRIMATION, RHINITIS, DULLNESS, DIZZINESS, AND ATAXIA. OTHER EFFECTS OF FATIGUE, NAUSEA, VOMITING, DIARRHEA, STOMACH PAINS, MALAISE, HEADACHE, FEVER, TACHYCARDIA, URINARY INCONTINENCE, CONSTIPATION, LEUKOPENIA, MYALGIA, AND TRANSIENT UNCONSCIOUSNESS MAY OCCUR. A DELAYED PERIPHERAL NEUROPATHY MAY DEVELOP CHARACTERIZED BY PARASTHESIAS, SEVERE PAIN, SYMMETRICAL MOTOR AND SENSORY DEFICITS, WEAKNESS, MYOTONIA, FASCICULATIONS, AND IN SOME CASES PARALYSIS OF THE EXTREMITIES. THE DISABILITY MAY BE PROLONGED AND RECOVERY INCOMPLETE. **CHRONIC EXPOSURE-** IN ADDITION TO THE EFFECTS LISTED IN ACUTE EXPOSURE, OCCUPATIONAL EXPOSURE TO 2,4-D AND ITS DERIVATIVES HAS PRODUCED A SWEET TASTE IN THE MOUTH, HYPERACUSIA, LOWERED SENSITIVITY TO TASTE AND SMELL, INCREASED SALIVATION, VERTIGO, SOMNOLENCE, ANOREXIA, HEAVINESS OF THE LEGS. OTHER EFFECTS HAVE INCLUDED HYPOTENSION, BRADYCARDIA AND OTHER CARDIOVASCULAR SYSTEM CHANGES, PAIN IN THE REGION OF THE LIVER AND STOMACH, AND CHANGES IN THE DIGESTIVE FUNCTION, LIVER FUNCTION AND METABOLIC PROCESSES. A CASE REPORT DESCRIBED A CHILD WITH MULTIPLE CONGENITAL ANOMALIES AND SEVERE MENTAL RETRADATION OF UNCERTAIN CAUSE BORN TO PARENTS HEAVILY EXPOSED TO 2,4-D WHILE SPRAYING TREES. AN INCREASED PREVALENCE OF SLOWED NERVE CONDUCTION VELOCITY WITH NO ASSOCIATED SYMPTOMS WAS REPORTED IN A STUDY OF CHEMICAL WORKERS EMPLOYED IN THE PRODUCTION OF 2,4-D AND 2,4,5-T. EPIDEMIOLOGICAL STUDIES REVEALED A SIGNIFICANT INCREASE IN SOFT-TISSUE SARCOMAS, MALIGNANT LYMPHOMAS, AND BRONCHIAL CARCINOMAS IN WORKERS EXPOSED TO CHLOROPHENOXY HERBICIDES INCLUDING 2,4-D.

FIRST AID- REMOVE FROM EXPOSURE AREA TO FRESH AIR IMMEDIATELY. IF BREATHING HAS STOPPED, GIVE ARTIFICIAL RESPIRATION. MAINTAIN AIRWAY AND BLOOD PRESSURE AND ADMINISTER OXYGEN IF AVAILABLE: KEEP AFFECTED PERSON WARM AND AT REST. TREAT SYMPTOMATICALLY AND SUPPORTIVELY. ADMINISTRATION OF OXYGEN SHOULD BE PERFORMED BY QUALIFIED PERSONNEL. GET MEDICAL ATTENTION IMMEDIATELY.

SKIN CONTACT: 2,4-DICHLOROPHENOXYACETIC ACID: IRRITANT. **ACUTE EXPOSURE-** MAY CAUSE IRRITATION. IF SUFFICIENT AMOUNTS ARE ABSORBED THROUGH THE SKIN, EFFECTS, INCLUDING PERIPHERAL NEUROPATHY, AS DESCRIBED IN ACUTE INHALATION MAY OCCUR. **CHRONIC EXPOSURE-** PROLONGED OR REPEATED EXPOSURE MAY CAUSE DERMATITIS AND EFFECTS AS DESCRIBED IN CHRONIC INHALATION. NEOPLASMS OF THE SKIN HAVE BEEN SHOWN TO BE PROMOTED BY 2,4-D IN SEVERAL STUDIES.

FIRST AID- REMOVE CONTAMINATED CLOTHING AND SHOES IMMEDIATELY. WASH AFFECTED AREA WITH SOAP OR MILD DETERGENT AND LARGE AMOUNTS OF WATER UNTIL NO EVIDENCE OF CHEMICAL REMAINS (APPROXIMATELY 15-20 MINUTES). GET MEDICAL ATTENTION IMMEDIATELY.

EYE CONTACT: 2,4-DICHLOROPHENOXYACETIC ACID: IRRITANT. **ACUTE EXPOSURE-** THIS MATERIAL APPLIED TO THE EYES OF RABBITS PRODUCED SEVERE IRRITATION. **CHRONIC EXPOSURE-** PROLONGED OR REPEATED EXPOSURE TO IRRITANTS MAY CAUSE CONJUNCTIVITIS.

FIRST AID- WASH EYES IMMEDIATELY WITH LARGE AMOUNTS OF WATER OR NORMAL SALINE, OCCASIONALLY LIFTING UPPER AND LOWER LIDS, UNTIL NO EVIDENCE OF CHEMICAL REMAINS (APPROXIMATELY 15-20 MINUTES). GET MEDICAL ATTENTION IMMEDIATELY.

INGESTION: 2,4-DICHLOROPHENOXYACETIC ACID: TOXIC. **ACUTE EXPOSURE-** INGESTION OF 2,4-D AND ITS DERIVATIVES MAY CAUSE IRRITATION OF THE MOUTH, THROAT, AND GASTROINTESTINAL TRACT, NAUSEA, VOMITING, CHEST AND ABDOMINAL PAIN, AND DIARRHEA. INGESTION OF VERY LARGE DOSES MAY PRODUCE METABOLIC ACIDOSIS, FEVER OR SUBNORMAL TEMPERATURES, HYPERVENTILATION, HYPOTENSION, VASODILATION, FLUSHING OF THE SKIN, SWEATING, CARDIAC ARRHYTHMIAS, TACHYCARDIA, LETHARGY, WEAKNESS, INTERCOSTAL PARALYSIS, RENAL AND HEPATIC DYSFUNCTION, MYOTONIA, COMA, AND CONVULSIONS. DAMAGE TO SKELETAL MUSCLE MAY BE MANIFEST BY MUSCLE TWITCHING AND ACHING WITH ELEVATED SERUM ENZYMES AND MYOGLOBIN IN THE BLOOD AND URINE. IMPAIRED MEMORY AND CHANGES IN COLOR VISION WERE REPORTED IN ONE CASE. DEATH MAY BE DUE TO CIRCULATORY COLLAPSE. **CHRONIC EXPOSURE-** DECREASED BODY WEIGHT, INCREASED LIVER WEIGHT, AND MICROSCOPIC HEPATOCELLULAR SWELLING WERE NOTED IN A STUDY OF RATS RECEIVING 50 MG/KG/DAY FOR 113 DAYS. THREE OF FOUR DOGS REPEATEDLY RECEIVING 20 MG/KG DIED WITHIN 18-49 DAYS; REPORTED EFFECTS INCLUDED WEIGHT LOSS, ATAXIA, INCREASED MUSCLE TONUS, AND A TERMINAL FALL IN LYMPHOCYTE COUNT PRIOR TO DEATH. IN A THREE-GENERATION STUDY OF RATS RECEIVING 1500 PPM IN THE DIET, DECREASED WEIGHT AND SURVIVAL RATE OF THE OFFSPRINGS WERE OBSERVED. FETAL SKELETAL ABNORMALITIES AND SUBCUTANEOUS EDEMA WERE REPORTED IN A STUDY OF PREGNANT RATS RECEIVING DOSES ABOVE 25 MG/KG. FETAL MORTALITY, FETAL WEIGHT REDUCTION, AND SKELETAL ABNORMALITIES WERE NOTED IN STUDIES OF PREGNANT MICE.

FIRST AID- IF THE PERSON IS CONSCIOUS AND NOT CONVULSING, INDUCE EMESIS BY GIVING SYRUP OF IPECAC (KEEPING THE HEAD BELOW THE HIPS TO PREVENT ASPIRATION) FOLLOWED BY WATER. REPEAT IN 20 MINUTES IF NOT EFFECTIVE INITIALLY. IN PATIENTS WITH DEPRESSED RESPIRATION OR IF EMESIS IS NOT PRODUCED, PERFORM GASTRIC LAVAGE WITH ACTIVATED CHARCOAL. FOLLOW WITH A SALINE CATHARTIC (DREISBACH, HANDBOOK OF POISONING, 12TH ED.). TREAT SYMPTOMATICALLY AND SUPPORTIVELY. GASTRIC LAVAGE SHOULD BE PERFORMED BY QUALIFIED MEDICAL PERSONNEL. GET MEDICAL ATTENTION IMMEDIATELY.

ANTIDOTE: NO SPECIFIC ANTIDOTE. TREAT SYMPTOMATICALLY AND SUPPORTIVELY.

REACTIVITY

REACTIVITY: STABLE UNDER NORMAL TEMPERATURES AND PRESSURES.

INCOMPATIBILITIES: 2,4-DICHLOROPHENOXYACETIC ACID: METALS: MAY CORRODE. OXIDIZERS (STRONG): FIRE AND EXPLOSION HAZARD.

DECOMPOSITION: THERMAL DECOMPOSITION PRODUCTS MAY INCLUDE HIGHLY TOXIC FUMES OF PHOSGENE, TOXIC AND CORROSIVE FUMES OF CHLORIDES, AND OXIDES OF CARBON.

POLYMERIZATION: HAZARDOUS POLYMERIZATION HAS NOT BEEN REPORTED TO OCCUR UNDER NORMAL TEMPERATURES AND PRESSURES.

STORAGE AND DISPOSAL

OBSERVE ALL FEDERAL, STATE AND LOCAL REGULATIONS WHEN STORING OR DISPOSING OF THIS SUBSTANCE. FOR ASSISTANCE, CONTACT THE DISTRICT DIRECTOR OF THE ENVIRONMENTAL PROTECTION AGENCY.

****STORAGE****

STORE IN ACCORDANCE WITH 40 CFR 165 RECOMMENDED PROCEDURES FOR THE DISPOSAL AND STORAGE OF PESTICIDES AND PESTICIDE CONTAINERS.
STORE AWAY FROM INCOMPATIBLE SUBSTANCES.

****DISPOSAL****

DISPOSAL MUST BE IN ACCORDANCE WITH 40 CFR 165 RECOMMENDED PROCEDURES FOR THE DISPOSAL AND STORAGE OF PESTICIDES AND PESTICIDE CONTAINERS.
DISPOSAL MUST BE IN ACCORDANCE WITH STANDARDS APPLICABLE TO GENERATORS OF HAZARDOUS WASTE, 40CFR 262. EPA HAZARDOUS WASTE NUMBER U240.

2,4-D - REGULATORY LEVEL: 10.0 MG/L MATERIALS WHICH CONTAIN THE ABOVE SUBSTANCE AT OR ABOVE THE REGULATORY LEVEL MEET THE EPA CHARACTERISTIC OF TOXICITY, AND MUST BE DISPOSED OF IN ACCORDANCE WITH 40 CFR PART 262. EPA HAZARDOUS WASTE NUMBER D016.

CONDITIONS TO AVOID

MAY BURN BUT DOES NOT IGNITE READILY. CONTAINERS MAY EXPLODE IN HEAT OF FIRE.

SPILL AND LEAK PROCEDURES

SOIL SPILL: DIG HOLDING AREA SUCH AS LAGOON, POND OR PIT FOR CONTAINMENT. USE PROTECTIVE COVER SUCH AS A PLASTIC SHEET TO PREVENT MATERIAL FROM DISSOLVING IN FIRE EXTINGUISHING WATER OR RAIN.

WATER SPILL: TRAP SPILLED MATERIAL AT BOTTOM IN DEEP WATER POCKETS, EXCAVATED HOLDING AREAS OR WITHIN SAND BAG BARRIERS.
USE ACTIVATED CARBON TO ABSORB SPILLED SUBSTANCE THAT IS DISSOLVED.
USE SUCTION HOSES TO REMOVE TRAPPED SPILL MATERIAL.
USE MECHANICAL DREDGES OR LIFTS TO EXTRACT IMMOBILIZED MASSES OF POLLUTION AND PRECIPITATES.

OCCUPATIONAL SPILL: DO NOT TOUCH SPILLED MATERIAL. STOP LEAK IF YOU CAN DO IT WITHOUT RISK. USE WATER SPRAY TO REDUCE VAPORS. FOR SMALL SPILLS, TAKE UP WITH SAND OR OTHER ABSORBENT MATERIAL AND PLACE INTO CONTAINERS FOR LATER DISPOSAL. FOR SMALL DRY SPILLS, WITH A CLEAN SHOVEL PLACE MATERIAL INTO CLEAN, DRY CONTAINERS AND COVER. MOVE CONTAINERS FROM SPILL AREA. FOR LARGER SPILLS, DIKE FAR AHEAD OF SPILL FOR LATER DISPOSAL. KEEP UNNECESSARY PEOPLE AWAY. ISOLATE HAZARD AREA AND DENY ENTRY. VENTILATE CLOSED SPACES BEFORE ENTERING.
REPORTABLE QUANTITY (RQ): 100 POUNDS THE SUPERFUND AMENDMENTS AND REAUTHORIZATION ACT (SARA) SECTION 304 REQUIRES THAT A RELEASE EQUAL TO OR GREATER THAN THE REPORTABLE QUANTITY FOR THIS SUBSTANCE BE IMMEDIATELY REPORTED TO THE LOCAL EMERGENCY PLANNING COMMITTEE AND THE STATE EMERGENCY RESPONSE COMMISSION (40 CFR 355.40). IF THE RELEASE OF THIS SUBSTANCE IS REPORTABLE UNDER CERCLA SECTION 103, THE NATIONAL RESPONSE CENTER MUST BE NOTIFIED IMMEDIATELY AT (800) 424-8802 OR (202) 426-2675 IN THE METROPOLITAN WASHINGTON, D.C. AREA (40 CFR 302.6).

PROTECTIVE EQUIPMENT

VENTILATION: PROVIDE LOCAL EXHAUST VENTILATION AND/OR GENERAL DILUTION VENTILATION TO MEET PUBLISHED EXPOSURE LIMITS.

RESPIRATOR: THE FOLLOWING RESPIRATORS AND MAXIMUM USE CONCENTRATIONS ARE RECOMMENDATIONS BY THE U.S. DEPARTMENT OF HEALTH AND HUMAN SERVICES, NIOSH POCKET GUIDE TO CHEMICAL HAZARDS; NIOSH CRITERIA DOCUMENTS OR BY THE U.S. DEPARTMENT OF LABOR, 29 CFR 1910 SUBPART Z.
THE SPECIFIC RESPIRATOR SELECTED MUST BE BASED ON CONTAMINATION LEVELS FOUND IN THE WORK PLACE, MUST NOT EXCEED THE WORKING LIMITS OF THE RESPIRATOR AND BE JOINTLY APPROVED BY THE NATIONAL INSTITUTE FOR OCCUPATIONAL SAFETY AND HEALTH AND THE MINE SAFETY AND HEALTH ADMINISTRATION (NIOSH-MSHA).
2,4-DICHLOROPHENOXY ACETIC ACID:
AT ANY DETECTABLE CONCENTRATION: SELF-CONTAINED BREATHING APPARATUS WITH FULL FACEPIECE OPERATED IN PRESSURE-DEMAND OR OTHER POSITIVE PRESSURE MODE. SUPPLIED-AIR RESPIRATOR WITH FULL FACEPIECE OPERATED IN PRESSURE-DEMAND OR OTHER POSITIVE PRESSURE MODE IN COMBINATION WITH AN AUXILIARY SELF-CONTAINED BREATHING APPARATUS OPERATED IN PRESSURE-DEMAND OR OTHER POSITIVE PRESSURE MODE.
ESCAPE- ANY AIR-PURIFYING FULL FACEPIECE RESPIRATOR (GAS MASK) WITH A CHIN-STYLE OR FRONT- OR BACK-MOUNTED ORGANIC VAPOR CANISTER HAVING A HIGH-EFFICIENCY PARTICULATE FILTER. ANY APPROPRIATE ESCAPE-TYPE SELF-CONTAINED BREATHING APPARATUS.
FOR FIREFIGHTING AND OTHER IMMEDIATELY DANGEROUS TO LIFE OR HEALTH CONDITIONS:
SELF-CONTAINED BREATHING APPARATUS WITH FULL FACEPIECE OPERATED IN PRESSURE-DEMAND OR OTHER POSITIVE PRESSURE MODE.
SUPPLIED-AIR RESPIRATOR WITH FULL FACEPIECE AND OPERATED IN PRESSURE-DEMAND OR OTHER POSITIVE PRESSURE MODE IN COMBINATION WITH AN AUXILIARY SELF-CONTAINED BREATHING APPARATUS OPERATED IN PRESSURE-DEMAND OR OTHER POSITIVE PRESSURE MODE.

CLOTHING: EMPLOYEE MUST WEAR APPROPRIATE PROTECTIVE (IMPERVIOUS) CLOTHING AND EQUIPMENT TO PREVENT REPEATED OR PROLONGED SKIN CONTACT WITH THIS SUBSTANCE.

GLOVES: EMPLOYEE MUST WEAR APPROPRIATE PROTECTIVE GLOVES TO PREVENT CONTACT WITH THIS SUBSTANCE.

EYE PROTECTION: EMPLOYEE MUST WEAR SPLASH-PROOF OR DUST-RESISTANT SAFETY GOGGLES TO PREVENT EYE CONTACT WITH THIS SUBSTANCE.
EMERGENCY EYE WASH: WHERE THERE IS ANY POSSIBILITY THAT AN EMPLOYEE'S EYES MAY BE EXPOSED TO THIS SUBSTANCE, THE EMPLOYER SHOULD PROVIDE AN EYE WASH FOUNTAIN WITHIN THE IMMEDIATE WORK AREA FOR EMERGENCY USE.

AUTHORIZED BY- OCCUPATIONAL HEALTH SERVICES, INC.
CREATION DATE: 10/05/89 ***REVISION DATE:*** 07/13/90

MATERIAL SAFETY DATA SHEET

OCCUPATIONAL HEALTH SERVICES, INC.
AGRICULTURE AND PESTICIDE DIVISION
450 SEVENTH AVENUE, SUITE 2407
NEW YORK, NEW YORK 10123
1-800-445-MSDS OR (212) 967-1100

EMERGENCY CONTACT:
JOHN S. BRANSFORD, JR. (615) 292-1180

SUBSTANCE IDENTIFICATION

CAS-NUMBER 51-28-5

SUBSTANCE: 2,4-DINITROPHENOL

TRADE NAMES/SYNONYMS: PHENOL, 2,4-DINITRO-; ALPHA-DINITROPHENOL; DINITROPHENOL; 1-HYDROXY-2,4-DINITROBENZENE; 2,4-DNP; ALDIFEN; STCC 4916626; RCRA P048; UN 1320; C6H4N2O5; PST28620

CHEMICAL FAMILY: PHENOL
NITRO

MOLECULAR FORMULA: (N-O2)2-C6-H3-O-H

MOLECULAR WEIGHT: 184.11

CERCLA RATINGS (SCALE 0-3): HEALTH=U FIRE=2 REACTIVITY=3 PERSISTENCE=2

NFPA RATINGS (SCALE 0-4): HEALTH=U FIRE=2 REACTIVITY=4

COMPONENTS AND CONTAMINANTS

COMPONENT: 2,4-DINITROPHENOL ***PERCENT:*** 100.0
CAS# 51-28-5

OTHER CONTAMINANTS: MAY CONTAIN 15% WATER TO REDUCE DETONATION SENSITIVITY

EXPOSURE LIMITS: NO OCCUPATIONAL EXPOSURE LIMITS ESTABLISHED BY OSHA, ACGIH, OR NIOSH.
2,4-DINITROPHENOL: 10 POUNDS CERCLA SECTION 103 REPORTABLE QUANTITY SUBJECT TO SARA SECTION 313 ANNUAL TOXIC CHEMICAL RELEASE REPORTING

PHYSICAL DATA

DESCRIPTION: YELLOWISH TO YELLOW CRYSTALLINE SOLID WITH A SWEET MUSTY ODOR AND A BITTER TASTE.

MELTING POINT: 239-241 F (115-116 C)

SPECIFIC GRAVITY: 1.683 ***SOLUBILITY IN WATER:*** 0.06% @ 25 C

VAPOR DENSITY: 6.35

SOLVENT SOLUBILITY: SOLUBLE IN ETHANOL, BENZENE, ACETONE, ETHER, PYRIDINE, ETHYL ACETATE, AQUEOUS ALKALINE SOLUTIONS; MODERATELY SOLUBLE IN CHLOROFORM, TOLUENE; SLIGHTLY SOLUBLE IN CARBON TETRACHLORIDE.

FIRE AND EXPLOSION DATA

FIRE AND EXPLOSION HAZARD: UNKNOWN FIRE AND EXPLOSION HAZARD.
DANGEROUS EXPLOSION HAZARD WHEN EXPOSED TO HEAT OR FLAME.
DUST-AIR MIXTURES MAY IGNITE OR EXPLODE.
DUE TO LOW ELECTROCONDUCTIVITY OF THE SUBSTANCE, FLOW OR AGITATION MAY GENERATE ELECTROSTATIC CHARGES RESULTING IN SPARKS WITH POSSIBLE IGNITION.

FIREFIGHTING MEDIA: FLOOD WITH WATER, IF NO WATER AVAILABLE USE DRY CHEMICAL OR DIRT.
FOR LARGER FIRES, WITHDRAW FROM AREA AND LET FIRE BURN (1987 EMERGENCY RESPONSE GUIDEBOOK, DOT P 5800.4).

FIREFIGHTING: DO NOT MOVE CONTAINERS IF EXPOSURE TO HEAT HAS OCCURRED.
FOR MASSIVE FIRE IN STORAGE AREA, USE UNMANNED HOSE HOLDER OR MONITOR NOZZLES; ELSE WITHDRAW FROM AREA AND LET FIRE BURN (1987 EMERGENCY RESPONSE GUIDEBOOK, DOT P 5800.4, GUIDE PAGE 36).
FLOOD WITH WATER, DANGEROUSLY EXPLOSIVE. COOL CONTAINERS WITH FLOODING AMOUNTS OF WATER, APPLY FROM AS FAR A DISTANCE AS POSSIBLE.
EVACUATE TO A RADIUS OF 500 FEET FOR UNCONTROLLABLE FIRES.

TRANSPORTATION DATA

DEPARTMENT OF TRANSPORTATION HAZARD CLASSIFICATION 49 CFR 172.101: POISON B

DEPARTMENT OF TRANSPORTATION LABELING REQUIREMENTS 49 CFR 172.101 AND SUBPART E: POISON
DEPARTMENT OF TRANSPORTATION PACKAGING REQUIREMENTS: 49 CFR 173.365 EXCEPTIONS: 49 CFR 173.364

TOXICITY

2,4-DINITROPHENOL: IRRITATION DATA: 300 MG/4 WEEKS INTERMITTENT SKIN-RABBIT MILD. TOXICITY DATA: 300 MG/M3/30 MONTHS INHALATION-DOG LCLO; 700 MG/KG SKIN-GUINEA PIG LDLO; 4300 UG/KG ORAL-HUMAN LDLO; 30 MG/KG ORAL-RAT LD50; 45 MG/KG ORAL-MOUSE LD50; 30 MG/KG ORAL-RABBIT LD50; 81 MG/KG ORAL-GUINEA PIG LD50; 75 MG/KG ORAL-CAT LD50; 30 MG/KG ORAL-DOG LDLO; 25 MG/KG SUBCUTANEOUS-RAT LD50; 20 MG/KG SUBCUTANEOUS-RABBIT LDLO; 25 MG/KG SUBCUTANEOUS GUINEA PIG LDLO; 20 MG/KG SUBCUTANEOUS-DOG LDLO; 15 MG/KG INTRAVENOUS-DOG LDLO; 20 MG/KG INTRAPERITONEAL-RAT LD50; 26 MG/KG INTRAPERITONEAL-MOUSE LD50; 28 MG/KG INTRAPERITONEAL-GUINEA PIG LD50; MUTAGENIC DATA (RTECS); REPRODUCTIVE EFFECTS DATA (RTECS). CARCINOGEN STATUS: NONE. ACUTE TOXICITY LEVEL: HIGHLY TOXIC BY INGESTION. TARGET EFFECTS: SENSITIZER. POISONING MAY INCREASE THE METABOLIC RATE AND AFFECT THE NERVOUS SYSTEM, LIVER, AND KIDNEYS. AT INCREASED RISK FROM EXPOSURE: ALCOHOLICS AND PERSONS WITH RENAL OR HEPATIC DISEASES. ADDITIONAL DATA: HOT ENVIRONMENTS MAY ENHANCE ABSORPTION AND THE TOXIC EFFECTS.

HEALTH EFFECTS AND FIRST AID

INHALATION: DINITROPHENOL: **ACUTE EXPOSURE-** MAY BE ABSORBED WITH SYMPTOMS OCCURRING SUDDENLY AND UP TO 2 DAYS AFTER CESSATION OF EXPOSURE. SYMPTOMS MAY INCLUDE FATIGUE, WEAKNESS, FEVER, THIRST, NAUSEA, VOMITING, HEADACHES, FLUSHED SKIN, PROSTRATION, EXCESSIVE PERSPIRATION, TACHYCARDIA, TACHYPNEA, AND DYSPNEA. APPREHENSION, RESTLESSNESS, ANXIETY, MANIC BEHAVIOR, OR UNCONSCIOUSNESS MAY INDICATE CEREBRAL INJURY. CONVULSIONS MAY OCCUR IN THE MOST SEVERE POISONINGS. ANOXIA WITH CYANOSIS, LIVIDITY AND METABOLIC ACIDOSIS, SEVERE HYPERPYREXIA, DEHYDRATION, AND MUSCULAR TREMORS MAY BE FOLLOWED BY CIRCULATORY OR RESPIRATORY COLLAPSE AND COMA. DEGENERATIVE CHANGES IN THE HEART, RENAL TUBULES AND LIVER PARENCHYMA MAY OCCUR. THERE MAY BE ALBUMINURIA, PYURIA, HEMATURIA, JAUNDICE, AND INCREASED BUN. SOME ISOMERS OF DINITROPHENOL MAY PRODUCE METHEMOGLOBIN. THE EFFECTS FROM POISONING ARE RAPID AND DEATH OR RECOVERY GENERALLY OCCURS WITHIN 24 TO 48 HOURS. FATAL NITROPHENOL POISONING IS FOLLOWED BY INSTANTANEOUS RIGOR MORTIS. **CHRONIC EXPOSURE-** IN ADDITION TO THE SYMPTOMS OF ACUTE EXPOSURE, PROLONGED OR REPEATED EXPOSURE MAY CAUSE WEIGHT LOSS, CATARACT FORMATION, AND LIVER AND KIDNEY DAMAGE. YELLOW STAINING OF THE SCLERAE AND URINE INDICATES ABSORPTION OF POTENTIALLY TOXIC AMOUNTS.
FIRST AID- REMOVE FROM EXPOSURE AREA TO FRESH AIR IMMEDIATELY. IF BREATHING HAS STOPPED, PERFORM ARTIFICIAL RESPIRATION. ADMINISTER OXYGEN. TREAT SYMPTOMATICALLY AND SUPPORTIVELY. GET MEDICAL ATTENTION IMMEDIATELY.

SKIN CONTACT: DINITROPHENOL: SENSITIZER. **ACUTE EXPOSURE-** MAY CAUSE IRRITATION. CONTACT MAY RESULT IN YELLOW STAINING OF THE SKIN AHD HAIR. SYSTEMIC EFFECTS, AS DESCRIBED IN ACUTE INHALATION, MAY OCCUR IF SUFFICIENT AMOUNTS ARE ABSORBED THROUGH THE SKIN. **CHRONIC EXPOSURE-** REPEATED OR PROLONGED CONTACT MAY RESULT IN DERMATITIS DUE TO IRRITATION OR ALLERGIC SENSITIVITY. IN ADDITION TO THE SYMPTOMS OF ACUTE EXPOSURE, CHRONIC ABSORPTION MAY CAUSE FATIGUE, WEIGHT LOSS, CATARACT FORMATION AND LIVER AND KIDNEY DAMAGE. YELLOW STAINING OF THE SCLERAE AND URINE INDICATES ABSORPTION OF POTENTIALLY TOXIC AMOUNTS.
FIRST AID- REMOVE CONTAMINATED CLOTHING AND SHOES IMMEDIATELY. THEN REMOVE SKIN AND HAIR CONTAMINATION BY SCRUBBING WITH SOAP AND WATER. IF BODY TEMPERATURE IS ELEVATED, REDUCE TO 37 C BY SPONGE BATH, IMMERSION IN COOL WATER OR BY APPLYING COOLING BLANKET. IF BODY TEMPERATURE IS ABOVE 40 C, ICE WATER IS NECESSARY (DREISBACH, HANDBOOK OF POISONING, 12TH EDITION; MORGAN, EPA RECOGNITION AND MANAGEMENT OF PESTICIDE POISONINGS, 3RD EDITION). GET MEDICAL ATTENTION IMMEDIATELY.

EYE CONTACT: DINITROPHENOL: **ACUTE EXPOSURE-** MAY CAUSE REDNESS, PAIN, AND IRRITATION OF THE EYE. **CHRONIC EXPOSURE-** PROLONGED OR REPEATED EXPOSURE TO IRRITANTS MAY CAUSE CONJUNCTIVITIS. CATARACTS WERE PRODUCED IN RABBIT EYES BY LOCAL ADMINISTRATION OR INJECTION.
FIRST AID- WASH EYES IMMEDIATELY WITH LARGE AMOUNTS OF WATER OR NORMAL SALINE, OCCASIONALLY LIFTING UPPER AND LOWER LIDS, UNTIL NO EVIDENCE OF CHEMICAL REMAINS (APPROXIMATELY 15-20 MINUTES). GET MEDICAL ATTENTION IMMEDIATELY.

INGESTION: 2,4-DINITROPHENOL: HIGHLY TOXIC. REPRODUCTIVE EFFECTS WERE REPORTED IN ANIMALS.
DINITROPHENOL: **ACUTE EXPOSURE-** MAY CAUSE EFFECTS ON THE METABOLIC RATE, CENTRAL NERVOUS SYSTEM AND LIVER AND KIDNEY RESULTING IN SIGNS AND SYMPTOMS AS DESCRIBED IN ACUTE INHALATION. **CHRONIC EXPOSURE-** IN ADDITION TO THE SYMPTOMS OF ACUTE EXPOSURE, REPEATED INGESTION MAY CAUSE AN INITIAL SENSE OF WELL-BEING THEN ANOREXIA, DIARRHEA, DIZZINESS, RESTLESSNESS, FATIGUE, WEIGHT LOSS, SKIN ERUPTIONS, PERIPHERAL NEURITIS, LIVER AND KIDNEY DAMAGE, CARDIOVASCULAR COMPLICATIONS, GRANULOCYTOPENIA, AND CATARACT FORMATION. YELLOW STAINING OF THE SCLERAE AND URINE INDICATES ABSORPTION OF POTENTIALLY TOXIC AMOUNTS.
FIRST AID- REMOVE INGESTED POISON BY THOROUGH GASTRIC LAVAGE WITH SATURATED BICARBONATE SOLUTION. IF GASTRIC LAVAGE CANNOT BE ACCOMPLISHED IMMEDIATELY, GIVE SYRUP OF IPECAC TO INDUCE EMESIS AND FOLLOW WITH SALINE CATHARTIC. IF BODY TEMPERATURE IS ELEVATED, REDUCE TO 37 C BY IMMERSION IN COOL WATER OR BY APPLYING COOLING BLANKET. IF BODY TEMPERATURE IS ABOVE 40 C, ICE WATER IS NECESSARY (DREISBACH, HANDBOOK OF POISONING, 12TH ED.). ADMINISTRATION OF GASTRIC LAVAGE SHOULD BE PERFORMED BY QUALIFIED MEDICAL PERSONNEL. GET MEDICAL ATTENTION IMMEDIATELY.
ANTIDOTE: NO SPECIFIC ANTIDOTE. TREAT SYMPTOMATICALLY AND SUPPORTIVELY.

REACTIVITY

REACTIVITY: DRY MATERIAL MAY DETONATE ON EXPOSURE TO HEAT OR SHOCK. MATERIAL MAY BE WET WITH WATER FOR STABILITY DURING STORAGE AND TRANSPORT.
INCOMPATIBILITIES: DINITROPHENOL: ALKALIES: MAY FORM EXPLOSIVE SALTS. AMMONIA: MAY FORM EXPLOSIVE SALTS. COMBUSTIBLE SUBSTANCES: MAY REACT VIOLENTLY. METALS (HEAVY) AND THEIR SALTS: MAY FORM EXTREMELY SENSITIVE COMPOUNDS. OXIDIZERS: MAY REACT VIOLENTLY. REDUCING AGENTS: MAY REACT VIOLENTLY. SODIUM AND COMPOUNDS: MAY FORM EXTREMELY SENSITIVE COMPOUNDS.
DECOMPOSITION: THERMAL DECOMPOSITION PRODUCTS MAY INCLUDE TOXIC OXIDES OF CARBON AND NITROGEN.
POLYMERIZATION: HAZARDOUS POLYMERIZATION HAS NOT BEEN REPORTED TO OCCUR UNDER NORMAL TEMPERATURES AND PRESSURES.

STORAGE AND DISPOSAL

OBSERVE ALL FEDERAL, STATE AND LOCAL REGULATIONS WHEN STORING OR DISPOSING OF THIS SUBSTANCE. FOR ASSISTANCE, CONTACT THE DISTRICT DIRECTOR OF THE ENVIRONMENTAL PROTECTION AGENCY.

STORAGE

STORE AWAY FROM INCOMPATIBLE SUBSTANCES.
KEEP IN A TIGHTLY CLOSED CONTAINER. STORE IN A COOL, DRY, VENTILATED AREA.

DISPOSAL

DISPOSAL MUST BE IN ACCORDANCE WITH STANDARDS APPLICABLE TO GENERATORS OF HAZARDOUS WASTE, 40CFR 262. EPA HAZARDOUS WASTE NUMBER P048.

CONDITIONS TO AVOID

AVOID CONTACT WITH HEAT, SPARKS, FLAMES, OR OTHER SOURCES OF IGNITION. MAY BE EXPLOSIVE WHEN DRY; AVOID OVERHEATING OR HEATING TO THE POINT OF DRYNESS. DO NOT CONTAMINATE WATER SOURCES.

SPILL AND LEAK PROCEDURES

SOIL SPILL: DIG HOLDING AREA SUCH AS LAGOON, POND OR PIT FOR CONTAINMENT. USE PROTECTIVE COVER SUCH AS A PLASTIC SHEET TO PREVENT MATERIAL FROM DISSOLVING IN FIRE EXTINGUISHING WATER OR RAIN.
WATER SPILL: TRAP SPILLED MATERIAL AT BOTTOM IN DEEP WATER POCKETS, EXCAVATED HOLDING AREAS OR WITHIN SAND BAG BARRIERS.
USE ACTIVATED CARBON TO ABSORB SPILLED SUBSTANCE THAT IS DISSOLVED.
USE SUCTION HOSES TO REMOVE TRAPPED SPILL MATERIAL.
USE MECHANICAL DREDGES OR LIFTS TO EXTRACT IMMOBILIZED MASSES OF POLLUTION AND PRECIPITATES.
OCCUPATIONAL SPILL: SHUT OFF IGNITION SOUCES. DO NOT TOUCH SPILLED MATERIAL. FOR SMALL SPILLS, FLUSH AREA WITH FLOODING AMOUNTS OF WATER. FOR LARGER SPILLS, WET DOWN WITH WATER AND DIKE FOR LATER DISPOSAL. NO SMOKING, FLAMES OR FLARES IN HAZARD AREA! KEEP UNNECESSARY PEOPLE AWAY. ISOLATE HAZARD AREA AND DENY ENTRY.
REPORTABLE QUANTITY (RQ): 10 POUNDS THE SUPERFUND AMENDMENTS AND

REAUTHORIZATION ACT (SARA) SECTION 304 REQUIRES THAT A RELEASE EQUAL TO OR GREATER THAN THE REPORTABLE QUANTITY FOR THIS SUBSTANCE BE IMMEDIATELY REPORTED TO THE LOCAL EMERGENCY PLANNING COMMITTEE AND THE STATE EMERGENCY RESPONSE COMMISSION (40 CFR 355.40). IF THE RELEASE OF THIS SUBSTANCE IS REPORTABLE UNDER CERCLA SECTION 103, THE NATIONAL RESPONSE CENTER MUST BE NOTIFIED IMMEDIATELY AT (800) 424-8802 OR (202) 426-2675 IN THE METROPOLITAN WASHINGTON, D.C. AREA (40 CFR 302.6).

PROTECTIVE EQUIPMENT

VENTILATION: PROVIDE LOCAL EXHAUST OR PROCESS ENCLOSURE VENTILATION. VENTILATION EQUIPMENT MUST BE EXPLOSION-PROOF.

RESPIRATOR: THE FOLLOWING RESPIRATORS ARE RECOMMENDED BASED ON INFORMATION FOUND IN THE PHYSICAL DATA, TOXICITY AND HEALTH EFFECTS SECTIONS. THEY ARE RANKED IN ORDER FROM MINIMUM TO MAXIMUM RESPIRATORY PROTECTION. THE SPECIFIC RESPIRATOR SELECTED MUST BE BASED ON CONTAMINATION LEVELS FOUND IN THE WORK PLACE, MUST NOT EXCEED THE WORKING LIMITS OF THE RESPIRATOR AND BE JOINTLY APPROVED BY THE NATIONAL INSTITUTE FOR OCCUPATIONAL SAFETY AND HEALTH AND THE MINE SAFETY AND HEALTH ADMINISTRATION (NIOSH-MSHA).

TYPE 'C' SUPPLIED-AIR RESPIRATOR WITH A FULL FACEPIECE OPERATED IN PRESSURE-DEMAND OR OTHER POSITIVE PRESSURE MODE OR WITH A FULL FACEPIECE, HELMET OR HOOD OPERATED IN CONTINOUS-FLOW MODE.

SELF-CONTAINED BREATHING APPARATUS WITH A FULL FACEPIECE OPERATED IN PRESSURE-DEMAND OR OTHER POSITIVE PRESSURE MODE.

FOR FIREFIGHTING AND OTHER IMMEDIATELY DANGEROUS TO LIFE OR HEALTH CONDITIONS:

SELF-CONTAINED BREATHING APPARATUS WITH FULL FACEPIECE OPERATED IN PRESSURE-DEMAND OR OTHER POSITIVE PRESSURE MODE.

SUPPLIED-AIR RESPIRATOR WITH FULL FACEPIECE AND OPERATED IN PRESSURE-DEMAND OR OTHER POSITIVE PRESSURE MODE IN COMBINATION WITH AN AUXILIARY SELF-CONTAINED BREATHING APPARATUS OPERATED IN PRESSURE-DEMAND OR OTHER POSITIVE PRESSURE MODE.

CLOTHING: EMPLOYEE MUST WEAR APPROPRIATE PROTECTIVE (IMPERVIOUS) CLOTHING AND EQUIPMENT TO PREVENT ANY POSSIBILITY OF SKIN CONTACT WITH THIS SUBSTANCE.

GLOVES: EMPLOYEE MUST WEAR APPROPRIATE PROTECTIVE GLOVES TO PREVENT CONTACT WITH THIS SUBSTANCE.

EYE PROTECTION: EMPLOYEE MUST WEAR SPLASH-PROOF OR DUST-RESISTANT SAFETY GOGGLES AND A FACESHIELD TO PREVENT CONTACT WITH THIS SUBSTANCE.

EMERGENCY WASH FACILITIES: WHERE THERE IS ANY POSSIBILITY THAT AN EMPLOYEE'S EYES AND/OR SKIN MAY BE EXPOSED TO THIS SUBSTANCE, THE EMPLOYER SHOULD PROVIDE AN EYE WASH FOUNTAIN AND QUICK DRENCH SHOWER WITHIN THE IMMEDIATE WORK AREA FOR EMERGENCY USE.

AUTHORIZED BY- OCCUPATIONAL HEALTH SERVICES, INC.

CREATION DATE: 10/05/89 ***REVISION DATE:*** 05/14/90

MATERIAL SAFETY DATA SHEET

OCCUPATIONAL HEALTH SERVICES, INC.
AGRICULTURE AND PESTICIDE DIVISION
450 SEVENTH AVENUE, SUITE 2407
NEW YORK, NEW YORK 10123
1-800-445-MSDS OR (212) 967-1100

EMERGENCY CONTACT:
JOHN S. BRANSFORD, JR. (615) 292-1180

SUBSTANCE IDENTIFICATION

CAS-NUMBER 105-67-9

SUBSTANCE: **2,4-XYLENOL**

TRADE NAMES/SYNONYMS: PHENOL, 2,4-DIMETHYL; 2,4-DIMETHYLPHENOL; 4,6-DIMETHYLPHENOL; M-XYLENOL; HYDROXY-2,4-DIMETHYLBENZENE; HYDROXYDIMETHYLBENZENE; DIMETHYLPHENOL; XYLENOL; RCRA U101; STCC 4941193; UN 2261; C8H10O; PST28670

CHEMICAL FAMILY: HYDROXYL, AROMATIC

MOLECULAR FORMULA: (C-H3)2-C6-H3-O-H

MOLECULAR WEIGHT: 122.17

CERCLA RATINGS (SCALE 0-3): HEALTH=U FIRE=1 REACTIVITY=0 PERSISTENCE=1

NFPA RATINGS (SCALE 0-4): HEALTH=U FIRE=1 REACTIVITY=0

COMPONENTS AND CONTAMINANTS

COMPONENT: 2,4-XYLENOL ***PERCENT:*** 100.0

CAS# 105-67-9

OTHER CONTAMINANTS: NONE

EXPOSURE LIMITS: NO OCCUPATIONAL EXPOSURE LIMITS ESTABLISHED BY OSHA, ACGIH, OR NIOSH.

2,4-XYLENOL: 100 POUNDS CERCLA SECTION 103 REPORTABLE QUANTITY SUBJECT TO SARA SECTION 313 ANNUAL TOXIC CHEMICAL RELEASE REPORTING

PHYSICAL DATA

DESCRIPTION: COLORLESS TO WHITE CRYSTALLINE SOLID. ***BOILING POINT:*** 410 F (210 C)

MELTING POINT: 81-82 F (27-28 C) ***SPECIFIC GRAVITY:*** 0.9650

SOLUBILITY IN WATER: SLIGHTLY SOLUBLE

SOLVENT SOLUBILITY: SOLUBLE IN ALCOHOL, ETHER, CHLOROFORM, BENZENE, OTHER ORGANIC SOLVENTS, SODIUM HYDROXIDE SOLUTION.

FIRE AND EXPLOSION DATA

FIRE AND EXPLOSION HAZARD: SLIGHT FIRE HAZARD WHEN EXPOSED TO HEAT OR FLAME.

FLASH POINT: >230 F (>110 C) (CC)

FIREFIGHTING MEDIA: DRY CHEMICAL, CARBON DIOXIDE, HALON, WATER SPRAY OR STANDARD FOAM (1987 EMERGENCY RESPONSE GUIDEBOOK, DOT P 5800.4). FOR LARGER FIRES, USE WATER SPRAY, FOG OR STANDARD FOAM (1987 EMERGENCY RESPONSE GUIDEBOOK, DOT P 5800.4).

FIREFIGHTING: MOVE CONTAINERS FROM FIRE AREA IF POSSIBLE. FIGHT FIRE FROM MAXIMUM DISTANCE. STAY AWAY FROM STORAGE TANK ENDS. DIKE FIRE CONTROL WATER FOR LATER DISPOSAL. DO NOT SCATTER MATERIAL (1987 EMERGENCY RESPONSE GUIDEBOOK, DOT P 5800.4, GUIDE PAGE 55). EXTINGUISH ONLY IF FLOW CAN BE STOPPED; USE WATER IN FLOODING AMOUNTS AS FOG, COOL CONTAINERS WITH FLOODING QUANTITIES OF WATER, APPLY FROM AS FAR A DISTANCE AS POSSIBLE. AVOID BREATHING TOXIC VAPORS, KEEP UPWIND.

TRANSPORTATION DATA

DEPARTMENT OF TRANSPORTATION HAZARD CLASSIFICATION 49 CFR 172.101: ORM-A

DEPARTMENT OF TRANSPORTATION LABELING REQUIREMENTS 49 CFR 172.101 AND SUBPART E: NONE

DEPARTMENT OF TRANSPORTATION PACKAGING REQUIREMENTS: 49 CFR 173.510 EXCEPTIONS: 49 CFR 173.505

TOXICITY

2,4-XYLENOL (2,4-DIMETHYLPHENOL): TOXICITY DATA: 1040 MG/KG SKIN-RAT LD50; 3200 MG/KG ORAL-RAT LD50; 809 MG/KG ORAL-MOUSE LD50; 183 MG/KG INTRAPERITONEAL-MOUSE LD50; 100 MG/KG INTRAVENOUS-MOUSE LD50; TUMORIGENIC DATA (RTECS). CARCINOGEN STATUS: NONE. LOCAL EFFECTS: CORROSIVE- SKIN, EYE; IRRITANT- INHALATION. ACUTE TOXICITY LEVEL: MODERATELY TOXIC BY DERMAL ABSORPTION AND INGESTION. TARGET EFFECTS: NO DATA AVAILABLE.

HEALTH EFFECTS AND FIRST AID

INHALATION: 2,4-XYLENOL (2,4-DIMETHYLPHENOL): IRRITANT. **ACUTE EXPOSURE-** MAY CAUSE IRRITATION OF THE RESPIRATORY TRACT. SOME PHENOL DERIVATIVES AFFECT THE BLOOD AND THE RESPIRATORY, CIRCULATORY, AND CARDIOVASCULAR SYSTEMS. **CHRONIC EXPOSURE-** NO DATA AVAILABLE.

FIRST AID- REMOVE FROM EXPOSURE AREA TO FRESH AIR IMMEDIATELY. IF BREATHING HAS STOPPED, PERFORM ARTIFICIAL RESPIRATION. KEEP PERSON WARM AND AT REST. TREAT SYMPTOMATICALLY AND SUPPORTIVELY. GET MEDICAL ATTENTION IMMEDIATELY.

SKIN CONTACT: 2,4-XYLENOL (2,4-DIMETHYLPHENOL): CORROSIVE. **ACUTE EXPOSURE-** MAY CAUSE SEVERE IRRITATION AND BURNS. MAY BE ABSORBED THROUGH THE SKIN. SOME PHENOL DERIVATIVES AFFECT THE BLOOD AND THE RESPIRATORY, CIRCULATORY, AND CARDIOVASCULAR SYSTEMS. **CHRONIC EXPOSURE-** EFFECTS DEPEND ON CONCENTRATION AND DURATION OF EXPOSURE. REPEATED OR PROLONGED CONTACT WITH CORROSIVE SUBSTANCES MAY RESULT IN DERMATITIS OR EFFECTS SIMILAR TO ACUTE EXPOSURE.

FIRST AID- REMOVE CONTAMINATED CLOTHING AND SHOES IMMEDIATELY. WASH AFFECTED AREA WITH SOAP OR MILD DETERGENT AND LARGE AMOUNTS OF WATER UNTIL NO EVIDENCE OF CHEMICAL REMAINS (AT LEAST 15-20 MINUTES). IN CASE OF CHEMICAL BURNS, COVER AREA WITH STERILE, DRY DRESSING. BANDAGE SECURELY, BUT NOT TOO TIGHTLY. GET MEDICAL ATTENTION IMMEDIATELY.

EYE CONTACT: 2,4-XYLENOL (2,4-DIMETHYLPHENOL): CORROSIVE. **ACUTE EXPOSURE-** MAY CAUSE SEVERE IRRITATION AND BURNS. **CHRONIC EXPOSURE-** EFFECTS DEPEND ON CONCENTRATION AND DURATION OF EXPOSURE. REPEATED OR

PROLONGED CONTACT WITH CORROSIVE SUBSTANCES MAY RESULT IN CONJUNCTIVITIS OR EFFECTS SIMILAR TO ACUTE EXPOSURE.

FIRST AID- WASH EYES IMMEDIATELY WITH LARGE AMOUNTS OF WATER, OCCASIONALLY LIFTING UPPER AND LOWER LIDS, UNTIL NO EVIDENCE OF CHEMICAL REMAINS (AT LEAST 15-20 MINUTES). CONTINUE IRRIGATING WITH NORMAL SALINE UNTIL THE PH HAS RETURNED TO NORMAL (30-60 MINUTES). COVER WITH STERILE BANDAGES. GET MEDICAL ATTENTION IMMEDIATELY.

INGESTION: 2,4-XYLENOL (2,4-DIMETHYLPHENOL): **ACUTE EXPOSURE**- SOME PHENOL DERIVATIVES AFFECT THE BLOOD AND THE RESPIRATORY, CIRCULATORY, AND CARDIOVASCULAR SYSTEMS. **CHRONIC EXPOSURE**- NO DATA AVAILABLE.

FIRST AID- TREAT SYMPTOMATICALLY AND SUPPORTIVELY. GET MEDICAL ATTENTION IMMEDIATELY. IF VOMITING OCCURS, KEEP HEAD LOWER THAN HIPS TO PREVENT ASPIRATION.

ANTIDOTE: NO SPECIFIC ANTIDOTE. TREAT SYMPTOMATICALLY AND SUPPORTIVELY.

REACTIVITY

REACTIVITY: STABLE UNDER NORMAL TEMPERATURES AND PRESSURES.

INCOMPATIBILITIES: 2,4-XYLENOL (2,4-DIMETHYLPHENOL): OXIDIZERS (STRONG): FIRE AND EXPLOSION HAZARD.

DECOMPOSITION: THERMAL DECOMPOSITION PRODUCTS MAY INCLUDE TOXIC OXIDES OF CARBON.

POLYMERIZATION: HAZARDOUS POLYMERIZATION HAS NOT BEEN REPORTED TO OCCUR UNDER NORMAL TEMPERATURES AND PRESSURES.

STORAGE AND DISPOSAL

OBSERVE ALL FEDERAL, STATE AND LOCAL REGULATIONS WHEN STORING OR DISPOSING OF THIS SUBSTANCE. FOR ASSISTANCE, CONTACT THE DISTRICT DIRECTOR OF THE ENVIRONMENTAL PROTECTION AGENCY.

****STORAGE****

STORE AWAY FROM INCOMPATIBLE SUBSTANCES.

****DISPOSAL****

DISPOSAL MUST BE IN ACCORDANCE WITH STANDARDS APPLICABLE TO GENERATORS OF HAZARDOUS WASTE, 40CFR 262. EPA HAZARDOUS WASTE NUMBER U101.

CONDITIONS TO AVOID

MAY BURN BUT DOES NOT IGNITE READILY. CONTAINERS MAY EXPLODE IN HEAT OF FIRE.

SPILL AND LEAK PROCEDURES

SOIL SPILL: DIG HOLDING AREA SUCH AS LAGOON, POND OR PIT FOR CONTAINMENT. USE PROTECTIVE COVER SUCH AS A PLASTIC SHEET TO PREVENT MATERIAL FROM DISSOLVING IN FIRE EXTINGUISHING WATER OR RAIN.

AIR SPILL: APPLY WATER SPRAY TO KNOCK DOWN VAPORS.

WATER SPILL: LIMIT SPILL MOTION AND DISPERSION WITH NATURAL BARRIERS OR OIL SPILL CONTROL BOOMS.

USE ACTIVATED CARBON TO ABSORB SPILLED SUBSTANCE THAT IS DISSOLVED.

USE SUCTION HOSES TO REMOVE TRAPPED SPILL MATERIAL.

USE MECHANICAL DREDGES OR LIFTS TO EXTRACT IMMOBILIZED MASSES OF POLLUTION AND PRECIPITATES.

OCCUPATIONAL SPILL: DO NOT TOUCH SPILLED MATERIAL. STOP LEAK IF YOU CAN DO IT WITHOUT RISK. USE WATER SPRAY TO REDUCE VAPORS. FOR SMALL SPILLS, TAKE UP WITH SAND OR OTHER ABSORBENT MATERIAL AND PLACE INTO CONTAINERS FOR LATER DISPOSAL. FOR SMALL DRY SPILLS, WITH A CLEAN SHOVEL PLACE MATERIAL INTO CLEAN, DRY CONTAINERS AND COVER. MOVE CONTAINERS FROM SPILL AREA. FOR LARGER SPILLS, DIKE FAR AHEAD OF SPILL FOR LATER DISPOSAL. KEEP UNNECESSARY PEOPLE AWAY. ISOLATE HAZARD AREA AND DENY ENTRY. VENTILATE CLOSED SPACES BEFORE ENTERING.

REPORTABLE QUANTITY (RQ): 100 POUNDS THE SUPERFUND AMENDMENTS AND REAUTHORIZATION ACT (SARA) SECTION 304 REQUIRES THAT A RELEASE EQUAL TO OR GREATER THAN THE REPORTABLE QUANTITY FOR THIS SUBSTANCE BE IMMEDIATELY REPORTED TO THE LOCAL EMERGENCY PLANNING COMMITTEE AND THE STATE EMERGENCY RESPONSE COMMISSION (40 CFR 355.40). IF THE RELEASE OF THIS SUBSTANCE IS REPORTABLE UNDER CERCLA SECTION 103, THE NATIONAL RESPONSE CENTER MUST BE NOTIFIED IMMEDIATELY AT (800) 424-8802 OR (202) 426-2675 IN THE METROPOLITAN WASHINGTON, D.C. AREA (40 CFR 302.6).

PROTECTIVE EQUIPMENT

VENTILATION: PROVIDE LOCAL EXHAUST OR PROCESS ENCLOSURE VENTILATION SYSTEM.

RESPIRATOR: THE FOLLOWING RESPIRATORS ARE RECOMMENDED BASED ON INFORMATION FOUND IN THE PHYSICAL DATA, TOXICITY AND HEALTH EFFECTS SECTIONS. THEY ARE RANKED IN ORDER FROM MINIMUM TO MAXIMUM RESPIRATORY PROTECTION. THE SPECIFIC RESPIRATOR SELECTED MUST BE BASED ON CONTAMINATION LEVELS FOUND IN THE WORK PLACE, MUST NOT EXCEED THE WORKING LIMITS OF THE RESPIRATOR AND BE JOINTLY APPROVED BY THE NATIONAL INSTITUTE FOR OCCUPATIONAL SAFETY AND HEALTH AND THE MINE SAFETY AND HEALTH ADMINISTRATION (NIOSH-MSHA).

DUST AND MIST RESPIRATOR WITH A FULL FACEPIECE.

AIR-PURIFYING FULL FACEPIECE RESPIRATOR WITH A HIGH-EFFICIENCY PARTICULATE FILTER.

POWERED AIR-PURIFYING RESPIRATOR WITH A TIGHT-FITTING FACEPIECE AND HIGH-EFFICIENCY PARTICULATE FILTER.

TYPE 'C' SUPPLIED-AIR RESPIRATOR WITH A FULL FACEPIECE OPERATED IN PRESSURE-DEMAND OR OTHER POSITIVE PRESSURE MODE OR WITH A FULL FACEPIECE, HELMET OR HOOD OPERATED IN CONTINUOUS-FLOW MODE.

SELF-CONTAINED BREATHING APPARATUS WITH A FULL FACEPIECE OPERATED IN PRESSURE-DEMAND OR OTHER POSITIVE PRESSURE MODE.

FOR FIREFIGHTING AND OTHER IMMEDIATELY DANGEROUS TO LIFE OR HEALTH CONDITIONS:

SELF-CONTAINED BREATHING APPARATUS WITH FULL FACEPIECE OPERATED IN PRESSURE-DEMAND OR OTHER POSITIVE PRESSURE MODE.

SUPPLIED-AIR RESPIRATOR WITH FULL FACEPIECE AND OPERATED IN PRESSURE-DEMAND OR OTHER POSITIVE PRESSURE MODE IN COMBINATION WITH AN AUXILIARY SELF-CONTAINED BREATHING APPARATUS OPERATED IN PRESSURE-DEMAND OR OTHER POSITIVE PRESSURE MODE.

CLOTHING: EMPLOYEE MUST WEAR APPROPRIATE PROTECTIVE (IMPERVIOUS) CLOTHING AND EQUIPMENT TO PREVENT ANY POSSIBILITY OF SKIN CONTACT WITH THIS SUBSTANCE.

GLOVES: EMPLOYEE MUST WEAR APPROPRIATE PROTECTIVE GLOVES TO PREVENT CONTACT WITH THIS SUBSTANCE.

EYE PROTECTION: EMPLOYEE MUST WEAR SPLASH-PROOF OR DUST-RESISTANT SAFETY GOGGLES AND A FACESHIELD TO PREVENT CONTACT WITH THIS SUBSTANCE.

EMERGENCY WASH FACILITIES: WHERE THERE IS ANY POSSIBILITY THAT AN EMPLOYEE'S EYES AND/OR SKIN MAY BE EXPOSED TO THIS SUBSTANCE, THE EMPLOYER SHOULD PROVIDE AN EYE WASH FOUNTAIN AND QUICK DRENCH SHOWER WITHIN THE IMMEDIATE WORK AREA FOR EMERGENCY USE.

AUTHORIZED BY- OCCUPATIONAL HEALTH SERVICES, INC.

CREATION DATE: 02/08/90 ***REVISION DATE:*** 05/25/90

MATERIAL SAFETY DATA SHEET

OCCUPATIONAL HEALTH SERVICES, INC.
AGRICULTURE AND PESTICIDE DIVISION
450 SEVENTH AVENUE, SUITE 2407
NEW YORK, NEW YORK 10123
1-800-445-MSDS OR (212) 967-1100

EMERGENCY CONTACT:
JOHN S. BRANSFORD, JR. (615) 292-1180

SUBSTANCE IDENTIFICATION

CAS-NUMBER 93-76-5

SUBSTANCE: **2,4,5-TRICHLOROPHENOXYACETIC ACID**

TRADE NAMES/SYNONYMS: 2,4,5-T; BCF-BUSHKILLER; FORST U 46; FORTEX; TRIOXON; VERTON 2T; U232; PST28690

CHEMICAL FAMILY: CARBOXYLIC ACID, AROMATIC HALOGEN

MOLECULAR FORMULA: C8-H5-CL3-O3

MOLECULAR WEIGHT: 255.48

CERCLA RATINGS (SCALE 0-3): HEALTH=3 FIRE=0 REACTIVITY=0 PERSISTENCE=3

NFPA RATINGS (SCALE 0-4): HEALTH=3 FIRE=0 REACTIVITY=0

COMPONENTS AND CONTAMINANTS

COMPONENT: 2,4,5-TRICHLOROPHENOXYACETIC ACID ***PERCENT:*** 100
CAS# 93-76-5

OTHER CONTAMINANTS: MAY CONTAIN <0.1 PPM 2,3,7,8-TETRACHLORODIBENZO-PARA-DIOXIN

EXPOSURE LIMITS: 2,4,5-TRICHLOROPHENOXYACETIC ACID: 10 MG/M3 OSHA TWA 10 MG/M3 ACGIH TWA
1000 POUNDS CERCLA SECTION 103 REPORTABLE QUANTITY

PHYSICAL DATA

DESCRIPTION: WHITE CRYSTALS ***BOILING POINT:*** DECOMPOSES ABOVE MELTING POINT

MELTING POINT: 316 F (158 C) ***SPECIFIC GRAVITY:*** 1.803

VAPOR PRESSURE: <0.01 MMHG @ 25 C ***SOLUBILITY IN WATER:*** 0.03% @ 25 C
SOLVENT SOLUBILITY: BENZENE, ALCOHOL

FIRE AND EXPLOSION DATA

FIRE AND EXPLOSION HAZARD: NEGLIGIBLE FIRE HAZARD WHEN EXPOSED TO HEAT OR FLAME.

FIREFIGHTING MEDIA: DRY CHEMICAL, CARBON DIOXIDE, HALON, WATER SPRAY OR ALCOHOL FOAM (1987 EMERGENCY RESPONSE GUIDEBOOK, DOT P 5800.4).
FOR LARGER FIRES, USE WATER SPRAY, FOG OR STANDARD FOAM (1987 EMERGENCY RESPONSE GUIDEBOOK, DOT P 5800.4).

FIREFIGHTING: MOVE CONTAINERS FROM FIRE AREA IF POSSIBLE. COOL CONTAINERS EXPOSED TO FLAMES WITH WATER FROM SIDE UNTIL WELL AFTER FIRE IS OUT. STAY AWAY FROM STORAGE TANK ENDS (1987 EMERGENCY RESPONSE GUIDEBOOK, DOT P 5800.4, GUIDE PAGE 59).
USE AGENTS SUITABLE FOR TYPE OF FIRE. AVOID BREATHING VAPORS OR DUSTS, KEEP UPWIND.

TRANSPORTATION DATA

DEPARTMENT OF TRANSPORTATION HAZARD CLASSIFICATION 49 CFR 172.101: ORM-A
DEPARTMENT OF TRANSPORTATION LABELING REQUIREMENTS 49 CFR 172.101 AND SUBPART E: NONE
DEPARTMENT OF TRANSPORTATION PACKAGING REQUIREMENTS: 49 CFR 173.510 EXCEPTIONS: 49 CFR 173.505

TOXICITY

2,4,5-TRICHLOROPHENOXYACETIC ACID: TOXICITY DATA: 1535 MG/KG SKIN-RAT LD50; 300 MG/KG ORAL-RAT LD50; 242 MG/KG ORAL-MOUSE LD50; 100 MG/KG ORAL-DOG LD50; 425 MG/KG ORAL-HAMSTER LD50; 381 MG/KG ORAL-GUINEA PIG LD50; 500 MG/KG ORAL-MAMMAL LD50; 500 MG/KG UNREPORTED-RAT LD50; MUTAGENIC DATA (RTECS); REPRODUCTIVE EFFECTS DATA (RTECS); TUMORIGENIC DATA (RTECS). CARCINOGEN STATUS: HUMAN LIMITED EVIDENCE*, ANIMAL INADEQUATE EVIDENCE (IARC GROUP-2B*) * FOR CHLOROPHENOXY HERBICIDES. STUDIES REVEALED A SIGNIFICANT INCREASE IN SOFT-TISSUE SARCOMAS, MALIGNANT LYMPHOMAS AND BRONCHIAL CARCINOMAS IN WORKERS EXPOSED TO CHLOROPHENOXY HERBICIDES. LOCAL EFFECTS: IRRITANT- INHALATION, SKIN, AND EYES. ACUTE TOXICITY LEVEL: TOXIC BY INGESTION; MODERATELY TOXIC BY DERMAL ABSORPTION. TARGET EFFECTS: POISONING MAY AFFECT THE GASTROINTESTINAL TRACT AND CARDIOVASCULAR SYSTEM. AT INCREASED RISK FROM EXPOSURE: PERSONS WITH PREEXISTING LIVER, GASTROINTESTINAL TRACT OR SKIN DISORDERS. ADDITIONAL DATA: STIMULANTS SUCH AS EPINEPHRINE MAY INDUCE VENTRICULAR FIBRILLATION.

HEALTH EFFECTS AND FIRST AID

INHALATION: 2,4,5-TRICHLOROPHENOXYACETIC ACID: IRRITANT. 5000 MG/M3 IMMEDIATELY DANGEROUS TO LIFE OR HEALTH. **ACUTE EXPOSURE-** MAY CAUSE IRRITATION WITH SORE THROAT AND BURNING SENSATIONS IN THE NASOPHARYNX AND CHEST, COUGHING, LACRIMATION, RHINITIS, DULLNESS, DIZZINESS, AND ATAXIA. IF SUFFICIENT AMOUNTS ARE ABSORBED THROUGH THE LUNGS, EFFECTS AS DESCRIBED IN ACUTE INGESTION MAY OCCUR. **CHRONIC EXPOSURE-** OCCUPATIONAL EXPOSURE TO 2,4,5-T AND ITS DERIVATIVES HAS PRODUCED HEADACHE, DECREASED AUDITORY ACUITY, GASTROINTESTINAL SYMPTOMS OF NAUSEA, VOMITING, DIARRHEA, ABDOMINAL PAINS, AND BLOOD IN THE STOOL, CHLORACNE, PORPHYRIA CUTANEA TARDIA, HYPERTRICHOSIS, HYPERPIGMENTATION, INCREASED SKIN FRAGILITY, LIVER DISORDERS, PERSONALITY CHANGES, AND PERIPHERAL NEUROPATHY. MANY OF THESE EFFECTS MAY BE DUE TO DIOXINS, ESPECIALLY TCDD, AS CONTAMINANTS. EPIDEMIOLOGICAL STUDIES HAVE INDICATED AN ASSOCIATION BETWEEN EXPOSURE TO 2,4,5-T COMPOUNDS AND AN INCREASED PREVALENCE OF REPORTED SEXUAL DYSFUNCTION AND DECREASED LIBIDO, ABNORMAL SENSORY FINDINGS, GASTROINTESTINAL TRACT ULCER, AND BIRTH MALFORMATIONS OF THE FEET. AN INCREASED PREVALENCE OF SLOWED NERVE CONDUCTION VELOCITY WITH NO ASSOCIATED SYMPTOMS WAS REPORTED IN A STUDY OF CHEMICAL WORKERS EMPLOYED IN THE PRODUCTION OF 2,4-D AND 2,4,5-T. EPIDEMIOLOGICAL STUDIES REVEALED A SIGNIFICANT INCREASE IN SOFT-TISSUE SARCOMAS, MALIGNANT LYMPHOMAS, AND BRONCHIAL CARCINOMAS IN WORKERS EXPOSED TO CHLOROPHENOXY HERBICIDES INCLUDING 2,4,5-T.
FIRST AID- REMOVE FROM EXPOSURE AREA TO FRESH AIR IMMEDIATELY. IF BREATHING HAS STOPPED, PERFORM ARTIFICIAL RESPIRATION. KEEP PERSON WARM AND AT REST. TREAT SYMPTOMATICALLY AND SUPPORTIVELY. GET MEDICAL ATTENTION IMMEDIATELY.

SKIN CONTACT: 2,4,5-TRICHLOROPHENOXYACETIC ACID: IRRITANT. **ACUTE EXPOSURE-** MAY CAUSE IRRITATION. IF SUFFICIENT AMOUNTS ARE ABSORBED THROUGH THE SKIN, EFFECTS AS DESCRIBED IN ACUTE INGESTION MAY OCCUR. **CHRONIC EXPOSURE-** PROLONGED OR REPEATED EXPOSURE MAY CAUSE DERMATITIS AND EFFECTS AS DESCRIBED IN CHRONIC INHALATION.
FIRST AID- REMOVE CONTAMINATED CLOTHING AND SHOES IMMEDIATELY. WASH AFFECTED AREA WITH SOAP OR MILD DETERGENT AND LARGE AMOUNTS OF WATER UNTIL NO EVIDENCE OF CHEMICAL REMAINS (APPROXIMATELY 15-20 MINUTES). GET MEDICAL ATTENTION IMMEDIATELY.

EYE CONTACT: 2,4,5-TRICHLOROPHENOXYACETIC ACID: IRRITANT. **ACUTE EXPOSURE-** MAY CAUSE IRRITATION. **CHRONIC EXPOSURE-** MAY CAUSE CONJUNCTIVITIS AFTER REPEATED OR PROLONGED EXPOSURE.
FIRST AID- WASH EYES IMMEDIATELY WITH LARGE AMOUNTS OF WATER OR NORMAL SALINE, OCCASIONALLY LIFTING UPPER AND LOWER LIDS, UNTIL NO EVIDENCE OF CHEMICAL REMAINS (APPROXIMATELY 15-20 MINUTES). GET MEDICAL ATTENTION IMMEDIATELY.

INGESTION: 2,4,5-TRICHLOROPHENOXYACETIC ACID: TOXIC. **ACUTE EXPOSURE-** INGESTION OF 2,4,5-T AND ITS DERIVATIVES MAY CAUSE IRRITATION OF THE MOUTH, THROAT, AND GASTROINTESTINAL TRACT, NAUSEA, VOMITING, CHEST AND ABDOMINAL PAIN, AND DIARRHEA. INGESTION OF VERY LARGE DOSES MAY PRODUCE METABOLIC ACIDOSIS, FEVER OR SUBNORMAL TEMPERATURES, HYPERVENTILATION, HYPOTENSION, VASODILATION, FLUSHING OF THE SKIN, SWEATING, CARDIAC ARRHYTHMIAS, TACHYCARDIA, LETHARGY, WEAKNESS, INTERCOSTAL PARALYSIS, RENAL AND HEPATIC DYSFUNCTION, MYOTONIA, COMA, AND CONVULSIONS. DAMAGE TO SKELETAL MUSCLE MAY BE MANIFEST BY MUSCLE TWITCHING AND ACHING WITH ELEVATED SERUM ENZYMES AND MYOGLOBIN IN THE BLOOD AND URINE. DEATH MAY BE DUE TO CIRCULATORY COLLAPSE. **CHRONIC EXPOSURE-** STUDIES HAVE ESTABLISHED THAT 2,4,5-TRICHLOROPHENOXYACETIC ACID IS FETOTOXIC AND TERATOGENIC AT DOSES AS LOW AS 35 MG/KG IN MICE; 4.6 MG/KG IN RATS; AND 20 MG/KG IN HAMSTERS. CHRONIC INGESTION OF 2,4,5-TRICHLOROPHENOXYACETIC ACID IN MICE PRODUCED A SIGNIFICANT INCREASE IN THE INCIDENCE OF NEOPLASTIC LESIONS.
FIRST AID- IF THE PERSON IS CONSCIOUS AND NOT CONVULSING, INDUCE EMESIS BY GIVING SYRUP OF IPECAC (KEEPING THE HEAD BELOW THE HIPS TO PREVENT ASPIRATION) FOLLOWED BY WATER. REPEAT IN 20 MINUTES IF NOT EFFECTIVE INITIALLY. IN PATIENTS WITH DEPRESSED RESPIRATION OR IF EMESIS IS NOT PRODUCED, PERFORM GASTRIC LAVAGE WITH ACTIVATED CHARCOAL. FOLLOW WITH A SALINE CATHARTIC (DREISBACH, HANDBOOK OF POISONING, 12TH ED.). TREAT SYMPTOMATICALLY AND SUPPORTIVELY. GASTRIC LAVAGE SHOULD BE PERFORMED BY QUALIFIED MEDICAL PERSONNEL. GET MEDICAL ATTENTION IMMEDIATELY.

ANTIDOTE: NO SPECIFIC ANTIDOTE. TREAT SYMPTOMATICALLY AND SUPPORTIVELY.

REACTIVITY

REACTIVITY: STABLE UNDER NORMAL TEMPERATURES AND PRESSURES.

INCOMPATIBILITIES: 2,4,5-TRICHLOROPHENOXYACETIC ACID: COMMON METALS: MAY CAUSE CORROSION. STRONG OXIDIZERS: MAY CAUSE FIRE AND EXPLOSION.

DECOMPOSITION: THERMAL DECOMPOSITION MAY RELEASE CORROSIVE FUMES OF HYDROGEN CHLORIDE AND TOXIC OXIDES OF CARBON.

POLYMERIZATION: HAZARDOUS POLYMERIZATION HAS NOT BEEN REPORTED TO OCCUR UNDER NORMAL TEMPERATURES AND PRESSURES.

STORAGE AND DISPOSAL

OBSERVE ALL FEDERAL, STATE AND LOCAL REGULATIONS WHEN STORING OR DISPOSING OF THIS SUBSTANCE. FOR ASSISTANCE, CONTACT THE DISTRICT DIRECTOR OF THE ENVIRONMENTAL PROTECTION AGENCY.

****STORAGE****

STORE IN ACCORDANCE WITH 40 CFR 165 RECOMMENDED PROCEDURES FOR THE DISPOSAL AND STORAGE OF PESTICIDES AND PESTICIDE CONTAINERS.

****DISPOSAL****

DISPOSAL MUST BE IN ACCORDANCE WITH 40 CFR 165 RECOMMENDED PROCEDURES FOR THE DISPOSAL AND STORAGE OF PESTICIDES AND PESTICIDE CONTAINERS.

CONDITIONS TO AVOID

MAY BURN BUT DOES NOT IGNITE READILY. CONTAINERS MAY EXPLODE IN HEAT OF FIRE.

SPILL AND LEAK PROCEDURES

SOIL SPILL: DIG A PIT, POND, LAGOON OR HOLDING AREA TO CONTAIN LIQUID OR SOLID MATERIAL. COVER SOLIDS WITH A PLASTIC SHEET TO PREVENT DISSOLVING IN RAIN OR FIREFIGHTING WATER.

WATER SPILL: USE SUCTION HOSES TO REMOVE TRAPPED SPILL MATERIAL.
IF DISSOLVED, AT A CONCENTRATION OF 10 PPM OR GREATER, APPLY ACTIVATED CARBON AT TEN TIMES THE AMOUNT THAT HAS BEEN SPILLED.
USE MECHANICAL DREDGES OR LIFTS TO EXTRACT IMMOBILIZED MASSES OF POLLUTION AND PRECIPITATES.

OCCUPATIONAL SPILL: DO NOT TOUCH SPILLED MATERIAL. STOP LEAK IF YOU CAN DO IT WITHOUT RISK. USE WATER SPRAY TO REDUCE VAPORS. FOR SMALL SPILLS, TAKE UP WITH SAND OR OTHER ABSORBENT MATERIAL AND PLACE INTO CONTAINERS FOR LATER DISPOSAL. FOR SMALL DRY SPILLS, WITH A CLEAN SHOVEL PLACE MATERIAL INTO CLEAN, DRY CONTAINERS AND COVER. MOVE CONTAINERS FROM SPILL AREA. FOR LARGER SPILLS, DIKE FAR AHEAD OF SPILL FOR LATER DISPOSAL. KEEP UNNECESSARY PEOPLE AWAY. ISOLATE HAZARD AREA AND DENY ENTRY. VENTILATE CLOSED SPACES BEFORE ENTERING. REPORTABLE QUANTITY (RQ): 1000 POUNDS THE SUPERFUND AMENDMENTS AND REAUTHORIZATION ACT (SARA) SECTION 304 REQUIRES THAT A RELEASE EQUAL TO OR GREATER THAN THE REPORTABLE QUANTITY FOR THIS SUBSTANCE BE IMMEDIATELY REPORTED TO THE LOCAL EMERGENCY PLANNING COMMITTEE AND THE STATE EMERGENCY RESPONSE COMMISSION (40 CFR 355.40). IF THE RELEASE OF THIS SUBSTANCE IS REPORTABLE UNDER CERCLA SECTION 103, THE NATIONAL RESPONSE CENTER MUST BE NOTIFIED IMMEDIATELY AT (800) 424-8802 OR (202) 426-2675 IN THE METROPOLITAN WASHINGTON, D.C. AREA (40 CFR 302.6).

PROTECTIVE EQUIPMENT

VENTILATION: PROVIDE LOCAL EXHAUST OR PROCESS ENCLOSURE VENTILATION TO MEET PUBLISHED EXPOSURE LIMITS.

RESPIRATOR: THE FOLLOWING RESPIRATORS AND MAXIMUM USE CONCENTRATIONS ARE RECOMMENDATIONS BY THE U.S. DEPARTMENT OF HEALTH AND HUMAN SERVICES, NIOSH POCKET GUIDE TO CHEMICAL HAZARDS; NIOSH CRITERIA DOCUMENTS OR BY THE U.S. DEPARTMENT OF LABOR, 29 CFR 1910 SUBPART Z. THE SPECIFIC RESPIRATOR SELECTED MUST BE BASED ON CONTAMINATION LEVELS FOUND IN THE WORK PLACE, MUST NOT EXCEED THE WORKING LIMITS OF THE RESPIRATOR AND BE JOINTLY APPROVED BY THE NATIONAL INSTITUTE FOR OCCUPATIONAL SAFETY AND HEALTH AND THE MINE SAFETY AND HEALTH ADMINISTRATION (NIOSH-MSHA).

2,4,5-TRICHLOROPHENOXYACETIC ACID: 50 MG/M3- ANY DUST AND MIST RESPIRATOR EXCEPT SINGLE-USE RESPIRATORS.

100 MG/M3- ANY DUST AND MIST RESPIRATOR EXCEPT SINGLE-USE AND QUARTER-MASK RESPIRATORS. ANY SUPPLIED-AIR RESPIRATOR. ANY SELF-CONTAINED BREATHING APPARATUS.

250 MG/M3- ANY SUPPLIED-AIR RESPIRATOR OPERATED IN A CONTINUOUS FLOW MODE. ANY POWERED AIR-PURIFYING RESPIRATOR WITH A DUST AND MIST FILTER.

500 MG/M3- ANY AIR-PURIFYING FULL FACEPIECE RESPIRATOR WITH A HIGH-EFFICIENCY PARTICULATE FILTER. ANY SUPPLIED-AIR RESPIRATOR WITH A FULL FACEPIECE. ANY POWERED AIR-PURIFYING RESPIRATOR WITH A TIGHT-FITTING FACEPIECE AND A HIGH-EFFICIENCY PARTICULATE FILTER. ANY SELF-CONTAINED BREATHING APPARATUS WITH A FULL FACEPIECE. ANY SUPPLIED-AIR RESPIRATOR WITH A TIGHT-FITTING FACEPIECE OPERATED IN A CONTINUOUS FLOW MODE.

5000 MG/M3- ANY SUPPLIED-AIR RESPIRATOR WITH A HALF-MASK AND OPERATED IN A PRESSURE-DEMAND OR OTHER POSITIVE PRESSURE MODE

ESCAPE- ANY AIR-PURFYING FULL FACEPIECE RESPIRATOR WITH A HIGH-EFFICIENCY PARTICULATE FILTER. ANY APPROPRIATE ESCAPE-TYPE SELF-CONTAINED BREATHING APPARATUS.

FOR FIREFIGHTING AND OTHER IMMEDIATELY DANGEROUS TO LIFE OR HEALTH CONDITIONS:

SELF-CONTAINED BREATHING APPARATUS WITH FULL FACEPIECE OPERATED IN PRESSURE-DEMAND OR OTHER POSITIVE PRESSURE MODE.

SUPPLIED-AIR RESPIRATOR WITH FULL FACEPIECE AND OPERATED IN PRESSURE-DEMAND OR OTHER POSITIVE PRESSURE MODE IN COMBINATION WITH AN AUXILIARY SELF-CONTAINED BREATHING APPARATUS OPERATED IN PRESSURE-DEMAND OR OTHER POSITIVE PRESSURE MODE.

CLOTHING: EMPLOYEE MUST WEAR APPROPRIATE PROTECTIVE (IMPERVIOUS) CLOTHING AND EQUIPMENT TO PREVENT REPEATED OR PROLONGED SKIN CONTACT WITH THIS SUBSTANCE.

GLOVES: EMPLOYEE MUST WEAR APPROPRIATE PROTECTIVE GLOVES TO PREVENT CONTACT WITH THIS SUBSTANCE.

EYE PROTECTION: EMPLOYEE MUST WEAR SPLASH-PROOF OR DUST-RESISTANT SAFETY GOGGLES TO PREVENT EYE CONTACT WITH THIS SUBSTANCE.

EMERGENCY EYE WASH: WHERE THERE IS ANY POSSIBILITY THAT AN EMPLOYEE'S EYES MAY BE EXPOSED TO THIS SUBSTANCE, THE EMPLOYER SHOULD PROVIDE AN EYE WASH FOUNTAIN WITHIN THE IMMEDIATE WORK AREA FOR EMERGENCY USE.

AUTHORIZED BY- OCCUPATIONAL HEALTH SERVICES, INC.

CREATION DATE: 10/05/89 ***REVISION DATE:*** 07/12/90

MATERIAL SAFETY DATA SHEET

OCCUPATIONAL HEALTH SERVICES, INC.
AGRICULTURE AND PESTICIDE DIVISION
450 SEVENTH AVENUE, SUITE 2407
NEW YORK, NEW YORK 10123
1-800-445-MSDS OR (212) 967-1100

EMERGENCY CONTACT:
JOHN S. BRANSFORD, JR. (615) 292-1180

SUBSTANCE IDENTIFICATION

CAS-NUMBER 95-95-4

SUBSTANCE: 2,4,5-TRICHLOROPHENOL

TRADE NAMES/SYNONYMS: 2,4,5-TRICHLORO PHENOL; DOWICIDE 2; PREVENTOL I; TCP; U230; NA 2020; PST28700

CHEMICAL FAMILY: PHENOL
HALOGEN COMPOUND, AROMATIC

MOLECULAR FORMULA: C6-H3-CL3-O

MOLECULAR WEIGHT: 197.44

CERCLA RATINGS (SCALE 0-3): HEALTH=2 FIRE=0 REACTIVITY=0 PERSISTENCE=3

NFPA RATINGS (SCALE 0-4): HEALTH=1 FIRE=1 REACTIVITY=0

COMPONENTS AND CONTAMINANTS

COMPONENT: 2,4,5-TRICHLOROPHENOL ***PERCENT:*** 100
CAS# 95-95-4

OTHER CONTAMINANTS: NONE

EXPOSURE LIMITS: NO OCCUPATIONAL EXPOSURE LIMITS ESTABLISHED BY OSHA, ACGIH, OR NIOSH.
2,4,5-TRICHLOROPHENOL: 10 POUNDS CERCLA SECTION 103 REPORTABLE QUANTITY SUBJECT TO SARA SECTION 313 ANNUAL TOXIC CHEMICAL RELEASE REPORTING

PHYSICAL DATA

DESCRIPTION: COLORLESS NEEDLES OR GRAY FLAKES WITH A STRONG PHENOLIC ODOR

BOILING POINT: 486 F (252 C) ***MELTING POINT:*** 142-145 F (61-63 C)

SPECIFIC GRAVITY: 1.7 @ 25/4 C ***VAPOR PRESSURE:*** 1 MMHG @ 72 C

SOLUBILITY IN WATER: <0.2%

SOLVENT SOLUBILITY: ALCOHOL, ACETONE, ETHER, BENZENE, CARBON TETRACHLORIDE

FIRE AND EXPLOSION DATA

FIRE AND EXPLOSION HAZARD: NEGLIGIBLE FIRE HAZARD WHEN EXPOSED TO HEAT OR FLAME.

FIREFIGHTING MEDIA: DRY CHEMICAL, CARBON DIOXIDE, HALON, WATER SPRAY OR STANDARD FOAM (1987 EMERGENCY RESPONSE GUIDEBOOK, DOT P 5800.4).
FOR LARGER FIRES, USE WATER SPRAY, FOG OR STANDARD FOAM (1987 EMERGENCY RESPONSE GUIDEBOOK, DOT P 5800.4).

FIREFIGHTING: MOVE CONTAINERS FROM FIRE AREA IF POSSIBLE (1987 EMERGENCY RESPONSE GUIDEBOOK, DOT P 5800.4, GUIDE PAGE 53).
USE AGENTS SUITABLE FOR TYPE OF FIRE. AVOID BREATHING HAZARDOUS VAPORS, KEEP UPWIND.

TRANSPORTATION DATA

DEPARTMENT OF TRANSPORTATION HAZARD CLASSIFICATION 49 CFR 172.101: ORM-A

DEPARTMENT OF TRANSPORTATION LABELING REQUIREMENTS 49 CFR 172.101 AND SUBPART E: NONE

DEPARTMENT OF TRANSPORTATION PACKAGING REQUIREMENTS: 49 CFR 173.510 EXCEPTIONS: 49 CFR 173.505

TOXICITY

2,4,5-TRICHLOROPHENOL: TOXICITY DATA: 820 MG/KG ORAL-RAT LD50; 600 MG/KG ORAL-MOUSE LD50; 1 GM/KG ORAL-GUINEA PIG LD50; 2260 MG/KG SUBCUTANEOUS-RAT LD50; 56 MG/KG INTRAVENOUS-MOUSE LD50; 355 MG/KG INTRAPERITONEAL-RAT LD50; 150 MG/KG UNREPORTED-MAMMAL LD50; MUTAGENIC DATA (RTECS); REPRODUCTIVE EFFECTS DATA (RTECS); TUMORIGENIC DATA (RTECS). CARCINOGEN STATUS: HUMAN LIMITED EVIDENCE, ANIMAL INADEQUATE EVIDENCE (IARC GROUP-2B). CASES OF SOFT-TISSUE SARCOMA, APPARENTLY SUBSTANTIALLY IN EXCESS OF THE EXPECTED NUMBER HAVE BEEN REPORTED IN COHORTS OF MEN INVOLVED IN THE MANUFACTURE OF TRICHLOROPHENOLS (MAINLY, IF NOT ENTIRELY, 2,4,5-TRICHLOROPHENOL). IN THESE CASES, EXPOSURE TO TRICHLOROPHENOLS COULD NOT BE DISTINGUISHED WITH ANY CERTAINTY FROM EXPOSURE TO TETRACHLORODIBENZO-DIOXIN (TCDD). LOCAL EFFECTS: CORROSIVE- SKIN; IRRITANT- INHALATION AND EYES. ACUTE TOXICITY LEVEL: MODERATELY TOXIC BY INGESTION. TARGET EFFECTS: POISONING MAY AFFECT THE LIVER AND KIDNEYS.

HEALTH EFFECTS AND FIRST AID

INHALATION: 2,4,5-TRICHLOROPHENOL: IRRITANT. **ACUTE EXPOSURE-** MAY CAUSE IRRITATION OF MUCOUS MEMBRANES OF THE NOSE AND THROAT, INTENSE THIRST, PROFUSE SWEATING, NAUSEA, CYANOSIS, HYPERNEA, HEMOLYSIS, CONVULSIONS, COMA, PULMONARY EDEMA FOLLOWED BY PNEUMONIA, AND OTHER SYMPTOMS AS IN ACUTE INGESTION. LIVER AND KIDNEY DAMAGE MAY OCCUR. **CHRONIC EXPOSURE-** REPEATED OR PROLONGED EXPOSURE MAY CAUSE SYMPTOMS AS IN ACUTE EXPOSURE.

FIRST AID- REMOVE FROM EXPOSURE AREA TO FRESH AIR IMMEDIATELY. IF BREATHING HAS STOPPED, PERFORM ARTIFICIAL RESPIRATION. KEEP PERSON WARM AND AT REST. TREAT SYMPTOMATICALLY AND SUPPORTIVELY. GET MEDICAL ATTENTION IMMEDIATELY.

SKIN CONTACT: 2,4,5-TRICHLOROPHENOL: CORROSIVE. **ACUTE EXPOSURE-** MAY CAUSE IRRITATION, WITH PAIN, REDNESS, AND EDEMA; NAUSEA; ABDOMINAL PAIN; VOMITING; DIARRHEA; INTENSE THIRST; PROFUSE SWEATING; HYPERACTIVITY; STUPOR; CYANOSIS; HEMOLYSIS; HYPERNEA; BLOOD PRESSURE FALL; CONVULSIONS; COMA; PULMONARY EDEMA FOLLOWED BY PNEUMONIA. DEATH IS POSSIBLE FROM RESPIRATORY FAILURE. LIVER AND KIDNEY DAMAGE WITH JAUNDICE AND OLIGURIA OR ANURIA ARE POSSIBLE. **CHRONIC EXPOSURE-** EFFECTS DEPEND ON CONCENTRATION AND DURATION OF EXPOSURE. REPEATED OR PROLONGED CONTACT MAY CAUSE DERMATITIS, CHLORACNE, MILD TO MODERATE CHEMICAL BURNS IN MAN, OR EFFECTS AS IN ACUTE POISONING. AS EVALUATED BY RTECS, ADMINISTRATION TO MICE BY SKIN EXPOSURE RESULTED IN A STATISTICALLY SIGNIFICANT INCREASE IN THE INCIDENCE OF NEOPLASTIC TUMORS OF THE SKIN AND APPENDAGES.

FIRST AID- REMOVE CONTAMINATED CLOTHING AND SHOES IMMEDIATELY. WASH AFFECTED AREA WITH SOAP OR MILD DETERGENT AND LARGE AMOUNTS OF WATER UNTIL NO EVIDENCE OF CHEMICAL REMAINS (AT LEAST 15-20 MINUTES). IN CASE OF CHEMICAL BURNS, COVER AREA WITH STERILE, DRY DRESSING. BANDAGE SECURELY, BUT NOT TOO TIGHTLY. GET MEDICAL ATTENTION IMMEDIATELY.

EYE CONTACT: 2,4,5-TRICHLOROPHENOL: IRRITANT. **ACUTE EXPOSURE-** MAY CAUSE IRRITATION, WITH PAIN, REDNESS, AND SWELLING; IRITIS; AND POSSIBLE CORNEAL INJURY. **CHRONIC EXPOSURE-** REPEATED OR PROLONGED EXPOSURE MAY CAUSE CONJUNCTIVITIS.

FIRST AID- WASH EYES IMMEDIATELY WITH LARGE AMOUNTS OF WATER OR NORMAL SALINE, OCCASIONALLY LIFTING UPPER AND LOWER LIDS, UNTIL NO EVIDENCE OF CHEMICAL REMAINS (APPROXIMATELY 15-20 MINUTES). GET MEDICAL ATTENTION IMMEDIATELY.

INGESTION: 2,4,5-TRICHLOROPHENOL: IRRITANT. **ACUTE EXPOSURE-** MAY CAUSE ABDOMINAL PAIN, NAUSEA, VOMITING, DIARRHEA, INTENSE THIRST, PROFUSE SWEATING, HYPERACTIVITY, STUPOR, CYANOSIS, HEMOLYSIS, HYPERNEA, BLOOD PRESSURE FALL, CONVULSIONS, COMA, AND PULMONARY EDEMA FOLLOWED BY PNEUMONIA. DEATH DUE TO RESPIRATORY FAILURE IS POSSIBLE. LIVER AND KIDNEY DAMAGE WITH JAUNDICE AND OLIGURIA OR ANURIA ARE POSSIBLE. **CHRONIC EXPOSURE-** EFFECTS ON THE NEWBORN HAVE BEEN REPORTED FROM REPEATED OR PROLONGED INGESTION IN MICE. REPEATED OR PROLONGED EXPOSURE MAY CAUSE SYMPTOMS AS IN ACUTE INGESTION.

FIRST AID- MAINTAIN OPEN AIRWAY. GET MEDICAL ATTENTION. TREAT SHOCK. IF CONSCIOUS, USE GASTRIC LAVAGE WITH A CONCENTRATED SOLUTION OF SODIUM BICARBONATE, OR 5% DISODIUM PHOSPHATE DIHYDRATE, OR MILK. AFTER LAVAGE, RETAIN 100-300 MILLILITERS OF SOLUTION IN STOMACH TO FORM POORLY ABSORBED IRON COMPOUNDS. ADMINISTER RECTAL LAVAGE WITH ONE OF THE ABOVE SOLUTIONS, IF THERE IS DIARRHEA, HYPERPERISTALSIS OF INTESTINAL TRACT, OR 3 OR MORE HOUR LAPSE SINCE INGESTION.IN CRITICAL CASES, ADMINISTER CHELATING AGENT SUCH AS EDETATE OR DIETHYLENETRIAMINE-PENTA-ACETIC ACID, OR DEFEROXAMINE MESYLATE (ARENA, POISONING, 4TH EDITION, 1979).

ANTIDOTE: NO SPECIFIC ANTIDOTE. TREAT SYMPTOMATICALLY AND SUPPORTIVELY.

REACTIVITY

REACTIVITY: STABLE UNDER NORMAL TEMPERATURES AND PRESSURES.

INCOMPATIBILITIES: 2,4,5-TRICHLOROPHENOLS: ALKALINE MEDIA: REACTS AT HIGH TEMPERATURES RELEASING DIOXIN. OXIDIZERS: REACTS.

DECOMPOSITION: THERMAL DECOMPOSITION MAY RELEASE CORROSIVE FUMES OF HYDROGEN CHLORIDE OR TOXIC CHLORINE GAS.

POLYMERIZATION: HAZARDOUS POLYMERIZATION HAS NOT BEEN REPORTED TO OCCUR UNDER NORMAL TEMPERATURES AND PRESSURES.

STORAGE AND DISPOSAL

OBSERVE ALL FEDERAL, STATE AND LOCAL REGULATIONS WHEN STORING OR DISPOSING OF THIS SUBSTANCE. FOR ASSISTANCE, CONTACT THE DISTRICT DIRECTOR OF THE ENVIRONMENTAL PROTECTION AGENCY.

****STORAGE****

STORE AWAY FROM INCOMPATIBLE SUBSTANCES.

****DISPOSAL****

DISPOSAL MUST BE IN ACCORDANCE WITH STANDARDS APPLICABLE TO GENERATORS OF HAZARDOUS WASTE, 40CFR 262. EPA HAZARDOUS WASTE NUMBER U230.

2,4,5-TRICHLOROPHENOL - REGULATORY LEVEL: 400.0 MG/L MATERIALS WHICH CONTAIN THE ABOVE SUBSTANCE AT OR ABOVE THE REGULATORY LEVEL MEET THE EPA CHARACTERISTIC OF TOXICITY, AND MUST BE DISPOSED OF IN ACCORDANCE WITH 40 CFR PART 262. EPA HAZARDOUS WASTE NUMBER D041.

CONDITIONS TO AVOID

MAY BURN BUT DOES NOT IGNITE READILY.

SPILL AND LEAK PROCEDURES

SOIL SPILL: DIG A HOLDING AREA SUCH AS PIT, POND OR LAGOON TO CONTAIN SPILLED MATERIAL. USE PROTECTIVE COVER SUCH AS A PLASTIC SHEET TO PREVENT DISSOLVING IN FIREFIGHTING WATER OR RAIN.

WATER SPILL: USE NATURAL DEEP WATER POCKETS, EXCAVATED LAGOONS, OR SAND BAG BARRIERS TO TRAP MATERIAL AT BOTTOM. USE ACTIVATED CARBON AT 10 TIMES THE SPILLED AMOUNT IF IT IS DISSOLVED AT 10 PPM OR GREATER CONCENTRATION. REMOVE TRAPPED MATERIAL WITH SUCTION HOSES. USE MECHANICAL DREDGES OR LIFTS TO REMOVE IMMOBILIZED MASSES OF POLLUTION AND PRECIPITATES.

OCCUPATIONAL SPILL: DO NOT TOUCH SPILLED MATERIAL. STOP LEAK IF YOU CAN DO IT WITHOUT RISK. FOR SMALL SPILLS, TAKE UP WITH SAND OR OTHER ABSORBENT MATERIAL AND PLACE INTO CONTAINERS FOR LATER DISPOSAL. FOR SMALL DRY SPILLS, WITH A CLEAN SHOVEL PLACE MATERIAL INTO CLEAN, DRY CONTAINER AND COVER. MOVE CONTAINERS FROM SPILL AREA. FOR LARGER SPILLS, DIKE FAR AHEAD OF SPILL FOR LATER DISPOSAL. KEEP UNNECESSARY PEOPLE AWAY. ISOLATE HAZARD AREA AND DENY ENTRY.

REPORTABLE QUANTITY (RQ): 10 POUNDS THE SUPERFUND AMENDMENTS AND REAUTHORIZATION ACT (SARA) SECTION 304 REQUIRES THAT A RELEASE EQUAL TO OR GREATER THAN THE REPORTABLE QUANTITY FOR THIS SUBSTANCE BE IMMEDIATELY REPORTED TO THE LOCAL EMERGENCY PLANNING COMMITTEE AND THE STATE EMERGENCY RESPONSE COMMISSION (40 CFR 355.40). IF THE RELEASE OF THIS SUBSTANCE IS REPORTABLE UNDER CERCLA SECTION 103, THE NATIONAL RESPONSE CENTER MUST BE NOTIFIED IMMEDIATELY AT (800) 424-8802 OR (202) 426-2675 IN THE METROPOLITAN WASHINGTON, D.C. AREA (40 CFR 302.6).

PROTECTIVE EQUIPMENT

VENTILATION: PROVIDE LOCAL EXHAUST OR PROCESS ENCLOSURE VENTILATION SYSTEM.

RESPIRATOR: THE FOLLOWING RESPIRATORS ARE RECOMMENDED BASED ON INFORMATION FOUND IN THE PHYSICAL DATA, TOXICITY AND HEALTH EFFECTS SECTIONS. THEY ARE RANKED IN ORDER FROM MINIMUM TO MAXIMUM RESPIRATORY PROTECTION. THE SPECIFIC RESPIRATOR SELECTED MUST BE BASED ON CONTAMINATION LEVELS FOUND IN THE WORK PLACE, MUST NOT EXCEED THE WORKING LIMITS OF THE RESPIRATOR AND BE JOINTLY APPROVED BY THE NATIONAL INSTITUTE FOR OCCUPATIONAL SAFETY AND HEALTH AND THE MINE SAFETY AND HEALTH ADMINISTRATION (NIOSH-MSHA).

CHEMICAL CARTRIDGE RESPIRATOR WITH AN ORGANIC VAPOR CARTRIDGE(S) WITH A FULL FACEPIECE AND ORGANIC VAPOR CARTRIDGE(S) IN COMBINATION WITH A DUST AND MIST FILTER.

POWERED AIR-PURIFYING RESPIRATOR WITH A TIGHT-FITTING FACEPIECE AND ORGANIC VAPOR CARTRIDGE(S) IN COMBINATION WITH A HIGH-EFFICIENCY PARTICULATE FILTER.

TYPE 'C' SUPPLIED-AIR RESPIRATOR WITH A FULL FACEPIECE OPERATED IN A PRESSURE-DEMAND OR OTHER POSITIVE PRESSURE MODE.

SELF-CONTAINED BREATHING APPARATUS WITH A FULL FACEPIECE OPERATED IN PRESSURE-DEMAND OR OTHER POSITIVE PRESSURE MODE.

FOR FIREFIGHTING AND OTHER IMMEDIATELY DANGEROUS TO LIFE OR HEALTH CONDITIONS:

SELF-CONTAINED BREATHING APPARATUS WITH FULL FACEPIECE OPERATED IN PRESSURE-DEMAND OR OTHER POSITIVE PRESSURE MODE.

SUPPLIED-AIR RESPIRATOR WITH FULL FACEPIECE AND OPERATED IN PRESSURE-DEMAND OR OTHER POSITIVE PRESSURE MODE IN COMBINATION WITH AN AUXILIARY SELF-CONTAINED BREATHING APPARATUS OPERATED IN PRESSURE-DEMAND OR OTHER POSITIVE PRESSURE MODE.

CLOTHING: EMPLOYEE MUST WEAR APPROPRIATE PROTECTIVE (IMPERVIOUS) CLOTHING AND EQUIPMENT TO PREVENT ANY POSSIBILITY OF SKIN CONTACT WITH THIS SUBSTANCE.

GLOVES: EMPLOYEE MUST WEAR APPROPRIATE PROTECTIVE GLOVES TO PREVENT CONTACT WITH THIS SUBSTANCE.

EYE PROTECTION: EMPLOYEE MUST WEAR SPLASH-PROOF OR DUST-RESISTANT SAFETY GOGGLES TO PREVENT EYE CONTACT WITH THIS SUBSTANCE. EMERGENCY EYE WASH: WHERE THERE IS ANY POSSIBILITY THAT AN EMPLOYEE'S EYES MAY BE EXPOSED TO THIS SUBSTANCE, THE EMPLOYER SHOULD PROVIDE AN EYE WASH FOUNTAIN WITHIN THE IMMEDIATE WORK AREA FOR EMERGENCY USE.

AUTHORIZED BY- OCCUPATIONAL HEALTH SERVICES, INC.
CREATION DATE: 10/05/89 ***REVISION DATE:*** 07/13/90

MATERIAL SAFETY DATA SHEET

OCCUPATIONAL HEALTH SERVICES, INC.
AGRICULTURE AND PESTICIDE DIVISION
450 SEVENTH AVENUE, SUITE 2407
NEW YORK, NEW YORK 10123
1-800-445-MSDS OR (212) 967-1100

EMERGENCY CONTACT:
JOHN S. BRANSFORD, JR. (615) 292-1180

SUBSTANCE IDENTIFICATION

CAS-NUMBER 99-30-9
SUBSTANCE: **2,6-DICHLORO-4-NITROANILINE**
TRADE NAMES/SYNONYMS: BENZENAMINE, 2,6-DICHLORO-4-NITRO-; ALLISAN; DCNA; 2,6-DICHLORO-4-NITROBENZENAMINE; ANILINE, 2,6-DICHLORO-4-NITRO-; DICHLORAN; DICLORAN; RESISAN; BOTRAN; C6H4CL2N2O2; PST28910
CHEMICAL FAMILY: AMINE, AROMATIC HALOGEN
MOLECULAR FORMULA: CL2-(N-O2)-C6-H2-N-H2
MOLECULAR WEIGHT: 207.02
CERCLA RATINGS (SCALE 0-3): HEALTH=U FIRE=1 REACTIVITY=0 PERSISTENCE=3
NFPA RATINGS (SCALE 0-4): HEALTH=U FIRE=1 REACTIVITY=0

COMPONENTS AND CONTAMINANTS

COMPONENT: 2,6-DICHLORO-4-NITROANILINE ***PERCENT:*** 100.0
CAS# 99-30-9
OTHER CONTAMINANTS: NONE
EXPOSURE LIMITS: NO OCCUPATIONAL EXPOSURE LIMITS ESTABLISHED BY OSHA, ACGIH, OR NIOSH.

PHYSICAL DATA

DESCRIPTION: YELLOW TO BROWNISH-YELLOW CRYSTALLINE SOLID WITH AN AROMATIC ODOR.
BOILING POINT: 266 F (130 C) @ 2 MMHG ***MELTING POINT:*** 376-383 F (191-195 C)
SPECIFIC GRAVITY: NOT AVAILABLE ***VAPOR PRESSURE:*** NEGLIGIBLE
SOLUBILITY IN WATER: 0.0007%
SOLVENT SOLUBILITY: SOLUBLE IN ALCOHOL, ACETONE, CHLOROFORM, ETHYL ACETATE; SLIGHTLY SOLUBLE IN BENZENE, CYCLOHEXANE, OTHER NON-POLAR SOLVENTS.

FIRE AND EXPLOSION DATA

FIRE AND EXPLOSION HAZARD: SLIGHT FIRE HAZARD WHEN EXPOSED TO HEAT OR FLAME.
FIREFIGHTING MEDIA: DRY CHEMICAL, CARBON DIOXIDE, HALON, WATER SPRAY OR STANDARD FOAM (1987 EMERGENCY RESPONSE GUIDEBOOK, DOT P 5800.4).
FOR LARGER FIRES, USE WATER SPRAY, FOG OR STANDARD FOAM (1987 EMERGENCY RESPONSE GUIDEBOOK, DOT P 5800.4).
FIREFIGHTING: MOVE CONTAINER FROM FIRE AREA IF POSSIBLE. DO NOT SCATTER SPILLED MATERIAL WITH HIGH PRESSURE WATER STREAMS. DIKE FIRE CONTROL WATER FOR LATER DISPOSAL (1987 EMERGENCY RESPONSE GUIDEBOOK, DOT P 5800.4, GUIDE PAGE 31).
USE AGENTS SUITABLE FOR TYPE OF SURROUNDING FIRE. AVOID BREATHING HAZARDOUS VAPORS, KEEP UPWIND.

TOXICITY

2,6-DICHLORO-4-NITROANILINE: TOXICITY DATA: 1500 MG/KG ORAL-RAT LDLO; 1500 MG/KG ORAL-MOUSE LD50; 1450 MG/KG ORAL-GUINEA PIG LD50; 56 MG/KG INTRAVENOUS-MOUSE LD50; 1500 MG/KG UNREPORTED-MAMMAL LD50; MUTAGENIC DATA (RTECS); TUMORIGENIC DATA (RTECS). CARCINOGEN STATUS: NONE. LOCAL EFFECTS: IRRITANT- SKIN. ACUTE TOXICITY LEVEL: MODERATELY TOXIC BY INGESTION. TARGET EFFECTS: NO DATA AVAILABLE.

HEALTH EFFECTS AND FIRST AID

INHALATION: 2,6-DICHLORO-4-NITROANILINE: **ACUTE EXPOSURE-** MAY BE IRRITATING TO MUCOUS MEMBRANES. **CHRONIC EXPOSURE-** NO DATA AVAILABLE.
FIRST AID- REMOVE FROM EXPOSURE AREA TO FRESH AIR IMMEDIATELY. IF BREATHING HAS STOPPED, PERFORM ARTIFICIAL RESPIRATION. KEEP PERSON WARM AND AT REST. TREAT SYMPTOMATICALLY AND SUPPORTIVELY. GET MEDICAL ATTENTION IMMEDIATELY.

SKIN CONTACT: 2,6-DICHLORO-4-NITROANILINE: IRRITANT. **ACUTE EXPOSURE-** MAY CAUSE IRRITATION WITH REDNESS AND ITCHING. MAY CAUSE SENSITIZATION REACTIONS IN PREVIOUSLY EXPOSED INDIVIDUALS. **CHRONIC EXPOSURE-** REPEATED AND PROLONGED EXPOSURE TO IRRITANTS MAY CAUSE DERMATITIS. SENSITIZATION REACTIONS IN PREVIOUSLY EXPOSED INDIVIDUALS MAY OCCUR.
FIRST AID- REMOVE CONTAMINATED CLOTHING AND SHOES IMMEDIATELY. WASH AFFECTED AREA WITH SOAP OR MILD DETERGENT AND LARGE AMOUNTS OF WATER UNTIL NO EVIDENCE OF CHEMICAL REMAINS (APPROXIMATELY 15-20 MINUTES). GET MEDICAL ATTENTION IMMEDIATELY.

EYE CONTACT: 2,6-DICHLORO-4-NITROANILINE: **ACUTE EXPOSURE-** MAY CAUSE IRRITATION. **CHRONIC EXPOSURE-** DIRECT APPLICATION OF DUST OR OF 5% SOLUTION TO THE EYES OF DOGS FOR 3 MONTHS HAD NO EFFECT ON THE CORNEA OR THE CONJUNCTIVA. PLACING 20 TO 30 MG OF 2,6-DICHLORO-4-NITROANILINE, DAILY, INTO THE INFERIOR CUL-DE-SAC OF THE EYE CAUSED CENTRAL CORNEAL LESIONS TO BE PRODUCED WITHIN SEVERAL WEEKS.
FIRST AID- WASH EYES IMMEDIATELY WITH LARGE AMOUNTS OF WATER OR NORMAL SALINE, OCCASIONALLY LIFTING UPPER AND LOWER LIDS, UNTIL NO EVIDENCE OF CHEMICAL REMAINS (APPROXIMATELY 15-20 MINUTES). GET MEDICAL ATTENTION IMMEDIATELY.

INGESTION: 2,6-DICHLORO-4-NITROANILINE: **ACUTE EXPOSURE-** A SINGLE DOSE OF 2,6-DICHLORO-4-NITROANILINE PRODUCED SIGNIFICANT ENLARGEMENT OF THE LIVER AND INDUCTION OF LIVER MICROSOMAL ENZYMES IN RATS. **CHRONIC EXPOSURE-** TWENTY MEN RECEIVED 0.14 MG/KG/DAY FOR 90 DAYS WITHOUT ANY CLINICAL EFFECTS. RATS TOLERATED 400 MG/KG/DAY BUT 160 MG/KG/DAY WAS FATAL TO MONKEYS DURING A 3 MONTH STUDY. THE MONKEY LIVERS SHOWED CENTROLOBULAR FATTY INFILTRATION WITH SWELLING OF MITOCHONDRIA AND DISTORTION OF CRISTAE. REPEATED ORAL DOSES PRODUCED SIGNIFICANT ENLARGEMENT OF THE LIVER IN RATS. DOGS GIVEN 24 MG/KG OF 2,6-DICHLORO-4-NITROANILINE DAILY FOR 55 DAYS DEVELOPED CORNEAL AND LENS OPACITIES WHEN EXPOSED TO NATURAL SUNLIGHT. THE INJURIES WERE IRREVERSIBLE. AT HIGH DOSAGE LEVELS, SOME DOGS SHOWED HEINZ BODIES IN THEIR ERYTHROCYTES AND AN INCREASED PROPORTION OF RETICULOCYTES.
FIRST AID- REMOVE BY GASTRIC LAVAGE OR EMESIS. FOLLOW WITH A SALINE CATHARTIC (UPJOHN MSDS). MAINTAIN BLOOD PRESSURE, AIRWAY, AND GIVE OXYGEN IF RESPIRATION IS DEPRESSED. DO NOT PERFORM GASTRIC LAVAGE OR EMESIS IF VICTIM IS UNCONSCIUS. GET MEDICAL ATTENTION IMMEDIATELY. ADMINISTRATION OF GASTRIC LAVAGE OR OXYGEN SHOULD BE PERFORMED BY QUALIFIED MEDICAL PERSONNEL.
ANTIDOTE: NO SPECIFIC ANTIDOTE. TREAT SYMPTOMATICALLY AND SUPPORTIVELY.

REACTIVITY

REACTIVITY: STABLE UNDER NORMAL TEMPERATURES AND PRESSURES.
INCOMPATIBILITIES: BOTRAN: ACID ANHYDRIDES: MAY REACT VIOLENTLY. ACID CHLORIDES: POSSIBLE VIOLENT REACTION. ACIDS (STRONG): MAY REACT VIOLENTLY. OXIDIZERS (STRONG): FIRE AND EXPLOSION HAZARD. SEE ALSO NITROAROMATICS.
NITROAROMATICS: ALKALIES: POSSIBLE VIOLENT DECOMPOSITION OR EXPLOSION WHEN HEATED. CHLORINE TRIFLUORIDE: SOLUTIONS ARE EXTREMELY SHOCK SENSITIVE.
DECOMPOSITION: THERMAL DECOMPOSITION PRODUCTS MAY INCLUDE TOXIC OXIDES OF NITROGEN AND CARBON AND TOXIC AND CORROSIVE FUMES OF CHLORIDES.
POLYMERIZATION: HAZARDOUS POLYMERIZATION HAS NOT BEEN REPORTED TO OCCUR UNDER NORMAL TEMPERATURES AND PRESSURES.

STORAGE AND DISPOSAL

OBSERVE ALL FEDERAL, STATE AND LOCAL REGULATIONS WHEN STORING OR DISPOSING OF THIS SUBSTANCE. FOR ASSISTANCE, CONTACT THE DISTRICT DIRECTOR OF THE ENVIRONMENTAL PROTECTION AGENCY.

****STORAGE****

STORE IN ACCORDANCE WITH 40 CFR 165 RECOMMENDED PROCEDURES FOR THE DISPOSAL AND STORAGE OF PESTICIDES AND PESTICIDE CONTAINERS.
STORE AWAY FROM INCOMPATIBLE SUBSTANCES.

DISPOSAL

DISPOSAL MUST BE IN ACCORDANCE WITH 40 CFR 165 RECOMMENDED PROCEDURES FOR THE DISPOSAL AND STORAGE OF PESTICIDES AND PESTICIDE CONTAINERS.

CONDITIONS TO AVOID

MAY BURN BUT DOES NOT IGNITE READILY. AVOID CONTACT WITH STRONG OXIDIZERS, EXCESSIVE HEAT, SPARKS, OR OPEN FLAME.

SPILL AND LEAK PROCEDURES

OCCUPATIONAL SPILL: SWEEP UP AND PLACE IN SUITABLE CLEAN, DRY CONTAINERS FOR RECLAMATION OR LATER DISPOSAL. DO NOT FLUSH SPILLED MATERIAL INTO SEWER. KEEP UNNECESSARY PEOPLE AWAY.

PROTECTIVE EQUIPMENT

VENTILATION: PROVIDE LOCAL EXHAUST OR GENERAL DILUTION VENTILATION SYSTEM.

RESPIRATOR: THE FOLLOWING RESPIRATORS ARE RECOMMENDED BASED ON INFORMATION FOUND IN THE PHYSICAL DATA, TOXICITY AND HEALTH EFFECTS SECTIONS. THEY ARE RANKED IN ORDER FROM MINIMUM TO MAXIMUM RESPIRATORY PROTECTION. THE SPECIFIC RESPIRATOR SELECTED MUST BE BASED ON CONTAMINATION LEVELS FOUND IN THE WORK PLACE, MUST NOT EXCEED THE WORKING LIMITS OF THE RESPIRATOR AND BE JOINTLY APPROVED BY THE NATIONAL INSTITUTE FOR OCCUPATIONAL SAFETY AND HEALTH AND THE MINE SAFETY AND HEALTH ADMINISTRATION (NIOSH-MSHA).

CHEMICAL CARTRIDGE RESPIRATOR WITH AN ORGANIC VAPOR CARTRIDGE(S) WITH A FULL FACEPIECE AND ORGANIC VAPOR CARTRIDGE(S) IN COMBINATION WITH A DUST AND MIST FILTER.

POWERED AIR-PURIFYING RESPIRATOR WITH A TIGHT-FITTING FACEPIECE AND ORGANIC VAPOR CARTRIDGE(S) IN COMBINATION WITH A HIGH-EFFICIENCY PARTICULATE FILTER.

TYPE 'C' SUPPLIED-AIR RESPIRATOR WITH A FULL FACEPIECE OPERATED IN A PRESSURE-DEMAND OR OTHER POSITIVE PRESSURE MODE.

SELF-CONTAINED BREATHING APPARATUS WITH A FULL FACEPIECE OPERATED IN PRESSURE-DEMAND OR OTHER POSITIVE PRESSURE MODE.

FOR FIREFIGHTING AND OTHER IMMEDIATELY DANGEROUS TO LIFE OR HEALTH CONDITIONS:

SELF-CONTAINED BREATHING APPARATUS WITH FULL FACEPIECE OPERATED IN PRESSURE-DEMAND OR OTHER POSITIVE PRESSURE MODE.

SUPPLIED-AIR RESPIRATOR WITH FULL FACEPIECE AND OPERATED IN PRESSURE-DEMAND OR OTHER POSITIVE PRESSURE MODE IN COMBINATION WITH AN AUXILIARY SELF-CONTAINED BREATHING APPARATUS OPERATED IN PRESSURE-DEMAND OR OTHER POSITIVE PRESSURE MODE.

CLOTHING: EMPLOYEE MUST WEAR APPROPRIATE PROTECTIVE (IMPERVIOUS) CLOTHING AND EQUIPMENT TO PREVENT REPEATED OR PROLONGED SKIN CONTACT WITH THIS SUBSTANCE.

GLOVES: EMPLOYEE MUST WEAR APPROPRIATE PROTECTIVE GLOVES TO PREVENT CONTACT WITH THIS SUBSTANCE.

EYE PROTECTION: EMPLOYEE MUST WEAR SPLASH-PROOF OR DUST-RESISTANT SAFETY GOGGLES TO PREVENT EYE CONTACT WITH THIS SUBSTANCE.

EMERGENCY EYE WASH: WHERE THERE IS ANY POSSIBILITY THAT AN EMPLOYEE'S EYES MAY BE EXPOSED TO THIS SUBSTANCE, THE EMPLOYER SHOULD PROVIDE AN EYE WASH FOUNTAIN WITHIN THE IMMEDIATE WORK AREA FOR EMERGENCY USE.

AUTHORIZED BY- OCCUPATIONAL HEALTH SERVICES, INC.
CREATION DATE: 10/05/89 ***REVISION DATE:*** 05/31/90

MATERIAL SAFETY DATA SHEET

OCCUPATIONAL HEALTH SERVICES, INC.
AGRICULTURE AND PESTICIDE DIVISION
450 SEVENTH AVENUE, SUITE 2407
NEW YORK, NEW YORK 10123
1-800-445-MSDS OR (212) 967-1100

EMERGENCY CONTACT:
JOHN S. BRANSFORD, JR. (615) 292-1180

SUBSTANCE IDENTIFICATION

CAS-NUMBER 133-90-4

SUBSTANCE: **CHLORAMBEN**

TRADE NAMES/SYNONYMS: BENZOIC ACID, 3-AMINO-2,5-DICHLORO-; 3-AMINO-2,5-DICHLOROBENZOIC ACID; AMBEN; AMBIBEN; AMIBEN; AMIBIN; AMOBEN; CHLORAMBENE; VEGIBEN; C7H5CL2NO2; PST29084

CHEMICAL FAMILY: CARBOXYLIC ACID, AROMATIC
HALOGEN
AMINE

MOLECULAR FORMULA: (CL2)-(H2-N)-C6-H2-C-O2-H

MOLECULAR WEIGHT: 206.03

CERCLA RATINGS (SCALE 0-3): HEALTH=3 FIRE=1 REACTIVITY=0 PERSISTENCE=1

NFPA RATINGS (SCALE 0-4): HEALTH=U FIRE=1 REACTIVITY=0

COMPONENTS AND CONTAMINANTS

COMPONENT: CHLORAMBEN ***PERCENT:*** 100
CAS# 133-90-4

EXPOSURE LIMITS: NO OCCUPATIONAL EXPOSURE LIMITS ESTABLISHED BY OSHA, ACGIH, OR NIOSH.
CHLORAMBEN: SUBJECT TO SARA SECTION 313 ANNUAL TOXIC CHEMICAL RELEASE REPORTING

PHYSICAL DATA

DESCRIPTION: ODORLESS, COLORLESS TO WHITE CRYSTALLINE, AMPORPHOUS SOLID; MAY TURN A PINK TO PURPLE COLOR UPON LONG EXPOSURE TO LIGHT

MELTING POINT: 392-394 F (200-201 C) ***SPECIFIC GRAVITY:*** NOT AVAILABLE

VAPOR PRESSURE: 0.007 MMHG @ 100 C ***PH:*** 2.95 (SAT. SOLN)

SOLUBILITY IN WATER: 0.07% @ 25 C

SOLVENT SOLUBILITY: SOLUBLE IN ACETONE, DIMETHYLSULFOXIDE, DIETHYLCARBITOL, METHANOL, ISOPROPANOL, ETHANOL, DIMETHYLFORMAMIDE, DIOXANE, BUTYL CELLOSOLVE; MODERATELY SOLUBLE IN ETHER, ETHYL ACETATE, DIETHYLENE GLYCOL, PINE OIL,
ISOOCTANOL; VERY SLIGHTLY SOLUBLE IN TOLUENE, BENZENE, AND CHLOROFORM.

FIRE AND EXPLOSION DATA

FIRE AND EXPLOSION HAZARD: SLIGHT FIRE HAZARD WHEN EXPOSED TO HEAT OR FLAME.

FIREFIGHTING MEDIA: DRY CHEMICAL, CARBON DIOXIDE, HALON, WATER SPRAY OR STANDARD FOAM (1987 EMERGENCY RESPONSE GUIDEBOOK, DOT P 5800.4).
FOR LARGER FIRES, USE WATER SPRAY, FOG OR STANDARD FOAM (1987 EMERGENCY RESPONSE GUIDEBOOK, DOT P 5800.4).

FIREFIGHTING: MOVE CONTAINER FROM FIRE AREA IF POSSIBLE. DO NOT SCATTER SPILLED MATERIAL WITH HIGH PRESSURE WATER STREAMS. DIKE FIRE CONTROL WATER FOR LATER DISPOSAL (1987 EMERGENCY RESPONSE GUIDEBOOK, DOT P 5800.4, GUIDE PAGE 31).
USE AGENTS SUITABLE FOR TYPE OF SURROUNDING FIRE. AVOID BREATHING HAZARDOUS VAPORS, KEEP UPWIND.

TOXICITY

CHLORAMBEN: TOXICITY DATA: 3136 MG/KG SKIN-RABBIT LD50; 3500 MG/KG ORAL-RAT LD50; 3725 MG/KG ORAL-MOUSE LD50; MUTAGENIC DATA (RTECS); TUMORIGENIC DATA (RTECS). CARCINOGEN STATUS: NONE. LOCAL EFFECTS: IRRITANT- EYE. ACUTE TOXICITY LEVEL: MODERATELY TOXIC BY INGESTION; SLIGHTLY TOXIC BY DERMAL ABSORPTION. TARGET EFFECTS: NO DATA AVAILABLE.

HEALTH EFFECTS AND FIRST AID

INHALATION: CHLORAMBEN: **ACUTE EXPOSURE-** NO DATA AVAILABLE. **CHRONIC EXPOSURE-** NO DATA AVAILABLE.

FIRST AID- REMOVE FROM EXPOSURE AREA TO FRESH AIR IMMEDIATELY. IF BREATHING HAS STOPPED, PERFORM ARTIFICIAL RESPIRATION. KEEP PERSON WARM AND AT REST. TREAT SYMPTOMATICALLY AND SUPPORTIVELY. GET MEDICAL ATTENTION IMMEDIATELY.

SKIN CONTACT: CHLORAMBEN: **ACUTE EXPOSURE-** APPLIED TO RABBIT SKIN, THIS MATERIAL PRODUCED MILD TO MODERATE ERYTHEMA AND MILD EDEMA THAT SUBSIDED WITHIN 2 DAYS AND DEPRESSION CHARACTERIZED BY INACTIVITY. **CHRONIC EXPOSURE-** NO DATA AVAILABLE.

FIRST AID- REMOVE CONTAMINATED CLOTHING AND SHOES IMMEDIATELY. WASH AFFECTED AREA WITH SOAP OR MILD DETERGENT AND LARGE AMOUNTS OF WATER UNTIL NO EVIDENCE OF CHEMICAL REMAINS (APPROXIMATELY 15-20 MINUTES). GET MEDICAL ATTENTION IMMEDIATELY.

EYE CONTACT: CHLORAMBEN: IRRITANT. **ACUTE EXPOSURE-** SODIUM CHLORAMBEN (85% CHLORAMBIC ACID EQUIVALENT) WAS MILDLY TO MODERATELY IRRITATING TO RABBIT EYES; THE IRRITATION HAD CLEARED WITHIN 7 DAYS. **CHRONIC EXPOSURE-** PROLONGED OR REPEATED EXPOSURE TO IRRITANTS MAY CAUSE CONJUNCTIVITIS.

FIRST AID- WASH EYES IMMEDIATELY WITH LARGE AMOUNTS OF WATER OR NORMAL SALINE, OCCASIONALLY LIFTING UPPER AND LOWER LIDS, UNTIL NO EVIDENCE OF CHEMICAL REMAINS (APPROXIMATELY 15-20 MINUTES). GET MEDICAL ATTENTION IMMEDIATELY.

INGESTION: CHLORAMBEN: **ACUTE EXPOSURE**- EFFECTS PRODUCED IN RATS FROM LETHAL DOSES INCLUDED DEPRESSION CHARACTERIZED BY INACTIVITY AND ATAXIA, LABORED RESPIRATION, SPRAWLING OF LIMBS, PTOSIS, LACK OF COORDINATION AND EXCESSIVE URINATION. GROSS PATHOLOGIC CHANGES INCLUDED CONGESTED LUNGS, KIDNEYS, AND ADRENALS. **CHRONIC EXPOSURE**- HEPATOCELLULAR ALTERATIONS HAVE BEEN REPORTED IN MICE AND DOGS. AN INCREASED INCIDENCE OF HEPATOCELLULAR CARCINOMAS IN FEMALES WAS OBSERVED IN AN ONCOGENIC STUDY OF MICE. INCREASED FETAL MORTALITY AND DECREASED FETAL SKELETAL DEVELOPMENT WERE OBSERVED IN A STUDY OF PREGNANT RATS.

FIRST AID- IF THE PERSON IS CONSCIOUS AND NOT CONVULSING, REMOVE BY GIVING SYRUP OF IPECAC (IF VOMITING OCCURS, KEEP THE HEAD BELOW THE HIPS TO PREVENT ASPIRATION). GIVE ACTIVATED CHARCOAL FOLLOWED BY GASTRIC LAVAGE. FOLLOW WITH A SALINE CATHARTIC. DO NOT GIVE FATS OR OILS. INTESTINAL LAVAGE WITH 20% MANNITOL (200 ML) BY STOMACH TUBE IS ALSO USEFUL. GIVE ARTIFICIAL RESPIRATION WITH OXYGEN IF RESPIRATION IS DEPRESSED (DREISBACH, HANDBOOK OF POISONING, 12TH ED.). TREAT SYMPTOMATICALLY AND SUPPORTIVELY. LAVAGE AND ADMINISTRATION OF OXYGEN SHOULD BE PERFORMED BY QUALIFIED MEDICAL PERSONNEL. GET MEDICAL ATTENTION IMMEDIATELY.

ANTIDOTE: NO SPECIFIC ANTIDOTE. TREAT SYMPTOMATICALLY AND SUPPORTIVELY.

REACTIVITY

REACTIVITY: STABLE UNDER NORMAL TEMPERATURES AND PRESSURES.

INCOMPATIBILITIES: CHLORAMBEN: OXIDIZERS (STRONG): FIRE AND EXPLOSION HAZARD. SODIUM HYPOCHLORITE SOLUTION (BLEACH): DECOMPOSES.

DECOMPOSITION: THERMAL DECOMPOSITION PRODUCTS MAY INCLUDE TOXIC OXIDES OF NITROGEN AND CARBON AND TOXIC AND CORROSIVE FUMES OF CHLORIDES.

POLYMERIZATION: HAZARDOUS POLYMERIZATION HAS NOT BEEN REPORTED TO OCCUR UNDER NORMAL TEMPERATURES AND PRESSURES.

STORAGE AND DISPOSAL

OBSERVE ALL FEDERAL, STATE AND LOCAL REGULATIONS WHEN STORING OR DISPOSING OF THIS SUBSTANCE. FOR ASSISTANCE, CONTACT THE DISTRICT DIRECTOR OF THE ENVIRONMENTAL PROTECTION AGENCY.

STORAGE

STORE IN ACCORDANCE WITH 40 CFR 165 RECOMMENDED PROCEDURES FOR THE DISPOSAL AND STORAGE OF PESTICIDES AND PESTICIDE CONTAINERS.

STORE AWAY FROM INCOMPATIBLE SUBSTANCES.

DISPOSAL

DISPOSAL MUST BE IN ACCORDANCE WITH 40 CFR 165 RECOMMENDED PROCEDURES FOR THE DISPOSAL AND STORAGE OF PESTICIDES AND PESTICIDE CONTAINERS.

CONDITIONS TO AVOID

MAY BURN BUT DOES NOT IGNITE READILY. AVOID CONTACT WITH STRONG OXIDIZERS, EXCESSIVE HEAT, SPARKS, OR OPEN FLAME.

SPILL AND LEAK PROCEDURES

OCCUPATIONAL SPILL: SWEEP UP AND PLACE IN SUITABLE CLEAN, DRY CONTAINERS FOR RECLAMATION OR LATER DISPOSAL. DO NOT FLUSH SPILLED MATERIAL INTO SEWER. KEEP UNNECESSARY PEOPLE AWAY.

PROTECTIVE EQUIPMENT

VENTILATION: PROVIDE LOCAL EXHAUST OR GENERAL DILUTION VENTILATION SYSTEM.

RESPIRATOR: THE FOLLOWING RESPIRATORS ARE RECOMMENDED BASED ON INFORMATION FOUND IN THE PHYSICAL DATA, TOXICITY AND HEALTH EFFECTS SECTIONS. THEY ARE RANKED IN ORDER FROM MINIMUM TO MAXIMUM RESPIRATORY PROTECTION. THE SPECIFIC RESPIRATOR SELECTED MUST BE BASED ON CONTAMINATION LEVELS FOUND IN THE WORK PLACE, MUST NOT EXCEED THE WORKING LIMITS OF THE RESPIRATOR AND BE JOINTLY APPROVED BY THE NATIONAL INSTITUTE FOR OCCUPATIONAL SAFETY AND HEALTH AND THE MINE SAFETY AND HEALTH ADMINISTRATION (NIOSH-MSHA).

CHEMICAL CARTRIDGE RESPIRATOR WITH AN ORGANIC VAPOR CARTRIDGE(S) IN COMBINATION WITH A DUST AND MIST FILTER.

GAS MASK WITH ORGANIC VAPOR CANISTER (CHIN-STYLE OR FRONT- OR BACK-MOUNTED CANISTER) WITH A DUST AND MIST FILTER.

GAS MASK WITH ORGANIC VAPOR CANISTER (CHIN-STYLE OR FRONT- OR BACK-MOUNTED CANISTER) WITH A PARTICULATE FILTER.

POWERED AIR-PURIFYING RESPIRATOR WITH A HIGH-EFFICIENCY FILTER.

TYPE 'C' SUPPLIED-AIR RESPIRATOR WITH A FULL FACEPIECE OPERATED IN A PRESSURE-DEMAND OR OTHER POSITIVE PRESSURE MODE.

SELF-CONTAINED BREATHING APPARATUS WITH A FULL FACEPIECE OPERATED IN PRESSURE-DEMAND OR OTHER POSITIVE PRESSURE MODE.

FOR FIREFIGHTING AND OTHER IMMEDIATELY DANGEROUS TO LIFE OR HEALTH CONDITIONS:

SELF-CONTAINED BREATHING APPARATUS WITH FULL FACEPIECE OPERATED IN PRESSURE-DEMAND OR OTHER POSITIVE PRESSURE MODE.

SUPPLIED-AIR RESPIRATOR WITH FULL FACEPIECE AND OPERATED IN PRESSURE-DEMAND OR OTHER POSITIVE PRESSURE MODE IN COMBINATION WITH AN AUXILIARY SELF-CONTAINED BREATHING APPARATUS OPERATED IN PRESSURE-DEMAND OR OTHER POSITIVE PRESSURE MODE.

CLOTHING: EMPLOYEE MUST WEAR APPROPRIATE PROTECTIVE (IMPERVIOUS) CLOTHING AND EQUIPMENT TO PREVENT REPEATED OR PROLONGED SKIN CONTACT WITH THIS SUBSTANCE.

GLOVES: EMPLOYEE MUST WEAR APPROPRIATE PROTECTIVE GLOVES TO PREVENT CONTACT WITH THIS SUBSTANCE.

EYE PROTECTION: EMPLOYEE MUST WEAR SPLASH-PROOF OR DUST-RESISTANT SAFETY GOGGLES TO PREVENT EYE CONTACT WITH THIS SUBSTANCE.

EMERGENCY EYE WASH: WHERE THERE IS ANY POSSIBILITY THAT AN EMPLOYEE'S EYES MAY BE EXPOSED TO THIS SUBSTANCE, THE EMPLOYER SHOULD PROVIDE AN EYE WASH FOUNTAIN WITHIN THE IMMEDIATE WORK AREA FOR EMERGENCY USE.

AUTHORIZED BY- OCCUPATIONAL HEALTH SERVICES, INC.

CREATION DATE: 10/04/89 ***REVISION DATE:*** 05/31/90

MATERIAL SAFETY DATA SHEET

OCCUPATIONAL HEALTH SERVICES, INC.
AGRICULTURE AND PESTICIDE DIVISION
450 SEVENTH AVENUE, SUITE 2407
NEW YORK, NEW YORK 10123
1-800-445-MSDS OR (212) 967-1100

EMERGENCY CONTACT:
JOHN S. BRANSFORD, JR. (615) 292-1180

SUBSTANCE IDENTIFICATION

CAS-NUMBER 133-32-4

SUBSTANCE: **3-INDOLEBUTYRIC ACID**

TRADE NAMES/SYNONYMS: 1H-INDOLE-3-BUTANOIC ACID; HORMEX; IBA; HORMODIN; INDOLEBUTYRIC ACID; BETA-INDOLEBUTYRIC ACID; BETA-IBA; INDOLE-3-BUTANOIC ACID; BETA-INDOLYLBUTRIC ACID; 3-INDOLYLBUTRIC ACID; BP-936; PST29325

CHEMICAL FAMILY: HETEROCYCLIC NITROGEN

MOLECULAR FORMULA: C12-H13-N-O2

MOLECULAR WEIGHT: 203.26

CERCLA RATINGS (SCALE 0-3): HEALTH=3 FIRE=0 REACTIVITY=0 PERSISTENCE=3

NFPA RATINGS (SCALE 0-4): HEALTH=3 FIRE=0 REACTIVITY=0

COMPONENTS AND CONTAMINANTS

COMPONENT: 3-INDOLEBUTYRIC ACID ***PERCENT:*** 100
CAS# 133-32-4

OTHER CONTAMINANTS: NONE

EXPOSURE LIMITS: NO OCCUPATIONAL EXPOSURE LIMITS ESTABLISHED BY OSHA, ACGIH, OR NIOSH.

PHYSICAL DATA

DESCRIPTION: WHITE TO SLIGHTLY YELLOW CRYSTALS OR POWDER WITH A SLIGHT, CHARACTERISTIC ODOR. ***MELTING POINT:*** 255-257 (124-125 C)

SOLUBILITY IN WATER: INSOLUBLE

SOLVENT SOLUBILITY: SOLUBLE IN ETHANOL, ACETONE, ETHER, KETONES, ALCOHOLS; INSOLUBLE IN CHLOROFORM

FIRE AND EXPLOSION DATA

FIRE AND EXPLOSION HAZARD: NEGLIGIBLE FIRE HAZARD WHEN EXPOSED TO HEAT OR FLAME.

FIREFIGHTING MEDIA: DRY CHEMICAL, CARBON DIOXIDE, HALON, WATER SPRAY OR STANDARD FOAM (1987 EMERGENCY RESPONSE GUIDEBOOK, DOT P 5800.4). FOR LARGER FIRES, USE WATER SPRAY, FOG OR STANDARD FOAM (1987 EMERGENCY RESPONSE GUIDEBOOK, DOT P 5800.4).

FIREFIGHTING: NO ACUTE HAZARD. MOVE CONTAINER FROM FIRE AREA IF POSSIBLE. AVOID BREATHING VAPORS OR DUSTS; KEEP UPWIND.

TOXICITY

3-INDOLEBUTYRIC ACID: TOXICITY DATA: 100 MG/KG ORAL-MOUSE LD50; 100 MG/KG INTRAPERITONEAL-MOUSE LDLO; MUTAGENIC DATA (RTECS). CARCINOGEN STATUS: NONE. ACUTE TOXICITY LEVEL: TOXIC BY INGESTION. TARGET EFFECTS: NO DATA AVAILABLE.

HEALTH EFFECTS AND FIRST AID

INHALATION: **ACUTE EXPOSURE-** NO DATA AVAILABLE. **CHRONIC EXPOSURE-** NO DATA AVAILABLE.

FIRST AID- REMOVE FROM EXPOSURE AREA TO FRESH AIR IMMEDIATELY. IF BREATHING HAS STOPPED, PERFORM ARTIFICIAL RESPIRATION. KEEP PERSON WARM AND AT REST. TREAT SYMPTOMATICALLY AND SUPPORTIVELY. GET MEDICAL ATTENTION IMMEDIATELY.

SKIN CONTACT: **ACUTE EXPOSURE-** NO DATA AVAILABLE, MAY CAUSE IRRITATION. **CHRONIC EXPOSURE-** NO DATA AVAILABLE.

FIRST AID- REMOVE CONTAMINATED CLOTHING AND SHOES IMMEDIATELY. WASH AFFECTED AREA WITH SOAP OR MILD DETERGENT AND LARGE AMOUNTS OF WATER UNTIL NO EVIDENCE OF CHEMICAL REMAINS (APPROXIMATELY 15-20 MINUTES). GET MEDICAL ATTENTION IMMEDIATELY.

EYE CONTACT: **ACUTE EXPOSURE-** MAY CAUSE IRRITATION. NO EFFECTS REPORTED IN HUMANS. **CHRONIC EXPOSURE-** NO DATA AVAILABLE.

FIRST AID- WASH EYES IMMEDIATELY WITH LARGE AMOUNTS OF WATER OR NORMAL SALINE, OCCASIONALLY LIFTING UPPER AND LOWER LIDS, UNTIL NO EVIDENCE OF CHEMICAL REMAINS (APPROXIMATELY 15-20 MINUTES). GET MEDICAL ATTENTION IMMEDIATELY.

INGESTION: **ACUTE EXPOSURE-** NO DATA AVAILABLE. **CHRONIC EXPOSURE-** NO DATA AVAILABLE.

FIRST AID- WHEN THIS CHEMICAL HAS BEEN SWALLOWED AND PERSON IS CONSCIOUS, IMMEDIATELY GIVE PERSON LARGE AMOUNTS OF WATER. AFTER WATER HAS BEEN SWALLOWED, TRY TO GET THE VICTIM TO VOMIT BY HAVING HIM TO TOUCH THE BACK OF HIS THROAT WITH HIS FINGER. DO NOT MAKE AN UNCONSCIOUS PERSON VOMIT. GET MEDICAL ATTENTION IMMEDIATELY.

REACTIVITY

REACTIVITY: STABLE UNDER NORMAL TEMPERATURES AND PRESSURES.

INCOMPATIBILITIES: NONE KNOWN.

DECOMPOSITION: THERMAL DECOMPOSITION PRODUCTS MAY INCLUDE TOXIC OXIDES OF CARBON AND NITROGEN.

POLYMERIZATION: HAZARDOUS POLYMERIZATION HAS NOT BEEN REPORTED TO OCCUR UNDER NORMAL TEMPERATURES AND PRESSURES.

STORAGE AND DISPOSAL

OBSERVE ALL FEDERAL, STATE AND LOCAL REGULATIONS WHEN STORING OR DISPOSING OF THIS SUBSTANCE. FOR ASSISTANCE, CONTACT THE DISTRICT DIRECTOR OF THE ENVIRONMENTAL PROTECTION AGENCY.

CONDITIONS TO AVOID

NONE REPORTED.

SPILL AND LEAK PROCEDURES

OCCUPATIONAL SPILL: SWEEP UP AND PLACE IN SUITABLE (FIBERBOARD) CONTAINERS FOR RECLAMATION OR LATER DISPOSAL.

PROTECTIVE EQUIPMENT

VENTILATION: PROVIDE GENERAL DILUTION VENTILATION.

RESPIRATOR: THE FOLLOWING RESPIRATORS ARE RECOMMENDED BASED ON INFORMATION FOUND IN THE PHYSICAL DATA, TOXICITY AND HEALTH EFFECTS SECTIONS. THEY ARE RANKED IN ORDER FROM MINIMUM TO MAXIMUM RESPIRATORY PROTECTION. THE SPECIFIC RESPIRATOR SELECTED MUST BE BASED ON CONTAMINATION LEVELS FOUND IN THE WORK PLACE, MUST NOT EXCEED THE WORKING LIMITS OF THE RESPIRATOR AND BE JOINTLY APPROVED BY THE NATIONAL INSTITUTE FOR OCCUPATIONAL SAFETY AND HEALTH AND THE MINE SAFETY AND HEALTH ADMINISTRATION (NIOSH-MSHA).

DUST AND MIST RESPIRATOR WITH A FULL FACEPIECE.

AIR-PURIFYING FULL FACEPIECE RESPIRATOR WITH A HIGH-EFFICIENCY PARTICULATE FILTER.

POWERED AIR-PURIFYING RESPIRATOR WITH A TIGHT-FITTING FACEPIECE AND HIGH-EFFICIENCY PARTICULATE FILTER.

TYPE 'C' SUPPLIED-AIR RESPIRATOR WITH A FULL FACEPIECE OPERATED IN PRESSURE-DEMAND OR OTHER POSITIVE PRESSURE MODE OR WITH A FULL FACEPIECE, HELMET OR HOOD OPERATED IN CONTINUOUS-FLOW MODE.

SELF-CONTAINED BREATHING APPARATUS WITH A FULL FACEPIECE OPERATED IN PRESSURE-DEMAND OR OTHER POSITIVE PRESSURE MODE.

FOR FIREFIGHTING AND OTHER IMMEDIATELY DANGEROUS TO LIFE OR HEALTH CONDITIONS:

SELF-CONTAINED BREATHING APPARATUS WITH FULL FACEPIECE OPERATED IN PRESSURE-DEMAND OR OTHER POSITIVE PRESSURE MODE.

SUPPLIED-AIR RESPIRATOR WITH FULL FACEPIECE AND OPERATED IN PRESSURE-DEMAND OR OTHER POSITIVE PRESSURE MODE IN COMBINATION WITH AN AUXILIARY SELF-CONTAINED BREATHING APPARATUS OPERATED IN PRESSURE-DEMAND OR OTHER POSITIVE PRESSURE MODE.

CLOTHING: PROTECTIVE CLOTHING NOT REQUIRED. AVOID REPEATED OR PROLONGED CONTACT WITH THIS SUBSTANCE.

GLOVES: PROTECTIVE GLOVES ARE NOT REQUIRED BUT RECOMMENDED.

EYE PROTECTION: EMPLOYEE MUST WEAR SPLASH-PROOF OR DUST-RESISTANT SAFETY GOGGLES TO PREVENT EYE CONTACT WITH THIS SUBSTANCE.

EMERGENCY EYE WASH: WHERE THERE IS ANY POSSIBILITY THAT AN EMPLOYEE'S EYES MAY BE EXPOSED TO THIS SUBSTANCE, THE EMPLOYER SHOULD PROVIDE AN EYE WASH FOUNTAIN WITHIN THE IMMEDIATE WORK AREA FOR EMERGENCY USE.

AUTHORIZED BY- OCCUPATIONAL HEALTH SERVICES, INC.

CREATION DATE: 10/05/89 ***REVISION DATE:*** 05/25/90

MATERIAL SAFETY DATA SHEET

OCCUPATIONAL HEALTH SERVICES, INC.
AGRICULTURE AND PESTICIDE DIVISION
450 SEVENTH AVENUE, SUITE 2407
NEW YORK, NEW YORK 10123
1-800-445-MSDS OR (212) 967-1100

EMERGENCY CONTACT:
JOHN S. BRANSFORD, JR. (615) 292-1180

SUBSTANCE IDENTIFICATION

CAS-NUMBER 64-00-6

SUBSTANCE: **3-ISOPROPYLPHENYL N-METHYLCARBAMATE**

TRADE NAMES/SYNONYMS: PHENOL, 3-(1-METHYLETHYL)-, METHYLCARBAMATE; 3-(1-METHYLETHYL)PHENOL METHYLCARBAMATE; CARBAMIC ACID, METHYL-, M-CUMENYL ESTER; METHYLCARBAMIC ACID M-CUMENYL ESTER; M-CUMENOL METHYLCARBAMATE; M-CUMENYL METHYLCARBAMATE; M-ISOPROPYLPHENOL METHYLCARBAMATE; M-ISOPROPYLPHENYL METHYLCARBAMATE; 3-ISOPROPYLPHENYL METHYLCARBAMATE; ENT 25500; H 5727; H 8757; HERCULES 5727; HERCULES AC 5727; OMS 15; OMS 162; UC 10854; C11H15NO2; PST29423

CHEMICAL FAMILY: CARBAMATE
AROMATIC

MOLECULAR FORMULA: C11-H15-N-O2

MOLECULAR WEIGHT: 193.27

CERCLA RATINGS (SCALE 0-3): HEALTH=3 FIRE=1 REACTIVITY=0 PERSISTENCE=2

NFPA RATINGS (SCALE 0-4): HEALTH=4 FIRE=1 REACTIVITY=0

COMPONENTS AND CONTAMINANTS

COMPONENT: 3-ISOPROPYLPHENYL N-METHYLCARBAMATE ***PERCENT:*** 100.0
CAS# 64-00-6

OTHER CONTAMINANTS: NONE

EXPOSURE LIMITS: NO OCCUPATIONAL EXPOSURE LIMITS ESTABLISHED BY OSHA, ACGIH, OR NIOSH.

3-ISOPROPYLPHENYL N-METHYLCARBAMATE: 500/10,000 POUNDS SARA SECTION 302 THRESHOLD PLANNING QUANTITY 1 POUND SARA SECTION 304 REPORTABLE QUANTITY

PHYSICAL DATA

DESCRIPTION: ODORLESS, WHITE CRYSTALLINE SOLID.

MELTING POINT: 162-165 F (72-74 C) ***SPECIFIC GRAVITY:*** NOT AVAILABLE

SOLUBILITY IN WATER: 85 PPM @ 30 C

SOLVENT SOLUBILITY: SOLUBLE IN ISOPHORONE, XYLENE, TOLUENE, ISOPROPANOL, ACETONE AND DIMETHYLFORMAMIDE; PRACTICALLY INSOLUBLE IN DEOBASE AND CYCLOHEXANE.

FIRE AND EXPLOSION DATA

FIRE AND EXPLOSION HAZARD: SLIGHT FIRE HAZARD WHEN EXPOSED TO HEAT OR FLAME.

FIREFIGHTING MEDIA: DRY CHEMICAL, CARBON DIOXIDE, HALON, WATER SPRAY OR STANDARD FOAM (1987 EMERGENCY RESPONSE GUIDEBOOK, DOT P 5800.4). FOR LARGER FIRES, USE WATER SPRAY, FOG OR STANDARD FOAM (1987 EMERGENCY RESPONSE GUIDEBOOK, DOT P 5800.4).

FIREFIGHTING: MOVE CONTAINERS FROM FIRE AREA IF POSSIBLE (1987 EMERGENCY RESPONSE GUIDEBOOK, DOT P 5800.4, GUIDE PAGE 53).
EXTINGUISH USING AGENT SUITABLE FOR TYPE OF SURROUNDING FIRE. AVOID BREATHING VAPORS AND DUSTS. KEEP UPWIND.

TRANSPORTATION DATA

DEPARTMENT OF TRANSPORTATION HAZARD CLASSIFICATION 49 CFR 172.101: POISON B
DEPARTMENT OF TRANSPORTATION LABELING REQUIREMENTS 49 CFR 172.101 AND SUBPART E: POISON
DEPARTMENT OF TRANSPORTATION PACKAGING REQUIREMENTS: 49 CFR 173.346 EXCEPTIONS: 49 CFR 173.345

TOXICITY

3-ISOPROPYLPHENYL N-METHYLCARBAMATE: TOXICITY DATA: 40 MG/KG SKIN-RABBIT LD50; 113 MG/KG SKIN-RAT LD50; 16 MG/KG ORAL-RAT LD50; 16 MG/KG ORAL-MOUSE LD50; 10 MG/KG ORAL-GUINEA PIG LDLO; 3150 UG/KG INTRAVENOUS-RAT LD50; 1410 UG/KG INTRAVENOUS-MOUSE LD50; 14,200 UG/KG INTRAPERITONEAL-RAT LD50; 3100 UG/KG INTRAPERITONEAL-MOUSE LD50; 14 MG/KG INTRAMUSCULAR-RAT LD50; 13 MG/KG INTRAMUSCULAR-DOG LDLO; 41 MG/KG UNREPORTED-RAT LD50. CARCINOGEN STATUS: NONE. ACUTE TOXICITY LEVEL: HIGHLY TOXIC BY DERMAL ABSORPTION AND INGESTION. TARGET EFFECTS: CHOLINESTERASE INHIBITOR. AT INCREASED RISK FROM EXPOSURE: PERSONS WITH ASTHMA, DIABETES, CARDIOVASCULAR DISEASE, MECHANICAL OBSTRUCTION OF THE GASTROINTESTINAL OR UROGENITAL TRACT, AND THOSE IN VAGOTONIC STATES.*

* MAY BE BASED ON GENERAL INFORMATION ON CARBAMATES.

HEALTH EFFECTS AND FIRST AID

INHALATION: 3-ISOPROPYLPHENYL N-METHYLCARBAMATE: SEE INFORMATION ON CARBAMATES. EXPOSURE OF MALE RATS TO 45 MG/M3 PRODUCED INHIBITION OF BRAIN CHOLINESTERASE TO ABOUT 56% OF NORMAL IN 10 MINUTES, AND 25% IN 120 MINUTES.
CARBAMATES: CHOLINESTERASE INHIBITOR. **ACUTE EXPOSURE-** WHEN INHALED, THE FIRST EFFECTS OF CHOLINESTERASE INHIBITION ARE USUALLY RESPIRATORY AND MAY INCLUDE NASAL HYPEREMIA AND WATERY DISCHARGE, CHEST DISCOMFORT, DYSPNEA, AND WHEEZING DUE TO INCREASED BRONCHIAL SECRETIONS AND BRONCHOCONSTRICTION. OTHER SYSTEMIC EFFECTS MAY BEGIN WITHIN A FEW MINUTES OR SEVERAL HOURS OF EXPOSURE. SYMPTOMS MAY INCLUDE NAUSEA, VOMITING, DIARRHEA, ABDOMINAL CRAMPS, HEADACHE, VERTIGO, OCULAR PAIN, CILIARY MUSCLE SPASM, BLURRING OR DIMNESS OF VISION, MIOSIS, OR IN SOME CASES MYDRIASIS, LACRIMATION, SALIVATION, SWEATING, AND CONFUSION. OTHER REPORTED CENTRAL NERVOUS SYSTEM OR NEUROMUSCULAR EFFECTS INCLUDE ATAXIA, SLURRED SPEECH, AREFLEXIA, WEAKNESS, FATIGUE, TWITCHING, FASCICULATION, TREMOR, AND EVENTUALLY PARALYSIS OF THE EXTREMITIES AND POSSIBLY OF THE RESPIRATORY MUSCLES. IN SEVERE CASES, THERE MAY ALSO BE INVOLUNTARY DEFECATION AND URINATION, BRADYCARDIA, HYPOTENSION, PULMONARY EDEMA, CONVULSIONS, COMA, AND DEATH FROM RESPIRATORY FAILURE OR CARDIAC ARREST. CARBAMATES GENERALLY DO NOT ACCUMULATE IN MAMMALIAN TISSUE AND THE CHOLINESTERASE INHIBITION REVERSES RATHER RAPIDLY. IN NON-FATAL CASES, THE ILLNESS GENERALLY LASTS LESS THAN 24 HOURS. **CHRONIC EXPOSURE-** PROLONGED OR REPEATED EXPOSURE MAY CAUSE EFFECTS AS DESCRIBED IN ACUTE EXPOSURE.

FIRST AID- REMOVE FROM EXPOSURE AREA TO FRESH AIR IMMEDIATELY. IF BREATHING HAS STOPPED, GIVE ARTIFICIAL RESPIRATION. MAINTAIN AIRWAY AND BLOOD PRESSURE AND ADMINISTER OXYGEN IF AVAILABLE. KEEP AFFECTED PERSON WARM AND AT REST. TREAT SYMPTOMATICALLY AND SUPPORTIVELY. ADMINISTRATION OF OXYGEN SHOULD BE PERFORMED BY QUALIFIED PERSONNEL. GET MEDICAL ATTENTION IMMEDIATELY.

SKIN CONTACT: 3-ISOPROPYLPHENYL N-METHYLCARBAMATE: HIGHLY TOXIC. SEE INFORMATION ON CARBAMATES. SKIN ERUPTIONS, WHICH WERE LIMITED TO AREAS OF DIRECT CONTACT, HAVE BEEN REPORTED. THE RASHES WERE IRRITATING AND LASTED 2 OR 3 WEEKS.
CARBAMATES: CHOLINESTERASE INHIBITOR. **ACUTE EXPOSURE-** SOME COMPOUNDS MAY CAUSE IRRITATION. LOCALIZED SWEATING AND FASCICULATIONS MAY OCCUR AT THE SITE OF CONTACT. IF SUFFICIENT AMOUNTS ARE ABSORBED THROUGH THE SKIN, OTHER EFFECTS OF CHOLINESTERASE INHIBITION MAY OCCUR AS DESCRIBED IN ACUTE INHALATION; SYMPTOMS MAY BE DELAYED FOR 2-3 HOURS, USUALLY NO MORE THAN 8 HOURS. **CHRONIC EXPOSURE-** REPEATED OR PROLONGED EXPOSURE MAY CAUSE EFFECTS AS DESCRIBED IN ACUTE EXPOSURE.

FIRST AID- REMOVE CONTAMINATED CLOTHING IMMEDIATELY. WASH CONTAMINATED AREAS WITH SOAP AND WATER FOLLOWED BY ALCOHOL (ARENA, POISONING, 4TH ED.). EMERGENCY PERSONNEL SHOULD WEAR GLOVES AND AVOID CONTAMINATION. TREAT RESPIRATORY DIFFICULTY WITH ARTIFICIAL RESPIRATION. GET MEDICAL ATTENTION IMMEDIATELY.

EYE CONTACT: 3-ISOPROPYLPHENYL N-METHYLCARBAMATE: SEE INFORMATION ON CARBAMATES.
CARBAMATES: CHOLINESTERASE INHIBITOR. **ACUTE EXPOSURE-** DIRECT CONTACT MAY CAUSE PAIN, HYPEREMIA, LACRIMATION, TWITCHING OF THE EYELIDS, MIOSIS, AND CILIARY MUSCLE SPASM WITH LOSS OF ACCOMODATION, BLURRED OR DIMMED VISION AND BROWACHE. SOMETIMES MYDRIASIS MAY OCCUR INSTEAD OF MIOSIS. WITH SUFFICIENT EXPOSURE, OTHER SYMPTOMS OF CHOLINESTERASE INHIBITION MAY OCCUR AS DESCRIBED IN ACUTE INHALATION. **CHRONIC EXPOSURE-** PROLONGED EXPOSURE MAY CAUSE EFFECTS AS DESCRIBED IN ACUTE EXPOSURE. SOME COMPOUNDS HAVE CAUSED TOXIC EFFECTS ON THE CRYSTALLINE LENS, CONJUNCTIVAL THICKENING AND OBSTRUCTION OF NASOLACRIMAL CANALS WHEN USED AS MIOTIC EYE DROPS.

FIRST AID- IRRIGATE EYES WITH WATER OR SALINE SOLUTION. IF SYMPTOMS OF POISONING OCCUR, TREAT RESPIRATORY DIFFICULTY WITH ARTIFICIAL RESPIRATION AND OXYGEN. OBSERVE PATIENT FOR AT LEAST 24-36 HOURS (GOSSELIN, CLINICAL TOXICOLOGY OF COMMERCIAL PRODUCTS, 5TH ED.). GET MEDICAL ATTENTION IMMEDIATELY. OXYGEN SHOULD BE ADMINISTERED BY QUALIFIED MEDICAL PERSONNEL.

INGESTION: 3-ISOPROPYLPHENYL N-METHYLCARBAMATE: HIGHLY TOXIC. SEE INFORMATION ON CARBAMATES.
CARBAMATES: CHOLINESTERASE INHIBITOR. **ACUTE EXPOSURE-** WHEN INGESTED, THE FIRST EFFECTS MAY BE NAUSEA, VOMITING, ANOREXIA, ABDOMINAL CRAMPS, AND DIARRHEA. WITH ABSORPTION FROM THE GASTROINTESTINAL TRACT, THE OTHER EFFECTS OF CHOLINESTERASE INHIBITION AS DESCRIBED IN ACUTE INHALATION MAY OCCUR; SYMPTOMS MAY BEGIN WITHIN MINUTES OR BE DELAYED SEVERAL HOURS. **CHRONIC EXPOSURE-** REPEATED INGESTION MAY CAUSE EFFECTS AS DESCRIBED IN ACUTE EXPOSURE.

FIRST AID- IF PERSON IS ALERT AND RESPIRATION IS NOT DEPRESSED, GIVE SYRUP OF IPECAC FOLLOWED BY WATER (IF VOMITING OCCURS, KEEP HEAD BELOW HIPS TO PREVENT ASPIRATION). IF CONSCIOUSNESS LEVEL DECLINES OR VOMITING HAS NOT OCCURRED IN 15 MINUTES EMPTY STOMACH BY GASTRIC LAVAGE WITH THE AID OF CUFFED ENDOTRACHEAL TUBE USING ISOTONIC SALINE OR 5% SODIUM BICARBONATE FOLLOW WITH ACTIVATED CHARCOAL. ESTABLISH AND MAINTAIN AIRWAY. TREAT RESPIRATORY DIFFICULTY WITH ARTIFICIAL RESPIRATION AND OXYGEN. DO NOT GIVE MORPHINE, AMINOPHYLLINE, PHENOTHIAZINES, RESERPINE, FUROSEMIDE, OR ETHACRYNIC ACID (MORGAN, RECOGNITION AND MANAGEMENT OF PESTICIDE POISONINGS, 3RD ED.). TREAT SYMPTOMATICALLY AND SUPPORTIVELY. ADMINISTRATION OF OXYGEN AND LAVAGE MUST BE PERFORMED BY QUALIFIED MEDICAL PERSONNEL. GET MEDICAL ATTENTION IMMEDIATELY.

ANTIDOTE: THE FOLLOWING ANTIDOTE HAS BEEN RECOMMENDED. HOWEVER, THE DECISION AS TO WHETHER THE SEVERITY OF POISONING REQUIRES ADMINISTRATION OF ANY ANTIDOTE AND ACTUAL DOSE REQUIRED SHOULD BE MADE BY QUALIFIED MEDICAL PERSONNEL.
FOR CHOLINESTERASE INHIBITORS: ESTABLISH CLEAR AIRWAY AND TISSUE OXYGENATION BY ASPIRATION OF SECRETIONS, AND IF NECESSARY, BY ASSISTED PULMONARY VENTILATION WITH OXYGEN. IMPROVE TISSUE OXYGENATION AS MUCH AS POSSIBLE BEFORE ADMINISTERING ATROPINE TO MINIMIZE THE RISK OF VENTRICULAR FIBRILLATION. ADMINISTER ATROPINE SULFATE INTRAVENOUSLY, OR INTRAMUSCULARLY IF IV INJECTION IS NOT POSSIBLE. IN MODERATELY SEVERE POISONING ADMINISTER ATROPINE SULFATE, 0.4-2.0 MG REPEATED EVERY 15 MINUTES UNTIL ATROPINIZATION IS ACHIEVED (TACHYCARDIA, FLUSHING, DRY MOUTH, MYDRIASIS). MAINTAIN ATROPINIZATION BY REPEATED DOSES FOR 2-12 HOURS, OR LONGER, DEPENDING ON THE SEVERITY OF POISONING. THE APPEARANCE OF RALES IN THE LUNG BASES, MIOSIS, SALIVATION, NAUSEA, BRADYCARDIA, ARE ALL INDICATIONS OF INADEQUATE ATROPINIZATION. SEVERELY POISONED INDIVIDUALS MAY EXHIBIT REMARKABLE TOLERANCE TO ATROPINE; TWO OR MORE TIMES THE DOSAGES SUGGESTED ABOVE MAY BE NEEDED. PERSONS NOT POISONED OR ONLY SLIGHTLY POISONED, HOWEVER, MAY DEVELOP SIGNS OF ATROPINE TOXICITY FROM SUCH LARGE DOSAGES: FEVER, MUSCLE FIBRILLATIONS, AND DELIRIUM ARE THE MAIN SIGNS OF ATROPINE TOXICITY. IF THESE SIGNS APPEAR WHILE THE PATIENT IS FULLY ATROPINIZED, ATROPINE ADMINISTRATION SHOULD BE DISCONTINUED, AT LEAST TEMPORARILY. OBSERVE TREATED PATIENTS CLOSELY AT LEAST 24 HOURS TO INSURE THAT SYMPTOMS (POSSIBLY PULMONARY EDEMA) DO NOT RECUR AS ATROPINIZATION WEARS OFF. IN VERY SEVERE POISONINGS, METABOLIC DISPOSITION OF TOXICANT MAY REQUIRE SEVERAL HOURS OR DAYS DURING WHICH ATROPINIZATION MUST BE MAINTAINED. MARKEDLY LOWER LEVELS OF URINARY METABOLITES INDICATE THAT ATROPINE DOSAGE CAN BE TAPERED OFF. AS

DOSAGE IS REDUCED, CHECK THE LUNG BASES FREQUENTLY FOR RALES. IF RALES ARE HEARD OR OTHER SYMPTOMS RETURN, RE-ESTABLISH ATROPINIZATION PROMPTLY (MORGAN, RECOGNITION AND MANAGEMENT OF PESTICIDE POISONINGS, 3RD ED.). ADMINISTRATION OF ANTIDOTE MUST BE PERFORMED BY QUALIFIED MEDICAL PERSONNEL.

REACTIVITY

REACTIVITY: STABLE UNDER NORMAL TEMPERATURES AND PRESSURES.

INCOMPATIBILITIES: 3-ISOPROPYLPHENYL N-METHYLCARBAMATE: ALKALIES: INCOMPATIBLE. OXIDIZERS (STRONG): FIRE AND EXPLOSION HAZARD.

DECOMPOSITION: THERMAL DECOMPOSITION PRODUCTS MAY INCLUDE TOXIC OXIDES OF CARBON AND NITROGEN.

POLYMERIZATION: HAZARDOUS POLYMERIZATION HAS NOT BEEN REPORTED TO OCCUR UNDER NORMAL TEMPERATURES AND PRESSURES.

STORAGE AND DISPOSAL

OBSERVE ALL FEDERAL, STATE AND LOCAL REGULATIONS WHEN STORING OR DISPOSING OF THIS SUBSTANCE. FOR ASSISTANCE, CONTACT THE DISTRICT DIRECTOR OF THE ENVIRONMENTAL PROTECTION AGENCY.

****STORAGE****

STORE IN ACCORDANCE WITH 40 CFR 165 RECOMMENDED PROCEDURES FOR THE DISPOSAL AND STORAGE OF PESTICIDES AND PESTICIDE CONTAINERS.

STORE AWAY FROM INCOMPATIBLE SUBSTANCES.

THRESHOLD PLANNING QUANTITY (TPQ): THE SUPERFUND AMENDMENTS AND REAUTHORIZATION ACT (SARA) SECTION 302 REQUIRES THAT EACH FACILITY WHERE ANY EXTREMELY HAZARDOUS SUBSTANCE IS PRESENT IN A QUANTITY EQUAL TO OR GREATER THAN THE TPQ ESTABLISHED FOR THAT SUBSTANCE NOTIFY THE STATE EMERGENCY RESPONSE COMMISSION FOR THE STATE IN WHICH IT IS LOCATED. SECTION 303 OF SARA REQUIRES THESE FACILITIES TO PARTICIPATE IN LOCAL EMERGENCY RESPONSE PLANNING (40 CFR 355.30).

****DISPOSAL****

DISPOSAL MUST BE IN ACCORDANCE WITH 40 CFR 165 RECOMMENDED PROCEDURES FOR THE DISPOSAL AND STORAGE OF PESTICIDES AND PESTICIDE CONTAINERS.

CONDITIONS TO AVOID

MAY BURN BUT DOES NOT IGNITE READILY.

SPILL AND LEAK PROCEDURES

OCCUPATIONAL SPILL: DO NOT TOUCH SPILLED MATERIAL. STOP LEAK IF YOU CAN DO IT WITHOUT RISK. FOR SMALL SPILLS, TAKE UP WITH SAND OR OTHER ABSORBENT MATERIAL AND PLACE INTO CONTAINERS FOR LATER DISPOSAL. FOR SMALL DRY SPILLS, WITH A CLEAN SHOVEL PLACE MATERIAL INTO CLEAN, DRY CONTAINER AND COVER. MOVE CONTAINERS FROM SPILL AREA. FOR LARGER SPILLS, DIKE FAR AHEAD OF SPILL FOR LATER DISPOSAL. KEEP UNNECESSARY PEOPLE AWAY. ISOLATE HAZARD AREA AND DENY ENTRY.

REPORTABLE QUANTITY (RQ): 1 POUND THE SUPERFUND AMENDMENTS AND REAUTHORIZATION ACT (SARA) SECTION 304 REQUIRES THAT A RELEASE EQUAL TO OR GREATER THAN THE REPORTABLE QUANTITY FOR THIS SUBSTANCE BE IMMEDIATELY REPORTED TO THE LOCAL EMERGENCY PLANNING COMMITTEE AND THE STATE EMERGENCY RESPONSE COMMISSION (40 CFR 355.40). IF THE RELEASE OF THIS SUBSTANCE IS REPORTABLE UNDER CERCLA SECTION 103, THE NATIONAL RESPONSE CENTER MUST BE NOTIFIED IMMEDIATELY AT (800) 424-8802 OR (202) 426-2675 IN THE METROPOLITAN WASHINGTON, D.C. AREA (40 CFR 302.6).

PROTECTIVE EQUIPMENT

VENTILATION: PROVIDE LOCAL EXHAUST OR GENERAL DILUTION VENTILATION SYSTEM.

RESPIRATOR: THE FOLLOWING RESPIRATORS ARE RECOMMENDED BASED ON INFORMATION FOUND IN THE PHYSICAL DATA, TOXICITY AND HEALTH EFFECTS SECTIONS. THEY ARE RANKED IN ORDER FROM MINIMUM TO MAXIMUM RESPIRATORY PROTECTION. THE SPECIFIC RESPIRATOR SELECTED MUST BE BASED ON CONTAMINATION LEVELS FOUND IN THE WORK PLACE, MUST NOT EXCEED THE WORKING LIMITS OF THE RESPIRATOR AND BE JOINTLY APPROVED BY THE NATIONAL INSTITUTE FOR OCCUPATIONAL SAFETY AND HEALTH AND THE MINE SAFETY AND HEALTH ADMINISTRATION (NIOSH-MSHA).

TYPE 'C' SUPPLIED-AIR RESPIRATOR WITH A FULL FACEPIECE OPERATED IN PRESSURE-DEMAND OR OTHER POSITIVE PRESSURE MODE OR WITH A FULL FACEPIECE, HELMET OR HOOD OPERATED IN CONTINOUS-FLOW MODE.

SELF-CONTAINED BREATHING APPARATUS WITH A FULL FACEPIECE OPERATED IN PRESSURE-DEMAND OR OTHER POSITIVE PRESSURE MODE.

FOR FIREFIGHTING AND OTHER IMMEDIATELY DANGEROUS TO LIFE OR HEALTH CONDITIONS:

SELF-CONTAINED BREATHING APPARATUS WITH FULL FACEPIECE OPERATED IN PRESSURE-DEMAND OR OTHER POSITIVE PRESSURE MODE.

SUPPLIED-AIR RESPIRATOR WITH FULL FACEPIECE AND OPERATED IN PRESSURE-DEMAND OR OTHER POSITIVE PRESSURE MODE IN COMBINATION WITH AN AUXILIARY SELF-CONTAINED BREATHING APPARATUS OPERATED IN PRESSURE-DEMAND OR OTHER POSITIVE PRESSURE MODE.

CLOTHING: EMPLOYEE MUST WEAR APPROPRIATE PROTECTIVE (IMPERVIOUS) CLOTHING AND EQUIPMENT TO PREVENT ANY POSSIBILITY OF SKIN CONTACT WITH THIS SUBSTANCE.

GLOVES: EMPLOYEE MUST WEAR APPROPRIATE PROTECTIVE GLOVES TO PREVENT CONTACT WITH THIS SUBSTANCE.

EYE PROTECTION: EMPLOYEE MUST WEAR SPLASH-PROOF OR DUST-RESISTANT SAFETY GOGGLES AND A FACESHIELD TO PREVENT CONTACT WITH THIS SUBSTANCE.

EMERGENCY WASH FACILITIES: WHERE THERE IS ANY POSSIBILITY THAT AN EMPLOYEE'S EYES AND/OR SKIN MAY BE EXPOSED TO THIS SUBSTANCE, THE EMPLOYER SHOULD PROVIDE AN EYE WASH FOUNTAIN AND QUICK DRENCH SHOWER WITHIN THE IMMEDIATE WORK AREA FOR EMERGENCY USE.

AUTHORIZED BY- OCCUPATIONAL HEALTH SERVICES, INC.

CREATION DATE: 10/05/89 ***REVISION DATE:*** 06/12/90

MATERIAL SAFETY DATA SHEET

OCCUPATIONAL HEALTH SERVICES, INC.
AGRICULTURE AND PESTICIDE DIVISION
450 SEVENTH AVENUE, SUITE 2407
NEW YORK, NEW YORK 10123
1-800-445-MSDS OR (212) 967-1100

EMERGENCY CONTACT:
JOHN S. BRANSFORD, JR. (615) 292-1180

SUBSTANCE IDENTIFICATION

CAS-NUMBER 1079-33-0

SUBSTANCE: 4-BENZOTHIENYL METHYLCARBAMATE

TRADE NAMES/SYNONYMS: BENZO(B)THIOPHENE-4-OL, METHYLCARBAMATE; CARBAMIC ACID, METHYL-, BENZO(B)THIEN-4-YL ESTER; METHYLCARBAMIC ACID BENZO(B)THIEN-4-YL ESTER; BENZO(B)THIEN-4-YL METHYLCARBAMATE; 4-BENZOTHIENYL-N-METHYLCARBAMATE; MCA 600; MOBAM; OMS 708; ENT 27041; C10H9NO2S; PST29855

CHEMICAL FAMILY: CARBAMATE

MOLECULAR FORMULA: C10-H9-N-O2-S

MOLECULAR WEIGHT: 207.26

CERCLA RATINGS (SCALE 0-3): HEALTH=3 FIRE=1 REACTIVITY=0 PERSISTENCE=1

NFPA RATINGS (SCALE 0-4): HEALTH=3 FIRE=1 REACTIVITY=0

COMPONENTS AND CONTAMINANTS

COMPONENT: 4-BENZOTHIENYL METHYLCARBAMATE ***PERCENT:*** 100.0
CAS# 1079-33-0

OTHER CONTAMINANTS: NONE

EXPOSURE LIMITS: NO OCCUPATIONAL EXPOSURE LIMITS ESTABLISHED BY OSHA, ACGIH, OR NIOSH.

PHYSICAL DATA

DESCRIPTION: ODORLESS, WHITE, CRYSTALLINE SOLID.

MELTING POINT: 259-266 F (126-130 C) ***SPECIFIC GRAVITY:*** NOT AVAILABLE

VAPOR PRESSURE: NEGLIGIBLE ***SOLUBILITY IN WATER:*** <0.1%

SOLVENT SOLUBILITY: SOLUBLE IN DIMETHYLSULFOXIDE, ACETONE, TOLUIDINE, TRIETHYLENE GLYCOL, ACETONITRILE, DIOXANE, METHYLENE CHLORIDE, ALCOHOLS, ETHYL ACETATE, AND ETHYLENE GLYCOL, METHYL ETHYL KETONE, AND CARBON TETRACHLORIDE.

FIRE AND EXPLOSION DATA

FIRE AND EXPLOSION HAZARD: SLIGHT FIRE HAZARD WHEN EXPOSED TO HEAT OR FLAME.

FIREFIGHTING MEDIA: DRY CHEMICAL, CARBON DIOXIDE, HALON, WATER SPRAY OR STANDARD FOAM (1987 EMERGENCY RESPONSE GUIDEBOOK, DOT P 5800.4). FOR LARGER FIRES, USE WATER SPRAY, FOG OR STANDARD FOAM (1987 EMERGENCY RESPONSE GUIDEBOOK, DOT P 5800.4).

FIREFIGHTING: MOVE CONTAINERS FROM FIRE AREA IF POSSIBLE. FIGHT FIRE FROM MAXIMUM DISTANCE. STAY AWAY FROM STORAGE TANK ENDS. DIKE FIRE CONTROL WATER FOR LATER DISPOSAL. DO NOT SCATTER MATERIAL (1987 EMERGENCY RESPONSE GUIDEBOOK, DOT P 5800.4, GUIDE PAGE 55). EXTINGUISH USING AGENTS SUITABLE FOR TYPE OF SURROUNDING FIRE. USE

FLOODING AMOUNTS OF WATER AS FOG. AVOID BREATHING TOXIC DUST AND FUMES FROM BURNING MATERIAL; KEEP UPWIND.

TOXICITY

4-BENZOTHIENYL METHYLCARBAMATE: TOXICITY DATA: 70 MG/KG ORAL-RAT LD50; 50 MG/KG ORAL-GUINEA PIG LDLO; 25 MG/KG SUBCUTANEOUS-GUINEA PIG LDLO; 24,800 UG/KG INTRAVENOUS-RAT LD50; 40,800 UG/KG INTRAPERITONEAL-RAT LD50; 234 MG/KG UNREPORTED-RAT LD50.. CARCINOGEN STATUS: NONE. ACUTE TOXICITY LEVEL: TOXIC BY INGESTION. TARGET EFFECTS: CHOLINESTERASE INHIBITOR. AT INCREASED RISK FROM EXPOSURE: PERSONS WITH ASTHMA, DIABETES, CARDIOVASCULAR DISEASE, MECHANICAL OBSTRUCTION OF THE GASTROINTESTINAL OR UROGENITAL TRACT, AND THOSE IN VAGOTONIC STATES.*

* MAY BE BASED ON GENERAL INFORMATION ON CARBAMATES.

HEALTH EFFECTS AND FIRST AID

INHALATION: 4-BENZOTHIENYL METHYLCARBAMATE: SEE INFORMATION ON CARBAMATES.

CARBAMATES: CHOLINESTERASE INHIBITOR. **ACUTE EXPOSURE-** WHEN INHALED, THE FIRST EFFECTS OF CHOLINESTERASE INHIBITION ARE USUALLY RESPIRATORY AND MAY INCLUDE NASAL HYPEREMIA AND WATERY DISCHARGE, CHEST DISCOMFORT, DYSPNEA, AND WHEEZING DUE TO INCREASED BRONCHIAL SECRETIONS AND BRONCHOCONSTRICTION. OTHER SYSTEMIC EFFECTS MAY BEGIN WITHIN A FEW MINUTES OR SEVERAL HOURS OF EXPOSURE. SYMPTOMS MAY INCLUDE NAUSEA, VOMITING, DIARRHEA, ABDOMINAL CRAMPS, HEADACHE, VERTIGO, OCULAR PAIN, CILIARY MUSCLE SPASM, BLURRING OR DIMNESS OF VISION, MIOSIS, OR IN SOME CASES MYDRIASIS, LACRIMATION, SALIVATION, SWEATING, AND CONFUSION. OTHER REPORTED CENTRAL NERVOUS SYSTEM OR NEUROMUSCULAR EFFECTS INCLUDE ATAXIA, SLURRED SPEECH, AREFLEXIA, WEAKNESS, FATIGUE, TWITCHING, FASCICULATION, TREMOR, AND EVENTUALLY PARALYSIS OF THE EXTREMITIES AND POSSIBLY OF THE RESPIRATORY MUSCLES. IN SEVERE CASES, THERE MAY ALSO BE INVOLUNTARY DEFECATION AND URINATION, BRADYCARDIA, HYPOTENSION, PULMONARY EDEMA, CONVULSIONS, COMA, AND DEATH FROM RESPIRATORY FAILURE OR CARDIAC ARREST. CARBAMATES GENERALLY DO NOT ACCUMULATE IN MAMMALIAN TISSUE AND THE CHOLINESTERASE INHIBITION REVERSES RATHER RAPIDLY. IN NON-FATAL CASES, THE ILLNESS GENERALLY LASTS LESS THAN 24 HOURS. **CHRONIC EXPOSURE-** PROLONGED OR REPEATED EXPOSURE MAY CAUSE EFFECTS AS DESCRIBED IN ACUTE EXPOSURE.

FIRST AID- REMOVE FROM EXPOSURE AREA TO FRESH AIR IMMEDIATELY. IF BREATHING HAS STOPPED, GIVE ARTIFICIAL RESPIRATION. MAINTAIN AIRWAY AND BLOOD PRESSURE AND ADMINISTER OXYGEN IF AVAILABLE. KEEP AFFECTED PERSON WARM AND AT REST. TREAT SYMPTOMATICALLY AND SUPPORTIVELY. ADMINISTRATION OF OXYGEN SHOULD BE PERFORMED BY QUALIFIED PERSONNEL. GET MEDICAL ATTENTION IMMEDIATELY.

SKIN CONTACT: 4-BENZOTHIENYL METHYLCARBAMATE: SEE INFORMATION ON CARBAMATES.

CARBAMATES: CHOLINESTERASE INHIBITOR. **ACUTE EXPOSURE-** SOME COMPOUNDS MAY CAUSE IRRITATION. LOCALIZED SWEATING AND FASCICULATIONS MAY OCCUR AT THE SITE OF CONTACT. IF SUFFICIENT AMOUNTS ARE ABSORBED THROUGH THE SKIN, OTHER EFFECTS OF CHOLINESTERASE INHIBITION MAY OCCUR AS DESCRIBED IN ACUTE INHALATION; SYMPTOMS MAY BE DELAYED FOR 2-3 HOURS, USUALLY NO MORE THAN 8 HOURS. **CHRONIC EXPOSURE-** REPEATED OR PROLONGED EXPOSURE MAY CAUSE EFFECTS AS DESCRIBED IN ACUTE EXPOSURE.

FIRST AID- REMOVE CONTAMINATED CLOTHING IMMEDIATELY. WASH CONTAMINATED AREAS WITH SOAP AND WATER FOLLOWED BY ALCOHOL (ARENA, POISONING, 4TH ED.). EMERGENCY PERSONNEL SHOULD WEAR GLOVES AND AVOID CONTAMINATION. TREAT RESPIRATORY DIFFICULTY WITH ARTIFICIAL RESPIRATION. GET MEDICAL ATTENTION IMMEDIATELY.

EYE CONTACT: 4-BENZOTHIENYL METHYLCARBAMATE: SEE INFORMATION ON CARBAMATES.

CARBAMATES: CHOLINESTERASE INHIBITOR. **ACUTE EXPOSURE-** DIRECT CONTACT MAY CAUSE PAIN, HYPEREMIA, LACRIMATION, TWITCHING OF THE EYELIDS, MIOSIS, AND CILIARY MUSCLE SPASM WITH LOSS OF ACCOMODATION, BLURRED OR DIMMED VISION AND BROWACHE. SOMETIMES MYDRIASIS MAY OCCUR INSTEAD OF MIOSIS. WITH SUFFICIENT EXPOSURE, OTHER SYMPTOMS OF CHOLINESTERASE INHIBITION MAY OCCUR AS DESCRIBED IN ACUTE INHALATION. **CHRONIC EXPOSURE-** PROLONGED EXPOSURE MAY CAUSE EFFECTS AS DESCRIBED IN ACUTE EXPOSURE. SOME COMPOUNDS HAVE CAUSED TOXIC EFFECTS ON THE CRYSTALLINE LENS, CONJUNCTIVAL THICKENING AND OBSTRUCTION OF NASOLACRIMAL CANALS WHEN USED AS MIOTIC EYE DROPS.

FIRST AID- IRRIGATE EYES WITH WATER OR SALINE SOLUTION. IF SYMPTOMS OF POISONING OCCUR, TREAT RESPIRATORY DIFFICULTY WITH ARTIFICIAL RESPIRATION AND OXYGEN. OBSERVE PATIENT FOR AT LEAST 24-36 HOURS (GOSSELIN, CLINICAL TOXICOLOGY OF COMMERCIAL PRODUCTS, 5TH ED.). GET MEDICAL ATTENTION IMMEDIATELY. OXYGEN SHOULD BE ADMINISTERED BY QUALIFIED MEDICAL PERSONNEL.

INGESTION: 4-BENZOTHIENYL METHYLCARBAMATE: TOXIC. BRIEF CHOLINESTERASE INHIBITION WAS NOTED IN RATS FED 1 MG/KG. SEE INFORMATION ON CARBAMATES.

CARBAMATES: CHOLINESTERASE INHIBITOR. **ACUTE EXPOSURE-** WHEN INGESTED, THE FIRST EFFECTS MAY BE NAUSEA, VOMITING, ANOREXIA, ABDOMINAL CRAMPS, AND DIARRHEA. WITH ABSORPTION FROM THE GASTROINTESTINAL TRACT, THE OTHER EFFECTS OF CHOLINESTERASE INHIBITION AS DESCRIBED IN ACUTE INHALATION MAY OCCUR; SYMPTOMS MAY BEGIN WITHIN MINUTES OR BE DELAYED SEVERAL HOURS. **CHRONIC EXPOSURE-** REPEATED INGESTION MAY CAUSE EFFECTS AS DESCRIBED IN ACUTE EXPOSURE.

FIRST AID- IF PERSON IS ALERT AND RESPIRATION IS NOT DEPRESSED, GIVE SYRUP OF IPECAC FOLLOWED BY WATER (IF VOMITING OCCURS, KEEP HEAD BELOW HIPS TO PREVENT ASPIRATION). IF CONSCIOUSNESS LEVEL DECLINES OR VOMITING HAS NOT OCCURRED IN 15 MINUTES EMPTY STOMACH BY GASTRIC LAVAGE WITH THE AID OF CUFFED ENDOTRACHEAL TUBE USING ISOTONIC SALINE OR 5% SODIUM BICARBONATE FOLLOW WITH ACTIVATED CHARCOAL. ESTABLISH AND MAINTAIN AIRWAY. TREAT RESPIRATORY DIFFICULTY WITH ARTIFICIAL RESPIRATION AND OXYGEN. DO NOT GIVE MORPHINE, AMINOPHYLLINE, PHENOTHIAZINES, RESERPINE, FUROSEMIDE, OR ETHACRYNIC ACID (MORGAN, RECOGNITION AND MANAGEMENT OF PESTICIDE POISONINGS, 3RD ED.). TREAT SYMPTOMATICALLY AND SUPPORTIVELY. ADMINISTRATION OF OXYGEN AND LAVAGE MUST BE PERFORMED BY QUALIFIED MEDICAL PERSONNEL. GET MEDICAL ATTENTION IMMEDIATELY.

ANTIDOTE: THE FOLLOWING ANTIDOTE HAS BEEN RECOMMENDED. HOWEVER, THE DECISION AS TO WHETHER THE SEVERITY OF POISONING REQUIRES ADMINISTRATION OF ANY ANTIDOTE AND ACTUAL DOSE REQUIRED SHOULD BE MADE BY QUALIFIED MEDICAL PERSONNEL.

FOR CHOLINESTERASE INHIBITORS: ESTABLISH CLEAR AIRWAY AND TISSUE OXYGENATION BY ASPIRATION OF SECRETIONS, AND IF NECESSARY, BY ASSISTED PULMONARY VENTILATION WITH OXYGEN. IMPROVE TISSUE OXYGENATION AS MUCH AS POSSIBLE BEFORE ADMINISTERING ATROPINE TO MINIMIZE THE RISK OF VENTRICULAR FIBRILLATION. ADMINISTER ATROPINE SULFATE INTRAVENOUSLY, OR INTRAMUSCULARLY IF IV INJECTION IS NOT POSSIBLE. IN MODERATELY SEVERE POISONING ADMINISTER ATROPINE SULFATE, 0.4-2.0 MG REPEATED EVERY 15 MINUTES UNTIL ATROPINIZATION IS ACHIEVED (TACHYCARDIA, FLUSHING, DRY MOUTH, MYDRIASIS). MAINTAIN ATROPINIZATION BY REPEATED DOSES FOR 2-12 HOURS, OR LONGER, DEPENDING ON THE SEVERITY OF POISONING. THE APPEARANCE OF RALES IN THE LUNG BASES, MIOSIS, SALIVATION, NAUSEA, BRADYCARDIA, ARE ALL INDICATIONS OF INADEQUATE ATROPINIZATION. SEVERELY POISONED INDIVIDUALS MAY EXHIBIT REMARKABLE TOLERANCE TO ATROPINE; TWO OR MORE TIMES THE DOSAGES SUGGESTED ABOVE MAY BE NEEDED. PERSONS NOT POISONED OR ONLY SLIGHTLY POISONED, HOWEVER, MAY DEVELOP SIGNS OF ATROPINE TOXICITY FROM SUCH LARGE DOSAGES: FEVER, MUSCLE FIBRILLATIONS, AND DELIRIUM ARE THE MAIN SIGNS OF ATROPINE TOXICITY. IF THESE SIGNS APPEAR WHILE THE PATIENT IS FULLY ATROPINIZED, ATROPINE ADMINISTRATION SHOULD BE DISCONTINUED, AT LEAST TEMPORARILY. OBSERVE TREATED PATIENTS CLOSELY AT LEAST 24 HOURS TO INSURE THAT SYMPTOMS (POSSIBLY PULMONARY EDEMA) DO NOT RECUR AS ATROPINIZATION WEARS OFF. IN VERY SEVERE POISONINGS, METABOLIC DISPOSITION OF TOXICANT MAY REQUIRE SEVERAL HOURS OR DAYS DURING WHICH ATROPINIZATION MUST BE MAINTAINED. MARKEDLY LOWER LEVELS OF URINARY METABOLITES INDICATE THAT ATROPINE DOSAGE CAN BE TAPERED OFF. AS DOSAGE IS REDUCED, CHECK THE LUNG BASES FREQUENTLY FOR RALES. IF RALES ARE HEARD OR OTHER SYMPTOMS RETURN, RE-ESTABLISH ATROPINIZATION PROMPTLY (MORGAN, RECOGNITION AND MANAGEMENT OF PESTICIDE POISONINGS, 3RD ED.). ADMINISTRATION OF ANTIDOTE MUST BE PERFORMED BY QUALIFIED MEDICAL PERSONNEL.

REACTIVITY

REACTIVITY: STABLE UNDER NORMAL TEMPERATURES AND PRESSURES.

INCOMPATIBILITIES: 4-BENZOTHIENYL METHYLCARBAMATE: BASES (STRONG): HYDROLYZES. OXIDIZERS (STRONG): FIRE AND EXPLOSION HAZARD.

DECOMPOSITION: THERMAL DECOMPOSITION PRODUCTS MAY INCLUDE TOXIC OXIDES OF CARBON, NITROGEN, AND SULFUR.

POLYMERIZATION: HAZARDOUS POLYMERIZATION HAS NOT BEEN REPORTED TO OCCUR UNDER NORMAL TEMPERATURES AND PRESSURES.

STORAGE AND DISPOSAL

OBSERVE ALL FEDERAL, STATE AND LOCAL REGULATIONS WHEN STORING OR DISPOSING OF THIS SUBSTANCE. FOR ASSISTANCE, CONTACT THE DISTRICT DIRECTOR OF THE ENVIRONMENTAL PROTECTION AGENCY.

STORAGE

STORE IN ACCORDANCE WITH 40 CFR 165 RECOMMENDED PROCEDURES FOR THE DISPOSAL AND STORAGE OF PESTICIDES AND PESTICIDE CONTAINERS.
STORE AWAY FROM INCOMPATIBLE SUBSTANCES.

DISPOSAL

DISPOSAL MUST BE IN ACCORDANCE WITH 40 CFR 165 RECOMMENDED PROCEDURES FOR THE DISPOSAL AND STORAGE OF PESTICIDES AND PESTICIDE CONTAINERS.

CONDITIONS TO AVOID

MAY BURN BUT DOES NOT IGNITE READILY. CONTAINERS MAY EXPLODE IN HEAT OF FIRE.

SPILL AND LEAK PROCEDURES

OCCUPATIONAL SPILL: DO NOT TOUCH SPILLED MATERIAL. STOP LEAK IF YOU CAN DO IT WITHOUT RISK. USE WATER SPRAY TO REDUCE VAPORS. FOR SMALL SPILLS, TAKE UP WITH SAND OR OTHER ABSORBENT MATERIAL AND PLACE INTO CONTAINERS FOR LATER DISPOSAL. FOR SMALL DRY SPILLS, WITH A CLEAN SHOVEL PLACE MATERIAL INTO CLEAN, DRY CONTAINERS AND COVER. MOVE CONTAINERS FROM SPILL AREA. FOR LARGER SPILLS, DIKE FAR AHEAD OF SPILL FOR LATER DISPOSAL. KEEP UNNECESSARY PEOPLE AWAY. ISOLATE HAZARD AREA AND DENY ENTRY. VENTILATE CLOSED SPACES BEFORE ENTERING.

PROTECTIVE EQUIPMENT

VENTILATION: PROVIDE LOCAL EXHAUST OR GENERAL DILUTION VENTILATION SYSTEM.

RESPIRATOR: THE FOLLOWING RESPIRATORS ARE RECOMMENDED BASED ON INFORMATION FOUND IN THE PHYSICAL DATA, TOXICITY AND HEALTH EFFECTS SECTIONS. THEY ARE RANKED IN ORDER FROM MINIMUM TO MAXIMUM RESPIRATORY PROTECTION. THE SPECIFIC RESPIRATOR SELECTED MUST BE BASED ON CONTAMINATION LEVELS FOUND IN THE WORK PLACE, MUST NOT EXCEED THE WORKING LIMITS OF THE RESPIRATOR AND BE JOINTLY APPROVED BY THE NATIONAL INSTITUTE FOR OCCUPATIONAL SAFETY AND HEALTH AND THE MINE SAFETY AND HEALTH ADMINISTRATION (NIOSH-MSHA).
CHEMICAL CARTRIDGE RESPIRATOR WITH AN ORGANIC VAPOR CARTRIDGE(S) IN COMBINATION WITH A DUST AND MIST FILTER.
GAS MASK WITH ORGANIC VAPOR CANISTER (CHIN-STYLE OR FRONT- OR BACK-MOUNTED CANISTER) WITH A DUST AND MIST FILTER.
GAS MASK WITH ORGANIC VAPOR CANISTER (CHIN-STYLE OR FRONT- OR BACK-MOUNTED CANISTER) WITH A PARTICULATE FILTER.
POWERED AIR-PURIFYING RESPIRATOR WITH A HIGH-EFFICIENCY FILTER.
TYPE 'C' SUPPLIED-AIR RESPIRATOR WITH A FULL FACEPIECE OPERATED IN A PRESSURE-DEMAND OR OTHER POSITIVE PRESSURE MODE.
SELF-CONTAINED BREATHING APPARATUS WITH A FULL FACEPIECE OPERATED IN PRESSURE-DEMAND OR OTHER POSITIVE PRESSURE MODE.
FOR FIREFIGHTING AND OTHER IMMEDIATELY DANGEROUS TO LIFE OR HEALTH CONDITIONS:
SELF-CONTAINED BREATHING APPARATUS WITH FULL FACEPIECE OPERATED IN PRESSURE-DEMAND OR OTHER POSITIVE PRESSURE MODE.
SUPPLIED-AIR RESPIRATOR WITH FULL FACEPIECE AND OPERATED IN PRESSURE-DEMAND OR OTHER POSITIVE PRESSURE MODE IN COMBINATION WITH AN AUXILIARY SELF-CONTAINED BREATHING APPARATUS OPERATED IN PRESSURE-DEMAND OR OTHER POSITIVE PRESSURE MODE.

CLOTHING: EMPLOYEE MUST WEAR APPROPRIATE PROTECTIVE (IMPERVIOUS) CLOTHING AND EQUIPMENT TO PREVENT REPEATED OR PROLONGED SKIN CONTACT WITH THIS SUBSTANCE.

GLOVES: EMPLOYEE MUST WEAR APPROPRIATE PROTECTIVE GLOVES TO PREVENT CONTACT WITH THIS SUBSTANCE.

EYE PROTECTION: EMPLOYEE MUST WEAR SPLASH-PROOF OR DUST-RESISTANT SAFETY GOGGLES TO PREVENT EYE CONTACT WITH THIS SUBSTANCE.
EMERGENCY EYE WASH: WHERE THERE IS ANY POSSIBILITY THAT AN EMPLOYEE'S EYES MAY BE EXPOSED TO THIS SUBSTANCE, THE EMPLOYER SHOULD PROVIDE AN EYE WASH FOUNTAIN WITHIN THE IMMEDIATE WORK AREA FOR EMERGENCY USE.

AUTHORIZED BY- OCCUPATIONAL HEALTH SERVICES, INC.
CREATION DATE: 10/05/89 ***REVISION DATE:*** 06/12/90

MATERIAL SAFETY DATA SHEET

OCCUPATIONAL HEALTH SERVICES, INC. EMERGENCY CONTACT:
AGRICULTURE AND PESTICIDE DIVISION JOHN S. BRANSFORD, JR. (615) 292-1180
450 SEVENTH AVENUE, SUITE 2407
NEW YORK, NEW YORK 10123
1-800-445-MSDS OR (212) 967-1100

SUBSTANCE IDENTIFICATION

CAS-NUMBER 59-50-7

SUBSTANCE: **4-CHLORO-M-CRESOL**

TRADE NAMES/SYNONYMS: PHENOL, 4-CHLORO-3-METHYL-; 4-CHLORO-3-METHYLPHENOL; M-CRESOL, 4-CHLORO-; 3-METHYL-4-CHLOROPHENOL; 6-CHLORO-M-CRESOL; 6-CHLORO-3-HYDROXYTOLUENE; 2-CHLORO-5-HYDROXYTOLUENE; 4-CHLORO-1-HYDROXY-3-METHYLBENZENE; P-CHLORO-M-CRESOL; CHLOROCRESOL; P-CHLOROCRESOL; APTAL; BAKTOL; BAKTOLAN; CANDASEPTIC; OTTAFACT; PCMC; RCRA U039; UN 2669; C7H7CLO; PST29890

CHEMICAL FAMILY: HALOGEN COMPOUND, AROMATIC

MOLECULAR FORMULA: C7-H7-CL-O

MOLECULAR WEIGHT: 142.58

CERCLA RATINGS (SCALE 0-3): HEALTH=3 FIRE=0 REACTIVITY=0 PERSISTENCE=3

NFPA RATINGS (SCALE 0-4): HEALTH=3 FIRE=0 REACTIVITY=0

COMPONENTS AND CONTAMINANTS

COMPONENT: 4-CHLORO-M-CRESOL ***PERCENT:*** 100
CAS# 59-50-7

OTHER CONTAMINANTS: NONE.

EXPOSURE LIMITS: 4-CHLORO-M-CRESOL: NO OCCUPATIONAL EXPOSURE LIMITS ESTABLISHED BY OSHA, ACGIH, OR NIOSH.
5000 POUNDS CERCLA SECTION 103 REPORTABLE QUANTITY

PHYSICAL DATA

DESCRIPTION: WHITE, OR SLIGHTLY PINK CRYSTALS WITH A PHENOLIC ODOR; AQUEOUS SOLUTION TURNS YELLOW ON EXPOSURE TO LIGHT AND AIR.

BOILING POINT: 455 F (235 C)

MELTING POINT: 151-154 F (66-68 C) ***SOLUBILITY IN WATER:*** 0.38%

ODOR THRESHOLD: 3 PPM IN WATER

SOLVENT SOLUBILITY: ALCOHOL, BENZENE, CHLOROFORM, ETHER, ACETONE, TERPENES, PETROLEUM ETHER, FIXED OILS, AQUEOUS ALKALINE SOLUTIONS, ORGANIC SOLVENTS.

FIRE AND EXPLOSION DATA

FIRE AND EXPLOSION HAZARD: NEGLIGIBLE FIRE HAZARD WHEN EXPOSED TO HEAT OR FLAME.

FIREFIGHTING MEDIA: DRY CHEMICAL, CARBON DIOXIDE, HALON, WATER SPRAY OR STANDARD FOAM (1987 EMERGENCY RESPONSE GUIDEBOOK, DOT P 5800.4).
FOR LARGER FIRES, USE WATER SPRAY, FOG OR STANDARD FOAM (1987 EMERGENCY RESPONSE GUIDEBOOK, DOT P 5800.4).

FIREFIGHTING: MOVE CONTAINERS FROM FIRE AREA IF POSSIBLE (1987 EMERGENCY RESPONSE GUIDEBOOK, DOT P 5800.4, GUIDE PAGE 53).
EXTINGUISH ONLY IF FLOW CAN BE STOPPED. EXTINGUISH USING AGENT INDICATED. USE FLOODING AMOUNTS OF WATER AS A FOG. COOL CONTAINERS WITH FLOODING AMOUNTS OF WATER FROM AS FAR A DISTANCE AS POSSIBLE. AVOID BREATHING POISONOUS VAPORS, KEEP UPWIND. CONSIDER EVACUATION OF DOWNWIND AREA IF MATERIAL IS LEAKING.

TOXICITY

4-CHLORO-M-CRESOL: TOXICITY DATA: 1830 MG/KG ORAL-RAT LD50; 400 MG/KG SUBCUTANEOUS-RAT LD50; 200 MG/KG SUBCUTANEOUS-MOUSE LDLO; 30 MG/KG INTRAPERITONEAL-MOUSE LDLO; MUTAGENIC DATA (RTECS). CARCINOGEN STATUS: NONE. LOCAL EFFECTS: CORROSIVE- INHALATION, SKIN, AND EYES. ACUTE TOXICITY LEVEL: MODERATELY TOXIC BY INGESTION. TARGET EFFECTS: SENSITIZER- SKIN. POISONING MAY AFFECT THE LUNGS, LIVER, KIDNEYS, PANCREAS, SPLEEN, AND SKIN.

HEALTH EFFECTS AND FIRST AID

INHALATION: 4-CHLORO-M-CRESOL: ACUTE EXPOSURE- NO SPECIFIC DATA AVAILABLE. PHENOL DERIVATIVES MAY BE ABSORBED FROM THE LUNGS AND PRODUCE A RAPID DEVELOPMENT OF ADVERSE EFFECTS OF HEADACHE, DIZZINESS, DIMNESS OF VISION, TINNITUS, IRREGULAR AND RAPID RESPIRATION, WEAK PULSE, DYSPNEA, AND PROFOUND MUSCULAR WEAKNESS; MENTAL CONFUSION MAY ALSO OCCUR. PULMONARY EDEMA WITH SIGNS OF STERTOROUS BREATHING, MUCOUS RALES, RHONCHI, FROTHING AT NOSE AND MOUTH IS SOMETIMES OBSERVED. SERIOUS EFFECTS OF SHOCK, COLLAPSE, CONVULSIONS, CYANOSIS, AND COMA ARE POSSIBLE. RENAL COMPLICATIONS MAY DEVELOP AND SOMETIMES PROGRESS TO ACUTE FAILURE. DEATH MAY BE DUE TO RESPIRATORY, CIRCULATORY, OR CARDIAC FAILURE. DAMAGE TO THE

LIVER, PANCREAS, AND SPLEEN MAY OCCUR. SOME PHENOL DERIVATIVES HAVE BEEN IMPLICATED AS CAUSES OF METHEMOGLOBINEMIA OR HEINZ BODY HEMOLYTIC ANEMIA OR BOTH. **CHRONIC EXPOSURE-** REPEATED EXPOSURES TO PHENOL DERIVATIVES MAY RESULT IN GASTROINTESTINAL DISTURBANCES OF VOMITING, DIFFICULTY OF SWALLOWING, PTYALISM, DIARRHEA, AND ANOREXIA; NERVOUS DISORDERS OF HEADACHE, FAINTING, VERTIGO, AND MENTAL DISTURBANCES; AND DERMATITIS. THE URINE MAY HAVE A DARK-COLORED OR "SMOKY" APPEARANCE. DEATH MAY OCCUR WHEN THERE IS EXTENSIVE DAMAGE TO THE LIVER AND KIDNEYS.

FIRST AID- REMOVE FROM EXPOSURE AREA TO FRESH AIR IMMEDIATELY. IF BREATHING HAS STOPPED, GIVE ARTIFICIAL RESPIRATION. MAINTAIN AIRWAY AND BLOOD PRESSURE AND ADMINISTER OXYGEN IF AVAILABLE. KEEP AFFECTED PERSON WARM AND AT REST. TREAT SYMPTOMATICALLY AND SUPPORTIVELY. ADMINISTRATION OF OXYGEN SHOULD BE PERFORMED BY QUALIFIED PERSONNEL. GET MEDICAL ATTENTION IMMEDIATELY.

SKIN CONTACT: 4-CHLORO-M-CRESOL: SENSITIZER. **ACUTE EXPOSURE-** A 1.5% AQUEOUS SOLUTION HAS PRODUCED PRURITIC VESICULAR DERMATITIS IN SENSITIVE INDIVIDUALS; SYMPTOMS APPEARED IN 4 HOURS AND REGRESSED WITHIN 1 WEEK. SENSITIZATION MAY OCCUR IN PERSONS PREVIOUSLY EXPOSED. PHENOL DERIVATIVES MAY CAUSE SEVERE IRRITATION OF THE SKIN WITH INTENSE BURNING AND PAIN FOLLOWED BY LOCAL ANESTHESIA WITH A WHITE DISCOLORATION; THE AREA MAY SUBSEQUENTLY BECOME GANGRENOUS. PHENOL DERIVATIVES MAY BE ABSORBED THROUGH THE SKIN WITH THE RATE OF ABSORPTION DEPENDING UPON THE SIZE OF THE AREA EXPOSED RATHER THAN ON THE CONCENTRATION OF THE MATERIAL. EXTENSIVE SKIN CONTACT MAY BE FATAL. THE SYSTEMIC EFFECTS FROM EXPOSURE TO PHENOL DERIVATIVES ARE AS DESCRIBED IN ACUTE INHALATION. **CHRONIC EXPOSURE-** REPEATED CONTACT MAY LEAD TO SENSITIZATION DERMATITIS. CHRONIC SKIN EXPOSURE TO PHENOL DERIVATIVES MAY RESULT IN OCHRONOSIS, A PIGMENTARY DISORDER CHARACETERIZED BY A DARKENING OF THE SKIN, CONJUNCTIVA, AND CARTILAGE OF THE NOSE AND EARS. CHRONIC SKIN CONTACT WITH PHENOL DERIVATIVES MAY BE FATAL. THE SYSTEMIC EFFECTS FROM CHRONIC EXPOSURE TO PHENOL DERIVATIVES ARE AS DESCRIBED IN CHRONIC INHALATION.

FIRST AID- REMOVE CONTAMINATED CLOTHING AND SHOES IMMEDIATELY. WASH AFFECTED AREA WITH SOAP OR MILD DETERGENT AND LARGE AMOUNTS OF WATER UNTIL NO EVIDENCE OF CHEMICAL REMAINS (AT LEAST 15-20 MINUTES). IN CASE OF CHEMICAL BURNS, COVER AREA WITH STERILE, DRY DRESSING. BANDAGE SECURELY, BUT NOT TOO TIGHTLY. GET MEDICAL ATTENTION IMMEDIATELY.

EYE CONTACT: 4-CHLORO-M-CRESOL: **ACUTE EXPOSURE-** A 0.05% SOLUTION IN SALINE INJECTED INTO THE ANTERIOR CHAMBER OF RABBIT EYES PRODUCED OPACIFICATION. PHENOL DERIVATIVES ARE SEVERELY IRRITATING TO THE HUMAN EYE WITH POSSIBLE CONJUNCTIVAL SWELLING; THE CORNEA MAY BECOME WHITE AND HYPESTHETIC; SEVERE AND IRREVERSIBLE DAMAGE MAY OCCUR. **CHRONIC EXPOSURE-** NO DATA AVAILABLE.

FIRST AID- WASH EYES IMMEDIATELY WITH LARGE AMOUNTS OF WATER, OCCASIONALLY LIFTING UPPER AND LOWER LIDS, UNTIL NO EVIDENCE OF CHEMICAL REMAINS (AT LEAST 15-20 MINUTES). CONTINUE IRRIGATING WITH NORMAL SALINE UNTIL THE PH HAS RETURNED TO NORMAL (30-60 MINUTES). COVER WITH STERILE BANDAGES. GET MEDICAL ATTENTION IMMEDIATELY.

INGESTION: 4-CHLORO-M-CRESOL: **ACUTE EXPOSURE-** A LETHAL DOSE IN RATS WAS 1830 MG/KG. INGESTION OF PHENOL DERIVATIVES MAY CAUSE BURNING PAIN IN MOUTH AND THROAT, WHITE NECROTIC LESIONS IN MOUTH, ESOPHAGUS AND STOMACH, ABDOMINAL PAIN, VOMITING, AND BLOODY DIARRHEA. OTHER EFFECTS OF POISONING FROM PHENOL DERIVATIVES ARE AS DESCRIBED IN ACUTE INHALATION. **CHRONIC EXPOSURE-** REPEATED EXPOSURE TO PHENOL DERIVATIVES MAY CAUSE EFFECTS AS DESCRIBED IN ACUTE INGESTION.

FIRST AID- IN THE ABSENCE OF CORROSIVE INJURY, REMOVE POISON BY IPECAC EMESIS. ACTIVATED CHARCOAL IS ALSO USEFUL. FOLLOW WITH 60 ML OF CASTOR OIL, WHICH DISSOLVES PHENOL, RETARDS ITS ABSORPTION, AND HASTENS ITS REMOVAL. FOLLOW CASTOR OIL BY GIVING 30-60 ML OF FLEET'S PHOSPHO-SODA DILUTED 1:4 IN WATER. GASTRIC LAVAGE AND EMESIS ARE CONTRAINDICATED IN THE PRESENCE OF ESOPHAGEAL INJURY. (DREISBACH, HANDBOOK OF POISONING, 11TH ED.) GET MEDICAL ATTENTION IMMEDIATELY. TREATMENT SHOULD BE ADMINISTERED BY QUALIFIED PERSONNEL.

ANTIDOTE: NO SPECIFIC ANTIDOTE. TREAT SYMPTOMATICALLY AND SUPPORTIVELY.

REACTIVITY

REACTIVITY: STABLE UNDER NORMAL TEMPERATURES AND PRESSURES.

INCOMPATIBILITIES: 4-CHLORO-M-CRESOL: NO DATA AVAILABLE.

DECOMPOSITION: THERMAL DECOMPOSITION PRODUCTS MAY INCLUDE TOXIC AND CORROSIVE FUMES OF CHLORIDES AND PHOSGENE, AND TOXIC OXIDES OF CARBON.

POLYMERIZATION: HAZARDOUS POLYMERIZATION HAS NOT BEEN REPORTED TO OCCUR UNDER NORMAL TEMPERATURES AND PRESSURES.

STORAGE AND DISPOSAL

OBSERVE ALL FEDERAL, STATE AND LOCAL REGULATIONS WHEN STORING OR DISPOSING OF THIS SUBSTANCE. FOR ASSISTANCE, CONTACT THE DISTRICT DIRECTOR OF THE ENVIRONMENTAL PROTECTION AGENCY.

****DISPOSAL****

DISPOSAL MUST BE IN ACCORDANCE WITH STANDARDS APPLICABLE TO GENERATORS OF HAZARDOUS WASTE, 40CFR 262. EPA HAZARDOUS WASTE NUMBER U039.

CONDITIONS TO AVOID

MAY BURN BUT DOES NOT IGNITE READILY.

SPILL AND LEAK PROCEDURES

OCCUPATIONAL SPILL: DO NOT TOUCH SPILLED MATERIAL. STOP LEAK IF YOU CAN DO IT WITHOUT RISK. FOR SMALL SPILLS, TAKE UP WITH SAND OR OTHER ABSORBENT MATERIAL AND PLACE INTO CONTAINERS FOR LATER DISPOSAL. FOR SMALL DRY SPILLS, WITH A CLEAN SHOVEL PLACE MATERIAL INTO CLEAN, DRY CONTAINER AND COVER. MOVE CONTAINERS FROM SPILL AREA. FOR LARGER SPILLS, DIKE FAR AHEAD OF SPILL FOR LATER DISPOSAL. KEEP UNNECESSARY PEOPLE AWAY. ISOLATE HAZARD AREA AND DENY ENTRY.

REPORTABLE QUANTITY (RQ): 5000 POUNDS THE SUPERFUND AMENDMENTS AND REAUTHORIZATION ACT (SARA) SECTION 304 REQUIRES THAT A RELEASE EQUAL TO OR GREATER THAN THE REPORTABLE QUANTITY FOR THIS SUBSTANCE BE IMMEDIATELY REPORTED TO THE LOCAL EMERGENCY PLANNING COMMITTEE AND THE STATE EMERGENCY RESPONSE COMMISSION (40 CFR 355.40). IF THE RELEASE OF THIS SUBSTANCE IS REPORTABLE UNDER CERCLA SECTION 103, THE NATIONAL RESPONSE CENTER MUST BE NOTIFIED IMMEDIATELY AT (800) 424-8802 OR (202) 426-2675 IN THE METROPOLITAN WASHINGTON, D.C. AREA (40 CFR 302.6).

PROTECTIVE EQUIPMENT

VENTILATION: PROVIDE LOCAL EXHAUST OR GENERAL DILUTION VENTILATION SYSTEM.

RESPIRATOR: THE FOLLOWING RESPIRATORS AND MAXIMUM USE CONCENTRATIONS ARE RECOMMENDATIONS BY THE U.S. DEPARTMENT OF HEALTH AND HUMAN SERVICES, NIOSH POCKET GUIDE TO CHEMICAL HAZARDS; NIOSH CRITERIA DOCUMENTS OR BY THE U.S. DEPARTMENT OF LABOR, 29 CFR 1910 SUBPART Z. THE SPECIFIC RESPIRATOR SELECTED MUST BE BASED ON CONTAMINATION LEVELS FOUND IN THE WORK PLACE, MUST NOT EXCEED THE WORKING LIMITS OF THE RESPIRATOR AND BE JOINTLY APPROVED BY THE NATIONAL INSTITUTE FOR OCCUPATIONAL SAFETY AND HEALTH AND THE MINE SAFETY AND HEALTH ADMINISTRATION (NIOSH-MSHA).

DUST AND MIST RESPIRATOR WITH A FULL FACEPIECE.

AIR-PURIFYING FULL FACEPIECE RESPIRATOR WITH A HIGH-EFFICIENCY PARTICULATE FILTER.

POWERED AIR-PURIFYING RESPIRATOR WITH A TIGHT-FITTING FACEPIECE AND HIGH-EFFICIENCY PARTICULATE FILTER.

TYPE 'C' SUPPLIED-AIR RESPIRATOR WITH A FULL FACEPIECE OPERATED IN PRESSURE-DEMAND OR OTHER POSITIVE PRESSURE MODE OR WITH A FULL FACEPIECE, HELMET OR HOOD OPERATED IN CONTINUOUS-FLOW MODE.

SELF-CONTAINED BREATHING APPARATUS WITH A FULL FACEPIECE OPERATED IN PRESSURE-DEMAND OR OTHER POSITIVE PRESSURE MODE.

FOR FIREFIGHTING AND OTHER IMMEDIATELY DANGEROUS TO LIFE OR HEALTH CONDITIONS:

SELF-CONTAINED BREATHING APPARATUS WITH FULL FACEPIECE OPERATED IN PRESSURE-DEMAND OR OTHER POSITIVE PRESSURE MODE.

SUPPLIED-AIR RESPIRATOR WITH FULL FACEPIECE AND OPERATED IN PRESSURE-DEMAND OR OTHER POSITIVE PRESSURE MODE IN COMBINATION WITH AN AUXILIARY SELF-CONTAINED BREATHING APPARATUS OPERATED IN PRESSURE-DEMAND OR OTHER POSITIVE PRESSURE MODE.

CLOTHING: EMPLOYEE MUST WEAR APPROPRIATE PROTECTIVE (IMPERVIOUS) CLOTHING AND EQUIPMENT TO PREVENT ANY POSSIBILITY OF SKIN CONTACT WITH THIS SUBSTANCE.

GLOVES: EMPLOYEE MUST WEAR APPROPRIATE PROTECTIVE GLOVES TO PREVENT CONTACT WITH THIS SUBSTANCE.

EYE PROTECTION: EMPLOYEE MUST WEAR SPLASH-PROOF OR DUST-RESISTANT SAFETY GOGGLES AND A FACESHIELD TO PREVENT CONTACT WITH THIS SUBSTANCE.

EMERGENCY WASH FACILITIES: WHERE THERE IS ANY POSSIBILITY THAT AN EMPLOYEE'S EYES AND/OR SKIN MAY BE EXPOSED TO THIS SUBSTANCE, THE EMPLOYER SHOULD PROVIDE AN EYE WASH FOUNTAIN AND QUICK DRENCH SHOWER WITHIN THE IMMEDIATE WORK AREA FOR EMERGENCY USE.

AUTHORIZED BY- OCCUPATIONAL HEALTH SERVICES, INC.
CREATION DATE: 10/06/89 ***REVISION DATE:*** 05/29/90

MATERIAL SAFETY DATA SHEET

OCCUPATIONAL HEALTH SERVICES, INC.
AGRICULTURE AND PESTICIDE DIVISION
450 SEVENTH AVENUE, SUITE 2407
NEW YORK, NEW YORK 10123
1-800-445-MSDS OR (212) 967-1100

EMERGENCY CONTACT:
JOHN S. BRANSFORD, JR. (615) 292-1180

SUBSTANCE IDENTIFICATION

CAS-NUMBER 148-24-3
SUBSTANCE: **8-HYDROXYQUINOLINE**
TRADE NAMES/SYNONYMS: 8-QUINOLINOL; OXYQUINOLINE; HYDROXYBENZOPYRIDINE; OXY-BENZOPYRIDINE; PHENOPYRIDINE; OXINE; BIOQUIN; QUINOPHENOL; NCI-C55298; OXY-CHINOLIN; 8-OQ; 8-OXYQUINOLINE; TUMEX; O-261; PST30450
CHEMICAL FAMILY: QUINOLINE
MOLECULAR FORMULA: C9-H7-N-O
MOLECULAR WEIGHT: 145.17
CERCLA RATINGS (SCALE 0-3): HEALTH=3 FIRE=0 REACTIVITY=0 PERSISTENCE=1
NFPA RATINGS (SCALE 0-4): HEALTH=3 FIRE=0 REACTIVITY=0

COMPONENTS AND CONTAMINANTS

COMPONENT: 8-HYDROXYQUINOLINE ***PERCENT:*** 100
CAS# 148-24-3
OTHER CONTAMINANTS: NONE
EXPOSURE LIMITS: NO OCCUPATIONAL EXPOSURE LIMITS ESTABLISHED BY OSHA, ACGIH, OR NIOSH.

PHYSICAL DATA

DESCRIPTION: WHITE CRYSTALS OR CRYSTALLINE POWDER, DARKENS UPON EXPOSURE TO LIGHT
BOILING POINT: 512 F (267 C) SUBLIMES
MELTING POINT: 167 F (75 C) ***SPECIFIC GRAVITY:*** 1.0 @ 209 C
SOLUBILITY IN WATER: INSOLUBLE
SOLVENT SOLUBILITY: ACETONE, CHLOROFORM, BZ, DILUTE ALKALIES, ALCOHOL

FIRE AND EXPLOSION DATA

FIRE AND EXPLOSION HAZARD: SLIGHT FIRE HAZARD WHEN EXPOSED TO HEAT OR FLAME.
FLASH POINT: NONFLAMMABLE
FIREFIGHTING MEDIA: DRY CHEMICAL, CARBON DIOXIDE OR HALON (1987 EMERGENCY RESPONSE GUIDEBOOK, DOT P 5800.4).
FOR LARGER FIRES, USE WATER SPRAY, FOG OR STANDARD FOAM (1987 EMERGENCY RESPONSE GUIDEBOOK, DOT P 5800.4).
FIREFIGHTING: NO ACUTE HAZARD. MOVE CONTAINER FROM FIRE AREA IF POSSIBLE. AVOID BREATHING VAPORS OR DUSTS; KEEP UPWIND.

TOXICITY

8-HYDROXYQUINOLINE: TOXICITY DATA: 1200 MG/KG ORAL-RAT LD50; 20 GM/KG ORAL-MOUSE LD50; 1205 MG/KG ORAL-GUINEA PIG LD20; 83,600 UG/KG SUBCUTANEOUS-MOUSE LD50; 43 MG/KG INTRAPERITONEAL-MOUSE LD50; 1000 MG/KG UNREPORTED-MAMMAL LD50; MUTAGENIC DATA (RTECS); TUMORIGENIC DATA (RTECS). CARCINOGEN STATUS: ANIMAL INADEQUATE EVIDENCE (IARC GROUP-3). ACUTE TOXICITY DATA: MODERATELY TOXIC BY INGESTION. TARGET EFFECTS: METHEMOGLOBIN FORMER.

HEALTH EFFECTS AND FIRST AID

INHALATION: 8-HYDROXYQUINOLINE **ACUTE EXPOSURE-** SYMPTOMS INCLUDE CYANOSIS AT METHEMOGLOBIN LEVELS ABOVE 15%; HEADACHE, SHALLOW RESPIRATION AND DIZZINESS AT METHEMOGLOBIN LEVELS OF 40-50%; CONFUSION, HYPOTENSION, LETHARGY AND STUPOR AT 60%; AND CONVULSIONS, COMA, HYPOTENSION AND POSSIBLE DEATH AT METHEMOGLOBIN LEVELS OF 70% OR HIGHER. JAUNDICE, PAIN ON URINATION AND ANEMIA MAY APPEAR LATER. **CHRONIC EXPOSURE-** NERVOUS SYSTEM, LIVER, KIDNEY AND BONE MARROW MAY BE AFFECTED. WEIGHT LOSS, ANEMIA, WEAKNESS AND IRRITABILITY MAY ALSO OCCUR.
FIRST AID- REMOVE FROM EXPOSURE AREA TO FRESH AIR IMMEDIATELY. IF BREATHING HAS STOPPED, GIVE ARTIFICIAL RESPIRATION. MAINTAIN AIRWAY AND BLOOD PRESSURE AND ADMINISTER OXYGEN IF AVAILABLE. KEEP AFFECTED PERSON WARM AND AT REST. TREAT SYMPTOMATICALLY AND SUPPORTIVELY. ADMINISTRATION OF OXYGEN SHOULD BE PERFORMED BY QUALIFIED PERSONNEL. GET MEDICAL ATTENTION IMMEDIATELY.

SKIN CONTACT: 8-HYDROXYQUINOLINE: **ACUTE EXPOSURE-** SUBSTANCE MAY BE ABSORBED CAUSING CYANOSIS AT METHEMOGLOBIN LEVELS ABOVE 15%; HEADACHE, SHALLOW RESPIRATION AND DIZZINESS AT METHEMOGLOBIN LEVELS OF 40-50%; CONFUSION, LETHARGY, HYPOTENSION AND STUPOR AT 60%; AND CONVULSIONS, COMA, HYPOTENSION AND POSSIBLY DEATH AT METHEMOGLOBIN LEVELS OF 70% OR HIGHER. JAUNDICE, PAIN ON URINATION AND ANEMIA MAY APPEAR LATER. **CHRONIC EXPOSURE-** NERVOUS SYSTEM, LIVER, KIDNEY AND BONE MARROW MAY BE AFFECTED. WEIGHT LOSS, ANEMIA, WEAKNESS AND IRRITABILITY MAY ALSO OCCUR FROM PROLONGED EXPOSURE. **FIRST AID-** REMOVE CONTAMINATED CLOTHING AND SHOES IMMEDIATELY. WASH AFFECTED AREA WITH SOAP OR MILD DETERGENT AND LARGE AMOUNTS OF WATER UNTIL NO EVIDENCE OF CHEMICAL REMAINS (APPROXIMATELY 15-20 MINUTES). GET MEDICAL ATTENTION IMMEDIATELY.

EYE CONTACT: 8-HYDROXYQUINOLINE: IRRITANT. **ACUTE EXPOSURE-** DIRECT CONTACT MAY CAUSE REDNESS AND IRRITATION. **CHRONIC EXPOSURE-** PROLONGED OR REPEATED EXPOSURE MAY CAUSE CONJUNCTIVITIS.
FIRST AID- WASH EYES IMMEDIATELY WITH LARGE AMOUNTS OF WATER OR NORMAL SALINE, OCCASIONALLY LIFTING UPPER AND LOWER LIDS, UNTIL NO EVIDENCE OF CHEMICAL REMAINS (APPROXIMATELY 15-20 MINUTES). GET MEDICAL ATTENTION IMMEDIATELY.

INGESTION: 8-HYDROXYQUINOLINE: **ACUTE EXPOSURE-** DEPENDING UPON THE QUANTITY INGESTED, SYMPTOMS MAY INCLUDE CYANOSIS AT METHEMOGLOBIN LEVELS ABOVE 15%; HEADACHE, SHALLOW RESPIRATION AND DIZZINESS AT METHEMOGLOBIN LEVELS OF 40-50%; CONFUSION, HYPOTENSION, LETHARGY AND STUPOR AT 60%; AND CONVULSIONS, COMA, HYPOTENSION AND POSSIBLY DEATH AT METHEMOBLOBIN LEVELS OF 70% OR HIGHER. JAUNDICE, PAIN ON URINATION AND ANEMIA MAY APPEAR LATER. **CHRONIC EXPOSURE-** PROLONGED EXPOSURE FROM INGESTION MAY CAUSE NERVOUS SYSTEM, LIVER, KIDNEY AND BONE MARROW DAMAGE. WEIGHT LOSS, ANEMIA, WEAKNESS AND IRRITABILITY MAY ALSO OCCUR.
FIRST AID- IF THE PERSON IS CONSCIOUS AND NOT CONVULSING, INDUCE EMESIS BY GIVING SYRUP OF IPECAC FOLLOWED BY WATER. (IF VOMITING OCCURS KEEP THE HEAD BELOW THE HIPS TO PREVENT ASPIRATION). REPEAT IN 20 MINUTES IF NOT EFFECTIVE INITIALLY. GIVE ACTIVATED CHARCOAL. IN PATIENTS WITH DEPRESSED RESPIRATION OR IF EMESIS IS NOT PRODUCED, PERFORM GASTRIC LAVAGE CAUTIOUSLY (DREISBACH, HANDBOOK OF POISONING, 12TH ED.). TREAT SYMPTOMATICALLY AND SUPPORTIVELY. GASTRIC LAVAGE SHOULD BE PERFORMED BY QUALIFIED MEDICAL PERSONNEL. GET MEDICAL ATTENTION IMMEDIATELY.
ANTIDOTE: THE FOLLOWING ANTIDOTE HAS BEEN RECOMMENDED. HOWEVER, THE DECISION AS TO WHETHER THE SEVERITY OF POISONING REQUIRES ADMINISTRATION OF ANY ANTIDOTE AND ACTUAL DOSE REQUIRED SHOULD BE MADE BY QUALIFIED MEDICAL PERSONNEL.
METHEMOGLOBINEMIA: (WHEN METHEMOGLOBIN CONCENTRATION IS OVER 25-40% OR IN PRESENCE OF SYMPTOMS.) GIVE METHYLENE BLUE, 1% SOLUTION, 0.1 ML/KG INTRAVENOUSLY OVER A 10-MINUTE PERIOD. CYANOSIS MAY DISAPPEAR WITHIN MINUTES OR PERSIST LONGER DEPENDING ON DEGREE OF METHEMOGLOBINEMIA. INTRAVENOUS ADMINISTRATION OF THERAPEUTIC DOSES OF METHYLENE BLUE MAY CAUSE A RISE IN BLOOD PRESSURE, NAUSEA, AND DIZZINESS. LARGER DOSES (>500 MG) CAUSE VOMITING, DIARRHEA, CHEST PAIN, MENTAL CONFUSION, CYANOSIS, AND SWEATING. HEMOLYTIC ANEMIA HAS ALSO OCCURRED SEVERAL DAYS AFTER ADMINISTRATION. THESE EFFECTS ARE TEMPORARY, AND FATALITIES HAVE NOT BEEN REPORTED. IF METHYLENE BLUE IS NOT AVAILABLE, GIVE ASCORBIC ACID, 1 GRAM SLOWLY INTRAVENOUSLY. WITHOUT TREATMENT, METHEMOGLOBINEMIA LEVELS OF 20-30% REVERT TO NORMAL WITHIN 3 DAYS (DREISBACH, HANDBOOK OF POISONING, 12TH ED.). ANTIDOTE SHOULD BE ADMINISTERED BY QUALIFIED MEDICAL PERSONNEL.

REACTIVITY

REACTIVITY: STABLE UNDER NORMAL TEMPERATURES AND PRESSURES.
INCOMPATIBILITIES: NONE KNOWN.
DECOMPOSITION: THERMAL DECOMPOSITION MAY INCLUDE TOXIC OXIDES OF CARBON AND NITROGEN.
POLYMERIZATION: HAZARDOUS POLYMERIZATION HAS NOT BEEN REPORTED TO OCCUR UNDER NORMAL TEMPERATURES AND PRESSURES.

SPILL AND LEAK PROCEDURES

OCCUPATIONAL SPILL: NO SPECIAL PRECAUTIONS INDICATED.

PROTECTIVE EQUIPMENT

VENTILATION: PROVIDE LOCAL EXHAUST OR GENERAL DILUTION VENTILATION SYSTEM.

RESPIRATOR: HIGH LEVELS- DUST MASK.

FIREFIGHTING- SELF-CONTAINED BREATHING APPARATUS WITH A FULL FACE-PIECE OPERATED IN PRESSURE-DEMAND OR OTHER POSITIVE PRESSURE MODE.

CLOTHING: EMPLOYEE MUST WEAR APPROPRIATE PROTECTIVE (IMPERVIOUS) CLOTHING AND EQUIPMENT TO PREVENT ANY POSSIBILITY OF SKIN CONTACT WITH THIS SUBSTANCE.

GLOVES: EMPLOYEE MUST WEAR APPROPRIATE PROTECTIVE GLOVES TO PREVENT CONTACT WITH THIS SUBSTANCE.

EYE PROTECTION: EMPLOYEE MUST WEAR SPLASH-PROOF OR DUST-RESISTANT SAFETY GOGGLES TO PREVENT EYE CONTACT WITH THIS SUBSTANCE.

EMERGENCY EYE WASH: WHERE THERE IS ANY POSSIBILITY THAT AN EMPLOYEE'S EYES MAY BE EXPOSED TO THIS SUBSTANCE, THE EMPLOYER SHOULD PROVIDE AN EYE WASH FOUNTAIN WITHIN THE IMMEDIATE WORK AREA FOR EMERGENCY USE.

AUTHORIZED BY- OCCUPATIONAL HEALTH SERVICES, INC.
CREATION DATE: 11/16/89 ***REVISION DATE:*** 07/12/90

MATERIAL SAFETY DATA SHEET

OCCUPATIONAL HEALTH SERVICES, INC.
AGRICULTURE AND PESTICIDE DIVISION
450 SEVENTH AVENUE, SUITE 2407
NEW YORK, NEW YORK 10123
1-800-445-MSDS OR (212) 967-1100

EMERGENCY CONTACT:
JOHN S. BRANSFORD, JR. (615) 292-1180

SUBSTANCE IDENTIFICATION

CAS-NUMBER 58-36-6

SUBSTANCE: **10, 10'-OXYDIPHENOXARSINE**

TRADE NAMES/SYNONYMS: 10, 10-OXYBIS-PHENOXARSINE; 10, 10-OXIDIPHENOXARSINE; BIS(PHENOXARSIN-10-YL) ETHER; BIS(10-PHENOXARSINYL) OXIDE; BIS(10-PHENOXARSYL) OXIDE; DID 47; VINADINE; VINYZENE; PST30500

CHEMICAL FAMILY: XANTHENE

MOLECULAR FORMULA: C24-H16-AS2-O3

MOLECULAR WEIGHT: 502.23

CERCLA RATINGS (SCALE 0-3): HEALTH=3 FIRE=U REACTIVITY=U PERSISTENCE=2

NFPA RATINGS (SCALE 0-4): HEALTH=4 FIRE=U REACTIVITY=U

COMPONENTS AND CONTAMINANTS

COMPONENT: 10, 10'-OXYDIPHENOXARSINE ***PERCENT:*** 100.0
CAS# 58-36-6

OTHER CONTAMINANTS: NONE.

EXPOSURE LIMITS: ARSENIC, ORGANIC AND INSOLUBLE COMPOUNDS: 0.5 MG(AS)/M3 OSHA TWA

SUBJECT TO SARA SECTION 313 ANNUAL TOXIC CHEMICAL RELEASE REPORTING
10,10'-OXYDIPHENOXARSINE: 0.5 MG(AS)/M3 OSHA TWA
500/10,000 POUNDS SARA SECTION 302 THRESHOLD PLANNING QUANTITY 1 POUND SARA SECTION 304 REPORTABLE QUANTITY

PHYSICAL DATA

DESCRIPTION: COLORLESS CRYSTALS. ***BOILING POINT:*** 716 F (380 C) DECOMPOSES

MELTING POINT: 365 F (185 C) ***SPECIFIC GRAVITY:*** 1.40

SOLUBILITY IN WATER: 5 PPM

SOLVENT SOLUBILITY: SOLUBLE IN ALCOHOL, CHLOROFORM, AND METHYLENE CHLORIDE.

FIRE AND EXPLOSION DATA

FIRE AND EXPLOSION HAZARD: UNKNOWN FIRE AND EXPLOSION HAZARD.

FIREFIGHTING MEDIA: DRY CHEMICAL, CARBON DIOXIDE, HALON, WATER SPRAY OR STANDARD FOAM (1987 EMERGENCY RESPONSE GUIDEBOOK, DOT P 5800.4).

FOR LARGER FIRES, USE WATER SPRAY, FOG OR STANDARD FOAM (1987 EMERGENCY RESPONSE GUIDEBOOK, DOT P 5800.4).

FIREFIGHTING: MOVE CONTAINERS FROM FIRE AREA IF POSSIBLE (1987 EMERGENCY RESPONSE GUIDEBOOK, DOT P 5800.4, GUIDE PAGE 53).

USE AGENTS INDICATED. DO NOT USE WATER ON MATERIAL. FOR LARGE FIRES USE WATER IN FLOODING AMOUNTS AS FOG AND SPRAY. USE WATER TO ABSORB VAPORS. AVOID BREATHING POISONOUS VAPORS, KEEP UPWIND.

TRANSPORTATION DATA

DEPARTMENT OF TRANSPORTATION HAZARD CLASSIFICATION 49 CFR 172.101: POISON B

DEPARTMENT OF TRANSPORTATION LABELING REQUIREMENTS 49 CFR 172.101 AND SUBPART E: POISON

DEPARTMENT OF TRANSPORTATION PACKAGING REQUIREMENTS: 49 CFR 173.365 EXCEPTIONS: 49 CFR 173.364

TOXICITY

10, 10'-OXYDIPHENOXARSINE: IRRITATION DATA: 250 MG/5 DAYS SKIN-GUINEA PIG SEVERE. TOXICITY DATA: 141 MG/M3/2 HOURS INHALATION-GUINEA PIG LCLO; 40 MG/KG ORAL-RAT LD50; 24 MG/KG ORAL-GUINEA PIG LD50; 42 MG/KG ORAL-MOUSE LDLO. CARCINOGEN STATUS: NONE. NO ADEQUATE DATA ON ORGANIC ARSENICALS WERE AVAILABLE FOR EVALUATION. ACUTE TOXICITY LEVEL: HIGHLY TOXIC INGESTION. TARGET EFFECTS: POISONING MAY AFFECT THE PERIPHERAL NERVOUS SYSTEM AND BLOOD.

HEALTH EFFECTS AND FIRST AID

INHALATION: 10, 10'-OXYDIPHENOXARSINE: IRRITANT/HIGHLY TOXIC. **ACUTE EXPOSURE-** THE LOWEST REPORTED LETHAL DOSE OF THIS SUBSTANCE IN GUINEA PIGS WAS 141 MG/M3 FOR 2 HOURS. SYMPTOMS WERE NOT REPORTED. ACUTE ARSENIC POISONING BY INHALATION MAY CAUSE COUGH, CHEST PAIN, DIFFICULTY IN BREATHING, GIDDINESS, HEADACHE, AND EXTREME GENERAL WEAKNESS. LATER GASTROINTESTINAL SYMPTOMS SUCH AS NAUSEA AND VOMITING MAY OCCUR. **CHRONIC EXPOSURE-** NO DATA AVAILABLE .

FIRST AID- REMOVE FROM EXPOSURE AREA TO FRESH AIR IMMEDIATELY. IF BREATHING HAS STOPPED, PERFORM ARTIFICIAL RESPIRATION. KEEP PERSON WARM AND AT REST. TREAT SYMPTOMATICALLY AND SUPPORTIVELY. GET MEDICAL ATTENTION IMMEDIATELY.

SKIN CONTACT: 10, 10'-OXYDIPHENOXARSINE: IRRITANT. **ACUTE EXPOSURE-** APPLICATION OF 250 MG TO THE SKIN OF GUINEA PIGS FOR 5 DAYS CAUSED SEVERE IRRITATION. EXPOSURE TO ORGANIC ARSENIC COMPOUNDS MAY PRODUCE IRRITATION AND ALLERGIC CONTACT DERMATITIS. **CHRONIC EXPOSURE-** NO DATA AVAILABLE. CHRONIC SYSTEMIC POISONING MAY CAUSE BRONZING OF THE SKIN AND MEE'S LINES IN THE FINGERNAILS, AS WELL AS HYPERKERATOSES OF THE PALMS OF THE HANDS AND SOLES OF THE FEET.

FIRST AID- REMOVE CONTAMINATED CLOTHING AND SHOES IMMEDIATELY. WASH AFFECTED AREA WITH SOAP OR MILD DETERGENT AND LARGE AMOUNTS OF WATER UNTIL NO EVIDENCE OF CHEMICAL REMAINS (APPROXIMATELY 15-20 MINUTES). GET MEDICAL ATTENTION IMMEDIATELY.

EYE CONTACT: 10, 10'-OXYDIPHENOXARSINE: **ACUTE EXPOSURE-** NO DATA AVAILABLE. EYE EXPOSURE TO INORGANIC ARSENIC COMPOUNDS GENERALLY CAUSES IRRITATION AND CONJUNCTIVITIS, WHICH IS CHARACTERIZED BY ITCHING, BURNING AND WATERING OF THE EYES, WITH PHOTOPHOBIA AND SOMETIMES HYPEREMIA AND CHEMOSIS. **CHRONIC EXPOSURE-** NO DATA AVIALABLE. CHRONIC SYSTEMIC POISONING BY ARSENIC COMPOUNDS MAY ALSO PRODUCE CONJUNCTIVITIS, POSSIBLY DUE TO EXCRETION OF ARSENIC IN TEARS.

FIRST AID- WASH EYES IMMEDIATELY WITH LARGE AMOUNTS OF WATER OR NORMAL SALINE, OCCASIONALLY LIFTING UPPER AND LOWER LIDS, UNTIL NO EVIDENCE OF CHEMICAL REMAINS (APPROXIMATELY 15-20 MINUTES). GET MEDICAL ATTENTION IMMEDIATELY.

INGESTION: 10, 10'-OXYDIPENOXARSINE: HIGHLY TOXIC. **ACUTE EXPOSURE-** THE LETHAL DOSE OF THIS SUBSTANCE IN RATS WAS 42 MG/KG; SYMPTOMS WERE NOT REPORTED. ACUTE ORGANIC ARSENIC POISONING IS CHARACTERIZED BY BURNING AND DRYNESS OF THE MOUTH, ESOPHAGUS AND STOMACH. NAUSEA, PROTRACTED VOMITING, ABDOMINAL PAIN AND DIARRHEA OFTEN FOLLOW. OLIGURIA, SHOCK AND DEATH MAY DEVELOP IN SEVERE CASES. OCCASIONALLY, RESTLESSNESS, VERTIGO, MUSCLE SPASM, DELIRIUM, AND COMA MAY OCCUR. CONJUCTIVITIS AND SWELLING OF THE EYELIDS HAVE BEEN SEEN. **CHRONIC EXPOSURE-** CHRONIC ORGANIC ARSENIC INTOXICATION IS MANIFESTED BY MALAISE AND FATIGUE; NAUSEA AND VOMITING OR DIARRHEA MAY FREQUENTLY APPEAR. SKIN FINDINGS INCLUDE INCREASED PIGMENTATION AND HYPERKERITOSIS OF THE PALMS AND SOLES OF THE FEET. PARESTHESIA AND NUMBNESS OF THE HANDS AND FEET AND MUSCULAR WEAKNESS OF THE EXTREMITIES ARE COMMON. THE HEMATOLOGIC ABNORMALITIES DESCRIBED IN CHRONIC ARSENIC POISONING ARE BASOPHYLIC STIPPLING OF ERYTHROCYTES, HEMOLYTIC ANEMIA, LEUKOPENIA, AND BONE MARROW HYPOPLASIA. THESE SYMPTOMS MAY WORSEN INTO ACUTE MYELOGENOUS LEUKEMIA.

FIRST AID- REMOVE BY GASTRIC LAVAGE OR EMESIS. FOLLOW WITH A SALINE CATHARTIC. MAINTAIN BLOOD PRESSURE, AIRWAY, AND GIVE OXYGEN IF RESPIRATION IS DEPRESSED. DO NOT PERFORM GASTRIC LAVAGE OR EMESIS IF

VICTIM IS UNCONSCIOUS. GET MEDICAL ATTENTION IMMEDIATELY. (DREISBACH, HANDBOOK OF POISONING, 12TH ED.) ADMINISTRATION OF GASTRIC LAVAGE OR OXYGEN SHOULD BE PERFORMED BY QUALIFIED MEDICAL PERSONNEL.

ANTIDOTE: THE FOLLOWING ANTIDOTE HAS BEEN RECOMMENDED. HOWEVER, THE DECISION AS TO WHETHER THE SEVERITY OF POISONING REQUIRES ADMINISTRATION OF ANY ANTIDOTE AND ACTUAL DOSE REQUIRED SHOULD BE MADE BY QUALIFIED MEDICAL PERSONNEL.

ARSENIC POISONING: GIVE DIMERCAPROL, 3 MG/KG (OR 0.3 ML/KG) EVERY 4 HOURS FOR 2 DAYS AND THEN 2 MG/KG EVERY 2 HOURS FOR A TOTAL OF 10 DAYS. DIMERCAPROL IS AVAILABLE AS A 10% SOLUTION IN OIL FOR INTRAMUSCULAR ADMINISTRATION. NEXT, GIVE PENICILLAMINE, UP TO 100 MG/KG/DAY (MAXIMUM 1 G/DAY) DIVIDED INTO 4 DOSES FOR NO LONGER THAN 1 WEEK. IF A LONGER ADMINISTRATION PERIOD IS WARRANTED, DOSAGE SHOULD NOT EXCEED 40 MG/KG/DAY. GIVE THE DRUG ORALLY HALF AN HOUR BEFORE MEALS. DISCONTINUE ANTIDOTE WHEN URINE ARSENIC LEVEL FALLS BELOW 50 UG/24 HR. (DREISBACH, HANDBOOK OF POISONING, 12TH ED.). ANITDOTE SHOULD BE ADMINISTERED BY QUALIFIED MEDICAL PERSONNEL.

REACTIVITY

REACTIVITY: NO DATA AVAILABLE.

INCOMPATIBILITIES: 10, 10'-OXYDIPENOXARSINE: NO DATA AVAILABLE.

DECOMPOSITION: THERMAL DECOMPOSITION PRODUCTS MAY INCLUDE TOXIC OXIDES OF ARSENIC AND CARBON.

POLYMERIZATION: HAZARDOUS POLYMERIZATION HAS NOT BEEN REPORTED TO OCCUR UNDER NORMAL TEMPERATURES AND PRESSURES.

STORAGE AND DISPOSAL

OBSERVE ALL FEDERAL, STATE AND LOCAL REGULATIONS WHEN STORING OR DISPOSING OF THIS SUBSTANCE. FOR ASSISTANCE, CONTACT THE DISTRICT DIRECTOR OF THE ENVIRONMENTAL PROTECTION AGENCY.

STORAGE

THRESHOLD PLANNING QUANTITY (TPQ): THE SUPERFUND AMENDMENTS AND REAUTHORIZATION ACT (SARA) SECTION 302 REQUIRES THAT EACH FACILITY WHERE ANY EXTREMELY HAZARDOUS SUBSTANCE IS PRESENT IN A QUANTITY EQUAL TO OR GREATER THAN THE TPQ ESTABLISHED FOR THAT SUBSTANCE NOTIFY THE STATE EMERGENCY RESPONSE COMMISSION FOR THE STATE IN WHICH IT IS LOCATED. SECTION 303 OF SARA REQUIRES THESE FACILITIES TO PARTICIPATE IN LOCAL EMERGENCY RESPONSE PLANNING (40 CFR 355.30).

DISPOSAL

ARSENIC - REGULATORY LEVEL: 5.0 MG/L MATERIALS WHICH CONTAIN THE ABOVE SUBSTANCE AT OR ABOVE THE REGULATORY LEVEL MEET THE EPA CHARACTERISTIC OF TOXICITY, AND MUST BE DISPOSED OF IN ACCORDANCE WITH 40 CFR PART 262. EPA HAZARDOUS WASTE NUMBER D004.

CONDITIONS TO AVOID

NONE REPORTED.

SPILL AND LEAK PROCEDURES

OCCUPATIONAL SPILL: DO NOT TOUCH SPILLED MATERIAL. STOP LEAK IF YOU CAN DO IT WITHOUT RISK. FOR SMALL SPILLS, TAKE UP WITH SAND OR OTHER ABSORBENT MATERIAL AND PLACE INTO CONTAINERS FOR LATER DISPOSAL. FOR SMALL DRY SPILLS, WITH A CLEAN SHOVEL PLACE MATERIAL INTO CLEAN, DRY CONTAINER AND COVER. MOVE CONTAINERS FROM SPILL AREA. FOR LARGER SPILLS, DIKE FAR AHEAD OF SPILL FOR LATER DISPOSAL. KEEP UNNECESSARY PEOPLE AWAY. ISOLATE HAZARD AREA AND DENY ENTRY.

REPORTABLE QUANTITY (RQ): 1 POUND THE SUPERFUND AMENDMENTS AND REAUTHORIZATION ACT (SARA) SECTION 304 REQUIRES THAT A RELEASE EQUAL TO OR GREATER THAN THE REPORTABLE QUANTITY FOR THIS SUBSTANCE BE IMMEDIATELY REPORTED TO THE LOCAL EMERGENCY PLANNING COMMITTEE AND THE STATE EMERGENCY RESPONSE COMMISSION (40 CFR 355.40). IF THE RELEASE OF THIS SUBSTANCE IS REPORTABLE UNDER CERCLA SECTION 103, THE NATIONAL RESPONSE CENTER MUST BE NOTIFIED IMMEDIATELY AT (800) 424-8802 OR (202) 426-2675 IN THE METROPOLITAN WASHINGTON, D.C. AREA (40 CFR 302.6).

PROTECTIVE EQUIPMENT

VENTILATION: PROVIDE LOCAL EXHAUST OR PROCESS ENCLOSURE VENTILATION TO MEET PUBLISHED EXPOSURE LIMITS.

RESPIRATOR: THE FOLLOWING RESPIRATORS ARE RECOMMENDED BASED ON INFORMATION FOUND IN THE PHYSICAL DATA, TOXICITY AND HEALTH EFFECTS SECTIONS. THEY ARE RANKED IN ORDER FROM MINIMUM TO MAXIMUM RESPIRATORY PROTECTION. THE SPECIFIC RESPIRATOR SELECTED MUST BE BASED ON CONTAMINATION LEVELS FOUND IN THE WORK PLACE, MUST NOT EXCEED THE WORKING LIMITS OF THE RESPIRATOR AND BE JOINTLY APPROVED BY THE NATIONAL INSTITUTE FOR OCCUPATIONAL SAFETY AND HEALTH AND THE MINE SAFETY AND HEALTH ADMINISTRATION (NIOSH-MSHA).

AT ANY DETECTABLE CONCENTRATION:

SELF-CONTAINED BREATHING APPARATUS WITH FULL FACEPIECE OPERATED IN PRESSURE-DEMAND OR OTHER POSITIVE PRESSURE MODE. SUPPLIED-AIR RESPIRATOR WITH FULL FACEPIECE OPERATED IN PRESSURE-DEMAND OR OTHER POSITIVE PRESSURE MODE IN COMBINATION WITH AN AUXILIARY SELF-CONTAINED BREATHING APPARATUS OPERATED IN PRESSURE-DEMAND OR OTHER POSITIVE PRESSURE MODE. ESCAPE- AIR-PURIFYING FULL FACEPIECE RESPIRATOR (GAS MASK) WITH A CHIN-STYLE OR FRONT- OR BACK-MOUNTED ACID GAS CANISTER HAVING A HIGH-EFFICIENCY PARTICULATE FILTER. ESCAPE-TYPE SELF-CONTAINED BREATHING APPARATUS.

FOR FIREFIGHTING AND OTHER IMMEDIATELY DANGEROUS TO LIFE OR HEALTH CONDITIONS:

SELF-CONTAINED BREATHING APPARATUS WITH FULL FACEPIECE OPERATED IN PRESSURE-DEMAND OR OTHER POSITIVE PRESSURE MODE.

SUPPLIED-AIR RESPIRATOR WITH FULL FACEPIECE AND OPERATED IN PRESSURE-DEMAND OR OTHER POSITIVE PRESSURE MODE IN COMBINATION WITH AN AUXILIARY SELF-CONTAINED BREATHING APPARATUS OPERATED IN PRESSURE-DEMAND OR OTHER POSITIVE PRESSURE MODE.

CLOTHING: EMPLOYEE MUST WEAR APPROPRIATE PROTECTIVE (IMPERVIOUS) CLOTHING AND EQUIPMENT TO PREVENT ANY POSSIBILITY OF SKIN CONTACT WITH THIS SUBSTANCE.

GLOVES: EMPLOYEE MUST WEAR APPROPRIATE PROTECTIVE GLOVES TO PREVENT CONTACT WITH THIS SUBSTANCE.

EYE PROTECTION: EMPLOYEE MUST WEAR SPLASH-PROOF OR DUST-RESISTANT SAFETY GOGGLES AND A FACESHIELD TO PREVENT CONTACT WITH THIS SUBSTANCE.

EMERGENCY WASH FACILITIES: WHERE THERE IS ANY POSSIBILITY THAT AN EMPLOYEE'S EYES AND/OR SKIN MAY BE EXPOSED TO THIS SUBSTANCE, THE EMPLOYER SHOULD PROVIDE AN EYE WASH FOUNTAIN AND QUICK DRENCH SHOWER WITHIN THE IMMEDIATE WORK AREA FOR EMERGENCY USE.

AUTHORIZED BY- OCCUPATIONAL HEALTH SERVICES, INC.

CREATION DATE: 10/05/89 ***REVISION DATE:*** 07/13/90

MATERIAL SAFETY DATA SHEET

OCCUPATIONAL HEALTH SERVICES, INC.
AGRICULTURE AND PESTICIDE DIVISION
450 SEVENTH AVENUE, SUITE 2407
NEW YORK, NEW YORK 10123
1-800-445-MSDS OR (212) 967-1100

EMERGENCY CONTACT:
JOHN S. BRANSFORD, JR. (615) 292-1180

SUBSTANCE IDENTIFICATION

CAS-NUMBER 9005-65-6

SUBSTANCE: **POLYOXYETHYLENE (20) SORBITAN MONOOLEATE**

TRADE NAMES/SYNONYMS: TWEEN 80; ARMOTAN PMO-20; CAPMUL POE-O; EMSORB 6900; GLYCOSPERSE O-20 VEG; LIPOSORB O-20; POLYOXYETHYLENE SORBITAN MONOOLEATE; POLYSORBATE 80; PROTASORB O-20; SORBIMACROGOL OLEATE 300; LIPOSORB L-20; POLYSORBATE 80 B.P.C.; SORLATE; MONITAN; OLOTHORB; GLYCOSPERSE O-20X; GLYCOSPERSE O-20; T-164; PST40200

CHEMICAL FAMILY: POLYMER

MOLECULAR FORMULA: (C64-H123-O26)N MOL WT: (1308)N

CERCLA RATINGS (SCALE 0-3): HEALTH=2 FIRE=0 REACTIVITY=0 PERSISTENCE=0

NFPA RATINGS (SCALE 0-4): HEALTH=2 FIRE=0 REACTIVITY=0

COMPONENTS AND CONTAMINANTS

COMPONENT: POLYOXYETHYLENE (20) SORBITAN MONOOLEATE ***PERCENT:*** 100
CAS# 9005-65-6

OTHER CONTAMINANTS: NONE

EXPOSURE LIMITS: NO OCCUPATIONAL EXPOSURE LIMITS ESTABLISHED BY OSHA, ACGIH, OR NIOSH.

PHYSICAL DATA

DESCRIPTION: VISCOUS AMBER LIQUID ***BOILING POINT:*** NOT AVAILABLE

SPECIFIC GRAVITY: 1.1 ***VAPOR PRESSURE:*** NOT AVAILABLE

EVAPORATION RATE: (ETHER = 1) >1 ***PH:*** 5-7 (5% SOLUTION)

SOLUBILITY IN WATER: SOLUBLE ***VAPOR DENSITY:*** NOT AVAILABLE

SOLVENT SOLUBILITY: ALCOHOL, ETHYL ACETATE, TOLUENE, CORN OIL, ACETONE

FIRE AND EXPLOSION DATA

FIRE AND EXPLOSION HAZARD: NEGLIGIBLE FIRE HAZARD WHEN EXPOSED TO HEAT OR FLAME.

FLASH POINT: 600 F (316 C) ***FLAMMABILITY CLASS(OSHA):*** IIIB

FIREFIGHTING MEDIA: DRY CHEMICAL, CARBON DIOXIDE, HALON, WATER SPRAY OR STANDARD FOAM (1987 EMERGENCY RESPONSE GUIDEBOOK, DOT P 5800.4). FOR LARGER FIRES, USE WATER SPRAY, FOG OR STANDARD FOAM (1987 EMERGENCY RESPONSE GUIDEBOOK, DOT P 5800.4).

FIREFIGHTING: MOVE CONTAINER FROM FIRE AREA IF POSSIBLE. DO NOT SCATTER SPILLED MATERIAL WITH HIGH PRESSURE WATER STREAMS. DIKE FIRE CONTROL WATER FOR LATER DISPOSAL (1987 EMERGENCY RESPONSE GUIDEBOOK, DOT P 5800.4, GUIDE PAGE 31).
USE AGENTS SUITABLE FOR TYPE OF SURROUNDING FIRE. AVOID BREATHING HAZARDOUS VAPORS, KEEP UPWIND.

TOXICITY

POLYOXYETHYLENE (20) SORBITAN MONOOLEATE (TWEEN (R) 80): IRRITATION DATA: 150 MG EYE-RABBIT MILD. TOXICITY DATA: 25 GM/KG ORAL-MOUSE LD50; 1790 MG/KG INTRAVENOUS-RAT LD50; 4500 MG/KG INTRAVENOUS-MOUSE LD50; 500 MG/KG INTRAVENOUS-DOG LDLO; 500 MG/KG INTRAVENOUS-CAT LDLO; 6804 MG/KG INTRAPERITONEAL-RAT LD50; 7600 MG/KG INTRAPERITONEAL-MOUSE LD50; MUTAGENIC DATA (RTECS); REPRODUCTIVE EFFECTS DATA (RTECS); TUMORIGENIC DATA (RTECS). CARCINGEN STATUS: NONE. ACUTE TOXICITY LEVEL: RELATIVELY NONTOXIC BY INGESTION. TARGET EFFECTS: POISONING MAY AFFECT THE EYES AND DIGESTIVE SYSTEM.

HEALTH EFFECTS AND FIRST AID

INHALATION: POLYOXYETHYLENE (20) SORBITAN MONOOLEATE (TWEEN (R) 80): **ACUTE EXPOSURE-** INHALATION MAY CAUSE CHEMICAL PNEUMONITIS. **CHRONIC EXPOSURE-** NO DATA AVAILABLE.

FIRST AID- REMOVE FROM EXPOSURE AREA TO FRESH AIR IMMEDIATELY. IF BREATHING HAS STOPPED, PERFORM ARTIFICIAL RESPIRATION. KEEP PERSON WARM AND AT REST. TREAT SYMPTOMATICALLY AND SUPPORTIVELY. GET MEDICAL ATTENTION IMMEDIATELY.

SKIN CONTACT: POLYOXYETHYLENE (20) SORBITAN MONOOLEATE (TWEEN (R) 80): **ACUTE EXPOSURE-** NO DATA AVAILABLE. **CHRONIC EXPOSURE-** NO DATA AVAILABLE.

FIRST AID- REMOVE CONTAMINATED CLOTHING AND SHOES IMMEDIATELY. WASH AFFECTED AREA WITH SOAP OR MILD DETERGENT AND LARGE AMOUNTS OF WATER UNTIL NO EVIDENCE OF CHEMICAL REMAINS (APPROXIMATELY 15-20 MINUTES). GET MEDICAL ATTENTION IMMEDIATELY.

EYE CONTACT: POLYOXYETHYLENE (20) SORBITAN MONOOLEATE (TWEEN (R) 80): **ACUTE EXPOSURE-** 150 MG APPLIED TO RABBIT EYES CAUSED MILD IRRITATION. A 20% SOLUTION OF PH 5 TO 7 DROPPED IN HUMAN EYES WAS WELL TOLERATED. **CHRONIC EXPOSURE-** NO DATA AVAILABLE.

FIRST AID- WASH EYES IMMEDIATELY WITH LARGE AMOUNTS OF WATER OR NORMAL SALINE, OCCASIONALLY LIFTING UPPER AND LOWER LIDS, UNTIL NO EVIDENCE OF CHEMICAL REMAINS (APPROXIMATELY 15-20 MINUTES). GET MEDICAL ATTENTION IMMEDIATELY.

INGESTION: POLYOXYETHYLENE (20) SORBITAN MONOOLEATE (TWEEN (R) 80): **ACUTE EXPOSURE-** INGESTION OF LARGE QUANTITIES MAY CAUSE INTESTINAL OBSTRUCTION. ASPIRATION COULD CAUSE A CHEMICAL PNEUMONITIS. **CHRONIC EXPOSURE-** ADMINISTRATION OF 19.2 GM/KG FOR 2 DAYS CAUSED DIARRHEA BUT NO OTHER TOXIC EFFECTS.

FIRST AID- TREAT SYMPTOMATICALLY AND SUPPORTIVELY. GET MEDICAL ATTENTION.

ANTIDOTE: NO SPECIFIC ANTIDOTE. TREAT SYMPTOMATICALLY AND SUPPORTIVELY.

REACTIVITY

REACTIVITY: STABLE UNDER NORMAL TEMPERATURES AND PRESSURES.

INCOMPATIBILITIES: NONE KNOWN.

DECOMPOSITION: THERMAL DECOMPOSITION MAY RELEASE ACRID SMOKE AND IRRITATING FUMES.

POLYMERIZATION: HAZARDOUS POLYMERIZATION HAS NOT BEEN REPORTED TO OCCUR UNDER NORMAL TEMPERATURES AND PRESSURES.

CONDITIONS TO AVOID

NO REPORTS FOUND.

SPILL AND LEAK PROCEDURES

OCCUPATIONAL SPILL: TAKE UP WITH SUITABLE ABSORBENT MATERIAL.

PROTECTIVE EQUIPMENT

VENTILATION: PROVIDE LOCAL EXHAUST OR PROCESS ENCLOSURE VENTILATION SYSTEM.

RESPIRATOR: THE FOLLOWING RESPIRATORS ARE RECOMMENDED BASED ON INFORMATION FOUND IN THE PHYSICAL DATA, TOXICITY AND HEALTH EFFECTS SECTIONS. THEY ARE RANKED IN ORDER FROM MINIMUM TO MAXIMUM RESPIRATORY PROTECTION. THE SPECIFIC RESPIRATOR SELECTED MUST BE BASED ON CONTAMINATION LEVELS FOUND IN THE WORK PLACE, MUST NOT EXCEED THE WORKING LIMITS OF THE RESPIRATOR AND BE JOINTLY APPROVED BY THE NATIONAL INSTITUTE FOR OCCUPATIONAL SAFETY AND HEALTH AND THE MINE SAFETY AND HEALTH ADMINISTRATION (NIOSH-MSHA).
CHEMICAL CARTRIDGE RESPIRATOR WITH AN ORGANIC VAPOR CARTRIDGE(S) WITH A FULL FACEPIECE.
GAS MASK WITH ORGANIC VAPOR CANISTER (CHIN-STYLE OR FRONT- OR BACK-MOUNTED CANISTER) WITH A FULL FACEPIECE.
TYPE 'C' SUPPLIED-AIR RESPIRATOR WITH A FULL FACEPIECE OPERATED IN PRESSURE-DEMAND OR OTHER POSITIVE PRESSURE MODE OR WITH A FULL FACEPIECE, HELMET OR HOOD OPERATED IN CONTINUOUS-FLOW MODE.
SELF-CONTAINED BREATHING APPARATUS WITH A FULL FACEPIECE OPERATED IN PRESSURE-DEMAND OR OTHER POSITIVE PRESSURE MODE.
FOR FIREFIGHTING AND OTHER IMMEDIATELY DANGEROUS TO LIFE OR HEALTH CONDITIONS:
SELF-CONTAINED BREATHING APPARATUS WITH FULL FACEPIECE OPERATED IN PRESSURE-DEMAND OR OTHER POSITIVE PRESSURE MODE.
SUPPLIED-AIR RESPIRATOR WITH FULL FACEPIECE AND OPERATED IN PRESSURE-DEMAND OR OTHER POSITIVE PRESSURE MODE IN COMBINATION WITH AN AUXILIARY SELF-CONTAINED BREATHING APPARATUS OPERATED IN PRESSURE-DEMAND OR OTHER POSITIVE PRESSURE MODE.

CLOTHING: EMPLOYEE MUST WEAR APPROPRIATE PROTECTIVE (IMPERVIOUS) CLOTHING AND EQUIPMENT TO PREVENT REPEATED OR PROLONGED SKIN CONTACT WITH THIS SUBSTANCE.

GLOVES: EMPLOYEE MUST WEAR APPROPRIATE PROTECTIVE GLOVES TO PREVENT CONTACT WITH THIS SUBSTANCE.

EYE PROTECTION: EMPLOYEE MUST WEAR SPLASH-PROOF OR DUST-RESISTANT SAFETY GOGGLES TO PREVENT EYE CONTACT WITH THIS SUBSTANCE.
EMERGENCY EYE WASH: WHERE THERE IS ANY POSSIBILITY THAT AN EMPLOYEE'S EYES MAY BE EXPOSED TO THIS SUBSTANCE, THE EMPLOYER SHOULD PROVIDE AN EYE WASH FOUNTAIN WITHIN THE IMMEDIATE WORK AREA FOR EMERGENCY USE.

AUTHORIZED BY- OCCUPATIONAL HEALTH SERVICES, INC.
CREATION DATE: 10/04/89 ***REVISION DATE:*** 05/18/90

MATERIAL SAFETY DATA SHEET

OCCUPATIONAL HEALTH SERVICES, INC.
AGRICULTURE AND PESTICIDE DIVISION
450 SEVENTH AVENUE, SUITE 2407
NEW YORK, NEW YORK 10123
1-800-445-MSDS OR (212) 967-1100

EMERGENCY CONTACT:
JOHN S. BRANSFORD, JR. (615) 292-1180

SUBSTANCE IDENTIFICATION

CAS-NUMBER 50-00-0

SUBSTANCE: **FORMALDEHYDE SOLUTION, 37%**

TRADE NAMES/SYNONYMS: FORMALIN; FORMIC ALDEHYDE; PARAFORM; FORMALIN, (METHANOL-FREE); METHANAL; METHYL ALDEHYDE; METHYLENE GLYCOL; METHYLENE OXIDE; TETRAOXYMETHYLENE; OXOMETHANE; OXYMETHYLENE; RCRA U122; STCC 4913168; UN 2209; FORMALDEHYDE SOLUTION; CH2O; PST50003

CHEMICAL FAMILY: ALDEHYDE, ALIPHATIC
MIXTURE, AQUEOUS

MOLECULAR FORMULA: H-C-H-O

MOLECULAR WEIGHT: 30.03

CERCLA RATINGS (SCALE 0-3): HEALTH=3 FIRE=2 REACTIVITY=0 PERSISTENCE=0

NFPA RATINGS (SCALE 0-4): HEALTH=2 FIRE=2 REACTIVITY=0

COMPONENTS AND CONTAMINANTS

COMPONENT: FORMALDEHYDE ***PERCENT:*** 37.0
CAS# 50-00-0

COMPONENT: WATER ***PERCENT:*** 63.0

EXPOSURE LIMITS: FORMALDEHYDE: 1 PPM OSHA TWA; 2 PPM OSHA 15 MINUTE STEL; 0.5 PPM OSHA ACTION LEVEL 1 PPM ACGIH TWA; 2 PPM ACGIH STEL (NOTICE OF INTENDED CHANGES 1989-1990) ACGIH A2-SUSPECTED HUMAN CARCINOGEN. LOWEST FEASIBLE LIMIT NIOSH RECOMMENDED EXPOSURE CRITERIA
500 POUNDS SARA SECTION 302 THRESHOLD PLANNING QUANTITY 1000 POUNDS SARA SECTION 304 REPORTABLE QUANTITY 100 POUNDS CERCLA SECTION 103 REPORTABLE QUANTITY SUBJECT TO SARA SECTION 313 ANNUAL TOXIC CHEMICAL RELEASE REPORTING SUBJECT TO CALIFORNIA PROPOSITION 65 CANCER AND/OR REPRODUCTIVE TOXICITY WARNING AND RELEASE REQUIREMENTS- (JANUARY 1, 1988)

PHYSICAL DATA

DESCRIPTION: COLORLESS LIQUID WITH A PUNGENT ODOR. ***BOILING POINT:*** 214 F (101 C)
SPECIFIC GRAVITY: 1.1 ***VAPOR PRESSURE:*** NOT AVAILABLE
SOLUBILITY IN WATER: COMPLETE

FIRE AND EXPLOSION DATA

FIRE AND EXPLOSION HAZARD: MODERATE FIRE HAZARD WHEN EXPOSED TO HEAT OR FLAME.
VAPORS ARE HEAVIER THAN AIR AND MAY TRAVEL A CONSIDERABLE DISTANCE TO A SOURCE OF IGNITION AND FLASH BACK.
FLASH POINT: 185 F (85 C) (TCC) ***UPPER EXPLOSIVE LIMIT:*** 73%
LOWER EXPLOSIVE LIMIT: 7% ***FLAMMABILITY CLASS(OSHA):*** IIIA
FIREFIGHTING MEDIA: DRY CHEMICAL, CARBON DIOXIDE, HALON, WATER SPRAY OR STANDARD FOAM (1987 EMERGENCY RESPONSE GUIDEBOOK, DOT P 5800.4).
FOR LARGER FIRES, USE WATER SPRAY, FOG OR STANDARD FOAM (1987 EMERGENCY RESPONSE GUIDEBOOK, DOT P 5800.4).
ALCOHOL FOAM (NFPA 325M, FIRE HAZARD PROPERTIES OF FLAMMABLE LIQUIDS, GASES, AND VOLATILE SOLIDS, 1984).
FIREFIGHTING: MOVE CONTAINER FROM FIRE AREA IF POSSIBLE. COOL FIRE-EXPOSED CONTAINERS WITH WATER FROM SIDE UNTIL WELL AFTER FIRE IS OUT. STAY AWAY FROM STORAGE TANK ENDS. FOR MASSIVE FIRE IN STORAGE AREA, USE UNMANNED HOSE HOLDER OR MONITOR NOZZLES, ELSE WITHDRAW FROM AREA AND LET FIRE BURN. WITHDRAW IMMEDIATELY IN CASE OF RISING SOUND FROM VENTING SAFETY DEVICE OR ANY DISCOLORATION OF STORAGE TANK DUE TO FIRE (1987 EMERGENCY RESPONSE GUIDEBOOK, DOT P 5800.4, GUIDE PAGE 27).
EXTINGUISH ONLY IF FLOW CAN BE STOPPED; USE FLOODING AMOUNTS OF WATER AS A FOG, SOLID STREAMS MAY BE INEFFECTIVE. COOL CONTAINERS WITH FLOODING AMOUNTS OF WATER, APPLY FROM AS FAR A DISTANCE AS POSSIBLE. AVOID BREATHING VAPORS, KEEP UPWIND.

TRANSPORTATION DATA

FORMALDEHYDE SOLUTIONS: DEPARTMENT OF TRANSPORTATION HAZARD CLASSIFICATION 49 CFR 172.101: ORM-A (IN CONTAINERS OF 110 GALLONS OR LESS)
DEPARTMENT OF TRANSPORTATION LABELING REQUIREMENTS 49 CFR 172.101 AND SUBPART E: NONE
DEPARTMENT OF TRANSPORATION PACKAGING REQUIREMENTS: 49 CFR 173.510 EXCEPTIONS: 49 CFR 173.505
DEPARTMENT OF TRANSPORTATION HAZARD CLASSIFICATION 49 CFR 172.101: COMBUSTIBLE LIQUID (IN CONTAINERS OVER 110 GALLONS) DEPARTMENT OF TRANSPORTATION LABELING REQUIREMENTS 49 CFR 172.101 AND SUBPART E: NONE
DEPARTMENT OF TRANSPORATION PACKAGING REQUIREMENTS: 49CFR173.118A EXCEPTIONS: NONE

TOXICITY

FORMALDEHYDE: IRRITATION DATA: 150 UG/3 DAYS INTERMITTENT SKIN-HUMAN MILD; 2 MG/24 HOURS SKIN-RABBIT SEVERE; 540 MG OPEN SKIN-RABBIT MILD; 50 MG/24 HOURS SKIN-RABBIT MODERATE; 4 PPM/5 MINUTES EYE-HUMAN; 1 PPM/6 MINUTES NONSTANDARD EXPOSURE EYE-HUMAN MILD; 750 UG/24 HOURS EYE-RABBIT SEVERE; 750 UG EYE-RABBIT SEVERE; 10 MG EYE-RABBIT SEVERE. TOXICITY DATA: 17 MG/M3/30 MINUTES INHALATION-HUMAN TCLO; 300 UG/M3 INHALATION-MAN TCLO; 590 MG/M3 INHALATION-RAT LC50; 400 MG/M3/2 HOURS INHALATION-MOUSE LC50; 400 MG/M3/2 HOURS INHALATION-CAT LCLO; 92 MG/M3 INHALATION-MAMMAL LC50; 270 MG/KG SKIN-RABBIT LD50; 108 MG/KG ORAL-WOMAN LDLO; 800 MG/KG ORAL-RAT LD50; 42 MG/KG ORAL-MOUSE LD50; 260 MG/KG ORAL-GUINEA PIG LD50; 420 MG/KG SUBCUTANEOUS-RAT LD50; 300 MG/KG SUBCUTANEOUS-MOUSE LD50; 350 MG/KG SUBCUTANEOUS-DOG LDLO; 240 MG/KG SUBCUTANEOUS-RABBIT LDLO; 87 MG/KG INTRAVENOUS-RAT LD50; 48 MG/KG INTRAVENOUS-RABBIT LDLO; 30 MG/KG INTRAVENOUS-CAT LDLO; 70 MG/KG INTRAVENOUS-DOG LDLO; 16 MG/KG INTRAPERITONEAL-MOUSE LDLO; 477 MG/KG UNREPORTED-MAN LDLO; MUTAGENIC DATA (RTECS); REPRODUCTIVE EFFECTS DATA (RTECS); TUMORIGENIC DATA (RTECS). CARCINOGEN STATUS: OSHA CARCINOGEN; ANTICIPATED HUMAN CARCINOGEN (NTP); HUMAN LIMITED EVIDENCE, ANIMAL SUFFICIENT EVIDENCE (IARC GROUP-2A). EPIDEMIOLOGICAL STUDIES AND CASE REPORTS INDICATE AN EXCESS OCCURRENCE OF A NUMBER OF CANCERS, BUT EVIDENCE FOR INVOLVEMENT OF FORMALDEHYDE IS STRONGEST FOR NASAL AND NASOPHARYNGEAL CANCER. A SIGNIFICANT INCIDENCE OF SQUAMOUS CELL CARCINOMA OF THE NASAL CAVITY WAS INDUCED IN RATS EXPOSED TO FORMALDEHYDE GAS. LOCAL EFFECTS: CORROSIVE- INHALATION, SKIN, EYE, INGESTION. ACUTE TOXICITY LEVEL: HIGHLY TOXIC BY INHALATION; TOXIC BY DERMAL ABSORPTION; MODERATELY TOXIC BY INGESTION. TARGET EFFECTS: SENSITIZER- INHALATION, SKIN. POISONING MAY ALSO AFFECT THE KIDNEYS. AT INCREASED RISK FROM EXPOSURE: PERSONS WITH ASTHMA, CHRONIC SKIN DISEASE OR PREEXISTING LUNG DISEASE.

HEALTH EFFECTS AND FIRST AID

INHALATION: FORMALDEHYDE: CORROSIVE/SENSITIZER/CARCINOGEN/HIGHLY TOXIC.
ACUTE EXPOSURE- CONCENTRATIONS OF 0.1-5.0 PPM MAY CAUSE IRRITATION OF THE NOSE AND THROAT; 10-20 PPM MAY CAUSE DIFFICULTY IN BREATHING, A BURNING SENSATION IN THE NOSE AND THROAT, AND COUGHING; 25-50 PPM MAY CAUSE TISSUE DAMAGE AND SERIOUS RESPIRATORY TRACT INJURY SUCH AS PNEUMONITIS AND, RARELY, PULMONARY EDEMA. OTHER SYMPTOMS MAY INCLUDE SNEEZING, WHEEZING, PHARYNGITIS, TRACHEITIS, CHEST CONSTRICTION, BRONCHITIS, HEADACHE, DYSPHAGIA, EXCESSIVE THIRST, WEAKNESS, PALPITATIONS, NAUSEA AND VOMITING. VERY HIGH CONCENTRATIONS HAVE CAUSED HUMAN DEATHS. HYPERSENSITIVITY REACTIONS SUCH AS LARYNGEAL EDEMA, ASTHMATIC BRONCHITIS, SEVERE OBSTRUCTIVE TRACHEOBRONCHITIS, AND URTICARIA HAVE BEEN REPORTED IN PREVIOUSLY EXPOSED INDIVIDUALS. **CHRONIC EXPOSURE-** REPEATED OR PROLONGED EXPOSURE MAY CAUSE HEADACHE, RHINITIS, NAUSEA, DROWSINESS, RESPIRATORY IMPAIRMENT, KIDNEY INJURY, AND PULMONARY SENSITIZATION. NEUROPSYCHOLOGICAL EFFECTS MAY INCLUDE SLEEP DISORDERS, IRRITABILITY, ALTERED SENSE OF BALANCE, MEMORY DEFICITS, LOSS OF CONCENTRATION, AND MOOD ALTERATIONS. MENSTRUAL DISORDERS AND SECONDARY STERILITY HAVE OCCURRED IN WOMEN. REPRODUCTIVE EFFECTS HAVE BEEN REPORTED IN ANIMALS. OFFSPRING OF RATS EXPOSED CONTINUOUSLY DURING PREGNANCY DISPLAYED NO VISIBLE MALFORMATIONS. LITTER SIZES, DURATION OF PREGNANCY, AND WEIGHT OF FETAL ADRENALS AND KIDNEYS WERE INCREASED AND WEIGHT OF FETAL LUNGS AND LIVER WERE DECREASED. LONG TERM EXPOSURE TO FORMALDEHYDE IS REPORTED TO BE ASSOCIATED WITH AN INCREASED RISK OF CANCER OF THE NOSE AND ACCESSORY SINUSES AND NASOPHARYNGEAL AND OROPHARYNGEAL CANCER IN HUMANS. SLIGHT EXCESSES IN THE OCCURRENCE OF LUNG CANCER HAVE BEEN NOTED IN SEVERAL STUDIES; HOWEVER, THE INCREASES OF LUNG CANCERS DID NOT DISPLAY THE PATTERNS OF INCREASED RISK WITH VARIOUS MEASURES OF EXPOSURE USUALLY SEEN FOR OCCUPATIONAL CARCINOGENS. ANIMAL STUDIES SHOW THAT REPEATED EXPOSURE TO LEVELS OF 14.3 PPM INDUCED NASAL CAVITY SQUAMOUS CELL CARCINOMA IN RATS, AND ACUTE DEGENERATION, NECROSIS, INFLAMMATION, AND INCREASED CELL REPLICATION IN THE NASAL MUCOSA OF RATS AND MICE. THE INCIDENCES OF A VARIETY OF NON-NEOPLASTIC LESIONS WERE SIGNIFICANTLY INCREASED IN MICE AND RATS.
FIRST AID- REMOVE FROM EXPOSURE AREA TO FRESH AIR IMMEDIATELY. IF BREATHING HAS STOPPED, GIVE ARTIFICIAL RESPIRATION. MAINTAIN AIRWAY AND BLOOD PRESSURE AND ADMINISTER OXYGEN IF AVAILABLE. KEEP AFFECTED PERSON WARM AND AT REST. TREAT SYMPTOMATICALLY AND SUPPORTIVELY. ADMINISTRATION OF OXYGEN SHOULD BE PERFORMED BY QUALIFIED PERSONNEL. GET MEDICAL ATTENTION IMMEDIATELY.

SKIN CONTACT: FORMALDEHYDE: CORROSIVE/SENSITIZER/TOXIC. **ACUTE EXPOSURE-** VAPORS OR SOLUTIONS MAY CAUSE SMARTING, WHITE DISCOLORATION, ROUGHNESS, HARDNESS, ANESTHESIA, AND FIRST DEGREE BURNS. SENSITIZATION DERMATITIS CHARACTERIZED BY AN ECZEMATOUS, VESICULAR REACTION WHICH OCCURS SUDDENLY WITH ERUPTIONS ON THE EYELIDS, FACE, NECK, SCROTUM, AND ARMS, MAY OCCUR IN PREVIOUSLY EXPOSED INDIVIDUALS. URTICARIA HAS ALSO BEEN REPORTED. THE LETHAL DOSE IN RABBITS WAS 270 MG/KG. THE SYMPTOMS WERE NOT REPORTED. **CHRONIC EXPOSURE-** PROLONGED OR REPEATED EXPOSURE MAY CAUSE SECOND DEGREE BURNS, NUMBNESS, AN ITCHING RASH, FINGERNAIL DAMAGE, HARDENING AND TANNING OF THE SKIN AND SENSITIZATION. THE RESULTING DERMATITIS MAY BE EITHER A SUDDEN VESICULAR REACTION, OR MAY BE DELAYED SEVERAL YEARS WITH ERUPTIONS STARTING ON THE DIGITAL AREAS, WRISTS AND OTHER PARTS OF THE BODY. MICE DEVELOPED SEVERE LIVER DAMAGE FOLLOWING TREATMENT ON THE SKIN.
FIRST AID- REMOVE CONTAMINATED CLOTHING AND SHOES IMMEDIATELY. WASH AFFECTED AREA WITH SOAP OR MILD DETERGENT AND LARGE AMOUNTS OF WATER UNTIL NO EVIDENCE OF CHEMICAL REMAINS (AT LEAST 15-20 MINUTES). IN CASE OF CHEMICAL BURNS, COVER AREA WITH STERILE, DRY DRESSING. BANDAGE SECURELY, BUT NOT TOO TIGHTLY. GET MEDICAL ATTENTION IMMEDIATELY.

EYE CONTACT: FORMALDEHYDE: CORROSIVE. **ACUTE EXPOSURE-** CONCENTRATIONS OF 0.05-3.0 PPM MAY CAUSE IRRITATION WITH REDNESS, ITCHING, PAIN, BLURRED VISION, AND MILD LACRIMATION; 4-20 PPM MAY CAUSE PROFUSE LACRIMATION, AND OCULAR DAMAGE. AQUEOUS SOLUTIONS HAVE CAUSED EFFECTS RANGING FROM TRANSIENT, MINOR INJURY AND DISCOMFORT TO SEVERE, PERMANENT CORNEAL OPACIFICATION, AND LOSS OF VISION. CORNEAL OPACIFICATION MAY BE DELAYED FROM SEVERAL MINUTES TO HOURS. **CHRONIC EXPOSURE-** EFFECTS DEPEND ON THE CONCENTRATION AND DURATION OF EXPOSURE. REPEATED OR PROLONGED CONTACT WITH CORROSIVE SUBSTANCES MAY RESULT IN CONJUNCTIVITIS OR EFFECTS AS IN ACUTE EXPOSURE.

FIRST AID- WASH EYES IMMEDIATELY WITH LARGE AMOUNTS OF WATER, OCCASIONALLY LIFTING UPPER AND LOWER LIDS, UNTIL NO EVIDENCE OF CHEMICAL REMAINS (AT LEAST 15-20 MINUTES). CONTINUE IRRIGATING WITH NORMAL SALINE UNTIL THE PH HAS RETURNED TO NORMAL (30-60 MINUTES). COVER WITH STERILE BANDAGES. GET MEDICAL ATTENTION IMMEDIATELY.

INGESTION: FORMALDEHYDE: CORROSIVE. **ACUTE EXPOSURE-** INGESTION OF THE GAS IS NOT LIKELY TO OCCUR; HOWEVER, INGESTION OF SOLUTIONS MAY CAUSE BURNING OF THE MOUTH, THROAT AND STOMACH, DIFFICULTY SWALLOWING, NAUSEA, VOMITING AND DIARRHEA, POSSIBLY BLOODY, SEVERE ABDOMINAL PAIN, HEADACHE, HYPOTENSION, VERTIGO, STUPOR, CONVULSIONS, UNCONSCIOUSNESS AND COMA. DEGENERATIVE CHANGES OF THE LIVER, HEART AND BRAIN, AND DAMAGE OF THE SPLEEN, PANCREAS, CENTRAL NERVOUS SYSTEM , AND KIDNEYS WITH ALBUMINURIA, HEMATURIA, ANURIA, AND ACIDOSIS MAY OCCUR. ASPIRATION MAY RESULT IN CHEMICAL PNEUMONITIS. DELAYED STENOSIS OF THE UPPER GASTROINTESTINAL TRACT MAY ALSO OCCUR. DEATH MAY BE DELAYED FOR SEVERAL HOURS TO DAYS AND MAY BE DUE TO SHOCK OR CIRCULATORY OR RESPIRATORY FAILURE. A MEAN FATAL DOSE IN HUMANS IS 1-2 OUNCES OF A 37% SOLUTION. REPRODUCTIVE EFFECTS HAVE BEEN REPORTED IN ANIMALS. **CHRONIC EXPOSURE-** REPEATED INGESTION OF SMALL AMOUNTS OF FORMALDEHYDE MAY CAUSE GASTROINTESTINAL IRRITATION, VOMITING, AND DIZZINESS. SENSITIZATION REACTIONS HAVE BEEN REPORTED. MEN WHO INGESTED FORMALDEHYDE IN MILK FOR 15 DAYS COMPLAINED OF STOMACH OR INTESTINAL PAIN AND HEADACHE. OTHER REPORTED SYMPTOMS INCLUDED A BURNING SENSATION IN THE THROAT, A SLIGHT DECREASE IN BODY TEMPERATURE, AND, IN 4 OF THE MEN, AN ITCHING RASH ON THE CHEST AND THIGHS.

FIRST AID- DILUTE, INACTIVATE, OR ABSORB INGESTED FORMALDEHYDE BY GIVING MILK, ACTIVATED CHARCOAL, OR TAP WATER. DO NOT USE GASTRIC LAVAGE OR EMETICS. ANY ORGANIC MATERIAL WILL INACTIVATE FORMALDEHYDE (DREISBACH, HANDBOOK OF POISONING, 12TH ED.) GET MEDICAL ATTENTION IMMEDIATELY. TREATMENT SHOULD BE ADMINISTERED BY QUALIFIED MEDICAL PERSONNEL.

ANTIDOTE: NO SPECIFIC ANTIDOTE. TREAT SYMPTOMATICALLY AND SUPPORTIVELY.

REACTIVITY

REACTIVITY: FORMALDEHYDE SOLUTIONS ARE STABLE IN CLOSED CONTAINERS UNDER NORMAL TEMPERATURES AND PRESSURES; MAY OXIDIZE SLOWLY ON EXPOSURE TO AIR.

INCOMPATIBILITIES: FORMALDEHYDE: ACIDS (INORGANIC): FORMALDEHYDE SOLUTIONS REACT. ALKALIES (STRONG): FORMALDEHYDE SOLUTIONS REACT. AMMONIA: INCOMPATIBLE. ANHYDRIDES: FORMALDEHYDE SOLUTIONS REACT. ANILINE + PERCHLORIC ACID: ANILINE TREATED WITH PERCHLORIC ACID, THEN WITH FORMALDEHYDE, GIVES A RESINOUS PRODUCT WHICH BURNS WITH EXPLOSIVE VIOLENCE. BISULFIDES: INCOMPATIBLE. COPPER: FORMALDEHYDE SOLUTIONS MAY BE CORROSIVE. COPPER ALLOYS: FORMALDEHYDE SOLUTIONS MAY BE CORROSIVE. COPPER SALTS: FORMALDEHYDE SOLUTIONS MAY BE CORROSIVE. IODINE: INCOMPATIBLE. IRON PREPARATIONS: INCOMPATIBLE. ISOCYANATES: FORMALDEHYDE SOLUTIONS REACT. HYDROCHLORIC ACID: FORMS HIGHLY TOXIC BIS(CHLOROMETHYL) ETHER. HYDROGEN PEROXIDE: VIOLENT REACTION. NITROGEN DIOXIDE: SLOW REACTION BECOMES EXPLOSIVE AROUND 180 C. NITROMETHANE: FORMS EXPLOSIVE COMPOUND IN THE PRESENCE OF ALKALIES. OXIDES: FORMALDEHYDE SOLUTIONS REACT. OXIDIZERS (STRONG): FIRE AND EXPLOSION HAZARD. PEROXYFORMIC ACID (CONCENTRATED): VIOLENT OXIDATION REACTION. PHENOL: POLYMERIZATION REACTION WITH SUDDEN PRESSURE DEVELOPMENT. POTASSIUM PERMANGANATE: INCOMPATIBLE. SILVER SALTS: INCOMPATIBLE. STEEL: FORMALDEHYDE SOLUTIONS MAY BE CORROSIVE. UREA: FORMALDEHYDE SOLUTIONS REACT.

DECOMPOSITION: THERMAL DECOMPOSITION PRODUCTS MAY INCLUDE UNBURNED FORMALDEHYDE AND OTHER TOXIC PRODUCTS OF ORGANIC SUBSTANCES.

POLYMERIZATION: MAY UNDERGO A NON-HAZARDOUS SELF-POLYMERIZATION TO FORM PARAFORMALDEHYDE WHICH PRECIPITATES OUT OF SOLUTION. WILL POLYMERIZE WITH ACTIVE ORGANIC MATERIALS SUCH AS PHENOL WITH SUDDEN PRESSURE DEVELOPMENT.

STORAGE AND DISPOSAL

OBSERVE ALL FEDERAL, STATE AND LOCAL REGULATIONS WHEN STORING OR DISPOSING OF THIS SUBSTANCE. FOR ASSISTANCE, CONTACT THE DISTRICT DIRECTOR OF THE ENVIRONMENTAL PROTECTION AGENCY.

STORE IN ACCORDANCE WITH 29 CFR 1910.106.

BONDING AND GROUNDING: SUBSTANCES WITH LOW ELECTROCONDUCTIVITY, WHICH MAY BE IGNITED BY ELECTROSTATIC SPARKS, SHOULD BE STORED IN CONTAINERS WHICH MEET THE BONDING AND GROUNDING GUIDELINES SPECIFIED IN NFPA 77-1983, RECOMMENDED PRACTICE ON STATIC ELECTRICITY.

THRESHOLD PLANNING QUANTITY (TPQ): THE SUPERFUND AMENDMENTS AND REAUTHORIZATION ACT (SARA) SECTION 302 REQUIRES THAT EACH FACILITY WHERE ANY EXTREMELY HAZARDOUS SUBSTANCE IS PRESENT IN A QUANTITY EQUAL TO OR GREATER THAN THE TPQ ESTABLISHED FOR THAT SUBSTANCE NOTIFY THE STATE EMERGENCY RESPONSE COMMISSION FOR THE STATE IN WHICH IT IS LOCATED. SECTION 303 OF SARA REQUIRES THESE FACILITIES TO PARTICIPATE IN LOCAL EMERGENCY RESPONSE PLANNING (40 CFR 355.30).

STORE AWAY FROM INCOMPATIBLE SUBSTANCES.

CONDITIONS TO AVOID

AVOID CONTACT WITH HEAT, SPARKS, FLAMES, OR OTHER SOURCES OF IGNITION. VAPORS MAY BE EXPLOSIVE. AVOID OVERHEATING OF CONTAINERS; CONTAINERS MAY VIOLENTLY RUPTURE IN HEAT OF FIRE. AVOID CONTAMINATION OF WATER SOURCES.

SPILL AND LEAK PROCEDURES

SOIL SPILL: DIG A HOLDING AREA SUCH AS A PIT, POND OR LAGOON TO CONTAIN SPILL AND DIKE SURFACE FLOW USING BARRIER OF SOIL, SANDBAGS, FOAMED POLYURETHANE OR FOAMED CONCRETE. ABSORB LIQUID MASS WITH FLY ASH OR CEMENT POWDER.

USE SODIUM BISULFATE (NA-H-SO4) TO NEUTRALIZE SPILL.

AIR SPILL: KNOCK DOWN VAPORS WITH WATER SPRAY. KEEP UPWIND.

WATER SPILL: IF MATERIAL DISSOLVED, APPLY ACTIVATED CARBON. USE DREDGES OR LIFTS TO EXTRACT MASSES OF POLLUTION AND PRECIPITATES. APPLY UNIVERSAL GELLING AGENT TO IMMOBILIZE TRAPPED SPILL AND INCREASE EFFICIENCY OF REMOVAL. LIMIT SPILL MOTION AND DISPERSION WITH NATURAL BARRIERS OR OIL SPILL CONTROL BOOMS. USE SOAPS, DETERGENTS, ALCOHOLS OR OTHER SURFACE ACTIVE AGENT TO THICKEN SPILLED MATERIAL. USE SUCTION HOSES TO REMOVE TRAPPED SPILL MATERIAL.

THE CALIFORNIA SAFE DRINKING WATER AND TOXIC ENFORCEMENT ACT OF 1986 (PROPOSITION 65) PROHIBITS CONTAMINATING ANY KNOWN SOURCE OF DRINKING WATER WITH SUBSTANCES KNOWN TO CAUSE CANCER AND/OR REPRODUCTIVE TOXICITY.

OCCUPATIONAL SPILL: SHUT OFF IGNITION SOURCES. STOP LEAK IF YOU CAN DO IT WITHOUT RISK. USE WATER SPRAY TO REDUCE VAPORS. FOR SMALL SPILLS, TAKE UP WITH SAND OR OTHER ABSORBENT MATERIAL AND PLACE INTO CONTAINERS FOR LATER DISPOSAL. FOR LARGER SPILLS, DIKE FAR AHEAD OF SPILL FOR LATER DISPOSAL. NO SMOKING, FLAMES OR FLARES IN HAZARD AREA. KEEP UNNECESSARY PEOPLE AWAY; ISOLATE HAZARD AREA AND RESTRICT ENTRY.

PROTECTIVE EQUIPMENT

VENTILATION: PROVIDE LOCAL EXHAUST VENTILATION AND/OR GENERAL DILUTION VENTILATION TO MEET PUBLISHED EXPOSURE LIMITS.

RESPIRATOR: THE FOLLOWING RESPIRATORS ARE THE MINIMUM LEGAL REQUIREMENTS AS SET FORTH BY THE OCCUPATIONAL SAFETY AND HEALTH ADMINISTRATION FOUND IN 29 CFR 1910, SUBPART Z.

FORMALDEHYDE:

UP TO 10 PPM- FULL FACEPIECE WITH CARTRIDGES OR CANISTERS SPECIFICALLY APPROVED FOR PROTECTION AGAINST FORMALDEHYDE. A HALF-MASK RESPIRATOR WITH CARTRIDGES SPECIFICALLY APPROVED FOR PROTECTION AGAINST FORMALDEHYDE CAN BE SUBSTITUTED FOR THE FULL FACEPIECE RESPIRATOR PROVIDING THAT EFFECTIVE GAS-PROOF GOGGLES ARE PROVIDED AND USED IN COMBINATION WITH THE HALF-MASK RESPIRATOR.

UP TO 100 PPM- FULL-FACE MASK, CHEST OR BACK MOUNTED TYPE, WITH INDUSTRIAL SIZE CANISTER SPECIFICALLY APPROVED FOR PROTECTION AGAINST FORMALDEHYDE. TYPE C SUPPLIED AIR RESPIRATOR, DEMAND TYPE, WITH FULL FACEPIECE, HOOD, OR HELMET.

ABOVE 100 PPM OR UNKNOWN (EMERGENCIES)- SELF-CONTAINED BREATHING APPARATUS WITH POSITIVE PRESSURE FULL FACEPIECE. COMBINATION SUPPLIED-AIR FULL FACEPIECE POSITIVE PRESSURE RESPIRATOR WITH AUXILIARY SELF-CONTAINED AIR SUPPLY.

FIREFIGHTING- SELF-CONTAINED BREATHING APPARATUS WITH POSITIVE PRESSURE IN FULL FACEPIECE.

ESCAPE- SELF-CONTAINED BREATHING APPARATUS IN DEMAND OR PRESSURE DEMAND MODE. FULL-FACE MASK, FRONT OR BACK MOUNTED TYPE WITH INDUSTRIAL SIZE CANISTER SPECIFICALLY APPROVED FOR PROTECTION AGAINST FORMALDEHYDE.

THE FOLLOWING RESPIRATORS AND MAXIMUM USE CONCENTRATIONS ARE

RECOMMENDATIONS BY THE U.S. DEPARTMENT OF HEALTH AND HUMAN SERVICES, NIOSH POCKET GUIDE TO CHEMICAL HAZARDS, OR NIOSH CRITERIA DOCUMENTS. THE SPECIFIC RESPIRATOR SELECTED MUST BE BASED ON CONTAMINATION LEVELS FOUND IN THE WORK PLACE, MUST NOT EXCEED THE WORKING LIMITS OF THE RESPIRATOR AND BE JOINTLY APPROVED BY THE NATIONAL INSTITUTE FOR OCCUPATIONAL SAFETY AND HEALTH AND THE MINE SAFETY AND HEALTH ADMINISTRATION (NIOSH-MSHA).

AT ANY DETECTABLE CONCENTRATION:

ANY SELF-CONTAINED BREATHING APPARATUS WITH A FULL FACEPIECE OPERATED IN A PRESSURE-DEMAND OR OTHER POSITIVE PRESSURE MODE. ANY SUPPLIED-AIR RESPIRATOR WITH A FULL FACEPIECE OPERATED IN PRESSURE-DEMAND OR OTHER POSITIVE-PRESSURE MODE IN COMBINATION WITH AN AUXILIARY SELF-CONTAINED BREATHING APPARATUS OPERATED IN PRESSURE-DEMAND OR OTHER POSITIVE-PRESSURE MODE.

ESCAPE- ANY AIR-PURIFYING FULL FACEPIECE RESPIRATOR (GAS MASK) WITH A CHIN-STYLE OR FRONT- OR BACK-MOUNTED CANISTER PROVIDING PROTECTION AGAINST FORMALDEHYDE. ANY APPROPRIATE ESCAPE-TYPE SELF-CONTAINED BREATHING APPARATUS.

FOR FIREFIGHTING AND OTHER IMMEDIATELY DANGEROUS TO LIFE OR HEALTH CONDITIONS:

SELF-CONTAINED BREATHING APPARATUS WITH FULL FACEPIECE OPERATED IN PRESSURE-DEMAND OR OTHER POSITIVE PRESSURE MODE.

SUPPLIED-AIR RESPIRATOR WITH FULL FACEPIECE AND OPERATED IN PRESSURE-DEMAND OR OTHER POSITIVE PRESSURE MODE IN COMBINATION WITH AN AUXILIARY SELF-CONTAINED BREATHING APPARATUS OPERATED IN PRESSURE-DEMAND OR OTHER POSITIVE PRESSURE MODE.

CLOTHING: EMPLOYEE MUST WEAR APPROPRIATE PROTECTIVE (IMPERVIOUS) CLOTHING AND EQUIPMENT TO PREVENT ANY POSSIBILITY OF SKIN CONTACT WITH THIS SUBSTANCE.

GLOVES: EMPLOYEE MUST WEAR APPROPRIATE PROTECTIVE GLOVES TO PREVENT CONTACT WITH THIS SUBSTANCE.

EYE PROTECTION: EMPLOYEE MUST WEAR SPLASH-PROOF OR DUST-RESISTANT SAFETY GOGGLES AND A FACESHIELD TO PREVENT CONTACT WITH THIS SUBSTANCE.

EMERGENCY WASH FACILITIES: WHERE THERE IS ANY POSSIBILITY THAT AN EMPLOYEE'S EYES AND/OR SKIN MAY BE EXPOSED TO THIS SUBSTANCE, THE EMPLOYER SHOULD PROVIDE AN EYE WASH FOUNTAIN AND QUICK DRENCH SHOWER WITHIN THE IMMEDIATE WORK AREA FOR EMERGENCY USE.

AUTHORIZED BY- OCCUPATIONAL HEALTH SERVICES, INC.

CREATION DATE: 10/04/89 ***REVISION DATE:*** 07/03/90

MATERIAL SAFETY DATA SHEET

OCCUPATIONAL HEALTH SERVICES, INC.
AGRICULTURE AND PESTICIDE DIVISION
450 SEVENTH AVENUE, SUITE 2407
NEW YORK, NEW YORK 10123
1-800-445-MSDS OR (212) 967-1100

EMERGENCY CONTACT:
JOHN S. BRANSFORD, JR. (615) 292-1180

SUBSTANCE IDENTIFICATION

CAS-NUMBER 7784-46-5

SUBSTANCE: **SODIUM ARSENITE, LIQUID**

TRADE NAMES/SYNONYMS: SODIUM META-ARSENITE LIQUID (SOLUTION); SODIUM ORTHOARSENITE LIQUID; MONOSODIUM ARSENITE LIQUID; STCC 4923291; UN 1686; PST52136

CHEMICAL FAMILY: INORGANIC SALT

MOLECULAR FORMULA: AS-NA-O2

CERCLA RATINGS (SCALE 0-3): HEALTH=3 FIRE=0 REACTIVITY=0 PERSISTENCE=3

NFPA RATINGS (SCALE 0-4): HEALTH=3 FIRE=0 REACTIVITY=0

COMPONENTS AND CONTAMINANTS

COMPONENT: SODIUM ARSENITE ***PERCENT:*** VARIES
CAS# 7784-46-5

COMPONENT: WATER ***PERCENT:*** VARIES

OTHER CONTAMINANTS: NONE

EXPOSURE LIMITS: ARSENIC, INORGANIC AND SOLUBLE COMPOUNDS: 10 UG(AS)/M3 OSHA TWA 200 UG(AS)/M3 ACGIH TWA 2 UG(AS)/M3 NIOSH RECOMMENDED 15 MINUTE CEILING

SUBJECT TO SARA SECTION 313 ANNUAL TOXIC CHEMICAL RELEASE REPORTING

SUBJECT TO CALIFORNIA PROPOSITION 65 CANCER AND/OR REPRODUCTIVE TOXICITY WARNING AND RELEASE REQUIREMENTS- (FEBRUARY 27, 1987)

SODIUM ARSENITE: 500/10,000 POUNDS SARA SECTION 302 THRESHOLD PLANNING QUANTITY 1000 POUNDS SARA SECTION 304 REPORTABLE QUANTITY 1 POUND CERCLA SECTION 103 REPORTABLE QUANTITY

PHYSICAL DATA

DESCRIPTION: SODIUM ARSENITE, LIQUID IS THE WHITE POWDERED SODIUM ARSENITE DISSOLVED IN WATER. ***VAPOR PRESSURE:*** NOT AVAILABLE

EVAPORATION RATE: NOT AVAILABLE ***SOLUBILITY IN WATER:*** SOLUBLE

VAPOR DENSITY: NOT AVAILABLE

SOLVENT SOLUBILITY: SLIGHTLY SOLUBLE IN ALCOHOL.

FIRE AND EXPLOSION DATA

FIRE AND EXPLOSION HAZARD: NEGLIGIBLE FIRE HAZARD WHEN EXPOSED TO HEAT OR FLAME.

FIREFIGHTING MEDIA: DRY CHEMICAL, CARBON DIOXIDE, HALON, WATER SPRAY OR STANDARD FOAM (1987 EMERGENCY RESPONSE GUIDEBOOK, DOT P 5800.4).

FOR LARGER FIRES, USE WATER SPRAY, FOG OR STANDARD FOAM (1987 EMERGENCY RESPONSE GUIDEBOOK, DOT P 5800.4).

FIREFIGHTING: MOVE CONTAINERS FROM FIRE AREA IF POSSIBLE (1987 EMERGENCY RESPONSE GUIDEBOOK, DOT P 5800.4, GUIDE PAGE 54).

USE AGENTS SUITABLE FOR TYPE OF FIRE. USE FLOODING AMOUNTS OF WATER AS FOG. AVOID BREATHING POISONOUS VAPORS, KEEP UPWIND.

TRANSPORTATION DATA

DEPARTMENT OF TRANSPORTATION HAZARD CLASSIFICATION 49 CFR 172.101: POISON B

DEPARTMENT OF TRANSPORTATION LABELING REQUIREMENTS 49 CFR 172.101 AND SUBPART E: POISON

DEPARTMENT OF TRANSPORTATION PACKAGING REQUIREMENTS: 49 CFR 173.346 EXCEPTIONS: 49 CFR 173.345

TOXICITY

SODIUM ARSENITE: TOXICITY DATA: 150 MG/KG SKIN-RAT LD50; 1 MG/KG ORAL-CHILD TDLO; 2 MG/KG ORAL-CHILD LDLO; 41 MG/KG ORAL-RAT LD50; 12 MG/KG ORAL-RABBIT LDLO; 10 MG/KG ORAL-MAMMAL LD50; 6 MG/KG INTRAVENOUS-RAT LDLO; 7600 UG/KG INTRAVENOUS-RABBIT LD50; 7 MG/KG INTRAPERITONEAL-RAT LDLO; 1170 UG/KG INTRAPERITONEAL-MOUSE LD50; 14 MG/KG INTRAMUSCULAR-MOUSE LD50; MUTAGENIC DATA (RTECS); REPRODUCTIVE EFFECTS DATA (RTECS).

CARCINOGEN STATUS: OSHA CARCINOGEN; KNOWN HUMAN CARCINOGEN (NTP); HUMAN SUFFICIENT EVIDENCE, ANIMAL LIMITED EVIDENCE (IARC GROUP-1). AN INCREASED INCIDENCE OF SKIN AND LUNG CANCER HAS BEEN ASSOCIATED WITH INORGANIC ARSENIC COMPOUNDS THROUGH MEDICAL TREATMENT, CONTAMINATED DRINKING WATER OR OCCUPATIONAL EXPOSURE. CANCERS AT OTHER SITES HAVE ALSO BEEN REPORTED, BUT A CLEAR ASSOCIATION HAS NOT BEEN CONFIRMED. LOCAL EFFECTS: IRRITANT- INHALATION, SKIN, AND EYES.

ACUTE TOXICITY LEVEL: HIGHLY TOXIC BY DERMAL ABSORPTION AND INGESTION.

TARGET EFFECTS: SENSITIZER- SKIN; NEUROTOXIN. POISONING MAY AFFECT THE LIVER, KIDNEYS, BONE MARROW, AND CENTRAL NERVOUS AND GASTROINTESTINAL SYSTEMS.

HEALTH EFFECTS AND FIRST AID

INHALATION: SODIUM ARSENITE: IRRITANT/NEUROTOXIN/CARCINOGEN: **ACUTE EXPOSURE-** INHALATION OF INORGANIC ARSENIC COMPOUNDS IS THE MOST COMMON CAUSE OF POISONING IN INDUSTRIAL SITUATIONS. INITIALLY, THE WORKER COMPLAINS OF WEAKNESS, LOSS OF APPETITE, NAUSEA, VOMITING, A SENSE OF HEAVINESS IN THE STOMACH, AND DIARRHEA. LATER, THE WORKER MAY EXPERIENCE CATARRH OF THE MUCOUS MEMBRANES OF THE NOSE, LARYNX, AND RESPIRATORY PASSAGES. CORYZA, HOARSENESS, AND TRACHEOBRONCHITIS MAY OCCUR. PERSONS POISONED MAY HAVE A METALLIC TASTE IN THE MOUTH, AND A GARLIC ODOR TO THE BREATH. **CHRONIC EXPOSURE-** LONG TERM INHALATION OF ARSENIC CONTAINING DUSTS MAY LEAD TO NASAL SEPTUM PERFORATION. CHANGES OCCUR IN THE CENTRAL NERVOUS SYSTEM WHICH MAY BE IRREVERSIBLE. THE VICTIM MAY EXPERIENCE COLD HANDS AND FEET, A SENSATION OF PINS AND NEEDLES OR SHOOTING PAINS IN THE FEET, AND LOSS OF SENSATION IN THOSE AREAS. CHRONIC ARSENIC POISONING OFTEN CAUSES BRONZING OF THE SKIN AND MEE'S LINES IN THE FINGERNAILS. INORGANIC ARSENIC COMPOUNDS, SUCH AS SODIUM ARSENITE, HAVE BEEN SHOWN TO BE SKIN AND LUNG CARCINOGENS IN HUMANS.

FIRST AID- REMOVE FROM EXPOSURE AREA TO FRESH AIR IMMEDIATELY. IF BREATHING HAS STOPPED, GIVE ARTIFICIAL RESPIRATION. MAINTAIN AIRWAY AND BLOOD PRESSURE AND ADMINISTER OXYGEN IF AVAILABLE. KEEP AFFECTED PERSON WARM AND AT REST. TREAT SYMPTOMATICALLY AND SUPPORTIVELY. ADMINISTRATION OF OXYGEN SHOULD BE PERFORMED BY QUALIFIED PERSONNEL. GET MEDICAL ATTENTION IMMEDIATELY.

SKIN CONTACT: SODIUM ARSENITE: IRRITANT/SENSITIZER. **ACUTE EXPOSURE**- 150 MG/KG APPLIED TO THE SKIN OF RABBITS KILLED HALF OF THOSE SO TESTED. INORGANIC ARSENIC COMPOUNDS, SUCH AS SODIUM ARSENITE, IRRITATE THE SKIN. SENSITIZATION DERMATITIS MAY OCCUR IN PREVIOUSLY EXPOSED PERSONS, CHARACTERIZED BY ECZEMA WITH SCALING AND HYPERPIGMENTATION OF THE SKIN AND HYPERKERATOSIS OR TH PALMS OF THE HANDS AND THE SOLES OF THE FEET. INORGANIC ARSENIC COMPOUNDS ARE SLIGHTLY ABSORBED THROUGH THE SKIN WHEN ADMINISTERED IN A LIPID VEHICLE. POISONING HAS CAUSED ALOPECIA, BRONZING OF THE SKIN, AND BRITTLE FINGERNAILS. **CHRONIC EXPOSURE**- REPEATED EXPOSURE TO INORGANIC ARSENIC COMPOUNDS MAY RESULT IN SENSITIZATION DERMATITIS. THESE COMPOUNDS ARE SKIN AND LUNG CARCINOGENS; IT IS UNCLEAR WHETHER SKIN CONTACT CONTRIBUTES TO THE CARCINOGENICITY NORMALLY ATTRIBUTED TO INHALATION AND INGESTION.

FIRST AID- REMOVE CONTAMINATED CLOTHING AND SHOES IMMEDIATELY. WASH AFFECTED AREA WITH SOAP OR MILD DETERGENT AND LARGE AMOUNTS OF WATER UNTIL NO EVIDENCE OF CHEMICAL REMAINS (APPROXIMATELY 15-20 MINUTES). GET MEDICAL ATTENTION IMMEDIATELY.

EYE CONTACT: SODIUM ARSENITE: IRRITANT. **ACUTE EXPOSURE**- MAY CAUSE IRRITATION AND CONJUNCTIVITIS. POISONING HAS CAUSED EDEMA OF THE EYELIDS, CORNEAL NECROSIS AND VISUAL DISTURBANCES. **CHRONIC EXPOSURE**- REPEATED OR PROLONGED EXPOSURE TO INORGANIC ARSENIC DUSTS MAY CAUSE CONJUNCTIVITIS. POISONING FROM INHALATION AND INGESTION HAS CAUSED OPTIC NEURITIS.

FIRST AID- WASH EYES IMMEDIATELY WITH LARGE AMOUNTS OF WATER OR NORMAL SALINE, OCCASIONALLY LIFTING UPPER AND LOWER LIDS, UNTIL NO EVIDENCE OF CHEMICAL REMAINS (APPROXIMATELY 15-20 MINUTES). GET MEDICAL ATTENTION IMMEDIATELY.

INGESTION: SODIUM ARSENITE: NEUROTOXIN/CARCINOGEN/HIGHLY TOXIC. **ACUTE EXPOSURE**- A CHILD CONSUMING 1 MG/KG, AND A CHILD CONSUMING 2 MG/KG SODIUM ARSENITE EXPERIENCED NON-LETHAL TOXIC EFFECTS. HALF OF THE MAMMALS FED 10 MG/KG DIED. RABBITS FED 7500 UG/KG EXPERIENCED UNREPORTED NON-LETHAL TOXIC EFFECTS. HAMSTERS FED 5 MG/KG DURING THE 9TH DAY OF PREGNANCY HAD AN INCREASED INCIDENCE OF POST-IMPLANTATION MORTALITY. HAMSTERS FED 25 MG/KG SODIUM ARSENITE DURING THE 12TH DAY OF PREGANACY HAD STUNTED FETUSES, AND INCREASED INCIDENCE OF FETAL DEATH. MICE FED SODIUM ARSENITE DURING PREGNANCY ALSO EXPERIENCED FETAL DEATH, STUNTED OFFSPRING AND MALE OFFSPRING WITH REDUCED FERTILITY. NON-FATAL DOSES MAY CAUSE RESTLESSNESS, NAUSEA, VOMITING, HEADACHE, DIZZINESS, CHILLS, CRAMPS, IRRITABILITY, AND PARALYSIS. JAUNDICE, OLIGURIA, AND ANURIA MAY OCCUR WITHIN 1-3 DAYS. FATAL DOSES MAY CAUSE GASTROINTESTINAL DISTURBANCES, BURNING PAIN IN THE THROAT, VOMITING, WATERY OR BLOODY DIARRHEA WITH MUCOUS, HYPOTENSION, WEAKNESS, CONVULSIONS, COMA AND DEATH. **CHRONIC EXPOSURE**- CHRONIC POISONING MAY AFFECT THE CENTRAL NERVOUS SYSTEM, SKIN, GASTROINTESTINAL TRACT, CARDIOVASCULAR SYSTEM, KIDNEYS AND LIVER. ARSENIC TYPICALLY CAUSES BRONZING OF THE SKIN, MEE'S LINES IN THE FINGERNAILS, AND A FEELING OF PINS AND NEEDLES IN THE FEET. THE LOSS OF SENSATION IN THE HANDS AND FEET MAY WORSEN INTO GANGRENE. INORGANIC ARSENIC COMPOUNDS, SUCH AS SODIUM ARSENITE, HAVE BEEN POSITIVLY LINKED WITH SKIN AND LUNG CANCER IN HUMANS.

FIRST AID- REMOVE BY GASTRIC LAVAGE OR EMESIS. FOLLOW WITH A SALINE CATHARTIC. MAINTAIN BLOOD PRESSURE, AIRWAY, AND GIVE OXYGEN IF RESPIRATION IS DEPRESSED. DO NOT PERFORM GASTRIC LAVAGE OR EMESIS IF VICTIM IS UNCONSCIOUS. GET MEDICAL ATTENTION IMMEDIATELY. (DREISBACH, HANDBOOK OF POISONING, 12TH ED.) ADMINISTRATION OF GASTRIC LAVAGE OR OXYGEN SHOULD BE PERFORMED BY QUALIFIED MEDICAL PERSONNEL.

ANTIDOTE: THE FOLLOWING ANTIDOTE HAS BEEN RECOMMENDED. HOWEVER, THE DECISION AS TO WHETHER THE SEVERITY OF POISONING REQUIRES ADMINISTRATION OF ANY ANTIDOTE AND ACTUAL DOSE REQUIRED SHOULD BE MADE BY QUALIFIED MEDICAL PERSONNEL.

ARSENIC POISONING: GIVE DIMERCAPROL, 3 MG/KG (OR 0.3 ML/KG) EVERY 4 HOURS FOR 2 DAYS AND THEN 2 MG/KG EVERY 2 HOURS FOR A TOTAL OF 10 DAYS. DIMERCAPROL IS AVAILABLE AS A 10% SOLUTION IN OIL FOR INTRAMUSCULAR ADMINISTRATION. NEXT, GIVE PENICILLAMINE, UP TO 100 MG/KG/DAY (MAXIMUM 1 G/DAY) DIVIDED INTO 4 DOSES FOR NO LONGER THAN 1 WEEK. IF A LONGER ADMINISTRATION PERIOD IS WARRANTED, DOSAGE SHOULD NOT EXCEED 40 MG/KG/DAY. GIVE THE DRUG ORALLY HALF AN HOUR BEFORE MEALS. DISCONTINUE ANTIDOTE WHEN URINE ARSENIC LEVEL FALLS BELOW 50 UG/24 HR. (DREISBACH, HANDBOOK OF POISONING, 12TH ED.). ANITDOTE SHOULD BE ADMINISTERED BY QUALIFIED MEDICAL PERSONNEL.

REACTIVITY

REACTIVITY: STABLE UNDER NORMAL TEMPERATURES AND PRESSURES.

INCOMPATIBILITIES: NONE KNOWN.

DECOMPOSITION: THERMAL DECOMPOSITION PRODUCTS MAY INCLUDE TOXIC ARSINE GAS.

POLYMERIZATION: HAZARDOUS POLYMERIZATION HAS NOT BEEN REPORTED TO OCCUR UNDER NORMAL TEMPERATURES AND PRESSURES.

STORAGE AND DISPOSAL

OBSERVE ALL FEDERAL, STATE AND LOCAL REGULATIONS WHEN STORING OR DISPOSING OF THIS SUBSTANCE. FOR ASSISTANCE, CONTACT THE DISTRICT DIRECTOR OF THE ENVIRONMENTAL PROTECTION AGENCY.

****STORAGE****

THRESHOLD PLANNING QUANTITY (TPQ): THE SUPERFUND AMENDMENTS AND REAUTHORIZATION ACT (SARA) SECTION 302 REQUIRES THAT EACH FACILITY WHERE ANY EXTREMELY HAZARDOUS SUBSTANCE IS PRESENT IN A QUANTITY EQUAL TO OR GREATER THAN THE TPQ ESTABLISHED FOR THAT SUBSTANCE NOTIFY THE STATE EMERGENCY RESPONSE COMMISSION FOR THE STATE IN WHICH IT IS LOCATED. SECTION 303 OF SARA REQUIRES THESE FACILITIES TO PARTICIPATE IN LOCAL EMERGENCY RESPONSE PLANNING (40 CFR 355.30).

****DISPOSAL****

ARSENIC - REGULATORY LEVEL: 5.0 MG/L MATERIALS WHICH CONTAIN THE ABOVE SUBSTANCE AT OR ABOVE THE REGULATORY LEVEL MEET THE EPA CHARACTERISTIC OF TOXICITY, AND MUST BE DISPOSED OF IN ACCORDANCE WITH 40 CFR PART 262. EPA HAZARDOUS WASTE NUMBER D004.

CONDITIONS TO AVOID

MAY BURN BUT DOES NOT IGNITE READILY.

MAY BURN BUT DOES NOT IGNITE READILY. AVOID CONTACT WITH STRONG OXIDIZERS, EXCESSIVE HEAT, SPARKS, OR OPEN FLAME.

SPILL AND LEAK PROCEDURES

SOIL SPILL: DIG A HOLDING AREA SUCH AS PIT, POND OR LAGOON TO CONTAIN SPILL AND DIKE SURFACE FLOW WITH BARRIER OF SOIL, SANDBAGS, FOAMED POLYURETHANE OR FOAMED CONCRETE. ABSORB BULK LIQUID WITH FLY ASH, CEMENT POWDER, SAWDUST, OR COMMERCIAL SORBENTS.

DO NOT HANDLE PACKAGES WITHOUT FULL PROTECTIVE EQUIPMENT.

AIR SPILL: KNOCK DOWN VAPORS WITH WATER SPRAY. KEEP UPWIND.

WATER SPILL: NEUTRALIZE WITH AGRICULTURAL LIME, SLAKED LIME, CRUSHED LIMESTONE, OR SODIUM BICARBONATE.

ADD FERRIC CHLORIDE TO SPILL.

USE DREDGES OR LIFTS TO EXTRACT IMMOBILIZED MASSES OF POLLUTION AND PRECIPITATES. ADD SUITABLE AGENT TO NEUTRALIZE MATERIAL TO PH-7. ADD CALCIUM HYPOCHLORITE TO SPILL.

OCCUPATIONAL SPILL: DO NOT TOUCH SPILLED MATERIAL. STOP LEAK IF YOU CAN DO IT WITHOUT RISK. FOR SMALL SPILLS, TAKE UP WITH SAND OR OTHER ABSORBENT MATERIAL AND PLACE INTO CONTAINERS FOR LATER DISPOSAL. FOR SMALL DRY SPILLS, WITH A CLEAN SHOVEL PLACE MATERIAL INTO CLEAN, DRY CONTAINER AND COVER. MOVE CONTAINERS FROM SPILL AREA. FOR LARGER SPILLS, DIKE FAR AHEAD OF SPILL FOR LATER DISPOSAL. KEEP UNNECESSARY PEOPLE AWAY. ISOLATE HAZARD AREA AND DENY ENTRY.

DO NOT TOUCH SPILLED MATERIAL. STOP LEAK IF YOU CAN DO IT WITHOUT RISK. FOR SMALL SPILLS, TAKE UP WITH SAND OR OTHER ABSORBENT MATERIAL AND PLACE INTO CONTAINERS FOR LATER DISPOSAL. FOR SMALL DRY SPILLS, PLACE MATERIAL INTO A CLEAN, DRY CONTAINER WITH A CLEAN SHOVEL AND COVER. MOVE CONTAINERS FROM SPILL AREA. FOR LARGER SPILLS, DIKE FAR AHEAD OF SPILL FOR LATER DISPOSAL. KEEP UNNECESSARY PEOPLE AWAY. ISOLATE HAZARD AREA AND DENY ENTRY.

REPORTABLE QUANTITY (RQ): 1000 POUNDS THE SUPERFUND AMENDMENTS AND REAUTHORIZATION ACT (SARA) SECTION 304 REQUIRES THAT A RELEASE EQUAL TO OR GREATER THAN THE REPORTABLE QUANTITY FOR THIS SUBSTANCE BE IMMEDIATELY REPORTED TO THE LOCAL EMERGENCY PLANNING COMMITTEE AND THE STATE EMERGENCY RESPONSE COMMISSION (40 CFR 355.40). IF THE RELEASE OF THIS SUBSTANCE IS REPORTABLE UNDER CERCLA SECTION 103, THE NATIONAL RESPONSE CENTER MUST BE NOTIFIED IMMEDIATELY AT (800) 424-8802 OR (202) 426-2675 IN THE METROPOLITAN WASHINGTON, D.C. AREA (40 CFR 302.6).

PROTECTIVE EQUIPMENT

VENTILATION: PROVIDE LOCAL EXHAUST OR PROCESS ENCLOSURE VENTILATION TO MEET PUBLISHED EXPOSURE LIMITS.

ARSENIC (INORGANIC): VENTILATION SHOULD MEET THE REQUIREMENTS IN 29 CFR 1910.1018(G).

RESPIRATOR: THE FOLLOWING RESPIRATORS ARE THE MINIMUM LEGAL REQUIREMENTS AS SET FORTH BY THE OCCUPATIONAL SAFETY AND HEALTH ADMINISTRATION FOUND IN 29 CFR 1910, SUBPART Z.

RESPIRATORY PROTECTION FOR INORGANIC ARSENIC PARTICULATE EXCEPT THOSE WITH SIGNIFICANT VAPOR PRESSURE

CONCENTRATION OF INORGANIC ARSENIC (AS) REQUIRED RESPIRATOR OR CONDITION OF USE

UNKNOWN OR GREATER OR LESS THAN 20,000 UG/M3 (20 MG/M3) OR FIREFIGHTING — ANY FULL FACEPIECE, SELF CONTAINED BREATHING APPARATUS, OPERATED IN POSITIVE PRESSURE MODE.
NOT GREATER THAN 20,000 UG/M3 (20 MG/M3) — SUPPLIED-AIR RESPIRATOR WITH FULL FACEPIECE, HOOD OR HELMET OR SUIT AND OPERATED IN POSITIVE PRESSURE MODE.
NOT GREATER THAN 10,000 UG/M3 (10 MG/M3) — POWERED-AIR PURIFYING RESPIRATORS IN ALL INLET FACE COVERINGS WITH HIGH EFFICIENCY FILTERS; OR HALF-MASK SUPPLIED-AIR RESPIRATOR OPERATED IN POSITIVE PRESSURE MODE.
NOT GREATER THAN 500 UG/M3 — FULL FACEPIECE AIR-PURIFYING RESPIRATOR EQUIPPED WITH HIGH EFFICIENCY FILTERS; OR ANY FULL FACEPIECE SUPPLIED-AIR RESPIRATOR; OR ANY FULL FACEPIECE SELF-CONTAINED BREATHING APPARATUS. NOT GREATER THAN 100 UG/M3 — HALF-MASK AIR-PURIFYING RESPIRATOR EQUIPPED WITH HIGH EFFICIENCY FILTERS; OR ANY HALF-MASK SUPPLIED-AIR RESPIRATOR.
(HIGH EFFICIENCY FILTER- 99.97% EFFICIENCY AGAINST 0.3 MICROMETER MONODISPERSE DIETHYL-HEXYL PHTHALATE (DOP) PARTICLES)
RESPIRATORY PROTECTION FOR INORGANIC ARSENICALS (SUCH AS ARSENIC TRICHLORIDE OR ARSENIC PHOSPHIDE) WITH SIGNIFICANT VAPOR PRESSURE.
CONCENTRATION OF INORGANIC ARSENIC (AS) — REQUIRED RESPIRATOR OR CONDITION OF USE
UNKNOWN OR GREATER OR LESS THAN 20,000 UG/M3 (20 MG/M3) — ANY FULL FACEPIECE SELF-CONTAINED BREATHING APPARATUS OPERATED IN POSITIVE PRESSURE MODE.
NOT GREATER THAN 20,000 UG/M3 (20 MG/M3) — SUPPLIED-AIR RESPIRATOR WITH A FULL FACEPIECE, HOOD OR HELMET OR SUIT OPERATED IN POSITIVE PRESSURE MODE.
NOT GREATER THAN 10,000 UG/M3 (10 MG/M3) — HALF-MASK SUPPLIED AIR RESPIRATOR OPERATED IN POSITIVE PRESSURE MODE.
NOT GREATER THAN 500 UG/M3 — FRONT- OR BACK-MOUNTED GAS MASK EQUIPPED WITH HIGH-EFFICIENCY FILTERS AND ACID GAS CANISTER; OR ANY FULL FACEPIECE SUPPLIED AIR RESPIRATOR; OR ANY FULL FACEPIECE SELF-CONTAINED BREATHING APPARATUS.
NOT GREATER THAN 100 UG/M3 — HALF-MASK AIR-PURIFYING RESPIRATOR EQUIPPED WITH HIGH EFFICIENCY FILTER AND ACID GAS CARTRIDGE; OR ANY HALF-MASK SUPPLIED-AIR RESPIRATOR.
(HIGH EFFICIENCY FILTER- 99.97% EFFICIENCY AGAINST 0.3 MICROMETER MONODISPERSE DIETHYL-HEXYL PHTHALATE (DOP) PARTICLES) (HALF-MASK RESPIRATORS SHALL NOT BE USED FOR PROTECTION AGAINST ARSENIC TRICHLORIDE, AS IT IS RAPIDLY ABSORBED THROUGH THE SKIN).
FOR FIREFIGHTING AND OTHER IMMEDIATELY DANGEROUS TO LIFE OR HEALTH CONDITIONS:
SELF-CONTAINED BREATHING APPARATUS WITH FULL FACEPIECE OPERATED IN PRESSURE-DEMAND OR OTHER POSITIVE PRESSURE MODE.
SUPPLIED-AIR RESPIRATOR WITH FULL FACEPIECE AND OPERATED IN PRESSURE-DEMAND OR OTHER POSITIVE PRESSURE MODE IN COMBINATION WITH AN AUXILIARY SELF-CONTAINED BREATHING APPARATUS OPERATED IN PRESSURE-DEMAND OR OTHER POSITIVE PRESSURE MODE.

CLOTHING: EMPLOYEE MUST WEAR APPROPRIATE PROTECTIVE (IMPERVIOUS) CLOTHING AND EQUIPMENT TO PREVENT REPEATED OR PROLONGED SKIN CONTACT WITH THIS SUBSTANCE.
ARSENIC (INORGANIC): PROTECTIVE CLOTHING SHOULD MEET THE REQUIREMENTS FOR PROTECTIVE WORK CLOTHING AND EQUIPMENT IN 29 CFR 1910.1018(J).

GLOVES: EMPLOYEE MUST WEAR APPROPRIATE PROTECTIVE GLOVES TO PREVENT CONTACT WITH THIS SUBSTANCE.
ARSENIC (INORGANIC): PROTECTIVE GLOVES SHOULD MEET THE REQUIREMENTS FOR PROTECTIVE WORK CLOTHING AND EQUIPMENT IN 29 CFR 1910.1018(J).

EYE PROTECTION: EMPLOYEE MUST WEAR SPLASH-PROOF OR DUST-RESISTANT SAFETY GOGGLES TO PREVENT EYE CONTACT WITH THIS SUBSTANCE.
EMERGENCY EYE WASH: WHERE THERE IS ANY POSSIBILITY THAT AN EMPLOYEE'S EYES MAY BE EXPOSED TO THIS SUBSTANCE, THE EMPLOYER SHOULD PROVIDE AN EYE WASH FOUNTAIN WITHIN THE IMMEDIATE WORK AREA FOR EMERGENCY USE.
ARSENIC (INORGANIC): PROTECTIVE EYE EQUIPMENT SHOULD MEET THE REQUIREMENTS FOR PROTECTIVE WORK CLOTHING AND EQUIPMENT IN 29 CFR 1910.1018(J).

AUTHORIZED BY- OCCUPATIONAL HEALTH SERVICES, INC.
CREATION DATE: 10/05/89 ***REVISION DATE:*** 07/13/90

MATERIAL SAFETY DATA SHEET

OCCUPATIONAL HEALTH SERVICES, INC.
AGRICULTURE AND PESTICIDE DIVISION
450 SEVENTH AVENUE, SUITE 2407
NEW YORK, NEW YORK 10123
1-800-445-MSDS OR (212) 967-1100

EMERGENCY CONTACT:
JOHN S. BRANSFORD, JR. (615) 292-1180

SUBSTANCE IDENTIFICATION

CAS-NUMBER 67-97-0
SUBSTANCE: **CHOLECALCIFEROL**
TRADE NAMES/SYNONYMS: BP-858; (3BETA,5ZETA,7EPSILON)-9,10-SECOCHOLESTA-5,7,10(19)-TRIEN-3-OL; CALCIOL; DELSTEROL; DEPARAL; D3-VIGANTOL; OLEOVITAMIN D3; RICKETON; TRIVITAN; VIGORSAN; VITAMIN D3; VITINC DAN-DEE-3; PST60913
CHEMICAL FAMILY: AMINO ACID DERIVATIVE
MOLECULAR FORMULA: C27-H44-O
MOLECULAR WEIGHT: 384.62
CERCLA RATINGS (SCALE 0-3): HEALTH=3 FIRE=U REACTIVITY=0 PERSISTENCE=0
NFPA RATINGS (SCALE 0-4): HEALTH=3 FIRE=U REACTIVITY=0

COMPONENTS AND CONTAMINANTS

COMPONENT: CHOLECALCIFEROL ***PERCENT:*** 100
CAS# 67-97-0
EXPOSURE LIMITS: NO OCCUPATIONAL EXPOSURE LIMITS ESTABLISHED BY OSHA, ACGIH, OR NIOSH.

PHYSICAL DATA

DESCRIPTION: COLORLESS CRYSTALS. ***MELTING POINT:*** 183-187 F (84-87 C)
SPECIFIC GRAVITY: NOT AVAILABLE ***SOLUBILITY IN WATER:*** SLIGHTLY SOLUBLE
SOLVENT SOLUBILITY: MOST ORGANIC SOLVENTS

FIRE AND EXPLOSION DATA

FIRE AND EXPLOSION HAZARD: UNKNOWN FIRE AND EXPLOSION HAZARD.
FIREFIGHTING MEDIA: DRY CHEMICAL, CARBON DIOXIDE, WATER SPRAY OR FOAM FOR LARGER FIRES, USE WATER SPRAY, FOG OR ALCOHOL FOAM
FIREFIGHTING: MOVE CONTAINER FROM FIRE AREA IF POSSIBLE. DO NOT SCATTER SPILLED MATERIAL WITH MORE WATER THAN NEEDED FOR FIRE CONTROL. DIKE FIRE CONTROL WATER FOR LATER DISPOSAL
USE AGENTS SUITABLE FOR TYPE OF SURROUNDING FIRE. AVOID BREATHING HAZARDOUS VAPORS, KEEP UPWIND.

TOXICITY

CHOLECALCIFEROL: TOXICITY DATA: 39 MG/KG/34 WEEKS INTERMITTENT ORAL-INFANT TDLO; 42 MG/KG ORAL-RAT LD50; 80 MG/KG ORAL-DOG LD50; REPRODUCTIVE EFFECTS DATA (RTECS). CARCINOGEN STATUS: NONE. ACUTE TOXICITY LEVEL: HIGHLY TOXIC BY INGESTION. TARGET EFFECTS: POISONING MAY AFFECT THE KIDNEYS AND DISTURB THE SERUM CALCIUM AND PHOSPHORUS LEVELS. ADDITIONAL DATA: INTERACTIONS WITH MEDICATIONS HAVE BEEN REPORTED.

HEALTH EFFECTS AND FIRST AID

INHALATION: CHOLECALCIFEROL: **ACUTE EXPOSURE-** NO DATA AVAILABLE. **CHRONIC EXPOSURE-** NO DATA AVAILABLE.
FIRST AID- REMOVE FROM EXPOSURE AREA TO FRESH AIR IMMEDIATELY. IF BREATHING HAS STOPPED, PERFORM ARTIFICIAL RESPIRATION. KEEP PERSON WARM AND AT REST. TREAT SYMPTOMATICALLY AND SUPPORTIVELY. GET MEDICAL ATTENTION IMMEDIATELY.

SKIN CONTACT: CHOLECALCIFEROL: **ACUTE EXPOSURE-** NO DATA AVAILABLE. **CHRONIC EXPOSURE-** NO DATA AVAILABLE.
FIRST AID- REMOVE CONTAMINATED CLOTHING AND SHOES IMMEDIATELY. WASH AFFECTED AREA WITH SOAP OR MILD DETERGENT AND LARGE AMOUNTS OF WATER UNTIL NO EVIDENCE OF CHEMICAL REMAINS (APPROXIMATELY 15-20 MINUTES). GET MEDICAL ATTENTION IMMEDIATELY.

EYE CONTACT: CHOLECALCIFEROL: **ACUTE EXPOSURE-** NO DATA AVAILABLE. **CHRONIC EXPOSURE-** NO DATA AVAILABLE.
FIRST AID- WASH EYES IMMEDIATELY WITH LARGE AMOUNTS OF WATER OR NORMAL SALINE, OCCASIONALLY LIFTING UPPER AND LOWER LIDS, UNTIL NO EVIDENCE OF CHEMICAL REMAINS (APPROXIMATELY 15-20 MINUTES). GET MEDICAL ATTENTION IMMEDIATELY.

INGESTION: CHOLECALCIFEROL: HIGHLY TOXIC. **ACUTE EXPOSURE-** CHOLECALCIFEROL IS A FAT-SOLUBLE FORM OF VITAMIN D. VITAMIN D IS REQUIRED DAILY IN THE DIET IN AMOUNTS OF 5-10 UG. EXCESSIVE AMOUNTS MAY LEAD TO TOXICITY IN WHICH THE INITIAL SIGNS ARE THOSE ASSOCIATED WITH HYPERCALCEMIA AND CONSIST OF WEAKNESS, FATIGUE, LASSITUDE, HEADACHE, ANOREXIA, NAUSEA, VOMITING, AND DIARRHEA. OBTUNDATION AND COMA MAY DEVELOP. EARLY IMPAIRMENT OF RENAL FUNCTION FROM HYPERCALCEMIA IS MANIFEST BY POLYURIA, POLYDIPSIA, NOCTURIA, DECREASED URINARY CONCENTRATING ABILITY, AND PROTEINURIA. DEATH IS POSSIBLE FROM CARDIAC ARRHYTHMIAS. **CHRONIC EXPOSURE-** THE FOOD AND DRUG ADMINISTRATION LISTS IT AS A SUBSTANCE GENERALLY RECOGNIZED AS SAFE. CHRONIC INGESTION OF CHOLECALCIFEROL AT LEVELS OF 50,000-100,000 UG/DAY MAY RESULT IN SYMPTOMS AS THOSE OF ACUTE EXPOSURE. PARESTHESIAS, DEPRESSION, ELEVATED PHOSPHORUS LEVELS, AND ANEMIA MAY OCCUR. CALCIFICATION OF SOFT TISSUES MAY RESULT LEADING TO TO NEPHROLITHIASIS, DIFFUSE NEPHROCALCINOSIS, OR BOTH. RENAL FUNCTION MAY BE SEVERELY AND IRREVERSIBLY IMPAIRED. OTHER SITES OF CALCIFICATION MAY INCLUDE BLOOD VESSELS, HEART, LUNGS AND SKIN. SOME INDIVIDUALS MAY EXHIBIT HYPERTENSION. CALCIUM DEPOSITS HAVE ALSO BEEN REPORTED IN THE CORNEA AND CONJUNCTIVA; LESS COMMONLY, STRABISMUS, EPICANTHAL FOLDS, PAPILLEDEMA, SLOW PUPILLARY REACTION TO LIGHT, IRITIS, AND CATARACTS MAY RESULT. THERE IS A RELATIONSHIP BETWEEN EXCESS MATERNAL VITAMIN D INTAKE OR EXTREME SENSITIVITY TO THE VITAMIN AND NONFAMILIAL CONGENITAL SUPRAVALVULAR AORTIC STENOSIS. MATERNAL HYPERCALCEMIA MAY ALSO RESULT IN SUPPRESSION OF PARATHYROID FUNCTION IN THE NEWBORN, WITH RESULTANT HYPOCALCEMIA, TETANY, AND SEIZURES. EXCESSIVE DOSES OF VITAMIN D DURING PREGNANCY IS ALSO SUSPECTED OF CAUSING RETARDATION AND CONGENITAL HEART DEFECTS IN CHILDREN.

FIRST AID- IF EXTENSIVE VOMITING HAS NOT OCCURRED, THE SUBSTANCE SHOULD BE REMOVED BY EMESIS OR GASTRIC LAVAGE PROVIDED THAT THE PATIENT IS CONSCIOUS AND CONVULSIONS ARE NOT PRESENT. KEEP HEAD BELOW HIPS DURING VOMITING TO PREVENT ASPIRATION. DO NOT ATTEMPT TO MAKE AN UNCONSCIOUS PERSON VOMIT. TREAT SYMPTOMATICALLY AND SUPPORTIVELY. GET MEDICAL ATTENTION IMMEDIATELY (DREISBACH, HANDBOOK OF POISONING, 12TH ED.). TREATMENT SHOULD BE PERFORMED BY QUALIFIED MEDICAL PERSONNEL.

ANTIDOTE: NO SPECIFIC ANTIDOTE. TREAT SYMPTOMATICALLY AND SUPPORTIVELY.

REACTIVITY

REACTIVITY: STABLE UNDER NORMAL TEMPERATURES AND PRESSURES.

INCOMPATIBILITIES: NONE KNOWN.

DECOMPOSITION: THERMAL DECOMPOSITION MAY RELEASE TOXIC AND/OR HAZARDOUS GASES.

POLYMERIZATION: HAZARDOUS POLYMERIZATION HAS NOT BEEN REPORTED TO OCCUR UNDER NORMAL TEMPERATURES AND PRESSURES.

CONDITIONS TO AVOID

NONE REPORTED.

SPILL AND LEAK PROCEDURES

OCCUPATIONAL SPILL: SWEEP UP AND PLACE IN SUITABLE CLEAN, DRY CONTAINERS FOR RECLAMATION OR LATER DISPOSAL. DO NOT FLUSH SPILLED MATERIAL INTO SEWER. KEEP UNNECESSARY PEOPLE AWAY.

PROTECTIVE EQUIPMENT

VENTILATION: PROVIDE LOCAL EXHAUST OR PROCESS ENCLOSURE VENTILATION SYSTEM.

RESPIRATOR: THE FOLLOWING RESPIRATORS ARE RECOMMENDED BASED ON INFORMATION FOUND IN THE PHYSICAL DATA, TOXICITY AND HEALTH EFFECTS SECTIONS. THEY ARE RANKED IN ORDER FROM MINIMUM TO MAXIMUM RESPIRATORY PROTECTION. THE SPECIFIC RESPIRATOR SELECTED MUST BE BASED ON CONTAMINATION LEVELS FOUND IN THE WORK PLACE, MUST NOT EXCEED THE WORKING LIMITS OF THE RESPIRATOR AND BE JOINTLY APPROVED BY THE NATIONAL INSTITUTE FOR OCCUPATIONAL SAFETY AND HEALTH AND THE MINE SAFETY AND HEALTH ADMINISTRATION (NIOSH-MSHA).

TYPE 'C' SUPPLIED-AIR RESPIRATOR WITH A FULL FACEPIECE OPERATED IN PRESSURE-DEMAND OR OTHER POSITIVE PRESSURE MODE OR WITH A FULL FACEPIECE, HELMET OR HOOD OPERATED IN CONTINOUS-FLOW MODE.

SELF-CONTAINED BREATHING APPARATUS WITH A FULL FACEPIECE OPERATED IN PRESSURE-DEMAND OR OTHER POSITIVE PRESSURE MODE.

FOR FIREFIGHTING AND OTHER IMMEDIATELY DANGEROUS TO LIFE OR HEALTH CONDITIONS:

SELF-CONTAINED BREATHING APPARATUS WITH FULL FACEPIECE OPERATED IN PRESSURE-DEMAND OR OTHER POSITIVE PRESSURE MODE.

SUPPLIED-AIR RESPIRATOR WITH FULL FACEPIECE AND OPERATED IN PRESSURE-DEMAND OR OTHER POSITIVE PRESSURE MODE IN COMBINATION WITH AN AUXILIARY SELF-CONTAINED BREATHING APPARATUS OPERATED IN PRESSURE-DEMAND OR OTHER POSITIVE PRESSURE MODE.

CLOTHING: EMPLOYEE MUST WEAR APPROPRIATE PROTECTIVE (IMPERVIOUS) CLOTHING AND EQUIPMENT TO PREVENT REPEATED OR PROLONGED SKIN CONTACT WITH THIS SUBSTANCE.

GLOVES: EMPLOYEE MUST WEAR APPROPRIATE PROTECTIVE GLOVES TO PREVENT CONTACT WITH THIS SUBSTANCE.

EYE PROTECTION: EMPLOYEE MUST WEAR SPLASH-PROOF OR DUST-RESISTANT SAFETY GOGGLES TO PREVENT EYE CONTACT WITH THIS SUBSTANCE.

EMERGENCY EYE WASH: WHERE THERE IS ANY POSSIBILITY THAT AN EMPLOYEE'S EYES MAY BE EXPOSED TO THIS SUBSTANCE, THE EMPLOYER SHOULD PROVIDE AN EYE WASH FOUNTAIN WITHIN THE IMMEDIATE WORK AREA FOR EMERGENCY USE.

AUTHORIZED BY- OCCUPATIONAL HEALTH SERVICES, INC.

CREATION DATE: 10/04/89 ***REVISION DATE:*** 05/31/90

MATERIAL SAFETY DATA SHEET

OCCUPATIONAL HEALTH SERVICES, INC.
AGRICULTURE AND PESTICIDE DIVISION
450 SEVENTH AVENUE, SUITE 2407
NEW YORK, NEW YORK 10123
1-800-445-MSDS OR (212) 967-1100

EMERGENCY CONTACT:
JOHN S. BRANSFORD, JR. (615) 292-1180

SUBSTANCE IDENTIFICATION

CAS-NUMBER 60238-56-4

SUBSTANCE: **CHLORTHIOPHOS**

TRADE NAMES/SYNONYMS: PHOSPHOROTHIOIC ACID, O-(DICHLORO(METHYLTHIO)PHENYL) O,O-DIETHYL ESTER; O,O-DIETHYL-O-(DICHLORO(METHYLTHIO)PHENYL PHOSPHOROTHIOATE; ENT 27635; C11H15CL2O3PS2; PST64913

CHEMICAL FAMILY: HALOGEN COMPOUND, AROMATIC PHOSPHOROTHIOATE

MOLECULAR FORMULA: C11-H15-O3-P-S2-CL2

MOLECULAR WEIGHT: 361.25

CERCLA RATINGS (SCALE 0-3): HEALTH=3 FIRE=U REACTIVITY=0 PERSISTENCE=3

NFPA RATINGS (SCALE 0-4): HEALTH=4 FIRE=U REACTIVITY=0

COMPONENTS AND CONTAMINANTS

COMPONENT: O-(2,5-DICHLORO-4-(METHYLTHIO)PHENYL) O,O-DIETHYLESTER PHOSPHOROTHIOIC ACID ***PERCENT:*** 73.0

COMPONENT: O-(2,4-DICHLORO-5-(METHYLTHIO)PHENYL) O,O-DIETHYLESTER PHOSPHOROTHIOIC ACID ***PERCENT:*** 14.0

COMPONENT: O-(4,5-DICHLORO-2-(METHYLTHIO)PHENYL) O,O-DIETHYLESTER PHOSPHOROTHIOIC ACID ***PERCENT:*** 13.0

OTHER CONTAMINANTS: MAY CONTAIN 10 PPB 2,3,7,8-TETRACHLORODIBENZO-PARA-DIOXIN

EXPOSURE LIMITS: NO OCCUPATIONAL EXPOSURE LIMITS ESTABLISHED BY OSHA, ACGIH, OR NIOSH.

CHLORTHIOPHOS: 500 POUNDS SARA SECTION 302 THRESHOLD PLANNING QUANTITY 1 POUND SARA SECTION 304 REPORTABLE QUANTITY

PHYSICAL DATA

DESCRIPTION: CRYSTALLINE SOLID OR YELLOW-BROWN LIQUID.

BOILING POINT: 307-316 F (153-158 C) @ 0.1 MMHG

MELTING POINT: >77 F (>25 C)

SPECIFIC GRAVITY: NOT AVAILABLE ***VAPOR PRESSURE:*** NOT AVAILABLE

SOLUBILITY IN WATER: VERY SLIGHTLY SOLUBLE

SOLVENT SOLUBILITY: SOLUBLE IN ACETONE, BENZENE, CHLOROFORM, CYCLOHEXANONE, DIOXANE, ALCOHOL, METHYLENE CHLORIDE AND TOLUENE.

FIRE AND EXPLOSION DATA

FIRE AND EXPLOSION HAZARD: UNKNOWN FIRE AND EXPLOSION HAZARD.

FLASH POINT: NOT AVAILABLE

FIREFIGHTING MEDIA: DRY CHEMICAL, CARBON DIOXIDE, HALON, WATER SPRAY OR STANDARD FOAM (1987 EMERGENCY RESPONSE GUIDEBOOK, DOT P 5800.4).

FOR LARGER FIRES, USE WATER SPRAY, FOG OR STANDARD FOAM (1987 EMERGENCY RESPONSE GUIDEBOOK, DOT P 5800.4).

FIREFIGHTING: MOVE CONTAINERS FROM FIRE AREA IF POSSIBLE. COOL CONTAINERS EXPOSED TO FLAMES WITH WATER FROM SIDE UNTIL WELL AFTER FIRE IS OUT. FIGHT FIRE FROM MAXIMUM DISTANCE. STAY AWAY FROM STORAGE TANK ENDS. DIKE FIRE CONTROL WATER FOR LATER DISPOSAL. DO NOT SCATTER MATERIAL. (1987 EMERGENCY RESPONSE GUIDEBOOK, DOT P 5800.4, GUIDE PAGE 57). EXTINGUISH ONLY IF FLOW CAN BE STOPPED. USE FLOODING AMOUNTS OF WATER AS A FOG; SOLID STREAMS MAY BE INEFFECTIVE. COOL CONTAINERS WITH FLOODING AMOUNTS OF WATER FROM AS FAR A DISTANCE AS POSSIBLE. AVOID BREATHING POISONOUS VAPORS, KEEP UPWIND.

TRANSPORTATION DATA

DEPARTMENT OF TRANSPORTATION HAZARD CLASSIFICATION 49 CFR 172.101: POISON B

DEPARTMENT OF TRANSPORTATION LABELING REQUIREMENTS 49 CFR 172.101 AND SUBPART E: POISON

DEPARTMENT OF TRANSPORTATION PACKAGING REQUIREMENTS: 49 CFR 173.346 EXCEPTIONS: 49 CFR 173.345

TOXICITY

CHLORTHIOPHOS: TOXICITY DATA: 50 MG/KG SKIN-RABBIT LD50; 121 MG/KG SKIN-RAT LD50; 7800 UG/KG ORAL-RAT LD50; 91400 UG/KG ORAL-MOUSE LD50. CARCINOGEN STATUS: NONE. ACUTE TOXICITY LEVEL: HIGHLY TOXIC BY DERMAL ABSORPTION AND INGESTION. TARGET EFFECTS: CHOLINESTERASE INHIBITOR. POISONING MAY AFFECT THE NERVOUS SYSTEM. AT INCREASED RISK FROM EXPOSURE: PERSONS WITH RESPIRATORY AILMENTS, RECENT EXPOSURE TO CHOLINESTERASE INHIBITORS OR IMPAIRED CHOLINESTERASE PRODUCTION, OR LIVER MALFUNCTION.* ADDITIONAL DATA: MAY CROSS THE PLACENTA. HIGH ENVIRONMENTAL TEMPERATURES OR EXPOSURE OF THE CHEMICAL TO VISIBLE OR ULTRAVIOLET LIGHT MAY ENHANCE THE TOXICITY. INTERACTIONS WITH MEDICATIONS MAY OCCUR.*

* MAY BE BASED ON GENERAL INFORMATION ON ORGANOPHOSPHATES.

HEALTH EFFECTS AND FIRST AID

INHALATION: CHLORTHIOPHOS: SEE INFORMATION ON ORGANOPHOSPHATES.
ORGANOPHOSPHATES: CHOLINESTERASE INHIBITOR. **ACUTE EXPOSURE-** WHEN INHALED, THE FIRST EFFECTS OF CHOLINESTERASE INHIBITORS ARE USUALLY RESPIRATORY AND MAY INCLUDE NASAL HYPEREMIA AND WATERY DISCHARGE, COUGH, CHEST DISCOMFORT, DYSPNEA, AND WHEEZING DUE TO INCREASED BRONCHIAL SECRETIONS AND BRONCHOCONSTRICTION. IF SUFFICIENT AMOUNTS ARE ABSORBED, OTHER SYSTEMIC EFFECTS MAY BEGIN WITHIN A FEW MINUTES OR BE DELAYED FOR UP TO 12 HOURS. SYMPTOMS MAY INCLUDE PALLOR, NAUSEA, VOMITING, DIARRHEA, ABDOMINAL CRAMPS, HEADACHE, DIZZINESS, OCULAR PAIN, BLURRED VISION, MIOSIS OR IN SOME CASES, ESPECIALLY INITIALLY, MYDRIASIS, LACRIMATION, SALIVATION, SWEATING, AND CONFUSION. OTHER REPORTED CENTRAL NERVOUS SYSTEM OR NEUROMUSCULAR EFFECTS MAY INCLUDE ATAXIA, SLURRED SPEECH, AREFLEXIA, WEAKNESS, FATIGUE, FASCICULATIONS, TWITCHING, TREMORS POSSIBLY OF THE TONGUE AND EYELIDS, AND EVENTUALLY PARALYSIS OF THE EXTREMITIES AND POSSIBLY OF THE RESPIRATORY MUSCLES. IN SEVERE CASES THERE MAY ALSO BE INVOLUNTARY DEFECATION AND URINATION, CYANOSIS, PSYCHOSIS, HYPERGLYCEMIA, ACUTE PANCREATITIS, CARDIAC IRREGULARITIES, PULMONARY EDEMA, UNCONSCIOUSNESS, CONVULSIONS, AND COMA. DEATH IS PRIMARILY DUE TO RESPIRATORY FAILURE, ALTHOUGH CARDIOVASCULAR EFFECTS INCLUDING CARDIAC ARREST MAY ALSO BE IMPLICATED. LONG TERM SEQUELAE ARE RARE BUT MAY INCLUDE NEUROPSYCHIATRIC DISORDERS AND MYOPATHY WITH MUSCLE TENDERNESS. SOME ORGANOPHOSPHATES MAY CAUSE A DELAYED NEUROPATHY BEGINNING 1-4 WEEKS AFTER AN ACUTE EXPOSURE WHICH MAY OR MAY NOT HAVE CAUSED ACUTE CHOLINERGIC EFFECTS. NUMBNESS, TINGLING, WEAKNESS AND CRAMPING BEGINNING SYMMETRICALLY IN THE LOWER LIMBS MAY PROGRESS TO ATAXIA AND PARALYSIS. IN SEVERE CASES, UPPER LIMB INVOLVEMENT IS POSSIBLE AND FLACCID PARALYSIS MAY PROGRESS TO SPASTIC PARALYSIS WITH EXAGGERATED REFLEXES. IMPROVEMENT MAY OCCUR OVER MONTHS TO YEARS, BUT SOME RESIDUAL IMPAIRMENT USUALLY REMAINS. **CHRONIC EXPOSURE-** REPEATED OR PROLONGED EXPOSURE MAY RESULT IN THE EFFECTS OF ACUTE EXPOSURE INCLUDING THE DELAYED NEUROPATHY. OTHER EFFECTS REPORTED IN WORKERS REPEATEDLY EXPOSED INCLUDE IMPAIRED MEMORY AND CONCENTRATION, ACUTE PSYCHOSIS, SEVERE DEPRESSIONS, IRRITABILTY, CONFUSION, APATHY, EMOTIONAL LABILITY, SOCIAL WITHDRAWAL, CONFUSION, HEADACHE, SPEECH DIFFICULTIES, DELAYED REACTION TIMES, SPATIAL DISORIENTATION, NIGHTMARES, SLEEPWALKING, AND DROWSINESS OR INSOMNIA. AN INFLUENZA-LIKE CONDITION WITH HEADACHE, NAUSEA, WEAKNESS, ANOREXIA AND MALAISE HAS ALSO BEEN REPORTED.

FIRST AID- REMOVE FROM EXPOSURE AREA TO FRESH AIR IMMEDIATELY. IF BREATHING HAS STOPPED, GIVE ARTIFICIAL RESPIRATION. MAINTAIN AIRWAY AND BLOOD PRESSURE AND ADMINISTER OXYGEN IF AVAILABLE. KEEP AFFECTED PERSON WARM AND AT REST. TREAT SYMPTOMATICALLY AND SUPPORTIVELY. ADMINISTRATION OF OXYGEN SHOULD BE PERFORMED BY QUALIFIED PERSONNEL. GET MEDICAL ATTENTION IMMEDIATELY.

SKIN CONTACT: CHLORTHIOPHOS: HIGHLY TOXIC. SEE INFORMATION ON ORGANOPHOSPHATES.
ORGANOPHOSPHATES: CHOLINESTERASE INHIBITOR. **ACUTE EXPOSURE-** LOCALIZED SWEATING AND FASCICULATIONS MAY OCCUR AT THE SITE OF CONTACT. IF SUFFICIENT AMOUNTS ARE ABSORBED, OTHER EFFECTS OF CHOLINESTERASE INHIBITION AS DESCRIBED IN ACUTE INHALATION MAY OCCUR. SYMPTOMS MAY BE DELAYED 2-3 HOURS, BUT USUALLY NO MORE THAN 12 HOURS. THE RATE OF ABSORPTION IS INCREASED BY THE PRESENCE OF DERMATITIS OR HIGH AMBIENT TEMPERATURES. DELAYED NEUROPATHY IS ALSO POSSIBLE. **CHRONIC EXPOSURE-** REPEATED OR PROLONGED EXPOSURE MAY CAUSE EFFECTS AS DESCRIBED IN ACUTE EXPOSURE. SOME ORGANOPHOSPHATES MAY CAUSE SENSITIZATION.

FIRST AID- REMOVE CONTAMINATED CLOTHING IMMEDIATELY. WASH CONTAMINATED AREAS WITH SOAP AND WATER FOLLOWED BY ALCOHOL (ARENA, POISONING, 4TH ED.). EMERGENCY PERSONNEL SHOULD WEAR GLOVES AND AVOID CONTAMINATION. TREAT RESPIRATORY DIFFICULTY WITH ARTIFICIAL RESPIRATION. GET MEDICAL ATTENTION IMMEDIATELY.

EYE CONTACT: CHLORTHIOPHOS: SEE INFORMATION ON ORGANOPHOSPATES.
ORGANOPHOSPHATES: CHOLINESTERASE INHIBITOR. **ACUTE EXPOSURE-** DIRECT CONTACT MAY CAUSE PAIN, HYPEREMIA, LACRIMATION, TWITCHING OF THE EYELIDS, MIOSIS, AND CILIARY MUSCLE SPASM WITH LOSS OF ACCOMODATION, BLURRED OR DIMMED VISION AND BROWACHE. SOMETIMES MYDRIASIS MAY OCCUR INSTEAD OF MIOSIS. WITH SUFFICIENT EXPOSURE, OTHER SYMPTOMS OF CHOLINESTERASE INHIBITION AS DESCRIBED IN ACUTE INHALATION MAY OCCUR. **CHRONIC EXPOSURE-** REPEATED OR PROLONGED EXPOSURE MAY CAUSE EFFECTS AS DESCRIBED IN ACUTE EXPOSURE. SOME COMPOUNDS HAVE CAUSED TOXIC EFFECTS ON THE CRYSTALLINE LENS, CONJUNCTIVAL THICKENING AND OBSTRUCTION OF THE NASOLACRIMAL CANALS WHEN USED AS MIOTIC EYEDROPS.

FIRST AID- IRRIGATE EYES WITH WATER OR SALINE SOLUTION. IF SYMPTOMS OF POISONING OCCUR, TREAT RESPIRATORY DIFFICULTY WITH ARTIFICIAL RESPIRATION AND OXYGEN. OBSERVE PATIENT FOR AT LEAST 24-36 HOURS (GOSSELIN, CLINICAL TOXICOLOGY OF COMMERCIAL PRODUCTS, 5TH ED.). GET MEDICAL ATTENTION IMMEDIATELY. OXYGEN SHOULD BE ADMINISTERED BY QUALIFIED MEDICAL PERSONNEL.

INGESTION: CHLORTHIOPHOS: HIGHLY TOXIC. IN AN ACUTE DELAYED NEUROTOXICITY STUDY WITH HENS, SLIGHT AXONAL DEGENERATION WAS SEEN AT 90 MG/KG. SEE INFORMATION ON ORGANOPHOSPHATES.
ORGANOPHOSPHATES: CHOLINESTERASE INHIBITOR. **ACUTE EXPOSURE-** WHEN INGESTED, THE FIRST EFFECTS MAY BE NAUSEA, VOMITING, ANOREXIA, ABDOMINAL CRAMPS AND DIARRHEA. GASTROINTESTINAL ABSORPTION MAY CAUSE SYMPTOMS OF CHOLINESTERASE INHIBITION AS DESCRIBED IN ACUTE INHALATION. SYMPTOMS MAY BEGIN WITHIN MINUTES OR BE DELAYED FOR HOURS. DELAYED EFFECTS INCLUDING NEUROPATHY MAY ALSO OCCUR. **CHRONIC EXPOSURE-** REPEATED INGESTION MAY CAUSE EFFECTS AS DESCRIBED IN ACUTE EXPOSURE.

FIRST AID- IF PERSON IS ALERT AND RESPIRATION IS NOT DEPRESSED, GIVE SYRUP OF IPECAC FOLLOWED BY WATER (IF VOMITING OCCURS, KEEP HEAD BELOW HIPS TO PREVENT ASPIRATION). IF CONSCIOUSNESS LEVEL DECLINES OR VOMITING HAS NOT OCCURRED IN 15 MINUTES EMPTY STOMACH BY GASTRIC LAVAGE WITH THE AID OF CUFFED ENDOTRACHEAL TUBE USING ISOTONIC SALINE OR 5% SODIUM BICARBONATE FOLLOW WITH ACTIVATED CHARCOAL. ESTABLISH AND MAINTAIN AIRWAY. TREAT RESPIRATORY DIFFICULTY WITH ARTIFICIAL RESPIRATION AND OXYGEN. DO NOT GIVE MORPHINE, AMINOPHYLLINE, PHENOTHIAZINES, RESERPINE, FUROSEMIDE, OR ETHACRYNIC ACID (MORGAN, RECOGNITION AND MANAGEMENT OF PESTICIDE POISONINGS, 3RD ED.). TREAT SYMPTOMATICALLY AND SUPPORTIVELY. ADMINISTRATION OF OXYGEN AND LAVAGE MUST BE PERFORMED BY QUALIFIED MEDICAL PERSONNEL. GET MEDICAL ATTENTION IMMEDIATELY.

ANTIDOTE: THE FOLLOWING ANTIDOTE(S) HAVE BEEN RECOMMENDED. HOWEVER, THE DECISION AS TO WHETHER THE SEVERITY OF POISONING REQUIRES ADMINISTRATION OF ANY ANTIDOTE AND ACTUAL DOSE REQUIRED SHOULD BE MADE BY QUALIFIED MEDICAL PERSONNEL.
FOR CHOLINESTERASE INHIBITORS: ESTABLISH CLEAR AIRWAY AND TISSUE OXYGENATION BY ASPIRATION OF SECRETIONS, AND IF NECESSARY, BY ASSISTED PULMONARY VENTILATION WITH OXYGEN. IMPROVE TISSUE OXYGENATION AS MUCH AS POSSIBLE BEFORE ADMINISTERING ATROPINE TO MINIMIZE THE RISK OF VENTRICULAR FIBRILLATION. ADMINISTER ATROPINE SULFATE INTRAVENOUSLY, OR INTRAMUSCULARLY IF IV INJECTION IS NOT POSSIBLE. IN MODERATELY SEVERE POISONING ADMINISTER ATROPINE SULFATE, 0.4-2.0 MG REPEATED EVERY 15 MINUTES UNTIL ATROPINIZATION IS ACHIEVED (TACHYCARDIA, FLUSHING, DRY MOUTH, MYDRIASIS). MAINTAIN ATROPINIZATION BY REPEATED DOSES FOR 2-12

HOURS, OR LONGER, DEPENDING ON THE SEVERITY OF POISONING. THE APPEARANCE OF RALES IN THE LUNG BASES, MIOSIS, SALIVATION, NAUSEA, BRADYCARDIA, ARE ALL INDICATIONS OF INADEQUATE ATROPINIZATION. SEVERELY POISONED INDIVIDUALS MAY EXHIBIT REMARKABLE TOLERANCE TO ATROPINE; TWO OR MORE TIMES THE DOSAGES SUGGESTED ABOVE MAY BE NEEDED. PERSONS NOT POISONED OR ONLY SLIGHTLY POISONED, HOWEVER, MAY DEVELOP SIGNS OF ATROPINE TOXICITY FROM SUCH LARGE DOSAGES: FEVER, MUSCLE FIBRILLATIONS, AND DELIRIUM ARE THE MAIN SIGNS OF ATROPINE TOXICITY. IF THESE SIGNS APPEAR WHILE THE PATIENT IS FULLY ATROPINIZED, ATROPINE ADMINISTRATION SHOULD BE DISCONTINUED, AT LEAST TEMPORARILY. OBSERVE TREATED PATIENTS CLOSELY AT LEAST 24 HOURS TO INSURE THAT SYMPTOMS (POSSIBLY PULMONARY EDEMA) DO NOT RECUR AS ATROPINIZATION WEARS OFF. IN VERY SEVERE POISONINGS, METABOLIC DISPOSITION OF TOXICANT MAY REQUIRE SEVERAL HOURS OR DAYS DURING WHICH ATROPINIZATION MUST BE MAINTAINED. MARKEDLY LOWER LEVELS OF URINARY METABOLITES INDICATE THAT ATROPINE DOSAGE CAN BE TAPERED OFF. AS DOSAGE IS REDUCED, CHECK THE LUNG BASES FREQUENTLY FOR RALES. IF RALES ARE HEARD OR OTHER SYMPTOMS RETURN, RE-ESTABLISH ATROPINIZATION PROMPTLY (MORGAN, RECOGNITION AND MANAGEMENT OF PESTICIDE POISONINGS, 3RD ED.). ADMINISTRATION OF ANTIDOTE MUST BE PERFORMED BY QUALIFIED MEDICAL PERSONNEL.

IN CASES OF SEVERE POISONING BY ORGANOPHOSPHATE PESTICIDES IN WHICH RESPIRATORY DEPRESSION, MUSCLE WEAKNESS AND TWITCHINGS ARE SEVERE, GIVE PRALIDOXIME (PROTOPAM-AYERST, 2-PAM), 1.0 GRAM INTRAVENOUSLY AT NO MORE THAN 0.5 GRAM PER MINUTE. DOSAGE OF PRALIDOXIME MAY BE REPEATED IN 1-2 HOURS, THEN AT 10-12 HOUR INTERVALS IF NEEDED. IN VERY SEVERE POISONINGS, DOSAGE RATES MAY BE DOUBLED. TREATMENT WITH PRALIDOXIME WILL BE MOST EFFECTIVE IF GIVEN WITHIN THIRTY-SIX HOURS AFTER POISONING (MORGAN, RECOGNITION AND MANAGEMENT OF PESTICIDE POISONINGS, 3RD ED.). ANTIDOTE SHOULD BE ADMINISTERED BY QUALIFIED MEDICAL PERSONNEL.

REACTIVITY

REACTIVITY: STABLE UNDER NORMAL TEMPERATURES AND PRESSURES.

INCOMPATIBILITIES: CHLORTHIOPHOS: OXIDIZERS (STRONG): FIRE AND EXPLOSION HAZARD.

DECOMPOSITION: THERMAL DECOMPOSITION MAY RELEASE TOXIC OXIDES OF CARBON, SULFUR, PHOSPHORUS AND TOXIC FUMES OF CHLORINE.

POLYMERIZATION: HAZARDOUS POLYMERIZATION HAS NOT BEEN REPORTED TO OCCUR UNDER NORMAL TEMPERATURES AND PRESSURES.

STORAGE AND DISPOSAL

OBSERVE ALL FEDERAL, STATE AND LOCAL REGULATIONS WHEN STORING OR DISPOSING OF THIS SUBSTANCE. FOR ASSISTANCE, CONTACT THE DISTRICT DIRECTOR OF THE ENVIRONMENTAL PROTECTION AGENCY.

STORAGE

STORE IN ACCORDANCE WITH 40 CFR 165 RECOMMENDED PROCEDURES FOR THE DISPOSAL AND STORAGE OF PESTICIDES AND PESTICIDE CONTAINERS.

THRESHOLD PLANNING QUANTITY (TPQ): THE SUPERFUND AMENDMENTS AND REAUTHORIZATION ACT (SARA) SECTION 302 REQUIRES THAT EACH FACILITY WHERE ANY EXTREMELY HAZARDOUS SUBSTANCE IS PRESENT IN A QUANTITY EQUAL TO OR GREATER THAN THE TPQ ESTABLISHED FOR THAT SUBSTANCE NOTIFY THE STATE EMERGENCY RESPONSE COMMISSION FOR THE STATE IN WHICH IT IS LOCATED. SECTION 303 OF SARA REQUIRES THESE FACILITIES TO PARTICIPATE IN LOCAL EMERGENCY RESPONSE PLANNING (40 CFR 355.30).

DISPOSAL

DISPOSAL MUST BE IN ACCORDANCE WITH 40 CFR 165 RECOMMENDED PROCEDURES FOR THE DISPOSAL AND STORAGE OF PESTICIDES AND PESTICIDE CONTAINERS.

CONDITIONS TO AVOID

MAY BE IGNITED BY HEAT, SPARKS OR FLAMES. CONTAINER MAY EXPLODE IN HEAT OF FIRE. VAPOR EXPLOSION AND POISON HAZARD INDOORS, OUTDOORS OR IN SEWERS.

SPILL AND LEAK PROCEDURES

OCCUPATIONAL SPILL: SHUT OFF IGNITION SOURCES. DO NOT TOUCH SPILLED MATERIAL. STOP LEAK IF YOU CAN DO IT WITHOUT RISK. USE WATER SPRAY TO REDUCE VAPORS. FOR SMALL SPILLS, TAKE UP WITH SAND OR OTHER ABSORBENT MATERIAL AND PLACE INTO CONTAINERS FOR LATER DISPOSAL. FOR SMALL DRY SPILLS, WITH CLEAN SHOVEL PLACE MATERIAL INTO CLEAN, DRY CONTAINERS AND COVER. MOVE CONTAINERS FROM SPILL AREA. FOR LARGER SPILLS, DIKE FAR AHEAD OF SPILL FOR LATER DISPOSAL. NO SMOKING, FLAMES OR FLARES IN HAZARD AREA! KEEP UNNECESSARY PEOPLE AWAY. ISOLATE HAZARD AREA AND DENY ENTRY. VENTILATE CLOSED SPACES BEFORE ENTERING.

REPORTABLE QUANTITY (RQ): 1 POUND THE SUPERFUND AMENDMENTS AND REAUTHORIZATION ACT (SARA) SECTION 304 REQUIRES THAT A RELEASE EQUAL TO OR GREATER THAN THE REPORTABLE QUANTITY FOR THIS SUBSTANCE BE IMMEDIATELY REPORTED TO THE LOCAL EMERGENCY PLANNING COMMITTEE AND THE STATE EMERGENCY RESPONSE COMMISSION (40 CFR 355.40). IF THE RELEASE OF THIS SUBSTANCE IS REPORTABLE UNDER CERCLA SECTION 103, THE NATIONAL RESPONSE CENTER MUST BE NOTIFIED IMMEDIATELY AT (800) 424-8802 OR (202) 426-2675 IN THE METROPOLITAN WASHINGTON, D.C. AREA (40 CFR 302.6).

PROTECTIVE EQUIPMENT

VENTILATION: PROCESS ENCLOSURE RECOMMENDED.

RESPIRATOR: THE FOLLOWING RESPIRATORS ARE RECOMMENDED BASED ON INFORMATION FOUND IN THE PHYSICAL DATA, TOXICITY AND HEALTH EFFECTS SECTIONS. THEY ARE RANKED IN ORDER FROM MINIMUM TO MAXIMUM RESPIRATORY PROTECTION. THE SPECIFIC RESPIRATOR SELECTED MUST BE BASED ON CONTAMINATION LEVELS FOUND IN THE WORK PLACE, MUST NOT EXCEED THE WORKING LIMITS OF THE RESPIRATOR AND BE JOINTLY APPROVED BY THE NATIONAL INSTITUTE FOR OCCUPATIONAL SAFETY AND HEALTH AND THE MINE SAFETY AND HEALTH ADMINISTRATION (NIOSH-MSHA).

TYPE 'C' SUPPLIED-AIR RESPIRATOR WITH A FULL FACEPIECE OPERATED IN PRESSURE-DEMAND OR OTHER POSITIVE PRESSURE MODE OR WITH A FULL FACEPIECE, HELMET OR HOOD OPERATED IN CONTINOUS-FLOW MODE.

SELF-CONTAINED BREATHING APPARATUS WITH A FULL FACEPIECE OPERATED IN PRESSURE-DEMAND OR OTHER POSITIVE PRESSURE MODE.

FOR FIREFIGHTING AND OTHER IMMEDIATELY DANGEROUS TO LIFE OR HEALTH CONDITIONS:

SELF-CONTAINED BREATHING APPARATUS WITH FULL FACEPIECE OPERATED IN PRESSURE-DEMAND OR OTHER POSITIVE PRESSURE MODE.

SUPPLIED-AIR RESPIRATOR WITH FULL FACEPIECE AND OPERATED IN PRESSURE-DEMAND OR OTHER POSITIVE PRESSURE MODE IN COMBINATION WITH AN AUXILIARY SELF-CONTAINED BREATHING APPARATUS OPERATED IN PRESSURE-DEMAND OR OTHER POSITIVE PRESSURE MODE.

CLOTHING: EMPLOYEE MUST WEAR APPROPRIATE PROTECTIVE (IMPERVIOUS) CLOTHING AND EQUIPMENT TO PREVENT ANY POSSIBILITY OF SKIN CONTACT WITH THIS SUBSTANCE.

GLOVES: EMPLOYEE MUST WEAR APPROPRIATE PROTECTIVE GLOVES TO PREVENT CONTACT WITH THIS SUBSTANCE.

EYE PROTECTION: EMPLOYEE MUST WEAR SPLASH-PROOF OR DUST-RESISTANT SAFETY GOGGLES AND A FACESHIELD TO PREVENT CONTACT WITH THIS SUBSTANCE.

EMERGENCY WASH FACILITIES: WHERE THERE IS ANY POSSIBILITY THAT AN EMPLOYEE'S EYES AND/OR SKIN MAY BE EXPOSED TO THIS SUBSTANCE, THE EMPLOYER SHOULD PROVIDE AN EYE WASH FOUNTAIN AND QUICK DRENCH SHOWER WITHIN THE IMMEDIATE WORK AREA FOR EMERGENCY USE.

AUTHORIZED BY- OCCUPATIONAL HEALTH SERVICES, INC.

CREATION DATE: 10/04/89 ***REVISION DATE:*** 04/27/90

MATERIAL SAFETY DATA SHEET

OCCUPATIONAL HEALTH SERVICES, INC.
AGRICULTURE AND PESTICIDE DIVISION
450 SEVENTH AVENUE, SUITE 2407
NEW YORK, NEW YORK 10123
1-800-445-MSDS OR (212) 967-1100

EMERGENCY CONTACT:
JOHN S. BRANSFORD, JR. (615) 292-1180

SUBSTANCE IDENTIFICATION

CAS-NUMBER 321-54-0

SUBSTANCE: **COROXON**

TRADE NAMES/SYNONYMS: 3-CHLORO-7-HYDROXY-4-METHYLCOUMARIN DIETHYL PHOSPHATE; 3-CHLORO-4-METHYLCOUMARIN-7-YL DIETHYL PHOSPHATE; O,O-DIETHYL-O-(3-CHLORO-4-METHYLCOUMARIN-7-YL-)PHOSPHATE; 3-CHLORO-4-METHYL-2-OXO-2H-1-BENZOPYRAN-7-YL DIETHYL ESTER PHOSPHORIC ACID; CORALOX; COUMAPHOS O-ANALOG; COUMAPHOSOXON; C14H16CLO6P; PST65468

CHEMICAL FAMILY: ORGANOPHOSPHATE

MOLECULAR FORMULA: C14-H16-CL-O6-P

MOLECULAR WEIGHT: 346.72

CERCLA RATINGS (SCALE 0-3): HEALTH = 3 FIRE = 0 REACTIVITY = U PERSISTENCE = 0
NFPA RATINGS (SCALE 0-4): HEALTH = 3 FIRE = 0 REACTIVITY = U

COMPONENTS AND CONTAMINANTS

COMPONENT: COROXON ***PERCENT:*** 100
CAS# 321-54-0
EXPOSURE LIMITS: NO OCCUPATIONAL EXPOSURE LIMITS ESTABLISHED BY OSHA, ACGIH, OR NIOSH.

PHYSICAL DATA

DESCRIPTION: WHITE CRYSTALLINE SOLID ***MELTING POINT:*** 162 F (72 C)
SPECIFIC GRAVITY: NOT AVAILABLE ***SOLUBILITY IN WATER:*** 0.02%

FIRE AND EXPLOSION DATA

FIRE AND EXPLOSION HAZARD: NEGLIGIBLE FIRE HAZARD WHEN EXPOSED TO HEAT OR FLAME.
FIREFIGHTING MEDIA: DRY CHEMICAL, CARBON DIOXIDE, HALON, WATER SPRAY OR STANDARD FOAM (1987 EMERGENCY RESPONSE GUIDEBOOK, DOT P 5800.4). FOR LARGER FIRES, USE WATER SPRAY, FOG OR STANDARD FOAM (1987 EMERGENCY RESPONSE GUIDEBOOK, DOT P 5800.4).
FIREFIGHTING: MOVE CONTAINERS FROM FIRE AREA IF POSSIBLE. FIGHT FIRE FROM MAXIMUM DISTANCE. STAY AWAY FROM STORAGE TANK ENDS. DIKE FIRE CONTROL WATER FOR LATER DISPOSAL. DO NOT SCATTER MATERIAL (1987 EMERGENCY RESPONSE GUIDEBOOK, DOT P 5800.4, GUIDE PAGE 55).

TRANSPORTATION DATA

DEPARTMENT OF TRANSPORTATION HAZARD CLASSIFICATION 49 CFR 172.101: POISON B
DEPARTMENT OF TRANSPORTATION LABELING REQUIREMENTS 49 CFR 172.101 AND SUBPART E: POISON
DEPARTMENT OF TRANSPORTATION PACKAGING REQUIREMENTS: 49 {CFR 173.377 EXCEPTIONS: 49 CFR 173.377

TOXICITY

COROXON: TOXICITY DATA: 10 MG/KG ORAL-RAT LD50. CARCINOGEN STATUS: NONE. ACUTE TOXICITY LEVEL: HIGHLY TOXIC BY INGESTION. TARGET EFFECTS: CHOLINESTERASE INHIBITOR. POISONING MAY AFFECT THE NERVOUS SYSTEM.* AT INCREASED RISK FROM EXPOSURE: PERSONS WITH RESPIRATORY AILMENTS, RECENT EXPOSURE TO CHOLINESTERASE INHIBITORS OR IMPAIRED CHOLINESTERASE PRODUCTION, OR LIVER MALFUNCTION.* ADDITIONAL DATA: MAY CROSS THE PLACENTA. HIGH ENVIRONMENTAL TEMPERATURES OR EXPOSURE OF THE CHEMICAL TO VISIBLE OR ULTRAVIOLET LIGHT MAY ENHANCE THE TOXICITY. INTERACTIONS WITH MEDICATIONS MAY OCCUR.*
* MAY BE BASED ON GENERAL INFORMATION ON ORGANOPHOSPHATES.

HEALTH EFFECTS AND FIRST AID

INHALATION: COROXON: SEE INFORMATION ON ORGANOPHOSPHATES.
ORGANOPHOSPHATES: CHOLINESTERASE INHIBITOR. **ACUTE EXPOSURE-** WHEN INHALED, THE FIRST EFFECTS OF CHOLINESTERASE INHIBITORS ARE USUALLY RESPIRATORY AND MAY INCLUDE NASAL HYPEREMIA AND WATERY DISCHARGE, COUGH, CHEST DISCOMFORT, DYSPNEA, AND WHEEZING DUE TO INCREASED BRONCHIAL SECRETIONS AND BRONCHOCONSTRICTION. IF SUFFICIENT AMOUNTS ARE ABSORBED, OTHER SYSTEMIC EFFECTS MAY BEGIN WITHIN A FEW MINUTES OR BE DELAYED FOR UP TO 12 HOURS. SYMPTOMS MAY INCLUDE PALLOR, NAUSEA, VOMITING, DIARRHEA, ABDOMINAL CRAMPS, HEADACHE, DIZZINESS, OCULAR PAIN, BLURRED VISION, MIOSIS OR IN SOME CASES, ESPECIALLY INITIALLY, MYDRIASIS, LACRIMATION, SALIVATION, SWEATING, AND CONFUSION. OTHER REPORTED CENTRAL NERVOUS SYSTEM OR NEUROMUSCULAR EFFECTS MAY INCLUDE ATAXIA, SLURRED SPEECH, AREFLEXIA, WEAKNESS, FATIGUE, FASCICULATIONS, TWITCHING, TREMORS POSSIBLY OF THE TONGUE AND EYELIDS, AND EVENTUALLY PARALYSIS OF THE EXTREMITIES AND POSSIBLY OF THE RESPIRATORY MUSCLES. IN SEVERE CASES THERE MAY ALSO BE INVOLUNTARY DEFECATION AND URINATION, CYANOSIS, PSYCHOSIS, HYPERGLYCEMIA, ACUTE PANCREATITIS, CARDIAC IRREGULARITIES, PULMONARY EDEMA, UNCONSCIOUSNESS, CONVULSIONS, AND COMA. DEATH IS PRIMARILY DUE TO RESPIRATORY FAILURE, ALTHOUGH CARDIOVASCULAR EFFECTS INCLUDING CARDIAC ARREST MAY ALSO BE IMPLICATED. LONG TERM SEQUELAE ARE RARE BUT MAY INCLUDE NEUROPSYCHIATRIC DISORDERS AND MYOPATHY WITH MUSCLE TENDERNESS. SOME ORGANOPHOSPHATES MAY CAUSE A DELAYED NEUROPATHY BEGINNING 1-4 WEEKS AFTER AN ACUTE EXPOSURE WHICH MAY OR MAY NOT HAVE CAUSED ACUTE CHOLINERGIC EFFECTS. NUMBNESS, TINGLING, WEAKNESS AND CRAMPING BEGINNING SYMMETRICALLY IN THE LOWER LIMBS MAY PROGRESS TO ATAXIA AND PARALYSIS. IN SEVERE CASES, UPPER LIMB INVOLVEMENT IS POSSIBLE AND FLACCID PARALYSIS MAY PROGRESS TO SPASTIC PARALYSIS WITH EXAGGERATED REFLEXES. IMPROVEMENT MAY OCCUR OVER MONTHS TO YEARS, BUT SOME RESIDUAL IMPAIRMENT USUALLY REMAINS.
CHRONIC EXPOSURE- REPEATED OR PROLONGED EXPOSURE MAY RESULT IN THE EFFECTS OF ACUTE EXPOSURE INCLUDING THE DELAYED NEUROPATHY. OTHER EFFECTS REPORTED IN WORKERS REPEATEDLY EXPOSED INCLUDE IMPAIRED MEMORY AND CONCENTRATION, ACUTE PSYCHOSIS, SEVERE DEPRESSIONS, IRRITABILTY, CONFUSION, APATHY, EMOTIONAL LABILITY, SOCIAL WITHDRAWAL, CONFUSION, HEADACHE, SPEECH DIFFICULTIES, DELAYED REACTION TIMES, SPATIAL DISORIENTATION, NIGHTMARES, SLEEPWALKING, AND DROWSINESS OR INSOMNIA. AN INFLUENZA-LIKE CONDITION WITH HEADACHE, NAUSEA, WEAKNESS, ANOREXIA AND MALAISE HAS ALSO BEEN REPORTED.
FIRST AID- REMOVE FROM EXPOSURE AREA TO FRESH AIR IMMEDIATELY. IF BREATHING HAS STOPPED, GIVE ARTIFICIAL RESPIRATION. MAINTAIN AIRWAY AND BLOOD PRESSURE AND ADMINISTER OXYGEN IF AVAILABLE. KEEP AFFECTED PERSON WARM AND AT REST. TREAT SYMPTOMATICALLY AND SUPPORTIVELY. ADMINISTRATION OF OXYGEN SHOULD BE PERFORMED BY QUALIFIED PERSONNEL. GET MEDICAL ATTENTION IMMEDIATELY.

SKIN CONTACT: COROXON: SEE INFORMATION ON ORGANOPHOSPHATES.
ORGANOPHOSPHATES: CHOLINESTERASE INHIBITOR. **ACUTE EXPOSURE-** LOCALIZED SWEATING AND FASCICULATIONS MAY OCCUR AT THE SITE OF CONTACT. IF SUFFICIENT AMOUNTS ARE ABSORBED, OTHER EFFECTS OF CHOLINESTERASE INHIBITION AS DESCRIBED IN ACUTE INHALATION MAY OCCUR. SYMPTOMS MAY BE DELAYED 2-3 HOURS, BUT USUALLY NO MORE THAN 12 HOURS. THE RATE OF ABSORPTION IS INCREASED BY THE PRESENCE OF DERMATITIS OR HIGH AMBIENT TEMPERATURES. DELAYED NEUROPATHY IS ALSO POSSIBLE. **CHRONIC EXPOSURE-** REPEATED OR PROLONGED EXPOSURE MAY CAUSE EFFECTS AS DESCRIBED IN ACUTE EXPOSURE. SOME ORGANOPHOSPHATES MAY CAUSE SENSITIZATION.
FIRST AID- REMOVE CONTAMINATED CLOTHING IMMEDIATELY. WASH CONTAMINATED AREAS WITH SOAP AND WATER FOLLOWED BY ALCOHOL (ARENA, POISONING, 4TH ED.). EMERGENCY PERSONNEL SHOULD WEAR GLOVES AND AVOID CONTAMINATION. TREAT RESPIRATORY DIFFICULTY WITH ARTIFICIAL RESPIRATION. GET MEDICAL ATTENTION IMMEDIATELY.

EYE CONTACT: COROXON: SEE INFORMATION ON ORGANOPHOSPHATES.
ORGANOPHOSPHATES: CHOLINESTERASE INHIBITOR. **ACUTE EXPOSURE-** DIRECT CONTACT MAY CAUSE PAIN, HYPEREMIA, LACRIMATION, TWITCHING OF THE EYELIDS, MIOSIS, AND CILIARY MUSCLE SPASM WITH LOSS OF ACCOMODATION, BLURRED OR DIMMED VISION AND BROWACHE. SOMETIMES MYDRIASIS MAY OCCUR INSTEAD OF MIOSIS. WITH SUFFICIENT EXPOSURE, OTHER SYMPTOMS OF CHOLINESTERASE INHIBITION AS DESCRIBED IN ACUTE INHALATION MAY OCCUR. **CHRONIC EXPOSURE-** REPEATED OR PROLONGED EXPOSURE MAY CAUSE EFFECTS AS DESCRIBED IN ACUTE EXPOSURE. SOME COMPOUNDS HAVE CAUSED TOXIC EFFECTS ON THE CRYSTALLINE LENS, CONJUNCTIVAL THICKENING AND OBSTRUCTION OF THE NASOLACRIMAL CANALS WHEN USED AS MIOTIC EYEDROPS.
FIRST AID- IRRIGATE EYES WITH WATER OR SALINE SOLUTION. IF SYMPTOMS OF POISONING OCCUR, TREAT RESPIRATORY DIFFICULTY WITH ARTIFICIAL RESPIRATION AND OXYGEN. OBSERVE PATIENT FOR AT LEAST 24-36 HOURS (GOSSELIN, CLINICAL TOXICOLOGY OF COMMERCIAL PRODUCTS, 5TH ED.). GET MEDICAL ATTENTION IMMEDIATELY. OXYGEN SHOULD BE ADMINISTERED BY QUALIFIED MEDICAL PERSONNEL.

INGESTION: COROXON: HIGHLY TOXIC. SEE INFORMATION ON ORGANOPHOSPHATES.
ORGANOPHOSPHATES: CHOLINESTERASE INHIBITOR. **ACUTE EXPOSURE-** WHEN INGESTED, THE FIRST EFFECTS MAY BE NAUSEA, VOMITING, ANOREXIA, ABDOMINAL CRAMPS AND DIARRHEA. GASTROINTESTINAL ABSORPTION MAY CAUSE SYMPTOMS OF CHOLINESTERASE INHIBITION AS DESCRIBED IN ACUTE INHALATION. SYMPTOMS MAY BEGIN WITHIN MINUTES OR BE DELAYED FOR HOURS. DELAYED EFFECTS INCLUDING NEUROPATHY MAY ALSO OCCUR. **CHRONIC EXPOSURE-** REPEATED INGESTION MAY CAUSE EFFECTS AS DESCRIBED IN ACUTE EXPOSURE.
FIRST AID- IF PERSON IS ALERT AND RESPIRATION IS NOT DEPRESSED, GIVE SYRUP OF IPECAC FOLLOWED BY WATER (IF VOMITING OCCURS, KEEP HEAD BELOW HIPS TO PREVENT ASPIRATION). IF CONSCIOUSNESS LEVEL DECLINES OR VOMITING HAS NOT OCCURRED IN 15 MINUTES EMPTY STOMACH BY GASTRIC LAVAGE WITH THE AID OF CUFFED ENDOTRACHEAL TUBE USING ISOTONIC SALINE OR 5% SODIUM BICARBONATE FOLLOW WITH ACTIVATED CHARCOAL. ESTABLISH AND MAINTAIN AIRWAY. TREAT RESPIRATORY DIFFICULTY WITH ARTIFICIAL RESPIRATION AND OXYGEN. DO NOT GIVE MORPHINE, AMINOPHYLLINE, PHENOTHIAZINES, RESERPINE, FUROSEMIDE, OR ETHACRYNIC ACID (MORGAN, RECOGNITION AND MANAGEMENT OF PESTICIDE POISONINGS, 3RD ED.). TREAT SYMPTOMATICALLY AND SUPPORTIVELY. ADMINISTRATION OF OXYGEN AND LAVAGE MUST BE PERFORMED BY QUALIFIED MEDICAL PERSONNEL. GET MEDICAL ATTENTION IMMEDIATELY.
ANTIDOTE: THE FOLLOWING ANTIDOTE(S) HAVE BEEN RECOMMENDED. HOWEVER, THE DECISION AS TO WHETHER THE SEVERITY OF POISONING REQUIRES

ADMINISTRATION OF ANY ANTIDOTE AND ACTUAL DOSE REQUIRED SHOULD BE MADE BY QUALIFIED MEDICAL PERSONNEL.
FOR CHOLINESTERASE INHIBITORS: ESTABLISH CLEAR AIRWAY AND TISSUE OXYGENATION BY ASPIRATION OF SECRETIONS, AND IF NECESSARY, BY ASSISTED PULMONARY VENTILATION WITH OXYGEN. IMPROVE TISSUE OXYGENATION AS MUCH AS POSSIBLE BEFORE ADMINISTERING ATROPINE TO MINIMIZE THE RISK OF VENTRICULAR FIBRILLATION. ADMINISTER ATROPINE SULFATE INTRAVENOUSLY, OR INTRAMUSCULARLY IF IV INJECTION IS NOT POSSIBLE. IN MODERATELY SEVERE POISONING ADMINISTER ATROPINE SULFATE, 0.4-2.0 MG REPEATED EVERY 15 MINUTES UNTIL ATROPINIZATION IS ACHIEVED (TACHYCARDIA, FLUSHING, DRY MOUTH, MYDRIASIS). MAINTAIN ATROPINIZATION BY REPEATED DOSES FOR 2-12 HOURS, OR LONGER, DEPENDING ON THE SEVERITY OF POISONING. THE APPEARANCE OF RALES IN THE LUNG BASES, MIOSIS, SALIVATION, NAUSEA, BRADYCARDIA, ARE ALL INDICATIONS OF INADEQUATE ATROPINIZATION.
SEVERELY POISONED INDIVIDUALS MAY EXHIBIT REMARKABLE TOLERANCE TO ATROPINE; TWO OR MORE TIMES THE DOSAGES SUGGESTED ABOVE MAY BE NEEDED. PERSONS NOT POISONED OR ONLY SLIGHTLY POISONED, HOWEVER, MAY DEVELOP SIGNS OF ATROPINE TOXICITY FROM SUCH LARGE DOSAGES: FEVER, MUSCLE FIBRILLATIONS, AND DELIRIUM ARE THE MAIN SIGNS OF ATROPINE TOXICITY. IF THESE SIGNS APPEAR WHILE THE PATIENT IS FULLY ATROPINIZED, ATROPINE ADMINISTRATION SHOULD BE DISCONTINUED, AT LEAST TEMPORARILY. OBSERVE TREATED PATIENTS CLOSELY AT LEAST 24 HOURS TO INSURE THAT SYMPTOMS (POSSIBLY PULMONARY EDEMA) DO NOT RECUR AS ATROPINIZATION WEARS OFF. IN VERY SEVERE POISONINGS, METABOLIC DISPOSITION OF TOXICANT MAY REQUIRE SEVERAL HOURS OR DAYS DURING WHICH ATROPINIZATION MUST BE MAINTAINED. MARKEDLY LOWER LEVELS OF URINARY METABOLITES INDICATE THAT ATROPINE DOSAGE CAN BE TAPERED OFF. AS DOSAGE IS REDUCED, CHECK THE LUNG BASES FREQUENTLY FOR RALES. IF RALES ARE HEARD OR OTHER SYMPTOMS RETURN, RE-ESTABLISH ATROPINIZATION PROMPTLY (MORGAN, RECOGNITION AND MANAGEMENT OF PESTICIDE POISONINGS, 3RD ED.). ADMINISTRATION OF ANTIDOTE MUST BE PERFORMED BY QUALIFIED MEDICAL PERSONNEL.
IN CASES OF SEVERE POISONING BY ORGANOPHOSPHATE PESTICIDES IN WHICH RESPIRATORY DEPRESSION, MUSCLE WEAKNESS AND TWITCHINGS ARE SEVERE, GIVE PRALIDOXIME (PROTOPAM-AYERST, 2-PAM), 1.0 GRAM INTRAVENOUSLY AT NO MORE THAN 0.5 GRAM PER MINUTE. DOSAGE OF PRALIDOXIME MAY BE REPEATED IN 1-2 HOURS, THEN AT 10-12 HOUR INTERVALS IF NEEDED. IN VERY SEVERE POISONINGS, DOSAGE RATES MAY BE DOUBLED. TREATMENT WITH PRALIDOXIME WILL BE MOST EFFECTIVE IF GIVEN WITHIN THIRTY-SIX HOURS AFTER POISONING (MORGAN, RECOGNITION AND MANAGEMENT OF PESTICIDE POISONINGS, 3RD ED.). ANTIDOTE SHOULD BE ADMINISTERED BY QUALIFIED MEDICAL PERSONNEL.

REACTIVITY

REACTIVITY: NO SPECIFIC DATA AVAILABLE. HOWEVER, A NUMBER OF PHOSPHATE AND THIOPHOSPHATE ESTERS ARE OF LIMITED THERMAL STABILITY AND UNDERGO HIGHLY EXOTHERMIC SELF-ACCELERATING DECOMPOSITION REACTIONS.

INCOMPATIBILITIES: COROXON: NO DATA AVAILABLE.

DECOMPOSITION: THERMAL DECOMPOSITION MAY RELEASE TOXIC AND/OR HAZARDOUS GASES.

POLYMERIZATION: HAZARDOUS POLYMERIZATION HAS NOT BEEN REPORTED TO OCCUR UNDER NORMAL TEMPERATURES AND PRESSURES.

STORAGE AND DISPOSAL

OBSERVE ALL FEDERAL, STATE AND LOCAL REGULATIONS WHEN STORING OR DISPOSING OF THIS SUBSTANCE. FOR ASSISTANCE, CONTACT THE DISTRICT DIRECTOR OF THE ENVIRONMENTAL PROTECTION AGENCY.

STORAGE

STORE IN ACCORDANCE WITH 40 CFR 165 RECOMMENDED PROCEDURES FOR THE DISPOSAL AND STORAGE OF PESTICIDES AND PESTICIDE CONTAINERS.

DISPOSAL

DISPOSAL MUST BE IN ACCORDANCE WITH 40 CFR 165 RECOMMENDED PROCEDURES FOR THE DISPOSAL AND STORAGE OF PESTICIDES AND PESTICIDE CONTAINERS.

CONDITIONS TO AVOID

MAY BURN BUT DOES NOT IGNITE READILY. CONTAINERS MAY EXPLODE IN HEAT OF FIRE.

SPILL AND LEAK PROCEDURES

OCCUPATIONAL SPILL: DO NOT TOUCH SPILLED MATERIAL. STOP LEAK IF YOU CAN DO IT WITHOUT RISK. USE WATER SPRAY TO REDUCE VAPORS. FOR SMALL SPILLS, TAKE UP WITH SAND OR OTHER ABSORBENT MATERIAL AND PLACE INTO CONTAINERS FOR LATER DISPOSAL. FOR SMALL DRY SPILLS, WITH A CLEAN SHOVEL PLACE MATERIAL INTO CLEAN, DRY CONTAINERS AND COVER. MOVE CONTAINERS FROM SPILL AREA. FOR LARGER SPILLS, DIKE FAR AHEAD OF SPILL FOR LATER DISPOSAL. KEEP UNNECESSARY PEOPLE AWAY. ISOLATE HAZARD AREA AND DENY ENTRY. VENTILATE CLOSED SPACES BEFORE ENTERING.

PROTECTIVE EQUIPMENT

VENTILATION: PROCESS ENCLOSURE RECOMMENDED.

RESPIRATOR: THE FOLLOWING RESPIRATORS ARE RECOMMENDED BASED ON INFORMATION FOUND IN THE PHYSICAL DATA, TOXICITY AND HEALTH EFFECTS SECTIONS. THEY ARE RANKED IN ORDER FROM MINIMUM TO MAXIMUM RESPIRATORY PROTECTION. THE SPECIFIC RESPIRATOR SELECTED MUST BE BASED ON CONTAMINATION LEVELS FOUND IN THE WORK PLACE, MUST NOT EXCEED THE WORKING LIMITS OF THE RESPIRATOR AND BE JOINTLY APPROVED BY THE NATIONAL INSTITUTE FOR OCCUPATIONAL SAFETY AND HEALTH AND THE MINE SAFETY AND HEALTH ADMINISTRATION (NIOSH-MSHA).
TYPE 'C' SUPPLIED-AIR RESPIRATOR WITH A FULL FACEPIECE OPERATED IN PRESSURE-DEMAND OR OTHER POSITIVE PRESSURE MODE OR WITH A FULL FACEPIECE, HELMET OR HOOD OPERATED IN CONTINOUS-FLOW MODE.
SELF-CONTAINED BREATHING APPARATUS WITH A FULL FACEPIECE OPERATED IN PRESSURE-DEMAND OR OTHER POSITIVE PRESSURE MODE. FOR FIREFIGHTING AND OTHER IMMEDIATELY DANGEROUS TO LIFE OR HEALTH CONDITIONS:
SELF-CONTAINED BREATHING APPARATUS WITH FULL FACEPIECE OPERATED IN PRESSURE-DEMAND OR OTHER POSITIVE PRESSURE MODE.
SUPPLIED-AIR RESPIRATOR WITH FULL FACEPIECE AND OPERATED IN PRESSURE-DEMAND OR OTHER POSITIVE PRESSURE MODE IN COMBINATION WITH AN AUXILIARY SELF-CONTAINED BREATHING APPARATUS OPERATED IN PRESSURE-DEMAND OR OTHER POSITIVE PRESSURE MODE.

CLOTHING: EMPLOYEE MUST WEAR APPROPRIATE PROTECTIVE (IMPERVIOUS) CLOTHING AND EQUIPMENT TO PREVENT ANY POSSIBILITY OF SKIN CONTACT WITH THIS SUBSTANCE.

GLOVES: EMPLOYEE MUST WEAR APPROPRIATE PROTECTIVE GLOVES TO PREVENT CONTACT WITH THIS SUBSTANCE.

EYE PROTECTION: EMPLOYEE MUST WEAR SPLASH-PROOF OR DUST-RESISTANT SAFETY GOGGLES AND A FACESHIELD TO PREVENT CONTACT WITH THIS SUBSTANCE.
EMERGENCY WASH FACILITIES: WHERE THERE IS ANY POSSIBILITY THAT AN EMPLOYEE'S EYES AND/OR SKIN MAY BE EXPOSED TO THIS SUBSTANCE, THE EMPLOYER SHOULD PROVIDE AN EYE WASH FOUNTAIN AND QUICK DRENCH SHOWER WITHIN THE IMMEDIATE WORK AREA FOR EMERGENCY USE.

AUTHORIZED BY- OCCUPATIONAL HEALTH SERVICES, INC.
CREATION DATE: 10/04/89 ***REVISION DATE:*** 04/24/90

MATERIAL SAFETY DATA SHEET

OCCUPATIONAL HEALTH SERVICES, INC.
AGRICULTURE AND PESTICIDE DIVISION
450 SEVENTH AVENUE, SUITE 2407
NEW YORK, NEW YORK 10123
1-800-445-MSDS OR (212) 967-1100

EMERGENCY CONTACT:
JOHN S. BRANSFORD, JR. (615) 292-1180

SUBSTANCE IDENTIFICATION

CAS-NUMBER 104-15-4

SUBSTANCE: **P-TOLUENESULFONIC ACID**

TRADE NAMES/SYNONYMS: 4-METHYLBENZENESULFONIC ACID; 4-TOLUENESULFONIC ACID; P-METHYLPHENYLSULFONIC ACID; BENZENESULFONIC ACID, 4-METHYL-; P-METHYLBENZENESULFONIC ACID; TOLUENESULFONIC ACID; P-TOLUENESULPHONIC ACID; P-TOLYSULFONIC ACID; TOSIC ACID; PST67915

CHEMICAL FAMILY: SULFONIC ACID

MOLECULAR FORMULA: C7-H8-O3-S

MOLECULAR WEIGHT: 172.21

CERCLA RATINGS (SCALE 0-3): HEALTH=3 FIRE=1 REACTIVITY=1 PERSISTENCE=1

NFPA RATINGS (SCALE 0-4): HEALTH=3 FIRE=1 REACTIVITY=1

COMPONENTS AND CONTAMINANTS

COMPONENT: P-TOLUENESULFONIC ACID ***PERCENT:*** 100
CAS# 104-15-4

OTHER CONTAMINANTS: NONE

EXPOSURE LIMITS: NO OCCUPATIONAL EXPOSURE LIMITS ESTABLISHED BY OSHA, ACGIH, OR NIOSH.

PHYSICAL DATA

DESCRIPTION: ODORLESS, COLORLESS, HYGROSCOPIC MONOCLINIC LEAFLETS OR PRISMS.
BOILING POINT: 284 F (140 C) ***MELTING POINT:*** 219-221 F (104-105 C)
SPECIFIC GRAVITY: 1.24 ***VAPOR PRESSURE:*** 27 MMHG @ 140 C
SOLUBILITY IN WATER: 67% ***VAPOR DENSITY:*** 6.0
SOLVENT SOLUBILITY: VERY SOLUBLE IN ETHANOL, ETHER

FIRE AND EXPLOSION DATA

FIRE AND EXPLOSION HAZARD: SLIGHT FIRE HAZARD WHEN EXPOSED TO HEAT OR FLAME.
FLASH POINT: 363 F (184 C)
FIREFIGHTING MEDIA: DRY CHEMICAL, CARBON DIOXIDE, HALON, WATER SPRAY OR STANDARD FOAM (1987 EMERGENCY RESPONSE GUIDEBOOK, DOT P 5800.4). FOR LARGER FIRES, USE WATER SPRAY, FOG OR STANDARD FOAM (1987 EMERGENCY RESPONSE GUIDEBOOK, DOT P 5800.4).
FIREFIGHTING: MOVE CONTAINERS FROM FIRE AREA IF POSSIBLE. COOL CONTAINERS EXPOSED TO FLAMES WITH WATER FROM SIDE UNTIL WELL AFTER FIRE IS OUT. STAY AWAY FROM STORAGE TANK ENDS (1987 EMERGENCY RESPONSE GUIDEBOOK, DOT P 5800.4, GUIDE PAGE 60).
EXTINGUISH USING AGENT INDICATED; DO NOT USE WATER DIRECTLY ON MATERIAL. IF LARGE AMOUNTS OF COMBUSTIBLE MATERIALS ARE INVOLVED, USE WATER SPRAY OR FOG IN FLOODING AMOUNTS. AVOID BREATHING CORROSIVE DUSTS AND FUMES FROM BURNING MATERIAL, KEEP UPWIND.
WATER OR FOAM MAY CAUSE FROTHING (NFPA 325M, FIRE HAZARD PROPERTIES OF FLAMMABLE LIQUIDS, GASES, AND VOLATILE SOLIDS, 1984)

TRANSPORTATION DATA

DEPARTMENT OF TRANSPORTATION HAZARD CLASSIFICATION 49 CFR 172.101: CORROSIVE MATERIAL
DEPARTMENT OF TRANSPORTATION LABELING REQUIREMENTS 49 CFR 172.101 AND SUBPART E: CORROSIVE

TOXICITY

P-TOLUENESULFONIC ACID: TOXICITY DATA: 2480 MG/KG ORAL-RAT LD50; 400 MG/KG ORAL-MOUSE LD50. CARCINOGEN STATUS: NONE. LOCAL EFFECTS: CORROSIVE- INHALATION, SKIN, AND EYES. ACUTE TOXICITY LEVEL: MODERATELY TOXIC BY INGESTION. TARGET EFFECTS: NONE. AT INCREASED RISK FROM EXPOSURE: PERSONS WITH PRE-EXISTING SKIN OR CHRONIC RESPIRATORY DISEASE.

HEALTH EFFECTS AND FIRST AID

INHALATION: P-TOLUENESULFONIC ACID: CORROSIVE/HIGHLY TOXIC. **ACUTE EXPOSURE-** ACID FUMES MAY CAUSE SEVERE MUCOUS MEMBRANE IRRITATION, COUGHING, CHOKING, DYSPNEA, HEADACHE, DIZZINESS AND WEAKNESS. DELAYED SYMPTOMS MAY INCLUDE PULMONARY EDEMA, CHEST TIGHTNESS, FROTHY SPUTUM, CYANOSIS, RALES, AND HYPOTENSION. **CHRONIC EXPOSURE-** PROLONGED EXPOSURE TO ACID FUMES MAY CAUSE DENTAL EROSION, NECROSIS OF THE JAW, NASAL ULCERATION, BRONCHIAL IRRITATION, COUGHING, BRONCHIAL PNEUMONIA, AND GASTROINTESTINAL DISTURBANCES.
FIRST AID- REMOVE FROM EXPOSURE AREA TO FRESH AIR IMMEDIATELY. IF BREATHING HAS STOPPED, GIVE ARTIFICIAL RESPIRATION. MAINTAIN AIRWAY AND BLOOD PRESSURE AND ADMINISTER OXYGEN IF AVAILABLE. KEEP AFFECTED PERSON WARM AND AT REST. TREAT SYMPTOMATICALLY AND SUPPORTIVELY. ADMINISTRATION OF OXYGEN SHOULD BE PERFORMED BY QUALIFIED PERSONNEL. GET MEDICAL ATTENTION IMMEDIATELY.

SKIN CONTACT: P-TOLUENESULFONIC ACID: CORROSIVE. **ACUTE EXPOSURE-** CONTACT WITH ACIDS MAY CAUSE SEVERE IRRITATION AND PAIN WITH BURNS, VESICULATION, AND BROWNISH OR YELLOWISH STAINS. **CHRONIC EXPOSURE-** DEPENDING ON CONCENTRATION OR DURATION OF EXPOSURE, REPEATED OR PROLONGED CONTACT MAY CAUSE EFFECTS AS WITH ACUTE EXPOSURE.
FIRST AID- REMOVE CONTAMINATED CLOTHING AND SHOES IMMEDIATELY. WASH AFFECTED AREA WITH SOAP OR MILD DETERGENT AND LARGE AMOUNTS OF WATER UNTIL NO EVIDENCE OF CHEMICAL REMAINS (AT LEAST 15-20 MINUTES). IN CASE OF CHEMICAL BURNS, COVER AREA WITH STERILE, DRY DRESSING. BANDAGE SECURELY, BUT NOT TOO TIGHTLY. GET MEDICAL ATTENTION IMMEDIATELY.

EYE CONTACT: P-TOLUENESULFONIC ACID: CORROSIVE. **ACUTE EXPOSURE-** LIQUID OR FUMES OF ACIDS MAY CAUSE CORNEAL AND CONJUNCTIVAL EDEMA, IRITIS, CORNEAL EROSION AND OPACITY, PAIN, LACRIMATION, BLURRED VISION, AND PHOTOPHOBIA. **CHRONIC EXPOSURE-** DEPENDING ON CONCENTRATION AND DURATION OF EXPOSURE, REPEATED OR PROLONGED CONTACT MAY CAUSE EFFECTS AS WITH ACUTE EXPOSURE.
FIRST AID- WASH EYES IMMEDIATELY WITH LARGE AMOUNTS OF WATER, OCCASIONALLY LIFTING UPPER AND LOWER LIDS, UNTIL NO EVIDENCE OF CHEMICAL REMAINS (AT LEAST 15-20 MINUTES). CONTINUE IRRIGATING WITH NORMAL SALINE UNTIL THE PH HAS RETURNED TO NORMAL (30-60 MINUTES). COVER WITH STERILE BANDAGES. GET MEDICAL ATTENTION IMMEDIATELY.

INGESTION: P-TOLUENESULFONIC ACID: CORROSIVE. **ACUTE EXPOSURE-** ACIDS MAY CAUSE SEVERE BURNING PAIN IN THE MOUTH, THROAT AND ABDOMEN FOLLOWED BY NAUSEA, VOMITING, HEMATEMESIS, DIARRHEA, BLOODY STOOLS, HEMATURIA, ALBUMINURIA AND POSSIBLY ASPHYXIA. PERFORATION OF THE ESOPHAGUS AND STOMACH MAY OCCUR. NEPHROSIS IS ALSO POSSIBLE. DEATH MAY OCCUR FROM CARDIOVASCULAR COLLAPSE. **CHRONIC EXPOSURE-** NO DATA AVAILABLE.
FIRST AID- DO NOT USE GASTRIC LAVAGE OR EMESIS. DILUTE THE ACID IMMEDIATELY BY DRINKING LARGE QUANTITIES OF WATER OR MILK. IF VOMITING PERSISTS, ADMINISTER FLUIDS REPEATEDLY. INGESTED ACID MUST BE DILUTED APPROXIMATELY 100 FOLD TO RENDER IT HARMLESS TO TISSUES. MAINTAIN AIRWAY AND TREAT SHOCK (DREISBACH, HANDBOOK OF POISONING, 12TH ED.). GET MEDICAL ATTENTION IMMEDIATELY. IF VOMITING OCCURS, KEEP HEAD BELOW HIPS TO HELP PREVENT ASPIRATION.
ANTIDOTE: NO SPECIFIC ANTIDOTE. TREAT SYMPTOMATICALLY AND SUPPORTIVELY.

REACTIVITY

REACTIVITY: MAY REACT EXOTHERMICALLY WITH WATER TO FORM A STRONG ACID.
INCOMPATIBILITIES: P-TOLUENESULFONIC ACID: BASES: VIOLENT REACTION. M-THIOCRESOL: POSSIBLE EXPLOSION.
DECOMPOSITION: THERMAL DECOMPOSITION MAY RELEASE TOXIC OXIDES OF SULFUR.
POLYMERIZATION: HAZARDOUS POLYMERIZATION HAS NOT BEEN REPORTED TO OCCUR UNDER NORMAL TEMPERATURES AND PRESSURES.

STORAGE AND DISPOSAL

OBSERVE ALL FEDERAL, STATE AND LOCAL REGULATIONS WHEN STORING OR DISPOSING OF THIS SUBSTANCE.

STORAGE

STORE AWAY FROM INCOMPATIBLE SUBSTANCES.

DISPOSAL

DISPOSAL MUST BE IN ACCORDANCE WITH STANDARDS APPLICABLE TO GENERATORS OF HAZARDOUS WASTE, 40 CFR 262. EPA HAZARDOUS WASTE NUMBER D002

CONDITIONS TO AVOID

MAY BURN BUT DOES NOT IGNITE READILY. FLAMMABLE, POISONOUS GASES MAY ACCUMULATE IN TANKS AND HOPPER CARS. MAY IGNITE COMBUSTIBLES (WOOD, PAPER, OIL, ETC.).

SPILL AND LEAK PROCEDURES

OCCUPATIONAL SPILL: DO NOT TOUCH SPILLED MATERIAL. STOP LEAK IF YOU CAN DO IT WITHOUT RISK. FOR SMALL SPILLS, TAKE UP WITH SAND OR OTHER ABSORBENT MATERIAL AND PLACE INTO CONTAINERS FOR LATER DISPOSAL. FOR SMALL DRY SPILLS, WITH CLEAN SHOVEL PLACE MATERIAL INTO CLEAN, DRY CONTAINER AND COVER. MOVE CONTAINERS FROM SPILL AREA. FOR LARGER SPILLS, DIKE FAR AHEAD OF SPILL FOR LATER DISPOSAL. KEEP UNNECESSARY PEOPLE AWAY. ISOLATE HAZARD AREA AND DENY ENTRY.

PROTECTIVE EQUIPMENT

VENTILATION: PROVIDE LOCAL EXHAUST OR PROCESS ENCLOSURE VENTILATION SYSTEM.
RESPIRATOR: THE FOLLOWING RESPIRATORS ARE RECOMMENDED BASED ON INFORMATION FOUND IN THE PHYSICAL DATA, TOXICITY AND HEALTH EFFECTS SECTIONS. THEY ARE RANKED IN ORDER FROM MINIMUM TO MAXIMUM RESPIRATORY PROTECTION. THE SPECIFIC RESPIRATOR SELECTED MUST BE BASED ON CONTAMINATION LEVELS FOUND IN THE WORK PLACE, MUST NOT EXCEED THE WORKING LIMITS OF THE RESPIRATOR AND BE JOINTLY APPROVED BY THE NATIONAL INSTITUTE FOR OCCUPATIONAL SAFETY AND HEALTH AND THE MINE SAFETY AND HEALTH ADMINISTRATION (NIOSH-MSHA).
CHEMICAL CARTRIDGE RESPIRATOR WITH FULL FACEPIECE AND ORGANIC VAPOR CARTRIDGE(S) IN COMBINATION WITH A DUST AND MIST FILTER.
CHEMICAL CARTRIDGE RESPIRATOR WITH FULL FACEPIECE AND ORGANIC VAPOR CARTRIDGE(S) IN COMBINATION WITH A HIGH-EFFICIENCY PARTICULATE FILTER.
GAS MASK WITH ORGANIC VAPOR CANISTER (CHIN-STYLE OR FRONT- OR BACK-MOUNTED CANISTER) WITH A FULL FACEPIECE AND A HIGH-EFFICIENCY PARTICULATE FILTER.
POWERED AIR-PURIFYING RESPIRATOR WITH TIGHT-FITTING FACEPIECE AND ORGANIC VAPOR CARTRIDGE(S) IN COMBINATION WITH A HIGH-EFFICIENCY PARTICULATE FILTER.
TYPE 'C' SUPPLIED-AIR RESPIRATOR WITH A FULL FACEPIECE OPERATED IN PRESSURE-DEMAND OR OTHER POSITIVE PRESSURE MODE OR WITH A FULL

FACEPIECE, HELMET OR HOOD OPERATED IN CONTINUOUS-FLOW MODE.
SELF-CONTAINED BREATHING APPARATUS WITH A FULL FACEPIECE OPERATED IN PRESSURE-DEMAND OR OTHER POSITIVE PRESSURE MODE.
FOR FIREFIGHTING AND OTHER IMMEDIATELY DANGEROUS TO LIFE OR HEALTH CONDITIONS:
SELF-CONTAINED BREATHING APPARATUS WITH FULL FACEPIECE OPERATED IN PRESSURE-DEMAND OR OTHER POSITIVE PRESSURE MODE.
SUPPLIED-AIR RESPIRATOR WITH FULL FACEPIECE AND OPERATED IN PRESSURE-DEMAND OR OTHER POSITIVE PRESSURE MODE IN COMBINATION WITH AN AUXILIARY SELF-CONTAINED BREATHING APPARATUS OPERATED IN PRESSURE-DEMAND OR OTHER POSITIVE PRESSURE MODE.

CLOTHING: EMPLOYEE MUST WEAR APPROPRIATE PROTECTIVE (IMPERVIOUS) CLOTHING AND EQUIPMENT TO PREVENT ANY POSSIBILITY OF SKIN CONTACT WITH THIS SUBSTANCE.

GLOVES: EMPLOYEE MUST WEAR APPROPRIATE PROTECTIVE GLOVES TO PREVENT CONTACT WITH THIS SUBSTANCE.

EYE PROTECTION: EMPLOYEE MUST WEAR SPLASH-PROOF OR DUST-RESISTANT SAFETY GOGGLES AND A FACESHIELD TO PREVENT CONTACT WITH THIS SUBSTANCE. EMERGENCY WASH FACILITIES: WHERE THERE IS ANY POSSIBILITY THAT AN EMPLOYEE'S EYES AND/OR SKIN MAY BE EXPOSED TO THIS SUBSTANCE, THE EMPLOYER SHOULD PROVIDE AN EYE WASH FOUNTAIN AND QUICK DRENCH SHOWER WITHIN THE IMMEDIATE WORK AREA FOR EMERGENCY USE.

AUTHORIZED BY- OCCUPATIONAL HEALTH SERVICES, INC.
CREATION DATE: 02/08/90 ***REVISION DATE:*** 05/11/90

MATERIAL SAFETY DATA SHEET

OCCUPATIONAL HEALTH SERVICES, INC.
AGRICULTURE AND PESTICIDE DIVISION
450 SEVENTH AVENUE, SUITE 2407
NEW YORK, NEW YORK 10123
1-800-445-MSDS OR (212) 967-1100

EMERGENCY CONTACT:
JOHN S. BRANSFORD, JR. (615) 292-1180

SUBSTANCE IDENTIFICATION

CAS-NUMBER 8051-02-3

SUBSTANCE: **SABADILLA ALKALOIDS**

TRADE NAMES/SYNONYMS: VERATRINE (MIXTURE); CEVADINE MIXTURE WITH VERATRIDINE; VERATRIDINE MIXTURE WITH CEVADINE; VERATRINE; PST71010

CHEMICAL FAMILY: ALKALOID

CERCLA RATINGS (SCALE 0-3): HEALTH=2 FIRE=1 REACTIVITY=0 PERSISTENCE=1

NFPA RATINGS (SCALE 0-4): HEALTH=2 FIRE=1 REACTIVITY=0

COMPONENTS AND CONTAMINANTS

COMPONENT: SABADILLA ALKALOIDS ***PERCENT:*** 100.0
CAS# 8051-02-3

OTHER CONTAMINANTS: NONE

EXPOSURE LIMITS: NO OCCUPATIONAL EXPOSURE LIMITS ESTABLISHED BY OSHA, ACGIH, OR NIOSH.

PHYSICAL DATA

DESCRIPTION: WHITE OR GRAYISH WHITE POWDER.

MELTING POINT: 293-311 F (145-155 C) ***SPECIFIC GRAVITY:*** NOT AVAILABLE

SOLUBILITY IN WATER: 0.06%

SOLVENT SOLUBILITY: SOLUBLE IN ALCOHOL, AMYL ALCOHOL, BENZENE, CHLOROFORM, ETHER, AND DILUTE ACIDS; SLIGHTLY SOLUBLE IN GLYCEROL AND OLIVE OIL; INSOLUBLE IN PETROLEUM ETHER.

FIRE AND EXPLOSION DATA

FIRE AND EXPLOSION HAZARD: SLIGHT FIRE HAZARD WHEN EXPOSED TO HEAT OR FLAME.

FIREFIGHTING MEDIA: DRY CHEMICAL, CARBON DIOXIDE, HALON, WATER SPRAY OR STANDARD FOAM (1987 EMERGENCY RESPONSE GUIDEBOOK, DOT P 5800.4). FOR LARGER FIRES, USE WATER SPRAY, FOG OR STANDARD FOAM (1987 EMERGENCY RESPONSE GUIDEBOOK, DOT P 5800.4).

FIREFIGHTING: MOVE CONTAINER FROM FIRE AREA IF POSSIBLE. DO NOT SCATTER SPILLED MATERIAL WITH HIGH PRESSURE WATER STREAMS. DIKE FIRE CONTROL WATER FOR LATER DISPOSAL (1987 EMERGENCY RESPONSE GUIDEBOOK, DOT P 5800.4, GUIDE PAGE 31).
USE AGENTS SUITABLE FOR TYPE OF SURROUNDING FIRE. AVOID BREATHING HAZARDOUS VAPORS, KEEP UPWIND.

TOXICITY

SABADILLA ALKALOIDS: TOXICITY DATA: 143 MG/KG ORAL-HUMAN LDLO; 4000 MG/KG ORAL-RAT LD50; 2 MG/KG ORAL-DOG LDLO; 2500 UG/KG ORAL-CAT LDLO; 10 MG/KG SUBCUTANEOUS-MOUSE LDLO; 7500 UG/KG INTRAPERITONEAL-MOUSE LD50; 500 UG/KG UNREPORTED-RABBIT LDLO; 1000 UG/KG UNREPORTED-GUINEA PIG LDLO; REPRODUCTIVE EFFECTS DATA (RTECS). CARCINOGEN STATUS: NONE. LOCAL EFFECTS: IRRITANT- INHALATION, SKIN, AND EYES. ACUTE TOXICITY LEVEL: MODERATELY TOXIC BY INGESTION. TARGET EFFECTS: NO DATA AVAILABLE.

HEALTH EFFECTS AND FIRST AID

INHALATION: SABADILLA ALKALOIDS: IRRITANT. **ACUTE EXPOSURE-** INHALATION OF DUSTS MAY CAUSE MUCOUS MEMBRANE IRRITATION AND VIOLENT SNEEZING. **CHRONIC EXPOSURE-** NO DATA AVAILABLE.

FIRST AID- REMOVE FROM EXPOSURE AREA TO FRESH AIR IMMEDIATELY. IF BREATHING HAS STOPPED, PERFORM ARTIFICIAL RESPIRATION. KEEP PERSON WARM AND AT REST. TREAT SYMPTOMATICALLY AND SUPPORTIVELY. GET MEDICAL ATTENTION IMMEDIATELY.

SKIN CONTACT: SABADILLA ALKALOIDS: IRRITANT. **ACUTE EXPOSURE-** CONTACT MAY CAUSE IRRITATION. **CHRONIC EXPOSURE-** REPEATED OR PROLONGED EXPOSURE TO IRRITANTS MAY CAUSE DERMATITIS.

FIRST AID- REMOVE CONTAMINATED CLOTHING AND SHOES IMMEDIATELY. WASH AFFECTED AREA WITH SOAP OR MILD DETERGENT AND LARGE AMOUNTS OF WATER UNTIL NO EVIDENCE OF CHEMICAL REMAINS (APPROXIMATELY 15-20 MINUTES). GET MEDICAL ATTENTION IMMEDIATELY.

EYE CONTACT: SABADILLA ALKALOIDS: IRRITANT. **ACUTE EXPOSURE-** CONTACT MAY CAUSE IRRITATION WITH LACRIMATION AND INFLAMMATION OF THE CONJUNCTIVA. **CHRONIC EXPOSURE-** REPEATED OR PROLONGED EXPOSURE TO IRRITANTS MAY CAUSE CONJUNCTIVITIS.

FIRST AID- WASH EYES IMMEDIATELY WITH LARGE AMOUNTS OF WATER OR NORMAL SALINE, OCCASIONALLY LIFTING UPPER AND LOWER LIDS, UNTIL NO EVIDENCE OF CHEMICAL REMAINS (APPROXIMATELY 15-20 MINUTES). GET MEDICAL ATTENTION IMMEDIATELY.

INGESTION: SABADILLA ALKALOIDS: **ACUTE EXPOSURE-** INGESTION MAY CAUSE BURNING OF THE MOUTH AND STOMACH, ABDOMINAL PAIN, NAUSEA, VOMITING, SALIVATION AND DIARRHEA. GENERALIZED CENTRAL EXCITATION WITH GIDDINESS FOLLOWED BY DEPRESSION, ACUTE ANXIETY, DILATED PUPILS, HEADACHE, VERTIGO, WEAKNESS, DROWSINESS, SLOW AND FEEBLE PULSE, EXTREME HYPOTENSION, OFTEN SEVERE CARDIAC ARRHYTHMIAS, TWITCHING, CONVULSIONS, HYPOTHERMIA AND SELDOM COMA MAY ALSO OCCUR. DEATH DUE TO RESPIRATORY OR CARDIOVASCULAR COLLAPSE HAS BEEN REPORTED. THE PROBABLE LETHAL DOSE FOR AN ADULT IS 10 GRAMS. EFFECTS ON THE EMBRYO OR FETUS HAVE BEEN REPORTED FROM INGESTION 7 DAYS AFTER CONCEPTION IN RABBITS. **CHRONIC EXPOSURE-** REPEATED EXPOSURE MAY CAUSE EFFECTS AS DETAILED IN ACUTE EXPOSURE.

FIRST AID- TREAT SYMPTOMATICALLY AND SUPPORTIVELY. GET MEDICAL ATTENTION IMMEDIATELY. IF VOMITING OCCURS, KEEP HEAD LOWER THAN HIPS TO PREVENT ASPIRATION.

ANTIDOTE: NO SPECIFIC ANTIDOTE. TREAT SYMPTOMATICALLY AND SUPPORTIVELY.

REACTIVITY

REACTIVITY: STABLE UNDER NORMAL TEMPERATURES AND PRESSURES.

INCOMPATIBILITIES: SABADILLA ALKALOIDS: OXIDIZERS (STRONG): FIRE AND EXPLOSION HAZARD.

DECOMPOSITION: THERMAL DECOMPOSITION PRODUCTS MAY INCLUDE TOXIC OXIDES OF CARBON AND NITROGEN.

POLYMERIZATION: HAZARDOUS POLYMERIZATION HAS NOT BEEN REPORTED TO OCCUR UNDER NORMAL TEMPERATURES AND PRESSURES.

STORAGE AND DISPOSAL

OBSERVE ALL FEDERAL, STATE AND LOCAL REGULATIONS WHEN STORING OR DISPOSING OF THIS SUBSTANCE. FOR ASSISTANCE, CONTACT THE DISTRICT DIRECTOR OF THE ENVIRONMENTAL PROTECTION AGENCY.

****STORAGE****

STORE AWAY FROM INCOMPATIBLE SUBSTANCES.

CONDITIONS TO AVOID

MAY BURN BUT DOES NOT IGNITE READILY. AVOID CONTACT WITH STRONG OXIDIZERS, EXCESSIVE HEAT, SPARKS, OR OPEN FLAME.

SPILL AND LEAK PROCEDURES

OCCUPATIONAL SPILL: STOP LEAK IF YOU CAN DO IT WITHOUT RISK. FOR SMALL SPILLS, TAKE UP WITH SAND OR OTHER ABSORBENT MATERIAL AND PLACE INTO CLEAN, DRY CONTAINERS FOR LATER DISPOSAL. KEEP UNNECESSARY PEOPLE AWAY. ISOLATE HAZARD AREA AND DENY ENTRY.

PROTECTIVE EQUIPMENT

VENTILATION: PROVIDE LOCAL EXHAUST OR GENERAL DILUTION VENTILATION SYSTEM.

RESPIRATOR: THE FOLLOWING RESPIRATORS ARE RECOMMENDED BASED ON INFORMATION FOUND IN THE PHYSICAL DATA, TOXICITY AND HEALTH EFFECTS SECTIONS. THEY ARE RANKED IN ORDER FROM MINIMUM TO MAXIMUM RESPIRATORY PROTECTION. THE SPECIFIC RESPIRATOR SELECTED MUST BE BASED ON CONTAMINATION LEVELS FOUND IN THE WORK PLACE, MUST NOT EXCEED THE WORKING LIMITS OF THE RESPIRATOR AND BE JOINTLY APPROVED BY THE NATIONAL INSTITUTE FOR OCCUPATIONAL SAFETY AND HEALTH AND THE MINE SAFETY AND HEALTH ADMINISTRATION (NIOSH-MSHA).

DUST AND MIST RESPIRATOR WITH A FULL FACEPIECE.

AIR-PURIFYING FULL FACEPIECE RESPIRATOR WITH A HIGH-EFFICIENCY PARTICULATE FILTER.

POWERED AIR-PURIFYING RESPIRATOR WITH A TIGHT-FITTING FACEPIECE AND HIGH-EFFICIENCY PARTICULATE FILTER.

TYPE 'C' SUPPLIED-AIR RESPIRATOR WITH A FULL FACEPIECE OPERATED IN PRESSURE-DEMAND OR OTHER POSITIVE PRESSURE MODE OR WITH A FULL FACEPIECE, HELMET OR HOOD OPERATED IN CONTINUOUS-FLOW MODE.

SELF-CONTAINED BREATHING APPARATUS WITH A FULL FACEPIECE OPERATED IN PRESSURE-DEMAND OR OTHER POSITIVE PRESSURE MODE.

FOR FIREFIGHTING AND OTHER IMMEDIATELY DANGEROUS TO LIFE OR HEALTH CONDITIONS:

SELF-CONTAINED BREATHING APPARATUS WITH FULL FACEPIECE OPERATED IN PRESSURE-DEMAND OR OTHER POSITIVE PRESSURE MODE.

SUPPLIED-AIR RESPIRATOR WITH FULL FACEPIECE AND OPERATED IN PRESSURE-DEMAND OR OTHER POSITIVE PRESSURE MODE IN COMBINATION WITH AN AUXILIARY SELF-CONTAINED BREATHING APPARATUS OPERATED IN PRESSURE-DEMAND OR OTHER POSITIVE PRESSURE MODE.

CLOTHING: EMPLOYEE MUST WEAR APPROPRIATE PROTECTIVE (IMPERVIOUS) CLOTHING AND EQUIPMENT TO PREVENT REPEATED OR PROLONGED SKIN CONTACT WITH THIS SUBSTANCE.

GLOVES: EMPLOYEE MUST WEAR APPROPRIATE PROTECTIVE GLOVES TO PREVENT CONTACT WITH THIS SUBSTANCE.

EYE PROTECTION: EMPLOYEE MUST WEAR SPLASH-PROOF OR DUST-RESISTANT SAFETY GOGGLES TO PREVENT EYE CONTACT WITH THIS SUBSTANCE.

EMERGENCY EYE WASH: WHERE THERE IS ANY POSSIBILITY THAT AN EMPLOYEE'S EYES MAY BE EXPOSED TO THIS SUBSTANCE, THE EMPLOYER SHOULD PROVIDE AN EYE WASH FOUNTAIN WITHIN THE IMMEDIATE WORK AREA FOR EMERGENCY USE.

AUTHORIZED BY- OCCUPATIONAL HEALTH SERVICES, INC.

CREATION DATE: 10/05/89 ***REVISION DATE:*** 05/29/90

MATERIAL SAFETY DATA SHEET

OCCUPATIONAL HEALTH SERVICES, INC.
AGRICULTURE AND PESTICIDE DIVISION
450 SEVENTH AVENUE, SUITE 2407
NEW YORK, NEW YORK 10123
1-800-445-MSDS OR (212) 967-1100

EMERGENCY CONTACT:
JOHN S. BRANSFORD, JR. (615) 292-1180

SUBSTANCE IDENTIFICATION

CAS-NUMBER 28434-00-6

SUBSTANCE: BIOALLETHRIN

TRADE NAMES/SYNONYMS: CYCLOPROPANECARBOXYLIC ACID, 2,2-DIMETHYL-3-(2-METHYL-1-PROPENYL)-, 2-METHYL-4-OXO-3-(2-PROPENYL)-2-CYCLOPENTEN-1-YL ESTER, (1R-(1ALPHA (S*), 3 BETA))-; (1R(1 ALPHA(S*), 3 BETA))-2,2-DIMETHYL-3-(2-METHYL-1-PROPENYL)-CYCLO -PROPANECARBOXYLIC ACID-2-METHYL-4-OXO-3-(2-PROPENYL)-2-CYCLOPENTEN -1-YL ESTER; CYCLOPROPANECARBOXYLIC ACID, 2,2-DIMETHYL-3-(2-METHYLPROPENYL)-, TRANS -(+)-, ESTER WITH (+)-2-ALLYL-4-HYDROXY-3-METHYL-2-CYCLOPENTEN-1-ONE; TRANS-(+)-2,2-DIMETHYL-3-(2-METHYLPROPENYL)-CYCLOPROPANECARBOXYLIC ACID ESTER WITH (+)-2-ALLYL-4-HYDROXY-3-METHYL-2-CYCLOPENTEN-1-ONE; TRANS-(+)-ALLETHRIN; D-TRANS-ALLETHRIN; ALLETHRIN I; S-BIOALLETHRIN; ESBIOL; C19H26O3; PST71013

CHEMICAL FAMILY: CARBOXYLIC ACID ESTER

MOLECULAR FORMULA: C19-H26-O3

MOLECULAR WEIGHT: 302.45

CERCLA RATINGS (SCALE 0-3): HEALTH=3 FIRE=1 REACTIVITY=0 PERSISTENCE=2

NFPA RATINGS (SCALE 0-4): HEALTH=4 FIRE=1 REACTIVITY=0

COMPONENTS AND CONTAMINANTS

COMPONENT: BIOALLETHRIN ***PERCENT:*** 100.0
CAS# 28434-00-6

OTHER CONTAMINANTS: NONE

EXPOSURE LIMITS: NO OCCUPATIONAL EXPOSURE LIMITS ESTABLISHED BY OSHA, ACGIH, OR NIOSH.

PHYSICAL DATA

DESCRIPTION: YELLOW VISCOUS LIQUID WITH A SLIGHT AROMATIC ODOR.

MELTING POINT: NOT AVAILABLE ***SPECIFIC GRAVITY:*** 1.00-1.020

SOLUBILITY IN WATER: SPARINGLY SOLUBLE

SOLVENT SOLUBILITY: SOLUBLE ACETONE, ALCOHOL, BENZENE, CARBON TETRACHLORIDE, ETHANOL, ETHYLENE DICHLORIDE, HEXANE, NITROMETHANE, PETROLEUM ETHER, REFINED KEROSENE, ISOPARIFFINIC SOLVENTS, AND OTHER ORGANIC SOLVENTS.

FIRE AND EXPLOSION DATA

FIRE AND EXPLOSION HAZARD: SLIGHT FIRE HAZARD WHEN EXPOSED TO HEAT OR FLAME.

FLASH POINT: 248 F (120 C) (OC) ***FLAMMABILITY CLASS(OSHA):*** IIIB

FIREFIGHTING MEDIA: DRY CHEMICAL, CARBON DIOXIDE, HALON, WATER SPRAY OR STANDARD FOAM (1987 EMERGENCY RESPONSE GUIDEBOOK, DOT P 5800.4). FOR LARGER FIRES, USE WATER SPRAY, FOG OR STANDARD FOAM (1987 EMERGENCY RESPONSE GUIDEBOOK, DOT P 5800.4).

FIREFIGHTING: MOVE CONTAINER FROM FIRE AREA IF POSSIBLE. DO NOT SCATTER SPILLED MATERIAL WITH HIGH PRESSURE WATER STREAMS. DIKE FIRE CONTROL WATER FOR LATER DISPOSAL (1987 EMERGENCY RESPONSE GUIDEBOOK, DOT P 5800.4, GUIDE PAGE 31).

USE AGENTS SUITABLE FOR TYPE OF SURROUNDING FIRE. AVOID BREATHING HAZARDOUS VAPORS, KEEP UPWIND.

TOXICITY

BIOALLETHRIN: TOXICITY DATA: 1600 MG/M3/3 HOURS INHALATION-RAT LC50; 2720 MG/M3/3 HOURS INHALATION-MOUSE LC50; 25 GM/KG SKIN-RAT LD50; 1545 MG/KG SKIN-RABBIT LD50; 430 MG/KG ORAL-RAT LD50; 250 MG/KG ORAL-MOUSE LD50; 2600 MG/KG SUBCUTANEOUS-MOUSE LD50. CARCINOGEN STATUS: NONE. ACUTE TOXICITY LEVEL: HIGHLY TOXIC BY INHALATION; TOXIC BY INGESTION; MODERATELY TOXIC BY DERMAL ABSORPTION. TARGET EFFECTS: POISONING MAY AFFECT THE CENTRAL NERVOUS SYSTEM.

HEALTH EFFECTS AND FIRST AID

INHALATION: BIOALLETHRIN: HIGHLY TOXIC. THE REPORTED LETHAL DOSE IN RATS WAS 1600 MG/M3/3 HOURS. SEE INFORMATION ON PYRETHROIDS.

PYRETHROIDS: **ACUTE EXPOSURE-** HEAVY EXPOSURE TO A MIST OF SOME PYRETHROIDS HAS PRODUCED HYPERSENSITIVIITY, ATAXIA, AND URINARY INCONTINENCE. CONVULSIONS MAY ALSO BE POSSIBLE. **CHRONIC EXPOSURE-** ANIMALS EXPOSED TO AEROSOLS OF SOME PYRETHROIDS FOR 3-4 HOURS/DAY FOR UP TO 4 WEEKS DID NOT EXHIBIT ANY SIGNIFICANT COMPOUND RELATED FINDINGS.

FIRST AID- REMOVE FROM EXPOSURE AREA TO FRESH AIR IMMEDIATELY. IF BREATHING HAS STOPPED, PERFORM ARTIFICIAL RESPIRATION. KEEP PERSON WARM AND AT REST. TREAT SYMPTOMATICALLY AND SUPPORTIVELY. GET MEDICAL ATTENTION IMMEDIATELY.

SKIN CONTACT: BIOALLETHRIN: SEE INFORMATION ON PYRETHROIDS.

PYRETHROIDS: **ACUTE EXPOSURE-** BASED ON ANIMAL AND HUMAN STUDIES AND HUMAN EXPERIENCES WITH SOME PYRETHROIDS, PRIMARY IRRITATION IS UNLIKELY. CUTANEOUS PARESTHESIAS MAY OCCUR INCLUDING NUMBNESS, ITCHING, BURNING, TINGLING AND WARMTH WITHOUT SIGNS OF IRRITATION. THESE EFFECTS MAY BE DELAYED FOR 30 MINUTES OR MORE AND LAST LESS THAN 24 HOURS. **CHRONIC EXPOSURE-** TESTS WITH SOME PYRETHROIDS ON HUMANS AND ANIMALS INDICATE SENSITIZATION IS UNLIKELY.

FIRST AID- REMOVE CONTAMINATED CLOTHING AND SHOES IMMEDIATELY. WASH AFFECTED AREA WITH SOAP OR MILD DETERGENT AND LARGE AMOUNTS OF WATER UNTIL NO EVIDENCE OF CHEMICAL REMAINS (APPROXIMATELY 15-20 MINUTES). GET MEDICAL ATTENTION IMMEDIATELY.

EYE CONTACT: BIOALLETHRIN: SEE INFORMATION ON PYRETHROIDS.
PYRETHROIDS: **ACUTE EXPOSURE-** MASSIVE INSTILLATION OF SOME PYRETHROIDS INTO RABBIT EYES PRODUCED ONLY A SLIGHT, TRANSIENT CONGESTION OF THE CONJUNCTIVA OR LACRIMATION. **CHRONIC EXPOSURE-** NO DATA AVAILABLE.
FIRST AID- WASH EYES IMMEDIATELY WITH LARGE AMOUNTS OF WATER OR NORMAL SALINE, OCCASIONALLY LIFTING UPPER AND LOWER LIDS, UNTIL NO EVIDENCE OF CHEMICAL REMAINS (APPROXIMATELY 15-20 MINUTES). GET MEDICAL ATTENTION IMMEDIATELY.

INGESTION: BIOALLETHRIN: TOXIC. THE REPORTED LETHAL DOSE IN RATS WAS 430 MG/KG. SEE INFORMATION ON PYRETHROIDS.
PYRETHROIDS: **ACUTE EXPOSURE-** SOME PYRETHROIDS HAVE PRODUCED HYPERSENSITIVITY, NERVOUS IRRITABILITY, TREMORS, ATAXIA, AND URINARY INCONTINENCE IN ANIMALS. CONVULSIONS MAY ALSO BE POSSIBLE. **CHRONIC EXPOSURE-** INCREASED KIDNEY AND LIVER WEIGHTS AND HEPATIC HISTOPATHOLOGICAL CHANGES WERE NOTED IN ANIMALS CHRONICALLY FED SOME PYRETHROIDS.
FIRST AID- IF EXTENSIVE VOMITING HAS NOT OCCURRED, THE SUBSTANCE SHOULD BE REMOVED BY EMESIS OR GASTRIC LAVAGE PROVIDED THAT THE PATIENT IS CONSCIOUS AND CONVULSIONS ARE NOT PRESENT. KEEP HEAD BELOW HIPS DURING VOMITING TO PREVENT ASPIRATION. DO NOT ATTEMPT TO MAKE AN UNCONSCIOUS PERSON VOMIT. TREAT SYMPTOMATICALLY AND SUPPORTIVELY. GET MEDICAL ATTENTION IMMEDIATELY (DREISBACH, HANDBOOK OF POISONING, 12TH ED.). TREATMENT SHOULD BE PERFORMED BY QUALIFIED MEDICAL PERSONNEL.
ANTIDOTE: NO SPECIFIC ANTIDOTE. TREAT SYMPTOMATICALLY AND SUPPORTIVELY.

REACTIVITY

REACTIVITY: STABLE UNDER NORMAL TEMPERATURES AND PRESSURES.
INCOMPATIBILITIES: BIOALLETHRIN: ACIDS (STRONG): HYDROLYZES. ALKALIES (STRONG): HYDROLYZES. OXIDIZERS (STRONG): FIRE AND EXPLOSION HAZARD.
DECOMPOSITION: THERMAL DECOMPOSITION PRODUCTS MAY INCLUDE TOXIC OXIDES OF CARBON.
POLYMERIZATION: HAZARDOUS POLYMERIZATION HAS NOT BEEN REPORTED TO OCCUR UNDER NORMAL TEMPERATURES AND PRESSURES.

STORAGE AND DISPOSAL

OBSERVE ALL FEDERAL, STATE AND LOCAL REGULATIONS WHEN STORING OR DISPOSING OF THIS SUBSTANCE. FOR ASSISTANCE, CONTACT THE DISTRICT DIRECTOR OF THE ENVIRONMENTAL PROTECTION AGENCY.

****STORAGE****

STORE IN ACCORDANCE WITH 40 CFR 165 RECOMMENDED PROCEDURES FOR THE DISPOSAL AND STORAGE OF PESTICIDES AND PESTICIDE CONTAINERS.
STORE AWAY FROM INCOMPATIBLE SUBSTANCES.
STORE IN A COOL, DRY PLACE; KEEP CONTAINER TIGHTLY CLOSED WHEN NOT IN USE.

****DISPOSAL****

DISPOSAL MUST BE IN ACCORDANCE WITH 40 CFR 165 RECOMMENDED PROCEDURES FOR THE DISPOSAL AND STORAGE OF PESTICIDES AND PESTICIDE CONTAINERS.

CONDITIONS TO AVOID

MAY BURN BUT DOES NOT IGNITE READILY. AVOID CONTACT WITH STRONG OXIDIZERS, EXCESSIVE HEAT, SPARKS, OR OPEN FLAME.

SPILL AND LEAK PROCEDURES

OCCUPATIONAL SPILL: STOP LEAK IF YOU CAN DO IT WITHOUT RISK. FOR SMALL SPILLS, TAKE UP WITH SAND OR OTHER ABSORBENT MATERIAL AND PLACE INTO CLEAN, DRY CONTAINERS FOR LATER DISPOSAL. KEEP UNNECESSARY PEOPLE AWAY. ISOLATE HAZARD AREA AND DENY ENTRY.

PROTECTIVE EQUIPMENT

VENTILATION: PROCESS ENCLOSURE RECOMMENDED.
RESPIRATOR: THE FOLLOWING RESPIRATORS ARE RECOMMENDED BASED ON INFORMATION FOUND IN THE PHYSICAL DATA, TOXICITY AND HEALTH EFFECTS SECTIONS. THEY ARE RANKED IN ORDER FROM MINIMUM TO MAXIMUM RESPIRATORY PROTECTION. THE SPECIFIC RESPIRATOR SELECTED MUST BE BASED ON CONTAMINATION LEVELS FOUND IN THE WORK PLACE, MUST NOT EXCEED THE WORKING LIMITS OF THE RESPIRATOR AND BE JOINTLY APPROVED BY THE NATIONAL INSTITUTE FOR OCCUPATIONAL SAFETY AND HEALTH AND THE MINE SAFETY AND HEALTH ADMINISTRATION (NIOSH-MSHA).
TYPE 'C' SUPPLIED-AIR RESPIRATOR WITH A FULL FACEPIECE OPERATED IN PRESSURE-DEMAND OR OTHER POSITIVE PRESSURE MODE OR WITH A FULL FACEPIECE, HELMET OR HOOD OPERATED IN CONTINOUS-FLOW MODE.
SELF-CONTAINED BREATHING APPARATUS WITH A FULL FACEPIECE OPERATED IN PRESSURE-DEMAND OR OTHER POSITIVE PRESSURE MODE.
FOR FIREFIGHTING AND OTHER IMMEDIATELY DANGEROUS TO LIFE OR HEALTH CONDITIONS:
SELF-CONTAINED BREATHING APPARATUS WITH FULL FACEPIECE OPERATED IN PRESSURE-DEMAND OR OTHER POSITIVE PRESSURE MODE.
SUPPLIED-AIR RESPIRATOR WITH FULL FACEPIECE AND OPERATED IN PRESSURE-DEMAND OR OTHER POSITIVE PRESSURE MODE IN COMBINATION WITH AN AUXILIARY SELF-CONTAINED BREATHING APPARATUS OPERATED IN PRESSURE-DEMAND OR OTHER POSITIVE PRESSURE MODE.
CLOTHING: EMPLOYEE MUST WEAR APPROPRIATE PROTECTIVE (IMPERVIOUS) CLOTHING AND EQUIPMENT TO PREVENT REPEATED OR PROLONGED SKIN CONTACT WITH THIS SUBSTANCE.
GLOVES: EMPLOYEE MUST WEAR APPROPRIATE PROTECTIVE GLOVES TO PREVENT CONTACT WITH THIS SUBSTANCE.
EYE PROTECTION: EMPLOYEE MUST WEAR SPLASH-PROOF OR DUST-RESISTANT SAFETY GOGGLES TO PREVENT EYE CONTACT WITH THIS SUBSTANCE.
EMERGENCY EYE WASH: WHERE THERE IS ANY POSSIBILITY THAT AN EMPLOYEE'S EYES MAY BE EXPOSED TO THIS SUBSTANCE, THE EMPLOYER SHOULD PROVIDE AN EYE WASH FOUNTAIN WITHIN THE IMMEDIATE WORK AREA FOR EMERGENCY USE.

AUTHORIZED BY- OCCUPATIONAL HEALTH SERVICES, INC.
CREATION DATE: 10/04/89 ***REVISION DATE:*** 05/17/90

MATERIAL SAFETY DATA SHEET

OCCUPATIONAL HEALTH SERVICES, INC.
AGRICULTURE AND PESTICIDE DIVISION
450 SEVENTH AVENUE, SUITE 2407
NEW YORK, NEW YORK 10123
1-800-445-MSDS OR (212) 967-1100

EMERGENCY CONTACT:
JOHN S. BRANSFORD, JR. (615) 292-1180

SUBSTANCE IDENTIFICATION

CAS-NUMBER 8007-70-3
SUBSTANCE: **OIL OF ANISE**
TRADE NAMES/SYNONYMS: OILS, ANISE; ANISEED OIL; ANISE OIL; STAR ANISE OIL; PST71028
CHEMICAL FAMILY: ESSENTIAL OIL
CERCLA RATINGS (SCALE 0-3): HEALTH=2 FIRE=1 REACTIVITY=0 PERSISTENCE=1
NFPA RATINGS (SCALE 0-4): HEALTH=2 FIRE=1 REACTIVITY=0

COMPONENTS AND CONTAMINANTS

COMPONENT: OIL OF ANISE ***PERCENT:*** 100
CAS# 8007-70-3
OTHER CONTAMINANTS: NONE
EXPOSURE LIMITS: NO OCCUPATIONAL EXPOSURE LIMITS ESTABLISHED BY OSHA, ACGIH, OR NIOSH.

PHYSICAL DATA

DESCRIPTION: COLORLESS OR PALE YELLOW LIQUID. ***BOILING POINT:*** NOT AVAILABLE
SPECIFIC GRAVITY: 0.978-0.988 @ 25 C ***SOLUBILITY IN WATER:*** SLIGHTLY SOLUBLE
SOLVENT SOLUBILITY: SOLUBLE IN ETHER, CHLOROFORM, AND ALCOHOL. ALCOHOL.

FIRE AND EXPLOSION DATA

FIRE AND EXPLOSION HAZARD: SLIGHT FIRE HAZARD WHEN EXPOSED TO HEAT OR FLAME.
FIREFIGHTING MEDIA: DRY CHEMICAL, CARBON DIOXIDE, HALON, WATER SPRAY OR STANDARD FOAM (1987 EMERGENCY RESPONSE GUIDEBOOK, DOT P 5800.4).
FOR LARGER FIRES, USE WATER SPRAY, FOG OR STANDARD FOAM (1987 EMERGENCY RESPONSE GUIDEBOOK, DOT P 5800.4).
FIREFIGHTING: MOVE CONTAINER FROM FIRE AREA IF POSSIBLE. DO NOT SCATTER SPILLED MATERIAL WITH HIGH PRESSURE WATER STREAMS. DIKE FIRE CONTROL WATER FOR LATER DISPOSAL (1987 EMERGENCY RESPONSE GUIDEBOOK, DOT P 5800.4, GUIDE PAGE 31).
USE AGENTS SUITABLE FOR TYPE OF SURROUNDING FIRE. AVOID BREATHING HAZARDOUS VAPORS, KEEP UPWIND.

TOXICITY

OIL OF ANISE: TOXICITY DATA: 2250 MG/KG ORAL-RAT LD50; MUTAGENIC DATA (RTECS). CARCINOGEN STATUS: NONE. LOCAL EFFECTS: IRRITANT- SKIN. ACUTE

TOXICITY LEVEL: MODERATELY TOXIC BY INGESTION. TARGET EFFECTS: NO DATA AVAILABLE.

HEALTH EFFECTS AND FIRST AID

INHALATION: OIL OF ANISE: **ACUTE EXPOSURE-** INHALATION OF VOLATILE OILS MAY CAUSE DIZZINESS, RAPID, SHALLOW BREATHING, TACHYCARDIA, BRONCHIAL IRRITATION AND UNCONSCIOUSNESS OR CONVULSIONS. COMPLICATIONS MAY INCLUDE ANURIA, PULMONARY EDEMA, AND BRONCHIAL PNEUMONIA. **CHRONIC EXPOSURE-** NO DATA AVAILABLE.

FIRST AID- REMOVE FROM EXPOSURE AREA TO FRESH AIR IMMEDIATELY. IF BREATHING HAS STOPPED, PERFORM ARTIFICIAL RESPIRATION. KEEP PERSON WARM AND AT REST. TREAT SYMPTOMATICALLY AND SUPPORTIVELY. GET MEDICAL ATTENTION IMMEDIATELY.

SKIN CONTACT: OIL OF ANISE: IRRITANT. **ACUTE EXPOSURE-** CONTACT MAY CAUSE DERMATITIS. HYPERSENSITIVITY REACTIONS MAY OCCUR IN PERSONS PREVIOUSLY EXPOSED. **CHRONIC EXPOSURE-** REPEATED EXPOSURE MAY POSSIBLY RESULT IN SENSITIZATION.

FIRST AID- REMOVE CONTAMINATED CLOTHING AND SHOES IMMEDIATELY. WASH AFFECTED AREA WITH SOAP OR MILD DETERGENT AND LARGE AMOUNTS OF WATER UNTIL NO EVIDENCE OF CHEMICAL REMAINS (APPROXIMATELY 15-20 MINUTES). GET MEDICAL ATTENTION IMMEDIATELY.

EYE CONTACT: OIL OF ANISE: **ACUTE EXPOSURE-** NO DATA AVAILABLE. **CHRONIC EXPOSURE-** NO DATA AVAILABLE.

FIRST AID- WASH EYES IMMEDIATELY WITH LARGE AMOUNTS OF WATER OR NORMAL SALINE, OCCASIONALLY LIFTING UPPER AND LOWER LIDS, UNTIL NO EVIDENCE OF CHEMICAL REMAINS (APPROXIMATELY 15-20 MINUTES). GET MEDICAL ATTENTION IMMEDIATELY.

INGESTION: OIL OF ANISE: **ACUTE EXPOSURE-** INGESTION OF VOLATILE OILS MAY CAUSE ABDOMINAL BURNING, NAUSEA AND VOMITING, DIARRHEA, DYSURIA, HEMATURIA, UNCONSCIOUSNESS, SHALLOW RESPIRATION, AND CONVULSIONS. COMPLICATIONS MAY INCLUDE ANURIA, PULMONARY EDEMA, AND BRONCHIAL PNEUMONIA. PATHOLOGIC FINDINGS FROM INGESTION OF VOLATILE OILS INCLUDE RENAL DEGENERATIVE CHANGES AND INTENSE CONGESTION AND EDEMA IN THE LUNGS, BRAIN AND GASTRIC MUCOSA. **CHRONIC EXPOSURE-** NO DATA AVAILABLE.

FIRST AID- GIVE 120-240 ML OF MILK; THEN REMOVE BY GASTRIC LAVAGE OR EMESIS, TAKING CARE TO PREVENT ASPIRATION. FOLLOW THESE PROCEDURES BY ADMINISTERING 30-60 ML OF FLEET'S PHOSPHO-SODA DILUTED 1:4 IN WATER. PERFORM ARTIFICIAL RESPIRATION IF NECESSARY. GET MEDICAL ATTENTION (DREISBACH, HANDBOOK OF POISONING, 12TH ED.). FIRST AID SHOULD BE PERFORMED BY QUALIFIED MEDICAL PERSONNEL.

ANTIDOTE: NO SPECIFIC ANTIDOTE. TREAT SYMPTOMATICALLY AND SUPPORTIVELY.

REACTIVITY

REACTIVITY: STABLE UNDER NORMAL TEMPERATURES AND PRESSURES.

INCOMPATIBILITIES: OIL OF ANISE: OXIDIZERS (STRONG): FIRE AND EXPLOSION HAZARD.

DECOMPOSITION: THERMAL DECOMPOSITION MAY RELEASE ACRID SMOKE AND IRRITATING FUMES.

POLYMERIZATION: HAZARDOUS POLYMERIZATION HAS NOT BEEN REPORTED TO OCCUR UNDER NORMAL TEMPERATURES AND PRESSURES.

STORAGE AND DISPOSAL

OBSERVE ALL FEDERAL, STATE AND LOCAL REGULATIONS WHEN STORING OR DISPOSING OF THIS SUBSTANCE. FOR ASSISTANCE, CONTACT THE DISTRICT DIRECTOR OF THE ENVIRONMENTAL PROTECTION AGENCY.

****STORAGE****

STORE IN A COOL, DRY PLACE; KEEP CONTAINER TIGHTLY CLOSED WHEN NOT IN USE.

CONDITIONS TO AVOID

MAY BURN BUT DOES NOT IGNITE READILY. AVOID CONTACT WITH STRONG OXIDIZERS, EXCESSIVE HEAT, SPARKS, OR OPEN FLAME.

SPILL AND LEAK PROCEDURES

OCCUPATIONAL SPILL: STOP LEAK IF YOU CAN DO IT WITHOUT RISK. FOR SMALL SPILLS, TAKE UP WITH SAND OR OTHER ABSORBENT MATERIAL AND PLACE INTO CLEAN, DRY CONTAINERS FOR LATER DISPOSAL. KEEP UNNECESSARY PEOPLE AWAY. ISOLATE HAZARD AREA AND DENY ENTRY.

PROTECTIVE EQUIPMENT

VENTILATION: PROVIDE LOCAL EXHAUST OR GENERAL DILUTION VENTILATION SYSTEM.

RESPIRATOR: THE FOLLOWING RESPIRATORS ARE RECOMMENDED BASED ON INFORMATION FOUND IN THE PHYSICAL DATA, TOXICITY AND HEALTH EFFECTS SECTIONS. THEY ARE RANKED IN ORDER FROM MINIMUM TO MAXIMUM RESPIRATORY PROTECTION. THE SPECIFIC RESPIRATOR SELECTED MUST BE BASED ON CONTAMINATION LEVELS FOUND IN THE WORK PLACE, MUST NOT EXCEED THE WORKING LIMITS OF THE RESPIRATOR AND BE JOINTLY APPROVED BY THE NATIONAL INSTITUTE FOR OCCUPATIONAL SAFETY AND HEALTH AND THE MINE SAFETY AND HEALTH ADMINISTRATION (NIOSH-MSHA).

CHEMICAL CARTRIDGE RESPIRATOR WITH AN ORGANIC VAPOR CARTRIDGE(S) WITH A FULL FACEPIECE.

GAS MASK WITH ORGANIC VAPOR CANISTER (CHIN-STYLE OR FRONT- OR BACK-MOUNTED CANISTER) WITH A FULL FACEPIECE.

TYPE 'C' SUPPLIED-AIR RESPIRATOR WITH A FULL FACEPIECE OPERATED IN PRESSURE-DEMAND OR OTHER POSITIVE PRESSURE MODE OR WITH A FULL FACEPIECE, HELMET OR HOOD OPERATED IN CONTINUOUS-FLOW MODE.

SELF-CONTAINED BREATHING APPARATUS WITH A FULL FACEPIECE OPERATED IN PRESSURE-DEMAND OR OTHER POSITIVE PRESSURE MODE.

FOR FIREFIGHTING AND OTHER IMMEDIATELY DANGEROUS TO LIFE OR HEALTH CONDITIONS:

SELF-CONTAINED BREATHING APPARATUS WITH FULL FACEPIECE OPERATED IN PRESSURE-DEMAND OR OTHER POSITIVE PRESSURE MODE.

SUPPLIED-AIR RESPIRATOR WITH FULL FACEPIECE AND OPERATED IN PRESSURE-DEMAND OR OTHER POSITIVE PRESSURE MODE IN COMBINATION WITH AN AUXILIARY SELF-CONTAINED BREATHING APPARATUS OPERATED IN PRESSURE-DEMAND OR OTHER POSITIVE PRESSURE MODE.

CLOTHING: EMPLOYEE MUST WEAR APPROPRIATE PROTECTIVE (IMPERVIOUS) CLOTHING AND EQUIPMENT TO PREVENT REPEATED OR PROLONGED SKIN CONTACT WITH THIS SUBSTANCE.

GLOVES: EMPLOYEE MUST WEAR APPROPRIATE PROTECTIVE GLOVES TO PREVENT CONTACT WITH THIS SUBSTANCE.

EYE PROTECTION: EMPLOYEE MUST WEAR SPLASH-PROOF OR DUST-RESISTANT SAFETY GOGGLES TO PREVENT EYE CONTACT WITH THIS SUBSTANCE.

EMERGENCY EYE WASH: WHERE THERE IS ANY POSSIBILITY THAT AN EMPLOYEE'S EYES MAY BE EXPOSED TO THIS SUBSTANCE, THE EMPLOYER SHOULD PROVIDE AN EYE WASH FOUNTAIN WITHIN THE IMMEDIATE WORK AREA FOR EMERGENCY USE.

AUTHORIZED BY- OCCUPATIONAL HEALTH SERVICES, INC.

CREATION DATE: 02/08/90 ***REVISION DATE:*** 05/17/90

MATERIAL SAFETY DATA SHEET

OCCUPATIONAL HEALTH SERVICES, INC.
AGRICULTURE AND PESTICIDE DIVISION
450 SEVENTH AVENUE, SUITE 2407
NEW YORK, NEW YORK 10123
1-800-445-MSDS OR (212) 967-1100

EMERGENCY CONTACT:
JOHN S. BRANSFORD, JR. (615) 292-1180

SUBSTANCE IDENTIFICATION

CAS-NUMBER 298-39-5

***SUBSTANCE:* STREPTOMYCIN SULFATE (1:3) SALT**

TRADE NAMES/SYNONYMS: D-STREPTAMINE, O-2-DEOXY-2-(METHYLAMINO)-ALPHA-L-GLUCOPYRANOSYL-(1->2) -O-5-DEOXY-3-C-FORMYL-ALPHA-L-LYXOFURANOSYL-(1->4)-N,N'-BIS (AMINOIMINOMETHYL)-SULFATE (1:3) (SALT); STRYEIN; PST71042

CHEMICAL FAMILY: ANTIBIOTIC

MOLECULAR FORMULA: C21-H39-N7-O12.3H2-O4-S

MOLECULAR WEIGHT: 1457.58

CERCLA RATINGS (SCALE 0-3): HEALTH=3 FIRE=U REACTIVITY=0 PERSISTENCE=2

NFPA RATINGS (SCALE 0-4): HEALTH=3 FIRE=U REACTIVITY=0

COMPONENTS AND CONTAMINANTS

COMPONENT: STREPTOMYCIN SULFATE (1:3) SALT ***PERCENT:*** 100
CAS# 298-39-5

OTHER CONTAMINANTS: NONE

EXPOSURE LIMITS: NO OCCUPATIONAL EXPOSURE LIMITS ESTABLISHED BY OSHA, ACGIH, OR NIOSH.

PHYSICAL DATA

DESCRIPTION: WHITE TO LIGHT GRAY OR PALE BUFF HYGROSCOPIC POWDER WITH A FAINT AMINE-LIKE ODOR.
MELTING POINT: NOT AVAILABLE
SPECIFIC GRAVITY: NOT AVAILABLE ***PH:*** 4.5-7.0 (20% SOLN)
SOLUBILITY IN WATER: SOLUBLE
SOLVENT SOLUBILITY: SOLUBLE IN METHANOL, ETHANOL, ISOPROPANOL, PETROLEUM ETHER, CARBON TETRACHLORIDE, ETHER, CHLOROFORM

FIRE AND EXPLOSION DATA

FIRE AND EXPLOSION HAZARD: UNKNOWN FIRE AND EXPLOSION HAZARD.
FIREFIGHTING MEDIA: DRY CHEMICAL, CARBON DIOXIDE, WATER SPRAY OR FOAM FOR LARGER FIRES, USE WATER SPRAY, FOG OR ALCOHOL FOAM
FIREFIGHTING: MOVE CONTAINER FROM FIRE AREA IF POSSIBLE. DO NOT SCATTER SPILLED MATERIAL WITH MORE WATER THAN NEEDED FOR FIRE CONTROL. DIKE FIRE CONTROL WATER FOR LATER DISPOSAL
USE AGENTS SUITABLE FOR TYPE OF SURROUNDING FIRE. AVOID BREATHING HAZARDOUS VAPORS, KEEP UPWIND.

TOXICITY

STREPTOMYCIN SULFATE: TOXICITY DATA: 430 MG/KG ORAL-RAT LD50; 430 MG/KG ORAL-MOUSE LD50; 800 MG/KG SUBCUTANEOUS-RAT LD50; 970 MG/KG SUBCUTANEOUS-MOUSE LD50; REPRODUCTIVE EFFECTS DATA (RTECS).
CARCINOGEN STATUS: NONE. ACUTE TOXICITY LEVEL: TOXIC BY INGESTION. TARGET EFFECTS: SENSITIZER- RESPIRATORY, DERMAL. AT INCREASED RISK FROM EXPOSURE: PERSONS WITH IMPAIRED KIDNEY FUNCTION. ADDITIONAL DATA: PARENTERAL ADMINISTRATION OF STREPTOMYCIN MAY AFFECT THE BLOOD, KIDNEYS AND NERVOUS SYSTEM, ESPECIALLY THE VESTIBULAR BRANCH OF THE AUDITORY NERVE. RECOVERY IS GENERALLY COMPLETE FOLLOWING DISCONTINUANCE OF THE DRUG; HOWEVER, LONG TERM THERAPY HAS RESULTED IN LOSS OF HEARING. STREPTOMYCIN IS REPORTED TO HAVE INDUCED APLASTIC ANEMIA, PANCYTOPENIA, AND HEMOLYSIS OF RED BLOOD CELLS IN SENSITIZED AND NONSENSITIZED INDIVIDUALS. MAY CROSS THE PLACENTA. INTERACTIONS WITH MEDICATIONS HAVE BEEN REPORTED.

HEALTH EFFECTS AND FIRST AID

INHALATION: STREPTOMYCIN SULFATE: SENSITIZER. **ACUTE EXPOSURE-** DUSTS MAY CAUSE IRRITATION OF THE MUCOUS MEMBRANES. ALLERGIC REACTIONS MAY OCCUR IN PREVIOUSLY SENSITIZED INDIVIDUALS. ABSORPTION THROUGH THE LUNGS MAY OCCUR. PALLOR, CYANOSIS, WHEEZING, COLLAPSE, FROTHY SPUTUM, PULMONARY EDEMA, AND DEATH IN RESPIRATORY FAILURE MAY OCCUR WITHIN SECONDS TO MINUTES AFTER THE APPLICATION OF STREPTOMYCIN TO THE MUCOUS MEMBRANES. DELAYED REACTIONS MAY CONSIST OF FEVER, SKIN ERUPTIONS AND PHARYNGEAL OR LARYNGEAL EDEMA. **CHRONIC EXPOSURE-** REPEATED OR PROLONGED EXPOSURE MAY RESULT IN SENSITIZATION.
FIRST AID- REMOVE FROM EXPOSURE AREA TO FRESH AIR IMMEDIATELY. IF BREATHING HAS STOPPED, PERFORM ARTIFICIAL RESPIRATION. KEEP PERSON WARM AND AT REST. TREAT SYMPTOMATICALLY AND SUPPORTIVELY. GET MEDICAL ATTENTION IMMEDIATELY.

SKIN CONTACT: STREPTOMYCIN SULFATE: SENSITIZER. **ACUTE EXPOSURE-** EXCESSIVE AMOUNTS OF DUST MAY BE IRRITATING AND MAY CAUSE CONTACT DERMATITIS, SKIN RASH, URTICARIA, AND EXFOLIATIVE DERMATITIS IN SENSITIZED INDIVIDUALS HANDLING STREPTOMYCIN WITHOUT GLOVES. INTOXICATION MAY OCCUR WHEN AMINOGLYCOSIDES ARE APPLIED TOPICALLY TO LARGE WOUNDS, BURNS, OR CUTANEOUS ULCERS, PARTICULARLY IF THERE IS RENAL INSUFFICIENCY. **CHRONIC EXPOSURE-** TOPICALLY, STREPTOMYCIN HAS CAUSED A HIGH INCIDENCE OF SENSITIZATION. PROLONGED CONTACT IN THE SENSITIZED INDIVIDUAL MAY PRODUCE DEEP FISSURES AND HYPERKERATOSES WITH SUPERIMPOSED ECZEMATIZATION.
FIRST AID- REMOVE CONTAMINATED CLOTHING AND SHOES IMMEDIATELY. WASH AFFECTED AREA WITH SOAP OR MILD DETERGENT AND LARGE AMOUNTS OF WATER UNTIL NO EVIDENCE OF CHEMICAL REMAINS (APPROXIMATELY 15-20 MINUTES). GET MEDICAL ATTENTION IMMEDIATELY.

EYE CONTACT: STRETOMYCIN SULFATE: **ACUTE EXPOSURE-** DUSTS MAY BE IRRITATING. **CHRONIC EXPOSURE-** STREPTOMYCIN MAY CAUSE CONTACT DERMATITIS OF THE EYELID. THIS PRESUMABLY IS CAUSED FROM RUBBING THE EYES WITH CONTAMINATED FINGERS. GREEN COLOR BLINDNESS, NYSTAGMUS, OSCILLOPSIA OR OTHER VISUAL DISTURBANCES MAY OCCUR AS A SYSTEMIC EFFECT DUE TO PARENTERAL ADMINISTRATION.
FIRST AID- WASH EYES IMMEDIATELY WITH LARGE AMOUNTS OF WATER OR NORMAL SALINE, OCCASIONALLY LIFTING UPPER AND LOWER LIDS, UNTIL NO EVIDENCE OF CHEMICAL REMAINS (APPROXIMATELY 15-20 MINUTES). GET MEDICAL ATTENTION IMMEDIATELY.

INGESTION: STREPTOMYCIN SULFATE: TOXIC. **ACUTE EXPOSURE-** STREPTOMYCIN MAY BE ADMINISTERED ORALLY. HOWEVER THIS ROUTE IS INEFFECTIVE AGAINST SYSTEMIC INFECTIONS. A LOW DOSE WAS LETHAL TO HAMSTERS; HOWEVER, THERE IS SOME EVIDENCE THAT HAMSTERS MAY BE MORE SUSCEPTIBLE TO ANTIBIOTICS THAN OTHER SPECIES AND THE TOXIC EFFECTS MAY BY ASSOCIATED WITH INTESTINAL FLORA RATHER THAN ABSORPTION OF THE STREPTOMYCIN. THE AMINOGLYCOSIDES ARE HIGHLY POLAR CATIONS; THEY ARE THUS VERY POORLY ABSORBED FROM THE INTESTINAL TRACT. LESS THAN 1% OF A DOSE IS ABSORBED FOLLOWING ORAL ADMINISTRATION. AMINOGLYCOSIDES ARE NOT INACTIVATED IN THE INTESTINE, AND ARE ELIMINATED QUANTITATIVELY IN THE FECES. ORAL ADMINISTRATION OF STREPTOMYCIN CAN CAUSE ANAPHYLACTOID REACTIONS CHARACTERIZED BY NAUSEA AND VOMITING, ABDOMINAL PAIN AND CRAMPING, LOCALIZED EDEMA, CYANOSIS, RESPIRATORY DISTRESS, CONVULSIONS, SEVERE CHEST PAIN AND DEATH IN RESPIRATORY FAILURE. **CHRONIC EXPOSURE-** REPEATED ORAL ADMINISTRATION MAY RESULT IN HYPOVITAMINOSIS AND STREPTOMYCIN ACCUMULATION TO TOXIC CONCENTRATIONS IN PATIENTS WITH RENAL IMPAIRMENT. THE MOST COMMON UNTOWARD REACTION TO THE ADMINISTRATION OF ANTIBIOTICS IS THE OVERGROWTH OF ORGANISMS NOT AFFECTED BY THE ANTIBIOTIC AGENT. IN SOME CASES THESE ORGANISMS PRODUCE TOXINS THAT CAN CAUSE VOMITING, DIARRHEA AND CARDIOVASCULAR COLLAPSE. A MULTIGENERATION STUDY RESULTED IN EFFECTS ON FEMALE FERTILITY AND THE NEWBORN IN RATS ADMINISTERED STREPTOMYCIN SULFATE (2:3) SALT.
FIRST AID- IF ANAPHYLAXIS OCCURS, THE ANTIDOTE SHOULD BE ADMINISTERED BY QUALIFIED MEDICAL PERSONNEL. IF STREPTOMYCIN IS BEING GIVEN FOR THERAPEUTIC PURPOSES, DISCONTINUE USE OF THE DRUG. GET MEDICAL ATTENTION IMMEDIATELY. (DREISBACH HANDBOOK OF POISONING, 11TH ED.)
ANTIDOTE: NO SPECIFIC ANTIDOTE. TREAT SYMPTOMATICALLY AND SUPPORTIVELY.

REACTIVITY

REACTIVITY: STABLE UNDER NORMAL TEMPERATURES AND PRESSURES.
INCOMPATIBILITIES: STREPTOMYCIN SULFATE: ACIDS (STRONG): INCOMPATIBLE. OXIDIZERS (STRONG): FIRE AND EXPLOSION HAZARD.
DECOMPOSITION: THERMAL DECOMPOSITION MAY RELEASE TOXIC OXIDES OF NITROGEN, CARBON AND SULFUR.
POLYMERIZATION: HAZARDOUS POLYMERIZATION HAS NOT BEEN REPORTED TO OCCUR UNDER NORMAL TEMPERATURES AND PRESSURES.

STORAGE AND DISPOSAL

OBSERVE ALL FEDERAL, STATE AND LOCAL REGULATIONS WHEN STORING OR DISPOSING OF THIS SUBSTANCE. FOR ASSISTANCE, CONTACT THE DISTRICT DIRECTOR OF THE ENVIRONMENTAL PROTECTION AGENCY.

CONDITIONS TO AVOID

NONE REPORTED.

SPILL AND LEAK PROCEDURES

OCCUPATIONAL SPILL: SWEEP UP AND PLACE IN SUITABLE CLEAN, DRY CONTAINERS FOR RECLAMATION OR LATER DISPOSAL. DO NOT FLUSH SPILLED MATERIAL INTO SEWER. KEEP UNNECESSARY PEOPLE AWAY.

PROTECTIVE EQUIPMENT

VENTILATION: PROVIDE LOCAL EXHAUST OR PROCESS ENCLOSURE VENTILATION SYSTEM.
RESPIRATOR: THE FOLLOWING RESPIRATORS ARE RECOMMENDED BASED ON INFORMATION FOUND IN THE PHYSICAL DATA, TOXICITY AND HEALTH EFFECTS SECTIONS. THEY ARE RANKED IN ORDER FROM MINIMUM TO MAXIMUM RESPIRATORY PROTECTION. THE SPECIFIC RESPIRATOR SELECTED MUST BE BASED ON CONTAMINATION LEVELS FOUND IN THE WORK PLACE, MUST NOT EXCEED THE WORKING LIMITS OF THE RESPIRATOR AND BE JOINTLY APPROVED BY THE NATIONAL INSTITUTE FOR OCCUPATIONAL SAFETY AND HEALTH AND THE MINE SAFETY AND HEALTH ADMINISTRATION (NIOSH-MSHA).
TYPE 'C' SUPPLIED-AIR RESPIRATOR WITH A FULL FACEPIECE OPERATED IN PRESSURE-DEMAND OR OTHER POSITIVE PRESSURE MODE OR WITH A FULL FACEPIECE, HELMET OR HOOD OPERATED IN CONTINOUS-FLOW MODE.
SELF-CONTAINED BREATHING APPARATUS WITH A FULL FACEPIECE OPERATED IN PRESSURE-DEMAND OR OTHER POSITIVE PRESSURE MODE.
FOR FIREFIGHTING AND OTHER IMMEDIATELY DANGEROUS TO LIFE OR HEALTH CONDITIONS:
SELF-CONTAINED BREATHING APPARATUS WITH FULL FACEPIECE OPERATED IN PRESSURE-DEMAND OR OTHER POSITIVE PRESSURE MODE.
SUPPLIED-AIR RESPIRATOR WITH FULL FACEPIECE AND OPERATED IN PRESSURE-DEMAND OR OTHER POSITIVE PRESSURE MODE IN COMBINATION WITH AN AUXILIARY SELF-CONTAINED BREATHING APPARATUS OPERATED IN PRESSURE-DEMAND OR OTHER POSITIVE PRESSURE MODE.

CLOTHING: EMPLOYEE MUST WEAR APPROPRIATE PROTECTIVE (IMPERVIOUS) CLOTHING AND EQUIPMENT TO PREVENT REPEATED OR PROLONGED SKIN CONTACT WITH THIS SUBSTANCE.
GLOVES: EMPLOYEE MUST WEAR APPROPRIATE PROTECTIVE GLOVES TO PREVENT CONTACT WITH THIS SUBSTANCE.
EYE PROTECTION: EMPLOYEE MUST WEAR SPLASH-PROOF OR DUST-RESISTANT SAFETY GOGGLES TO PREVENT EYE CONTACT WITH THIS SUBSTANCE.
EMERGENCY EYE WASH: WHERE THERE IS ANY POSSIBILITY THAT AN EMPLOYEE'S EYES MAY BE EXPOSED TO THIS SUBSTANCE, THE EMPLOYER SHOULD PROVIDE AN EYE WASH FOUNTAIN WITHIN THE IMMEDIATE WORK AREA FOR EMERGENCY USE.

AUTHORIZED BY- OCCUPATIONAL HEALTH SERVICES, INC.
CREATION DATE: 10/05/89 ***REVISION DATE:*** 05/31/90

MATERIAL SAFETY DATA SHEET

OCCUPATIONAL HEALTH SERVICES, INC.
AGRICULTURE AND PESTICIDE DIVISION
450 SEVENTH AVENUE, SUITE 2407
NEW YORK, NEW YORK 10123
1-800-445-MSDS OR (212) 967-1100

EMERGENCY CONTACT:
JOHN S. BRANSFORD, JR. (615) 292-1180

SUBSTANCE IDENTIFICATION

CAS-NUMBER 58-27-5
SUBSTANCE: **MENADIONE**
TRADE NAMES/SYNONYMS: BP-870; 2-METHYL-1,4-NAPHTHALENEDION; 2-METHYL-1,4-NAPHTHOQUINONE; VITAMIN K; AQUINONE; MENAQUINONE O; KAYQUINONE; VITAMIN K3; K-THROMBYL; VITAMIN K2 (O); THYLOQUINONE; PST71050
CHEMICAL FAMILY: NAPHTHALENE QUINONE
MOLECULAR FORMULA: C11-H8-O2
MOLECULAR WEIGHT: 172.17
CERCLA RATINGS (SCALE 0-3): HEALTH=3 FIRE=U REACTIVITY=0 PERSISTENCE=0
NFPA RATINGS (SCALE 0-4): HEALTH=3 FIRE=U REACTIVITY=0

COMPONENTS AND CONTAMINANTS

COMPONENT: MENADIONE ***PERCENT:*** 100
CAS# 58-27-5
OTHER CONTAMINANTS: NONE
EXPOSURE LIMITS: NO OCCUPATIONAL EXPOSURE LIMITS ESTABLISHED BY OSHA, ACGIH, OR NIOSH.

PHYSICAL DATA

DESCRIPTION: BRIGHT YELLOW CRYSTALS WITH A VERY FAINT ACRID ODOR
MELTING POINT: 189-193 F (105-107 C) ***SPECIFIC GRAVITY:*** NOT AVAILABLE
SOLUBILITY IN WATER: INSOLUBLE
SOLVENT SOLUBILITY: BENZENE, CHLOROFORM, CARBON TETRACHLORIDE, ALCOHOL, VEGETABLE OILS
DECOMPOSES BY U.V. LIGHT

FIRE AND EXPLOSION DATA

FIRE AND EXPLOSION HAZARD: UNKNOWN FIRE AND EXPLOSION HAZARD.
FIREFIGHTING MEDIA: DRY CHEMICAL, CARBON DIOXIDE, WATER SPRAY OR FOAM FOR LARGER FIRES, USE WATER SPRAY, FOG OR ALCOHOL FOAM
FIREFIGHTING: MOVE CONTAINER FROM FIRE AREA IF POSSIBLE. DO NOT SCATTER SPILLED MATERIAL WITH MORE WATER THAN NEEDED FOR FIRE CONTROL. DIKE FIRE CONTROL WATER FOR LATER DISPOSAL
USE AGENTS SUITABLE FOR TYPE OF SURROUNDING FIRE. AVOID BREATHING HAZARDOUS VAPORS, KEEP UPWIND.

TOXICITY

MENADIONE: TOXICITY DATA: 500 MG/KG ORAL-MOUSE LD50; 230 MG/KG ORAL-RABBIT LDLO; 138 MG/KG SUBCUTANEOUS-MOUSE LD50; 50 MG/KG INTRAPERITONEAL-MOUSE LD50; 75 MG/KG INTRAPERITONEAL-RAT LD50; MUTAGENIC DATA (RTECS); REPRODUCTIVE EFFECTS DATA (RTECS); TUMORIGENIC DATA (RTECS). CARCINOGEN STATUS: NONE. LOCAL EFFECTS: IRRITANT-INHALATION AND SKIN. ACUTE TOXICITY LEVEL: TOXIC BY INGESTION. TARGET EFFECTS: POISONING MAY AFFECT THE LIVER AND KIDNEYS. ADDITIONAL DATA: INTERACTIONS WITH MEDICATIONS HAVE BEEN REPORTED.

HEALTH EFFECTS AND FIRST AID

INHALATION: MENADIONE: **ACUTE EXPOSURE-** MAY CAUSE IRRITATION OF THE RESPIRATORY TRACT. **CHRONIC EXPOSURE-** NO DATA AVAILABLE.
FIRST AID- REMOVE FROM EXPOSURE AREA TO FRESH AIR IMMEDIATELY. IF BREATHING HAS STOPPED, PERFORM ARTIFICIAL RESPIRATION. KEEP PERSON WARM AND AT REST. TREAT SYMPTOMATICALLY AND SUPPORTIVELY. GET MEDICAL ATTENTION IMMEDIATELY.

SKIN CONTACT: MENADIONE: **ACUTE EXPOSURE-** MAY CAUSE IRRITATION AND BLISTERING. **CHRONIC EXPOSURE-** REPEATED AND PROLONGED CONTACT WITH IRRITANTS MAY CAUSE DERMATITIS. REPEATED ADMINISTRATION TO THE SKIN OF MICE PRODUCED SKIN TUMORS.
FIRST AID- REMOVE CONTAMINATED CLOTHING AND SHOES IMMEDIATELY. WASH AFFECTED AREA WITH SOAP OR MILD DETERGENT AND LARGE AMOUNTS OF WATER UNTIL NO EVIDENCE OF CHEMICAL REMAINS (APPROXIMATELY 15-20 MINUTES). GET MEDICAL ATTENTION IMMEDIATELY.

EYE CONTACT: MENADIONE: **ACUTE EXPOSURE-** MENADIONE HAS BEEN TESTED IN RABBIT EYES IN THE FORM OF A WATER-SOLUBLE DERIVATIVE, MENADIONE SODIUM BISULFATE, WHICH MAY CAUSE IMMEDIATE DISCOMFORT AND CONJUNCTIVAL CONGESTION, BUT THE EYES RAPIDLY RETURN TO NORMAL. **CHRONIC EXPOSURE-** NO DATA AVAILABLE.
FIRST AID- WASH EYES IMMEDIATELY WITH LARGE AMOUNTS OF WATER OR NORMAL SALINE, OCCASIONALLY LIFTING UPPER AND LOWER LIDS, UNTIL NO EVIDENCE OF CHEMICAL REMAINS (APPROXIMATELY 15-20 MINUTES). GET MEDICAL ATTENTION IMMEDIATELY.

INGESTION: MENADIONE: TOXIC. **ACUTE EXPOSURE-** EXCESSIVE DOSES HAVE CAUSED DECREASED LIVER FUNCTION AND HYPOTHROMBINEMIA IN ADULTS. IT MAY PRODUCE TOXIC EFFECTS IN INFANTS RESULTING IN ANEMIA WITH HEINZ BODY, HYPERBILIRUBINEMIA AND KERNICTERUS. LARGE DOSES CAN CAUSE HEMOLYSIS IN PERSONS WITH GLUCOSE-6-PHOSPHATE DEHYDROGENASE DEFICIENCY. LARGE DOSES PRODUCED ANEMIA, POLYCYTHEMIA, SPLENOMEGALY, RENAL AND HEPATIC DAMAGE AND DEATH IN ANIMALS. **CHRONIC EXPOSURE-** FETAL DEVELOPMENTAL ABNORMALITIES HAVE BEEN REPORTED FROM 3 GM/KG ADMINISTERED DURING THE 1ST-20TH DAY OF PREGNANCY IN RATS.
FIRST AID- TREAT SYMPTOMATICALLY AND SUPPORTIVELY. GET MEDICAL ATTENTION IMMEDIATELY. IF VOMITING OCCURS, KEEP HEAD LOWER THAN HIPS TO PREVENT ASPIRATION.
ANTIDOTE: NO SPECIFIC ANTIDOTE. TREAT SYMPTOMATICALLY AND SUPPORTIVELY.

REACTIVITY

REACTIVITY: STABLE UNDER NORMAL TEMPERATURES AND PRESSURES.
INCOMPATIBILITIES: MENADIONE: NO DATA AVAILABLE.
DECOMPOSITION: THERMAL DECOMPOSITION MAY RELEASE TOXIC AND/OR HAZARDOUS GASES.
POLYMERIZATION: HAZARDOUS POLYMERIZATION HAS NOT BEEN REPORTED TO OCCUR UNDER NORMAL TEMPERATURES AND PRESSURES.

STORAGE AND DISPOSAL

STORE IN A COOL PLACE PROTECTED FROM LIGHT.

CONDITIONS TO AVOID

NONE REPORTED.

SPILL AND LEAK PROCEDURES

OCCUPATIONAL SPILL: SWEEP UP AND PLACE IN SUITABLE CLEAN, DRY CONTAINERS FOR RECLAMATION OR LATER DISPOSAL. DO NOT FLUSH SPILLED MATERIAL INTO SEWER. KEEP UNNECESSARY PEOPLE AWAY.

PROTECTIVE EQUIPMENT

VENTILATION: PROVIDE LOCAL EXHAUST OR PROCESS ENCLOSURE VENTILATION. VENTILATION EQUIPMENT MUST BE EXPLOSION-PROOF.
RESPIRATOR: THE FOLLOWING RESPIRATORS ARE RECOMMENDED BASED ON INFORMATION FOUND IN THE PHYSICAL DATA, TOXICITY AND HEALTH EFFECTS SECTIONS. THEY ARE RANKED IN ORDER FROM MINIMUM TO MAXIMUM RESPIRATORY PROTECTION. THE SPECIFIC RESPIRATOR SELECTED MUST BE BASED ON CONTAMINATION LEVELS FOUND IN THE WORK PLACE, MUST NOT EXCEED THE WORKING LIMITS OF THE RESPIRATOR AND BE JOINTLY APPROVED BY THE NATIONAL INSTITUTE FOR OCCUPATIONAL SAFETY AND HEALTH AND THE MINE SAFETY AND HEALTH ADMINISTRATION (NIOSH-MSHA).
DUST AND MIST RESPIRATOR WITH A FULL FACEPIECE.
AIR-PURIFYING FULL FACEPIECE RESPIRATOR WITH A HIGH-EFFICIENCY PARTICULATE FILTER.
POWERED AIR-PURIFYING RESPIRATOR WITH A TIGHT-FITTING FACEPIECE AND

HIGH-EFFICIENCY PARTICULATE FILTER.
TYPE 'C' SUPPLIED-AIR RESPIRATOR WITH A FULL FACEPIECE OPERATED IN PRESSURE-DEMAND OR OTHER POSITIVE PRESSURE MODE OR WITH A FULL FACEPIECE, HELMET OR HOOD OPERATED IN CONTINUOUS-FLOW MODE.
SELF-CONTAINED BREATHING APPARATUS WITH A FULL FACEPIECE OPERATED IN PRESSURE-DEMAND OR OTHER POSITIVE PRESSURE MODE.
FOR FIREFIGHTING AND OTHER IMMEDIATELY DANGEROUS TO LIFE OR HEALTH CONDITIONS:
SELF-CONTAINED BREATHING APPARATUS WITH FULL FACEPIECE OPERATED IN PRESSURE-DEMAND OR OTHER POSITIVE PRESSURE MODE.
SUPPLIED-AIR RESPIRATOR WITH FULL FACEPIECE AND OPERATED IN PRESSURE-DEMAND OR OTHER POSITIVE PRESSURE MODE IN COMBINATION WITH AN AUXILIARY SELF-CONTAINED BREATHING APPARATUS OPERATED IN PRESSURE-DEMAND OR OTHER POSITIVE PRESSURE MODE.

CLOTHING: EMPLOYEE MUST WEAR APPROPRIATE PROTECTIVE (IMPERVIOUS) CLOTHING AND EQUIPMENT TO PREVENT REPEATED OR PROLONGED SKIN CONTACT WITH THIS SUBSTANCE.

GLOVES: EMPLOYEE MUST WEAR APPROPRIATE PROTECTIVE GLOVES TO PREVENT CONTACT WITH THIS SUBSTANCE.

EYE PROTECTION: EMPLOYEE MUST WEAR SPLASH-PROOF OR DUST-RESISTANT SAFETY GOGGLES TO PREVENT EYE CONTACT WITH THIS SUBSTANCE.
EMERGENCY EYE WASH: WHERE THERE IS ANY POSSIBILITY THAT AN EMPLOYEE'S EYES MAY BE EXPOSED TO THIS SUBSTANCE, THE EMPLOYER SHOULD PROVIDE AN EYE WASH FOUNTAIN WITHIN THE IMMEDIATE WORK AREA FOR EMERGENCY USE.

AUTHORIZED BY- OCCUPATIONAL HEALTH SERVICES, INC.
CREATION DATE: 10/04/89 ***REVISION DATE:*** 05/31/90

MATERIAL SAFETY DATA SHEET

OCCUPATIONAL HEALTH SERVICES, INC.
AGRICULTURE AND PESTICIDE DIVISION
450 SEVENTH AVENUE, SUITE 2407
NEW YORK, NEW YORK 10123
1-800-445-MSDS OR (212) 967-1100

EMERGENCY CONTACT:
JOHN S. BRANSFORD, JR. (615) 292-1180

SUBSTANCE IDENTIFICATION

CAS-NUMBER 2104-96-3

SUBSTANCE: **BROMOPHOS**

TRADE NAMES/SYNONYMS: PHOSPHOROTHIOIC ACID, O-(4-BROMO-2,5-DICHLOROPHENYL) O,O-DIMETHYL; ESTER; O-(4-BROMO-2,5-DICHLOROPHENYL) O,O-DIMETHYL PHOSPHOROTHIOATE; 4-BROMO-2,5-DICHLOROPHENYL DIMETHYL PHOSPHOROTHIONATE; O-4-BROMO-2,5-DICHLOROPHENYL O,O-DIMETHYL PHOSPHOROTHIOATE; O,O-DIMETHYL-O-(2,5-DICHLORO-4-BROMOPHENYL)THIOPHOSPHATE; BROMOPHOS-METHYL; BROMOVUR; CELA S 1942; DRILLZID; EL 400; METABROM; NEXAGAN; NEXION; OMEXAN; S 1942; SOVINEXION; OMS 658; ENT 27162; PST71064

CHEMICAL FAMILY: ORGANOPHOSPHATE

MOLECULAR FORMULA: C8-H8-BR-CL2-O3-P-S

MOLECULAR WEIGHT: 366.00

CERCLA RATINGS (SCALE 0-3): HEALTH=2 FIRE=0 REACTIVITY=U PERSISTENCE=3

NFPA RATINGS (SCALE 0-4): HEALTH=2 FIRE=0 REACTIVITY=U

COMPONENTS AND CONTAMINANTS

COMPONENT: BROMOPHOS ***PERCENT:*** 100
CAS# 2104-96-3

EXPOSURE LIMITS: NO OCCUPATIONAL EXPOSURE LIMITS ESTABLISHED BY OSHA, ACGIH, OR NIOSH.

PHYSICAL DATA

DESCRIPTION: COLORLESS CRYSTALLINE SOLID

BOILING POINT: 284-288 F (140-141 C) @ 0.01 MMHG

MELTING POINT: 127-129 F (53-54 C) ***SPECIFIC GRAVITY:*** 1.32

VAPOR PRESSURE: 0.00013 MMHG @ 30 C ***SOLUBILITY IN WATER:*** 40 PPM

SOLVENT SOLUBILITY: SOLUBLE IN CARBON TETRACHLORIDE, ETHER, TOLUENE, KETONES, DICHLOROMETHANE, METHANOL, XYLENE, AROMATIC HYDROCARBONS, HALOGENATED HYDROCARBONS, MOST ORGANIC SOLVENTS

FIRE AND EXPLOSION DATA

FIRE AND EXPLOSION HAZARD: NEGLIGIBLE FIRE HAZARD WHEN EXPOSED TO HEAT OR FLAME.

FIREFIGHTING MEDIA: DRY CHEMICAL, CARBON DIOXIDE, HALON, WATER SPRAY OR STANDARD FOAM (1987 EMERGENCY RESPONSE GUIDEBOOK, DOT P 5800.4).
FOR LARGER FIRES, USE WATER SPRAY, FOG OR STANDARD FOAM (1987 EMERGENCY RESPONSE GUIDEBOOK, DOT P 5800.4).

FIREFIGHTING: MOVE CONTAINERS FROM FIRE AREA IF POSSIBLE. FIGHT FIRE FROM MAXIMUM DISTANCE. STAY AWAY FROM STORAGE TANK ENDS. DIKE FIRE CONTROL WATER FOR LATER DISPOSAL. DO NOT SCATTER MATERIAL (1987 EMERGENCY RESPONSE GUIDEBOOK, DOT P 5800.4, GUIDE PAGE 55).
EXTINGUISH USING AGENT SUITABLE FOR TYPE OF SURROUNDING FIRE. AVOID BREATHING VAPORS AND DUSTS. KEEP UPWIND.

TOXICITY

BROMPHOS: TOXICITY DATA: 2181 MG/KG SKIN-RABBIT LD50; 2820 MG/KG SKIN-MAMMAL LD50; 1600 MG/KG ORAL-RAT LD50; 2829 MG/KG ORAL-MOUSE LD50; 720 MG/KG ORAL-RABBIT LD50; 1500 MG/KG ORAL-GUINEA PIG LD50; 750 MG/KG ORAL-CAT LDLO; 1625 MG/KG INTRAPERITONEAL-RAT LDLO; 1040 MG/KG INTRAPERITONEAL-MOUSE LD50; 3750 MG/KG UNREPORTED-MAMMAL LD50; MUTAGENIC DATA (RTECS); REPRODUCTIVE EFFECTS DATA (RTECS). CARCINOGEN STATUS: NONE. ACUTE TOXICITY LEVEL: MODERATELY TOXIC BY INGESTION; SLIGHTLY TOXIC BY DERMAL ABSORPTION. TARGET EFFECTS: CHOLINESTERASE INHIBITOR. POISONING MAY AFFECT THE NERVOUS SYSTEM.* AT INCREASED RISK FROM EXPOSURE: PERSONS WITH RESPIRATORY AILMENTS, RECENT EXPOSURE TO CHOLINESTERASE INHIBITORS OR IMPAIRED CHOLINESTERASE PRODUCTION, OR LIVER MALFUNCTION.* ADDITIONAL DATA: MAY CROSS THE PLACENTA. HIGH ENVIRONMENTAL TEMPERATURES OR EXPOSURE OF THE CHEMICAL TO VISIBLE OR ULTRAVIOLET LIGHT MAY ENHANCE THE TOXICITY. INTERACTIONS WITH MEDICATIONS MAY OCCUR.*
* MAY BE BASED ON GENERAL INFORMATION ON ORGANOPHOSPHATES.

HEALTH EFFECTS AND FIRST AID

INHALATION: BROMOPHOS: SEE INFORMATION ON ORGANOPHOSPHATES.
ORGANOPHOSPHATES: CHOLINESTERASE INHIBITOR. **ACUTE EXPOSURE-** WHEN INHALED, THE FIRST EFFECTS OF CHOLINESTERASE INHIBITORS ARE USUALLY RESPIRATORY AND MAY INCLUDE NASAL HYPEREMIA AND WATERY DISCHARGE, COUGH, CHEST DISCOMFORT, DYSPNEA, AND WHEEZING DUE TO INCREASED BRONCHIAL SECRETIONS AND BRONCHOCONSTRICTION. IF SUFFICIENT AMOUNTS ARE ABSORBED, OTHER SYSTEMIC EFFECTS MAY BEGIN WITHIN A FEW MINUTES OR BE DELAYED FOR UP TO 12 HOURS. SYMPTOMS MAY INCLUDE PALLOR, NAUSEA, VOMITING, DIARRHEA, ABDOMINAL CRAMPS, HEADACHE, DIZZINESS, OCULAR PAIN, BLURRED VISION, MIOSIS OR IN SOME CASES, ESPECIALLY INITIALLY, MYDRIASIS, LACRIMATION, SALIVATION, SWEATING, AND CONFUSION. OTHER REPORTED CENTRAL NERVOUS SYSTEM OR NEUROMUSCULAR EFFECTS MAY INCLUDE ATAXIA, SLURRED SPEECH, AREFLEXIA, WEAKNESS, FATIGUE, FASCICULATIONS, TWITCHING, TREMORS POSSIBLY OF THE TONGUE AND EYELIDS, AND EVENTUALLY PARALYSIS OF THE EXTREMITIES AND POSSIBLY OF THE RESPIRATORY MUSCLES. IN SEVERE CASES THERE MAY ALSO BE INVOLUNTARY DEFECATION AND URINATION, CYANOSIS, PSYCHOSIS, HYPERGLYCEMIA, ACUTE PANCREATITIS, CARDIAC IRREGULARITIES, PULMONARY EDEMA, UNCONSCIOUSNESS, CONVULSIONS, AND COMA. DEATH IS PRIMARILY DUE TO RESPIRATORY FAILURE, ALTHOUGH CARDIOVASCULAR EFFECTS INCLUDING CARDIAC ARREST MAY ALSO BE IMPLICATED. LONG TERM SEQUELAE ARE RARE BUT MAY INCLUDE NEUROPSYCHIATRIC DISORDERS AND MYOPATHY WITH MUSCLE TENDERNESS. SOME ORGANOPHOSPHATES MAY CAUSE A DELAYED NEUROPATHY BEGINNING 1-4 WEEKS AFTER AN ACUTE EXPOSURE WHICH MAY OR MAY NOT HAVE CAUSED ACUTE CHOLINERGIC EFFECTS. NUMBNESS, TINGLING, WEAKNESS AND CRAMPING BEGINNING SYMMETRICALLY IN THE LOWER LIMBS MAY PROGRESS TO ATAXIA AND PARALYSIS. IN SEVERE CASES, UPPER LIMB INVOLVEMENT IS POSSIBLE AND FLACCID PARALYSIS MAY PROGRESS TO SPASTIC PARALYSIS WITH EXAGGERATED REFLEXES. IMPROVEMENT MAY OCCUR OVER MONTHS TO YEARS, BUT SOME RESIDUAL IMPAIRMENT USUALLY REMAINS.
CHRONIC EXPOSURE- REPEATED OR PROLONGED EXPOSURE MAY RESULT IN THE EFFECTS OF ACUTE EXPOSURE INCLUDING THE DELAYED NEUROPATHY. OTHER EFFECTS REPORTED IN WORKERS REPEATEDLY EXPOSED INCLUDE IMPAIRED MEMORY AND CONCENTRATION, ACUTE PSYCHOSIS, SEVERE DEPRESSIONS, IRRITABILTY, CONFUSION, APATHY, EMOTIONAL LABILITY, SOCIAL WITHDRAWAL, CONFUSION, HEADACHE, SPEECH DIFFICULTIES, DELAYED REACTION TIMES, SPATIAL DISORIENTATION, NIGHTMARES, SLEEPWALKING, AND DROWSINESS OR INSOMNIA. AN INFLUENZA-LIKE CONDITION WITH HEADACHE, NAUSEA, WEAKNESS, ANOREXIA AND MALAISE HAS ALSO BEEN REPORTED.

FIRST AID- REMOVE FROM EXPOSURE AREA TO FRESH AIR IMMEDIATELY. IF BREATHING HAS STOPPED, GIVE ARTIFICIAL RESPIRATION. MAINTAIN AIRWAY AND BLOOD PRESSURE AND ADMINISTER OXYGEN IF AVAILABLE. KEEP AFFECTED PERSON WARM AND AT REST. TREAT SYMPTOMATICALLY AND SUPPORTIVELY.

ADMINISTRATION OF OXYGEN SHOULD BE PERFORMED BY QUALIFIED PERSONNEL. GET MEDICAL ATTENTION IMMEDIATELY.

SKIN CONTACT: BROMOPHOS: SEE INFORMATION ON ORGANOPHOSPHATES. ORGANOPHOSPHATES: CHOLINESTERASE INHIBITOR. **ACUTE EXPOSURE-** LOCALIZED SWEATING AND FASCICULATIONS MAY OCCUR AT THE SITE OF CONTACT. IF SUFFICIENT AMOUNTS ARE ABSORBED, OTHER EFFECTS OF CHOLINESTERASE INHIBITION AS DESCRIBED IN ACUTE INHALATION MAY OCCUR. SYMPTOMS MAY BE DELAYED 2-3 HOURS, BUT USUALLY NO MORE THAN 12 HOURS. THE RATE OF ABSORPTION IS INCREASED BY THE PRESENCE OF DERMATITIS OR HIGH AMBIENT TEMPERATURES. DELAYED NEUROPATHY IS ALSO POSSIBLE. **CHRONIC EXPOSURE-** REPEATED OR PROLONGED EXPOSURE MAY CAUSE EFFECTS AS DESCRIBED IN ACUTE EXPOSURE. SOME ORGANOPHOSPHATES MAY CAUSE SENSITIZATION.

FIRST AID- REMOVE CONTAMINATED CLOTHING IMMEDIATELY. WASH CONTAMINATED AREAS WITH SOAP AND WATER FOLLOWED BY ALCOHOL (ARENA, POISONING, 4TH ED.). EMERGENCY PERSONNEL SHOULD WEAR GLOVES AND AVOID CONTAMINATION. TREAT RESPIRATORY DIFFICULTY WITH ARTIFICIAL RESPIRATION. GET MEDICAL ATTENTION IMMEDIATELY.

EYE CONTACT: BROMOPHOS: SEE INFORMATION ON ORGANOPHOSPHATES. ORGANOPHOSPHATES: CHOLINESTERASE INHIBITOR. **ACUTE EXPOSURE-** DIRECT CONTACT MAY CAUSE PAIN, HYPEREMIA, LACRIMATION, TWITCHING OF THE EYELIDS, MIOSIS, AND CILIARY MUSCLE SPASM WITH LOSS OF ACCOMODATION, BLURRED OR DIMMED VISION AND BROWACHE. SOMETIMES MYDRIASIS MAY OCCUR INSTEAD OF MIOSIS. WITH SUFFICIENT EXPOSURE, OTHER SYMPTOMS OF CHOLINESTERASE INHIBITION AS DESCRIBED IN ACUTE INHALATION MAY OCCUR. **CHRONIC EXPOSURE-** REPEATED OR PROLONGED EXPOSURE MAY CAUSE EFFECTS AS DESCRIBED IN ACUTE EXPOSURE. SOME COMPOUNDS HAVE CAUSED TOXIC EFFECTS ON THE CRYSTALLINE LENS, CONJUNCTIVAL THICKENING AND OBSTRUCTION OF THE NASOLACRIMAL CANALS WHEN USED AS MIOTIC EYEDROPS.

FIRST AID- IRRIGATE EYES WITH WATER OR SALINE SOLUTION. IF SYMPTOMS OF POISONING OCCUR, TREAT RESPIRATORY DIFFICULTY WITH ARTIFICIAL RESPIRATION AND OXYGEN. OBSERVE PATIENT FOR AT LEAST 24-36 HOURS (GOSSELIN, CLINICAL TOXICOLOGY OF COMMERCIAL PRODUCTS, 5TH ED.). GET MEDICAL ATTENTION IMMEDIATELY. OXYGEN SHOULD BE ADMINISTERED BY QUALIFIED MEDICAL PERSONNEL.

INGESTION: BROMOPHOS: A REPRODUCTION STUDY IN RATS REPORTED INCREASED STILLBIRTHS AND DECREASED PUP WEIGHT AT DOSAGE OF 80 MG/KG/DAY. IN OTHER RAT STUDIES, A DOSE OF 188 MG/KG/DAY PRODUCED HYDROPIC SWELLING OF HEPATIC CELLS AND A DOSE OF 1250 MG/KG/DAY PRODUCED HYALINE DROPLETS IN TUBULAR CELLS AND PROTEIN IN KIDNEY TUBULES. IN DOGS, IMPAIRED SPERMATOGENESIS WAS OBSERVED AT A DOSE OF 175 MG/KG/DAY. SEE INFORMATION ON ORGANOPHOSPHATES.
ORGANOPHOSPHATES: CHOLINESTERASE INHIBITOR. **ACUTE EXPOSURE-** WHEN INGESTED, THE FIRST EFFECTS MAY BE NAUSEA, VOMITING, ANOREXIA, ABDOMINAL CRAMPS AND DIARRHEA. GASTROINTESTINAL ABSORPTION MAY CAUSE SYMPTOMS OF CHOLINESTERASE INHIBITION AS DESCRIBED IN ACUTE INHALATION. SYMPTOMS MAY BEGIN WITHIN MINUTES OR BE DELAYED FOR HOURS. DELAYED EFFECTS INCLUDING NEUROPATHY MAY ALSO OCCUR. **CHRONIC EXPOSURE-** REPEATED INGESTION MAY CAUSE EFFECTS AS DESCRIBED IN ACUTE EXPOSURE.

FIRST AID- IF PERSON IS ALERT AND RESPIRATION IS NOT DEPRESSED, GIVE SYRUP OF IPECAC FOLLOWED BY WATER (IF VOMITING OCCURS, KEEP HEAD BELOW HIPS TO PREVENT ASPIRATION). IF CONSCIOUSNESS LEVEL DECLINES OR VOMITING HAS NOT OCCURRED IN 15 MINUTES EMPTY STOMACH BY GASTRIC LAVAGE WITH THE AID OF CUFFED ENDOTRACHEAL TUBE USING ISOTONIC SALINE OR 5% SODIUM BICARBONATE FOLLOW WITH ACTIVATED CHARCOAL. ESTABLISH AND MAINTAIN AIRWAY. TREAT RESPIRATORY DIFFICULTY WITH ARTIFICIAL RESPIRATION AND OXYGEN. DO NOT GIVE MORPHINE, AMINOPHYLLINE, PHENOTHIAZINES, RESERPINE, FUROSEMIDE, OR ETHACRYNIC ACID (MORGAN, RECOGNITION AND MANAGEMENT OF PESTICIDE POISONINGS, 3RD ED.). TREAT SYMPTOMATICALLY AND SUPPORTIVELY. ADMINISTRATION OF OXYGEN AND LAVAGE MUST BE PERFORMED BY QUALIFIED MEDICAL PERSONNEL. GET MEDICAL ATTENTION IMMEDIATELY.

ANTIDOTE: THE FOLLOWING ANTIDOTE(S) HAVE BEEN RECOMMENDED. HOWEVER, THE DECISION AS TO WHETHER THE SEVERITY OF POISONING REQUIRES ADMINISTRATION OF ANY ANTIDOTE AND ACTUAL DOSE REQUIRED SHOULD BE MADE BY QUALIFIED MEDICAL PERSONNEL.
FOR CHOLINESTERASE INHIBITORS: ESTABLISH CLEAR AIRWAY AND TISSUE OXYGENATION BY ASPIRATION OF SECRETIONS, AND IF NECESSARY, BY ASSISTED PULMONARY VENTILATION WITH OXYGEN. IMPROVE TISSUE OXYGENATION AS MUCH AS POSSIBLE BEFORE ADMINISTERING ATROPINE TO MINIMIZE THE RISK OF VENTRICULAR FIBRILLATION. ADMINISTER ATROPINE SULFATE INTRAVENOUSLY, OR INTRAMUSCULARLY IF IV INJECTION IS NOT POSSIBLE. IN MODERATELY SEVERE POISONING ADMINISTER ATROPINE SULFATE, 0.4-2.0 MG REPEATED EVERY 15 MINUTES UNTIL ATROPINIZATION IS ACHIEVED (TACHYCARDIA, FLUSHING, DRY MOUTH, MYDRIASIS). MAINTAIN ATROPINIZATION BY REPEATED DOSES FOR 2-12 HOURS, OR LONGER, DEPENDING ON THE SEVERITY OF POISONING. THE APPEARANCE OF RALES IN THE LUNG BASES, MIOSIS, SALIVATION, NAUSEA, BRADYCARDIA, ARE ALL INDICATIONS OF INADEQUATE ATROPINIZATION. SEVERELY POISONED INDIVIDUALS MAY EXHIBIT REMARKABLE TOLERANCE TO ATROPINE; TWO OR MORE TIMES THE DOSAGES SUGGESTED ABOVE MAY BE NEEDED. PERSONS NOT POISONED OR ONLY SLIGHTLY POISONED, HOWEVER, MAY DEVELOP SIGNS OF ATROPINE TOXICITY FROM SUCH LARGE DOSAGES: FEVER, MUSCLE FIBRILLATIONS, AND DELIRIUM ARE THE MAIN SIGNS OF ATROPINE TOXICITY. IF THESE SIGNS APPEAR WHILE THE PATIENT IS FULLY ATROPINIZED, ATROPINE ADMINISTRATION SHOULD BE DISCONTINUED, AT LEAST TEMPORARILY. OBSERVE TREATED PATIENTS CLOSELY AT LEAST 24 HOURS TO INSURE THAT SYMPTOMS (POSSIBLY PULMONARY EDEMA) DO NOT RECUR AS ATROPINIZATION WEARS OFF. IN VERY SEVERE POISONINGS, METABOLIC DISPOSITION OF TOXICANT MAY REQUIRE SEVERAL HOURS OR DAYS DURING WHICH ATROPINIZATION MUST BE MAINTAINED. MARKEDLY LOWER LEVELS OF URINARY METABOLITES INDICATE THAT ATROPINE DOSAGE CAN BE TAPERED OFF. AS DOSAGE IS REDUCED, CHECK THE LUNG BASES FREQUENTLY FOR RALES. IF RALES ARE HEARD OR OTHER SYMPTOMS RETURN, RE-ESTABLISH ATROPINIZATION PROMPTLY (MORGAN, RECOGNITION AND MANAGEMENT OF PESTICIDE POISONINGS, 3RD ED.). ADMINISTRATION OF ANTIDOTE MUST BE PERFORMED BY QUALIFIED MEDICAL PERSONNEL.
IN CASES OF SEVERE POISONING BY ORGANOPHOSPHATE PESTICIDES IN WHICH RESPIRATORY DEPRESSION, MUSCLE WEAKNESS AND TWITCHINGS ARE SEVERE, GIVE PRALIDOXIME (PROTOPAM-AYERST, 2-PAM), 1.0 GRAM INTRAVENOUSLY AT NO MORE THAN 0.5 GRAM PER MINUTE. DOSAGE OF PRALIDOXIME MAY BE REPEATED IN 1-2 HOURS, THEN AT 10-12 HOUR INTERVALS IF NEEDED. IN VERY SEVERE POISONINGS, DOSAGE RATES MAY BE DOUBLED. TREATMENT WITH PRALIDOXIME WILL BE MOST EFFECTIVE IF GIVEN WITHIN THIRTY-SIX HOURS AFTER POISONING (MORGAN, RECOGNITION AND MANAGEMENT OF PESTICIDE POISONINGS, 3RD ED.). ANTIDOTE SHOULD BE ADMINISTERED BY QUALIFIED MEDICAL PERSONNEL.

REACTIVITY

REACTIVITY: NO SPECIFIC DATA AVAILABLE. HOWEVER, A NUMBER OF PHOSPHATE AND THIOPHOSPHATE ESTERS ARE OF LIMITED THERMAL STABILITY AND UNDERGO HIGHLY EXOTHERMIC SELF-ACCELERATING DECOMPOSITION REACTIONS.

INCOMPATIBILITIES: BROMOPHOS: ALKALINE CONDITIONS (PH >9): MAY CAUSE HYDROLYSIS. ORGANOMETAL FUNGICIDES: INCOMPATIBLE. SULFUR: INCOMPATIBLE.

DECOMPOSITION: THERMAL DECOMPOSITION MAY RELEASE TOXIC OXIDES OF SULFUR, PHOSPHOROUS AND HAZARDOUS FUMES OF HYDROGEN BROMIDE AND HYDROGEN CHLORIDE.

POLYMERIZATION: HAZARDOUS POLYMERIZATION HAS NOT BEEN REPORTED TO OCCUR UNDER NORMAL TEMPERATURES AND PRESSURES.

STORAGE AND DISPOSAL

OBSERVE ALL FEDERAL, STATE AND LOCAL REGULATIONS WHEN STORING OR DISPOSING OF THIS SUBSTANCE. FOR ASSISTANCE, CONTACT THE DISTRICT DIRECTOR OF THE ENVIRONMENTAL PROTECTION AGENCY.

STORAGE

STORE IN ACCORDANCE WITH 40 CFR 165 RECOMMENDED PROCEDURES FOR THE DISPOSAL AND STORAGE OF PESTICIDES AND PESTICIDE CONTAINERS.
STORE AWAY FROM INCOMPATIBLE SUBSTANCES.

DISPOSAL

DISPOSAL MUST BE IN ACCORDANCE WITH 40 CFR 165 RECOMMENDED PROCEDURES FOR THE DISPOSAL AND STORAGE OF PESTICIDES AND PESTICIDE CONTAINERS.

CONDITIONS TO AVOID

NONE REPORTED.

SPILL AND LEAK PROCEDURES

OCCUPATIONAL SPILL: DO NOT TOUCH SPILLED MATERIAL. STOP LEAK IF YOU CAN DO IT WITHOUT RISK. USE WATER SPRAY TO REDUCE VAPORS. FOR SMALL SPILLS, TAKE UP WITH SAND OR OTHER ABSORBENT MATERIAL AND PLACE INTO CONTAINERS FOR LATER DISPOSAL. FOR SMALL DRY SPILLS, WITH A CLEAN SHOVEL PLACE MATERIAL INTO CLEAN, DRY CONTAINERS AND COVER. MOVE CONTAINERS FROM SPILL AREA. FOR LARGER SPILLS, DIKE FAR AHEAD OF SPILL FOR LATER DISPOSAL. KEEP UNNECESSARY PEOPLE AWAY. ISOLATE HAZARD AREA AND DENY ENTRY. VENTILATE CLOSED SPACES BEFORE ENTERING.

PROTECTIVE EQUIPMENT

VENTILATION: PROVIDE LOCAL EXHAUST OR GENERAL DILUTION VENTILATION SYSTEM.

RESPIRATOR: THE FOLLOWING RESPIRATORS ARE RECOMMENDED BASED ON INFORMATION FOUND IN THE PHYSICAL DATA, TOXICITY AND HEALTH EFFECTS SECTIONS. THEY ARE RANKED IN ORDER FROM MINIMUM TO MAXIMUM RESPIRATORY PROTECTION. THE SPECIFIC RESPIRATOR SELECTED MUST BE BASED ON CONTAMINATION LEVELS FOUND IN THE WORK PLACE, MUST NOT EXCEED THE WORKING LIMITS OF THE RESPIRATOR AND BE JOINTLY APPROVED BY THE NATIONAL INSTITUTE FOR OCCUPATIONAL SAFETY AND HEALTH AND THE MINE SAFETY AND HEALTH ADMINISTRATION (NIOSH-MSHA).

CHEMICAL CARTRIDGE RESPIRATOR WITH PESTICIDE CARTRIDGE.

GAS MASK WITH A PESTICIDE CANISTER (CHIN-STYLE OR FRONT- OR BACK-MOUNTED CANISTER).

TYPE 'C' SUPPLIED-AIR RESPIRATOR OPERATED IN THE PRESSURE-DEMAND OR OTHER POSITIVE PRESSURE OR CONTINUOUS-FLOW MODE.

SELF-CONTAINED BREATHING APPARATUS.

FOR FIREFIGHTING AND OTHER IMMEDIATELY DANGEROUS TO LIFE OR HEALTH CONDITIONS:

SELF-CONTAINED BREATHING APPARATUS WITH FULL FACEPIECE OPERATED IN PRESSURE-DEMAND OR OTHER POSITIVE PRESSURE MODE.

SUPPLIED-AIR RESPIRATOR WITH FULL FACEPIECE AND OPERATED IN PRESSURE-DEMAND OR OTHER POSITIVE PRESSURE MODE IN COMBINATION WITH AN AUXILIARY SELF-CONTAINED BREATHING APPARATUS OPERATED IN PRESSURE-DEMAND OR OTHER POSITIVE PRESSURE MODE.

CLOTHING: EMPLOYEE MUST WEAR APPROPRIATE PROTECTIVE (IMPERVIOUS) CLOTHING AND EQUIPMENT TO PREVENT REPEATED OR PROLONGED SKIN CONTACT WITH THIS SUBSTANCE.

GLOVES: EMPLOYEE MUST WEAR APPROPRIATE PROTECTIVE GLOVES TO PREVENT CONTACT WITH THIS SUBSTANCE.

EYE PROTECTION: EMPLOYEE MUST WEAR SPLASH-PROOF OR DUST-RESISTANT SAFETY GOGGLES TO PREVENT EYE CONTACT WITH THIS SUBSTANCE.

EMERGENCY EYE WASH: WHERE THERE IS ANY POSSIBILITY THAT AN EMPLOYEE'S EYES MAY BE EXPOSED TO THIS SUBSTANCE, THE EMPLOYER SHOULD PROVIDE AN EYE WASH FOUNTAIN WITHIN THE IMMEDIATE WORK AREA FOR EMERGENCY USE.

AUTHORIZED BY- OCCUPATIONAL HEALTH SERVICES, INC.

CREATION DATE: 10/04/89 ***REVISION DATE:*** 05/01/90

MATERIAL SAFETY DATA SHEET

OCCUPATIONAL HEALTH SERVICES, INC.
AGRICULTURE AND PESTICIDE DIVISION
450 SEVENTH AVENUE, SUITE 2407
NEW YORK, NEW YORK 10123
1-800-445-MSDS OR (212) 967-1100

EMERGENCY CONTACT:
JOHN S. BRANSFORD, JR. (615) 292-1180

SUBSTANCE IDENTIFICATION

CAS-NUMBER 314-42-1

SUBSTANCE: **ISOCIL**

TRADE NAMES/SYNONYMS: 2,4(1H,3H)-PYRIMIDINEDIONE, 5-BROMO-6-METHYL-3-(1-METHYLETHYL)-; 5-BROMO-6-METHYL-3-(1-METHYLETHYL)-2,4(1H,3H)-PYRIMIDINEDIONE; URACIL, 5-BROMO-3-ISOPROPYL-6-METHYL-; 5-BROMO-3-ISOPROPYL-6-METHYLURACIL; H 82; HYVAR; ISOPROCIL; C8H11BRN2O2; PST71090

CHEMICAL FAMILY: HETEROCYCLIC NITROGEN HALOGEN COMPOUND, AROMATIC

MOLECULAR FORMULA: C8-H11-BR-N2-O2

MOLECULAR WEIGHT: 247.12

CERCLA RATINGS (SCALE 0-3): HEALTH=2 FIRE=1 REACTIVITY=0 PERSISTENCE=1

NFPA RATINGS (SCALE 0-4): HEALTH=2 FIRE=1 REACTIVITY=0

COMPONENTS AND CONTAMINANTS

COMPONENT: ISOCIL ***PERCENT:*** 100.0

CAS# 314-42-1

OTHER CONTAMINANTS: NONE

EXPOSURE LIMITS: NO OCCUPATIONAL EXPOSURE LIMITS ESTABLISHED BY OSHA, ACGIH, OR NIOSH.

PHYSICAL DATA

DESCRIPTION: CRYSTALLINE SOLID. ***MELTING POINT:*** 316-318 F (158-159 C)

SPECIFIC GRAVITY: NOT AVAILABLE ***SOLUBILITY IN WATER:*** NOT AVAILABLE

SOLVENT SOLUBILITY: SOLUBLE IN ABSOLUTE ALCOHOL.

FIRE AND EXPLOSION DATA

FIRE AND EXPLOSION HAZARD: SLIGHT FIRE HAZARD WHEN EXPOSED TO HEAT OR FLAME.

FIREFIGHTING MEDIA: DRY CHEMICAL, CARBON DIOXIDE, HALON, WATER SPRAY OR STANDARD FOAM (1987 EMERGENCY RESPONSE GUIDEBOOK, DOT P 5800.4).

FOR LARGER FIRES, USE WATER SPRAY, FOG OR STANDARD FOAM (1987 EMERGENCY RESPONSE GUIDEBOOK, DOT P 5800.4).

FIREFIGHTING: MOVE CONTAINER FROM FIRE AREA IF POSSIBLE. DO NOT SCATTER SPILLED MATERIAL WITH HIGH PRESSURE WATER STREAMS. DIKE FIRE CONTROL WATER FOR LATER DISPOSAL (1987 EMERGENCY RESPONSE GUIDEBOOK, DOT P 5800.4, GUIDE PAGE 31).

USE AGENTS SUITABLE FOR TYPE OF SURROUNDING FIRE. AVOID BREATHING HAZARDOUS VAPORS, KEEP UPWIND.

TOXICITY

ISOCIL: TOXICITY DATA: 3400 MG/KG ORAL-RAT LD50; 3750 MG/KG ORAL-MOUSE LDLO. CARCINOGEN STATUS: NONE. ACUTE TOXICITY LEVEL: MODERATELY TOXIC BY INGESTION. TARGET EFFECTS: NO DATA AVAILABLE.

HEALTH EFFECTS AND FIRST AID

INHALATION: ISOCIL: **ACUTE EXPOSURE-** SOME URACIL DERIVATIVE HERBICIDES ARE IRRITATING TO THE MUCOUS MEMBRANES. **CHRONIC EXPOSURE-** NO DATA AVAILABLE.

FIRST AID- REMOVE FROM EXPOSURE AREA TO FRESH AIR IMMEDIATELY. IF BREATHING HAS STOPPED, PERFORM ARTIFICIAL RESPIRATION. KEEP PERSON WARM AND AT REST. TREAT SYMPTOMATICALLY AND SUPPORTIVELY. GET MEDICAL ATTENTION IMMEDIATELY.

SKIN CONTACT: ISOCIL: **ACUTE EXPOSURE-** MAY CAUSE SKIN IRRITATION. **CHRONIC EXPOSURE-** NO DATA AVAILABLE.

FIRST AID- REMOVE CONTAMINATED CLOTHING AND SHOES IMMEDIATELY. WASH AFFECTED AREA WITH SOAP OR MILD DETERGENT AND LARGE AMOUNTS OF WATER UNTIL NO EVIDENCE OF CHEMICAL REMAINS (APPROXIMATELY 15-20 MINUTES). GET MEDICAL ATTENTION IMMEDIATELY.

EYE CONTACT: ISOCIL: **ACUTE EXPOSURE-** MAY CAUSE EYE IRRITATION. **CHRONIC EXPOSURE-** NO DATA AVAILABLE.

FIRST AID- WASH EYES IMMEDIATELY WITH LARGE AMOUNTS OF WATER OR NORMAL SALINE, OCCASIONALLY LIFTING UPPER AND LOWER LIDS, UNTIL NO EVIDENCE OF CHEMICAL REMAINS (APPROXIMATELY 15-20 MINUTES). GET MEDICAL ATTENTION IMMEDIATELY.

INGESTION: ISOCIL: **ACUTE EXPOSURE-** A LETHAL DOSE IN RATS WAS 3400 MG/KG. WITHIN FOUR HOURS OF INGESTING 250 MG/KG, SHEEP DISPLAYED TYMPANY AND STILTED GAIT. **CHRONIC EXPOSURE-** NO DATA AVAILABLE.

FIRST AID- TREAT SYMPTOMATICALLY AND SUPPORTIVELY. GET MEDICAL ATTENTION IMMEDIATELY. IF VOMITING OCCURS, KEEP HEAD LOWER THAN HIPS TO PREVENT ASPIRATION.

ANTIDOTE: NO SPECIFIC ANTIDOTE. TREAT SYMPTOMATICALLY AND SUPPORTIVELY.

REACTIVITY

REACTIVITY: STABLE UNDER NORMAL TEMPERATURES AND PRESSURES.

INCOMPATIBILITIES: ISOCIL: OXIDIZERS (STRONG): FIRE AND EXPLOSION HAZARD.

DECOMPOSITION: THERMAL DECOMPOSITION PRODUCTS MAY INCLUDE TOXIC AND CORROSIVE FUMES OF BROMIDES, AND TOXIC OXIDES OF CARBON AND NITROGEN.

POLYMERIZATION: HAZARDOUS POLYMERIZATION HAS NOT BEEN REPORTED TO OCCUR UNDER NORMAL TEMPERATURES AND PRESSURES.

STORAGE AND DISPOSAL

OBSERVE ALL FEDERAL, STATE AND LOCAL REGULATIONS WHEN STORING OR DISPOSING OF THIS SUBSTANCE. FOR ASSISTANCE, CONTACT THE DISTRICT DIRECTOR OF THE ENVIRONMENTAL PROTECTION AGENCY.

****STORAGE****

STORE IN ACCORDANCE WITH 40 CFR 165 RECOMMENDED PROCEDURES FOR THE DISPOSAL AND STORAGE OF PESTICIDES AND PESTICIDE CONTAINERS.

STORE AWAY FROM INCOMPATIBLE SUBSTANCES.

****DISPOSAL****

DISPOSAL MUST BE IN ACCORDANCE WITH 40 CFR 165 RECOMMENDED PROCEDURES FOR THE DISPOSAL AND STORAGE OF PESTICIDES AND PESTICIDE CONTAINERS.

CONDITIONS TO AVOID

MAY BURN BUT DOES NOT IGNITE READILY. AVOID CONTACT WITH STRONG OXIDIZERS, EXCESSIVE HEAT, SPARKS, OR OPEN FLAME.

SPILL AND LEAK PROCEDURES

OCCUPATIONAL SPILL: STOP LEAK IF YOU CAN DO IT WITHOUT RISK. FOR SMALL SPILLS, TAKE UP WITH SAND OR OTHER ABSORBENT MATERIAL AND PLACE INTO CLEAN, DRY CONTAINERS FOR LATER DISPOSAL. KEEP UNNECESSARY PEOPLE AWAY. ISOLATE HAZARD AREA AND DENY ENTRY.

PROTECTIVE EQUIPMENT

VENTILATION: PROVIDE LOCAL EXHAUST OR GENERAL DILUTION VENTILATION SYSTEM.

RESPIRATOR: THE FOLLOWING RESPIRATORS ARE RECOMMENDED BASED ON INFORMATION FOUND IN THE PHYSICAL DATA, TOXICITY AND HEALTH EFFECTS SECTIONS. THEY ARE RANKED IN ORDER FROM MINIMUM TO MAXIMUM RESPIRATORY PROTECTION. THE SPECIFIC RESPIRATOR SELECTED MUST BE BASED ON CONTAMINATION LEVELS FOUND IN THE WORK PLACE, MUST NOT EXCEED THE WORKING LIMITS OF THE RESPIRATOR AND BE JOINTLY APPROVED BY THE NATIONAL INSTITUTE FOR OCCUPATIONAL SAFETY AND HEALTH AND THE MINE SAFETY AND HEALTH ADMINISTRATION (NIOSH-MSHA).

CHEMICAL CARTRIDGE RESPIRATOR WITH AN ORGANIC VAPOR CARTRIDGE(S) WITH A FULL FACEPIECE AND ORGANIC VAPOR CARTRIDGE(S) IN COMBINATION WITH A DUST AND MIST FILTER.

POWERED AIR-PURIFYING RESPIRATOR WITH A TIGHT-FITTING FACEPIECE AND ORGANIC VAPOR CARTRIDGE(S) IN COMBINATION WITH A HIGH-EFFICIENCY PARTICULATE FILTER.

TYPE 'C' SUPPLIED-AIR RESPIRATOR WITH A FULL FACEPIECE OPERATED IN A PRESSURE-DEMAND OR OTHER POSITIVE PRESSURE MODE.

SELF-CONTAINED BREATHING APPARATUS WITH A FULL FACEPIECE OPERATED IN PRESSURE-DEMAND OR OTHER POSITIVE PRESSURE MODE.

FOR FIREFIGHTING AND OTHER IMMEDIATELY DANGEROUS TO LIFE OR HEALTH CONDITIONS:

SELF-CONTAINED BREATHING APPARATUS WITH FULL FACEPIECE OPERATED IN PRESSURE-DEMAND OR OTHER POSITIVE PRESSURE MODE.

SUPPLIED-AIR RESPIRATOR WITH FULL FACEPIECE AND OPERATED IN PRESSURE-DEMAND OR OTHER POSITIVE PRESSURE MODE IN COMBINATION WITH AN AUXILIARY SELF-CONTAINED BREATHING APPARATUS OPERATED IN PRESSURE-DEMAND OR OTHER POSITIVE PRESSURE MODE.

CLOTHING: EMPLOYEE MUST WEAR APPROPRIATE PROTECTIVE (IMPERVIOUS) CLOTHING AND EQUIPMENT TO PREVENT REPEATED OR PROLONGED SKIN CONTACT WITH THIS SUBSTANCE.

GLOVES: EMPLOYEE MUST WEAR APPROPRIATE PROTECTIVE GLOVES TO PREVENT CONTACT WITH THIS SUBSTANCE.

EYE PROTECTION: EMPLOYEE MUST WEAR SPLASH-PROOF OR DUST-RESISTANT SAFETY GOGGLES TO PREVENT EYE CONTACT WITH THIS SUBSTANCE.

EMERGENCY EYE WASH: WHERE THERE IS ANY POSSIBILITY THAT AN EMPLOYEE'S EYES MAY BE EXPOSED TO THIS SUBSTANCE, THE EMPLOYER SHOULD PROVIDE AN EYE WASH FOUNTAIN WITHIN THE IMMEDIATE WORK AREA FOR EMERGENCY USE.

AUTHORIZED BY- OCCUPATIONAL HEALTH SERVICES, INC.

CREATION DATE: 10/04/89 ***REVISION DATE:*** 05/14/90

MATERIAL SAFETY DATA SHEET

OCCUPATIONAL HEALTH SERVICES, INC.
AGRICULTURE AND PESTICIDE DIVISION
450 SEVENTH AVENUE, SUITE 2407
NEW YORK, NEW YORK 10123
1-800-445-MSDS OR (212) 967-1100

EMERGENCY CONTACT:
JOHN S. BRANSFORD, JR. (615) 292-1180

SUBSTANCE IDENTIFICATION

CAS-NUMBER 5902-51-2

SUBSTANCE: **TERBACIL**

TRADE NAMES/SYNONYMS: 2,4(1H,3H)-PYRIMIDINEDIONE, 5-CHLORO-3-(1,1-DIMETHYLETHYL)-6-METHYL-; 5-CHLORO-3-(1,1-DIMETHYLETHYL)-6-METHYL-2,4(1H,3H)-PYRIMIDINEDIONE; URACIL, 3-TERT-BUTYL-5-CHLORO-6-METHYL-; 3-TERT-BUTYL-5-CHLORO-6-METHYLURACIL; DU PONT 732; EXPERIMENTAL HERBICIDE 732; SINBAR; TURBACIL; C9H13CLN2O2; PST71099

CHEMICAL FAMILY: HETEROCYCLIC NITROGEN HALOGEN COMPOUND, AROMATIC

MOLECULAR FORMULA: C9-H13-CL-N2-O2

MOLECULAR WEIGHT: 216.65

CERCLA RATINGS (SCALE 0-3): HEALTH=1 FIRE=1 REACTIVITY=0 PERSISTENCE=0

NFPA RATINGS (SCALE 0-4): HEALTH=1 FIRE=1 REACTIVITY=0

COMPONENTS AND CONTAMINANTS

COMPONENT: TERBACIL ***PERCENT:*** 100.0
CAS# 5902-51-2

OTHER CONTAMINANTS: NONE

EXPOSURE LIMITS: NO OCCUPATIONAL EXPOSURE LIMITS ESTABLISHED BY OSHA, ACGIH, OR NIOSH.

PHYSICAL DATA

DESCRIPTION: ODORLESS, WHITE CRYSTALLINE SOLID.

MELTING POINT: 347-351 F (175-177 C) ***SPECIFIC GRAVITY:*** 1.34

VAPOR PRESSURE: NEGLIGIBLE ***SOLUBILITY IN WATER:*** 0.071% @ 25 C

SOLVENT SOLUBILITY: SOLUBLE IN DIMETHYLFORMAMIDE, DIMETHYLACETAMIDE, CYCLO- HEXANONE; MODERATELY SOLUBLE IN METHYL ISOBUTYL KETONE, BUTYL ACETATE, XYLENE.

FIRE AND EXPLOSION DATA

FIRE AND EXPLOSION HAZARD: SLIGHT FIRE HAZARD WHEN EXPOSED TO HEAT OR FLAME.

FIREFIGHTING MEDIA: DRY CHEMICAL, CARBON DIOXIDE, HALON, WATER SPRAY OR STANDARD FOAM (1987 EMERGENCY RESPONSE GUIDEBOOK, DOT P 5800.4). FOR LARGER FIRES, USE WATER SPRAY, FOG OR STANDARD FOAM (1987 EMERGENCY RESPONSE GUIDEBOOK, DOT P 5800.4).

FIREFIGHTING: MOVE CONTAINER FROM FIRE AREA IF POSSIBLE. DO NOT SCATTER SPILLED MATERIAL WITH HIGH PRESSURE WATER STREAMS. DIKE FIRE CONTROL WATER FOR LATER DISPOSAL (1987 EMERGENCY RESPONSE GUIDEBOOK, DOT P 5800.4, GUIDE PAGE 31).

USE AGENTS SUITABLE FOR TYPE OF SURROUNDING FIRE. AVOID BREATHING HAZARDOUS VAPORS, KEEP UPWIND.

TOXICITY

TERBACIL: TOXICITY DATA: 7500 MG/KG ORAL-RAT LD50; 5000 MG/KG UNREPORTED-MAMMAL LD50. CARCINOGEN STATUS: NONE. ACUTE TOXICITY LEVEL: SLIGHTLY TOXIC BY INGESTION. TARGET EFFECTS: NO DATA AVAILABLE.

HEALTH EFFECTS AND FIRST AID

INHALATION: TERBACIL: **ACUTE EXPOSURE-** MAY CAUSE IRRITATION OF THE NOSE, THROAT, AND MUCOUS MEMBRANES. **CHRONIC EXPOSURE-** NO DATA AVAILABLE.

FIRST AID- REMOVE FROM EXPOSURE AREA TO FRESH AIR IMMEDIATELY. IF BREATHING HAS STOPPED, PERFORM ARTIFICIAL RESPIRATION. KEEP PERSON WARM AND AT REST. TREAT SYMPTOMATICALLY AND SUPPORTIVELY. GET MEDICAL ATTENTION IMMEDIATELY.

SKIN CONTACT: TERBACIL: **ACUTE EXPOSURE-** 5000 MG/KG APPLIED TO RABBIT SKIN DID NOT PRODUCE ANY SIGNS OF SYSTEMIC TOXICITY OR IRRITATION. **CHRONIC EXPOSURE-** NO DATA AVAILABLE.

FIRST AID- REMOVE CONTAMINATED CLOTHING AND SHOES IMMEDIATELY. WASH AFFECTED AREA WITH SOAP OR MILD DETERGENT AND LARGE AMOUNTS OF WATER UNTIL NO EVIDENCE OF CHEMICAL REMAINS (APPROXIMATELY 15-20 MINUTES). GET MEDICAL ATTENTION IMMEDIATELY.

EYE CONTACT: TERBACIL: **ACUTE EXPOSURE-** THIS MATERIAL WAS MILDLY IRRITATING TO RABBIT EYES. **CHRONIC EXPOSURE-** NO DATA AVAILABLE.

FIRST AID- WASH EYES IMMEDIATELY WITH LARGE AMOUNTS OF WATER OR NORMAL SALINE, OCCASIONALLY LIFTING UPPER AND LOWER LIDS, UNTIL NO EVIDENCE OF CHEMICAL REMAINS (APPROXIMATELY 15-20 MINUTES). GET MEDICAL ATTENTION IMMEDIATELY.

INGESTION: TERBACIL: **ACUTE EXPOSURE-** CLINICAL SIGNS OF POISONING IN RATS WERE INITIAL WEIGHT LOSS, PALLOR, PROSTRATION, AND RAPID RESPIRATION. IN DOGS, 5 GM/KG PRODUCED EMESIS AND LACK OF PUPILLARY RESPONSE; NO DEATHS OCCURRED DUE TO REPEATED EMESIS. **CHRONIC EXPOSURE-** LOWER RATE OF WEIGHT GAIN, LIVER ENLARGEMENT, AND SLIGHT HISTOPATHOLOGICAL CHANGES IN THE LIVER WERE OBSERVED IN A STUDY OF RATS FED AT 2500 TO 10,000 PPM; IN DOGS FED HIGH DOSES, A SLIGHT INCREASE IN LIVER WEIGHT WAS NOTED. INCIDENCES OF HYDROPHENPHROSIS WERE OBSERVED IN ONE TERATOLOGY STUDY OF LABORATORY ANIMALS.

FIRST AID- REMOVE BY GASTRIC LAVAGE AND CATHARSIS. MAINTAIN BLOOD PRESSURE AND AIRWAY. GIVE OXYGEN IF RESPIRATION IS DEPRESSED. DO NOT PERFORM GASTRIC LAVAGE IF VICTIM IS UNCONSCIOUS. GET MEDICAL ATTENTION

IMMEDIATELY (DREISBACH, HANDBOOK OF POISONING, 12TH ED.).
ADMINISTRATION OF LAVAGE OR OXYGEN SHOULD BE PERFORMED BY QUALIFIED MEDICAL PERSONNEL.
ANTIDOTE: NO SPECIFIC ANTIDOTE. TREAT SYMPTOMATICALLY AND SUPPORTIVELY.

REACTIVITY

REACTIVITY: STABLE UNDER NORMAL TEMPERATURES AND PRESSURES.
INCOMPATIBILITIES: TERBACIL: OXIDIZERS (STRONG): FIRE AND EXPLSION HAZARD.
DECOMPOSITION: THERMAL DECOMPOSITION PRODUCTS MAY INCLUDE TOXIC OXIDES OF NITROGEN AND CARBON AND TOXIC AND CORROSIVE FUMES OF CHLORIDES.
POLYMERIZATION: HAZARDOUS POLYMERIZATION HAS NOT BEEN REPORTED TO OCCUR UNDER NORMAL TEMPERATURES AND PRESSURES.

STORAGE AND DISPOSAL

OBSERVE ALL FEDERAL, STATE AND LOCAL REGULATIONS WHEN STORING OR DISPOSING OF THIS SUBSTANCE. FOR ASSISTANCE, CONTACT THE DISTRICT DIRECTOR OF THE ENVIRONMENTAL PROTECTION AGENCY.

STORAGE

STORE IN ACCORDANCE WITH 40 CFR 165 RECOMMENDED PROCEDURES FOR THE DISPOSAL AND STORAGE OF PESTICIDES AND PESTICIDE CONTAINERS.
STORE AWAY FROM INCOMPATIBLE SUBSTANCES.

DISPOSAL

DISPOSAL MUST BE IN ACCORDANCE WITH 40 CFR 165 RECOMMENDED PROCEDURES FOR THE DISPOSAL AND STORAGE OF PESTICIDES AND PESTICIDE CONTAINERS.

CONDITIONS TO AVOID

MAY BURN BUT DOES NOT IGNITE READILY. AVOID CONTACT WITH STRONG OXIDIZERS, EXCESSIVE HEAT, SPARKS, OR OPEN FLAME.

SPILL AND LEAK PROCEDURES

OCCUPATIONAL SPILL: STOP LEAK IF YOU CAN DO IT WITHOUT RISK. FOR SMALL SPILLS, TAKE UP WITH SAND OR OTHER ABSORBENT MATERIAL AND PLACE INTO CLEAN, DRY CONTAINERS FOR LATER DISPOSAL. KEEP UNNECESSARY PEOPLE AWAY. ISOLATE HAZARD AREA AND DENY ENTRY.

PROTECTIVE EQUIPMENT

VENTILATION: PROVIDE GENERAL DILUTION VENTILATION.
RESPIRATOR: THE FOLLOWING RESPIRATORS ARE RECOMMENDED BASED ON INFORMATION FOUND IN THE PHYSICAL DATA, TOXICITY AND HEALTH EFFECTS SECTIONS. THEY ARE RANKED IN ORDER FROM MINIMUM TO MAXIMUM RESPIRATORY PROTECTION. THE SPECIFIC RESPIRATOR SELECTED MUST BE BASED ON CONTAMINATION LEVELS FOUND IN THE WORK PLACE, MUST NOT EXCEED THE WORKING LIMITS OF THE RESPIRATOR AND BE JOINTLY APPROVED BY THE NATIONAL INSTITUTE FOR OCCUPATIONAL SAFETY AND HEALTH AND THE MINE SAFETY AND HEALTH ADMINISTRATION (NIOSH-MSHA).
CHEMICAL CARTRIDGE RESPIRATOR WITH AN ORGANIC VAPOR CARTRIDGE(S) IN COMBINATION WITH A DUST AND MIST FILTER.
GAS MASK WITH ORGANIC VAPOR CANISTER (CHIN-STYLE OR FRONT- OR BACK-MOUNTED CANISTER) WITH A DUST AND MIST FILTER.
GAS MASK WITH ORGANIC VAPOR CANISTER (CHIN-STYLE OR FRONT- OR BACK-MOUNTED CANISTER) WITH A PARTICULATE FILTER.
POWERED AIR-PURIFYING RESPIRATOR WITH A HIGH-EFFICIENCY FILTER.
TYPE 'C' SUPPLIED-AIR RESPIRATOR WITH A FULL FACEPIECE OPERATED IN A PRESSURE-DEMAND OR OTHER POSITIVE PRESSURE MODE.
SELF-CONTAINED BREATHING APPARATUS WITH A FULL FACEPIECE OPERATED IN PRESSURE-DEMAND OR OTHER POSITIVE PRESSURE MODE.
FOR FIREFIGHTING AND OTHER IMMEDIATELY DANGEROUS TO LIFE OR HEALTH CONDITIONS:
SELF-CONTAINED BREATHING APPARATUS WITH FULL FACEPIECE OPERATED IN PRESSURE-DEMAND OR OTHER POSITIVE PRESSURE MODE.
SUPPLIED-AIR RESPIRATOR WITH FULL FACEPIECE AND OPERATED IN PRESSURE-DEMAND OR OTHER POSITIVE PRESSURE MODE IN COMBINATION WITH AN AUXILIARY SELF-CONTAINED BREATHING APPARATUS OPERATED IN PRESSURE-DEMAND OR OTHER POSITIVE PRESSURE MODE.
CLOTHING: EMPLOYEE MUST WEAR APPROPRIATE PROTECTIVE (IMPERVIOUS) CLOTHING AND EQUIPMENT TO PREVENT REPEATED OR PROLONGED SKIN CONTACT WITH THIS SUBSTANCE.
GLOVES: EMPLOYEE MUST WEAR APPROPRIATE PROTECTIVE GLOVES TO PREVENT CONTACT WITH THIS SUBSTANCE.
EYE PROTECTION: EMPLOYEE MUST WEAR SPLASH-PROOF OR DUST-RESISTANT SAFETY GOGGLES TO PREVENT EYE CONTACT WITH THIS SUBSTANCE.
EMERGENCY EYE WASH: WHERE THERE IS ANY POSSIBILITY THAT AN EMPLOYEE'S EYES MAY BE EXPOSED TO THIS SUBSTANCE, THE EMPLOYER SHOULD PROVIDE AN EYE WASH FOUNTAIN WITHIN THE IMMEDIATE WORK AREA FOR EMERGENCY USE.

AUTHORIZED BY- OCCUPATIONAL HEALTH SERVICES, INC.
CREATION DATE: 10/05/89 ***REVISION DATE:*** 05/15/90

MATERIAL SAFETY DATA SHEET

OCCUPATIONAL HEALTH SERVICES, INC.
AGRICULTURE AND PESTICIDE DIVISION
450 SEVENTH AVENUE, SUITE 2407
NEW YORK, NEW YORK 10123
1-800-445-MSDS OR (212) 967-1100

EMERGENCY CONTACT:
JOHN S. BRANSFORD, JR. (615) 292-1180

SUBSTANCE IDENTIFICATION

CAS-NUMBER 8018-01-7
SUBSTANCE: <u>MANCOZEB</u>
TRADE NAMES/SYNONYMS: MANGANESE, ((1,2-ETHANEDIYLBIS(CARBAMODITHIOATO))(2-))-, MIXTURE WITH ((1,2-ETHANEDIYLBIS(CARBAMODITHIOATO))(2-))ZINC; CARBAMIC ACID, ETHYLENEBIS(DITHIO , MANGANESE ZINC COMPLEX; ETHYLENEBIS(DITHIOCARBAMIC ACID) MANGANESE ZINC COMPLEX; MANGANESE ETHYLENEBIS(DITHIOCARBAMATE) (POLYMERIC) COMPLEX WITH ZINC SALT; ((1,2-ETHANEDIYLBIS(CARBAMODITHIOATO))(2-))MANGANESE MIXTURE WITH ((1,2-ETHANEDIYLBIS(CARBAMODITHIOATO))(2-))ZINC; (ETHYLENEBIS(DITHIOCARBAMATO))MANGANESE MIXTURE WITH (ETHYLENEBIS(DITHIOCARBAMATO))ZINC; DITHANE M-45; FORE; MANEB-ZINC; MANZATE 200; MANZEB; RCRA U114; PST71120
CHEMICAL FAMILY: THIOCARBAMATE
METAL SALT
MOLECULAR FORMULA: (C4-H6-N2-S4.MN)X.(ZN)Z
MOLECULAR WEIGHT: 541.04
CERCLA RATINGS (SCALE 0-3): HEALTH=2 FIRE=1 REACTIVITY=0 PERSISTENCE=0
NFPA RATINGS (SCALE 0-4): HEALTH=U FIRE=1 REACTIVITY=0

COMPONENTS AND CONTAMINANTS

COMPONENT: MANCOZEB ***PERCENT:*** 100.0
CAS# 8018-01-7
OTHER CONTAMINANTS: ETHYLENE DIAMINE, ETHYLENE THIOUREA
EXPOSURE LIMITS: MANCOZEB: 1 MG/M3 ROHM AND HAAS RECOMMENDED TWA
SUBJECT TO CALIFORNIA PROPOSITION 65 CANCER AND/OR REPRODUCTIVE TOXICITY WARNING AND RELEASE REQUIREMENTS- (JANUARY 1, 1990)
MANGANESE COMPOUNDS (AS MN): 5 MG/M3 OSHA CEILING 5 MG/M3 ACGIH TWA
SUBJECT TO SARA 313 ANNUAL TOXIC CHEMICAL RELEASE REPORTING.

PHYSICAL DATA

DESCRIPTION: GREYISH-YELLOW POWDER WITH MUSTY ODOR.
MELTING POINT: 378-399 F (192-204 C) DECOMPOSES ***SPECIFIC GRAVITY:*** 0.35-0.55
VAPOR PRESSURE: NEGLIGIBLE ***SOLUBILITY IN WATER:*** DISPERSIBLE
SOLVENT SOLUBILITY: INSOLUBLE IN MOST ORGANIC SOLVENTS

FIRE AND EXPLOSION DATA

FIRE AND EXPLOSION HAZARD: SLIGHT FIRE HAZARD WHEN EXPOSED TO HEAT OR FLAME.
DUST-AIR MIXTURES MAY IGNITE OR EXPLODE.
FLASH POINT: 280 F (138 C) (OC) ***LOWER EXPLOSIVE LIMIT:*** 16 OZ/FT3
AUTOIGNITION TEMP.: 270 F (132 C) (LAYER)
FIREFIGHTING MEDIA: DRY CHEMICAL, CARBON DIOXIDE, HALON, WATER SPRAY OR STANDARD FOAM (1987 EMERGENCY RESPONSE GUIDEBOOK, DOT P 5800.4).
FOR LARGER FIRES, USE WATER SPRAY, FOG OR STANDARD FOAM (1987 EMERGENCY RESPONSE GUIDEBOOK, DOT P 5800.4).
FIREFIGHTING: MOVE CONTAINERS FROM FIRE AREA IF POSSIBLE. FIGHT FIRE FROM MAXIMUM DISTANCE. STAY AWAY FROM STORAGE TANK ENDS. DIKE FIRE CONTROL WATER FOR LATER DISPOSAL. DO NOT SCATTER MATERIAL (1987 EMERGENCY RESPONSE GUIDEBOOK, DOT P 5800.4, GUIDE PAGE 55).
EXTINGUISH FIRE USING AGENTS SUITABLE FOR TYPE OF SURROUNDING FIRE. USE WATER IN FLOODING AMOUNTS AS FOG. USE ALCOHOL FOAM, CARBON DIOXIDE OR DRY CHEMICAL. AVOID BREATHING TOXIC VAPORS, KEEP UPWIND.

STORAGE AND DISPOSAL

OBSERVE ALL FEDERAL, STATE AND LOCAL REGULATIONS WHEN STORING OR DISPOSING OF THIS SUBSTANCE. FOR ASSISTANCE, CONTACT THE DISTRICT DIRECTOR OF THE ENVIRONMENTAL PROTECTION AGENCY.

STORAGE

STORE IN ACCORDANCE WITH 40 CFR 165 RECOMMENDED PROCEDURES FOR THE DISPOSAL AND STORAGE OF PESTICIDES AND PESTICIDE CONTAINERS.
STORE AWAY FROM INCOMPATIBLE SUBSTANCES.
DO NOT STORE AT TEMPERATURES OVER 86 F (30 C). PROTECT PRODUCT FROM MOISTURE AND SOLAR RADIATION.
STORE AWAY FROM FOOD, DRINK, TOBACCO AND FEED PRODUCTS.
DO NOT STORE BAGS IN STACKS OF 10 OR MORE BAGS.

DISPOSAL

DISPOSAL MUST BE IN ACCORDANCE WITH STANDARDS APPLICABLE TO GENERATORS OF HAZARDOUS WASTE, 40CFR 262. EPA HAZARDOUS WASTE NUMBER U114.

CONDITIONS TO AVOID

MAY BURN BUT DOES NOT IGNITE READILY. CONTAINERS MAY EXPLODE IN HEAT OF FIRE.

SPILL AND LEAK PROCEDURES

WATER SPILL: THE CALIFORNIA SAFE DRINKING WATER AND TOXIC ENFORCEMENT ACT OF 1986 (PROPOSITION 65) PROHIBITS CONTAMINATING ANY KNOWN SOURCE OF DRINKING WATER WITH SUBSTANCES KNOWN TO CAUSE CANCER AND/OR REPRODUCTIVE TOXICITY.

OCCUPATIONAL SPILL: DO NOT TOUCH SPILLED MATERIAL. STOP LEAK IF YOU CAN DO IT WITHOUT RISK. USE WATER SPRAY TO REDUCE VAPORS. FOR SMALL SPILLS, TAKE UP WITH SAND OR OTHER ABSORBENT MATERIAL AND PLACE INTO CONTAINERS FOR LATER DISPOSAL. FOR SMALL DRY SPILLS, WITH A CLEAN SHOVEL PLACE MATERIAL INTO CLEAN, DRY CONTAINERS AND COVER. MOVE CONTAINERS FROM SPILL AREA. FOR LARGER SPILLS, DIKE FAR AHEAD OF SPILL FOR LATER DISPOSAL. KEEP UNNECESSARY PEOPLE AWAY. ISOLATE HAZARD AREA AND DENY ENTRY. VENTILATE CLOSED SPACES BEFORE ENTERING.

PROTECTIVE EQUIPMENT

VENTILATION: PROVIDE LOCAL EXHAUST OR GENERAL DILUTION VENTILATION SYSTEM.

RESPIRATOR: THE FOLLOWING RESPIRATORS ARE RECOMMENDED BASED ON INFORMATION FOUND IN THE PHYSICAL DATA, TOXICITY AND HEALTH EFFECTS SECTIONS. THEY ARE RANKED IN ORDER FROM MINIMUM TO MAXIMUM RESPIRATORY PROTECTION. THE SPECIFIC RESPIRATOR SELECTED MUST BE BASED ON CONTAMINATION LEVELS FOUND IN THE WORK PLACE, MUST NOT EXCEED THE WORKING LIMITS OF THE RESPIRATOR AND BE JOINTLY APPROVED BY THE NATIONAL INSTITUTE FOR OCCUPATIONAL SAFETY AND HEALTH AND THE MINE SAFETY AND HEALTH ADMINISTRATION (NIOSH-MSHA).
CHEMICAL CARTRIDGE RESPIRATOR WITH AN ORGANIC VAPOR CARTRIDGE(S) WITH A FULL FACEPIECE AND ORGANIC VAPOR CARTRIDGE(S) IN COMBINATION WITH A DUST AND MIST FILTER.
POWERED AIR-PURIFYING RESPIRATOR WITH A TIGHT-FITTING FACEPIECE AND ORGANIC VAPOR CARTRIDGE(S) IN COMBINATION WITH A HIGH-EFFICIENCY PARTICULATE FILTER.
TYPE 'C' SUPPLIED-AIR RESPIRATOR WITH A FULL FACEPIECE OPERATED IN A PRESSURE-DEMAND OR OTHER POSITIVE PRESSURE MODE.
SELF-CONTAINED BREATHING APPARATUS WITH A FULL FACEPIECE OPERATED IN PRESSURE-DEMAND OR OTHER POSITIVE PRESSURE MODE.
FOR FIREFIGHTING AND OTHER IMMEDIATELY DANGEROUS TO LIFE OR HEALTH CONDITIONS:
SELF-CONTAINED BREATHING APPARATUS WITH FULL FACEPIECE OPERATED IN PRESSURE-DEMAND OR OTHER POSITIVE PRESSURE MODE.
SUPPLIED-AIR RESPIRATOR WITH FULL FACEPIECE AND OPERATED IN PRESSURE-DEMAND OR OTHER POSITIVE PRESSURE MODE IN COMBINATION WITH AN AUXILIARY SELF-CONTAINED BREATHING APPARATUS OPERATED IN PRESSURE-DEMAND OR OTHER POSITIVE PRESSURE MODE.

CLOTHING: EMPLOYEE MUST WEAR APPROPRIATE PROTECTIVE (IMPERVIOUS) CLOTHING AND EQUIPMENT TO PREVENT REPEATED OR PROLONGED SKIN CONTACT WITH THIS SUBSTANCE.

GLOVES: EMPLOYEE MUST WEAR APPROPRIATE PROTECTIVE GLOVES TO PREVENT CONTACT WITH THIS SUBSTANCE.

EYE PROTECTION: EMPLOYEE MUST WEAR SPLASH-PROOF OR DUST-RESISTANT SAFETY GOGGLES TO PREVENT EYE CONTACT WITH THIS SUBSTANCE.
EMERGENCY EYE WASH: WHERE THERE IS ANY POSSIBILITY THAT AN EMPLOYEE'S EYES MAY BE EXPOSED TO THIS SUBSTANCE, THE EMPLOYER SHOULD PROVIDE AN EYE WASH FOUNTAIN WITHIN THE IMMEDIATE WORK AREA FOR EMERGENCY USE.

AUTHORIZED BY- OCCUPATIONAL HEALTH SERVICES, INC.
CREATION DATE: 10/04/89 ***REVISION DATE:*** 05/18/90

MATERIAL SAFETY DATA SHEET

OCCUPATIONAL HEALTH SERVICES, INC.
AGRICULTURE AND PESTICIDE DIVISION
450 SEVENTH AVENUE, SUITE 2407
NEW YORK, NEW YORK 10123
1-800-445-MSDS OR (212) 967-1100

EMERGENCY CONTACT:
JOHN S. BRANSFORD, JR. (615) 292-1180

SUBSTANCE IDENTIFICATION

CAS-NUMBER 50-31-7

SUBSTANCE: **2,3,6-TRICHLOROBENZOIC ACID**

TRADE NAMES/SYNONYMS: BENZOIC ACID, 2,3,6-TRICHLORO-; BENZAC; 2,3,6-TBA; TCB; TCBA; 2,3,6-TCBA; TRYSBEN; TRICHLOROBENZOIC ACID; C7H3CL3O2; PST71134

CHEMICAL FAMILY: CARBOXYLIC ACID, AROMATIC HALOGEN

MOLECULAR FORMULA: CL3-C6-H2-C-O-O-H

MOLECULAR WEIGHT: 225.46

CERCLA RATINGS (SCALE 0-3): HEALTH=2 FIRE=1 REACTIVITY=0 PERSISTENCE=3

NFPA RATINGS (SCALE 0-4): HEALTH=U FIRE=1 REACTIVITY=0

COMPONENTS AND CONTAMINANTS

COMPONENT: 2,3,6-TRICHLOROBENZOIC ACID ***PERCENT:*** 100.0
CAS# 50-31-7

OTHER CONTAMINANTS: NONE

EXPOSURE LIMITS: NO OCCUPATIONAL EXPOSURE LIMITS ESTABLISHED BY OSHA, ACGIH, OR NIOSH.

PHYSICAL DATA

DESCRIPTION: SOLID. ***MELTING POINT:*** 255-257 F (124-125 C)
SPECIFIC GRAVITY: NOT AVAILABLE ***SOLUBILITY IN WATER:*** SOLUBLE
SOLVENT SOLUBILITY: SOLUBLE IN ETHER.

FIRE AND EXPLOSION DATA

FIRE AND EXPLOSION HAZARD: SLIGHT FIRE HAZARD WHEN EXPOSED TO HEAT OR FLAME.

FIREFIGHTING MEDIA: DRY CHEMICAL, CARBON DIOXIDE, HALON, WATER SPRAY OR STANDARD FOAM (1987 EMERGENCY RESPONSE GUIDEBOOK, DOT P 5800.4).
FOR LARGER FIRES, USE WATER SPRAY, FOG OR STANDARD FOAM (1987 EMERGENCY RESPONSE GUIDEBOOK, DOT P 5800.4).

FIREFIGHTING: MOVE CONTAINERS FROM FIRE AREA IF POSSIBLE (1987 EMERGENCY RESPONSE GUIDEBOOK, DOT P 5800.4, GUIDE PAGE 53).
EXTINGUISH FIRE USING AGENTS SUITABLE FOR TYPE OF SURROUNDING FIRE. USE WATER IN FLOODING AMOUNTS AS A FOG. AVOID BREATHING DUSTS AND FUMES FROM BURNING MATERIAL; KEEP UPWIND.

TOXICITY

2,3,6-TRICHLOROBENZOIC ACID: TOXICITY DATA: 650 MG/KG ORAL-RAT LD50; 600 MG/KG ORAL-RABBIT LD50; 1218 MG/KG ORAL-GUINEA PIG LD50; 1000 MG/KG INTRAPERITONEAL-RAT LD50; 178 MG/KG INTRAPERITONEAL-MOUSE LD50; 1500 MG/KG SUBCUTANEOUS-MOUSE LD50; 700 MG/KG UNREPORTED-MAMMAL LD50. CARCINOGEN STATUS: NONE. ACUTE TOXICITY LEVEL: MODERATELY TOXIC BY INGESTION. TARGET EFFECTS: NO DATA AVAILABLE. ADDITIONAL DATA: CHRONIC EXPOSURE MAY PRODUCE SLEEP DISORDERS.

HEALTH EFFECTS AND FIRST AID

INHALATION: 2,3,6-TRICHLOROBENZOIC ACID: **ACUTE EXPOSURE**- MAY CAUSE IRRITATION TO THE MUCOUS MEMBRANES. **CHRONIC EXPOSURE**- NO DATA AVAILABLE.

FIRST AID- REMOVE FROM EXPOSURE AREA TO FRESH AIR IMMEDIATELY. IF BREATHING HAS STOPPED, PERFORM ARTIFICIAL RESPIRATION. KEEP PERSON WARM AND AT REST. TREAT SYMPTOMATICALLY AND SUPPORTIVELY. GET MEDICAL ATTENTION IMMEDIATELY.

SKIN CONTACT: 2,3,6-TRICHLOROBENZOIC ACID: **ACUTE EXPOSURE**- MAY CAUSE IRRITATION. **CHRONIC EXPOSURE**- A SECOND APPLICATION RESULTED IN ERYTHEMA AND EDEMA IN RABBITS.

FIRST AID- REMOVE CONTAMINATED CLOTHING AND SHOES IMMEDIATELY. WASH AFFECTED AREA WITH SOAP OR MILD DETERGENT AND LARGE AMOUNTS OF WATER UNTIL NO EVIDENCE OF CHEMICAL REMAINS (APPROXIMATELY 15-20 MINUTES). GET MEDICAL ATTENTION IMMEDIATELY.

EYE CONTACT: 2,3,6-TRICHLOROBENZOIC ACID: **ACUTE EXPOSURE**- MAY CAUSE IRRITATION. **CHRONIC EXPOSURE**- NO DATA AVAILABLE.
FIRST AID- WASH EYES IMMEDIATELY WITH LARGE AMOUNTS OF WATER OR NORMAL SALINE, OCCASIONALLY LIFTING UPPER AND LOWER LIDS, UNTIL NO EVIDENCE OF CHEMICAL REMAINS (APPROXIMATELY 15-20 MINUTES). GET MEDICAL ATTENTION IMMEDIATELY.

INGESTION: 2,3,6-TRICHLOROBENZOIC ACID: **ACUTE EXPOSURE**- INGESTION OF TRICHLOROBENZOIC ACID CAUSED SALIVATION, TREMOR, DEPRESSION, TYMPANITES, LUNG CONGESTION AND HEMORRHAGING, AND KIDNEY INFLAMMATION IN CATTLE AND SHEEP. **CHRONIC EXPOSURE**- NO DATA AVAILABLE.
FIRST AID- REMOVE BY GASTRIC LAVAGE OR EMESIS. MAINTAIN BLOOD PRESSURE AND AIRWAY. DO NOT PERFORM GASTRIC LAVAGE OR EMESIS IF VICTIM IS UNCONSCIOUS. DO NOT GIVE STIMULANTS WHICH MAY INDUCE VENTRICULAR FIBRILLATION. GET MEDICAL ATTENTION IMMEDIATELY. (DREISBACH, HANDBOOK OF POISONING, 11TH EDITION) ADMINISTRATION OF GASTRIC LAVAGE SHOULD BE PERFORMED BY QUALIFIED MEDICAL PERSONNEL.
ANTIDOTE: NO SPECIFIC ANTIDOTE. TREAT SYMPTOMATICALLY AND SUPPORTIVELY.

REACTIVITY

REACTIVITY: STABLE UNDER NORMAL TEMPERATURES AND PRESSURES.
INCOMPATIBILITIES: 2,3,6-TRICHLOROBENZOIC ACID: OXIDIZERS (STRONG): FIRE AND EXPLOSION HAZARD.
DECOMPOSITION: THERMAL DECOMPOSITION PRODUCTS MAY INCLUDE TOXIC AND CORROSIVE FUMES OF CHLORIDES AND TOXIC OXIDES OF CARBON.
POLYMERIZATION: HAZARDOUS POLYMERIZATION HAS NOT BEEN REPORTED TO OCCUR UNDER NORMAL TEMPERATURES AND PRESSURES.

STORAGE AND DISPOSAL

OBSERVE ALL FEDERAL, STATE AND LOCAL REGULATIONS WHEN STORING OR DISPOSING OF THIS SUBSTANCE. FOR ASSISTANCE, CONTACT THE DISTRICT DIRECTOR OF THE ENVIRONMENTAL PROTECTION AGENCY.

****STORAGE****

STORE IN ACCORDANCE WITH 40 CFR 165 RECOMMENDED PROCEDURES FOR THE DISPOSAL AND STORAGE OF PESTICIDES AND PESTICIDE CONTAINERS.
STORE AWAY FROM INCOMPATIBLE SUBSTANCES.

****DISPOSAL****

DISPOSAL MUST BE IN ACCORDANCE WITH 40 CFR 165 RECOMMENDED PROCEDURES FOR THE DISPOSAL AND STORAGE OF PESTICIDES AND PESTICIDE CONTAINERS.

CONDITIONS TO AVOID

MAY BURN BUT DOES NOT IGNITE READILY.

SPILL AND LEAK PROCEDURES

OCCUPATIONAL SPILL: DO NOT TOUCH SPILLED MATERIAL. STOP LEAK IF YOU CAN DO IT WITHOUT RISK. FOR SMALL SPILLS, TAKE UP WITH SAND OR OTHER ABSORBENT MATERIAL AND PLACE INTO CONTAINERS FOR LATER DISPOSAL. FOR SMALL DRY SPILLS, WITH A CLEAN SHOVEL PLACE MATERIAL INTO CLEAN, DRY CONTAINER AND COVER. MOVE CONTAINERS FROM SPILL AREA. FOR LARGER SPILLS, DIKE FAR AHEAD OF SPILL FOR LATER DISPOSAL. KEEP UNNECESSARY PEOPLE AWAY. ISOLATE HAZARD AREA AND DENY ENTRY.

PROTECTIVE EQUIPMENT

VENTILATION: PROVIDE LOCAL EXHAUST OR GENERAL DILUTION VENTILATION SYSTEM.
RESPIRATOR: THE FOLLOWING RESPIRATORS ARE RECOMMENDED BASED ON INFORMATION FOUND IN THE PHYSICAL DATA, TOXICITY AND HEALTH EFFECTS SECTIONS. THEY ARE RANKED IN ORDER FROM MINIMUM TO MAXIMUM RESPIRATORY PROTECTION. THE SPECIFIC RESPIRATOR SELECTED MUST BE BASED ON CONTAMINATION LEVELS FOUND IN THE WORK PLACE, MUST NOT EXCEED THE WORKING LIMITS OF THE RESPIRATOR AND BE JOINTLY APPROVED BY THE NATIONAL INSTITUTE FOR OCCUPATIONAL SAFETY AND HEALTH AND THE MINE SAFETY AND HEALTH ADMINISTRATION (NIOSH-MSHA).
CHEMICAL CARTRIDGE RESPIRATOR WITH AN ORGANIC VAPOR CARTRIDGE(S) WITH A FULL FACEPIECE AND ORGANIC VAPOR CARTRIDGE(S) IN COMBINATION WITH A DUST AND MIST FILTER.
POWERED AIR-PURIFYING RESPIRATOR WITH A TIGHT-FITTING FACEPIECE AND ORGANIC VAPOR CARTRIDGE(S) IN COMBINATION WITH A HIGH-EFFICIENCY PARTICULATE FILTER.
TYPE 'C' SUPPLIED-AIR RESPIRATOR WITH A FULL FACEPIECE OPERATED IN A PRESSURE-DEMAND OR OTHER POSITIVE PRESSURE MODE.
SELF-CONTAINED BREATHING APPARATUS WITH A FULL FACEPIECE OPERATED IN PRESSURE-DEMAND OR OTHER POSITIVE PRESSURE MODE.
FOR FIREFIGHTING AND OTHER IMMEDIATELY DANGEROUS TO LIFE OR HEALTH CONDITIONS:
SELF-CONTAINED BREATHING APPARATUS WITH FULL FACEPIECE OPERATED IN PRESSURE-DEMAND OR OTHER POSITIVE PRESSURE MODE.
SUPPLIED-AIR RESPIRATOR WITH FULL FACEPIECE AND OPERATED IN PRESSURE-DEMAND OR OTHER POSITIVE PRESSURE MODE IN COMBINATION WITH AN AUXILIARY SELF-CONTAINED BREATHING APPARATUS OPERATED IN PRESSURE-DEMAND OR OTHER POSITIVE PRESSURE MODE.
CLOTHING: EMPLOYEE MUST WEAR APPROPRIATE PROTECTIVE (IMPERVIOUS) CLOTHING AND EQUIPMENT TO PREVENT REPEATED OR PROLONGED SKIN CONTACT WITH THIS SUBSTANCE.
GLOVES: EMPLOYEE MUST WEAR APPROPRIATE PROTECTIVE GLOVES TO PREVENT CONTACT WITH THIS SUBSTANCE.
EYE PROTECTION: EMPLOYEE MUST WEAR SPLASH-PROOF OR DUST-RESISTANT SAFETY GOGGLES TO PREVENT EYE CONTACT WITH THIS SUBSTANCE.
EMERGENCY EYE WASH: WHERE THERE IS ANY POSSIBILITY THAT AN EMPLOYEE'S EYES MAY BE EXPOSED TO THIS SUBSTANCE, THE EMPLOYER SHOULD PROVIDE AN EYE WASH FOUNTAIN WITHIN THE IMMEDIATE WORK AREA FOR EMERGENCY USE.

AUTHORIZED BY- OCCUPATIONAL HEALTH SERVICES, INC.
CREATION DATE: 02/08/90 ***REVISION DATE:*** 05/07/90

MATERIAL SAFETY DATA SHEET

OCCUPATIONAL HEALTH SERVICES, INC.
AGRICULTURE AND PESTICIDE DIVISION
450 SEVENTH AVENUE, SUITE 2407
NEW YORK, NEW YORK 10123
1-800-445-MSDS OR (212) 967-1100

EMERGENCY CONTACT:
JOHN S. BRANSFORD, JR. (615) 292-1180

SUBSTANCE IDENTIFICATION

CAS-NUMBER 2078-42-4
SUBSTANCE: **SODIUM 2,3,6-TRICHLOROBENZOIC ACID**
TRADE NAMES/SYNONYMS: BENZOIC ACID, 2,3,6-TRICHLORO-, SODIUM SALT; 2,3,6-TRICHLOROBENZOIC ACID, SODIUM SALT; SODIUM 2,3,6-TRICHLOROBENZOATE; C7H2CL3NAO2; PST71136
CHEMICAL FAMILY: SALT
HALOGEN COMPOUND, AROMATIC
MOLECULAR FORMULA: CL3-C6-H2-C-O-O-NA
MOLECULAR WEIGHT: 247.46
CERCLA RATINGS (SCALE 0-3): HEALTH=U FIRE=1 REACTIVITY=0 PERSISTENCE=3
NFPA RATINGS (SCALE 0-4): HEALTH=U FIRE=1 REACTIVITY=0

COMPONENTS AND CONTAMINANTS

COMPONENT: SODIUM 2,3,6-TRICHLOROBENZOIC ACID ***PERCENT:*** 100.0
CAS# 2078-42-4
OTHER CONTAMINANTS: NONE
EXPOSURE LIMITS: NO OCCUPATIONAL EXPOSURE LIMITS ESTABLISHED BY OSHA, ACGIH, OR NIOSH.

PHYSICAL DATA

DESCRIPTION: SOLID. ***MELTING POINT:*** NOT AVAILABLE
SPECIFIC GRAVITY: NOT AVAILABLE ***SOLUBILITY IN WATER:*** 44% @ 25 C

FIRE AND EXPLOSION DATA

FIRE AND EXPLOSION HAZARD: SLIGHT FIRE HAZARD WHEN EXPOSED TO HEAT OR FLAME.
FIREFIGHTING MEDIA: DRY CHEMICAL, CARBON DIOXIDE, HALON, WATER SPRAY OR STANDARD FOAM (1987 EMERGENCY RESPONSE GUIDEBOOK, DOT P 5800.4).
FOR LARGER FIRES, USE WATER SPRAY, FOG OR STANDARD FOAM (1987 EMERGENCY RESPONSE GUIDEBOOK, DOT P 5800.4).
FIREFIGHTING: MOVE CONTAINER FROM FIRE AREA IF POSSIBLE. DO NOT SCATTER SPILLED MATERIAL WITH HIGH PRESSURE WATER STREAMS. DIKE FIRE CONTROL WATER FOR LATER DISPOSAL (1987 EMERGENCY RESPONSE GUIDEBOOK, DOT P 5800.4, GUIDE PAGE 31).

USE AGENTS SUITABLE FOR TYPE OF SURROUNDING FIRE. AVOID BREATHING HAZARDOUS VAPORS, KEEP UPWIND.

TOXICITY

SODIUM 2,3,6-TRICHLOROBENZOIC ACID: CARCINOGEN STATUS: NONE. ACUTE TOXICITY LEVEL: NO DATA AVAILABLE. TARGET EFFECTS: NO DATA AVAILABLE.

HEALTH EFFECTS AND FIRST AID

INHALATION: SODIUM 2,3,6-TRICHLOROBENZOIC ACID: **ACUTE EXPOSURE-** NO DATA AVAILABLE. **CHRONIC EXPOSURE-** NO DATA AVAILABLE.

FIRST AID- REMOVE FROM EXPOSURE AREA TO FRESH AIR IMMEDIATELY. IF BREATHING HAS STOPPED, PERFORM ARTIFICIAL RESPIRATION. KEEP PERSON WARM AND AT REST. TREAT SYMPTOMATICALLY AND SUPPORTIVELY. GET MEDICAL ATTENTION IMMEDIATELY.

SKIN CONTACT: SODIUM 2,3,6-TRICHLOROBENZOIC ACID: **ACUTE EXPOSURE-** NO DATA AVAILABLE. **CHRONIC EXPOSURE-** NO DATA AVAILABLE.

FIRST AID- REMOVE CONTAMINATED CLOTHING AND SHOES IMMEDIATELY. WASH AFFECTED AREA WITH SOAP OR MILD DETERGENT AND LARGE AMOUNTS OF WATER UNTIL NO EVIDENCE OF CHEMICAL REMAINS (APPROXIMATELY 15-20 MINUTES). GET MEDICAL ATTENTION IMMEDIATELY.

EYE CONTACT: SODIUM 2,3,6-TRICHLOROBENZOIC ACID: **ACUTE EXPOSURE-** NO DATA AVAILABLE. **CHRONIC EXPOSURE-** NO DATA AVAILABLE.

FIRST AID- WASH EYES IMMEDIATELY WITH LARGE AMOUNTS OF WATER OR NORMAL SALINE, OCCASIONALLY LIFTING UPPER AND LOWER LIDS, UNTIL NO EVIDENCE OF CHEMICAL REMAINS (APPROXIMATELY 15-20 MINUTES). GET MEDICAL ATTENTION IMMEDIATELY.

INGESTION: SODIUM 2,3,6-TRICHLOROBENZOIC ACID: **ACUTE EXPOSURE-** NO DATA AVAILABLE. **CHRONIC EXPOSURE-** NO DATA AVAILABLE.

FIRST AID- TREAT SYMPTOMATICALLY AND SUPPORTIVELY. GET MEDICAL ATTENTION IMMEDIATELY. IF VOMITING OCCURS, KEEP HEAD LOWER THAN HIPS TO PREVENT ASPIRATION.

ANTIDOTE: NO SPECIFIC ANTIDOTE. TREAT SYMPTOMATICALLY AND SUPPORTIVELY.

REACTIVITY

REACTIVITY: STABLE UNDER NORMAL TEMPERATURES AND PRESSURES.

INCOMPATIBILITIES: SODIUM 2,3,6-TRICHLOROBENZOIC ACID: OXIDIZERS (STRONG): FIRE AND EXPLOSION HAZARD.

DECOMPOSITION: THERMAL DECOMPOSITION PRODUCTS MAY INCLUDE TOXIC AND CORROSIVE FUMES OF CHLORIDES AND TOXIC OXIDES OF CARBON.

POLYMERIZATION: HAZARDOUS POLYMERIZATION HAS NOT BEEN REPORTED TO OCCUR UNDER NORMAL TEMPERATURES AND PRESSURES.

STORAGE AND DISPOSAL

OBSERVE ALL FEDERAL, STATE AND LOCAL REGULATIONS WHEN STORING OR DISPOSING OF THIS SUBSTANCE. FOR ASSISTANCE, CONTACT THE DISTRICT DIRECTOR OF THE ENVIRONMENTAL PROTECTION AGENCY.

****STORAGE****

STORE IN ACCORDANCE WITH 40 CFR 165 RECOMMENDED PROCEDURES FOR THE DISPOSAL AND STORAGE OF PESTICIDES AND PESTICIDE CONTAINERS.
STORE AWAY FROM INCOMPATIBLE SUBSTANCES.

****DISPOSAL****

DISPOSAL MUST BE IN ACCORDANCE WITH 40 CFR 165 RECOMMENDED PROCEDURES FOR THE DISPOSAL AND STORAGE OF PESTICIDES AND PESTICIDE CONTAINERS.

CONDITIONS TO AVOID

MAY BURN BUT DOES NOT IGNITE READILY. AVOID CONTACT WITH STRONG OXIDIZERS, EXCESSIVE HEAT, SPARKS, OR OPEN FLAME.

SPILL AND LEAK PROCEDURES

OCCUPATIONAL SPILL: SWEEP UP AND PLACE IN SUITABLE CLEAN, DRY CONTAINERS FOR RECLAMATION OR LATER DISPOSAL. DO NOT FLUSH SPILLED MATERIAL INTO SEWER. KEEP UNNECESSARY PEOPLE AWAY.

PROTECTIVE EQUIPMENT

VENTILATION: PROVIDE LOCAL EXHAUST OR PROCESS ENCLOSURE VENTILATION SYSTEM.

RESPIRATOR: THE FOLLOWING RESPIRATORS ARE RECOMMENDED BASED ON INFORMATION FOUND IN THE PHYSICAL DATA, TOXICITY AND HEALTH EFFECTS SECTIONS. THEY ARE RANKED IN ORDER FROM MINIMUM TO MAXIMUM RESPIRATORY PROTECTION. THE SPECIFIC RESPIRATOR SELECTED MUST BE BASED ON CONTAMINATION LEVELS FOUND IN THE WORK PLACE, MUST NOT EXCEED THE WORKING LIMITS OF THE RESPIRATOR AND BE JOINTLY APPROVED BY THE NATIONAL INSTITUTE FOR OCCUPATIONAL SAFETY AND HEALTH AND THE MINE SAFETY AND HEALTH ADMINISTRATION (NIOSH-MSHA).
CHEMICAL CARTRIDGE RESPIRATOR WITH AN ORGANIC VAPOR CARTRIDGE(S) WITH A FULL FACEPIECE AND ORGANIC VAPOR CARTRIDGE(S) IN COMBINATION WITH A DUST AND MIST FILTER.
POWERED AIR-PURIFYING RESPIRATOR WITH A TIGHT-FITTING FACEPIECE AND ORGANIC VAPOR CARTRIDGE(S) IN COMBINATION WITH A HIGH-EFFICIENCY PARTICULATE FILTER.
TYPE 'C' SUPPLIED-AIR RESPIRATOR WITH A FULL FACEPIECE OPERATED IN A PRESSURE-DEMAND OR OTHER POSITIVE PRESSURE MODE.
SELF-CONTAINED BREATHING APPARATUS WITH A FULL FACEPIECE OPERATED IN PRESSURE-DEMAND OR OTHER POSITIVE PRESSURE MODE.
FOR FIREFIGHTING AND OTHER IMMEDIATELY DANGEROUS TO LIFE OR HEALTH CONDITIONS:
SELF-CONTAINED BREATHING APPARATUS WITH FULL FACEPIECE OPERATED IN PRESSURE-DEMAND OR OTHER POSITIVE PRESSURE MODE.
SUPPLIED-AIR RESPIRATOR WITH FULL FACEPIECE AND OPERATED IN PRESSURE-DEMAND OR OTHER POSITIVE PRESSURE MODE IN COMBINATION WITH AN AUXILIARY SELF-CONTAINED BREATHING APPARATUS OPERATED IN PRESSURE-DEMAND OR OTHER POSITIVE PRESSURE MODE.

CLOTHING: EMPLOYEE MUST WEAR APPROPRIATE PROTECTIVE (IMPERVIOUS) CLOTHING AND EQUIPMENT TO PREVENT REPEATED OR PROLONGED SKIN CONTACT WITH THIS SUBSTANCE.

GLOVES: EMPLOYEE MUST WEAR APPROPRIATE PROTECTIVE GLOVES TO PREVENT CONTACT WITH THIS SUBSTANCE.

EYE PROTECTION: EMPLOYEE MUST WEAR SPLASH-PROOF OR DUST-RESISTANT SAFETY GOGGLES TO PREVENT EYE CONTACT WITH THIS SUBSTANCE.
EMERGENCY EYE WASH: WHERE THERE IS ANY POSSIBILITY THAT AN EMPLOYEE'S EYES MAY BE EXPOSED TO THIS SUBSTANCE, THE EMPLOYER SHOULD PROVIDE AN EYE WASH FOUNTAIN WITHIN THE IMMEDIATE WORK AREA FOR EMERGENCY USE.

AUTHORIZED BY- OCCUPATIONAL HEALTH SERVICES, INC.
CREATION DATE: 10/05/89 ***REVISION DATE:*** 05/31/90

MATERIAL SAFETY DATA SHEET

OCCUPATIONAL HEALTH SERVICES, INC.
AGRICULTURE AND PESTICIDE DIVISION
450 SEVENTH AVENUE, SUITE 2407
NEW YORK, NEW YORK 10123
1-800-445-MSDS OR (212) 967-1100

EMERGENCY CONTACT:
JOHN S. BRANSFORD, JR. (615) 292-1180

SUBSTANCE IDENTIFICATION

CAS-NUMBER 103-17-3

***SUBSTANCE:* CHLORBENSIDE**

TRADE NAMES/SYNONYMS: BENZENE, 1-CHLORO-4-(((4-CHLOROPHENYL)METHYL)THIO)-; 1-CHLORO-4-(((4-CHLOROPHEYL)METHYL)THIO)BENZENE; SULFIDE, P-CHLOROBENZYL P-CHLOROPHENYL; P-CHLOROBENZYL P-CHLOROPHENYL SULFIDE; 4-CHLOROBENZYL 4-CHLOROPHENYL SULFIDE; CHLORPARACIDE; CHLORACID; CHLORBENSID; CHLORSULPHACIDE; MITOX; C13H10CL2S; PST71139

CHEMICAL FAMILY: HALOGEN COMPOUND, AROMATIC THIO

MOLECULAR FORMULA: CL-C6-H4-C-H2-S-C6-H4-CL

MOLECULAR WEIGHT: 269.20

CERCLA RATINGS (SCALE 0-3): HEALTH=2 FIRE=1 REACTIVITY=0 PERSISTENCE=3

NFPA RATINGS (SCALE 0-4): HEALTH=U FIRE=1 REACTIVITY=0

COMPONENTS AND CONTAMINANTS

COMPONENT: CHLORBENSIDE ***PERCENT:*** 100.0
CAS# 103-17-3

OTHER CONTAMINANTS: NONE

EXPOSURE LIMITS: NO OCCUPATIONAL EXPOSURE LIMITS ESTABLISHED BY OSHA, ACGIH, OR NIOSH.

PHYSICAL DATA

DESCRIPTION: CRYSTALS WITH AN ALMOND-LIKE ODOR.

MELTING POINT: 167-169 F (75-76 C) ***SPECIFIC GRAVITY:*** 1.4210 @ 25 C

VAPOR PRESSURE: NEGLIGIBLE ***SOLUBILITY IN WATER:*** >0.02%

SOLVENT SOLUBILITY: SOLUBLE IN ACETONE, BENZENE, TOLUENE, XYLENE AND PETROLEUM ETHER; MODERATELY SOLUBLE IN ETHANOL AND KEROSENE.

FIRE AND EXPLOSION DATA

FIRE AND EXPLOSION HAZARD: SLIGHT FIRE HAZARD WHEN EXPOSED TO HEAT OR FLAME.

FIREFIGHTING MEDIA: DRY CHEMICAL, CARBON DIOXIDE, HALON, WATER SPRAY OR STANDARD FOAM (1987 EMERGENCY RESPONSE GUIDEBOOK, DOT P 5800.4). FOR LARGER FIRES, USE WATER SPRAY, FOG OR STANDARD FOAM (1987 EMERGENCY RESPONSE GUIDEBOOK, DOT P 5800.4).

FIREFIGHTING: MOVE CONTAINER FROM FIRE AREA IF POSSIBLE. DO NOT SCATTER SPILLED MATERIAL WITH HIGH PRESSURE WATER STREAMS. DIKE FIRE CONTROL WATER FOR LATER DISPOSAL (1987 EMERGENCY RESPONSE GUIDEBOOK, DOT P 5800.4, GUIDE PAGE 31).
USE AGENTS SUITABLE FOR TYPE OF SURROUNDING FIRE. AVOID BREATHING HAZARDOUS VAPORS, KEEP UPWIND.

TOXICITY

CHLORBENSIDE: TOXICITY DATA: 2000 MG/KG ORAL-RAT LD50; 3000 MG/KG UNREPORTED-MOUSE LD50. CARCINOGEN STATUS: NONE. LOCAL EFFECTS: IRRITANT- SKIN. ACUTE TOXICITY LEVEL: MODERATELY TOXIC BY INGESTION. TARGET EFFECTS: POISONING MAY AFFECT THE KIDNEYS, LIVER, HEART, AND CENTRAL NERVOUS SYSTEM.* ADDITIONAL DATA: STIMULANTS SUCH AS EPINEPHRINE MAY INDUCE VENTRICULAR FIBRILLATION.*
* MAY BE BASED ON GENERAL CHLORINATED HYDROCARBON INSECTICIDE INFORMATION.

HEALTH EFFECTS AND FIRST AID

INHALATION: CHLORBENSIDE: **ACUTE EXPOSURE-** DUSTS OF CHLORINATED HYDROCARBON INSECTICIDES MAY CAUSE IRRITATION OF THE RESPIRATORY TRACT. IF SUFFICIENT AMOUNTS ARE ABSORBED, SYSTEMIC TOXICITY AS DETAILED IN ACUTE INGESTION MAY OCCUR. **CHRONIC EXPOSURE-** NO DATA AVAILABLE.

FIRST AID- REMOVE FROM EXPOSURE AREA TO FRESH AIR IMMEDIATELY. IF BREATHING HAS STOPPED, PERFORM ARTIFICIAL RESPIRATION. KEEP PERSON WARM AND AT REST. TREAT SYMPTOMATICALLY AND SUPPORTIVELY. GET MEDICAL ATTENTION IMMEDIATELY.

SKIN CONTACT: CHLORBENSIDE: IRRITANT. **ACUTE EXPOSURE-** MAY CAUSE IRRITATION. SOME CHLORINATED HYDROCARBON INSECTICIDES MAY BE ABSORBED THROUGH THE SKIN. **CHRONIC EXPOSURE-** REPEATED AND PROLONGED CONTACT WITH IRRITANTS MAY CAUSE DERMATITIS.

FIRST AID- REMOVE CONTAMINATED CLOTHING AND SHOES IMMEDIATELY. WASH AFFECTED AREA WITH SOAP OR MILD DETERGENT AND LARGE AMOUNTS OF WATER UNTIL NO EVIDENCE OF CHEMICAL REMAINS (APPROXIMATELY 15-20 MINUTES). GET MEDICAL ATTENTION IMMEDIATELY.

EYE CONTACT: CHLORBENSIDE: **ACUTE EXPOSURE-** DUSTS OF CHLORINATED HYDROCARBON INSECTICIDES MAY CAUSE IRRITATION. **CHRONIC EXPOSURE-** NO DATA AVAILABLE.

FIRST AID- WASH EYES IMMEDIATELY WITH LARGE AMOUNTS OF WATER OR NORMAL SALINE, OCCASIONALLY LIFTING UPPER AND LOWER LIDS, UNTIL NO EVIDENCE OF CHEMICAL REMAINS (APPROXIMATELY 15-20 MINUTES). GET MEDICAL ATTENTION IMMEDIATELY.

INGESTION: CHLORBENSIDE: **ACUTE EXPOSURE-** INGESTION OF CHLORINATED HYDROCARBON INSECTISIDES MAY RESULT IN CENTRAL NERVOUS SYSTEM EFFECTS. SYMPTOMS MAY INCLUDE DIZZINESS, HEADACHE, NAUSEA, ABDOMINAL PAIN, VOMITING, ANOREXIA, APPREHENSION, CONFUSION, AND IRRITABILITY. MUSCLE WEAKNESS, PARESTHESIAS, HYPERREFLEXIA, TREMOR, FASCICULATIONS, ATAXIA, CONVULSIVE SEIZURES, STUPOR, AND COMA MAY RESULT. IN SEVERE CASES, THE CONVULSIONS MAY BE CONTINUOUS WITH FEVER, DYSPNEA WITH VIGOROUS, RAPID HEART BEAT, AND DEATH MAY OCCUR FROM RESPIRATORY FAILURE OR VENTRICULAR FIBRILLATION. **CHRONIC EXPOSURE-** LIVER AND KIDNEY INJURIES HAVE BEEN PRODUCED IN ANIMAL STUDIES.

FIRST AID- IF THE PERSON IS CONSCIOUS AND NOT CONVULSING, REMOVE BY GIVING SYRUP OF IPECAC (IF VOMITING OCCURS, KEEP THE HEAD BELOW THE HIPS TO PREVENT ASPIRATION). GIVE ACTIVATED CHARCOAL FOLLOWED BY GASTRIC LAVAGE. FOLLOW WITH A SALINE CATHARTIC. DO NOT GIVE FATS OR OILS. INTESTINAL LAVAGE WITH 20% MANNITOL (200 ML) BY STOMACH TUBE IS ALSO USEFUL. GIVE ARTIFICIAL RESPIRATION WITH OXYGEN IF RESPIRATION IS DEPRESSED (DREISBACH, HANDBOOK OF POISONING, 12TH ED.). TREAT SYMPTOMATICALLY AND SUPPORTIVELY. LAVAGE AND ADMINISTRATION OF OXYGEN SHOULD BE PERFORMED BY QUALIFIED MEDICAL PERSONNEL. GET MEDICAL ATTENTION IMMEDIATELY.

ANTIDOTE: NO SPECIFIC ANTIDOTE. TREAT SYMPTOMATICALLY AND SUPPORTIVELY.

REACTIVITY

REACTIVITY: STABLE UNDER NORMAL TEMPERATURES AND PRESSURES.

INCOMPATIBILITIES: CHLORBENSIDE: OXIDIZERS (STRONG): FIRE AND EXPLOSION HAZARD.

DECOMPOSITION: THERMAL DECOMPOSITION PRODUCTS MAY INCLUDE TOXIC AND CORROSIVE FUMES OF CHLORIDES, AND TOXIC OXIDES OF SULFUR AND CARBON.

POLYMERIZATION: HAZARDOUS POLYMERIZATION HAS NOT BEEN REPORTED TO OCCUR UNDER NORMAL TEMPERATURES AND PRESSURES.

STORAGE AND DISPOSAL

OBSERVE ALL FEDERAL, STATE AND LOCAL REGULATIONS WHEN STORING OR DISPOSING OF THIS SUBSTANCE. FOR ASSISTANCE, CONTACT THE DISTRICT DIRECTOR OF THE ENVIRONMENTAL PROTECTION AGENCY.

STORAGE

STORE IN ACCORDANCE WITH 40 CFR 165 RECOMMENDED PROCEDURES FOR THE DISPOSAL AND STORAGE OF PESTICIDES AND PESTICIDE CONTAINERS.
STORE AWAY FROM INCOMPATIBLE SUBSTANCES.

DISPOSAL

DISPOSAL MUST BE IN ACCORDANCE WITH 40 CFR 165 RECOMMENDED PROCEDURES FOR THE DISPOSAL AND STORAGE OF PESTICIDES AND PESTICIDE CONTAINERS.

CONDITIONS TO AVOID

MAY BURN BUT DOES NOT IGNITE READILY. AVOID CONTACT WITH STRONG OXIDIZERS, EXCESSIVE HEAT, SPARKS, OR OPEN FLAME.

SPILL AND LEAK PROCEDURES

OCCUPATIONAL SPILL: SWEEP UP AND PLACE IN SUITABLE CLEAN, DRY CONTAINERS FOR RECLAMATION OR LATER DISPOSAL. DO NOT FLUSH SPILLED MATERIAL INTO SEWER. KEEP UNNECESSARY PEOPLE AWAY.

PROTECTIVE EQUIPMENT

VENTILATION: PROVIDE LOCAL EXHAUST OR GENERAL DILUTION VENTILATION SYSTEM.

RESPIRATOR: THE FOLLOWING RESPIRATORS ARE RECOMMENDED BASED ON INFORMATION FOUND IN THE PHYSICAL DATA, TOXICITY AND HEALTH EFFECTS SECTIONS. THEY ARE RANKED IN ORDER FROM MINIMUM TO MAXIMUM RESPIRATORY PROTECTION. THE SPECIFIC RESPIRATOR SELECTED MUST BE BASED ON CONTAMINATION LEVELS FOUND IN THE WORK PLACE, MUST NOT EXCEED THE WORKING LIMITS OF THE RESPIRATOR AND BE JOINTLY APPROVED BY THE NATIONAL INSTITUTE FOR OCCUPATIONAL SAFETY AND HEALTH AND THE MINE SAFETY AND HEALTH ADMINISTRATION (NIOSH-MSHA).
CHEMICAL CARTRIDGE RESPIRATOR WITH AN ORGANIC VAPOR CARTRIDGE(S) WITH A FULL FACEPIECE AND ORGANIC VAPOR CARTRIDGE(S) IN COMBINATION WITH A DUST AND MIST FILTER. POWERED AIR-PURIFYING RESPIRATOR WITH A TIGHT-FITTING FACEPIECE AND ORGANIC VAPOR CARTRIDGE(S) IN COMBINATION WITH A HIGH-EFFICIENCY PARTICULATE FILTER.
TYPE 'C' SUPPLIED-AIR RESPIRATOR WITH A FULL FACEPIECE OPERATED IN A PRESSURE-DEMAND OR OTHER POSITIVE PRESSURE MODE.
SELF-CONTAINED BREATHING APPARATUS WITH A FULL FACEPIECE OPERATED IN PRESSURE-DEMAND OR OTHER POSITIVE PRESSURE MODE.
FOR FIREFIGHTING AND OTHER IMMEDIATELY DANGEROUS TO LIFE OR HEALTH CONDITIONS:
SELF-CONTAINED BREATHING APPARATUS WITH FULL FACEPIECE OPERATED IN PRESSURE-DEMAND OR OTHER POSITIVE PRESSURE MODE.
SUPPLIED-AIR RESPIRATOR WITH FULL FACEPIECE AND OPERATED IN PRESSURE-DEMAND OR OTHER POSITIVE PRESSURE MODE IN COMBINATION WITH AN AUXILIARY SELF-CONTAINED BREATHING APPARATUS OPERATED IN PRESSURE-DEMAND OR OTHER POSITIVE PRESSURE MODE.

CLOTHING: EMPLOYEE MUST WEAR APPROPRIATE PROTECTIVE (IMPERVIOUS) CLOTHING AND EQUIPMENT TO PREVENT REPEATED OR PROLONGED SKIN CONTACT WITH THIS SUBSTANCE.

GLOVES: EMPLOYEE MUST WEAR APPROPRIATE PROTECTIVE GLOVES TO PREVENT CONTACT WITH THIS SUBSTANCE.

EYE PROTECTION: EMPLOYEE MUST WEAR SPLASH-PROOF OR DUST-RESISTANT SAFETY GOGGLES TO PREVENT EYE CONTACT WITH THIS SUBSTANCE.
EMERGENCY EYE WASH: WHERE THERE IS ANY POSSIBILITY THAT AN EMPLOYEE'S EYES MAY BE EXPOSED TO THIS SUBSTANCE, THE EMPLOYER SHOULD PROVIDE AN EYE WASH FOUNTAIN WITHIN THE IMMEDIATE WORK AREA FOR EMERGENCY USE.

AUTHORIZED BY- OCCUPATIONAL HEALTH SERVICES, INC.
CREATION DATE: 10/04/89 ***REVISION DATE:*** 05/31/90

MATERIAL SAFETY DATA SHEET

OCCUPATIONAL HEALTH SERVICES, INC.
AGRICULTURE AND PESTICIDE DIVISION
450 SEVENTH AVENUE, SUITE 2407
NEW YORK, NEW YORK 10123
1-800-445-MSDS OR (212) 967-1100

EMERGENCY CONTACT:
JOHN S. BRANSFORD, JR. (615) 292-1180

SUBSTANCE IDENTIFICATION

CAS-NUMBER 101-27-9

SUBSTANCE: **BARBAN**

TRADE NAMES/SYNONYMS: CARBAMIC ACID, (3-CHLOROPHENYL)-, 4-CHLORO-2-BUTYNYL ESTER; CARBANILIC ACID, M-CHLORO-, 4-CHLORO-2-BUTYNYL ESTER; (3-CHLOROPHENYL)CARBAMIC ACID 4-CHLORO-2-BUTYNYL ESTER; M-CHLOROCARBANILIC ACID, 4-CHLORO-2-BUTYNYL ESTER; 4-CHLORO-2-BUTYNYL N-(3-CHLOROPHENYL)CARBAMATE; CHLORO-2-BUTYNLY M-CHLOROCARBANILATE; 4-CHLOROBUT-2-YNYL 3-CHLOROCARBANILATE; 4-CHLOROBUT-2-YNYL 3-CHLOROPHENYLCARBAMATE; 4-CHLORO-2-BUTYNYL 3-CHLOROPHENYLCARBAMATE; 4-CHLORO-2-BUTYNYL M-CHLOROPHENYLCARBAMATE; A 980; BARBANE; CARBYNE; CBN; S 847; C11H9CL2NO2; PST71143

CHEMICAL FAMILY: CARBAMATE

MOLECULAR FORMULA: CL-C6-H4-N-H-C-O2-C-H2-C3-H2-CL

MOLECULAR WEIGHT: 258.11

CERCLA RATINGS (SCALE 0-3): HEALTH = 3 FIRE = 2 REACTIVITY = 0 PERSISTENCE = 1

NFPA RATINGS (SCALE 0-4): HEALTH = U FIRE = 2 REACTIVITY = 0

COMPONENTS AND CONTAMINANTS

COMPONENT: BARBAN ***PERCENT:*** 100
CAS# 101-27-9

EXPOSURE LIMITS: NO OCCUPATIONAL EXPOSURE LIMITS ESTABLISHED BY OSHA, ACGIH, OR NIOSH.

PHYSICAL DATA

DESCRIPTION: COLORLESS, CRYSTALLINE SOLID

MELTING POINT: 167 F (75 C) (DECOMPOSES) ***SPECIFIC GRAVITY:*** 1.403

VAPOR PRESSURE: NEGLIGIBLE ***SOLUBILITY IN WATER:*** 11 PPM

SOLVENT SOLUBILITY: SOLUBLE IN BENZENE, N-BUTYLBENZENE, TOLUENE, XYLENE, ETHYLENE DICHLORIDE, ISOPHORONE, GLYCEROL FORMAL, PROPYLENE GLYCOL; SLIGHTLY SOLUBLE IN N-HEXANE, 2,2,4-TRIMETHYLPENTANE, N-DODECANE, KEROSENE

FIRE AND EXPLOSION DATA

FIRE AND EXPLOSION HAZARD: MODERATE FIRE HAZARD WHEN EXPOSED TO HEAT OR FLAME.

FLASH POINT: 177.8 F (81 C)

FIREFIGHTING MEDIA: DRY CHEMICAL, CARBON DIOXIDE, HALON, WATER SPRAY OR STANDARD FOAM (1987 EMERGENCY RESPONSE GUIDEBOOK, DOT P 5800.4).
FOR LARGER FIRES, USE WATER SPRAY, FOG OR STANDARD FOAM (1987 EMERGENCY RESPONSE GUIDEBOOK, DOT P 5800.4).

FIREFIGHTING: MOVE CONTAINER FROM FIRE AREA IF POSSIBLE. DO NOT SCATTER SPILLED MATERIAL WITH HIGH PRESSURE WATER STREAMS. DIKE FIRE CONTROL WATER FOR LATER DISPOSAL (1987 EMERGENCY RESPONSE GUIDEBOOK, DOT P 5800.4, GUIDE PAGE 31).
USE AGENTS SUITABLE FOR TYPE OF SURROUNDING FIRE. AVOID BREATHING HAZARDOUS VAPORS, KEEP UPWIND.

TOXICITY

BARBAN: TOXICITY DATA: 27400 MG/M3/4 HOURS INHALATION-RAT LC50; 23000 MG/KG SKIN-RABBIT LD50; 527 MG/KG ORAL-RAT LD50; 322 MG/KG ORAL-MOUSE LD50; 600 MG/KG ORAL-RABBIT LD50; 240 MG/KG ORAL-GUINEA PIG LD50; MUTAGENIC DATA (RTECS). CARCINOGEN STATUS: NONE. LOCAL EFFECTS: IRRITANT- EYE, SKIN AND MUCOUS MEMBRANE. ACUTE TOXICITY LEVEL: MODERATELY TOXIC BY INHALATION AND INGESTION; RELATIVELY NONTOXIC BY INHALATION. TARGET EFFECTS: SENSITIZER-SKIN. POISONING MAY AFFECT THE LIVER AND KIDNEYS. ADDITIONAL DATA: IN ANIMAL STUDIES, BARBAN IS A WEAK CHOLINESTERASE INHIBITOR AND A METHEMOGLOBIN FORMER.

HEALTH EFFECTS AND FIRST AID

INHALATION: BARBAN: IRRITANT. **ACUTE EXPOSURE-** MAY CAUSE IRRITATION OF THE MUCOUS MEMBRANE. EFFECTS ON BLOOD CHOLINESTERASE ACTIVITY WERE REPORTED IN RATS FOLLOWING EXPOSURE TO 80 MG/M3 FOR 4 HOURS. **CHRONIC EXPOSURE-** PROLONGED OR REPEATED EXPOSURE MAY CAUSE IRRITATION TO THE MUCOUS MEMBRANES.

FIRST AID- REMOVE FROM EXPOSURE AREA TO FRESH AIR IMMEDIATELY. IF BREATHING HAS STOPPED, PERFORM ARTIFICIAL RESPIRATION. KEEP PERSON WARM AND AT REST. TREAT SYMPTOMATICALLY AND SUPPORTIVELY. GET MEDICAL ATTENTION IMMEDIATELY.

SKIN CONTACT: BARBAN: IRRITANT/SENSITIZER. **ACUTE EXPOSURE-** MAY CAUSE IRRITATION. SENSITIZATION DERMATITIS MAY OCCUR IN PERSONS PREVIOUSLY EXPOSED. **CHRONIC EXPOSURE-** PROLONGED OR REPEATED EXPOSURE MAY CAUSE SENSITIZATION DERMATITIS. LOCAL IRRITATING EFFECTS FOLLOWED BY WEIGHT LOSS AND PATHOLOGICAL CHANGES IN THE BLOOD WERE PRODUCED BY REPEATED APPLICATION OF BARBAN TO THE SKIN OF RABBITS AND GUINEA PIGS. REPEATED CONTACT WITH 5% WATER EMULSION RESULTS IN SEVERE SKIN IRRITATION IN RABBITS.

FIRST AID- REMOVE CONTAMINATED CLOTHING AND SHOES IMMEDIATELY. WASH AFFECTED AREA WITH SOAP OR MILD DETERGENT AND LARGE AMOUNTS OF WATER UNTIL NO EVIDENCE OF CHEMICAL REMAINS (APPROXIMATELY 15-20 MINUTES). GET MEDICAL ATTENTION IMMEDIATELY.

EYE CONTACT: BARBAN: IRRITANT. **ACUTE EXPOSURE-** THIS MATERIAL PRODUCED TRANSIENT IRRITATION WHEN APPLIED TO THE EYES OF RABBITS. **CHRONIC EXPOSURE-** PROLONGED OR REPEATED EXPOSURE TO IRRITANTS MAY CAUSE CONJUNCTIVITIS.

FIRST AID- WASH EYES IMMEDIATELY WITH LARGE AMOUNTS OF WATER OR NORMAL SALINE, OCCASIONALLY LIFTING UPPER AND LOWER LIDS, UNTIL NO EVIDENCE OF CHEMICAL REMAINS (APPROXIMATELY 15-20 MINUTES). GET MEDICAL ATTENTION IMMEDIATELY.

INGESTION: BARBAN: **ACUTE EXPOSURE-** A LETHAL DOSE IN RATS WAS 527 MG/KG. **CHRONIC EXPOSURE-** DAILY ADMINISTRATION TO GUINEA PIGS AND RABBITS FOR 4 TO 6 MONTHS WAS REPORTED TO HAVE CAUSED FATTY DYSTROPHY OF THE LIVER AND KIDNEYS, HEMOSIDEROSIS OF SPLEEN AND VASCULAR HYPEREMIA OF LIVER, BRAIN, KIDNEYS, SPLEEN, AND GASTRIC MUCOSA. DAILY DOSES OF 20 TO 40 MG/KG TO RABBITS CAUSED A SIGNIFICANT DECREASE IN LIVER GLYCOGEN CONTENT.

FIRST AID- IF THE PERSON IS CONSCIOUS AND NOT CONVULSING, REMOVE BY GASTRIC LAVAGE AND FOLLOW WITH A CATHARTIC (DREISBACH, HANDBOOK OF POISONING, 12TH ED.). TREAT SYMPTOMATICALLY AND SUPPORTIVELY. GASTRIC LAVAGE SHOULD BE PERFORMED BY QUALIFIED MEDICAL PERSONNEL. GET MEDICAL ATTENTION IMMEDIATELY.

ANTIDOTE: NO SPECIFIC ANTIDOTE. TREAT SYMPTOMATICALLY AND SUPPORTIVELY.

REACTIVITY

REACTIVITY: STABLE UNDER NORMAL TEMPERATURES AND PRESSURES.

INCOMPATIBILITIES: BARBAN: ALKALI: HYDROLYZES ACID: HYDROLYZES

DECOMPOSITION: THERMAL DECOMPOSITION PRODUCTS MAY INCLUDE TOXIC OXIDES OF NITROGEN AND CARBON AND TOXIC AND CORROSIVE FUMES OF CHLORIDES.

POLYMERIZATION: HAZARDOUS POLYMERIZATION HAS NOT BEEN REPORTED TO OCCUR UNDER NORMAL TEMPERATURES AND PRESSURES.

STORAGE AND DISPOSAL

OBSERVE ALL FEDERAL, STATE AND LOCAL REGULATIONS WHEN STORING OR DISPOSING OF THIS SUBSTANCE. FOR ASSISTANCE, CONTACT THE DISTRICT DIRECTOR OF THE ENVIRONMENTAL PROTECTION AGENCY.

****STORAGE****

STORE IN ACCORDANCE WITH 40 CFR 165 RECOMMENDED PROCEDURES FOR THE DISPOSAL AND STORAGE OF PESTICIDES AND PESTICIDE CONTAINERS.
STORE AWAY FROM INCOMPATIBLE SUBSTANCES.

****DISPOSAL****

DISPOSAL MUST BE IN ACCORDANCE WITH 40 CFR 165 RECOMMENDED PROCEDURES FOR THE DISPOSAL AND STORAGE OF PESTICIDES AND PESTICIDE CONTAINERS.

CONDITIONS TO AVOID

MAY BURN BUT DOES NOT IGNITE READILY. AVOID CONTACT WITH STRONG OXIDIZERS, EXCESSIVE HEAT, SPARKS, OR OPEN FLAME.

SPILL AND LEAK PROCEDURES

OCCUPATIONAL SPILL: SWEEP UP AND PLACE IN SUITABLE CLEAN, DRY CONTAINERS FOR RECLAMATION OR LATER DISPOSAL. DO NOT FLUSH SPILLED MATERIAL INTO SEWER. KEEP UNNECESSARY PEOPLE AWAY.

PROTECTIVE EQUIPMENT

VENTILATION: PROVIDE LOCAL EXHAUST OR GENERAL DILUTION VENTILATION SYSTEM.

RESPIRATOR: THE FOLLOWING RESPIRATORS ARE RECOMMENDED BASED ON INFORMATION FOUND IN THE PHYSICAL DATA, TOXICITY AND HEALTH EFFECTS SECTIONS. THEY ARE RANKED IN ORDER FROM MINIMUM TO MAXIMUM RESPIRATORY PROTECTION. THE SPECIFIC RESPIRATOR SELECTED MUST BE BASED ON CONTAMINATION LEVELS FOUND IN THE WORK PLACE, MUST NOT EXCEED THE WORKING LIMITS OF THE RESPIRATOR AND BE JOINTLY APPROVED BY THE NATIONAL INSTITUTE FOR OCCUPATIONAL SAFETY AND HEALTH AND THE MINE SAFETY AND HEALTH ADMINISTRATION (NIOSH-MSHA).

CHEMICAL CARTRIDGE RESPIRATOR WITH AN ORGANIC VAPOR CARTRIDGE(S) WITH A FULL FACEPIECE AND ORGANIC VAPOR CARTRIDGE(S) IN COMBINATION WITH A DUST AND MIST FILTER. POWERED AIR-PURIFYING RESPIRATOR WITH A TIGHT-FITTING FACEPIECE AND ORGANIC VAPOR CARTRIDGE(S) IN COMBINATION WITH A HIGH-EFFICIENCY PARTICULATE FILTER.

TYPE 'C' SUPPLIED-AIR RESPIRATOR WITH A FULL FACEPIECE OPERATED IN A PRESSURE-DEMAND OR OTHER POSITIVE PRESSURE MODE.

SELF-CONTAINED BREATHING APPARATUS WITH A FULL FACEPIECE OPERATED IN PRESSURE-DEMAND OR OTHER POSITIVE PRESSURE MODE.

FOR FIREFIGHTING AND OTHER IMMEDIATELY DANGEROUS TO LIFE OR HEALTH CONDITIONS:

SELF-CONTAINED BREATHING APPARATUS WITH FULL FACEPIECE OPERATED IN PRESSURE-DEMAND OR OTHER POSITIVE PRESSURE MODE.

SUPPLIED-AIR RESPIRATOR WITH FULL FACEPIECE AND OPERATED IN PRESSURE-DEMAND OR OTHER POSITIVE PRESSURE MODE IN COMBINATION WITH AN AUXILIARY SELF-CONTAINED BREATHING APPARATUS OPERATED IN PRESSURE-DEMAND OR OTHER POSITIVE PRESSURE MODE.

CLOTHING: EMPLOYEE MUST WEAR APPROPRIATE PROTECTIVE (IMPERVIOUS) CLOTHING AND EQUIPMENT TO PREVENT REPEATED OR PROLONGED SKIN CONTACT WITH THIS SUBSTANCE.

GLOVES: EMPLOYEE MUST WEAR APPROPRIATE PROTECTIVE GLOVES TO PREVENT CONTACT WITH THIS SUBSTANCE.

EYE PROTECTION: EMPLOYEE MUST WEAR SPLASH-PROOF OR DUST-RESISTANT SAFETY GOGGLES TO PREVENT EYE CONTACT WITH THIS SUBSTANCE.

EMERGENCY EYE WASH: WHERE THERE IS ANY POSSIBILITY THAT AN EMPLOYEE'S EYES MAY BE EXPOSED TO THIS SUBSTANCE, THE EMPLOYER SHOULD PROVIDE AN EYE WASH FOUNTAIN WITHIN THE IMMEDIATE WORK AREA FOR EMERGENCY USE.

AUTHORIZED BY- OCCUPATIONAL HEALTH SERVICES, INC.

CREATION DATE: 10/04/89 ***REVISION DATE:*** 05/31/90

MATERIAL SAFETY DATA SHEET

OCCUPATIONAL HEALTH SERVICES, INC.	EMERGENCY CONTACT:
AGRICULTURE AND PESTICIDE DIVISION	JOHN S. BRANSFORD, JR. (615) 292-1180
450 SEVENTH AVENUE, SUITE 2407	
NEW YORK, NEW YORK 10123	
1-800-445-MSDS OR (212) 967-1100	

SUBSTANCE IDENTIFICATION

CAS-NUMBER 999-81-5

SUBSTANCE: **CHLORMEQUAT CHLORIDE**

TRADE NAMES/SYNONYMS: ETHANAMINIUM, 2-CHLORO-N,N,N-TRIMETHYL-, CHLORIDE; AMMONIUM, (2-CHLOROETHYL)TRIMETHYL-, CHLORIDE 2-CHLORO-N,N,N-TRIMETHYLETHANAMINIUM CHLORIDE; (2-CHLOROETHYL)TRIMETHYLAMMONIUM CHLORIDE; 2-CHLOROETHYLTRIMETHYLAMMONIUM CHLORIDE; CHLORCHOLINE CHLORIDE; CHLOROCHOLINE CHLORIDE; CCC; CYCOCEL; CYCOGAN; AC 38,555; C5H13CL2N; PST71147

CHEMICAL FAMILY: QUATERNARY AMMONIUM COMPOUND

MOLECULAR FORMULA: (C-H3)3-N-(C-H2-C-H2-CL)-CL

MOLECULAR WEIGHT: 158.07

CERCLA RATINGS (SCALE 0-3): HEALTH=3 FIRE=1 REACTIVITY=0 PERSISTENCE=1

NFPA RATINGS (SCALE 0-4): HEALTH=3 FIRE=1 REACTIVITY=0

COMPONENTS AND CONTAMINANTS

COMPONENT: CHLORMEQUAT CHLORIDE ***PERCENT:*** 100.0

CAS# 999-81-5

EXPOSURE LIMITS: NO OCCUPATIONAL EXPOSURE LIMITS ESTABLISHED BY OSHA, ACGIH, OR NIOSH.

CHLORMEQUAT CHLORIDE: 100/10,000 POUNDS SARA SECTION 302 THRESHOLD PLANNING QUANTITY 1 POUND SARA SECTION 304 REPORTABLE QUANTITY.

PHYSICAL DATA

DESCRIPTION: WHITE TO YELLOWISH, HYGROSCOPIC, CRYSTALLINE SOLID WITH A FAINT FISHY ODOR.

MELTING POINT: 462 F (239 C) DECOMPOSES

SPECIFIC GRAVITY: NOT AVAILABLE ***VAPOR PRESSURE:*** NEGLIGIBLE

SOLUBILITY IN WATER: 100%

SOLVENT SOLUBILITY: SOLUBLE IN ETHANOL AND LOWER ALCOHOLS; VERY SLIGHTLY SOLUBLE IN ACETONE, CHLOROFORM; INSOLUBLE IN ETHER, HYDROCARBONS, CYCLOHEXANE.

FIRE AND EXPLOSION DATA

FIRE AND EXPLOSION HAZARD: SLIGHT FIRE HAZARD WHEN EXPOSED TO HEAT OR FLAME.

FIREFIGHTING MEDIA: DRY CHEMICAL, CARBON DIOXIDE, HALON, WATER SPRAY OR STANDARD FOAM (1987 EMERGENCY RESPONSE GUIDEBOOK, DOT P 5800.4). FOR LARGER FIRES, USE WATER SPRAY, FOG OR STANDARD FOAM (1987 EMERGENCY RESPONSE GUIDEBOOK, DOT P 5800.4).

FIREFIGHTING: MOVE CONTAINERS FROM FIRE AREA IF POSSIBLE (1987 EMERGENCY RESPONSE GUIDEBOOK, DOT P 5800.4, GUIDE PAGE 53).

EXTINGUISH USING AGENT SUITABLE FOR TYPE OF SURROUNDING FIRE. AVOID BREATHING VAPORS AND DUSTS. KEEP UPWIND.

TOXICITY

CHLORMEQUAT CHLORIDE: IRRITATION DATA: 500 MG/24 HOURS SKIN-RABBIT MILD. TOXICITY DATA: >5200 MG/M3 INHALATION-RAT LC50 (85JFAN); 232 MG/KG SKIN-RABBIT LD50; 440 MG/KG SKIN-MAMMAL LD50; 10 MG/KG ORAL-HUMAN LDLO; 670 MG/KG ORAL-RAT LD50 (85JFAN); 883 MG/KG ORAL-RAT LD50; 70 MG/KG ORAL-RABBIT LD50; 54 MG/KG ORAL-MOUSE LD50; 7 MG/KG ORAL-CAT LD50; 615 MG/KG ORAL-GUINEA PIG LD50; 670 MG/KG ORAL-MAMMAL LD50; 50 MG/KG ORAL-DOG LD50; 1 MG/KG INTRAVENOUS-HUMAN LDLO; 12,500 UG/KG INTRAVENOUS-RAT LD50; 4 MG/KG INTRAVENOUS-RABBIT LDLO; 7 MG/KG INTRAVENOUS-MOUSE LD50; 1200 UG/KG INTRAVENOUS-CAT LDLO; 64 MG/KG INTRAPERITONEAL-RAT LD50; 62 MG/KG INTRAPERITONEAL-MOUSE LD50; MUTAGENIC DATA (RTECS); TUMORIGENIC DATA (RTECS). CARCINOGEN STATUS: NONE. ACUTE TOXICITY LEVEL: TOXIC BY DERMAL ABSORPTION; MODERATELY TOXIC BY INGESTION. TARGET EFFECTS: NO DATA AVAILABLE. ADDITIONAL DATA: IN BOTH ACUTE AND CHRONIC STUDIES, KIDNEY LESIONS WERE OBSERVED IN DOGS AND RATS.

HEALTH EFFECTS AND FIRST AID

INHALATION: CHLORMEQUAT CHLORIDE: **ACUTE EXPOSURE-** A LETHAL CONCENTRATION IN RATS WAS GREATER THAN 5200 MG/M3. **CHRONIC EXPOSURE-** NO DATA AVAILABLE.

FIRST AID- REMOVE FROM EXPOSURE AREA TO FRESH AIR IMMEDIATELY. IF BREATHING HAS STOPPED, PERFORM ARTIFICIAL RESPIRATION. KEEP PERSON WARM AND AT REST. TREAT SYMPTOMATICALLY AND SUPPORTIVELY. GET MEDICAL ATTENTION IMMEDIATELY.

SKIN CONTACT: CHLORMEQUAT CHLORIDE: TOXIC. **ACUTE EXPOSURE-** 500 MG APPLIED TO RABBIT SKIN WAS MILDLY IRRITATING. A LETHAL DOSE IN RABBITS BY DERMAL ABSORPTION WAS 232 MG/KG. **CHRONIC EXPOSURE-** LONG TERM ABSORPTION OF CHLORMEQUAT CHLORIDE MAY BE HARMFUL.

FIRST AID- REMOVE CONTAMINATED CLOTHING AND SHOES IMMEDIATELY. WASH AFFECTED AREA WITH SOAP OR MILD DETERGENT AND LARGE AMOUNTS OF WATER UNTIL NO EVIDENCE OF CHEMICAL REMAINS (APPROXIMATELY 15-20 MINUTES). GET MEDICAL ATTENTION IMMEDIATELY.

EYE CONTACT: CHLORMEQUAT CHLORIDE: **ACUTE EXPOSURE-** THIS MATERIAL WAS MILDLY IRRITATING TO RABBIT EYES. **CHRONIC EXPOSURE-** NO DATA AVAILABLE.

FIRST AID- WASH EYES IMMEDIATELY WITH LARGE AMOUNTS OF WATER OR NORMAL SALINE, OCCASIONALLY LIFTING UPPER AND LOWER LIDS, UNTIL NO EVIDENCE OF CHEMICAL REMAINS (APPROXIMATELY 15-20 MINUTES). GET MEDICAL ATTENTION IMMEDIATELY.

INGESTION: CHLORMEQUAT CHLORIDE: TOXIC. **ACUTE EXPOSURE-** A LETHAL DOSE IN RATS WAS 670 MG/KG; SYMPTOMS WERE NOT REPORTED. **CHRONIC EXPOSURE-** SOME SIGNS OF CHOLINERGIC EFFECT WERE OBSERVED IN A 2-YEAR STUDY OF

DOGS AT 1000 PPM LEVEL. ADVERSE EFFECTS ON SPERMATOGENSIS IN THE OFFSPRING OF RATS WERE REPORTED IN A REPRODUCTION STUDY. AS EVALUATED BY RTECS, ORAL ADMINISTRATION TO MICE RESULTED IN A STATISTICALLY SIGNIFICANT INCREASE IN THE INCIDENCE OF NEOPLASTIC TUMORS OF THE LIVER.

FIRST AID- TREAT SYMPTOMATICALLY AND SUPPORTIVELY. GET MEDICAL ATTENTION IMMEDIATELY. IF VOMITING OCCURS, KEEP HEAD LOWER THAN HIPS TO PREVENT ASPIRATION.

ANTIDOTE: NO SPECIFIC ANTIDOTE. TREAT SYMPTOMATICALLY AND SUPPORTIVELY.

REACTIVITY

REACTIVITY: STABLE UNDER NORMAL TEMPERATURES AND PRESSURES.

INCOMPATIBILITIES: CHLORMEQUAT CHLORIDE: METALS (UNPROTECTIVE): MAY BE CORRODED. OXIDIZERS (STRONG): FIRE AND EXPLOSION HAZARD.

DECOMPOSITION: THERMAL DECOMPOSITION PRODUCTS MAY INCLUDE TOXIC OXIDES OF NITROGEN AND CARBON AND TOXIC AND CORROSIVE FUMES OF CHLORIDES.

POLYMERIZATION: HAZARDOUS POLYMERIZATION HAS NOT BEEN REPORTED TO OCCUR UNDER NORMAL TEMPERATURES AND PRESSURES.

STORAGE AND DISPOSAL

OBSERVE ALL FEDERAL, STATE AND LOCAL REGULATIONS WHEN STORING OR DISPOSING OF THIS SUBSTANCE. FOR ASSISTANCE, CONTACT THE DISTRICT DIRECTOR OF THE ENVIRONMENTAL PROTECTION AGENCY.

****STORAGE****

STORE IN ACCORDANCE WITH 40 CFR 165 RECOMMENDED PROCEDURES FOR THE DISPOSAL AND STORAGE OF PESTICIDES AND PESTICIDE CONTAINERS.
STORE AWAY FROM INCOMPATIBLE SUBSTANCES.
THRESHOLD PLANNING QUANTITY (TPQ): THE SUPERFUND AMENDMENTS AND REAUTHORIZATION ACT (SARA) SECTION 302 REQUIRES THAT EACH FACILITY WHERE ANY EXTREMELY HAZARDOUS SUBSTANCE IS PRESENT IN A QUANTITY EQUAL TO OR GREATER THAN THE TPQ ESTABLISHED FOR THAT SUBSTANCE NOTIFY THE STATE EMERGENCY RESPONSE COMMISSION FOR THE STATE IN WHICH IT IS LOCATED. SECTION 303 OF SARA REQUIRES THESE FACILITIES TO PARTICIPATE IN LOCAL EMERGENCY RESPONSE PLANNING (40 CFR 355.30).

****DISPOSAL****

DISPOSAL MUST BE IN ACCORDANCE WITH 40 CFR 165 RECOMMENDED PROCEDURES FOR THE DISPOSAL AND STORAGE OF PESTICIDES AND PESTICIDE CONTAINERS.

CONDITIONS TO AVOID

MAY BURN BUT DOES NOT IGNITE READILY.

SPILL AND LEAK PROCEDURES

OCCUPATIONAL SPILL: DO NOT TOUCH SPILLED MATERIAL. STOP LEAK IF YOU CAN DO IT WITHOUT RISK. FOR SMALL SPILLS, TAKE UP WITH SAND OR OTHER ABSORBENT MATERIAL AND PLACE INTO CONTAINERS FOR LATER DISPOSAL. FOR SMALL DRY SPILLS, WITH A CLEAN SHOVEL PLACE MATERIAL INTO CLEAN, DRY CONTAINER AND COVER. MOVE CONTAINERS FROM SPILL AREA. FOR LARGER SPILLS, DIKE FAR AHEAD OF SPILL FOR LATER DISPOSAL. KEEP UNNECESSARY PEOPLE AWAY. ISOLATE HAZARD AREA AND DENY ENTRY.
REPORTABLE QUANTITY (RQ): 1 POUND THE SUPERFUND AMENDMENTS AND REAUTHORIZATION ACT (SARA) SECTION 304 REQUIRES THAT A RELEASE EQUAL TO OR GREATER THAN THE REPORTABLE QUANTITY FOR THIS SUBSTANCE BE IMMEDIATELY REPORTED TO THE LOCAL EMERGENCY PLANNING COMMITTEE AND THE STATE EMERGENCY RESPONSE COMMISSION (40 CFR 355.40). IF THE RELEASE OF THIS SUBSTANCE IS REPORTABLE UNDER CERCLA SECTION 103, THE NATIONAL RESPONSE CENTER MUST BE NOTIFIED IMMEDIATELY AT (800) 424-8802 OR (202) 426-2675 IN THE METROPOLITAN WASHINGTON, D.C. AREA (40 CFR 302.6).

PROTECTIVE EQUIPMENT

VENTILATION: PROVIDE LOCAL EXHAUST OR PROCESS ENCLOSURE VENTILATION SYSTEM.

RESPIRATOR: THE FOLLOWING RESPIRATORS ARE RECOMMENDED BASED ON INFORMATION FOUND IN THE PHYSICAL DATA, TOXICITY AND HEALTH EFFECTS SECTIONS. THEY ARE RANKED IN ORDER FROM MINIMUM TO MAXIMUM RESPIRATORY PROTECTION. THE SPECIFIC RESPIRATOR SELECTED MUST BE BASED ON CONTAMINATION LEVELS FOUND IN THE WORK PLACE, MUST NOT EXCEED THE WORKING LIMITS OF THE RESPIRATOR AND BE JOINTLY APPROVED BY THE NATIONAL INSTITUTE FOR OCCUPATIONAL SAFETY AND HEALTH AND THE MINE SAFETY AND HEALTH ADMINISTRATION (NIOSH-MSHA).
TYPE 'C' SUPPLIED-AIR RESPIRATOR WITH A FULL FACEPIECE OPERATED IN PRESSURE-DEMAND OR OTHER POSITIVE PRESSURE MODE OR WITH A FULL FACEPIECE, HELMET OR HOOD OPERATED IN CONTINOUS-FLOW MODE.
SELF-CONTAINED BREATHING APPARATUS WITH A FULL FACEPIECE OPERATED IN PRESSURE-DEMAND OR OTHER POSITIVE PRESSURE MODE.
FOR FIREFIGHTING AND OTHER IMMEDIATELY DANGEROUS TO LIFE OR HEALTH CONDITIONS:
SELF-CONTAINED BREATHING APPARATUS WITH FULL FACEPIECE OPERATED IN PRESSURE-DEMAND OR OTHER POSITIVE PRESSURE MODE.
SUPPLIED-AIR RESPIRATOR WITH FULL FACEPIECE AND OPERATED IN PRESSURE-DEMAND OR OTHER POSITIVE PRESSURE MODE IN COMBINATION WITH AN AUXILIARY SELF-CONTAINED BREATHING APPARATUS OPERATED IN PRESSURE-DEMAND OR OTHER POSITIVE PRESSURE MODE.

CLOTHING: EMPLOYEE MUST WEAR APPROPRIATE PROTECTIVE (IMPERVIOUS) CLOTHING AND EQUIPMENT TO PREVENT ANY POSSIBILITY OF SKIN CONTACT WITH THIS SUBSTANCE.

GLOVES: EMPLOYEE MUST WEAR APPROPRIATE PROTECTIVE GLOVES TO PREVENT CONTACT WITH THIS SUBSTANCE.

EYE PROTECTION: EMPLOYEE MUST WEAR SPLASH-PROOF OR DUST-RESISTANT SAFETY GOGGLES WITH OR WITHOUT A FACESHIELD TO PREVENT CONTACT WITH THIS SUBSTANCE.
EMERGENCY EYE WASH: WHERE THERE IS ANY POSSIBILITY THAT AN EMPLOYEE'S EYES MAY BE EXPOSED TO THIS SUBSTANCE, THE EMPLOYER SHOULD PROVIDE AN EYE WASH FOUNTAIN WITHIN THE IMMEDIATE WORK AREA FOR EMERGENCY USE.

AUTHORIZED BY- OCCUPATIONAL HEALTH SERVICES, INC.
CREATION DATE: 02/08/90 ***REVISION DATE:*** 05/16/90

MATERIAL SAFETY DATA SHEET

OCCUPATIONAL HEALTH SERVICES, INC.
AGRICULTURE AND PESTICIDE DIVISION
450 SEVENTH AVENUE, SUITE 2407
NEW YORK, NEW YORK 10123
1-800-445-MSDS OR (212) 967-1100

EMERGENCY CONTACT:
JOHN S. BRANSFORD, JR. (615) 292-1180

SUBSTANCE IDENTIFICATION

CAS-NUMBER 101-21-3

SUBSTANCE: **CHLORPROPHAM**

TRADE NAMES/SYNONYMS: CARBAMIC ACID, (3-CHLOROPHENYL)-, 1-METHYLETHYL ESTER; CARBANILIC ACID, M-CHLORO-, ISOPROPYL ESTER; (3-CHLOROPHENYL)CARBAMIC ACID 1-METHYLETHYL ESTER; M-CHLOROCARBANILIC ACID ISOPROPYL ESTER; ISOPROPYL M-CHLOROCARBANILATE; ISOPROPYL 3-CHLOROCARBANILATE; ISOPROPYL N-(3-CHLOROPHENYL)CARBAMATE; ISORPOPYL 3-CHLOROPHENYLCARBAMATE; 1-METHYLETHYL (3-CHLOROPHENYL)CARBAMATE; BUD NIP; CHLOR IPC; CHLORO-IPC; CHLOROPROPHAM; CIPC; FURLOE; BEET-KLEEN; SPROUT-NIP; ENT 18060; C10H12CLNO2; PST71148

CHEMICAL FAMILY: CARBAMATE

MOLECULAR FORMULA: (CL-C6-H4)-N-H-C-O2-C-H-(C-H3)2

MOLECULAR WEIGHT: 213.66

CERCLA RATINGS (SCALE 0-3): HEALTH=3 FIRE=1 REACTIVITY=0 PERSISTENCE=1

NFPA RATINGS (SCALE 0-4): HEALTH=U FIRE=1 REACTIVITY=0

COMPONENTS AND CONTAMINANTS

COMPONENT: CHLORPROPHAM ***PERCENT:*** 100.0
CAS# 101-21-3

EXPOSURE LIMITS: NO OCCUPATIONAL EXPOSURE LIMITS ESTABLISHED BY OSHA, ACGIH, OR NIOSH.

PHYSICAL DATA

DESCRIPTION: WHITE, CRYSTALLINE SOLID.

BOILING POINT: 300 F (149 C) @ 2 MMHG

MELTING POINT: 106 F (41 C) ***SPECIFIC GRAVITY:*** 1.180 @ 30 C

VAPOR PRESSURE: NEGLIGIBLE @ 25 C ***SOLUBILITY IN WATER:*** 89 PPM @ 25 C

SOLVENT SOLUBILITY: SOLUBLE IN BUTYROLACTONE, BENZENE, XYLENE, CHLOROFORM, KETONES, ACETONE, METHANOL, ETHANOL, ISOPROPYL ALCOHOL, KEROSENE, ESTERS, HEAVY AROMATIC NAPHTHA, AROMATIC HYDROCARBONS, MOST ORGANIC SOLVENTS AND OILS.

FIRE AND EXPLOSION DATA

FIRE AND EXPLOSION HAZARD: SLIGHT FIRE HAZARD WHEN EXPOSED TO HEAT OR FLAME.

FIREFIGHTING MEDIA: DRY CHEMICAL, CARBON DIOXIDE, HALON, WATER SPRAY OR STANDARD FOAM (1987 EMERGENCY RESPONSE GUIDEBOOK, DOT P 5800.4).

FOR LARGER FIRES, USE WATER SPRAY, FOG OR STANDARD FOAM (1987 EMERGENCY RESPONSE GUIDEBOOK, DOT P 5800.4).

FIREFIGHTING: MOVE CONTAINER FROM FIRE AREA IF POSSIBLE. DO NOT SCATTER SPILLED MATERIAL WITH HIGH PRESSURE WATER STREAMS. DIKE FIRE CONTROL WATER FOR LATER DISPOSAL (1987 EMERGENCY RESPONSE GUIDEBOOK, DOT P 5800.4, GUIDE PAGE 31).
USE AGENTS SUITABLE FOR TYPE OF SURROUNDING FIRE. AVOID BREATHING HAZARDOUS VAPORS, KEEP UPWIND.

TOXICITY

CHLORPROPHAM: TOXICITY DATA: 1200 MG/KG ORAL-RAT LD50; 5000 MG/KG ORAL-RABBIT LD50; 700 MG/KG INTRAPERITONEAL-RAT LD50; 2600 MG/KG INTRAPERITONEAL-MOUSE LD50; 3350 MG/KG UNREPORTED-RAT LD50; 3000 MG/KG UNREPORTED-MAMMAL LD50; MUTAGENIC DATA (RTECS): REPRODUCTIVE EFFECTS DATA (RTECS); TUMORIGENIC DATA (RTECS). CARCINOGEN STATUS: ANIMAL INADEQUATE EVIDENCE (IARC GROUP-3). CHLORPROPHAM ACTED AS AN INITIATOR OF SKIN CARCINOGENESIS IN MICE. A SUBSEQUENT EXPERIMENT DID NOT CONFIRM THIS RESULT. ACUTE TOXICITY: MODERATELY TOXIC BY INGESTION. TARGET EFFECTS: NO DATA AVAILABLE. ADDITIONAL DATA: MAY CROSS THE PLACENTA.

HEALTH EFFECTS AND FIRST AID

INHALATION: CHLORPROPHAM: **ACUTE EXPOSURE-** NO DEATHS WERE OBSERVED IN RATS EXPOSED TO A CONCENTRATION OF 64 MG/M3/6 HOURS. **CHRONIC EXPOSURE-** NO DATA AVAILABLE.

FIRST AID- REMOVE FROM EXPOSURE AREA TO FRESH AIR IMMEDIATELY. IF BREATHING HAS STOPPED, PERFORM ARTIFICIAL RESPIRATION. KEEP PERSON WARM AND AT REST. TREAT SYMPTOMATICALLY AND SUPPORTIVELY. GET MEDICAL ATTENTION IMMEDIATELY.

SKIN CONTACT: CHLORPROPHAM: **ACUTE EXPOSURE-** MAY CAUSE IRRITATION. **CHRONIC EXPOSURE-** NO DATA AVAILABLE.

FIRST AID- REMOVE CONTAMINATED CLOTHING AND SHOES IMMEDIATELY. WASH AFFECTED AREA WITH SOAP OR MILD DETERGENT AND LARGE AMOUNTS OF WATER UNTIL NO EVIDENCE OF CHEMICAL REMAINS (APPROXIMATELY 15-20 MINUTES). GET MEDICAL ATTENTION IMMEDIATELY.

EYE CONTACT: CHLORPROPHAM: **ACUTE EXPOSURE-** MAY CAUSE IRRITATION. **CHRONIC EXPOSURE-** NO DATA AVAILABLE.

FIRST AID- WASH EYES IMMEDIATELY WITH LARGE AMOUNTS OF WATER OR NORMAL SALINE, OCCASIONALLY LIFTING UPPER AND LOWER LIDS, UNTIL NO EVIDENCE OF CHEMICAL REMAINS (APPROXIMATELY 15-20 MINUTES). GET MEDICAL ATTENTION IMMEDIATELY.

INGESTION: CHLORPROPHAM: **ACUTE EXPOSURE-** INITIAL SYMPTOMS OF POISONING IN LABORATORY ANIMALS INCLUDED LISTLESSNESS, ATAXIA, EPISTAXIS, EXOPHTHALMOS, HEMODACRYORRHEA AND HEMORHINORRHEA. THESE SYMPTOMS PROGRESSED TO DYSPNEA, PROSTRATION, ANURIA, GLYCOSURIA, PROTEINURIA, HYPERTHERMIA, AND DEATH. AUTOPSY FINDINGS SHOWED GASTROENTERITIS WITH OCCASIONAL CONGESTION OF BRAIN, LUNGS AND OTHER ORGANS AND DEGENERATIVE CHANGES IN THE KIDNEY AND LIVER. **CHRONIC EXPOSURE-** RETARDED GROWTH, INCREASED MORTALITY, INCREASED WEIGHTS OF LIVER, KIDNEY, AND SPLEEN, AND SPLENIC CONGESTION WERE OBSERVED IN ANIMALS RECEIVING CHLORPROPHAM. SLIGHT FETOTOXIC AND MATERNAL EFFECTS WERE REPORTED IN A THREE GENERATION STUDY WITH RATS. ORALLY ADMINISTERED CHLORPROPHAM ACTED AS AN INITIATOR OF SKIN CARCINOGENESIS IN MICE. A SUBSEQUENT EXPERIMENT DID NOT CONFIRM THIS RESULT.

FIRST AID- IF THE PERSON IS CONSCIOUS AND NOT CONVULSING, REMOVE BY GASTRIC LAVAGE AND FOLLOW WITH A CATHARTIC (DREISBACH, HANDBOOK OF POISONING, 12TH ED.). TREAT SYMPTOMATICALLY AND SUPPORTIVELY. GASTRIC LAVAGE SHOULD BE PERFORMED BY QUALIFIED MEDICAL PERSONNEL. GET MEDICAL ATTENTION IMMEDIATELY.

ANTIDOTE: NO SPECIFIC ANTIDOTE. TREAT SYMPTOMATICALLY AND SUPPORTIVELY.

REACTIVITY

REACTIVITY: STABLE UNDER NORMAL TEMPERATURES AND PRESSURES.

INCOMPATIBILITIES: CHLORPROPHAM: OXIDIZERS (STRONG): FIRE AND EXPLOSION HAZARD.

DECOMPOSITION: THERMAL DECOMPOSITION PRODUCTS MAY INCLUDE HIGHLY TOXIC FUMES OF PHOSGENE, TOXIC AND CORROSIVE FUMES OF CHLORIDES, AND OXIDES OF CARBON.

POLYMERIZATION: HAZARDOUS POLYMERIZATION HAS NOT BEEN REPORTED TO OCCUR UNDER NORMAL TEMPERATURES AND PRESSURES.

STORAGE AND DISPOSAL

OBSERVE ALL FEDERAL, STATE AND LOCAL REGULATIONS WHEN STORING OR DISPOSING OF THIS SUBSTANCE. FOR ASSISTANCE, CONTACT THE DISTRICT DIRECTOR OF THE ENVIRONMENTAL PROTECTION AGENCY.

****STORAGE****

STORE IN ACCORDANCE WITH 40 CFR 165 RECOMMENDED PROCEDURES FOR THE DISPOSAL AND STORAGE OF PESTICIDES AND PESTICIDE CONTAINERS.
STORE AWAY FROM INCOMPATIBLE SUBSTANCES.

****DISPOSAL****

DISPOSAL MUST BE IN ACCORDANCE WITH 40 CFR 165 RECOMMENDED PROCEDURES FOR THE DISPOSAL AND STORAGE OF PESTICIDES AND PESTICIDE CONTAINERS.

CONDITIONS TO AVOID

MAY BURN BUT DOES NOT IGNITE READILY. AVOID CONTACT WITH STRONG OXIDIZERS, EXCESSIVE HEAT, SPARKS, OR OPEN FLAME.

SPILL AND LEAK PROCEDURES

OCCUPATIONAL SPILL: SWEEP UP AND PLACE IN SUITABLE CLEAN, DRY CONTAINERS FOR RECLAMATION OR LATER DISPOSAL. DO NOT FLUSH SPILLED MATERIAL INTO SEWER. KEEP UNNECESSARY PEOPLE AWAY.

PROTECTIVE EQUIPMENT

VENTILATION: PROVIDE LOCAL EXHAUST OR GENERAL DILUTION VENTILATION SYSTEM.

RESPIRATOR: THE FOLLOWING RESPIRATORS ARE RECOMMENDED BASED ON INFORMATION FOUND IN THE PHYSICAL DATA, TOXICITY AND HEALTH EFFECTS SECTIONS. THEY ARE RANKED IN ORDER FROM MINIMUM TO MAXIMUM RESPIRATORY PROTECTION. THE SPECIFIC RESPIRATOR SELECTED MUST BE BASED ON CONTAMINATION LEVELS FOUND IN THE WORK PLACE, MUST NOT EXCEED THE WORKING LIMITS OF THE RESPIRATOR AND BE JOINTLY APPROVED BY THE NATIONAL INSTITUTE FOR OCCUPATIONAL SAFETY AND HEALTH AND THE MINE SAFETY AND HEALTH ADMINISTRATION (NIOSH-MSHA).
CHEMICAL CARTRIDGE RESPIRATOR WITH AN ORGANIC VAPOR CARTRIDGE(S) IN COMBINATION WITH A DUST AND MIST FILTER.
GAS MASK WITH ORGANIC VAPOR CANISTER (CHIN-STYLE OR FRONT- OR BACK-MOUNTED CANISTER) WITH A DUST AND MIST FILTER.
GAS MASK WITH ORGANIC VAPOR CANISTER (CHIN-STYLE OR FRONT- OR BACK-MOUNTED CANISTER) WITH A PARTICULATE FILTER.
POWERED AIR-PURIFYING RESPIRATOR WITH A HIGH-EFFICIENCY FILTER.
TYPE 'C' SUPPLIED-AIR RESPIRATOR WITH A FULL FACEPIECE OPERATED IN A PRESSURE-DEMAND OR OTHER POSITIVE PRESSURE MODE.
SELF-CONTAINED BREATHING APPARATUS WITH A FULL FACEPIECE OPERATED IN PRESSURE-DEMAND OR OTHER POSITIVE PRESSURE MODE.
FOR FIREFIGHTING AND OTHER IMMEDIATELY DANGEROUS TO LIFE OR HEALTH CONDITIONS:
SELF-CONTAINED BREATHING APPARATUS WITH FULL FACEPIECE OPERATED IN PRESSURE-DEMAND OR OTHER POSITIVE PRESSURE MODE.
SUPPLIED-AIR RESPIRATOR WITH FULL FACEPIECE AND OPERATED IN PRESSURE-DEMAND OR OTHER POSITIVE PRESSURE MODE IN COMBINATION WITH AN AUXILIARY SELF-CONTAINED BREATHING APPARATUS OPERATED IN PRESSURE-DEMAND OR OTHER POSITIVE PRESSURE MODE.

CLOTHING: EMPLOYEE MUST WEAR APPROPRIATE PROTECTIVE (IMPERVIOUS) CLOTHING AND EQUIPMENT TO PREVENT REPEATED OR PROLONGED SKIN CONTACT WITH THIS SUBSTANCE.

GLOVES: EMPLOYEE MUST WEAR APPROPRIATE PROTECTIVE GLOVES TO PREVENT CONTACT WITH THIS SUBSTANCE.

EYE PROTECTION: EMPLOYEE MUST WEAR SPLASH-PROOF OR DUST-RESISTANT SAFETY GOGGLES TO PREVENT EYE CONTACT WITH THIS SUBSTANCE.
EMERGENCY EYE WASH: WHERE THERE IS ANY POSSIBILITY THAT AN EMPLOYEE'S EYES MAY BE EXPOSED TO THIS SUBSTANCE, THE EMPLOYER SHOULD PROVIDE AN EYE WASH FOUNTAIN WITHIN THE IMMEDIATE WORK AREA FOR EMERGENCY USE.

AUTHORIZED BY- OCCUPATIONAL HEALTH SERVICES, INC.
CREATION DATE: 04/18/90 ***REVISION DATE:*** 07/12/90

MATERIAL SAFETY DATA SHEET

OCCUPATIONAL HEALTH SERVICES, INC.
AGRICULTURE AND PESTICIDE DIVISION
450 SEVENTH AVENUE, SUITE 2407

EMERGENCY CONTACT:
JOHN S. BRANSFORD, JR. (615) 292-1180

NEW YORK, NEW YORK 10123
1-800-445-MSDS OR (212) 967-1100

SUBSTANCE IDENTIFICATION

CAS-NUMBER 4104-14-7
SUBSTANCE: **PHOSACETIM**
TRADE NAMES/SYNONYMS: PHOSPHORAMIDOTHIOIC ACID, (1-IMINOETHYL)-, O,O-BIS(P-CHLOROPHENYL) ESTER; PHOSPHORAMIDOTHIOIC ACID, ACETIMIDOYL-, O,O-BIS(P-CHLOROPHENYL) ESTER; O,O-BIS(P-CHLOROPHENYL)ACETIMIDOYLPHOSPHORAMIDOTHIOATE; O,O-BIS(4-CHLOROPHENYL) (1-IMINOETHYL)PHOSPHORAMIDOTHIOATE; O,O-BIS(4-CHLOROPHENYL) N-ACETIMIDOYLPHOSPHORAMIDOTHIOATE; GOPHACIDE; O,O-BIS(4-CHLOROPHENYL) (1-IMINOETHYL)PHOSPHORAMIDOTHIOIC ACID; (1-IMINOETHYL)PHOSPHORAMIDOTHIOIC ACID O,O-BIS(4-CHLOROPHENYL) ESTER; ACETIMIDOYLPHOSPHORAMIDOTHIOIC ACID O,O-BIS(P-CHLOROPHENYL) ESTER; C14H13CL2N2O2PS; PST71150
CHEMICAL FAMILY: ORGANOPHOSPHATE
HALOGEN COMPOUND, AROMATIC
MOLECULAR FORMULA: (CL-C6-H4-O)2-P-(S)-N-(H)-C-(N-H)-C-H3
MOLECULAR WEIGHT: 375.22
CERCLA RATINGS (SCALE 0-3): HEALTH=3 FIRE=1 REACTIVITY=0
PERSISTENCE=3
NFPA RATINGS (SCALE 0-4): HEALTH=4 FIRE=1 REACTIVITY=0

COMPONENTS AND CONTAMINANTS

COMPONENT: PHOSACETIM ***PERCENT:*** 100.0
CAS# 4104-14-7
OTHER CONTAMINANTS: NONE
EXPOSURE LIMITS: NO OCCUPATIONAL EXPOSURE LIMITS ESTABLISHED BY OSHA, ACGIH, OR NIOSH.
PHOSACETIM: 100/10,000 POUNDS SARA SECTION 302 THRESHOLD PLANNING QUANTITY 1 POUND SARA SECTION 304 REPORTABLE QUANTITY

PHYSICAL DATA

DESCRIPTION: WHITE CRYSTALLINE POWDER.
MELTING POINT: 219-223 F (104-106 C)
SPECIFIC GRAVITY: NOT AVAILABLE ***SOLUBILITY IN WATER:*** NOT AVAILABLE
SOLVENT SOLUBILITY: SOLUBLE IN CHLORINATED HYDROCARBONS; SLIGHTLY SOLUBLE IN ALCOHOL, BENZENE AND ETHER.

FIRE AND EXPLOSION DATA

FIRE AND EXPLOSION HAZARD: UNKNOWN FIRE AND EXPLOSION HAZARD.
DUST-AIR MIXTURES MAY IGNITE OR EXPLODE.
FIREFIGHTING MEDIA: DRY CHEMICAL, CARBON DIOXIDE, HALON, WATER SPRAY OR STANDARD FOAM (1987 EMERGENCY RESPONSE GUIDEBOOK, DOT P 5800.4).
FOR LARGER FIRES, USE WATER SPRAY, FOG OR STANDARD FOAM (1987 EMERGENCY RESPONSE GUIDEBOOK, DOT P 5800.4).
FIREFIGHTING: MOVE CONTAINERS FROM FIRE AREA IF POSSIBLE (1987 EMERGENCY RESPONSE GUIDEBOOK, DOT P 5800.4, GUIDE PAGE 53).
EXTINGUISH USING AGENT SUITABLE FOR TYPE OF SURROUNDING FIRE. AVOID BREATHING VAPORS AND DUSTS. KEEP UPWIND.

TRANSPORTATION DATA

DEPARTMENT OF TRANSPORTATION HAZARD CLASSIFICATION 49 CFR 172.101: POISON B
DEPARTMENT OF TRANSPORTATION LABELING REQUIREMENTS 49 CFR 172.101 AND SUBPART E: POISON
DEPARTMENT OF TRANSPORTATION PACKAGING REQUIREMENTS: 49 CFR 173.365 EXCEPTIONS: 49 CFR 173.364

TOXICITY

PHOSACETIM: TOXICITY DATA: 25 MG/KG SKIN-RAT LD50; 3700 UG/KG ORAL-RAT LD50; 12 MG/KG ORAL-MOUSE LD50; 20 MG/KG ORAL-GUINEA PIG LD50; 23 MG/KG ORAL-DOG LD50; 3500 UG/KG INTRAPERITONEAL-RAT; 5500 UG/KG INTRAPERITONEAL-MOUSE LD50; 14 MG/KG INTRAPERITONEAL-GUINEA PIG LD50. CARCINOGEN STATUS: NONE. ACUTE TOXICITY LEVEL: HIGHLY TOXIC BY DERMAL ABSORPTION AND INGESTION. TARGET EFFECTS: CHOLINESTERASE INHIBITOR. POISONING MAY AFFECT THE NERVOUS SYSTEM.* AT INCREASED RISK FROM EXPOSURE: PERSONS WITH RESPIRATORY AILMENTS, RECENT EXPOSURE TO CHOLINESTERASE INHIBITORS OR IMPAIRED CHOLINESTERASE PRODUCTION, OR LIVER MALFUNCTION.* ADDITIONAL DATA: MAY CROSS THE PLACENTA. HIGH ENVIRONMENTAL TEMPERATURES OR EXPOSURE OF THE CHEMICAL TO VISIBLE OR ULTRAVIOLET LIGHT MAY ENHANCE THE TOXICITY. INTERACTIONS WITH MEDICATIONS MAY OCCUR.*
* MAY BE BASED ON GENERAL INFORMATION ON ORGANOPHOSPHATES.

HEALTH EFFECTS AND FIRST AID

INHALATION: PHOSACETIM: SEE INFORMATION ON ORGANOPHOSPHATES.
ORGANOPHOSPHATES: CHOLINESTERASE INHIBITOR. **ACUTE EXPOSURE-** WHEN INHALED, THE FIRST EFFECTS OF CHOLINESTERASE INHIBITORS ARE USUALLY RESPIRATORY AND MAY INCLUDE NASAL HYPEREMIA AND WATERY DISCHARGE, COUGH, CHEST DISCOMFORT, DYSPNEA, AND WHEEZING DUE TO INCREASED BRONCHIAL SECRETIONS AND BRONCHOCONSTRICTION. IF SUFFICIENT AMOUNTS ARE ABSORBED, OTHER SYSTEMIC EFFECTS MAY BEGIN WITHIN A FEW MINUTES OR BE DELAYED FOR UP TO 12 HOURS. SYMPTOMS MAY INCLUDE PALLOR, NAUSEA, VOMITING, DIARRHEA, ABDOMINAL CRAMPS, HEADACHE, DIZZINESS, OCULAR PAIN, BLURRED VISION, MIOSIS OR IN SOME CASES, ESPECIALLY INITIALLY, MYDRIASIS, LACRIMATION, SALIVATION, SWEATING, AND CONFUSION. OTHER REPORTED CENTRAL NERVOUS SYSTEM OR NEUROMUSCULAR EFFECTS MAY INCLUDE ATAXIA, SLURRED SPEECH, AREFLEXIA, WEAKNESS, FATIGUE, FASCICULATIONS, TWITCHING, TREMORS POSSIBLY OF THE TONGUE AND EYELIDS, AND EVENTUALLY PARALYSIS OF THE EXTREMITIES AND POSSIBLY OF THE RESPIRATORY MUSCLES. IN SEVERE CASES THERE MAY ALSO BE INVOLUNTARY DEFECATION AND URINATION, CYANOSIS, PSYCHOSIS, HYPERGLYCEMIA, ACUTE PANCREATITIS, CARDIAC IRREGULARITIES, PULMONARY EDEMA, UNCONSCIOUSNESS, CONVULSIONS, AND COMA. DEATH IS PRIMARILY DUE TO RESPIRATORY FAILURE, ALTHOUGH CARDIOVASCULAR EFFECTS INCLUDING CARDIAC ARREST MAY ALSO BE IMPLICATED. LONG TERM SEQUELAE ARE RARE BUT MAY INCLUDE NEUROPSYCHIATRIC DISORDERS AND MYOPATHY WITH MUSCLE TENDERNESS. SOME ORGANOPHOSPHATES MAY CAUSE A DELAYED NEUROPATHY BEGINNING 1-4 WEEKS AFTER AN ACUTE EXPOSURE WHICH MAY OR MAY NOT HAVE CAUSED ACUTE CHOLINERGIC EFFECTS. NUMBNESS, TINGLING, WEAKNESS AND CRAMPING BEGINNING SYMMETRICALLY IN THE LOWER LIMBS MAY PROGRESS TO ATAXIA AND PARALYSIS. IN SEVERE CASES, UPPER LIMB INVOLVEMENT IS POSSIBLE AND FLACCID PARALYSIS MAY PROGRESS TO SPASTIC PARALYSIS WITH EXAGGERATED REFLEXES. IMPROVEMENT MAY OCCUR OVER MONTHS TO YEARS, BUT SOME RESIDUAL IMPAIRMENT USUALLY REMAINS.
CHRONIC EXPOSURE- REPEATED OR PROLONGED EXPOSURE MAY RESULT IN THE EFFECTS OF ACUTE EXPOSURE INCLUDING THE DELAYED NEUROPATHY. OTHER EFFECTS REPORTED IN WORKERS REPEATEDLY EXPOSED INCLUDE IMPAIRED MEMORY AND CONCENTRATION, ACUTE PSYCHOSIS, SEVERE DEPRESSIONS, IRRITABILTY, CONFUSION, APATHY, EMOTIONAL LABILITY, SOCIAL WITHDRAWAL, CONFUSION, HEADACHE, SPEECH DIFFICULTIES, DELAYED REACTION TIMES, SPATIAL DISORIENTATION, NIGHTMARES, SLEEPWALKING, AND DROWSINESS OR INSOMNIA. AN INFLUENZA-LIKE CONDITION WITH HEADACHE, NAUSEA, WEAKNESS, ANOREXIA AND MALAISE HAS ALSO BEEN REPORTED.
FIRST AID- REMOVE FROM EXPOSURE AREA TO FRESH AIR IMMEDIATELY. IF BREATHING HAS STOPPED, GIVE ARTIFICIAL RESPIRATION. MAINTAIN AIRWAY AND BLOOD PRESSURE AND ADMINISTER OXYGEN IF AVAILABLE. KEEP AFFECTED PERSON WARM AND AT REST. TREAT SYMPTOMATICALLY AND SUPPORTIVELY. ADMINISTRATION OF OXYGEN SHOULD BE PERFORMED BY QUALIFIED PERSONNEL. GET MEDICAL ATTENTION IMMEDIATELY.

SKIN CONTACT: PHOSACETIM: HIGHLY TOXIC. SEE INFORMATION ON ORGANOPHOSPHATES.
ORGANOPHOSPHATES: CHOLINESTERASE INHIBITOR. **ACUTE EXPOSURE-** LOCALIZED SWEATING AND FASCICULATIONS MAY OCCUR AT THE SITE OF CONTACT. IF SUFFICIENT AMOUNTS ARE ABSORBED, OTHER EFFECTS OF CHOLINESTERASE INHIBITION AS DESCRIBED IN ACUTE INHALATION MAY OCCUR. SYMPTOMS MAY BE DELAYED 2-3 HOURS, BUT USUALLY NO MORE THAN 12 HOURS. THE RATE OF ABSORPTION IS INCREASED BY THE PRESENCE OF DERMATITIS OR HIGH AMBIENT TEMPERATURES. DELAYED NEUROPATHY IS ALSO POSSIBLE. **CHRONIC EXPOSURE-** REPEATED OR PROLONGED EXPOSURE MAY CAUSE EFFECTS AS DESCRIBED IN ACUTE EXPOSURE. SOME ORGANOPHOSPHATES MAY CAUSE SENSITIZATION.
FIRST AID- REMOVE CONTAMINATED CLOTHING IMMEDIATELY. WASH CONTAMINATED AREAS WITH SOAP AND WATER FOLLOWED BY ALCOHOL (ARENA, POISONING, 4TH ED.). EMERGENCY PERSONNEL SHOULD WEAR GLOVES AND AVOID CONTAMINATION. TREAT RESPIRATORY DIFFICULTY WITH ARTIFICIAL RESPIRATION. GET MEDICAL ATTENTION IMMEDIATELY.

EYE CONTACT: PHOSACETIM: SEE INFORMATION ON ORGANOPHOSPHATES.
ORGANOPHOSPHATES: CHOLINESTERASE INHIBITOR. **ACUTE EXPOSURE-** DIRECT CONTACT MAY CAUSE PAIN, HYPEREMIA, LACRIMATION, TWITCHING OF THE EYELIDS, MIOSIS, AND CILIARY MUSCLE SPASM WITH LOSS OF ACCOMODATION, BLURRED OR DIMMED VISION AND BROWACHE. SOMETIMES MYDRIASIS MAY OCCUR INSTEAD OF MIOSIS. WITH SUFFICIENT EXPOSURE, OTHER SYMPTOMS OF CHOLINESTERASE INHIBITION AS DESCRIBED IN ACUTE INHALATION MAY OCCUR. **CHRONIC EXPOSURE-** REPEATED OR PROLONGED EXPOSURE MAY CAUSE EFFECTS AS DESCRIBED IN ACUTE EXPOSURE. SOME COMPOUNDS HAVE CAUSED TOXIC EFFECTS ON THE CRYSTALLINE LENS, CONJUNCTIVAL THICKENING AND

OBSTRUCTION OF THE NASOLACRIMAL CANALS WHEN USED AS MIOTIC EYEDROPS.

FIRST AID- IRRIGATE EYES WITH WATER OR SALINE SOLUTION. IF SYMPTOMS OF POISONING OCCUR, TREAT RESPIRATORY DIFFICULTY WITH ARTIFICIAL RESPIRATION AND OXYGEN. OBSERVE PATIENT FOR AT LEAST 24-36 HOURS (GOSSELIN, CLINICAL TOXICOLOGY OF COMMERCIAL PRODUCTS, 5TH ED.). GET MEDICAL ATTENTION IMMEDIATELY. OXYGEN SHOULD BE ADMINISTERED BY QUALIFIED MEDICAL PERSONNEL.

INGESTION: PHOSACETIM: HIGHLY TOXIC. SEE INFORMATION ON ORGANOPHOSPHATES.

ORGANOPHOSPHATES: CHOLINESTERASE INHIBITOR. **ACUTE EXPOSURE-** WHEN INGESTED, THE FIRST EFFECTS MAY BE NAUSEA, VOMITING, ANOREXIA, ABDOMINAL CRAMPS AND DIARRHEA. GASTROINTESTINAL ABSORPTION MAY CAUSE SYMPTOMS OF CHOLINESTERASE INHIBITION AS DESCRIBED IN ACUTE INHALATION. SYMPTOMS MAY BEGIN WITHIN MINUTES OR BE DELAYED FOR HOURS. DELAYED EFFECTS INCLUDING NEUROPATHY MAY ALSO OCCUR. **CHRONIC EXPOSURE-** REPEATED INGESTION MAY CAUSE EFFECTS AS DESCRIBED IN ACUTE EXPOSURE.

FIRST AID- IF PERSON IS ALERT AND RESPIRATION IS NOT DEPRESSED, GIVE SYRUP OF IPECAC FOLLOWED BY WATER (IF VOMITING OCCURS, KEEP HEAD BELOW HIPS TO PREVENT ASPIRATION). IF CONSCIOUSNESS LEVEL DECLINES OR VOMITING HAS NOT OCCURRED IN 15 MINUTES EMPTY STOMACH BY GASTRIC LAVAGE WITH THE AID OF CUFFED ENDOTRACHEAL TUBE USING ISOTONIC SALINE OR 5% SODIUM BICARBONATE FOLLOW WITH ACTIVATED CHARCOAL. ESTABLISH AND MAINTAIN AIRWAY. TREAT RESPIRATORY DIFFICULTY WITH ARTIFICIAL RESPIRATION AND OXYGEN. DO NOT GIVE MORPHINE, AMINOPHYLLINE, PHENOTHIAZINES, RESERPINE, FUROSEMIDE, OR ETHACRYNIC ACID (MORGAN, RECOGNITION AND MANAGEMENT OF PESTICIDE POISONINGS, 3RD ED.). TREAT SYMPTOMATICALLY AND SUPPORTIVELY. ADMINISTRATION OF OXYGEN AND LAVAGE MUST BE PERFORMED BY QUALIFIED MEDICAL PERSONNEL. GET MEDICAL ATTENTION IMMEDIATELY.

ANTIDOTE: THE FOLLOWING ANTIDOTE(S) HAVE BEEN RECOMMENDED. HOWEVER, THE DECISION AS TO WHETHER THE SEVERITY OF POISONING REQUIRES ADMINISTRATION OF ANY ANTIDOTE AND ACTUAL DOSE REQUIRED SHOULD BE MADE BY QUALIFIED MEDICAL PERSONNEL.

FOR CHOLINESTERASE INHIBITORS: ESTABLISH CLEAR AIRWAY AND TISSUE OXYGENATION BY ASPIRATION OF SECRETIONS, AND IF NECESSARY, BY ASSISTED PULMONARY VENTILATION WITH OXYGEN. IMPROVE TISSUE OXYGENATION AS MUCH AS POSSIBLE BEFORE ADMINISTERING ATROPINE TO MINIMIZE THE RISK OF VENTRICULAR FIBRILLATION. ADMINISTER ATROPINE SULFATE INTRAVENOUSLY, OR INTRAMUSCULARLY IF IV INJECTION IS NOT POSSIBLE. IN MODERATELY SEVERE POISONING ADMINISTER ATROPINE SULFATE, 0.4-2.0 MG REPEATED EVERY 15 MINUTES UNTIL ATROPINIZATION IS ACHIEVED (TACHYCARDIA, FLUSHING, DRY MOUTH, MYDRIASIS). MAINTAIN ATROPINIZATION BY REPEATED DOSES FOR 2-12 HOURS, OR LONGER, DEPENDING ON THE SEVERITY OF POISONING. THE APPEARANCE OF RALES IN THE LUNG BASES, MIOSIS, SALIVATION, NAUSEA, BRADYCARDIA, ARE ALL INDICATIONS OF INADEQUATE ATROPINIZATION. SEVERELY POISONED INDIVIDUALS MAY EXHIBIT REMARKABLE TOLERANCE TO ATROPINE; TWO OR MORE TIMES THE DOSAGES SUGGESTED ABOVE MAY BE NEEDED. PERSONS NOT POISONED OR ONLY SLIGHTLY POISONED, HOWEVER, MAY DEVELOP SIGNS OF ATROPINE TOXICITY FROM SUCH LARGE DOSAGES: FEVER, MUSCLE FIBRILLATIONS, AND DELIRIUM ARE THE MAIN SIGNS OF ATROPINE TOXICITY. IF THESE SIGNS APPEAR WHILE THE PATIENT IS FULLY ATROPINIZED, ATROPINE ADMINISTRATION SHOULD BE DISCONTINUED, AT LEAST TEMPORARILY. OBSERVE TREATED PATIENTS CLOSELY AT LEAST 24 HOURS TO INSURE THAT SYMPTOMS (POSSIBLY PULMONARY EDEMA) DO NOT RECUR AS ATROPINIZATION WEARS OFF. IN VERY SEVERE POISONINGS, METABOLIC DISPOSITION OF TOXICANT MAY REQUIRE SEVERAL HOURS OR DAYS DURING WHICH ATROPINIZATION MUST BE MAINTAINED. MARKEDLY LOWER LEVELS OF URINARY METABOLITES INDICATE THAT ATROPINE DOSAGE CAN BE TAPERED OFF. AS DOSAGE IS REDUCED, CHECK THE LUNG BASES FREQUENTLY FOR RALES. IF RALES ARE HEARD OR OTHER SYMPTOMS RETURN, RE-ESTABLISH ATROPINIZATION PROMPTLY (MORGAN, RECOGNITION AND MANAGEMENT OF PESTICIDE POISONINGS, 3RD ED.). ADMINISTRATION OF ANTIDOTE MUST BE PERFORMED BY QUALIFIED MEDICAL PERSONNEL.

IN CASES OF SEVERE POISONING BY ORGANOPHOSPHATE PESTICIDES IN WHICH RESPIRATORY DEPRESSION, MUSCLE WEAKNESS AND TWITCHINGS ARE SEVERE, GIVE PRALIDOXIME (PROTOPAM-AYERST, 2-PAM), 1.0 GRAM INTRAVENOUSLY AT NO MORE THAN 0.5 GRAM PER MINUTE. DOSAGE OF PRALIDOXIME MAY BE REPEATED IN 1-2 HOURS, THEN AT 10-12 HOUR INTERVALS IF NEEDED. IN VERY SEVERE POISONINGS, DOSAGE RATES MAY BE DOUBLED. TREATMENT WITH PRALIDOXIME WILL BE MOST EFFECTIVE IF GIVEN WITHIN THIRTY-SIX HOURS AFTER POISONING (MORGAN, RECOGNITION AND MANAGEMENT OF PESTICIDE POISONINGS, 3RD ED.). ANTIDOTE SHOULD BE ADMINISTERED BY QUALIFIED MEDICAL PERSONNEL.

REACTIVITY

REACTIVITY: STABLE UNDER NORMAL TEMPERATURES AND PRESSURES.

INCOMPATIBILITIES: PHOSACETIM: OXIDIZERS (STRONG): FIRE AND EXPLOSION HAZARD.

DECOMPOSITION: THERMAL DECOMPOSITION MAY RELEASE TOXIC OXIDES OF CARBON, NITROGEN, SULFUR, AND PHOSPHORUS AND TOXIC FUMES OF CHLORIDE.

POLYMERIZATION: HAZARDOUS POLYMERIZATION HAS NOT BEEN REPORTED TO OCCUR UNDER NORMAL TEMPERATURES AND PRESSURES.

STORAGE AND DISPOSAL

OBSERVE ALL FEDERAL, STATE AND LOCAL REGULATIONS WHEN STORING OR DISPOSING OF THIS SUBSTANCE. FOR ASSISTANCE, CONTACT THE DISTRICT DIRECTOR OF THE ENVIRONMENTAL PROTECTION AGENCY.

STORAGE

STORE IN ACCORDANCE WITH 40 CFR 165 RECOMMENDED PROCEDURES FOR THE DISPOSAL AND STORAGE OF PESTICIDES AND PESTICIDE CONTAINERS.

STORE AWAY FROM INCOMPATIBLE SUBSTANCES.

THRESHOLD PLANNING QUANTITY (TPQ): THE SUPERFUND AMENDMENTS AND REAUTHORIZATION ACT (SARA) SECTION 302 REQUIRES THAT EACH FACILITY WHERE ANY EXTREMELY HAZARDOUS SUBSTANCE IS PRESENT IN A QUANTITY EQUAL TO OR GREATER THAN THE TPQ ESTABLISHED FOR THAT SUBSTANCE NOTIFY THE STATE EMERGENCY RESPONSE COMMISSION FOR THE STATE IN WHICH IT IS LOCATED. SECTION 303 OF SARA REQUIRES THESE FACILITIES TO PARTICIPATE IN LOCAL EMERGENCY RESPONSE PLANNING (40 CFR 355.30).

DISPOSAL

DISPOSAL MUST BE IN ACCORDANCE WITH 40 CFR 165 RECOMMENDED PROCEDURES FOR THE DISPOSAL AND STORAGE OF PESTICIDES AND PESTICIDE CONTAINERS.

CONDITIONS TO AVOID

MAY BURN BUT DOES NOT IGNITE READILY.

SPILL AND LEAK PROCEDURES

OCCUPATIONAL SPILL: DO NOT TOUCH SPILLED MATERIAL. STOP LEAK IF YOU CAN DO IT WITHOUT RISK. FOR SMALL SPILLS, TAKE UP WITH SAND OR OTHER ABSORBENT MATERIAL AND PLACE INTO CONTAINERS FOR LATER DISPOSAL. FOR SMALL DRY SPILLS, WITH A CLEAN SHOVEL PLACE MATERIAL INTO CLEAN, DRY CONTAINER AND COVER. MOVE CONTAINERS FROM SPILL AREA. FOR LARGER SPILLS, DIKE FAR AHEAD OF SPILL FOR LATER DISPOSAL. KEEP UNNECESSARY PEOPLE AWAY. ISOLATE HAZARD AREA AND DENY ENTRY.

REPORTABLE QUANTITY (RQ): 1 POUND THE SUPERFUND AMENDMENTS AND REAUTHORIZATION ACT (SARA) SECTION 304 REQUIRES THAT A RELEASE EQUAL TO OR GREATER THAN THE REPORTABLE QUANTITY FOR THIS SUBSTANCE BE IMMEDIATELY REPORTED TO THE LOCAL EMERGENCY PLANNING COMMITTEE AND THE STATE EMERGENCY RESPONSE COMMISSION (40 CFR 355.40). IF THE RELEASE OF THIS SUBSTANCE IS REPORTABLE UNDER CERCLA SECTION 103, THE NATIONAL RESPONSE CENTER MUST BE NOTIFIED IMMEDIATELY AT (800) 424-8802 OR (202) 426-2675 IN THE METROPOLITAN WASHINGTON, D.C. AREA (40 CFR 302.6).

PROTECTIVE EQUIPMENT

VENTILATION: PROCESS ENCLOSURE RECOMMENDED.

RESPIRATOR: THE FOLLOWING RESPIRATORS ARE RECOMMENDED BASED ON INFORMATION FOUND IN THE PHYSICAL DATA, TOXICITY AND HEALTH EFFECTS SECTIONS. THEY ARE RANKED IN ORDER FROM MINIMUM TO MAXIMUM RESPIRATORY PROTECTION. THE SPECIFIC RESPIRATOR SELECTED MUST BE BASED ON CONTAMINATION LEVELS FOUND IN THE WORK PLACE, MUST NOT EXCEED THE WORKING LIMITS OF THE RESPIRATOR AND BE JOINTLY APPROVED BY THE NATIONAL INSTITUTE FOR OCCUPATIONAL SAFETY AND HEALTH AND THE MINE SAFETY AND HEALTH ADMINISTRATION (NIOSH-MSHA).

TYPE 'C' SUPPLIED-AIR RESPIRATOR WITH A FULL FACEPIECE OPERATED IN PRESSURE-DEMAND OR OTHER POSITIVE PRESSURE MODE OR WITH A FULL FACEPIECE, HELMET OR HOOD OPERATED IN CONTINOUS-FLOW MODE.

SELF-CONTAINED BREATHING APPARATUS WITH A FULL FACEPIECE OPERATED IN PRESSURE-DEMAND OR OTHER POSITIVE PRESSURE MODE.

FOR FIREFIGHTING AND OTHER IMMEDIATELY DANGEROUS TO LIFE OR HEALTH CONDITIONS:

SELF-CONTAINED BREATHING APPARATUS WITH FULL FACEPIECE OPERATED IN PRESSURE-DEMAND OR OTHER POSITIVE PRESSURE MODE.

SUPPLIED-AIR RESPIRATOR WITH FULL FACEPIECE AND OPERATED IN PRESSURE-DEMAND OR OTHER POSITIVE PRESSURE MODE IN COMBINATION WITH AN AUXILIARY SELF-CONTAINED BREATHING APPARATUS OPERATED IN PRESSURE-DEMAND OR OTHER POSITIVE PRESSURE MODE.

CLOTHING: EMPLOYEE MUST WEAR APPROPRIATE PROTECTIVE (IMPERVIOUS) CLOTHING AND EQUIPMENT TO PREVENT ANY POSSIBILITY OF SKIN CONTACT WITH THIS SUBSTANCE.

GLOVES: EMPLOYEE MUST WEAR APPROPRIATE PROTECTIVE GLOVES TO PREVENT CONTACT WITH THIS SUBSTANCE.

EYE PROTECTION: EMPLOYEE MUST WEAR SPLASH-PROOF OR DUST-RESISTANT SAFETY GOGGLES AND A FACESHIELD TO PREVENT CONTACT WITH THIS SUBSTANCE.

EMERGENCY WASH FACILITIES: WHERE THERE IS ANY POSSIBILITY THAT AN EMPLOYEE'S EYES AND/OR SKIN MAY BE EXPOSED TO THIS SUBSTANCE, THE EMPLOYER SHOULD PROVIDE AN EYE WASH FOUNTAIN AND QUICK DRENCH SHOWER WITHIN THE IMMEDIATE WORK AREA FOR EMERGENCY USE.

AUTHORIZED BY- OCCUPATIONAL HEALTH SERVICES, INC.
CREATION DATE: 10/04/89 ***REVISION DATE:*** 07/10/90

MATERIAL SAFETY DATA SHEET

OCCUPATIONAL HEALTH SERVICES, INC.
AGRICULTURE AND PESTICIDE DIVISION
450 SEVENTH AVENUE, SUITE 2407
NEW YORK, NEW YORK 10123
1-800-445-MSDS OR (212) 967-1100

EMERGENCY CONTACT:
JOHN S. BRANSFORD, JR. (615) 292-1180

SUBSTANCE IDENTIFICATION

CAS-NUMBER 93-71-0

SUBSTANCE: **ALLIDOCHLOR**

TRADE NAMES/SYNONYMS: ACETAMIDE, 2-CHLORO-N,N-DI-2-PROPENYL-; ACETAMIDE, N,N-DIALLYL-2-CHLORO-; N,N-DIALLYL-2-CHLOROACETAMIDE; 2-CHLORO-N,N-DI-2-PROPENYLACETAMIDE; N,N-DIALLYLCHLOROACETAMIDE; 2-CHLORO-N,N-DIALLYLACETAMIDE; CHLOROACETAMIDE, N,N-DIALLYL-; ALIDOCHLORE; CDAA; CP 6,343; RANDOX; C8H12CLNO; PST71155

CHEMICAL FAMILY: AMIDE
HALOGEN COMPOUND, ALIPHATIC

MOLECULAR FORMULA: CL-C-H2-C-O-N-(C-H2-C-H-C-H2)2

MOLECULAR WEIGHT: 173.64

CERCLA RATINGS (SCALE 0-3): HEALTH=3 FIRE=U REACTIVITY=0 PERSISTENCE=2

NFPA RATINGS (SCALE 0-4): HEALTH=U FIRE=U REACTIVITY=0

COMPONENTS AND CONTAMINANTS

COMPONENT: ALLIDOCHLOR ***PERCENT:*** 100.0
CAS# 93-71-0

OTHER CONTAMINANTS: NONE

EXPOSURE LIMITS: NO OCCUPATIONAL EXPOSURE LIMITS ESTABLISHED BY OSHA, ACGIH, OR NIOSH.

PHYSICAL DATA

DESCRIPTION: AMBER-COLORED, OILY LIQUID.

BOILING POINT: 198 F (92 C) @ 0.7 MMHG

SPECIFIC GRAVITY: 1.09 @ 25 C ***VAPOR PRESSURE:*** 0.0094 MMHG @ 20 C

SOLUBILITY IN WATER: 1.97% @ 25 C

SOLVENT SOLUBILITY: SOLUBLE IN ETHANOL, CHLOROBENZENE, CHLOROFORM, CYCLOHEXANONE, HEXANE, KEROSENE, AND XYLENE.
DECOMPOSES @ 257 F (125 C)

FIRE AND EXPLOSION DATA

FIRE AND EXPLOSION HAZARD: SLIGHT FIRE HAZARD WHEN EXPOSED TO HEAT OR FLAME.

FLASH POINT: NOT AVAILABLE

FIREFIGHTING MEDIA: DRY CHEMICAL, CARBON DIOXIDE, HALON, WATER SPRAY OR STANDARD FOAM (1987 EMERGENCY RESPONSE GUIDEBOOK, DOT P 5800.4).
FOR LARGER FIRES, USE WATER SPRAY, FOG OR STANDARD FOAM (1987 EMERGENCY RESPONSE GUIDEBOOK, DOT P 5800.4).

FIREFIGHTING: MOVE CONTAINER FROM FIRE AREA IF POSSIBLE. COOL FIRE-EXPOSED CONTAINERS WITH WATER FROM SIDE UNTIL WELL AFTER FIRE IS OUT. STAY AWAY FROM STORAGE TANK ENDS. FOR MASSIVE FIRE IN STORAGE AREA, USE UNMANNED HOSE HOLDER OR MONITOR NOZZLES, ELSE WITHDRAW FROM AREA AND LET FIRE BURN. WITHDRAW IMMEDIATELY IN CASE OF RISING SOUND FROM VENTING SAFETY DEVICE OR ANY DISCOLORATION OF STORAGE TANK DUE TO FIRE (1987 EMERGENCY RESPONSE GUIDEBOOK, DOT P 5800.4, GUIDE PAGE 27). EXTINGUISH ONLY IF FLOW CAN BE STOPPED; USE FLOODING AMOUNTS OF WATER AS A FOG, SOLID STREAMS MAY BE INEFFECTIVE. COOL CONTAINERS WITH FLOODING AMOUNTS OF WATER, APPLY FROM AS FAR A DISTANCE AS POSSIBLE. AVOID BREATHING VAPORS, KEEP UPWIND.

TOXICITY

ALLIDOCHLOR: TOXICITY DATA: 360 MG/KG SKIN-RAT LD50; 700 MG/KG ORAL-RAT LD50; 266 MG/KG ORAL-RAT LD50 (THE FDA SURVEILLANCE INDEX, SUPPLEMENT NO 12, 1987). CARCINOGEN STATUS: NONE. LOCAL EFFECTS: IRRITANT-SKIN, EYE. ACUTE TOXICITY LEVEL: TOXIC BY DERMAL ABSORPTION AND INGESTION. TARGET EFFECTS: NO DATA AVAILABLE.

HEALTH EFFECTS AND FIRST AID

INHALATION: ALLIDOCHLOR: **ACUTE EXPOSURE-** NO DATA AVAILABLE. **CHRONIC EXPOSURE-** NO DATA AVAILABLE.

FIRST AID- REMOVE FROM EXPOSURE AREA TO FRESH AIR IMMEDIATELY. IF BREATHING HAS STOPPED, PERFORM ARTIFICIAL RESPIRATION. KEEP PERSON WARM AND AT REST. TREAT SYMPTOMATICALLY AND SUPPORTIVELY. GET MEDICAL ATTENTION IMMEDIATELY.

SKIN CONTACT: ALIDOCHLOR: IRRITANT/TOXIC. **ACUTE EXPOSURE-** MAY CAUSE SEVERE SKIN IRRITATION AND AN ACHING OR BURNING SENSATION DUE TO THE ABILITY OF THIS MATERIAL TO SENSITIZE THE EXPOSED AREA TO TEMPERATURE CHANGES; THIS SENSATION MAY LAST FOR SEVERAL HOURS AFTER EXPOSURE. A LETHAL DOSE IN RATS BY DERMAL ABSORPTION WAS 360 MG/KG; NO SYMPTOMS WERE REPORTED. **CHRONIC EXPOSURE-** NO DATA AVAILABLE.

FIRST AID- REMOVE CONTAMINATED CLOTHING AND SHOES IMMEDIATELY. WASH AFFECTED AREA WITH SOAP OR MILD DETERGENT AND LARGE AMOUNTS OF WATER UNTIL NO EVIDENCE OF CHEMICAL REMAINS (APPROXIMATELY 15-20 MINUTES). GET MEDICAL ATTENTION IMMEDIATELY.

EYE CONTACT: ALLIDOCHLOR: IRRITANT. **ACUTE EXPOSURE-** MAY CAUSE SEVERE EYE IRRITATION, POSSIBLY WITH SERIOUS OCULAR DAMAGE. **CHRONIC EXPOSURE-** NO DATA AVAILABLE.

FIRST AID- WASH EYES IMMEDIATELY WITH LARGE AMOUNTS OF WATER OR NORMAL SALINE, OCCASIONALLY LIFTING UPPER AND LOWER LIDS, UNTIL NO EVIDENCE OF CHEMICAL REMAINS (APPROXIMATELY 15-20 MINUTES). GET MEDICAL ATTENTION IMMEDIATELY.

INGESTION: ALLIDOCHLOR: TOXIC. **ACUTE EXPOSURE-** A LETHAL DOSE IN RATS WAS 266 MG/KG; SYMPTOMS WERE NOT REPORTED. **CHRONIC EXPOSURE-** NO DATA AVAILABLE.

FIRST AID- REMOVE BY GASTRIC LAVAGE AND CATHARSIS. MAINTAIN BLOOD PRESSURE AND AIRWAY. GIVE OXYGEN IF RESPIRATION IS DEPRESSED. DO NOT PERFORM GASTRIC LAVAGE IF VICTIM IS UNCONSCIOUS. GET MEDICAL ATTENTION IMMEDIATELY (DREISBACH, HANDBOOK OF POISONING, 12TH ED.).
ADMINISTRATION OF LAVAGE OR OXYGEN SHOULD BE PERFORMED BY QUALIFIED MEDICAL PERSONNEL.

ANTIDOTE: NO SPECIFIC ANTIDOTE. TREAT SYMPTOMATICALLY AND SUPPORTIVELY.

REACTIVITY

REACTIVITY: STABLE UNDER NORMAL TEMPERATURES AND PRESSURES.

INCOMPATIBILITIES: ALLIDOCHLOR: MINERAL ACIDS: DECOMPOSES. MINERAL BASES: DECOMPOSES. OXIDIZERS (STRONG): FIRE AND EXPLOSION HAZARD.

DECOMPOSITION: THERMAL DECOMPOSITION PRODUCTS MAY INCLUDE TOXIC OXIDES OF NITROGEN AND CARBON AND TOXIC AND CORROSIVE FUMES OF CHLORIDES.

POLYMERIZATION: HAZARDOUS POLYMERIZATION HAS NOT BEEN REPORTED TO OCCUR UNDER NORMAL TEMPERATURES AND PRESSURES.

STORAGE AND DISPOSAL

OBSERVE ALL FEDERAL, STATE AND LOCAL REGULATIONS WHEN STORING OR DISPOSING OF THIS SUBSTANCE. FOR ASSISTANCE, CONTACT THE DISTRICT DIRECTOR OF THE ENVIRONMENTAL PROTECTION AGENCY.

****STORAGE****

STORE IN ACCORDANCE WITH 40 CFR 165 RECOMMENDED PROCEDURES FOR THE DISPOSAL AND STORAGE OF PESTICIDES AND PESTICIDE CONTAINERS.
STORE AWAY FROM INCOMPATIBLE SUBSTANCES.

****DISPOSAL****

DISPOSAL MUST BE IN ACCORDANCE WITH 40 CFR 165 RECOMMENDED PROCEDURES FOR THE DISPOSAL AND STORAGE OF PESTICIDES AND PESTICIDE CONTAINERS.

CONDITIONS TO AVOID

AVOID CONTACT WITH HEAT, SPARKS, FLAMES, OR OTHER SOURCES OF IGNITION. VAPORS MAY BE EXPLOSIVE. AVOID OVERHEATING OF CONTAINERS; CONTAINERS MAY VIOLENTLY RUPTURE IN HEAT OF FIRE. AVOID CONTAMINATION OF WATER SOURCES.

SPILL AND LEAK PROCEDURES

OCCUPATIONAL SPILL: SHUT OFF IGNITION SOURCES. STOP LEAK IF YOU CAN DO IT WITHOUT RISK. USE WATER SPRAY TO REDUCE VAPORS. FOR SMALL SPILLS, TAKE UP WITH SAND OR OTHER ABSORBENT MATERIAL AND PLACE INTO CONTAINERS FOR LATER DISPOSAL. FOR LARGER SPILLS, DIKE FAR AHEAD OF SPILL FOR LATER DISPOSAL. NO SMOKING, FLAMES OR FLARES IN HAZARD AREA. KEEP UNNECESSARY PEOPLE AWAY; ISOLATE HAZARD AREA AND RESTRICT ENTRY.

PROTECTIVE EQUIPMENT

VENTILATION: PROVIDE LOCAL EXHAUST OR PROCESS ENCLOSURE VENTILATION SYSTEM.

RESPIRATOR: THE FOLLOWING RESPIRATORS ARE RECOMMENDED BASED ON INFORMATION FOUND IN THE PHYSICAL DATA, TOXICITY AND HEALTH EFFECTS SECTIONS. THEY ARE RANKED IN ORDER FROM MINIMUM TO MAXIMUM RESPIRATORY PROTECTION. THE SPECIFIC RESPIRATOR SELECTED MUST BE BASED ON CONTAMINATION LEVELS FOUND IN THE WORK PLACE, MUST NOT EXCEED THE WORKING LIMITS OF THE RESPIRATOR AND BE JOINTLY APPROVED BY THE NATIONAL INSTITUTE FOR OCCUPATIONAL SAFETY AND HEALTH AND THE MINE SAFETY AND HEALTH ADMINISTRATION (NIOSH-MSHA).

TYPE 'C' SUPPLIED-AIR RESPIRATOR WITH A FULL FACEPIECE OPERATED IN PRESSURE-DEMAND OR OTHER POSITIVE PRESSURE MODE OR WITH A FULL FACEPIECE, HELMET OR HOOD OPERATED IN CONTINOUS-FLOW MODE. SELF-CONTAINED BREATHING APPARATUS WITH A FULL FACEPIECE OPERATED IN PRESSURE-DEMAND OR OTHER POSITIVE PRESSURE MODE.

FOR FIREFIGHTING AND OTHER IMMEDIATELY DANGEROUS TO LIFE OR HEALTH CONDITIONS:

SELF-CONTAINED BREATHING APPARATUS WITH FULL FACEPIECE OPERATED IN PRESSURE-DEMAND OR OTHER POSITIVE PRESSURE MODE.

SUPPLIED-AIR RESPIRATOR WITH FULL FACEPIECE AND OPERATED IN PRESSURE-DEMAND OR OTHER POSITIVE PRESSURE MODE IN COMBINATION WITH AN AUXILIARY SELF-CONTAINED BREATHING APPARATUS OPERATED IN PRESSURE-DEMAND OR OTHER POSITIVE PRESSURE MODE.

CLOTHING: EMPLOYEE MUST WEAR APPROPRIATE PROTECTIVE (IMPERVIOUS) CLOTHING AND EQUIPMENT TO PREVENT ANY POSSIBILITY OF SKIN CONTACT WITH THIS SUBSTANCE.

GLOVES: EMPLOYEE MUST WEAR APPROPRIATE PROTECTIVE GLOVES TO PREVENT CONTACT WITH THIS SUBSTANCE.

EYE PROTECTION: EMPLOYEE MUST WEAR SPLASH-PROOF OR DUST-RESISTANT SAFETY GOGGLES WITH OR WITHOUT A FACESHIELD TO PREVENT CONTACT WITH THIS SUBSTANCE.

EMERGENCY EYE WASH: WHERE THERE IS ANY POSSIBILITY THAT AN EMPLOYEE'S EYES MAY BE EXPOSED TO THIS SUBSTANCE, THE EMPLOYER SHOULD PROVIDE AN EYE WASH FOUNTAIN WITHIN THE IMMEDIATE WORK AREA FOR EMERGENCY USE.

AUTHORIZED BY- OCCUPATIONAL HEALTH SERVICES, INC.
CREATION DATE: 10/04/89 ***REVISION DATE:*** 10/31/89

MATERIAL SAFETY DATA SHEET

OCCUPATIONAL HEALTH SERVICES, INC.
AGRICULTURE AND PESTICIDE DIVISION
450 SEVENTH AVENUE, SUITE 2407
NEW YORK, NEW YORK 10123
1-800-445-MSDS OR (212) 967-1100

EMERGENCY CONTACT:
JOHN S. BRANSFORD, JR. (615) 292-1180

SUBSTANCE IDENTIFICATION

CAS-NUMBER 8001-50-1
SUBSTANCE: **STROBANE**
TRADE NAMES/SYNONYMS: TERPENE POLYCHLORINATE; POLYCHLOROTERPENES; PST71162
CHEMICAL FAMILY: TERPENE
HALOGEN
MOLECULAR WEIGHT: VARIES
CERCLA RATINGS (SCALE 0-3): HEALTH=3 FIRE=1 REACTIVITY=0 PERSISTENCE=3
NFPA RATINGS (SCALE 0-4): HEALTH=4 FIRE=1 REACTIVITY=0

COMPONENTS AND CONTAMINANTS

COMPONENT: STROBANE ***PERCENT:*** 100.0
CAS# 8001-50-1

OTHER CONTAMINANTS: NONE
EXPOSURE LIMITS: NO OCCUPATIONAL EXPOSURE LIMITS ESTABLISHED BY OSHA, ACGIH, OR NIOSH.

PHYSICAL DATA

DESCRIPTION: VISCOUS, AMBER LIQUID. ***BOILING POINT:*** NOT AVAILABLE
SPECIFIC GRAVITY: 1.6267 ***VAPOR PRESSURE:*** NEGLIGIBLE
SOLUBILITY IN WATER: INSOLUBLE
SOLVENT SOLUBILITY: SOLUBLE WITH AROMATIC AND ALIPHATIC HYDROCARBONS; SLIGHTLY SOLUBLE IN ALCOHOL.

FIRE AND EXPLOSION DATA

FIRE AND EXPLOSION HAZARD: SLIGHT FIRE HAZARD WHEN EXPOSED TO HEAT OR FLAME.

FIREFIGHTING MEDIA: DRY CHEMICAL, CARBON DIOXIDE, HALON, WATER SPRAY OR STANDARD FOAM (1987 EMERGENCY RESPONSE GUIDEBOOK, DOT P 5800.4). FOR LARGER FIRES, USE WATER SPRAY, FOG OR STANDARD FOAM (1987 EMERGENCY RESPONSE GUIDEBOOK, DOT P 5800.4).

FIREFIGHTING: MOVE CONTAINERS FROM FIRE AREA IF POSSIBLE. FIGHT FIRE FROM MAXIMUM DISTANCE. STAY AWAY FROM STORAGE TANK ENDS. DIKE FIRE CONTROL WATER FOR LATER DISPOSAL. DO NOT SCATTER MATERIAL (1987 EMERGENCY RESPONSE GUIDEBOOK, DOT P 5800.4, GUIDE PAGE 55). EXTINGUISH ONLY IF FLOW CAN BE STOPPED. EXTINGUISH USING AGENT INDICATED. USE FLOODING AMOUNTS OF WATER AS A FOG. COOL CONTAINERS WITH FLOODING AMOUNTS OF WATER FROM AS FAR A DISTANCE AS POSSIBLE. AVOID BREATHING POISONOUS VAPORS, KEEP UPWIND. CONSIDER EVACUATION OF DOWNWIND AREA IF MATERIAL IS LEAKING.

TOXICITY

STROBANE: TOXICITY DATA: 600 MG/M3/4 HOURS INHALATION-CAT LC100 (85GMAT); 1000-1500 MG/KG SKIN-RABBIT LD100 (85GMAT); 200 MG/KG ORAL-RAT LD50; 200 MG/KG ORAL-MOUSE LD50; 200 MG/KG ORAL-DOG LD50; 250 MG/KG UNREPORTED-RAT LD50; TUMORIGENIC DATA (RTECS). CARCINOGEN STATUS: ANIMAL LIMITED EVIDENCE (IARC GROUP-3). ORAL ADMINISTRATION PRODUCED AN INCREASED INCIDENCE OF HEPATOMAS IN ONE STRAIN OF MALE MICE. A SUGGESTION THAT STROBANE ALSO INCREASED THE INCIDENCE OF MALIGNANT LYMPHOMAS HAS NOT BEEN CONFIRMED. ACUTE TOXICITY LEVEL: HIGHLY TOXIC BY INHALATION; TOXIC BY DERMAL ABSORPTION, INGESTION. TARGET EFFECTS: CONVULSANT. POISONING MAY ALSO AFFECT THE LIVER AND KIDNEYS.* ADDITIONAL DATA: MAY BE EXCRETED IN BREAST MILK. STIMULANTS SUCH AS EPINEPHRINE MAY INDUCE VENTRICULAR FIBRILLATION.*

* MAY BE BASED ON GENERAL INFORMATION ON ORGANOCHLORINE PESTICIDES.

HEALTH EFFECTS AND FIRST AID

INHALATION: STROBANE: CONVULSANT/HIGHLY TOXIC. **ACUTE EXPOSURE**- SYMPTOMS OF ORGANOCHLORINE PESTICIDE POISONING MAY BE DELAYED FROM 30 MINUTES TO SEVERAL HOURS. THEY MAY INCLUDE NAUSEA, VOMITING, DIARRHEA, STOMACH PAIN, HEADACHE, DIZZINESS, ATAXIA, PARESTHESIAS, RESTLESSNESS, IRRITABILITY, CONFUSION, AND TREMORS PROGRESSING TO STUPOR, COMA AND EPILEPTIFORM OR TONIC-CLONIC CONVULSIONS WITH FROTHING AT THE MOUTH, FACIAL CONGESTION, VIOLENT CONVULSIVE MOVEMENTS OR STIFFNESS OF THE LIMBS. THE TREMORS MAY START AT THE EYELIDS AND FACIAL MUSCLES AND DESCEND TOWARD THE TRUNK AND LIMBS. IN SEVERE CASES, THE CONVULSIONS MAY BE CONTINUOUS AND ACCOMPANIED BY INCREASED BODY TEMPERATURE, UNCONSCIOUSNESS, LABORED BREATHING WITH VIGOROUS AND RAPID HEARTBEAT AND GENERALIZED DEPRESSION. ANOXIA, METABOLIC ACIDOSIS, RESPIRATORY COLLAPSE AND DEATH MAY OCCUR. TOXIC HEPATITIS, TOXIC NEPHROPATHY, PROLONGED TOXIC POLYNEURITIS, ANEMIA AND HEMORRHAGIC DIATHESIS HAVE ALSO BEEN REPORTED. SOME ORGANOCHLORINE PESTICIDES INCREASE MYOCARDIAL IRRITABILITY. **CHRONIC EXPOSURE**- ORGANOCHLORINE PESTICIDES ARE CENTRAL NERVOUS SYSTEM STIMULANTS. OCCUPATIONAL EXPOSURE HAS BEEN REPORTED TO CAUSE POLYNEURITIS, ENCEPHALOPOLYNEURITIS AND NEUROVEGETATIVE SYNDROMES WITH HEADACHE, DIZZINESS, PARESTHESIAS AND TREMORS OF THE LIMBS, VASCULAR LABILITY, NEUROCIRCULATORY DISTURBANCES, AND, LESS FREQUENTLY, COLIC PAINS AND DYSKINESIA OF THE BILE DUCTS. OTHER EFFECTS MAY INCLUDE ANOREXIA AND WEIGHT LOSS, LIVER AND KIDNEY DAMAGE, CARDIOVASCULAR DISTURBANCES WITH RAPID HEARTBEAT, INCREASED HEART VOLUME, HOLLOW HEART TONES AND OPPRESSION AND PAIN IN THE REGION OF THE HEART. BLOOD DISTURBANCES INCLUDING THROMBOCYTOPENIA, PANCYTOPENIA, AGRANULOCYTOSIS, HEMOLYSIS AND CAPILLARY DISORDERS MANIFESTED AS PURPURA HAVE ALSO OCCURRED. REVERSIBLE BEHAVIORAL CHANGES SUCH AS DISTURBANCES OF SENSORY AND EQUILIBRIUM FUNCTIONS HAVE BEEN REPORTED. PROLONGED EXPOSURE HAS RESULTED IN EOSINOPENIA, NEUTROPENIA WITH LYMPHOCYTOSIS, AND HYPOCHROMIC ANEMIA.

FIRST AID- REMOVE FROM EXPOSURE AREA TO FRESH AIR IMMEDIATELY. IF BREATHING HAS STOPPED, PERFORM ARTIFICIAL RESPIRATION. KEEP PERSON WARM AND AT REST. TREAT SYMPTOMATICALLY AND SUPPORTIVELY. GET MEDICAL ATTENTION IMMEDIATELY.

SKIN CONTACT: STROBANE: TOXIC. **ACUTE EXPOSURE-** MAY CAUSE MILD IRRITATION. ORGANOCHLORINE PESTICIDES MAY BE ABSORBED THROUGH THE SKIN. SYMPTOMS OF ORGANOCHLORINE PESTICIDE POISONING ARE DESCRIBED IN ACUTE INHALATION. **CHRONIC EXPOSURE-** REPEATED APPLICATIONS OF A 5% SOLUTION OF STROBANE AT 1-4 CC/KG CAUSED TOXICITY IN RABBITS. ORGANOCHLORINE PESTICIDES MAY ACCUMULATE IN BODY TISSUES.
FIRST AID- REMOVE CONTAMINATED CLOTHING AND SHOES IMMEDIATELY. WASH AFFECTED AREA WITH SOAP OR MILD DETERGENT AND LARGE AMOUNTS OF WATER UNTIL NO EVIDENCE OF CHEMICAL REMAINS (APPROXIMATELY 15-20 MINUTES). GET MEDICAL ATTENTION IMMEDIATELY.

EYE CONTACT: STROBANE: **ACUTE EXPOSURE-** SOME ORGANOCHLORINE PESTICIDES CAUSE IRRITATION. **CHRONIC EXPOSURE-** NO DATA AVAILABLE.
FIRST AID- WASH EYES IMMEDIATELY WITH LARGE AMOUNTS OF WATER OR NORMAL SALINE, OCCASIONALLY LIFTING UPPER AND LOWER LIDS, UNTIL NO EVIDENCE OF CHEMICAL REMAINS (APPROXIMATELY 15-20 MINUTES). GET MEDICAL ATTENTION IMMEDIATELY.

INGESTION: STROBANE: CONVULSANT/CARCINOGEN/TOXIC. **ACUTE EXPOSURE-** INGESTION OF ORGANOCHLORINE PESTICIDES MAY CAUSE SYMPTOMS AS DETAILED IN ACUTE INHALATION. **CHRONIC EXPOSURE-** A STATISTICALLY SIGNIFICANT NUMBER OF HEPATOMAS WERE SEEN IN ONE STRAIN OF MALE MICE ADMINISTERED STROBANE UP TO 80 WEEKS. MALIGNANT LYMPHOMAS WERE ALSO SEEN IN ONE STRAIN OF MALE AND FEMALE MICE. IN ANOTHER STUDY, AN INCREASED INCIDENCE OF RETICULUM CELL SARCOMAS WAS REPORTED IN MICE.
FIRST AID- IF THE PERSON IS CONSCIOUS AND NOT CONVULSING, REMOVE BY GIVING SYRUP OF IPECAC (IF VOMITING OCCURS, KEEP THE HEAD BELOW THE HIPS TO PREVENT ASPIRATION). GIVE ACTIVATED CHARCOAL FOLLOWED BY GASTRIC LAVAGE. FOLLOW WITH A SALINE CATHARTIC. DO NOT GIVE FATS OR OILS. INTESTINAL LAVAGE WITH 20% MANNITOL (200 ML) BY STOMACH TUBE IS ALSO USEFUL. GIVE ARTIFICIAL RESPIRATION WITH OXYGEN IF RESPIRATION IS DEPRESSED (DREISBACH, HANDBOOK OF POISONING, 12TH ED.). TREAT SYMPTOMATICALLY AND SUPPORTIVELY. LAVAGE AND ADMINISTRATION OF OXYGEN SHOULD BE PERFORMED BY QUALIFIED MEDICAL PERSONNEL. GET MEDICAL ATTENTION IMMEDIATELY.
ANTIDOTE: NO SPECIFIC ANTIDOTE. TREAT SYMPTOMATICALLY AND SUPPORTIVELY.

REACTIVITY

REACTIVITY: STABLE UNDER NORMAL TEMPERATURES AND PRESSURES.
INCOMPATIBILITIES: STROBANE: BASES (STRONG): INCOMPATIBLE. OXIDIZERS (STRONG): FIRE AND EXPLOSION HAZARD.
DECOMPOSITION: THERMAL DECOMPOSITION PRODUCTS MAY INCLUDE TOXIC AND CORROSIVE FUMES OF CHLORIDES AND TOXIC OXIDES OF CARBON.
POLYMERIZATION: HAZARDOUS POLYMERIZATION HAS NOT BEEN REPORTED TO OCCUR UNDER NORMAL TEMPERATURES AND PRESSURES.

STORAGE AND DISPOSAL

OBSERVE ALL FEDERAL, STATE AND LOCAL REGULATIONS WHEN STORING OR DISPOSING OF THIS SUBSTANCE. FOR ASSISTANCE, CONTACT THE DISTRICT DIRECTOR OF THE ENVIRONMENTAL PROTECTION AGENCY.

STORAGE

STORE IN ACCORDANCE WITH 40 CFR 165 RECOMMENDED PROCEDURES FOR THE DISPOSAL AND STORAGE OF PESTICIDES AND PESTICIDE CONTAINERS.
STORE AWAY FROM INCOMPATIBLE SUBSTANCES.

DISPOSAL

DISPOSAL MUST BE IN ACCORDANCE WITH 40 CFR 165 RECOMMENDED PROCEDURES FOR THE DISPOSAL AND STORAGE OF PESTICIDES AND PESTICIDE CONTAINERS.

CONDITIONS TO AVOID

MAY BURN BUT DOES NOT IGNITE READILY. CONTAINERS MAY EXPLODE IN HEAT OF FIRE.

SPILL AND LEAK PROCEDURES

OCCUPATIONAL SPILL: DO NOT TOUCH SPILLED MATERIAL. STOP LEAK IF YOU CAN DO IT WITHOUT RISK. USE WATER SPRAY TO REDUCE VAPORS. FOR SMALL SPILLS, TAKE UP WITH SAND OR OTHER ABSORBENT MATERIAL AND PLACE INTO CONTAINERS FOR LATER DISPOSAL. FOR SMALL DRY SPILLS, WITH A CLEAN SHOVEL PLACE MATERIAL INTO CLEAN, DRY CONTAINERS AND COVER. MOVE CONTAINERS FROM SPILL AREA. FOR LARGER SPILLS, DIKE FAR AHEAD OF SPILL FOR LATER DISPOSAL. KEEP UNNECESSARY PEOPLE AWAY. ISOLATE HAZARD AREA AND DENY ENTRY. VENTILATE CLOSED SPACES BEFORE ENTERING.

PROTECTIVE EQUIPMENT

VENTILATION: PROCESS ENCLOSURE RECOMMENDED.
RESPIRATOR: THE FOLLOWING RESPIRATORS ARE RECOMMENDED BASED ON INFORMATION FOUND IN THE PHYSICAL DATA, TOXICITY AND HEALTH EFFECTS SECTIONS. THEY ARE RANKED IN ORDER FROM MINIMUM TO MAXIMUM RESPIRATORY PROTECTION. THE SPECIFIC RESPIRATOR SELECTED MUST BE BASED ON CONTAMINATION LEVELS FOUND IN THE WORK PLACE, MUST NOT EXCEED THE WORKING LIMITS OF THE RESPIRATOR AND BE JOINTLY APPROVED BY THE NATIONAL INSTITUTE FOR OCCUPATIONAL SAFETY AND HEALTH AND THE MINE SAFETY AND HEALTH ADMINISTRATION (NIOSH-MSHA).
TYPE 'C' SUPPLIED-AIR RESPIRATOR WITH A FULL FACEPIECE OPERATED IN PRESSURE-DEMAND OR OTHER POSITIVE PRESSURE MODE OR WITH A FULL FACEPIECE, HELMET OR HOOD OPERATED IN CONTINOUS-FLOW MODE.
SELF-CONTAINED BREATHING APPARATUS WITH A FULL FACEPIECE OPERATED IN PRESSURE-DEMAND OR OTHER POSITIVE PRESSURE MODE.
FOR FIREFIGHTING AND OTHER IMMEDIATELY DANGEROUS TO LIFE OR HEALTH CONDITIONS:
SELF-CONTAINED BREATHING APPARATUS WITH FULL FACEPIECE OPERATED IN PRESSURE-DEMAND OR OTHER POSITIVE PRESSURE MODE.
SUPPLIED-AIR RESPIRATOR WITH FULL FACEPIECE AND OPERATED IN PRESSURE-DEMAND OR OTHER POSITIVE PRESSURE MODE IN COMBINATION WITH AN AUXILIARY SELF-CONTAINED BREATHING APPARATUS OPERATED IN PRESSURE-DEMAND OR OTHER POSITIVE PRESSURE MODE.
CLOTHING: EMPLOYEE MUST WEAR APPROPRIATE PROTECTIVE (IMPERVIOUS) CLOTHING AND EQUIPMENT TO PREVENT ANY POSSIBILITY OF SKIN CONTACT WITH THIS SUBSTANCE.
GLOVES: EMPLOYEE MUST WEAR APPROPRIATE PROTECTIVE GLOVES TO PREVENT CONTACT WITH THIS SUBSTANCE.
EYE PROTECTION: EMPLOYEE MUST WEAR SPLASH-PROOF OR DUST-RESISTANT SAFETY GOGGLES AND A FACESHIELD TO PREVENT CONTACT WITH THIS SUBSTANCE.
EMERGENCY WASH FACILITIES: WHERE THERE IS ANY POSSIBILITY THAT AN EMPLOYEE'S EYES AND/OR SKIN MAY BE EXPOSED TO THIS SUBSTANCE, THE EMPLOYER SHOULD PROVIDE AN EYE WASH FOUNTAIN AND QUICK DRENCH SHOWER WITHIN THE IMMEDIATE WORK AREA FOR EMERGENCY USE.

AUTHORIZED BY- OCCUPATIONAL HEALTH SERVICES, INC.
CREATION DATE: 03/30/90 ***REVISION DATE:*** 07/12/90

MATERIAL SAFETY DATA SHEET

OCCUPATIONAL HEALTH SERVICES, INC.
AGRICULTURE AND PESTICIDE DIVISION
450 SEVENTH AVENUE, SUITE 2407
NEW YORK, NEW YORK 10123
1-800-445-MSDS OR (212) 967-1100

EMERGENCY CONTACT:
JOHN S. BRANSFORD, JR. (615) 292-1180

SUBSTANCE IDENTIFICATION

CAS-NUMBER 2307-68-8
SUBSTANCE: **PENTANOCHLOR**
TRADE NAMES/SYNONYMS: PENTANAMIDE, N-(3-CHLORO-4-METHYLPHENYL)-2-METHYL-; P-VALEROTOLUIDIDE, 3'-CHLORO-2-METHYL-; N-(3-CHLORO-4-METHYLPHENYL)-2-METHYLPENTANAMIDE; 3'-CHLORO-2-METHYL-P-VALEROTOLUIDIDE; 3'-CHLORO-2-METHYLVALER-P-TOLUIDIDE; N-(3-CHLORO-P-TOLYL)-2-METHYLVALERAMIDE; CHLORPENTAN; CMMP; DUTOM; HORTOX; NIAGARA 4512; SOLAN; SOLANE; C13H18CLNO; PST71164
CHEMICAL FAMILY: AMIDE, AROMATIC
HALOGEN COMPOUND, AROMATIC
MOLECULAR FORMULA: C13-H18-CL-N-O
MOLECULAR WEIGHT: 239.77
CERCLA RATINGS (SCALE 0-3): HEALTH=1 FIRE=1 REACTIVITY=0 PERSISTENCE=1
NFPA RATINGS (SCALE 0-4): HEALTH=U FIRE=1 REACTIVITY=0

COMPONENTS AND CONTAMINANTS

COMPONENT: PENTANOCHLOR ***PERCENT:*** 100.0
CAS# 2307-68-8
OTHER CONTAMINANTS: NONE

EXPOSURE LIMITS: NO OCCUPATIONAL EXPOSURE LIMITS ESTABLISHED BY OSHA, ACGIH, OR NIOSH.

PHYSICAL DATA

DESCRIPTION: COLORLESS SOLID. ***MELTING POINT:*** 185-187 F (85-86 C)
SPECIFIC GRAVITY: NOT AVAILABLE ***SOLUBILITY IN WATER:*** 0.0008-0.0009%
SOLVENT SOLUBILITY: SOLUBLE IN DI-ISOBUTYL KETONE, METHYLPENTANONE, PINE OIL, TRIMETHYLCYCLOHEXENONE, AND XYLENE.

FIRE AND EXPLOSION DATA

FIRE AND EXPLOSION HAZARD: SLIGHT FIRE HAZARD WHEN EXPOSED TO HEAT OR FLAME.
FIREFIGHTING MEDIA: DRY CHEMICAL, CARBON DIOXIDE, HALON, WATER SPRAY OR STANDARD FOAM (1987 EMERGENCY RESPONSE GUIDEBOOK, DOT P 5800.4). FOR LARGER FIRES, USE WATER SPRAY, FOG OR STANDARD FOAM (1987 EMERGENCY RESPONSE GUIDEBOOK, DOT P 5800.4).
FIREFIGHTING: MOVE CONTAINER FROM FIRE AREA IF POSSIBLE. DO NOT SCATTER SPILLED MATERIAL WITH HIGH PRESSURE WATER STREAMS. DIKE FIRE CONTROL WATER FOR LATER DISPOSAL (1987 EMERGENCY RESPONSE GUIDEBOOK, DOT P 5800.4, GUIDE PAGE 31).
USE AGENTS SUITABLE FOR TYPE OF SURROUNDING FIRE. AVOID BREATHING HAZARDOUS VAPORS, KEEP UPWIND.

TOXICITY

PENTANOCHLOR: TOXICITY DATA: 5100 MG/KG ORAL-RAT LD50; 1800 MG/KG ORAL-MOUSE LD50. CARCINOGEN STATUS: NONE. ACUTE TOXICITY LEVEL: SLIGHTLY TOXIC BY INGESTION. TARGET EFFECTS: NO DATA AVAILABLE.

HEALTH EFFECTS AND FIRST AID

INHALATION: PENTANOCHLOR: **ACUTE EXPOSURE-** METHEMOGLOBINEMIA WAS PRODUCED IN RATS EXPOSED TO 28 MG/M3/4 HOURS. **CHRONIC EXPOSURE-** NO DATA AVAILABLE.
FIRST AID- REMOVE FROM EXPOSURE AREA TO FRESH AIR IMMEDIATELY. IF BREATHING HAS STOPPED, PERFORM ARTIFICIAL RESPIRATION. KEEP PERSON WARM AND AT REST. TREAT SYMPTOMATICALLY AND SUPPORTIVELY. GET MEDICAL ATTENTION IMMEDIATELY.

SKIN CONTACT: PENTANOCHLOR: **ACUTE EXPOSURE-** THIS MATERIAL WAS MILDLY IRRITATING TO RABBIT SKIN. A LETHAL DOSE IN RABBITS BY DERMAL ABSORPTION WAS GREATER THAN 10 GM/KG. **CHRONIC EXPOSURE-** NO DATA AVAILABLE.
FIRST AID- REMOVE CONTAMINATED CLOTHING AND SHOES IMMEDIATELY. WASH AFFECTED AREA WITH SOAP OR MILD DETERGENT AND LARGE AMOUNTS OF WATER UNTIL NO EVIDENCE OF CHEMICAL REMAINS (APPROXIMATELY 15-20 MINUTES). GET MEDICAL ATTENTION IMMEDIATELY.

EYE CONTACT: PENTANOCHLOR: **ACUTE EXPOSURE-** NO DATA AVAILABLE. **CHRONIC EXPOSURE-** NO DATA AVAILABLE.
FIRST AID- WASH EYES IMMEDIATELY WITH LARGE AMOUNTS OF WATER OR NORMAL SALINE, OCCASIONALLY LIFTING UPPER AND LOWER LIDS, UNTIL NO EVIDENCE OF CHEMICAL REMAINS (APPROXIMATELY 15-20 MINUTES). GET MEDICAL ATTENTION IMMEDIATELY.

INGESTION: PENTANOCHLOR: **ACUTE EXPOSURE-** INGESTION BY RATS PRODUCED EFFECTS OF PTOSIS, LABORED RESPIRATION, ATAXIA, SALIVATION, CENTRAL NERVOUS DEPRESSION, COMA, AND DEATH. AUTOPSY REVEALED CONGESTION OF LUNGS, KIDNEYS AND ADRENALS. NO GROSS PATHOLOGY WAS OBSERVED IN THE SURVIVORS. **CHRONIC EXPOSURE-** EFFECTS OF GROWTH RETARDATION, ENLARGED LIVERS, ABNORMAL BLOOD PIGMENT, AND DEPRESSED RED CELL COUNTS, HEMOGLOBIN LEVELS AND HEMATOCRITS WERE OBSERVED IN A STUDY OF RATS FED A DIETARY LEVEL OF 2% FOR 140 DAYS.
FIRST AID- TREAT SYMPTOMATICALLY AND SUPPORTIVELY. GET MEDICAL ATTENTION IMMEDIATELY. IF VOMITING OCCURS, KEEP HEAD LOWER THAN HIPS TO PREVENT ASPIRATION.
ANTIDOTE: NO SPECIFIC ANTIDOTE. TREAT SYMPTOMATICALLY AND SUPPORTIVELY.

REACTIVITY

REACTIVITY: STABLE UNDER NORMAL TEMPERATURES AND PRESSURES.
INCOMPATIBILITIES: PENTANOCHLOR: OXIDIZERS (STRONG): FIRE AND EXPLOSION HAZARD.
DECOMPOSITION: THERMAL DECOMPOSITION PRODUCTS MAY INCLUDE TOXIC OXIDES OF NITROGEN AND CARBON AND TOXIC AND CORROSIVE FUMES OF CHLORIDES.
POLYMERIZATION: HAZARDOUS POLYMERIZATION HAS NOT BEEN REPORTED TO OCCUR UNDER NORMAL TEMPERATURES AND PRESSURES.

STORAGE AND DISPOSAL

OBSERVE ALL FEDERAL, STATE AND LOCAL REGULATIONS WHEN STORING OR DISPOSING OF THIS SUBSTANCE. FOR ASSISTANCE, CONTACT THE DISTRICT DIRECTOR OF THE ENVIRONMENTAL PROTECTION AGENCY.

****STORAGE****

STORE IN ACCORDANCE WITH 40 CFR 165 RECOMMENDED PROCEDURES FOR THE DISPOSAL AND STORAGE OF PESTICIDES AND PESTICIDE CONTAINERS.
STORE AWAY FROM INCOMPATIBLE SUBSTANCES.

****DISPOSAL****

DISPOSAL MUST BE IN ACCORDANCE WITH 40 CFR 165 RECOMMENDED PROCEDURES FOR THE DISPOSAL AND STORAGE OF PESTICIDES AND PESTICIDE CONTAINERS.

CONDITIONS TO AVOID

MAY BURN BUT DOES NOT IGNITE READILY. AVOID CONTACT WITH STRONG OXIDIZERS, EXCESSIVE HEAT, SPARKS, OR OPEN FLAME.

SPILL AND LEAK PROCEDURES

OCCUPATIONAL SPILL: SWEEP UP AND PLACE IN SUITABLE CLEAN, DRY CONTAINERS FOR RECLAMATION OR LATER DISPOSAL. DO NOT FLUSH SPILLED MATERIAL INTO SEWER. KEEP UNNECESSARY PEOPLE AWAY.

PROTECTIVE EQUIPMENT

VENTILATION: PROVIDE GENERAL DILUTION VENTILATION.
RESPIRATOR: THE FOLLOWING RESPIRATORS ARE RECOMMENDED BASED ON INFORMATION FOUND IN THE PHYSICAL DATA, TOXICITY AND HEALTH EFFECTS SECTIONS. THEY ARE RANKED IN ORDER FROM MINIMUM TO MAXIMUM RESPIRATORY PROTECTION. THE SPECIFIC RESPIRATOR SELECTED MUST BE BASED ON CONTAMINATION LEVELS FOUND IN THE WORK PLACE, MUST NOT EXCEED THE WORKING LIMITS OF THE RESPIRATOR AND BE JOINTLY APPROVED BY THE NATIONAL INSTITUTE FOR OCCUPATIONAL SAFETY AND HEALTH AND THE MINE SAFETY AND HEALTH ADMINISTRATION (NIOSH-MSHA).
CHEMICAL CARTRIDGE RESPIRATOR WITH AN ORGANIC VAPOR CARTRIDGE(S) IN COMBINATION WITH A DUST AND MIST FILTER.
GAS MASK WITH ORGANIC VAPOR CANISTER (CHIN-STYLE OR FRONT- OR BACK-MOUNTED CANISTER) WITH A DUST AND MIST FILTER.
GAS MASK WITH ORGANIC VAPOR CANISTER (CHIN-STYLE OR FRONT- OR BACK-MOUNTED CANISTER) WITH A PARTICULATE FILTER.
POWERED AIR-PURIFYING RESPIRATOR WITH A HIGH-EFFICIENCY FILTER.
TYPE 'C' SUPPLIED-AIR RESPIRATOR WITH A FULL FACEPIECE OPERATED IN A PRESSURE-DEMAND OR OTHER POSITIVE PRESSURE MODE.
SELF-CONTAINED BREATHING APPARATUS WITH A FULL FACEPIECE OPERATED IN PRESSURE-DEMAND OR OTHER POSITIVE PRESSURE MODE.
FOR FIREFIGHTING AND OTHER IMMEDIATELY DANGEROUS TO LIFE OR HEALTH CONDITIONS:
SELF-CONTAINED BREATHING APPARATUS WITH FULL FACEPIECE OPERATED IN PRESSURE-DEMAND OR OTHER POSITIVE PRESSURE MODE.
SUPPLIED-AIR RESPIRATOR WITH FULL FACEPIECE AND OPERATED IN PRESSURE-DEMAND OR OTHER POSITIVE PRESSURE MODE IN COMBINATION WITH AN AUXILIARY SELF-CONTAINED BREATHING APPARATUS OPERATED IN PRESSURE-DEMAND OR OTHER POSITIVE PRESSURE MODE.
CLOTHING: EMPLOYEE MUST WEAR APPROPRIATE PROTECTIVE (IMPERVIOUS) CLOTHING AND EQUIPMENT TO PREVENT REPEATED OR PROLONGED SKIN CONTACT WITH THIS SUBSTANCE.
GLOVES: EMPLOYEE MUST WEAR APPROPRIATE PROTECTIVE GLOVES TO PREVENT CONTACT WITH THIS SUBSTANCE.
EYE PROTECTION: EMPLOYEE MUST WEAR SPLASH-PROOF OR DUST-RESISTANT SAFETY GOGGLES TO PREVENT EYE CONTACT WITH THIS SUBSTANCE.
EMERGENCY EYE WASH: WHERE THERE IS ANY POSSIBILITY THAT AN EMPLOYEE'S EYES MAY BE EXPOSED TO THIS SUBSTANCE, THE EMPLOYER SHOULD PROVIDE AN EYE WASH FOUNTAIN WITHIN THE IMMEDIATE WORK AREA FOR EMERGENCY USE.

AUTHORIZED BY- OCCUPATIONAL HEALTH SERVICES, INC.
CREATION DATE: 10/04/89 ***REVISION DATE:*** 05/31/90

MATERIAL SAFETY DATA SHEET

OCCUPATIONAL HEALTH SERVICES, INC.
AGRICULTURE AND PESTICIDE DIVISION
450 SEVENTH AVENUE, SUITE 2407

EMERGENCY CONTACT:
JOHN S. BRANSFORD, JR. (615) 292-1180

NEW YORK, NEW YORK 10123
1-800-445-MSDS OR (212) 967-1100

SUBSTANCE IDENTIFICATION

CAS-NUMBER 8052-42-4
SUBSTANCE: **BITUMEN**
TRADE NAMES/SYNONYMS: ASPHALTUM; ASPHALT; JUDEAN PITCH; MINERAL PITCH; PETROLEUM PITCH; ROAD ASPHALT; ROAD TAR; TRINIDAD PITCH; PETROLEUM ASPHALT; NA 1999; PST71177
CERCLA RATINGS (SCALE 0-3): HEALTH=3 FIRE=1 REACTIVITY=0 PERSISTENCE=3
NFPA RATINGS (SCALE 0-4): HEALTH=0 FIRE=1 REACTIVITY=0

COMPONENTS AND CONTAMINANTS

COMPONENT: BITUMEN ***PERCENT:*** >99
CAS# 8052-42-4
OTHER CONTAMINANTS: MAY CONTAIN SULFUR AND TRACES OF NICKEL, IRON OR VANADIUM
EXPOSURE LIMITS: BITUMEN (PETROLEUM) FUMES: 5 MG/M3 ACGIH TWA 5 MG/M3 NIOSH RECOMMENDED 15 MINUTE CEILING
HYDROGEN SULFIDE: 10 PPM (14 MG/M3) OSHA TWA; 15 PPM (21 MG/M3) OSHA STEL 10 PPM (14 MG/M3) ACGIH TWA; 15 PPM (21 MG/M3) ACGIH STEL 10 PPM NIOSH RECOMMENDED 10 MINUTE CEILING
500 POUNDS SARA SECTION 302 THRESHOLD PLANNING QUANTITY 100 POUNDS SARA SECTION 304 REPORTABLE QUANTITY 100 POUNDS CERCLA SECTION 103 REPORTABLE QUANTITY

PHYSICAL DATA

DESCRIPTION: BLACK OR BROWN MASS OR VISCOUS LIQUID (ASPHALT)
BOILING POINT: >700 F (>300 C) (ASPHALT) ***SPECIFIC GRAVITY:*** 1.1 (ASPHALT)
SOLUBILITY IN WATER: INSOLUBLE (ASPHALT)
SOLVENT SOLUBILITY: OIL, TURPENTINE, PETROLEUM, CARBON DISULFIDE, CHLOROFORM, ETHER, ACETONE; INSOLUBLE IN ALCOHOL

FIRE AND EXPLOSION DATA

FIRE AND EXPLOSION HAZARD: SLIGHT FIRE HAZARD WHEN EXPOSED TO HEAT OR FLAME.
FLASH POINT: 400 F (204 C) (CC) (ASPHALT)
AUTOIGNITION TEMP.: 905 F (485 C) (ASPHALT) ***FLAMMABILITY CLASS(OSHA):*** IIIB
FIREFIGHTING MEDIA: DRY CHEMICAL, CARBON DIOXIDE, HALON, WATER SPRAY OR STANDARD FOAM (1987 EMERGENCY RESPONSE GUIDEBOOK, DOT P 5800.4).
FOR LARGER FIRES, USE WATER SPRAY, FOG OR STANDARD FOAM (1987 EMERGENCY RESPONSE GUIDEBOOK, DOT P 5800.4).
FIREFIGHTING: MOVE CONTAINER FROM FIRE AREA IF POSSIBLE. COOL FIRE-EXPOSED CONTAINERS WITH WATER FROM SIDE UNTIL WELL AFTER FIRE IS OUT. STAY AWAY FROM STORAGE TANK ENDS. FOR MASSIVE FIRE IN STORAGE AREA, USE UNMANNED HOSE HOLDER OR MONITOR NOZZLES, ELSE WITHDRAW FROM AREA AND LET FIRE BURN. WITHDRAW IMMEDIATELY IN CASE OF RISING SOUND FROM VENTING SAFETY DEVICE OR ANY DISCOLORATION OF STORAGE TANK DUE TO FIRE (1987 EMERGENCY RESPONSE GUIDEBOOK, DOT P 5800.4, GUIDE PAGE 27).
EXTINGUISH ONLY IF FLOW CAN BE STOPPED; USE WATER IN FLOODING AMOUNTS AS FOG SOLID STREAMS MAY NOT BE EFFECTIVE. COOL CONTAINERS WITH FLOODING AMOUNTS OF WATER, APPLY FROM AS FAR A DISTANCE AS POSSIBLE. AVOID BREATHING TOXIC VAPORS, KEEP UPWIND.
WATER OR FOAM MAY CAUSE FROTHING (NFPA 325M, FIRE HAZARD PROPERTIES OF FLAMMABLE LIQUIDS, GASES, AND VOLATILE SOLIDS, 1984)

TRANSPORTATION DATA

DEPARTMENT OF TRANSPORTATION HAZARD CLASSIFICATION 49 CFR 172.101: ORM-C
DEPARTMENT OF TRANSPORTATION LABELING REQUIREMENTS 49 CFR 172.101 AND SUBPART E: NONE
DEPARTMENT OF TRANSPORTATION PACKAGING REQUIREMENTS: NONE EXCEPTIONS: NONE

TOXICITY

BITUMEN: TOXICITY DATA: MUTAGENIC DATA (IARC); TUMORIGENIC DATA (RTECS). CARCINOGEN STATUS: HUMAN INADEQUATE EVIDENCE (IARC GROUP-3 FOR BITUMENS); ANIMAL SUFFICIENT EVIDENCE (IARC GROUP-2B FOR EXTRACTS OF STEAM-REFINED AND AIR-REFINED BITUMENS); ANIMAL LIMITED EVIDENCE (FOR STEAM-REFINED AND CRACKING-RESIDUE BITUMENS); ANIMAL INADEQUATE EVIDENCE (FOR AIR-REFINED BITUMENS). THERE IS INADEQUATE EVIDENCE THAT BITUMENS ALONE ARE CARCINOGENIC TO HUMANS. THERE IS SUFFICIENT EVIDENCE OF CARCINOGENICITY OF EXTRACTS OF STEAM-REFINED BITUMENS, AIR-REFINED BITUMENS, AND POOLED MIXTURES OF STEAM- AND AIR-REFINED BITUMENS IN EXPERIMENTAL ANIMALS. THERE IS LIMITED EVIDENCE FOR THE CARCINOGENICITY OF UNDILUTED STEAM-REFINED BITUMENS AND FOR CRACKING-RESIDUE BITUMENS IN EXPERIMENTAL ANIMALS. THERE IS INADEQUATE EVIDENCE FOR THE CARCINOGENICITY OF UNDILUTED AIR-REFINED BITUMENS IN EXPERIMENTAL ANIMALS. LOCAL EFFECTS: IRRITANT: INHALATION, SKIN, AND EYES. ACUTE TOXICITY LEVEL: NO DATA AVAILABLE. TARGET EFFECTS: POISONING MAY AFFECT THE RESPIRATORY SYSTEM.

HEALTH EFFECTS AND FIRST AID

INHALATION: BITUMEN: IRRITANT. **ACUTE EXPOSURE-** INHALATION OF FUMES FROM HOT BITUMEN MAY CAUSE IRRITATION OF THE MUCOUS MEMBRANES. WHEN HEATED, HYDROGEN SULFIDE, AND EXTREMELY TOXIC AND FLAMMABLE GAS MAY BE RELEASED AND ACCUMULATE IN ENCLOSED SPACES. HYDROGEN SULFIDE IS EXTREMELY IRRITATING AND AT 500-1000 PPM MAY CAUSE COMA, CONVULSIONS AND DEATH WITHIN 30 MINUTES. AT VERY HIGH CONCENTRATIONS, RESPIRATORY PARALYSIS AND DEATH FROM ASPHYXIA ARE IMMEDIATE. **CHRONIC EXPOSURE-** MICE WHICH INHALED AN AEROSOL OF PETROLEUM ASPHALT AND SMOKE FROM HEATED PETROLEUM ASPHALT SUFFERED CONGESTION, ACUTE BRONCHITIS, PNEUMONITIS, BRONCHIAL DILATION, ABSCESS FORMATION, EPITHELIAL ATROPHY AND NECROSIS. GUINEA PIGS AND RATS INHALING FUMES FROM HEATED ASPHALT SHOWED EFFECTS SUCH AS CHRONIC FIBROSING PNEUMONITIS WITH PERIBRONCHIAL ADENOMATOSIS; ONLY THE RATS DEVELOPED SQUAMOUS CELL METAPLASIA.
FIRST AID- REMOVE FROM EXPOSURE AREA TO FRESH AIR IMMEDIATELY. IF BREATHING HAS STOPPED, GIVE ARTIFICIAL RESPIRATION. MAINTAIN AIRWAY AND BLOOD PRESSURE AND ADMINISTER OXYGEN IF AVAILABLE. KEEP AFFECTED PERSON WARM AND AT REST. TREAT SYMPTOMATICALLY AND S UPPORTIVELY. ADMINISTRATION OF OXYGEN SHOULD BE PERFORMED BY QUALIFIED PERSONNEL. GET MEDICAL ATTENTION IMMEDIATELY.

SKIN CONTACT: BITUMEN: IRRITANT/CARCINOGEN. **ACUTE EXPOSURE-** CONTACT WITH FUMES FROM HOT BITUMEN MAY CAUSE IRRITATION. DIRECT CONTACT WITH HOT BITUMEN MAY CAUSE THERMAL BURNS. **CHRONIC EXPOSURE-** REPEATED OR PROLONGED CONTACT WITH FUMES FROM HOT BITUMEN MAY CAUSE DERMATITIS AND ACNE-LIKE LESIONS AS WELL AS MILD KERATOSES. THE GREENISH-YELLOW FUMES GIVEN OFF WHEN BITUMEN IS BOILED CAN CAUSE PHOTO-SENSITIZATION AND MELANOSIS. IN SOME STUDIES, REPEATED SKIN APPLICATION OF VARIOUS TYES OF BITUMENS RSULTED IN TUMORS IN MICE.
FIRST AID- IF CONTACT IS NOT WITH MOLTEN MATERIAL, REMOVE CONTAMINATED CLOTHING AND SHOES IMMEDIATELY. WASH AFFECTED AREA WITH SOAP OR MILD DETERGENT AND LARGE AMOUNTS OF WATER UNTIL NO EVIDENCE OF CHEMICAL REMAINS (APPROXIMATELY 15-20 MINUTES). GET MEDICAL ATTENTION IMMEDIATELY. BURNS FROM CONTACT WITH MOLTEN MATERIAL SHOULD BE TREATED LIKE THERMAL BURNS. COOL AFFECTED AREA AS QUICKLY AS POSSIBLE BY DRENCHING OR IMMERSING IN WATER UNTIL MATERIAL SOLIDIFIES. DO NOT ATTEMPT TO REMOVE SOLIDIFIED MATERIAL. COVER AREA WITH STERILE, DRY DRESSING. GET MEDICAL ATTENTION IMMEDIATELY.

EYE CONTACT: BITUMEN: IRRITANT. **ACUTE EXPOSURE-** FUMES FROM HOT BITUMEN MAY CAUSE IRRITATION. DIRECT CONTACT WITH HOT BITUMEN MAY CAUSE THERMAL BURNS. **CHRONIC EXPOSURE-** REPEATED OR PROLONGED EXPOSURE TO BITUMEN FUMES MAY CAUSE CONJUNCTIVITIS.
FIRST AID- WASH EYES IMMEDIATELY WITH LARGE AMOUNTS OF WATER, OCCASIONALLY LIFTING UPPER AND LOWER LIDS, UNTIL NO EVIDENCE OF CHEMICAL REMAINS (AT LEAST 15-20 MINUTES). CONTINUE IRRIGATING WITH NORMAL SALINE UNTIL THE PH HAS RETURNED TO NORMAL (30-60 MINUTES). COVER WITH STERILE BANDAGES. GET MEDICAL ATTENTION IMMEDIATELY.

INGESTION: BITUMEN: **ACUTE EXPOSURE-** MAY CAUSE NAUSEA AND IRRITATION OF THE GASTROINTESTINAL TRACT. **CHRONIC EXPOSURE-** ASPHALT WORKERS WHO WERE IN THE HABIT OF CHEWING ASPHALT AND SOMETIMES SWALLOWING IT HAVE BEEN REPORTED TO HAVE PYLORIC OBSTRUCTION BECAUSE THE INDIGESTIBLE MASS ACCUMULATES IN THE STOMACH FORMING A STONY CONCRETION.
FIRST AID- TREAT SYMPTOMATICALLY AND SUPPORTIVELY. GET MEDICAL ATTENTION IMMEDIATELY. IF VOMITING OCCURS, KEEP HEAD LOWER THAN HIPS TO PREVENT ASPIRATION.
ANTIDOTE: NO SPECIFIC ANTIDOTE. TREAT SYMPTOMATICALLY AND SUPPORTIVELY.

REACTIVITY

REACTIVITY: STABLE UNDER NORMAL TEMPERATURES AND PRESSURES.
INCOMPATIBILITIES: BITUMEN: FLUORINE: BURNS WITH SPATTERING AND SMALL FLAMES. NAPHTHA: READILY IGNITES. VOLATILE SOLVENTS: READILY IGNITES.
DECOMPOSITION: THERMAL DECOMPOSITION MAY RELEASE TOXIC AND/OR HAZARDOUS GASES.
POLYMERIZATION: HAZARDOUS POLYMERIZATION HAS NOT BEEN REPORTED TO OCCUR UNDER NORMAL TEMPERATURES AND PRESSURES.

CONDITIONS TO AVOID

AVOID CONTACT WITH HEAT, SPARKS, FLAMES, OR OTHER SOURCES OF IGNITION. VAPORS MAY BE EXPLOSIVE. AVOID OVERHEATING OF CONTAINERS; CONTAINERS MAY VIOLENTLY RUPTURE IN HEAT OF FIRE. AVOID CONTAMINATION OF WATER SOURCES.

SPILL AND LEAK PROCEDURES

OCCUPATIONAL SPILL: SHUT OFF IGNITION SOURCES. STOP LEAK IF YOU CAN DO IT WITHOUT RISK. USE WATER SPRAY TO REDUCE VAPORS. FOR SMALL SPILLS, TAKE UP WITH SAND OR OTHER ABSORBENT MATERIAL AND PLACE INTO CONTAINERS FOR LATER DISPOSAL. FOR LARGER SPILLS, DIKE FAR AHEAD OF SPILL FOR LATER DISPOSAL. NO SMOKING, FLAMES OR FLARES IN HAZARD AREA. KEEP UNNECESSARY PEOPLE AWAY; ISOLATE HAZARD AREA AND RESTRICT ENTRY.

PROTECTIVE EQUIPMENT

VENTILATION: PROVIDE LOCAL EXHAUST VENTILATION SYSTEM TO MEET PUBLISHED EXPOSURE LIMITS.

RESPIRATOR: THE FOLLOWING RESPIRATORS ARE RECOMMENDED BASED ON INFORMATION FOUND IN THE PHYSICAL DATA, TOXICITY AND HEALTH EFFECTS SECTIONS. THEY ARE RANKED IN ORDER FROM MINIMUM TO MAXIMUM RESPIRATORY PROTECTION. THE SPECIFIC RESPIRATOR SELECTED MUST BE BASED ON CONTAMINATION LEVELS FOUND IN THE WORK PLACE, MUST NOT EXCEED THE WORKING LIMITS OF THE RESPIRATOR AND BE JOINTLY APPROVED BY THE NATIONAL INSTITUTE FOR OCCUPATIONAL SAFETY AND HEALTH AND THE MINE SAFETY AND HEALTH ADMINISTRATION (NIOSH-MSHA).

TYPE 'C' SUPPLIED-AIR RESPIRATOR WITH A FULL FACEPIECE OPERATED IN PRESSURE-DEMAND OR OTHER POSITIVE PRESSURE MODE OR WITH A FULL FACEPIECE, HELMET OR HOOD OPERATED IN CONTINOUS-FLOW MODE.

SELF-CONTAINED BREATHING APPARATUS WITH A FULL FACEPIECE OPERATED IN PRESSURE-DEMAND OR OTHER POSITIVE PRESSURE MODE.

FOR FIREFIGHTING AND OTHER IMMEDIATELY DANGEROUS TO LIFE OR HEALTH CONDITIONS:

SELF-CONTAINED BREATHING APPARATUS WITH FULL FACEPIECE OPERATED IN PRESSURE-DEMAND OR OTHER POSITIVE PRESSURE MODE.

SUPPLIED-AIR RESPIRATOR WITH FULL FACEPIECE AND OPERATED IN PRESSURE-DEMAND OR OTHER POSITIVE PRESSURE MODE IN COMBINATION WITH AN AUXILIARY SELF-CONTAINED BREATHING APPARATUS OPERATED IN PRESSURE-DEMAND OR OTHER POSITIVE PRESSURE MODE.

CLOTHING: EMPLOYEE MUST WEAR APPROPRIATE PROTECTIVE (IMPERVIOUS) CLOTHING AND EQUIPMENT TO PREVENT REPEATED OR PROLONGED SKIN CONTACT WITH THIS SUBSTANCE.

GLOVES: EMPLOYEE MUST WEAR APPROPRIATE PROTECTIVE GLOVES TO PREVENT CONTACT WITH THIS SUBSTANCE.

EYE PROTECTION: EMPLOYEE MUST WEAR SPLASH-PROOF OR DUST-RESISTANT SAFETY GOGGLES WITH OR WITHOUT A FACESHIELD TO PREVENT CONTACT WITH THIS SUBSTANCE.

EMERGENCY EYE WASH: WHERE THERE IS ANY POSSIBILITY THAT AN EMPLOYEE'S EYES MAY BE EXPOSED TO THIS SUBSTANCE, THE EMPLOYER SHOULD PROVIDE AN EYE WASH FOUNTAIN WITHIN THE IMMEDIATE WORK AREA FOR EMERGENCY USE.

AUTHORIZED BY- OCCUPATIONAL HEALTH SERVICES, INC.

CREATION DATE: 10/04/89 ***REVISION DATE:*** 07/12/90

MATERIAL SAFETY DATA SHEET

OCCUPATIONAL HEALTH SERVICES, INC.
AGRICULTURE AND PESTICIDE DIVISION
450 SEVENTH AVENUE, SUITE 2407
NEW YORK, NEW YORK 10123
1-800-445-MSDS OR (212) 967-1100

EMERGENCY CONTACT:
JOHN S. BRANSFORD, JR. (615) 292-1180

SUBSTANCE IDENTIFICATION

CAS-NUMBER 8000-29-1

SUBSTANCE: **OIL OF CITRONELLA**

TRADE NAMES/SYNONYMS: OILS, CITRONELLA; CITRONELLA OIL; CITRONELLA; PST71180

CHEMICAL FAMILY: ESSENTIAL OIL

CERCLA RATINGS (SCALE 0-3): HEALTH = 1 FIRE = 2 REACTIVITY = 0
PERSISTENCE = 1

NFPA RATINGS (SCALE 0-4): HEALTH = 1 FIRE = 2 REACTIVITY = 0

COMPONENTS AND CONTAMINANTS

COMPONENT: OIL OF CITRONELLA ***PERCENT:*** 100.0
CAS# 8000-29-1

OTHER CONTAMINANTS: NONE

EXPOSURE LIMITS: NO OCCUPATIONAL EXPOSURE LIMITS ESTABLISHED BY OSHA, ACGIH, OR NIOSH.

PHYSICAL DATA

DESCRIPTION: ALMOST COLORLESS TO PALE YELLOW LIQUID WITH A PUNGENT CITRUS-LIKE ODOR.

BOILING POINT: 392 F (200 C) ***SPECIFIC GRAVITY:*** 0.897-0.912

VAPOR PRESSURE: .000098 MMHG @ 20 C ***SOLUBILITY IN WATER:*** SLIGHTLY SOLUBLE

SOLVENT SOLUBILITY: SOLUBLE IN ALCOHOL.

FIRE AND EXPLOSION DATA

FIRE AND EXPLOSION HAZARD: MODERATE FIRE HAZARD WHEN EXPOSED TO HEAT OR FLAME.

FLASH POINT: >176 F (>80 C) ***FLAMMABILITY CLASS(OSHA):*** IIIA

FIREFIGHTING MEDIA: DRY CHEMICAL, CARBON DIOXIDE, HALON, WATER SPRAY OR STANDARD FOAM (1987 EMERGENCY RESPONSE GUIDEBOOK, DOT P 5800.4). FOR LARGER FIRES, USE WATER SPRAY, FOG OR STANDARD FOAM (1987 EMERGENCY RESPONSE GUIDEBOOK, DOT P 5800.4). ***FIREFIGHTING:*** MOVE CONTAINER FROM FIRE AREA IF POSSIBLE. COOL FIRE-EXPOSED CONTAINERS WITH WATER FROM SIDE UNTIL WELL AFTER FIRE IS OUT. STAY AWAY FROM STORAGE TANK ENDS. FOR MASSIVE FIRE IN STORAGE AREA, USE UNMANNED HOSE HOLDER OR MONITOR NOZZLES, ELSE WITHDRAW FROM AREA AND LET FIRE BURN. WITHDRAW IMMEDIATELY IN CASE OF RISING SOUND FROM VENTING SAFETY DEVICE OR ANY DISCOLORATION OF STORAGE TANK DUE TO FIRE (1987 EMERGENCY RESPONSE GUIDEBOOK, DOT P 5800.4, GUIDE PAGE 27). EXTINGUISH ONLY IF FLOW CAN BE STOPPED; USE FLOODING AMOUNTS OF WATER AS A FOG, SOLID STREAMS MAY BE INEFFECTIVE. COOL CONTAINERS WITH FLOODING AMOUNTS OF WATER, APPLY FROM AS FAR A DISTANCE AS POSSIBLE. AVOID BREATHING VAPORS, KEEP UPWIND.

TOXICITY

OIL OF CITRONELLA: IRRITATION DATA: 500 MG/24 HOURS SKIN-RABBIT; 100 MG EYE-RABBIT. TOXICITY DATA: 4700 MG/KG SKIN-RABBIT LD50; 7200 MG/KG ORAL-RAT LD50; 4600 MG/KG ORAL-MOUSE LD50; 713 MG/KG INTRAPERITONEAL-RAT LD50; MUTAGENIC DATA (RTECS). CARCINOGEN STATUS: NONE. LOCAL EFFECTS: IRRITANT- SKIN. ACUTE TOXICITY LEVEL: SLIGHTLY TOXIC BY DERMAL ABSORPTION AND INGESTION. TARGET EFFECTS: NO DATA AVAILABLE.

HEALTH EFFECTS AND FIRST AID

INHALATION: OIL OF CITRONELLA: **ACUTE EXPOSURE-** INHALATION MAY CAUSE MUCOUS MEMBRANE IRRITATION, SORE THROAT AND COUGHING. VOLATILE OILS MAY CAUSE DIZZINESS, RAPID, SHALLOW BREATHING, TACHYCARDIA, BRONCHIAL IRRITATION AND UNCONSCIOUSNESS OR CONVULSIONS. COMPLICATIONS MAY INCLUDE ANURIA, PULMONARY EDEMA, AND BRONCHIAL PNEUMONIA. **CHRONIC EXPOSURE-** NO DATA AVAILABLE.

FIRST AID- REMOVE FROM EXPOSURE AREA TO FRESH AIR IMMEDIATELY. IF BREATHING HAS STOPPED, PERFORM ARTIFICIAL RESPIRATION. KEEP PERSON WARM AND AT REST. TREAT SYMPTOMATICALLY AND SUPPORTIVELY. GET MEDICAL ATTENTION IMMEDIATELY.

SKIN CONTACT: OIL OF CITRONELLA: IRRITANT. **ACUTE EXPOSURE-** CONTACT MAY CAUSE IRRITATION. DERMAL APPLICATION PRODUCED DEATH IN RABBITS. **CHRONIC EXPOSURE-** REPEATED OR PROLONGED EXPOSURE MAY CAUSE DERMATITIS.

FIRST AID- REMOVE CONTAMINATED CLOTHING AND SHOES IMMEDIATELY. WASH AFFECTED AREA WITH SOAP OR MILD DETERGENT AND LARGE AMOUNTS OF WATER UNTIL NO EVIDENCE OF CHEMICAL REMAINS (APPROXIMATELY 15-20 MINUTES). GET MEDICAL ATTENTION IMMEDIATELY.

EYE CONTACT: OIL OF CITRONELLA: **ACUTE EXPOSURE-** APPLICATION OF A DROP TO RABBIT EYES CAUSED ONLY SLIGHT TRANSIENT INJURY, GRADED 3 ON A SCALE OF 1 TO 10 AFTER 24 HOURS. **CHRONIC EXPOSURE-** NO DATA AVAILABLE.

FIRST AID- WASH EYES IMMEDIATELY WITH LARGE AMOUNTS OF WATER OR NORMAL SALINE, OCCASIONALLY LIFTING UPPER AND LOWER LIDS, UNTIL NO EVIDENCE OF CHEMICAL REMAINS (APPROXIMATELY 15-20 MINUTES). GET MEDICAL ATTENTION IMMEDIATELY.

INGESTION: OIL OF CITRONELLA: **ACUTE EXPOSURE-** INGESTION OF VOLATILE OILS MAY CAUSE ABDOMINAL BURNING, NAUSEA AND VOMITING, DIARRHEA, DYSURIA, HEMATURIA, UNCONSCIOUSNESS, SHALLOW RESPIRATION, AND CONVULSIONS. COMPLICATIONS MAY INCLUDE ANURIA, PULMONARY EDEMA, AND BRONCHIAL PNEUMONIA. PATHOLOGIC FINDINGS FROM INGESTION OF VOLATILE OILS INCLUDE RENAL DEGENERATIVE CHANGES AND INTENSE CONGESTION AND EDEMA IN THE LUNGS, BRAIN AND GASTRIC MUCOSA. **CHRONIC EXPOSURE-** NO DATA AVAILABLE.

FIRST AID- GIVE 120-240 ML OF MILK; THEN REMOVE BY GASTRIC LAVAGE OR EMESIS, TAKING CARE TO PREVENT ASPIRATION. FOLLOW THESE PROCEDURES BY ADMINISTERING 30-60 ML OF FLEET'S PHOSPHO-SODA DILUTED 1:4 IN WATER. PERFORM ARTIFICIAL RESPIRATION IF NECESSARY. GET MEDICAL ATTENTION (DREISBACH, HANDBOOK OF POISONING, 12TH ED.). FIRST AID SHOULD BE PERFORMED BY QUALIFIED MEDICAL PERSONNEL.

ANTIDOTE: NO SPECIFIC ANTIDOTE. TREAT SYMPTOMATICALLY AND SUPPORTIVELY.

REACTIVITY

REACTIVITY: STABLE UNDER NORMAL TEMPERATURES AND PRESSURES.

INCOMPATIBILITIES: OIL OF CITRONELLA: OXIDIZERS (STRONG): FIRE AND EXPLOSION HAZARD.

DECOMPOSITION: THERMAL DECOMPOSITION MAY RELEASE ACRID SMOKE AND IRRITATING FUMES.

POLYMERIZATION: HAZARDOUS POLYMERIZATION HAS NOT BEEN REPORTED TO OCCUR UNDER NORMAL TEMPERATURES AND PRESSURES.

STORAGE AND DISPOSAL

OBSERVE ALL FEDERAL, STATE AND LOCAL REGULATIONS WHEN STORING OR DISPOSING OF THIS SUBSTANCE. FOR ASSISTANCE, CONTACT THE DISTRICT DIRECTOR OF THE ENVIRONMENTAL PROTECTION AGENCY.

STORAGE

STORE IN ACCORDANCE WITH 29 CFR 1910.106. STORE IN A COOL, DRY PLACE; KEEP CONTAINER TIGHTLY CLOSED WHEN NOT IN USE.

CONDITIONS TO AVOID

AVOID CONTACT WITH HEAT, SPARKS, FLAMES, OR OTHER SOURCES OF IGNITION. VAPORS MAY BE EXPLOSIVE. AVOID OVERHEATING OF CONTAINERS; CONTAINERS MAY VIOLENTLY RUPTURE IN HEAT OF FIRE. AVOID CONTAMINATION OF WATER SOURCES.

SPILL AND LEAK PROCEDURES

OCCUPATIONAL SPILL: SHUT OFF IGNITION SOURCES. STOP LEAK IF YOU CAN DO IT WITHOUT RISK. USE WATER SPRAY TO REDUCE VAPORS. FOR SMALL SPILLS, TAKE UP WITH SAND OR OTHER ABSORBENT MATERIAL AND PLACE INTO CONTAINERS FOR LATER DISPOSAL. FOR LARGER SPILLS, DIKE FAR AHEAD OF SPILL FOR LATER DISPOSAL. NO SMOKING, FLAMES OR FLARES IN HAZARD AREA. KEEP UNNECESSARY PEOPLE AWAY; ISOLATE HAZARD AREA AND RESTRICT ENTRY.

PROTECTIVE EQUIPMENT

VENTILATION: PROVIDE LOCAL EXHAUST OR GENERAL DILUTION VENTILATION SYSTEM.

RESPIRATOR: THE FOLLOWING RESPIRATORS ARE RECOMMENDED BASED ON INFORMATION FOUND IN THE PHYSICAL DATA, TOXICITY AND HEALTH EFFECTS SECTIONS. THEY ARE RANKED IN ORDER FROM MINIMUM TO MAXIMUM RESPIRATORY PROTECTION. THE SPECIFIC RESPIRATOR SELECTED MUST BE BASED ON CONTAMINATION LEVELS FOUND IN THE WORK PLACE, MUST NOT EXCEED THE WORKING LIMITS OF THE RESPIRATOR AND BE JOINTLY APPROVED BY THE NATIONAL INSTITUTE FOR OCCUPATIONAL SAFETY AND HEALTH AND THE MINE SAFETY AND HEALTH ADMINISTRATION (NIOSH-MSHA).

CHEMICAL CARTRIDGE RESPIRATOR WITH AN ORGANIC VAPOR CARTRIDGE(S) WITH A FULL FACEPIECE.

GAS MASK WITH ORGANIC VAPOR CANISTER (CHIN-STYLE OR FRONT- OR BACK-MOUNTED CANISTER) WITH A FULL FACEPIECE.

TYPE 'C' SUPPLIED-AIR RESPIRATOR WITH A FULL FACEPIECE OPERATED IN PRESSURE-DEMAND OR OTHER POSITIVE PRESSURE MODE OR WITH A FULL FACEPIECE, HELMET OR HOOD OPERATED IN CONTINUOUS-FLOW MODE.

SELF-CONTAINED BREATHING APPARATUS WITH A FULL FACEPIECE OPERATED IN PRESSURE-DEMAND OR OTHER POSITIVE PRESSURE MODE.

FOR FIREFIGHTING AND OTHER IMMEDIATELY DANGEROUS TO LIFE OR HEALTH CONDITIONS:

SELF-CONTAINED BREATHING APPARATUS WITH FULL FACEPIECE OPERATED IN PRESSURE-DEMAND OR OTHER POSITIVE PRESSURE MODE.

SUPPLIED-AIR RESPIRATOR WITH FULL FACEPIECE AND OPERATED IN PRESSURE-DEMAND OR OTHER POSITIVE PRESSURE MODE IN COMBINATION WITH AN AUXILIARY SELF-CONTAINED BREATHING APPARATUS OPERATED IN PRESSURE-DEMAND OR OTHER POSITIVE PRESSURE MODE.

CLOTHING: EMPLOYEE MUST WEAR APPROPRIATE PROTECTIVE (IMPERVIOUS) CLOTHING AND EQUIPMENT TO PREVENT REPEATED OR PROLONGED SKIN CONTACT WITH THIS SUBSTANCE.

GLOVES: EMPLOYEE MUST WEAR APPROPRIATE PROTECTIVE GLOVES TO PREVENT CONTACT WITH THIS SUBSTANCE.

EYE PROTECTION: EMPLOYEE MUST WEAR SPLASH-PROOF OR DUST-RESISTANT SAFETY GOGGLES TO PREVENT EYE CONTACT WITH THIS SUBSTANCE.

EMERGENCY EYE WASH: WHERE THERE IS ANY POSSIBILITY THAT AN EMPLOYEE'S EYES MAY BE EXPOSED TO THIS SUBSTANCE, THE EMPLOYER SHOULD PROVIDE AN EYE WASH FOUNTAIN WITHIN THE IMMEDIATE WORK AREA FOR EMERGENCY USE.

AUTHORIZED BY- OCCUPATIONAL HEALTH SERVICES, INC.
CREATION DATE: 10/04/89 ***REVISION DATE:*** 05/18/90

MATERIAL SAFETY DATA SHEET

OCCUPATIONAL HEALTH SERVICES, INC.
AGRICULTURE AND PESTICIDE DIVISION
450 SEVENTH AVENUE, SUITE 2407
NEW YORK, NEW YORK 10123
1-800-445-MSDS OR (212) 967-1100

EMERGENCY CONTACT:
JOHN S. BRANSFORD, JR. (615) 292-1180

SUBSTANCE IDENTIFICATION

CAS-NUMBER 8021-39-4

SUBSTANCE: **WOOD CREOSOTE**

TRADE NAMES/SYNONYMS: CREASOTE; CREOSOTE, WOOD; PST71221

CHEMICAL FAMILY: MIXTURE

CERCLA RATINGS (SCALE 0-3): HEALTH=3 FIRE=2 REACTIVITY=0 PERSISTENCE=1

NFPA RATINGS (SCALE 0-4): HEALTH=2 FIRE=2 REACTIVITY=0

COMPONENTS AND CONTAMINANTS

COMPONENT: WOOD CREOSOTE ***PERCENT:*** 100.0
CAS# 8021-39-4

OTHER CONTAMINANTS: NONE

EXPOSURE LIMITS: COAL TAR PITCH VOLATILES (POLYCYCLIC AROMATIC HYDROCARBONS): 0.2 MG/M3 OSHA TWA (AS BENZENE SOLUBLES) 0.2 MG/M3 ACGIH TWA (AS BENZENE SOLUBLES) ACGIH A1-CONFIRMED HUMAN CARCINOGEN. 0.1 MG/M3 NIOSH RECOMMENDED 10 HOUR TWA (CYCLOHEXANE-EXTRACTABLE FRACTION)

WOOD CREOSOTE: SUBJECT TO CALIFORNIA PROPOSITION 65 CANCER AND/OR REPRODUCTIVE TOXICITY WARNING AND RELEASE REQUIREMENTS- (FEBRUARY 27, 1987)

PHYSICAL DATA

DESCRIPTION: ALMOST COLORLESS TO BROWN, OILY LIQUID WITH A CHARACTERISTIC SMOKY ODOR AND CAUSTIC, BURNING TASTE

BOILING POINT: 195-400 F (383-752 C)

SPECIFIC GRAVITY: >1.076 ***EVAPORATION RATE:*** NOT AVAILABLE

SOLUBILITY IN WATER: SLIGHTLY SOLUBLE

SOLVENT SOLUBILITY: SOLUBLE IN GLYCEROL, GLACIAL ACETIC ACID, FIXED ALKALI HYDROXIDE SOLUTIONS, ALCOHOL, CHLOROFORM, ETHER, OILS

FIRE AND EXPLOSION DATA

FIRE AND EXPLOSION HAZARD: MODERATE FIRE HAZARD WHEN EXPOSED TO HEAT OR FLAME.

FLASH POINT: 165 F (73 C) ***AUTOIGNITION TEMP.:*** 637 F (336 C)

FLAMMABILITY CLASS(OSHA): IIIA

FIREFIGHTING MEDIA: DRY CHEMICAL, CARBON DIOXIDE, HALON, WATER SPRAY OR STANDARD FOAM (1987 EMERGENCY RESPONSE GUIDEBOOK, DOT P 5800.4). FOR LARGER FIRES, USE WATER SPRAY, FOG OR STANDARD FOAM (1987 EMERGENCY RESPONSE GUIDEBOOK, DOT P 5800.4).

FIREFIGHTING: MOVE CONTAINER FROM FIRE AREA IF POSSIBLE. COOL FIRE-EXPOSED CONTAINERS WITH WATER FROM SIDE UNTIL WELL AFTER FIRE IS OUT. STAY AWAY FROM STORAGE TANK ENDS. FOR MASSIVE FIRE IN STORAGE AREA, USE UNMANNED HOSE HOLDER OR MONITOR NOZZLES, ELSE WITHDRAW FROM AREA AND LET FIRE BURN. WITHDRAW IMMEDIATELY IN CASE OF RISING SOUND FROM VENTING SAFETY DEVICE OR ANY DISCOLORATION OF STORAGE TANK DUE TO FIRE (1987 EMERGENCY RESPONSE GUIDEBOOK, DOT P 5800.4, GUIDE PAGE 27). EXTINGUISH ONLY IF FLOW CAN BE STOPPED; USE FLOODING AMOUNTS OF WATER AS A FOG, SOLID STREAMS MAY BE INEFFECTIVE. COOL CONTAINERS

WITH FLOODING AMOUNTS OF WATER, APPLY FROM AS FAR A DISTANCE AS POSSIBLE. AVOID BREATHING VAPORS, KEEP UPWIND.

TRANSPORTATION DATA

DEPARTMENT OF TRANSPORTATION HAZARD CLASSIFICATION 49 CFR 172.101: COMBUSTIBLE LIQUID
DEPARTMENT OF TRANSPORTATION LABELING REQUIREMENTS 49 CFR 172.101 AND SUBPART E: NONE
DEPARTMENT OF TRANSPORTATION PACKAGING REQUIREMENTS: NONE
EXCEPTIONS: 49 CFR 173.118A

TOXICITY

WOOD CREOSOTE: TOXICITY DATA: REPRODUCTIVE EFFECTS DATA (RTECS). CARCINOGEN STATUS: KNOWN HUMAN CARCINOGEN (NTP) (SOOTS, TARS, MINERAL OILS); HUMAN LIMITED EVIDENCE, ANIMAL SUFFICIENT EVIDENCE (IARC GROUP-2A FOR CRESOTES). THERE IS SUFFICIENT EVIDENCE THAT SOOTS, TARS, AND SOME MINERAL OILS ARE CARCINOGENIC IN HUMANS AND IN EXPERIMENTAL ANIMALS. SCROTAL CANCER AND OTHER SKIN CANCER IN WORKERS HAS BEEN ASSOCIATED WITH CREOSOTE EXPOSURE. SKIN APPLICATION OF CREOSOTES TO MICE PRODUCED SKIN TUMORS, INCLUDING CARCINOMAS; ONE TYPE ALSO PRODUCED LUNG TUMORS. LOCAL EFFECTS: CORROSIVE- SKIN AND EYES; IRRITANT- INHALATION. ACUTE TOXICITY LEVEL: NO DATA AVAILABLE. TARGET EFFECTS: NO DATA AVAILABLE.

HEALTH EFFECTS AND FIRST AID

INHALATION: WOOD CREOSOTE: IRRITANT. **ACUTE EXPOSURE-** MAY CAUSE MODERATE RESPIRATORY TRACT IRRITATION. IN ONE STUDY OF WORKERS WHO DEVELOPED CREOSOTE BURNS, A SMALL PERCENT ALSO COMPLAINED OF DEPRESSION, WEAKNESS, SEVERE HEADACHE, SLIGHT CONFUSION, VERTIGO, SALIVATION, AND NAUSEA. IT IS UNCLEAR WHETHER THE ROUTE OF EXPOSURE WAS SKIN CONTACT OR INHALATION OR BOTH. **CHRONIC EXPOSURE-** A STUDY OF WORKERS SPRAYING WARMED CREOSOTE WITH CONCENTRATIONS UP TO 0.01 MG/L REPORTED HEADACHES, GIDDINESS, NAUSEA, VOMITING, AND SALIVATION.
FIRST AID- REMOVE FROM EXPOSURE AREA TO FRESH AIR IMMEDIATELY. IF BREATHING HAS STOPPED, PERFORM ARTIFICIAL RESPIRATION. KEEP PERSON WARM AND AT REST. TREAT SYMPTOMATICALLY AND SUPPORTIVELY. GET MEDICAL ATTENTION IMMEDIATELY.

SKIN CONTACT: WOOD CREOSOTE: CORROSIVE/CARCINOGEN. **ACUTE EXPOSURE-** THE LIQUID AND VAPORS ARE STRONG IRRITANTS AND MAY CAUSE BURNING, ITCHING, LOCAL ERYTHEMA PROGESSING TO A BRONZE PIGMENTATION, PAPULAR AND VESICULAR ERUPTIONS, ULCERATION, AND DESQUAMATION. PHOTOSENSITIZATION OCCURS, ESPECIALLY IN FAIR-SKINNED PERSONS. PROLONGED CONTACT MAY CAUSE BURNS. IT IS READILY ABSORBED THROUGH THE SKIN AND MAY CAUSE SYSTEMIC ILLNESS WITH SALIVATION, NAUSEA, VOMITING, HEADACHE, THREADY PULSE, RESPIRATORY DISTRESS, LOSS OF PUPILLARY REFLEXES, HYPOTHERMIA, MILD CONVULSIONS, AND CYANOSIS. DEPRESSION, WEAKNESS, SLIGHT CONFUSION, NAUSEA, AND VERTIGO WERE ALSO REPORTED FROM ONE STUDY IN WHICH IT WAS NOT CLEAR WHETHER THE ROUTE OF EXPOSURE WAS INHALATION OR SKIN CONTACT OR BOTH. **CHRONIC EXPOSURE-** REPEATED OR PROLONGED EXPOSURE MAY CAUSE DARKENING OF THE SKIN AND DERMATITIS. IF SUFFICIENT AMOUNTS ARE ABSORBED, SYSTEMIC SYMPTOMS AS WITH ACUTE EXPOSURE MAY OCCUR. FIVE CREOSOTES OR CREOSOTE OILS PRODUCED SKIN TUMORS WHEN APPLIED TO THE SKIN OF MICE; ONE ALSO PRODUCED LUNG TUMORS. HUMAN MORTALITY ANALYSIS OF CREOSOTE-EXPOSED BRICKMAKERS INDICATED INCREASED RISK OF MORTALITY FROM SCROTAL CANCER. MALIGNANT EPITHELIOMAS, ABOUT ONE-THIRD OF WHICH WERE SCROTAL, HAVE BEEN REPORTED IN SEVERAL CASE REPORTS OF WORKERS EXPOSED TO CREOSOTE.
FIRST AID- REMOVE CONTAMINATED CLOTHING AND SHOES IMMEDIATELY. WASH AFFECTED AREA WITH SOAP OR MILD DETERGENT AND LARGE AMOUNTS OF WATER UNTIL NO EVIDENCE OF CHEMICAL REMAINS (AT LEAST 15-20 MINUTES). IN CASE OF CHEMICAL BURNS, COVER AREA WITH STERILE, DRY DRESSING. BANDAGE SECURELY, BUT NOT TOO TIGHTLY. GET MEDICAL ATTENTION IMMEDIATELY.

EYE CONTACT: WOOD CREOSOTE: CORROSIVE. **ACUTE EXPOSURE-** LIQUID CONTACT HAS CAUSED PAINFUL PROTRACTED KERATOCONJUNCTIVITIS INVOLVING LOSS OF CORNEAL EPITHELIUM, CLOUDING OF THE CORNEA, MIOSIS AND LONG-LASTING IRRITABILITY AND PHOTOPHOBIA. OTHER SYMPTOMS WHICH HAVE BEEN REPORTED FROM EXPOSURE TO CREOSOTE-TREATED PARTICLES INCLUDE ABRASION OF THE CORNEA WITH SOME PERMANENT SCARRING, HYPEREMIA, AND PRONOUCED SEROUS SECRETION. **CHRONIC EXPOSURE-** REPEATED OR PROLONGED EXPOSURE MAY CAUSE CONJUNCTIVITIS.
FIRST AID- WASH EYES IMMEDIATELY WITH LARGE AMOUNTS OF WATER, OCCASIONALLY LIFTING UPPER AND LOWER LIDS, UNTIL NO EVIDENCE OF CHEMICAL REMAINS (AT LEAST 15-20 MINUTES). CONTINUE IRRIGATING WITH NORMAL SALINE UNTIL THE PH HAS RETURNED TO NORMAL (30-60 MINUTES). COVER WITH STERILE BANDAGES. GET MEDICAL ATTENTION IMMEDIATELY.

INGESTION: WOOD CREOSOTE: **ACUTE EXPOSURE-** HAS CAUSED INTENSE IRRITATION AND CONGESTION OF THE ENTIRE GASTROENTERIC TRACT. SALIVATION, NAUSEA, VOMITING, RESPIRATORY DISTRESS, THREADY PULSE, VERTIGO, HEADACHE, LOSS OF PUPILLARY REFLEXES, HYPOTHERMIA, CYANOSIS AND MILD CONVULSIONS MAY ALSO OCCUR. DEATH FROM LARGE DOSES APPEARS LARGELY DUE TO CARDIOVASCULAR COLLAPSE. **CHRONIC EXPOSURE-** REPEATED INGESTION OF SMALL DOSES MAY RESULT IN CHRONIC INTOXICATION CHARACTERIZED BY DISTUBANCES OF VISION AND DIGESTION INCLUDING INCREASED PERISTALSIS AND BLOODY STOOLS. IN ONE CASE, HYPERTENSION AND GENERAL CARDIOVASCULAR COLLAPSE WERE REPORTED. OTHER SYMPTOMS OF ACUTE EXPOSURE ARE ALSO POSSIBLE. MATERNAL REPRODUCTIVE EFFECTS HAVE BEEN REPORTED IN MICE FOLLOWING REPEATED EXPOSURES PRIOR TO MATING. PATERNAL REPRODUCTIVE EFFECTS HAVE BEEN REPORTED IN MICE AND RATS FOLLOWING REPEATED EXPOSURES PRIOR TO MATING.
FIRST AID- IF THE PATIENT IS ALERT AND ABLE TO SWALLOW, GIVE A SLURRY OF ACTIVATED CHARCOAL IN WATER. DO NOT GIVE EMETICS. CAREFUL GASTRIC LAVAGE WITH WATER IS RECOMMENDED IF THERE ARE NO DEEP BURNS IN THE MOUTH OR PHARYNX. OLDER RECOMMENDATIONS TO LAVAGE WITH OLIVE OR OTHER VEGETABLE OILS DO NOT APPEAR TO BE SUBSTANTIATED. IN ANY CASE AVOID MINERAL OIL AND ALCOHOL. (GOSSELIN, CLINICAL TOXICOLOGY OF COMMERCIAL PRODUCTS, 5TH ED.). LAVAGE MUST BE PERFORMED BY QUALIFIED MEDICAL PERSONNEL.
ANTIDOTE: NO SPECIFIC ANTIDOTE. TREAT SYMPTOMATICALLY AND SUPPORTIVELY.

REACTIVITY

REACTIVITY: STABLE UNDER NORMAL TEMPERATURES AND PRESSURES.
INCOMPATIBILITIES: WOOD CREOSOTE: ACACIA: INCOMPATIBLE. ALBUMIN: INCOMPATIBLE. CHLOROSULFONIC ACID: INCREASE IN TEMPERATURE AND PRESSURE WHEN MIXED IN CLOSED CONTAINER. CUPRIC SALTS: INCOMPATIBLE. FERRIC SALTS: INCOMPATIBLE. GOLD SALTS: INCOMPATIBLE. OXIDIZERS: FIRE AND EXPLOSION HAZARD. SILVER SALTS: INCOMPATIBLE.
DECOMPOSITION: THERMAL DECOMPOSITION PRODUCTS MAY INCLUDE TOXIC OXIDES OF CARBON.
POLYMERIZATION: HAZARDOUS POLYMERIZATION HAS NOT BEEN REPORTED TO OCCUR UNDER NORMAL TEMPERATURES AND PRESSURES.

STORAGE AND DISPOSAL

OBSERVE ALL FEDERAL, STATE AND LOCAL REGULATIONS WHEN STORING OR DISPOSING OF THIS SUBSTANCE. FOR ASSISTANCE, CONTACT THE DISTRICT DIRECTOR OF THE ENVIRONMENTAL PROTECTION AGENCY.

STORAGE

STORE IN ACCORDANCE WITH 29 CFR 1910.106.
BONDING AND GROUNDING: SUBSTANCES WITH LOW ELECTROCONDUCTIVITY, WHICH MAY BE IGNITED BY ELECTROSTATIC SPARKS, SHOULD BE STORED IN CONTAINERS WHICH MEET THE BONDING AND GROUNDING GUIDELINES SPECIFIED IN NFPA 77-1983, RECOMMENDED PRACTICE ON STATIC ELECTRICITY.
STORE AWAY FROM INCOMPATIBLE SUBSTANCES.

DISPOSAL

DISPOSAL MUST BE IN ACCORDANCE WITH STANDARDS APPLICABLE TO GENERATORS OF HAZARDOUS WASTE, 40CFR 262. EPA HAZARDOUS WASTE NUMBER U051.

CONDITIONS TO AVOID

AVOID CONTACT WITH HEAT, SPARKS, FLAMES, OR OTHER SOURCES OF IGNITION. VAPORS MAY BE EXPLOSIVE. AVOID OVERHEATING OF CONTAINERS; CONTAINERS MAY VIOLENTLY RUPTURE IN HEAT OF FIRE. AVOID CONTAMINATION OF WATER SOURCES.

SPILL AND LEAK PROCEDURES

WATER SPILL: THE CALIFORNIA SAFE DRINKING WATER AND TOXIC ENFORCEMENT ACT OF 1986 (PROPOSITION 65) PROHIBITS CONTAMINATING ANY KNOWN SOURCE OF DRINKING WATER WITH SUBSTANCES KNOWN TO CAUSE CANCER AND/OR REPRODUCTIVE TOXICITY.
OCCUPATIONAL SPILL: SHUT OFF IGNITION SOURCES. STOP LEAK IF YOU CAN DO IT WITHOUT RISK. USE WATER SPRAY TO REDUCE VAPORS. FOR SMALL SPILLS, TAKE UP WITH SAND OR OTHER ABSORBENT MATERIAL AND PLACE INTO CONTAINERS FOR LATER DISPOSAL. FOR LARGER SPILLS, DIKE FAR AHEAD OF SPILL FOR LATER DISPOSAL. NO SMOKING, FLAMES OR FLARES IN HAZARD AREA. KEEP UNNECESSARY PEOPLE AWAY; ISOLATE HAZARD AREA AND RESTRICT ENTRY.

PROTECTIVE EQUIPMENT

VENTILATION: PROVIDE LOCAL EXHAUST OR PROCESS ENCLOSURE VENTILATION SYSTEM.

RESPIRATOR: THE FOLLOWING RESPIRATORS ARE RECOMMENDED BASED ON INFORMATION FOUND IN THE PHYSICAL DATA, TOXICITY AND HEALTH EFFECTS SECTIONS. THEY ARE RANKED IN ORDER FROM MINIMUM TO MAXIMUM RESPIRATORY PROTECTION. THE SPECIFIC RESPIRATOR SELECTED MUST BE BASED ON CONTAMINATION LEVELS FOUND IN THE WORK PLACE, MUST NOT EXCEED THE WORKING LIMITS OF THE RESPIRATOR AND BE JOINTLY APPROVED BY THE NATIONAL INSTITUTE FOR OCCUPATIONAL SAFETY AND HEALTH AND THE MINE SAFETY AND HEALTH ADMINISTRATION (NIOSH-MSHA).

TYPE 'C' SUPPLIED-AIR RESPIRATOR WITH A FULL FACEPIECE OPERATED IN PRESSURE-DEMAND OR OTHER POSITIVE PRESSURE MODE OR WITH A FULL FACEPIECE, HELMET OR HOOD OPERATED IN CONTINOUS-FLOW MODE.

SELF-CONTAINED BREATHING APPARATUS WITH A FULL FACEPIECE OPERATED IN PRESSURE-DEMAND OR OTHER POSITIVE PRESSURE MODE.

FOR FIREFIGHTING AND OTHER IMMEDIATELY DANGEROUS TO LIFE OR HEALTH CONDITIONS:

SELF-CONTAINED BREATHING APPARATUS WITH FULL FACEPIECE OPERATED IN PRESSURE-DEMAND OR OTHER POSITIVE PRESSURE MODE.

SUPPLIED-AIR RESPIRATOR WITH FULL FACEPIECE AND OPERATED IN PRESSURE-DEMAND OR OTHER POSITIVE PRESSURE MODE IN COMBINATION WITH AN AUXILIARY SELF-CONTAINED BREATHING APPARATUS OPERATED IN PRESSURE-DEMAND OR OTHER POSITIVE PRESSURE MODE.

CLOTHING: EMPLOYEE MUST WEAR APPROPRIATE PROTECTIVE (IMPERVIOUS) CLOTHING AND EQUIPMENT TO PREVENT ANY POSSIBILITY OF SKIN CONTACT WITH THIS SUBSTANCE.

GLOVES: EMPLOYEE MUST WEAR APPROPRIATE PROTECTIVE GLOVES TO PREVENT CONTACT WITH THIS SUBSTANCE.

EYE PROTECTION: EMPLOYEE MUST WEAR SPLASH-PROOF OR DUST-RESISTANT SAFETY GOGGLES AND A FACESHIELD TO PREVENT CONTACT WITH THIS SUBSTANCE.

EMERGENCY WASH FACILITIES: WHERE THERE IS ANY POSSIBILITY THAT AN EMPLOYEE'S EYES AND/OR SKIN MAY BE EXPOSED TO THIS SUBSTANCE, THE EMPLOYER SHOULD PROVIDE AN EYE WASH FOUNTAIN AND QUICK DRENCH SHOWER WITHIN THE IMMEDIATE WORK AREA FOR EMERGENCY USE.

AUTHORIZED BY- OCCUPATIONAL HEALTH SERVICES, INC.
CREATION DATE: 10/05/89 ***REVISION DATE:*** 07/12/90

MATERIAL SAFETY DATA SHEET

OCCUPATIONAL HEALTH SERVICES, INC.
AGRICULTURE AND PESTICIDE DIVISION
450 SEVENTH AVENUE, SUITE 2407
NEW YORK, NEW YORK 10123
1-800-445-MSDS OR (212) 967-1100

EMERGENCY CONTACT:
JOHN S. BRANSFORD, JR. (615) 292-1180

SUBSTANCE IDENTIFICATION

CAS-NUMBER 1111-67-7

SUBSTANCE: **COPPER THIOCYANATE**

TRADE NAMES/SYNONYMS: THIOCYANIC ACID, COPPER(1 +) SALT; COPPER MONOTHIOCYANATE; COPPER(1 +) THIOCYANATE; COPPER THIOCYANATE (CU(NCS)); CUPROUS THIOCYANATE; CUPROUS THIOCYANATE (CUCNS); CCUNS; PST71224

CHEMICAL FAMILY: THIOCYANATE

MOLECULAR FORMULA: CU-S-C-N

MOLECULAR WEIGHT: 121.62

CERCLA RATINGS (SCALE 0-3): HEALTH = U FIRE = 1 REACTIVITY = 0 PERSISTENCE = 3

NFPA RATINGS (SCALE 0-4): HEALTH = U FIRE = 1 REACTIVITY = 0

COMPONENTS AND CONTAMINANTS

COMPONENT: COPPER THIOCYANATE ***PERCENT:*** 100
CAS# 1111-67-7

OTHER CONTAMINANTS: NONE

EXPOSURE LIMITS: COPPER DUST AND MIST (AS CU): 1 MG/M3 OSHA TWA 1 MG/M3 ACGIH TWA

SUBJECT TO SARA SECTION 313 ANNUAL TOXIC CHEMICAL RELEASE REPORTING

PHYSICAL DATA

DESCRIPTION: WHITE TO YELLOW AMORPHOUS POWDER.

MELTING POINT: 1983 F (1084 C)

SPECIFIC GRAVITY: 2.843 ***SOLUBILITY IN WATER:*** 500 PPM

SOLVENT SOLUBILITY: SOLUBLE IN AMMONIUM HYDROXIDE, ETHER AND ALKALI THIOCYANATES. SLIGHTLY SOLUBLE IN ACETIC ACID. INSOLUBLE IN ALCOHOL AND ACETONE. DECOMPOSED BY CONCENTRATED MINERAL ACIDS.

FIRE AND EXPLOSION DATA

FIRE AND EXPLOSION HAZARD: SLIGHT FIRE HAZARD WHEN EXPOSED TO HEAT OR FLAME.

FIREFIGHTING MEDIA: DRY CHEMICAL, CARBON DIOXIDE, HALON, WATER SPRAY OR STANDARD FOAM (1987 EMERGENCY RESPONSE GUIDEBOOK, DOT P 5800.4). FOR LARGER FIRES, USE WATER SPRAY, FOG OR STANDARD FOAM (1987 EMERGENCY RESPONSE GUIDEBOOK, DOT P 5800.4).

FIREFIGHTING: MOVE CONTAINERS FROM FIRE AREA IF POSSIBLE (1987 EMERGENCY RESPONSE GUIDEBOOK, DOT P 5800.4, GUIDE PAGE 53).

EXTINGUISH USING AGENTS SUITABLE FOR SURROUNDING FIRE. APPLY WATER IN FLOODING QUANTITIES AS A FOG. AVOID CONTAMINATION OF WATER SOURCES. KEEP UPWIND AND AVOID BREATHING DUST AND FUMES.

TOXICITY

COPPER THIOCYANATE: CARCINOGEN STATUS: NONE. ACUTE TOXICITY LEVEL: NO DATA AVAILABLE. TARGET EFFECTS: POISONING MAY AFFECT THE EYES, SKIN, RESPIRATORY TRACT, LIVER, KIDNEY, SLPEEN, GASTROINTESTINAL TRACT, NERVOUS SYSTEM, AND THYROID GLAND. AT INCREASED RISK FROM EXPOSURE: PERSONS WITH PREEXISTING RESPIRATORY, LIVER, SKIN, KIDNEY, AND HEMATOPOIETIC DISEASES OR WILSON'S DISEASE.

HEALTH EFFECTS AND FIRST AID

INHALATION: COPPER THIOCYANATE: **ACUTE EXPOSURE-** INHALATION OF COPPER DUST MAY CAUSE IRRITATION OF THE UPPER RESPIRATORY TRACT OR AN ILLNESS SIMILAR TO THE COMMON COLD WITH SENSATIONS OF CHILLS AND STUFFINESS OF THE HEAD. **CHRONIC EXPOSURE-** PROLONGED INHALATION OF DUST OR MIST OF COPPER SALTS MAY CAUSE CONGESTION OF THE NASAL MUCOUS MEMBRANES, SOMETIMES OF THE PHARYNX, AND ON OCCASIONS ULCERATION AND PERFORATION OF THE NASAL SEPTUM. ATROPHIC CHANGES IN THE MUCOUS MEMBRANES WERE NOTED IN SUBJECTS EXPOSED TO COMPLEX COPPER SALTS FOR LONG PERIODS OF TIME. INHALATION OF COPPER COMPOUNDS HAS CAUSED INJURY TO THE LUNGS AND LIVER WITH HEMOCHROMATOSIS IN ANIMALS.

FIRST AID- REMOVE FROM EXPOSURE AREA TO FRESH AIR IMMEDIATELY. IF BREATHING HAS STOPPED, PERFORM ARTIFICIAL RESPIRATION. KEEP PERSON WARM AND AT REST. TREAT SYMPTOMATICALLY AND SUPPORTIVELY. GET MEDICAL ATTENTION IMMEDIATELY.

SKIN CONTACT: COPPER THIOCYANATE: **ACUTE EXPOSURE-** DIRECT CONTACT WITH COPPER COMPOUNDS MAY CAUSE IRRITATION. COPPER SALTS HAVE BEEN REPORTED TO CAUSE ITCHING PAPULOVESICULATION, SKIN DISCOLORATION, AND ECZEMATOID LESIONS. **CHRONIC EXPOSURE-** REPEATED AND PROLONGED CONTACT WITH SOME COPPER SALTS HAS RESULTED IN IRRITATION, NECROSIS, AND GREENISH SKIN DISCOLORATION. ALLERGIC CONTACT DERMATITIS, ALTHOUGH RARE, HAS BEEN REPORTED.

FIRST AID- REMOVE CONTAMINATED CLOTHING AND SHOES IMMEDIATELY. WASH AFFECTED AREA WITH SOAP OR MILD DETERGENT AND LARGE AMOUNTS OF WATER UNTIL NO EVIDENCE OF CHEMICAL REMAINS (APPROXIMATELY 15-20 MINUTES). GET MEDICAL ATTENTION IMMEDIATELY.

EYE CONTACT: COPPER THIOCYANATE: **ACUTE EXPOSURE-** SOME COPPER SALTS HAVE BEEN REPORTED TO CAUSE CONJUNCTIVITIS, CORNEAL ULCERATIONS, AND TURBIDITY POSSIBLY WITH PALPEBRAL EDEMA. COPPER PARTICLES EMBEDDED IN THE EYE MAY RESULT IN A PRONOUNCED FOREIGN-BODY RESPONSE WITH CHARACTERISTIC DISCOLORATION OF OCULAR TISSUE. **CHRONIC EXPOSURE-** NO DATA AVAILABLE.

FIRST AID- WASH EYES IMMEDIATELY WITH LARGE AMOUNTS OF WATER OR NORMAL SALINE, OCCASIONALLY LIFTING UPPER AND LOWER LIDS, UNTIL NO EVIDENCE OF CHEMICAL REMAINS (APPROXIMATELY 15-20 MINUTES). GET MEDICAL ATTENTION IMMEDIATELY.

INGESTION: COPPER THIOCYANATE: **ACUTE EXPOSURE-** INGESTION OF COPPER SALTS MAY CAUSE AN IMMEDIATE METALLIC TASTE, SALIVATION, NAUSEA, EPIGASTRIC BURNING, VOMITING, DIARRHEA, ULCERS, HEMORRHAGIC GASTRITIS, ANURIA, COMA, CONVULSIONS, AND DEATH. IF SUFFICIENT VOMITING DOES NOT OCCUR, SOME COPPER SALTS MAY CAUSE SYSTEMIC EFFECTS INCLUDING CAPILLARY DAMAGE, SHOCK, KIDNEY AND LIVER INJURY, CENTRAL NERVOUS SYSTEM EXCITATION FOLLOWED BY DEPRESSION, AND DEATH. THIOCYANATES MAY CAUSE NAUSEA, VOMITING, GASTRIC PAIN AND HEMORRHAGE, WEAKNESS, EXTREME CEREBRAL EXCITEMENT, DELIRIUM, DISORIENTATION, CONFUSION,

PSYCHOTIC BEHAVIOR, HIGH FEVER, EXTENSOR MUSCLE SPASTICITY, ANGINA, TOXIC HEPATITIS, CONVULSIONS, COMA AND DEATH. THE PROBABLE LETHAL DOSE OF A THIOCYANATE SALT IS BETWEEN 15-30 GRAMS, WITH DEATH IN 10-48 HOURS. PATHOLOGICAL FINDINGS INCLUDE MYOCARDIAL DAMAGE, FOCAL BRAIN DAMAGE, THYROID ENLARGEMENT AND THROMBOPHLEBITIS. PERSISTENT ALBUMINURIA OR ANURIA HAS BEEN REPORTED IN NON-FATAL ANIMAL POISONING. **CHRONIC EXPOSURE-** REPEATED OR PROLONGED INGESTION OF COPPER SALTS HAS PRODUCED HEMOLYTIC ANEMIA AND LIVER, KIDNEY, AND SPLEEN DAMAGE IN ANIMALS. PROLONGED ABSORPTION OF THIOCYANATES MAY CAUSE VARIOUS SKIN DISORDERS, CORYZA, WEAKNESS, FATIGUE, VERTIGO, NAUSEA, VOMITING, DIARRHEA, CONFUSION, DISORIENTATION, AND APHASIAS. THYROID ENLARGEMENT, APLASTIC ANEMIA, AND ABNORMAL BLEEDING MAY ALSO OCCUR.

FIRST AID- REMOVE BY GASTRIC LAVAGE OR EMESIS. MAINTAIN BLOOD PRESSURE AND AIRWAY. GIVE OXYGEN IF RESPIRATION IS DEPRESSED. DO NOT PERFORM GASTRIC LAVAGE OR EMESIS IF VICTIM IS UNCONSCIOUS. GET MEDICAL ATTENTION IMMEDIATELY (DREISBACH, HANDBOOK OF POISONING, 11TH ED.). ADMINISTRATION OF GASTRIC LAVAGE OR OXYGEN SHOULD BE PERFORMED BY QUALIFIED MEDICAL PERSONNEL.

ANTIDOTE: THE FOLLOWING ANTIDOTE HAS BEEN RECOMMENDED. HOWEVER, THE DECISION AS TO WHETHER THE SEVERITY OF POISONING REQUIRES ADMINISTRATION OF ANY ANTIDOTE AND ACTUAL DOSE REQUIRED SHOULD BE MADE BY QUALIFIED MEDICAL PERSONNEL.

COPPER POISONING: GIVE CALCIUM DISODIUM EDETATE 15-25 MG/KG (0.08-0.125 ML OF 20% SOLUTION PER KILOGRAM BODY WEIGHT) IN 250-500 ML OF 5% DEXTROSE INTRAVENOUSLY OVER A 1 TO 2 HOUR PERIOD TWICE DAILY. THE MAXIMUM DOSE SHOULD NOT EXCEED 50 MG/KG/DAY. THE DRUG SHOULD BE GIVEN IN 5-DAY COURSES WITH A REST PERIOD OF AT LEAST 2 DAYS BETWEEN COURSES. AFTER THE FIRST COURSE, SUBSEQUENT COURSES SHOULD NOT EXCEED 50 MG/KG/DAY. DAILY URINALYSES SHOULD NOT BE DONE DURING THE TREATMENT PERIOD. THE DOSAGE SHOULD BE REDUCED IF ANY UNUSUAL URINARY FINDINGS APPEAR. INTRAVENOUS ADMINISTRATION IS CONTRAINDICATED IN THE PRESENCE OF ELEVATED CEREBROSPINAL FLUID PRESSURE. PENICILLAMINE IS ALSO EFFECTIVE IN COPPER POISONING. GIVE UP TO 100 MG/KG/DAY (MAXIMUM 1 G/DAY) DIVIDED INTO 4 DOSES FOR NO LONGER THAN 1 WEEK. IF A LONGER ADMINISTRATION PERIOD IS WARRANTED, DOSAGE SHOULD NOT EXCEED 40 MG/KG/DAY. GIVE THE DRUG ORALLY, HALF AN HOUR BEFORE MEALS (DREISBACH, HANDBOOK OF POISONING, 12TH ED.). ANTIDOTE SHOULD BE ADMINISTERED BY QUALIFIED MEDICAL PERSONNEL.

REACTIVITY

REACTIVITY: STABLE UNDER NORMAL TEMPERATURES AND PRESSURES.

INCOMPATIBILITIES: COPPER THIOCYANATE: MINERAL ACIDS: DECOMPOSES. SEE ALSO COPPER SALTS AND THIOCYANATES.

COPPER SALTS: ACETYLENE: MAY FORM EXPLOSIVE ACETYLIDES. HYDRAZINE: DECOMPOSES. NITROMETHANE: FORMS EXPLOSIVE MIXTURES.

THIOCYANATES: CHLORATES: EXPLOSIVE MIXTURE. NITRATES: EXPLOSIVE MIXTURE. NITRIC ACID: EXPLOSION REACTION. ORGANIC PEROXIDES: EXPLOSION REACTION. OXIDIZERS: EXPLOSION REACTION. PEROXIDES: EXPLOSION REACTION. POTASSIUM CHLORATE: EXPLOSIVE MIXTURE. SODIUM CHLORATE: EXPLOSIVE MIXTURE.

DECOMPOSITION: THERMAL DECOMPOSITION MAY RELEASE TOXIC AND/OR HAZARDOUS GASES.

POLYMERIZATION: HAZARDOUS POLYMERIZATION HAS NOT BEEN REPORTED TO OCCUR UNDER NORMAL TEMPERATURES AND PRESSURES.

STORAGE AND DISPOSAL

OBSERVE ALL FEDERAL, STATE AND LOCAL REGULATIONS WHEN STORING OR DISPOSING OF THIS SUBSTANCE. FOR ASSISTANCE, CONTACT THE DISTRICT DIRECTOR OF THE ENVIRONMENTAL PROTECTION AGENCY.

STORAGE

STORE AWAY FROM INCOMPATIBLE SUBSTANCES.

STORE IN ACCORDANCE WITH 40 CFR 165 RECOMMENDED PROCEDURES FOR THE DISPOSAL AND STORAGE OF PESTICIDES AND PESTICIDE CONTAINERS.

DISPOSAL

DISPOSAL MUST BE IN ACCORDANCE WITH 40 CFR 165 RECOMMENDED PROCEDURES FOR THE DISPOSAL AND STORAGE OF PESTICIDES AND PESTICIDE CONTAINERS.

CONDITIONS TO AVOID

MAY BURN BUT DOES NOT IGNITE READILY.

SPILL AND LEAK PROCEDURES

OCCUPATIONAL SPILL: DO NOT TOUCH SPILLED MATERIAL. STOP LEAK IF YOU CAN DO IT WITHOUT RISK. FOR SMALL SPILLS, TAKE UP WITH SAND OR OTHER ABSORBENT MATERIAL AND PLACE INTO CONTAINERS FOR LATER DISPOSAL. FOR SMALL DRY SPILLS, WITH A CLEAN SHOVEL PLACE MATERIAL INTO CLEAN, DRY CONTAINER AND COVER. MOVE CONTAINERS FROM SPILL AREA. FOR LARGER SPILLS, DIKE FAR AHEAD OF SPILL FOR LATER DISPOSAL. KEEP UNNECESSARY PEOPLE AWAY. ISOLATE HAZARD AREA AND DENY ENTRY.

PROTECTIVE EQUIPMENT

VENTILATION: PROVIDE LOCAL EXHAUST VENTILATION AND/OR GENERAL DILUTION VENTILATION TO MEET PUBLISHED EXPOSURE LIMITS.

RESPIRATOR: THE FOLLOWING RESPIRATORS AND MAXIMUM USE CONCENTRATIONS ARE RECOMMENDATIONS BY THE U.S. DEPARTMENT OF HEALTH AND HUMAN SERVICES, NIOSH POCKET GUIDE TO CHEMICAL HAZARDS; NIOSH CRITERIA DOCUMENTS OR BY THE U.S. DEPARTMENT OF LABOR, 29 CFR 1910 SUBPART Z. THE SPECIFIC RESPIRATOR SELECTED MUST BE BASED ON CONTAMINATION LEVELS FOUND IN THE WORK PLACE, MUST NOT EXCEED THE WORKING LIMITS OF THE RESPIRATOR AND BE JOINTLY APPROVED BY THE NATIONAL INSTITUTE FOR OCCUPATIONAL SAFETY AND HEALTH AND THE MINE SAFETY AND HEALTH ADMINISTRATION (NIOSH-MSHA).

COPPER DUST AND MIST (AS CU):

5 MG/M3- ANY DUST AND MIST RESPIRATOR EXCEPT SINGLE-USE RESPIRATORS.

10 MG/M3- ANY DUST AND MIST RESPIRATOR EXCEPT SINGLE-USE AND QUARTER-MASK RESPIRATORS. ANY SUPPLIED-AIR RESPIRATOR. ANY SELF-CONTAINED BREATHING APPARATUS.

25 MG/M3- ANY POWERED AIR-PURIFYING RESPIRATOR WITH A DUST AND MIST FILTER. ANY SUPPLIED-AIR RESPIRATOR OPERATED IN A CONTINUOUS FLOW MODE.

50 MG/M3- ANY AIR-PURIFYING FULL FACEPIECE RESPIRATOR WITH A HIGH-EFFICIENCY PARTICULATE FILTER. ANY SELF-CONTAINED BREATHING APPARATUS WITH A FULL FACEPIECE. ANY SUPPLIED-AIR RESPIRATOR WITH A FULL FACEPIECE. ANY POWERED AIR-PURIFYING RESPIRATOR WITH A TIGHT-FITTING FACEPIECE AND A HIGH-EFFICIENCY PARTICULATE FILTER.

1000 MG/M3- ANY SUPPLIED-AIR RESPIRATOR WITH A HALF-MASK AND OPERATED IN A PRESSURE-DEMAND OR OTHER POSITIVE PRESSURE MODE. 2000 MG/M3- ANY SUPPLIED-AIR RESPIRATOR WITH A FULL FACEPIECE AND OPERATED IN A PRESSURE-DEMAND OR OTHER POSITIVE PRESSURE MODE.

ESCAPE- ANY AIR-PURIFYING FULL FACEPIECE RESPIRATOR WITH A HIGH-EFFICIENCY PARTICULATE FILTER. ANY APPROPRIATE ESCAPE-TYPE SELF-CONTAINED BREATHING APPARATUS.

FOR FIREFIGHTING AND OTHER IMMEDIATELY DANGEROUS TO LIFE OR HEALTH CONDITIONS:

SELF-CONTAINED BREATHING APPARATUS WITH FULL FACEPIECE OPERATED IN PRESSURE-DEMAND OR OTHER POSITIVE PRESSURE MODE.

SUPPLIED-AIR RESPIRATOR WITH FULL FACEPIECE AND OPERATED IN PRESSURE-DEMAND OR OTHER POSITIVE PRESSURE MODE IN COMBINATION WITH AN AUXILIARY SELF-CONTAINED BREATHING APPARATUS OPERATED IN PRESSURE-DEMAND OR OTHER POSITIVE PRESSURE MODE.

CLOTHING: EMPLOYEE MUST WEAR APPROPRIATE PROTECTIVE (IMPERVIOUS) CLOTHING AND EQUIPMENT TO PREVENT REPEATED OR PROLONGED SKIN CONTACT WITH THIS SUBSTANCE.

GLOVES: EMPLOYEE MUST WEAR APPROPRIATE PROTECTIVE GLOVES TO PREVENT CONTACT WITH THIS SUBSTANCE.

EYE PROTECTION: EMPLOYEE MUST WEAR SPLASH-PROOF OR DUST-RESISTANT SAFETY GOGGLES TO PREVENT EYE CONTACT WITH THIS SUBSTANCE.

EMERGENCY EYE WASH: WHERE THERE IS ANY POSSIBILITY THAT AN EMPLOYEE'S EYES MAY BE EXPOSED TO THIS SUBSTANCE, THE EMPLOYER SHOULD PROVIDE AN EYE WASH FOUNTAIN WITHIN THE IMMEDIATE WORK AREA FOR EMERGENCY USE.

AUTHORIZED BY- OCCUPATIONAL HEALTH SERVICES, INC.

CREATION DATE: 11/16/89 ***REVISION DATE:*** 05/18/90

MATERIAL SAFETY DATA SHEET

OCCUPATIONAL HEALTH SERVICES, INC.
AGRICULTURE AND PESTICIDE DIVISION
450 SEVENTH AVENUE, SUITE 2407
NEW YORK, NEW YORK 10123
1-800-445-MSDS OR (212) 967-1100

EMERGENCY CONTACT:
JOHN S. BRANSFORD, JR. (615) 292-1180

SUBSTANCE IDENTIFICATION

CAS-NUMBER 2675-77-6

SUBSTANCE: CHLORONEB

TRADE NAMES/SYNONYMS: 1,4-DICHLORO-2,5-DIMETHOXYBENZENE; BENZENE, 1,4-DICHLORO-2,5-DIMETHOXY-; DEMOSAN; TERRANEB SP; C8H8CL2O2; PST71229
CHEMICAL FAMILY: HALOGEN COMPOUND, AROMATIC ETHER
MOLECULAR FORMULA: CL2-C6-H2-(O-C-H3)2
MOLECULAR WEIGHT: 207.1
CERCLA RATINGS (SCALE 0-3): HEALTH=1 FIRE=1 REACTIVITY=0 PERSISTENCE=3
NFPA RATINGS (SCALE 0-4): HEALTH=1 FIRE=1 REACTIVITY=0

COMPONENTS AND CONTAMINANTS

COMPONENT: CHLORONEB ***PERCENT:*** 100
CAS# 2675-77-6
OTHER CONTAMINANTS: NONE
EXPOSURE LIMITS: NO OCCUPATIONAL EXPOSURE LIMITS ESTABLISHED BY OSHA, ACGIH, OR NIOSH.

PHYSICAL DATA

DESCRIPTION: COLORLESS CRYSTALLINE SOLID WITH A MUSTY ODOR.
BOILING POINT: 514 F (268 C) ***MELTING POINT:*** 271-275 F (133-135 C)
SPECIFIC GRAVITY: NOT AVAILABLE ***VAPOR PRESSURE:*** 0.003 MMHG @ 25 C
SOLUBILITY IN WATER: 8 PPM @ 25 C
SOLVENT SOLUBILITY: SOLUBLE IN ACETONE, METHYLENE CHLORIDE, XYLENE, DIMETHYLFORMAMIDE

FIRE AND EXPLOSION DATA

FIRE AND EXPLOSION HAZARD: SLIGHT FIRE HAZARD WHEN EXPOSED TO HEAT OR FLAME.
FIREFIGHTING MEDIA: DRY CHEMICAL, CARBON DIOXIDE, HALON, WATER SPRAY OR STANDARD FOAM (1987 EMERGENCY RESPONSE GUIDEBOOK, DOT P 5800.4).
FOR LARGER FIRES, USE WATER SPRAY, FOG OR STANDARD FOAM (1987 EMERGENCY RESPONSE GUIDEBOOK, DOT P 5800.4).
FIREFIGHTING: MOVE CONTAINERS FROM FIRE AREA IF POSSIBLE. FIGHT FIRE FROM MAXIMUM DISTANCE. STAY AWAY FROM STORAGE TANK ENDS. DIKE FIRE CONTROL WATER FOR LATER DISPOSAL. DO NOT SCATTER MATERIAL (1987 EMERGENCY RESPONSE GUIDEBOOK, DOT P 5800.4, GUIDE PAGE 55).
USE AGENTS SUITABLE FOR TYPE OF FIRE. COOL CONTAINERS WITH FLOODING AMOUNTS OF WATER. AVOID BREATHING VAPORS OR DUSTS, KEEP UPWIND.

TOXICITY

CHLORONEB: TOXICITY DATA: 25,000 MG/M3 INHALATION-RAT LC50 (EPA PESTICIDE REGISTRATION STANDARD FOR CHLORONEB, 1980); 11 GM/KG ORAL-RAT LD50; MUTAGENIC DATA (RTECS). CARCINOGEN STATUS: NONE. ACUTE TOXICITY LEVEL: MODERATELY TOXIC BY INHALATION AND SLIGHTLY TOXIC BY INGESTION. TARGET EFFECTS: NO DATA AVAILABLE.

HEALTH EFFECTS AND FIRST AID

INHALATION: CHLORONEB: **ACUTE EXPOSURE-** A LETHAL CONCENTRATION IN MALE RATS WAS 25,200 MG/M3; REPORTED EFFECTS FROM EXPOSURE WERE HYPEREMIA, UNRESPONSIVENESS, MYDRIASIS, AND RESPIRATORY IRREGULARITIES. HYPEREMIA AND HYPERPNEA WERE OBSERVED AT SUBLETHAL CONCENTRATIONS. **CHRONIC EXPOSURE-** NO DATA AVAILABLE.
FIRST AID- REMOVE FROM EXPOSURE AREA TO FRESH AIR IMMEDIATELY. IF BREATHING HAS STOPPED, PERFORM ARTIFICIAL RESPIRATION. KEEP PERSON WARM AND AT REST. TREAT SYMPTOMATICALLY AND SUPPORTIVELY. GET MEDICAL ATTENTION IMMEDIATELY.

SKIN CONTACT: CHLORONEB: **ACUTE EXPOSURE-** TECHNICAL CHLORONEB WAS VERY SLIGHTLY IRRITATING TO INTACT AND ABRADED RABBIT SKIN. **CHRONIC EXPOSURE-** SLIGHTLY LOWER WEIGHT GAIN WAS THE ONLY OBSERVABLE EFFECT PRODUCED FROM REPEATED APPLICATION OF 5 GM/KG TO RABBIT SKIN. REPEATED APPLICATION OF A 50% AQUEOUS SUSPENSION OF THE WETTABLE POWDER DID NOT PRODUCE SKIN SENSITIZATION IN GUINEA PIGS.
FIRST AID- REMOVE CONTAMINATED CLOTHING AND SHOES IMMEDIATELY. WASH AFFECTED AREA WITH SOAP OR MILD DETERGENT AND LARGE AMOUNTS OF WATER UNTIL NO EVIDENCE OF CHEMICAL REMAINS (APPROXIMATELY 15-20 MINUTES). GET MEDICAL ATTENTION IMMEDIATELY.

EYE CONTACT: CHLORONEB: **ACUTE EXPOSURE-** THIS MATERIAL WAS NOT IRRITATING TO RABBIT EYES. **CHRONIC EXPOSURE-** NO DATA AVAILABLE.
FIRST AID- WASH EYES IMMEDIATELY WITH LARGE AMOUNTS OF WATER OR NORMAL SALINE, OCCASIONALLY LIFTING UPPER AND LOWER LIDS, UNTIL NO EVIDENCE OF CHEMICAL REMAINS (APPROXIMATELY 15-20 MINUTES). GET MEDICAL ATTENTION IMMEDIATELY.

INGESTION: CHLORONEB: **ACUTE EXPOSURE-** IN RATS, INGESTION OF 5 GM/KG PRODUCED EFFECTS OF DIARRHEA, STAINED FACE AND PERINEAL AREA, AND WEIGHT LOSS. GROSS PATHOLOGIC CHANGES INCLUDED HEAVY LIVER, KIDNEYS WITH HYDRONEPHROSIS, CORNEAL OPACITY, AND LUNGS THAT WERE DULL-RED AND GRAY MOTTLED WITH GRAY FOCI. **CHRONIC EXPOSURE-** PATHOLOGICAL ALTERATIONS AND WEIGHT INCREASES OF THE LIVER AND KIDNEY AND EFFECTS ON THE HEMATOPOIETIC SYSTEM WERE OBSERVED IN A SUBCHRONIC ORAL STUDY IN RATS. MORPHOLOGIC CHANGES IN THE THYROID, PATHOLOGICAL ALTERATIONS AND WEIGHT INCREASES IN THE LIVER, AND GASTRITIS DEVELOPED IN DOGS AFTER INGESTING HIGH ORAL DOSES FOR TWO YEARS.
FIRST AID- IF THE PERSON IS CONSCIOUS AND NOT CONVULSING, REMOVE BY GIVING SYRUP OF IPECAC (IF VOMITING OCCURS, KEEP THE HEAD BELOW THE HIPS TO PREVENT ASPIRATION). GIVE ACTIVATED CHARCOAL FOLLOWED BY GASTRIC LAVAGE. FOLLOW WITH A SALINE CATHARTIC. DO NOT GIVE FATS OR OILS. INTESTINAL LAVAGE WITH 20% MANNITOL (200 ML) BY STOMACH TUBE IS ALSO USEFUL. GIVE ARTIFICIAL RESPIRATION WITH OXYGEN IF RESPIRATION IS DEPRESSED (DREISBACH, HANDBOOK OF POISONING, 12TH ED.). TREAT SYMPTOMATICALLY AND SUPPORTIVELY. LAVAGE AND ADMINISTRATION OF OXYGEN SHOULD BE PERFORMED BY QUALIFIED MEDICAL PERSONNEL. GET MEDICAL ATTENTION IMMEDIATELY.
ANTIDOTE: NO SPECIFIC ANTIDOTE. TREAT SYMPTOMATICALLY AND SUPPORTIVELY.

REACTIVITY

REACTIVITY: STABLE UNDER NORMAL TEMPERATURES AND PRESSURES.
INCOMPATIBILITIES: CHLORONEB: NO DATA AVAILABLE.
DECOMPOSITION: THERMAL DECOMPOSITION PRODUCTS MAY INCLUDE HIGHLY TOXIC FUMES OF PHOSGENE, TOXIC AND CORROSIVE FUMES OF CHLORIDES, AND OXIDES OF CARBON.
POLYMERIZATION: HAZARDOUS POLYMERIZATION HAS NOT BEEN REPORTED TO OCCUR UNDER NORMAL TEMPERATURES AND PRESSURES.

STORAGE AND DISPOSAL

OBSERVE ALL FEDERAL, STATE AND LOCAL REGULATIONS WHEN STORING OR DISPOSING OF THIS SUBSTANCE. FOR ASSISTANCE, CONTACT THE DISTRICT DIRECTOR OF THE ENVIRONMENTAL PROTECTION AGENCY.

STORAGE

STORE IN ACCORDANCE WITH 40 CFR 165 RECOMMENDED PROCEDURES FOR THE DISPOSAL AND STORAGE OF PESTICIDES AND PESTICIDE CONTAINERS.

DISPOSAL

DISPOSAL MUST BE IN ACCORDANCE WITH 40 CFR 165 RECOMMENDED PROCEDURES FOR THE DISPOSAL AND STORAGE OF PESTICIDES AND PESTICIDE CONTAINERS.

CONDITIONS TO AVOID

MAY BURN BUT DOES NOT IGNITE READILY. CONTAINERS MAY EXPLODE IN HEAT OF FIRE.

SPILL AND LEAK PROCEDURES

OCCUPATIONAL SPILL: DO NOT TOUCH SPILLED MATERIAL. STOP LEAK IF YOU CAN DO IT WITHOUT RISK. USE WATER SPRAY TO REDUCE VAPORS. FOR SMALL SPILLS, TAKE UP WITH SAND OR OTHER ABSORBENT MATERIAL AND PLACE INTO CONTAINERS FOR LATER DISPOSAL. FOR SMALL DRY SPILLS, WITH A CLEAN SHOVEL PLACE MATERIAL INTO CLEAN, DRY CONTAINERS AND COVER. MOVE CONTAINERS FROM SPILL AREA. FOR LARGER SPILLS, DIKE FAR AHEAD OF SPILL FOR LATER DISPOSAL. KEEP UNNECESSARY PEOPLE AWAY. ISOLATE HAZARD AREA AND DENY ENTRY. VENTILATE CLOSED SPACES BEFORE ENTERING.

PROTECTIVE EQUIPMENT

VENTILATION: PROVIDE GENERAL DILUTION VENTILATION.
RESPIRATOR: THE FOLLOWING RESPIRATORS ARE RECOMMENDED BASED ON INFORMATION FOUND IN THE PHYSICAL DATA, TOXICITY AND HEALTH EFFECTS SECTIONS. THEY ARE RANKED IN ORDER FROM MINIMUM TO MAXIMUM RESPIRATORY PROTECTION. THE SPECIFIC RESPIRATOR SELECTED MUST BE BASED ON CONTAMINATION LEVELS FOUND IN THE WORK PLACE, MUST NOT EXCEED THE WORKING LIMITS OF THE RESPIRATOR AND BE JOINTLY APPROVED BY THE NATIONAL INSTITUTE FOR OCCUPATIONAL SAFETY AND HEALTH AND THE MINE SAFETY AND HEALTH ADMINISTRATION (NIOSH-MSHA).
CHEMICAL CARTRIDGE RESPIRATOR WITH AN ORGANIC VAPOR CARTRIDGE(S) IN COMBINATION WITH A DUST AND MIST FILTER.
GAS MASK WITH ORGANIC VAPOR CANISTER (CHIN-STYLE OR FRONT- OR BACK-MOUNTED CANISTER) WITH A DUST AND MIST FILTER.
GAS MASK WITH ORGANIC VAPOR CANISTER (CHIN-STYLE OR FRONT- OR BACK-MOUNTED CANISTER) WITH A PARTICULATE FILTER.
POWERED AIR-PURIFYING RESPIRATOR WITH A HIGH-EFFICIENCY FILTER.
TYPE 'C' SUPPLIED-AIR RESPIRATOR WITH A FULL FACEPIECE OPERATED IN A PRESSURE-DEMAND OR OTHER POSITIVE PRESSURE MODE.
SELF-CONTAINED BREATHING APPARATUS WITH A FULL FACEPIECE OPERATED IN

PRESSURE-DEMAND OR OTHER POSITIVE PRESSURE MODE.
FOR FIREFIGHTING AND OTHER IMMEDIATELY DANGEROUS TO LIFE OR HEALTH CONDITIONS:
SELF-CONTAINED BREATHING APPARATUS WITH FULL FACEPIECE OPERATED IN PRESSURE-DEMAND OR OTHER POSITIVE PRESSURE MODE.
SUPPLIED-AIR RESPIRATOR WITH FULL FACEPIECE AND OPERATED IN PRESSURE-DEMAND OR OTHER POSITIVE PRESSURE MODE IN COMBINATION WITH AN AUXILIARY SELF-CONTAINED BREATHING APPARATUS OPERATED IN PRESSURE-DEMAND OR OTHER POSITIVE PRESSURE MODE.

CLOTHING: EMPLOYEE MUST WEAR APPROPRIATE PROTECTIVE (IMPERVIOUS) CLOTHING AND EQUIPMENT TO PREVENT REPEATED OR PROLONGED SKIN CONTACT WITH THIS SUBSTANCE.

GLOVES: EMPLOYEE MUST WEAR APPROPRIATE PROTECTIVE GLOVES TO PREVENT CONTACT WITH THIS SUBSTANCE.

EYE PROTECTION: EMPLOYEE MUST WEAR SPLASH-PROOF OR DUST-RESISTANT SAFETY GOGGLES TO PREVENT EYE CONTACT WITH THIS SUBSTANCE.
EMERGENCY EYE WASH: WHERE THERE IS ANY POSSIBILITY THAT AN EMPLOYEE'S EYES MAY BE EXPOSED TO THIS SUBSTANCE, THE EMPLOYER SHOULD PROVIDE AN EYE WASH FOUNTAIN WITHIN THE IMMEDIATE WORK AREA FOR EMERGENCY USE.

AUTHORIZED BY- OCCUPATIONAL HEALTH SERVICES, INC.
CREATION DATE: 10/04/89 ***REVISION DATE:*** 05/10/90

MATERIAL SAFETY DATA SHEET

OCCUPATIONAL HEALTH SERVICES, INC.
AGRICULTURE AND PESTICIDE DIVISION
450 SEVENTH AVENUE, SUITE 2407
NEW YORK, NEW YORK 10123
1-800-445-MSDS OR (212) 967-1100

EMERGENCY CONTACT:
JOHN S. BRANSFORD, JR. (615) 292-1180

SUBSTANCE IDENTIFICATION

CAS-NUMBER 299-85-4

SUBSTANCE: O-2,4-DICHLOROPHENYL O-METHYL ISOPROPYLPHOSPHORAMIDOTHIOATE

TRADE NAMES/SYNONYMS: PHOSPHORAMIDOTHIOIC ACID, (1-METHYLETHYL)-, O-(2,4-DICHLOROPHENYL) O-METHYL ESTER; (1-METHYLETHYL)PHOSPHORAMIDOTHIOIC ACID, O-(2,4-DICHLOROPHENYL) O-METHYL ESTER; PHOSPHORAMIDOTHIOIC ACID, ISOPROPYL-, O-(2,4-DICHLOROPHENYL) O-METHYL ESTER; ISOPROPYLPHOSPHORAMIDOTHIOIC ACID, O-(2,4-DICHLOROPHENYL) O-METHYL ESTER; O-(2,4-DICHLOROPHENYL) O-METHYL ISOPROPYLPHOSPHORAMIDOTHIOATE; O-(2,4-DICHLOROPHENYL) O-METHYL (1-METHYLETHYL)PHOSPHORAMIDOTHIOATE; DMPA; DOW 1329; K 22023; ZYTRON; OMS 115; ENT 25647; C10H14CL2NO2PS; PST71236

CHEMICAL FAMILY: PHOSPHOROTHIOATE

MOLECULAR FORMULA: C10-H14-CL2-N-O2-P-S

MOLECULAR WEIGHT: 314.18

CERCLA RATINGS (SCALE 0-3): HEALTH=3 FIRE=1 REACTIVITY=0 PERSISTENCE=1

NFPA RATINGS (SCALE 0-4): HEALTH=3 FIRE=1 REACTIVITY=0

COMPONENTS AND CONTAMINANTS

COMPONENT: O-2,4-DICHLOROPHENYL O-METHYL ISOPROPYLPHOS-PHORAMIDOTHIOATE ***PERCENT:*** 100.0
CAS# 299-85-4

OTHER CONTAMINANTS: NONE

EXPOSURE LIMITS: NO OCCUPATIONAL EXPOSURE LIMITS ESTABLISHED BY OSHA, ACGIH, OR NIOSH.

PHYSICAL DATA

DESCRIPTION: WHITE CRYSTALLINE SOLID. ***MELTING POINT:*** 124 F (51 C)

SPECIFIC GRAVITY: NOT AVAILABLE ***VAPOR PRESSURE:*** 2 MMHG @ 150 C

SOLUBILITY IN WATER: 0.0005% @ 25 C

SOLVENT SOLUBILITY: SOLUBLE IN ACETONE, BENZENE, CARBON TETRACHLORIDE AND MOST ORGANIC SOLVENTS

FIRE AND EXPLOSION DATA

FIRE AND EXPLOSION HAZARD: SLIGHT FIRE HAZARD WHEN EXPOSED TO HEAT OR FLAME.

FIREFIGHTING MEDIA: DRY CHEMICAL, CARBON DIOXIDE, HALON, WATER SPRAY OR STANDARD FOAM (1987 EMERGENCY RESPONSE GUIDEBOOK, DOT P 5800.4).
FOR LARGER FIRES, USE WATER SPRAY, FOG OR STANDARD FOAM (1987 EMERGENCY RESPONSE GUIDEBOOK, DOT P 5800.4).

FIREFIGHTING: MOVE CONTAINERS FROM FIRE AREA IF POSSIBLE. FIGHT FIRE FROM MAXIMUM DISTANCE. STAY AWAY FROM STORAGE TANK ENDS. DIKE FIRE CONTROL WATER FOR LATER DISPOSAL. DO NOT SCATTER MATERIAL (1987 EMERGENCY RESPONSE GUIDEBOOK, DOT P 5800.4, GUIDE PAGE 55).
EXTINGUISH ONLY IF FLOW CAN BE STOPPED; USE FLOODING AMOUNTS OF WATER AS FOG, SOLID STREAMS MAY BE INEFFECTIVE. COOL CONTAINERS WITH FLOODING AMOUNTS OF WATER FROM AS FAR A DISTANCE AS POSSIBLE. USE WATER SPRAY TO ABSORB TOXIC VAPORS. AVOID BREATHING TOXIC VAPORS; KEEP UPWIND. CONSIDER EVACUATION OF DOWNWIND AREA IF MATERIAL IS LEAKING.

TOXICITY

O-2,4-DICHLOROPHENYL O-METHYL ISOPROPYLPHOSPHORAMIDOTHIOATE:
TOXICITY DATA: 1680 MG/KG SKIN-RABBIT LD50; 270 MG/KG ORAL-RAT LD50; 210 MG/KG ORAL-GUINEA PIG LD50; 1000 MG/KG UNREPORTED-DOG LD50.
CARCINOGEN STATUS: NONE. ACUTE TOXICITY LEVEL: TOXIC BY INGESTION AND MODERATELY TOXIC BY DERMAL ABSORPTION. TARGET EFFECTS: CHOLINESTERASE INHIBITOR. POISONING MAY AFFECT THE NERVOUS SYSTEM.* AT INCREASED RISK FROM EXPOSURE: PERSONS WITH RESPIRATORY AILMENTS, RECENT EXPOSURE TO CHOLINESTERASE INHIBITORS OR IMPAIRED CHOLINESTERASE PRODUCTION, OR LIVER MALFUNCTION.* ADDITIONAL DATA: MAY CROSS THE PLACENTA. HIGH ENVIRONMENTAL TEMPERATURES OR EXPOSURE OF THE CHEMICAL TO VISIBLE OR ULTRAVIOLET LIGHT MAY ENHANCE THE TOXICITY. INTERACTIONS WITH MEDICATIONS MAY OCCUR.*
* MAY BE BASED ON GENERAL INFORMATION ON ORGANOPHOSPHATES.

HEALTH EFFECTS AND FIRST AID

INHALATION: O-2,4-DICHLOROPHENYL O-METHYL ISOPROPYLPHOSPHORAMIDOTHIOATE: SEE INFORMATION ON ORGANOPHOSPHATES.
ORGANOPHOSPHATES: CHOLINESTERASE INHIBITOR. **ACUTE EXPOSURE**- WHEN INHALED, THE FIRST EFFECTS OF CHOLINESTERASE INHIBITORS ARE USUALLY RESPIRATORY AND MAY INCLUDE NASAL HYPEREMIA AND WATERY DISCHARGE, COUGH, CHEST DISCOMFORT, DYSPNEA, AND WHEEZING DUE TO INCREASED BRONCHIAL SECRETIONS AND BRONCHOCONSTRICTION. IF SUFFICIENT AMOUNTS ARE ABSORBED, OTHER SYSTEMIC EFFECTS MAY BEGIN WITHIN A FEW MINUTES OR BE DELAYED FOR UP TO 12 HOURS. SYMPTOMS MAY INCLUDE PALLOR, NAUSEA, VOMITING, DIARRHEA, ABDOMINAL CRAMPS, HEADACHE, DIZZINESS, OCULAR PAIN, BLURRED VISION, MIOSIS OR IN SOME CASES, ESPECIALLY INITIALLY, MYDRIASIS, LACRIMATION, SALIVATION, SWEATING, AND CONFUSION. OTHER REPORTED CENTRAL NERVOUS SYSTEM OR NEUROMUSCULAR EFFECTS MAY INCLUDE ATAXIA, SLURRED SPEECH, AREFLEXIA, WEAKNESS, FATIGUE, FASCICULATIONS, TWITCHING, TREMORS POSSIBLY OF THE TONGUE AND EYELIDS, AND EVENTUALLY PARALYSIS OF THE EXTREMITIES AND POSSIBLY OF THE RESPIRATORY MUSCLES. IN SEVERE CASES THERE MAY ALSO BE INVOLUNTARY DEFECATION AND URINATION, CYANOSIS, PSYCHOSIS, HYPERGLYCEMIA, ACUTE PANCREATITIS, CARDIAC IRREGULARITIES, PULMONARY EDEMA, UNCONSCIOUSNESS, CONVULSIONS, AND COMA. DEATH IS PRIMARILY DUE TO RESPIRATORY FAILURE, ALTHOUGH CARDIOVASCULAR EFFECTS INCLUDING CARDIAC ARREST MAY ALSO BE IMPLICATED. LONG TERM SEQUELAE ARE RARE BUT MAY INCLUDE NEUROPSYCHIATRIC DISORDERS AND MYOPATHY WITH MUSCLE TENDERNESS. SOME ORGANOPHOSPHATES MAY CAUSE A DELAYED NEUROPATHY BEGINNING 1-4 WEEKS AFTER AN ACUTE EXPOSURE WHICH MAY OR MAY NOT HAVE CAUSED ACUTE CHOLINERGIC EFFECTS. NUMBNESS, TINGLING, WEAKNESS AND CRAMPING BEGINNING SYMMETRICALLY IN THE LOWER LIMBS MAY PROGRESS TO ATAXIA AND PARALYSIS. IN SEVERE CASES, UPPER LIMB INVOLVEMENT IS POSSIBLE AND FLACCID PARALYSIS MAY PROGRESS TO SPASTIC PARALYSIS WITH EXAGGERATED REFLEXES. IMPROVEMENT MAY OCCUR OVER MONTHS TO YEARS, BUT SOME RESIDUAL IMPAIRMENT USUALLY REMAINS.
CHRONIC EXPOSURE- REPEATED OR PROLONGED EXPOSURE MAY RESULT IN THE EFFECTS OF ACUTE EXPOSURE INCLUDING THE DELAYED NEUROPATHY. OTHER EFFECTS REPORTED IN WORKERS REPEATEDLY EXPOSED INCLUDE IMPAIRED MEMORY AND CONCENTRATION, ACUTE PSYCHOSIS, SEVERE DEPRESSIONS, IRRITABILTY, CONFUSION, APATHY, EMOTIONAL LABILITY, SOCIAL WITHDRAWAL, CONFUSION, HEADACHE, SPEECH DIFFICULTIES, DELAYED REACTION TIMES, SPATIAL DISORIENTATION, NIGHTMARES, SLEEPWALKING, AND DROWSINESS OR INSOMNIA. AN INFLUENZA-LIKE CONDITION WITH HEADACHE, NAUSEA, WEAKNESS, ANOREXIA AND MALAISE HAS ALSO BEEN REPORTED.

FIRST AID- REMOVE FROM EXPOSURE AREA TO FRESH AIR IMMEDIATELY. IF BREATHING HAS STOPPED, GIVE ARTIFICIAL RESPIRATION. MAINTAIN AIRWAY AND BLOOD PRESSURE AND ADMINISTER OXYGEN IF AVAILABLE. KEEP AFFECTED PERSON WARM AND AT REST. TREAT SYMPTOMATICALLY AND SUPPORTIVELY.

ADMINISTRATION OF OXYGEN SHOULD BE PERFORMED BY QUALIFIED PERSONNEL. GET MEDICAL ATTENTION IMMEDIATELY.

SKIN CONTACT: O-2,4-DICHLOROPHENYL O-METHYL ISOPROPYLPHOSPHORAMIDOTHIOATE: SEE INFORMATION ON ORGANOPHOSPHATES.
ORGANOPHOSPHATES: CHOLINESTERASE INHIBITOR. **ACUTE EXPOSURE-** LOCALIZED SWEATING AND FASCICULATIONS MAY OCCUR AT THE SITE OF CONTACT. IF SUFFICIENT AMOUNTS ARE ABSORBED, OTHER EFFECTS OF CHOLINESTERASE INHIBITION AS DESCRIBED IN ACUTE INHALATION MAY OCCUR. SYMPTOMS MAY BE DELAYED 2-3 HOURS, BUT USUALLY NO MORE THAN 12 HOURS. THE RATE OF ABSORPTION IS INCREASED BY THE PRESENCE OF DERMATITIS OR HIGH AMBIENT TEMPERATURES. DELAYED NEUROPATHY IS ALSO POSSIBLE. **CHRONIC EXPOSURE-** REPEATED OR PROLONGED EXPOSURE MAY CAUSE EFFECTS AS DESCRIBED IN ACUTE EXPOSURE. SOME ORGANOPHOSPHATES MAY CAUSE SENSITIZATION.
FIRST AID- REMOVE CONTAMINATED CLOTHING IMMEDIATELY. WASH CONTAMINATED AREAS WITH SOAP AND WATER FOLLOWED BY ALCOHOL (ARENA, POISONING, 4TH ED.). EMERGENCY PERSONNEL SHOULD WEAR GLOVES AND AVOID CONTAMINATION. TREAT RESPIRATORY DIFFICULTY WITH ARTIFICIAL RESPIRATION. GET MEDICAL ATTENTION IMMEDIATELY.

EYE CONTACT: O-2,4-DICHLOROPHENYL O-METHYL ISOPROPYLPHOSPHORAMIDOTHIOATE: SEE INFORMATION ON ORGANOPHOSPHATES.
ORGANOPHOSPHATES: CHOLINESTERASE INHIBITOR. **ACUTE EXPOSURE-** DIRECT CONTACT MAY CAUSE PAIN, HYPEREMIA, LACRIMATION, TWITCHING OF THE EYELIDS, MIOSIS, AND CILIARY MUSCLE SPASM WITH LOSS OF ACCOMODATION, BLURRED OR DIMMED VISION AND BROWACHE. SOMETIMES MYDRIASIS MAY OCCUR INSTEAD OF MIOSIS. WITH SUFFICIENT EXPOSURE, OTHER SYMPTOMS OF CHOLINESTERASE INHIBITION AS DESCRIBED IN ACUTE INHALATION MAY OCCUR. **CHRONIC EXPOSURE-** REPEATED OR PROLONGED EXPOSURE MAY CAUSE EFFECTS AS DESCRIBED IN ACUTE EXPOSURE. SOME COMPOUNDS HAVE CAUSED TOXIC EFFECTS ON THE CRYSTALLINE LENS, CONJUNCTIVAL THICKENING AND OBSTRUCTION OF THE NASOLACRIMAL CANALS WHEN USED AS MIOTIC EYEDROPS.
FIRST AID- IRRIGATE EYES WITH WATER OR SALINE SOLUTION. IF SYMPTOMS OF POISONING OCCUR, TREAT RESPIRATORY DIFFICULTY WITH ARTIFICIAL RESPIRATION AND OXYGEN. OBSERVE PATIENT FOR AT LEAST 24-36 HOURS (GOSSELIN, CLINICAL TOXICOLOGY OF COMMERCIAL PRODUCTS, 5TH ED.). GET MEDICAL ATTENTION IMMEDIATELY. OXYGEN SHOULD BE ADMINISTERED BY QUALIFIED MEDICAL PERSONNEL.

INGESTION: O-2,4-DICHLOROPHENYL O-METHYL ISOPROPYLPHOSPHORAMIDOTHIOATE: TOXIC. SINGLE DOSES IN CHICKENS PRODUCED DEATHS OVER A 7-DAY PERIOD WITH ASSOCIATED LETHARGY AND ATAXIA. SEE INFORMATION ON ORGANOPHOSPHATES.
ORGANOPHOSPHATES: CHOLINESTERASE INHIBITOR. **ACUTE EXPOSURE-** WHEN INGESTED, THE FIRST EFFECTS MAY BE NAUSEA, VOMITING, ANOREXIA, ABDOMINAL CRAMPS AND DIARRHEA. GASTROINTESTINAL ABSORPTION MAY CAUSE SYMPTOMS OF CHOLINESTERASE INHIBITION AS DESCRIBED IN ACUTE INHALATION. SYMPTOMS MAY BEGIN WITHIN MINUTES OR BE DELAYED FOR HOURS. DELAYED EFFECTS INCLUDING NEUROPATHY MAY ALSO OCCUR. **CHRONIC EXPOSURE-** REPEATED INGESTION MAY CAUSE EFFECTS AS DESCRIBED IN ACUTE EXPOSURE.
FIRST AID- IF PERSON IS ALERT AND RESPIRATION IS NOT DEPRESSED, GIVE SYRUP OF IPECAC FOLLOWED BY WATER (IF VOMITING OCCURS, KEEP HEAD BELOW HIPS TO PREVENT ASPIRATION). IF CONSCIOUSNESS LEVEL DECLINES OR VOMITING HAS NOT OCCURRED IN 15 MINUTES EMPTY STOMACH BY GASTRIC LAVAGE WITH THE AID OF CUFFED ENDOTRACHEAL TUBE USING ISOTONIC SALINE OR 5% SODIUM BICARBONATE FOLLOW WITH ACTIVATED CHARCOAL. ESTABLISH AND MAINTAIN AIRWAY. TREAT RESPIRATORY DIFFICULTY WITH ARTIFICIAL RESPIRATION AND OXYGEN. DO NOT GIVE MORPHINE, AMINOPHYLLINE, PHENOTHIAZINES, RESERPINE, FUROSEMIDE, OR ETHACRYNIC ACID (MORGAN, RECOGNITION AND MANAGEMENT OF PESTICIDE POISONINGS, 3RD ED.). TREAT SYMPTOMATICALLY AND SUPPORTIVELY. ADMINISTRATION OF OXYGEN AND LAVAGE MUST BE PERFORMED BY QUALIFIED MEDICAL PERSONNEL. GET MEDICAL ATTENTION IMMEDIATELY.
ANTIDOTE: THE FOLLOWING ANTIDOTE(S) HAVE BEEN RECOMMENDED. HOWEVER, THE DECISION AS TO WHETHER THE SEVERITY OF POISONING REQUIRES ADMINISTRATION OF ANY ANTIDOTE AND ACTUAL DOSE REQUIRED SHOULD BE MADE BY QUALIFIED MEDICAL PERSONNEL.
FOR CHOLINESTERASE INHIBITORS: ESTABLISH CLEAR AIRWAY AND TISSUE OXYGENATION BY ASPIRATION OF SECRETIONS, AND IF NECESSARY, BY ASSISTED PULMONARY VENTILATION WITH OXYGEN. IMPROVE TISSUE OXYGENATION AS MUCH AS POSSIBLE BEFORE ADMINISTERING ATROPINE TO MINIMIZE THE RISK OF VENTRICULAR FIBRILLATION. ADMINISTER ATROPINE SULFATE INTRAVENOUSLY, OR INTRAMUSCULARLY IF IV INJECTION IS NOT POSSIBLE. IN MODERATELY SEVERE POISONING ADMINISTER ATROPINE SULFATE, 0.4-2.0 MG REPEATED EVERY 15 MINUTES UNTIL ATROPINIZATION IS ACHIEVED (TACHYCARDIA, FLUSHING, DRY MOUTH, MYDRIASIS). MAINTAIN ATROPINIZATION BY REPEATED DOSES FOR 2-12 HOURS, OR LONGER, DEPENDING ON THE SEVERITY OF POISONING. THE APPEARANCE OF RALES IN THE LUNG BASES, MIOSIS, SALIVATION, NAUSEA, BRADYCARDIA, ARE ALL INDICATIONS OF INADEQUATE ATROPINIZATION. SEVERELY POISONED INDIVIDUALS MAY EXHIBIT REMARKABLE TOLERANCE TO ATROPINE; TWO OR MORE TIMES THE DOSAGES SUGGESTED ABOVE MAY BE NEEDED. PERSONS NOT POISONED OR ONLY SLIGHTLY POISONED, HOWEVER, MAY DEVELOP SIGNS OF ATROPINE TOXICITY FROM SUCH LARGE DOSAGES: FEVER, MUSCLE FIBRILLATIONS, AND DELIRIUM ARE THE MAIN SIGNS OF ATROPINE TOXICITY. IF THESE SIGNS APPEAR WHILE THE PATIENT IS FULLY ATROPINIZED, ATROPINE ADMINISTRATION SHOULD BE DISCONTINUED, AT LEAST TEMPORARILY. OBSERVE TREATED PATIENTS CLOSELY AT LEAST 24 HOURS TO INSURE THAT SYMPTOMS (POSSIBLY PULMONARY EDEMA) DO NOT RECUR AS ATROPINIZATION WEARS OFF. IN VERY SEVERE POISONINGS, METABOLIC DISPOSITION OF TOXICANT MAY REQUIRE SEVERAL HOURS OR DAYS DURING WHICH ATROPINIZATION MUST BE MAINTAINED. MARKEDLY LOWER LEVELS OF URINARY METABOLITES INDICATE THAT ATROPINE DOSAGE CAN BE TAPERED OFF. AS DOSAGE IS REDUCED, CHECK THE LUNG BASES FREQUENTLY FOR RALES. IF RALES ARE HEARD OR OTHER SYMPTOMS RETURN, RE-ESTABLISH ATROPINIZATION PROMPTLY (MORGAN, RECOGNITION AND MANAGEMENT OF PESTICIDE POISONINGS, 3RD ED.). ADMINISTRATION OF ANTIDOTE MUST BE PERFORMED BY QUALIFIED MEDICAL PERSONNEL.
IN CASES OF SEVERE POISONING BY ORGANOPHOSPHATE PESTICIDES IN WHICH RESPIRATORY DEPRESSION, MUSCLE WEAKNESS AND TWITCHINGS ARE SEVERE, GIVE PRALIDOXIME (PROTOPAM-AYERST, 2-PAM), 1.0 GRAM INTRAVENOUSLY AT NO MORE THAN 0.5 GRAM PER MINUTE. DOSAGE OF PRALIDOXIME MAY BE REPEATED IN 1-2 HOURS, THEN AT 10-12 HOUR INTERVALS IF NEEDED. IN VERY SEVERE POISONINGS, DOSAGE RATES MAY BE DOUBLED. TREATMENT WITH PRALIDOXIME WILL BE MOST EFFECTIVE IF GIVEN WITHIN THIRTY-SIX HOURS AFTER POISONING (MORGAN, RECOGNITION AND MANAGEMENT OF PESTICIDE POISONINGS, 3RD ED.). ANTIDOTE SHOULD BE ADMINISTERED BY QUALIFIED MEDICAL PERSONNEL.

REACTIVITY

REACTIVITY: STABLE UNDER NORMAL TEMPERATURES AND PRESSURES.
INCOMPATIBILITIES: O-2,4-DICHLOROPHENYL O-METHYL ISOPROPYLPHOSPHORAMIDOTHIOATE: OXIDIZERS (STRONG): FIRE AND EXPLOSION HAZARD.
DECOMPOSITION: THERMAL DECOMPOSITION PRODUCTS MAY INCLUDE TOXIC AND CORROSIVE FUMES OF CHLORIDES, AND TOXIC OXIDES OF PHOSPHORUS, NITROGEN AND SULFUR.
POLYMERIZATION: HAZARDOUS POLYMERIZATION HAS NOT BEEN REPORTED TO OCCUR UNDER NORMAL TEMPERATURES AND PRESSURES.

STORAGE AND DISPOSAL

OBSERVE ALL FEDERAL, STATE AND LOCAL REGULATIONS WHEN STORING OR DISPOSING OF THIS SUBSTANCE. FOR ASSISTANCE, CONTACT THE DISTRICT DIRECTOR OF THE ENVIRONMENTAL PROTECTION AGENCY.

STORAGE

STORE IN ACCORDANCE WITH 40 CFR 165 RECOMMENDED PROCEDURES FOR THE DISPOSAL AND STORAGE OF PESTICIDES AND PESTICIDE CONTAINERS.
STORE AWAY FROM INCOMPATIBLE SUBSTANCES.

DISPOSAL

DISPOSAL MUST BE IN ACCORDANCE WITH 40 CFR 165 RECOMMENDED PROCEDURES FOR THE DISPOSAL AND STORAGE OF PESTICIDES AND PESTICIDE CONTAINERS.

CONDITIONS TO AVOID

MAY BURN BUT DOES NOT IGNITE READILY. CONTAINERS MAY EXPLODE IN HEAT OF FIRE.

SPILL AND LEAK PROCEDURES

OCCUPATIONAL SPILL: DO NOT TOUCH SPILLED MATERIAL. STOP LEAK IF YOU CAN DO IT WITHOUT RISK. USE WATER SPRAY TO REDUCE VAPORS. FOR SMALL SPILLS, TAKE UP WITH SAND OR OTHER ABSORBENT MATERIAL AND PLACE INTO CONTAINERS FOR LATER DISPOSAL. FOR SMALL DRY SPILLS, WITH A CLEAN SHOVEL PLACE MATERIAL INTO CLEAN, DRY CONTAINERS AND COVER. MOVE CONTAINERS FROM SPILL AREA. FOR LARGER SPILLS, DIKE FAR AHEAD OF SPILL FOR LATER DISPOSAL. KEEP UNNECESSARY PEOPLE AWAY. ISOLATE HAZARD AREA AND DENY ENTRY. VENTILATE CLOSED SPACES BEFORE ENTERING.

PROTECTIVE EQUIPMENT

VENTILATION: PROVIDE LOCAL EXHAUST OR PROCESS ENCLOSURE VENTILATION SYSTEM.

RESPIRATOR: THE FOLLOWING RESPIRATORS ARE RECOMMENDED BASED ON INFORMATION FOUND IN THE PHYSICAL DATA, TOXICITY AND HEALTH EFFECTS SECTIONS. THEY ARE RANKED IN ORDER FROM MINIMUM TO MAXIMUM RESPIRATORY PROTECTION. THE SPECIFIC RESPIRATOR SELECTED MUST BE BASED ON CONTAMINATION LEVELS FOUND IN THE WORK PLACE, MUST NOT EXCEED THE WORKING LIMITS OF THE RESPIRATOR AND BE JOINTLY APPROVED BY THE NATIONAL INSTITUTE FOR OCCUPATIONAL SAFETY AND HEALTH AND THE MINE SAFETY AND HEALTH ADMINISTRATION (NIOSH-MSHA).
TYPE 'C' SUPPLIED-AIR RESPIRATOR WITH A FULL FACEPIECE OPERATED IN PRESSURE-DEMAND OR OTHER POSITIVE PRESSURE MODE OR WITH A FULL FACEPIECE, HELMET OR HOOD OPERATED IN CONTINOUS-FLOW MODE.
SELF-CONTAINED BREATHING APPARATUS WITH A FULL FACEPIECE OPERATED IN PRESSURE-DEMAND OR OTHER POSITIVE PRESSURE MODE.
FOR FIREFIGHTING AND OTHER IMMEDIATELY DANGEROUS TO LIFE OR HEALTH CONDITIONS:
SELF-CONTAINED BREATHING APPARATUS WITH FULL FACEPIECE OPERATED IN PRESSURE-DEMAND OR OTHER POSITIVE PRESSURE MODE.
SUPPLIED-AIR RESPIRATOR WITH FULL FACEPIECE AND OPERATED IN PRESSURE-DEMAND OR OTHER POSITIVE PRESSURE MODE IN COMBINATION WITH AN AUXILIARY SELF-CONTAINED BREATHING APPARATUS OPERATED IN PRESSURE-DEMAND OR OTHER POSITIVE PRESSURE MODE.

CLOTHING: EMPLOYEE MUST WEAR APPROPRIATE PROTECTIVE (IMPERVIOUS) CLOTHING AND EQUIPMENT TO PREVENT REPEATED OR PROLONGED SKIN CONTACT WITH THIS SUBSTANCE.

GLOVES: EMPLOYEE MUST WEAR APPROPRIATE PROTECTIVE GLOVES TO PREVENT CONTACT WITH THIS SUBSTANCE.

EYE PROTECTION: EMPLOYEE MUST WEAR SPLASH-PROOF OR DUST-RESISTANT SAFETY GOGGLES TO PREVENT EYE CONTACT WITH THIS SUBSTANCE.
EMERGENCY EYE WASH: WHERE THERE IS ANY POSSIBILITY THAT AN EMPLOYEE'S EYES MAY BE EXPOSED TO THIS SUBSTANCE, THE EMPLOYER SHOULD PROVIDE AN EYE WASH FOUNTAIN WITHIN THE IMMEDIATE WORK AREA FOR EMERGENCY USE.

AUTHORIZED BY- OCCUPATIONAL HEALTH SERVICES, INC.
CREATION DATE: 10/04/89 ***REVISION DATE:*** 04/27/90

MATERIAL SAFETY DATA SHEET

OCCUPATIONAL HEALTH SERVICES, INC.
AGRICULTURE AND PESTICIDE DIVISION
450 SEVENTH AVENUE, SUITE 2407
NEW YORK, NEW YORK 10123
1-800-445-MSDS OR (212) 967-1100

EMERGENCY CONTACT:
JOHN S. BRANSFORD, JR. (615) 292-1180

SUBSTANCE IDENTIFICATION

CAS-NUMBER 127-20-8

SUBSTANCE: **SODIUM DALAPON**

TRADE NAMES/SYNONYMS: PROPANOIC ACID, 2,2-DICHLORO-, SODIUM SALT; 2,2-DICHLOROPROPANOIC ACID SODIUM SALT; PROPIONIC ACID, 2,2-DICHLORO-, SODIUM SALT; 2,2-DICHLOROPROPIONIC ACID SODIUM SALT; ANTIGRAMIGNA; DALAPON SODIUM; DALAPON SODIUM SALT; DOWPON; PROPINATE; SODIUM DICHLOROPROPIONATE; SODIUM ALPHA, ALPHA-DICHLOROPROPIONATE; SODIUM 2,2-DICHLOROPROPIONATE; SODIUM 2,2-DICHLOROPROPIONIC ACID; TAFAPON; DALAPON-SODIUM; C3H3CL2NAO2; PST71239

CHEMICAL FAMILY: SALT

MOLECULAR FORMULA: C3-H3-CL2-NA-O2

MOLECULAR WEIGHT: 165.0

CERCLA RATINGS (SCALE 0-3): HEALTH=U FIRE=1 REACTIVITY=0 PERSISTENCE=3

NFPA RATINGS (SCALE 0-4): HEALTH=U FIRE=1 REACTIVITY=0

COMPONENTS AND CONTAMINANTS

COMPONENT: SODIUM DALAPON ***PERCENT:*** 100.0
CAS# 127-20-8

OTHER CONTAMINANTS: NONE

EXPOSURE LIMITS: NO OCCUPATIONAL EXPOSURE LIMITS ESTABLISHED BY OSHA, ACGIH, OR NIOSH.

PHYSICAL DATA

DESCRIPTION: HYGROSCOPIC CRYSTALLINE POWDER.

MELTING POINT: NOT AVAILABLE

SPECIFIC GRAVITY: NOT AVAILABLE ***SOLUBILITY IN WATER:*** 45%

SOLVENT SOLUBILITY: SOLUBLE IN ETHANOL, METHANOL; SLIGHTLY SOLUBLE IN ACETONE; VERY SLIGHTLY SOLUBLE IN BENZENE, ETHER.
DECOMPOSES WITHOUT MELTING @ 333 F (167 C)

FIRE AND EXPLOSION DATA

FIRE AND EXPLOSION HAZARD: SLIGHT FIRE HAZARD WHEN EXPOSED TO HEAT OR FLAME.

FIREFIGHTING MEDIA: DRY CHEMICAL, CARBON DIOXIDE, HALON, WATER SPRAY OR STANDARD FOAM (1987 EMERGENCY RESPONSE GUIDEBOOK, DOT P 5800.4).
FOR LARGER FIRES, USE WATER SPRAY, FOG OR STANDARD FOAM (1987 EMERGENCY RESPONSE GUIDEBOOK, DOT P 5800.4).

FIREFIGHTING: MOVE CONTAINER FROM FIRE AREA IF POSSIBLE. DO NOT SCATTER SPILLED MATERIAL WITH HIGH PRESSURE WATER STREAMS. DIKE FIRE CONTROL WATER FOR LATER DISPOSAL (1987 EMERGENCY RESPONSE GUIDEBOOK, DOT P 5800.4, GUIDE PAGE 31).
USE AGENTS SUITABLE FOR TYPE OF SURROUNDING FIRE. AVOID BREATHING HAZARDOUS VAPORS, KEEP UPWIND.

TOXICITY

SODIUM DALAPON: TOXICITY DATA: 3860 MG/KG ORAL-RAT LD50; 3400 MG/KG ORAL-RABBIT LD50; 3400 MG/KG ORAL-GUINEA PIG LD50; 4 GM/KG ORAL-MAMMAL LD50; 3650 MG/KG UNREPORTED-MOUSE LD50; 6600 MG/KG UNREPORTED-MAMMAL LD50; MUTAGENIC DATA (RTECS). CARCINOGEN STATUS: NONE. LOCAL EFFECTS: IRRITANT- EYE, SKIN. ACUTE TOXICITY LEVEL: MODERATELY TOXIC BY INGESTION. TARGET EFFECTS: POISONING MAY AFFECT THE LIVER, KIDNEYS, THYROID, AND PITUITARY.

HEALTH EFFECTS AND FIRST AID

INHALATION: SODIUM DALAPON: **ACUTE EXPOSURE-** MAY CAUSE IRRITATION OF THE RESPIRATORY TRACT. IF SUFFICIENT AMOUNTS ARE ABSORBED, SYSTEMIC EFFECTS MAY INCLUDE LETHARGY, GASTROINTESTINAL TRACT DISTURBANCES WITH VOMITING AND DIARRHEA, ANOREXIA, DEPRESSION, UNBALANCED GAIT, BRADYCARDIA, KIDNEY AND LIVER CHANGES, AND THYROID AND PITUITARY DYSFUNCTION. **CHRONIC EXPOSURE-** REPEATED OR PROLONGED EXPOSURE MAY CAUSE LIVER AND KIDNEY CHANGES.

FIRST AID- REMOVE FROM EXPOSURE AREA TO FRESH AIR IMMEDIATELY. IF BREATHING HAS STOPPED, PERFORM ARTIFICIAL RESPIRATION. KEEP PERSON WARM AND AT REST. TREAT SYMPTOMATICALLY AND SUPPORTIVELY. GET MEDICAL ATTENTION IMMEDIATELY.

SKIN CONTACT: SODIUM DALAPON: IRRITANT. **ACUTE EXPOSURE-** MAY CAUSE CONTACT DERMATITIS. DIRECT CONTACT WITH DUST WHILE SWEATING MAY CAUSE A MILD BURNING SENSATION. **CHRONIC EXPOSURE-** REPEATED OR PROLONGED CONTACT MAY CAUSE DERMATITIS.

FIRST AID- REMOVE CONTAMINATED CLOTHING AND SHOES IMMEDIATELY. WASH AFFECTED AREA WITH SOAP OR MILD DETERGENT AND LARGE AMOUNTS OF WATER UNTIL NO EVIDENCE OF CHEMICAL REMAINS (APPROXIMATELY 15-20 MINUTES). GET MEDICAL ATTENTION IMMEDIATELY.

EYE CONTACT: SODIUM DALAPON: IRRITANT. **ACUTE EXPOSURE-** DIRECT CONTACT WITH SOLID FORM OR CONCENTRATED LIQUID MAY CAUSE IRRITATION AND PAIN, BUT SERIOUS DAMAGE IS NOT LIKELY. **CHRONIC EXPOSURE-** REPEATED OR PROLONGED EXPOSURE TO IRRITANTS MAY CAUSE CONJUNCTIVITIS.

FIRST AID- WASH EYES IMMEDIATELY WITH LARGE AMOUNTS OF WATER OR NORMAL SALINE, OCCASIONALLY LIFTING UPPER AND LOWER LIDS, UNTIL NO EVIDENCE OF CHEMICAL REMAINS (APPROXIMATELY 15-20 MINUTES). GET MEDICAL ATTENTION IMMEDIATELY.

INGESTION: SODIUM DALAPON: **ACUTE EXPOSURE-** INGESTION MAY CAUSE GASTROINTESTINAL TRACT DISTURBANCES WITH VOMITING AND DIARRHEA. IF SUFFICIENT AMOUNTS ARE ABSORBED, SYSTEMIC EFFECTS MAY INCLUDE LETHARGY, ANOREXIA, DEPRESSION, UNBALANCED GAIT, BRADYCARDIA, KIDNEY AND LIVER CHANGES, AND THYROID AND PITUITARY DYSFUNCTION. **CHRONIC EXPOSURE-** PROLONGED INGESTION OF 50 MG/KG/DAY PRODUCED NO LESIONS EXCEPT INCREASED KIDNEY WEIGHTS IN DOGS AND CATS.

FIRST AID- REMOVE BY GASTRIC LAVAGE AND CATHARSIS. MAINTAIN BLOOD PRESSURE AND AIRWAY. GIVE OXYGEN IF RESPIRATION IS DEPRESSED. DO NOT PERFORM GASTRIC LAVAGE IF VICTIM IS UNCONSCIOUS. GET MEDICAL ATTENTION IMMEDIATELY (DREISBACH, HANDBOOK OF POISONING, 12TH ED.).
ADMINISTRATION OF LAVAGE OR OXYGEN SHOULD BE PERFORMED BY QUALIFIED MEDICAL PERSONNEL.

ANTIDOTE: NO SPECIFIC ANTIDOTE. TREAT SYMPTOMATICALLY AND SUPPORTIVELY.

REACTIVITY

REACTIVITY: STABLE UNDER NORMAL TEMPERATURES AND PRESSURES.

INCOMPATIBILITIES: SODIUM DALAPON: IRON: CORRODES IN THE PRESENCE OF MOISTURE. OXIDIZERS (STRONG): FIRE AND EXPLOSION HAZARD.

DECOMPOSITION: THERMAL DECOMPOSITION PRODUCTS MAY INCLUDE TOXIC AND CORROSIVE FUMES OF CHLORIDES AND TOXIC OXIDES OF CARBON.

POLYMERIZATION: HAZARDOUS POLYMERIZATION HAS NOT BEEN REPORTED TO OCCUR UNDER NORMAL TEMPERATURES AND PRESSURES.

STORAGE AND DISPOSAL

OBSERVE ALL FEDERAL, STATE AND LOCAL REGULATIONS WHEN STORING OR DISPOSING OF THIS SUBSTANCE. FOR ASSISTANCE, CONTACT THE DISTRICT DIRECTOR OF THE ENVIRONMENTAL PROTECTION AGENCY.

****STORAGE****

STORE IN ACCORDANCE WITH 40 CFR 165 RECOMMENDED PROCEDURES FOR THE DISPOSAL AND STORAGE OF PESTICIDES AND PESTICIDE CONTAINERS.
STORE AWAY FROM INCOMPATIBLE SUBSTANCES.

****DISPOSAL****

DISPOSAL MUST BE IN ACCORDANCE WITH 40 CFR 165 RECOMMENDED PROCEDURES FOR THE DISPOSAL AND STORAGE OF PESTICIDES AND PESTICIDE CONTAINERS.

CONDITIONS TO AVOID

MAY BURN BUT DOES NOT IGNITE READILY. AVOID CONTACT WITH STRONG OXIDIZERS, EXCESSIVE HEAT, SPARKS, OR OPEN FLAME.

SPILL AND LEAK PROCEDURES

OCCUPATIONAL SPILL: SWEEP UP AND PLACE IN SUITABLE CLEAN, DRY CONTAINERS FOR RECLAMATION OR LATER DISPOSAL. DO NOT FLUSH SPILLED MATERIAL INTO SEWER. KEEP UNNECESSARY PEOPLE AWAY.

PROTECTIVE EQUIPMENT

VENTILATION: PROVIDE LOCAL EXHAUST OR GENERAL DILUTION VENTILATION SYSTEM.

RESPIRATOR: THE FOLLOWING RESPIRATORS ARE RECOMMENDED BASED ON INFORMATION FOUND IN THE PHYSICAL DATA, TOXICITY AND HEALTH EFFECTS SECTIONS. THEY ARE RANKED IN ORDER FROM MINIMUM TO MAXIMUM RESPIRATORY PROTECTION. THE SPECIFIC RESPIRATOR SELECTED MUST BE BASED ON CONTAMINATION LEVELS FOUND IN THE WORK PLACE, MUST NOT EXCEED THE WORKING LIMITS OF THE RESPIRATOR AND BE JOINTLY APPROVED BY THE NATIONAL INSTITUTE FOR OCCUPATIONAL SAFETY AND HEALTH AND THE MINE SAFETY AND HEALTH ADMINISTRATION (NIOSH-MSHA).
CHEMICAL CARTRIDGE RESPIRATOR WITH AN ORGANIC VAPOR CARTRIDGE(S) WITH A FULL FACEPIECE AND ORGANIC VAPOR CARTRIDGE(S) IN COMBINATION WITH A DUST AND MIST FILTER.
POWERED AIR-PURIFYING RESPIRATOR WITH A TIGHT-FITTING FACEPIECE AND ORGANIC VAPOR CARTRIDGE(S) IN COMBINATION WITH A HIGH-EFFICIENCY PARTICULATE FILTER.
TYPE 'C' SUPPLIED-AIR RESPIRATOR WITH A FULL FACEPIECE OPERATED IN A PRESSURE-DEMAND OR OTHER POSITIVE PRESSURE MODE.
SELF-CONTAINED BREATHING APPARATUS WITH A FULL FACEPIECE OPERATED IN PRESSURE-DEMAND OR OTHER POSITIVE PRESSURE MODE.
FOR FIREFIGHTING AND OTHER IMMEDIATELY DANGEROUS TO LIFE OR HEALTH CONDITIONS:
SELF-CONTAINED BREATHING APPARATUS WITH FULL FACEPIECE OPERATED IN PRESSURE-DEMAND OR OTHER POSITIVE PRESSURE MODE.
SUPPLIED-AIR RESPIRATOR WITH FULL FACEPIECE AND OPERATED IN PRESSURE-DEMAND OR OTHER POSITIVE PRESSURE MODE IN COMBINATION WITH AN AUXILIARY SELF-CONTAINED BREATHING APPARATUS OPERATED IN PRESSURE-DEMAND OR OTHER POSITIVE PRESSURE MODE.

CLOTHING: EMPLOYEE MUST WEAR APPROPRIATE PROTECTIVE (IMPERVIOUS) CLOTHING AND EQUIPMENT TO PREVENT REPEATED OR PROLONGED SKIN CONTACT WITH THIS SUBSTANCE.

GLOVES: EMPLOYEE MUST WEAR APPROPRIATE PROTECTIVE GLOVES TO PREVENT CONTACT WITH THIS SUBSTANCE.

EYE PROTECTION: EMPLOYEE MUST WEAR SPLASH-PROOF OR DUST-RESISTANT SAFETY GOGGLES TO PREVENT EYE CONTACT WITH THIS SUBSTANCE.
EMERGENCY EYE WASH: WHERE THERE IS ANY POSSIBILITY THAT AN EMPLOYEE'S EYES MAY BE EXPOSED TO THIS SUBSTANCE, THE EMPLOYER SHOULD PROVIDE AN EYE WASH FOUNTAIN WITHIN THE IMMEDIATE WORK AREA FOR EMERGENCY USE.

AUTHORIZED BY- OCCUPATIONAL HEALTH SERVICES, INC.
CREATION DATE: 10/05/89 ***REVISION DATE:*** 05/31/90

MATERIAL SAFETY DATA SHEET

OCCUPATIONAL HEALTH SERVICES, INC.
AGRICULTURE AND PESTICIDE DIVISION
450 SEVENTH AVENUE, SUITE 2407
NEW YORK, NEW YORK 10123
1-800-445-MSDS OR (212) 967-1100

EMERGENCY CONTACT:
JOHN S. BRANSFORD, JR. (615) 292-1180

SUBSTANCE IDENTIFICATION

CAS-NUMBER 1982-69-0

SUBSTANCE: **SODIUM DICAMBA**

TRADE NAMES/SYNONYMS: BENZOIC ACID, 3,6-DICHLORO-2-METHOXY-, SODIUM SALT; 3,6-DICHLORO-2-METHOXYBENZOIC ACID SODIUM SALT; O-ANISIC ACID, 3,6-DICHLORO-, SODIUM SALT; 3,6-DICHLORO-O-ANISIC ACID SODIUM SALT; DICAMBA SODIUM SALT; C8H5CL2NAO3; PST71250

CHEMICAL FAMILY: CARBOXYLIC ACID, AROMATIC SALT

MOLECULAR FORMULA: C8-H5-CL2-O3.NA

MOLECULAR WEIGHT: 243.0

CERCLA RATINGS (SCALE 0-3): HEALTH=U FIRE=1 REACTIVITY=0 PERSISTENCE=1

NFPA RATINGS (SCALE 0-4): HEALTH=U FIRE=1 REACTIVITY=0

COMPONENTS AND CONTAMINANTS

COMPONENT: SODIUM DICAMBA ***PERCENT:*** 100.0
CAS# 1982-69-0

OTHER CONTAMINANTS: NONE

EXPOSURE LIMITS: NO OCCUPATIONAL EXPOSURE LIMITS ESTABLISHED BY OSHA, ACGIH, OR NIOSH.

PHYSICAL DATA

DESCRIPTION: CRYSTALLINE SOLID. ***MELTING POINT:*** NOT AVAILABLE
SPECIFIC GRAVITY: NOT AVAILABLE ***SOLUBILITY IN WATER:*** 36%

FIRE AND EXPLOSION DATA

FIRE AND EXPLOSION HAZARD: SLIGHT FIRE HAZARD WHEN EXPOSED TO HEAT OR FLAME.

FIREFIGHTING MEDIA: DRY CHEMICAL, CARBON DIOXIDE, HALON, WATER SPRAY OR STANDARD FOAM (1987 EMERGENCY RESPONSE GUIDEBOOK, DOT P 5800.4).
FOR LARGER FIRES, USE WATER SPRAY, FOG OR STANDARD FOAM (1987 EMERGENCY RESPONSE GUIDEBOOK, DOT P 5800.4).

FIREFIGHTING: MOVE CONTAINER FROM FIRE AREA IF POSSIBLE. DO NOT SCATTER SPILLED MATERIAL WITH HIGH PRESSURE WATER STREAMS. DIKE FIRE CONTROL WATER FOR LATER DISPOSAL (1987 EMERGENCY RESPONSE GUIDEBOOK, DOT P 5800.4, GUIDE PAGE 31).
USE AGENTS SUITABLE FOR TYPE OF SURROUNDING FIRE. AVOID BREATHING HAZARDOUS VAPORS, KEEP UPWIND.

TOXICITY

SODIUM DICAMBA: CARCINOGEN STATUS: NONE. ACUTE TOXICITY LEVEL: NO DATA AVAILABLE. TARGET EFFECTS: NO DATA AVAILABLE.

HEALTH EFFECTS AND FIRST AID

INHALATION: SODIUM DICAMBA: **ACUTE EXPOSURE**- NO DATA AVAILABLE. **CHRONIC EXPOSURE**- NO DATA AVAILABLE.

FIRST AID- REMOVE FROM EXPOSURE AREA TO FRESH AIR IMMEDIATELY. IF BREATHING HAS STOPPED, PERFORM ARTIFICIAL RESPIRATION. KEEP PERSON WARM AND AT REST. TREAT SYMPTOMATICALLY AND SUPPORTIVELY. GET MEDICAL ATTENTION IMMEDIATELY.

SKIN CONTACT: SODIUM DICAMBA: **ACUTE EXPOSURE**- NO SPECIFIC DATA AVAILABLE. DICAMBA CAUSED MILD IRRITATION TO RABBIT SKIN. **CHRONIC EXPOSURE**- NO DATA AVAILABLE.

FIRST AID- REMOVE CONTAMINATED CLOTHING AND SHOES IMMEDIATELY. WASH AFFECTED AREA WITH SOAP OR MILD DETERGENT AND LARGE AMOUNTS OF WATER UNTIL NO EVIDENCE OF CHEMICAL REMAINS (APPROXIMATELY 15-20 MINUTES). GET MEDICAL ATTENTION IMMEDIATELY.

EYE CONTACT: SODIUM DICAMBA: **ACUTE EXPOSURE**- NO DATA AVAILABLE. **CHRONIC EXPOSURE**- NO DATA AVAILABLE.

FIRST AID- WASH EYES IMMEDIATELY WITH LARGE AMOUNTS OF WATER OR NORMAL SALINE, OCCASIONALLY LIFTING UPPER AND LOWER LIDS, UNTIL NO EVIDENCE OF CHEMICAL REMAINS (APPROXIMATELY 15-20 MINUTES). GET MEDICAL ATTENTION IMMEDIATELY.

INGESTION: SODIUM DICAMBA: **ACUTE EXPOSURE**- INGESTION OF DICAMBA CAUSED MYOTONIC MUSCULAR SPASMS, URINARY INCONTINENCE, DYSPNEA, EXHAUSTION, CYANOSIS, AND DEATH IN RATS. MINOR LUNG HEMORRHAGES WERE NOTED IN SOME ANIMALS. **CHRONIC EXPOSURE**- NO SPECIFIC DATA AVAILABLE. ANIMAL STUDIES INDICATE DICAMBA SALTS MAY PRODUCE HEPATIC NECROSIS.

FIRST AID- TREAT SYMPTOMATICALLY AND SUPPORTIVELY. GET MEDICAL ATTENTION IMMEDIATELY. IF VOMITING OCCURS, KEEP HEAD LOWER THAN HIPS TO PREVENT ASPIRATION.

ANTIDOTE: NO SPECIFIC ANTIDOTE. TREAT SYMPTOMATICALLY AND SUPPORTIVELY.

REACTIVITY

REACTIVITY: STABLE UNDER NORMAL TEMPERATURES AND PRESSURES.

INCOMPATIBILITIES: SODIUM DICAMBA: OXIDIZERS (STRONG): FIRE AND EXPLOSION HAZARD.

DECOMPOSITION: THERMAL DECOMPOSITION PRODUCTS MAY INCLUDE TOXIC AND CORROSIVE FUMES OF CHLORIDES AND TOXIC OXIDES OF CARBON.

POLYMERIZATION: HAZARDOUS POLYMERIZATION HAS NOT BEEN REPORTED TO OCCUR UNDER NORMAL TEMPERATURES AND PRESSURES.

STORAGE AND DISPOSAL

OBSERVE ALL FEDERAL, STATE AND LOCAL REGULATIONS WHEN STORING OR DISPOSING OF THIS SUBSTANCE. FOR ASSISTANCE, CONTACT THE DISTRICT DIRECTOR OF THE ENVIRONMENTAL PROTECTION AGENCY.

****STORAGE****

STORE IN ACCORDANCE WITH 40 CFR 165 RECOMMENDED PROCEDURES FOR THE DISPOSAL AND STORAGE OF PESTICIDES AND PESTICIDE CONTAINERS.
STORE AWAY FROM INCOMPATIBLE SUBSTANCES.

****DISPOSAL****

DISPOSAL MUST BE IN ACCORDANCE WITH 40 CFR 165 RECOMMENDED PROCEDURES FOR THE DISPOSAL AND STORAGE OF PESTICIDES AND PESTICIDE CONTAINERS.

CONDITIONS TO AVOID

MAY BURN BUT DOES NOT IGNITE READILY. AVOID CONTACT WITH STRONG OXIDIZERS, EXCESSIVE HEAT, SPARKS, OR OPEN FLAME.

SPILL AND LEAK PROCEDURES

OCCUPATIONAL SPILL: SWEEP UP AND PLACE IN SUITABLE CLEAN, DRY CONTAINERS FOR RECLAMATION OR LATER DISPOSAL. DO NOT FLUSH SPILLED MATERIAL INTO SEWER. KEEP UNNECESSARY PEOPLE AWAY.

PROTECTIVE EQUIPMENT

VENTILATION: PROVIDE LOCAL EXHAUST OR PROCESS ENCLOSURE VENTILATION SYSTEM.

RESPIRATOR: THE FOLLOWING RESPIRATORS ARE RECOMMENDED BASED ON INFORMATION FOUND IN THE PHYSICAL DATA, TOXICITY AND HEALTH EFFECTS SECTIONS. THEY ARE RANKED IN ORDER FROM MINIMUM TO MAXIMUM RESPIRATORY PROTECTION. THE SPECIFIC RESPIRATOR SELECTED MUST BE BASED ON CONTAMINATION LEVELS FOUND IN THE WORK PLACE, MUST NOT EXCEED THE WORKING LIMITS OF THE RESPIRATOR AND BE JOINTLY APPROVED BY THE NATIONAL INSTITUTE FOR OCCUPATIONAL SAFETY AND HEALTH AND THE MINE SAFETY AND HEALTH ADMINISTRATION (NIOSH-MSHA).

CHEMICAL CARTRIDGE RESPIRATOR WITH AN ORGANIC VAPOR CARTRIDGE(S) WITH A FULL FACEPIECE AND ORGANIC VAPOR CARTRIDGE(S) IN COMBINATION WITH A DUST AND MIST FILTER.

POWERED AIR-PURIFYING RESPIRATOR WITH A TIGHT-FITTING FACEPIECE AND ORGANIC VAPOR CARTRIDGE(S) IN COMBINATION WITH A HIGH-EFFICIENCY PARTICULATE FILTER.

TYPE 'C' SUPPLIED-AIR RESPIRATOR WITH A FULL FACEPIECE OPERATED IN A PRESSURE-DEMAND OR OTHER POSITIVE PRESSURE MODE.

SELF-CONTAINED BREATHING APPARATUS WITH A FULL FACEPIECE OPERATED IN PRESSURE-DEMAND OR OTHER POSITIVE PRESSURE MODE.

FOR FIREFIGHTING AND OTHER IMMEDIATELY DANGEROUS TO LIFE OR HEALTH CONDITIONS:

SELF-CONTAINED BREATHING APPARATUS WITH FULL FACEPIECE OPERATED IN PRESSURE-DEMAND OR OTHER POSITIVE PRESSURE MODE.

SUPPLIED-AIR RESPIRATOR WITH FULL FACEPIECE AND OPERATED IN PRESSURE-DEMAND OR OTHER POSITIVE PRESSURE MODE IN COMBINATION WITH AN AUXILIARY SELF-CONTAINED BREATHING APPARATUS OPERATED IN PRESSURE-DEMAND OR OTHER POSITIVE PRESSURE MODE.

CLOTHING: EMPLOYEE MUST WEAR APPROPRIATE PROTECTIVE (IMPERVIOUS) CLOTHING AND EQUIPMENT TO PREVENT REPEATED OR PROLONGED SKIN CONTACT WITH THIS SUBSTANCE.

GLOVES: EMPLOYEE MUST WEAR APPROPRIATE PROTECTIVE GLOVES TO PREVENT CONTACT WITH THIS SUBSTANCE.

EYE PROTECTION: EMPLOYEE MUST WEAR SPLASH-PROOF OR DUST-RESISTANT SAFETY GOGGLES TO PREVENT EYE CONTACT WITH THIS SUBSTANCE.
EMERGENCY EYE WASH: WHERE THERE IS ANY POSSIBILITY THAT AN EMPLOYEE'S EYES MAY BE EXPOSED TO THIS SUBSTANCE, THE EMPLOYER SHOULD PROVIDE AN EYE WASH FOUNTAIN WITHIN THE IMMEDIATE WORK AREA FOR EMERGENCY USE.

AUTHORIZED BY- OCCUPATIONAL HEALTH SERVICES, INC.
CREATION DATE: 10/05/89 ***REVISION DATE:*** 05/31/90

MATERIAL SAFETY DATA SHEET

OCCUPATIONAL HEALTH SERVICES, INC.
AGRICULTURE AND PESTICIDE DIVISION
450 SEVENTH AVENUE, SUITE 2407
NEW YORK, NEW YORK 10123
1-800-445-MSDS OR (212) 967-1100

EMERGENCY CONTACT:
JOHN S. BRANSFORD, JR. (615) 292-1180

SUBSTANCE IDENTIFICATION

CAS-NUMBER 1076-46-6

SUBSTANCE: **CHLORAMBEN AMMONIUM SALT**

TRADE NAMES/SYNONYMS: BENZOIC ACID, 3-AMINO-2,5-DICHLORO-, MONOAMMONIUM SALT; 3-AMINO-2,5-DICHLOROBENZOIC ACID, MONOAMMONIUM SALT; AMMONIUM 3-AMINO-2,5-DICHLOROBENZOATE; AMIBEN AMMONIUM SALT; C7H8CL2N2O2; PST71252

CHEMICAL FAMILY: CARBOXYLIC ACID, AROMATIC, SALT
HALOGEN
AMINE

MOLECULAR FORMULA: (CL2)-(H2-N)-C6-H2-C-O2.(N-H4)

MOLECULAR WEIGHT: 223.07

CERCLA RATINGS (SCALE 0-3): HEALTH=U FIRE=1 REACTIVITY=0 PERSISTENCE=1

NFPA RATINGS (SCALE 0-4): HEALTH=U FIRE=1 REACTIVITY=0

COMPONENTS AND CONTAMINANTS

COMPONENT: CHLORAMBEN AMMONIUM SALT ***PERCENT:*** 100.0
CAS# 1076-46-6

OTHER CONTAMINANTS: NONE

EXPOSURE LIMITS: NO OCCUPATIONAL EXPOSURE LIMITS ESTABLISHED BY OSHA, ACGIH, OR NIOSH.

PHYSICAL DATA

DESCRIPTION: SOLID. ***MELTING POINT:*** 381-387 F (194-197 C)

SPECIFIC GRAVITY: NOT AVAILABLE ***SOLUBILITY IN WATER:*** 30 %

SOLVENT SOLUBILITY: MODERATELY SOLUBLE IN ETHANOL, ISOPROPANOL.

FIRE AND EXPLOSION DATA

FIRE AND EXPLOSION HAZARD: SLIGHT FIRE HAZARD WHEN EXPOSED TO HEAT OR FLAME. DUST-AIR MIXTURES MAY IGNITE OR EXPLODE.

FIREFIGHTING MEDIA: DRY CHEMICAL, CARBON DIOXIDE, HALON, WATER SPRAY OR STANDARD FOAM (1987 EMERGENCY RESPONSE GUIDEBOOK, DOT P 5800.4).
FOR LARGER FIRES, USE WATER SPRAY, FOG OR STANDARD FOAM (1987 EMERGENCY RESPONSE GUIDEBOOK, DOT P 5800.4).

FIREFIGHTING: MOVE CONTAINER FROM FIRE AREA IF POSSIBLE. DO NOT SCATTER SPILLED MATERIAL WITH HIGH PRESSURE WATER STREAMS. DIKE FIRE CONTROL WATER FOR LATER DISPOSAL (1987 EMERGENCY RESPONSE GUIDEBOOK, DOT P 5800.4, GUIDE PAGE 31).
USE AGENTS SUITABLE FOR TYPE OF SURROUNDING FIRE. AVOID BREATHING HAZARDOUS VAPORS, KEEP UPWIND.

TOXICITY

CHLORAMBEN AMMONIUM SALT: CARCINOGEN STATUS: NONE. ACUTE TOXICITY LEVEL: NO DATA AVAILABLE. TARGET EFFECTS: NO DATA AVAILABLE.

HEALTH EFFECTS AND FIRST AID

INHALATION: CHLORAMBEN AMMONIUM SALT: **ACUTE EXPOSURE-** NO DATA AVAILABLE. **CHRONIC EXPOSURE-** NO DATA AVAILABLE.

FIRST AID- REMOVE FROM EXPOSURE AREA TO FRESH AIR IMMEDIATELY. IF BREATHING HAS STOPPED, PERFORM ARTIFICIAL RESPIRATION. KEEP PERSON WARM AND AT REST. TREAT SYMPTOMATICALLY AND SUPPORTIVELY. GET MEDICAL ATTENTION IMMEDIATELY.

SKIN CONTACT: CHLORAMBEN AMMONIUM SALT: **ACUTE EXPOSURE-** NO DATA AVAILABLE. **CHRONIC EXPOSURE-** NO DATA AVAILABLE.

FIRST AID- REMOVE CONTAMINATED CLOTHING AND SHOES IMMEDIATELY. WASH AFFECTED AREA WITH SOAP OR MILD DETERGENT AND LARGE AMOUNTS OF WATER UNTIL NO EVIDENCE OF CHEMICAL REMAINS (APPROXIMATELY 15-20 MINUTES). GET MEDICAL ATTENTION IMMEDIATELY.

EYE CONTACT: CHLORAMBEN AMMONIUM SALT: **ACUTE EXPOSURE-** NO DATA AVAILABLE. **CHRONIC EXPOSURE-** NO DATA AVAILABLE.

FIRST AID- WASH EYES IMMEDIATELY WITH LARGE AMOUNTS OF WATER OR NORMAL SALINE, OCCASIONALLY LIFTING UPPER AND LOWER LIDS, UNTIL NO EVIDENCE OF CHEMICAL REMAINS (APPROXIMATELY 15-20 MINUTES). GET MEDICAL ATTENTION IMMEDIATELY.

INGESTION: CHLORAMBEN AMMONIUM SALT: **ACUTE EXPOSURE-** SYMPTOMS OF POISONING FROM DOSES UP TO 21.5 ML/KG INCLUDED DEPRESSION, GASPING, LABORED RESPIRATION, ATAXIA, SPRAWLING OF THE LIMBS, DEPRESSED RIGHTING AND PLACEMENT REFLEXES, AND MUSCULAR STIFFNESS. CONGESTION OF THE LUNGS, KIDNEYS, ADRENAL, AND PANCREAS; PALE APPEARING SPLEEN; AND INFLAMMATION OF THE DIAPHRAGM, PERITONEUM, AND PYLORIC PORTION OF THE STOMACH WAS OBSERVED AT NECROPSY. **CHRONIC EXPOSURE-** CHLORAMBEN PRODUCED HEPATOCELLULAR ALTERATIONS IN DOGS AND MICE. AN INCREASED INCIDENCE OF HEPATOCELLULAR CARCINOMA IN FEMALES WAS OBSERVED IN AN ONCOGENIC STUDY OF MICE RECEIVING CHLORAMBEN. INCREASED FETAL MORTALITY AND DECREASED FETAL SKELETAL DEVELOPMENT WAS OBSERVED IN A STUDY OF PREGNANT RATS FED CHLORAMBEN.

FIRST AID- TREAT SYMPTOMATICALLY AND SUPPORTIVELY. GET MEDICAL ATTENTION IMMEDIATELY. IF VOMITING OCCURS, KEEP HEAD LOWER THAN HIPS TO PREVENT ASPIRATION.

ANTIDOTE: NO SPECIFIC ANTIDOTE. TREAT SYMPTOMATICALLY AND SUPPORTIVELY.

REACTIVITY

REACTIVITY: STABLE UNDER NORMAL TEMPERATURES AND PRESSURES.

INCOMPATIBILITIES: CHLORAMBEN AMMONIUM SALT: OXIDIZERS (STRONG): FIRE AND EXPLOSION HAZARD.

DECOMPOSITION: THERMAL DECOMPOSITION PRODUCTS MAY INCLUDE TOXIC OXIDES OF NITROGEN AND CARBON AND TOXIC AND CORROSIVE FUMES OF CHLORIDES.

POLYMERIZATION: HAZARDOUS POLYMERIZATION HAS NOT BEEN REPORTED TO OCCUR UNDER NORMAL TEMPERATURES AND PRESSURES.

STORAGE AND DISPOSAL

OBSERVE ALL FEDERAL, STATE AND LOCAL REGULATIONS WHEN STORING OR DISPOSING OF THIS SUBSTANCE. FOR ASSISTANCE, CONTACT THE DISTRICT DIRECTOR OF THE ENVIRONMENTAL PROTECTION AGENCY.

****STORAGE****

STORE IN ACCORDANCE WITH 40 CFR 165 RECOMMENDED PROCEDURES FOR THE DISPOSAL AND STORAGE OF PESTICIDES AND PESTICIDE CONTAINERS.
STORE AWAY FROM INCOMPATIBLE SUBSTANCES.

****DISPOSAL****

DISPOSAL MUST BE IN ACCORDANCE WITH 40 CFR 165 RECOMMENDED PROCEDURES FOR THE DISPOSAL AND STORAGE OF PESTICIDES AND PESTICIDE CONTAINERS.

CONDITIONS TO AVOID

MAY BURN BUT DOES NOT IGNITE READILY. AVOID CONTACT WITH STRONG OXIDIZERS, EXCESSIVE HEAT, SPARKS, OR OPEN FLAME.

SPILL AND LEAK PROCEDURES

OCCUPATIONAL SPILL: SWEEP UP AND PLACE IN SUITABLE CLEAN, DRY CONTAINERS FOR RECLAMATION OR LATER DISPOSAL. DO NOT FLUSH SPILLED MATERIAL INTO SEWER. KEEP UNNECESSARY PEOPLE AWAY.

PROTECTIVE EQUIPMENT

VENTILATION: PROVIDE LOCAL EXHAUST OR GENERAL DILUTION VENTILATION SYSTEM.

RESPIRATOR: THE FOLLOWING RESPIRATORS ARE RECOMMENDED BASED ON INFORMATION FOUND IN THE PHYSICAL DATA, TOXICITY AND HEALTH EFFECTS SECTIONS. THEY ARE RANKED IN ORDER FROM MINIMUM TO MAXIMUM RESPIRATORY PROTECTION. THE SPECIFIC RESPIRATOR SELECTED MUST BE BASED ON CONTAMINATION LEVELS FOUND IN THE WORK PLACE, MUST NOT EXCEED THE WORKING LIMITS OF THE RESPIRATOR AND BE JOINTLY APPROVED BY THE NATIONAL INSTITUTE FOR OCCUPATIONAL SAFETY AND HEALTH AND THE MINE SAFETY AND HEALTH ADMINISTRATION (NIOSH-MSHA).

CHEMICAL CARTRIDGE RESPIRATOR WITH AN ORGANIC VAPOR CARTRIDGE(S) WITH A FULL FACEPIECE AND ORGANIC VAPOR CARTRIDGE(S) IN COMBINATION WITH A DUST AND MIST FILTER.

POWERED AIR-PURIFYING RESPIRATOR WITH A TIGHT-FITTING FACEPIECE AND ORGANIC VAPOR CARTRIDGE(S) IN COMBINATION WITH A HIGH-EFFICIENCY PARTICULATE FILTER.

TYPE 'C' SUPPLIED-AIR RESPIRATOR WITH A FULL FACEPIECE OPERATED IN A PRESSURE-DEMAND OR OTHER POSITIVE PRESSURE MODE.

SELF-CONTAINED BREATHING APPARATUS WITH A FULL FACEPIECE OPERATED IN PRESSURE-DEMAND OR OTHER POSITIVE PRESSURE MODE.

FOR FIREFIGHTING AND OTHER IMMEDIATELY DANGEROUS TO LIFE OR HEALTH CONDITIONS:

SELF-CONTAINED BREATHING APPARATUS WITH FULL FACEPIECE OPERATED IN PRESSURE-DEMAND OR OTHER POSITIVE PRESSURE MODE.

SUPPLIED-AIR RESPIRATOR WITH FULL FACEPIECE AND OPERATED IN PRESSURE-DEMAND OR OTHER POSITIVE PRESSURE MODE IN COMBINATION WITH AN AUXILIARY SELF-CONTAINED BREATHING APPARATUS OPERATED IN PRESSURE-DEMAND OR OTHER POSITIVE PRESSURE MODE.

CLOTHING: EMPLOYEE MUST WEAR APPROPRIATE PROTECTIVE (IMPERVIOUS) CLOTHING AND EQUIPMENT TO PREVENT REPEATED OR PROLONGED SKIN CONTACT WITH THIS SUBSTANCE.

GLOVES: EMPLOYEE MUST WEAR APPROPRIATE PROTECTIVE GLOVES TO PREVENT CONTACT WITH THIS SUBSTANCE.

EYE PROTECTION: EMPLOYEE MUST WEAR SPLASH-PROOF OR DUST-RESISTANT SAFETY GOGGLES TO PREVENT EYE CONTACT WITH THIS SUBSTANCE.
EMERGENCY EYE WASH: WHERE THERE IS ANY POSSIBILITY THAT AN EMPLOYEE'S EYES MAY BE EXPOSED TO THIS SUBSTANCE, THE EMPLOYER SHOULD PROVIDE AN EYE WASH FOUNTAIN WITHIN THE IMMEDIATE WORK AREA FOR EMERGENCY USE.

AUTHORIZED BY- OCCUPATIONAL HEALTH SERVICES, INC.
CREATION DATE: 04/13/90 ***REVISION DATE:*** 05/31/90

MATERIAL SAFETY DATA SHEET

OCCUPATIONAL HEALTH SERVICES, INC.
AGRICULTURE AND PESTICIDE DIVISION
450 SEVENTH AVENUE, SUITE 2407
NEW YORK, NEW YORK 10123
1-800-445-MSDS OR (212) 967-1100

EMERGENCY CONTACT:
JOHN S. BRANSFORD, JR. (615) 292-1180

SUBSTANCE IDENTIFICATION

CAS-NUMBER 7286-84-2

SUBSTANCE: **CHLORAMBEN METHYL ESTER**

TRADE NAMES/SYNONYMS: BENZOIC ACID, 3-AMINO-2,5-DICHLORO-, METHYL ESTER; 3-AMINO-2,5-DICHLOROBENZOIC ACID, METHYL ESTER; METHYL 3-AMINO-2,5-DICHLOROBENZOATE; AMIBEN METHYL ESTER; CHLORAMBEN METHYL; METHYL CHLORAMBEN; C8H7CL2NO2; PST71255

CHEMICAL FAMILY: ESTER, CARBOXYLIC, AROMATIC
HALOGEN
AMINE

MOLECULAR FORMULA: (CL2)-(H2-N)-C6-H2-C-O2-C-H3

MOLECULAR WEIGHT: 220.06

CERCLA RATINGS (SCALE 0-3): HEALTH=U FIRE=1 REACTIVITY=0 PERSISTENCE=1

NFPA RATINGS (SCALE 0-4): HEALTH=U FIRE=1 REACTIVITY=0

COMPONENTS AND CONTAMINANTS

COMPONENT: CHLORAMBEN METHYL ESTER ***PERCENT:*** 100.0
CAS# 7286-84-2

OTHER CONTAMINANTS: NONE

EXPOSURE LIMITS: NO OCCUPATIONAL EXPOSURE LIMITS ESTABLISHED BY OSHA, ACGIH, OR NIOSH.

PHYSICAL DATA

DESCRIPTION: OFF-WHITE CRYSTALLINE SOLID.
MELTING POINT: 145-147 F (63-64 C)
SPECIFIC GRAVITY: NOT AVAILABLE ***SOLUBILITY IN WATER:*** 0.01%
SOLVENT SOLUBILITY: SOLUBLE IN ALCOHOL, ACETONE, ETHER, AND AROMATIC SOLVENTS.

FIRE AND EXPLOSION DATA

FIRE AND EXPLOSION HAZARD: SLIGHT FIRE HAZARD WHEN EXPOSED TO HEAT OR FLAME.
DUST-AIR MIXTURES MAY IGNITE OR EXPLODE.
FIREFIGHTING MEDIA: DRY CHEMICAL, CARBON DIOXIDE, HALON, WATER SPRAY OR STANDARD FOAM (1987 EMERGENCY RESPONSE GUIDEBOOK, DOT P 5800.4).
FOR LARGER FIRES, USE WATER SPRAY, FOG OR STANDARD FOAM (1987 EMERGENCY RESPONSE GUIDEBOOK, DOT P 5800.4).
FIREFIGHTING: MOVE CONTAINER FROM FIRE AREA IF POSSIBLE. DO NOT SCATTER SPILLED MATERIAL WITH HIGH PRESSURE WATER STREAMS. DIKE FIRE CONTROL WATER FOR LATER DISPOSAL (1987 EMERGENCY RESPONSE GUIDEBOOK, DOT P 5800.4, GUIDE PAGE 31).
USE AGENTS SUITABLE FOR TYPE OF SURROUNDING FIRE. AVOID BREATHING HAZARDOUS VAPORS, KEEP UPWIND.

TOXICITY

CHLORAMBEN METHYL ESTER: TOXICITY DATA: 1,710 MG/KG ORAL-RAT LD50 (EPA, CHLORAMBEN PESTICIDE REGISTRATION STANDARD, JULY, 1981).
CARCINOGEN STATUS: NONE. ACUTE TOXICITY LEVEL: MODERATELY TOXIC BY INGESTION. TARGET EFFECTS: NO DATA AVAILABLE.

HEALTH EFFECTS AND FIRST AID

INHALATION: CHLORAMBEN METHYL ESTER: **ACUTE EXPOSURE-** NO DATA AVAILABLE. **CHRONIC EXPOSURE-** NO DATA AVAILABLE.
FIRST AID- REMOVE FROM EXPOSURE AREA TO FRESH AIR IMMEDIATELY. IF BREATHING HAS STOPPED, PERFORM ARTIFICIAL RESPIRATION. KEEP PERSON WARM AND AT REST. TREAT SYMPTOMATICALLY AND SUPPORTIVELY. GET MEDICAL ATTENTION IMMEDIATELY.

SKIN CONTACT: CHLORAMBEN METHYL ESTER: **ACUTE EXPOSURE-** NO DATA AVAILABLE. **CHRONIC EXPOSURE-** NO DATA AVAILABLE.
FIRST AID- REMOVE CONTAMINATED CLOTHING AND SHOES IMMEDIATELY. WASH AFFECTED AREA WITH SOAP OR MILD DETERGENT AND LARGE AMOUNTS OF WATER UNTIL NO EVIDENCE OF CHEMICAL REMAINS (APPROXIMATELY 15-20 MINUTES). GET MEDICAL ATTENTION IMMEDIATELY.

EYE CONTACT: CHLORAMBEN METHYL ESTER: **ACUTE EXPOSURE-** MAY CAUSE IRRITATION. **CHRONIC EXPOSURE-** PROLONGED OR REPEATED EXPOSURE MAY CAUSE CONJUNCTIVITIS.
FIRST AID- WASH EYES IMMEDIATELY WITH LARGE AMOUNTS OF WATER OR NORMAL SALINE, OCCASIONALLY LIFTING UPPER AND LOWER LIDS, UNTIL NO EVIDENCE OF CHEMICAL REMAINS (APPROXIMATELY 15-20 MINUTES). GET MEDICAL ATTENTION IMMEDIATELY.

INGESTION: CHLORAMBEN METHYL ESTER: **ACUTE EXPOSURE-** A LETHAL DOSE IN RATS PRODUCED EFFECTS OF DEPRESSION, GASPING, LARBORED RESPIRATION, ATAXIA, SPRAWLING OF LIMBS, DEPRESSED RIGHTING AND PLACEMENT REFLEXES, AND MUSCULAR STIFFNESS. MAJOR NECROPSY FINDINGS INCLUDED CONGESTION OF THE LUNGS, LIVER, KIDNEYS, AND PANCREAS; PALE-APPEARING SPLEEN AND GASTROINTESTINAL INFLAMMATION. **CHRONIC EXPOSURE-** CHLORAMBEN PRODUCED HEPATOCELLULAR ALTERATIONS IN DOGS AND MICE. AN INCREASED INCIDENCE OF HEPATOCELLULAR CARCINOMA IN FEMALES WAS OBSERVED IN AN ONCOGENIC STUDY OF MICE RECEIVING CHLORAMBEN. INCREASED FETAL MORTALITY AND DECREASED FETAL SKELETAL DEVELOPMENT WERE OBSERVED IN A STUDY OF PREGNANT RATS.
FIRST AID- TREAT SYMPTOMATICALLY AND SUPPORTIVELY. GET MEDICAL ATTENTION IMMEDIATELY. IF VOMITING OCCURS, KEEP HEAD LOWER THAN HIPS TO PREVENT ASPIRATION.
ANTIDOTE: NO SPECIFIC ANTIDOTE. TREAT SYMPTOMATICALLY AND SUPPORTIVELY.

REACTIVITY

REACTIVITY: STABLE UNDER NORMAL TEMPERATURES AND PRESSURES.
INCOMPATIBILITIES: CHLORAMBEN METHYL ESTER: OXIDIZERS (STRONG): FIRE AND EXPLOSION HAZARD.
DECOMPOSITION: THERMAL DECOMPOSITION PRODUCTS MAY INCLUDE TOXIC OXIDES OF NITROGEN AND CARBON AND TOXIC AND CORROSIVE FUMES OF CHLORIDES.
POLYMERIZATION: HAZARDOUS POLYMERIZATION HAS NOT BEEN REPORTED TO OCCUR UNDER NORMAL TEMPERATURES AND PRESSURES.

STORAGE AND DISPOSAL

OBSERVE ALL FEDERAL, STATE AND LOCAL REGULATIONS WHEN STORING OR DISPOSING OF THIS SUBSTANCE. FOR ASSISTANCE, CONTACT THE DISTRICT DIRECTOR OF THE ENVIRONMENTAL PROTECTION AGENCY.

****STORAGE****

STORE IN ACCORDANCE WITH 40 CFR 165 RECOMMENDED PROCEDURES FOR THE DISPOSAL AND STORAGE OF PESTICIDES AND PESTICIDE CONTAINERS.
STORE AWAY FROM INCOMPATIBLE SUBSTANCES.

****DISPOSAL****

DISPOSAL MUST BE IN ACCORDANCE WITH 40 CFR 165 RECOMMENDED PROCEDURES FOR THE DISPOSAL AND STORAGE OF PESTICIDES AND PESTICIDE CONTAINERS.

CONDITIONS TO AVOID

MAY BURN BUT DOES NOT IGNITE READILY. AVOID CONTACT WITH STRONG OXIDIZERS, EXCESSIVE HEAT, SPARKS, OR OPEN FLAME.

SPILL AND LEAK PROCEDURES

OCCUPATIONAL SPILL: SWEEP UP AND PLACE IN SUITABLE CLEAN, DRY CONTAINERS FOR RECLAMATION OR LATER DISPOSAL. DO NOT FLUSH SPILLED MATERIAL INTO SEWER. KEEP UNNECESSARY PEOPLE AWAY.

PROTECTIVE EQUIPMENT

VENTILATION: PROVIDE LOCAL EXHAUST OR GENERAL DILUTION VENTILATION SYSTEM.
RESPIRATOR: THE FOLLOWING RESPIRATORS ARE RECOMMENDED BASED ON INFORMATION FOUND IN THE PHYSICAL DATA, TOXICITY AND HEALTH EFFECTS SECTIONS. THEY ARE RANKED IN ORDER FROM MINIMUM TO MAXIMUM RESPIRATORY PROTECTION. THE SPECIFIC RESPIRATOR SELECTED MUST BE BASED ON CONTAMINATION LEVELS FOUND IN THE WORK PLACE, MUST NOT EXCEED THE WORKING LIMITS OF THE RESPIRATOR AND BE JOINTLY APPROVED BY THE NATIONAL INSTITUTE FOR OCCUPATIONAL SAFETY AND HEALTH AND THE MINE SAFETY AND HEALTH ADMINISTRATION (NIOSH-MSHA).
CHEMICAL CARTRIDGE RESPIRATOR WITH AN ORGANIC VAPOR CARTRIDGE(S) WITH A FULL FACEPIECE AND ORGANIC VAPOR CARTRIDGE(S) IN COMBINATION WITH A DUST AND MIST FILTER.
POWERED AIR-PURIFYING RESPIRATOR WITH A TIGHT-FITTING FACEPIECE AND ORGANIC VAPOR CARTRIDGE(S) IN COMBINATION WITH A HIGH-EFFICIENCY PARTICULATE FILTER.
TYPE 'C' SUPPLIED-AIR RESPIRATOR WITH A FULL FACEPIECE OPERATED IN A PRESSURE-DEMAND OR OTHER POSITIVE PRESSURE MODE.
SELF-CONTAINED BREATHING APPARATUS WITH A FULL FACEPIECE OPERATED IN PRESSURE-DEMAND OR OTHER POSITIVE PRESSURE MODE.
FOR FIREFIGHTING AND OTHER IMMEDIATELY DANGEROUS TO LIFE OR HEALTH CONDITIONS:
SELF-CONTAINED BREATHING APPARATUS WITH FULL FACEPIECE OPERATED IN PRESSURE-DEMAND OR OTHER POSITIVE PRESSURE MODE.
SUPPLIED-AIR RESPIRATOR WITH FULL FACEPIECE AND OPERATED IN PRESSURE-DEMAND OR OTHER POSITIVE PRESSURE MODE IN COMBINATION WITH AN AUXILIARY SELF-CONTAINED BREATHING APPARATUS OPERATED IN PRESSURE-DEMAND OR OTHER POSITIVE PRESSURE MODE.
CLOTHING: EMPLOYEE MUST WEAR APPROPRIATE PROTECTIVE (IMPERVIOUS) CLOTHING AND EQUIPMENT TO PREVENT REPEATED OR PROLONGED SKIN CONTACT WITH THIS SUBSTANCE.
GLOVES: EMPLOYEE MUST WEAR APPROPRIATE PROTECTIVE GLOVES TO PREVENT CONTACT WITH THIS SUBSTANCE.
EYE PROTECTION: EMPLOYEE MUST WEAR SPLASH-PROOF OR DUST-RESISTANT SAFETY GOGGLES TO PREVENT EYE CONTACT WITH THIS SUBSTANCE.
EMERGENCY EYE WASH: WHERE THERE IS ANY POSSIBILITY THAT AN EMPLOYEE'S EYES MAY BE EXPOSED TO THIS SUBSTANCE, THE EMPLOYER SHOULD PROVIDE AN EYE WASH FOUNTAIN WITHIN THE IMMEDIATE WORK AREA FOR EMERGENCY USE.

AUTHORIZED BY- OCCUPATIONAL HEALTH SERVICES, INC.
CREATION DATE: 04/13/90 ***REVISION DATE:*** 05/31/90

MATERIAL SAFETY DATA SHEET

OCCUPATIONAL HEALTH SERVICES, INC.
AGRICULTURE AND PESTICIDE DIVISION
450 SEVENTH AVENUE, SUITE 2407
NEW YORK, NEW YORK 10123
1-800-445-MSDS OR (212) 967-1100

EMERGENCY CONTACT:
JOHN S. BRANSFORD, JR. (615) 292-1180

SUBSTANCE IDENTIFICATION

CAS-NUMBER 1954-81-0

SUBSTANCE: **CHLORAMBEN, SODIUM SALT**

TRADE NAMES/SYNONYMS: BENZOIC ACID, 3-AMINO-2,5-DICHLORO-, MONOSODIUM SALT; 3-AMINO-2,5-DICHLOROBENZOIC ACID, MONOSODIUM SALT; AMIBEN SODIUM SALT; SODIUM CHLORAMBEN; SODIUM SALT OF CHLORAMBEN; C7H4CL2NANO2; PST71256

CHEMICAL FAMILY: CARBOXYLIC ACID, AROMATIC, SALT
HALOGEN
AMINE

MOLECULAR FORMULA: (CL2)-(H2-N)-C6-H2-C-O2.NA

MOLECULAR WEIGHT: 229.02

CERCLA RATINGS (SCALE 0-3): HEALTH=U FIRE=1 REACTIVITY=0 PERSISTENCE=1

NFPA RATINGS (SCALE 0-4): HEALTH=U FIRE=1 REACTIVITY=0

COMPONENTS AND CONTAMINANTS

COMPONENT: CHLORAMBEN, SODIUM SALT ***PERCENT:*** 100.0
CAS# 1954-81-0

OTHER CONTAMINANTS: NONE

EXPOSURE LIMITS: NO OCCUPATIONAL EXPOSURE LIMITS ESTABLISHED BY OSHA, ACGIH, OR NIOSH.

PHYSICAL DATA

DESCRIPTION: CRYSTALLINE SOLID. ***MELTING POINT:*** 520 F (271 C)

SPECIFIC GRAVITY: NOT AVAILABLE ***SOLUBILITY IN WATER:*** SOLUBLE

SOLVENT SOLUBILITY: INSOLUBLE IN AROMATIC SOLVENTS.

FIRE AND EXPLOSION DATA

FIRE AND EXPLOSION HAZARD: SLIGHT FIRE HAZARD WHEN EXPOSED TO HEAT OR FLAME.
DUST-AIR MIXTURES MAY IGNITE OR EXPLODE.

FIREFIGHTING MEDIA: DRY CHEMICAL, CARBON DIOXIDE, HALON, WATER SPRAY OR STANDARD FOAM (1987 EMERGENCY RESPONSE GUIDEBOOK, DOT P 5800.4).
FOR LARGER FIRES, USE WATER SPRAY, FOG OR STANDARD FOAM (1987 EMERGENCY RESPONSE GUIDEBOOK, DOT P 5800.4).

FIREFIGHTING: MOVE CONTAINER FROM FIRE AREA IF POSSIBLE. DO NOT SCATTER SPILLED MATERIAL WITH HIGH PRESSURE WATER STREAMS. DIKE FIRE CONTROL WATER FOR LATER DISPOSAL (1987 EMERGENCY RESPONSE GUIDEBOOK, DOT P 5800.4, GUIDE PAGE 31).
USE AGENTS SUITABLE FOR TYPE OF SURROUNDING FIRE. AVOID BREATHING HAZARDOUS VAPORS, KEEP UPWIND.

TOXICITY

CHLORAMBEN, SODIUM SALT: TOXICITY DATA: >200 MG/L INHALATION-RAT LC50 (EPA, CHLORAMBEN PESTICIDE REGISTRATION STANDARD, JULY, 1981); >5000 MG/KG SKIN-RABBIT LC50 (EPA, CHLORAMBEN PESTICIDE REGISTRATION STANDARD, JULY, 1981). 3330 MG/KG ORAL-RAT LD50 (UNION CARBIDE MSDS). CARCINOGEN STATUS: NONE. LOCAL EFFECTS: IRRITANT- EYE. ACUTE TOXICITY LEVEL: MODERATELY TOXIC BY INGESTION; SLIGHTLY TOXIC BY INHALATION AND DERMAL ABSORPTION. TARGET EFFECTS: NO DATA AVAILABLE.

HEALTH EFFECTS AND FIRST AID

INHALATION: CHLORAMBEN, SODIUM SALT: **ACUTE EXPOSURE-** THE LC50 REPORTED IN RATS WAS GREATER THAN 20 MG/L. **CHRONIC EXPOSURE-** NO DATA AVAILABLE.

FIRST AID- REMOVE FROM EXPOSURE AREA TO FRESH AIR IMMEDIATELY. IF BREATHING HAS STOPPED, PERFORM ARTIFICIAL RESPIRATION. KEEP PERSON WARM AND AT REST. TREAT SYMPTOMATICALLY AND SUPPORTIVELY. GET MEDICAL ATTENTION IMMEDIATELY.

SKIN CONTACT: CHLORAMBEN, SODIUM SALT: **ACUTE EXPOSURE-** THIS MATERIAL WAS VERY SLIGHTLY IRRITATING TO INTACT AND ABRADED RABBIT SKIN. **CHRONIC EXPOSURE-** NO DATA AVAILABLE.

FIRST AID- REMOVE CONTAMINATED CLOTHING AND SHOES IMMEDIATELY. WASH AFFECTED AREA WITH SOAP OR MILD DETERGENT AND LARGE AMOUNTS OF WATER UNTIL NO EVIDENCE OF CHEMICAL REMAINS (APPROXIMATELY 15-20 MINUTES). GET MEDICAL ATTENTION IMMEDIATELY.

EYE CONTACT: CHLORAMBEN, SODIUM SALT: IRRITANT. **ACUTE EXPOSURE-** THIS MATERIAL WAS MILDLY TO MODERATELY IRRITATING TO RABBIT EYES; THE IRRITATION WAS COMPLETELY CLEARED WITHIN 7 DAYS. **CHRONIC EXPOSURE-** PROLONGED OR REPEATED EXPOSURE TO IRRITANTS MAY CAUSE CONJUNCTIVITIS.

FIRST AID- WASH EYES IMMEDIATELY WITH LARGE AMOUNTS OF WATER OR NORMAL SALINE, OCCASIONALLY LIFTING UPPER AND LOWER LIDS, UNTIL NO EVIDENCE OF CHEMICAL REMAINS (APPROXIMATELY 15-20 MINUTES). GET MEDICAL ATTENTION IMMEDIATELY.

INGESTION: CHLORAMBEN, SODIUM SALT: **ACUTE EXPOSURE-** EFFECTS PRODUCED IN RATS FROM LETHAL DOSES OF CHLORAMBEN INCLUDED DEPRESSION CHARACTERIZED BY INACTIVITY AND ATAXIA, LABORED RESPIRATION, SPRAWLING OF LIMBS, PTOSIS, LACK OF COORDINATION AND EXCESSIVE URINATION. GROSS PATHOLOGIC CHANGES INCLUDED CONGESTED LUNGS, LUNGS, KIDNEYS, AND ADRENALS. **CHRONIC EXPOSURE-** CHLORAMBEN PRODUCED HEPATOCELLULAR ALTERATIONS IN DOGS AND MICE. AN INCREASED INCIDENCE OF HEPATOCELLULAR CARCINOMA IN FEMALES WAS OBSERVED IN AN ONCOGENIC STUDY OF MICE RECEIVING CHLORAMBEN. INCREASED FETAL MORTALITY AND DECREASED FETAL SKELETAL DEVELOPMENT WERE OBSERVED IN A STUDY OF PREGNANT RATS.

FIRST AID- TREAT SYMPTOMATICALLY AND SUPPORTIVELY. GET MEDICAL ATTENTION IMMEDIATELY. IF VOMITING OCCURS, KEEP HEAD LOWER THAN HIPS TO PREVENT ASPIRATION.

ANTIDOTE: NO SPECIFIC ANTIDOTE. TREAT SYMPTOMATICALLY AND SUPPORTIVELY.

REACTIVITY

REACTIVITY: STABLE UNDER NORMAL TEMPERATURES AND PRESSURES.

INCOMPATIBILITIES: CHLORAMBEN, SODIUM SALT: OXIDIZERS (STRONG): FIRE AND EXPLOSION HAZARD.

DECOMPOSITION: THERMAL DECOMPOSITION PRODUCTS MAY INCLUDE TOXIC OXIDES OF NITROGEN AND CARBON AND TOXIC AND CORROSIVE FUMES OF CHLORIDES.

POLYMERIZATION: HAZARDOUS POLYMERIZATION HAS NOT BEEN REPORTED TO OCCUR UNDER NORMAL TEMPERATURES AND PRESSURES.

STORAGE AND DISPOSAL

OBSERVE ALL FEDERAL, STATE AND LOCAL REGULATIONS WHEN STORING OR DISPOSING OF THIS SUBSTANCE. FOR ASSISTANCE, CONTACT THE DISTRICT DIRECTOR OF THE ENVIRONMENTAL PROTECTION AGENCY.

****STORAGE****

STORE IN ACCORDANCE WITH 40 CFR 165 RECOMMENDED PROCEDURES FOR THE DISPOSAL AND STORAGE OF PESTICIDES AND PESTICIDE CONTAINERS.
STORE AWAY FROM INCOMPATIBLE SUBSTANCES.

****DISPOSAL****

DISPOSAL MUST BE IN ACCORDANCE WITH 40 CFR 165 RECOMMENDED PROCEDURES FOR THE DISPOSAL AND STORAGE OF PESTICIDES AND PESTICIDE CONTAINERS.

CONDITIONS TO AVOID

MAY BURN BUT DOES NOT IGNITE READILY. AVOID CONTACT WITH STRONG OXIDIZERS, EXCESSIVE HEAT, SPARKS, OR OPEN FLAME.

SPILL AND LEAK PROCEDURES

OCCUPATIONAL SPILL: SWEEP UP AND PLACE IN SUITABLE CLEAN, DRY CONTAINERS FOR RECLAMATION OR LATER DISPOSAL. DO NOT FLUSH SPILLED MATERIAL INTO SEWER. KEEP UNNECESSARY PEOPLE AWAY.

PROTECTIVE EQUIPMENT

VENTILATION: PROVIDE LOCAL EXHAUST OR GENERAL DILUTION VENTILATION SYSTEM.

RESPIRATOR: THE FOLLOWING RESPIRATORS ARE RECOMMENDED BASED ON INFORMATION FOUND IN THE PHYSICAL DATA, TOXICITY AND HEALTH EFFECTS SECTIONS. THEY ARE RANKED IN ORDER FROM MINIMUM TO MAXIMUM RESPIRATORY PROTECTION. THE SPECIFIC RESPIRATOR SELECTED MUST BE BASED ON CONTAMINATION LEVELS FOUND IN THE WORK PLACE, MUST NOT EXCEED THE WORKING LIMITS OF THE RESPIRATOR AND BE JOINTLY APPROVED BY THE NATIONAL INSTITUTE FOR OCCUPATIONAL SAFETY AND HEALTH AND THE MINE SAFETY AND HEALTH ADMINISTRATION (NIOSH-MSHA).
CHEMICAL CARTRIDGE RESPIRATOR WITH AN ORGANIC VAPOR CARTRIDGE(S) WITH A FULL FACEPIECE AND ORGANIC VAPOR CARTRIDGE(S) IN COMBINATION WITH A DUST AND MIST FILTER.
POWERED AIR-PURIFYING RESPIRATOR WITH A TIGHT-FITTING FACEPIECE AND ORGANIC VAPOR CARTRIDGE(S) IN COMBINATION WITH A HIGH-EFFICIENCY PARTICULATE FILTER.

TYPE 'C' SUPPLIED-AIR RESPIRATOR WITH A FULL FACEPIECE OPERATED IN A PRESSURE-DEMAND OR OTHER POSITIVE PRESSURE MODE.
SELF-CONTAINED BREATHING APPARATUS WITH A FULL FACEPIECE OPERATED IN PRESSURE-DEMAND OR OTHER POSITIVE PRESSURE MODE.
FOR FIREFIGHTING AND OTHER IMMEDIATELY DANGEROUS TO LIFE OR HEALTH CONDITIONS: SELF-CONTAINED BREATHING APPARATUS WITH FULL FACEPIECE OPERATED IN PRESSURE-DEMAND OR OTHER POSITIVE PRESSURE MODE.
SUPPLIED-AIR RESPIRATOR WITH FULL FACEPIECE AND OPERATED IN PRESSURE-DEMAND OR OTHER POSITIVE PRESSURE MODE IN COMBINATION WITH AN AUXILIARY SELF-CONTAINED BREATHING APPARATUS OPERATED IN PRESSURE-DEMAND OR OTHER POSITIVE PRESSURE MODE.

CLOTHING: EMPLOYEE MUST WEAR APPROPRIATE PROTECTIVE (IMPERVIOUS) CLOTHING AND EQUIPMENT TO PREVENT REPEATED OR PROLONGED SKIN CONTACT WITH THIS SUBSTANCE.

GLOVES: EMPLOYEE MUST WEAR APPROPRIATE PROTECTIVE GLOVES TO PREVENT CONTACT WITH THIS SUBSTANCE.

EYE PROTECTION: EMPLOYEE MUST WEAR SPLASH-PROOF OR DUST-RESISTANT SAFETY GOGGLES TO PREVENT EYE CONTACT WITH THIS SUBSTANCE.
EMERGENCY EYE WASH: WHERE THERE IS ANY POSSIBILITY THAT AN EMPLOYEE'S EYES MAY BE EXPOSED TO THIS SUBSTANCE, THE EMPLOYER SHOULD PROVIDE AN EYE WASH FOUNTAIN WITHIN THE IMMEDIATE WORK AREA FOR EMERGENCY USE.

AUTHORIZED BY- OCCUPATIONAL HEALTH SERVICES, INC.
CREATION DATE: 04/13/90 ***REVISION DATE:*** 05/31/90

MATERIAL SAFETY DATA SHEET

OCCUPATIONAL HEALTH SERVICES, INC.
AGRICULTURE AND PESTICIDE DIVISION
450 SEVENTH AVENUE, SUITE 2407
NEW YORK, NEW YORK 10123
1-800-445-MSDS OR (212) 967-1100

EMERGENCY CONTACT:
JOHN S. BRANSFORD, JR. (615) 292-1180

SUBSTANCE IDENTIFICATION

CAS-NUMBER 1928-45-6

SUBSTANCE: **2,4-D PROPYLENE GLYCOL BUTYL ETHER ESTER**

TRADE NAMES/SYNONYMS: ACETIC ACID, (2,4-DICHLOROPHENOXY)-, 3-BUTOXYPROPYL ESTER; (2,4-DICHLOROPHENOXY)ACETIC ACID 3-BUTOXYPROPYL ESTER; 2,4-D BUTOXYPROPYL ESTER; 2,4-DICHLOROPHENOXY ACETIC ACID, PROPYLENE GLYCOL BUTYL ETHER ESTER; RCRA U240; C15H20CL2O4; PST71294

CHEMICAL FAMILY: ESTER, CARBOXYLIC, AROMATIC HALOGEN

MOLECULAR FORMULA: CL2-C6-H3-O-C-H2-C-(O2)-(C-H2)3-O-C4-H9

MOLECULAR WEIGHT: 335.23

CERCLA RATINGS (SCALE 0-3): HEALTH=2 FIRE=U REACTIVITY=0 PERSISTENCE=3

NFPA RATINGS (SCALE 0-4): HEALTH=U FIRE=U REACTIVITY=0

COMPONENTS AND CONTAMINANTS

COMPONENT: 2,4-D PROPYLENE GLYCOL BUTYL ETHER ESTER ***PERCENT:*** 100.0
CAS# 1928-45-6

OTHER CONTAMINANTS: NONE

EXPOSURE LIMITS: NO OCCUPATIONAL EXPOSURE LIMITS ESTABLISHED BY OSHA, ACGIH, OR NIOSH.
2,4-D, SALTS AND ESTERS: 100 POUNDS CERCLA SECTION 103 REPORTABLE QUANTITY

PHYSICAL DATA

DESCRIPTION: AMBER LIQUID. ***BOILING POINT:*** NOT AVAILABLE

SPECIFIC GRAVITY: NOT AVAILABLE ***VAPOR PRESSURE:*** NOT AVAILABLE

SOLUBILITY IN WATER: SLIGHTLY SOLUBLE

SOLVENT SOLUBILITY: SOLUBLE IN SOME PETROLEUM OILS.

FIRE AND EXPLOSION DATA

FIRE AND EXPLOSION HAZARD: UNKNOWN FIRE AND EXPLOSION HAZARD.

FLASH POINT: NOT AVAILABLE

FIREFIGHTING MEDIA: DRY CHEMICAL, CARBON DIOXIDE, HALON, WATER SPRAY OR STANDARD FOAM (1987 EMERGENCY RESPONSE GUIDEBOOK, DOT P 5800.4).
FOR LARGER FIRES, USE WATER SPRAY, FOG OR STANDARD FOAM (1987 EMERGENCY RESPONSE GUIDEBOOK, DOT P 5800.4).

FIREFIGHTING: MOVE CONTAINER FROM FIRE AREA IF POSSIBLE. DIKE FIRE CONTROL WATER FOR LATER DISPOSAL; DO NOT SCATTER THE MATERIAL. COOL FIRE-EXPOSED CONTAINERS WITH WATER FROM SIDE UNTIL WELL AFTER FIRE IS OUT. STAY AWAY FROM STORAGE TANK ENDS. WITHDRAW IMMEDIATELY IN CASE OF RISING SOUND FROM VENTING SAFETY DEVICE OR ANY DISCOLORATION OF STORAGE TANK DUE TO FIRE (1987 EMERGENCY RESPONSE GUIDEBOOK, DOT P 5800.4, GUIDE PAGE 28).
EXTINGUISH ONLY IF FLOW CAN BE STOPPED. USE FLOODING AMOUNTS OF WATER AS A FOG; SOLID STREAMS MAY BE INEFFECTIVE. COOL CONTAINERS WITH FLOODING AMOUNTS OF WATER FROM AS FAR A DISTANCE AS POSSIBLE. AVOID BREATHING POISONOUS VAPORS, KEEP UPWIND.

TOXICITY

2,4-D PROPYLENE GLYCOL BUTYL ETHER ESTER: TOXICITY DATA: 500 MG/KG ORAL-RAT LD50; REPRODUCTIVE EFFECTS DATA (RTECS). CARCINOGEN STATUS: HUMAN LIMITED EVIDENCE (IARC GROUP-2B FOR CHLOROPHENOXY HERBICIDES). STUDIES REVEALED A SIGNIFICANT INCREASE IN SOFT-TISSUE SARCOMAS, MALIGNANT LYMPHOMAS AND BRONCHIAL CARCINOMAS IN WORKERS EXPOSED TO CHLOROPHENOXY HERBICIDES. ACUTE TOXICITY LEVEL: TOXIC BY INGESTION. TARGET EFFECTS: POISONING MAY AFFECT THE GASTROINTESTINAL TRACT AND THE CARDIOVASCULAR AND NERVOUS SYSTEMS.* AT INCREASED RISK FROM EXPOSURE: PERSONS WITH LIVER, KIDNEY, CARDIOVASCULAR OR SKIN DISEASES, AND CONVULSIVE DISORDERS OR NEUROPATHY.*
* MAY BE BASED ON GENERAL INFORMATION ON DICHLOROPHENOXY DERIVATIVES.

HEALTH EFFECTS AND FIRST AID

INHALATION: 2,4-D PROPYLENE GLYCOL BUTYL ETHER ESTER: SEE INFORMATION ON 2,4-D AND DERIVATIVES.
2,4-D AND DERIVATIVES: **ACUTE EXPOSURE-** EXPOSURE TO 2,4-D AND ITS DERIVATIVES MAY CAUSE IRRITATION WITH SORE THROAT AND BURNING SENSATIONS IN THE NASOPHARYNX AND CHEST, COUGHING, LACRIMATION, RHINITIS, DULLNESS, DIZZINESS, AND ATAXIA. OTHER EFFECTS OF FATIGUE, NAUSEA, VOMITING, DIARRHEA, STOMACH PAINS, MALAISE, HEADACHE, FEVER, TACHYCARDIA, URINARY INCONTINENCE, CONSTIPATION, LEUKOPENIA, MYALGIA, AND TRANSIENT UNCONSCIOUSNESS MAY OCCUR. A DELAYED PERIPHERAL NEUROPATHY MAY DEVELOP CHARACTERIZED BY PARESTHESIAS, SEVERE PAIN, SYMMETRICAL MOTOR AND SENSORY DEFICITS, WEAKNESS, MYOTONIA, FASCICULATIONS, AND IN SOME CASES PARALYSIS OF THE EXTREMITIES. THE DISABILITY MAY BE PROLONGED AND RECOVERY INCOMPLETE. **CHRONIC EXPOSURE-** IN ADDITION TO THE EFFECTS LISTED IN ACUTE EXPOSURE, OCCUPATIONAL EXPOSURE TO 2,4-D AND ITS DERIVATIVES HAS PRODUCED A SWEET TASTE IN THE MOUTH, HYPERACUSIA, LOWERED SENSITIVITY TO TASTE AND SMELL, INCREASED SALIVATION, VERTIGO, SOMNOLENCE, ANOREXIA, HEAVINESS OF THE LEGS. OTHER EFFECTS HAVE INCLUDED HYPOTENSION, BRADYCARDIA AND OTHER CARDIOVASCULAR SYSTEM CHANGES, PAIN IN THE REGION OF THE LIVER AND STOMACH, AND CHANGES IN THE DIGESTIVE FUNCTION, LIVER FUNCTION AND METABOLIC PROCESSES. A CASE REPORT DESCRIBED A CHILD WITH MULTIPLE CONGENITAL ANOMALIES AND SEVERE MENTAL RETARDATION OF UNCERTAIN CAUSE BORN TO PARENTS HEAVILY EXPOSED TO 2,4-D WHILE SPRAYING TREES. AN INCREASED PREVALENCE OF SLOWED NERVE CONDUCTION VELOCITY WITH NO ASSOCIATED SYMPTOMS WAS REPORTED IN A STUDY OF CHEMICAL WORKERS EMPLOYED IN THE PRODUCTION OF 2,4-D AND 2,4,5-T. EPIDEMIOLOGICAL STUDIES REVEALED A SIGNIFICANT INCREASE IN SOFT-TISSUE SARCOMAS, MALIGNANT LYMPHOMAS, AND BRONCHIAL CARCINOMAS IN WORKERS EXPOSED TO CHLOROPHENOXY HERBICIDES INCLUDING 2,4-D.

FIRST AID- REMOVE FROM EXPOSURE AREA TO FRESH AIR IMMEDIATELY. IF BREATHING HAS STOPPED, PERFORM ARTIFICIAL RESPIRATION. KEEP PERSON WARM AND AT REST. TREAT SYMPTOMATICALLY AND SUPPORTIVELY. GET MEDICAL ATTENTION IMMEDIATELY.

SKIN CONTACT: 2,4-D PROPYLENE GLYCOL BUTYL ETHER ESTER: SEE INFORMATION ON 2,4-D AND DERIVATIVES.
2,4-D AND DERIVATIVES: **ACUTE EXPOSURE-** MAY CAUSE IRRITATION. IF SUFFICIENT AMOUNTS ARE ABSORBED THROUGH THE SKIN, EFFECTS, INCLUDING PERIPHERAL NEUROPATHY, AS DESCRIBED IN ACUTE INHALATION MAY OCCUR. **CHRONIC EXPOSURE-** PROLONGED OR REPEATED EXPOSURE MAY CAUSE DERMATITIS AND EFFECTS AS DESCRIBED IN CHRONIC INHALATION.

FIRST AID- REMOVE CONTAMINATED CLOTHING AND SHOES IMMEDIATELY. WASH AFFECTED AREA WITH SOAP OR MILD DETERGENT AND LARGE AMOUNTS OF WATER UNTIL NO EVIDENCE OF CHEMICAL REMAINS (APPROXIMATELY 15-20 MINUTES). GET MEDICAL ATTENTION IMMEDIATELY.

EYE CONTACT: 2,4-D PROPYLENE GLYCOL BUTYL ETHER ESTER: SEE INFORMATION ON 2,4-D AND DERIVATIVES.

2,4-D AND DERIVATIVES: **ACUTE EXPOSURE**- MAY CAUSE IRRITATION. **CHRONIC EXPOSURE**- NO DATA AVAILABLE.

FIRST AID- WASH EYES IMMEDIATELY WITH LARGE AMOUNTS OF WATER OR NORMAL SALINE, OCCASIONALLY LIFTING UPPER AND LOWER LIDS, UNTIL NO EVIDENCE OF CHEMICAL REMAINS (APPROXIMATELY 15-20 MINUTES). GET MEDICAL ATTENTION IMMEDIATELY.

INGESTION: 2,4-D PROPYLENE GLYCOL BUTYL ETHER ESTER: TOXIC. REPRODUCTIVE EFFECTS HAVE BEEN REPORTED IN ANIMALS. SEE INFORMATION ON 2,4-D AND DERIVATIVES.

2,4-D AND DERIVATIVES: **ACUTE EXPOSURE**- INGESTION OF 2,4-D AND ITS DERIVATIVES MAY CAUSE IRRITATION OF THE MOUTH, THROAT, AND GASTROINTESTINAL TRACT, NAUSEA, VOMITING, CHEST AND ABDOMINAL PAIN, AND DIARRHEA. INGESTION OF VERY LARGE DOSES MAY PRODUCE METABOLIC ACIDOSIS, FEVER OR SUBNORMAL TEMPERATURES, HYPERVENTILATION, HYPOTENSION, VASODILATION, FLUSHING OF THE SKIN, SWEATING, CARDIAC ARRHYTHMIAS, TACHYCARDIA, LETHARGY, WEAKNESS, INTERCOSTAL PARALYSIS, RENAL AND HEPATIC DYSFUNCTION, MYOTONIA, COMA, AND CONVULSIONS. DAMAGE TO SKELETAL MUSCLE MAY BE MANIFEST BY MUSCLE TWITCHING AND ACHING WITH ELEVATED SERUM ENZYMES AND MYOGLOBIN IN THE BLOOD AND URINE. IMPAIRED MEMORY AND CHANGES IN COLOR VISION WERE REPORTED IN ONE CASE OF POISONING. DEATH MAY BE DUE TO CIRCULATORY COLLAPSE. **CHRONIC EXPOSURE**- NO DATA AVAILABLE.

FIRST AID- IF THE PERSON IS CONSCIOUS AND NOT CONVULSING, INDUCE EMESIS BY GIVING SYRUP OF IPECAC (KEEPING THE HEAD BELOW THE HIPS TO PREVENT ASPIRATION) FOLLOWED BY WATER. REPEAT IN 20 MINUTES IF NOT EFFECTIVE INITIALLY. IN PATIENTS WITH DEPRESSED RESPIRATION OR IF EMESIS IS NOT PRODUCED, PERFORM GASTRIC LAVAGE WITH ACTIVATED CHARCOAL. FOLLOW WITH A SALINE CATHARTIC (DREISBACH, HANDBOOK OF POISONING, 12TH ED.). TREAT SYMPTOMATICALLY AND SUPPORTIVELY. GASTRIC LAVAGE SHOULD BE PERFORMED BY QUALIFIED MEDICAL PERSONNEL. GET MEDICAL ATTENTION IMMEDIATELY.

ANTIDOTE: NO SPECIFIC ANTIDOTE. TREAT SYMPTOMATICALLY AND SUPPORTIVELY.

REACTIVITY

REACTIVITY: STABLE UNDER NORMAL TEMPERATURES AND PRESSURES.

INCOMPATIBILITIES: 2,4-D PROPYLENE GLYCOL BUTYL ETHER ESTER: OXIDIZERS (STRONG): FIRE AND EXPLOSION HAZARD.

DECOMPOSITION: THERMAL DECOMPOSITION PRODUCTS MAY INCLUDE TOXIC AND CORROSIVE FUMES OF CHLORIDES AND TOXIC OXIDES OF CARBON.

POLYMERIZATION: HAZARDOUS POLYMERIZATION HAS NOT BEEN REPORTED TO OCCUR UNDER NORMAL TEMPERATURES AND PRESSURES.

STORAGE AND DISPOSAL

OBSERVE ALL FEDERAL, STATE AND LOCAL REGULATIONS WHEN STORING OR DISPOSING OF THIS SUBSTANCE. FOR ASSISTANCE, CONTACT THE DISTRICT DIRECTOR OF THE ENVIRONMENTAL PROTECTION AGENCY.

****STORAGE****

STORE IN ACCORDANCE WITH 40 CFR 165 RECOMMENDED PROCEDURES FOR THE DISPOSAL AND STORAGE OF PESTICIDES AND PESTICIDE CONTAINERS.

STORE AWAY FROM INCOMPATIBLE SUBSTANCES.

****DISPOSAL****

DISPOSAL MUST BE IN ACCORDANCE WITH 40 CFR 165 RECOMMENDED PROCEDURES FOR THE DISPOSAL AND STORAGE OF PESTICIDES AND PESTICIDE CONTAINERS.

DISPOSAL MUST BE IN ACCORDANCE WITH STANDARDS APPLICABLE TO GENERATORS OF HAZARDOUS WASTE, 40CFR 262. EPA HAZARDOUS WASTE NUMBER U240.

2,4-D - REGULATORY LEVEL: 10.0 MG/L MATERIALS WHICH CONTAIN THE ABOVE SUBSTANCE AT OR ABOVE THE REGULATORY LEVEL MEET THE EPA CHARACTERISTIC OF TOXICITY, AND MUST BE DISPOSED OF IN ACCORDANCE WITH 40 CFR PART 262. EPA HAZARDOUS WASTE NUMBER D016.

CONDITIONS TO AVOID

AVOID CONTACT WITH HEAT, SPARKS, FLAMES OR OTHER IGNITION SOURCES. VAPORS MAY BE EXPLOSIVE. MATERIAL IS POISONOUS; AVOID INHALATION OF VAPORS OR CONTACT WITH SKIN. DO NOT ALLOW MATERIAL TO CONTAMINATE WATER SOURCES.

SPILL AND LEAK PROCEDURES

OCCUPATIONAL SPILL: SHUT OFF IGNITION SOURCES. DO NOT TOUCH SPILLED MATERIAL. STOP LEAK IF YOU CAN DO IT WITHOUT RISK. USE WATER SPRAY TO REDUCE VAPORS. FOR SMALL SPILLS, TAKE UP WITH SAND OR OTHER ABSORBENT MATERIAL AND PLACE INTO CONTAINERS FOR LATER DISPOSAL. FOR LARGER SPILLS, DIKE FAR AHEAD OF SPILL FOR LATER DISPOSAL. NO SMOKING, FLAMES OR FLARES IN HAZARD AREA! KEEP UNNECESSARY PEOPLE AWAY; ISOLATE HAZARD AREA AND DENY ENTRY.

REPORTABLE QUANTITY (RQ): 100 POUNDS THE SUPERFUND AMENDMENTS AND REAUTHORIZATION ACT (SARA) SECTION 304 REQUIRES THAT A RELEASE EQUAL TO OR GREATER THAN THE REPORTABLE QUANTITY FOR THIS SUBSTANCE BE IMMEDIATELY REPORTED TO THE LOCAL EMERGENCY PLANNING COMMITTEE AND THE STATE EMERGENCY RESPONSE COMMISSION (40 CFR 355.40). IF THE RELEASE OF THIS SUBSTANCE IS REPORTABLE UNDER CERCLA SECTION 103, THE NATIONAL RESPONSE CENTER MUST BE NOTIFIED IMMEDIATELY AT (800) 424-8802 OR (202) 426-2675 IN THE METROPOLITAN WASHINGTON, D.C. AREA (40 CFR 302.6).

PROTECTIVE EQUIPMENT

VENTILATION: PROVIDE LOCAL EXHAUST OR GENERAL DILUTION VENTILATION SYSTEM.

RESPIRATOR: THE FOLLOWING RESPIRATORS ARE RECOMMENDED BASED ON INFORMATION FOUND IN THE PHYSICAL DATA, TOXICITY AND HEALTH EFFECTS SECTIONS. THEY ARE RANKED IN ORDER FROM MINIMUM TO MAXIMUM RESPIRATORY PROTECTION. THE SPECIFIC RESPIRATOR SELECTED MUST BE BASED ON CONTAMINATION LEVELS FOUND IN THE WORK PLACE, MUST NOT EXCEED THE WORKING LIMITS OF THE RESPIRATOR AND BE JOINTLY APPROVED BY THE NATIONAL INSTITUTE FOR OCCUPATIONAL SAFETY AND HEALTH AND THE MINE SAFETY AND HEALTH ADMINISTRATION (NIOSH-MSHA).

TYPE 'C' SUPPLIED-AIR RESPIRATOR WITH A FULL FACEPIECE OPERATED IN PRESSURE-DEMAND OR OTHER POSITIVE PRESSURE MODE OR WITH A FULL FACEPIECE, HELMET OR HOOD OPERATED IN CONTINOUS-FLOW MODE.

SELF-CONTAINED BREATHING APPARATUS WITH A FULL FACEPIECE OPERATED IN PRESSURE-DEMAND OR OTHER POSITIVE PRESSURE MODE.

FOR FIREFIGHTING AND OTHER IMMEDIATELY DANGEROUS TO LIFE OR HEALTH CONDITIONS:

SELF-CONTAINED BREATHING APPARATUS WITH FULL FACEPIECE OPERATED IN PRESSURE-DEMAND OR OTHER POSITIVE PRESSURE MODE.

SUPPLIED-AIR RESPIRATOR WITH FULL FACEPIECE AND OPERATED IN PRESSURE-DEMAND OR OTHER POSITIVE PRESSURE MODE IN COMBINATION WITH AN AUXILIARY SELF-CONTAINED BREATHING APPARATUS OPERATED IN PRESSURE-DEMAND OR OTHER POSITIVE PRESSURE MODE.

CLOTHING: EMPLOYEE MUST WEAR APPROPRIATE PROTECTIVE (IMPERVIOUS) CLOTHING AND EQUIPMENT TO PREVENT REPEATED OR PROLONGED SKIN CONTACT WITH THIS SUBSTANCE.

GLOVES: EMPLOYEE MUST WEAR APPROPRIATE PROTECTIVE GLOVES TO PREVENT CONTACT WITH THIS SUBSTANCE.

EYE PROTECTION: EMPLOYEE MUST WEAR SPLASH-PROOF OR DUST-RESISTANT SAFETY GOGGLES TO PREVENT EYE CONTACT WITH THIS SUBSTANCE.

EMERGENCY EYE WASH: WHERE THERE IS ANY POSSIBILITY THAT AN EMPLOYEE'S EYES MAY BE EXPOSED TO THIS SUBSTANCE, THE EMPLOYER SHOULD PROVIDE AN EYE WASH FOUNTAIN WITHIN THE IMMEDIATE WORK AREA FOR EMERGENCY USE.

AUTHORIZED BY- OCCUPATIONAL HEALTH SERVICES, INC.

CREATION DATE: 05/22/90 ***REVISION DATE:*** 07/13/90

MATERIAL SAFETY DATA SHEET

OCCUPATIONAL HEALTH SERVICES, INC.	EMERGENCY CONTACT:
AGRICULTURE AND PESTICIDE DIVISION	JOHN S. BRANSFORD, JR. (615) 292-1180
450 SEVENTH AVENUE, SUITE 2407	
NEW YORK, NEW YORK 10123	
1-800-445-MSDS OR (212) 967-1100	

SUBSTANCE IDENTIFICATION

CAS-NUMBER 94-80-4

SUBSTANCE: **BUTYL 2,4-DICHLOROPHENOXYACETATE**

TRADE NAMES/SYNONYMS: ACETIC ACID, (2,4-DICHLOROPHENOXY)-, BUTYL ESTER; BUTYL 2,4-D; BUTYL DICHLOROPHENOXYACETATE; BUTYL (2,4-DICHLOROPHENOXY)ACETATE; 2,4-DBE; 2,4-D BUTYL ESTER; N-BUTYL 2,4-DICHLOROPHENOXY ACETATE; 2,4-D, N-BUTYL ESTER; LIRONOX; C12H14CL2O3; PST71295

CHEMICAL FAMILY: HALOGEN COMPOUND, AROMATIC ESTER

MOLECULAR FORMULA: C6-H3-CL2-O-C-H2-C-O2-C-H2-C3-H7

MOLECULAR WEIGHT: 277.16

CERCLA RATINGS (SCALE 0-3): HEALTH=3 FIRE=2 REACTIVITY=0 PERSISTENCE=2

NFPA RATINGS (SCALE 0-4): HEALTH=U FIRE=2 REACTIVITY=0

COMPONENTS AND CONTAMINANTS

COMPONENT: BUTYL 2,4-DICHLOROPHENOXYACETATE ***PERCENT:*** 100.0
CAS# 94-80-4

OTHER CONTAMINANTS: NONE

EXPOSURE LIMITS: NO OCCUPATIONAL EXPOSURE LIMITS ESTABLISHED BY OSHA, ACGIH, OR NIOSH.
2,4-D, SALTS AND ESTERS: 100 POUNDS CERCLA SECTION 103 REPORTABLE QUANTITY

PHYSICAL DATA

DESCRIPTION: CLEAR TO LIGHT BROWN LIQUID WITH AN ODOR OF FUEL OIL.

BOILING POINT: 295-297 F (146-147 C) @ 1 MMHG

SPECIFIC GRAVITY: 1.235-1.245 @ 20 C ***VAPOR PRESSURE:*** NOT AVAILABLE

SOLUBILITY IN WATER: SLIGHTLY SOLUBLE

SOLVENT SOLUBILITY: SOLUBLE IN ETHYL ALCOHOL.

FIRE AND EXPLOSION DATA

FIRE AND EXPLOSION HAZARD: MODERATE FIRE HAZARD WHEN EXPOSED TO HEAT OR FLAME.
VAPOR-AIR MIXTURES ARE EXPLOSIVE ABOVE FLASH POINT.

FLASH POINT: >175 F (>79 C) ***FLAMMABILITY CLASS(OSHA):*** IIIA

FIREFIGHTING MEDIA: DRY CHEMICAL, CARBON DIOXIDE, HALON, WATER SPRAY OR STANDARD FOAM (1987 EMERGENCY RESPONSE GUIDEBOOK, DOT P 5800.4).
FOR LARGER FIRES, USE WATER SPRAY, FOG OR STANDARD FOAM (1987 EMERGENCY RESPONSE GUIDEBOOK, DOT P 5800.4).

FIREFIGHTING: MOVE CONTAINER FROM FIRE AREA IF POSSIBLE. COOL FIRE-EXPOSED CONTAINERS WITH WATER FROM SIDE UNTIL WELL AFTER FIRE IS OUT. STAY AWAY FROM STORAGE TANK ENDS. FOR MASSIVE FIRE IN STORAGE AREA, USE UNMANNED HOSE HOLDER OR MONITOR NOZZLES, ELSE WITHDRAW FROM AREA AND LET FIRE BURN. WITHDRAW IMMEDIATELY IN CASE OF RISING SOUND FROM VENTING SAFETY DEVICE OR ANY DISCOLORATION OF STORAGE TANK DUE TO FIRE (1987 EMERGENCY RESPONSE GUIDEBOOK, DOT P 5800.4, GUIDE PAGE 27). EXTINGUISH ONLY IF FLOW CAN BE STOPPED; USE FLOODING AMOUNTS OF WATER AS A FOG, SOLID STREAMS MAY BE INEFFECTIVE. COOL CONTAINERS WITH FLOODING AMOUNTS OF WATER, APPLY FROM AS FAR A DISTANCE AS POSSIBLE. AVOID BREATHING VAPORS, KEEP UPWIND.

TRANSPORTATION DATA

DEPARTMENT OF TRANSPORTATION HAZARD CLASSIFICATION 49 CFR 172.101: COMBUSTIBLE LIQUID
DEPARTMENT OF TRANSPORTATION LABELING REQUIREMENTS 49 CFR 172.101 AND SUBPART E: NONE
DEPARTMENT OF TRANSPORTATION PACKAGING REQUIREMENTS: NONE
EXCEPTIONS: 49 CFR 173.118A

TOXICITY

BUTYL 2,4-DICHLOROPHENOXYACETATE: TOXICITY DATA: 600 MG/KG ORAL-RAT LD50; 500 MG/KG ORAL-RAT LD50 (EPA); 425 MG/KG ORAL-MOUSE LD50; 780 MG/KG ORAL-CAT LD50; 920 MG/KG UNREPORTED-RAT LD50; 380 MG/KG UNREPORTED-MOUSE LD50; REPRODUCTIVE EFFECTS DATA (RTECS). CARCINOGEN STATUS: HUMAN LIMITED EVIDENCE (IARC GROUP-2B FOR CHLOROPHENOXY HERBICIDES). STUDIES REVEALED A SIGNIFICANT INCREASE IN SOFT-TISSUE SARCOMAS, MALIGNANT LYMPHOMAS AND BRONCHIAL CARCINOMAS IN WORKERS EXPOSED TO CHLOROPHENOXY HERBICIDES. ACUTE TOXICITY LEVEL: TOXIC BY INGESTION. TARGET EFFECTS: POISONING MAY AFFECT THE GASTROINTESTINAL TRACT AND THE CARDIOVASCULAR AND NERVOUS SYSTEMS.* AT INCREASED RISK FROM EXPOSURE: PERSONS WITH LIVER, KIDNEY, CARDIOVASCULAR, OR SKIN DISEASES, AND CONVULSIVE DISORDERS OR NEUROPATHY.*
* MAY BE BASED ON GENERAL INFORMATION ON DICHLOROPHENOXY DERIVATIVES.

HEALTH EFFECTS AND FIRST AID

INHALATION: BUTYL 2,4-DICHLOROPHENOXYACETATE: SEE INFORMATION ON 2,4-D AND DERIVATIVES.
2,4-D AND DERIVATIVES: **ACUTE EXPOSURE**- EXPOSURE TO 2,4-D AND ITS DERIVATIVES MAY CAUSE IRRITATION WITH SORE THROAT AND BURNING SENSATIONS IN THE NASOPHARYNX AND CHEST, COUGHING, LACRIMATION, RHINITIS, DULLNESS, DIZZINESS, AND ATAXIA. OTHER EFFECTS OF FATIGUE, NAUSEA, VOMITING, DIARRHEA, STOMACH PAINS, MALAISE, HEADACHE, FEVER, TACHYCARDIA, URINARY INCONTINENCE, CONSTIPATION, LEUKOPENIA, MYALGIA, AND TRANSIENT UNCONSCIOUSNESS MAY OCCUR. A DELAYED PERIPHERAL NEUROPATHY MAY DEVELOP CHARACTERIZED BY PARESTHESIAS, SEVERE PAIN, SYMMETRICAL MOTOR AND SENSORY DEFICITS, WEAKNESS, MYOTONIA, FASCICULATIONS, AND IN SOME CASES PARALYSIS OF THE EXTREMITIES. THE DISABILITY MAY BE PROLONGED AND RECOVERY INCOMPLETE. **CHRONIC EXPOSURE**- IN ADDITION TO THE EFFECTS LISTED IN ACUTE EXPOSURE, OCCUPATIONAL EXPOSURE TO 2,4-D AND ITS DERIVATIVES HAS PRODUCED A SWEET TASTE IN THE MOUTH, HYPERACUSIA, LOWERED SENSITIVITY TO TASTE AND SMELL, INCREASED SALIVATION, VERTIGO, SOMNOLENCE, ANOREXIA, HEAVINESS OF THE LEGS. OTHER EFFECTS HAVE INCLUDED HYPOTENSION, BRADYCARDIA AND OTHER CARDIOVASCULAR SYSTEM CHANGES, PAIN IN THE REGION OF THE LIVER AND STOMACH, AND CHANGES IN THE DIGESTIVE FUNCTION, LIVER FUNCTION AND METABOLIC PROCESSES. A CASE REPORT DESCRIBED A CHILD WITH MULTIPLE CONGENITAL ANOMALIES AND SEVERE MENTAL RETARDATION OF UNCERTAIN CAUSE BORN TO PARENTS HEAVILY EXPOSED TO 2,4-D WHILE SPRAYING TREES. AN INCREASED PREVALENCE OF SLOWED NERVE CONDUCTION VELOCITY WITH NO ASSOCIATED SYMPTOMS WAS REPORTED IN A STUDY OF CHEMICAL WORKERS EMPLOYED IN THE PRODUCTION OF 2,4-D AND 2,4,5-T. EPIDEMIOLOGICAL STUDIES REVEALED A SIGNIFICANT INCREASE IN SOFT-TISSUE SARCOMAS, MALIGNANT LYMPHOMAS, AND BRONCHIAL CARCINOMAS IN WORKERS EXPOSED TO CHLOROPHENOXY HERBICIDES INCLUDING 2,4-D.

FIRST AID- REMOVE FROM EXPOSURE AREA TO FRESH AIR IMMEDIATELY. IF BREATHING HAS STOPPED, PERFORM ARTIFICIAL RESPIRATION. KEEP PERSON WARM AND AT REST. TREAT SYMPTOMATICALLY AND SUPPORTIVELY. GET MEDICAL ATTENTION IMMEDIATELY.

SKIN CONTACT: BUTYL 2,4-DICHLOROPHENOXYACETATE: APPLICATION OF 200 MG/KG PRODUCED MILD DEPRESSION IN MICE; 500 MG/KG RESULTED IN MODERATE TO SEVERE DEPRESSION, MYOTONIA, IMMUNOSUPPRESSIVE EFFECTS, AND PERIVASCULAR EDEMA AND GANGLION CELL NECROSIS OF THE CENTRAL NERVOUS SYSTEM. SEE INFORMATION ON 2,4-D AND DERIVATIVES.
2,4-D AND DERIVATIVES: **ACUTE EXPOSURE**- MAY CAUSE IRRITATION. IF SUFFICIENT AMOUNTS ARE ABSORBED THROUGH THE SKIN, EFFECTS, INCLUDING PERIPHERAL NEUROPATHY, AS DESCRIBED IN ACUTE INHALATION MAY OCCUR. **CHRONIC EXPOSURE**- PROLONGED OR REPEATED EXPOSURE MAY CAUSE DERMATITIS AND EFFECTS AS DESCRIBED IN CHRONIC INHALATION.

FIRST AID- REMOVE CONTAMINATED CLOTHING AND SHOES IMMEDIATELY. WASH AFFECTED AREA WITH SOAP OR MILD DETERGENT AND LARGE AMOUNTS OF WATER UNTIL NO EVIDENCE OF CHEMICAL REMAINS (APPROXIMATELY 15-20 MINUTES). GET MEDICAL ATTENTION IMMEDIATELY.

EYE CONTACT: BUTYL 2,4-DICHLOROPHENOXYACETATE: SEE INFORMATION ON 2,4-D AND DERIVATIVES.
2,4-D AND DERIVATIVES: **ACUTE EXPOSURE**- MAY CAUSE IRRITATION. **CHRONIC EXPOSURE**- NO DATA AVAILABLE.

FIRST AID- WASH EYES IMMEDIATELY WITH LARGE AMOUNTS OF WATER OR NORMAL SALINE, OCCASIONALLY LIFTING UPPER AND LOWER LIDS, UNTIL NO EVIDENCE OF CHEMICAL REMAINS (APPROXIMATELY 15-20 MINUTES). GET MEDICAL ATTENTION IMMEDIATELY.

INGESTION: BUTYL 2,4-DICHLOROPHENOXYACETATE: TOXIC. PIGS FED 50-300 MG/KG FOR UP TO 103 DAYS EXHIBITED ATAXIA, LOSS OF APPETITE, AND LIVER AND KIDNEY CHANGES. AN INCREASED INCIDENCE OF SKELETAL DEFECTS AND DECREASED LACTATION AND VIABILITY OF OFFSPRING WERE REPORTED FROM A STUDY OF PREGNANT RATS FED 100-150 MG/KG/DAY. EFFECTS OF AN INCREASED RATE OF STILLBIRTHS AND IMPAIRED SPERM QUALITY AND SEXUAL ACTIVITY IN THE MALES WERE OBSERVED IN SHEEPS AFTER GRAZING IN TREATED FIELDS. OTHER REPRODUCTIVE EFFECTS HAVE ALSO BEEN REPORTED IN ANIMALS. SEE INFORMATION ON 2,4-D AND DERIVATIVES.
2,4-D AND DERIVATIVES: **ACUTE EXPOSURE**- INGESTION OF 2,4-D AND ITS DERIVATIVES MAY CAUSE IRRITATION OF THE MOUTH, THROAT, AND GASTROINTESTINAL TRACT, NAUSEA, VOMITING, CHEST AND ABDOMINAL PAIN, AND DIARRHEA. INGESTION OF VERY LARGE DOSES MAY PRODUCE METABOLIC ACIDOSIS, FEVER OR SUBNORMAL TEMPERATURES, HYPERVENTILATION, HYPOTENSION, VASODILATION, FLUSHING OF THE SKIN, SWEATING, CARDIAC ARRHYTHMIAS, TACHYCARDIA, LETHARGY, WEAKNESS, INTERCOSTAL PARALYSIS, RENAL AND HEPATIC DYSFUNCTION, MYOTONIA, COMA, AND CONVULSIONS. DAMAGE TO SKELETAL MUSCLE MAY BE MANIFEST BY MUSCLE TWITCHING AND ACHING WITH ELEVATED SERUM ENZYMES AND MYOGLOBIN IN THE BLOOD AND URINE. IMPAIRED MEMORY AND CHANGES IN COLOR VISION WERE REPORTED IN ONE CASE OF POISONING. DEATH MAY BE DUE TO CIRCULATORY COLLAPSE. **CHRONIC EXPOSURE**- NO DATA AVAILABLE.

FIRST AID- IF THE PERSON IS CONSCIOUS AND NOT CONVULSING, INDUCE EMESIS BY GIVING SYRUP OF IPECAC (KEEPING THE HEAD BELOW THE HIPS TO PREVENT ASPIRATION) FOLLOWED BY WATER. REPEAT IN 20 MINUTES IF NOT EFFECTIVE INITIALLY. IN PATIENTS WITH DEPRESSED RESPIRATION OR IF EMESIS IS NOT PRODUCED, PERFORM GASTRIC LAVAGE WITH ACTIVATED CHARCOAL. FOLLOW WITH A SALINE CATHARTIC (DREISBACH, HANDBOOK OF POISONING, 12TH ED.).

TREAT SYMPTOMATICALLY AND SUPPORTIVELY. GASTRIC LAVAGE SHOULD BE PERFORMED BY QUALIFIED MEDICAL PERSONNEL. GET MEDICAL ATTENTION IMMEDIATELY.

ANTIDOTE: NO SPECIFIC ANTIDOTE. TREAT SYMPTOMATICALLY AND SUPPORTIVELY.

REACTIVITY

REACTIVITY: STABLE UNDER NORMAL TEMPERATURES AND PRESSURES.

INCOMPATIBILITIES: BUTYL 2,4-DICHLOROPHENOXYACETATE: OXIDIZERS (STRONG): FIRE AND EXPLOSION HAZARD.

DECOMPOSITION: THERMAL DECOMPOSITION PRODUCTS MAY INCLUDE TOXIC AND CORROSIVE FUMES OF CHLORIDES AND TOXIC OXIDES OF CARBON.

POLYMERIZATION: HAZARDOUS POLYMERIZATION HAS NOT BEEN REPORTED TO OCCUR UNDER NORMAL TEMPERATURES AND PRESSURES.

STORAGE AND DISPOSAL

OBSERVE ALL FEDERAL, STATE AND LOCAL REGULATIONS WHEN STORING OR DISPOSING OF THIS SUBSTANCE. FOR ASSISTANCE, CONTACT THE DISTRICT DIRECTOR OF THE ENVIRONMENTAL PROTECTION AGENCY.

****STORAGE****

STORE IN ACCORDANCE WITH 29 CFR 1910.106.

BONDING AND GROUNDING: SUBSTANCES WITH LOW ELECTROCONDUCTIVITY, WHICH MAY BE IGNITED BY ELECTROSTATIC SPARKS, SHOULD BE STORED IN CONTAINERS WHICH MEET THE BONDING AND GROUNDING GUIDELINES SPECIFIED IN NFPA 77-1983, RECOMMENDED PRACTICE ON STATIC ELECTRICITY.

STORE IN ACCORDANCE WITH 40 CFR 165 RECOMMENDED PROCEDURES FOR THE DISPOSAL AND STORAGE OF PESTICIDES AND PESTICIDE CONTAINERS.

STORE AWAY FROM INCOMPATIBLE SUBSTANCES.

****DISPOSAL****

DISPOSAL MUST BE IN ACCORDANCE WITH 40 CFR 165 RECOMMENDED PROCEDURES FOR THE DISPOSAL AND STORAGE OF PESTICIDES AND PESTICIDE CONTAINERS.

DISPOSAL MUST BE IN ACCORDANCE WITH STANDARDS APPLICABLE TO GENERATORS OF HAZARDOUS WASTE, 40CFR 262. EPA HAZARDOUS WASTE NUMBER U240.

2,4-D - REGULATORY LEVEL: 10.0 MG/L MATERIALS WHICH CONTAIN THE ABOVE SUBSTANCE AT OR ABOVE THE REGULATORY LEVEL MEET THE EPA CHARACTERISTIC OF TOXICITY, AND MUST BE DISPOSED OF IN ACCORDANCE WITH 40 CFR PART 262. EPA HAZARDOUS WASTE NUMBER D016.

CONDITIONS TO AVOID

AVOID CONTACT WITH HEAT, SPARKS, FLAMES, OR OTHER SOURCES OF IGNITION. VAPORS MAY BE EXPLOSIVE. AVOID OVERHEATING OF CONTAINERS; CONTAINERS MAY VIOLENTLY RUPTURE IN HEAT OF FIRE. AVOID CONTAMINATION OF WATER SOURCES.

SPILL AND LEAK PROCEDURES

OCCUPATIONAL SPILL: SHUT OFF IGNITION SOURCES. STOP LEAK IF YOU CAN DO IT WITHOUT RISK. USE WATER SPRAY TO REDUCE VAPORS. FOR SMALL SPILLS, TAKE UP WITH SAND OR OTHER ABSORBENT MATERIAL AND PLACE INTO CONTAINERS FOR LATER DISPOSAL. FOR LARGER SPILLS, DIKE FAR AHEAD OF SPILL FOR LATER DISPOSAL. NO SMOKING, FLAMES OR FLARES IN HAZARD AREA. KEEP UNNECESSARY PEOPLE AWAY; ISOLATE HAZARD AREA AND RESTRICT ENTRY.

REPORTABLE QUANTITY (RQ): 100 POUNDS THE SUPERFUND AMENDMENTS AND REAUTHORIZATION ACT (SARA) SECTION 304 REQUIRES THAT A RELEASE EQUAL TO OR GREATER THAN THE REPORTABLE QUANTITY FOR THIS SUBSTANCE BE IMMEDIATELY REPORTED TO THE LOCAL EMERGENCY PLANNING COMMITTEE AND THE STATE EMERGENCY RESPONSE COMMISSION (40 CFR 355.40). IF THE RELEASE OF THIS SUBSTANCE IS REPORTABLE UNDER CERCLA SECTION 103, THE NATIONAL RESPONSE CENTER MUST BE NOTIFIED IMMEDIATELY AT (800) 424-8802 OR (202) 426-2675 IN THE METROPOLITAN WASHINGTON, D.C. AREA (40 CFR 302.6).

PROTECTIVE EQUIPMENT

VENTILATION: PROVIDE LOCAL EXHAUST OR PROCESS ENCLOSURE VENTILATION SYSTEM.

RESPIRATOR: THE FOLLOWING RESPIRATORS ARE RECOMMENDED BASED ON INFORMATION FOUND IN THE PHYSICAL DATA, TOXICITY AND HEALTH EFFECTS SECTIONS. THEY ARE RANKED IN ORDER FROM MINIMUM TO MAXIMUM RESPIRATORY PROTECTION. THE SPECIFIC RESPIRATOR SELECTED MUST BE BASED ON CONTAMINATION LEVELS FOUND IN THE WORK PLACE, MUST NOT EXCEED THE WORKING LIMITS OF THE RESPIRATOR AND BE JOINTLY APPROVED BY THE NATIONAL INSTITUTE FOR OCCUPATIONAL SAFETY AND HEALTH AND THE MINE SAFETY AND HEALTH ADMINISTRATION (NIOSH-MSHA).

CHEMICAL CARTRIDGE RESPIRATOR WITH FULL FACEPIECE AND PESTICIDE CARTRIDGE.

TYPE 'C' SUPPLIED-AIR RESPIRATOR WITH A FULL FACEPIECE OPERATED IN PRESSURE-DEMAND OR OTHER POSITIVE PRESSURE MODE OR WITH A FULL FACEPIECE, HELMET OR HOOD OPERATED IN CONTINUOUS-FLOW MODE.

SELF-CONTAINED BREATHING APPARATUS OPERATED IN PRESSURE-DEMAND OR OTHER POSITIVE PRESSURE MODE.

FOR FIREFIGHTING AND OTHER IMMEDIATELY DANGEROUS TO LIFE OR HEALTH CONDITIONS:

SELF-CONTAINED BREATHING APPARATUS WITH FULL FACEPIECE OPERATED IN PRESSURE-DEMAND OR OTHER POSITIVE PRESSURE MODE.

SUPPLIED-AIR RESPIRATOR WITH FULL FACEPIECE AND OPERATED IN PRESSURE-DEMAND OR OTHER POSITIVE PRESSURE MODE IN COMBINATION WITH AN AUXILIARY SELF-CONTAINED BREATHING APPARATUS OPERATED IN PRESSURE-DEMAND OR OTHER POSITIVE PRESSURE MODE.

CLOTHING: EMPLOYEE MUST WEAR APPROPRIATE PROTECTIVE (IMPERVIOUS) CLOTHING AND EQUIPMENT TO PREVENT REPEATED OR PROLONGED SKIN CONTACT WITH THIS SUBSTANCE.

GLOVES: EMPLOYEE MUST WEAR APPROPRIATE PROTECTIVE GLOVES TO PREVENT CONTACT WITH THIS SUBSTANCE.

EYE PROTECTION: EMPLOYEE MUST WEAR SPLASH-PROOF OR DUST-RESISTANT SAFETY GOGGLES TO PREVENT EYE CONTACT WITH THIS SUBSTANCE.

EMERGENCY EYE WASH: WHERE THERE IS ANY POSSIBILITY THAT AN EMPLOYEE'S EYES MAY BE EXPOSED TO THIS SUBSTANCE, THE EMPLOYER SHOULD PROVIDE AN EYE WASH FOUNTAIN WITHIN THE IMMEDIATE WORK AREA FOR EMERGENCY USE.

AUTHORIZED BY- OCCUPATIONAL HEALTH SERVICES, INC.

CREATION DATE: 03/30/90 ***REVISION DATE:*** 08/06/90

MATERIAL SAFETY DATA SHEET

OCCUPATIONAL HEALTH SERVICES, INC.
AGRICULTURE AND PESTICIDE DIVISION
450 SEVENTH AVENUE, SUITE 2407
NEW YORK, NEW YORK 10123
1-800-445-MSDS OR (212) 967-1100

EMERGENCY CONTACT:
JOHN S. BRANSFORD, JR. (615) 292-1180

SUBSTANCE IDENTIFICATION

CAS-NUMBER 1928-38-7

SUBSTANCE: METHYL 2,4-DICHLOROPHENOXY ACETATE

TRADE NAMES/SYNONYMS: 2,4-D METHYL ESTER; ACETIC ACID, (2,4-DICHLOROPHENOXY)-, METHYL ESTER; (2,4-DICHLOROPHENOXY)METHYL ACETATE; (2,4-DICHLOROPHENOXY)ACETIC ACID METHYL ESTER; RCRA U240; C9H8CL2O3; PST71307

CHEMICAL FAMILY: HALOGEN COMPOUND, AROMATIC ESTER, NON-CARBOXYLIC

MOLECULAR FORMULA: C6-H3-(CL)2-(O-C-H2-C-O2-C-H3)

MOLECULAR WEIGHT: 235.07

CERCLA RATINGS (SCALE 0-3): HEALTH=3 FIRE=1 REACTIVITY=0 PERSISTENCE=2

NFPA RATINGS (SCALE 0-4): HEALTH=U FIRE=1 REACTIVITY=0

COMPONENTS AND CONTAMINANTS

COMPONENT: METHYL 2,4-DICHLOROPHENOXY ACETATE ***PERCENT:*** 100.0
CAS# 1928-38-7

OTHER CONTAMINANTS: NONE

EXPOSURE LIMITS: NO OCCUPATIONAL EXPOSURE LIMITS ESTABLISHED BY OSHA, ACGIH, OR NIOSH.

2,4-D, SALTS AND ESTERS: 100 POUNDS CERCLA SECTION 103 REPORTABLE QUANTITY

PHYSICAL DATA

DESCRIPTION: WHITE POWDER. ***MELTING POINT:*** 104 F (40 C)

SPECIFIC GRAVITY: NOT AVAILABLE ***SOLUBILITY IN WATER:*** NOT AVAILABLE

FIRE AND EXPLOSION DATA

FIRE AND EXPLOSION HAZARD: SLIGHT FIRE HAZARD WHEN EXPOSED TO HEAT OR FLAME.

DUST-AIR MIXTURES MAY IGNITE OR EXPLODE.

FIREFIGHTING MEDIA: DRY CHEMICAL, CARBON DIOXIDE, HALON, WATER SPRAY OR STANDARD FOAM (1987 EMERGENCY RESPONSE GUIDEBOOK, DOT P 5800.4).

FOR LARGER FIRES, USE WATER SPRAY, FOG OR STANDARD FOAM (1987 EMERGENCY RESPONSE GUIDEBOOK, DOT P 5800.4).

FIREFIGHTING: MOVE CONTAINERS FROM FIRE AREA IF POSSIBLE (1987 EMERGENCY RESPONSE GUIDEBOOK, DOT P 5800.4, GUIDE PAGE 53).
EXTINGUISH USING AGENT SUITABLE FOR TYPE OF SURROUNDING FIRE. AVOID BREATHING VAPORS AND DUSTS. KEEP UPWIND.

TOXICITY

METHYL 2,4-DICHLOROPHENOXY ACETATE: TOXICITY DATA: 500 MG/KG ORAL-RAT LD50 (EPA); REPRODUCTIVE EFFECTS DATA (RTECS). CARCINOGEN STATUS: HUMAN LIMITED EVIDENCE (IARC GROUP-2B FOR CHLOROPHENOXY HERBICIDES). STUDIES REVEALED A SIGNIFICANT INCREASE IN SOFT-TISSUE SARCOMAS, MALIGNANT LYMPHOMAS AND BRONCHIAL CARCINOMAS IN WORKERS EXPOSED TO CHLOROPHENOXY HERBICIDES. ACUTE TOXICITY LEVEL: TOXIC BY INGESTION. TARGET EFFECTS: POISONING MAY AFFECT THE GASTROINTESTINAL TRACT AND THE CARDIOVASCULAR AND NERVOUS SYSTEMS.* AT INCREASED RISK FROM EXPOSURE: PERSONS WITH LIVER, KIDNEY, CARDIOVASCULAR, OR SKIN DISEASES, AND CONVULSIVE DISORDERS OR NEUROPATHY.* ADDITIONAL DATA: STIMULANTS SUCH AS EPINEPHRINE MAY INDUCE VENTRICULAR FIBRILLATION.
* MAY BE BASED ON GENERAL INFORMATION ON DICHLOROPHENOXY DERIVATIVES.

HEALTH EFFECTS AND FIRST AID

INHALATION: METHYL 2,4-DICHLOROPHENOXY ACETATE: SEE INFORMATION ON 2,4-D AND DERIVATIVES.
2,4-D AND DERIVATIVES: **ACUTE EXPOSURE-** EXPOSURE TO 2,4-D AND ITS DERIVATIVES MAY CAUSE IRRITATION WITH SORE THROAT AND BURNING SENSATIONS IN THE NASOPHARYNX AND CHEST, COUGHING, LACRIMATION, RHINITIS, DULLNESS, DIZZINESS, AND ATAXIA. OTHER EFFECTS OF FATIGUE, NAUSEA, VOMITING, DIARRHEA, STOMACH PAINS, MALAISE, HEADACHE, FEVER, TACHYCARDIA, URINARY INCONTINENCE, CONSTIPATION, LEUKOPENIA, MYALGIA, AND TRANSIENT UNCONSCIOUSNESS MAY OCCUR. A DELAYED PERIPHERAL NEUROPATHY MAY DEVELOP CHARACTERIZED BY PARESTHESIAS, SEVERE PAIN, SYMMETRICAL MOTOR AND SENSORY DEFICITS, WEAKNESS, MYOTONIA, FASCICULATIONS, AND IN SOME CASES PARALYSIS OF THE EXTREMITIES. THE DISABILITY MAY BE PROLONGED AND RECOVERY INCOMPLETE. **CHRONIC EXPOSURE-** IN ADDITION TO THE EFFECTS LISTED IN ACUTE EXPOSURE, OCCUPATIONAL EXPOSURE TO 2,4-D AND ITS DERIVATIVES HAS PRODUCED A SWEET TASTE IN THE MOUTH, HYPERACUSIA, LOWERED SENSITIVITY TO TASTE AND SMELL, INCREASED SALIVATION, VERTIGO, SOMNOLENCE, ANOREXIA, HEAVINESS OF THE LEGS. OTHER EFFECTS HAVE INCLUDED HYPOTENSION, BRADYCARDIA AND OTHER CARDIOVASCULAR SYSTEM CHANGES, PAIN IN THE REGION OF THE LIVER AND STOMACH, AND CHANGES IN THE DIGESTIVE FUNCTION, LIVER FUNCTION AND METABOLIC PROCESSES. A CASE REPORT DESCRIBED A CHILD WITH MULTIPLE CONGENITAL ANOMALIES AND SEVERE MENTAL RETARDATION OF UNCERTAIN CAUSE BORN TO PARENTS HEAVILY EXPOSED TO 2,4-D WHILE SPRAYING TREES. AN INCREASED PREVALENCE OF SLOWED NERVE CONDUCTION VELOCITY WITH NO ASSOCIATED SYMPTOMS WAS REPORTED IN A STUDY OF CHEMICAL WORKERS EMPLOYED IN THE PRODUCTION OF 2,4-D AND 2,4,5-T. EPIDEMIOLOGICAL STUDIES REVEALED A SIGNIFICANT INCREASE IN SOFT-TISSUE SARCOMAS, MALIGNANT LYMPHOMAS, AND BRONCHIAL CARCINOMAS IN WORKERS EXPOSED TO CHLOROPHENOXY HERBICIDES INCLUDING 2,4-D.
FIRST AID- REMOVE FROM EXPOSURE AREA TO FRESH AIR IMMEDIATELY. IF BREATHING HAS STOPPED, PERFORM ARTIFICIAL RESPIRATION. KEEP PERSON WARM AND AT REST. TREAT SYMPTOMATICALLY AND SUPPORTIVELY. GET MEDICAL ATTENTION IMMEDIATELY.

SKIN CONTACT: METHYL 2,4-DICHLOROPHENOXY ACETATE: SEE INFORMATION ON 2,4-D AND DERIVATIVES.
2,4-D AND DERIVATIVES: **ACUTE EXPOSURE-** MAY CAUSE IRRITATION. IF SUFFICIENT AMOUNTS ARE ABSORBED THROUGH THE SKIN, EFFECTS, INCLUDING PERIPHERAL NEUROPATHY, AS DESCRIBED IN ACUTE INHALATION MAY OCCUR. **CHRONIC EXPOSURE-** PROLONGED OR REPEATED EXPOSURE MAY CAUSE DERMATITIS AND EFFECTS AS DESCRIBED IN CHRONIC INHALATION.
FIRST AID- REMOVE CONTAMINATED CLOTHING AND SHOES IMMEDIATELY. WASH AFFECTED AREA WITH SOAP OR MILD DETERGENT AND LARGE AMOUNTS OF WATER UNTIL NO EVIDENCE OF CHEMICAL REMAINS (APPROXIMATELY 15-20 MINUTES). GET MEDICAL ATTENTION IMMEDIATELY.

EYE CONTACT: METHYL 2,4-DICHLOROPHENOXY ACETATE: SEE INFORMATION ON 2,4-D AND DERIVATIVES.
2,4-D AND DERIVATIVES: **ACUTE EXPOSURE-** MAY CAUSE IRRITATION. **CHRONIC EXPOSURE-** NO DATA AVAILABLE.
FIRST AID- WASH EYES IMMEDIATELY WITH LARGE AMOUNTS OF WATER OR NORMAL SALINE, OCCASIONALLY LIFTING UPPER AND LOWER LIDS, UNTIL NO EVIDENCE OF CHEMICAL REMAINS (APPROXIMATELY 15-20 MINUTES). GET MEDICAL ATTENTION IMMEDIATELY.

INGESTION: METHYL 2,4-DICHLOROPHENOXY ACETATE: TOXIC. SEE INFORMATION ON 2,4-D AND DERIVATIVES.
2,4-D AND DERIVATIVES: **ACUTE EXPOSURE-** INGESTION OF 2,4-D AND ITS DERIVATIVES MAY CAUSE IRRITATION OF THE MOUTH, THROAT, AND GASTROINTESTINAL TRACT, NAUSEA, VOMITING, CHEST AND ABDOMINAL PAIN, AND DIARRHEA. INGESTION OF VERY LARGE DOSES MAY PRODUCE METABOLIC ACIDOSIS, FEVER OR SUBNORMAL TEMPERATURES, HYPERVENTILATION, HYPOTENSION, VASODILATION, FLUSHING OF THE SKIN, SWEATING, CARDIAC ARRHYTHMIAS, TACHYCARDIA, LETHARGY, WEAKNESS, INTERCOSTAL PARALYSIS, RENAL AND HEPATIC DYSFUNCTION, MYOTONIA, COMA, AND CONVULSIONS. DAMAGE TO SKELETAL MUSCLE MAY BE MANIFEST BY MUSCLE TWITCHING AND ACHING WITH ELEVATED SERUM ENZYMES AND MYOGLOBIN IN THE BLOOD AND URINE. IMPAIRED MEMORY AND CHANGES IN COLOR VISION WERE REPORTED IN ONE CASE OF POISONING. DEATH MAY BE DUE TO CIRCULATORY COLLAPSE. **CHRONIC EXPOSURE-** NO DATA AVAILABLE.
FIRST AID- IF THE PERSON IS CONSCIOUS AND NOT CONVULSING, INDUCE EMESIS BY GIVING SYRUP OF IPECAC (KEEPING THE HEAD BELOW THE HIPS TO PREVENT ASPIRATION) FOLLOWED BY WATER. REPEAT IN 20 MINUTES IF NOT EFFECTIVE INITIALLY. IN PATIENTS WITH DEPRESSED RESPIRATION OR IF EMESIS IS NOT PRODUCED, PERFORM GASTRIC LAVAGE WITH ACTIVATED CHARCOAL. FOLLOW WITH A SALINE CATHARTIC (DREISBACH, HANDBOOK OF POISONING, 12TH ED.). TREAT SYMPTOMATICALLY AND SUPPORTIVELY. GASTRIC LAVAGE SHOULD BE PERFORMED BY QUALIFIED MEDICAL PERSONNEL. GET MEDICAL ATTENTION IMMEDIATELY.
ANTIDOTE: NO SPECIFIC ANTIDOTE. TREAT SYMPTOMATICALLY AND SUPPORTIVELY.

REACTIVITY

REACTIVITY: STABLE UNDER NORMAL TEMPERATURES AND PRESSURES.
INCOMPATIBILITIES: METHYL 2,4-DICHLOROPHENOXY ACETATE: OXIDIZERS (STRONG): FIRE AND EXPLOSION HAZARD.
DECOMPOSITION: THERMAL DECOMPOSITION PRODUCTS MAY INCLUDE TOXIC AND CORROSIVE FUMES OF CHLORIDES AND TOXIC OXIDES OF CARBON.
POLYMERIZATION: HAZARDOUS POLYMERIZATION HAS NOT BEEN REPORTED TO OCCUR UNDER NORMAL TEMPERATURES AND PRESSURES.

STORAGE AND DISPOSAL

OBSERVE ALL FEDERAL, STATE AND LOCAL REGULATIONS WHEN STORING OR DISPOSING OF THIS SUBSTANCE. FOR ASSISTANCE, CONTACT THE DISTRICT DIRECTOR OF THE ENVIRONMENTAL PROTECTION AGENCY.

STORAGE

STORE IN ACCORDANCE WITH 40 CFR 165 RECOMMENDED PROCEDURES FOR THE DISPOSAL AND STORAGE OF PESTICIDES AND PESTICIDE CONTAINERS.
STORE AWAY FROM INCOMPATIBLE SUBSTANCES.

DISPOSAL

DISPOSAL MUST BE IN ACCORDANCE WITH 40 CFR 165 RECOMMENDED PROCEDURES FOR THE DISPOSAL AND STORAGE OF PESTICIDES AND PESTICIDE CONTAINERS.
DISPOSAL MUST BE IN ACCORDANCE WITH STANDARDS APPLICABLE TO GENERATORS OF HAZARDOUS WASTE, 40CFR 262. EPA HAZARDOUS WASTE NUMBER U240.
2,4-D - REGULATORY LEVEL: 10.0 MG/L MATERIALS WHICH CONTAIN THE ABOVE SUBSTANCE AT OR ABOVE THE REGULATORY LEVEL MEET THE EPA CHARACTERISTIC OF TOXICITY, AND MUST BE DISPOSED OF IN ACCORDANCE WITH 40 CFR PART 262. EPA HAZARDOUS WASTE NUMBER D016.

CONDITIONS TO AVOID

MAY BURN BUT DOES NOT IGNITE READILY.

SPILL AND LEAK PROCEDURES

OCCUPATIONAL SPILL: DO NOT TOUCH SPILLED MATERIAL. STOP LEAK IF YOU CAN DO IT WITHOUT RISK. FOR SMALL SPILLS, TAKE UP WITH SAND OR OTHER ABSORBENT MATERIAL AND PLACE INTO CONTAINERS FOR LATER DISPOSAL. FOR SMALL DRY SPILLS, WITH A CLEAN SHOVEL PLACE MATERIAL INTO CLEAN, DRY CONTAINER AND COVER. MOVE CONTAINERS FROM SPILL AREA. FOR LARGER SPILLS, DIKE FAR AHEAD OF SPILL FOR LATER DISPOSAL. KEEP UNNECESSARY PEOPLE AWAY. ISOLATE HAZARD AREA AND DENY ENTRY.
REPORTABLE QUANTITY (RQ): 100 POUNDS THE SUPERFUND AMENDMENTS AND REAUTHORIZATION ACT (SARA) SECTION 304 REQUIRES THAT A RELEASE EQUAL TO OR GREATER THAN THE REPORTABLE QUANTITY FOR THIS SUBSTANCE BE IMMEDIATELY REPORTED TO THE LOCAL EMERGENCY PLANNING COMMITTEE AND THE STATE EMERGENCY RESPONSE COMMISSION (40 CFR 355.40). IF THE RELEASE OF THIS SUBSTANCE IS REPORTABLE UNDER CERCLA SECTION 103, THE NATIONAL RESPONSE CENTER MUST BE NOTIFIED IMMEDIATELY AT (800) 424-8802 OR (202) 426-2675 IN THE METROPOLITAN WASHINGTON, D.C. AREA (40 CFR 302.6).

PROTECTIVE EQUIPMENT

VENTILATION: PROVIDE LOCAL EXHAUST OR PROCESS ENCLOSURE VENTILATION SYSTEM.

RESPIRATOR: THE FOLLOWING RESPIRATORS ARE RECOMMENDED BASED ON INFORMATION FOUND IN THE PHYSICAL DATA, TOXICITY AND HEALTH EFFECTS SECTIONS. THEY ARE RANKED IN ORDER FROM MINIMUM TO MAXIMUM RESPIRATORY PROTECTION. THE SPECIFIC RESPIRATOR SELECTED MUST BE BASED ON CONTAMINATION LEVELS FOUND IN THE WORK PLACE, MUST NOT EXCEED THE WORKING LIMITS OF THE RESPIRATOR AND BE JOINTLY APPROVED BY THE NATIONAL INSTITUTE FOR OCCUPATIONAL SAFETY AND HEALTH AND THE MINE SAFETY AND HEALTH ADMINISTRATION (NIOSH-MSHA).

TYPE 'C' SUPPLIED-AIR RESPIRATOR WITH A FULL FACEPIECE OPERATED IN PRESSURE-DEMAND OR OTHER POSITIVE PRESSURE MODE OR WITH A FULL FACEPIECE, HELMET OR HOOD OPERATED IN CONTINOUS-FLOW MODE.

SELF-CONTAINED BREATHING APPARATUS WITH A FULL FACEPIECE OPERATED IN PRESSURE-DEMAND OR OTHER POSITIVE PRESSURE MODE. FOR FIREFIGHTING AND OTHER IMMEDIATELY DANGEROUS TO LIFE OR HEALTH CONDITIONS:

SELF-CONTAINED BREATHING APPARATUS WITH FULL FACEPIECE OPERATED IN PRESSURE-DEMAND OR OTHER POSITIVE PRESSURE MODE.

SUPPLIED-AIR RESPIRATOR WITH FULL FACEPIECE AND OPERATED IN PRESSURE-DEMAND OR OTHER POSITIVE PRESSURE MODE IN COMBINATION WITH AN AUXILIARY SELF-CONTAINED BREATHING APPARATUS OPERATED IN PRESSURE-DEMAND OR OTHER POSITIVE PRESSURE MODE.

CLOTHING: EMPLOYEE MUST WEAR APPROPRIATE PROTECTIVE (IMPERVIOUS) CLOTHING AND EQUIPMENT TO PREVENT ANY POSSIBILITY OF SKIN CONTACT WITH THIS SUBSTANCE.

GLOVES: EMPLOYEE MUST WEAR APPROPRIATE PROTECTIVE GLOVES TO PREVENT CONTACT WITH THIS SUBSTANCE.

EYE PROTECTION: EMPLOYEE MUST WEAR SPLASH-PROOF OR DUST-RESISTANT SAFETY GOGGLES AND A FACESHIELD TO PREVENT CONTACT WITH THIS SUBSTANCE.

EMERGENCY WASH FACILITIES: WHERE THERE IS ANY POSSIBILITY THAT AN EMPLOYEE'S EYES AND/OR SKIN MAY BE EXPOSED TO THIS SUBSTANCE, THE EMPLOYER SHOULD PROVIDE AN EYE WASH FOUNTAIN AND QUICK DRENCH SHOWER WITHIN THE IMMEDIATE WORK AREA FOR EMERGENCY USE.

AUTHORIZED BY- OCCUPATIONAL HEALTH SERVICES, INC.
CREATION DATE: 06/04/90 ***REVISION DATE:*** 07/13/90

MATERIAL SAFETY DATA SHEET

OCCUPATIONAL HEALTH SERVICES, INC.
AGRICULTURE AND PESTICIDE DIVISION
450 SEVENTH AVENUE, SUITE 2407
NEW YORK, NEW YORK 10123
1-800-445-MSDS OR (212) 967-1100

EMERGENCY CONTACT:
JOHN S. BRANSFORD, JR. (615) 292-1180

SUBSTANCE IDENTIFICATION

CAS-NUMBER 132-66-1

SUBSTANCE: **NAPTALAM**

TRADE NAMES/SYNONYMS: BENZOIC ACID, 2-((1-NAPHTHALENYLAMINO)CARBONYL)-; PHTHALAMIC ACID, N-1-NAPHTHYL-; 2-((1-NAPHTHALENYLAMINO)CARBONYL)BENZOIC ACID; N-1-NAPHTHYLPHTHALAMIC ACID; N-ALPHA-NAPHTHYLPHTHALAMIC ACID; 1-NAPHTHYLPHTHALAMIC ACID; ALPHA-NAPHTHYLPHTHALAMIC ACID; ALANAP; ANALAP-1; ANALAPE; NPA; C18H13NO3; PST71340

CHEMICAL FAMILY: CARBOXYLIC ACID
NAPHTHALENE

MOLECULAR FORMULA: H-O2-C-C6-H4-C-O-N-H-C10-H7

MOLECULAR WEIGHT: 291.31

CERCLA RATINGS (SCALE 0-3): HEALTH=1 FIRE=1 REACTIVITY=0 PERSISTENCE=1

NFPA RATINGS (SCALE 0-4): HEALTH=U FIRE=1 REACTIVITY=0

COMPONENTS AND CONTAMINANTS

COMPONENT: NAPTALAM ***PERCENT:*** 100.0
CAS# 132-66-1

OTHER CONTAMINANTS: NONE

EXPOSURE LIMITS: NO OCCUPATIONAL EXPOSURE LIMITS ESTABLISHED BY OSHA, ACGIH, OR NIOSH.

PHYSICAL DATA

DESCRIPTION: COLORLESS TO WHITE CRYSTALLINE SOLID.

MELTING POINT: 397 F (203 C)

SPECIFIC GRAVITY: 1.362 ***VOLATILITY:*** NEG ***SOLUBILITY IN WATER:*** 0.02%

SOLVENT SOLUBILITY: SOLUBLE IN ALKALINE SOLUTIONS; SLIGHTLY SOLUBLE IN ACETONE, ETHANOL, AND BENZENE.

FIRE AND EXPLOSION DATA

FIRE AND EXPLOSION HAZARD: SLIGHT FIRE HAZARD WHEN EXPOSED TO HEAT OR FLAME.

FIREFIGHTING MEDIA: DRY CHEMICAL, CARBON DIOXIDE, HALON, WATER SPRAY OR STANDARD FOAM (1987 EMERGENCY RESPONSE GUIDEBOOK, DOT P 5800.4). FOR LARGER FIRES, USE WATER SPRAY, FOG OR STANDARD FOAM (1987 EMERGENCY RESPONSE GUIDEBOOK, DOT P 5800.4).

FIREFIGHTING: MOVE CONTAINER FROM FIRE AREA IF POSSIBLE. DO NOT SCATTER SPILLED MATERIAL WITH HIGH PRESSURE WATER STREAMS. DIKE FIRE CONTROL WATER FOR LATER DISPOSAL (1987 EMERGENCY RESPONSE GUIDEBOOK, DOT P 5800.4, GUIDE PAGE 31).
USE AGENTS SUITABLE FOR TYPE OF SURROUNDING FIRE. AVOID BREATHING HAZARDOUS VAPORS, KEEP UPWIND.

TOXICITY

NAPTALAM: TOXICITY DATA: 8200 MG/KG ORAL-RAT LD50. CARCINOGEN STATUS: NONE. HOWEVER, OCCUPATIONAL EXPOSURE TO 1-NAPHTHYLAMINE, A METABOLITE AND DEGRADATION PRODUCT OF NAPTALAM, IS STRONGLY ASSOCIATED WITH BLADDER CANCER IN HUMANS. ACUTE TOXICITY LEVEL: SLIGHTLY TOXIC BY INGESTION. TARGET EFFECTS: NO DATA AVAILABLE.

HEALTH EFFECTS AND FIRST AID

INHALATION: NAPTALAM: **ACUTE EXPOSURE-** A LETHAL CONCENTRATION IN RATS WAS GREATER THAN 2070 MG/M3. **CHRONIC EXPOSURE-** OCCUPATIONAL EXPOSURE TO 1-NAPHTHYLAMINE, A METABOLITE AND DEGRADATION PRODUCT OF NAPTALAM, IS ASSOCIATED WITH THE DEVELOPMENT OF BLADDER CANCER IN HUMANS.

FIRST AID- REMOVE FROM EXPOSURE AREA TO FRESH AIR IMMEDIATELY. IF BREATHING HAS STOPPED, PERFORM ARTIFICIAL RESPIRATION. KEEP PERSON WARM AND AT REST. TREAT SYMPTOMATICALLY AND SUPPORTIVELY. GET MEDICAL ATTENTION IMMEDIATELY.

SKIN CONTACT: NAPTALAM: **ACUTE EXPOSURE-** THIS MATERIAL WAS REPORTED TO BE NONIRRITATING TO THE SKIN. A LETHAL DOSE IN RABBITS BY DERMAL ABSORPTION WAS GREATER THAN 2000 MG/KG. **CHRONIC EXPOSURE-** OCCUPATIONAL EXPOSURE TO 1-NAPHTHYLAMINE, A METABOLITE AND DEGRADATION PRODUCT OF NAPTALAM, IS ASSOCIATED WITH THE DEVELOPMENT OF BLADDER CANCER IN HUMANS.

FIRST AID- REMOVE CONTAMINATED CLOTHING AND SHOES IMMEDIATELY. WASH AFFECTED AREA WITH SOAP OR MILD DETERGENT AND LARGE AMOUNTS OF WATER UNTIL NO EVIDENCE OF CHEMICAL REMAINS (APPROXIMATELY 15-20 MINUTES). GET MEDICAL ATTENTION IMMEDIATELY.

EYE CONTACT: NAPTALAM: **ACUTE EXPOSURE-** MAY CAUSE EYE IRRITATION. **CHRONIC EXPOSURE-** NO DATA AVAILABLE.

FIRST AID- WASH EYES IMMEDIATELY WITH LARGE AMOUNTS OF WATER OR NORMAL SALINE, OCCASIONALLY LIFTING UPPER AND LOWER LIDS, UNTIL NO EVIDENCE OF CHEMICAL REMAINS (APPROXIMATELY 15-20 MINUTES). GET MEDICAL ATTENTION IMMEDIATELY.

INGESTION: NAPTALAM: **ACUTE EXPOSURE-** A LETHAL DOSE IN RATS WAS 8200 MG/KG; SYMPTOMS WERE NOT REPORTED. **CHRONIC EXPOSURE-** NO DATA AVAILABLE.

FIRST AID- REMOVE BY GASTRIC LAVAGE AND CATHARSIS. MAINTAIN BLOOD PRESSURE AND AIRWAY. GIVE OXYGEN IF RESPIRATION IS DEPRESSED. DO NOT PERFORM GASTRIC LAVAGE IF VICTIM IS UNCONSCIOUS. GET MEDICAL ATTENTION IMMEDIATELY (DREISBACH, HANDBOOK OF POISONING, 12TH ED.). ADMINISTRATION OF LAVAGE OR OXYGEN SHOULD BE PERFORMED BY QUALIFIED MEDICAL PERSONNEL.

ANTIDOTE: NO SPECIFIC ANTIDOTE. TREAT SYMPTOMATICALLY AND SUPPORTIVELY.

REACTIVITY

REACTIVITY: STABLE UNDER NORMAL TEMPERATURES AND PRESSURES.

INCOMPATIBILITIES: NAPTALAM: ACIDS (STRONG): HYDROLYZES. BASES (STRONG): HYDROLYZES. OXIDIZERS (STRONG): FIRE AND EXPLOSION HAZARD.

DECOMPOSITION: THERMAL DECOMPOSITION PRODUCTS MAY INCLUDE TOXIC OXIDES OF CARBON AND NITROGEN.

POLYMERIZATION: HAZARDOUS POLYMERIZATION HAS NOT BEEN REPORTED TO OCCUR UNDER NORMAL TEMPERATURES AND PRESSURES.

STORAGE AND DISPOSAL

OBSERVE ALL FEDERAL, STATE AND LOCAL REGULATIONS WHEN STORING OR DISPOSING OF THIS SUBSTANCE. FOR ASSISTANCE, CONTACT THE DISTRICT DIRECTOR OF THE ENVIRONMENTAL PROTECTION AGENCY.

****STORAGE****

STORE IN ACCORDANCE WITH 40 CFR 165 RECOMMENDED PROCEDURES FOR THE DISPOSAL AND STORAGE OF PESTICIDES AND PESTICIDE CONTAINERS.
STORE AWAY FROM INCOMPATIBLE SUBSTANCES.

****DISPOSAL****

DISPOSAL MUST BE IN ACCORDANCE WITH 40 CFR 165 RECOMMENDED PROCEDURES FOR THE DISPOSAL AND STORAGE OF PESTICIDES AND PESTICIDE CONTAINERS.

CONDITIONS TO AVOID

MAY BURN BUT DOES NOT IGNITE READILY. AVOID CONTACT WITH STRONG OXIDIZERS, EXCESSIVE HEAT, SPARKS, OR OPEN FLAME.

SPILL AND LEAK PROCEDURES

OCCUPATIONAL SPILL: SWEEP UP AND PLACE IN SUITABLE CLEAN, DRY CONTAINERS FOR RECLAMATION OR LATER DISPOSAL. DO NOT FLUSH SPILLED MATERIAL INTO SEWER. KEEP UNNECESSARY PEOPLE AWAY.

PROTECTIVE EQUIPMENT

VENTILATION: PROVIDE GENERAL DILUTION VENTILATION.

RESPIRATOR: THE FOLLOWING RESPIRATORS ARE RECOMMENDED BASED ON INFORMATION FOUND IN THE PHYSICAL DATA, TOXICITY AND HEALTH EFFECTS SECTIONS. THEY ARE RANKED IN ORDER FROM MINIMUM TO MAXIMUM RESPIRATORY PROTECTION. THE SPECIFIC RESPIRATOR SELECTED MUST BE BASED ON CONTAMINATION LEVELS FOUND IN THE WORK PLACE, MUST NOT EXCEED THE WORKING LIMITS OF THE RESPIRATOR AND BE JOINTLY APPROVED BY THE NATIONAL INSTITUTE FOR OCCUPATIONAL SAFETY AND HEALTH AND THE MINE SAFETY AND HEALTH ADMINISTRATION (NIOSH-MSHA).
CHEMICAL CARTRIDGE RESPIRATOR WITH AN ORGANIC VAPOR CARTRIDGE(S) IN COMBINATION WITH A DUST AND MIST FILTER.
GAS MASK WITH ORGANIC VAPOR CANISTER (CHIN-STYLE OR FRONT- OR BACK-MOUNTED CANISTER) WITH A DUST AND MIST FILTER.
GAS MASK WITH ORGANIC VAPOR CANISTER (CHIN-STYLE OR FRONT- OR BACK-MOUNTED CANISTER) WITH A PARTICULATE FILTER.
POWERED AIR-PURIFYING RESPIRATOR WITH A HIGH-EFFICIENCY FILTER.
TYPE 'C' SUPPLIED-AIR RESPIRATOR WITH A FULL FACEPIECE OPERATED IN A PRESSURE-DEMAND OR OTHER POSITIVE PRESSURE MODE.
SELF-CONTAINED BREATHING APPARATUS WITH A FULL FACEPIECE OPERATED IN PRESSURE-DEMAND OR OTHER POSITIVE PRESSURE MODE.
FOR FIREFIGHTING AND OTHER IMMEDIATELY DANGEROUS TO LIFE OR HEALTH CONDITIONS:
SELF-CONTAINED BREATHING APPARATUS WITH FULL FACEPIECE OPERATED IN PRESSURE-DEMAND OR OTHER POSITIVE PRESSURE MODE.
SUPPLIED-AIR RESPIRATOR WITH FULL FACEPIECE AND OPERATED IN PRESSURE-DEMAND OR OTHER POSITIVE PRESSURE MODE IN COMBINATION WITH AN AUXILIARY SELF-CONTAINED BREATHING APPARATUS OPERATED IN PRESSURE-DEMAND OR OTHER POSITIVE PRESSURE MODE.

CLOTHING: EMPLOYEE MUST WEAR APPROPRIATE PROTECTIVE (IMPERVIOUS) CLOTHING AND EQUIPMENT TO PREVENT REPEATED OR PROLONGED SKIN CONTACT WITH THIS SUBSTANCE.

GLOVES: EMPLOYEE MUST WEAR APPROPRIATE PROTECTIVE GLOVES TO PREVENT CONTACT WITH THIS SUBSTANCE.

EYE PROTECTION: EMPLOYEE MUST WEAR SPLASH-PROOF OR DUST-RESISTANT SAFETY GOGGLES TO PREVENT EYE CONTACT WITH THIS SUBSTANCE.
EMERGENCY EYE WASH: WHERE THERE IS ANY POSSIBILITY THAT AN EMPLOYEE'S EYES MAY BE EXPOSED TO THIS SUBSTANCE, THE EMPLOYER SHOULD PROVIDE AN EYE WASH FOUNTAIN WITHIN THE IMMEDIATE WORK AREA FOR EMERGENCY USE.

AUTHORIZED BY- OCCUPATIONAL HEALTH SERVICES, INC.
CREATION DATE: 10/04/89 ***REVISION DATE:*** 05/31/90

MATERIAL SAFETY DATA SHEET

OCCUPATIONAL HEALTH SERVICES, INC.
AGRICULTURE AND PESTICIDE DIVISION
450 SEVENTH AVENUE, SUITE 2407
NEW YORK, NEW YORK 10123
1-800-445-MSDS OR (212) 967-1100

EMERGENCY CONTACT:
JOHN S. BRANSFORD, JR. (615) 292-1180

SUBSTANCE IDENTIFICATION

CAS-NUMBER 132-67-2

SUBSTANCE: **NAPTALAM SODIUM**

TRADE NAMES/SYNONYMS: BENZOIC ACID, 2-((1-NAPHTHALENYLAMINO)CARBONYL)-, MONOSODIUM SALT; PHTHALAMIC ACID, N-1-NAPHTHYL-, MONOSODIUM SALT; 2-((1-NAPHTHALENYLAMINO)CARBONYL)BENZOIC ACID MONOSODIUM SALT; N-1-NAPHTHYLPHTHALAMIC ACID, MONOSODIUM SALT; SODIUM 2-((1-NAPHTHALENYLAMINO)CARBONYL)BENZOATE; SODIUM N-1-NAPHTHYLPHTHALAMATE; SODIUM N-1-NAPHTHYLPHTHALAMIC ACID; SODIUM NAPTALAM; ALANAP; ALANAP 3; SODIUM NPA; NPA-3; ACP-322; NAPTALAM; C18H12NANO3; PST71341

CHEMICAL FAMILY: NAPHTHALENE SALT

MOLECULAR FORMULA: C18-H12-N-O3.NA

MOLECULAR WEIGHT: 313.30

CERCLA RATINGS (SCALE 0-3): HEALTH=2 FIRE=1 REACTIVITY=0 PERSISTENCE=2

NFPA RATINGS (SCALE 0-4): HEALTH=U FIRE=1 REACTIVITY=0

COMPONENTS AND CONTAMINANTS

COMPONENT: SODIUM NAPTALAM ***PERCENT:*** 100.0
CAS# 132-67-2

OTHER CONTAMINANTS: NONE

EXPOSURE LIMITS: NO OCCUPATIONAL EXPOSURE LIMITS ESTABLISHED BY OSHA, ACGIH, OR NIOSH.

PHYSICAL DATA

DESCRIPTION: PURPLE CRYSTALLINE SOLID. ***MELTING POINT:*** NOT AVAILABLE

SPECIFIC GRAVITY: NOT AVAILABLE ***SOLUBILITY IN WATER:*** 30%

FIRE AND EXPLOSION DATA

FIRE AND EXPLOSION HAZARD: SLIGHT FIRE HAZARD WHEN EXPOSED TO HEAT OR FLAME.

FIREFIGHTING MEDIA: DRY CHEMICAL, CARBON DIOXIDE, HALON, WATER SPRAY OR STANDARD FOAM (1987 EMERGENCY RESPONSE GUIDEBOOK, DOT P 5800.4).
FOR LARGER FIRES, USE WATER SPRAY, FOG OR STANDARD FOAM (1987 EMERGENCY RESPONSE GUIDEBOOK, DOT P 5800.4).

FIREFIGHTING: MOVE CONTAINER FROM FIRE AREA IF POSSIBLE. DO NOT SCATTER SPILLED MATERIAL WITH HIGH PRESSURE WATER STREAMS. DIKE FIRE CONTROL WATER FOR LATER DISPOSAL (1987 EMERGENCY RESPONSE GUIDEBOOK, DOT P 5800.4, GUIDE PAGE 31).
USE AGENTS SUITABLE FOR TYPE OF SURROUNDING FIRE. AVOID BREATHING HAZARDOUS VAPORS, KEEP UPWIND.

TOXICITY

NAPTALAM SODIUM TOXICITY DATA: 1770 MG/KG ORAL-RAT LD50. CARCINOGEN STATUS: NONE. HOWEVER, OCCUPATIONAL EXPOSURE TO 1-NAPHTHYLAMINE, A METABOLITE AND DEGRADATION PRODUCT OF NAPTALAM, IS STRONGLY ASSOCIATED WITH BLADDER CANCER IN HUMANS. ACUTE TOXICITY LEVEL: MODERATELY TOXIC BY INGESTION. TARGET EFFECTS: NO DATA AVAILABLE.

HEALTH EFFECTS AND FIRST AID

INHALATION: NAPTALAM SODIUM: **ACUTE EXPOSURE-** NO DATA AVAILABLE.
CHRONIC EXPOSURE- OCCUPATIONAL EXPOSURE TO 1-NAPHTHYLAMINE, A METABOLITE AND DEGRADATION PRODUCT OF NAPTALAM, IS ASSOCIATED WITH THE DEVELOPMENT OF BLADDER CANCER IN HUMANS.

FIRST AID- REMOVE FROM EXPOSURE AREA TO FRESH AIR IMMEDIATELY. IF BREATHING HAS STOPPED, PERFORM ARTIFICIAL RESPIRATION. KEEP PERSON WARM AND AT REST. TREAT SYMPTOMATICALLY AND SUPPORTIVELY. GET MEDICAL ATTENTION IMMEDIATELY.

SKIN CONTACT: NAPTALAM SODIUM: **ACUTE EXPOSURE-** NO DATA AVAILABLE.
CHRONIC EXPOSURE- OCCUPATIONAL EXPOSURE TO 1-NAPHTHYLAMINE, A METABOLITE AND DEGRADATION PRODUCT OF NAPTALAM, IS ASSOCIATED WITH THE DEVELOPMENT OF BLADDER CANCER IN HUMANS.

FIRST AID- REMOVE CONTAMINATED CLOTHING AND SHOES IMMEDIATELY. WASH AFFECTED AREA WITH SOAP OR MILD DETERGENT AND LARGE AMOUNTS OF WATER UNTIL NO EVIDENCE OF CHEMICAL REMAINS (APPROXIMATELY 15-20 MINUTES). GET MEDICAL ATTENTION IMMEDIATELY.

EYE CONTACT: NAPTALAM SODIUM: **ACUTE EXPOSURE-** NO DATA AVAILABLE.
CHRONIC EXPOSURE- NO DATA AVAILABLE.

FIRST AID- WASH EYES IMMEDIATELY WITH LARGE AMOUNTS OF WATER OR NORMAL SALINE, OCCASIONALLY LIFTING UPPER AND LOWER LIDS, UNTIL NO EVIDENCE OF CHEMICAL REMAINS (APPROXIMATELY 15-20 MINUTES). GET MEDICAL ATTENTION IMMEDIATELY.

INGESTION: NAPTALAM SODIUM: ACUTE EXPOSURE- A LETHAL DOSE IN RATS WAS 1770 MG/KG; SYMPTOMS WERE NOT REPORTED. CHRONIC EXPOSURE- SLIGHTLY LOWERED HEART/BODY AND SPLEEN/BODY WEIGHT RATIOS WERE NOTED IN A 13-WEEK STUDY OF RATS RECEIVING 5000 PPM IN THE DIET.

FIRST AID- REMOVE BY GASTRIC LAVAGE AND CATHARSIS. MAINTAIN BLOOD PRESSURE AND AIRWAY. GIVE OXYGEN IF RESPIRATION IS DEPRESSED. DO NOT PERFORM GASTRIC LAVAGE IF VICTIM IS UNCONSCIOUS. GET MEDICAL ATTENTION IMMEDIATELY (DREISBACH, HANDBOOK OF POISONING, 12TH ED.).
ADMINISTRATION OF LAVAGE OR OXYGEN SHOULD BE PERFORMED BY QUALIFIED MEDICAL PERSONNEL.

ANTIDOTE: NO SPECIFIC ANTIDOTE. TREAT SYMPTOMATICALLY AND SUPPORTIVELY.

REACTIVITY

REACTIVITY: STABLE UNDER NORMAL TEMPERATURES AND PRESSURES.

INCOMPATIBILITIES: NAPTALAM-SODIUM: OXIDIZERS (STRONG): FIRE AND EXPLOSION HAZARD.

DECOMPOSITION: THERMAL DECOMPOSITION PRODUCTS MAY INCLUDE TOXIC OXIDES OF CARBON AND NITROGEN.

POLYMERIZATION: HAZARDOUS POLYMERIZATION HAS NOT BEEN REPORTED TO OCCUR UNDER NORMAL TEMPERATURES AND PRESSURES.

STORAGE AND DISPOSAL

OBSERVE ALL FEDERAL, STATE AND LOCAL REGULATIONS WHEN STORING OR DISPOSING OF THIS SUBSTANCE. FOR ASSISTANCE, CONTACT THE DISTRICT DIRECTOR OF THE ENVIRONMENTAL PROTECTION AGENCY.

****STORAGE****

STORE IN ACCORDANCE WITH 40 CFR 165 RECOMMENDED PROCEDURES FOR THE DISPOSAL AND STORAGE OF PESTICIDES AND PESTICIDE CONTAINERS.
STORE AWAY FROM INCOMPATIBLE SUBSTANCES.

****DISPOSAL****

DISPOSAL MUST BE IN ACCORDANCE WITH 40 CFR 165 RECOMMENDED PROCEDURES FOR THE DISPOSAL AND STORAGE OF PESTICIDES AND PESTICIDE CONTAINERS.

CONDITIONS TO AVOID

MAY BURN BUT DOES NOT IGNITE READILY. AVOID CONTACT WITH STRONG OXIDIZERS, EXCESSIVE HEAT, SPARKS, OR OPEN FLAME.

SPILL AND LEAK PROCEDURES

OCCUPATIONAL SPILL: SWEEP UP AND PLACE IN SUITABLE CLEAN, DRY CONTAINERS FOR RECLAMATION OR LATER DISPOSAL. DO NOT FLUSH SPILLED MATERIAL INTO SEWER. KEEP UNNECESSARY PEOPLE AWAY.

PROTECTIVE EQUIPMENT

VENTILATION: PROVIDE LOCAL EXHAUST OR GENERAL DILUTION VENTILATION SYSTEM.

RESPIRATOR: THE FOLLOWING RESPIRATORS ARE RECOMMENDED BASED ON INFORMATION FOUND IN THE PHYSICAL DATA, TOXICITY AND HEALTH EFFECTS SECTIONS. THEY ARE RANKED IN ORDER FROM MINIMUM TO MAXIMUM RESPIRATORY PROTECTION. THE SPECIFIC RESPIRATOR SELECTED MUST BE BASED ON CONTAMINATION LEVELS FOUND IN THE WORK PLACE, MUST NOT EXCEED THE WORKING LIMITS OF THE RESPIRATOR AND BE JOINTLY APPROVED BY THE NATIONAL INSTITUTE FOR OCCUPATIONAL SAFETY AND HEALTH AND THE MINE SAFETY AND HEALTH ADMINISTRATION (NIOSH-MSHA).
CHEMICAL CARTRIDGE RESPIRATOR WITH AN ORGANIC VAPOR CARTRIDGE(S) WITH A FULL FACEPIECE AND ORGANIC VAPOR CARTRIDGE(S) IN COMBINATION WITH A DUST AND MIST FILTER.
POWERED AIR-PURIFYING RESPIRATOR WITH A TIGHT-FITTING FACEPIECE AND ORGANIC VAPOR CARTRIDGE(S) IN COMBINATION WITH A HIGH-EFFICIENCY PARTICULATE FILTER.
TYPE 'C' SUPPLIED-AIR RESPIRATOR WITH A FULL FACEPIECE OPERATED IN A PRESSURE-DEMAND OR OTHER POSITIVE PRESSURE MODE.
SELF-CONTAINED BREATHING APPARATUS WITH A FULL FACEPIECE OPERATED IN PRESSURE-DEMAND OR OTHER POSITIVE PRESSURE MODE.
FOR FIREFIGHTING AND OTHER IMMEDIATELY DANGEROUS TO LIFE OR HEALTH CONDITIONS:
SELF-CONTAINED BREATHING APPARATUS WITH FULL FACEPIECE OPERATED IN PRESSURE-DEMAND OR OTHER POSITIVE PRESSURE MODE.
SUPPLIED-AIR RESPIRATOR WITH FULL FACEPIECE AND OPERATED IN PRESSURE-DEMAND OR OTHER POSITIVE PRESSURE MODE IN COMBINATION WITH AN AUXILIARY SELF-CONTAINED BREATHING APPARATUS OPERATED IN PRESSURE-DEMAND OR OTHER POSITIVE PRESSURE MODE.

CLOTHING: EMPLOYEE MUST WEAR APPROPRIATE PROTECTIVE (IMPERVIOUS) CLOTHING AND EQUIPMENT TO PREVENT REPEATED OR PROLONGED SKIN CONTACT WITH THIS SUBSTANCE.

GLOVES: EMPLOYEE MUST WEAR APPROPRIATE PROTECTIVE GLOVES TO PREVENT CONTACT WITH THIS SUBSTANCE.

EYE PROTECTION: EMPLOYEE MUST WEAR SPLASH-PROOF OR DUST-RESISTANT SAFETY GOGGLES TO PREVENT EYE CONTACT WITH THIS SUBSTANCE.
EMERGENCY EYE WASH: WHERE THERE IS ANY POSSIBILITY THAT AN EMPLOYEE'S EYES MAY BE EXPOSED TO THIS SUBSTANCE, THE EMPLOYER SHOULD PROVIDE AN EYE WASH FOUNTAIN WITHIN THE IMMEDIATE WORK AREA FOR EMERGENCY USE.

AUTHORIZED BY- OCCUPATIONAL HEALTH SERVICES, INC.
CREATION DATE: 10/04/89 ***REVISION DATE:*** 05/31/90

MATERIAL SAFETY DATA SHEET

OCCUPATIONAL HEALTH SERVICES, INC.
AGRICULTURE AND PESTICIDE DIVISION
450 SEVENTH AVENUE, SUITE 2407
NEW YORK, NEW YORK 10123
1-800-445-MSDS OR (212) 967-1100

EMERGENCY CONTACT:
JOHN S. BRANSFORD, JR. (615) 292-1180

SUBSTANCE IDENTIFICATION

CAS-NUMBER 97-16-5

SUBSTANCE: GENITE

TRADE NAMES/SYNONYMS: PHENOL, 2,4-DICHLORO-, BENZENESULFONATE; 2,4-DICHLOROPHENOL BENZENESULFONATE; BENZENESULFONIC ACID, 2,4-DICHLOROPHENYL ESTER; 2,4-DICHLOROPHENYL BENZENESULFONATE; 2,4-DICHLOROPHENYL BENZENESULPHONATE; BENZENESULFONIC ACID 2,4-DICHLOROPHENYL ESTER; EM 923; GENITOL; GENITOL 923; C12H8CL2O3S; PST71350

CHEMICAL FAMILY: SULFONATE

MOLECULAR FORMULA: C6-H5-S-O3(C6-H3-CL2)

MOLECULAR WEIGHT: 303.16

CERCLA RATINGS (SCALE 0-3): HEALTH=3 FIRE=1 REACTIVITY=0 PERSISTENCE=3

NFPA RATINGS (SCALE 0-4): HEALTH=3 FIRE=1 REACTIVITY=0

COMPONENTS AND CONTAMINANTS

COMPONENT: GENITE ***PERCENT:*** 100
CAS# 97-16-5

OTHER CONTAMINANTS: NONE

EXPOSURE LIMITS: NO OCCUPATIONAL EXPOSURE LIMITS ESTABLISHED BY OSHA, ACGIH, OR NIOSH.

PHYSICAL DATA

DESCRIPTION: WAXY SOLID. ***MELTING POINT:*** 113-115 F (45-46 C)

SPECIFIC GRAVITY: NOT AVAILABLE ***VAPOR PRESSURE:*** 0.00027 MMHG @ 30 C

SOLUBILITY IN WATER: INSOLUBLE

SOLVENT SOLUBILITY: SOLUBLE IN ACETONE, CHLOROFORM, METHYLENE CHLORIDE.

FIRE AND EXPLOSION DATA

FIRE AND EXPLOSION HAZARD: SLIGHT FIRE HAZARD WHEN EXPOSED TO HEAT OR FLAME.

FIREFIGHTING MEDIA: DRY CHEMICAL, CARBON DIOXIDE, HALON, WATER SPRAY OR STANDARD FOAM (1987 EMERGENCY RESPONSE GUIDEBOOK, DOT P 5800.4).
FOR LARGER FIRES, USE WATER SPRAY, FOG OR STANDARD FOAM (1987 EMERGENCY RESPONSE GUIDEBOOK, DOT P 5800.4).

FIREFIGHTING: MOVE CONTAINERS FROM FIRE AREA IF POSSIBLE (1987 EMERGENCY RESPONSE GUIDEBOOK, DOT P 5800.4, GUIDE PAGE 53).
EXTINGUISH FIRE USING AGENTS SUITABLE FOR TYPE OF SURROUNDING FIRE. USE WATER IN FLOODING AMOUNTS AS A FOG. AVOID BREATHING DUSTS AND FUMES FROM BURNING MATERIAL; KEEP UPWIND.

TOXICITY

GENITE: TOXICITY DATA: 1 GM/KG ORAL-RAT LD50; 700 MG/KG ORAL-RABBIT LD50; 620 MG/KG ORAL-DOG LDLO; 115 MG/KG INTRAVENOUS-RABBIT LD50; 1400 MG/KG UNREPORTED-RAT LD50; TUMORIGENIC DATA (RTECS). CARCINOGEN

STATUS: NONE. ACUTE TOXICITY LEVEL: MODERATELY TOXIC BY INGESTION.
TARGET EFFECTS: NO DATA AVAILABLE.

HEALTH EFFECTS AND FIRST AID

INHALATION: GENITE: **ACUTE EXPOSURE-** NO DATA AVAILABLE. **CHRONIC EXPOSURE-** NO DATA AVAILABLE.
FIRST AID- REMOVE FROM EXPOSURE AREA TO FRESH AIR IMMEDIATELY. IF BREATHING HAS STOPPED, PERFORM ARTIFICIAL RESPIRATION. KEEP PERSON WARM AND AT REST. TREAT SYMPTOMATICALLY AND SUPPORTIVELY. GET MEDICAL ATTENTION IMMEDIATELY.

SKIN CONTACT: GENITE: **ACUTE EXPOSURE-** MAY BE ABSORBED THROUGH THE INTACT SKIN OF RABBITS. **CHRONIC EXPOSURE-** NO DATA AVAILABLE.
FIRST AID- REMOVE CONTAMINATED CLOTHING AND SHOES IMMEDIATELY. WASH AFFECTED AREA WITH SOAP OR MILD DETERGENT AND LARGE AMOUNTS OF WATER UNTIL NO EVIDENCE OF CHEMICAL REMAINS (APPROXIMATELY 15-20 MINUTES). GET MEDICAL ATTENTION IMMEDIATELY.

EYE CONTACT: GENITE: **ACUTE EXPOSURE-** NO DATA AVAILABLE. **CHRONIC EXPOSURE-** NO DATA AVAILABLE.
FIRST AID- WASH EYES IMMEDIATELY WITH LARGE AMOUNTS OF WATER OR NORMAL SALINE, OCCASIONALLY LIFTING UPPER AND LOWER LIDS, UNTIL NO EVIDENCE OF CHEMICAL REMAINS (APPROXIMATELY 15-20 MINUTES). GET MEDICAL ATTENTION IMMEDIATELY.

INGESTION: GENITE: **ACUTE EXPOSURE-** A DOSE OF 1000 MG/KG WAS LETHAL IN SOME RATS. LETHAL DOSES IN ANIMALS PRODUCED VOMITING, UNSTEADINESS, GENERALIZED WEAKNESS, AND FINE TREMORS FOLLOWED BY DEATH 1 TO 4 DAYS LATER. RABBITS AND DOGS SHOWED MARKEDLY DILATED HEARTS AND HEMORRHAGIC AREAS THROUGHOUT THE GASTROINTESTINAL TRACT. **CHRONIC EXPOSURE-** NO DATA AVAILABLE.
FIRST AID- TREAT SYMPTOMATICALLY AND SUPPORTIVELY. GET MEDICAL ATTENTION IMMEDIATELY. IF VOMITING OCCURS, KEEP HEAD LOWER THAN HIPS TO PREVENT ASPIRATION.
ANTIDOTE: NO SPECIFIC ANTIDOTE. TREAT SYMPTOMATICALLY AND SUPPORTIVELY.

REACTIVITY

REACTIVITY: STABLE UNDER NORMAL TEMPERATURES AND PRESSURES.
INCOMPATIBILITIES: GENITE: NO DATA AVAILABLE.
DECOMPOSITION: THERMAL DECOMPOSITION PRODUCTS MAY INCLUDE TOXIC OXIDES OF SULFUR AND TOXIC AND CORROSIVE FUMES OF CHLORIDES.
POLYMERIZATION: HAZARDOUS POLYMERIZATION HAS NOT BEEN REPORTED TO OCCUR UNDER NORMAL TEMPERATURES AND PRESSURES.

STORAGE AND DISPOSAL

OBSERVE ALL FEDERAL, STATE AND LOCAL REGULATIONS WHEN STORING OR DISPOSING OF THIS SUBSTANCE. FOR ASSISTANCE, CONTACT THE DISTRICT DIRECTOR OF THE ENVIRONMENTAL PROTECTION AGENCY.

STORAGE

STORE IN ACCORDANCE WITH 40 CFR 165 RECOMMENDED PROCEDURES FOR THE DISPOSAL AND STORAGE OF PESTICIDES AND PESTICIDE CONTAINERS.

DISPOSAL

DISPOSAL MUST BE IN ACCORDANCE WITH 40 CFR 165 RECOMMENDED PROCEDURES FOR THE DISPOSAL AND STORAGE OF PESTICIDES AND PESTICIDE CONTAINERS.

CONDITIONS TO AVOID

MAY BURN BUT DOES NOT IGNITE READILY.

SPILL AND LEAK PROCEDURES

OCCUPATIONAL SPILL: DO NOT TOUCH SPILLED MATERIAL. STOP LEAK IF YOU CAN DO IT WITHOUT RISK. FOR SMALL SPILLS, TAKE UP WITH SAND OR OTHER ABSORBENT MATERIAL AND PLACE INTO CONTAINERS FOR LATER DISPOSAL. FOR SMALL DRY SPILLS, WITH A CLEAN SHOVEL PLACE MATERIAL INTO CLEAN, DRY CONTAINER AND COVER. MOVE CONTAINERS FROM SPILL AREA. FOR LARGER SPILLS, DIKE FAR AHEAD OF SPILL FOR LATER DISPOSAL. KEEP UNNECESSARY PEOPLE AWAY. ISOLATE HAZARD AREA AND DENY ENTRY.

PROTECTIVE EQUIPMENT

VENTILATION: PROVIDE LOCAL EXHAUST OR PROCESS ENCLOSURE VENTILATION SYSTEM.
RESPIRATOR: THE FOLLOWING RESPIRATORS ARE RECOMMENDED BASED ON INFORMATION FOUND IN THE PHYSICAL DATA, TOXICITY AND HEALTH EFFECTS SECTIONS. THEY ARE RANKED IN ORDER FROM MINIMUM TO MAXIMUM RESPIRATORY PROTECTION. THE SPECIFIC RESPIRATOR SELECTED MUST BE BASED ON CONTAMINATION LEVELS FOUND IN THE WORK PLACE, MUST NOT EXCEED THE WORKING LIMITS OF THE RESPIRATOR AND BE JOINTLY APPROVED BY THE NATIONAL INSTITUTE FOR OCCUPATIONAL SAFETY AND HEALTH AND THE MINE SAFETY AND HEALTH ADMINISTRATION (NIOSH-MSHA).
CHEMICAL CARTRIDGE RESPIRATOR WITH AN ORGANIC VAPOR CARTRIDGE(S) WITH A FULL FACEPIECE AND ORGANIC VAPOR CARTRIDGE(S) IN COMBINATION WITH A DUST AND MIST FILTER.
POWERED AIR-PURIFYING RESPIRATOR WITH A TIGHT-FITTING FACEPIECE AND ORGANIC VAPOR CARTRIDGE(S) IN COMBINATION WITH A HIGH-EFFICIENCY PARTICULATE FILTER.
TYPE 'C' SUPPLIED-AIR RESPIRATOR WITH A FULL FACEPIECE OPERATED IN A PRESSURE-DEMAND OR OTHER POSITIVE PRESSURE MODE.
SELF-CONTAINED BREATHING APPARATUS WITH A FULL FACEPIECE OPERATED IN PRESSURE-DEMAND OR OTHER POSITIVE PRESSURE MODE.
FOR FIREFIGHTING AND OTHER IMMEDIATELY DANGEROUS TO LIFE OR HEALTH CONDITIONS:
SELF-CONTAINED BREATHING APPARATUS WITH FULL FACEPIECE OPERATED IN PRESSURE-DEMAND OR OTHER POSITIVE PRESSURE MODE.
SUPPLIED-AIR RESPIRATOR WITH FULL FACEPIECE AND OPERATED IN PRESSURE-DEMAND OR OTHER POSITIVE PRESSURE MODE IN COMBINATION WITH AN AUXILIARY SELF-CONTAINED BREATHING APPARATUS OPERATED IN PRESSURE-DEMAND OR OTHER POSITIVE PRESSURE MODE.
CLOTHING: EMPLOYEE MUST WEAR APPROPRIATE PROTECTIVE (IMPERVIOUS) CLOTHING AND EQUIPMENT TO PREVENT REPEATED OR PROLONGED SKIN CONTACT WITH THIS SUBSTANCE.
GLOVES: EMPLOYEE MUST WEAR APPROPRIATE PROTECTIVE GLOVES TO PREVENT CONTACT WITH THIS SUBSTANCE.
EYE PROTECTION: EMPLOYEE MUST WEAR SPLASH-PROOF OR DUST-RESISTANT SAFETY GOGGLES TO PREVENT EYE CONTACT WITH THIS SUBSTANCE.
EMERGENCY EYE WASH: WHERE THERE IS ANY POSSIBILITY THAT AN EMPLOYEE'S EYES MAY BE EXPOSED TO THIS SUBSTANCE, THE EMPLOYER SHOULD PROVIDE AN EYE WASH FOUNTAIN WITHIN THE IMMEDIATE WORK AREA FOR EMERGENCY USE.

AUTHORIZED BY- OCCUPATIONAL HEALTH SERVICES, INC.
CREATION DATE: 11/17/89 ***REVISION DATE:*** 05/18/90

MATERIAL SAFETY DATA SHEET

OCCUPATIONAL HEALTH SERVICES, INC.
AGRICULTURE AND PESTICIDE DIVISION
450 SEVENTH AVENUE, SUITE 2407
NEW YORK, NEW YORK 10123
1-800-445-MSDS OR (212) 967-1100

EMERGENCY CONTACT:
JOHN S. BRANSFORD, JR. (615) 292-1180

SUBSTANCE IDENTIFICATION

CAS-NUMBER 8001-26-1
SUBSTANCE: **LINSEED OIL**
TRADE NAMES/SYNONYMS: LINSEED OIL, BLEACHED; FLAXSEED OIL; OLEUM LINI; LINSEED OIL, RAW; PST71365
CHEMICAL FAMILY: ESSENTIAL OIL
CERCLA RATINGS (SCALE 0-3): HEALTH=0 FIRE=1 REACTIVITY=0 PERSISTENCE=1
NFPA RATINGS (SCALE 0-4): HEALTH=0 FIRE=1 REACTIVITY=0

COMPONENTS AND CONTAMINANTS

COMPONENT: LINSEED OIL ***PERCENT:*** 100.0
CAS# 8001-26-1
OTHER CONTAMINANTS: NONE
EXPOSURE LIMITS: NO OCCUPATIONAL EXPOSURE LIMITS ESTABLISHED BY OSHA, ACGIH, OR NIOSH.

PHYSICAL DATA

DESCRIPTION: YELLOW TO BROWN LIQUID WITH A PECULIAR ODOR AND BLAND TASTE.
BOILING POINT: >600 F (>316 C) ***MELTING POINT:*** -11 F (-24 C)
SPECIFIC GRAVITY: 0.925-0.935 ***SOLUBILITY IN WATER:*** INSOLUBLE
SOLVENT SOLUBILITY: SOLUBLE IN ETHER, CHLOROFORM, CARBON DISULFIDE, BENZENE PETROLEUM ETHER, OIL, AND TURPENTINE; SLIGHTLY SOLUBLE IN ALCOHOL.

FIRE AND EXPLOSION DATA

FIRE AND EXPLOSION HAZARD: SLIGHT FIRE HAZARD WHEN EXPOSED TO HEAT OR FLAME.

FLASH POINT: 432 F (222 C) (CC) ***AUTOIGNITION TEMP.:*** 650 F (343 C)

FLAMMABILITY CLASS(OSHA): IIIB

FIREFIGHTING MEDIA: DRY CHEMICAL, CARBON DIOXIDE, HALON, WATER SPRAY OR STANDARD FOAM (1987 EMERGENCY RESPONSE GUIDEBOOK, DOT P 5800.4). FOR LARGER FIRES, USE WATER SPRAY, FOG OR STANDARD FOAM (1987 EMERGENCY RESPONSE GUIDEBOOK, DOT P 5800.4).

FIREFIGHTING: MOVE CONTAINER FROM FIRE AREA IF POSSIBLE. DO NOT SCATTER SPILLED MATERIAL WITH HIGH PRESSURE WATER STREAMS. DIKE FIRE CONTROL WATER FOR LATER DISPOSAL (1987 EMERGENCY RESPONSE GUIDEBOOK, DOT P 5800.4, GUIDE PAGE 31).

USE AGENTS SUITABLE FOR TYPE OF SURROUNDING FIRE. AVOID BREATHING HAZARDOUS VAPORS, KEEP UPWIND.

WATER OR FOAM MAY CAUSE FROTHING (NFPA 325M, FIRE HAZARD PROPERTIES OF FLAMMABLE LIQUIDS, GASES, AND VOLATILE SOLIDS, 1984)

TOXICITY

LINSEED OIL: IRRITATION DATA: 300 MG/3 DAYS INTERMITTENT SKIN-HUMAN MODERATE. CARCINOGEN STATUS: NONE. LOCAL EFFECTS: IRRITANT-SKIN. ACUTE TOXICITY LEVEL: NO DATA AVAILABLE. TARGET EFFECTS: NO DATA AVAILABLE.

AT INCREASED RISK FROM EXPOSURE: PERSONS WHO EXHIBIT HYPERSENSITIVITY.

HEALTH EFFECTS AND FIRST AID

INHALATION: LINSEED OIL: **ACUTE EXPOSURE-** INHALATION MAY RESULT IN CHEMICAL PNEUMONITIS. AN ALLERGIC ASTHMATIC REACTION IN PREVIOUSLY EXPOSED INDIVIDUALS MAY OCCUR. **CHRONIC EXPOSURE-** REPEATED OR PROLONGED EXPOSURE MAY RESULT IN SENSITIZATION.

FIRST AID- REMOVE FROM EXPOSURE AREA TO FRESH AIR IMMEDIATELY. IF BREATHING HAS STOPPED, PERFORM ARTIFICIAL RESPIRATION. KEEP PERSON WARM AND AT REST. TREAT SYMPTOMATICALLY AND SUPPORTIVELY. GET MEDICAL ATTENTION IMMEDIATELY.

SKIN CONTACT: LINSEED OIL: IRRITANT. **ACUTE EXPOSURE-** RARELY, CONTACT MAY CAUSE A HYPERSENSITIVITY REACTION IN PREVIOUSLY EXPOSED INDIVIDUALS. **CHRONIC EXPOSURE-** REPEATED OR PROLONGED CONTACT MAY CAUSE IRRITATION AND RESULT IN SENSITIZATION.

FIRST AID- REMOVE CONTAMINATED CLOTHING AND SHOES IMMEDIATELY. WASH AFFECTED AREA WITH SOAP OR MILD DETERGENT AND LARGE AMOUNTS OF WATER UNTIL NO EVIDENCE OF CHEMICAL REMAINS (APPROXIMATELY 15-20 MINUTES). GET MEDICAL ATTENTION IMMEDIATELY.

EYE CONTACT: LINSEED OIL: **ACUTE EXPOSURE-** NO DATA AVAILABLE. **CHRONIC EXPOSURE-** NO DATA AVAILABLE.

FIRST AID- WASH EYES IMMEDIATELY WITH LARGE AMOUNTS OF WATER OR NORMAL SALINE, OCCASIONALLY LIFTING UPPER AND LOWER LIDS, UNTIL NO EVIDENCE OF CHEMICAL REMAINS (APPROXIMATELY 15-20 MINUTES). GET MEDICAL ATTENTION IMMEDIATELY.

INGESTION: LINSEED OIL: **ACUTE EXPOSURE-** INGESTION OF AMOUNTS GREATER THAN 1 OUNCE MAY PRODUCE A LAXATIVE EFFECT. VERY LARGE QUANTITIES MAY CAUSE INTESTINAL OBSTRUCTION. ASPIRATION MAY RESULT IN CHEMICAL PNEUMONITIS. **CHRONIC EXPOSURE-** NO DATA AVAILABLE.

FIRST AID- TREAT SYMPTOMATICALLY AND SUPPORTIVELY. GET MEDICAL ATTENTION IMMEDIATELY. IF VOMITING OCCURS, KEEP HEAD LOWER THAN HIPS TO PREVENT ASPIRATION.

ANTIDOTE: NO SPECIFIC ANTIDOTE. TREAT SYMPTOMATICALLY AND SUPPORTIVELY.

REACTIVITY

REACTIVITY: STABLE UNDER NORMAL TEMPERATURES AND PRESSURES.

INCOMPATIBILITIES: LINSEED OIL: CHLORINE (LIQUID): EXPLOSIVE REACTION. OXIDIZERS (STRONG): FIRE AND EXPLOSION HAZARD.

DECOMPOSITION: THERMAL DECOMPOSITION MAY RELEASE ACRID SMOKE AND IRRITATING FUMES.

POLYMERIZATION: LINSEED OIL: SLOWLY POLYMERIZES ON EXPOSURE TO AIR.

STORAGE AND DISPOSAL

OBSERVE ALL FEDERAL, STATE AND LOCAL REGULATIONS WHEN STORING OR DISPOSING OF THIS SUBSTANCE. FOR ASSISTANCE, CONTACT THE DISTRICT DIRECTOR OF THE ENVIRONMENTAL PROTECTION AGENCY.

****STORAGE****

STORE AWAY FROM INCOMPATIBLE SUBSTANCES.

CONDITIONS TO AVOID

MAY BURN BUT DOES NOT IGNITE READILY. AVOID CONTACT WITH STRONG OXIDIZERS, EXCESSIVE HEAT, SPARKS, OR OPEN FLAME.

SPILL AND LEAK PROCEDURES

OCCUPATIONAL SPILL: STOP LEAK IF YOU CAN DO IT WITHOUT RISK. FOR SMALL SPILLS, TAKE UP WITH SAND OR OTHER ABSORBENT MATERIAL AND PLACE INTO CLEAN, DRY CONTAINERS FOR LATER DISPOSAL. KEEP UNNECESSARY PEOPLE AWAY. ISOLATE HAZARD AREA AND DENY ENTRY.

PROTECTIVE EQUIPMENT

VENTILATION: PROVIDE GENERAL DILUTION VENTILATION.

RESPIRATOR: THE FOLLOWING RESPIRATORS ARE RECOMMENDED BASED ON INFORMATION FOUND IN THE PHYSICAL DATA, TOXICITY AND HEALTH EFFECTS SECTIONS. THEY ARE RANKED IN ORDER FROM MINIMUM TO MAXIMUM RESPIRATORY PROTECTION. THE SPECIFIC RESPIRATOR SELECTED MUST BE BASED ON CONTAMINATION LEVELS FOUND IN THE WORK PLACE, MUST NOT EXCEED THE WORKING LIMITS OF THE RESPIRATOR AND BE JOINTLY APPROVED BY THE NATIONAL INSTITUTE FOR OCCUPATIONAL SAFETY AND HEALTH AND THE MINE SAFETY AND HEALTH ADMINISTRATION (NIOSH-MSHA).

CHEMICAL CARTRIDGE RESPIRATOR WITH AN ORGANIC VAPOR CARTRIDGE(S) WITH A FULL FACEPIECE.

GAS MASK WITH ORGANIC VAPOR CANISTER (CHIN-STYLE OR FRONT- OR BACK-MOUNTED CANISTER) WITH A FULL FACEPIECE.

TYPE 'C' SUPPLIED-AIR RESPIRATOR WITH A FULL FACEPIECE OPERATED IN PRESSURE-DEMAND OR OTHER POSITIVE PRESSURE MODE OR WITH A FULL FACEPIECE, HELMET OR HOOD OPERATED IN CONTINUOUS-FLOW MODE.

SELF-CONTAINED BREATHING APPARATUS WITH A FULL FACEPIECE OPERATED IN PRESSURE-DEMAND OR OTHER POSITIVE PRESSURE MODE.

FOR FIREFIGHTING AND OTHER IMMEDIATELY DANGEROUS TO LIFE OR HEALTH CONDITIONS:

SELF-CONTAINED BREATHING APPARATUS WITH FULL FACEPIECE OPERATED IN PRESSURE-DEMAND OR OTHER POSITIVE PRESSURE MODE.

SUPPLIED-AIR RESPIRATOR WITH FULL FACEPIECE AND OPERATED IN PRESSURE-DEMAND OR OTHER POSITIVE PRESSURE MODE IN COMBINATION WITH AN AUXILIARY SELF-CONTAINED BREATHING APPARATUS OPERATED IN PRESSURE-DEMAND OR OTHER POSITIVE PRESSURE MODE.

CLOTHING: EMPLOYEE MUST WEAR APPROPRIATE PROTECTIVE (IMPERVIOUS) CLOTHING AND EQUIPMENT TO PREVENT REPEATED OR PROLONGED SKIN CONTACT WITH THIS SUBSTANCE.

GLOVES: EMPLOYEE MUST WEAR APPROPRIATE PROTECTIVE GLOVES TO PREVENT CONTACT WITH THIS SUBSTANCE.

EYE PROTECTION: EMPLOYEE MUST WEAR SPLASH-PROOF OR DUST-RESISTANT SAFETY GOGGLES TO PREVENT EYE CONTACT WITH THIS SUBSTANCE.

EMERGENCY EYE WASH: WHERE THERE IS ANY POSSIBILITY THAT AN EMPLOYEE'S EYES MAY BE EXPOSED TO THIS SUBSTANCE, THE EMPLOYER SHOULD PROVIDE AN EYE WASH FOUNTAIN WITHIN THE IMMEDIATE WORK AREA FOR EMERGENCY USE.

AUTHORIZED BY- OCCUPATIONAL HEALTH SERVICES, INC.
CREATION DATE: 02/08/90 ***REVISION DATE:*** 05/18/90

MATERIAL SAFETY DATA SHEET

OCCUPATIONAL HEALTH SERVICES, INC.
AGRICULTURE AND PESTICIDE DIVISION
450 SEVENTH AVENUE, SUITE 2407
NEW YORK, NEW YORK 10123
1-800-445-MSDS OR (212) 967-1100

EMERGENCY CONTACT:
JOHN S. BRANSFORD, JR. (615) 292-1180

SUBSTANCE IDENTIFICATION

CAS-NUMBER 72-56-0

***SUBSTANCE:* ETHYLAN**

TRADE NAMES/SYNONYMS: BENZENE, 1,1'-(2,2-DICHLOROETHYLIDENE)BIS(4-ETHYL-; 1,1'-(2,2-DICHLOROETHYLIDENE)BIS(4-ETHYLBENZENE); ETHANE, 1,1-DICHLORO-2,2-BIS(P-ETHYLPHENYL)-; 1,1-DICHLORO-2,2-BIS(P-ETHYLPHENYL)ETHANE; 2,2-BIS(P-ETHYLPHENYL)-1,1-DICHLOROETHANE; DI(P-ETHYLPHENYL)DICHLOROETHANE; 1,1-DICHLORO-2,2-DI-(4-ETHYLPHENYL)ETHANE; 1,1-(2,2-DICHLOROETHYLIDENE)BIS(4-ETHYLBENZENE); DIETHYLDIPHENYL DICHLOROETHANE; PERTHANE; Q 137; ENT 17082; ETHYLAN (INSECTICIDE); C18H20CL2; PST71373

CHEMICAL FAMILY: HALOGEN COMPOUND, AROMATIC

MOLECULAR FORMULA: C2-H5-C6-H4-C-H-(C-CL2-H)-C6-H4-C2-H5

MOLECULAR WEIGHT: 307.28
CERCLA RATINGS (SCALE 0-3): HEALTH=3 FIRE=1 REACTIVITY=0
PERSISTENCE=3
NFPA RATINGS (SCALE 0-4): HEALTH=U FIRE=1 REACTIVITY=0

COMPONENTS AND CONTAMINANTS

COMPONENT: ETHYLAN ***PERCENT:*** 100.0
CAS# 72-56-0
OTHER CONTAMINANTS: NONE
EXPOSURE LIMITS: NO OCCUPATIONAL EXPOSURE LIMITS ESTABLISHED BY OSHA, ACGIH, OR NIOSH.

PHYSICAL DATA

DESCRIPTION: WHITE CRYSTALS. ***MELTING POINT:*** 133-135 F (56-57 C)
SPECIFIC GRAVITY: NOT AVAILABLE ***SOLUBILITY IN WATER:*** ALMOST INSOLUBLE
SOLVENT SOLUBILITY: SOLUBLE IN MOST ORGANIC SOLVENTS.

FIRE AND EXPLOSION DATA

FIRE AND EXPLOSION HAZARD: SLIGHT FIRE HAZARD WHEN EXPOSED TO HEAT OR FLAME.
DUST-AIR MIXTURES MAY IGNITE OR EXPLODE.
FIREFIGHTING MEDIA: DRY CHEMICAL, CARBON DIOXIDE, HALON, WATER SPRAY OR STANDARD FOAM (1987 EMERGENCY RESPONSE GUIDEBOOK, DOT P 5800.4).
FOR LARGER FIRES, USE WATER SPRAY, FOG OR STANDARD FOAM (1987 EMERGENCY RESPONSE GUIDEBOOK, DOT P 5800.4).
FIREFIGHTING: MOVE CONTAINER FROM FIRE AREA IF POSSIBLE. DO NOT SCATTER SPILLED MATERIAL WITH HIGH PRESSURE WATER STREAMS. DIKE FIRE CONTROL WATER FOR LATER DISPOSAL (1987 EMERGENCY RESPONSE GUIDEBOOK, DOT P 5800.4, GUIDE PAGE 31).
USE AGENTS SUITABLE FOR TYPE OF SURROUNDING FIRE. AVOID BREATHING HAZARDOUS VAPORS, KEEP UPWIND.

TOXICITY

ETHYLAN: TOXICITY DATA: APPROXIMATELY 10,000 MG/KG SKIN-RAT LD50 (MCEWEN, THE USE AND SIGNIFICANCE OF PESTICIDE IN THE ENVIRONMENT, 1979); 6600 MG/KG ORAL-RAT LD50; 6600 MG/KG ORAL-MOUSE LD50; 73 MG/KG INTRAVENOUS-RAT LD50; 173 MG/KG INTRAVENOUS-MOUSE LD50; MUTAGENIC DATA (RTECS); REPRODUCTIVE EFFECTS DATA (RTECS); TUMORIGENIC DATA (RTECS). CARCINOGEN STATUS: NONE. ACUTE TOXICITY LEVEL: SLIGHTLY TOXIC BY DERMAL ABSORPTION AND INGESTION. TARGET EFFECTS: POISONING MAY AFFECT THE FUNCTION OF THE ADRENAL CORTEX. ADDITIONAL DATA: INTERACTIONS WITH MEDICATIONS MAY OCCUR. MAY BE EXCRETED IN BREAST MILK. STIMULANTS SUCH AS EPHINEPHRINE OR EPHEDRINE MAY INDUCE VENTRICULAR FIBRILLATION.*
* MAY BE BASED ON GENERAL INFORMATION ON ORGANOCHLORINE PESTICIDES.

HEALTH EFFECTS AND FIRST AID

INHALATION: ETHYLAN: **ACUTE EXPOSURE-** NO DATA AVAILABLE. **CHRONIC EXPOSURE-** NO DATA AVAILABLE.
FIRST AID- REMOVE FROM EXPOSURE AREA TO FRESH AIR IMMEDIATELY. IF BREATHING HAS STOPPED, PERFORM ARTIFICIAL RESPIRATION. KEEP PERSON WARM AND AT REST. TREAT SYMPTOMATICALLY AND SUPPORTIVELY. GET MEDICAL ATTENTION IMMEDIATELY.

SKIN CONTACT: ETHYLAN: **ACUTE EXPOSURE-** ANIMAL STUDIES INDICATE THAT SKIN ABSORPTION MAY OCCUR. **CHRONIC EXPOSURE-** ETHYLAN WAS NOT LETHAL TO RABBITS BY DERMAL ABSORPTION WHEN APPLIED AT THE RATE OF 3 ML/KG/DAY IN A 30% SOLUTION FOR 13 WEEKS.
FIRST AID- REMOVE CONTAMINATED CLOTHING AND SHOES IMMEDIATELY. WASH AFFECTED AREA WITH SOAP OR MILD DETERGENT AND LARGE AMOUNTS OF WATER UNTIL NO EVIDENCE OF CHEMICAL REMAINS (APPROXIMATELY 15-20 MINUTES). GET MEDICAL ATTENTION IMMEDIATELY.

EYE CONTACT: ETHYLAN: **ACUTE EXPOSURE-** NO DATA AVAILABLE. **CHRONIC EXPOSURE-** NO DATA AVAILABLE.
FIRST AID- WASH EYES IMMEDIATELY WITH LARGE AMOUNTS OF WATER OR NORMAL SALINE, OCCASIONALLY LIFTING UPPER AND LOWER LIDS, UNTIL NO EVIDENCE OF CHEMICAL REMAINS (APPROXIMATELY 15-20 MINUTES). GET MEDICAL ATTENTION IMMEDIATELY.

INGESTION: ETHYLAN: **ACUTE EXPOSURE-** A LETHAL DOSE IN RATS WAS 6600 MG/KG; SYMPTOMS WERE NOT REPORTED. **CHRONIC EXPOSURE-** THERAPEUTIC DOSAGES AS HIGH AS 300 MG/KG/DAY HAVE BEEN GIVEN TO PATIENTS. REPORTED ADVERSE EFFECTS INCLUDED DIARRHEA, VOMITING, NAUSEA, SKIN RASH, THROMBOCYTOPENIA AND LEUCOPENIA; PLASMA 17-HYDROXYCORTICOSTEROID LEVELS WERE MARKEDLY DEPRESSED BUT NOT BELOW NORMAL. A DIETARY LEVEL OF 5000 PPM WAS LETHAL TO DOGS WITH 22 WEEKS; 1,000 PPM PRODUCED SOME ATROPHY OF THE ADRENALS. AN INCREASED INCIDENCE OF HEPATOCELLULAR AND CHOLANGIOCELLULAR CARCINOMAS WAS OBSERVED IN MICE FED ETHYLAN FOR 2 YEARS.
FIRST AID- IF THE PERSON IS CONSCIOUS AND NOT CONVULSING, REMOVE BY GIVING SYRUP OF IPECAC (IF VOMITING OCCURS, KEEP THE HEAD BELOW THE HIPS TO PREVENT ASPIRATION). GIVE ACTIVATED CHARCOAL FOLLOWED BY GASTRIC LAVAGE. FOLLOW WITH A SALINE CATHARTIC. DO NOT GIVE FATS OR OILS. INTESTINAL LAVAGE WITH 20% MANNITOL (200 ML) BY STOMACH TUBE IS ALSO USEFUL. GIVE ARTIFICIAL RESPIRATION WITH OXYGEN IF RESPIRATION IS DEPRESSED (DREISBACH, HANDBOOK OF POISONING, 12TH ED.). TREAT SYMPTOMATICALLY AND SUPPORTIVELY. LAVAGE AND ADMINISTRATION OF OXYGEN SHOULD BE PERFORMED BY QUALIFIED MEDICAL PERSONNEL. GET MEDICAL ATTENTION IMMEDIATELY.
ANTIDOTE: NO SPECIFIC ANTIDOTE. TREAT SYMPTOMATICALLY AND SUPPORTIVELY.

REACTIVITY

REACTIVITY: STABLE UNDER NORMAL TEMPERATURES AND PRESSURES.
INCOMPATIBILITIES: ETHYLAN: OXIDIZERS (STRONG): FIRE AND EXPLOSION HAZARD.
DECOMPOSITION: THERMAL DECOMPOSITION PRODUCTS MAY INCLUDE TOXIC AND CORROSIVE FUMES OF CHLORIDES AND TOXIC OXIDES OF CARBON.
POLYMERIZATION: HAZARDOUS POLYMERIZATION HAS NOT BEEN REPORTED TO OCCUR UNDER NORMAL TEMPERATURES AND PRESSURES.

STORAGE AND DISPOSAL

OBSERVE ALL FEDERAL, STATE AND LOCAL REGULATIONS WHEN STORING OR DISPOSING OF THIS SUBSTANCE. FOR ASSISTANCE, CONTACT THE DISTRICT DIRECTOR OF THE ENVIRONMENTAL PROTECTION AGENCY.

STORAGE

STORE IN ACCORDANCE WITH 40 CFR 165 RECOMMENDED PROCEDURES FOR THE DISPOSAL AND STORAGE OF PESTICIDES AND PESTICIDE CONTAINERS.
STORE AWAY FROM INCOMPATIBLE SUBSTANCES.

DISPOSAL

DISPOSAL MUST BE IN ACCORDANCE WITH 40 CFR 165 RECOMMENDED PROCEDURES FOR THE DISPOSAL AND STORAGE OF PESTICIDES AND PESTICIDE CONTAINERS.

CONDITIONS TO AVOID

MAY BURN BUT DOES NOT IGNITE READILY. AVOID CONTACT WITH STRONG OXIDIZERS, EXCESSIVE HEAT, SPARKS, OR OPEN FLAME.

SPILL AND LEAK PROCEDURES

OCCUPATIONAL SPILL: SWEEP UP AND PLACE IN SUITABLE CLEAN, DRY CONTAINERS FOR RECLAMATION OR LATER DISPOSAL. DO NOT FLUSH SPILLED MATERIAL INTO SEWER. KEEP UNNECESSARY PEOPLE AWAY.

PROTECTIVE EQUIPMENT

VENTILATION: PROVIDE LOCAL EXHAUST OR GENERAL DILUTION VENTILATION SYSTEM.
RESPIRATOR: THE FOLLOWING RESPIRATORS ARE RECOMMENDED BASED ON INFORMATION FOUND IN THE PHYSICAL DATA, TOXICITY AND HEALTH EFFECTS SECTIONS. THEY ARE RANKED IN ORDER FROM MINIMUM TO MAXIMUM RESPIRATORY PROTECTION. THE SPECIFIC RESPIRATOR SELECTED MUST BE BASED ON CONTAMINATION LEVELS FOUND IN THE WORK PLACE, MUST NOT EXCEED THE WORKING LIMITS OF THE RESPIRATOR AND BE JOINTLY APPROVED BY THE NATIONAL INSTITUTE FOR OCCUPATIONAL SAFETY AND HEALTH AND THE MINE SAFETY AND HEALTH ADMINISTRATION (NIOSH-MSHA).
CHEMICAL CARTRIDGE RESPIRATOR WITH AN ORGANIC VAPOR CARTRIDGE(S) IN COMBINATION WITH A DUST AND MIST FILTER.
GAS MASK WITH ORGANIC VAPOR CANISTER (CHIN-STYLE OR FRONT- OR BACK-MOUNTED CANISTER) WITH A DUST AND MIST FILTER.
GAS MASK WITH ORGANIC VAPOR CANISTER (CHIN-STYLE OR FRONT- OR BACK-MOUNTED CANISTER) WITH A PARTICULATE FILTER.
POWERED AIR-PURIFYING RESPIRATOR WITH A HIGH-EFFICIENCY FILTER.
TYPE 'C' SUPPLIED-AIR RESPIRATOR WITH A FULL FACEPIECE OPERATED IN A PRESSURE-DEMAND OR OTHER POSITIVE PRESSURE MODE.
SELF-CONTAINED BREATHING APPARATUS WITH A FULL FACEPIECE OPERATED IN PRESSURE-DEMAND OR OTHER POSITIVE PRESSURE MODE.
FOR FIREFIGHTING AND OTHER IMMEDIATELY DANGEROUS TO LIFE OR HEALTH CONDITIONS:
SELF-CONTAINED BREATHING APPARATUS WITH FULL FACEPIECE OPERATED IN PRESSURE-DEMAND OR OTHER POSITIVE PRESSURE MODE.
SUPPLIED-AIR RESPIRATOR WITH FULL FACEPIECE AND OPERATED IN PRESSURE-DEMAND OR OTHER POSITIVE PRESSURE MODE IN COMBINATION WITH AN AUXILIARY SELF-CONTAINED BREATHING APPARATUS OPERATED IN PRESSURE-DEMAND OR OTHER POSITIVE PRESSURE MODE.

CLOTHING: EMPLOYEE MUST WEAR APPROPRIATE PROTECTIVE (IMPERVIOUS) CLOTHING AND EQUIPMENT TO PREVENT REPEATED OR PROLONGED SKIN CONTACT WITH THIS SUBSTANCE.
GLOVES: EMPLOYEE MUST WEAR APPROPRIATE PROTECTIVE GLOVES TO PREVENT CONTACT WITH THIS SUBSTANCE.
EYE PROTECTION: EMPLOYEE MUST WEAR SPLASH-PROOF OR DUST-RESISTANT SAFETY GOGGLES TO PREVENT EYE CONTACT WITH THIS SUBSTANCE.
EMERGENCY EYE WASH: WHERE THERE IS ANY POSSIBILITY THAT AN EMPLOYEE'S EYES MAY BE EXPOSED TO THIS SUBSTANCE, THE EMPLOYER SHOULD PROVIDE AN EYE WASH FOUNTAIN WITHIN THE IMMEDIATE WORK AREA FOR EMERGENCY USE.

AUTHORIZED BY- OCCUPATIONAL HEALTH SERVICES, INC.
CREATION DATE: 01/31/90 ***REVISION DATE:*** 05/31/90

MATERIAL SAFETY DATA SHEET

OCCUPATIONAL HEALTH SERVICES, INC.
AGRICULTURE AND PESTICIDE DIVISION
450 SEVENTH AVENUE, SUITE 2407
NEW YORK, NEW YORK 10123
1-800-445-MSDS OR (212) 967-1100

EMERGENCY CONTACT:
JOHN S. BRANSFORD, JR. (615) 292-1180

SUBSTANCE IDENTIFICATION

CAS-NUMBER 7359-55-9
SUBSTANCE: **THIONAZIN OXYGEN ANALOG**
TRADE NAMES/SYNONYMS: PHOSPHORIC ACID, DIETHYL PYRAZINYL ESTER; ETHYL PYRAZINYL PHOSPHATE; DIETHYL 2-PYRAZINYL PHOSPHATE; THIONAZIN-O-ANALOG; THIONAZIN-OXON; DIETHYL PYRAZINYL PHOSPHATE; C8H13N2O4P; PST71377
CHEMICAL FAMILY: ORGANOPHOSPHATE
MOLECULAR FORMULA: (C2-H5-O)2-P-(O)-O-C4-N2-H3
MOLECULAR WEIGHT: 232.18
CERCLA RATINGS (SCALE 0-3): HEALTH=3 FIRE=U REACTIVITY=0 PERSISTENCE=0
NFPA RATINGS (SCALE 0-4): HEALTH=3 FIRE=U REACTIVITY=0

COMPONENTS AND CONTAMINANTS

COMPONENT: THIONAZIN OXYGEN ANALOG ***PERCENT:*** 100.0
CAS# 7359-55-9
OTHER CONTAMINANTS: NONE
EXPOSURE LIMITS: NO OCCUPATIONAL EXPOSURE LIMITS ESTABLISHED BY OSHA, ACGIH, OR NIOSH.

PHYSICAL DATA

DESCRIPTION: DARK AMBER, VISCOUS LIQUID. ***BOILING POINT:*** NOT AVAILABLE
SPECIFIC GRAVITY: NOT AVAILABLE ***EVAPORATION RATE:*** NOT AVAILABLE
SOLUBILITY IN WATER: NOT AVAILABLE

FIRE AND EXPLOSION DATA

FIRE AND EXPLOSION HAZARD: UNKNOWN FIRE AND EXPLOSION HAZARD.
FIREFIGHTING MEDIA: DRY CHEMICAL, CARBON DIOXIDE, HALON, WATER SPRAY OR STANDARD FOAM (1987 EMERGENCY RESPONSE GUIDEBOOK, DOT P 5800.4).
FOR LARGER FIRES, USE WATER SPRAY, FOG OR STANDARD FOAM (1987 EMERGENCY RESPONSE GUIDEBOOK, DOT P 5800.4).
FIREFIGHTING: MOVE CONTAINER FROM FIRE AREA IF POSSIBLE. DIKE FIRE CONTROL WATER FOR LATER DISPOSAL; DO NOT SCATTER THE MATERIAL. COOL FIRE-EXPOSED CONTAINERS WITH WATER FROM SIDE UNTIL WELL AFTER FIRE IS OUT. STAY AWAY FROM STORAGE TANK ENDS. WITHDRAW IMMEDIATELY IN CASE OF RISING SOUND FROM VENTING SAFETY DEVICE OR ANY DISCOLORATION OF STORAGE TANK DUE TO FIRE (1987 EMERGENCY RESPONSE GUIDEBOOK, DOT P 5800.4, GUIDE PAGE 28).
EXTINGUISH ONLY IF FLOW CAN BE STOPPED. USE FLOODING AMOUNTS OF WATER AS A FOG; SOLID STREAMS MAY BE INEFFECTIVE. COOL CONTAINERS WITH FLOODING AMOUNTS OF WATER FROM AS FAR A DISTANCE AS POSSIBLE. AVOID BREATHING POISONOUS VAPORS, KEEP UPWIND.

TRANSPORTATION DATA

DEPARTMENT OF TRANSPORTATION HAZARD CLASSIFICATION 49 CFR 172.101: POISON B
DEPARTMENT OF TRANSPORTATION LABELING REQUIREMENTS 49 CFR 172.101 AND SUBPART E: POISON
DEPARTMENT OF TRANSPORTATION PACKAGING REQUIREMENTS: 49 CFR 173.359
EXCEPTIONS: 49 CFR 173.359

TOXICITY

THIONAZIN OXYGEN ANALOG: TOXICITY DATA: 4 MG/KG ORAL-RAT LD50 (EPA). CARCINOGEN STATUS: NONE. ACUTE TOXICITY LEVEL: HIGHLY TOXIC BY INGESTION. TARGET EFFECTS: CHOLINESTERASE INHIBITOR. POISONING MAY AFFECT THE NERVOUS SYSTEM.* AT INCREASED RISK FROM EXPOSURE: PERSONS WITH RESPIRATORY AILMENTS, RECENT EXPOSURE TO CHOLINESTERASE INHIBITORS OR IMPAIRED CHOLINESTERASE PRODUCTION, OR LIVER MALFUNCTION.* ADDITIONAL DATA: MAY CROSS THE PLACENTA. HIGH ENVIRONMENTAL TEMPERATURES OR EXPOSURE OF THE CHEMICAL TO VISIBLE OR ULTRAVIOLET LIGHT MAY ENHANCE THE TOXICITY. INTERACTIONS WITH MEDICATIONS MAY OCCUR.*
* MAY BE BASED ON GENERAL INFORMATION ON ORGANOPHOSPHATES.

HEALTH EFFECTS AND FIRST AID

INHALATION: THIONAZIN OXYGEN ANALOG: SEE INFORMATION ON ORGANOPHOSPHATES.
ORGANOPHOSPHATES: CHOLINESTERASE INHIBITOR. **ACUTE EXPOSURE-** WHEN INHALED, THE FIRST EFFECTS OF CHOLINESTERASE INHIBITORS ARE USUALLY RESPIRATORY AND MAY INCLUDE NASAL HYPEREMIA AND WATERY DISCHARGE, COUGH, CHEST DISCOMFORT, DYSPNEA, AND WHEEZING DUE TO INCREASED BRONCHIAL SECRETIONS AND BRONCHOCONSTRICTION. IF SUFFICIENT AMOUNTS ARE ABSORBED, OTHER SYSTEMIC EFFECTS MAY BEGIN WITHIN A FEW MINUTES OR BE DELAYED FOR UP TO 12 HOURS. SYMPTOMS MAY INCLUDE PALLOR, NAUSEA, VOMITING, DIARRHEA, ABDOMINAL CRAMPS, HEADACHE, DIZZINESS, OCULAR PAIN, BLURRED VISION, MIOSIS OR IN SOME CASES, ESPECIALLY INITIALLY, MYDRIASIS, LACRIMATION, SALIVATION, SWEATING, AND CONFUSION. OTHER REPORTED CENTRAL NERVOUS SYSTEM OR NEUROMUSCULAR EFFECTS MAY INCLUDE ATAXIA, SLURRED SPEECH, AREFLEXIA, WEAKNESS, FATIGUE, FASCICULATIONS, TWITCHING, TREMORS POSSIBLY OF THE TONGUE AND EYELIDS, AND EVENTUALLY PARALYSIS OF THE EXTREMITIES AND POSSIBLY OF THE RESPIRATORY MUSCLES. IN SEVERE CASES THERE MAY ALSO BE INVOLUNTARY DEFECATION AND URINATION, CYANOSIS, PSYCHOSIS, HYPERGLYCEMIA, ACUTE PANCREATITIS, CARDIAC IRREGULARITIES, PULMONARY EDEMA, UNCONSCIOUSNESS, CONVULSIONS, AND COMA. DEATH IS PRIMARILY DUE TO RESPIRATORY FAILURE, ALTHOUGH CARDIOVASCULAR EFFECTS INCLUDING CARDIAC ARREST MAY ALSO BE IMPLICATED. LONG TERM SEQUELAE ARE RARE BUT MAY INCLUDE NEUROPSYCHIATRIC DISORDERS AND MYOPATHY WITH MUSCLE TENDERNESS. SOME ORGANOPHOSPHATES MAY CAUSE A DELAYED NEUROPATHY BEGINNING 1-4 WEEKS AFTER AN ACUTE EXPOSURE WHICH MAY OR MAY NOT HAVE CAUSED ACUTE CHOLINERGIC EFFECTS. NUMBNESS, TINGLING, WEAKNESS AND CRAMPING BEGINNING SYMMETRICALLY IN THE LOWER LIMBS MAY PROGRESS TO ATAXIA AND PARALYSIS. IN SEVERE CASES, UPPER LIMB INVOLVEMENT IS POSSIBLE AND FLACCID PARALYSIS MAY PROGRESS TO SPASTIC PARALYSIS WITH EXAGGERATED REFLEXES. IMPROVEMENT MAY OCCUR OVER MONTHS TO YEARS, BUT SOME RESIDUAL IMPAIRMENT USUALLY REMAINS.
CHRONIC EXPOSURE- REPEATED OR PROLONGED EXPOSURE MAY RESULT IN THE EFFECTS OF ACUTE EXPOSURE INCLUDING THE DELAYED NEUROPATHY. OTHER EFFECTS REPORTED IN WORKERS REPEATEDLY EXPOSED INCLUDE IMPAIRED MEMORY AND CONCENTRATION, ACUTE PSYCHOSIS, SEVERE DEPRESSIONS, IRRITABILTY, CONFUSION, APATHY, EMOTIONAL LABILITY, SOCIAL WITHDRAWAL, CONFUSION, HEADACHE, SPEECH DIFFICULTIES, DELAYED REACTION TIMES, SPATIAL DISORIENTATION, NIGHTMARES, SLEEPWALKING, AND DROWSINESS OR INSOMNIA. AN INFLUENZA-LIKE CONDITION WITH HEADACHE, NAUSEA, WEAKNESS, ANOREXIA AND MALAISE HAS ALSO BEEN REPORTED.
FIRST AID- REMOVE FROM EXPOSURE AREA TO FRESH AIR IMMEDIATELY. IF BREATHING HAS STOPPED, GIVE ARTIFICIAL RESPIRATION. MAINTAIN AIRWAY AND BLOOD PRESSURE AND ADMINISTER OXYGEN IF AVAILABLE. KEEP AFFECTED PERSON WARM AND AT REST. TREAT SYMPTOMATICALLY AND SUPPORTIVELY. ADMINISTRATION OF OXYGEN SHOULD BE PERFORMED BY QUALIFIED PERSONNEL. GET MEDICAL ATTENTION IMMEDIATELY.

SKIN CONTACT: THIONAZIN OXYGEN ANALOG: SEE INFORMATION ON ORGANOPHOSPHATES.
ORGANOPHOSPHATES: CHOLINESTERASE INHIBITOR. **ACUTE EXPOSURE-** LOCALIZED SWEATING AND FASCICULATIONS MAY OCCUR AT THE SITE OF CONTACT. IF SUFFICIENT AMOUNTS ARE ABSORBED, OTHER EFFECTS OF CHOLINESTERASE INHIBITION AS DESCRIBED IN ACUTE INHALATION MAY OCCUR. SYMPTOMS MAY BE DELAYED 2-3 HOURS, BUT USUALLY NO MORE THAN 12 HOURS. THE RATE OF ABSORPTION IS INCREASED BY THE PRESENCE OF DERMATITIS OR HIGH AMBIENT TEMPERATURES. DELAYED NEUROPATHY IS ALSO POSSIBLE. **CHRONIC EXPOSURE-** REPEATED OR PROLONGED EXPOSURE MAY

CAUSE EFFECTS AS DESCRIBED IN ACUTE EXPOSURE. SOME ORGANOPHOSPHATES MAY CAUSE SENSITIZATION.

FIRST AID- REMOVE CONTAMINATED CLOTHING IMMEDIATELY. WASH CONTAMINATED AREAS WITH SOAP AND WATER FOLLOWED BY ALCOHOL (ARENA, POISONING, 4TH ED.). EMERGENCY PERSONNEL SHOULD WEAR GLOVES AND AVOID CONTAMINATION. TREAT RESPIRATORY DIFFICULTY WITH ARTIFICIAL RESPIRATION. GET MEDICAL ATTENTION IMMEDIATELY.

EYE CONTACT: THIONAZIN OXYGEN ANALOG: SEE INFORMATION ON ORGANOPHOSPHATES.
ORGANOPHOSPHATES: CHOLINESTERASE INHIBITOR. **ACUTE EXPOSURE**- DIRECT CONTACT MAY CAUSE PAIN, HYPEREMIA, LACRIMATION, TWITCHING OF THE EYELIDS, MIOSIS, AND CILIARY MUSCLE SPASM WITH LOSS OF ACCOMODATION, BLURRED OR DIMMED VISION AND BROWACHE. SOMETIMES MYDRIASIS MAY OCCUR INSTEAD OF MIOSIS. WITH SUFFICIENT EXPOSURE, OTHER SYMPTOMS OF CHOLINESTERASE INHIBITION AS DESCRIBED IN ACUTE INHALATION MAY OCCUR. **CHRONIC EXPOSURE**- REPEATED OR PROLONGED EXPOSURE MAY CAUSE EFFECTS AS DESCRIBED IN ACUTE EXPOSURE. SOME COMPOUNDS HAVE CAUSED TOXIC EFFECTS ON THE CRYSTALLINE LENS, CONJUNCTIVAL THICKENING AND OBSTRUCTION OF THE NASOLACRIMAL CANALS WHEN USED AS MIOTIC EYEDROPS.

FIRST AID- IRRIGATE EYES WITH WATER OR SALINE SOLUTION. IF SYMPTOMS OF POISONING OCCUR, TREAT RESPIRATORY DIFFICULTY WITH ARTIFICIAL RESPIRATION AND OXYGEN. OBSERVE PATIENT FOR AT LEAST 24-36 HOURS (GOSSELIN, CLINICAL TOXICOLOGY OF COMMERCIAL PRODUCTS, 5TH ED.). GET MEDICAL ATTENTION IMMEDIATELY. OXYGEN SHOULD BE ADMINISTERED BY QUALIFIED MEDICAL PERSONNEL.

INGESTION: THIONAZIN OXYGEN ANALOG: HIGHLY TOXIC. A LETHAL DOSE REPORTED IN RATS WAS 4 MG/KG. SEE INFORMATION ON ORGANOPHOSPHATES.
ORGANOPHOSPHATES: CHOLINESTERASE INHIBITOR. **ACUTE EXPOSURE**- WHEN INGESTED, THE FIRST EFFECTS MAY BE NAUSEA, VOMITING, ANOREXIA, ABDOMINAL CRAMPS AND DIARRHEA. GASTROINTESTINAL ABSORPTION MAY CAUSE SYMPTOMS OF CHOLINESTERASE INHIBITION AS DESCRIBED IN ACUTE INHALATION. SYMPTOMS MAY BEGIN WITHIN MINUTES OR BE DELAYED FOR HOURS. DELAYED EFFECTS INCLUDING NEUROPATHY MAY ALSO OCCUR. **CHRONIC EXPOSURE**- REPEATED INGESTION MAY CAUSE EFFECTS AS DESCRIBED IN ACUTE EXPOSURE.

FIRST AID- IF PERSON IS ALERT AND RESPIRATION IS NOT DEPRESSED, GIVE SYRUP OF IPECAC FOLLOWED BY WATER (IF VOMITING OCCURS, KEEP HEAD BELOW HIPS TO PREVENT ASPIRATION). IF CONSCIOUSNESS LEVEL DECLINES OR VOMITING HAS NOT OCCURRED IN 15 MINUTES EMPTY STOMACH BY GASTRIC LAVAGE WITH THE AID OF CUFFED ENDOTRACHEAL TUBE USING ISOTONIC SALINE OR 5% SODIUM BICARBONATE FOLLOW WITH ACTIVATED CHARCOAL. ESTABLISH AND MAINTAIN AIRWAY. TREAT RESPIRATORY DIFFICULTY WITH ARTIFICIAL RESPIRATION AND OXYGEN. DO NOT GIVE MORPHINE, AMINOPHYLLINE, PHENOTHIAZINES, RESERPINE, FUROSEMIDE, OR ETHACRYNIC ACID (MORGAN, RECOGNITION AND MANAGEMENT OF PESTICIDE POISONINGS, 3RD ED.). TREAT SYMPTOMATICALLY AND SUPPORTIVELY. ADMINISTRATION OF OXYGEN AND LAVAGE MUST BE PERFORMED BY QUALIFIED MEDICAL PERSONNEL. GET MEDICAL ATTENTION IMMEDIATELY.

ANTIDOTE: THE FOLLOWING ANTIDOTE(S) HAVE BEEN RECOMMENDED. HOWEVER, THE DECISION AS TO WHETHER THE SEVERITY OF POISONING REQUIRES ADMINISTRATION OF ANY ANTIDOTE AND ACTUAL DOSE REQUIRED SHOULD BE MADE BY QUALIFIED MEDICAL PERSONNEL.
FOR CHOLINESTERASE INHIBITORS: ESTABLISH CLEAR AIRWAY AND TISSUE OXYGENATION BY ASPIRATION OF SECRETIONS, AND IF NECESSARY, BY ASSISTED PULMONARY VENTILATION WITH OXYGEN. IMPROVE TISSUE OXYGENATION AS MUCH AS POSSIBLE BEFORE ADMINISTERING ATROPINE TO MINIMIZE THE RISK OF VENTRICULAR FIBRILLATION. ADMINISTER ATROPINE SULFATE INTRAVENOUSLY, OR INTRAMUSCULARLY IF IV INJECTION IS NOT POSSIBLE. IN MODERATELY SEVERE POISONING ADMINISTER ATROPINE SULFATE, 0.4-2.0 MG REPEATED EVERY 15 MINUTES UNTIL ATROPINIZATION IS ACHIEVED (TACHYCARDIA, FLUSHING, DRY MOUTH, MYDRIASIS). MAINTAIN ATROPINIZATION BY REPEATED DOSES FOR 2-12 HOURS, OR LONGER, DEPENDING ON THE SEVERITY OF POISONING. THE APPEARANCE OF RALES IN THE LUNG BASES, MIOSIS, SALIVATION, NAUSEA, BRADYCARDIA, ARE ALL INDICATIONS OF INADEQUATE ATROPINIZATION. SEVERELY POISONED INDIVIDUALS MAY EXHIBIT REMARKABLE TOLERANCE TO ATROPINE; TWO OR MORE TIMES THE DOSAGES SUGGESTED ABOVE MAY BE NEEDED. PERSONS NOT POISONED OR ONLY SLIGHTLY POISONED, HOWEVER, MAY DEVELOP SIGNS OF ATROPINE TOXICITY FROM SUCH LARGE DOSAGES: FEVER, MUSCLE FIBRILLATIONS, AND DELIRIUM ARE THE MAIN SIGNS OF ATROPINE TOXICITY. IF THESE SIGNS APPEAR WHILE THE PATIENT IS FULLY ATROPINIZED, ATROPINE ADMINISTRATION SHOULD BE DISCONTINUED, AT LEAST TEMPORARILY. OBSERVE TREATED PATIENTS CLOSELY AT LEAST 24 HOURS TO INSURE THAT SYMPTOMS (POSSIBLY PULMONARY EDEMA) DO NOT RECUR AS ATROPINIZATION WEARS OFF. IN VERY SEVERE POISONINGS, METABOLIC DISPOSITION OF TOXICANT MAY REQUIRE SEVERAL HOURS OR DAYS DURING WHICH ATROPINIZATION MUST BE MAINTAINED. MARKEDLY LOWER LEVELS OF URINARY METABOLITES INDICATE THAT ATROPINE DOSAGE CAN BE TAPERED OFF. AS DOSAGE IS REDUCED, CHECK THE LUNG BASES FREQUENTLY FOR RALES. IF RALES ARE HEARD OR OTHER SYMPTOMS RETURN, RE-ESTABLISH ATROPINIZATION PROMPTLY (MORGAN, RECOGNITION AND MANAGEMENT OF PESTICIDE POISONINGS, 3RD ED.). ADMINISTRATION OF ANTIDOTE MUST BE PERFORMED BY QUALIFIED MEDICAL PERSONNEL.
IN CASES OF SEVERE POISONING BY ORGANOPHOSPHATE PESTICIDES IN WHICH RESPIRATORY DEPRESSION, MUSCLE WEAKNESS AND TWITCHINGS ARE SEVERE, GIVE PRALIDOXIME (PROTOPAM-AYERST, 2-PAM), 1.0 GRAM INTRAVENOUSLY AT NO MORE THAN 0.5 GRAM PER MINUTE. DOSAGE OF PRALIDOXIME MAY BE REPEATED IN 1-2 HOURS, THEN AT 10-12 HOUR INTERVALS IF NEEDED. IN VERY SEVERE POISONINGS, DOSAGE RATES MAY BE DOUBLED. TREATMENT WITH PRALIDOXIME WILL BE MOST EFFECTIVE IF GIVEN WITHIN THIRTY-SIX HOURS AFTER POISONING (MORGAN, RECOGNITION AND MANAGEMENT OF PESTICIDE POISONINGS, 3RD ED.). ANTIDOTE SHOULD BE ADMINISTERED BY QUALIFIED MEDICAL PERSONNEL.

REACTIVITY

REACTIVITY: STABLE UNDER NORMAL TEMPERATURES AND PRESSURES.

INCOMPATIBILITIES: THIONAZIN OXYGEN ANALOG: OXIDIZERS (STRONG): FIRE AND EXPLOSION HAZARD.

DECOMPOSITION: THERMAL DECOMPOSITION MAY RELEASE TOXIC OXIDES OF NITROGEN, PHOSPHORUS AND CARBON.

POLYMERIZATION: HAZARDOUS POLYMERIZATION HAS NOT BEEN REPORTED TO OCCUR UNDER NORMAL TEMPERATURES AND PRESSURES.

STORAGE AND DISPOSAL

OBSERVE ALL FEDERAL, STATE AND LOCAL REGULATIONS WHEN STORING OR DISPOSING OF THIS SUBSTANCE. FOR ASSISTANCE, CONTACT THE DISTRICT DIRECTOR OF THE ENVIRONMENTAL PROTECTION AGENCY.

STORAGE

STORE IN ACCORDANCE WITH 40 CFR 165 RECOMMENDED PROCEDURES FOR THE DISPOSAL AND STORAGE OF PESTICIDES AND PESTICIDE CONTAINERS.
STORE AWAY FROM INCOMPATIBLE SUBSTANCES.

DISPOSAL

DISPOSAL MUST BE IN ACCORDANCE WITH 40 CFR 165 RECOMMENDED PROCEDURES FOR THE DISPOSAL AND STORAGE OF PESTICIDES AND PESTICIDE CONTAINERS.

CONDITIONS TO AVOID

AVOID CONTACT WITH HEAT, SPARKS, FLAMES OR OTHER IGNITION SOURCES. VAPORS MAY BE EXPLOSIVE. MATERIAL IS POISONOUS; AVOID INHALATION OF VAPORS OR CONTACT WITH SKIN. DO NOT ALLOW MATERIAL TO CONTAMINATE WATER SOURCES.

SPILL AND LEAK PROCEDURES

OCCUPATIONAL SPILL: SHUT OFF IGNITION SOURCES. DO NOT TOUCH SPILLED MATERIAL. STOP LEAK IF YOU CAN DO IT WITHOUT RISK. USE WATER SPRAY TO REDUCE VAPORS. FOR SMALL SPILLS, TAKE UP WITH SAND OR OTHER ABSORBENT MATERIAL AND PLACE INTO CONTAINERS FOR LATER DISPOSAL. FOR LARGER SPILLS, DIKE FAR AHEAD OF SPILL FOR LATER DISPOSAL. NO SMOKING, FLAMES OR FLARES IN HAZARD AREA! KEEP UNNECESSARY PEOPLE AWAY; ISOLATE HAZARD AREA AND DENY ENTRY.

PROTECTIVE EQUIPMENT

VENTILATION: PROCESS ENCLOSURE RECOMMENDED.

RESPIRATOR: THE FOLLOWING RESPIRATORS ARE RECOMMENDED BASED ON INFORMATION FOUND IN THE PHYSICAL DATA, TOXICITY AND HEALTH EFFECTS SECTIONS. THEY ARE RANKED IN ORDER FROM MINIMUM TO MAXIMUM RESPIRATORY PROTECTION. THE SPECIFIC RESPIRATOR SELECTED MUST BE BASED ON CONTAMINATION LEVELS FOUND IN THE WORK PLACE, MUST NOT EXCEED THE WORKING LIMITS OF THE RESPIRATOR AND BE JOINTLY APPROVED BY THE NATIONAL INSTITUTE FOR OCCUPATIONAL SAFETY AND HEALTH AND THE MINE SAFETY AND HEALTH ADMINISTRATION (NIOSH-MSHA).
TYPE 'C' SUPPLIED-AIR RESPIRATOR WITH A FULL FACEPIECE OPERATED IN PRESSURE-DEMAND OR OTHER POSITIVE PRESSURE MODE OR WITH A FULL FACEPIECE, HELMET OR HOOD OPERATED IN CONTINOUS-FLOW MODE.
SELF-CONTAINED BREATHING APPARATUS WITH A FULL FACEPIECE OPERATED IN PRESSURE-DEMAND OR OTHER POSITIVE PRESSURE MODE.
FOR FIREFIGHTING AND OTHER IMMEDIATELY DANGEROUS TO LIFE OR HEALTH CONDITIONS:
SELF-CONTAINED BREATHING APPARATUS WITH FULL FACEPIECE OPERATED IN PRESSURE-DEMAND OR OTHER POSITIVE PRESSURE MODE.

SUPPLIED-AIR RESPIRATOR WITH FULL FACEPIECE AND OPERATED IN PRESSURE-DEMAND OR OTHER POSITIVE PRESSURE MODE IN COMBINATION WITH AN AUXILIARY SELF-CONTAINED BREATHING APPARATUS OPERATED IN PRESSURE-DEMAND OR OTHER POSITIVE PRESSURE MODE.

CLOTHING: EMPLOYEE MUST WEAR APPROPRIATE PROTECTIVE (IMPERVIOUS) CLOTHING AND EQUIPMENT TO PREVENT ANY POSSIBILITY OF SKIN CONTACT WITH THIS SUBSTANCE.

GLOVES: EMPLOYEE MUST WEAR APPROPRIATE PROTECTIVE GLOVES TO PREVENT CONTACT WITH THIS SUBSTANCE.

EYE PROTECTION: EMPLOYEE MUST WEAR SPLASH-PROOF OR DUST-RESISTANT SAFETY GOGGLES AND A FACESHIELD TO PREVENT CONTACT WITH THIS SUBSTANCE.

EMERGENCY WASH FACILITIES: WHERE THERE IS ANY POSSIBILITY THAT AN EMPLOYEE'S EYES AND/OR SKIN MAY BE EXPOSED TO THIS SUBSTANCE, THE EMPLOYER SHOULD PROVIDE AN EYE WASH FOUNTAIN AND QUICK DRENCH SHOWER WITHIN THE IMMEDIATE WORK AREA FOR EMERGENCY USE.

AUTHORIZED BY- OCCUPATIONAL HEALTH SERVICES, INC.
CREATION DATE: 10/27/89 ***REVISION DATE:*** 05/03/90

MATERIAL SAFETY DATA SHEET

OCCUPATIONAL HEALTH SERVICES, INC.
AGRICULTURE AND PESTICIDE DIVISION
450 SEVENTH AVENUE, SUITE 2407
NEW YORK, NEW YORK 10123
1-800-445-MSDS OR (212) 967-1100

EMERGENCY CONTACT:
JOHN S. BRANSFORD, JR. (615) 292-1180

SUBSTANCE IDENTIFICATION

CAS-NUMBER 2164-09-2

SUBSTANCE: DICRYL

TRADE NAMES/SYNONYMS: 2-PROPENAMIDE, N-(3,4-DICHLOROPHENYL)-2-METHYL-; N-(3,4-DICHLOROPHENYL)-2-METHYL-2-PROPENAMIDE; ACRYLANILIDE, 3',4'-DICHLORO-2-METHYL-; 3',4'-DICHLORO-2-METHYLACRYLANILIDE; 3',4'-DICHLOROMETHACRYLAMIDE; NIAGARA 4556; CHLORANOCRYL; DCMA; C10H9CL2NO; PST71378

CHEMICAL FAMILY: ANILINE DERIVATIVE
HALOGEN

MOLECULAR FORMULA: (CL)2-C6-H3-N-H-O-C-C-(C-H3)-C-H2

MOLECULAR WEIGHT: 230.10

CERCLA RATINGS (SCALE 0-3): HEALTH=U FIRE=1 REACTIVITY=0 PERSISTENCE=1

NFPA RATINGS (SCALE 0-4): HEALTH=U FIRE=1 REACTIVITY=0

COMPONENTS AND CONTAMINANTS

COMPONENT: DICRYL ***PERCENT:*** 100.0
CAS# 2164-09-2

OTHER CONTAMINANTS: MAY CONTAIN TRACES OF 3,4,3',4'-TETRACHLOROAZOBENZENE

EXPOSURE LIMITS: NO OCCUPATIONAL EXPOSURE LIMITS ESTABLISHED BY OSHA, ACGIH, OR NIOSH.

PHYSICAL DATA

DESCRIPTION: WHITE CRYSTALLINE SOLID. ***MELTING POINT:*** 262 F (128 C)

SPECIFIC GRAVITY: NOT AVAILABLE ***SOLUBILITY IN WATER:*** INSOLUBLE

SOLVENT SOLUBILITY: SOLUBLE IN ACETONE, ALCOHOL, ISOPHORONE, DIMETHYL SULFOXIDE.

FIRE AND EXPLOSION DATA

FIRE AND EXPLOSION HAZARD: SLIGHT FIRE HAZARD WHEN EXPOSED TO HEAT OR FLAME.
DUST-AIR MIXTURES MAY IGNITE OR EXPLODE.

FIREFIGHTING MEDIA: DRY CHEMICAL, CARBON DIOXIDE, HALON, WATER SPRAY OR STANDARD FOAM (1987 EMERGENCY RESPONSE GUIDEBOOK, DOT P 5800.4).
FOR LARGER FIRES, USE WATER SPRAY, FOG OR STANDARD FOAM (1987 EMERGENCY RESPONSE GUIDEBOOK, DOT P 5800.4).

FIREFIGHTING: MOVE CONTAINER FROM FIRE AREA IF POSSIBLE. DO NOT SCATTER SPILLED MATERIAL WITH HIGH PRESSURE WATER STREAMS. DIKE FIRE CONTROL WATER FOR LATER DISPOSAL (1987 EMERGENCY RESPONSE GUIDEBOOK, DOT P 5800.4, GUIDE PAGE 31).
USE AGENTS SUITABLE FOR TYPE OF SURROUNDING FIRE. AVOID BREATHING HAZARDOUS VAPORS, KEEP UPWIND.

TOXICITY

DICRYL: TOXICITY DATA: 10 GM/KG SKIN-RABBIT LD50; 1780 MG/KG SKIN-RAT LD50; 1800 MG/KG ORAL-RAT LD50; 410 MG/KG ORAL-MOUSE LD50. CARCINOGEN STATUS: NONE. ACUTE TOXICITY LEVEL: MODERATELY TOXIC BY INGESTION; SLIGHTLY TOXIC BY DERMAL ABSORPTION. TARGET EFFECTS: POISONING MAY AFFECT THE BLOOD.* ADDITIONAL DATA: PRESENCE OF CERTAIN CONTAMINANTS MAY CAUSE CHLORACNE.
* BASED ON INFORMATION ON A RELATED SUBSTANCE.

HEALTH EFFECTS AND FIRST AID

INHALATION: DICRYL: **ACUTE EXPOSURE-** NO SPECIFIC DATA AVAILABLE. 3,4-DICHLOROANILINE, A RELATED SUBSTANCE, CAUSES METHEMOGLOBINEMIA WITH CYANOSIS. **CHRONIC EXPOSURE-** NO DATA AVAILABLE.

FIRST AID- REMOVE FROM EXPOSURE AREA TO FRESH AIR IMMEDIATELY. IF BREATHING HAS STOPPED, PERFORM ARTIFICIAL RESPIRATION. KEEP PERSON WARM AND AT REST. TREAT SYMPTOMATICALLY AND SUPPORTIVELY. GET MEDICAL ATTENTION IMMEDIATELY.

SKIN CONTACT: DICRYL: **ACUTE EXPOSURE-** NO SPECIFIC DATA AVAILABLE. 3,4-DICHLOROANILINE, A RELATED SUBSTANCE, CAUSES METHEMOGLOBINEMIA WITH CYANOSIS. **CHRONIC EXPOSURE-** NO DATA AVAILABLE.

FIRST AID- REMOVE CONTAMINATED CLOTHING AND SHOES IMMEDIATELY. WASH AFFECTED AREA WITH SOAP OR MILD DETERGENT AND LARGE AMOUNTS OF WATER UNTIL NO EVIDENCE OF CHEMICAL REMAINS (APPROXIMATELY 15-20 MINUTES). GET MEDICAL ATTENTION IMMEDIATELY.

EYE CONTACT: DICRYL: **ACUTE EXPOSURE-** NO DATA AVAILABLE. **CHRONIC EXPOSURE-** NO DATA AVAILABLE.

FIRST AID- WASH EYES IMMEDIATELY WITH LARGE AMOUNTS OF WATER OR NORMAL SALINE, OCCASIONALLY LIFTING UPPER AND LOWER LIDS, UNTIL NO EVIDENCE OF CHEMICAL REMAINS (APPROXIMATELY 15-20 MINUTES). GET MEDICAL ATTENTION IMMEDIATELY.

INGESTION: DICRYL: **ACUTE EXPOSURE-** NO SPECIFIC DATA AVAILABLE. 3,4-DICHLOROANILINE, A RELATED SUBSTANCE, CAUSES METHEMOGLOBINEMIA WITH CYANOSIS. **CHRONIC EXPOSURE-** NO DATA AVAILABLE.

FIRST AID- TREAT SYMPTOMATICALLY AND SUPPORTIVELY. GET MEDICAL ATTENTION IMMEDIATELY. IF VOMITING OCCURS, KEEP HEAD LOWER THAN HIPS TO PREVENT ASPIRATION.

ANTIDOTE: NO SPECIFIC ANTIDOTE. TREAT SYMPTOMATICALLY AND SUPPORTIVELY.

REACTIVITY

REACTIVITY: STABLE UNDER NORMAL TEMPERATURES AND PRESSURES.

INCOMPATIBILITIES: DICRYL: OXIDIZERS (STRONG): FIRE AND EXPLOSION HAZARD.

DECOMPOSITION: THERMAL DECOMPOSITION PRODUCTS MAY INCLUDE TOXIC OXIDES OF NITROGEN AND CARBON AND TOXIC AND CORROSIVE FUMES OF CHLORIDES.

POLYMERIZATION: HAZARDOUS POLYMERIZATION HAS NOT BEEN REPORTED TO OCCUR UNDER NORMAL TEMPERATURES AND PRESSURES.

STORAGE AND DISPOSAL

OBSERVE ALL FEDERAL, STATE AND LOCAL REGULATIONS WHEN STORING OR DISPOSING OF THIS SUBSTANCE. FOR ASSISTANCE, CONTACT THE DISTRICT DIRECTOR OF THE ENVIRONMENTAL PROTECTION AGENCY.

****STORAGE****

STORE IN ACCORDANCE WITH 40 CFR 165 RECOMMENDED PROCEDURES FOR THE DISPOSAL AND STORAGE OF PESTICIDES AND PESTICIDE CONTAINERS.
STORE AWAY FROM INCOMPATIBLE SUBSTANCES.

****DISPOSAL****

DISPOSAL MUST BE IN ACCORDANCE WITH 40 CFR 165 RECOMMENDED PROCEDURES FOR THE DISPOSAL AND STORAGE OF PESTICIDES AND PESTICIDE CONTAINERS.

CONDITIONS TO AVOID

MAY BURN BUT DOES NOT IGNITE READILY. AVOID CONTACT WITH STRONG OXIDIZERS, EXCESSIVE HEAT, SPARKS, OR OPEN FLAME.

SPILL AND LEAK PROCEDURES

OCCUPATIONAL SPILL: SWEEP UP AND PLACE IN SUITABLE CLEAN, DRY CONTAINERS FOR RECLAMATION OR LATER DISPOSAL. DO NOT FLUSH SPILLED MATERIAL INTO SEWER. KEEP UNNECESSARY PEOPLE AWAY.

PROTECTIVE EQUIPMENT

VENTILATION: PROVIDE LOCAL EXHAUST OR PROCESS ENCLOSURE VENTILATION SYSTEM.

RESPIRATOR: THE FOLLOWING RESPIRATORS AND MAXIMUM USE CONCENTRATIONS ARE RECOMMENDATIONS BY THE U.S. DEPARTMENT OF HEALTH AND HUMAN SERVICES, NIOSH POCKET GUIDE TO CHEMICAL HAZARDS; NIOSH CRITERIA DOCUMENTS OR BY THE U.S. DEPARTMENT OF LABOR, 29 CFR 1910 SUBPART Z. THE SPECIFIC RESPIRATOR SELECTED MUST BE BASED ON CONTAMINATION LEVELS FOUND IN THE WORK PLACE, MUST NOT EXCEED THE WORKING LIMITS OF THE RESPIRATOR AND BE JOINTLY APPROVED BY THE NATIONAL INSTITUTE FOR OCCUPATIONAL SAFETY AND HEALTH AND THE MINE SAFETY AND HEALTH ADMINISTRATION (NIOSH-MSHA).

THE FOLLOWING RESPIRATORS ARE RECOMMENDED BASED ON INFORMATION FOUND IN THE PHYSICAL DATA, TOXICITY AND HEALTH EFFECTS SECTIONS. THEY ARE RANKED IN ORDER FROM MINIMUM TO MAXIMUM RESPIRATORY PROTECTION. THE SPECIFIC RESPIRATOR SELECTED MUST BE BASED ON CONTAMINATION LEVELS FOUND IN THE WORK PLACE, MUST NOT EXCEED THE WORKING LIMITS OF THE RESPIRATOR AND BE JOINTLY APPROVED BY THE NATIONAL INSTITUTE FOR OCCUPATIONAL SAFETY AND HEALTH AND THE MINE SAFETY AND HEALTH ADMINISTRATION (NIOSH-MSHA).

FOR FIREFIGHTING AND OTHER IMMEDIATELY DANGEROUS TO LIFE OR HEALTH CONDITIONS:

SELF-CONTAINED BREATHING APPARATUS WITH FULL FACEPIECE OPERATED IN PRESSURE-DEMAND OR OTHER POSITIVE PRESSURE MODE.

SUPPLIED-AIR RESPIRATOR WITH FULL FACEPIECE AND OPERATED IN PRESSURE-DEMAND OR OTHER POSITIVE PRESSURE MODE IN COMBINATION WITH AN AUXILIARY SELF-CONTAINED BREATHING APPARATUS OPERATED IN PRESSURE-DEMAND OR OTHER POSITIVE PRESSURE MODE.

CLOTHING: EMPLOYEE MUST WEAR APPROPRIATE PROTECTIVE (IMPERVIOUS) CLOTHING AND EQUIPMENT TO PREVENT REPEATED OR PROLONGED SKIN CONTACT WITH THIS SUBSTANCE.

GLOVES: EMPLOYEE MUST WEAR APPROPRIATE PROTECTIVE GLOVES TO PREVENT CONTACT WITH THIS SUBSTANCE.

EYE PROTECTION: EMPLOYEE MUST WEAR SPLASH-PROOF OR DUST-RESISTANT SAFETY GOGGLES TO PREVENT EYE CONTACT WITH THIS SUBSTANCE.

EMERGENCY EYE WASH: WHERE THERE IS ANY POSSIBILITY THAT AN EMPLOYEE'S EYES MAY BE EXPOSED TO THIS SUBSTANCE, THE EMPLOYER SHOULD PROVIDE AN EYE WASH FOUNTAIN WITHIN THE IMMEDIATE WORK AREA FOR EMERGENCY USE.

AUTHORIZED BY- OCCUPATIONAL HEALTH SERVICES, INC.

CREATION DATE: 03/22/90 ***REVISION DATE:*** 05/31/90

MATERIAL SAFETY DATA SHEET

OCCUPATIONAL HEALTH SERVICES, INC.
AGRICULTURE AND PESTICIDE DIVISION
450 SEVENTH AVENUE, SUITE 2407
NEW YORK, NEW YORK 10123
1-800-445-MSDS OR (212) 967-1100

EMERGENCY CONTACT:
JOHN S. BRANSFORD, JR. (615) 292-1180

SUBSTANCE IDENTIFICATION

CAS-NUMBER 500-28-7

SUBSTANCE: CHLORTHION

TRADE NAMES/SYNONYMS: PHOSPHOROTHIOIC ACID, O-(3-CHLORO-4-NITROPHENYL) O,O-DIMETHYL ESTER; O-3-CHLORO-4-NITROPHENYL O,O-DIMETHYL PHOSPHOROTHIOATE; O-(3-CHLORO-4-NITROPHENYL) O,O-DIMETHYL PHOSPHOROTHIOATE; O,O-DIMETHYL O-(3-CHLORO-4-NITROPHENYL) THIONOPHOSPHATE; P-NITRO-M-CHLOROPHENYL DIMETHYL THIONOPHOSPHATE; O,O-DIMETHYL O-3-CHLORO-4-NITROPHENYL THIONOPHOSPHATE; O,O-DIMETHYL-O-(3-CHLORO-4-NITROPHENYL)PHOSPHOROTHIOATE; 3-CHLORO-4-NITROPHENYL DIMETHYL PHOSPHOROTHIONATE; BAYER 22190; BAYER 22/190; CHLOROTHION; CHLORTHION METHYL; COMPOUND 22/190; METHYLCHLOROTHION; OMS 217; PST71379

CHEMICAL FAMILY: ORGANOPHOSPHATE

MOLECULAR FORMULA: C8-H9-CL-N-O5-P-S

MOLECULAR WEIGHT: 297.66

CERCLA RATINGS (SCALE 0-3): HEALTH=2 FIRE=0 REACTIVITY=2 PERSISTENCE=1

NFPA RATINGS (SCALE 0-4): HEALTH=2 FIRE=0 REACTIVITY=2

COMPONENTS AND CONTAMINANTS

COMPONENT: CHLORTHION ***PERCENT:*** 100
CAS# 500-28-7

EXPOSURE LIMITS: NO OCCUPATIONAL EXPOSURE LIMITS ESTABLISHED BY OSHA, ACGIH, OR NIOSH.

PHYSICAL DATA

DESCRIPTION: YELLOW CRYSTALLINE POWDER

BOILING POINT: 234 F (112 C) (0.04 MMHG)

MELTING POINT: 70 F (21 C) ***SPECIFIC GRAVITY:*** 1.437

VAPOR PRESSURE: 0.000007 MMHG @ 30 C ***SOLUBILITY IN WATER:*** 40 PPM

SOLVENT SOLUBILITY: SOLUBLE IN ALCOHOL, ETHER, BENZENE, TOLUENE, OILS, AROMATIC HYDROCARBONS

DECOMPOSES ABOUT 302 F (150 C)

FIRE AND EXPLOSION DATA

FIRE AND EXPLOSION HAZARD: NEGLIGIBLE FIRE HAZARD WHEN EXPOSED TO HEAT OR FLAME.

FIREFIGHTING MEDIA: DRY CHEMICAL, CARBON DIOXIDE, HALON, WATER SPRAY OR STANDARD FOAM (1987 EMERGENCY RESPONSE GUIDEBOOK, DOT P 5800.4).

FOR LARGER FIRES, USE WATER SPRAY, FOG OR STANDARD FOAM (1987 EMERGENCY RESPONSE GUIDEBOOK, DOT P 5800.4).

FIREFIGHTING: MOVE CONTAINERS FROM FIRE AREA IF POSSIBLE. FIGHT FIRE FROM MAXIMUM DISTANCE. STAY AWAY FROM STORAGE TANK ENDS. DIKE FIRE CONTROL WATER FOR LATER DISPOSAL. DO NOT SCATTER MATERIAL (1987 EMERGENCY RESPONSE GUIDEBOOK, DOT P 5800.4, GUIDE PAGE 55).

EXTINGUISH USING AGENT SUITABLE FOR TYPE OF SURROUNDING FIRE. AVOID BREATHING VAPORS AND DUSTS. KEEP UPWIND.

TOXICITY

CHLORTHION: TOXICITY DATA: 1500 MG/KG SKIN-RAT LD50; 625 MG/KG ORAL-RAT LD50; 794 MG/KG ORAL-MOUSE LD50; 1 GM/KG ORAL-RABBIT LDLO; 750 MG/KG INTRAPERITONEAL-RAT LD50; 525 MG/KG INTRAPERITONEAL-GUINEA PIG LD50; 880 MG/KG UNREPORTED-RAT LD50. CARCINOGEN STATUS: NONE. ACUTE TOXICITY LEVEL: MODERATELY TOXIC BY INGESTION AND DERMAL ABSORPTION. TARGET EFFECTS: CHOLINESTERASE INHIBITOR. POISONING MAY AFFECT THE NERVOUS SYSTEM.* AT INCREASED RISK FROM EXPOSURE: PERSONS WITH RESPIRATORY AILMENTS, RECENT EXPOSURE TO CHOLINESTERASE INHIBITORS OR IMPAIRED CHOLINESTERASE PRODUCTION, OR LIVER MALFUNCTION.* ADDITIONAL DATA: MAY CROSS THE PLACENTA. HIGH ENVIRONMENTAL TEMPERATURES OR EXPOSURE OF THE CHEMICAL TO VISIBLE OR ULTRAVIOLET LIGHT MAY ENHANCE THE TOXICITY. INTERACTIONS WITH MEDICATIONS MAY OCCUR.*

* MAY BE BASED ON GENERAL INFORMATION ON ORGANOPHOSPHATES.

HEALTH EFFECTS AND FIRST AID

INHALATION: CHLORTHION: SEE INFORMATION ON ORGANOPHOSPHATES.

ORGANOPHOSPHATES: CHOLINESTERASE INHIBITOR. ACUTE EXPOSURE- WHEN INHALED, THE FIRST EFFECTS OF CHOLINESTERASE INHIBITORS ARE USUALLY RESPIRATORY AND MAY INCLUDE NASAL HYPEREMIA AND WATERY DISCHARGE, COUGH, CHEST DISCOMFORT, DYSPNEA, AND WHEEZING DUE TO INCREASED BRONCHIAL SECRETIONS AND BRONCHOCONSTRICTION. IF SUFFICIENT AMOUNTS ARE ABSORBED, OTHER SYSTEMIC EFFECTS MAY BEGIN WITHIN A FEW MINUTES OR BE DELAYED FOR UP TO 12 HOURS. SYMPTOMS MAY INCLUDE PALLOR, NAUSEA, VOMITING, DIARRHEA, ABDOMINAL CRAMPS, HEADACHE, DIZZINESS, OCULAR PAIN, BLURRED VISION, MIOSIS OR IN SOME CASES, ESPECIALLY INITIALLY, MYDRIASIS, LACRIMATION, SALIVATION, SWEATING, AND CONFUSION. OTHER REPORTED CENTRAL NERVOUS SYSTEM OR NEUROMUSCULAR EFFECTS MAY INCLUDE ATAXIA, SLURRED SPEECH, AREFLEXIA, WEAKNESS, FATIGUE, FASCICULATIONS, TWITCHING, TREMORS POSSIBLY OF THE TONGUE AND EYELIDS, AND EVENTUALLY PARALYSIS OF THE EXTREMITIES AND POSSIBLY OF THE RESPIRATORY MUSCLES. IN SEVERE CASES THERE MAY ALSO BE INVOLUNTARY DEFECATION AND URINATION, CYANOSIS, PSYCHOSIS, HYPERGLYCEMIA, ACUTE PANCREATITIS, CARDIAC IRREGULARITIES, PULMONARY EDEMA, UNCONSCIOUSNESS, CONVULSIONS, AND COMA. DEATH IS PRIMARILY DUE TO RESPIRATORY FAILURE, ALTHOUGH CARDIOVASCULAR EFFECTS INCLUDING CARDIAC ARREST MAY ALSO BE IMPLICATED. LONG TERM SEQUELAE ARE RARE BUT MAY INCLUDE NEUROPSYCHIATRIC DISORDERS AND MYOPATHY WITH MUSCLE TENDERNESS. SOME ORGANOPHOSPHATES MAY CAUSE A DELAYED NEUROPATHY BEGINNING 1-4 WEEKS AFTER AN ACUTE EXPOSURE WHICH MAY OR MAY NOT HAVE CAUSED ACUTE CHOLINERGIC EFFECTS. NUMBNESS, TINGLING, WEAKNESS AND CRAMPING BEGINNING SYMMETRICALLY IN THE LOWER LIMBS MAY PROGRESS TO ATAXIA AND PARALYSIS. IN SEVERE CASES, UPPER LIMB INVOLVEMENT IS POSSIBLE AND FLACCID PARALYSIS MAY PROGRESS TO SPASTIC PARALYSIS WITH EXAGGERATED REFLEXES. IMPROVEMENT MAY OCCUR OVER MONTHS TO YEARS, BUT SOME RESIDUAL IMPAIRMENT USUALLY REMAINS.

CHRONIC EXPOSURE- REPEATED OR PROLONGED EXPOSURE MAY RESULT IN THE EFFECTS OF ACUTE EXPOSURE INCLUDING THE DELAYED NEUROPATHY. OTHER EFFECTS REPORTED IN WORKERS REPEATEDLY EXPOSED INCLUDE IMPAIRED MEMORY AND CONCENTRATION, ACUTE PSYCHOSIS, SEVERE DEPRESSIONS, IRRITABILTY, CONFUSION, APATHY, EMOTIONAL LABILITY, SOCIAL WITHDRAWAL, CONFUSION, HEADACHE, SPEECH DIFFICULTIES, DELAYED REACTION TIMES, SPATIAL DISORIENTATION, NIGHTMARES, SLEEPWALKING, AND DROWSINESS OR INSOMNIA. AN INFLUENZA-LIKE CONDITION WITH HEADACHE, NAUSEA, WEAKNESS, ANOREXIA AND MALAISE HAS ALSO BEEN REPORTED.

FIRST AID- REMOVE FROM EXPOSURE AREA TO FRESH AIR IMMEDIATELY. IF BREATHING HAS STOPPED, GIVE ARTIFICIAL RESPIRATION. MAINTAIN AIRWAY AND BLOOD PRESSURE AND ADMINISTER OXYGEN IF AVAILABLE. KEEP AFFECTED PERSON WARM AND AT REST. TREAT SYMPTOMATICALLY AND SUPPORTIVELY. ADMINISTRATION OF OXYGEN SHOULD BE PERFORMED BY QUALIFIED PERSONNEL. GET MEDICAL ATTENTION IMMEDIATELY.

SKIN CONTACT: CHLORTHION: SEE INFORMATION ON ORGANOPHOSPHATES. ORGANOPHOSPHATES: CHOLINESTERASE INHIBITOR. **ACUTE EXPOSURE-** LOCALIZED SWEATING AND FASCICULATIONS MAY OCCUR AT THE SITE OF CONTACT. IF SUFFICIENT AMOUNTS ARE ABSORBED, OTHER EFFECTS OF CHOLINESTERASE INHIBITION AS DESCRIBED IN ACUTE INHALATION MAY OCCUR. SYMPTOMS MAY BE DELAYED 2-3 HOURS, BUT USUALLY NO MORE THAN 12 HOURS. THE RATE OF ABSORPTION IS INCREASED BY THE PRESENCE OF DERMATITIS OR HIGH AMBIENT TEMPERATURES. DELAYED NEUROPATHY IS ALSO POSSIBLE. **CHRONIC EXPOSURE-** REPEATED OR PROLONGED EXPOSURE MAY CAUSE EFFECTS AS DESCRIBED IN ACUTE EXPOSURE. SOME ORGA NOPHOSPHATES MAY CAUSE SENSITIZATION.

FIRST AID- REMOVE CONTAMINATED CLOTHING IMMEDIATELY. WASH CONTAMINATED AREAS WITH SOAP AND WATER FOLLOWED BY ALCOHOL (ARENA, POISONING, 4TH ED.). EMERGENCY PERSONNEL SHOULD WEAR GLOVES AND AVOID CONTAMINATION. TREAT RESPIRATORY DIFFICULTY WITH ARTIFICIAL RESPIRATION. GET MEDICAL ATTENTION IMMEDIATELY.

EYE CONTACT: CHLORTHION: SEE INFORMATION ON ORGANOPHOSPHATES. ORGANOPHOSPHATES: CHOLINESTERASE INHIBITOR. **ACUTE EXPOSURE-** DIRECT CONTACT MAY CAUSE PAIN, HYPEREMIA, LACRIMATION, TWITCHING OF THE EYELIDS, MIOSIS, AND CILIARY MUSCLE SPASM WITH LOSS OF ACCOMODATION, BLURRED OR DIMMED VISION AND BROWACHE. SOMETIMES MYDRIASIS MAY OCCUR INSTEAD OF MIOSIS. WITH SUFFICIENT EXPOSURE, OTHER SYMPTOMS OF CHOLINESTERASE INHIBITION AS DESCRIBED IN ACUTE INHALATION MAY OCCUR. **CHRONIC EXPOSURE-** REPEATED OR PROLONGED EXPOSURE MAY CAUSE EFFECTS AS DESCRIBED IN ACUTE EXPOSURE. SOME COMPOUNDS HAVE CAUSED TOXIC EFFECTS ON THE CRYSTALLINE LENS, CONJUNCTIVAL THICKENING AND OBSTRUCTION OF THE NASOLACRIMAL CANALS WHEN USED AS MIOTIC EYEDROPS.

FIRST AID- IRRIGATE EYES WITH WATER OR SALINE SOLUTION. IF SYMPTOMS OF POISONING OCCUR, TREAT RESPIRATORY DIFFICULTY WITH ARTIFICIAL RESPIRATION AND OXYGEN. OBSERVE PATIENT FOR AT LEAST 24-36 HOURS (GOSSELIN, CLINICAL TOXICOLOGY OF COMMERCIAL PRODUCTS, 5TH ED.). GET MEDICAL ATTENTION IMMEDIATELY. OXYGEN SHOULD BE ADMINISTERED BY QUALIFIED MEDICAL PERSONNEL.

INGESTION: CHLORTHION: A DAILY DOSE OF 50 MG/KG/DAY PRODUCED 50 PERCENT CHOLINESTERASE INHIBITION IN RATS. A DOSAGE OF 200 MG/KG/DAY PRODUCED 75 PERCENT CHOLINESTERASE INHIBITION AND WAS NOT TOLERATED FOR MORE THAN 5 TO 10 DAYS IN RATS. SEE INFORMATION ON ORGANOPHOSPHATES. ORGANOPHOSPHATES: CHOLINESTERASE INHIBITOR. **ACUTE EXPOSURE-** WHEN INGESTED, THE FIRST EFFECTS MAY BE NAUSEA, VOMITING, ANOREXIA, ABDOMINAL CRAMPS AND DIARRHEA. GASTROINTESTINAL ABSORPTION MAY CAUSE SYMPTOMS OF CHOLINESTERASE INHIBITION AS DESCRIBED IN ACUTE INHALATION. SYMPTOMS MAY BEGIN WITHIN MINUTES OR BE DELAYED FOR HOURS. DELAYED EFFECTS INCLUDING NEUROPATHY MAY ALSO OCCUR. **CHRONIC EXPOSURE-** REPEATED INGESTION MAY CAUSE EFFECTS AS DESCRIBED IN ACUTE EXPOSURE.

FIRST AID- IF PERSON IS ALERT AND RESPIRATION IS NOT DEPRESSED, GIVE SYRUP OF IPECAC FOLLOWED BY WATER (IF VOMITING OCCURS, KEEP HEAD BELOW HIPS TO PREVENT ASPIRATION). IF CONSCIOUSNESS LEVEL DECLINES OR VOMITING HAS NOT OCCURRED IN 15 MINUTES EMPTY STOMACH BY GASTRIC LAVAGE WITH THE AID OF CUFFED ENDOTRACHEAL TUBE USING ISOTONIC SALINE OR 5% SODIUM BICARBONATE FOLLOW WITH ACTIVATED CHARCOAL. ESTABLISH AND MAINTAIN AIRWAY. TREAT RESPIRATORY DIFFICULTY WITH ARTIFICIAL RESPIRATION AND OXYGEN. DO NOT GIVE MORPHINE, AMINOPHYLLINE, PHENOTHIAZINES, RESERPINE, FUROSEMIDE, OR ETHACRYNIC ACID (MORGAN, RECOGNITION AND MANAGEMENT OF PESTICIDE POISONINGS, 3RD ED.). TREAT SYMPTOMATICALLY AND SUPPORTIVELY. ADMINISTRATION OF OXYGEN AND LAVAGE MUST BE PERFORMED BY QUALIFIED MEDICAL PERSONNEL. GET MEDICAL ATTENTION IMMEDIATELY.

ANTIDOTE: THE FOLLOWING ANTIDOTE(S) HAVE BEEN RECOMMENDED. HOWEVER, THE DECISION AS TO WHETHER THE SEVERITY OF POISONING REQUIRES ADMINISTRATION OF ANY ANTIDOTE AND ACTUAL DOSE REQUIRED SHOULD BE MADE BY QUALIFIED MEDICAL PERSONNEL.

FOR CHOLINESTERASE INHIBITORS: ESTABLISH CLEAR AIRWAY AND TISSUE OXYGENATION BY ASPIRATION OF SECRETIONS, AND IF NECESSARY, BY ASSISTED PULMONARY VENTILATION WITH OXYGEN. IMPROVE TISSUE OXYGENATION AS MUCH AS POSSIBLE BEFORE ADMINISTERING ATROPINE TO MINIMIZE THE RISK OF VENTRICULAR FIBRILLATION. ADMINISTER ATROPINE SULFATE INTRAVENOUSLY, OR INTRAMUSCULARLY IF IV INJECTION IS NOT POSSIBLE. IN MODERATELY SEVERE POISONING ADMINISTER ATROPINE SULFATE, 0.4-2.0 MG REPEATED EVERY 15 MINUTES UNTIL ATROPINIZATION IS ACHIEVED (TACHYCARDIA, FLUSHING, DRY MOUTH, MYDRIASIS). MAINTAIN ATROPINIZATION BY REPEATED DOSES FOR 2-12 HOURS, OR LONGER, DEPENDING ON THE SEVERITY OF POISONING. THE APPEARANCE OF RALES IN THE LUNG BASES, MIOSIS, SALIVATION, NAUSEA, BRADYCARDIA, ARE ALL INDICATIONS OF INADEQUATE ATROPINIZATION. SEVERELY POISONED INDIVIDUALS MAY EXHIBIT REMARKABLE TOLERANCE TO ATROPINE; TWO OR MORE TIMES THE DOSAGES SUGGESTED ABOVE MAY BE NEEDED. PERSONS NOT POISONED OR ONLY SLIGHTLY POISONED, HOWEVER, MAY DEVELOP SIGNS OF ATROPINE TOXICITY FROM SUCH LARGE DOSAGES: FEVER, MUSCLE FIBRILLATIONS, AND DELIRIUM ARE THE MAIN SIGNS OF ATROPINE TOXICITY. IF THESE SIGNS APPEAR WHILE THE PATIENT IS FULLY ATROPINIZED, ATROPINE ADMINISTRATION SHOULD BE DISCONTINUED, AT LEAST TEMPORARILY. OBSERVE TREATED PATIENTS CLOSELY AT LEAST 24 HOURS TO INSURE THAT SYMPTOMS (POSSIBLY PULMONARY EDEMA) DO NOT RECUR AS ATROPINIZATION WEARS OFF. IN VERY SEVERE POISONINGS, METABOLIC DISPOSITION OF TOXICANT MAY REQUIRE SEVERAL HOURS OR DAYS DURING WHICH ATROPINIZATION MUST BE MAINTAINED. MARKEDLY LOWER LEVELS OF URINARY METABOLITES INDICATE THAT ATROPINE DOSAGE CAN BE TAPERED OFF. AS DOSAGE IS REDUCED, CHECK THE LUNG BASES FREQUENTLY FOR RALES. IF RALES ARE HEARD OR OTHER SYMPTOMS RETURN, RE-ESTABLISH ATROPINIZATION PROMPTLY (MORGAN, RECOGNITION AND MANAGEMENT OF PESTICIDE POISONINGS, 3RD ED.). ADMINISTRATION OF ANTIDOTE MUST BE PERFORMED BY QUALIFIED MEDICAL PERSONNEL.

IN CASES OF SEVERE POISONING BY ORGANOPHOSPHATE PESTICIDES IN WHICH RESPIRATORY DEPRESSION, MUSCLE WEAKNESS AND TWITCHINGS ARE SEVERE, GIVE PRALIDOXIME (PROTOPAM-AYERST, 2-PAM), 1.0 GRAM INTRAVENOUSLY AT NO MORE THAN 0.5 GRAM PER MINUTE. DOSAGE OF PRALIDOXIME MAY BE REPEATED IN 1-2 HOURS, THEN AT 10-12 HOUR INTERVALS IF NEEDED. IN VERY SEVERE POISONINGS, DOSAGE RATES MAY BE DOUBLED. TREATMENT WITH PRALIDOXIME WILL BE MOST EFFECTIVE IF GIVEN WITHIN THIRTY-SIX HOURS AFTER POISONING (MORGAN, RECOGNITION AND MANAGEMENT OF PESTICIDE POISONINGS, 3RD ED.). ANTIDOTE SHOULD BE ADMINISTERED BY QUALIFIED MEDICAL PERSONNEL.

REACTIVITY

REACTIVITY: THE MATERIAL MAY BECOME UNSTABLE AT ELEVATED TEMPERATURES. THERMAL DECOMPOSITION MAY BECOME SELF-ACCELERATING AND RESULT IN THE RUPTURE OF THE CONTAINER.

INCOMPATIBILITIES: CHLORTHION: ALKALIS: HYDROLYZED.

DECOMPOSITION: THERMAL DECOMPOSITION MAY RELEASE TOXIC OXIDES OF SULFUR, PHOSPHORUS, AND NITROGEN AND CORROSIVE HYDROGEN CHLORIDE.

POLYMERIZATION: HAZARDOUS POLYMERIZATION HAS NOT BEEN REPORTED TO OCCUR UNDER NORMAL TEMPERATURES AND PRESSURES.

STORAGE AND DISPOSAL

OBSERVE ALL FEDERAL, STATE AND LOCAL REGULATIONS WHEN STORING OR DISPOSING OF THIS SUBSTANCE. FOR ASSISTANCE, CONTACT THE DISTRICT DIRECTOR OF THE ENVIRONMENTAL PROTECTION AGENCY.

STORAGE

STORE IN ACCORDANCE WITH 40 CFR 165 RECOMMENDED PROCEDURES FOR THE DISPOSAL AND STORAGE OF PESTICIDES AND PESTICIDE CONTAINERS.
STORE AWAY FROM INCOMPATIBLE SUBSTANCES.

DISPOSAL

DISPOSAL MUST BE IN ACCORDANCE WITH 40 CFR 165 RECOMMENDED PROCEDURES FOR THE DISPOSAL AND STORAGE OF PESTICIDES AND PESTICIDE CONTAINERS.

CONDITIONS TO AVOID

DO NOT HEAT TO DECOMPOSITION.

SPILL AND LEAK PROCEDURES

OCCUPATIONAL SPILL: DO NOT TOUCH SPILLED MATERIAL. STOP LEAK IF YOU CAN DO IT WITHOUT RISK. USE WATER SPRAY TO REDUCE VAPORS. FOR SMALL SPILLS, TAKE UP WITH SAND OR OTHER ABSORBENT MATERIAL AND PLACE INTO CONTAINERS FOR LATER DISPOSAL. FOR SMALL DRY SPILLS, WITH A CLEAN

SHOVEL PLACE MATERIAL INTO CLEAN, DRY CONTAINERS AND COVER. MOVE CONTAINERS FROM SPILL AREA. FOR LARGER SPILLS, DIKE FAR AHEAD OF SPILL FOR LATER DISPOSAL. KEEP UNNECESSARY PEOPLE AWAY. ISOLATE HAZARD AREA AND DENY ENTRY. VENTILATE CLOSED SPACES BEFORE ENTERING.

PROTECTIVE EQUIPMENT

VENTILATION: PROVIDE LOCAL EXHAUST OR GENERAL DILUTION VENTILATION SYSTEM.

RESPIRATOR: THE FOLLOWING RESPIRATORS ARE RECOMMENDED BASED ON INFORMATION FOUND IN THE PHYSICAL DATA, TOXICITY AND HEALTH EFFECTS SECTIONS. THEY ARE RANKED IN ORDER FROM MINIMUM TO MAXIMUM RESPIRATORY PROTECTION. THE SPECIFIC RESPIRATOR SELECTED MUST BE BASED ON CONTAMINATION LEVELS FOUND IN THE WORK PLACE, MUST NOT EXCEED THE WORKING LIMITS OF THE RESPIRATOR AND BE JOINTLY APPROVED BY THE NATIONAL INSTITUTE FOR OCCUPATIONAL SAFETY AND HEALTH AND THE MINE SAFETY AND HEALTH ADMINISTRATION (NIOSH-MSHA).

CHEMICAL CARTRIDGE RESPIRATOR WITH AN ORGANIC VAPOR CARTRIDGE(S) IN COMBINATION WITH A DUST AND MIST FILTER.

GAS MASK WITH ORGANIC VAPOR CANISTER (CHIN-STYLE OR FRONT- OR BACK-MOUNTED CANISTER) WITH A DUST AND MIST FILTER.

GAS MASK WITH ORGANIC VAPOR CANISTER (CHIN-STYLE OR FRONT- OR BACK-MOUNTED CANISTER) WITH A PARTICULATE FILTER.

POWERED AIR-PURIFYING RESPIRATOR WITH A HIGH-EFFICIENCY FILTER.

TYPE 'C' SUPPLIED-AIR RESPIRATOR WITH A FULL FACEPIECE OPERATED IN A PRESSURE-DEMAND OR OTHER POSITIVE PRESSURE MODE.

SELF-CONTAINED BREATHING APPARATUS WITH A FULL FACEPIECE OPERATED IN PRESSURE-DEMAND OR OTHER POSITIVE PRESSURE MODE.

FOR FIREFIGHTING AND OTHER IMMEDIATELY DANGEROUS TO LIFE OR HEALTH CONDITIONS:

SELF-CONTAINED BREATHING APPARATUS WITH FULL FACEPIECE OPERATED IN PRESSURE-DEMAND OR OTHER POSITIVE PRESSURE MODE.

SUPPLIED-AIR RESPIRATOR WITH FULL FACEPIECE AND OPERATED IN PRESSURE-DEMAND OR OTHER POSITIVE PRESSURE MODE IN COMBINATION WITH AN AUXILIARY SELF-CONTAINED BREATHING APPARATUS OPERATED IN PRESSURE-DEMAND OR OTHER POSITIVE PRESSURE MODE.

CLOTHING: EMPLOYEE MUST WEAR APPROPRIATE PROTECTIVE (IMPERVIOUS) CLOTHING AND EQUIPMENT TO PREVENT REPEATED OR PROLONGED SKIN CONTACT WITH THIS SUBSTANCE.

GLOVES: EMPLOYEE MUST WEAR APPROPRIATE PROTECTIVE GLOVES TO PREVENT CONTACT WITH THIS SUBSTANCE.

EYE PROTECTION: EMPLOYEE MUST WEAR SPLASH-PROOF OR DUST-RESISTANT SAFETY GOGGLES TO PREVENT EYE CONTACT WITH THIS SUBSTANCE.

EMERGENCY EYE WASH: WHERE THERE IS ANY POSSIBILITY THAT AN EMPLOYEE'S EYES MAY BE EXPOSED TO THIS SUBSTANCE, THE EMPLOYER SHOULD PROVIDE AN EYE WASH FOUNTAIN WITHIN THE IMMEDIATE WORK AREA FOR EMERGENCY USE.

AUTHORIZED BY- OCCUPATIONAL HEALTH SERVICES, INC.

CREATION DATE: 10/04/89 ***REVISION DATE:*** 05/07/90

MATERIAL SAFETY DATA SHEET

OCCUPATIONAL HEALTH SERVICES, INC.
AGRICULTURE AND PESTICIDE DIVISION
450 SEVENTH AVENUE, SUITE 2407
NEW YORK, NEW YORK 10123
1-800-445-MSDS OR (212) 967-1100

EMERGENCY CONTACT:
JOHN S. BRANSFORD, JR. (615) 292-1180

SUBSTANCE IDENTIFICATION

CAS-NUMBER 2463-84-5

SUBSTANCE: **DICAPTHON**

TRADE NAMES/SYNONYMS: PHOSPHOROTHIOIC ACID, O-(2-CHLORO-4-NITROPHENYL) O,O-DIMETHYL ESTER; O-(2-CHLORO-4-NITROPHENYL) O,O-DIMETHYLPHOSPHOROTHIOATE; O,O-DIMETHYL O-(2-CHLORO-4-NITROPHENYL)PHOSPHOROTHIOATE; O,O-DIMETHYL-O-(2-CHLORO-4-NITROPHENYL)THIONOPHOSPHATE; P-NITRO-O-CHLOROPHENYL DIMETHYL THIONOPHOSPHATE; AMERICAN CYANAMID 4,124; DICAPTAN; DICAPTHION; ISOCHLOROTHION; ISOCHLORTHION; ISOMERIC CHLORHTION; ENT 17,035; OMS 214; C8H9CLNO5PS; PST71380

CHEMICAL FAMILY: PHOSPHOROTHIOATE

MOLECULAR FORMULA: (C-H3-O)2-P-(S)-O-C6-H3-(CL)-N-O2

MOLECULAR WEIGHT: 297.68

CERCLA RATINGS (SCALE 0-3): HEALTH=3 FIRE=1 REACTIVITY=0 PERSISTENCE=1

NFPA RATINGS (SCALE 0-4): HEALTH=3 FIRE=1 REACTIVITY=0

COMPONENTS AND CONTAMINANTS

COMPONENT: DICAPTHON ***PERCENT:*** 100.0

CAS# 2463-84-5

OTHER CONTAMINANTS: NONE

EXPOSURE LIMITS: NO OCCUPATIONAL EXPOSURE LIMITS ESTABLISHED BY OSHA, ACGIH, OR NIOSH.

PHYSICAL DATA

DESCRIPTION: WHITE CRYSTALLINE SOLID. ***MELTING POINT:*** 127 F (53 C)

SPECIFIC GRAVITY: NOT AVAILABLE ***SOLUBILITY IN WATER:*** 0.0035%

SOLVENT SOLUBILITY: SOLUBLE IN ACETONE, CYCLOHEXANE, CYCLOHEXANONE, ETHYL ACETATE, TOLUENE, XYLENE, ETHYLENE GLYCOL, PROPYLENE GLYCOL, AND SOME OILS.

FIRE AND EXPLOSION DATA

FIRE AND EXPLOSION HAZARD: SLIGHT FIRE HAZARD WHEN EXPOSED TO HEAT OR FLAME.

FIREFIGHTING MEDIA: DRY CHEMICAL, CARBON DIOXIDE, HALON, WATER SPRAY OR STANDARD FOAM (1987 EMERGENCY RESPONSE GUIDEBOOK, DOT P 5800.4). FOR LARGER FIRES, USE WATER SPRAY, FOG OR STANDARD FOAM (1987 EMERGENCY RESPONSE GUIDEBOOK, DOT P 5800.4).

FIREFIGHTING: MOVE CONTAINERS FROM FIRE AREA IF POSSIBLE. FIGHT FIRE FROM MAXIMUM DISTANCE. STAY AWAY FROM STORAGE TANK ENDS. DIKE FIRE CONTROL WATER FOR LATER DISPOSAL. DO NOT SCATTER MATERIAL (1987 EMERGENCY RESPONSE GUIDEBOOK, DOT P 5800.4, GUIDE PAGE 55). EXTINGUISH ONLY IF FLOW CAN BE STOPPED; USE FLOODING AMOUNTS OF WATER AS FOG, SOLID STREAMS MAY BE INEFFECTIVE. COOL CONTAINERS WITH FLOODING AMOUNTS OF WATER FROM AS FAR A DISTANCE AS POSSIBLE. USE WATER SPRAY TO ABSORB TOXIC VAPORS. AVOID BREATHING TOXIC VAPORS; KEEP UPWIND. CONSIDER EVACUATION OF DOWNWIND AREA IF MATERIAL IS LEAKING.

TOXICITY

DICAPTHON: TOXICITY DATA: 790 MG/KG SKIN-RAT LD50; 284 MG/KG ORAL-RAT LD50; 331 MG/KG ORAL-MOUSE LD50; 65 MG/KG INTRAPERITONEAL-MOUSE LD50. CARCINOGEN STATUS: NONE. ACUTE TOXICITY: TOXIC BY DERMAL ABSORPTION AND INGESTION. TARGET EFFECTS: CHOLINESTERASE INHIBITOR. POISONING MAY AFFECT THE NERVOUS SYSTEM.* AT INCREASED RISK FROM EXPOSURE: PERSONS WITH RESPIRATORY AILMENTS, RECENT EXPOSURE TO CHOLINESTERASE INHIBITORS OR IMPAIRED CHOLINESTERASE PRODUCTION, OR LIVER MALFUNCTION.* ADDITIONAL DATA: MAY CROSS THE PLACENTA. HIGH ENVIRONMENTAL TEMPERATURES OR EXPOSURE OF THE CHEMICAL TO VISIBLE OR ULTRAVIOLET LIGHT MAY ENHANCE THE TOXICITY. INTERACTIONS WITH MEDICATIONS MAY OCCUR.*

* MAY BE BASED ON GENERAL INFORMATION ON ORGANOPHOSPHATES.

HEALTH EFFECTS AND FIRST AID

INHALATION: DICAPTHON: SEE INFORMATION ON ORGANOPHOSPHATES.

ORGANOPHOSPHATES: CHOLINESTERASE INHIBITOR. **ACUTE EXPOSURE**- WHEN INHALED, THE FIRST EFFECTS OF CHOLINESTERASE INHIBITORS ARE USUALLY RESPIRATORY AND MAY INCLUDE NASAL HYPEREMIA AND WATERY DISCHARGE, COUGH, CHEST DISCOMFORT, DYSPNEA, AND WHEEZING DUE TO INCREASED BRONCHIAL SECRETIONS AND BRONCHOCONSTRICTION. IF SUFFICIENT AMOUNTS ARE ABSORBED, OTHER SYSTEMIC EFFECTS MAY BEGIN WITHIN A FEW MINUTES OR BE DELAYED FOR UP TO 12 HOURS. SYMPTOMS MAY INCLUDE PALLOR, NAUSEA, VOMITING, DIARRHEA, ABDOMINAL CRAMPS, HEADACHE, DIZZINESS, OCULAR PAIN, BLURRED VISION, MIOSIS OR IN SOME CASES, ESPECIALLY INITIALLY, MYDRIASIS, LACRIMATION, SALIVATION, SWEATING, AND CONFUSION. OTHER REPORTED CENTRAL NERVOUS SYSTEM OR NEUROMUSCULAR EFFECTS MAY INCLUDE ATAXIA, SLURRED SPEECH, AREFLEXIA, WEAKNESS, FATIGUE, FASCICULATIONS, TWITCHING, TREMORS POSSIBLY OF THE TONGUE AND EYELIDS, AND EVENTUALLY PARALYSIS OF THE EXTREMITIES AND POSSIBLY OF THE RESPIRATORY MUSCLES. IN SEVERE CASES THERE MAY ALSO BE INVOLUNTARY DEFECATION AND URINATION, CYANOSIS, PSYCHOSIS, HYPERGLYCEMIA, ACUTE PANCREATITIS, CARDIAC IRREGULARITIES, PULMONARY EDEMA, UNCONSCIOUSNESS, CONVULSIONS, AND COMA. DEATH IS PRIMARILY DUE TO RESPIRATORY FAILURE, ALTHOUGH CARDIOVASCULAR EFFECTS INCLUDING CARDIAC ARREST MAY ALSO BE IMPLICATED. LONG TERM SEQUELAE ARE RARE BUT MAY INCLUDE NEUROPSYCHIATRIC DISORDERS AND MYOPATHY WITH MUSCLE TENDERNESS. SOME ORGANOPHOSPHATES MAY CAUSE A DELAYED NEUROPATHY BEGINNING 1-4 WEEKS AFTER AN ACUTE EXPOSURE WHICH MAY OR

MAY NOT HAVE CAUSED ACUTE CHOLINERGIC EFFECTS. NUMBNESS, TINGLING, WEAKNESS AND CRAMPING BEGINNING SYMMETRICALLY IN THE LOWER LIMBS MAY PROGRESS TO ATAXIA AND PARALYSIS. IN SEVERE CASES, UPPER LIMB INVOLVEMENT IS POSSIBLE AND FLACCID PARALYSIS MAY PROGRESS TO SPASTIC PARALYSIS WITH EXAGGERATED REFLEXES. IMPROVEMENT MAY OCCUR OVER MONTHS TO YEARS, BUT SOME RESIDUAL IMPAIRMENT USUALLY REMAINS. **CHRONIC EXPOSURE-** REPEATED OR PROLONGED EXPOSURE MAY RESULT IN THE EFFECTS OF ACUTE EXPOSURE INCLUDING THE DELAYED NEUROPATHY. OTHER EFFECTS REPORTED IN WORKERS REPEATEDLY EXPOSED INCLUDE IMPAIRED MEMORY AND CONCENTRATION, ACUTE PSYCHOSIS, SEVERE DEPRESSIONS, IRRITABILTY, CONFUSION, APATHY, EMOTIONAL LABILITY, SOCIAL WITHDRAWAL, CONFUSION, HEADACHE, SPEECH DIFFICULTIES, DELAYED REACTION TIMES, SPATIAL DISORIENTATION, NIGHTMARES, SLEEPWALKING, AND DROWSINESS OR INSOMNIA. AN INFLUENZA-LIKE CONDITION WITH HEADACHE, NAUSEA, WEAKNESS, ANOREXIA AND MALAISE HAS ALSO BEEN REPORTED.

FIRST AID- REMOVE FROM EXPOSURE AREA TO FRESH AIR IMMEDIATELY. IF BREATHING HAS STOPPED, GIVE ARTIFICIAL RESPIRATION. MAINTAIN AIRWAY AND BLOOD PRESSURE AND ADMINISTER OXYGEN IF AVAILABLE. KEEP AFFECTED PERSON WARM AND AT REST. TREAT SYMPTOMATICALLY AND SUPPORTIVELY. ADMINISTRATION OF OXYGEN SHOULD BE PERFORMED BY QUALIFIED PERSONNEL. GET MEDICAL ATTENTION IMMEDIATELY.

SKIN CONTACT: DICAPTHON: TOXIC. SEE INFORMATION ON ORGANOPHOSPHATES. ORGANOPHOSPHATES: CHOLINESTERASE INHIBITOR. **ACUTE EXPOSURE-** LOCALIZED SWEATING AND FASCICULATIONS MAY OCCUR AT THE SITE OF CONTACT. IF SUFFICIENT AMOUNTS ARE ABSORBED, OTHER EFFECTS OF CHOLINESTERASE INHIBITION AS DESCRIBED IN ACUTE INHALATION MAY OCCUR. SYMPTOMS MAY BE DELAYED 2-3 HOURS, BUT USUALLY NO MORE THAN 12 HOURS. THE RATE OF ABSORPTION IS INCREASED BY THE PRESENCE OF DERMATITIS OR HIGH AMBIENT TEMPERATURES. DELAYED NEUROPATHY IS ALSO POSSIBLE. **CHRONIC EXPOSURE-** REPEATED OR PROLONGED EXPOSURE MAY CAUSE EFFECTS AS DESCRIBED IN ACUTE EXPOSURE. SOME ORGANOPHOSPHATES MAY CAUSE SENSITIZATION.

FIRST AID- REMOVE CONTAMINATED CLOTHING IMMEDIATELY. WASH CONTAMINATED AREAS WITH SOAP AND WATER FOLLOWED BY ALCOHOL (ARENA, POISONING, 4TH ED.). EMERGENCY PERSONNEL SHOULD WEAR GLOVES AND AVOID CONTAMINATION. TREAT RESPIRATORY DIFFICULTY WITH ARTIFICIAL RESPIRATION. GET MEDICAL ATTENTION IMMEDIATELY.

EYE CONTACT: DICAPTHON: SEE INFORMATION ON ORGANOPHOSPHATES. ORGANOPHOSPHATES: CHOLINESTERASE INHIBITOR. **ACUTE EXPOSURE-** DIRECT CONTACT MAY CAUSE PAIN, HYPEREMIA, LACRIMATION, TWITCHING OF THE EYELIDS, MIOSIS, AND CILIARY MUSCLE SPASM WITH LOSS OF ACCOMODATION, BLURRED OR DIMMED VISION AND BROWACHE. SOMETIMES MYDRIASIS MAY OCCUR INSTEAD OF MIOSIS. WITH SUFFICIENT EXPOSURE, OTHER SYMPTOMS OF CHOLINESTERASE INHIBITION AS DESCRIBED IN ACUTE INHALATION MAY OCCUR. **CHRONIC EXPOSURE-** REPEATED OR PROLONGED EXPOSURE MAY CAUSE EFFECTS AS DESCRIBED IN ACUTE EXPOSURE. SOME COMPOUNDS HAVE CAUSED TOXIC EFFECTS ON THE CRYSTALLINE LENS, CONJUNCTIVAL THICKENING AND OBSTRUCTION OF THE NASOLACRIMAL CANALS WHEN USED AS MIOTIC EYEDROPS.

FIRST AID- IRRIGATE EYES WITH WATER OR SALINE SOLUTION. IF SYMPTOMS OF POISONING OCCUR, TREAT RESPIRATORY DIFFICULTY WITH ARTIFICIAL RESPIRATION AND OXYGEN. OBSERVE PATIENT FOR AT LEAST 24-36 HOURS (GOSSELIN, CLINICAL TOXICOLOGY OF COMMERCIAL PRODUCTS, 5TH ED.). GET MEDICAL ATTENTION IMMEDIATELY. OXYGEN SHOULD BE ADMINISTERED BY QUALIFIED MEDICAL PERSONNEL.

INGESTION: DICAPTHON: TOXIC. RATS FED A 25 PPM DIET FOR 1 YEAR SHOWED NO RETARDANCE IN GROWTH. SEE INFORMATION ON ORGANOPHOSPHATES. ORGANOPHOSPHATES: CHOLINESTERASE INHIBITOR. **ACUTE EXPOSURE-** WHEN INGESTED, THE FIRST EFFECTS MAY BE NAUSEA, VOMITING, ANOREXIA, ABDOMINAL CRAMPS AND DIARRHEA. GASTROINTESTINAL ABSORPTION MAY CAUSE SYMPTOMS OF CHOLINESTERASE INHIBITION AS DESCRIBED IN ACUTE INHALATION. SYMPTOMS MAY BEGIN WITHIN MINUTES OR BE DELAYED FOR HOURS. DELAYED EFFECTS INCLUDING NEUROPATHY MAY ALSO OCCUR. **CHRONIC EXPOSURE-** REPEATED INGESTION MAY CAUSE EFFECTS AS DESCRIBED IN ACUTE EXPOSURE.

FIRST AID- IF PERSON IS ALERT AND RESPIRATION IS NOT DEPRESSED, GIVE SYRUP OF IPECAC FOLLOWED BY WATER (IF VOMITING OCCURS, KEEP HEAD BELOW HIPS TO PREVENT ASPIRATION). IF CONSCIOUSNESS LEVEL DECLINES OR VOMITING HAS NOT OCCURRED IN 15 MINUTES EMPTY STOMACH BY GASTRIC LAVAGE WITH THE AID OF CUFFED ENDOTRACHEAL TUBE USING ISOTONIC SALINE OR 5% SODIUM BICARBONATE FOLLOW WITH ACTIVATED CHARCOAL. ESTABLISH AND MAINTAIN AIRWAY. TREAT RESPIRATORY DIFFICULTY WITH ARTIFICIAL RESPIRATION AND OXYGEN. DO NOT GIVE MORPHINE, AMINOPHYLLINE, PHENOTHIAZINES, RESERPINE, FUROSEMIDE, OR ETHACRYNIC ACID (MORGAN, RECOGNITION AND MANAGEMENT OF PESTICIDE POISONINGS, 3RD ED.). TREAT SYMPTOMATICALLY AND SUPPORTIVELY. ADMINISTRATION OF OXYGEN AND LAVAGE MUST BE PERFORMED BY QUALIFIED MEDICAL PERSONNEL. GET MEDICAL ATTENTION IMMEDIATELY.

ANTIDOTE: THE FOLLOWING ANTIDOTE(S) HAVE BEEN RECOMMENDED. HOWEVER, THE DECISION AS TO WHETHER THE SEVERITY OF POISONING REQUIRES ADMINISTRATION OF ANY ANTIDOTE AND ACTUAL DOSE REQUIRED SHOULD BE MADE BY QUALIFIED MEDICAL PERSONNEL.

FOR CHOLINESTERASE INHIBITORS: ESTABLISH CLEAR AIRWAY AND TISSUE OXYGENATION BY ASPIRATION OF SECRETIONS, AND IF NECESSARY, BY ASSISTED PULMONARY VENTILATION WITH OXYGEN. IMPROVE TISSUE OXYGENATION AS MUCH AS POSSIBLE BEFORE ADMINISTERING ATROPINE TO MINIMIZE THE RISK OF VENTRICULAR FIBRILLATION. ADMINISTER ATROPINE SULFATE INTRAVENOUSLY, OR INTRAMUSCULARLY IF IV INJECTION IS NOT POSSIBLE. IN MODERATELY SEVERE POISONING ADMINISTER ATROPINE SULFATE, 0.4-2.0 MG REPEATED EVERY 15 MINUTES UNTIL ATROPINIZATION IS ACHIEVED (TACHYCARDIA, FLUSHING, DRY MOUTH, MYDRIASIS). MAINTAIN ATROPINIZATION BY REPEATED DOSES FOR 2-12 HOURS, OR LONGER, DEPENDING ON THE SEVERITY OF POISONING. THE APPEARANCE OF RALES IN THE LUNG BASES, MIOSIS, SALIVATION, NAUSEA, BRADYCARDIA, ARE ALL INDICATIONS OF INADEQUATE ATROPINIZATION. SEVERELY POISONED INDIVIDUALS MAY EXHIBIT REMARKABLE TOLERANCE TO ATROPINE; TWO OR MORE TIMES THE DOSAGES SUGGESTED ABOVE MAY BE NEEDED. PERSONS NOT POISONED OR ONLY SLIGHTLY POISONED, HOWEVER, MAY DEVELOP SIGNS OF ATROPINE TOXICITY FROM SUCH LARGE DOSAGES: FEVER, MUSCLE FIBRILLATIONS, AND DELIRIUM ARE THE MAIN SIGNS OF ATROPINE TOXICITY. IF THESE SIGNS APPEAR WHILE THE PATIENT IS FULLY ATROPINIZED, ATROPINE ADMINISTRATION SHOULD BE DISCONTINUED, AT LEAST TEMPORARILY. OBSERVE TREATED PATIENTS CLOSELY AT LEAST 24 HOURS TO INSURE THAT SYMPTOMS (POSSIBLY PULMONARY EDEMA) DO NOT RECUR AS ATROPINIZATION WEARS OFF. IN VERY SEVERE POISONINGS, METABOLIC DISPOSITION OF TOXICANT MAY REQUIRE SEVERAL HOURS OR DAYS DURING WHICH ATROPINIZATION MUST BE MAINTAINED. MARKEDLY LOWER LEVELS OF URINARY METABOLITES INDICATE THAT ATROPINE DOSAGE CAN BE TAPERED OFF. AS DOSAGE IS REDUCED, CHECK THE LUNG BASES FREQUENTLY FOR RALES. IF RALES ARE HEARD OR OTHER SYMPTOMS RETURN, RE-ESTABLISH ATROPINIZATION PROMPTLY (MORGAN, RECOGNITION AND MANAGEMENT OF PESTICIDE POISONINGS, 3RD ED.). ADMINISTRATION OF ANTIDOTE MUST BE PERFORMED BY QUALIFIED MEDICAL PERSONNEL.

IN CASES OF SEVERE POISONING BY ORGANOPHOSPHATE PESTICIDES IN WHICH RESPIRATORY DEPRESSION, MUSCLE WEAKNESS AND TWITCHINGS ARE SEVERE, GIVE PRALIDOXIME (PROTOPAM-AYERST, 2-PAM), 1.0 GRAM INTRAVENOUSLY AT NO MORE THAN 0.5 GRAM PER MINUTE. DOSAGE OF PRALIDOXIME MAY BE REPEATED IN 1-2 HOURS, THEN AT 10-12 HOUR INTERVALS IF NEEDED. IN VERY SEVERE POISONINGS, DOSAGE RATES MAY BE DOUBLED. TREATMENT WITH PRALIDOXIME WILL BE MOST EFFECTIVE IF GIVEN WITHIN THIRTY-SIX HOURS AFTER POISONING (MORGAN, RECOGNITION AND MANAGEMENT OF PESTICIDE POISONINGS, 3RD ED.). ANTIDOTE SHOULD BE ADMINISTERED BY QUALIFIED MEDICAL PERSONNEL.

REACTIVITY

REACTIVITY: STABLE UNDER NORMAL TEMPERATURES AND PRESSURES.

INCOMPATIBILITIES: DICAPTHON: OXIDIZERS (STRONG): FIRE AND EXPLOSION HAZARD.

DECOMPOSITION: THERMAL DECOMPOSITION PRODUCTS MAY INCLUDE TOXIC AND CORROSIVE FUMES OF CHLORIDES, AND TOXIC OXIDES OF PHOSPHORUS, NITROGEN AND SULFUR.

POLYMERIZATION: HAZARDOUS POLYMERIZATION HAS NOT BEEN REPORTED TO OCCUR UNDER NORMAL TEMPERATURES AND PRESSURES.

STORAGE AND DISPOSAL

OBSERVE ALL FEDERAL, STATE AND LOCAL REGULATIONS WHEN STORING OR DISPOSING OF THIS SUBSTANCE. FOR ASSISTANCE, CONTACT THE DISTRICT DIRECTOR OF THE ENVIRONMENTAL PROTECTION AGENCY.

****STORAGE****

STORE IN ACCORDANCE WITH 40 CFR 165 RECOMMENDED PROCEDURES FOR THE DISPOSAL AND STORAGE OF PESTICIDES AND PESTICIDE CONTAINERS. STORE AWAY FROM INCOMPATIBLE SUBSTANCES.

****DISPOSAL****

DISPOSAL MUST BE IN ACCORDANCE WITH 40 CFR 165 RECOMMENDED PROCEDURES FOR THE DISPOSAL AND STORAGE OF PESTICIDES AND PESTICIDE CONTAINERS.

CONDITIONS TO AVOID

MAY BURN BUT DOES NOT IGNITE READILY. CONTAINERS MAY EXPLODE IN HEAT OF FIRE.

SPILL AND LEAK PROCEDURES

OCCUPATIONAL SPILL: DO NOT TOUCH SPILLED MATERIAL. STOP LEAK IF YOU CAN DO IT WITHOUT RISK. USE WATER SPRAY TO REDUCE VAPORS. FOR SMALL SPILLS, TAKE UP WITH SAND OR OTHER ABSORBENT MATERIAL AND PLACE INTO CONTAINERS FOR LATER DISPOSAL. FOR SMALL DRY SPILLS, WITH A CLEAN SHOVEL PLACE MATERIAL INTO CLEAN, DRY CONTAINERS AND COVER. MOVE CONTAINERS FROM SPILL AREA. FOR LARGER SPILLS, DIKE FAR AHEAD OF SPILL FOR LATER DISPOSAL. KEEP UNNECESSARY PEOPLE AWAY. ISOLATE HAZARD AREA AND DENY ENTRY. VENTILATE CLOSED SPACES BEFORE ENTERING.

PROTECTIVE EQUIPMENT

VENTILATION: PROVIDE LOCAL EXHAUST OR PROCESS ENCLOSURE VENTILATION SYSTEM.

RESPIRATOR: THE FOLLOWING RESPIRATORS ARE RECOMMENDED BASED ON INFORMATION FOUND IN THE PHYSICAL DATA, TOXICITY AND HEALTH EFFECTS SECTIONS. THEY ARE RANKED IN ORDER FROM MINIMUM TO MAXIMUM RESPIRATORY PROTECTION. THE SPECIFIC RESPIRATOR SELECTED MUST BE BASED ON CONTAMINATION LEVELS FOUND IN THE WORK PLACE, MUST NOT EXCEED THE WORKING LIMITS OF THE RESPIRATOR AND BE JOINTLY APPROVED BY THE NATIONAL INSTITUTE FOR OCCUPATIONAL SAFETY AND HEALTH AND THE MINE SAFETY AND HEALTH ADMINISTRATION (NIOSH-MSHA).

TYPE 'C' SUPPLIED-AIR RESPIRATOR WITH A FULL FACEPIECE OPERATED IN PRESSURE-DEMAND OR OTHER POSITIVE PRESSURE MODE OR WITH A FULL FACEPIECE, HELMET OR HOOD OPERATED IN CONTINOUS-FLOW MODE.

SELF-CONTAINED BREATHING APPARATUS WITH A FULL FACEPIECE OPERATED IN PRESSURE-DEMAND OR OTHER POSITIVE PRESSURE MODE.

FOR FIREFIGHTING AND OTHER IMMEDIATELY DANGEROUS TO LIFE OR HEALTH CONDITIONS:

SELF-CONTAINED BREATHING APPARATUS WITH FULL FACEPIECE OPERATED IN PRESSURE-DEMAND OR OTHER POSITIVE PRESSURE MODE.

SUPPLIED-AIR RESPIRATOR WITH FULL FACEPIECE AND OPERATED IN PRESSURE-DEMAND OR OTHER POSITIVE PRESSURE MODE IN COMBINATION WITH AN AUXILIARY SELF-CONTAINED BREATHING APPARATUS OPERATED IN PRESSURE-DEMAND OR OTHER POSITIVE PRESSURE MODE.

CLOTHING: EMPLOYEE MUST WEAR APPROPRIATE PROTECTIVE (IMPERVIOUS) CLOTHING AND EQUIPMENT TO PREVENT ANY POSSIBILITY OF SKIN CONTACT WITH THIS SUBSTANCE.

GLOVES: EMPLOYEE MUST WEAR APPROPRIATE PROTECTIVE GLOVES TO PREVENT CONTACT WITH THIS SUBSTANCE.

EYE PROTECTION: EMPLOYEE MUST WEAR SPLASH-PROOF OR DUST-RESISTANT SAFETY GOGGLES WITH OR WITHOUT A FACESHIELD TO PREVENT CONTACT WITH THIS SUBSTANCE.

EMERGENCY EYE WASH: WHERE THERE IS ANY POSSIBILITY THAT AN EMPLOYEE'S EYES MAY BE EXPOSED TO THIS SUBSTANCE, THE EMPLOYER SHOULD PROVIDE AN EYE WASH FOUNTAIN WITHIN THE IMMEDIATE WORK AREA FOR EMERGENCY USE.

AUTHORIZED BY- OCCUPATIONAL HEALTH SERVICES, INC.
CREATION DATE: 10/04/89 ***REVISION DATE:*** 04/26/90

MATERIAL SAFETY DATA SHEET

OCCUPATIONAL HEALTH SERVICES, INC.
AGRICULTURE AND PESTICIDE DIVISION
450 SEVENTH AVENUE, SUITE 2407
NEW YORK, NEW YORK 10123
1-800-445-MSDS OR (212) 967-1100

EMERGENCY CONTACT:
JOHN S. BRANSFORD, JR. (615) 292-1180

SUBSTANCE IDENTIFICATION

CAS-NUMBER 128-04-1

SUBSTANCE: **SODIUM DIMETHYLDITHIOCARBAMATE**

TRADE NAMES/SYNONYMS: CARBAMODITHIOIC ACID, DIMETHYL-, SODIUM SALT; DIMETHYLCARBAMODITHIOIC ACID, SODIUM SALT; CARBAMIC ACID, DIMETHYLDITHIO-, SODIUM SALT; DIMETHYLDITHIOCARBAMIC ACID, SODIUM SALT; SODIUM DIMETHYLAMINOCARBODITHIOATE; SODIUM N,N-DIMETHYLDITHIOCARBAMATE; SDDC; DIBAM; PST71383

CHEMICAL FAMILY: THIOCARBAMATE

MOLECULAR FORMULA: C3-H6-N-S2.NA

MOLECULAR WEIGHT: 143.21

CERCLA RATINGS (SCALE 0-3): HEALTH=2 FIRE=U REACTIVITY=U PERSISTENCE=1

NFPA RATINGS (SCALE 0-4): HEALTH=2 FIRE=U REACTIVITY=U

COMPONENTS AND CONTAMINANTS

COMPONENT: SODIUM DIMETHYLDITHIOCARBAMATE ***PERCENT:*** 100
CAS# 128-04-1

OTHER CONTAMINANTS: NONE

EXPOSURE LIMITS: NO OCCUPATIONAL EXPOSURE LIMITS ESTABLISHED BY OSHA, ACGIH, OR NIOSH.

PHYSICAL DATA

DESCRIPTION: CRYSTALS (THE 40% SOLUTION IS AMBER TO LIGHT GREEN).

MELTING POINT: NOT AVAILABLE ***SPECIFIC GRAVITY:*** 1.17-1.20 (40% SOLN)

SOLUBILITY IN WATER: SOLUBLE

FIRE AND EXPLOSION DATA

FIRE AND EXPLOSION HAZARD: UNKNOWN FIRE AND EXPLOSION HAZARD.

FIREFIGHTING MEDIA: DRY CHEMICAL, CARBON DIOXIDE, WATER SPRAY OR FOAM FOR LARGER FIRES, USE WATER SPRAY, FOG OR ALCOHOL FOAM

FIREFIGHTING: USE AGENTS SUITABLE FOR TYPE OF SURROUNDING FIRE. AVOID BREATHING HAZARDOUS VAPORS, KEEP UPWIND.

TOXICITY

SODIUM DIMETHYLDITHIOCARBAMATE: TOXICITY DATA: 1000 MG/KG ORAL-RAT LD50; 1500 MG/KG ORAL-MOUSE LD50; 1000 MG/KG INTRAPERITONEAL-RAT LD50; 573 MG/KG INTRAPERITONEAL-MOUSE LD50; MUTAGENIC DATA (RTECS). CARCINOGEN STATUS: NONE. ACUTE TOXICITY LEVEL: MODERATELY TOXIC BY INGESTION. TARGET EFFECTS: NO DATA AVAILABLE. ADDITIONAL DATA: INTERACTIONS WITH ALCOHOL MAY OCCUR.

HEALTH EFFECTS AND FIRST AID

INHALATION: SODIUM DIMETHYLDITHIOCARBAMATE **ACUTE EXPOSURE-** INHALATION OF DITHIOCARBAMATES HAVE PRODUCED IRRITATION OF RESPIRATORY TRACT WITH SYMPTOMS OF NASAL STUFFINESS, HOARSENESS, COUGH, AND RARELY, PNEUMONITIS. **CHRONIC EXPOSURE-** NO DATA AVAILABLE.

FIRST AID- REMOVE FROM EXPOSURE AREA TO FRESH AIR IMMEDIATELY. IF BREATHING HAS STOPPED, PERFORM ARTIFICIAL RESPIRATION. KEEP PERSON WARM AND AT REST. TREAT SYMPTOMATICALLY AND SUPPORTIVELY. GET MEDICAL ATTENTION IMMEDIATELY.

SKIN CONTACT: SODIUM DIMETHYLDITHIOCARBAMATE: **ACUTE EXPOSURE-** EXPOSURE TO DITHIOCARBAMATES HAVE CAUSED IRRITATION. DITHIOCARBAMSTES MAY CAUSE ITCHING, REDNESS, AND ECZEMATOID DERMATITIS IN PREDISPOSED INDIVIDUALS. **CHRONIC EXPOSURE-** PROLONGED OR REPEATED EXPOSURE TO DITHIOCARBAMATES MAY CAUSE DERMATITIS AND SENSITIZATION IN SOME INDIVIDUALS.

FIRST AID- REMOVE CONTAMINATED CLOTHING AND SHOES IMMEDIATELY. WASH AFFECTED AREA WITH SOAP OR MILD DETERGENT AND LARGE AMOUNTS OF WATER UNTIL NO EVIDENCE OF CHEMICAL REMAINS (APPROXIMATELY 15-20 MINUTES). GET MEDICAL ATTENTION IMMEDIATELY.

EYE CONTACT: SODIUM DIMETHYLDITHIOCARBAMATE: **ACUTE EXPOSURE-** EXPOSURE TO DITHIOCARBAMATES HAVE CAUSED IRRITATION OF THE EYES. **CHRONIC EXPOSURE-** NO DATA AVAILABLE.

FIRST AID- WASH EYES IMMEDIATELY WITH LARGE AMOUNTS OF WATER OR NORMAL SALINE, OCCASIONALLY LIFTING UPPER AND LOWER LIDS, UNTIL NO EVIDENCE OF CHEMICAL REMAINS (APPROXIMATELY 15-20 MINUTES). GET MEDICAL ATTENTION IMMEDIATELY.

INGESTION: SODIUM DIMETHYLDITHIOCARBAMATE: **ACUTE EXPOSURE-** A LETHAL DOSE IN RATS WAS 1000 MG/KG. INGESTION OF DITHIOCARBAMATES MAY CAUSE NAUSEA, VOMITING, DIARRHEA, ANOREXIA, HEADACHE, LETHARGY, DIZZINESS, ATAXIA, CONFUSION, DROWSINESS, EMOTIONAL LABILITY, AND COMA. IN ANIMALS STUDIES, MUSCLE WEAKNESS AND ASCENDING PARALYSIS PROGRESSED TO RESPIRATORY PARALYSIS AND DEATH. **CHRONIC EXPOSURE-** IN A 3-GENERATION REPRODUCTIVE STUDY OF RATS, NO REPRODUCTIVE EFFECTS WERE OBSERVED AT DOSES UP TO 350 MG/KG/DAY.

FIRST AID- IF VIGOROUS EMESIS HAS NOT ALREADY OCCURRED AND VICTIM IS FULLY ALERT, GIVE SYRUP OF IPECAC, FOLLOWED BY 1-2 GLASSES OF WATER TO INDUCE VOMITING (ADULTS, 12 YEARS AND OLDER: 30 ML; CHILDREN UNDER 12: 15 ML). IF CONSCIOUSNESS LEVEL DECLINES OR VOMITING HAS NOT OCCURRED IN 15 MINUTES, EMPTY THE STOMACH BY INTUBATION, ASPIRATION, AND LAVAGE, USING ALL AVAILABLE MEANS TO AVOID ASPIRATION OF VOMITUS. AFTER ASPIRATION OF THE STOMACH AND WASHING WITH ISOTONIC SALINE OR SODIUM BICARBONATE, INSTILL 30-50 GM OF ACTIVATED CHARCOAL IN 3-4 OUNCES OF WATER THROUGH THE STOMACH TUBE TO LIMIT ABSORPTION OF REMAINING TOXICANT. IF THE IRRITANT PROPERTIES OF THE TOXICANT FAIL TO PRODUCE A

BOWEL MOVEMENT IN 4 HOURS, ADMINISTER SODIUM OR MAGNESIUM SULFATE AS A CATHARTIC: 0.25 GM/KG BODY WEIGHT IN 1-6 OUNCES OF WATER. ADMINISTER GLUCOSE-CONTAINING FLUIDS INTRAVENOUSLY TO ACCELERATE EXCRETION OF TOXICANT. (MORGAN, RECOGNITION AND MANAGEMENT OF PESTICIDE POISONINGS, THIRD EDITION) GET MEDICAL ATTENTION. TREATMENT SHOULD BE BE ADMINISTERED BY QUALIFIED MEDICAL PERSONNEL.

ANTIDOTE: NO SPECIFIC ANTIDOTE. TREAT SYMPTOMATICALLY AND SUPPORTIVELY.

REACTIVITY

REACTIVITY: THE DITHIOCARBAMATES ARE RATHER UNSTABLE IN THE PRESENCE OF HEAT OR MOISTURE.

INCOMPATIBILITIES: SODIUM DIMETHYLDITHIOCARBAMATES: NO DATA AVAILABLE.

DECOMPOSITION: THERMAL DECOMPOSITION PRODUCTS MAY INCLUDE TOXIC OXIDES OF NITROGEN, SULFUR AND SODIUM.

POLYMERIZATION: HAZARDOUS POLYMERIZATION HAS NOT BEEN REPORTED TO OCCUR UNDER NORMAL TEMPERATURES AND PRESSURES.

STORAGE AND DISPOSAL

OBSERVE ALL FEDERAL, STATE AND LOCAL REGULATIONS WHEN STORING OR DISPOSING OF THIS SUBSTANCE. FOR ASSISTANCE, CONTACT THE DISTRICT DIRECTOR OF THE ENVIRONMENTAL PROTECTION AGENCY.

STORAGE

STORE IN ACCORDANCE WITH 40 CFR 165 RECOMMENDED PROCEDURES FOR THE DISPOSAL AND STORAGE OF PESTICIDES AND PESTICIDE CONTAINERS.

DISPOSAL

DISPOSAL MUST BE IN ACCORDANCE WITH 40 CFR 165 RECOMMENDED PROCEDURES FOR THE DISPOSAL AND STORAGE OF PESTICIDES AND PESTICIDE CONTAINERS.

CONDITIONS TO AVOID

NONE REPORTED.

SPILL AND LEAK PROCEDURES

OCCUPATIONAL SPILL: NO SPECIAL PRECAUTIONS INDICATED.

PROTECTIVE EQUIPMENT

VENTILATION: PROVIDE LOCAL EXHAUST VENTILATION SYSTEM.

RESPIRATOR: THE FOLLOWING RESPIRATORS ARE RECOMMENDED BASED ON INFORMATION FOUND IN THE PHYSICAL DATA, TOXICITY AND HEALTH EFFECTS SECTIONS. THEY ARE RANKED IN ORDER FROM MINIMUM TO MAXIMUM RESPIRATORY PROTECTION. THE SPECIFIC RESPIRATOR SELECTED MUST BE BASED ON CONTAMINATION LEVELS FOUND IN THE WORK PLACE, MUST NOT EXCEED THE WORKING LIMITS OF THE RESPIRATOR AND BE JOINTLY APPROVED BY THE NATIONAL INSTITUTE FOR OCCUPATIONAL SAFETY AND HEALTH AND THE MINE SAFETY AND HEALTH ADMINISTRATION (NIOSH-MSHA).

CHEMICAL CARTRIDGE RESPIRATOR WITH FULL FACEPIECE AND PESTICIDE CARTRIDGE.

TYPE 'C' SUPPLIED-AIR RESPIRATOR WITH A FULL FACEPIECE OPERATED IN PRESSURE-DEMAND OR OTHER POSITIVE PRESSURE MODE OR WITH A FULL FACEPIECE, HELMET OR HOOD OPERATED IN CONTINUOUS-FLOW MODE.

SELF-CONTAINED BREATHING APPARATUS OPERATED IN PRESSURE-DEMAND OR OTHER POSITIVE PRESSURE MODE.

FOR FIREFIGHTING AND OTHER IMMEDIATELY DANGEROUS TO LIFE OR HEALTH CONDITIONS:

SELF-CONTAINED BREATHING APPARATUS WITH FULL FACEPIECE OPERATED IN PRESSURE-DEMAND OR OTHER POSITIVE PRESSURE MODE.

SUPPLIED-AIR RESPIRATOR WITH FULL FACEPIECE AND OPERATED IN PRESSURE-DEMAND OR OTHER POSITIVE PRESSURE MODE IN COMBINATION WITH AN AUXILIARY SELF-CONTAINED BREATHING APPARATUS OPERATED IN PRESSURE-DEMAND OR OTHER POSITIVE PRESSURE MODE.

CLOTHING: EMPLOYEE MUST WEAR APPROPRIATE PROTECTIVE (IMPERVIOUS) CLOTHING AND EQUIPMENT TO PREVENT REPEATED OR PROLONGED SKIN CONTACT WITH THIS SUBSTANCE.

GLOVES: EMPLOYEE MUST WEAR APPROPRIATE PROTECTIVE GLOVES TO PREVENT CONTACT WITH THIS SUBSTANCE.

EYE PROTECTION: EMPLOYEE MUST WEAR SPLASH-PROOF OR DUST-RESISTANT SAFETY GOGGLES TO PREVENT EYE CONTACT WITH THIS SUBSTANCE.

EMERGENCY EYE WASH: WHERE THERE IS ANY POSSIBILITY THAT AN EMPLOYEE'S EYES MAY BE EXPOSED TO THIS SUBSTANCE, THE EMPLOYER SHOULD PROVIDE AN EYE WASH FOUNTAIN WITHIN THE IMMEDIATE WORK AREA FOR EMERGENCY USE.

AUTHORIZED BY- OCCUPATIONAL HEALTH SERVICES, INC.

CREATION DATE: 10/05/89 ***REVISION DATE:*** 05/03/90

MATERIAL SAFETY DATA SHEET

OCCUPATIONAL HEALTH SERVICES, INC.
AGRICULTURE AND PESTICIDE DIVISION
450 SEVENTH AVENUE, SUITE 2407
NEW YORK, NEW YORK 10123
1-800-445-MSDS OR (212) 967-1100

EMERGENCY CONTACT:
JOHN S. BRANSFORD, JR. (615) 292-1180

SUBSTANCE IDENTIFICATION

CAS-NUMBER 3861-41-4

SUBSTANCE: **BROMOXYNIL BUTYRATE**

TRADE NAMES/SYNONYMS: BUTANOIC ACID, 2,6-DIBROMO-4-CYANOPHENYL ESTER; BUTYRIC ACID, ESTER WITH 3,5-DIBROMO-4-HYDROXYBENZONITRILE; C11H9BR2NO2; PST71388

CHEMICAL FAMILY: ESTER
HALOGEN COMPOUND, AROMATIC
NITRILE, AROMATIC

MOLECULAR FORMULA: C-N-C6-H2-BR2-O-C-O-(C-H2)2-C-H3

CERCLA RATINGS (SCALE 0-3): HEALTH=U FIRE=1 REACTIVITY=0 PERSISTENCE=3

NFPA RATINGS (SCALE 0-4): HEALTH=U FIRE=1 REACTIVITY=0

COMPONENTS AND CONTAMINANTS

COMPONENT: BROMOXYNIL BUTYRATE ***PERCENT:*** 100
CAS# 3861-41-4

EXPOSURE LIMITS: NO OCCUPATIONAL EXPOSURE LIMITS ESTABLISHED BY OSHA, ACGIH, OR NIOSH.

PHYSICAL DATA

DESCRIPTION: SOLID ***MELTING POINT:*** NOT AVAILABLE

SPECIFIC GRAVITY: NOT AVAILABLE ***SOLUBILITY IN WATER:*** NOT AVAILABLE

FIRE AND EXPLOSION DATA

FIRE AND EXPLOSION HAZARD: SLIGHT FIRE HAZARD WHEN EXPOSED TO HEAT OR FLAME.

FIREFIGHTING MEDIA: DRY CHEMICAL, CARBON DIOXIDE, HALON, WATER SPRAY OR STANDARD FOAM (1987 EMERGENCY RESPONSE GUIDEBOOK, DOT P 5800.4).
FOR LARGER FIRES, USE WATER SPRAY, FOG OR STANDARD FOAM (1987 EMERGENCY RESPONSE GUIDEBOOK, DOT P 5800.4).

FIREFIGHTING: MOVE CONTAINERS FROM FIRE AREA IF POSSIBLE (1987 EMERGENCY RESPONSE GUIDEBOOK, DOT P 5800.4, GUIDE PAGE 53).
EXTINGUISH FIRE USING AGENTS SUITABLE FOR TYPE OF SURROUNDING FIRE. USE WATER IN FLOODING AMOUNTS AS A FOG. AVOID BREATHING DUSTS AND FUMES FROM BURNING MATERIAL; KEEP UPWIND.

TOXICITY

BROMOXYNIL BUTYRATE: CARCINOGEN STATUS: NONE. ACUTE TOXICITY LEVEL: NO DATA AVAILABLE. TARGET EFFECTS: NO DATA AVAILABLE.

HEALTH EFFECTS AND FIRST AID

INHALATION: BROMOXYNIL BUTYRATE: **ACUTE EXPOSURE**- NO DATA AVAILABLE. **CHRONIC EXPOSURE**- NO DATA AVAILABLE.

FIRST AID- REMOVE FROM EXPOSURE AREA TO FRESH AIR IMMEDIATELY. IF BREATHING HAS STOPPED, PERFORM ARTIFICIAL RESPIRATION. KEEP PERSON WARM AND AT REST. TREAT SYMPTOMATICALLY AND SUPPORTIVELY. GET MEDICAL ATTENTION IMMEDIATELY.

SKIN CONTACT: BROMOXYNIL BUTYRATE: **ACUTE EXPOSURE**- NO DATA AVAILABLE. A LETHAL DOSE OF BROMOXYNIL OCTANOATE IN RABBITS BY DERMAL ABSORPTION WAS 1675 MG/KG. **CHRONIC EXPOSURE**- NO DATA AVAILABLE.

FIRST AID- REMOVE CONTAMINATED CLOTHING AND SHOES IMMEDIATELY. WASH AFFECTED AREA WITH SOAP OR MILD DETERGENT AND LARGE AMOUNTS OF WATER UNTIL NO EVIDENCE OF CHEMICAL REMAINS (APPROXIMATELY 15-20 MINUTES). GET MEDICAL ATTENTION IMMEDIATELY.

EYE CONTACT: BROMOXYNIL BUTYRATE: **ACUTE EXPOSURE**- BROMOXYNIL, APPLIED TO THE EYES OF RABBITS, PRODUCED TRANSIENT IRRITATION. **CHRONIC EXPOSURE**- NO DATA AVAILABLE.

FIRST AID- WASH EYES IMMEDIATELY WITH LARGE AMOUNTS OF WATER OR NORMAL SALINE, OCCASIONALLY LIFTING UPPER AND LOWER LIDS, UNTIL NO EVIDENCE OF CHEMICAL REMAINS (APPROXIMATELY 15-20 MINUTES). GET MEDICAL ATTENTION IMMEDIATELY.

INGESTION: BROMOXYNIL BUTYRATE: **ACUTE EXPOSURE-** NO DATA AVAILABLE. A LETHAL DOSE OF BROMOXYNIL OCTANOATE IN RATS WAS 250 MG/KG; NO SYMPTOMS WERE REPORTED. **CHRONIC EXPOSURE-** NO DATA AVAILABLE.

FIRST AID- REMOVE BY GASTRIC LAVAGE AND CATHARSIS. MAINTAIN BLOOD PRESSURE AND AIRWAY. GIVE OXYGEN IF RESPIRATION IS DEPRESSED. DO NOT PERFORM GASTRIC LAVAGE IF VICTIM IS UNCONSCIOUS. GET MEDICAL ATTENTION IMMEDIATELY (DREISBACH, HANDBOOK OF POISONING, 12TH ED.). ADMINISTRATION OF LAVAGE OR OXYGEN SHOULD BE PERFORMED BY QUALIFIED MEDICAL PERSONNEL.

ANTIDOTE: NO SPECIFIC ANTIDOTE. TREAT SYMPTOMATICALLY AND SUPPORTIVELY.

REACTIVITY

REACTIVITY: STABLE UNDER NORMAL TEMPERATURES AND PRESSURES.

INCOMPATIBILITIES: BROMOXYNIL BUTYRATE: NO DATA AVAILABLE.

DECOMPOSITION: THERMAL DECOMPOSITION MAY RELEASE CORROSIVE BROMINE AND TOXIC OXIDES OF NITROGEN.

POLYMERIZATION: HAZARDOUS POLYMERIZATION HAS NOT BEEN REPORTED TO OCCUR UNDER NORMAL TEMPERATURES AND PRESSURES.

STORAGE AND DISPOSAL

OBSERVE ALL FEDERAL, STATE AND LOCAL REGULATIONS WHEN STORING OR DISPOSING OF THIS SUBSTANCE. FOR ASSISTANCE, CONTACT THE DISTRICT DIRECTOR OF THE ENVIRONMENTAL PROTECTION AGENCY.

****STORAGE****

STORE IN ACCORDANCE WITH 40 CFR 165 RECOMMENDED PROCEDURES FOR THE DISPOSAL AND STORAGE OF PESTICIDES AND PESTICIDE CONTAINERS.

****DISPOSAL****

DISPOSAL MUST BE IN ACCORDANCE WITH 40 CFR 165 RECOMMENDED PROCEDURES FOR THE DISPOSAL AND STORAGE OF PESTICIDES AND PESTICIDE CONTAINERS.

CONDITIONS TO AVOID

MAY BURN BUT DOES NOT IGNITE READILY.

SPILL AND LEAK PROCEDURES

OCCUPATIONAL SPILL: DO NOT TOUCH SPILLED MATERIAL. STOP LEAK IF YOU CAN DO IT WITHOUT RISK. FOR SMALL SPILLS, TAKE UP WITH SAND OR OTHER ABSORBENT MATERIAL AND PLACE INTO CONTAINERS FOR LATER DISPOSAL. FOR SMALL DRY SPILLS, WITH A CLEAN SHOVEL PLACE MATERIAL INTO CLEAN, DRY CONTAINER AND COVER. MOVE CONTAINERS FROM SPILL AREA. FOR LARGER SPILLS, DIKE FAR AHEAD OF SPILL FOR LATER DISPOSAL. KEEP UNNECESSARY PEOPLE AWAY. ISOLATE HAZARD AREA AND DENY ENTRY.

PROTECTIVE EQUIPMENT

VENTILATION: PROVIDE LOCAL EXHAUST OR GENERAL DILUTION VENTILATION SYSTEM.

RESPIRATOR: THE FOLLOWING RESPIRATORS ARE RECOMMENDED BASED ON INFORMATION FOUND IN THE PHYSICAL DATA, TOXICITY AND HEALTH EFFECTS SECTIONS. THEY ARE RANKED IN ORDER FROM MINIMUM TO MAXIMUM RESPIRATORY PROTECTION. THE SPECIFIC RESPIRATOR SELECTED MUST BE BASED ON CONTAMINATION LEVELS FOUND IN THE WORK PLACE, MUST NOT EXCEED THE WORKING LIMITS OF THE RESPIRATOR AND BE JOINTLY APPROVED BY THE NATIONAL INSTITUTE FOR OCCUPATIONAL SAFETY AND HEALTH AND THE MINE SAFETY AND HEALTH ADMINISTRATION (NIOSH-MSHA).

CHEMICAL CARTRIDGE RESPIRATOR WITH AN ORGANIC VAPOR CARTRIDGE(S) WITH A FULL FACEPIECE AND ORGANIC VAPOR CARTRIDGE(S) IN COMBINATION WITH A DUST AND MIST FILTER.

POWERED AIR-PURIFYING RESPIRATOR WITH A TIGHT-FITTING FACEPIECE AND ORGANIC VAPOR CARTRIDGE(S) IN COMBINATION WITH A HIGH-EFFICIENCY PARTICULATE FILTER.

TYPE 'C' SUPPLIED-AIR RESPIRATOR WITH A FULL FACEPIECE OPERATED IN A PRESSURE-DEMAND OR OTHER POSITIVE PRESSURE MODE.

SELF-CONTAINED BREATHING APPARATUS WITH A FULL FACEPIECE OPERATED IN PRESSURE-DEMAND OR OTHER POSITIVE PRESSURE MODE.

FOR FIREFIGHTING AND OTHER IMMEDIATELY DANGEROUS TO LIFE OR HEALTH CONDITIONS:

SELF-CONTAINED BREATHING APPARATUS WITH FULL FACEPIECE OPERATED IN PRESSURE-DEMAND OR OTHER POSITIVE PRESSURE MODE.

SUPPLIED-AIR RESPIRATOR WITH FULL FACEPIECE AND OPERATED IN PRESSURE-DEMAND OR OTHER POSITIVE PRESSURE MODE IN COMBINATION WITH AN AUXILIARY SELF-CONTAINED BREATHING APPARATUS OPERATED IN PRESSURE-DEMAND OR OTHER POSITIVE PRESSURE MODE.

CLOTHING: EMPLOYEE MUST WEAR APPROPRIATE PROTECTIVE (IMPERVIOUS) CLOTHING AND EQUIPMENT TO PREVENT REPEATED OR PROLONGED SKIN CONTACT WITH THIS SUBSTANCE.

GLOVES: EMPLOYEE MUST WEAR APPROPRIATE PROTECTIVE GLOVES TO PREVENT CONTACT WITH THIS SUBSTANCE.

EYE PROTECTION: EMPLOYEE MUST WEAR SPLASH-PROOF OR DUST-RESISTANT SAFETY GOGGLES TO PREVENT EYE CONTACT WITH THIS SUBSTANCE. EMERGENCY EYE WASH: WHERE THERE IS ANY POSSIBILITY THAT AN EMPLOYEE'S EYES MAY BE EXPOSED TO THIS SUBSTANCE, THE EMPLOYER SHOULD PROVIDE AN EYE WASH FOUNTAIN WITHIN THE IMMEDIATE WORK AREA FOR EMERGENCY USE.

AUTHORIZED BY- OCCUPATIONAL HEALTH SERVICES, INC.

CREATION DATE: 10/04/89 ***REVISION DATE:*** 05/18/90

MATERIAL SAFETY DATA SHEET

OCCUPATIONAL HEALTH SERVICES, INC.
AGRICULTURE AND PESTICIDE DIVISION
450 SEVENTH AVENUE, SUITE 2407
NEW YORK, NEW YORK 10123
1-800-445-MSDS OR (212) 967-1100

EMERGENCY CONTACT:
JOHN S. BRANSFORD, JR. (615) 292-1180

SUBSTANCE IDENTIFICATION

CAS-NUMBER 4482-55-7

SUBSTANCE: **FENURON-TCA**

TRADE NAMES/SYNONYMS: ACETIC ACID, TRICHLORO-, COMPOUND WITH N,N-DIMETHYL-N'- -PHENYLUREA (1:1); ACETIC ACID, TRICHLORO-, COMPUND WITH 1,1-DIMETHYL-; 3-PHENYLUREA (1:1); TRICHLOROACETIC ACID COMPOUND WITH N,N-DIMETHYL-N'-PHENYLUREA; TRICHLOROACETIC ACID COMPOUND WITH 1,1-DIMETHYL-3-PHENYLUREA; 1,1-DIMETHYL-3-PHENYLURONIUM TRICHLOROACETATE; 1,1-DIMETHYL-3-PHENYLUREA TRICHLOROACETATE; N,N-DIMETHYL-N'-PHENYLUREA TRICHLOROACETATE; FENURON TRICHLOROACETATE; FENURON TCA; DOZER; GC-2603; URAB; C11H13CL3N2O3; PST71389

CHEMICAL FAMILY: SUBSTITUTED UREA
HALOGEN COMPOUND, AROMATIC

MOLECULAR FORMULA: C9-H12-N2-O.C2-H-CL3-O2

MOLECULAR WEIGHT: 327.61

CERCLA RATINGS (SCALE 0-3): HEALTH=2 FIRE=1 REACTIVITY=0 PERSISTENCE=0

NFPA RATINGS (SCALE 0-4): HEALTH=2 FIRE=1 REACTIVITY=0

COMPONENTS AND CONTAMINANTS

COMPONENT: FENURON-TCA ***PERCENT:*** 100.0
CAS# 4482-55-7

OTHER CONTAMINANTS: NONE

EXPOSURE LIMITS: NO OCCUPATIONAL EXPOSURE LIMITS ESTABLISHED BY OSHA, ACGIH, OR NIOSH.

PHYSICAL DATA

DESCRIPTION: COLORLESS OR WHITE CRYSTALLINE SOLID.

MELTING POINT: 149-154 F (65-68 C) ***SPECIFIC GRAVITY:*** NOT AVAILABLE

SOLUBILITY IN WATER: 0.48%

SOLVENT SOLUBILITY: SOLUBLE IN DICHLOROETHANE, TRICHLOROETHYLENE, ACETONE, AND AROMATIC SOLVENTS; SLIGHTLY SOLUBLE IN PETROLEUM OILS.

FIRE AND EXPLOSION DATA

FIRE AND EXPLOSION HAZARD: SLIGHT FIRE HAZARD WHEN EXPOSED TO HEAT OR FLAME.

FIREFIGHTING MEDIA: DRY CHEMICAL, CARBON DIOXIDE, HALON, WATER SPRAY OR STANDARD FOAM (1987 EMERGENCY RESPONSE GUIDEBOOK, DOT P 5800.4). FOR LARGER FIRES, USE WATER SPRAY, FOG OR STANDARD FOAM (1987 EMERGENCY RESPONSE GUIDEBOOK, DOT P 5800.4).

FIREFIGHTING: MOVE CONTAINERS FROM FIRE AREA IF POSSIBLE. FIGHT FIRE FROM MAXIMUM DISTANCE. STAY AWAY FROM STORAGE TANK ENDS. DIKE FIRE CONTROL WATER FOR LATER DISPOSAL. DO NOT SCATTER MATERIAL (1987 EMERGENCY RESPONSE GUIDEBOOK, DOT P 5800.4, GUIDE PAGE 55). EXTINGUISH USING AGENT SUITABLE FOR TYPE OF SURROUNDING FIRE. USE WATER IN FLOODING QUANTITIES AS FOG. KEEP SPARKS, FLAMES AND OTHER SOURCES OF IGNITION AWAY. KEEP MATERIAL OUT OF WATER SOURCES AND

SEWERS. DO NOT TOUCH MATERIAL AND AVOID BREATHING DUSTS AND FUMES FROM BURNING MATERIAL. KEEP UPWIND.

TOXICITY

FENURON-TCA: TOXICITY DATA: 4 GM/KG ORAL-RAT LD50. CARCINOGEN STATUS: NONE. ACUTE TOXICITY LEVEL: MODERATELY TOXIC BY INGESTION. TARGET EFFECTS: NO DATA AVAILABLE.

HEALTH EFFECTS AND FIRST AID

INHALATION: FENURON-TCA: **ACUTE EXPOSURE-** MAY CAUSE IRRITATION TO THE MUCOUS MEMBRANES. **CHRONIC EXPOSURE-** NO DATA AVAILABLE.

FIRST AID- REMOVE FROM EXPOSURE AREA TO FRESH AIR IMMEDIATELY. IF BREATHING HAS STOPPED, PERFORM ARTIFICIAL RESPIRATION. KEEP PERSON WARM AND AT REST. TREAT SYMPTOMATICALLY AND SUPPORTIVELY. GET MEDICAL ATTENTION IMMEDIATELY.

SKIN CONTACT: FENURON-TCA: **ACUTE EXPOSURE-** MAY CAUSE SKIN IRRITATION. **CHRONIC EXPOSURE-** NO DATA AVAILABLE.

FIRST AID- REMOVE CONTAMINATED CLOTHING AND SHOES IMMEDIATELY. WASH AFFECTED AREA WITH SOAP OR MILD DETERGENT AND LARGE AMOUNTS OF WATER UNTIL NO EVIDENCE OF CHEMICAL REMAINS (APPROXIMATELY 15-20 MINUTES). GET MEDICAL ATTENTION IMMEDIATELY.

EYE CONTACT: FENURON-TCA: **ACUTE EXPOSURE-** MAY CAUSE IRRITATION. **CHRONIC EXPOSURE-** NO DATA AVAILABLE.

FIRST AID- WASH EYES IMMEDIATELY WITH LARGE AMOUNTS OF WATER OR NORMAL SALINE, OCCASIONALLY LIFTING UPPER AND LOWER LIDS, UNTIL NO EVIDENCE OF CHEMICAL REMAINS (APPROXIMATELY 15-20 MINUTES). GET MEDICAL ATTENTION IMMEDIATELY.

INGESTION: FENURON-TCA: **ACUTE EXPOSURE-** A LETHAL DOSE IN RATS WAS 4 GM/KG. **CHRONIC EXPOSURE-** NO DATA AVAILABLE.

FIRST AID- TREAT SYMPTOMATICALLY AND SUPPORTIVELY. GET MEDICAL ATTENTION IMMEDIATELY. IF VOMITING OCCURS, KEEP HEAD LOWER THAN HIPS TO PREVENT ASPIRATION.

ANTIDOTE: NO SPECIFIC ANTIDOTE. TREAT SYMPTOMATICALLY AND SUPPORTIVELY.

REACTIVITY

REACTIVITY: STABLE UNDER NORMAL TEMPERATURES AND PRESSURES.

INCOMPATIBILITIES: FENURON-TCA: OXIDIZERS (STRONG): FIRE AND EXPLOSION HAZARD.

DECOMPOSITION: THERMAL DECOMPOSITION PRODUCTS MAY INCLUDE TOXIC OXIDES OF NITROGEN AND CARBON AND TOXIC AND CORROSIVE FUMES OF CHLORIDES.

POLYMERIZATION: HAZARDOUS POLYMERIZATION HAS NOT BEEN REPORTED TO OCCUR UNDER NORMAL TEMPERATURES AND PRESSURES.

STORAGE AND DISPOSAL

OBSERVE ALL FEDERAL, STATE AND LOCAL REGULATIONS WHEN STORING OR DISPOSING OF THIS SUBSTANCE. FOR ASSISTANCE, CONTACT THE DISTRICT DIRECTOR OF THE ENVIRONMENTAL PROTECTION AGENCY.

STORAGE

STORE IN ACCORDANCE WITH 40 CFR 165 RECOMMENDED PROCEDURES FOR THE DISPOSAL AND STORAGE OF PESTICIDES AND PESTICIDE CONTAINERS.
STORE AWAY FROM INCOMPATIBLE SUBSTANCES.

DISPOSAL

DISPOSAL MUST BE IN ACCORDANCE WITH 40 CFR 165 RECOMMENDED PROCEDURES FOR THE DISPOSAL AND STORAGE OF PESTICIDES AND PESTICIDE CONTAINERS.

CONDITIONS TO AVOID

MAY BURN BUT DOES NOT IGNITE READILY. CONTAINERS MAY EXPLODE IN HEAT OF FIRE.

SPILL AND LEAK PROCEDURES

OCCUPATIONAL SPILL: DO NOT TOUCH SPILLED MATERIAL. STOP LEAK IF YOU CAN DO IT WITHOUT RISK. USE WATER SPRAY TO REDUCE VAPORS. FOR SMALL SPILLS, TAKE UP WITH SAND OR OTHER ABSORBENT MATERIAL AND PLACE INTO CONTAINERS FOR LATER DISPOSAL. FOR SMALL DRY SPILLS, WITH A CLEAN SHOVEL PLACE MATERIAL INTO CLEAN, DRY CONTAINERS AND COVER. MOVE CONTAINERS FROM SPILL AREA. FOR LARGER SPILLS, DIKE FAR AHEAD OF SPILL FOR LATER DISPOSAL. KEEP UNNECESSARY PEOPLE AWAY. ISOLATE HAZARD AREA AND DENY ENTRY. VENTILATE CLOSED SPACES BEFORE ENTERING.

PROTECTIVE EQUIPMENT

VENTILATION: PROVIDE LOCAL EXHAUST OR GENERAL DILUTION VENTILATION SYSTEM.

RESPIRATOR: THE FOLLOWING RESPIRATORS ARE RECOMMENDED BASED ON INFORMATION FOUND IN THE PHYSICAL DATA, TOXICITY AND HEALTH EFFECTS SECTIONS. THEY ARE RANKED IN ORDER FROM MINIMUM TO MAXIMUM RESPIRATORY PROTECTION. THE SPECIFIC RESPIRATOR SELECTED MUST BE BASED ON CONTAMINATION LEVELS FOUND IN THE WORK PLACE, MUST NOT EXCEED THE WORKING LIMITS OF THE RESPIRATOR AND BE JOINTLY APPROVED BY THE NATIONAL INSTITUTE FOR OCCUPATIONAL SAFETY AND HEALTH AND THE MINE SAFETY AND HEALTH ADMINISTRATION (NIOSH-MSHA).
CHEMICAL CARTRIDGE RESPIRATOR WITH AN ORGANIC VAPOR CARTRIDGE(S) WITH A FULL FACEPIECE AND ORGANIC VAPOR CARTRIDGE(S) IN COMBINATION WITH A DUST AND MIST FILTER.
POWERED AIR-PURIFYING RESPIRATOR WITH A TIGHT-FITTING FACEPIECE AND ORGANIC VAPOR CARTRIDGE(S) IN COMBINATION WITH A HIGH-EFFICIENCY PARTICULATE FILTER.
TYPE 'C' SUPPLIED-AIR RESPIRATOR WITH A FULL FACEPIECE OPERATED IN A PRESSURE-DEMAND OR OTHER POSITIVE PRESSURE MODE.
SELF-CONTAINED BREATHING APPARATUS WITH A FULL FACEPIECE OPERATED IN PRESSURE-DEMAND OR OTHER POSITIVE PRESSURE MODE.
FOR FIREFIGHTING AND OTHER IMMEDIATELY DANGEROUS TO LIFE OR HEALTH CONDITIONS:
SELF-CONTAINED BREATHING APPARATUS WITH FULL FACEPIECE OPERATED IN PRESSURE-DEMAND OR OTHER POSITIVE PRESSURE MODE.
SUPPLIED-AIR RESPIRATOR WITH FULL FACEPIECE AND OPERATED IN PRESSURE-DEMAND OR OTHER POSITIVE PRESSURE MODE IN COMBINATION WITH AN AUXILIARY SELF-CONTAINED BREATHING APPARATUS OPERATED IN PRESSURE-DEMAND OR OTHER POSITIVE PRESSURE MODE.

CLOTHING: EMPLOYEE MUST WEAR APPROPRIATE PROTECTIVE (IMPERVIOUS) CLOTHING AND EQUIPMENT TO PREVENT REPEATED OR PROLONGED SKIN CONTACT WITH THIS SUBSTANCE.

GLOVES: EMPLOYEE MUST WEAR APPROPRIATE PROTECTIVE GLOVES TO PREVENT CONTACT WITH THIS SUBSTANCE.

EYE PROTECTION: EMPLOYEE MUST WEAR SPLASH-PROOF OR DUST-RESISTANT SAFETY GOGGLES TO PREVENT EYE CONTACT WITH THIS SUBSTANCE.
EMERGENCY EYE WASH: WHERE THERE IS ANY POSSIBILITY THAT AN EMPLOYEE'S EYES MAY BE EXPOSED TO THIS SUBSTANCE, THE EMPLOYER SHOULD PROVIDE AN EYE WASH FOUNTAIN WITHIN THE IMMEDIATE WORK AREA FOR EMERGENCY USE.

AUTHORIZED BY- OCCUPATIONAL HEALTH SERVICES, INC.
CREATION DATE: 10/04/89 ***REVISION DATE:*** 05/11/90

MATERIAL SAFETY DATA SHEET

OCCUPATIONAL HEALTH SERVICES, INC.
AGRICULTURE AND PESTICIDE DIVISION
450 SEVENTH AVENUE, SUITE 2407
NEW YORK, NEW YORK 10123
1-800-445-MSDS OR (212) 967-1100

EMERGENCY CONTACT:
JOHN S. BRANSFORD, JR. (615) 292-1180

SUBSTANCE IDENTIFICATION

CAS-NUMBER 21564-17-0

SUBSTANCE: **2-(THIOCYANOMETHYLTHIO)BENZOTHIAZOLE**

TRADE NAMES/SYNONYMS: (2-BENZOTHIAZOLYLTHIO)METHYL ESTER, THIOCYANIC ACID; ALENTISAN; BENTHIAZOLE; BUSAN; BUSAN 15; BUSAN 30; BUSAN 70; BUSAN 71; BUSAN 72; BUSAN 30-1; BUSAN 30A; BUSAN 72A; BUSAN 30I; ICHIBAN; KVK 733059; SUPERDAVLOXAN; TCMTB; PST71392

CHEMICAL FAMILY: THIAZOLE
THIOCYANATE

MOLECULAR FORMULA: C9-H6-N2-S

MOLECULAR WEIGHT: 283.35

CERCLA RATINGS (SCALE 0-3): HEALTH=2 FIRE=U REACTIVITY=U PERSISTENCE=2

NFPA RATINGS (SCALE 0-4): HEALTH=2 FIRE=U REACTIVITY=U

COMPONENTS AND CONTAMINANTS

COMPONENT: 2-(THIOCYANOMETHYLTHIO)BENZOTHIAZOLE ***PERCENT:*** 100
CAS# 21564-17-0

OTHER CONTAMINANTS: NONE

EXPOSURE LIMITS: NO OCCUPATIONAL EXPOSURE LIMITS ESTABLISHED BY OSHA, ACGIH, OR NIOSH.

PHYSICAL DATA

DESCRIPTION: DARK BROWN LIQUID WITH A PUNGENT ODOR.
BOILING POINT: 300 F (149 C) ***SPECIFIC GRAVITY:*** 1.38 ***PH:*** 6-7
SOLUBILITY IN WATER: SLIGHTLY SOLUBLE

FIRE AND EXPLOSION DATA

FIRE AND EXPLOSION HAZARD: UNKNOWN FIRE AND EXPLOSION HAZARD.
FLASH POINT: 250 F (121 C) ***FLAMMABILITY CLASS(OSHA):*** IIIB
FIREFIGHTING MEDIA: DRY CHEMICAL, CARBON DIOXIDE, HALON, WATER SPRAY OR STANDARD FOAM (1987 EMERGENCY RESPONSE GUIDEBOOK, DOT P 5800.4). FOR LARGER FIRES, USE WATER SPRAY, FOG OR STANDARD FOAM (1987 EMERGENCY RESPONSE GUIDEBOOK, DOT P 5800.4).
FIREFIGHTING: MOVE CONTAINERS FROM FIRE AREA IF POSSIBLE (1987 EMERGENCY RESPONSE GUIDEBOOK, DOT P 5800.4, GUIDE PAGE 53).
USE AGENTS SUITABLE FOR TYPE OF SURROUNDING FIRE. AVOID BREATHING HAZARDOUS VAPORS, KEEP UPWIND.

TOXICITY

2-(THIOCYANOMETHYLTHIO)BENZOTHIAZOLE: TOXICITY DATA: 10 GM/KG SKIN-RABBIT LD50; 1590 MG/KG ORAL-RAT LD50. CARCINOGEN STATUS: NONE. LOCAL EFFECTS: CORROSIVE- EYE; IRRITANT- SKIN. ACUTE TOXICITY LEVEL: MODERATELY TOXIC BY INGESTION AND SLIGHTLY TOXIC BY DERMAL ABSORPTION. TARGET EFFECTS: SENSITIZER- SKIN. POISONING MAY AFFECT THE CENTRAL NERVOUS SYSTEM AND HEART.

HEALTH EFFECTS AND FIRST AID

INHALATION: 2-(THIOCYANOMETHYLTHIO)BENZOTHIAZOLE: **ACUTE EXPOSURE-** NO DATA AVAILABLE. **CHRONIC EXPOSURE-** NO DATA AVAILABLE.
FIRST AID- REMOVE FROM EXPOSURE AREA TO FRESH AIR IMMEDIATELY. IF BREATHING HAS STOPPED, PERFORM ARTIFICIAL RESPIRATION. KEEP PERSON WARM AND AT REST. TREAT SYMPTOMATICALLY AND SUPPORTIVELY. GET MEDICAL ATTENTION IMMEDIATELY.

SKIN CONTACT: 2-(THIOCYANOMETHYLTHIO)BENZOTHIAZOLE: IRRITANT/SENSITIZER. **ACUTE EXPOSURE-** THE LETHAL DOSE OF THIS COMPOUND BY SKIN ABSORPTION WAS MEASURED TO BE 10 GM/KG. SYMPTOMS WERE NOT REPORTED. THIS SUBSTANCE IRRITATES THE SKIN AND IS A SENSITIZER. **CHRONIC EXPOSURE-** NO DATA AVAILABLE. REPEATED OR PROLONGED CONTACT MAY RESULT IN SENSITIZATION DERMATITIS.
FIRST AID- REMOVE CONTAMINATED CLOTHING AND SHOES IMMEDIATELY. WASH AFFECTED AREA WITH SOAP OR MILD DETERGENT AND LARGE AMOUNTS OF WATER UNTIL NO EVIDENCE OF CHEMICAL REMAINS (APPROXIMATELY 15-20 MINUTES). GET MEDICAL ATTENTION IMMEDIATELY.

EYE CONTACT: 2-(THIOCYANOMETHYLTHIO)BENZOTHIAZOLE: CORROSIVE. **ACUTE EXPOSURE-** THIS SUBSTANCE MAY CAUSE BURNS TO THE EYES UPON CONTACT. **CHRONIC EXPOSURE-** DEPENDING ON THE CONCENTRATION AND DURATION OF CONTACT, EFFECTS AS IN ACUTE EXPOSURE MAY OCCUR WITH REPEATED OR PROLONGED CONTACT.
FIRST AID- WASH EYES IMMEDIATELY WITH LARGE AMOUNTS OF WATER OR NORMAL SALINE, OCCASIONALLY LIFTING UPPER AND LOWER LIDS, UNTIL NO EVIDENCE OF CHEMICAL REMAINS (APPROXIMATELY 15-20 MINUTES). GET MEDICAL ATTENTION IMMEDIATELY.

INGESTION: 2-(THIOCYANOMETHYLTHIO)BENZOTHIAZOLE: **ACUTE EXPOSURE-** THE LETHAL DOSE OF THIS SUBSTANCE IN RATS WAS 1590 MG/KG; THE LETHAL DOSE IN DUCKS WAS 1310 MG/KG. SYMPTOMS WERE NOT REPORTED FOR EITHER SPECIES. ACUTE POISONING BY THIOCYANATES MAY RESULT IN MENTAL CONFUSION, HALLUCINATIONS, DELIRIUM, PSYCHOTIC BEHAVIOR, HYPOTENSION, MUSCULAR SPASMS, CONVULSIONS, AND DEATH. **CHRONIC EXPOSURE-** NO SPECIFIC DATA AVAILABLE. CHRONIC EXPOSURE TO THIOCYANATES MAY RESULT IN URTICARIA, DERMATITIS, ABNORMAL BLEEDING, THYROID ENLARGEMENT, DERMATITIS, AND HIVES.
FIRST AID- TREAT SYMPTOMATICALLY AND SUPPORTIVELY. GET MEDICAL ATTENTION IMMEDIATELY. IF VOMITING OCCURS, KEEP HEAD LOWER THAN HIPS TO PREVENT ASPIRATION.
ANTIDOTE: NO SPECIFIC ANTIDOTE. TREAT SYMPTOMATICALLY AND SUPPORTIVELY.

REACTIVITY

REACTIVITY: NO DATA AVAILABLE.
INCOMPATIBILITIES: THIOCYANATES: CHLORATES: MAY EXPLODE WHEN FUSED AT A TEMPERATURE ABOVE 750 F, OR WHEN TOUCHED BY FLAMES OR SPARKS. NITRATES: MAY EXPLODE WHEN FUSED AT A TEMPERATURE ABOVE 750 F, OR WHEN TOUCHED BY FLAMES OR SPARKS. NITRIC ACID: WHEN A THIOCYANATE SOLUTION CAME INTO CONTACT WITH NITRIC ACID, AN EXPLOSION OCCURRED. ORGANIC PEROXIDES: MAY EXPLODE. OXIDIZING AGENTS: MAY EXPLODE. PEROXIDES: MAY EXPLODE. POTASSIUM CHLORATE: MAY EXPLODE WHEN FUSED AT A TEMPERATURE ABOVE 750 F, OR WHEN TOUCHED BY FLAMES OR SPARKS. SODIUM CHLORATE: MAY EXPLODE WHEN FUSED AT A TEMPERATURE ABOVE 750 F, OR WHEN TOUCHED BY FLAMES OR SPARKS.
DECOMPOSITION: THERMAL DECOMPOSITION MAY RELEASE TOXIC AND/OR HAZARDOUS GASES.
POLYMERIZATION: HAZARDOUS POLYMERIZATION HAS NOT BEEN REPORTED TO OCCUR UNDER NORMAL TEMPERATURES AND PRESSURES.

STORAGE AND DISPOSAL

OBSERVE ALL FEDERAL, STATE AND LOCAL REGULATIONS WHEN STORING OR DISPOSING OF THIS SUBSTANCE. FOR ASSISTANCE, CONTACT THE DISTRICT DIRECTOR OF THE ENVIRONMENTAL PROTECTION AGENCY.

****STORAGE****

STORE AWAY FROM INCOMPATIBLE SUBSTANCES.

CONDITIONS TO AVOID

NONE REPORTED.

SPILL AND LEAK PROCEDURES

OCCUPATIONAL SPILL: STOP LEAK IF YOU CAN DO IT WITHOUT RISK. FOR SMALL SPILLS, TAKE UP WITH SAND OR OTHER ABSORBENT MATERIAL AND PLACE INTO CLEAN, DRY CONTAINERS FOR LATER DISPOSAL. KEEP UNNECESSARY PEOPLE AWAY. ISOLATE HAZARD AREA AND DENY ENTRY.

PROTECTIVE EQUIPMENT

VENTILATION: PROVIDE LOCAL EXHAUST OR GENERAL DILUTION VENTILATION SYSTEM.
RESPIRATOR: THE FOLLOWING RESPIRATORS ARE RECOMMENDED BASED ON INFORMATION FOUND IN THE PHYSICAL DATA, TOXICITY AND HEALTH EFFECTS SECTIONS. THEY ARE RANKED IN ORDER FROM MINIMUM TO MAXIMUM RESPIRATORY PROTECTION. THE SPECIFIC RESPIRATOR SELECTED MUST BE BASED ON CONTAMINATION LEVELS FOUND IN THE WORK PLACE, MUST NOT EXCEED THE WORKING LIMITS OF THE RESPIRATOR AND BE JOINTLY APPROVED BY THE NATIONAL INSTITUTE FOR OCCUPATIONAL SAFETY AND HEALTH AND THE MINE SAFETY AND HEALTH ADMINISTRATION (NIOSH-MSHA).
TYPE 'C' SUPPLIED-AIR RESPIRATOR WITH A FULL FACEPIECE OPERATED IN PRESSURE-DEMAND OR OTHER POSITIVE PRESSURE MODE OR WITH A FULL FACEPIECE, HELMET OR HOOD OPERATED IN CONTINOUS-FLOW MODE.
SELF-CONTAINED BREATHING APPARATUS WITH A FULL FACEPIECE OPERATED IN PRESSURE-DEMAND OR OTHER POSITIVE PRESSURE MODE.
FOR FIREFIGHTING AND OTHER IMMEDIATELY DANGEROUS TO LIFE OR HEALTH CONDITIONS:
SELF-CONTAINED BREATHING APPARATUS WITH FULL FACEPIECE OPERATED IN PRESSURE-DEMAND OR OTHER POSITIVE PRESSURE MODE.
SUPPLIED-AIR RESPIRATOR WITH FULL FACEPIECE AND OPERATED IN PRESSURE-DEMAND OR OTHER POSITIVE PRESSURE MODE IN COMBINATION WITH AN AUXILIARY SELF-CONTAINED BREATHING APPARATUS OPERATED IN PRESSURE-DEMAND OR OTHER POSITIVE PRESSURE MODE.
CLOTHING: EMPLOYEE MUST WEAR APPROPRIATE PROTECTIVE (IMPERVIOUS) CLOTHING AND EQUIPMENT TO PREVENT REPEATED OR PROLONGED SKIN CONTACT WITH THIS SUBSTANCE.
GLOVES: EMPLOYEE MUST WEAR APPROPRIATE PROTECTIVE GLOVES TO PREVENT CONTACT WITH THIS SUBSTANCE.
EYE PROTECTION: EMPLOYEE MUST WEAR SPLASH-PROOF OR DUST-RESISTANT SAFETY GOGGLES TO PREVENT EYE CONTACT WITH THIS SUBSTANCE.
EMERGENCY EYE WASH: WHERE THERE IS ANY POSSIBILITY THAT AN EMPLOYEE'S EYES MAY BE EXPOSED TO THIS SUBSTANCE, THE EMPLOYER SHOULD PROVIDE AN EYE WASH FOUNTAIN WITHIN THE IMMEDIATE WORK AREA FOR EMERGENCY USE.

AUTHORIZED BY- OCCUPATIONAL HEALTH SERVICES, INC.
CREATION DATE: 10/05/89 ***REVISION DATE:*** 05/11/90

MATERIAL SAFETY DATA SHEET

OCCUPATIONAL HEALTH SERVICES, INC.
AGRICULTURE AND PESTICIDE DIVISION
450 SEVENTH AVENUE, SUITE 2407
NEW YORK, NEW YORK 10123
1-800-445-MSDS OR (212) 967-1100

EMERGENCY CONTACT:
JOHN S. BRANSFORD, JR. (615) 292-1180

SUBSTANCE IDENTIFICATION

CAS-NUMBER 126-22-7

SUBSTANCE: **BUTONATE**

TRADE NAMES/SYNONYMS: BUTANOIC ACID, 2,2,2-TRICHLORO-1-(DIMETHOXYPHOSPHINYL)ETHYL ESTER; BUTYRIC ACID, ESTER WITH DIMETHYL(2,2,2-TRICHLORO-1-HYDROXYETHYL) PHOSPHONATE; 2,2,2-TRICHLORO-1-(DIMETHOXYPHOSPHINYL)ETHYL BUTANOATE; BUTYRATE ESTER OF DIMETHYL (2,2,2-TRICHLORO-1-HYDROXYETHYL)PHOSPHONATE; O,O-DIMETHYL 2,2,2-TRICHLORO-1-N-BUTYRYLOXYETHYLPHOSPHONATE; O,O-DIMETHYL-2,2,2-TRICHLORO-1-PHOSPHONOETHYL BUTYRATE; F 139; T 113; TRIBUFON; ENT 20852; C8H14CL3O5P; PST71399

CHEMICAL FAMILY: ORGANOPHOSPHATE

MOLECULAR FORMULA: (C-H3-O)2-P-(O)-C-H-(C-CL3)-O2-C-C3-H7

MOLECULAR WEIGHT: 327.55

CERCLA RATINGS (SCALE 0-3): HEALTH=U FIRE=U REACTIVITY=0 PERSISTENCE=1

NFPA RATINGS (SCALE 0-4): HEALTH=U FIRE=U REACTIVITY=0

COMPONENTS AND CONTAMINANTS

COMPONENT: BUTONATE ***PERCENT:*** 100.0
CAS# 126-22-7

OTHER CONTAMINANTS: NONE

EXPOSURE LIMITS: NO OCCUPATIONAL EXPOSURE LIMITS ESTABLISHED BY OSHA, ACGIH, OR NIOSH.

PHYSICAL DATA

DESCRIPTION: COLORLESS, OILY LIQUID WITH A SLIGHT ESTER ODOR.

BOILING POINT: 264 F (129 C) @ 0.5 MMHG ***SPECIFIC GRAVITY:*** 1.3998

SOLUBILITY IN WATER: MODERATELY SOLUBLE

SOLVENT SOLUBILITY: SOLUBLE IN MOST ORGANIC SOLVENTS.

FIRE AND EXPLOSION DATA

FIRE AND EXPLOSION HAZARD: UNKNOWN FIRE AND EXPLOSION HAZARD.

FIREFIGHTING MEDIA: DRY CHEMICAL, CARBON DIOXIDE, HALON, WATER SPRAY OR STANDARD FOAM (1987 EMERGENCY RESPONSE GUIDEBOOK, DOT P 5800.4). FOR LARGER FIRES, USE WATER SPRAY, FOG OR STANDARD FOAM (1987 EMERGENCY RESPONSE GUIDEBOOK, DOT P 5800.4).

FIREFIGHTING: MOVE CONTAINER FROM FIRE AREA IF POSSIBLE. DIKE FIRE CONTROL WATER FOR LATER DISPOSAL; DO NOT SCATTER THE MATERIAL. COOL FIRE-EXPOSED CONTAINERS WITH WATER FROM SIDE UNTIL WELL AFTER FIRE IS OUT. STAY AWAY FROM STORAGE TANK ENDS. WITHDRAW IMMEDIATELY IN CASE OF RISING SOUND FROM VENTING SAFETY DEVICE OR ANY DISCOLORATION OF STORAGE TANK DUE TO FIRE (1987 EMERGENCY RESPONSE GUIDEBOOK, DOT P 5800.4, GUIDE PAGE 28).
EXTINGUISH ONLY IF FLOW CAN BE STOPPED. USE FLOODING AMOUNTS OF WATER AS A FOG; SOLID STREAMS MAY BE INEFFECTIVE. COOL CONTAINERS WITH FLOODING AMOUNTS OF WATER FROM AS FAR A DISTANCE AS POSSIBLE. AVOID BREATHING POISONOUS VAPORS, KEEP UPWIND.

TOXICITY

BUTONATE: TOXICITY DATA: 7 GM/KG SKIN-RAT LD50; 3080 MG/KG SKIN-DOG LD50; 1100 MG/KG ORAL-RAT LD50; 760 MG/KG ORAL-MOUSE LD50; 950 MG/KG ORAL-GUINEA PIG LD50; 3000 MG/KG SUBCUTANEOUS-RAT LD50; 700 MG/KG INTRAPERITONEAL-RAT LD50; 700 MG/KG UNREPORTED-RAT LD50; MUTAGENIC DATA (RTECS). CARCINOGEN STATUS: NONE. ACUTE TOXICITY: MODERATELY TOXIC BY INGESTION; SLIGHTLY TOXIC BY DERMAL ABSORPTION. TARGET EFFECTS: CHOLINESTERASE INHIBITOR. POISONING MAY AFFECT THE NERVOUS SYSTEM.* AT INCREASED RISK FROM EXPOSURE: PERSONS WITH RESPIRATORY AILMENTS, RECENT EXPOSURE TO CHOLINESTERASE INHIBITORS OR IMPAIRED CHOLINESTERASE PRODUCTION, OR LIVER MALFUNCTION.* ADDITIONAL DATA: MAY CROSS THE PLACENTA. HIGH ENVIRONMENTAL TEMPERATURES OR EXPOSURE OF THE CHEMICAL TO VISIBLE OR ULTRAVIOLET LIGHT MAY ENHANCE THE TOXICITY. INTERACTIONS WITH MEDICATIONS MAY OCCUR.*
* MAY BE BASED ON GENERAL INFORMATION ON ORGANOPHOSPHATES.

HEALTH EFFECTS AND FIRST AID

INHALATION: BUTONATE: SEE INFORMATION ON ORGANOPHOSPHATES.
ORGANOPHOSPHATES: CHOLINESTERASE INHIBITOR. **ACUTE EXPOSURE-** WHEN INHALED, THE FIRST EFFECTS OF CHOLINESTERASE INHIBITORS ARE USUALLY RESPIRATORY AND MAY INCLUDE NASAL HYPEREMIA AND WATERY DISCHARGE, COUGH, CHEST DISCOMFORT, DYSPNEA, AND WHEEZING DUE TO INCREASED BRONCHIAL SECRETIONS AND BRONCHOCONSTRICTION. IF SUFFICIENT AMOUNTS ARE ABSORBED, OTHER SYSTEMIC EFFECTS MAY BEGIN WITHIN A FEW MINUTES OR BE DELAYED FOR UP TO 12 HOURS. SYMPTOMS MAY INCLUDE PALLOR, NAUSEA, VOMITING, DIARRHEA, ABDOMINAL CRAMPS, HEADACHE, DIZZINESS, OCULAR PAIN, BLURRED VISION, MIOSIS OR IN SOME CASES, ESPECIALLY INITIALLY, MYDRIASIS, LACRIMATION, SALIVATION, SWEATING, AND CONFUSION. OTHER REPORTED CENTRAL NERVOUS SYSTEM OR NEUROMUSCULAR EFFECTS MAY INCLUDE ATAXIA, SLURRED SPEECH, AREFLEXIA, WEAKNESS, FATIGUE, FASCICULATIONS, TWITCHING, TREMORS POSSIBLY OF THE TONGUE AND EYELIDS, AND EVENTUALLY PARALYSIS OF THE EXTREMITIES AND POSSIBLY OF THE RESPIRATORY MUSCLES. IN SEVERE CASES THERE MAY ALSO BE INVOLUNTARY DEFECATION AND URINATION, CYANOSIS, PSYCHOSIS, HYPERGLYCEMIA, ACUTE PANCREATITIS, CARDIAC IRREGULARITIES, PULMONARY EDEMA, UNCONSCIOUSNESS, CONVULSIONS, AND COMA. DEATH IS PRIMARILY DUE TO RESPIRATORY FAILURE, ALTHOUGH CARDIOVASCULAR EFFECTS INCLUDING CARDIAC ARREST MAY ALSO BE IMPLICATED. LONG TERM SEQUELAE ARE RARE BUT MAY INCLUDE NEUROPSYCHIATRIC DISORDERS AND MYOPATHY WITH MUSCLE TENDERNESS. SOME ORGANOPHOSPHATES MAY CAUSE A DELAYED NEUROPATHY BEGINNING 1-4 WEEKS AFTER AN ACUTE EXPOSURE WHICH MAY OR MAY NOT HAVE CAUSED ACUTE CHOLINERGIC EFFECTS. NUMBNESS, TINGLING, WEAKNESS AND CRAMPING BEGINNING SYMMETRICALLY IN THE LOWER LIMBS MAY PROGRESS TO ATAXIA AND PARALYSIS. IN SEVERE CASES, UPPER LIMB INVOLVEMENT IS POSSIBLE AND FLACCID PARALYSIS MAY PROGRESS TO SPASTIC PARALYSIS WITH EXAGGERATED REFLEXES. IMPROVEMENT MAY OCCUR OVER MONTHS TO YEARS, BUT SOME RESIDUAL IMPAIRMENT USUALLY REMAINS.
CHRONIC EXPOSURE- REPEATED OR PROLONGED EXPOSURE MAY RESULT IN THE EFFECTS OF ACUTE EXPOSURE INCLUDING THE DELAYED NEUROPATHY. OTHER EFFECTS REPORTED IN WORKERS REPEATEDLY EXPOSED INCLUDE IMPAIRED MEMORY AND CONCENTRATION, ACUTE PSYCHOSIS, SEVERE DEPRESSIONS, IRRITABILTY, CONFUSION, APATHY, EMOTIONAL LABILITY, SOCIAL WITHDRAWAL, CONFUSION, HEADACHE, SPEECH DIFFICULTIES, DELAYED REACTION TIMES, SPATIAL DISORIENTATION, NIGHTMARES, SLEEPWALKING, AND DROWSINESS OR INSOMNIA. AN INFLUENZA-LIKE CONDITION WITH HEADACHE, NAUSEA, WEAKNESS, ANOREXIA AND MALAISE HAS ALSO BEEN REPORTED.

FIRST AID- REMOVE FROM EXPOSURE AREA TO FRESH AIR IMMEDIATELY. IF BREATHING HAS STOPPED, GIVE ARTIFICIAL RESPIRATION. MAINTAIN AIRWAY AND BLOOD PRESSURE AND ADMINISTER OXYGEN IF AVAILABLE. KEEP AFFECTED PERSON WARM AND AT REST. TREAT SYMPTOMATICALLY AND SUPPORTIVELY. ADMINISTRATION OF OXYGEN SHOULD BE PERFORMED BY QUALIFIED PERSONNEL. GET MEDICAL ATTENTION IMMEDIATELY.

SKIN CONTACT: BUTONATE: SEE INFORMATION ON ORGANOPHOSPHATES.
ORGANOPHOSPHATES: CHOLINESTERASE INHIBITOR. **ACUTE EXPOSURE-** LOCALIZED SWEATING AND FASCICULATIONS MAY OCCUR AT THE SITE OF CONTACT. IF SUFFICIENT AMOUNTS ARE ABSORBED, OTHER EFFECTS OF CHOLINESTERASE INHIBITION AS DESCRIBED IN ACUTE INHALATION MAY OCCUR. SYMPTOMS MAY BE DELAYED 2-3 HOURS, BUT USUALLY NO MORE THAN 12 HOURS. THE RATE OF ABSORPTION IS INCREASED BY THE PRESENCE OF DERMATITIS OR HIGH AMBIENT TEMPERATURES. DELAYED NEUROPATHY IS ALSO POSSIBLE. **CHRONIC EXPOSURE-** REPEATED OR PROLONGED EXPOSURE MAY CAUSE EFFECTS AS DESCRIBED IN ACUTE EXPOSURE. SOME ORGANOPHOSPHATES MAY CAUSE SENSITIZATION.

FIRST AID- REMOVE CONTAMINATED CLOTHING IMMEDIATELY. WASH CONTAMINATED AREAS WITH SOAP AND WATER FOLLOWED BY ALCOHOL (ARENA, POISONING, 4TH ED.). EMERGENCY PERSONNEL SHOULD WEAR GLOVES AND AVOID CONTAMINATION. TREAT RESPIRATORY DIFFICULTY WITH ARTIFICIAL RESPIRATION. GET MEDICAL ATTENTION IMMEDIATELY.

EYE CONTACT: BUTONATE: SEE INFORMATION ON ORGANOPHOSPHATES.
ORGANOPHOSPHATES: CHOLINESTERASE INHIBITOR. **ACUTE EXPOSURE-** DIRECT CONTACT MAY CAUSE PAIN, HYPEREMIA, LACRIMATION, TWITCHING OF THE EYELIDS, MIOSIS, AND CILIARY MUSCLE SPASM WITH LOSS OF ACCOMODATION, BLURRED OR DIMMED VISION AND BROWACHE. SOMETIMES MYDRIASIS MAY OCCUR INSTEAD OF MIOSIS. WITH SUFFICIENT EXPOSURE, OTHER SYMPTOMS OF CHOLINESTERASE INHIBITION AS DESCRIBED IN ACUTE INHALATION MAY OCCUR. **CHRONIC EXPOSURE-** REPEATED OR PROLONGED EXPOSURE MAY CAUSE EFFECTS AS DESCRIBED IN ACUTE EXPOSURE. SOME COMPOUNDS HAVE CAUSED TOXIC EFFECTS ON THE CRYSTALLINE LENS, CONJUNCTIVAL THICKENING AND OBSTRUCTION OF THE NASOLACRIMAL CANALS WHEN USED AS MIOTIC EYEDROPS.

FIRST AID- IRRIGATE EYES WITH WATER OR SALINE SOLUTION. IF SYMPTOMS OF POISONING OCCUR, TREAT RESPIRATORY DIFFICULTY WITH ARTIFICIAL RESPIRATION AND OXYGEN. OBSERVE PATIENT FOR AT LEAST 24-36 HOURS (GOSSELIN, CLINICAL TOXICOLOGY OF COMMERCIAL PRODUCTS, 5TH ED.). GET MEDICAL ATTENTION IMMEDIATELY. OXYGEN SHOULD BE ADMINISTERED BY QUALIFIED MEDICAL PERSONNEL.

INGESTION: BUTONATE: SEE INFORMATION ON ORGANOPHOSPHATES.
ORGANOPHOSPHATES: CHOLINESTERASE INHIBITOR. **ACUTE EXPOSURE-** WHEN INGESTED, THE FIRST EFFECTS MAY BE NAUSEA, VOMITING, ANOREXIA,

ABDOMINAL CRAMPS AND DIARRHEA. GASTROINTESTINAL ABSORPTION MAY CAUSE SYMPTOMS OF CHOLINESTERASE INHIBITION AS DESCRIBED IN ACUTE INHALATION. SYMPTOMS MAY BEGIN WITHIN MINUTES OR BE DELAYED FOR HOURS. DELAYED EFFECTS INCLUDING NEUROPATHY MAY ALSO OCCUR. **CHRONIC EXPOSURE-** REPEATED INGESTION MAY CAUSE EFFECTS AS DESCRIBED IN ACUTE EXPOSURE.

FIRST AID- IF PERSON IS ALERT AND RESPIRATION IS NOT DEPRESSED, GIVE SYRUP OF IPECAC FOLLOWED BY WATER (IF VOMITING OCCURS, KEEP HEAD BELOW HIPS TO PREVENT ASPIRATION). IF CONSCIOUSNESS LEVEL DECLINES OR VOMITING HAS NOT OCCURRED IN 15 MINUTES EMPTY STOMACH BY GASTRIC LAVAGE WITH THE AID OF CUFFED ENDOTRACHEAL TUBE USING ISOTONIC SALINE OR 5% SODIUM BICARBONATE FOLLOW WITH ACTIVATED CHARCOAL. ESTABLISH AND MAINTAIN AIRWAY. TREAT RESPIRATORY DIFFICULTY WITH ARTIFICIAL RESPIRATION AND OXYGEN. DO NOT GIVE MORPHINE, AMINOPHYLLINE, PHENOTHIAZINES, RESERPINE, FUROSEMIDE, OR ETHACRYNIC ACID (MORGAN, RECOGNITION AND MANAGEMENT OF PESTICIDE POISONINGS, 3RD ED.). TREAT SYMPTOMATICALLY AND SUPPORTIVELY. ADMINISTRATION OF OXYGEN AND LAVAGE MUST BE PERFORMED BY QUALIFIED MEDICAL PERSONNEL. GET MEDICAL ATTENTION IMMEDIATELY.

ANTIDOTE: THE FOLLOWING ANTIDOTE(S) HAVE BEEN RECOMMENDED. HOWEVER, THE DECISION AS TO WHETHER THE SEVERITY OF POISONING REQUIRES ADMINISTRATION OF ANY ANTIDOTE AND ACTUAL DOSE REQUIRED SHOULD BE MADE BY QUALIFIED MEDICAL PERSONNEL.

FOR CHOLINESTERASE INHIBITORS: ESTABLISH CLEAR AIRWAY AND TISSUE OXYGENATION BY ASPIRATION OF SECRETIONS, AND IF NECESSARY, BY ASSISTED PULMONARY VENTILATION WITH OXYGEN. IMPROVE TISSUE OXYGENATION AS MUCH AS POSSIBLE BEFORE ADMINISTERING ATROPINE TO MINIMIZE THE RISK OF VENTRICULAR FIBRILLATION. ADMINISTER ATROPINE SULFATE INTRAVENOUSLY, OR INTRAMUSCULARLY IF IV INJECTION IS NOT POSSIBLE. IN MODERATELY SEVERE POISONING ADMINISTER ATROPINE SULFATE, 0.4-2.0 MG REPEATED EVERY 15 MINUTES UNTIL ATROPINIZATION IS ACHIEVED (TACHYCARDIA, FLUSHING, DRY MOUTH, MYDRIASIS). MAINTAIN ATROPINIZATION BY REPEATED DOSES FOR 2-12 HOURS, OR LONGER, DEPENDING ON THE SEVERITY OF POISONING. THE APPEARANCE OF RALES IN THE LUNG BASES, MIOSIS, SALIVATION, NAUSEA, BRADYCARDIA, ARE ALL INDICATIONS OF INADEQUATE ATROPINIZATION. SEVERELY POISONED INDIVIDUALS MAY EXHIBIT REMARKABLE TOLERANCE TO ATROPINE; TWO OR MORE TIMES THE DOSAGES SUGGESTED ABOVE MAY BE NEEDED. PERSONS NOT POISONED OR ONLY SLIGHTLY POISONED, HOWEVER, MAY DEVELOP SIGNS OF ATROPINE TOXICITY FROM SUCH LARGE DOSAGES: FEVER, MUSCLE FIBRILLATIONS, AND DELIRIUM ARE THE MAIN SIGNS OF ATROPINE TOXICITY. IF THESE SIGNS APPEAR WHILE THE PATIENT IS FULLY ATROPINIZED, ATROPINE ADMINISTRATION SHOULD BE DISCONTINUED, AT LEAST TEMPORARILY. OBSERVE TREATED PATIENTS CLOSELY AT LEAST 24 HOURS TO INSURE THAT SYMPTOMS (POSSIBLY PULMONARY EDEMA) DO NOT RECUR AS ATROPINIZATION WEARS OFF. IN VERY SEVERE POISONINGS, METABOLIC DISPOSITION OF TOXICANT MAY REQUIRE SEVERAL HOURS OR DAYS DURING WHICH ATROPINIZATION MUST BE MAINTAINED. MARKEDLY LOWER LEVELS OF URINARY METABOLITES INDICATE THAT ATROPINE DOSAGE CAN BE TAPERED OFF. AS DOSAGE IS REDUCED, CHECK THE LUNG BASES FREQUENTLY FOR RALES. IF RALES ARE HEARD OR OTHER SYMPTOMS RETURN, RE-ESTABLISH ATROPINIZATION PROMPTLY (MORGAN, RECOGNITION AND MANAGEMENT OF PESTICIDE POISONINGS, 3RD ED.). ADMINISTRATION OF ANTIDOTE MUST BE PERFORMED BY QUALIFIED MEDICAL PERSONNEL.

IN CASES OF SEVERE POISONING BY ORGANOPHOSPHATE PESTICIDES IN WHICH RESPIRATORY DEPRESSION, MUSCLE WEAKNESS AND TWITCHINGS ARE SEVERE, GIVE PRALIDOXIME (PROTOPAM-AYERST, 2-PAM), 1.0 GRAM INTRAVENOUSLY AT NO MORE THAN 0.5 GRAM PER MINUTE. DOSAGE OF PRALIDOXIME MAY BE REPEATED IN 1-2 HOURS, THEN AT 10-12 HOUR INTERVALS IF NEEDED. IN VERY SEVERE POISONINGS, DOSAGE RATES MAY BE DOUBLED. TREATMENT WITH PRALIDOXIME WILL BE MOST EFFECTIVE IF GIVEN WITHIN THIRTY-SIX HOURS AFTER POISONING (MORGAN, RECOGNITION AND MANAGEMENT OF PESTICIDE POISONINGS, 3RD ED.). ANTIDOTE SHOULD BE ADMINISTERED BY QUALIFIED MEDICAL PERSONNEL.

REACTIVITY

REACTIVITY: STABLE UNDER NORMAL TEMPERATURES AND PRESSURES.

INCOMPATIBILITIES: BUTONATE: ALKALI: MAY HYDROLYZE. OXIDIZERS (STRONG): FIRE AND EXPLOSION HAZARD.

DECOMPOSITION: THERMAL DECOMPOSITION PRODUCTS MAY INCLUDE TOXIC ANC CORROSIVE FUMES OF CHLORIDES AND TOXIC OXIDES OF PHOSPHORUS.

POLYMERIZATION: HAZARDOUS POLYMERIZATION HAS NOT BEEN REPORTED TO OCCUR UNDER NORMAL TEMPERATURES AND PRESSURES.

STORAGE AND DISPOSAL

OBSERVE ALL FEDERAL, STATE AND LOCAL REGULATIONS WHEN STORING OR DISPOSING OF THIS SUBSTANCE. FOR ASSISTANCE, CONTACT THE DISTRICT DIRECTOR OF THE ENVIRONMENTAL PROTECTION AGENCY.

****STORAGE****

STORE IN ACCORDANCE WITH 40 CFR 165 RECOMMENDED PROCEDURES FOR THE DISPOSAL AND STORAGE OF PESTICIDES AND PESTICIDE CONTAINERS.
STORE AWAY FROM INCOMPATIBLE SUBSTANCES.

****DISPOSAL****

DISPOSAL MUST BE IN ACCORDANCE WITH 40 CFR 165 RECOMMENDED PROCEDURES FOR THE DISPOSAL AND STORAGE OF PESTICIDES AND PESTICIDE CONTAINERS.

CONDITIONS TO AVOID

AVOID CONTACT WITH HEAT, SPARKS, FLAMES OR OTHER IGNITION SOURCES. VAPORS MAY BE EXPLOSIVE. MATERIAL IS POISONOUS; AVOID INHALATION OF VAPORS OR CONTACT WITH SKIN. DO NOT ALLOW MATERIAL TO CONTAMINATE WATER SOURCES.

SPILL AND LEAK PROCEDURES

OCCUPATIONAL SPILL: SHUT OFF IGNITION SOURCES. DO NOT TOUCH SPILLED MATERIAL. STOP LEAK IF YOU CAN DO IT WITHOUT RISK. USE WATER SPRAY TO REDUCE VAPORS. FOR SMALL SPILLS, TAKE UP WITH SAND OR OTHER ABSORBENT MATERIAL AND PLACE INTO CONTAINERS FOR LATER DISPOSAL. FOR LARGER SPILLS, DIKE FAR AHEAD OF SPILL FOR LATER DISPOSAL. NO SMOKING, FLAMES OR FLARES IN HAZARD AREA! KEEP UNNECESSARY PEOPLE AWAY; ISOLATE HAZARD AREA AND DENY ENTRY.

PROTECTIVE EQUIPMENT

VENTILATION: PROVIDE GENERAL DILUTION VENTILATION.

RESPIRATOR: THE FOLLOWING RESPIRATORS ARE RECOMMENDED BASED ON INFORMATION FOUND IN THE PHYSICAL DATA, TOXICITY AND HEALTH EFFECTS SECTIONS. THEY ARE RANKED IN ORDER FROM MINIMUM TO MAXIMUM RESPIRATORY PROTECTION. THE SPECIFIC RESPIRATOR SELECTED MUST BE BASED ON CONTAMINATION LEVELS FOUND IN THE WORK PLACE, MUST NOT EXCEED THE WORKING LIMITS OF THE RESPIRATOR AND BE JOINTLY APPROVED BY THE NATIONAL INSTITUTE FOR OCCUPATIONAL SAFETY AND HEALTH AND THE MINE SAFETY AND HEALTH ADMINISTRATION (NIOSH-MSHA).

CHEMICAL CARTRIDGE RESPIRATOR WITH PESTICIDE CARTRIDGE.

GAS MASK WITH A PESTICIDE CANISTER (CHIN-STYLE OR FRONT- OR BACK-MOUNTED CANISTER).

TYPE 'C' SUPPLIED-AIR RESPIRATOR OPERATED IN THE PRESSURE-DEMAND OR OTHER POSITIVE PRESSURE OR CONTINUOUS-FLOW MODE.

SELF-CONTAINED BREATHING APPARATUS.

FOR FIREFIGHTING AND OTHER IMMEDIATELY DANGEROUS TO LIFE OR HEALTH CONDITIONS:

SELF-CONTAINED BREATHING APPARATUS WITH FULL FACEPIECE OPERATED IN PRESSURE-DEMAND OR OTHER POSITIVE PRESSURE MODE.

SUPPLIED-AIR RESPIRATOR WITH FULL FACEPIECE AND OPERATED IN PRESSURE-DEMAND OR OTHER POSITIVE PRESSURE MODE IN COMBINATION WITH AN AUXILIARY SELF-CONTAINED BREATHING APPARATUS OPERATED IN PRESSURE-DEMAND OR OTHER POSITIVE PRESSURE MODE.

CLOTHING: EMPLOYEE MUST WEAR APPROPRIATE PROTECTIVE (IMPERVIOUS) CLOTHING AND EQUIPMENT TO PREVENT REPEATED OR PROLONGED SKIN CONTACT WITH THIS SUBSTANCE.

GLOVES: EMPLOYEE MUST WEAR APPROPRIATE PROTECTIVE GLOVES TO PREVENT CONTACT WITH THIS SUBSTANCE.

EYE PROTECTION: EMPLOYEE MUST WEAR SPLASH-PROOF OR DUST-RESISTANT SAFETY GOGGLES TO PREVENT EYE CONTACT WITH THIS SUBSTANCE.

EMERGENCY EYE WASH: WHERE THERE IS ANY POSSIBILITY THAT AN EMPLOYEE'S EYES MAY BE EXPOSED TO THIS SUBSTANCE, THE EMPLOYER SHOULD PROVIDE AN EYE WASH FOUNTAIN WITHIN THE IMMEDIATE WORK AREA FOR EMERGENCY USE.

AUTHORIZED BY- OCCUPATIONAL HEALTH SERVICES, INC.
CREATION DATE: 10/04/89 ***REVISION DATE:*** 05/01/90

MATERIAL SAFETY DATA SHEET

OCCUPATIONAL HEALTH SERVICES, INC.
AGRICULTURE AND PESTICIDE DIVISION
450 SEVENTH AVENUE, SUITE 2407
NEW YORK, NEW YORK 10123
1-800-445-MSDS OR (212) 967-1100

EMERGENCY CONTACT:
JOHN S. BRANSFORD, JR. (615) 292-1180

SUBSTANCE IDENTIFICATION

CAS-NUMBER 18530-56-8

SUBSTANCE: **NOREA**

TRADE NAMES/SYNONYMS: UREA, N,N-DIMETHYL-N'-(OCTAHYDRO-4,7-METHANO-1H-INDEN-5-YL)-, (3A ALPHA, 4 ALPHA, 5 ALPHA, 7 ALPHA, 7A ALPHA)-; UREA, 3-(HEXAHYDRO-4,7-METHANOINDAN-5-YL)-1,1-DIMETHYL-, ENDO,EXO-5-; ENDO,EXO-5-3-(HEXAHYDRO-4,7-METHANOINDAN-5-YL)-1,1-DIMETHYLUREA; (3A ALPHA, 4 ALPHA, 5 ALPHA, 7ALPHA, 7A ALPHA)-N,N-DIMETHYL-N'- (OCTAHYDRO-4,7-METHANO-1H-INDEN-5-YL)UREA; 1,1-DIMETHYL-3-(PERHYDRO-4,7-METHANOINDEN-5-YL)UREA; 3-(HEXAHYDRO-4,7-METHANOINDAN-5-YL)-1,1-DIMETHYLUREA; N,N-DIMETHYL-N'-(OCTAHYDRO-4,7-METHANO-1H-INDEN-5-YL)UREA; N'-(HEXAHYDRO-4,7-METHANOINDAN-5-YL)-N,N-DIMETHYLUREA; HERBAN; HERCULES 7531; NORURON; C13H22N2O; PST71400

CHEMICAL FAMILY: SUBSTITUTED UREA

MOLECULAR FORMULA: C10-H15-N-H-C-O-N-(C-H3)2

MOLECULAR WEIGHT: 222.32

CERCLA RATINGS (SCALE 0-3): HEALTH=2 FIRE=1 REACTIVITY=0 PERSISTENCE=1

NFPA RATINGS (SCALE 0-4): HEALTH=2 FIRE=1 REACTIVITY=0

COMPONENTS AND CONTAMINANTS

COMPONENT: NOREA ***PERCENT:*** 100.0

CAS# 18530-56-8

OTHER CONTAMINANTS: NONE

EXPOSURE LIMITS: NO OCCUPATIONAL EXPOSURE LIMITS ESTABLISHED BY OSHA, ACGIH, OR NIOSH.

PHYSICAL DATA

DESCRIPTION: WHITE CRYSTALLINE SOLID. ***MELTING POINT:*** 349-352 F (176-178 C)

SPECIFIC GRAVITY: 1.162 @ 25 C ***SOLUBILITY IN WATER:*** 150 PPM

SOLVENT SOLUBILITY: SOLUBLE IN ACETONE, CYCLOHEXANONE, ALCOHOL; SLIGHTLY SOLUBLE IN BENZENE, TOLUENE, XYLENE, KEROSENE; INSOLUBLE IN HEXANE.

FIRE AND EXPLOSION DATA

FIRE AND EXPLOSION HAZARD: SLIGHT FIRE HAZARD WHEN EXPOSED TO HEAT OR FLAME.

FIREFIGHTING MEDIA: DRY CHEMICAL, CARBON DIOXIDE, HALON, WATER SPRAY OR STANDARD FOAM (1987 EMERGENCY RESPONSE GUIDEBOOK, DOT P 5800.4). FOR LARGER FIRES, USE WATER SPRAY, FOG OR STANDARD FOAM (1987 EMERGENCY RESPONSE GUIDEBOOK, DOT P 5800.4).

FIREFIGHTING: MOVE CONTAINERS FROM FIRE AREA IF POSSIBLE. FIGHT FIRE FROM MAXIMUM DISTANCE. STAY AWAY FROM STORAGE TANK ENDS. DIKE FIRE CONTROL WATER FOR LATER DISPOSAL. DO NOT SCATTER MATERIAL (1987 EMERGENCY RESPONSE GUIDEBOOK, DOT P 5800.4, GUIDE PAGE 55). EXTINGUISH USING AGENT SUITABLE FOR TYPE OF SURROUNDING FIRE. USE WATER IN FLOODING QUANTITIES AS FOG. KEEP SPARKS, FLAMES AND OTHER SOURCES OF IGNITION AWAY. KEEP MATERIAL OUT OF WATER SOURCES AND SEWERS. DO NOT TOUCH MATERIAL AND AVOID BREATHING DUSTS AND FUMES FROM BURNING MATERIAL. KEEP UPWIND.

TOXICITY

NOREA: TOXICITY DATA: 723 MG/KG SKIN-RABBIT LD50; 23 GM/KG SKIN-RAT LD50; 2 GM/KG ORAL-RAT LD50; 4600 MG/KG ORAL-MOUSE LD50; 3700 MG/KG ORAL-DOG LD50. CARCINOGEN STATUS: NONE. ACUTE TOXICITY LEVEL: TOXIC BY DERMAL ABSORPTION; MODERATELY TOXIC BY INGESTION. TARGET EFFECTS: NO DATA AVAILABLE.

HEALTH EFFECTS AND FIRST AID

INHALATION: NOREA: **ACUTE EXPOSURE-** A CONCENTRATION OF 60,000 MG/M3/6 HOURS WAS LETHAL TO 50% OF A GROUP OF MICE; NO SYMPTOMS WERE OBSERVED IN RATS AND GUINEA PIGS EXPOSED TO THIS SAME CONCENTRATION. MANY SUBSTITUTED UREA HERBICIDES ARE MODERATELY IRRITATING TO THE MUCOUS MEMBRANES. **CHRONIC EXPOSURE-** NO DATA AVAILABLE.

FIRST AID- REMOVE FROM EXPOSURE AREA TO FRESH AIR IMMEDIATELY. IF BREATHING HAS STOPPED, PERFORM ARTIFICIAL RESPIRATION. KEEP PERSON WARM AND AT REST. TREAT SYMPTOMATICALLY AND SUPPORTIVELY. GET MEDICAL ATTENTION IMMEDIATELY.

SKIN CONTACT: NOREA: TOXIC. **ACUTE EXPOSURE-** A LETHAL DOSE IN RABBITS BY DERMAL ABSORPTION WAS 723 MG/KG. MANY SUBSTITUTED UREA HERBICIDES ARE MODERATELY IRRITATING TO THE SKIN. **CHRONIC EXPOSURE-** NO DATA AVAILABLE.

FIRST AID- REMOVE CONTAMINATED CLOTHING AND SHOES IMMEDIATELY. WASH AFFECTED AREA WITH SOAP OR MILD DETERGENT AND LARGE AMOUNTS OF WATER UNTIL NO EVIDENCE OF CHEMICAL REMAINS (APPROXIMATELY 15-20 MINUTES). GET MEDICAL ATTENTION IMMEDIATELY.

EYE CONTACT: NOREA: **ACUTE EXPOSURE-** THIS MATERIAL WAS NOT IRRITATING TO RABBIT EYES. **CHRONIC EXPOSURE-** NO DATA AVAILABLE.

FIRST AID- WASH EYES IMMEDIATELY WITH LARGE AMOUNTS OF WATER OR NORMAL SALINE, OCCASIONALLY LIFTING UPPER AND LOWER LIDS, UNTIL NO EVIDENCE OF CHEMICAL REMAINS (APPROXIMATELY 15-20 MINUTES). GET MEDICAL ATTENTION IMMEDIATELY.

INGESTION: NOREA: **ACUTE EXPOSURE-** A LETHAL DOSE IN RATS WAS 2000 MG/KG. SYMPTOMS OF CENTRAL NERVOUS DEPRESSION INCLUDING SEDATION, ATAXIA, LOSS OF RIGHTING REFLEX, DYSPNEA, COMA AND CONVULSIONS WERE DISPLAYED IN LABORATORY ANIMALS FED DOSES CONTAINING 4-10% OF THIS MATERIAL. **CHRONIC EXPOSURE-** MODERATE HISTOLOGICAL DAMAGE AND MILD ISCHEMIA OF THE KIDNEYS WERE OBSERVED IN A 90-DAY STUDY OF RATS FED A DIETARY LEVEL OF 3000 PPM AND ABOVE.

FIRST AID- TREAT SYMPTOMATICALLY AND SUPPORTIVELY. GET MEDICAL ATTENTION IMMEDIATELY. IF VOMITING OCCURS, KEEP HEAD LOWER THAN HIPS TO PREVENT ASPIRATION.

ANTIDOTE: NO SPECIFIC ANTIDOTE. TREAT SYMPTOMATICALLY AND SUPPORTIVELY.

REACTIVITY

REACTIVITY: STABLE UNDER NORMAL TEMPERATURES AND PRESSURES.

INCOMPATIBILITIES: NOREA: ACIDS: MAY HYDROLYZE AT ELEVATED TEMPERATURES. BASES: MAY HYDROLYZE AT EVEVATED TEMPERATURES. OXIDIZERS (STRONG): FIRE AND EXPLOSION HAZARD.

DECOMPOSITION: THERMAL DECOMPOSITION PRODUCTS MAY INCLUDE TOXIC OXIDES OF CARBON AND NITROGEN.

POLYMERIZATION: HAZARDOUS POLYMERIZATION HAS NOT BEEN REPORTED TO OCCUR UNDER NORMAL TEMPERATURES AND PRESSURES.

STORAGE AND DISPOSAL

OBSERVE ALL FEDERAL, STATE AND LOCAL REGULATIONS WHEN STORING OR DISPOSING OF THIS SUBSTANCE. FOR ASSISTANCE, CONTACT THE DISTRICT DIRECTOR OF THE ENVIRONMENTAL PROTECTION AGENCY.

STORAGE

STORE IN ACCORDANCE WITH 40 CFR 165 RECOMMENDED PROCEDURES FOR THE DISPOSAL AND STORAGE OF PESTICIDES AND PESTICIDE CONTAINERS. STORE AWAY FROM INCOMPATIBLE SUBSTANCES.

DISPOSAL

DISPOSAL MUST BE IN ACCORDANCE WITH 40 CFR 165 RECOMMENDED PROCEDURES FOR THE DISPOSAL AND STORAGE OF PESTICIDES AND PESTICIDE CONTAINERS.

CONDITIONS TO AVOID

MAY BURN BUT DOES NOT IGNITE READILY. CONTAINERS MAY EXPLODE IN HEAT OF FIRE.

SPILL AND LEAK PROCEDURES

OCCUPATIONAL SPILL: DO NOT TOUCH SPILLED MATERIAL. STOP LEAK IF YOU CAN DO IT WITHOUT RISK. USE WATER SPRAY TO REDUCE VAPORS. FOR SMALL SPILLS, TAKE UP WITH SAND OR OTHER ABSORBENT MATERIAL AND PLACE INTO CONTAINERS FOR LATER DISPOSAL. FOR SMALL DRY SPILLS, WITH A CLEAN SHOVEL PLACE MATERIAL INTO CLEAN, DRY CONTAINERS AND COVER. MOVE CONTAINERS FROM SPILL AREA. FOR LARGER SPILLS, DIKE FAR AHEAD OF SPILL FOR LATER DISPOSAL. KEEP UNNECESSARY PEOPLE AWAY. ISOLATE HAZARD AREA AND DENY ENTRY. VENTILATE CLOSED SPACES BEFORE ENTERING.

PROTECTIVE EQUIPMENT

VENTILATION: PROVIDE LOCAL EXHAUST OR PROCESS ENCLOSURE VENTILATION SYSTEM.

RESPIRATOR: THE FOLLOWING RESPIRATORS ARE RECOMMENDED BASED ON INFORMATION FOUND IN THE PHYSICAL DATA, TOXICITY AND HEALTH EFFECTS SECTIONS. THEY ARE RANKED IN ORDER FROM MINIMUM TO MAXIMUM RESPIRATORY PROTECTION. THE SPECIFIC RESPIRATOR SELECTED MUST BE BASED ON CONTAMINATION LEVELS FOUND IN THE WORK PLACE, MUST NOT EXCEED THE WORKING LIMITS OF THE RESPIRATOR AND BE JOINTLY APPROVED BY THE NATIONAL INSTITUTE FOR OCCUPATIONAL SAFETY AND HEALTH AND THE MINE SAFETY AND HEALTH ADMINISTRATION (NIOSH-MSHA).

TYPE 'C' SUPPLIED-AIR RESPIRATOR WITH A FULL FACEPIECE OPERATED IN PRESSURE-DEMAND OR OTHER POSITIVE PRESSURE MODE OR WITH A FULL FACEPIECE, HELMET OR HOOD OPERATED IN CONTINOUS-FLOW MODE.

SELF-CONTAINED BREATHING APPARATUS WITH A FULL FACEPIECE OPERATED IN PRESSURE-DEMAND OR OTHER POSITIVE PRESSURE MODE.

FOR FIREFIGHTING AND OTHER IMMEDIATELY DANGEROUS TO LIFE OR HEALTH CONDITIONS:

SELF-CONTAINED BREATHING APPARATUS WITH FULL FACEPIECE OPERATED IN

PRESSURE-DEMAND OR OTHER POSITIVE PRESSURE MODE.

SUPPLIED-AIR RESPIRATOR WITH FULL FACEPIECE AND OPERATED IN PRESSURE-DEMAND OR OTHER POSITIVE PRESSURE MODE IN COMBINATION WITH AN AUXILIARY SELF-CONTAINED BREATHING APPARATUS OPERATED IN PRESSURE-DEMAND OR OTHER POSITIVE PRESSURE MODE.

CLOTHING: EMPLOYEE MUST WEAR APPROPRIATE PROTECTIVE (IMPERVIOUS) CLOTHING AND EQUIPMENT TO PREVENT ANY POSSIBILITY OF SKIN CONTACT WITH THIS SUBSTANCE.

GLOVES: EMPLOYEE MUST WEAR APPROPRIATE PROTECTIVE GLOVES TO PREVENT CONTACT WITH THIS SUBSTANCE.

EYE PROTECTION: EMPLOYEE MUST WEAR SPLASH-PROOF OR DUST-RESISTANT SAFETY GOGGLES WITH OR WITHOUT A FACESHIELD TO PREVENT CONTACT WITH THIS SUBSTANCE.

EMERGENCY EYE WASH: WHERE THERE IS ANY POSSIBILITY THAT AN EMPLOYEE'S EYES MAY BE EXPOSED TO THIS SUBSTANCE, THE EMPLOYER SHOULD PROVIDE AN EYE WASH FOUNTAIN WITHIN THE IMMEDIATE WORK AREA FOR EMERGENCY USE.

AUTHORIZED BY- OCCUPATIONAL HEALTH SERVICES, INC.

CREATION DATE: 10/04/89 ***REVISION DATE:*** 05/08/90

MATERIAL SAFETY DATA SHEET

OCCUPATIONAL HEALTH SERVICES, INC.
AGRICULTURE AND PESTICIDE DIVISION
450 SEVENTH AVENUE, SUITE 2407
NEW YORK, NEW YORK 10123
1-800-445-MSDS OR (212) 967-1100

EMERGENCY CONTACT:
JOHN S. BRANSFORD, JR. (615) 292-1180

SUBSTANCE IDENTIFICATION

CAS-NUMBER 39300-45-3

SUBSTANCE: **DINOCAP**

TRADE NAMES/SYNONYMS: 2-BUTENOIC ACID, 2(OR 4)-ISOOCTYL-4,6(OR 2,6)-DINITROPHENYL ESTER; DINITROCAPRYL CROTONATE; ARATHANE; CAPRANE; CARATHANE; CROTOTHANE; DNOCP; CPC; ISOCOTHANE; ISOCTHANE; KARATHANE; MILDEX; CR1639; ENT 24,727; C18H24N2O6; PST71402

CHEMICAL FAMILY: NITRO ESTER, CARBOXYLIC, AROMATIC

MOLECULAR FORMULA: C18-H24-N2-O6

MOLECULAR WEIGHT: 364.39

CERCLA RATINGS (SCALE 0-3): HEALTH=3 FIRE=2 REACTIVITY=3 PERSISTENCE=1

NFPA RATINGS (SCALE 0-4): HEALTH=U FIRE=2 REACTIVITY=3

COMPONENTS AND CONTAMINANTS

COMPONENT: DINOCAP ***PERCENT:*** 100.0
CAS# 39300-45-3

OTHER CONTAMINANTS: NONE

EXPOSURE LIMITS: NO OCCUPATIONAL EXPOSURE LIMITS ESTABLISHED BY OSHA, ACGIH, OR NIOSH.

DINOCAP: 0.2 MG/M3 ROHM AND HAAS RECOMMENDED TWA; 0.6 MG/M3 ROHM AND HAAS RECOMMENDED STEL

SUBJECT TO CALFORNIA PROPOSITION 65 CANCER AND/OR REPRODUCTIVE TOXICITY WARNING AND RELEASE REQUIREMENTS-(APRIL 1,1990)

PHYSICAL DATA

DESCRIPTION: DARK RED OR BROWN LIQUID WITH A MUSTY ODOR.

BOILING POINT: 280-284 F (138-140 C) @ 0.05 MMHG ***SPECIFIC GRAVITY:*** 1.10

VISCOSITY: 500-1000 CPS @ 20 C ***VOLATILITY:*** 2%

EVAPORATION RATE: (BUTYL ACETATE=1) <1 ***PH:*** 3-5

SOLUBILITY IN WATER: ALMOST INSOLUBLE ***VAPOR DENSITY:*** >1

SOLVENT SOLUBILITY: SOLUBLE IN BENZENE, PENTANE, CHLOROFORM, ETHER, AND MANY ORGANIC SOLVENTS.

FIRE AND EXPLOSION DATA

FIRE AND EXPLOSION HAZARD: MODERATE FIRE HAZARD WHEN EXPOSED TO HEAT OR FLAME.

VAPORS ARE HEAVIER THAN AIR AND MAY TRAVEL A CONSIDERABLE DISTANCE TO A SOURCE OF IGNITION AND FLASH BACK.

FLASH POINT: 190 F (88 C) (TOC) ***FLAMMABILITY CLASS(OSHA):*** IIIA

FIREFIGHTING MEDIA: DRY CHEMICAL, CARBON DIOXIDE, HALON, WATER SPRAY OR STANDARD FOAM (1987 EMERGENCY RESPONSE GUIDEBOOK, DOT P 5800.4). FOR LARGER FIRES, USE WATER SPRAY, FOG OR STANDARD FOAM (1987 EMERGENCY RESPONSE GUIDEBOOK, DOT P 5800.4).

FIREFIGHTING: MOVE CONTAINER FROM FIRE AREA IF POSSIBLE. COOL FIRE-EXPOSED CONTAINERS WITH WATER FROM SIDE UNTIL WELL AFTER FIRE IS OUT. STAY AWAY FROM STORAGE TANK ENDS. FOR MASSIVE FIRE IN STORAGE AREA, USE UNMANNED HOSE HOLDER OR MONITOR NOZZLES, ELSE WITHDRAW FROM AREA AND LET FIRE BURN. WITHDRAW IMMEDIATELY IN CASE OF RISING SOUND FROM VENTING SAFETY DEVICE OR ANY DISCOLORATION OF STORAGE TANK DUE TO FIRE (1987 EMERGENCY RESPONSE GUIDEBOOK, DOT P 5800.4, GUIDE PAGE 27). EXTINGUISH ONLY IF FLOW CAN BE STOPPED; USE FLOODING AMOUNTS OF WATER AS A FOG, SOLID STREAMS MAY BE INEFFECTIVE. COOL CONTAINERS WITH FLOODING AMOUNTS OF WATER, APPLY FROM AS FAR A DISTANCE AS POSSIBLE. AVOID BREATHING VAPORS, KEEP UPWIND.

TRANSPORTATION DATA

DEPARTMENT OF TRANSPORTATION HAZARD CLASSIFICATION 49 CFR 172.101: COMBUSTIBLE LIQUID

DEPARTMENT OF TRANSPORTATION LABELING REQUIREMENTS 49 CFR 172.101 AND SUBPART E: NONE

DEPARTMENT OF TRANSPORTATION PACKAGING REQUIREMENTS: NONE EXCEPTIONS: 49 CFR 173.118A

TOXICITY

DINOCAP: TOXICITY DATA: 9400 MG/KG SKIN-RABBIT LD50; 980 MG/KG ORAL-RAT LD50; 2000 MG/KG ORAL-RABBIT LD50; 49500 UG/KG ORAL-MOUSE LD50; 100 MG/KG ORAL-DOG LD50; 23 MG/KG INTRAVENOUS-RAT LD50; MUTAGENIC DATA (RTECS): REPRODUCTIVE EFFECTS DATA (RTECS); TUMORIGENIC DATA (RTECS). CARCINOGEN STATUS: NONE. LOCAL EFFECTS: CORROSIVE- EYE; IRRITANT-INHALATION, SKIN. ACUTE TOXICITY LEVEL: MODERATELY TOXIC BY INGESTION; SLIGHTLY TOXIC BY DERMAL ABSORPTION. TARGET EFFECTS: SENSITIZER-DERMAL. POISONING MAY INCREASE THE METABOLIC RATE AND AFFECT THE NERVOUS SYSTEM, LIVER, AND KIDNEYS.* AT INCREASED RISK FROM EXPOSURE: ALCOHOLICS AND PERSONS WITH RENAL OR HEPATIC DISEASES.* ADDITIONAL DATA: HOT ENVIRONMENTS MAY ENHANCE ABSORPTION AND THE TOXIC EFFECTS.*

*MAY BE BASED ON GROUP INFORMATION ON DINITROPHENOL DERIVATIVES.

HEALTH EFFECTS AND FIRST AID

INHALATION: DINOCAP: IRRITANT. SEE INFORMATION ON DINITROPHENOL DERIVATIVES. VAPOR OR MIST MAY IRRITATE THE NOSE AND THROAT.

DINITROPHENOL DERIVATIVES: **ACUTE EXPOSURE-** MAY BE ABSORBED WITH SYMPTOMS OCCURRING SUDDENLY AND UP TO 2 DAYS AFTER CESSATION OF EXPOSURE. SYMPTOMS MAY INCLUDE FATIGUE, WEAKNESS, FEVER, THIRST, NAUSEA, VOMITING, HEADACHES, FLUSHED SKIN, PROSTRATION, EXCESSIVE PERSPIRATION, TACHYCARDIA, TACHYPNEA, AND DYSPNEA. APPREHENSION, RESTLESSNESS, ANXIETY, MANIC BEHAVIOR, OR UNCONSCIOUSNESS MAY INDICATE CEREBRAL INJURY. CONVULSIONS MAY OCCUR IN THE MOST SEVERE POISONINGS. ANOXIA WITH CYANOSIS, LIVIDITY AND METABOLIC ACIDOSIS, SEVERE HYPERPYREXIA, DEHYDRATION, AND MUSCULAR TREMORS MAY BE FOLLOWED BY CIRCULATORY OR RESPIRATORY COLLAPSE AND COMA. DEGENERATIVE CHANGES IN THE HEART, RENAL TUBULES AND LIVER PARENCHYMA MAY OCCUR. THERE MAY BE ALBUMINURIA, PYURIA, HEMATURIA, JAUNDICE, AND INCREASED BUN. THE EFFECTS FROM POISONING ARE RAPID AND DEATH OR RECOVERY GENERALLY OCCURS WITHIN 24 TO 48 HOURS. FATAL DINITROPHENOL POISONING IS FOLLOWED BY INSTANTANEOUS RIGOR MORTIS.

CHRONIC EXPOSURE- IN ADDITION TO THE SYMPTOMS OF ACUTE EXPOSURE, PROLONGED OR REPEATED EXPOSURE MAY CAUSE WEIGHT LOSS, CATARACT FORMATION, AND LIVER AND KIDNEY DAMAGE. YELLOW STAINING OF THE SCLERAE AND URINE INDICATES ABSORPTION OF POTENTIALLY TOXIC AMOUNTS.

FIRST AID- REMOVE FROM EXPOSURE AREA TO FRESH AIR IMMEDIATELY. IF BREATHING HAS STOPPED, PERFORM ARTIFICIAL RESPIRATION. ADMINISTER OXYGEN. TREAT SYMPTOMATICALLY AND SUPPORTIVELY. GET MEDICAL ATTENTION IMMEDIATELY.

SKIN CONTACT: DINOCAP: IRRITANT/SENSITIZER. SEE INFORMATION ON DINITROPHENOL DERIVATIVES. MAY CAUSE IRRITATION AND ALLERGIC SKIN REACTIONS. REDUCED FETAL WEIGHT AND AN INCREASED INCIDENCE OF SKULL ABNORMALITIES WERE REPORTED IN A STUDY OF PREGNANT RABBITS RECEIVING A DERMAL DOSE AT A LEVEL OF 100 MG/KG/DAY.

DINITROPHENOL DERIVATIVES: **ACUTE EXPOSURE-** MAY CAUSE IRRITATION. CONTACT MAY RESULT IN YELLOW STAINING OF THE SKIN AHD HAIR. SOME DERIVATIVES MAY BE ABSORBED THROUGH THE SKIN WITH SYMPTOMS OCCURRING SUDDENLY AND UP TO 2 DAYS AFTER CESSATION OF EXPOSURE AND PRODUCE EFFECTS ON THE METABOLIC RATE, CENTRAL NERVOUS SYSTEM AND LIVER AND KIDNEY RESULTING IN SIGNS AND SYMPTOMS AS DESCRIBED IN ACUTE

INHALATION. **CHRONIC EXPOSURE-** REPEATED OR PROLONGED CONTACT MAY RESULT IN DERMATITIS DUE TO IRRITATION OR ALLERGIC SENSITIVITY. IN ADDITION TO THE SYMPTOMS OF ACUTE EXPOSURE, CHRONIC ABSORPTION MAY CAUSE FATIGUE, WEIGHT LOSS, CATARACT FORMATION AND LIVER AND KIDNEY DAMAGE. YELLOW STAINING OF THE SCLERAE AND URINE INDICATES ABSORPTION OF POTENTIALLY TOXIC AMOUNTS.

FIRST AID- REMOVE CONTAMINATED CLOTHING AND SHOES IMMEDIATELY. THEN REMOVE SKIN AND HAIR CONTAMINATION BY SCRUBBING WITH SOAP AND WATER. IF BODY TEMPERATURE IS ELEVATED, REDUCE TO 37 C BY SPONGE BATH, IMMERSION IN COOL WATER OR BY APPLYING COOLING BLANKET. IF BODY TEMPERATURE IS ABOVE 40 C, ICE WATER IS NECESSARY (DREISBACH, HANDBOOK OF POISONING, 12TH EDITION; MORGAN, EPA RECOGNITION AND MANAGEMENT OF PESTICIDE POISONINGS, 3RD EDITION). GET MEDICAL ATTENTION IMMEDIATELY.

EYE CONTACT: DINOCAP: CORROSIVE. **ACUTE EXPOSURE-** MAY CAUSE SEVERE IRRITATION OF THE EYES WITH POSSIBLE PERMANENT INJURY. **CHRONIC EXPOSURE-** EFFECTS DEPEND ON CONCENTRATION AND DURATION OF EXPOSURE. REPEATED OR PROLONGED CONTACT WITH CORROSIVE SUBSTANCES MAY RESULT IN CONJUNCTIVITIS OR EFFECTS AS IN ACUTE EXPOSURE.

FIRST AID- WASH EYES IMMEDIATELY WITH LARGE AMOUNTS OF WATER, OCCASIONALLY LIFTING UPPER AND LOWER LIDS, UNTIL NO EVIDENCE OF CHEMICAL REMAINS (AT LEAST 15-20 MINUTES). CONTINUE IRRIGATING WITH NORMAL SALINE UNTIL THE PH HAS RETURNED TO NORMAL (30-60 MINUTES). COVER WITH STERILE BANDAGES. GET MEDICAL ATTENTION IMMEDIATELY.

INGESTION: DINOCAP: SEE INFORMATION OF DINITROPHENOL DERIVATIVES. INCREASED MORTALITY AND LIVER CELL NECROSIS WERE OBSERVED AMONG DOGS RECEIVING A DIETARY LEVEL OF 250 OR 1000 PPM FOR 1 YEAR. FETOTOXIC EFFECTS WERE OBSERVED IN HAMSTERS AT OR NEAR DOSES THAT CAUSED MATERNAL TOXICITY. AN INCREASED IN CLEFT PALATE, MODERATE TO SEVERE HYDRONEPHROSIS, AND A DECREASED IN SKELETAL OSSIFICATION WERE OBSERVED IN THE OFFSPRING OF MICE FED DINOCAP DURING PREGNANCY. IN TWO TERATOLOGY STUDIES OF RABBITS, EFFECTS OF DECREASED WEIGHT GAIN, DECREASED IMPLANTATION EFFICIENCY, DECREASED VIABILITY INDEX, INCREASED RESORPTIONS, AND MALFORMATIONS OF THE FETAL NEURAL TUBE AND SKULL WERE NOTED.

DINITROPHENOL DERIVATIVES: **ACUTE EXPOSURE-** MAY CAUSE EFFECTS ON THE METABOLIC RATE, CENTRAL NERVOUS SYSTEM AND LIVER AND KIDNEY RESULTING IN SIGNS AND SYMPTOMS AS DESCRIBED IN ACUTE INHALATION. **CHRONIC EXPOSURE-** IN ADDITION TO THE SYMPTOMS OF ACUTE EXPOSURE, REPEATED INGESTION MAY CAUSE AN INITIAL SENSE OF WELL-BEING THEN ANOREXIA, DIARRHEA, DIZZINESS, RESTLESSNESS, FATIGUE, WEIGHT LOSS, SKIN ERUPTIONS, PERIPHERAL NEURITIS, LIVER AND KIDNEY DAMAGE, CARDIOVASCULAR COMPLICATIONS, GRANULOCYTOPENIA, AND CATARACT FORMATION. YELLOW STAINING OF THE SCLERAE AND URINE INDICATES ABSORPTION OF POTENTIALLY TOXIC AMOUNTS.

FIRST AID- REMOVE INGESTED POISON BY THOROUGH GASTRIC LAVAGE WITH SATURATED BICARBONATE SOLUTION. IF GASTRIC LAVAGE CANNOT BE ACCOMPLISHED IMMEDIATELY, GIVE SYRUP OF IPECAC TO INDUCE EMESIS AND FOLLOW WITH SALINE CATHARTIC. IF BODY TEMPERATURE IS ELEVATED, REDUCE TO 37 C BY IMMERSION IN COOL WATER OR BY APPLYING COOLING BLANKET. IF BODY TEMPERATURE IS ABOVE 40 C, ICE WATER IS NECESSARY (DREISBACH, HANDBOOK OF POISONING, 12TH ED.). ADMINISTRATION OF GASTRIC LAVAGE SHOULD BE PERFORMED BY QUALIFIED MEDICAL PERSONNEL. GET MEDICAL ATTENTION IMMEDIATELY.

ANTIDOTE: NO SPECIFIC ANTIDOTE. TREAT SYMPTOMATICALLY AND SUPPORTIVELY.

REACTIVITY

REACTIVITY: HEATING FOR MORE THAN 48 HOURS AT TEMPERATURES ABOVE 90 F (32 C) MAY RESULT IN EXPLOSIVE DECOMPOSITION.

INCOMPATIBILITIES: DINOCAP: ACIDS (INORGANIC): INCOMPATIBLE. ALKANOLAMINES: INCOMPATIBLE. AMINES: INCOMPATIBLE. CAUSTICS: INCOMPATIBLE. HALOGENATED COMPOUNDS: INCOMPATIBLE. IRON: INCOMPATIBLE. LIME SULFUR: INCOMPATIBLE. OIL AND OIL-BASED SPRAYS: INCOMPATIBLE. OXIDIZERS (STRONG): FIRE AND EXPLOSION HAZARD.

DECOMPOSITION: THERMAL DECOMPOSITION PRODUCTS MAY INCLUDE TOXIC OXIDES OF CARBON AND NITROGEN.

POLYMERIZATION: HAZARDOUS POLYMERIZATION HAS NOT BEEN REPORTED TO OCCUR UNDER NORMAL TEMPERATURES AND PRESSURES.

STORAGE AND DISPOSAL

OBSERVE ALL FEDERAL, STATE AND LOCAL REGULATIONS WHEN STORING OR DISPOSING OF THIS SUBSTANCE. FOR ASSISTANCE, CONTACT THE DISTRICT DIRECTOR OF THE ENVIRONMENTAL PROTECTION AGENCY.

****STORAGE****

STORE IN ACCORDANCE WITH 29 CFR 1910.106.

STORE IN ACCORDANCE WITH 40 CFR 165 RECOMMENDED PROCEDURES FOR THE DISPOSAL AND STORAGE OF PESTICIDES AND PESTICIDE CONTAINERS.

STORE AWAY FROM INCOMPATIBLE SUBSTANCES.

STORE IN A TIGHTLY CLOSED CONTAINER AT TEMPERATURES NOT EXCEEDING 39 F (4 C).

****DISPOSAL****

DISPOSAL MUST BE IN ACCORDANCE WITH STANDARDS APPLICABLE TO GENERATORS OF HAZARDOUS WASTE, 40 CFR 262. EPA HAZARDOUS WASTE NUMBER D003. 100 POUND CERCLA SECTION 103 REPORTABLE QUANTITY.

DISPOSAL MUST BE IN ACCORDANCE WITH 40 CFR 165 RECOMMENDED PROCEDURES FOR THE DISPOSAL AND STORAGE OF PESTICIDES AND PESTICIDE CONTAINERS.

CONDITIONS TO AVOID

AVOID CONTACT WITH HEAT, SPARKS, FLAMES, OR OTHER SOURCES OF IGNITION. VAPORS MAY BE EXPLOSIVE. AVOID OVERHEATING OF CONTAINERS; CONTAINERS MAY VIOLENTLY RUPTURE IN HEAT OF FIRE. AVOID CONTAMINATION OF WATER SOURCES.

SPILL AND LEAK PROCEDURES

WATER SPILL: THE CALIFORNIA SAFE DRINKING WATER AND TOXIC ENFORCEMENT ACT OF 1986 (PROPOSITION 65) PROHIBITS CONTAMINATING ANY KNOWN SOURCE OF DRINKING WATER WITH SUBSTANCES KNOWN TO CAUSE CANCER AND/OR REPRODUCTIVE TOXICITY.

OCCUPATIONAL SPILL: SHUT OFF IGNITION SOURCES. STOP LEAK IF YOU CAN DO IT WITHOUT RISK. USE WATER SPRAY TO REDUCE VAPORS. FOR SMALL SPILLS, TAKE UP WITH SAND OR OTHER ABSORBENT MATERIAL AND PLACE INTO CONTAINERS FOR LATER DISPOSAL. FOR LARGER SPILLS, DIKE FAR AHEAD OF SPILL FOR LATER DISPOSAL. NO SMOKING, FLAMES OR FLARES IN HAZARD AREA. KEEP UNNECESSARY PEOPLE AWAY; ISOLATE HAZARD AREA AND RESTRICT ENTRY.

PROTECTIVE EQUIPMENT

VENTILATION: PROVIDE LOCAL EXHAUST OR GENERAL DILUTION VENTILATION SYSTEM.

RESPIRATOR: THE FOLLOWING RESPIRATORS ARE RECOMMENDED BASED ON INFORMATION FOUND IN THE PHYSICAL DATA, TOXICITY AND HEALTH EFFECTS SECTIONS. THEY ARE RANKED IN ORDER FROM MINIMUM TO MAXIMUM RESPIRATORY PROTECTION. THE SPECIFIC RESPIRATOR SELECTED MUST BE BASED ON CONTAMINATION LEVELS FOUND IN THE WORK PLACE, MUST NOT EXCEED THE WORKING LIMITS OF THE RESPIRATOR AND BE JOINTLY APPROVED BY THE NATIONAL INSTITUTE FOR OCCUPATIONAL SAFETY AND HEALTH AND THE MINE SAFETY AND HEALTH ADMINISTRATION (NIOSH-MSHA).

CHEMICAL CARTRIDGE RESPIRATOR WITH FULL FACEPIECE AND PESTICIDE CARTRIDGE.

TYPE 'C' SUPPLIED-AIR RESPIRATOR WITH A FULL FACEPIECE OPERATED IN PRESSURE-DEMAND OR OTHER POSITIVE PRESSURE MODE OR WITH A FULL FACEPIECE, HELMET OR HOOD OPERATED IN CONTINUOUS-FLOW MODE.

SELF-CONTAINED BREATHING APPARATUS OPERATED IN PRESSURE-DEMAND OR OTHER POSITIVE PRESSURE MODE.

FOR FIREFIGHTING AND OTHER IMMEDIATELY DANGEROUS TO LIFE OR HEALTH CONDITIONS:

SELF-CONTAINED BREATHING APPARATUS WITH FULL FACEPIECE OPERATED IN PRESSURE-DEMAND OR OTHER POSITIVE PRESSURE MODE.

SUPPLIED-AIR RESPIRATOR WITH FULL FACEPIECE AND OPERATED IN PRESSURE-DEMAND OR OTHER POSITIVE PRESSURE MODE IN COMBINATION WITH AN AUXILIARY SELF-CONTAINED BREATHING APPARATUS OPERATED IN PRESSURE-DEMAND OR OTHER POSITIVE PRESSURE MODE.

CLOTHING: EMPLOYEE MUST WEAR APPROPRIATE PROTECTIVE (IMPERVIOUS) CLOTHING AND EQUIPMENT TO PREVENT REPEATED OR PROLONGED SKIN CONTACT WITH THIS SUBSTANCE.

GLOVES: EMPLOYEE MUST WEAR APPROPRIATE PROTECTIVE GLOVES TO PREVENT CONTACT WITH THIS SUBSTANCE.

EYE PROTECTION: EMPLOYEE MUST WEAR SPLASH-PROOF OR DUST-RESISTANT SAFETY GOGGLES AND A FACESHIELD TO PREVENT CONTACT WITH THIS SUBSTANCE.

EMERGENCY WASH FACILITIES: WHERE THERE IS ANY POSSIBILITY THAT AN EMPLOYEE'S EYES AND/OR SKIN MAY BE EXPOSED TO THIS SUBSTANCE, THE EMPLOYER SHOULD PROVIDE AN EYE WASH FOUNTAIN AND QUICK DRENCH SHOWER WITHIN THE IMMEDIATE WORK AREA FOR EMERGENCY USE.

AUTHORIZED BY- OCCUPATIONAL HEALTH SERVICES, INC.

CREATION DATE: 10/04/89 ***REVISION DATE:*** 07/11/90

MATERIAL SAFETY DATA SHEET

OCCUPATIONAL HEALTH SERVICES, INC.
AGRICULTURE AND PESTICIDE DIVISION
450 SEVENTH AVENUE, SUITE 2407
NEW YORK, NEW YORK 10123
1-800-445-MSDS OR (212) 967-1100

EMERGENCY CONTACT:
JOHN S. BRANSFORD, JR. (615) 292-1180

SUBSTANCE IDENTIFICATION

CAS-NUMBER 88-30-2

SUBSTANCE: **ALPHA, ALPHA, ALPHA-TRIFLUORO-4-NITRO-M-CRESOL**

TRADE NAMES/SYNONYMS: PHENOL, 4-NITRO-3-(TRIFLUOROMETHYL)-; 4-NITRO-3-(TRIFLUOROMETHYL)PHENOL; M-CRESOL, ALPHA,ALPHA,ALPHA-TRIFLUORO-4-NITRO-; 3-TRIFLUOROMETHYL-4-NITROPHENOL; LAMPRECID; TFM; C7H4F3NO3; PST71405

CHEMICAL FAMILY: NITRO
CRESOL
HALOGEN

MOLECULAR FORMULA: C7-H4-F3-N-O3

MOLECULAR WEIGHT: 207.11

CERCLA RATINGS (SCALE 0-3): HEALTH=3 FIRE=1 REACTIVITY=0 PERSISTENCE=2

NFPA RATINGS (SCALE 0-4): HEALTH=3 FIRE=1 REACTIVITY=0

COMPONENTS AND CONTAMINANTS

COMPONENT: ALPHA,ALPHA,ALPHA-TRIFLUORO-4-NITRO-M-CRESOL ***PERCENT:*** 100.0
CAS# 88-30-2

OTHER CONTAMINANTS: NONE

EXPOSURE LIMITS: NO OCCUPATIONAL EXPOSURE LIMITS ESTABLISHED BY OSHA, ACGIH, OR NIOSH.

PHYSICAL DATA

DESCRIPTION: CRYSTALS. ***MELTING POINT:*** 165-169 F (74-76 C)

SPECIFIC GRAVITY: NOT AVAILABLE ***SOLUBILITY IN WATER:*** NOT AVAILABLE

FIRE AND EXPLOSION DATA

FIRE AND EXPLOSION HAZARD: SLIGHT FIRE HAZARD WHEN EXPOSED TO HEAT OR FLAME.

FIREFIGHTING MEDIA: DRY CHEMICAL, CARBON DIOXIDE, HALON, WATER SPRAY OR STANDARD FOAM (1987 EMERGENCY RESPONSE GUIDEBOOK, DOT P 5800.4).
FOR LARGER FIRES, USE WATER SPRAY, FOG OR STANDARD FOAM (1987 EMERGENCY RESPONSE GUIDEBOOK, DOT P 5800.4).

FIREFIGHTING: MOVE CONTAINER FROM FIRE AREA IF POSSIBLE. DO NOT SCATTER SPILLED MATERIAL WITH HIGH PRESSURE WATER STREAMS. DIKE FIRE CONTROL WATER FOR LATER DISPOSAL (1987 EMERGENCY RESPONSE GUIDEBOOK, DOT P 5800.4, GUIDE PAGE 31).
USE AGENTS SUITABLE FOR TYPE OF SURROUNDING FIRE. AVOID BREATHING HAZARDOUS VAPORS, KEEP UPWIND.

TOXICITY

ALPHA, ALPHA, ALPHA-TRIFLUORO-4-NITRO-M-CRESOL: TOXICITY DATA: 500 MG/KG ORAL-MAMMAL LD50; 86 MG/KG INTRAVENOUS-MOUSE LDLO; 40 MG/KG INTRAPERITONEAL-RAT LDLO; 25 MG/KG INTRAPERITONEAL-MOUSE LD50.
CARCINOGEN STATUS: NONE. ACUTE TOXICITY LEVEL: TOXIC BY INGESTION.
TARGET EFFECTS: NO DATA AVAILABLE.

HEALTH EFFECTS AND FIRST AID

INHALATION: ALPHA, ALPHA, ALPHA-TRIFLUORO-4-NITRO-M-CRESOL: **ACUTE EXPOSURE**- NO DATA AVAILABLE. **CHRONIC EXPOSURE**- NO DATA AVAILABLE.

FIRST AID- REMOVE FROM EXPOSURE AREA TO FRESH AIR IMMEDIATELY. IF BREATHING HAS STOPPED, PERFORM ARTIFICIAL RESPIRATION. KEEP PERSON WARM AND AT REST. TREAT SYMPTOMATICALLY AND SUPPORTIVELY. GET MEDICAL ATTENTION IMMEDIATELY.

SKIN CONTACT: ALPHA, ALPHA, ALPHA-TRIFLUORO-4-NITRO-M-CRESOL: **ACUTE EXPOSURE**- NO DATA AVAILABLE. **CHRONIC EXPOSURE**- NO DATA AVAILABLE.

FIRST AID- REMOVE CONTAMINATED CLOTHING AND SHOES IMMEDIATELY. WASH AFFECTED AREA WITH SOAP OR MILD DETERGENT AND LARGE AMOUNTS OF WATER UNTIL NO EVIDENCE OF CHEMICAL REMAINS (APPROXIMATELY 15-20 MINUTES). GET MEDICAL ATTENTION IMMEDIATELY.

EYE CONTACT: ALPHA, ALPHA, ALPHA-TRIFLUORO-4-NITRO-M-CRESOL: **ACUTE EXPOSURE**- NO DATA AVAILABLE. **CHRONIC EXPOSURE**- NO DATA AVAILABLE.

FIRST AID- WASH EYES IMMEDIATELY WITH LARGE AMOUNTS OF WATER OR NORMAL SALINE, OCCASIONALLY LIFTING UPPER AND LOWER LIDS, UNTIL NO EVIDENCE OF CHEMICAL REMAINS (APPROXIMATELY 15-20 MINUTES). GET MEDICAL ATTENTION IMMEDIATELY.

INGESTION: ALPHA, ALPHA, ALPHA-TRIFLUORO-4-NITRO-M-CRESOL: TOXIC. **ACUTE EXPOSURE**- 500 MG/KG IS THE LETHAL DOSE IN MAMMALS. THE SYMPTOMS WERE NOT REPORTED. **CHRONIC EXPOSURE**- NO DATA AVAILABLE.

FIRST AID- TREAT SYMPTOMATICALLY AND SUPPORTIVELY. GET MEDICAL ATTENTION IMMEDIATELY. IF VOMITING OCCURS, KEEP HEAD LOWER THAN HIPS TO PREVENT ASPIRATION.

ANTIDOTE: NO SPECIFIC ANTIDOTE. TREAT SYMPTOMATICALLY AND SUPPORTIVELY.

REACTIVITY

REACTIVITY: STABLE UNDER NORMAL TEMPERATURES AND PRESSURES.

INCOMPATIBILITIES: ALPHA,ALPHA,ALPHA-TRIFLUORO-4-NITRO-M-CRESOL: OXIDIZERS (STRONG): FIRE AND EXPLOSION HAZARD.

DECOMPOSITION: THERMAL DECOMPOSITION PRODUCTS MAY INCLUDE HIGHLY TOXIC FUMES OF FLUORIDES AND OXIDES OF NITROGEN AND CARBON.

POLYMERIZATION: HAZARDOUS POLYMERIZATION HAS NOT BEEN REPORTED TO OCCUR UNDER NORMAL TEMPERATURES AND PRESSURES.

STORAGE AND DISPOSAL

OBSERVE ALL FEDERAL, STATE AND LOCAL REGULATIONS WHEN STORING OR DISPOSING OF THIS SUBSTANCE. FOR ASSISTANCE, CONTACT THE DISTRICT DIRECTOR OF THE ENVIRONMENTAL PROTECTION AGENCY.

****STORAGE****

STORE IN ACCORDANCE WITH 40 CFR 165 RECOMMENDED PROCEDURES FOR THE DISPOSAL AND STORAGE OF PESTICIDES AND PESTICIDE CONTAINERS.
STORE AWAY FROM INCOMPATIBLE SUBSTANCES.

****DISPOSAL****

DISPOSAL MUST BE IN ACCORDANCE WITH 40 CFR 165 RECOMMENDED PROCEDURES FOR THE DISPOSAL AND STORAGE OF PESTICIDES AND PESTICIDE CONTAINERS.

CONDITIONS TO AVOID

MAY BURN BUT DOES NOT IGNITE READILY. AVOID CONTACT WITH STRONG OXIDIZERS, EXCESSIVE HEAT, SPARKS, OR OPEN FLAME.

SPILL AND LEAK PROCEDURES

OCCUPATIONAL SPILL: SWEEP UP AND PLACE IN SUITABLE CLEAN, DRY CONTAINERS FOR RECLAMATION OR LATER DISPOSAL. DO NOT FLUSH SPILLED MATERIAL INTO SEWER. KEEP UNNECESSARY PEOPLE AWAY.

PROTECTIVE EQUIPMENT

VENTILATION: PROVIDE LOCAL EXHAUST OR PROCESS ENCLOSURE VENTILATION SYSTEM.

RESPIRATOR: THE FOLLOWING RESPIRATORS ARE RECOMMENDED BASED ON INFORMATION FOUND IN THE PHYSICAL DATA, TOXICITY AND HEALTH EFFECTS SECTIONS. THEY ARE RANKED IN ORDER FROM MINIMUM TO MAXIMUM RESPIRATORY PROTECTION. THE SPECIFIC RESPIRATOR SELECTED MUST BE BASED ON CONTAMINATION LEVELS FOUND IN THE WORK PLACE, MUST NOT EXCEED THE WORKING LIMITS OF THE RESPIRATOR AND BE JOINTLY APPROVED BY THE NATIONAL INSTITUTE FOR OCCUPATIONAL SAFETY AND HEALTH AND THE MINE SAFETY AND HEALTH ADMINISTRATION (NIOSH-MSHA).
TYPE 'C' SUPPLIED-AIR RESPIRATOR WITH A FULL FACEPIECE OPERATED IN PRESSURE-DEMAND OR OTHER POSITIVE PRESSURE MODE OR WITH A FULL FACEPIECE, HELMET OR HOOD OPERATED IN CONTINOUS-FLOW MODE.
SELF-CONTAINED BREATHING APPARATUS WITH A FULL FACEPIECE OPERATED IN PRESSURE-DEMAND OR OTHER POSITIVE PRESSURE MODE.
FOR FIREFIGHTING AND OTHER IMMEDIATELY DANGEROUS TO LIFE OR HEALTH CONDITIONS:
SELF-CONTAINED BREATHING APPARATUS WITH FULL FACEPIECE OPERATED IN PRESSURE-DEMAND OR OTHER POSITIVE PRESSURE MODE.
SUPPLIED-AIR RESPIRATOR WITH FULL FACEPIECE AND OPERATED IN PRESSURE-DEMAND OR OTHER POSITIVE PRESSURE MODE IN COMBINATION WITH AN AUXILIARY SELF-CONTAINED BREATHING APPARATUS OPERATED IN PRESSURE-DEMAND OR OTHER POSITIVE PRESSURE MODE.

CLOTHING: EMPLOYEE MUST WEAR APPROPRIATE PROTECTIVE (IMPERVIOUS) CLOTHING AND EQUIPMENT TO PREVENT REPEATED OR PROLONGED SKIN CONTACT WITH THIS SUBSTANCE.

GLOVES: EMPLOYEE MUST WEAR APPROPRIATE PROTECTIVE GLOVES TO PREVENT CONTACT WITH THIS SUBSTANCE.

EYE PROTECTION: EMPLOYEE MUST WEAR SPLASH-PROOF OR DUST-RESISTANT SAFETY GOGGLES TO PREVENT EYE CONTACT WITH THIS SUBSTANCE.
EMERGENCY EYE WASH: WHERE THERE IS ANY POSSIBILITY THAT AN EMPLOYEE'S

EYES MAY BE EXPOSED TO THIS SUBSTANCE, THE EMPLOYER SHOULD PROVIDE AN EYE WASH FOUNTAIN WITHIN THE IMMEDIATE WORK AREA FOR EMERGENCY USE.

AUTHORIZED BY- OCCUPATIONAL HEALTH SERVICES, INC.
CREATION DATE: 10/04/89 ***REVISION DATE:*** 05/31/90

MATERIAL SAFETY DATA SHEET

OCCUPATIONAL HEALTH SERVICES, INC.
AGRICULTURE AND PESTICIDE DIVISION
450 SEVENTH AVENUE, SUITE 2407
NEW YORK, NEW YORK 10123
1-800-445-MSDS OR (212) 967-1100

EMERGENCY CONTACT:
JOHN S. BRANSFORD, JR. (615) 292-1180

SUBSTANCE IDENTIFICATION

CAS-NUMBER 957-51-7
SUBSTANCE: DIPHENAMID
TRADE NAMES/SYNONYMS: BENZENEACETAMIDE, N,N-DIMETHYL-ALPHA-PHENYL-; ACETAMIDE, N,N-DIMETHYL-2,2-DIPHENYL-; N,N-DIMETHYLDIPHENYLACETAMIDE; N,N-DIMETHYL-ALPHA-PHENYLBENZENEACETAMIDE; N,N-DIMETHYL-2,2-DIPHENYLACETAMIDE; 2,2-DIPHENYL-N,N-DIMETHYLACETAMIDE; DIPHENAMIDE; DYMID; ENIDE; FENAM; L 34314; C16H17NO; PST71406
CHEMICAL FAMILY: AMIDE, AROMATIC
MOLECULAR FORMULA: (C6-H5)2-C-H-C-O-N-(C-H3)2
MOLECULAR WEIGHT: 239.30
CERCLA RATINGS (SCALE 0-3): HEALTH=2 FIRE=1 REACTIVITY=0 PERSISTENCE=2
NFPA RATINGS (SCALE 0-4): HEALTH=U FIRE=1 REACTIVITY=0

COMPONENTS AND CONTAMINANTS

COMPONENT: DIPHENAMID ***PERCENT:*** 100.0
CAS# 957-51-7
OTHER CONTAMINANTS: NONE
EXPOSURE LIMITS: NO OCCUPATIONAL EXPOSURE LIMITS ESTABLISHED BY OSHA, ACGIH, OR NIOSH.

PHYSICAL DATA

DESCRIPTION: WHITE TO OFF-WHITE CRYSTALLINE SOLID.
MELTING POINT: 275-277 F (135-136 C) ***SPECIFIC GRAVITY:*** 1.17 @ 23 C
VAPOR PRESSURE: NEGLIGIBLE ***SOLUBILITY IN WATER:*** 0.026% @ 27 C
SOLVENT SOLUBILITY: SOLUBLE IN ACETONE, DIMETHYL FORMAMIDE, AND PHENYL CELLOSOLVE; MODERATELY SOLUBLE IN XYLENE AND POLAR ORGANIC SOLVENTS. DECOMPOSES ABOVE 410 F (210 C)

FIRE AND EXPLOSION DATA

FIRE AND EXPLOSION HAZARD: SLIGHT FIRE HAZARD WHEN EXPOSED TO HEAT OR FLAME.
FIREFIGHTING MEDIA: DRY CHEMICAL, CARBON DIOXIDE, HALON, WATER SPRAY OR STANDARD FOAM (1987 EMERGENCY RESPONSE GUIDEBOOK, DOT P 5800.4).
FOR LARGER FIRES, USE WATER SPRAY, FOG OR STANDARD FOAM (1987 EMERGENCY RESPONSE GUIDEBOOK, DOT P 5800.4).
FIREFIGHTING: MOVE CONTAINER FROM FIRE AREA IF POSSIBLE. DO NOT SCATTER SPILLED MATERIAL WITH HIGH PRESSURE WATER STREAMS. DIKE FIRE CONTROL WATER FOR LATER DISPOSAL (1987 EMERGENCY RESPONSE GUIDEBOOK, DOT P 5800.4, GUIDE PAGE 31).
USE AGENTS SUITABLE FOR TYPE OF SURROUNDING FIRE. AVOID BREATHING HAZARDOUS VAPORS, KEEP UPWIND.

TOXICITY

DIPHENAMID: TOXICITY DATA: 685 MG/KG ORAL-RAT LD50; 600 MG/KG ORAL-MOUSE LD50; 1500 MG/KG ORAL-RABBIT LD50; 1000 MG/KG ORAL-MONKEY LD50; 1000 MG/KG ORAL-DOG LD50; 800 MG/KG SUBCUTANEOUS-MOUSE LD50; 500 MG/KG INTRAPERITONEAL-MOUSE LD50; 700 MG/KG UNREPORTED-MOUSE LD50; MUTAGENIC DATA (RTECS). CARCINOGEN STATUS: NONE. ACUTE TOXICITY LEVEL: MODERATELY TOXIC BY INGESTION. TARGET EFFECTS: NO DATA AVAILABLE.

HEALTH EFFECTS AND FIRST AID

INHALATION: DIPHENAMID: **ACUTE EXPOSURE-** NO EFFECTS WERE OBSERVED IN RATS EXPOSED FOR 1 HOUR TO A DUST CLOUD CONTAINING 3100 MG/M3. **CHRONIC EXPOSURE-** NO DATA AVAILABLE.
FIRST AID- REMOVE FROM EXPOSURE AREA TO FRESH AIR IMMEDIATELY. IF BREATHING HAS STOPPED, PERFORM ARTIFICIAL RESPIRATION. KEEP PERSON WARM AND AT REST. TREAT SYMPTOMATICALLY AND SUPPORTIVELY. GET MEDICAL ATTENTION IMMEDIATELY.

SKIN CONTACT: DIPHENAMID: **ACUTE EXPOSURE-** THIS MATERIAL WAS REPORTED NOT TO BE A SKIN IRRITANT OR SENSITIZER. A LETHAL DOSE IN RABBITS BY DERMAL ABSORPTION WAS GREATER THAN 6 GM/KG. **CHRONIC EXPOSURE-** NO DATA AVAILABLE.
FIRST AID- REMOVE CONTAMINATED CLOTHING AND SHOES IMMEDIATELY. WASH AFFECTED AREA WITH SOAP OR MILD DETERGENT AND LARGE AMOUNTS OF WATER UNTIL NO EVIDENCE OF CHEMICAL REMAINS (APPROXIMATELY 15-20 MINUTES). GET MEDICAL ATTENTION IMMEDIATELY.

EYE CONTACT: DIPHENAMID: **ACUTE EXPOSURE-** A 1% SUSPENSION APPLIED TO RABBIT EYES WAS NOT IRRITATING. **CHRONIC EXPOSURE-** NO DATA AVAILABLE.
FIRST AID- WASH EYES IMMEDIATELY WITH LARGE AMOUNTS OF WATER OR NORMAL SALINE, OCCASIONALLY LIFTING UPPER AND LOWER LIDS, UNTIL NO EVIDENCE OF CHEMICAL REMAINS (APPROXIMATELY 15-20 MINUTES). GET MEDICAL ATTENTION IMMEDIATELY.

INGESTION: DIPHENAMID: **ACUTE EXPOSURE-** EFFECTS OF ATAXIA AND INCREASED EXCITABILITY WERE PRODUCED IN POISONED RATS; INITIAL CENTRAL NERVOUS DEPRESSION FOLLOWED BY CLONIC-TONIC SPASMS WAS OBSERVED IN MICE. EMESIS WAS EXHIBITED IN MONKEYS AND DOGS. **CHRONIC EXPOSURE-** INCREASED LIVER AND THYROID WEIGHTS WERE OBSERVED IN A 101-WEEK STUDY OF RATS FED DOSAGES UP TO 30 MG/KG. IN A 101-WEEK STUDY OF DOGS, INCREASED LIVER/BODY WEIGHT RATIOS AND INFLAMMATORY HEPATIC CELL INFILTRATES WERE NOTED AT A LEVEL OF 10 MG/KG; A DIETARY LEVEL OF 200 MG/KG WAS LETHAL TO DOGS IN A 72-DAY PERIOD. FETAL LIVER CONGESTION AND OTHER ADVERSE HEPATIC EFFECTS WERE REPORTED FROM A 3-GENERATION REPRODUCTION STUDY OF RATS RECEIVING DIPHENAMID AT LEVELS UP TO 30 MG/KG.
FIRST AID- REMOVE BY GASTRIC LAVAGE AND CATHARSIS. MAINTAIN BLOOD PRESSURE AND AIRWAY. GIVE OXYGEN IF RESPIRATION IS DEPRESSED. DO NOT PERFORM GASTRIC LAVAGE IF VICTIM IS UNCONSCIOUS. GET MEDICAL ATTENTION IMMEDIATELY (DREISBACH, HANDBOOK OF POISONING, 12TH ED.). ADMINISTRATION OF LAVAGE OR OXYGEN SHOULD BE PERFORMED BY QUALIFIED MEDICAL PERSONNEL.
ANTIDOTE: NO SPECIFIC ANTIDOTE. TREAT SYMPTOMATICALLY AND SUPPORTIVELY.

REACTIVITY

REACTIVITY: STABLE UNDER NORMAL TEMPERATURES AND PRESSURES.
INCOMPATIBILITIES: DIPHENAMID: OXIDIZERS (STRONG): FIRE AND EXPLOSION HAZARD.
DECOMPOSITION: THERMAL DECOMPOSITION PRODUCTS MAY INCLUDE TOXIC OXIDES OF CARBON AND NITROGEN.
POLYMERIZATION: HAZARDOUS POLYMERIZATION HAS NOT BEEN REPORTED TO OCCUR UNDER NORMAL TEMPERATURES AND PRESSURES.

STORAGE AND DISPOSAL

OBSERVE ALL FEDERAL, STATE AND LOCAL REGULATIONS WHEN STORING OR DISPOSING OF THIS SUBSTANCE. FOR ASSISTANCE, CONTACT THE DISTRICT DIRECTOR OF THE ENVIRONMENTAL PROTECTION AGENCY.

STORAGE

STORE IN ACCORDANCE WITH 40 CFR 165 RECOMMENDED PROCEDURES FOR THE DISPOSAL AND STORAGE OF PESTICIDES AND PESTICIDE CONTAINERS.
STORE AWAY FROM INCOMPATIBLE SUBSTANCES.

DISPOSAL

DISPOSAL MUST BE IN ACCORDANCE WITH 40 CFR 165 RECOMMENDED PROCEDURES FOR THE DISPOSAL AND STORAGE OF PESTICIDES AND PESTICIDE CONTAINERS.

CONDITIONS TO AVOID

MAY BURN BUT DOES NOT IGNITE READILY. AVOID CONTACT WITH STRONG OXIDIZERS, EXCESSIVE HEAT, SPARKS, OR OPEN FLAME.

SPILL AND LEAK PROCEDURES

OCCUPATIONAL SPILL: SWEEP UP AND PLACE IN SUITABLE CLEAN, DRY CONTAINERS FOR RECLAMATION OR LATER DISPOSAL. DO NOT FLUSH SPILLED MATERIAL INTO SEWER. KEEP UNNECESSARY PEOPLE AWAY.

PROTECTIVE EQUIPMENT

VENTILATION: PROVIDE LOCAL EXHAUST OR GENERAL DILUTION VENTILATION SYSTEM.

RESPIRATOR: THE FOLLOWING RESPIRATORS ARE RECOMMENDED BASED ON INFORMATION FOUND IN THE PHYSICAL DATA, TOXICITY AND HEALTH EFFECTS SECTIONS. THEY ARE RANKED IN ORDER FROM MINIMUM TO MAXIMUM RESPIRATORY PROTECTION. THE SPECIFIC RESPIRATOR SELECTED MUST BE BASED ON CONTAMINATION LEVELS FOUND IN THE WORK PLACE, MUST NOT EXCEED THE WORKING LIMITS OF THE RESPIRATOR AND BE JOINTLY APPROVED BY THE NATIONAL INSTITUTE FOR OCCUPATIONAL SAFETY AND HEALTH AND THE MINE SAFETY AND HEALTH ADMINISTRATION (NIOSH-MSHA).

CHEMICAL CARTRIDGE RESPIRATOR WITH AN ORGANIC VAPOR CARTRIDGE(S) IN COMBINATION WITH A DUST AND MIST FILTER.

GAS MASK WITH ORGANIC VAPOR CANISTER (CHIN-STYLE OR FRONT- OR BACK-MOUNTED CANISTER) WITH A DUST AND MIST FILTER.

GAS MASK WITH ORGANIC VAPOR CANISTER (CHIN-STYLE OR FRONT- OR BACK-MOUNTED CANISTER) WITH A PARTICULATE FILTER.

POWERED AIR-PURIFYING RESPIRATOR WITH A HIGH-EFFICIENCY FILTER.

TYPE 'C' SUPPLIED-AIR RESPIRATOR WITH A FULL FACEPIECE OPERATED IN A PRESSURE-DEMAND OR OTHER POSITIVE PRESSURE MODE.

SELF-CONTAINED BREATHING APPARATUS WITH A FULL FACEPIECE OPERATED IN PRESSURE-DEMAND OR OTHER POSITIVE PRESSURE MODE.

FOR FIREFIGHTING AND OTHER IMMEDIATELY DANGEROUS TO LIFE OR HEALTH CONDITIONS:

SELF-CONTAINED BREATHING APPARATUS WITH FULL FACEPIECE OPERATED IN PRESSURE-DEMAND OR OTHER POSITIVE PRESSURE MODE.

SUPPLIED-AIR RESPIRATOR WITH FULL FACEPIECE AND OPERATED IN PRESSURE-DEMAND OR OTHER POSITIVE PRESSURE MODE IN COMBINATION WITH AN AUXILIARY SELF-CONTAINED BREATHING APPARATUS OPERATED IN PRESSURE-DEMAND OR OTHER POSITIVE PRESSURE MODE.

CLOTHING: EMPLOYEE MUST WEAR APPROPRIATE PROTECTIVE (IMPERVIOUS) CLOTHING AND EQUIPMENT TO PREVENT REPEATED OR PROLONGED SKIN CONTACT WITH THIS SUBSTANCE.

GLOVES: EMPLOYEE MUST WEAR APPROPRIATE PROTECTIVE GLOVES TO PREVENT CONTACT WITH THIS SUBSTANCE.

EYE PROTECTION: EMPLOYEE MUST WEAR SPLASH-PROOF OR DUST-RESISTANT SAFETY GOGGLES TO PREVENT EYE CONTACT WITH THIS SUBSTANCE.

EMERGENCY EYE WASH: WHERE THERE IS ANY POSSIBILITY THAT AN EMPLOYEE'S EYES MAY BE EXPOSED TO THIS SUBSTANCE, THE EMPLOYER SHOULD PROVIDE AN EYE WASH FOUNTAIN WITHIN THE IMMEDIATE WORK AREA FOR EMERGENCY USE.

AUTHORIZED BY- OCCUPATIONAL HEALTH SERVICES, INC.

CREATION DATE: 10/04/89 ***REVISION DATE:*** 05/31/90

MATERIAL SAFETY DATA SHEET

OCCUPATIONAL HEALTH SERVICES, INC.
AGRICULTURE AND PESTICIDE DIVISION
450 SEVENTH AVENUE, SUITE 2407
NEW YORK, NEW YORK 10123
1-800-445-MSDS OR (212) 967-1100

EMERGENCY CONTACT:
JOHN S. BRANSFORD, JR. (615) 292-1180

SUBSTANCE IDENTIFICATION

CAS-NUMBER 2312-76-7

SUBSTANCE: **DINITRO-O-CRESOL SODIUM SALT**

TRADE NAMES/SYNONYMS: PHENOL, 2-METHYL-4,6-DINITRO-, SODIUM SALT; 2-METHYL-4,6-DINITROPHENOL SODIUM SALT; O-CRESOL, 4,6-DINITRO-, SODIUM SALT; 4,6-DINITRO-O-CRESOL SODIUM SALT; SODIUM, ((4,6-DINITRO-O-TOLYL)OXY)-; ((4,6-DINITRO-O-TOLYL)OXY)SODIUM; SODIUM 4,6-DINITRO-O-CRESYLATE; DINITRO-ORTHO-CRESOL SODIUM SALT; DNOC SODIUM SALT; RCRA P047; C7H5N2NAO5; PST71411

CHEMICAL FAMILY: CRESOL
NITRO
SALT

MOLECULAR FORMULA: (N-O2)2-C-H3-C6-H2-O.NA

MOLECULAR WEIGHT: 220.12

CERCLA RATINGS (SCALE 0-3): HEALTH=3 FIRE=1 REACTIVITY=3 PERSISTENCE=1

NFPA RATINGS (SCALE 0-4): HEALTH=4 FIRE=1 REACTIVITY=4

COMPONENTS AND CONTAMINANTS

COMPONENT: DINITRO-O-CRESOL SODIUM SALT ***PERCENT:*** 100.0
CAS# 2312-76-7

OTHER CONTAMINANTS: MAY CONTAIN UP TO 10% WATER TO REDUCE DETONATION SENSITIVITY.

EXPOSURE LIMITS: DINITRO-O-CRESOL SALTS: 0.2 MG/M3 NIOSH RECOMMENDED 10 HOUR TWA

10 POUNDS CERCLA SECTION 103 REPORTABLE QUANTITY

PHYSICAL DATA

DESCRIPTION: RED POWDER. ***MELTING POINT:*** NOT AVAILABLE

SPECIFIC GRAVITY: NOT AVAILABLE ***SOLUBILITY IN WATER:*** SOLUBLE

FIRE AND EXPLOSION DATA

FIRE AND EXPLOSION HAZARD: SLIGHT FIRE HAZARD WHEN EXPOSED TO HEAT OR FLAME.

DUST-AIR MIXTURES MAY IGNITE OR EXPLODE.

DANGEROUS EXPLOSION HAZARD WHEN EXPOSED TO HEAT OR FLAME.

FIREFIGHTING MEDIA: DRY CHEMICAL, CARBON DIOXIDE, HALON, WATER SPRAY OR STANDARD FOAM (1987 EMERGENCY RESPONSE GUIDEBOOK, DOT P 5800.4).

FOR LARGER FIRES, USE WATER SPRAY, FOG OR STANDARD FOAM (1987 EMERGENCY RESPONSE GUIDEBOOK, DOT P 5800.4).

FIREFIGHTING: MOVE CONTAINERS FROM FIRE AREA IF POSSIBLE. COOL CONTAINERS EXPOSED TO FLAMES WITH WATER FROM SIDE UNTIL WELL AFTER FIRE IS OUT. STAY AWAY FROM STORAGE TANK ENDS. FOR MASSIVE FIRE IN STORAGE AREA, USE UNMANNED HOSE HOLDER OR MONITOR NOZZLES; ELSE WITHDRAW FROM AREA AND LET FIRE BURN (1987 EMERGENCY RESPONSE GUIDEBOOK, DOT P 5800.4, GUIDE PAGE 56).

EXTINGUISH ONLY IF FLOW CAN BE STOPPED. USE WATER IN FLOODING AMOUNTS AS A FOG; SOLID STREAMS MAY NOT BE EFFECTIVE. COOL CONTAINERS WITH FLOODING QUANTITIES OF WATER APPLIED FROM AS FAR A DISTANCE AS POSSIBLE. AVOID BREATHING TOXIC VAPORS, KEEP UPWIND.

TRANSPORTATION DATA

DEPARTMENT OF TRANSPORTATION HAZARD CLASSIFICATION 49 CFR 172.101: POISON B

DEPARTMENT OF TRANSPORTATION LABELING REQUIREMENTS 49 CFR 172.101 AND SUBPART E: POISON

DEPARTMENT OF TRANSPORTATION PACKAGING REQUIREMENTS: 49 CFR 173.365 EXCEPTIONS: 49 CFR 173.364

TOXICITY

DINITRO-O-CRESOL SODIUM SALT: TOXICITY DATA: 200 MG/KG SKIN-RAT LD50; 26 MG/KG ORAL-RAT LD50; 200 MG/KG ORAL-MAMMAL LD50; 200 MG/KG ORAL-DOMESTIC ANIMAL LD50; 20 MG/KG SUBCUTANEOUS-RAT LDLO; MUTAGENIC DATA (RTECS). CARCINOGEN STATUS: NONE. ACUTE TOXICITY LEVEL: HIGHLY TOXIC BY DERMAL ABSORPTION AND INGESTION. TARGET EFFECTS: POISONING MAY INCREASE THE METABOLIC RATE AND AFFECT THE NERVOUS SYSTEM, LIVER, AND KIDNEY. AT INCREASED RISK FROM EXPOSURE: ALCOHOLICS AND PERSONS WITH RENAL OR HEPATIC DISEASES. ADDITIONAL DATA: HOT ENVIRONMENTS MAY ENHANCE ABSORPTION AND THE TOXIC EFFECTS.

HEALTH EFFECTS AND FIRST AID

INHALATION: DINITRO-O-CRESOL SODIUM SALT: SEE INFORMATION ON DINITROPHENOL DERIVATIVES.

DINITROPHENOL DERIVATIVES: **ACUTE EXPOSURE-** MAY BE ABSORBED WITH SYMPTOMS OCCURRING SUDDENLY AND UP TO 2 DAYS AFTER CESSATION OF EXPOSURE. SYMPTOMS MAY INCLUDE FATIGUE, WEAKNESS, FEVER, THIRST, NAUSEA, VOMITING, HEADACHES, FLUSHED SKIN, PROSTRATION, EXCESSIVE PERSPIRATION, TACHYCARDIA, TACHYPNEA, AND DYSPNEA. APPREHENSION, RESTLESSNESS, ANXIETY, MANIC BEHAVIOR, OR UNCONSCIOUSNESS MAY INDICATE CEREBRAL INJURY. CONVULSIONS MAY OCCUR IN THE MOST SEVERE POISONINGS. ANOXIA WITH CYANOSIS, LIVIDITY AND METABOLIC ACIDOSIS, SEVERE HYPERPYREXIA, DEHYDRATION, AND MUSCULAR TREMORS MAY BE FOLLOWED BY CIRCULATORY OR RESPIRATORY COLLAPSE AND COMA. DEGENERATIVE CHANGES IN THE HEART, RENAL TUBULES AND LIVER PARENCHYMA MAY OCCUR. THERE MAY BE ALBUMINURIA, PYURIA, HEMATURIA, JAUNDICE, AND INCREASED BUN. THE EFFECTS FROM POISONING ARE RAPID AND DEATH OR RECOVERY GENERALLY OCCURS WITHIN 24 TO 48 HOURS. FATAL DINITROPHENOL POISONING IS FOLLOWED BY INSTANTANEOUS RIGOR MORTIS.

CHRONIC EXPOSURE- IN ADDITION TO THE SYMPTOMS OF ACUTE EXPOSURE, PROLONGED OR REPEATED EXPOSURE MAY CAUSE WEIGHT LOSS, CATARACT FORMATION, AND LIVER AND KIDNEY DAMAGE. YELLOW STAINING OF THE SCLERAE AND URINE INDICATES ABSORPTION OF POTENTIALLY TOXIC AMOUNTS.

FIRST AID- REMOVE FROM EXPOSURE AREA TO FRESH AIR IMMEDIATELY. IF BREATHING HAS STOPPED, PERFORM ARTIFICIAL RESPIRATION. ADMINISTER OXYGEN. TREAT SYMPTOMATICALLY AND SUPPORTIVELY. GET MEDICAL ATTENTION IMMEDIATELY.

SKIN CONTACT: DINITRO-O-CRESOL SODIUM SALT: HIGHLY TOXIC. SEE INFORMATION ON DINITROPHENOL DERIVATIVES.

DINITROPHENOL DERIVATIVES: **ACUTE EXPOSURE**- MAY CAUSE IRRITATION. CONTACT MAY RESULT IN YELLOW STAINING OF THE SKIN AHD HAIR. SOME DERIVATIVES MAY BE ABSORBED THROUGH THE SKIN WITH SYMPTOMS OCCURRING SUDDENLY AND UP TO 2 DAYS AFTER CESSATION OF EXPOSURE AND PRODUCE EFFECTS ON THE METABOLIC RATE, CENTRAL NERVOUS SYSTEM AND LIVER AND KIDNEY RESULTING IN SIGNS AND SYMPTOMS AS DESCRIBED IN ACUTE INHALATION. **CHRONIC EXPOSURE**- REPEATED OR PROLONGED CONTACT MAY RESULT IN DERMATITIS DUE TO IRRITATION OR ALLERGIC SENSITIVITY. IN ADDITION TO THE SYMPTOMS OF ACUTE EXPOSURE, CHRONIC ABSORPTION MAY CAUSE FATIGUE, WEIGHT LOSS, CATARACT FORMATION AND LIVER AND KIDNEY DAMAGE. YELLOW STAINING OF THE SCLERAE AND URINE INDICATES ABSORPTION OF POTENTIALLY TOXIC AMOUNTS.

FIRST AID- REMOVE CONTAMINATED CLOTHING AND SHOES IMMEDIATELY. THEN REMOVE SKIN AND HAIR CONTAMINATION BY SCRUBBING WITH SOAP AND WATER. IF BODY TEMPERATURE IS ELEVATED, REDUCE TO 37 C BY SPONGE BATH, IMMERSION IN COOL WATER OR BY APPLYING COOLING BLANKET. IF BODY TEMPERATURE IS ABOVE 40 C, ICE WATER IS NECESSARY (DREISBACH, HANDBOOK OF POISONING, 12TH EDITION; MORGAN, EPA RECOGNITION AND MANAGEMENT OF PESTICIDE POISONINGS, 3RD EDITION). GET MEDICAL ATTENTION IMMEDIATELY.

EYE CONTACT: DINITRO-O-CRESOL SODIUM SALT: **ACUTE EXPOSURE**- MAY CAUSE IRRITATION. **CHRONIC EXPOSURE**- PROLONGED OR REPEATED EXPOSURE MAY CAUSE CONJUNCTIVITIS.

FIRST AID- WASH EYES IMMEDIATELY WITH LARGE AMOUNTS OF WATER OR NORMAL SALINE, OCCASIONALLY LIFTING UPPER AND LOWER LIDS, UNTIL NO EVIDENCE OF CHEMICAL REMAINS (APPROXIMATELY 15-20 MINUTES). GET MEDICAL ATTENTION IMMEDIATELY.

INGESTION: DINITRO-O-CRESOL SODIUM SALT: HIGHLY TOXIC. SEE INFORMATION ON DINITROPHENOL DERIVATIVES.

DINITROPHENOL DERIVATIVES: **ACUTE EXPOSURE**- MAY CAUSE EFFECTS ON THE METABOLIC RATE, CENTRAL NERVOUS SYSTEM AND LIVER AND KIDNEY RESULTING IN SIGNS AND SYMPTOMS AS DESCRIBED IN ACUTE INHALATION. **CHRONIC EXPOSURE**- IN ADDITION TO THE SYMPTOMS OF ACUTE EXPOSURE, REPEATED INGESTION MAY CAUSE AN INITIAL SENSE OF WELL-BEING THEN ANOREXIA, DIARRHEA, DIZZINESS, RESTLESSNESS, FATIGUE, WEIGHT LOSS, SKIN ERUPTIONS, PERIPHERAL NEURITIS, LIVER AND KIDNEY DAMAGE, CARDIOVASCULAR COMPLICATIONS, GRANULOCYTOPENIA, AND CATARACT FORMATION. YELLOW STAINING OF THE SCLERAE AND URINE INDICATES ABSORPTION OF POTENTIALLY TOXIC AMOUNTS.

FIRST AID- REMOVE INGESTED POISON BY THOROUGH GASTRIC LAVAGE WITH SATURATED BICARBONATE SOLUTION. IF GASTRIC LAVAGE CANNOT BE ACCOMPLISHED IMMEDIATELY, GIVE SYRUP OF IPECAC TO INDUCE EMESIS AND FOLLOW WITH SALINE CATHARTIC. IF BODY TEMPERATURE IS ELEVATED, REDUCE TO 37 C BY IMMERSION IN COOL WATER OR BY APPLYING COOLING BLANKET. IF BODY TEMPERATURE IS ABOVE 40 C, ICE WATER IS NECESSARY (DREISBACH, HANDBOOK OF POISONING, 12TH ED.). ADMINISTRATION OF GASTRIC LAVAGE SHOULD BE PERFORMED BY QUALIFIED MEDICAL PERSONNEL. GET MEDICAL ATTENTION IMMEDIATELY.

ANTIDOTE: NO SPECIFIC ANTIDOTE. TREAT SYMPTOMATICALLY AND SUPPORTIVELY.

REACTIVITY

REACTIVITY: DINITRO-O-CRESOL SODIUM SALT: DRY MATERIAL MAY DETONATE ON EXPOSURE TO HEAT OR SHOCK. MATERIAL MAY BE WET WITH WATER FOR STABILITY DURING STORAGE AND TRANSPORT.

INCOMPATIBILITIES: DINITRO-O-CRESOL SODIUM SALT: OXIDIZERS (STRONG): FIRE AND EXPLOSION HAZARD.

DECOMPOSITION: THERMAL DECOMPOSITION PRODUCTS MAY INCLUDE TOXIC OXIDES OF CARBON AND NITROGEN.

POLYMERIZATION: HAZARDOUS POLYMERIZATION HAS NOT BEEN REPORTED TO OCCUR UNDER NORMAL TEMPERATURES AND PRESSURES.

STORAGE AND DISPOSAL

OBSERVE ALL FEDERAL, STATE AND LOCAL REGULATIONS WHEN STORING OR DISPOSING OF THIS SUBSTANCE. FOR ASSISTANCE, CONTACT THE DISTRICT DIRECTOR OF THE ENVIRONMENTAL PROTECTION AGENCY.

****STORAGE****

STORE IN ACCORDANCE WITH 40 CFR 165 RECOMMENDED PROCEDURES FOR THE DISPOSAL AND STORAGE OF PESTICIDES AND PESTICIDE CONTAINERS.

STORE AWAY FROM INCOMPATIBLE SUBSTANCES.

****DISPOSAL****

DISPOSAL MUST BE IN ACCORDANCE WITH STANDARDS APPLICABLE TO GENERATORS OF HAZARDOUS WASTE, 40 CFR 262. EPA HAZARDOUS WASTE NUMBER P047

DISPOSAL MUST BE IN ACCORDANCE WITH 40 CFR 165 RECOMMENDED PROCEDURES FOR THE DISPOSAL AND STORAGE OF PESTICIDES AND PESTICIDE CONTAINERS.

CONDITIONS TO AVOID

MAY BURN BUT DOES NOT IGNITE READILY. MAY EXPLODE FROM FRICTION, HEAT OR CONTAMINATION.

SPILL AND LEAK PROCEDURES

OCCUPATIONAL SPILL: DO NOT TOUCH SPILLED MATERIAL. STOP LEAK IF YOU CAN DO IT WITHOUT RISK. USE WATER SPRAY TO REDUCE VAPORS. FOR SMALL SPILLS, TAKE UP WITH SAND OR OTHER ABSORBENT MATERIAL AND PLACE INTO CONTAINERS FOR LATER DISPOSAL. FOR SMALL DRY SPILLS, WITH CLEAN SHOVEL PLACE MATERIAL INTO CLEAN, DRY CONTAINERS AND COVER. MOVE CONTAINERS FROM SPILL AREA. FOR LARGER SPILLS, DIKE FAR AHEAD OF SPILL FOR LATER DISPOSAL. KEEP UNNECESSARY PEOPLE AWAY. ISOLATE HAZARD AREA AND DENY ENTRY. VENTILATE CLOSED SPACES BEFORE ENTERING.

REPORTABLE QUANTITY (RQ): 10 POUNDS THE SUPERFUND AMENDMENTS AND REAUTHORIZATION ACT (SARA) SECTION 304 REQUIRES THAT A RELEASE EQUAL TO OR GREATER THAN THE REPORTABLE QUANTITY FOR THIS SUBSTANCE BE IMMEDIATELY REPORTED TO THE LOCAL EMERGENCY PLANNING COMMITTEE AND THE STATE EMERGENCY RESPONSE COMMISSION (40 CFR 355.40). IF THE RELEASE OF THIS SUBSTANCE IS REPORTABLE UNDER CERCLA SECTION 103, THE NATIONAL RESPONSE CENTER MUST BE NOTIFIED IMMEDIATELY AT (800) 424-8802 OR (202) 426-2675 IN THE METROPOLITAN WASHINGTON, D.C. AREA (40 CFR 302.6).

PROTECTIVE EQUIPMENT

VENTILATION: PROVIDE LOCAL EXHAUST OR PROCESS ENCLOSURE VENTILATION TO MEET THE PUBLISHED EXPOSURE LIMITS. VENTILATION EQUIPMENT MUST BE EXPLOSION-PROOF.

RESPIRATOR: THE FOLLOWING RESPIRATORS AND MAXIMUM USE CONCENTRATIONS ARE RECOMMENDATIONS BY THE U.S. DEPARTMENT OF HEALTH AND HUMAN SERVICES, NIOSH POCKET GUIDE TO CHEMICAL HAZARDS; NIOSH CRITERIA DOCUMENTS OR BY THE U.S. DEPARTMENT OF LABOR, 29 CFR 1910 SUBPART Z. THE SPECIFIC RESPIRATOR SELECTED MUST BE BASED ON CONTAMINATION LEVELS FOUND IN THE WORK PLACE, MUST NOT EXCEED THE WORKING LIMITS OF THE RESPIRATOR AND BE JOINTLY APPROVED BY THE NATIONAL INSTITUTE FOR OCCUPATIONAL SAFETY AND HEALTH AND THE MINE SAFETY AND HEALTH ADMINISTRATION (NIOSH-MSHA).

DINITRO-ORTHO-CRESOL:

2 MG/M3- ANY DUST AND MIST RESPIRATOR WITH A FULL FACEPIECE.

5 MG/M3- ANY POWERED AIR-PURIFYING RESPIRATOR WITH A DUST AND MIST FILTER. ANY SUPPLIED-AIR RESPIRATOR OPERATED IN A CONTINUOUS FLOW MODE. ANY AIR-PURIFYING FULL FACEPIECE RESPIRATOR WITH A HIGH-EFFICIENCY PARTICULATE FILTER. ANY SUPPLIED-AIR RESPIRATOR WITH A FULL FACEPIECE. ANY SELF-CONTAINED BREATHING APPARATUS WITH A FULL FACEPIECE.

ESCAPE- ANY AIR-PURIFYING FULL FACEPIECE RESPIRATOR WITH A HIGH-EFFICIENCY PARTICULATE FILTER. ANY APPROPRIATE ESCAPE-TYPE SELF-CONTAINED BREATHING APPARATUS.

FOR FIREFIGHTING AND OTHER IMMEDIATELY DANGEROUS TO LIFE OR HEALTH CONDITIONS:

SELF-CONTAINED BREATHING APPARATUS WITH FULL FACEPIECE OPERATED IN PRESSURE-DEMAND OR OTHER POSITIVE PRESSURE MODE.

SUPPLIED-AIR RESPIRATOR WITH FULL FACEPIECE AND OPERATED IN PRESSURE-DEMAND OR OTHER POSITIVE PRESSURE MODE IN COMBINATION WITH AN AUXILIARY SELF-CONTAINED BREATHING APPARATUS OPERATED IN PRESSURE-DEMAND OR OTHER POSITIVE PRESSURE MODE.

CLOTHING: EMPLOYEE MUST WEAR APPROPRIATE PROTECTIVE (IMPERVIOUS) CLOTHING AND EQUIPMENT TO PREVENT ANY POSSIBILITY OF SKIN CONTACT WITH THIS SUBSTANCE.

GLOVES: EMPLOYEE MUST WEAR APPROPRIATE PROTECTIVE GLOVES TO PREVENT CONTACT WITH THIS SUBSTANCE.

EYE PROTECTION: EMPLOYEE MUST WEAR SPLASH-PROOF OR DUST-RESISTANT SAFETY GOGGLES AND A FACESHIELD TO PREVENT CONTACT WITH THIS SUBSTANCE.

EMERGENCY WASH FACILITIES: WHERE THERE IS ANY POSSIBILITY THAT AN EMPLOYEE'S EYES AND/OR SKIN MAY BE EXPOSED TO THIS SUBSTANCE, THE EMPLOYER SHOULD PROVIDE AN EYE WASH FOUNTAIN AND QUICK DRENCH SHOWER WITHIN THE IMMEDIATE WORK AREA FOR EMERGENCY USE.

AUTHORIZED BY- OCCUPATIONAL HEALTH SERVICES, INC.

CREATION DATE: 04/20/90 ***REVISION DATE:*** 04/20/90

MATERIAL SAFETY DATA SHEET

OCCUPATIONAL HEALTH SERVICES, INC.
AGRICULTURE AND PESTICIDE DIVISION
450 SEVENTH AVENUE, SUITE 2407
NEW YORK, NEW YORK 10123
1-800-445-MSDS OR (212) 967-1100

EMERGENCY CONTACT:
JOHN S. BRANSFORD, JR. (615) 292-1180

SUBSTANCE IDENTIFICATION

CAS-NUMBER 137-42-8

SUBSTANCE: **SODIUM METHYLDITHIOCARBAMATE**

TRADE NAMES/SYNONYMS: N-METHYLDITHIOCARBAMIC ACID, SODIUM SALT; VAPAM; CARBAMODITHIOIC ACID, METHYL-, MONOSODIUM SALT; CARBAMIC ACID, METHYLDITHIO-, MONOSODIUM SALT; METHYLCARBAMODITHIOIC ACID, MONOSODIUM SALT; METHYLDITHIOCARBAMIC ACID, MONOSODIUM SALT; SODIUM METHYLCARBAMODITHIOATE; SODIUM N-METHYLDITHIOCARBAMATE; SODIUM MONOMETHYLDITHIOCARBAMATE; VPM; SMDC; METAM SODIUM; METHAM SODIUM; METAM-SODIUM; CARBAM; SODIUM METHAM; SODIUM METAM; PST71430

CHEMICAL FAMILY: THIOCARBAMATE

MOLECULAR FORMULA: C2-H4-N-S2.NA

MOLECULAR WEIGHT: 129.18

CERCLA RATINGS (SCALE 0-3): HEALTH=3 FIRE=U REACTIVITY=0 PERSISTENCE=1

NFPA RATINGS (SCALE 0-4): HEALTH=3 FIRE=U REACTIVITY=0

COMPONENTS AND CONTAMINANTS

COMPONENT: SODIUM METHYLDITHIOCARBAMATE ***PERCENT:*** 100
CAS# 137-42-8

OTHER CONTAMINANTS: NONE

EXPOSURE LIMITS: NO OCCUPATIONAL EXPOSURE LIMITS ESTABLISHED BY OSHA, ACGIH, OR NIOSH.

PHYSICAL DATA

DESCRIPTION: COLORLESS TO WHITE CRYSTALLINE POWDER OR CRYSTALS WITH AN UNPLEASANT ODOR WHICH IS SIMILAR TO CARBON DISULFIDE.

MELTING POINT: NOT AVAILABLE

SPECIFIC GRAVITY: NOT AVAILABLE ***SOLUBILITY IN WATER:*** 72.2%

SOLVENT SOLUBILITY: MODERATELY SOLUBLE IN ETHANOL, METHANOL; SLIGHTLY SOLUBLE IN OTHER ORGANIC SOLVENTS

FIRE AND EXPLOSION DATA

FIRE AND EXPLOSION HAZARD: UNKNOWN FIRE AND EXPLOSION HAZARD.

FIREFIGHTING MEDIA: DRY CHEMICAL, CARBON DIOXIDE, WATER SPRAY OR FOAM FOR LARGER FIRES, USE WATER SPRAY, FOG OR ALCOHOL FOAM

FIREFIGHTING: USE AGENTS SUITABLE FOR TYPE OF SURROUNDING FIRE. AVOID BREATHING HAZARDOUS VAPORS, KEEP UPWIND.

TOXICITY

SODIUM METHYLDITHIOCARBAMATE: TOXICITY DATA: 800 MG/KG SKIN-RABBIT LD50; 636 MG/KG SKIN-RAT LD50; 450 MG/KG ORAL-RAT LD50; 50 MG/KG ORAL-MOUSE LD50; 320 MG/KG ORAL-RABBIT LD50; 815 MG/KG ORAL-GUINEA PIG LD50; 700 MG/KG SUBCUTANEOUS-RAT LD50; 266 MG/KG SUBCUTANEOUS-MOUSE LD50; 320 MG/KG SUBCUTANEOUS-RABBIT LD50; 815 MG/KG SUBCUTANEOUS-GUINEA PIG LD50; 500 MG/KG INTRAPERITONEAL-MOUSE LD50; 550 MG/KG UNREPORTED-RAT LD50; 285 MG/KG UNREPORTED-MOUSE LD50. CARCINOGEN STATUS: NONE. LOCAL EFFECTS: IRRITANT- INHALATION, SKIN, AND EYES. ACUTE TOXICITY LEVEL: TOXIC BY DERMAL ABSORPTION AND INGESTION. TARGET EFFECTS: NO DATA AVAILABLE. ADDITIONAL DATA: INTERACTIONS WITH ALCOHOL MAY OCCUR.

HEALTH EFFECTS AND FIRST AID

INHALATION: SODIUM METHYLDITHIOCARBAMATE IRRITANT. **ACUTE EXPOSURE-** MAY CAUSE IRRITATION. INHALATION OF DITHIOCARBAMATES HAVE PRODUCED IRRITATION OF RESPIRATORY TRACT WITH SYMPTOMS OF NASAL STUFFINESS, HOARSENESS, COUGH, AND RARELY PNEUMONITIS. **CHRONIC EXPOSURE-** PROLONGED OR REPEATED EXPOSURE MAY CAUSE IRRITATION.

FIRST AID- REMOVE FROM EXPOSURE AREA TO FRESH AIR IMMEDIATELY. IF BREATHING HAS STOPPED, PERFORM ARTIFICIAL RESPIRATION. KEEP PERSON WARM AND AT REST. TREAT SYMPTOMATICALLY AND SUPPORTIVELY. GET MEDICAL ATTENTION IMMEDIATELY.

SKIN CONTACT: SODIUM METHYLDITHIOCARBAMATE: IRRITANT/TOXIC. **ACUTE EXPOSURE-** MAY CAUSE IRRITATION. ANIMAL STUDIES INDICATED THAT HARMFUL AMOUNTS MAY BE ABSORBED THROUGH THE SKIN. A LETHAL DOSE IN RABBITS WAS 800 MG/KG. DITHIOCARBAMATES MAY CAUSE ITCHING, REDNESS, AND ECZEMATOID DERMATITIS IN PREDISPOSED INDIVIDUALS. **CHRONIC EXPOSURE-** PROLONGED OR REPEATED EXPOSURE MAY CAUSE DERMATITIS. REPEATED CONTACT WITH DITHIOCARBAMATES MAY CAUSE SENSITIZATION IN SOME INDIVIDUALS.

FIRST AID- REMOVE CONTAMINATED CLOTHING AND SHOES IMMEDIATELY. WASH AFFECTED AREA WITH SOAP OR MILD DETERGENT AND LARGE AMOUNTS OF WATER UNTIL NO EVIDENCE OF CHEMICAL REMAINS (APPROXIMATELY 15-20 MINUTES). GET MEDICAL ATTENTION IMMEDIATELY.

EYE CONTACT: SODIUM METHYLDITHIOCARBAMATE: IRRITANT. **ACUTE EXPOSURE-** MAY CAUSE IRRITATION. **CHRONIC EXPOSURE-** REPEATED OR PROLONGED CONTACT MAY CAUSE CONJUNCTIVITIS.

FIRST AID- WASH EYES IMMEDIATELY WITH LARGE AMOUNTS OF WATER OR NORMAL SALINE, OCCASIONALLY LIFTING UPPER AND LOWER LIDS, UNTIL NO EVIDENCE OF CHEMICAL REMAINS (APPROXIMATELY 15-20 MINUTES). GET MEDICAL ATTENTION IMMEDIATELY.

INGESTION: SODIUM METHYLDITHIOCARBAMATE: **ACUTE EXPOSURE-** A LETHAL DOSE IN RATS WAS 1700 MG/KG. INGESTION OF DITHIOCARBAMATES MAY CAUSE NAUSEA, VOMITING, DIARRHEA, ANOREXIA, HEADACHE, LETHARGY, DIZZINESS, ATAXIA, CONFUSION, DROWSINESS, EMOTIONAL LABILITY, AND COMA. IN ANIMALS STUDIES, MUSCLE WEAKNESS AND ASCENDING PARALYSIS PROGRESSED TO RESPIRATORY PARALYSIS AND DEATH. **CHRONIC EXPOSURE-** NO DATA AVAILABLE.

FIRST AID- IF VIGOROUS EMESIS HAS NOT ALREADY OCCURRED AND VICTIM IS FULLY ALERT, GIVE SYRUP OF IPECAC, FOLLOWED BY 1-2 GLASSES OF WATER TO INDUCE VOMITING (ADULTS, 12 YEARS AND OLDER: 30 ML; CHILDREN UNDER 12: 15 ML). IF CONSCIOUSNESS LEVEL DECLINES OR VOMITING HAS NOT OCCURRED IN 15 MINUTES, EMPTY THE STOMACH BY INTUBATION, ASPIRATION, AND LAVAGE, USING ALL AVAILABLE MEANS TO AVOID ASPIRATION OF VOMITUS. AFTER ASPIRATION OF THE STOMACH AND WASHING WITH ISOTONIC SALINE OR SODIUM BICARBONATE, INSTILL 30-50 GM OF ACTIVATED CHARCOAL IN 3-4 OUNCES OF WATER THROUGH THE STOMACH TUBE TO LIMIT ABSORPTION OF REMAINING TOXICANT. IF THE IRRITANT PROPERTIES OF THE TOXICANT FAIL TO PRODUCE A BOWEL MOVEMENT IN 4 HOURS, ADMINISTER SODIUM OR MAGNESIUM SULFATE AS A CATHARTIC: 0.25 GM/KG BODY WEIGHT IN 1-6 OUNCES OF WATER. ADMINISTER GLUCOSE-CONTAINING FLUIDS INTRAVENOUSLY TO ACCELERATE EXCRETION OF TOXICANT. (MORGAN, RECOGNITION AND MANAGEMENT OF PESTICIDE POISONINGS, THIRD EDITION) GET MEDICAL ATTENTION. TREATMENT SHOULD BE BE ADMINISTERED BY QUALIFIED MEDICAL PERSONNEL.

ANTIDOTE: NO SPECIFIC ANTIDOTE. TREAT SYMPTOMATICALLY AND SUPPORTIVELY.

REACTIVITY

REACTIVITY: STABLE UNDER NORMAL TEMPERATURES AND PRESSURES.

INCOMPATIBILITIES: SODIUM METHYLDITHIOCARBAMATE: ACIDS: DECOMPOSE IN AQUEOUS SOLUTION. HEAVY METAL SALTS: DECOMPOSE IN AQUEOUS SOLUTION.

DECOMPOSITION: THERMAL DECOMPOSITION PRODUCTS MAY INCLUDE TOXIC OXIDES OF NITROGEN.

POLYMERIZATION: HAZARDOUS POLYMERIZATION HAS NOT BEEN REPORTED TO OCCUR UNDER NORMAL TEMPERATURES AND PRESSURES.

STORAGE AND DISPOSAL

OBSERVE ALL FEDERAL, STATE AND LOCAL REGULATIONS WHEN STORING OR DISPOSING OF THIS SUBSTANCE. FOR ASSISTANCE, CONTACT THE DISTRICT DIRECTOR OF THE ENVIRONMENTAL PROTECTION AGENCY.

STORAGE

STORE IN ACCORDANCE WITH 40 CFR 165 RECOMMENDED PROCEDURES FOR THE DISPOSAL AND STORAGE OF PESTICIDES AND PESTICIDE CONTAINERS. STORE AWAY FROM INCOMPATIBLE SUBSTANCES.

DISPOSAL

DISPOSAL MUST BE IN ACCORDANCE WITH 40 CFR 165 RECOMMENDED PROCEDURES FOR THE DISPOSAL AND STORAGE OF PESTICIDES AND PESTICIDE CONTAINERS.

CONDITIONS TO AVOID

NONE REPORTED.

SPILL AND LEAK PROCEDURES

OCCUPATIONAL SPILL: NO SPECIAL PRECAUTIONS INDICATED.

PROTECTIVE EQUIPMENT

VENTILATION: PROVIDE LOCAL EXHAUST OR PROCESS ENCLOSURE VENTILATION SYSTEM.

RESPIRATOR: THE FOLLOWING RESPIRATORS ARE RECOMMENDED BASED ON INFORMATION FOUND IN THE PHYSICAL DATA, TOXICITY AND HEALTH EFFECTS SECTIONS. THEY ARE RANKED IN ORDER FROM MINIMUM TO MAXIMUM RESPIRATORY PROTECTION. THE SPECIFIC RESPIRATOR SELECTED MUST BE BASED ON CONTAMINATION LEVELS FOUND IN THE WORK PLACE, MUST NOT EXCEED THE WORKING LIMITS OF THE RESPIRATOR AND BE JOINTLY APPROVED BY THE NATIONAL INSTITUTE FOR OCCUPATIONAL SAFETY AND HEALTH AND THE MINE SAFETY AND HEALTH ADMINISTRATION (NIOSH-MSHA).
TYPE 'C' SUPPLIED-AIR RESPIRATOR WITH A FULL FACEPIECE OPERATED IN PRESSURE-DEMAND OR OTHER POSITIVE PRESSURE MODE OR WITH A FULL FACEPIECE, HELMET OR HOOD OPERATED IN CONTINOUS-FLOW MODE.
SELF-CONTAINED BREATHING APPARATUS WITH A FULL FACEPIECE OPERATED IN PRESSURE-DEMAND OR OTHER POSITIVE PRESSURE MODE.
FOR FIREFIGHTING AND OTHER IMMEDIATELY DANGEROUS TO LIFE OR HEALTH CONDITIONS:
SELF-CONTAINED BREATHING APPARATUS WITH FULL FACEPIECE OPERATED IN PRESSURE-DEMAND OR OTHER POSITIVE PRESSURE MODE.
SUPPLIED-AIR RESPIRATOR WITH FULL FACEPIECE AND OPERATED IN PRESSURE-DEMAND OR OTHER POSITIVE PRESSURE MODE IN COMBINATION WITH AN AUXILIARY SELF-CONTAINED BREATHING APPARATUS OPERATED IN PRESSURE-DEMAND OR OTHER POSITIVE PRESSURE MODE.

CLOTHING: EMPLOYEE MUST WEAR APPROPRIATE PROTECTIVE (IMPERVIOUS) CLOTHING AND EQUIPMENT TO PREVENT ANY POSSIBILITY OF SKIN CONTACT WITH THIS SUBSTANCE.

GLOVES: EMPLOYEE MUST WEAR APPROPRIATE PROTECTIVE GLOVES TO PREVENT CONTACT WITH THIS SUBSTANCE.

EYE PROTECTION: EMPLOYEE MUST WEAR SPLASH-PROOF OR DUST-RESISTANT SAFETY GOGGLES AND A FACESHIELD TO PREVENT CONTACT WITH THIS SUBSTANCE.
EMERGENCY WASH FACILITIES: WHERE THERE IS ANY POSSIBILITY THAT AN EMPLOYEE'S EYES AND/OR SKIN MAY BE EXPOSED TO THIS SUBSTANCE, THE EMPLOYER SHOULD PROVIDE AN EYE WASH FOUNTAIN AND QUICK DRENCH SHOWER WITHIN THE IMMEDIATE WORK AREA FOR EMERGENCY USE.

AUTHORIZED BY- OCCUPATIONAL HEALTH SERVICES, INC.
CREATION DATE: 10/05/89 ***REVISION DATE:*** 05/09/90

MATERIAL SAFETY DATA SHEET

OCCUPATIONAL HEALTH SERVICES, INC.
AGRICULTURE AND PESTICIDE DIVISION
450 SEVENTH AVENUE, SUITE 2407
NEW YORK, NEW YORK 10123
1-800-445-MSDS OR (212) 967-1100

EMERGENCY CONTACT:
JOHN S. BRANSFORD, JR. (615) 292-1180

SUBSTANCE IDENTIFICATION

CAS-NUMBER 139-41-3
SUBSTANCE: **SODIUM DIHYDROXYETHYLGLYCINE**
TRADE NAMES/SYNONYMS: GLYCINE, N,N-BIS(2-HYDROXYETHYL)-, MONOSODIUM SALT; N,N-BIS(2-HYDROXYETHYL)GLYCINE MONOSODIUM SALT; HAMPSHIRE DEG; MONAQUEST IA; SODIUM DIETHANOLGLYCINATE; C6H12NNAO4; PST71447
CHEMICAL FAMILY: SALT
MOLECULAR FORMULA: NA-O-O-C-C-H2-N-(C-H2-C-H2-OH)2
MOLECULAR WEIGHT: 185.16
CERCLA RATINGS (SCALE 0-3): HEALTH=U FIRE=U REACTIVITY=0 PERSISTENCE=0
NFPA RATINGS (SCALE 0-4): HEALTH=U FIRE=U REACTIVITY=0

COMPONENTS AND CONTAMINANTS

COMPONENT: SODIUM DIHYDROXYETHYLGLYCINE ***PERCENT:*** 100.0
CAS# 139-41-3
OTHER CONTAMINANTS: NONE
EXPOSURE LIMITS: NO OCCUPATIONAL EXPOSURE LIMITS ESTABLISHED BY OSHA, ACGIH, OR NIOSH.

PHYSICAL DATA

DESCRIPTION: CLEAR, STRAW-COLORED LIQUID. ***MELTING POINT:*** 14 F (-10 C)
SPECIFIC GRAVITY: 1.204 @ 25 C ***SOLUBILITY IN WATER:*** NOT AVAILABLE

FIRE AND EXPLOSION DATA

FIRE AND EXPLOSION HAZARD: UNKNOWN FIRE AND EXPLOSION HAZARD.
FLASH POINT: NOT AVAILABLE
FIREFIGHTING MEDIA: DRY CHEMICAL, CARBON DIOXIDE, HALON, WATER SPRAY OR STANDARD FOAM (1987 EMERGENCY RESPONSE GUIDEBOOK, DOT P 5800.4). FOR LARGER FIRES, USE WATER SPRAY, FOG OR STANDARD FOAM (1987 EMERGENCY RESPONSE GUIDEBOOK, DOT P 5800.4).
FIREFIGHTING: MOVE CONTAINER FROM FIRE AREA IF POSSIBLE. COOL FIRE-EXPOSED CONTAINERS WITH WATER FROM SIDE UNTIL WELL AFTER FIRE IS OUT. STAY AWAY FROM STORAGE TANK ENDS. FOR MASSIVE FIRE IN STORAGE AREA, USE UNMANNED HOSE HOLDER OR MONITOR NOZZLES, ELSE WITHDRAW FROM AREA AND LET FIRE BURN. WITHDRAW IMMEDIATELY IN CASE OF RISING SOUND FROM VENTING SAFETY DEVICE OR ANY DISCOLORATION OF STORAGE TANK DUE TO FIRE (1987 EMERGENCY RESPONSE GUIDEBOOK, DOT P 5800.4, GUIDE PAGE 27). EXTINGUISH ONLY IF FLOW CAN BE STOPPED; USE FLOODING AMOUNTS OF WATER AS A FOG, SOLID STREAMS MAY BE INEFFECTIVE. COOL CONTAINERS WITH FLOODING AMOUNTS OF WATER, APPLY FROM AS FAR A DISTANCE AS POSSIBLE. AVOID BREATHING VAPORS, KEEP UPWIND.

TOXICITY

SODIUM DIHYDROXYETHYLGLYCINE: CARCINOGEN STATUS: NONE. ACUTE TOXICITY LEVEL: NO DATA AVAILABLE. TARGET EFFECTS: NO DATA AVAILABLE.

HEALTH EFFECTS AND FIRST AID

INHALATION: SODIUM DIHYDROXYETHYLGLYCINE: **ACUTE EXPOSURE**- NO DATA AVAILABLE. **CHRONIC EXPOSURE**- NO DATA AVAILABLE.
FIRST AID- REMOVE FROM EXPOSURE AREA TO FRESH AIR IMMEDIATELY. IF BREATHING HAS STOPPED, PERFORM ARTIFICIAL RESPIRATION. KEEP PERSON WARM AND AT REST. TREAT SYMPTOMATICALLY AND SUPPORTIVELY. GET MEDICAL ATTENTION IMMEDIATELY.

SKIN CONTACT: SODIUM DIHYDROXYETHYLGLYCINE: **ACUTE EXPOSURE**- NO DATA AVAILABLE. **CHRONIC EXPOSURE**- NO DATA AVAILABLE.
FIRST AID- REMOVE CONTAMINATED CLOTHING AND SHOES IMMEDIATELY. WASH AFFECTED AREA WITH SOAP OR MILD DETERGENT AND LARGE AMOUNTS OF WATER UNTIL NO EVIDENCE OF CHEMICAL REMAINS (APPROXIMATELY 15-20 MINUTES). GET MEDICAL ATTENTION IMMEDIATELY.

EYE CONTACT: SODIUM DIHYDROXYETHYLGLYCINE: **ACUTE EXPOSURE**- NO DATA AVAILABLE. **CHRONIC EXPOSURE**- NO DATA AVAILABLE.
FIRST AID- WASH EYES IMMEDIATELY WITH LARGE AMOUNTS OF WATER OR NORMAL SALINE, OCCASIONALLY LIFTING UPPER AND LOWER LIDS, UNTIL NO EVIDENCE OF CHEMICAL REMAINS (APPROXIMATELY 15-20 MINUTES). GET MEDICAL ATTENTION IMMEDIATELY.

INGESTION: SODIUM DIHYDROXYETHYLGLYCINE: **ACUTE EXPOSURE**- NO DATA AVAILABLE. **CHRONIC EXPOSURE**- NO DATA AVAILABLE.
FIRST AID- TREAT SYMPTOMATICALLY AND SUPPORTIVELY. GET MEDICAL ATTENTION IMMEDIATELY. IF VOMITING OCCURS, KEEP HEAD LOWER THAN HIPS TO PREVENT ASPIRATION.
ANTIDOTE: NO SPECIFIC ANTIDOTE. TREAT SYMPTOMATICALLY AND SUPPORTIVELY.

REACTIVITY

REACTIVITY: STABLE UNDER NORMAL TEMPERATURES AND PRESSURES.
INCOMPATIBILITIES: SODIUM DIHYDROXYETHYLGLYCINE: OXIDIZERS (STRONG): FIRE AND EXPLOSION HAZARD.
DECOMPOSITION: THERMAL DECOMPOSITION PRODUCTS MAY INCLUDE TOXIC OXIDES OF CARBON.
POLYMERIZATION: HAZARDOUS POLYMERIZATION HAS NOT BEEN REPORTED TO OCCUR UNDER NORMAL TEMPERATURES AND PRESSURES.

STORAGE AND DISPOSAL

OBSERVE ALL FEDERAL, STATE AND LOCAL REGULATIONS WHEN STORING OR DISPOSING OF THIS SUBSTANCE. FOR ASSISTANCE, CONTACT THE DISTRICT DIRECTOR OF THE ENVIRONMENTAL PROTECTION AGENCY.

STORAGE

STORE AWAY FROM INCOMPATIBLE SUBSTANCES.

CONDITIONS TO AVOID

AVOID CONTACT WITH HEAT, SPARKS, FLAMES, OR OTHER SOURCES OF IGNITION. VAPORS MAY BE EXPLOSIVE. AVOID OVERHEATING OF CONTAINERS; CONTAINERS MAY VIOLENTLY RUPTURE IN HEAT OF FIRE. AVOID CONTAMINATION OF WATER SOURCES.

SPILL AND LEAK PROCEDURES

OCCUPATIONAL SPILL: SHUT OFF IGNITION SOURCES. STOP LEAK IF YOU CAN DO IT WITHOUT RISK. USE WATER SPRAY TO REDUCE VAPORS. FOR SMALL SPILLS, TAKE UP WITH SAND OR OTHER ABSORBENT MATERIAL AND PLACE INTO CONTAINERS

FOR LATER DISPOSAL. FOR LARGER SPILLS, DIKE FAR AHEAD OF SPILL FOR LATER DISPOSAL. NO SMOKING, FLAMES OR FLARES IN HAZARD AREA. KEEP UNNECESSARY PEOPLE AWAY; ISOLATE HAZARD AREA AND RESTRICT ENTRY.

PROTECTIVE EQUIPMENT

VENTILATION: PROVIDE LOCAL EXHAUST OR PROCESS ENCLOSURE VENTILATION. VENTILATION EQUIPMENT MUST BE EXPLOSION-PROOF.

RESPIRATOR: THE FOLLOWING RESPIRATORS ARE RECOMMENDED BASED ON INFORMATION FOUND IN THE PHYSICAL DATA, TOXICITY AND HEALTH EFFECTS SECTIONS. THEY ARE RANKED IN ORDER FROM MINIMUM TO MAXIMUM RESPIRATORY PROTECTION. THE SPECIFIC RESPIRATOR SELECTED MUST BE BASED ON CONTAMINATION LEVELS FOUND IN THE WORK PLACE, MUST NOT EXCEED THE WORKING LIMITS OF THE RESPIRATOR AND BE JOINTLY APPROVED BY THE NATIONAL INSTITUTE FOR OCCUPATIONAL SAFETY AND HEALTH AND THE MINE SAFETY AND HEALTH ADMINISTRATION (NIOSH-MSHA).

CHEMICAL CARTRIDGE RESPIRATOR WITH AN ORGANIC VAPOR CARTRIDGE(S) WITH AN ACID GAS CARTRIDGE(S) AND A FULL FACEPIECE.

GAS MASK WITH ORGANIC VAPOR CANISTER (CHIN-STYLE OR FRONT- OR BACK-MOUNTED CANISTER), WITH A FULL FACEPIECE, PROVIDING PROTECTION AGAINST ACID GASES.

TYPE 'C' SUPPLIED-AIR RESPIRATOR WITH A FULL FACEPIECE OPERATED IN PRESSURE-DEMAND OR OTHER POSITIVE PRESSURE MODE OR WITH A FULL FACEPIECE, HELMET OR HOOD OPERATED IN CONTINUOUS-FLOW MODE.

SELF-CONTAINED BREATHING APPARATUS WITH A FULL FACEPIECE OPERATED IN PRESSURE-DEMAND OR OTHER POSITIVE PRESSURE MODE.

FOR FIREFIGHTING AND OTHER IMMEDIATELY DANGEROUS TO LIFE OR HEALTH CONDITIONS:

SELF-CONTAINED BREATHING APPARATUS WITH FULL FACEPIECE OPERATED IN PRESSURE-DEMAND OR OTHER POSITIVE PRESSURE MODE.

SUPPLIED-AIR RESPIRATOR WITH FULL FACEPIECE AND OPERATED IN PRESSURE-DEMAND OR OTHER POSITIVE PRESSURE MODE IN COMBINATION WITH AN AUXILIARY SELF-CONTAINED BREATHING APPARATUS OPERATED IN PRESSURE-DEMAND OR OTHER POSITIVE PRESSURE MODE.

CLOTHING: EMPLOYEE MUST WEAR APPROPRIATE PROTECTIVE (IMPERVIOUS) CLOTHING AND EQUIPMENT TO PREVENT REPEATED OR PROLONGED SKIN CONTACT WITH THIS SUBSTANCE.

GLOVES: EMPLOYEE MUST WEAR APPROPRIATE PROTECTIVE GLOVES TO PREVENT CONTACT WITH THIS SUBSTANCE.

EYE PROTECTION: EMPLOYEE MUST WEAR SPLASH-PROOF OR DUST-RESISTANT SAFETY GOGGLES TO PREVENT EYE CONTACT WITH THIS SUBSTANCE.

EMERGENCY EYE WASH: WHERE THERE IS ANY POSSIBILITY THAT AN EMPLOYEE'S EYES MAY BE EXPOSED TO THIS SUBSTANCE, THE EMPLOYER SHOULD PROVIDE AN EYE WASH FOUNTAIN WITHIN THE IMMEDIATE WORK AREA FOR EMERGENCY USE.

AUTHORIZED BY- OCCUPATIONAL HEALTH SERVICES, INC.

CREATION DATE: 11/15/89 ***REVISION DATE:*** 01/09/90

MATERIAL SAFETY DATA SHEET

OCCUPATIONAL HEALTH SERVICES, INC.
AGRICULTURE AND PESTICIDE DIVISION
450 SEVENTH AVENUE, SUITE 2407
NEW YORK, NEW YORK 10123
1-800-445-MSDS OR (212) 967-1100

EMERGENCY CONTACT:
JOHN S. BRANSFORD, JR. (615) 292-1180

SUBSTANCE IDENTIFICATION

CAS-NUMBER 8000-48-4

SUBSTANCE: OIL OF EUCALYPTUS

TRADE NAMES/SYNONYMS: OILS, EUCALYPTUS; DINKUM OIL; EUCALYPTUS OIL; PST71453

CHEMICAL FAMILY: ESSENTIAL OIL

CERCLA RATINGS (SCALE 0-3): HEALTH=2 FIRE=U REACTIVITY=0 PERSISTENCE=1

NFPA RATINGS (SCALE 0-4): HEALTH=2 FIRE=U REACTIVITY=0

COMPONENTS AND CONTAMINANTS

COMPONENT: OIL OF EUCALYPTUS ***PERCENT:*** 100
CAS# 8000-48-4

OTHER CONTAMINANTS: NONE

EXPOSURE LIMITS: NO OCCUPATIONAL EXPOSURE LIMITS ESTABLISHED BY OSHA, ACGIH, OR NIOSH.

PHYSICAL DATA

DESCRIPTION: COLORLESS TO PALE YELLOW LIQUID WITH CAMPHOR-LIKE ODOR AND SPICY, COOL TASTE.

BOILING POINT: NOT AVAILABLE

SPECIFIC GRAVITY: 0.905-0.925 @ 25 C

SOLUBILITY IN WATER: ALMOST INSOLUBLE

SOLVENT SOLUBILITY: SOLUBLE IN ALCOHOL, OILS, AND FATS.

FIRE AND EXPLOSION DATA

FIRE AND EXPLOSION HAZARD: UNKNOWN FIRE AND EXPLOSION HAZARD.

FIREFIGHTING MEDIA: DRY CHEMICAL, CARBON DIOXIDE, HALON, WATER SPRAY OR STANDARD FOAM (1987 EMERGENCY RESPONSE GUIDEBOOK, DOT P 5800.4). FOR LARGER FIRES, USE WATER SPRAY, FOG OR STANDARD FOAM (1987 EMERGENCY RESPONSE GUIDEBOOK, DOT P 5800.4).

FIREFIGHTING: MOVE CONTAINER FROM FIRE AREA IF POSSIBLE. COOL FIRE-EXPOSED CONTAINERS WITH WATER FROM SIDE UNTIL WELL AFTER FIRE IS OUT. STAY AWAY FROM STORAGE TANK ENDS. FOR MASSIVE FIRE IN STORAGE AREA, USE UNMANNED HOSE HOLDER OR MONITOR NOZZLES, ELSE WITHDRAW FROM AREA AND LET FIRE BURN. WITHDRAW IMMEDIATELY IN CASE OF RISING SOUND FROM VENTING SAFETY DEVICE OR ANY DISCOLORATION OF STORAGE TANK DUE TO FIRE (1987 EMERGENCY RESPONSE GUIDEBOOK, DOT P 5800.4, GUIDE PAGE 27). EXTINGUISH ONLY IF FLOW CAN BE STOPPED; USE FLOODING AMOUNTS OF WATER AS A FOG, SOLID STREAMS MAY BE INEFFECTIVE. COOL CONTAINERS WITH FLOODING AMOUNTS OF WATER, APPLY FROM AS FAR A DISTANCE AS POSSIBLE. AVOID BREATHING VAPORS, KEEP UPWIND.

TOXICITY

OIL OF EUCALYPTUS: IRRITATION DATA: 500 MG/24 HOURS SKIN-RABBIT MODERATE. TOXICITY DATA: 2480 MG/KG SKIN-RABBIT LD50; 375 MG/KG ORAL-MAN LDLO; 218 MG/KG ORAL-CHILD TDLO; 2480 MG/KG ORAL-RAT LD50. CARCINOGEN STATUS: NONE. LOCAL EFFECTS: IRRITANT- SKIN. ACUTE TOXICITY LEVEL: MODERATELY TOXIC BY INGESTION; SLIGHTLY TOXIC BY DERMAL ABSORPTION. TARGET EFFECTS: POISONING MAY AFFECT THE CENTRAL NERVOUS SYSTEM.

HEALTH EFFECTS AND FIRST AID

INHALATION: OIL OF EUCALYPTUS: **ACUTE EXPOSURE-** INHALATION OF VOLATILE OILS MAY CAUSE DIZZINESS, RAPID, SHALLOW BREATHING, TACHYCARDIA, BRONCHIAL IRRITATION AND UNCONSCIOUSNESS OR CONVULSIONS. COMPLICATIONS MAY INCLUDE ANURIA, PULMONARY EDEMA, AND BRONCHIAL PNEUMONIA. **CHRONIC EXPOSURE-** NO DATA AVAILABLE.

FIRST AID- REMOVE FROM EXPOSURE AREA TO FRESH AIR IMMEDIATELY. IF BREATHING HAS STOPPED, PERFORM ARTIFICIAL RESPIRATION. KEEP PERSON WARM AND AT REST. TREAT SYMPTOMATICALLY AND SUPPORTIVELY. GET MEDICAL ATTENTION IMMEDIATELY.

SKIN CONTACT: OIL OF EUCALYPTUS: IRRITANT. **ACUTE EXPOSURE-** CONTACT HAS PRODUCED MODERATE IRRITATION IN RABBITS. **CHRONIC EXPOSURE-** REPEATED OR PROLONGED EXPOSURE TO IRRITANTS MAY CAUSE DERMATITIS.

FIRST AID- REMOVE CONTAMINATED CLOTHING AND SHOES IMMEDIATELY. WASH AFFECTED AREA WITH SOAP OR MILD DETERGENT AND LARGE AMOUNTS OF WATER UNTIL NO EVIDENCE OF CHEMICAL REMAINS (APPROXIMATELY 15-20 MINUTES). GET MEDICAL ATTENTION IMMEDIATELY.

EYE CONTACT: OIL OF EUCALYPTUS: **ACUTE EXPOSURE-** DIRECT CONTACT WITH VOLATILE OILS MAY CAUSE IRRITATION. **CHRONIC EXPOSURE-** NO DATA AVAILABLE.

FIRST AID- WASH EYES IMMEDIATELY WITH LARGE AMOUNTS OF WATER OR NORMAL SALINE, OCCASIONALLY LIFTING UPPER AND LOWER LIDS, UNTIL NO EVIDENCE OF CHEMICAL REMAINS (APPROXIMATELY 15-20 MINUTES). GET MEDICAL ATTENTION IMMEDIATELY.

INGESTION: OIL OF EUCALYPTUS: NARCOTIC. **ACUTE EXPOSURE-** INGESTION MAY CAUSE A EUCALYPTUS ODOR OF THE BREATH AND URINE, VERTIGO, ATAXIA, MUSCLE WEAKNESS, CEREBRAL DEPRESSION, INSENSIBILITY, DELIRIUM, STUPOR, PALLOR, DYSPNEA, CYANOSIS, RESPIRATORY STRIDOR, EXTREME MIOSIS, CIRCULATORY COLLAPSE AND COMA. RARELY, SYMPTOMS MAY BE DELAYED UP TO 2 HOURS. GIDDINESS, CONFUSION, INCOORDINATION, FAINTNESS, PERSISTENT DROWSINESS, PROFOUND SLEEP, A SUFFOCATING SENSATION, PULSELESSNESS AND RESIDUAL DIZZINESS HAVE ALSO BEEN REPORTED. ADDITIONAL EFFECTS DUE TO VOLATILE OILS MAY INCLUDE ABDOMINAL BURNING, NAUSEA AND VOMITING, DIARRHEA, DYSURIA, HEMATURIA, UNCONSCIOUSNESS, SHALLOW RESPIRATION, AND CONVULSIONS. COMPLICATIONS MAY INCLUDE ANURIA, PULMONARY EDEMA, AND BRONCHIAL PNEUMONIA. PATHOLOGIC FINDINGS FROM INGESTION

OF VOLATILE OILS INCLUDE RENAL DEGENERATIVE CHANGES AND INTENSE CONGESTION AND EDEMA IN THE LUNGS, BRAIN AND GASTRIC MUCOSA. **CHRONIC EXPOSURE-** NO DATA AVAILABLE.

FIRST AID- GIVE 120-240 ML OF MILK; THEN REMOVE BY GASTRIC LAVAGE OR EMESIS, TAKING CARE TO PREVENT ASPIRATION. FOLLOW THESE PROCEDURES BY ADMINISTERING 30-60 ML OF FLEET'S PHOSPHO-SODA DILUTED 1:4 IN WATER. PERFORM ARTIFICIAL RESPIRATION IF NECESSARY. GET MEDICAL ATTENTION (DREISBACH, HANDBOOK OF POISONING, 12TH ED.). FIRST AID SHOULD BE PERFORMED BY QUALIFIED MEDICAL PERSONNEL.

ANTIDOTE: NO SPECIFIC ANTIDOTE. TREAT SYMPTOMATICALLY AND SUPPORTIVELY.

REACTIVITY

REACTIVITY: STABLE UNDER NORMAL TEMPERATURES AND PRESSURES.

INCOMPATIBILITIES: OIL OF EUCALYTUS: OXIDIZERS (STRONG): FIRE AND EXPLOSION HAZARD.

DECOMPOSITION: THERMAL DECOMPOSITION MAY RELEASE ACRID SMOKE AND IRRITATING FUMES.

POLYMERIZATION: HAZARDOUS POLYMERIZATION HAS NOT BEEN REPORTED TO OCCUR UNDER NORMAL TEMPERATURES AND PRESSURES.

STORAGE AND DISPOSAL

OBSERVE ALL FEDERAL, STATE AND LOCAL REGULATIONS WHEN STORING OR DISPOSING OF THIS SUBSTANCE. FOR ASSISTANCE, CONTACT THE DISTRICT DIRECTOR OF THE ENVIRONMENTAL PROTECTION AGENCY. STORE IN A COOL PLACE PROTECTED FROM LIGHT.

CONDITIONS TO AVOID

AVOID CONTACT WITH HEAT, SPARKS, FLAMES, OR OTHER SOURCES OF IGNITION. VAPORS MAY BE EXPLOSIVE. AVOID OVERHEATING OF CONTAINERS; CONTAINERS MAY VIOLENTLY RUPTURE IN HEAT OF FIRE. AVOID CONTAMINATION OF WATER SOURCES.

SPILL AND LEAK PROCEDURES

OCCUPATIONAL SPILL: SHUT OFF IGNITION SOURCES. STOP LEAK IF YOU CAN DO IT WITHOUT RISK. USE WATER SPRAY TO REDUCE VAPORS. FOR SMALL SPILLS, TAKE UP WITH SAND OR OTHER ABSORBENT MATERIAL AND PLACE INTO CONTAINERS FOR LATER DISPOSAL. FOR LARGER SPILLS, DIKE FAR AHEAD OF SPILL FOR LATER DISPOSAL. NO SMOKING, FLAMES OR FLARES IN HAZARD AREA. KEEP UNNECESSARY PEOPLE AWAY; ISOLATE HAZARD AREA AND RESTRICT ENTRY.

PROTECTIVE EQUIPMENT

VENTILATION: PROVIDE LOCAL EXHAUST OR GENERAL DILUTION VENTILATION. VENTILATION EQUIPMENT MUST BE EXPLOSION-PROOF.

RESPIRATOR: THE FOLLOWING RESPIRATORS ARE RECOMMENDED BASED ON INFORMATION FOUND IN THE PHYSICAL DATA, TOXICITY AND HEALTH EFFECTS SECTIONS. THEY ARE RANKED IN ORDER FROM MINIMUM TO MAXIMUM RESPIRATORY PROTECTION. THE SPECIFIC RESPIRATOR SELECTED MUST BE BASED ON CONTAMINATION LEVELS FOUND IN THE WORK PLACE, MUST NOT EXCEED THE WORKING LIMITS OF THE RESPIRATOR AND BE JOINTLY APPROVED BY THE NATIONAL INSTITUTE FOR OCCUPATIONAL SAFETY AND HEALTH AND THE MINE SAFETY AND HEALTH ADMINISTRATION (NIOSH-MSHA).

CHEMICAL CARTRIDGE RESPIRATOR WITH AN ORGANIC VAPOR CARTRIDGE(S) WITH A FULL FACEPIECE.

GAS MASK WITH ORGANIC VAPOR CANISTER (CHIN-STYLE OR FRONT- OR BACK-MOUNTED CANISTER) WITH A FULL FACEPIECE.

TYPE 'C' SUPPLIED-AIR RESPIRATOR WITH A FULL FACEPIECE OPERATED IN PRESSURE-DEMAND OR OTHER POSITIVE PRESSURE MODE OR WITH A FULL FACEPIECE, HELMET OR HOOD OPERATED IN CONTINUOUS-FLOW MODE.

SELF-CONTAINED BREATHING APPARATUS WITH A FULL FACEPIECE OPERATED IN PRESSURE-DEMAND OR OTHER POSITIVE PRESSURE MODE.

FOR FIREFIGHTING AND OTHER IMMEDIATELY DANGEROUS TO LIFE OR HEALTH CONDITIONS:

SELF-CONTAINED BREATHING APPARATUS WITH FULL FACEPIECE OPERATED IN PRESSURE-DEMAND OR OTHER POSITIVE PRESSURE MODE.

SUPPLIED-AIR RESPIRATOR WITH FULL FACEPIECE AND OPERATED IN PRESSURE-DEMAND OR OTHER POSITIVE PRESSURE MODE IN COMBINATION WITH AN AUXILIARY SELF-CONTAINED BREATHING APPARATUS OPERATED IN PRESSURE-DEMAND OR OTHER POSITIVE PRESSURE MODE.

CLOTHING: EMPLOYEE MUST WEAR APPROPRIATE PROTECTIVE (IMPERVIOUS) CLOTHING AND EQUIPMENT TO PREVENT REPEATED OR PROLONGED SKIN CONTACT WITH THIS SUBSTANCE.

GLOVES: EMPLOYEE MUST WEAR APPROPRIATE PROTECTIVE GLOVES TO PREVENT CONTACT WITH THIS SUBSTANCE.

EYE PROTECTION: EMPLOYEE MUST WEAR SPLASH-PROOF OR DUST-RESISTANT SAFETY GOGGLES TO PREVENT EYE CONTACT WITH THIS SUBSTANCE.

EMERGENCY EYE WASH: WHERE THERE IS ANY POSSIBILITY THAT AN EMPLOYEE'S EYES MAY BE EXPOSED TO THIS SUBSTANCE, THE EMPLOYER SHOULD PROVIDE AN EYE WASH FOUNTAIN WITHIN THE IMMEDIATE WORK AREA FOR EMERGENCY USE.

AUTHORIZED BY- OCCUPATIONAL HEALTH SERVICES, INC.
CREATION DATE: 02/08/90 ***REVISION DATE:*** 05/18/90

MATERIAL SAFETY DATA SHEET

OCCUPATIONAL HEALTH SERVICES, INC.
AGRICULTURE AND PESTICIDE DIVISION
450 SEVENTH AVENUE, SUITE 2407
NEW YORK, NEW YORK 10123
1-800-445-MSDS OR (212) 967-1100

EMERGENCY CONTACT:
JOHN S. BRANSFORD, JR. (615) 292-1180

SUBSTANCE IDENTIFICATION

CAS-NUMBER 8007-44-1

SUBSTANCE: **PENNYROYAL OIL**

TRADE NAMES/SYNONYMS: OILS, PENNYROYAL, HEDEOMA PULEGIOIDES; AMERICAN PENNYROYAL OIL; OIL OF HEDEOMA; OIL OF PENNYROYAL; OIL OF PENNYROYAL-AMERICAN; PST71456

CHEMICAL FAMILY: ESSENTIAL OIL

CERCLA RATINGS (SCALE 0-3): HEALTH=3 FIRE=U REACTIVITY=0 PERSISTENCE=1

NFPA RATINGS (SCALE 0-4): HEALTH=3 FIRE=U REACTIVITY=0

COMPONENTS AND CONTAMINANTS

COMPONENT: PENNYROYAL OIL ***PERCENT:*** 100.0
CAS# 8007-44-1

OTHER CONTAMINANTS: NONE

EXPOSURE LIMITS: NO OCCUPATIONAL EXPOSURE LIMITS ESTABLISHED BY OSHA, ACGIH, OR NIOSH.

PHYSICAL DATA

DESCRIPTION: LIGHT YELLOW TO REDDISH LIQUID WITH A MINT-LIKE ODOR.

BOILING POINT: NOT AVAILABLE ***SPECIFIC GRAVITY:*** 0.920-0.935 @ 25 C

SOLUBILITY IN WATER: SLIGHTLY SOLUBLE

SOLVENT SOLUBILITY: SOLUBLE IN FIXED OILS, ALCOHOL, CHLOROFORM, ETHER, PROPYLENE GLYCOL; MINERAL OIL; ALMOST INSOLUBLE IN GLYCERIN.

FIRE AND EXPLOSION DATA

FIRE AND EXPLOSION HAZARD: UNKNOWN FIRE AND EXPLOSION HAZARD.

FIREFIGHTING MEDIA: DRY CHEMICAL, CARBON DIOXIDE, HALON, WATER SPRAY OR STANDARD FOAM (1987 EMERGENCY RESPONSE GUIDEBOOK, DOT P 5800.4). FOR LARGER FIRES, USE WATER SPRAY, FOG OR STANDARD FOAM (1987 EMERGENCY RESPONSE GUIDEBOOK, DOT P 5800.4).

FIREFIGHTING: MOVE CONTAINER FROM FIRE AREA IF POSSIBLE. COOL FIRE-EXPOSED CONTAINERS WITH WATER FROM SIDE UNTIL WELL AFTER FIRE IS OUT. STAY AWAY FROM STORAGE TANK ENDS. FOR MASSIVE FIRE IN STORAGE AREA, USE UNMANNED HOSE HOLDER OR MONITOR NOZZLES, ELSE WITHDRAW FROM AREA AND LET FIRE BURN. WITHDRAW IMMEDIATELY IN CASE OF RISING SOUND FROM VENTING SAFETY DEVICE OR ANY DISCOLORATION OF STORAGE TANK DUE TO FIRE (1987 EMERGENCY RESPONSE GUIDEBOOK, DOT P 5800.4, GUIDE PAGE 27). EXTINGUISH ONLY IF FLOW CAN BE STOPPED; USE FLOODING AMOUNTS OF WATER AS A FOG, SOLID STREAMS MAY BE INEFFECTIVE. COOL CONTAINERS WITH FLOODING AMOUNTS OF WATER, APPLY FROM AS FAR A DISTANCE AS POSSIBLE. AVOID BREATHING VAPORS, KEEP UPWIND.

TOXICITY

PENNYROYAL OIL: IRRITATION DATA: 100% SKIN-MOUSE MODERATE. TOXICITY DATA: 400 MG/KG ORAL-RAT LD50. CARCINOGEN STATUS: NONE. LOCAL EFFECTS: IRRITANT- SKIN. ACUTE TOXICITY LEVEL: TOXIC BY INGESTION. TARGET EFFECTS: NO DATA AVAILABLE.

HEALTH EFFECTS AND FIRST AID

INHALATION: PENNYROYAL OIL: **ACUTE EXPOSURE-** INHALATION OF VOLATILE OILS MAY CAUSE DIZZINESS, RAPID, SHALLOW BREATHING, TACHYCARDIA, BRONCHIAL IRRITATION AND UNCONSCIOUSNESS OR CONVULSIONS. COMPLICATIONS MAY INCLUDE ANURIA, PULMONARY EDEMA, AND BRONCHIAL PNEUMONIA. **CHRONIC EXPOSURE-** NO DATA AVAILABLE.

FIRST AID- REMOVE FROM EXPOSURE AREA TO FRESH AIR IMMEDIATELY. IF BREATHING HAS STOPPED, PERFORM ARTIFICIAL RESPIRATION. KEEP PERSON WARM AND AT REST. TREAT SYMPTOMATICALLY AND SUPPORTIVELY. GET MEDICAL ATTENTION IMMEDIATELY.

SKIN CONTACT: PENNYROYAL OIL: IRRITANT. **ACUTE EXPOSURE-** CONTACT WITH THE PURE OIL HAS PRODUCED MODERATE IRRITATION IN MICE. **CHRONIC EXPOSURE-** REPEATED OR PROLONGED EXPOSURE TO IRRITANTS MAY CAUSE DERMATITIS.
FIRST AID- REMOVE CONTAMINATED CLOTHING AND SHOES IMMEDIATELY. WASH AFFECTED AREA WITH SOAP OR MILD DETERGENT AND LARGE AMOUNTS OF WATER UNTIL NO EVIDENCE OF CHEMICAL REMAINS (APPROXIMATELY 15-20 MINUTES). GET MEDICAL ATTENTION IMMEDIATELY.

EYE CONTACT: PENNYROYAL OIL: **ACUTE EXPOSURE-** DIRECT CONTACT WITH VOLATILE OILS MAY CAUSE IRRITATION. **CHRONIC EXPOSURE-** REPEATED OR PROLONGED EXPOSURE TO IRRITANTS MAY CAUSE CONJUNCTIVITIS.
FIRST AID- WASH EYES IMMEDIATELY WITH LARGE AMOUNTS OF WATER OR NORMAL SALINE, OCCASIONALLY LIFTING UPPER AND LOWER LIDS, UNTIL NO EVIDENCE OF CHEMICAL REMAINS (APPROXIMATELY 15-20 MINUTES). GET MEDICAL ATTENTION IMMEDIATELY.

INGESTION: PENNYROYAL OIL: TOXIC. **ACUTE EXPOSURE-** INGESTION OF 30 ML OF PENNYROYAL OIL BY AN 18 YEAR OLD GIRL CAUSED VOMITING, ABDOMINAL PAIN, HEMATEMESIS, SHOCK, DISSEMINATED INTRAVASCULAR COAGULATION, MASSIVE HEPATIC NECROSIS, RENAL FAILURE AND DEATH ON THE SEVENTH DAY. ADDITIONAL SYMPTOMS INCLUDING CONFUSION, DELIRIUM, RESTLESSNESS, TWITCHING, TOXIC ENCEPHALOPATHY, MYDRIASIS AND PERIPHERAL VASOMOTOR COLLAPSE MAY OCCUR. A CASE OF FRANK EPILEPTIFORM CONVULSIONS HAS BEEN REPORTED. ADDITIONAL SYMTPOMS DUE TO VOLATILE OILS MAY INCLUDE ABDOMINAL BURNING, NAUSEA AND VOMITING, DIARRHEA, DYSURIA, HEMATURIA, UNCONSCIOUSNESS, SHALLOW RESPIRATION, AND CONVULSIONS. COMPLICATIONS MAY INCLUDE ANURIA, PULMONARY EDEMA, AND BRONCHIAL PNEUMONIA. PATHOLOGIC FINDINGS FROM INGESTION OF VOLATILE OILS INCLUDE RENAL DEGENERATIVE CHANGES AND INTENSE CONGESTION AND EDEMA IN THE LUNGS, BRAIN AND GASTRIC MUCOSA. **CHRONIC EXPOSURE-** NO DATA AVAILABLE.
FIRST AID- GIVE 120-240 ML OF MILK; THEN REMOVE BY GASTRIC LAVAGE OR EMESIS, TAKING CARE TO PREVENT ASPIRATION. FOLLOW THESE PROCEDURES BY ADMINISTERING 30-60 ML OF FLEET'S PHOSPHO-SODA DILUTED 1:4 IN WATER. PERFORM ARTIFICIAL RESPIRATION IF NECESSARY. GET MEDICAL ATTENTION (DREISBACH, HANDBOOK OF POISONING, 12TH ED.). FIRST AID SHOULD BE PERFORMED BY QUALIFIED MEDICAL PERSONNEL.
ANTIDOTE: NO SPECIFIC ANTIDOTE. TREAT SYMPTOMATICALLY AND SUPPORTIVELY.

REACTIVITY

REACTIVITY: STABLE UNDER NORMAL TEMPERATURES AND PRESSURES.
INCOMPATIBILITIES: PENNYROYAL OIL: OXIDIZERS (STRONG): FIRE AND EXPLOSION HAZARD.
DECOMPOSITION: THERMAL DECOMPOSITION MAY RELEASE ACRID SMOKE AND IRRITATING FUMES.
POLYMERIZATION: HAZARDOUS POLYMERIZATION HAS NOT BEEN REPORTED TO OCCUR UNDER NORMAL TEMPERATURES AND PRESSURES.

STORAGE AND DISPOSAL

OBSERVE ALL FEDERAL, STATE AND LOCAL REGULATIONS WHEN STORING OR DISPOSING OF THIS SUBSTANCE. FOR ASSISTANCE, CONTACT THE DISTRICT DIRECTOR OF THE ENVIRONMENTAL PROTECTION AGENCY.

****STORAGE****

STORE AWAY FROM INCOMPATIBLE SUBSTANCES.
STORE IN A COOL, DRY PLACE; KEEP CONTAINER TIGHTLY CLOSED WHEN NOT IN USE.

CONDITIONS TO AVOID

AVOID CONTACT WITH HEAT, SPARKS, FLAMES, OR OTHER SOURCES OF IGNITION. VAPORS MAY BE EXPLOSIVE. AVOID OVERHEATING OF CONTAINERS; CONTAINERS MAY VIOLENTLY RUPTURE IN HEAT OF FIRE. AVOID CONTAMINATION OF WATER SOURCES.

SPILL AND LEAK PROCEDURES

OCCUPATIONAL SPILL: SHUT OFF IGNITION SOURCES. STOP LEAK IF YOU CAN DO IT WITHOUT RISK. USE WATER SPRAY TO REDUCE VAPORS. FOR SMALL SPILLS, TAKE UP WITH SAND OR OTHER ABSORBENT MATERIAL AND PLACE INTO CONTAINERS FOR LATER DISPOSAL. FOR LARGER SPILLS, DIKE FAR AHEAD OF SPILL FOR LATER DISPOSAL. NO SMOKING, FLAMES OR FLARES IN HAZARD AREA. KEEP UNNECESSARY PEOPLE AWAY; ISOLATE HAZARD AREA AND RESTRICT ENTRY.

PROTECTIVE EQUIPMENT

VENTILATION: PROVIDE LOCAL EXHAUST OR PROCESS ENCLOSURE VENTILATION. VENTILATION EQUIPMENT MUST BE EXPLOSION-PROOF.
RESPIRATOR: THE FOLLOWING RESPIRATORS ARE RECOMMENDED BASED ON INFORMATION FOUND IN THE PHYSICAL DATA, TOXICITY AND HEALTH EFFECTS SECTIONS. THEY ARE RANKED IN ORDER FROM MINIMUM TO MAXIMUM RESPIRATORY PROTECTION. THE SPECIFIC RESPIRATOR SELECTED MUST BE BASED ON CONTAMINATION LEVELS FOUND IN THE WORK PLACE, MUST NOT EXCEED THE WORKING LIMITS OF THE RESPIRATOR AND BE JOINTLY APPROVED BY THE NATIONAL INSTITUTE FOR OCCUPATIONAL SAFETY AND HEALTH AND THE MINE SAFETY AND HEALTH ADMINISTRATION (NIOSH-MSHA).
CHEMICAL CARTRIDGE RESPIRATOR WITH AN ORGANIC VAPOR CARTRIDGE(S) WITH A FULL FACEPIECE.
GAS MASK WITH ORGANIC VAPOR CANISTER (CHIN-STYLE OR FRONT- OR BACK-MOUNTED CANISTER) WITH A FULL FACEPIECE.
TYPE 'C' SUPPLIED-AIR RESPIRATOR WITH A FULL FACEPIECE OPERATED IN PRESSURE-DEMAND OR OTHER POSITIVE PRESSURE MODE OR WITH A FULL FACEPIECE, HELMET OR HOOD OPERATED IN CONTINUOUS-FLOW MODE. SELF-CONTAINED BREATHING APPARATUS WITH A FULL FACEPIECE OPERATED IN PRESSURE-DEMAND OR OTHER POSITIVE PRESSURE MODE.
FOR FIREFIGHTING AND OTHER IMMEDIATELY DANGEROUS TO LIFE OR HEALTH CONDITIONS:
SELF-CONTAINED BREATHING APPARATUS WITH FULL FACEPIECE OPERATED IN PRESSURE-DEMAND OR OTHER POSITIVE PRESSURE MODE.
SUPPLIED-AIR RESPIRATOR WITH FULL FACEPIECE AND OPERATED IN PRESSURE-DEMAND OR OTHER POSITIVE PRESSURE MODE IN COMBINATION WITH AN AUXILIARY SELF-CONTAINED BREATHING APPARATUS OPERATED IN PRESSURE-DEMAND OR OTHER POSITIVE PRESSURE MODE.
CLOTHING: EMPLOYEE MUST WEAR APPROPRIATE PROTECTIVE (IMPERVIOUS) CLOTHING AND EQUIPMENT TO PREVENT REPEATED OR PROLONGED SKIN CONTACT WITH THIS SUBSTANCE.
GLOVES: EMPLOYEE MUST WEAR APPROPRIATE PROTECTIVE GLOVES TO PREVENT CONTACT WITH THIS SUBSTANCE.
EYE PROTECTION: EMPLOYEE MUST WEAR SPLASH-PROOF OR DUST-RESISTANT SAFETY GOGGLES TO PREVENT EYE CONTACT WITH THIS SUBSTANCE.
EMERGENCY EYE WASH: WHERE THERE IS ANY POSSIBILITY THAT AN EMPLOYEE'S EYES MAY BE EXPOSED TO THIS SUBSTANCE, THE EMPLOYER SHOULD PROVIDE AN EYE WASH FOUNTAIN WITHIN THE IMMEDIATE WORK AREA FOR EMERGENCY USE.

AUTHORIZED BY- OCCUPATIONAL HEALTH SERVICES, INC.
CREATION DATE: 10/04/89 ***REVISION DATE:*** 05/18/90

MATERIAL SAFETY DATA SHEET

OCCUPATIONAL HEALTH SERVICES, INC.
AGRICULTURE AND PESTICIDE DIVISION
450 SEVENTH AVENUE, SUITE 2407
NEW YORK, NEW YORK 10123
1-800-445-MSDS OR (212) 967-1100

EMERGENCY CONTACT:
JOHN S. BRANSFORD, JR. (615) 292-1180

SUBSTANCE IDENTIFICATION

CAS-NUMBER 94-96-2
SUBSTANCE: **2-ETHYL-1,3-HEXANEDIOL**
TRADE NAMES/SYNONYMS: 1,3-HEXANEDIOL, 2-ETHYL-; ETHOHEXADIOL; 2-ETHYLHEXANEDIOL; ETHYL HEXYLENE GLYCOL; 2-ETHYL-3-PROPYL-1,3-PROPANEDIOL; OCTYLENE GLYCOL; RUTGERS 612; C8H18O2; PST71458
CHEMICAL FAMILY: GLYCOL
MOLECULAR FORMULA: C3-H7-C-H-(O-H)-C-H-(C2-H5)-C-H2-O-H
MOLECULAR WEIGHT: 146.23
CERCLA RATINGS (SCALE 0-3): HEALTH=2 FIRE=1 REACTIVITY=0 PERSISTENCE=0
NFPA RATINGS (SCALE 0-4): HEALTH=1 FIRE=1 REACTIVITY=0

COMPONENTS AND CONTAMINANTS

COMPONENT: 2-ETHYL-1,3-HEXANEDIOL ***PERCENT:*** 100.0
CAS# 94-96-2
OTHER CONTAMINANTS: NONE
EXPOSURE LIMITS: NO OCCUPATIONAL EXPOSURE LIMITS ESTABLISHED BY OSHA, ACGIH, OR NIOSH.

PHYSICAL DATA

DESCRIPTION: ODORLESS, COLORLESS, SLIGHTLY OILY, HYGROSCOPIC, VISCOUS LIQUID.

BOILING POINT: 471 F (244 C) ***MELTING POINT:*** -40 F (-40 C)

SPECIFIC GRAVITY: 0.9325 @ 22 C ***VISCOSITY:*** 0.323 CPS @ 20 C

VAPOR PRESSURE: <0.01 MMHG @ 20 C ***SOLUBILITY IN WATER:*** 0.6%

VAPOR DENSITY: 5.03

SOLVENT SOLUBILITY: SOLUBLE IN ETHANOL, ETHER, ISOPROPANOL, PROPYLENE GLYCOL, AND CASTOR OIL.

FIRE AND EXPLOSION DATA

FIRE AND EXPLOSION HAZARD: SLIGHT FIRE HAZARD WHEN EXPOSED TO HEAT OR FLAME.

FLASH POINT: 260 F (127 C) (OC) ***AUTOIGNITION TEMP.:*** 680 F (360 C)

FLAMMABILITY CLASS(OSHA): IIIB

FIREFIGHTING MEDIA: DRY CHEMICAL, CARBON DIOXIDE, HALON, WATER SPRAY OR STANDARD FOAM (1987 EMERGENCY RESPONSE GUIDEBOOK, DOT P 5800.4).
FOR LARGER FIRES, USE WATER SPRAY, FOG OR STANDARD FOAM (1987 EMERGENCY RESPONSE GUIDEBOOK, DOT P 5800.4).
ALCOHOL FOAM (NFPA 325M, FIRE HAZARD PROPERTIES OF FLAMMABLE LIQUIDS, GASES, AND VOLATILE SOLIDS, 1984).

FIREFIGHTING: MOVE CONTAINER FROM FIRE AREA IF POSSIBLE. DO NOT SCATTER SPILLED MATERIAL WITH HIGH PRESSURE WATER STREAMS. DIKE FIRE CONTROL WATER FOR LATER DISPOSAL (1987 EMERGENCY RESPONSE GUIDEBOOK, DOT P 5800.4, GUIDE PAGE 31).
USE AGENTS SUITABLE FOR TYPE OF SURROUNDING FIRE. AVOID BREATHING HAZARDOUS VAPORS, KEEP UPWIND.
WATER OR FOAM MAY CAUSE FROTHING (NFPA 325M, FIRE HAZARD PROPERTIES OF FLAMMABLE LIQUIDS, GASES, AND VOLATILE SOLIDS, 1984)

TOXICITY

2-ETHYL-1,3-HEXANEDIOL: IRRITATION DATA: 500 MG SKIN-RABBIT MILD; 5 MG EYES-RABBIT SEVERE. TOXICITY DATA: 2 GM/KG SKIN-RABBIT LD50; 9422 MG/KG SKIN-GUINEA PIG LD50; 1400 MG/KG ORAL-RAT LD50; 1900 MG/KG ORAL-MOUSE LD50; 2600 MG/KG ORAL-RABBIT LD50; 1790 MG/KG ORAL-GUINEA PIG LD50. CARCINOGEN STATUS: NONE. LOCAL EFFECTS: IRRITANT- INHALATION AND EYES. ACUTE TOXICITY LEVEL: MODERATELY TOXIC BY DERMAL ABSORPTION AND INGESTION. TARGET EFFECTS: NO DATA AVAILABLE.

HEALTH EFFECTS AND FIRST AID

INHALATION: 2-ETHYL-1,3-HEXANEDIOL: IRRITANT. **ACUTE EXPOSURE-** MAY CAUSE IRRITATION TO THE MUCOUS MEMBRANES OF THE RESPIRATORY TRACT. RATS EXPOSED TO SATURATED VAPORS FOR 2 HOURS SURVIVED; THOSE EXPOSED FOR 8 HOURS DIED. NO SYMPTOMS WERE AVAILABLE. **CHRONIC EXPOSURE-** NO DATA AVAILABLE.

FIRST AID- REMOVE FROM EXPOSURE AREA TO FRESH AIR IMMEDIATELY. IF BREATHING HAS STOPPED, PERFORM ARTIFICIAL RESPIRATION. KEEP PERSON WARM AND AT REST. TREAT SYMPTOMATICALLY AND SUPPORTIVELY. GET MEDICAL ATTENTION IMMEDIATELY.

SKIN CONTACT: 2-ETHYL-1,3-HEXANEDIOL: **ACUTE EXPOSURE-** SOMEWHAT IRRITATING TO THE SKIN OF RABBITS, BUT HUMAN SKIN APPEARS TO BE QUITE RESISTANT. IT IS SLOWLY ABSORBED THROUGH THE SKIN; ONCE ABSORBED, MAY CAUSE NARCOSIS. **CHRONIC EXPOSURE-** CONTINUED CONTACT WITH RABBIT SKIN CAUSED APPRECIABLE IRRITATION. THE ANIMALS THAT DIED EXHIBITED MODERATE LIVER AND KIDNEY INJURY.

FIRST AID- REMOVE CONTAMINATED CLOTHING AND SHOES IMMEDIATELY. WASH AFFECTED AREA WITH SOAP OR MILD DETERGENT AND LARGE AMOUNTS OF WATER UNTIL NO EVIDENCE OF CHEMICAL REMAINS (APPROXIMATELY 15-20 MINUTES). GET MEDICAL ATTENTION IMMEDIATELY.

EYE CONTACT: 2-ETHYL-1,3-HEXANEDIOL: IRRITANT. **ACUTE EXPOSURE-** MAY CAUSE IRRITATION. APPLICATION TO RABBIT EYES CAUSED SEVERE IRRITATION AND CORNEAL INJURY. **CHRONIC EXPOSURE-** REPEATED AND PROLONGED CONTACT WITH IRRITANTS MAY CAUSE CONJUNCTIVITIS.

FIRST AID- WASH EYES IMMEDIATELY WITH LARGE AMOUNTS OF WATER OR NORMAL SALINE, OCCASIONALLY LIFTING UPPER AND LOWER LIDS, UNTIL NO EVIDENCE OF CHEMICAL REMAINS (APPROXIMATELY 15-20 MINUTES). GET MEDICAL ATTENTION IMMEDIATELY.

INGESTION: 2-ETHYL-1,3-HEXANEDIOL: **ACUTE EXPOSURE-** MAY CAUSE GASTROINTESTINAL IRRITATION AND CENTRAL NERVOUS SYSTEM DEPRESSION. LARGE DOSES IN RATS CAUSED DEEP NARCOSIS AND WAS BELIEVED TO BE THE CAUSE OF DEATH. DEATH WAS ACCOMPANIED BY SEVERE KIDNEY AND LIVER DAMAGE. **CHRONIC EXPOSURE-** RATS FED DIETS CONTAINING 2.0, 4.0 AND 8.0 PERCENT OF 2-ETHYL-1,3-HEXANEDIOL WERE REPORTED TO SHOW DEPRESSED GROWTH. AT THE 8.0 PERCENT LEVEL, ALL ANIMALS WERE DEAD WITHIN 18 WEEKS, WITH DEATH DUE TO INANITION.

FIRST AID- REMOVE BY GASTRIC LAVAGE AND CATHARSIS. MAINTAIN BLOOD PRESSURE AND AIRWAY. GIVE OXYGEN IF RESPIRATION IS DEPRESSED. DO NOT PERFORM GASTRIC LAVAGE IF VICTIM IS UNCONSCIOUS. GET MEDICAL ATTENTION IMMEDIATELY (DREISBACH, HANDBOOK OF POISONING, 12TH ED.).
ADMINISTRATION OF LAVAGE OR OXYGEN SHOULD BE PERFORMED BY QUALIFIED MEDICAL PERSONNEL.

ANTIDOTE: NO SPECIFIC ANTIDOTE. TREAT SYMPTOMATICALLY AND SUPPORTIVELY.

REACTIVITY

REACTIVITY: STABLE UNDER NORMAL TEMPERATURES AND PRESSURES.

INCOMPATIBILITIES: 2-ETHYL-1,3-HEXANEDIOL: OXIDIZERS (STRONG): FIRE AND EXPLOSION HAZARD.

DECOMPOSITION: THERMAL DECOMPOSITION PRODUCTS MAY INCLUDE TOXIC OXIDES OF CARBON.

POLYMERIZATION: HAZARDOUS POLYMERIZATION HAS NOT BEEN REPORTED TO OCCUR UNDER NORMAL TEMPERATURES AND PRESSURES.

STORAGE AND DISPOSAL

OBSERVE ALL FEDERAL, STATE AND LOCAL REGULATIONS WHEN STORING OR DISPOSING OF THIS SUBSTANCE. FOR ASSISTANCE, CONTACT THE DISTRICT DIRECTOR OF THE ENVIRONMENTAL PROTECTION AGENCY.

****STORAGE****

STORE IN ACCORDANCE WITH 40 CFR 165 RECOMMENDED PROCEDURES FOR THE DISPOSAL AND STORAGE OF PESTICIDES AND PESTICIDE CONTAINERS.
STORE AWAY FROM INCOMPATIBLE SUBSTANCES.

****DISPOSAL****

DISPOSAL MUST BE IN ACCORDANCE WITH 40 CFR 165 RECOMMENDED PROCEDURES FOR THE DISPOSAL AND STORAGE OF PESTICIDES AND PESTICIDE CONTAINERS.

CONDITIONS TO AVOID

MAY BURN BUT DOES NOT IGNITE READILY. AVOID CONTACT WITH STRONG OXIDIZERS, EXCESSIVE HEAT, SPARKS, OR OPEN FLAME.

SPILL AND LEAK PROCEDURES

OCCUPATIONAL SPILL: STOP LEAK IF YOU CAN DO IT WITHOUT RISK. FOR SMALL SPILLS, TAKE UP WITH SAND OR OTHER ABSORBENT MATERIAL AND PLACE INTO CLEAN, DRY CONTAINERS FOR LATER DISPOSAL. KEEP UNNECESSARY PEOPLE AWAY. ISOLATE HAZARD AREA AND DENY ENTRY.

PROTECTIVE EQUIPMENT

VENTILATION: PROVIDE LOCAL EXHAUST OR GENERAL DILUTION VENTILATION SYSTEM.

RESPIRATOR: THE FOLLOWING RESPIRATORS ARE RECOMMENDED BASED ON INFORMATION FOUND IN THE PHYSICAL DATA, TOXICITY AND HEALTH EFFECTS SECTIONS. THEY ARE RANKED IN ORDER FROM MINIMUM TO MAXIMUM RESPIRATORY PROTECTION. THE SPECIFIC RESPIRATOR SELECTED MUST BE BASED ON CONTAMINATION LEVELS FOUND IN THE WORK PLACE, MUST NOT EXCEED THE WORKING LIMITS OF THE RESPIRATOR AND BE JOINTLY APPROVED BY THE NATIONAL INSTITUTE FOR OCCUPATIONAL SAFETY AND HEALTH AND THE MINE SAFETY AND HEALTH ADMINISTRATION (NIOSH-MSHA).
CHEMICAL CARTRIDGE RESPIRATOR WITH FULL FACEPIECE AND PESTICIDE CARTRIDGE.
TYPE 'C' SUPPLIED-AIR RESPIRATOR WITH A FULL FACEPIECE OPERATED IN PRESSURE-DEMAND OR OTHER POSITIVE PRESSURE MODE OR WITH A FULL FACEPIECE, HELMET OR HOOD OPERATED IN CONTINUOUS-FLOW MODE.
SELF-CONTAINED BREATHING APPARATUS OPERATED IN PRESSURE-DEMAND OR OTHER POSITIVE PRESSURE MODE.
FOR FIREFIGHTING AND OTHER IMMEDIATELY DANGEROUS TO LIFE OR HEALTH CONDITIONS:
SELF-CONTAINED BREATHING APPARATUS WITH FULL FACEPIECE OPERATED IN PRESSURE-DEMAND OR OTHER POSITIVE PRESSURE MODE.
SUPPLIED-AIR RESPIRATOR WITH FULL FACEPIECE AND OPERATED IN PRESSURE-DEMAND OR OTHER POSITIVE PRESSURE MODE IN COMBINATION WITH AN AUXILIARY SELF-CONTAINED BREATHING APPARATUS OPERATED IN PRESSURE-DEMAND OR OTHER POSITIVE PRESSURE MODE.

CLOTHING: EMPLOYEE MUST WEAR APPROPRIATE PROTECTIVE (IMPERVIOUS) CLOTHING AND EQUIPMENT TO PREVENT REPEATED OR PROLONGED SKIN CONTACT WITH THIS SUBSTANCE.

GLOVES: EMPLOYEE MUST WEAR APPROPRIATE PROTECTIVE GLOVES TO PREVENT CONTACT WITH THIS SUBSTANCE.

EYE PROTECTION: EMPLOYEE MUST WEAR SPLASH-PROOF OR DUST-RESISTANT SAFETY GOGGLES TO PREVENT EYE CONTACT WITH THIS SUBSTANCE.
EMERGENCY EYE WASH: WHERE THERE IS ANY POSSIBILITY THAT AN EMPLOYEE'S

EYES MAY BE EXPOSED TO THIS SUBSTANCE, THE EMPLOYER SHOULD PROVIDE AN EYE WASH FOUNTAIN WITHIN THE IMMEDIATE WORK AREA FOR EMERGENCY USE.

AUTHORIZED BY- OCCUPATIONAL HEALTH SERVICES, INC.
CREATION DATE: 10/05/89 ***REVISION DATE:*** 05/17/90

MATERIAL SAFETY DATA SHEET

OCCUPATIONAL HEALTH SERVICES, INC.
AGRICULTURE AND PESTICIDE DIVISION
450 SEVENTH AVENUE, SUITE 2407
NEW YORK, NEW YORK 10123
1-800-445-MSDS OR (212) 967-1100

EMERGENCY CONTACT:
JOHN S. BRANSFORD, JR. (615) 292-1180

SUBSTANCE IDENTIFICATION

CAS-NUMBER 1134-23-2
SUBSTANCE: CYCLOATE
TRADE NAMES/SYNONYMS: CARBAMOTHIOIC ACID, CYCLOHEXYLETHYL-, S-ETHYL ESTER; CYCLOHEXYLETHYLCARBAMOTHIOIC ACID S-ETHYL ESTER; CYCLOHEXANECARBAMIC ACID, N-ETHYLTHIO-, S-ETHYL ESTER; N-ETHYLTHIOCYLCLOHEXANECARBAMIC ACID S-ETHYL ESTER; S-ETHYL N-CYCLOHEXYL-N-ETHYL(THIOCARBAMATE); S-ETHYL CYCLOHEXYLETHYLCARBAMOTHIOATE; S-ETHYLCYCLOHEXYLETHYLTHIOCARBAMATE; S-ETHYL N-ETHYLTHIOCYCLOHEXANECARBAMATE; HEXYLTHIOCARBAM; RO-NEET; ETSAN; EUREX; R 2063; RONIT; SABET; PST71469
CHEMICAL FAMILY: THIOCARBAMATE
MOLECULAR FORMULA: C11-H21-N-O-S
MOLECULAR WEIGHT: 215.37
CERCLA RATINGS (SCALE 0-3): HEALTH=2 FIRE=U REACTIVITY=0 PERSISTENCE=1
NFPA RATINGS (SCALE 0-4): HEALTH=2 FIRE=U REACTIVITY=0

COMPONENTS AND CONTAMINANTS

COMPONENT: CYCLOATE ***PERCENT:*** 100
CAS# 1134-23-2
OTHER CONTAMINANTS: NONE
EXPOSURE LIMITS: NO OCCUPATIONAL EXPOSURE LIMITS ESTABLISHED BY OSHA, ACGIH, OR NIOSH.

PHYSICAL DATA

DESCRIPTION: COLORLESS LIQUID WITH AROMATIC ODOR
BOILING POINT: 293 F (145 C) 10 MMHG ***MELTING POINT:*** 54 F (12 C)
SPECIFIC GRAVITY: 1.016 @ 30/4 C ***VAPOR PRESSURE:*** 0.0062 MMHG @ 25
SOLUBILITY IN WATER: 0.0085%
SOLVENT SOLUBILITY: SOLUBLE IN ACETONE, BENZENE, ETHANOL, KEROSENE, 4-METHYLPENTAN-2-ONE, XYLENE, METHANOL, ISOPROPANOL, AND MOST ORGANIC SOLVENTS

FIRE AND EXPLOSION DATA

FIRE AND EXPLOSION HAZARD: UNKNOWN FIRE AND EXPLOSION HAZARD.
FIREFIGHTING MEDIA: DRY CHEMICAL, CARBON DIOXIDE, WATER SPRAY OR FOAM FOR LARGER FIRES, USE WATER SPRAY, FOG OR ALCOHOL FOAM
FIREFIGHTING: MOVE CONTAINER FROM FIRE AREA IF POSSIBLE. DO NOT SCATTER SPILLED MATERIAL WITH MORE WATER THAN NEEDED FOR FIRE CONTROL. DIKE FIRE CONTROL WATER FOR LATER DISPOSAL
USE AGENTS SUITABLE FOR TYPE OF SURROUNDING FIRE. AVOID BREATHING HAZARDOUS VAPORS, KEEP UPWIND.

TOXICITY

CYCLOATE: TOXICITY DATA: 3 GM/KG SKIN-RABBIT LD50; 2467 MG/KG SKIN-RAT LD50; 1678 MG/KG ORAL-RAT LD50; 1275 MG/KG ORAL-MOUSE LD50; 1600 MG/KG ORAL-GUINEA PIG LD50; 2325 MG/KG UNREPORTED-RAT LD50; 2300 MG/KG UNREPORTED-MOUSE LD50; 2300 MG/KG UNREPORTED-MAMMAL LD50; MUTAGENIC DATA (RTECS). CARCINOGEN STATUS: NONE. ACUTE TOXICITY DATA: MODERATELY TOXIC BY INGESTION AND SLIGHTLY TOXIC BY DERMAL ABSORPTION. TARGET EFFECTS: NO DATA AVAILABLE.

HEALTH EFFECTS AND FIRST AID

INHALATION: CYCLOATE: **ACUTE EXPOSURE-** INHALATION OF EXCESSIVE AMOUNTS OF SOME THIOCARBAMATES CAUSES SCRATCHY THROAT, SNEEZING, AND COUGHING. **CHRONIC EXPOSURE-** NO ADVERSE EFFECTS WERE REPORTED FROM WORKERS EXPOSED TO AEROSOLS AND VAPORS CONCENTRATIONS AS HIGH AS 6.2 MG/M3 FOR 5 CONSECUTIVE DAYS.
FIRST AID- REMOVE FROM EXPOSURE AREA TO FRESH AIR IMMEDIATELY. IF BREATHING HAS STOPPED, PERFORM ARTIFICIAL RESPIRATION. KEEP PERSON WARM AND AT REST. TREAT SYMPTOMATICALLY AND SUPPORTIVELY. GET MEDICAL ATTENTION IMMEDIATELY.

SKIN CONTACT: CYCLOATE: **ACUTE EXPOSURE-** MAY CAUSE IRRITATION. A LETHAL DOSE IN RABBITS BY DERMAL ABSORPTION WAS 3 GM/KG. **CHRONIC EXPOSURE-** REPEATED DERMAL APPLICATION OF 115 MG/KG/DAY PRODUCED HYPEREMIA AND EDEMA OF THE SKIN OF RABBITS.
FIRST AID- REMOVE CONTAMINATED CLOTHING AND SHOES IMMEDIATELY. WASH AFFECTED AREA WITH SOAP OR MILD DETERGENT AND LARGE AMOUNTS OF WATER UNTIL NO EVIDENCE OF CHEMICAL REMAINS (APPROXIMATELY 15-20 MINUTES). GET MEDICAL ATTENTION IMMEDIATELY.

EYE CONTACT: CYCLOATE: **ACUTE EXPOSURE-** MAY CAUSE IRRITATION. **CHRONIC EXPOSURE-** PROLONGED OR REPEATED EXPOSURE TO IRRITANTS MAY CAUSE CONJUNCTIVITIS.
FIRST AID- WASH EYES IMMEDIATELY WITH LARGE AMOUNTS OF WATER OR NORMAL SALINE, OCCASIONALLY LIFTING UPPER AND LOWER LIDS, UNTIL NO EVIDENCE OF CHEMICAL REMAINS (APPROXIMATELY 15-20 MINUTES). GET MEDICAL ATTENTION IMMEDIATELY.

INGESTION: CYCLOATE: **ACUTE EXPOSURE-** A LETHAL DOSE IN RATS WAS 2000 MG/KG. **CHRONIC EXPOSURE-** A DOSE OF 232 MG/KG/DAY FOR 4 MONTHS WAS LETHAL TO 20% OF THE RATS. IN A 2-YEAR FEEDING STUDY USING RATS, A DOSE OF 8 MG/KG/DAY PRODUCED PERIPHERAL NEUROPATHY AND NEUROMYOPATHY INVOLVING SCIATIC NERVE AND SURROUNDING MUSCLES. DECREASED RELATIVE HEART WEIGHT WAS OBSERVED IN MALE RATS AT DOSE LEVELS AS LOW AS 20 MG/KG/DAY. IN A 13-WEEK STUDY OF RATS FED A DIETARY LEVEL OF 55 MG/KG/DAY, EFFECTS OF DECREASED OVARIAN WEIGHTS AND INCREASED BODY WEIGHT GAIN IN THE FEMALE AND INCREASED LIVER WEIGHT GAIN IN THE MALES WERE REPORTED; 500 MG/KG/DAY PRODUCED HISTOPATHOLOGIC CHANGES IN THE LIVER AND KIDNEYS IN MALE RATS. THE RESULTS FROM DELAYED NEUROTOXICITY STUDIES IN HENS WERE NEGATIVE.
FIRST AID- GIVE SYRUP OF IPECAC, FOLLOWED BY 1-2 GLASSES OF WATER, TO INDUCE VOMITING (ADULTS: 30 ML). FOLLOWING EMESIS, ADMINISTER 30-50 GRAMS ACTIVATED CHARCOAL. FOLLOW CHARCOAL WITH SODIUM OR MAGNESIUM SULFATE, 250 MG/KG, TO REMOVE TOXICANT FROM THE GUT BY CATHARSIS (EPA, RECOGNITION AND MANAGEMENT OF PESTICIDE POISONINGS, 3RD ED.). FIRST AID SHOULD BE ADMINISTERED UNDER THE DIRECTION OF QUALIFIED MEDICAL PERSONNEL. GET MEDICAL ATTENTION.
ANTIDOTE: NO SPECIFIC ANTIDOTE. TREAT SYMPTOMATICALLY AND SUPPORTIVELY.

REACTIVITY

REACTIVITY: STABLE UNDER NORMAL TEMPERATURES AND PRESSURES.
INCOMPATIBILITIES: CYCLOATE: NO DATA AVAILABLE.
DECOMPOSITION: THERMAL DECOMPOSITION MAY RELEASE TOXIC OXIDES OF NITROGEN AND SULFUR.
POLYMERIZATION: HAZARDOUS POLYMERIZATION HAS NOT BEEN REPORTED TO OCCUR UNDER NORMAL TEMPERATURES AND PRESSURES.

STORAGE AND DISPOSAL

OBSERVE ALL FEDERAL, STATE AND LOCAL REGULATIONS WHEN STORING OR DISPOSING OF THIS SUBSTANCE. FOR ASSISTANCE, CONTACT THE DISTRICT DIRECTOR OF THE ENVIRONMENTAL PROTECTION AGENCY.

STORAGE

STORE IN ACCORDANCE WITH 40 CFR 165 RECOMMENDED PROCEDURES FOR THE DISPOSAL AND STORAGE OF PESTICIDES AND PESTICIDE CONTAINERS.

DISPOSAL

DISPOSAL MUST BE IN ACCORDANCE WITH 40 CFR 165 RECOMMENDED PROCEDURES FOR THE DISPOSAL AND STORAGE OF PESTICIDES AND PESTICIDE CONTAINERS.

CONDITIONS TO AVOID

NONE REPORTED.

SPILL AND LEAK PROCEDURES

OCCUPATIONAL SPILL: STOP LEAK IF YOU CAN DO IT WITHOUT RISK. FOR SMALL SPILLS, TAKE UP WITH SAND OR OTHER ABSORBENT MATERIAL AND PLACE INTO CLEAN, DRY CONTAINERS FOR LATER DISPOSAL. KEEP UNNECESSARY PEOPLE AWAY. ISOLATE HAZARD AREA AND DENY ENTRY.

PROTECTIVE EQUIPMENT

VENTILATION: PROVIDE LOCAL EXHAUST VENTILATION SYSTEM.

RESPIRATOR: THE FOLLOWING RESPIRATORS ARE RECOMMENDED BASED ON INFORMATION FOUND IN THE PHYSICAL DATA, TOXICITY AND HEALTH EFFECTS SECTIONS. THEY ARE RANKED IN ORDER FROM MINIMUM TO MAXIMUM RESPIRATORY PROTECTION. THE SPECIFIC RESPIRATOR SELECTED MUST BE BASED ON CONTAMINATION LEVELS FOUND IN THE WORK PLACE, MUST NOT EXCEED THE WORKING LIMITS OF THE RESPIRATOR AND BE JOINTLY APPROVED BY THE NATIONAL INSTITUTE FOR OCCUPATIONAL SAFETY AND HEALTH AND THE MINE SAFETY AND HEALTH ADMINISTRATION (NIOSH-MSHA).

CHEMICAL CARTRIDGE RESPIRATOR WITH FULL FACEPIECE AND PESTICIDE CARTRIDGE.

TYPE 'C' SUPPLIED-AIR RESPIRATOR WITH A FULL FACEPIECE OPERATED IN PRESSURE-DEMAND OR OTHER POSITIVE PRESSURE MODE OR WITH A FULL FACEPIECE, HELMET OR HOOD OPERATED IN CONTINUOUS-FLOW MODE.

SELF-CONTAINED BREATHING APPARATUS OPERATED IN PRESSURE-DEMAND OR OTHER POSITIVE PRESSURE MODE.

FOR FIREFIGHTING AND OTHER IMMEDIATELY DANGEROUS TO LIFE OR HEALTH CONDITIONS: SELF-CONTAINED BREATHING APPARATUS WITH FULL FACEPIECE OPERATED IN PRESSURE-DEMAND OR OTHER POSITIVE PRESSURE MODE.

SUPPLIED-AIR RESPIRATOR WITH FULL FACEPIECE AND OPERATED IN PRESSURE-DEMAND OR OTHER POSITIVE PRESSURE MODE IN COMBINATION WITH AN AUXILIARY SELF-CONTAINED BREATHING APPARATUS OPERATED IN PRESSURE-DEMAND OR OTHER POSITIVE PRESSURE MODE.

CLOTHING: EMPLOYEE MUST WEAR APPROPRIATE PROTECTIVE (IMPERVIOUS) CLOTHING AND EQUIPMENT TO PREVENT REPEATED OR PROLONGED SKIN CONTACT WITH THIS SUBSTANCE.

GLOVES: EMPLOYEE MUST WEAR APPROPRIATE PROTECTIVE GLOVES TO PREVENT CONTACT WITH THIS SUBSTANCE.

EYE PROTECTION: EMPLOYEE MUST WEAR SPLASH-PROOF OR DUST-RESISTANT SAFETY GOGGLES TO PREVENT EYE CONTACT WITH THIS SUBSTANCE.

EMERGENCY EYE WASH: WHERE THERE IS ANY POSSIBILITY THAT AN EMPLOYEE'S EYES MAY BE EXPOSED TO THIS SUBSTANCE, THE EMPLOYER SHOULD PROVIDE AN EYE WASH FOUNTAIN WITHIN THE IMMEDIATE WORK AREA FOR EMERGENCY USE.

AUTHORIZED BY- OCCUPATIONAL HEALTH SERVICES, INC.

CREATION DATE: 02/08/90 ***REVISION DATE:*** 06/04/90

MATERIAL SAFETY DATA SHEET

OCCUPATIONAL HEALTH SERVICES, INC.
AGRICULTURE AND PESTICIDE DIVISION
450 SEVENTH AVENUE, SUITE 2407
NEW YORK, NEW YORK 10123
1-800-445-MSDS OR (212) 967-1100

EMERGENCY CONTACT:
JOHN S. BRANSFORD, JR. (615) 292-1180

SUBSTANCE IDENTIFICATION

CAS-NUMBER 759-94-4

SUBSTANCE: **S-ETHYL DIPROPYLTHIOCARBAMATE**

TRADE NAMES/SYNONYMS: CARBAMOTHIOIC ACID, DIPROPYL-, S-ETHYL ESTER; DIPROPYLCARBAMOTHIOIC ACID S-ETHYL ESTER; CARBAMIC ACID, DIPROPYLTHIO-, S-ETHYL ESTER; DIPROPYLTHIOCARBAMIC ACID S-ETHYL ESTER; S-ETHYL DIPROPYLCARBAMOTHIOATE; ETHYL DI-N-PROPYLTHIOLCARBAMATE; S-ETHYL DI-N,N-PROPYLTHIOLCARBAMATE; EPTC; EPTAM; FDA 1541; R 1608; STAUFFER R 1608; TORBIN; C9H19NOS; PST71470

CHEMICAL FAMILY: THIOCARBAMATE

MOLECULAR FORMULA: C9-H19-N-O-S

MOLECULAR WEIGHT: 189.31

CERCLA RATINGS (SCALE 0-3): HEALTH=3 FIRE=1 REACTIVITY=0 PERSISTENCE=0

NFPA RATINGS (SCALE 0-4): HEALTH=3 FIRE=1 REACTIVITY=0

COMPONENTS AND CONTAMINANTS

COMPONENT: EPTC ***PERCENT:*** 100

CAS# 759-94-4

OTHER CONTAMINANTS: NONE

EXPOSURE LIMITS: NO OCCUPATIONAL EXPOSURE LIMITS ESTABLISHED BY OSHA, ACGIH, OR NIOSH.

PHYSICAL DATA

DESCRIPTION: CLEAR COLORLESS LIQUID WITH AN AROMATIC ODOR

BOILING POINT: 455 F (235 C) ***SPECIFIC GRAVITY:*** 0.9546 @ 30/4 C

VAPOR PRESSURE: 0.034 MMHG @ 35 C ***SOLUBILITY IN WATER:*** 0.0365%

SOLVENT SOLUBILITY: SOLUBLE IN BENZENE, ALCOHOL, TOLUENE, XYLENE, ACETONE HEXANE, KEROSENE, 4-METHYL PENTAN-2-ONE, METHANOL, ISOPROPYL ALCOHOL, ETHANOL, MOST ORGANIC SOLVENTS

FIRE AND EXPLOSION DATA

FIRE AND EXPLOSION HAZARD: SLIGHT FIRE HAZARD WHEN EXPOSED TO HEAT OR FLAME.

FLASH POINT: 241 F (116 C) ***FLAMMABILITY CLASS(OSHA):*** IIIB

FIREFIGHTING MEDIA: DRY CHEMICAL, CARBON DIOXIDE, WATER SPRAY OR FOAM FOR LARGER FIRES, USE WATER SPRAY, FOG OR ALCOHOL FOAM

FIREFIGHTING: MOVE CONTAINER FROM FIRE AREA IF POSSIBLE. DO NOT SCATTER SPILLED MATERIAL WITH MORE WATER THAN NEEDED FOR FIRE CONTROL. DIKE FIRE CONTROL WATER FOR LATER DISPOSAL

USE AGENTS SUITABLE FOR TYPE OF SURROUNDING FIRE. AVOID BREATHING HAZARDOUS VAPORS, KEEP UPWIND.

TOXICITY

S-ETHYL DIPROPYLTHIOCARBAMATE: TOXICITY DATA: 135 MG/M3/90 MINUTES INHALATION-HUMAN TCLO; 200 MG/M3/4 HOURS INHALATION-RAT LCLO; 400 MG/M3/4 HOURS INHALATION-CAT LCLO; 1460 MG/KG SKIN-RABBIT LD50; 3200 MG/KG SKIN-RAT LD50; 750 MG/KG ORAL-MOUSE LD50; 112 MG/KG ORAL-CAT LD50; 2640 MG/KG ORAL-RABBIT LD50; 916 MG/KG ORAL-RAT LD50 (FDA SURVEILLANCE INDEX, PB82-913201); 320 MG/KG INTRAVENOUS-MOUSE LD50; 58 MG/KG INTRAPERITONEAL-MOUSE LD50; MUTAGENIC DATA (RTECS). CARCINOGEN STATUS: NONE. ACUTE TOXICITY LEVEL: MODERATELY TOXIC BY DERMAL ABSORPTION AND INGESTION. TARGET EFFECTS: ANIMAL STUDIES INDICATED THAT S-ETHYL DIPROPYLTHIOCARBAMATE MAY BE A WEAK CHOLINESTERASE INHIBITOR.

HEALTH EFFECTS AND FIRST AID

INHALATION: S-ETHYL DIPROPYLTHIOCARBAMATE: **ACUTE EXPOSURE-** COMPLAINTS OF HEADACHE, NAUSEA, GENERAL MALAISE, AND IMPAIRED WORKING CAPACITY WERE REPORTED AMONG SOME EXPOSED WORKERS. ANIMAL STUDIES INDICATED THAT S-ETHYL DIPROPYLTHIOCARBAMATE MAY BE A WEAK CHOLINESTERASE INHIBITOR. EARLY SYMPTOMS OF CHOLINESTERASE INHIBITION ARE BLURRED VISION, FATIGUE, HEADACHE, VERTIGO, NAUSEA, MIOSIS, ABDOMINAL CRAMPS AND DIARRHEA. SEVERE INHIBITION OF CHOLINESTERASE MAY CAUSE EXCESSIVE SWEATING, TEARING, BRADYCARDIA, GIDDINESS, SLURRED SPEECH, CONFUSION, PULMONARY EDEMA, CONVULSIONS AND COMA. **CHRONIC EXPOSURE-** NO DATA AVAILABLE.

FIRST AID- REMOVE FROM EXPOSURE AREA TO FRESH AIR IMMEDIATELY. IF BREATHING HAS STOPPED, PERFORM ARTIFICIAL RESPIRATION. KEEP PERSON WARM AND AT REST. TREAT SYMPTOMATICALLY AND SUPPORTIVELY. GET MEDICAL ATTENTION IMMEDIATELY.

SKIN CONTACT: S-ETHYL DIPROPYLTHIOCARBAMATE: **ACUTE EXPOSURE-** MAY CAUSE IRRITATION. A LETHAL DOSE IN RABBITS BY DERMAL ABSORPTION WAS 1460 MG/KG. ANIMAL STUDIES INDICATED THAT S-ETHYL DIPROPYLTHIOCARBAMATE MAY BE A WEAK CHOLINESTERASE INHIBITOR. **CHRONIC EXPOSURE-** IN A 21-DAY STUDY OF RABBITS, REPEATED APPLICATIONS OF S-ETHYL DIPROPYLTHIOCARBAMATE AT A DOSAGE LEVEL OF 300 MG/KG/DAY PRODUCED SOME CHOLINESTERASE INHIBITION AND SOME WEIGHT LOSS; NO DEATHS WERE REPORTED.

FIRST AID- REMOVE CONTAMINATED CLOTHING AND SHOES IMMEDIATELY. WASH AFFECTED AREA WITH SOAP OR MILD DETERGENT AND LARGE AMOUNTS OF WATER UNTIL NO EVIDENCE OF CHEMICAL REMAINS (APPROXIMATELY 15-20 MINUTES). GET MEDICAL ATTENTION IMMEDIATELY.

EYE CONTACT: S-ETHYL DIPROPYLTHIOCARBAMATE: **ACUTE EXPOSURE-** MAY CAUSE IRRITATION. **CHRONIC EXPOSURE-** PROLONGED OR REPEATED EXPOSURE MAY CAUSE IRRITATION.

FIRST AID- WASH EYES IMMEDIATELY WITH LARGE AMOUNTS OF WATER OR NORMAL SALINE, OCCASIONALLY LIFTING UPPER AND LOWER LIDS, UNTIL NO EVIDENCE OF CHEMICAL REMAINS (APPROXIMATELY 15-20 MINUTES). GET MEDICAL ATTENTION IMMEDIATELY.

INGESTION: S-ETHYL DIPROPYLTHIOCARBAMATE: **ACUTE EXPOSURE-** A LETHAL DOSE IN RATS WAS 916 MG/KG. ANIMAL STUDIES INDICATED THAT S-ETHYL DIPROPYLTHIOCARBAMATE MAY BE A WEAK CHOLINESTERASE INHIBITOR. POISONED ANIMALS DISPLAYED EXCITEMENT, SALIVATION, LACRIMATION, BLEPHAROSPASM, AND DEPRESSION. **CHRONIC EXPOSURE-** EXCITABILITY AND SOME BODY WEIGHT LOSS WAS OBSERVED IN RATS FED 300 MG/KG/DAY FOR 21

DAYS. IN A 16 WEEK STUDY OF DOGS FED 1800 PPM, EFFECTS OF BRAIN CHOLINESTERASE INHIBITION AND GASTRIC MUCOSAL CHANGES WERE REPORTED.

FIRST AID- GIVE SYRUP OF IPECAC, FOLLOWED BY 1-2 GLASSES OF WATER, TO INDUCE VOMITING (ADULTS: 30 ML). FOLLOWING EMESIS, ADMINISTER 30-50 GRAMS ACTIVATED CHARCOAL. FOLLOW CHARCOAL WITH SODIUM OR MAGNESIUM SULFATE, 250 MG/KG, TO REMOVE TOXICANT FROM THE GUT BY CATHARSIS (EPA, RECOGNITION AND MANAGEMENT OF PESTICIDE POISONINGS, 3RD ED.). FIRST AID SHOULD BE ADMINISTERED UNDER THE DIRECTION OF QUALIFIED MEDICAL PERSONNEL. GET MEDICAL ATTENTION.

ANTIDOTE: NO SPECIFIC ANTIDOTE. TREAT SYMPTOMATICALLY AND SUPPORTIVELY.

REACTIVITY

REACTIVITY: STABLE UNDER NORMAL TEMPERATURES AND PRESSURES.

INCOMPATIBILITIES: S-ETHYL DIPROPYLTHIOCARBAMATE: NO DATA AVAILABLE.

DECOMPOSITION: THERMAL DECOMPOSITION MAY RELEASE TOXIC OXIDES OF NITROGEN AND SULFUR.

POLYMERIZATION: HAZARDOUS POLYMERIZATION HAS NOT BEEN REPORTED TO OCCUR UNDER NORMAL TEMPERATURES AND PRESSURES.

STORAGE AND DISPOSAL

OBSERVE ALL FEDERAL, STATE AND LOCAL REGULATIONS WHEN STORING OR DISPOSING OF THIS SUBSTANCE. FOR ASSISTANCE, CONTACT THE DISTRICT DIRECTOR OF THE ENVIRONMENTAL PROTECTION AGENCY.

STORAGE

STORE IN ACCORDANCE WITH 40 CFR 165 RECOMMENDED PROCEDURES FOR THE DISPOSAL AND STORAGE OF PESTICIDES AND PESTICIDE CONTAINERS.

DISPOSAL

DISPOSAL MUST BE IN ACCORDANCE WITH 40 CFR 165 RECOMMENDED PROCEDURES FOR THE DISPOSAL AND STORAGE OF PESTICIDES AND PESTICIDE CONTAINERS.

CONDITIONS TO AVOID

MAY BURN BUT DOES NOT IGNITE READILY. AVOID CONTACT WITH STRONG OXIDIZERS, EXCESSIVE HEAT, SPARKS, OR OPEN FLAME.

SPILL AND LEAK PROCEDURES

OCCUPATIONAL SPILL: STOP LEAK IF YOU CAN DO IT WITHOUT RISK. FOR SMALL SPILLS, TAKE UP WITH SAND OR OTHER ABSORBENT MATERIAL AND PLACE INTO CLEAN, DRY CONTAINERS FOR LATER DISPOSAL. KEEP UNNECESSARY PEOPLE AWAY. ISOLATE HAZARD AREA AND DENY ENTRY.

PROTECTIVE EQUIPMENT

VENTILATION: PROVIDE LOCAL EXHAUST OR GENERAL DILUTION VENTILATION SYSTEM.

RESPIRATOR: THE FOLLOWING RESPIRATORS ARE RECOMMENDED BASED ON INFORMATION FOUND IN THE PHYSICAL DATA, TOXICITY AND HEALTH EFFECTS SECTIONS. THEY ARE RANKED IN ORDER FROM MINIMUM TO MAXIMUM RESPIRATORY PROTECTION. THE SPECIFIC RESPIRATOR SELECTED MUST BE BASED ON CONTAMINATION LEVELS FOUND IN THE WORK PLACE, MUST NOT EXCEED THE WORKING LIMITS OF THE RESPIRATOR AND BE JOINTLY APPROVED BY THE NATIONAL INSTITUTE FOR OCCUPATIONAL SAFETY AND HEALTH AND THE MINE SAFETY AND HEALTH ADMINISTRATION (NIOSH-MSHA).

CHEMICAL CARTRIDGE RESPIRATOR WITH FULL FACEPIECE AND PESTICIDE CARTRIDGE.

TYPE 'C' SUPPLIED-AIR RESPIRATOR WITH A FULL FACEPIECE OPERATED IN PRESSURE-DEMAND OR OTHER POSITIVE PRESSURE MODE OR WITH A FULL FACEPIECE, HELMET OR HOOD OPERATED IN CONTINUOUS-FLOW MODE. SELF-CONTAINED BREATHING APPARATUS OPERATED IN PRESSURE-DEMAND OR OTHER POSITIVE PRESSURE MODE.

FOR FIREFIGHTING AND OTHER IMMEDIATELY DANGEROUS TO LIFE OR HEALTH CONDITIONS:

SELF-CONTAINED BREATHING APPARATUS WITH FULL FACEPIECE OPERATED IN PRESSURE-DEMAND OR OTHER POSITIVE PRESSURE MODE.

SUPPLIED-AIR RESPIRATOR WITH FULL FACEPIECE AND OPERATED IN PRESSURE-DEMAND OR OTHER POSITIVE PRESSURE MODE IN COMBINATION WITH AN AUXILIARY SELF-CONTAINED BREATHING APPARATUS OPERATED IN PRESSURE-DEMAND OR OTHER POSITIVE PRESSURE MODE.

CLOTHING: EMPLOYEE MUST WEAR APPROPRIATE PROTECTIVE (IMPERVIOUS) CLOTHING AND EQUIPMENT TO PREVENT REPEATED OR PROLONGED SKIN CONTACT WITH THIS SUBSTANCE.

GLOVES: EMPLOYEE MUST WEAR APPROPRIATE PROTECTIVE GLOVES TO PREVENT CONTACT WITH THIS SUBSTANCE.

EYE PROTECTION: EMPLOYEE MUST WEAR SPLASH-PROOF OR DUST-RESISTANT SAFETY GOGGLES TO PREVENT EYE CONTACT WITH THIS SUBSTANCE.

EMERGENCY EYE WASH: WHERE THERE IS ANY POSSIBILITY THAT AN EMPLOYEE'S EYES MAY BE EXPOSED TO THIS SUBSTANCE, THE EMPLOYER SHOULD PROVIDE AN EYE WASH FOUNTAIN WITHIN THE IMMEDIATE WORK AREA FOR EMERGENCY USE.

AUTHORIZED BY- OCCUPATIONAL HEALTH SERVICES, INC.

CREATION DATE: 10/05/89 ***REVISION DATE:*** 05/16/90

MATERIAL SAFETY DATA SHEET

OCCUPATIONAL HEALTH SERVICES, INC.
AGRICULTURE AND PESTICIDE DIVISION
450 SEVENTH AVENUE, SUITE 2407
NEW YORK, NEW YORK 10123
1-800-445-MSDS OR (212) 967-1100

EMERGENCY CONTACT:
JOHN S. BRANSFORD, JR. (615) 292-1180

SUBSTANCE IDENTIFICATION

CAS-NUMBER 2212-67-1

***SUBSTANCE:* MOLINATE**

TRADE NAMES/SYNONYMS: 1H-AZEPINE-1-CARBOTHIOIC ACID, HEXAHYDRO-, S-ETHYL ESTER; HEXAHYDRO-1H-AZEPINE-1-CARBOTHIOIC ACID S-ETHYL ESTER; S-ETHYL AZEPANE-1-CARBOTHIOATE; S-ETHYL PERHYDROAZEPIN-1-CARBOTHIOATE; S-ETHYL N,N-HEXAMETHYLENETHIOCARBAMATE; S-ETHYL PERHYDROAZEPINE-1-THIOCARBOXYLATE; S-ETHYL HEXAHYDRO-1H-AZEPINE-1-CARBOTHIOATE; FELAN; HYDRAM; JALAN; ORDRAM; R-4572; YALAN; YULAN; PST71471

CHEMICAL FAMILY: THIOCARBAMATE

MOLECULAR FORMULA: C9-H15-N-O-S

MOLECULAR WEIGHT: 187.3

CERCLA RATINGS (SCALE 0-3): HEALTH=2 FIRE=U REACTIVITY=0 PERSISTENCE=0

NFPA RATINGS (SCALE 0-4): HEALTH=2 FIRE=U REACTIVITY=0

COMPONENTS AND CONTAMINANTS

COMPONENT: MOLINATE ***PERCENT:*** 100.0
CAS# 2212-67-1

OTHER CONTAMINANTS: NONE

EXPOSURE LIMITS: NO OCCUPATIONAL EXPOSURE LIMITS ESTABLISHED BY OSHA, ACGIH, OR NIOSH.

PHYSICAL DATA

DESCRIPTION: CLEAR LIQUID WITH AN AROMATIC ODOR

BOILING POINT: 396 F (202 C) @ 10 MMHG ***SPECIFIC GRAVITY:*** 1.06 20/20 C

VAPOR PRESSURE: 0.0056 MMHG @ 25 C ***SOLUBILITY IN WATER:*** 0.088 %

SOLVENT SOLUBILITY: SOLUBLE IN ACETONE, BENZENE, 2-PROPANOL, METHANOL, XYLENE, ETHANOL, KEROSENE, 4-METHYLPENTAN-2-ONE

FIRE AND EXPLOSION DATA

FIRE AND EXPLOSION HAZARD: UNKNOWN FIRE AND EXPLOSION HAZARD.

FIREFIGHTING MEDIA: DRY CHEMICAL, CARBON DIOXIDE, WATER SPRAY OR FOAM FOR LARGER FIRES, USE WATER SPRAY, FOG OR ALCOHOL FOAM

FIREFIGHTING: MOVE CONTAINER FROM FIRE AREA IF POSSIBLE. DO NOT SCATTER SPILLED MATERIAL WITH MORE WATER THAN NEEDED FOR FIRE CONTROL. DIKE FIRE CONTROL WATER FOR LATER DISPOSAL

TOXICITY

MOLINATE: TOXICITY DATA: 200 MG/M3 INHALATION-RAT LCLO; 200 MG/M3 INHALATION-CAT LDLO; 3536 MG/KG SKIN-RABBIT LD50; 1167 MG/KG SKIN-RAT LD50; 369 MG/KG ORAL-RAT LD50; 530 MG/KG ORAL-MOUSE LD50; 1167 MG/KG SUBCUTANEOUS-RAT LD50; 720 MG/KG UNREPORTED-MAMMAL LD50; 720 MG/KG UNREPORTED-RAT LD50; MUTAGENIC DATA (RTECS); REPRODUCTIVE EFFECTS DATA (RTECS). CARCINOGEN STATUS: NONE. ACUTE TOXICITY LEVEL: TOXIC BY INGESTION; SLIGHTLY TOXIC BY DERMAL ABSORPTION. TARGET EFFECTS: SENSITIZER- SKIN.

HEALTH EFFECTS AND FIRST AID

INHALATION: MOLINATE: ACUTE EXPOSURE- A CONCENTRATION OF 200 MG/M3 WAS LETHAL TO SOME RATS AND CATS. EXPOSURE TO LARGE AMOUNTS OF THIOCARBAMATES MAY CAUSE ITCHING, SCRATCHY THROAT, SNEEZING, AND COUGHING. CHRONIC EXPOSURE- NO CLINICAL SYMPTOMS OR LABORATORY TEST DEVIATIONS WERE OBSERVED 3 DAYS AFTER DAILY OCCUPATIONAL EXPOSURE TO 0.2-5 MG/M3. ADVERSE EFFECTS ON FERTILITY AND THE REPRODUCTIVE SYSTEM WERE REPORTED FROM A CHRONIC INHALATION STUDY OF MALE RATS.

FIRST AID- REMOVE FROM EXPOSURE AREA TO FRESH AIR IMMEDIATELY. IF BREATHING HAS STOPPED, PERFORM ARTIFICIAL RESPIRATION. KEEP PERSON WARM AND AT REST. TREAT SYMPTOMATICALLY AND SUPPORTIVELY. GET MEDICAL ATTENTION IMMEDIATELY.

SKIN CONTACT: MOLINATE: SENSITIZER. **ACUTE EXPOSURE**- MAY CAUSE IRRITATION. A LETHAL DOSE IN RABBITS BY DERMAL ABSORPTION WAS 3536 MG/KG. SENSITIZATION MAY OCCUR IN PERSONS PREVIOUSLY EXPOSED. **CHRONIC EXPOSURE**- PROLONGED OR REPEATED EXPOSURE MAY CAUSE SENSITIZATION DERMATITIS.

FIRST AID- REMOVE CONTAMINATED CLOTHING AND SHOES IMMEDIATELY. WASH AFFECTED AREA WITH SOAP OR MILD DETERGENT AND LARGE AMOUNTS OF WATER UNTIL NO EVIDENCE OF CHEMICAL REMAINS (APPROXIMATELY 15-20 MINUTES). GET MEDICAL ATTENTION IMMEDIATELY.

EYE CONTACT: MOLINATE: **ACUTE EXPOSURE**- MAY CAUSE IRRITATION. **CHRONIC EXPOSURE**- PROLONGED OR REPEATED EXPOSURE MAY CAUSE CONJUNCTIVITIS.

FIRST AID- WASH EYES IMMEDIATELY WITH LARGE AMOUNTS OF WATER OR NORMAL SALINE, OCCASIONALLY LIFTING UPPER AND LOWER LIDS, UNTIL NO EVIDENCE OF CHEMICAL REMAINS (APPROXIMATELY 15-20 MINUTES). GET MEDICAL ATTENTION IMMEDIATELY.

INGESTION: MOLINATE: **ACUTE EXPOSURE**- MAY CAUSE NAUSEA, DIARRHEA, ABDOMINAL PAIN, FEVER, WEAKNESS, AND CONJUNCTIVITIS. A LETHAL DOSE IN RATS WAS 501 MG/KG. **CHRONIC EXPOSURE**- IN ANIMAL STUDIES, INHIBITED THYROID FUNCTION AND DECREASED ENERGY METABOLISM WERE OBSERVED. GONADOTOXICITY AND EMBRYOTOXICITY WERE OBSERVED IN ANIMAL STUDIES IN RUSSIA.

FIRST AID- GIVE SYRUP OF IPECAC, FOLLOWED BY 1-2 GLASSES OF WATER, TO INDUCE VOMITING (ADULTS: 30 ML). FOLLOWING EMESIS, ADMINISTER 30-50 GRAMS ACTIVATED CHARCOAL. FOLLOW CHARCOAL WITH SODIUM OR MAGNESIUM SULFATE, 250 MG/KG, TO REMOVE TOXICANT FROM THE GUT BY CATHARSIS (EPA, RECOGNITION AND MANAGEMENT OF PESTICIDE POISONINGS, 3RD ED.). FIRST AID SHOULD BE ADMINISTERED UNDER THE DIRECTION OF QUALIFIED MEDICAL PERSONNEL. GET MEDICAL ATTENTION.

REACTIVITY

REACTIVITY: STABLE UNDER NORMAL TEMPERATURES AND PRESSURES.

INCOMPATIBILITIES: MOLINATE: SULFURIC ACID: MAY CAUSE HYDROLYSIS.

DECOMPOSITION: THERMAL DECOMPOSITION MAY RELEASE TOXIC OXIDES OF NITROGEN AND SULFUR.

POLYMERIZATION: HAZARDOUS POLYMERIZATION HAS NOT BEEN REPORTED TO OCCUR UNDER NORMAL TEMPERATURES AND PRESSURES.

STORAGE AND DISPOSAL

OBSERVE ALL FEDERAL, STATE AND LOCAL REGULATIONS WHEN STORING OR DISPOSING OF THIS SUBSTANCE. FOR ASSISTANCE, CONTACT THE DISTRICT DIRECTOR OF THE ENVIRONMENTAL PROTECTION AGENCY.

STORAGE

STORE IN ACCORDANCE WITH 40 CFR 165 RECOMMENDED PROCEDURES FOR THE DISPOSAL AND STORAGE OF PESTICIDES AND PESTICIDE CONTAINERS.
STORE AWAY FROM INCOMPATIBLE SUBSTANCES.

DISPOSAL

DISPOSAL MUST BE IN ACCORDANCE WITH 40 CFR 165 RECOMMENDED PROCEDURES FOR THE DISPOSAL AND STORAGE OF PESTICIDES AND PESTICIDE CONTAINERS.

CONDITIONS TO AVOID

NONE REPORTED.

SPILL AND LEAK PROCEDURES

OCCUPATIONAL SPILL: STOP LEAK IF YOU CAN DO IT WITHOUT RISK. FOR SMALL SPILLS, TAKE UP WITH SAND OR OTHER ABSORBENT MATERIAL AND PLACE INTO CLEAN, DRY CONTAINERS FOR LATER DISPOSAL. KEEP UNNECESSARY PEOPLE AWAY. ISOLATE HAZARD AREA AND DENY ENTRY.

PROTECTIVE EQUIPMENT

VENTILATION: PROVIDE LOCAL EXHAUST OR PROCESS ENCLOSURE VENTILATION SYSTEM.

RESPIRATOR: THE FOLLOWING RESPIRATORS ARE RECOMMENDED BASED ON INFORMATION FOUND IN THE PHYSICAL DATA, TOXICITY AND HEALTH EFFECTS SECTIONS. THEY ARE RANKED IN ORDER FROM MINIMUM TO MAXIMUM RESPIRATORY PROTECTION. THE SPECIFIC RESPIRATOR SELECTED MUST BE BASED ON CONTAMINATION LEVELS FOUND IN THE WORK PLACE, MUST NOT EXCEED THE WORKING LIMITS OF THE RESPIRATOR AND BE JOINTLY APPROVED BY THE NATIONAL INSTITUTE FOR OCCUPATIONAL SAFETY AND HEALTH AND THE MINE SAFETY AND HEALTH ADMINISTRATION (NIOSH-MSHA).
CHEMICAL CARTRIDGE RESPIRATOR WITH FULL FACEPIECE AND PESTICIDE CARTRIDGE.
TYPE 'C' SUPPLIED-AIR RESPIRATOR WITH A FULL FACEPIECE OPERATED IN PRESSURE-DEMAND OR OTHER POSITIVE PRESSURE MODE OR WITH A FULL FACEPIECE, HELMET OR HOOD OPERATED IN CONTINUOUS-FLOW MODE.
SELF-CONTAINED BREATHING APPARATUS OPERATED IN PRESSURE-DEMAND OR OTHER POSITIVE PRESSURE MODE.
FOR FIREFIGHTING AND OTHER IMMEDIATELY DANGEROUS TO LIFE OR HEALTH CONDITIONS:
SELF-CONTAINED BREATHING APPARATUS WITH FULL FACEPIECE OPERATED IN PRESSURE-DEMAND OR OTHER POSITIVE PRESSURE MODE.
SUPPLIED-AIR RESPIRATOR WITH FULL FACEPIECE AND OPERATED IN PRESSURE-DEMAND OR OTHER POSITIVE PRESSURE MODE IN COMBINATION WITH AN AUXILIARY SELF-CONTAINED BREATHING APPARATUS OPERATED IN PRESSURE-DEMAND OR OTHER POSITIVE PRESSURE MODE.

CLOTHING: EMPLOYEE MUST WEAR APPROPRIATE PROTECTIVE (IMPERVIOUS) CLOTHING AND EQUIPMENT TO PREVENT REPEATED OR PROLONGED SKIN CONTACT WITH THIS SUBSTANCE.

GLOVES: EMPLOYEE MUST WEAR APPROPRIATE PROTECTIVE GLOVES TO PREVENT CONTACT WITH THIS SUBSTANCE.

EYE PROTECTION: EMPLOYEE MUST WEAR SPLASH-PROOF OR DUST-RESISTANT SAFETY GOGGLES TO PREVENT EYE CONTACT WITH THIS SUBSTANCE.
EMERGENCY EYE WASH: WHERE THERE IS ANY POSSIBILITY THAT AN EMPLOYEE'S EYES MAY BE EXPOSED TO THIS SUBSTANCE, THE EMPLOYER SHOULD PROVIDE AN EYE WASH FOUNTAIN WITHIN THE IMMEDIATE WORK AREA FOR EMERGENCY USE.

AUTHORIZED BY- OCCUPATIONAL HEALTH SERVICES, INC.
CREATION DATE: 10/04/89 ***REVISION DATE:*** 05/11/90

MATERIAL SAFETY DATA SHEET

OCCUPATIONAL HEALTH SERVICES, INC.
AGRICULTURE AND PESTICIDE DIVISION
450 SEVENTH AVENUE, SUITE 2407
NEW YORK, NEW YORK 10123
1-800-445-MSDS OR (212) 967-1100

EMERGENCY CONTACT:
JOHN S. BRANSFORD, JR. (615) 292-1180

SUBSTANCE IDENTIFICATION

CAS-NUMBER 1114-71-2

SUBSTANCE: **PEBULATE**

TRADE NAMES/SYNONYMS: CARBAMOTHIOIC ACID, BUTYLETHYL-, S-PROPYL ESTER; BUTYLETHYLCARBAMOTHIOIC ACID S-PROPYL ESTER; CARBAMIC ACID, BUTYLETHYLTHIO-, S-PROPYL ESTER; BUTYLETHYLTHIOCARBAMIC ACID S-PROPYL ESTER; S-PROPYL BUTYLETHYLTHIOCARBAMATE; THIOCARBAMIC ACID, N-BUTYL-N-ETHYL, S-PROPYL ESTER; S-PROPYL BUTYL(ETHYL)THIOCARBAMATE; S-PROPYL BUTYLETHYLCARBAMOTHIOATE; PROPYL ETHYL-N-BUTYLTHIOCARBAMATE; N-PROPYL ETHYL-N-BUTYLTHIOLCARBAMATE; N-BUTYL-N-ETHYLTHIOCARBAMIC ACID S-PROPYL ESTER; PEBC; R 2061; STAUFFER R 2061; TILLAM; PST71472

CHEMICAL FAMILY: THIOCARBAMATE

MOLECULAR FORMULA: C10-H21-N-O-S

MOLECULAR WEIGHT: 203.38

CERCLA RATINGS (SCALE 0-3): HEALTH=2 FIRE=U REACTIVITY=0 PERSISTENCE=0

NFPA RATINGS (SCALE 0-4): HEALTH=2 FIRE=U REACTIVITY=0

COMPONENTS AND CONTAMINANTS

COMPONENT: PEBULATE ***PERCENT:*** 100
CAS# 1114-71-2

OTHER CONTAMINANTS: NONE

EXPOSURE LIMITS: NO OCCUPATIONAL EXPOSURE LIMITS ESTABLISHED BY OSHA, ACGIH, OR NIOSH.

PHYSICAL DATA

DESCRIPTION: CLEAR, COLORLESS LIQUID WITH AN AROMATIC ODOR

BOILING POINT: 288 F (142 C) @ 20 MMHG ***SPECIFIC GRAVITY:*** 0.0956

VAPOR PRESSURE: 0.035 MMHG @ 25 C ***SOLUBILITY IN WATER:*** 0.006%

SOLVENT SOLUBILITY: SOLUBLE IN ACETONE, ETHANOL, KEROSENE, BENZENE, 4-METHYLPENTAN-2-ONE, XYLENE, METHANOL, TOLUENE, ISOPROPANOL, METHYL ISOBUTYL KETONE, AND MOST ORGANIC SOLVENTS

FIRE AND EXPLOSION DATA

FIRE AND EXPLOSION HAZARD: UNKNOWN FIRE AND EXPLOSION HAZARD.

FIREFIGHTING MEDIA: DRY CHEMICAL, CARBON DIOXIDE, WATER SPRAY OR FOAM FOR LARGER FIRES, USE WATER SPRAY, FOG OR ALCOHOL FOAM

FIREFIGHTING: MOVE CONTAINER FROM FIRE AREA IF POSSIBLE. DO NOT SCATTER SPILLED MATERIAL WITH MORE WATER THAN NEEDED FOR FIRE CONTROL. DIKE FIRE CONTROL WATER FOR LATER DISPOSAL
USE AGENTS SUITABLE FOR TYPE OF SURROUNDING FIRE. AVOID BREATHING HAZARDOUS VAPORS, KEEP UPWIND.

TOXICITY

PEBULATE: TOXICITY DATA: 4640 MG/KG SKIN-RABBIT LD50; 2 GM/KG SKIN-RAT LD50; 921 MG/KG ORAL-RAT LD50; 1652 MG/KG ORAL-MOUSE LD50; 1125 MG/KG UNREPORTED-RAT LD50; 713 MG/KG UNREPORTED-MAMMAL LD50; 750 MG/KG UNREPORTED-MOUSE LD50; 750 MG/KG UNREPORTED-CAT LD50; MUTAGENIC DATA (RTECS); TUMORIGENIC DATA (RTECS). CARCINOGEN STATUS: NONE. ACUTE TOXICITY LEVEL: MODERATELY TOXIC BY INGESTION; SLIGHTLY TOXIC BY DERMAL ABSORPTION. TARGET EFFECTS: AN ANIMAL STUDY INDICATES THAT PEBULATE MAY BE A WEAK CHOLINESTERASE INHIBITOR.

HEALTH EFFECTS AND FIRST AID

INHALATION: PEBULATE: **ACUTE EXPOSURE-** AN ANIMAL STUDY INDICATED THAT PEBULATE MAY BE A WEAK CHOLINESTERASE INHIBITOR. EARLY SYMPTOMS OF CHOLINESTERASE INHIBITION ARE BLURRED VISION, FATIGUE, HEADACHE, VERTIGO, NAUSEA, MIOSIS, ABDOMINAL CRAMPS AND DIARRHEA. SEVERE INHIBITION OF CHOLINESTERASE MAY CAUSE EXCESSIVE SWEATING, TEARING, BRADYCARDIA, GIDDINESS, SLURRED SPEECH, CONFUSION, PULMONARY EDEMA, CONVULSIONS AND COMA. INHALATION OF EXCESSIVE AMOUNTS OF SOME THIOCARBAMATES CAUSES SCRATCHY THROAT, SNEEZING, AND COUGHING. **CHRONIC EXPOSURE-** NO DATA AVAILABLE.

FIRST AID- REMOVE FROM EXPOSURE AREA TO FRESH AIR IMMEDIATELY. IF BREATHING HAS STOPPED, PERFORM ARTIFICIAL RESPIRATION. KEEP PERSON WARM AND AT REST. TREAT SYMPTOMATICALLY AND SUPPORTIVELY. GET MEDICAL ATTENTION IMMEDIATELY.

SKIN CONTACT: PEBULATE: **ACUTE EXPOSURE-** A LETHAL DOSE IN RATS BY DERMAL ABSORPTION WAS 4640 MG/KG. AN ANIMAL STUDY INDICATED THAT PEBULATE MAY BE A WEAK CHOLINESTERASE INHIBITOR. SOME THIOCARBAMATES ARE MODERATELY IRRITATING TO THE SKIN. **CHRONIC EXPOSURE-** NO DATA AVAILABLE.

FIRST AID- REMOVE CONTAMINATED CLOTHING AND SHOES IMMEDIATELY. WASH AFFECTED AREA WITH SOAP OR MILD DETERGENT AND LARGE AMOUNTS OF WATER UNTIL NO EVIDENCE OF CHEMICAL REMAINS (APPROXIMATELY 15-20 MINUTES). GET MEDICAL ATTENTION IMMEDIATELY.

EYE CONTACT: PEBULATE: **ACUTE EXPOSURE-** MAY CAUSE IRRITATION. **CHRONIC EXPOSURE-** PROLONGED OR REPEATED EXPOSURE TO IRRITANTS MAY CAUSE CONJUNCTIVITIS.

FIRST AID- WASH EYES IMMEDIATELY WITH LARGE AMOUNTS OF WATER OR NORMAL SALINE, OCCASIONALLY LIFTING UPPER AND LOWER LIDS, UNTIL NO EVIDENCE OF CHEMICAL REMAINS (APPROXIMATELY 15-20 MINUTES). GET MEDICAL ATTENTION IMMEDIATELY.

INGESTION: PEBULATE: **ACUTE EXPOSURE-** A LETHAL DOSE IN RATS WAS 921 MG/KG. LARGE DOSES ARE SUSPECTED OF INCREASING SUSCEPTIBILITY OF LABORATORY ANIMALS TO INFECTIONS. AN ANIMAL STUDY INDICATED THAT PEBULATE MAY BE A WEAK CHOLINESTERASE INHIBITOR. EARLY SYMPTOMS OF CHOLINESTERASE INHIBITION ARE BLURRED VISION, FATIGUE, HEADACHE, VERTIGO, NAUSEA, MIOSIS, ABDOMINAL CRAMPS, AND DIARRHEA. SEVERE INHIBITION OF CHOLINESTERASE MAY CAUSE EXCESSIVE SWEATING, TEARING, BRADYCARDIA, GIDDINESS, SLURRED SPEECH, CONFUSION, PULMONARY EDEMA, CONVULSIONS AND COMA. **CHRONIC EXPOSURE-** DECREASES IN OXIDATIVE METABOLISM WERE OBSERVED IN A 16-WEEK STUDY OF RATS. REPEATED DOSES OF 100 MG/KG WERE LETHAL IN COWS AFTER SIX DAYS. NECROPSY FINDINGS INCLUDED CONGESTION OF THYROID, SPLEEN, ADRENAL AND LUNG PARENCHYMA, ACUTE TOXIC TUBULAR NEPHRITIS WITH HEMORRHAGING, AND COAGULATIVE NECROSIS OF THE LIVER.

FIRST AID- GIVE SYRUP OF IPECAC, FOLLOWED BY 1-2 GLASSES OF WATER, TO INDUCE VOMITING (ADULTS: 30 ML). FOLLOWING EMESIS, ADMINISTER 30-50 GRAMS ACTIVATED CHARCOAL. FOLLOW CHARCOAL WITH SODIUM OR MAGNESIUM SULFATE, 250 MG/KG, TO REMOVE TOXICANT FROM THE GUT BY CATHARSIS (EPA, RECOGNITION AND MANAGEMENT OF PESTICIDE POISONINGS, 3RD ED.). FIRST AID SHOULD BE ADMINISTERED UNDER THE DIRECTION OF QUALIFIED MEDICAL PERSONNEL. GET MEDICAL ATTENTION.

ANTIDOTE: NO SPECIFIC ANTIDOTE. TREAT SYMPTOMATICALLY AND SUPPORTIVELY.

REACTIVITY

REACTIVITY: STABLE UNDER NORMAL TEMPERATURES AND PRESSURES.

INCOMPATIBILITIES: PEBULATE: NO DATA AVAILABLE.

DECOMPOSITION: THERMAL DECOMPOSITION MAY RELEASE TOXIC OXIDES OF NITROGEN AND SULFUR.

POLYMERIZATION: HAZARDOUS POLYMERIZATION HAS NOT BEEN REPORTED TO OCCUR UNDER NORMAL TEMPERATURES AND PRESSURES.

STORAGE AND DISPOSAL

OBSERVE ALL FEDERAL, STATE AND LOCAL REGULATIONS WHEN STORING OR DISPOSING OF THIS SUBSTANCE. FOR ASSISTANCE, CONTACT THE DISTRICT DIRECTOR OF THE ENVIRONMENTAL PROTECTION AGENCY.

****STORAGE****

STORE IN ACCORDANCE WITH 40 CFR 165 RECOMMENDED PROCEDURES FOR THE DISPOSAL AND STORAGE OF PESTICIDES AND PESTICIDE CONTAINERS.

****DISPOSAL****

DISPOSAL MUST BE IN ACCORDANCE WITH 40 CFR 165 RECOMMENDED PROCEDURES FOR THE DISPOSAL AND STORAGE OF PESTICIDES AND PESTICIDE CONTAINERS.

CONDITIONS TO AVOID

NONE REPORTED.

SPILL AND LEAK PROCEDURES

OCCUPATIONAL SPILL: STOP LEAK IF YOU CAN DO IT WITHOUT RISK. FOR SMALL SPILLS, TAKE UP WITH SAND OR OTHER ABSORBENT MATERIAL AND PLACE INTO CLEAN, DRY CONTAINERS FOR LATER DISPOSAL. KEEP UNNECESSARY PEOPLE AWAY. ISOLATE HAZARD AREA AND DENY ENTRY.

PROTECTIVE EQUIPMENT

VENTILATION: PROVIDE LOCAL EXHAUST VENTILATION SYSTEM.

RESPIRATOR: THE FOLLOWING RESPIRATORS ARE RECOMMENDED BASED ON INFORMATION FOUND IN THE PHYSICAL DATA, TOXICITY AND HEALTH EFFECTS SECTIONS. THEY ARE RANKED IN ORDER FROM MINIMUM TO MAXIMUM RESPIRATORY PROTECTION. THE SPECIFIC RESPIRATOR SELECTED MUST BE BASED ON CONTAMINATION LEVELS FOUND IN THE WORK PLACE, MUST NOT EXCEED THE WORKING LIMITS OF THE RESPIRATOR AND BE JOINTLY APPROVED BY THE NATIONAL INSTITUTE FOR OCCUPATIONAL SAFETY AND HEALTH AND THE MINE SAFETY AND HEALTH ADMINISTRATION (NIOSH-MSHA).
CHEMICAL CARTRIDGE RESPIRATOR WITH FULL FACEPIECE AND PESTICIDE CARTRIDGE.
TYPE 'C' SUPPLIED-AIR RESPIRATOR WITH A FULL FACEPIECE OPERATED IN PRESSURE-DEMAND OR OTHER POSITIVE PRESSURE MODE OR WITH A FULL FACEPIECE, HELMET OR HOOD OPERATED IN CONTINUOUS-FLOW MODE.
SELF-CONTAINED BREATHING APPARATUS OPERATED IN PRESSURE-DEMAND OR OTHER POSITIVE PRESSURE MODE.
FOR FIREFIGHTING AND OTHER IMMEDIATELY DANGEROUS TO LIFE OR HEALTH CONDITIONS:
SELF-CONTAINED BREATHING APPARATUS WITH FULL FACEPIECE OPERATED IN PRESSURE-DEMAND OR OTHER POSITIVE PRESSURE MODE.
SUPPLIED-AIR RESPIRATOR WITH FULL FACEPIECE AND OPERATED IN PRESSURE-DEMAND OR OTHER POSITIVE PRESSURE MODE IN COMBINATION WITH AN AUXILIARY SELF-CONTAINED BREATHING APPARATUS OPERATED IN PRESSURE-DEMAND OR OTHER POSITIVE PRESSURE MODE.

CLOTHING: EMPLOYEE MUST WEAR APPROPRIATE PROTECTIVE (IMPERVIOUS) CLOTHING AND EQUIPMENT TO PREVENT REPEATED OR PROLONGED SKIN CONTACT WITH THIS SUBSTANCE.

GLOVES: EMPLOYEE MUST WEAR APPROPRIATE PROTECTIVE GLOVES TO PREVENT CONTACT WITH THIS SUBSTANCE.

EYE PROTECTION: EMPLOYEE MUST WEAR SPLASH-PROOF OR DUST-RESISTANT SAFETY GOGGLES TO PREVENT EYE CONTACT WITH THIS SUBSTANCE.
EMERGENCY EYE WASH: WHERE THERE IS ANY POSSIBILITY THAT AN EMPLOYEE'S EYES MAY BE EXPOSED TO THIS SUBSTANCE, THE EMPLOYER SHOULD PROVIDE AN EYE WASH FOUNTAIN WITHIN THE IMMEDIATE WORK AREA FOR EMERGENCY USE.

AUTHORIZED BY- OCCUPATIONAL HEALTH SERVICES, INC.
CREATION DATE: 10/04/89 ***REVISION DATE:*** 05/07/90

MATERIAL SAFETY DATA SHEET

OCCUPATIONAL HEALTH SERVICES, INC.
AGRICULTURE AND PESTICIDE DIVISION
450 SEVENTH AVENUE, SUITE 2407
NEW YORK, NEW YORK 10123
1-800-445-MSDS OR (212) 967-1100

EMERGENCY CONTACT:
JOHN S. BRANSFORD, JR. (615) 292-1180

SUBSTANCE IDENTIFICATION

CAS-NUMBER 1929-77-7
SUBSTANCE: VERNOLATE
TRADE NAMES/SYNONYMS: CARBAMOTHIOIC ACID, DIPROPYL-, S-PROPYL ESTER; DIPROPYLCARBAMOTHIOIC ACID S-PROPYL ESTER; CARBAMIC ACID, DIPROPYLTHIO-, S-PROPYL ESTER; DIPROPYLTHIOCARBAMIC ACID S-PROPYL ESTER; S-PROPYL DIPROPYLCARBAMOTHIOATE; S-PROPYL DIPROPYL(THIOCARBAMATE); S-PROPYL DIPROPYLTHIOCARBAMATE; PROPYL DIPROPYLTHIOLCARBAMATE; PERBULATE; PPTC; R-1607; VANALATE; VERNAM; PST71473
CHEMICAL FAMILY: THIOCARBAMATE
MOLECULAR FORMULA: C10-C21-N-O-S
MOLECULAR WEIGHT: 203.35
CERCLA RATINGS (SCALE 0-3): HEALTH=2 FIRE=U REACTIVITY=0 PERSISTENCE=0
NFPA RATINGS (SCALE 0-4): HEALTH=2 FIRE=U REACTIVITY=0

COMPONENTS AND CONTAMINANTS

COMPONENT: VERNOLATE ***PERCENT:*** 100
CAS# 1929-77-7
OTHER CONTAMINANTS: NONE
EXPOSURE LIMITS: NO OCCUPATIONAL EXPOSURE LIMITS ESTABLISHED BY OSHA, ACGIH, OR NIOSH.

PHYSICAL DATA

DESCRIPTION: CLEAR LIQUID WITH A FAINT AROMATIC ODOR
BOILING POINT: 302 F (150 C) @ 30 MMHG ***SPECIFIC GRAVITY:*** 0.9440 AT 30/4 C
VAPOR PRESSURE: 0.0104 MMHG @ 25 C ***SOLUBILITY IN WATER:*** 0.0107% AT 25 C
SOLVENT SOLUBILITY: SOLUBLE IN ACETONE, ETHANOL, KEROSENE, XYLENE, METHYL ISOBUTYL KETONE, 4-METHYLPENTAN-2-ONE, MOST ORGANIC SOLVENTS

FIRE AND EXPLOSION DATA

FIRE AND EXPLOSION HAZARD: UNKNOWN FIRE AND EXPLOSION HAZARD.
FIREFIGHTING MEDIA: DRY CHEMICAL, CARBON DIOXIDE, WATER SPRAY OR FOAM FOR LARGER FIRES, USE WATER SPRAY, FOG OR ALCOHOL FOAM
FIREFIGHTING: MOVE CONTAINER FROM FIRE AREA IF POSSIBLE. DO NOT SCATTER SPILLED MATERIAL WITH MORE WATER THAN NEEDED FOR FIRE CONTROL. DIKE FIRE CONTROL WATER FOR LATER DISPOSAL
USE AGENTS SUITABLE FOR TYPE OF SURROUNDING FIRE. AVOID BREATHING HAZARDOUS VAPORS, KEEP UPWIND.

TOXICITY

VERNOLATE: TOXICITY DATA: 1200 MG/KG ORAL-RAT LD50; MUTAGENIC DATA (RTECS). CARCINOGEN STATUS: NONE. ACUTE TOXICITY LEVEL: MODERATELY TOXIC BY INGESTION. TARGET EFFECTS: NO DATA AVAILABLE.

HEALTH EFFECTS AND FIRST AID

INHALATION: VERNOLATE: **ACUTE EXPOSURE-** INHALATION OF EXCESSIVE AMOUNTS OF SOME THIOCARBAMATES CAUSES SCRATCHY THROAT, SNEEZING, AND COUGHING. **CHRONIC EXPOSURE-** NO DATA AVAILABLE.
FIRST AID- REMOVE FROM EXPOSURE AREA TO FRESH AIR IMMEDIATELY. IF BREATHING HAS STOPPED, PERFORM ARTIFICIAL RESPIRATION. KEEP PERSON WARM AND AT REST. TREAT SYMPTOMATICALLY AND SUPPORTIVELY. GET MEDICAL ATTENTION IMMEDIATELY.

SKIN CONTACT: VERNOLATE: **ACUTE EXPOSURE-** A LETHAL DOSE IN RABBITS BY DERMAL ABSORPTION IS GREATER THAN 2955 MG/KG. **CHRONIC EXPOSURE-** NO DATA AVAILABLE.
FIRST AID- REMOVE CONTAMINATED CLOTHING AND SHOES IMMEDIATELY. WASH AFFECTED AREA WITH SOAP OR MILD DETERGENT AND LARGE AMOUNTS OF WATER UNTIL NO EVIDENCE OF CHEMICAL REMAINS (APPROXIMATELY 15-20 MINUTES). GET MEDICAL ATTENTION IMMEDIATELY.

EYE CONTACT: VERNOLATE: **ACUTE EXPOSURE-** MAY CAUSE IRRITATION. **CHRONIC EXPOSURE-** PROLONGED OR REPEATED EXPOSURE MAY CAUSE IRRITATION.
FIRST AID- WASH EYES IMMEDIATELY WITH LARGE AMOUNTS OF WATER OR NORMAL SALINE, OCCASIONALLY LIFTING UPPER AND LOWER LIDS, UNTIL NO EVIDENCE OF CHEMICAL REMAINS (APPROXIMATELY 15-20 MINUTES). GET MEDICAL ATTENTION IMMEDIATELY.

INGESTION: VERNOLATE: **ACUTE EXPOSURE-** A LETHAL DOSE IN RATS WAS 1200 MG/KG. **CHRONIC EXPOSURE-** A DOSE OF 80 MG/KG/DAY FOR 51 WEEKS PRODUCED A SIGNIFICANTLY INCREASED MORTALITY IN MALE RATS DUE TO HEMORRHAGE. A DOSE OF 20 MG/KG/DAY FOR 51 WEEKS PRODUCED AN INCREASE IN BLOOD CLOTTING TIME. NO DELAYED NEUROTOXICITY WAS OBSERVED IN A STUDY OF HENS. IN A 24 MONTH STUDY OF MICE, NO ONCOGENIC EFFECTS WERE OBSERVED AT LEVELS AS HIGH AS 100 MG/KG/DAY.
FIRST AID- GIVE SYRUP OF IPECAC, FOLLOWED BY 1-2 GLASSES OF WATER, TO INDUCE VOMITING (ADULTS: 30 ML). FOLLOWING EMESIS, ADMINISTER 30-50 GRAMS ACTIVATED CHARCOAL. FOLLOW CHARCOAL WITH SODIUM OR MAGNESIUM SULFATE, 250 MG/KG, TO REMOVE TOXICANT FROM THE GUT BY CATHARSIS (EPA, RECOGNITION AND MANAGEMENT OF PESTICIDE POISONINGS, 3RD ED.). FIRST AID SHOULD BE ADMINISTERED UNDER THE DIRECTION OF QUALIFIED MEDICAL PERSONNEL. GET MEDICAL ATTENTION.
ANTIDOTE: NO SPECIFIC ANTIDOTE. TREAT SYMPTOMATICALLY AND SUPPORTIVELY.

REACTIVITY

REACTIVITY: STABLE UNDER NORMAL TEMPERATURES AND PRESSURES.
INCOMPATIBILITIES: VERNOLATE: NO DATA AVAILABLE.
DECOMPOSITION: THERMAL DECOMPOSITION MAY RELEASE TOXIC OXIDES OF NITROGEN AND SULFUR.
POLYMERIZATION: HAZARDOUS POLYMERIZATION HAS NOT BEEN REPORTED TO OCCUR UNDER NORMAL TEMPERATURES AND PRESSURES.

STORAGE AND DISPOSAL

OBSERVE ALL FEDERAL, STATE AND LOCAL REGULATIONS WHEN STORING OR DISPOSING OF THIS SUBSTANCE. FOR ASSISTANCE, CONTACT THE DISTRICT DIRECTOR OF THE ENVIRONMENTAL PROTECTION AGENCY.

STORAGE

STORE IN ACCORDANCE WITH 40 CFR 165 RECOMMENDED PROCEDURES FOR THE DISPOSAL AND STORAGE OF PESTICIDES AND PESTICIDE CONTAINERS.

DISPOSAL

DISPOSAL MUST BE IN ACCORDANCE WITH 40 CFR 165 RECOMMENDED PROCEDURES FOR THE DISPOSAL AND STORAGE OF PESTICIDES AND PESTICIDE CONTAINERS.

CONDITIONS TO AVOID

NONE REPORTED.

SPILL AND LEAK PROCEDURES

OCCUPATIONAL SPILL: STOP LEAK IF YOU CAN DO IT WITHOUT RISK. FOR SMALL SPILLS, TAKE UP WITH SAND OR OTHER ABSORBENT MATERIAL AND PLACE INTO CLEAN, DRY CONTAINERS FOR LATER DISPOSAL. KEEP UNNECESSARY PEOPLE AWAY. ISOLATE HAZARD AREA AND DENY ENTRY.

PROTECTIVE EQUIPMENT

VENTILATION: PROVIDE LOCAL EXHAUST VENTILATION SYSTEM.
RESPIRATOR: THE FOLLOWING RESPIRATORS ARE RECOMMENDED BASED ON INFORMATION FOUND IN THE PHYSICAL DATA, TOXICITY AND HEALTH EFFECTS SECTIONS. THEY ARE RANKED IN ORDER FROM MINIMUM TO MAXIMUM RESPIRATORY PROTECTION. THE SPECIFIC RESPIRATOR SELECTED MUST BE BASED ON CONTAMINATION LEVELS FOUND IN THE WORK PLACE, MUST NOT EXCEED THE WORKING LIMITS OF THE RESPIRATOR AND BE JOINTLY APPROVED BY THE NATIONAL INSTITUTE FOR OCCUPATIONAL SAFETY AND HEALTH AND THE MINE SAFETY AND HEALTH ADMINISTRATION (NIOSH-MSHA).
CHEMICAL CARTRIDGE RESPIRATOR WITH FULL FACEPIECE AND PESTICIDE CARTRIDGE.
TYPE 'C' SUPPLIED-AIR RESPIRATOR WITH A FULL FACEPIECE OPERATED IN PRESSURE-DEMAND OR OTHER POSITIVE PRESSURE MODE OR WITH A FULL FACEPIECE, HELMET OR HOOD OPERATED IN CONTINUOUS-FLOW MODE.
SELF-CONTAINED BREATHING APPARATUS OPERATED IN PRESSURE-DEMAND OR OTHER POSITIVE PRESSURE MODE.
FOR FIREFIGHTING AND OTHER IMMEDIATELY DANGEROUS TO LIFE OR HEALTH CONDITIONS:
SELF-CONTAINED BREATHING APPARATUS WITH FULL FACEPIECE OPERATED IN PRESSURE-DEMAND OR OTHER POSITIVE PRESSURE MODE.
SUPPLIED-AIR RESPIRATOR WITH FULL FACEPIECE AND OPERATED IN PRESSURE-DEMAND OR OTHER POSITIVE PRESSURE MODE IN COMBINATION WITH AN AUXILIARY SELF-CONTAINED BREATHING APPARATUS OPERATED IN PRESSURE-DEMAND OR OTHER POSITIVE PRESSURE MODE.

CLOTHING: EMPLOYEE MUST WEAR APPROPRIATE PROTECTIVE (IMPERVIOUS) CLOTHING AND EQUIPMENT TO PREVENT REPEATED OR PROLONGED SKIN CONTACT WITH THIS SUBSTANCE.
GLOVES: EMPLOYEE MUST WEAR APPROPRIATE PROTECTIVE GLOVES TO PREVENT CONTACT WITH THIS SUBSTANCE.
EYE PROTECTION: EMPLOYEE MUST WEAR SPLASH-PROOF OR DUST-RESISTANT SAFETY GOGGLES TO PREVENT EYE CONTACT WITH THIS SUBSTANCE. EMERGENCY EYE WASH: WHERE THERE IS ANY POSSIBILITY THAT AN EMPLOYEE'S EYES MAY BE EXPOSED TO THIS SUBSTANCE, THE EMPLOYER SHOULD PROVIDE AN EYE WASH FOUNTAIN WITHIN THE IMMEDIATE WORK AREA FOR EMERGENCY USE.

AUTHORIZED BY- OCCUPATIONAL HEALTH SERVICES, INC.
CREATION DATE: 10/05/89 ***REVISION DATE:*** 05/09/90

MATERIAL SAFETY DATA SHEET

OCCUPATIONAL HEALTH SERVICES, INC.
AGRICULTURE AND PESTICIDE DIVISION
450 SEVENTH AVENUE, SUITE 2407
NEW YORK, NEW YORK 10123
1-800-445-MSDS OR (212) 967-1100

EMERGENCY CONTACT:
JOHN S. BRANSFORD, JR. (615) 292-1180

SUBSTANCE IDENTIFICATION

CAS-NUMBER 2008-41-5
SUBSTANCE: **BUTYLATE**
TRADE NAMES/SYNONYMS: CARBAMOTHIOIC ACID, BIS(2-METHYLPROPYL)-, S-ETHYL ESTER; BIS(2-METHYLPROPYL)CARBAMOTHIOIC ACID S-ETHYL ESTER; CARBAMIC ACID, DIISOBUTYLTHIO-, S-ETHYL ESTER; DIISOBUTYLTHIOCARBAMIC ACID S-ETHYL ESTER; S-ETHYL DI-ISOBUTYLTHIOCARBAMATE; S-ETHYL DI-ISOBUTYL(THIOCARBAMATE); S-ETHYL BIS(2-METHYLPROPYL)CARBAMOTHIOATE; S-ETHYL DIISOBUTYLTHIOCARBAMATE; S-ETHYL N,N-DIISOBUTYLTHIOCARBAMATE; ETHYL N,N-DIISOBUTYLTHIOCARBAMATE; ANELDA; BUTILATE; DIISOCARB; R 1910; STAUFFER R 1910; SUTAN; PST71474
CHEMICAL FAMILY: THIOCARBAMATE
MOLECULAR FORMULA: C11-H23-N-O-S
MOLECULAR WEIGHT: 217.37
CERCLA RATINGS (SCALE 0-3): HEALTH=2 FIRE=U REACTIVITY=0 PERSISTENCE=1
NFPA RATINGS (SCALE 0-4): HEALTH=2 FIRE=U REACTIVITY=0

COMPONENTS AND CONTAMINANTS

COMPONENT: BUTYLATE ***PERCENT:*** 100
CAS# 2008-41-5
OTHER CONTAMINANTS: NONE
EXPOSURE LIMITS: NO OCCUPATIONAL EXPOSURE LIMITS ESTABLISHED BY OSHA, ACGIH, OR NIOSH.

PHYSICAL DATA

DESCRIPTION: CLEAR AMBER TO YELLOW LIQUID WITH AN AROMATIC ODOR
BOILING POINT: 160 F (71 C) @ 10 MMHG ***SPECIFIC GRAVITY:*** 0.9402
VAPOR PRESSURE: 0.0013 MMHG @ 25 C ***SOLUBILITY IN WATER:*** 0.0036-0.0046%
SOLVENT SOLUBILITY: SOLUBLE IN KEROSENE, ACETONE, ETHYL ALCOHOL, XYLENE, 4-METHYLPENTAN-2-ONE, AND MANY ORGANIC SOLVENTS

FIRE AND EXPLOSION DATA

FIRE AND EXPLOSION HAZARD: UNKNOWN FIRE AND EXPLOSION HAZARD.
FIREFIGHTING MEDIA: DRY CHEMICAL, CARBON DIOXIDE, WATER SPRAY OR FOAM FOR LARGER FIRES, USE WATER SPRAY, FOG OR ALCOHOL FOAM
FIREFIGHTING: MOVE CONTAINER FROM FIRE AREA IF POSSIBLE. DO NOT SCATTER SPILLED MATERIAL WITH MORE WATER THAN NEEDED FOR FIRE CONTROL. DIKE FIRE CONTROL WATER FOR LATER DISPOSAL
USE AGENTS SUITABLE FOR TYPE OF SURROUNDING FIRE. AVOID BREATHING HAZARDOUS VAPORS, KEEP UPWIND.

TOXICITY

BUTYLATE: 4000 MG/KG ORAL-RAT LD50; 3500 MG/KG ORAL-RAT LD50 (MEISTER, FARM CHEMICALS HANDBOOK, 1987); 1659 MG/KG ORAL-GUINEA PIG LD50 (FDA SURVEILLANCE INDEX, PB 82-913299); MUTAGENIC DATA (RTECS). CARCINOGEN STATUS: NONE. BUTYLATE MAY CAUSE IRRITATION OF THE SKIN AND MUCOUS MEMBRANES.

HEALTH EFFECTS AND FIRST AID

INHALATION: BUTYLATE: **ACUTE EXPOSURE-** INHALATION OF EXCESSIVE AMOUNTS OF SOME THIOCARBAMATES CAUSES SCRATCHY THROAT, SNEEZING, AND COUGHING. **CHRONIC EXPOSURE-** NO DATA AVAILABLE.
FIRST AID- REMOVE FROM EXPOSURE AREA TO FRESH AIR IMMEDIATELY. IF BREATHING HAS STOPPED, PERFORM ARTIFICIAL RESPIRATION. KEEP PERSON WARM AND AT REST. TREAT SYMPTOMATICALLY AND SUPPORTIVELY. GET MEDICAL ATTENTION IMMEDIATELY.

SKIN CONTACT: BUTYLATE: **ACUTE EXPOSURE-** THIS MATERIAL WAS MILDLY IRRITATING TO SKINS OF RABBITS. A LETHAL DOSE IN RABBITS BY DERMAL ABSORPTION WAS GREATER THAN 5000 MG/KG. **CHRONIC EXPOSURE-** NO DATA AVAILABLE.
FIRST AID- REMOVE CONTAMINATED CLOTHING AND SHOES IMMEDIATELY. WASH AFFECTED AREA WITH SOAP OR MILD DETERGENT AND LARGE AMOUNTS OF WATER UNTIL NO EVIDENCE OF CHEMICAL REMAINS (APPROXIMATELY 15-20 MINUTES). GET MEDICAL ATTENTION IMMEDIATELY.

EYE CONTACT: BUTYLATE: **ACUTE EXPOSURE-** THIS MATERIAL WAS NOT IRRITATING IN RABBIT EYES. **CHRONIC EXPOSURE-** NO DATA AVAILABLE.
FIRST AID- WASH EYES IMMEDIATELY WITH LARGE AMOUNTS OF WATER OR NORMAL SALINE, OCCASIONALLY LIFTING UPPER AND LOWER LIDS, UNTIL NO EVIDENCE OF CHEMICAL REMAINS (APPROXIMATELY 15-20 MINUTES). GET MEDICAL ATTENTION IMMEDIATELY.

INGESTION: BUTYLATE: **ACUTE EXPOSURE-** A LETHAL DOSE IN RATS WAS 4000 MG/KG. **CHRONIC EXPOSURE-** NO ADVERSE EFFECTS WERE OBSERVED IN CHRONIC FEEDING STUDIES OF DOGS AT 40 MG/KG/DAY AND OF RATS AT 32 MG/KG/DAY.
FIRST AID- GIVE SYRUP OF IPECAC, FOLLOWED BY 1-2 GLASSES OF WATER, TO INDUCE VOMITING (ADULTS: 30 ML). FOLLOWING EMESIS, ADMINISTER 30-50 GRAMS ACTIVATED CHARCOAL. FOLLOW CHARCOAL WITH SODIUM OR MAGNESIUM SULFATE, 250 MG/KG, TO REMOVE TOXICANT FROM THE GUT BY CATHARSIS (EPA, RECOGNITION AND MANAGEMENT OF PESTICIDE POISONINGS, 3RD ED.). FIRST AID SHOULD BE ADMINISTERED UNDER THE DIRECTION OF QUALIFIED MEDICAL PERSONNEL. GET MEDICAL ATTENTION.
ANTIDOTE: NO SPECIFIC ANTIDOTE. TREAT SYMPTOMATICALLY AND SUPPORTIVELY.

REACTIVITY

REACTIVITY: STABLE UNDER NORMAL TEMPERATURES AND PRESSURES.
INCOMPATIBILITIES: BUTYLATE: NO DATA AVAILABLE.
DECOMPOSITION: THERMAL DECOMPOSITION MAY RELEASE TOXIC OXIDES OF NITROGEN AND SULFUR.
POLYMERIZATION: HAZARDOUS POLYMERIZATION HAS NOT BEEN REPORTED TO OCCUR UNDER NORMAL TEMPERATURES AND PRESSURES.

STORAGE AND DISPOSAL

OBSERVE ALL FEDERAL, STATE AND LOCAL REGULATIONS WHEN STORING OR DISPOSING OF THIS SUBSTANCE. FOR ASSISTANCE, CONTACT THE DISTRICT DIRECTOR OF THE ENVIRONMENTAL PROTECTION AGENCY.

****STORAGE****

STORE IN ACCORDANCE WITH 40 CFR 165 RECOMMENDED PROCEDURES FOR THE DISPOSAL AND STORAGE OF PESTICIDES AND PESTICIDE CONTAINERS.

****DISPOSAL****

DISPOSAL MUST BE IN ACCORDANCE WITH 40 CFR 165 RECOMMENDED PROCEDURES FOR THE DISPOSAL AND STORAGE OF PESTICIDES AND PESTICIDE CONTAINERS.

CONDITIONS TO AVOID

NONE REPORTED.

SPILL AND LEAK PROCEDURES

OCCUPATIONAL SPILL: STOP LEAK IF YOU CAN DO IT WITHOUT RISK. FOR SMALL SPILLS, TAKE UP WITH SAND OR OTHER ABSORBENT MATERIAL AND PLACE INTO CLEAN, DRY CONTAINERS FOR LATER DISPOSAL. KEEP UNNECESSARY PEOPLE AWAY. ISOLATE HAZARD AREA AND DENY ENTRY.

PROTECTIVE EQUIPMENT

VENTILATION: PROVIDE LOCAL EXHAUST VENTILATION SYSTEM.
RESPIRATOR: THE FOLLOWING RESPIRATORS ARE RECOMMENDED BASED ON INFORMATION FOUND IN THE PHYSICAL DATA, TOXICITY AND HEALTH EFFECTS SECTIONS. THEY ARE RANKED IN ORDER FROM MINIMUM TO MAXIMUM RESPIRATORY PROTECTION. THE SPECIFIC RESPIRATOR SELECTED MUST BE BASED ON CONTAMINATION LEVELS FOUND IN THE WORK PLACE, MUST NOT EXCEED THE WORKING LIMITS OF THE RESPIRATOR AND BE JOINTLY APPROVED BY THE NATIONAL INSTITUTE FOR OCCUPATIONAL SAFETY AND HEALTH AND THE MINE

SAFETY AND HEALTH ADMINISTRATION (NIOSH-MSHA).
CHEMICAL CARTRIDGE RESPIRATOR WITH FULL FACEPIECE AND PESTICIDE CARTRIDGE.
TYPE 'C' SUPPLIED-AIR RESPIRATOR WITH A FULL FACEPIECE OPERATED IN PRESSURE-DEMAND OR OTHER POSITIVE PRESSURE MODE OR WITH A FULL FACEPIECE, HELMET OR HOOD OPERATED IN CONTINUOUS-FLOW MODE.
SELF-CONTAINED BREATHING APPARATUS OPERATED IN PRESSURE-DEMAND OR OTHER POSITIVE PRESSURE MODE.
FOR FIREFIGHTING AND OTHER IMMEDIATELY DANGEROUS TO LIFE OR HEALTH CONDITIONS:
SELF-CONTAINED BREATHING APPARATUS WITH FULL FACEPIECE OPERATED IN PRESSURE-DEMAND OR OTHER POSITIVE PRESSURE MODE.
SUPPLIED-AIR RESPIRATOR WITH FULL FACEPIECE AND OPERATED IN PRESSURE-DEMAND OR OTHER POSITIVE PRESSURE MODE IN COMBINATION WITH AN AUXILIARY SELF-CONTAINED BREATHING APPARATUS OPERATED IN PRESSURE-DEMAND OR OTHER POSITIVE PRESSURE MODE.

CLOTHING: EMPLOYEE MUST WEAR APPROPRIATE PROTECTIVE (IMPERVIOUS) CLOTHING AND EQUIPMENT TO PREVENT REPEATED OR PROLONGED SKIN CONTACT WITH THIS SUBSTANCE.

GLOVES: EMPLOYEE MUST WEAR APPROPRIATE PROTECTIVE GLOVES TO PREVENT CONTACT WITH THIS SUBSTANCE.

EYE PROTECTION: EMPLOYEE MUST WEAR SPLASH-PROOF OR DUST-RESISTANT SAFETY GOGGLES TO PREVENT EYE CONTACT WITH THIS SUBSTANCE.
EMERGENCY EYE WASH: WHERE THERE IS ANY POSSIBILITY THAT AN EMPLOYEE'S EYES MAY BE EXPOSED TO THIS SUBSTANCE, THE EMPLOYER SHOULD PROVIDE AN EYE WASH FOUNTAIN WITHIN THE IMMEDIATE WORK AREA FOR EMERGENCY USE.

AUTHORIZED BY- OCCUPATIONAL HEALTH SERVICES, INC.
CREATION DATE: 10/04/89 ***REVISION DATE:*** 10/31/89

MATERIAL SAFETY DATA SHEET

OCCUPATIONAL HEALTH SERVICES, INC.
AGRICULTURE AND PESTICIDE DIVISION
450 SEVENTH AVENUE, SUITE 2407
NEW YORK, NEW YORK 10123
1-800-445-MSDS OR (212) 967-1100

EMERGENCY CONTACT:
JOHN S. BRANSFORD, JR. (615) 292-1180

SUBSTANCE IDENTIFICATION

CAS-NUMBER 109-62-6
SUBSTANCE: **ETHYLMERCURY ACETATE**
TRADE NAMES/SYNONYMS: (ACETATO-O)ETHYLMERCURY; (ACETATO)ETHYLMERCURY; ACETOXYETHYLMERCURY; ETHYLMERCURIC ACETATE; MERCURY, (ACETATO-O)ETHYL-; MERCURY, (ACETATO)ETHYL-; MERCURY, ACETOXYETHYL-; C4H8HGO2; PST71476
CHEMICAL FAMILY: ORGANOMETALLIC
MOLECULAR FORMULA: C2-H5-HG-O2-C-C-H3
MOLECULAR WEIGHT: 288.71
CERCLA RATINGS (SCALE 0-3): HEALTH=U FIRE=1 REACTIVITY=0 PERSISTENCE=3
NFPA RATINGS (SCALE 0-4): HEALTH=U FIRE=1 REACTIVITY=0

COMPONENTS AND CONTAMINANTS

COMPONENT: ETHYLMERCURY ACETATE ***PERCENT:*** 100
CAS# 109-62-6
OTHER CONTAMINANTS: NONE
EXPOSURE LIMITS: ORGANO(ALKYL)MERCURY COMPOUNDS, AS HG: 0.01 MG/M3 OSHA TWA (SKIN); 0.03 MG/M3 OSHA STEL 0.01 MG/M3 ACGIH TWA (SKIN); 0.03 MG/M3 ACGIH STEL
SUBJECT TO SARA SECTION 313 ANNUAL TOXIC CHEMICAL RELEASE REPORTING
SUBJECT TO CALIFORNIA PROPOSITION 65 CANCER AND/OR REPRODUCTIVE TOXICITY WARNING AND RELEASE REQUIREMENTS- (JULY 1, 1990)

PHYSICAL DATA

DESCRIPTION: WHITE, CRYSTALLINE SOLID. ***MELTING POINT:*** 352 F (178 C)
SPECIFIC GRAVITY: NOT AVAILABLE ***SOLUBILITY IN WATER:*** SLIGHTLY SOLUBLE
SOLVENT SOLUBILITY: SOLUBLE IN ORGANIC SOLVENTS.

FIRE AND EXPLOSION DATA

FIRE AND EXPLOSION HAZARD: SLIGHT FIRE HAZARD WHEN EXPOSED TO HEAT OR FLAME.

FIREFIGHTING MEDIA: DRY CHEMICAL, CARBON DIOXIDE, HALON, WATER SPRAY OR STANDARD FOAM (1987 EMERGENCY RESPONSE GUIDEBOOK, DOT P 5800.4).
FOR LARGER FIRES, USE WATER SPRAY, FOG OR STANDARD FOAM (1987 EMERGENCY RESPONSE GUIDEBOOK, DOT P 5800.4).

FIREFIGHTING: MOVE CONTAINERS FROM FIRE AREA IF POSSIBLE (1987 EMERGENCY RESPONSE GUIDEBOOK, DOT P 5800.4, GUIDE PAGE 53).
EXTINGUISH USING AGENTS SUITABLE FOR SURROUNDING FIRE. APPLY WATER IN FLOODING QUANTITIES AS A FOG. AVOID CONTAMINATING WATER SOURCES AND SEWERS. AVOID BREATHING HAZARDOUS VAPORS; KEEP UPWIND.

TRANSPORTATION DATA

DEPARTMENT OF TRANSPORTATION HAZARD CLASSIFICATION 49 CFR 172.101: POISON B
DEPARTMENT OF TRANSPORTATION LABELING REQUIREMENTS 49 CFR 172.101 AND SUBPART E: POISON
DEPARTMENT OF TRANSPORTATION PACKAGING REQUIREMENTS: 49 CFR 173.365 EXCEPTIONS: 49 CFR 173.364

TOXICITY

ETHYLMERCURY ACETATE: TOXICITY DATA: 29 MG/KG ORAL-CHICKEN LD50.
CARCINOGEN STATUS: NONE. ACUTE TOXICITY LEVEL: INSUFFICIENT DATA.
TARGET EFFECTS: NEUROTOXIN; TERATOGEN. POISONING MAY ALSO AFFECT THE LIVER, BRAIN, KIDNEYS AND CARDIOVASCULAR SYSTEM.* ADDITIONAL DATA: ALCOHOL MAY ENHANCE THE TOXIC EFFECTS. MAY CROSS THE PLACENTA AND BE EXCRETED IN BREAST MILK. CROSS SENSITIZATION REACTIONS MAY OCCUR WITH METALLIC OR INORGANIC MERCURY COMPOUNDS.*
* MAY BE BASED ON GENERAL INFORMATION ON ALKYL MERCURY COMPOUNDS.

HEALTH EFFECTS AND FIRST AID

INHALATION: ETHYLMERCURY ACETATE: SEE INFORMATION ON ALKYL MERCURY COMPOUNDS.
ALKYL MERCURY COMPOUNDS: NEUROTOXIN. 10 MG(HG)/M3 IMMEDIATELY DANGEROUS TO LIFE OR HEALTH. **ACUTE EXPOSURE-** DUST OR VAPORS MAY BE IRRITATING TO THE RESPIRATORY TRACT. SYSTEMIC POISONING AND DEATH, AS DESCRIBED IN CHRONIC INHALATION, MAY OCCUR. **CHRONIC EXPOSURE-** REPEATED OR PROLONGED EXPOSURE MAY CAUSE RESPIRATORY TRACT IRRITATION. SYSTEMIC SYMPTOMS, OFTEN INSIDIOUS, MAY BEGIN AFTER A LATENCY PERIOD, DEPENDING ON THE SEVERITY OF EXPOSURE, RANGING FROM WEEKS TO YEARS AFTER THE INITIAL EXPOSURE. THE ONSET MAY BEGIN WITH FATIGUE, HEADACHE, PARESTHESIAS OF THE TONGUE, AROUND THE LIPS, AND OF THE HANDS AND FEET, ATAXIA OF THE ARMS AND LEGS, FINE TREMORS IN THE HANDS, ARMS, AND FEET WHICH MAY BECOME CONVULSIVE, ATHETOSIS, ARTHRALGIA, AND AN UNSTEADY GAIT WHICH IS SPASTIC IN NATURE. VISUAL EFFECTS MAY INCLUDE TUNNEL VISION, SCOTOMATA, AND BLINDNESS WITH OPTIC NERVE ATROPHY. SLURRED SPEECH WITH DIFFICULT PRONUNCIATION AND IMPAIRED HEARING ARE ALSO COMMON. GASTROINTESTINAL DISTURBANCES MAY OCCUR WITH NAUSEA, VOMITING, DIARRHEA OR CONSTIPATION, COLIC, EPIGASTRIC PAIN, CATARRHAL GINGIVITIS, BLUE LINE ON THE GUM, AND APHTHOUS STOMATITIS. EMOTIONAL INSTABILITY, MEMORY LOSS, LOSS OF LIBIDO, DEPRESSION, HALLUCINATIONS, IRRITABILITY, ANXIETY, CONFUSION, INSOMNIA, EXCITATION, AND BOUTS OF GROANING, MOANING, SHOUTING, OR CRYING MAY OCCUR. MENTAL DETERIORATION MAY PROGRESS TO STUPOR AND COMA. OTHER EFFECTS MAY INCLUDE DIZZINESS, LACRIMATION, HYPERSALIVATION, ECZEMA, PRURITIS, EXFOLIATIVE DERMATITIS, RENAL DAMAGE, INCONTINENCE, POLYURIA, OLIGURIA, POLYDYPSIA, DEHYDRATION, WEIGHT LOSS, LIVER DAMAGE, BRADYCARDIA AND OTHER SIGNS OF CARDIAC INVOLVEMENT. WITH SEVERE INTOXICATION, CLONIC SEIZURES, PARALYSIS, COMA AND DEATH MAY OCCUR. THE DURATION OF ILLNESS IN FATAL CASES HAS RANGED FROM 1 MONTH TO 15 YEARS, WITH INFECTION, ASPIRATION PNEUMONIA OR INANITION AS THE CAUSE OF DEATH IN PROTRACTED CASES. IN MILD POISONING, SYMPTOMS MAY ALSO PERSIST FOR YEARS. REPRODUCTIVE EFFECTS MAY OCCUR AS DESCRIBED IN CHRONIC INGESTION.

FIRST AID- REMOVE FROM EXPOSURE AREA TO FRESH AIR IMMEDIATELY. IF BREATHING HAS STOPPED, PERFORM ARTIFICIAL RESPIRATION. KEEP PERSON WARM AND AT REST. TREAT SYMPTOMATICALLY AND SUPPORTIVELY. GET MEDICAL ATTENTION IMMEDIATELY.

SKIN CONTACT: ETHYLMERCURY ACETATE: SEE INFORMATION ON ALKYL MERCURY COMPOUNDS.
ALKYL MERCURY COMPOUNDS: NEUROTOXIN. **ACUTE EXPOSURE-** SYMPTOMS OF SKIN CONTACT MAY BE DELAYED FOR SEVERAL HOURS AND THEN BEGIN WITH A SENSATION OF WARMTH AND REDNESS WHICH MAY PROGRESS TO BURNS AND BLISTERING. HEALING MAY TAKE SEVERAL WEEKS. SYSTEMIC POISONING AND DEATH, AS DESCRIBED IN CHRONIC INHALATION, MAY OCCUR DUE TO SKIN ABSORPTION. **CHRONIC EXPOSURE-** REPEATED OR PROLONGED CONTACT MAY

RESULT IN DERMATITIS OR EFFECTS AS DESCRIBED IN ACUTE EXPOSURE. SKIN SENSITIZATION HAS BEEN REPORTED FROM CONTACT WITH SOME ALKYL MERCURY COMPOUNDS.

FIRST AID- REMOVE CONTAMINATED CLOTHING AND SHOES IMMEDIATELY. WASH AFFECTED AREA WITH SOAP OR MILD DETERGENT AND LARGE AMOUNTS OF WATER UNTIL NO EVIDENCE OF CHEMICAL REMAINS (APPROXIMATELY 15-20 MINUTES). GET MEDICAL ATTENTION IMMEDIATELY.

EYE CONTACT: ETHYLMERCURY ACETATE: SEE INFORMATION ON ALKYL MERCURY COMPOUNDS.

ALKYL MERCURY COMPOUNDS: **ACUTE EXPOSURE**- DUSTS OR VAPORS MAY CAUSE IRRITATION. **CHRONIC EXPOSURE**- NO DATA AVAILABLE.

FIRST AID- WASH EYES IMMEDIATELY WITH LARGE AMOUNTS OF WATER OR NORMAL SALINE, OCCASIONALLY LIFTING UPPER AND LOWER LIDS, UNTIL NO EVIDENCE OF CHEMICAL REMAINS (APPROXIMATELY 15-20 MINUTES). GET MEDICAL ATTENTION IMMEDIATELY.

INGESTION: ETHYLMERCURY ACETATE: SEE INFORMATION ON ALKYL MERCURY COMPOUNDS.

ALKYL MERCURY COMPOUNDS: NEUROTOXIN/TERATOGEN. **ACUTE EXPOSURE**- IF A TOXIC DOSE HAS BEEN ABSORBED AND RETAINED FOR A PERIOD OF TIME, SYSTEMIC POISONING AND DEATH AS DESCRIBED IN CHRONIC INHALATION MAY OCCUR. **CHRONIC EXPOSURE**- REPEATED OR PROLONGED EXPOSURE MAY RESULT IN POISONING AS DESCRIBED IN CHRONIC INHALATION. WOMEN EXPOSED TO SOME ALKYL MERCURY COMPOUNDS WHILE PREGNANT OR PERHAPS SEVERAL YEARS BEFORE PREGNANCY HAVE HAD CHILDREN WITH IMPAIRMENT OF MOTOR AND MENTAL DEVELOPMENT OF VARIOUS DEGREES WITH FRETFULLNESS, IRRITABILITY, EXCESSIVE CRYING, DECREASED BIRTH WEIGHT AND MUSCLE TONE, CEREBRAL PALSY, DEAFNESS, BLINDNESS, MICROCEPHALY, AND MENTAL RETARDATION. POSTNATAL EXPOSURE THROUGH BREAST MILK MAY ALSO OCCUR.

FIRST AID- IF THE PERSON IS CONSCIOUS AND NOT CONVULSING, INDUCE EMESIS BY GIVING SYRUP OF IPECAC (KEEPING THE HEAD BELOW THE HIPS TO PREVENT ASPIRATION), FOLLOWED BY WATER. REPEAT IN 20 MINUTES IF NOT EFFECTIVE INITIALLY. IN PATIENTS WITH DEPRESSED RESPIRATION OR IF EMESIS IS NOT PRODUCED, PERFORM GASTRIC LAVAGE CAUTIOUSLY. FOLLOW WITH A SALINE CATHARTIC (DREISBACH, HANDBOOK OF POISONING, 12TH ED.). TREAT SYMPTOMATICALLY AND SUPPORTIVELY. GASTRIC LAVAGE SHOULD BE PERFORMED BY QUALIFIED MEDICAL PERSONNEL. GET MEDICAL ATTENTION IMMEDIATELY.

ANTIDOTE: THE FOLLOWING ANTIDOTE HAS BEEN RECOMMENDED. HOWEVER, THE DECISION AS TO WHETHER THE SEVERITY OF POISONING REQUIRES ADMINISTRATION OF ANY ANTIDOTE AND ACTUAL DOSE REQUIRED SHOULD BE MADE BY QUALIFIED MEDICAL PERSONNEL.

POISONING FROM ORGANIC MERCURY COMPOUNDS: GIVE N-ACETYL-D,L-PENICILLAMINE (OR IF NOT AVAILABLE D-PENICILLAMINE) BY MOUTH, 250 MG, 4 TIMES DAILY FOR 5-10 DAYS. DIMERCAPROL IS LESS EFFECTIVE AND MAY BE CONTRAINDICATED (GOSSELIN, CLINICAL TOXICOLOGY OF COMMERCIAL PRODUCTS, 5TH EDITION). ANTIDOTE SHOULD BE ADMINISTERED BY QUALIFIED MEDICAL PERSONNEL.

REACTIVITY

REACTIVITY: STABLE UNDER NORMAL TEMPERATURES AND PRESSURES.

INCOMPATIBILITIES: ETHYLMERCURY ACETATE: OXIDIZERS (STRONG): MAY CAUSE FIRE AND EXPLOSION HAZARD.

DECOMPOSITION: THERMAL DECOMPOSITION MAY RELEASE TOXIC AND/OR HAZARDOUS GASES.

POLYMERIZATION: HAZARDOUS POLYMERIZATION HAS NOT BEEN REPORTED TO OCCUR UNDER NORMAL TEMPERATURES AND PRESSURES.

STORAGE AND DISPOSAL

OBSERVE ALL FEDERAL, STATE AND LOCAL REGULATIONS WHEN STORING OR DISPOSING OF THIS SUBSTANCE. FOR ASSISTANCE, CONTACT THE DISTRICT DIRECTOR OF THE ENVIRONMENTAL PROTECTION AGENCY.

STORAGE

STORE IN ACCORDANCE WITH 40 CFR 165 RECOMMENDED PROCEDURES FOR THE DISPOSAL AND STORAGE OF PESTICIDES AND PESTICIDE CONTAINERS.

STORE AWAY FROM INCOMPATIBLE SUBSTANCES.

DISPOSAL

DISPOSAL MUST BE IN ACCORDANCE WITH 40 CFR 165 RECOMMENDED PROCEDURES FOR THE DISPOSAL AND STORAGE OF PESTICIDES AND PESTICIDE CONTAINERS.

MERCURY - REGULATORY LEVEL: 0.2 MG/L MATERIALS WHICH CONTAIN THE ABOVE SUBSTANCE AT OR ABOVE THE REGULATORY LEVEL MEET THE EPA CHARACTERISTIC OF TOXICITY, AND MUST BE DISPOSED OF IN ACCORDANCE WITH 40 CFR PART 262. EPA HAZARDOUS WASTE NUMBER D009.

CONDITIONS TO AVOID

MAY BURN BUT DOES NOT IGNITE READILY.

SPILL AND LEAK PROCEDURES

WATER SPILL: THE CALIFORNIA SAFE DRINKING WATER AND TOXIC ENFORCEMENT ACT OF 1986 (PROPOSITION 65) PROHIBITS CONTAMINATING ANY KNOWN SOURCE OF DRINKING WATER WITH SUBSTANCES KNOWN TO CAUSE CANCER AND/OR REPRODUCTIVE TOXICITY.

OCCUPATIONAL SPILL: DO NOT TOUCH SPILLED MATERIAL. STOP LEAK IF YOU CAN DO IT WITHOUT RISK. FOR SMALL SPILLS, TAKE UP WITH SAND OR OTHER ABSORBENT MATERIAL AND PLACE INTO CONTAINERS FOR LATER DISPOSAL. FOR SMALL DRY SPILLS, WITH A CLEAN SHOVEL PLACE MATERIAL INTO CLEAN, DRY CONTAINER AND COVER. MOVE CONTAINERS FROM SPILL AREA. FOR LARGER SPILLS, DIKE FAR AHEAD OF SPILL FOR LATER DISPOSAL. KEEP UNNECESSARY PEOPLE AWAY. ISOLATE HAZARD AREA AND DENY ENTRY.

PROTECTIVE EQUIPMENT

VENTILATION: PROVIDE LOCAL EXHAUST OR PROCESS ENCLOSURE VENTILATION TO MEET PUBLISHED EXPOSURE LIMITS.

RESPIRATOR: THE FOLLOWING RESPIRATORS AND MAXIMUM USE CONCENTRATIONS ARE RECOMMENDATIONS BY THE U.S. DEPARTMENT OF HEALTH AND HUMAN SERVICES, NIOSH POCKET GUIDE TO CHEMICAL HAZARDS; NIOSH CRITERIA DOCUMENTS OR BY THE U.S. DEPARTMENT OF LABOR, 29 CFR 1910 SUBPART Z. THE SPECIFIC RESPIRATOR SELECTED MUST BE BASED ON CONTAMINATION LEVELS FOUND IN THE WORK PLACE, MUST NOT EXCEED THE WORKING LIMITS OF THE RESPIRATOR AND BE JOINTLY APPROVED BY THE NATIONAL INSTITUTE FOR OCCUPATIONAL SAFETY AND HEALTH AND THE MINE SAFETY AND HEALTH ADMINISTRATION (NIOSH-MSHA).

MERCURY, (ORGANO) ALKYL COMPOUNDS (AS HG):

0.1 MG/M3- ANY SUPPLIED-AIR RESPIRATOR. ANY SELF-CONTAINED BREATHING APPARATUS.

0.25 MG/M3- ANY SUPPLIED-AIR RESPIRATOR OPERATED IN A CONTINUOUS FLOW MODE.

0.5 MG/M3- ANY SUPPLIED-AIR RESPIRATOR WITH A FULL FACEPIECE. ANY SELF-CONTAINED BREATHING APPARATUS WITH A FULL FACEPIECE. ANY SUPPLIED-AIR RESPIRATOR WITH A TIGHT-FITTING FACEPIECE OPERATED IN A CONTINUOUS FLOW MODE.

10 MG/M3- ANY SUPPLIED-AIR RESPIRATOR WITH A HALF-MASK AND OPERATED IN A PRESSURE-DEMAND OR OTHER POSITIVE PRESSURE MODE.

ESCAPE- ANY APPROPRIATE ESCAPE-TYPE SELF-CONTAINED BREATHING APPARATUS.

FOR FIREFIGHTING AND OTHER IMMEDIATELY DANGEROUS TO LIFE OR HEALTH CONDITIONS:

SELF-CONTAINED BREATHING APPARATUS WITH FULL FACEPIECE OPERATED IN PRESSURE-DEMAND OR OTHER POSITIVE PRESSURE MODE.

SUPPLIED-AIR RESPIRATOR WITH FULL FACEPIECE AND OPERATED IN PRESSURE-DEMAND OR OTHER POSITIVE PRESSURE MODE IN COMBINATION WITH AN AUXILIARY SELF-CONTAINED BREATHING APPARATUS OPERATED IN PRESSURE-DEMAND OR OTHER POSITIVE PRESSURE MODE.

CLOTHING: EMPLOYEE MUST WEAR APPROPRIATE PROTECTIVE (IMPERVIOUS) CLOTHING AND EQUIPMENT TO PREVENT ANY POSSIBILITY OF SKIN CONTACT WITH THIS SUBSTANCE.

GLOVES: EMPLOYEE MUST WEAR APPROPRIATE PROTECTIVE GLOVES TO PREVENT CONTACT WITH THIS SUBSTANCE.

EYE PROTECTION: EMPLOYEE MUST WEAR SPLASH-PROOF OR DUST-RESISTANT SAFETY GOGGLES AND A FACESHIELD TO PREVENT CONTACT WITH THIS SUBSTANCE.

EMERGENCY WASH FACILITIES: WHERE THERE IS ANY POSSIBILITY THAT AN EMPLOYEE'S EYES AND/OR SKIN MAY BE EXPOSED TO THIS SUBSTANCE, THE EMPLOYER SHOULD PROVIDE AN EYE WASH FOUNTAIN AND QUICK DRENCH SHOWER WITHIN THE IMMEDIATE WORK AREA FOR EMERGENCY USE.

AUTHORIZED BY- OCCUPATIONAL HEALTH SERVICES, INC.

CREATION DATE: 10/04/89 ***REVISION DATE:*** 07/13/90

MATERIAL SAFETY DATA SHEET

OCCUPATIONAL HEALTH SERVICES, INC.
AGRICULTURE AND PESTICIDE DIVISION
450 SEVENTH AVENUE, SUITE 2407

EMERGENCY CONTACT:
JOHN S. BRANSFORD, JR. (615) 292-1180

NEW YORK, NEW YORK 10123
1-800-445-MSDS OR (212) 967-1100

SUBSTANCE IDENTIFICATION

CAS-NUMBER 2235-25-8
SUBSTANCE: **ETHYLMERCURIC PHOSPHATE**
TRADE NAMES/SYNONYMS: MERCURATE(2), ETHYL(PHOSPHATO(3-)-O-)-, DIHYDROGEN; MERCURY, (DIHYDROGEN PHOSPHATO)ETHYL-; ETHYL(PHOSPHATO(3-)-O-)-MERCURATE(2-), DIHYDROGEN; (DIHYDROGEN PHOSPHATO)ETHYLMERCURY; ETHYL MERCURY PHOSPHATE; EMP; LIGNASAN; C2H7HGO4P; PST71479
CHEMICAL FAMILY: ORGANOMETALLIC PHOSPHATE
MOLECULAR FORMULA: C2-H7-HG-O4-P
MOLECULAR WEIGHT: 326.65
CERCLA RATINGS (SCALE 0-3): HEALTH=3 FIRE=1 REACTIVITY=0 PERSISTENCE=3
NFPA RATINGS (SCALE 0-4): HEALTH=3 FIRE=1 REACTIVITY=0

COMPONENTS AND CONTAMINANTS

COMPONENT: ETHYLMERCURIC PHOSPHATE ***PERCENT:*** 100.0
CAS# 2235-25-8
OTHER CONTAMINANTS: NONE
EXPOSURE LIMITS: ORGANO(ALKYL)MERCURY COMPOUNDS, AS HG: 0.01 MG/M3 OSHA TWA (SKIN); 0.03 MG/M3 OSHA STEL 0.01 MG/M3 ACGIH TWA (SKIN); 0.03 MG/M3 ACGIH STEL
SUBJECT TO SARA SECTION 313 ANNUAL TOXIC CHEMICAL RELEASE REPORTING
SUBJECT TO CALIFORNIA PROPOSITION 65 CANCER AND/OR REPRODUCTIVE TOXICITY WARNING AND RELEASE REQUIREMENTS- (JULY 1, 1990)

PHYSICAL DATA

DESCRIPTION: SOLID. ***MELTING POINT:*** NOT AVAILABLE
SPECIFIC GRAVITY: NOT AVAILABLE ***SOLUBILITY IN WATER:*** NOT AVAILABLE

FIRE AND EXPLOSION DATA

FIRE AND EXPLOSION HAZARD: SLIGHT FIRE HAZARD WHEN EXPOSED TO HEAT OR FLAME.
FIREFIGHTING MEDIA: DRY CHEMICAL, CARBON DIOXIDE, HALON, WATER SPRAY OR STANDARD FOAM (1987 EMERGENCY RESPONSE GUIDEBOOK, DOT P 5800.4).
FOR LARGER FIRES, USE WATER SPRAY, FOG OR STANDARD FOAM (1987 EMERGENCY RESPONSE GUIDEBOOK, DOT P 5800.4).
FIREFIGHTING: MOVE CONTAINERS FROM FIRE AREA IF POSSIBLE (1987 EMERGENCY RESPONSE GUIDEBOOK, DOT P 5800.4, GUIDE PAGE 53).
EXTINGUISH USING AGENT SUITABLE FOR TYPE OF SURROUNDING FIRE. AVOID BREATHING VAPORS AND DUSTS. KEEP UPWIND.

TRANSPORTATION DATA

DEPARTMENT OF TRANSPORTATION HAZARD CLASSIFICATION 49 CFR 172.101: POISON B
DEPARTMENT OF TRANSPORTATION LABELING REQUIREMENTS 49 CFR 172.101 AND SUBPART E: POISON
DEPARTMENT OF TRANSPORTATION PACKAGING REQUIREMENTS: 49 CFR 173.365 EXCEPTIONS: 49 CFR 173.364

TOXICITY

ETHYLMERCURIC PHOSPHATE: TOXICITY DATA: 8614 UG/KG/13 WEEKS ORAL-HUMAN LDLO; 48 MG/KG ORAL-RAT LD50; 48 MG/KG ORAL-MOUSE LD50; 76 MG/KG SUBCUTANEOUS-MOUSE LD50; REPRODUCTIVE EFFECTS DATA (RTECS).
CARCINOGEN STATUS: NONE. ACUTE TOXICITY LEVEL: HIGHLY TOXIC BY INGESTION. TARGET EFFECTS: NEUROTOXIN; TERATOGEN. POISONING MAY ALSO AFFECT THE LIVER, BRAIN, KIDNEYS, AND CARDIOVASCULAR SYSTEM.*
ADDITIONAL DATA: ALCOHOL MAY ENHANCE THE TOXIC EFFECTS. MAY CROSS THE PLACENTA AND BE EXCRETED IN BREAST MILK. CROSS SENSITIZATION REACTIONS MAY OCCUR WITH METALLIC OR INORGANIC MERCURY COMPOUNDS.*
* MAY BE BASED ON GENERAL INFORMATION ON ALKYL MERCURY COMPOUNDS.

HEALTH EFFECTS AND FIRST AID

INHALATION: ETHYLMERCURIC PHOSPHATE: SEE INFORMATION ON ALKYL MERCURY COMPOUNDS. ALKYL MERCURY COMPOUNDS: NEUROTOXIN. 10 MG(HG)/M3 IMMEDIATELY DANGEROUS TO LIFE OR HEALTH. **ACUTE EXPOSURE-** DUST OR VAPORS MAY BE IRRITATING TO THE RESPIRATORY TRACT. SYSTEMIC POISONING AND DEATH, AS DESCRIBED IN CHRONIC INHALATION, MAY OCCUR. **CHRONIC EXPOSURE-** REPEATED OR PROLONGED EXPOSURE MAY CAUSE RESPIRATORY TRACT IRRITATION. SYSTEMIC SYMPTOMS, OFTEN INSIDIOUS, MAY BEGIN AFTER A LATENCY PERIOD, DEPENDING ON THE SEVERITY OF EXPOSURE, RANGING FROM WEEKS TO YEARS AFTER THE INITIAL EXPOSURE. THE ONSET MAY BEGIN WITH FATIGUE, HEADACHE, PARESTHESIAS OF THE TONGUE, AROUND THE LIPS, AND OF THE HANDS AND FEET, ATAXIA OF THE ARMS AND LEGS, FINE TREMORS IN THE HANDS, ARMS, AND FEET WHICH MAY BECOME CONVULSIVE, ATHETOSIS, ARTHRALGIA, AND AN UNSTEADY GAIT WHICH IS SPASTIC IN NATURE. VISUAL EFFECTS MAY INCLUDE TUNNEL VISION, SCOTOMATA, AND BLINDNESS WITH OPTIC NERVE ATROPHY. SLURRED SPEECH WITH DIFFICULT PRONUNCIATION AND IMPAIRED HEARING ARE ALSO COMMON. GASTROINTESTINAL DISTURBANCES MAY OCCUR WITH NAUSEA, VOMITING, DIARRHEA OR CONSTIPATION, COLIC, EPIGASTRIC PAIN, CATARRHAL GINGIVITIS, BLUE LINE ON THE GUM, AND APHTHOUS STOMATITIS. EMOTIONAL INSTABILITY, MEMORY LOSS, LOSS OF LIBIDO, DEPRESSION, HALLUCINATIONS, IRRITABILITY, ANXIETY, CONFUSION, INSOMNIA, EXCITATION, AND BOUTS OF GROANING, MOANING, SHOUTING, OR CRYING MAY OCCUR. MENTAL DETERIORATION MAY PROGRESS TO STUPOR AND COMA. OTHER EFFECTS MAY INCLUDE DIZZINESS, LACRIMATION, HYPERSALIVATION, ECZEMA, PRURITIS, EXFOLIATIVE DERMATITIS, RENAL DAMAGE, INCONTINENCE, POLYURIA, OLIGURIA, POLYDYPSIA, DEHYDRATION, WEIGHT LOSS, LIVER DAMAGE, BRADYCARDIA AND OTHER SIGNS OF CARDIAC INVOLVEMENT. WITH SEVERE INTOXICATION, CLONIC SEIZURES, PARALYSIS, COMA AND DEATH MAY OCCUR. THE DURATION OF ILLNESS IN FATAL CASES HAS RANGED FROM 1 MONTH TO 15 YEARS, WITH INFECTION, ASPIRATION PNEUMONIA OR INANITION AS THE CAUSE OF DEATH IN PROTRACTED CASES. IN MILD POISONING, SYMPTOMS MAY ALSO PERSIST FOR YEARS. REPRODUCTIVE EFFECTS MAY OCCUR AS DESCRIBED IN CHRONIC INGESTION.
FIRST AID- REMOVE FROM EXPOSURE AREA TO FRESH AIR IMMEDIATELY. IF BREATHING HAS STOPPED, PERFORM ARTIFICIAL RESPIRATION. KEEP PERSON WARM AND AT REST. TREAT SYMPTOMATICALLY AND SUPPORTIVELY. GET MEDICAL ATTENTION IMMEDIATELY.

SKIN CONTACT: ETHYLMERCURIC PHOSPHATE: SEE INFORMATION ON ALKYL MERCURY COMPOUNDS.
ALKYL MERCURY COMPOUNDS: NEUROTOXIN. **ACUTE EXPOSURE-** SYMPTOMS OF SKIN CONTACT MAY BE DELAYED FOR SEVERAL HOURS AND THEN BEGIN WITH A SENSATION OF WARMTH AND REDNESS WHICH MAY PROGRESS TO BURNS AND BLISTERING. HEALING MAY TAKE SEVERAL WEEKS. SYSTEMIC POISONING AND DEATH, AS DESCRIBED IN CHRONIC INHALATION, MAY OCCUR DUE TO SKIN ABSORPTION. **CHRONIC EXPOSURE-** REPEATED OR PROLONGED CONTACT MAY RESULT IN DERMATITIS OR EFFECTS AS DESCRIBED IN ACUTE EXPOSURE. SKIN SENSITIZATION HAS BEEN REPORTED FROM CONTACT WITH SOME ALKYL MERCURY COMPOUNDS.
FIRST AID- REMOVE CONTAMINATED CLOTHING AND SHOES IMMEDIATELY. WASH AFFECTED AREA WITH SOAP OR MILD DETERGENT AND LARGE AMOUNTS OF WATER UNTIL NO EVIDENCE OF CHEMICAL REMAINS (APPROXIMATELY 15-20 MINUTES). GET MEDICAL ATTENTION IMMEDIATELY.

EYE CONTACT: ETHYLMERCURIC PHOSPHATE: SEE INFORMATION ON ALKYL MERCURY COMPOUNDS.
ALKYL MERCURY COMPOUNDS: **ACUTE EXPOSURE-** DUSTS OR VAPORS MAY CAUSE IRRITATION. **CHRONIC EXPOSURE-** NO DATA AVAILABLE.
FIRST AID- WASH EYES IMMEDIATELY WITH LARGE AMOUNTS OF WATER OR NORMAL SALINE, OCCASIONALLY LIFTING UPPER AND LOWER LIDS, UNTIL NO EVIDENCE OF CHEMICAL REMAINS (APPROXIMATELY 15-20 MINUTES). GET MEDICAL ATTENTION IMMEDIATELY.

INGESTION: ETHYLMERCURIC PHOSPHATE: HIGHLY TOXIC. SEE INFORMATION ON ALKYL MERCURY COMPOUNDS.
ALKYL MERCURY COMPOUNDS: NEUROTOXIN/TERATOGEN. **ACUTE EXPOSURE-** IF A TOXIC DOSE HAS BEEN ABSORBED AND RETAINED FOR A PERIOD OF TIME, SYSTEMIC POISONING AND DEATH AS DESCRIBED IN CHRONIC INHALATION MAY OCCUR. **CHRONIC EXPOSURE-** REPEATED OR PROLONGED EXPOSURE MAY RESULT IN POISONING AS DESCRIBED IN CHRONIC INHALATION. WOMEN EXPOSED TO SOME ALKYL MERCURY COMPOUNDS WHILE PREGNANT OR PERHAPS SEVERAL YEARS BEFORE PREGNANCY HAVE HAD CHILDREN WITH IMPAIRMENT OF MOTOR AND MENTAL DEVELOPMENT OF VARIOUS DEGREES WITH FRETFULLNESS, IRRITABILITY, EXCESSIVE CRYING, DECREASED BIRTH WEIGHT AND MUSCLE TONE, CEREBRAL PALSY, DEAFNESS, BLINDNESS, MICROCEPHALY, AND MENTAL RETARDATION. POSTNATAL EXPOSURE THROUGH BREAST MILK MAY ALSO OCCUR.
FIRST AID- IF THE PERSON IS CONSCIOUS AND NOT CONVULSING, INDUCE EMESIS BY GIVING SYRUP OF IPECAC (KEEPING THE HEAD BELOW THE HIPS TO PREVENT ASPIRATION), FOLLOWED BY WATER. REPEAT IN 20 MINUTES IF NOT EFFECTIVE INITIALLY. IN PATIENTS WITH DEPRESSED RESPIRATION OR IF EMESIS IS NOT PRODUCED, PERFORM GASTRIC LAVAGE CAUTIOUSLY. FOLLOW WITH A SALINE CATHARTIC (DREISBACH, HANDBOOK OF POISONING, 12TH ED.). TREAT SYMPTOMATICALLY AND SUPPORTIVELY. GASTRIC LAVAGE SHOULD BE PERFORMED BY QUALIFIED MEDICAL PERSONNEL. GET MEDICAL ATTENTION IMMEDIATELY.

ANTIDOTE: THE FOLLOWING ANTIDOTE(S) HAVE BEEN RECOMMENDED. HOWEVER, THE DECISION AS TO WHETHER THE SEVERITY OF POISONING REQUIRES ADMINISTRATION OF ANY ANTIDOTE AND ACTUAL DOSE REQUIRED SHOULD BE MADE BY QUALIFIED MEDICAL PERSONNEL.
POISONING FROM ORGANIC MERCURY COMPOUNDS: GIVE N-ACETYL-D,L-PENICILLAMINE (OR IF NOT AVAILABLE D-PENICILLAMINE) BY MOUTH, 250 MG, 4 TIMES DAILY FOR 5-10 DAYS. DIMERCAPROL IS LESS EFFECTIVE AND MAY BE CONTRAINDICATED (GOSSELIN, CLINICAL TOXICOLOGY OF COMMERCIAL PRODUCTS, 5TH EDITION). ANTIDOTE SHOULD BE ADMINISTERED BY QUALIFIED MEDICAL PERSONNEL.
PHOSPHATES: FOR HYPOCALCEMIA, AFTER PHOSPHATE INGESTION, GIVE CALCIUM GLUCONATE, 5 ML OF 10% SOLUTION SLOWLY INTRAVENOUSLY, TO RESTORE IONIC CALCIUM TO NORMAL LEVEL (DREISBACH, HANDBOOK OF POISONING, 12TH ED.). ANTIDOTE SHOULD BE ADMINISTERED BY QUALIFIED MEDICAL PERSONNEL.

REACTIVITY

REACTIVITY: STABLE UNDER NORMAL TEMPERATURES AND PRESSURES.
INCOMPATIBILITIES: ETHYLMERCURIC PHOSPHATE: OXIDIZERS (STRONG): MAY CAUSE FIRE AND EXPLOSION HAZARD.
DECOMPOSITION: THERMAL DECOMPOSITION MAY RELEASE TOXIC FUMES OF MERCURY AND TOXIC OXIDES OF PHOSPHORUS.
POLYMERIZATION: HAZARDOUS POLYMERIZATION HAS NOT BEEN REPORTED TO OCCUR UNDER NORMAL TEMPERATURES AND PRESSURES.

STORAGE AND DISPOSAL

OBSERVE ALL FEDERAL, STATE AND LOCAL REGULATIONS WHEN STORING OR DISPOSING OF THIS SUBSTANCE. FOR ASSISTANCE, CONTACT THE DISTRICT DIRECTOR OF THE ENVIRONMENTAL PROTECTION AGENCY.

STORAGE

STORE IN ACCORDANCE WITH 40 CFR 165 RECOMMENDED PROCEDURES FOR THE DISPOSAL AND STORAGE OF PESTICIDES AND PESTICIDE CONTAINERS.
STORE AWAY FROM INCOMPATIBLE SUBSTANCES.

DISPOSAL

DISPOSAL MUST BE IN ACCORDANCE WITH 40 CFR 165 RECOMMENDED PROCEDURES FOR THE DISPOSAL AND STORAGE OF PESTICIDES AND PESTICIDE CONTAINERS.
MERCURY - REGULATORY LEVEL: 0.2 MG/L MATERIALS WHICH CONTAIN THE ABOVE SUBSTANCE AT OR ABOVE THE REGULATORY LEVEL MEET THE EPA CHARACTERISTIC OF TOXICITY, AND MUST BE DISPOSED OF IN ACCORDANCE WITH 40 CFR PART 262. EPA HAZARDOUS WASTE NUMBER D009.

CONDITIONS TO AVOID

MAY BURN BUT DOES NOT IGNITE READILY.

SPILL AND LEAK PROCEDURES

WATER SPILL: THE CALIFORNIA SAFE DRINKING WATER AND TOXIC ENFORCEMENT ACT OF 1986 (PROPOSITION 65) PROHIBITS CONTAMINATING ANY KNOWN SOURCE OF DRINKING WATER WITH SUBSTANCES KNOWN TO CAUSE CANCER AND/OR REPRODUCTIVE TOXICITY.
OCCUPATIONAL SPILL: DO NOT TOUCH SPILLED MATERIAL. STOP LEAK IF YOU CAN DO IT WITHOUT RISK. FOR SMALL SPILLS, TAKE UP WITH SAND OR OTHER ABSORBENT MATERIAL AND PLACE INTO CONTAINERS FOR LATER DISPOSAL. FOR SMALL DRY SPILLS, WITH A CLEAN SHOVEL PLACE MATERIAL INTO CLEAN, DRY CONTAINER AND COVER. MOVE CONTAINERS FROM SPILL AREA. FOR LARGER SPILLS, DIKE FAR AHEAD OF SPILL FOR LATER DISPOSAL. KEEP UNNECESSARY PEOPLE AWAY. ISOLATE HAZARD AREA AND DENY ENTRY.

PROTECTIVE EQUIPMENT

VENTILATION: PROVIDE LOCAL EXHAUST OR PROCESS ENCLOSURE VENTILATION TO MEET PUBLISHED EXPOSURE LIMITS.
RESPIRATOR: THE FOLLOWING RESPIRATORS AND MAXIMUM USE CONCENTRATIONS ARE RECOMMENDATIONS BY THE U.S. DEPARTMENT OF HEALTH AND HUMAN SERVICES, NIOSH POCKET GUIDE TO CHEMICAL HAZARDS; NIOSH CRITERIA DOCUMENTS OR BY THE U.S. DEPARTMENT OF LABOR, 29 CFR 1910 SUBPART Z. THE SPECIFIC RESPIRATOR SELECTED MUST BE BASED ON CONTAMINATION LEVELS FOUND IN THE WORK PLACE, MUST NOT EXCEED THE WORKING LIMITS OF THE RESPIRATOR AND BE JOINTLY APPROVED BY THE NATIONAL INSTITUTE FOR OCCUPATIONAL SAFETY AND HEALTH AND THE MINE SAFETY AND HEALTH ADMINISTRATION (NIOSH-MSHA).
MERCURY, (ORGANO) ALKYL COMPOUNDS (AS HG):
0.1 MG/M3- ANY SUPPLIED-AIR RESPIRATOR. ANY SELF-CONTAINED BREATHING APPARATUS.
0.25 MG/M3- ANY SUPPLIED-AIR RESPIRATOR OPERATED IN A CONTINUOUS FLOW MODE.
0.5 MG/M3- ANY SUPPLIED-AIR RESPIRATOR WITH A FULL FACEPIECE. ANY SELF-CONTAINED BREATHING APPARATUS WITH A FULL FACEPIECE. ANY SUPPLIED-AIR RESPIRATOR WITH A TIGHT-FITTING FACEPIECE OPERATED IN A CONTINUOUS FLOW MODE.
10 MG/M3- ANY SUPPLIED-AIR RESPIRATOR WITH A HALF-MASK AND OPERATED IN A PRESSURE-DEMAND OR OTHER POSITIVE PRESSURE MODE.
ESCAPE- ANY APPROPRIATE ESCAPE-TYPE SELF-CONTAINED BREATHING APPARATUS.
FOR FIREFIGHTING AND OTHER IMMEDIATELY DANGEROUS TO LIFE OR HEALTH CONDITIONS:
SELF-CONTAINED BREATHING APPARATUS WITH FULL FACEPIECE OPERATED IN PRESSURE-DEMAND OR OTHER POSITIVE PRESSURE MODE.
SUPPLIED-AIR RESPIRATOR WITH FULL FACEPIECE AND OPERATED IN PRESSURE-DEMAND OR OTHER POSITIVE PRESSURE MODE IN COMBINATION WITH AN AUXILIARY SELF-CONTAINED BREATHING APPARATUS OPERATED IN PRESSURE-DEMAND OR OTHER POSITIVE PRESSURE MODE.
CLOTHING: EMPLOYEE MUST WEAR APPROPRIATE PROTECTIVE (IMPERVIOUS) CLOTHING AND EQUIPMENT TO PREVENT ANY POSSIBILITY OF SKIN CONTACT WITH THIS SUBSTANCE.
GLOVES: EMPLOYEE MUST WEAR APPROPRIATE PROTECTIVE GLOVES TO PREVENT CONTACT WITH THIS SUBSTANCE.
EYE PROTECTION: EMPLOYEE MUST WEAR SPLASH-PROOF OR DUST-RESISTANT SAFETY GOGGLES AND A FACESHIELD TO PREVENT CONTACT WITH THIS SUBSTANCE.
EMERGENCY WASH FACILITIES: WHERE THERE IS ANY POSSIBILITY THAT AN EMPLOYEE'S EYES AND/OR SKIN MAY BE EXPOSED TO THIS SUBSTANCE, THE EMPLOYER SHOULD PROVIDE AN EYE WASH FOUNTAIN AND QUICK DRENCH SHOWER WITHIN THE IMMEDIATE WORK AREA FOR EMERGENCY USE.

AUTHORIZED BY- OCCUPATIONAL HEALTH SERVICES, INC.
CREATION DATE: 10/04/89 ***REVISION DATE:*** 07/13/90

MATERIAL SAFETY DATA SHEET

OCCUPATIONAL HEALTH SERVICES, INC.
AGRICULTURE AND PESTICIDE DIVISION
450 SEVENTH AVENUE, SUITE 2407
NEW YORK, NEW YORK 10123
1-800-445-MSDS OR (212) 967-1100

EMERGENCY CONTACT:
JOHN S. BRANSFORD, JR. (615) 292-1180

SUBSTANCE IDENTIFICATION

CAS-NUMBER 126-15-8
SUBSTANCE: **2,3,4,5-BIS(2-BUTYLENE)TETRAHYDRO-2-FURALDEHYDE**
TRADE NAMES/SYNONYMS: 4A(4H)-DIBENZOFURANCARBOXALDEHYDE, 1,5A,6,9,9A,9B-HEXAHYDRO-; 1,5A,6,9,9A,9B-HEXAHYDRO-4A(4H)-DIBENZOFURANCARBOXALDEHYDE; 1,4,4A,5A,6,9,9A,9B-OCTAHYDRODIBENZOFURAN-4A-CARBALDEHYDE; BISBUTENYLENETETRAHYDROFURFURAL; DIBUTYLENE TETRAFURFURAL; 2,3:4,5-BIS(2-BUTYLENE)TETRAHYDROFURFURAL; BUTADIENE-FURFURAL COPOLYMER; MGK REPELLENT 11; R-11; REPEL 111; PHILLIPS REPELLENT 11; INSECT REPELLENT-11; R 11; MGK 11; ENT 17596; C13H16O2; PST71487
CHEMICAL FAMILY: BENZOFURAN DERIVATIVE
ALDEHYDE, ALIPHATIC
MOLECULAR FORMULA: C13-H16-O2
MOLECULAR WEIGHT: 204.26
CERCLA RATINGS (SCALE 0-3): HEALTH=2 FIRE=U REACTIVITY=0 PERSISTENCE=2
NFPA RATINGS (SCALE 0-4): HEALTH=U FIRE=U REACTIVITY=0

COMPONENTS AND CONTAMINANTS

COMPONENT: 2,3,4,5-BIS(2-BUTYLENE)TETRAHYDRO-2-FURALDEHYDE ***PERCENT:*** 100.0
CAS# 126-15-8
EXPOSURE LIMITS: NO OCCUPATIONAL EXPOSURE LIMITS ESTABLISHED BY OSHA, ACGIH, OR NIOSH.

PHYSICAL DATA

DESCRIPTION: PALE YELLOW LIQUID WITH A FRUITY ODOR.
BOILING POINT: 585 F (307 C) ***MELTING POINT:*** -112 F (-80 C)
SPECIFIC GRAVITY: 1.120 ***VAPOR PRESSURE:*** NOT AVAILABLE
SOLUBILITY IN WATER: PRACTICALLY INSOLUBLE

SOLVENT SOLUBILITY: SOLUBLE IN ETHANOL, PETROLEUM OILS, TOLUENE, AND XYLENE; PRACTICALLY INSOLUBLE IN DILUTE ALKALI.

FIRE AND EXPLOSION DATA

FIRE AND EXPLOSION HAZARD: UNKNOWN FIRE AND EXPLOSION HAZARD.

FIREFIGHTING MEDIA: DRY CHEMICAL, CARBON DIOXIDE, HALON, WATER SPRAY OR STANDARD FOAM (1987 EMERGENCY RESPONSE GUIDEBOOK, DOT P 5800.4). FOR LARGER FIRES, USE WATER SPRAY, FOG OR STANDARD FOAM (1987 EMERGENCY RESPONSE GUIDEBOOK, DOT P 5800.4).

FIREFIGHTING: MOVE CONTAINER FROM FIRE AREA IF POSSIBLE. COOL FIRE-EXPOSED CONTAINERS WITH WATER FROM SIDE UNTIL WELL AFTER FIRE IS OUT. STAY AWAY FROM STORAGE TANK ENDS. FOR MASSIVE FIRE IN STORAGE AREA, USE UNMANNED HOSE HOLDER OR MONITOR NOZZLES, ELSE WITHDRAW FROM AREA AND LET FIRE BURN. WITHDRAW IMMEDIATELY IN CASE OF RISING SOUND FROM VENTING SAFETY DEVICE OR ANY DISCOLORATION OF STORAGE TANK DUE TO FIRE (1987 EMERGENCY RESPONSE GUIDEBOOK, DOT P 5800.4, GUIDE PAGE 27). EXTINGUISH ONLY IF FLOW CAN BE STOPPED; USE FLOODING AMOUNTS OF WATER AS A FOG, SOLID STREAMS MAY BE INEFFECTIVE. COOL CONTAINERS WITH FLOODING AMOUNTS OF WATER, APPLY FROM AS FAR A DISTANCE AS POSSIBLE. AVOID BREATHING VAPORS, KEEP UPWIND.

TOXICITY

2,3,4,5-BIS(2-BUTYLENE)TETRAHYDRO-2-FURALDEHYDE: TOXICITY DATA: >2000 MG/KG SKIN-RABBIT LD50 (PEMNDP); 2500 MG/KG ORAL-RAT LD50; 2 GM/KG INTRAVENOUS-RAT LD50. CARCINOGEN STATUS: NONE. ACUTE TOXICITY LEVEL: MODERATELY TOXIC BY INGESTION; SLIGHTLY TOXIC BY DERMAL ABSORPTION. TARGET EFFECTS: NO DATA AVAILABLE.

HEALTH EFFECTS AND FIRST AID

INHALATION: 2,3,4,5-BIS(2-BUTYLENE)TETRAHYDRO-2-FURALDEHYDE: **ACUTE EXPOSURE-** NO DATA AVAILABLE. **CHRONIC EXPOSURE-** NO DATA AVAILABLE.

FIRST AID- REMOVE FROM EXPOSURE AREA TO FRESH AIR IMMEDIATELY. IF BREATHING HAS STOPPED, PERFORM ARTIFICIAL RESPIRATION. KEEP PERSON WARM AND AT REST. TREAT SYMPTOMATICALLY AND SUPPORTIVELY. GET MEDICAL ATTENTION IMMEDIATELY.

SKIN CONTACT: 2,3,4,5-BIS(2-BUTYLENE)TETRAHYDRO-2-FURALDEHYDE: **ACUTE EXPOSURE-** THE LD50 FOR RABBITS WAS GREATER THAN 2000 MG/KG. **CHRONIC EXPOSURE-** NO DATA AVAILABLE.

FIRST AID- REMOVE CONTAMINATED CLOTHING AND SHOES IMMEDIATELY. WASH AFFECTED AREA WITH SOAP OR MILD DETERGENT AND LARGE AMOUNTS OF WATER UNTIL NO EVIDENCE OF CHEMICAL REMAINS (APPROXIMATELY 15-20 MINUTES). GET MEDICAL ATTENTION IMMEDIATELY.

EYE CONTACT: 2,3,4,5-BIS(2-BUTYLENE)TETRAHYDRO-2-FURALDEHYDE: **ACUTE EXPOSURE-** NO DATA AVAILABLE. **CHRONIC EXPOSURE-** NO DATA AVAILABLE.

FIRST AID- WASH EYES IMMEDIATELY WITH LARGE AMOUNTS OF WATER OR NORMAL SALINE, OCCASIONALLY LIFTING UPPER AND LOWER LIDS, UNTIL NO EVIDENCE OF CHEMICAL REMAINS (APPROXIMATELY 15-20 MINUTES). GET MEDICAL ATTENTION IMMEDIATELY.

INGESTION: 2,3,4,5-BIS(2-BUTYLENE)TETRAHYDRO-2-FURALDEHYDE: **ACUTE EXPOSURE-** THE LETHAL DOSE REPORTED IN RATS WAS 2500 MG/KG; SYMPTOMS WERE NOT REPORTED. **CHRONIC EXPOSURE-** ADVERSE REPRODUCTIVE EFFECTS, OVARIAN ATROPHY, AND ONCOGENICITY WERE OBSERVED IN ANIMAL STUDIES.

FIRST AID- IF THE PERSON IS CONSCIOUS AND NOT CONVULSING, REMOVE BY GASTRIC LAVAGE AND FOLLOW WITH A CATHARTIC (DREISBACH, HANDBOOK OF POISONING, 12TH ED.). TREAT SYMPTOMATICALLY AND SUPPORTIVELY. GASTRIC LAVAGE SHOULD BE PERFORMED BY QUALIFIED MEDICAL PERSONNEL. GET MEDICAL ATTENTION IMMEDIATELY.

ANTIDOTE: NO SPECIFIC ANTIDOTE. TREAT SYMPTOMATICALLY AND SUPPORTIVELY.

REACTIVITY

REACTIVITY: STABLE UNDER NORMAL TEMPERATURES AND PRESSURES.

INCOMPATIBILITIES: 2,3,4,5-BIS(2-BUTYLENE)TETRAHYDRO-2-FURALDEHYDE: OXIDIZERS (STRONG): FIRE AND EXPLOSION HAZARD.

DECOMPOSITION: THERMAL DECOMPOSITION PRODUCTS MAY INCLUDE TOXIC OXIDES OF CARBON.

POLYMERIZATION: HAZARDOUS POLYMERIZATION HAS NOT BEEN REPORTED TO OCCUR UNDER NORMAL TEMPERATURES AND PRESSURES.

STORAGE AND DISPOSAL

OBSERVE ALL FEDERAL, STATE AND LOCAL REGULATIONS WHEN STORING OR DISPOSING OF THIS SUBSTANCE. FOR ASSISTANCE, CONTACT THE DISTRICT DIRECTOR OF THE ENVIRONMENTAL PROTECTION AGENCY.

****STORAGE****

STORE IN ACCORDANCE WITH 40 CFR 165 RECOMMENDED PROCEDURES FOR THE DISPOSAL AND STORAGE OF PESTICIDES AND PESTICIDE CONTAINERS. STORE AWAY FROM INCOMPATIBLE SUBSTANCES.

****DISPOSAL****

DISPOSAL MUST BE IN ACCORDANCE WITH 40 CFR 165 RECOMMENDED PROCEDURES FOR THE DISPOSAL AND STORAGE OF PESTICIDES AND PESTICIDE CONTAINERS.

CONDITIONS TO AVOID

AVOID CONTACT WITH HEAT, SPARKS, FLAMES, OR OTHER SOURCES OF IGNITION. VAPORS MAY BE EXPLOSIVE. AVOID OVERHEATING OF CONTAINERS; CONTAINERS MAY VIOLENTLY RUPTURE IN HEAT OF FIRE. AVOID CONTAMINATION OF WATER SOURCES.

SPILL AND LEAK PROCEDURES

OCCUPATIONAL SPILL: SHUT OFF IGNITION SOURCES. STOP LEAK IF YOU CAN DO IT WITHOUT RISK. USE WATER SPRAY TO REDUCE VAPORS. FOR SMALL SPILLS, TAKE UP WITH SAND OR OTHER ABSORBENT MATERIAL AND PLACE INTO CONTAINERS FOR LATER DISPOSAL. FOR LARGER SPILLS, DIKE FAR AHEAD OF SPILL FOR LATER DISPOSAL. NO SMOKING, FLAMES OR FLARES IN HAZARD AREA. KEEP UNNECESSARY PEOPLE AWAY; ISOLATE HAZARD AREA AND RESTRICT ENTRY.

PROTECTIVE EQUIPMENT

VENTILATION: PROVIDE LOCAL EXHAUST OR GENERAL DILUTION VENTILATION. VENTILATION EQUIPMENT MUST BE EXPLOSION-PROOF.

RESPIRATOR: THE FOLLOWING RESPIRATORS ARE RECOMMENDED BASED ON INFORMATION FOUND IN THE PHYSICAL DATA, TOXICITY AND HEALTH EFFECTS SECTIONS. THEY ARE RANKED IN ORDER FROM MINIMUM TO MAXIMUM RESPIRATORY PROTECTION. THE SPECIFIC RESPIRATOR SELECTED MUST BE BASED ON CONTAMINATION LEVELS FOUND IN THE WORK PLACE, MUST NOT EXCEED THE WORKING LIMITS OF THE RESPIRATOR AND BE JOINTLY APPROVED BY THE NATIONAL INSTITUTE FOR OCCUPATIONAL SAFETY AND HEALTH AND THE MINE SAFETY AND HEALTH ADMINISTRATION (NIOSH-MSHA).

CHEMICAL CARTRIDGE RESPIRATOR WITH FULL FACEPIECE AND PESTICIDE CARTRIDGE.

TYPE 'C' SUPPLIED-AIR RESPIRATOR WITH A FULL FACEPIECE OPERATED IN PRESSURE-DEMAND OR OTHER POSITIVE PRESSURE MODE OR WITH A FULL FACEPIECE, HELMET OR HOOD OPERATED IN CONTINUOUS-FLOW MODE.

SELF-CONTAINED BREATHING APPARATUS OPERATED IN PRESSURE-DEMAND OR OTHER POSITIVE PRESSURE MODE.

FOR FIREFIGHTING AND OTHER IMMEDIATELY DANGEROUS TO LIFE OR HEALTH CONDITIONS:

SELF-CONTAINED BREATHING APPARATUS WITH FULL FACEPIECE OPERATED IN PRESSURE-DEMAND OR OTHER POSITIVE PRESSURE MODE.

SUPPLIED-AIR RESPIRATOR WITH FULL FACEPIECE AND OPERATED IN PRESSURE-DEMAND OR OTHER POSITIVE PRESSURE MODE IN COMBINATION WITH AN AUXILIARY SELF-CONTAINED BREATHING APPARATUS OPERATED IN PRESSURE-DEMAND OR OTHER POSITIVE PRESSURE MODE.

CLOTHING: EMPLOYEE MUST WEAR APPROPRIATE PROTECTIVE (IMPERVIOUS) CLOTHING AND EQUIPMENT TO PREVENT REPEATED OR PROLONGED SKIN CONTACT WITH THIS SUBSTANCE.

GLOVES: EMPLOYEE MUST WEAR APPROPRIATE PROTECTIVE GLOVES TO PREVENT CONTACT WITH THIS SUBSTANCE.

EYE PROTECTION: EMPLOYEE MUST WEAR SPLASH-PROOF OR DUST-RESISTANT SAFETY GOGGLES TO PREVENT EYE CONTACT WITH THIS SUBSTANCE.

EMERGENCY EYE WASH: WHERE THERE IS ANY POSSIBILITY THAT AN EMPLOYEE'S EYES MAY BE EXPOSED TO THIS SUBSTANCE, THE EMPLOYER SHOULD PROVIDE AN EYE WASH FOUNTAIN WITHIN THE IMMEDIATE WORK AREA FOR EMERGENCY USE.

AUTHORIZED BY- OCCUPATIONAL HEALTH SERVICES, INC.

CREATION DATE: 04/30/90 ***REVISION DATE:*** 04/30/90

MATERIAL SAFETY DATA SHEET

OCCUPATIONAL HEALTH SERVICES, INC.
AGRICULTURE AND PESTICIDE DIVISION
450 SEVENTH AVENUE, SUITE 2407
NEW YORK, NEW YORK 10123
1-800-445-MSDS OR (212) 967-1100

EMERGENCY CONTACT:
JOHN S. BRANSFORD, JR. (615) 292-1180

SUBSTANCE IDENTIFICATION

CAS-NUMBER 125-67-7

SUBSTANCE: POTASSIUM GIBBERELLATE

TRADE NAMES/SYNONYMS: GIBB-3-ENE-1,10-DICARBOXYLIC ACID, 2,4A,7-TRIHYDROXY-1-METHYL-8- METHYLENE-, 1,4A-LACTONE, MONOPOTASSIUM SALT, (1 ALPHA, 2 BETA, 4A(ALPHA), 4B(BETA), 10 BETA)-; (1 ALPHA, 2 BETA, 4A(ALPHA), 4B(BETA), 10 BETA)-2,4A,7-TRIHYDROXY-1-METHYL-8-GIBB-3-ENE-1,10-DICARBOXYLIC ACID, 1,4A-LACTONE, MONOPOTASSIUM SALT; GIBBERELLIC ACID , MONOPOTASSIUM SALT; GIBREL; GIBBERELLIC ACID POTASSIUM SALT; GIBBERELLIN A3 POTASSIUM SALT; C19H21KO6; PST71492

CHEMICAL FAMILY: SOAP

MOLECULAR FORMULA: C19-H21-O6-K

MOLECULAR WEIGHT: 384.48

CERCLA RATINGS (SCALE 0-3): HEALTH=U FIRE=1 REACTIVITY=0 PERSISTENCE=2

NFPA RATINGS (SCALE 0-4): HEALTH=U FIRE=1 REACTIVITY=0

COMPONENTS AND CONTAMINANTS

COMPONENT: POTASSIUM GIBBERELLATE ***PERCENT:*** 100.0
CAS# 125-67-7

OTHER CONTAMINANTS: NONE

EXPOSURE LIMITS: NO OCCUPATIONAL EXPOSURE LIMITS ESTABLISHED BY OSHA, ACGIH, OR NIOSH.

PHYSICAL DATA

DESCRIPTION: WHITE, BULKY POWDER. ***MELTING POINT:*** NOT AVAILABLE

SPECIFIC GRAVITY: NOT AVAILABLE ***PH:*** 5.5-6.5 @ 5% SOLN

SOLUBILITY IN WATER: 5%

FIRE AND EXPLOSION DATA

FIRE AND EXPLOSION HAZARD: SLIGHT FIRE HAZARD WHEN EXPOSED TO HEAT OR FLAME.

FIREFIGHTING MEDIA: DRY CHEMICAL, CARBON DIOXIDE, HALON, WATER SPRAY OR STANDARD FOAM (1987 EMERGENCY RESPONSE GUIDEBOOK, DOT P 5800.4). FOR LARGER FIRES, USE WATER SPRAY, FOG OR STANDARD FOAM (1987 EMERGENCY RESPONSE GUIDEBOOK, DOT P 5800.4).

FIREFIGHTING: MOVE CONTAINER FROM FIRE AREA IF POSSIBLE. DO NOT SCATTER SPILLED MATERIAL WITH HIGH PRESSURE WATER STREAMS. DIKE FIRE CONTROL WATER FOR LATER DISPOSAL (1987 EMERGENCY RESPONSE GUIDEBOOK, DOT P 5800.4, GUIDE PAGE 31).
USE AGENTS SUITABLE FOR TYPE OF SURROUNDING FIRE. AVOID BREATHING HAZARDOUS VAPORS, KEEP UPWIND.

TOXICITY

POTASSIUM GIBBERELLATE: TOXICITY DATA: MUTAGENIC DATA (RTECS).
CARCINOGEN STATUS: NONE. ACUTE TOXICITY LEVEL: NO DATA AVAILABLE.
TARGET EFFECTS: POISONING BY POTASSIUM SALTS MAY AFFECT THE HEART.

HEALTH EFFECTS AND FIRST AID

INHALATION: POTASSIUM GIBBERELLATE: **ACUTE EXPOSURE-** NO DATA AVAILABLE. MAY BE IRRITATING TO THE MUCOUS MEMBRANES. **CHRONIC EXPOSURE-** NO DATA AVAILABLE.

FIRST AID- REMOVE FROM EXPOSURE AREA TO FRESH AIR IMMEDIATELY. IF BREATHING HAS STOPPED, PERFORM ARTIFICIAL RESPIRATION. KEEP PERSON WARM AND AT REST. TREAT SYMPTOMATICALLY AND SUPPORTIVELY. GET MEDICAL ATTENTION IMMEDIATELY.

SKIN CONTACT: POTASSIUM GIBBERELLATE: **ACUTE EXPOSURE-** NO DATA AVAILABLE. MAY BE IRRITATING. **CHRONIC EXPOSURE-** NO DATA AVAILABLE.

FIRST AID- REMOVE CONTAMINATED CLOTHING AND SHOES IMMEDIATELY. WASH AFFECTED AREA WITH SOAP OR MILD DETERGENT AND LARGE AMOUNTS OF WATER UNTIL NO EVIDENCE OF CHEMICAL REMAINS (APPROXIMATELY 15-20 MINUTES). GET MEDICAL ATTENTION IMMEDIATELY.

EYE CONTACT: POTASSIUM GIBBERELLATE: **ACUTE EXPOSURE-** NO DATA AVAILABLE. MAY BE IRRITATING. **CHRONIC EXPOSURE-** NO DATA AVAILABLE.

FIRST AID- WASH EYES IMMEDIATELY WITH LARGE AMOUNTS OF WATER OR NORMAL SALINE, OCCASIONALLY LIFTING UPPER AND LOWER LIDS, UNTIL NO EVIDENCE OF CHEMICAL REMAINS (APPROXIMATELY 15-20 MINUTES). GET MEDICAL ATTENTION IMMEDIATELY.

INGESTION: POTASSIUM GIBBERELLATE: **ACUTE EXPOSURE-** POISONING BY POTASSIUM SALTS IS RARE BECAUSE A LARGE SINGLE DOSE USUALLY CAUSES VOMITING, AND IN THE ABSENCE OF PRE-EXISTING KIDNEY DAMAGE, POTASSIUM IS RAPIDLY EXCRETED. HOWEVER, IF SUFFICIENT AMOUNTS ARE ABSORBED IT MAY DISTURB THE RHYTHM OF THE HEART AND EVENTUALLY WEAKEN CARDIAC CONTRACTILITY. SKELETAL MUSCLE WEAKNESS AND FLACCID PARALYSIS MAY OCCUR IN SEVERE CASES. **CHRONIC EXPOSURE-** NO DATA AVAILABLE.

FIRST AID- TREAT SYMPTOMATICALLY AND SUPPORTIVELY. GET MEDICAL ATTENTION IMMEDIATELY. IF VOMITING OCCURS, KEEP HEAD LOWER THAN HIPS TO PREVENT ASPIRATION.

ANTIDOTE: NO SPECIFIC ANTIDOTE. TREAT SYMPTOMATICALLY AND SUPPORTIVELY.

REACTIVITY

REACTIVITY: STABLE UNDER NORMAL TEMPERATURES AND PRESSURES.

INCOMPATIBILITIES: POTASSIUM GIBBERELLATE: OXIDIZERS (STRONG): FIRE AND EXPLOSION HAZARD.

DECOMPOSITION: THERMAL DECOMPOSITION MAY RELEASE TOXIC AND/OR HAZARDOUS GASES.

POLYMERIZATION: HAZARDOUS POLYMERIZATION HAS NOT BEEN REPORTED TO OCCUR UNDER NORMAL TEMPERATURES AND PRESSURES.

STORAGE AND DISPOSAL

OBSERVE ALL FEDERAL, STATE AND LOCAL REGULATIONS WHEN STORING OR DISPOSING OF THIS SUBSTANCE. FOR ASSISTANCE, CONTACT THE DISTRICT DIRECTOR OF THE ENVIRONMENTAL PROTECTION AGENCY.

STORAGE

STORE IN ACCORDANCE WITH 40 CFR 165 RECOMMENDED PROCEDURES FOR THE DISPOSAL AND STORAGE OF PESTICIDES AND PESTICIDE CONTAINERS.
STORE AWAY FROM INCOMPATIBLE SUBSTANCES.

DISPOSAL

DISPOSAL MUST BE IN ACCORDANCE WITH 40 CFR 165 RECOMMENDED PROCEDURES FOR THE DISPOSAL AND STORAGE OF PESTICIDES AND PESTICIDE CONTAINERS.

CONDITIONS TO AVOID

MAY BURN BUT DOES NOT IGNITE READILY. AVOID CONTACT WITH STRONG OXIDIZERS, EXCESSIVE HEAT, SPARKS, OR OPEN FLAME.

SPILL AND LEAK PROCEDURES

OCCUPATIONAL SPILL: SWEEP UP AND PLACE IN SUITABLE CLEAN, DRY CONTAINERS FOR RECLAMATION OR LATER DISPOSAL. DO NOT FLUSH SPILLED MATERIAL INTO SEWER. KEEP UNNECESSARY PEOPLE AWAY.

PROTECTIVE EQUIPMENT

VENTILATION: PROVIDE LOCAL EXHAUST OR GENERAL DILUTION VENTILATION SYSTEM.

RESPIRATOR: THE FOLLOWING RESPIRATORS ARE RECOMMENDED BASED ON INFORMATION FOUND IN THE PHYSICAL DATA, TOXICITY AND HEALTH EFFECTS SECTIONS. THEY ARE RANKED IN ORDER FROM MINIMUM TO MAXIMUM RESPIRATORY PROTECTION. THE SPECIFIC RESPIRATOR SELECTED MUST BE BASED ON CONTAMINATION LEVELS FOUND IN THE WORK PLACE, MUST NOT EXCEED THE WORKING LIMITS OF THE RESPIRATOR AND BE JOINTLY APPROVED BY THE NATIONAL INSTITUTE FOR OCCUPATIONAL SAFETY AND HEALTH AND THE MINE SAFETY AND HEALTH ADMINISTRATION (NIOSH-MSHA).
CHEMICAL CARTRIDGE RESPIRATOR WITH AN ORGANIC VAPOR CARTRIDGE(S) WITH A FULL FACEPIECE AND ORGANIC VAPOR CARTRIDGE(S) IN COMBINATION WITH A DUST AND MIST FILTER.
POWERED AIR-PURIFYING RESPIRATOR WITH A TIGHT-FITTING FACEPIECE AND ORGANIC VAPOR CARTRIDGE(S) IN COMBINATION WITH A HIGH-EFFICIENCY PARTICULATE FILTER.
TYPE 'C' SUPPLIED-AIR RESPIRATOR WITH A FULL FACEPIECE OPERATED IN A PRESSURE-DEMAND OR OTHER POSITIVE PRESSURE MODE.
SELF-CONTAINED BREATHING APPARATUS WITH A FULL FACEPIECE OPERATED IN PRESSURE-DEMAND OR OTHER POSITIVE PRESSURE MODE.
FOR FIREFIGHTING AND OTHER IMMEDIATELY DANGEROUS TO LIFE OR HEALTH CONDITIONS:
SELF-CONTAINED BREATHING APPARATUS WITH FULL FACEPIECE OPERATED IN PRESSURE-DEMAND OR OTHER POSITIVE PRESSURE MODE.
SUPPLIED-AIR RESPIRATOR WITH FULL FACEPIECE AND OPERATED IN PRESSURE-DEMAND OR OTHER POSITIVE PRESSURE MODE IN COMBINATION WITH AN AUXILIARY SELF-CONTAINED BREATHING APPARATUS OPERATED IN PRESSURE-DEMAND OR OTHER POSITIVE PRESSURE MODE.

CLOTHING: EMPLOYEE MUST WEAR APPROPRIATE PROTECTIVE (IMPERVIOUS) CLOTHING AND EQUIPMENT TO PREVENT REPEATED OR PROLONGED SKIN CONTACT WITH THIS SUBSTANCE.

GLOVES: EMPLOYEE MUST WEAR APPROPRIATE PROTECTIVE GLOVES TO PREVENT CONTACT WITH THIS SUBSTANCE.

EYE PROTECTION: EMPLOYEE MUST WEAR SPLASH-PROOF OR DUST-RESISTANT SAFETY GOGGLES TO PREVENT EYE CONTACT WITH THIS SUBSTANCE.
EMERGENCY EYE WASH: WHERE THERE IS ANY POSSIBILITY THAT AN EMPLOYEE'S

EYES MAY BE EXPOSED TO THIS SUBSTANCE, THE EMPLOYER SHOULD PROVIDE AN EYE WASH FOUNTAIN WITHIN THE IMMEDIATE WORK AREA FOR EMERGENCY USE.

AUTHORIZED BY- OCCUPATIONAL HEALTH SERVICES, INC.
CREATION DATE: 02/08/90 ***REVISION DATE:*** 05/31/90

MATERIAL SAFETY DATA SHEET

OCCUPATIONAL HEALTH SERVICES, INC.
AGRICULTURE AND PESTICIDE DIVISION
450 SEVENTH AVENUE, SUITE 2407
NEW YORK, NEW YORK 10123
1-800-445-MSDS OR (212) 967-1100

EMERGENCY CONTACT:
JOHN S. BRANSFORD, JR. (615) 292-1180

SUBSTANCE IDENTIFICATION

CAS-NUMBER 10402-15-0
SUBSTANCE: **COPPER CITRATE**
TRADE NAMES/SYNONYMS: 1,2,3-PROPANETRICARBOXYLIC ACID, 2-HYDROXY-, COPPER SALT; 2-HYDROXY-1,2,3-PROPANETRICARBOXYLIC ACID, COPPER SALT; CITRIC ACID, COPPER SALT; PST71496
CHEMICAL FAMILY: SALT
CERCLA RATINGS (SCALE 0-3): HEALTH=U FIRE=1 REACTIVITY=0 PERSISTENCE=3
NFPA RATINGS (SCALE 0-4): HEALTH=U FIRE=1 REACTIVITY=0

COMPONENTS AND CONTAMINANTS

COMPONENT: COPPER CITRATE ***PERCENT:*** 100
CAS# 10402-15-0
OTHER CONTAMINANTS: NONE
EXPOSURE LIMITS: COPPER DUST AND MIST (AS CU): 1 MG/M3 OSHA TWA 1 MG/M3 ACGIH TWA
SUBJECT TO SARA SECTION 313 ANNUAL TOXIC CHEMICAL RELEASE REPORTING

PHYSICAL DATA

DESCRIPTION: BLUISH-GREEN POWDER. ***MELTING POINT:*** NOT AVAILABLE
SPECIFIC GRAVITY: NOT AVAILABLE ***SOLUBILITY IN WATER:*** NOT AVAILABLE
SOLVENT SOLUBILITY: SOLUBLE IN DILUTE ACIDS.

FIRE AND EXPLOSION DATA

FIRE AND EXPLOSION HAZARD: SLIGHT FIRE HAZARD WHEN EXPOSED TO HEAT OR FLAME.
FIREFIGHTING MEDIA: DRY CHEMICAL, CARBON DIOXIDE, HALON, WATER SPRAY OR STANDARD FOAM (1987 EMERGENCY RESPONSE GUIDEBOOK, DOT P 5800.4).
FOR LARGER FIRES, USE WATER SPRAY, FOG OR STANDARD FOAM (1987 EMERGENCY RESPONSE GUIDEBOOK, DOT P 5800.4).
FIREFIGHTING: MOVE CONTAINERS FROM FIRE AREA IF POSSIBLE (1987 EMERGENCY RESPONSE GUIDEBOOK, DOT P 5800.4, GUIDE PAGE 53).
EXTINGUISH USING AGENTS SUITABLE FOR SURROUNDING FIRE. APPLY WATER IN FLOODING QUANTITIES AS A FOG. AVOID CONTAMINATION OF WATER SOURCES. KEEP UPWIND AND AVOID BREATHING DUST AND FUMES.

TOXICITY

COPPER CITRATE: CARCINOGEN STATUS: NONE. ACUTE TOXICITY LEVEL: NO DATA AVAILABLE. TARGET EFFECTS: POISONING MAY AFFECT THE EYES, SKIN, RESPIRATORY TRACT, LIVER, KIDNEY, SPLEEN, OR THE DIGESTIVE TRACT. AT INCREASED RISK FROM EXPOSURE: PERSONS WITH PREEXISTING RESPIRATORY, LIVER, SKIN, KIDNEY, HEMATOPOIETIC, OR WILSON'S DISEASES.

HEALTH EFFECTS AND FIRST AID

INHALATION: COPPER CITRATE: **ACUTE EXPOSURE-** INHALATION OF COPPER DUST MAY CAUSE IRRITATION OF THE UPPER RESPIRATORY TRACT OR AN ILLNESS SIMILAR TO THE COMMON COLD WITH SENSATIONS OF CHILLS AND STUFFINESS OF THE HEAD. **CHRONIC EXPOSURE-** PROLONGED INHALATION OF DUST OR MIST OF COPPER SALTS MAY CAUSE CONGESTION OF THE NASAL MUCOUS MEMBRANES, SOMETIMES OF THE PHARYNX, AND ON OCCASIONS ULCERATION AND PERFORATION OF THE NASAL SEPTUM. ATROPHIC CHANGES IN THE MUCOUS MEMBRANES WERE NOTED IN SUBJECTS EXPOSED TO COMPLEX COPPER SALTS FOR LONG PERIODS OF TIME. INHALATION OF COPPER COMPOUNDS HAS CAUSED INJURY TO THE LUNGS AND LIVER WITH HEMOCHROMATOSIS IN ANIMALS.
FIRST AID- REMOVE FROM EXPOSURE AREA TO FRESH AIR IMMEDIATELY. IF BREATHING HAS STOPPED, PERFORM ARTIFICIAL RESPIRATION. KEEP PERSON WARM AND AT REST. TREAT SYMPTOMATICALLY AND SUPPORTIVELY. GET MEDICAL ATTENTION IMMEDIATELY.

SKIN CONTACT: COPPER CITRATE: **ACUTE EXPOSURE-** DIRECT CONTACT WITH COPPER COMPOUNDS MAY CAUSE IRRITATION. COPPER SALTS HAVE BEEN REPORTED TO CAUSE ITCHING PAPULOVESICULATION, SKIN DISCOLORATION, AND ECZEMATOID LESIONS. **CHRONIC EXPOSURE-** REPEATED AND PROLONGED CONTACT WITH SOME COPPER SALTS HAS RESULTED IN IRRITATION, NECROSIS, AND GREENISH SKIN DISCOLORATION. ALLERGIC CONTACT DERMATITIS, ALTHOUGH RARE, HAS BEEN REPORTED.
FIRST AID- REMOVE CONTAMINATED CLOTHING AND SHOES IMMEDIATELY. WASH AFFECTED AREA WITH SOAP OR MILD DETERGENT AND LARGE AMOUNTS OF WATER UNTIL NO EVIDENCE OF CHEMICAL REMAINS (APPROXIMATELY 15-20 MINUTES). GET MEDICAL ATTENTION IMMEDIATELY.

EYE CONTACT: COPPER CITRATE: **ACUTE EXPOSURE-** SOME COPPER SALTS HAVE BEEN REPORTED TO CAUSE CONJUNCTIVITIS, CORNEAL ULCERATIONS, AND TURBIDITY POSSIBLY WITH PALPEBRAL EDEMA. COPPER PARTICLES EMBEDDED IN THE EYE MAY RESULT IN A PRONOUNCED FOREIGN-BODY RESPONSE WITH CHARACTERISTIC DISCOLORATION OF OCULAR TISSUE. **CHRONIC EXPOSURE-** NO DATA AVAILABLE.
FIRST AID- WASH EYES IMMEDIATELY WITH LARGE AMOUNTS OF WATER OR NORMAL SALINE, OCCASIONALLY LIFTING UPPER AND LOWER LIDS, UNTIL NO EVIDENCE OF CHEMICAL REMAINS (APPROXIMATELY 15-20 MINUTES). GET MEDICAL ATTENTION IMMEDIATELY.

INGESTION: COPPER CITRATE: **ACUTE EXPOSURE-** INGESTION OF COPPER SALTS MAY CAUSE AN IMMEDIATE METALLIC TASTE, SALIVATION, NAUSEA, EPIGASTRIC BURNING, VOMITING, DIARRHEA, ULCERS, HEMORRHAGIC GASTRITIS, ANURIA, COMA, CONVULSIONS, AND DEATH. IF SUFFICIENT VOMITING DOES NOT OCCUR, SOME COPPER SALTS MAY CAUSE SYSTEMIC EFFECTS INCLUDING CAPILLARY DAMAGE, SHOCK, KIDNEY AND LIVER INJURY, CENTRAL NERVOUS SYSTEM EXCITATION FOLLOWED BY DEPRESSION, AND DEATH. **CHRONIC EXPOSURE-** REPEATED AND PROLONGED INGESTION OF COPPER SALTS HAS PRODUCED HEMOLYTIC ANEMIA AND LIVER, KIDNEY, AND SPLEEN DAMAGE IN ANIMALS.
FIRST AID- DILUTE THE POISON IMMEDIATELY WITH LARGE AMOUNTS OF WATER OR MILK AND REMOVE BY GASTRIC LAVAGE UNLESS THE VICTIM IS ALREADY VOMITING. (DREISBACH, HANDBOOK OF POISONING, 12TH ED.) GET MEDICAL ATTENTION IMMEDIATELY. ADMINISTRATION OF GASTRIC LAVAGE SHOULD BE PERFORMED BY QUALIFIED MEDICAL PERSONNEL.
ANTIDOTE: THE FOLLOWING ANTIDOTE HAS BEEN RECOMMENDED. HOWEVER, THE DECISION AS TO WHETHER THE SEVERITY OF POISONING REQUIRES ADMINISTRATION OF ANY ANTIDOTE AND ACTUAL DOSE REQUIRED SHOULD BE MADE BY QUALIFIED MEDICAL PERSONNEL.
COPPER POISONING: GIVE CALCIUM DISODIUM EDETATE 15-25 MG/KG (0.08-0.125 ML OF 20% SOLUTION PER KILOGRAM BODY WEIGHT) IN 250-500 ML OF 5% DEXTROSE INTRAVENOUSLY OVER A 1 TO 2 HOUR PERIOD TWICE DAILY. THE MAXIMUM DOSE SHOULD NOT EXCEED 50 MG/KG/DAY. THE DRUG SHOULD BE GIVEN IN 5-DAY COURSES WITH A REST PERIOD OF AT LEAST 2 DAYS BETWEEN COURSES. AFTER THE FIRST COURSE, SUBSEQUENT COURSES SHOULD NOT EXCEED 50 MG/KG/DAY. DAILY URINALYSES SHOULD NOT BE DONE DURING THE TREATMENT PERIOD. THE DOSAGE SHOULD BE REDUCED IF ANY UNUSUAL URINARY FINDINGS APPEAR. INTRAVENOUS ADMINISTRATION IS CONTRAINDICATED IN THE PRESENCE OF ELEVATED CEREBROSPINAL FLUID PRESSURE. PENICILLAMINE IS ALSO EFFECTIVE IN COPPER POISONING. GIVE UP TO 100 MG/KG/DAY (MAXIMUM 1 G/DAY) DIVIDED INTO 4 DOSES FOR NO LONGER THAN 1 WEEK. IF A LONGER ADMINISTRATION PERIOD IS WARRANTED, DOSAGE SHOULD NOT EXCEED 40 MG/KG/DAY. GIVE THE DRUG ORALLY, HALF AN HOUR BEFORE MEALS (DREISBACH, HANDBOOK OF POISONING, 12TH ED.). ANTIDOTE SHOULD BE ADMINISTERED BY QUALIFIED MEDICAL PERSONNEL.

REACTIVITY

REACTIVITY: STABLE UNDER NORMAL TEMPERATURES AND PRESSURES.
INCOMPATIBILITIES: COPPER CITRATE: OXIDIZERS (STRONG): FIRE AND EXPLOSION HAZARD. SEE ALSO COPPER SALTS.
COPPER SALTS: ACETYLENE: MAY FORM EXPLOSIVE ACETYLIDES. HYDRAZINE: DECOMPOSES. NITROMETHANE: FORMS EXPLOSIVE MIXTURES.
DECOMPOSITION: THERMAL DECOMPOSITION MAY RELEASE TOXIC AND/OR HAZARDOUS GASES.
POLYMERIZATION: HAZARDOUS POLYMERIZATION HAS NOT BEEN REPORTED TO OCCUR UNDER NORMAL TEMPERATURES AND PRESSURES.

STORAGE AND DISPOSAL

OBSERVE ALL FEDERAL, STATE AND LOCAL REGULATIONS WHEN STORING OR DISPOSING OF THIS SUBSTANCE. FOR ASSISTANCE, CONTACT THE DISTRICT DIRECTOR OF THE ENVIRONMENTAL PROTECTION AGENCY.

STORAGE

STORE IN ACCORDANCE WITH 40 CFR 165 RECOMMENDED PROCEDURES FOR THE DISPOSAL AND STORAGE OF PESTICIDES AND PESTICIDE CONTAINERS.
STORE AWAY FROM INCOMPATIBLE SUBSTANCES.

DISPOSAL

DISPOSAL MUST BE IN ACCORDANCE WITH 40 CFR 165 RECOMMENDED PROCEDURES FOR THE DISPOSAL AND STORAGE OF PESTICIDES AND PESTICIDE CONTAINERS.

CONDITIONS TO AVOID

MAY BURN BUT DOES NOT IGNITE READILY.

SPILL AND LEAK PROCEDURES

OCCUPATIONAL SPILL: DO NOT TOUCH SPILLED MATERIAL. STOP LEAK IF YOU CAN DO IT WITHOUT RISK. FOR SMALL SPILLS, TAKE UP WITH SAND OR OTHER ABSORBENT MATERIAL AND PLACE INTO CONTAINERS FOR LATER DISPOSAL. FOR SMALL DRY SPILLS, WITH A CLEAN SHOVEL PLACE MATERIAL INTO CLEAN, DRY CONTAINER AND COVER. MOVE CONTAINERS FROM SPILL AREA. FOR LARGER SPILLS, DIKE FAR AHEAD OF SPILL FOR LATER DISPOSAL. KEEP UNNECESSARY PEOPLE AWAY. ISOLATE HAZARD AREA AND DENY ENTRY.

PROTECTIVE EQUIPMENT

VENTILATION: PROVIDE LOCAL EXHAUST OR PROCESS ENCLOSURE VENTILATION TO MEET PUBLISHED EXPOSURE LIMITS.

RESPIRATOR: THE FOLLOWING RESPIRATORS ARE RECOMMENDED BASED ON INFORMATION FOUND IN THE PHYSICAL DATA, TOXICITY AND HEALTH EFFECTS SECTIONS. THEY ARE RANKED IN ORDER FROM MINIMUM TO MAXIMUM RESPIRATORY PROTECTION. THE SPECIFIC RESPIRATOR SELECTED MUST BE BASED ON CONTAMINATION LEVELS FOUND IN THE WORK PLACE, MUST NOT EXCEED THE WORKING LIMITS OF THE RESPIRATOR AND BE JOINTLY APPROVED BY THE NATIONAL INSTITUTE FOR OCCUPATIONAL SAFETY AND HEALTH AND THE MINE SAFETY AND HEALTH ADMINISTRATION (NIOSH-MSHA).
CHEMICAL CARTRIDGE RESPIRATOR WITH AN ORGANIC VAPOR CARTRIDGE(S) WITH A HIGH-EFFICIENCY PARTICULATE FILTER AND FULL FACEPIECE.
HIGH-EFFICIENCY PARTICULATE RESPIRATOR WITH A FULL FACEPIECE.
POWERED AIR-PURIFYING RESPIRATOR WITH A HIGH-EFFICIENCY FILTER WITH A FULL FACEPIECE.
TYPE 'C' SUPPLIED-AIR RESPIRATOR WITH A FULL FACEPIECE OPERATED IN PRESSURE-DEMAND OR OTHER POSITIVE PRESSURE MODE OR WITH A FULL FACEPIECE, HELMET OR HOOD OPERATED IN CONTINUOUS-FLOW MODE.
SELF-CONTAINED BREATHING APPARATUS WITH A FULL FACEPIECE OPERATED IN PRESSURE-DEMAND OR OTHER POSITIVE PRESSURE MODE.
FOR FIREFIGHTING AND OTHER IMMEDIATELY DANGEROUS TO LIFE OR HEALTH CONDITIONS:
SELF-CONTAINED BREATHING APPARATUS WITH FULL FACEPIECE OPERATED IN PRESSURE-DEMAND OR OTHER POSITIVE PRESSURE MODE.
SUPPLIED-AIR RESPIRATOR WITH FULL FACEPIECE AND OPERATED IN PRESSURE-DEMAND OR OTHER POSITIVE PRESSURE MODE IN COMBINATION WITH AN AUXILIARY SELF-CONTAINED BREATHING APPARATUS OPERATED IN PRESSURE-DEMAND OR OTHER POSITIVE PRESSURE MODE.

CLOTHING: EMPLOYEE MUST WEAR APPROPRIATE PROTECTIVE (IMPERVIOUS) CLOTHING AND EQUIPMENT TO PREVENT REPEATED OR PROLONGED SKIN CONTACT WITH THIS SUBSTANCE.

GLOVES: EMPLOYEE MUST WEAR APPROPRIATE PROTECTIVE GLOVES TO PREVENT CONTACT WITH THIS SUBSTANCE.

EYE PROTECTION: EMPLOYEE MUST WEAR SPLASH-PROOF OR DUST-RESISTANT SAFETY GOGGLES TO PREVENT EYE CONTACT WITH THIS SUBSTANCE.
EMERGENCY EYE WASH: WHERE THERE IS ANY POSSIBILITY THAT AN EMPLOYEE'S EYES MAY BE EXPOSED TO THIS SUBSTANCE, THE EMPLOYER SHOULD PROVIDE AN EYE WASH FOUNTAIN WITHIN THE IMMEDIATE WORK AREA FOR EMERGENCY USE.

AUTHORIZED BY- OCCUPATIONAL HEALTH SERVICES, INC.
CREATION DATE: 10/04/89 ***REVISION DATE:*** 05/18/90

MATERIAL SAFETY DATA SHEET

OCCUPATIONAL HEALTH SERVICES, INC.
AGRICULTURE AND PESTICIDE DIVISION
450 SEVENTH AVENUE, SUITE 2407
NEW YORK, NEW YORK 10123
1-800-445-MSDS OR (212) 967-1100

EMERGENCY CONTACT:
JOHN S. BRANSFORD, JR. (615) 292-1180

SUBSTANCE IDENTIFICATION

CAS-NUMBER 126-96-5

SUBSTANCE: **SODIUM DIACETATE**

TRADE NAMES/SYNONYMS: ACETIC ACID, SODIUM SALT (2:1); ACETIC ACID, SODIUM SALT, COMPOUND WITH ACETIC ACID (1:1); DYKON; SODIUM ACID ACETATE; SODIUM HYDROGEN DIACETATE; ACETIC ACID, SODIUM SALT; C4H7NAO4; PST71497

CHEMICAL FAMILY: ACETATE

MOLECULAR FORMULA: C-H3-C-O-O-NA.C-H3-C-O-O-H

MOLECULAR WEIGHT: 142.09

CERCLA RATINGS (SCALE 0-3): HEALTH=U FIRE=1 REACTIVITY=0 PERSISTENCE=0

NFPA RATINGS (SCALE 0-4): HEALTH=U FIRE=1 REACTIVITY=0

COMPONENTS AND CONTAMINANTS

COMPONENT: SODIUM DIACETATE ***PERCENT:*** 100.0
CAS# 126-96-5

OTHER CONTAMINANTS: NONE

EXPOSURE LIMITS: NO OCCUPATIONAL EXPOSURE LIMITS ESTABLISHED BY OSHA, ACGIH, OR NIOSH.

PHYSICAL DATA

DESCRIPTION: WHITE, HYGROSCOPIC, CRYSTALLINE SOLID WITH AN ODOR OF ACETIC ACID.

MELTING POINT: NOT AVAILABLE ***SPECIFIC GRAVITY:*** NOT AVAILABLE

PH: 4.5-5.0 @ 10% SOLN ***SOLUBILITY IN WATER:*** 100%

SOLVENT SOLUBILITY: SLIGHTLY SOLUBLE IN ALCOHOL; INSOLUBLE IN ETHER. DECOMPOSES ABOVE 150 C

FIRE AND EXPLOSION DATA

FIRE AND EXPLOSION HAZARD: SLIGHT FIRE HAZARD WHEN EXPOSED TO HEAT OR FLAME.

FIREFIGHTING MEDIA: DRY CHEMICAL, CARBON DIOXIDE, HALON, WATER SPRAY OR STANDARD FOAM (1987 EMERGENCY RESPONSE GUIDEBOOK, DOT P 5800.4).
FOR LARGER FIRES, USE WATER SPRAY, FOG OR STANDARD FOAM (1987 EMERGENCY RESPONSE GUIDEBOOK, DOT P 5800.4).

FIREFIGHTING: MOVE CONTAINER FROM FIRE AREA IF POSSIBLE. DO NOT SCATTER SPILLED MATERIAL WITH HIGH PRESSURE WATER STREAMS. DIKE FIRE CONTROL WATER FOR LATER DISPOSAL (1987 EMERGENCY RESPONSE GUIDEBOOK, DOT P 5800.4, GUIDE PAGE 31).
USE AGENTS SUITABLE FOR TYPE OF SURROUNDING FIRE. AVOID BREATHING HAZARDOUS VAPORS, KEEP UPWIND.

TOXICITY

SODIUM DIACETATE: CARCINOGEN STATUS: NONE. ACUTE TOXICITY LEVEL: NO DATA AVAILABLE. TARGET EFFECTS: NO DATA AVAILABLE.

HEALTH EFFECTS AND FIRST AID

INHALATION: SODIUM DIACETATE: **ACUTE EXPOSURE-** CONTACT WITH MUCOUS MEMBRANES MAY CAUSE IRRITATION, POSSIBLY SEVERE. **CHRONIC EXPOSURE-** NO DATA AVAILABLE.

FIRST AID- REMOVE FROM EXPOSURE AREA TO FRESH AIR IMMEDIATELY. IF BREATHING HAS STOPPED, PERFORM ARTIFICIAL RESPIRATION. KEEP PERSON WARM AND AT REST. TREAT SYMPTOMATICALLY AND SUPPORTIVELY. GET MEDICAL ATTENTION IMMEDIATELY.

SKIN CONTACT: SODIUM DIACETATE: **ACUTE EXPOSURE-** CONTACT WITH MOIST SKIN MAY CAUSE IRRITATION, POSSIBLY SEVERE. **CHRONIC EXPOSURE-** NO DATA AVAILABLE.

FIRST AID- REMOVE CONTAMINATED CLOTHING AND SHOES IMMEDIATELY. WASH AFFECTED AREA WITH SOAP OR MILD DETERGENT AND LARGE AMOUNTS OF WATER UNTIL NO EVIDENCE OF CHEMICAL REMAINS (APPROXIMATELY 15-20 MINUTES). GET MEDICAL ATTENTION IMMEDIATELY.

EYE CONTACT: SODIUM DIACETATE: **ACUTE EXPOSURE-** CONTACT MAY CAUSE IRRITATION, POSSIBLY SEVERE. **CHRONIC EXPOSURE-** NO DATA AVAILABLE.

FIRST AID- WASH EYES IMMEDIATELY WITH LARGE AMOUNTS OF WATER OR NORMAL SALINE, OCCASIONALLY LIFTING UPPER AND LOWER LIDS, UNTIL NO EVIDENCE OF CHEMICAL REMAINS (APPROXIMATELY 15-20 MINUTES). GET MEDICAL ATTENTION IMMEDIATELY.

INGESTION: SODIUM DIACETATE: **ACUTE EXPOSURE**- INGESTION MAY CAUSE GASTROINTESTINAL IRRITATION, POSSIBLY SEVERE. **CHRONIC EXPOSURE**- NO DATA AVAILABLE.

FIRST AID- TREAT SYMPTOMATICALLY AND SUPPORTIVELY. GET MEDICAL ATTENTION IMMEDIATELY. IF VOMITING OCCURS, KEEP HEAD LOWER THAN HIPS TO PREVENT ASPIRATION.

ANTIDOTE: NO SPECIFIC ANTIDOTE. TREAT SYMPTOMATICALLY AND SUPPORTIVELY.

REACTIVITY

REACTIVITY: STABLE UNDER NORMAL TEMPERATURES AND PRESSURES.

INCOMPATIBILITIES: SODIUM DIACETATE: OXIDIZERS (STRONG): FIRE AND EXPLOSION HAZARD.

DECOMPOSITION: THERMAL DECOMPOSITION MAY RELEASE TOXIC AND/OR HAZARDOUS GASES.

POLYMERIZATION: HAZARDOUS POLYMERIZATION HAS NOT BEEN REPORTED TO OCCUR UNDER NORMAL TEMPERATURES AND PRESSURES.

STORAGE AND DISPOSAL

OBSERVE ALL FEDERAL, STATE AND LOCAL REGULATIONS WHEN STORING OR DISPOSING OF THIS SUBSTANCE. FOR ASSISTANCE, CONTACT THE DISTRICT DIRECTOR OF THE ENVIRONMENTAL PROTECTION AGENCY.

****STORAGE****

STORE IN ACCORDANCE WITH 40 CFR 165 RECOMMENDED PROCEDURES FOR THE DISPOSAL AND STORAGE OF PESTICIDES AND PESTICIDE CONTAINERS.

STORE IN TIGHTLY CLOSED CONTAINERS; PREVENT EXPOSURE TO MOISTURE.

STORE AWAY FROM INCOMPATIBLE SUBSTANCES.

****DISPOSAL****

DISPOSAL MUST BE IN ACCORDANCE WITH 40 CFR 165 RECOMMENDED PROCEDURES FOR THE DISPOSAL AND STORAGE OF PESTICIDES AND PESTICIDE CONTAINERS.

CONDITIONS TO AVOID

MAY BURN BUT DOES NOT IGNITE READILY. AVOID CONTACT WITH STRONG OXIDIZERS, EXCESSIVE HEAT, SPARKS, OR OPEN FLAME.

SPILL AND LEAK PROCEDURES

OCCUPATIONAL SPILL: SWEEP UP AND PLACE IN SUITABLE CLEAN, DRY CONTAINERS FOR RECLAMATION OR LATER DISPOSAL. DO NOT FLUSH SPILLED MATERIAL INTO SEWER. KEEP UNNECESSARY PEOPLE AWAY.

PROTECTIVE EQUIPMENT

VENTILATION: PROVIDE LOCAL EXHAUST OR PROCESS ENCLOSURE VENTILATION SYSTEM.

RESPIRATOR: THE FOLLOWING RESPIRATORS ARE RECOMMENDED BASED ON INFORMATION FOUND IN THE PHYSICAL DATA, TOXICITY AND HEALTH EFFECTS SECTIONS. THEY ARE RANKED IN ORDER FROM MINIMUM TO MAXIMUM RESPIRATORY PROTECTION. THE SPECIFIC RESPIRATOR SELECTED MUST BE BASED ON CONTAMINATION LEVELS FOUND IN THE WORK PLACE, MUST NOT EXCEED THE WORKING LIMITS OF THE RESPIRATOR AND BE JOINTLY APPROVED BY THE NATIONAL INSTITUTE FOR OCCUPATIONAL SAFETY AND HEALTH AND THE MINE SAFETY AND HEALTH ADMINISTRATION (NIOSH-MSHA).

CHEMICAL CARTRIDGE RESPIRATOR WITH AN ORGANIC VAPOR CARTRIDGE(S) WITH A FULL FACEPIECE AND ORGANIC VAPOR CARTRIDGE(S) IN COMBINATION WITH A DUST AND MIST FILTER.

POWERED AIR-PURIFYING RESPIRATOR WITH A TIGHT-FITTING FACEPIECE AND ORGANIC VAPOR CARTRIDGE(S) IN COMBINATION WITH A HIGH-EFFICIENCY PARTICULATE FILTER.

TYPE 'C' SUPPLIED-AIR RESPIRATOR WITH A FULL FACEPIECE OPERATED IN A PRESSURE-DEMAND OR OTHER POSITIVE PRESSURE MODE.

SELF-CONTAINED BREATHING APPARATUS WITH A FULL FACEPIECE OPERATED IN PRESSURE-DEMAND OR OTHER POSITIVE PRESSURE MODE.

FOR FIREFIGHTING AND OTHER IMMEDIATELY DANGEROUS TO LIFE OR HEALTH CONDITIONS:

SELF-CONTAINED BREATHING APPARATUS WITH FULL FACEPIECE OPERATED IN PRESSURE-DEMAND OR OTHER POSITIVE PRESSURE MODE.

SUPPLIED-AIR RESPIRATOR WITH FULL FACEPIECE AND OPERATED IN PRESSURE-DEMAND OR OTHER POSITIVE PRESSURE MODE IN COMBINATION WITH AN AUXILIARY SELF-CONTAINED BREATHING APPARATUS OPERATED IN PRESSURE-DEMAND OR OTHER POSITIVE PRESSURE MODE.

CLOTHING: EMPLOYEE MUST WEAR APPROPRIATE PROTECTIVE (IMPERVIOUS) CLOTHING AND EQUIPMENT TO PREVENT REPEATED OR PROLONGED SKIN CONTACT WITH THIS SUBSTANCE.

GLOVES: EMPLOYEE MUST WEAR APPROPRIATE PROTECTIVE GLOVES TO PREVENT CONTACT WITH THIS SUBSTANCE.

EYE PROTECTION: EMPLOYEE MUST WEAR SPLASH-PROOF OR DUST-RESISTANT SAFETY GOGGLES TO PREVENT EYE CONTACT WITH THIS SUBSTANCE.

EMERGENCY EYE WASH: WHERE THERE IS ANY POSSIBILITY THAT AN EMPLOYEE'S EYES MAY BE EXPOSED TO THIS SUBSTANCE, THE EMPLOYER SHOULD PROVIDE AN EYE WASH FOUNTAIN WITHIN THE IMMEDIATE WORK AREA FOR EMERGENCY USE.

AUTHORIZED BY- OCCUPATIONAL HEALTH SERVICES, INC.

CREATION DATE: 11/15/89 ***REVISION DATE:*** 05/31/90

MATERIAL SAFETY DATA SHEET

OCCUPATIONAL HEALTH SERVICES, INC.
AGRICULTURE AND PESTICIDE DIVISION
450 SEVENTH AVENUE, SUITE 2407
NEW YORK, NEW YORK 10123
1-800-445-MSDS OR (212) 967-1100

EMERGENCY CONTACT:
JOHN S. BRANSFORD, JR. (615) 292-1180

SUBSTANCE IDENTIFICATION

CAS-NUMBER 2032-59-9

SUBSTANCE: **AMINOCARB**

TRADE NAMES/SYNONYMS: PHENOL, 4-(DIMETHYLAMINO)-3-METHYL-, METHYLCARBAMATE (ESTER); CARBAMIC ACID, METHYL-,4-(DIMETHYLAMINO)-M-TOLYL ESTER; METHYLCARBAMIC ACID, 4-(DIMETHYLAMINO)-M-TOLYL ESTER; 4-(DIMETHYLAMINO)-3-METHYLPHENOL METHYLCARBAMATE (ESTER); 4-DIMETHYLAMINO-M-TOLYL METHYLCARBAMATE; 4-(DIMETHYLAMINO)-M-TOLYL METHYLCARBAMATE; 4-DIMETHYLAMINO-3-CRESYL METHYLCARBAMATE; 4-DIMETHYLAMINO-M-CRESYL METHYLCARBAMATE; 4-DIMETHYLAMINO-3-METHYL-PHENYL-N-METHYLCARBAMATE; MATACIL; BAYER 44646; OMS 17K0; ENT 25,784; C11H16N2O2; PST71500

CHEMICAL FAMILY: CARBAMATE ESTER

MOLECULAR FORMULA: (C-H3)2-N-C6-H3-C-H3-O2-C-N-H-C-H3

MOLECULAR WEIGHT: 208.26

CERCLA RATINGS (SCALE 0-3): HEALTH=3 FIRE=1 REACTIVITY=0 PERSISTENCE=1

NFPA RATINGS (SCALE 0-4): HEALTH=3 FIRE=1 REACTIVITY=0

COMPONENTS AND CONTAMINANTS

COMPONENT: AMINOCARB ***PERCENT:*** 100

CAS# 2032-59-9

EXPOSURE LIMITS: NO OCCUPATIONAL EXPOSURE LIMITS ESTABLISHED BY OSHA, ACGIH, OR NIOSH.

PHYSICAL DATA

DESCRIPTION: COLORLESS CRYSTALLINE SOLID ***MELTING POINT:*** 199-20 F (93-94 C)

SPECIFIC GRAVITY: NOT AVAILABLE ***VAPOR PRESSURE:*** 0.000013 MMHG @ 20 C

SOLUBILITY IN WATER: SLIGHTLY SOLUBLE

SOLVENT SOLUBILITY: SOLUBLE IN ACETONE, METHANOL, AND MOST POLAR ORGANIC SOLVENTS; MODERATELY SOLUBLE IN AROMATIC SOLVENTS

FIRE AND EXPLOSION DATA

FIRE AND EXPLOSION HAZARD: SLIGHT FIRE HAZARD WHEN EXPOSED TO HEAT OR FLAME.

FIREFIGHTING MEDIA: DRY CHEMICAL, CARBON DIOXIDE, HALON, WATER SPRAY OR STANDARD FOAM (1987 EMERGENCY RESPONSE GUIDEBOOK, DOT P 5800.4). FOR LARGER FIRES, USE WATER SPRAY, FOG OR STANDARD FOAM (1987 EMERGENCY RESPONSE GUIDEBOOK, DOT P 5800.4).

FIREFIGHTING: MOVE CONTAINERS FROM FIRE AREA IF POSSIBLE. FIGHT FIRE FROM MAXIMUM DISTANCE. STAY AWAY FROM STORAGE TANK ENDS. DIKE FIRE CONTROL WATER FOR LATER DISPOSAL. DO NOT SCATTER MATERIAL (1987 EMERGENCY RESPONSE GUIDEBOOK, DOT P 5800.4, GUIDE PAGE 55). EXTINGUISH USING AGENTS SUITABLE FOR TYPE OF SURROUNDING FIRE. USE FLOODING AMOUNTS OF WATER AS FOG. AVOID BREATHING TOXIC DUST AND FUMES FROM BURNING MATERIAL; KEEP UPWIND.

TRANSPORTATION DATA

DEPARTMENT OF TRANSPORTATION HAZARD CLASSIFICATION 49 CFR 172.101: POISON B

DEPARTMENT OF TRANSPORTATION LABELING REQUIREMENTS 49 CFR 172.101 AND SUBPART E: POISON

DEPARTMENT OF TRANSPORTATION PACKAGING REQUIREMENTS: 49 CFR 173.365 EXCEPTIONS: 49 CFR 173.364

TOXICITY

AMINOCARB: TOXICITY DATA: 275 MG/KG SKIN-RAT LD50; 31 MG/KG SKIN-MOUSE LD50; 30 MG/KG ORAL-RAT LD50; 50 MG/KG ORAL-GUINEA PIG LDLO; 94 MG/KG ORAL-MOUSE LDLO; 6900 UG/KG SUBCUTANEOUS-MOUSE LD50; 50 MG/KG SUBCUTANEOUS-GUINEA PIG LDLO; 4700 UG/KG INTRAPERITONEAL-MOUSE LD50; 21 MG/KG INTRAPERITONEAL-RAT LD50; 50 MG/KG UNREPORTED-RAT LD50; MUTAGENIC DATA (RTECS). CARCINOGEN STATUS: NONE. ACUTE TOXICITY LEVEL: HIGHLY TOXIC BY INGESTION AND DERMAL ABSORPTION. TARGET EFFECTS: CHOLINESTERASE INHIBITOR. AT INCREASED RISK FROM EXPOSURE: PERSONS WITH ASTHMA, DIABETES, CARDIOVASCULAR DISEASE, MECHANICAL OBSTRUCTION OF THE GASTROINTESTINAL OR UROGENITAL TRACT, AND THOSE IN VAGOTONIC STATES.*

* MAY BE BASED ON GENERAL INFORMATION ON CARBAMATES.

HEALTH EFFECTS AND FIRST AID

INHALATION: AMINOCARB: SEE INFORMATION ON CARBAMATES.
CARBAMATES: CHOLINESTERASE INHIBITOR. **ACUTE EXPOSURE-** WHEN INHALED, THE FIRST EFFECTS OF CHOLINESTERASE INHIBITION ARE USUALLY RESPIRATORY AND MAY INCLUDE NASAL HYPEREMIA AND WATERY DISCHARGE, CHEST DISCOMFORT, DYSPNEA, AND WHEEZING DUE TO INCREASED BRONCHIAL SECRETIONS AND BRONCHOCONSTRICTION. OTHER SYSTEMIC EFFECTS MAY BEGIN WITHIN A FEW MINUTES OR SEVERAL HOURS OF EXPOSURE. SYMPTOMS MAY INCLUDE NAUSEA, VOMITING, DIARRHEA, ABDOMINAL CRAMPS, HEADACHE, VERTIGO, OCULAR PAIN, CILIARY MUSCLE SPASM, BLURRING OR DIMNESS OF VISION, MIOSIS, OR IN SOME CASES MYDRIASIS, LACRIMATION, SALIVATION, SWEATING, AND CONFUSION. OTHER REPORTED CENTRAL NERVOUS SYSTEM OR NEUROMUSCULAR EFFECTS INCLUDE ATAXIA, SLURRED SPEECH, AREFLEXIA, WEAKNESS, FATIGUE, TWITCHING, FASCICULATION, TREMOR, AND EVENTUALLY PARALYSIS OF THE EXTREMITIES AND POSSIBLY OF THE RESPIRATORY MUSCLES. IN SEVERE CASES, THERE MAY ALSO BE INVOLUNTARY DEFECATION AND URINATION, BRADYCARDIA, HYPOTENSION, PULMONARY EDEMA, CONVULSIONS, COMA, AND DEATH FROM RESPIRATORY FAILURE OR CARDIAC ARREST. CARBAMATES GENERALLY DO NOT ACCUMULATE IN MAMMALIAN TISSUE AND THE CHOLINESTERASE INHIBITION REVERSES RATHER RAPIDLY. IN NON-FATAL CASES, THE ILLNESS GENERALLY LASTS LESS THAN 24 HOURS. **CHRONIC EXPOSURE-** PROLONGED OR REPEATED EXPOSURE MAY CAUSE EFFECTS AS DESCRIBED IN ACUTE EXPOSURE.

FIRST AID- REMOVE FROM EXPOSURE AREA TO FRESH AIR IMMEDIATELY. IF BREATHING HAS STOPPED, GIVE ARTIFICIAL RESPIRATION. MAINTAIN AIRWAY AND BLOOD PRESSURE AND ADMINISTER OXYGEN IF AVAILABLE. KEEP AFFECTED PERSON WARM AND AT REST. TREAT SYMPTOMATICALLY AND SUPPORTIVELY. ADMINISTRATION OF OXYGEN SHOULD BE PERFORMED BY QUALIFIED PERSONNEL. GET MEDICAL ATTENTION IMMEDIATELY.

SKIN CONTACT: AMINOCARB: HIGHLY TOXIC. SEE INFORMATION ON CARBAMATES.
CARBAMATES: CHOLINESTERASE INHIBITOR. **ACUTE EXPOSURE-** SOME COMPOUNDS MAY CAUSE IRRITATION. LOCALIZED SWEATING AND FASCICULATIONS MAY OCCUR AT THE SITE OF CONTACT. IF SUFFICIENT AMOUNTS ARE ABSORBED THROUGH THE SKIN, OTHER EFFECTS OF CHOLINESTERASE INHIBITION MAY OCCUR AS DESCRIBED IN ACUTE INHALATION; SYMPTOMS MAY BE DELAYED FOR 2-3 HOURS, USUALLY NO MORE THAN 8 HOURS. **CHRONIC EXPOSURE-** REPEATED OR PROLONGED EXPOSURE MAY CAUSE EFFECTS AS DESCRIBED IN ACUTE EXPOSURE.

FIRST AID- REMOVE CONTAMINATED CLOTHING IMMEDIATELY. WASH CONTAMINATED AREAS WITH SOAP AND WATER FOLLOWED BY ALCOHOL (ARENA, POISONING, 4TH ED.). EMERGENCY PERSONNEL SHOULD WEAR GLOVES AND AVOID CONTAMINATION. TREAT RESPIRATORY DIFFICULTY WITH ARTIFICIAL RESPIRATION. GET MEDICAL ATTENTION IMMEDIATELY.

EYE CONTACT: AMINOCARB: SEE INFORMATION ON CARBAMATES.
CARBAMATES: CHOLINESTERASE INHIBITOR. **ACUTE EXPOSURE-** DIRECT CONTACT MAY CAUSE PAIN, HYPEREMIA, LACRIMATION, TWITCHING OF THE EYELIDS, MIOSIS, AND CILIARY MUSCLE SPASM WITH LOSS OF ACCOMODATION, BLURRED OR DIMMED VISION AND BROWACHE. SOMETIMES MYDRIASIS MAY OCCUR INSTEAD OF MIOSIS. WITH SUFFICIENT EXPOSURE, OTHER SYMPTOMS OF CHOLINESTERASE INHIBITION MAY OCCUR AS DESCRIBED IN ACUTE INHALATION. **CHRONIC EXPOSURE-** PROLONGED EXPOSURE MAY CAUSE EFFECTS AS DESCRIBED IN ACUTE EXPOSURE. SOME COMPOUNDS HAVE CAUSED TOXIC EFFECTS ON THE CRYSTALLINE LENS, CONJUNCTIVAL THICKENING AND OBSTRUCTION OF NASOLACRIMAL CANALS WHEN USED AS MIOTIC EYE DROPS.

FIRST AID- IRRIGATE EYES WITH WATER OR SALINE SOLUTION. IF SYMPTOMS OF POISONING OCCUR, TREAT RESPIRATORY DIFFICULTY WITH ARTIFICIAL RESPIRATION AND OXYGEN. OBSERVE PATIENT FOR AT LEAST 24-36 HOURS (GOSSELIN, CLINICAL TOXICOLOGY OF COMMERCIAL PRODUCTS, 5TH ED.). GET MEDICAL ATTENTION IMMEDIATELY. OXYGEN SHOULD BE ADMINISTERED BY QUALIFIED MEDICAL PERSONNEL.

INGESTION: AMINOCARB: HIGHLY TOXIC. SEE INFORMATION ON CARBAMATES.
CARBAMATES: CHOLINESTERASE INHIBITOR. **ACUTE EXPOSURE-** WHEN INGESTED, THE FIRST EFFECTS MAY BE NAUSEA, VOMITING, ANOREXIA, ABDOMINAL CRAMPS, AND DIARRHEA. WITH ABSORPTION FROM THE GASTROINTESTINAL TRACT, THE OTHER EFFECTS OF CHOLINESTERASE INHIBITION AS DESCRIBED IN ACUTE INHALATION MAY OCCUR; SYMPTOMS MAY BEGIN WITHIN MINUTES OR BE DELAYED SEVERAL HOURS. **CHRONIC EXPOSURE-** REPEATED INGESTION MAY CAUSE EFFECTS AS DESCRIBED IN ACUTE EXPOSURE.

FIRST AID- IF PERSON IS ALERT AND RESPIRATION IS NOT DEPRESSED, GIVE SYRUP OF IPECAC FOLLOWED BY WATER (IF VOMITING OCCURS, KEEP HEAD BELOW HIPS TO PREVENT ASPIRATION). IF CONSCIOUSNESS LEVEL DECLINES OR VOMITING HAS NOT OCCURRED IN 15 MINUTES EMPTY STOMACH BY GASTRIC LAVAGE WITH THE AID OF CUFFED ENDOTRACHEAL TUBE USING ISOTONIC SALINE OR 5% SODIUM BICARBONATE FOLLOW WITH ACTIVATED CHARCOAL. ESTABLISH AND MAINTAIN AIRWAY. TREAT RESPIRATORY DIFFICULTY WITH ARTIFICIAL RESPIRATION AND OXYGEN. DO NOT GIVE MORPHINE, AMINOPHYLLINE, PHENOTHIAZINES, RESERPINE, FUROSEMIDE, OR ETHACRYNIC ACID (MORGAN, RECOGNITION AND MANAGEMENT OF PESTICIDE POISONINGS, 3RD ED.). TREAT SYMPTOMATICALLY AND SUPPORTIVELY. ADMINISTRATION OF OXYGEN AND LAVAGE MUST BE PERFORMED BY QUALIFIED MEDICAL PERSONNEL. GET MEDICAL ATTENTION IMMEDIATELY.

ANTIDOTE: THE FOLLOWING ANTIDOTE HAS BEEN RECOMMENDED. HOWEVER, THE DECISION AS TO WHETHER THE SEVERITY OF POISONING REQUIRES ADMINISTRATION OF ANY ANTIDOTE AND ACTUAL DOSE REQUIRED SHOULD BE MADE BY QUALIFIED MEDICAL PERSONNEL.
FOR CHOLINESTERASE INHIBITORS: ESTABLISH CLEAR AIRWAY AND TISSUE OXYGENATION BY ASPIRATION OF SECRETIONS, AND IF NECESSARY, BY ASSISTED PULMONARY VENTILATION WITH OXYGEN. IMPROVE TISSUE OXYGENATION AS MUCH AS POSSIBLE BEFORE ADMINISTERING ATROPINE TO MINIMIZE THE RISK OF VENTRICULAR FIBRILLATION. ADMINISTER ATROPINE SULFATE INTRAVENOUSLY, OR INTRAMUSCULARLY IF IV INJECTION IS NOT POSSIBLE. IN MODERATELY SEVERE POISONING ADMINISTER ATROPINE SULFATE, 0.4-2.0 MG REPEATED EVERY 15 MINUTES UNTIL ATROPINIZATION IS ACHIEVED (TACHYCARDIA, FLUSHING, DRY MOUTH, MYDRIASIS). MAINTAIN ATROPINIZATION BY REPEATED DOSES FOR 2-12 HOURS, OR LONGER, DEPENDING ON THE SEVERITY OF POISONING. THE APPEARANCE OF RALES IN THE LUNG BASES, MIOSIS, SALIVATION, NAUSEA, BRADYCARDIA, ARE ALL INDICATIONS OF INADEQUATE ATROPINIZATION. SEVERELY POISONED INDIVIDUALS MAY EXHIBIT REMARKABLE TOLERANCE TO ATROPINE; TWO OR MORE TIMES THE DOSAGES SUGGESTED ABOVE MAY BE NEEDED. PERSONS NOT POISONED OR ONLY SLIGHTLY POISONED, HOWEVER, MAY DEVELOP SIGNS OF ATROPINE TOXICITY FROM SUCH LARGE DOSAGES: FEVER, MUSCLE FIBRILLATIONS, AND DELIRIUM ARE THE MAIN SIGNS OF ATROPINE TOXICITY. IF THESE SIGNS APPEAR WHILE THE PATIENT IS FULLY ATROPINIZED, ATROPINE ADMINISTRATION SHOULD BE DISCONTINUED, AT LEAST TEMPORARILY. OBSERVE TREATED PATIENTS CLOSELY AT LEAST 24 HOURS TO INSURE THAT SYMPTOMS (POSSIBLY PULMONARY EDEMA) DO NOT RECUR AS ATROPINIZATION WEARS OFF. IN VERY SEVERE POISONINGS, METABOLIC DISPOSITION OF TOXICANT MAY REQUIRE SEVERAL HOURS OR DAYS DURING WHICH ATROPINIZATION MUST BE MAINTAINED. MARKEDLY LOWER LEVELS OF URINARY METABOLITES INDICATE THAT ATROPINE DOSAGE CAN BE TAPERED OFF. AS DOSAGE IS REDUCED, CHECK THE LUNG BASES FREQUENTLY FOR RALES. IF RALES ARE HEARD OR OTHER SYMPTOMS RETURN, RE-ESTABLISH ATROPINIZATION PROMPTLY (MORGAN, RECOGNITION AND MANAGEMENT OF PESTICIDE POISONINGS, 3RD ED.). ADMINISTRATION OF ANTIDOTE MUST BE PERFORMED BY QUALIFIED MEDICAL PERSONNEL.

REACTIVITY

REACTIVITY: STABLE UNDER NORMAL TEMPERATURES AND PRESSURES.

INCOMPATIBILITIES: AMINOCARB: ALKALI: HYDROLYZES.

DECOMPOSITION: THERMAL DECOMPOSITION PRODUCTS MAY INCLUDE TOXIC OXIDES OF CARBON AND NITROGEN.

POLYMERIZATION: HAZARDOUS POLYMERIZATION HAS NOT BEEN REPORTED TO OCCUR UNDER NORMAL TEMPERATURES AND PRESSURES.

STORAGE AND DISPOSAL

OBSERVE ALL FEDERAL, STATE AND LOCAL REGULATIONS WHEN STORING OR DISPOSING OF THIS SUBSTANCE. FOR ASSISTANCE, CONTACT THE DISTRICT DIRECTOR OF THE ENVIRONMENTAL PROTECTION AGENCY.

STORAGE

STORE IN ACCORDANCE WITH 40 CFR 165 RECOMMENDED PROCEDURES FOR THE DISPOSAL AND STORAGE OF PESTICIDES AND PESTICIDE CONTAINERS.
STORE AWAY FROM INCOMPATIBLE SUBSTANCES.

DISPOSAL

DISPOSAL MUST BE IN ACCORDANCE WITH 40 CFR 165 RECOMMENDED PROCEDURES FOR THE DISPOSAL AND STORAGE OF PESTICIDES AND PESTICIDE CONTAINERS.

CONDITIONS TO AVOID

MAY BURN BUT DOES NOT IGNITE READILY. CONTAINERS MAY EXPLODE IN HEAT OF FIRE.

SPILL AND LEAK PROCEDURES

OCCUPATIONAL SPILL: DO NOT TOUCH SPILLED MATERIAL. STOP LEAK IF YOU CAN DO IT WITHOUT RISK. USE WATER SPRAY TO REDUCE VAPORS. FOR SMALL SPILLS, TAKE UP WITH SAND OR OTHER ABSORBENT MATERIAL AND PLACE INTO CONTAINERS FOR LATER DISPOSAL. FOR SMALL DRY SPILLS, WITH A CLEAN SHOVEL PLACE MATERIAL INTO CLEAN, DRY CONTAINERS AND COVER. MOVE CONTAINERS FROM SPILL AREA. FOR LARGER SPILLS, DIKE FAR AHEAD OF SPILL FOR LATER DISPOSAL. KEEP UNNECESSARY PEOPLE AWAY. ISOLATE HAZARD AREA AND DENY ENTRY. VENTILATE CLOSED SPACES BEFORE ENTERING.

PROTECTIVE EQUIPMENT

VENTILATION: PROVIDE LOCAL EXHAUST OR PROCESS ENCLOSURE VENTILATION SYSTEM.

RESPIRATOR: THE FOLLOWING RESPIRATORS ARE RECOMMENDED BASED ON INFORMATION FOUND IN THE PHYSICAL DATA, TOXICITY AND HEALTH EFFECTS SECTIONS. THEY ARE RANKED IN ORDER FROM MINIMUM TO MAXIMUM RESPIRATORY PROTECTION. THE SPECIFIC RESPIRATOR SELECTED MUST BE BASED ON CONTAMINATION LEVELS FOUND IN THE WORK PLACE, MUST NOT EXCEED THE WORKING LIMITS OF THE RESPIRATOR AND BE JOINTLY APPROVED BY THE NATIONAL INSTITUTE FOR OCCUPATIONAL SAFETY AND HEALTH AND THE MINE SAFETY AND HEALTH ADMINISTRATION (NIOSH-MSHA).

TYPE 'C' SUPPLIED-AIR RESPIRATOR WITH A FULL FACEPIECE OPERATED IN PRESSURE-DEMAND OR OTHER POSITIVE PRESSURE MODE OR WITH A FULL FACEPIECE, HELMET OR HOOD OPERATED IN CONTINOUS-FLOW MODE.

SELF-CONTAINED BREATHING APPARATUS WITH A FULL FACEPIECE OPERATED IN PRESSURE-DEMAND OR OTHER POSITIVE PRESSURE MODE.

FOR FIREFIGHTING AND OTHER IMMEDIATELY DANGEROUS TO LIFE OR HEALTH CONDITIONS:

SELF-CONTAINED BREATHING APPARATUS WITH FULL FACEPIECE OPERATED IN PRESSURE-DEMAND OR OTHER POSITIVE PRESSURE MODE.

SUPPLIED-AIR RESPIRATOR WITH FULL FACEPIECE AND OPERATED IN PRESSURE-DEMAND OR OTHER POSITIVE PRESSURE MODE IN COMBINATION WITH AN AUXILIARY SELF-CONTAINED BREATHING APPARATUS OPERATED IN PRESSURE-DEMAND OR OTHER POSITIVE PRESSURE MODE.

CLOTHING: EMPLOYEE MUST WEAR APPROPRIATE PROTECTIVE (IMPERVIOUS) CLOTHING AND EQUIPMENT TO PREVENT ANY POSSIBILITY OF SKIN CONTACT WITH THIS SUBSTANCE.

GLOVES: EMPLOYEE MUST WEAR APPROPRIATE PROTECTIVE GLOVES TO PREVENT CONTACT WITH THIS SUBSTANCE.

EYE PROTECTION: EMPLOYEE MUST WEAR SPLASH-PROOF OR DUST-RESISTANT SAFETY GOGGLES AND A FACESHIELD TO PREVENT CONTACT WITH THIS SUBSTANCE.

EMERGENCY WASH FACILITIES: WHERE THERE IS ANY POSSIBILITY THAT AN EMPLOYEE'S EYES AND/OR SKIN MAY BE EXPOSED TO THIS SUBSTANCE, THE EMPLOYER SHOULD PROVIDE AN EYE WASH FOUNTAIN AND QUICK DRENCH SHOWER WITHIN THE IMMEDIATE WORK AREA FOR EMERGENCY USE.

AUTHORIZED BY- OCCUPATIONAL HEALTH SERVICES, INC.
CREATION DATE: 10/04/89 ***REVISION DATE:*** 06/12/90

MATERIAL SAFETY DATA SHEET

OCCUPATIONAL HEALTH SERVICES, INC.
AGRICULTURE AND PESTICIDE DIVISION
450 SEVENTH AVENUE, SUITE 2407
NEW YORK, NEW YORK 10123
1-800-445-MSDS OR (212) 967-1100

EMERGENCY CONTACT:
JOHN S. BRANSFORD, JR. (615) 292-1180

SUBSTANCE IDENTIFICATION

CAS-NUMBER 122-42-9

SUBSTANCE: **PROPHAM**

TRADE NAMES/SYNONYMS: CARBAMIC ACID, PHENYL-, 1-METHYLETHYL ESTER; CARBANILIC ACID, ISOPROPYL ESTER; PHENYLCARBAMIC ACID 1-METHYLETHYL ESTER; ISOPROPYL CARBANILATE; ISOPROPYL PHENYLCARBAMATE; ISOPROPYL PHENYL URETHANE; 1-METHYLETHYL PHENYLCARBAMATE; N-PHENYL ISOPROPYL CARBAMATE; O-ISOPROPYL N-PHENYL CARBAMATE; BAN-HOE (FORMULATION); CHEM-HOE (FORMULATION); INPC; IPC; IPPC; PROFAM; PREMALOX (FORMULATION); TUBERITE (FORMULATION); C10H13NO2; PST71564

CHEMICAL FAMILY: CARBAMATE

MOLECULAR FORMULA: C6-H5-N-H-C-O2-CH-(C-H3)2

MOLECULAR WEIGHT: 179.22

CERCLA RATINGS (SCALE 0-3): HEALTH=3 FIRE=1 REACTIVITY=0 PERSISTENCE=1

NFPA RATINGS (SCALE 0-4): HEALTH=U FIRE=1 REACTIVITY=0

COMPONENTS AND CONTAMINANTS

COMPONENT: PROPHAM ***PERCENT:*** 100.0
CAS# 122-42-9

EXPOSURE LIMITS: NO OCCUPATIONAL EXPOSURE LIMITS ESTABLISHED BY OSHA, ACGIH, OR NIOSH.

PHYSICAL DATA

DESCRIPTION: COLORLESS, CRYSTALLINE SOLID WITH A FAINT AMINE-LIKE ODOR.

MELTING POINT: 194 F (90 C) ***SPECIFIC GRAVITY:*** 1.09 @ 30 C

SOLUBILITY IN WATER: 32-250 PPM

SOLVENT SOLUBILITY: SOLUBLE IN CARBON DISULFIDE, ACETONE, BENZENE, XYLENE, ETHANOL, ISOPROPYL ALCOHOL, CYCLOHEXANE, DICHLOROMETHANE, ETHER, ESTERS, AND MOST ORGANIC SOLVENTS; SLIGHTLY SOLUBLE IN KEROSENE AND DIESEL OIL.

SUBLIMES ABOVE 302 F (150 C)

FIRE AND EXPLOSION DATA

FIRE AND EXPLOSION HAZARD: SLIGHT FIRE HAZARD WHEN EXPOSED TO HEAT OR FLAME.

FIREFIGHTING MEDIA: DRY CHEMICAL, CARBON DIOXIDE, HALON, WATER SPRAY OR STANDARD FOAM (1987 EMERGENCY RESPONSE GUIDEBOOK, DOT P 5800.4).

FOR LARGER FIRES, USE WATER SPRAY, FOG OR STANDARD FOAM (1987 EMERGENCY RESPONSE GUIDEBOOK, DOT P 5800.4).

FIREFIGHTING: MOVE CONTAINER FROM FIRE AREA IF POSSIBLE. DO NOT SCATTER SPILLED MATERIAL WITH HIGH PRESSURE WATER STREAMS. DIKE FIRE CONTROL WATER FOR LATER DISPOSAL (1987 EMERGENCY RESPONSE GUIDEBOOK, DOT P 5800.4, GUIDE PAGE 31).

USE AGENTS SUITABLE FOR TYPE OF SURROUNDING FIRE. AVOID BREATHING HAZARDOUS VAPORS, KEEP UPWIND.

TOXICITY

PROPHAM: TOXICITY DATA: 714 MG/KG ORAL-HUMAN LDLO; 1000 MG/KG ORAL-RAT LD50; 2160 MG/KG ORAL-MOUSE LD50; 600 MG/KG INTRAPERITONEAL-RAT LD50; >3000 MG/KG SKIN-RABBIT LD50 (EPA, PESTICIDE FACT SHEET 1987); 200 MG/KG INTRAPERITONEAL-MOUSE LD50; 1000 MG/KG UNREPORTED-MAMMAL LD50; MUTAGENIC DATA (RTECS); REPRODUCTIVE EFFECTS DATA (RTECS); TUMORIGENIC DATA (RTECS). CARCINOGEN STATUS: ANIMAL INADEQUATE EVIDENCE (IARC GROUP-3). ORALLY ADMINISTERED PROPHAM ACTED AS AN INITIATOR IN TWO-STAGE CARCINOGENESIS STUDIES IN MICE. ACUTE TOXICITY: MODERATELY TOXIC BY INGESTION; SLIGHTLY TOXIC BY DERMAL ABSORPTION. TARGET EFFECTS: NO DATA AVAILABLE.

HEALTH EFFECTS AND FIRST AID

INHALATION: PROPHAM: **ACUTE EXPOSURE-** NO DEATHS WERE OBSERVED IN RATS EXPOSED TO A CONCENTRATION OF 55 MG/M3/6 HOURS. **CHRONIC EXPOSURE-** OCCUPATIONAL EXPOSURE TO ANILINE AND OTHER CHEMICALS DURING THE MANUFACTURE OF PROPHAM PRODUCED A RISE IN METHEMOGLOBIN CONTENT, THE APPEARANCE OF HEINZ CORPULSCLES, AND THE DEVELOPMENT OF UNSTABLE ANEMIA.

FIRST AID- REMOVE FROM EXPOSURE AREA TO FRESH AIR IMMEDIATELY. IF BREATHING HAS STOPPED, PERFORM ARTIFICIAL RESPIRATION. KEEP PERSON WARM AND AT REST. TREAT SYMPTOMATICALLY AND SUPPORTIVELY. GET MEDICAL ATTENTION IMMEDIATELY.

SKIN CONTACT: PROPHAM: **ACUTE EXPOSURE-** THE LD50 IN RABBITS WAS GREATER THAN 3000 MG/KG. **CHRONIC EXPOSURE-** OCCUPATIONAL EXPOSURE TO ANILINE AND OTHER CHEMICALS DURING THE MANUFACTURE OF PROPHAM PRODUCED A RISE IN METHEMOGLOBIN CONTENT, THE APPEARANCE OF HEINZ CORPUSCLES, AND THE DEVELOPMENT OF UNSTABLE ANEMIA.

FIRST AID- REMOVE CONTAMINATED CLOTHING AND SHOES IMMEDIATELY. WASH AFFECTED AREA WITH SOAP OR MILD DETERGENT AND LARGE AMOUNTS OF WATER UNTIL NO EVIDENCE OF CHEMICAL REMAINS (APPROXIMATELY 15-20 MINUTES). GET MEDICAL ATTENTION IMMEDIATELY.

EYE CONTACT: PROPHAM: **ACUTE EXPOSURE-** NO DATA AVAILABLE. **CHRONIC EXPOSURE-** NO DATA AVAILABLE.
FIRST AID- WASH EYES IMMEDIATELY WITH LARGE AMOUNTS OF WATER OR NORMAL SALINE, OCCASIONALLY LIFTING UPPER AND LOWER LIDS, UNTIL NO EVIDENCE OF CHEMICAL REMAINS (APPROXIMATELY 15-20 MINUTES). GET MEDICAL ATTENTION IMMEDIATELY.

INGESTION: PROPHAM: **ACUTE EXPOSURE-** SYMPTOMS OF POISONING IN RATS, REPORTED IN ONE STUDY OF PROPHAM OF UNSPECIFIED PURITY, INCLUDED CHANGES IN THE BLOOD, METHEMOGLOBIN FORMATION, DEVELOPMENT OF ANEMIA WITH RETICULOCYTOSIS AND POLYCHROMATOPHILIA, AND LYMPHOCYTOSIS. **CHRONIC EXPOSURE-** DECREASED BODY WEIGHT AND CHANGES IN THE BLOOD WERE OBSERVED IN RATS ADMINISTERED PROPHAM OF UNSPECIFIED PURITY.
FIRST AID- IF THE PERSON IS CONSCIOUS AND NOT CONVULSING, REMOVE BY GASTRIC LAVAGE AND FOLLOW WITH A CATHARTIC (DREISBACH, HANDBOOK OF POISONING, 12TH ED.). TREAT SYMPTOMATICALLY AND SUPPORTIVELY. GASTRIC LAVAGE SHOULD BE PERFORMED BY QUALIFIED MEDICAL PERSONNEL. GET MEDICAL ATTENTION IMMEDIATELY.
ANTIDOTE: NO SPECIFIC ANTIDOTE. TREAT SYMPTOMATICALLY AND SUPPORTIVELY.

REACTIVITY

REACTIVITY: STABLE UNDER NORMAL TEMPERATURES AND PRESSURES.
INCOMPATIBILITIES: PROPHAM: OXIDIZERS (STRONG): FIRE AND EXPLOSION HAZARD.
DECOMPOSITION: THERMAL DECOMPOSITION PRODUCTS MAY INCLUDE TOXIC OXIDES OF CARBON AND NITROGEN.
POLYMERIZATION: HAZARDOUS POLYMERIZATION HAS NOT BEEN REPORTED TO OCCUR UNDER NORMAL TEMPERATURES AND PRESSURES.

STORAGE AND DISPOSAL

OBSERVE ALL FEDERAL, STATE AND LOCAL REGULATIONS WHEN STORING OR DISPOSING OF THIS SUBSTANCE. FOR ASSISTANCE, CONTACT THE DISTRICT DIRECTOR OF THE ENVIRONMENTAL PROTECTION AGENCY.

STORAGE

STORE IN ACCORDANCE WITH 40 CFR 165 RECOMMENDED PROCEDURES FOR THE DISPOSAL AND STORAGE OF PESTICIDES AND PESTICIDE CONTAINERS.
STORE AWAY FROM INCOMPATIBLE SUBSTANCES.

DISPOSAL

DISPOSAL MUST BE IN ACCORDANCE WITH 40 CFR 165 RECOMMENDED PROCEDURES FOR THE DISPOSAL AND STORAGE OF PESTICIDES AND PESTICIDE CONTAINERS.

CONDITIONS TO AVOID

MAY BURN BUT DOES NOT IGNITE READILY. AVOID CONTACT WITH STRONG OXIDIZERS, EXCESSIVE HEAT, SPARKS, OR OPEN FLAME.

SPILL AND LEAK PROCEDURES

OCCUPATIONAL SPILL: SWEEP UP AND PLACE IN SUITABLE CLEAN, DRY CONTAINERS FOR RECLAMATION OR LATER DISPOSAL. DO NOT FLUSH SPILLED MATERIAL INTO SEWER. KEEP UNNECESSARY PEOPLE AWAY.

PROTECTIVE EQUIPMENT

VENTILATION: PROVIDE LOCAL EXHAUST OR GENERAL DILUTION VENTILATION SYSTEM.
RESPIRATOR: THE FOLLOWING RESPIRATORS ARE RECOMMENDED BASED ON INFORMATION FOUND IN THE PHYSICAL DATA, TOXICITY AND HEALTH EFFECTS SECTIONS. THEY ARE RANKED IN ORDER FROM MINIMUM TO MAXIMUM RESPIRATORY PROTECTION. THE SPECIFIC RESPIRATOR SELECTED MUST BE BASED ON CONTAMINATION LEVELS FOUND IN THE WORK PLACE, MUST NOT EXCEED THE WORKING LIMITS OF THE RESPIRATOR AND BE JOINTLY APPROVED BY THE NATIONAL INSTITUTE FOR OCCUPATIONAL SAFETY AND HEALTH AND THE MINE SAFETY AND HEALTH ADMINISTRATION (NIOSH-MSHA).
CHEMICAL CARTRIDGE RESPIRATOR WITH AN ORGANIC VAPOR CARTRIDGE(S) IN COMBINATION WITH A DUST AND MIST FILTER.
GAS MASK WITH ORGANIC VAPOR CANISTER (CHIN-STYLE OR FRONT- OR BACK-MOUNTED CANISTER) WITH A DUST AND MIST FILTER.
GAS MASK WITH ORGANIC VAPOR CANISTER (CHIN-STYLE OR FRONT- OR BACK-MOUNTED CANISTER) WITH A PARTICULATE FILTER.
POWERED AIR-PURIFYING RESPIRATOR WITH A HIGH-EFFICIENCY FILTER.
TYPE 'C' SUPPLIED-AIR RESPIRATOR WITH A FULL FACEPIECE OPERATED IN A PRESSURE-DEMAND OR OTHER POSITIVE PRESSURE MODE.
SELF-CONTAINED BREATHING APPARATUS WITH A FULL FACEPIECE OPERATED IN PRESSURE-DEMAND OR OTHER POSITIVE PRESSURE MODE.
FOR FIREFIGHTING AND OTHER IMMEDIATELY DANGEROUS TO LIFE OR HEALTH CONDITIONS:
SELF-CONTAINED BREATHING APPARATUS WITH FULL FACEPIECE OPERATED IN PRESSURE-DEMAND OR OTHER POSITIVE PRESSURE MODE.
SUPPLIED-AIR RESPIRATOR WITH FULL FACEPIECE AND OPERATED IN PRESSURE-DEMAND OR OTHER POSITIVE PRESSURE MODE IN COMBINATION WITH AN AUXILIARY SELF-CONTAINED BREATHING APPARATUS OPERATED IN PRESSURE-DEMAND OR OTHER POSITIVE PRESSURE MODE.
CLOTHING: EMPLOYEE MUST WEAR APPROPRIATE PROTECTIVE (IMPERVIOUS) CLOTHING AND EQUIPMENT TO PREVENT REPEATED OR PROLONGED SKIN CONTACT WITH THIS SUBSTANCE.
GLOVES: EMPLOYEE MUST WEAR APPROPRIATE PROTECTIVE GLOVES TO PREVENT CONTACT WITH THIS SUBSTANCE.
EYE PROTECTION: EMPLOYEE MUST WEAR SPLASH-PROOF OR DUST-RESISTANT SAFETY GOGGLES TO PREVENT EYE CONTACT WITH THIS SUBSTANCE.
EMERGENCY EYE WASH: WHERE THERE IS ANY POSSIBILITY THAT AN EMPLOYEE'S EYES MAY BE EXPOSED TO THIS SUBSTANCE, THE EMPLOYER SHOULD PROVIDE AN EYE WASH FOUNTAIN WITHIN THE IMMEDIATE WORK AREA FOR EMERGENCY USE.

AUTHORIZED BY- OCCUPATIONAL HEALTH SERVICES, INC.
CREATION DATE: 11/14/89 ***REVISION DATE:*** 07/12/90

MATERIAL SAFETY DATA SHEET

OCCUPATIONAL HEALTH SERVICES, INC.
AGRICULTURE AND PESTICIDE DIVISION
450 SEVENTH AVENUE, SUITE 2407
NEW YORK, NEW YORK 10123
1-800-445-MSDS OR (212) 967-1100

EMERGENCY CONTACT:
JOHN S. BRANSFORD, JR. (615) 292-1180

SUBSTANCE IDENTIFICATION

CAS-NUMBER 119-12-0
SUBSTANCE: **PYRIDAPHENTHION**
TRADE NAMES/SYNONYMS: PHOSPHOROTHIOIC ACID, O-(1,6-DIHYDRO-6-OXO-1-PHENYL-3-PYRIDAZINYL) O,O-DIETHYL ESTER; O-(1,6-DIHYDRO-6-OXO-1-PHENYL-3-PYRIDAZINYL) O,O-DIETHYL PHOSPHOROTHIOATE; PHOSPHOROTHIOIC ACID, O,O-DIETHYL ESTER, O-ESTER WITH 6-HYDROXY -2-PHENYL-3(2H)-PYRIDAZINONE; O,O-DIETHYLPHOSPHOROTHIOATE, O-ESTER WITH 6-HYDROXY-2-PHENYL -3(2H)-PYRIDAZINONE; OFUNACK; OFNACK; PYRIDAFENTHION; C14H17N2O4PS; PST71604
CHEMICAL FAMILY: PHOSPHOROTHIOATE
MOLECULAR FORMULA: C14-H17-N2-O4-P-S
MOLECULAR WEIGHT: 340.36
CERCLA RATINGS (SCALE 0-3): HEALTH=2 FIRE=1 REACTIVITY=0 PERSISTENCE=1
NFPA RATINGS (SCALE 0-4): HEALTH=2 FIRE=1 REACTIVITY=0

COMPONENTS AND CONTAMINANTS

COMPONENT: PYRIDAPHENTHION ***PERCENT:*** 100.0
CAS# 119-12-0
OTHER CONTAMINANTS: NONE
EXPOSURE LIMITS: NO OCCUPATIONAL EXPOSURE LIMITS ESTABLISHED BY OSHA, ACGIH, OR NIOSH.

PHYSICAL DATA

DESCRIPTION: YELLOW CRYSTALLINE POWDER.
MELTING POINT: 131-133 F (55-56 C)
SPECIFIC GRAVITY: NOT AVAILABLE ***SOLUBILITY IN WATER:*** INSOLUBLE
SOLVENT SOLUBILITY: SOLUBLE IN MOST ORGANIC SOLVENTS.

FIRE AND EXPLOSION DATA

FIRE AND EXPLOSION HAZARD: SLIGHT FIRE HAZARD WHEN EXPOSED TO HEAT OR FLAME.
FIREFIGHTING MEDIA: DRY CHEMICAL, CARBON DIOXIDE, HALON, WATER SPRAY OR STANDARD FOAM (1987 EMERGENCY RESPONSE GUIDEBOOK, DOT P 5800.4).
FOR LARGER FIRES, USE WATER SPRAY, FOG OR STANDARD FOAM (1987 EMERGENCY RESPONSE GUIDEBOOK, DOT P 5800.4).
FIREFIGHTING: MOVE CONTAINERS FROM FIRE AREA IF POSSIBLE. FIGHT FIRE FROM MAXIMUM DISTANCE. STAY AWAY FROM STORAGE TANK ENDS. DIKE FIRE CONTROL WATER FOR LATER DISPOSAL. DO NOT SCATTER MATERIAL (1987 EMERGENCY RESPONSE GUIDEBOOK, DOT P 5800.4, GUIDE PAGE 55).
EXTINGUISH ONLY IF FLOW CAN BE STOPPED; USE FLOODING AMOUNTS OF WATER AS FOG, SOLID STREAMS MAY BE INEFFECTIVE. COOL CONTAINERS WITH

FLOODING AMOUNTS OF WATER FROM AS FAR A DISTANCE AS POSSIBLE. USE WATER SPRAY TO ABSORB TOXIC VAPORS. AVOID BREATHING TOXIC VAPORS; KEEP UPWIND. CONSIDER EVACUATION OF DOWNWIND AREA IF MATERIAL IS LEAKING.

TOXICITY

PYRIDAPHENTHION: TOXICITY DATA: 769 MG/KG ORAL-RAT LD50; 459 MG/KG ORAL-MOUSE LD50; 2100 MG/KG SKIN-RAT LD50; 64 MG/KG INTRAPERITONEAL-MOUSE LD50. CARCINOGEN STATUS: NONE. ACUTE TOXICITY: MODERATELY TOXIC BY INGESTION; SLIGHTLY TOXIC BY DERMAL ABSORPTION. TARGET EFFECTS: CHOLINESTERASE INHIBITOR. POISONING MAY AFFECT THE NERVOUS SYSTEM.* AT INCREASED RISK FROM EXPOSURE: PERSONS WITH RESPIRATORY AILMENTS, RECENT EXPOSURE TO CHOLINESTERASE INHIBITORS OR IMPAIRED CHOLINESTERASE PRODUCTION, OR LIVER MALFUNCTION.* ADDITIONAL DATA: MAY CROSS THE PLACENTA. HIGH ENVIRONMENTAL TEMPERATURES OR EXPOSURE OF THE CHEMICAL TO VISIBLE OR ULTRAVIOLET LIGHT MAY ENHANCE THE TOXICITY. INTERACTIONS WITH MEDICATIONS MAY OCCUR.*

* MAY BE BASED ON GENERAL INFORMATION ON ORGANOPHOSPHATES.

HEALTH EFFECTS AND FIRST AID

INHALATION: PYRIDAPHENTHION: SEE INFORMATION ON ORGANOPHOSPHATES. ORGANOPHOSPHATES: CHOLINESTERASE INHIBITOR. **ACUTE EXPOSURE-** WHEN INHALED, THE FIRST EFFECTS OF CHOLINESTERASE INHIBITORS ARE USUALLY RESPIRATORY AND MAY INCLUDE NASAL HYPEREMIA AND WATERY DISCHARGE, COUGH, CHEST DISCOMFORT, DYSPNEA, AND WHEEZING DUE TO INCREASED BRONCHIAL SECRETIONS AND BRONCHOCONSTRICTION. IF SUFFICIENT AMOUNTS ARE ABSORBED, OTHER SYSTEMIC EFFECTS MAY BEGIN WITHIN A FEW MINUTES OR BE DELAYED FOR UP TO 12 HOURS. SYMPTOMS MAY INCLUDE PALLOR, NAUSEA, VOMITING, DIARRHEA, ABDOMINAL CRAMPS, HEADACHE, DIZZINESS, OCULAR PAIN, BLURRED VISION, MIOSIS OR IN SOME CASES, ESPECIALLY INITIALLY, MYDRIASIS, LACRIMATION, SALIVATION, SWEATING, AND CONFUSION. OTHER REPORTED CENTRAL NERVOUS SYSTEM OR NEUROMUSCULAR EFFECTS MAY INCLUDE ATAXIA, SLURRED SPEECH, AREFLEXIA, WEAKNESS, FATIGUE, FASCICULATIONS, TWITCHING, TREMORS POSSIBLY OF THE TONGUE AND EYELIDS, AND EVENTUALLY PARALYSIS OF THE EXTREMITIES AND POSSIBLY OF THE RESPIRATORY MUSCLES. IN SEVERE CASES THERE MAY ALSO BE INVOLUNTARY DEFECATION AND URINATION, CYANOSIS, PSYCHOSIS, HYPERGLYCEMIA, ACUTE PANCREATITIS, CARDIAC IRREGULARITIES, PULMONARY EDEMA, UNCONSCIOUSNESS, CONVULSIONS, AND COMA. DEATH IS PRIMARILY DUE TO RESPIRATORY FAILURE, ALTHOUGH CARDIOVASCULAR EFFECTS INCLUDING CARDIAC ARREST MAY ALSO BE IMPLICATED. LONG TERM SEQUELAE ARE RARE BUT MAY INCLUDE NEUROPSYCHIATRIC DISORDERS AND MYOPATHY WITH MUSCLE TENDERNESS. SOME ORGANOPHOSPHATES MAY CAUSE A DELAYED NEUROPATHY BEGINNING 1-4 WEEKS AFTER AN ACUTE EXPOSURE WHICH MAY OR MAY NOT HAVE CAUSED ACUTE CHOLINERGIC EFFECTS. NUMBNESS, TINGLING, WEAKNESS AND CRAMPING BEGINNING SYMMETRICALLY IN THE LOWER LIMBS MAY PROGRESS TO ATAXIA AND PARALYSIS. IN SEVERE CASES, UPPER LIMB INVOLVEMENT IS POSSIBLE AND FLACCID PARALYSIS MAY PROGRESS TO SPASTIC PARALYSIS WITH EXAGGERATED REFLEXES. IMPROVEMENT MAY OCCUR OVER MONTHS TO YEARS, BUT SOME RESIDUAL IMPAIRMENT USUALLY REMAINS. **CHRONIC EXPOSURE-** REPEATED OR PROLONGED EXPOSURE MAY RESULT IN THE EFFECTS OF ACUTE EXPOSURE INCLUDING THE DELAYED NEUROPATHY. OTHER EFFECTS REPORTED IN WORKERS REPEATEDLY EXPOSED INCLUDE IMPAIRED MEMORY AND CONCENTRATION, ACUTE PSYCHOSIS, SEVERE DEPRESSIONS, IRRITABILTY, CONFUSION, APATHY, EMOTIONAL LABILITY, SOCIAL WITHDRAWAL, CONFUSION, HEADACHE, SPEECH DIFFICULTIES, DELAYED REACTION TIMES, SPATIAL DISORIENTATION, NIGHTMARES, SLEEPWALKING, AND DROWSINESS OR INSOMNIA. AN INFLUENZA-LIKE CONDITION WITH HEADACHE, NAUSEA, WEAKNESS, ANOREXIA AND MALAISE HAS ALSO BEEN REPORTED.

FIRST AID- REMOVE FROM EXPOSURE AREA TO FRESH AIR IMMEDIATELY. IF BREATHING HAS STOPPED, GIVE ARTIFICIAL RESPIRATION. MAINTAIN AIRWAY AND BLOOD PRESSURE AND ADMINISTER OXYGEN IF AVAILABLE. KEEP AFFECTED PERSON WARM AND AT REST. TREAT SYMPTOMATICALLY AND SUPPORTIVELY. ADMINISTRATION OF OXYGEN SHOULD BE PERFORMED BY QUALIFIED PERSONNEL. GET MEDICAL ATTENTION IMMEDIATELY.

SKIN CONTACT: PYRIDAPHENTHION: SEE INFORMATION ON ORGANOPOHOSPHATES. ORGANOPHOSPHATES: CHOLINESTERASE INHIBITOR. **ACUTE EXPOSURE-** LOCALIZED SWEATING AND FASCICULATIONS MAY OCCUR AT THE SITE OF CONTACT. IF SUFFICIENT AMOUNTS ARE ABSORBED, OTHER EFFECTS OF CHOLINESTERASE INHIBITION AS DESCRIBED IN ACUTE INHALATION MAY OCCUR. SYMPTOMS MAY BE DELAYED 2-3 HOURS, BUT USUALLY NO MORE THAN 12 HOURS. THE RATE OF ABSORPTION IS INCREASED BY THE PRESENCE OF DERMATITIS OR HIGH AMBIENT TEMPERATURES. DELAYED NEUROPATHY IS ALSO POSSIBLE. **CHRONIC EXPOSURE-** REPEATED OR PROLONGED EXPOSURE MAY CAUSE EFFECTS AS DESCRIBED IN ACUTE EXPOSURE. SOME ORGANOPHOSPHATES MAY CAUSE SENSITIZATION.

FIRST AID- REMOVE CONTAMINATED CLOTHING IMMEDIATELY. WASH CONTAMINATED AREAS WITH SOAP AND WATER FOLLOWED BY ALCOHOL (ARENA, POISONING, 4TH ED.). EMERGENCY PERSONNEL SHOULD WEAR GLOVES AND AVOID CONTAMINATION. TREAT RESPIRATORY DIFFICULTY WITH ARTIFICIAL RESPIRATION. GET MEDICAL ATTENTION IMMEDIATELY.

EYE CONTACT: PYRIDAPHENTHION: SEE INFORMATION ON ORGANOPHOSPHATES. ORGANOPHOSPHATES: CHOLINESTERASE INHIBITOR. **ACUTE EXPOSURE-** DIRECT CONTACT MAY CAUSE PAIN, HYPEREMIA, LACRIMATION, TWITCHING OF THE EYELIDS, MIOSIS, AND CILIARY MUSCLE SPASM WITH LOSS OF ACCOMODATION, BLURRED OR DIMMED VISION AND BROWACHE. SOMETIMES MYDRIASIS MAY OCCUR INSTEAD OF MIOSIS. WITH SUFFICIENT EXPOSURE, OTHER SYMPTOMS OF CHOLINESTERASE INHIBITION AS DESCRIBED IN ACUTE INHALATION MAY OCCUR. **CHRONIC EXPOSURE-** REPEATED OR PROLONGED EXPOSURE MAY CAUSE EFFECTS AS DESCRIBED IN ACUTE EXPOSURE. SOME COMPOUNDS HAVE CAUSED TOXIC EFFECTS ON THE CRYSTALLINE LENS, CONJUNCTIVAL THICKENING AND OBSTRUCTION OF THE NASOLACRIMAL CANALS WHEN USED AS MIOTIC EYEDROPS.

FIRST AID- IRRIGATE EYES WITH WATER OR SALINE SOLUTION. IF SYMPTOMS OF POISONING OCCUR, TREAT RESPIRATORY DIFFICULTY WITH ARTIFICIAL RESPIRATION AND OXYGEN. OBSERVE PATIENT FOR AT LEAST 24-36 HOURS (GOSSELIN, CLINICAL TOXICOLOGY OF COMMERCIAL PRODUCTS, 5TH ED.). GET MEDICAL ATTENTION IMMEDIATELY. OXYGEN SHOULD BE ADMINISTERED BY QUALIFIED MEDICAL PERSONNEL.

INGESTION: PYRIDAPHENTHION: SEE INFORMATION ON ORGANOPHOSPHATES. ORGANOPHOSPHATES: CHOLINESTERASE INHIBITOR. **ACUTE EXPOSURE-** WHEN INGESTED, THE FIRST EFFECTS MAY BE NAUSEA, VOMITING, ANOREXIA, ABDOMINAL CRAMPS AND DIARRHEA. GASTROINTESTINAL ABSORPTION MAY CAUSE SYMPTOMS OF CHOLINESTERASE INHIBITION AS DESCRIBED IN ACUTE INHALATION. SYMPTOMS MAY BEGIN WITHIN MINUTES OR BE DELAYED FOR HOURS. DELAYED EFFECTS INCLUDING NEUROPATHY MAY ALSO OCCUR. **CHRONIC EXPOSURE-** REPEATED INGESTION MAY CAUSE EFFECTS AS DESCRIBED IN ACUTE EXPOSURE.

FIRST AID- IF PERSON IS ALERT AND RESPIRATION IS NOT DEPRESSED, GIVE SYRUP OF IPECAC FOLLOWED BY WATER (IF VOMITING OCCURS, KEEP HEAD BELOW HIPS TO PREVENT ASPIRATION). IF CONSCIOUSNESS LEVEL DECLINES OR VOMITING HAS NOT OCCURRED IN 15 MINUTES EMPTY STOMACH BY GASTRIC LAVAGE WITH THE AID OF CUFFED ENDOTRACHEAL TUBE USING ISOTONIC SALINE OR 5% SODIUM BICARBONATE FOLLOW WITH ACTIVATED CHARCOAL. ESTABLISH AND MAINTAIN AIRWAY. TREAT RESPIRATORY DIFFICULTY WITH ARTIFICIAL RESPIRATION AND OXYGEN. DO NOT GIVE MORPHINE, AMINOPHYLLINE, PHENOTHIAZINES, RESERPINE, FUROSEMIDE, OR ETHACRYNIC ACID (MORGAN, RECOGNITION AND MANAGEMENT OF PESTICIDE POISONINGS, 3RD ED.). TREAT SYMPTOMATICALLY AND SUPPORTIVELY. ADMINISTRATION OF OXYGEN AND LAVAGE MUST BE PERFORMED BY QUALIFIED MEDICAL PERSONNEL. GET MEDICAL ATTENTION IMMEDIATELY.

ANTIDOTE: THE FOLLOWING ANTIDOTE(S) HAVE BEEN RECOMMENDED. HOWEVER, THE DECISION AS TO WHETHER THE SEVERITY OF POISONING REQUIRES ADMINISTRATION OF ANY ANTIDOTE AND ACTUAL DOSE REQUIRED SHOULD BE MADE BY QUALIFIED MEDICAL PERSONNEL.

FOR CHOLINESTERASE INHIBITORS: ESTABLISH CLEAR AIRWAY AND TISSUE OXYGENATION BY ASPIRATION OF SECRETIONS, AND IF NECESSARY, BY ASSISTED PULMONARY VENTILATION WITH OXYGEN. IMPROVE TISSUE OXYGENATION AS MUCH AS POSSIBLE BEFORE ADMINISTERING ATROPINE TO MINIMIZE THE RISK OF VENTRICULAR FIBRILLATION. ADMINISTER ATROPINE SULFATE INTRAVENOUSLY, OR INTRAMUSCULARLY IF IV INJECTION IS NOT POSSIBLE. IN MODERATELY SEVERE POISONING ADMINISTER ATROPINE SULFATE, 0.4-2.0 MG REPEATED EVERY 15 MINUTES UNTIL ATROPINIZATION IS ACHIEVED (TACHYCARDIA, FLUSHING, DRY MOUTH, MYDRIASIS). MAINTAIN ATROPINIZATION BY REPEATED DOSES FOR 2-12 HOURS, OR LONGER, DEPENDING ON THE SEVERITY OF POISONING. THE APPEARANCE OF RALES IN THE LUNG BASES, MIOSIS, SALIVATION, NAUSEA, BRADYCARDIA, ARE ALL INDICATIONS OF INADEQUATE ATROPINIZATION. SEVERELY POISONED INDIVIDUALS MAY EXHIBIT REMARKABLE TOLERANCE TO ATROPINE; TWO OR MORE TIMES THE DOSAGES SUGGESTED ABOVE MAY BE NEEDED. PERSONS NOT POISONED OR ONLY SLIGHTLY POISONED, HOWEVER, MAY DEVELOP SIGNS OF ATROPINE TOXICITY FROM SUCH LARGE DOSAGES: FEVER, MUSCLE FIBRILLATIONS, AND DELIRIUM ARE THE MAIN SIGNS OF ATROPINE TOXICITY. IF THESE SIGNS APPEAR WHILE THE PATIENT IS FULLY ATROPINIZED, ATROPINE ADMINISTRATION SHOULD BE DISCONTINUED, AT LEAST TEMPORARILY. OBSERVE TREATED PATIENTS CLOSELY AT LEAST 24 HOURS TO INSURE THAT SYMPTOMS (POSSIBLY PULMONARY EDEMA) DO NOT RECUR AS ATROPINIZATION WEARS OFF. IN VERY SEVERE POISONINGS, METABOLIC DISPOSITION OF TOXICANT MAY REQUIRE SEVERAL HOURS OR DAYS DURING WHICH ATROPINIZATION MUST BE MAINTAINED. MARKEDLY LOWER LEVELS OF URINARY METABOLITES INDICATE THAT ATROPINE DOSAGE CAN BE TAPERED OFF. AS

DOSAGE IS REDUCED, CHECK THE LUNG BASES FREQUENTLY FOR RALES. IF RALES ARE HEARD OR OTHER SYMPTOMS RETURN, RE-ESTABLISH ATROPINIZATION PROMPTLY (MORGAN, RECOGNITION AND MANAGEMENT OF PESTICIDE POISONINGS, 3RD ED.). ADMINISTRATION OF ANTIDOTE MUST BE PERFORMED BY QUALIFIED MEDICAL PERSONNEL.
IN CASES OF SEVERE POISONING BY ORGANOPHOSPHATE PESTICIDES IN WHICH RESPIRATORY DEPRESSION, MUSCLE WEAKNESS AND TWITCHINGS ARE SEVERE, GIVE PRALIDOXIME (PROTOPAM-AYERST, 2-PAM), 1.0 GRAM INTRAVENOUSLY AT NO MORE THAN 0.5 GRAM PER MINUTE. DOSAGE OF PRALIDOXIME MAY BE REPEATED IN 1-2 HOURS, THEN AT 10-12 HOUR INTERVALS IF NEEDED. IN VERY SEVERE POISONINGS, DOSAGE RATES MAY BE DOUBLED. TREATMENT WITH PRALIDOXIME WILL BE MOST EFFECTIVE IF GIVEN WITHIN THIRTY-SIX HOURS AFTER POISONING (MORGAN, RECOGNITION AND MANAGEMENT OF PESTICIDE POISONINGS, 3RD ED.). ANTIDOTE SHOULD BE ADMINISTERED BY QUALIFIED MEDICAL PERSONNEL.

REACTIVITY

REACTIVITY: STABLE UNDER NORMAL TEMPERATURES AND PRESSURES.
INCOMPATIBILITIES: PYRIDAPHENTHION: OXIDIZERS (STRONG): FIRE AND EXPLOSION HAZARD.
DECOMPOSITION: THERMAL DECOMPOSITION PRODUCTS MAY INCLUDE TOXIC OXIDES OF NITROGEN, CARBON, PHOSPHORUS, AND SULFUR.
POLYMERIZATION: HAZARDOUS POLYMERIZATION HAS NOT BEEN REPORTED TO OCCUR UNDER NORMAL TEMPERATURES AND PRESSURES.

STORAGE AND DISPOSAL

OBSERVE ALL FEDERAL, STATE AND LOCAL REGULATIONS WHEN STORING OR DISPOSING OF THIS SUBSTANCE. FOR ASSISTANCE, CONTACT THE DISTRICT DIRECTOR OF THE ENVIRONMENTAL PROTECTION AGENCY.

STORAGE

STORE IN ACCORDANCE WITH 40 CFR 165 RECOMMENDED PROCEDURES FOR THE DISPOSAL AND STORAGE OF PESTICIDES AND PESTICIDE CONTAINERS.
STORE AWAY FROM INCOMPATIBLE SUBSTANCES.

DISPOSAL

DISPOSAL MUST BE IN ACCORDANCE WITH 40 CFR 165 RECOMMENDED PROCEDURES FOR THE DISPOSAL AND STORAGE OF PESTICIDES AND PESTICIDE CONTAINERS.

CONDITIONS TO AVOID

MAY BURN BUT DOES NOT IGNITE READILY. CONTAINERS MAY EXPLODE IN HEAT OF FIRE.

SPILL AND LEAK PROCEDURES

OCCUPATIONAL SPILL: DO NOT TOUCH SPILLED MATERIAL. STOP LEAK IF YOU CAN DO IT WITHOUT RISK. USE WATER SPRAY TO REDUCE VAPORS. FOR SMALL SPILLS, TAKE UP WITH SAND OR OTHER ABSORBENT MATERIAL AND PLACE INTO CONTAINERS FOR LATER DISPOSAL. FOR SMALL DRY SPILLS, WITH A CLEAN SHOVEL PLACE MATERIAL INTO CLEAN, DRY CONTAINERS AND COVER. MOVE CONTAINERS FROM SPILL AREA. FOR LARGER SPILLS, DIKE FAR AHEAD OF SPILL FOR LATER DISPOSAL. KEEP UNNECESSARY PEOPLE AWAY. ISOLATE HAZARD AREA AND DENY ENTRY. VENTILATE CLOSED SPACES BEFORE ENTERING.

PROTECTIVE EQUIPMENT

VENTILATION: PROVIDE LOCAL EXHAUST OR GENERAL DILUTION VENTILATION SYSTEM.
RESPIRATOR: THE FOLLOWING RESPIRATORS ARE RECOMMENDED BASED ON INFORMATION FOUND IN THE PHYSICAL DATA, TOXICITY AND HEALTH EFFECTS SECTIONS. THEY ARE RANKED IN ORDER FROM MINIMUM TO MAXIMUM RESPIRATORY PROTECTION. THE SPECIFIC RESPIRATOR SELECTED MUST BE BASED ON CONTAMINATION LEVELS FOUND IN THE WORK PLACE, MUST NOT EXCEED THE WORKING LIMITS OF THE RESPIRATOR AND BE JOINTLY APPROVED BY THE NATIONAL INSTITUTE FOR OCCUPATIONAL SAFETY AND HEALTH AND THE MINE SAFETY AND HEALTH ADMINISTRATION (NIOSH-MSHA).
CHEMICAL CARTRIDGE RESPIRATOR WITH AN ORGANIC VAPOR CARTRIDGE(S) IN COMBINATION WITH A DUST AND MIST FILTER.
GAS MASK WITH ORGANIC VAPOR CANISTER (CHIN-STYLE OR FRONT- OR BACK-MOUNTED CANISTER) WITH A DUST AND MIST FILTER.
GAS MASK WITH ORGANIC VAPOR CANISTER (CHIN-STYLE OR FRONT- OR BACK-MOUNTED CANISTER) WITH A PARTICULATE FILTER.
POWERED AIR-PURIFYING RESPIRATOR WITH A HIGH-EFFICIENCY FILTER.
TYPE 'C' SUPPLIED-AIR RESPIRATOR WITH A FULL FACEPIECE OPERATED IN A PRESSURE-DEMAND OR OTHER POSITIVE PRESSURE MODE.
SELF-CONTAINED BREATHING APPARATUS WITH A FULL FACEPIECE OPERATED IN PRESSURE-DEMAND OR OTHER POSITIVE PRESSURE MODE.
FOR FIREFIGHTING AND OTHER IMMEDIATELY DANGEROUS TO LIFE OR HEALTH CONDITIONS:
SELF-CONTAINED BREATHING APPARATUS WITH FULL FACEPIECE OPERATED IN PRESSURE-DEMAND OR OTHER POSITIVE PRESSURE MODE.
SUPPLIED-AIR RESPIRATOR WITH FULL FACEPIECE AND OPERATED IN PRESSURE-DEMAND OR OTHER POSITIVE PRESSURE MODE IN COMBINATION WITH AN AUXILIARY SELF-CONTAINED BREATHING APPARATUS OPERATED IN PRESSURE-DEMAND OR OTHER POSITIVE PRESSURE MODE.
CLOTHING: EMPLOYEE MUST WEAR APPROPRIATE PROTECTIVE (IMPERVIOUS) CLOTHING AND EQUIPMENT TO PREVENT REPEATED OR PROLONGED SKIN CONTACT WITH THIS SUBSTANCE.
GLOVES: EMPLOYEE MUST WEAR APPROPRIATE PROTECTIVE GLOVES TO PREVENT CONTACT WITH THIS SUBSTANCE.
EYE PROTECTION: EMPLOYEE MUST WEAR SPLASH-PROOF OR DUST-RESISTANT SAFETY GOGGLES TO PREVENT EYE CONTACT WITH THIS SUBSTANCE.
EMERGENCY EYE WASH: WHERE THERE IS ANY POSSIBILITY THAT AN EMPLOYEE'S EYES MAY BE EXPOSED TO THIS SUBSTANCE, THE EMPLOYER SHOULD PROVIDE AN EYE WASH FOUNTAIN WITHIN THE IMMEDIATE WORK AREA FOR EMERGENCY USE.

AUTHORIZED BY- OCCUPATIONAL HEALTH SERVICES, INC.
CREATION DATE: 10/04/89 ***REVISION DATE:*** 05/07/90

MATERIAL SAFETY DATA SHEET

OCCUPATIONAL HEALTH SERVICES, INC.
AGRICULTURE AND PESTICIDE DIVISION
450 SEVENTH AVENUE, SUITE 2407
NEW YORK, NEW YORK 10123
1-800-445-MSDS OR (212) 967-1100

EMERGENCY CONTACT:
JOHN S. BRANSFORD, JR. (615) 292-1180

SUBSTANCE IDENTIFICATION

CAS-NUMBER 97-23-4
SUBSTANCE: **2,2'-METHYLENEBIS(4-CHLOROPHENOL)**
TRADE NAMES/SYNONYMS: PHENOL, 2,2'-METHYLENEBIS(4-CHLORO-; ANTHIPHEN; DIPHENYLMETHANE, 5,5'-DICHLORO-2,2'-HYDROXY-; BIS(CHLOROHYDROXYPHENYL)METHANE; DICHLOROPHENE; DICHLOROPHEN; 2,2'-HYDROXY-5,5'-DICHLOROPHENYLMETHANE; GINGIVIT; HALENOL; HYOSAN; KORIUM; PANACIDE; PARABIS; PLATH-LYSE; PREVENTAL; PREVENTOL; TENIATOL; SUPER MOSSTOX; VERMITHANA; C13H10CL2O2; PST71611
CHEMICAL FAMILY: PHENOL
HALOGEN
MOLECULAR FORMULA: (CL-H-O-C6-H3)2-C-H2
MOLECULAR WEIGHT: 269.13
CERCLA RATINGS (SCALE 0-3): HEALTH=3 FIRE=1 REACTIVITY=0 PERSISTENCE=2
NFPA RATINGS (SCALE 0-4): HEALTH=U FIRE=1 REACTIVITY=0

COMPONENTS AND CONTAMINANTS

COMPONENT: 2,2'-METHYLENEBIS(4-CHLOROPHENOL) ***PERCENT:*** 100.0
CAS# 97-23-4
OTHER CONTAMINANTS: NONE
EXPOSURE LIMITS: NO OCCUPATIONAL EXPOSURE LIMITS ESTABLISHED BY OSHA, ACGIH, OR NIOSH.

PHYSICAL DATA

DESCRIPTION: WHITE TO LIGHT TAN, FREE-FLOWING POWDER OR CRYSTALS WITH A WEAKLY PHENOLIC ODOR.
MELTING POINT: 351-352 F (177-178 C)
SPECIFIC GRAVITY: NOT AVAILABLE ***VAPOR PRESSURE:*** NEGLIGIBLE
SOLUBILITY IN WATER: 3% @ 25 C
SOLVENT SOLUBILITY: SOLUBLE IN ALCOHOLS, ACETONE, ETHER, PETROLEUM ETHER, AND ISOPROPYL ETHER; SLIGHTLY SOLUBLE IN BENZENE, TOLUENE, AND CARBON TETRACHLORIDE; SOLUBLE WITH DECOMPOSITION IN ALKALINE SOLUTIONS.

FIRE AND EXPLOSION DATA

FIRE AND EXPLOSION HAZARD: SLIGHT FIRE HAZARD WHEN EXPOSED TO HEAT OR FLAME.
FIREFIGHTING MEDIA: DRY CHEMICAL, CARBON DIOXIDE, HALON, WATER SPRAY OR STANDARD FOAM (1987 EMERGENCY RESPONSE GUIDEBOOK, DOT P 5800.4).
FOR LARGER FIRES, USE WATER SPRAY, FOG OR STANDARD FOAM (1987 EMERGENCY RESPONSE GUIDEBOOK, DOT P 5800.4).

FIREFIGHTING: MOVE CONTAINER FROM FIRE AREA IF POSSIBLE. DO NOT SCATTER SPILLED MATERIAL WITH HIGH PRESSURE WATER STREAMS. DIKE FIRE CONTROL WATER FOR LATER DISPOSAL (1987 EMERGENCY RESPONSE GUIDEBOOK, DOT P 5800.4, GUIDE PAGE 31).
USE AGENTS SUITABLE FOR TYPE OF SURROUNDING FIRE. AVOID BREATHING HAZARDOUS VAPORS, KEEP UPWIND.

TOXICITY

2,2'-METHYLENEBIS(4-CHLOROPHENOL): IRRITATION DATA: 500 MG/24 HOURS SKIN-RABBIT MILD; 50 UG/24 HOURS EYE-RABBIT SEVERE. TOXICITY DATA: 1506 MG/KG ORAL-RAT LD50; 1 GM/KG ORAL-MOUSE LD50; 1250 MG/KG ORAL-GUINEA PIG LD50; 2000 MG/KG ORAL-DOG LD50; 17 MG/KG INTRAVENOUS-RAT LD50; MUTAGENIC DATA (RTECS). CARCINOGEN STATUS: NONE. LOCAL EFFECTS: CORROSIVE-EYE. ACUTE TOXICITY LEVEL: MODERATELY TOXIC BY INGESTION. TARGET EFFECTS: SENSITIZER- DERMAL AND ORAL. AT INCREASED RISK FROM EXPOSURE: PERSONS WITH LIVER DISEASE.

HEALTH EFFECTS AND FIRST AID

INHALATION: 2,2'-METHYLENEBIS(4-CHLOROPHENOL): **ACUTE EXPOSURE-** NO SPECIFIC DATA AVAILABLE. SOME PHENOL DERIVATIVES AFFECT THE BLOOD AND THE RESPIRATORY, CIRCULATORY AND CARDIOVASCULAR SYSTEMS. **CHRONIC EXPOSURE-** NO DATA AVAILABLE.

FIRST AID- REMOVE FROM EXPOSURE AREA TO FRESH AIR IMMEDIATELY. IF BREATHING HAS STOPPED, PERFORM ARTIFICIAL RESPIRATION. KEEP PERSON WARM AND AT REST. TREAT SYMPTOMATICALLY AND SUPPORTIVELY. GET MEDICAL ATTENTION IMMEDIATELY.

SKIN CONTACT: 2,2'-METHYLENEBIS(4-CHLOROPHENOL): SENSITIZER. **ACUTE EXPOSURE-** CONTACT MAY CAUSE IRRITATION. SENSITIZATION DERMATITIS MAY OCCUR IN PREVIOUSLY EXPOSED INDIVIDUALS. AS WITH OTHER PHENOL DERIVATIVES, IF ABSORPTION TAKES PLACE, SYSTEMIC TOXICITY MAY OCCUR. **CHRONIC EXPOSURE-** REPEATED AND PROLONGED CONTACT MAY LEAD TO SENSITIZATION DERMATITIS.

FIRST AID- REMOVE CONTAMINATED CLOTHING AND SHOES IMMEDIATELY. WASH AFFECTED AREA WITH SOAP OR MILD DETERGENT AND LARGE AMOUNTS OF WATER UNTIL NO EVIDENCE OF CHEMICAL REMAINS (APPROXIMATELY 15-20 MINUTES). FOLLOW WITH APPLICATION OF CASTOR OIL OR 10% ETHYL ALCOHOL. (ARENA, POISONING, 4TH ED.) GET MEDICAL ATTENTION.

EYE CONTACT: 2,2'-METHYLENEBIS(4-CHLOROPHENOL): CORROSIVE. **ACUTE EXPOSURE-** APPLICATION OF 50 UG TO RABBIT EYES FOR 24 HOURS CAUSED SEVERE IRRITATION. DIRECT CONTACT WITH CORROSIVE SUBSTANCES MAY CAUSE IRRITATION, PAIN, AND BURNS, POSSIBLY SEVERE. THE DEGREE OF INJURY DEPENDS ON THE CONCENTRATION AND DURATION OF CONTACT. THE FULL EXTENT OF THE INJURY MAY NOT BE IMMEDIATELY APPARENT. **CHRONIC EXPOSURE-** EFFECTS DEPEND ON CONCENTRATION AND DURATION OF EXPOSURE. REPEATED OR PROLONGED CONTACT WITH CORROSIVE SUBSTANCES MAY RESULT IN CONJUNCTIVITIS OR EFFECTS AS IN ACUTE EXPOSURE.

FIRST AID- WASH EYES IMMEDIATELY WITH LARGE AMOUNTS OF WATER, OCCASIONALLY LIFTING UPPER AND LOWER LIDS, UNTIL NO EVIDENCE OF CHEMICAL REMAINS (AT LEAST 15-20 MINUTES). CONTINUE IRRIGATING WITH NORMAL SALINE UNTIL THE PH HAS RETURNED TO NORMAL (30-60 MINUTES). COVER WITH STERILE BANDAGES. GET MEDICAL ATTENTION IMMEDIATELY.

INGESTION: 2,2'-METHYLENEBIS(4-CHLOROPHENOL): SENSITIZER. **ACUTE EXPOSURE-** MAY CAUSE ANOREXIA, NAUSEA, VOMITING, ABDOMINAL CRAMPS AND DIARRHEA. SENSITIZATION MAY OCCUR IN PREVIOUSLY EXPOSED INDIVIDUALS. SOME PHENOL DERIVATIVES AFFECT THE BLOOD AND THE RESPIRATORY, CIRCULATORY, AND CARDIOVASCULAR SYSTEMS. **CHRONIC EXPOSURE-** REPEATED AND PROLONGED EXPOSURE MAY LEAD TO SENSITIZATION REACTIONS INCLUDING CIRCUMORAL DERMATITIS, INFLAMMATION OF THE ORAL MUCOSA, AND LIPS, CHERRY-RED TONGUE, LOSS OF TASTE, AND NUMBNESS. THE LIPS MAY BECOME DRY AND SCALY AND FISSURING AT THE CORNERS OF THE MOUTH MAY OCCUR. RATS RECEIVING 2000 MG/KG IN THEIR DIET FOR 90 DAYS SHOWED NO EVIDENCE OF TOXICITY.

FIRST AID- IF THE PATIENT IS ALERT AND ABLE TO SWALLOW, GIVE A SLURRY OF ACTIVATED CHARCOAL IN WATER. DO NOT GIVE EMETICS. CAREFUL GASTRIC LAVAGE WITH WATER IS RECOMMENDED IF THERE ARE NO DEEP BURNS IN THE MOUTH OR PHARYNX. OLDER RECOMMENDATIONS TO LAVAGE WITH OLIVE OR OTHER VEGETABLE OILS DO NOT APPEAR TO BE SUBSTANTIATED. IN ANY CASE AVOID MINERAL OIL AND ALCOHOL. (GOSSELIN, CLINICAL TOXICOLOGY OF COMMERCIAL PRODUCTS, 5TH ED.). LAVAGE MUST BE PERFORMED BY QUALIFIED MEDICAL PERSONNEL.

ANTIDOTE: NO SPECIFIC ANTIDOTE. TREAT SYMPTOMATICALLY AND SUPPORTIVELY.

REACTIVITY

REACTIVITY: STABLE UNDER NORMAL TEMPERATURES AND PRESSURES.
INCOMPATIBILITIES: 2,2'-METHYLENEBIS(4-CHLOROPHENOL): OXIDIZERS (STRONG): FIRE AND EXPLOSION HAZARD.
DECOMPOSITION: THERMAL DECOMPOSITION PRODUCTS MAY INCLUDE TOXIC AND CORROSIVE FUMES OF CHLORIDES AND TOXIC OXIDES OF CARBON.
POLYMERIZATION: HAZARDOUS POLYMERIZATION HAS NOT BEEN REPORTED TO OCCUR UNDER NORMAL TEMPERATURES AND PRESSURES.

STORAGE AND DISPOSAL

OBSERVE ALL FEDERAL, STATE AND LOCAL REGULATIONS WHEN STORING OR DISPOSING OF THIS SUBSTANCE. FOR ASSISTANCE, CONTACT THE DISTRICT DIRECTOR OF THE ENVIRONMENTAL PROTECTION AGENCY.

****STORAGE****

STORE IN ACCORDANCE WITH 40 CFR 165 RECOMMENDED PROCEDURES FOR THE DISPOSAL AND STORAGE OF PESTICIDES AND PESTICIDE CONTAINERS.
STORE AWAY FROM INCOMPATIBLE SUBSTANCES.

****DISPOSAL****

DISPOSAL MUST BE IN ACCORDANCE WITH 40 CFR 165 RECOMMENDED PROCEDURES FOR THE DISPOSAL AND STORAGE OF PESTICIDES AND PESTICIDE CONTAINERS.

CONDITIONS TO AVOID

MAY BURN BUT DOES NOT IGNITE READILY. AVOID CONTACT WITH STRONG OXIDIZERS, EXCESSIVE HEAT, SPARKS, OR OPEN FLAME.

SPILL AND LEAK PROCEDURES

OCCUPATIONAL SPILL: SWEEP UP AND PLACE IN SUITABLE CLEAN, DRY CONTAINERS FOR RECLAMATION OR LATER DISPOSAL. DO NOT FLUSH SPILLED MATERIAL INTO SEWER. KEEP UNNECESSARY PEOPLE AWAY.

PROTECTIVE EQUIPMENT

VENTILATION: PROVIDE LOCAL EXHAUST OR GENERAL DILUTION VENTILATION SYSTEM.

RESPIRATOR: THE FOLLOWING RESPIRATORS ARE RECOMMENDED BASED ON INFORMATION FOUND IN THE PHYSICAL DATA, TOXICITY AND HEALTH EFFECTS SECTIONS. THEY ARE RANKED IN ORDER FROM MINIMUM TO MAXIMUM RESPIRATORY PROTECTION. THE SPECIFIC RESPIRATOR SELECTED MUST BE BASED ON CONTAMINATION LEVELS FOUND IN THE WORK PLACE, MUST NOT EXCEED THE WORKING LIMITS OF THE RESPIRATOR AND BE JOINTLY APPROVED BY THE NATIONAL INSTITUTE FOR OCCUPATIONAL SAFETY AND HEALTH AND THE MINE SAFETY AND HEALTH ADMINISTRATION (NIOSH-MSHA).
CHEMICAL CARTRIDGE RESPIRATOR WITH AN ORGANIC VAPOR CARTRIDGE(S) WITH A FULL FACEPIECE AND ORGANIC VAPOR CARTRIDGE(S) IN COMBINATION WITH A DUST AND MIST FILTER.
POWERED AIR-PURIFYING RESPIRATOR WITH A TIGHT-FITTING FACEPIECE AND ORGANIC VAPOR CARTRIDGE(S) IN COMBINATION WITH A HIGH-EFFICIENCY PARTICULATE FILTER.
TYPE 'C' SUPPLIED-AIR RESPIRATOR WITH A FULL FACEPIECE OPERATED IN A PRESSURE-DEMAND OR OTHER POSITIVE PRESSURE MODE.
SELF-CONTAINED BREATHING APPARATUS WITH A FULL FACEPIECE OPERATED IN PRESSURE-DEMAND OR OTHER POSITIVE PRESSURE MODE.
FOR FIREFIGHTING AND OTHER IMMEDIATELY DANGEROUS TO LIFE OR HEALTH CONDITIONS:
SELF-CONTAINED BREATHING APPARATUS WITH FULL FACEPIECE OPERATED IN PRESSURE-DEMAND OR OTHER POSITIVE PRESSURE MODE.
SUPPLIED-AIR RESPIRATOR WITH FULL FACEPIECE AND OPERATED IN PRESSURE-DEMAND OR OTHER POSITIVE PRESSURE MODE IN COMBINATION WITH AN AUXILIARY SELF-CONTAINED BREATHING APPARATUS OPERATED IN PRESSURE-DEMAND OR OTHER POSITIVE PRESSURE MODE.

CLOTHING: EMPLOYEE MUST WEAR APPROPRIATE PROTECTIVE (IMPERVIOUS) CLOTHING AND EQUIPMENT TO PREVENT REPEATED OR PROLONGED SKIN CONTACT WITH THIS SUBSTANCE.

GLOVES: EMPLOYEE MUST WEAR APPROPRIATE PROTECTIVE GLOVES TO PREVENT CONTACT WITH THIS SUBSTANCE.

EYE PROTECTION: EMPLOYEE MUST WEAR SPLASH-PROOF OR DUST-RESISTANT SAFETY GOGGLES AND A FACESHIELD TO PREVENT CONTACT WITH THIS SUBSTANCE.
EMERGENCY WASH FACILITIES: WHERE THERE IS ANY POSSIBILITY THAT AN EMPLOYEE'S EYES AND/OR SKIN MAY BE EXPOSED TO THIS SUBSTANCE, THE EMPLOYER SHOULD PROVIDE AN EYE WASH FOUNTAIN AND QUICK DRENCH SHOWER WITHIN THE IMMEDIATE WORK AREA FOR EMERGENCY USE.

AUTHORIZED BY- OCCUPATIONAL HEALTH SERVICES, INC.
CREATION DATE: 10/05/89 ***REVISION DATE:*** 05/31/90

MATERIAL SAFETY DATA SHEET

OCCUPATIONAL HEALTH SERVICES, INC.
AGRICULTURE AND PESTICIDE DIVISION
450 SEVENTH AVENUE, SUITE 2407
NEW YORK, NEW YORK 10123
1-800-445-MSDS OR (212) 967-1100

EMERGENCY CONTACT:
JOHN S. BRANSFORD, JR. (615) 292-1180

SUBSTANCE IDENTIFICATION

CAS-NUMBER 117-18-0
SUBSTANCE: TECNAZENE
TRADE NAMES/SYNONYMS: BENZENE, 1,2,4,5-TETRACHLORO-3-NITRO-; 1,2,4,5-TETRACHLORO-3-NITRO-BENZENE; FOLOSAN; FUSAREX; MYFUSAN; TCNB; TECNAZEN; TETRACHLORONITROBENZENE; C6HCL4NO2; PST71616
CHEMICAL FAMILY: NITRO
HALOGEN COMPOUND, AROMATIC
MOLECULAR FORMULA: C6-H-CL4-N-O2
MOLECULAR WEIGHT: 260.88
CERCLA RATINGS (SCALE 0-3): HEALTH=3 FIRE=1 REACTIVITY=0 PERSISTENCE=3
NFPA RATINGS (SCALE 0-4): HEALTH=U FIRE=1 REACTIVITY=0

COMPONENTS AND CONTAMINANTS

COMPONENT: TECNAZENE ***PERCENT:*** 100.0
CAS# 117-18-0
OTHER CONTAMINANTS: NONE
EXPOSURE LIMITS: NO OCCUPATIONAL EXPOSURE LIMITS ESTABLISHED BY OSHA, ACGIH, OR NIOSH.

PHYSICAL DATA

DESCRIPTION: COLORLESS CRYSTALS. ***BOILING POINT:*** 579 F (304 C)
MELTING POINT: 208-214 F (98-101 C) ***SPECIFIC GRAVITY:*** NOT AVAILABLE
SOLUBILITY IN WATER: INSOLUBLE
SOLVENT SOLUBILITY: SOLUBLE IN BENZENE, CARBON DISULFIDE AND CHLOROFORM; MODERATELY SOLUBLE IN ETHANOL.

FIRE AND EXPLOSION DATA

FIRE AND EXPLOSION HAZARD: SLIGHT FIRE HAZARD WHEN EXPOSED TO HEAT OR FLAME.
FIREFIGHTING MEDIA: DRY CHEMICAL, CARBON DIOXIDE, HALON, WATER SPRAY OR STANDARD FOAM (1987 EMERGENCY RESPONSE GUIDEBOOK, DOT P 5800.4).
FOR LARGER FIRES, USE WATER SPRAY, FOG OR STANDARD FOAM (1987 EMERGENCY RESPONSE GUIDEBOOK, DOT P 5800.4).
FIREFIGHTING: MOVE CONTAINER FROM FIRE AREA IF POSSIBLE. DO NOT SCATTER SPILLED MATERIAL WITH HIGH PRESSURE WATER STREAMS. DIKE FIRE CONTROL WATER FOR LATER DISPOSAL (1987 EMERGENCY RESPONSE GUIDEBOOK, DOT P 5800.4, GUIDE PAGE 31).
USE AGENTS SUITABLE FOR TYPE OF SURROUNDING FIRE. AVOID BREATHING HAZARDOUS VAPORS, KEEP UPWIND.

TOXICITY

TECNAZENE: TOXICITY DATA: 7500 MG/KG ORAL-RAT LD50; 250 MG/KG UNREPORTED-RAT LD50; MUTAGENIC DATA (RTECS). CARCINOGEN STATUS: NONE. ACUTE TOXICITY LEVEL: SLIGHTLY TOXIC BY INGESTION. TARGET EFFECTS: POISONING MAY AFFECT THE HEART, LIVER, KIDNEYS, AND CENTRAL NERVOUS SYSTEM.* ADDITIONAL DATA: USE OF STIMULANTS SUCH AS EPINEPHRINE MAY CAUSE VENTRICULAR FIBRILLATION.*
*MAY BE BASED ON GENERAL INFORMATION ON HYDROCARBONS.

HEALTH EFFECTS AND FIRST AID

INHALATION: TECNAZENE: <u>ACUTE EXPOSURE</u>- MAY CAUSE IRRITATION. <u>CHRONIC EXPOSURE</u>- NO DATA AVAILABLE.
FIRST AID- REMOVE FROM EXPOSURE AREA TO FRESH AIR IMMEDIATELY. IF BREATHING HAS STOPPED, PERFORM ARTIFICIAL RESPIRATION. KEEP PERSON WARM AND AT REST. TREAT SYMPTOMATICALLY AND SUPPORTIVELY. GET MEDICAL ATTENTION IMMEDIATELY.

SKIN CONTACT: TECNAZENE: <u>ACUTE EXPOSURE</u>- CONTACT MAY CAUSE IRRITATION. <u>CHRONIC EXPOSURE</u>- NO DATA AVAILABLE.
FIRST AID- REMOVE CONTAMINATED CLOTHING AND SHOES IMMEDIATELY. WASH AFFECTED AREA WITH SOAP OR MILD DETERGENT AND LARGE AMOUNTS OF WATER UNTIL NO EVIDENCE OF CHEMICAL REMAINS (APPROXIMATELY 15-20 MINUTES). GET MEDICAL ATTENTION IMMEDIATELY.

EYE CONTACT: TECNAZENE: <u>ACUTE EXPOSURE</u>- CONTACT MAY CAUSE IRRITATION. <u>CHRONIC EXPOSURE</u>- NO DATA AVAILABLE.
FIRST AID- WASH EYES IMMEDIATELY WITH LARGE AMOUNTS OF WATER OR NORMAL SALINE, OCCASIONALLY LIFTING UPPER AND LOWER LIDS, UNTIL NO EVIDENCE OF CHEMICAL REMAINS (APPROXIMATELY 15-20 MINUTES). GET MEDICAL ATTENTION IMMEDIATELY.

INGESTION: TECNAZENE: <u>ACUTE EXPOSURE</u>- INGESTION OF HALOBENZENE DERIVATIVES MAY CAUSE VOMITING, TREMORS, AND CONVULSIONS. THE MOST CHARACTERISTIC FINDING IN EXPERIMENTAL ANIMALS IS LIVER DAMAGE. <u>CHRONIC EXPOSURE</u>- NO ILL EFFECTS WERE NOTED IN RATS RECEIVING 57 MG/KG DAILY OR MICE RECEIVING 215 MG/KG DAILY.
FIRST AID- IF THE PERSON IS CONSCIOUS AND NOT CONVULSING, REMOVE BY GIVING SYRUP OF IPECAC (IF VOMITING OCCURS, KEEP THE HEAD BELOW THE HIPS TO PREVENT ASPIRATION). GIVE ACTIVATED CHARCOAL FOLLOWED BY GASTRIC LAVAGE. FOLLOW WITH A SALINE CATHARTIC. DO NOT GIVE FATS OR OILS. INTESTINAL LAVAGE WITH 20% MANNITOL (200 ML) BY STOMACH TUBE IS ALSO USEFUL. GIVE ARTIFICIAL RESPIRATION WITH OXYGEN IF RESPIRATION IS DEPRESSED (DREISBACH, HANDBOOK OF POISONING, 12TH ED.). TREAT SYMPTOMATICALLY AND SUPPORTIVELY. LAVAGE AND ADMINISTRATION OF OXYGEN SHOULD BE PERFORMED BY QUALIFIED MEDICAL PERSONNEL. GET MEDICAL ATTENTION IMMEDIATELY.
ANTIDOTE: NO SPECIFIC ANTIDOTE. TREAT SYMPTOMATICALLY AND SUPPORTIVELY.

REACTIVITY

REACTIVITY: STABLE UNDER NORMAL TEMPERATURES AND PRESSURES.
INCOMPATIBILITIES: TECNAZENE: OXIDIZERS (STRONG): FIRE AND EXPLOSION HAZARD.
DECOMPOSITION: THERMAL DECOMPOSITION PRODUCTS MAY INCLUDE TOXIC AND CORROSIVE FUMES OF CHLORIDES, AND TOXIC OXIDES OF NITROGEN AND CARBON.
POLYMERIZATION: HAZARDOUS POLYMERIZATION HAS NOT BEEN REPORTED TO OCCUR UNDER NORMAL TEMPERATURES AND PRESSURES.

STORAGE AND DISPOSAL

OBSERVE ALL FEDERAL, STATE AND LOCAL REGULATIONS WHEN STORING OR DISPOSING OF THIS SUBSTANCE. FOR ASSISTANCE, CONTACT THE DISTRICT DIRECTOR OF THE ENVIRONMENTAL PROTECTION AGENCY.

STORAGE

STORE IN ACCORDANCE WITH 40 CFR 165 RECOMMENDED PROCEDURES FOR THE DISPOSAL AND STORAGE OF PESTICIDES AND PESTICIDE CONTAINERS. STORE AWAY FROM INCOMPATIBLE SUBSTANCES.

DISPOSAL

DISPOSAL MUST BE IN ACCORDANCE WITH 40 CFR 165 RECOMMENDED PROCEDURES FOR THE DISPOSAL AND STORAGE OF PESTICIDES AND PESTICIDE CONTAINERS.

CONDITIONS TO AVOID

MAY BURN BUT DOES NOT IGNITE READILY. AVOID CONTACT WITH STRONG OXIDIZERS, EXCESSIVE HEAT, SPARKS, OR OPEN FLAME.

SPILL AND LEAK PROCEDURES

OCCUPATIONAL SPILL: SWEEP UP AND PLACE IN SUITABLE CLEAN, DRY CONTAINERS FOR RECLAMATION OR LATER DISPOSAL. DO NOT FLUSH SPILLED MATERIAL INTO SEWER. KEEP UNNECESSARY PEOPLE AWAY.

PROTECTIVE EQUIPMENT

VENTILATION: PROVIDE LOCAL EXHAUST OR GENERAL DILUTION VENTILATION SYSTEM.
RESPIRATOR: THE FOLLOWING RESPIRATORS ARE RECOMMENDED BASED ON INFORMATION FOUND IN THE PHYSICAL DATA, TOXICITY AND HEALTH EFFECTS SECTIONS. THEY ARE RANKED IN ORDER FROM MINIMUM TO MAXIMUM RESPIRATORY PROTECTION. THE SPECIFIC RESPIRATOR SELECTED MUST BE BASED ON CONTAMINATION LEVELS FOUND IN THE WORK PLACE, MUST NOT EXCEED THE WORKING LIMITS OF THE RESPIRATOR AND BE JOINTLY APPROVED BY THE NATIONAL INSTITUTE FOR OCCUPATIONAL SAFETY AND HEALTH AND THE MINE SAFETY AND HEALTH ADMINISTRATION (NIOSH-MSHA).
CHEMICAL CARTRIDGE RESPIRATOR WITH AN ORGANIC VAPOR CARTRIDGE(S) WITH A FULL FACEPIECE AND ORGANIC VAPOR CARTRIDGE(S) IN COMBINATION WITH A DUST AND MIST FILTER.
POWERED AIR-PURIFYING RESPIRATOR WITH A TIGHT-FITTING FACEPIECE AND ORGANIC VAPOR CARTRIDGE(S) IN COMBINATION WITH A HIGH-EFFICIENCY PARTICULATE FILTER.
TYPE 'C' SUPPLIED-AIR RESPIRATOR WITH A FULL FACEPIECE OPERATED IN A

PRESSURE-DEMAND OR OTHER POSITIVE PRESSURE MODE.
SELF-CONTAINED BREATHING APPARATUS WITH A FULL FACEPIECE OPERATED IN PRESSURE-DEMAND OR OTHER POSITIVE PRESSURE MODE.
FOR FIREFIGHTING AND OTHER IMMEDIATELY DANGEROUS TO LIFE OR HEALTH CONDITIONS:
SELF-CONTAINED BREATHING APPARATUS WITH FULL FACEPIECE OPERATED IN PRESSURE-DEMAND OR OTHER POSITIVE PRESSURE MODE.
SUPPLIED-AIR RESPIRATOR WITH FULL FACEPIECE AND OPERATED IN PRESSURE-DEMAND OR OTHER POSITIVE PRESSURE MODE IN COMBINATION WITH AN AUXILIARY SELF-CONTAINED BREATHING APPARATUS OPERATED IN PRESSURE-DEMAND OR OTHER POSITIVE PRESSURE MODE.

CLOTHING: EMPLOYEE MUST WEAR APPROPRIATE PROTECTIVE (IMPERVIOUS) CLOTHING AND EQUIPMENT TO PREVENT REPEATED OR PROLONGED SKIN CONTACT WITH THIS SUBSTANCE.

GLOVES: EMPLOYEE MUST WEAR APPROPRIATE PROTECTIVE GLOVES TO PREVENT CONTACT WITH THIS SUBSTANCE.

EYE PROTECTION: EMPLOYEE MUST WEAR SPLASH-PROOF OR DUST-RESISTANT SAFETY GOGGLES TO PREVENT EYE CONTACT WITH THIS SUBSTANCE.
EMERGENCY EYE WASH: WHERE THERE IS ANY POSSIBILITY THAT AN EMPLOYEE'S EYES MAY BE EXPOSED TO THIS SUBSTANCE, THE EMPLOYER SHOULD PROVIDE AN EYE WASH FOUNTAIN WITHIN THE IMMEDIATE WORK AREA FOR EMERGENCY USE.

AUTHORIZED BY- OCCUPATIONAL HEALTH SERVICES, INC.
CREATION DATE: 10/05/89 ***REVISION DATE:*** 05/31/90

MATERIAL SAFETY DATA SHEET

OCCUPATIONAL HEALTH SERVICES, INC.
AGRICULTURE AND PESTICIDE DIVISION
450 SEVENTH AVENUE, SUITE 2407
NEW YORK, NEW YORK 10123
1-800-445-MSDS OR (212) 967-1100

EMERGENCY CONTACT:
JOHN S. BRANSFORD, JR. (615) 292-1180

SUBSTANCE IDENTIFICATION

CAS-NUMBER 2122-70-5
SUBSTANCE: **ETHYL 1-NAPHTHALENEACETATE**
TRADE NAMES/SYNONYMS: 1-NAPHTHALENEACETIC ACID, ETHYL ESTER; NAPHTHALENEACETIC ACID, ETHYL ESTER; ETHYL 1-NAPHTHYLACETATE; NAA ETHYL ESTER; C14H14O2; PST71628
CHEMICAL FAMILY: ESTER, CARBOXYLIC, AROMATIC
MOLECULAR FORMULA: C14-H14-O2
MOLECULAR WEIGHT: 214.26
CERCLA RATINGS (SCALE 0-3): HEALTH=2 FIRE=U REACTIVITY=0 PERSISTENCE=2
NFPA RATINGS (SCALE 0-4): HEALTH=2 FIRE=U REACTIVITY=0

COMPONENTS AND CONTAMINANTS

COMPONENT: ETHYL 1-NAPHTHALENEACETIC ACID ***PERCENT:*** 100.0
CAS# 2122-70-5
OTHER CONTAMINANTS: NONE
EXPOSURE LIMITS: NO OCCUPATIONAL EXPOSURE LIMITS ESTABLISHED BY OSHA, ACGIH, OR NIOSH.

PHYSICAL DATA

DESCRIPTION: COLORLESS OILY LIQUID.
BOILING POINT: 428-437 F (220-225 C) @ 20 MMHG
SPECIFIC GRAVITY: 1.106 @ 25 C
SOLUBILITY IN WATER: ALMOST INSOLUBLE
SOLVENT SOLUBILITY: VERY SOLUBLE IN ACETONE, ETHANOL, ISOPROPANOL; SLIGHTLY SOLUBLE IN KEROSENE AND DIESEL OIL.

FIRE AND EXPLOSION DATA

FIRE AND EXPLOSION HAZARD: UNKNOWN FIRE AND EXPLOSION HAZARD.
FIREFIGHTING MEDIA: DRY CHEMICAL, CARBON DIOXIDE, HALON, WATER SPRAY OR ALCOHOL FOAM (1987 EMERGENCY RESPONSE GUIDEBOOK, DOT P 5800.4).
FOR LARGER FIRES, USE WATER SPRAY, FOG OR ALCOHOL FOAM (1987 EMERGENCY RESPONSE GUIDEBOOK, DOT P 5800.4).
FIREFIGHTING: MOVE CONTAINER FROM FIRE AREA IF POSSIBLE. COOL FIRE-EXPOSED CONTAINERS WITH WATER FROM SIDE UNTIL WELL AFTER FIRE IS OUT. STAY AWAY FROM STORAGE TANK ENDS. FOR MASSIVE FIRE IN STORAGE AREA, USE UNMANNED HOSE HOLDER OR MONITOR NOZZLES, ELSE WITHDRAW FROM AREA AND LET FIRE BURN. WITHDRAW IMMEDIATELY IN CASE OF RISING SOUND FROM VENTING SAFETY DEVICE OR ANY DISCOLORATION OF STORAGE TANK DUE TO FIRE (1987 EMERGENCY RESPONSE GUIDEBOOK, DOT P 5800.4, GUIDE PAGE 26). EXTINGUISH ONLY IF FLOW CAN BE STOPPED. USE FLOODING AMOUNTS OF WATER AS FOG; SOLID STREAMS MAY BE INEFFECTIVE. COOL CONTAINERS WITH FLOODING AMOUNTS OF WATER FROM AS FAR A DISTANCE AS POSSIBLE. AVOID BREATHING VAPORS; KEEP UPWIND.

TOXICITY

ETHYL 1-NAPHTHALENEACETATE: TOXICITY DATA: 3580 MG/KG ORAL-RAT LD50. CARCINOGEN STATUS: NONE. ACUTE TOXICITY LEVEL: MODERATELY TOXIC BY INGESTION. TARGET EFFECTS: NO DATA AVAILABLE.

HEALTH EFFECTS AND FIRST AID

INHALATION: ETHYL 1-NAPHTHALENEACETATE: **ACUTE EXPOSURE-** NO DATA AVAILABLE. **CHRONIC EXPOSURE-** NO DATA AVAILABLE.
FIRST AID- REMOVE FROM EXPOSURE AREA TO FRESH AIR IMMEDIATELY. IF BREATHING HAS STOPPED, PERFORM ARTIFICIAL RESPIRATION. KEEP PERSON WARM AND AT REST. TREAT SYMPTOMATICALLY AND SUPPORTIVELY. GET MEDICAL ATTENTION IMMEDIATELY.

SKIN CONTACT: ETHYL 1-NAPHTHALENEACETATE: **ACUTE EXPOSURE-** NO DATA AVAILABLE. **CHRONIC EXPOSURE-** NO DATA AVAILABLE.
FIRST AID- REMOVE CONTAMINATED CLOTHING AND SHOES IMMEDIATELY. WASH AFFECTED AREA WITH SOAP OR MILD DETERGENT AND LARGE AMOUNTS OF WATER UNTIL NO EVIDENCE OF CHEMICAL REMAINS (APPROXIMATELY 15-20 MINUTES). GET MEDICAL ATTENTION IMMEDIATELY.

EYE CONTACT: ETHYL 1-NAPHTHALENEACETATE: **ACUTE EXPOSURE-** NO DATA AVAILABLE. **CHRONIC EXPOSURE-** NO DATA AVAILABLE.
FIRST AID- WASH EYES IMMEDIATELY WITH LARGE AMOUNTS OF WATER OR NORMAL SALINE, OCCASIONALLY LIFTING UPPER AND LOWER LIDS, UNTIL NO EVIDENCE OF CHEMICAL REMAINS (APPROXIMATELY 15-20 MINUTES). GET MEDICAL ATTENTION IMMEDIATELY.

INGESTION: ETHYL 1-NAPHTHALENEACETATE: **ACUTE EXPOSURE-** THE LETHAL DOSE REPORTED IN RATS WAS 3580 MG/KG. THE SYMPTOMS WERE NOT REPORTED. **CHRONIC EXPOSURE-** NO DATA AVAILABLE.
FIRST AID- TREAT SYMPTOMATICALLY AND SUPPORTIVELY. GET MEDICAL ATTENTION IMMEDIATELY. IF VOMITING OCCURS, KEEP HEAD LOWER THAN HIPS TO PREVENT ASPIRATION.
ANTIDOTE: NO SPECIFIC ANTIDOTE. TREAT SYMPTOMATICALLY AND SUPPORTIVELY.

REACTIVITY

REACTIVITY: STABLE UNDER NORMAL TEMPERATURES AND PRESSURES.
INCOMPATIBILITIES: ETHYL 1-NAPHTHALENEACETATE: OXIDIZERS (STRONG): FIRE AND EXPLOSION HAZARD. SEE ALSO ESTERS.
ESTERS: NITRATES: POSSIBLE EXPLOSIVE REACTION.
DECOMPOSITION: THERMAL DECOMPOSITION PRODUCTS MAY INCLUDE TOXIC OXIDES OF CARBON.
POLYMERIZATION: HAZARDOUS POLYMERIZATION HAS NOT BEEN REPORTED TO OCCUR UNDER NORMAL TEMPERATURES AND PRESSURES.

STORAGE AND DISPOSAL

OBSERVE ALL FEDERAL, STATE AND LOCAL REGULATIONS WHEN STORING OR DISPOSING OF THIS SUBSTANCE. FOR ASSISTANCE, CONTACT THE DISTRICT DIRECTOR OF THE ENVIRONMENTAL PROTECTION AGENCY.

STORAGE

STORE IN ACCORDANCE WITH 40 CFR 165 RECOMMENDED PROCEDURES FOR THE DISPOSAL AND STORAGE OF PESTICIDES AND PESTICIDE CONTAINERS.
STORE AWAY FROM INCOMPATIBLE SUBSTANCES.

DISPOSAL

DISPOSAL MUST BE IN ACCORDANCE WITH 40 CFR 165 RECOMMENDED PROCEDURES FOR THE DISPOSAL AND STORAGE OF PESTICIDES AND PESTICIDE CONTAINERS.

CONDITIONS TO AVOID

AVOID CONTACT WITH HEAT, SPARKS, FLAMES, OR OTHER SOURCES OF IGNITION. VAPORS MAY BE EXPLOSIVE AND POISONOUS; DO NOT ALLOW UNNECESSARY PERSONNEL IN AREA. DO NOT OVERHEAT CONTAINERS; CONTAINERS MAY VIOLENTLY RUPTURE AND TRAVEL A CONSIDERABLE DISTANCE IN HEAT OF FIRE.

SPILL AND LEAK PROCEDURES

OCCUPATIONAL SPILL: SHUT OFF IGNITION SOURCES. STOP LEAK IF YOU CAN DO IT WITHOUT RISK. USE WATER SPRAY TO REDUCE VAPORS. FOR SMALL SPILLS, TAKE

UP WITH SAND OR OTHER ABSORBENT MATERIAL AND PLACE INTO CONTAINERS FOR LATER DISPOSAL. FOR LARGER SPILLS, DIKE FAR AHEAD OF SPILL FOR LATER DISPOSAL. NO SMOKING, FLAMES OR FLARES IN HAZARD AREA. KEEP UNNECESSARY PEOPLE AWAY; ISOLATE HAZARD AREA AND DENY ENTRY.

PROTECTIVE EQUIPMENT

VENTILATION: PROVIDE LOCAL EXHAUST OR GENERAL DILUTION VENTILATION. VENTILATION EQUIPMENT MUST BE EXPLOSION-PROOF.

RESPIRATOR: THE FOLLOWING RESPIRATORS ARE RECOMMENDED BASED ON INFORMATION FOUND IN THE PHYSICAL DATA, TOXICITY AND HEALTH EFFECTS SECTIONS. THEY ARE RANKED IN ORDER FROM MINIMUM TO MAXIMUM RESPIRATORY PROTECTION. THE SPECIFIC RESPIRATOR SELECTED MUST BE BASED ON CONTAMINATION LEVELS FOUND IN THE WORK PLACE, MUST NOT EXCEED THE WORKING LIMITS OF THE RESPIRATOR AND BE JOINTLY APPROVED BY THE NATIONAL INSTITUTE FOR OCCUPATIONAL SAFETY AND HEALTH AND THE MINE SAFETY AND HEALTH ADMINISTRATION (NIOSH-MSHA).

CHEMICAL CARTRIDGE RESPIRATOR WITH AN ORGANIC VAPOR CARTRIDGE(S) WITH AN ACID GAS CARTRIDGE(S) AND A FULL FACEPIECE.

GAS MASK WITH ORGANIC VAPOR CANISTER (CHIN-STYLE OR FRONT- OR BACK-MOUNTED CANISTER), WITH A FULL FACEPIECE, PROVIDING PROTECTION AGAINST ACID GASES.

TYPE 'C' SUPPLIED-AIR RESPIRATOR WITH A FULL FACEPIECE OPERATED IN PRESSURE-DEMAND OR OTHER POSITIVE PRESSURE MODE OR WITH A FULL FACEPIECE, HELMET OR HOOD OPERATED IN CONTINUOUS-FLOW MODE.

SELF-CONTAINED BREATHING APPARATUS WITH A FULL FACEPIECE OPERATED IN PRESSURE-DEMAND OR OTHER POSITIVE PRESSURE MODE.

FOR FIREFIGHTING AND OTHER IMMEDIATELY DANGEROUS TO LIFE OR HEALTH CONDITIONS:

SELF-CONTAINED BREATHING APPARATUS WITH FULL FACEPIECE OPERATED IN PRESSURE-DEMAND OR OTHER POSITIVE PRESSURE MODE.

SUPPLIED-AIR RESPIRATOR WITH FULL FACEPIECE AND OPERATED IN PRESSURE-DEMAND OR OTHER POSITIVE PRESSURE MODE IN COMBINATION WITH AN AUXILIARY SELF-CONTAINED BREATHING APPARATUS OPERATED IN PRESSURE-DEMAND OR OTHER POSITIVE PRESSURE MODE.

CLOTHING: EMPLOYEE MUST WEAR APPROPRIATE PROTECTIVE (IMPERVIOUS) CLOTHING AND EQUIPMENT TO PREVENT REPEATED OR PROLONGED SKIN CONTACT WITH THIS SUBSTANCE.

GLOVES: EMPLOYEE MUST WEAR APPROPRIATE PROTECTIVE GLOVES TO PREVENT CONTACT WITH THIS SUBSTANCE.

EYE PROTECTION: EMPLOYEE MUST WEAR SPLASH-PROOF OR DUST-RESISTANT SAFETY GOGGLES TO PREVENT EYE CONTACT WITH THIS SUBSTANCE.

EMERGENCY EYE WASH: WHERE THERE IS ANY POSSIBILITY THAT AN EMPLOYEE'S EYES MAY BE EXPOSED TO THIS SUBSTANCE, THE EMPLOYER SHOULD PROVIDE AN EYE WASH FOUNTAIN WITHIN THE IMMEDIATE WORK AREA FOR EMERGENCY USE.

AUTHORIZED BY- OCCUPATIONAL HEALTH SERVICES, INC.

CREATION DATE: 10/04/89 ***REVISION DATE:*** 05/11/90

MATERIAL SAFETY DATA SHEET

OCCUPATIONAL HEALTH SERVICES, INC.
AGRICULTURE AND PESTICIDE DIVISION
450 SEVENTH AVENUE, SUITE 2407
NEW YORK, NEW YORK 10123
1-800-445-MSDS OR (212) 967-1100

EMERGENCY CONTACT:
JOHN S. BRANSFORD, JR. (615) 292-1180

SUBSTANCE IDENTIFICATION

CAS-NUMBER 117-26-0

SUBSTANCE: BULAN

TRADE NAMES/SYNONYMS: BENZENE, 1,1'-(2-NITROBUTYLIDENE)BIS(4-CHLORO-; BUTANE, 1,1-BIS(P-CHLOROPHENYL)-2-NITRO-; 1,1'-(2-NITROBUTYLIDENE)BIS(4-CHLOROBENZENE); 1,1-BIS(P-CHLOROPHENYL)2-NITROBUTANE; ENT 18,065; CS 674A; STCC 4921670; C16H15CL2NO2; PST71635

CHEMICAL FAMILY: HALOGEN COMPOUND, AROMATIC

MOLECULAR FORMULA: C-H3-C-H2-C-(N-O2)-H-C-(C6-H4-CL)2-H

MOLECULAR WEIGHT: 324.22

CERCLA RATINGS (SCALE 0-3): HEALTH=3 FIRE=1 REACTIVITY=0 PERSISTENCE=3

NFPA RATINGS (SCALE 0-4): HEALTH=U FIRE=1 REACTIVITY=0

COMPONENTS AND CONTAMINANTS

COMPONENT: BULAN ***PERCENT:*** 100.0

CAS# 117-26-0

OTHER CONTAMINANTS: NONE

EXPOSURE LIMITS: NO OCCUPATIONAL EXPOSURE LIMITS ESTABLISHED BY OSHA, ACGIH, OR NIOSH.

PHYSICAL DATA

DESCRIPTION: WHITE POWDER. ***MELTING POINT:*** 144 F (62 C)

SPECIFIC GRAVITY: NOT AVAILABLE ***SOLUBILITY IN WATER:*** NOT AVAILABLE

FIRE AND EXPLOSION DATA

FIRE AND EXPLOSION HAZARD: SLIGHT FIRE HAZARD WHEN EXPOSED TO HEAT OR FLAME.

FIREFIGHTING MEDIA: DRY CHEMICAL, CARBON DIOXIDE, HALON, WATER SPRAY OR STANDARD FOAM (1987 EMERGENCY RESPONSE GUIDEBOOK, DOT P 5800.4). FOR LARGER FIRES, USE WATER SPRAY, FOG OR STANDARD FOAM (1987 EMERGENCY RESPONSE GUIDEBOOK, DOT P 5800.4).

FIREFIGHTING: MOVE CONTAINER FROM FIRE AREA IF POSSIBLE. DO NOT SCATTER SPILLED MATERIAL WITH HIGH PRESSURE WATER STREAMS. DIKE FIRE CONTROL WATER FOR LATER DISPOSAL (1987 EMERGENCY RESPONSE GUIDEBOOK, DOT P 5800.4, GUIDE PAGE 31).

USE AGENTS SUITABLE FOR TYPE OF SURROUNDING FIRE. AVOID BREATHING HAZARDOUS VAPORS, KEEP UPWIND.

TOXICITY

BULAN: TOXICITY DATA: 300 MG/KG ORAL-RAT LD50. CARCINOGEN STATUS: NONE. ACUTE TOXICITY LEVEL: TOXIC BY INGESTION. TARGET EFFECTS: POISONING MAY AFFECT THE BLOOD, CENTRAL NERVOUS AND CARDIOVASCULAR SYSTEMS, LIVER AND KIDNEYS.* AT INCREASED RISK FROM EXPOSURE: PERSONS WITH CONVULSIVE DISORDERS OR LIVER OR BLOOD DISEASES.* ADDITIONAL DATA: MAY BE STORED IN ADIPOSE TISSUES FOR MONTHS OR YEARS; MAY ALSO BE EXCRETED IN BREAST MILK. STIMULANTS SUCH AS EPINEPHRINE MAY INDUCE VENTRICULAR FIBRILLATION.*

* MAY BE BASED ON GENERAL INFORMATION ON ORGANOCHLORINE PESTICIDES.

HEALTH EFFECTS AND FIRST AID

INHALATION: BULAN: **ACUTE EXPOSURE-** SOME ORGANOCHLORINE PESTICIDES CAUSE IRRITATION; IF SUFFICIENT AMOUNTS ARE ABSORBED THROUGH THE RESPIRATORY TRACT, SYMPTOMS AS DETAILED IN ACUTE INGESTION MAY OCCUR. **CHRONIC EXPOSURE-** PROLONGED OR REPEATED EXPOSURE MAY CAUSE EFFECTS AS DETAILED IN CHRONIC INGESTION.

FIRST AID- REMOVE FROM EXPOSURE AREA TO FRESH AIR IMMEDIATELY. IF BREATHING HAS STOPPED, PERFORM ARTIFICIAL RESPIRATION. KEEP PERSON WARM AND AT REST. TREAT SYMPTOMATICALLY AND SUPPORTIVELY. GET MEDICAL ATTENTION IMMEDIATELY.

SKIN CONTACT: BULAN: **ACUTE EXPOSURE-** MAY BE ABSORBED THROUGH INTACT SKIN AND, IF ABSORBED, MAY CAUSE EFFECTS AS DESCRIBED IN ACUTE INGESTION. SOME ORGANOCHLORINE PESTICIDES CAUSE IRRITATION. **CHRONIC EXPOSURE-** REPEATED OR PROLONGED EXPOSURE MAY CAUSE EFFECTS AS DESCRIBED IN CHRONIC INGESTION.

FIRST AID- REMOVE CONTAMINATED CLOTHING AND SHOES IMMEDIATELY. WASH AFFECTED AREA WITH SOAP OR MILD DETERGENT AND LARGE AMOUNTS OF WATER UNTIL NO EVIDENCE OF CHEMICAL REMAINS (APPROXIMATELY 15-20 MINUTES). GET MEDICAL ATTENTION IMMEDIATELY.

EYE CONTACT: BULAN: **ACUTE EXPOSURE-** SOME ORGANOCHLORINE PESTICIDES CAUSE IRRITATION. **CHRONIC EXPOSURE-** NO DATA AVAILABLE.

FIRST AID- WASH EYES IMMEDIATELY WITH LARGE AMOUNTS OF WATER OR NORMAL SALINE, OCCASIONALLY LIFTING UPPER AND LOWER LIDS, UNTIL NO EVIDENCE OF CHEMICAL REMAINS (APPROXIMATELY 15-20 MINUTES). GET MEDICAL ATTENTION IMMEDIATELY.

INGESTION: BULAN: TOXIC. **ACUTE EXPOSURE-** THE LETHAL DOSE REPORTED IN RATS WAS 300 MG/KG. THE SYMPTOMS WERE NOT REPORTED. SYSTEMIC EFFECTS ARE SIMILAR TO THOSE OF DDT, MAY BE DELAYED FOR SEVERAL HOURS, AND ARE CHARACTERIZED BY PARESTHESIAS OF THE TONGUE, LIPS, AND FACE FOLLOWED BY TREMOR, A SENSE OF APPREHENSION, DIZZINESS, CONFUSION, HEADACHE, FATIGUE, ATAXIA, NYSTAGMUS, INCREASED RESPIRATION, AND HYPEREXCITEABILITY, BLOOD DISORDERS, AND CARDIAC IRREGULARITIES. INGESTION OF VERY LARGE AMOUNTS MAY CAUSE PROMPT VOMITING WITH NAUSEA AND DIARRHEA. CONVULSIONS MAY ALTERNATE WITH PERIODS OF COMA, AND PARTIAL PARALYSIS. DEATH MAY BE DUE TO RESPIRATORY FAILURE. **CHRONIC EXPOSURE-** REPEATED INGESTION MAY CAUSE SYMPTOMS AS DETAILED IN ACUTE EXPOSURE. IN ADDITION, DDT HAS BEEN REPORTED TO CAUSE

ANOREXIA, LOSS OF WEIGHT, ANEMIA, MILD ANXIETY, NERVOUS TENSION, FEAR, MYOCLONIC JERKS. LIVER AND KIDNEY DAMAGE MAY ALSO OCCUR. IF MODERATE AMOUNTS ARE ABSORBED OVER SEVERAL DAYS, BODY CONCENTRATION MAY BECOME HIGH WITHOUT CAUSING SYMPTOMS.

FIRST AID- IF THE PERSON IS CONSCIOUS AND NOT CONVULSING, REMOVE BY GIVING SYRUP OF IPECAC (IF VOMITING OCCURS, KEEP THE HEAD BELOW THE HIPS TO PREVENT ASPIRATION). GIVE ACTIVATED CHARCOAL FOLLOWED BY GASTRIC LAVAGE. FOLLOW WITH A SALINE CATHARTIC. DO NOT GIVE FATS OR OILS. INTESTINAL LAVAGE WITH 20% MANNITOL (200 ML) BY STOMACH TUBE IS ALSO USEFUL. GIVE ARTIFICIAL RESPIRATION WITH OXYGEN IF RESPIRATION IS DEPRESSED (DREISBACH, HANDBOOK OF POISONING, 12TH ED.). TREAT SYMPTOMATICALLY AND SUPPORTIVELY. LAVAGE AND ADMINISTRATION OF OXYGEN SHOULD BE PERFORMED BY QUALIFIED MEDICAL PERSONNEL. GET MEDICAL ATTENTION IMMEDIATELY.

ANTIDOTE: NO SPECIFIC ANTIDOTE. TREAT SYMPTOMATICALLY AND SUPPORTIVELY.

REACTIVITY

REACTIVITY: STABLE UNDER NORMAL TEMPERATURES AND PRESSURES.

INCOMPATIBILITIES: BULAN: OXIDIZERS (STRONG): FIRE AND EXPLOSION HAZARD.

DECOMPOSITION: THERMAL DECOMPOSITION PRODUCTS MAY INCLUDE TOXIC OXIDES OF NITROGEN AND CARBON AND TOXIC AND CORROSIVE FUMES OF CHLORIDES.

POLYMERIZATION: HAZARDOUS POLYMERIZATION HAS NOT BEEN REPORTED TO OCCUR UNDER NORMAL TEMPERATURES AND PRESSURES.

STORAGE AND DISPOSAL

OBSERVE ALL FEDERAL, STATE AND LOCAL REGULATIONS WHEN STORING OR DISPOSING OF THIS SUBSTANCE. FOR ASSISTANCE, CONTACT THE DISTRICT DIRECTOR OF THE ENVIRONMENTAL PROTECTION AGENCY.

STORAGE

STORE IN ACCORDANCE WITH 40 CFR 165 RECOMMENDED PROCEDURES FOR THE DISPOSAL AND STORAGE OF PESTICIDES AND PESTICIDE CONTAINERS.
STORE AWAY FROM INCOMPATIBLE SUBSTANCES.

DISPOSAL

DISPOSAL MUST BE IN ACCORDANCE WITH 40 CFR 165 RECOMMENDED PROCEDURES FOR THE DISPOSAL AND STORAGE OF PESTICIDES AND PESTICIDE CONTAINERS.

CONDITIONS TO AVOID

MAY BURN BUT DOES NOT IGNITE READILY. AVOID CONTACT WITH STRONG OXIDIZERS, EXCESSIVE HEAT, SPARKS, OR OPEN FLAME.

SPILL AND LEAK PROCEDURES

OCCUPATIONAL SPILL: SWEEP UP AND PLACE IN SUITABLE CLEAN, DRY CONTAINERS FOR RECLAMATION OR LATER DISPOSAL. DO NOT FLUSH SPILLED MATERIAL INTO SEWER. KEEP UNNECESSARY PEOPLE AWAY.

PROTECTIVE EQUIPMENT

VENTILATION: PROVIDE LOCAL EXHAUST OR GENERAL DILUTION VENTILATION SYSTEM.

RESPIRATOR: THE FOLLOWING RESPIRATORS ARE RECOMMENDED BASED ON INFORMATION FOUND IN THE PHYSICAL DATA, TOXICITY AND HEALTH EFFECTS SECTIONS. THEY ARE RANKED IN ORDER FROM MINIMUM TO MAXIMUM RESPIRATORY PROTECTION. THE SPECIFIC RESPIRATOR SELECTED MUST BE BASED ON CONTAMINATION LEVELS FOUND IN THE WORK PLACE, MUST NOT EXCEED THE WORKING LIMITS OF THE RESPIRATOR AND BE JOINTLY APPROVED BY THE NATIONAL INSTITUTE FOR OCCUPATIONAL SAFETY AND HEALTH AND THE MINE SAFETY AND HEALTH ADMINISTRATION (NIOSH-MSHA).
CHEMICAL CARTRIDGE RESPIRATOR WITH AN ORGANIC VAPOR CARTRIDGE(S) WITH A FULL FACEPIECE AND ORGANIC VAPOR CARTRIDGE(S) IN COMBINATION WITH A DUST AND MIST FILTER. POWERED AIR-PURIFYING RESPIRATOR WITH A TIGHT-FITTING FACEPIECE AND ORGANIC VAPOR CARTRIDGE(S) IN COMBINATION WITH A HIGH-EFFICIENCY PARTICULATE FILTER.
TYPE 'C' SUPPLIED-AIR RESPIRATOR WITH A FULL FACEPIECE OPERATED IN A PRESSURE-DEMAND OR OTHER POSITIVE PRESSURE MODE.
SELF-CONTAINED BREATHING APPARATUS WITH A FULL FACEPIECE OPERATED IN PRESSURE-DEMAND OR OTHER POSITIVE PRESSURE MODE.
FOR FIREFIGHTING AND OTHER IMMEDIATELY DANGEROUS TO LIFE OR HEALTH CONDITIONS:
SELF-CONTAINED BREATHING APPARATUS WITH FULL FACEPIECE OPERATED IN PRESSURE-DEMAND OR OTHER POSITIVE PRESSURE MODE.
SUPPLIED-AIR RESPIRATOR WITH FULL FACEPIECE AND OPERATED IN PRESSURE-DEMAND OR OTHER POSITIVE PRESSURE MODE IN COMBINATION WITH AN AUXILIARY SELF-CONTAINED BREATHING APPARATUS OPERATED IN PRESSURE-DEMAND OR OTHER POSITIVE PRESSURE MODE.

CLOTHING: PROTECTIVE CLOTHING NOT REQUIRED. AVOID REPEATED OR PROLONGED CONTACT WITH THIS SUBSTANCE.

GLOVES: EMPLOYEE MUST WEAR APPROPRIATE PROTECTIVE GLOVES TO PREVENT CONTACT WITH THIS SUBSTANCE.

EYE PROTECTION: EMPLOYEE MUST WEAR SPLASH-PROOF OR DUST-RESISTANT SAFETY GOGGLES TO PREVENT EYE CONTACT WITH THIS SUBSTANCE.
EMERGENCY EYE WASH: WHERE THERE IS ANY POSSIBILITY THAT AN EMPLOYEE'S EYES MAY BE EXPOSED TO THIS SUBSTANCE, THE EMPLOYER SHOULD PROVIDE AN EYE WASH FOUNTAIN WITHIN THE IMMEDIATE WORK AREA FOR EMERGENCY USE.

AUTHORIZED BY- OCCUPATIONAL HEALTH SERVICES, INC.
CREATION DATE: 10/04/89 ***REVISION DATE:*** 05/31/90

MATERIAL SAFETY DATA SHEET

OCCUPATIONAL HEALTH SERVICES, INC.
AGRICULTURE AND PESTICIDE DIVISION
450 SEVENTH AVENUE, SUITE 2407
NEW YORK, NEW YORK 10123
1-800-445-MSDS OR (212) 967-1100

EMERGENCY CONTACT:
JOHN S. BRANSFORD, JR. (615) 292-1180

SUBSTANCE IDENTIFICATION

CAS-NUMBER 3734-97-2

SUBSTANCE: AMITON OXALATE

TRADE NAMES/SYNONYMS: PHOSPHOROTHIOIC ACID, S-(2-(DIETHYLAMINO)ETHYL) O,O-DIETHYL ESTER, ETHANEDIOATE; PHOSPHOROTHIOIC ACID, S-(2-(DIETHYLAMINO)ETHYL) O,O-DIETHYL ESTER, OXALATE; PHOSPHOROTHIOIC ACID, S-(2-(DIETHYLAMINO)ETHYL) O,O-DIETHYL ESTER, HYDROGEN OXALATE; CHIPMAN R-6,199; CITRAM; TETRAM; TETRAM MONOOXALATE; ENT 20,993; PST71642

CHEMICAL FAMILY: PHOSPHOROTHIOATE
AMINE, ALIPHATIC
OXALATE

MOLECULAR FORMULA: C10-H24-N-O3-P-S.C2-H2-O4

MOLECULAR WEIGHT: 359.42

CERCLA RATINGS (SCALE 0-3): HEALTH=3 FIRE=U REACTIVITY=U PERSISTENCE=1

NFPA RATINGS (SCALE 0-4): HEALTH=3 FIRE=U REACTIVITY=U

COMPONENTS AND CONTAMINANTS

COMPONENT: AMITON OXALATE ***PERCENT:*** 100.0
CAS# 3734-97-2

OTHER CONTAMINANTS: NONE

EXPOSURE LIMITS: AMITON OXALATE: NO OCCUPATIONAL EXPOSURE LIMITS ESTABLISHED BY OSHA, ACGIH, OR NIOSH.
100/10,000 POUNDS SARA SECTION 302 THRESHOLD PLANNING QUANTITY 1 POUND SARA SECTION 304 REPORTABLE QUANTITY

PHYSICAL DATA

DESCRIPTION: CRYSTALLINE SOLID ***SPECIFIC GRAVITY:*** NOT AVAILABLE

SOLUBILITY IN WATER: NOT AVAILABLE

FIRE AND EXPLOSION DATA

FIRE AND EXPLOSION HAZARD: UNKNOWN FIRE AND EXPLOSION HAZARD.

FIREFIGHTING MEDIA: DRY CHEMICAL, CARBON DIOXIDE, HALON, WATER SPRAY OR STANDARD FOAM (1987 EMERGENCY RESPONSE GUIDEBOOK, DOT P 5800.4).
FOR LARGER FIRES, USE WATER SPRAY, FOG OR STANDARD FOAM (1987 EMERGENCY RESPONSE GUIDEBOOK, DOT P 5800.4).

FIREFIGHTING: MOVE CONTAINERS FROM FIRE AREA IF POSSIBLE (1987 EMERGENCY RESPONSE GUIDEBOOK, DOT P 5800.4, GUIDE PAGE 53).
EXTINGUISH ONLY IF FLOW CAN BE STOPPED. EXTINGUISH USING AGENT INDICATED. USE FLOODING AMOUNTS OF WATER AS A FOG. COOL CONTAINERS WITH FLOODING AMOUNTS OF WATER FROM AS FAR A DISTANCE AS POSSIBLE. AVOID BREATHING POISONOUS VAPORS, KEEP UPWIND. CONSIDER EVACUATION OF DOWNWIND AREA IF MATERIAL IS LEAKING.

TRANSPORTATION DATA

DEPARTMENT OF TRANSPORTATION HAZARD CLASSIFICATION 49 CFR 172.101: POISON B
DEPARTMENT OF TRANSPORTATION LABELING REQUIREMENTS 49 CFR 172.101 AND SUBPART E: POISON

DEPARTMENT OF TRANSPORTATION PACKAGING REQUIREMENTS: 49 CFR 173.365 EXCEPTIONS: 49 CFR 173.364

TOXICITY

AMITON OXALATE: TOXICITY DATA: 3 MG/KG ORAL-RAT LD50; 500 UG/KG INTRAPERITONEAL-MOUSE LD50. CARCINOGEN STATUS: NONE. ACUTE TOXICITY LEVEL: HIGHLY TOXIC BY INGESTION. TARGET EFFECTS: CHOLINESTERASE INHIBITOR. POISONING MAY AFFECT THE NERVOUS SYSTEM.* AT INCREASED RISK FROM EXPOSURE: PERSONS WITH RESPIRATORY AILMENTS, RECENT EXPOSURE TO CHOLINESTERASE INHIBITORS OR IMPAIRED CHOLINESTERASE PRODUCTION, OR LIVER MALFUNCTION.* ADDITIONAL DATA: MAY CROSS THE PLACENTA. HIGH ENVIRONMENTAL TEMPERATURES OR EXPOSURE OF THE CHEMICAL TO VISIBLE OR ULTRAVIOLET LIGHT MAY ENHANCE THE TOXICITY. INTERACTIONS WITH MEDICATIONS MAY OCCUR.*

* MAY BE BASED ON GENERAL INFORMATION ON ORGANOPHOSPHATES.

HEALTH EFFECTS AND FIRST AID

INHALATION: AMITON OXALATE: SEE INFORMATION ON ORGANOPHOSPHATES. ORGANOPHOSPHATES: CHOLINESTERASE INHIBITOR. **ACUTE EXPOSURE-** WHEN INHALED, THE FIRST EFFECTS OF CHOLINESTERASE INHIBITORS ARE USUALLY RESPIRATORY AND MAY INCLUDE NASAL HYPEREMIA AND WATERY DISCHARGE, COUGH, CHEST DISCOMFORT, DYSPNEA, AND WHEEZING DUE TO INCREASED BRONCHIAL SECRETIONS AND BRONCHOCONSTRICTION. IF SUFFICIENT AMOUNTS ARE ABSORBED, OTHER SYSTEMIC EFFECTS MAY BEGIN WITHIN A FEW MINUTES OR BE DELAYED FOR UP TO 12 HOURS. SYMPTOMS MAY INCLUDE PALLOR, NAUSEA, VOMITING, DIARRHEA, ABDOMINAL CRAMPS, HEADACHE, DIZZINESS, OCULAR PAIN, BLURRED VISION, MIOSIS OR IN SOME CASES, ESPECIALLY INITIALLY, MYDRIASIS, LACRIMATION, SALIVATION, SWEATING, AND CONFUSION. OTHER REPORTED CENTRAL NERVOUS SYSTEM OR NEUROMUSCULAR EFFECTS MAY INCLUDE ATAXIA, SLURRED SPEECH, AREFLEXIA, WEAKNESS, FATIGUE, FASCICULATIONS, TWITCHING, TREMORS POSSIBLY OF THE TONGUE AND EYELIDS, AND EVENTUALLY PARALYSIS OF THE EXTREMITIES AND POSSIBLY OF THE RESPIRATORY MUSCLES. IN SEVERE CASES THERE MAY ALSO BE INVOLUNTARY DEFECATION AND URINATION, CYANOSIS, PSYCHOSIS, HYPERGLYCEMIA, ACUTE PANCREATITIS, CARDIAC IRREGULARITIES, PULMONARY EDEMA, UNCONSCIOUSNESS, CONVULSIONS, AND COMA. DEATH IS PRIMARILY DUE TO RESPIRATORY FAILURE, ALTHOUGH CARDIOVASCULAR EFFECTS INCLUDING CARDIAC ARREST MAY ALSO BE IMPLICATED. LONG TERM SEQUELAE ARE RARE BUT MAY INCLUDE NEUROPSYCHIATRIC DISORDERS AND MYOPATHY WITH MUSCLE TENDERNESS. SOME ORGANOPHOSPHATES MAY CAUSE A DELAYED NEUROPATHY BEGINNING 1-4 WEEKS AFTER AN ACUTE EXPOSURE WHICH MAY OR MAY NOT HAVE CAUSED ACUTE CHOLINERGIC EFFECTS. NUMBNESS, TINGLING, WEAKNESS AND CRAMPING BEGINNING SYMMETRICALLY IN THE LOWER LIMBS MAY PROGRESS TO ATAXIA AND PARALYSIS. IN SEVERE CASES, UPPER LIMB INVOLVEMENT IS POSSIBLE AND FLACCID PARALYSIS MAY PROGRESS TO SPASTIC PARALYSIS WITH EXAGGERATED REFLEXES. IMPROVEMENT MAY OCCUR OVER MONTHS TO YEARS, BUT SOME RESIDUAL IMPAIRMENT USUALLY REMAINS. **CHRONIC EXPOSURE-** REPEATED OR PROLONGED EXPOSURE MAY RESULT IN THE EFFECTS OF ACUTE EXPOSURE INCLUDING THE DELAYED NEUROPATHY. OTHER EFFECTS REPORTED IN WORKERS REPEATEDLY EXPOSED INCLUDE IMPAIRED MEMORY AND CONCENTRATION, ACUTE PSYCHOSIS, SEVERE DEPRESSIONS, IRRITABILTY, CONFUSION, APATHY, EMOTIONAL LABILITY, SOCIAL WITHDRAWAL, CONFUSION, HEADACHE, SPEECH DIFFICULTIES, DELAYED REACTION TIMES, SPATIAL DISORIENTATION, NIGHTMARES, SLEEPWALKING, AND DROWSINESS OR INSOMNIA. AN INFLUENZA-LIKE CONDITION WITH HEADACHE, NAUSEA, WEAKNESS, ANOREXIA AND MALAISE HAS ALSO BEEN REPORTED.

FIRST AID- REMOVE FROM EXPOSURE AREA TO FRESH AIR IMMEDIATELY. IF BREATHING HAS STOPPED, GIVE ARTIFICIAL RESPIRATION. MAINTAIN AIRWAY AND BLOOD PRESSURE AND ADMINISTER OXYGEN IF AVAILABLE. KEEP AFFECTED PERSON WARM AND AT REST. TREAT SYMPTOMATICALLY AND SUPPORTIVELY. ADMINISTRATION OF OXYGEN SHOULD BE PERFORMED BY QUALIFIED PERSONNEL. GET MEDICAL ATTENTION IMMEDIATELY.

SKIN CONTACT: AMITON OXALATE: SEE INFORMATION ON ORGANOPHOSPHATES. ORGANOPHOSPHATES: CHOLINESTERASE INHIBITOR. **ACUTE EXPOSURE-** LOCALIZED SWEATING AND FASCICULATIONS MAY OCCUR AT THE SITE OF CONTACT. IF SUFFICIENT AMOUNTS ARE ABSORBED, OTHER EFFECTS OF CHOLINESTERASE INHIBITION AS DESCRIBED IN ACUTE INHALATION MAY OCCUR. SYMPTOMS MAY BE DELAYED 2-3 HOURS, BUT USUALLY NO MORE THAN 12 HOURS. THE RATE OF ABSORPTION IS INCREASED BY THE PRESENCE OF DERMATITIS OR HIGH AMBIENT TEMPERATURES. DELAYED NEUROPATHY IS ALSO POSSIBLE. **CHRONIC EXPOSURE-** REPEATED OR PROLONGED EXPOSURE MAY CAUSE EFFECTS AS DESCRIBED IN ACUTE EXPOSURE. SOME ORGANOPHOSPHATES MAY CAUSE SENSITIZATION.

FIRST AID- REMOVE CONTAMINATED CLOTHING IMMEDIATELY. WASH CONTAMINATED AREAS WITH SOAP AND WATER FOLLOWED BY ALCOHOL (ARENA, POISONING, 4TH ED.). EMERGENCY PERSONNEL SHOULD WEAR GLOVES AND AVOID CONTAMINATION. TREAT RESPIRATORY DIFFICULTY WITH ARTIFICIAL RESPIRATION. GET MEDICAL ATTENTION IMMEDIATELY.

EYE CONTACT: AMITON OXALATE: SEE INFORMATION ON ORGANOPHOSPHATES. ORGANOPHOSPHATES: CHOLINESTERASE INHIBITOR. **ACUTE EXPOSURE-** DIRECT CONTACT MAY CAUSE PAIN, HYPEREMIA, LACRIMATION, TWITCHING OF THE EYELIDS, MIOSIS, AND CILIARY MUSCLE SPASM WITH LOSS OF ACCOMODATION, BLURRED OR DIMMED VISION AND BROWACHE. SOMETIMES MYDRIASIS MAY OCCUR INSTEAD OF MIOSIS. WITH SUFFICIENT EXPOSURE, OTHER SYMPTOMS OF CHOLINESTERASE INHIBITION AS DESCRIBED IN ACUTE INHALATION MAY OCCUR. **CHRONIC EXPOSURE-** REPEATED OR PROLONGED EXPOSURE MAY CAUSE EFFECTS AS DESCRIBED IN ACUTE EXPOSURE. SOME COMPOUNDS HAVE CAUSED TOXIC EFFECTS ON THE CRYSTALLINE LENS, CONJUNCTIVAL THICKENING AND OBSTRUCTION OF THE NASOLACRIMAL CANALS WHEN USED AS MIOTIC EYEDROPS.

FIRST AID- IRRIGATE EYES WITH WATER OR SALINE SOLUTION. IF SYMPTOMS OF POISONING OCCUR, TREAT RESPIRATORY DIFFICULTY WITH ARTIFICIAL RESPIRATION AND OXYGEN. OBSERVE PATIENT FOR AT LEAST 24-36 HOURS (GOSSELIN, CLINICAL TOXICOLOGY OF COMMERCIAL PRODUCTS, 5TH ED.). GET MEDICAL ATTENTION IMMEDIATELY. OXYGEN SHOULD BE ADMINISTERED BY QUALIFIED MEDICAL PERSONNEL.

INGESTION: AMITON OXALATE: HIGHLY TOXIC. SEE INFORMATION ON ORGANOPHOSPHATES.

ORGANOPHOSPHATES: CHOLINESTERASE INHIBITOR. **ACUTE EXPOSURE-** WHEN INGESTED, THE FIRST EFFECTS MAY BE NAUSEA, VOMITING, ANOREXIA, ABDOMINAL CRAMPS AND DIARRHEA. GASTROINTESTINAL ABSORPTION MAY CAUSE SYMPTOMS OF CHOLINESTERASE INHIBITION AS DESCRIBED IN ACUTE INHALATION. SYMPTOMS MAY BEGIN WITHIN MINUTES OR BE DELAYED FOR HOURS. DELAYED EFFECTS INCLUDING NEUROPATHY MAY ALSO OCCUR. **CHRONIC EXPOSURE-** REPEATED INGESTION MAY CAUSE EFFECTS AS DESCRIBED IN ACUTE EXPOSURE.

FIRST AID- IF PERSON IS ALERT AND RESPIRATION IS NOT DEPRESSED, GIVE SYRUP OF IPECAC FOLLOWED BY WATER (IF VOMITING OCCURS, KEEP HEAD BELOW HIPS TO PREVENT ASPIRATION). IF CONSCIOUSNESS LEVEL DECLINES OR VOMITING HAS NOT OCCURRED IN 15 MINUTES EMPTY STOMACH BY GASTRIC LAVAGE WITH THE AID OF CUFFED ENDOTRACHEAL TUBE USING ISOTONIC SALINE OR 5% SODIUM BICARBONATE FOLLOW WITH ACTIVATED CHARCOAL. ESTABLISH AND MAINTAIN AIRWAY. TREAT RESPIRATORY DIFFICULTY WITH ARTIFICIAL RESPIRATION AND OXYGEN. DO NOT GIVE MORPHINE, AMINOPHYLLINE, PHENOTHIAZINES, RESERPINE, FUROSEMIDE, OR ETHACRYNIC ACID (MORGAN, RECOGNITION AND MANAGEMENT OF PESTICIDE POISONINGS, 3RD ED.). TREAT SYMPTOMATICALLY AND SUPPORTIVELY. ADMINISTRATION OF OXYGEN AND LAVAGE MUST BE PERFORMED BY QUALIFIED MEDICAL PERSONNEL. GET MEDICAL ATTENTION IMMEDIATELY.

ANTIDOTE: THE FOLLOWING ANTIDOTE(S) HAVE BEEN RECOMMENDED. HOWEVER, THE DECISION AS TO WHETHER THE SEVERITY OF POISONING REQUIRES ADMINISTRATION OF ANY ANTIDOTE AND ACTUAL DOSE REQUIRED SHOULD BE MADE BY QUALIFIED MEDICAL PERSONNEL.

FOR CHOLINESTERASE INHIBITORS: ESTABLISH CLEAR AIRWAY AND TISSUE OXYGENATION BY ASPIRATION OF SECRETIONS, AND IF NECESSARY, BY ASSISTED PULMONARY VENTILATION WITH OXYGEN. IMPROVE TISSUE OXYGENATION AS MUCH AS POSSIBLE BEFORE ADMINISTERING ATROPINE TO MINIMIZE THE RISK OF VENTRICULAR FIBRILLATION. ADMINISTER ATROPINE SULFATE INTRAVENOUSLY, OR INTRAMUSCULARLY IF IV INJECTION IS NOT POSSIBLE. IN MODERATELY SEVERE POISONING ADMINISTER ATROPINE SULFATE, 0.4-2.0 MG REPEATED EVERY 15 MINUTES UNTIL ATROPINIZATION IS ACHIEVED (TACHYCARDIA, FLUSHING, DRY MOUTH, MYDRIASIS). MAINTAIN ATROPINIZATION BY REPEATED DOSES FOR 2-12 HOURS, OR LONGER, DEPENDING ON THE SEVERITY OF POISONING. THE APPEARANCE OF RALES IN THE LUNG BASES, MIOSIS, SALIVATION, NAUSEA, BRADYCARDIA, ARE ALL INDICATIONS OF INADEQUATE ATROPINIZATION. SEVERELY POISONED INDIVIDUALS MAY EXHIBIT REMARKABLE TOLERANCE TO ATROPINE; TWO OR MORE TIMES THE DOSAGES SUGGESTED ABOVE MAY BE NEEDED. PERSONS NOT POISONED OR ONLY SLIGHTLY POISONED, HOWEVER, MAY DEVELOP SIGNS OF ATROPINE TOXICITY FROM SUCH LARGE DOSAGES: FEVER, MUSCLE FIBRILLATIONS, AND DELIRIUM ARE THE MAIN SIGNS OF ATROPINE TOXICITY. IF THESE SIGNS APPEAR WHILE THE PATIENT IS FULLY ATROPINIZED, ATROPINE ADMINISTRATION SHOULD BE DISCONTINUED, AT LEAST TEMPORARILY. OBSERVE TREATED PATIENTS CLOSELY AT LEAST 24 HOURS TO INSURE THAT SYMPTOMS (POSSIBLY PULMONARY EDEMA) DO NOT RECUR AS ATROPINIZATION WEARS OFF. IN VERY SEVERE POISONINGS, METABOLIC DISPOSITION OF TOXICANT MAY REQUIRE SEVERAL HOURS OR DAYS DURING WHICH

ATROPINIZATION MUST BE MAINTAINED. MARKEDLY LOWER LEVELS OF URINARY METABOLITES INDICATE THAT ATROPINE DOSAGE CAN BE TAPERED OFF. AS DOSAGE IS REDUCED, CHECK THE LUNG BASES FREQUENTLY FOR RALES. IF RALES ARE HEARD OR OTHER SYMPTOMS RETURN, RE-ESTABLISH ATROPINIZATION PROMPTLY (MORGAN, RECOGNITION AND MANAGEMENT OF PESTICIDE POISONINGS, 3RD ED.). ADMINISTRATION OF ANTIDOTE MUST BE PERFORMED BY QUALIFIED MEDICAL PERSONNEL.

IN CASES OF SEVERE POISONING BY ORGANOPHOSPHATE PESTICIDES IN WHICH RESPIRATORY DEPRESSION, MUSCLE WEAKNESS AND TWITCHINGS ARE SEVERE, GIVE PRALIDOXIME (PROTOPAM-AYERST, 2-PAM), 1.0 GRAM INTRAVENOUSLY AT NO MORE THAN 0.5 GRAM PER MINUTE. DOSAGE OF PRALIDOXIME MAY BE REPEATED IN 1-2 HOURS, THEN AT 10-12 HOUR INTERVALS IF NEEDED. IN VERY SEVERE POISONINGS, DOSAGE RATES MAY BE DOUBLED. TREATMENT WITH PRALIDOXIME WILL BE MOST EFFECTIVE IF GIVEN WITHIN THIRTY-SIX HOURS AFTER POISONING (MORGAN, RECOGNITION AND MANAGEMENT OF PESTICIDE POISONINGS, 3RD ED.). ANTIDOTE SHOULD BE ADMINISTERED BY QUALIFIED MEDICAL PERSONNEL.

REACTIVITY

REACTIVITY: STABLE UNDER NORMAL TEMPERATURES AND PRESSURES.
INCOMPATIBILITIES: AMITON OXALATE: NO DATA AVAILABLE.
DECOMPOSITION: THERMAL DECOMPOSITION MAY RELEASE TOXIC AND/OR HAZARDOUS GASES.
POLYMERIZATION: HAZARDOUS POLYMERIZATION HAS NOT BEEN REPORTED TO OCCUR UNDER NORMAL TEMPERATURES AND PRESSURES.

STORAGE AND DISPOSAL

OBSERVE ALL FEDERAL, STATE AND LOCAL REGULATIONS WHEN STORING OR DISPOSING OF THIS SUBSTANCE. FOR ASSISTANCE, CONTACT THE DISTRICT DIRECTOR OF THE ENVIRONMENTAL PROTECTION AGENCY.

STORAGE

STORE IN ACCORDANCE WITH 40 CFR 165 RECOMMENDED PROCEDURES FOR THE DISPOSAL AND STORAGE OF PESTICIDES AND PESTICIDE CONTAINERS.
THRESHOLD PLANNING QUANTITY (TPQ): THE SUPERFUND AMENDMENTS AND REAUTHORIZATION ACT (SARA) SECTION 302 REQUIRES THAT EACH FACILITY WHERE ANY EXTREMELY HAZARDOUS SUBSTANCE IS PRESENT IN A QUANTITY EQUAL TO OR GREATER THAN THE TPQ ESTABLISHED FOR THAT SUBSTANCE NOTIFY THE STATE EMERGENCY RESPONSE COMMISSION FOR THE STATE IN WHICH IT IS LOCATED. SECTION 303 OF SARA REQUIRES THESE FACILITIES TO PARTICIPATE IN LOCAL EMERGENCY RESPONSE PLANNING (40 CFR 355.30).

DISPOSAL

DISPOSAL MUST BE IN ACCORDANCE WITH 40 CFR 165 RECOMMENDED PROCEDURES FOR THE DISPOSAL AND STORAGE OF PESTICIDES AND PESTICIDE CONTAINERS.

CONDITIONS TO AVOID

NONE REPORTED.

SPILL AND LEAK PROCEDURES

OCCUPATIONAL SPILL: DO NOT TOUCH SPILLED MATERIAL. STOP LEAK IF YOU CAN DO IT WITHOUT RISK. FOR SMALL SPILLS, TAKE UP WITH SAND OR OTHER ABSORBENT MATERIAL AND PLACE INTO CONTAINERS FOR LATER DISPOSAL. FOR SMALL DRY SPILLS, WITH A CLEAN SHOVEL PLACE MATERIAL INTO CLEAN, DRY CONTAINER AND COVER. MOVE CONTAINERS FROM SPILL AREA. FOR LARGER SPILLS, DIKE FAR AHEAD OF SPILL FOR LATER DISPOSAL. KEEP UNNECESSARY PEOPLE AWAY. ISOLATE HAZARD AREA AND DENY ENTRY.
REPORTABLE QUANTITY (RQ): 1 POUND THE SUPERFUND AMENDMENTS AND REAUTHORIZATION ACT (SARA) SECTION 304 REQUIRES THAT A RELEASE EQUAL TO OR GREATER THAN THE REPORTABLE QUANTITY FOR THIS SUBSTANCE BE IMMEDIATELY REPORTED TO THE LOCAL EMERGENCY PLANNING COMMITTEE AND THE STATE EMERGENCY RESPONSE COMMISSION (40 CFR 355.40). IF THE RELEASE OF THIS SUBSTANCE IS REPORTABLE UNDER CERCLA SECTION 103, THE NATIONAL RESPONSE CENTER MUST BE NOTIFIED IMMEDIATELY AT (800) 424-8802 OR (202) 426-2675 IN THE METROPOLITAN WASHINGTON, D.C. AREA (40 CFR 302.6).

PROTECTIVE EQUIPMENT

VENTILATION: PROVIDE LOCAL EXHAUST OR PROCESS ENCLOSURE VENTILATION SYSTEM.
RESPIRATOR: THE FOLLOWING RESPIRATORS ARE RECOMMENDED BASED ON INFORMATION FOUND IN THE PHYSICAL DATA, TOXICITY AND HEALTH EFFECTS SECTIONS. THEY ARE RANKED IN ORDER FROM MINIMUM TO MAXIMUM RESPIRATORY PROTECTION. THE SPECIFIC RESPIRATOR SELECTED MUST BE BASED ON CONTAMINATION LEVELS FOUND IN THE WORK PLACE, MUST NOT EXCEED THE WORKING LIMITS OF THE RESPIRATOR AND BE JOINTLY APPROVED BY THE NATIONAL INSTITUTE FOR OCCUPATIONAL SAFETY AND HEALTH AND THE MINE SAFETY AND HEALTH ADMINISTRATION (NIOSH-MSHA).
TYPE 'C' SUPPLIED-AIR RESPIRATOR WITH A FULL FACEPIECE OPERATED IN PRESSURE-DEMAND OR OTHER POSITIVE PRESSURE MODE OR WITH A FULL FACEPIECE, HELMET OR HOOD OPERATED IN CONTINOUS-FLOW MODE.
SELF-CONTAINED BREATHING APPARATUS WITH A FULL FACEPIECE OPERATED IN PRESSURE-DEMAND OR OTHER POSITIVE PRESSURE MODE.
FOR FIREFIGHTING AND OTHER IMMEDIATELY DANGEROUS TO LIFE OR HEALTH CONDITIONS:
SELF-CONTAINED BREATHING APPARATUS WITH FULL FACEPIECE OPERATED IN PRESSURE-DEMAND OR OTHER POSITIVE PRESSURE MODE.
SUPPLIED-AIR RESPIRATOR WITH FULL FACEPIECE AND OPERATED IN PRESSURE-DEMAND OR OTHER POSITIVE PRESSURE MODE IN COMBINATION WITH AN AUXILIARY SELF-CONTAINED BREATHING APPARATUS OPERATED IN PRESSURE-DEMAND OR OTHER POSITIVE PRESSURE MODE.
CLOTHING: EMPLOYEE MUST WEAR APPROPRIATE PROTECTIVE (IMPERVIOUS) CLOTHING AND EQUIPMENT TO PREVENT ANY POSSIBILITY OF SKIN CONTACT WITH THIS SUBSTANCE.
GLOVES: EMPLOYEE MUST WEAR APPROPRIATE PROTECTIVE GLOVES TO PREVENT CONTACT WITH THIS SUBSTANCE.
EYE PROTECTION: EMPLOYEE MUST WEAR SPLASH-PROOF OR DUST-RESISTANT SAFETY GOGGLES AND A FACESHIELD TO PREVENT CONTACT WITH THIS SUBSTANCE.
EMERGENCY WASH FACILITIES: WHERE THERE IS ANY POSSIBILITY THAT AN EMPLOYEE'S EYES AND/OR SKIN MAY BE EXPOSED TO THIS SUBSTANCE, THE EMPLOYER SHOULD PROVIDE AN EYE WASH FOUNTAIN AND QUICK DRENCH SHOWER WITHIN THE IMMEDIATE WORK AREA FOR EMERGENCY USE.

AUTHORIZED BY- OCCUPATIONAL HEALTH SERVICES, INC.
CREATION DATE: 10/04/89 ***REVISION DATE:*** 04/26/90

MATERIAL SAFETY DATA SHEET

OCCUPATIONAL HEALTH SERVICES, INC.
AGRICULTURE AND PESTICIDE DIVISION
450 SEVENTH AVENUE, SUITE 2407
NEW YORK, NEW YORK 10123
1-800-445-MSDS OR (212) 967-1100

EMERGENCY CONTACT:
JOHN S. BRANSFORD, JR. (615) 292-1180

SUBSTANCE IDENTIFICATION

CAS-NUMBER 298-03-3
SUBSTANCE: DEMETON-O
TRADE NAMES/SYNONYMS: PHOSPHOROTHIOIC ACID, O,O-DIETHYL O-(2-(ETHYLTHIO)ETHYL)ESTER; DIETHYL 2-(ETHYLTHIO)ETHYL)PHOSPHOROTHIONATE; DIETHYL 2-ETHTHIOETHYL THIONOPHOSPHATE; O,O-DIETHYL O-(2-ETHTHIOETHYL) PHOSPHOROTHIOATE; O,O-DIETHYL O-2-(ETHYLTHIO)ETHYL PHOSPHOROTHIOATE; DEMETONTHIONE; PST71646
CHEMICAL FAMILY: ORGANOPHOSPHATE
MOLECULAR FORMULA: C8-H19-O3-P-S2
MOLECULAR WEIGHT: 258.36
CERCLA RATINGS (SCALE 0-3): HEALTH=3 FIRE=U REACTIVITY=0 PERSISTENCE=0
NFPA RATINGS (SCALE 0-4): HEALTH=3 FIRE=U REACTIVITY=0

COMPONENTS AND CONTAMINANTS

COMPONENT: DEMETON-O ***PERCENT:*** 100.0
CAS# 298-03-3
OTHER CONTAMINANTS: NONE
EXPOSURE LIMITS: DEMETON: 0.1 MG/M3 OSHA TWA (SKIN) 0.01 PPM (0.1 MG/M3) ACGIH TWA (SKIN)

PHYSICAL DATA

DESCRIPTION: COLORLESS, OILY LIQUID ***BOILING POINT:*** 223 F (106 C) @ .4 MMHG
SPECIFIC GRAVITY: 1.1193 ***VAPOR PRESSURE:*** 0.00025 MMHG @ 20 C
SOLUBILITY IN WATER: 0.01%
SOLVENT SOLUBILITY: MOST ORGANIC SOLVENTS

FIRE AND EXPLOSION DATA

FIRE AND EXPLOSION HAZARD: UNKNOWN FIRE AND EXPLOSION HAZARD.
FIREFIGHTING MEDIA: DRY CHEMICAL, CARBON DIOXIDE, HALON, WATER SPRAY OR STANDARD FOAM (1987 EMERGENCY RESPONSE GUIDEBOOK, DOT P 5800.4).
FOR LARGER FIRES, USE WATER SPRAY, FOG OR STANDARD FOAM (1987 EMERGENCY RESPONSE GUIDEBOOK, DOT P 5800.4).

FIREFIGHTING: MOVE CONTAINERS FROM FIRE AREA IF POSSIBLE. FIGHT FIRE FROM MAXIMUM DISTANCE. STAY AWAY FROM STORAGE TANK ENDS. DIKE FIRE CONTROL WATER FOR LATER DISPOSAL. DO NOT SCATTER MATERIAL (1987 EMERGENCY RESPONSE GUIDEBOOK, DOT P 5800.4, GUIDE PAGE 55). EXTINGUISH ONLY IF FLOW CAN BE STOPPED; USE FLOODING AMOUNTS OF WATER AS FOG, SOLID STREAMS MAY BE INEFFECTIVE. COOL CONTAINERS WITH FLOODING AMOUNTS OF WATER FROM AS FAR A DISTANCE AS POSSIBLE. USE WATER SPRAY TO ABSORB TOXIC VAPORS. AVOID BREATHING TOXIC VAPORS; KEEP UPWIND. CONSIDER EVACUATION OF DOWNWIND AREA IF MATERIAL IS LEAKING.

TRANSPORTATION DATA

DEPARTMENT OF TRANSPORTATION HAZARD CLASSIFICATION 49 CFR 172.101: POISON B

DEPARTMENT OF TRANSPORTATION LABELING REQUIREMENTS 49 CFR 172.101 AND SUBPART E: POISON

DEPARTMENT OF TRANSPORTATION PACKAGING REQUIREMENTS: 49 CFR 173.346 EXCEPTIONS: 49 CFR 173.345

TOXICITY

DEMETON-O; TOXICITY DATA: 7500 UG/KG ORAL-RAT LD50; 15 MG/KG SUBCUTANEOUS-MOUSE LD50; 10 MG/KG INTRAPERITONEAL-HAMSTER LD50; MUTAGENIC DATA (RTECS). CARCINOGEN STATUS: NONE. ACUTE TOXICITY LEVEL: HIGHLY TOXIC BY INGESTION. TARGET EFFECTS: CHOLINESTERASE INHIBITOR. AT INCREASED RISK FROM EXPOSURE: PERSONS WITH RESPIRATORY AILMENTS, RECENT EXPOSURE TO CHOLINESTERASE INHIBITORS OR IMPAIRED CHOLINESTERASE PRODUCTION, OR LIVER MALFUNCTION.* ADDITIONAL DATA: MAY CROSS THE PLACENTA. HIGH ENVIRONMENTAL TEMPERATURES OR EXPOSURE OF THE CHEMICAL TO VISIBLE OR ULTRAVIOLET LIGHT MAY ENHANCE THE TOXICITY. INTERACTIONS WITH MEDICATIONS MAY OCCUR.*

* MAY BE BASED ON GENERAL INFORMATION ON ORGANOPHOSPHATES.

HEALTH EFFECTS AND FIRST AID

INHALATION: DEMETON-O: 20 MG/M3 IMMEDIATELY DANGEROUS TO LIFE OR HEALTH. ALTHOUGH THERE IS NO DATA ON THE ISOMER, DEMETON-O, THE MIXTURE OF THE ISOMERS, DEMETON IS HIGHLY TOXIC. SEE INFORMATION ON ORGANOPHOSPHATES.

ORGANOPHOSPHATES: CHOLINESTERASE INHIBITOR. **ACUTE EXPOSURE-** WHEN INHALED, THE FIRST EFFECTS OF CHOLINESTERASE INHIBITORS ARE USUALLY RESPIRATORY AND MAY INCLUDE NASAL HYPEREMIA AND WATERY DISCHARGE, COUGH, CHEST DISCOMFORT, DYSPNEA, AND WHEEZING DUE TO INCREASED BRONCHIAL SECRETIONS AND BRONCHOCONSTRICTION. IF SUFFICIENT AMOUNTS ARE ABSORBED, OTHER SYSTEMIC EFFECTS MAY BEGIN WITHIN A FEW MINUTES OR BE DELAYED FOR UP TO 12 HOURS. SYMPTOMS MAY INCLUDE PALLOR, NAUSEA, VOMITING, DIARRHEA, ABDOMINAL CRAMPS, HEADACHE, DIZZINESS, OCULAR PAIN, BLURRED VISION, MIOSIS OR IN SOME CASES, ESPECIALLY INITIALLY, MYDRIASIS, LACRIMATION, SALIVATION, SWEATING, AND CONFUSION. OTHER REPORTED CENTRAL NERVOUS SYSTEM OR NEUROMUSCULAR EFFECTS MAY INCLUDE ATAXIA, SLURRED SPEECH, AREFLEXIA, WEAKNESS, FATIGUE, FASCICULATIONS, TWITCHING, TREMORS POSSIBLY OF THE TONGUE AND EYELIDS, AND EVENTUALLY PARALYSIS OF THE EXTREMITIES AND POSSIBLY OF THE RESPIRATORY MUSCLES. IN SEVERE CASES THERE MAY ALSO BE INVOLUNTARY DEFECATION AND URINATION, CYANOSIS, PSYCHOSIS, HYPERGLYCEMIA, ACUTE PANCREATITIS, CARDIAC IRREGULARITIES, PULMONARY EDEMA, UNCONSCIOUSNESS, CONVULSIONS, AND COMA. DEATH IS PRIMARILY DUE TO RESPIRATORY FAILURE, ALTHOUGH CARDIOVASCULAR EFFECTS INCLUDING CARDIAC ARREST MAY ALSO BE IMPLICATED. LONG TERM SEQUELAE ARE RARE BUT MAY INCLUDE NEUROPSYCHIATRIC DISORDERS AND MYOPATHY WITH MUSCLE TENDERNESS. **CHRONIC EXPOSURE-** REPEATED OR PROLONGED EXPOSURE MAY RESULT IN THE EFFECTS OF ACUTE EXPOSURE. OTHER EFFECTS REPORTED IN WORKERS REPEATEDLY EXPOSED INCLUDE IMPAIRED MEMORY AND CONCENTRATION, ACUTE PSYCHOSIS, SEVERE DEPRESSIONS, IRRITABILTY, CONFUSION, APATHY, EMOTIONAL LABILITY, SOCIAL WITHDRAWAL, CONFUSION, HEADACHE, SPEECH DIFFICULTIES, DELAYED REACTION TIMES, SPATIAL DISORIENTATION, NIGHTMARES, SLEEPWALKING, AND DROWSINESS OR INSOMNIA. AN INFLUENZA-LIKE CONDITION WITH HEADACHE, NAUSEA, WEAKNESS, ANOREXIA AND MALAISE HAS ALSO BEEN REPORTED.

FIRST AID- REMOVE FROM EXPOSURE AREA TO FRESH AIR IMMEDIATELY. IF BREATHING HAS STOPPED, GIVE ARTIFICIAL RESPIRATION. MAINTAIN AIRWAY AND BLOOD PRESSURE AND ADMINISTER OXYGEN IF AVAILABLE. KEEP AFFECTED PERSON WARM AND AT REST. TREAT SYMPTOMATICALLY AND SUPPORTIVELY. ADMINISTRATION OF OXYGEN SHOULD BE PERFORMED BY QUALIFIED PERSONNEL. GET MEDICAL ATTENTION IMMEDIATELY.

SKIN CONTACT: DEMETON-O: ALTHOUGH THERE IS NO DATA ON THE ISOMER, DEMETON-O, THE MIXTURE OF ISOMERS, DEMETON IS HIGHLY TOXIC BY SKIN ABSORPTION. SEE INFORMATION ON ORGANOPHOSPHATES.

ORGANOPHOSPHATES: CHOLINESTERASE INHIBITOR. **ACUTE EXPOSURE-** LOCALIZED SWEATING AND FASCICULATIONS MAY OCCUR AT THE SITE OF CONTACT. IF SUFFICIENT AMOUNTS ARE ABSORBED, OTHER EFFECTS OF CHOLINESTERASE INHIBITION AS DESCRIBED IN ACUTE INHALATION MAY OCCUR. SYMPTOMS MAY BE DELAYED 2-3 HOURS, BUT USUALLY NO MORE THAN 12 HOURS. THE RATE OF ABSORPTION IS INCREASED BY THE PRESENCE OF DERMATITIS OR HIGH AMBIENT TEMPERATURES. **CHRONIC EXPOSURE-** REPEATED OR PROLONGED EXPOSURE MAY CAUSE EFFECTS AS DESCRIBED IN ACUTE EXPOSURE. SOME ORGANOPHOSPHATES MAY CAUSE SENSITIZATION.

FIRST AID- REMOVE CONTAMINATED CLOTHING IMMEDIATELY. WASH CONTAMINATED AREAS WITH SOAP AND WATER FOLLOWED BY ALCOHOL (ARENA, POISONING, 4TH ED.). EMERGENCY PERSONNEL SHOULD WEAR GLOVES AND AVOID CONTAMINATION. TREAT RESPIRATORY DIFFICULTY WITH ARTIFICIAL RESPIRATION. GET MEDICAL ATTENTION IMMEDIATELY.

EYE CONTACT: DEMETON-O: SEE INFORMATION ON ORGANOPHOSPHATES.

ORGANOPHOSPHATES: CHOLINESTERASE INHIBITOR. **ACUTE EXPOSURE-** DIRECT CONTACT MAY CAUSE PAIN, HYPEREMIA, LACRIMATION, TWITCHING OF THE EYELIDS, MIOSIS, AND CILIARY MUSCLE SPASM WITH LOSS OF ACCOMODATION, BLURRED OR DIMMED VISION AND BROWACHE. SOMETIMES MYDRIASIS MAY OCCUR INSTEAD OF MIOSIS. WITH SUFFICIENT EXPOSURE, OTHER SYMPTOMS OF CHOLINESTERASE INHIBITION AS DESCRIBED IN ACUTE INHALATION MAY OCCUR. **CHRONIC EXPOSURE-** REPEATED OR PROLONGED EXPOSURE MAY CAUSE EFFECTS AS DESCRIBED IN ACUTE EXPOSURE. SOME COMPOUNDS HAVE CAUSED TOXIC EFFECTS ON THE CRYSTALLINE LENS, CONJUNCTIVAL THICKENING AND OBSTRUCTION OF THE NASOLACRIMAL CANALS WHEN USED AS MIOTIC EYEDROPS.

FIRST AID- IRRIGATE EYES WITH WATER OR SALINE SOLUTION. IF SYMPTOMS OF POISONING OCCUR, TREAT RESPIRATORY DIFFICULTY WITH ARTIFICIAL RESPIRATION AND OXYGEN. OBSERVE PATIENT FOR AT LEAST 24-36 HOURS (GOSSELIN, CLINICAL TOXICOLOGY OF COMMERCIAL PRODUCTS, 5TH ED.). GET MEDICAL ATTENTION IMMEDIATELY. OXYGEN SHOULD BE ADMINISTERED BY QUALIFIED MEDICAL PERSONNEL.

INGESTION: DEMETON-O: HIGHLY TOXIC. IN ONE STUDY OF 5 MEN WHO EACH INGESTED 7.125 MG PER DAY OF THE TECHNICAL DEMETON FOR 25 DAYS, 39.8% AND 15.9% DEPRESSIONS IN PLASMA AND ERYTHROCYTE CHOLINESTERASE ACTIVITY WERE OBSERVED. THIS MATERIAL DOES NOT INDUCE DELAYED NEUROTOXIC SIGNS OF POISONING IN HENS OR POTENTIATE THE ACUTE TOXICITY OF OTHER ANTI-CHOLINESTERASE ORGANOPHOSPHATES OR CARBAMATE INSECTICIDES. SEE INFORMATION ON ORGANOPHOSPHATES.

ORGANOPHOSPHATES: CHOLINESTERASE INHIBITOR. **ACUTE EXPOSURE-** WHEN INGESTED, THE FIRST EFFECTS MAY BE NAUSEA, VOMITING, ANOREXIA, ABDOMINAL CRAMPS AND DIARRHEA. GASTROINTESTINAL ABSORPTION MAY CAUSE THE SYMPTOMS OF CHOLINESTERASE INHIBITION AS DESCRIBED IN ACUTE INHALATION. SYMPTOMS MAY BEGIN WITHIN MINUTES OR BE DELAYED. **CHRONIC EXPOSURE-** REPEATED INGESTION MAY CAUSE EFFECTS AS DESCRIBED IN ACUTE EXPOSURE.

FIRST AID- IF PERSON IS ALERT AND RESPIRATION IS NOT DEPRESSED, GIVE SYRUP OF IPECAC FOLLOWED BY WATER (IF VOMITING OCCURS, KEEP HEAD BELOW HIPS TO PREVENT ASPIRATION). IF CONSCIOUSNESS LEVEL DECLINES OR VOMITING HAS NOT OCCURRED IN 15 MINUTES EMPTY STOMACH BY GASTRIC LAVAGE WITH THE AID OF CUFFED ENDOTRACHEAL TUBE USING ISOTONIC SALINE OR 5% SODIUM BICARBONATE FOLLOW WITH ACTIVATED CHARCOAL. ESTABLISH AND MAINTAIN AIRWAY. TREAT RESPIRATORY DIFFICULTY WITH ARTIFICIAL RESPIRATION AND OXYGEN. DO NOT GIVE MORPHINE, AMINOPHYLLINE, PHENOTHIAZINES, RESERPINE, FUROSEMIDE, OR ETHACRYNIC ACID (MORGAN, RECOGNITION AND MANAGEMENT OF PESTICIDE POISONINGS, 3RD ED.). TREAT SYMPTOMATICALLY AND SUPPORTIVELY. ADMINISTRATION OF OXYGEN AND LAVAGE MUST BE PERFORMED BY QUALIFIED MEDICAL PERSONNEL. GET MEDICAL ATTENTION IMMEDIATELY.

ANTIDOTE: THE FOLLOWING ANTIDOTE(S) HAVE BEEN RECOMMENDED. HOWEVER, THE DECISION AS TO WHETHER THE SEVERITY OF POISONING REQUIRES ADMINISTRATION OF ANY ANTIDOTE AND ACTUAL DOSE REQUIRED SHOULD BE MADE BY QUALIFIED MEDICAL PERSONNEL.

FOR CHOLINESTERASE INHIBITORS: ESTABLISH CLEAR AIRWAY AND TISSUE OXYGENATION BY ASPIRATION OF SECRETIONS, AND IF NECESSARY, BY ASSISTED PULMONARY VENTILATION WITH OXYGEN. IMPROVE TISSUE OXYGENATION AS MUCH AS POSSIBLE BEFORE ADMINISTERING ATROPINE TO MINIMIZE THE RISK OF VENTRICULAR FIBRILLATION. ADMINISTER ATROPINE SULFATE INTRAVENOUSLY, OR INTRAMUSCULARLY IF IV INJECTION IS NOT POSSIBLE. IN MODERATELY SEVERE POISONING ADMINISTER ATROPINE SULFATE, 0.4-2.0 MG REPEATED EVERY 15 MINUTES UNTIL ATROPINIZATION IS ACHIEVED (TACHYCARDIA, FLUSHING, DRY MOUTH, MYDRIASIS). MAINTAIN ATROPINIZATION BY REPEATED DOSES FOR 2-12 HOURS, OR LONGER, DEPENDING ON THE SEVERITY OF POISONING. THE APPEARANCE OF RALES IN THE LUNG BASES, MIOSIS, SALIVATION, NAUSEA,

BRADYCARDIA, ARE ALL INDICATIONS OF INADEQUATE ATROPINIZATION. SEVERELY POISONED INDIVIDUALS MAY EXHIBIT REMARKABLE TOLERANCE TO ATROPINE; TWO OR MORE TIMES THE DOSAGES SUGGESTED ABOVE MAY BE NEEDED. PERSONS NOT POISONED OR ONLY SLIGHTLY POISONED, HOWEVER, MAY DEVELOP SIGNS OF ATROPINE TOXICITY FROM SUCH LARGE DOSAGES: FEVER, MUSCLE FIBRILLATIONS, AND DELIRIUM ARE THE MAIN SIGNS OF ATROPINE TOXICITY. IF THESE SIGNS APPEAR WHILE THE PATIENT IS FULLY ATROPINIZED, ATROPINE ADMINISTRATION SHOULD BE DISCONTINUED, AT LEAST TEMPORARILY. OBSERVE TREATED PATIENTS CLOSELY AT LEAST 24 HOURS TO INSURE THAT SYMPTOMS (POSSIBLY PULMONARY EDEMA) DO NOT RECUR AS ATROPINIZATION WEARS OFF. IN VERY SEVERE POISONINGS, METABOLIC DISPOSITION OF TOXICANT MAY REQUIRE SEVERAL HOURS OR DAYS DURING WHICH ATROPINIZATION MUST BE MAINTAINED. MARKEDLY LOWER LEVELS OF URINARY METABOLITES INDICATE THAT ATROPINE DOSAGE CAN BE TAPERED OFF. AS DOSAGE IS REDUCED, CHECK THE LUNG BASES FREQUENTLY FOR RALES. IF RALES ARE HEARD OR OTHER SYMPTOMS RETURN, RE-ESTABLISH ATROPINIZATION PROMPTLY (MORGAN, RECOGNITION AND MANAGEMENT OF PESTICIDE POISONINGS, 3RD ED.). ADMINISTRATION OF ANTIDOTE MUST BE PERFORMED BY QUALIFIED MEDICAL PERSONNEL.

IN CASES OF SEVERE POISONING BY ORGANOPHOSPHATE PESTICIDES IN WHICH RESPIRATORY DEPRESSION, MUSCLE WEAKNESS AND TWITCHINGS ARE SEVERE, GIVE PRALIDOXIME (PROTOPAM-AYERST, 2-PAM), 1.0 GRAM INTRAVENOUSLY AT NO MORE THAN 0.5 GRAM PER MINUTE. DOSAGE OF PRALIDOXIME MAY BE REPEATED IN 1-2 HOURS, THEN AT 10-12 HOUR INTERVALS IF NEEDED. IN VERY SEVERE POISONINGS, DOSAGE RATES MAY BE DOUBLED. TREATMENT WITH PRALIDOXIME WILL BE MOST EFFECTIVE IF GIVEN WITHIN THIRTY-SIX HOURS AFTER POISONING (MORGAN, RECOGNITION AND MANAGEMENT OF PESTICIDE POISONINGS, 3RD ED.). ANTIDOTE SHOULD BE ADMINISTERED BY QUALIFIED MEDICAL PERSONNEL.

REACTIVITY

REACTIVITY: STABLE UNDER NORMAL TEMPERATURES AND PRESSURES; HYDROLYZED BY BOILING WATER.

INCOMPATIBILITIES: DEMETON-O: ALKALINE CONDITIONS: MAY CAUSE HYDROLYSIS. BORDEAUX:INCOMPATIBLE CALCIUM ARSENATE: INCOMPATIBLE. CYPREX: INCOMPATIBLE. LIME OR LIME SULFUR: INCOMPATIBLE. MERCURY COMPOUNDS (WATER SOLUBLE): INCOMPATIBLE. PARIS GREEN: INCOMPATIBLE PLASTICS, RUBBER, AND COATINGS: SOME FORMS MAY BE ATTACKED. STRONG OXIDIZERS: MAY CAUSE FIRE OR EXPLOSION. UREA: INCOMPATIBLE. ZINC ARSENATE: INCOMPATIBLE.

DECOMPOSITION: THERMAL DECOMPOSITION MAY RELEASE TOXIC OXIDES OF PHOSPHORUS AND SULFUR.

POLYMERIZATION: HAZARDOUS POLYMERIZATION HAS NOT BEEN REPORTED TO OCCUR UNDER NORMAL TEMPERATURES AND PRESSURES.

STORAGE AND DISPOSAL

OBSERVE ALL FEDERAL, STATE AND LOCAL REGULATIONS WHEN STORING OR DISPOSING OF THIS SUBSTANCE. FOR ASSISTANCE, CONTACT THE DISTRICT DIRECTOR OF THE ENVIRONMENTAL PROTECTION AGENCY.

****STORAGE****

STORE IN ACCORDANCE WITH 40 CFR 165 RECOMMENDED PROCEDURES FOR THE DISPOSAL AND STORAGE OF PESTICIDES AND PESTICIDE CONTAINERS.

STORE AWAY FROM INCOMPATIBLE SUBSTANCES.

THRESHOLD PLANNING QUANTITY (TPQ): THE SUPERFUND AMENDMENTS AND REAUTHORIZATION ACT (SARA) SECTION 302 REQUIRES THAT EACH FACILITY WHERE ANY EXTREMELY HAZARDOUS SUBSTANCE IS PRESENT IN A QUANTITY EQUAL TO OR GREATER THAN THE TPQ ESTABLISHED FOR THAT SUBSTANCE NOTIFY THE STATE EMERGENCY RESPONSE COMMISSION FOR THE STATE IN WHICH IT IS LOCATED. SECTION 303 OF SARA REQUIRES THESE FACILITIES TO PARTICIPATE IN LOCAL EMERGENCY RESPONSE PLANNING (40 CFR 355.30).

****DISPOSAL****

DISPOSAL MUST BE IN ACCORDANCE WITH 40 CFR 165 RECOMMENDED PROCEDURES FOR THE DISPOSAL AND STORAGE OF PESTICIDES AND PESTICIDE CONTAINERS.

CONDITIONS TO AVOID

NONE REPORTED.

SPILL AND LEAK PROCEDURES

OCCUPATIONAL SPILL: DO NOT TOUCH SPILLED MATERIAL. STOP LEAK IF YOU CAN DO IT WITHOUT RISK. USE WATER SPRAY TO REDUCE VAPORS. FOR SMALL SPILLS, TAKE UP WITH SAND OR OTHER ABSORBENT MATERIAL AND PLACE INTO CONTAINERS FOR LATER DISPOSAL. FOR SMALL DRY SPILLS, WITH A CLEAN SHOVEL PLACE MATERIAL INTO CLEAN, DRY CONTAINERS AND COVER. MOVE CONTAINERS FROM SPILL AREA. FOR LARGER SPILLS, DIKE FAR AHEAD OF SPILL FOR LATER DISPOSAL. KEEP UNNECESSARY PEOPLE AWAY. ISOLATE HAZARD AREA AND DENY ENTRY. VENTILATE CLOSED SPACES BEFORE ENTERING.

REPORTABLE QUANTITY (RQ): 1 POUND THE SUPERFUND AMENDMENTS AND REAUTHORIZATION ACT (SARA) SECTION 304 REQUIRES THAT A RELEASE EQUAL TO OR GREATER THAN THE REPORTABLE QUANTITY FOR THIS SUBSTANCE BE IMMEDIATELY REPORTED TO THE LOCAL EMERGENCY PLANNING COMMITTEE AND THE STATE EMERGENCY RESPONSE COMMISSION (40 CFR 355.40). IF THE RELEASE OF THIS SUBSTANCE IS REPORTABLE UNDER CERCLA SECTION 103, THE NATIONAL RESPONSE CENTER MUST BE NOTIFIED IMMEDIATELY AT (800) 424-8802 OR (202) 426-2675 IN THE METROPOLITAN WASHINGTON, D.C. AREA (40 CFR 302.6).

PROTECTIVE EQUIPMENT

VENTILATION: PROCESS ENCLOSURE RECOMMENDED TO MEET PUBLISHED EXPOSURE LIMITS.

RESPIRATOR: THE FOLLOWING RESPIRATORS AND MAXIMUM USE CONCENTRATIONS ARE RECOMMENDATIONS BY THE U.S. DEPARTMENT OF HEALTH AND HUMAN SERVICES, NIOSH POCKET GUIDE TO CHEMICAL HAZARDS; NIOSH CRITERIA DOCUMENTS OR BY THE U.S. DEPARTMENT OF LABOR, 29 CFR 1910 SUBPART Z. THE SPECIFIC RESPIRATOR SELECTED MUST BE BASED ON CONTAMINATION LEVELS FOUND IN THE WORK PLACE, MUST NOT EXCEED THE WORKING LIMITS OF THE RESPIRATOR AND BE JOINTLY APPROVED BY THE NATIONAL INSTITUTE FOR OCCUPATIONAL SAFETY AND HEALTH AND THE MINE SAFETY AND HEALTH ADMINISTRATION (NIOSH-MSHA).

DEMETON: 1 MG/M3- ANY SUPPLIED-AIR RESPIRATOR. ANY SELF-CONTAINED BREATHING APPARATUS.

2.5 MG/M3- ANY SUPPLIED-AIR RESPIRATOR OPERATED IN A CONTINUOUS FLOW MODE.

5 MG/M3- ANY SELF-CONTAINED BREATHING APPARATUS WITH A FULL FACEPIECE. ANY SUPPLIED-AIR RESPIRATOR WITH A FULL FACEPIECE. ANY SUPPLIED-AIR RESPIRATOR WITH A TIGHT-FITTING FACEPIECE OPERATED IN A CONTINUOUS FLOW MODE.

20 MG/M3- ANY SUPPLIED-AIR RESPIRATOR WITH A HALF-MASK AND OPERATED IN A PRESSURE-DEMAND OR OTHER POSITIVE PRESSURE MODE.

ESCAPE- ANY AIR-PURIFYING FULL FACEPIECE RESPIRATOR (GAS MASK) WITH A CHIN-STYLE OR FRONT- OR BACK-MOUNTED ORGANIC VAPOR CANISTER HAVING A HIGH-EFFICIENCY PARTICULATE FILTER. ANY APPROPRIATE ESCAPE-TYPE SELF-CONTAINED BREATHING APPARATUS.

FOR FIREFIGHTING AND OTHER IMMEDIATELY DANGEROUS TO LIFE OR HEALTH CONDITIONS: SELF-CONTAINED BREATHING APPARATUS WITH FULL FACEPIECE OPERATED IN PRESSURE-DEMAND OR OTHER POSITIVE PRESSURE MODE. SUPPLIED-AIR RESPIRATOR WITH FULL FACEPIECE AND OPERATED IN PRESSURE-DEMAND OR OTHER POSITIVE PRESSURE MODE IN COMBINATION WITH AN AUXILIARY SELF-CONTAINED BREATHING APPARATUS OPERATED IN PRESSURE-DEMAND OR OTHER POSITIVE PRESSURE MODE.

CLOTHING: EMPLOYEE MUST WEAR APPROPRIATE PROTECTIVE (IMPERVIOUS) CLOTHING AND EQUIPMENT TO PREVENT ANY POSSIBILITY OF SKIN CONTACT WITH THIS SUBSTANCE.

GLOVES: EMPLOYEE MUST WEAR APPROPRIATE PROTECTIVE GLOVES TO PREVENT CONTACT WITH THIS SUBSTANCE.

EYE PROTECTION: EMPLOYEE MUST WEAR SPLASH-PROOF OR DUST-RESISTANT SAFETY GOGGLES AND A FACESHIELD TO PREVENT CONTACT WITH THIS SUBSTANCE.

EMERGENCY WASH FACILITIES: WHERE THERE IS ANY POSSIBILITY THAT AN EMPLOYEE'S EYES AND/OR SKIN MAY BE EXPOSED TO THIS SUBSTANCE, THE EMPLOYER SHOULD PROVIDE AN EYE WASH FOUNTAIN AND QUICK DRENCH SHOWER WITHIN THE IMMEDIATE WORK AREA FOR EMERGENCY USE.

AUTHORIZED BY- OCCUPATIONAL HEALTH SERVICES, INC.
CREATION DATE: 10/04/89 ***REVISION DATE:*** 06/20/90

MATERIAL SAFETY DATA SHEET

OCCUPATIONAL HEALTH SERVICES, INC.
AGRICULTURE AND PESTICIDE DIVISION
450 SEVENTH AVENUE, SUITE 2407
NEW YORK, NEW YORK 10123
1-800-445-MSDS OR (212) 967-1100

EMERGENCY CONTACT:
JOHN S. BRANSFORD, JR. (615) 292-1180

SUBSTANCE IDENTIFICATION

CAS-NUMBER 126-75-0
SUBSTANCE: **DEMETON-S**

TRADE NAMES/SYNONYMS: PHOSPHOROTHIOIC ACID, O,O-DIETHYL S-(2-(ETHYLTHIO)ETHYL)ESTER; DIETHYL S-(2-ETHIOETHYL)THIOPHOSPHATE; O,O-DIETHYL S-(2-ETHTHIOETHYL) PHOSPHOROTHIOATE; O,O-DIETHYL S-ETHYL-2-ETHYLMERCAPTOPHOSPHOROTHIOLATE; O,O-DIETHYL S-2-(ETHYLTHIO)ETHYL PHOSPHOROTHIOATE; O,O-DIETHYL S-(2-(ETHYLTHIO)ETHYL)PHOSPHOROTHIOLATE; ETHANETHIOL, 2-(ETHYLTHIO)-, S-ESTER WITH O,O-DIETHYL PHOSPHOROTHIOATE; DEMETONTHIOL; DEMETON THIOLO; ETHYLTHIONODEMETON; IS; ISOSYSTOX; SYSTOX-THIOL; THIOLDEMETON; PST71646
CHEMICAL FAMILY: ORGANOPHOSPHATE
MOLECULAR FORMULA: C8-H19-O3-P-S2
MOLECULAR WEIGHT: 258.36
CERCLA RATINGS (SCALE 0-3): HEALTH=3 FIRE=U REACTIVITY=0 PERSISTENCE=0
NFPA RATINGS (SCALE 0-4): HEALTH=3 FIRE=U REACTIVITY=0

COMPONENTS AND CONTAMINANTS

COMPONENT: DEMETON-S ***PERCENT:*** 100.0
CAS# 126-75-0
OTHER CONTAMINANTS: NONE
EXPOSURE LIMITS: DEMETON: 0.1 MG/M3 OSHA TWA (SKIN) 0.01 PPM (0.1 MG/M3) ACGIH TWA (SKIN)

PHYSICAL DATA

DESCRIPTION: COLORLESS, OILY LIQUID ***BOILING POINT:*** 212 F (100 C) @ .25 MMHG
SPECIFIC GRAVITY: 1.1325 ***VAPOR PRESSURE:*** 0.00026 MMHG @ 20 C
SOLUBILITY IN WATER: 0.2%
SOLVENT SOLUBILITY: MOST ORGANIC SOLVENTS

FIRE AND EXPLOSION DATA

FIRE AND EXPLOSION HAZARD: UNKNOWN FIRE AND EXPLOSION HAZARD.
FIREFIGHTING MEDIA: DRY CHEMICAL, CARBON DIOXIDE, HALON, WATER SPRAY OR STANDARD FOAM (1987 EMERGENCY RESPONSE GUIDEBOOK, DOT P 5800.4). FOR LARGER FIRES, USE WATER SPRAY, FOG OR STANDARD FOAM (1987 EMERGENCY RESPONSE GUIDEBOOK, DOT P 5800.4).
FIREFIGHTING: MOVE CONTAINERS FROM FIRE AREA IF POSSIBLE. FIGHT FIRE FROM MAXIMUM DISTANCE. STAY AWAY FROM STORAGE TANK ENDS. DIKE FIRE CONTROL WATER FOR LATER DISPOSAL. DO NOT SCATTER MATERIAL (1987 EMERGENCY RESPONSE GUIDEBOOK, DOT P 5800.4, GUIDE PAGE 55). EXTINGUISH ONLY IF FLOW CAN BE STOPPED; USE FLOODING AMOUNTS OF WATER AS FOG, SOLID STREAMS MAY BE INEFFECTIVE. COOL CONTAINERS WITH FLOODING AMOUNTS OF WATER FROM AS FAR A DISTANCE AS POSSIBLE. USE WATER SPRAY TO ABSORB TOXIC VAPORS. AVOID BREATHING TOXIC VAPORS; KEEP UPWIND. CONSIDER EVACUATION OF DOWNWIND AREA IF MATERIAL IS LEAKING.

TRANSPORTATION DATA

DEPARTMENT OF TRANSPORTATION HAZARD CLASSIFICATION 49 CFR 172.101: POISON B
DEPARTMENT OF TRANSPORTATION LABELING REQUIREMENTS 49 CFR 172.101 AND SUBPART E: POISON
DEPARTMENT OF TRANSPORTATION PACKAGING REQUIREMENTS: 49 CFR 173.346 EXCEPTIONS: 49 CFR 173.345

TOXICITY

DEMETON-S; TOXICITY DATA: 1500 UG/KG ORAL-RAT LD50; 6 MG/KG SUBCUTANEOUS-MOUSE LD50; 1700 UG/KG INTRAVENOUS-RAT LD50; 1500 UG/KG INTRAPERITONEAL-RAT LD50; 174 UG/KG INTRAPERITONEAL-MOUSE LD50; 5500 UG/KG INTRAPERITONEAL-GUINEA PIG LD50. CARCINOGEN STATUS: NONE. ACUTE TOXICITY LEVEL: HIGHLY TOXIC BY INGESTION. TARGET EFFECTS: CHOLINESTERASE INHIBITOR. AT INCREASED RISK FROM EXPOSURE: PERSONS WITH RESPIRATORY AILMENTS, RECENT EXPOSURE TO CHOLINESTERASE INHIBITORS OR IMPAIRED CHOLINESTERASE PRODUCTION, OR LIVER MALFUNCTION.* ADDITIONAL DATA: MAY CROSS THE PLACENTA. HIGH ENVIRONMENTAL TEMPERATURES OR EXPOSURE OF THE CHEMICAL TO VISIBLE OR ULTRAVIOLET LIGHT MAY ENHANCE THE TOXICITY. INTERACTIONS WITH MEDICATIONS MAY OCCUR.*
* MAY BE BASED ON GENERAL INFORMATION ON ORGANOPHOSPHATES.

HEALTH EFFECTS AND FIRST AID

INHALATION: DEMETON-S: 20 MG/M3 IMMEDIATELY DANGEROUS TO LIFE OR HEALTH. ALTHOUGH THERE IS NO DATA ON THE ISOMER, DEMETON-S, THE MIXTURE OF ISOMERS, DEMETON IS HIGHLY TOXIC. SEE INFORMATION ON ORGANOPHOSPHATES.
ORGANOPHOSPHATES: CHOLINESTERASE INHIBITOR. **ACUTE EXPOSURE-** WHEN INHALED, THE FIRST EFFECTS OF CHOLINESTERASE INHIBITORS ARE USUALLY RESPIRATORY AND MAY INCLUDE NASAL HYPEREMIA AND WATERY DISCHARGE, COUGH, CHEST DISCOMFORT, DYSPNEA, AND WHEEZING DUE TO INCREASED BRONCHIAL SECRETIONS AND BRONCHOCONSTRICTION. IF SUFFICIENT AMOUNTS ARE ABSORBED, OTHER SYSTEMIC EFFECTS MAY BEGIN WITHIN A FEW MINUTES OR BE DELAYED FOR UP TO 12 HOURS. SYMPTOMS MAY INCLUDE PALLOR, NAUSEA, VOMITING, DIARRHEA, ABDOMINAL CRAMPS, HEADACHE, DIZZINESS, OCULAR PAIN, BLURRED VISION, MIOSIS OR IN SOME CASES, ESPECIALLY INITIALLY, MYDRIASIS, LACRIMATION, SALIVATION, SWEATING, AND CONFUSION. OTHER REPORTED CENTRAL NERVOUS SYSTEM OR NEUROMUSCULAR EFFECTS MAY INCLUDE ATAXIA, SLURRED SPEECH, AREFLEXIA, WEAKNESS, FATIGUE, FASCICULATIONS, TWITCHING, TREMORS POSSIBLY OF THE TONGUE AND EYELIDS, AND EVENTUALLY PARALYSIS OF THE EXTREMITIES AND POSSIBLY OF THE RESPIRATORY MUSCLES. IN SEVERE CASES THERE MAY ALSO BE INVOLUNTARY DEFECATION AND URINATION, CYANOSIS, PSYCHOSIS, HYPERGLYCEMIA, ACUTE PANCREATITIS, CARDIAC IRREGULARITIES, PULMONARY EDEMA, UNCONSCIOUSNESS, CONVULSIONS, AND COMA. DEATH IS PRIMARILY DUE TO RESPIRATORY FAILURE, ALTHOUGH CARDIOVASCULAR EFFECTS INCLUDING CARDIAC ARREST MAY ALSO BE IMPLICATED. LONG TERM SEQUELAE ARE RARE BUT MAY INCLUDE NEUROPSYCHIATRIC DISORDERS AND MYOPATHY WITH MUSCLE TENDERNESS. **CHRONIC EXPOSURE-** REPEATED OR PROLONGED EXPOSURE MAY RESULT IN THE EFFECTS OF ACUTE EXPOSURE. OTHER EFFECTS REPORTED IN WORKERS REPEATEDLY EXPOSED INCLUDE IMPAIRED MEMORY AND CONCENTRATION, ACUTE PSYCHOSIS, SEVERE DEPRESSIONS, IRRITABILTY, CONFUSION, APATHY, EMOTIONAL LABILITY, SOCIAL WITHDRAWAL, CONFUSION, HEADACHE, SPEECH DIFFICULTIES, DELAYED REACTION TIMES, SPATIAL DISORIENTATION, NIGHTMARES, SLEEPWALKING, AND DROWSINESS OR INSOMNIA. AN INFLUENZA-LIKE CONDITION WITH HEADACHE, NAUSEA, WEAKNESS, ANOREXIA AND MALAISE HAS ALSO BEEN REPORTED.
FIRST AID- REMOVE FROM EXPOSURE AREA TO FRESH AIR IMMEDIATELY. IF BREATHING HAS STOPPED, GIVE ARTIFICIAL RESPIRATION. MAINTAIN AIRWAY AND BLOOD PRESSURE AND ADMINISTER OXYGEN IF AVAILABLE. KEEP AFFECTED PERSON WARM AND AT REST. TREAT SYMPTOMATICALLY AND SUPPORTIVELY. ADMINISTRATION OF OXYGEN SHOULD BE PERFORMED BY QUALIFIED PERSONNEL. GET MEDICAL ATTENTION IMMEDIATELY.

SKIN CONTACT: DEMETON-S: ALTHOUGH THERE IS NO DATA ON THE ISOMER, DEMETON-S, THE MIXTURE OF ISOMERS, DEMETON IS HIGHLY TOXIC BY SKIN ABSORPTION. SEE INFORMATION ON ORGANOPHOSPHATES.
ORGANOPHOSPHATES: CHOLINESTERASE INHIBITOR. **ACUTE EXPOSURE-** LOCALIZED SWEATING AND FASCICULATIONS MAY OCCUR AT THE SITE OF CONTACT. IF SUFFICIENT AMOUNTS ARE ABSORBED, OTHER EFFECTS OF CHOLINESTERASE INHIBITION AS DESCRIBED IN ACUTE INHALATION MAY OCCUR. SYMPTOMS MAY BE DELAYED 2-3 HOURS, BUT USUALLY NO MORE THAN 12 HOURS. THE RATE OF ABSORPTION IS INCREASED BY THE PRESENCE OF DERMATITIS OR HIGH AMBIENT TEMPERATURES. **CHRONIC EXPOSURE-** REPEATED OR PROLONGED EXPOSURE MAY CAUSE EFFECTS AS DESCRIBED IN ACUTE EXPOSURE. SOME ORGANOPHOSPHATES MAY CAUSE SENSITIZATION.
FIRST AID- REMOVE CONTAMINATED CLOTHING IMMEDIATELY. WASH CONTAMINATED AREAS WITH SOAP AND WATER FOLLOWED BY ALCOHOL (ARENA, POISONING, 4TH ED.). EMERGENCY PERSONNEL SHOULD WEAR GLOVES AND AVOID CONTAMINATION. TREAT RESPIRATORY DIFFICULTY WITH ARTIFICIAL RESPIRATION. GET MEDICAL ATTENTION IMMEDIATELY.

EYE CONTACT: DEMETON-S: SEE INFORMATION ON ORGANOPHOSPHATES.
ORGANOPHOSPHATES: CHOLINESTERASE INHIBITOR. **ACUTE EXPOSURE-** DIRECT CONTACT MAY CAUSE PAIN, HYPEREMIA, LACRIMATION, TWITCHING OF THE EYELIDS, MIOSIS, AND CILIARY MUSCLE SPASM WITH LOSS OF ACCOMODATION, BLURRED OR DIMMED VISION AND BROWACHE. SOMETIMES MYDRIASIS MAY OCCUR INSTEAD OF MIOSIS. WITH SUFFICIENT EXPOSURE, OTHER SYMPTOMS OF CHOLINESTERASE INHIBITION AS DESCRIBED IN ACUTE INHALATION MAY OCCUR. **CHRONIC EXPOSURE-** REPEATED OR PROLONGED EXPOSURE MAY CAUSE EFFECTS AS DESCRIBED IN ACUTE EXPOSURE. SOME COMPOUNDS HAVE CAUSED TOXIC EFFECTS ON THE CRYSTALLINE LENS, CONJUNCTIVAL THICKENING AND OBSTRUCTION OF THE NASOLACRIMAL CANALS WHEN USED AS MIOTIC EYEDROPS.
FIRST AID- IRRIGATE EYES WITH WATER OR SALINE SOLUTION. IF SYMPTOMS OF POISONING OCCUR, TREAT RESPIRATORY DIFFICULTY WITH ARTIFICIAL RESPIRATION AND OXYGEN. OBSERVE PATIENT FOR AT LEAST 24-36 HOURS (GOSSELIN, CLINICAL TOXICOLOGY OF COMMERCIAL PRODUCTS, 5TH ED.). GET MEDICAL ATTENTION IMMEDIATELY. OXYGEN SHOULD BE ADMINISTERED BY QUALIFIED MEDICAL PERSONNEL.

INGESTION: DEMETON-S: HIGHLY TOXIC. IN ONE STUDY OF 5 MEN WHO EACH INGESTED 7.125 MG PER DAY OF THE TECHNICAL DEMETON FOR 25 DAYS, 39.8% AND 15.9% DEPRESSIONS IN PLASMA AND ERYTHROCYTE CHOLINESTERASE ACTIVITY WERE OBSERVED. THIS MATERIAL DOES NOT INDUCE DELAYED NEUROTOXIC SIGNS OF POISONING IN HENS OR POTENTIATE THE ACUTE TOXICITY

OF OTHER ANTI-CHOLINESTERASE ORGANOPHOSPHATES OR CARBAMATE INSECTICIDES. SEE INFORMATION ON ORGANOPHOSPHATES.
ORGANOPHOSPHATES: CHOLINESTERASE INHIBITOR. ACUTE EXPOSURE- WHEN INGESTED, THE FIRST EFFECTS MAY BE NAUSEA, VOMITING, ANOREXIA, ABDOMINAL CRAMPS AND DIARRHEA. GASTROINTESTINAL ABSORPTION MAY CAUSE THE SYMPTOMS OF CHOLINESTERASE INHIBITION AS DESCRIBED IN ACUTE INHALATION. SYMPTOMS MAY BEGIN WITHIN MINUTES OR BE DELAYED. CHRONIC EXPOSURE- REPEATED INGESTION MAY CAUSE EFFECTS AS DESCRIBED IN ACUTE EXPOSURE.

FIRST AID- IF PERSON IS ALERT AND RESPIRATION IS NOT DEPRESSED, GIVE SYRUP OF IPECAC FOLLOWED BY WATER (IF VOMITING OCCURS, KEEP HEAD BELOW HIPS TO PREVENT ASPIRATION). IF CONSCIOUSNESS LEVEL DECLINES OR VOMITING HAS NOT OCCURRED IN 15 MINUTES EMPTY STOMACH BY GASTRIC LAVAGE WITH THE AID OF CUFFED ENDOTRACHEAL TUBE USING ISOTONIC SALINE OR 5% SODIUM BICARBONATE FOLLOW WITH ACTIVATED CHARCOAL. ESTABLISH AND MAINTAIN AIRWAY. TREAT RESPIRATORY DIFFICULTY WITH ARTIFICIAL RESPIRATION AND OXYGEN. DO NOT GIVE MORPHINE, AMINOPHYLLINE, PHENOTHIAZINES, RESERPINE, FUROSEMIDE, OR ETHACRYNIC ACID (MORGAN, RECOGNITION AND MANAGEMENT OF PESTICIDE POISONINGS, 3RD ED.). TREAT SYMPTOMATICALLY AND SUPPORTIVELY. ADMINISTRATION OF OXYGEN AND LAVAGE MUST BE PERFORMED BY QUALIFIED MEDICAL PERSONNEL. GET MEDICAL ATTENTION IMMEDIATELY.

ANTIDOTE: THE FOLLOWING ANTIDOTE(S) HAVE BEEN RECOMMENDED. HOWEVER, THE DECISION AS TO WHETHER THE SEVERITY OF POISONING REQUIRES ADMINISTRATION OF ANY ANTIDOTE AND ACTUAL DOSE REQUIRED SHOULD BE MADE BY QUALIFIED MEDICAL PERSONNEL.
FOR CHOLINESTERASE INHIBITORS: ESTABLISH CLEAR AIRWAY AND TISSUE OXYGENATION BY ASPIRATION OF SECRETIONS, AND IF NECESSARY, BY ASSISTED PULMONARY VENTILATION WITH OXYGEN. IMPROVE TISSUE OXYGENATION AS MUCH AS POSSIBLE BEFORE ADMINISTERING ATROPINE TO MINIMIZE THE RISK OF VENTRICULAR FIBRILLATION. ADMINISTER ATROPINE SULFATE INTRAVENOUSLY, OR INTRAMUSCULARLY IF IV INJECTION IS NOT POSSIBLE. IN MODERATELY SEVERE POISONING ADMINISTER ATROPINE SULFATE, 0.4-2.0 MG REPEATED EVERY 15 MINUTES UNTIL ATROPINIZATION IS ACHIEVED (TACHYCARDIA, FLUSHING, DRY MOUTH, MYDRIASIS). MAINTAIN ATROPINIZATION BY REPEATED DOSES FOR 2-12 HOURS, OR LONGER, DEPENDING ON THE SEVERITY OF POISONING. THE APPEARANCE OF RALES IN THE LUNG BASES, MIOSIS, SALIVATION, NAUSEA, BRADYCARDIA, ARE ALL INDICATIONS OF INADEQUATE ATROPINIZATION. SEVERELY POISONED INDIVIDUALS MAY EXHIBIT REMARKABLE TOLERANCE TO ATROPINE; TWO OR MORE TIMES THE DOSAGES SUGGESTED ABOVE MAY BE NEEDED. PERSONS NOT POISONED OR ONLY SLIGHTLY POISONED, HOWEVER, MAY DEVELOP SIGNS OF ATROPINE TOXICITY FROM SUCH LARGE DOSAGES: FEVER, MUSCLE FIBRILLATIONS, AND DELIRIUM ARE THE MAIN SIGNS OF ATROPINE TOXICITY. IF THESE SIGNS APPEAR WHILE THE PATIENT IS FULLY ATROPINIZED, ATROPINE ADMINISTRATION SHOULD BE DISCONTINUED, AT LEAST TEMPORARILY. OBSERVE TREATED PATIENTS CLOSELY AT LEAST 24 HOURS TO INSURE THAT SYMPTOMS (POSSIBLY PULMONARY EDEMA) DO NOT RECUR AS ATROPINIZATION WEARS OFF. IN VERY SEVERE POISONINGS, METABOLIC DISPOSITION OF TOXICANT MAY REQUIRE SEVERAL HOURS OR DAYS DURING WHICH ATROPINIZATION MUST BE MAINTAINED. MARKEDLY LOWER LEVELS OF URINARY METABOLITES INDICATE THAT ATROPINE DOSAGE CAN BE TAPERED OFF. AS DOSAGE IS REDUCED, CHECK THE LUNG BASES FREQUENTLY FOR RALES. IF RALES ARE HEARD OR OTHER SYMPTOMS RETURN, RE-ESTABLISH ATROPINIZATION PROMPTLY (MORGAN, RECOGNITION AND MANAGEMENT OF PESTICIDE POISONINGS, 3RD ED.). ADMINISTRATION OF ANTIDOTE MUST BE PERFORMED BY QUALIFIED MEDICAL PERSONNEL.
IN CASES OF SEVERE POISONING BY ORGANOPHOSPHATE PESTICIDES IN WHICH RESPIRATORY DEPRESSION, MUSCLE WEAKNESS AND TWITCHINGS ARE SEVERE, GIVE PRALIDOXIME (PROTOPAM-AYERST, 2-PAM), 1.0 GRAM INTRAVENOUSLY AT NO MORE THAN 0.5 GRAM PER MINUTE. DOSAGE OF PRALIDOXIME MAY BE REPEATED IN 1-2 HOURS, THEN AT 10-12 HOUR INTERVALS IF NEEDED. IN VERY SEVERE POISONINGS, DOSAGE RATES MAY BE DOUBLED. TREATMENT WITH PRALIDOXIME WILL BE MOST EFFECTIVE IF GIVEN WITHIN THIRTY-SIX HOURS AFTER POISONING (MORGAN, RECOGNITION AND MANAGEMENT OF PESTICIDE POISONINGS, 3RD ED.). ANTIDOTE SHOULD BE ADMINISTERED BY QUALIFIED MEDICAL PERSONNEL.

REACTIVITY

REACTIVITY: STABLE UNDER NORMAL TEMPERATURES AND PRESSURES; HYDROLYZED BY BOILING WATER.

INCOMPATIBILITIES: DEMETON-S: ALKALINE CONDITIONS: MAY CAUSE HYDROLYSIS. BORDEAUX:INCOMPATIBLE CALCIUM ARSENATE: INCOMPATIBLE. CYPREX: INCOMPATIBLE. LIME OR LIME SULFUR: INCOMPATIBLE. MERCURY COMPOUND (WATER SOLUBLE): INCOMPATIBLE. PARIS GREEN: INCOMPATIBLE PLASTICS, RUBBER, AND COATINGS: SOME FORMS MAY BE ATTACKED. STRONG OXIDIZERS: MAY CAUSE FIRE OR EXPLOSION. UREA: INCOMPATIBLE. ZINC ARSENATE: INCOMPATIBLE.

DECOMPOSITION: THERMAL DECOMPOSITION MAY RELEASE TOXIC OXIDES OF PHOSPHORUS AND SULFUR.

POLYMERIZATION: HAZARDOUS POLYMERIZATION HAS NOT BEEN REPORTED TO OCCUR UNDER NORMAL TEMPERATURES AND PRESSURES.

STORAGE AND DISPOSAL

OBSERVE ALL FEDERAL, STATE AND LOCAL REGULATIONS WHEN STORING OR DISPOSING OF THIS SUBSTANCE. FOR ASSISTANCE, CONTACT THE DISTRICT DIRECTOR OF THE ENVIRONMENTAL PROTECTION AGENCY.

STORAGE

STORE IN ACCORDANCE WITH 40 CFR 165 RECOMMENDED PROCEDURES FOR THE DISPOSAL AND STORAGE OF PESTICIDES AND PESTICIDE CONTAINERS.
STORE AWAY FROM INCOMPATIBLE SUBSTANCES.
THRESHOLD PLANNING QUANTITY (TPQ): THE SUPERFUND AMENDMENTS AND REAUTHORIZATION ACT (SARA) SECTION 302 REQUIRES THAT EACH FACILITY WHERE ANY EXTREMELY HAZARDOUS SUBSTANCE IS PRESENT IN A QUANTITY EQUAL TO OR GREATER THAN THE TPQ ESTABLISHED FOR THAT SUBSTANCE NOTIFY THE STATE EMERGENCY RESPONSE COMMISSION FOR THE STATE IN WHICH IT IS LOCATED. SECTION 303 OF SARA REQUIRES THESE FACILITIES TO PARTICIPATE IN LOCAL EMERGENCY RESPONSE PLANNING (40 CFR 355.30).

DISPOSAL

DISPOSAL MUST BE IN ACCORDANCE WITH 40 CFR 165 RECOMMENDED PROCEDURES FOR THE DISPOSAL AND STORAGE OF PESTICIDES AND PESTICIDE CONTAINERS.

CONDITIONS TO AVOID

NONE REPORTED.

SPILL AND LEAK PROCEDURES

OCCUPATIONAL SPILL: DO NOT TOUCH SPILLED MATERIAL. STOP LEAK IF YOU CAN DO IT WITHOUT RISK. USE WATER SPRAY TO REDUCE VAPORS. FOR SMALL SPILLS, TAKE UP WITH SAND OR OTHER ABSORBENT MATERIAL AND PLACE INTO CONTAINERS FOR LATER DISPOSAL. FOR SMALL DRY SPILLS, WITH A CLEAN SHOVEL PLACE MATERIAL INTO CLEAN, DRY CONTAINERS AND COVER. MOVE CONTAINERS FROM SPILL AREA. FOR LARGER SPILLS, DIKE FAR AHEAD OF SPILL FOR LATER DISPOSAL. KEEP UNNECESSARY PEOPLE AWAY. ISOLATE HAZARD AREA AND DENY ENTRY. VENTILATE CLOSED SPACES BEFORE ENTERING.
REPORTABLE QUANTITY (RQ): 1 POUND THE SUPERFUND AMENDMENTS AND REAUTHORIZATION ACT (SARA) SECTION 304 REQUIRES THAT A RELEASE EQUAL TO OR GREATER THAN THE REPORTABLE QUANTITY FOR THIS SUBSTANCE BE IMMEDIATELY REPORTED TO THE LOCAL EMERGENCY PLANNING COMMITTEE AND THE STATE EMERGENCY RESPONSE COMMISSION (40 CFR 355.40). IF THE RELEASE OF THIS SUBSTANCE IS REPORTABLE UNDER CERCLA SECTION 103, THE NATIONAL RESPONSE CENTER MUST BE NOTIFIED IMMEDIATELY AT (800) 424-8802 OR (202) 426-2675 IN THE METROPOLITAN WASHINGTON, D.C. AREA (40 CFR 302.6).

PROTECTIVE EQUIPMENT

VENTILATION: PROCESS ENCLOSURE RECOMMENDED TO MEET PUBLISHED EXPOSURE LIMITS.

RESPIRATOR: THE FOLLOWING RESPIRATORS AND MAXIMUM USE CONCENTRATIONS ARE RECOMMENDATIONS BY THE U.S. DEPARTMENT OF HEALTH AND HUMAN SERVICES, NIOSH POCKET GUIDE TO CHEMICAL HAZARDS; NIOSH CRITERIA DOCUMENTS OR BY THE U.S. DEPARTMENT OF LABOR, 29 CFR 1910 SUBPART Z. THE SPECIFIC RESPIRATOR SELECTED MUST BE BASED ON CONTAMINATION LEVELS FOUND IN THE WORK PLACE, MUST NOT EXCEED THE WORKING LIMITS OF THE RESPIRATOR AND BE JOINTLY APPROVED BY THE NATIONAL INSTITUTE FOR OCCUPATIONAL SAFETY AND HEALTH AND THE MINE SAFETY AND HEALTH ADMINISTRATION (NIOSH-MSHA).
DEMETON: 1 MG/M3- ANY SUPPLIED-AIR RESPIRATOR. ANY SELF-CONTAINED BREATHING APPARATUS.
2.5 MG/M3- ANY SUPPLIED-AIR RESPIRATOR OPERATED IN A CONTINUOUS FLOW MODE.
5 MG/M3- ANY SELF-CONTAINED BREATHING APPARATUS WITH A FULL FACEPIECE. ANY SUPPLIED-AIR RESPIRATOR WITH A FULL FACEPIECE. ANY SUPPLIED-AIR RESPIRATOR WITH A TIGHT-FITTING FACEPIECE OPERATED IN A CONTINUOUS FLOW MODE.
20 MG/M3- ANY SUPPLIED-AIR RESPIRATOR WITH A HALF-MASK AND OPERATED IN A PRESSURE-DEMAND OR OTHER POSITIVE PRESSURE MODE.
ESCAPE- ANY AIR-PURIFYING FULL FACEPIECE RESPIRATOR (GAS MASK) WITH A CHIN-STYLE OR FRONT- OR BACK-MOUNTED ORGANIC VAPOR CANISTER HAVING A HIGH-EFFICIENCY PARTICULATE FILTER. ANY APPROPRIATE ESCAPE-TYPE SELF-CONTAINED BREATHING APPARATUS.
FOR FIREFIGHTING AND OTHER IMMEDIATELY DANGEROUS TO LIFE OR HEALTH CONDITIONS:
SELF-CONTAINED BREATHING APPARATUS WITH FULL FACEPIECE OPERATED IN PRESSURE-DEMAND OR OTHER POSITIVE PRESSURE MODE.

SUPPLIED-AIR RESPIRATOR WITH FULL FACEPIECE AND OPERATED IN PRESSURE-DEMAND OR OTHER POSITIVE PRESSURE MODE IN COMBINATION WITH AN AUXILIARY SELF-CONTAINED BREATHING APPARATUS OPERATED IN PRESSURE-DEMAND OR OTHER POSITIVE PRESSURE MODE.

CLOTHING: EMPLOYEE MUST WEAR APPROPRIATE PROTECTIVE (IMPERVIOUS) CLOTHING AND EQUIPMENT TO PREVENT ANY POSSIBILITY OF SKIN CONTACT WITH THIS SUBSTANCE.

GLOVES: EMPLOYEE MUST WEAR APPROPRIATE PROTECTIVE GLOVES TO PREVENT CONTACT WITH THIS SUBSTANCE.

EYE PROTECTION: EMPLOYEE MUST WEAR SPLASH-PROOF OR DUST-RESISTANT SAFETY GOGGLES AND A FACESHIELD TO PREVENT CONTACT WITH THIS SUBSTANCE.

EMERGENCY WASH FACILITIES: WHERE THERE IS ANY POSSIBILITY THAT AN EMPLOYEE'S EYES AND/OR SKIN MAY BE EXPOSED TO THIS SUBSTANCE, THE EMPLOYER SHOULD PROVIDE AN EYE WASH FOUNTAIN AND QUICK DRENCH SHOWER WITHIN THE IMMEDIATE WORK AREA FOR EMERGENCY USE.

AUTHORIZED BY- OCCUPATIONAL HEALTH SERVICES, INC.
CREATION DATE: 10/04/89 ***REVISION DATE:*** 06/20/90

MATERIAL SAFETY DATA SHEET

OCCUPATIONAL HEALTH SERVICES, INC.
AGRICULTURE AND PESTICIDE DIVISION
450 SEVENTH AVENUE, SUITE 2407
NEW YORK, NEW YORK 10123
1-800-445-MSDS OR (212) 967-1100

EMERGENCY CONTACT:
JOHN S. BRANSFORD, JR. (615) 292-1180

SUBSTANCE IDENTIFICATION

CAS-NUMBER 953-17-3

SUBSTANCE: **METHYL CARBOPHENOTHION**

TRADE NAMES/SYNONYMS: PHOSPHORODITHIOIC ACID, S-(((4-CHLOROPHENYL)THIO)METHYL) O,O-DIMETHYL ESTER; PHOSPHORODITHIOIC ACID, S-(((P-CHLOROPHENYL)THIO)METHYL) O,O-DIMETHYL ESTER; O,O-DIMETHYL-S-4-CHLOROPHENYL-THIOMETHYL PHOSPHOROTHIONATE; S-4-CHLOROPHENYLTHIOMETHYL O,O-DIMETHYL PHOSPHORODITHIOATE; S-((P-CHLOROPHENYL)THIO)METHYL) O,O-DIMETHYL PHOSPHORODITHIOATE; S-(P-CHLOROPHENYLTHIOMETHYL)DIMETHYL PHOSPHOROTHIOLOTHIONATE; O,O-DIMETHYL-S-PARA-CHLOROPHENYLTHIOMETHYL PHOSPHORODITHIOATE; CARBOPHENOTHION METHYL; METHYL TRITHION; STAUFFER R 1492; TRITHION-METHYL; ENT 25,586; C9H12CLO2PS3; PST71647

CHEMICAL FAMILY: ORGANOPHOSPHATE
HALOGEN COMPOUND, AROMATIC

MOLECULAR FORMULA: C9-H12-CL-O2-P-S3

MOLECULAR WEIGHT: 314.81

CERCLA RATINGS (SCALE 0-3): HEALTH=3 FIRE=0 REACTIVITY=0 PERSISTENCE=2

NFPA RATINGS (SCALE 0-4): HEALTH=3 FIRE=0 REACTIVITY=0

COMPONENTS AND CONTAMINANTS

COMPONENT: METHYL CARBOPHENOTHION ***PERCENT:*** 100
CAS# 953-17-3

EXPOSURE LIMITS: NO OCCUPATIONAL EXPOSURE LIMITS ESTABLISHED BY OSHA, ACGIH, OR NIOSH.

PHYSICAL DATA

DESCRIPTION: LIGHT YELLOW LIQUID ***BOILING POINT:*** 257 F (125 C) @ 0.01 MMHG

SPECIFIC GRAVITY: 1.360 @ 20 C ***EVAPORATION RATE:*** NOT AVAILABLE

SOLUBILITY IN WATER: 1 PPM

SOLVENT SOLUBILITY: SOLUBLE IN MOST ORGANIC SOLVENTS

FIRE AND EXPLOSION DATA

FIRE AND EXPLOSION HAZARD: NEGLIGIBLE FIRE HAZARD WHEN EXPOSED TO HEAT OR FLAME.

FIREFIGHTING MEDIA: DRY CHEMICAL, CARBON DIOXIDE, HALON, WATER SPRAY OR STANDARD FOAM (1987 EMERGENCY RESPONSE GUIDEBOOK, DOT P 5800.4). FOR LARGER FIRES, USE WATER SPRAY, FOG OR STANDARD FOAM (1987 EMERGENCY RESPONSE GUIDEBOOK, DOT P 5800.4).

FIREFIGHTING: MOVE CONTAINERS FROM FIRE AREA IF POSSIBLE. FIGHT FIRE FROM MAXIMUM DISTANCE. STAY AWAY FROM STORAGE TANK ENDS. DIKE FIRE CONTROL WATER FOR LATER DISPOSAL. DO NOT SCATTER MATERIAL (1987 EMERGENCY RESPONSE GUIDEBOOK, DOT P 5800.4, GUIDE PAGE 55). EXTINGUISH USING AGENT SUITABLE FOR TYPE OF SURROUNDING FIRE. AVOID BREATHING VAPORS AND DUSTS. KEEP UPWIND.

TRANSPORTATION DATA

DEPARTMENT OF TRANSPORTATION HAZARD CLASSIFICATION 49 CFR 172.101: POISON B

DEPARTMENT OF TRANSPORTATION LABELING REQUIREMENTS 49 CFR 172.101 AND SUBPART E: POISON

DEPARTMENT OF TRANSPORTATION PACKAGING REQUIREMENTS: 49 CFR 173.346 EXCEPTIONS: 49 CFR 173.345

TOXICITY

METHYL CARBOPHENOTHION: TOXICITY DATA: 2420 MG/KG SKIN-RABBIT LD50; 190 MG/KG SKIN-RAT LD50; 48 MG/KG ORAL-RAT LD50; 112 MG/KG ORAL-MOUSE LD50; 180 MG/KG UNREPORTED-RAT LD50. CARCINOGEN STATUS: NONE. ACUTE TOXICITY LEVEL: HIGHLY TOXIC BY INGESTION; SLIGHTLY TOXIC BY DERMAL ABSORPTION. TARGET EFFECTS: CHOLINESTERASE INHIBITOR. POISONING MAY AFFECT THE NERVOUS SYSTEM.* AT INCREASED RISK FROM EXPOSURE: PERSONS WITH RESPIRATORY AILMENTS, RECENT EXPOSURE TO CHOLINESTERASE INHIBITORS OR IMPAIRED CHOLINESTERASE PRODUCTION, OR LIVER MALFUNCTION.* ADDITIONAL DATA: MAY CROSS THE PLACENTA. HIGH ENVIRONMENTAL TEMPERATURES OR EXPOSURE OF THE CHEMICAL TO VISIBLE OR ULTRAVIOLET LIGHT MAY ENHANCE THE TOXICITY. INTERACTIONS WITH MEDICATIONS MAY OCCUR.*

* MAY BE BASED ON GENERAL INFORMATION ON ORGANOPHOSPHATES.

HEALTH EFFECTS AND FIRST AID

INHALATION: METHYL CARBOPHENOTHION: SEE INFORMATION ON ORGANOPHOSPHATES.

ORGANOPHOSPHATES: CHOLINESTERASE INHIBITOR. ACUTE EXPOSURE- WHEN INHALED, THE FIRST EFFECTS OF CHOLINESTERASE INHIBITORS ARE USUALLY RESPIRATORY AND MAY INCLUDE NASAL HYPEREMIA AND WATERY DISCHARGE, COUGH, CHEST DISCOMFORT, DYSPNEA, AND WHEEZING DUE TO INCREASED BRONCHIAL SECRETIONS AND BRONCHOCONSTRICTION. IF SUFFICIENT AMOUNTS ARE ABSORBED, OTHER SYSTEMIC EFFECTS MAY BEGIN WITHIN A FEW MINUTES OR BE DELAYED FOR UP TO 12 HOURS. SYMPTOMS MAY INCLUDE PALLOR, NAUSEA, VOMITING, DIARRHEA, ABDOMINAL CRAMPS, HEADACHE, DIZZINESS, OCULAR PAIN, BLURRED VISION, MIOSIS OR IN SOME CASES, ESPECIALLY INITIALLY, MYDRIASIS, LACRIMATION, SALIVATION, SWEATING, AND CONFUSION. OTHER REPORTED CENTRAL NERVOUS SYSTEM OR NEUROMUSCULAR EFFECTS MAY INCLUDE ATAXIA, SLURRED SPEECH, AREFLEXIA, WEAKNESS, FATIGUE, FASCICULATIONS, TWITCHING, TREMORS POSSIBLY OF THE TONGUE AND EYELIDS, AND EVENTUALLY PARALYSIS OF THE EXTREMITIES AND POSSIBLY OF THE RESPIRATORY MUSCLES. IN SEVERE CASES THERE MAY ALSO BE INVOLUNTARY DEFECATION AND URINATION, CYANOSIS, PSYCHOSIS, HYPERGLYCEMIA, ACUTE PANCREATITIS, CARDIAC IRREGULARITIES, PULMONARY EDEMA, UNCONSCIOUSNESS, CONVULSIONS, AND COMA. DEATH IS PRIMARILY DUE TO RESPIRATORY FAILURE, ALTHOUGH CARDIOVASCULAR EFFECTS INCLUDING CARDIAC ARREST MAY ALSO BE IMPLICATED. LONG TERM SEQUELAE ARE RARE BUT MAY INCLUDE NEUROPSYCHIATRIC DISORDERS AND MYOPATHY WITH MUSCLE TENDERNESS. SOME ORGANOPHOSPHATES MAY CAUSE A DELAYED NEUROPATHY BEGINNING 1-4 WEEKS AFTER AN ACUTE EXPOSURE WHICH MAY OR MAY NOT HAVE CAUSED ACUTE CHOLINERGIC EFFECTS. NUMBNESS, TINGLING, WEAKNESS AND CRAMPING BEGINNING SYMMETRICALLY IN THE LOWER LIMBS MAY PROGRESS TO ATAXIA AND PARALYSIS. IN SEVERE CASES, UPPER LIMB INVOLVEMENT IS POSSIBLE AND FLACCID PARALYSIS MAY PROGRESS TO SPASTIC PARALYSIS WITH EXAGGERATED REFLEXES. IMPROVEMENT MAY OCCUR OVER MONTHS TO YEARS, BUT SOME RESIDUAL IMPAIRMENT USUALLY REMAINS. CHRONIC EXPOSURE- REPEATED OR PROLONGED EXPOSURE MAY RESULT IN THE EFFECTS OF ACUTE EXPOSURE INCLUDING THE DELAYED NEUROPATHY. OTHER EFFECTS REPORTED IN WORKERS REPEATEDLY EXPOSED INCLUDE IMPAIRED MEMORY AND CONCENTRATION, ACUTE PSYCHOSIS, SEVERE DEPRESSIONS, IRRITABILTY, CONFUSION, APATHY, EMOTIONAL LABILITY, SOCIAL WITHDRAWAL, CONFUSION, HEADACHE, SPEECH DIFFICULTIES, DELAYED REACTION TIMES, SPATIAL DISORIENTATION, NIGHTMARES, SLEEPWALKING, AND DROWSINESS OR INSOMNIA. AN INFLUENZA-LIKE CONDITION WITH HEADACHE, NAUSEA, WEAKNESS, ANOREXIA AND MALAISE HAS ALSO BEEN REPORTED.

FIRST AID- REMOVE FROM EXPOSURE AREA TO FRESH AIR IMMEDIATELY. IF BREATHING HAS STOPPED, GIVE ARTIFICIAL RESPIRATION. MAINTAIN AIRWAY AND BLOOD PRESSURE AND ADMINISTER OXYGEN IF AVAILABLE. KEEP AFFECTED PERSON WARM AND AT REST. TREAT SYMPTOMATICALLY AND SUPPORTIVELY. ADMINISTRATION OF OXYGEN SHOULD BE PERFORMED BY QUALIFIED PERSONNEL. GET MEDICAL ATTENTION IMMEDIATELY.

SKIN CONTACT: METHYL CARBOPHENOTHION: SEE INFORMATION ON ORGANOPHOSPHATES.
ORGANOPHOSPHATES: CHOLINESTERASE INHIBITOR. **ACUTE EXPOSURE-** LOCALIZED SWEATING AND FASCICULATIONS MAY OCCUR AT THE SITE OF CONTACT. IF SUFFICIENT AMOUNTS ARE ABSORBED, OTHER EFFECTS OF CHOLINESTERASE INHIBITION AS DESCRIBED IN ACUTE INHALATION MAY OCCUR. SYMPTOMS MAY BE DELAYED 2-3 HOURS, BUT USUALLY NO MORE THAN 12 HOURS. THE RATE OF ABSORPTION IS INCREASED BY THE PRESENCE OF DERMATITIS OR HIGH AMBIENT TEMPERATURES. DELAYED NEUROPATHY IS ALSO POSSIBLE. **CHRONIC EXPOSURE-** REPEATED OR PROLONGED EXPOSURE MAY CAUSE EFFECTS AS DESCRIBED IN ACUTE EXPOSURE. SOME ORGANOPHOSPHATES MAY CAUSE SENSITIZATION.
FIRST AID- REMOVE CONTAMINATED CLOTHING IMMEDIATELY. WASH CONTAMINATED AREAS WITH SOAP AND WATER FOLLOWED BY ALCOHOL (ARENA, POISONING, 4TH ED.). EMERGENCY PERSONNEL SHOULD WEAR GLOVES AND AVOID CONTAMINATION. TREAT RESPIRATORY DIFFICULTY WITH ARTIFICIAL RESPIRATION. GET MEDICAL ATTENTION IMMEDIATELY.

EYE CONTACT: METHYL CARBOPHENOTHION: SEE INFORMATION ON ORGANOPHOSPHATES.
ORGANOPHOSPHATES: CHOLINESTERASE INHIBITOR. **ACUTE EXPOSURE-** DIRECT CONTACT MAY CAUSE PAIN, HYPEREMIA, LACRIMATION, TWITCHING OF THE EYELIDS, MIOSIS, AND CILIARY MUSCLE SPASM WITH LOSS OF ACCOMODATION, BLURRED OR DIMMED VISION AND BROWACHE. SOMETIMES MYDRIASIS MAY OCCUR INSTEAD OF MIOSIS. WITH SUFFICIENT EXPOSURE, OTHER SYMPTOMS OF CHOLINESTERASE INHIBITION AS DESCRIBED IN ACUTE INHALATION MAY OCCUR. **CHRONIC EXPOSURE-** REPEATED OR PROLONGED EXPOSURE MAY CAUSE EFFECTS AS DESCRIBED IN ACUTE EXPOSURE. SOME COMPOUNDS HAVE CAUSED TOXIC EFFECTS ON THE CRYSTALLINE LENS, CONJUNCTIVAL THICKENING AND OBSTRUCTION OF THE NASOLACRIMAL CANALS WHEN USED AS MIOTIC EYEDROPS.
FIRST AID- IRRIGATE EYES WITH WATER OR SALINE SOLUTION. IF SYMPTOMS OF POISONING OCCUR, TREAT RESPIRATORY DIFFICULTY WITH ARTIFICIAL RESPIRATION AND OXYGEN. OBSERVE PATIENT FOR AT LEAST 24-36 HOURS (GOSSELIN, CLINICAL TOXICOLOGY OF COMMERCIAL PRODUCTS, 5TH ED.). GET MEDICAL ATTENTION IMMEDIATELY. OXYGEN SHOULD BE ADMINISTERED BY QUALIFIED MEDICAL PERSONNEL.

INGESTION: METHYL CARBOPHENOTHION: HIGHLY TOXIC. SEE INFORMATION ON ORGANOPHOSPHATES.
ORGANOPHOSPHATES: CHOLINESTERASE INHIBITOR. **ACUTE EXPOSURE-** WHEN INGESTED, THE FIRST EFFECTS MAY BE NAUSEA, VOMITING, ANOREXIA, ABDOMINAL CRAMPS AND DIARRHEA. GASTROINTESTINAL ABSORPTION MAY CAUSE SYMPTOMS OF CHOLINESTERASE INHIBITION AS DESCRIBED IN ACUTE INHALATION. SYMPTOMS MAY BEGIN WITHIN MINUTES OR BE DELAYED FOR HOURS. DELAYED EFFECTS INCLUDING NEUROPATHY MAY ALSO OCCUR. **CHRONIC EXPOSURE-** REPEATED INGESTION MAY CAUSE EFFECTS AS DESCRIBED IN ACUTE EXPOSURE.
FIRST AID- IF PERSON IS ALERT AND RESPIRATION IS NOT DEPRESSED, GIVE SYRUP OF IPECAC FOLLOWED BY WATER (IF VOMITING OCCURS, KEEP HEAD BELOW HIPS TO PREVENT ASPIRATION). IF CONSCIOUSNESS LEVEL DECLINES OR VOMITING HAS NOT OCCURRED IN 15 MINUTES EMPTY STOMACH BY GASTRIC LAVAGE WITH THE AID OF CUFFED ENDOTRACHEAL TUBE USING ISOTONIC SALINE OR 5% SODIUM BICARBONATE FOLLOW WITH ACTIVATED CHARCOAL. ESTABLISH AND MAINTAIN AIRWAY. TREAT RESPIRATORY DIFFICULTY WITH ARTIFICIAL RESPIRATION AND OXYGEN. DO NOT GIVE MORPHINE, AMINOPHYLLINE, PHENOTHIAZINES, RESERPINE, FUROSEMIDE, OR ETHACRYNIC ACID (MORGAN, RECOGNITION AND MANAGEMENT OF PESTICIDE POISONINGS, 3RD ED.). TREAT SYMPTOMATICALLY AND SUPPORTIVELY. ADMINISTRATION OF OXYGEN AND LAVAGE MUST BE PERFORMED BY QUALIFIED MEDICAL PERSONNEL. GET MEDICAL ATTENTION IMMEDIATELY.
ANTIDOTE: THE FOLLOWING ANTIDOTE(S) HAVE BEEN RECOMMENDED. HOWEVER, THE DECISION AS TO WHETHER THE SEVERITY OF POISONING REQUIRES ADMINISTRATION OF ANY ANTIDOTE AND ACTUAL DOSE REQUIRED SHOULD BE MADE BY QUALIFIED MEDICAL PERSONNEL.
FOR CHOLINESTERASE INHIBITORS: ESTABLISH CLEAR AIRWAY AND TISSUE OXYGENATION BY ASPIRATION OF SECRETIONS, AND IF NECESSARY, BY ASSISTED PULMONARY VENTILATION WITH OXYGEN. IMPROVE TISSUE OXYGENATION AS MUCH AS POSSIBLE BEFORE ADMINISTERING ATROPINE TO MINIMIZE THE RISK OF VENTRICULAR FIBRILLATION. ADMINISTER ATROPINE SULFATE INTRAVENOUSLY, OR INTRAMUSCULARLY IF IV INJECTION IS NOT POSSIBLE. IN MODERATELY SEVERE POISONING ADMINISTER ATROPINE SULFATE, 0.4-2.0 MG REPEATED EVERY 15 MINUTES UNTIL ATROPINIZATION IS ACHIEVED (TACHYCARDIA, FLUSHING, DRY MOUTH, MYDRIASIS). MAINTAIN ATROPINIZATION BY REPEATED DOSES FOR 2-12 HOURS, OR LONGER, DEPENDING ON THE SEVERITY OF POISONING. THE APPEARANCE OF RALES IN THE LUNG BASES, MIOSIS, SALIVATION, NAUSEA, BRADYCARDIA, ARE ALL INDICATIONS OF INADEQUATE ATROPINIZATION. SEVERELY POISONED INDIVIDUALS MAY EXHIBIT REMARKABLE TOLERANCE TO ATROPINE; TWO OR MORE TIMES THE DOSAGES SUGGESTED ABOVE MAY BE NEEDED. PERSONS NOT POISONED OR ONLY SLIGHTLY POISONED, HOWEVER, MAY DEVELOP SIGNS OF ATROPINE TOXICITY FROM SUCH LARGE DOSAGES: FEVER, MUSCLE FIBRILLATIONS, AND DELIRIUM ARE THE MAIN SIGNS OF ATROPINE TOXICITY. IF THESE SIGNS APPEAR WHILE THE PATIENT IS FULLY ATROPINIZED, ATROPINE ADMINISTRATION SHOULD BE DISCONTINUED, AT LEAST TEMPORARILY. OBSERVE TREATED PATIENTS CLOSELY AT LEAST 24 HOURS TO INSURE THAT SYMPTOMS (POSSIBLY PULMONARY EDEMA) DO NOT RECUR AS ATROPINIZATION WEARS OFF. IN VERY SEVERE POISONINGS, METABOLIC DISPOSITION OF TOXICANT MAY REQUIRE SEVERAL HOURS OR DAYS DURING WHICH ATROPINIZATION MUST BE MAINTAINED. MARKEDLY LOWER LEVELS OF URINARY METABOLITES INDICATE THAT ATROPINE DOSAGE CAN BE TAPERED OFF. AS DOSAGE IS REDUCED, CHECK THE LUNG BASES FREQUENTLY FOR RALES. IF RALES ARE HEARD OR OTHER SYMPTOMS RETURN, RE-ESTABLISH ATROPINIZATION PROMPTLY (MORGAN, RECOGNITION AND MANAGEMENT OF PESTICIDE POISONINGS, 3RD ED.). ADMINISTRATION OF ANTIDOTE MUST BE PERFORMED BY QUALIFIED MEDICAL PERSONNEL.
IN CASES OF SEVERE POISONING BY ORGANOPHOSPHATE PESTICIDES IN WHICH RESPIRATORY DEPRESSION, MUSCLE WEAKNESS AND TWITCHINGS ARE SEVERE, GIVE PRALIDOXIME (PROTOPAM-AYERST, 2-PAM), 1.0 GRAM INTRAVENOUSLY AT NO MORE THAN 0.5 GRAM PER MINUTE. DOSAGE OF PRALIDOXIME MAY BE REPEATED IN 1-2 HOURS, THEN AT 10-12 HOUR INTERVALS IF NEEDED. IN VERY SEVERE POISONINGS, DOSAGE RATES MAY BE DOUBLED. TREATMENT WITH PRALIDOXIME WILL BE MOST EFFECTIVE IF GIVEN WITHIN THIRTY-SIX HOURS AFTER POISONING (MORGAN, RECOGNITION AND MANAGEMENT OF PESTICIDE POISONINGS, 3RD ED.). ANTIDOTE SHOULD BE ADMINISTERED BY QUALIFIED MEDICAL PERSONNEL.

REACTIVITY

REACTIVITY: STABLE UNDER NORMAL TEMPERATURES AND PRESSURES.
INCOMPATIBILITIES: METHYL CARBOPHENOTHION: NO DATA AVAILABLE.
DECOMPOSITION: THERMAL DECOMPOSITION PRODUCTS MAY INCLUDE TOXIC AND HAZARDOUS FUMES OF CHLORINE AND OXIDES OF OXIDES OF SULFUR AND PHOSPHORUS.
POLYMERIZATION: HAZARDOUS POLYMERIZATION HAS NOT BEEN REPORTED TO OCCUR UNDER NORMAL TEMPERATURES AND PRESSURES.

STORAGE AND DISPOSAL

OBSERVE ALL FEDERAL, STATE AND LOCAL REGULATIONS WHEN STORING OR DISPOSING OF THIS SUBSTANCE. FOR ASSISTANCE, CONTACT THE DISTRICT DIRECTOR OF THE ENVIRONMENTAL PROTECTION AGENCY.

****STORAGE****

STORE IN ACCORDANCE WITH 40 CFR 165 RECOMMENDED PROCEDURES FOR THE DISPOSAL AND STORAGE OF PESTICIDES AND PESTICIDE CONTAINERS.

****DISPOSAL****

DISPOSAL MUST BE IN ACCORDANCE WITH 40 CFR 165 RECOMMENDED PROCEDURES FOR THE DISPOSAL AND STORAGE OF PESTICIDES AND PESTICIDE CONTAINERS.

CONDITIONS TO AVOID

MAY BURN BUT DOES NOT IGNITE READILY. CONTAINERS MAY EXPLODE IN HEAT OF FIRE.

SPILL AND LEAK PROCEDURES

OCCUPATIONAL SPILL: DO NOT TOUCH SPILLED MATERIAL. STOP LEAK IF YOU CAN DO IT WITHOUT RISK. USE WATER SPRAY TO REDUCE VAPORS. FOR SMALL SPILLS, TAKE UP WITH SAND OR OTHER ABSORBENT MATERIAL AND PLACE INTO CONTAINERS FOR LATER DISPOSAL. FOR SMALL DRY SPILLS, WITH A CLEAN SHOVEL PLACE MATERIAL INTO CLEAN, DRY CONTAINERS AND COVER. MOVE CONTAINERS FROM SPILL AREA. FOR LARGER SPILLS, DIKE FAR AHEAD OF SPILL FOR LATER DISPOSAL. KEEP UNNECESSARY PEOPLE AWAY. ISOLATE HAZARD AREA AND DENY ENTRY. VENTILATE CLOSED SPACES BEFORE ENTERING.

PROTECTIVE EQUIPMENT

VENTILATION: PROCESS ENCLOSURE RECOMMENDED.
RESPIRATOR: THE FOLLOWING RESPIRATORS ARE RECOMMENDED BASED ON INFORMATION FOUND IN THE PHYSICAL DATA, TOXICITY AND HEALTH EFFECTS SECTIONS. THEY ARE RANKED IN ORDER FROM MINIMUM TO MAXIMUM RESPIRATORY PROTECTION. THE SPECIFIC RESPIRATOR SELECTED MUST BE BASED ON CONTAMINATION LEVELS FOUND IN THE WORK PLACE, MUST NOT EXCEED THE WORKING LIMITS OF THE RESPIRATOR AND BE JOINTLY APPROVED BY THE NATIONAL INSTITUTE FOR OCCUPATIONAL SAFETY AND HEALTH AND THE MINE SAFETY AND HEALTH ADMINISTRATION (NIOSH-MSHA).
TYPE 'C' SUPPLIED-AIR RESPIRATOR WITH A FULL FACEPIECE OPERATED IN PRESSURE-DEMAND OR OTHER POSITIVE PRESSURE MODE OR WITH A FULL

FACEPIECE, HELMET OR HOOD OPERATED IN CONTINOUS-FLOW MODE.
SELF-CONTAINED BREATHING APPARATUS WITH A FULL FACEPIECE OPERATED IN PRESSURE-DEMAND OR OTHER POSITIVE PRESSURE MODE.
FOR FIREFIGHTING AND OTHER IMMEDIATELY DANGEROUS TO LIFE OR HEALTH CONDITIONS:
SELF-CONTAINED BREATHING APPARATUS WITH FULL FACEPIECE OPERATED IN PRESSURE-DEMAND OR OTHER POSITIVE PRESSURE MODE.
SUPPLIED-AIR RESPIRATOR WITH FULL FACEPIECE AND OPERATED IN PRESSURE-DEMAND OR OTHER POSITIVE PRESSURE MODE IN COMBINATION WITH AN AUXILIARY SELF-CONTAINED BREATHING APPARATUS OPERATED IN PRESSURE-DEMAND OR OTHER POSITIVE PRESSURE MODE.

CLOTHING: EMPLOYEE MUST WEAR APPROPRIATE PROTECTIVE (IMPERVIOUS) CLOTHING AND EQUIPMENT TO PREVENT ANY POSSIBILITY OF SKIN CONTACT WITH THIS SUBSTANCE.

GLOVES: EMPLOYEE MUST WEAR APPROPRIATE PROTECTIVE GLOVES TO PREVENT CONTACT WITH THIS SUBSTANCE.

EYE PROTECTION: EMPLOYEE MUST WEAR SPLASH-PROOF OR DUST-RESISTANT SAFETY GOGGLES WITH OR WITHOUT A FACESHIELD TO PREVENT CONTACT WITH THIS SUBSTANCE.
EMERGENCY EYE WASH: WHERE THERE IS ANY POSSIBILITY THAT AN EMPLOYEE'S EYES MAY BE EXPOSED TO THIS SUBSTANCE, THE EMPLOYER SHOULD PROVIDE AN EYE WASH FOUNTAIN WITHIN THE IMMEDIATE WORK AREA FOR EMERGENCY USE.

AUTHORIZED BY- OCCUPATIONAL HEALTH SERVICES, INC.
CREATION DATE: 10/04/89 ***REVISION DATE:*** 05/01/90

MATERIAL SAFETY DATA SHEET

OCCUPATIONAL HEALTH SERVICES, INC.
AGRICULTURE AND PESTICIDE DIVISION
450 SEVENTH AVENUE, SUITE 2407
NEW YORK, NEW YORK 10123
1-800-445-MSDS OR (212) 967-1100

EMERGENCY CONTACT:
JOHN S. BRANSFORD, JR. (615) 292-1180

SUBSTANCE IDENTIFICATION

CAS-NUMBER 17210-55-8
SUBSTANCE: **TEMEPHOS SULFOXIDE**
TRADE NAMES/SYNONYMS: PHOSPHOROTHIOIC ACID, O,O'-(SULFINYLDI-4,1-PHENYLENE) O,O,O',O'- TETRAMETHYL ESTER; PHOSPHOROTHIOIC ACID, O,O'-(SULFINYLDI-P-PHENYLENE) O,O,O',O'- TETRAMETHYL ESTER; ABATE, SULFOXIDE; C16H20O7P2S3; PST71651
CHEMICAL FAMILY: ORGANOPHOSPHATE SULFOXIDE
MOLECULAR FORMULA: ((C-H3-O)2-P-(S)-O-C6-H4)2-S-(O)
MOLECULAR WEIGHT: 482.46
CERCLA RATINGS (SCALE 0-3): HEALTH=3 FIRE=1 REACTIVITY=0 PERSISTENCE=0
NFPA RATINGS (SCALE 0-4): HEALTH=U FIRE=1 REACTIVITY=0

COMPONENTS AND CONTAMINANTS

COMPONENT: TEMEPHOS SULFOXIDE ***PERCENT:*** 100.0
CAS# 17210-55-8
OTHER CONTAMINANTS: NONE
EXPOSURE LIMITS: NO OCCUPATIONAL EXPOSURE LIMITS ESTABLISHED BY OSHA, ACGIH, OR NIOSH.

PHYSICAL DATA

DESCRIPTION: WHITE FLUFFY POWDER. ***MELTING POINT:*** NOT AVAILABLE
SPECIFIC GRAVITY: NOT AVAILABLE ***SOLUBILITY IN WATER:*** NOT AVAILABLE

FIRE AND EXPLOSION DATA

FIRE AND EXPLOSION HAZARD: SLIGHT FIRE HAZARD WHEN EXPOSED TO HEAT OR FLAME.
FIREFIGHTING MEDIA: DRY CHEMICAL, CARBON DIOXIDE, HALON, WATER SPRAY OR STANDARD FOAM (1987 EMERGENCY RESPONSE GUIDEBOOK, DOT P 5800.4).
FOR LARGER FIRES, USE WATER SPRAY, FOG OR STANDARD FOAM (1987 EMERGENCY RESPONSE GUIDEBOOK, DOT P 5800.4).
FIREFIGHTING: MOVE CONTAINERS FROM FIRE AREA IF POSSIBLE (1987 EMERGENCY RESPONSE GUIDEBOOK, DOT P 5800.4, GUIDE PAGE 53).
EXTINGUISH USING AGENT SUITABLE FOR TYPE OF SURROUNDING FIRE. AVOID BREATHING VAPORS AND DUSTS. KEEP UPWIND.

TOXICITY

TEMEPHOS SULFOXIDE: TOXICITY DATA: 190 MG/KG ORAL-RAT LD50 (EPA).
CARCINOGEN STATUS: NONE. ACUTE TOXICITY LEVEL: TOXIC BY INGESTION.
TARGET EFFECTS: CHOLINESTERASE INHIBITOR. POISONING MAY AFFECT THE NERVOUS SYSTEM.* AT INCREASED RISK FROM EXPOSURE: PERSONS WITH RESPIRATORY AILMENTS, RECENT EXPOSURE TO CHOLINESTERASE INHIBITORS OR IMPAIRED CHOLINESTERASE PRODUCTION, OR LIVER MALFUNCTION.* ADDITIONAL DATA: MAY CROSS THE PLACENTA. HIGH ENVIRONMENTAL TEMPERATURES OR EXPOSURE OF THE CHEMICAL TO VISIBLE OR ULTRAVIOLET LIGHT MAY ENHANCE THE TOXICITY. INTERACTIONS WITH MEDICATIONS MAY OCCUR.*
* MAY BE BASED ON GENERAL INFORMATION ON ORGANOPHOSPHATES.

HEALTH EFFECTS AND FIRST AID

INHALATION: TEMEPHOS SULFOXIDE: SEE INFORMATION ON ORGANOPHOSPHATES.
ORGANOPHOSPHATES: CHOLINESTERASE INHIBITOR. **ACUTE EXPOSURE**- WHEN INHALED, THE FIRST EFFECTS OF CHOLINESTERASE INHIBITORS ARE USUALLY RESPIRATORY AND MAY INCLUDE NASAL HYPEREMIA AND WATERY DISCHARGE, COUGH, CHEST DISCOMFORT, DYSPNEA, AND WHEEZING DUE TO INCREASED BRONCHIAL SECRETIONS AND BRONCHOCONSTRICTION. IF SUFFICIENT AMOUNTS ARE ABSORBED, OTHER SYSTEMIC EFFECTS MAY BEGIN WITHIN A FEW MINUTES OR BE DELAYED FOR UP TO 12 HOURS. SYMPTOMS MAY INCLUDE PALLOR, NAUSEA, VOMITING, DIARRHEA, ABDOMINAL CRAMPS, HEADACHE, DIZZINESS, OCULAR PAIN, BLURRED VISION, MIOSIS OR IN SOME CASES, ESPECIALLY INITIALLY, MYDRIASIS, LACRIMATION, SALIVATION, SWEATING, AND CONFUSION. OTHER REPORTED CENTRAL NERVOUS SYSTEM OR NEUROMUSCULAR EFFECTS MAY INCLUDE ATAXIA, SLURRED SPEECH, AREFLEXIA, WEAKNESS, FATIGUE, FASCICULATIONS, TWITCHING, TREMORS POSSIBLY OF THE TONGUE AND EYELIDS, AND EVENTUALLY PARALYSIS OF THE EXTREMITIES AND POSSIBLY OF THE RESPIRATORY MUSCLES. IN SEVERE CASES THERE MAY ALSO BE INVOLUNTARY DEFECATION AND URINATION, CYANOSIS, PSYCHOSIS, HYPERGLYCEMIA, ACUTE PANCREATITIS, CARDIAC IRREGULARITIES, PULMONARY EDEMA, UNCONSCIOUSNESS, CONVULSIONS, AND COMA. DEATH IS PRIMARILY DUE TO RESPIRATORY FAILURE, ALTHOUGH CARDIOVASCULAR EFFECTS INCLUDING CARDIAC ARREST MAY ALSO BE IMPLICATED. LONG TERM SEQUELAE ARE RARE BUT MAY INCLUDE NEUROPSYCHIATRIC DISORDERS AND MYOPATHY WITH MUSCLE TENDERNESS. SOME ORGANOPHOSPHATES MAY CAUSE A DELAYED NEUROPATHY BEGINNING 1-4 WEEKS AFTER AN ACUTE EXPOSURE WHICH MAY OR MAY NOT HAVE CAUSED ACUTE CHOLINERGIC EFFECTS. NUMBNESS, TINGLING, WEAKNESS AND CRAMPING BEGINNING SYMMETRICALLY IN THE LOWER LIMBS MAY PROGRESS TO ATAXIA AND PARALYSIS. IN SEVERE CASES, UPPER LIMB INVOLVEMENT IS POSSIBLE AND FLACCID PARALYSIS MAY PROGRESS TO SPASTIC PARALYSIS WITH EXAGGERATED REFLEXES. IMPROVEMENT MAY OCCUR OVER MONTHS TO YEARS, BUT SOME RESIDUAL IMPAIRMENT USUALLY REMAINS.
CHRONIC EXPOSURE- REPEATED OR PROLONGED EXPOSURE MAY RESULT IN THE EFFECTS OF ACUTE EXPOSURE INCLUDING THE DELAYED NEUROPATHY. OTHER EFFECTS REPORTED IN WORKERS REPEATEDLY EXPOSED INCLUDE IMPAIRED MEMORY AND CONCENTRATION, ACUTE PSYCHOSIS, SEVERE DEPRESSIONS, IRRITABILTY, CONFUSION, APATHY, EMOTIONAL LABILITY, SOCIAL WITHDRAWAL, CONFUSION, HEADACHE, SPEECH DIFFICULTIES, DELAYED REACTION TIMES, SPATIAL DISORIENTATION, NIGHTMARES, SLEEPWALKING, AND DROWSINESS OR INSOMNIA. AN INFLUENZA-LIKE CONDITION WITH HEADACHE, NAUSEA, WEAKNESS, ANOREXIA AND MALAISE HAS ALSO BEEN REPORTED.
FIRST AID- REMOVE FROM EXPOSURE AREA TO FRESH AIR IMMEDIATELY. IF BREATHING HAS STOPPED, GIVE ARTIFICIAL RESPIRATION. MAINTAIN AIRWAY AND BLOOD PRESSURE AND ADMINISTER OXYGEN IF AVAILABLE. KEEP AFFECTED PERSON WARM AND AT REST. TREAT SYMPTOMATICALLY AND SUPPORTIVELY. ADMINISTRATION OF OXYGEN SHOULD BE PERFORMED BY QUALIFIED PERSONNEL. GET MEDICAL ATTENTION IMMEDIATELY.

SKIN CONTACT: TEMEPHOS SULFOXIDE: SEE INFORMATION ON ORGANOPHOSPHATES.
ORGANOPHOSPHATES: CHOLINESTERASE INHIBITOR. **ACUTE EXPOSURE**- LOCALIZED SWEATING AND FASCICULATIONS MAY OCCUR AT THE SITE OF CONTACT. IF SUFFICIENT AMOUNTS ARE ABSORBED, OTHER EFFECTS OF CHOLINESTERASE INHIBITION AS DESCRIBED IN ACUTE INHALATION MAY OCCUR. SYMPTOMS MAY BE DELAYED 2-3 HOURS, BUT USUALLY NO MORE THAN 12 HOURS. THE RATE OF ABSORPTION IS INCREASED BY THE PRESENCE OF DERMATITIS OR HIGH AMBIENT TEMPERATURES. DELAYED NEUROPATHY IS ALSO POSSIBLE. **CHRONIC EXPOSURE**- REPEATED OR PROLONGED EXPOSURE MAY CAUSE EFFECTS AS DESCRIBED IN ACUTE EXPOSURE. SOME ORGANOPHOSPHATES MAY CAUSE SENSITIZATION.
FIRST AID- REMOVE CONTAMINATED CLOTHING IMMEDIATELY. WASH CONTAMINATED AREAS WITH SOAP AND WATER FOLLOWED BY ALCOHOL (ARENA, POISONING, 4TH ED.). EMERGENCY PERSONNEL SHOULD WEAR GLOVES AND

AVOID CONTAMINATION. TREAT RESPIRATORY DIFFICULTY WITH ARTIFICIAL RESPIRATION. GET MEDICAL ATTENTION IMMEDIATELY.

EYE CONTACT: TEMEPHOS SULFOXIDE: SEE INFORMATION ON ORGANOPHOSPHATES. ORGANOPHOSPHATES: CHOLINESTERASE INHIBITOR. **ACUTE EXPOSURE-** DIRECT CONTACT MAY CAUSE PAIN, HYPEREMIA, LACRIMATION, TWITCHING OF THE EYELIDS, MIOSIS, AND CILIARY MUSCLE SPASM WITH LOSS OF ACCOMODATION, BLURRED OR DIMMED VISION AND BROWACHE. SOMETIMES MYDRIASIS MAY OCCUR INSTEAD OF MIOSIS. WITH SUFFICIENT EXPOSURE, OTHER SYMPTOMS OF CHOLINESTERASE INHIBITION AS DESCRIBED IN ACUTE INHALATION MAY OCCUR. **CHRONIC EXPOSURE-** REPEATED OR PROLONGED EXPOSURE MAY CAUSE EFFECTS AS DESCRIBED IN ACUTE EXPOSURE. SOME COMPOUNDS HAVE CAUSED TOXIC EFFECTS ON THE CRYSTALLINE LENS, CONJUNCTIVAL THICKENING AND OBSTRUCTION OF THE NASOLACRIMAL CANALS WHEN USED AS MIOTIC EYEDROPS.

FIRST AID- IRRIGATE EYES WITH WATER OR SALINE SOLUTION. IF SYMPTOMS OF POISONING OCCUR, TREAT RESPIRATORY DIFFICULTY WITH ARTIFICIAL RESPIRATION AND OXYGEN. OBSERVE PATIENT FOR AT LEAST 24-36 HOURS (GOSSELIN, CLINICAL TOXICOLOGY OF COMMERCIAL PRODUCTS, 5TH ED.). GET MEDICAL ATTENTION IMMEDIATELY. OXYGEN SHOULD BE ADMINISTERED BY QUALIFIED MEDICAL PERSONNEL.

INGESTION: TEMEPHOS SULFOXIDE: TOXIC. THE LETHAL DOSE REPORTED IN RATS WAS 190 MG/KG. SEE INFORMATION ON ORGANOPHOSPHATES. ORGANOPHOSPHATES: CHOLINESTERASE INHIBITOR. **ACUTE EXPOSURE-** WHEN INGESTED, THE FIRST EFFECTS MAY BE NAUSEA, VOMITING, ANOREXIA, ABDOMINAL CRAMPS AND DIARRHEA. GASTROINTESTINAL ABSORPTION MAY CAUSE SYMPTOMS OF CHOLINESTERASE INHIBITION AS DESCRIBED IN ACUTE INHALATION. SYMPTOMS MAY BEGIN WITHIN MINUTES OR BE DELAYED FOR HOURS. DELAYED EFFECTS INCLUDING NEUROPATHY MAY ALSO OCCUR. **CHRONIC EXPOSURE-** REPEATED INGESTION MAY CAUSE EFFECTS AS DESCRIBED IN ACUTE EXPOSURE.

FIRST AID- IF PERSON IS ALERT AND RESPIRATION IS NOT DEPRESSED, GIVE SYRUP OF IPECAC FOLLOWED BY WATER (IF VOMITING OCCURS, KEEP HEAD BELOW HIPS TO PREVENT ASPIRATION). IF CONSCIOUSNESS LEVEL DECLINES OR VOMITING HAS NOT OCCURRED IN 15 MINUTES EMPTY STOMACH BY GASTRIC LAVAGE WITH THE AID OF CUFFED ENDOTRACHEAL TUBE USING ISOTONIC SALINE OR 5% SODIUM BICARBONATE FOLLOW WITH ACTIVATED CHARCOAL. ESTABLISH AND MAINTAIN AIRWAY. TREAT RESPIRATORY DIFFICULTY WITH ARTIFICIAL RESPIRATION AND OXYGEN. DO NOT GIVE MORPHINE, AMINOPHYLLINE, PHENOTHIAZINES, RESERPINE, FUROSEMIDE, OR ETHACRYNIC ACID (MORGAN, RECOGNITION AND MANAGEMENT OF PESTICIDE POISONINGS, 3RD ED.). TREAT SYMPTOMATICALLY AND SUPPORTIVELY. ADMINISTRATION OF OXYGEN AND LAVAGE MUST BE PERFORMED BY QUALIFIED MEDICAL PERSONNEL. GET MEDICAL ATTENTION IMMEDIATELY.

ANTIDOTE: THE FOLLOWING ANTIDOTE(S) HAVE BEEN RECOMMENDED. HOWEVER, THE DECISION AS TO WHETHER THE SEVERITY OF POISONING REQUIRES ADMINISTRATION OF ANY ANTIDOTE AND ACTUAL DOSE REQUIRED SHOULD BE MADE BY QUALIFIED MEDICAL PERSONNEL.

FOR CHOLINESTERASE INHIBITORS: ESTABLISH CLEAR AIRWAY AND TISSUE OXYGENATION BY ASPIRATION OF SECRETIONS, AND IF NECESSARY, BY ASSISTED PULMONARY VENTILATION WITH OXYGEN. IMPROVE TISSUE OXYGENATION AS MUCH AS POSSIBLE BEFORE ADMINISTERING ATROPINE TO MINIMIZE THE RISK OF VENTRICULAR FIBRILLATION. ADMINISTER ATROPINE SULFATE INTRAVENOUSLY, OR INTRAMUSCULARLY IF IV INJECTION IS NOT POSSIBLE. IN MODERATELY SEVERE POISONING ADMINISTER ATROPINE SULFATE, 0.4-2.0 MG REPEATED EVERY 15 MINUTES UNTIL ATROPINIZATION IS ACHIEVED (TACHYCARDIA, FLUSHING, DRY MOUTH, MYDRIASIS). MAINTAIN ATROPINIZATION BY REPEATED DOSES FOR 2-12 HOURS, OR LONGER, DEPENDING ON THE SEVERITY OF POISONING. THE APPEARANCE OF RALES IN THE LUNG BASES, MIOSIS, SALIVATION, NAUSEA, BRADYCARDIA, ARE ALL INDICATIONS OF INADEQUATE ATROPINIZATION. SEVERELY POISONED INDIVIDUALS MAY EXHIBIT REMARKABLE TOLERANCE TO ATROPINE; TWO OR MORE TIMES THE DOSAGES SUGGESTED ABOVE MAY BE NEEDED. PERSONS NOT POISONED OR ONLY SLIGHTLY POISONED, HOWEVER, MAY DEVELOP SIGNS OF ATROPINE TOXICITY FROM SUCH LARGE DOSAGES: FEVER, MUSCLE FIBRILLATIONS, AND DELIRIUM ARE THE MAIN SIGNS OF ATROPINE TOXICITY. IF THESE SIGNS APPEAR WHILE THE PATIENT IS FULLY ATROPINIZED, ATROPINE ADMINISTRATION SHOULD BE DISCONTINUED, AT LEAST TEMPORARILY. OBSERVE TREATED PATIENTS CLOSELY AT LEAST 24 HOURS TO INSURE THAT SYMPTOMS (POSSIBLY PULMONARY EDEMA) DO NOT RECUR AS ATROPINIZATION WEARS OFF. IN VERY SEVERE POISONINGS, METABOLIC DISPOSITION OF TOXICANT MAY REQUIRE SEVERAL HOURS OR DAYS DURING WHICH ATROPINIZATION MUST BE MAINTAINED. MARKEDLY LOWER LEVELS OF URINARY METABOLITES INDICATE THAT ATROPINE DOSAGE CAN BE TAPERED OFF. AS DOSAGE IS REDUCED, CHECK THE LUNG BASES FREQUENTLY FOR RALES. IF RALES ARE HEARD OR OTHER SYMPTOMS RETURN, RE-ESTABLISH ATROPINIZATION PROMPTLY (MORGAN, RECOGNITION AND MANAGEMENT OF PESTICIDE POISONINGS, 3RD ED.). ADMINISTRATION OF ANTIDOTE MUST BE PERFORMED BY QUALIFIED MEDICAL PERSONNEL.

IN CASES OF SEVERE POISONING BY ORGANOPHOSPHATE PESTICIDES IN WHICH RESPIRATORY DEPRESSION, MUSCLE WEAKNESS AND TWITCHINGS ARE SEVERE, GIVE PRALIDOXIME (PROTOPAM-AYERST, 2-PAM), 1.0 GRAM INTRAVENOUSLY AT NO MORE THAN 0.5 GRAM PER MINUTE. DOSAGE OF PRALIDOXIME MAY BE REPEATED IN 1-2 HOURS, THEN AT 10-12 HOUR INTERVALS IF NEEDED. IN VERY SEVERE POISONINGS, DOSAGE RATES MAY BE DOUBLED. TREATMENT WITH PRALIDOXIME WILL BE MOST EFFECTIVE IF GIVEN WITHIN THIRTY-SIX HOURS AFTER POISONING (MORGAN, RECOGNITION AND MANAGEMENT OF PESTICIDE POISONINGS, 3RD ED.). ANTIDOTE SHOULD BE ADMINISTERED BY QUALIFIED MEDICAL PERSONNEL.

REACTIVITY

REACTIVITY: STABLE UNDER NORMAL TEMPERATURES AND PRESSURES.

INCOMPATIBILITIES: TEMEPHOS SULFOXIDE: OXIDIZERS (STRONG): FIRE AND EXPLOSION HAZARD.

DECOMPOSITION: THERMAL DECOMPOSITION PRODUCTS MAY INCLUDE TOXIC OXIDES OF CARBON, SULFUR, AND PHOSPHORUS.

POLYMERIZATION: HAZARDOUS POLYMERIZATION HAS NOT BEEN REPORTED TO OCCUR UNDER NORMAL TEMPERATURES AND PRESSURES.

STORAGE AND DISPOSAL

OBSERVE ALL FEDERAL, STATE AND LOCAL REGULATIONS WHEN STORING OR DISPOSING OF THIS SUBSTANCE. FOR ASSISTANCE, CONTACT THE DISTRICT DIRECTOR OF THE ENVIRONMENTAL PROTECTION AGENCY.

STORAGE

STORE AWAY FROM INCOMPATIBLE SUBSTANCES.

CONDITIONS TO AVOID

MAY BURN BUT DOES NOT IGNITE READILY.

SPILL AND LEAK PROCEDURES

OCCUPATIONAL SPILL: DO NOT TOUCH SPILLED MATERIAL. STOP LEAK IF YOU CAN DO IT WITHOUT RISK. FOR SMALL SPILLS, TAKE UP WITH SAND OR OTHER ABSORBENT MATERIAL AND PLACE INTO CONTAINERS FOR LATER DISPOSAL. FOR SMALL DRY SPILLS, WITH A CLEAN SHOVEL PLACE MATERIAL INTO CLEAN, DRY CONTAINER AND COVER. MOVE CONTAINERS FROM SPILL AREA. FOR LARGER SPILLS, DIKE FAR AHEAD OF SPILL FOR LATER DISPOSAL. KEEP UNNECESSARY PEOPLE AWAY. ISOLATE HAZARD AREA AND DENY ENTRY.

PROTECTIVE EQUIPMENT

VENTILATION: PROVIDE LOCAL EXHAUST OR PROCESS ENCLOSURE VENTILATION SYSTEM.

RESPIRATOR: THE FOLLOWING RESPIRATORS ARE RECOMMENDED BASED ON INFORMATION FOUND IN THE PHYSICAL DATA, TOXICITY AND HEALTH EFFECTS SECTIONS. THEY ARE RANKED IN ORDER FROM MINIMUM TO MAXIMUM RESPIRATORY PROTECTION. THE SPECIFIC RESPIRATOR SELECTED MUST BE BASED ON CONTAMINATION LEVELS FOUND IN THE WORK PLACE, MUST NOT EXCEED THE WORKING LIMITS OF THE RESPIRATOR AND BE JOINTLY APPROVED BY THE NATIONAL INSTITUTE FOR OCCUPATIONAL SAFETY AND HEALTH AND THE MINE SAFETY AND HEALTH ADMINISTRATION (NIOSH-MSHA).

CHEMICAL CARTRIDGE RESPIRATOR WITH AN ORGANIC VAPOR CARTRIDGE(S) WITH A FULL FACEPIECE AND ORGANIC VAPOR CARTRIDGE(S) IN COMBINATION WITH A DUST AND MIST FILTER.

POWERED AIR-PURIFYING RESPIRATOR WITH A TIGHT-FITTING FACEPIECE AND ORGANIC VAPOR CARTRIDGE(S) IN COMBINATION WITH A HIGH-EFFICIENCY PARTICULATE FILTER.

TYPE 'C' SUPPLIED-AIR RESPIRATOR WITH A FULL FACEPIECE OPERATED IN A PRESSURE-DEMAND OR OTHER POSITIVE PRESSURE MODE.

SELF-CONTAINED BREATHING APPARATUS WITH A FULL FACEPIECE OPERATED IN PRESSURE-DEMAND OR OTHER POSITIVE PRESSURE MODE.

FOR FIREFIGHTING AND OTHER IMMEDIATELY DANGEROUS TO LIFE OR HEALTH CONDITIONS:

SELF-CONTAINED BREATHING APPARATUS WITH FULL FACEPIECE OPERATED IN PRESSURE-DEMAND OR OTHER POSITIVE PRESSURE MODE.

SUPPLIED-AIR RESPIRATOR WITH FULL FACEPIECE AND OPERATED IN PRESSURE-DEMAND OR OTHER POSITIVE PRESSURE MODE IN COMBINATION WITH AN AUXILIARY SELF-CONTAINED BREATHING APPARATUS OPERATED IN PRESSURE-DEMAND OR OTHER POSITIVE PRESSURE MODE.

CLOTHING: EMPLOYEE MUST WEAR APPROPRIATE PROTECTIVE (IMPERVIOUS) CLOTHING AND EQUIPMENT TO PREVENT ANY POSSIBILITY OF SKIN CONTACT WITH THIS SUBSTANCE.

GLOVES: EMPLOYEE MUST WEAR APPROPRIATE PROTECTIVE GLOVES TO PREVENT CONTACT WITH THIS SUBSTANCE.

EYE PROTECTION: EMPLOYEE MUST WEAR SPLASH-PROOF OR DUST-RESISTANT SAFETY GOGGLES AND A FACESHIELD TO PREVENT CONTACT WITH THIS SUBSTANCE.
EMERGENCY WASH FACILITIES: WHERE THERE IS ANY POSSIBILITY THAT AN EMPLOYEE'S EYES AND/OR SKIN MAY BE EXPOSED TO THIS SUBSTANCE, THE EMPLOYER SHOULD PROVIDE AN EYE WASH FOUNTAIN AND QUICK DRENCH SHOWER WITHIN THE IMMEDIATE WORK AREA FOR EMERGENCY USE.

AUTHORIZED BY- OCCUPATIONAL HEALTH SERVICES, INC.
CREATION DATE: 11/17/89 ***REVISION DATE:*** 05/07/90

MATERIAL SAFETY DATA SHEET

OCCUPATIONAL HEALTH SERVICES, INC.	EMERGENCY CONTACT:
AGRICULTURE AND PESTICIDE DIVISION	JOHN S. BRANSFORD, JR. (615) 292-1180
450 SEVENTH AVENUE, SUITE 2407	
NEW YORK, NEW YORK 10123	
1-800-445-MSDS OR (212) 967-1100	

SUBSTANCE IDENTIFICATION

CAS-NUMBER 5598-13-0
SUBSTANCE: **CHLORPYRIFOS-METHYL**
TRADE NAMES/SYNONYMS: PHOSPHOROTHIOIC ACID, O,O-DIMETHYL O-(3,5,6-TRICHLORO-2-PYRIDINYL) ESTER; PHOSPHOROTHIOIC ACID, O,O-DIMETHYL O-(3,5,6-TRICHLORO-2-PYRIDYL)ESTER; O,O-DIMETHYL O-3,5,6-TRICHLORO-2-PYRIDYL PHOSPHOROTHIOATE; O,O-DIMETHYL O-(3,5,6-TRICHLORO-2-PYRIDINYL) PHOSPHOROTHIOATE; DOWCO 214; DURSBAN METHYL; METHYL CHLORPYRIFOS; METHYL DURSBAN; NOLTRAN; OMS 1155; RELDAN; ENT 27520; PST71652
MOLECULAR FORMULA: C7-H7-CL3-N-O3-P-S
MOLECULAR WEIGHT: 322.53
CERCLA RATINGS (SCALE 0-3): HEALTH=2 FIRE=U REACTIVITY=U PERSISTENCE=1
NFPA RATINGS (SCALE 0-4): HEALTH=2 FIRE=U REACTIVITY=U

COMPONENTS AND CONTAMINANTS

COMPONENT: CHLORPYRIFOS-METHYL ***PERCENT:*** 100.0
CAS# 5598-13-0
OTHER CONTAMINANTS: NONE
EXPOSURE LIMITS: NO OCCUPATIONAL EXPOSURE LIMITS ESTABLISHED BY OSHA, ACGIH, OR NIOSH.

PHYSICAL DATA

DESCRIPTION: COLORLESS CRYSTALS WITH A SLIGHT MERCAPTAN ODOR
MELTING POINT: 114-116 F (46-47 C) ***SPECIFIC GRAVITY:*** NOT AVAILABLE
VAPOR PRESSURE: 0.0000422 MMHG ***SOLUBILITY IN WATER:*** 4 MG/L
SOLVENT SOLUBILITY: SOLUBLE IN ACETONE, BENZENE, CHLOROFORM, HEXANE, METHANOL

FIRE AND EXPLOSION DATA

FIRE AND EXPLOSION HAZARD: UNKNOWN FIRE AND EXPLOSION HAZARD.
FIREFIGHTING MEDIA: DRY CHEMICAL, CARBON DIOXIDE, HALON, WATER SPRAY OR STANDARD FOAM (1987 EMERGENCY RESPONSE GUIDEBOOK, DOT P 5800.4).
FOR LARGER FIRES, USE WATER SPRAY, FOG OR STANDARD FOAM (1987 EMERGENCY RESPONSE GUIDEBOOK, DOT P 5800.4).
FIREFIGHTING: MOVE CONTAINERS FROM FIRE AREA IF POSSIBLE. FIGHT FIRE FROM MAXIMUM DISTANCE. STAY AWAY FROM STORAGE TANK ENDS. DIKE FIRE CONTROL WATER FOR LATER DISPOSAL. DO NOT SCATTER MATERIAL (1987 EMERGENCY RESPONSE GUIDEBOOK, DOT P 5800.4, GUIDE PAGE 55).
EXTINGUISH USING AGENT SUITABLE FOR TYPE OF SURROUNDING FIRE. AVOID BREATHING VAPORS AND DUSTS. KEEP UPWIND.

TOXICITY

CHLORPYRIFOS-METHYL: IRRITATION DATA: 500 MG/24 HOURS SKIN-RABBIT MILD. TOXOCITY DATA: 3713 MG/KG SKIN-RAT LD50; 1828 MG/KG ORAL-RAT LD50; 2000 MG/KG ORAL-RABBIT LD50; 2032 MG/KG ORAL-MOUSE LD50; 2250 MG/KG ORAL-GUINEA PIG LD50; 6900 MG/KG SUBCUTANEOUS-RAT LD50; 23,800 MG/KG SUBCUTANEOUS-MOUSE LD50; 2325 MG/KG INTRAPERITONEAL-MOUSE LD50; REPRODUCTIVE EFFECTS DATA (RTECS). CARCINOGEN STATUS: NONE. ACUTE TOXICITY LEVEL: MODERATELY TOXIC BY INGESTION AND DERMAL ABSORPTION. TARGET EFFECTS: CHOLINESTERASE INHIBITOR. AT INCREASED RISK FROM EXPOSURE: PERSONS WITH RESPIRATORY AILMENTS, RECENT EXPOSURE TO CHOLINESTERASE INHIBITORS OR IMPAIRED CHOLINESTERASE PRODUCTION, OR LIVER MALFUNCTION.* ADDITIONAL DATA: MAY CROSS THE PLACENTA. HIGH ENVIRONMENTAL TEMPERATURES OR EXPOSURE OF THE CHEMICAL TO VISIBLE OR ULTRAVIOLET LIGHT MAY ENHANCE THE TOXICITY. INTERACTIONS WITH MEDICATIONS MAY OCCUR.*
* MAY BE BASED ON GENERAL INFORMATION ON ORGANOPHOSPHATES.

HEALTH EFFECTS AND FIRST AID

INHALATION: CHLORPYRIFOS-METHYL: SEE INFORMATION ON ORGANOPHOSPHATES.
ORGANOPHOSPHATES: CHOLINESTERASE INHIBITOR. **ACUTE EXPOSURE-** WHEN INHALED, THE FIRST EFFECTS OF CHOLINESTERASE INHIBITORS ARE USUALLY RESPIRATORY AND MAY INCLUDE NASAL HYPEREMIA AND WATERY DISCHARGE, COUGH, CHEST DISCOMFORT, DYSPNEA, AND WHEEZING DUE TO INCREASED BRONCHIAL SECRETIONS AND BRONCHOCONSTRICTION. IF SUFFICIENT AMOUNTS ARE ABSORBED, OTHER SYSTEMIC EFFECTS MAY BEGIN WITHIN A FEW MINUTES OR BE DELAYED FOR UP TO 12 HOURS. SYMPTOMS MAY INCLUDE PALLOR, NAUSEA, VOMITING, DIARRHEA, ABDOMINAL CRAMPS, HEADACHE, DIZZINESS, OCULAR PAIN, BLURRED VISION, MIOSIS OR IN SOME CASES, ESPECIALLY INITIALLY, MYDRIASIS, LACRIMATION, SALIVATION, SWEATING, AND CONFUSION. OTHER REPORTED CENTRAL NERVOUS SYSTEM OR NEUROMUSCULAR EFFECTS MAY INCLUDE ATAXIA, SLURRED SPEECH, AREFLEXIA, WEAKNESS, FATIGUE, FASCICULATIONS, TWITCHING, TREMORS POSSIBLY OF THE TONGUE AND EYELIDS, AND EVENTUALLY PARALYSIS OF THE EXTREMITIES AND POSSIBLY OF THE RESPIRATORY MUSCLES. IN SEVERE CASES THERE MAY ALSO BE INVOLUNTARY DEFECATION AND URINATION, CYANOSIS, PSYCHOSIS, HYPERGLYCEMIA, ACUTE PANCREATITIS, CARDIAC IRREGULARITIES, PULMONARY EDEMA, UNCONSCIOUSNESS, CONVULSIONS, AND COMA. DEATH IS PRIMARILY DUE TO RESPIRATORY FAILURE, ALTHOUGH CARDIOVASCULAR EFFECTS INCLUDING CARDIAC ARREST MAY ALSO BE IMPLICATED. LONG TERM SEQUELAE ARE RARE BUT MAY INCLUDE NEUROPSYCHIATRIC DISORDERS AND MYOPATHY WITH MUSCLE TENDERNESS. **CHRONIC EXPOSURE-** REPEATED OR PROLONGED EXPOSURE MAY RESULT IN THE EFFECTS OF ACUTE EXPOSURE. OTHER EFFECTS REPORTED IN WORKERS REPEATEDLY EXPOSED INCLUDE IMPAIRED MEMORY AND CONCENTRATION, ACUTE PSYCHOSIS, SEVERE DEPRESSIONS, IRRITABILTY, CONFUSION, APATHY, EMOTIONAL LABILITY, SOCIAL WITHDRAWAL, CONFUSION, HEADACHE, SPEECH DIFFICULTIES, DELAYED REACTION TIMES, SPATIAL DISORIENTATION, NIGHTMARES, SLEEPWALKING, AND DROWSINESS OR INSOMNIA. AN INFLUENZA-LIKE CONDITION WITH HEADACHE, NAUSEA, WEAKNESS, ANOREXIA AND MALAISE HAS ALSO BEEN REPORTED.
FIRST AID- REMOVE FROM EXPOSURE AREA TO FRESH AIR IMMEDIATELY. IF BREATHING HAS STOPPED, GIVE ARTIFICIAL RESPIRATION. MAINTAIN AIRWAY AND BLOOD PRESSURE AND ADMINISTER OXYGEN IF AVAILABLE. KEEP AFFECTED PERSON WARM AND AT REST. TREAT SYMPTOMATICALLY AND SUPPORTIVELY. ADMINISTRATION OF OXYGEN SHOULD BE PERFORMED BY QUALIFIED PERSONNEL. GET MEDICAL ATTENTION IMMEDIATELY.

SKIN CONTACT: CHLORPYRIFOS-METHYL: SEE INFORMATION ON ORGANOPHOSPHATES.
ORGANOPHOSPHATES: CHOLINESTERASE INHIBITOR. **ACUTE EXPOSURE-** LOCALIZED SWEATING AND FASCICULATIONS MAY OCCUR AT THE SITE OF CONTACT. IF SUFFICIENT AMOUNTS ARE ABSORBED, OTHER EFFECTS OF CHOLINESTERASE INHIBITION AS DESCRIBED IN ACUTE INHALATION MAY OCCUR. SYMPTOMS MAY BE DELAYED 2-3 HOURS, BUT USUALLY NO MORE THAN 12 HOURS. THE RATE OF ABSORPTION IS INCREASED BY THE PRESENCE OF DERMATITIS OR HIGH AMBIENT TEMPERATURES. **CHRONIC EXPOSURE-** REPEATED OR PROLONGED EXPOSURE MAY CAUSE EFFECTS AS DESCRIBED IN ACUTE EXPOSURE. SOME ORGANOPHOSPHATES MAY CAUSE SENSITIZATION.
FIRST AID- REMOVE CONTAMINATED CLOTHING IMMEDIATELY. WASH CONTAMINATED AREAS WITH SOAP AND WATER FOLLOWED BY ALCOHOL (ARENA, POISONING, 4TH ED.). EMERGENCY PERSONNEL SHOULD WEAR GLOVES AND AVOID CONTAMINATION. TREAT RESPIRATORY DIFFICULTY WITH ARTIFICIAL RESPIRATION. GET MEDICAL ATTENTION IMMEDIATELY.

EYE CONTACT: CHLORPYRIFOS-METHYL: SEE INFORMATION ON ORGANOPHOSPHATES.
ORGANOPHOSPHATES: CHOLINESTERASE INHIBITOR. **ACUTE EXPOSURE-** DIRECT CONTACT MAY CAUSE PAIN, HYPEREMIA, LACRIMATION, TWITCHING OF THE EYELIDS, MIOSIS, AND CILIARY MUSCLE SPASM WITH LOSS OF ACCOMODATION, BLURRED OR DIMMED VISION AND BROWACHE. SOMETIMES MYDRIASIS MAY OCCUR INSTEAD OF MIOSIS. WITH SUFFICIENT EXPOSURE, OTHER SYMPTOMS OF CHOLINESTERASE INHIBITION AS DESCRIBED IN ACUTE INHALATION MAY OCCUR. **CHRONIC EXPOSURE-** REPEATED OR PROLONGED EXPOSURE MAY CAUSE EFFECTS AS DESCRIBED IN ACUTE EXPOSURE. SOME COMPOUNDS HAVE CAUSED TOXIC EFFECTS ON THE CRYSTALLINE LENS, CONJUNCTIVAL THICKENING AND OBSTRUCTION OF THE NASOLACRIMAL CANALS WHEN USED AS MIOTIC EYEDROPS.

FIRST AID- IRRIGATE EYES WITH WATER OR SALINE SOLUTION. IF SYMPTOMS OF POISONING OCCUR, TREAT RESPIRATORY DIFFICULTY WITH ARTIFICIAL RESPIRATION AND OXYGEN. OBSERVE PATIENT FOR AT LEAST 24-36 HOURS (GOSSELIN, CLINICAL TOXICOLOGY OF COMMERCIAL PRODUCTS, 5TH ED.). GET MEDICAL ATTENTION IMMEDIATELY. OXYGEN SHOULD BE ADMINISTERED BY QUALIFIED MEDICAL PERSONNEL.

INGESTION: CHLORPYRIFOS-METHYL: NO APPARENT CLINICAL EVIDENCE OF NEUROTOXICITY WAS OBSERVED IN HENS GIVEN A LARGE DOSE OF CHLORPYRIFOS-METHYL. HISTOLOGICAL EXAMINATION OF NERVOUS TISSUE WAS NOT CONDUCTED. TERATOGENICITY STUDIES IN THE RAT REVEALED NO ADVERSE EFFECTS AT DIETARY INTAKE LEVELS OF UP TO 250 MG/KG. SEE INFORMATION ON ORGANOPHOSPHATES.

ORGANOPHOSPHATES: CHOLINESTERASE INHIBITOR. **ACUTE EXPOSURE**- WHEN INGESTED, THE FIRST EFFECTS MAY BE NAUSEA, VOMITING, ANOREXIA, ABDOMINAL CRAMPS AND DIARRHEA. GASTROINTESTINAL ABSORPTION MAY CAUSE THE SYMPTOMS OF CHOLINESTERASE INHIBITION AS DESCRIBED IN ACUTE INHALATION. SYMPTOMS MAY BEGIN WITHIN MINUTES OR BE DELAYED. **CHRONIC EXPOSURE**- REPEATED INGESTION MAY CAUSE EFFECTS AS DESCRIBED IN ACUTE EXPOSURE.

FIRST AID- IF PERSON IS ALERT AND RESPIRATION IS NOT DEPRESSED, GIVE SYRUP OF IPECAC FOLLOWED BY WATER (IF VOMITING OCCURS, KEEP HEAD BELOW HIPS TO PREVENT ASPIRATION). IF CONSCIOUSNESS LEVEL DECLINES OR VOMITING HAS NOT OCCURRED IN 15 MINUTES EMPTY STOMACH BY GASTRIC LAVAGE WITH THE AID OF CUFFED ENDOTRACHEAL TUBE USING ISOTONIC SALINE OR 5% SODIUM BICARBONATE FOLLOW WITH ACTIVATED CHARCOAL. ESTABLISH AND MAINTAIN AIRWAY. TREAT RESPIRATORY DIFFICULTY WITH ARTIFICIAL RESPIRATION AND OXYGEN. DO NOT GIVE MORPHINE, AMINOPHYLLINE, PHENOTHIAZINES, RESERPINE, FUROSEMIDE, OR ETHACRYNIC ACID (MORGAN, RECOGNITION AND MANAGEMENT OF PESTICIDE POISONINGS, 3RD ED.). TREAT SYMPTOMATICALLY AND SUPPORTIVELY. ADMINISTRATION OF OXYGEN AND LAVAGE MUST BE PERFORMED BY QUALIFIED MEDICAL PERSONNEL. GET MEDICAL ATTENTION IMMEDIATELY.

ANTIDOTE: THE FOLLOWING ANTIDOTE(S) HAVE BEEN RECOMMENDED. HOWEVER, THE DECISION AS TO WHETHER THE SEVERITY OF POISONING REQUIRES ADMINISTRATION OF ANY ANTIDOTE AND ACTUAL DOSE REQUIRED SHOULD BE MADE BY QUALIFIED MEDICAL PERSONNEL.

FOR CHOLINESTERASE INHIBITORS: ESTABLISH CLEAR AIRWAY AND TISSUE OXYGENATION BY ASPIRATION OF SECRETIONS, AND IF NECESSARY, BY ASSISTED PULMONARY VENTILATION WITH OXYGEN. IMPROVE TISSUE OXYGENATION AS MUCH AS POSSIBLE BEFORE ADMINISTERING ATROPINE TO MINIMIZE THE RISK OF VENTRICULAR FIBRILLATION. ADMINISTER ATROPINE SULFATE INTRAVENOUSLY, OR INTRAMUSCULARLY IF IV INJECTION IS NOT POSSIBLE. IN MODERATELY SEVERE POISONING ADMINISTER ATROPINE SULFATE, 0.4-2.0 MG REPEATED EVERY 15 MINUTES UNTIL ATROPINIZATION IS ACHIEVED (TACHYCARDIA, FLUSHING, DRY MOUTH, MYDRIASIS). MAINTAIN ATROPINIZATION BY REPEATED DOSES FOR 2-12 HOURS, OR LONGER, DEPENDING ON THE SEVERITY OF POISONING. THE APPEARANCE OF RALES IN THE LUNG BASES, MIOSIS, SALIVATION, NAUSEA, BRADYCARDIA, ARE ALL INDICATIONS OF INADEQUATE ATROPINIZATION. SEVERELY POISONED INDIVIDUALS MAY EXHIBIT REMARKABLE TOLERANCE TO ATROPINE; TWO OR MORE TIMES THE DOSAGES SUGGESTED ABOVE MAY BE NEEDED. PERSONS NOT POISONED OR ONLY SLIGHTLY POISONED, HOWEVER, MAY DEVELOP SIGNS OF ATROPINE TOXICITY FROM SUCH LARGE DOSAGES: FEVER, MUSCLE FIBRILLATIONS, AND DELIRIUM ARE THE MAIN SIGNS OF ATROPINE TOXICITY. IF THESE SIGNS APPEAR WHILE THE PATIENT IS FULLY ATROPINIZED, ATROPINE ADMINISTRATION SHOULD BE DISCONTINUED, AT LEAST TEMPORARILY. OBSERVE TREATED PATIENTS CLOSELY AT LEAST 24 HOURS TO INSURE THAT SYMPTOMS (POSSIBLY PULMONARY EDEMA) DO NOT RECUR AS ATROPINIZATION WEARS OFF. IN VERY SEVERE POISONINGS, METABOLIC DISPOSITION OF TOXICANT MAY REQUIRE SEVERAL HOURS OR DAYS DURING WHICH ATROPINIZATION MUST BE MAINTAINED. MARKEDLY LOWER LEVELS OF URINARY METABOLITES INDICATE THAT ATROPINE DOSAGE CAN BE TAPERED OFF. AS DOSAGE IS REDUCED, CHECK THE LUNG BASES FREQUENTLY FOR RALES. IF RALES ARE HEARD OR OTHER SYMPTOMS RETURN, RE-ESTABLISH ATROPINIZATION PROMPTLY (MORGAN, RECOGNITION AND MANAGEMENT OF PESTICIDE POISONINGS, 3RD ED.). ADMINISTRATION OF ANTIDOTE MUST BE PERFORMED BY QUALIFIED MEDICAL PERSONNEL.

IN CASES OF SEVERE POISONING BY ORGANOPHOSPHATE PESTICIDES IN WHICH RESPIRATORY DEPRESSION, MUSCLE WEAKNESS AND TWITCHINGS ARE SEVERE, GIVE PRALIDOXIME (PROTOPAM-AYERST, 2-PAM), 1.0 GRAM INTRAVENOUSLY AT NO MORE THAN 0.5 GRAM PER MINUTE. DOSAGE OF PRALIDOXIME MAY BE REPEATED IN 1-2 HOURS, THEN AT 10-12 HOUR INTERVALS IF NEEDED. IN VERY SEVERE POISONINGS, DOSAGE RATES MAY BE DOUBLED. TREATMENT WITH PRALIDOXIME WILL BE MOST EFFECTIVE IF GIVEN WITHIN THIRTY-SIX HOURS AFTER POISONING (MORGAN, RECOGNITION AND MANAGEMENT OF PESTICIDE POISONINGS, 3RD ED.). ANTIDOTE SHOULD BE ADMINISTERED BY QUALIFIED MEDICAL PERSONNEL.

REACTIVITY

REACTIVITY: STABLE UNDER NORMAL TEMPERATURES AND PRESSURES.

INCOMPATIBILITIES: CHLORPYRIFOS-METHYL: ACIDIC CONDITIONS (PH4-6): MAY CAUSE HYDROLYSIS. ALKALINE CONDITIONS (PH8-10): MAY CAUSE HYDROLYSIS.

DECOMPOSITION: THERMAL DECOMPOSITION MAY RELEASE CORROSIVE HYDROGEN CHLORIDE AND TOXIC OXIDES OF NITROGEN, PHOSPHORUS AND SULFUR.

POLYMERIZATION: HAZARDOUS POLYMERIZATION HAS NOT BEEN REPORTED TO OCCUR UNDER NORMAL TEMPERATURES AND PRESSURES.

STORAGE AND DISPOSAL

OBSERVE ALL FEDERAL, STATE AND LOCAL REGULATIONS WHEN STORING OR DISPOSING OF THIS SUBSTANCE. FOR ASSISTANCE, CONTACT THE DISTRICT DIRECTOR OF THE ENVIRONMENTAL PROTECTION AGENCY.

****STORAGE****

STORE IN ACCORDANCE WITH 40 CFR 165 RECOMMENDED PROCEDURES FOR THE DISPOSAL AND STORAGE OF PESTICIDES AND PESTICIDE CONTAINERS.

STORE AWAY FROM INCOMPATIBLE SUBSTANCES.

****DISPOSAL****

DISPOSAL MUST BE IN ACCORDANCE WITH 40 CFR 165 RECOMMENDED PROCEDURES FOR THE DISPOSAL AND STORAGE OF PESTICIDES AND PESTICIDE CONTAINERS.

CONDITIONS TO AVOID

NONE REPORTED.

SPILL AND LEAK PROCEDURES

OCCUPATIONAL SPILL: DO NOT TOUCH SPILLED MATERIAL. STOP LEAK IF YOU CAN DO IT WITHOUT RISK. USE WATER SPRAY TO REDUCE VAPORS. FOR SMALL SPILLS, TAKE UP WITH SAND OR OTHER ABSORBENT MATERIAL AND PLACE INTO CONTAINERS FOR LATER DISPOSAL. FOR SMALL DRY SPILLS, WITH A CLEAN SHOVEL PLACE MATERIAL INTO CLEAN, DRY CONTAINERS AND COVER. MOVE CONTAINERS FROM SPILL AREA. FOR LARGER SPILLS, DIKE FAR AHEAD OF SPILL FOR LATER DISPOSAL. KEEP UNNECESSARY PEOPLE AWAY. ISOLATE HAZARD AREA AND DENY ENTRY. VENTILATE CLOSED SPACES BEFORE ENTERING.

PROTECTIVE EQUIPMENT

VENTILATION: PROVIDE LOCAL EXHAUST VENTILATION SYSTEM.

RESPIRATOR: THE FOLLOWING RESPIRATORS ARE RECOMMENDED BASED ON INFORMATION FOUND IN THE PHYSICAL DATA, TOXICITY AND HEALTH EFFECTS SECTIONS. THEY ARE RANKED IN ORDER FROM MINIMUM TO MAXIMUM RESPIRATORY PROTECTION. THE SPECIFIC RESPIRATOR SELECTED MUST BE BASED ON CONTAMINATION LEVELS FOUND IN THE WORK PLACE, MUST NOT EXCEED THE WORKING LIMITS OF THE RESPIRATOR AND BE JOINTLY APPROVED BY THE NATIONAL INSTITUTE FOR OCCUPATIONAL SAFETY AND HEALTH AND THE MINE SAFETY AND HEALTH ADMINISTRATION (NIOSH-MSHA).

CHEMICAL CARTRIDGE RESPIRATOR WITH AN ORGANIC VAPOR CARTRIDGE(S) WITH A FULL FACEPIECE AND ORGANIC VAPOR CARTRIDGE(S) IN COMBINATION WITH A DUST AND MIST FILTER.

POWERED AIR-PURIFYING RESPIRATOR WITH A TIGHT-FITTING FACEPIECE AND ORGANIC VAPOR CARTRIDGE(S) IN COMBINATION WITH A HIGH-EFFICIENCY PARTICULATE FILTER.

TYPE 'C' SUPPLIED-AIR RESPIRATOR WITH A FULL FACEPIECE OPERATED IN A PRESSURE-DEMAND OR OTHER POSITIVE PRESSURE MODE.

SELF-CONTAINED BREATHING APPARATUS WITH A FULL FACEPIECE OPERATED IN PRESSURE-DEMAND OR OTHER POSITIVE PRESSURE MODE.

FOR FIREFIGHTING AND OTHER IMMEDIATELY DANGEROUS TO LIFE OR HEALTH CONDITIONS:

SELF-CONTAINED BREATHING APPARATUS WITH FULL FACEPIECE OPERATED IN PRESSURE-DEMAND OR OTHER POSITIVE PRESSURE MODE.

SUPPLIED-AIR RESPIRATOR WITH FULL FACEPIECE AND OPERATED IN PRESSURE-DEMAND OR OTHER POSITIVE PRESSURE MODE IN COMBINATION WITH AN AUXILIARY SELF-CONTAINED BREATHING APPARATUS OPERATED IN PRESSURE-DEMAND OR OTHER POSITIVE PRESSURE MODE.

CLOTHING: EMPLOYEE MUST WEAR APPROPRIATE PROTECTIVE (IMPERVIOUS) CLOTHING AND EQUIPMENT TO PREVENT REPEATED OR PROLONGED SKIN CONTACT WITH THIS SUBSTANCE.

GLOVES: EMPLOYEE MUST WEAR APPROPRIATE PROTECTIVE GLOVES TO PREVENT CONTACT WITH THIS SUBSTANCE.

EYE PROTECTION: EMPLOYEE MUST WEAR SPLASH-PROOF OR DUST-RESISTANT SAFETY GOGGLES TO PREVENT EYE CONTACT WITH THIS SUBSTANCE.

EMERGENCY EYE WASH: WHERE THERE IS ANY POSSIBILITY THAT AN EMPLOYEE'S EYES MAY BE EXPOSED TO THIS SUBSTANCE, THE EMPLOYER SHOULD PROVIDE AN EYE WASH FOUNTAIN WITHIN THE IMMEDIATE WORK AREA FOR EMERGENCY USE.

AUTHORIZED BY- OCCUPATIONAL HEALTH SERVICES, INC.
CREATION DATE: 10/04/89 ***REVISION DATE:*** 06/20/90

MATERIAL SAFETY DATA SHEET

OCCUPATIONAL HEALTH SERVICES, INC.
AGRICULTURE AND PESTICIDE DIVISION
450 SEVENTH AVENUE, SUITE 2407
NEW YORK, NEW YORK 10123
1-800-445-MSDS OR (212) 967-1100

EMERGENCY CONTACT:
JOHN S. BRANSFORD, JR. (615) 292-1180

SUBSTANCE IDENTIFICATION

CAS-NUMBER 19750-95-9
SUBSTANCE: **CHLORDIMEFORM HYDROCHLORIDE**
TRADE NAMES/SYNONYMS: METHANIMIDAMIDE, N'-(4-CHLORO-2-METHYLPHENYL)-N,N-DIMETHYL-, MONOHYDROCHLORIDE; FORMAMIDINE, N'-(4-CHLORO-2-METHYLPHENYL)-N,N-DIMETHYL-, MONOHYDROCHLORIDE; N'-(4-CHLORO-2-METHYLPHENYL)-N,N-DIMETHYLMETHANIMIDAMIDE MONOHYDROCHLORIDE; N'-(4-CHLOARO-2-METHYLPHENYL)-N,N-DIMETHYLFORMAMIDINE MONOHYDROCHLORIDE; N'-(4-CHLORO-2-METHYLPHENYL)-N,N-DIMETHYLFORMAMIDINIUMCHLORIDE; CHLORDIMEFORM MONOHYDROCHLORIDE; CHLOROPHENAMIDINE HYDROCHLORIDE; CHLORPHENAMIDINE MONOHYDROCHLORIDE; GALECRON, MONOHYDROCHLORIDE; SPANON MONOHYDROCHLORIDE; ENT 27567; C10H14CL2N2; PST71656
CHEMICAL FAMILY: HALOGEN COMPOUND, AROMATIC AMIDINE
MOLECULAR FORMULA: CL-C-H3-C6-H3-N-C-H-N-(C-H3)2.H-CL
MOLECULAR WEIGHT: 233.14
CERCLA RATINGS (SCALE 0-3): HEALTH=3 FIRE=1 REACTIVITY=0 PERSISTENCE=3
NFPA RATINGS (SCALE 0-4): HEALTH=3 FIRE=1 REACTIVITY=0

COMPONENTS AND CONTAMINANTS

COMPONENT: CHLORDIMEFORM HYDROCHLORIDE ***PERCENT:*** 100
CAS# 19750-95-9
OTHER CONTAMINANTS: NONE
EXPOSURE LIMITS: NO OCCUPATIONAL EXPOSURE LIMITS ESTABLISHED BY OSHA, ACGIH, OR NIOSH.

PHYSICAL DATA

DESCRIPTION: COLORLESS POWDER WITH AN AMINE-LIKE ODOR
MELTING POINT: 435-439 F (224-226 C) DECOMPOSES
SPECIFIC GRAVITY: NOT AVAILABLE
VAPOR PRESSURE: NEGLIGIBLE ***SOLUBILITY IN WATER:*** >50%
SOLVENT SOLUBILITY: SOLUBLE IN METHANOL, VERY SLIGHTLY SOLUBLE IN CHLOROFORM

FIRE AND EXPLOSION DATA

FIRE AND EXPLOSION HAZARD: SLIGHT FIRE HAZARD WHEN EXPOSED TO HEAT OR FLAME.
FIREFIGHTING MEDIA: DRY CHEMICAL, CARBON DIOXIDE, HALON, WATER SPRAY OR STANDARD FOAM (1987 EMERGENCY RESPONSE GUIDEBOOK, DOT P 5800.4). FOR LARGER FIRES, USE WATER SPRAY, FOG OR STANDARD FOAM (1987 EMERGENCY RESPONSE GUIDEBOOK, DOT P 5800.4).
FIREFIGHTING: MOVE CONTAINERS FROM FIRE AREA IF POSSIBLE. FIGHT FIRE FROM MAXIMUM DISTANCE. STAY AWAY FROM STORAGE TANK ENDS. DIKE FIRE CONTROL WATER FOR LATER DISPOSAL. DO NOT SCATTER MATERIAL (1987 EMERGENCY RESPONSE GUIDEBOOK, DOT P 5800.4, GUIDE PAGE 55). USE AGENTS SUITABLE FOR TYPE OF FIRE. COOL CONTAINERS WITH FLOODING AMOUNTS OF WATER. AVOID BREATHING VAPORS OR DUSTS, KEEP UPWIND.

TOXICITY

CHLORDIMEFORM HYDROCHLORIDE: IRRITATION DATA: 100 MG EYE-RABBIT MILD. TOXICITY DATA: 4000 MG/KG SKIN-RAT LD50; 225 MG/KG ORAL-RAT LD50; 290 MG/KG ORAL-MOUSE LD50; 625 MG/KG ORAL-RABBIT LD50; 85500 UG/KG INTRAPERITONEAL-MOUSE LD50. CARCINOGEN STATUS: ANIMAL INADEQUATE EVIDENCE (IARC GROUP-3). THE AVAILABLE DATA ARE INSUFFICIENT TO EVALUATE THE CARCINOGENICITY OF CHLORDIMEFORM TO HUMANS. HOWEVER, RESULTS OF EXPERIMENTS IN MICE PROVIDE SUFFICIENT EVIDENCE THAT PARA-CHLORO-ORTHO-TOLUIDINE, A METABOLITE OF CHLORDIMEFORM, IS CARCINOGENIC TO EXPERIMENTAL ANIMALS. ACUTE TOXICITY LEVEL: TOXIC BY INGESTION AND SLIGHTLY TOXIC BY DERMAL ABSORPTION. TARGET EFFECTS: POISONING MAY AFFECT THE URINARY BLADDER.

HEALTH EFFECTS AND FIRST AID

INHALATION: CHLORDIMEFORM HYDROCHLORIDE: **ACUTE EXPOSURE-** MAY CAUSE NAUSEA, VOMITING AND LETHARGY. MASSIVE EXPOSURE TO CHLORDIMEFORM MAY CAUSE EFFECTS AS LISTED IN CHRONIC EXPOSURE. **CHRONIC EXPOSURE-** SYMPTOMS OF INCREASE URINARY FREQUENCY, GROSS HEMATURIA, URETHRAL DISCHARGE, ABDOMINAL AND BACK PAIN, AND A HOT SENSATION ALL OVER WERE REPORTED AMONG WORKERS EXPOSED TO CHLORDIMEFORM. OTHER EFFECTS OF BLADDER IRRITATION, SLEEPINESS, SKIN RASH, ANOREXIA, DIZZINESS, AND A SWEET TASTE IN THE MOUTH ALSO OCCURRED. AN UROLOGICAL EXAMINATION OF THREE HOSPITALIZED WORKERS REVEALED HEMATURIA AND PYURIA, PROTEINURIA, LOW CREATININE CLEARANCE, DECREASED SERUM COMPLEMENT LEVEL, ELEVATED SERUM GLUTAMIC OXALOACETIC TRANSAMINASE, SMALL URINARY BLADDER CAPACITY AND URETERAL REFLUX; SEVERE HEMORRHAGIC CYSTITIS WAS DETERMINED BY CYSTOSCOPIC EXAMINATION. THESE EFFECTS WERE COMPLETELY REVERSED WITHIN A THREE TO EIGHT WEEK PERIOD.
FIRST AID- REMOVE FROM EXPOSURE AREA TO FRESH AIR IMMEDIATELY. IF BREATHING HAS STOPPED, PERFORM ARTIFICIAL RESPIRATION. KEEP PERSON WARM AND AT REST. TREAT SYMPTOMATICALLY AND SUPPORTIVELY. GET MEDICAL ATTENTION IMMEDIATELY.

SKIN CONTACT: CHLORDIMEFORM HYDROCHLORIDE: **ACUTE EXPOSURE-** THIS MATERIAL WAS SLIGHTLY IRRITATING TO THE SKIN OF RABBITS. A LETHAL DOSE BY DERMAL ABSORPTION IN RABBITS WAS 4000 MG/KG. A LETHAL DOSE OF A METABOLITE OF CHLORDIMEFORM, 4-CHLORO-O-TOLUIDINE, PRODUCED HEMORRHAGE OF THE BLADDER MUCOSA IN CATS; A CONDITION THAT IS NOT PRODUCED BY CHLORDIMEFORM OR ITS METABOLITES IN OTHER ANIMALS. **CHRONIC EXPOSURE-** SYMPTOMS OF INCREASE URINARY FREQUENCY, GROSS HEMATURIA, URETHRAL DISCHARGE, ABDOMINAL AND BACK PAIN, AND A HOT SENSATION ALL OVER WERE REPORTED AMONG WORKERS EXPOSED TO CHLORDIMEFORM. OTHER EFFECTS OF BLADDER IRRITATION, SLEEPINESS, SKIN RASH, ANOREXIA, DIZZINESS, AND A SWEET TASTE IN THE MOUTH ALSO OCCURRED. AN UROLOGICAL EXAMINATION OF THREE HOSPITALIZED WORKERS REVEALED HEMATURIA AND PYURIA, PROTEINURIA, LOW CREATININE CLEARANCE, DECREASED SERUM COMPLEMENT LEVEL, ELEVATED SERUM GLUTAMIC OXALOACETIC TRANSAMINASE, SMALL URINARY BLADDER CAPACITY AND URETERAL REFLUX; SEVERE HEMORRHAGIC CYSTITIS WAS DETERMINED BY CYSTOSCOPIC EXAMINATION. THESE EFFECTS WERE COMPLETELY REVERSED WITHIN A THREE TO EIGHT WEEK PERIOD.
FIRST AID- REMOVE CONTAMINATED CLOTHING AND SHOES IMMEDIATELY. WASH AFFECTED AREA WITH SOAP OR MILD DETERGENT AND LARGE AMOUNTS OF WATER UNTIL NO EVIDENCE OF CHEMICAL REMAINS (APPROXIMATELY 15-20 MINUTES). GET MEDICAL ATTENTION IMMEDIATELY.

EYE CONTACT: CHLORDIMEFORM HYDROCHLORIDE: **ACUTE EXPOSURE-** A 100 MG APPLIED TO THE EYES OF RABBITS WAS MILDLY IRRITATING. **CHRONIC EXPOSURE-** NO DATA AVAILABLE.
FIRST AID- WASH EYES IMMEDIATELY WITH LARGE AMOUNTS OF WATER OR NORMAL SALINE, OCCASIONALLY LIFTING UPPER AND LOWER LIDS, UNTIL NO EVIDENCE OF CHEMICAL REMAINS (APPROXIMATELY 15-20 MINUTES). GET MEDICAL ATTENTION IMMEDIATELY.

INGESTION: CHLORDIMEFORM HYDROCHLORIDE: TOXIC. **ACUTE EXPOSURE-** A LETHAL DOSE IN RAT WAS 225 MG/KG. **CHRONIC EXPOSURE-** EFFECTS OF REDUCED FOOD CONSUMPTION, DECREASED BLOOD GLUCOSE, HEMOLYTIC ANEMIA AND BLOOD VESSEL NEOPLASMS WAS OBSERVED IN STUDIES OF MICE REPEATEDLY FED CHLORDIMEFORM HYDROCHLORIDE. IN RATS STUDIES, EFFECTS FROM REPEATED ADMINISTRATION OF THIS MATERIAL INCLUDED REDUCED FOOD CONSUMPTION AND BODY WEIGHTS, DECREASED OVERNIGHT URINE, DECREASED BLOOD GLUCOSE, AND INCREASED METHEMOGLOBIN FORMATION. IN A LIFETIME FEEDING STUDY OF MICE, HEMANGIOENDOTHELIOMA (A CANCER DERIVED FROM BLOOD VESSELS) WAS OBSERVED AT DIETARY LEVELS OF 100 AND 500 PPM; NO ONCOGENIC EFFECTS WERE REPORTED IN RATS AT THESE LEVELS. PARA-CHLORO-ORTHO-TOLUIDINE, A METABOLITE OF CHLORDIMEFORM, PRODUCED CARCINOGENIC EFFECTS IN MICE.
FIRST AID- REMOVE BY GASTRIC LAVAGE AND CATHARSIS. MAINTAIN BLOOD PRESSURE AND AIRWAY. GIVE OXYGEN IF RESPIRATION IS DEPRESSED. DO NOT PERFORM GASTRIC LAVAGE IF VICTIM IS UNCONSCIOUS. GET MEDICAL ATTENTION IMMEDIATELY (DREISBACH, HANDBOOK OF POISONING, 12TH ED.). ADMINISTRATION OF LAVAGE OR OXYGEN SHOULD BE PERFORMED BY QUALIFIED MEDICAL PERSONNEL.
ANTIDOTE: NO SPECIFIC ANTIDOTE. TREAT SYMPTOMATICALLY AND SUPPORTIVELY.

REACTIVITY

REACTIVITY: STABLE UNDER NORMAL TEMPERATURES AND PRESSURES.
INCOMPATIBILITIES: CHLORDIMEFORM HYDROCHLORIDE: NO DATA AVAILABLE.
DECOMPOSITION: THERMAL DECOMPOSITION PRODUCTS MAY INCLUDE TOXIC AND CORROSIVE FUMES OF CHLORIDES AND PHOSGENE, AND TOXIC OXIDES OF CARBON.
POLYMERIZATION: HAZARDOUS POLYMERIZATION HAS NOT BEEN REPORTED TO OCCUR UNDER NORMAL TEMPERATURES AND PRESSURES.

STORAGE AND DISPOSAL

OBSERVE ALL FEDERAL, STATE AND LOCAL REGULATIONS WHEN STORING OR DISPOSING OF THIS SUBSTANCE. FOR ASSISTANCE, CONTACT THE DISTRICT DIRECTOR OF THE ENVIRONMENTAL PROTECTION AGENCY.

STORAGE

STORE IN ACCORDANCE WITH 40 CFR 165 RECOMMENDED PROCEDURES FOR THE DISPOSAL AND STORAGE OF PESTICIDES AND PESTICIDE CONTAINERS.
STORE IN A COOL, DRY PLACE; KEEP CONTAINER TIGHTLY CLOSED WHEN NOT IN USE.

DISPOSAL

DISPOSAL MUST BE IN ACCORDANCE WITH 40 CFR 165 RECOMMENDED PROCEDURES FOR THE DISPOSAL AND STORAGE OF PESTICIDES AND PESTICIDE CONTAINERS.

CONDITIONS TO AVOID

MAY BURN BUT DOES NOT IGNITE READILY. CONTAINERS MAY EXPLODE IN HEAT OF FIRE.

SPILL AND LEAK PROCEDURES

OCCUPATIONAL SPILL: DO NOT TOUCH SPILLED MATERIAL. STOP LEAK IF YOU CAN DO IT WITHOUT RISK. USE WATER SPRAY TO REDUCE VAPORS. FOR SMALL SPILLS, TAKE UP WITH SAND OR OTHER ABSORBENT MATERIAL AND PLACE INTO CONTAINERS FOR LATER DISPOSAL. FOR SMALL DRY SPILLS, WITH A CLEAN SHOVEL PLACE MATERIAL INTO CLEAN, DRY CONTAINERS AND COVER. MOVE CONTAINERS FROM SPILL AREA. FOR LARGER SPILLS, DIKE FAR AHEAD OF SPILL FOR LATER DISPOSAL. KEEP UNNECESSARY PEOPLE AWAY. ISOLATE HAZARD AREA AND DENY ENTRY. VENTILATE CLOSED SPACES BEFORE ENTERING.

PROTECTIVE EQUIPMENT

VENTILATION: PROVIDE LOCAL EXHAUST OR GENERAL DILUTION VENTILATION SYSTEM.
RESPIRATOR: THE FOLLOWING RESPIRATORS ARE RECOMMENDED BASED ON INFORMATION FOUND IN THE PHYSICAL DATA, TOXICITY AND HEALTH EFFECTS SECTIONS. THEY ARE RANKED IN ORDER FROM MINIMUM TO MAXIMUM RESPIRATORY PROTECTION. THE SPECIFIC RESPIRATOR SELECTED MUST BE BASED ON CONTAMINATION LEVELS FOUND IN THE WORK PLACE, MUST NOT EXCEED THE WORKING LIMITS OF THE RESPIRATOR AND BE JOINTLY APPROVED BY THE NATIONAL INSTITUTE FOR OCCUPATIONAL SAFETY AND HEALTH AND THE MINE SAFETY AND HEALTH ADMINISTRATION (NIOSH-MSHA).
CHEMICAL CARTRIDGE RESPIRATOR WITH AN ORGANIC VAPOR CARTRIDGE(S) WITH A FULL FACEPIECE AND ORGANIC VAPOR CARTRIDGE(S) IN COMBINATION WITH A DUST AND MIST FILTER.
POWERED AIR-PURIFYING RESPIRATOR WITH A TIGHT-FITTING FACEPIECE AND ORGANIC VAPOR CARTRIDGE(S) IN COMBINATION WITH A HIGH-EFFICIENCY PARTICULATE FILTER.
TYPE 'C' SUPPLIED-AIR RESPIRATOR WITH A FULL FACEPIECE OPERATED IN A PRESSURE-DEMAND OR OTHER POSITIVE PRESSURE MODE.
SELF-CONTAINED BREATHING APPARATUS WITH A FULL FACEPIECE OPERATED IN PRESSURE-DEMAND OR OTHER POSITIVE PRESSURE MODE.
FOR FIREFIGHTING AND OTHER IMMEDIATELY DANGEROUS TO LIFE OR HEALTH CONDITIONS:
SELF-CONTAINED BREATHING APPARATUS WITH FULL FACEPIECE OPERATED IN PRESSURE-DEMAND OR OTHER POSITIVE PRESSURE MODE.
SUPPLIED-AIR RESPIRATOR WITH FULL FACEPIECE AND OPERATED IN PRESSURE-DEMAND OR OTHER POSITIVE PRESSURE MODE IN COMBINATION WITH AN AUXILIARY SELF-CONTAINED BREATHING APPARATUS OPERATED IN PRESSURE-DEMAND OR OTHER POSITIVE PRESSURE MODE.
CLOTHING: EMPLOYEE MUST WEAR APPROPRIATE PROTECTIVE (IMPERVIOUS) CLOTHING AND EQUIPMENT TO PREVENT REPEATED OR PROLONGED SKIN CONTACT WITH THIS SUBSTANCE.
GLOVES: EMPLOYEE MUST WEAR APPROPRIATE PROTECTIVE GLOVES TO PREVENT CONTACT WITH THIS SUBSTANCE.
EYE PROTECTION: EMPLOYEE MUST WEAR SPLASH-PROOF OR DUST-RESISTANT SAFETY GOGGLES TO PREVENT EYE CONTACT WITH THIS SUBSTANCE.
EMERGENCY EYE WASH: WHERE THERE IS ANY POSSIBILITY THAT AN EMPLOYEE'S EYES MAY BE EXPOSED TO THIS SUBSTANCE, THE EMPLOYER SHOULD PROVIDE AN EYE WASH FOUNTAIN WITHIN THE IMMEDIATE WORK AREA FOR EMERGENCY USE.

AUTHORIZED BY- OCCUPATIONAL HEALTH SERVICES, INC.
CREATION DATE: 10/04/89 ***REVISION DATE:*** 07/12/90

MATERIAL SAFETY DATA SHEET

OCCUPATIONAL HEALTH SERVICES, INC.
AGRICULTURE AND PESTICIDE DIVISION
450 SEVENTH AVENUE, SUITE 2407
NEW YORK, NEW YORK 10123
1-800-445-MSDS OR (212) 967-1100

EMERGENCY CONTACT:
JOHN S. BRANSFORD, JR. (615) 292-1180

SUBSTANCE IDENTIFICATION

CAS-NUMBER 7091-57-8
SUBSTANCE: **8-QUINOLINOL BENZOATE**
TRADE NAMES/SYNONYMS: BENZOIC ACID, COMPOUND WITH 8-QUINOLINOL (1:1); 8-HYDROXYQUINOLINE BENZOATE (SALT); OXINE BENZOATE; OXYQUINOLINE BENZOATE; C16H13NO3; PST71657
CHEMICAL FAMILY: QUINOLINE
MOLECULAR FORMULA: C9-H7-N-O.C7-H6-O2
MOLECULAR WEIGHT: 267.00
CERCLA RATINGS (SCALE 0-3): HEALTH=U FIRE=1 REACTIVITY=0 PERSISTENCE=2
NFPA RATINGS (SCALE 0-4): HEALTH=U FIRE=1 REACTIVITY=0

COMPONENTS AND CONTAMINANTS

COMPONENT: 8-QUINOLINOL BENZOATE ***PERCENT:*** 100.0
CAS# 7091-57-8
OTHER CONTAMINANTS: NONE
EXPOSURE LIMITS: NO OCCUPATIONAL EXPOSURE LIMITS ESTABLISHED BY OSHA, ACGIH, OR NIOSH.

PHYSICAL DATA

DESCRIPTION: SOLID. ***MELTING POINT:*** 133-142 F (56-61 C)
SPECIFIC GRAVITY: NOT AVAILABLE ***SOLUBILITY IN WATER:*** NOT AVAILABLE

FIRE AND EXPLOSION DATA

FIRE AND EXPLOSION HAZARD: SLIGHT FIRE HAZARD WHEN EXPOSED TO HEAT OR FLAME.
FIREFIGHTING MEDIA: DRY CHEMICAL, CARBON DIOXIDE, HALON, WATER SPRAY OR STANDARD FOAM (1987 EMERGENCY RESPONSE GUIDEBOOK, DOT P 5800.4).
FOR LARGER FIRES, USE WATER SPRAY, FOG OR STANDARD FOAM (1987 EMERGENCY RESPONSE GUIDEBOOK, DOT P 5800.4).
FIREFIGHTING: MOVE CONTAINERS FROM FIRE AREA IF POSSIBLE (1987 EMERGENCY RESPONSE GUIDEBOOK, DOT P 5800.4, GUIDE PAGE 53).
EXTINGUISH ONLY IF FLOW CAN BE STOPPED; USE FLOODING AMOUNTS OF WATER AS FOG, SOLID STREAMS MAY NOT BE EFFECTIVE. COOL CONTAINERS WITH FLOODING AMOUNTS OF WATER, APPLY FROM AS FAR A DISTANCE AS POSSIBLE. AVOID BREATHING POISONOUS VAPORS, KEEP UPWIND.

TOXICITY

8-QUINOLINOL BENZOATE: CARCINOGEN STATUS: NONE. ACUTE TOXICITY DATA: NO DATA AVAILABLE. TARGET EFFECTS: NO DATA AVAILABLE.

HEALTH EFFECTS AND FIRST AID

INHALATION: 8-QUINOLINOL BENZOATE: **ACUTE EXPOSURE-** NO DATA AVAILABLE.
CHRONIC EXPOSURE- NO DATA AVAILABLE.
FIRST AID- REMOVE FROM EXPOSURE AREA TO FRESH AIR IMMEDIATELY. IF BREATHING HAS STOPPED, PERFORM ARTIFICIAL RESPIRATION. KEEP PERSON WARM AND AT REST. TREAT SYMPTOMATICALLY AND SUPPORTIVELY. GET MEDICAL ATTENTION IMMEDIATELY.

SKIN CONTACT: 8-QUINOLINOL BENZOATE: **ACUTE EXPOSURE-** NO DATA AVAILABLE.
CHRONIC EXPOSURE- NO DATA AVAILABLE.
FIRST AID- REMOVE CONTAMINATED CLOTHING AND SHOES IMMEDIATELY. WASH AFFECTED AREA WITH SOAP OR MILD DETERGENT AND LARGE AMOUNTS OF WATER UNTIL NO EVIDENCE OF CHEMICAL REMAINS (APPROXIMATELY 15-20 MINUTES). GET MEDICAL ATTENTION IMMEDIATELY.

EYE CONTACT: 8-QUINOLINOL BENZOATE: **ACUTE EXPOSURE**- NO DATA AVAILABLE. **CHRONIC EXPOSURE**- NO DATA AVAILABLE.

FIRST AID- WASH EYES IMMEDIATELY WITH LARGE AMOUNTS OF WATER OR NORMAL SALINE, OCCASIONALLY LIFTING UPPER AND LOWER LIDS, UNTIL NO EVIDENCE OF CHEMICAL REMAINS (APPROXIMATELY 15-20 MINUTES). GET MEDICAL ATTENTION IMMEDIATELY.

INGESTION: 8-QUINOLINOL BENZOATE: **ACUTE EXPOSURE**- NO DATA AVAILABLE. **CHRONIC EXPOSURE**- NO DATA AVAILABLE.

FIRST AID- TREAT SYMPTOMATICALLY AND SUPPORTIVELY. GET MEDICAL ATTENTION IMMEDIATELY. IF VOMITING OCCURS, KEEP HEAD LOWER THAN HIPS TO PREVENT ASPIRATION.

ANTIDOTE: NO SPECIFIC ANTIDOTE. TREAT SYMPTOMATICALLY AND SUPPORTIVELY.

REACTIVITY

REACTIVITY: STABLE UNDER NORMAL TEMPERATURES AND PRESSURES.

INCOMPATIBILITIES: 8-QUINOLINOL BENZOATE: OXIDIZERS (STRONG): FIRE AND EXPLOSION HAZARD.

DECOMPOSITION: THERMAL DECOMPOSITION PRODUCTS MAY INCLUDE TOXIC OXIDES OF CARBON AND NITROGEN.

POLYMERIZATION: HAZARDOUS POLYMERIZATION HAS NOT BEEN REPORTED TO OCCUR UNDER NORMAL TEMPERATURES AND PRESSURES.

STORAGE AND DISPOSAL

OBSERVE ALL FEDERAL, STATE AND LOCAL REGULATIONS WHEN STORING OR DISPOSING OF THIS SUBSTANCE. FOR ASSISTANCE, CONTACT THE DISTRICT DIRECTOR OF THE ENVIRONMENTAL PROTECTION AGENCY.

****STORAGE****

STORE IN ACCORDANCE WITH 40 CFR 165 RECOMMENDED PROCEDURES FOR THE DISPOSAL AND STORAGE OF PESTICIDES AND PESTICIDE CONTAINERS.
STORE AWAY FROM INCOMPATIBLE SUBSTANCES.

****DISPOSAL****

DISPOSAL MUST BE IN ACCORDANCE WITH 40 CFR 165 RECOMMENDED PROCEDURES FOR THE DISPOSAL AND STORAGE OF PESTICIDES AND PESTICIDE CONTAINERS.

CONDITIONS TO AVOID

MAY BURN BUT DOES NOT IGNITE READILY.

SPILL AND LEAK PROCEDURES

OCCUPATIONAL SPILL: DO NOT TOUCH SPILLED MATERIAL. STOP LEAK IF YOU CAN DO IT WITHOUT RISK. FOR SMALL SPILLS, TAKE UP WITH SAND OR OTHER ABSORBENT MATERIAL AND PLACE INTO CONTAINERS FOR LATER DISPOSAL. FOR SMALL DRY SPILLS, WITH A CLEAN SHOVEL PLACE MATERIAL INTO CLEAN, DRY CONTAINER AND COVER. MOVE CONTAINERS FROM SPILL AREA. FOR LARGER SPILLS, DIKE FAR AHEAD OF SPILL FOR LATER DISPOSAL. KEEP UNNECESSARY PEOPLE AWAY. ISOLATE HAZARD AREA AND DENY ENTRY.

PROTECTIVE EQUIPMENT

VENTILATION: PROVIDE LOCAL EXHAUST OR PROCESS ENCLOSURE VENTILATION SYSTEM.

RESPIRATOR: THE FOLLOWING RESPIRATORS ARE RECOMMENDED BASED ON INFORMATION FOUND IN THE PHYSICAL DATA, TOXICITY AND HEALTH EFFECTS SECTIONS. THEY ARE RANKED IN ORDER FROM MINIMUM TO MAXIMUM RESPIRATORY PROTECTION. THE SPECIFIC RESPIRATOR SELECTED MUST BE BASED ON CONTAMINATION LEVELS FOUND IN THE WORK PLACE, MUST NOT EXCEED THE WORKING LIMITS OF THE RESPIRATOR AND BE JOINTLY APPROVED BY THE NATIONAL INSTITUTE FOR OCCUPATIONAL SAFETY AND HEALTH AND THE MINE SAFETY AND HEALTH ADMINISTRATION (NIOSH-MSHA).
DUST AND MIST RESPIRATOR WITH A FULL FACEPIECE.
AIR-PURIFYING FULL FACEPIECE RESPIRATOR WITH A HIGH-EFFICIENCY PARTICULATE FILTER.
POWERED AIR-PURIFYING RESPIRATOR WITH A TIGHT-FITTING FACEPIECE AND HIGH-EFFICIENCY PARTICULATE FILTER.
TYPE 'C' SUPPLIED-AIR RESPIRATOR WITH A FULL FACEPIECE OPERATED IN PRESSURE-DEMAND OR OTHER POSITIVE PRESSURE MODE OR WITH A FULL FACEPIECE, HELMET OR HOOD OPERATED IN CONTINUOUS FLOW MODE.
SELF-CONTAINED BREATHING APPARATUS WITH A FULL FACEPIECE OPERATED IN PRESSURE-DEMAND OR OTHER POSITIVE PRESSURE MODE.
FOR FIREFIGHTING AND OTHER IMMEDIATELY DANGEROUS TO LIFE OR HEALTH CONDITIONS:
SELF-CONTAINED BREATHING APPARATUS WITH FULL FACEPIECE OPERATED IN PRESSURE-DEMAND OR OTHER POSITIVE PRESSURE MODE.
SUPPLIED-AIR RESPIRATOR WITH FULL FACEPIECE AND OPERATED IN PRESSURE-DEMAND OR OTHER POSITIVE PRESSURE MODE IN COMBINATION WITH AN AUXILIARY SELF-CONTAINED BREATHING APPARATUS OPERATED IN PRESSURE-DEMAND OR OTHER POSITIVE PRESSURE MODE.

CLOTHING: EMPLOYEE MUST WEAR APPROPRIATE PROTECTIVE (IMPERVIOUS) CLOTHING AND EQUIPMENT TO PREVENT REPEATED OR PROLONGED SKIN CONTACT WITH THIS SUBSTANCE.

GLOVES: EMPLOYEE MUST WEAR APPROPRIATE PROTECTIVE GLOVES TO PREVENT CONTACT WITH THIS SUBSTANCE.

EYE PROTECTION: EMPLOYEE MUST WEAR SPLASH-PROOF OR DUST-RESISTANT SAFETY GOGGLES TO PREVENT EYE CONTACT WITH THIS SUBSTANCE.
EMERGENCY EYE WASH: WHERE THERE IS ANY POSSIBILITY THAT AN EMPLOYEE'S EYES MAY BE EXPOSED TO THIS SUBSTANCE, THE EMPLOYER SHOULD PROVIDE AN EYE WASH FOUNTAIN WITHIN THE IMMEDIATE WORK AREA FOR EMERGENCY USE.

AUTHORIZED BY- OCCUPATIONAL HEALTH SERVICES, INC.
CREATION DATE: 11/16/89 ***REVISION DATE:*** 05/29/90

MATERIAL SAFETY DATA SHEET

OCCUPATIONAL HEALTH SERVICES, INC.
AGRICULTURE AND PESTICIDE DIVISION
450 SEVENTH AVENUE, SUITE 2407
NEW YORK, NEW YORK 10123
1-800-445-MSDS OR (212) 967-1100

EMERGENCY CONTACT:
JOHN S. BRANSFORD, JR. (615) 292-1180

SUBSTANCE IDENTIFICATION

CAS-NUMBER 80-00-2

SUBSTANCE: **P-CHLOROPHENYL PHENYL SULFONE**

TRADE NAMES/SYNONYMS: BENZENE, 1-CHLORO-4-(PHENYLSULFONYL)-; 1-CHLORO-4-(PHENYLSULFONYL)BENZENE; SULFONE, P-CHLOROPHENYL PHENYL-; P-CHLORODIPHENYL SULFONE; 4-CHLORODIPHENYL SULFONE; 4-CHLOROPHENYL PHENYL SULFONE; SULPHENONE; SULFENON; C12H9CLO2S; PST71663

CHEMICAL FAMILY: SULFONYL
HALOGEN COMPOUND, AROMATIC

MOLECULAR FORMULA: CL-C6-H4-S-(O)2-C6-H5

MOLECULAR WEIGHT: 252.73

CERCLA RATINGS (SCALE 0-3): HEALTH=2 FIRE=1 REACTIVITY=0 PERSISTENCE=1

NFPA RATINGS (SCALE 0-4): HEALTH=U FIRE=1 REACTIVITY=0

COMPONENTS AND CONTAMINANTS

COMPONENT: P-CHLOROPHENYL PHENYL SULFONE ***PERCENT:*** 100.0
CAS# 80-00-2

OTHER CONTAMINANTS: NONE

EXPOSURE LIMITS: NO OCCUPATIONAL EXPOSURE LIMITS ESTABLISHED BY OSHA, ACGIH, OR NIOSH.

PHYSICAL DATA

DESCRIPTION: TASTELESS, CRYSTALLINE SOLID WITH A SLIGHT AROMATIC ODOR.

MELTING POINT: 194-201 F (90-94 C) ***SOLUBILITY IN WATER:*** INSOLUBLE

SOLVENT SOLUBILITY: SOLUBLE IN ACETONE, DIOXANE, ISOPROPANOL, BENZENE, TOLUENE, XYLENE. MODERATELY SOLUBLE IN CARBON TETRACHLORIDE. SLIGHTLY SOLUBLE IN HEXANE, PETROLEUM OILS.

FIRE AND EXPLOSION DATA

FIRE AND EXPLOSION HAZARD: SLIGHT FIRE HAZARD WHEN EXPOSED TO HEAT OR FLAME. DUST-AIR MIXTURES MAY IGNITE OR EXPLODE.

FIREFIGHTING MEDIA: DRY CHEMICAL, CARBON DIOXIDE, HALON, WATER SPRAY OR STANDARD FOAM (1987 EMERGENCY RESPONSE GUIDEBOOK, DOT P 5800.4).
FOR LARGER FIRES, USE WATER SPRAY, FOG OR STANDARD FOAM (1987 EMERGENCY RESPONSE GUIDEBOOK, DOT P 5800.4).

FIREFIGHTING: MOVE CONTAINER FROM FIRE AREA IF POSSIBLE. DO NOT SCATTER SPILLED MATERIAL WITH HIGH PRESSURE WATER STREAMS. DIKE FIRE CONTROL WATER FOR LATER DISPOSAL (1987 EMERGENCY RESPONSE GUIDEBOOK, DOT P 5800.4, GUIDE PAGE 31).
USE AGENTS SUITABLE FOR TYPE OF SURROUNDING FIRE. AVOID BREATHING HAZARDOUS VAPORS, KEEP UPWIND.

TOXICITY

P-CHLOROPHENYL PHENYL SULFONE: TOXICITY DATA: 1400 MG/KG ORAL-RAT LD50; 2700 MG/KG ORAL-MOUSE LD50; 500 MG/KG INTRAPERITONEAL-RAT LDLO; 1000 MG/KG INTRAPERITONEAL-MOUSE LD50. CARCINOGEN STATUS: NONE.

ACUTE TOXICITY LEVEL: MODERATELY TOXIC BY INGESTION. TARGET EFFECTS: NO DATA AVAILABLE.

HEALTH EFFECTS AND FIRST AID

INHALATION: P-CHLOROPHENYL PHENYL SULFONE: **ACUTE EXPOSURE-** NO DATA AVAILABLE. **CHRONIC EXPOSURE-** NO DATA AVAILABLE.
FIRST AID- REMOVE FROM EXPOSURE AREA TO FRESH AIR IMMEDIATELY. IF BREATHING HAS STOPPED, PERFORM ARTIFICIAL RESPIRATION. KEEP PERSON WARM AND AT REST. TREAT SYMPTOMATICALLY AND SUPPORTIVELY. GET MEDICAL ATTENTION IMMEDIATELY.

SKIN CONTACT: P-CHLOROPHENYL PHENYL SULFONE: **ACUTE EXPOSURE-** NO IRRITATION OCCURRED WHEN DRY OR MOISTENED P-CHLOROPHENYL PHENYL SULFONE WAS APPLIED TO RABBIT SKIN. **CHRONIC EXPOSURE-** REPEATED SKIN TESTS IN RABBITS AND GUINEA PIGS RESULTED IN NO IRRITATION.
FIRST AID- REMOVE CONTAMINATED CLOTHING AND SHOES IMMEDIATELY. WASH AFFECTED AREA WITH SOAP OR MILD DETERGENT AND LARGE AMOUNTS OF WATER UNTIL NO EVIDENCE OF CHEMICAL REMAINS (APPROXIMATELY 15-20 MINUTES). GET MEDICAL ATTENTION IMMEDIATELY.

EYE CONTACT: P-CHLOROPHENYL PHENYL SULFONE: **ACUTE EXPOSURE-** APPLICATION OF SUSPENSIONS TO RABBIT EYES CAUSED TRANSIENT IRRITATION. **CHRONIC EXPOSURE-** NO DATA AVAILABLE.
FIRST AID- WASH EYES IMMEDIATELY WITH LARGE AMOUNTS OF WATER OR NORMAL SALINE, OCCASIONALLY LIFTING UPPER AND LOWER LIDS, UNTIL NO EVIDENCE OF CHEMICAL REMAINS (APPROXIMATELY 15-20 MINUTES). GET MEDICAL ATTENTION IMMEDIATELY.

INGESTION: P-CHLOROPHENYL PHENYL SULFONE: **ACUTE EXPOSURE-** THE LETHAL DOSE REPORTED IN RATS WAS 1400 MG/KG. THE SYMPTOMS WERE NOT REPORTED. **CHRONIC EXPOSURE-** FEEDING 1000 PPM TO RATS FOR 2 YEARS RESULTED IN LOWER BODY WEIGHT AND INCREASED LIVER WEIGHTS IN MALE RATS. DAILY ORAL DOSES OF 100 MG/KG TO DOGS CAUSED LOSS OF APPETITE AND WEIGHT.
FIRST AID- IF THE PERSON IS CONSCIOUS AND NOT CONVULSING, REMOVE BY GIVING SYRUP OF IPECAC (IF VOMITING OCCURS, KEEP THE HEAD BELOW THE HIPS TO PREVENT ASPIRATION). GIVE ACTIVATED CHARCOAL FOLLOWED BY GASTRIC LAVAGE. FOLLOW WITH A SALINE CATHARTIC. DO NOT GIVE FATS OR OILS. INTESTINAL LAVAGE WITH 20% MANNITOL (200 ML) BY STOMACH TUBE IS ALSO USEFUL. GIVE ARTIFICIAL RESPIRATION WITH OXYGEN IF RESPIRATION IS DEPRESSED (DREISBACH, HANDBOOK OF POISONING, 12TH ED.). TREAT SYMPTOMATICALLY AND SUPPORTIVELY. LAVAGE AND ADMINISTRATION OF OXYGEN SHOULD BE PERFORMED BY QUALIFIED MEDICAL PERSONNEL. GET MEDICAL ATTENTION IMMEDIATELY.
ANTIDOTE: NO SPECIFIC ANTIDOTE. TREAT SYMPTOMATICALLY AND SUPPORTIVELY.

REACTIVITY

REACTIVITY: STABLE UNDER NORMAL TEMPERATURES AND PRESSURES.
INCOMPATIBILITIES: P-CHLOROPHENYL PHENYL SULFONE: OXIDIZERS (STRONG): FIRE AND EXPLOSION HAZARD.
DECOMPOSITION: THERMAL DECOMPOSITION PRODUCTS MAY INCLUDE TOXIC OXIDES OF CARBON AND SULFUR, AND TOXIC AND CORROSIVE FUMES OF CHLORIDES.
POLYMERIZATION: HAZARDOUS POLYMERIZATION HAS NOT BEEN REPORTED TO OCCUR UNDER NORMAL TEMPERATURES AND PRESSURES.

STORAGE AND DISPOSAL

OBSERVE ALL FEDERAL, STATE AND LOCAL REGULATIONS WHEN STORING OR DISPOSING OF THIS SUBSTANCE. FOR ASSISTANCE, CONTACT THE DISTRICT DIRECTOR OF THE ENVIRONMENTAL PROTECTION AGENCY.

STORAGE

STORE IN ACCORDANCE WITH 40 CFR 165 RECOMMENDED PROCEDURES FOR THE DISPOSAL AND STORAGE OF PESTICIDES AND PESTICIDE CONTAINERS. STORE AWAY FROM INCOMPATIBLE SUBSTANCES.

DISPOSAL

DISPOSAL MUST BE IN ACCORDANCE WITH 40 CFR 165 RECOMMENDED PROCEDURES FOR THE DISPOSAL AND STORAGE OF PESTICIDES AND PESTICIDE CONTAINERS.

CONDITIONS TO AVOID

MAY BURN BUT DOES NOT IGNITE READILY. AVOID CONTACT WITH STRONG OXIDIZERS, EXCESSIVE HEAT, SPARKS, OR OPEN FLAME.

SPILL AND LEAK PROCEDURES

OCCUPATIONAL SPILL: SWEEP UP AND PLACE IN SUITABLE CLEAN, DRY CONTAINERS FOR RECLAMATION OR LATER DISPOSAL. DO NOT FLUSH SPILLED MATERIAL INTO SEWER. KEEP UNNECESSARY PEOPLE AWAY.

PROTECTIVE EQUIPMENT

VENTILATION: PROVIDE LOCAL EXHAUST OR GENERAL DILUTION VENTILATION SYSTEM.
RESPIRATOR: THE FOLLOWING RESPIRATORS ARE RECOMMENDED BASED ON INFORMATION FOUND IN THE PHYSICAL DATA, TOXICITY AND HEALTH EFFECTS SECTIONS. THEY ARE RANKED IN ORDER FROM MINIMUM TO MAXIMUM RESPIRATORY PROTECTION. THE SPECIFIC RESPIRATOR SELECTED MUST BE BASED ON CONTAMINATION LEVELS FOUND IN THE WORK PLACE, MUST NOT EXCEED THE WORKING LIMITS OF THE RESPIRATOR AND BE JOINTLY APPROVED BY THE NATIONAL INSTITUTE FOR OCCUPATIONAL SAFETY AND HEALTH AND THE MINE SAFETY AND HEALTH ADMINISTRATION (NIOSH-MSHA).
CHEMICAL CARTRIDGE RESPIRATOR WITH AN ORGANIC VAPOR CARTRIDGE(S) WITH A FULL FACEPIECE AND ORGANIC VAPOR CARTRIDGE(S) IN COMBINATION WITH A DUST AND MIST FILTER.
POWERED AIR-PURIFYING RESPIRATOR WITH A TIGHT-FITTING FACEPIECE AND ORGANIC VAPOR CARTRIDGE(S) IN COMBINATION WITH A HIGH-EFFICIENCY PARTICULATE FILTER.
TYPE 'C' SUPPLIED-AIR RESPIRATOR WITH A FULL FACEPIECE OPERATED IN A PRESSURE-DEMAND OR OTHER POSITIVE PRESSURE MODE.
SELF-CONTAINED BREATHING APPARATUS WITH A FULL FACEPIECE OPERATED IN PRESSURE-DEMAND OR OTHER POSITIVE PRESSURE MODE.
FOR FIREFIGHTING AND OTHER IMMEDIATELY DANGEROUS TO LIFE OR HEALTH CONDITIONS:
SELF-CONTAINED BREATHING APPARATUS WITH FULL FACEPIECE OPERATED IN PRESSURE-DEMAND OR OTHER POSITIVE PRESSURE MODE.
SUPPLIED-AIR RESPIRATOR WITH FULL FACEPIECE AND OPERATED IN PRESSURE-DEMAND OR OTHER POSITIVE PRESSURE MODE IN COMBINATION WITH AN AUXILIARY SELF-CONTAINED BREATHING APPARATUS OPERATED IN PRESSURE-DEMAND OR OTHER POSITIVE PRESSURE MODE.
CLOTHING: EMPLOYEE MUST WEAR APPROPRIATE PROTECTIVE (IMPERVIOUS) CLOTHING AND EQUIPMENT TO PREVENT REPEATED OR PROLONGED SKIN CONTACT WITH THIS SUBSTANCE.
GLOVES: EMPLOYEE MUST WEAR APPROPRIATE PROTECTIVE GLOVES TO PREVENT CONTACT WITH THIS SUBSTANCE.
EYE PROTECTION: EMPLOYEE MUST WEAR SPLASH-PROOF OR DUST-RESISTANT SAFETY GOGGLES TO PREVENT EYE CONTACT WITH THIS SUBSTANCE.
EMERGENCY EYE WASH: WHERE THERE IS ANY POSSIBILITY THAT AN EMPLOYEE'S EYES MAY BE EXPOSED TO THIS SUBSTANCE, THE EMPLOYER SHOULD PROVIDE AN EYE WASH FOUNTAIN WITHIN THE IMMEDIATE WORK AREA FOR EMERGENCY USE.

AUTHORIZED BY- OCCUPATIONAL HEALTH SERVICES, INC.
CREATION DATE: 03/30/90 ***REVISION DATE:*** 05/31/90

MATERIAL SAFETY DATA SHEET

OCCUPATIONAL HEALTH SERVICES, INC.
AGRICULTURE AND PESTICIDE DIVISION
450 SEVENTH AVENUE, SUITE 2407
NEW YORK, NEW YORK 10123
1-800-445-MSDS OR (212) 967-1100

EMERGENCY CONTACT:
JOHN S. BRANSFORD, JR. (615) 292-1180

SUBSTANCE IDENTIFICATION

CAS-NUMBER 2074-50-2
SUBSTANCE: **PARAQUAT DIMETHYL SULFATE**
TRADE NAMES/SYNONYMS: 4,4'-BIPYRIDINIUM, 1,1'-DIMETHYL-, BIS(METHYL SULFATE); 1,1'-DIMETHYL-4,4'-BIPYRIDINIUM BIS(METHYL SULFATE); GRAMOXONE METHYL SULFATE; PARAQUAT BIS(METHYL SULFATE); PARAQUAT DIMETHOSULFATE; PARAQUAT DIMETHYL SULPHATE; PARAQUAT I; PARAQUAT METHOXULFATE; PARAQUAT METHYLSULFATE; PARAQUAT; C14H20N2O8S2; PST71670
CHEMICAL FAMILY: BIPYRIDYL COMPOUND SALT
MOLECULAR FORMULA: C12-H14-N2.2(C-H3-S-O4)
MOLECULAR WEIGHT: 408.48
CERCLA RATINGS (SCALE 0-3): HEALTH=3 FIRE=U REACTIVITY=0 PERSISTENCE=2
NFPA RATINGS (SCALE 0-4): HEALTH=U FIRE=U REACTIVITY=0

COMPONENTS AND CONTAMINANTS

COMPONENT: PARAQUAT DIMETHYL SULFATE ***PERCENT:*** 100.0
CAS# 2074-50-2

OTHER CONTAMINANTS: NONE

EXPOSURE LIMITS: PARAQUAT: 0.1 MG/M3 OSHA TWA (SKIN) (RESPIRIBLE PARTICLES) 0.1 MG/M3 ACGIH TWA (RESPIRABLE PARTICLES, <5 UM) 0.5 MG/M3 ACGIH TWA (NON-RESPIRABLE PARTICLES, >5 UM)
PARAQUAT DIMETHYL SULFATE: 10/10,000 POUNDS SARA SECTION 302 THRESHOLD PLANNING QUANTITY 1 POUND SARA SECTION 304 REPORTABLE QUANTITY

PHYSICAL DATA

DESCRIPTION: HYGROSCOPIC, WHITE CRYSTALLINE SOLID.

BOILING POINT: 347-356 F (175-180 C) DECOMPOSES

SPECIFIC GRAVITY: NOT AVAILABLE

SOLUBILITY IN WATER: SOLUBLE

SOLVENT SOLUBILITY: SLIGHTLY SOLUBLE IN LOWER ALCOHOLS; INSOLUBLE IN ACETONE, ETHANOL, ORGANIC SOLVENTS.

FIRE AND EXPLOSION DATA

FIRE AND EXPLOSION HAZARD: UNKNOWN FIRE AND EXPLOSION HAZARD.

FIREFIGHTING MEDIA: DRY CHEMICAL, CARBON DIOXIDE, WATER SPRAY OR FOAM FOR LARGER FIRES, USE WATER SPRAY, FOG OR ALCOHOL FOAM

FIREFIGHTING: MOVE CONTAINER FROM FIRE AREA IF POSSIBLE. DO NOT SCATTER SPILLED MATERIAL WITH MORE WATER THAN NEEDED FOR FIRE CONTROL. DIKE FIRE CONTROL WATER FOR LATER DISPOSAL
USE AGENTS SUITABLE FOR TYPE OF SURROUNDING FIRE. AVOID BREATHING HAZARDOUS VAPORS, KEEP UPWIND.

TOXICITY

PARAQUAT DIMETHYL SULFATE: TOXICITY DATA: 100 MG/KG ORAL-RAT LD50; 30 MG/KG ORAL-GUINEA PIG LD50; 35 MG/KG ORAL-CAT LD50; 25 MG/KG ORAL-DOG LD50; 35 MG/KG INTRAPERITONEAL-RAT LD50. CARCINOGEN STATUS: NONE. LOCAL EFFECTS: CORROSIVE- EYE, INGESTION; IRRITANT- INHALATION, SKIN. ACUTE TOXICITY: TOXIC BY INGESTION. TARGET EFFECTS: POISONING MAY AFFECT THE LUNGS, LIVER, AND KIDNEYS. ADDITIONAL DATA: THE ADMINISTRATION OF OXYGEN MAY AGGRAVATE THE PARAQUAT-INDUCED LUNG DAMAGE.

HEALTH EFFECTS AND FIRST AID

INHALATION: PARAQUAT DIMETHYL SULFATE: IRRITANT. 1.5 MG/M3 IMMEDIATELY DANGEROUS TO LIFE OR HEALTH. **ACUTE EXPOSURE-** EXPOSURE TO THE SPRAY MIST OF PARAQUAT AND ITS SALTS HAS PRODUCED IN WORKERS, IRRITATION AND INFLAMMATION OF THE MOUTH AND UPPER RESPIRATORY TRACT, COUGH, NOSEBLEEDS, CHEST PAIN, ASTHMATIC ATTACKS, FRONTAL HEADACHE, VOMITING, AND PAIN AND SWELLING OF THE JOINTS. INHALATION OF A SUFFICIENT QUANTITY MAY CAUSE SYSTEMIC POISONING WITH SYMPTOMS OF HEPATIC, RENAL AND RESPIRATORY INSUFFICIENCY AS DESCRIBED IN ACUTE INGESTION. AN AEROSOL OF PARAQUAT DICHLORIDE ADMINISTERED IN THE RESPIRABLE SIZE RANGE OF 3 UM TO 5 UM AT A CONCENTRATION OF 1 MG/M3 FOR 6 HOURS WAS LETHAL IN RATS. PARTICLES SMALLER OR GREATER THAN THE 3 UM TO 5 UM SIZE RANGE ARE NOT AS EFFECTIVE AT REACHING THE LOWER RESPIRATORY PASSAGES AND THEREBY DO NOT PRODUCED AS SEVERE A POISONING. **CHRONIC EXPOSURE-** PROLONGED OR REPEATED EXPOSURE MAY CAUSE SYMPTOMS AS DESCRIBED IN ACUTE EXPOSURE. PULMONARY, LIVER AND KIDNEY DAMAGE AND LEUKOPENIA WERE OBSERVED IN RATS EXPOSED TO 1.1 MG/M3/DAY FOR 5 MONTHS. EXPOSURE TO 100 MG/M3 OF NONRESPIRABLE SIZE PARTICLES OF PARAQUAT DICHLORIDE FOR 6 HOURS/DAY, 5 DAYS A WEEK FOR 3 WEEKS WAS TOLERATED BY RATS, DOGS AND GUINEA PIGS WITH SOME REPORTS OF NOSEBLEEDS.

FIRST AID- REMOVE FROM EXPOSURE AREA TO FRESH AIR IMMEDIATELY. IF BREATHING HAS STOPPED, PERFORM ARTIFICIAL RESPIRATION. KEEP PERSON WARM AND AT REST. TREAT SYMPTOMATICALLY AND SUPPORTIVELY. GET MEDICAL ATTENTION IMMEDIATELY. OXYGEN THERAPY MAY ENHANCE THE TOXICITY. QUALIFIED MEDICAL PERSONNEL SHOULD CONSIDER THE NEED VERSUS THE INCREASED RISK OF OXYGEN ADMINISTRATION.

SKIN CONTACT: PARAQUAT DIMETHYL SULFATE: IRRITANT. **ACUTE EXPOSURE-** PARAQUAT AND ITS SALTS MAY CAUSE SEVERE IRRITATION AND DERMATITIS WITH ERYTHEMA, EDEMA AND EXUDATION. THEY ALSO CAN DELAY HEALING OF CUTS AND WOUNDS. THEY MAY BE ABSORBED THROUGHT THE SKIN AND PRODUCED SYSTEMIC POISONING WITH SYMPTOMS OF RENAL, HEPATIC AND RESPIRATORY INSUFFICIENCY AS DESCRIBED IN ACUTE INGESTION. SEVERAL CASES OF LETHAL POISONING FROM DERMAL ABSORPTION OF PARAQUAT AND ITS SALTS ARE DOCUMENTED. **CHRONIC EXPOSURE-** PROLONGED OR REPEATED EXPOSURE MAY CAUSE EFFECTS AS DESCRIBED IN ACUTE EXPOSURE. PROLONGED OR REPEATED EXPOSURE MAY ALSO PRODUCE FISSURING OF THE SKIN OF THE HANDS, AND CRACKING, DISCOLORATION, AND SOMETIMES LOSS OF THE FINGERNAILS. REGENERATION OF THE NAILS WILL OCCUR AFTER CESSATION OF EXPOSURE TO PARAQUAT AND ITS SALTS. PREMALIGNANT SKIN LESIONS OF HYPERPIGMENTED MACULES AND HYPERKERATOSIS WERE OBSERVED AMONG WORKERS INVOLVED IN THE MANUFACTURE OF PARAQUAT. ANALYSIS OF THE DATA SUGGESTED THAT EXPOSURE TO BIPYRIDINE PRECURSORS ALONG WITH SUNLIGHT, RATHER THAN PARAQUAT, WAS RESPONSIBLE.

FIRST AID- REMOVE CONTAMINATED CLOTHING AND SHOES IMMEDIATELY. WASH AFFECTED AREA WITH SOAP OR MILD DETERGENT AND LARGE AMOUNTS OF WATER UNTIL NO EVIDENCE OF CHEMICAL REMAINS (APPROXIMATELY 15-20 MINUTES). GET MEDICAL ATTENTION IMMEDIATELY.

EYE CONTACT: PARAQUAT DIMETHYL SULFATE: CORROSIVE. **ACUTE EXPOSURE-** PARAQUAT AND ITS SALTS MAY PRODUCE SEVERE, PROGRESSIVE INFLAMMATION OF THE EYES WHICH MAY PEAK 12 TO 24 HOURS AFTER EXPOSURE. LOSS OF CONJUNCTIVAL EPITHELIUM AND SUPERFICIAL LAYERS OF THE CORNEA MAY OCCUR AND SEVERE CASES MAY RESULT IN PROTRACTED OPACIFICATION OF THE CORNEA. THE ADDITION OF SURFACTANTS TO PARAQUAT SALTS MAY INCREASE THE IRRITATING EFFECTS. 48.4 MG OF PARAQUAT DICHLORIDE APPLIED TO THE EYES OF RABBITS WAS LETHAL. **CHRONIC EXPOSURE-** PROLONGED OR REPEATED EXPOSURE MAY CAUSE EFFECTS AS DESCRIBED IN ACUTE EXPOSURE.

FIRST AID- WASH EYES IMMEDIATELY WITH LARGE AMOUNTS OF WATER, OCCASIONALLY LIFTING UPPER AND LOWER LIDS, UNTIL NO EVIDENCE OF CHEMICAL REMAINS (AT LEAST 15-20 MINUTES). CONTINUE IRRIGATING WITH NORMAL SALINE UNTIL THE PH HAS RETURNED TO NORMAL (30-60 MINUTES). COVER WITH STERILE BANDAGES. GET MEDICAL ATTENTION IMMEDIATELY.

INGESTION: PARAQUAT DIMETHYL SULFATE: CORROSIVE/TOXIC. **ACUTE EXPOSURE-** INGESTION MAY CAUSE INITIAL SYMPTOMS OF BURNING DISCOMFORT OR PAIN IN MOUTH, PHARYNX, ESOPHAGUS AND ABDOMEN, HEADACHE, NAUSEA, DIARRHEA WITH BLOODY STOOLS, AND REPEATED VOMITING WITH HEMATEMESIS. SEVERE POISONING MAY RESULT IN PULMONARY OR CEREBRAL HEMORRHAGE OR IN RENAL, HEPATIC OR CARDIAC FAILURE WHICH IS FATAL WITHIN SEVERAL DAYS OF POISONING. IN INGESTION OF SMALLER AMOUNTS OR DILUTE SOLUTIONS, INITIAL SYMPTOMS MAY BE FOLLOWED WITHIN 24 HOURS BY SORE THROAT, EXCORIATED LIPS, ULCERS OF THE TONGUE, BUCCAL MUCOSA AND PHARYNX. WITHIN 2 TO 6 DAYS, RENAL FAILURE, INDICATED BY PROTEINURIA AND OLIGURIA, MAY OCCUR WITH POSSIBLE HEPATIC INSUFFICIENCY WITH EFFECTS OF ANOREXIA, JAUNDICE AND PULMONARY INVOLVEMENT WITH DYSPNEA, RALES, AND EDEMA. NECROSIS OF THE ADRENAL CORTEX WITH SIGNS OF FEVER, ABDOMINAL PAIN, LETHARGY, SOMNOLENCE, HYPOVOLEMIC VASCULAR SHOCK, AND CYANOSIS FROM HYPOXIA OR METHEMOGLOBINEMIA ARE ALSO POSSIBLE. SURVIVAL AT THIS POINT MAY OCCUR WITH COMPLETE RECOVERY OR WITH A LATENT PERIOD OF 2 WEEKS IN WHICH THERE IS AN APPEARANCE OF RECOVERY WITH IMPROVED KIDNEY FUNCTION. IF THE EFFECTS OF POISONING PROGRESSES, A RAPID DEVELOPMENT OF PULMONARY FIBROSIS WILL OCCUR WITH THE GRADUAL DETERIORATION OF PULMONARY FUNCTION. THE PULMONARY FUNCTION MAY DETERIORATE TO THE POINT OF CYANOSIS. DEATH MAY RESULT FROM RESPIRATORY FAILURE. SURVIVORS HAVE EXPERIENCED COMPLETE RECOVERY, HOWEVER, PULMONARY FUNCTION TESTS MAY BE ABNORMAL FOR MONTHS. IN FIVE CASES OF POISONING, FATAL APLASTIC ANEMIA WAS REPORTED. A DOSE AS LITTLE AS 14 MG/KG CAN BE FATAL TO HUMANS. **CHRONIC EXPOSURE-** A SIGNIFICANT INCREASE IN EYE LESIONS WAS OBSERVED IN RATS FED 75 AND 150 PPM FOR 110 WEEKS. MORTALITY IN MALE RATS AT 75 PPM EXCEEDED 50%. A SIGNIFICANT INCREASE IN POSTNANTAL MORTALITY OF THE OFFSPRING WAS OBSERVED IN A STUDY OF PREGNANT MICE FED PARAQUAT. A SLIGHT INCREASE IN THE INCIDENCE OF RENAL HYDROPIC DEGENERATION OF THE OFFSPRING WAS NOTED IN A THREE-GENERATION STUDY OF RATS.

FIRST AID- INTUBATE THE STOMACH, ASPIRATE CONTENTS, THEN LAVAGE WITH AT LEAST TWO LITERS OF A SLURRY OF ADSORBENT IN NORMAL SALINE. THEN, SLOWLY INSTILL SEVERAL HUNDRED ADDITIONAL ML OF ADSORBENT SLURRY, ALLOWING THE STOMACH AND INTESTINE TO ACCOMMODATE THIS VOLUME WITHOUT OVERDISTENSION AND VOMITING. THE IDEAL ADSORBENT IS BENTONITE. IF NOT IMMEDIATELY AVAILABLE, USE ACTIVATED CHARCOAL. AS SOON AS BENTONITE HAS BEEN OBTAINED, ADMINISTER IT AS RAPIDLY AS THE PATIENT WILL TOLERATE IT. IF PATIENT CANNOT SWALLOW BENTONITE, ADMINISTER IT BY STOMACH TUBE AT THE HIGHEST CONCENTRATION THAT WILL FLOW THROUGH THE TUBE. INITIATE SALINE CATHARSIS. GIVE SODIUM SULFATE AND REPEAT IN TWO HOURS IF NO BOWEL MOVEMENT HAS OCCURRED. MAGNESIUM SALTS ARE PROBABLY CONTRAINDICATED, BECAUSE OF THE RISK OF MAGNESIUM RETENTION IN THE PRESENCE OF IMPAIRED RENAL FUNCTION. CONTINUE ADMINISTERING BENTONITE SUSPENSION AND SODIUM SULFATE UNTIL THE GUT HAS BEEN THOROUGHLY FLUSHED. HEMODIALYSIS AND/OR HEMOPERFUSION OVER SPECIALLY COATED CHARCOAL IS AN EFFECTIVE PROCEDURE FOR REMOVING POISONING FROM THE BLOOD. OXYGEN THERAPY

MAY ENHANCE THE TOXICITY. (MORGAN, RECOGNITION AND MANAGEMENT OF PESTICIDE POISONINGS, THIRD EDITION). TREATMENT SHOULD BE PERFORMED BY QUALIFIED MEDICAL PERSONNEL. GET MEDICAL ATTENTION IMMEDIATELY.

ANTIDOTE: NO SPECIFIC ANTIDOTE. TREAT SYMPTOMATICALLY AND SUPPORTIVELY.

REACTIVITY

REACTIVITY: STABLE UNDER NORMAL TEMPERATURES AND PRESSURES.

INCOMPATIBILITIES: PARAQUAT DIMETHYL SULFATE: ALKALINE SOLUTIONS: HYDROLYZE. ANIONIC SURFACTANT: INACTIVATE. CLAYS (INERT): INACTIVATE. METALS: CORRODE. OXIDIZERS (STRONG): FIRE AND EXPLOSION HAZARD.

DECOMPOSITION: THERMAL DECOMPOSITION MAY RELEASE TOXIC AND/OR HAZARDOUS GASES.

POLYMERIZATION: HAZARDOUS POLYMERIZATION HAS NOT BEEN REPORTED TO OCCUR UNDER NORMAL TEMPERATURES AND PRESSURES.

STORAGE AND DISPOSAL

OBSERVE ALL FEDERAL, STATE AND LOCAL REGULATIONS WHEN STORING OR DISPOSING OF THIS SUBSTANCE. FOR ASSISTANCE, CONTACT THE DISTRICT DIRECTOR OF THE ENVIRONMENTAL PROTECTION AGENCY.

****STORAGE****

STORE IN ACCORDANCE WITH 40 CFR 165 RECOMMENDED PROCEDURES FOR THE DISPOSAL AND STORAGE OF PESTICIDES AND PESTICIDE CONTAINERS.

STORE AWAY FROM INCOMPATIBLE SUBSTANCES.

THRESHOLD PLANNING QUANTITY (TPQ): THE SUPERFUND AMENDMENTS AND REAUTHORIZATION ACT (SARA) SECTION 302 REQUIRES THAT EACH FACILITY WHERE ANY EXTREMELY HAZARDOUS SUBSTANCE IS PRESENT IN A QUANTITY EQUAL TO OR GREATER THAN THE TPQ ESTABLISHED FOR THAT SUBSTANCE NOTIFY THE STATE EMERGENCY RESPONSE COMMISSION FOR THE STATE IN WHICH IT IS LOCATED. SECTION 303 OF SARA REQUIRES THESE FACILITIES TO PARTICIPATE IN LOCAL EMERGENCY RESPONSE PLANNING (40 CFR 355.30).

****DISPOSAL****

DISPOSAL MUST BE IN ACCORDANCE WITH 40 CFR 165 RECOMMENDED PROCEDURES FOR THE DISPOSAL AND STORAGE OF PESTICIDES AND PESTICIDE CONTAINERS.

CONDITIONS TO AVOID

NONE REPORTED.

SPILL AND LEAK PROCEDURES

OCCUPATIONAL SPILL: SWEEP UP AND PLACE IN SUITABLE CLEAN, DRY CONTAINERS FOR RECLAMATION OR LATER DISPOSAL. DO NOT FLUSH SPILLED MATERIAL INTO SEWER. KEEP UNNECESSARY PEOPLE AWAY.

REPORTABLE QUANTITY (RQ): 1 POUND THE SUPERFUND AMENDMENTS AND REAUTHORIZATION ACT (SARA) SECTION 304 REQUIRES THAT A RELEASE EQUAL TO OR GREATER THAN THE REPORTABLE QUANTITY FOR THIS SUBSTANCE BE IMMEDIATELY REPORTED TO THE LOCAL EMERGENCY PLANNING COMMITTEE AND THE STATE EMERGENCY RESPONSE COMMISSION (40 CFR 355.40). IF THE RELEASE OF THIS SUBSTANCE IS REPORTABLE UNDER CERCLA SECTION 103, THE NATIONAL RESPONSE CENTER MUST BE NOTIFIED IMMEDIATELY AT (800) 424-8802 OR (202) 426-2675 IN THE METROPOLITAN WASHINGTON, D.C. AREA (40 CFR 302.6).

PROTECTIVE EQUIPMENT

VENTILATION: PROVIDE LOCAL EXHAUST OR PROCESS ENCLOSURE VENTILATION TO MEET THE PUBLISHED EXPOSURE LIMITS. VENTILATION EQUIPMENT MUST BE EXPLOSION-PROOF.

RESPIRATOR: THE FOLLOWING RESPIRATORS AND MAXIMUM USE CONCENTRATIONS ARE RECOMMENDATIONS BY THE U.S. DEPARTMENT OF HEALTH AND HUMAN SERVICES, NIOSH POCKET GUIDE TO CHEMICAL HAZARDS; NIOSH CRITERIA DOCUMENTS OR BY THE U.S. DEPARTMENT OF LABOR, 29 CFR 1910 SUBPART Z. THE SPECIFIC RESPIRATOR SELECTED MUST BE BASED ON CONTAMINATION LEVELS FOUND IN THE WORK PLACE, MUST NOT EXCEED THE WORKING LIMITS OF THE RESPIRATOR AND BE JOINTLY APPROVED BY THE NATIONAL INSTITUTE FOR OCCUPATIONAL SAFETY AND HEALTH AND THE MINE SAFETY AND HEALTH ADMINISTRATION (NIOSH-MSHA).

PARAQUAT COMPOUNDS: 1 MG/M3- ANY CHEMICAL CARTRIDGE RESPIRATOR WITH ORGANIC VAPOR CARTRIDGE(S) IN COMBINATION WITH A DUST, MIST, AND FUME FILTER. ANY SUPPLIED-AIR RESPIRATOR. ANY SELF-CONTAINED BREATHING APPARATUS.

1.5 MG/M3- ANY CHEMICAL CARTRIDGE RESPIRATOR WITH A FULL FACEPIECE AND ORGANIC VAPOR CARTRIDGE(S) IN COMBINATION WITH A DUST, MIST, AND FUME FILTER. ANY SUPPLIED-AIR RESPIRATOR OPERATED IN A CONTINUOUS FLOW MODE. ANY SELF-CONTAINED BREATHING APPARATUS WITH A FULL FACEPIECE. ANY SUPPLIED-AIR RESPIRATOR WITH A FULL FACEPIECE. ANY POWERED AIR-PURIFYING RESPIRATOR WITH ORGANIC VAPOR CARTRIDGE(S) IN COMBINATION WITH A DUST, MIST, AND FUME FILTER.

ESCAPE- ANY AIR-PURIFYING FULL FACEPIECE RESPIRATOR (GAS MASK) WITH A CHIN-STYLE OR FRONT- OR BACK-MOUNTED ORGANIC VAPOR CANISTER HAVING A HIGH-EFFICIENCY PARTICULATE FILTER. ANY APPROPRIATE ESCAPE-TYPE SELF-CONTAINED BREATHING APPARATUS.

FOR FIREFIGHTING AND OTHER IMMEDIATELY DANGEROUS TO LIFE OR HEALTH CONDITIONS:

SELF-CONTAINED BREATHING APPARATUS WITH FULL FACEPIECE OPERATED IN PRESSURE-DEMAND OR OTHER POSITIVE PRESSURE MODE.

SUPPLIED-AIR RESPIRATOR WITH FULL FACEPIECE AND OPERATED IN PRESSURE-DEMAND OR OTHER POSITIVE PRESSURE MODE IN COMBINATION WITH AN AUXILIARY SELF-CONTAINED BREATHING APPARATUS OPERATED IN PRESSURE-DEMAND OR OTHER POSITIVE PRESSURE MODE.

CLOTHING: EMPLOYEE MUST WEAR APPROPRIATE PROTECTIVE (IMPERVIOUS) CLOTHING AND EQUIPMENT TO PREVENT ANY POSSIBILITY OF SKIN CONTACT WITH THIS SUBSTANCE.

GLOVES: EMPLOYEE MUST WEAR APPROPRIATE PROTECTIVE GLOVES TO PREVENT CONTACT WITH THIS SUBSTANCE.

EYE PROTECTION: EMPLOYEE MUST WEAR SPLASH-PROOF OR DUST-RESISTANT SAFETY GOGGLES AND A FACESHIELD TO PREVENT CONTACT WITH THIS SUBSTANCE.

EMERGENCY WASH FACILITIES: WHERE THERE IS ANY POSSIBILITY THAT AN EMPLOYEE'S EYES AND/OR SKIN MAY BE EXPOSED TO THIS SUBSTANCE, THE EMPLOYER SHOULD PROVIDE AN EYE WASH FOUNTAIN AND QUICK DRENCH SHOWER WITHIN THE IMMEDIATE WORK AREA FOR EMERGENCY USE.

AUTHORIZED BY- OCCUPATIONAL HEALTH SERVICES, INC.

CREATION DATE: 10/04/89 ***REVISION DATE:*** 05/31/90

MATERIAL SAFETY DATA SHEET

OCCUPATIONAL HEALTH SERVICES, INC.
AGRICULTURE AND PESTICIDE DIVISION
450 SEVENTH AVENUE, SUITE 2407
NEW YORK, NEW YORK 10123
1-800-445-MSDS OR (212) 967-1100

EMERGENCY CONTACT:
JOHN S. BRANSFORD, JR. (615) 292-1180

SUBSTANCE IDENTIFICATION

CAS-NUMBER 4685-14-7

SUBSTANCE: **PARAQUAT ION**

TRADE NAMES/SYNONYMS: 4,4'-BIPYRIDINIUM, 1,1'-DIMETHYL-; 1,1'-DIMETHYL-4,4'-BIPYRIDINIUM; N,N'-DIMETHYL-GAMMA,GAMMA'-DIPYRIDYLIUM; DIMETHYL VIOLOGEN; METHYL VIOLOGEN (2+); PARAQUAT DICATION; PARAQUAT; C12H14N2; PST71671

CHEMICAL FAMILY: BIPYRIDYL COMPOUND

MOLECULAR FORMULA: C12-H14-N2

MOLECULAR WEIGHT: 186.25

CERCLA RATINGS (SCALE 0-3): HEALTH=3 FIRE=U REACTIVITY=0 PERSISTENCE=2

NFPA RATINGS (SCALE 0-4): HEALTH=U FIRE=U REACTIVITY=0

COMPONENTS AND CONTAMINANTS

COMPONENT: PARAQUAT ION ***PERCENT:*** 100.0
CAS# 4685-14-7

OTHER CONTAMINANTS: NONE

EXPOSURE LIMITS: PARAQUAT: 0.1 MG/M3 OSHA TWA (SKIN) (RESPIRIBLE PARTICLES) 0.1 MG/M3 ACGIH TWA (RESPIRABLE PARTICLES, <5 UM) 0.5 MG/M3 ACGIH TWA (NON-RESPIRABLE PARTICLES, >5 UM)

PHYSICAL DATA

DESCRIPTION: WHITE CRYSTALLINE SOLID.

BOILING POINT: 347-356 F (175-180 C) DECOMPOSES

SPECIFIC GRAVITY: 1.24-1.26 20/20 C ***VAPOR PRESSURE:*** <0.0000001 MMHG

SOLUBILITY IN WATER: SOLUBLE

SOLVENT SOLUBILITY: SLIGHTLY SOLUBLE IN LOWER ALCOHOLS; INSOLUBLE IN HYDROCARBONS

FIRE AND EXPLOSION DATA

FIRE AND EXPLOSION HAZARD: UNKNOWN FIRE AND EXPLOSION HAZARD.

FIREFIGHTING MEDIA: DRY CHEMICAL, CARBON DIOXIDE, WATER SPRAY OR FOAM FOR LARGER FIRES, USE WATER SPRAY, FOG OR ALCOHOL FOAM

FIREFIGHTING: MOVE CONTAINER FROM FIRE AREA IF POSSIBLE. DO NOT SCATTER SPILLED MATERIAL WITH MORE WATER THAN NEEDED FOR FIRE CONTROL. DIKE

FIRE CONTROL WATER FOR LATER DISPOSAL
USE AGENTS SUITABLE FOR TYPE OF SURROUNDING FIRE. AVOID BREATHING HAZARDOUS VAPORS, KEEP UPWIND.

TOXICITY

PARAQUAT ION: TOXICITY DATA: 236 MG/KG SKIN-RABBIT LD50; 100 MG/KG ORAL-RAT LD50; 120 MG/KG ORAL-MOUSE LD50; 25 MG/KG ORAL-DOG LD50; 35 MG/KG ORAL-CAT LD50; 70 MG/KG ORAL-MAMMAL LD50; 30 MG/KG ORAL-GUINEA PIG LD50; 14,800 UG/KG INTRAPERITONEAL-RAT LD50; 250 MG/KG UNREPORTED-RAT LD50; 198 MG/KG UNREPORTED-MOUSE LD50; MUTAGENIC DATA (RTECS). CARCINOGEN STATUS: NONE. LOCAL EFFECTS: CORROSIVE- EYE, INGESTION; IRRITANT- INHALATION, SKIN. ACUTE TOXICITY: TOXIC BY DERMAL ABSORPTION AND INGESTION. TARGET EFFECTS: POISONING MAY AFFECT THE LUNGS, LIVER AND KIDNEYS. ADDITIONAL DATA: THE ADMINISTRATION OF OXYGEN MAY AGGRAVATE THE PARAQUAT-INDUCED LUNG DAMAGE.

HEALTH EFFECTS AND FIRST AID

INHALATION: PARAQUAT ION: IRRITANT. 1.5 MG/M3 IMMEDIATELY DANGEROUS TO LIFE OR HEALTH. **ACUTE EXPOSURE-** EXPOSURE TO THE SPRAY MIST OF PARAQUAT AND ITS SALTS HAS PRODUCED IN WORKERS, IRRITATION AND INFLAMMATION OF THE MOUTH AND UPPER RESPIRATORY TRACT, COUGH, NOSEBLEED, CHEST PAIN, ASTHMATIC ATTACKS, FRONTAL HEADACHE, VOMITING, AND PAIN AND SWELLING OF THE JOINTS. INHALATION OF A SUFFICIENT QUANTITY MAY CAUSE SYSTEMIC POISONING WITH SYMPTOMS OF HEPATIC, RENAL AND RESPIRATORY INSUFFICIENCY AS DESCRIBED IN ACUTE INGESTION. AN AEROSOL OF PARAQUAT AS THE DICHLORIDE SALT ADMINISTERED IN THE RESPIRABLE SIZE RANGE OF 3 UM TO 5 UM AT A CONCENTRATION OF 1 MG/M3 FOR 6 HOURS WAS LETHAL IN RATS. PARTICLES SMALLER OR GREATER THAN THE 3 UM TO 5 UM SIZE RANGE ARE NOT AS EFFECTIVE AT REACHING THE LOWER RESPIRATORY PASSAGES AND THEREBY DO NOT PRODUCE AS SEVERE A POISONING. **CHRONIC EXPOSURE-** PROLONGED OR REPEATED EXPOSURE MAY CAUSE SYMPTOMS AS DESCRIBED IN ACUTE EXPOSURE. PULMONARY, LIVER AND KIDNEY DAMAGE AND LEUKOPENIA WERE OBSERVED IN RATS EXPOSED TO 1.1 MG/M3/DAY FOR 5 MONTHS. EXPOSURE TO 100 MG/3 OF NONRESPIRABLE SIZE PARTICLES OF PARAQUAT FOR 6 HOURS/DAY, 5 DAYS A WEEK FOR 3 WEEKS WAS TOLERATED BY RATS, DOGS AND GUINEA PIGS WITH SOME REPORTS OF NOSEBLEEDS.

FIRST AID- REMOVE FROM EXPOSURE AREA TO FRESH AIR IMMEDIATELY. IF BREATHING HAS STOPPED, PERFORM ARTIFICIAL RESPIRATION. KEEP PERSON WARM AND AT REST. TREAT SYMPTOMATICALLY AND SUPPORTIVELY. GET MEDICAL ATTENTION IMMEDIATELY. OXYGEN THERAPY MAY ENHANCE THE TOXICITY. QUALIFIED MEDICAL PERSONNEL SHOULD CONSIDER THE NEED VERSUS THE INCREASED RISK OF OXYGEN ADMINISTRATION.

SKIN CONTACT: PARAQUAT ION: IRRITANT. **ACUTE EXPOSURE-** PARAQUAT AND ITS SALTS MAY CAUSE SEVERE IRRITATION AND DERMATITIS WITH ERYTHEMA, EDEMA AND EXUDATION. THEY ALSO CAN DELAY HEALING OF CUTS AND WOUNDS. THEY MAY BE ABSORBED THROUGH THE SKIN AND PRODUCED SYSTEMIC POISONING WITH SYMPTOMS OF RENAL, HEPATIC AND RESPIRATORY INSUFFICIENCY AS DESCRIBED IN ACUTE INGESTION. SEVERAL CASES OF LETHAL POISONING FROM DERMAL ABSORPTION OF PARAQUAT AND ITS SALTS ARE DOCUMENTED. **CHRONIC EXPOSURE-** PROLONGED OR REPEATED EXPOSURE MAY CAUSE EFFECTS AS DESCRIBED IN ACUTE EXPOSURE. PROLONGED OR REPEATED EXPOSURE MAY ALSO PRODUCE FISSURING OF THE SKIN OF THE HANDS, AND CRACKING, DISCOLORATION, AND SOMETIMES LOSS OF THE FINGERNAILS. REGENERATION OF THE NAILS WILL OCCUR AFTER CESSATION OF EXPOSURE TO PARAQUAT AND ITS SALTS. PREMALIGNANT SKIN LESIONS OF HYPERPIGMENTED MACULES AND HYPERKERATOSIS WERE OBSERVED AMONG WORKERS INVOLVED IN THE MANUFACTURE OF PARAQUAT. ANALYSIS OF THE DATA SUGGESTED THAT EXPOSURE TO BIPYRIDINE PRECURSORS ALONG WITH SUNLIGHT, RATHER THAN PARAQUAT, WAS RESPONSIBLE.

FIRST AID- REMOVE CONTAMINATED CLOTHING AND SHOES IMMEDIATELY. WASH AFFECTED AREA WITH SOAP OR MILD DETERGENT AND LARGE AMOUNTS OF WATER UNTIL NO EVIDENCE OF CHEMICAL REMAINS (APPROXIMATELY 15-20 MINUTES). GET MEDICAL ATTENTION IMMEDIATELY.

EYE CONTACT: PARAQUAT ION: CORROSIVE. **ACUTE EXPOSURE-** PARAQUAT AND ITS SALTS MAY PRODUCE SEVERE, PROGRESSIVE INFLAMMATION OF THE EYES WHICH MAY PEAK 12 TO 24 HOURS AFTER EXPOSURE. LOSS OF CONJUNCTIVAL EPITHELIUM AND SUPERFICIAL LAYERS OF THE CORNEA MAY OCCUR AND SEVERE CASES MAY RESULT IN PROTRACTED OPACIFICATION OF THE CORNEA. THE ADDITION OF SURFACTANTS TO PARAQUAT SALTS MAY INCREASE THE IRRITATING EFFECTS. 48.4 MG OF PARAQUAT AS THE DICHLORIDE SALT APPLIED TO THE EYES OF RABBITS WAS LETHAL. **CHRONIC EXPOSURE-** PROLONGED OR REPEATED EXPOSURE MAY CAUSE EFFECTS AS DESCRIBED IN ACUTE EXPOSURE.

FIRST AID- WASH EYES IMMEDIATELY WITH LARGE AMOUNTS OF WATER, OCCASIONALLY LIFTING UPPER AND LOWER LIDS, UNTIL NO EVIDENCE OF CHEMICAL REMAINS (AT LEAST 15-20 MINUTES). CONTINUE IRRIGATING WITH NORMAL SALINE UNTIL THE PH HAS RETURNED TO NORMAL (30-60 MINUTES). COVER WITH STERILE BANDAGES. GET MEDICAL ATTENTION IMMEDIATELY.

INGESTION: PARAQUAT ION: CORROSIVE/TOXIC. **ACUTE EXPOSURE-** INGESTION MAY CAUSE INITIAL SYMPTOMS OF BURNING, DISCOMFORT OR PAIN IN MOUTH, PHARYNX, ESOPHAGUS AND ABDOMEN, HEADACHE, NAUSEA, DIARRHEA WITH BLOODY STOOLS, AND REPEATED VOMITING WITH HEMATEMESIS. SEVERE POISONING MAY RESULT IN PULMONARY OR CEREBRAL HEMORRHAGE OR IN RENAL, HEPATIC OR CARDIAC FAILURE WHICH IS FATAL WITHIN SEVERAL DAYS OF POISONING. IN INGESTION OF SMALLER AMOUNTS OR DILUTE SOLUTIONS, INITIAL SYMPTOMS MAY BE FOLLOWED WITHIN 24 HOURS BY SORE THROAT, EXCORIATED LIPS, ULCERS OF THE TONGUE, BUCCAL MUCOSA AND PHARYNX. WITHIN 2 TO 6 DAYS, RENAL FAILURE, INDICATED BY PROTEINURIA AND OLIGURIA, MAY OCCUR WITH POSSIBLE HEPATIC INSUFFICIENCY WITH EFFECTS OF ANOREXIA, JAUNDICE AND PULMONARY INVOLVEMENT WITH DYSPNEA, RALES, AND EDEMA. NECROSIS OF THE ADRENAL CORTEX WITH SIGNS OF FEVER, ABDOMINAL PAIN, LETHARGY, SOMNOLENCE, HYPOVOLEMIC VASCULAR SHOCK AND CYANOSIS FROM HYPOXIA OR METHEMOGLOBINEMIA ARE ALSO POSSIBLE. SURVIVAL AT THIS POINT MAY OCCUR WITH COMPLETE RECOVERY OR WITH A LATENT PERIOD OF 2 WEEKS IN WHICH THERE IS AN APPEARANCE OF RECOVERY WITH IMPROVED KIDNEY FUNCTION. IF THE EFFECTS OF POISONING PROGRESS, A RAPID DEVELOPMENT OF PULMONARY FIBROSIS WILL OCCUR WITH THE GRADUAL DETERIORATION OF PULMONARY FUNCTION. THE PULMONARY FUNCTION MAY DETERIORATE TO THE POINT OF CYANOSIS. DEATH MAY RESULT FROM RESPIRATORY FAILURE. SURVIVORS HAVE EXPERIENCED COMPLETE RECOVERY, HOWEVER, PULMONARY FUNCTION TESTS MAY BE ABNORMAL FOR MONTHS. IN FIVE CASES OF POISONING, FATAL APLASTIC ANEMIA WAS REPORTED. A DOSE AS LITTLE AS 14 MG/KG CAN BE FATAL IN HUMANS. **CHRONIC EXPOSURE-** A SIGNIFICANT INCREASE IN EYE LESIONS WAS OBSERVED IN RATS FED 75 AND 150 PPM FOR 110 WEEKS. MORTALITY IN MALE RATS AT 175 PPM EXCEEDED 50%. A SIGNIFICANT INCREASE IN POSTNATAL MORTALITY OF THE OFFSPRING WAS OBSERVED IN A STUDY OF PREGNANT MICE FED PARAQUAT. A SLIGHT INCREASE IN THE INCIDENCE OF RENAL HYDROPIC DEGENERATION OF THE OFFSPRING WAS NOTED IN A THREE-GENERATION STUDY OF RATS.

FIRST AID- INTUBATE THE STOMACH, ASPIRATE CONTENTS, THEN LAVAGE WITH AT LEAST TWO LITERS OF A SLURRY OF ADSORBENT IN NORMAL SALINE. THEN, SLOWLY INSTILL SEVERAL HUNDRED ADDITIONAL ML OF ADSORBENT SLURRY, ALLOWING THE STOMACH AND INTESTINE TO ACCOMMODATE THIS VOLUME WITHOUT OVERDISTENSION AND VOMITING. THE IDEAL ADSORBENT IS BENTONITE. IF NOT IMMEDIATELY AVAILABLE, USE ACTIVATED CHARCOAL. AS SOON AS BENTONITE HAS BEEN OBTAINED, ADMINISTER IT AS RAPIDLY AS THE PATIENT WILL TOLERATE IT. IF PATIENT CANNOT SWALLOW BENTONITE, ADMINISTER IT BY STOMACH TUBE AT THE HIGHEST CONCENTRATION THAT WILL FLOW THROUGH THE TUBE. INITIATE SALINE CATHARSIS. GIVE SODIUM SULFATE AND REPEAT IN TWO HOURS IF NO BOWEL MOVEMENT HAS OCCURRED. MAGNESIUM SALTS ARE PROBABLY CONTRAINDICATED, BECAUSE OF THE RISK OF MAGNESIUM RETENTION IN THE PRESENCE OF IMPAIRED RENAL FUNCTION. CONTINUE ADMINISTERING BENTONITE SUSPENSION AND SODIUM SULFATE UNTIL THE GUT HAS BEEN THOROUGHLY FLUSHED. HEMODIALYSIS AND/OR HEMOPERFUSION OVER SPECIALLY COATED CHARCOAL IS AN EFFECTIVE PROCEDURE FOR REMOVING POISONING FROM THE BLOOD. OXYGEN THERAPY MAY ENHANCE THE TOXICITY. (MORGAN, RECOGNITION AND MANAGEMENT OF PESTICIDE POISONINGS, THIRD EDITION). TREATMENT SHOULD BE PERFORMED BY QUALIFIED MEDICAL PERSONNEL. GET MEDICAL ATTENTION IMMEDIATELY.

ANTIDOTE: NO SPECIFIC ANTIDOTE. TREAT SYMPTOMATICALLY AND SUPPORTIVELY.

REACTIVITY

REACTIVITY: STABLE UNDER NORMAL TEMPERATURES AND PRESSURES.

INCOMPATIBILITIES: PARAQUAT ION: ALAKINE SOLUTIONS: HYDROLYZE. ANIONIC SURFACTANT: INACTIVATE. CLAY (INERT): INACTIVATE. METALS: CORRODE. OXIDIZERS (STRONG): FIRE AND EXPLOSION HAZARD.

DECOMPOSITION: THERMAL DECOMPOSITION MAY RELEASE TOXIC AND/OR HAZARDOUS GASES.

POLYMERIZATION: HAZARDOUS POLYMERIZATION HAS NOT BEEN REPORTED TO OCCUR UNDER NORMAL TEMPERATURES AND PRESSURES.

STORAGE AND DISPOSAL

OBSERVE ALL FEDERAL, STATE AND LOCAL REGULATIONS WHEN STORING OR DISPOSING OF THIS SUBSTANCE. FOR ASSISTANCE, CONTACT THE DISTRICT DIRECTOR OF THE ENVIRONMENTAL PROTECTION AGENCY.

****STORAGE****

STORE IN ACCORDANCE WITH 40 CFR 165 RECOMMENDED PROCEDURES FOR THE DISPOSAL AND STORAGE OF PESTICIDES AND PESTICIDE CONTAINERS.
STORE AWAY FROM INCOMPATIBLE SUBSTANCES.

DISPOSAL

DISPOSAL MUST BE IN ACCORDANCE WITH 40 CFR 165 RECOMMENDED PROCEDURES FOR THE DISPOSAL AND STORAGE OF PESTICIDES AND PESTICIDE CONTAINERS.

CONDITIONS TO AVOID

NONE REPORTED.

SPILL AND LEAK PROCEDURES

OCCUPATIONAL SPILL: SWEEP UP AND PLACE IN SUITABLE CLEAN, DRY CONTAINERS FOR RECLAMATION OR LATER DISPOSAL. DO NOT FLUSH SPILLED MATERIAL INTO SEWER. KEEP UNNECESSARY PEOPLE AWAY.

PROTECTIVE EQUIPMENT

VENTILATION: PROVIDE LOCAL EXHAUST OR PROCESS ENCLOSURE VENTILATION TO MEET THE PUBLISHED EXPOSURE LIMITS. VENTILATION EQUIPMENT MUST BE EXPLOSION-PROOF.

RESPIRATOR: THE FOLLOWING RESPIRATORS AND MAXIMUM USE CONCENTRATIONS ARE RECOMMENDATIONS BY THE U.S. DEPARTMENT OF HEALTH AND HUMAN SERVICES, NIOSH POCKET GUIDE TO CHEMICAL HAZARDS; NIOSH CRITERIA DOCUMENTS OR BY THE U.S. DEPARTMENT OF LABOR, 29 CFR 1910 SUBPART Z. THE SPECIFIC RESPIRATOR SELECTED MUST BE BASED ON CONTAMINATION LEVELS FOUND IN THE WORK PLACE, MUST NOT EXCEED THE WORKING LIMITS OF THE RESPIRATOR AND BE JOINTLY APPROVED BY THE NATIONAL INSTITUTE FOR OCCUPATIONAL SAFETY AND HEALTH AND THE MINE SAFETY AND HEALTH ADMINISTRATION (NIOSH-MSHA).

PARAQUAT COMPOUNDS: 1 MG/M3- ANY CHEMICAL CARTRIDGE RESPIRATOR WITH ORGANIC VAPOR CARTRIDGE(S) IN COMBINATION WITH A DUST, MIST, AND FUME FILTER. ANY SUPPLIED-AIR RESPIRATOR. ANY SELF-CONTAINED BREATHING APPARATUS.

1.5 MG/M3- ANY CHEMICAL CARTRIDGE RESPIRATOR WITH A FULL FACEPIECE AND ORGANIC VAPOR CARTRIDGE(S) IN COMBINATION WITH A DUST, MIST, AND FUME FILTER. ANY SUPPLIED-AIR RESPIRATOR OPERATED IN A CONTINUOUS FLOW MODE. ANY SELF-CONTAINED BREATHING APPARATUS WITH A FULL FACEPIECE. ANY SUPPLIED-AIR RESPIRATOR WITH A FULL FACEPIECE. ANY POWERED AIR-PURIFYING RESPIRATOR WITH ORGANIC VAPOR CARTRIDGE(S) IN COMBINATION WITH A DUST, MIST, AND FUME FILTER.

ESCAPE- ANY AIR-PURIFYING FULL FACEPIECE RESPIRATOR (GAS MASK) WITH A CHIN-STYLE OR FRONT- OR BACK-MOUNTED ORGANIC VAPOR CANISTER HAVING A HIGH-EFFICIENCY PARTICULATE FILTER. ANY APPROPRIATE ESCAPE-TYPE SELF-CONTAINED BREATHING APPARATUS.

FOR FIREFIGHTING AND OTHER IMMEDIATELY DANGEROUS TO LIFE OR HEALTH CONDITIONS:

SELF-CONTAINED BREATHING APPARATUS WITH FULL FACEPIECE OPERATED IN PRESSURE-DEMAND OR OTHER POSITIVE PRESSURE MODE.

SUPPLIED-AIR RESPIRATOR WITH FULL FACEPIECE AND OPERATED IN PRESSURE-DEMAND OR OTHER POSITIVE PRESSURE MODE IN COMBINATION WITH AN AUXILIARY SELF-CONTAINED BREATHING APPARATUS OPERATED IN PRESSURE-DEMAND OR OTHER POSITIVE PRESSURE MODE.

CLOTHING: EMPLOYEE MUST WEAR APPROPRIATE PROTECTIVE (IMPERVIOUS) CLOTHING AND EQUIPMENT TO PREVENT ANY POSSIBILITY OF SKIN CONTACT WITH THIS SUBSTANCE.

GLOVES: EMPLOYEE MUST WEAR APPROPRIATE PROTECTIVE GLOVES TO PREVENT CONTACT WITH THIS SUBSTANCE.

EYE PROTECTION: EMPLOYEE MUST WEAR SPLASH-PROOF OR DUST-RESISTANT SAFETY GOGGLES AND A FACESHIELD TO PREVENT CONTACT WITH THIS SUBSTANCE.

EMERGENCY WASH FACILITIES: WHERE THERE IS ANY POSSIBILITY THAT AN EMPLOYEE'S EYES AND/OR SKIN MAY BE EXPOSED TO THIS SUBSTANCE, THE EMPLOYER SHOULD PROVIDE AN EYE WASH FOUNTAIN AND QUICK DRENCH SHOWER WITHIN THE IMMEDIATE WORK AREA FOR EMERGENCY USE.

AUTHORIZED BY- OCCUPATIONAL HEALTH SERVICES, INC.

CREATION DATE: 10/04/89 ***REVISION DATE:*** 05/31/90

MATERIAL SAFETY DATA SHEET

OCCUPATIONAL HEALTH SERVICES, INC.
AGRICULTURE AND PESTICIDE DIVISION
450 SEVENTH AVENUE, SUITE 2407
NEW YORK, NEW YORK 10123

EMERGENCY CONTACT:
JOHN S. BRANSFORD, JR. (615) 292-1180
1-800-445-MSDS OR (212) 967-1100

SUBSTANCE IDENTIFICATION

CAS-NUMBER 85-97-2

SUBSTANCE: **6-CHLORO-2-PHENYLPHENOL**

TRADE NAMES/SYNONYMS: 6-CHLOROXENOL; 2-HYDROXY-3-CHLOROBIPHENYL; C12H9CLO; PST71680

CHEMICAL FAMILY: PHENOL HALOGEN

MOLECULAR FORMULA: C6-H5-CL-C6-H3-O-H

MOLECULAR WEIGHT: 204.66

CERCLA RATINGS (SCALE 0-3): HEALTH=U FIRE=U REACTIVITY=0 PERSISTENCE=2

NFPA RATINGS (SCALE 0-4): HEALTH=U FIRE=U REACTIVITY=0

COMPONENTS AND CONTAMINANTS

COMPONENT: 6-CHLORO-2-PHENYLPHENOL ***PERCENT:*** 100.0
CAS# 85-97-2

OTHER CONTAMINANTS: NONE

EXPOSURE LIMITS: NO OCCUPATIONAL EXPOSURE LIMITS ESTABLISHED BY OSHA, ACGIH, OR NIOSH.

PHYSICAL DATA

DESCRIPTION: COLORLESS TO PALE YELLOW STRAW-COLORED VISCOUS LIQUID.

BOILING POINT: 603-604 F (317-318 C) (DECOMPOSES) ***MELTING POINT:*** 43 F (6 C)

SPECIFIC GRAVITY: 1.24 ***VAPOR PRESSURE:*** NOT AVAILABLE

SOLUBILITY IN WATER: INSOLUBLE

SOLVENT SOLUBILITY: SOLUBLE IN ALKALIES, BENZENE, ETHANOL, AND ETHER.

FIRE AND EXPLOSION DATA

FIRE AND EXPLOSION HAZARD: UNKNOWN FIRE AND EXPLOSION HAZARD.

FLASH POINT: NOT AVAILABLE

FIREFIGHTING MEDIA: DRY CHEMICAL, CARBON DIOXIDE, HALON, WATER SPRAY OR STANDARD FOAM (1987 EMERGENCY RESPONSE GUIDEBOOK, DOT P 5800.4). FOR LARGER FIRES, USE WATER SPRAY, FOG OR STANDARD FOAM (1987 EMERGENCY RESPONSE GUIDEBOOK, DOT P 5800.4).

FIREFIGHTING: MOVE CONTAINERS FROM FIRE AREA IF POSSIBLE. FIGHT FIRE FROM MAXIMUM DISTANCE. STAY AWAY FROM STORAGE TANK ENDS. DIKE FIRE CONTROL WATER FOR LATER DISPOSAL. DO NOT SCATTER MATERIAL (1987 EMERGENCY RESPONSE GUIDEBOOK, DOT P 5800.4, GUIDE PAGE 55).
USE AGENTS SUITABLE FOR TYPE OF FIRE. AVOID BREATHING VAPORS OR DUSTS, KEEP UPWIND.

TOXICITY

6-CHLORO-2-PHENYLPHENOL: CARCINOGEN STATUS: NONE. ACUTE TOXICITY LEVEL: NO DATA AVAILABLE. TARGET EFFECTS: NO DATA AVAILABLE.

HEALTH EFFECTS AND FIRST AID

INHALATION: 6-CHLORO-2-PHENYLPHENOL: **ACUTE EXPOSURE-** NO SPECIFIC DATA AVAILABLE. MONOCHLOROPHENOLS ARE SLIGHTLY LESS TOXIC THAN PHENOL. HOWEVER, THEY MAY BE SOMEWHAT MORE POTENT THAN PHENOL IN ELICITING CONVULSIONS. SOME PHENOL DERIVATIVES EFFECT THE BLOOD, AND THE RESPIRATORY, CIRCULATORY AND CARDIOVASCULAR SYSTEMS. **CHRONIC EXPOSURE-** NO DATA AVAILABLE.

FIRST AID- REMOVE FROM EXPOSURE AREA TO FRESH AIR IMMEDIATELY. IF BREATHING HAS STOPPED, PERFORM ARTIFICIAL RESPIRATION. KEEP PERSON WARM AND AT REST. TREAT SYMPTOMATICALLY AND SUPPORTIVELY. GET MEDICAL ATTENTION IMMEDIATELY.

SKIN CONTACT: 6-CHLORO-2-PHENYLPHENOL: **ACUTE EXPOSURE-** NO SPECIFIC DATA AVAILABLE. MONOCHLOROPHENOLS ARE SLIGHTLY LESS TOXIC THAN PHENOL. HOWEVER, THEY MAY BE SOMEWHAT MORE POTENT THAN PHENOL IN ELICITING CONVULSIONS. SOME PHENOL DERIVATIVES EFFECT THE BLOOD, AND THE RESPIRATORY, CIRCULATORY AND CARDIOVASCULAR SYSTEMS. **CHRONIC EXPOSURE-** NO DATA AVAILABLE.

FIRST AID- REMOVE CONTAMINATED CLOTHING AND SHOES IMMEDIATELY. WASH AFFECTED AREA WITH SOAP OR MILD DETERGENT AND LARGE AMOUNTS OF WATER UNTIL NO EVIDENCE OF CHEMICAL REMAINS (APPROXIMATELY 15-20 MINUTES). GET MEDICAL ATTENTION IMMEDIATELY.

EYE CONTACT: 6-CHLORO-2-PHENYLPHENOL: **ACUTE EXPOSURE-** NO DATA AVAILABLE. **CHRONIC EXPOSURE-** NO DATA AVAILABLE.

FIRST AID- WASH EYES IMMEDIATELY WITH LARGE AMOUNTS OF WATER OR NORMAL SALINE, OCCASIONALLY LIFTING UPPER AND LOWER LIDS, UNTIL NO EVIDENCE OF CHEMICAL REMAINS (APPROXIMATELY 15-20 MINUTES). GET MEDICAL ATTENTION IMMEDIATELY.

INGESTION: 6-CHLORO-2-PHENYLPHENOL: **ACUTE EXPOSURE-** NO SPECIFIC DATA AVAILABLE. MONOCHLOROPHENOLS ARE SLIGHTLY LESS TOXIC THAN PHENOL. HOWEVER, THEY MAY BE SOMEWHAT MORE POTENT THAN PHENOL IN ELICITING CONVULSIONS. SOME PHENOL DERIVATIVES EFFECT THE BLOOD, AND THE RESPIRATORY, CIRCULATORY AND CARDIOVASCULAR SYSTEMS. **CHRONIC EXPOSURE-** NO DATA AVAILABLE.

FIRST AID- TREAT SYMPTOMATICALLY AND SUPPORTIVELY. GET MEDICAL ATTENTION IMMEDIATELY. IF VOMITING OCCURS, KEEP HEAD LOWER THAN HIPS TO PREVENT ASPIRATION.

ANTIDOTE: NO SPECIFIC ANTIDOTE. TREAT SYMPTOMATICALLY AND SUPPORTIVELY.

REACTIVITY

REACTIVITY: STABLE UNDER NORMAL TEMPERATURES AND PRESSURES.

INCOMPATIBILITIES: 6-CHLORO-2-PHENYLPHENOL: OXIDIZERS (STRONG): FIRE AND EXPLOSION HAZARD.

DECOMPOSITION: THERMAL DECOMPOSITION PRODUCTS MAY INCLUDE TOXIC AND CORROSIVE FUMES OF CHLORIDES AND TOXIC OXIDES OF CARBON.

POLYMERIZATION: HAZARDOUS POLYMERIZATION HAS NOT BEEN REPORTED TO OCCUR UNDER NORMAL TEMPERATURES AND PRESSURES.

STORAGE AND DISPOSAL

OBSERVE ALL FEDERAL, STATE AND LOCAL REGULATIONS WHEN STORING OR DISPOSING OF THIS SUBSTANCE. FOR ASSISTANCE, CONTACT THE DISTRICT DIRECTOR OF THE ENVIRONMENTAL PROTECTION AGENCY.

STORAGE

STORE IN ACCORDANCE WITH 40 CFR 165 RECOMMENDED PROCEDURES FOR THE DISPOSAL AND STORAGE OF PESTICIDES AND PESTICIDE CONTAINERS.
STORE AWAY FROM INCOMPATIBLE SUBSTANCES.

DISPOSAL

DISPOSAL MUST BE IN ACCORDANCE WITH 40 CFR 165 RECOMMENDED PROCEDURES FOR THE DISPOSAL AND STORAGE OF PESTICIDES AND PESTICIDE CONTAINERS.

CONDITIONS TO AVOID

MAY BURN BUT DOES NOT IGNITE READILY. CONTAINERS MAY EXPLODE IN HEAT OF FIRE.

SPILL AND LEAK PROCEDURES

OCCUPATIONAL SPILL: DO NOT TOUCH SPILLED MATERIAL. STOP LEAK IF YOU CAN DO IT WITHOUT RISK. USE WATER SPRAY TO REDUCE VAPORS. FOR SMALL SPILLS, TAKE UP WITH SAND OR OTHER ABSORBENT MATERIAL AND PLACE INTO CONTAINERS FOR LATER DISPOSAL. FOR SMALL DRY SPILLS, WITH A CLEAN SHOVEL PLACE MATERIAL INTO CLEAN, DRY CONTAINERS AND COVER. MOVE CONTAINERS FROM SPILL AREA. FOR LARGER SPILLS, DIKE FAR AHEAD OF SPILL FOR LATER DISPOSAL. KEEP UNNECESSARY PEOPLE AWAY. ISOLATE HAZARD AREA AND DENY ENTRY. VENTILATE CLOSED SPACES BEFORE ENTERING.

PROTECTIVE EQUIPMENT

VENTILATION: PROVIDE LOCAL EXHAUST OR PROCESS ENCLOSURE VENTILATION. VENTILATION EQUIPMENT MUST BE EXPLOSION-PROOF.

RESPIRATOR: THE FOLLOWING RESPIRATORS ARE RECOMMENDED BASED ON INFORMATION FOUND IN THE PHYSICAL DATA, TOXICITY AND HEALTH EFFECTS SECTIONS. THEY ARE RANKED IN ORDER FROM MINIMUM TO MAXIMUM RESPIRATORY PROTECTION. THE SPECIFIC RESPIRATOR SELECTED MUST BE BASED ON CONTAMINATION LEVELS FOUND IN THE WORK PLACE, MUST NOT EXCEED THE WORKING LIMITS OF THE RESPIRATOR AND BE JOINTLY APPROVED BY THE NATIONAL INSTITUTE FOR OCCUPATIONAL SAFETY AND HEALTH AND THE MINE SAFETY AND HEALTH ADMINISTRATION (NIOSH-MSHA).
CHEMICAL CARTRIDGE RESPIRATOR WITH FULL FACEPIECE AND PESTICIDE CARTRIDGE.
TYPE 'C' SUPPLIED-AIR RESPIRATOR WITH A FULL FACEPIECE OPERATED IN PRESSURE-DEMAND OR OTHER POSITIVE PRESSURE MODE OR WITH A FULL FACEPIECE, HELMET OR HOOD OPERATED IN CONTINUOUS-FLOW MODE.
SELF-CONTAINED BREATHING APPARATUS OPERATED IN PRESSURE-DEMAND OR OTHER POSITIVE PRESSURE MODE.
FOR FIREFIGHTING AND OTHER IMMEDIATELY DANGEROUS TO LIFE OR HEALTH CONDITIONS:
SELF-CONTAINED BREATHING APPARATUS WITH FULL FACEPIECE OPERATED IN PRESSURE-DEMAND OR OTHER POSITIVE PRESSURE MODE.
SUPPLIED-AIR RESPIRATOR WITH FULL FACEPIECE AND OPERATED IN PRESSURE-DEMAND OR OTHER POSITIVE PRESSURE MODE IN COMBINATION WITH AN AUXILIARY SELF-CONTAINED BREATHING APPARATUS OPERATED IN PRESSURE-DEMAND OR OTHER POSITIVE PRESSURE MODE.

CLOTHING: EMPLOYEE MUST WEAR APPROPRIATE PROTECTIVE (IMPERVIOUS) CLOTHING AND EQUIPMENT TO PREVENT REPEATED OR PROLONGED SKIN CONTACT WITH THIS SUBSTANCE.

GLOVES: EMPLOYEE MUST WEAR APPROPRIATE PROTECTIVE GLOVES TO PREVENT CONTACT WITH THIS SUBSTANCE.

EYE PROTECTION: EMPLOYEE MUST WEAR SPLASH-PROOF OR DUST-RESISTANT SAFETY GOGGLES TO PREVENT EYE CONTACT WITH THIS SUBSTANCE.
EMERGENCY EYE WASH: WHERE THERE IS ANY POSSIBILITY THAT AN EMPLOYEE'S EYES MAY BE EXPOSED TO THIS SUBSTANCE, THE EMPLOYER SHOULD PROVIDE AN EYE WASH FOUNTAIN WITHIN THE IMMEDIATE WORK AREA FOR EMERGENCY USE.

AUTHORIZED BY- OCCUPATIONAL HEALTH SERVICES, INC.
CREATION DATE: 10/05/89 ***REVISION DATE:*** 05/18/90

MATERIAL SAFETY DATA SHEET

OCCUPATIONAL HEALTH SERVICES, INC.
AGRICULTURE AND PESTICIDE DIVISION
450 SEVENTH AVENUE, SUITE 2407
NEW YORK, NEW YORK 10123
1-800-445-MSDS OR (212) 967-1100

EMERGENCY CONTACT:
JOHN S. BRANSFORD, JR. (615) 292-1180

SUBSTANCE IDENTIFICATION

CAS-NUMBER 25167-83-3

SUBSTANCE: **TETRACHLOROPHENOL**

TRADE NAMES/SYNONYMS: PHENOL, TETRACHLORO-; C6H2CL4O; PST71689

CHEMICAL FAMILY: PHENOL

MOLECULAR FORMULA: C6-H2-CL4-O

MOLECULAR WEIGHT: 231.88

CERCLA RATINGS (SCALE 0-3): HEALTH=3 FIRE=1 REACTIVITY=0 PERSISTENCE=3

NFPA RATINGS (SCALE 0-4): HEALTH=3 FIRE=1 REACTIVITY=0

COMPONENTS AND CONTAMINANTS

COMPONENT: TETRACHLOROPHENOL ***PERCENT:*** 100.0
CAS# 25167-83-3

OTHER CONTAMINANTS: NONE

EXPOSURE LIMITS: NO OCCUPATIONAL EXPOSURE LIMITS ESTABLISHED BY OSHA, ACGIH, OR NIOSH.

PHYSICAL DATA

DESCRIPTION: BROWN SOLID WITH PHENOLIC ODOR. ***MELTING POINT:*** 122 F (50 C)

SPECIFIC GRAVITY: 1.65 @ 60 C ***SOLUBILITY IN WATER:*** NOT AVAILABLE

FIRE AND EXPLOSION DATA

FIRE AND EXPLOSION HAZARD: SLIGHT FIRE HAZARD WHEN EXPOSED TO HEAT OR FLAME.

FIREFIGHTING MEDIA: DRY CHEMICAL, CARBON DIOXIDE, HALON, WATER SPRAY OR STANDARD FOAM (1987 EMERGENCY RESPONSE GUIDEBOOK, DOT P 5800.4).
FOR LARGER FIRES, USE WATER SPRAY, FOG OR STANDARD FOAM (1987 EMERGENCY RESPONSE GUIDEBOOK, DOT P 5800.4).

FIREFIGHTING: MOVE CONTAINERS FROM FIRE AREA IF POSSIBLE (1987 EMERGENCY RESPONSE GUIDEBOOK, DOT P 5800.4, GUIDE PAGE 53).
USE AGENTS SUITABLE FOR TYPE OF FIRE. AVOID BREATHING HAZARDOUS VAPORS, KEEP UPWIND.

TOXICITY

TETRACHLOROPHENOL: TOXICITY DATA: 140 MG/KG ORAL-RAT LD50; 210 MG/KG SUBCUTANEOUS-RAT LD50. CARCINOGEN STATUS: NONE. LOCAL EFFECTS: IRRITANT- EYE. ACUTE TOXICITY LEVEL: TOXIC BY INGESTION. TARGET EFFECTS: POISONING MAY AFFECT THE CENTRAL NERVOUS SYSTEM.

HEALTH EFFECTS AND FIRST AID

INHALATION: TETRACHLOROPHENOL: **ACUTE EXPOSURE-** DUST MAY BE IRRITATING TO THE NOSE AND THROAT. **CHRONIC EXPOSURE-** NO DATA AVAILABLE.

FIRST AID- REMOVE FROM EXPOSURE AREA TO FRESH AIR IMMEDIATELY. IF BREATHING HAS STOPPED, PERFORM ARTIFICIAL RESPIRATION. KEEP PERSON WARM AND AT REST. TREAT SYMPTOMATICALLY AND SUPPORTIVELY. GET MEDICAL ATTENTION IMMEDIATELY.

SKIN CONTACT: TETRACHLOROPHENOL: **ACUTE EXPOSURE-** CONTACT WITH TETRACHLOROPHENOLS MAY CAUSE PHOTOALLERGIC CONTACT DERMATITIS.

CHRONIC EXPOSURE- CONTACT WITH TETRACHLOROPHENOLS MAY CAUSE DERMATOSES, INCLUDING PAPULOFOLLICULAR LESIONS, COMEDONES, SEBACEOUS CYSTS, AND MARKED HYPERKERATOSIS.

FIRST AID- REMOVE CONTAMINATED CLOTHING AND SHOES IMMEDIATELY. WASH AFFECTED AREA WITH SOAP OR MILD DETERGENT AND LARGE AMOUNTS OF WATER UNTIL NO EVIDENCE OF CHEMICAL REMAINS (APPROXIMATELY 15-20 MINUTES). GET MEDICAL ATTENTION IMMEDIATELY.

EYE CONTACT: TETRACHLOROPHENOL: IRRITANT. **ACUTE EXPOSURE-** CONTACT WITH ANIMAL EYES CAUSED SEVERE IRRITATION. **CHRONIC EXPOSURE-** REPEATED AND PROLONGED CONTACT WITH IRRITANTS MAY CAUSE CONJUNCTIVITIS.

FIRST AID- WASH EYES IMMEDIATELY WITH LARGE AMOUNTS OF WATER OR NORMAL SALINE, OCCASIONALLY LIFTING UPPER AND LOWER LIDS, UNTIL NO EVIDENCE OF CHEMICAL REMAINS (APPROXIMATELY 15-20 MINUTES). GET MEDICAL ATTENTION IMMEDIATELY.

INGESTION: TETRACHLOROPHENOL: TOXIC. **ACUTE EXPOSURE-** THE LETHAL DOSE FOR RATS IS 140 MG/KG. INTOXICATION WITH TETRACHLOROPHENOLS IN RATS MAY LEAD TO RESTLESSNESS, INCREASED RATE OF RESPIRATION, RAPIDLY DEVELOPING MOTOR WEAKNESS, TREMORS, CLONIC CONVULSIONS, DYSPNEA, COMA AND DEATH. TETRACHLOROPHENOLS MAY CAUSE INTERFERENCE WITH OXIDATIVE PHOSPHORYLATION. **CHRONIC EXPOSURE-** NO DATA AVAILABLE.

FIRST AID- IN THE ABSENCE OF CORROSIVE INJURY, REMOVE POISON BY IPECAC EMESIS. ACTIVATED CHARCOAL IS ALSO USEFUL. FOLLOW WITH 240 ML OF MILK. GASTRIC LAVAGE AND EMESIS ARE CONTRAINDICATED IN THE PRESENCE OF ESOPHAGEAL INJURY (DREISBACH, HANDBOOK OF POISONING, 12TH EDITION). GET MEDICAL ATTENTION IMMEDIATELY.

ANTIDOTE: NO SPECIFIC ANTIDOTE. TREAT SYMPTOMATICALLY AND SUPPORTIVELY.

REACTIVITY

REACTIVITY: STABLE UNDER NORMAL TEMPERATURES AND PRESSURES.

INCOMPATIBILITIES: TETRACHLOROPHENOL: OXIDIZERS (STRONG): FIRE AND EXPLOSION HAZARD.

DECOMPOSITION: THERMAL DECOMPOSITION PRODUCTS MAY INCLUDE TOXIC AND CORROSIVE FUMES OF CHLORIDES AND TOXIC OXIDES OF CARBON.

POLYMERIZATION: HAZARDOUS POLYMERIZATION HAS NOT BEEN REPORTED TO OCCUR UNDER NORMAL TEMPERATURES AND PRESSURES.

STORAGE AND DISPOSAL

OBSERVE ALL FEDERAL, STATE AND LOCAL REGULATIONS WHEN STORING OR DISPOSING OF THIS SUBSTANCE. FOR ASSISTANCE, CONTACT THE DISTRICT DIRECTOR OF THE ENVIRONMENTAL PROTECTION AGENCY.

STORAGE

STORE AWAY FROM INCOMPATIBLE SUBSTANCES.

CONDITIONS TO AVOID

MAY BURN BUT DOES NOT IGNITE READILY.

SPILL AND LEAK PROCEDURES

OCCUPATIONAL SPILL: DO NOT TOUCH SPILLED MATERIAL. STOP LEAK IF YOU CAN DO IT WITHOUT RISK. FOR SMALL SPILLS, TAKE UP WITH SAND OR OTHER ABSORBENT MATERIAL AND PLACE INTO CONTAINERS FOR LATER DISPOSAL. FOR SMALL DRY SPILLS, WITH A CLEAN SHOVEL PLACE MATERIAL INTO CLEAN, DRY CONTAINER AND COVER. MOVE CONTAINERS FROM SPILL AREA. FOR LARGER SPILLS, DIKE FAR AHEAD OF SPILL FOR LATER DISPOSAL. KEEP UNNECESSARY PEOPLE AWAY. ISOLATE HAZARD AREA AND DENY ENTRY.

PROTECTIVE EQUIPMENT

VENTILATION: PROVIDE LOCAL EXHAUST OR PROCESS ENCLOSURE VENTILATION SYSTEM.

RESPIRATOR: THE FOLLOWING RESPIRATORS ARE RECOMMENDED BASED ON INFORMATION FOUND IN THE PHYSICAL DATA, TOXICITY AND HEALTH EFFECTS SECTIONS. THEY ARE RANKED IN ORDER FROM MINIMUM TO MAXIMUM RESPIRATORY PROTECTION. THE SPECIFIC RESPIRATOR SELECTED MUST BE BASED ON CONTAMINATION LEVELS FOUND IN THE WORK PLACE, MUST NOT EXCEED THE WORKING LIMITS OF THE RESPIRATOR AND BE JOINTLY APPROVED BY THE NATIONAL INSTITUTE FOR OCCUPATIONAL SAFETY AND HEALTH AND THE MINE SAFETY AND HEALTH ADMINISTRATION (NIOSH-MSHA).

DUST AND MIST RESPIRATOR WITH A FULL FACEPIECE.

AIR-PURIFYING FULL FACEPIECE RESPIRATOR WITH A HIGH-EFFICIENCY PARTICULATE FILTER.

POWERED AIR-PURIFYING RESPIRATOR WITH A TIGHT-FITTING FACEPIECE AND HIGH-EFFICIENCY PARTICULATE FILTER.

TYPE 'C' SUPPLIED-AIR RESPIRATOR WITH A FULL FACEPIECE OPERATED IN PRESSURE-DEMAND OR OTHER POSITIVE PRESSURE MODE OR WITH A FULL FACEPIECE, HELMET OR HOOD OPERATED IN CONTINUOUS-FLOW MODE.

SELF-CONTAINED BREATHING APPARATUS WITH A FULL FACEPIECE OPERATED IN PRESSURE-DEMAND OR OTHER POSITIVE PRESSURE MODE.

FOR FIREFIGHTING AND OTHER IMMEDIATELY DANGEROUS TO LIFE OR HEALTH CONDITIONS:

SELF-CONTAINED BREATHING APPARATUS WITH FULL FACEPIECE OPERATED IN PRESSURE-DEMAND OR OTHER POSITIVE PRESSURE MODE.

SUPPLIED-AIR RESPIRATOR WITH FULL FACEPIECE AND OPERATED IN PRESSURE-DEMAND OR OTHER POSITIVE PRESSURE MODE IN COMBINATION WITH AN AUXILIARY SELF-CONTAINED BREATHING APPARATUS OPERATED IN PRESSURE-DEMAND OR OTHER POSITIVE PRESSURE MODE.

CLOTHING: EMPLOYEE MUST WEAR APPROPRIATE PROTECTIVE (IMPERVIOUS) CLOTHING AND EQUIPMENT TO PREVENT REPEATED OR PROLONGED SKIN CONTACT WITH THIS SUBSTANCE.

GLOVES: EMPLOYEE MUST WEAR APPROPRIATE PROTECTIVE GLOVES TO PREVENT CONTACT WITH THIS SUBSTANCE.

EYE PROTECTION: EMPLOYEE MUST WEAR SPLASH-PROOF OR DUST-RESISTANT SAFETY GOGGLES TO PREVENT EYE CONTACT WITH THIS SUBSTANCE.

EMERGENCY EYE WASH: WHERE THERE IS ANY POSSIBILITY THAT AN EMPLOYEE'S EYES MAY BE EXPOSED TO THIS SUBSTANCE, THE EMPLOYER SHOULD PROVIDE AN EYE WASH FOUNTAIN WITHIN THE IMMEDIATE WORK AREA FOR EMERGENCY USE.

AUTHORIZED BY- OCCUPATIONAL HEALTH SERVICES, INC.

CREATION DATE: 02/08/90 ***REVISION DATE:*** 05/25/90

MATERIAL SAFETY DATA SHEET

OCCUPATIONAL HEALTH SERVICES, INC.
AGRICULTURE AND PESTICIDE DIVISION
450 SEVENTH AVENUE, SUITE 2407
NEW YORK, NEW YORK 10123
1-800-445-MSDS OR (212) 967-1100

EMERGENCY CONTACT:
JOHN S. BRANSFORD, JR. (615) 292-1180

SUBSTANCE IDENTIFICATION

CAS-NUMBER 80-46-6

SUBSTANCE: **4-TERT-AMYLPHENOL**

TRADE NAMES/SYNONYMS: 4-(1,1-DIMETHYLPROPYL)PHENOL; P-TERT-PENTYLPHENOL; P-T-AMYLPHENOL; PENTAPHEN; P-(ALPHA, ALPHA-DIMETHYLPROPYL)PHENOL; AMILFENOL; 2-METHYL-2-P-HYDROXYPHENYLBUTANE; PST71715

CHEMICAL FAMILY: PHENOL

MOLECULAR FORMULA: C11-H16-O

MOLECULAR WEIGHT: 164.27

CERCLA RATINGS (SCALE 0-3): HEALTH=2 FIRE=1 REACTIVITY=0 PERSISTENCE=1

NFPA RATINGS (SCALE 0-4): HEALTH=2 FIRE=1 REACTIVITY=0

COMPONENTS AND CONTAMINANTS

COMPONENT: 4-TERT-AMYLPHENOL ***PERCENT:*** 100
CAS# 80-46-6

OTHER CONTAMINANTS: NONE

EXPOSURE LIMITS: NO OCCUPATIONAL EXPOSURE LIMITS ESTABLISHED BY OSHA, ACGIH, OR NIOSH.

PHYSICAL DATA

DESCRIPTION: COLORLESS TO WHITE NEEDLES. ***BOILING POINT:*** 491 F (255 C)

MELTING POINT: 190-192 F (88-89 C) ***SPECIFIC GRAVITY:*** 0.9

SOLUBILITY IN WATER: INSOLUBLE

SOLVENT SOLUBILITY: SOLUBLE IN ALCOHOL, ETHER, BENZENE, CHLOROFORM

FIRE AND EXPLOSION DATA

FIRE AND EXPLOSION HAZARD: SLIGHT FIRE HAZARD WHEN EXPOSED TO HEAT OR FLAME.

FLASH POINT: 232 F (111 C) (OC) ***FLAMMABILITY CLASS(OSHA):*** IIIB

FIREFIGHTING MEDIA: DRY CHEMICAL, CARBON DIOXIDE, HALON, WATER SPRAY OR STANDARD FOAM (1987 EMERGENCY RESPONSE GUIDEBOOK, DOT P 5800.4).

FOR LARGER FIRES, USE WATER SPRAY, FOG OR STANDARD FOAM (1987 EMERGENCY RESPONSE GUIDEBOOK, DOT P 5800.4).

FIREFIGHTING: MOVE CONTAINER FROM FIRE AREA IF POSSIBLE. DO NOT SCATTER SPILLED MATERIAL WITH HIGH PRESSURE WATER STREAMS. DIKE FIRE CONTROL

WATER FOR LATER DISPOSAL (1987 EMERGENCY RESPONSE GUIDEBOOK, DOT P 5800.4, GUIDE PAGE 31).
USE AGENTS SUITABLE FOR TYPE OF SURROUNDING FIRE. AVOID BREATHING HAZARDOUS VAPORS, KEEP UPWIND.
WATER OR FOAM MAY CAUSE FROTHING (NFPA 325M, FIRE HAZARD PROPERTIES OF FLAMMABLE LIQUIDS, GASES, AND VOLATILE SOLIDS, 1984)

TOXICITY

4-TERT-AMYLPHENOL: IRRITATION DATA: 100 UG/24 HOURS OPEN SKIN-RABBIT; 1% EYE-RABBIT SEVERE; 500 MG EYE-RABBIT SEVERE. TOXICITY DATA: 2000 MG/KG SKIN-RABBIT LD50; 1830 MG/KG ORAL-RAT LD50. CARCINOGEN STATUS: NONE. LOCAL EFFECTS: CORROSIVE- SKIN AND EYES. ACUTE TOXICITY LEVEL: MODERATELY TOXIC BY DERMAL ABSORPTION AND INGESTION. TARGET EFFECTS: NO DATA AVAILABLE.

HEALTH EFFECTS AND FIRST AID

INHALATION: 4-TERT-AMYLPHENOL: **ACUTE EXPOSURE-** NO DATA AVAILABLE. **CHRONIC EXPOSURE-** NO DATA AVAILABLE.
FIRST AID- REMOVE FROM EXPOSURE AREA TO FRESH AIR IMMEDIATELY. IF BREATHING HAS STOPPED, PERFORM ARTIFICIAL RESPIRATION. KEEP PERSON WARM AND AT REST. TREAT SYMPTOMATICALLY AND SUPPORTIVELY. GET MEDICAL ATTENTION IMMEDIATELY.

SKIN CONTACT: 4-TERT-AMYLPHENOL: CORROSIVE. **ACUTE EXPOSURE-** APPLICATION OF 0.01 ML OF UNDILUTED 4-TERT-AMYLPHENOL TO RABBIT SKIN FOR 24 HOURS PRODUCED NECROSIS AND WAS RATED 6 ON A SCALE OF 1 TO 10. A MODERATE DOSE APPLIED TO RABBIT SKIN WAS LETHAL TO 50% OF THE ANIMALS TESTED. NO SYMPOMS WERE REPORTED. HOWEVER, PHENOL DERIVATIVES MAY CAUSE PROFUSE SWEATING, INTENSE THRIST, NAUSEA AND VOMITING, DIARRHEA, CYANOSIS FROM METHEMOGLOBINEMIA, HYPERACTIVITY, STUPOR, FALL IN BLOOD PRESSURE, HYPERPNEA, ABDOMINAL PAIN, HEMOLYSIS, CONVULSIONS, COMA, AND PULMONARY EDEMA FOLLOWED BY PNEUMONIA. CARDIOVASCULAR COLLAPSE AND SHOCK DEVELOP QUICKLY. IF DEATH FROM RESPIRATORY FAILURE IS NOT IMMEDIATE, SEVERE RENAL DAMAGE MAY OCCUR WITH JAUNDICE AND ANURIA OR OLIGURIA. PATHOLOGIC FINDINGS ARE CEREBRAL EDEMA, DEGENERATIVE CHANGES IN THE LIVER AND KIDNEY AND POSSIBLE BLADDER NECROSIS. **CHRONIC EXPOSURE-** REPEATED OR PROLONGED CONTACT WITH IRRITANTS MAY CAUSE DERMATITIS.
FIRST AID- REMOVE CONTAMINATED CLOTHING AND SHOES IMMEDIATELY. WASH AFFECTED AREA WITH SOAP OR MILD DETERGENT AND LARGE AMOUNTS OF WATER UNTIL NO EVIDENCE OF CHEMICAL REMAINS (AT LEAST 15-20 MINUTES). IN CASE OF CHEMICAL BURNS, COVER AREA WITH STERILE, DRY DRESSING. BANDAGE SECURELY, BUT NOT TOO TIGHTLY. GET MEDICAL ATTENTION IMMEDIATELY.

EYE CONTACT: 4-TERT-AMYLPHENOL: CORROSIVE. **ACUTE EXPOSURE-** APPLICATION OF 0.5 ML OF A 1% SOLUTION PRODUCED SEVERE BURNS IN RABBIT EYES. THE EFFECTS SCORED 10 ON A SCALE OF 1-10 FOR CORNEAL INJURY. **CHRONIC EXPOSURE-** EFFECTS ARE DEPENDENT UPON CONCENTRATION AND DURATION OF EXPOSURE. CONJUNCTIVITIS OR EFFECTS SIMILAR TO THOSE FOR ACUTE EXPOSURE MAY OCCUR.
FIRST AID- WASH EYES IMMEDIATELY WITH LARGE AMOUNTS OF WATER, OCCASIONALLY LIFTING UPPER AND LOWER LIDS, UNTIL NO EVIDENCE OF CHEMICAL REMAINS (AT LEAST 15-20 MINUTES). CONTINUE IRRIGATING WITH NORMAL SALINE UNTIL THE PH HAS RETURNED TO NORMAL (30-60 MINUTES). COVER WITH STERILE BANDAGES. GET MEDICAL ATTENTION IMMEDIATELY.

INGESTION: 4-TERT-AMYLPHENOL: **ACUTE EXPOSURE-** A MODERATE DOSE WAS REQUIRED TO BE LETHAL TO 50% OF THE RATS TESTED. NO SYMPTOMS WERE REPORTED. HOWEVER, PHENOL DERIVATIVES MAY CAUSE PROFUSE SWEATING, INTENSE THIRST, NAUSEA AND VOMITING, DIARRHEA, CYANOSIS FROM METHEMOGLOBINEMIA, HYPERACTIVITY, STUPOR, FALL IN BLOOD PRESSURE, HYPERPNEA, ABDOMINAL PAIN, HEMOLYSIS, CONVULSIONS, COMA, AND PULMONARY EDEMA FOLLOWED BY PNEUMONIA. CARDIOVASCULAR COLLAPSE AND SHOCK DEVELOP QUICKLY. IF DEATH FROM RESPIRATORY FAILURE IS NOT IMMEDIATE, SEVERE RENAL DAMAGE MAY OCCUR WITH JAUNDICE AND ANURIA OR OLIGURIA. PATHOLOGIC FINDINGS ARE NECROSIS OF MUCOUS MEMBRANES, CEREBRAL EDEMA, DEGENERATIVE CHANGES IN THE LIVER AND KIDNEY AND POSSIBLE BLADDER NECROSIS. **CHRONIC EXPOSURE-** NO DATA AVAILABLE.
FIRST AID- IN THE ABSENCE OF CORROSIVE INJURY, REMOVE POISON BY IPECAC EMESIS. ACTIVATED CHARCOAL IS ALSO USEFUL. FOLLOW WITH 240 ML OF MILK. GASTRIC LAVAGE AND EMESIS ARE CONTRAINDICATED IN THE PRESENCE OF ESOPHAGEAL INJURY (DREISBACH, HANDBOOK OF POISONING, 12TH EDITION). GET MEDICAL ATTENTION IMMEDIATELY.
ANTIDOTE: NO SPECIFIC ANTIDOTE. TREAT SYMPTOMATICALLY AND SUPPORTIVELY.

REACTIVITY

REACTIVITY: STABLE UNDER NORMAL TEMPERATURES AND PRESSURES.
INCOMPATIBILITIES: 4-TERT-AMYLPHENOL: OXIDIZING MATERIALS: MAY REACT.
DECOMPOSITION: THERMAL DECOMPOSITION MAY RELEASE TOXIC AND/OR HAZARDOUS GASES.
POLYMERIZATION: HAZARDOUS POLYMERIZATION HAS NOT BEEN REPORTED TO OCCUR UNDER NORMAL TEMPERATURES AND PRESSURES.

CONDITIONS TO AVOID

MAY BURN BUT DOES NOT IGNITE READILY. AVOID CONTACT WITH STRONG OXIDIZERS, EXCESSIVE HEAT, SPARKS, OR OPEN FLAME.

SPILL AND LEAK PROCEDURES

OCCUPATIONAL SPILL: SWEEP UP AND PLACE IN SUITABLE CLEAN, DRY CONTAINERS FOR RECLAMATION OR LATER DISPOSAL. DO NOT FLUSH SPILLED MATERIAL INTO SEWER. KEEP UNNECESSARY PEOPLE AWAY.

PROTECTIVE EQUIPMENT

VENTILATION: PROVIDE LOCAL EXHAUST OR GENERAL DILUTION VENTILATION SYSTEM.
RESPIRATOR: THE FOLLOWING RESPIRATORS ARE RECOMMENDED BASED ON INFORMATION FOUND IN THE PHYSICAL DATA, TOXICITY AND HEALTH EFFECTS SECTIONS. THEY ARE RANKED IN ORDER FROM MINIMUM TO MAXIMUM RESPIRATORY PROTECTION. THE SPECIFIC RESPIRATOR SELECTED MUST BE BASED ON CONTAMINATION LEVELS FOUND IN THE WORK PLACE, MUST NOT EXCEED THE WORKING LIMITS OF THE RESPIRATOR AND BE JOINTLY APPROVED BY THE NATIONAL INSTITUTE FOR OCCUPATIONAL SAFETY AND HEALTH AND THE MINE SAFETY AND HEALTH ADMINISTRATION (NIOSH-MSHA).
DUST AND MIST RESPIRATOR WITH A FULL FACEPIECE.
AIR-PURIFYING FULL FACEPIECE RESPIRATOR WITH A HIGH-EFFICIENCY PARTICULATE FILTER.
POWERED AIR-PURIFYING RESPIRATOR WITH A TIGHT-FITTING FACEPIECE AND HIGH-EFFICIENCY PARTICULATE FILTER.
TYPE 'C' SUPPLIED-AIR RESPIRATOR WITH A FULL FACEPIECE OPERATED IN PRESSURE-DEMAND OR OTHER POSITIVE PRESSURE MODE OR WITH A FULL FACEPIECE, HELMET OR HOOD OPERATED IN CONTINUOUS-FLOW MODE.
SELF-CONTAINED BREATHING APPARATUS WITH A FULL FACEPIECE OPERATED IN PRESSURE-DEMAND OR OTHER POSITIVE PRESSURE MODE.
FOR FIREFIGHTING AND OTHER IMMEDIATELY DANGEROUS TO LIFE OR HEALTH CONDITIONS:
SELF-CONTAINED BREATHING APPARATUS WITH FULL FACEPIECE OPERATED IN PRESSURE-DEMAND OR OTHER POSITIVE PRESSURE MODE.
SUPPLIED-AIR RESPIRATOR WITH FULL FACEPIECE AND OPERATED IN PRESSURE-DEMAND OR OTHER POSITIVE PRESSURE MODE IN COMBINATION WITH AN AUXILIARY SELF-CONTAINED BREATHING APPARATUS OPERATED IN PRESSURE-DEMAND OR OTHER POSITIVE PRESSURE MODE.
CLOTHING: EMPLOYEE MUST WEAR APPROPRIATE PROTECTIVE (IMPERVIOUS) CLOTHING AND EQUIPMENT TO PREVENT ANY POSSIBILITY OF SKIN CONTACT WITH THIS SUBSTANCE.
GLOVES: EMPLOYEE MUST WEAR APPROPRIATE PROTECTIVE GLOVES TO PREVENT CONTACT WITH THIS SUBSTANCE.
EYE PROTECTION: EMPLOYEE MUST WEAR SPLASH-PROOF OR DUST-RESISTANT SAFETY GOGGLES AND A FACESHIELD TO PREVENT CONTACT WITH THIS SUBSTANCE.
EMERGENCY WASH FACILITIES: WHERE THERE IS ANY POSSIBILITY THAT AN EMPLOYEE'S EYES AND/OR SKIN MAY BE EXPOSED TO THIS SUBSTANCE, THE EMPLOYER SHOULD PROVIDE AN EYE WASH FOUNTAIN AND QUICK DRENCH SHOWER WITHIN THE IMMEDIATE WORK AREA FOR EMERGENCY USE.

AUTHORIZED BY- OCCUPATIONAL HEALTH SERVICES, INC.
CREATION DATE: 10/05/89 ***REVISION DATE:*** 05/31/90

MATERIAL SAFETY DATA SHEET

OCCUPATIONAL HEALTH SERVICES, INC.
AGRICULTURE AND PESTICIDE DIVISION
450 SEVENTH AVENUE, SUITE 2407
NEW YORK, NEW YORK 10123
1-800-445-MSDS OR (212) 967-1100

EMERGENCY CONTACT:
JOHN S. BRANSFORD, JR. (615) 292-1180

SUBSTANCE IDENTIFICATION

CAS-NUMBER 13347-42-7

***SUBSTANCE:* 4-CHLORO-2-CYCLOPENTYLPHENOL**

TRADE NAMES/SYNONYMS: PHENOL, 4-CHLORO-2-CYCLOPENTYL-; DOWICIDE 9; C11H13CLO; PST71731

CHEMICAL FAMILY: PHENOL
HALOGEN COMPOUND, ALICYCLIC

MOLECULAR FORMULA: C11-H13-CL-O

MOLECULAR WEIGHT: 196.68

CERCLA RATINGS (SCALE 0-3): HEALTH=2 FIRE=U REACTIVITY=0 PERSISTENCE=3

NFPA RATINGS (SCALE 0-4): HEALTH=U FIRE=U REACTIVITY=0

COMPONENTS AND CONTAMINANTS

COMPONENT: 4-CHLORO-2-CYCLOPENTYLPHENOL ***PERCENT:*** 100.0
CAS# 13347-42-7

OTHER CONTAMINANTS: NONE

EXPOSURE LIMITS: NO OCCUPATIONAL EXPOSURE LIMITS ESTABLISHED BY OSHA, ACGIH, OR NIOSH.

PHYSICAL DATA

DESCRIPTION: LIQUID. ***BOILING POINT:*** 358-365 F (181-185 C) @ 18 MMHG

SPECIFIC GRAVITY: NOT AVAILABLE ***VAPOR PRESSURE:*** NOT AVAILABLE

SOLUBILITY IN WATER: NOT AVAILABLE

FIRE AND EXPLOSION DATA

FIRE AND EXPLOSION HAZARD: UNKNOWN FIRE AND EXPLOSION HAZARD.

FIREFIGHTING MEDIA: DRY CHEMICAL, CARBON DIOXIDE, HALON, WATER SPRAY OR STANDARD FOAM (1987 EMERGENCY RESPONSE GUIDEBOOK, DOT P 5800.4). FOR LARGER FIRES, USE WATER SPRAY, FOG OR STANDARD FOAM (1987 EMERGENCY RESPONSE GUIDEBOOK, DOT P 5800.4).

FIREFIGHTING: MOVE CONTAINERS FROM FIRE AREA IF POSSIBLE. FIGHT FIRE FROM MAXIMUM DISTANCE. STAY AWAY FROM STORAGE TANK ENDS. DIKE FIRE CONTROL WATER FOR LATER DISPOSAL. DO NOT SCATTER MATERIAL (1987 EMERGENCY RESPONSE GUIDEBOOK, DOT P 5800.4, GUIDE PAGE 55).
USE AGENTS SUITABLE FOR TYPE OF FIRE. AVOID BREATHING VAPORS OR DUSTS, KEEP UPWIND.

TOXICITY

4-CHLORO-2-CYCLOPENTYLPHENOL: IRRITATION DATA: 25 MG SKIN-HUMAN MILD; 100 MG EYE-RABBIT SEVERE. TOXICITY DATA: 850 MG/KG SKIN-RABBIT LD50; 420 MG/KG ORAL-RAT LDLO; 420 MG/KG ORAL-RABBIT LDLO; 420 MG/KG ORAL-GUINEA PIG LDLO. CARCINOGEN STATUS: NONE. LOCAL EFFECTS: IRRITANT- SKIN AND EYES. ACUTE TOXICITY LEVEL: TOXIC BY DERMAL ABSORPTION. TARGET EFFECTS: NO DATA AVAILABLE.

HEALTH EFFECTS AND FIRST AID

INHALATION: 4-CHLORO-2-CYCLOPENTYLPHENOL: **ACUTE EXPOSURE-** VAPORS AND MISTS MAY BE IRRITATING TO THE RESPIRATORY TRACT. BELIEVED TO RESEMBLE PHENOL IN ITS SYSTEMIC EFFECTS AND THUS, MAY CAUSE EFFECTS ON THE RESPIRATORY, CENTRAL NERVOUS AND CARDIOVASCULAR SYSTEMS, AND ON THE BLOOD. **CHRONIC EXPOSURE-** NO SPECIFIC DATA AVAILABLE. AS WITH PHENOL, EXCESSIVE EXPOSURE MAY CAUSE EXTENSIVE LIVER AND KIDNEY DAMAGE.

FIRST AID- REMOVE FROM EXPOSURE AREA TO FRESH AIR IMMEDIATELY. IF BREATHING HAS STOPPED, PERFORM ARTIFICIAL RESPIRATION. KEEP PERSON WARM AND AT REST. TREAT SYMPTOMATICALLY AND SUPPORTIVELY. GET MEDICAL ATTENTION IMMEDIATELY.

SKIN CONTACT: 4-CHLORO-2-CYCLOPENTYLPHENOL: IRRITANT/TOXIC. **ACUTE EXPOSURE-** CONTACT OF CONCENTRATED MATERIAL ON SKIN MAY CAUSE REDNESS AND MODERATE BURNS. 25 MG CAUSED MILD IRRITATION ON HUMAN SKIN. 850 MG/KG IS THE LETHAL DOSE FOR RABBITS. BELIEVED TO RESEMBLE PHENOL, IN SYSTEMIC TOXICITY. ABSORPTION MAY CAUSE SYSTEMIC EFFECTS DESCRIBED IN ACUTE INHALATION. **CHRONIC EXPOSURE-** REPEATED AND PROLONGED EXPOSURE TO IRRITANTS MAY CAUSE DERMITITIS. AS WITH PHENOL, REPEATED AND PROLONGED EXPOSURE MAY CAUSE LIVER AND KIDNEY DAMAGE.

FIRST AID- REMOVE CONTAMINATED CLOTHING AND SHOES IMMEDIATELY. WASH AFFECTED AREA WITH SOAP OR MILD DETERGENT AND LARGE AMOUNTS OF WATER UNTIL NO EVIDENCE OF CHEMICAL REMAINS (APPROXIMATELY 15-20 MINUTES). GET MEDICAL ATTENTION IMMEDIATELY.

EYE CONTACT: 4-CHLORO-2-CYCLOPENTYLPHENOL: IRRITANT. **ACUTE EXPOSURE-** MAY BE IRRITATING, CAUSING CONJUNCTIVAL INFLAMMATION AND CORNEAL INJURY. 100 MG CAUSED SEVERE IRRITATION OF RABBIT EYES. **CHRONIC EXPOSURE-** REPEATED AND PROLONGED EXPOSURE TO IRRITANTS MAY CAUSE CONJUNCTIVITIS.

FIRST AID- WASH EYES IMMEDIATELY WITH LARGE AMOUNTS OF WATER OR NORMAL SALINE, OCCASIONALLY LIFTING UPPER AND LOWER LIDS, UNTIL NO EVIDENCE OF CHEMICAL REMAINS (APPROXIMATELY 15-20 MINUTES). GET MEDICAL ATTENTION IMMEDIATELY.

INGESTION: 4-CHLORO-2-CYCLOPENTYLPHENOL: **ACUTE EXPOSURE-** 420 MG/KG IS THE LETHAL DOSE FOR RATS. BELIEVED TO RESEMBLE PHENOL, MAY CAUSE SYSTEMIC EFFECTS DESCRIBED IN ACUTE INHALATION. **CHRONIC EXPOSURE-** NO SPECIFIC DATA AVAILABLE. AS WITH PHENOL, REPEATED AND PROLONGED EXPOSURE MAY RESULT IN LIVER AND KIDNEY DAMAGE IN ADDITION TO ACUTE INHALATION SYSTEMIC EFFECTS.

FIRST AID- IF THE PATIENT IS ALERT AND ABLE TO SWALLOW, GIVE A SLURRY OF ACTIVATED CHARCOAL IN WATER. DO NOT GIVE EMETICS. CAREFUL GASTRIC LAVAGE WITH WATER IS RECOMMENDED IF THERE ARE NO DEEP BURNS IN THE MOUTH OR PHARYNX. OLDER RECOMMENDATIONS TO LAVAGE WITH OLIVE OR OTHER VEGETABLE OILS DO NOT APPEAR TO BE SUBSTANTIATED. IN ANY CASE AVOID MINERAL OIL AND ALCOHOL. (GOSSELIN, CLINICAL TOXICOLOGY OF COMMERCIAL PRODUCTS, 5TH ED.). LAVAGE MUST BE PERFORMED BY QUALIFIED MEDICAL PERSONNEL.

ANTIDOTE: NO SPECIFIC ANTIDOTE. TREAT SYMPTOMATICALLY AND SUPPORTIVELY.

REACTIVITY

REACTIVITY: STABLE UNDER NORMAL TEMPERATURES AND PRESSURES.

INCOMPATIBILITIES: 4-CHLORO-2-CYCLOPENTYLPHENOL: OXIDIZERS (STRONG): FIRE AND EXPLOSION HAZARD.

DECOMPOSITION: THERMAL DECOMPOSITION PRODUCTS MAY INCLUDE TOXIC AND CORROSIVE FUMES OF CHLORIDES AND TOXIC OXIDES OF CARBON.

POLYMERIZATION: HAZARDOUS POLYMERIZATION HAS NOT BEEN REPORTED TO OCCUR UNDER NORMAL TEMPERATURES AND PRESSURES.

STORAGE AND DISPOSAL

OBSERVE ALL FEDERAL, STATE AND LOCAL REGULATIONS WHEN STORING OR DISPOSING OF THIS SUBSTANCE. FOR ASSISTANCE, CONTACT THE DISTRICT DIRECTOR OF THE ENVIRONMENTAL PROTECTION AGENCY.

****STORAGE****

STORE IN ACCORDANCE WITH 40 CFR 165 RECOMMENDED PROCEDURES FOR THE DISPOSAL AND STORAGE OF PESTICIDES AND PESTICIDE CONTAINERS.
STORE AWAY FROM INCOMPATIBLE SUBSTANCES.

****DISPOSAL****

DISPOSAL MUST BE IN ACCORDANCE WITH 40 CFR 165 RECOMMENDED PROCEDURES FOR THE DISPOSAL AND STORAGE OF PESTICIDES AND PESTICIDE CONTAINERS.

CONDITIONS TO AVOID

MAY BURN BUT DOES NOT IGNITE READILY. CONTAINERS MAY EXPLODE IN HEAT OF FIRE.

SPILL AND LEAK PROCEDURES

OCCUPATIONAL SPILL: DO NOT TOUCH SPILLED MATERIAL. STOP LEAK IF YOU CAN DO IT WITHOUT RISK. USE WATER SPRAY TO REDUCE VAPORS. FOR SMALL SPILLS, TAKE UP WITH SAND OR OTHER ABSORBENT MATERIAL AND PLACE INTO CONTAINERS FOR LATER DISPOSAL. FOR SMALL DRY SPILLS, WITH A CLEAN SHOVEL PLACE MATERIAL INTO CLEAN, DRY CONTAINERS AND COVER. MOVE CONTAINERS FROM SPILL AREA. FOR LARGER SPILLS, DIKE FAR AHEAD OF SPILL FOR LATER DISPOSAL. KEEP UNNECESSARY PEOPLE AWAY. ISOLATE HAZARD AREA AND DENY ENTRY. VENTILATE CLOSED SPACES BEFORE ENTERING.

PROTECTIVE EQUIPMENT

VENTILATION: PROVIDE LOCAL EXHAUST OR PROCESS ENCLOSURE VENTILATION. VENTILATION EQUIPMENT MUST BE EXPLOSION-PROOF.

RESPIRATOR: THE FOLLOWING RESPIRATORS ARE RECOMMENDED BASED ON INFORMATION FOUND IN THE PHYSICAL DATA, TOXICITY AND HEALTH EFFECTS SECTIONS. THEY ARE RANKED IN ORDER FROM MINIMUM TO MAXIMUM RESPIRATORY PROTECTION. THE SPECIFIC RESPIRATOR SELECTED MUST BE BASED ON CONTAMINATION LEVELS FOUND IN THE WORK PLACE, MUST NOT EXCEED THE WORKING LIMITS OF THE RESPIRATOR AND BE JOINTLY APPROVED BY THE NATIONAL INSTITUTE FOR OCCUPATIONAL SAFETY AND HEALTH AND THE MINE SAFETY AND HEALTH ADMINISTRATION (NIOSH-MSHA).
TYPE 'C' SUPPLIED-AIR RESPIRATOR WITH A FULL FACEPIECE OPERATED IN PRESSURE-DEMAND OR OTHER POSITIVE PRESSURE MODE OR WITH A FULL FACEPIECE, HELMET OR HOOD OPERATED IN CONTINOUS-FLOW MODE.
SELF-CONTAINED BREATHING APPARATUS WITH A FULL FACEPIECE OPERATED IN PRESSURE-DEMAND OR OTHER POSITIVE PRESSURE MODE.
FOR FIREFIGHTING AND OTHER IMMEDIATELY DANGEROUS TO LIFE OR HEALTH CONDITIONS:

SELF-CONTAINED BREATHING APPARATUS WITH FULL FACEPIECE OPERATED IN PRESSURE-DEMAND OR OTHER POSITIVE PRESSURE MODE.
SUPPLIED-AIR RESPIRATOR WITH FULL FACEPIECE AND OPERATED IN PRESSURE-DEMAND OR OTHER POSITIVE PRESSURE MODE IN COMBINATION WITH AN AUXILIARY SELF-CONTAINED BREATHING APPARATUS OPERATED IN PRESSURE-DEMAND OR OTHER POSITIVE PRESSURE MODE.

CLOTHING: EMPLOYEE MUST WEAR APPROPRIATE PROTECTIVE (IMPERVIOUS) CLOTHING AND EQUIPMENT TO PREVENT ANY POSSIBILITY OF SKIN CONTACT WITH THIS SUBSTANCE.

GLOVES: EMPLOYEE MUST WEAR APPROPRIATE PROTECTIVE GLOVES TO PREVENT CONTACT WITH THIS SUBSTANCE.

EYE PROTECTION: EMPLOYEE MUST WEAR SPLASH-PROOF OR DUST-RESISTANT SAFETY GOGGLES AND A FACESHIELD TO PREVENT CONTACT WITH THIS SUBSTANCE.
EMERGENCY WASH FACILITIES: WHERE THERE IS ANY POSSIBILITY THAT AN EMPLOYEE'S EYES AND/OR SKIN MAY BE EXPOSED TO THIS SUBSTANCE, THE EMPLOYER SHOULD PROVIDE AN EYE WASH FOUNTAIN AND QUICK DRENCH SHOWER WITHIN THE IMMEDIATE WORK AREA FOR EMERGENCY USE.

AUTHORIZED BY- OCCUPATIONAL HEALTH SERVICES, INC.
CREATION DATE: 10/05/89 ***REVISION DATE:*** 05/09/90

MATERIAL SAFETY DATA SHEET

OCCUPATIONAL HEALTH SERVICES, INC.
AGRICULTURE AND PESTICIDE DIVISION
450 SEVENTH AVENUE, SUITE 2407
NEW YORK, NEW YORK 10123
1-800-445-MSDS OR (212) 967-1100

EMERGENCY CONTACT:
JOHN S. BRANSFORD, JR. (615) 292-1180

SUBSTANCE IDENTIFICATION

CAS-NUMBER 97-24-5

SUBSTANCE: **2,2'-THIOBIS(4-CHLOROPHENOL)**

TRADE NAMES/SYNONYMS: PHENOL, 2,2'-THIOBIS(4-CHLORO-; BIS(2-HYDROXY-5-CHLOROPHENYL)SULFIDE; D 25 ANTIMYKOTIKUM; FENTICHLOR; FENTICLOR; MEFLORIN; NOVEX; OKSID; OVITROL; S7; 2,2'-DIHYDROXY-5,5'-DICHLORODIPHENYL SULFIDE; C12H8CL2O2S; PST71737

CHEMICAL FAMILY: PHENOL
HALOGEN
THIO

MOLECULAR FORMULA: C12-H8-CL2-O2-S

MOLECULAR WEIGHT: 287.18

CERCLA RATINGS (SCALE 0-3): HEALTH=U FIRE=1 REACTIVITY=0 PERSISTENCE=2

NFPA RATINGS (SCALE 0-4): HEALTH=U FIRE=1 REACTIVITY=0

COMPONENTS AND CONTAMINANTS

COMPONENT: 2,2-THIOBIS(4-CHLOROPHENOL) ***PERCENT:*** 100.0
CAS# 97-24-5

OTHER CONTAMINANTS: NONE

EXPOSURE LIMITS: NO OCCUPATIONAL EXPOSURE LIMITS ESTABLISHED BY OSHA, ACGIH, OR NIOSH.

PHYSICAL DATA

DESCRIPTION: FINE NEEDLES. ***MELTING POINT:*** 347 F (175 C)

SPECIFIC GRAVITY: NOT AVAILABLE ***SOLUBILITY IN WATER:*** NOT AVAILABLE

SOLVENT SOLUBILITY: SOLUBLE IN ALCOHOL, HOT BENZENE, AND SODIUM HYDROXIDE.

FIRE AND EXPLOSION DATA

FIRE AND EXPLOSION HAZARD: SLIGHT FIRE HAZARD WHEN EXPOSED TO HEAT OR FLAME.

FIREFIGHTING MEDIA: DRY CHEMICAL, CARBON DIOXIDE, HALON, WATER SPRAY OR STANDARD FOAM (1987 EMERGENCY RESPONSE GUIDEBOOK, DOT P 5800.4).
FOR LARGER FIRES, USE WATER SPRAY, FOG OR STANDARD FOAM (1987 EMERGENCY RESPONSE GUIDEBOOK, DOT P 5800.4).

FIREFIGHTING: MOVE CONTAINER FROM FIRE AREA IF POSSIBLE. DO NOT SCATTER SPILLED MATERIAL WITH HIGH PRESSURE WATER STREAMS. DIKE FIRE CONTROL WATER FOR LATER DISPOSAL (1987 EMERGENCY RESPONSE GUIDEBOOK, DOT P 5800.4, GUIDE PAGE 31).
USE AGENTS SUITABLE FOR TYPE OF SURROUNDING FIRE. AVOID BREATHING HAZARDOUS VAPORS, KEEP UPWIND.

TOXICITY

2,2'-THIOBIS(4-CHLOROPHENOL): TOXICITY DATA: 250 MG/KG INTRAPERITONEAL-MOUSE LDLO. CARCINOGEN STATUS: NONE. ACUTE TOXICITY LEVEL: NO DATA AVAILABLE BY OCCUPATIONAL ROUTE OF EXPOSURE. TARGET EFFECTS: NO DATA AVAILABLE.

HEALTH EFFECTS AND FIRST AID

INHALATION: 2,2'-THIOBIS(4-CHLOROPHENOL): **ACUTE EXPOSURE**- NO DATA AVAILABLE. **CHRONIC EXPOSURE**- NO DATA AVAILABLE.

FIRST AID- REMOVE FROM EXPOSURE AREA TO FRESH AIR IMMEDIATELY. IF BREATHING HAS STOPPED, PERFORM ARTIFICIAL RESPIRATION. KEEP PERSON WARM AND AT REST. TREAT SYMPTOMATICALLY AND SUPPORTIVELY. GET MEDICAL ATTENTION IMMEDIATELY.

SKIN CONTACT: 2,2'-THIOBIS(4-CHLOROPHENOL): **ACUTE EXPOSURE**- PHOTOSENSITIVE REACTION MAY OCCUR IN PREVIOUSLY EXPOSED INDIVIDUALS. **CHRONIC EXPOSURE**- PROLONGED OR REPEATED EXPOSURE MAY PRODUCE PHOTOALLERGIC CONTACT DERMATITIS.

FIRST AID- REMOVE CONTAMINATED CLOTHING AND SHOES IMMEDIATELY. WASH AFFECTED AREA WITH SOAP OR MILD DETERGENT AND LARGE AMOUNTS OF WATER UNTIL NO EVIDENCE OF CHEMICAL REMAINS (APPROXIMATELY 15-20 MINUTES). FOLLOW WITH APPLICATION OF CASTOR OIL OR 10% ETHYL ALCOHOL. (ARENA, POISONING, 4TH ED.) GET MEDICAL ATTENTION.

EYE CONTACT: 2,2'-THIOBIS(4-CHLOROPHENOL): **ACUTE EXPOSURE**- NO DATA AVAILABLE. **CHRONIC EXPOSURE**- NO DATA AVAILABLE.

FIRST AID- WASH EYES IMMEDIATELY WITH LARGE AMOUNTS OF WATER OR NORMAL SALINE, OCCASIONALLY LIFTING UPPER AND LOWER LIDS, UNTIL NO EVIDENCE OF CHEMICAL REMAINS (APPROXIMATELY 15-20 MINUTES). GET MEDICAL ATTENTION IMMEDIATELY.

INGESTION: 2,2'-THIOBIS(4-CHLOROPHENOL): **ACUTE EXPOSURE**- NO DATA AVAILABLE. **CHRONIC EXPOSURE**- NO DATA AVAILABLE.

FIRST AID- IF THE PATIENT IS ALERT AND ABLE TO SWALLOW, GIVE A SLURRY OF ACTIVATED CHARCOAL IN WATER. DO NOT GIVE EMETICS. CAREFUL GASTRIC LAVAGE WITH WATER IS RECOMMENDED IF THERE ARE NO DEEP BURNS IN THE MOUTH OR PHARYNX. OLDER RECOMMENDATIONS TO LAVAGE WITH OLIVE OR OTHER VEGETABLE OILS DO NOT APPEAR TO BE SUBSTANTIATED. IN ANY CASE AVOID MINERAL OIL AND ALCOHOL. (GOSSELIN, CLINICAL TOXICOLOGY OF COMMERCIAL PRODUCTS, 5TH ED.). LAVAGE MUST BE PERFORMED BY QUALIFIED MEDICAL PERSONNEL.

ANTIDOTE: NO SPECIFIC ANTIDOTE. TREAT SYMPTOMATICALLY AND SUPPORTIVELY.

REACTIVITY

REACTIVITY: STABLE UNDER NORMAL TEMPERATURES AND PRESSURES.

INCOMPATIBILITIES: 2,2'-THIOBIS(4-CHLOROPHENOL): OXIDIZERS (STRONG): FIRE AND EXPLOSION HAZARD.

DECOMPOSITION: THERMAL DECOMPOSITION MAY YIELD HIGHLY TOXIC OXIDES OF SULFUR, CHLORIDE FUMES, AND PHOSGENE.

POLYMERIZATION: HAZARDOUS POLYMERIZATION HAS NOT BEEN REPORTED TO OCCUR UNDER NORMAL TEMPERATURES AND PRESSURES.

STORAGE AND DISPOSAL

OBSERVE ALL FEDERAL, STATE AND LOCAL REGULATIONS WHEN STORING OR DISPOSING OF THIS SUBSTANCE. FOR ASSISTANCE, CONTACT THE DISTRICT DIRECTOR OF THE ENVIRONMENTAL PROTECTION AGENCY.

STORAGE

STORE IN ACCORDANCE WITH 40 CFR 165 RECOMMENDED PROCEDURES FOR THE DISPOSAL AND STORAGE OF PESTICIDES AND PESTICIDE CONTAINERS.
STORE AWAY FROM INCOMPATIBLE SUBSTANCES.

DISPOSAL

DISPOSAL MUST BE IN ACCORDANCE WITH 40 CFR 165 RECOMMENDED PROCEDURES FOR THE DISPOSAL AND STORAGE OF PESTICIDES AND PESTICIDE CONTAINERS.

CONDITIONS TO AVOID

MAY BURN BUT DOES NOT IGNITE READILY. AVOID CONTACT WITH STRONG OXIDIZERS, EXCESSIVE HEAT, SPARKS, OR OPEN FLAME.

SPILL AND LEAK PROCEDURES

OCCUPATIONAL SPILL: SWEEP UP AND PLACE IN SUITABLE CLEAN, DRY CONTAINERS FOR RECLAMATION OR LATER DISPOSAL. DO NOT FLUSH SPILLED MATERIAL INTO SEWER. KEEP UNNECESSARY PEOPLE AWAY.

PROTECTIVE EQUIPMENT

VENTILATION: PROVIDE LOCAL EXHAUST OR PROCESS ENCLOSURE VENTILATION SYSTEM.

RESPIRATOR: THE FOLLOWING RESPIRATORS ARE RECOMMENDED BASED ON INFORMATION FOUND IN THE PHYSICAL DATA, TOXICITY AND HEALTH EFFECTS SECTIONS. THEY ARE RANKED IN ORDER FROM MINIMUM TO MAXIMUM RESPIRATORY PROTECTION. THE SPECIFIC RESPIRATOR SELECTED MUST BE BASED ON CONTAMINATION LEVELS FOUND IN THE WORK PLACE, MUST NOT EXCEED THE WORKING LIMITS OF THE RESPIRATOR AND BE JOINTLY APPROVED BY THE NATIONAL INSTITUTE FOR OCCUPATIONAL SAFETY AND HEALTH AND THE MINE SAFETY AND HEALTH ADMINISTRATION (NIOSH-MSHA).

CHEMICAL CARTRIDGE RESPIRATOR WITH AN ORGANIC VAPOR CARTRIDGE(S) WITH A FULL FACEPIECE AND ORGANIC VAPOR CARTRIDGE(S) IN COMBINATION WITH A DUST AND MIST FILTER.

POWERED AIR-PURIFYING RESPIRATOR WITH A TIGHT-FITTING FACEPIECE AND ORGANIC VAPOR CARTRIDGE(S) IN COMBINATION WITH A HIGH-EFFICIENCY PARTICULATE FILTER.

TYPE 'C' SUPPLIED-AIR RESPIRATOR WITH A FULL FACEPIECE OPERATED IN A PRESSURE-DEMAND OR OTHER POSITIVE PRESSURE MODE.

SELF-CONTAINED BREATHING APPARATUS WITH A FULL FACEPIECE OPERATED IN PRESSURE-DEMAND OR OTHER POSITIVE PRESSURE MODE.

FOR FIREFIGHTING AND OTHER IMMEDIATELY DANGEROUS TO LIFE OR HEALTH CONDITIONS:

SELF-CONTAINED BREATHING APPARATUS WITH FULL FACEPIECE OPERATED IN PRESSURE-DEMAND OR OTHER POSITIVE PRESSURE MODE.

SUPPLIED-AIR RESPIRATOR WITH FULL FACEPIECE AND OPERATED IN PRESSURE-DEMAND OR OTHER POSITIVE PRESSURE MODE IN COMBINATION WITH AN AUXILIARY SELF-CONTAINED BREATHING APPARATUS OPERATED IN PRESSURE-DEMAND OR OTHER POSITIVE PRESSURE MODE.

CLOTHING: EMPLOYEE MUST WEAR APPROPRIATE PROTECTIVE (IMPERVIOUS) CLOTHING AND EQUIPMENT TO PREVENT REPEATED OR PROLONGED SKIN CONTACT WITH THIS SUBSTANCE.

GLOVES: EMPLOYEE MUST WEAR APPROPRIATE PROTECTIVE GLOVES TO PREVENT CONTACT WITH THIS SUBSTANCE.

EYE PROTECTION: EMPLOYEE MUST WEAR SPLASH-PROOF OR DUST-RESISTANT SAFETY GOGGLES TO PREVENT EYE CONTACT WITH THIS SUBSTANCE.

EMERGENCY EYE WASH: WHERE THERE IS ANY POSSIBILITY THAT AN EMPLOYEE'S EYES MAY BE EXPOSED TO THIS SUBSTANCE, THE EMPLOYER SHOULD PROVIDE AN EYE WASH FOUNTAIN WITHIN THE IMMEDIATE WORK AREA FOR EMERGENCY USE.

AUTHORIZED BY- OCCUPATIONAL HEALTH SERVICES, INC.

CREATION DATE: 11/16/89 ***REVISION DATE:*** 05/31/90

MATERIAL SAFETY DATA SHEET

OCCUPATIONAL HEALTH SERVICES, INC.
AGRICULTURE AND PESTICIDE DIVISION
450 SEVENTH AVENUE, SUITE 2407
NEW YORK, NEW YORK 10123
1-800-445-MSDS OR (212) 967-1100

EMERGENCY CONTACT:
JOHN S. BRANSFORD, JR. (615) 292-1180

SUBSTANCE IDENTIFICATION

CAS-NUMBER 6273-99-0

***SUBSTANCE:* PHENYLMERCURIC BORATE**

TRADE NAMES/SYNONYMS: MERCURY, (MU-(ORTHOBORATO(2-)-O:O'))DIPHENYLDI-; (MU-(ORTHOBORATO-O:O'))DIPHENYLDIMERCURY; MERCURY, (MU-(HYDROGEN ORTHOBORATO))DIPHENYLDI-; (MU-(HYDROGEN ORTHOBORATO)DIPHENYLDIMERCURY; PHENYLMERCURY BORATE; C12H11BHG2O3; PST71754

CHEMICAL FAMILY: ORGANOMETALLIC SALT

MOLECULAR FORMULA: (C6-H5-HG-O)2-B-O-H

MOLECULAR WEIGHT: 615.12

CERCLA RATINGS (SCALE 0-3): HEALTH=U FIRE=1 REACTIVITY=0 PERSISTENCE=3

NFPA RATINGS (SCALE 0-4): HEALTH=U FIRE=1 REACTIVITY=0

COMPONENTS AND CONTAMINANTS

COMPONENT: PHENYLMERCURIC BORATE ***PERCENT:*** 100.0
CAS# 6273-99-0

OTHER CONTAMINANTS: NONE

EXPOSURE LIMITS: MERCURY, ALL FORMS EXCEPT ALKYL (AS HG): 0.05 MG/M3 OSHA TWA (VAPOR); 0.1 MG/M3 OSHA CEILING (SKIN) 0.05 MG/M3 ACGIH TWA (VAPOR); 0.10 MG/M3 ACGIH TWA (ARYL & INORGANIC)-(SKIN) 0.05 MG/M3 NIOSH RECOMMENDED 10 HOUR TWA

SUBJECT TO SARA SECTION 313 ANNUAL TOXIC CHEMICAL RELEASE REPORTING

SUBJECT TO CALIFORNIA PROPOSITION 65 CANCER AND/OR REPRODUCTIVE TOXICITY WARNING AND RELEASE REQUIREMENTS- (JULY 1, 1990)

PHYSICAL DATA

DESCRIPTION: WHITE POWDER. ***MELTING POINT:*** 257 F (125 C)

SPECIFIC GRAVITY: NOT AVAILABLE ***SOLUBILITY IN WATER:*** SLIGHTLY SOLUBLE

FIRE AND EXPLOSION DATA

FIRE AND EXPLOSION HAZARD: SLIGHT FIRE HAZARD WHEN EXPOSED TO HEAT OR FLAME.

DUST-AIR MIXTURES MAY IGNITE OR EXPLODE.

FIREFIGHTING MEDIA: DRY CHEMICAL, CARBON DIOXIDE, HALON, WATER SPRAY OR STANDARD FOAM (1987 EMERGENCY RESPONSE GUIDEBOOK, DOT P 5800.4).

FOR LARGER FIRES, USE WATER SPRAY, FOG OR STANDARD FOAM (1987 EMERGENCY RESPONSE GUIDEBOOK, DOT P 5800.4).

FIREFIGHTING: MOVE CONTAINERS FROM FIRE AREA IF POSSIBLE (1987 EMERGENCY RESPONSE GUIDEBOOK, DOT P 5800.4, GUIDE PAGE 53).

EXTINGUISH USING AGENT SUITABLE FOR TYPE OF SURROUNDING FIRE. AVOID BREATHING VAPORS AND DUSTS. KEEP UPWIND.

TRANSPORTATION DATA

DEPARTMENT OF TRANSPORTATION HAZARD CLASSIFICATION 49 CFR 172.101: POISON B

DEPARTMENT OF TRANSPORTATION LABELING REQUIREMENTS 49 CFR 172.101 AND SUBPART E: POISON

DEPARTMENT OF TRANSPORTATION PACKAGING REQUIREMENTS: 49 CFR 173.365 EXCEPTIONS: 49 CFR 173.364

TOXICITY

PHENYLMERCURY BORATE: CARCINOGEN STATUS: NONE. LOCAL EFFECTS: CORROSIVE- INHALATION, SKIN, EYE, AND INGESTION. ACUTE TOXICITY LEVEL: NO DATA AVAILABLE. TARGET EFFECTS: NEUROTOXIN; NEPHROTOXIN. POISONING MAY ALSO AFFECT THE GASTROINTESTINAL TRACT. AT INCREASED RISK FROM EXPOSURE: PERSONS WITH NERVOUS SYSTEM DISORDERS OR CHRONIC RESPIRATORY OR KIDNEY DISEASE.* ADDITIONAL DATA: CROSS-SENSITIZATION REACTIONS MAY OCCUR BETWEEN METALLIC MERCURY AND THE ORGANIC AND INORGANIC MERCURY COMPOUNDS. MAY CROSS THE PLACENTA. REPRODUCTIVE EFFECTS HAVE BEEN REPORTED FROM SOME MERCURY COMPOUNDS.*

* MAY BE BASED ON GENERAL INFORMATION ON MERCURY COMPOUNDS.

HEALTH EFFECTS AND FIRST AID

INHALATION: PHENYLMERCURY BORATE: CORROSIVE. SEE INFORMATION ON ARYL MERCURY COMPOUNDS.

ARYL MERCURY COMPOUNDS: NEUROTOXIN/NEPHROTOXIN. 28 MG(HG)/M3 IMMEDIATELY DANGEROUS TO LIFE OR HEALTH. **ACUTE EXPOSURE**- INHALATION OF HIGH LEVELS MAY CAUSE LUNG DAMAGE. WITH SUFFICIENT ABSORPTION OF MERCURY COMPOUNDS A DELAYED SECOND STAGE OF TOXIC SYMPTOMS MAY DEVELOP CHARACTERIZED BY STOMATITIS, COLITIS, TUBULAR NEPHRITIS AND SEVERE ANURIA WITH UREMIA. **CHRONIC EXPOSURE**- REPEATED INHALATION OF ARYL MERCURY COMPOUNDS MAY CAUSE EFFECTS SIMILAR TO THOSE OF INORGANIC MERCURY. RENAL INVOLVEMENT MAY BE INDICATED BY PROTEINURIA WHICH, IN SEVERE CASES, MAY PROGRESS TO NEPHROTIC SYNDROME WITH EDEMA. LIVER EFFECTS MAY ALSO OCCUR. FINE "INTENTION" TREMORS MAY DEVELOP IN THE HANDS AND THEN BECOME EVIDENT IN THE FACE, ARMS AND LEGS. PARESTHESIAS, NEURALGIA, ABNORMAL REFLEXES, SPEECH AND SENSORY DISORDERS, ATAXIA, UNSTEADY GAIT, DISTURBANCE OF HANDWRITING, AND VISUAL EFFECTS MAY OCCUR. SALIVATION, METALLIC TASTE, GINGIVITIS, STOMATITIS, LOOSENING OF THE TEETH, BLUE LINE ON THE GUMS, ANOREXIA WEIGHT LOSS, ABDOMINAL PAIN, VOMITING, DIARRHEA, RHINITIS, COUGH, CHEST PAIN, DYSPNEA AND FEVER HAVE BEEN REPORTED. ERETHISM MAY DEVELOP AND BE CHARACTERIZED BY ABNORMAL SHYNESS, BLUSHING, DEPRESSION OR DESPONDENCY, RESENTMENT OF CRITICISM, IRRITABILITY, EXCITABILITY, ANXIETY, HEADACHE, PERSPIRATION, FATIGUE, MUSCLE WEAKNESS, AND DROWSINESS OR INSOMNIA. IN SEVERE CASES, HALLUCINATIONS, LOSS OF MEMORY AND MENTAL DETERIORATION MAY OCCUR. SYSTEMIC ABSORPTION MAY REPRODUCE OR EXACERBATE ALLERGIC CONTACT DERMATITIS. ACRODYNIA HAS BEEN REPORTED FROM EXPOSURE TO A PHENYLMERCURY COMPOUND IN PAINT AND MAY HAVE BEEN A HYPERSENSITIVITY REACTION.

FIRST AID- REMOVE FROM EXPOSURE AREA TO FRESH AIR IMMEDIATELY. IF BREATHING HAS STOPPED, GIVE ARTIFICIAL RESPIRATION. MAINTAIN AIRWAY AND

BLOOD PRESSURE AND ADMINISTER OXYGEN IF AVAILABLE. KEEP AFFECTED PERSON WARM AND AT REST. TREAT SYMPTOMATICALLY AND SUPPORTIVELY. ADMINISTRATION OF OXYGEN SHOULD BE PERFORMED BY QUALIFIED PERSONNEL. GET MEDICAL ATTENTION IMMEDIATELY.

SKIN CONTACT: PHENYLMERCURY BORATE: CORROSIVE/SENSITIZER. MAY CAUSE REDNESS, PAIN, AND SERIOUS BURNS. SEE INFORMATION ON ARYL MERCURY COMPOUNDS.

ARYL MERCURY COMPOUND: **ACUTE EXPOSURE**- SOME MERCURY COMPOUNDS CAUSE PRIMARY SKIN IRRITATION. CONCENTRATED SOLUTIONS OF SOME ARYL MERCURY COMPOUNDS CAUSE BURNS AND BLISTERS. SENSITIZATION REACTIONS MAY OCCUR IN PREVIOUSLY EXPOSED PERSONS. TOPICAL APPLICATION OF SOME ARYL MERCURY COMPOUNDS HAVE PRODUCED SIGNS OF SYSTEMIC TOXICITY. **CHRONIC EXPOSURE**- REPEATED OR PROLONGED EXPOSURE TO SOME ARYL MERCURY COMPOUNDS MAY CAUSE CONTACT OR SENSITIZATION DERMATITIS. ABSORPTION THROUGH THE SKIN MAY CONTRIBUTE TO THE SYSTEMIC EFFECTS OF MERCURY ABSORPTION FROM OTHER ROUTES.

FIRST AID- REMOVE CONTAMINATED CLOTHING AND SHOES IMMEDIATELY. WASH AFFECTED AREA WITH SOAP OR MILD DETERGENT AND LARGE AMOUNTS OF WATER UNTIL NO EVIDENCE OF CHEMICAL REMAINS (AT LEAST 15-20 MINUTES). IN CASE OF CHEMICAL BURNS, COVER AREA WITH STERILE, DRY DRESSING. BANDAGE SECURELY, BUT NOT TOO TIGHTLY. GET MEDICAL ATTENTION IMMEDIATELY.

EYE CONTACT: PHENYLMERCURY BORATE: CORROSIVE. SEE INFORMATION ON ARYL MERCURY COMPOUNDS.

ARYL MERCURY COMPOUNDS: **ACUTE EXPOSURE**- SOLUTIONS OF SOME ARYL MERCURY COMPOUNDS HAVE CAUSED IRRITATION AND CORNEAL INJURY. **CHRONIC EXPOSURE**- REPEATED OR PROLONGED CONTACT WITH SOME ARYL MERCURY COMPOUNDS HAS CAUSED MERCURIALENTIS WITH MERCURY DEPOSITION IN THE LENS.

FIRST AID- WASH EYES IMMEDIATELY WITH LARGE AMOUNTS OF WATER, OCCASIONALLY LIFTING UPPER AND LOWER LIDS, UNTIL NO EVIDENCE OF CHEMICAL REMAINS (AT LEAST 15-20 MINUTES). CONTINUE IRRIGATING WITH NORMAL SALINE UNTIL THE PH HAS RETURNED TO NORMAL (30-60 MINUTES). COVER WITH STERILE BANDAGES. GET MEDICAL ATTENTION IMMEDIATELY.

INGESTION: PHENYLMERCURY BORATE: CORROSIVE. SEE INFORMATION ON ARYL MERCURY COMPOUNDS.

ARYL MERCURY COMPOUNDS: NEUROTOXIN/NEPHROTOXIN. **ACUTE EXPOSURE**- INGESTION OF SUFFICIENT AMOUNTS OF SOME MERCURY COMPOUNDS MAY CAUSE A BURNING OF THE MOUTH AND THROAT, THIRST, SALIVATION, METALLIC TASTE, NAUSEA, VOMITING, BLOODY DIARRHEA, SHOCK, AND CIRCULATORY COLLAPSE WHICH MAY BE FATAL WITHIN A FEW HOURS. IN NONFATAL CASES, DELAYED EFFECTS INCLUDING SWELLING OF THE SALIVARY GLANDS, STOMATITIS, COLITIS, LIVER DAMAGE, AND RENAL TUBULAR NECROSIS WITH TRANSIENT POLYURIA, HEMATURIA, ANURIA AND UREMIA MAY OCCUR IN 1-3 DAYS. IN THIS PHASE, DEATH MAY OCCUR DUE TO COMPLETE RENAL FAILURE. **CHRONIC EXPOSURE**- REPEATED INGESTION MAY RESULT IN TOXIC EFFECTS AS DETAILED IN CHRONIC INHALATION.

FIRST AID- IF THE PERSON IS CONSCIOUS AND NOT CONVULSING, INDUCE EMESIS BY GIVING SYRUP OF IPECAC (KEEPING THE HEAD BELOW THE HIPS TO PREVENT ASPIRATION), FOLLOWED BY WATER. REPEAT IN 20 MINUTES IF NOT EFFECTIVE INITIALLY. IN PATIENTS WITH DEPRESSED RESPIRATION OR IF EMESIS IS NOT PRODUCED, PERFORM GASTRIC LAVAGE CAUTIOUSLY. FOLLOW WITH A SALINE CATHARTIC (DREISBACH, HANDBOOK OF POISONING, 12TH ED.). TREAT SYMPTOMATICALLY AND SUPPORTIVELY. GASTRIC LAVAGE SHOULD BE PERFORMED BY QUALIFIED MEDICAL PERSONNEL. GET MEDICAL ATTENTION IMMEDIATELY.

ANTIDOTE: THE FOLLOWING ANTIDOTE HAS BEEN RECOMMENDED. HOWEVER, THE DECISION AS TO WHETHER THE SEVERITY OF POISONING REQUIRES ADMINISTRATION OF ANY ANTIDOTE AND ACTUAL DOSE REQUIRED SHOULD BE MADE BY QUALIFIED MEDICAL PERSONNEL.

MERCURY POISONING: GIVE DIMERCAPROL, 3 MG/KG (OR 0.3 ML/10 KG) EVERY 4 HOURS FOR THE FIRST 2 DAYS AND THEN 2 MG/KG EVERY 12 HOURS FOR A TOTAL OF 10 DAYS IF NECESSARY. DIMERCAPROL IS AVAILABLE AS A 10% SOLUTION IN OIL FOR INTRAMUSCULAR ADMINISTRATION. HEMODIALYSIS WILL SPEED THE REMOVAL OF THE MERCURY-DIMERCAPROL COMPLEX. PENICILLAMINE IS ALSO EFFECTIVE. GIVE UP TO 100 MG/KG/DAY (MAXIMUM 1 GR/DAY) DIVIDED INTO 4 DOSES FOR NO LONGER THAN 1 WEEK. IF A LONGER ADMINISTRATION PERIOD IS WARRANTED, DOSAGE SHOULD NOT EXCEED 40 MG/KG/DAY. GIVE THE DRUG ORALLY HALF AN HOUR BEFORE MEALS. A CHELATING AGENT SHOULD BE BE CONTINUED UNTIL THE URINE-MERCURY LEVEL FALLS BELOW 50 UG/24 HOURS (DREISBACH, HANDBOOK OF POISONING, 12TH ED.). ANTIDOTE SHOULD BE ADMINISTERED BY QUALIFIED MEDICAL PERSONNEL.

REACTIVITY

REACTIVITY: STABLE UNDER NORMAL TEMPERATURES AND PRESSURES.

INCOMPATIBILITIES: PHENYLMERCURY BORATE: OXIDIZERS (STRONG): FIRE AND EXPLOSION HAZARD.

DECOMPOSITION: THERMAL DECOMPOSITION PRODUCTS MAY INCLUDE TOXIC MERCURY VAPOR AND OXIDES OF BORON AND CARBON.

POLYMERIZATION: HAZARDOUS POLYMERIZATION HAS NOT BEEN REPORTED TO OCCUR UNDER NORMAL TEMPERATURES AND PRESSURES.

STORAGE AND DISPOSAL

OBSERVE ALL FEDERAL, STATE AND LOCAL REGULATIONS WHEN STORING OR DISPOSING OF THIS SUBSTANCE. FOR ASSISTANCE, CONTACT THE DISTRICT DIRECTOR OF THE ENVIRONMENTAL PROTECTION AGENCY.

STORAGE

STORE AWAY FROM INCOMPATIBLE SUBSTANCES.

DISPOSAL

MERCURY - REGULATORY LEVEL: 0.2 MG/L MATERIALS WHICH CONTAIN THE ABOVE SUBSTANCE AT OR ABOVE THE REGULATORY LEVEL MEET THE EPA CHARACTERISTIC OF TOXICITY, AND MUST BE DISPOSED OF IN ACCORDANCE WITH 40 CFR PART 262. EPA HAZARDOUS WASTE NUMBER D009.

CONDITIONS TO AVOID

MAY BURN BUT DOES NOT IGNITE READILY.

SPILL AND LEAK PROCEDURES

WATER SPILL: THE CALIFORNIA SAFE DRINKING WATER AND TOXIC ENFORCEMENT ACT OF 1986 (PROPOSITION 65) PROHIBITS CONTAMINATING ANY KNOWN SOURCE OF DRINKING WATER WITH SUBSTANCES KNOWN TO CAUSE CANCER AND/OR REPRODUCTIVE TOXICITY.

OCCUPATIONAL SPILL: DO NOT TOUCH SPILLED MATERIAL. STOP LEAK IF YOU CAN DO IT WITHOUT RISK. FOR SMALL SPILLS, TAKE UP WITH SAND OR OTHER ABSORBENT MATERIAL AND PLACE INTO CONTAINERS FOR LATER DISPOSAL. FOR SMALL DRY SPILLS, WITH A CLEAN SHOVEL PLACE MATERIAL INTO CLEAN, DRY CONTAINER AND COVER. MOVE CONTAINERS FROM SPILL AREA. FOR LARGER SPILLS, DIKE FAR AHEAD OF SPILL FOR LATER DISPOSAL. KEEP UNNECESSARY PEOPLE AWAY. ISOLATE HAZARD AREA AND DENY ENTRY.

PROTECTIVE EQUIPMENT

VENTILATION: PROVIDE LOCAL EXHAUST OR PROCESS ENCLOSURE VENTILATION TO MEET PUBLISHED EXPOSURE LIMITS.

RESPIRATOR: THE FOLLOWING RESPIRATORS AND MAXIMUM USE CONCENTRATIONS ARE RECOMMENDATIONS BY THE U.S. DEPARTMENT OF HEALTH AND HUMAN SERVICES, NIOSH POCKET GUIDE TO CHEMICAL HAZARDS; NIOSH CRITERIA DOCUMENTS OR BY THE U.S. DEPARTMENT OF LABOR, 29 CFR 1910 SUBPART Z. THE SPECIFIC RESPIRATOR SELECTED MUST BE BASED ON CONTAMINATION LEVELS FOUND IN THE WORK PLACE, MUST NOT EXCEED THE WORKING LIMITS OF THE RESPIRATOR AND BE JOINTLY APPROVED BY THE NATIONAL INSTITUTE FOR OCCUPATIONAL SAFETY AND HEALTH AND THE MINE SAFETY AND HEALTH ADMINISTRATION (NIOSH-MSHA).

MERCURY, ALL FORMS EXCEPT ALKYL (AS HG):

0.5 MG/M3- ANY AIR-PURIFYING RESPIRATOR WITH A HIGH-EFFICIENCY PARTICULATE FILTER. ANY SUPPLIED-AIR RESPIRATOR. ANY SELF-CONTAINED BREATHING APPARATUS.

1.25 MG/M3- ANY SUPPLIED-AIR RESPIRATOR OPERATED IN A CONTINUOUS FLOW MODE. ANY POWERED AIR-PURIFYING RESPIRATOR WITH A HIGH-EFFICIENCY PARTICULATE FILTER.

2.5 MG/M3- ANY SUPPLIED-AIR RESPIRATOR WITH A FULL FACEPIECE. ANY SELF-CONTAINED BREATHING APPARATUS WITH A FULL FACEPIECE. ANY AIR-PURIFYING FULL FACEPIECE RESPIRATOR WITH A HIGH-EFFICIENCY PARTICULATE FILTER. ANY POWERED AIR-PURIFYING RESPIRATOR WITH A TIGHT-FITTING FACEPIECE AND A HIGH-EFFICIENCY PARTICULATE FILTER. ANY SUPPLIED-AIR RESPIRATOR WITH A TIGHT-FITTING FACEPIECE OPERATED IN A CONTINUOUS FLOW MODE.

28 MG/M3- ANY SUPPLIED-AIR RESPIRATOR WITH A HALF-MASK AND OPERATED IN A PRESSURE-DEMAND OR OTHER POSITIVE PRESSURE MODE.

ESCAPE- ANY AIR-PURIFYING FULL FACEPIECE RESPIRATOR WITH A HIGH-EFFICIENCY PARTICULATE FILTER. ANY APPROPRIATE ESCAPE-TYPE SELF-CONTAINED BREATHING APPARATUS.

FOR FIREFIGHTING AND OTHER IMMEDIATELY DANGEROUS TO LIFE OR HEALTH CONDITIONS: SELF-CONTAINED BREATHING APPARATUS WITH FULL FACEPIECE OPERATED IN PRESSURE-DEMAND OR OTHER POSITIVE PRESSURE MODE. SUPPLIED-AIR RESPIRATOR WITH FULL FACEPIECE AND OPERATED IN PRESSURE-DEMAND OR OTHER POSITIVE PRESSURE MODE IN COMBINATION WITH AN

AUXILIARY SELF-CONTAINED BREATHING APPARATUS OPERATED IN PRESSURE-DEMAND OR OTHER POSITIVE PRESSURE MODE.

CLOTHING: EMPLOYEE MUST WEAR APPROPRIATE PROTECTIVE (IMPERVIOUS) CLOTHING AND EQUIPMENT TO PREVENT ANY POSSIBILITY OF SKIN CONTACT WITH THIS SUBSTANCE.

GLOVES: EMPLOYEE MUST WEAR APPROPRIATE PROTECTIVE GLOVES TO PREVENT CONTACT WITH THIS SUBSTANCE.

EYE PROTECTION: EMPLOYEE MUST WEAR SPLASH-PROOF OR DUST-RESISTANT SAFETY GOGGLES AND A FACESHIELD TO PREVENT CONTACT WITH THIS SUBSTANCE.

EMERGENCY WASH FACILITIES: WHERE THERE IS ANY POSSIBILITY THAT AN EMPLOYEE'S EYES AND/OR SKIN MAY BE EXPOSED TO THIS SUBSTANCE, THE EMPLOYER SHOULD PROVIDE AN EYE WASH FOUNTAIN AND QUICK DRENCH SHOWER WITHIN THE IMMEDIATE WORK AREA FOR EMERGENCY USE.

AUTHORIZED BY- OCCUPATIONAL HEALTH SERVICES, INC.

CREATION DATE: 02/07/90 ***REVISION DATE:*** 07/13/90

MATERIAL SAFETY DATA SHEET

OCCUPATIONAL HEALTH SERVICES, INC.
AGRICULTURE AND PESTICIDE DIVISION
450 SEVENTH AVENUE, SUITE 2407
NEW YORK, NEW YORK 10123
1-800-445-MSDS OR (212) 967-1100

EMERGENCY CONTACT:
JOHN S. BRANSFORD, JR. (615) 292-1180

SUBSTANCE IDENTIFICATION

CAS-NUMBER 23319-66-6

SUBSTANCE: **PHENYL MERCURIC TRIETHANOL AMMONIUM LACTATE**

TRADE NAMES/SYNONYMS: MERCURY(1+), (2,2',2''-NITRILOTRIS(ETHANOL)-N,O,O',O'') PHENYL-, SALT WITH 2-HYDROXYPROPANOIC ACID(1:1); (2,2',2''-NITRILOTRIS(ETHANOL)-N,O,O',O'')PHENYLMERCURY(1+), SALT WITH 2-HYDROXYPROPANOIC ACID(1:1); TRIS(2-HYDROXYETHYL)PHENYLMERCURIAMMONIUM LACTATE; PURATURF; C15H25HGNO6; PST71768

CHEMICAL FAMILY: SALT

MOLECULAR FORMULA: C12-H20-HG-N-O3-.C3-H5-O3

MOLECULAR WEIGHT: 516.00

CERCLA RATINGS (SCALE 0-3): HEALTH=3 FIRE=1 REACTIVITY=0 PERSISTENCE=3

NFPA RATINGS (SCALE 0-4): HEALTH=3 FIRE=1 REACTIVITY=0

COMPONENTS AND CONTAMINANTS

COMPONENT: PHENYL MERCURIC TRIETHANOL AMMONIUM LACTATE ***PERCENT:*** 100
CAS# 23319-66-6

OTHER CONTAMINANTS: NONE

EXPOSURE LIMITS: MERCURY, ALL FORMS EXCEPT ALKYL (AS HG): 0.05 MG/M3 OSHA TWA (VAPOR); 0.1 MG/M3 OSHA CEILING (SKIN) 0.05 MG/M3 ACGIH TWA (VAPOR); 0.10 MG/M3 ACGIH TWA (ARYL & INORGANIC)-(SKIN) 0.05 MG/M3 NIOSH RECOMMENDED 10 HOUR TWA

SUBJECT TO SARA SECTION 313 ANNUAL TOXIC CHEMICAL RELEASE REPORTING

SUBJECT TO CALIFORNIA PROPOSITION 65 CANCER AND/OR REPRODUCTIVE TOXICITY WARNING AND RELEASE REQUIREMENTS- (JULY 1, 1990)

PHYSICAL DATA

DESCRIPTION: WHITE, CRYSTALLINE SOLID. ***MELTING POINT:*** NOT AVAILABLE

SPECIFIC GRAVITY: NOT AVAILABLE ***SOLUBILITY IN WATER:*** SOLUBLE

FIRE AND EXPLOSION DATA

FIRE AND EXPLOSION HAZARD: SLIGHT FIRE HAZARD WHEN EXPOSED TO HEAT OR FLAME.

FIREFIGHTING MEDIA: DRY CHEMICAL, CARBON DIOXIDE, HALON, WATER SPRAY OR STANDARD FOAM (1987 EMERGENCY RESPONSE GUIDEBOOK, DOT P 5800.4). FOR LARGER FIRES, USE WATER SPRAY, FOG OR STANDARD FOAM (1987 EMERGENCY RESPONSE GUIDEBOOK, DOT P 5800.4).

FIREFIGHTING: MOVE CONTAINERS FROM FIRE AREA IF POSSIBLE. FIGHT FIRE FROM MAXIMUM DISTANCE. STAY AWAY FROM STORAGE TANK ENDS. DIKE FIRE CONTROL WATER FOR LATER DISPOSAL. DO NOT SCATTER MATERIAL (1987 EMERGENCY RESPONSE GUIDEBOOK, DOT P 5800.4, GUIDE PAGE 55).

EXTINGUISH USING AGENTS SUITABLE FOR SURROUNDING FIRE. APPLY WATER IN FLOODING QUANTITIES AS A FOG. AVOID CONTAMINATING WATER SOURCES AND SEWERS. AVOID BREATHING HAZARDOUS VAPORS; KEEP UPWIND.

TRANSPORTATION DATA

DEPARTMENT OF TRANSPORTATION HAZARD CLASSIFICATION 49 CFR 172.101: POISON B

DEPARTMENT OF TRANSPORTATION LABELING REQUIREMENTS 49 CFR 172.101 AND SUBPART E: POISON

DEPARTMENT OF TRANSPORTATION PACKAGING REQUIREMENTS: 49 CFR 173.365 EXCEPTIONS: 49 CFR 173.364

TOXICITY

PHENYL MERCURIC TRIETHANOL AMMONIUM LACTATE: TOXICITY DATA: 30 MG/KG ORAL-RAT LD50. CARCINOGEN STATUS: NONE. ACUTE TOXICITY LEVEL: HIGHLY TOXIC BY INGESTION. TARGET EFFECTS: SENSITIZER- PULMONARY AND SKIN; NEUROTOXIN; NEPHROTOXIN. AT INCREASED RISK FROM EXPOSURE: PERSONS WITH CHRONIC RESPIRATORY DISEASE, NERVOUS SYSTEM DISORDERS AND KIDNEY DISEASE.

HEALTH EFFECTS AND FIRST AID

INHALATION: PHENYL MERCURIC TRIETHANOL AMMONIUM LACTATE: SENSITIZER/NEUROTOXIN/NEPHROTOXIN. 28 MG/M3 IMMEDIATELY DANGEROUS TO LIFE OR HEALTH. **ACUTE EXPOSURE-** INHALATION OF HIGH LEVELS OF MERCURY COMPOUNDS MAY CAUSE ALMOST IMMEDIATE DYSPNEA, COUGH, FEVER, NAUSEA, VOMITING, DIARRHEA, HEADACHE, STOMATITIS, SALIVATION, GINGIVITIS, A METALLIC TASTE, AND CARDIAC ABNORMALITIES. RESPIRATORY IRRITATION MAY OCCUR WITH CHEST PAIN AND TIGHTNESS. SYMPTOMS MAY RESOLVE OR MAY PROGRESS TO NECROTIZING BRONCHIOLITIS, PNEUMONITIS, PULMONARY EDEMA, PNEUMOTHORAX, INTERSTITIAL INTERSTITIAL FIBROSIS. ACIDOSIS, RENAL DAMAGE AND DEATH MAY OCCUR. ALLERGIC REACTIONS THAT MAY OCCUR IN PREVIOUSLY EXPOSED PERSONS INCLUDE DERMATITIS, ENCEPHALITIS, AND DEATH. **CHRONIC EXPOSURE-** REPEATED INHALATION OF MERCURY COMPOUNDS MAY CAUSE MERCURIALISM, WHICH IS CHARACTERIZED BY FINE TREMORS AND ERETHISM. TREMORS MAY AFFECT THE HANDS FIRST, BUT MAY ALSO BECOME EVIDENT IN THE FACE, ARMS, AND LEGS. ERETHISM MAY BE MANIFESTED BY ABNORMAL SHYNESS, BLUSHING, SELF-CONSCIOUSNESS, DEPRESSION OR DESPONDENCY, RESENTMENT OF CRITICISM, IRRITABILITY OR EXCITABILITY, HEADACHE, FATIGUE, AND INSOMNIA. IN SEVERE CASES, HALLUCINATIONS, LOSS OF MEMORY AND MENTAL DETERIORATION MAY OCCUR. CONCENTRATIONS AS LOW AS 0.03 MG/M3 HAVE INDUCED PSYCHIATRIC SYMPTOMS IN HUMANS. RENAL INVOLVEMENT MAY BE INDICATED BY PROTEINURIA, ALBUMINURIA, ENZYMURIA, AND ANURIA. OTHER EFFECTS MAY INCLUDE SALIVATION, GINGIVITIS, STOMATITIS, LOOSENING OF THE TEETH, BLUE LINES ON THE GUMS, DIARRHEA, WEIGHT LOSS, ANOREXIA, SPEECH AND SENSORY DISORDERS, UNSTEADY GAIT, CHRONIC PNEUMONITIS AND MILD ANEMIA. REPEATED EXPOSURE TO MERCURY AND ITS COMPOUNDS MAY RESULT IN SENSITIZATION. MERCURY IS EXCRETED IN BREAST MILK.

FIRST AID- REMOVE FROM EXPOSURE AREA TO FRESH AIR IMMEDIATELY. IF BREATHING HAS STOPPED, PERFORM ARTIFICIAL RESPIRATION. KEEP PERSON WARM AND AT REST. TREAT SYMPTOMATICALLY AND SUPPORTIVELY. GET MEDICAL ATTENTION IMMEDIATELY.

SKIN CONTACT: PHENYL MERCURIC TRIETHANOL AMMONIUM LACTATE: SENSITIZER/NEUROTOXIN/NEPHROTOXIN. **ACUTE EXPOSURE-** MERCURY COMPOUNDS MAY CAUSE SKIN IRRITATION. SMALL AMOUNTS OF MERCURY MAY BE ABSORBED THROUGH INTACT SKIN. ALLERGIC REACTIONS THAT MAY OCCUR INCLUDE DERMATITIS, ENCEPHALITIS, AND DEATH. **CHRONIC EXPOSURE-** PROLONGED OR REPEATED EXPOSURE TO MERCURY COMPOUNDS MAY RESULT IN DERMAL SENSITIZATION AND SYSTEMIC EFFECTS AS DETAILED IN CHRONIC INHALATION.

FIRST AID- REMOVE CONTAMINATED CLOTHING AND SHOES IMMEDIATELY. WASH AFFECTED AREA WITH SOAP OR MILD DETERGENT AND LARGE AMOUNTS OF WATER UNTIL NO EVIDENCE OF CHEMICAL REMAINS (APPROXIMATELY 15-20 MINUTES). GET MEDICAL ATTENTION IMMEDIATELY.

EYE CONTACT: PHENYL MERCURIC TRIETHANOL AMMONIUM LACTATE: **ACUTE EXPOSURE-** MERCURY COMPOUNDS MAY CAUSE IRRITATION. **CHRONIC EXPOSURE-** MERCURY EXPOSURE FROM INHALATION, INGESTION, OR SKIN CONTACT MAY BE INDICATED BY MERCURIALENTIS, DISCOLORATION OF THE CRYSTALLINE LENS, ON SLIT LAMP EXAMINATION OF THE EYES.

FIRST AID- WASH EYES IMMEDIATELY WITH LARGE AMOUNTS OF WATER OR NORMAL SALINE, OCCASIONALLY LIFTING UPPER AND LOWER LIDS, UNTIL NO EVIDENCE OF CHEMICAL REMAINS (APPROXIMATELY 15-20 MINUTES). GET MEDICAL ATTENTION IMMEDIATELY.

INGESTION: PHENYL MERCURIC TRIETHANOL AMMONIUM LACTATE: NEUROTOXIN/NEPHROTOXIN/HIGHLY TOXIC. **ACUTE EXPOSURE-** INGESTION OF

MERCURY COMPOUNDS MAY CAUSE A BURNING OF THE MOUTH AND THROAT, THIRST, NAUSEA AND VOMITING. MAY ALSO CAUSE SIGNS AND SYMPTOMS AS DETAILED IN CHRONIC INHALATION. THE MEDIAN LETHAL DOSE IS RATS WAS 30 MG/KG. **CHRONIC EXPOSURE**- REPEATED INGESTION MAY RESULT IN TOXIC EFFECTS AS DETAILED IN CHRONIC INHALATION.

FIRST AID- REMOVE BY GASTRIC LAVAGE OR EMESIS. MAINTAIN BLOOD PRESSURE AND AIRWAY. GIVE OXYGEN IF RESPIRATION IS DEPRESSED. DO NOT PERFORM GASTRIC LAVAGE OR EMESIS IF VICTIM IS UNCONSCIOUS. GET MEDICAL ATTENTION IMMEDIATELY (DREISBACH, HANDBOOK OF POISONING, 11TH ED.). ADMINISTRATION OF GASTRIC LAVAGE OR OXYGEN SHOULD BE PERFORMED BY QUALIFIED MEDICAL PERSONNEL.

ANTIDOTE: THE FOLLOWING ANTIDOTE HAS BEEN RECOMMENDED. HOWEVER, THE DECISION AS TO WHETHER THE SEVERITY OF POISONING REQUIRES ADMINISTRATION OF ANY ANTIDOTE AND ACTUAL DOSE REQUIRED SHOULD BE MADE BY QUALIFIED MEDICAL PERSONNEL.

MERCURY POISONING: GIVE DIMERCAPROL, 3 MG/KG (OR 0.3 ML/10 KG) EVERY 4 HOURS FOR THE FIRST 2 DAYS AND THEN 2 MG/KG EVERY 12 HOURS FOR A TOTAL OF 10 DAYS IF NECESSARY. DIMERCAPROL IS AVAILABLE AS A 10% SOLUTION IN OIL FOR INTRAMUSCULAR ADMINISTRATION. HEMODIALYSIS WILL SPEED THE REMOVAL OF THE MERCURY-DIMERCAPROL COMPLEX. PENICILLAMINE IS ALSO EFFECTIVE. GIVE UP TO 100 MG/KG/DAY (MAXIMUM 1 GR/DAY) DIVIDED INTO 4 DOSES FOR NO LONGER THAN 1 WEEK. IF A LONGER ADMINISTRATION PERIOD IS WARRANTED, DOSAGE SHOULD NOT EXCEED 40 MG/KG/DAY. GIVE THE DRUG ORALLY HALF AN HOUR BEFORE MEALS. A CHELATING AGENT SHOULD BE BE CONTINUED UNTIL THE URINE-MERCURY LEVEL FALLS BELOW 50 UG/24 HOURS (DREISBACH, HANDBOOK OF POISONING, 12TH ED.). ANTIDOTE SHOULD BE ADMINISTERED BY QUALIFIED MEDICAL PERSONNEL.

REACTIVITY

REACTIVITY: STABLE UNDER NORMAL TEMPERATURES AND PRESSURES.

INCOMPATIBILITIES: PHENYL MERCURIC TRIETHANOL AMMONIUM: NO SPECIFIC DATA AVAILABLE. SEE MERCURY SALTS.

MERCURY SALTS: ACETYLENE: FORMS SHOCK-SENSITIVE ACETYLIDES. BUTYNEDIOL + ACIDS: VIOLENT DECOMPOSITION. NITROMETHANE: FORMS EXPLOSIVE COMPOUND.

DECOMPOSITION: THERMAL DECOMPOSITION PRODUCTS MAY INCLUDE TOXIC VAPORS OF MERCURY.

POLYMERIZATION: HAZARDOUS POLYMERIZATION HAS NOT BEEN REPORTED TO OCCUR UNDER NORMAL TEMPERATURES AND PRESSURES.

STORAGE AND DISPOSAL

OBSERVE ALL FEDERAL, STATE AND LOCAL REGULATIONS WHEN STORING OR DISPOSING OF THIS SUBSTANCE. FOR ASSISTANCE, CONTACT THE DISTRICT DIRECTOR OF THE ENVIRONMENTAL PROTECTION AGENCY.

STORAGE

STORE AWAY FROM INCOMPATIBLE SUBSTANCES.

STORE IN ACCORDANCE WITH 40 CFR 165 RECOMMENDED PROCEDURES FOR THE DISPOSAL AND STORAGE OF PESTICIDES AND PESTICIDE CONTAINERS.

DISPOSAL

DISPOSAL MUST BE IN ACCORDANCE WITH 40 CFR 165 RECOMMENDED PROCEDURES FOR THE DISPOSAL AND STORAGE OF PESTICIDES AND PESTICIDE CONTAINERS.

MERCURY - REGULATORY LEVEL: 0.2 MG/L MATERIALS WHICH CONTAIN THE ABOVE SUBSTANCE AT OR ABOVE THE REGULATORY LEVEL MEET THE EPA CHARACTERISTIC OF TOXICITY, AND MUST BE DISPOSED OF IN ACCORDANCE WITH 40 CFR PART 262. EPA HAZARDOUS WASTE NUMBER D009.

CONDITIONS TO AVOID

MAY BURN BUT DOES NOT IGNITE READILY. CONTAINERS MAY EXPLODE IN HEAT OF FIRE.

SPILL AND LEAK PROCEDURES

WATER SPILL: THE CALIFORNIA SAFE DRINKING WATER AND TOXIC ENFORCEMENT ACT OF 1986 (PROPOSITION 65) PROHIBITS CONTAMINATING ANY KNOWN SOURCE OF DRINKING WATER WITH SUBSTANCES KNOWN TO CAUSE CANCER AND/OR REPRODUCTIVE TOXICITY.

OCCUPATIONAL SPILL: DO NOT TOUCH SPILLED MATERIAL. STOP LEAK IF YOU CAN DO IT WITHOUT RISK. USE WATER SPRAY TO REDUCE VAPORS. FOR SMALL SPILLS, TAKE UP WITH SAND OR OTHER ABSORBENT MATERIAL AND PLACE INTO CONTAINERS FOR LATER DISPOSAL. FOR SMALL DRY SPILLS, WITH A CLEAN SHOVEL PLACE MATERIAL INTO CLEAN, DRY CONTAINERS AND COVER. MOVE CONTAINERS FROM SPILL AREA. FOR LARGER SPILLS, DIKE FAR AHEAD OF SPILL FOR LATER DISPOSAL. KEEP UNNECESSARY PEOPLE AWAY. ISOLATE HAZARD AREA AND DENY ENTRY. VENTILATE CLOSED SPACES BEFORE ENTERING.

PROTECTIVE EQUIPMENT

VENTILATION: PROVIDE LOCAL EXHAUST OR PROCESS ENCLOSURE VENTILATION TO MEET PUBLISHED EXPOSURE LIMITS.

RESPIRATOR: THE FOLLOWING RESPIRATORS AND MAXIMUM USE CONCENTRATIONS ARE RECOMMENDATIONS BY THE U.S. DEPARTMENT OF HEALTH AND HUMAN SERVICES, NIOSH POCKET GUIDE TO CHEMICAL HAZARDS; NIOSH CRITERIA DOCUMENTS OR BY THE U.S. DEPARTMENT OF LABOR, 29 CFR 1910 SUBPART Z. THE SPECIFIC RESPIRATOR SELECTED MUST BE BASED ON CONTAMINATION LEVELS FOUND IN THE WORK PLACE, MUST NOT EXCEED THE WORKING LIMITS OF THE RESPIRATOR AND BE JOINTLY APPROVED BY THE NATIONAL INSTITUTE FOR OCCUPATIONAL SAFETY AND HEALTH AND THE MINE SAFETY AND HEALTH ADMINISTRATION (NIOSH-MSHA).

MERCURY, ALL FORMS EXCEPT ALKYL (AS HG):

0.5 MG/M3- ANY AIR-PURIFYING RESPIRATOR WITH A HIGH-EFFICIENCY PARTICULATE FILTER. ANY SUPPLIED-AIR RESPIRATOR. ANY SELF-CONTAINED BREATHING APPARATUS.

1.25 MG/M3- ANY SUPPLIED-AIR RESPIRATOR OPERATED IN A CONTINUOUS FLOW MODE. ANY POWERED AIR-PURIFYING RESPIRATOR WITH A HIGH-EFFICIENCY PARTICULATE FILTER.

2.5 MG/M3- ANY SUPPLIED-AIR RESPIRATOR WITH A FULL FACEPIECE. ANY SELF-CONTAINED BREATHING APPARATUS WITH A FULL FACEPIECE. ANY AIR-PURIFYING FULL FACEPIECE RESPIRATOR WITH A HIGH-EFFICIENCY PARTICULATE FILTER. ANY POWERED AIR-PURIFYING RESPIRATOR WITH A TIGHT-FITTING FACEPIECE AND A HIGH-EFFICIENCY PARTICULATE FILTER. ANY SUPPLIED-AIR RESPIRATOR WITH A TIGHT-FITTING FACEPIECE OPERATED IN A CONTINUOUS FLOW MODE.

28 MG/M3- ANY SUPPLIED-AIR RESPIRATOR WITH A HALF-MASK AND OPERATED IN A PRESSURE-DEMAND OR OTHER POSITIVE PRESSURE MODE.

ESCAPE- ANY AIR-PURIFYING FULL FACEPIECE RESPIRATOR WITH A HIGH-EFFICIENCY PARTICULATE FILTER. ANY APPROPRIATE ESCAPE-TYPE SELF-CONTAINED BREATHING APPARATUS.

FOR FIREFIGHTING AND OTHER IMMEDIATELY DANGEROUS TO LIFE OR HEALTH CONDITIONS:

SELF-CONTAINED BREATHING APPARATUS WITH FULL FACEPIECE OPERATED IN PRESSURE-DEMAND OR OTHER POSITIVE PRESSURE MODE.

SUPPLIED-AIR RESPIRATOR WITH FULL FACEPIECE AND OPERATED IN PRESSURE-DEMAND OR OTHER POSITIVE PRESSURE MODE IN COMBINATION WITH AN AUXILIARY SELF-CONTAINED BREATHING APPARATUS OPERATED IN PRESSURE-DEMAND OR OTHER POSITIVE PRESSURE MODE.

CLOTHING: EMPLOYEE MUST WEAR APPROPRIATE PROTECTIVE (IMPERVIOUS) CLOTHING AND EQUIPMENT TO PREVENT REPEATED OR PROLONGED SKIN CONTACT WITH THIS SUBSTANCE.

GLOVES: EMPLOYEE MUST WEAR APPROPRIATE PROTECTIVE GLOVES TO PREVENT CONTACT WITH THIS SUBSTANCE.

EYE PROTECTION: EMPLOYEE MUST WEAR SPLASH-PROOF OR DUST-RESISTANT SAFETY GOGGLES TO PREVENT EYE CONTACT WITH THIS SUBSTANCE.

EMERGENCY EYE WASH: WHERE THERE IS ANY POSSIBILITY THAT AN EMPLOYEE'S EYES MAY BE EXPOSED TO THIS SUBSTANCE, THE EMPLOYER SHOULD PROVIDE AN EYE WASH FOUNTAIN WITHIN THE IMMEDIATE WORK AREA FOR EMERGENCY USE.

AUTHORIZED BY- OCCUPATIONAL HEALTH SERVICES, INC.

CREATION DATE: 10/04/89 ***REVISION DATE:*** 07/13/90

MATERIAL SAFETY DATA SHEET

OCCUPATIONAL HEALTH SERVICES, INC.
AGRICULTURE AND PESTICIDE DIVISION
450 SEVENTH AVENUE, SUITE 2407
NEW YORK, NEW YORK 10123
1-800-445-MSDS OR (212) 967-1100

EMERGENCY CONTACT:
JOHN S. BRANSFORD, JR. (615) 292-1180

SUBSTANCE IDENTIFICATION

CAS-NUMBER 104-60-9

SUBSTANCE: PHENYLMERCURIC OLEATE

TRADE NAMES/SYNONYMS: (Z)-(9-OCTADECENOATO-O)PHENYLMERCURY; (OLEATO)PHENYLMERCURY; (OLEOYLOXY)PHENYLMERCURY; PHENYLMERCURY OLEATE; MERCURY, (9-OCTADECENOATO-O)PHENYL-, (Z)-; MERCURY, (OLEATO)PHENYL; MERCURY, (OLEOYLOXY)PHENYL-; C24H38HGO2; PST71769

CHEMICAL FAMILY: SALT

MOLECULAR FORMULA: C24-H38-HG-O2

MOLECULAR WEIGHT: 559.21

CERCLA RATINGS (SCALE 0-3): HEALTH=3 FIRE=1 REACTIVITY=0 PERSISTENCE=3
NFPA RATINGS (SCALE 0-4): HEALTH=3 FIRE=1 REACTIVITY=0

COMPONENTS AND CONTAMINANTS

COMPONENT: PHENYLMERCURIC OLEATE ***PERCENT:*** 100
CAS# 104-60-9

OTHER CONTAMINANTS: NONE

EXPOSURE LIMITS: MERCURY, ALL FORMS EXCEPT ALKYL (AS HG): 0.05 MG/M3 OSHA TWA (VAPOR); 0.1 MG/M3 OSHA CEILING (SKIN) 0.05 MG/M3 ACGIH TWA (VAPOR); 0.10 MG/M3 ACGIH TWA (ARYL & INORGANIC)-(SKIN) 0.05 MG/M3 NIOSH RECOMMENDED 10 HOUR TWA
SUBJECT TO SARA SECTION 313 ANNUAL TOXIC CHEMICAL RELEASE REPORTING
SUBJECT TO CALIFORNIA PROPOSITION 65 CANCER AND/OR REPRODUCTIVE TOXICITY WARNING AND RELEASE REQUIREMENTS- (JULY 1, 1990)

PHYSICAL DATA

DESCRIPTION: WHITE, CRYSTALLINE POWDER. ***MELTING POINT:*** 113 F (45 C)
SPECIFIC GRAVITY: NOT AVAILABLE ***SOLUBILITY IN WATER:*** INSOLUBLE
SOLVENT SOLUBILITY: SOLUBLE IN ORGANIC SOLVENTS AND SOME OILS.

FIRE AND EXPLOSION DATA

FIRE AND EXPLOSION HAZARD: SLIGHT FIRE HAZARD WHEN EXPOSED TO HEAT OR FLAME.

FIREFIGHTING MEDIA: DRY CHEMICAL, CARBON DIOXIDE, HALON, WATER SPRAY OR STANDARD FOAM (1987 EMERGENCY RESPONSE GUIDEBOOK, DOT P 5800.4).
FOR LARGER FIRES, USE WATER SPRAY, FOG OR STANDARD FOAM (1987 EMERGENCY RESPONSE GUIDEBOOK, DOT P 5800.4).

FIREFIGHTING: MOVE CONTAINERS FROM FIRE AREA IF POSSIBLE. FIGHT FIRE FROM MAXIMUM DISTANCE. STAY AWAY FROM STORAGE TANK ENDS. DIKE FIRE CONTROL WATER FOR LATER DISPOSAL. DO NOT SCATTER MATERIAL (1987 EMERGENCY RESPONSE GUIDEBOOK, DOT P 5800.4, GUIDE PAGE 55).
EXTINGUISH USING AGENTS SUITABLE FOR SURROUNDING FIRE. APPLY WATER IN FLOODING QUANTITIES AS A FOG. AVOID CONTAMINATING WATER SOURCES AND SEWERS. AVOID BREATHING HAZARDOUS VAPORS; KEEP UPWIND.

TRANSPORTATION DATA

DEPARTMENT OF TRANSPORTATION HAZARD CLASSIFICATION 49 CFR 172.101: POISON B
DEPARTMENT OF TRANSPORTATION LABELING REQUIREMENTS 49 CFR 172.101 AND SUBPART E: POISON
DEPARTMENT OF TRANSPORTATION PACKAGING REQUIREMENTS: 49 CFR 173.365 EXCEPTIONS: 49 CFR 173.364

TOXICITY

PHENYLMERCURIC OLEATE: TOXICITY DATA: 48,400 UG/KG ORAL-RAT LD50. CARCINOGEN STATUS: NONE. ACUTE TOXICITY LEVEL: HIGHLY TOXIC BY INGESTION. TARGET EFFECTS: SENSITIZER- PULMONARY AND SKIN; NEUROTOXIN, AND NEPHROTOXIN. AT INCREASED RISK FROM EXPOSURE: PERSONS WITH CHRONIC RESPIRATORY DISEASE, NERVOUS SYSTEM DISORDERS AND KIDNEY DISEASE.

HEALTH EFFECTS AND FIRST AID

INHALATION: PHENYLMERCURIC OLEATE: SENSITIZER/NEUROTOXIN/NEPHROTOXIN. 28 MG/M3 IMMEDIATELY DANGEROUS TO LIFE OR HEALTH. **ACUTE EXPOSURE-** INHALATION OF HIGH LEVELS OF MERCURY COMPOUNDS MAY CAUSE ALMOST IMMEDIATE DYSPNEA, COUGH, FEVER, NAUSEA, VOMITING, DIARRHEA, HEADACHE, STOMATITIS, SALIVATION, GINGIVITIS, A METALLIC TASTE, AND CARDIAC ABNORMALITIES. RESPIRATORY IRRITATION MAY OCCUR WITH CHEST PAIN AND TIGHTNESS. SYMPTOMS MAY RESOLVE OR MAY PROGRESS TO NECROTIZING BRONCHIOLITIS, PNEUMONITIS, PULMONARY EDEMA, PNEUMOTHORAX AND INTERSTITIAL FIBROSIS. ACIDOSIS, RENAL DAMAGE AND DEATH MAY OCCUR. ALLERGIC REACTIONS THAT MAY OCCUR IN PREVIOUSLY EXPOSED PERSONS INCLUDE DERMATITIS, ENCEPHALITIS, AND DEATH. **CHRONIC EXPOSURE-** REPEATED INHALATION OF MERCURY COMPOUNDS MAY CAUSE MERCURIALISM, WHICH IS CHARACTERIZED BY FINE TREMORS AND ERETHISM. TREMORS MAY AFFECT THE HANDS FIRST, BUT MAY ALSO BECOME EVIDENT IN THE FACE, ARMS, AND LEGS. ERETHISM MAY BE MANIFESTED BY ABNORMAL SHYNESS, BLUSHING, SELF-CONSCIOUSNESS, DEPRESSION OR DESPONDENCY, RESENTMENT OF CRITICISM, IRRITABILITY OR EXCITABILITY, HEADACHE, FATIGUE, AND INSOMNIA. IN SEVERE CASES, HALLUCINATIONS, LOSS OF MEMORY AND MENTAL DETERIORATION MAY OCCUR. CONCENTRATIONS AS LOW AS 0.03 MG/M3 HAVE INDUCED PSYCHIATRIC SYMPTOMS IN HUMANS. RENAL INVOLVEMENT MAY BE INDICATED BY PROTEINURIA, ALBUMINURIA, ENZYMURIA, AND ANURIA. OTHER EFFECTS MAY INCLUDE SALIVATION, GINGIVITIS, STOMATITIS, LOOSENING OF THE TEETH, BLUE LINES ON THE GUMS, DIARRHEA, WEIGHT LOSS, ANOREXIA, SPEECH AND SENSORY DISORDERS, UNSTEADY GAIT, CHRONIC PNEUMONITIS AND MILD ANEMIA. REPEATED EXPOSURE TO MERCURY AND ITS COMPOUNDS MAY RESULT IN SENSITIZATION. MERCURY IS EXCRETED IN BREAST MILK.

FIRST AID- REMOVE FROM EXPOSURE AREA TO FRESH AIR IMMEDIATELY. IF BREATHING HAS STOPPED, PERFORM ARTIFICIAL RESPIRATION. KEEP PERSON WARM AND AT REST. TREAT SYMPTOMATICALLY AND SUPPORTIVELY. GET MEDICAL ATTENTION IMMEDIATELY.

SKIN CONTACT: PHENYLMERCURIC OLEATE: SENSITIZER/NEUROTOXIN/NEPHROTOXIN. **ACUTE EXPOSURE-** CONTACT WITH SOME PHENYLMERCURIC SALTS MAY RESULT IN IRRITATION WITH POSSIBLE SKIN BURNS. **CHRONIC EXPOSURE-** REPEATED OR PROLONGED EXPOSURE TO MERCURIC SALTS MAY RESULT IN DERMATITIS, SENSITIZATION, AND MERCURIALISM WITH SYMPTOMS SIMILAR TO THOSE IN CHRONIC INHALATION.

FIRST AID- REMOVE CONTAMINATED CLOTHING AND SHOES IMMEDIATELY. WASH AFFECTED AREA WITH SOAP OR MILD DETERGENT AND LARGE AMOUNTS OF WATER UNTIL NO EVIDENCE OF CHEMICAL REMAINS (APPROXIMATELY 15-20 MINUTES). GET MEDICAL ATTENTION IMMEDIATELY.

EYE CONTACT: PHENYLMERCURIC OLEATE: **ACUTE EXPOSURE-** MERCURY COMPOUNDS MAY CAUSE IRRITATION. **CHRONIC EXPOSURE-** MERCURY EXPOSURE FROM INHALATION, INGESTION, OR SKIN CONTACT MAY BE INDICATED BY MERCURIALENTIS, DISCOLORATION OF THE CRYSTALLINE LENS, ON SLIT LAMP EXAMINATION OF THE EYES.

FIRST AID- WASH EYES IMMEDIATELY WITH LARGE AMOUNTS OF WATER OR NORMAL SALINE, OCCASIONALLY LIFTING UPPER AND LOWER LIDS, UNTIL NO EVIDENCE OF CHEMICAL REMAINS (APPROXIMATELY 15-20 MINUTES). GET MEDICAL ATTENTION IMMEDIATELY.

INGESTION: PHENYLMERCURIC OLEATE: NEUROTOXIN/NEPHROTOXIN/HIGHLY TOXIC. **ACUTE EXPOSURE-** INGESTION OF MERCURY COMPOUNDS MAY CAUSE A BURNING OF THE MOUTH AND THROAT, THIRST, NAUSEA AND VOMITING. MAY ALSO CAUSE SIGNS AND SYMPTOMS AS DETAILED IN CHRONIC INHALATION. THE MEDIAN LETHAL DOSE IN RATS WAS 48,400 UG/KG. **CHRONIC EXPOSURE-** REPEATED INGESTION MAY RESULT IN TOXIC EFFECTS AS DETAILED IN CHRONIC INHALATION.

FIRST AID- REMOVE BY GASTRIC LAVAGE OR EMESIS. MAINTAIN BLOOD PRESSURE AND AIRWAY. GIVE OXYGEN IF RESPIRATION IS DEPRESSED. DO NOT PERFORM GASTRIC LAVAGE OR EMESIS IF VICTIM IS UNCONSCIOUS. GET MEDICAL ATTENTION IMMEDIATELY (DREISBACH, HANDBOOK OF POISONING, 11TH ED.). ADMINISTRATION OF GASTRIC LAVAGE OR OXYGEN SHOULD BE PERFORMED BY QUALIFIED MEDICAL PERSONNEL.

ANTIDOTE: THE FOLLOWING ANTIDOTE HAS BEEN RECOMMENDED. HOWEVER, THE DECISION AS TO WHETHER THE SEVERITY OF POISONING REQUIRES ADMINISTRATION OF ANY ANTIDOTE AND ACTUAL DOSE REQUIRED SHOULD BE MADE BY QUALIFIED MEDICAL PERSONNEL.
MERCURY POISONING: GIVE DIMERCAPROL, 3 MG/KG (OR 0.3 ML/10 KG) EVERY 4 HOURS FOR THE FIRST 2 DAYS AND THEN 2 MG/KG EVERY 12 HOURS FOR A TOTAL OF 10 DAYS IF NECESSARY. DIMERCAPROL IS AVAILABLE AS A 10% SOLUTION IN OIL FOR INTRAMUSCULAR ADMINISTRATION. HEMODIALYSIS WILL SPEED THE REMOVAL OF THE MERCURY-DIMERCAPROL COMPLEX. PENICILLAMINE IS ALSO EFFECTIVE. GIVE UP TO 100 MG/KG/DAY (MAXIMUM 1 GR/DAY) DIVIDED INTO 4 DOSES FOR NO LONGER THAN 1 WEEK. IF A LONGER ADMINISTRATION PERIOD IS WARRANTED, DOSAGE SHOULD NOT EXCEED 40 MG/KG/DAY. GIVE THE DRUG ORALLY HALF AN HOUR BEFORE MEALS. A CHELATING AGENT SHOULD BE BE CONTINUED UNTIL THE URINE-MERCURY LEVEL FALLS BELOW 50 UG/24 HOURS (DREISBACH, HANDBOOK OF POISONING, 12TH ED.). ANTIDOTE SHOULD BE ADMINISTERED BY QUALIFIED MEDICAL PERSONNEL.

REACTIVITY

REACTIVITY: STABLE UNDER NORMAL TEMPERATURES AND PRESSURES.

INCOMPATIBILITIES: PHENYLMERCURIC OLEATE: NO SPECIFIC DATA AVAILABLE. SEE MERCURY SALTS.
MERCURY SALTS: ACETYLENE: FORMS SHOCK-SENSITIVE ACETYLIDES.
BUTYNEDIOL + ACIDS: VIOLENT DECOMPOSITION. NITROMETHANE: FORMS EXPLOSIVE COMPOUND.

DECOMPOSITION: THERMAL DECOMPOSITION MAY RELEASE TOXIC AND/OR HAZARDOUS GASES.

POLYMERIZATION: HAZARDOUS POLYMERIZATION HAS NOT BEEN REPORTED TO OCCUR UNDER NORMAL TEMPERATURES AND PRESSURES.

STORAGE AND DISPOSAL

OBSERVE ALL FEDERAL, STATE AND LOCAL REGULATIONS WHEN STORING OR DISPOSING OF THIS SUBSTANCE. FOR ASSISTANCE, CONTACT THE DISTRICT DIRECTOR OF THE ENVIRONMENTAL PROTECTION AGENCY.

STORAGE

STORE IN ACCORDANCE WITH 40 CFR 165 RECOMMENDED PROCEDURES FOR THE DISPOSAL AND STORAGE OF PESTICIDES AND PESTICIDE CONTAINERS.
STORE AWAY FROM INCOMPATIBLE SUBSTANCES.

DISPOSAL

DISPOSAL MUST BE IN ACCORDANCE WITH 40 CFR 165 RECOMMENDED PROCEDURES FOR THE DISPOSAL AND STORAGE OF PESTICIDES AND PESTICIDE CONTAINERS.
MERCURY - REGULATORY LEVEL: 0.2 MG/L MATERIALS WHICH CONTAIN THE ABOVE SUBSTANCE AT OR ABOVE THE REGULATORY LEVEL MEET THE EPA CHARACTERISTIC OF TOXICITY, AND MUST BE DISPOSED OF IN ACCORDANCE WITH 40 CFR PART 262. EPA HAZARDOUS WASTE NUMBER D009.

CONDITIONS TO AVOID

MAY BURN BUT DOES NOT IGNITE READILY. CONTAINERS MAY EXPLODE IN HEAT OF FIRE.

SPILL AND LEAK PROCEDURES

WATER SPILL: THE CALIFORNIA SAFE DRINKING WATER AND TOXIC ENFORCEMENT ACT OF 1986 (PROPOSITION 65) PROHIBITS CONTAMINATING ANY KNOWN SOURCE OF DRINKING WATER WITH SUBSTANCES KNOWN TO CAUSE CANCER AND/OR REPRODUCTIVE TOXICITY.

OCCUPATIONAL SPILL: DO NOT TOUCH SPILLED MATERIAL. STOP LEAK IF YOU CAN DO IT WITHOUT RISK. USE WATER SPRAY TO REDUCE VAPORS. FOR SMALL SPILLS, TAKE UP WITH SAND OR OTHER ABSORBENT MATERIAL AND PLACE INTO CONTAINERS FOR LATER DISPOSAL. FOR SMALL DRY SPILLS, WITH A CLEAN SHOVEL PLACE MATERIAL INTO CLEAN, DRY CONTAINERS AND COVER. MOVE CONTAINERS FROM SPILL AREA. FOR LARGER SPILLS, DIKE FAR AHEAD OF SPILL FOR LATER DISPOSAL. KEEP UNNECESSARY PEOPLE AWAY. ISOLATE HAZARD AREA AND DENY ENTRY. VENTILATE CLOSED SPACES BEFORE ENTERING.

PROTECTIVE EQUIPMENT

VENTILATION: PROVIDE LOCAL EXHAUST OR PROCESS ENCLOSURE VENTILATION TO MEET PUBLISHED EXPOSURE LIMITS.

RESPIRATOR: THE FOLLOWING RESPIRATORS AND MAXIMUM USE CONCENTRATIONS ARE RECOMMENDATIONS BY THE U.S. DEPARTMENT OF HEALTH AND HUMAN SERVICES, NIOSH POCKET GUIDE TO CHEMICAL HAZARDS; NIOSH CRITERIA DOCUMENTS OR BY THE U.S. DEPARTMENT OF LABOR, 29 CFR 1910 SUBPART Z. THE SPECIFIC RESPIRATOR SELECTED MUST BE BASED ON CONTAMINATION LEVELS FOUND IN THE WORK PLACE, MUST NOT EXCEED THE WORKING LIMITS OF THE RESPIRATOR AND BE JOINTLY APPROVED BY THE NATIONAL INSTITUTE FOR OCCUPATIONAL SAFETY AND HEALTH AND THE MINE SAFETY AND HEALTH ADMINISTRATION (NIOSH-MSHA). MERCURY, ALL FORMS EXCEPT ALKYL (AS HG):
0.5 MG/M3- ANY AIR-PURIFYING RESPIRATOR WITH A HIGH-EFFICIENCY PARTICULATE FILTER. ANY SUPPLIED-AIR RESPIRATOR. ANY SELF-CONTAINED BREATHING APPARATUS.
1.25 MG/M3- ANY SUPPLIED-AIR RESPIRATOR OPERATED IN A CONTINUOUS FLOW MODE. ANY POWERED AIR-PURIFYING RESPIRATOR WITH A HIGH-EFFICIENCY PARTICULATE FILTER.
2.5 MG/M3- ANY SUPPLIED-AIR RESPIRATOR WITH A FULL FACEPIECE. ANY SELF-CONTAINED BREATHING APPARATUS WITH A FULL FACEPIECE. ANY AIR-PURIFYING FULL FACEPIECE RESPIRATOR WITH A HIGH-EFFICIENCY PARTICULATE FILTER. ANY POWERED AIR-PURIFYING RESPIRATOR WITH A TIGHT-FITTING FACEPIECE AND A HIGH-EFFICIENCY PARTICULATE FILTER. ANY SUPPLIED-AIR RESPIRATOR WITH A TIGHT-FITTING FACEPIECE OPERATED IN A CONTINUOUS FLOW MODE.
28 MG/M3- ANY SUPPLIED-AIR RESPIRATOR WITH A HALF-MASK AND OPERATED IN A PRESSURE-DEMAND OR OTHER POSITIVE PRESSURE MODE.
ESCAPE- ANY AIR-PURIFYING FULL FACEPIECE RESPIRATOR WITH A HIGH-EFFICIENCY PARTICULATE FILTER. ANY APPROPRIATE ESCAPE-TYPE SELF-CONTAINED BREATHING APPARATUS.
FOR FIREFIGHTING AND OTHER IMMEDIATELY DANGEROUS TO LIFE OR HEALTH CONDITIONS:
SELF-CONTAINED BREATHING APPARATUS WITH FULL FACEPIECE OPERATED IN PRESSURE-DEMAND OR OTHER POSITIVE PRESSURE MODE.
SUPPLIED-AIR RESPIRATOR WITH FULL FACEPIECE AND OPERATED IN PRESSURE-DEMAND OR OTHER POSITIVE PRESSURE MODE IN COMBINATION WITH AN AUXILIARY SELF-CONTAINED BREATHING APPARATUS OPERATED IN PRESSURE-DEMAND OR OTHER POSITIVE PRESSURE MODE.

CLOTHING: EMPLOYEE MUST WEAR APPROPRIATE PROTECTIVE (IMPERVIOUS) CLOTHING AND EQUIPMENT TO PREVENT REPEATED OR PROLONGED SKIN CONTACT WITH THIS SUBSTANCE.

GLOVES: EMPLOYEE MUST WEAR APPROPRIATE PROTECTIVE GLOVES TO PREVENT CONTACT WITH THIS SUBSTANCE.

EYE PROTECTION: EMPLOYEE MUST WEAR SPLASH-PROOF OR DUST-RESISTANT SAFETY GOGGLES TO PREVENT EYE CONTACT WITH THIS SUBSTANCE.
EMERGENCY EYE WASH: WHERE THERE IS ANY POSSIBILITY THAT AN EMPLOYEE'S EYES MAY BE EXPOSED TO THIS SUBSTANCE, THE EMPLOYER SHOULD PROVIDE AN EYE WASH FOUNTAIN WITHIN THE IMMEDIATE WORK AREA FOR EMERGENCY USE.

AUTHORIZED BY- OCCUPATIONAL HEALTH SERVICES, INC.
CREATION DATE: 10/04/89 ***REVISION DATE:*** 07/13/90

MATERIAL SAFETY DATA SHEET

OCCUPATIONAL HEALTH SERVICES, INC.
AGRICULTURE AND PESTICIDE DIVISION
450 SEVENTH AVENUE, SUITE 2407
NEW YORK, NEW YORK 10123
1-800-445-MSDS OR (212) 967-1100

EMERGENCY CONTACT:
JOHN S. BRANSFORD, JR. (615) 292-1180

SUBSTANCE IDENTIFICATION

CAS-NUMBER 5281-13-0
SUBSTANCE: PIPROTAL
TRADE NAMES/SYNONYMS: 5-(BIS(2-(2-BUTOXYETHOXY)ETHOXY)METHYL)-1,3-BENZODIOXOLE; PIPERONAL, BIS(2-(2-BUTOXYETHOXY)ETHYL)ACETAL; 1,3-BENZODIOXOLE, 5-(BIS(2-(2-BUTOXYETHOXY)ETHOXY)METHYL)-; 1-BIS(2-(2-BUTOXYETHOXY)ETHOXY)METHYL-3,4-METHYLENEDIOXYBENZENE; PIPERONAL BIS(2-(2-BUTOXYETHOXY)ETHYL)ACETAL; TROPITAL; ENT 28344; C24H4008; PST71828
CHEMICAL FAMILY: BENZOFURAN DERIVATIVE
MOLECULAR FORMULA: C24-H40-O8
MOLECULAR WEIGHT: 456.64
CERCLA RATINGS (SCALE 0-3): HEALTH=2 FIRE=U REACTIVITY=0 PERSISTENCE=3
NFPA RATINGS (SCALE 0-4): HEALTH=2 FIRE=U REACTIVITY=0

COMPONENTS AND CONTAMINANTS

COMPONENT: PIPROTAL ***PERCENT:*** 100.0
CAS# 5281-13-0
OTHER CONTAMINANTS: NONE
EXPOSURE LIMITS: NO OCCUPATIONAL EXPOSURE LIMITS ESTABLISHED BY OSHA, ACGIH, OR NIOSH.

PHYSICAL DATA

DESCRIPTION: NOT AVAILABLE ***SPECIFIC GRAVITY:*** NOT AVAILABLE
SOLUBILITY IN WATER: NOT AVAILABLE

FIRE AND EXPLOSION DATA

FIRE AND EXPLOSION HAZARD: UNKNOWN FIRE AND EXPLOSION HAZARD.

FIREFIGHTING MEDIA: DRY CHEMICAL, CARBON DIOXIDE, HALON, WATER SPRAY OR STANDARD FOAM (1987 EMERGENCY RESPONSE GUIDEBOOK, DOT P 5800.4).
FOR LARGER FIRES, USE WATER SPRAY, FOG OR STANDARD FOAM (1987 EMERGENCY RESPONSE GUIDEBOOK, DOT P 5800.4).

FIREFIGHTING: MOVE CONTAINERS FROM FIRE AREA IF POSSIBLE (1987 EMERGENCY RESPONSE GUIDEBOOK, DOT P 5800.4, GUIDE PAGE 53).
EXTINGUISH USING AGENT SUITABLE FOR TYPE OF SURROUNDING FIRE. AVOID BREATHING VAPORS AND DUSTS. KEEP UPWIND.

TOXICITY

PIPROTAL: TOXICITY DATA: 2939 MG/KG ORAL-RAT LD50. CARCINOGEN STATUS: NONE. ACUTE TOXICITY LEVEL: MODERATELY TOXIC BY INGESTION. TARGET EFFECTS: NO DATA AVAILABLE. ADDITIONAL DATA: PIPROTAL MAY ENHANCE THE TOXICITY OF PYRETHRUMS AND CARBAMATE INSECTICIDES.

HEALTH EFFECTS AND FIRST AID

INHALATION: PIPROTAL: **ACUTE EXPOSURE**- NO DATA AVAILABLE. **CHRONIC EXPOSURE**- NO DATA AVAILABLE.

FIRST AID- REMOVE FROM EXPOSURE AREA TO FRESH AIR IMMEDIATELY. IF BREATHING HAS STOPPED, PERFORM ARTIFICIAL RESPIRATION. KEEP PERSON WARM AND AT REST. TREAT SYMPTOMATICALLY AND SUPPORTIVELY. GET MEDICAL ATTENTION IMMEDIATELY.

SKIN CONTACT: PIPROTAL: **ACUTE EXPOSURE**- NO DATA AVAILABLE. **CHRONIC EXPOSURE**- NO DATA AVAILABLE.

FIRST AID- REMOVE CONTAMINATED CLOTHING AND SHOES IMMEDIATELY. WASH AFFECTED AREA WITH SOAP OR MILD DETERGENT AND LARGE AMOUNTS OF

WATER UNTIL NO EVIDENCE OF CHEMICAL REMAINS (APPROXIMATELY 15-20 MINUTES). GET MEDICAL ATTENTION IMMEDIATELY.

EYE CONTACT: PIPROTAL: **ACUTE EXPOSURE-** NO DATA AVAILABLE. **CHRONIC EXPOSURE-** NO DATA AVAILABLE.
FIRST AID- WASH EYES IMMEDIATELY WITH LARGE AMOUNTS OF WATER OR NORMAL SALINE, OCCASIONALLY LIFTING UPPER AND LOWER LIDS, UNTIL NO EVIDENCE OF CHEMICAL REMAINS (APPROXIMATELY 15-20 MINUTES). GET MEDICAL ATTENTION IMMEDIATELY.

INGESTION: PIPROTAL: **ACUTE EXPOSURE-** A LETHAL DOSE IN RATS WAS 2939 MG/KG; NO SYMPTOMS WERE REPORTED. **CHRONIC EXPOSURE-** NO DATA AVAILABLE.
FIRST AID- TREAT SYMPTOMATICALLY AND SUPPORTIVELY. GET MEDICAL ATTENTION IMMEDIATELY. IF VOMITING OCCURS, KEEP HEAD LOWER THAN HIPS TO PREVENT ASPIRATION.
ANTIDOTE: NO SPECIFIC ANTIDOTE. TREAT SYMPTOMATICALLY AND SUPPORTIVELY.

REACTIVITY

REACTIVITY: STABLE UNDER NORMAL TEMPERATURES AND PRESSURES.
INCOMPATIBILITIES: PIPROTAL: OXIDIZERS (STRONG): FIRE AND EXPLOSION HAZARD.
DECOMPOSITION: THERMAL DECOMPOSITION MAY RELEASE TOXIC AND/OR HAZARDOUS GASES.
POLYMERIZATION: HAZARDOUS POLYMERIZATION HAS NOT BEEN REPORTED TO OCCUR UNDER NORMAL TEMPERATURES AND PRESSURES.

STORAGE AND DISPOSAL

OBSERVE ALL FEDERAL, STATE AND LOCAL REGULATIONS WHEN STORING OR DISPOSING OF THIS SUBSTANCE. FOR ASSISTANCE, CONTACT THE DISTRICT DIRECTOR OF THE ENVIRONMENTAL PROTECTION AGENCY.

STORAGE

STORE IN ACCORDANCE WITH 40 CFR 165 RECOMMENDED PROCEDURES FOR THE DISPOSAL AND STORAGE OF PESTICIDES AND PESTICIDE CONTAINERS.
STORE AWAY FROM INCOMPATIBLE SUBSTANCES.

DISPOSAL

DISPOSAL MUST BE IN ACCORDANCE WITH 40 CFR 165 RECOMMENDED PROCEDURES FOR THE DISPOSAL AND STORAGE OF PESTICIDES AND PESTICIDE CONTAINERS.

CONDITIONS TO AVOID

NONE REPORTED.

SPILL AND LEAK PROCEDURES

OCCUPATIONAL SPILL: DO NOT TOUCH SPILLED MATERIAL. STOP LEAK IF YOU CAN DO IT WITHOUT RISK. FOR SMALL SPILLS, TAKE UP WITH SAND OR OTHER ABSORBENT MATERIAL AND PLACE INTO CONTAINERS FOR LATER DISPOSAL. FOR SMALL DRY SPILLS, WITH A CLEAN SHOVEL PLACE MATERIAL INTO CLEAN, DRY CONTAINER AND COVER. MOVE CONTAINERS FROM SPILL AREA. FOR LARGER SPILLS, DIKE FAR AHEAD OF SPILL FOR LATER DISPOSAL. KEEP UNNECESSARY PEOPLE AWAY. ISOLATE HAZARD AREA AND DENY ENTRY.

PROTECTIVE EQUIPMENT

VENTILATION: PROVIDE LOCAL EXHAUST VENTILATION SYSTEM.
RESPIRATOR: THE FOLLOWING RESPIRATORS ARE RECOMMENDED BASED ON INFORMATION FOUND IN THE PHYSICAL DATA, TOXICITY AND HEALTH EFFECTS SECTIONS. THEY ARE RANKED IN ORDER FROM MINIMUM TO MAXIMUM RESPIRATORY PROTECTION. THE SPECIFIC RESPIRATOR SELECTED MUST BE BASED ON CONTAMINATION LEVELS FOUND IN THE WORK PLACE, MUST NOT EXCEED THE WORKING LIMITS OF THE RESPIRATOR AND BE JOINTLY APPROVED BY THE NATIONAL INSTITUTE FOR OCCUPATIONAL SAFETY AND HEALTH AND THE MINE SAFETY AND HEALTH ADMINISTRATION (NIOSH-MSHA).
TYPE 'C' SUPPLIED-AIR RESPIRATOR WITH A FULL FACEPIECE OPERATED IN PRESSURE-DEMAND OR OTHER POSITIVE PRESSURE MODE OR WITH A FULL FACEPIECE, HELMET OR HOOD OPERATED IN CONTINOUS-FLOW MODE.
SELF-CONTAINED BREATHING APPARATUS WITH A FULL FACEPIECE OPERATED IN PRESSURE-DEMAND OR OTHER POSITIVE PRESSURE MODE.
FOR FIREFIGHTING AND OTHER IMMEDIATELY DANGEROUS TO LIFE OR HEALTH CONDITIONS:
SELF-CONTAINED BREATHING APPARATUS WITH FULL FACEPIECE OPERATED IN PRESSURE-DEMAND OR OTHER POSITIVE PRESSURE MODE.
SUPPLIED-AIR RESPIRATOR WITH FULL FACEPIECE AND OPERATED IN PRESSURE-DEMAND OR OTHER POSITIVE PRESSURE MODE IN COMBINATION WITH AN AUXILIARY SELF-CONTAINED BREATHING APPARATUS OPERATED IN PRESSURE-DEMAND OR OTHER POSITIVE PRESSURE MODE.
CLOTHING: EMPLOYEE MUST WEAR APPROPRIATE PROTECTIVE (IMPERVIOUS) CLOTHING AND EQUIPMENT TO PREVENT REPEATED OR PROLONGED SKIN CONTACT WITH THIS SUBSTANCE.
GLOVES: EMPLOYEE MUST WEAR APPROPRIATE PROTECTIVE GLOVES TO PREVENT CONTACT WITH THIS SUBSTANCE.
EYE PROTECTION: EMPLOYEE MUST WEAR SPLASH-PROOF OR DUST-RESISTANT SAFETY GOGGLES TO PREVENT EYE CONTACT WITH THIS SUBSTANCE.
EMERGENCY EYE WASH: WHERE THERE IS ANY POSSIBILITY THAT AN EMPLOYEE'S EYES MAY BE EXPOSED TO THIS SUBSTANCE, THE EMPLOYER SHOULD PROVIDE AN EYE WASH FOUNTAIN WITHIN THE IMMEDIATE WORK AREA FOR EMERGENCY USE.

AUTHORIZED BY- OCCUPATIONAL HEALTH SERVICES, INC.
CREATION DATE: 10/04/89 ***REVISION DATE:*** 05/14/90

MATERIAL SAFETY DATA SHEET

OCCUPATIONAL HEALTH SERVICES, INC.
AGRICULTURE AND PESTICIDE DIVISION
450 SEVENTH AVENUE, SUITE 2407
NEW YORK, NEW YORK 10123
1-800-445-MSDS OR (212) 967-1100

EMERGENCY CONTACT:
JOHN S. BRANSFORD, JR. (615) 292-1180

SUBSTANCE IDENTIFICATION

CAS-NUMBER 53516-76-0
SUBSTANCE: **ALKYLDIMETHYLBENZYLAMMONIUM CHLORIDE (60%C14, 30% C16, 5% C18, 5% C12)**
TRADE NAMES/SYNONYMS: BTC; BENZALKONIUM CHLORIDE; QUATERNARY AMMONIUM COMPOUNDS, BENZYL-C12-C18-ALKYLDIMETHYL, CHLORIDES; PST71834
CHEMICAL FAMILY: QUATERNARY AMMONIUM COMPOUND
CERCLA RATINGS (SCALE 0-3): HEALTH=3 FIRE=1 REACTIVITY=0 PERSISTENCE=2
NFPA RATINGS (SCALE 0-4): HEALTH=U FIRE=1 REACTIVITY=0

COMPONENTS AND CONTAMINANTS

COMPONENT: ALKYLDIMETHYLBENZYLAMMONIUM CHLORIDE ***PERCENT:*** 100.0
(60% C14,30% C16, 5% C18, 5% C12)
CAS# 53516-76-0
OTHER CONTAMINANTS: 100.0
EXPOSURE LIMITS: NO OCCUPATIONAL EXPOSURE LIMITS ESTABLISHED BY OSHA, ACGIH, OR NIOSH.

PHYSICAL DATA

DESCRIPTION: WHITE OR YELLOWISH-WHITE, AMORPHOUS POWDER OR GELATINOUS PIECES WITH AN AROMATIC ODOR AND VERY BITTER TASTE.
MELTING POINT: NOT AVAILABLE
SPECIFIC GRAVITY: NOT AVAILABLE ***SOLUBILITY IN WATER:*** SOLUBLE
SOLVENT SOLUBILITY: SOLUBLE IN ALCOHOL AND ACETONE; SLIGHTLY SOLUBLE IN BENZENE; VERY SLIGHTLY SOLUBLE IN ETHER.

FIRE AND EXPLOSION DATA

FIRE AND EXPLOSION HAZARD: SLIGHT FIRE HAZARD WHEN EXPOSED TO HEAT OR FLAME.
DUST-AIR MIXTURES MAY IGNITE OR EXPLODE.
FIREFIGHTING MEDIA: DRY CHEMICAL, CARBON DIOXIDE, HALON, WATER SPRAY OR STANDARD FOAM (1987 EMERGENCY RESPONSE GUIDEBOOK, DOT P 5800.4).
FOR LARGER FIRES, USE WATER SPRAY, FOG OR STANDARD FOAM (1987 EMERGENCY RESPONSE GUIDEBOOK, DOT P 5800.4).
FIREFIGHTING: MOVE CONTAINER FROM FIRE AREA IF POSSIBLE. DO NOT SCATTER SPILLED MATERIAL WITH HIGH PRESSURE WATER STREAMS. DIKE FIRE CONTROL WATER FOR LATER DISPOSAL (1987 EMERGENCY RESPONSE GUIDEBOOK, DOT P 5800.4, GUIDE PAGE 31).
USE AGENTS SUITABLE FOR TYPE OF SURROUNDING FIRE. AVOID BREATHING HAZARDOUS VAPORS, KEEP UPWIND.

TOXICITY

ALKYLDIMETHYLBENZYLAMMONIUM CHLORIDE: IRRITATION DATA: 150 UG/3 DAYS INTERMITTENT SKIN-HUMAN MILD; 50 UG EYE-HUMAN SEVERE; 2 MG/24 HOURS EYE-MONKEY SEVERE; 50 MG/24 HOURS SKIN-RABBIT MODERATE; 100 UG EYE-RABBIT; 1 MG/24 HOURS EYE-RABBIT SEVERE; 10 MG EYE-RABBIT MILD. TOXICITY DATA: 1560 MG/KG SKIN-RAT LD50; 266 MG/KG ORAL-WOMAN TDLO; 240 MG/KG ORAL-RAT LD50; 175 MG/KG ORAL-MOUSE LD50; 200 MG/KG ORAL-GUINEA PIG LD50; 400 MG/KG SUBCUTANEOUS-RAT LD50; 64 MG/KG SUBCUTANEOUS-MOUSE

LD50; 13900 UG/KG INTRAVENOUS-RAT LD50; 10 MG/KG INTRAVENOUS-MOUSE LD50; 14500 UG/KG INTRAPERITONEAL-RAT LD50; 10 MG/KG INTRAPERITONEAL-MOUSE LDLO; 10 MG/KG INTRAPERITONEAL-GUINEA PIG LDLO; 7 MG/KG INTRAPERITONEAL-DOG LDLO; 12 MG/KG PARENTERAL-WOMAN LDLO; MUTAGENIC DATA (RTECS); REPRODUCTIVE EFFECTS DATA (RTECS). CARCINOGEN STATUS: NONE. LOCAL EFFECTS: CORROSIVE- INHALATION, SKIN, EYES, INGESTION. ACUTE TOXICITY: TOXIC BY INGESTION; MODERATELY TOXIC BY DERMAL ABSORPTION. TARGET EFFECTS: SENSITIZER- SKIN, EYE.

HEALTH EFFECTS AND FIRST AID

INHALATION: ALKYLDIMETHYLBENZYLAMMONIUM CHLORIDE: CORROSIVE. **ACUTE EXPOSURE-** CONCENTRATIONS AS LOW AS 0.1-0.5% MAY CAUSE IRRITATION OF THE MUCOUS MEMBRANES. STRONG AQUEOUS SOLUTIONS, 10-20%, HAVE PRODUCED SUPERFICIAL NECROSIS OF THE MUCOUS MEMBRANES. **CHRONIC EXPOSURE-** REPEATED OR PROLONGED EXPOSURE MAY CAUSE EFFECTS AS THOSE LISTED IN ACUTE EXPOSURE. ASTHMA DUE TO OCCUPATIONAL EXPOSURE HAS BEEN REPORTED.

FIRST AID- REMOVE FROM EXPOSURE AREA TO FRESH AIR IMMEDIATELY. IF BREATHING HAS STOPPED, GIVE ARTIFICIAL RESPIRATION. MAINTAIN AIRWAY AND BLOOD PRESSURE AND ADMINISTER OXYGEN IF AVAILABLE. KEEP AFFECTED PERSON WARM AND AT REST. TREAT SYMPTOMATICALLY AND SUPPORTIVELY. ADMINISTRATION OF OXYGEN SHOULD BE PERFORMED BY QUALIFIED PERSONNEL. GET MEDICAL ATTENTION IMMEDIATELY.

SKIN CONTACT: ALKYLDIMETHYLBENZYLAMMONIUM CHLORIDE: CORROSIVE/SENSITIZER. **ACUTE EXPOSURE-** CONCENTRATIONS EXCEEDING 1% CAN IRRITATE THE SKIN. CONCENTRATED AQUEOUS SOLUTIONS OF 10% ARE PRIMARY SKIN IRRITANTS. DAMAGE TO THE EPIDERMIS MAY OCCUR. SEVERE SKIN DAMAGE HAS BEEN REPORTED IN LABORATORY ANIMALS. **CHRONIC EXPOSURE-** ALLERGIC CONTACT DERMATITIS HAS OCCURRED IN INDIVIDUALS REPEATEDLY EXPOSED TO THIS MATERIAL.

FIRST AID- REMOVE CONTAMINATED CLOTHING AND SHOES IMMEDIATELY. WASH AFFECTED AREA WITH SOAP OR MILD DETERGENT AND LARGE AMOUNTS OF WATER UNTIL NO EVIDENCE OF CHEMICAL REMAINS (AT LEAST 15-20 MINUTES). IN CASE OF CHEMICAL BURNS, COVER AREA WITH STERILE, DRY DRESSING. BANDAGE SECURELY, BUT NOT TOO TIGHTLY. GET MEDICAL ATTENTION IMMEDIATELY.

EYE CONTACT: ALKYLDIMETHYLBENZYLAMMONIUM CHLORIDE: CORROSIVE/SENSITIZER. **ACUTE EXPOSURE-** A DROP OF 0.1% CONCENTRATION IN HUMAN EYES CAUSED MILD DISCOMFORT WHICH PERSISTED FOR 2 OR 3 HOURS AS A SLIGHT, SCRATCHY, FOREIGN-BODY TYPE SENSATION. HIGHER CONCENTRATIONS IN HUMAN EYES, SUCH AS 10%, CAN CAUSE VERY SERIOUS DAMAGE TO THE WHOLE CORNEA. IRRIGATION OF THE SURFACE OF RABBIT EYES WITH A 0.1% SOLUTION FOR 15 MINUTES PRODUCED SEVERE INJURY OF THE ENDOTHELIUM AND MUCH SWELLING. THE CORNEAS OF RABBIT EYES BECAME BLUE AND SWOLLEN, THEN COMPLETELY OPAQUE AND VASCULARIZED WITH THE FORMATION OF SCAR TISSUE AT THE 10% CONCENTRATION. **CHRONIC EXPOSURE-** ALLERGIC CONJUNCTIVITIS HAS DEVELOPED IN SOME INDIVIDUALS AFTER USING OPHTHALMIC SOLUTIONS CONTAINING THIS MATERIAL. A 0.1% CONCENTRATION APPLIED TO RABBIT EYES AS DROPS 2 OR 3 TIMES A DAY FOR 1 TO 3 MONTHS HAS CAUSED THICKENING AND ROUGHENING OF THE CORNEAL EPITHELIUM, WITH SUPERFICIAL VASCULARIZATION, BUT NO DEEPER DAMAGE.

FIRST AID- WASH EYES IMMEDIATELY WITH LARGE AMOUNTS OF WATER, OCCASIONALLY LIFTING UPPER AND LOWER LIDS, UNTIL NO EVIDENCE OF CHEMICAL REMAINS (AT LEAST 15-20 MINUTES). CONTINUE IRRIGATING WITH NORMAL SALINE UNTIL THE PH HAS RETURNED TO NORMAL (30-60 MINUTES). COVER WITH STERILE BANDAGES. GET MEDICAL ATTENTION IMMEDIATELY.

INGESTION: ALKYLDIMETHYLBENZYLAMMONIUM CHLORIDE: CORROSIVE/TOXIC. **ACUTE EXPOSURE-** CONCENTRATED SOLUTIONS MAY CAUSE AN IMMEDIATE BURNING PAIN IN THE MOUTH, THROAT, AND ABDOMEN WITH PROFUSE SALIVATION. EXPOSED AREAS OF MUCOUS MEMBRANES MAY ULCERATE. VOMITING MAY OCCUR, POSSIBLY WITH BLOOD. SIGNS OF CIRCULATORY SHOCK INCLUDING HYPOTENSION, LABORED BREATHING, AND CYANOSIS MAY OCCUR. RAPIDLY DEVELOPING APPREHENSION, RESTLESSNESS, CONFUSION, AND WEAKNESS MAY RESULT. WEAK CONVULSIVE MOVEMENTS MAY PRECEDE CENTRAL NERVOUS SYSTEM DEPRESSION. EROSION, ULCERATION AND PETECHIAL HEMORRHAGES MAY OCCUR THROUGHOUT THE SMALL INTESTINES. GLOTTIC, BRAIN, AND PULMONARY EDEMA HAVE BEEN REPORTED. DEATH MAY OCCUR WITHIN 1-2 HOURS AFTER INGESTION DUE TO ASPHYXIATION BECAUSE OF PARALYSIS OF THE MUSCLES OF RESPIRATION OR TO CARDIOVASCULAR COLLAPSE. EVEN IN PROMPT DEATH, CLOUDY SWELLING, PATCHY NECROSIS AND FATTY INFILTRATION OCCUR IN SUCH VISCERAL ORGANS AS HEART, LIVER, AND KIDNEYS. RENAL FAILURE MAY DEVELOP IN INDIVIDUALS THAT SURVIVED A PERIOD OF SEVERE HYPOTENSION. **CHRONIC EXPOSURE-** RATS REPEATEDLY FED THIS MATERIAL FOR SEVERAL WEEKS DIED OF INANITION ASSOCIATED WITH CHRONIC DIARRHEA; THE ONLY LESION FOUND WAS FOCAL HEMORRHAGIC NECROSIS OF THE GASTRIC MUCOSA. REPEATED ADMINISTRATION OF A 0.5% CONCENTRATION IN THE DIET WAS LETHAL TO RATS. REPEATED DOSAGES OF 25 MG/KG IN WATER WAS LETHAL TO ALL THREE DOGS TESTED; EFFECTS OF CONDITIONED SALIVATION, VOMITING, ENTERITIS, PULMONARY HEMORRHAGE, AND INFLAMMATION AND SLOUGHING OF THE MUCOSA WERE REPORTED.

FIRST AID- GIVE MILK OR ACTIVATED CHARCOAL AND REMOVE BY CATHARSIS WITH FLEET'S PHOSPHO-SODA, 15-60 ML DILUTED 1:4 WITH WATER. LAVAGE AND EMESIS ARE CONTRAINDICATED IN THE PRESENCE OF ESOPHAGEAL INJURY. GASTRIC LAVAGE SHOULD BE PERFORMED BY QUALIFIED MEDICAL PERSONNEL. GET MEDICAL ATTENTION IMMEDIATELY (DREISBACH, HANDBOOK OF POISONING, 12TH ED.). MAINTAIN AIRWAY, BLOOD PRESSURE AND RESPIRATION.

ANTIDOTE: NO SPECIFIC ANTIDOTE. TREAT SYMPTOMATICALLY AND SUPPORTIVELY.

REACTIVITY

REACTIVITY: STABLE UNDER NORMAL TEMPERATURES AND PRESSURES.

INCOMPATIBILITIES: ALKYLDIMETHYLBENZYLAMMONIUM CHLORIDE: OXIDIZERS (STRONG): FIRE AND EXPLOSION HAZARD.

DECOMPOSITION: THERMAL DECOMPOSITION PRODUCTS MAY INCLUDE TOXIC OXIDES OF NITROGEN AND CARBON AND TOXIC AND CORROSIVE FUMES OF CHLORIDES.

POLYMERIZATION: HAZARDOUS POLYMERIZATION HAS NOT BEEN REPORTED TO OCCUR UNDER NORMAL TEMPERATURES AND PRESSURES.

STORAGE AND DISPOSAL

OBSERVE ALL FEDERAL, STATE AND LOCAL REGULATIONS WHEN STORING OR DISPOSING OF THIS SUBSTANCE. FOR ASSISTANCE, CONTACT THE DISTRICT DIRECTOR OF THE ENVIRONMENTAL PROTECTION AGENCY.

STORAGE

STORE AWAY FROM INCOMPATIBLE SUBSTANCES.

CONDITIONS TO AVOID

MAY BURN BUT DOES NOT IGNITE READILY. AVOID CONTACT WITH STRONG OXIDIZERS, EXCESSIVE HEAT, SPARKS, OR OPEN FLAME.

SPILL AND LEAK PROCEDURES

OCCUPATIONAL SPILL: SWEEP UP AND PLACE IN SUITABLE CLEAN, DRY CONTAINERS FOR RECLAMATION OR LATER DISPOSAL. DO NOT FLUSH SPILLED MATERIAL INTO SEWER. KEEP UNNECESSARY PEOPLE AWAY.

PROTECTIVE EQUIPMENT

VENTILATION: PROVIDE LOCAL EXHAUST OR GENERAL DILUTION VENTILATION SYSTEM.

RESPIRATOR: THE FOLLOWING RESPIRATORS ARE RECOMMENDED BASED ON INFORMATION FOUND IN THE PHYSICAL DATA, TOXICITY AND HEALTH EFFECTS SECTIONS. THEY ARE RANKED IN ORDER FROM MINIMUM TO MAXIMUM RESPIRATORY PROTECTION. THE SPECIFIC RESPIRATOR SELECTED MUST BE BASED ON CONTAMINATION LEVELS FOUND IN THE WORK PLACE, MUST NOT EXCEED THE WORKING LIMITS OF THE RESPIRATOR AND BE JOINTLY APPROVED BY THE NATIONAL INSTITUTE FOR OCCUPATIONAL SAFETY AND HEALTH AND THE MINE SAFETY AND HEALTH ADMINISTRATION (NIOSH-MSHA).

DUST AND MIST RESPIRATOR WITH A FULL FACEPIECE.

AIR-PURIFYING FULL FACEPIECE RESPIRATOR WITH A HIGH-EFFICIENCY PARTICULATE FILTER.

POWERED AIR-PURIFYING RESPIRATOR WITH A TIGHT-FITTING FACEPIECE AND HIGH-EFFICIENCY PARTICULATE FILTER.

TYPE 'C' SUPPLIED-AIR RESPIRATOR WITH A FULL FACEPIECE OPERATED IN PRESSURE-DEMAND OR OTHER POSITIVE PRESSURE MODE OR WITH A FULL FACEPIECE, HELMET OR HOOD OPERATED IN CONTINUOUS-FLOW MODE.

SELF-CONTAINED BREATHING APPARATUS WITH A FULL FACEPIECE OPERATED IN PRESSURE-DEMAND OR OTHER POSITIVE PRESSURE MODE.

FOR FIREFIGHTING AND OTHER IMMEDIATELY DANGEROUS TO LIFE OR HEALTH CONDITIONS:

SELF-CONTAINED BREATHING APPARATUS WITH FULL FACEPIECE OPERATED IN PRESSURE-DEMAND OR OTHER POSITIVE PRESSURE MODE.

SUPPLIED-AIR RESPIRATOR WITH FULL FACEPIECE AND OPERATED IN PRESSURE-DEMAND OR OTHER POSITIVE PRESSURE MODE IN COMBINATION WITH AN AUXILIARY SELF-CONTAINED BREATHING APPARATUS OPERATED IN PRESSURE-DEMAND OR OTHER POSITIVE PRESSURE MODE.

CLOTHING: EMPLOYEE MUST WEAR APPROPRIATE PROTECTIVE (IMPERVIOUS) CLOTHING AND EQUIPMENT TO PREVENT ANY POSSIBILITY OF SKIN CONTACT WITH THIS SUBSTANCE.

GLOVES: EMPLOYEE MUST WEAR APPROPRIATE PROTECTIVE GLOVES TO PREVENT CONTACT WITH THIS SUBSTANCE.

EYE PROTECTION: EMPLOYEE MUST WEAR SPLASH-PROOF OR DUST-RESISTANT SAFETY GOGGLES AND A FACESHIELD TO PREVENT CONTACT WITH THIS SUBSTANCE. EMERGENCY WASH FACILITIES: WHERE THERE IS ANY POSSIBILITY THAT AN EMPLOYEE'S EYES AND/OR SKIN MAY BE EXPOSED TO THIS SUBSTANCE, THE EMPLOYER SHOULD PROVIDE AN EYE WASH FOUNTAIN AND QUICK DRENCH SHOWER WITHIN THE IMMEDIATE WORK AREA FOR EMERGENCY USE.

AUTHORIZED BY- OCCUPATIONAL HEALTH SERVICES, INC.
CREATION DATE: 03/30/90 ***REVISION DATE:*** 05/31/90

MATERIAL SAFETY DATA SHEET

OCCUPATIONAL HEALTH SERVICES, INC.
AGRICULTURE AND PESTICIDE DIVISION
450 SEVENTH AVENUE, SUITE 2407
NEW YORK, NEW YORK 10123
1-800-445-MSDS OR (212) 967-1100

EMERGENCY CONTACT:
JOHN S. BRANSFORD, JR. (615) 292-1180

SUBSTANCE IDENTIFICATION

CAS-NUMBER 68424-85-1
SUBSTANCE: ALKYLDIMETHYLBENZYLAMMONIUM CHLORIDE (50% C14, 40% C12, 10% C16)
TRADE NAMES/SYNONYMS: QUATERNARY AMMONIUM COMPOUNDS, BENZYL-C12-16-ALKYLDIMETHYL, CHLORIDES; BENZALKONIUM CHLORIDE; PST71835
CHEMICAL FAMILY: QUATERNARY AMMONIUM COMPOUND
CERCLA RATINGS (SCALE 0-3): HEALTH=3 FIRE=1 REACTIVITY=0 PERSISTENCE=2
NFPA RATINGS (SCALE 0-4): HEALTH=U FIRE=1 REACTIVITY=0

COMPONENTS AND CONTAMINANTS

COMPONENT: ALKYLDIMETHYLBENZYLAMMONIUM CHLORIDE (50% C14, 40% C12, 10% C16) ***PERCENT:*** 100.0
CAS# 68424-85-1
OTHER CONTAMINANTS: NONE
EXPOSURE LIMITS: NO OCCUPATIONAL EXPOSURE LIMITS ESTABLISHED BY OSHA, ACGIH, OR NIOSH.

PHYSICAL DATA

DESCRIPTION: WHITE OR YELLOWISH-WHITE, AMORPHOUS POWDER OR GELATINOUS PIECES WITH AN AROMATIC ODOR AND A VERY BITTER TASTE.
MELTING POINT: NOT AVAILABLE
SPECIFIC GRAVITY: NOT AVAILABLE ***SOLUBILITY IN WATER:*** SOLUBLE
SOLVENT SOLUBILITY: SOLUBLE IN ALCOHOL AND ACETONE; SLIGHTLY SOLUBLE IN BENZENE. VERY SLIGHTLY SOLUBLE IN ETHER.

FIRE AND EXPLOSION DATA

FIRE AND EXPLOSION HAZARD: SLIGHT FIRE HAZARD WHEN EXPOSED TO HEAT OR FLAME.
DUST-AIR MIXTURES MAY IGNITE OR EXPLODE.
FIREFIGHTING MEDIA: DRY CHEMICAL, CARBON DIOXIDE, HALON, WATER SPRAY OR STANDARD FOAM (1987 EMERGENCY RESPONSE GUIDEBOOK, DOT P 5800.4).
FOR LARGER FIRES, USE WATER SPRAY, FOG OR STANDARD FOAM (1987 EMERGENCY RESPONSE GUIDEBOOK, DOT P 5800.4).
FIREFIGHTING: MOVE CONTAINER FROM FIRE AREA IF POSSIBLE. DO NOT SCATTER SPILLED MATERIAL WITH HIGH PRESSURE WATER STREAMS. DIKE FIRE CONTROL WATER FOR LATER DISPOSAL (1987 EMERGENCY RESPONSE GUIDEBOOK, DOT P 5800.4, GUIDE PAGE 31).
USE AGENTS SUITABLE FOR TYPE OF SURROUNDING FIRE. AVOID BREATHING HAZARDOUS VAPORS, KEEP UPWIND.

TOXICITY

ALKYLDIMETHYLBENZYLAMMONIUM CHLORIDE: IRRITATION DATA: 150 UG/3 DAYS INTERMITTENT SKIN-HUMAN MILD; 50 UG EYE-HUMAN SEVERE; 2 MG/24 HOURS EYE-MONKEY SEVERE; 50 MG/24 HOURS SKIN-RABBIT MODERATE; 100 UG EYE-RABBIT; 1 MG/24 HOURS EYE-RABBIT SEVERE; 10 MG EYE-RABBIT MILD. TOXICITY DATA: 1560 MG/KG SKIN-RAT LD50; 266 MG/KG ORAL-WOMAN TDLO; 240 MG/KG ORAL-RAT LD50; 175 MG/KG ORAL-MOUSE LD50; 200 MG/KG ORAL-GUINEA PIG LD50; 400 MG/KG SUBCUTANEOUS-RAT LD50; 64 MG/KG SUBCUTANEOUS-MOUSE LD50; 13900 UG/KG INTRAVENOUS-RAT LD50; 10 MG/KG INTRAVENOUS-MOUSE LD50; 14500 UG/KG INTRAPERITONEAL-RAT LD50; 10 MG/KG INTRAPERITONEAL-MOUSE LDLO; 10 MG/KG INTRAPERITONEAL-GUINEA PIG LDLO; 7 MG/KG INTRAPERITONEAL-DOG LDLO; 12 MG/KG PARENTERAL-WOMAN LDLO; MUTAGENIC DATA (RTECS); REPRODUCTIVE EFFECTS DATA (RTECS). CARCINOGEN STATUS: NONE. LOCAL EFFECTS: CORROSIVE- INHALATION, SKIN, EYES, INGESTION. ACUTE TOXICITY: TOXIC BY INGESTION; MODERATELY TOXIC BY DERMAL ABSORPTION. TARGET EFFECTS: SENSITIZER- SKIN, EYE.

HEALTH EFFECTS AND FIRST AID

INHALATION: ALKYLDIMETHYLBENZYLAMMONIUM CHLORIDE: CORROSIVE. **ACUTE EXPOSURE-** CONCENTRATIONS AS LOW AS 0.1-0.5% MAY CAUSE IRRITATION OF THE MUCOUS MEMBRANES. STRONG AQUEOUS SOLUTIONS, 10-20%, HAVE PRODUCED SUPERFICIAL NECROSIS OF THE MUCOUS MEMBRANES. **CHRONIC EXPOSURE-** REPEATED OR PROLONGED EXPOSURE MAY CAUSE EFFECTS AS THOSE LISTED IN ACUTE EXPOSURE. ASTHMA DUE TO OCCUPATIONAL EXPOSURE HAS BEEN REPORTED.
FIRST AID- REMOVE FROM EXPOSURE AREA TO FRESH AIR IMMEDIATELY. IF BREATHING HAS STOPPED, GIVE ARTIFICIAL RESPIRATION. MAINTAIN AIRWAY AND BLOOD PRESSURE AND ADMINISTER OXYGEN IF AVAILABLE. KEEP AFFECTED PERSON WARM AND AT REST. TREAT SYMPTOMATICALLY AND SUPPORTIVELY. ADMINISTRATION OF OXYGEN SHOULD BE PERFORMED BY QUALIFIED PERSONNEL. GET MEDICAL ATTENTION IMMEDIATELY.

SKIN CONTACT: ALKYLDIMETHYLBENZYLAMMONIUM CHLORIDE: CORROSIVE/SENSITIZER. **ACUTE EXPOSURE-** CONCENTRATIONS EXCEEDING 1% CAN IRRITATE THE SKIN. CONCENTRATED AQUEOUS SOLUTIONS OF 10% ARE PRIMARY SKIN IRRITANTS. DAMAGE TO THE EPIDERMIS MAY OCCUR. SEVERE SKIN DAMAGE HAS BEEN REPORTED IN LABORATORY ANIMALS. **CHRONIC EXPOSURE-** ALLERGIC CONTACT DERMATITIS HAS OCCURRED IN INDIVIDUALS REPEATEDLY EXPOSED TO THIS MATERIAL.
FIRST AID- REMOVE CONTAMINATED CLOTHING AND SHOES IMMEDIATELY. WASH AFFECTED AREA WITH SOAP OR MILD DETERGENT AND LARGE AMOUNTS OF WATER UNTIL NO EVIDENCE OF CHEMICAL REMAINS (AT LEAST 15-20 MINUTES). IN CASE OF CHEMICAL BURNS, COVER AREA WITH STERILE, DRY DRESSING. BANDAGE SECURELY, BUT NOT TOO TIGHTLY. GET MEDICAL ATTENTION IMMEDIATELY.

EYE CONTACT: ALKYLDIMETHYLBENZYLAMMONIUM CHLORIDE: CORROSIVE/SENSITIZER. **ACUTE EXPOSURE-** A DROP OF 0.1% CONCENTRATION IN HUMAN EYES CAUSED MILD DISCOMFORT WHICH PERSISTED FOR 2 OR 3 HOURS AS A SLIGHT, SCRATCHY, FOREIGN-BODY TYPE SENSATION. HIGHER CONCENTRATIONS IN HUMAN EYES, SUCH AS 10%, CAN CAUSE VERY SERIOUS DAMAGE TO THE WHOLE CORNEA. IRRIGATION OF THE SURFACE OF RABBIT EYES WITH A 0.1% SOLUTION FOR 15 MINUTES PRODUCED SEVERE INJURY OF THE ENDOTHELIUM AND MUCH SWELLING. THE CORNEAS OF RABBIT EYES BECAME BLUE AND SWOLLEN, THEN COMPLETELY OPAQUE AND VASCULARIZED WITH THE FORMATION OF SCAR TISSUE AT THE 10% CONCENTRATION. **CHRONIC EXPOSURE-** ALLERGIC CONJUNCTIVITIS HAS DEVELOPED IN SOME INDIVIDUALS AFTER USING OPHTHALMIC SOLUTIONS CONTAINING THIS MATERIAL. A 0.1% CONCENTRATION APPLIED TO RABBIT EYES AS DROPS 2 OR 3 TIMES A DAY FOR 1 TO 3 MONTHS HAS CAUSED THICKENING AND ROUGHENING OF THE CORNEAL EPITHELIUM, WITH SUPERFICIAL VASCULARIZATION, BUT NO DEEPER DAMAGE.
FIRST AID- WASH EYES IMMEDIATELY WITH LARGE AMOUNTS OF WATER, OCCASIONALLY LIFTING UPPER AND LOWER LIDS, UNTIL NO EVIDENCE OF CHEMICAL REMAINS (AT LEAST 15-20 MINUTES). CONTINUE IRRIGATING WITH NORMAL SALINE UNTIL THE PH HAS RETURNED TO NORMAL (30-60 MINUTES). COVER WITH STERILE BANDAGES. GET MEDICAL ATTENTION IMMEDIATELY.

INGESTION: ALKYLDIMETHYLBENZYLAMMONIUM CHLORIDE: CORROSIVE/TOXIC. **ACUTE EXPOSURE-** CONCENTRATED SOLUTIONS MAY CAUSE AN IMMEDIATE BURNING PAIN IN THE MOUTH, THROAT, AND ABDOMEN WITH PROFUSE SALIVATION. EXPOSED AREAS OF MUCOUS MEMBRANES MAY ULCERATE. VOMITING MAY OCCUR, POSSIBLY WITH BLOOD. SIGNS OF CIRCULATORY SHOCK INCLUDING HYPOTENSION, LABORED BREATHING, AND CYANOSIS MAY OCCUR. RAPIDLY DEVELOPING APPREHENSION, RESTLESSNESS, CONFUSION, AND WEAKNESS MAY RESULT. WEAK CONVULSIVE MOVEMENTS MAY PRECEDE CENTRAL NERVOUS SYSTEM DEPRESSION. EROSION, ULCERATION AND PETECHIAL HEMORRHAGES MAY OCCUR THROUGHOUT THE SMALL INTESTINES. GLOTTIC, BRAIN, AND PULMONARY EDEMA HAVE BEEN REPORTED. DEATH MAY OCCUR WITHIN 1-2 HOURS AFTER INGESTION DUE TO ASPHYXIATION BECAUSE OF PARALYSIS OF THE MUSCLES OF RESPIRATION OR TO CARDIOVASCULAR COLLAPSE. EVEN IN PROMPT DEATH, CLOUDY SWELLING, PATCHY NECROSIS AND FATTY INFILTRATION OCCUR IN SUCH VISCERAL ORGANS AS HEART, LIVER, AND KIDNEYS. RENAL FAILURE MAY DEVELOP IN INDIVIDUALS THAT SURVIVED A PERIOD OF SEVERE HYPOTENSION. **CHRONIC EXPOSURE-** RATS REPEATEDLY FED THIS MATERIAL FOR SEVERAL WEEKS DIED OF INANITION ASSOCIATED WITH CHRONIC DIARRHEA; THE ONLY LESION FOUND WAS FOCAL HEMORRHAGIC

NECROSIS OF THE GASTRIC MUCOSA. REPEATED ADMINISTRATION OF A 0.5% CONCENTRATION IN THE DIET WAS LETHAL TO RATS. REPEATED DOSAGES OF 25 MG/KG IN WATER WAS LETHAL TO ALL THREE DOGS TESTED; EFFECTS OF CONDITIONED SALIVATION, VOMITING, ENTERITIS, PULMONARY HEMORRHAGE, AND INFLAMMATION AND SLOUGHING OF THE MUCOSA WERE REPORTED.

FIRST AID- GIVE MILK OR ACTIVATED CHARCOAL AND REMOVE BY CATHARSIS WITH FLEET'S PHOSPHO-SODA, 15-60 ML DILUTED 1:4 WITH WATER. LAVAGE AND EMESIS ARE CONTRAINDICATED IN THE PRESENCE OF ESOPHAGEAL INJURY. GASTRIC LAVAGE SHOULD BE PERFORMED BY QUALIFIED MEDICAL PERSONNEL. GET MEDICAL ATTENTION IMMEDIATELY (DREISBACH, HANDBOOK OF POISONING, 12TH ED.). MAINTAIN AIRWAY, BLOOD PRESSURE AND RESPIRATION.

ANTIDOTE: NO SPECIFIC ANTIDOTE. TREAT SYMPTOMATICALLY AND SUPPORTIVELY.

REACTIVITY

REACTIVITY: STABLE UNDER NORMAL TEMPERATURES AND PRESSURES.

INCOMPATIBILITIES: ALKYLDIMETHYLBENZYLAMMONIUM CHLORIDE: OXIDIZERS (STRONG): FIRE AND EXPLOSION HAZARD.

DECOMPOSITION: THERMAL DECOMPOSITION PRODUCTS MAY INCLUDE TOXIC AND CORROSIVE FUMES OF CHLORIDES AND TOXIC OXIDES OF CARBON.

POLYMERIZATION: HAZARDOUS POLYMERIZATION HAS NOT BEEN REPORTED TO OCCUR UNDER NORMAL TEMPERATURES AND PRESSURES.

STORAGE AND DISPOSAL

OBSERVE ALL FEDERAL, STATE AND LOCAL REGULATIONS WHEN STORING OR DISPOSING OF THIS SUBSTANCE. FOR ASSISTANCE, CONTACT THE DISTRICT DIRECTOR OF THE ENVIRONMENTAL PROTECTION AGENCY.

****STORAGE****

STORE AWAY FROM INCOMPATIBLE SUBSTANCES.

CONDITIONS TO AVOID

MAY BURN BUT DOES NOT IGNITE READILY. AVOID CONTACT WITH STRONG OXIDIZERS, EXCESSIVE HEAT, SPARKS, OR OPEN FLAME.

SPILL AND LEAK PROCEDURES

OCCUPATIONAL SPILL: SWEEP UP AND PLACE IN SUITABLE CLEAN, DRY CONTAINERS FOR RECLAMATION OR LATER DISPOSAL. DO NOT FLUSH SPILLED MATERIAL INTO SEWER. KEEP UNNECESSARY PEOPLE AWAY.

PROTECTIVE EQUIPMENT

VENTILATION: PROVIDE LOCAL EXHAUST OR GENERAL DILUTION VENTILATION SYSTEM.

RESPIRATOR: THE FOLLOWING RESPIRATORS ARE RECOMMENDED BASED ON INFORMATION FOUND IN THE PHYSICAL DATA, TOXICITY AND HEALTH EFFECTS SECTIONS. THEY ARE RANKED IN ORDER FROM MINIMUM TO MAXIMUM RESPIRATORY PROTECTION. THE SPECIFIC RESPIRATOR SELECTED MUST BE BASED ON CONTAMINATION LEVELS FOUND IN THE WORK PLACE, MUST NOT EXCEED THE WORKING LIMITS OF THE RESPIRATOR AND BE JOINTLY APPROVED BY THE NATIONAL INSTITUTE FOR OCCUPATIONAL SAFETY AND HEALTH AND THE MINE SAFETY AND HEALTH ADMINISTRATION (NIOSH-MSHA).

DUST AND MIST RESPIRATOR WITH A FULL FACEPIECE.

AIR-PURIFYING FULL FACEPIECE RESPIRATOR WITH A HIGH-EFFICIENCY PARTICULATE FILTER.

POWERED AIR-PURIFYING RESPIRATOR WITH A TIGHT-FITTING FACEPIECE AND HIGH-EFFICIENCY PARTICULATE FILTER.

TYPE 'C' SUPPLIED-AIR RESPIRATOR WITH A FULL FACEPIECE OPERATED IN PRESSURE-DEMAND OR OTHER POSITIVE PRESSURE MODE OR WITH A FULL FACEPIECE, HELMET OR HOOD OPERATED IN CONTINUOUS-FLOW MODE.

SELF-CONTAINED BREATHING APPARATUS WITH A FULL FACEPIECE OPERATED IN PRESSURE-DEMAND OR OTHER POSITIVE PRESSURE MODE.

FOR FIREFIGHTING AND OTHER IMMEDIATELY DANGEROUS TO LIFE OR HEALTH CONDITIONS:

SELF-CONTAINED BREATHING APPARATUS WITH FULL FACEPIECE OPERATED IN PRESSURE-DEMAND OR OTHER POSITIVE PRESSURE MODE.

SUPPLIED-AIR RESPIRATOR WITH FULL FACEPIECE AND OPERATED IN PRESSURE-DEMAND OR OTHER POSITIVE PRESSURE MODE IN COMBINATION WITH AN AUXILIARY SELF-CONTAINED BREATHING APPARATUS OPERATED IN PRESSURE-DEMAND OR OTHER POSITIVE PRESSURE MODE.

CLOTHING: EMPLOYEE MUST WEAR APPROPRIATE PROTECTIVE (IMPERVIOUS) CLOTHING AND EQUIPMENT TO PREVENT ANY POSSIBILITY OF SKIN CONTACT WITH THIS SUBSTANCE.

GLOVES: EMPLOYEE MUST WEAR APPROPRIATE PROTECTIVE GLOVES TO PREVENT CONTACT WITH THIS SUBSTANCE.

EYE PROTECTION: EMPLOYEE MUST WEAR SPLASH-PROOF OR DUST-RESISTANT SAFETY GOGGLES AND A FACESHIELD TO PREVENT CONTACT WITH THIS SUBSTANCE.

EMERGENCY WASH FACILITIES: WHERE THERE IS ANY POSSIBILITY THAT AN EMPLOYEE'S EYES AND/OR SKIN MAY BE EXPOSED TO THIS SUBSTANCE, THE EMPLOYER SHOULD PROVIDE AN EYE WASH FOUNTAIN AND QUICK DRENCH SHOWER WITHIN THE IMMEDIATE WORK AREA FOR EMERGENCY USE.

AUTHORIZED BY- OCCUPATIONAL HEALTH SERVICES, INC.

CREATION DATE: 03/30/90 ***REVISION DATE:*** 05/31/90

MATERIAL SAFETY DATA SHEET

OCCUPATIONAL HEALTH SERVICES, INC.
AGRICULTURE AND PESTICIDE DIVISION
450 SEVENTH AVENUE, SUITE 2407
NEW YORK, NEW YORK 10123
1-800-445-MSDS OR (212) 967-1100

EMERGENCY CONTACT:
JOHN S. BRANSFORD, JR. (615) 292-1180

SUBSTANCE IDENTIFICATION

CAS-NUMBER 8023-53-8

SUBSTANCE: **DICHLOROBENZALKONIUM CHLORIDE**

TRADE NAMES/SYNONYMS: TETROSAN; ALKYL DIMETHYL 3,4-DICHLOROBENZYL AMMONIUM CHLORIDE; PST71839

CHEMICAL FAMILY: QUATERNARY AMMONIUM COMPOUND HALOGEN COMPOUND, AROMATIC

MOLECULAR FORMULA: (C8-H17 TO C18-H37) C9-H11-CL2-N.CL

MOLECULAR WEIGHT: 352.7 TO 492.8

CERCLA RATINGS (SCALE 0-3): HEALTH=2 FIRE=U REACTIVITY=U PERSISTENCE=2

NFPA RATINGS (SCALE 0-4): HEALTH=2 FIRE=U REACTIVITY=U

COMPONENTS AND CONTAMINANTS

COMPONENT: DICHLOROBENZALKONIUM CHLORIDE ***PERCENT:*** 100
CAS# 8023-53-8

OTHER CONTAMINANTS: NONE

EXPOSURE LIMITS: NO OCCUPATIONAL EXPOSURE LIMITS ESTABLISHED BY OSHA, ACGIH, OR NIOSH.

PHYSICAL DATA

DESCRIPTION: CRYSTALLINE SOLID WITH A VERY BITTER TASTE.

MELTING POINT: NOT AVAILABLE ***SPECIFIC GRAVITY:*** NOT AVAILABLE

SOLUBILITY IN WATER: SOLUBLE

SOLVENT SOLUBILITY: SOLUBLE IN ALCOHOL.

FIRE AND EXPLOSION DATA

FIRE AND EXPLOSION HAZARD: UNKNOWN FIRE AND EXPLOSION HAZARD.

FIREFIGHTING MEDIA: DRY CHEMICAL, CARBON DIOXIDE, WATER SPRAY OR FOAM FOR LARGER FIRES, USE WATER SPRAY, FOG OR ALCOHOL FOAM

FIREFIGHTING: MOVE CONTAINER FROM FIRE AREA IF POSSIBLE. DO NOT SCATTER SPILLED MATERIAL WITH MORE WATER THAN NEEDED FOR FIRE CONTROL. DIKE FIRE CONTROL WATER FOR LATER DISPOSAL

USE AGENTS SUITABLE FOR TYPE OF SURROUNDING FIRE. AVOID BREATHING HAZARDOUS VAPORS, KEEP UPWIND.

TOXICITY

DICHLOROBENZALKONIUM CHLORIDE: IRRITATION DATA: 1% EYE-RABBIT SEVERE. TOXICITY DATA: 730 MG/KG ORAL-RAT LD50; 2000 MG/KG ORAL-MOUSE LD50; 316 MG/KG ORAL-GUINEA PIG LD50; 50 MG/KG INTRAVENOUS-MOUSE LD50. CARCINOGEN STATUS: NONE. LOCAL EFFECTS: CORROSIVE- EYES. ACUTE TOXICITY LEVEL: MODERATELY TOXIC BY INGESTION. TARGET EFFECTS: NO DATA AVAILABLE.

HEALTH EFFECTS AND FIRST AID

INHALATION: DICHLOROBENZALKONIUM CHLORIDE: **ACUTE EXPOSURE-** NO SPECIFIC DATA AVAILABLE. PERSONS INHALING BENZALKONIUM CHLORIDE HAVE EXPERIENCED ASTHMA ON OCCASION. **CHRONIC EXPOSURE-** NO DATA AVAILABLE.

FIRST AID- REMOVE FROM EXPOSURE AREA TO FRESH AIR IMMEDIATELY. IF BREATHING HAS STOPPED, PERFORM ARTIFICIAL RESPIRATION. KEEP PERSON WARM AND AT REST. TREAT SYMPTOMATICALLY AND SUPPORTIVELY. GET MEDICAL ATTENTION IMMEDIATELY.

SKIN CONTACT: DICHLOROBENZALKONIUM CHLORIDE: **ACUTE EXPOSURE-** NO SPECIFIC DATA AVAILABLE. AQUEOUS SOLUTIONS OF 10% OR GREATER OF BENZALKONIUM CHLORIDE ARE PRIMARY SKIN IRRITANTS. AT ANTISEPTIC

CONCENTRATIONS, QUATERNARY AMMONIUM AGENTS ARE USUALLY NONIRRITATING. OCCASIONALLY, ALLERGIC REACTIONS ARE REPORTED. QUATERNARY AMMONIUM COMPOUNDS TEND TO FORM A FILM UNDER WHICH BACTERIA MAY REMAIN VIABLE. SOAP DEACTIVATES BACTERICIDAL AND BACTERIOSTATIC PROPERTIES. CONCURRENT USE OF ANTIBIOTICS MAY RESULT IN SENSITIZATION. **CHRONIC EXPOSURE-** THE CATIONIC SURFACTANTS INTERACT WITH KERATIN AND CAUSE EPIDERMAL DAMAGE, AS WELL AS CAUSE OCCASIONAL ALLERGIC RESPONSES WHEN USED OVER A LONG PERIOD.

FIRST AID- REMOVE CONTAMINATED CLOTHING AND SHOES IMMEDIATELY. WASH AFFECTED AREA WITH SOAP OR MILD DETERGENT AND LARGE AMOUNTS OF WATER UNTIL NO EVIDENCE OF CHEMICAL REMAINS (APPROXIMATELY 15-20 MINUTES). GET MEDICAL ATTENTION IMMEDIATELY.

EYE CONTACT: DICHLOROBENZALKONIUM CHLORIDE: CORROSIVE. **ACUTE EXPOSURE-** APPLICATION OF A 1% SOLUTION TO THE EYES OF RABBITS CAUSED SEVERE IRRITATION. APPLICATION OF A 0.1% SOLUTION OF BENZALKONIUM CHLORIDE TO HUMAN EYES RESULTED IN A SCRATCHY, FOREIGN-BODY TYPE OF SENSATION, THAT PERSISTED FOR SEVERAL HOURS. **CHRONIC EXPOSURE-** OCCASIONAL CASES OF ALLERGIC CONJUNCTIVITIS HAVE BEEN REPORTED AS A RESULT OF EYE CONTACT WITH BENZALKONIUM CHLORIDE. WHEN 0.1% BENZALKONIUM CHLORIDE WAS APPLIED TO RABBIT EYES TWO OR THREE TIMES A DAY FOR ONE TO THREE MONTHS, A THICKENING AND ROUGHENING OF THE CORNEAL EPITHELIUM WITH SUPERFICIAL VASCULARIZATION RESULTED, BUT NO DEEPER DAMAGE OCCURRED.

FIRST AID- WASH EYES IMMEDIATELY WITH LARGE AMOUNTS OF WATER OR NORMAL SALINE, OCCASIONALLY LIFTING UPPER AND LOWER LIDS, UNTIL NO EVIDENCE OF CHEMICAL REMAINS (APPROXIMATELY 15-20 MINUTES). GET MEDICAL ATTENTION IMMEDIATELY.

INGESTION: DICHLOROBENZALKONIUM CHLORIDE: **ACUTE EXPOSURE-** THE LETHAL DOSE OF DICHLOROBENZALKONIUM CHLORIDE IN RATS WAS 730 MG/KG. BENZALKONIUM CHLORIDE HAS BEEN REPORTED TO HAVE A LOW SYSTEMIC TOXICITY, BUT POISONING FROM INGESTION HAS OCCURRED. INGESTION OF A CONCENTRATED SOLUTION OF BENZALKONIUM CHLORIDE MAY RESULT IN AN IMMEDIATE BURNING PAIN IN THE MOUTH, THROAT, AND ABDOMEN, WITH PROFUSE SALIVATION. VICTIMS MAY ALSO EXPERIENCE HYPOTENSION, APPREHENSION, RESTLESSNESS, CONFUSION, WEAKNESS, AND CENTRAL NERVOUS SYSTEM DEPRESSION. **CHRONIC EXPOSURE-** IN CHRONIC EXPOSURES OF SEVERAL WEEKS, THE ONLY LESION FOUND IN FATALLY ILL RATS WAS FOCAL HEMORRHAGIC NECROSIS OF THE GASTRIC MUCOSA; THESE ANIMALS DIED OF INANITION ASSOCIATED WITH CHRONIC DIARRHEA.

FIRST AID- IT IS UNLIKELY THAT EMERGENCY TREATMENT WILL BE REQUIRED. IF ADVERSE EFFECTS OCCUR, TREAT SYMPTOMATICALLY AND SUPPORTIVELY AND GET MEDICAL ATTENTION.

ANTIDOTE: NO SPECIFIC ANTIDOTE. TREAT SYMPTOMATICALLY AND SUPPORTIVELY.

REACTIVITY

REACTIVITY: NO DATA AVAILABLE.

INCOMPATIBILITIES: DICHLOROBENZALKONIUM CHLORIDE: NO DATA AVAILABLE.

DECOMPOSITION: THERMAL DECOMPOSITION PRODUCTS MAY INCLUDE TOXIC AND HAZARDOUS FUMES OF CHLORINE, HYDROGEN CHLORIDE, AMMONIA, AND OXIDES OF NITROGEN.

POLYMERIZATION: HAZARDOUS POLYMERIZATION HAS NOT BEEN REPORTED TO OCCUR UNDER NORMAL TEMPERATURES AND PRESSURES.

STORAGE AND DISPOSAL

OBSERVE ALL FEDERAL, STATE AND LOCAL REGULATIONS WHEN STORING OR DISPOSING OF THIS SUBSTANCE. FOR ASSISTANCE, CONTACT THE DISTRICT DIRECTOR OF THE ENVIRONMENTAL PROTECTION AGENCY.

CONDITIONS TO AVOID

NONE REPORTED.

SPILL AND LEAK PROCEDURES

OCCUPATIONAL SPILL: SWEEP UP AND PLACE IN SUITABLE CLEAN, DRY CONTAINERS FOR RECLAMATION OR LATER DISPOSAL. DO NOT FLUSH SPILLED MATERIAL INTO SEWER. KEEP UNNECESSARY PEOPLE AWAY.

PROTECTIVE EQUIPMENT

VENTILATION: PROVIDE LOCAL EXHAUST OR GENERAL DILUTION VENTILATION SYSTEM.

RESPIRATOR: THE FOLLOWING RESPIRATORS ARE RECOMMENDED BASED ON INFORMATION FOUND IN THE PHYSICAL DATA, TOXICITY AND HEALTH EFFECTS SECTIONS. THEY ARE RANKED IN ORDER FROM MINIMUM TO MAXIMUM RESPIRATORY PROTECTION. THE SPECIFIC RESPIRATOR SELECTED MUST BE BASED ON CONTAMINATION LEVELS FOUND IN THE WORK PLACE, MUST NOT EXCEED THE WORKING LIMITS OF THE RESPIRATOR AND BE JOINTLY APPROVED BY THE NATIONAL INSTITUTE FOR OCCUPATIONAL SAFETY AND HEALTH AND THE MINE SAFETY AND HEALTH ADMINISTRATION (NIOSH-MSHA).

DUST AND MIST RESPIRATOR WITH A FULL FACEPIECE.

AIR-PURIFYING FULL FACEPIECE RESPIRATOR WITH A HIGH-EFFICIENCY PARTICULATE FILTER.

POWERED AIR-PURIFYING RESPIRATOR WITH A TIGHT-FITTING FACEPIECE AND HIGH-EFFICIENCY PARTICULATE FILTER.

TYPE 'C' SUPPLIED-AIR RESPIRATOR WITH A FULL FACEPIECE OPERATED IN PRESSURE-DEMAND OR OTHER POSITIVE PRESSURE MODE OR WITH A FULL FACEPIECE, HELMET OR HOOD OPERATED IN CONTINUOUS-FLOW MODE.

SELF-CONTAINED BREATHING APPARATUS WITH A FULL FACEPIECE OPERATED IN PRESSURE-DEMAND OR OTHER POSITIVE PRESSURE MODE.

FOR FIREFIGHTING AND OTHER IMMEDIATELY DANGEROUS TO LIFE OR HEALTH CONDITIONS:

SELF-CONTAINED BREATHING APPARATUS WITH FULL FACEPIECE OPERATED IN PRESSURE-DEMAND OR OTHER POSITIVE PRESSURE MODE.

SUPPLIED-AIR RESPIRATOR WITH FULL FACEPIECE AND OPERATED IN PRESSURE-DEMAND OR OTHER POSITIVE PRESSURE MODE IN COMBINATION WITH AN AUXILIARY SELF-CONTAINED BREATHING APPARATUS OPERATED IN PRESSURE-DEMAND OR OTHER POSITIVE PRESSURE MODE.

CLOTHING: EMPLOYEE MUST WEAR APPROPRIATE PROTECTIVE (IMPERVIOUS) CLOTHING AND EQUIPMENT TO PREVENT REPEATED OR PROLONGED SKIN CONTACT WITH THIS SUBSTANCE.

GLOVES: EMPLOYEE MUST WEAR APPROPRIATE PROTECTIVE GLOVES TO PREVENT CONTACT WITH THIS SUBSTANCE.

EYE PROTECTION: EMPLOYEE MUST WEAR SPLASH-PROOF OR DUST-RESISTANT SAFETY GOGGLES TO PREVENT EYE CONTACT WITH THIS SUBSTANCE.

EMERGENCY EYE WASH: WHERE THERE IS ANY POSSIBILITY THAT AN EMPLOYEE'S EYES MAY BE EXPOSED TO THIS SUBSTANCE, THE EMPLOYER SHOULD PROVIDE AN EYE WASH FOUNTAIN WITHIN THE IMMEDIATE WORK AREA FOR EMERGENCY USE.

AUTHORIZED BY- OCCUPATIONAL HEALTH SERVICES, INC.

CREATION DATE: 10/04/89 ***REVISION DATE:*** 05/31/90

MATERIAL SAFETY DATA SHEET

OCCUPATIONAL HEALTH SERVICES, INC.
AGRICULTURE AND PESTICIDE DIVISION
450 SEVENTH AVENUE, SUITE 2407
NEW YORK, NEW YORK 10123
1-800-445-MSDS OR (212) 967-1100

EMERGENCY CONTACT:
JOHN S. BRANSFORD, JR. (615) 292-1180

SUBSTANCE IDENTIFICATION

CAS-NUMBER 121-54-0

***SUBSTANCE:* BENZETHONIUM CHLORIDE**

TRADE NAMES/SYNONYMS: BENZENEMETHANAMINIUM, N,N-DIMETHYL-N-(2-(2-(4-(1,1,3, 3-TETRAMETHYLBUTYL)PHENOXY)ETHOXY)ETHYL)-, CHLORIDE; N,N-DIMETHYL-N-(2-(2-(4-(1,1,3,3-TETRAMETHYLBUTYL)PHENOXY)ETHOXY) ETHYL)BENZENEMETHANAMINIUM CHLORIDE; AMMONIUM, BENZYLDIMETHYL(2-(2-(P-(1,1,3,3-TETRAMETHYLBUTYL)PHENOXY) ETHOXY)ETHYL)-, CHLORIDE; HYAMINE 1622; ANTIGERM 77; BZT; PHEMERIDE; PHEMEROL; PHEMEROL CHLORIDE; BENZYLDIMETHYL (2-(2-(P-(1,1,3,3-TETRAMETHYLBUTYL)PHENOXY)ETHOXY) ETHYL)AMMONIUM CHLORIDE; C27H42CLNO2; PST71851

CHEMICAL FAMILY: QUATERNARY AMMONIUM COMPOUND

MOLECULAR FORMULA: C27-H42-N-O2-CL

MOLECULAR WEIGHT: 448.15

CERCLA RATINGS (SCALE 0-3): HEALTH=3 FIRE=1 REACTIVITY=0 PERSISTENCE=2

NFPA RATINGS (SCALE 0-4): HEALTH=3 FIRE=1 REACTIVITY=0

COMPONENTS AND CONTAMINANTS

COMPONENT: BENZETHONIUM CHLORIDE ***PERCENT:*** 100
CAS# 121-54-0

OTHER CONTAMINANTS: NONE

EXPOSURE LIMITS: NO OCCUPATIONAL EXPOSURE LIMITS ESTABLISHED BY OSHA, ACGIH, OR NIOSH.

PHYSICAL DATA

DESCRIPTION: ODORLESS, COLORLESS PLATES.

MELTING POINT: 327-331 F (164-166 C)
SPECIFIC GRAVITY: NOT AVAILABLE. ***PH:*** 4.8-5.5 @ 1% SOLN
SOLUBILITY IN WATER: SOLUBLE
SOLVENT SOLUBILITY: SOLUBLE IN ALCOHOL, ACETONE, CHLOROFORM; SLIGHTLY SOLUBLE IN ETHER.

FIRE AND EXPLOSION DATA

FIRE AND EXPLOSION HAZARD: SLIGHT FIRE HAZARD WHEN EXPOSED TO HEAT OR FLAME.

FIREFIGHTING MEDIA: DRY CHEMICAL, CARBON DIOXIDE, HALON, WATER SPRAY OR STANDARD FOAM (1987 EMERGENCY RESPONSE GUIDEBOOK, DOT P 5800.4). FOR LARGER FIRES, USE WATER SPRAY, FOG OR STANDARD FOAM (1987 EMERGENCY RESPONSE GUIDEBOOK, DOT P 5800.4).

FIREFIGHTING: MOVE CONTAINER FROM FIRE AREA IF POSSIBLE. DO NOT SCATTER SPILLED MATERIAL WITH HIGH PRESSURE WATER STREAMS. DIKE FIRE CONTROL WATER FOR LATER DISPOSAL (1987 EMERGENCY RESPONSE GUIDEBOOK, DOT P 5800.4, GUIDE PAGE 31).
USE AGENTS SUITABLE FOR TYPE OF SURROUNDING FIRE. AVOID BREATHING HAZARDOUS VAPORS, KEEP UPWIND.

TOXICITY

BENZETHONIUM CHLORIDE: IRRITATION DATA: 30 UG EYE-RABBIT SEVERE. TOXICITY DATA: 368 MG/KG ORAL-RAT LD50; 338 MG/KG ORAL-MOUSE LD50; 16,500 UG/KG INTRAPERITONEAL-RAT LD50; 7813 UG/KG INTRAPERITONEAL-MOUSE LD50; 19 MG/KG INTRAVENOUS-RAT LD50; 30 MG/KG INTRAVENOUS-MOUSE LD50; 119 MG/KG SUBCUTANEOUS-RAT LD50; 420 MG/KG UNREPORTED-RAT LD50; MUTAGENIC DATA (RTECS); TUMORIGENIC DATA (RTECS). CARCINOGEN STATUS: NONE. LOCAL EFFECTS: CORROSIVE- INHALATION, SKIN, AND EYES. ACUTE TOXICITY LEVEL: TOXIC BY INGESTION. TARGET EFFECTS: NO DATA AVAILABLE.

HEALTH EFFECTS AND FIRST AID

INHALATION: BENZETHONIUM CHLORIDE: CORROSIVE. **ACUTE EXPOSURE-** SOLUTIONS OF CATIONIC SURFACTANTS WITH CONCENTRATIONS OF 10% OR GREATER MAY CAUSE CORROSION OF THE MUCOUS MEMBRANES WITH WHICH THEY COME IN CONTACT; DILUTE SOLUTIONS MAY CAUSE IRRITATION. **CHRONIC EXPOSURE-** NO DATA AVAILABLE.

FIRST AID- REMOVE FROM EXPOSURE AREA TO FRESH AIR IMMEDIATELY. IF BREATHING HAS STOPPED, GIVE ARTIFICIAL RESPIRATION. MAINTAIN AIRWAY AND BLOOD PRESSURE AND ADMINISTER OXYGEN IF AVAILABLE. KEEP AFFECTED PERSON WARM AND AT REST. TREAT SYMPTOMATICALLY AND SUPPORTIVELY. ADMINISTRATION OF OXYGEN SHOULD BE PERFORMED BY QUALIFIED PERSONNEL. GET MEDICAL ATTENTION IMMEDIATELY.

SKIN CONTACT: BENZETHONIUM CHLORIDE: CORROSIVE. **ACUTE EXPOSURE-** CONTACT WITH SOLUTIONS OF CATIONIC SURFACTANTS WITH A CONCENTRATION OF 10% OR LESS MAY CAUSE IRRITATION AND MINOR EPIDERMAL DAMAGE. CUTANEOUS NECROSIS HAS BEEN REPORTED WITH CONCENTRATED SOLUTIONS. RARELY, HYPERSENSITIVITY REACTIONS MAY OCCUR IN PERSONS PREVIOUSLY EXPOSED. **CHRONIC EXPOSURE-** EFFECTS ARE DEPENDENT UPON CONCENTRATION AND DURATION OF EXPOSURE. DERMATITIS OR EFFECTS SIMILAR TO THOSE FOR ACUTE EXPOSURE MAY OCCUR. REPEATED EXPOSURE HAS RARELY BEEN REPORTED TO CAUSE SENSITIZATION SUCH AS ALLERGIC AXILLARY DERMATITIS DUE TO USE IN A ROLL-ON DEODORANT.

FIRST AID- REMOVE CONTAMINATED CLOTHING AND SHOES IMMEDIATELY. WASH AFFECTED AREA WITH SOAP OR MILD DETERGENT AND LARGE AMOUNTS OF WATER UNTIL NO EVIDENCE OF CHEMICAL REMAINS (AT LEAST 15-20 MINUTES). IN CASE OF CHEMICAL BURNS, COVER AREA WITH STERILE, DRY DRESSING. BANDAGE SECURELY, BUT NOT TOO TIGHTLY. GET MEDICAL ATTENTION IMMEDIATELY.

EYE CONTACT: BENZETHONIUM CHLORIDE: CORROSIVE. **ACUTE EXPOSURE-** APPLICATION OF 30 UG TO RABBIT EYES PRODUCED SEVERE IRRITATION. APPLICATION OF CATIONIC SURFACTANTS IN CONCENTRATIONS OF 0.1 TO 1.0% IN WATER HAVE BEEN SIGNIFICANTLY IRRITATING OR INJURIOUS TO RABBIT EYES. **CHRONIC EXPOSURE-** EFFECTS ARE DEPENDENT UPON CONCENTRATION AND DURATION OF EXPOSURE. CONJUNCTIVITIS OR EFFECTS SIMILAR TO THOSE FOR ACUTE EXPOSURE MAY OCCUR.

FIRST AID- WASH EYES IMMEDIATELY WITH LARGE AMOUNTS OF WATER, OCCASIONALLY LIFTING UPPER AND LOWER LIDS, UNTIL NO EVIDENCE OF CHEMICAL REMAINS (AT LEAST 15-20 MINUTES). CONTINUE IRRIGATING WITH NORMAL SALINE UNTIL THE PH HAS RETURNED TO NORMAL (30-60 MINUTES). COVER WITH STERILE BANDAGES. GET MEDICAL ATTENTION IMMEDIATELY.

INGESTION: BENZETHONIUM CHLORIDE: CORROSIVE/TOXIC. **ACUTE EXPOSURE-** INGESTION OF QUANTERNARY AMMONIUM COMPOUNDS MAY CAUSE NAUSEA, VOMITING, RESTLESSNESS, CONFUSION, HYPOTENSION, CONVULSIONS, SKELETAL MUSCLE WEAKNESS OR PARALYSIS, RESPIRATORY DIFFICULTY AND PARALYSIS, CYANOSIS, COLLAPSE, AND COMA. OTHER REPORTED SYMPTOMS INCLUDE CHILLS, SHORTNESS OF BREATH, APPREHENSION, ARRYTHMIAS, OLIGURIA, AND CIRCULATORY SHOCK. THE HUMAN FATAL DOSE IS APPROXIMATELY 1-3 GRAMS. DEATH, DUE TO ASPHYXIA, GENERALLY OCCURS WITHIN 1-3 HOURS. FINDINGS IN HUMAN FATALITIES HAVE INCLUDED SEVERE CORROSION OF THE UPPER ALIMENTARY TRACT, EROSION, ULCERATION AND PETECHIAL HEMORRHAGES OF THE SMALL INTESTINE, GLOTTAL AND PULMONARY EDEMA. PATHOLOGIC FINDINGS, EVEN IN CASES OF PROMPT DEATH, MAY INCLUDE CLOUDY SWELLING, PATCHY NECROSIS AND FATTY INFILTRATION IN THE VISCERAL ORGANS SUCH AS THE HEART, LIVER AND KIDNEYS. BRAIN EDEMA AND HEMORRHAGE HAVE ALSO BEEN REPORTED. **CHRONIC EXPOSURE-** STUDIES DONE ON RELATED COMPOUNDS INDICATE THAT ANIMALS WHICH DIED FROM REPEATED FEEDING OVER SEVERAL WEEKS HAD FOCAL HEMORRHAGIC NECROSIS OF THE GASTRIC MUCOSA AND APPARENTLY DIED OF INANITION ASSOCIATED WITH CHRONIC DIARRHEA.

FIRST AID- GIVE MILK OR ACTIVATED CHARCOAL AND REMOVE BY CATHARSIS WITH FLEET'S PHOSPHO-SODA, 15-60 ML DILUTED 1:4 WITH WATER. LAVAGE AND EMESIS ARE CONTRAINDICATED IN THE PRESENCE OF ESOPHAGEAL INJURY. GASTRIC LAVAGE SHOULD BE PERFORMED BY QUALIFIED MEDICAL PERSONNEL. GET MEDICAL ATTENTION IMMEDIATELY (DREISBACH, HANDBOOK OF POISONING, 12TH ED.). MAINTAIN AIRWAY, BLOOD PRESSURE AND RESPIRATION.

ANTIDOTE: NO SPECIFIC ANTIDOTE. TREAT SYMPTOMATICALLY AND SUPPORTIVELY.

REACTIVITY

REACTIVITY: STABLE UNDER NORMAL TEMPERATURES AND PRESSURES.

INCOMPATIBILITIES: BENZETHONIUM CHLORIDE: NONIONIC DETERGENTS: INCOMPATIBLE. SOAPS: INCOMPATIBLE.

DECOMPOSITION: THERMAL DECOMPOSITION PRODUCTS MAY INCLUDE TOXIC OXIDES OF NITROGEN.

POLYMERIZATION: HAZARDOUS POLYMERIZATION HAS NOT BEEN REPORTED TO OCCUR UNDER NORMAL TEMPERATURES AND PRESSURES.

STORAGE AND DISPOSAL

OBSERVE ALL FEDERAL, STATE AND LOCAL REGULATIONS WHEN STORING OR DISPOSING OF THIS SUBSTANCE. FOR ASSISTANCE, CONTACT THE DISTRICT DIRECTOR OF THE ENVIRONMENTAL PROTECTION AGENCY.

****STORAGE****

STORE AWAY FROM INCOMPATIBLE SUBSTANCES.

CONDITIONS TO AVOID

MAY BURN BUT DOES NOT IGNITE READILY. AVOID CONTACT WITH STRONG OXIDIZERS, EXCESSIVE HEAT, SPARKS, OR OPEN FLAME.

SPILL AND LEAK PROCEDURES

OCCUPATIONAL SPILL: SWEEP UP AND PLACE IN SUITABLE CLEAN, DRY CONTAINERS FOR RECLAMATION OR LATER DISPOSAL. DO NOT FLUSH SPILLED MATERIAL INTO SEWER. KEEP UNNECESSARY PEOPLE AWAY.

PROTECTIVE EQUIPMENT

VENTILATION: PROVIDE LOCAL EXHAUST OR PROCESS ENCLOSURE VENTILATION SYSTEM.

RESPIRATOR: THE FOLLOWING RESPIRATORS ARE RECOMMENDED BASED ON INFORMATION FOUND IN THE PHYSICAL DATA, TOXICITY AND HEALTH EFFECTS SECTIONS. THEY ARE RANKED IN ORDER FROM MINIMUM TO MAXIMUM RESPIRATORY PROTECTION. THE SPECIFIC RESPIRATOR SELECTED MUST BE BASED ON CONTAMINATION LEVELS FOUND IN THE WORK PLACE, MUST NOT EXCEED THE WORKING LIMITS OF THE RESPIRATOR AND BE JOINTLY APPROVED BY THE NATIONAL INSTITUTE FOR OCCUPATIONAL SAFETY AND HEALTH AND THE MINE SAFETY AND HEALTH ADMINISTRATION (NIOSH-MSHA).
TYPE 'C' SUPPLIED-AIR RESPIRATOR WITH A FULL FACEPIECE OPERATED IN PRESSURE-DEMAND OR OTHER POSITIVE PRESSURE MODE OR WITH A FULL FACEPIECE, HELMET OR HOOD OPERATED IN CONTINOUS-FLOW MODE.
SELF-CONTAINED BREATHING APPARATUS WITH A FULL FACEPIECE OPERATED IN PRESSURE-DEMAND OR OTHER POSITIVE PRESSURE MODE.
FOR FIREFIGHTING AND OTHER IMMEDIATELY DANGEROUS TO LIFE OR HEALTH CONDITIONS:
SELF-CONTAINED BREATHING APPARATUS WITH FULL FACEPIECE OPERATED IN PRESSURE-DEMAND OR OTHER POSITIVE PRESSURE MODE.
SUPPLIED-AIR RESPIRATOR WITH FULL FACEPIECE AND OPERATED IN PRESSURE-DEMAND OR OTHER POSITIVE PRESSURE MODE IN COMBINATION WITH AN AUXILIARY SELF-CONTAINED BREATHING APPARATUS OPERATED IN PRESSURE-DEMAND OR OTHER POSITIVE PRESSURE MODE.

CLOTHING: EMPLOYEE MUST WEAR APPROPRIATE PROTECTIVE (IMPERVIOUS) CLOTHING AND EQUIPMENT TO PREVENT ANY POSSIBILITY OF SKIN CONTACT WITH THIS SUBSTANCE.

GLOVES: EMPLOYEE MUST WEAR APPROPRIATE PROTECTIVE GLOVES TO PREVENT CONTACT WITH THIS SUBSTANCE.

EYE PROTECTION: EMPLOYEE MUST WEAR SPLASH-PROOF OR DUST-RESISTANT SAFETY GOGGLES AND A FACESHIELD TO PREVENT CONTACT WITH THIS SUBSTANCE.

EMERGENCY WASH FACILITIES: WHERE THERE IS ANY POSSIBILITY THAT AN EMPLOYEE'S EYES AND/OR SKIN MAY BE EXPOSED TO THIS SUBSTANCE, THE EMPLOYER SHOULD PROVIDE AN EYE WASH FOUNTAIN AND QUICK DRENCH SHOWER WITHIN THE IMMEDIATE WORK AREA FOR EMERGENCY USE.

AUTHORIZED BY- OCCUPATIONAL HEALTH SERVICES, INC.
CREATION DATE: 05/03/90 ***REVISION DATE:*** 05/31/90

MATERIAL SAFETY DATA SHEET

OCCUPATIONAL HEALTH SERVICES, INC.
AGRICULTURE AND PESTICIDE DIVISION
450 SEVENTH AVENUE, SUITE 2407
NEW YORK, NEW YORK 10123
1-800-445-MSDS OR (212) 967-1100

EMERGENCY CONTACT:
JOHN S. BRANSFORD, JR. (615) 292-1180

SUBSTANCE IDENTIFICATION

CAS-NUMBER 1330-85-4

***SUBSTANCE:* DODECYLBENZYLTRIMETHYLAMMONIUM CHLORIDE**

TRADE NAMES/SYNONYMS: BENZENEMETHANAMINIUM, AR-DODECYL-N,N,N-TRIMETHYL-, CHLORIDE; AR-DODECYL-N,N,N-TRIMETHYLBENZENEMETHANAMINIUM CHLORIDE; AMMONIUM, (DODECYLBENZYL)TRIMETHYL-, CHLORIDE; (DODECYLBENZYL)TRIMETHYLAMMONIUM CHLORIDE; HALIMIDE; C22H40CLN; PST71854

CHEMICAL FAMILY: QUATERNARY AMMONIUM COMPOUND
CATIONIC SURFACTANT

MOLECULAR FORMULA: C22-H40-N.CL

MOLECULAR WEIGHT: 354.03

CERCLA RATINGS (SCALE 0-3): HEALTH=U FIRE=1 REACTIVITY=0 PERSISTENCE=1

NFPA RATINGS (SCALE 0-4): HEALTH=U FIRE=1 REACTIVITY=0

COMPONENTS AND CONTAMINANTS

COMPONENT: DODECYLBENZYLTRIMETHYLAMMONIUM CHLORIDE ***PERCENT:*** 100.0
CAS# 1330-85-4

OTHER CONTAMINANTS: NONE

EXPOSURE LIMITS: NO OCCUPATIONAL EXPOSURE LIMITS ESTABLISHED BY OSHA, ACGIH, OR NIOSH.

PHYSICAL DATA

DESCRIPTION: PALE YELLOW, GLASSY SOLID. ***MELTING POINT:*** NOT AVAILABLE
SPECIFIC GRAVITY: NOT AVAILABLE ***SOLUBILITY IN WATER:*** SOLUBLE

FIRE AND EXPLOSION DATA

FIRE AND EXPLOSION HAZARD: SLIGHT FIRE HAZARD WHEN EXPOSED TO HEAT OR FLAME.

FIREFIGHTING MEDIA: DRY CHEMICAL, CARBON DIOXIDE, HALON, WATER SPRAY OR STANDARD FOAM (1987 EMERGENCY RESPONSE GUIDEBOOK, DOT P 5800.4).
FOR LARGER FIRES, USE WATER SPRAY, FOG OR STANDARD FOAM (1987 EMERGENCY RESPONSE GUIDEBOOK, DOT P 5800.4).

FIREFIGHTING: MOVE CONTAINER FROM FIRE AREA IF POSSIBLE. DO NOT SCATTER SPILLED MATERIAL WITH HIGH PRESSURE WATER STREAMS. DIKE FIRE CONTROL WATER FOR LATER DISPOSAL (1987 EMERGENCY RESPONSE GUIDEBOOK, DOT P 5800.4, GUIDE PAGE 31).
USE AGENTS SUITABLE FOR TYPE OF SURROUNDING FIRE. AVOID BREATHING HAZARDOUS VAPORS, KEEP UPWIND.

TOXICITY

DODECYLBENZYLTRIMETHYLAMMONIUM CHLORIDE: CARCINOGEN STATUS: NONE. ACUTE TOXICITY: NO DATA AVAILABLE. TARGET EFFECTS: NO DATA AVAILABLE.

HEALTH EFFECTS AND FIRST AID

INHALATION: DODECYLBENZYLTRIMETHYLAMMONIUM CHLORIDE: SEE INFORMATION ON CATIONIC SURFACTANTS.
CATIONIC SURFACTANTS: **ACUTE EXPOSURE**- CONCENTRATIONS OF MANY CATIONIC SURFACTANTS AS LOW AS 0.1 TO 0.5% ARE IRRITATING TO THE MUCOUS MEMBRANES. 1% SOLUTIONS MAY PRODUCE SIGNIFICANT IRRITATION, AND CONCENTRATED SOLUTIONS (>10%), MAY HAVE CAUSTIC QUALITIES.
CHRONIC EXPOSURE- NO DATA AVAILABLE.

FIRST AID- REMOVE FROM EXPOSURE AREA TO FRESH AIR IMMEDIATELY. IF BREATHING HAS STOPPED, GIVE ARTIFICIAL RESPIRATION. MAINTAIN AIRWAY AND BLOOD PRESSURE AND ADMINISTER OXYGEN IF AVAILABLE. KEEP AFFECTED PERSON WARM AND AT REST. TREAT SYMPTOMATICALLY AND S UPPORTIVELY. ADMINISTRATION OF OXYGEN SHOULD BE PERFORMED BY QUALIFIED PERSONNEL. GET MEDICAL ATTENTION IMMEDIATELY.

SKIN CONTACT: DODECYLBENZYLTRIMETHYLAMMONIUM CHLORIDE: SEE INFORMATION ON CATIONIC SURFACTANTS.
CATIONIC SURFACTANTS: **ACUTE EXPOSURE**- 1% SOLUTIONS OF MANY CATIONIC SURFACTANTS PRODUCE IRRITATION AND CONCENTRATED SOLUTIONS (>10%), HAVE CAUSTIC QUALITIES. **CHRONIC EXPOSURE**- PROLONGED OR REPEATED EXPOSURE TO SOME CATIONIC SURFACTANTS HAS RESULTED IN ALLERGIC REACTIONS.

FIRST AID- REMOVE CONTAMINATED CLOTHING AND SHOES IMMEDIATELY. WASH AFFECTED AREA WITH SOAP OR MILD DETERGENT AND LARGE AMOUNTS OF WATER UNTIL NO EVIDENCE OF CHEMICAL REMAINS (AT LEAST 15-20 MINUTES). IN CASE OF CHEMICAL BURNS, COVER AREA WITH STERILE, DRY DRESSING. BANDAGE SECURELY, BUT NOT TOO TIGHTLY. GET MEDICAL ATTENTION IMMEDIATELY.

EYE CONTACT: DODECYLBENZYLTRIMETHYLAMMONIUM CHLORIDE: SEE INFORMATION ON CATIONIC SURFACTANTS.
CATIONIC SURFACTANTS: **ACUTE EXPOSURE**- 1% SOLUTIONS, AND POSSIBLY AS LOW AS 0.1%, OF MANY CATIONIC SURFACTANTS PRODUCE SIGNIFICANT IRRITATION. HIGH CONCENTRATIONS (>10%), OF SOME CATIONIC SURFACTANTS CAUSE SEVERE BURNS WITH PERMANENT OPACITY AND VASCULARIZATION.
CHRONIC EXPOSURE- NO DATA AVAILABLE.

FIRST AID- WASH EYES IMMEDIATELY WITH LARGE AMOUNTS OF WATER, OCCASIONALLY LIFTING UPPER AND LOWER LIDS, UNTIL NO EVIDENCE OF CHEMICAL REMAINS (AT LEAST 15-20 MINUTES). CONTINUE IRRIGATING WITH NORMAL SALINE UNTIL THE PH HAS RETURNED TO NORMAL (30-60 MINUTES). COVER WITH STERILE BANDAGES. GET MEDICAL ATTENTION IMMEDIATELY.

INGESTION: DODECYLBENZYLTRIMETHYLAMMONIUM CHLORIDE: SEE INFORMATION ON CATIONIC SURFACTANTS.
CATIONIC SURFACTANTS: **ACUTE EXPOSURE**- CONCENTRATED SOLUTIONS (>10%), OF MANY CATIONIC SURFACTANTS, CAUSE CORROSIVE DAMAGE TO THE MUCOUS MEMBRANES AND ESOPHAGUS, NAUSEA, AND VOMITING. IF SUFFICIENT QUANTITIES ARE INGESTED OTHER SIGNS AND SYMPTOMS REFERABLE TO THE CENTRAL NERVOUS SYSTEM OR CIRCULATORY SHOCK MAY DEVELOP INCLUDING RESTLESSNESS, CONFUSION, HYPOTENSION, MUSCLE WEAKNESS, COLLAPSE, CONVULSIONS, RESPIRATORY PARALYSIS, CYANOSIS, AND COMA. DEATH MAY OCCUR WITHIN 1-4 HOURS. THE ESTIMATED FATAL HUMAN DOSE IS BETWEEN 1-3 GRAMS. **CHRONIC EXPOSURE**- NO DATA AVAILABLE.

FIRST AID- GIVE MILK OR ACTIVATED CHARCOAL AND REMOVE BY CATHARSIS WITH FLEET'S PHOSPHO-SODA, 15-60 ML DILUTED 1:4 WITH WATER. LAVAGE AND EMESIS ARE CONTRAINDICATED IN THE PRESENCE OF ESOPHAGEAL INJURY. GASTRIC LAVAGE SHOULD BE PERFORMED BY QUALIFIED MEDICAL PERSONNEL. GET MEDICAL ATTENTION IMMEDIATELY (DREISBACH, HANDBOOK OF POISONING, 12TH ED.). MAINTAIN AIRWAY, BLOOD PRESSURE AND RESPIRATION.

ANTIDOTE: NO SPECIFIC ANTIDOTE. TREAT SYMPTOMATICALLY AND SUPPORTIVELY.

REACTIVITY

REACTIVITY: STABLE UNDER NORMAL TEMPERATURES AND PRESSURES.

INCOMPATIBILITIES: DODECYLBENZYLTRIMETHYLAMMONIUM CHLORIDE: OXIDIZERS (STRONG): FIRE AND EXPLOSION HAZARD.

DECOMPOSITION: THERMAL DECOMPOSITION PRODUCTS MAY INCLUDE TOXIC OXIDES OF NITROGEN AND CARBON AND TOXIC AND CORROSIVE FUMES OF CHLORIDES.

POLYMERIZATION: HAZARDOUS POLYMERIZATION HAS NOT BEEN REPORTED TO OCCUR UNDER NORMAL TEMPERATURES AND PRESSURES.

STORAGE AND DISPOSAL

OBSERVE ALL FEDERAL, STATE AND LOCAL REGULATIONS WHEN STORING OR DISPOSING OF THIS SUBSTANCE. FOR ASSISTANCE, CONTACT THE DISTRICT DIRECTOR OF THE ENVIRONMENTAL PROTECTION AGENCY.

STORAGE

STORE IN ACCORDANCE WITH 40 CFR 165 RECOMMENDED PROCEDURES FOR THE DISPOSAL AND STORAGE OF PESTICIDES AND PESTICIDE CONTAINERS.
STORE AWAY FROM INCOMPATIBLE SUBSTANCES.

****DISPOSAL****

DISPOSAL MUST BE IN ACCORDANCE WITH 40 CFR 165 RECOMMENDED PROCEDURES FOR THE DISPOSAL AND STORAGE OF PESTICIDES AND PESTICIDE CONTAINERS.

CONDITIONS TO AVOID

MAY BURN BUT DOES NOT IGNITE READILY. AVOID CONTACT WITH STRONG OXIDIZERS, EXCESSIVE HEAT, SPARKS, OR OPEN FLAME.

SPILL AND LEAK PROCEDURES

OCCUPATIONAL SPILL: SWEEP UP AND PLACE IN SUITABLE CLEAN, DRY CONTAINERS FOR RECLAMATION OR LATER DISPOSAL. DO NOT FLUSH SPILLED MATERIAL INTO SEWER. KEEP UNNECESSARY PEOPLE AWAY.

PROTECTIVE EQUIPMENT

VENTILATION: PROVIDE LOCAL EXHAUST OR GENERAL DILUTION VENTILATION SYSTEM.

RESPIRATOR: THE FOLLOWING RESPIRATORS ARE RECOMMENDED BASED ON INFORMATION FOUND IN THE PHYSICAL DATA, TOXICITY AND HEALTH EFFECTS SECTIONS. THEY ARE RANKED IN ORDER FROM MINIMUM TO MAXIMUM RESPIRATORY PROTECTION. THE SPECIFIC RESPIRATOR SELECTED MUST BE BASED ON CONTAMINATION LEVELS FOUND IN THE WORK PLACE, MUST NOT EXCEED THE WORKING LIMITS OF THE RESPIRATOR AND BE JOINTLY APPROVED BY THE NATIONAL INSTITUTE FOR OCCUPATIONAL SAFETY AND HEALTH AND THE MINE SAFETY AND HEALTH ADMINISTRATION (NIOSH-MSHA).

DUST AND MIST RESPIRATOR WITH A FULL FACEPIECE.

AIR-PURIFYING FULL FACEPIECE RESPIRATOR WITH A HIGH-EFFICIENCY PARTICULATE FILTER.

POWERED AIR-PURIFYING RESPIRATOR WITH A TIGHT-FITTING FACEPIECE AND HIGH-EFFICIENCY PARTICULATE FILTER.

TYPE 'C' SUPPLIED-AIR RESPIRATOR WITH A FULL FACEPIECE OPERATED IN PRESSURE-DEMAND OR OTHER POSITIVE PRESSURE MODE OR WITH A FULL FACEPIECE, HELMET OR HOOD OPERATED IN CONTINUOUS-FLOW MODE.

SELF-CONTAINED BREATHING APPARATUS WITH A FULL FACEPIECE OPERATED IN PRESSURE-DEMAND OR OTHER POSITIVE PRESSURE MODE.

FOR FIREFIGHTING AND OTHER IMMEDIATELY DANGEROUS TO LIFE OR HEALTH CONDITIONS:

SELF-CONTAINED BREATHING APPARATUS WITH FULL FACEPIECE OPERATED IN PRESSURE-DEMAND OR OTHER POSITIVE PRESSURE MODE.

SUPPLIED-AIR RESPIRATOR WITH FULL FACEPIECE AND OPERATED IN PRESSURE-DEMAND OR OTHER POSITIVE PRESSURE MODE IN COMBINATION WITH AN AUXILIARY SELF-CONTAINED BREATHING APPARATUS OPERATED IN PRESSURE-DEMAND OR OTHER POSITIVE PRESSURE MODE.

CLOTHING: EMPLOYEE MUST WEAR APPROPRIATE PROTECTIVE (IMPERVIOUS) CLOTHING AND EQUIPMENT TO PREVENT ANY POSSIBILITY OF SKIN CONTACT WITH THIS SUBSTANCE.

GLOVES: EMPLOYEE MUST WEAR APPROPRIATE PROTECTIVE GLOVES TO PREVENT CONTACT WITH THIS SUBSTANCE.

EYE PROTECTION: EMPLOYEE MUST WEAR SPLASH-PROOF OR DUST-RESISTANT SAFETY GOGGLES AND A FACESHIELD TO PREVENT CONTACT WITH THIS SUBSTANCE.

EMERGENCY WASH FACILITIES: WHERE THERE IS ANY POSSIBILITY THAT AN EMPLOYEE'S EYES AND/OR SKIN MAY BE EXPOSED TO THIS SUBSTANCE, THE EMPLOYER SHOULD PROVIDE AN EYE WASH FOUNTAIN AND QUICK DRENCH SHOWER WITHIN THE IMMEDIATE WORK AREA FOR EMERGENCY USE.

AUTHORIZED BY- OCCUPATIONAL HEALTH SERVICES, INC.

CREATION DATE: 05/22/90 ***REVISION DATE:*** 05/31/90

MATERIAL SAFETY DATA SHEET

OCCUPATIONAL HEALTH SERVICES, INC.
AGRICULTURE AND PESTICIDE DIVISION
450 SEVENTH AVENUE, SUITE 2407
NEW YORK, NEW YORK 10123
1-800-445-MSDS OR (212) 967-1100

EMERGENCY CONTACT:
JOHN S. BRANSFORD, JR. (615) 292-1180

SUBSTANCE IDENTIFICATION

CAS-NUMBER 25155-18-4

SUBSTANCE: **METHYLBENZETHONIUM CHLORIDE**

TRADE NAMES/SYNONYMS: BENZENEMETHANAMINIUM, N,N-DIMETHYL-N-(2-(2-(METHYL-4-(1,1,3,3- TETRAMETHYLBUTYL)PHENOXY)ETHOXY)ETHYL)-, CHLORIDE; N,N-DIMETHYL-N-(2-(2-(METHYL-4-(1,1,3,3-TETRAMETHYLBUTYL)PHENOXY)ETHOXY)ETHYL)BENZENEMETHANAMINIUM CHLORIDE; AMMONIUM, BENZYLDIMETHYL(2-(2-((4-(1,1,3,3-TETRAMETHYLBUTYL)TOLYL)OXY)ETHOXY)ETHYL)-, CHLORIDE; BENZYLDIMETHYL(2-(2-((4-(1,1,3,3 TETRAMETHYLBUTYL)TOLYL)OXY)ETHOXY)ETHYL)AMMONIUM CHLORIDE; AMMONIUM, BENZYLDIMETHYL(2-(2-(P-1,1,3,3-TETRAMETHYLBUTYLCRESOXY)ETHOXY)ETHYL)-, CHLORIDE; BENZYLDIMETHYL(2-(2-(P-1,1,3,3-TETRAMETHYLBUTYLCRESOXY)ETHOXY)ETHYL)AMMONIUM CHLORIDE; HYAMINE 10X; DIMETHYLBENZYLAMMONIUM, (2-(2-(P-OCTYLCRESOXY)ETHOXY)ETHYL)-, CHLORIDE; (2-(2-(P-OCTYLCRESOXY)ETHOXY)ETHYL)DIMETHYLBENZYLAMMONIUM CHLORIDE; DIAPARENE CHLORIDE; BACTINE; C28H44CLNO2; PST71862

CHEMICAL FAMILY: QUATERNARY AMMONIUM COMPOUND CATIONIC SURFACTANT

MOLECULAR FORMULA: C28-H44-N-O2.CL

MOLECULAR WEIGHT: 462.12

CERCLA RATINGS (SCALE 0-3): HEALTH=1 FIRE=1 REACTIVITY=0 PERSISTENCE=0

NFPA RATINGS (SCALE 0-4): HEALTH=U FIRE=1 REACTIVITY=0

COMPONENTS AND CONTAMINANTS

COMPONENT: METHYLBENZETHONIUM CHLORIDE ***PERCENT:*** 100.0
CAS# 25155-18-4

OTHER CONTAMINANTS: NONE

EXPOSURE LIMITS: NO OCCUPATIONAL EXPOSURE LIMITS ESTABLISHED BY OSHA, ACGIH, OR NIOSH.

PHYSICAL DATA

DESCRIPTION: ODORLESS, COLORLESS, CRYSTALLINE SOLID WITH A BITTER TASTE.

MELTING POINT: 322-325 F (161-163 C) ***SPECIFIC GRAVITY:*** NOT AVAILABLE

SOLUBILITY IN WATER: SOLUBLE

SOLVENT SOLUBILITY: SOLUBLE IN ALCOHOL, CELLOSOLVE, CHLOROFORM; INSOLUBLE IN CARBON TETRACHLORIDE, ETHER.

FIRE AND EXPLOSION DATA

FIRE AND EXPLOSION HAZARD: SLIGHT FIRE HAZARD WHEN EXPOSED TO HEAT OR FLAME.

FIREFIGHTING MEDIA: DRY CHEMICAL, CARBON DIOXIDE, HALON, WATER SPRAY OR STANDARD FOAM (1987 EMERGENCY RESPONSE GUIDEBOOK, DOT P 5800.4).
FOR LARGER FIRES, USE WATER SPRAY, FOG OR STANDARD FOAM (1987 EMERGENCY RESPONSE GUIDEBOOK, DOT P 5800.4).

FIREFIGHTING: MOVE CONTAINER FROM FIRE AREA IF POSSIBLE. DO NOT SCATTER SPILLED MATERIAL WITH HIGH PRESSURE WATER STREAMS. DIKE FIRE CONTROL WATER FOR LATER DISPOSAL (1987 EMERGENCY RESPONSE GUIDEBOOK, DOT P 5800.4, GUIDE PAGE 31).
USE AGENTS SUITABLE FOR TYPE OF SURROUNDING FIRE. AVOID BREATHING HAZARDOUS VAPORS, KEEP UPWIND.

TOXICITY

METHYLBENZETHONIUM CHLORIDE: TOXICITY DATA: 55 GM/KG ORAL-RAT LD50; 55 MG/KG ORAL-CAT LD50. CARCINOGEN STATUS: NONE. ACUTE TOXICITY: RELATIVELY NONTOXIC BY INGESTION. TARGET EFFECTS: NO DATA AVAILABLE.

HEALTH EFFECTS AND FIRST AID

INHALATION: METHYLBENZETHONIUM CHLORIDE: SEE INFORMATION ON CATIONIC SURFACTANTS.
CATIONIC SURFACTANTS: **ACUTE EXPOSURE**- CONCENTRATIONS OF MANY CATIONIC SURFACTANTS AS LOW AS 0.1 TO 0.5% ARE IRRITATING TO THE MUCOUS MEMBRANES. 1% SOLUTIONS MAY PRODUCE SIGNIFICANT IRRITATION, AND CONCENTRATED SOLUTIONS (>10%), MAY HAVE CAUSTIC QUALITIES.
CHRONIC EXPOSURE- NO DATA AVAILABLE.

FIRST AID- REMOVE FROM EXPOSURE AREA TO FRESH AIR IMMEDIATELY. IF BREATHING HAS STOPPED, GIVE ARTIFICIAL RESPIRATION. MAINTAIN AIRWAY AND BLOOD PRESSURE AND ADMINISTER OXYGEN IF AVAILABLE. KEEP AFFECTED PERSON WARM AND AT REST. TREAT SYMPTOMATICALLY AND SUPPORTIVELY. ADMINISTRATION OF OXYGEN SHOULD BE PERFORMED BY QUALIFIED PERSONNEL. GET MEDICAL ATTENTION IMMEDIATELY.

SKIN CONTACT: METHYLBENZETHONIUM CHLORIDE: SEE INFORMATION ON CATIONIC SURFACTANTS.
CATIONIC SURFACTANTS: **ACUTE EXPOSURE**- 1% SOLUTIONS OF MANY CATIONIC SURFACTANTS PRODUCE IRRITATION AND CONCENTRATED SOLUTIONS (>10%), HAVE CAUSTIC QUALITIES. **CHRONIC EXPOSURE**- PROLONGED OR REPEATED

EXPOSURE TO SOME CATIONIC SURFACTANTS HAS RESULTED IN ALLERGIC REACTIONS.
FIRST AID- REMOVE CONTAMINATED CLOTHING AND SHOES IMMEDIATELY. WASH AFFECTED AREA WITH SOAP OR MILD DETERGENT AND LARGE AMOUNTS OF WATER UNTIL NO EVIDENCE OF CHEMICAL REMAINS (AT LEAST 15-20 MINUTES). IN CASE OF CHEMICAL BURNS, COVER AREA WITH STERILE, DRY DRESSING. BANDAGE SECURELY, BUT NOT TOO TIGHTLY. GET MEDICAL ATTENTION IMMEDIATELY.

EYE CONTACT: METHYLBENZETHONIUM CHLORIDE: SEE INFORMATION ON CATIONIC SURFACTANTS.
CATIONIC SURFACTANTS: **ACUTE EXPOSURE**- 1% SOLUTIONS, AND POSSIBLY AS LOW AS 0.1%, OF MANY CATIONIC SURFACTANTS PRODUCE SIGNIFICANT IRRITATION. HIGH CONCENTRATIONS (>10%), OF SOME CATIONIC SURFACTANTS CAUSE SEVERE BURNS WITH PERMANENT OPACITY AND VASCULARIZATION. **CHRONIC EXPOSURE**- NO DATA AVAILABLE.
FIRST AID- WASH EYES IMMEDIATELY WITH LARGE AMOUNTS OF WATER, OCCASIONALLY LIFTING UPPER AND LOWER LIDS, UNTIL NO EVIDENCE OF CHEMICAL REMAINS (AT LEAST 15-20 MINUTES). CONTINUE IRRIGATING WITH NORMAL SALINE UNTIL THE PH HAS RETURNED TO NORMAL (30-60 MINUTES). COVER WITH STERILE BANDAGES. GET MEDICAL ATTENTION IMMEDIATELY.

INGESTION: METHYLBENZETHONIUM CHLORIDE: SEE INFORMATION ON CATIONIC SURFACTANTS.
CATIONIC SURFACTANTS: **ACUTE EXPOSURE**- CONCENTRATED SOLUTIONS (>10%), OF MANY CATIONIC SURFACTANTS, CAUSE CORROSIVE DAMAGE TO THE MUCOUS MEMBRANES AND ESOPHAGUS, NAUSEA, AND VOMITING. IF SUFFICIENT QUANTITIES ARE INGESTED OTHER SIGNS AND SYMPTOMS REFERABLE TO THE CENTRAL NERVOUS SYSTEM OR CIRCULATORY SHOCK MAY DEVELOP INCLUDING RESTLESSNESS, CONFUSION, HYPOTENSION, MUSCLE WEAKNESS, COLLAPSE, CONVULSIONS, RESPIRATORY PARALYSIS, CYANOSIS, AND COMA. DEATH MAY OCCUR WITHIN 1-4 HOURS. THE ESTIMATED FATAL HUMAN DOSE IS BETWEEN 1-3 GRAMS. **CHRONIC EXPOSURE**- NO DATA AVAILABLE.
FIRST AID- GIVE MILK OR ACTIVATED CHARCOAL AND REMOVE BY CATHARSIS WITH FLEET'S PHOSPHO-SODA, 15-60 ML DILUTED 1:4 WITH WATER. LAVAGE AND EMESIS ARE CONTRAINDICATED IN THE PRESENCE OF ESOPHAGEAL INJURY. GASTRIC LAVAGE SHOULD BE PERFORMED BY QUALIFIED MEDICAL PERSONNEL. GET MEDICAL ATTENTION IMMEDIATELY (DREISBACH, HANDBOOK OF POISONING, 12TH ED.). MAINTAIN AIRWAY, BLOOD PRESSURE AND RESPIRATION.
ANTIDOTE: NO SPECIFIC ANTIDOTE. TREAT SYMPTOMATICALLY AND SUPPORTIVELY.

REACTIVITY

REACTIVITY: STABLE UNDER NORMAL TEMPERATURES AND PRESSURES.
INCOMPATIBILITIES: METHYLBENZETHONIUM CHLORIDE: ANIONIC AGENTS: INCOMPATABLE. OXIDIZERS (STRONG): FIRE AND EXPLOSION HAZARD.
DECOMPOSITION: THERMAL DECOMPOSITION PRODUCTS MAY INCLUDE TOXIC OXIDES OF NITROGEN AND CARBON AND TOXIC AND CORROSIVE FUMES OF CHLORIDES.
POLYMERIZATION: HAZARDOUS POLYMERIZATION HAS NOT BEEN REPORTED TO OCCUR UNDER NORMAL TEMPERATURES AND PRESSURES.

STORAGE AND DISPOSAL

OBSERVE ALL FEDERAL, STATE AND LOCAL REGULATIONS WHEN STORING OR DISPOSING OF THIS SUBSTANCE. FOR ASSISTANCE, CONTACT THE DISTRICT DIRECTOR OF THE ENVIRONMENTAL PROTECTION AGENCY.

STORAGE

STORE AWAY FROM INCOMPATIBLE SUBSTANCES.

CONDITIONS TO AVOID

MAY BURN BUT DOES NOT IGNITE READILY. AVOID CONTACT WITH STRONG OXIDIZERS, EXCESSIVE HEAT, SPARKS, OR OPEN FLAME.

SPILL AND LEAK PROCEDURES

OCCUPATIONAL SPILL: SWEEP UP AND PLACE IN SUITABLE CLEAN, DRY CONTAINERS FOR RECLAMATION OR LATER DISPOSAL. DO NOT FLUSH SPILLED MATERIAL INTO SEWER. KEEP UNNECESSARY PEOPLE AWAY.

PROTECTIVE EQUIPMENT

VENTILATION: PROVIDE LOCAL EXHAUST OR GENERAL DILUTION VENTILATION SYSTEM.
RESPIRATOR: THE FOLLOWING RESPIRATORS ARE RECOMMENDED BASED ON INFORMATION FOUND IN THE PHYSICAL DATA, TOXICITY AND HEALTH EFFECTS SECTIONS. THEY ARE RANKED IN ORDER FROM MINIMUM TO MAXIMUM RESPIRATORY PROTECTION. THE SPECIFIC RESPIRATOR SELECTED MUST BE BASED ON CONTAMINATION LEVELS FOUND IN THE WORK PLACE, MUST NOT EXCEED THE WORKING LIMITS OF THE RESPIRATOR AND BE JOINTLY APPROVED BY THE NATIONAL INSTITUTE FOR OCCUPATIONAL SAFETY AND HEALTH AND THE MINE SAFETY AND HEALTH ADMINISTRATION (NIOSH-MSHA).
DUST AND MIST RESPIRATOR WITH A FULL FACEPIECE.
AIR-PURIFYING FULL FACEPIECE RESPIRATOR WITH A HIGH-EFFICIENCY PARTICULATE FILTER.
POWERED AIR-PURIFYING RESPIRATOR WITH A TIGHT-FITTING FACEPIECE AND HIGH-EFFICIENCY PARTICULATE FILTER.
TYPE 'C' SUPPLIED-AIR RESPIRATOR WITH A FULL FACEPIECE OPERATED IN PRESSURE-DEMAND OR OTHER POSITIVE PRESSURE MODE OR WITH A FULL FACEPIECE, HELMET OR HOOD OPERATED IN CONTINUOUS-FLOW MODE.
SELF-CONTAINED BREATHING APPARATUS WITH A FULL FACEPIECE OPERATED IN PRESSURE-DEMAND OR OTHER POSITIVE PRESSURE MODE.
FOR FIREFIGHTING AND OTHER IMMEDIATELY DANGEROUS TO LIFE OR HEALTH CONDITIONS:
SELF-CONTAINED BREATHING APPARATUS WITH FULL FACEPIECE OPERATED IN PRESSURE-DEMAND OR OTHER POSITIVE PRESSURE MODE.
SUPPLIED-AIR RESPIRATOR WITH FULL FACEPIECE AND OPERATED IN PRESSURE-DEMAND OR OTHER POSITIVE PRESSURE MODE IN COMBINATION WITH AN AUXILIARY SELF-CONTAINED BREATHING APPARATUS OPERATED IN PRESSURE-DEMAND OR OTHER POSITIVE PRESSURE MODE.
CLOTHING: EMPLOYEE MUST WEAR APPROPRIATE PROTECTIVE (IMPERVIOUS) CLOTHING AND EQUIPMENT TO PREVENT ANY POSSIBILITY OF SKIN CONTACT WITH THIS SUBSTANCE.
GLOVES: EMPLOYEE MUST WEAR APPROPRIATE PROTECTIVE GLOVES TO PREVENT CONTACT WITH THIS SUBSTANCE.
EYE PROTECTION: EMPLOYEE MUST WEAR SPLASH-PROOF OR DUST-RESISTANT SAFETY GOGGLES AND A FACESHIELD TO PREVENT CONTACT WITH THIS SUBSTANCE.
EMERGENCY WASH FACILITIES: WHERE THERE IS ANY POSSIBILITY THAT AN EMPLOYEE'S EYES AND/OR SKIN MAY BE EXPOSED TO THIS SUBSTANCE, THE EMPLOYER SHOULD PROVIDE AN EYE WASH FOUNTAIN AND QUICK DRENCH SHOWER WITHIN THE IMMEDIATE WORK AREA FOR EMERGENCY USE.

AUTHORIZED BY- OCCUPATIONAL HEALTH SERVICES, INC.
CREATION DATE: 05/22/90 ***REVISION DATE:*** 05/31/90

MATERIAL SAFETY DATA SHEET

OCCUPATIONAL HEALTH SERVICES, INC.
AGRICULTURE AND PESTICIDE DIVISION
450 SEVENTH AVENUE, SUITE 2407
NEW YORK, NEW YORK 10123
1-800-445-MSDS OR (212) 967-1100

EMERGENCY CONTACT:
JOHN S. BRANSFORD, JR. (615) 292-1180

SUBSTANCE IDENTIFICATION

CAS-NUMBER 1698-60-8
***SUBSTANCE:* PYRAZON**
TRADE NAMES/SYNONYMS: 3(2H)-PYRIDAZINONE, 5-AMINO-4-CHLORO-2-PHENYL-; 5-AMINO-4-CHLORO-2-PHENYL-3(2H)-PYRIDAZINONE; 5-AMINO-4-CHLORO-2-PHENYLPYRIDAZIN-3(2H)-ONE; CHLORIDAZON; CHLORIDAZONE; H-119; PAC; PCA; PYRAMIN; C10H8CLN3O; PST71928
CHEMICAL FAMILY: PYRIDAZINE
HALOGEN
AROMATIC
MOLECULAR FORMULA: C10-H8-CL-N3-O
MOLECULAR WEIGHT: 221.66
CERCLA RATINGS (SCALE 0-3): HEALTH=2 FIRE=1 REACTIVITY=0 PERSISTENCE=2
NFPA RATINGS (SCALE 0-4): HEALTH=U FIRE=1 REACTIVITY=0

COMPONENTS AND CONTAMINANTS

COMPONENT: PYRAZON ***PERCENT:*** 100.0
CAS# 1698-60-8
EXPOSURE LIMITS: NO OCCUPATIONAL EXPOSURE LIMITS ESTABLISHED BY OSHA, ACGIH, OR NIOSH.

PHYSICAL DATA

DESCRIPTION: PALE YELLOW TO BROWN CRYSTALLINE SOLID.
MELTING POINT: 401-403 F (205-206 C) (DECOMPOSES)
SPECIFIC GRAVITY: NOT AVAILABLE ***VAPOR PRESSURE:*** NEGLIGIBLE
SOLUBILITY IN WATER: 0.04%

SOLVENT SOLUBILITY: MODERATELY SOLUBLE IN METHANOL AND ACETONE; SLIGHTLY SOLUBLE IN ETHYL ACETATE, DICHLOROMETHANE, AND CHLOROFORM; VERY SLIGHTLY SOLUBLE IN BENZENE, ETHER, AND CYCLOHEXANE.

FIRE AND EXPLOSION DATA

FIRE AND EXPLOSION HAZARD: SLIGHT FIRE HAZARD WHEN EXPOSED TO HEAT OR FLAME.
DUST-AIR MIXTURES MAY IGNITE OR EXPLODE.

FIREFIGHTING MEDIA: DRY CHEMICAL, CARBON DIOXIDE, HALON, WATER SPRAY OR STANDARD FOAM (1987 EMERGENCY RESPONSE GUIDEBOOK, DOT P 5800.4).
FOR LARGER FIRES, USE WATER SPRAY, FOG OR STANDARD FOAM (1987 EMERGENCY RESPONSE GUIDEBOOK, DOT P 5800.4).

FIREFIGHTING: MOVE CONTAINER FROM FIRE AREA IF POSSIBLE. DO NOT SCATTER SPILLED MATERIAL WITH HIGH PRESSURE WATER STREAMS. DIKE FIRE CONTROL WATER FOR LATER DISPOSAL (1987 EMERGENCY RESPONSE GUIDEBOOK, DOT P 5800.4, GUIDE PAGE 31).
USE AGENTS SUITABLE FOR TYPE OF SURROUNDING FIRE. AVOID BREATHING HAZARDOUS VAPORS, KEEP UPWIND.

TOXICITY

PYRAZON: IRRITATION DATA: 500 MG/24 HOURS EYE-RABBIT MILD. TOXICITY DATA: 2500 MG/KG SKIN-RABBIT LD50; 647 MG/KG ORAL-RAT LD50; 1000 MG/KG ORAL-MOUSE LD50; 2000 MG/KG ORAL-RABBIT LD50; 760 MG/KG ORAL-GUINEA PIG LD50; 600 MG/KG INTRAPERITONEAL-RAT LD50; 410 MG/KG INTRAPERITONEAL-MOUSE LD50; >30800 MG/M3/4 HOURS INHALATION-RAT LC50 (85JFAN); 2 GM/KG UNREPORTED-MAMMAL LD50; REPRODUCTIVE EFFECTS DATA (RTECS). CARCINOGEN STATUS: NONE. ACUTE TOXICITY LEVEL: MODERATELY TOXIC BY INHALATION AND INGESTION; SLIGHTLY TOXIC BY DERMAL ABSORPTION. TARGET EFFECTS: NO DATA AVAILABLE.

HEALTH EFFECTS AND FIRST AID

INHALATION: PYRAZON: **ACUTE EXPOSURE-** THE LC50 FOR RATS WAS GREATER THAN 30800 MG/M3/4 HOURS. **CHRONIC EXPOSURE-** NO DATA AVAILABLE.

FIRST AID- REMOVE FROM EXPOSURE AREA TO FRESH AIR IMMEDIATELY. IF BREATHING HAS STOPPED, PERFORM ARTIFICIAL RESPIRATION. KEEP PERSON WARM AND AT REST. TREAT SYMPTOMATICALLY AND SUPPORTIVELY. GET MEDICAL ATTENTION IMMEDIATELY.

SKIN CONTACT: PYRAZON: **ACUTE EXPOSURE-** THIS MATERIAL WAS SLIGHTLY IRRITATING TO RABBIT SKIN. SENSITIZATION MAY OCCUR IN PREVIOUSLY EXPOSED PERSONS. **CHRONIC EXPOSURE-** PROLONGED OR REPEATED EXPOSURE MAY CAUSE SENSTITIZATION DERMATITIS. BLOOD ALTERATIONS FOLLOWING DERMAL APPLICATIONS HAVE BEEN DESCRIBED IN THE RUSSIAN LITERATURE.

FIRST AID- REMOVE CONTAMINATED CLOTHING AND SHOES IMMEDIATELY. WASH AFFECTED AREA WITH SOAP OR MILD DETERGENT AND LARGE AMOUNTS OF WATER UNTIL NO EVIDENCE OF CHEMICAL REMAINS (APPROXIMATELY 15-20 MINUTES). GET MEDICAL ATTENTION IMMEDIATELY.

EYE CONTACT: PYRAZON: **ACUTE EXPOSURE-** MAY BE SEVERELY IRRITATING TO THE EYE. **CHRONIC EXPOSURE-** NO DATA AVAILABLE.

FIRST AID- WASH EYES IMMEDIATELY WITH LARGE AMOUNTS OF WATER OR NORMAL SALINE, OCCASIONALLY LIFTING UPPER AND LOWER LIDS, UNTIL NO EVIDENCE OF CHEMICAL REMAINS (APPROXIMATELY 15-20 MINUTES). GET MEDICAL ATTENTION IMMEDIATELY.

INGESTION: PYRAZON: **ACUTE EXPOSURE-** A LETHAL DOSE REPORTED IN RATS WAS 647 MG/KG; SYMPTOMS WERE NOT REPORTED. **CHRONIC EXPOSURE-** NO OBSERVABLE EFFECTS WERE NOTED IN 2-YEAR STUDIES OF RATS RECEIVING A 300 MG/KG DIET AND DOGS RECEIVING A 1500 MG/KG DIET.

FIRST AID- IF THE PERSON IS CONSCIOUS AND NOT CONVULSING, REMOVE BY GASTRIC LAVAGE AND FOLLOW WITH A CATHARTIC (DREISBACH, HANDBOOK OF POISONING, 12TH ED.). TREAT SYMPTOMATICALLY AND SUPPORTIVELY. GASTRIC LAVAGE SHOULD BE PERFORMED BY QUALIFIED MEDICAL PERSONNEL. GET MEDICAL ATTENTION IMMEDIATELY.

ANTIDOTE: NO SPECIFIC ANTIDOTE. TREAT SYMPTOMATICALLY AND SUPPORTIVELY.

REACTIVITY

REACTIVITY: STABLE UNDER NORMAL TEMPERATURES AND PRESSURES.

INCOMPATIBILITIES: PYRAZON: OXIDIZERS (STRONG): FIRE AND EXPLOSION HAZARD.

DECOMPOSITION: THERMAL DECOMPOSITION PRODUCTS MAY INCLUDE TOXIC OXIDES OF NITROGEN AND CARBON AND TOXIC AND CORROSIVE FUMES OF CHLORIDES.

POLYMERIZATION: HAZARDOUS POLYMERIZATION HAS NOT BEEN REPORTED TO OCCUR UNDER NORMAL TEMPERATURES AND PRESSURES.

STORAGE AND DISPOSAL

OBSERVE ALL FEDERAL, STATE AND LOCAL REGULATIONS WHEN STORING OR DISPOSING OF THIS SUBSTANCE. FOR ASSISTANCE, CONTACT THE DISTRICT DIRECTOR OF THE ENVIRONMENTAL PROTECTION AGENCY.

****STORAGE****

STORE IN ACCORDANCE WITH 40 CFR 165 RECOMMENDED PROCEDURES FOR THE DISPOSAL AND STORAGE OF PESTICIDES AND PESTICIDE CONTAINERS.
STORE AWAY FROM INCOMPATIBLE SUBSTANCES.

****DISPOSAL****

DISPOSAL MUST BE IN ACCORDANCE WITH 40 CFR 165 RECOMMENDED PROCEDURES FOR THE DISPOSAL AND STORAGE OF PESTICIDES AND PESTICIDE CONTAINERS.

CONDITIONS TO AVOID

MAY BURN BUT DOES NOT IGNITE READILY. AVOID CONTACT WITH STRONG OXIDIZERS, EXCESSIVE HEAT, SPARKS, OR OPEN FLAME.

SPILL AND LEAK PROCEDURES

OCCUPATIONAL SPILL: SWEEP UP AND PLACE IN SUITABLE CLEAN, DRY CONTAINERS FOR RECLAMATION OR LATER DISPOSAL. DO NOT FLUSH SPILLED MATERIAL INTO SEWER. KEEP UNNECESSARY PEOPLE AWAY.

PROTECTIVE EQUIPMENT

VENTILATION: PROVIDE LOCAL EXHAUST OR GENERAL DILUTION VENTILATION SYSTEM.

RESPIRATOR: THE FOLLOWING RESPIRATORS ARE RECOMMENDED BASED ON INFORMATION FOUND IN THE PHYSICAL DATA, TOXICITY AND HEALTH EFFECTS SECTIONS. THEY ARE RANKED IN ORDER FROM MINIMUM TO MAXIMUM RESPIRATORY PROTECTION. THE SPECIFIC RESPIRATOR SELECTED MUST BE BASED ON CONTAMINATION LEVELS FOUND IN THE WORK PLACE, MUST NOT EXCEED THE WORKING LIMITS OF THE RESPIRATOR AND BE JOINTLY APPROVED BY THE NATIONAL INSTITUTE FOR OCCUPATIONAL SAFETY AND HEALTH AND THE MINE SAFETY AND HEALTH ADMINISTRATION (NIOSH-MSHA).
CHEMICAL CARTRIDGE RESPIRATOR WITH AN ORGANIC VAPOR CARTRIDGE(S) IN COMBINATION WITH A DUST AND MIST FILTER.
GAS MASK WITH ORGANIC VAPOR CANISTER (CHIN-STYLE OR FRONT- OR BACK-MOUNTED CANISTER) WITH A DUST AND MIST FILTER.
GAS MASK WITH ORGANIC VAPOR CANISTER (CHIN-STYLE OR FRONT- OR BACK-MOUNTED CANISTER) WITH A PARTICULATE FILTER.
POWERED AIR-PURIFYING RESPIRATOR WITH A HIGH-EFFICIENCY FILTER.
TYPE 'C' SUPPLIED-AIR RESPIRATOR WITH A FULL FACEPIECE OPERATED IN A PRESSURE-DEMAND OR OTHER POSITIVE PRESSURE MODE.
SELF-CONTAINED BREATHING APPARATUS WITH A FULL FACEPIECE OPERATED IN PRESSURE-DEMAND OR OTHER POSITIVE PRESSURE MODE.
FOR FIREFIGHTING AND OTHER IMMEDIATELY DANGEROUS TO LIFE OR HEALTH CONDITIONS:
SELF-CONTAINED BREATHING APPARATUS WITH FULL FACEPIECE OPERATED IN PRESSURE-DEMAND OR OTHER POSITIVE PRESSURE MODE.
SUPPLIED-AIR RESPIRATOR WITH FULL FACEPIECE AND OPERATED IN PRESSURE-DEMAND OR OTHER POSITIVE PRESSURE MODE IN COMBINATION WITH AN AUXILIARY SELF-CONTAINED BREATHING APPARATUS OPERATED IN PRESSURE-DEMAND OR OTHER POSITIVE PRESSURE MODE.

CLOTHING: EMPLOYEE MUST WEAR APPROPRIATE PROTECTIVE (IMPERVIOUS) CLOTHING AND EQUIPMENT TO PREVENT REPEATED OR PROLONGED SKIN CONTACT WITH THIS SUBSTANCE.

GLOVES: EMPLOYEE MUST WEAR APPROPRIATE PROTECTIVE GLOVES TO PREVENT CONTACT WITH THIS SUBSTANCE.

EYE PROTECTION: EMPLOYEE MUST WEAR SPLASH-PROOF OR DUST-RESISTANT SAFETY GOGGLES TO PREVENT EYE CONTACT WITH THIS SUBSTANCE.
EMERGENCY EYE WASH: WHERE THERE IS ANY POSSIBILITY THAT AN EMPLOYEE'S EYES MAY BE EXPOSED TO THIS SUBSTANCE, THE EMPLOYER SHOULD PROVIDE AN EYE WASH FOUNTAIN WITHIN THE IMMEDIATE WORK AREA FOR EMERGENCY USE.

AUTHORIZED BY- OCCUPATIONAL HEALTH SERVICES, INC.
CREATION DATE: 03/23/90 ***REVISION DATE:*** 05/31/90

MATERIAL SAFETY DATA SHEET

OCCUPATIONAL HEALTH SERVICES, INC.
AGRICULTURE AND PESTICIDE DIVISION

EMERGENCY CONTACT:
JOHN S. BRANSFORD, JR. (615) 292-1180

450 SEVENTH AVENUE, SUITE 2407
NEW YORK, NEW YORK 10123
1-800-445-MSDS OR (212) 967-1100

SUBSTANCE IDENTIFICATION

CAS-NUMBER 12789-03-6
SUBSTANCE: **CHLORDANE (COMMERCIAL)**
TRADE NAMES/SYNONYMS:
1,2,4,5,6,7,8,8-OCTACHLORO-2,3,3A,4,7,7A-HEXAHYDRO-4,7-METHANO-1H -INDENE; 1,2,4,5,6,7,8,8-OCTACHLORO-3A,4,7,7A-TETRAHYDRO-4,7-METHANOINDAN; CHLORINDAN; CHLORDAN; CHLORDANE; CORTILAN-NEU; HCS 3260; TAT; TOXICHLOR; ENT 9,932; ENT 25,552-X; RCRA U036; NCI-COOO99; NA 2762; C10H6CL8; PST71948
CHEMICAL FAMILY: HALOGEN COMPOUND, AROMATIC
MOLECULAR FORMULA: C10-H6-CL8
MOLECULAR WEIGHT: 409.76
CERCLA RATINGS (SCALE 0-3): HEALTH=3 FIRE=0 REACTIVITY=0 PERSISTENCE=3
NFPA RATINGS (SCALE 0-4): HEALTH=4 FIRE=0 REACTIVITY=0

COMPONENTS AND CONTAMINANTS

COMPONENT: CHLORDANE ***PERCENT:*** 60.0-75.0
CAS# 57-74-9
COMPONENT: HEPTACHLOR ***PERCENT:*** 0-10.0
CAS# 76-44-8
COMPONENT: RELATED COMPOUNDS ***PERCENT:*** 1-30.0
EXPOSURE LIMITS: CHLORDANE: 0.5 MG/M3 OSHA TWA (SKIN) 0.5 MG/M3 ACGIH TWA (SKIN); 2 MG/M3 ACGIH STEL (NOTICE OF INTENDED CHANGES 1988-89) 1000 POUNDS SARA SECTION 302 THRESHOLD PLANNING QUANTITY 1 POUND SARA SECTION 304 REPORTABLE QUANTITY 1 POUND CERCLA SECTION 103 REPORTABLE QUANTITY SUBJECT TO SARA SECTION 313 ANNUAL TOXIC CHEMICAL RELEASE REPORTING SUBJECT TO CALIFORNIA PROPOSITION 65 CANCER AND/OR REPRODUCTIVE TOXICITY WARNING AND RELEASE REQUIREMENTS- (JULY 1, 1988)
HEPTACHLOR: 0.5 MG/M3 OSHA TWA (SKIN) 0.5 MG/M3 ACGIH TWA (SKIN) 1 POUND CERCLA SECTION 103 REPORTABLE QUANTITY SUBJECT TO SARA SECTION 313 ANNUAL TOXIC CHEMICAL RELEASE REPORTING SUBJECT TO CALIFORNIA PROPOSITION 65 CANCER AND/OR REPRODUCTIVE TOXICITY WARNING AND RELEASE REQUIREMENTS- (JULY 1, 1988)

PHYSICAL DATA

DESCRIPTION: VISCOUS, AMBER-COLORED LIQUID.
BOILING POINT: 347 F (175 C) @ 2 MMHG (DECOMPOSES)
SPECIFIC GRAVITY: 1.59-1.63
VISCOSITY: 69 POISES @ 25 C ***VAPOR PRESSURE:*** 0.00001 MMHG @ 25 C
EVAPORATION RATE: NOT AVAILABLE ***SOLUBILITY IN WATER:*** 0.1 PPM @ 25 C
VAPOR DENSITY: 14
SOLVENT SOLUBILITY: SOLUBLE IN ALIPHATIC AND AROMATIC HYDROCARBON SOLVENTS INCLUDING KEROSENE.

FIRE AND EXPLOSION DATA

FIRE AND EXPLOSION HAZARD: NEGLIGIBLE FIRE HAZARD WHEN EXPOSED TO HEAT OR FLAME.
FIREFIGHTING MEDIA: DRY CHEMICAL, CARBON DIOXIDE, HALON, WATER SPRAY OR STANDARD FOAM (1987 EMERGENCY RESPONSE GUIDEBOOK, DOT P 5800.4). FOR LARGER FIRES, USE WATER SPRAY, FOG OR STANDARD FOAM (1987 EMERGENCY RESPONSE GUIDEBOOK, DOT P 5800.4).
FIREFIGHTING: MOVE CONTAINERS FROM FIRE AREA IF POSSIBLE. FIGHT FIRE FROM MAXIMUM DISTANCE. STAY AWAY FROM STORAGE TANK ENDS. DIKE FIRE CONTROL WATER FOR LATER DISPOSAL. DO NOT SCATTER MATERIAL (1987 EMERGENCY RESPONSE GUIDEBOOK, DOT P 5800.4, GUIDE PAGE 55). EXTINGUISH ONLY IF FLOW CAN BE STOPPED. EXTINGUISH USING AGENT INDICATED. USE FLOODING AMOUNTS OF WATER AS A FOG. COOL CONTAINERS WITH FLOODING AMOUNTS OF WATER FROM AS FAR A DISTANCE AS POSSIBLE. AVOID BREATHING POISONOUS VAPORS, KEEP UPWIND. CONSIDER EVACUATION OF DOWNWIND AREA IF MATERIAL IS LEAKING.

TOXICITY

CHLORDANE (COMMERCIAL): TOXICITY DATA: 283 MG/KG ORAL-RAT LD50; MUTAGENIC DATA (RTECS). CARCINOGEN STATUS: NONE. ACUTE TOXICITY LEVEL: TOXIC BY INGESTION. TARGET EFFECTS: POISONING MAY AFFECT THE LIVER, KIDNEYS, AND BLOOD.
CHLORDANE: TOXICITY DATA: 100 MG/M3/4 HOURS INHALATION-CAT LC50; 428 MG/KG SKIN-HUMAN LDLO; 780 MG/KG SKIN-RABBIT LD50; 690 MG/KG SKIN-RAT LD50; 29 MG/KG ORAL-HUMAN LDLO; 3071 UG/KG ORAL-MAN TDLO; 120 UG/KG ORAL-WOMAN LDLO; 200 MG/KG ORAL-RAT LD50; 145 MG/KG ORAL-MOUSE LD50; 100 MG/KG ORAL-RABBIT LD50; 1720 MG/KG ORAL-HAMSTER LD50; 180 MG/KG ORAL-MAMMAL LD50; 50 MG/KG ORAL-DOMESTIC ANIMAL LD50; 100 MG/KG INTRAVENOUS-MOUSE LD50; 10 MG/KG INTRAVENOUS-RABBIT LDLO; 343 MG/KG INTRAPERITONEAL-RAT LD50; 240 MG/KG INTRAPERITONEAL-MOUSE LDLO; 118 MG/KG UNREPORTED-MAN LDLO; MUTAGENIC DATA (RTECS); REPRODUCTIVE EFFECTS DATA (RTECS); TUMORIGENIC DATA (RTECS). CARCINOGEN STATUS: HUMAN INADEQUATE EVIDENCE; ANIMAL LIMITED EVIDENCE (IARC GROUP-3). HEPATOCELLULAR CARCINOMAS WERE PRODUCED IN MICE BY ORAL ADMINISTRATION. ACUTE TOXICITY LEVEL: HIGHLY TOXIC BY INHALATION; TOXIC BY DERMAL ABSORPTION AND INGESTION. TARGET EFFECTS: CONVULSANT. POISONING MAY ALSO AFFECT THE LIVER, KIDNEYS, AND BLOOD. AT INCREASED RISK FROM EXPOSURE: PERSONS WITH CONVULSIVE DISORDERS. ADDITIONAL DATA: CHLORDANE MAY BE STORED IN ADIPOSE TISSUE; INTENSE ACTIVITY AND STARVATION MAY MOBILIZE THE PESTICIDE RESULTING IN THE REAPPEARANCE OF TOXIC SYMPTOMS. IT CROSSES THE PLACENTA AND MAY BE EXCRETED IN HUMAN MILK. STUDIES OF 2 GROUPS OF WORKERS, ONE INVOLVED IN THE MANUFACTURE OF CHLORDANE, HEPTACHLOR, AND ENDRIN AND THE OTHER OF CHLORDANE AND HEPTACHLOR, REVEALED A STATISTICALLY SIGNIFICANT INCREASE IN DEATHS FROM CEREBROVASCULAR DISEASE IN THE FORMER BUT NOT THE LATTER; THE FORMER STUDY HAD METHODOLOGICAL DEFICIENCIES.
HEPTACHLOR: TOXICITY DATA: 150 MG/M3/4 HOURS INHALATION-CAT LCLO; 200 MG/M3/4 HOURS INHALATION-MAMMAL LCLO; 119 MG/KG SKIN-RAT LD50; 1 GM/KG SKIN-GUINEA PIG LDLO; 40 MG/KG ORAL-RAT LD50; 116 MG/KG ORAL-GUINEA PIG LD50; 68 MG/KG ORAL-MOUSE LD50; 100 MG/KG ORAL-HAMSTER LD50; 50 MG/KG ORAL-CAT LDLO; 20 MG/KG INTRAVENOUS-MOUSE LDLO; 27 MG/KG INTRAPERITONEAL-RAT LD50; 130 MG/KG INTRAPERITONEAL-MOUSE LD50; 60 MG/KG UNREPORTED-MAMMAL LD50; MUTAGENIC DATA (RTECS); TUMORIGENIC DATA (RTECS). CARCINOGEN STATUS: HUMAN INADEQUATE EVIDENCE, ANIMAL LIMITED EVIDENCE (IARC GROUP-3). ORAL ADMINISTRATION OF HEPTACHLOR CONTAINING ABOUT 20% CHLORDANE PRODUCED LIVER CARCINOMAS IN MICE AND A SUGGESTION OF CARCINOGENIC EFFECTS ON THE THYROID IN FEMALE RATS. ACUTE TOXICITY LEVEL: HIGHLY TOXIC BY DERMAL ABSORPTION AND INGESTION. TARGET EFFECTS: CONVULSANT; HEPATOTOXIN. AT INCREASED RISK FROM EXPOSURE: PERSONS WITH CONVULSIVE DISORDERS AND LIVER DAMAGE. ADDITIONAL DATA: HEPTACHLOR AND ITS METABOLITE, HEPTACHLOR EPOXIDE, ACCUMULATE IN ADIPOSE TISSUE; INTENSE ACTIVITY AND STARVATION MAY MOBILIZE THE PESTICIDE RESULTING IN THE REAPPEARANCE OF TOXIC SYMPTOMS. HEPTACHLOR CROSSES THE PLACENTA AND IS EXCRETED IN HUMAN MILK. STUDIES OF 2 GROUPS OF WORKERS, ONE INVOLVED IN THE MANUFACTURE OF CHLORDANE, HEPTACHLOR, AND ENDRIN AND THE OTHER OF CHLORDANE AND HEPTACHLOR, REVEALED A STATISTICALLY SIGNIFICANT INCREASE IN DEATHS FROM CEREBROVASCULAR DISEASE IN THE FORMER BUT NOT THE LATTER; THE FORMER STUDY HAD METHODOLOGICAL DEFICIENCIES. STIMULANTS SUCH AS EPINEPHRINE MAY INDUCE VENTRICULAR FIBRILLATIONS.

HEALTH EFFECTS AND FIRST AID

INHALATION: CHLORDANE: CONVULSANT/HIGHLY TOXIC. 500 MG/M3 IMMEDIATELY DANGEROUS TO LIFE OR HEALTH. **ACUTE EXPOSURE-** SYMPTOMS OF BLURRED VISION, COUGH, CONFUSION, ATAXIA, HEADACHE, WEAKNESS, DIZZINESS, AND DELIRIUM WERE REPORTED FROM INHALATION EXPOSURE TO CHLORDANE. SYMPTOMS OF CENTRAL NERVOUS SYSTEM STIMULATION MAY ALSO OCCUR AS DETAILED IN ACUTE INGESTION. **CHRONIC EXPOSURE-** HUMAN EXPOSURE TO VAPORS OF 7 PERCENT CHLORDANE FOR 15 MINUTES AT 3-DAY INTERVALS FOR PERIODS OF 15 WEEKS AND REPEATED A YEAR LATER, DID NOT RESULT IN SYMPTOMS OF TOXICITY. IN ADDITION TO THE SYMPTOMS OF ACUTE EXPOSURE, CHRONIC EXPOSURE OF HUMANS TO TECHNICAL CHLORDANE CONTAINING HEPTACHLOR AND OTHER CHEMICALS HAS CAUSED LIGHTHEADEDNESS, NAUSEA, COUGH, CHEST COMPLAINTS, TREMORS, ARTHRALGIAS, FATIGUE, THROMBOCYTOPENIC PURPURA, AND MARKED BRUISING. PANCYTOPENIA, APLASTIC, HEMOLYTIC, AND MEGALOBLASTIC ANEMIAS, LEUKEMIA, AND DEATH HAVE ALSO BEEN REPORTED. EXPOSURE OF MONKEYS TO 100-1,000 UG/M3 FOR 90 DAYS INDUCED A STATISTICALLY SIGNIFICANT INCIDENCE OF LEUKOPENIA AND THROMBOCYTOPENIA, WITH EFFECTS OCCURRING AT THE LOWEST DOSE TESTED.
HEPTACHLOR: 100 MG/M3 IMMEDIATELY DANGEROUS TO LIFE OR HEALTH. CONVULSANT. **ACUTE EXPOSURE-** MAY BE ABSORBED THROUGH THE LUNGS TO PRODUCE SYMPTOMS CHARACTERISTIC OF CHLORINATED CYCLODIENE PESTICIDES INCLUDING MUSCLE TWITCHING, MYOCLONIC JERKING, AND CONVULSIVE SEIZURES. THE CONVULSIONS MAY OCCUR WITH PERIODS OF UNCONSCIOUSNESS. OTHER SYMPTOMS MAY INCLUDE HEADACHE, NAUSEA, VOMITING, MALAISE, AND DIZZINESS. IN CASES OF GROSS OVEREXPOSURE, CONVULSIONS MAY OCCUR WITHOUT ANY PRIOR SYMPTOMS. ABNORMAL EEG PATTERNS MAY BE OBSERVED AND MAY PERSIST FOR WEEKS OR MONTHS WHILE NO OTHER OBSERVABLE SIGNS OF POISONING MAY EXIST. **CHRONIC EXPOSURE-** IN ADDITION TO THE SYMPTOMS OF ACUTE EXPOSURE, CHRONIC EXPOSURE OF HUMANS TO TECHNICAL CHLORDANE CONTAINING HEPTACHLOR AND OTHER

CHEMICALS HAS CAUSED LIGHTHEADEDNESS, NAUSEA, COUGH, CHEST COMPLAINTS, TREMORS, ARTHRALGIAS, FATIGUE, THROMBOCYTOPENIC PURPURA, AND MARKED BRUISING. PANCYTOPENIA, APLASTIC, HEMOLYTIC, AND MEGALOBLASTIC ANEMIAS, LEUKEMIA, AND DEATH HAVE ALSO BEEN REPORTED.

FIRST AID- REMOVE FROM EXPOSURE AREA TO FRESH AIR IMMEDIATELY. IF BREATHING HAS STOPPED, GIVE ARTIFICIAL RESPIRATION. MAINTAIN AIRWAY AND BLOOD PRESSURE AND ADMINISTER OXYGEN IF AVAILABLE. KEEP AFFECTED PERSON WARM AND AT REST. TREAT SYMPTOMATICALLY AND SUPPORTIVELY. ADMINISTRATION OF OXYGEN SHOULD BE PERFORMED BY QUALIFIED PERSONNEL. GET MEDICAL ATTENTION IMMEDIATELY.

SKIN CONTACT: CHLORDANE: CONVULSANT/TOXIC. **ACUTE EXPOSURE-** MAY BE IRRITATING. SKIN ABSORPTION HAS CAUSED BLURRED VISION, CONFUSION, ATAXIA, HEADACHE, DIZZINESS, WEAKNESS, AND DELIRIUM. IN SEVERE POISONING, CONVULSIONS MAY DEVELOP AND COMA AND DEATH ARE POSSIBLE. IN ONE CASE OF OCCUPATIONAL EXPOSURE, A WOMAN BECAME CONFUSED AND DEVELOPED CONVULSIONS 40 MINUTES AFTER SPILLING A SOLUTION CONTAINING 25% CHLORDANE AND 26% DDT ON HER CLOTHING. SHE DIED SHORTLY THEREAFTER FROM RESPIRATORY FAILURE. **CHRONIC EXPOSURE-** REPEATED CONTACT CAUSED EPISODES OF PARESTHESIA, TWITCHING OF THE RIGHT HAND AND ARM, GRAND MAL SEIZURES, AND UNCONSCIOUSNESS. OTHER EFFECTS MAY OCCUR AS DETAILED IN CHRONIC INHALATION. REPEATED APPLICATION OF 50 MG/KG TO THE SKIN OF RATS FOR 3 OR 4 DAYS CAUSED 100% FATALITIES.
HEPTACHLOR: CONVULSANT/HIGHLY TOXIC. **ACUTE EXPOSURE-** A LETHAL DOSE IN RABBITS FROM DERMAL ABSORPTION OF DRY POWDER WAS 2000 MG/KG; REPORTED SYMPTOMS WERE SEVERE ANOREXIA, HYPEREXCITABILITY, CONVULSIONS, AND DEATH. THE LETHAL DOSE IN RATS FROM DERMAL ABSORPTION OF HEPTACHLOR IN XYLENE WAS 195 MG/KG. CHLORINATED CYCLODIENE PESTICIDES ARE ABSORBED FROM THE SKIN AND MAY PRODUCE CENTRAL NERVOUS SYSTEM EFFECTS WITH SYMPTOMS OF MOTOR HYPEREXCITABILITY THAT MAY INCLUDE MUSCLE TWITCHING, MYOCLONIC JERKING, AND CONVULSIVE SEIZURES. THE CONVULSIONS MAY OCCUR WITH PERIODS OF UNCONSCIOUSNESS. OTHER SYMPTOMS MAY INCLUDE HEADACHE, NAUSEA, VOMITING, MALAISE, AND DIZZINESS. IN CASES CF GROSS OVEREXPOSURE, CONVULSIONS MAY OCCUR WITHOUT ANY PRIOR SYMPTOMS. ABNORMAL EEG PATTERNS MAY BE OBSERVED; THESE CHANGES IN EEG PATTERNS MAY PERSIST FOR WEEKS OR MONTHS WHILE NO OTHER OBSERVABLE SIGNS OF POISONING MAY EXIST. **CHRONIC EXPOSURE-** PROLONGED OR REPEATED EXPOSURE MAY CAUSE EFFECTS AS DETAILED IN CHRONIC INHALATION. WHEN APPLIED TO RABBITS AS A 20% SOLUTION IN DIMETHYL PHTHALATE, THE APPROXIMATE LETHAL DOSE WAS LESS THAN 780 MG/KG BUT WHEN IT WAS APPLIED IN REPEATED SMALLER DOSES, THE APPROXIMATE LD50 WAS LESS THAN 20 MG/KG PER DAY AND THERE WERE NO SURVIVORS AFTER 14 DOSES OF 28 MG/KG.

FIRST AID- REMOVE CONTAMINATED CLOTHING AND SHOES IMMEDIATELY. WASH AFFECTED AREA WITH SOAP OR MILD DETERGENT AND LARGE AMOUNTS OF WATER UNTIL NO EVIDENCE OF CHEMICAL REMAINS (APPROXIMATELY 15-20 MINUTES). GET MEDICAL ATTENTION IMMEDIATELY.

EYE CONTACT: CHLORDANE: **ACUTE EXPOSURE-** MAY BE IRRITATING. **CHRONIC EXPOSURE-** NO DATA AVAILABLE.
HEPTACHLOR: **ACUTE EXPOSURE-** NO DATA AVAILABLE. **CHRONIC EXPOSURE-** NO DATA AVAILABLE.

FIRST AID- WASH EYES IMMEDIATELY WITH LARGE AMOUNTS OF WATER OR NORMAL SALINE, OCCASIONALLY LIFTING UPPER AND LOWER LIDS, UNTIL NO EVIDENCE OF CHEMICAL REMAINS (APPROXIMATELY 15-20 MINUTES). GET MEDICAL ATTENTION IMMEDIATELY.

INGESTION: CHLORDANE: CONVULSANT/LIMITED ANIMAL CARCINOGEN/TOXIC. **ACUTE EXPOSURE-** MAY CAUSE ABDOMINAL PAIN, NAUSEA, VOMITING, AND DIARRHEA. CHLORDANE MAY STIMULATE THE CENTRAL NERVOUS SYSTEM WITH CONVULSIONS SOMETIMES APPEARING AS THE FIRST SYMPTOM OF POISONING. SYMPTOMS OF HEADACHE, BLURRED VISION, HYPEREXCITABILITY, MUSCLE TWITCHING, TREMOR, INCOORDINATION, AND ATAXIA MAY ALSO OCCUR. IN SEVERE CASES OF POISONING, COMA AND DEATH ARE POSSIBLE. EEG PATTERNS SUGGEST THAT DEATH IS DUE TO RESPIRATORY ARREST BETWEEN OR DURING CONVULSIVE EPISODES. CHLORDANE MAY BE EXCRETED SLOWLY FROM THE BODY; THE SERUM HALF-LIFE IN ONE CHILD WAS 88 DAYS. **CHRONIC EXPOSURE-** IN A TWO-YEAR FEEDING STUDY IN RATS, A DIETARY CONCENTRATION OF 150 PPM PRODUCED A NOTED RETARDATION OF GROWTH, LIVER AND KIDNEY DAMAGE, MYOCARDIAL DAMAGE, AND MILD INJURY TO THE LUNGS; MARKED DAMAGE TO THE LUNGS AND INCREASED MORTALITY WERE OBSERVED AT DIETARY CONCENTRATIONS OF 300 PPM. SIMILAR EFFECTS WERE REPORTED IN RABBITS ADMINISTERED 5 MG/KG/DAY. CHLORDANE PRODUCED LIVER NEOPLASMS IN MICE FOLLOWING ORAL ADMINISTRATION; RESULTS FOR RATS WERE INCONCLUSIVE. ORAL ADMINISTRATION OF CHLORDANE ENHANCED THE INCIDENCE OF LIVER TUMORS INDUCED IN MICE BY ORAL ADMINISTRATION OF N-NITROSODIETHYLAMINE. REPRODUCTIVE EFFECTS REPORTED IN ANIMALS INCLUDE DECREASED VIABILTIY OF OFFSPRING IN MICE FED 100 MG/KG/DAY FOR 4 MONTHS; DECREASED FERTILITY IN RATS AND MICE; AND EXCITABILITY AND TREMORS IN OFFSPRING WHEN KEPT WITH TREATED MOTHERS, BUT NOT WITH UNTREATED FEMALES.
HEPTACHLOR: CONVULSANT/HEPATOTOXIN/CARCINOGEN/HIGHLY TOXIC. **ACUTE EXPOSURE-** MAY CAUSE NAUSEA, VOMITING, DIARRHEA, AND GASTROINTESTINAL IRRITATION. IN ANIMAL STUDIES, INGESTION PRODUCED NEUROTOXIC EFFECTS OF HYPOACTIVITY, ATAXIA, TREMORS AND CONVULSIONS, CHANGES IN EEG PATTERNS, AND DEATH. SIMILAR EFFECTS HAVE BEEN OBSERVED IN HUMANS EXPOSED TO CHLORINATED CYCLODIENE PESTICIDES. IN RATS, ACUTE ORAL DOSES PRODUCED LIVER NECROSIS, CELL VACUOLIZATION, LIVER STEATOSIS, AND INCREASED RELATIVE LIVER WEIGHT. OTHER EFFECTS INCLUDED ELEVATED SERUM LEVELS OF ALDOLASE, GLUTAMIC-PYRUVIC TRANSAMINASE, BILIRUBIN, ALKALINE PHOSPHATASE, AND CHOLESTEROL. **CHRONIC EXPOSURE-** LONG-TERM EXPOSURES PRODUCED RENAL TOXICITY, HEMATOLOGIC EFFECTS, AND ADRENOTOXICITY IN ANIMALS. REPEATED ADMINISTRATION TO RATS PRODUCED CHRONIC CONVULSIONS, OPISTHOTONOS, HYPERREFLEXIA, RAPID RESPIRATION, AND CATARACTS. HISTOLOGIC EVIDENCE OF SEVERE LIVER DAMAGE, INCREASED LIVER WEIGHT, INCREASED LEVELS OF SERUM COMPONENTS INDICATIVE OF HEPATIC DAMAGE, AND DECREASED BODY WEIGHTS WERE ALSO OBSERVED IN ANIMAL STUDIES. A DAILY INTAKE OF 1 MG/KG FOR ALMOST A YEAR WAS LETHAL IN DOGS. MALE AND FEMALE MICE THAT RECEIVED HEPTACHLOR IN THE DIET FOR 10 WEEKS WERE UNABLE TO PRODUCE A NEW GENERATION. DECREASED PREGNANCY RATES WERE REPORTED FOLLOWING ORAL ADMINISTRATION OF HEPTACHLOR TO MALE AND FEMALE RATS FOR TWO GENERATIONS. IN MALE AND FEMALE RATS FED HEPTACHLOR, HEPTACHLOR EPOXIDE, OR A MIXTURE OF THE TWO FOR THREE GENERATIONS, THE NUMBER OF RESORBED FETUSES INCREASED AND FERTILITY DECREASED WITH SUCCEEDING GENERATIONS. ORAL ADMINISTRATION OF HEPTACHLOR CONTAINING 20% CHLORDANE PRODUCED LIVER CARCINOMAS IN MICE AND A SUGGESTION OF CARCINOGENIC EFFECTS ON THE THYROID IN FEMALE RATS.

FIRST AID- IF THE PERSON IS CONSCIOUS AND NOT CONVULSING, REMOVE BY GIVING SYRUP OF IPECAC (IF VOMITING OCCURS, KEEP THE HEAD BELOW THE HIPS TO PREVENT ASPIRATION). GIVE ACTIVATED CHARCOAL FOLLOWED BY GASTRIC LAVAGE. FOLLOW WITH A SALINE CATHARTIC. DO NOT GIVE FATS OR OILS. INTESTINAL LAVAGE WITH 20% MANNITOL (200 ML) BY STOMACH TUBE IS ALSO USEFUL. GIVE ARTIFICIAL RESPIRATION WITH OXYGEN IF RESPIRATION IS DEPRESSED (DREISBACH, HANDBOOK OF POISONING, 12TH ED.). TREAT SYMPTOMATICALLY AND SUPPORTIVELY. LAVAGE AND ADMINISTRATION OF OXYGEN SHOULD BE PERFORMED BY QUALIFIED MEDICAL PERSONNEL. GET MEDICAL ATTENTION IMMEDIATELY.

REACTIVITY

REACTIVITY: STABLE UNDER NORMAL TEMPERATURES AND PRESSURES.

INCOMPATIBILITIES: CHLORDANE: ALKALIES (WEAK): DECOMPOSES. OXIDIZERS (STRONG): FIRE AND EXPLOSION HAZARD. PLASTICS, RUBBER, COATINGS: MAY BE ATTACKED.
HEPTACHLOR: ALKALI (STRONG): INCOMPATIBLE. IRON AND RUST: CONTACT WITH MELTED HEPTACHLOR MAY PRODUCE TOXIC HYDROGEN CHLORIDE GAS.

DECOMPOSITION: THERMAL DECOMPOSITION PRODUCTS MAY INCLUDE TOXIC AND CORROSIVE FUMES OF CHLORIDES AND PHOSGENE, AND TOXIC OXIDES OF CARBON.

POLYMERIZATION: HAZARDOUS POLYMERIZATION HAS NOT BEEN REPORTED TO OCCUR UNDER NORMAL TEMPERATURES AND PRESSURES.

STORAGE AND DISPOSAL

OBSERVE ALL FEDERAL, STATE AND LOCAL REGULATIONS WHEN STORING OR DISPOSING OF THIS SUBSTANCE. FOR ASSISTANCE, CONTACT THE DISTRICT DIRECTOR OF THE ENVIRONMENTAL PROTECTION AGENCY.

****STORAGE****

STORE IN ACCORDANCE WITH 40 CFR 165 RECOMMENDED PROCEDURES FOR THE DISPOSAL AND STORAGE OF PESTICIDES AND PESTICIDE CONTAINERS.
STORE AWAY FROM INCOMPATIBLE SUBSTANCES.
THRESHOLD PLANNING QUANTITY (TPQ): THE SUPERFUND AMENDMENTS AND REAUTHORIZATION ACT (SARA) SECTION 302 REQUIRES THAT EACH FACILITY WHERE ANY EXTREMELY HAZARDOUS SUBSTANCE IS PRESENT IN A QUANTITY EQUAL TO OR GREATER THAN THE TPQ ESTABLISHED FOR THAT SUBSTANCE NOTIFY THE STATE EMERGENCY RESPONSE COMMISSION FOR THE STATE IN WHICH IT IS LOCATED. SECTION 303 OF SARA REQUIRES THESE FACILITIES TO PARTICIPATE IN LOCAL EMERGENCY RESPONSE PLANNING (40 CFR 355.30).

****DISPOSAL****

DISPOSAL MUST BE IN ACCORDANCE WITH 40 CFR 165 RECOMMENDED PROCEDURES FOR THE DISPOSAL AND STORAGE OF PESTICIDES AND PESTICIDE CONTAINERS.

DISPOSAL MUST BE IN ACCORDANCE WITH STANDARDS APPLICABLE TO GENERATORS OF HAZARDOUS WASTE, 40CFR 262. EPA HAZARDOUS WASTE NUMBER U036.
HEPTACHLOR (AND ITS HYDROXIDE) - REGULATORY LEVEL: 0.008 MG/L MATERIALS WHICH CONTAIN THE ABOVE SUBSTANCE AT OR ABOVE THE REGULATORY LEVEL MEET THE EPA CHARACTERISTIC OF TOXICITY, AND MUST BE DISPOSED OF IN ACCORDANCE WITH 40 CFR PART 262. EPA HAZARDOUS WASTE NUMBER D031.
CHLORDANE - REGULATORY LEVEL: 0.03 MG/L MATERIALS WHICH CONTAIN THE ABOVE SUBSTANCE AT OR ABOVE THE REGULATORY LEVEL MEET THE EPA CHARACTERISTIC OF TOXICITY, AND MUST BE DISPOSED OF IN ACCORDANCE WITH 40 CFR PART 262. EPA HAZARDOUS WASTE NUMBER D020.

CONDITIONS TO AVOID

MAY BURN BUT DOES NOT IGNITE READILY. CONTAINERS MAY EXPLODE IN HEAT OF FIRE.

SPILL AND LEAK PROCEDURES

SOIL SPILL: DIG A HOLDING AREA SUCH AS A PIT, POND OR LAGOON TO CONTAIN SPILL AND DIKE SURFACE FLOW USING BARRIER OF SOIL, SANDBAGS, FOAMED POLYURETHANE OR FOAMED CONCRETE. ABSORB LIQUID MASS WITH FLY ASH OR CEMENT POWDER.
IMMOBILIZE SPILL WITH UNIVERSAL GELLING AGENT.

AIR SPILL: KNOCK DOWN VAPORS WITH WATER SPRAY. KEEP UPWIND.
COMBUSTION PRODUCTS INCLUDE CORROSIVE OR TOXIC VAPORS.

WATER SPILL: TRAP SPILLED MATERIAL AT BOTTOM IN DEEP WATER POCKETS, EXCAVATED HOLDING AREAS OR WITHIN SAND BAG BARRIERS.
USE ACTIVATED CARBON TO ABSORB SPILLED SUBSTANCE THAT IS DISSOLVED.
USE MECHANICAL DREDGES OR LIFTS TO EXTRACT IMMOBILIZED MASSES OF POLLUTION AND PRECIPITATES.
THE CALIFORNIA SAFE DRINKING WATER AND TOXIC ENFORCEMENT ACT OF 1986 (PROPOSITION 65) PROHIBITS CONTAMINATING ANY KNOWN SOURCE OF DRINKING WATER WITH SUBSTANCES KNOWN TO CAUSE CANCER AND/OR REPRODUCTIVE TOXICITY.

OCCUPATIONAL SPILL: DO NOT TOUCH SPILLED MATERIAL. STOP LEAK IF YOU CAN DO IT WITHOUT RISK. USE WATER SPRAY TO REDUCE VAPORS. FOR SMALL SPILLS, TAKE UP WITH SAND OR OTHER ABSORBENT MATERIAL AND PLACE INTO CONTAINERS FOR LATER DISPOSAL. FOR SMALL DRY SPILLS, WITH A CLEAN SHOVEL PLACE MATERIAL INTO CLEAN, DRY CONTAINERS AND COVER. MOVE CONTAINERS FROM SPILL AREA. FOR LARGER SPILLS, DIKE FAR AHEAD OF SPILL FOR LATER DISPOSAL. KEEP UNNECESSARY PEOPLE AWAY. ISOLATE HAZARD AREA AND DENY ENTRY. VENTILATE CLOSED SPACES BEFORE ENTERING.
REPORTABLE QUANTITY (RQ): 1 POUND THE SUPERFUND AMENDMENTS AND REAUTHORIZATION ACT (SARA) SECTION 304 REQUIRES THAT A RELEASE EQUAL TO OR GREATER THAN THE REPORTABLE QUANTITY FOR THIS SUBSTANCE BE IMMEDIATELY REPORTED TO THE LOCAL EMERGENCY PLANNING COMMITTEE AND THE STATE EMERGENCY RESPONSE COMMISSION (40 CFR 355.40). IF THE RELEASE OF THIS SUBSTANCE IS REPORTABLE UNDER CERCLA SECTION 103, THE NATIONAL RESPONSE CENTER MUST BE NOTIFIED IMMEDIATELY AT (800) 424-8802 OR (202) 426-2675 IN THE METROPOLITAN WASHINGTON, D.C. AREA (40 CFR 302.6).

PROTECTIVE EQUIPMENT

VENTILATION: PROVIDE LOCAL EXHAUST VENTILATION AND/OR GENERAL DILUTION VENTILATION TO MEET PUBLISHED EXPOSURE LIMITS.

RESPIRATOR: THE FOLLOWING RESPIRATORS AND MAXIMUM USE CONCENTRATIONS ARE RECOMMENDATIONS BY THE U.S. DEPARTMENT OF HEALTH AND HUMAN SERVICES, NIOSH POCKET GUIDE TO CHEMICAL HAZARDS; NIOSH CRITERIA DOCUMENTS OR BY THE U.S. DEPARTMENT OF LABOR, 29 CFR 1910 SUBPART Z. THE SPECIFIC RESPIRATOR SELECTED MUST BE BASED ON CONTAMINATION LEVELS FOUND IN THE WORK PLACE, MUST NOT EXCEED THE WORKING LIMITS OF THE RESPIRATOR AND BE JOINTLY APPROVED BY THE NATIONAL INSTITUTE FOR OCCUPATIONAL SAFETY AND HEALTH AND THE MINE SAFETY AND HEALTH ADMINISTRATION (NIOSH-MSHA).
CHLORDANE:
5 MG/M3- ANY CHEMICAL CARTRIDGE RESPIRATOR WITH ORGANIC VAPOR CARTRIDGE(S) IN COMBINATION WITH A DUST, MIST, AND FUME FILTER. ANY SUPPLIED-AIR RESPIRATOR. ANY SELF-CONTAINED BREATHING APPARATUS.
12.5 MG/M3- ANY SUPPLIED-AIR RESPIRATOR OPERATED IN A CONTINUOUS FLOW MODE. ANY POWERED AIR-PURIFYING RESPIRATOR WITH ORGANIC VAPOR CARTRIDGE(S) IN COMBINATION WITH A DUST, MIST, AND FUME FILTER.
25 MG/M3- ANY CHEMICAL CARTRIDGE RESPIRATOR WITH A FULL FACEPIECE AND ORGANIC VAPOR CARTRIDGE(S) IN COMBINATION WITH A HIGH-EFFICIENCY PARTICULATE FILTER. ANY SUPPLIED-AIR RESPIRATOR WITH A FULL FACEPIECE. ANY SELF-CONTAINED BREATHING APPARATUS WITH A FULL FACEPIECE. ANY POWDERED AIR-PURIFYING RESPIRATOR WITH A TIGHT-FITTING FACEPIECE AND ORGANIC VAPOR CARTRIDGE(S) IN COMBINATION WITH A HIGH-EFFICIENCY PARTICULATE FILTER. ANY AIR-PURIFYING FULL FACEPIECE RESPIRATOR (GAS MASK) WITH A CHIN-STYLE OR FRONT- OR BACK-MOUNTED ORGANIC VAPOR CANISTER HAVING A HIGH-EFFICIENCY PARTICULATE FILTER.
500 MG/M3- ANY SUPPLIED-AIR RESPIRATOR WITH A HALF-MASK AND OPERATED IN A PRESSURE-DEMAND OR OTHER POSITIVE PRESSURE MODE.
ESCAPE- ANY AIR-PURIFYING FULL FACEPIECE RESPIRATOR (GAS MASK) WITH A CHIN-STYLE OR FRONT- OR BACK-MOUNTED ORGANIC VAPOR CANISTER HAVING A HIGH-EFFICIENCY PARTICULATE FILTER. ANY APPROPRIATE ESCAPE-TYPE SELF-CONTAINED BREATHING APPARATUS.
FOR FIREFIGHTING AND OTHER IMMEDIATELY DANGEROUS TO LIFE OR HEALTH CONDITIONS:
SELF-CONTAINED BREATHING APPARATUS WITH FULL FACEPIECE OPERATED IN PRESSURE-DEMAND OR OTHER POSITIVE PRESSURE MODE.
SUPPLIED-AIR RESPIRATOR WITH FULL FACEPIECE AND OPERATED IN PRESSURE-DEMAND OR OTHER POSITIVE PRESSURE MODE IN COMBINATION WITH AN AUXILIARY SELF-CONTAINED BREATHING APPARATUS OPERATED IN PRESSURE-DEMAND OR OTHER POSITIVE PRESSURE MODE.

CLOTHING: EMPLOYEE MUST WEAR APPROPRIATE PROTECTIVE (IMPERVIOUS) CLOTHING AND EQUIPMENT TO PREVENT ANY POSSIBILITY OF SKIN CONTACT WITH THIS SUBSTANCE.

GLOVES: EMPLOYEE MUST WEAR APPROPRIATE PROTECTIVE GLOVES TO PREVENT CONTACT WITH THIS SUBSTANCE.

EYE PROTECTION: EMPLOYEE MUST WEAR SPLASH-PROOF OR DUST-RESISTANT SAFETY GOGGLES AND A FACESHIELD TO PREVENT CONTACT WITH THIS SUBSTANCE.
EMERGENCY WASH FACILITIES: WHERE THERE IS ANY POSSIBILITY THAT AN EMPLOYEE'S EYES AND/OR SKIN MAY BE EXPOSED TO THIS SUBSTANCE, THE EMPLOYER SHOULD PROVIDE AN EYE WASH FOUNTAIN AND QUICK DRENCH SHOWER WITHIN THE IMMEDIATE WORK AREA FOR EMERGENCY USE.

AUTHORIZED BY- OCCUPATIONAL HEALTH SERVICES, INC.
CREATION DATE: 10/04/89 ***REVISION DATE:*** 07/13/90

MATERIAL SAFETY DATA SHEET

OCCUPATIONAL HEALTH SERVICES, INC.
AGRICULTURE AND PESTICIDE DIVISION
450 SEVENTH AVENUE, SUITE 2407
NEW YORK, NEW YORK 10123
1-800-445-MSDS OR (212) 967-1100

EMERGENCY CONTACT:
JOHN S. BRANSFORD, JR. (615) 292-1180

SUBSTANCE IDENTIFICATION

CAS-NUMBER 597-09-1
SUBSTANCE: 2-NITRO-2-ETHYL-1,3-PROPANEDIOL
TRADE NAMES/SYNONYMS: 1,3-PROPANEDIOL, 2-ETHYL-2-NITRO-; C5H11NO4; PST71953
CHEMICAL FAMILY: GLYCOL
NITRO
MOLECULAR FORMULA: (H-O-C-H2)2-C-(N-O2)-C2-H5
MOLECULAR WEIGHT: 149.15
CERCLA RATINGS (SCALE 0-3): HEALTH=U FIRE=1 REACTIVITY=0 PERSISTENCE=1
NFPA RATINGS (SCALE 0-4): HEALTH=U FIRE=1 REACTIVITY=0

COMPONENTS AND CONTAMINANTS

COMPONENT: 2-NITRO-2-ETHYL-1,3-PROPANEDIOL ***PERCENT:*** 100.0
CAS# 597-09-1
OTHER CONTAMINANTS: NONE
EXPOSURE LIMITS: NO OCCUPATIONAL EXPOSURE LIMITS ESTABLISHED BY OSHA, ACGIH, OR NIOSH.

PHYSICAL DATA

DESCRIPTION: WHITE CRYSTALLINE SOLID.
BOILING POINT: DECOMPOSES @ 10 MMHG
MELTING POINT: 135-136 F (57-58 C) ***SPECIFIC GRAVITY:*** NOT AVAILABLE
PH: 5.48 @ 0.1M SOLN ***SOLUBILITY IN WATER:*** VERY SOLUBLE
SOLVENT SOLUBILITY: SOLUBLE IN ALCOHOL, ETHER, AND MOST ORGANIC SOLVENTS.

FIRE AND EXPLOSION DATA

FIRE AND EXPLOSION HAZARD: SLIGHT FIRE HAZARD WHEN EXPOSED TO HEAT OR FLAME.

FIREFIGHTING MEDIA: DRY CHEMICAL, CARBON DIOXIDE, HALON, WATER SPRAY OR STANDARD FOAM (1987 EMERGENCY RESPONSE GUIDEBOOK, DOT P 5800.4). FOR LARGER FIRES, USE WATER SPRAY, FOG OR STANDARD FOAM (1987 EMERGENCY RESPONSE GUIDEBOOK, DOT P 5800.4).

FIREFIGHTING: MOVE CONTAINER FROM FIRE AREA IF POSSIBLE. DO NOT SCATTER SPILLED MATERIAL WITH HIGH PRESSURE WATER STREAMS. DIKE FIRE CONTROL WATER FOR LATER DISPOSAL (1987 EMERGENCY RESPONSE GUIDEBOOK, DOT P 5800.4, GUIDE PAGE 31). USE AGENTS SUITABLE FOR TYPE OF SURROUNDING FIRE. AVOID BREATHING HAZARDOUS VAPORS, KEEP UPWIND.

TOXICITY

2-NITRO-2-ETHYL-1,3-PROPANEDIOL: CARCINOGEN STATUS: NONE. ACUTE TOXICITY DATA: NO DATA AVAILABLE. TARGET EFFECTS: NO DATA AVAILABLE.

HEALTH EFFECTS AND FIRST AID

INHALATION: 2-NITRO-2-ETHYL-1,3-PROPANEDIOL: **ACUTE EXPOSURE-** NO DATA AVAILABLE. **CHRONIC EXPOSURE-** NO DATA AVAILABLE.

FIRST AID- REMOVE FROM EXPOSURE AREA TO FRESH AIR IMMEDIATELY. IF BREATHING HAS STOPPED, PERFORM ARTIFICIAL RESPIRATION. KEEP PERSON WARM AND AT REST. TREAT SYMPTOMATICALLY AND SUPPORTIVELY. GET MEDICAL ATTENTION IMMEDIATELY.

SKIN CONTACT: 2-NITRO-2-ETHYL-1,3-PROPANEDIOL: **ACUTE EXPOSURE-** NO DATA AVAILABLE. **CHRONIC EXPOSURE-** NO DATA AVAILABLE.

FIRST AID- REMOVE CONTAMINATED CLOTHING AND SHOES IMMEDIATELY. WASH AFFECTED AREA WITH SOAP OR MILD DETERGENT AND LARGE AMOUNTS OF WATER UNTIL NO EVIDENCE OF CHEMICAL REMAINS (APPROXIMATELY 15-20 MINUTES). GET MEDICAL ATTENTION IMMEDIATELY.

EYE CONTACT: 2-NITRO-2-ETHYL-1,3-PROPANEDIOL: **ACUTE EXPOSURE-** NO DATA AVAILABLE. **CHRONIC EXPOSURE-** NO DATA AVAILABLE.

FIRST AID- WASH EYES IMMEDIATELY WITH LARGE AMOUNTS OF WATER OR NORMAL SALINE, OCCASIONALLY LIFTING UPPER AND LOWER LIDS, UNTIL NO EVIDENCE OF CHEMICAL REMAINS (APPROXIMATELY 15-20 MINUTES). GET MEDICAL ATTENTION IMMEDIATELY.

INGESTION: 2-NITRO-2-ETHYL-1,3-PROPANEDIOL: **ACUTE EXPOSURE-** NO DATA AVAILABLE. **CHRONIC EXPOSURE-** NO DATA AVAILABLE.

FIRST AID- TREAT SYMPTOMATICALLY AND SUPPORTIVELY. GET MEDICAL ATTENTION IMMEDIATELY. IF VOMITING OCCURS, KEEP HEAD LOWER THAN HIPS TO PREVENT ASPIRATION.

ANTIDOTE: NO SPECIFIC ANTIDOTE. TREAT SYMPTOMATICALLY AND SUPPORTIVELY.

REACTIVITY

REACTIVITY: STABLE UNDER NORMAL TEMPERATURES AND PRESSURES.

INCOMPATIBILITIES: 2-NITRO-2-ETHYL-1,3-PROPANEDIOL: OXIDIZERS (STRONG): FIRE AND EXPLOSION HAZARD.

DECOMPOSITION: THERMAL DECOMPOSITION PRODUCTS MAY INCLUDE TOXIC OXIDES OF CARBON AND NITROGEN.

POLYMERIZATION: HAZARDOUS POLYMERIZATION HAS NOT BEEN REPORTED TO OCCUR UNDER NORMAL TEMPERATURES AND PRESSURES.

STORAGE AND DISPOSAL

OBSERVE ALL FEDERAL, STATE AND LOCAL REGULATIONS WHEN STORING OR DISPOSING OF THIS SUBSTANCE. FOR ASSISTANCE, CONTACT THE DISTRICT DIRECTOR OF THE ENVIRONMENTAL PROTECTION AGENCY.

****STORAGE****

STORE AWAY FROM INCOMPATIBLE SUBSTANCES.

CONDITIONS TO AVOID

MAY BURN BUT DOES NOT IGNITE READILY. AVOID CONTACT WITH STRONG OXIDIZERS, EXCESSIVE HEAT, SPARKS, OR OPEN FLAME.

SPILL AND LEAK PROCEDURES

OCCUPATIONAL SPILL: SWEEP UP AND PLACE IN SUITABLE CLEAN, DRY CONTAINERS FOR RECLAMATION OR LATER DISPOSAL. DO NOT FLUSH SPILLED MATERIAL INTO SEWER. KEEP UNNECESSARY PEOPLE AWAY.

PROTECTIVE EQUIPMENT

VENTILATION: PROVIDE LOCAL EXHAUST OR PROCESS ENCLOSURE VENTILATION SYSTEM.

RESPIRATOR: THE FOLLOWING RESPIRATORS ARE RECOMMENDED BASED ON INFORMATION FOUND IN THE PHYSICAL DATA, TOXICITY AND HEALTH EFFECTS SECTIONS. THEY ARE RANKED IN ORDER FROM MINIMUM TO MAXIMUM RESPIRATORY PROTECTION. THE SPECIFIC RESPIRATOR SELECTED MUST BE BASED ON CONTAMINATION LEVELS FOUND IN THE WORK PLACE, MUST NOT EXCEED THE WORKING LIMITS OF THE RESPIRATOR AND BE JOINTLY APPROVED BY THE NATIONAL INSTITUTE FOR OCCUPATIONAL SAFETY AND HEALTH AND THE MINE SAFETY AND HEALTH ADMINISTRATION (NIOSH-MSHA).

DUST AND MIST RESPIRATOR WITH A FULL FACEPIECE.

AIR-PURIFYING FULL FACEPIECE RESPIRATOR WITH A HIGH-EFFICIENCY PARTICULATE FILTER.

POWERED AIR-PURIFYING RESPIRATOR WITH A TIGHT-FITTING FACEPIECE AND HIGH-EFFICIENCY PARTICULATE FILTER.

TYPE 'C' SUPPLIED-AIR RESPIRATOR WITH A FULL FACEPIECE OPERATED IN PRESSURE-DEMAND OR OTHER POSITIVE PRESSURE MODE OR WITH A FULL FACEPIECE, HELMET OR HOOD OPERATED IN CONTINUOUS-FLOW MODE.

SELF-CONTAINED BREATHING APPARATUS WITH A FULL FACEPIECE OPERATED IN PRESSURE-DEMAND OR OTHER POSITIVE PRESSURE MODE.

FOR FIREFIGHTING AND OTHER IMMEDIATELY DANGEROUS TO LIFE OR HEALTH CONDITIONS:

SELF-CONTAINED BREATHING APPARATUS WITH FULL FACEPIECE OPERATED IN PRESSURE-DEMAND OR OTHER POSITIVE PRESSURE MODE.

SUPPLIED-AIR RESPIRATOR WITH FULL FACEPIECE AND OPERATED IN PRESSURE-DEMAND OR OTHER POSITIVE PRESSURE MODE IN COMBINATION WITH AN AUXILIARY SELF-CONTAINED BREATHING APPARATUS OPERATED IN PRESSURE-DEMAND OR OTHER POSITIVE PRESSURE MODE.

CLOTHING: EMPLOYEE MUST WEAR APPROPRIATE PROTECTIVE (IMPERVIOUS) CLOTHING AND EQUIPMENT TO PREVENT REPEATED OR PROLONGED SKIN CONTACT WITH THIS SUBSTANCE.

GLOVES: EMPLOYEE MUST WEAR APPROPRIATE PROTECTIVE GLOVES TO PREVENT CONTACT WITH THIS SUBSTANCE.

EYE PROTECTION: EMPLOYEE MUST WEAR SPLASH-PROOF OR DUST-RESISTANT SAFETY GOGGLES TO PREVENT EYE CONTACT WITH THIS SUBSTANCE. EMERGENCY EYE WASH: WHERE THERE IS ANY POSSIBILITY THAT AN EMPLOYEE'S EYES MAY BE EXPOSED TO THIS SUBSTANCE, THE EMPLOYER SHOULD PROVIDE AN EYE WASH FOUNTAIN WITHIN THE IMMEDIATE WORK AREA FOR EMERGENCY USE.

AUTHORIZED BY- OCCUPATIONAL HEALTH SERVICES, INC.
CREATION DATE: 10/05/89 ***REVISION DATE:*** 05/31/90

MATERIAL SAFETY DATA SHEET

OCCUPATIONAL HEALTH SERVICES, INC.
AGRICULTURE AND PESTICIDE DIVISION
450 SEVENTH AVENUE, SUITE 2407
NEW YORK, NEW YORK 10123
1-800-445-MSDS OR (212) 967-1100

EMERGENCY CONTACT:
JOHN S. BRANSFORD, JR. (615) 292-1180

SUBSTANCE IDENTIFICATION

CAS-NUMBER 26002-80-2

SUBSTANCE: **PHENOTHRIN**

TRADE NAMES/SYNONYMS: CYCLOPROPANECARBOXYLIC ACID, 2,2-DIMETHYL-3-(2-METHYL-1-PROPENYL)-, (3-PHENOXYPHENYL)METHYL ESTER; CYCLOPROPANECARBOXYLIC ACID, 2,2-DIMETHYL-3-(2-METHYLPROPENYL)-, M-PHENOXYBENZYL ESTER; 2,2-DIMETHYL-3-(2-METHYL-1-PROPENYL)CYCLOPROPANECARBOXYLIC ACID (3-PHENOXYPHENYL)METHYL ESTER; 2,2-DIMETHYL-3-(2-METHYLPROPENYL)CYCLOPROPANECARBOXYLIC ACID M-PHENOXYBENZYL ESTER; 3-PHENOXYBENZYL (1RS,3RS;1RS,3SR)-2,2-DIMETHYL-3-(2-METHYLPROP-1-ENYL) CYCLOPROPANECARBOXYLATE; 2,2-DIMETHYL-3-(2-METHYL-1-PROPENYL)CYCLOPROPANECARBOXYLATE; M-PHENOXYBENZYL 2,2-DIMETHYL-3-(2-METHYLPROPENYL)CYCLOPROPANE- CARBOXYLATE; 3-PHENOXYBENZYL(1RS)-CIS-TRANS-2,2-DIMETHYL-3-(2-METHYLPROP-1-ENYL)-CYCLOPROPANECARBOXYLATE; 3-PHENOXYBENZYL (+-)-CIS-TRANS-CHRYSANTHEMATE; SUMITHRIN; OMS 1809; ENT 27972; C23H26O3; PST71954

CHEMICAL FAMILY: PYRETHROID (SYNTHETIC)

MOLECULAR FORMULA: C23-H26-O3

MOLECULAR WEIGHT: 350.46

CERCLA RATINGS (SCALE 0-3): HEALTH=U FIRE=U REACTIVITY=0 PERSISTENCE=1

NFPA RATINGS (SCALE 0-4): HEALTH=U FIRE=U REACTIVITY=0

COMPONENTS AND CONTAMINANTS

COMPONENT: PHENOTHRIN ***PERCENT:*** 100.0
CAS# 26002-80-2

EXPOSURE LIMITS: NO OCCUPATIONAL EXPOSURE LIMITS ESTABLISHED BY OSHA, ACGIH, OR NIOSH.
PYRETHROIDS: 1 POUND CERCLA SECTION 103 REPORTABLE QUANTITY

PHYSICAL DATA

DESCRIPTION: PALE YELLOW TO YELLOW-BROWN LIQUID.
BOILING POINT: NOT AVAILABLE
SPECIFIC GRAVITY: 1.061 @ 25 C ***VAPOR PRESSURE:*** NEGLIGIBLE
SOLUBILITY IN WATER: 2 PPM
SOLVENT SOLUBILITY: SOLUBLE IN HEXANE, METHANOL, XYLENE, ACETONE, STABLE IN MOST ORGANIC SOLVENTS.

FIRE AND EXPLOSION DATA

FIRE AND EXPLOSION HAZARD: UNKNOWN FIRE AND EXPLOSION HAZARD.
FIREFIGHTING MEDIA: DRY CHEMICAL, CARBON DIOXIDE, HALON, WATER SPRAY OR STANDARD FOAM (1987 EMERGENCY RESPONSE GUIDEBOOK, DOT P 5800.4).
FOR LARGER FIRES, USE WATER SPRAY, FOG OR STANDARD FOAM (1987 EMERGENCY RESPONSE GUIDEBOOK, DOT P 5800.4).
FIREFIGHTING: MOVE CONTAINER FROM FIRE AREA IF POSSIBLE. COOL FIRE-EXPOSED CONTAINERS WITH WATER FROM SIDE UNTIL WELL AFTER FIRE IS OUT. STAY AWAY FROM STORAGE TANK ENDS. FOR MASSIVE FIRE IN STORAGE AREA, USE UNMANNED HOSE HOLDER OR MONITOR NOZZLES, ELSE WITHDRAW FROM AREA AND LET FIRE BURN. WITHDRAW IMMEDIATELY IN CASE OF RISING SOUND FROM VENTING SAFETY DEVICE OR ANY DISCOLORATION OF STORAGE TANK DUE TO FIRE (1987 EMERGENCY RESPONSE GUIDEBOOK, DOT P 5800.4, GUIDE PAGE 27). EXTINGUISH ONLY IF FLOW CAN BE STOPPED; USE FLOODING AMOUNTS OF WATER AS A FOG, SOLID STREAMS MAY BE INEFFECTIVE. COOL CONTAINERS WITH FLOODING AMOUNTS OF WATER, APPLY FROM AS FAR A DISTANCE AS POSSIBLE. AVOID BREATHING VAPORS, KEEP UPWIND.

TOXICITY

PHENOTHRIN: TOXICITY DATA: 10 GM/KG ORAL-MOUSE LD50; >10,000 MG/KG SKIN-RAT LD50 (PEMNDP 8,654,87). CARCINOGEN STATUS: NONE. ACUTE TOXICITY DATA: SLIGHTLY TOXIC BY INGESTION. TARGET EFFECTS: POISONING MAY AFFECT THE CENTRAL NERVOUS SYSTEM.*
* MAY BE BASED ON GENERAL INFORMATION ON PYRETHROIDS.

HEALTH EFFECTS AND FIRST AID

INHALATION: PHENOTHRIN: SEE INFORMATION ON PYRETHROIDS.
PYRETHROIDS: **ACUTE EXPOSURE-** HEAVY EXPOSURE TO A MIST OF SOME PYRETHROIDS HAS PRODUCED HYPERSENSITIVIITY, ATAXIA, AND URINARY INCONTINENCE. CONVULSIONS MAY ALSO BE POSSIBLE. **CHRONIC EXPOSURE-** ANIMALS EXPOSED TO AEROSOLS OF SOME PYRETHROIDS FOR 3-4 HOURS/DAY FOR UP TO 4 WEEKS DID NOT EXHIBIT ANY SIGNIFICANT COMPOUND RELATED FINDINGS.
FIRST AID- REMOVE FROM EXPOSURE AREA TO FRESH AIR IMMEDIATELY. IF BREATHING HAS STOPPED, PERFORM ARTIFICIAL RESPIRATION. KEEP PERSON WARM AND AT REST. TREAT SYMPTOMATICALLY AND SUPPORTIVELY. GET MEDICAL ATTENTION IMMEDIATELY.

SKIN CONTACT: PHENOTHRIN: SEE INFORMATION ON PYRETHROIDS.
PYRETHROIDS: **ACUTE EXPOSURE-** BASED ON ANIMAL AND HUMAN STUDIES AND HUMAN EXPERIENCES WITH SOME PYRETHROIDS, PRIMARY IRRITATION IS UNLIKELY. CUTANEOUS PARESTHESIAS MAY OCCUR INCLUDING NUMBNESS, ITCHING, BURNING, TINGLING AND WARMTH WITHOUT SIGNS OF IRRITATION. THESE EFFECTS MAY BE DELAYED FOR 30 MINUTES OR MORE AND LAST LESS THAN 24 HOURS. **CHRONIC EXPOSURE-** TESTS WITH SOME PYRETHROIDS ON HUMANS AND ANIMALS INDICATE SENSITIZATION IS UNLIKELY.
FIRST AID- REMOVE CONTAMINATED CLOTHING AND SHOES IMMEDIATELY. WASH AFFECTED AREA WITH SOAP OR MILD DETERGENT AND LARGE AMOUNTS OF WATER UNTIL NO EVIDENCE OF CHEMICAL REMAINS (APPROXIMATELY 15-20 MINUTES). GET MEDICAL ATTENTION IMMEDIATELY.

EYE CONTACT: PHENOTHRIN: SEE INFORMATION ON PYRETHROIDS.
PYRETHROIDS: **ACUTE EXPOSURE-** MASSIVE INSTILLATION OF SOME PYRETHROIDS INTO RABBIT EYES PRODUCED ONLY A SLIGHT, TRANSIENT CONGESTION OF THE CONJUNCTIVA OR LACRIMATION. **CHRONIC EXPOSURE-** NO DATA AVAILABLE.
FIRST AID- WASH EYES IMMEDIATELY WITH LARGE AMOUNTS OF WATER OR NORMAL SALINE, OCCASIONALLY LIFTING UPPER AND LOWER LIDS, UNTIL NO EVIDENCE OF CHEMICAL REMAINS (APPROXIMATELY 15-20 MINUTES). GET MEDICAL ATTENTION IMMEDIATELY.

INGESTION: PHENOTHRIN: SEE INFORMATION ON PYRETHROIDS.
PYRETHROIDS: **ACUTE EXPOSURE-** SOME PYRETHROIDS HAVE PRODUCED HYPERSENSITIVITY, NERVOUS IRRITABILITY, TREMORS, ATAXIA, AND URINARY INCONTINENCE IN ANIMALS. CONVULSIONS MAY ALSO BE POSSIBLE. **CHRONIC EXPOSURE-** INCREASED KIDNEY AND LIVER WEIGHTS AND HEPATIC HISTOPATHOLOGICAL CHANGES WERE NOTED IN ANIMALS CHRONICALLY FED SOME PYRETHROIDS.
FIRST AID- REMOVE BY GASTRIC LAVAGE AND CATHARSIS. MAINTAIN BLOOD PRESSURE AND AIRWAY. GIVE OXYGEN IF RESPIRATION IS DEPRESSED. DO NOT PERFORM GASTRIC LAVAGE IF VICTIM IS UNCONSCIOUS. GET MEDICAL ATTENTION IMMEDIATELY (DREISBACH, HANDBOOK OF POISONING, 12TH ED.).
ADMINISTRATION OF LAVAGE OR OXYGEN SHOULD BE PERFORMED BY QUALIFIED MEDICAL PERSONNEL.
ANTIDOTE: NO SPECIFIC ANTIDOTE. TREAT SYMPTOMATICALLY AND SUPPORTIVELY.

REACTIVITY

REACTIVITY: STABLE UNDER NORMAL TEMPERATURES AND PRESSURES.
INCOMPATIBILITIES: PHENOTHRIN: OXIDIZERS (STRONG): FIRE AND EXPLOSION HAZARD.
DECOMPOSITION: THERMAL DECOMPOSITION PRODUCTS MAY INCLUDE TOXIC OXIDES OF CARBON.
POLYMERIZATION: HAZARDOUS POLYMERIZATION HAS NOT BEEN REPORTED TO OCCUR UNDER NORMAL TEMPERATURES AND PRESSURES.

STORAGE AND DISPOSAL

OBSERVE ALL FEDERAL, STATE AND LOCAL REGULATIONS WHEN STORING OR DISPOSING OF THIS SUBSTANCE. FOR ASSISTANCE, CONTACT THE DISTRICT DIRECTOR OF THE ENVIRONMENTAL PROTECTION AGENCY.

STORAGE

STORE IN ACCORDANCE WITH 40 CFR 165 RECOMMENDED PROCEDURES FOR THE DISPOSAL AND STORAGE OF PESTICIDES AND PESTICIDE CONTAINERS.
STORE AWAY FROM INCOMPATIBLE SUBSTANCES.

DISPOSAL

DISPOSAL MUST BE IN ACCORDANCE WITH 40 CFR 165 RECOMMENDED PROCEDURES FOR THE DISPOSAL AND STORAGE OF PESTICIDES AND PESTICIDE CONTAINERS.

CONDITIONS TO AVOID

AVOID CONTACT WITH HEAT, SPARKS, FLAMES, OR OTHER SOURCES OF IGNITION. VAPORS MAY BE EXPLOSIVE. AVOID OVERHEATING OF CONTAINERS; CONTAINERS MAY VIOLENTLY RUPTURE IN HEAT OF FIRE. AVOID CONTAMINATION OF WATER SOURCES.

SPILL AND LEAK PROCEDURES

SOIL SPILL: DIG HOLDING AREA SUCH AS LAGOON, POND OR PIT FOR CONTAINMENT. DIKE FLOW OF SPILLED MATERIAL USING SOIL OR SANDBAGS OR FOAMED BARRIERS SUCH AS POLYURETHANE OR CONCRETE.
USE CEMENT POWDER OR FLY ASH TO ABSORB LIQUID MASS.
WATER SPILL: USE ACTIVATED CARBON TO ABSORB SPILLED SUBSTANCE THAT IS DISSOLVED.
USE MECHANICAL DREDGES OR LIFTS TO EXTRACT IMMOBILIZED MASSES OF POLLUTION AND PRECIPITATES.
OCCUPATIONAL SPILL: SHUT OFF IGNITION SOURCES. STOP LEAK IF YOU CAN DO IT WITHOUT RISK. USE WATER SPRAY TO REDUCE VAPORS. FOR SMALL SPILLS, TAKE UP WITH SAND OR OTHER ABSORBENT MATERIAL AND PLACE INTO CONTAINERS FOR LATER DISPOSAL. FOR LARGER SPILLS, DIKE FAR AHEAD OF SPILL FOR LATER DISPOSAL. NO SMOKING, FLAMES OR FLARES IN HAZARD AREA. KEEP UNNECESSARY PEOPLE AWAY; ISOLATE HAZARD AREA AND RESTRICT ENTRY.

PROTECTIVE EQUIPMENT

VENTILATION: PROVIDE GENERAL DILUTION VENTILATION.
RESPIRATOR: THE FOLLOWING RESPIRATORS ARE RECOMMENDED BASED ON INFORMATION FOUND IN THE PHYSICAL DATA, TOXICITY AND HEALTH EFFECTS SECTIONS. THEY ARE RANKED IN ORDER FROM MINIMUM TO MAXIMUM RESPIRATORY PROTECTION. THE SPECIFIC RESPIRATOR SELECTED MUST BE BASED ON CONTAMINATION LEVELS FOUND IN THE WORK PLACE, MUST NOT EXCEED THE WORKING LIMITS OF THE RESPIRATOR AND BE JOINTLY APPROVED BY THE NATIONAL INSTITUTE FOR OCCUPATIONAL SAFETY AND HEALTH AND THE MINE SAFETY AND HEALTH ADMINISTRATION (NIOSH-MSHA).
CHEMICAL CARTRIDGE RESPIRATOR WITH PESTICIDE CARTRIDGE.
GAS MASK WITH A PESTICIDE CANISTER (CHIN-STYLE OR FRONT- OR BACK-MOUNTED CANISTER).
TYPE 'C' SUPPLIED-AIR RESPIRATOR OPERATED IN THE PRESSURE-DEMAND OR OTHER POSITIVE PRESSURE OR CONTINUOUS-FLOW MODE.
SELF-CONTAINED BREATHING APPARATUS.
FOR FIREFIGHTING AND OTHER IMMEDIATELY DANGEROUS TO LIFE OR HEALTH CONDITIONS:
SELF-CONTAINED BREATHING APPARATUS WITH FULL FACEPIECE OPERATED IN PRESSURE-DEMAND OR OTHER POSITIVE PRESSURE MODE.
SUPPLIED-AIR RESPIRATOR WITH FULL FACEPIECE AND OPERATED IN PRESSURE-

DEMAND OR OTHER POSITIVE PRESSURE MODE IN COMBINATION WITH AN AUXILIARY SELF-CONTAINED BREATHING APPARATUS OPERATED IN PRESSURE-DEMAND OR OTHER POSITIVE PRESSURE MODE.

CLOTHING: EMPLOYEE MUST WEAR APPROPRIATE PROTECTIVE (IMPERVIOUS) CLOTHING AND EQUIPMENT TO PREVENT REPEATED OR PROLONGED SKIN CONTACT WITH THIS SUBSTANCE.

GLOVES: EMPLOYEE MUST WEAR APPROPRIATE PROTECTIVE GLOVES TO PREVENT CONTACT WITH THIS SUBSTANCE.

EYE PROTECTION: EMPLOYEE MUST WEAR SPLASH-PROOF OR DUST-RESISTANT SAFETY GOGGLES TO PREVENT EYE CONTACT WITH THIS SUBSTANCE. EMERGENCY EYE WASH: WHERE THERE IS ANY POSSIBILITY THAT AN EMPLOYEE'S EYES MAY BE EXPOSED TO THIS SUBSTANCE, THE EMPLOYER SHOULD PROVIDE AN EYE WASH FOUNTAIN WITHIN THE IMMEDIATE WORK AREA FOR EMERGENCY USE.

AUTHORIZED BY- OCCUPATIONAL HEALTH SERVICES, INC.
CREATION DATE: 04/16/90 ***REVISION DATE:*** 04/16/90

MATERIAL SAFETY DATA SHEET

OCCUPATIONAL HEALTH SERVICES, INC.	EMERGENCY CONTACT:
AGRICULTURE AND PESTICIDE DIVISION	JOHN S. BRANSFORD, JR. (615) 292-1180
450 SEVENTH AVENUE, SUITE 2407	
NEW YORK, NEW YORK 10123	
1-800-445-MSDS OR (212) 967-1100	

SUBSTANCE IDENTIFICATION

CAS-NUMBER 485-31-4

SUBSTANCE: BINAPACRYL

TRADE NAMES/SYNONYMS: 2-BUTENOIC ACID, 3-METHYL-, 2-(1-METHYLPROPYL)-4,6-DINITROPHENYL ESTER; 3-METHYL-2-BUTENOIC ACID-2-(1-METHYLPROPYL)-4,6-DINITROPHENYL ESTER; CROTONIC ACID, 3-METHYL-, 2-SEC-BUTYL-4,6-DINITROPHENYL ESTER; 3-METHYLCROTONIC ACID-2-SEC-BUTYL-4,6-DINITROPHENYL ESTER; 2-SEC-BUTYL-4,6-DINITROPHENYL-3-METHYL-2-BUTENOATE; ACRICID; ENDOSAN; HOE 2784; MOROCIDE; NIA 9044; DAPACRYL; ENT 25,793; C15H18N2O6; PST71960

CHEMICAL FAMILY: ESTER, CARBOXYLIC, AROMATIC NITRO

MOLECULAR FORMULA: C15-H18-N2-O6

MOLECULAR WEIGHT: 322.31

CERCLA RATINGS (SCALE 0-3): HEALTH=3 FIRE=1 REACTIVITY=U PERSISTENCE=1

NFPA RATINGS (SCALE 0-4): HEALTH=3 FIRE=1 REACTIVITY=U

COMPONENTS AND CONTAMINANTS

COMPONENT: BINAPACRYL ***PERCENT:*** 100.0
CAS# 485-31-4

OTHER CONTAMINANTS: NONE

EXPOSURE LIMITS: NO OCCUPATIONAL EXPOSURE LIMITS ESTABLISHED BY OSHA, ACGIH, OR NIOSH.

PHYSICAL DATA

DESCRIPTION: COLORLESS, CRYSTALLINE POWDER.

MELTING POINT: 151-153 F (66-67 C)

SPECIFIC GRAVITY: 1.2 ***VAPOR PRESSURE:*** 0.0001 @ 60 C

SOLUBILITY IN WATER: 1 PPM

SOLVENT SOLUBILITY: SOLUBLE IN ACETONE, XYLENE, ETHANOL, KEROSENE, HEXANE, DICHLOROMETHANE, ETHYL ACETATE AND TOLUENE; MODERATELY SOLUBLE IN METHANOL.

FIRE AND EXPLOSION DATA

FIRE AND EXPLOSION HAZARD: SLIGHT FIRE HAZARD WHEN EXPOSED TO HEAT OR FLAME.

FIREFIGHTING MEDIA: DRY CHEMICAL, CARBON DIOXIDE, HALON, WATER SPRAY OR STANDARD FOAM (1987 EMERGENCY RESPONSE GUIDEBOOK, DOT P 5800.4). FOR LARGER FIRES, USE WATER SPRAY, FOG OR STANDARD FOAM (1987 EMERGENCY RESPONSE GUIDEBOOK, DOT P 5800.4).

FIREFIGHTING: MOVE CONTAINERS FROM FIRE AREA IF POSSIBLE (1987 EMERGENCY RESPONSE GUIDEBOOK, DOT P 5800.4, GUIDE PAGE 53). EXTINGUISH USING AGENT SUITABLE FOR TYPE OF SURROUNDING FIRE. AVOID BREATHING VAPORS AND DUSTS. KEEP UPWIND.

TOXICITY

BINAPACRYL: TOXICITY DATA: 750 MG/KG SKIN-RABBIT LD50; 720 MG/KG SKIN-RAT LD50; 750 MG/KG SKIN-MOUSE LD50; 58 MG/KG ORAL-RAT LD50; 1600 MG/KG ORAL-MOUSE LD50; 200 MG/KG ORAL-GUINEA PIG LD50; 50 MG/KG ORAL-DOG LD50; MUTAGENIC DATA (RTECS). CARCINOGEN STATUS: NONE. ACUTE TOXICITY LEVEL: TOXIC BY DERMAL ABSORPTION AND INGESTION. TARGET EFFECTS: POISONING MAY INCREASE THE METABOLIC RATE AND AFFECT THE NERVOUS SYSTEM, LIVER, AND KIDNEYS.* AT INCREASED RISK FROM EXPOSURE: ALCOHOLICS AND PERSONS WITH RENAL OR HEPATIC DISEASES.* ADDITIONAL DATA: HOT ENVIRONMENTS MAY ENHANCE ABSORPTION AND THE TOXIC EFFECTS:*

* MAY BE BASED ON GENERAL INFORMATION ON DINITROPHENOL DERIVATIVES.

HEALTH EFFECTS AND FIRST AID

INHALATION: BINAPACRYL: SEE INFORMATION ON DINITROPHENOL DERIVATIVES.
DINITROPHENOL DERIVATIVES: **ACUTE EXPOSURE-** MAY BE ABSORBED WITH SYMPTOMS OCCURRING SUDDENLY AND UP TO 2 DAYS AFTER CESSATION OF EXPOSURE. SYMPTOMS MAY INCLUDE FATIGUE, WEAKNESS, FEVER, THIRST, NAUSEA, VOMITING, HEADACHES, FLUSHED SKIN, PROSTRATION, EXCESSIVE PERSPIRATION, TACHYCARDIA, TACHYPNEA, AND DYSPNEA. APPREHENSION, RESTLESSNESS, ANXIETY, MANIC BEHAVIOR, OR UNCONSCIOUSNESS MAY INDICATE CEREBRAL INJURY. CONVULSIONS MAY OCCUR IN THE MOST SEVERE POISONINGS. ANOXIA WITH CYANOSIS, LIVIDITY AND METABOLIC ACIDOSIS, SEVERE HYPERPYREXIA, DEHYDRATION, AND MUSCULAR TREMORS MAY BE FOLLOWED BY CIRCULATORY OR RESPIRATORY COLLAPSE AND COMA. DEGENERATIVE CHANGES IN THE HEART, RENAL TUBULES AND LIVER PARENCHYMA MAY OCCUR. THERE MAY BE ALBUMINURIA, PYURIA, HEMATURIA, JAUNDICE, AND INCREASED BUN. THE EFFECTS FROM POISONING ARE RAPID AND DEATH OR RECOVERY GENERALLY OCCURS WITHIN 24 TO 48 HOURS. FATAL DINITROPHENOL POISONING IS FOLLOWED BY INSTANTANEOUS RIGOR MORTIS.
CHRONIC EXPOSURE- IN ADDITION TO THE SYMPTOMS OF ACUTE EXPOSURE, PROLONGED OR REPEATED EXPOSURE MAY CAUSE WEIGHT LOSS, CATARACT FORMATION, AND LIVER AND KIDNEY DAMAGE. YELLOW STAINING OF THE SCLERAE AND URINE INDICATES ABSORPTION OF POTENTIALLY TOXIC AMOUNTS.

FIRST AID- REMOVE FROM EXPOSURE AREA TO FRESH AIR IMMEDIATELY. IF BREATHING HAS STOPPED, PERFORM ARTIFICIAL RESPIRATION. ADMINISTER OXYGEN. TREAT SYMPTOMATICALLY AND SUPPORTIVELY. GET MEDICAL ATTENTION IMMEDIATELY.

SKIN CONTACT: BINAPACRYL: TOXIC. SEE INFORMATION ON DINITROPHENOL DERIVATIVES.
DINITROPHENOL DERIVATIVES: **ACUTE EXPOSURE-** MAY CAUSE IRRITATION. CONTACT MAY RESULT IN YELLOW STAINING OF THE SKIN AHD HAIR. SOME DERIVATIVES MAY BE ABSORBED THROUGH THE SKIN WITH SYMPTOMS OCCURRING SUDDENLY AND UP TO 2 DAYS AFTER CESSATION OF EXPOSURE AND PRODUCE EFFECTS ON THE METABOLIC RATE, CENTRAL NERVOUS SYSTEM AND LIVER AND KIDNEY RESULTING IN SIGNS AND SYMPTOMS AS DESCRIBED IN ACUTE INHALATION. **CHRONIC EXPOSURE-** REPEATED OR PROLONGED CONTACT MAY RESULT IN DERMATITIS DUE TO IRRITATION OR ALLERGIC SENSITIVITY. IN ADDITION TO THE SYMPTOMS OF ACUTE EXPOSURE, CHRONIC ABSORPTION MAY CAUSE FATIGUE, WEIGHT LOSS, CATARACT FORMATION AND LIVER AND KIDNEY DAMAGE. YELLOW STAINING OF THE SCLERAE AND URINE INDICATES ABSORPTION OF POTENTIALLY TOXIC AMOUNTS.

FIRST AID- REMOVE CONTAMINATED CLOTHING AND SHOES IMMEDIATELY. THEN REMOVE SKIN AND HAIR CONTAMINATION BY SCRUBBING WITH SOAP AND WATER. IF BODY TEMPERATURE IS ELEVATED, REDUCE TO 37 C BY SPONGE BATH, IMMERSION IN COOL WATER OR BY APPLYING COOLING BLANKET. IF BODY TEMPERATURE IS ABOVE 40 C, ICE WATER IS NECESSARY (DREISBACH, HANDBOOK OF POISONING, 12TH EDITION; MORGAN, EPA RECOGNITION AND MANAGEMENT OF PESTICIDE POISONINGS, 3RD EDITION). GET MEDICAL ATTENTION IMMEDIATELY.

EYE CONTACT: BINAPACRYL: **ACUTE EXPOSURE-** MAY BE SLIGHTLY IRRITATING.
CHRONIC EXPOSURE- NO DATA AVAILABLE.

FIRST AID- WASH EYES IMMEDIATELY WITH LARGE AMOUNTS OF WATER OR NORMAL SALINE, OCCASIONALLY LIFTING UPPER AND LOWER LIDS, UNTIL NO EVIDENCE OF CHEMICAL REMAINS (APPROXIMATELY 15-20 MINUTES). GET MEDICAL ATTENTION IMMEDIATELY.

INGESTION: BINAPACRYL: TOXIC. SEE INFORMATION ON DINITROPHENOL DERIVATIVES. REPEATED DAILY ORAL ADMINISTRATION OF 25 MG/KG TO DOGS RESULTED IN DEPRESSION, CONTINUOUS PARESIS OF THE HINDQUARTERS, AND DEATH WITHIN 6 MONTHS.
DINITROPHENOL DERIVATIVES: **ACUTE EXPOSURE-** MAY CAUSE EFFECTS ON THE METABOLIC RATE, CENTRAL NERVOUS SYSTEM AND LIVER AND KIDNEY

RESULTING IN SIGNS AND SYMPTOMS AS DESCRIBED IN ACUTE INHALATION.
CHRONIC EXPOSURE- IN ADDITION TO THE SYMPTOMS OF ACUTE EXPOSURE, REPEATED INGESTION MAY CAUSE AN INITIAL SENSE OF WELL-BEING THEN ANOREXIA, DIARRHEA, DIZZINESS, RESTLESSNESS, FATIGUE, WEIGHT LOSS, SKIN ERUPTIONS, PERIPHERAL NEURITIS, LIVER AND KIDNEY DAMAGE, CARDIOVASCULAR COMPLICATIONS, GRANULOCYTOPENIA, AND CATARACT FORMATION. YELLOW STAINING OF THE SCLERAE AND URINE INDICATES ABSORPTION OF POTENTIALLY TOXIC AMOUNTS.

FIRST AID- REMOVE INGESTED POISON BY THOROUGH GASTRIC LAVAGE WITH SATURATED BICARBONATE SOLUTION. IF GASTRIC LAVAGE CANNOT BE ACCOMPLISHED IMMEDIATELY, GIVE SYRUP OF IPECAC TO INDUCE EMESIS AND FOLLOW WITH SALINE CATHARTIC. IF BODY TEMPERATURE IS ELEVATED, REDUCE TO 37 C BY IMMERSION IN COOL WATER OR BY APPLYING COOLING BLANKET. IF BODY TEMPERATURE IS ABOVE 40 C, ICE WATER IS NECESSARY (DREISBACH, HANDBOOK OF POISONING, 12TH ED.). ADMINISTRATION OF GASTRIC LAVAGE SHOULD BE PERFORMED BY QUALIFIED MEDICAL PERSONNEL. GET MEDICAL ATTENTION IMMEDIATELY.

ANTIDOTE: NO SPECIFIC ANTIDOTE. TREAT SYMPTOMATICALLY AND SUPPORTIVELY.

REACTIVITY

REACTIVITY: NO DATA AVAILABLE.

INCOMPATIBILITIES: BINAPACRYL: ACIDS (STRONG): INCOMPATIBLE. ALKALIES: INCOMPATIBLE. OXIDIZERS (STRONG): FIRE AND EXPLOSION HAZARD.

DECOMPOSITION: THERMAL DECOMPOSITION PRODUCTS MAY INCLUDE TOXIC OXIDES OF CARBON AND NITROGEN.

POLYMERIZATION: HAZARDOUS POLYMERIZATION HAS NOT BEEN REPORTED TO OCCUR UNDER NORMAL TEMPERATURES AND PRESSURES.

STORAGE AND DISPOSAL

OBSERVE ALL FEDERAL, STATE AND LOCAL REGULATIONS WHEN STORING OR DISPOSING OF THIS SUBSTANCE. FOR ASSISTANCE, CONTACT THE DISTRICT DIRECTOR OF THE ENVIRONMENTAL PROTECTION AGENCY.

STORAGE

STORE IN ACCORDANCE WITH 40 CFR 165 RECOMMENDED PROCEDURES FOR THE DISPOSAL AND STORAGE OF PESTICIDES AND PESTICIDE CONTAINERS.
STORE AWAY FROM INCOMPATIBLE SUBSTANCES.

DISPOSAL

DISPOSAL MUST BE IN ACCORDANCE WITH 40 CFR 165 RECOMMENDED PROCEDURES FOR THE DISPOSAL AND STORAGE OF PESTICIDES AND PESTICIDE CONTAINERS.

CONDITIONS TO AVOID

MAY BURN BUT DOES NOT IGNITE READILY.

SPILL AND LEAK PROCEDURES

OCCUPATIONAL SPILL: DO NOT TOUCH SPILLED MATERIAL. STOP LEAK IF YOU CAN DO IT WITHOUT RISK. FOR SMALL SPILLS, TAKE UP WITH SAND OR OTHER ABSORBENT MATERIAL AND PLACE INTO CONTAINERS FOR LATER DISPOSAL. FOR SMALL DRY SPILLS, WITH A CLEAN SHOVEL PLACE MATERIAL INTO CLEAN, DRY CONTAINER AND COVER. MOVE CONTAINERS FROM SPILL AREA. FOR LARGER SPILLS, DIKE FAR AHEAD OF SPILL FOR LATER DISPOSAL. KEEP UNNECESSARY PEOPLE AWAY. ISOLATE HAZARD AREA AND DENY ENTRY.

PROTECTIVE EQUIPMENT

VENTILATION: PROVIDE LOCAL EXHAUST VENTILATION SYSTEM.

RESPIRATOR: THE FOLLOWING RESPIRATORS ARE RECOMMENDED BASED ON INFORMATION FOUND IN THE PHYSICAL DATA, TOXICITY AND HEALTH EFFECTS SECTIONS. THEY ARE RANKED IN ORDER FROM MINIMUM TO MAXIMUM RESPIRATORY PROTECTION. THE SPECIFIC RESPIRATOR SELECTED MUST BE BASED ON CONTAMINATION LEVELS FOUND IN THE WORK PLACE, MUST NOT EXCEED THE WORKING LIMITS OF THE RESPIRATOR AND BE JOINTLY APPROVED BY THE NATIONAL INSTITUTE FOR OCCUPATIONAL SAFETY AND HEALTH AND THE MINE SAFETY AND HEALTH ADMINISTRATION (NIOSH-MSHA).

TYPE 'C' SUPPLIED-AIR RESPIRATOR WITH A FULL FACEPIECE OPERATED IN PRESSURE-DEMAND OR OTHER POSITIVE PRESSURE MODE OR WITH A FULL FACEPIECE, HELMET OR HOOD OPERATED IN CONTINOUS-FLOW MODE.

SELF-CONTAINED BREATHING APPARATUS WITH A FULL FACEPIECE OPERATED IN PRESSURE-DEMAND OR OTHER POSITIVE PRESSURE MODE.

FOR FIREFIGHTING AND OTHER IMMEDIATELY DANGEROUS TO LIFE OR HEALTH CONDITIONS:

SELF-CONTAINED BREATHING APPARATUS WITH FULL FACEPIECE OPERATED IN PRESSURE-DEMAND OR OTHER POSITIVE PRESSURE MODE.

SUPPLIED-AIR RESPIRATOR WITH FULL FACEPIECE AND OPERATED IN PRESSURE-DEMAND OR OTHER POSITIVE PRESSURE MODE IN COMBINATION WITH AN AUXILIARY SELF-CONTAINED BREATHING APPARATUS OPERATED IN PRESSURE-DEMAND OR OTHER POSITIVE PRESSURE MODE.

CLOTHING: EMPLOYEE MUST WEAR APPROPRIATE PROTECTIVE (IMPERVIOUS) CLOTHING AND EQUIPMENT TO PREVENT ANY POSSIBILITY OF SKIN CONTACT WITH THIS SUBSTANCE.

GLOVES: EMPLOYEE MUST WEAR APPROPRIATE PROTECTIVE GLOVES TO PREVENT CONTACT WITH THIS SUBSTANCE.

EYE PROTECTION: EMPLOYEE MUST WEAR SPLASH-PROOF OR DUST-RESISTANT SAFETY GOGGLES AND A FACESHIELD TO PREVENT CONTACT WITH THIS SUBSTANCE.

EMERGENCY WASH FACILITIES: WHERE THERE IS ANY POSSIBILITY THAT AN EMPLOYEE'S EYES AND/OR SKIN MAY BE EXPOSED TO THIS SUBSTANCE, THE EMPLOYER SHOULD PROVIDE AN EYE WASH FOUNTAIN AND QUICK DRENCH SHOWER WITHIN THE IMMEDIATE WORK AREA FOR EMERGENCY USE.

AUTHORIZED BY- OCCUPATIONAL HEALTH SERVICES, INC.
CREATION DATE: 10/04/89 ***REVISION DATE:*** 04/18/90

MATERIAL SAFETY DATA SHEET

OCCUPATIONAL HEALTH SERVICES, INC.
AGRICULTURE AND PESTICIDE DIVISION
450 SEVENTH AVENUE, SUITE 2407
NEW YORK, NEW YORK 10123
1-800-445-MSDS OR (212) 967-1100

EMERGENCY CONTACT:
JOHN S. BRANSFORD, JR. (615) 292-1180

SUBSTANCE IDENTIFICATION

CAS-NUMBER 867-27-6

SUBSTANCE: **DEMETON-O-METHYL**

TRADE NAMES/SYNONYMS: PHOSPHOROTHIOIC ACID, O-(2-(ETHYLTHIO)ETHYL) O,O-DIMETHYL ESTER; PHOSPHOROTHIOIC ACID, 2-(ETHYLTHIO)ETHYL O,O-DIMETHYL ESTER; O,O-DIMETHYL O-2-(ETHYLTHIO)ETHYL PHOSPHOROTHIOATE; O,O-DIMETHYL O-(2-(ETHYLTHIO)ETHYL) PHOSPHOROTHIOATE; METHYL-O-DEMETON; PST71969

CHEMICAL FAMILY: ORGANOPHOSPHATE

MOLECULAR FORMULA: C6-H15-O3-P-S2

MOLECULAR WEIGHT: 230.30

CERCLA RATINGS (SCALE 0-3): HEALTH=3 FIRE=0 REACTIVITY=0 PERSISTENCE=0

NFPA RATINGS (SCALE 0-4): HEALTH=3 FIRE=0 REACTIVITY=0

COMPONENTS AND CONTAMINANTS

COMPONENT: DEMETON-O-METHYL ***PERCENT:*** 100
CAS# 867-27-6

EXPOSURE LIMITS: METHYL DEMETON: 0.5 MG/M3 OSHA TWA (SKIN) 0.5 MG/M3 ACGIH TWA (SKIN)

PHYSICAL DATA

DESCRIPTION: PALE YELLOW LIQUID WITH AN UNPLEASANT ODOR

BOILING POINT: 165 F (74 C) @ 0.15 MMHG ***SPECIFIC GRAVITY:*** 1.1904

EVAPORATION RATE: NOT AVAILABLE ***SOLUBILITY IN WATER:*** 0.33%

SOLVENT SOLUBILITY: SOLUBLE IN MOST ORGANIC SOLVENTS

FIRE AND EXPLOSION DATA

FIRE AND EXPLOSION HAZARD: NEGLIGIBLE FIRE HAZARD WHEN EXPOSED TO HEAT OR FLAME.

FIREFIGHTING MEDIA: DRY CHEMICAL, CARBON DIOXIDE, HALON, WATER SPRAY OR STANDARD FOAM (1987 EMERGENCY RESPONSE GUIDEBOOK, DOT P 5800.4). FOR LARGER FIRES, USE WATER SPRAY, FOG OR STANDARD FOAM (1987 EMERGENCY RESPONSE GUIDEBOOK, DOT P 5800.4).

FIREFIGHTING: MOVE CONTAINERS FROM FIRE AREA IF POSSIBLE. FIGHT FIRE FROM MAXIMUM DISTANCE. STAY AWAY FROM STORAGE TANK ENDS. DIKE FIRE CONTROL WATER FOR LATER DISPOSAL. DO NOT SCATTER MATERIAL (1987 EMERGENCY RESPONSE GUIDEBOOK, DOT P 5800.4, GUIDE PAGE 55). EXTINGUISH USING AGENT SUITABLE FOR TYPE OF SURROUNDING FIRE. AVOID BREATHING VAPORS AND DUSTS. KEEP UPWIND.

TOXICITY

DEMETON-O-METHYL: TOXICITY DATA: 20 MG/M3 INHALATION-CAT LCLO; 75 MG/KG SKIN-RABBIT LDLO; 75 MG/KG ORAL-RAT LD50; 46 MG/KG ORAL-MOUSE LD50; 30 MG/KG ORAL-CAT LDLO; 216 MG/KG INTRAVENOUS-RAT LD50; 3500 UG/KG UNREPORTED-MOUSE LD50; REPRODUCTIVE EFFECTS DATA (RTECS). CARCINOGEN STATUS: NONE. ACUTE TOXICITY LEVEL: TOXIC BY INGESTION.

TARGET EFFECTS: CHOLINESTERASE INHIBITOR. POISONING MAY AFFECT THE NERVOUS SYSTEM.* AT INCREASED RISK FROM EXPOSURE: PERSONS WITH RESPIRATORY AILMENTS, RECENT EXPOSURE TO CHOLINESTERASE INHIBITORS OR IMPAIRED CHOLINESTERASE PRODUCTION, OR LIVER MALFUNCTION.* ADDITIONAL DATA: MAY CROSS THE PLACENTA. HIGH ENVIRONMENTAL TEMPERATURES OR EXPOSURE OF THE CHEMICAL TO VISIBLE OR ULTRAVIOLET LIGHT MAY ENHANCE THE TOXICITY. INTERACTIONS WITH MEDICATIONS MAY OCCUR.*

* MAY BE BASED ON GENERAL INFORMATION ON ORGANOPHOSPHATES.

HEALTH EFFECTS AND FIRST AID

INHALATION: DEMETON-O-METHYL: ADVERSE EFFECTS ON FERTILITY, FETOTOXICITY, AND FETAL DEVELOPMENTAL ABNORMALITIES WERE REPORTED FROM A CHRONIC INHALATION STUDY OF PREGNANT RATS. SEE INFORMATION ON ORGANOPHOSPHATES.

ORGANOPHOSPHATES: CHOLINESTERASE INHIBITOR. **ACUTE EXPOSURE-** WHEN INHALED, THE FIRST EFFECTS OF CHOLINESTERASE INHIBITORS ARE USUALLY RESPIRATORY AND MAY INCLUDE NASAL HYPEREMIA AND WATERY DISCHARGE, COUGH, CHEST DISCOMFORT, DYSPNEA, AND WHEEZING DUE TO INCREASED BRONCHIAL SECRETIONS AND BRONCHOCONSTRICTION. IF SUFFICIENT AMOUNTS ARE ABSORBED, OTHER SYSTEMIC EFFECTS MAY BEGIN WITHIN A FEW MINUTES OR BE DELAYED FOR UP TO 12 HOURS. SYMPTOMS MAY INCLUDE PALLOR, NAUSEA, VOMITING, DIARRHEA, ABDOMINAL CRAMPS, HEADACHE, DIZZINESS, OCULAR PAIN, BLURRED VISION, MIOSIS OR IN SOME CASES, ESPECIALLY INITIALLY, MYDRIASIS, LACRIMATION, SALIVATION, SWEATING, AND CONFUSION. OTHER REPORTED CENTRAL NERVOUS SYSTEM OR NEUROMUSCULAR EFFECTS MAY INCLUDE ATAXIA, SLURRED SPEECH, AREFLEXIA, WEAKNESS, FATIGUE, FASCICULATIONS, TWITCHING, TREMORS POSSIBLY OF THE TONGUE AND EYELIDS, AND EVENTUALLY PARALYSIS OF THE EXTREMITIES AND POSSIBLY OF THE RESPIRATORY MUSCLES. IN SEVERE CASES THERE MAY ALSO BE INVOLUNTARY DEFECATION AND URINATION, CYANOSIS, PSYCHOSIS, HYPERGLYCEMIA, ACUTE PANCREATITIS, CARDIAC IRREGULARITIES, PULMONARY EDEMA, UNCONSCIOUSNESS, CONVULSIONS, AND COMA. DEATH IS PRIMARILY DUE TO RESPIRATORY FAILURE, ALTHOUGH CARDIOVASCULAR EFFECTS INCLUDING CARDIAC ARREST MAY ALSO BE IMPLICATED. LONG TERM SEQUELAE ARE RARE BUT MAY INCLUDE NEUROPSYCHIATRIC DISORDERS AND MYOPATHY WITH MUSCLE TENDERNESS. SOME ORGANOPHOSPHATES MAY CAUSE A DELAYED NEUROPATHY BEGINNING 1-4 WEEKS AFTER AN ACUTE EXPOSURE WHICH MAY OR MAY NOT HAVE CAUSED ACUTE CHOLINERGIC EFFECTS. NUMBNESS, TINGLING, WEAKNESS AND CRAMPING BEGINNING SYMMETRICALLY IN THE LOWER LIMBS MAY PROGRESS TO ATAXIA AND PARALYSIS. IN SEVERE CASES, UPPER LIMB INVOLVEMENT IS POSSIBLE AND FLACCID PARALYSIS MAY PROGRESS TO SPASTIC PARALYSIS WITH EXAGGERATED REFLEXES. IMPROVEMENT MAY OCCUR OVER MONTHS TO YEARS, BUT SOME RESIDUAL IMPAIRMENT USUALLY REMAINS. **CHRONIC EXPOSURE-** REPEATED OR PROLONGED EXPOSURE MAY RESULT IN THE EFFECTS OF ACUTE EXPOSURE INCLUDING THE DELAYED NEUROPATHY. OTHER EFFECTS REPORTED IN WORKERS REPEATEDLY EXPOSED INCLUDE IMPAIRED MEMORY AND CONCENTRATION, ACUTE PSYCHOSIS, SEVERE DEPRESSIONS, IRRITABILTY, CONFUSION, APATHY, EMOTIONAL LABILITY, SOCIAL WITHDRAWAL, CONFUSION, HEADACHE, SPEECH DIFFICULTIES, DELAYED REACTION TIMES, SPATIAL DISORIENTATION, NIGHTMARES, SLEEPWALKING, AND DROWSINESS OR INSOMNIA. AN INFLUENZA-LIKE CONDITION WITH HEADACHE, NAUSEA, WEAKNESS, ANOREXIA AND MALAISE HAS ALSO BEEN REPORTED.

FIRST AID- REMOVE FROM EXPOSURE AREA TO FRESH AIR IMMEDIATELY. IF BREATHING HAS STOPPED, GIVE ARTIFICIAL RESPIRATION. MAINTAIN AIRWAY AND BLOOD PRESSURE AND ADMINISTER OXYGEN IF AVAILABLE. KEEP AFFECTED PERSON WARM AND AT REST. TREAT SYMPTOMATICALLY AND SUPPORTIVELY. ADMINISTRATION OF OXYGEN SHOULD BE PERFORMED BY QUALIFIED PERSONNEL. GET MEDICAL ATTENTION IMMEDIATELY.

SKIN CONTACT: DEMETON-O-METHYL: SEE INFORMATION ON ORGANOPHOSPHATES.

ORGANOPHOSPHATES: CHOLINESTERASE INHIBITOR. **ACUTE EXPOSURE-** LOCALIZED SWEATING AND FASCICULATIONS MAY OCCUR AT THE SITE OF CONTACT. IF SUFFICIENT AMOUNTS ARE ABSORBED, OTHER EFFECTS OF CHOLINESTERASE INHIBITION AS DESCRIBED IN ACUTE INHALATION MAY OCCUR. SYMPTOMS MAY BE DELAYED 2-3 HOURS, BUT USUALLY NO MORE THAN 12 HOURS. THE RATE OF ABSORPTION IS INCREASED BY THE PRESENCE OF DERMATITIS OR HIGH AMBIENT TEMPERATURES. DELAYED NEUROPATHY IS ALSO POSSIBLE. **CHRONIC EXPOSURE-** REPEATED OR PROLONGED EXPOSURE MAY CAUSE EFFECTS AS DESCRIBED IN ACUTE EXPOSURE. SOME ORGANOPHOSPHATES MAY CAUSE SENSITIZATION.

FIRST AID- REMOVE CONTAMINATED CLOTHING IMMEDIATELY. WASH CONTAMINATED AREAS WITH SOAP AND WATER FOLLOWED BY ALCOHOL (ARENA, POISONING, 4TH ED.). EMERGENCY PERSONNEL SHOULD WEAR GLOVES AND AVOID CONTAMINATION. TREAT RESPIRATORY DIFFICULTY WITH ARTIFICIAL RESPIRATION. GET MEDICAL ATTENTION IMMEDIATELY.

EYE CONTACT: DEMETON-O-METHYL: SEE INFORMATION ON ORGANOPHOSPHATES.

ORGANOPHOSPHATES: CHOLINESTERASE INHIBITOR. **ACUTE EXPOSURE-** DIRECT CONTACT MAY CAUSE PAIN, HYPEREMIA, LACRIMATION, TWITCHING OF THE EYELIDS, MIOSIS, AND CILIARY MUSCLE SPASM WITH LOSS OF ACCOMODATION, BLURRED OR DIMMED VISION AND BROWACHE. SOMETIMES MYDRIASIS MAY OCCUR INSTEAD OF MIOSIS. WITH SUFFICIENT EXPOSURE, OTHER SYMPTOMS OF CHOLINESTERASE INHIBITION AS DESCRIBED IN ACUTE INHALATION MAY OCCUR. **CHRONIC EXPOSURE-** REPEATED OR PROLONGED EXPOSURE MAY CAUSE EFFECTS AS DESCRIBED IN ACUTE EXPOSURE. SOME COMPOUNDS HAVE CAUSED TOXIC EFFECTS ON THE CRYSTALLINE LENS, CONJUNCTIVAL THICKENING AND OBSTRUCTION OF THE NASOLACRIMAL CANALS WHEN USED AS MIOTIC EYEDROPS.

FIRST AID- IRRIGATE EYES WITH WATER OR SALINE SOLUTION. IF SYMPTOMS OF POISONING OCCUR, TREAT RESPIRATORY DIFFICULTY WITH ARTIFICIAL RESPIRATION AND OXYGEN. OBSERVE PATIENT FOR AT LEAST 24-36 HOURS (GOSSELIN, CLINICAL TOXICOLOGY OF COMMERCIAL PRODUCTS, 5TH ED.). GET MEDICAL ATTENTION IMMEDIATELY. OXYGEN SHOULD BE ADMINISTERED BY QUALIFIED MEDICAL PERSONNEL.

INGESTION: DEMETON-O-METHYL: TOXIC. SEE INFORMATION ON ORGANOPHOSPHATES.

ORGANOPHOSPHATES: CHOLINESTERASE INHIBITOR. **ACUTE EXPOSURE-** WHEN INGESTED, THE FIRST EFFECTS MAY BE NAUSEA, VOMITING, ANOREXIA, ABDOMINAL CRAMPS AND DIARRHEA. GASTROINTESTINAL ABSORPTION MAY CAUSE SYMPTOMS OF CHOLINESTERASE INHIBITION AS DESCRIBED IN ACUTE INHALATION. SYMPTOMS MAY BEGIN WITHIN MINUTES OR BE DELAYED FOR HOURS. DELAYED EFFECTS INCLUDING NEUROPATHY MAY ALSO OCCUR. **CHRONIC EXPOSURE-** REPEATED INGESTION MAY CAUSE EFFECTS AS DESCRIBED IN ACUTE EXPOSURE.

FIRST AID- IF PERSON IS ALERT AND RESPIRATION IS NOT DEPRESSED, GIVE SYRUP OF IPECAC FOLLOWED BY WATER (IF VOMITING OCCURS, KEEP HEAD BELOW HIPS TO PREVENT ASPIRATION). IF CONSCIOUSNESS LEVEL DECLINES OR VOMITING HAS NOT OCCURRED IN 15 MINUTES EMPTY STOMACH BY GASTRIC LAVAGE WITH THE AID OF CUFFED ENDOTRACHEAL TUBE USING ISOTONIC SALINE OR 5% SODIUM BICARBONATE FOLLOW WITH ACTIVATED CHARCOAL. ESTABLISH AND MAINTAIN AIRWAY. TREAT RESPIRATORY DIFFICULTY WITH ARTIFICIAL RESPIRATION AND OXYGEN. DO NOT GIVE MORPHINE, AMINOPHYLLINE, PHENOTHIAZINES, RESERPINE, FUROSEMIDE, OR ETHACRYNIC ACID (MORGAN, RECOGNITION AND MANAGEMENT OF PESTICIDE POISONINGS, 3RD ED.). TREAT SYMPTOMATICALLY AND SUPPORTIVELY. ADMINISTRATION OF OXYGEN AND LAVAGE MUST BE PERFORMED BY QUALIFIED MEDICAL PERSONNEL. GET MEDICAL ATTENTION IMMEDIATELY.

ANTIDOTE: THE FOLLOWING ANTIDOTE(S) HAVE BEEN RECOMMENDED. HOWEVER, THE DECISION AS TO WHETHER THE SEVERITY OF POISONING REQUIRES ADMINISTRATION OF ANY ANTIDOTE AND ACTUAL DOSE REQUIRED SHOULD BE MADE BY QUALIFIED MEDICAL PERSONNEL.

FOR CHOLINESTERASE INHIBITORS: ESTABLISH CLEAR AIRWAY AND TISSUE OXYGENATION BY ASPIRATION OF SECRETIONS, AND IF NECESSARY, BY ASSISTED PULMONARY VENTILATION WITH OXYGEN. IMPROVE TISSUE OXYGENATION AS MUCH AS POSSIBLE BEFORE ADMINISTERING ATROPINE TO MINIMIZE THE RISK OF VENTRICULAR FIBRILLATION. ADMINISTER ATROPINE SULFATE INTRAVENOUSLY, OR INTRAMUSCULARLY IF IV INJECTION IS NOT POSSIBLE. IN MODERATELY SEVERE POISONING ADMINISTER ATROPINE SULFATE, 0.4-2.0 MG REPEATED EVERY 15 MINUTES UNTIL ATROPINIZATION IS ACHIEVED (TACHYCARDIA, FLUSHING, DRY MOUTH, MYDRIASIS). MAINTAIN ATROPINIZATION BY REPEATED DOSES FOR 2-12 HOURS, OR LONGER, DEPENDING ON THE SEVERITY OF POISONING. THE APPEARANCE OF RALES IN THE LUNG BASES, MIOSIS, SALIVATION, NAUSEA, BRADYCARDIA, ARE ALL INDICATIONS OF INADEQUATE ATROPINIZATION. SEVERELY POISONED INDIVIDUALS MAY EXHIBIT REMARKABLE TOLERANCE TO ATROPINE; TWO OR MORE TIMES THE DOSAGES SUGGESTED ABOVE MAY BE NEEDED. PERSONS NOT POISONED OR ONLY SLIGHTLY POISONED, HOWEVER, MAY DEVELOP SIGNS OF ATROPINE TOXICITY FROM SUCH LARGE DOSAGES: FEVER, MUSCLE FIBRILLATIONS, AND DELIRIUM ARE THE MAIN SIGNS OF ATROPINE TOXICITY. IF THESE SIGNS APPEAR WHILE THE PATIENT IS FULLY ATROPINIZED, ATROPINE ADMINISTRATION SHOULD BE DISCONTINUED, AT LEAST TEMPORARILY. OBSERVE TREATED PATIENTS CLOSELY AT LEAST 24 HOURS TO INSURE THAT SYMPTOMS (POSSIBLY PULMONARY EDEMA) DO NOT RECUR AS ATROPINIZATION WEARS OFF. IN VERY SEVERE POISONINGS, METABOLIC DISPOSITION OF TOXICANT MAY REQUIRE SEVERAL HOURS OR DAYS DURING WHICH ATROPINIZATION MUST BE MAINTAINED. MARKEDLY LOWER LEVELS OF URINARY METABOLITES INDICATE THAT ATROPINE DOSAGE CAN BE TAPERED OFF. AS DOSAGE IS REDUCED, CHECK THE LUNG BASES FREQUENTLY FOR RALES. IF RALES ARE HEARD OR OTHER SYMPTOMS RETURN, RE-ESTABLISH ATROPINIZATION PROMPTLY (MORGAN, RECOGNITION AND MANAGEMENT OF PESTICIDE POISONINGS, 3RD ED.). ADMINISTRATION OF ANTIDOTE MUST BE PERFORMED BY QUALIFIED MEDICAL PERSONNEL.

IN CASES OF SEVERE POISONING BY ORGANOPHOSPHATE PESTICIDES IN WHICH RESPIRATORY DEPRESSION, MUSCLE WEAKNESS AND TWITCHINGS ARE SEVERE, GIVE PRALIDOXIME (PROTOPAM-AYERST, 2-PAM), 1.0 GRAM INTRAVENOUSLY AT NO MORE THAN 0.5 GRAM PER MINUTE. DOSAGE OF PRALIDOXIME MAY BE REPEATED IN 1-2 HOURS, THEN AT 10-12 HOUR INTERVALS IF NEEDED. IN VERY SEVERE POISONINGS, DOSAGE RATES MAY BE DOUBLED. TREATMENT WITH PRALIDOXIME WILL BE MOST EFFECTIVE IF GIVEN WITHIN THIRTY-SIX HOURS AFTER POISONING (MORGAN, RECOGNITION AND MANAGEMENT OF PESTICIDE POISONINGS, 3RD ED.). ANTIDOTE SHOULD BE ADMINISTERED BY QUALIFIED MEDICAL PERSONNEL.

REACTIVITY

REACTIVITY: STABLE UNDER NORMAL TEMPERATURES AND PRESSURES.

INCOMPATIBILITIES: DEMETON-O-METHYL: ALKALI: HYDROLYZE. STRONG OXIDIZERS: INCOMPATIBLE.

DECOMPOSITION: THERMAL DECOMPOSITION MAY RELEASE TOXIC OXIDES OF PHOSPHORUS AND SULFUR.

POLYMERIZATION: HAZARDOUS POLYMERIZATION HAS NOT BEEN REPORTED TO OCCUR UNDER NORMAL TEMPERATURES AND PRESSURES.

STORAGE AND DISPOSAL

OBSERVE ALL FEDERAL, STATE AND LOCAL REGULATIONS WHEN STORING OR DISPOSING OF THIS SUBSTANCE. FOR ASSISTANCE, CONTACT THE DISTRICT DIRECTOR OF THE ENVIRONMENTAL PROTECTION AGENCY.

STORAGE

STORE IN ACCORDANCE WITH 40 CFR 165 RECOMMENDED PROCEDURES FOR THE DISPOSAL AND STORAGE OF PESTICIDES AND PESTICIDE CONTAINERS.

STORE AWAY FROM INCOMPATIBLE SUBSTANCES.

DISPOSAL

DISPOSAL MUST BE IN ACCORDANCE WITH 40 CFR 165 RECOMMENDED PROCEDURES FOR THE DISPOSAL AND STORAGE OF PESTICIDES AND PESTICIDE CONTAINERS.

CONDITIONS TO AVOID

NONE REPORTED.

SPILL AND LEAK PROCEDURES

OCCUPATIONAL SPILL: DO NOT TOUCH SPILLED MATERIAL. STOP LEAK IF YOU CAN DO IT WITHOUT RISK. USE WATER SPRAY TO REDUCE VAPORS. FOR SMALL SPILLS, TAKE UP WITH SAND OR OTHER ABSORBENT MATERIAL AND PLACE INTO CONTAINERS FOR LATER DISPOSAL. FOR SMALL DRY SPILLS, WITH A CLEAN SHOVEL PLACE MATERIAL INTO CLEAN, DRY CONTAINERS AND COVER. MOVE CONTAINERS FROM SPILL AREA. FOR LARGER SPILLS, DIKE FAR AHEAD OF SPILL FOR LATER DISPOSAL. KEEP UNNECESSARY PEOPLE AWAY. ISOLATE HAZARD AREA AND DENY ENTRY. VENTILATE CLOSED SPACES BEFORE ENTERING.

PROTECTIVE EQUIPMENT

VENTILATION: PROVIDE LOCAL EXHAUST OR PROCESS ENCLOSURE VENTILATION TO MEET PUBLISHED EXPOSURE LIMITS.

RESPIRATOR: THE FOLLOWING RESPIRATORS ARE RECOMMENDED BASED ON INFORMATION FOUND IN THE PHYSICAL DATA, TOXICITY AND HEALTH EFFECTS SECTIONS. THEY ARE RANKED IN ORDER FROM MINIMUM TO MAXIMUM RESPIRATORY PROTECTION. THE SPECIFIC RESPIRATOR SELECTED MUST BE BASED ON CONTAMINATION LEVELS FOUND IN THE WORK PLACE, MUST NOT EXCEED THE WORKING LIMITS OF THE RESPIRATOR AND BE JOINTLY APPROVED BY THE NATIONAL INSTITUTE FOR OCCUPATIONAL SAFETY AND HEALTH AND THE MINE SAFETY AND HEALTH ADMINISTRATION (NIOSH-MSHA).

TYPE 'C' SUPPLIED-AIR RESPIRATOR WITH A FULL FACEPIECE OPERATED IN PRESSURE-DEMAND OR OTHER POSITIVE PRESSURE MODE OR WITH A FULL FACEPIECE, HELMET OR HOOD OPERATED IN CONTINOUS-FLOW MODE.

SELF-CONTAINED BREATHING APPARATUS WITH A FULL FACEPIECE OPERATED IN PRESSURE-DEMAND OR OTHER POSITIVE PRESSURE MODE.

FOR FIREFIGHTING AND OTHER IMMEDIATELY DANGEROUS TO LIFE OR HEALTH CONDITIONS:

SELF-CONTAINED BREATHING APPARATUS WITH FULL FACEPIECE OPERATED IN PRESSURE-DEMAND OR OTHER POSITIVE PRESSURE MODE.

SUPPLIED-AIR RESPIRATOR WITH FULL FACEPIECE AND OPERATED IN PRESSURE-DEMAND OR OTHER POSITIVE PRESSURE MODE IN COMBINATION WITH AN AUXILIARY SELF-CONTAINED BREATHING APPARATUS OPERATED IN PRESSURE-DEMAND OR OTHER POSITIVE PRESSURE MODE.

CLOTHING: EMPLOYEE MUST WEAR APPROPRIATE PROTECTIVE (IMPERVIOUS) CLOTHING AND EQUIPMENT TO PREVENT ANY POSSIBILITY OF SKIN CONTACT WITH THIS SUBSTANCE.

GLOVES: EMPLOYEE MUST WEAR APPROPRIATE PROTECTIVE GLOVES TO PREVENT CONTACT WITH THIS SUBSTANCE.

EYE PROTECTION: EMPLOYEE MUST WEAR SPLASH-PROOF OR DUST-RESISTANT SAFETY GOGGLES AND A FACESHIELD TO PREVENT CONTACT WITH THIS SUBSTANCE.

EMERGENCY WASH FACILITIES: WHERE THERE IS ANY POSSIBILITY THAT AN EMPLOYEE'S EYES AND/OR SKIN MAY BE EXPOSED TO THIS SUBSTANCE, THE EMPLOYER SHOULD PROVIDE AN EYE WASH FOUNTAIN AND QUICK DRENCH SHOWER WITHIN THE IMMEDIATE WORK AREA FOR EMERGENCY USE.

AUTHORIZED BY- OCCUPATIONAL HEALTH SERVICES, INC.

CREATION DATE: 10/04/89 ***REVISION DATE:*** 04/27/90

MATERIAL SAFETY DATA SHEET

OCCUPATIONAL HEALTH SERVICES, INC.
AGRICULTURE AND PESTICIDE DIVISION
450 SEVENTH AVENUE, SUITE 2407
NEW YORK, NEW YORK 10123
1-800-445-MSDS OR (212) 967-1100

EMERGENCY CONTACT:
JOHN S. BRANSFORD, JR. (615) 292-1180

SUBSTANCE IDENTIFICATION

CAS-NUMBER 13932-13-3

SUBSTANCE: POTASSIUM TETRATHIONATE

TRADE NAMES/SYNONYMS: TETRATHIONIC ACID, DIPOTASSIUM SALT; POTASSIUM TETRATHIONATE (K2S4O6); K2O6S4; PST72015

CHEMICAL FAMILY: SOAP

MOLECULAR FORMULA: K2-S4-O6

MOLECULAR WEIGHT: 302.43

CERCLA RATINGS (SCALE 0-3): HEALTH=U FIRE=1 REACTIVITY=0 PERSISTENCE=2

NFPA RATINGS (SCALE 0-4): HEALTH=U FIRE=1 REACTIVITY=0

COMPONENTS AND CONTAMINANTS

COMPONENT: POTASSIUM TETRATHIONATE ***PERCENT:*** 100.0
CAS# 13932-13-3

OTHER CONTAMINANTS: NONE

EXPOSURE LIMITS: NO OCCUPATIONAL EXPOSURE LIMITS ESTABLISHED BY OSHA, ACGIH, OR NIOSH.

PHYSICAL DATA

DESCRIPTION: COLORLESS MONOCLINIC CRYSTALLINE SOLID.

MELTING POINT: NOT AVAILABLE ***SPECIFIC GRAVITY:*** 2.296

SOLUBILITY IN WATER: VERY SOLUBLE

SOLVENT SOLUBILITY: INSOLUBLE IN ALCOHOL.

FIRE AND EXPLOSION DATA

FIRE AND EXPLOSION HAZARD: SLIGHT FIRE HAZARD WHEN EXPOSED TO HEAT OR FLAME.

FIREFIGHTING MEDIA: DRY CHEMICAL, CARBON DIOXIDE, HALON, WATER SPRAY OR STANDARD FOAM (1987 EMERGENCY RESPONSE GUIDEBOOK, DOT P 5800.4). FOR LARGER FIRES, USE WATER SPRAY, FOG OR STANDARD FOAM (1987 EMERGENCY RESPONSE GUIDEBOOK, DOT P 5800.4).

FIREFIGHTING: MOVE CONTAINER FROM FIRE AREA IF POSSIBLE. DO NOT SCATTER SPILLED MATERIAL WITH HIGH PRESSURE WATER STREAMS. DIKE FIRE CONTROL WATER FOR LATER DISPOSAL (1987 EMERGENCY RESPONSE GUIDEBOOK, DOT P 5800.4, GUIDE PAGE 31).

USE AGENTS SUITABLE FOR TYPE OF SURROUNDING FIRE. AVOID BREATHING HAZARDOUS VAPORS, KEEP UPWIND.

TOXICITY

POTASSIUM TETRATHIONATE: CARCINOGEN STATUS: NONE. ACUTE TOXICITY LEVEL: NO DATA AVAILABLE. TARGET EFFECTS: POISONING BY POTASSIUM SALTS MAY AFFECT THE HEART.

HEALTH EFFECTS AND FIRST AID

INHALATION: POTASSIUM TETRATHIONATE: **ACUTE EXPOSURE-** NO DATA AVAILABLE. MAY BE IRRITATING TO THE MUCOUS MEMBRANES. **CHRONIC EXPOSURE-** NO DATA AVAILABLE.

FIRST AID- REMOVE FROM EXPOSURE AREA TO FRESH AIR IMMEDIATELY. IF BREATHING HAS STOPPED, PERFORM ARTIFICIAL RESPIRATION. KEEP PERSON WARM AND AT REST. TREAT SYMPTOMATICALLY AND SUPPORTIVELY. GET MEDICAL ATTENTION IMMEDIATELY.

SKIN CONTACT: POTASSIUM TETRATHIONATE: **ACUTE EXPOSURE**- NO DATA AVAILABLE. MAY BE IRRITATING. **CHRONIC EXPOSURE**- NO DATA AVAILABLE.
FIRST AID- REMOVE CONTAMINATED CLOTHING AND SHOES IMMEDIATELY. WASH AFFECTED AREA WITH SOAP OR MILD DETERGENT AND LARGE AMOUNTS OF WATER UNTIL NO EVIDENCE OF CHEMICAL REMAINS (APPROXIMATELY 15-20 MINUTES). GET MEDICAL ATTENTION IMMEDIATELY.

EYE CONTACT: POTASSIUM TETRATHIONATE: **ACUTE EXPOSURE**- NO DATA AVAILABLE. MAY BE IRRITATING. **CHRONIC EXPOSURE**- NO DATA AVAILABLE.
FIRST AID- WASH EYES IMMEDIATELY WITH LARGE AMOUNTS OF WATER OR NORMAL SALINE, OCCASIONALLY LIFTING UPPER AND LOWER LIDS, UNTIL NO EVIDENCE OF CHEMICAL REMAINS (APPROXIMATELY 15-20 MINUTES). GET MEDICAL ATTENTION IMMEDIATELY.

INGESTION: POTASSIUM TETRATHIONATE: **ACUTE EXPOSURE**- POISONING BY POTASSIUM SALTS IS RARE BECAUSE A LARGE SINGLE DOSE USUALLY CAUSES VOMITING, AND IN THE ABSENCE OF PRE-EXISTING KIDNEY DAMAGE, POTASSIUM IS RAPIDLY EXCRETED. HOWEVER, IF SUFFICIENT AMOUNTS ARE ABSORBED IT MAY DISTURB THE RHYTHM OF THE HEART AND EVENTUALLY WEAKEN CARDIAC CONTRACTILITY. SKELETAL MUSCLE WEAKNESS AND FLACCID PARALYSIS MAY OCCUR IN SEVERE CASES. **CHRONIC EXPOSURE**- NO DATA AVAILABLE.
FIRST AID- TREAT SYMPTOMATICALLY AND SUPPORTIVELY. GET MEDICAL ATTENTION IMMEDIATELY. IF VOMITING OCCURS, KEEP HEAD LOWER THAN HIPS TO PREVENT ASPIRATION.
ANTIDOTE: NO SPECIFIC ANTIDOTE. TREAT SYMPTOMATICALLY AND SUPPORTIVELY.

REACTIVITY

REACTIVITY: STABLE UNDER NORMAL TEMPERATURES AND PRESSURES.
INCOMPATIBILITIES: POTASSIUN TETRATHIONATE: OXIDIZERS (STRONG): FIRE AND EXPLOSION HAZARD.
DECOMPOSITION: THERMAL DECOMPOSITION MAY RELEASE TOXIC AND/OR HAZARDOUS GASES.
POLYMERIZATION: HAZARDOUS POLYMERIZATION HAS NOT BEEN REPORTED TO OCCUR UNDER NORMAL TEMPERATURES AND PRESSURES.

STORAGE AND DISPOSAL

OBSERVE ALL FEDERAL, STATE AND LOCAL REGULATIONS WHEN STORING OR DISPOSING OF THIS SUBSTANCE. FOR ASSISTANCE, CONTACT THE DISTRICT DIRECTOR OF THE ENVIRONMENTAL PROTECTION AGENCY.

STORAGE

STORE IN ACCORDANCE WITH 40 CFR 165 RECOMMENDED PROCEDURES FOR THE DISPOSAL AND STORAGE OF PESTICIDES AND PESTICIDE CONTAINERS.
STORE AWAY FROM INCOMPATIBLE SUBSTANCES.

DISPOSAL

DISPOSAL MUST BE IN ACCORDANCE WITH 40 CFR 165 RECOMMENDED PROCEDURES FOR THE DISPOSAL AND STORAGE OF PESTICIDES AND PESTICIDE CONTAINERS.

CONDITIONS TO AVOID

MAY BURN BUT DOES NOT IGNITE READILY. AVOID CONTACT WITH STRONG OXIDIZERS, EXCESSIVE HEAT, SPARKS, OR OPEN FLAME.

SPILL AND LEAK PROCEDURES

OCCUPATIONAL SPILL: SWEEP UP AND PLACE IN SUITABLE CLEAN, DRY CONTAINERS FOR RECLAMATION OR LATER DISPOSAL. DO NOT FLUSH SPILLED MATERIAL INTO SEWER. KEEP UNNECESSARY PEOPLE AWAY.

PROTECTIVE EQUIPMENT

VENTILATION: PROVIDE LOCAL EXHAUST OR GENERAL DILUTION VENTILATION SYSTEM.
RESPIRATOR: THE FOLLOWING RESPIRATORS ARE RECOMMENDED BASED ON INFORMATION FOUND IN THE PHYSICAL DATA, TOXICITY AND HEALTH EFFECTS SECTIONS. THEY ARE RANKED IN ORDER FROM MINIMUM TO MAXIMUM RESPIRATORY PROTECTION. THE SPECIFIC RESPIRATOR SELECTED MUST BE BASED ON CONTAMINATION LEVELS FOUND IN THE WORK PLACE, MUST NOT EXCEED THE WORKING LIMITS OF THE RESPIRATOR AND BE JOINTLY APPROVED BY THE NATIONAL INSTITUTE FOR OCCUPATIONAL SAFETY AND HEALTH AND THE MINE SAFETY AND HEALTH ADMINISTRATION (NIOSH-MSHA).
CHEMICAL CARTRIDGE RESPIRATOR WITH AN ORGANIC VAPOR CARTRIDGE(S) WITH A FULL FACEPIECE AND ORGANIC VAPOR CARTRIDGE(S) IN COMBINATION WITH A DUST AND MIST FILTER.
POWERED AIR-PURIFYING RESPIRATOR WITH A TIGHT-FITTING FACEPIECE AND ORGANIC VAPOR CARTRIDGE(S) IN COMBINATION WITH A HIGH-EFFICIENCY PARTICULATE FILTER.
TYPE 'C' SUPPLIED-AIR RESPIRATOR WITH A FULL FACEPIECE OPERATED IN A PRESSURE-DEMAND OR OTHER POSITIVE PRESSURE MODE.
SELF-CONTAINED BREATHING APPARATUS WITH A FULL FACEPIECE OPERATED IN PRESSURE-DEMAND OR OTHER POSITIVE PRESSURE MODE.
FOR FIREFIGHTING AND OTHER IMMEDIATELY DANGEROUS TO LIFE OR HEALTH CONDITIONS:
SELF-CONTAINED BREATHING APPARATUS WITH FULL FACEPIECE OPERATED IN PRESSURE-DEMAND OR OTHER POSITIVE PRESSURE MODE.
SUPPLIED-AIR RESPIRATOR WITH FULL FACEPIECE AND OPERATED IN PRESSURE-DEMAND OR OTHER POSITIVE PRESSURE MODE IN COMBINATION WITH AN AUXILIARY SELF-CONTAINED BREATHING APPARATUS OPERATED IN PRESSURE-DEMAND OR OTHER POSITIVE PRESSURE MODE.
CLOTHING: EMPLOYEE MUST WEAR APPROPRIATE PROTECTIVE (IMPERVIOUS) CLOTHING AND EQUIPMENT TO PREVENT REPEATED OR PROLONGED SKIN CONTACT WITH THIS SUBSTANCE.
GLOVES: EMPLOYEE MUST WEAR APPROPRIATE PROTECTIVE GLOVES TO PREVENT CONTACT WITH THIS SUBSTANCE.
EYE PROTECTION: EMPLOYEE MUST WEAR SPLASH-PROOF OR DUST-RESISTANT SAFETY GOGGLES TO PREVENT EYE CONTACT WITH THIS SUBSTANCE.
EMERGENCY EYE WASH: WHERE THERE IS ANY POSSIBILITY THAT AN EMPLOYEE'S EYES MAY BE EXPOSED TO THIS SUBSTANCE, THE EMPLOYER SHOULD PROVIDE AN EYE WASH FOUNTAIN WITHIN THE IMMEDIATE WORK AREA FOR EMERGENCY USE.

AUTHORIZED BY- OCCUPATIONAL HEALTH SERVICES, INC.
CREATION DATE: 11/17/89 ***REVISION DATE:*** 05/31/90

MATERIAL SAFETY DATA SHEET

OCCUPATIONAL HEALTH SERVICES, INC.
AGRICULTURE AND PESTICIDE DIVISION
450 SEVENTH AVENUE, SUITE 2407
NEW YORK, NEW YORK 10123
1-800-445-MSDS OR (212) 967-1100

EMERGENCY CONTACT:
JOHN S. BRANSFORD, JR. (615) 292-1180

SUBSTANCE IDENTIFICATION

CAS-NUMBER 59-40-5
SUBSTANCE: **SULFAQUINOXALINE**
TRADE NAMES/SYNONYMS: BENZENESULFONAMIDE, 4-AMINO-N-2-QUINOXALINYL-; 4-AMINO-N-2-QUINOXALINYL-BENZENESULFONAMIDE; SULFANILAMIDE, N'-2-QUINOXALINYL-; N'-2-QUINOXALINYLSULFANILAMIDE; SULFABENZPYRAZINE; SULFALINE; 2-SULFANILAMIDOBENZOPYRAZINE; 2-(P-SULFANILAMIDO)QUINOZALINE; SULPHAQUINOXALINE; N1-(2-QUINOXALINYL)SULFANILAMIDE; C14H12N4O2S; PST72046
CHEMICAL FAMILY: SULFONAMIDE
MOLECULAR FORMULA: C14-H12-N4-O2-S
MOLECULAR WEIGHT: 300.33
CERCLA RATINGS (SCALE 0-3): HEALTH=2 FIRE=1 REACTIVITY=0 PERSISTENCE=2
NFPA RATINGS (SCALE 0-4): HEALTH=2 FIRE=1 REACTIVITY=0

COMPONENTS AND CONTAMINANTS

COMPONENT: SULFAQUINOXALINE ***PERCENT:*** 100
CAS# 59-40-5
OTHER CONTAMINANTS: NONE
EXPOSURE LIMITS: NO OCCUPATIONAL EXPOSURE LIMITS ESTABLISHED BY OSHA, ACGIH, OR NIOSH.

PHYSICAL DATA

DESCRIPTION: MINUTE CRYSTALS. ***MELTING POINT:*** 477-478 F (247-248 C)
SOLUBILITY IN WATER: 7.5 PPM
SOLVENT SOLUBILITY: SOLUBLE IN ALCOHOL, ACETONE, AQUEOUS SODIUM CARBONATE, SODIUM HYDROXIDE SOLUTIONS, ACETONITRILE SOLUTIONS.

FIRE AND EXPLOSION DATA

FIRE AND EXPLOSION HAZARD: SLIGHT FIRE HAZARD WHEN EXPOSED TO HEAT OR FLAME.

FIREFIGHTING MEDIA: DRY CHEMICAL, CARBON DIOXIDE, HALON, WATER SPRAY OR STANDARD FOAM (1987 EMERGENCY RESPONSE GUIDEBOOK, DOT P 5800.4). FOR LARGER FIRES, USE WATER SPRAY, FOG OR STANDARD FOAM (1987 EMERGENCY RESPONSE GUIDEBOOK, DOT P 5800.4).

FIREFIGHTING: MOVE CONTAINERS FROM FIRE AREA IF POSSIBLE (1987 EMERGENCY RESPONSE GUIDEBOOK, DOT P 5800.4, GUIDE PAGE 53). EXTINGUISH FIRE USING AGENTS SUITABLE FOR TYPE OF SURROUNDING FIRE. USE WATER IN FLOODING AMOUNTS AS A FOG. AVOID BREATHING DUSTS AND FUMES FROM BURNING MATERIAL; KEEP UPWIND.

TOXICITY

SULFAQUINOXALINE: TOXICITY DATA: 1370 MG/KG ORAL-RAT LD50; 15 GM/KG ORAL-MOUSE LD50. CARCINOGEN STATUS: NONE. ACUTE TOXICITY DATA: MODERATELY TOXIC BY INGESTION. TARGET EFFECTS: SENSITIZER. POISONING MAY AFFECT THE KIDNEYS, LIVER, BONE MARROW AND THE HEART.* AT INCREASED RISK FROM EXPOSURE: PERSONS WITH LIVER OR KIDNEY DYSFUNCTION; SEVERE ALLERGY OR BRONCHIAL ASTHMA; GLUCOSE-6-PHOSPHATE DEHYDROGENASE DEFICIENCY; DIABETICS; PREEXISTING PORPHYRIA; AND DARK-SKINNED INDIVIDUALS.*

* MAY BE BASED ON GENERAL INFORMATION ON SULFONAMIDE DRUGS.

HEALTH EFFECTS AND FIRST AID

INHALATION: SULFAQUINOXALINE: **ACUTE EXPOSURE-** HYPERSENSITIVITY REACTIONS MAY OCCUR IN PREVIOUSLY EXPOSED INDIVIDUALS. **CHRONIC EXPOSURE-** SULFONAMIDE ABSORPTION IS VARIABLE; IF SUFFICIENT QUANTITIES ARE ABSORBED, SYSTEMIC POISONING AND SENSITIZATION MAY RESULT AS DETAILED IN CHRONIC INGESTION.

FIRST AID- REMOVE FROM EXPOSURE AREA TO FRESH AIR IMMEDIATELY. IF BREATHING HAS STOPPED, PERFORM ARTIFICIAL RESPIRATION. KEEP PERSON WARM AND AT REST. TREAT SYMPTOMATICALLY AND SUPPORTIVELY. GET MEDICAL ATTENTION IMMEDIATELY.

SKIN CONTACT: SULFAQUINOXALINE: **ACUTE EXPOSURE-** HYPERSENSITIVITY REACTIONS MAY OCCUR IN PERSONS PREVIOUSLY EXPOSED. **CHRONIC EXPOSURE-** SULFONAMIDE ABSORPTION IS VARIABLE; IF SUFFICIENT QUANTITIES ARE ABSORBED, SYSTEMIC POISONING AND SENSITIZATION MAY RESULT AS DETAILED IN CHRONIC INGESTION.

FIRST AID- REMOVE CONTAMINATED CLOTHING AND SHOES IMMEDIATELY. WASH AFFECTED AREA WITH SOAP OR MILD DETERGENT AND LARGE AMOUNTS OF WATER UNTIL NO EVIDENCE OF CHEMICAL REMAINS (APPROXIMATELY 15-20 MINUTES). GET MEDICAL ATTENTION IMMEDIATELY.

EYE CONTACT: SULFAQUINOXALINE: **ACUTE EXPOSURE-** CONTACT WITH SULFONAMIDES MAY CAUSE HEADACHE OR BROWACHE, ACUTE TRANSIENT MYOPIA WITH BLURRED VISION AND TEMPORARY IMPAIRMENT OF DEPTH PERCEPTION, LOCAL IRRITATION, REACTIVE HYPEREMIA, BURNING AND TRANSIENT STINGING. HYPERSENSITIVITY REACTIONS MAY OCCUR IN PERSONS PREVIOUSLY EXPOSED. **CHRONIC EXPOSURE-** REPEATED CONTACT MAY CAUSE CONJUNCTIVITIS AND KERATITIS. INFLAMMATION AND CHEMOSIS OF THE CONJUNCTIVA HAVE COMMONLY BEEN ACCOMPANIED BY SWELLING OF THE LIDS AND IN MORE SEVERE CASES BY PHOTOPHOBIA, LACRIMATION AND DISCHARGE. IN SEVERE CASES, CHANGES IN THE CONJUNCTIVA RESEMBLING PEMPHIGUS HAVE PRODUCED SYMBLEPHARON. RARELY RETINAL AND PRERETINAL HEMORRHAGES HAVE BEEN OBSERVED. SENSITIZATION MAY OCCUR AND BE MANIFESTED BY ERYTHEMA MULTIFORM, EXFOLIATIVE DERMATITIS, TOXIC EPIDERMAL NECROLYSIS, FEVER, SKIN RASH, GASTROINTESTINAL DISTURBANCES AND BONE MARROW DEPRESSION.

FIRST AID- WASH EYES IMMEDIATELY WITH LARGE AMOUNTS OF WATER OR NORMAL SALINE, OCCASIONALLY LIFTING UPPER AND LOWER LIDS, UNTIL NO EVIDENCE OF CHEMICAL REMAINS (APPROXIMATELY 15-20 MINUTES). GET MEDICAL ATTENTION IMMEDIATELY.

INGESTION: SULFAQUINOXALINE: **ACUTE EXPOSURE-** HYPERSENSITIVITY REACTIONS MAY OCCUR IN PREVIOUSLY EXPOSED INDIVIDUALS. ANIMALS GIVEN SINGLE TOXIC DOSES OF SULFONAMIDES EXHIBITED SALIVATION, HYPERPNEA, EXCITEMENT, MUSCULAR WEAKNESS, ATAXIA, ATHETOTIC MOVEMENTS, CLONIC CONVULSION, PARALYSIS AND DEATH FROM RESPIRATORY FAILURE. **CHRONIC EXPOSURE-** REPEATED INGESTION OF SULFONAMIDES MAY CAUSE NAUSEA, EMESIS, ABDOMINAL PAINS, DIARRHEA, ANOREXIA, ACIDOSIS, PANCREATITIS, MYOPIA, STOMATITIS, IMPAIRED FOLIC ACID ABSORPTION, HEPATITIS AND HEPATOCELLULAR NECROSIS. CENTRAL NERVOUS SYSTEM EFFECTS MAY INCLUDE: HEADACHE, PERIPHERAL NEUROPATHY, MENTAL DEPRESSION, CONVULSIONS, MUSCULAR PARALYSIS, ATAXIA, HALLUCINATIONS, TINNITUS, VERTIGO, INSOMNIA, HEARING LOSS, DROWSINESS, UNCONSCIOUSNESS, TRANSIENT LESIONS OF THE POSTERIOR SPINAL COLUMN AND TRANSVERSE MYELITIS. CRYSTALLURIA, HEMATURIA, PROTEINURIA, PAIN ON URINATION, TUBULAR NECROSIS, NEPHROTIC SYNDROME, TOXIC NEPHROSIS WITH OLIGURIA OR ANURIA, AND AZOTEMIA MAY OCCUR. BLOOD DYSCRASIAS MAY INCLUDE AGRANULOCYTOSIS, APLASTIC ANEMIA, THROMBOCYTOPENIA, LEUKOPENIA, NEUTROPENIA OR PANCYTOPENIA, HEMOLYTIC ANEMIA, PURPURA, HYPOPROTHROMBINEMIA, CYANOSIS, METHEMOGLOBINEMIA, MEGALOBLASTIC ANEMIA, HEINZ BODY ANEMIA AND PETECHIAE. IN ADDITION, SULFONAMIDES MAY CAUSE DRUG FEVER, CHILLS, ALOPECIA, OLIGOSPERMIA, INFERTILITY, PRECIPITATION OF PERIARTERITIS NODOSUM, LUPUS-ERYTHEMATOSUS, RARELY GOITER PRODUCTION, DIURESIS AND HYPOGLYCEMIA. REPEATED EXPOSURE MAY RESULT IN SENSITIZATION REACTIONS CHARACTERIZED BY ERYTHEMA MULTIFORM, PARAPSORIASIS, VARIOLIFORMIS ACUTA, GENERALIZED SKIN ERUPTIONS, EPIDERMAL NECROLYSIS, ECZEMA, URTICARIA, SERUM SICKNESS, PRURITIS, EXFOLIATIVE DERMATITIS, ANAPHYLACTOID REACTIONS, ANGIOEDEMA, PERIORBITAL EDEMA, CONJUNCTIVAL AND SCLERAL INFLAMMATION, ARTHRALGIA, ALLERGIC MYOCARDITIS, DECREASED PULMONARY FUNCTION AND EOSINOPHILIC PNEUMONIA. SEVERE REACTIONS MAY INCLUDE IRREVERSIBLE NEUROMUSCULAR AND CENTRAL NERVOUS SYSTEM CHANGES AND FIBROSING ALVEOLITIS. SULFONAMIDES CROSS THE PLACENTAL BARRIER; ARE EXCRETED IN BREAST MILK AND MAY CAUSE JAUNDICE, HEMOLYTIC ANEMIA AND KERNICTERUS IN THE NEWBORN. DEATHS ASSOCIATED WITH THE ADMINISTRATION OF SULFONAMIDES HAVE BEEN REPORTED FROM HYPERSENSITIVITY REACTIONS, AGRANULOCYTOSIS, APLASTIC ANEMIA, OTHER BLOOD DYSCRASIAS, AND RENAL AND HEPATIC DAMAGE. DOSES OF 2-5 GRAMS DAILY MAY PRODUCE TOXICITY OR FATALITIES. PATHOLOGIC FINDINGS MAY INCLUDE CRYSTALLINE DEPOSITS IN THE KIDNEY TUBULES, CALICES, AND URETERS, AND NECROTIC OR INFLAMMATORY LESIONS IN THE LIVER, HEART, KIDNEYS, BONE MARROW OR OTHER ORGANS. THE BONE MARROW MAY BE LACKING IN MYELOID ELEMENTS OR MAY BE COMPLETELY APLASTIC.

FIRST AID- REMOVE BY GASTRIC LAVAGE OR EMESIS. MAINTAIN BLOOD PRESSURE AND AIRWAY. GIVE OXYGEN IF RESPIRATION IS DEPRESSED. DO NOT PERFORM GASTRIC LAVAGE OR EMESIS IF VICTIM IS UNCONSCIOUS. GET MEDICAL ATTENTION IMMEDIATELY (DREISBACH, HANDBOOK OF POISONING, 11TH ED.). ADMINISTRATION OF GASTRIC LAVAGE OR OXYGEN SHOULD BE PERFORMED BY QUALIFIED MEDICAL PERSONNEL.

REACTIVITY

REACTIVITY: STABLE UNDER NORMAL TEMPERATURES AND PRESSURES.

INCOMPATIBILITIES: SULFAQUINOXALINE: NO DATA AVAILABLE.

DECOMPOSITION: THERMAL DECOMPOSITION MAY RELEASE TOXIC OXIDES OF NITROGEN AND SULFUR.

POLYMERIZATION: HAZARDOUS POLYMERIZATION HAS NOT BEEN REPORTED TO OCCUR UNDER NORMAL TEMPERATURES AND PRESSURES.

STORAGE AND DISPOSAL

OBSERVE ALL FEDERAL, STATE AND LOCAL REGULATIONS WHEN STORING OR DISPOSING OF THIS SUBSTANCE. FOR ASSISTANCE, CONTACT THE DISTRICT DIRECTOR OF THE ENVIRONMENTAL PROTECTION AGENCY.

STORAGE

STORE IN ACCORDANCE WITH 40 CFR 165 RECOMMENDED PROCEDURES FOR THE DISPOSAL AND STORAGE OF PESTICIDES AND PESTICIDE CONTAINERS.

DISPOSAL

DISPOSAL MUST BE IN ACCORDANCE WITH 40 CFR 165 RECOMMENDED PROCEDURES FOR THE DISPOSAL AND STORAGE OF PESTICIDES AND PESTICIDE CONTAINERS.

CONDITIONS TO AVOID

MAY BURN BUT DOES NOT IGNITE READILY.

SPILL AND LEAK PROCEDURES

OCCUPATIONAL SPILL: DO NOT TOUCH SPILLED MATERIAL. STOP LEAK IF YOU CAN DO IT WITHOUT RISK. FOR SMALL SPILLS, TAKE UP WITH SAND OR OTHER ABSORBENT MATERIAL AND PLACE INTO CONTAINERS FOR LATER DISPOSAL. FOR SMALL DRY SPILLS, WITH A CLEAN SHOVEL PLACE MATERIAL INTO CLEAN, DRY CONTAINER AND COVER. MOVE CONTAINERS FROM SPILL AREA. FOR LARGER SPILLS, DIKE FAR AHEAD OF SPILL FOR LATER DISPOSAL. KEEP UNNECESSARY PEOPLE AWAY. ISOLATE HAZARD AREA AND DENY ENTRY.

PROTECTIVE EQUIPMENT

VENTILATION: PROVIDE LOCAL EXHAUST OR GENERAL DILUTION VENTILATION SYSTEM.

RESPIRATOR: THE FOLLOWING RESPIRATORS ARE RECOMMENDED BASED ON INFORMATION FOUND IN THE PHYSICAL DATA, TOXICITY AND HEALTH EFFECTS SECTIONS. THEY ARE RANKED IN ORDER FROM MINIMUM TO MAXIMUM RESPIRATORY PROTECTION. THE SPECIFIC RESPIRATOR SELECTED MUST BE BASED ON CONTAMINATION LEVELS FOUND IN THE WORK PLACE, MUST NOT EXCEED THE WORKING LIMITS OF THE RESPIRATOR AND BE JOINTLY APPROVED BY THE

NATIONAL INSTITUTE FOR OCCUPATIONAL SAFETY AND HEALTH AND THE MINE SAFETY AND HEALTH ADMINISTRATION (NIOSH-MSHA).
DUST AND MIST RESPIRATOR WITH A FULL FACEPIECE.
AIR-PURIFYING FULL FACEPIECE RESPIRATOR WITH A HIGH-EFFICIENCY PARTICULATE FILTER.
POWERED AIR-PURIFYING RESPIRATOR WITH A TIGHT-FITTING FACEPIECE AND HIGH-EFFICIENCY PARTICULATE FILTER.
TYPE 'C' SUPPLIED-AIR RESPIRATOR WITH A FULL FACEPIECE OPERATED IN PRESSURE-DEMAND OR OTHER POSITIVE PRESSURE MODE OR WITH A FULL FACEPIECE, HELMET OR HOOD OPERATED IN CONTINUOUS-FLOW MODE.
SELF-CONTAINED BREATHING APPARATUS WITH A FULL FACEPIECE OPERATED IN PRESSURE-DEMAND OR OTHER POSITIVE PRESSURE MODE.
FOR FIREFIGHTING AND OTHER IMMEDIATELY DANGEROUS TO LIFE OR HEALTH CONDITIONS:
SELF-CONTAINED BREATHING APPARATUS WITH FULL FACEPIECE OPERATED IN PRESSURE-DEMAND OR OTHER POSITIVE PRESSURE MODE.
SUPPLIED-AIR RESPIRATOR WITH FULL FACEPIECE AND OPERATED IN PRESSURE-DEMAND OR OTHER POSITIVE PRESSURE MODE IN COMBINATION WITH AN AUXILIARY SELF-CONTAINED BREATHING APPARATUS OPERATED IN PRESSURE-DEMAND OR OTHER POSITIVE PRESSURE MODE.

CLOTHING: EMPLOYEE MUST WEAR APPROPRIATE PROTECTIVE (IMPERVIOUS) CLOTHING AND EQUIPMENT TO PREVENT REPEATED OR PROLONGED SKIN CONTACT WITH THIS SUBSTANCE.

GLOVES: EMPLOYEE MUST WEAR APPROPRIATE PROTECTIVE GLOVES TO PREVENT CONTACT WITH THIS SUBSTANCE.

EYE PROTECTION: EMPLOYEE MUST WEAR SPLASH-PROOF OR DUST-RESISTANT SAFETY GOGGLES TO PREVENT EYE CONTACT WITH THIS SUBSTANCE.
EMERGENCY EYE WASH: WHERE THERE IS ANY POSSIBILITY THAT AN EMPLOYEE'S EYES MAY BE EXPOSED TO THIS SUBSTANCE, THE EMPLOYER SHOULD PROVIDE AN EYE WASH FOUNTAIN WITHIN THE IMMEDIATE WORK AREA FOR EMERGENCY USE.

AUTHORIZED BY- OCCUPATIONAL HEALTH SERVICES, INC.
CREATION DATE: 10/05/89 ***REVISION DATE:*** 05/29/90

MATERIAL SAFETY DATA SHEET

OCCUPATIONAL HEALTH SERVICES, INC.
AGRICULTURE AND PESTICIDE DIVISION
450 SEVENTH AVENUE, SUITE 2407
NEW YORK, NEW YORK 10123
1-800-445-MSDS OR (212) 967-1100

EMERGENCY CONTACT:
JOHN S. BRANSFORD, JR. (615) 292-1180

SUBSTANCE IDENTIFICATION

CAS-NUMBER 72-14-0

SUBSTANCE: SULFATHIAZOLE

TRADE NAMES/SYNONYMS: BENZENESULFONAMIDE, 4-AMINO-N-2-THIAZOLYL; 4-AMINO-N-2-THIAZOLYLBENZENESULFONAMIDE; SULFANILAMIDE, N1-2-THIAZOLYL-; N1-2-THIAZOLYLSULFANILAMIDE; SULFANILAMIDE, N1-4-THIAZOLIN-2-YLIDENE-; N1-4-THIAZOLIN-2-YLIDENESULFANILAMIDE; AZOQUIMIOL; AZOSEPTALE; CIBAZOL; DUATEX; ELEUDRON; ESTAFILOL; NORSULFAZOL; SULFANILAMIDETHIAZOLE; 2-SULFANILAMIDOTHIAZOLE; 2-SULFATHIAZOLE; SULPHATHIAZOLE; N1-(2-THIAZOLYL)SULFANILAMIDE; 2-(SULFANILYLAMINO)THIAZOLE; C9H9N3O2S2; PST72047

CHEMICAL FAMILY: THIAZOLE

MOLECULAR FORMULA: C9-H9-N3-O2-S2

MOLECULAR WEIGHT: 255.31

CERCLA RATINGS (SCALE 0-3): HEALTH=3 FIRE=1 REACTIVITY=0 PERSISTENCE=2

NFPA RATINGS (SCALE 0-4): HEALTH=3 FIRE=1 REACTIVITY=0

COMPONENTS AND CONTAMINANTS

COMPONENT: SULFATHIAZOLE ***PERCENT:*** 100
CAS# 72-14-0

OTHER CONTAMINANTS: NONE

EXPOSURE LIMITS: NO OCCUPATIONAL EXPOSURE LIMITS ESTABLISHED BY OSHA, ACGIH, OR NIOSH.

PHYSICAL DATA

DESCRIPTION: ODORLESS WHITE TO BROWN CRYSTALS, GRANULES OR POWDER.

MELTING POINT: 397 F (203 C) ***SPECIFIC GRAVITY:*** NOT AVAILABLE

SOLUBILITY IN WATER: 60% @ 26 C

SOLVENT SOLUBILITY: SOLUBLE IN ALCOHOL, ACETONE, DILUTE MINERAL ACIDS, POTASSIUM HYDROXIDE, SODIUM HYDROXIDE, AMMONIUM HYDROXIDE.

FIRE AND EXPLOSION DATA

FIRE AND EXPLOSION HAZARD: SLIGHT FIRE HAZARD WHEN EXPOSED TO HEAT OR FLAME.

FIREFIGHTING MEDIA: DRY CHEMICAL, CARBON DIOXIDE, HALON, WATER SPRAY OR STANDARD FOAM (1987 EMERGENCY RESPONSE GUIDEBOOK, DOT P 5800.4).
FOR LARGER FIRES, USE WATER SPRAY, FOG OR STANDARD FOAM (1987 EMERGENCY RESPONSE GUIDEBOOK, DOT P 5800.4).

FIREFIGHTING: MOVE CONTAINER FROM FIRE AREA IF POSSIBLE. DO NOT SCATTER SPILLED MATERIAL WITH HIGH PRESSURE WATER STREAMS. DIKE FIRE CONTROL WATER FOR LATER DISPOSAL (1987 EMERGENCY RESPONSE GUIDEBOOK, DOT P 5800.4, GUIDE PAGE 31).
USE AGENTS SUITABLE FOR TYPE OF SURROUNDING FIRE. AVOID BREATHING HAZARDOUS VAPORS, KEEP UPWIND.

TOXICITY

SULFATHIAZOLE: TOXICITY DATA: 4500 MG/KG ORAL-MOUSE LD50; 1450 MG/KG SUBCUTANEOUS-MOUSE LD50; 1370 MG/KG INTRAVENOUS-RAT LD50; 990 MG/KG INTRAVENOUS-MOUSE LD50; 1250 MG/KG INTRAPERITONEAL-RAT LDLO; 400 MG/KG INTRAPERITONEAL-MOUSE LD50; 1000 MG/KG PARENTERAL-RAT LDLO; 250 MG/KG/23 DAYS INTERMITTENT UNREPORTED-MAN LDLO; MUTAGENIC DATA (RTECS); REPRODUCTIVE EFFECTS DATA (RTECS); TUMORIGENIC DATA (RTECS).
CARCINOGEN STATUS: NONE. LOCAL EFFECTS: IRRITANT- EYE. ACUTE TOXICITY LEVEL: MODERATELY TOXIC BY INGESTION. TARGET EFFECTS: SENSITIZER-PULMONARY, SKIN, AND INGESTION. POISONING MAY AFFECT THE KIDNEYS, LIVER, BONE MARROW AND HEART. AT INCREASED RISK FROM EXPOSURE: PERSONS WITH LIVER OR KIDNEY DYSFUNCTION, SEVERE ALLERGY OR BRONCHIAL ASTHMA, GLUCOSE-6-PHOSPHATE DEHYDROGENASE DEFICIENCY, DIABETICS, PREEXISTING PORPHYRIA, AND DARK-SKINNED INDIVIDUALS. ADDITIONAL DATA: CROSS-SENSITIZATION REACTIONS BETWEEN DIFFERENT SULFONAMIDES MAY OCCUR. INTERACTIONS WITH MEDICATIONS HAVE BEEN REPORTED.

HEALTH EFFECTS AND FIRST AID

INHALATION: SULFATHIAZOLE: SENSITIZER. **ACUTE EXPOSURE-** HYPERSENSITIVITY REACTIONS MAY OCCUR IN PREVIOUSLY EXPOSED INDIVIDUALS. **CHRONIC EXPOSURE-** SULFONAMIDE ABSORPTION IS VARIABLE; IF SUFFICIENT QUANTITIES ARE ABSORBED, SYSTEMIC POISONING AND SENSITIZATION MAY RESULT AS DETAILED IN CHRONIC INGESTION.

FIRST AID- REMOVE FROM EXPOSURE AREA TO FRESH AIR IMMEDIATELY. IF BREATHING HAS STOPPED, PERFORM ARTIFICIAL RESPIRATION. KEEP PERSON WARM AND AT REST. TREAT SYMPTOMATICALLY AND SUPPORTIVELY. GET MEDICAL ATTENTION IMMEDIATELY.

SKIN CONTACT: SULFATHIAZOLE: SENSITIZER. **ACUTE EXPOSURE-** HYPERSENSITIVITY REACTIONS MAY OCCUR IN PERSONS PREVIOUSLY EXPOSED. **CHRONIC EXPOSURE-** SULFONAMIDE ABSORPTION IS VARIABLE; IF SUFFICIENT QUANTITIES ARE ABSORBED, SYSTEMIC POISONING AND SENSITIZATION MAY RESULT AS DETAILED IN CHRONIC INGESTION.

FIRST AID- REMOVE CONTAMINATED CLOTHING AND SHOES IMMEDIATELY. WASH AFFECTED AREA WITH SOAP OR MILD DETERGENT AND LARGE AMOUNTS OF WATER UNTIL NO EVIDENCE OF CHEMICAL REMAINS (APPROXIMATELY 15-20 MINUTES). GET MEDICAL ATTENTION IMMEDIATELY.

EYE CONTACT: SULFATHIAZOLE: IRRITANT/SENSITIZER: **ACUTE EXPOSURE-** CONTACT WITH SULFONAMIDES MAY CAUSE HEADACHE OR BROWACHE, BLURRED VISION AND TEMPORARY IMPAIRMENT OF DEPTH PERCEPTION, LOCAL IRRITATION, REACTIVE HYPEREMIA, BURNING AND TRANSIENT STINGING. HYPERSENSITIVITY REACTIONS MAY OCCUR IN PERSONS PREVIOUSLY EXPOSED. **CHRONIC EXPOSURE-** REPEATED CONTACT MAY CAUSE CONJUNCTIVITIS AND KERATITIS. INFLAMMATION AND CHEMOSIS OF THE CONJUNCTIVA HAVE COMMONLY BEEN ACCOMPANIED BY SWELLING OF THE LIDS AND IN MORE SEVERE CASES BY PHOTOPHOBIA, LACRIMATION AND DISCHARGE. IN SEVERE CASES, CHANGES IN THE CONJUNCTIVA RESEMBLING PEMPHIGUS HAVE PRODUCED SYMBLEPHARON. RARELY RETINAL AND PRERETINAL HEMORRHAGES HAVE BEEN OBSERVED. XANTHOPSIA, OR YELLOW VISION HAVE BEEN NOTED IN A SINGLE INSTANCE AFTER TAKING SULFATHIAZOLE. SYSTEMIC EFFECTS AND SENSITIZATION REACTIONS MAY OCCUR AS DETAILED IN CHRONIC INGESTION.

FIRST AID- WASH EYES IMMEDIATELY WITH LARGE AMOUNTS OF WATER OR NORMAL SALINE, OCCASIONALLY LIFTING UPPER AND LOWER LIDS, UNTIL NO EVIDENCE OF CHEMICAL REMAINS (APPROXIMATELY 15-20 MINUTES). GET MEDICAL ATTENTION IMMEDIATELY.

INGESTION: SULFATHIAZOLE: SENSITIZER. **ACUTE EXPOSURE**- HYPERSENSITIVITY REACTIONS MAY OCCUR IN PREVIOUSLY EXPOSED INDIVIDUALS. INGESTION OF LARGE DOSES MAY PRODUCE SYSTEMIC POISONING AS DETAILED IN CHRONIC INGESTION. ANIMALS GIVEN SINGLE TOXIC DOSES OF SULFONAMIDES EXHIBITED SALIVATION, HYPERPNEA, EXCITEMENT, MUSCULAR WEAKNESS, ATAXIA, ATHETOTIC MOVEMENTS, CLONIC CONVULSION, PARALYSIS AND DEATH FROM RESPIRATORY FAILURE. **CHRONIC EXPOSURE**- REPEATED INGESTION OF SULFONAMIDES MAY CAUSE NAUSEA, EMESIS, ABDOMINAL PAINS, DIARRHEA, ANOREXIA, ACIDOSIS, PANCREATITIS, MYOPIA, STOMATITIS, IMPAIRED FOLIC ACID ABSORPTION, HEPATITIS AND HEPATOCELLULAR NECROSIS. CENTRAL NERVOUS SYSTEM EFFECTS MAY INCLUDE: HEADACHE, PERIPHERAL NEUROPATHY, MENTAL DEPRESSION, CONVULSIONS, MUSCULAR PARALYSIS, ATAXIA, HALLUCINATIONS, TINNITUS, VERTIGO, INSOMNIA, HEARING LOSS, DROWSINESS, UNCONSCIOUSNESS, TRANSIENT LESIONS OF THE POSTERIOR SPINAL COLUMN AND TRANSVERSE MYELITIS. CRYSTALLURIA, HEMATURIA, PROTEINURIA, PAIN ON URINATION, TUBULAR NECROSIS, NEPHROTIC SYNDROME, TOXIC NEPHROSIS WITH OLIGURIA OR ANURIA, AND AZOTEMIA MAY OCCUR. BLOOD DYSCRASIAS MAY INCLUDE AGRANULOCYTOSIS, APLASTIC ANEMIA, THROMBOCYTOPENIA, LEUKOPENIA, NEUTROPENIA OR PANCYTOPENIA, HEMOLYTIC ANEMIA, PURPURA, HYPOPROTHROMBINEMIA, CYANOSIS, METHEMOGLOBINEMIA, MEGALOBLASTIC ANEMIA, HEINZ BODY ANEMIA AND PETECHIAE. IN ADDITION, SULFONAMIDES MAY CAUSE DRUG FEVER, CHILLS, ALOPECIA, OLIGOSPERMIA, INFERTILITY, PRECIPITATION OF PERIARTERITIS NODOSUM, LUPUS-ERYTHEMATOSUS, RARELY GOITER PRODUCTION, DIURESIS AND HYPOGLYCEMIA. REPEATED EXPOSURE MAY RESULT IN SENSITIZATION REACTIONS CHARACTERIZED BY ERYTHEMA MULTIFORM, PARAPSORIASIS, VARIOLIFORMIS ACUTA, GENERALIZED SKIN ERUPTIONS, EPIDERMAL NECROLYSIS, ECZEMA, URTICARIA, SERUM SICKNESS, PRURITIS, EXFOLIATIVE DERMATITIS, ANAPHYLACTOID REACTIONS, ANGIOEDEMA, PERIORBITAL EDEMA, CONJUNCTIVAL AND SCLERAL INFLAMMATION, ARTHRALGIA, ALLERGIC MYOCARDITIS, DECREASED PULMONARY FUNCTION AND EOSINOPHILIC PNEUMONIA. SEVERE REACTIONS MAY INCLUDE IRREVERSIBLE NEUROMUSCULAR AND CENTRAL NERVOUS SYSTEM CHANGES AND FIBROSING ALVEOLITIS. SULFONAMIDES CROSS THE PLACENTAL BARRIER; ARE EXCRETED IN BREAST MILK AND MAY CAUSE JAUNDICE, HEMOLYTIC ANEMIA AND KERNICTERUS IN THE NEWBORN. DEATHS ASSOCIATED WITH THE ADMINISTRATION OF SULFONAMIDES HAVE BEEN REPORTED FROM HYPERSENSITIVITY REACTIONS, AGRANULOCYTOSIS, APLASTIC ANEMIA, OTHER BLOOD DYSCRASIAS, AND RENAL AND HEPATIC DAMAGE. DOSES OF 2-5 GRAMS DAILY MAY PRODUCE TOXICITY OR FATALITIES. PATHOLOGIC FINDINGS MAY INCLUDE CRYSTALLINE DEPOSITS IN THE KIDNEY TUBULES, CALICES, AND URETERS, AND NECROTIC OR INFLAMMATORY LESIONS IN THE LIVER, HEART, KIDNEYS, BONE MARROW OR OTHER ORGANS. THE BONE MARROW MAY BE LACKING IN MYELOID ELEMENTS OR MAY BE COMPLETELY APLASTIC. REPEATED USE OF ANTIBIOTICS MAY LEAD TO THE DEVELOPMENT OF VAGINAL, ORAL, PHARYNGEAL, INTESTINAL AND SYSTEMIC SUPRAINFECTIONS DUE TO THE OVERGROWTH OF ORGANISMS NOT AFFECTED BY THE ANTIBIOTIC AGENT. IN SOME CASES, THESE ORGANISMS PRODUCE TOXINS THAT CAUSE SEVERE VOMITING, DIARRHEA AND CIRCULATORY COLLAPSE.

FIRST AID- REMOVE BY GASTRIC LAVAGE OR EMESIS. MAINTAIN BLOOD PRESSURE AND AIRWAY. GIVE OXYGEN IF RESPIRATION IS DEPRESSED. DO NOT PERFORM GASTRIC LAVAGE OR EMESIS IF VICTIM IS UNCONSCIOUS. GET MEDICAL ATTENTION IMMEDIATELY (DREISBACH, HANDBOOK OF POISONING, 11TH ED.). ADMINISTRATION OF GASTRIC LAVAGE OR OXYGEN SHOULD BE PERFORMED BY QUALIFIED MEDICAL PERSONNEL.

ANTIDOTE: NO SPECIFIC ANTIDOTE. TREAT SYMPTOMATICALLY AND SUPPORTIVELY.

REACTIVITY

REACTIVITY: STABLE UNDER NORMAL TEMPERATURES AND PRESSURES.

INCOMPATIBILITIES: SULFATHIAZOLE: NO DATA AVAILABLE.

DECOMPOSITION: THERMAL DECOMPOSITION MAY RELEASE TOXIC OXIDES OF NITROGEN AND SULFUR.

POLYMERIZATION: HAZARDOUS POLYMERIZATION HAS NOT BEEN REPORTED TO OCCUR UNDER NORMAL TEMPERATURES AND PRESSURES.

STORAGE AND DISPOSAL

OBSERVE ALL FEDERAL, STATE AND LOCAL REGULATIONS WHEN STORING OR DISPOSING OF THIS SUBSTANCE. FOR ASSISTANCE, CONTACT THE DISTRICT DIRECTOR OF THE ENVIRONMENTAL PROTECTION AGENCY.

CONDITIONS TO AVOID

MAY BURN BUT DOES NOT IGNITE READILY. AVOID CONTACT WITH STRONG OXIDIZERS, EXCESSIVE HEAT, SPARKS, OR OPEN FLAME.

SPILL AND LEAK PROCEDURES

OCCUPATIONAL SPILL: STOP LEAK IF YOU CAN DO IT WITHOUT RISK. FOR SMALL SPILLS, TAKE UP WITH SAND OR OTHER ABSORBENT MATERIAL AND PLACE INTO CLEAN, DRY CONTAINERS FOR LATER DISPOSAL. KEEP UNNECESSARY PEOPLE AWAY. ISOLATE HAZARD AREA AND DENY ENTRY.

PROTECTIVE EQUIPMENT

VENTILATION: PROVIDE LOCAL EXHAUST OR PROCESS ENCLOSURE VENTILATION SYSTEM.

RESPIRATOR: THE FOLLOWING RESPIRATORS ARE RECOMMENDED BASED ON INFORMATION FOUND IN THE PHYSICAL DATA, TOXICITY AND HEALTH EFFECTS SECTIONS. THEY ARE RANKED IN ORDER FROM MINIMUM TO MAXIMUM RESPIRATORY PROTECTION. THE SPECIFIC RESPIRATOR SELECTED MUST BE BASED ON CONTAMINATION LEVELS FOUND IN THE WORK PLACE, MUST NOT EXCEED THE WORKING LIMITS OF THE RESPIRATOR AND BE JOINTLY APPROVED BY THE NATIONAL INSTITUTE FOR OCCUPATIONAL SAFETY AND HEALTH AND THE MINE SAFETY AND HEALTH ADMINISTRATION (NIOSH-MSHA).

DUST AND MIST RESPIRATOR WITH A FULL FACEPIECE.

AIR-PURIFYING FULL FACEPIECE RESPIRATOR WITH A HIGH-EFFICIENCY PARTICULATE FILTER.

POWERED AIR-PURIFYING RESPIRATOR WITH A TIGHT-FITTING FACEPIECE AND HIGH-EFFICIENCY PARTICULATE FILTER.

TYPE 'C' SUPPLIED-AIR RESPIRATOR WITH A FULL FACEPIECE OPERATED IN PRESSURE-DEMAND OR OTHER POSITIVE PRESSURE MODE OR WITH A FULL FACEPIECE, HELMET OR HOOD OPERATED IN CONTINUOUS-FLOW MODE.

SELF-CONTAINED BREATHING APPARATUS WITH A FULL FACEPIECE OPERATED IN PRESSURE-DEMAND OR OTHER POSITIVE PRESSURE MODE.

FOR FIREFIGHTING AND OTHER IMMEDIATELY DANGEROUS TO LIFE OR HEALTH CONDITIONS:

SELF-CONTAINED BREATHING APPARATUS WITH FULL FACEPIECE OPERATED IN PRESSURE-DEMAND OR OTHER POSITIVE PRESSURE MODE.

SUPPLIED-AIR RESPIRATOR WITH FULL FACEPIECE AND OPERATED IN PRESSURE-DEMAND OR OTHER POSITIVE PRESSURE MODE IN COMBINATION WITH AN AUXILIARY SELF-CONTAINED BREATHING APPARATUS OPERATED IN PRESSURE-DEMAND OR OTHER POSITIVE PRESSURE MODE.

CLOTHING: EMPLOYEE MUST WEAR APPROPRIATE PROTECTIVE (IMPERVIOUS) CLOTHING AND EQUIPMENT TO PREVENT REPEATED OR PROLONGED SKIN CONTACT WITH THIS SUBSTANCE.

GLOVES: EMPLOYEE MUST WEAR APPROPRIATE PROTECTIVE GLOVES TO PREVENT CONTACT WITH THIS SUBSTANCE.

EYE PROTECTION: EMPLOYEE MUST WEAR SPLASH-PROOF OR DUST-RESISTANT SAFETY GOGGLES TO PREVENT EYE CONTACT WITH THIS SUBSTANCE.

EMERGENCY EYE WASH: WHERE THERE IS ANY POSSIBILITY THAT AN EMPLOYEE'S EYES MAY BE EXPOSED TO THIS SUBSTANCE, THE EMPLOYER SHOULD PROVIDE AN EYE WASH FOUNTAIN WITHIN THE IMMEDIATE WORK AREA FOR EMERGENCY USE.

AUTHORIZED BY- OCCUPATIONAL HEALTH SERVICES, INC.

CREATION DATE: 10/05/89 ***REVISION DATE:*** 05/29/90

MATERIAL SAFETY DATA SHEET

OCCUPATIONAL HEALTH SERVICES, INC.
AGRICULTURE AND PESTICIDE DIVISION
450 SEVENTH AVENUE, SUITE 2407
NEW YORK, NEW YORK 10123
1-800-445-MSDS OR (212) 967-1100

EMERGENCY CONTACT:
JOHN S. BRANSFORD, JR. (615) 292-1180

SUBSTANCE IDENTIFICATION

CAS-NUMBER 2303-17-5

SUBSTANCE: **TRIALLATE**

TRADE NAMES/SYNONYMS: CARBAMOTHIOIC ACID, BIS(1-METHYLETHYL)-, S-(2,3,3-TRICHLORO-2- PROPENYL) ESTER; BIS(1-METHYLETHYL)CARBAMOTHIOIC ACID S-(2,3,3-TRICHLORO--2-PROPENYL) ESTER; CARBAMIC ACID, DIISOPROPYLTHIO-, S-(2,3,3-TRICHLOROALLYL) ESTER; DIISOPROPYLTHIOCARBAMIC ACID S-(2,3,3-TRICHLOROALLYL) ESTER; S-2,3,3-TRICHLOROALLYL DI-ISOPROPYL(THIOCARBAMATE); S-2,3,3-TRICHLOROALLYL DI-ISOPROPYL THIOCARBAMATE; S-(2,3,3-TRICHLORO-2-PROPENYL) BIS(1-METHYLETHYL)CARBAMOTHIOATE; S-(2,3,3-TRICHLOROALLYL) DIISOPROPYLTHIOCARBAMATE; S-(2,3,3-TRICHLOROALLYL)DIISOPROPYLTHIOCARBAMATE; AVADEX BW; CP 23426; DIPTHAL; FAR-GO; TRI-ALLATE; PST72050

CHEMICAL FAMILY: THIOCARBAMATE

MOLECULAR FORMULA: C10-H16-CL3-N-O-S

MOLECULAR WEIGHT: 304.68
CERCLA RATINGS (SCALE 0-3): HEALTH = 2 FIRE = U REACTIVITY = 0 PERSISTENCE = 3
NFPA RATINGS (SCALE 0-4): HEALTH = 2 FIRE = U REACTIVITY = 0

COMPONENTS AND CONTAMINANTS

COMPONENT: TRIALLATE ***PERCENT:*** 100
CAS# 2303-17-5
OTHER CONTAMINANTS: NONE
EXPOSURE LIMITS: NO OCCUPATIONAL EXPOSURE LIMITS ESTABLISHED BY OSHA, ACGIH, OR NIOSH.

PHYSICAL DATA

DESCRIPTION: AMBER OILY LIQUID ***BOILING POINT:*** 329 F (165 C) AT 6.0 MMHG
MELTING POINT: 86 F (30 C) ***SPECIFIC GRAVITY:*** 1.273 25/15.6 C
VAPOR PRESSURE: 0.00012 MMHG @ 25 C ***SOLUBILITY IN WATER:*** 0.0004%
SOLVENT SOLUBILITY: SOLUBLE IN ACETONE, ETHANOL, MOST ORGANIC SOLVENTS DECOMPOSES ABOVE 200 C

FIRE AND EXPLOSION DATA

FIRE AND EXPLOSION HAZARD: UNKNOWN FIRE AND EXPLOSION HAZARD.
FIREFIGHTING MEDIA: DRY CHEMICAL, CARBON DIOXIDE, WATER SPRAY OR FOAM FOR LARGER FIRES, USE WATER SPRAY, FOG OR ALCOHOL FOAM
FIREFIGHTING: MOVE CONTAINER FROM FIRE AREA IF POSSIBLE. DO NOT SCATTER SPILLED MATERIAL WITH MORE WATER THAN NEEDED FOR FIRE CONTROL. DIKE FIRE CONTROL WATER FOR LATER DISPOSAL
USE AGENTS SUITABLE FOR TYPE OF SURROUNDING FIRE. AVOID BREATHING HAZARDOUS VAPORS, KEEP UPWIND.

TOXICITY

TRIALLATE: TOXICITY DATA: 400 MG/M3/4 HOURS INHALATION-CAT LCLO; 2225 MG/KG SKIN-RABBIT LD50; 3500 MG/KG SKIN-RAT LDLO; 800 MG/KG ORAL-RAT LD50; 930 MG/KG ORAL-MOUSE LD50; 1471 MG/KG UNREPORTED-RAT LD50; 832 MG/KG UNREPORTED-MOUSE LD50; MUTAGENIC DATA (RTECS). CARCINOGEN STATUS: NONE. ACUTE TOXICITY LEVEL: MODERATELY TOXIC BY INGESTION; SLIGHTLY TOXIC BY DERMAL ABSORPTION. TARGET EFFECTS: AN ANIMAL STUDY INDICATES THAT TRIALLATE MAY BE A WEAK CHOLINESTERASE INHIBITOR.

HEALTH EFFECTS AND FIRST AID

INHALATION: TRIALLATE: ACUTE EXPOSURE- A CONCENTRATION OF 400 MG/KG/4 HOURS WAS LETHAL IN SOME CATS. INHALATION OF EXCESSIVE AMOUNTS OF SOME THIOCARBAMATES CAUSES SCRATCHY THROAT, SNEEZING, AND COUGHING. AN ANIMAL STUDY INDICATED THAT TRIALLATE MAY BE A WEAK CHOLINESTERASE INHIBITOR. EARLY SYMPTOMS OF CHOLINESTERASE INHIBITION ARE BLURRED VISION, FATIGUE, HEADACHE, VERTIGO, NAUSEA, MIOSIS, ABDOMINAL CRAMPS AND DIARRHEA. SEVERE INHIBITION OF CHOLINESTERASE MAY CAUSE EXCESSIVE SWEATING, TEARING, BRADYCARDIA, GIDDINESS, SLURRED SPEECH, CONFUSION, PULMONARY EDEMA, CONVULSIONS AND COMA. CHRONIC EXPOSURE- NO DATA AVAILABLE.
FIRST AID- REMOVE FROM EXPOSURE AREA TO FRESH AIR IMMEDIATELY. IF BREATHING HAS STOPPED, PERFORM ARTIFICIAL RESPIRATION. KEEP PERSON WARM AND AT REST. TREAT SYMPTOMATICALLY AND SUPPORTIVELY. GET MEDICAL ATTENTION IMMEDIATELY.

SKIN CONTACT: TRIALLATE: ACUTE EXPOSURE- THIS MATERIAL WAS MODERATELY IRRITATING TO SKIN OF RABBITS. A LETHAL DOSE IN RATS BY DERMAL ABSORPTION WAS 2225 MG/KG. AN ANIMAL STUDY INDICATED THAT TRIALLATE MAY BE A WEAK CHOLINESTERASE INHIBITOR. EFFECTS OF CHOLINESTERASE INHIBITION ARE AS DESCRIBED IN ACUTE INHALATION. CHRONIC EXPOSURE- NO DATA AVAILABLE.
FIRST AID- REMOVE CONTAMINATED CLOTHING AND SHOES IMMEDIATELY. WASH AFFECTED AREA WITH SOAP OR MILD DETERGENT AND LARGE AMOUNTS OF WATER UNTIL NO EVIDENCE OF CHEMICAL REMAINS (APPROXIMATELY 15-20 MINUTES). GET MEDICAL ATTENTION IMMEDIATELY.

EYE CONTACT: TRIALLATE: ACUTE EXPOSURE- THIS MATERIAL WAS SLIGHTLY IRRITATING TO RABBIT EYES. CHRONIC EXPOSURE- NO DATA AVAILABLE.
FIRST AID- WASH EYES IMMEDIATELY WITH LARGE AMOUNTS OF WATER OR NORMAL SALINE, OCCASIONALLY LIFTING UPPER AND LOWER LIDS, UNTIL NO EVIDENCE OF CHEMICAL REMAINS (APPROXIMATELY 15-20 MINUTES). GET MEDICAL ATTENTION IMMEDIATELY.

INGESTION: TRIALLATE: ACUTE EXPOSURE- A LETHAL DOSE IN RATS WAS 1471 MG/KG. AN ANIMAL STUDY INDICATED THAT TRIALLATE MAY BE A WEAK CHOLINESTERASE INHIBITOR. EARLY SYMPTOMS OF CHOLINESTERASE INHIBITION ARE BLURRED VISION, FATIGUE, HEADACHE, VERTIGO, NAUSEA, MIOSIS, ABDOMINAL CRAMPS, AND DIARRHEA. SEVERE INHIBITION OF CHOLINESTERASE MAY CAUSE EXCESSIVE SWEATING, TEARING, BRADYCARDIA, GIDDINESS, SLURRED SPEECH, CONFUSION, PULMONARY EDEMA, CONVULSIONS AND COMA. CHRONIC EXPOSURE- IN A CHRONIC INGESTION STUDY DONE IN RUSSIA, DEGENERATIVE NECROTIC CHANGES IN LIVER, KIDNEYS AND REPRODUCTIVE ORGANS WERE OBSERVED IN CHICKENS.
FIRST AID- GIVE SYRUP OF IPECAC, FOLLOWED BY 1-2 GLASSES OF WATER, TO INDUCE VOMITING (ADULTS: 30 ML). FOLLOWING EMESIS, ADMINISTER 30-50 GRAMS ACTIVATED CHARCOAL. FOLLOW CHARCOAL WITH SODIUM OR MAGNESIUM SULFATE, 250 MG/KG, TO REMOVE TOXICANT FROM THE GUT BY CATHARSIS (EPA, RECOGNITION AND MANAGEMENT OF PESTICIDE POISONINGS, 3RD ED.). FIRST AID SHOULD BE ADMINISTERED UNDER THE DIRECTION OF QUALIFIED MEDICAL PERSONNEL. GET MEDICAL ATTENTION.
ANTIDOTE: NO SPECIFIC ANTIDOTE. TREAT SYMPTOMATICALLY AND SUPPORTIVELY.

REACTIVITY

REACTIVITY: STABLE UNDER NORMAL TEMPERATURES AND PRESSURES.
INCOMPATIBILITIES: TRIALLATE: NO DATA AVAILABLE.
DECOMPOSITION: THERMAL DECOMPOSITION PRODUCTS MAY INCLUDE TOXIC AND HAZARDOUS FUMES OF HYDROGEN CHLORIDE AND OXIDES OF SULFUR AND NITROGEN.
POLYMERIZATION: HAZARDOUS POLYMERIZATION HAS NOT BEEN REPORTED TO OCCUR UNDER NORMAL TEMPERATURES AND PRESSURES.

STORAGE AND DISPOSAL

OBSERVE ALL FEDERAL, STATE AND LOCAL REGULATIONS WHEN STORING OR DISPOSING OF THIS SUBSTANCE. FOR ASSISTANCE, CONTACT THE DISTRICT DIRECTOR OF THE ENVIRONMENTAL PROTECTION AGENCY.

****STORAGE****

STORE IN ACCORDANCE WITH 40 CFR 165 RECOMMENDED PROCEDURES FOR THE DISPOSAL AND STORAGE OF PESTICIDES AND PESTICIDE CONTAINERS.

****DISPOSAL****

DISPOSAL MUST BE IN ACCORDANCE WITH 40 CFR 165 RECOMMENDED PROCEDURES FOR THE DISPOSAL AND STORAGE OF PESTICIDES AND PESTICIDE CONTAINERS.

CONDITIONS TO AVOID

NONE REPORTED.

SPILL AND LEAK PROCEDURES

OCCUPATIONAL SPILL: STOP LEAK IF YOU CAN DO IT WITHOUT RISK. FOR SMALL SPILLS, TAKE UP WITH SAND OR OTHER ABSORBENT MATERIAL AND PLACE INTO CLEAN, DRY CONTAINERS FOR LATER DISPOSAL. KEEP UNNECESSARY PEOPLE AWAY. ISOLATE HAZARD AREA AND DENY ENTRY.

PROTECTIVE EQUIPMENT

VENTILATION: PROVIDE LOCAL EXHAUST OR GENERAL DILUTION VENTILATION SYSTEM.
RESPIRATOR: THE FOLLOWING RESPIRATORS ARE RECOMMENDED BASED ON INFORMATION FOUND IN THE PHYSICAL DATA, TOXICITY AND HEALTH EFFECTS SECTIONS. THEY ARE RANKED IN ORDER FROM MINIMUM TO MAXIMUM RESPIRATORY PROTECTION. THE SPECIFIC RESPIRATOR SELECTED MUST BE BASED ON CONTAMINATION LEVELS FOUND IN THE WORK PLACE, MUST NOT EXCEED THE WORKING LIMITS OF THE RESPIRATOR AND BE JOINTLY APPROVED BY THE NATIONAL INSTITUTE FOR OCCUPATIONAL SAFETY AND HEALTH AND THE MINE SAFETY AND HEALTH ADMINISTRATION (NIOSH-MSHA).
CHEMICAL CARTRIDGE RESPIRATOR WITH FULL FACEPIECE AND PESTICIDE CARTRIDGE.
TYPE 'C' SUPPLIED-AIR RESPIRATOR WITH A FULL FACEPIECE OPERATED IN PRESSURE-DEMAND OR OTHER POSITIVE PRESSURE MODE OR WITH A FULL FACEPIECE, HELMET OR HOOD OPERATED IN CONTINUOUS-FLOW MODE.
SELF-CONTAINED BREATHING APPARATUS OPERATED IN PRESSURE-DEMAND OR OTHER POSITIVE PRESSURE MODE.
FOR FIREFIGHTING AND OTHER IMMEDIATELY DANGEROUS TO LIFE OR HEALTH CONDITIONS:
SELF-CONTAINED BREATHING APPARATUS WITH FULL FACEPIECE OPERATED IN PRESSURE-DEMAND OR OTHER POSITIVE PRESSURE MODE.
SUPPLIED-AIR RESPIRATOR WITH FULL FACEPIECE AND OPERATED IN PRESSURE-DEMAND OR OTHER POSITIVE PRESSURE MODE IN COMBINATION WITH AN AUXILIARY SELF-CONTAINED BREATHING APPARATUS OPERATED IN PRESSURE-DEMAND OR OTHER POSITIVE PRESSURE MODE.
CLOTHING: EMPLOYEE MUST WEAR APPROPRIATE PROTECTIVE (IMPERVIOUS) CLOTHING AND EQUIPMENT TO PREVENT REPEATED OR PROLONGED SKIN CONTACT WITH THIS SUBSTANCE.
GLOVES: EMPLOYEE MUST WEAR APPROPRIATE PROTECTIVE GLOVES TO PREVENT CONTACT WITH THIS SUBSTANCE.

EYE PROTECTION: EMPLOYEE MUST WEAR SPLASH-PROOF OR DUST-RESISTANT SAFETY GOGGLES TO PREVENT EYE CONTACT WITH THIS SUBSTANCE. EMERGENCY EYE WASH: WHERE THERE IS ANY POSSIBILITY THAT AN EMPLOYEE'S EYES MAY BE EXPOSED TO THIS SUBSTANCE, THE EMPLOYER SHOULD PROVIDE AN EYE WASH FOUNTAIN WITHIN THE IMMEDIATE WORK AREA FOR EMERGENCY USE.

AUTHORIZED BY- OCCUPATIONAL HEALTH SERVICES, INC.
CREATION DATE: 10/05/89 ***REVISION DATE:*** 05/11/90

MATERIAL SAFETY DATA SHEET

OCCUPATIONAL HEALTH SERVICES, INC.
AGRICULTURE AND PESTICIDE DIVISION
450 SEVENTH AVENUE, SUITE 2407
NEW YORK, NEW YORK 10123
1-800-445-MSDS OR (212) 967-1100

EMERGENCY CONTACT:
JOHN S. BRANSFORD, JR. (615) 292-1180

SUBSTANCE IDENTIFICATION

CAS-NUMBER 10124-65-9
SUBSTANCE: POTASSIUM LAURATE
TRADE NAMES/SYNONYMS: DODECANOIC ACID, POTASSIUM SALT; LAURIC ACID, POTASSIUM SALT; POTASSIUM DODECANOATE; POTASSIUM N-DODECANOATE; C12H23KO2; PST72072
CHEMICAL FAMILY: SOAP
MOLECULAR FORMULA: K-O-O-C-C11-H23
MOLECULAR WEIGHT: 238.41
CERCLA RATINGS (SCALE 0-3): HEALTH=U FIRE=1 REACTIVITY=0 PERSISTENCE=2
NFPA RATINGS (SCALE 0-4): HEALTH=U FIRE=1 REACTIVITY=0

COMPONENTS AND CONTAMINANTS

COMPONENT: POTASSIUM LAURATE ***PERCENT:*** 100.0
CAS# 10124-65-9
OTHER CONTAMINANTS: NONE
EXPOSURE LIMITS: NO OCCUPATIONAL EXPOSURE LIMITS ESTABLISHED BY OSHA, ACGIH, OR NIOSH.

PHYSICAL DATA

DESCRIPTION: LIGHT TAN AMORPHOUS SOLID. ***MELTING POINT:*** NOT AVAILABLE
SPECIFIC GRAVITY: NOT AVAILABLE ***SOLUBILITY IN WATER:*** SOLUBLE
SOLVENT SOLUBILITY: SOLUBLE IN ALCOHOL.

FIRE AND EXPLOSION DATA

FIRE AND EXPLOSION HAZARD: SLIGHT FIRE HAZARD WHEN EXPOSED TO HEAT OR FLAME.
FIREFIGHTING MEDIA: DRY CHEMICAL, CARBON DIOXIDE, HALON, WATER SPRAY OR STANDARD FOAM (1987 EMERGENCY RESPONSE GUIDEBOOK, DOT P 5800.4). FOR LARGER FIRES, USE WATER SPRAY, FOG OR STANDARD FOAM (1987 EMERGENCY RESPONSE GUIDEBOOK, DOT P 5800.4).
FIREFIGHTING: MOVE CONTAINER FROM FIRE AREA IF POSSIBLE. DO NOT SCATTER SPILLED MATERIAL WITH HIGH PRESSURE WATER STREAMS. DIKE FIRE CONTROL WATER FOR LATER DISPOSAL (1987 EMERGENCY RESPONSE GUIDEBOOK, DOT P 5800.4, GUIDE PAGE 31).
USE AGENTS SUITABLE FOR TYPE OF SURROUNDING FIRE. AVOID BREATHING HAZARDOUS VAPORS, KEEP UPWIND.

TOXICITY

POTASSIUM LAURATE: IRRITATION DATA: 9560 MG SKIN-HUMAN. CARCINOGEN STATUS: NONE. LOCAL EFFECTS: IRRITANT- SKIN. ACUTE TOXICITY DATA: NO DATA AVAILABLE. TARGET EFFECTS: POISONING BY POTASSIUM SALTS MAY AFFECT THE HEART.

HEALTH EFFECTS AND FIRST AID

INHALATION: POTASSIUM LAURATE: **ACUTE EXPOSURE-** NO DATA AVAILABLE. MAY BE IRRITATING TO THE MUCOUS MEMBRANES. **CHRONIC EXPOSURE-** NO DATA AVAILABLE.
FIRST AID- REMOVE FROM EXPOSURE AREA TO FRESH AIR IMMEDIATELY. IF BREATHING HAS STOPPED, PERFORM ARTIFICIAL RESPIRATION. KEEP PERSON WARM AND AT REST. TREAT SYMPTOMATICALLY AND SUPPORTIVELY. GET MEDICAL ATTENTION IMMEDIATELY.

SKIN CONTACT: POTASSIUM LAURATE: **ACUTE EXPOSURE-** DIRECT CONTACT HAS BEEN REPORTED TO CAUSE IRRITATION. **CHRONIC EXPOSURE-** NO DATA AVAILABLE.
FIRST AID- REMOVE CONTAMINATED CLOTHING AND SHOES IMMEDIATELY. WASH AFFECTED AREA WITH SOAP OR MILD DETERGENT AND LARGE AMOUNTS OF WATER UNTIL NO EVIDENCE OF CHEMICAL REMAINS (APPROXIMATELY 15-20 MINUTES). GET MEDICAL ATTENTION IMMEDIATELY.

EYE CONTACT: POTASSIUM LAURATE: **ACUTE EXPOSURE-** NO DATA AVAILABLE. MAY BE IRRITATING. **CHRONIC EXPOSURE-** NO DATA AVAILABLE.
FIRST AID- WASH EYES IMMEDIATELY WITH LARGE AMOUNTS OF WATER OR NORMAL SALINE, OCCASIONALLY LIFTING UPPER AND LOWER LIDS, UNTIL NO EVIDENCE OF CHEMICAL REMAINS (APPROXIMATELY 15-20 MINUTES). GET MEDICAL ATTENTION IMMEDIATELY.

INGESTION: POTASSIUM LAURATE: **ACUTE EXPOSURE-** POISONING BY POTASSIUM SALTS IS RARE BECAUSE A LARGE SINGLE DOSE USUALLY CAUSES VOMITING, AND IN THE ABSENCE OF PRE-EXISTING KIDNEY DAMAGE, POTASSIUM IS RAPIDLY EXCRETED. HOWEVER, IF SUFFICIENT AMOUNTS ARE ABSORBED IT MAY DISTURB THE RHYTHM OF THE HEART AND EVENTUALLY WEAKEN CARDIAC CONTRACTILITY. SKELETAL MUSCLE WEAKNESS AND FLACCID PARALYSIS MAY OCCUR IN SEVERE CASES. **CHRONIC EXPOSURE-** NO DATA AVAILABLE.
FIRST AID- TREAT SYMPTOMATICALLY AND SUPPORTIVELY. GET MEDICAL ATTENTION IMMEDIATELY. IF VOMITING OCCURS, KEEP HEAD LOWER THAN HIPS TO PREVENT ASPIRATION.
ANTIDOTE: NO SPECIFIC ANTIDOTE. TREAT SYMPTOMATICALLY AND SUPPORTIVELY.

REACTIVITY

REACTIVITY: STABLE UNDER NORMAL TEMPERATURES AND PRESSURES.
INCOMPATIBILITIES: POTASSIUM LAURATE: OXIDIZERS (STRONG): FIRE AND EXPLOSION HAZARD.
DECOMPOSITION: THERMAL DECOMPOSITION MAY RELEASE ACRID SMOKE AND IRRITATING FUMES.
POLYMERIZATION: HAZARDOUS POLYMERIZATION HAS NOT BEEN REPORTED TO OCCUR UNDER NORMAL TEMPERATURES AND PRESSURES.

STORAGE AND DISPOSAL

OBSERVE ALL FEDERAL, STATE AND LOCAL REGULATIONS WHEN STORING OR DISPOSING OF THIS SUBSTANCE. FOR ASSISTANCE, CONTACT THE DISTRICT DIRECTOR OF THE ENVIRONMENTAL PROTECTION AGENCY.

STORAGE

STORE IN ACCORDANCE WITH 40 CFR 165 RECOMMENDED PROCEDURES FOR THE DISPOSAL AND STORAGE OF PESTICIDES AND PESTICIDE CONTAINERS.
STORE AWAY FROM INCOMPATIBLE SUBSTANCES.

DISPOSAL

DISPOSAL MUST BE IN ACCORDANCE WITH 40 CFR 165 RECOMMENDED PROCEDURES FOR THE DISPOSAL AND STORAGE OF PESTICIDES AND PESTICIDE CONTAINERS.

CONDITIONS TO AVOID

MAY BURN BUT DOES NOT IGNITE READILY. AVOID CONTACT WITH STRONG OXIDIZERS, EXCESSIVE HEAT, SPARKS, OR OPEN FLAME.

SPILL AND LEAK PROCEDURES

OCCUPATIONAL SPILL: SWEEP UP AND PLACE IN SUITABLE CLEAN, DRY CONTAINERS FOR RECLAMATION OR LATER DISPOSAL. DO NOT FLUSH SPILLED MATERIAL INTO SEWER. KEEP UNNECESSARY PEOPLE AWAY.

PROTECTIVE EQUIPMENT

VENTILATION: PROVIDE LOCAL EXHAUST OR GENERAL DILUTION VENTILATION SYSTEM.
RESPIRATOR: THE FOLLOWING RESPIRATORS ARE RECOMMENDED BASED ON INFORMATION FOUND IN THE PHYSICAL DATA, TOXICITY AND HEALTH EFFECTS SECTIONS. THEY ARE RANKED IN ORDER FROM MINIMUM TO MAXIMUM RESPIRATORY PROTECTION. THE SPECIFIC RESPIRATOR SELECTED MUST BE BASED ON CONTAMINATION LEVELS FOUND IN THE WORK PLACE, MUST NOT EXCEED THE WORKING LIMITS OF THE RESPIRATOR AND BE JOINTLY APPROVED BY THE NATIONAL INSTITUTE FOR OCCUPATIONAL SAFETY AND HEALTH AND THE MINE SAFETY AND HEALTH ADMINISTRATION (NIOSH-MSHA).
CHEMICAL CARTRIDGE RESPIRATOR WITH AN ORGANIC VAPOR CARTRIDGE(S) WITH A FULL FACEPIECE AND ORGANIC VAPOR CARTRIDGE(S) IN COMBINATION WITH A DUST AND MIST FILTER.
POWERED AIR-PURIFYING RESPIRATOR WITH A TIGHT-FITTING FACEPIECE AND ORGANIC VAPOR CARTRIDGE(S) IN COMBINATION WITH A HIGH-EFFICIENCY PARTICULATE FILTER.

TYPE 'C' SUPPLIED-AIR RESPIRATOR WITH A FULL FACEPIECE OPERATED IN A PRESSURE-DEMAND OR OTHER POSITIVE PRESSURE MODE.
SELF-CONTAINED BREATHING APPARATUS WITH A FULL FACEPIECE OPERATED IN PRESSURE-DEMAND OR OTHER POSITIVE PRESSURE MODE.
FOR FIREFIGHTING AND OTHER IMMEDIATELY DANGEROUS TO LIFE OR HEALTH CONDITIONS:
SELF-CONTAINED BREATHING APPARATUS WITH FULL FACEPIECE OPERATED IN PRESSURE-DEMAND OR OTHER POSITIVE PRESSURE MODE.
SUPPLIED-AIR RESPIRATOR WITH FULL FACEPIECE AND OPERATED IN PRESSURE-DEMAND OR OTHER POSITIVE PRESSURE MODE IN COMBINATION WITH AN AUXILIARY SELF-CONTAINED BREATHING APPARATUS OPERATED IN PRESSURE-DEMAND OR OTHER POSITIVE PRESSURE MODE.

CLOTHING: EMPLOYEE MUST WEAR APPROPRIATE PROTECTIVE (IMPERVIOUS) CLOTHING AND EQUIPMENT TO PREVENT REPEATED OR PROLONGED SKIN CONTACT WITH THIS SUBSTANCE.

GLOVES: EMPLOYEE MUST WEAR APPROPRIATE PROTECTIVE GLOVES TO PREVENT CONTACT WITH THIS SUBSTANCE.

EYE PROTECTION: EMPLOYEE MUST WEAR SPLASH-PROOF OR DUST-RESISTANT SAFETY GOGGLES TO PREVENT EYE CONTACT WITH THIS SUBSTANCE.
EMERGENCY EYE WASH: WHERE THERE IS ANY POSSIBILITY THAT AN EMPLOYEE'S EYES MAY BE EXPOSED TO THIS SUBSTANCE, THE EMPLOYER SHOULD PROVIDE AN EYE WASH FOUNTAIN WITHIN THE IMMEDIATE WORK AREA FOR EMERGENCY USE.

AUTHORIZED BY- OCCUPATIONAL HEALTH SERVICES, INC.
CREATION DATE: 02/08/90 ***REVISION DATE:*** 05/31/90

MATERIAL SAFETY DATA SHEET

OCCUPATIONAL HEALTH SERVICES, INC.
AGRICULTURE AND PESTICIDE DIVISION
450 SEVENTH AVENUE, SUITE 2407
NEW YORK, NEW YORK 10123
1-800-445-MSDS OR (212) 967-1100

EMERGENCY CONTACT:
JOHN S. BRANSFORD, JR. (615) 292-1180

SUBSTANCE IDENTIFICATION

CAS-NUMBER 13429-27-1
SUBSTANCE: POTASSIUM MYRISTATE
TRADE NAMES/SYNONYMS: TETRADECANOIC ACID, POTASSIUM SALT; MYRISTIC ACID POTASSIUM SALT; POTASSIUM TETRADECANOATE; C14H27KO2; PST72073
CHEMICAL FAMILY: SOAP
MOLECULAR FORMULA: K-C14-H27-O2
MOLECULAR WEIGHT: 266.23
CERCLA RATINGS (SCALE 0-3): HEALTH=U FIRE=1 REACTIVITY=0 PERSISTENCE=2
NFPA RATINGS (SCALE 0-4): HEALTH=U FIRE=1 REACTIVITY=0

COMPONENTS AND CONTAMINANTS

COMPONENT: POTASSIUM MYRISTATE ***PERCENT:*** 100.0
CAS# 13429-27-1
OTHER CONTAMINANTS: NONE
EXPOSURE LIMITS: NO OCCUPATIONAL EXPOSURE LIMITS ESTABLISHED BY OSHA, ACGIH, OR NIOSH.

PHYSICAL DATA

DESCRIPTION: WHITE, WAXY SOLID. ***MELTING POINT:*** 307 F (153 C)
SPECIFIC GRAVITY: NOT AVAILABLE ***SOLUBILITY IN WATER:*** NOT AVAILABLE
SOLVENT SOLUBILITY: SOLUBLE IN ALCOHOL.

FIRE AND EXPLOSION DATA

FIRE AND EXPLOSION HAZARD: SLIGHT FIRE HAZARD WHEN EXPOSED TO HEAT OR FLAME.

FIREFIGHTING MEDIA: DRY CHEMICAL, CARBON DIOXIDE, HALON, WATER SPRAY OR STANDARD FOAM (1987 EMERGENCY RESPONSE GUIDEBOOK, DOT P 5800.4). FOR LARGER FIRES, USE WATER SPRAY, FOG OR STANDARD FOAM (1987 EMERGENCY RESPONSE GUIDEBOOK, DOT P 5800.4).

FIREFIGHTING: MOVE CONTAINER FROM FIRE AREA IF POSSIBLE. DO NOT SCATTER SPILLED MATERIAL WITH HIGH PRESSURE WATER STREAMS. DIKE FIRE CONTROL WATER FOR LATER DISPOSAL (1987 EMERGENCY RESPONSE GUIDEBOOK, DOT P 5800.4, GUIDE PAGE 31).
USE AGENTS SUITABLE FOR TYPE OF SURROUNDING FIRE. AVOID BREATHING HAZARDOUS VAPORS, KEEP UPWIND.

TOXICITY

POTASSIUM MYRISTATE: CARCINOGEN STATUS: NONE. ACUTE TOXICITY LEVEL: NO DATA AVAILABLE. TARGET EFFECTS: POISONING BY POTASSIUM SALTS MAY AFFECT THE HEART.

HEALTH EFFECTS AND FIRST AID

INHALATION: POTASSIUM MYRISTATE: **ACUTE EXPOSURE-** NO DATA AVAILABLE. MAY BE IRRITATING TO THE MUCOUS MEMBRANES. **CHRONIC EXPOSURE-** NO DATA AVAILABLE.

FIRST AID- REMOVE FROM EXPOSURE AREA TO FRESH AIR IMMEDIATELY. IF BREATHING HAS STOPPED, PERFORM ARTIFICIAL RESPIRATION. KEEP PERSON WARM AND AT REST. TREAT SYMPTOMATICALLY AND SUPPORTIVELY. GET MEDICAL ATTENTION IMMEDIATELY.

SKIN CONTACT: POTASSIUM MYRISTATE: **ACUTE EXPOSURE-** NO DATA AVAILABLE. MAY BE IRRITATING. **CHRONIC EXPOSURE-** NO DATA AVAILABLE.

FIRST AID- REMOVE CONTAMINATED CLOTHING AND SHOES IMMEDIATELY. WASH AFFECTED AREA WITH SOAP OR MILD DETERGENT AND LARGE AMOUNTS OF WATER UNTIL NO EVIDENCE OF CHEMICAL REMAINS (APPROXIMATELY 15-20 MINUTES). GET MEDICAL ATTENTION IMMEDIATELY.

EYE CONTACT: POTASSIUM MYRISTATE: **ACUTE EXPOSURE-** NO DATA AVAILABLE. MAY BE IRRITATING. **CHRONIC EXPOSURE-** NO DATA AVAILABLE.

FIRST AID- WASH EYES IMMEDIATELY WITH LARGE AMOUNTS OF WATER OR NORMAL SALINE, OCCASIONALLY LIFTING UPPER AND LOWER LIDS, UNTIL NO EVIDENCE OF CHEMICAL REMAINS (APPROXIMATELY 15-20 MINUTES). GET MEDICAL ATTENTION IMMEDIATELY.

INGESTION: POTASSIUM MYRISTATE: **ACUTE EXPOSURE-** NO SPECIFIC DATA AVAILABLE. POISONING BY POTASSIUM SALTS IS RARE BECAUSE A LARGE SINGLE DOSE USUALLY CAUSES VOMITING, AND IN THE ABSENCE OF PRE-EXISTING KIDNEY DAMAGE, POTASSIUM IS RAPIDLY EXCRETED. HOWEVER, IF SUFFICIENT AMOUNTS ARE ABSORBED IT MAY DISTURB THE RHYTHM OF THE HEART AND EVENTUALLY WEAKEN CARDIAC CONTRACTILITY. SKELETAL MUSCLE WEAKNESS AND FLACCID PARALYSIS MAY OCCUR IN SEVERE CASES. **CHRONIC EXPOSURE-** NO DATA AVAILABLE.

FIRST AID- TREAT SYMPTOMATICALLY AND SUPPORTIVELY. GET MEDICAL ATTENTION IMMEDIATELY. IF VOMITING OCCURS, KEEP HEAD LOWER THAN HIPS TO PREVENT ASPIRATION.

ANTIDOTE: NO SPECIFIC ANTIDOTE. TREAT SYMPTOMATICALLY AND SUPPORTIVELY.

REACTIVITY

REACTIVITY: STABLE UNDER NORMAL TEMPERATURES AND PRESSURES.
INCOMPATIBILITIES: POTASSIUM MYRISTATE: OXIDIZERS (STRONG): FIRE AND EXPLOSION HAZARD.
DECOMPOSITION: THERMAL DECOMPOSITION MAY RELEASE TOXIC AND/OR HAZARDOUS GASES.
POLYMERIZATION: HAZARDOUS POLYMERIZATION HAS NOT BEEN REPORTED TO OCCUR UNDER NORMAL TEMPERATURES AND PRESSURES.

STORAGE AND DISPOSAL

OBSERVE ALL FEDERAL, STATE AND LOCAL REGULATIONS WHEN STORING OR DISPOSING OF THIS SUBSTANCE. FOR ASSISTANCE, CONTACT THE DISTRICT DIRECTOR OF THE ENVIRONMENTAL PROTECTION AGENCY.

STORAGE

STORE IN ACCORDANCE WITH 40 CFR 165 RECOMMENDED PROCEDURES FOR THE DISPOSAL AND STORAGE OF PESTICIDES AND PESTICIDE CONTAINERS.
STORE AWAY FROM INCOMPATIBLE SUBSTANCES.

DISPOSAL

DISPOSAL MUST BE IN ACCORDANCE WITH 40 CFR 165 RECOMMENDED PROCEDURES FOR THE DISPOSAL AND STORAGE OF PESTICIDES AND PESTICIDE CONTAINERS.

CONDITIONS TO AVOID

MAY BURN BUT DOES NOT IGNITE READILY. AVOID CONTACT WITH STRONG OXIDIZERS, EXCESSIVE HEAT, SPARKS, OR OPEN FLAME.

SPILL AND LEAK PROCEDURES

OCCUPATIONAL SPILL: SWEEP UP AND PLACE IN SUITABLE CLEAN, DRY CONTAINERS FOR RECLAMATION OR LATER DISPOSAL. DO NOT FLUSH SPILLED MATERIAL INTO SEWER. KEEP UNNECESSARY PEOPLE AWAY.

PROTECTIVE EQUIPMENT

VENTILATION: PROVIDE LOCAL EXHAUST OR GENERAL DILUTION VENTILATION SYSTEM.

RESPIRATOR: THE FOLLOWING RESPIRATORS ARE RECOMMENDED BASED ON INFORMATION FOUND IN THE PHYSICAL DATA, TOXICITY AND HEALTH EFFECTS SECTIONS. THEY ARE RANKED IN ORDER FROM MINIMUM TO MAXIMUM RESPIRATORY PROTECTION. THE SPECIFIC RESPIRATOR SELECTED MUST BE BASED ON CONTAMINATION LEVELS FOUND IN THE WORK PLACE, MUST NOT EXCEED THE WORKING LIMITS OF THE RESPIRATOR AND BE JOINTLY APPROVED BY THE NATIONAL INSTITUTE FOR OCCUPATIONAL SAFETY AND HEALTH AND THE MINE SAFETY AND HEALTH ADMINISTRATION (NIOSH-MSHA).

CHEMICAL CARTRIDGE RESPIRATOR WITH AN ORGANIC VAPOR CARTRIDGE(S) WITH A FULL FACEPIECE AND ORGANIC VAPOR CARTRIDGE(S) IN COMBINATION WITH A DUST AND MIST FILTER.

POWERED AIR-PURIFYING RESPIRATOR WITH A TIGHT-FITTING FACEPIECE AND ORGANIC VAPOR CARTRIDGE(S) IN COMBINATION WITH A HIGH-EFFICIENCY PARTICULATE FILTER.

TYPE 'C' SUPPLIED-AIR RESPIRATOR WITH A FULL FACEPIECE OPERATED IN A PRESSURE-DEMAND OR OTHER POSITIVE PRESSURE MODE.

SELF-CONTAINED BREATHING APPARATUS WITH A FULL FACEPIECE OPERATED IN PRESSURE-DEMAND OR OTHER POSITIVE PRESSURE MODE.

FOR FIREFIGHTING AND OTHER IMMEDIATELY DANGEROUS TO LIFE OR HEALTH CONDITIONS:

SELF-CONTAINED BREATHING APPARATUS WITH FULL FACEPIECE OPERATED IN PRESSURE-DEMAND OR OTHER POSITIVE PRESSURE MODE.

SUPPLIED-AIR RESPIRATOR WITH FULL FACEPIECE AND OPERATED IN PRESSURE-DEMAND OR OTHER POSITIVE PRESSURE MODE IN COMBINATION WITH AN AUXILIARY SELF-CONTAINED BREATHING APPARATUS OPERATED IN PRESSURE-DEMAND OR OTHER POSITIVE PRESSURE MODE.

CLOTHING: EMPLOYEE MUST WEAR APPROPRIATE PROTECTIVE (IMPERVIOUS) CLOTHING AND EQUIPMENT TO PREVENT REPEATED OR PROLONGED SKIN CONTACT WITH THIS SUBSTANCE.

GLOVES: EMPLOYEE MUST WEAR APPROPRIATE PROTECTIVE GLOVES TO PREVENT CONTACT WITH THIS SUBSTANCE.

EYE PROTECTION: EMPLOYEE MUST WEAR SPLASH-PROOF OR DUST-RESISTANT SAFETY GOGGLES TO PREVENT EYE CONTACT WITH THIS SUBSTANCE.

EMERGENCY EYE WASH: WHERE THERE IS ANY POSSIBILITY THAT AN EMPLOYEE'S EYES MAY BE EXPOSED TO THIS SUBSTANCE, THE EMPLOYER SHOULD PROVIDE AN EYE WASH FOUNTAIN WITHIN THE IMMEDIATE WORK AREA FOR EMERGENCY USE.

AUTHORIZED BY- OCCUPATIONAL HEALTH SERVICES, INC.

CREATION DATE: 02/08/90 ***REVISION DATE:*** 05/31/90

MATERIAL SAFETY DATA SHEET

OCCUPATIONAL HEALTH SERVICES, INC.
AGRICULTURE AND PESTICIDE DIVISION
450 SEVENTH AVENUE, SUITE 2407
NEW YORK, NEW YORK 10123
1-800-445-MSDS OR (212) 967-1100

EMERGENCY CONTACT:
JOHN S. BRANSFORD, JR. (615) 292-1180

SUBSTANCE IDENTIFICATION

CAS-NUMBER 7492-30-0

SUBSTANCE: **POTASSIUM RICINOLEATE**

TRADE NAMES/SYNONYMS: 9-OCTADECENOIC ACID, 12-HYDROXY-, MONOPOTASSIUM SALT; 12-HYDROXY-9-OCTADECENOIC ACID, MONOPOTASSIUM SALT; 9-OCTADECENOIC ACID, 12-HYDROXY-, MONOPOTASSIUM SALT, (R-(Z))-; (R-(Z))-12-HYDROXY-9-OCTADECENOIC ACID, MONOPOTASSIUM SALT; RICINOLEIC ACID, MONOPOTASSIUM SALT; C18H33KO3; PST72074

CHEMICAL FAMILY: SOAP

MOLECULAR FORMULA: C17-H32-O-H-C-O-O-K

MOLECULAR WEIGHT: 336.53

CERCLA RATINGS (SCALE 0-3): HEALTH=U FIRE=1 REACTIVITY=0 PERSISTENCE=2

NFPA RATINGS (SCALE 0-4): HEALTH=U FIRE=1 REACTIVITY=0

COMPONENTS AND CONTAMINANTS

COMPONENT: POTASSIUM RICINOLEATE ***PERCENT:*** 100.0
CAS# 7492-30-0

OTHER CONTAMINANTS: NONE

EXPOSURE LIMITS: NO OCCUPATIONAL EXPOSURE LIMITS ESTABLISHED BY OSHA, ACGIH, OR NIOSH.

PHYSICAL DATA

DESCRIPTION: WHITE, AMORPHOUS SOLID. ***MELTING POINT:*** NOT AVAILABLE

SPECIFIC GRAVITY: NOT AVAILABLE ***SOLUBILITY IN WATER:*** SOLUBLE

FIRE AND EXPLOSION DATA

FIRE AND EXPLOSION HAZARD: SLIGHT FIRE HAZARD WHEN EXPOSED TO HEAT OR FLAME.

FIREFIGHTING MEDIA: DRY CHEMICAL, CARBON DIOXIDE, HALON, WATER SPRAY OR STANDARD FOAM (1987 EMERGENCY RESPONSE GUIDEBOOK, DOT P 5800.4). FOR LARGER FIRES, USE WATER SPRAY, FOG OR STANDARD FOAM (1987 EMERGENCY RESPONSE GUIDEBOOK, DOT P 5800.4).

FIREFIGHTING: MOVE CONTAINER FROM FIRE AREA IF POSSIBLE. DO NOT SCATTER SPILLED MATERIAL WITH HIGH PRESSURE WATER STREAMS. DIKE FIRE CONTROL WATER FOR LATER DISPOSAL (1987 EMERGENCY RESPONSE GUIDEBOOK, DOT P 5800.4, GUIDE PAGE 31).

USE AGENTS SUITABLE FOR TYPE OF SURROUNDING FIRE. AVOID BREATHING HAZARDOUS VAPORS, KEEP UPWIND.

TOXICITY

POTASSIUM RICINOLEATE: CARCINOGEN STATUS: NONE. ACUTE TOXICITY LEVEL: NO DATA AVAILABLE. TARGET EFFECTS: POISONING BY POTASSIUM SALTS MAY AFFECT THE HEART.

HEALTH EFFECTS AND FIRST AID

INHALATION: POTASSIUM RICINOLEATE: **ACUTE EXPOSURE-** NO DATA AVAILABLE. MAY BE IRRITATING TO THE MUCOUS MEMBRANES. **CHRONIC EXPOSURE-** NO DATA AVAILABLE.

FIRST AID- REMOVE FROM EXPOSURE AREA TO FRESH AIR IMMEDIATELY. IF BREATHING HAS STOPPED, PERFORM ARTIFICIAL RESPIRATION. KEEP PERSON WARM AND AT REST. TREAT SYMPTOMATICALLY AND SUPPORTIVELY. GET MEDICAL ATTENTION IMMEDIATELY.

SKIN CONTACT: POTASSIUM RICINOLEATE: **ACUTE EXPOSURE-** NO DATA AVAILABLE. MAY BE IRRITATING. **CHRONIC EXPOSURE-** NO DATA AVAILABLE.

FIRST AID- REMOVE CONTAMINATED CLOTHING AND SHOES IMMEDIATELY. WASH AFFECTED AREA WITH SOAP OR MILD DETERGENT AND LARGE AMOUNTS OF WATER UNTIL NO EVIDENCE OF CHEMICAL REMAINS (APPROXIMATELY 15-20 MINUTES). GET MEDICAL ATTENTION IMMEDIATELY.

EYE CONTACT: POTASSIUM RICINOLEATE: **ACUTE EXPOSURE-** NO DATA AVAILABLE. MAY BE IRRITATING. **CHRONIC EXPOSURE-** NO DATA AVAILABLE.

FIRST AID- WASH EYES IMMEDIATELY WITH LARGE AMOUNTS OF WATER OR NORMAL SALINE, OCCASIONALLY LIFTING UPPER AND LOWER LIDS, UNTIL NO EVIDENCE OF CHEMICAL REMAINS (APPROXIMATELY 15-20 MINUTES). GET MEDICAL ATTENTION IMMEDIATELY.

INGESTION: POTASSIUM RICINOLEATE: **ACUTE EXPOSURE-** POISONING BY POTASSIUM SALTS IS RARE BECAUSE A LARGE SINGLE DOSE USUALLY CAUSES VOMITING, AND IN THE ABSENCE OF PRE-EXISTING KIDNEY DAMAGE, POTASSIUM IS RAPIDLY EXCRETED. HOWEVER, IF SUFFICIENT AMOUNTS ARE ABSORBED IT MAY DISTURB THE RHYTHM OF THE HEART AND EVENTUALLY WEAKEN CARDIAC CONTRACTILITY. SKELETAL MUSCLE WEAKNESS AND FLACCID PARALYSIS MAY OCCUR IN SEVERE CASES. **CHRONIC EXPOSURE-** NO DATA AVAILABLE.

FIRST AID- TREAT SYMPTOMATICALLY AND SUPPORTIVELY. GET MEDICAL ATTENTION IMMEDIATELY. IF VOMITING OCCURS, KEEP HEAD LOWER THAN HIPS TO PREVENT ASPIRATION.

ANTIDOTE: NO SPECIFIC ANTIDOTE. TREAT SYMPTOMATICALLY AND SUPPORTIVELY.

REACTIVITY

REACTIVITY: STABLE UNDER NORMAL TEMPERATURES AND PRESSURES.

INCOMPATIBILITIES: POTASSIUM RICINOLEATE: OXIDIZERS (STRONG): FIRE AND EXPLOSION HAZARD.

DECOMPOSITION: THERMAL DECOMPOSITION MAY RELEASE TOXIC AND/OR HAZARDOUS GASES.

POLYMERIZATION: HAZARDOUS POLYMERIZATION HAS NOT BEEN REPORTED TO OCCUR UNDER NORMAL TEMPERATURES AND PRESSURES.

STORAGE AND DISPOSAL

OBSERVE ALL FEDERAL, STATE AND LOCAL REGULATIONS WHEN STORING OR DISPOSING OF THIS SUBSTANCE. FOR ASSISTANCE, CONTACT THE DISTRICT DIRECTOR OF THE ENVIRONMENTAL PROTECTION AGENCY.

STORAGE

STORE IN ACCORDANCE WITH 40 CFR 165 RECOMMENDED PROCEDURES FOR THE DISPOSAL AND STORAGE OF PESTICIDES AND PESTICIDE CONTAINERS.
STORE AWAY FROM INCOMPATIBLE SUBSTANCES.

DISPOSAL

DISPOSAL MUST BE IN ACCORDANCE WITH 40 CFR 165 RECOMMENDED PROCEDURES FOR THE DISPOSAL AND STORAGE OF PESTICIDES AND PESTICIDE CONTAINERS.

CONDITIONS TO AVOID

MAY BURN BUT DOES NOT IGNITE READILY. AVOID CONTACT WITH STRONG OXIDIZERS, EXCESSIVE HEAT, SPARKS, OR OPEN FLAME.

SPILL AND LEAK PROCEDURES

OCCUPATIONAL SPILL: SWEEP UP AND PLACE IN SUITABLE CLEAN, DRY CONTAINERS FOR RECLAMATION OR LATER DISPOSAL. DO NOT FLUSH SPILLED MATERIAL INTO SEWER. KEEP UNNECESSARY PEOPLE AWAY.

PROTECTIVE EQUIPMENT

VENTILATION: PROVIDE LOCAL EXHAUST OR GENERAL DILUTION VENTILATION SYSTEM.

RESPIRATOR: THE FOLLOWING RESPIRATORS ARE RECOMMENDED BASED ON INFORMATION FOUND IN THE PHYSICAL DATA, TOXICITY AND HEALTH EFFECTS SECTIONS. THEY ARE RANKED IN ORDER FROM MINIMUM TO MAXIMUM RESPIRATORY PROTECTION. THE SPECIFIC RESPIRATOR SELECTED MUST BE BASED ON CONTAMINATION LEVELS FOUND IN THE WORK PLACE, MUST NOT EXCEED THE WORKING LIMITS OF THE RESPIRATOR AND BE JOINTLY APPROVED BY THE NATIONAL INSTITUTE FOR OCCUPATIONAL SAFETY AND HEALTH AND THE MINE SAFETY AND HEALTH ADMINISTRATION (NIOSH-MSHA).
CHEMICAL CARTRIDGE RESPIRATOR WITH AN ORGANIC VAPOR CARTRIDGE(S) WITH A FULL FACEPIECE AND ORGANIC VAPOR CARTRIDGE(S) IN COMBINATION WITH A DUST AND MIST FILTER.
POWERED AIR-PURIFYING RESPIRATOR WITH A TIGHT-FITTING FACEPIECE AND ORGANIC VAPOR CARTRIDGE(S) IN COMBINATION WITH A HIGH-EFFICIENCY PARTICULATE FILTER.
TYPE 'C' SUPPLIED-AIR RESPIRATOR WITH A FULL FACEPIECE OPERATED IN A PRESSURE-DEMAND OR OTHER POSITIVE PRESSURE MODE.
SELF-CONTAINED BREATHING APPARATUS WITH A FULL FACEPIECE OPERATED IN PRESSURE-DEMAND OR OTHER POSITIVE PRESSURE MODE.
FOR FIREFIGHTING AND OTHER IMMEDIATELY DANGEROUS TO LIFE OR HEALTH CONDITIONS:
SELF-CONTAINED BREATHING APPARATUS WITH FULL FACEPIECE OPERATED IN PRESSURE-DEMAND OR OTHER POSITIVE PRESSURE MODE.
SUPPLIED-AIR RESPIRATOR WITH FULL FACEPIECE AND OPERATED IN PRESSURE-DEMAND OR OTHER POSITIVE PRESSURE MODE IN COMBINATION WITH AN AUXILIARY SELF-CONTAINED BREATHING APPARATUS OPERATED IN PRESSURE-DEMAND OR OTHER POSITIVE PRESSURE MODE.

CLOTHING: EMPLOYEE MUST WEAR APPROPRIATE PROTECTIVE (IMPERVIOUS) CLOTHING AND EQUIPMENT TO PREVENT REPEATED OR PROLONGED SKIN CONTACT WITH THIS SUBSTANCE.

GLOVES: EMPLOYEE MUST WEAR APPROPRIATE PROTECTIVE GLOVES TO PREVENT CONTACT WITH THIS SUBSTANCE.

EYE PROTECTION: EMPLOYEE MUST WEAR SPLASH-PROOF OR DUST-RESISTANT SAFETY GOGGLES TO PREVENT EYE CONTACT WITH THIS SUBSTANCE.
EMERGENCY EYE WASH: WHERE THERE IS ANY POSSIBILITY THAT AN EMPLOYEE'S EYES MAY BE EXPOSED TO THIS SUBSTANCE, THE EMPLOYER SHOULD PROVIDE AN EYE WASH FOUNTAIN WITHIN THE IMMEDIATE WORK AREA FOR EMERGENCY USE.

AUTHORIZED BY- OCCUPATIONAL HEALTH SERVICES, INC.
CREATION DATE: 02/08/90 ***REVISION DATE:*** 05/31/90

MATERIAL SAFETY DATA SHEET

OCCUPATIONAL HEALTH SERVICES, INC.
AGRICULTURE AND PESTICIDE DIVISION
450 SEVENTH AVENUE, SUITE 2407
NEW YORK, NEW YORK 10123
1-800-445-MSDS OR (212) 967-1100

EMERGENCY CONTACT:
JOHN S. BRANSFORD, JR. (615) 292-1180

SUBSTANCE IDENTIFICATION

CAS-NUMBER 1984-06-1

SUBSTANCE: **SODIUM CAPRYLATE**

TRADE NAMES/SYNONYMS: OCTANOIC ACID, SODIUM SALT; CAPRYLIC ACID SODIUM SALT; SODIUM OCTANOATE; SODIUM N-OCTANOATE; SODIUM OCTOATE; C8H15NAO2; PST72105

CHEMICAL FAMILY: SOAP

MOLECULAR FORMULA: C-H3-(C-H2)6-C-O-O.NA

MOLECULAR WEIGHT: 166.20

CERCLA RATINGS (SCALE 0-3): HEALTH=U FIRE=1 REACTIVITY=0 PERSISTENCE=1

NFPA RATINGS (SCALE 0-4): HEALTH=U FIRE=1 REACTIVITY=0

COMPONENTS AND CONTAMINANTS

COMPONENT: SODIUM CAPRYLATE ***PERCENT:*** 100.0
CAS# 1984-06-1

OTHER CONTAMINANTS: NONE

EXPOSURE LIMITS: NO OCCUPATIONAL EXPOSURE LIMITS ESTABLISHED BY OSHA, ACGIH, OR NIOSH.

PHYSICAL DATA

DESCRIPTION: WHITE POWDER. ***MELTING POINT:*** NOT AVAILABLE
SPECIFIC GRAVITY: NOT AVAILABLE ***SOLUBILITY IN WATER:*** 5%

FIRE AND EXPLOSION DATA

FIRE AND EXPLOSION HAZARD: SLIGHT FIRE HAZARD WHEN EXPOSED TO HEAT OR FLAME.

FIREFIGHTING MEDIA: DRY CHEMICAL, CARBON DIOXIDE, HALON, WATER SPRAY OR STANDARD FOAM (1987 EMERGENCY RESPONSE GUIDEBOOK, DOT P 5800.4).
FOR LARGER FIRES, USE WATER SPRAY, FOG OR STANDARD FOAM (1987 EMERGENCY RESPONSE GUIDEBOOK, DOT P 5800.4).

FIREFIGHTING: MOVE CONTAINER FROM FIRE AREA IF POSSIBLE. DO NOT SCATTER SPILLED MATERIAL WITH HIGH PRESSURE WATER STREAMS. DIKE FIRE CONTROL WATER FOR LATER DISPOSAL (1987 EMERGENCY RESPONSE GUIDEBOOK, DOT P 5800.4, GUIDE PAGE 31).
USE AGENTS SUITABLE FOR TYPE OF SURROUNDING FIRE. AVOID BREATHING HAZARDOUS VAPORS, KEEP UPWIND.

TOXICITY

SODIUM CAPRYLATE: TOXICITY DATA: MUTAGENIC DATA (RTECS). CARCINOGEN STATUS: NONE. ACUTE TOXICITY LEVEL: NO DATA AVAILABLE. TARGET EFFECTS: NO DATA AVAILBLE.

HEALTH EFFECTS AND FIRST AID

INHALATION: SODIUM CAPRYLATE: **ACUTE EXPOSURE**- SOAPS MAY CAUSE MILD MUCOUS MEMBRANE IRRITATION. **CHRONIC EXPOSURE**- NO DATA AVAILABLE.
FIRST AID- REMOVE FROM EXPOSURE AREA TO FRESH AIR IMMEDIATELY. IF BREATHING HAS STOPPED, PERFORM ARTIFICIAL RESPIRATION. KEEP PERSON WARM AND AT REST. TREAT SYMPTOMATICALLY AND SUPPORTIVELY. GET MEDICAL ATTENTION IMMEDIATELY.

SKIN CONTACT: SODIUM CAPRYLATE: **ACUTE EXPOSURE**- SOAPS MAY REMOVE OILS FROM THE SKIN CAUSING REDNESS, SORENESS AND PAPULAR DERMATITIS. **CHRONIC EXPOSURE**- NO DATA AVAILABLE.
FIRST AID- REMOVE CONTAMINATED CLOTHING AND SHOES IMMEDIATELY. WASH AFFECTED AREA WITH SOAP OR MILD DETERGENT AND LARGE AMOUNTS OF WATER UNTIL NO EVIDENCE OF CHEMICAL REMAINS (APPROXIMATELY 15-20 MINUTES). GET MEDICAL ATTENTION IMMEDIATELY.

EYE CONTACT: SODIUM CAPRYLATE: **ACUTE EXPOSURE**- SOAPS MAY CAUSE MUCOUS MEMBRANE IRRITATION. **CHRONIC EXPOSURE**- NO DATA AVAILABLE.
FIRST AID- WASH EYES IMMEDIATELY WITH LARGE AMOUNTS OF WATER OR NORMAL SALINE, OCCASIONALLY LIFTING UPPER AND LOWER LIDS, UNTIL NO EVIDENCE OF CHEMICAL REMAINS (APPROXIMATELY 15-20 MINUTES). GET MEDICAL ATTENTION IMMEDIATELY.

INGESTION: SODIUM CAPRYLATE: **ACUTE EXPOSURE**- SOAPS MAY CAUSE MILD GASTROINTESTINAL IRRITATION. INGESTION MAY PRODUCE NAUSEA, VOMITING, DIARRHEA AND ABDOMINAL PAIN. **CHRONIC EXPOSURE**- NO DATA AVAILABLE.
FIRST AID- TREAT SYMPTOMATICALLY AND SUPPORTIVELY. GET MEDICAL ATTENTION IMMEDIATELY. IF VOMITING OCCURS, KEEP HEAD LOWER THAN HIPS TO PREVENT ASPIRATION.

ANTIDOTE: NO SPECIFIC ANTIDOTE. TREAT SYMPTOMATICALLY AND SUPPORTIVELY.

REACTIVITY

REACTIVITY: STABLE UNDER NORMAL TEMPERATURES AND PRESSURES.

INCOMPATIBILITIES: SODIUM CAPRYLATE: OXIDIZERS (STRONG): FIRE AND EXPLOSION HAZARD.
DECOMPOSITION: THERMAL DECOMPOSITION PRODUCTS MAY INCLUDE TOXIC OXIDES OF CARBON.
POLYMERIZATION: HAZARDOUS POLYMERIZATION HAS NOT BEEN REPORTED TO OCCUR UNDER NORMAL TEMPERATURES AND PRESSURES.

STORAGE AND DISPOSAL

OBSERVE ALL FEDERAL, STATE AND LOCAL REGULATIONS WHEN STORING OR DISPOSING OF THIS SUBSTANCE. FOR ASSISTANCE, CONTACT THE DISTRICT DIRECTOR OF THE ENVIRONMENTAL PROTECTION AGENCY.

STORAGE

STORE IN ACCORDANCE WITH 40 CFR 165 RECOMMENDED PROCEDURES FOR THE DISPOSAL AND STORAGE OF PESTICIDES AND PESTICIDE CONTAINERS.
STORE AWAY FROM INCOMPATIBLE SUBSTANCES.

DISPOSAL

DISPOSAL MUST BE IN ACCORDANCE WITH 40 CFR 165 RECOMMENDED PROCEDURES FOR THE DISPOSAL AND STORAGE OF PESTICIDES AND PESTICIDE CONTAINERS.

CONDITIONS TO AVOID

MAY BURN BUT DOES NOT IGNITE READILY. AVOID CONTACT WITH STRONG OXIDIZERS, EXCESSIVE HEAT, SPARKS, OR OPEN FLAME.

SPILL AND LEAK PROCEDURES

OCCUPATIONAL SPILL: SWEEP UP AND PLACE IN SUITABLE CLEAN, DRY CONTAINERS FOR RECLAMATION OR LATER DISPOSAL. DO NOT FLUSH SPILLED MATERIAL INTO SEWER. KEEP UNNECESSARY PEOPLE AWAY.

PROTECTIVE EQUIPMENT

VENTILATION: PROVIDE LOCAL EXHAUST OR PROCESS ENCLOSURE VENTILATION SYSTEM.
RESPIRATOR: THE FOLLOWING RESPIRATORS ARE RECOMMENDED BASED ON INFORMATION FOUND IN THE PHYSICAL DATA, TOXICITY AND HEALTH EFFECTS SECTIONS. THEY ARE RANKED IN ORDER FROM MINIMUM TO MAXIMUM RESPIRATORY PROTECTION. THE SPECIFIC RESPIRATOR SELECTED MUST BE BASED ON CONTAMINATION LEVELS FOUND IN THE WORK PLACE, MUST NOT EXCEED THE WORKING LIMITS OF THE RESPIRATOR AND BE JOINTLY APPROVED BY THE NATIONAL INSTITUTE FOR OCCUPATIONAL SAFETY AND HEALTH AND THE MINE SAFETY AND HEALTH ADMINISTRATION (NIOSH-MSHA).
CHEMICAL CARTRIDGE RESPIRATOR WITH AN ORGANIC VAPOR CARTRIDGE(S) WITH A FULL FACEPIECE AND ORGANIC VAPOR CARTRIDGE(S) IN COMBINATION WITH A DUST AND MIST FILTER.
POWERED AIR-PURIFYING RESPIRATOR WITH A TIGHT-FITTING FACEPIECE AND ORGANIC VAPOR CARTRIDGE(S) IN COMBINATION WITH A HIGH-EFFICIENCY PARTICULATE FILTER.
TYPE 'C' SUPPLIED-AIR RESPIRATOR WITH A FULL FACEPIECE OPERATED IN A PRESSURE-DEMAND OR OTHER POSITIVE PRESSURE MODE.
SELF-CONTAINED BREATHING APPARATUS WITH A FULL FACEPIECE OPERATED IN PRESSURE-DEMAND OR OTHER POSITIVE PRESSURE MODE.
FOR FIREFIGHTING AND OTHER IMMEDIATELY DANGEROUS TO LIFE OR HEALTH CONDITIONS:
SELF-CONTAINED BREATHING APPARATUS WITH FULL FACEPIECE OPERATED IN PRESSURE-DEMAND OR OTHER POSITIVE PRESSURE MODE.
SUPPLIED-AIR RESPIRATOR WITH FULL FACEPIECE AND OPERATED IN PRESSURE-DEMAND OR OTHER POSITIVE PRESSURE MODE IN COMBINATION WITH AN AUXILIARY SELF-CONTAINED BREATHING APPARATUS OPERATED IN PRESSURE-DEMAND OR OTHER POSITIVE PRESSURE MODE.
CLOTHING: EMPLOYEE MUST WEAR APPROPRIATE PROTECTIVE (IMPERVIOUS) CLOTHING AND EQUIPMENT TO PREVENT REPEATED OR PROLONGED SKIN CONTACT WITH THIS SUBSTANCE.
GLOVES: EMPLOYEE MUST WEAR APPROPRIATE PROTECTIVE GLOVES TO PREVENT CONTACT WITH THIS SUBSTANCE.
EYE PROTECTION: EMPLOYEE MUST WEAR SPLASH-PROOF OR DUST-RESISTANT SAFETY GOGGLES TO PREVENT EYE CONTACT WITH THIS SUBSTANCE.
EMERGENCY EYE WASH: WHERE THERE IS ANY POSSIBILITY THAT AN EMPLOYEE'S EYES MAY BE EXPOSED TO THIS SUBSTANCE, THE EMPLOYER SHOULD PROVIDE AN EYE WASH FOUNTAIN WITHIN THE IMMEDIATE WORK AREA FOR EMERGENCY USE.

AUTHORIZED BY- OCCUPATIONAL HEALTH SERVICES, INC.
CREATION DATE: 10/05/89 ***REVISION DATE:*** 05/31/90

MATERIAL SAFETY DATA SHEET

OCCUPATIONAL HEALTH SERVICES, INC.
AGRICULTURE AND PESTICIDE DIVISION
450 SEVENTH AVENUE, SUITE 2407
NEW YORK, NEW YORK 10123
1-800-445-MSDS OR (212) 967-1100

EMERGENCY CONTACT:
JOHN S. BRANSFORD, JR. (615) 292-1180

SUBSTANCE IDENTIFICATION

CAS-NUMBER 143-18-0
SUBSTANCE: **POTASSIUM OLEATE**
TRADE NAMES/SYNONYMS: 9-OCTADECENOIC ACID (Z)-,POTASSIUM SALT; POTASSIUM SALT 9-OCTADECENOIC ACID (Z); OLEIC ACID, POTASSIUM SALT; POTASSIUM CIS-9-OCTADECENOIC ACID; TRENAMINE D 200; TRENAMINE D 201; FR 14; PST72131
CHEMICAL FAMILY: ESTER, CARBOXYLIC, ALIPHATIC
MOLECULAR FORMULA: C18-H33-O2.K
MOLECULAR WEIGHT: 320.57
CERCLA RATINGS (SCALE 0-3): HEALTH=2 FIRE=2 REACTIVITY=0 PERSISTENCE=1
NFPA RATINGS (SCALE 0-4): HEALTH=2 FIRE=2 REACTIVITY=0

COMPONENTS AND CONTAMINANTS

COMPONENT: POTASSIUM OLEATE ***PERCENT:*** 100.0
CAS# 143-18-0
EXPOSURE LIMITS: NO OCCUPATIONAL EXPOSURE LIMITS ESTABLISHED BY OSHA, ACGIH, OR NIOSH.

PHYSICAL DATA

DESCRIPTION: YELLOWISH OR BROWNISH SOFT PASTE WITH A SOAPY ODOR.
MELTING POINT: 455-464 F (235-240 C) ***SPECIFIC GRAVITY:*** >1.1 ***PH:*** ALKALINE
SOLUBILITY IN WATER: SOLUBLE
SOLVENT SOLUBILITY: SOLUBLE IN ALCOHOL

FIRE AND EXPLOSION DATA

FIRE AND EXPLOSION HAZARD: MODERATE FIRE HAZARD WHEN EXPOSED TO HEAT OR FLAME.
FLASH POINT: 140 F (60 C) ***FLAMMABILITY CLASS(OSHA):*** IIIA
FIREFIGHTING MEDIA: DRY CHEMICAL, CARBON DIOXIDE, WATER SPRAY OR FOAM FOR LARGER FIRES, USE WATER SPRAY, FOG OR ALCOHOL FOAM
FIREFIGHTING: MOVE CONTAINER FROM FIRE AREA IF POSSIBLE. DO NOT SCATTER SPILLED MATERIAL WITH MORE WATER THAN NEEDED FOR FIRE CONTROL. DIKE FIRE CONTROL WATER FOR LATER DISPOSAL
USE AGENTS SUITABLE FOR TYPE OF SURROUNDING FIRE. AVOID BREATHING HAZARDOUS VAPORS, KEEP UPWIND.

TRANSPORTATION DATA

DEPARTMENT OF TRANSPORTATION HAZARD CLASSIFICATION 49 CFR 172.101: COMBUSTIBLE LIQUID
DEPARTMENT OF TRANSPORTATION LABELING REQUIREMENTS 49 CFR 172.101 AND SUBPART E: NONE

TOXICITY

POTASSIUM OLEATE: IRRITATION DATA: 12 MG/48 HOURS EYE-RABBIT. CARCINOGEN STATUS: NONE. LOCAL EFFECTS: IRRITANT- EYE. ACUTE TOXICITY LEVEL: NO DATA AVAILABLE. TARGET EFFECTS: NO DATA AVAILABLE.

HEALTH EFFECTS AND FIRST AID

INHALATION: POTASSIUM OLEATE: **ACUTE EXPOSURE-** INHALATION OF DUST MAY CAUSE IRRITATION TO THE NOSE AND THROAT, COUGHING AND SNEEZING.
CHRONIC EXPOSURE- NO DATA AVAILABLE.
FIRST AID- REMOVE FROM EXPOSURE AREA TO FRESH AIR IMMEDIATELY. IF BREATHING HAS STOPPED, PERFORM ARTIFICIAL RESPIRATION. KEEP PERSON WARM AND AT REST. TREAT SYMPTOMATICALLY AND SUPPORTIVELY. GET MEDICAL ATTENTION IMMEDIATELY.

SKIN CONTACT: POTASSIUM OLEATE: **ACUTE EXPOSURE-** MAY BE IRRITATING.
CHRONIC EXPOSURE- MAY CAUSE IRRITATION, REDNESS, SORENESS AND PAPULAR DERMATITIS DUE TO THE DEFATTING ACTION ON THE SKIN. IN SENSITIVE PERSONS, ANIONIC DETERGENTS MAY CAUSE THICKENING OF THE SKIN WITH WEEPING, CRACKING, SCALING AND BLISTERING.
FIRST AID- REMOVE CONTAMINATED CLOTHING AND SHOES IMMEDIATELY. WASH AFFECTED AREA WITH SOAP OR MILD DETERGENT AND LARGE AMOUNTS OF

WATER UNTIL NO EVIDENCE OF CHEMICAL REMAINS (APPROXIMATELY 15-20 MINUTES). GET MEDICAL ATTENTION IMMEDIATELY.

EYE CONTACT: POTASSIUM OLEATE: IRRITANT. **ACUTE EXPOSURE-** MAY CAUSE IRRITATION, STINGING PAIN, AND TEARING. **CHRONIC EXPOSURE-** NO DATA AVAILABLE.

FIRST AID- WASH EYES IMMEDIATELY WITH LARGE AMOUNTS OF WATER OR NORMAL SALINE, OCCASIONALLY LIFTING UPPER AND LOWER LIDS, UNTIL NO EVIDENCE OF CHEMICAL REMAINS (APPROXIMATELY 15-20 MINUTES). GET MEDICAL ATTENTION IMMEDIATELY.

INGESTION: POTASSIUM OLEATE: **ACUTE EXPOSURE-** MAY CAUSE GASTROINTESTINAL IRRITATION WITH NAUSEA, VOMITING, AND DIARRHEA. **CHRONIC EXPOSURE-** NO DATA AVAILABLE.

FIRST AID- TREAT SYMPTOMATICALLY AND SUPPORTIVELY. GET MEDICAL ATTENTION IMMEDIATELY. IF VOMITING OCCURS, KEEP HEAD LOWER THAN HIPS TO PREVENT ASPIRATION.

ANTIDOTE: NO SPECIFIC ANTIDOTE. TREAT SYMPTOMATICALLY AND SUPPORTIVELY.

REACTIVITY

REACTIVITY: STABLE UNDER NORMAL TEMPERATURES AND PRESSURES.

INCOMPATIBILITIES: POTASSIUM OLEATE: NO DATA AVAILABLE.

DECOMPOSITION: THERMAL DECOMPOSITION MAY RELEASE ACRID SMOKE AND IRRITATING FUMES.

POLYMERIZATION: HAZARDOUS POLYMERIZATION HAS NOT BEEN REPORTED TO OCCUR UNDER NORMAL TEMPERATURES AND PRESSURES.

STORAGE AND DISPOSAL

OBSERVE ALL FEDERAL, STATE AND LOCAL REGULATIONS WHEN STORING OR DISPOSING OF THIS SUBSTANCE. FOR ASSISTANCE, CONTACT THE DISTRICT DIRECTOR OF THE ENVIRONMENTAL PROTECTION AGENCY.

****STORAGE****

STORE IN ACCORDANCE WITH 29 CFR 1910.106.

BONDING AND GROUNDING: SUBSTANCES WITH LOW ELECTROCONDUCTIVITY, WHICH MAY BE IGNITED BY ELECTROSTATIC SPARKS, SHOULD BE STORED IN CONTAINERS WHICH MEET THE BONDING AND GROUNDING GUIDELINES SPECIFIED IN NFPA 77-1983, RECOMMENDED PRACTICE ON STATIC ELECTRICITY.

****DISPOSAL****

DISPOSAL MUST BE IN ACCORDANCE WITH STANDARDS APPLICABLE TO GENERATORS OF HAZARDOUS WASTE, 40 CFR 262. EPA HAZARDOUS WASTE NUMBER D001. 100 POUND CERCLA SECTION 103 REPORTABLE QUANTITY.

CONDITIONS TO AVOID

NONE REPORTED.

SPILL AND LEAK PROCEDURES

OCCUPATIONAL SPILL: STOP LEAK IF YOU CAN DO IT WITHOUT RISK. FOR SMALL SPILLS, TAKE UP WITH SAND OR OTHER ABSORBENT MATERIAL AND PLACE INTO CLEAN, DRY CONTAINERS FOR LATER DISPOSAL. KEEP UNNECESSARY PEOPLE AWAY. ISOLATE HAZARD AREA AND DENY ENTRY.

PROTECTIVE EQUIPMENT

VENTILATION: PROVIDE LOCAL EXHAUST VENTILATION SYSTEM.

RESPIRATOR: THE FOLLOWING RESPIRATORS ARE RECOMMENDED BASED ON INFORMATION FOUND IN THE PHYSICAL DATA, TOXICITY AND HEALTH EFFECTS SECTIONS. THEY ARE RANKED IN ORDER FROM MINIMUM TO MAXIMUM RESPIRATORY PROTECTION. THE SPECIFIC RESPIRATOR SELECTED MUST BE BASED ON CONTAMINATION LEVELS FOUND IN THE WORK PLACE, MUST NOT EXCEED THE WORKING LIMITS OF THE RESPIRATOR AND BE JOINTLY APPROVED BY THE NATIONAL INSTITUTE FOR OCCUPATIONAL SAFETY AND HEALTH AND THE MINE SAFETY AND HEALTH ADMINISTRATION (NIOSH-MSHA).

CHEMICAL CARTRIDGE RESPIRATOR WITH AN ORGANIC VAPOR CARTRIDGE(S) WITH A FULL FACEPIECE.

GAS MASK WITH ORGANIC VAPOR CANISTER (CHIN-STYLE OR FRONT- OR BACK-MOUNTED CANISTER) WITH A FULL FACEPIECE.

TYPE 'C' SUPPLIED-AIR RESPIRATOR WITH A FULL FACEPIECE OPERATED IN PRESSURE-DEMAND OR OTHER POSITIVE PRESSURE MODE OR WITH A FULL FACEPIECE, HELMET OR HOOD OPERATED IN CONTINUOUS-FLOW MODE.

SELF-CONTAINED BREATHING APPARATUS WITH A FULL FACEPIECE OPERATED IN PRESSURE-DEMAND OR OTHER POSITIVE PRESSURE MODE.

FOR FIREFIGHTING AND OTHER IMMEDIATELY DANGEROUS TO LIFE OR HEALTH CONDITIONS:

SELF-CONTAINED BREATHING APPARATUS WITH FULL FACEPIECE OPERATED IN PRESSURE-DEMAND OR OTHER POSITIVE PRESSURE MODE.

SUPPLIED-AIR RESPIRATOR WITH FULL FACEPIECE AND OPERATED IN PRESSURE-DEMAND OR OTHER POSITIVE PRESSURE MODE IN COMBINATION WITH AN AUXILIARY SELF-CONTAINED BREATHING APPARATUS OPERATED IN PRESSURE-DEMAND OR OTHER POSITIVE PRESSURE MODE.

CLOTHING: EMPLOYEE MUST WEAR APPROPRIATE PROTECTIVE (IMPERVIOUS) CLOTHING AND EQUIPMENT TO PREVENT REPEATED OR PROLONGED SKIN CONTACT WITH THIS SUBSTANCE.

GLOVES: EMPLOYEE MUST WEAR APPROPRIATE PROTECTIVE GLOVES TO PREVENT CONTACT WITH THIS SUBSTANCE.

EYE PROTECTION: EMPLOYEE MUST WEAR SPLASH-PROOF OR DUST-RESISTANT SAFETY GOGGLES TO PREVENT EYE CONTACT WITH THIS SUBSTANCE.

EMERGENCY EYE WASH: WHERE THERE IS ANY POSSIBILITY THAT AN EMPLOYEE'S EYES MAY BE EXPOSED TO THIS SUBSTANCE, THE EMPLOYER SHOULD PROVIDE AN EYE WASH FOUNTAIN WITHIN THE IMMEDIATE WORK AREA FOR EMERGENCY USE.

AUTHORIZED BY- OCCUPATIONAL HEALTH SERVICES, INC.

CREATION DATE: 02/08/90 ***REVISION DATE:*** 05/08/90

MATERIAL SAFETY DATA SHEET

OCCUPATIONAL HEALTH SERVICES, INC.
AGRICULTURE AND PESTICIDE DIVISION
450 SEVENTH AVENUE, SUITE 2407
NEW YORK, NEW YORK 10123
1-800-445-MSDS OR (212) 967-1100

EMERGENCY CONTACT:
JOHN S. BRANSFORD, JR. (615) 292-1180

SUBSTANCE IDENTIFICATION

CAS-NUMBER 3244-90-4

***SUBSTANCE:* O,O,O',O'-TETRAPROPYL DITHIOPYROPHOSPHATE**

TRADE NAMES/SYNONYMS: THIODIPHOSPHORIC ACID (((HO)2P(S))2O), TETRAPROPYL ESTER; THIOPYROPHOSPHORIC ACID (((HO)2PS)2O), TETRAPROPYL ESTER; PROPYL THIOPYROPHSOPHATE (((PRO)2P(S))2O); TETRA-N-PROPYL DITHIOPYROPHOSPHATE; O,O,O,O-TETRA-N-PROPYL DITHIOPYROPHOSPHATE; TETRAPROPYL THIOPYROPHOSPHATE; TETRAPROPYL THIODIPHOSPHATE; ASPON; ASP 51; NPD; ENT 16894; C12H28O5P2S2; PST72135

CHEMICAL FAMILY: PHOSPHOROTHIOATE

MOLECULAR FORMULA: ((C-H3-C-H2-C-H2-O)2-P-(S))2-O)

MOLECULAR WEIGHT: 378.46

CERCLA RATINGS (SCALE 0-3): HEALTH=3 FIRE=1 REACTIVITY=0 PERSISTENCE=1

NFPA RATINGS (SCALE 0-4): HEALTH=3 FIRE=1 REACTIVITY=0

COMPONENTS AND CONTAMINANTS

COMPONENT: O,O,O',O'-TETRAPROPYL DITHIOPYROPHOSPHATE ***PERCENT:*** 100.0 CAS# 3244-90-4

OTHER CONTAMINANTS: NONE

EXPOSURE LIMITS: NO OCCUPATIONAL EXPOSURE LIMITS ESTABLISHED BY OSHA, ACGIH, OR NIOSH.

PHYSICAL DATA

DESCRIPTION: STRAW TO AMBER-COLORED LIQUID WITH FAINT AROMATIC ODOR.

BOILING POINT: 338 F (170 C) @ 1.0 MMHG ***MELTING POINT:*** <-40 F (<-40 C)

SPECIFIC GRAVITY: 1.119-1.123 ***VISCOSITY:*** 12.5 CPS @ 21 C

VAPOR PRESSURE: 0.000095 MMHG @ 25 C

SOLUBILITY IN WATER: 0.0003% @ 20 C

SOLVENT SOLUBILITY: SOLUBLE IN ACETONE, ETHANOL, KEROSENE, XYLENE, 4-METHYLPENTAN-2-ONE, AND MOST ORGANIC SOLVENTS; INSOLUBLE IN PETROLEUM OILS.

DECOMPOSES ABOVE 300 F (149 C)

FIRE AND EXPLOSION DATA

FIRE AND EXPLOSION HAZARD: SLIGHT FIRE HAZARD WHEN EXPOSED TO HEAT OR FLAME.

FLASH POINT: 300 F (149 C) (OC)

FIREFIGHTING MEDIA: DRY CHEMICAL, CARBON DIOXIDE, HALON, WATER SPRAY OR STANDARD FOAM (1987 EMERGENCY RESPONSE GUIDEBOOK, DOT P 5800.4).

FOR LARGER FIRES, USE WATER SPRAY, FOG OR STANDARD FOAM (1987 EMERGENCY RESPONSE GUIDEBOOK, DOT P 5800.4).

FIREFIGHTING: MOVE CONTAINERS FROM FIRE AREA IF POSSIBLE. FIGHT FIRE FROM MAXIMUM DISTANCE. STAY AWAY FROM STORAGE TANK ENDS. DIKE FIRE CONTROL WATER FOR LATER DISPOSAL. DO NOT SCATTER MATERIAL (1987 EMERGENCY RESPONSE GUIDEBOOK, DOT P 5800.4, GUIDE PAGE 55).

EXTINGUISH ONLY IF FLOW CAN BE STOPPED; USE FLOODING AMOUNTS OF WATER AS FOG, SOLID STREAMS MAY BE INEFFECTIVE. COOL CONTAINERS WITH FLOODING AMOUNTS OF WATER FROM AS FAR A DISTANCE AS POSSIBLE. USE WATER SPRAY TO ABSORB TOXIC VAPORS. AVOID BREATHING TOXIC VAPORS; KEEP UPWIND. CONSIDER EVACUATION OF DOWNWIND AREA IF MATERIAL IS LEAKING.

TOXICITY

O,O,O',O'-TETRAPROPYL DITHIOPYROPHOSPHATE: TOXICITY DATA: 3830 MG/KG SKIN-RABBIT LD50; 1800 MG/KG SKIN-RAT LD50; 450 MG/KG ORAL-RAT LD50; 3250 UG/KG INTRAVENOUS-MOUSE LD50; 1100 MG/KG INTRAPERITONEAL-RAT LD50; 8 MG/KG INTRAPERITONEAL-MOUSE LD50; 4410 UG/KG INTRAMUSCULAR-MOUSE LD50; 100 MG/KG UNREPORTED-RAT LD50. CARCINOGEN STATUS: NONE. ACUTE TOXICITY LEVEL: TOXIC BY INGESTION AND SLIGHTLY TOXIC BY DERMAL ABSORPTION. TARGET EFFECTS: CHOLINESTERASE INHIBITOR. POISONING MAY AFFECT THE NERVOUS SYSTEM.* AT INCREASED RISK FROM EXPOSURE: PERSONS WITH RESPIRATORY AILMENTS, RECENT EXPOSURE TO CHOLINESTERASE INHIBITORS OR IMPAIRED CHOLINESTERASE PRODUCTION, OR LIVER MALFUNCTION.* ADDITIONAL DATA: MAY CROSS THE PLACENTA. HIGH ENVIRONMENTAL TEMPERATURES OR EXPOSURE OF THE CHEMICAL TO VISIBLE OR ULTRAVIOLET LIGHT MAY ENHANCE THE TOXICITY. INTERACTIONS WITH MEDICATIONS MAY OCCUR.*

* MAY BE BASED ON GENERAL INFORMATION ON ORGANOPHOSPHATES.

HEALTH EFFECTS AND FIRST AID

INHALATION: O,O,O',O'-TETRAPROPYL DITHIOPYROPHOSPHATE: SEE INFORMATION ON ORGANOPHOSPHATES.

ORGANOPHOSPHATES: CHOLINESTERASE INHIBITOR. **ACUTE EXPOSURE-** WHEN INHALED, THE FIRST EFFECTS OF CHOLINESTERASE INHIBITORS ARE USUALLY RESPIRATORY AND MAY INCLUDE NASAL HYPEREMIA AND WATERY DISCHARGE, COUGH, CHEST DISCOMFORT, DYSPNEA, AND WHEEZING DUE TO INCREASED BRONCHIAL SECRETIONS AND BRONCHOCONSTRICTION. IF SUFFICIENT AMOUNTS ARE ABSORBED, OTHER SYSTEMIC EFFECTS MAY BEGIN WITHIN A FEW MINUTES OR BE DELAYED FOR UP TO 12 HOURS. SYMPTOMS MAY INCLUDE PALLOR, NAUSEA, VOMITING, DIARRHEA, ABDOMINAL CRAMPS, HEADACHE, DIZZINESS, OCULAR PAIN, BLURRED VISION, MIOSIS OR IN SOME CASES, ESPECIALLY INITIALLY, MYDRIASIS, LACRIMATION, SALIVATION, SWEATING, AND CONFUSION. OTHER REPORTED CENTRAL NERVOUS SYSTEM OR NEUROMUSCULAR EFFECTS MAY INCLUDE ATAXIA, SLURRED SPEECH, AREFLEXIA, WEAKNESS, FATIGUE, FASCICULATIONS, TWITCHING, TREMORS POSSIBLY OF THE TONGUE AND EYELIDS, AND EVENTUALLY PARALYSIS OF THE EXTREMITIES AND POSSIBLY OF THE RESPIRATORY MUSCLES. IN SEVERE CASES THERE MAY ALSO BE INVOLUNTARY DEFECATION AND URINATION, CYANOSIS, PSYCHOSIS, HYPERGLYCEMIA, ACUTE PANCREATITIS, CARDIAC IRREGULARITIES, PULMONARY EDEMA, UNCONSCIOUSNESS, CONVULSIONS, AND COMA. DEATH IS PRIMARILY DUE TO RESPIRATORY FAILURE, ALTHOUGH CARDIOVASCULAR EFFECTS INCLUDING CARDIAC ARREST MAY ALSO BE IMPLICATED. LONG TERM SEQUELAE ARE RARE BUT MAY INCLUDE NEUROPSYCHIATRIC DISORDERS AND MYOPATHY WITH MUSCLE TENDERNESS. SOME ORGANOPHOSPHATES MAY CAUSE A DELAYED NEUROPATHY BEGINNING 1-4 WEEKS AFTER AN ACUTE EXPOSURE WHICH MAY OR MAY NOT HAVE CAUSED ACUTE CHOLINERGIC EFFECTS. NUMBNESS, TINGLING, WEAKNESS AND CRAMPING BEGINNING SYMMETRICALLY IN THE LOWER LIMBS MAY PROGRESS TO ATAXIA AND PARALYSIS. IN SEVERE CASES, UPPER LIMB INVOLVEMENT IS POSSIBLE AND FLACCID PARALYSIS MAY PROGRESS TO SPASTIC PARALYSIS WITH EXAGGERATED REFLEXES. IMPROVEMENT MAY OCCUR OVER MONTHS TO YEARS, BUT SOME RESIDUAL IMPAIRMENT USUALLY REMAINS. **CHRONIC EXPOSURE-** REPEATED OR PROLONGED EXPOSURE MAY RESULT IN THE EFFECTS OF ACUTE EXPOSURE INCLUDING THE DELAYED NEUROPATHY. OTHER EFFECTS REPORTED IN WORKERS REPEATEDLY EXPOSED INCLUDE IMPAIRED MEMORY AND CONCENTRATION, ACUTE PSYCHOSIS, SEVERE DEPRESSIONS, IRRITABILTY, CONFUSION, APATHY, EMOTIONAL LABILITY, SOCIAL WITHDRAWAL, CONFUSION, HEADACHE, SPEECH DIFFICULTIES, DELAYED REACTION TIMES, SPATIAL DISORIENTATION, NIGHTMARES, SLEEPWALKING, AND DROWSINESS OR INSOMNIA. AN INFLUENZA-LIKE CONDITION WITH HEADACHE, NAUSEA, WEAKNESS, ANOREXIA AND MALAISE HAS ALSO BEEN REPORTED.

FIRST AID- REMOVE FROM EXPOSURE AREA TO FRESH AIR IMMEDIATELY. IF BREATHING HAS STOPPED, GIVE ARTIFICIAL RESPIRATION. MAINTAIN AIRWAY AND BLOOD PRESSURE AND ADMINISTER OXYGEN IF AVAILABLE. KEEP AFFECTED PERSON WARM AND AT REST. TREAT SYMPTOMATICALLY AND SUPPORTIVELY. ADMINISTRATION OF OXYGEN SHOULD BE PERFORMED BY QUALIFIED PERSONNEL. GET MEDICAL ATTENTION IMMEDIATELY.

SKIN CONTACT: O,O,O',O'-TETRAPROPYL DITHIOPYROPHOSPHATE: ANIMAL STUDIES INDICATED THAT SKIN EXPOSURE TO 13 TO 14% EMULSIFIABLE CONCENTRATE FORMULATIONS MAY CAUSE FROM MODERATE ERYTHEMA AND EDEMA TO SEVER IRRITATION. SEE INFORMATION ON ORGANOPHOSPHATES.

ORGANOPHOSPHATES: CHOLINESTERASE INHIBITOR. **ACUTE EXPOSURE-** LOCALIZED SWEATING AND FASCICULATIONS MAY OCCUR AT THE SITE OF CONTACT. IF SUFFICIENT AMOUNTS ARE ABSORBED, OTHER EFFECTS OF CHOLINESTERASE INHIBITION AS DESCRIBED IN ACUTE INHALATION MAY OCCUR. SYMPTOMS MAY BE DELAYED 2-3 HOURS, BUT USUALLY NO MORE THAN 12 HOURS. THE RATE OF ABSORPTION IS INCREASED BY THE PRESENCE OF DERMATITIS OR HIGH AMBIENT TEMPERATURES. DELAYED NEUROPATHY IS ALSO POSSIBLE. **CHRONIC EXPOSURE-** REPEATED OR PROLONGED EXPOSURE MAY CAUSE EFFECTS AS DESCRIBED IN ACUTE EXPOSURE. SOME ORGANOPHOSPHATES MAY CAUSE SENSITIZATION.

FIRST AID- REMOVE CONTAMINATED CLOTHING IMMEDIATELY. WASH CONTAMINATED AREAS WITH SOAP AND WATER FOLLOWED BY ALCOHOL (ARENA, POISONING, 4TH ED.). EMERGENCY PERSONNEL SHOULD WEAR GLOVES AND AVOID CONTAMINATION. TREAT RESPIRATORY DIFFICULTY WITH ARTIFICIAL RESPIRATION. GET MEDICAL ATTENTION IMMEDIATELY.

EYE CONTACT: O,O,O',O'-TETRAPROPYL DITHIOPYROPHOSPHATE: ANIMAL STUDIES INDICATED THAT EYE EXPOSURE TO 13 TO 14% EMULSIFIABLE CONCENTRATE FORMULATIONS MAY CAUSE IRREVERSIBLE CORNEAL OPACITY AND SEVERE EYE IRRITATION. SEE INFORMATION ON ORGANOPHOSPHATES.

ORGANOPHOSPHATES: CHOLINESTERASE INHIBITOR. **ACUTE EXPOSURE-** DIRECT CONTACT MAY CAUSE PAIN, HYPEREMIA, LACRIMATION, TWITCHING OF THE EYELIDS, MIOSIS, AND CILIARY MUSCLE SPASM WITH LOSS OF ACCOMODATION, BLURRED OR DIMMED VISION AND BROWACHE. SOMETIMES MYDRIASIS MAY OCCUR INSTEAD OF MIOSIS. WITH SUFFICIENT EXPOSURE, OTHER SYMPTOMS OF CHOLINESTERASE INHIBITION AS DESCRIBED IN ACUTE INHALATION MAY OCCUR. **CHRONIC EXPOSURE-** REPEATED OR PROLONGED EXPOSURE MAY CAUSE EFFECTS AS DESCRIBED IN ACUTE EXPOSURE. SOME COMPOUNDS HAVE CAUSED TOXIC EFFECTS ON THE CRYSTALLINE LENS, CONJUNCTIVAL THICKENING AND OBSTRUCTION OF THE NASOLACRIMAL CANALS WHEN USED AS MIOTIC EYEDROPS.

FIRST AID- IRRIGATE EYES WITH WATER OR SALINE SOLUTION. IF SYMPTOMS OF POISONING OCCUR, TREAT RESPIRATORY DIFFICULTY WITH ARTIFICIAL RESPIRATION AND OXYGEN. OBSERVE PATIENT FOR AT LEAST 24-36 HOURS (GOSSELIN, CLINICAL TOXICOLOGY OF COMMERCIAL PRODUCTS, 5TH ED.). GET MEDICAL ATTENTION IMMEDIATELY. OXYGEN SHOULD BE ADMINISTERED BY QUALIFIED MEDICAL PERSONNEL.

INGESTION: O,O,O',O'-TETRAPROPYL DITHIOPYROPHOSPHATE: TOXIC. SEE INFORMATION ON ORGANOPHOSPHATES.

ORGANOPHOSPHATES: CHOLINESTERASE INHIBITOR. **ACUTE EXPOSURE-** WHEN INGESTED, THE FIRST EFFECTS MAY BE NAUSEA, VOMITING, ANOREXIA, ABDOMINAL CRAMPS AND DIARRHEA. GASTROINTESTINAL ABSORPTION MAY CAUSE SYMPTOMS OF CHOLINESTERASE INHIBITION AS DESCRIBED IN ACUTE INHALATION. SYMPTOMS MAY BEGIN WITHIN MINUTES OR BE DELAYED FOR HOURS. DELAYED EFFECTS INCLUDING NEUROPATHY MAY ALSO OCCUR. **CHRONIC EXPOSURE-** REPEATED INGESTION MAY CAUSE EFFECTS AS DESCRIBED IN ACUTE EXPOSURE.

FIRST AID- IF PERSON IS ALERT AND RESPIRATION IS NOT DEPRESSED, GIVE SYRUP OF IPECAC FOLLOWED BY WATER (IF VOMITING OCCURS, KEEP HEAD BELOW HIPS TO PREVENT ASPIRATION). IF CONSCIOUSNESS LEVEL DECLINES OR VOMITING HAS NOT OCCURRED IN 15 MINUTES EMPTY STOMACH BY GASTRIC LAVAGE WITH THE AID OF CUFFED ENDOTRACHEAL TUBE USING ISOTONIC SALINE OR 5% SODIUM BICARBONATE FOLLOW WITH ACTIVATED CHARCOAL. ESTABLISH AND MAINTAIN AIRWAY. TREAT RESPIRATORY DIFFICULTY WITH ARTIFICIAL RESPIRATION AND OXYGEN. DO NOT GIVE MORPHINE, AMINOPHYLLINE, PHENOTHIAZINES, RESERPINE, FUROSEMIDE, OR ETHACRYNIC ACID (MORGAN, RECOGNITION AND MANAGEMENT OF PESTICIDE POISONINGS, 3RD ED.). TREAT SYMPTOMATICALLY AND SUPPORTIVELY. ADMINISTRATION OF OXYGEN AND LAVAGE MUST BE PERFORMED BY QUALIFIED MEDICAL PERSONNEL. GET MEDICAL ATTENTION IMMEDIATELY.

ANTIDOTE: THE FOLLOWING ANTIDOTE(S) HAVE BEEN RECOMMENDED. HOWEVER, THE DECISION AS TO WHETHER THE SEVERITY OF POISONING REQUIRES ADMINISTRATION OF ANY ANTIDOTE AND ACTUAL DOSE REQUIRED SHOULD BE MADE BY QUALIFIED MEDICAL PERSONNEL.

FOR CHOLINESTERASE INHIBITORS: ESTABLISH CLEAR AIRWAY AND TISSUE OXYGENATION BY ASPIRATION OF SECRETIONS, AND IF NECESSARY, BY ASSISTED PULMONARY VENTILATION WITH OXYGEN. IMPROVE TISSUE OXYGENATION AS MUCH AS POSSIBLE BEFORE ADMINISTERING ATROPINE TO MINIMIZE THE RISK OF VENTRICULAR FIBRILLATION. ADMINISTER ATROPINE SULFATE INTRAVENOUSLY, OR INTRAMUSCULARLY IF IV INJECTION IS NOT POSSIBLE. IN MODERATELY SEVERE POISONING ADMINISTER ATROPINE SULFATE, 0.4-2.0 MG REPEATED EVERY 15 MINUTES UNTIL ATROPINIZATION IS ACHIEVED (TACHYCARDIA, FLUSHING, DRY MOUTH, MYDRIASIS). MAINTAIN ATROPINIZATION BY REPEATED DOSES FOR 2-12 HOURS, OR LONGER, DEPENDING ON THE SEVERITY OF POISONING. THE APPEARANCE OF RALES IN THE LUNG BASES, MIOSIS, SALIVATION, NAUSEA, BRADYCARDIA, ARE ALL INDICATIONS OF INADEQUATE ATROPINIZATION.

SEVERELY POISONED INDIVIDUALS MAY EXHIBIT REMARKABLE TOLERANCE TO ATROPINE; TWO OR MORE TIMES THE DOSAGES SUGGESTED ABOVE MAY BE NEEDED. PERSONS NOT POISONED OR ONLY SLIGHTLY POISONED, HOWEVER, MAY DEVELOP SIGNS OF ATROPINE TOXICITY FROM SUCH LARGE DOSAGES: FEVER, MUSCLE FIBRILLATIONS, AND DELIRIUM ARE THE MAIN SIGNS OF ATROPINE TOXICITY. IF THESE SIGNS APPEAR WHILE THE PATIENT IS FULLY ATROPINIZED, ATROPINE ADMINISTRATION SHOULD BE DISCONTINUED, AT LEAST TEMPORARILY. OBSERVE TREATED PATIENTS CLOSELY AT LEAST 24 HOURS TO INSURE THAT SYMPTOMS (POSSIBLY PULMONARY EDEMA) DO NOT RECUR AS ATROPINIZATION WEARS OFF. IN VERY SEVERE POISONINGS, METABOLIC DISPOSITION OF TOXICANT MAY REQUIRE SEVERAL HOURS OR DAYS DURING WHICH ATROPINIZATION MUST BE MAINTAINED. MARKEDLY LOWER LEVELS OF URINARY METABOLITES INDICATE THAT ATROPINE DOSAGE CAN BE TAPERED OFF. AS DOSAGE IS REDUCED, CHECK THE LUNG BASES FREQUENTLY FOR RALES. IF RALES ARE HEARD OR OTHER SYMPTOMS RETURN, RE-ESTABLISH ATROPINIZATION PROMPTLY (MORGAN, RECOGNITION AND MANAGEMENT OF PESTICIDE POISONINGS, 3RD ED.). ADMINISTRATION OF ANTIDOTE MUST BE PERFORMED BY QUALIFIED MEDICAL PERSONNEL.

IN CASES OF SEVERE POISONING BY ORGANOPHOSPHATE PESTICIDES IN WHICH RESPIRATORY DEPRESSION, MUSCLE WEAKNESS AND TWITCHINGS ARE SEVERE, GIVE PRALIDOXIME (PROTOPAM-AYERST, 2-PAM), 1.0 GRAM INTRAVENOUSLY AT NO MORE THAN 0.5 GRAM PER MINUTE. DOSAGE OF PRALIDOXIME MAY BE REPEATED IN 1-2 HOURS, THEN AT 10-12 HOUR INTERVALS IF NEEDED. IN VERY SEVERE POISONINGS, DOSAGE RATES MAY BE DOUBLED. TREATMENT WITH PRALIDOXIME WILL BE MOST EFFECTIVE IF GIVEN WITHIN THIRTY-SIX HOURS AFTER POISONING (MORGAN, RECOGNITION AND MANAGEMENT OF PESTICIDE POISONINGS, 3RD ED.). ANTIDOTE SHOULD BE ADMINISTERED BY QUALIFIED MEDICAL PERSONNEL.

REACTIVITY

REACTIVITY: STABLE UNDER NORMAL TEMPERATURES AND PRESSURES.

INCOMPATIBILITIES: O,O,O',O'-TETRAPROPYL DITHIOPYROPHOSPHATE: OXIDIZERS (STRONG): FIRE AND EXPLOSION HAZARD. STEEL: MAY CORRODE.

DECOMPOSITION: THERMAL DECOMPOSITION PRODUCTS MAY INCLUDE TOXIC OXIDES OF CARBON, SULFUR, AND PHOSPHORUS.

POLYMERIZATION: HAZARDOUS POLYMERIZATION HAS NOT BEEN REPORTED TO OCCUR UNDER NORMAL TEMPERATURES AND PRESSURES.

STORAGE AND DISPOSAL

OBSERVE ALL FEDERAL, STATE AND LOCAL REGULATIONS WHEN STORING OR DISPOSING OF THIS SUBSTANCE. FOR ASSISTANCE, CONTACT THE DISTRICT DIRECTOR OF THE ENVIRONMENTAL PROTECTION AGENCY.

****STORAGE****

STORE IN ACCORDANCE WITH 40 CFR 165 RECOMMENDED PROCEDURES FOR THE DISPOSAL AND STORAGE OF PESTICIDES AND PESTICIDE CONTAINERS.
STORE AWAY FROM INCOMPATIBLE SUBSTANCES.
DO NOT STORE IN UNLINED STEEL CONTAINERS.

****DISPOSAL****

DISPOSAL MUST BE IN ACCORDANCE WITH 40 CFR 165 RECOMMENDED PROCEDURES FOR THE DISPOSAL AND STORAGE OF PESTICIDES AND PESTICIDE CONTAINERS.

CONDITIONS TO AVOID

MAY BURN BUT DOES NOT IGNITE READILY. CONTAINERS MAY EXPLODE IN HEAT OF FIRE.

SPILL AND LEAK PROCEDURES

OCCUPATIONAL SPILL: DO NOT TOUCH SPILLED MATERIAL. STOP LEAK IF YOU CAN DO IT WITHOUT RISK. USE WATER SPRAY TO REDUCE VAPORS. FOR SMALL SPILLS, TAKE UP WITH SAND OR OTHER ABSORBENT MATERIAL AND PLACE INTO CONTAINERS FOR LATER DISPOSAL. FOR SMALL DRY SPILLS, WITH A CLEAN SHOVEL PLACE MATERIAL INTO CLEAN, DRY CONTAINERS AND COVER. MOVE CONTAINERS FROM SPILL AREA. FOR LARGER SPILLS, DIKE FAR AHEAD OF SPILL FOR LATER DISPOSAL. KEEP UNNECESSARY PEOPLE AWAY. ISOLATE HAZARD AREA AND DENY ENTRY. VENTILATE CLOSED SPACES BEFORE ENTERING.

PROTECTIVE EQUIPMENT

VENTILATION: PROVIDE LOCAL EXHAUST OR PROCESS ENCLOSURE VENTILATION SYSTEM.

RESPIRATOR: THE FOLLOWING RESPIRATORS ARE RECOMMENDED BASED ON INFORMATION FOUND IN THE PHYSICAL DATA, TOXICITY AND HEALTH EFFECTS SECTIONS. THEY ARE RANKED IN ORDER FROM MINIMUM TO MAXIMUM RESPIRATORY PROTECTION. THE SPECIFIC RESPIRATOR SELECTED MUST BE BASED ON CONTAMINATION LEVELS FOUND IN THE WORK PLACE, MUST NOT EXCEED THE WORKING LIMITS OF THE RESPIRATOR AND BE JOINTLY APPROVED BY THE NATIONAL INSTITUTE FOR OCCUPATIONAL SAFETY AND HEALTH AND THE MINE SAFETY AND HEALTH ADMINISTRATION (NIOSH-MSHA).

TYPE 'C' SUPPLIED-AIR RESPIRATOR WITH A FULL FACEPIECE OPERATED IN PRESSURE-DEMAND OR OTHER POSITIVE PRESSURE MODE OR WITH A FULL FACEPIECE, HELMET OR HOOD OPERATED IN CONTINOUS-FLOW MODE.

SELF-CONTAINED BREATHING APPARATUS WITH A FULL FACEPIECE OPERATED IN PRESSURE-DEMAND OR OTHER POSITIVE PRESSURE MODE.

FOR FIREFIGHTING AND OTHER IMMEDIATELY DANGEROUS TO LIFE OR HEALTH CONDITIONS:

SELF-CONTAINED BREATHING APPARATUS WITH FULL FACEPIECE OPERATED IN PRESSURE-DEMAND OR OTHER POSITIVE PRESSURE MODE.

SUPPLIED-AIR RESPIRATOR WITH FULL FACEPIECE AND OPERATED IN PRESSURE-DEMAND OR OTHER POSITIVE PRESSURE MODE IN COMBINATION WITH AN AUXILIARY SELF-CONTAINED BREATHING APPARATUS OPERATED IN PRESSURE-DEMAND OR OTHER POSITIVE PRESSURE MODE.

CLOTHING: EMPLOYEE MUST WEAR APPROPRIATE PROTECTIVE (IMPERVIOUS) CLOTHING AND EQUIPMENT TO PREVENT REPEATED OR PROLONGED SKIN CONTACT WITH THIS SUBSTANCE.

GLOVES: EMPLOYEE MUST WEAR APPROPRIATE PROTECTIVE GLOVES TO PREVENT CONTACT WITH THIS SUBSTANCE.

EYE PROTECTION: EMPLOYEE MUST WEAR SPLASH-PROOF OR DUST-RESISTANT SAFETY GOGGLES TO PREVENT EYE CONTACT WITH THIS SUBSTANCE.

EMERGENCY EYE WASH: WHERE THERE IS ANY POSSIBILITY THAT AN EMPLOYEE'S EYES MAY BE EXPOSED TO THIS SUBSTANCE, THE EMPLOYER SHOULD PROVIDE AN EYE WASH FOUNTAIN WITHIN THE IMMEDIATE WORK AREA FOR EMERGENCY USE.

AUTHORIZED BY- OCCUPATIONAL HEALTH SERVICES, INC.
CREATION DATE: 10/04/89 ***REVISION DATE:*** 05/11/90

MATERIAL SAFETY DATA SHEET

OCCUPATIONAL HEALTH SERVICES, INC.
AGRICULTURE AND PESTICIDE DIVISION
450 SEVENTH AVENUE, SUITE 2407
NEW YORK, NEW YORK 10123
1-800-445-MSDS OR (212) 967-1100

EMERGENCY CONTACT:
JOHN S. BRANSFORD, JR. (615) 292-1180

SUBSTANCE IDENTIFICATION

CAS-NUMBER 118-75-2

SUBSTANCE: **CHLORANIL**

TRADE NAMES/SYNONYMS: 2,5-CYCLOHEXADIENE-1,4-DIONE, 2,3,5,6-TETRACHLORO-; 2,3,5,6-TETRACHLORO-2,5-CYCLOHEXADIENE-1,4-DIONE; P-BENZOQUINONE, 2,3,5,6-TETRACHLORO-; 2,3,5,6-TETRACHLORO-P-BENZOQUINONE; P-CHLORANIL; ALPHA-CHLORANIL; PSORISAN; QUINONE TETRACHLORIDE; RERANIL; SPERGON; TETRACHLOROBENZOQUINONE; TETRACHLORO-P-BENZOQUINONE; TETRACHLORO-1,4-BENZOQUINONE; 2,3,5,6-TETRACHLOROBENZOQUINONE; TETRACHLOROPARABENZOQUINONE; TETRACHLOROQUINONE; TETRACHLORO-P-QUINONE; 2,3,5,6-TETRACHLOROQUINONE; VULKLOR; C6CL4O2; PST72136

CHEMICAL FAMILY: QUINONE
HALOGEN

MOLECULAR FORMULA: O-C6-CL4-O

MOLECULAR WEIGHT: 245.88

CERCLA RATINGS (SCALE 0-3): HEALTH=3 FIRE=1 REACTIVITY=0 PERSISTENCE=3

NFPA RATINGS (SCALE 0-4): HEALTH=U FIRE=1 REACTIVITY=0

COMPONENTS AND CONTAMINANTS

COMPONENT: CHLORANIL ***PERCENT:*** 100.0
CAS# 118-75-2

OTHER CONTAMINANTS: NONE

EXPOSURE LIMITS: NO OCCUPATIONAL EXPOSURE LIMITS ESTABLISHED BY OSHA, ACGIH, OR NIOSH.

PHYSICAL DATA

DESCRIPTION: GOLDEN-YELLOW MONOCLINIC PRISMS OR PLATES.

MELTING POINT: 554 F (290 C) (IN VACUO) (SUBLIMES) ***SPECIFIC GRAVITY:*** 1.97

SOLUBILITY IN WATER: INSOLUBLE

SOLVENT SOLUBILITY: SOLUBLE IN ETHER; SPARINGLY SOLUBLE IN CHLOROFORM, CARBON TETRACHLORIDE, CARBON DISULFIDE; PRACTICALLY INSOLUBLE IN COLD PETROLEUM ETHER AND COLD ALCOHOL.

FIRE AND EXPLOSION DATA

FIRE AND EXPLOSION HAZARD: SLIGHT FIRE HAZARD WHEN EXPOSED TO HEAT OR FLAME.

FIREFIGHTING MEDIA: DRY CHEMICAL, CARBON DIOXIDE, HALON, WATER SPRAY OR STANDARD FOAM (1987 EMERGENCY RESPONSE GUIDEBOOK, DOT P 5800.4). FOR LARGER FIRES, USE WATER SPRAY, FOG OR STANDARD FOAM (1987 EMERGENCY RESPONSE GUIDEBOOK, DOT P 5800.4).

FIREFIGHTING: MOVE CONTAINER FROM FIRE AREA IF POSSIBLE. DO NOT SCATTER SPILLED MATERIAL WITH HIGH PRESSURE WATER STREAMS. DIKE FIRE CONTROL WATER FOR LATER DISPOSAL (1987 EMERGENCY RESPONSE GUIDEBOOK, DOT P 5800.4, GUIDE PAGE 31).
USE AGENTS SUITABLE FOR TYPE OF SURROUNDING FIRE. AVOID BREATHING HAZARDOUS VAPORS, KEEP UPWIND.

TOXICITY

CHLORANIL: TOXICITY DATA: 4000 MG/KG ORAL-RAT LD50; 500 MG/KG INTRAPERITONEAL-RAT LDLO; TUMORIGENIC DATA (RTECS). CARCINOGEN STATUS: NONE. LOCAL EFFECTS: IRRITANT- INHALATION, SKIN, EYE. ACUTE TOXICITY LEVEL: MODERATELY TOXIC BY INGESTION. TARGET EFFECTS: CENTRAL NERVOUS SYSTEM DEPRESSANT.

HEALTH EFFECTS AND FIRST AID

INHALATION: CHLORANIL: IRRITANT. **ACUTE EXPOSURE-** MAY CAUSE MUCOUS MEMBRANE IRRITATION. **CHRONIC EXPOSURE-** NO DATA AVAILABLE.

FIRST AID- REMOVE FROM EXPOSURE AREA TO FRESH AIR IMMEDIATELY. IF BREATHING HAS STOPPED, PERFORM ARTIFICIAL RESPIRATION. KEEP PERSON WARM AND AT REST. TREAT SYMPTOMATICALLY AND SUPPORTIVELY. GET MEDICAL ATTENTION IMMEDIATELY.

SKIN CONTACT: CHLORANIL: IRRITANT. **ACUTE EXPOSURE-** CONTACT MAY CAUSE IRRITATION. **CHRONIC EXPOSURE-** REPEATED OR PROLONGED CONTACT WITH IRRITANTS MAY CAUSE DERMATITIS.

FIRST AID- REMOVE CONTAMINATED CLOTHING AND SHOES IMMEDIATELY. WASH AFFECTED AREA WITH SOAP OR MILD DETERGENT AND LARGE AMOUNTS OF WATER UNTIL NO EVIDENCE OF CHEMICAL REMAINS (APPROXIMATELY 15-20 MINUTES). GET MEDICAL ATTENTION IMMEDIATELY.

EYE CONTACT: CHLORANIL: IRRITANT. **ACUTE EXPOSURE-** CONTACT MAY CAUSE IRRITATION. DUST APPLIED TO RABBIT EYES HAS BEEN REPORTED TO CAUSE "CORNEAL NECROSIS" THOUGH THE SEVERITY WAS NOT REPORTED. **CHRONIC EXPOSURE-** REPEATED OR PROLONGED CONTACT WITH IRRITANTS MAY CAUSE CONJUNCTIVITIS.

FIRST AID- WASH EYES IMMEDIATELY WITH LARGE AMOUNTS OF WATER OR NORMAL SALINE, OCCASIONALLY LIFTING UPPER AND LOWER LIDS, UNTIL NO EVIDENCE OF CHEMICAL REMAINS (APPROXIMATELY 15-20 MINUTES). GET MEDICAL ATTENTION IMMEDIATELY.

INGESTION: CHLORANIL: NARCOTIC. **ACUTE EXPOSURE-** VERY HIGH DOSES MAY PRODUCE WATERY DIARRHEA, CENTRAL NERVOUS SYSTEM DEPRESSION, COMA AND DEATH. **CHRONIC EXPOSURE-** AS EVALUATED BY RTECS, ADMINISTRATION TO MICE BY INGESTION RESULTED IN A STATISTICALLY SIGNIFICANT INCREASE IN THE INCIDENCE OF NEOPLASTIC TUMORS OF THE LIVER.

FIRST AID- TREAT SYMPTOMATICALLY AND SUPPORTIVELY. GET MEDICAL ATTENTION IMMEDIATELY. IF VOMITING OCCURS, KEEP HEAD LOWER THAN HIPS TO PREVENT ASPIRATION.

ANTIDOTE: NO SPECIFIC ANTIDOTE. TREAT SYMPTOMATICALLY AND SUPPORTIVELY.

REACTIVITY

REACTIVITY: STABLE UNDER NORMAL TEMPERATURES AND PRESSURES.

INCOMPATIBILITIES: CHLORANIL: OXIDIZERS (STRONG): FIRE AND EXPLOSION HAZARD.

DECOMPOSITION: THERMAL DECOMPOSITION PRODUCTS MAY INCLUDE TOXIC AND CORROSIVE FUMES OF CHLORIDES.

POLYMERIZATION: HAZARDOUS POLYMERIZATION HAS NOT BEEN REPORTED TO OCCUR UNDER NORMAL TEMPERATURES AND PRESSURES.

STORAGE AND DISPOSAL

OBSERVE ALL FEDERAL, STATE AND LOCAL REGULATIONS WHEN STORING OR DISPOSING OF THIS SUBSTANCE. FOR ASSISTANCE, CONTACT THE DISTRICT DIRECTOR OF THE ENVIRONMENTAL PROTECTION AGENCY.

****STORAGE****

STORE IN ACCORDANCE WITH 40 CFR 165 RECOMMENDED PROCEDURES FOR THE DISPOSAL AND STORAGE OF PESTICIDES AND PESTICIDE CONTAINERS.
STORE AWAY FROM INCOMPATIBLE SUBSTANCES.

****DISPOSAL****

DISPOSAL MUST BE IN ACCORDANCE WITH 40 CFR 165 RECOMMENDED PROCEDURES FOR THE DISPOSAL AND STORAGE OF PESTICIDES AND PESTICIDE CONTAINERS.

CONDITIONS TO AVOID

MAY BURN BUT DOES NOT IGNITE READILY. AVOID CONTACT WITH STRONG OXIDIZERS, EXCESSIVE HEAT, SPARKS, OR OPEN FLAME.

SPILL AND LEAK PROCEDURES

OCCUPATIONAL SPILL: STOP LEAK IF YOU CAN DO IT WITHOUT RISK. FOR SMALL SPILLS, TAKE UP WITH SAND OR OTHER ABSORBENT MATERIAL AND PLACE INTO CLEAN, DRY CONTAINERS FOR LATER DISPOSAL. KEEP UNNECESSARY PEOPLE AWAY. ISOLATE HAZARD AREA AND DENY ENTRY.

PROTECTIVE EQUIPMENT

VENTILATION: PROVIDE LOCAL EXHAUST OR PROCESS ENCLOSURE VENTILATION SYSTEM.

RESPIRATOR: THE FOLLOWING RESPIRATORS ARE RECOMMENDED BASED ON INFORMATION FOUND IN THE PHYSICAL DATA, TOXICITY AND HEALTH EFFECTS SECTIONS. THEY ARE RANKED IN ORDER FROM MINIMUM TO MAXIMUM RESPIRATORY PROTECTION. THE SPECIFIC RESPIRATOR SELECTED MUST BE BASED ON CONTAMINATION LEVELS FOUND IN THE WORK PLACE, MUST NOT EXCEED THE WORKING LIMITS OF THE RESPIRATOR AND BE JOINTLY APPROVED BY THE NATIONAL INSTITUTE FOR OCCUPATIONAL SAFETY AND HEALTH AND THE MINE SAFETY AND HEALTH ADMINISTRATION (NIOSH-MSHA).
CHEMICAL CARTRIDGE RESPIRATOR WITH AN ORGANIC VAPOR CARTRIDGE(S) WITH A FULL FACEPIECE AND ORGANIC VAPOR CARTRIDGE(S) IN COMBINATION WITH A DUST AND MIST FILTER.
POWERED AIR-PURIFYING RESPIRATOR WITH A TIGHT-FITTING FACEPIECE AND ORGANIC VAPOR CARTRIDGE(S) IN COMBINATION WITH A HIGH-EFFICIENCY PARTICULATE FILTER.
TYPE 'C' SUPPLIED-AIR RESPIRATOR WITH A FULL FACEPIECE OPERATED IN A PRESSURE-DEMAND OR OTHER POSITIVE PRESSURE MODE.
SELF-CONTAINED BREATHING APPARATUS WITH A FULL FACEPIECE OPERATED IN PRESSURE-DEMAND OR OTHER POSITIVE PRESSURE MODE.
FOR FIREFIGHTING AND OTHER IMMEDIATELY DANGEROUS TO LIFE OR HEALTH CONDITIONS: SELF-CONTAINED BREATHING APPARATUS WITH FULL FACEPIECE OPERATED IN PRESSURE-DEMAND OR OTHER POSITIVE PRESSURE MODE.
SUPPLIED-AIR RESPIRATOR WITH FULL FACEPIECE AND OPERATED IN PRESSURE-DEMAND OR OTHER POSITIVE PRESSURE MODE IN COMBINATION WITH AN AUXILIARY SELF-CONTAINED BREATHING APPARATUS OPERATED IN PRESSURE-DEMAND OR OTHER POSITIVE PRESSURE MODE.

CLOTHING: EMPLOYEE MUST WEAR APPROPRIATE PROTECTIVE (IMPERVIOUS) CLOTHING AND EQUIPMENT TO PREVENT REPEATED OR PROLONGED SKIN CONTACT WITH THIS SUBSTANCE.

GLOVES: EMPLOYEE MUST WEAR APPROPRIATE PROTECTIVE GLOVES TO PREVENT CONTACT WITH THIS SUBSTANCE.

EYE PROTECTION: EMPLOYEE MUST WEAR SPLASH-PROOF OR DUST-RESISTANT SAFETY GOGGLES TO PREVENT EYE CONTACT WITH THIS SUBSTANCE.
EMERGENCY EYE WASH: WHERE THERE IS ANY POSSIBILITY THAT AN EMPLOYEE'S EYES MAY BE EXPOSED TO THIS SUBSTANCE, THE EMPLOYER SHOULD PROVIDE AN EYE WASH FOUNTAIN WITHIN THE IMMEDIATE WORK AREA FOR EMERGENCY USE.

AUTHORIZED BY- OCCUPATIONAL HEALTH SERVICES, INC.
CREATION DATE: 10/04/89 ***REVISION DATE:*** 05/07/90

MATERIAL SAFETY DATA SHEET

OCCUPATIONAL HEALTH SERVICES, INC.
AGRICULTURE AND PESTICIDE DIVISION
450 SEVENTH AVENUE, SUITE 2407
NEW YORK, NEW YORK 10123
1-800-445-MSDS OR (212) 967-1100

EMERGENCY CONTACT:
JOHN S. BRANSFORD, JR. (615) 292-1180

SUBSTANCE IDENTIFICATION

CAS-NUMBER 580-48-3

SUBSTANCE: **CHLORAZINE**

TRADE NAMES/SYNONYMS: 1,3,5-TRIAZINE-2,4-DIAMINE, 6-CHLORO-N,N,N',N'-TETRAETHYL-; S-TRIAZINE, 2-CHLORO-4,6-BIS(DIETHYLAMINO)-; 6-CHLORO-N,N,N',N'-TETRAETHYL-1,3,5-TRIAZINE-2,4-DIAMINE; 2-CHLORO-4,6-BIS(DIETHYLAMINO)-S-TRIAZINE; 2-CHLORO-4,6-BIS(DIETHYLAMINO)-1,3,5-

TRIAZINE; 2,4-BIS(DIETHYLAMINO)-6-CHLORO-S-TRIAZINE; CHLORAZIN; G 25,804; C11H20CLN5; PST72143

CHEMICAL FAMILY: S-TRIAZINE

MOLECULAR FORMULA: ((C2-H5)2-N)2-C3-N3-CL

MOLECULAR WEIGHT: 257.77

CERCLA RATINGS (SCALE 0-3): HEALTH=2 FIRE=1 REACTIVITY=0 PERSISTENCE=3

NFPA RATINGS (SCALE 0-4): HEALTH=2 FIRE=1 REACTIVITY=0

COMPONENTS AND CONTAMINANTS

COMPONENT: CHLORAZINE ***PERCENT:*** 100.0

CAS# 580-48-3

OTHER CONTAMINANTS: NONE

EXPOSURE LIMITS: NO OCCUPATIONAL EXPOSURE LIMITS ESTABLISHED BY OSHA, ACGIH, OR NIOSH.

PHYSICAL DATA

DESCRIPTION: CRYSTALS OR OILY LIQUID.

BOILING POINT: 309-313 F (154-156 C) @ 9 MMHG ***MELTING POINT:*** 81 F (27 C)

SPECIFIC GRAVITY: 1.0956 ***SOLUBILITY IN WATER:*** INSOLUBLE

SOLVENT SOLUBILITY: SOLUBLE IN BENZENE, CHLOROFORM, LIGROIN, HYDROCARBONS, ALCOHOLS, AND KETONES.

FIRE AND EXPLOSION DATA

FIRE AND EXPLOSION HAZARD: SLIGHT FIRE HAZARD WHEN EXPOSED TO HEAT OR FLAME.

FIREFIGHTING MEDIA: DRY CHEMICAL, CARBON DIOXIDE, HALON, WATER SPRAY OR STANDARD FOAM (1987 EMERGENCY RESPONSE GUIDEBOOK, DOT P 5800.4). FOR LARGER FIRES, USE WATER SPRAY, FOG OR STANDARD FOAM (1987 EMERGENCY RESPONSE GUIDEBOOK, DOT P 5800.4).

FIREFIGHTING: MOVE CONTAINERS FROM FIRE AREA IF POSSIBLE. FIGHT FIRE FROM MAXIMUM DISTANCE. STAY AWAY FROM STORAGE TANK ENDS. DIKE FIRE CONTROL WATER FOR LATER DISPOSAL. DO NOT SCATTER MATERIAL (1987 EMERGENCY RESPONSE GUIDEBOOK, DOT P 5800.4, GUIDE PAGE 55). EXTINGUISH FIRE ONLY IF FLOW CAN BE STOPPED. APPLY WATER FROM AS FAR A DISTANCE AS POSSIBLE IN FLOODING QUANTITIES AS A FOG AS SOLID STREAMS MAY BE INEFFECTIVE. AVOID CONTAMINATING WATER SOURCES AND SEWERS. KEEP UPWIND; DO NOT BREATH FUMES.

TOXICITY

CHLORAZINE: TOXICITY DATA: 850 MG/KG ORAL-RAT LD50; 743 MG/KG ORAL-MOUSE LD50; 3500 MG/KG UNREPORTED-RAT LD50. CARCINOGEN STATUS: NONE. ACUTE TOXICITY DATA: MODERATELY TOXIC BY INGESTION. TARGET EFFECTS: NO DATA AVAILABLE.

HEALTH EFFECTS AND FIRST AID

INHALATION: CHLORAZINE: **ACUTE EXPOSURE-** NO DEATHS WERE PRODUCED AMONG RATS EXPOSED TO 800-1100 MG/M3/4 HOURS. SOME TRIAZINES ARE MILDLY IRRITATING TO THE UPPER RESPIRATORY TRACT. **CHRONIC EXPOSURE-** NO DATA AVAILABLE.

FIRST AID- REMOVE FROM EXPOSURE AREA TO FRESH AIR IMMEDIATELY. IF BREATHING HAS STOPPED, PERFORM ARTIFICIAL RESPIRATION. KEEP PERSON WARM AND AT REST. TREAT SYMPTOMATICALLY AND SUPPORTIVELY. GET MEDICAL ATTENTION IMMEDIATELY.

SKIN CONTACT: CHLORAZINE: **ACUTE EXPOSURE-** SOME TRIAZINES ARE MILDLY IRRITATING TO THE SKIN. **CHRONIC EXPOSURE-** NO DATA AVAILABLE.

FIRST AID- REMOVE CONTAMINATED CLOTHING AND SHOES IMMEDIATELY. WASH AFFECTED AREA WITH SOAP OR MILD DETERGENT AND LARGE AMOUNTS OF WATER UNTIL NO EVIDENCE OF CHEMICAL REMAINS (APPROXIMATELY 15-20 MINUTES). GET MEDICAL ATTENTION IMMEDIATELY.

EYE CONTACT: CHLORAZINE: **ACUTE EXPOSURE-** SOME TRIAZINES ARE MILDLY IRRITATING TO THE EYES. **CHRONIC EXPOSURE-** NO DATA AVAILABLE.

FIRST AID- WASH EYES IMMEDIATELY WITH LARGE AMOUNTS OF WATER OR NORMAL SALINE, OCCASIONALLY LIFTING UPPER AND LOWER LIDS, UNTIL NO EVIDENCE OF CHEMICAL REMAINS (APPROXIMATELY 15-20 MINUTES). GET MEDICAL ATTENTION IMMEDIATELY.

INGESTION: CHLORAZINE: **ACUTE EXPOSURE-** A LETHAL DOSE IN RATS WAS 850 MG/KG; SYMPTOMS WERE NOT REPORTED. **CHRONIC EXPOSURE-** NO DATA AVAILABLE.

FIRST AID- REMOVE BY GASTRIC LAVAGE AND CATHARSIS. MAINTAIN BLOOD PRESSURE AND AIRWAY. GIVE OXYGEN IF RESPIRATION IS DEPRESSED. DO NOT PERFORM GASTRIC LAVAGE IF VICTIM IS UNCONSCIOUS. GET MEDICAL ATTENTION IMMEDIATELY (DREISBACH, HANDBOOK OF POISONING, 12TH ED.). ADMINISTRATION OF LAVAGE OR OXYGEN SHOULD BE PERFORMED BY QUALIFIED MEDICAL PERSONNEL.

ANTIDOTE: NO SPECIFIC ANTIDOTE. TREAT SYMPTOMATICALLY AND SUPPORTIVELY.

REACTIVITY

REACTIVITY: STABLE UNDER NORMAL TEMPERATURES AND PRESSURES.

INCOMPATIBILITIES: CHLORAZINE: NO DATA AVAILABLE.

DECOMPOSITION: THERMAL DECOMPOSITION PRODUCTS MAY INCLUDE TOXIC OXIDES OF NITROGEN AND CARBON AND TOXIC AND CORROSIVE FUMES OF CHLORIDES.

POLYMERIZATION: HAZARDOUS POLYMERIZATION HAS NOT BEEN REPORTED TO OCCUR UNDER NORMAL TEMPERATURES AND PRESSURES.

STORAGE AND DISPOSAL

OBSERVE ALL FEDERAL, STATE AND LOCAL REGULATIONS WHEN STORING OR DISPOSING OF THIS SUBSTANCE. FOR ASSISTANCE, CONTACT THE DISTRICT DIRECTOR OF THE ENVIRONMENTAL PROTECTION AGENCY.

****STORAGE****

STORE IN ACCORDANCE WITH 40 CFR 165 RECOMMENDED PROCEDURES FOR THE DISPOSAL AND STORAGE OF PESTICIDES AND PESTICIDE CONTAINERS.

****DISPOSAL****

DISPOSAL MUST BE IN ACCORDANCE WITH 40 CFR 165 RECOMMENDED PROCEDURES FOR THE DISPOSAL AND STORAGE OF PESTICIDES AND PESTICIDE CONTAINERS.

CONDITIONS TO AVOID

MAY BURN BUT DOES NOT IGNITE READILY. CONTAINERS MAY EXPLODE IN HEAT OF FIRE.

SPILL AND LEAK PROCEDURES

OCCUPATIONAL SPILL: DO NOT TOUCH SPILLED MATERIAL. STOP LEAK IF YOU CAN DO IT WITHOUT RISK. USE WATER SPRAY TO REDUCE VAPORS. FOR SMALL SPILLS, TAKE UP WITH SAND OR OTHER ABSORBENT MATERIAL AND PLACE INTO CONTAINERS FOR LATER DISPOSAL. FOR SMALL DRY SPILLS, WITH A CLEAN SHOVEL PLACE MATERIAL INTO CLEAN, DRY CONTAINERS AND COVER. MOVE CONTAINERS FROM SPILL AREA. FOR LARGER SPILLS, DIKE FAR AHEAD OF SPILL FOR LATER DISPOSAL. KEEP UNNECESSARY PEOPLE AWAY. ISOLATE HAZARD AREA AND DENY ENTRY. VENTILATE CLOSED SPACES BEFORE ENTERING.

PROTECTIVE EQUIPMENT

VENTILATION: PROVIDE LOCAL EXHAUST OR GENERAL DILUTION VENTILATION SYSTEM.

RESPIRATOR: THE FOLLOWING RESPIRATORS ARE RECOMMENDED BASED ON INFORMATION FOUND IN THE PHYSICAL DATA, TOXICITY AND HEALTH EFFECTS SECTIONS. THEY ARE RANKED IN ORDER FROM MINIMUM TO MAXIMUM RESPIRATORY PROTECTION. THE SPECIFIC RESPIRATOR SELECTED MUST BE BASED ON CONTAMINATION LEVELS FOUND IN THE WORK PLACE, MUST NOT EXCEED THE WORKING LIMITS OF THE RESPIRATOR AND BE JOINTLY APPROVED BY THE NATIONAL INSTITUTE FOR OCCUPATIONAL SAFETY AND HEALTH AND THE MINE SAFETY AND HEALTH ADMINISTRATION (NIOSH-MSHA).

CHEMICAL CARTRIDGE RESPIRATOR WITH AN ORGANIC VAPOR CARTRIDGE(S) WITH A FULL FACEPIECE AND ORGANIC VAPOR CARTRIDGE(S) IN COMBINATION WITH A DUST AND MIST FILTER.

POWERED AIR-PURIFYING RESPIRATOR WITH A TIGHT-FITTING FACEPIECE AND ORGANIC VAPOR CARTRIDGE(S) IN COMBINATION WITH A HIGH-EFFICIENCY PARTICULATE FILTER.

TYPE 'C' SUPPLIED-AIR RESPIRATOR WITH A FULL FACEPIECE OPERATED IN A PRESSURE-DEMAND OR OTHER POSITIVE PRESSURE MODE.

SELF-CONTAINED BREATHING APPARATUS WITH A FULL FACEPIECE OPERATED IN PRESSURE-DEMAND OR OTHER POSITIVE PRESSURE MODE.

FOR FIREFIGHTING AND OTHER IMMEDIATELY DANGEROUS TO LIFE OR HEALTH CONDITIONS:

SELF-CONTAINED BREATHING APPARATUS WITH FULL FACEPIECE OPERATED IN PRESSURE-DEMAND OR OTHER POSITIVE PRESSURE MODE.

SUPPLIED-AIR RESPIRATOR WITH FULL FACEPIECE AND OPERATED IN PRESSURE-DEMAND OR OTHER POSITIVE PRESSURE MODE IN COMBINATION WITH AN AUXILIARY SELF-CONTAINED BREATHING APPARATUS OPERATED IN PRESSURE-DEMAND OR OTHER POSITIVE PRESSURE MODE.

CLOTHING: EMPLOYEE MUST WEAR APPROPRIATE PROTECTIVE (IMPERVIOUS) CLOTHING AND EQUIPMENT TO PREVENT REPEATED OR PROLONGED SKIN CONTACT WITH THIS SUBSTANCE.

GLOVES: EMPLOYEE MUST WEAR APPROPRIATE PROTECTIVE GLOVES TO PREVENT CONTACT WITH THIS SUBSTANCE.

EYE PROTECTION: EMPLOYEE MUST WEAR SPLASH-PROOF OR DUST-RESISTANT SAFETY GOGGLES TO PREVENT EYE CONTACT WITH THIS SUBSTANCE.

EMERGENCY EYE WASH: WHERE THERE IS ANY POSSIBILITY THAT AN EMPLOYEE'S EYES MAY BE EXPOSED TO THIS SUBSTANCE, THE EMPLOYER SHOULD PROVIDE AN EYE WASH FOUNTAIN WITHIN THE IMMEDIATE WORK AREA FOR EMERGENCY USE.

AUTHORIZED BY- OCCUPATIONAL HEALTH SERVICES, INC.
CREATION DATE: 10/04/89 ***REVISION DATE:*** 05/15/90

MATERIAL SAFETY DATA SHEET

OCCUPATIONAL HEALTH SERVICES, INC.
AGRICULTURE AND PESTICIDE DIVISION
450 SEVENTH AVENUE, SUITE 2407
NEW YORK, NEW YORK 10123
1-800-445-MSDS OR (212) 967-1100

EMERGENCY CONTACT:
JOHN S. BRANSFORD, JR. (615) 292-1180

SUBSTANCE IDENTIFICATION

CAS-NUMBER 22936-75-0
SUBSTANCE: **DIMETHAMETRYN**
TRADE NAMES/SYNONYMS: 1,3,5-TRIAZINE-2,4-DIAMINE, N-(1,2-DIMETHYLPROPYL)-N'-ETHYL-6 -(METHYLTHIO)-; S-TRIAZINE, 2-((1,2-DIMETHYLPROPYL)AMINO)-4-(ETHYLAMINO)-6 -(METHYLTHIO)-; N-(1,2-DIMETHYLPROPYL)-N'-ETHYL-6-(METHYLTHIO)-1,3,5-TRIAZINE -2,4-DIAMINE; 2-((1,2-DIMETHYLPROPYL)AMINO)-4-(ETHYLAMINO)-6-(METHYLTHIO)-S-TRIAZINE; 2-(1,2-DIMETHYLPROPYLAMINO)-4-(ETHYLAMINO)-6-(METHYLTHIO)-S-TRIAZINE; 2-(1,2-DIMETHYLPROPYLAMINO)-4-ETHYLAMINO-6-METHYLTHIO-1,3,5-TRIAZINE; C 18898; DIMETHAMETORIN; C11H21N5S; PST72145
CHEMICAL FAMILY: S-TRIAZINE
MOLECULAR FORMULA: C11-H21-N5-S
MOLECULAR WEIGHT: 255.43
CERCLA RATINGS (SCALE 0-3): HEALTH=2 FIRE=1 REACTIVITY=0 PERSISTENCE=2
NFPA RATINGS (SCALE 0-4): HEALTH=2 FIRE=1 REACTIVITY=0

COMPONENTS AND CONTAMINANTS

COMPONENT: DIMETHAMETRYN ***PERCENT:*** 100.0
CAS# 22936-75-0
OTHER CONTAMINANTS: NONE
EXPOSURE LIMITS: NO OCCUPATIONAL EXPOSURE LIMITS ESTABLISHED BY OSHA, ACGIH, OR NIOSH.

PHYSICAL DATA

DESCRIPTION: COLORLESS CRYSTALS.
BOILING POINT: 304-307 F (151-153 C) @ 0.05 MMHG ***MELTING POINT:*** 149 F (65 C)
SPECIFIC GRAVITY: 1.098 ***VAPOR PRESSURE:*** .0000014 MMHG @ 20 C
SOLUBILITY IN WATER: 50 PPM @ 20 C
SOLVENT SOLUBILITY: SOLUBLE IN ACETONE, DICHLOROMETHANE, METHANOL, TOLUENE, OCTAN-1-OL, AND HEXANE

FIRE AND EXPLOSION DATA

FIRE AND EXPLOSION HAZARD: SLIGHT FIRE HAZARD WHEN EXPOSED TO HEAT OR FLAME.
FIREFIGHTING MEDIA: DRY CHEMICAL, CARBON DIOXIDE, HALON, WATER SPRAY OR STANDARD FOAM (1987 EMERGENCY RESPONSE GUIDEBOOK, DOT P 5800.4). FOR LARGER FIRES, USE WATER SPRAY, FOG OR STANDARD FOAM (1987 EMERGENCY RESPONSE GUIDEBOOK, DOT P 5800.4).
FIREFIGHTING: MOVE CONTAINERS FROM FIRE AREA IF POSSIBLE (1987 EMERGENCY RESPONSE GUIDEBOOK, DOT P 5800.4, GUIDE PAGE 53).
EXTINGUISH USING AGENTS SUITABLE FOR SURROUNDING FIRE. USE FLOODING QUANTITIES OF WATER AS A FOG. KEEP MATERIAL OUT OF SEWERS AND WATER SOURCES. DO NOT TOUCH SPILLED MATERIAL. AVOID BREATHING HAZARDOUS FUMES; KEEP UPWIND.

TOXICITY

DIMETHAMETRYN: TOXICITY DATA: 3000 MG/KG ORAL-RAT LD50. CARCINOGEN STATUS: NONE. ACUTE TOXICITY LEVEL: MODERATELY TOXIC BY INGESTION. TARGET EFFECTS: NO DATA AVAILABLE.

HEALTH EFFECTS AND FIRST AID

INHALATION: DIMETHAMETRYN: **ACUTE EXPOSURE-** SOME TRIAZINES ARE MILDLY IRRITATING TO THE UPPER RESPIRATORY TRACT. **CHRONIC EXPOSURE-** NO DATA AVAILABLE.
FIRST AID- REMOVE FROM EXPOSURE AREA TO FRESH AIR IMMEDIATELY. IF BREATHING HAS STOPPED, PERFORM ARTIFICIAL RESPIRATION. KEEP PERSON WARM AND AT REST. TREAT SYMPTOMATICALLY AND SUPPORTIVELY. GET MEDICAL ATTENTION IMMEDIATELY.

SKIN CONTACT: DIMETHAMETRYN: **ACUTE EXPOSURE-** THIS MATERIAL WAS NOT IRRITATING TO RABBIT SKIN. A LETHAL DOSE IN RATS BY DERMAL ABSORPTION WAS GREATER THAN 2150 MG/KG. **CHRONIC EXPOSURE-** NO DATA AVAILABLE.
FIRST AID- REMOVE CONTAMINATED CLOTHING AND SHOES IMMEDIATELY. WASH AFFECTED AREA WITH SOAP OR MILD DETERGENT AND LARGE AMOUNTS OF WATER UNTIL NO EVIDENCE OF CHEMICAL REMAINS (APPROXIMATELY 15-20 MINUTES). GET MEDICAL ATTENTION IMMEDIATELY.

EYE CONTACT: DIMETHAMETRYN: **ACUTE EXPOSURE-** THIS MATERIAL WAS SLIGHTLY IRRITATING TO RABBIT EYES. **CHRONIC EXPOSURE-** NO DATA AVAILABLE.
FIRST AID- WASH EYES IMMEDIATELY WITH LARGE AMOUNTS OF WATER OR NORMAL SALINE, OCCASIONALLY LIFTING UPPER AND LOWER LIDS, UNTIL NO EVIDENCE OF CHEMICAL REMAINS (APPROXIMATELY 15-20 MINUTES). GET MEDICAL ATTENTION IMMEDIATELY.

INGESTION: DIMETHAMETRYN: **ACUTE EXPOSURE-** A LETHAL DOSE IN RATS WAS 3000 MG/KG; SYMPTOMS WERE NOT REPORTED. **CHRONIC EXPOSURE-** NO ADVERSE EFFECTS WERE NOTED IN A 90-DAY STUDY OF RATS FED 27 MG/KG/DAY AND DOGS FED 29 MG/KG/DAY.
FIRST AID- TREAT SYMPTOMATICALLY AND SUPPORTIVELY. GET MEDICAL ATTENTION IMMEDIATELY. IF VOMITING OCCURS, KEEP HEAD LOWER THAN HIPS TO PREVENT ASPIRATION.
ANTIDOTE: NO SPECIFIC ANTIDOTE. TREAT SYMPTOMATICALLY AND SUPPORTIVELY.

REACTIVITY

REACTIVITY: STABLE UNDER NORMAL TEMPERATURES AND PRESSURES.
INCOMPATIBILITIES: DIMETHAMETRYN: NO DATA AVAILABLE.
DECOMPOSITION: THERMAL DECOMPOSITION PRODUCTS MAY INCLUDE TOXIC OXIDES OF CARBON, NITROGEN, AND SULFUR.
POLYMERIZATION: HAZARDOUS POLYMERIZATION HAS NOT BEEN REPORTED TO OCCUR UNDER NORMAL TEMPERATURES AND PRESSURES.

STORAGE AND DISPOSAL

OBSERVE ALL FEDERAL, STATE AND LOCAL REGULATIONS WHEN STORING OR DISPOSING OF THIS SUBSTANCE. FOR ASSISTANCE, CONTACT THE DISTRICT DIRECTOR OF THE ENVIRONMENTAL PROTECTION AGENCY.

****STORAGE****

STORE IN ACCORDANCE WITH 40 CFR 165 RECOMMENDED PROCEDURES FOR THE DISPOSAL AND STORAGE OF PESTICIDES AND PESTICIDE CONTAINERS.

****DISPOSAL****

DISPOSAL MUST BE IN ACCORDANCE WITH 40 CFR 165 RECOMMENDED PROCEDURES FOR THE DISPOSAL AND STORAGE OF PESTICIDES AND PESTICIDE CONTAINERS.

CONDITIONS TO AVOID

MAY BURN BUT DOES NOT IGNITE READILY.

SPILL AND LEAK PROCEDURES

OCCUPATIONAL SPILL: DO NOT TOUCH SPILLED MATERIAL. STOP LEAK IF YOU CAN DO IT WITHOUT RISK. FOR SMALL SPILLS, TAKE UP WITH SAND OR OTHER ABSORBENT MATERIAL AND PLACE INTO CONTAINERS FOR LATER DISPOSAL. FOR SMALL DRY SPILLS, WITH A CLEAN SHOVEL PLACE MATERIAL INTO CLEAN, DRY CONTAINER AND COVER. MOVE CONTAINERS FROM SPILL AREA. FOR LARGER SPILLS, DIKE FAR AHEAD OF SPILL FOR LATER DISPOSAL. KEEP UNNECESSARY PEOPLE AWAY. ISOLATE HAZARD AREA AND DENY ENTRY.

PROTECTIVE EQUIPMENT

VENTILATION: PROVIDE LOCAL EXHAUST OR GENERAL DILUTION VENTILATION SYSTEM.
RESPIRATOR: THE FOLLOWING RESPIRATORS ARE RECOMMENDED BASED ON INFORMATION FOUND IN THE PHYSICAL DATA, TOXICITY AND HEALTH EFFECTS SECTIONS. THEY ARE RANKED IN ORDER FROM MINIMUM TO MAXIMUM RESPIRATORY PROTECTION. THE SPECIFIC RESPIRATOR SELECTED MUST BE BASED ON CONTAMINATION LEVELS FOUND IN THE WORK PLACE, MUST NOT EXCEED THE WORKING LIMITS OF THE RESPIRATOR AND BE JOINTLY APPROVED BY THE NATIONAL INSTITUTE FOR OCCUPATIONAL SAFETY AND HEALTH AND THE MINE SAFETY AND HEALTH ADMINISTRATION (NIOSH-MSHA).
CHEMICAL CARTRIDGE RESPIRATOR WITH AN ORGANIC VAPOR CARTRIDGE(S) IN COMBINATION WITH A DUST AND MIST FILTER.
GAS MASK WITH ORGANIC VAPOR CANISTER (CHIN-STYLE OR FRONT- OR BACK-

MOUNTED CANISTER) WITH A DUST AND MIST FILTER.
GAS MASK WITH ORGANIC VAPOR CANISTER (CHIN-STYLE OR FRONT- OR BACK-MOUNTED CANISTER) WITH A PARTICULATE FILTER.
POWERED AIR-PURIFYING RESPIRATOR WITH A HIGH-EFFICIENCY FILTER.
TYPE 'C' SUPPLIED-AIR RESPIRATOR WITH A FULL FACEPIECE OPERATED IN A PRESSURE-DEMAND OR OTHER POSITIVE PRESSURE MODE.
SELF-CONTAINED BREATHING APPARATUS WITH A FULL FACEPIECE OPERATED IN PRESSURE-DEMAND OR OTHER POSITIVE PRESSURE MODE.
FOR FIREFIGHTING AND OTHER IMMEDIATELY DANGEROUS TO LIFE OR HEALTH CONDITIONS:
SELF-CONTAINED BREATHING APPARATUS WITH FULL FACEPIECE OPERATED IN PRESSURE-DEMAND OR OTHER POSITIVE PRESSURE MODE.
SUPPLIED-AIR RESPIRATOR WITH FULL FACEPIECE AND OPERATED IN PRESSURE-DEMAND OR OTHER POSITIVE PRESSURE MODE IN COMBINATION WITH AN AUXILIARY SELF-CONTAINED BREATHING APPARATUS OPERATED IN PRESSURE-DEMAND OR OTHER POSITIVE PRESSURE MODE.

CLOTHING: EMPLOYEE MUST WEAR APPROPRIATE PROTECTIVE (IMPERVIOUS) CLOTHING AND EQUIPMENT TO PREVENT REPEATED OR PROLONGED SKIN CONTACT WITH THIS SUBSTANCE.

GLOVES: EMPLOYEE MUST WEAR APPROPRIATE PROTECTIVE GLOVES TO PREVENT CONTACT WITH THIS SUBSTANCE.

EYE PROTECTION: EMPLOYEE MUST WEAR SPLASH-PROOF OR DUST-RESISTANT SAFETY GOGGLES TO PREVENT EYE CONTACT WITH THIS SUBSTANCE.
EMERGENCY EYE WASH: WHERE THERE IS ANY POSSIBILITY THAT AN EMPLOYEE'S EYES MAY BE EXPOSED TO THIS SUBSTANCE, THE EMPLOYER SHOULD PROVIDE AN EYE WASH FOUNTAIN WITHIN THE IMMEDIATE WORK AREA FOR EMERGENCY USE.

AUTHORIZED BY- OCCUPATIONAL HEALTH SERVICES, INC.
CREATION DATE: 10/04/89 ***REVISION DATE:*** 05/11/90

MATERIAL SAFETY DATA SHEET

OCCUPATIONAL HEALTH SERVICES, INC.
AGRICULTURE AND PESTICIDE DIVISION
450 SEVENTH AVENUE, SUITE 2407
NEW YORK, NEW YORK 10123
1-800-445-MSDS OR (212) 967-1100

EMERGENCY CONTACT:
JOHN S. BRANSFORD, JR. (615) 292-1180

SUBSTANCE IDENTIFICATION

CAS-NUMBER 25537-26-2

SUBSTANCE: **BUTOXYPROPYL SILVEX**

TRADE NAMES/SYNONYMS: PROPIONIC ACID, 2-(2,4,5-TRICHLOROPHENOXY)-, 3-BUTOXYPROPYL ESTER; 2-(2,4,5-TRICHLOROPHENOXY)PROPIONIC ACID 3-BUTOXYPROPYL ESTER; SILVEX PGBE ESTER; SILVEX PROPYLENE GLYCOL BUTYL ETHER ESTER; PST72194

CHEMICAL FAMILY: ESTER, CARBOXYLIC, AROMATIC HALOGEN

MOLECULAR FORMULA: C16-H21-CL3-O4

CERCLA RATINGS (SCALE 0-3): HEALTH=3 FIRE=U REACTIVITY=0 PERSISTENCE=1

NFPA RATINGS (SCALE 0-4): HEALTH=U FIRE=U REACTIVITY=0

COMPONENTS AND CONTAMINANTS

COMPONENT: BUTOXYPROPYL SILVEX ***PERCENT:*** 100.0
CAS# 25537-26-2

OTHER CONTAMINANTS: NONE

EXPOSURE LIMITS: NO OCCUPATIONAL EXPOSURE LIMITS ESTABLISHED BY OSHA, ACGIH, OR NIOSH.

PHYSICAL DATA

DESCRIPTION: AMBER LIQUID. ***BOILING POINT:*** 621 F (327 C)

SPECIFIC GRAVITY: 1.22 ***VAPOR PRESSURE:*** 54 MMHG @ 229 C

SOLUBILITY IN WATER: INSOLUBLE

SOLVENT SOLUBILITY: SOLUBLE IN OIL.

FIRE AND EXPLOSION DATA

FIRE AND EXPLOSION HAZARD: UNKNOWN FIRE AND EXPLOSION HAZARD.

FLASH POINT: NOT AVAILABLE

FIREFIGHTING MEDIA: DRY CHEMICAL, CARBON DIOXIDE, HALON, WATER SPRAY OR STANDARD FOAM (1987 EMERGENCY RESPONSE GUIDEBOOK, DOT P 5800.4).
FOR LARGER FIRES, USE WATER SPRAY, FOG OR STANDARD FOAM (1987 EMERGENCY RESPONSE GUIDEBOOK, DOT P 5800.4).

FIREFIGHTING: MOVE CONTAINER FROM FIRE AREA IF POSSIBLE. COOL FIRE-EXPOSED CONTAINERS WITH WATER FROM SIDE UNTIL WELL AFTER FIRE IS OUT. STAY AWAY FROM STORAGE TANK ENDS. FOR MASSIVE FIRE IN STORAGE AREA, USE UNMANNED HOSE HOLDER OR MONITOR NOZZLES, ELSE WITHDRAW FROM AREA AND LET FIRE BURN. WITHDRAW IMMEDIATELY IN CASE OF RISING SOUND FROM VENTING SAFETY DEVICE OR ANY DISCOLORATION OF STORAGE TANK DUE TO FIRE (1987 EMERGENCY RESPONSE GUIDEBOOK, DOT P 5800.4, GUIDE PAGE 27). EXTINGUISH ONLY IF FLOW CAN BE STOPPED; USE FLOODING AMOUNTS OF WATER AS A FOG, SOLID STREAMS MAY BE INEFFECTIVE. COOL CONTAINERS WITH FLOODING AMOUNTS OF WATER, APPLY FROM AS FAR A DISTANCE AS POSSIBLE. AVOID BREATHING VAPORS, KEEP UPWIND.

TOXICITY

BUTOXYPROPYL SILVEX: TOXICITY DATA: 650 MG/KG ORAL-RAT LD50 (EPA). CARCINOGEN STATUS: HUMAN LIMITED EVIDENCE (IARC GROUP-2B FOR CHLOROPHENOXY HERBICIDES). STUDIES REVEALED A SIGNIFICANT INCREASE IN SOFT-TISSUE SARCOMAS, MALIGNANT LYMPHOMAS AND BRONCHIAL CARCINOMAS IN WORKERS EXPOSED TO CHLOROPHENOXY HERBICIDES. ACUTE TOXICITY LEVEL: MODERATELY TOXIC BY INGESTION. TARGET EFFECTS: POISONING MAY AFFECT THE GASTROINTESTINAL TRACT AND CARDIOVASCULAR SYSTEM.* AT INCREASED RISK FROM EXPOSURE: PERSONS WITH PREEXISTING LIVER, GASTROINTESTINAL TRACT OR SKIN DISORDERS.* ADDITIONAL DATA: STIMULANTS SUCH AS EPINEPHRINE MAY INDUCE VENTRICULAR FIBRILLATION.*
* MAY BE BASED ON GENERAL INFORMATION ON 2,4,5-T AND DERIVATIVES.

HEALTH EFFECTS AND FIRST AID

INHALATION: BUTOXYPROPYL SILVEX: SEE INFORMATION ON 2,4,5-T AND DERIVATIVES.
2,4,5-T AND DERIVATIVES: **ACUTE EXPOSURE-** MAY CAUSE IRRITATION WITH SORE THROAT AND BURNING SENSATIONS IN THE NASOPHARYNX AND CHEST, COUGHING, LACRIMATION, RHINITIS, DULLNESS, DIZZINESS, AND ATAXIA. IF SUFFICIENT AMOUNTS ARE ABSORBED THROUGH THE LUNGS, EFFECTS AS DESCRIBED IN ACUTE INGESTION MAY OCCUR. **CHRONIC EXPOSURE-** OCCUPATIONAL EXPOSURE TO 2,4,5-T AND ITS DERIVATIVES HAS PRODUCED HEADACHE, DECREASED AUDITORY ACUITY, GASTROINTESTINAL SYMPTOMS OF NAUSEA, VOMITING, DIARRHEA, ABDOMINAL PAINS, AND BLOOD IN THE STOOL, CHLORACNE, PORPHYRIA CUTANEA TARDIA, HYPERTRICHOSIS, HYPERPIGMENTATION, INCREASED SKIN FRAGILITY, LIVER DISORDERS, PERSONALITY CHANGES, AND PERIPHERAL NEUROPATHY. MANY OF THESE EFFECTS MAY BE DUE TO DIOXINS, ESPECIALLY TCDD, AS CONTAMINANTS. EPIDEMIOLOGICAL STUDIES HAVE INDICATED AN ASSOCIATION BETWEEN EXPOSURE TO 2,4,5-T COMPOUNDS AND AN INCREASED PREVALENCE OF REPORTED SEXUAL DYSFUNCTION AND DECREASED LIBIDO, ABNORMAL SENSORY FINDINGS, GASTROINTESTINAL TRACT ULCER, AND BIRTH MALFORMATIONS OF THE FEET. AN INCREASED PREVALENCE OF SLOWED NERVE CONDUCTION VELOCITY WITH NO ASSOCIATED SYMPTOMS WAS REPORTED IN A STUDY OF CHEMICAL WORKERS EMPLOYED IN THE PRODUCTION OF 2,4-D AND 2,4,5-T. EPIDEMIOLOGICAL STUDIES REVEALED A SIGNIFICANT INCREASE IN SOFT-TISSUE SARCOMAS, MALIGNANT LYMPHOMAS, AND BRONCHIAL CARCINOMAS IN WORKERS EXPOSED TO CHLOROPHENOXY HERBICIDES INCLUDING 2,4,5-T.

FIRST AID- REMOVE FROM EXPOSURE AREA TO FRESH AIR IMMEDIATELY. IF BREATHING HAS STOPPED, PERFORM ARTIFICIAL RESPIRATION. KEEP PERSON WARM AND AT REST. TREAT SYMPTOMATICALLY AND SUPPORTIVELY. GET MEDICAL ATTENTION IMMEDIATELY.

SKIN CONTACT: BUTOXYPROPYL SILVEX: SEE INFORMATION ON 2,4,5-T AND DERIVATIVES.
2,4,5-T AND DERIVATIVES: **ACUTE EXPOSURE-** MAY CAUSE IRRITATION. IF SUFFICIENT AMOUNTS ARE ABSORBED THROUGH THE SKIN, EFFECTS AS DESCRIBED IN ACUTE INGESTION MAY OCCUR. **CHRONIC EXPOSURE-** PROLONGED OR REPEATED EXPOSURE MAY CAUSE DERMATITIS AND EFFECTS AS DESCRIBED IN CHRONIC INHALATION.

FIRST AID- REMOVE CONTAMINATED CLOTHING AND SHOES IMMEDIATELY. WASH AFFECTED AREA WITH SOAP OR MILD DETERGENT AND LARGE AMOUNTS OF WATER UNTIL NO EVIDENCE OF CHEMICAL REMAINS (APPROXIMATELY 15-20 MINUTES). GET MEDICAL ATTENTION IMMEDIATELY.

EYE CONTACT: BUTOXYPROPYL SILVEX: SEE INFORMATION ON 2,4,5-T AND DERIVATIVES.
2,4,5-T AND DERIVATIVES: **ACUTE EXPOSURE-** MAY CAUSE IRRITATION. **CHRONIC EXPOSURE-** NO DATA AVAILABLE.

FIRST AID- WASH EYES IMMEDIATELY WITH LARGE AMOUNTS OF WATER OR NORMAL SALINE, OCCASIONALLY LIFTING UPPER AND LOWER LIDS, UNTIL NO EVIDENCE OF

CHEMICAL REMAINS (APPROXIMATELY 15-20 MINUTES). GET MEDICAL ATTENTION IMMEDIATELY.

INGESTION: BUTOXYPROPYL SILVEX: TEN DAILY DOSES OF 100 MG/KG WERE LETHAL TO SHEEP. SEE INFORMATION ON 2,4,5-T AND DERIVATIVES.

2,4,5-T AND DERIVATIVES: **ACUTE EXPOSURE-** MAY CAUSE IRRITATION OF THE MOUTH, THROAT, AND GASTROINTESTINAL TRACT, NAUSEA, VOMITING, CHEST AND ABDOMINAL PAIN, AND DIARRHEA. INGESTION OF VERY LARGE DOSES MAY PRODUCE METABOLIC ACIDOSIS, FEVER OR SUBNORMAL TEMPERATURES, HYPERVENTILATION, HYPOTENSION, VASODILATION, FLUSHING OF THE SKIN, SWEATING, CARDIAC ARRHYTHMIAS, TACHYCARDIA, LETHARGY, WEAKNESS, INTERCOSTAL PARALYSIS, RENAL AND HEPATIC DYSFUNCTION, MYOTONIA, COMA, AND CONVULSIONS. DAMAGE TO SKELETAL MUSCLE MAY BE MANIFEST BY MUSCLE TWITCHING AND ACHING WITH ELEVATED SERUM ENZYMES AND MYOGLOBIN IN THE BLOOD AND URINE. DEATH MAY BE DUE TO CIRCULATORY COLLAPSE. **CHRONIC EXPOSURE-** NO DATA AVAILABLE.

FIRST AID- IF THE PERSON IS CONSCIOUS AND NOT CONVULSING, INDUCE EMESIS BY GIVING SYRUP OF IPECAC (KEEPING THE HEAD BELOW THE HIPS TO PREVENT ASPIRATION) FOLLOWED BY WATER. REPEAT IN 20 MINUTES IF NOT EFFECTIVE INITIALLY. IN PATIENTS WITH DEPRESSED RESPIRATION OR IF EMESIS IS NOT PRODUCED, PERFORM GASTRIC LAVAGE WITH ACTIVATED CHARCOAL. FOLLOW WITH A SALINE CATHARTIC (DREISBACH, HANDBOOK OF POISONING, 12TH ED.). TREAT SYMPTOMATICALLY AND SUPPORTIVELY. GASTRIC LAVAGE SHOULD BE PERFORMED BY QUALIFIED MEDICAL PERSONNEL. GET MEDICAL ATTENTION IMMEDIATELY.

ANTIDOTE: NO SPECIFIC ANTIDOTE. TREAT SYMPTOMATICALLY AND SUPPORTIVELY.

REACTIVITY

REACTIVITY: STABLE UNDER NORMAL TEMPERATURES AND PRESSURES.

INCOMPATIBILITIES: BUTOXYPROPYL SILVEX: OXIDIZERS (STRONG): FIRE AND EXPLOSION HAZARD.

DECOMPOSITION: THERMAL DECOMPOSITION PRODUCTS MAY INCLUDE TOXIC SODIUM OXIDE AND TOXIC OXIDES OF CARBON.

POLYMERIZATION: HAZARDOUS POLYMERIZATION HAS NOT BEEN REPORTED TO OCCUR UNDER NORMAL TEMPERATURES AND PRESSURES.

STORAGE AND DISPOSAL

OBSERVE ALL FEDERAL, STATE AND LOCAL REGULATIONS WHEN STORING OR DISPOSING OF THIS SUBSTANCE. FOR ASSISTANCE, CONTACT THE DISTRICT DIRECTOR OF THE ENVIRONMENTAL PROTECTION AGENCY.

****STORAGE****

STORE AWAY FROM INCOMPATIBLE SUBSTANCES.

CONDITIONS TO AVOID

AVOID CONTACT WITH HEAT, SPARKS, FLAMES, OR OTHER SOURCES OF IGNITION. VAPORS MAY BE EXPLOSIVE. AVOID OVERHEATING OF CONTAINERS; CONTAINERS MAY VIOLENTLY RUPTURE IN HEAT OF FIRE. AVOID CONTAMINATION OF WATER SOURCES.

SPILL AND LEAK PROCEDURES

OCCUPATIONAL SPILL: SHUT OFF IGNITION SOURCES. STOP LEAK IF YOU CAN DO IT WITHOUT RISK. USE WATER SPRAY TO REDUCE VAPORS. FOR SMALL SPILLS, TAKE UP WITH SAND OR OTHER ABSORBENT MATERIAL AND PLACE INTO CONTAINERS FOR LATER DISPOSAL. FOR LARGER SPILLS, DIKE FAR AHEAD OF SPILL FOR LATER DISPOSAL. NO SMOKING, FLAMES OR FLARES IN HAZARD AREA. KEEP UNNECESSARY PEOPLE AWAY; ISOLATE HAZARD AREA AND RESTRICT ENTRY.

PROTECTIVE EQUIPMENT

VENTILATION: PROVIDE LOCAL EXHAUST OR PROCESS ENCLOSURE VENTILATION SYSTEM.

RESPIRATOR: THE FOLLOWING RESPIRATORS ARE RECOMMENDED BASED ON INFORMATION FOUND IN THE PHYSICAL DATA, TOXICITY AND HEALTH EFFECTS SECTIONS. THEY ARE RANKED IN ORDER FROM MINIMUM TO MAXIMUM RESPIRATORY PROTECTION. THE SPECIFIC RESPIRATOR SELECTED MUST BE BASED ON CONTAMINATION LEVELS FOUND IN THE WORK PLACE, MUST NOT EXCEED THE WORKING LIMITS OF THE RESPIRATOR AND BE JOINTLY APPROVED BY THE NATIONAL INSTITUTE FOR OCCUPATIONAL SAFETY AND HEALTH AND THE MINE SAFETY AND HEALTH ADMINISTRATION (NIOSH-MSHA).

CHEMICAL CARTRIDGE RESPIRATOR WITH FULL FACEPIECE AND PESTICIDE CARTRIDGE.

TYPE 'C' SUPPLIED-AIR RESPIRATOR WITH A FULL FACEPIECE OPERATED IN PRESSURE-DEMAND OR OTHER POSITIVE PRESSURE MODE OR WITH A FULL FACEPIECE, HELMET OR HOOD OPERATED IN CONTINUOUS-FLOW MODE.

SELF-CONTAINED BREATHING APPARATUS OPERATED IN PRESSURE-DEMAND OR OTHER POSITIVE PRESSURE MODE.

FOR FIREFIGHTING AND OTHER IMMEDIATELY DANGEROUS TO LIFE OR HEALTH CONDITIONS:

SELF-CONTAINED BREATHING APPARATUS WITH FULL FACEPIECE OPERATED IN PRESSURE-DEMAND OR OTHER POSITIVE PRESSURE MODE.

SUPPLIED-AIR RESPIRATOR WITH FULL FACEPIECE AND OPERATED IN PRESSURE-DEMAND OR OTHER POSITIVE PRESSURE MODE IN COMBINATION WITH AN AUXILIARY SELF-CONTAINED BREATHING APPARATUS OPERATED IN PRESSURE-DEMAND OR OTHER POSITIVE PRESSURE MODE.

CLOTHING: EMPLOYEE MUST WEAR APPROPRIATE PROTECTIVE (IMPERVIOUS) CLOTHING AND EQUIPMENT TO PREVENT REPEATED OR PROLONGED SKIN CONTACT WITH THIS SUBSTANCE.

GLOVES: EMPLOYEE MUST WEAR APPROPRIATE PROTECTIVE GLOVES TO PREVENT CONTACT WITH THIS SUBSTANCE.

EYE PROTECTION: EMPLOYEE MUST WEAR SPLASH-PROOF OR DUST-RESISTANT SAFETY GOGGLES TO PREVENT EYE CONTACT WITH THIS SUBSTANCE.

EMERGENCY EYE WASH: WHERE THERE IS ANY POSSIBILITY THAT AN EMPLOYEE'S EYES MAY BE EXPOSED TO THIS SUBSTANCE, THE EMPLOYER SHOULD PROVIDE AN EYE WASH FOUNTAIN WITHIN THE IMMEDIATE WORK AREA FOR EMERGENCY USE.

AUTHORIZED BY- OCCUPATIONAL HEALTH SERVICES, INC.

CREATION DATE: 03/23/90 ***REVISION DATE:*** 07/12/90

MATERIAL SAFETY DATA SHEET

OCCUPATIONAL HEALTH SERVICES, INC.
AGRICULTURE AND PESTICIDE DIVISION
450 SEVENTH AVENUE, SUITE 2407
NEW YORK, NEW YORK 10123
1-800-445-MSDS OR (212) 967-1100

EMERGENCY CONTACT:
JOHN S. BRANSFORD, JR. (615) 292-1180

SUBSTANCE IDENTIFICATION

CAS-NUMBER 845-52-3

SUBSTANCE: **2,4-BIS(3-METHOXYPROPYLAMINO)-6-METHYLTHIO-S-TRIAZINE**

TRADE NAMES/SYNONYMS: 1,3,5-TRIAZINE-2,4-DIAMINE, N,N'-BIS(3-METHOXYPROPYL)-6-(METHYLTHIO)-; S-TRIAZINE, 2,4-BIS((3-METHOXYPROPYL)AMINO)-6-(METHYLTHIO)-; N,N'-BIS(3-METHOXYPROPYL)-6-(METHYLTHIO)-1,3,5-TRIAZINE-2,4-DIAMINE; 2,4-BIS((3-METHOXYPROPYLAMINO)-6-(METHYLTHIO)-S-TRIAZINE; 2,4-BIS(3-METHOXYPROPYLAMINO)-6-(METHYLTHIO)-1,3,5-TRIAZINE; MPMT; CP 17029; LAMBAST; C12H23N5O2S; PST72212

CHEMICAL FAMILY: S-TRIAZINE

MOLECULAR FORMULA: (C-H3-O-(C-H2)3-N-H)2-C3-N3-S-C-H3

MOLECULAR WEIGHT: 301.46

CERCLA RATINGS (SCALE 0-3): HEALTH=2 FIRE=1 REACTIVITY=0 PERSISTENCE=2

NFPA RATINGS (SCALE 0-4): HEALTH=2 FIRE=1 REACTIVITY=0

COMPONENTS AND CONTAMINANTS

COMPONENT: 2,4-BIS(3-METHOXYPROPYLAMINO)-6-METHYLTHIO-S-TRIAZINE ***PERCENT:*** 100.0

CAS# 845-52-3

OTHER CONTAMINANTS: NONE

EXPOSURE LIMITS: NO OCCUPATIONAL EXPOSURE LIMITS ESTABLISHED BY OSHA, ACGIH, OR NIOSH.

PHYSICAL DATA

DESCRIPTION: WHITE SOLID ***MELTING POINT:*** 131 F (55 C)

SPECIFIC GRAVITY: NOT AVAILABLE ***SOLUBILITY IN WATER:*** INSOLUBLE

SOLVENT SOLUBILITY: SOLUBLE IN ACETONE AND BENZENE, SLIGHTLY SOLUBLE IN ETHANOL.

FIRE AND EXPLOSION DATA

FIRE AND EXPLOSION HAZARD: SLIGHT FIRE HAZARD WHEN EXPOSED TO HEAT OR FLAME.

FIREFIGHTING MEDIA: DRY CHEMICAL, CARBON DIOXIDE, HALON, WATER SPRAY OR STANDARD FOAM (1987 EMERGENCY RESPONSE GUIDEBOOK, DOT P 5800.4).

FOR LARGER FIRES, USE WATER SPRAY, FOG OR STANDARD FOAM (1987 EMERGENCY RESPONSE GUIDEBOOK, DOT P 5800.4).

FIREFIGHTING: MOVE CONTAINERS FROM FIRE AREA IF POSSIBLE (1987 EMERGENCY RESPONSE GUIDEBOOK, DOT P 5800.4, GUIDE PAGE 53).

EXTINGUISH USING AGENTS SUITABLE FOR SURROUNDING FIRE. USE FLOODING

QUANTITIES OF WATER AS A FOG. KEEP MATERIAL OUT OF SEWERS AND WATER SOURCES. DO NOT TOUCH SPILLED MATERIAL. AVOID BREATHING HAZARDOUS FUMES; KEEP UPWIND.

TOXICITY

2,4-BIS(3-METHOXYPROPYLAMINO)-6-METHYLTHIO-S-TRIAZINE: TOXICITY DATA: 1400 MG/KG ORAL-RAT LD50. CARCINOGEN STATUS: NONE. ACUTE TOXICITY DATA: MODERATELY TOXIC BY INGESTION. TARGET EFFECTS: NO DATA AVAILABLE.

HEALTH EFFECTS AND FIRST AID

INHALATION: 2,4-BIS(3-METHOXYPROPYLAMINO)-6-METHYLTHIO-S-TRIAZINE: **ACUTE EXPOSURE**- SOME TRIAZINES ARE MILDLY IRRITATING TO THE UPPER RESPIRATORY TRACT. **CHRONIC EXPOSURE**- NO DATA AVAILABLE.

FIRST AID- REMOVE FROM EXPOSURE AREA TO FRESH AIR IMMEDIATELY. IF BREATHING HAS STOPPED, PERFORM ARTIFICIAL RESPIRATION. KEEP PERSON WARM AND AT REST. TREAT SYMPTOMATICALLY AND SUPPORTIVELY. GET MEDICAL ATTENTION IMMEDIATELY.

SKIN CONTACT: 2,4-BIS(3-METHOXYPROPYLAMINO)-6-METHYLTHIO-S-TRIAZINE: **ACUTE EXPOSURE**- SOME TRIAZINES ARE MILDLY IRRITATING TO THE SKIN. **CHRONIC EXPOSURE**- NO DATA AVAILABLE.

FIRST AID- REMOVE CONTAMINATED CLOTHING AND SHOES IMMEDIATELY. WASH AFFECTED AREA WITH SOAP OR MILD DETERGENT AND LARGE AMOUNTS OF WATER UNTIL NO EVIDENCE OF CHEMICAL REMAINS (APPROXIMATELY 15-20 MINUTES). GET MEDICAL ATTENTION IMMEDIATELY.

EYE CONTACT: 2,4-BIS(3-METHOXYPROPYLAMINO)-6-METHYLTHIO-S-TRIAZINE: **ACUTE EXPOSURE**- SOME TRIAZINES ARE MILDLY IRRITATING TO THE EYES. **CHRONIC EXPOSURE**- NO DATA AVAILABLE.

FIRST AID- WASH EYES IMMEDIATELY WITH LARGE AMOUNTS OF WATER OR NORMAL SALINE, OCCASIONALLY LIFTING UPPER AND LOWER LIDS, UNTIL NO EVIDENCE OF CHEMICAL REMAINS (APPROXIMATELY 15-20 MINUTES). GET MEDICAL ATTENTION IMMEDIATELY.

INGESTION: 2,4-BIS(3-METHOXYPROPYLAMINO)-6-METHYLTHIO-S-TRIAZINE: **ACUTE EXPOSURE**- A LETHAL DOSE IN RATS WAS 1400 MG/KG. A SINGLE DOSE OF 250 MG/KG INGESTED BY SHEEP PRODUCED IMMEDIATE ATAXIA, UNCOORDINATION AND LAMENESS, FOLLOWED AFTER 2 HOURS BY EXTREME DEPRESSION. **CHRONIC EXPOSURE**- NO DATA AVAILABLE.

FIRST AID- TREAT SYMPTOMATICALLY AND SUPPORTIVELY. GET MEDICAL ATTENTION IMMEDIATELY. IF VOMITING OCCURS, KEEP HEAD LOWER THAN HIPS TO PREVENT ASPIRATION.

ANTIDOTE: NO SPECIFIC ANTIDOTE. TREAT SYMPTOMATICALLY AND SUPPORTIVELY.

REACTIVITY

REACTIVITY: STABLE UNDER NORMAL TEMPERATURES AND PRESSURES.

INCOMPATIBILITIES: 2,4-BIS(3-METHOXYPROPYLAMINO)-6-METHYLTHIO-S-TRIAZINE: NO DATA AVAILABLE.

DECOMPOSITION: THERMAL DECOMPOSITION PRODUCTS MAY INCLUDE TOXIC OXIDES OF CARBON, NITROGEN, AND SULFUR.

POLYMERIZATION: HAZARDOUS POLYMERIZATION HAS NOT BEEN REPORTED TO OCCUR UNDER NORMAL TEMPERATURES AND PRESSURES.

STORAGE AND DISPOSAL

OBSERVE ALL FEDERAL, STATE AND LOCAL REGULATIONS WHEN STORING OR DISPOSING OF THIS SUBSTANCE. FOR ASSISTANCE, CONTACT THE DISTRICT DIRECTOR OF THE ENVIRONMENTAL PROTECTION AGENCY.

STORAGE

STORE IN ACCORDANCE WITH 40 CFR 165 RECOMMENDED PROCEDURES FOR THE DISPOSAL AND STORAGE OF PESTICIDES AND PESTICIDE CONTAINERS.

DISPOSAL

DISPOSAL MUST BE IN ACCORDANCE WITH 40 CFR 165 RECOMMENDED PROCEDURES FOR THE DISPOSAL AND STORAGE OF PESTICIDES AND PESTICIDE CONTAINERS.

CONDITIONS TO AVOID

MAY BURN BUT DOES NOT IGNITE READILY.

SPILL AND LEAK PROCEDURES

OCCUPATIONAL SPILL: DO NOT TOUCH SPILLED MATERIAL. STOP LEAK IF YOU CAN DO IT WITHOUT RISK. FOR SMALL SPILLS, TAKE UP WITH SAND OR OTHER ABSORBENT MATERIAL AND PLACE INTO CONTAINERS FOR LATER DISPOSAL. FOR SMALL DRY SPILLS, WITH A CLEAN SHOVEL PLACE MATERIAL INTO CLEAN, DRY CONTAINER AND COVER. MOVE CONTAINERS FROM SPILL AREA. FOR LARGER SPILLS, DIKE FAR AHEAD OF SPILL FOR LATER DISPOSAL. KEEP UNNECESSARY PEOPLE AWAY. ISOLATE HAZARD AREA AND DENY ENTRY.

PROTECTIVE EQUIPMENT

VENTILATION: PROVIDE LOCAL EXHAUST OR GENERAL DILUTION VENTILATION SYSTEM.

RESPIRATOR: THE FOLLOWING RESPIRATORS ARE RECOMMENDED BASED ON INFORMATION FOUND IN THE PHYSICAL DATA, TOXICITY AND HEALTH EFFECTS SECTIONS. THEY ARE RANKED IN ORDER FROM MINIMUM TO MAXIMUM RESPIRATORY PROTECTION. THE SPECIFIC RESPIRATOR SELECTED MUST BE BASED ON CONTAMINATION LEVELS FOUND IN THE WORK PLACE, MUST NOT EXCEED THE WORKING LIMITS OF THE RESPIRATOR AND BE JOINTLY APPROVED BY THE NATIONAL INSTITUTE FOR OCCUPATIONAL SAFETY AND HEALTH AND THE MINE SAFETY AND HEALTH ADMINISTRATION (NIOSH-MSHA).

CHEMICAL CARTRIDGE RESPIRATOR WITH AN ORGANIC VAPOR CARTRIDGE(S) WITH A FULL FACEPIECE AND ORGANIC VAPOR CARTRIDGE(S) IN COMBINATION WITH A DUST AND MIST FILTER.

POWERED AIR-PURIFYING RESPIRATOR WITH A TIGHT-FITTING FACEPIECE AND ORGANIC VAPOR CARTRIDGE(S) IN COMBINATION WITH A HIGH-EFFICIENCY PARTICULATE FILTER.

TYPE 'C' SUPPLIED-AIR RESPIRATOR WITH A FULL FACEPIECE OPERATED IN A PRESSURE-DEMAND OR OTHER POSITIVE PRESSURE MODE.

SELF-CONTAINED BREATHING APPARATUS WITH A FULL FACEPIECE OPERATED IN PRESSURE-DEMAND OR OTHER POSITIVE PRESSURE MODE.

FOR FIREFIGHTING AND OTHER IMMEDIATELY DANGEROUS TO LIFE OR HEALTH CONDITIONS:

SELF-CONTAINED BREATHING APPARATUS WITH FULL FACEPIECE OPERATED IN PRESSURE-DEMAND OR OTHER POSITIVE PRESSURE MODE.

SUPPLIED-AIR RESPIRATOR WITH FULL FACEPIECE AND OPERATED IN PRESSURE-DEMAND OR OTHER POSITIVE PRESSURE MODE IN COMBINATION WITH AN AUXILIARY SELF-CONTAINED BREATHING APPARATUS OPERATED IN PRESSURE-DEMAND OR OTHER POSITIVE PRESSURE MODE.

CLOTHING: EMPLOYEE MUST WEAR APPROPRIATE PROTECTIVE (IMPERVIOUS) CLOTHING AND EQUIPMENT TO PREVENT REPEATED OR PROLONGED SKIN CONTACT WITH THIS SUBSTANCE.

GLOVES: EMPLOYEE MUST WEAR APPROPRIATE PROTECTIVE GLOVES TO PREVENT CONTACT WITH THIS SUBSTANCE.

EYE PROTECTION: EMPLOYEE MUST WEAR SPLASH-PROOF OR DUST-RESISTANT SAFETY GOGGLES TO PREVENT EYE CONTACT WITH THIS SUBSTANCE. EMERGENCY EYE WASH: WHERE THERE IS ANY POSSIBILITY THAT AN EMPLOYEE'S EYES MAY BE EXPOSED TO THIS SUBSTANCE, THE EMPLOYER SHOULD PROVIDE AN EYE WASH FOUNTAIN WITHIN THE IMMEDIATE WORK AREA FOR EMERGENCY USE.

AUTHORIZED BY- OCCUPATIONAL HEALTH SERVICES, INC.
CREATION DATE: 10/05/89 ***REVISION DATE:*** 05/10/90

MATERIAL SAFETY DATA SHEET

OCCUPATIONAL HEALTH SERVICES, INC.
AGRICULTURE AND PESTICIDE DIVISION
450 SEVENTH AVENUE, SUITE 2407
NEW YORK, NEW YORK 10123
1-800-445-MSDS OR (212) 967-1100

EMERGENCY CONTACT:
JOHN S. BRANSFORD, JR. (615) 292-1180

SUBSTANCE IDENTIFICATION

CAS-NUMBER 56-36-0

SUBSTANCE: **TRIBUTYLTIN ACETATE**

TRADE NAMES/SYNONYMS: STANNANE, (ACETYLOXY)TRIBUTYL-; (ACETYLOXY)TRIBUTYLSTANNANE; STANNANE, ACETOXYTRIBUTYL-; ACETOXYTRIBUTYLSTANNANE; ACETOXYTRIBUTYLTIN; TRIBUTYLACETOXYSTANNANE; TRIBUTYLSTANNYL ACETATE; TRI-N-BUTYLTIN ACETATE; C14H30O2SN; PST72220

CHEMICAL FAMILY: ORGANOMETALLIC ACETATE

MOLECULAR FORMULA: (C4-H9)3-SN-O-C-(O)-C-H3

MOLECULAR WEIGHT: 349.08

CERCLA RATINGS (SCALE 0-3): HEALTH=3 FIRE=1 REACTIVITY=0 PERSISTENCE=2

NFPA RATINGS (SCALE 0-4): HEALTH=U FIRE=1 REACTIVITY=0

COMPONENTS AND CONTAMINANTS

COMPONENT: TRIBUTYLTIN ACETATE ***PERCENT:*** 100
CAS# 56-36-0

OTHER CONTAMINANTS: NONE

EXPOSURE LIMITS: TIN, ORGANIC COMPOUNDS (AS SN): 0.1 MG/M3 OSHA TWA 0.1 MG/M3 ACGIH TWA (SKIN) (NOTICE OF INTENDED CHANGE 1988-89) 0.1 MG/M3 NIOSH RECOMMENDED 10 HOUR TWA

PHYSICAL DATA

DESCRIPTION: WHITE, CRYSTALLINE OR WAXY SOLID.

MELTING POINT: 176-181 F (80-83 C) ***SPECIFIC GRAVITY:*** 1.27

SOLUBILITY IN WATER: INSOLUBLE

SOLVENT SOLUBILITY: SOLUBLE IN BENZENE, METHANOL, CONCENTRATED ACIDS.

FIRE AND EXPLOSION DATA

FIRE AND EXPLOSION HAZARD: SLIGHT FIRE HAZARD WHEN EXPOSED TO HEAT OR FLAME.

FIREFIGHTING MEDIA: DRY CHEMICAL, CARBON DIOXIDE, HALON, WATER SPRAY OR STANDARD FOAM (1987 EMERGENCY RESPONSE GUIDEBOOK, DOT P 5800.4). FOR LARGER FIRES, USE WATER SPRAY, FOG OR STANDARD FOAM (1987 EMERGENCY RESPONSE GUIDEBOOK, DOT P 5800.4).

FIREFIGHTING: MOVE CONTAINERS FROM FIRE AREA IF POSSIBLE. FIGHT FIRE FROM MAXIMUM DISTANCE. STAY AWAY FROM STORAGE TANK ENDS. DIKE FIRE CONTROL WATER FOR LATER DISPOSAL. DO NOT SCATTER MATERIAL (1987 EMERGENCY RESPONSE GUIDEBOOK, DOT P 5800.4, GUIDE PAGE 55). EXTINGUISH USING AGENTS SUITABLE FOR SURROUNDING FIRE. APPLY WATER IN FLOODING QUANTITIES AS A FOG. AVOID CONTAMINATING WATER SOURCES AND SEWERS. AVOID BREATHING FUMES; KEEP UPWIND.

TOXICITY

TRIBUTYLTIN ACETATE: TOXICITY DATA: 99 MG/KG ORAL-RAT LD50; 46 MG/KG ORAL-MOUSE LD50; 40 MG/KG ORAL-RABBIT LDLO; 20 MG/KG ORAL-GUINEA PIG LDLO; 180 MG/KG INTRAVENOUS-MOUSE LD50; 10 MG/KG INTRAPERITONEAL-RAT LDLO; 500 MG/KG UNREPORTED-MAMMAL LD50. CARCINOGEN STATUS: NONE. LOCAL EFFECTS: IRRITANT- SKIN. ACUTE TOXICITY LEVEL: TOXIC BY INGESTION. TARGET EFFECTS: POISONING MAY AFFECT THE LIVER, KIDNEYS, AND SPLEEN. AT INCREASED RISK FROM EXPOSURE: PERSONS WITH PRE-EXISTING SKIN DISEASE.

HEALTH EFFECTS AND FIRST AID

INHALATION: TRIBUTYLTIN ACETATE: 200 MG(SN)/M3 IMMEDIATELY DANGEROUS TO LIFE OR HEALTH. **ACUTE EXPOSURE-** EXPOSURE TO VAPORS OR FUMES OF ORGANOTIN COMPOUNDS MAY CAUSE IRRITATION OF THE MOUTH AND RESPIRATORY TRACT, WITH SORE THROAT AND COUGHING. **CHRONIC EXPOSURE-** WORKERS EXPOSED TO TRIBUYLTIN OXIDE FOR 2 WEEKS EXHIBITED NASAL DISCHARGE AND BLEEDING, AND IRRITATION AND HEMORRHAGE OF THE NASAL MUCOSA AND SEPTUM.

FIRST AID- REMOVE FROM EXPOSURE AREA TO FRESH AIR IMMEDIATELY. IF BREATHING HAS STOPPED, PERFORM ARTIFICIAL RESPIRATION. KEEP PERSON WARM AND AT REST. TREAT SYMPTOMATICALLY AND SUPPORTIVELY. GET MEDICAL ATTENTION IMMEDIATELY.

SKIN CONTACT: TRIBUTYLTIN ACETATE: IRRITANT. **ACUTE EXPOSURE-** DIRECT CONTACT CAN CAUSE FOLLICULAR INFLAMMATION AND PUSTULATION, WHICH MAY BE DELAYED. TRIBUTYLTIN COMPOUNDS MAY CAUSE CAUSE CHEMICAL BURNS WHICH APPEAR 1 TO 8 HOURS AFTER CONTACT, CAUSE ITCHING WITHOUT PAIN, AND HEAL IN 7 TO 10 DAYS WITHOUT SCARRING. **CHRONIC EXPOSURE-** PROLONGED CONTACT WITH TRIBUTYLTIN COMPOUNDS THROUGH CONTAMINATED CLOTHING MAY CAUSE DIFFUSE, FAINT ERYTHEMATOUS ERUPTIONS WHICH ITCH. THESE LESIONS ARE USUALLY LOCATED ON THE LOWER ABDOMEN, THIGHS, GROIN, AND PERINEUM, AND HEAL RAPIDLY WHEN CONTACT IS DISCONTINUED.

FIRST AID- REMOVE CONTAMINATED CLOTHING AND SHOES IMMEDIATELY. WASH AFFECTED AREA WITH SOAP OR MILD DETERGENT AND LARGE AMOUNTS OF WATER UNTIL NO EVIDENCE OF CHEMICAL REMAINS (APPROXIMATELY 15-20 MINUTES). GET MEDICAL ATTENTION IMMEDIATELY.

EYE CONTACT: TRIBUTYLTIN ACETATE: **ACUTE EXPOSURE-** NO SPECIFIC DATA AVAILABLE. SOME TRIBUTYLTIN COMPOUNDS ARE EYE IRRITANTS, AND ACCIDENTAL SPLASHING INTO THE EYES HAS CAUSED LACRIMATION AND CONJUNCTIVAL ERYTHEMA AND EDEMA, WHICH LASTED SEVERAL DAYS BUT CAUSED NO PERMANENT INJURY. **CHRONIC EXPOSURE-** REPEATED OR PROLONGED EXPOSURE TO TRIBUTYLTIN COMPOUNDS MAY RESULT IN CONJUNCTIVITIS.

FIRST AID- WASH EYES IMMEDIATELY WITH LARGE AMOUNTS OF WATER OR NORMAL SALINE, OCCASIONALLY LIFTING UPPER AND LOWER LIDS, UNTIL NO EVIDENCE OF CHEMICAL REMAINS (APPROXIMATELY 15-20 MINUTES). GET MEDICAL ATTENTION IMMEDIATELY.

INGESTION: TRIBUTYLTIN ACETATE: TOXIC. **ACUTE EXPOSURE-** INGESTION BY MICE CAUSED DAMAGE TO THE LIVER, KIDNEY, AND SPLEEN, AND DEATH. **CHRONIC EXPOSURE-** NO SPECIFIC DATA AVAILABLE. REPEATED INGESTION OF TRIBUTYLTIN COMPOUNDS BY RATS CAUSED DEPLETION OF FAT STORES, BLOODY DISCHARGE FROM EYES AND NOSE, RAPID AND LABORED RESPIRATION, AND DEATH.

FIRST AID- IF EXTENSIVE VOMITING HAS NOT OCCURRED, THE SUBSTANCE SHOULD BE REMOVED BY EMESIS OR GASTRIC LAVAGE PROVIDED THAT THE PATIENT IS CONSCIOUS AND CONVULSIONS ARE NOT PRESENT. KEEP HEAD BELOW HIPS DURING VOMITING TO PREVENT ASPIRATION. DO NOT ATTEMPT TO MAKE AN UNCONSCIOUS PERSON VOMIT. TREAT SYMPTOMATICALLY AND SUPPORTIVELY. GET MEDICAL ATTENTION IMMEDIATELY (DREISBACH, HANDBOOK OF POISONING, 12TH ED.). TREATMENT SHOULD BE PERFORMED BY QUALIFIED MEDICAL PERSONNEL.

ANTIDOTE: NO SPECIFIC ANTIDOTE. TREAT SYMPTOMATICALLY AND SUPPORTIVELY.

REACTIVITY

REACTIVITY: STABLE UNDER NORMAL TEMPERATURES AND PRESSURES.

INCOMPATIBILITIES: TRIBUTYLTIN ACETATE: OXIDIZERS (STRONG): FIRE AND EXPLOSION HAZARD.

DECOMPOSITION: THERMAL DECOMPOSITION MAY RELEASE TOXIC AND/OR HAZARDOUS GASES.

POLYMERIZATION: HAZARDOUS POLYMERIZATION HAS NOT BEEN REPORTED TO OCCUR UNDER NORMAL TEMPERATURES AND PRESSURES.

STORAGE AND DISPOSAL

OBSERVE ALL FEDERAL, STATE AND LOCAL REGULATIONS WHEN STORING OR DISPOSING OF THIS SUBSTANCE. FOR ASSISTANCE, CONTACT THE DISTRICT DIRECTOR OF THE ENVIRONMENTAL PROTECTION AGENCY.

STORAGE

STORE IN ACCORDANCE WITH 40 CFR 165 RECOMMENDED PROCEDURES FOR THE DISPOSAL AND STORAGE OF PESTICIDES AND PESTICIDE CONTAINERS. STORE AWAY FROM INCOMPATIBLE SUBSTANCES.

DISPOSAL

DISPOSAL MUST BE IN ACCORDANCE WITH 40 CFR 165 RECOMMENDED PROCEDURES FOR THE DISPOSAL AND STORAGE OF PESTICIDES AND PESTICIDE CONTAINERS.

CONDITIONS TO AVOID

MAY BURN BUT DOES NOT IGNITE READILY. CONTAINERS MAY EXPLODE IN HEAT OF FIRE.

SPILL AND LEAK PROCEDURES

OCCUPATIONAL SPILL: DO NOT TOUCH SPILLED MATERIAL. STOP LEAK IF YOU CAN DO IT WITHOUT RISK. USE WATER SPRAY TO REDUCE VAPORS. FOR SMALL SPILLS, TAKE UP WITH SAND OR OTHER ABSORBENT MATERIAL AND PLACE INTO CONTAINERS FOR LATER DISPOSAL. FOR SMALL DRY SPILLS, WITH A CLEAN SHOVEL PLACE MATERIAL INTO CLEAN, DRY CONTAINERS AND COVER. MOVE CONTAINERS FROM SPILL AREA. FOR LARGER SPILLS, DIKE FAR AHEAD OF SPILL FOR LATER DISPOSAL. KEEP UNNECESSARY PEOPLE AWAY. ISOLATE HAZARD AREA AND DENY ENTRY. VENTILATE CLOSED SPACES BEFORE ENTERING.

PROTECTIVE EQUIPMENT

VENTILATION: PROVIDE LOCAL EXHAUST OR PROCESS ENCLOSURE VENTILATION TO MEET PUBLISHED EXPOSURE LIMITS.

RESPIRATOR: THE FOLLOWING RESPIRATORS AND MAXIMUM USE CONCENTRATIONS ARE RECOMMENDATIONS BY THE U.S. DEPARTMENT OF HEALTH AND HUMAN SERVICES, NIOSH POCKET GUIDE TO CHEMICAL HAZARDS; NIOSH CRITERIA DOCUMENTS OR BY THE U.S. DEPARTMENT OF LABOR, 29 CFR 1910 SUBPART Z. THE SPECIFIC RESPIRATOR SELECTED MUST BE BASED ON CONTAMINATION LEVELS FOUND IN THE WORK PLACE, MUST NOT EXCEED THE WORKING LIMITS OF THE RESPIRATOR AND BE JOINTLY APPROVED BY THE NATIONAL INSTITUTE FOR OCCUPATIONAL SAFETY AND HEALTH AND THE MINE SAFETY AND HEALTH ADMINISTRATION (NIOSH-MSHA).

TIN, ORGANIC COMPOUNDS (AS SN):

1 MG/M3- ANY CHEMICAL CARTRIDGE RESPIRATOR WITH ORGANIC VAPOR CARTRIDGES IN COMBINATION WITH A DUST AND MIST FILTER. ANY SUPPLIED-AIR RESPIRATOR. ANY SELF-CONTAINED BREATHING APPARATUS.

2.5 MG/M3- ANY SUPPLIED-AIR RESPIRATOR OPERATED IN A CONTINUOUS FLOW MODE. ANY POWERED AIR-PURIFYING RESPIRATOR WITH ORGANIC VAPOR CARTRIDGES IN COMBINATION WITH A DUST AND MIST FILTER.

5 MG/M3- ANY CHEMICAL CARTRIDGE RESPIRATOR WITH A FULL FACEPIECE AND ORGANIC VAPOR CARTRIDGES IN COMBINATION WITH A HIGH-EFFICIENCY PARTICULATE FILTER. ANY SUPPLIED-AIR RESPIRATOR WITH A FULL FACEPIECE. ANY SELF-CONTAINED BREATHING APPARATUS WITH A FULL FACEPIECE. ANY AIR-PURIFYING FULL FACEPIECE RESPIRATOR (GAS MASK) WITH A CHIN-STYLE OR

FRONT- OR BACK-MOUNTED ORGANIC VAPOR CANISTER HAVING A HIGH-EFFICIENCY PARTICULATE FILTER. ANY POWERED AIR-PURIFYING RESPIRATOR WITH A TIGHT-FITTING FACEPIECE AND ORGANIC VAPOR CARTRIDGES IN COMBINATION WITH A HIGH-EFFICIENCY PARTICULATE FILTER. ANY SUPPLIED-AIR RESPIRATOR WITH A TIGHT-FITTING FACEPIECE OPERATED IN A CONTINUOUS FLOW MODE.

200 MG/M3- ANY SUPPLIED-AIR RESPIRATOR WITH A FULL FACEPIECE OPERATED IN PRESSURE-DEMAND OR OTHER POSITIVE PRESSURE MODE.

ESCAPE- ANY AIR-PURIFYING FULL FACEPIECE RESPIRATOR (GAS MASK) WITH A CHIN-STYLE OR FRONT- OR BACK-MOUNTED ORGANIC VAPOR CANISTER HAVING A HIGH-EFFICIENCY PARTICULATE FILTER. ANY APPROPRIATE ESCAPE-TYPE SELF-CONTAINED BREATHING APPARATUS.

FOR FIREFIGHTING AND OTHER IMMEDIATELY DANGEROUS TO LIFE OR HEALTH CONDITIONS: SELF-CONTAINED BREATHING APPARATUS WITH FULL FACEPIECE OPERATED IN PRESSURE-DEMAND OR OTHER POSITIVE PRESSURE MODE. SUPPLIED-AIR RESPIRATOR WITH FULL FACEPIECE AND OPERATED IN PRESSURE-DEMAND OR OTHER POSITIVE PRESSURE MODE IN COMBINATION WITH AN AUXILIARY SELF-CONTAINED BREATHING APPARATUS OPERATED IN PRESSURE-DEMAND OR OTHER POSITIVE PRESSURE MODE.

CLOTHING: EMPLOYEE MUST WEAR APPROPRIATE PROTECTIVE (IMPERVIOUS) CLOTHING AND EQUIPMENT TO PREVENT ANY POSSIBILITY OF SKIN CONTACT WITH THIS SUBSTANCE.

GLOVES: EMPLOYEE MUST WEAR APPROPRIATE PROTECTIVE GLOVES TO PREVENT CONTACT WITH THIS SUBSTANCE.

EYE PROTECTION: EMPLOYEE MUST WEAR SPLASH-PROOF OR DUST-RESISTANT SAFETY GOGGLES AND A FACESHIELD TO PREVENT CONTACT WITH THIS SUBSTANCE.

EMERGENCY WASH FACILITIES: WHERE THERE IS ANY POSSIBILITY THAT AN EMPLOYEE'S EYES AND/OR SKIN MAY BE EXPOSED TO THIS SUBSTANCE, THE EMPLOYER SHOULD PROVIDE AN EYE WASH FOUNTAIN AND QUICK DRENCH SHOWER WITHIN THE IMMEDIATE WORK AREA FOR EMERGENCY USE.

AUTHORIZED BY- OCCUPATIONAL HEALTH SERVICES, INC.
CREATION DATE: 10/05/89 ***REVISION DATE:*** 11/09/89

MATERIAL SAFETY DATA SHEET

OCCUPATIONAL HEALTH SERVICES, INC.
AGRICULTURE AND PESTICIDE DIVISION
450 SEVENTH AVENUE, SUITE 2407
NEW YORK, NEW YORK 10123

EMERGENCY CONTACT:
JOHN S. BRANSFORD, JR. (615) 292-1180
1-800-445-MSDS OR (212) 967-1100

SUBSTANCE IDENTIFICATION

CAS-NUMBER 1461-22-9

SUBSTANCE: **TRIBUTYLTIN CHLORIDE**

TRADE NAMES/SYNONYMS: STANNANE, TRIBUTYLCHLORO-; TRIBUTYLCHLOROSTANNANE; CHLOROTRIBUTYLTIN; CHLOROTRIBUTYLSTANNANE; MONOCHLOROTRIBUTYLTIN; TRIBUTYLCHLOROTIN; C12H27CLSN; PST72222

CHEMICAL FAMILY: ORGANOMETALLIC

MOLECULAR FORMULA: (C4-H9)3-SN-CL

MOLECULAR WEIGHT: 325.49

CERCLA RATINGS (SCALE 0-3): HEALTH=3 FIRE=1 REACTIVITY=0 PERSISTENCE=2

NFPA RATINGS (SCALE 0-4): HEALTH=3 FIRE=1 REACTIVITY=0

COMPONENTS AND CONTAMINANTS

COMPONENT: TRIBUTYLTIN CHLORIDE ***PERCENT:*** 100
CAS# 1461-22-9

OTHER CONTAMINANTS: NONE

EXPOSURE LIMITS: TIN, ORGANIC COMPOUNDS (AS SN): 0.1 MG/M3 OSHA TWA 0.1 MG/M3 ACGIH TWA (SKIN) (NOTICE OF INTENDED CHANGE 1988-89) 0.1 MG/M3 NIOSH RECOMMENDED 10 HOUR TWA

PHYSICAL DATA

DESCRIPTION: COLORLESS LIQUID. ***BOILING POINT:*** 293-297 F (145-147 C) @ 5 MMHG

SPECIFIC GRAVITY: 1.20 ***SOLUBILITY IN WATER:*** SOLUBLE

SOLVENT SOLUBILITY: SOLUBLE IN ALCOHOL, HEPTANE, BENZENE, TOLUENE, ORGANIC SOLVENTS

FIRE AND EXPLOSION DATA

FIRE AND EXPLOSION HAZARD: SLIGHT FIRE HAZARD WHEN EXPOSED TO HEAT OR FLAME.

FLASH POINT: >230 F (>110 C) ***FLAMMABILITY CLASS(OSHA):*** IIIB

FIREFIGHTING MEDIA: DRY CHEMICAL, CARBON DIOXIDE, HALON, WATER SPRAY OR STANDARD FOAM (1987 EMERGENCY RESPONSE GUIDEBOOK, DOT P 5800.4). FOR LARGER FIRES, USE WATER SPRAY, FOG OR STANDARD FOAM (1987 EMERGENCY RESPONSE GUIDEBOOK, DOT P 5800.4).

FIREFIGHTING: MOVE CONTAINERS FROM FIRE AREA IF POSSIBLE. FIGHT FIRE FROM MAXIMUM DISTANCE. STAY AWAY FROM STORAGE TANK ENDS. DIKE FIRE CONTROL WATER FOR LATER DISPOSAL. DO NOT SCATTER MATERIAL (1987 EMERGENCY RESPONSE GUIDEBOOK, DOT P 5800.4, GUIDE PAGE 55). EXTINGUISH USING AGENTS SUITABLE FOR SURROUNDING FIRE. APPLY WATER IN FLOODING QUANTITIES AS A FOG. AVOID CONTAMINATING WATER SOURCES AND SEWERS. AVOID BREATHING FUMES; KEEP UPWIND.

TOXICITY

TRIBUTYLTIN CHLORIDE: IRRITATION DATA: 50 UG/24 HOURS EYE-RABBIT SEVERE. TOXICITY DATA: 70 MG/KG SKIN-RABBIT LDLO; 129 MG/KG ORAL-RAT LD50; 60 MG/KG ORAL-MOUSE LD50; 30 UG/KG ORAL-RABBIT LD50; 2300 MG/KG UNREPORTED-RAT LD50. CARCINOGEN STATUS: NONE. LOCAL EFFECTS: CORROSIVE- SKIN; IRRITANT- INHALATION AND EYES. ACUTE TOXICITY LEVEL: TOXIC BY INGESTION. TARGET EFFECTS: POISONING MAY AFFECT THE CENTRAL NERVOUS SYSTEM, LIVER, KIDNEYS, AND BLOOD. AT INCREASED RISK FROM EXPOSURE: PERSONS WITH PRE-EXISTING SKIN DISEASE.

HEALTH EFFECTS AND FIRST AID

INHALATION: TRIBUTYLTIN CHLORIDE: IRRITANT. 200 MG(SN)/M3 IMMEDIATELY DANGEROUS TO LIFE OR HEALTH. **ACUTE EXPOSURE-** VAPORS OR FUMES MAY CAUSE IRRITATION OF THE MUCOUS MEMBRANES WITH DELAYED SORE THROAT, COUGHING, SNEEZING, AND RETCHING. SOME ORGANOTIN COMPOUNDS MAY CAUSE PULMONARY EDEMA, GASTROINTESTINAL TRACT DISTURBANCES, AND LIVER AND KIDNEY DAMAGE. **CHRONIC EXPOSURE-** EXPOSURE TO 4-6 MG/M3/4 MONTHS PRODUCED INFLAMED EYES AND NOSTRILS, SEVERE LIVER DAMAGE, KIDNEY CHANGES, HYPEREMIA OF THE BRAIN, AND PRONOUNCED CEREBRAL EDEMA AND CELLULAR NECROSIS IN RATS. ANOSMIA, NOSEBLEED, AND OCCIPITAL HEADACHE WERE REPORTED IN ONE WORKER ENGAGED IN THE MANUFACTURE OF BUTYL TIN COMPOUNDS.

FIRST AID- REMOVE FROM EXPOSURE AREA TO FRESH AIR IMMEDIATELY. IF BREATHING HAS STOPPED, PERFORM ARTIFICIAL RESPIRATION. KEEP PERSON WARM AND AT REST. TREAT SYMPTOMATICALLY AND SUPPORTIVELY. GET MEDICAL ATTENTION IMMEDIATELY.

SKIN CONTACT: TRIBUTYLTIN CHLORIDE: IRRITANT. **ACUTE EXPOSURE-** DIRECT CONTACT WITH VAPOR OR LIQUID MAY CAUSE REDDENING AND SWELLING OF HAIR FOLLICLES, AND ITCHING, WHICH MAY BE DELAYED SEVERAL HOURS. THE REACTION MAY INTENSIFY WITH FORMATION OF PUSTULES OVER FOLLICULAR OPENINGS. IN CASE OF SEVERE BURNS, THERE MAY BE MODERATE PAIN, BUT PRIMARILY ITCHING. HEALING MAY BE COMPLETE WITHIN 7-10 DAYS. **CHRONIC EXPOSURE-** PROLONGED CONTACT MAY RESULT IN DIFFUSE ERYTHEMATOID DERMATITIS WITH PRURITIS AND SOME PUSTULAR ERUPTIONS. LESIONS GENERALLY DISAPPEAR RAPIDLY WHEN REMOVED FROM CONTACT. REPEATED APPLICATION TO RABBIT SKIN PRODUCED WEIGHT LOSS, LOSS OF APPETITE, ASTHENIA, ANEMIA, BLOOD DESTRUCTION, AND INDICATIONS OF SEVERE LIVER AND KIDNEY DAMAGE.

FIRST AID- REMOVE CONTAMINATED CLOTHING AND SHOES IMMEDIATELY. WASH AFFECTED AREA WITH SOAP OR MILD DETERGENT AND LARGE AMOUNTS OF WATER UNTIL NO EVIDENCE OF CHEMICAL REMAINS (AT LEAST 15-20 MINUTES).

EYE CONTACT: TRIBUTYLTIN CHLORIDE: IRRITANT. **ACUTE EXPOSURE-** APPLICATION OF 50 UG FOR 24 HOURS RESULTED IN SEVERE IRRITATION IN RABBITS. CONTACT WITH A BUTYLTIN COMPOUND PRODUCED LACRIMATION AND CONJUNCTIVAL EDEMA, LASTING SEVERAL DAYS, BUT WITH NO PERMANENT INJURY. CORNEAL OPACITIES HAVE BEEN REPORTED FROM CONTACT WITH SOME ORGANOTIN COMPOUNDS. **CHRONIC EXPOSURE-** PROLONGED EXPOSURE TO VAPORS PRODUCED INFLAMED EYES IN RABBITS. REPEATED EXPOSURE TO IRRITANTS MAY CAUSE CONJUNCTIVITIS.

FIRST AID- WASH EYES IMMEDIATELY WITH LARGE AMOUNTS OF WATER, OCCASIONALLY LIFTING UPPER AND LOWER LIDS, UNTIL NO EVIDENCE OF CHEMICAL REMAINS (AT LEAST 15-20 MINUTES).

INGESTION: TRIBUTYLTIN CHLORIDE: TOXIC. **ACUTE EXPOSURE-** INGESTION OF 129 MG/KG OF TRIBUTYLTIN CHLORIDE RESULTED IN DEATH IN RATS; 500 MG/KG PRODUCED DAMAGE TO THE LIVER, KIDNEYS, AND SPLEEN IN MICE. **CHRONIC EXPOSURE-** NO SPECIFIC DATA AVAILABLE. SOME ORGANOTIN COMPOUNDS HAVE PRODUCED WEAKNESS, TRANSIENT OR PERMANENT PARALYSIS, VERTIGO, VISUAL DISTURBANCES, PHOTOPHOBIA, ABDOMINAL PAIN, ENCEPHALOPATHY AND BRAIN

EDEMA, CLINICAL EFFECTS OF DEPRESSION, CONVULSIONS, FLACCID PARALYSIS, URINARY RETENTION, AND DEATH.

FIRST AID- TREAT SYMPTOMATICALLY AND SUPPORTIVELY. GET MEDICAL ATTENTION IMMEDIATELY (DREISBACH, HANDBOOK OF POISONING, 12TH ED.). TREATMENT SHOULD BE PERFORMED BY QUALIFIED MEDICAL PERSONNEL.

ANTIDOTE: NO SPECIFIC ANTIDOTE. TREAT SYMPTOMATICALLY AND SUPPORTIVELY.

REACTIVITY

REACTIVITY: STABLE UNDER NORMAL TEMPERATURES AND PRESSURES.

INCOMPATIBILITIES: TRIBUTYLTIN CHLORIDE: OXIDIZERS (STRONG): INCOMPATIBLE.

DECOMPOSITION: THERMAL DECOMPOSITION PRODUCTS MAY INCLUDE TOXIC AND CORROSIVE FUMES OF CHLORIDES AND TOXIC OXIDES OF CARBON.

POLYMERIZATION:WILL NOT OCCUR.

STORAGE AND DISPOSAL

OBSERVE ALL FEDERAL, STATE AND LOCAL REGULATIONS WHEN STORING OR DISPOSING OF THIS SUBSTANCE. FOR ASSISTANCE, CONTACT THE DISTRICT DIRECTOR OF THE ENVIRONMENTAL PROTECTION AGENCY.

STORAGE AND DISPOSAL MUST BE IN ACCORDANCE WITH 40 CFR 165.

CONDITIONS TO AVOID

MAY BURN BUT DOES NOT IGNITE READILY.

SPILL AND LEAK PROCEDURES

OCCUPATIONAL SPILL: DO NOT TOUCH SPILLED MATERIAL. STOP LEAK IF YOU CAN DO IT WITHOUT RISK. USE WATER SPRAY TO REDUCE VAPORS. FOR SMALL SPILLS, TAKE UP WITH SAND OR OTHER ABSORBENT MATERIAL AND PLACE INTO CONTAINERS FOR LATER DISPOSAL. FOR LARGER SPILLS, DIKE FAR AHEAD OF SPILL FOR LATER DISPOSAL. KEEP UNNECESSARY PEOPLE AWAY. ISOLATE HAZARD AREA AND DENY ENTRY. VENTILATE CLOSED SPACES BEFORE ENTERING.

PROTECTIVE EQUIPMENT

VENTILATION: PROVIDE LOCAL EXHAUST OR PROCESS ENCLOSURE VENTILATION TO MEET PUBLISHED EXPOSURE LIMITS.

RESPIRATOR: THE FOLLOWING RESPIRATORS AND MAXIMUM USE CONCENTRATIONS ARE RECOMMENDATIONS BY THE U.S. DEPARTMENT OF HEALTH AND HUMAN SERVICES, NIOSH POCKET GUIDE TO CHEMICAL HAZARDS; NIOSH CRITERIA DOCUMENTS OR BY THE U.S. DEPARTMENT OF LABOR, 29 CFR 1910 SUBPART Z. THE SPECIFIC RESPIRATOR SELECTED MUST BE BASED ON CONTAMINATION LEVELS FOUND IN THE WORK PLACE, MUST NOT EXCEED THE WORKING LIMITS OF THE RESPIRATOR AND BE JOINTLY APPROVED BY THE NATIONAL INSTITUTE FOR OCCUPATIONAL SAFETY AND HEALTH AND THE MINE SAFETY AND HEALTH ADMINISTRATION (NIOSH-MSHA).

TIN, ORGANIC COMPOUNDS (AS SN):

1 MG/M3- ANY CHEMICAL CARTRIDGE RESPIRATOR WITH ORGANIC VAPOR CARTRIDGES IN COMBINATION WITH A DUST AND MIST FILTER. ANY SUPPLIED-AIR RESPIRATOR. ANY SELF-CONTAINED BREATHING APPARATUS.

2.5 MG/M3- ANY SUPPLIED-AIR RESPIRATOR OPERATED IN A CONTINUOUS FLOW MODE. ANY POWERED AIR-PURIFYING RESPIRATOR WITH ORGANIC VAPOR CARTRIDGES IN COMBINATION WITH A DUST AND MIST FILTER.

5 MG/M3- ANY CHEMICAL CARTRIDGE RESPIRATOR WITH A FULL FACEPIECE AND ORGANIC VAPOR CARTRIDGES IN COMBINATION WITH A HIGH-EFFICIENCY PARTICULATE FILTER. ANY SUPPLIED-AIR RESPIRATOR WITH A FULL FACEPIECE. ANY SELF-CONTAINED BREATHING APPARATUS WITH A FULL FACEPIECE. ANY AIR-PURIFYING FULL FACEPIECE RESPIRATOR (GAS MASK) WITH A CHIN-STYLE OR FRONT- OR BACK-MOUNTED ORGANIC VAPOR CANISTER HAVING A HIGH-EFFICIENCY PARTICULATE FILTER. ANY POWERED AIR-PURIFYING RESPIRATOR WITH A TIGHT-FITTING FACEPIECE AND ORGANIC VAPOR CARTRIDGES IN COMBINATION WITH A HIGH-EFFICIENCY PARTICULATE FILTER. ANY SUPPLIED-AIR RESPIRATOR WITH A TIGHT-FITTING FACEPIECE OPERATED IN A CONTINUOUS FLOW MODE.

200 MG/M3- ANY SUPPLIED-AIR RESPIRATOR WITH A FULL FACEPIECE OPERATED IN PRESSURE-DEMAND OR OTHER POSITIVE PRESSURE MODE.

ESCAPE- ANY AIR-PURIFYING FULL FACEPIECE RESPIRATOR (GAS MASK) WITH A CHIN-STYLE OR FRONT- OR BACK-MOUNTED ORGANIC VAPOR CANISTER HAVING A HIGH-EFFICIENCY PARTICULATE FILTER. ANY APPROPRIATE ESCAPE-TYPE SELF-CONTAINED BREATHING APPARATUS.

FOR FIREFIGHTING AND OTHER IMMEDIATELY DANGEROUS TO LIFE OR HEALTH CONDITIONS:

SELF-CONTAINED BREATHING APPARATUS WITH FULL FACEPIECE OPERATED IN PRESSURE-DEMAND OR OTHER POSITIVE PRESSURE MODE.

SUPPLIED-AIR RESPIRATOR WITH FULL FACEPIECE AND OPERATED IN PRESSURE-DEMAND OR OTHER POSITIVE PRESSURE MODE IN COMBINATION WITH AN AUXILIARY SELF-CONTAINED BREATHING APPARATUS OPERATED IN PRESSURE-DEMAND OR OTHER POSITIVE PRESSURE MODE.

CLOTHING: EMPLOYEE MUST WEAR APPROPRIATE PROTECTIVE (IMPERVIOUS) CLOTHING AND EQUIPMENT TO PREVENT ANY POSSIBILITY OF SKIN CONTACT WITH THIS SUBSTANCE.

GLOVES: EMPLOYEE MUST WEAR APPROPRIATE PROTECTIVE GLOVES TO PREVENT CONTACT WITH THIS SUBSTANCE.

EYE PROTECTION: EMPLOYEE MUST WEAR SPLASH-PROOF OR DUST-RESISTANT SAFETY GOGGLES AND A FACESHIELD TO PREVENT CONTACT WITH THIS SUBSTANCE.

EMERGENCY WASH FACILITIES: WHERE THERE IS ANY POSSIBILITY THAT AN EMPLOYEE'S EYES AND/OR SKIN MAY BE EXPOSED TO THIS SUBSTANCE, THE EMPLOYER SHOULD PROVIDE AN EYE WASH FOUNTAIN AND QUICK DRENCH SHOWER WITHIN THE IMMEDIATE WORK AREA FOR EMERGENCY USE.

AUTHORIZED BY- OCCUPATIONAL HEALTH SERVICES, INC.

CREATION DATE: 10/05/89 ***REVISION DATE:*** 05/09/90

MATERIAL SAFETY DATA SHEET

OCCUPATIONAL HEALTH SERVICES, INC.
AGRICULTURE AND PESTICIDE DIVISION
450 SEVENTH AVENUE, SUITE 2407
NEW YORK, NEW YORK 10123

EMERGENCY CONTACT:
JOHN S. BRANSFORD, JR. (615) 292-1180
1-800-445-MSDS OR (212) 967-1100

SUBSTANCE IDENTIFICATION

CAS-NUMBER 1983-10-4

SUBSTANCE: TRIBUTYLTIN FLUORIDE

TRADE NAMES/SYNONYMS: STANNANE, TRIBUTYLFLUORO-; TIN, TRIBUTYLFLUORO-; FLUOROTRIBUTYLSTANNANE; TRIBUTYLFLUOROTIN; TRI-N-BUTYLSTANNYLFLUORIDE; TRI-N-BUTYLTIN FLUORIDE; FLUOROTRIBUTYLTIN; TRIBUTYLFLUOROSTANNANE; BIOMET; C12H27FSN; PST72227

CHEMICAL FAMILY: ORGANOMETALLIC

MOLECULAR FORMULA: (C4-H9)3-SN-F

MOLECULAR WEIGHT: 309.08

CERCLA RATINGS (SCALE 0-3): HEALTH=3 FIRE=1 REACTIVITY=0 PERSISTENCE=3

NFPA RATINGS (SCALE 0-4): HEALTH=4 FIRE=1 REACTIVITY=0

COMPONENTS AND CONTAMINANTS

COMPONENT: TRIBUTYLTIN FLUORIDE ***PERCENT:*** 100.0
CAS# 1983-10-4

OTHER CONTAMINANTS: NONE

EXPOSURE LIMITS: TIN, ORGANIC COMPOUNDS (AS SN): 0.1 MG/M3 OSHA TWA 0.1 MG/M3 ACGIH TWA (SKIN) (NOTICE OF INTENDED CHANGE 1988-89) 0.1 MG/M3 NIOSH RECOMMENDED 10 HOUR TWA

PHYSICAL DATA

DESCRIPTION: SOLID ***MELTING POINT:*** 424-426 F (218-219 C) (DECOMPOSES)

SPECIFIC GRAVITY: 1.27 @ 25 C ***SOLUBILITY IN WATER:*** NOT AVAILABLE

FIRE AND EXPLOSION DATA

FIRE AND EXPLOSION HAZARD: SLIGHT FIRE HAZARD WHEN EXPOSED TO HEAT OR FLAME.

FIREFIGHTING MEDIA: DRY CHEMICAL, CARBON DIOXIDE, HALON, WATER SPRAY OR STANDARD FOAM (1987 EMERGENCY RESPONSE GUIDEBOOK, DOT P 5800.4). FOR LARGER FIRES, USE WATER SPRAY, FOG OR STANDARD FOAM (1987 EMERGENCY RESPONSE GUIDEBOOK, DOT P 5800.4).

FIREFIGHTING: MOVE CONTAINERS FROM FIRE AREA IF POSSIBLE. FIGHT FIRE FROM MAXIMUM DISTANCE. STAY AWAY FROM STORAGE TANK ENDS. DIKE FIRE CONTROL WATER FOR LATER DISPOSAL. DO NOT SCATTER MATERIAL (1987 EMERGENCY RESPONSE GUIDEBOOK, DOT P 5800.4, GUIDE PAGE 55). EXTINGUISH USING AGENTS SUITABLE FOR SURROUNDING FIRE. APPLY WATER IN FLOODING QUANTITIES AS A FOG. AVOID CONTAMINATING WATER SOURCES AND SEWERS. AVOID BREATHING FUMES; KEEP UPWIND.

TOXICITY

TRIBUTYLTIN FLUORIDE: TOXICITY DATA: 5.3 MG/M3/4 HOURS INHALATION-RAT LC50 (38MKAJ); 320 MG/KG ORAL-MOUSE LDLO; 50 MG/KG ORAL-RABBIT LDLO. CARCINOGEN STATUS: NONE. LOCAL EFFECTS: IRRITANT- INHALATION, SKIN, EYES. ACUTE TOXICITY LEVEL: HIGHLY TOXIC BY INHALATION. TARGET EFFECTS: POISONING MAY AFFECT LIVER, KIDNEYS, SPLEEN, AND BLOOD. AT INCREASED RISK FROM EXPOSURE: PERSONS WITH PRE-EXISTING SKIN DISEASE.

HEALTH EFFECTS AND FIRST AID

INHALATION: TRIBUTYLTIN FLUORIDE: IRRITANT/HIGHLY TOXIC. 200 MG(SN)/M3 IMMEDIATELY DANGEROUS TO LIFE OR HEALTH. ACUTE EXPOSURE- WHEN

EXPOSED TO DUSTS AT 2.0-73.0 MG/M3 FOR 4 HOURS, RATS EXPERIENCED SNEEZING, WEAKNESS, CLEAR OR BLOODY NASAL DISCHARGE, PROSTRATION, AND DEATH. INDIVIDUALS EXPOSED TO VAPORS OR FUMES OF ORGANOTIN COMPOUNDS MAY DEVELOP IRRITATION OF THE MOUTH AND RESPRIATORY TRACT WITH SORE THROAT AND COUGHING. **CHRONIC EXPOSURE-** WORKERS EXPOSED TO TRIBUTYLTIN OXIDE FOR 2 WEEKS EXHIBITED NASAL DISCHARGE AND BLEEDING, AND IRRITATION AND HEMORRHAGE OF THE NASAL MUCOSA AND SEPTUM. CHRONIC EXPOSURE TO THE FUMES OF OTHER TRIBUTYLTIN HALIDES BY RATS RESULTED IN EDEMA OF THE SKIN AND TRACHEA, AND EDEMA, INFLAMMATION, BLEEDING AND CONGESTION OF THE BRONCHI AND LUNGS. SYSTEMIC EFFECTS IN THE CENTRAL NERVOUS SYSTEM, LIVER, AND KIDNEYS, AND DEATH WERE ALSO OBSERVED.

FIRST AID- REMOVE FROM EXPOSURE AREA TO FRESH AIR IMMEDIATELY. IF BREATHING HAS STOPPED, PERFORM ARTIFICIAL RESPIRATION. KEEP PERSON WARM AND AT REST. TREAT SYMPTOMATICALLY AND SUPPORTIVELY. GET MEDICAL ATTENTION IMMEDIATELY.

SKIN CONTACT: TRIBUTYLTIN FLUORIDE: IRRITANT. **ACUTE EXPOSURE-** TRIBUTYLTIN COMPOUNDS MAY CAUSE CHEMICAL BURNS WHICH USUALLY APPEAR 1 TO 8 HOURS AFTER CONTACT, CAUSE ITCHING WITHOUT MUCH PAIN, AND HEAL IN 7 TO 10 DAYS WITHOUT SCARRING. SINGLE APPLICATIONS OF OTHER TRIBUTYLTIN HALIDES TO THE SHAVED BACKS OF RABBITS AT 0.2-1.0 CC/KG CAUSED ANEMIA, BLOOD DESTRUCTION, AND DEATH. **CHRONIC EXPOSURE-** ADMINISTRATION OF 5-30% TRIBUTYLTIN FLUORIDE SOLUTIONS TO THE SHAVED BACKS OF MICE 3 DAYS/WEEK FOR 6 MONTHS CAUSED NON-NEOPLASTIC HYPERTROPHIC, INFLAMMATORY LESIONS. PROLONGED CONTACT WITH TRIBUTYLTIN COMPOUNDS BY MAN THROUGH CONTAMINATED CLOTHES HAS CAUSED FAINT ERYTHEMATOUS ERUPTIONS WHICH ITCH. THESE LESIONS ARE USUALLY LOCATED ON THE LOWER ABDOMEN, THIGHS, GROIN, AND PERINEUM, AND HEAL RAPIDLY WHEN CONTACT IS DISCONTINUED. PROLONGED AND REPEATED CONTACT WITH OTHER TRIBUTYLTIN HALIDES BY RABBITS CAUSED LOSS OF APETITE, ASTHENIA, AND ANEMIA, WITH LIVER AND KIDNEY DAMAGE, BLOOD DESTRUCTION, AND DEATH.

FIRST AID- REMOVE CONTAMINATED CLOTHING AND SHOES IMMEDIATELY. WASH AFFECTED AREA WITH SOAP OR MILD DETERGENT AND LARGE AMOUNTS OF WATER UNTIL NO EVIDENCE OF CHEMICAL REMAINS (APPROXIMATELY 15-20 MINUTES). GET MEDICAL ATTENTION IMMEDIATELY.

EYE CONTACT: TRIBUTYLTIN FLUORIDE: IRRITANT. **ACUTE EXPOSURE-** EXPOSURE TO DUSTS BY RATS AT 2.0-73.0 MG/M3 FOR 4 HOURS CAUSED LACRIMATION AND PTOSIS. SOME TRIBUTYLTIN COMPOUNDS ARE EYE IRRITANTS IN MAN, AND ACCIDENTAL SPLASHING INTO THE EYES HAS CAUSED LACRIMATION AND CONJUNCTIVAL ERYTHEMA AND EDEMA, WHICH LASTED FOR SEVERAL DAYS BUT CAUSED NO PERMANENT DAMAGE. **CHRONIC EXPOSURE-** REPEATED OR PROLONGED EXPOSURE TO TRIBUTYLTIN COMPOUNDS MAY RESULT IN CONJUNCTIVITIS.

FIRST AID- WASH EYES IMMEDIATELY WITH LARGE AMOUNTS OF WATER OR NORMAL SALINE, OCCASIONALLY LIFTING UPPER AND LOWER LIDS, UNTIL NO EVIDENCE OF CHEMICAL REMAINS (APPROXIMATELY 15-20 MINUTES). GET MEDICAL ATTENTION IMMEDIATELY.

INGESTION: TRIBUTYLTIN FLUORIDE: **ACUTE EXPOSURE-** NO SPECIFIC DATA AVAILABLE. INGESTION OF OTHER TRIBUTYLTIN HALIDES BY MICE CAUSED DAMAGE TO THE LIVER, KIDNEYS, AND SPLEEN, AND DEATH. **CHRONIC EXPOSURE-** NO SPECIFIC DATA AVAILABLE.

FIRST AID- TREAT SYMPTOMATICALLY AND SUPPORTIVELY. GET MEDICAL ATTENTION IMMEDIATELY. IF VOMITING OCCURS, KEEP HEAD LOWER THAN HIPS TO PREVENT ASPIRATION.

ANTIDOTE: NO SPECIFIC ANTIDOTE. TREAT SYMPTOMATICALLY AND SUPPORTIVELY.

REACTIVITY

REACTIVITY: STABLE UNDER NORMAL TEMPERATURES AND PRESSURES.

INCOMPATIBILITIES: TRIBUTYLTIN FLUORIDE: OXIDIZERS (STRONG): FIRE AND EXPLOSION HAZARD.

DECOMPOSITION: THERMAL DECOMPOSITION MAY RELEASE TOXIC AND/OR HAZARDOUS GASES.

POLYMERIZATION: WILL NOT OCCUR.

STORAGE AND DISPOSAL

OBSERVE ALL FEDERAL, STATE AND LOCAL REGULATIONS WHEN STORING OR DISPOSING OF THIS SUBSTANCE. FOR ASSISTANCE, CONTACT THE DISTRICT DIRECTOR OF THE ENVIRONMENTAL PROTECTION AGENCY.

STORAGE AND DISPOSAL MUST BE IN ACCORDANCE WITH 40 CFR 165.

CONDITIONS TO AVOID

MAY BURN BUT DOES NOT IGNITE READILY.

SPILL AND LEAK PROCEDURES

OCCUPATIONAL SPILL: DO NOT TOUCH SPILLED MATERIAL. FOR SMALL DRY SPILLS, WITH A CLEAN SHOVEL PLACE MATERIAL INTO CLEAN, DRY CONTAINERS AND COVER. MOVE CONTAINERS FROM SPILL AREA. FOR LARGER SPILLS, DIKE FAR AHEAD OF SPILL FOR LATER DISPOSAL. KEEP UNNECESSARY PEOPLE AWAY. ISOLATE HAZARD AREA AND DENY ENTRY. VENTILATE CLOSED SPACES BEFORE ENTERING.

PROTECTIVE EQUIPMENT

VENTILATION: PROCESS ENCLOSURE RECOMMENDED TO MEET PUBLISHED EXPOSURE LIMITS.

RESPIRATOR: THE FOLLOWING RESPIRATORS AND MAXIMUM USE CONCENTRATIONS ARE RECOMMENDATIONS BY THE U.S. DEPARTMENT OF HEALTH AND HUMAN SERVICES, NIOSH POCKET GUIDE TO CHEMICAL HAZARDS; NIOSH CRITERIA DOCUMENTS OR BY THE U.S. DEPARTMENT OF LABOR, 29 CFR 1910 SUBPART Z. THE SPECIFIC RESPIRATOR SELECTED MUST BE BASED ON CONTAMINATION LEVELS FOUND IN THE WORK PLACE, MUST NOT EXCEED THE WORKING LIMITS OF THE RESPIRATOR AND BE JOINTLY APPROVED BY THE NATIONAL INSTITUTE FOR OCCUPATIONAL SAFETY AND HEALTH AND THE MINE SAFETY AND HEALTH ADMINISTRATION (NIOSH-MSHA). TIN, ORGANIC COMPOUNDS (AS SN):

1 MG/M3- ANY CHEMICAL CARTRIDGE RESPIRATOR WITH ORGANIC VAPOR CARTRIDGES IN COMBINATION WITH A DUST AND MIST FILTER. ANY SUPPLIED-AIR RESPIRATOR. ANY SELF-CONTAINED BREATHING APPARATUS.

2.5 MG/M3- ANY SUPPLIED-AIR RESPIRATOR OPERATED IN A CONTINUOUS FLOW MODE. ANY POWERED AIR-PURIFYING RESPIRATOR WITH ORGANIC VAPOR CARTRIDGES IN COMBINATION WITH A DUST AND MIST FILTER.

5 MG/M3- ANY CHEMICAL CARTRIDGE RESPIRATOR WITH A FULL FACEPIECE AND ORGANIC VAPOR CARTRIDGES IN COMBINATION WITH A HIGH-EFFICIENCY PARTICULATE FILTER. ANY SUPPLIED-AIR RESPIRATOR WITH A FULL FACEPIECE. ANY SELF-CONTAINED BREATHING APPARATUS WITH A FULL FACEPIECE. ANY AIR-PURIFYING FULL FACEPIECE RESPIRATOR (GAS MASK) WITH A CHIN-STYLE OR FRONT- OR BACK-MOUNTED ORGANIC VAPOR CANISTER HAVING A HIGH-EFFICIENCY PARTICULATE FILTER. ANY POWERED AIR-PURIFYING RESPIRATOR WITH A TIGHT-FITTING FACEPIECE AND ORGANIC VAPOR CARTRIDGES IN COMBINATION WITH A HIGH-EFFICIENCY PARTICULATE FILTER. ANY SUPPLIED-AIR RESPIRATOR WITH A TIGHT-FITTING FACEPIECE OPERATED IN A CONTINUOUS FLOW MODE.

200 MG/M3- ANY SUPPLIED-AIR RESPIRATOR WITH A FULL FACEPIECE OPERATED IN PRESSURE-DEMAND OR OTHER POSITIVE PRESSURE MODE.

ESCAPE- ANY AIR-PURIFYING FULL FACEPIECE RESPIRATOR (GAS MASK) WITH A CHIN-STYLE OR FRONT- OR BACK-MOUNTED ORGANIC VAPOR CANISTER HAVING A HIGH-EFFICIENCY PARTICULATE FILTER. ANY APPROPRIATE ESCAPE-TYPE SELF-CONTAINED BREATHING APPARATUS.

FOR FIREFIGHTING AND OTHER IMMEDIATELY DANGEROUS TO LIFE OR HEALTH CONDITIONS:

SELF-CONTAINED BREATHING APPARATUS WITH FULL FACEPIECE OPERATED IN PRESSURE-DEMAND OR OTHER POSITIVE PRESSURE MODE.

SUPPLIED-AIR RESPIRATOR WITH FULL FACEPIECE AND OPERATED IN PRESSURE-DEMAND OR OTHER POSITIVE PRESSURE MODE IN COMBINATION WITH AN AUXILIARY SELF-CONTAINED BREATHING APPARATUS OPERATED IN PRESSURE-DEMAND OR OTHER POSITIVE PRESSURE MODE.

CLOTHING: EMPLOYEE MUST WEAR APPROPRIATE PROTECTIVE (IMPERVIOUS) CLOTHING AND EQUIPMENT TO PREVENT ANY POSSIBILITY OF SKIN CONTACT WITH THIS SUBSTANCE.

GLOVES: EMPLOYEE MUST WEAR APPROPRIATE PROTECTIVE GLOVES TO PREVENT CONTACT WITH THIS SUBSTANCE.

EYE PROTECTION: EMPLOYEE MUST WEAR SPLASH-PROOF OR DUST-RESISTANT SAFETY GOGGLES AND A FACESHIELD TO PREVENT CONTACT WITH THIS SUBSTANCE.

EMERGENCY WASH FACILITIES: WHERE THERE IS ANY POSSIBILITY THAT AN EMPLOYEE'S EYES AND/OR SKIN MAY BE EXPOSED TO THIS SUBSTANCE, THE EMPLOYER SHOULD PROVIDE AN EYE WASH FOUNTAIN AND QUICK DRENCH SHOWER WITHIN THE IMMEDIATE WORK AREA FOR EMERGENCY USE.

AUTHORIZED BY- OCCUPATIONAL HEALTH SERVICES, INC.
CREATION DATE: 10/05/89 ***REVISION DATE:*** 11/02/89

MATERIAL SAFETY DATA SHEET

OCCUPATIONAL HEALTH SERVICES, INC.
AGRICULTURE AND PESTICIDE DIVISION
450 SEVENTH AVENUE, SUITE 2407
NEW YORK, NEW YORK 10123

EMERGENCY CONTACT:
JOHN S. BRANSFORD, JR. (615) 292-1180

1-800-445-MSDS OR (212) 967-1100

SUBSTANCE IDENTIFICATION

CAS-NUMBER 961-11-5

SUBSTANCE: **TETRACHLORVINPHOS**

TRADE NAMES/SYNONYMS: PHOSPHORIC ACID, 2-CHLORO-1-(2,4,5-TRICHLOROPHENYL)ETHENYL DIMETHYL ESTER; 2-CHLORO-1-(2,4,5-TRICHLOROPHENYL)ETHENYL DIMETHYL PHOSPHATE; PHOSPHORIC ACID, 2-CHLORO-1-(2,4,5-TRICHLOROPHENYL)VINYL DIMETHYL ESTER; 2-CHLORO-1-(2,4,5-TRICHLOROPHENYL)VINYL DIMETHYL PHOSPHATE; STIROFOS; GARDONA; RABON; STIROPHOS; C10H9CL4O4P; PST72243

CHEMICAL FAMILY: ORGANOPHOSPHATE

MOLECULAR FORMULA: C10-H9-CL4-O4-P

MOLECULAR WEIGHT: 365.95

CERCLA RATINGS (SCALE 0-3): HEALTH=2 FIRE=1 REACTIVITY=0 PERSISTENCE=0

NFPA RATINGS (SCALE 0-4): HEALTH=2 FIRE=1 REACTIVITY=0

COMPONENTS AND CONTAMINANTS

COMPONENT: TETRACHLORVINPHOS ***PERCENT:*** 100.0
CAS# 961-11-5

OTHER CONTAMINANTS: NONE

EXPOSURE LIMITS: NO OCCUPATIONAL EXPOSURE LIMITS ESTABLISHED BY OSHA, ACGIH, OR NIOSH.
TETRACHLORVINPHOS: SUBJECT TO SARA SECTION 313 ANNUAL TOXIC CHEMICAL RELEASE REPORTING.

PHYSICAL DATA

DESCRIPTION: COLORLESS TO OFF-WHITE CRYSTALLINE SOLID.

MELTING POINT: 199-208 F (93-98 C) ***SPECIFIC GRAVITY:*** NOT AVAILABLE

VAPOR PRESSURE: NEGLIGIBLE ***SOLUBILITY IN WATER:*** 0.0011% @ 20 C

SOLVENT SOLUBILITY: SOLUBLE IN ACETONE, CHLOROFORM, DICHLOROMETHANE, AND XYLENE; VERY SLIGHTLY SOLUBLE IN AROMATIC HYDROCARBONS. DECOMPOSES SLOWLY AT 500 F (260 C).

FIRE AND EXPLOSION DATA

FIRE AND EXPLOSION HAZARD: SLIGHT FIRE HAZARD WHEN EXPOSED TO HEAT OR FLAME.

FIREFIGHTING MEDIA: DRY CHEMICAL, CARBON DIOXIDE, HALON, WATER SPRAY OR STANDARD FOAM (1987 EMERGENCY RESPONSE GUIDEBOOK, DOT P 5800.4). FOR LARGER FIRES, USE WATER SPRAY, FOG OR STANDARD FOAM (1987 EMERGENCY RESPONSE GUIDEBOOK, DOT P 5800.4).

FIREFIGHTING: MOVE CONTAINERS FROM FIRE AREA IF POSSIBLE. FIGHT FIRE FROM MAXIMUM DISTANCE. STAY AWAY FROM STORAGE TANK ENDS. DIKE FIRE CONTROL WATER FOR LATER DISPOSAL. DO NOT SCATTER MATERIAL (1987 EMERGENCY RESPONSE GUIDEBOOK, DOT P 5800.4, GUIDE PAGE 55). EXTINGUISH ONLY IF FLOW CAN BE STOPPED; USE FLOODING AMOUNTS OF WATER AS FOG, SOLID STREAMS MAY BE INEFFECTIVE. COOL CONTAINERS WITH FLOODING AMOUNTS OF WATER FROM AS FAR A DISTANCE AS POSSIBLE. USE WATER SPRAY TO ABSORB TOXIC VAPORS. AVOID BREATHING TOXIC VAPORS; KEEP UPWIND. CONSIDER EVACUATION OF DOWNWIND AREA IF MATERIAL IS LEAKING.

TOXICITY

TETRACHLORVINPHOS: TOXICITY DATA: >2500 MG/KG SKIN-RABBIT LD50 (FMCHA2); 4 GM/KG ORAL-RAT LD50; 4200 MG/KG ORAL-MOUSE LD50; 15 GM/KG SUBCUTANEOUS-MOUSE LD50; 1160 MG/KG INTRAPERITONEAL-RAT LD50; 1170 MG/KG INTRAPERITONEAL-MOUSE LD50; REPRODUCTIVE EFFECTS DATA (RTECS); TUMORIGENIC DATA (RTECS). CARCINOGEN STATUS: ANIMAL LIMITED EVIDENCE (IARC GROUP-3). BY ORAL ADMINISTRATION, TECHNICAL TETRACHLORVINPHOS PRODUCED HEPATOCELLULAR CARCINOMAS IN MALE MICE AND BENIGN AND MALIGNANT LIVER-CELL TUMORS IN FEMALE MICE. INCREASED INCIDENCES OF C-CELL ADENOMA OF THE THYROID AND OF CORTICAL ADENOMA OF THE ADRENAL WERE OBSERVED IN FEMALE RATS. ACUTE TOXICITY LEVEL: MODERATELY TOXIC BY INGESTION. TARGET EFFECTS: CHOLINESTERASE INHIBITOR. AT INCREASED RISK FROM EXPOSURE: PERSONS WITH RESPIRATORY AILMENTS, RECENT EXPOSURE TO CHOLINESTERASE INHIBITORS OR IMPAIRED CHOLINESTERASE PRODUCTION, OR LIVER MALFUNCTION.* ADDITIONAL DATA: TETRACHLORVINPHOS MAY POTENTIATE THE TOXICITY OF MALATHION, AZINPHOS-METHYL, CARBARYL, COUMAPHOS, DICROTOPHOS, DIMETHOATE, METHYL PARATHION, MEVINPHOS, PARATHION, PHOSPHAMIDON, AND RONNEL. MAY CROSS THE PLACENTA. HIGH ENVIRONMENTAL TEMPERATURES OR EXPOSURE OF THE CHEMICAL TO VISIBLE OR ULTRAVIOLET LIGHT MAY ENHANCE THE TOXICITY. INTERACTIONS WITH MEDICATIONS MAY OCCUR.*

* MAY BE BASED ON GENERAL INFORMATION ON ORGANOPHOSPHATES.

HEALTH EFFECTS AND FIRST AID

INHALATION: TETRACHLORVINPHOS: SEE INFORMATION ON ORGANOPHOSPHATES.
ORGANOPHOSPHATES: CHOLINESTERASE INHIBITOR. **ACUTE EXPOSURE-** WHEN INHALED, THE FIRST EFFECTS OF CHOLINESTERASE INHIBITORS ARE USUALLY RESPIRATORY AND MAY INCLUDE NASAL HYPEREMIA AND WATERY DISCHARGE, COUGH, CHEST DISCOMFORT, DYSPNEA, AND WHEEZING DUE TO INCREASED BRONCHIAL SECRETIONS AND BRONCHOCONSTRICTION. IF SUFFICIENT AMOUNTS ARE ABSORBED, OTHER SYSTEMIC EFFECTS MAY BEGIN WITHIN A FEW MINUTES OR BE DELAYED FOR UP TO 12 HOURS. SYMPTOMS MAY INCLUDE PALLOR, NAUSEA, VOMITING, DIARRHEA, ABDOMINAL CRAMPS, HEADACHE, DIZZINESS, OCULAR PAIN, BLURRED VISION, MIOSIS OR IN SOME CASES, ESPECIALLY INITIALLY, MYDRIASIS, LACRIMATION, SALIVATION, SWEATING, AND CONFUSION. OTHER REPORTED CENTRAL NERVOUS SYSTEM OR NEUROMUSCULAR EFFECTS MAY INCLUDE ATAXIA, SLURRED SPEECH, AREFLEXIA, WEAKNESS, FATIGUE, FASCICULATIONS, TWITCHING, TREMORS POSSIBLY OF THE TONGUE AND EYELIDS, AND EVENTUALLY PARALYSIS OF THE EXTREMITIES AND POSSIBLY OF THE RESPIRATORY MUSCLES. IN SEVERE CASES THERE MAY ALSO BE INVOLUNTARY DEFECATION AND URINATION, CYANOSIS, PSYCHOSIS, HYPERGLYCEMIA, ACUTE PANCREATITIS, CARDIAC IRREGULARITIES, PULMONARY EDEMA, UNCONSCIOUSNESS, CONVULSIONS, AND COMA. DEATH IS PRIMARILY DUE TO RESPIRATORY FAILURE, ALTHOUGH CARDIOVASCULAR EFFECTS INCLUDING CARDIAC ARREST MAY ALSO BE IMPLICATED. LONG TERM SEQUELAE ARE RARE BUT MAY INCLUDE NEUROPSYCHIATRIC DISORDERS AND MYOPATHY WITH MUSCLE TENDERNESS. **CHRONIC EXPOSURE-** REPEATED OR PROLONGED EXPOSURE MAY RESULT IN THE EFFECTS OF ACUTE EXPOSURE. OTHER EFFECTS REPORTED IN WORKERS REPEATEDLY EXPOSED INCLUDE IMPAIRED MEMORY AND CONCENTRATION, ACUTE PSYCHOSIS, SEVERE DEPRESSIONS, IRRITABILTY, CONFUSION, APATHY, EMOTIONAL LABILITY, SOCIAL WITHDRAWAL, CONFUSION, HEADACHE, SPEECH DIFFICULTIES, DELAYED REACTION TIMES, SPATIAL DISORIENTATION, NIGHTMARES, SLEEPWALKING, AND DROWSINESS OR INSOMNIA. AN INFLUENZA-LIKE CONDITION WITH HEADACHE, NAUSEA, WEAKNESS, ANOREXIA AND MALAISE HAS ALSO BEEN REPORTED.

FIRST AID- REMOVE FROM EXPOSURE AREA TO FRESH AIR IMMEDIATELY. IF BREATHING HAS STOPPED, GIVE ARTIFICIAL RESPIRATION. MAINTAIN AIRWAY AND BLOOD PRESSURE AND ADMINISTER OXYGEN IF AVAILABLE. KEEP AFFECTED PERSON WARM AND AT REST. TREAT SYMPTOMATICALLY AND SUPPORTIVELY. ADMINISTRATION OF OXYGEN SHOULD BE PERFORMED BY QUALIFIED PERSONNEL. GET MEDICAL ATTENTION IMMEDIATELY.

SKIN CONTACT: TETRACHLORVINPHOS: SEE INFORMATION ON ORGANOPHOSPHATES.
ORGANOPHOSPHATES: CHOLINESTERASE INHIBITOR. **ACUTE EXPOSURE-** LOCALIZED SWEATING AND FASCICULATIONS MAY OCCUR AT THE SITE OF CONTACT. IF SUFFICIENT AMOUNTS ARE ABSORBED, OTHER EFFECTS OF CHOLINESTERASE INHIBITION AS DESCRIBED IN ACUTE INHALATION MAY OCCUR. SYMPTOMS MAY BE DELAYED 2-3 HOURS, BUT USUALLY NO MORE THAN 12 HOURS. THE RATE OF ABSORPTION IS INCREASED BY THE PRESENCE OF DERMATITIS OR HIGH AMBIENT TEMPERATURES. **CHRONIC EXPOSURE-** REPEATED OR PROLONGED EXPOSURE MAY CAUSE EFFECTS AS DESCRIBED IN ACUTE EXPOSURE. SOME ORGANOPHOSPHATES MAY CAUSE SENSITIZATION.

FIRST AID- REMOVE CONTAMINATED CLOTHING IMMEDIATELY. WASH CONTAMINATED AREAS WITH SOAP AND WATER FOLLOWED BY ALCOHOL (ARENA, POISONING, 4TH ED.). EMERGENCY PERSONNEL SHOULD WEAR GLOVES AND AVOID CONTAMINATION. TREAT RESPIRATORY DIFFICULTY WITH ARTIFICIAL RESPIRATION. GET MEDICAL ATTENTION IMMEDIATELY.

EYE CONTACT: TETRACHLORVINPHOS: SEE INFORMATION ON ORAGANOPHOSPHATES.
ORGANOPHOSPHATES: CHOLINESTERASE INHIBITOR. **ACUTE EXPOSURE-** DIRECT CONTACT MAY CAUSE PAIN, HYPEREMIA, LACRIMATION, TWITCHING OF THE EYELIDS, MIOSIS, AND CILIARY MUSCLE SPASM WITH LOSS OF ACCOMODATION, BLURRED OR DIMMED VISION AND BROWACHE. SOMETIMES MYDRIASIS MAY OCCUR INSTEAD OF MIOSIS. WITH SUFFICIENT EXPOSURE, OTHER SYMPTOMS OF CHOLINESTERASE INHIBITION AS DESCRIBED IN ACUTE INHALATION MAY OCCUR. **CHRONIC EXPOSURE-** REPEATED OR PROLONGED EXPOSURE MAY CAUSE EFFECTS AS DESCRIBED IN ACUTE EXPOSURE. SOME COMPOUNDS HAVE CAUSED TOXIC EFFECTS ON THE CRYSTALLINE LENS, CONJUNCTIVAL THICKENING AND OBSTRUCTION OF THE NASOLACRIMAL CANALS WHEN USED AS MIOTIC EYEDROPS.

FIRST AID- IRRIGATE EYES WITH WATER OR SALINE SOLUTION. IF SYMPTOMS OF POISONING OCCUR, TREAT RESPIRATORY DIFFICULTY WITH ARTIFICIAL RESPIRATION AND OXYGEN. OBSERVE PATIENT FOR AT LEAST 24-36 HOURS (GOSSELIN, CLINICAL TOXICOLOGY OF COMMERCIAL PRODUCTS, 5TH ED.). GET MEDICAL ATTENTION IMMEDIATELY. OXYGEN SHOULD BE ADMINISTERED BY QUALIFIED MEDICAL PERSONNEL.

INGESTION: TETRACHLORVINPHOS:
NO SIGNS OF DELAYED NEUROTOXICITY WERE OBSERVED IN HENS FED AN ACUTE DOSE OF 1.5 GM/KG. ADVERSE EFFECTS ON THE LIVER WERE REPORTED IN

HUMANS RECEIVING A DAILY DOSE OF 12 OR 15 MG FOR 28 DAYS; LIVER FUNCTIONS. RETURNED TO NORMAL AFTER CESSATION OF TREATMENT. MINIMAL SIGNS OF CHOLINESTERASE INHIBITION WAS SEEN AT THE 15 MG LEVEL. NO SIGNS OF DELAYED NEUROTOXICITY WERE OBSERVED IN HENS RECEIVING A DAILY DOSE OF 300 MG/KG FOR 5 DAYS. REPRODUCTIVE EFFECTS HAVE BEEN REPORTED IN ANIMALS. TECHNICAL TETRACHLORVINPHOS PRODUCED HEPATOCELLULAR CARCINOMAS IN MALE MICE AND BENIGN AND MALIGNANT LIVER-CELL TUMORS IN FEMALE MICE. INCREASED INCIDENCES OF C-CELL ADENOMA OF THE THYROID AND OF CORTICAL ADENOMA OF THE ADRENEAL WERE FOUND IN FEMALE RATS; REDUCED BODY WIEGHTS AND DECREASE SURVIVAL WERE NOTED IN THE MALE RATS. SEE INFORMATION ON ORGANOPHOSPHATES.

ORGANOPHOSPHATES: CHOLINESTERASE INHIBITOR. **ACUTE EXPOSURE**- WHEN INGESTED, THE FIRST EFFECTS MAY BE NAUSEA, VOMITING, ANOREXIA, ABDOMINAL CRAMPS AND DIARRHEA. GASTROINTESTINAL ABSORPTION MAY CAUSE THE SYMPTOMS OF CHOLINESTERASE INHIBITION AS DESCRIBED IN ACUTE INHALATION. SYMPTOMS MAY BEGIN WITHIN MINUTES OR BE DELAYED. **CHRONIC EXPOSURE**- REPEATED INGESTION MAY CAUSE EFFECTS AS DESCRIBED IN ACUTE EXPOSURE.

FIRST AID- IF PERSON IS ALERT AND RESPIRATION IS NOT DEPRESSED, GIVE SYRUP OF IPECAC FOLLOWED BY WATER (IF VOMITING OCCURS, KEEP HEAD BELOW HIPS TO PREVENT ASPIRATION). IF CONSCIOUSNESS LEVEL DECLINES OR VOMITING HAS NOT OCCURRED IN 15 MINUTES EMPTY STOMACH BY GASTRIC LAVAGE WITH THE AID OF CUFFED ENDOTRACHEAL TUBE USING ISOTONIC SALINE OR 5% SODIUM BICARBONATE FOLLOW WITH ACTIVATED CHARCOAL. ESTABLISH AND MAINTAIN AIRWAY. TREAT RESPIRATORY DIFFICULTY WITH ARTIFICIAL RESPIRATION AND OXYGEN. DO NOT GIVE MORPHINE, AMINOPHYLLINE, PHENOTHIAZINES, RESERPINE, FUROSEMIDE, OR ETHACRYNIC ACID (MORGAN, RECOGNITION AND MANAGEMENT OF PESTICIDE POISONINGS, 3RD ED.). TREAT SYMPTOMATICALLY AND SUPPORTIVELY. ADMINISTRATION OF OXYGEN AND LAVAGE MUST BE PERFORMED BY QUALIFIED MEDICAL PERSONNEL. GET MEDICAL ATTENTION IMMEDIATELY.

ANTIDOTE: THE FOLLOWING ANTIDOTE(S) HAVE BEEN RECOMMENDED. HOWEVER, THE DECISION AS TO WHETHER THE SEVERITY OF POISONING REQUIRES ADMINISTRATION OF ANY ANTIDOTE AND ACTUAL DOSE REQUIRED SHOULD BE MADE BY QUALIFIED MEDICAL PERSONNEL.

FOR CHOLINESTERASE INHIBITORS: ESTABLISH CLEAR AIRWAY AND TISSUE OXYGENATION BY ASPIRATION OF SECRETIONS, AND IF NECESSARY, BY ASSISTED PULMONARY VENTILATION WITH OXYGEN. IMPROVE TISSUE OXYGENATION AS MUCH AS POSSIBLE BEFORE ADMINISTERING ATROPINE TO MINIMIZE THE RISK OF VENTRICULAR FIBRILLATION. ADMINISTER ATROPINE SULFATE INTRAVENOUSLY, OR INTRAMUSCULARLY IF IV INJECTION IS NOT POSSIBLE. IN MODERATELY SEVERE POISONING ADMINISTER ATROPINE SULFATE, 0.4-2.0 MG REPEATED EVERY 15 MINUTES UNTIL ATROPINIZATION IS ACHIEVED (TACHYCARDIA, FLUSHING, DRY MOUTH, MYDRIASIS). MAINTAIN ATROPINIZATION BY REPEATED DOSES FOR 2-12 HOURS, OR LONGER, DEPENDING ON THE SEVERITY OF POISONING. THE APPEARANCE OF RALES IN THE LUNG BASES, MIOSIS, SALIVATION, NAUSEA, BRADYCARDIA, ARE ALL INDICATIONS OF INADEQUATE ATROPINIZATION. SEVERELY POISONED INDIVIDUALS MAY EXHIBIT REMARKABLE TOLERANCE TO ATROPINE; TWO OR MORE TIMES THE DOSAGES SUGGESTED ABOVE MAY BE NEEDED. PERSONS NOT POISONED OR ONLY SLIGHTLY POISONED, HOWEVER, MAY DEVELOP SIGNS OF ATROPINE TOXICITY FROM SUCH LARGE DOSAGES: FEVER, MUSCLE FIBRILLATIONS, AND DELIRIUM ARE THE MAIN SIGNS OF ATROPINE TOXICITY. IF THESE SIGNS APPEAR WHILE THE PATIENT IS FULLY ATROPINIZED, ATROPINE ADMINISTRATION SHOULD BE DISCONTINUED, AT LEAST TEMPORARILY. OBSERVE TREATED PATIENTS CLOSELY AT LEAST 24 HOURS TO INSURE THAT SYMPTOMS (POSSIBLY PULMONARY EDEMA) DO NOT RECUR AS ATROPINIZATION WEARS OFF. IN VERY SEVERE POISONINGS, METABOLIC DISPOSITION OF TOXICANT MAY REQUIRE SEVERAL HOURS OR DAYS DURING WHICH ATROPINIZATION MUST BE MAINTAINED. MARKEDLY LOWER LEVELS OF URINARY METABOLITES INDICATE THAT ATROPINE DOSAGE CAN BE TAPERED OFF. AS DOSAGE IS REDUCED, CHECK THE LUNG BASES FREQUENTLY FOR RALES. IF RALES ARE HEARD OR OTHER SYMPTOMS RETURN, RE-ESTABLISH ATROPINIZATION PROMPTLY (MORGAN, RECOGNITION AND MANAGEMENT OF PESTICIDE POISONINGS, 3RD ED.). ADMINISTRATION OF ANTIDOTE MUST BE PERFORMED BY QUALIFIED MEDICAL PERSONNEL.

IN CASES OF SEVERE POISONING BY ORGANOPHOSPHATE PESTICIDES IN WHICH RESPIRATORY DEPRESSION, MUSCLE WEAKNESS AND TWITCHINGS ARE SEVERE, GIVE PRALIDOXIME (PROTOPAM-AYERST, 2-PAM), 1.0 GRAM INTRAVENOUSLY AT NO MORE THAN 0.5 GRAM PER MINUTE. DOSAGE OF PRALIDOXIME MAY BE REPEATED IN 1-2 HOURS, THEN AT 10-12 HOUR INTERVALS IF NEEDED. IN VERY SEVERE POISONINGS, DOSAGE RATES MAY BE DOUBLED. TREATMENT WITH PRALIDOXIME WILL BE MOST EFFECTIVE IF GIVEN WITHIN THIRTY-SIX HOURS AFTER POISONING (MORGAN, RECOGNITION AND MANAGEMENT OF PESTICIDE POISONINGS, 3RD ED.). ANTIDOTE SHOULD BE ADMINISTERED BY QUALIFIED MEDICAL PERSONNEL.

REACTIVITY

REACTIVITY: MAY BE SLOWLY HYDROLYZED BY WATER.

INCOMPATIBILITIES: TETRACHLORVINPHOS: ACIDS: SLOWLY HYDROLYZES. ALKALI: HYDROLYZES. OXIDIZERS (STRONG): FIRE AND EXPLOSION HAZARD.

DECOMPOSITION: THERMAL DECOMPOSITION PRODUCTS MAY INCLUDE TOXIC AND CORROSIVE FUMES OF CHLORIDES, AND TOXIC OXIDES OF CARBON AND PHOSPHORUS.

POLYMERIZATION: HAZARDOUS POLYMERIZATION HAS NOT BEEN REPORTED TO OCCUR UNDER NORMAL TEMPERATURES AND PRESSURES.

STORAGE AND DISPOSAL

OBSERVE ALL FEDERAL, STATE AND LOCAL REGULATIONS WHEN STORING OR DISPOSING OF THIS SUBSTANCE. FOR ASSISTANCE, CONTACT THE DISTRICT DIRECTOR OF THE ENVIRONMENTAL PROTECTION AGENCY.

****STORAGE****

STORE IN ACCORDANCE WITH 40 CFR 165 RECOMMENDED PROCEDURES FOR THE DISPOSAL AND STORAGE OF PESTICIDES AND PESTICIDE CONTAINERS.

STORE AWAY FROM INCOMPATIBLE SUBSTANCES.

****DISPOSAL****

DISPOSAL MUST BE IN ACCORDANCE WITH 40 CFR 165 RECOMMENDED PROCEDURES FOR THE DISPOSAL AND STORAGE OF PESTICIDES AND PESTICIDE CONTAINERS.

CONDITIONS TO AVOID

MAY BURN BUT DOES NOT IGNITE READILY. CONTAINERS MAY EXPLODE IN HEAT OF FIRE.

SPILL AND LEAK PROCEDURES

OCCUPATIONAL SPILL: DO NOT TOUCH SPILLED MATERIAL. STOP LEAK IF YOU CAN DO IT WITHOUT RISK. USE WATER SPRAY TO REDUCE VAPORS. FOR SMALL SPILLS, TAKE UP WITH SAND OR OTHER ABSORBENT MATERIAL AND PLACE INTO CONTAINERS FOR LATER DISPOSAL. FOR SMALL DRY SPILLS, WITH A CLEAN SHOVEL PLACE MATERIAL INTO CLEAN, DRY CONTAINERS AND COVER. MOVE CONTAINERS FROM SPILL AREA. FOR LARGER SPILLS, DIKE FAR AHEAD OF SPILL FOR LATER DISPOSAL. KEEP UNNECESSARY PEOPLE AWAY. ISOLATE HAZARD AREA AND DENY ENTRY. VENTILATE CLOSED SPACES BEFORE ENTERING.

PROTECTIVE EQUIPMENT

VENTILATION: PROVIDE LOCAL EXHAUST OR GENERAL DILUTION VENTILATION SYSTEM.

RESPIRATOR: THE FOLLOWING RESPIRATORS ARE RECOMMENDED BASED ON INFORMATION FOUND IN THE PHYSICAL DATA, TOXICITY AND HEALTH EFFECTS SECTIONS. THEY ARE RANKED IN ORDER FROM MINIMUM TO MAXIMUM RESPIRATORY PROTECTION. THE SPECIFIC RESPIRATOR SELECTED MUST BE BASED ON CONTAMINATION LEVELS FOUND IN THE WORK PLACE, MUST NOT EXCEED THE WORKING LIMITS OF THE RESPIRATOR AND BE JOINTLY APPROVED BY THE NATIONAL INSTITUTE FOR OCCUPATIONAL SAFETY AND HEALTH AND THE MINE SAFETY AND HEALTH ADMINISTRATION (NIOSH-MSHA).

CHEMICAL CARTRIDGE RESPIRATOR WITH AN ORGANIC VAPOR CARTRIDGE(S) IN COMBINATION WITH A DUST AND MIST FILTER.

GAS MASK WITH ORGANIC VAPOR CANISTER (CHIN-STYLE OR FRONT- OR BACK-MOUNTED CANISTER) WITH A DUST AND MIST FILTER.

GAS MASK WITH ORGANIC VAPOR CANISTER (CHIN-STYLE OR FRONT- OR BACK-MOUNTED CANISTER) WITH A PARTICULATE FILTER.

POWERED AIR-PURIFYING RESPIRATOR WITH A HIGH-EFFICIENCY FILTER.

TYPE 'C' SUPPLIED-AIR RESPIRATOR WITH A FULL FACEPIECE OPERATED IN A PRESSURE-DEMAND OR OTHER POSITIVE PRESSURE MODE.

SELF-CONTAINED BREATHING APPARATUS WITH A FULL FACEPIECE OPERATED IN PRESSURE-DEMAND OR OTHER POSITIVE PRESSURE MODE.

FOR FIREFIGHTING AND OTHER IMMEDIATELY DANGEROUS TO LIFE OR HEALTH CONDITIONS:

SELF-CONTAINED BREATHING APPARATUS WITH FULL FACEPIECE OPERATED IN PRESSURE-DEMAND OR OTHER POSITIVE PRESSURE MODE.

SUPPLIED-AIR RESPIRATOR WITH FULL FACEPIECE AND OPERATED IN PRESSURE-DEMAND OR OTHER POSITIVE PRESSURE MODE IN COMBINATION WITH AN AUXILIARY SELF-CONTAINED BREATHING APPARATUS OPERATED IN PRESSURE-DEMAND OR OTHER POSITIVE PRESSURE MODE.

CLOTHING: EMPLOYEE MUST WEAR APPROPRIATE PROTECTIVE (IMPERVIOUS) CLOTHING AND EQUIPMENT TO PREVENT REPEATED OR PROLONGED SKIN CONTACT WITH THIS SUBSTANCE.

GLOVES: EMPLOYEE MUST WEAR APPROPRIATE PROTECTIVE GLOVES TO PREVENT CONTACT WITH THIS SUBSTANCE.

EYE PROTECTION: EMPLOYEE MUST WEAR SPLASH-PROOF OR DUST-RESISTANT SAFETY GOGGLES TO PREVENT EYE CONTACT WITH THIS SUBSTANCE.

EMERGENCY EYE WASH: WHERE THERE IS ANY POSSIBILITY THAT AN EMPLOYEE'S EYES MAY BE EXPOSED TO THIS SUBSTANCE, THE EMPLOYER SHOULD PROVIDE

AN EYE WASH FOUNTAIN WITHIN THE IMMEDIATE WORK AREA FOR EMERGENCY USE.

AUTHORIZED BY- OCCUPATIONAL HEALTH SERVICES, INC.
CREATION DATE: 10/05/89 ***REVISION DATE:*** 07/12/90

MATERIAL SAFETY DATA SHEET

OCCUPATIONAL HEALTH SERVICES, INC.
AGRICULTURE AND PESTICIDE DIVISION
450 SEVENTH AVENUE, SUITE 2407
NEW YORK, NEW YORK 10123
1-800-445-MSDS OR (212) 967-1100

EMERGENCY CONTACT:
JOHN S. BRANSFORD, JR. (615) 292-1180

SUBSTANCE IDENTIFICATION

CAS-NUMBER 22248-79-9

SUBSTANCE: **(Z)-2-CHLORO-1-(2,4,5-TRICHLOROPHENYL)VINYL DIMETHYL PHOSPHATE**

TRADE NAMES/SYNONYMS: PHOSPHORIC ACID, 2-CHLORO-1-(2,4,5-TRICHLOROPHENYL)ETHENYL DIMETHYL ESTER, (Z)-; (Z)-2-CHLORO-1-(2,4,5-TRICHLOROPHENYL)ETHENYL DIMETHYL PHOSPHATE; PHOSPHORIC ACID, 2-CHLORO-1-(2,4,5-TRICHLOROPHENYL)VINYL DIMETHYL ESTER, (Z)-; CIS-GARDONA; CVMP; GARDONA; GARDONA, CIS; RABON; RABOND; SD 8447; STIROFOS; STIROPHOS; TETRACHLORVINPHOS; C10H9CL4O4P; PST72244

CHEMICAL FAMILY: ORGANOPHOSPHATE ESTER

MOLECULAR FORMULA: C10-H9-CL4-O4-P

MOLECULAR WEIGHT: 365.95

CERCLA RATINGS (SCALE 0-3): HEALTH=3 FIRE=1 REACTIVITY=0 PERSISTENCE=0

NFPA RATINGS (SCALE 0-4): HEALTH=3 FIRE=1 REACTIVITY=0

COMPONENTS AND CONTAMINANTS

COMPONENT: (Z)-2-CHLORO-1-(2,4,5-TRICHLOROPHENYL)VINYL DIMETHYL PHOSPHATE ***PERCENT:*** 100.0
CAS# 22248-79-9

OTHER CONTAMINANTS: NONE

EXPOSURE LIMITS: NO OCCUPATIONAL EXPOSURE LIMITS ESTABLISHED BY OSHA, ACGIH, OR NIOSH.

PHYSICAL DATA

DESCRIPTION: OFF-WHITE CRYSTALLINE SOLID. ***MELTING POINT:*** 208 F (98 C)

SPECIFIC GRAVITY: NOT AVAILABLE ***SOLUBILITY IN WATER:*** 0.0011%

SOLVENT SOLUBILITY: SOLUBLE IN CHLOROFORM, METHYLENE CHLORIDE, ACETONE, AND XYLENE; VERY SLIGHTLY SOLUBLE IN AROMATIC HYDROCARBONS. DECOMPOSES SLOWLY @ 500 F (260 C).

VAPOR PRESSURE: 0.000000042 MMHG @ 20 C

FIRE AND EXPLOSION DATA

FIRE AND EXPLOSION HAZARD: SLIGHT FIRE HAZARD WHEN EXPOSED TO HEAT OR FLAME.

FIREFIGHTING MEDIA: DRY CHEMICAL, CARBON DIOXIDE, HALON, WATER SPRAY OR STANDARD FOAM (1987 EMERGENCY RESPONSE GUIDEBOOK, DOT P 5800.4). FOR LARGER FIRES, USE WATER SPRAY, FOG OR STANDARD FOAM (1987 EMERGENCY RESPONSE GUIDEBOOK, DOT P 5800.4).

FIREFIGHTING: MOVE CONTAINERS FROM FIRE AREA IF POSSIBLE. FIGHT FIRE FROM MAXIMUM DISTANCE. STAY AWAY FROM STORAGE TANK ENDS. DIKE FIRE CONTROL WATER FOR LATER DISPOSAL. DO NOT SCATTER MATERIAL (1987 EMERGENCY RESPONSE GUIDEBOOK, DOT P 5800.4, GUIDE PAGE 55). EXTINGUISH ONLY IF FLOW CAN BE STOPPED; USE FLOODING AMOUNTS OF WATER AS FOG, SOLID STREAMS MAY BE INEFFECTIVE. COOL CONTAINERS WITH FLOODING AMOUNTS OF WATER FROM AS FAR A DISTANCE AS POSSIBLE. USE WATER SPRAY TO ABSORB TOXIC VAPORS. AVOID BREATHING TOXIC VAPORS; KEEP UPWIND. CONSIDER EVACUATION OF DOWNWIND AREA IF MATERIAL IS LEAKING.

TOXICITY

(Z)-2-CHLORO-1-(2,4,5-TRICHLOROPHENYL)VINYL DIMETHYL PHOSPHATE: TOXICITY DATA: 1500 MG/KG SKIN-RAT LD50; >2500 MG/KG SKIN-RABBIT LD50 (FMCHA2); 480 MG/KG ORAL-RAT LD50; 1600 MG/KG ORAL-GUINEA PIG LD50; 1379 MG/KG ORAL-MOUSE LD50; 360 MG/KG ORAL-CATTLE LD50; 7473 MG/KG UNREPORTED-RAT LD50; 4000 MG/KG UNREPORTED-MAMMAL LD50; MUTAGENIC DATA (RTECS); TUMORIGENIC DATA (NCI-CG-TR-33,78). CARCINOGEN STATUS: ANIMAL LIMITED EVIDENCE (IARC GROUP-3). BY ORAL ADMINISTRATION, TECHNICAL TETRACHLORVINPHOS PRODUCED HEPATOCELLULAR CARCINOMAS IN MALE MICE AND BENIGN AND MALIGNANT LIVER-CELL TUMORS IN FEMALE MICE. INCREASED INCIDENCES OF C-CELL ADENOMA OF THE THYROID AND OF CORTICAL ADENOMA OF THE ADRENAL WERE OBSERVED IN FEMALE RATS. ACUTE TOXICITY LEVEL: TOXIC BY INGESTION; MODERATELY TOXIC BY DERMAL ABSORPTION. TARGET EFFECTS: CHOLINESTERASE INHIBITOR. AT INCREASED RISK FROM EXPOSURE: PERSONS WITH RESPIRATORY AILMENTS, RECENT EXPOSURE TO CHOLINESTERASE INHIBITORS OR IMPAIRED CHOLINESTERASE PRODUCTION, OR LIVER MALFUNCTION.* ADDITIONAL DATA: TETRACHLORVINPHOS MAY POTENTIATE THE TOXICITY OF MALATHION, AZINPHOS-METHYL, CARBARYL, COUMAPHOS, DICROTOPHOS, DIMETHOATE, METHYL PARATHION, MEVINPHOS, PARATHION, PHOSPHAMIDON, AND RONNEL. MAY CROSS THE PLACENTA. HIGH ENVIRONMENTAL TEMPERATURES OR EXPOSURE OF THE CHEMICAL TO VISIBLE OR ULTRAVIOLET LIGHT MAY ENHANCE THE TOXICITY. INTERACTIONS WITH MEDICATIONS MAY OCCUR.*

* MAY BE BASED ON GENERAL INFORMATION ON ORGANOPHOSPHATES.

HEALTH EFFECTS AND FIRST AID

INHALATION: (Z)-2-CHLORO-1-(2,4,5-TRICHLOROPHENYL)VINYL DIMETHYL PHOSPHATE: SEE INFORMATION ON ORGANOPHOSPHATES.
ORGANOPHOSPHATES: CHOLINESTERASE INHIBITOR. **ACUTE EXPOSURE-** WHEN INHALED, THE FIRST EFFECTS OF CHOLINESTERASE INHIBITORS ARE USUALLY RESPIRATORY AND MAY INCLUDE NASAL HYPEREMIA AND WATERY DISCHARGE, COUGH, CHEST DISCOMFORT, DYSPNEA, AND WHEEZING DUE TO INCREASED BRONCHIAL SECRETIONS AND BRONCHOCONSTRICTION. IF SUFFICIENT AMOUNTS ARE ABSORBED, OTHER SYSTEMIC EFFECTS MAY BEGIN WITHIN A FEW MINUTES OR BE DELAYED FOR UP TO 12 HOURS. SYMPTOMS MAY INCLUDE PALLOR, NAUSEA, VOMITING, DIARRHEA, ABDOMINAL CRAMPS, HEADACHE, DIZZINESS, OCULAR PAIN, BLURRED VISION, MIOSIS OR IN SOME CASES, ESPECIALLY INITIALLY, MYDRIASIS, LACRIMATION, SALIVATION, SWEATING, AND CONFUSION. OTHER REPORTED CENTRAL NERVOUS SYSTEM OR NEUROMUSCULAR EFFECTS MAY INCLUDE ATAXIA, SLURRED SPEECH, AREFLEXIA, WEAKNESS, FATIGUE, FASCICULATIONS, TWITCHING, TREMORS POSSIBLY OF THE TONGUE AND EYELIDS, AND EVENTUALLY PARALYSIS OF THE EXTREMITIES AND POSSIBLY OF THE RESPIRATORY MUSCLES. IN SEVERE CASES THERE MAY ALSO BE INVOLUNTARY DEFECATION AND URINATION, CYANOSIS, PSYCHOSIS, HYPERGLYCEMIA, ACUTE PANCREATITIS, CARDIAC IRREGULARITIES, PULMONARY EDEMA, UNCONSCIOUSNESS, CONVULSIONS, AND COMA. DEATH IS PRIMARILY DUE TO RESPIRATORY FAILURE, ALTHOUGH CARDIOVASCULAR EFFECTS INCLUDING CARDIAC ARREST MAY ALSO BE IMPLICATED. LONG TERM SEQUELAE ARE RARE BUT MAY INCLUDE NEUROPSYCHIATRIC DISORDERS AND MYOPATHY WITH MUSCLE TENDERNESS. **CHRONIC EXPOSURE-** REPEATED OR PROLONGED EXPOSURE MAY RESULT IN THE EFFECTS OF ACUTE EXPOSURE. OTHER EFFECTS REPORTED IN WORKERS REPEATEDLY EXPOSED INCLUDE IMPAIRED MEMORY AND CONCENTRATION, ACUTE PSYCHOSIS, SEVERE DEPRESSIONS, IRRITABILTY, CONFUSION, APATHY, EMOTIONAL LABILITY, SOCIAL WITHDRAWAL, CONFUSION, HEADACHE, SPEECH DIFFICULTIES, DELAYED REACTION TIMES, SPATIAL DISORIENTATION, NIGHTMARES, SLEEPWALKING, AND DROWSINESS OR INSOMNIA. AN INFLUENZA-LIKE CONDITION WITH HEADACHE, NAUSEA, WEAKNESS, ANOREXIA AND MALAISE HAS ALSO BEEN REPORTED.

FIRST AID- REMOVE FROM EXPOSURE AREA TO FRESH AIR IMMEDIATELY. IF BREATHING HAS STOPPED, GIVE ARTIFICIAL RESPIRATION. MAINTAIN AIRWAY AND BLOOD PRESSURE AND ADMINISTER OXYGEN IF AVAILABLE. KEEP AFFECTED PERSON WARM AND AT REST. TREAT SYMPTOMATICALLY AND SUPPORTIVELY. ADMINISTRATION OF OXYGEN SHOULD BE PERFORMED BY QUALIFIED PERSONNEL. GET MEDICAL ATTENTION IMMEDIATELY.

SKIN CONTACT: (Z)-2-CHLORO-1-(2,4,5-TRICHLOROPHENYL)VINYL DIMETHYL PHOSPHATE: SEE INFORMATION ON ORGANOPHOSPHATES.
ORGANOPHOSPHATES: CHOLINESTERASE INHIBITOR. **ACUTE EXPOSURE-** LOCALIZED SWEATING AND FASCICULATIONS MAY OCCUR AT THE SITE OF CONTACT. IF SUFFICIENT AMOUNTS ARE ABSORBED, OTHER EFFECTS OF CHOLINESTERASE INHIBITION AS DESCRIBED IN ACUTE INHALATION MAY OCCUR. SYMPTOMS MAY BE DELAYED 2-3 HOURS, BUT USUALLY NO MORE THAN 12 HOURS. THE RATE OF ABSORPTION IS INCREASED BY THE PRESENCE OF DERMATITIS OR HIGH AMBIENT TEMPERATURES. **CHRONIC EXPOSURE-** REPEATED OR PROLONGED EXPOSURE MAY CAUSE EFFECTS AS DESCRIBED IN ACUTE EXPOSURE. SOME ORGANOPHOSPHATES MAY CAUSE SENSITIZATION.

FIRST AID- REMOVE CONTAMINATED CLOTHING IMMEDIATELY. WASH CONTAMINATED AREAS WITH SOAP AND WATER FOLLOWED BY ALCOHOL (ARENA, POISONING, 4TH ED.). EMERGENCY PERSONNEL SHOULD WEAR GLOVES AND AVOID CONTAMINATION. TREAT RESPIRATORY DIFFICULTY WITH ARTIFICIAL RESPIRATION. GET MEDICAL ATTENTION IMMEDIATELY.

EYE CONTACT: (Z)-2-CHLORO-1-(2,4,5-TRICHLOROPHENYL)VINYL DIMETHYL PHOSPHATE: SEE INFORMATION ON ORGANOPHOSPHATES.
ORGANOPHOSPHATES: CHOLINESTERASE INHIBITOR. **ACUTE EXPOSURE-** DIRECT CONTACT MAY CAUSE PAIN, HYPEREMIA, LACRIMATION, TWITCHING OF THE EYELIDS, MIOSIS, AND CILIARY MUSCLE SPASM WITH LOSS OF ACCOMODATION, BLURRED OR DIMMED VISION AND BROWACHE. SOMETIMES MYDRIASIS MAY OCCUR INSTEAD OF MIOSIS. WITH SUFFICIENT EXPOSURE, OTHER SYMPTOMS OF CHOLINESTERASE INHIBITION AS DESCRIBED IN ACUTE INHALATION MAY OCCUR. **CHRONIC EXPOSURE-** REPEATED OR PROLONGED EXPOSURE MAY CAUSE EFFECTS AS DESCRIBED IN ACUTE EXPOSURE. SOME COMPOUNDS HAVE CAUSED TOXIC EFFECTS ON THE CRYSTALLINE LENS, CONJUNCTIVAL THICKENING AND OBSTRUCTION OF THE NASOLACRIMAL CANALS WHEN USED AS MIOTIC EYEDROPS.

FIRST AID- IRRIGATE EYES WITH WATER OR SALINE SOLUTION. IF SYMPTOMS OF POISONING OCCUR, TREAT RESPIRATORY DIFFICULTY WITH ARTIFICIAL RESPIRATION AND OXYGEN. OBSERVE PATIENT FOR AT LEAST 24-36 HOURS (GOSSELIN, CLINICAL TOXICOLOGY OF COMMERCIAL PRODUCTS, 5TH ED.). GET MEDICAL ATTENTION IMMEDIATELY. OXYGEN SHOULD BE ADMINISTERED BY QUALIFIED MEDICAL PERSONNEL.

INGESTION: (Z)-2-CHLORO-1-(2,4,5-TRICHLOROPHENYL)VINYL DIMETHYL PHOSPHATE: TOXIC. NO SIGNS OF DELAYED NEUROTOXICITY WERE OBSERVED IN HENS FED AN ACUTE DOSE OF 1.5 MG/KG. MORPHOLOGICAL CHANGES IN THE LIVER, KIDNEY, LUNG AND BRAIN WERE NOTED IN CHICKENS ACUTELY INTOXICATED WITH TETRACHLORVINPHOS. ADVERSE EFFECTS ON THE LIVER WERE REPORTED IN HUMANS RECEIVING A DAILY DOSE OF 12 OR 15 MG FOR 28 DAYS; LIVER FUNCTIONS RETURNED TO NORMAL AFTER CESSATION OF TREATMENT. MINIMAL SIGNS OF CHOLINESTERASE INHIBITION WERE SEEN AT THE 15 MG LEVEL. NO SIGNS OF DELAYED NEUROTOXICITY WERE OBSERVED IN HENS RECEIVING A DAILY DOSE OF 300 MG/KG FOR 5 DAYS. CHOLINESTERASE INHIBITION, DECREASED HEMOGLOBIN, DEPRESSED BODY WEIGHTS, AND INCREASED LIVER, KIDNEY, SPLEEN, AND ADRENAL WEIGHTS WERE SEEN IN STUDIES OF RATS REPEATEDLY FED TETRACHLORVINPHOS. CHOLINESTERASE INHIBITION AND INCREASED LIVER AND KIDNEY WEIGHTS WERE ALSO OBSERVED IN STUDIES OF DOGS. TECHNICAL TETRACHLORVINPHOS PRODUCED HEPATOCELLULAR CARCINOMAS IN MALE MICE AND BENIGN AND MALIGNANT LIVER-CELL TUMORS IN FEMALE MICE. INCREASED INCIDENCES OF C-CELL ADENOMA OF THE THYROID AND OF CORTICAL ADENOMA OF THE ADRENAL WERE FOUND IN FEMALE RATS; REDUCED BODY WEIGHTS AND DECREASED SURVIVAL WERE NOTED IN THE MALE RATS. SEE INFORMATION ON ORGANOPHOSPHATES.
ORGANOPHOSPHATES: CHOLINESTERASE INHIBITOR. **ACUTE EXPOSURE-** WHEN INGESTED, THE FIRST EFFECTS MAY BE NAUSEA, VOMITING, ANOREXIA, ABDOMINAL CRAMPS AND DIARRHEA. GASTROINTESTINAL ABSORPTION MAY CAUSE THE SYMPTOMS OF CHOLINESTERASE INHIBITION AS DESCRIBED IN ACUTE INHALATION. SYMPTOMS MAY BEGIN WITHIN MINUTES OR BE DELAYED. **CHRONIC EXPOSURE-** REPEATED INGESTION MAY CAUSE EFFECTS AS DESCRIBED IN ACUTE EXPOSURE.

FIRST AID- IF PERSON IS ALERT AND RESPIRATION IS NOT DEPRESSED, GIVE SYRUP OF IPECAC FOLLOWED BY WATER (IF VOMITING OCCURS, KEEP HEAD BELOW HIPS TO PREVENT ASPIRATION). IF CONSCIOUSNESS LEVEL DECLINES OR VOMITING HAS NOT OCCURRED IN 15 MINUTES EMPTY STOMACH BY GASTRIC LAVAGE WITH THE AID OF CUFFED ENDOTRACHEAL TUBE USING ISOTONIC SALINE OR 5% SODIUM BICARBONATE FOLLOW WITH ACTIVATED CHARCOAL. ESTABLISH AND MAINTAIN AIRWAY. TREAT RESPIRATORY DIFFICULTY WITH ARTIFICIAL RESPIRATION AND OXYGEN. DO NOT GIVE MORPHINE, AMINOPHYLLINE, PHENOTHIAZINES, RESERPINE, FUROSEMIDE, OR ETHACRYNIC ACID (MORGAN, RECOGNITION AND MANAGEMENT OF PESTICIDE POISONINGS, 3RD ED.). TREAT SYMPTOMATICALLY AND SUPPORTIVELY. ADMINISTRATION OF OXYGEN AND LAVAGE MUST BE PERFORMED BY QUALIFIED MEDICAL PERSONNEL. GET MEDICAL ATTENTION IMMEDIATELY.

ANTIDOTE: THE FOLLOWING ANTIDOTE(S) HAVE BEEN RECOMMENDED. HOWEVER, THE DECISION AS TO WHETHER THE SEVERITY OF POISONING REQUIRES ADMINISTRATION OF ANY ANTIDOTE AND ACTUAL DOSE REQUIRED SHOULD BE MADE BY QUALIFIED MEDICAL PERSONNEL.
FOR CHOLINESTERASE INHIBITORS: ESTABLISH CLEAR AIRWAY AND TISSUE OXYGENATION BY ASPIRATION OF SECRETIONS, AND IF NECESSARY, BY ASSISTED PULMONARY VENTILATION WITH OXYGEN. IMPROVE TISSUE OXYGENATION AS MUCH AS POSSIBLE BEFORE ADMINISTERING ATROPINE TO MINIMIZE THE RISK OF VENTRICULAR FIBRILLATION. ADMINISTER ATROPINE SULFATE INTRAVENOUSLY, OR INTRAMUSCULARLY IF IV INJECTION IS NOT POSSIBLE. IN MODERATELY SEVERE POISONING ADMINISTER ATROPINE SULFATE, 0.4-2.0 MG REPEATED EVERY 15 MINUTES UNTIL ATROPINIZATION IS ACHIEVED (TACHYCARDIA, FLUSHING, DRY MOUTH, MYDRIASIS). MAINTAIN ATROPINIZATION BY REPEATED DOSES FOR 2-12 HOURS, OR LONGER, DEPENDING ON THE SEVERITY OF POISONING. THE APPEARANCE OF RALES IN THE LUNG BASES, MIOSIS, SALIVATION, NAUSEA, BRADYCARDIA, ARE ALL INDICATIONS OF INADEQUATE ATROPINIZATION. SEVERELY POISONED INDIVIDUALS MAY EXHIBIT REMARKABLE TOLERANCE TO ATROPINE; TWO OR MORE TIMES THE DOSAGES SUGGESTED ABOVE MAY BE NEEDED. PERSONS NOT POISONED OR ONLY SLIGHTLY POISONED, HOWEVER, MAY DEVELOP SIGNS OF ATROPINE TOXICITY FROM SUCH LARGE DOSAGES: FEVER, MUSCLE FIBRILLATIONS, AND DELIRIUM ARE THE MAIN SIGNS OF ATROPINE TOXICITY. IF THESE SIGNS APPEAR WHILE THE PATIENT IS FULLY ATROPINIZED, ATROPINE ADMINISTRATION SHOULD BE DISCONTINUED, AT LEAST TEMPORARILY. OBSERVE TREATED PATIENTS CLOSELY AT LEAST 24 HOURS TO INSURE THAT SYMPTOMS (POSSIBLY PULMONARY EDEMA) DO NOT RECUR AS ATROPINIZATION WEARS OFF. IN VERY SEVERE POISONINGS, METABOLIC DISPOSITION OF TOXICANT MAY REQUIRE SEVERAL HOURS OR DAYS DURING WHICH ATROPINIZATION MUST BE MAINTAINED. MARKEDLY LOWER LEVELS OF URINARY METABOLITES INDICATE THAT ATROPINE DOSAGE CAN BE TAPERED OFF. AS DOSAGE IS REDUCED, CHECK THE LUNG BASES FREQUENTLY FOR RALES. IF RALES ARE HEARD OR OTHER SYMPTOMS RETURN, RE-ESTABLISH ATROPINIZATION PROMPTLY (MORGAN, RECOGNITION AND MANAGEMENT OF PESTICIDE POISONINGS, 3RD ED.). ADMINISTRATION OF ANTIDOTE MUST BE PERFORMED BY QUALIFIED MEDICAL PERSONNEL.
IN CASES OF SEVERE POISONING BY ORGANOPHOSPHATE PESTICIDES IN WHICH RESPIRATORY DEPRESSION, MUSCLE WEAKNESS AND TWITCHINGS ARE SEVERE, GIVE PRALIDOXIME (PROTOPAM-AYERST, 2-PAM), 1.0 GRAM INTRAVENOUSLY AT NO MORE THAN 0.5 GRAM PER MINUTE. DOSAGE OF PRALIDOXIME MAY BE REPEATED IN 1-2 HOURS, THEN AT 10-12 HOUR INTERVALS IF NEEDED. IN VERY SEVERE POISONINGS, DOSAGE RATES MAY BE DOUBLED. TREATMENT WITH PRALIDOXIME WILL BE MOST EFFECTIVE IF GIVEN WITHIN THIRTY-SIX HOURS AFTER POISONING (MORGAN, RECOGNITION AND MANAGEMENT OF PESTICIDE POISONINGS, 3RD ED.). ANTIDOTE SHOULD BE ADMINISTERED BY QUALIFIED MEDICAL PERSONNEL.

REACTIVITY

REACTIVITY: MAY BE SLOWLY HYDROLYZED BY WATER.

INCOMPATIBILITIES: (Z)-2-CHLORO-1-(2,4,5-TRICHLOROPHENYL)VINYL DIMETHYL PHOSPHATE: ACIDS: SLOWLY HYDROLYZES. ALKALI: HYDROLYZES. OXIDIZERS (STRONG): FIRE AND EXPLOSION HAZARD.

DECOMPOSITION: THERMAL DECOMPOSITION PRODUCTS MAY INCLUDE TOXIC AND CORROSIVE FUMES OF CHLORIDES, AND TOXIC OXIDES OF CARBON AND PHOSPHORUS.

POLYMERIZATION: HAZARDOUS POLYMERIZATION HAS NOT BEEN REPORTED TO OCCUR UNDER NORMAL TEMPERATURES AND PRESSURES.

STORAGE AND DISPOSAL

OBSERVE ALL FEDERAL, STATE AND LOCAL REGULATIONS WHEN STORING OR DISPOSING OF THIS SUBSTANCE. FOR ASSISTANCE, CONTACT THE DISTRICT DIRECTOR OF THE ENVIRONMENTAL PROTECTION AGENCY.

****STORAGE****

STORE IN ACCORDANCE WITH 40 CFR 165 RECOMMENDED PROCEDURES FOR THE DISPOSAL AND STORAGE OF PESTICIDES AND PESTICIDE CONTAINERS.
STORE AWAY FROM INCOMPATIBLE SUBSTANCES.

****DISPOSAL****

DISPOSAL MUST BE IN ACCORDANCE WITH 40 CFR 165 RECOMMENDED PROCEDURES FOR THE DISPOSAL AND STORAGE OF PESTICIDES AND PESTICIDE CONTAINERS.

CONDITIONS TO AVOID

MAY BURN BUT DOES NOT IGNITE READILY. CONTAINERS MAY EXPLODE IN HEAT OF FIRE.

SPILL AND LEAK PROCEDURES

OCCUPATIONAL SPILL: DO NOT TOUCH SPILLED MATERIAL. STOP LEAK IF YOU CAN DO IT WITHOUT RISK. USE WATER SPRAY TO REDUCE VAPORS. FOR SMALL SPILLS, TAKE UP WITH SAND OR OTHER ABSORBENT MATERIAL AND PLACE INTO CONTAINERS FOR LATER DISPOSAL. FOR SMALL DRY SPILLS, WITH A CLEAN SHOVEL PLACE MATERIAL INTO CLEAN, DRY CONTAINERS AND COVER. MOVE CONTAINERS FROM SPILL AREA. FOR LARGER SPILLS, DIKE FAR AHEAD OF SPILL FOR LATER DISPOSAL. KEEP UNNECESSARY PEOPLE AWAY. ISOLATE HAZARD AREA AND DENY ENTRY. VENTILATE CLOSED SPACES BEFORE ENTERING.

PROTECTIVE EQUIPMENT

VENTILATION: PROVIDE LOCAL EXHAUST OR GENERAL DILUTION VENTILATION SYSTEM.

RESPIRATOR: THE FOLLOWING RESPIRATORS ARE RECOMMENDED BASED ON INFORMATION FOUND IN THE PHYSICAL DATA, TOXICITY AND HEALTH EFFECTS SECTIONS. THEY ARE RANKED IN ORDER FROM MINIMUM TO MAXIMUM RESPIRATORY PROTECTION. THE SPECIFIC RESPIRATOR SELECTED MUST BE BASED ON CONTAMINATION LEVELS FOUND IN THE WORK PLACE, MUST NOT EXCEED THE WORKING LIMITS OF THE RESPIRATOR AND BE JOINTLY APPROVED BY THE NATIONAL INSTITUTE FOR OCCUPATIONAL SAFETY AND HEALTH AND THE MINE

SAFETY AND HEALTH ADMINISTRATION (NIOSH-MSHA).
CHEMICAL CARTRIDGE RESPIRATOR WITH AN ORGANIC VAPOR CARTRIDGE(S) IN COMBINATION WITH A DUST AND MIST FILTER.
GAS MASK WITH ORGANIC VAPOR CANISTER (CHIN-STYLE OR FRONT- OR BACK-MOUNTED CANISTER) WITH A DUST AND MIST FILTER.
GAS MASK WITH ORGANIC VAPOR CANISTER (CHIN-STYLE OR FRONT- OR BACK-MOUNTED CANISTER) WITH A PARTICULATE FILTER.
POWERED AIR-PURIFYING RESPIRATOR WITH A HIGH-EFFICIENCY FILTER.
TYPE 'C' SUPPLIED-AIR RESPIRATOR WITH A FULL FACEPIECE OPERATED IN A PRESSURE-DEMAND OR OTHER POSITIVE PRESSURE MODE.
SELF-CONTAINED BREATHING APPARATUS WITH A FULL FACEPIECE OPERATED IN PRESSURE-DEMAND OR OTHER POSITIVE PRESSURE MODE.
FOR FIREFIGHTING AND OTHER IMMEDIATELY DANGEROUS TO LIFE OR HEALTH CONDITIONS:
SELF-CONTAINED BREATHING APPARATUS WITH FULL FACEPIECE OPERATED IN PRESSURE-DEMAND OR OTHER POSITIVE PRESSURE MODE.
SUPPLIED-AIR RESPIRATOR WITH FULL FACEPIECE AND OPERATED IN PRESSURE-DEMAND OR OTHER POSITIVE PRESSURE MODE IN COMBINATION WITH AN AUXILIARY SELF-CONTAINED BREATHING APPARATUS OPERATED IN PRESSURE-DEMAND OR OTHER POSITIVE PRESSURE MODE.

CLOTHING: EMPLOYEE MUST WEAR APPROPRIATE PROTECTIVE (IMPERVIOUS) CLOTHING AND EQUIPMENT TO PREVENT REPEATED OR PROLONGED SKIN CONTACT WITH THIS SUBSTANCE.

GLOVES: EMPLOYEE MUST WEAR APPROPRIATE PROTECTIVE GLOVES TO PREVENT CONTACT WITH THIS SUBSTANCE.

EYE PROTECTION: EMPLOYEE MUST WEAR SPLASH-PROOF OR DUST-RESISTANT SAFETY GOGGLES TO PREVENT EYE CONTACT WITH THIS SUBSTANCE.
EMERGENCY EYE WASH: WHERE THERE IS ANY POSSIBILITY THAT AN EMPLOYEE'S EYES MAY BE EXPOSED TO THIS SUBSTANCE, THE EMPLOYER SHOULD PROVIDE AN EYE WASH FOUNTAIN WITHIN THE IMMEDIATE WORK AREA FOR EMERGENCY USE.

AUTHORIZED BY- OCCUPATIONAL HEALTH SERVICES, INC.
CREATION DATE: 05/18/90 ***REVISION DATE:*** 07/12/90

MATERIAL SAFETY DATA SHEET

OCCUPATIONAL HEALTH SERVICES, INC.
AGRICULTURE AND PESTICIDE DIVISION
450 SEVENTH AVENUE, SUITE 2407
NEW YORK, NEW YORK 10123
1-800-445-MSDS OR (212) 967-1100

EMERGENCY CONTACT:
JOHN S. BRANSFORD, JR. (615) 292-1180

SUBSTANCE IDENTIFICATION

CAS-NUMBER 22350-76-1

SUBSTANCE: (E)-2-CHLORO-1-(2,4,5-TRICHLOROPHENYL)VINYL DIMETHYL PHOSPHATE

TRADE NAMES/SYNONYMS: PHOSPHORIC ACID, 2-CHLORO-1-(2,4,5-TRICHLOROPHENYL)ETHENYL DIMETHYL ESTER, (E)-; (E)-2-CHLORO-1-(2,4,5-TRICHLOROPHENYL)ETHENYL DIMETHYL PHOSPHATE; PHOSPHORIC ACID, 2-CHLORO-1-(2,4,5-TRICHLOROPHENYL)VINYL DIMETHYL ESTER, (E)-; GARDONA, TRANS-; TRANS-GARDONA; GARDONA; TETRACHLORVINPHOS; RABON; C10H9CL4O4P; PST72245

CHEMICAL FAMILY: ORGANOPHOSPHATE ESTER

MOLECULAR FORMULA: C10-H9-CL4-O4-P

MOLECULAR WEIGHT: 365.95

CERCLA RATINGS (SCALE 0-3): HEALTH=2 FIRE=1 REACTIVITY=0 PERSISTENCE=3

NFPA RATINGS (SCALE 0-4): HEALTH=2 FIRE=1 REACTIVITY=0

COMPONENTS AND CONTAMINANTS

COMPONENT: (E)-2-CHLORO-1-(2,4,5-TRICHLOROPHENYL)VINYL DIMETHYL PHOSPHATE ***PERCENT:*** 100.0
CAS# 22350-76-1

OTHER CONTAMINANTS: NONE

EXPOSURE LIMITS: NO OCCUPATIONAL EXPOSURE LIMITS ESTABLISHED BY OSHA, ACGIH, OR NIOSH.

PHYSICAL DATA

DESCRIPTION: CRYSTALLINE SOLID. ***MELTING POINT:*** 144 F (62 C)

SPECIFIC GRAVITY: NOT AVAILABLE ***SOLUBILITY IN WATER:*** NOT AVAILABLE

SOLVENT SOLUBILITY: NOT AVAILABLE

FIRE AND EXPLOSION DATA

FIRE AND EXPLOSION HAZARD: SLIGHT FIRE HAZARD WHEN EXPOSED TO HEAT OR FLAME.

FIREFIGHTING MEDIA: DRY CHEMICAL, CARBON DIOXIDE, HALON, WATER SPRAY OR STANDARD FOAM (1987 EMERGENCY RESPONSE GUIDEBOOK, DOT P 5800.4).
FOR LARGER FIRES, USE WATER SPRAY, FOG OR STANDARD FOAM (1987 EMERGENCY RESPONSE GUIDEBOOK, DOT P 5800.4).

FIREFIGHTING: MOVE CONTAINERS FROM FIRE AREA IF POSSIBLE. FIGHT FIRE FROM MAXIMUM DISTANCE. STAY AWAY FROM STORAGE TANK ENDS. DIKE FIRE CONTROL WATER FOR LATER DISPOSAL. DO NOT SCATTER MATERIAL (1987 EMERGENCY RESPONSE GUIDEBOOK, DOT P 5800.4, GUIDE PAGE 55).
EXTINGUISH ONLY IF FLOW CAN BE STOPPED; USE FLOODING AMOUNTS OF WATER AS FOG, SOLID STREAMS MAY BE INEFFECTIVE. COOL CONTAINERS WITH FLOODING AMOUNTS OF WATER FROM AS FAR A DISTANCE AS POSSIBLE. USE WATER SPRAY TO ABSORB TOXIC VAPORS. AVOID BREATHING TOXIC VAPORS; KEEP UPWIND. CONSIDER EVACUATION OF DOWNWIND AREA IF MATERIAL IS LEAKING.

TOXICITY

(E)-2-CHLORO-1-(2,4,5-TRICHLOROPHENYL)VINYL DIMETHYL PHOSPHATE: TOXICITY DATA: 4 GM/KG ORAL-RAT LD50 (85HSAI). CARCINOGEN STATUS: NONE. BY ORAL ADMINISTRATION, TECHNICAL TETRACHLORVINPHOS PRODUCED HEPATOCELLULAR CARCINOMAS IN MALE MICE AND BENIGN AND MALIGNANT LIVER-CELL TUMORS IN FEMALE MICE. INCREASED INCIDENCES OF C-CELL ADENOMA OF THE THYROID AND OF CORTICAL ADENOMA OF THE ADRENAL WERE OBSERVED IN FEMALE RATS. ACUTE TOXICITY LEVEL: MODERATELY TOXIC BY INGESTION. TARGET EFFECTS: CHOLINESTERASE INHIBITOR. AT INCREASED RISK FROM EXPOSURE: PERSONS WITH RESPIRATORY AILMENTS, RECENT EXPOSURE TO CHOLINESTERASE INHIBITORS OR IMPAIRED CHOLINESTERASE PRODUCTION, OR LIVER MALFUNCTION.* ADDITIONAL DATA: MAY CROSS THE PLACENTA. HIGH ENVIRONMENTAL TEMPERATURES OR EXPOSURE OF THE CHEMICAL TO VISIBLE OR ULTRAVIOLET LIGHT MAY ENHANCE THE TOXICITY. INTERACTIONS WITH MEDICATIONS MAY OCCUR.*
* MAY BE BASED ON GENERAL INFORMATION ON ORGANOPHOSPHATES.

HEALTH EFFECTS AND FIRST AID

INHALATION: (E)-2-CHLORO-1-(2,4,5-TRICHLOROPHENYL)VINYL DIMETHYL PHOSPHATE: SEE INFORMATION ON ORGANOPHOSPHATES.
ORGANOPHOSPHATES: CHOLINESTERASE INHIBITOR. **ACUTE EXPOSURE**- WHEN INHALED, THE FIRST EFFECTS OF CHOLINESTERASE INHIBITORS ARE USUALLY RESPIRATORY AND MAY INCLUDE NASAL HYPEREMIA AND WATERY DISCHARGE, COUGH, CHEST DISCOMFORT, DYSPNEA, AND WHEEZING DUE TO INCREASED BRONCHIAL SECRETIONS AND BRONCHOCONSTRICTION. IF SUFFICIENT AMOUNTS ARE ABSORBED, OTHER SYSTEMIC EFFECTS MAY BEGIN WITHIN A FEW MINUTES OR BE DELAYED FOR UP TO 12 HOURS. SYMPTOMS MAY INCLUDE PALLOR, NAUSEA, VOMITING, DIARRHEA, ABDOMINAL CRAMPS, HEADACHE, DIZZINESS, OCULAR PAIN, BLURRED VISION, MIOSIS OR IN SOME CASES, ESPECIALLY INITIALLY, MYDRIASIS, LACRIMATION, SALIVATION, SWEATING, AND CONFUSION. OTHER REPORTED CENTRAL NERVOUS SYSTEM OR NEUROMUSCULAR EFFECTS MAY INCLUDE ATAXIA, SLURRED SPEECH, AREFLEXIA, WEAKNESS, FATIGUE, FASCICULATIONS, TWITCHING, TREMORS POSSIBLY OF THE TONGUE AND EYELIDS, AND EVENTUALLY PARALYSIS OF THE EXTREMITIES AND POSSIBLY OF THE RESPIRATORY MUSCLES. IN SEVERE CASES THERE MAY ALSO BE INVOLUNTARY DEFECATION AND URINATION, CYANOSIS, PSYCHOSIS, HYPERGLYCEMIA, ACUTE PANCREATITIS, CARDIAC IRREGULARITIES, PULMONARY EDEMA, UNCONSCIOUSNESS, CONVULSIONS, AND COMA. DEATH IS PRIMARILY DUE TO RESPIRATORY FAILURE, ALTHOUGH CARDIOVASCULAR EFFECTS INCLUDING CARDIAC ARREST MAY ALSO BE IMPLICATED. LONG TERM SEQUELAE ARE RARE BUT MAY INCLUDE NEUROPSYCHIATRIC DISORDERS AND MYOPATHY WITH MUSCLE TENDERNESS. **CHRONIC EXPOSURE**- REPEATED OR PROLONGED EXPOSURE MAY RESULT IN THE EFFECTS OF ACUTE EXPOSURE. OTHER EFFECTS REPORTED IN WORKERS REPEATEDLY EXPOSED INCLUDE IMPAIRED MEMORY AND CONCENTRATION, ACUTE PSYCHOSIS, SEVERE DEPRESSIONS, IRRITABILTY, CONFUSION, APATHY, EMOTIONAL LABILITY, SOCIAL WITHDRAWAL, CONFUSION, HEADACHE, SPEECH DIFFICULTIES, DELAYED REACTION TIMES, SPATIAL DISORIENTATION, NIGHTMARES, SLEEPWALKING, AND DROWSINESS OR INSOMNIA. AN INFLUENZA-LIKE CONDITION WITH HEADACHE, NAUSEA, WEAKNESS, ANOREXIA AND MALAISE HAS ALSO BEEN REPORTED.

FIRST AID- REMOVE FROM EXPOSURE AREA TO FRESH AIR IMMEDIATELY. IF BREATHING HAS STOPPED, GIVE ARTIFICIAL RESPIRATION. MAINTAIN AIRWAY AND BLOOD PRESSURE AND ADMINISTER OXYGEN IF AVAILABLE. KEEP AFFECTED PERSON WARM AND AT REST. TREAT SYMPTOMATICALLY AND SUPPORTIVELY.

ADMINISTRATION OF OXYGEN SHOULD BE PERFORMED BY QUALIFIED PERSONNEL. GET MEDICAL ATTENTION IMMEDIATELY.

SKIN CONTACT: (E)-2-CHLORO-1-(2,4,5-TRICHLOROPHENYL)VINYL DIMETHYL PHOSPHATE: CHRONIC EXPOSURE TO TETRACHLORVINPHOS MAY LEAD TO SKIN SENSITIZATION. SEE INFORMATION ON ORGANOPHOSPHATES. ORGANOPHOSPHATES: CHOLINESTERASE INHIBITOR. **ACUTE EXPOSURE-** LOCALIZED SWEATING AND FASCICULATIONS MAY OCCUR AT THE SITE OF CONTACT. IF SUFFICIENT AMOUNTS ARE ABSORBED, OTHER EFFECTS OF CHOLINESTERASE INHIBITION AS DESCRIBED IN ACUTE INHALATION MAY OCCUR. SYMPTOMS MAY BE DELAYED 2-3 HOURS, BUT USUALLY NO MORE THAN 12 HOURS. THE RATE OF ABSORPTION IS INCREASED BY THE PRESENCE OF DERMATITIS OR HIGH AMBIENT TEMPERATURES. **CHRONIC EXPOSURE-** REPEATED OR PROLONGED EXPOSURE MAY CAUSE EFFECTS AS DESCRIBED IN ACUTE EXPOSURE. SOME ORGANOPHOSPHATES MAY CAUSE SENSITIZATION.

FIRST AID- REMOVE CONTAMINATED CLOTHING IMMEDIATELY. WASH CONTAMINATED AREAS WITH SOAP AND WATER FOLLOWED BY ALCOHOL (ARENA, POISONING, 4TH ED.). EMERGENCY PERSONNEL SHOULD WEAR GLOVES AND AVOID CONTAMINATION. TREAT RESPIRATORY DIFFICULTY WITH ARTIFICIAL RESPIRATION. GET MEDICAL ATTENTION IMMEDIATELY.

EYE CONTACT: (E)-2-CHLORO-1-(2,4,5-TRICHLOROPHENYL)VINYL DIMETHYL PHOSPHATE: SEE INFORMATION ON ORGANOPHOSPHATES. ORGANOPHOSPHATES: CHOLINESTERASE INHIBITOR. **ACUTE EXPOSURE-** DIRECT CONTACT MAY CAUSE PAIN, HYPEREMIA, LACRIMATION, TWITCHING OF THE EYELIDS, MIOSIS, AND CILIARY MUSCLE SPASM WITH LOSS OF ACCOMODATION, BLURRED OR DIMMED VISION AND BROWACHE. SOMETIMES MYDRIASIS MAY OCCUR INSTEAD OF MIOSIS. WITH SUFFICIENT EXPOSURE, OTHER SYMPTOMS OF CHOLINESTERASE INHIBITION AS DESCRIBED IN ACUTE INHALATION MAY OCCUR. **CHRONIC EXPOSURE-** REPEATED OR PROLONGED EXPOSURE MAY CAUSE EFFECTS AS DESCRIBED IN ACUTE EXPOSURE. SOME COMPOUNDS HAVE CAUSED TOXIC EFFECTS ON THE CRYSTALLINE LENS, CONJUNCTIVAL THICKENING AND OBSTRUCTION OF THE NASOLACRIMAL CANALS WHEN USED AS MIOTIC EYEDROPS.

FIRST AID- IRRIGATE EYES WITH WATER OR SALINE SOLUTION. IF SYMPTOMS OF POISONING OCCUR, TREAT RESPIRATORY DIFFICULTY WITH ARTIFICIAL RESPIRATION AND OXYGEN. OBSERVE PATIENT FOR AT LEAST 24-36 HOURS (GOSSELIN, CLINICAL TOXICOLOGY OF COMMERCIAL PRODUCTS, 5TH ED.). GET MEDICAL ATTENTION IMMEDIATELY. OXYGEN SHOULD BE ADMINISTERED BY QUALIFIED MEDICAL PERSONNEL.

INGESTION: (E)-2-CHLORO-1-(2,4,5-TRICHLOROPHENYL)VINYL DIMETHYL PHOSPHATE: NO SIGNS OF DELAYED NEUROTOXICITY WERE OBSERVED IN HENS FED TETRACHLORVINPHOS. MORPHOLOGICAL CHANGES IN THE LIVER, KIDNEY, LUNG AND BRAIN WERE NOTED IN CHICKENS ACUTELY INTOXICATED WITH TETRACHLORVINPHOS. ADVERSE EFFECTS ON THE LIVER WERE REPORTED IN HUMANS RECEIVING TETRACHLORVINPHOS AT A RATE OF 12 OR 15 MG/DAY FOR 28 DAYS. LIVER FUNCTIONS RETURNED TO NORMAL AFTER CESSATION OF TREATMENT. MINIMAL SIGNS OF CHOLINESTERASE INHIBITION WERE SEEN AT THE 15 MG LEVEL. NO SIGNS OF DELAYED NEUROTOXICITY WERE OBSERVED IN HENS RECEIVING 300 MG/KG/DAY TETRACHLORVINPHOS FOR 5 DAYS. CHOLINESTERASE INHIBITION, DECREASED HEMOGLOBIN, DEPRESSED BODY WEIGHTS, AND INCREASED LIVER, KIDNEY, SPLEEN, AND ADRENAL WEIGHTS WERE SEEN IN STUDIES OF RATS REPEATEDLY FED TETRACHLORVINPHOS. CHOLINESTERASE INHIBITION AND INCREASED LIVER AND KIDNEY WEIGHTS WERE ALSO OBSERVED IN STUDIES OF DOGS. TECHNICAL TETRACHLORVINPHOS PRODUCED HEPATOCELLULAR CARCINOMAS IN MALE MICE AND BENIGN AND MALIGNANT LIVER-CELL TUMORS IN FEMALE MICE. INCREASED INCIDENCES OF C-CELL ADENOMA OF THE THYROID AND OF CORTICAL ADENOMA OF THE ADRENAL WERE FOUND IN FEMALE RATS; REDUCED BODY WEIGHTS AND DECREASED SURVIVAL WERE NOTED IN THE MALE RATS. SEE INFORMATION ON ORGANOPHOSPHATES. ORGANOPHOSPHATES: CHOLINESTERASE INHIBITOR. **ACUTE EXPOSURE-** WHEN INGESTED, THE FIRST EFFECTS MAY BE NAUSEA, VOMITING, ANOREXIA, ABDOMINAL CRAMPS AND DIARRHEA. GASTROINTESTINAL ABSORPTION MAY CAUSE THE SYMPTOMS OF CHOLINESTERASE INHIBITION AS DESCRIBED IN ACUTE INHALATION. SYMPTOMS MAY BEGIN WITHIN MINUTES OR BE DELAYED. **CHRONIC EXPOSURE-** REPEATED INGESTION MAY CAUSE EFFECTS AS DESCRIBED IN ACUTE EXPOSURE.

FIRST AID- IF PERSON IS ALERT AND RESPIRATION IS NOT DEPRESSED, GIVE SYRUP OF IPECAC FOLLOWED BY WATER (IF VOMITING OCCURS, KEEP HEAD BELOW HIPS TO PREVENT ASPIRATION). IF CONSCIOUSNESS LEVEL DECLINES OR VOMITING HAS NOT OCCURRED IN 15 MINUTES EMPTY STOMACH BY GASTRIC LAVAGE WITH THE AID OF CUFFED ENDOTRACHEAL TUBE USING ISOTONIC SALINE OR 5% SODIUM BICARBONATE FOLLOW WITH ACTIVATED CHARCOAL. ESTABLISH AND MAINTAIN AIRWAY. TREAT RESPIRATORY DIFFICULTY WITH ARTIFICIAL RESPIRATION AND OXYGEN. DO NOT GIVE MORPHINE, AMINOPHYLLINE, PHENOTHIAZINES, RESERPINE, FUROSEMIDE, OR ETHACRYNIC ACID (MORGAN, RECOGNITION AND MANAGEMENT OF PESTICIDE POISONINGS, 3RD ED.). TREAT SYMPTOMATICALLY AND SUPPORTIVELY. ADMINISTRATION OF OXYGEN AND LAVAGE MUST BE PERFORMED BY QUALIFIED MEDICAL PERSONNEL. GET MEDICAL ATTENTION IMMEDIATELY.

ANTIDOTE: THE FOLLOWING ANTIDOTE(S) HAVE BEEN RECOMMENDED. HOWEVER, THE DECISION AS TO WHETHER THE SEVERITY OF POISONING REQUIRES ADMINISTRATION OF ANY ANTIDOTE AND ACTUAL DOSE REQUIRED SHOULD BE MADE BY QUALIFIED MEDICAL PERSONNEL.

FOR CHOLINESTERASE INHIBITORS: ESTABLISH CLEAR AIRWAY AND TISSUE OXYGENATION BY ASPIRATION OF SECRETIONS, AND IF NECESSARY, BY ASSISTED PULMONARY VENTILATION WITH OXYGEN. IMPROVE TISSUE OXYGENATION AS MUCH AS POSSIBLE BEFORE ADMINISTERING ATROPINE TO MINIMIZE THE RISK OF VENTRICULAR FIBRILLATION. ADMINISTER ATROPINE SULFATE INTRAVENOUSLY, OR INTRAMUSCULARLY IF IV INJECTION IS NOT POSSIBLE. IN MODERATELY SEVERE POISONING ADMINISTER ATROPINE SULFATE, 0.4-2.0 MG REPEATED EVERY 15 MINUTES UNTIL ATROPINIZATION IS ACHIEVED (TACHYCARDIA, FLUSHING, DRY MOUTH, MYDRIASIS). MAINTAIN ATROPINIZATION BY REPEATED DOSES FOR 2-12 HOURS, OR LONGER, DEPENDING ON THE SEVERITY OF POISONING. THE APPEARANCE OF RALES IN THE LUNG BASES, MIOSIS, SALIVATION, NAUSEA, BRADYCARDIA, ARE ALL INDICATIONS OF INADEQUATE ATROPINIZATION. SEVERELY POISONED INDIVIDUALS MAY EXHIBIT REMARKABLE TOLERANCE TO ATROPINE; TWO OR MORE TIMES THE DOSAGES SUGGESTED ABOVE MAY BE NEEDED. PERSONS NOT POISONED OR ONLY SLIGHTLY POISONED, HOWEVER, MAY DEVELOP SIGNS OF ATROPINE TOXICITY FROM SUCH LARGE DOSAGES: FEVER, MUSCLE FIBRILLATIONS, AND DELIRIUM ARE THE MAIN SIGNS OF ATROPINE TOXICITY. IF THESE SIGNS APPEAR WHILE THE PATIENT IS FULLY ATROPINIZED, ATROPINE ADMINISTRATION SHOULD BE DISCONTINUED, AT LEAST TEMPORARILY. OBSERVE TREATED PATIENTS CLOSELY AT LEAST 24 HOURS TO INSURE THAT SYMPTOMS (POSSIBLY PULMONARY EDEMA) DO NOT RECUR AS ATROPINIZATION WEARS OFF. IN VERY SEVERE POISONINGS, METABOLIC DISPOSITION OF TOXICANT MAY REQUIRE SEVERAL HOURS OR DAYS DURING WHICH ATROPINIZATION MUST BE MAINTAINED. MARKEDLY LOWER LEVELS OF URINARY METABOLITES INDICATE THAT ATROPINE DOSAGE CAN BE TAPERED OFF. AS DOSAGE IS REDUCED, CHECK THE LUNG BASES FREQUENTLY FOR RALES. IF RALES ARE HEARD OR OTHER SYMPTOMS RETURN, RE-ESTABLISH ATROPINIZATION PROMPTLY (MORGAN, RECOGNITION AND MANAGEMENT OF PESTICIDE POISONINGS, 3RD ED.). ADMINISTRATION OF ANTIDOTE MUST BE PERFORMED BY QUALIFIED MEDICAL PERSONNEL.

IN CASES OF SEVERE POISONING BY ORGANOPHOSPHATE PESTICIDES IN WHICH RESPIRATORY DEPRESSION, MUSCLE WEAKNESS AND TWITCHINGS ARE SEVERE, GIVE PRALIDOXIME (PROTOPAM-AYERST, 2-PAM), 1.0 GRAM INTRAVENOUSLY AT NO MORE THAN 0.5 GRAM PER MINUTE. DOSAGE OF PRALIDOXIME MAY BE REPEATED IN 1-2 HOURS, THEN AT 10-12 HOUR INTERVALS IF NEEDED. IN VERY SEVERE POISONINGS, DOSAGE RATES MAY BE DOUBLED. TREATMENT WITH PRALIDOXIME WILL BE MOST EFFECTIVE IF GIVEN WITHIN THIRTY-SIX HOURS AFTER POISONING (MORGAN, RECOGNITION AND MANAGEMENT OF PESTICIDE POISONINGS, 3RD ED.). ANTIDOTE SHOULD BE ADMINISTERED BY QUALIFIED MEDICAL PERSONNEL.

REACTIVITY

REACTIVITY: MAY BE SLOWLY HYDROLYZED BY WATER.

INCOMPATIBILITIES: (E)-2-CHLORO-1-(2,4,5-TRICHLOROPHENYL)VINYL DIMETHYL PHOSPHATE: ACIDS: SLOWLY HYDROLYZES. ALKALIES: HYDROLYZES. OXIDIZERS (STRONG): FIRE AND EXPLOSION HAZARD.

DECOMPOSITION: THERMAL DECOMPOSITION PRODUCTS MAY INCLUDE TOXIC AND CORROSIVE FUMES OF CHLORIDES, AND TOXIC OXIDES OF CARBON AND PHOSPHORUS.

POLYMERIZATION: HAZARDOUS POLYMERIZATION HAS NOT BEEN REPORTED TO OCCUR UNDER NORMAL TEMPERATURES AND PRESSURES.

STORAGE AND DISPOSAL

OBSERVE ALL FEDERAL, STATE AND LOCAL REGULATIONS WHEN STORING OR DISPOSING OF THIS SUBSTANCE. FOR ASSISTANCE, CONTACT THE DISTRICT DIRECTOR OF THE ENVIRONMENTAL PROTECTION AGENCY.

STORAGE

STORE IN ACCORDANCE WITH 40 CFR 165 RECOMMENDED PROCEDURES FOR THE DISPOSAL AND STORAGE OF PESTICIDES AND PESTICIDE CONTAINERS.
STORE AWAY FROM INCOMPATIBLE SUBSTANCES.

DISPOSAL

DISPOSAL MUST BE IN ACCORDANCE WITH 40 CFR 165 RECOMMENDED PROCEDURES FOR THE DISPOSAL AND STORAGE OF PESTICIDES AND PESTICIDE CONTAINERS.

CONDITIONS TO AVOID

MAY BURN BUT DOES NOT IGNITE READILY. CONTAINERS MAY EXPLODE IN HEAT OF FIRE.

SPILL AND LEAK PROCEDURES

OCCUPATIONAL SPILL: DO NOT TOUCH SPILLED MATERIAL. STOP LEAK IF YOU CAN DO IT WITHOUT RISK. USE WATER SPRAY TO REDUCE VAPORS. FOR SMALL SPILLS, TAKE UP WITH SAND OR OTHER ABSORBENT MATERIAL AND PLACE INTO CONTAINERS FOR LATER DISPOSAL. FOR SMALL DRY SPILLS, WITH A CLEAN SHOVEL PLACE MATERIAL INTO CLEAN, DRY CONTAINERS AND COVER. MOVE CONTAINERS FROM SPILL AREA. FOR LARGER SPILLS, DIKE FAR AHEAD OF SPILL FOR LATER DISPOSAL. KEEP UNNECESSARY PEOPLE AWAY. ISOLATE HAZARD AREA AND DENY ENTRY. VENTILATE CLOSED SPACES BEFORE ENTERING.

PROTECTIVE EQUIPMENT

VENTILATION: PROVIDE LOCAL EXHAUST OR GENERAL DILUTION VENTILATION SYSTEM.

RESPIRATOR: THE FOLLOWING RESPIRATORS ARE RECOMMENDED BASED ON INFORMATION FOUND IN THE PHYSICAL DATA, TOXICITY AND HEALTH EFFECTS SECTIONS. THEY ARE RANKED IN ORDER FROM MINIMUM TO MAXIMUM RESPIRATORY PROTECTION. THE SPECIFIC RESPIRATOR SELECTED MUST BE BASED ON CONTAMINATION LEVELS FOUND IN THE WORK PLACE, MUST NOT EXCEED THE WORKING LIMITS OF THE RESPIRATOR AND BE JOINTLY APPROVED BY THE NATIONAL INSTITUTE FOR OCCUPATIONAL SAFETY AND HEALTH AND THE MINE SAFETY AND HEALTH ADMINISTRATION (NIOSH-MSHA).

CHEMICAL CARTRIDGE RESPIRATOR WITH AN ORGANIC VAPOR CARTRIDGE(S) IN COMBINATION WITH A DUST AND MIST FILTER.

GAS MASK WITH ORGANIC VAPOR CANISTER (CHIN-STYLE OR FRONT- OR BACK-MOUNTED CANISTER) WITH A DUST AND MIST FILTER.

GAS MASK WITH ORGANIC VAPOR CANISTER (CHIN-STYLE OR FRONT- OR BACK-MOUNTED CANISTER) WITH A PARTICULATE FILTER.

POWERED AIR-PURIFYING RESPIRATOR WITH A HIGH-EFFICIENCY FILTER.

TYPE 'C' SUPPLIED-AIR RESPIRATOR WITH A FULL FACEPIECE OPERATED IN A PRESSURE-DEMAND OR OTHER POSITIVE PRESSURE MODE.

SELF-CONTAINED BREATHING APPARATUS WITH A FULL FACEPIECE OPERATED IN PRESSURE-DEMAND OR OTHER POSITIVE PRESSURE MODE.

FOR FIREFIGHTING AND OTHER IMMEDIATELY DANGEROUS TO LIFE OR HEALTH CONDITIONS:

SELF-CONTAINED BREATHING APPARATUS WITH FULL FACEPIECE OPERATED IN PRESSURE-DEMAND OR OTHER POSITIVE PRESSURE MODE.

SUPPLIED-AIR RESPIRATOR WITH FULL FACEPIECE AND OPERATED IN PRESSURE-DEMAND OR OTHER POSITIVE PRESSURE MODE IN COMBINATION WITH AN AUXILIARY SELF-CONTAINED BREATHING APPARATUS OPERATED IN PRESSURE-DEMAND OR OTHER POSITIVE PRESSURE MODE.

CLOTHING: EMPLOYEE MUST WEAR APPROPRIATE PROTECTIVE (IMPERVIOUS) CLOTHING AND EQUIPMENT TO PREVENT REPEATED OR PROLONGED SKIN CONTACT WITH THIS SUBSTANCE.

GLOVES: EMPLOYEE MUST WEAR APPROPRIATE PROTECTIVE GLOVES TO PREVENT CONTACT WITH THIS SUBSTANCE.

EYE PROTECTION: EMPLOYEE MUST WEAR SPLASH-PROOF OR DUST-RESISTANT SAFETY GOGGLES TO PREVENT EYE CONTACT WITH THIS SUBSTANCE.

EMERGENCY EYE WASH: WHERE THERE IS ANY POSSIBILITY THAT AN EMPLOYEE'S EYES MAY BE EXPOSED TO THIS SUBSTANCE, THE EMPLOYER SHOULD PROVIDE AN EYE WASH FOUNTAIN WITHIN THE IMMEDIATE WORK AREA FOR EMERGENCY USE.

AUTHORIZED BY- OCCUPATIONAL HEALTH SERVICES, INC.

CREATION DATE: 05/18/90 ***REVISION DATE:*** 06/20/90

MATERIAL SAFETY DATA SHEET

OCCUPATIONAL HEALTH SERVICES, INC.
AGRICULTURE AND PESTICIDE DIVISION
450 SEVENTH AVENUE, SUITE 2407
NEW YORK, NEW YORK 10123
1-800-445-MSDS OR (212) 967-1100

EMERGENCY CONTACT:
JOHN S. BRANSFORD, JR. (615) 292-1180

SUBSTANCE IDENTIFICATION

CAS-NUMBER 1918-18-9

SUBSTANCE: SWEP

TRADE NAMES/SYNONYMS: CARBAMIC ACID, (3,4-DICHLOROPHENYL)-, METHYL ESTER; CARBANILIC ACID, 3,4-DICHLORO, METHYL ESTER; (3,4-DICHLOROPHENYL)CARBAMIC ACID, METHYL ESTER; 3,4-DICHLOROCARBANILIC ACID, METHYL ESTER; METHYL 3,4-DICHLOROCARBANILATE; METHYL 3,4-DICHLOROPHENYLCARBAMATE; METHYL N-(3,4-DICHLOROPHENYL)CARBAMATE; C8H7CL2NO2; PST72247

CHEMICAL FAMILY: CARBAMATE

MOLECULAR FORMULA: C-H3-O-O-C-N-H-C6-H3-CL2

MOLECULAR WEIGHT: 220.06

CERCLA RATINGS (SCALE 0-3): HEALTH=2 FIRE=1 REACTIVITY=0 PERSISTENCE=1

NFPA RATINGS (SCALE 0-4): HEALTH=U FIRE=1 REACTIVITY=0

COMPONENTS AND CONTAMINANTS

COMPONENT: SWEP ***PERCENT:*** 100.0

CAS# 1918-18-9

EXPOSURE LIMITS: NO OCCUPATIONAL EXPOSURE LIMITS ESTABLISHED BY OSHA, ACGIH, OR NIOSH.

PHYSICAL DATA

DESCRIPTION: WHITE, CRYSTALLLINE SOLID.

MELTING POINT: 230-234 F (110-112 C)

SPECIFIC GRAVITY: NOT AVAILABLE ***SOLUBILITY IN WATER:*** INSOLUBLE

SOLVENT SOLUBILITY: SOLUBLE IN ACETONE AND DIMETHYLFORMAMIDE; INSOLUBLE IN KEROSENE.

FIRE AND EXPLOSION DATA

FIRE AND EXPLOSION HAZARD: SLIGHT FIRE HAZARD WHEN EXPOSED TO HEAT OR FLAME.

FIREFIGHTING MEDIA: DRY CHEMICAL, CARBON DIOXIDE, HALON, WATER SPRAY OR STANDARD FOAM (1987 EMERGENCY RESPONSE GUIDEBOOK, DOT P 5800.4).

FOR LARGER FIRES, USE WATER SPRAY, FOG OR STANDARD FOAM (1987 EMERGENCY RESPONSE GUIDEBOOK, DOT P 5800.4).

FIREFIGHTING: MOVE CONTAINER FROM FIRE AREA IF POSSIBLE. DO NOT SCATTER SPILLED MATERIAL WITH HIGH PRESSURE WATER STREAMS. DIKE FIRE CONTROL WATER FOR LATER DISPOSAL (1987 EMERGENCY RESPONSE GUIDEBOOK, DOT P 5800.4, GUIDE PAGE 31).

USE AGENTS SUITABLE FOR TYPE OF SURROUNDING FIRE. AVOID BREATHING HAZARDOUS VAPORS, KEEP UPWIND.

TOXICITY

SWEP: TOXICITY DATA: 2480 MG/KG SKIN-RABBIT LD50; 522 MG/KG ORAL-RAT LD50. CARCINOGEN STATUS: NONE. ACUTE TOXICITY: MODERATELY TOXIC BY INGESTION; SLIGHTLY TOXIC BY DERMAL ABSORPTION. TARGET EFFECTS: NO DATA AVAILABLE.

HEALTH EFFECTS AND FIRST AID

INHALATION: SWEP: **ACUTE EXPOSURE-** NO DATA AVAILABLE. **CHRONIC EXPOSURE-** NO DATA AVAILABLE.

FIRST AID- REMOVE FROM EXPOSURE AREA TO FRESH AIR IMMEDIATELY. IF BREATHING HAS STOPPED, PERFORM ARTIFICIAL RESPIRATION. KEEP PERSON WARM AND AT REST. TREAT SYMPTOMATICALLY AND SUPPORTIVELY. GET MEDICAL ATTENTION IMMEDIATELY.

SKIN CONTACT: SWEP: **ACUTE EXPOSURE-** A LETHAL DOSE IN RABBITS BY DERMAL ABSORPTION WAS 2480 MG/KG; NO SYMPTOMS WERE REPORTED. **CHRONIC EXPOSURE-** NO DATA AVAILABLE.

FIRST AID- REMOVE CONTAMINATED CLOTHING AND SHOES IMMEDIATELY. WASH AFFECTED AREA WITH SOAP OR MILD DETERGENT AND LARGE AMOUNTS OF WATER UNTIL NO EVIDENCE OF CHEMICAL REMAINS (APPROXIMATELY 15-20 MINUTES). GET MEDICAL ATTENTION IMMEDIATELY.

EYE CONTACT: SWEP: **ACUTE EXPOSURE-** NO DATA AVAILABLE. **CHRONIC EXPOSURE-** NO DATA AVAILABLE.

FIRST AID- WASH EYES IMMEDIATELY WITH LARGE AMOUNTS OF WATER OR NORMAL SALINE, OCCASIONALLY LIFTING UPPER AND LOWER LIDS, UNTIL NO EVIDENCE OF CHEMICAL REMAINS (APPROXIMATELY 15-20 MINUTES). GET MEDICAL ATTENTION IMMEDIATELY.

INGESTION: SWEP: **ACUTE EXPOSURE-** A LETHAL DOSE IN RATS WAS 522 MG/KG; SYMPTOMS WERE NOT REPORTED. **CHRONIC EXPOSURE-** NO DATA AVAILABLE.

FIRST AID- TREAT SYMPTOMATICALLY AND SUPPORTIVELY. GET MEDICAL ATTENTION IMMEDIATELY. IF VOMITING OCCURS, KEEP HEAD LOWER THAN HIPS TO PREVENT ASPIRATION.

ANTIDOTE: NO SPECIFIC ANTIDOTE. TREAT SYMPTOMATICALLY AND SUPPORTIVELY.

REACTIVITY

REACTIVITY: STABLE UNDER NORMAL TEMPERATURES AND PRESSURES.

INCOMPATIBILITIES: SWEP: OXIDIZERS (STRONG): FIRE AND EXPLOSION HAZARD.

DECOMPOSITION: THERMAL DECOMPOSITION PRODUCTS MAY INCLUDE TOXIC OXIDES OF NITROGEN AND CARBON AND TOXIC AND CORROSIVE FUMES OF CHLORIDES.
POLYMERIZATION: HAZARDOUS POLYMERIZATION HAS NOT BEEN REPORTED TO OCCUR UNDER NORMAL TEMPERATURES AND PRESSURES.

STORAGE AND DISPOSAL

OBSERVE ALL FEDERAL, STATE AND LOCAL REGULATIONS WHEN STORING OR DISPOSING OF THIS SUBSTANCE. FOR ASSISTANCE, CONTACT THE DISTRICT DIRECTOR OF THE ENVIRONMENTAL PROTECTION AGENCY.

STORAGE

STORE IN ACCORDANCE WITH 40 CFR 165 RECOMMENDED PROCEDURES FOR THE DISPOSAL AND STORAGE OF PESTICIDES AND PESTICIDE CONTAINERS.
STORE AWAY FROM INCOMPATIBLE SUBSTANCES.

DISPOSAL

DISPOSAL MUST BE IN ACCORDANCE WITH 40 CFR 165 RECOMMENDED PROCEDURES FOR THE DISPOSAL AND STORAGE OF PESTICIDES AND PESTICIDE CONTAINERS.

CONDITIONS TO AVOID

MAY BURN BUT DOES NOT IGNITE READILY. AVOID CONTACT WITH STRONG OXIDIZERS, EXCESSIVE HEAT, SPARKS, OR OPEN FLAME.

SPILL AND LEAK PROCEDURES

OCCUPATIONAL SPILL: SWEEP UP AND PLACE IN SUITABLE CLEAN, DRY CONTAINERS FOR RECLAMATION OR LATER DISPOSAL. DO NOT FLUSH SPILLED MATERIAL INTO SEWER. KEEP UNNECESSARY PEOPLE AWAY.

PROTECTIVE EQUIPMENT

VENTILATION: PROVIDE LOCAL EXHAUST OR GENERAL DILUTION VENTILATION SYSTEM.
RESPIRATOR: THE FOLLOWING RESPIRATORS ARE RECOMMENDED BASED ON INFORMATION FOUND IN THE PHYSICAL DATA, TOXICITY AND HEALTH EFFECTS SECTIONS. THEY ARE RANKED IN ORDER FROM MINIMUM TO MAXIMUM RESPIRATORY PROTECTION. THE SPECIFIC RESPIRATOR SELECTED MUST BE BASED ON CONTAMINATION LEVELS FOUND IN THE WORK PLACE, MUST NOT EXCEED THE WORKING LIMITS OF THE RESPIRATOR AND BE JOINTLY APPROVED BY THE NATIONAL INSTITUTE FOR OCCUPATIONAL SAFETY AND HEALTH AND THE MINE SAFETY AND HEALTH ADMINISTRATION (NIOSH-MSHA).
CHEMICAL CARTRIDGE RESPIRATOR WITH AN ORGANIC VAPOR CARTRIDGE(S) IN COMBINATION WITH A DUST AND MIST FILTER.
GAS MASK WITH ORGANIC VAPOR CANISTER (CHIN-STYLE OR FRONT- OR BACK-MOUNTED CANISTER) WITH A DUST AND MIST FILTER.
GAS MASK WITH ORGANIC VAPOR CANISTER (CHIN-STYLE OR FRONT- OR BACK-MOUNTED CANISTER) WITH A PARTICULATE FILTER.
POWERED AIR-PURIFYING RESPIRATOR WITH A HIGH-EFFICIENCY FILTER.
TYPE 'C' SUPPLIED-AIR RESPIRATOR WITH A FULL FACEPIECE OPERATED IN A PRESSURE-DEMAND OR OTHER POSITIVE PRESSURE MODE.
SELF-CONTAINED BREATHING APPARATUS WITH A FULL FACEPIECE OPERATED IN PRESSURE-DEMAND OR OTHER POSITIVE PRESSURE MODE.
FOR FIREFIGHTING AND OTHER IMMEDIATELY DANGEROUS TO LIFE OR HEALTH CONDITIONS:
SELF-CONTAINED BREATHING APPARATUS WITH FULL FACEPIECE OPERATED IN PRESSURE-DEMAND OR OTHER POSITIVE PRESSURE MODE.
SUPPLIED-AIR RESPIRATOR WITH FULL FACEPIECE AND OPERATED IN PRESSURE-DEMAND OR OTHER POSITIVE PRESSURE MODE IN COMBINATION WITH AN AUXILIARY SELF-CONTAINED BREATHING APPARATUS OPERATED IN PRESSURE-DEMAND OR OTHER POSITIVE PRESSURE MODE.
CLOTHING: EMPLOYEE MUST WEAR APPROPRIATE PROTECTIVE (IMPERVIOUS) CLOTHING AND EQUIPMENT TO PREVENT REPEATED OR PROLONGED SKIN CONTACT WITH THIS SUBSTANCE.
GLOVES: EMPLOYEE MUST WEAR APPROPRIATE PROTECTIVE GLOVES TO PREVENT CONTACT WITH THIS SUBSTANCE.
EYE PROTECTION: EMPLOYEE MUST WEAR SPLASH-PROOF OR DUST-RESISTANT SAFETY GOGGLES TO PREVENT EYE CONTACT WITH THIS SUBSTANCE.
EMERGENCY EYE WASH: WHERE THERE IS ANY POSSIBILITY THAT AN EMPLOYEE'S EYES MAY BE EXPOSED TO THIS SUBSTANCE, THE EMPLOYER SHOULD PROVIDE AN EYE WASH FOUNTAIN WITHIN THE IMMEDIATE WORK AREA FOR EMERGENCY USE.

AUTHORIZED BY- OCCUPATIONAL HEALTH SERVICES, INC.
CREATION DATE: 10/09/89 ***REVISION DATE:*** 05/31/90

MATERIAL SAFETY DATA SHEET

OCCUPATIONAL HEALTH SERVICES, INC.
AGRICULTURE AND PESTICIDE DIVISION
450 SEVENTH AVENUE, SUITE 2407
NEW YORK, NEW YORK 10123
1-800-445-MSDS OR (212) 967-1100

EMERGENCY CONTACT:
JOHN S. BRANSFORD, JR. (615) 292-1180

SUBSTANCE IDENTIFICATION

CAS-NUMBER 15457-05-3
SUBSTANCE: **FLUORODIFEN**
TRADE NAMES/SYNONYMS: 2,4'-DINITRO-4-TRIFLUOROMETHYL-DIPHENYL ETHER; BENZENE, 2-NITRO-1-(4-NITROPHENOXY)-4-(TRIFLUOROMETHYL)-; ETHER, P-NITROPHENYL ALPHA,ALPHA,ALPHA-TRIFLUORO-2-NITRO-P-TOLYL; 2-NITRO-1-(4-NITROPHENOXY)-4-(TRIFLUOROMETHYL)BENZENE; P-NITROPHENYL ALPHA,ALPHA,ALPHA-TRIFLUORO-2-NITRO-P-TOLYL ETHER; FLUORODIPHEN (FORMULATION); PREFORAN (FORMULATION); C13H7F3N2O5; PST72248
CHEMICAL FAMILY: ETHER, AROMATIC
NITRO
MOLECULAR FORMULA: C-F3-C6-H3-(N-O2)-O-C6-H4-N-O2
MOLECULAR WEIGHT: 328.22
CERCLA RATINGS (SCALE 0-3): HEALTH=1 FIRE=1 REACTIVITY=0 PERSISTENCE=3
NFPA RATINGS (SCALE 0-4): HEALTH=U FIRE=1 REACTIVITY=0

COMPONENTS AND CONTAMINANTS

COMPONENT: FLUORODIFEN ***PERCENT:*** 100.0
CAS# 15457-05-3
OTHER CONTAMINANTS: NONE
EXPOSURE LIMITS: NO OCCUPATIONAL EXPOSURE LIMITS ESTABLISHED BY OSHA, ACGIH, OR NIOSH.

PHYSICAL DATA

DESCRIPTION: YELLOW CRYSTALS. ***MELTING POINT:*** 201-203 F (94-95 C)
SPECIFIC GRAVITY: 1.59 ***VAPOR PRESSURE:*** NEGLIGIBLE
SOLUBILITY IN WATER: 2 PPM
SOLVENT SOLUBILITY: SOLUBLE IN ACETONE, DICHLOROMETHANE; MODERATELY SOLUBLE IN 1-OCTANOL; SLIGHTLY SOLUBLE IN METHANOL AND HEXANE.

FIRE AND EXPLOSION DATA

FIRE AND EXPLOSION HAZARD: SLIGHT FIRE HAZARD WHEN EXPOSED TO HEAT OR FLAME.
FIREFIGHTING MEDIA: DRY CHEMICAL, CARBON DIOXIDE, HALON, WATER SPRAY OR STANDARD FOAM (1987 EMERGENCY RESPONSE GUIDEBOOK, DOT P 5800.4).
FOR LARGER FIRES, USE WATER SPRAY, FOG OR STANDARD FOAM (1987 EMERGENCY RESPONSE GUIDEBOOK, DOT P 5800.4).
FIREFIGHTING: MOVE CONTAINER FROM FIRE AREA IF POSSIBLE. DO NOT SCATTER SPILLED MATERIAL WITH HIGH PRESSURE WATER STREAMS. DIKE FIRE CONTROL WATER FOR LATER DISPOSAL (1987 EMERGENCY RESPONSE GUIDEBOOK, DOT P 5800.4, GUIDE PAGE 31).
USE AGENTS SUITABLE FOR TYPE OF SURROUNDING FIRE. AVOID BREATHING HAZARDOUS VAPORS, KEEP UPWIND.

TOXICITY

FLUORODIFEN: IRRITATION DATA: 100 MG EYE-RABBIT MODERATE. TOXICITY DATA: >0.99 MG/L/6 HOURS INHALATION-RAT LC50 (PEMNDP); >3000 MG/KG SKIN-RAT LD50 (FMCHA2); 9 GM/KG ORAL-RAT LD50. CARCINOGEN STATUS: NONE. LOCAL EFFECTS: IRRITANT- EYE. ACUTE TOXICITY LEVEL: SLIGHTLY TOXIC BY DERMAL ABSORPTION, INGESTION. TARGET EFFECTS: NO DATA AVAILABLE.

HEALTH EFFECTS AND FIRST AID

INHALATION: FLUORODIFEN: **ACUTE EXPOSURE-** A LETHAL CONCENTRATION IN RATS WAS GREATER THAN 990 MG/M3/6 HOURS. **CHRONIC EXPOSURE-** NO DATA AVAILABLE.
FIRST AID- REMOVE FROM EXPOSURE AREA TO FRESH AIR IMMEDIATELY. IF BREATHING HAS STOPPED, PERFORM ARTIFICIAL RESPIRATION. KEEP PERSON WARM AND AT REST. TREAT SYMPTOMATICALLY AND SUPPORTIVELY. GET MEDICAL ATTENTION IMMEDIATELY.

SKIN CONTACT: FLUORODIFEN: **ACUTE EXPOSURE-** MAY CAUSE IRRITATION. **CHRONIC EXPOSURE-** NO DATA AVAILABLE.
FIRST AID- REMOVE CONTAMINATED CLOTHING AND SHOES IMMEDIATELY. WASH AFFECTED AREA WITH SOAP OR MILD DETERGENT AND LARGE AMOUNTS OF

WATER UNTIL NO EVIDENCE OF CHEMICAL REMAINS (APPROXIMATELY 15-20 MINUTES). GET MEDICAL ATTENTION IMMEDIATELY.

EYE CONTACT: FLUORODIFEN: IRRITANT. **ACUTE EXPOSURE-** APPLICATION OF 100 MG TO RABBIT EYES CAUSED MODERATE IRRITATION. **CHRONIC EXPOSURE-** REPEATED OR PROLONGED EXPOSURE TO IRRITANTS MAY CAUSE CONJUNCTIVITIS.
FIRST AID- WASH EYES IMMEDIATELY WITH LARGE AMOUNTS OF WATER OR NORMAL SALINE, OCCASIONALLY LIFTING UPPER AND LOWER LIDS, UNTIL NO EVIDENCE OF CHEMICAL REMAINS (APPROXIMATELY 15-20 MINUTES). GET MEDICAL ATTENTION IMMEDIATELY.

INGESTION: FLUORODIFEN: **ACUTE EXPOSURE-** THE LETHAL DOSE IN RATS WAS 9000 MG/KG. **CHRONIC EXPOSURE-** NO OBSERVABLE EFFECTS WERE REPORTED FROM 90-DAY STUDIES OF RATS FED 67 MG/KG/DAY OR DOGS FED 10 MG/KG/DAY. FLUORODIFEN IS SIMILAR IN STRUCTURE TO NITROFEN WHICH PRODUCED HEPATOCELLULAR CARCINOMAS IN MICE AND ADENOCARCINOMAS OF THE PANCREAS IN FEMALE RATS BY ORAL ADMINISTRATION.
FIRST AID- IF THE PERSON IS CONSCIOUS AND NOT CONVULSING, REMOVE BY GASTRIC LAVAGE AND FOLLOW WITH A CATHARTIC (DREISBACH, HANDBOOK OF POISONING, 12TH ED.). TREAT SYMPTOMATICALLY AND SUPPORTIVELY. GASTRIC LAVAGE SHOULD BE PERFORMED BY QUALIFIED MEDICAL PERSONNEL. GET MEDICAL ATTENTION IMMEDIATELY.
ANTIDOTE: NO SPECIFIC ANTIDOTE. TREAT SYMPTOMATICALLY AND SUPPORTIVELY.

REACTIVITY

REACTIVITY: STABLE UNDER NORMAL TEMPERATURES AND PRESSURES.
INCOMPATIBILITIES: FLUORODIFEN: OXIDIZERS (STRONG): FIRE AND EXPLOSION HAZARD.
DECOMPOSITION: THERMAL DECOMPOSITION PRODUCTS MAY INCLUDE HIGHLY TOXIC FUMES OF FLUORIDES AND OXIDES OF NITROGEN AND CARBON.
POLYMERIZATION: HAZARDOUS POLYMERIZATION HAS NOT BEEN REPORTED TO OCCUR UNDER NORMAL TEMPERATURES AND PRESSURES.

STORAGE AND DISPOSAL

OBSERVE ALL FEDERAL, STATE AND LOCAL REGULATIONS WHEN STORING OR DISPOSING OF THIS SUBSTANCE. FOR ASSISTANCE, CONTACT THE DISTRICT DIRECTOR OF THE ENVIRONMENTAL PROTECTION AGENCY.

****STORAGE****

STORE IN ACCORDANCE WITH 40 CFR 165 RECOMMENDED PROCEDURES FOR THE DISPOSAL AND STORAGE OF PESTICIDES AND PESTICIDE CONTAINERS.
STORE AWAY FROM INCOMPATIBLE SUBSTANCES.

****DISPOSAL****

DISPOSAL MUST BE IN ACCORDANCE WITH 40 CFR 165 RECOMMENDED PROCEDURES FOR THE DISPOSAL AND STORAGE OF PESTICIDES AND PESTICIDE CONTAINERS.

CONDITIONS TO AVOID

MAY BURN BUT DOES NOT IGNITE READILY. AVOID CONTACT WITH STRONG OXIDIZERS, EXCESSIVE HEAT, SPARKS, OR OPEN FLAME.

SPILL AND LEAK PROCEDURES

OCCUPATIONAL SPILL: SWEEP UP AND PLACE IN SUITABLE CLEAN, DRY CONTAINERS FOR RECLAMATION OR LATER DISPOSAL. DO NOT FLUSH SPILLED MATERIAL INTO SEWER. KEEP UNNECESSARY PEOPLE AWAY.

PROTECTIVE EQUIPMENT

VENTILATION: PROVIDE GENERAL DILUTION VENTILATION.
RESPIRATOR: THE FOLLOWING RESPIRATORS ARE RECOMMENDED BASED ON INFORMATION FOUND IN THE PHYSICAL DATA, TOXICITY AND HEALTH EFFECTS SECTIONS. THEY ARE RANKED IN ORDER FROM MINIMUM TO MAXIMUM RESPIRATORY PROTECTION. THE SPECIFIC RESPIRATOR SELECTED MUST BE BASED ON CONTAMINATION LEVELS FOUND IN THE WORK PLACE, MUST NOT EXCEED THE WORKING LIMITS OF THE RESPIRATOR AND BE JOINTLY APPROVED BY THE NATIONAL INSTITUTE FOR OCCUPATIONAL SAFETY AND HEALTH AND THE MINE SAFETY AND HEALTH ADMINISTRATION (NIOSH-MSHA).
CHEMICAL CARTRIDGE RESPIRATOR WITH AN ORGANIC VAPOR CARTRIDGE(S) WITH A FULL FACEPIECE AND ORGANIC VAPOR CARTRIDGE(S) IN COMBINATION WITH A DUST AND MIST FILTER.
POWERED AIR-PURIFYING RESPIRATOR WITH A TIGHT-FITTING FACEPIECE AND ORGANIC VAPOR CARTRIDGE(S) IN COMBINATION WITH A HIGH-EFFICIENCY PARTICULATE FILTER.
TYPE 'C' SUPPLIED-AIR RESPIRATOR WITH A FULL FACEPIECE OPERATED IN A PRESSURE-DEMAND OR OTHER POSITIVE PRESSURE MODE.
SELF-CONTAINED BREATHING APPARATUS WITH A FULL FACEPIECE OPERATED IN PRESSURE-DEMAND OR OTHER POSITIVE PRESSURE MODE.
FOR FIREFIGHTING AND OTHER IMMEDIATELY DANGEROUS TO LIFE OR HEALTH CONDITIONS:
SELF-CONTAINED BREATHING APPARATUS WITH FULL FACEPIECE OPERATED IN PRESSURE-DEMAND OR OTHER POSITIVE PRESSURE MODE.
SUPPLIED-AIR RESPIRATOR WITH FULL FACEPIECE AND OPERATED IN PRESSURE-DEMAND OR OTHER POSITIVE PRESSURE MODE IN COMBINATION WITH AN AUXILIARY SELF-CONTAINED BREATHING APPARATUS OPERATED IN PRESSURE-DEMAND OR OTHER POSITIVE PRESSURE MODE.
CLOTHING: EMPLOYEE MUST WEAR APPROPRIATE PROTECTIVE (IMPERVIOUS) CLOTHING AND EQUIPMENT TO PREVENT REPEATED OR PROLONGED SKIN CONTACT WITH THIS SUBSTANCE.
GLOVES: EMPLOYEE MUST WEAR APPROPRIATE PROTECTIVE GLOVES TO PREVENT CONTACT WITH THIS SUBSTANCE.
EYE PROTECTION: EMPLOYEE MUST WEAR SPLASH-PROOF OR DUST-RESISTANT SAFETY GOGGLES TO PREVENT EYE CONTACT WITH THIS SUBSTANCE.
EMERGENCY EYE WASH: WHERE THERE IS ANY POSSIBILITY THAT AN EMPLOYEE'S EYES MAY BE EXPOSED TO THIS SUBSTANCE, THE EMPLOYER SHOULD PROVIDE AN EYE WASH FOUNTAIN WITHIN THE IMMEDIATE WORK AREA FOR EMERGENCY USE.

AUTHORIZED BY- OCCUPATIONAL HEALTH SERVICES, INC.
CREATION DATE: 10/04/89 ***REVISION DATE:*** 05/31/90

MATERIAL SAFETY DATA SHEET

OCCUPATIONAL HEALTH SERVICES, INC.
AGRICULTURE AND PESTICIDE DIVISION
450 SEVENTH AVENUE, SUITE 2407
NEW YORK, NEW YORK 10123
1-800-445-MSDS OR (212) 967-1100

EMERGENCY CONTACT:
JOHN S. BRANSFORD, JR. (615) 292-1180

SUBSTANCE IDENTIFICATION

CAS-NUMBER 991-42-4
SUBSTANCE: **NORBORMIDE**
TRADE NAMES/SYNONYMS: 3A,4,7,7A-TETRAHYDRO-5-(HYDROXYPHENYL-2-PYRIDINYLMETHYL)-8-(PHENYL -2-PYRIDINYLMETHYLENE)-4,7-METHANO-1H-ISOINDOLE-1,3(2H)-DIONE; 5-(ALPHA-HYDROXY-ALPHA-2-PYRIDYLBENZYL)-7-(ALPHA-2 -PYRIDYLBENZYLIDENE)-5-NORBORNENE-2,3-DICARBOXIMIDE; MCN 1025; RATICATE; S 6999; SHOXIN; PST72254
CHEMICAL FAMILY: HETEROCYCLIC
MOLECULAR FORMULA: C33-H25-N3-O3
MOLECULAR WEIGHT: 511.61
CERCLA RATINGS (SCALE 0-3): HEALTH=3 FIRE=U REACTIVITY=0 PERSISTENCE=2
NFPA RATINGS (SCALE 0-4): HEALTH=3 FIRE=U REACTIVITY=0

COMPONENTS AND CONTAMINANTS

COMPONENT: NORBORMIDE ***PERCENT:*** 100.0
CAS# 991-42-4
OTHER CONTAMINANTS: NONE
EXPOSURE LIMITS: NORBORMIDE: NO OCCUPATIONAL EXPOSURE LIMITS ESTABLISHED BY OSHA, ACGIH, OR NIOSH.
100/10,000 POUNDS SARA SECTION 302 THRESHOLD PLANNING QUANTITY 1 POUND SARA SECTION 304 REPORTABLE QUANTITY

PHYSICAL DATA

DESCRIPTION: WHITE CRYSTALLINE POWDER
MELTING POINT: 374-388 F (190-198 C)
SOLUBILITY IN WATER: 60 PPM
SOLVENT SOLUBILITY: SLIGHTLY SOLUBLE IN CHLOROFORM; VERY SLIGHTLY SOLUBLE IN DIETHYL ETHER, ETHANOL, 0.1N HYDROCHLORIC ACID

FIRE AND EXPLOSION DATA

FIRE AND EXPLOSION HAZARD: UNKNOWN FIRE AND EXPLOSION HAZARD.
FIREFIGHTING MEDIA: DRY CHEMICAL, CARBON DIOXIDE, HALON, WATER SPRAY OR STANDARD FOAM (1987 EMERGENCY RESPONSE GUIDEBOOK, DOT P 5800.4).
FOR LARGER FIRES, USE WATER SPRAY, FOG OR STANDARD FOAM (1987 EMERGENCY RESPONSE GUIDEBOOK, DOT P 5800.4).
FIREFIGHTING: MOVE CONTAINERS FROM FIRE AREA IF POSSIBLE (1987 EMERGENCY RESPONSE GUIDEBOOK, DOT P 5800.4, GUIDE PAGE 53).

EXTINGUISH USING AGENT SUITABLE FOR TYPE OF SURROUNDING FIRE. AVOID BREATHING VAPORS AND DUSTS. KEEP UPWIND.

TRANSPORTATION DATA

DEPARTMENT OF TRANSPORTATION HAZARD CLASSIFICATION 49 CFR 172.101: POISON B

DEPARTMENT OF TRANSPORTATION LABELING REQUIREMENTS 49 CFR 172.101 AND SUBPART E: POISON

DEPARTMENT OF TRANSPORTATION PACKAGING REQUIREMENTS: 49 CFR 173.365 EXCEPTIONS: 49 CFR 173.364

TOXICITY

NORBORMIDE: TOXICITY DATA: 3800 UG/KG ORAL-RAT LD50; 2250 MG/KG ORAL-MOUSE LD50; 1 GM/KG ORAL-CAT LD50; 1 GM/KG ORAL-DOG LD50; 300 MG/KG ORAL-GUINEA PIG LD50; 140 MG/KG ORAL-HAMSTER LD50; 1 GM/KG ORAL-RABBIT LD50; 1 GM/KG ORAL-MONKEY LD50; 20 MG/KG INTRAPERITONEAL-RAT LD50; 250 UG/KG INTRAVENOUS-RAT LDLO. CARCINOGEN STATUS: NONE. ACUTE TOXICITY LEVEL: HIGHLY TOXIC BY INGESTION. TARGET EFFECTS: POISONING MAY AFFECT THE CIRCULATORY SYSTEM.

HEALTH EFFECTS AND FIRST AID

INHALATION: NORBORMIDE: **ACUTE EXPOSURE-** NO DATA AVAILABLE. **CHRONIC EXPOSURE-** NO DATA AVAILABLE.

FIRST AID- REMOVE FROM EXPOSURE AREA TO FRESH AIR IMMEDIATELY. IF BREATHING HAS STOPPED, PERFORM ARTIFICIAL RESPIRATION. KEEP PERSON WARM AND AT REST. TREAT SYMPTOMATICALLY AND SUPPORTIVELY. GET MEDICAL ATTENTION IMMEDIATELY.

SKIN CONTACT: NORBORMIDE: **ACUTE EXPOSURE-** NO DATA AVAILABLE. **CHRONIC EXPOSURE-** NO DATA AVAILABLE.

FIRST AID- REMOVE CONTAMINATED CLOTHING AND SHOES IMMEDIATELY. WASH AFFECTED AREA WITH SOAP OR MILD DETERGENT AND LARGE AMOUNTS OF WATER UNTIL NO EVIDENCE OF CHEMICAL REMAINS (APPROXIMATELY 15-20 MINUTES). GET MEDICAL ATTENTION IMMEDIATELY.

EYE CONTACT: NORBORMIDE: **ACUTE EXPOSURE-** NO DATA AVAILABLE. **CHRONIC EXPOSURE-** NO DATA AVAILABLE.

FIRST AID- WASH EYES IMMEDIATELY WITH LARGE AMOUNTS OF WATER OR NORMAL SALINE, OCCASIONALLY LIFTING UPPER AND LOWER LIDS, UNTIL NO EVIDENCE OF CHEMICAL REMAINS (APPROXIMATELY 15-20 MINUTES). GET MEDICAL ATTENTION IMMEDIATELY.

INGESTION: NORBORMIDE: HIGHLY TOXIC. **ACUTE EXPOSURE-** HUMANS INGESTING DOSES UP TO 300 MG SHOWED SLIGHT TRANSIENT DECREASES IN BODY TEMPERATURES AND BLOOD PRESSURES. THIS MATERIAL IS A RODENTICIDE THAT IS MORE TOXIC IN RATS THEN IN OTHER ANIMALS; A VERY LOW DOSE WAS LETHAL IN RATS, WHEREAS A MODERATE DOSE WAS LETHAL IN OTHER ANIMALS. IN RATS, NORBORMIDE PRODUCES A GENERALIZED, SUDDEN, AND INTENSE VASOCONSTRICTION WITH SIGNS OF INITIAL INCREASE IN MOTOR ACTIVITY ACCOMPANIED BY INCOORDINATION AND A GENERALIZED WEAKENING OF HIND EXTREMITIES. THESE EFFECTS ARE FOLLOWED BY DYSPNEA, A MARKED BLANCHING OF EARS, EYES, FEET AND TAIL, AND WITH CONVULSIONS PRECEDING DEATH. **CHRONIC EXPOSURE-** NO ADVERSE EFFECTS WERE REPORTED IN DOGS FED APPROXIMATELY 1,000 PPM FOR 60 DAYS.

FIRST AID- ADMINISTER SYRUP OF IPECAC, THEN 1-2 GLASSES OF WATER, TO INDUCE VOMITING. FOLLOW WITH ACTIVATED CHARCOAL, THEN 0.25 GM/KG SODIUM OR MAGNESIUM SULFATE IN 1-6 OUNCES WATER. GET MEDICAL ATTENTION. FIRST AID SHOULD BE ADMINISTERED BY QUALIFIED MEDICAL PERSONNEL. (MORGAN, RECOGNITION AND MANAGEMENT OF PESTICIDE POISONINGS, 3RD EDITION)

ANTIDOTE: NO SPECIFIC ANTIDOTE. TREAT SYMPTOMATICALLY AND SUPPORTIVELY.

REACTIVITY

REACTIVITY: STABLE UNDER NORMAL TEMPERATURES AND PRESSURES.

INCOMPATIBILITIES: NORBORMIDE: ALKALI: MAY CAUSE HYDROLYSIS.

DECOMPOSITION: THERMAL DECOMPOSITION PRODUCTS MAY INCLUDE TOXIC OXIDES OF NITROGEN.

POLYMERIZATION: HAZARDOUS POLYMERIZATION HAS NOT BEEN REPORTED TO OCCUR UNDER NORMAL TEMPERATURES AND PRESSURES.

STORAGE AND DISPOSAL

OBSERVE ALL FEDERAL, STATE AND LOCAL REGULATIONS WHEN STORING OR DISPOSING OF THIS SUBSTANCE. FOR ASSISTANCE, CONTACT THE DISTRICT DIRECTOR OF THE ENVIRONMENTAL PROTECTION AGENCY.

****STORAGE****

STORE IN ACCORDANCE WITH 40 CFR 165 RECOMMENDED PROCEDURES FOR THE DISPOSAL AND STORAGE OF PESTICIDES AND PESTICIDE CONTAINERS.

STORE AWAY FROM INCOMPATIBLE SUBSTANCES.

THRESHOLD PLANNING QUANTITY (TPQ): THE SUPERFUND AMENDMENTS AND REAUTHORIZATION ACT (SARA) SECTION 302 REQUIRES THAT EACH FACILITY WHERE ANY EXTREMELY HAZARDOUS SUBSTANCE IS PRESENT IN A QUANTITY EQUAL TO OR GREATER THAN THE TPQ ESTABLISHED FOR THAT SUBSTANCE NOTIFY THE STATE EMERGENCY RESPONSE COMMISSION FOR THE STATE IN WHICH IT IS LOCATED. SECTION 303 OF SARA REQUIRES THESE FACILITIES TO PARTICIPATE IN LOCAL EMERGENCY RESPONSE PLANNING (40 CFR 355.30).

****DISPOSAL****

DISPOSAL MUST BE IN ACCORDANCE WITH 40 CFR 165 RECOMMENDED PROCEDURES FOR THE DISPOSAL AND STORAGE OF PESTICIDES AND PESTICIDE CONTAINERS.

CONDITIONS TO AVOID

NONE REPORTED.

SPILL AND LEAK PROCEDURES

OCCUPATIONAL SPILL: DO NOT TOUCH SPILLED MATERIAL. STOP LEAK IF YOU CAN DO IT WITHOUT RISK. FOR SMALL SPILLS, TAKE UP WITH SAND OR OTHER ABSORBENT MATERIAL AND PLACE INTO CONTAINERS FOR LATER DISPOSAL. FOR SMALL DRY SPILLS, WITH A CLEAN SHOVEL PLACE MATERIAL INTO CLEAN, DRY CONTAINER AND COVER. MOVE CONTAINERS FROM SPILL AREA. FOR LARGER SPILLS, DIKE FAR AHEAD OF SPILL FOR LATER DISPOSAL. KEEP UNNECESSARY PEOPLE AWAY. ISOLATE HAZARD AREA AND DENY ENTRY.

REPORTABLE QUANTITY (RQ): 1 POUND THE SUPERFUND AMENDMENTS AND REAUTHORIZATION ACT (SARA) SECTION 304 REQUIRES THAT A RELEASE EQUAL TO OR GREATER THAN THE REPORTABLE QUANTITY FOR THIS SUBSTANCE BE IMMEDIATELY REPORTED TO THE LOCAL EMERGENCY PLANNING COMMITTEE AND THE STATE EMERGENCY RESPONSE COMMISSION (40 CFR 355.40). IF THE RELEASE OF THIS SUBSTANCE IS REPORTABLE UNDER CERCLA SECTION 103, THE NATIONAL RESPONSE CENTER MUST BE NOTIFIED IMMEDIATELY AT (800) 424-8802 OR (202) 426-2675 IN THE METROPOLITAN WASHINGTON, D.C. AREA (40 CFR 302.6).

PROTECTIVE EQUIPMENT

VENTILATION: PROVIDE LOCAL EXHAUST OR PROCESS ENCLOSURE VENTILATION SYSTEM.

RESPIRATOR: THE FOLLOWING RESPIRATORS ARE RECOMMENDED BASED ON INFORMATION FOUND IN THE PHYSICAL DATA, TOXICITY AND HEALTH EFFECTS SECTIONS. THEY ARE RANKED IN ORDER FROM MINIMUM TO MAXIMUM RESPIRATORY PROTECTION. THE SPECIFIC RESPIRATOR SELECTED MUST BE BASED ON CONTAMINATION LEVELS FOUND IN THE WORK PLACE, MUST NOT EXCEED THE WORKING LIMITS OF THE RESPIRATOR AND BE JOINTLY APPROVED BY THE NATIONAL INSTITUTE FOR OCCUPATIONAL SAFETY AND HEALTH AND THE MINE SAFETY AND HEALTH ADMINISTRATION (NIOSH-MSHA).

CHEMICAL CARTRIDGE RESPIRATOR WITH AN ORGANIC VAPOR CARTRIDGE(S)

WITH A FULL FACEPIECE AND ORGANIC VAPOR CARTRIDGE(S) IN COMBINATION WITH A DUST AND MIST FILTER.

POWERED AIR-PURIFYING RESPIRATOR WITH A TIGHT-FITTING FACEPIECE AND ORGANIC VAPOR CARTRIDGE(S) IN COMBINATION WITH A HIGH-EFFICIENCY PARTICULATE FILTER.

TYPE 'C' SUPPLIED-AIR RESPIRATOR WITH A FULL FACEPIECE OPERATED IN A PRESSURE-DEMAND OR OTHER POSITIVE PRESSURE MODE.

SELF-CONTAINED BREATHING APPARATUS WITH A FULL FACEPIECE OPERATED IN PRESSURE-DEMAND OR OTHER POSITIVE PRESSURE MODE.

FOR FIREFIGHTING AND OTHER IMMEDIATELY DANGEROUS TO LIFE OR HEALTH CONDITIONS:

SELF-CONTAINED BREATHING APPARATUS WITH FULL FACEPIECE OPERATED IN PRESSURE-DEMAND OR OTHER POSITIVE PRESSURE MODE.

SUPPLIED-AIR RESPIRATOR WITH FULL FACEPIECE AND OPERATED IN PRESSURE-DEMAND OR OTHER POSITIVE PRESSURE MODE IN COMBINATION WITH AN AUXILIARY SELF-CONTAINED BREATHING APPARATUS OPERATED IN PRESSURE-DEMAND OR OTHER POSITIVE PRESSURE MODE.

CLOTHING: EMPLOYEE MUST WEAR APPROPRIATE PROTECTIVE (IMPERVIOUS) CLOTHING AND EQUIPMENT TO PREVENT REPEATED OR PROLONGED SKIN CONTACT WITH THIS SUBSTANCE.

GLOVES: EMPLOYEE MUST WEAR APPROPRIATE PROTECTIVE GLOVES TO PREVENT CONTACT WITH THIS SUBSTANCE.

EYE PROTECTION: EMPLOYEE MUST WEAR SPLASH-PROOF OR DUST-RESISTANT SAFETY GOGGLES TO PREVENT EYE CONTACT WITH THIS SUBSTANCE.

EMERGENCY EYE WASH: WHERE THERE IS ANY POSSIBILITY THAT AN EMPLOYEE'S EYES MAY BE EXPOSED TO THIS SUBSTANCE, THE EMPLOYER SHOULD PROVIDE AN EYE WASH FOUNTAIN WITHIN THE IMMEDIATE WORK AREA FOR EMERGENCY USE.

AUTHORIZED BY- OCCUPATIONAL HEALTH SERVICES, INC.
CREATION DATE: 10/04/89 ***REVISION DATE:*** 05/18/90

MATERIAL SAFETY DATA SHEET

OCCUPATIONAL HEALTH SERVICES, INC.
AGRICULTURE AND PESTICIDE DIVISION
450 SEVENTH AVENUE, SUITE 2407
NEW YORK, NEW YORK 10123
1-800-445-MSDS OR (212) 967-1100

EMERGENCY CONTACT:
JOHN S. BRANSFORD, JR. (615) 292-1180

SUBSTANCE IDENTIFICATION

CAS-NUMBER 88-04-0
SUBSTANCE: 4-CHLORO-3,5-DIMETHYLPHENOL
TRADE NAMES/SYNONYMS: PHENOL, 4-CHLORO-3,5-DIMETHYL-; 3,5-XYLENOL, 4-CHLORO-; 4-CHLORO-3,5-XYLENOL; CHLOROXYLENOL; P-CHLORO-M-XYLENOL; BENZYTOL; ESPADOL; HUSEPT EXTRA; OTTASEPT; PCMX; C8H9CLO; PST72258
CHEMICAL FAMILY: PHENOL
HALOGEN COMPOUND, ALICYCLIC
MOLECULAR FORMULA: (C-H3)2-CL-C6-H2-O-H
MOLECULAR WEIGHT: 156.61
CERCLA RATINGS (SCALE 0-3): HEALTH=U FIRE=1 REACTIVITY=0 PERSISTENCE=3
NFPA RATINGS (SCALE 0-4): HEALTH=U FIRE=1 REACTIVITY=0

COMPONENTS AND CONTAMINANTS

COMPONENT: 4-CHLORO-3,5-XYLENOL ***PERCENT:*** 100.0
CAS# 88-04-0
OTHER CONTAMINANTS: NONE
EXPOSURE LIMITS: NO OCCUPATIONAL EXPOSURE LIMITS ESTABLISHED BY OSHA, ACGIH, OR NIOSH.

PHYSICAL DATA

DESCRIPTION: CRYSTALS WITH A PHENOLIC ODOR. ***BOILING POINT:*** 475 F (246 C)
MELTING POINT: 239-244 F (115-118 C) ***SPECIFIC GRAVITY:*** NOT AVAILABLE
SOLUBILITY IN WATER: 0.03% @ 20 C
SOLVENT SOLUBILITY: SOLUBLE IN ALCOHOL, ETHER, BENZENE, TERPENES, FIXED OILS, AND ALKALI HYDROXIDE SOLUTIONS.

FIRE AND EXPLOSION DATA

FIRE AND EXPLOSION HAZARD: SLIGHT FIRE HAZARD WHEN EXPOSED TO HEAT OR FLAME.
FIREFIGHTING MEDIA: DRY CHEMICAL, CARBON DIOXIDE, HALON, WATER SPRAY OR STANDARD FOAM (1987 EMERGENCY RESPONSE GUIDEBOOK, DOT P 5800.4).
FOR LARGER FIRES, USE WATER SPRAY, FOG OR STANDARD FOAM (1987 EMERGENCY RESPONSE GUIDEBOOK, DOT P 5800.4).
FIREFIGHTING: MOVE CONTAINERS FROM FIRE AREA IF POSSIBLE. FIGHT FIRE FROM MAXIMUM DISTANCE. STAY AWAY FROM STORAGE TANK ENDS. DIKE FIRE CONTROL WATER FOR LATER DISPOSAL. DO NOT SCATTER MATERIAL (1987 EMERGENCY RESPONSE GUIDEBOOK, DOT P 5800.4, GUIDE PAGE 55).
USE AGENTS SUITABLE FOR TYPE OF FIRE. AVOID BREATHING VAPORS OR DUSTS, KEEP UPWIND.

TOXICITY

4-CHLORO-3,5-DIMETHYLPHENOL: IRRITATION DATA: 100 MG EYE-RABBIT MODERATE. TOXICITY DATA: 3830 MG/KG ORAL-RAT LD50; 1600 MG/KG ORAL-MOUSE LDLO; 115 GM/KG INTRAPERITONEAL-MOUSE LD50; REPRODUCTIVE EFFECTS DATA (RTECS). CARCINOGEN STATUS: NONE. LOCAL EFFECTS: IRRITANT-SKIN AND EYES. ACUTE TOXICITY LEVEL: MODERATELY TOXIC BY INGESTION. TARGET EFFECTS: SENSITIZER- SKIN.

HEALTH EFFECTS AND FIRST AID

INHALATION: 4-CHLORO-3,5-DIMETHYLPHENOL: **ACUTE EXPOSURE-** NO DATA AVAILABLE. **CHRONIC EXPOSURE-** NO DATA AVAILABLE.
FIRST AID- REMOVE FROM EXPOSURE AREA TO FRESH AIR IMMEDIATELY. IF BREATHING HAS STOPPED, PERFORM ARTIFICIAL RESPIRATION. KEEP PERSON WARM AND AT REST. TREAT SYMPTOMATICALLY AND SUPPORTIVELY. GET MEDICAL ATTENTION IMMEDIATELY.

SKIN CONTACT: 4-CHLORO-3,5-DIMETHYLPHENOL: **ACUTE EXPOSURE-** MAY BE IRRITATING AND ABSORBED THROUGH THE SKIN. CONTACT ALLERGIC ECZEMA MAY OCCUR IN PREVIOSLY EXPOSED PERSONS. **CHRONIC EXPOSURE-** REPEATED EXPOSURES MAY CAUSE SENSITIZATION AND CONTACT DERMATITIS.
FIRST AID- REMOVE CONTAMINATED CLOTHING AND SHOES IMMEDIATELY. WASH AFFECTED AREA WITH SOAP OR MILD DETERGENT AND LARGE AMOUNTS OF WATER UNTIL NO EVIDENCE OF CHEMICAL REMAINS (APPROXIMATELY 15-20 MINUTES). GET MEDICAL ATTENTION IMMEDIATELY.

EYE CONTACT: 4-CHLORO-3,5-DIMETHYLPHENOL: IRRITANT. **ACUTE EXPOSURE-** MAY BE IRRITATING. 100 MG APPLIED TO RABBIT EYES CAUSED MODERATE IRRITATION. **CHRONIC EXPOSURE-** REPEATED AND PROLONGED EXPOSURE TO IRRITANTS MAY CAUSE CONJUNCTIVITIS.
FIRST AID- WASH EYES IMMEDIATELY WITH LARGE AMOUNTS OF WATER OR NORMAL SALINE, OCCASIONALLY LIFTING UPPER AND LOWER LIDS, UNTIL NO EVIDENCE OF CHEMICAL REMAINS (APPROXIMATELY 15-20 MINUTES). GET MEDICAL ATTENTION IMMEDIATELY.

INGESTION: 4-CHLORO-3,5-DIMETHYLPHENOL: **ACUTE EXPOSURE-** 3830 MG/KG IS THE LETHAL DOSE IN RATS. DEATH OF A WOMAN RESULTED FROM INGESTION OF 300 ML OF A HOUSEHOLD DISINFECTANT, DETTOL, CONTAINING 4.8% 4-CHLORO-3,5-DIMETHYLPHENOL, THE PRINCIPAL TOXIC COMPONENT. THERE WERE ISOLATED AREAS OF CORROSIVE STAINING OF THE LIPS, CHIN, MOUTH, ESOPHAGUS, TRACHEA AND BRONCHI. OTHER SYMPTOMS INCLUDED OBSTRUCTION OF UPPER AIR PASSAGES, PULMONARY EDEMA, BRONCHOPNEUMONIA, RENAL FAILURE AND UNCONSCIOUSNESS. **CHRONIC EXPOSURE-** EFFECTS ON THE EMBRYO AND FETAL DEVELOPMENTAL ABNORMALITIES HAVE BEEN REPORTED FROM INGESTION DURING THE FIRST THROUGH NINETEENTH DAY OF PREGNANCY IN RATS.
FIRST AID- TREAT SYMPTOMATICALLY AND SUPPORTIVELY. GET MEDICAL ATTENTION IMMEDIATELY. IF VOMITING OCCURS, KEEP HEAD LOWER THAN HIPS TO PREVENT ASPIRATION.
ANTIDOTE: NO SPECIFIC ANTIDOTE. TREAT SYMPTOMATICALLY AND SUPPORTIVELY.

REACTIVITY

REACTIVITY: STABLE UNDER NORMAL TEMPERATURES AND PRESSURES.
INCOMPATIBILITIES: 4-CHLORO-3,5-DIMETHYLPHENOL: OXIDIZERS (STRONG): FIRE AND EXPLOSION HAZARD.
DECOMPOSITION: THERMAL DECOMPOSITION PRODUCTS MAY INCLUDE TOXIC AND CORROSIVE FUMES OF CHLORIDES AND TOXIC OXIDES OF CARBON.
POLYMERIZATION: HAZARDOUS POLYMERIZATION HAS NOT BEEN REPORTED TO OCCUR UNDER NORMAL TEMPERATURES AND PRESSURES.

STORAGE AND DISPOSAL

OBSERVE ALL FEDERAL, STATE AND LOCAL REGULATIONS WHEN STORING OR DISPOSING OF THIS SUBSTANCE. FOR ASSISTANCE, CONTACT THE DISTRICT DIRECTOR OF THE ENVIRONMENTAL PROTECTION AGENCY.

STORAGE

STORE IN ACCORDANCE WITH 40 CFR 165 RECOMMENDED PROCEDURES FOR THE DISPOSAL AND STORAGE OF PESTICIDES AND PESTICIDE CONTAINERS.
STORE AWAY FROM INCOMPATIBLE SUBSTANCES.

DISPOSAL

DISPOSAL MUST BE IN ACCORDANCE WITH 40 CFR 165 RECOMMENDED PROCEDURES FOR THE DISPOSAL AND STORAGE OF PESTICIDES AND PESTICIDE CONTAINERS.

CONDITIONS TO AVOID

MAY BURN BUT DOES NOT IGNITE READILY. CONTAINERS MAY EXPLODE IN HEAT OF FIRE.

SPILL AND LEAK PROCEDURES

OCCUPATIONAL SPILL: DO NOT TOUCH SPILLED MATERIAL. STOP LEAK IF YOU CAN DO IT WITHOUT RISK. USE WATER SPRAY TO REDUCE VAPORS. FOR SMALL SPILLS, TAKE UP WITH SAND OR OTHER ABSORBENT MATERIAL AND PLACE INTO CONTAINERS FOR LATER DISPOSAL. FOR SMALL DRY SPILLS, WITH A CLEAN SHOVEL PLACE MATERIAL INTO CLEAN, DRY CONTAINERS AND COVER. MOVE CONTAINERS FROM SPILL AREA. FOR LARGER SPILLS, DIKE FAR AHEAD OF SPILL FOR LATER DISPOSAL. KEEP UNNECESSARY PEOPLE AWAY. ISOLATE HAZARD AREA AND DENY ENTRY. VENTILATE CLOSED SPACES BEFORE ENTERING.

PROTECTIVE EQUIPMENT

VENTILATION: PROVIDE LOCAL EXHAUST OR GENERAL DILUTION VENTILATION SYSTEM.
RESPIRATOR: THE FOLLOWING RESPIRATORS ARE RECOMMENDED BASED ON INFORMATION FOUND IN THE PHYSICAL DATA, TOXICITY AND HEALTH EFFECTS SECTIONS. THEY ARE RANKED IN ORDER FROM MINIMUM TO MAXIMUM RESPIRATORY PROTECTION. THE SPECIFIC RESPIRATOR SELECTED MUST BE BASED ON CONTAMINATION LEVELS FOUND IN THE WORK PLACE, MUST NOT EXCEED THE WORKING LIMITS OF THE RESPIRATOR AND BE JOINTLY APPROVED BY THE

NATIONAL INSTITUTE FOR OCCUPATIONAL SAFETY AND HEALTH AND THE MINE SAFETY AND HEALTH ADMINISTRATION (NIOSH-MSHA).
CHEMICAL CARTRIDGE RESPIRATOR WITH AN ORGANIC VAPOR CARTRIDGE(S) WITH A FULL FACEPIECE AND ORGANIC VAPOR CARTRIDGE(S) IN COMBINATION WITH A DUST AND MIST FILTER.
POWERED AIR-PURIFYING RESPIRATOR WITH A TIGHT-FITTING FACEPIECE AND ORGANIC VAPOR CARTRIDGE(S) IN COMBINATION WITH A HIGH-EFFICIENCY PARTICULATE FILTER.
TYPE 'C' SUPPLIED-AIR RESPIRATOR WITH A FULL FACEPIECE OPERATED IN A PRESSURE-DEMAND OR OTHER POSITIVE PRESSURE MODE.
SELF-CONTAINED BREATHING APPARATUS WITH A FULL FACEPIECE OPERATED IN PRESSURE-DEMAND OR OTHER POSITIVE PRESSURE MODE.
FOR FIREFIGHTING AND OTHER IMMEDIATELY DANGEROUS TO LIFE OR HEALTH CONDITIONS:
SELF-CONTAINED BREATHING APPARATUS WITH FULL FACEPIECE OPERATED IN PRESSURE-DEMAND OR OTHER POSITIVE PRESSURE MODE.
SUPPLIED-AIR RESPIRATOR WITH FULL FACEPIECE AND OPERATED IN PRESSURE-DEMAND OR OTHER POSITIVE PRESSURE MODE IN COMBINATION WITH AN AUXILIARY SELF-CONTAINED BREATHING APPARATUS OPERATED IN PRESSURE-DEMAND OR OTHER POSITIVE PRESSURE MODE.

CLOTHING: EMPLOYEE MUST WEAR APPROPRIATE PROTECTIVE (IMPERVIOUS) CLOTHING AND EQUIPMENT TO PREVENT REPEATED OR PROLONGED SKIN CONTACT WITH THIS SUBSTANCE.

GLOVES: EMPLOYEE MUST WEAR APPROPRIATE PROTECTIVE GLOVES TO PREVENT CONTACT WITH THIS SUBSTANCE.

EYE PROTECTION: EMPLOYEE MUST WEAR SPLASH-PROOF OR DUST-RESISTANT SAFETY GOGGLES TO PREVENT EYE CONTACT WITH THIS SUBSTANCE.
EMERGENCY EYE WASH: WHERE THERE IS ANY POSSIBILITY THAT AN EMPLOYEE'S EYES MAY BE EXPOSED TO THIS SUBSTANCE, THE EMPLOYER SHOULD PROVIDE AN EYE WASH FOUNTAIN WITHIN THE IMMEDIATE WORK AREA FOR EMERGENCY USE.

AUTHORIZED BY- OCCUPATIONAL HEALTH SERVICES, INC.
CREATION DATE: 10/05/89 ***REVISION DATE:*** 05/16/90

MATERIAL SAFETY DATA SHEET

OCCUPATIONAL HEALTH SERVICES, INC.
AGRICULTURE AND PESTICIDE DIVISION
450 SEVENTH AVENUE, SUITE 2407
NEW YORK, NEW YORK 10123
1-800-445-MSDS OR (212) 967-1100

EMERGENCY CONTACT:
JOHN S. BRANSFORD, JR. (615) 292-1180

SUBSTANCE IDENTIFICATION

CAS-NUMBER 55285-14-8
SUBSTANCE: CARBOSULFAN
TRADE NAMES/SYNONYMS: CARBAMIC ACID, ((DIBUTYLAMINO)THIO)METHYL-, 2,3-DIHYDRO-2,2-DIMETHYL- 7-BENZOFURANYL ESTER; ((DIBUTYLAMINO)THIO)METHYLCARBAMIC ACID 2,3-DIHYDRO-2,2-DIMETHYL-7-BENZOFURANYL ESTER; 2,3-DIHYDRO-2,2-DIMETHYLBENZOFURAN-7-YL(DIBUTYLAMINOTHIO) METHYLCARBAMATE; 2,3-DIHYDRO-2,2-DIMETHYL-7-BENZOFURANYL ((DIBUTYLAMINO)THIO) METHYLCARBAMATE; ADVANTAGE; DBSC; FMC 35001; MARSHAL; POSSE; C20H32N2O3S; PST72266
CHEMICAL FAMILY: CARBAMATE
MOLECULAR FORMULA: C20-H32-N2-O3-S
MOLECULAR WEIGHT: 380.50
CERCLA RATINGS (SCALE 0-3): HEALTH=3 FIRE=U REACTIVITY=0 PERSISTENCE=1
NFPA RATINGS (SCALE 0-4): HEALTH=3 FIRE=U REACTIVITY=0

COMPONENTS AND CONTAMINANTS

COMPONENT: CARBOSULFAN ***PERCENT:*** 100.0
CAS# 55285-14-8
OTHER CONTAMINANTS: NONE
EXPOSURE LIMITS: NO OCCUPATIONAL EXPOSURE LIMITS ESTABLISHED BY OSHA, ACGIH, OR NIOSH.

PHYSICAL DATA

DESCRIPTION: VISCOUS BROWN LIQUID. ***BOILING POINT:*** NOT AVAILABLE
SPECIFIC GRAVITY: 1.056 ***SOLUBILITY IN WATER:*** 0.003% @ 25 C
SOLVENT SOLUBILITY: SOLUBLE IN ORGANIC SOLVENTS.

FIRE AND EXPLOSION DATA

FIRE AND EXPLOSION HAZARD: UNKNOWN FIRE AND EXPLOSION HAZARD.
FLASH POINT: NOT AVAILABLE
FIREFIGHTING MEDIA: DRY CHEMICAL, CARBON DIOXIDE, HALON, WATER SPRAY OR STANDARD FOAM (1987 EMERGENCY RESPONSE GUIDEBOOK, DOT P 5800.4). FOR LARGER FIRES, USE WATER SPRAY, FOG OR STANDARD FOAM (1987 EMERGENCY RESPONSE GUIDEBOOK, DOT P 5800.4).
FIREFIGHTING: MOVE CONTAINER FROM FIRE AREA IF POSSIBLE. COOL FIRE-EXPOSED CONTAINERS WITH WATER FROM SIDE UNTIL WELL AFTER FIRE IS OUT. STAY AWAY FROM STORAGE TANK ENDS. FOR MASSIVE FIRE IN STORAGE AREA, USE UNMANNED HOSE HOLDER OR MONITOR NOZZLES, ELSE WITHDRAW FROM AREA AND LET FIRE BURN. WITHDRAW IMMEDIATELY IN CASE OF RISING SOUND FROM VENTING SAFETY DEVICE OR ANY DISCOLORATION OF STORAGE TANK DUE TO FIRE (1987 EMERGENCY RESPONSE GUIDEBOOK, DOT P 5800.4, GUIDE PAGE 27). EXTINGUISH ONLY IF FLOW CAN BE STOPPED; USE FLOODING AMOUNTS OF WATER AS A FOG, SOLID STREAMS MAY BE INEFFECTIVE. COOL CONTAINERS WITH FLOODING AMOUNTS OF WATER, APPLY FROM AS FAR A DISTANCE AS POSSIBLE. AVOID BREATHING VAPORS, KEEP UPWIND.

TOXICITY

CARBOSULFAN: TOXICITY DATA: 51 MG/KG ORAL-RAT LD50; 74 MG/KG ORAL-MOUSE LD50. CARCINOGEN STATUS: NONE. ACUTE TOXICITY LEVEL: TOXIC BY INGESTION. TARGET EFFECTS: CHOLINESTERASE INHIBITOR. AT INCREASED RISK FROM EXPOSURE: PERSONS WITH ASTHMA, DIABETES, CARDIOVASCULAR DISEASE, MECHANICAL OBSTRUCTION OF THE GASTROINTESTINAL OR UROGENITAL TRACT, AND THOSE IN VAGOTONIC STATES.*
* MAY BE BASED ON GENERAL INFORMATION ON CARBAMATES.

HEALTH EFFECTS AND FIRST AID

INHALATION: CARBOSULFAN: SEE INFORMATION ON CARBAMATES.
CARBAMATES: CHOLINESTERASE INHIBITOR. **ACUTE EXPOSURE**- WHEN INHALED, THE FIRST EFFECTS OF CHOLINESTERASE INHIBITION ARE USUALLY RESPIRATORY AND MAY INCLUDE NASAL HYPEREMIA AND WATERY DISCHARGE, CHEST DISCOMFORT, DYSPNEA, AND WHEEZING DUE TO INCREASED BRONCHIAL SECRETIONS AND BRONCHOCONSTRICTION. OTHER SYSTEMIC EFFECTS MAY BEGIN WITHIN A FEW MINUTES OR SEVERAL HOURS OF EXPOSURE. SYMPTOMS MAY INCLUDE NAUSEA, VOMITING, DIARRHEA, ABDOMINAL CRAMPS, HEADACHE, VERTIGO, OCULAR PAIN, CILIARY MUSCLE SPASM, BLURRING OR DIMNESS OF VISION, MIOSIS, OR IN SOME CASES MYDRIASIS, LACRIMATION, SALIVATION, SWEATING, AND CONFUSION. OTHER REPORTED CENTRAL NERVOUS SYSTEM OR NEUROMUSCULAR EFFECTS INCLUDE ATAXIA, SLURRED SPEECH, AREFLEXIA, WEAKNESS, FATIGUE, TWITCHING, FASCICULATION, TREMOR, AND EVENTUALLY PARALYSIS OF THE EXTREMITIES AND POSSIBLY OF THE RESPIRATORY MUSCLES. IN SEVERE CASES, THERE MAY ALSO BE INVOLUNTARY DEFECATION AND URINATION, BRADYCARDIA, HYPOTENSION, PULMONARY EDEMA, CONVULSIONS, COMA, AND DEATH FROM RESPIRATORY FAILURE OR CARDIAC ARREST. CARBAMATES GENERALLY DO NOT ACCUMULATE IN MAMMALIAN TISSUE AND THE CHOLINESTERASE INHIBITION REVERSES RATHER RAPIDLY. IN NON-FATAL CASES, THE ILLNESS GENERALLY LASTS LESS THAN 24 HOURS. **CHRONIC EXPOSURE**- PROLONGED OR REPEATED EXPOSURE MAY CAUSE EFFECTS AS DESCRIBED IN ACUTE EXPOSURE.

FIRST AID- REMOVE FROM EXPOSURE AREA TO FRESH AIR IMMEDIATELY. IF BREATHING HAS STOPPED, GIVE ARTIFICIAL RESPIRATION. MAINTAIN AIRWAY AND BLOOD PRESSURE AND ADMINISTER OXYGEN IF AVAILABLE. KEEP AFFECTED PERSON WARM AND AT REST. TREAT SYMPTOMATICALLY AND SUPPORTIVELY. ADMINISTRATION OF OXYGEN SHOULD BE PERFORMED BY QUALIFIED PERSONNEL. GET MEDICAL ATTENTION IMMEDIATELY.

SKIN CONTACT: CARBOSULFAN: MAY CAUSE SKIN IRRITATION. SEE INFORMATION ON CARBAMATES.
CARBAMATES: CHOLINESTERASE INHIBITOR. **ACUTE EXPOSURE**- SOME COMPOUNDS MAY CAUSE IRRITATION. LOCALIZED SWEATING AND FASCICULATIONS MAY OCCUR AT THE SITE OF CONTACT. IF SUFFICIENT AMOUNTS ARE ABSORBED THROUGH THE SKIN, OTHER EFFECTS OF CHOLINESTERASE INHIBITION MAY OCCUR AS DESCRIBED IN ACUTE INHALATION; SYMPTOMS MAY BE DELAYED FOR 2-3 HOURS, USUALLY NO MORE THAN 8 HOURS. **CHRONIC EXPOSURE**- REPEATED OR PROLONGED EXPOSURE MAY CAUSE EFFECTS AS DESCRIBED IN ACUTE EXPOSURE.

FIRST AID- REMOVE CONTAMINATED CLOTHING IMMEDIATELY. WASH CONTAMINATED AREAS WITH SOAP AND WATER FOLLOWED BY ALCOHOL (ARENA, POISONING, 4TH ED.). EMERGENCY PERSONNEL SHOULD WEAR GLOVES AND AVOID CONTAMINATION. TREAT RESPIRATORY DIFFICULTY WITH ARTIFICIAL RESPIRATION. GET MEDICAL ATTENTION IMMEDIATELY.

EYE CONTACT: CARBOSULFAN: MAY CAUSE EYE IRRITATION. SEE INFORMATION ON CARBAMATES.

CARBAMATES: CHOLINESTERASE INHIBITOR. **ACUTE EXPOSURE-** DIRECT CONTACT MAY CAUSE PAIN, HYPEREMIA, LACRIMATION, TWITCHING OF THE EYELIDS, MIOSIS, AND CILIARY MUSCLE SPASM WITH LOSS OF ACCOMODATION, BLURRED OR DIMMED VISION AND BROWACHE. SOMETIMES MYDRIASIS MAY OCCUR INSTEAD OF MIOSIS. WITH SUFFICIENT EXPOSURE, OTHER SYMPTOMS OF CHOLINESTERASE INHIBITION MAY OCCUR AS DESCRIBED IN ACUTE INHALATION. **CHRONIC EXPOSURE-** PROLONGED EXPOSURE MAY CAUSE EFFECTS AS DESCRIBED IN ACUTE EXPOSURE. SOME COMPOUNDS HAVE CAUSED TOXIC EFFECTS ON THE CRYSTALLINE LENS, CONJUNCTIVAL THICKENING AND OBSTRUCTION OF NASOLACRIMAL CANALS WHEN USED AS MIOTIC EYE DROPS.

FIRST AID- IRRIGATE EYES WITH WATER OR SALINE SOLUTION. IF SYMPTOMS OF POISONING OCCUR, TREAT RESPIRATORY DIFFICULTY WITH ARTIFICIAL RESPIRATION AND OXYGEN. OBSERVE PATIENT FOR AT LEAST 24-36 HOURS (GOSSELIN, CLINICAL TOXICOLOGY OF COMMERCIAL PRODUCTS, 5TH ED.). GET MEDICAL ATTENTION IMMEDIATELY. OXYGEN SHOULD BE ADMINISTERED BY QUALIFIED MEDICAL PERSONNEL.

INGESTION: CARBOSULFAN: TOXIC. SEE INFORMATION ON CARBAMATES.

CARBAMATES: CHOLINESTERASE INHIBITOR. **ACUTE EXPOSURE-** WHEN INGESTED, THE FIRST EFFECTS MAY BE NAUSEA, VOMITING, ANOREXIA, ABDOMINAL CRAMPS, AND DIARRHEA. WITH ABSORPTION FROM THE GASTROINTESTINAL TRACT, THE OTHER EFFECTS OF CHOLINESTERASE INHIBITION AS DESCRIBED IN ACUTE INHALATION MAY OCCUR; SYMPTOMS MAY BEGIN WITHIN MINUTES OR BE DELAYED SEVERAL HOURS. **CHRONIC EXPOSURE-** REPEATED INGESTION MAY CAUSE EFFECTS AS DESCRIBED IN ACUTE EXPOSURE.

FIRST AID- IF PERSON IS ALERT AND RESPIRATION IS NOT DEPRESSED, GIVE SYRUP OF IPECAC FOLLOWED BY WATER (IF VOMITING OCCURS, KEEP HEAD BELOW HIPS TO PREVENT ASPIRATION). IF CONSCIOUSNESS LEVEL DECLINES OR VOMITING HAS NOT OCCURRED IN 15 MINUTES EMPTY STOMACH BY GASTRIC LAVAGE WITH THE AID OF CUFFED ENDOTRACHEAL TUBE USING ISOTONIC SALINE OR 5% SODIUM BICARBONATE FOLLOW WITH ACTIVATED CHARCOAL. ESTABLISH AND MAINTAIN AIRWAY. TREAT RESPIRATORY DIFFICULTY WITH ARTIFICIAL RESPIRATION AND OXYGEN. DO NOT GIVE MORPHINE, AMINOPHYLLINE, PHENOTHIAZINES, RESERPINE, FUROSEMIDE, OR ETHACRYNIC ACID (MORGAN, RECOGNITION AND MANAGEMENT OF PESTICIDE POISONINGS, 3RD ED.). TREAT SYMPTOMATICALLY AND SUPPORTIVELY. ADMINISTRATION OF OXYGEN AND LAVAGE MUST BE PERFORMED BY QUALIFIED MEDICAL PERSONNEL. GET MEDICAL ATTENTION IMMEDIATELY.

ANTIDOTE: THE FOLLOWING ANTIDOTE HAS BEEN RECOMMENDED. HOWEVER, THE DECISION AS TO WHETHER THE SEVERITY OF POISONING REQUIRES ADMINISTRATION OF ANY ANTIDOTE AND ACTUAL DOSE REQUIRED SHOULD BE MADE BY QUALIFIED MEDICAL PERSONNEL.

FOR CHOLINESTERASE INHIBITORS: ESTABLISH CLEAR AIRWAY AND TISSUE OXYGENATION BY ASPIRATION OF SECRETIONS, AND IF NECESSARY, BY ASSISTED PULMONARY VENTILATION WITH OXYGEN. IMPROVE TISSUE OXYGENATION AS MUCH AS POSSIBLE BEFORE ADMINISTERING ATROPINE TO MINIMIZE THE RISK OF VENTRICULAR FIBRILLATION. ADMINISTER ATROPINE SULFATE INTRAVENOUSLY, OR INTRAMUSCULARLY IF IV INJECTION IS NOT POSSIBLE. IN MODERATELY SEVERE POISONING ADMINISTER ATROPINE SULFATE, 0.4-2.0 MG REPEATED EVERY 15 MINUTES UNTIL ATROPINIZATION IS ACHIEVED (TACHYCARDIA, FLUSHING, DRY MOUTH, MYDRIASIS). MAINTAIN ATROPINIZATION BY REPEATED DOSES FOR 2-12 HOURS, OR LONGER, DEPENDING ON THE SEVERITY OF POISONING. THE APPEARANCE OF RALES IN THE LUNG BASES, MIOSIS, SALIVATION, NAUSEA, BRADYCARDIA, ARE ALL INDICATIONS OF INADEQUATE ATROPINIZATION. SEVERELY POISONED INDIVIDUALS MAY EXHIBIT REMARKABLE TOLERANCE TO ATROPINE; TWO OR MORE TIMES THE DOSAGES SUGGESTED ABOVE MAY BE NEEDED. PERSONS NOT POISONED OR ONLY SLIGHTLY POISONED, HOWEVER, MAY DEVELOP SIGNS OF ATROPINE TOXICITY FROM SUCH LARGE DOSAGES: FEVER, MUSCLE FIBRILLATIONS, AND DELIRIUM ARE THE MAIN SIGNS OF ATROPINE TOXICITY. IF THESE SIGNS APPEAR WHILE THE PATIENT IS FULLY ATROPINIZED, ATROPINE ADMINISTRATION SHOULD BE DISCONTINUED, AT LEAST TEMPORARILY. OBSERVE TREATED PATIENTS CLOSELY AT LEAST 24 HOURS TO INSURE THAT SYMPTOMS (POSSIBLY PULMONARY EDEMA) DO NOT RECUR AS ATROPINIZATION WEARS OFF. IN VERY SEVERE POISONINGS, METABOLIC DISPOSITION OF TOXICANT MAY REQUIRE SEVERAL HOURS OR DAYS DURING WHICH ATROPINIZATION MUST BE MAINTAINED. MARKEDLY LOWER LEVELS OF URINARY METABOLITES INDICATE THAT ATROPINE DOSAGE CAN BE TAPERED OFF. AS DOSAGE IS REDUCED, CHECK THE LUNG BASES FREQUENTLY FOR RALES. IF RALES ARE HEARD OR OTHER SYMPTOMS RETURN, RE-ESTABLISH ATROPINIZATION PROMPTLY (MORGAN, RECOGNITION AND MANAGEMENT OF PESTICIDE POISONINGS, 3RD ED.). ADMINISTRATION OF ANTIDOTE MUST BE PERFORMED BY QUALIFIED MEDICAL PERSONNEL.

REACTIVITY

REACTIVITY: STABLE UNDER NORMAL TEMPERATURES AND PRESSURES.

INCOMPATIBILITIES: CARBOSULFAN: OXIDIZERS (STRONG): FIRE AND EXPLOSION HAZARD.

DECOMPOSITION: THERMAL DECOMPOSITION PRODUCTS MAY INCLUDE TOXIC OXIDES OF CARBON, NITROGEN, AND SULFUR.

POLYMERIZATION: HAZARDOUS POLYMERIZATION HAS NOT BEEN REPORTED TO OCCUR UNDER NORMAL TEMPERATURES AND PRESSURES.

STORAGE AND DISPOSAL

OBSERVE ALL FEDERAL, STATE AND LOCAL REGULATIONS WHEN STORING OR DISPOSING OF THIS SUBSTANCE. FOR ASSISTANCE, CONTACT THE DISTRICT DIRECTOR OF THE ENVIRONMENTAL PROTECTION AGENCY.

****STORAGE****

STORE IN ACCORDANCE WITH 40 CFR 165 RECOMMENDED PROCEDURES FOR THE DISPOSAL AND STORAGE OF PESTICIDES AND PESTICIDE CONTAINERS.
STORE AWAY FROM INCOMPATIBLE SUBSTANCES.

****DISPOSAL****

DISPOSAL MUST BE IN ACCORDANCE WITH 40 CFR 165 RECOMMENDED PROCEDURES FOR THE DISPOSAL AND STORAGE OF PESTICIDES AND PESTICIDE CONTAINERS.

CONDITIONS TO AVOID

AVOID CONTACT WITH HEAT, SPARKS, FLAMES, OR OTHER SOURCES OF IGNITION. VAPORS MAY BE EXPLOSIVE. AVOID OVERHEATING OF CONTAINERS; CONTAINERS MAY VIOLENTLY RUPTURE IN HEAT OF FIRE. AVOID CONTAMINATION OF WATER SOURCES.

SPILL AND LEAK PROCEDURES

OCCUPATIONAL SPILL: SHUT OFF IGNITION SOURCES. STOP LEAK IF YOU CAN DO IT WITHOUT RISK. USE WATER SPRAY TO REDUCE VAPORS. FOR SMALL SPILLS, TAKE UP WITH SAND OR OTHER ABSORBENT MATERIAL AND PLACE INTO CONTAINERS FOR LATER DISPOSAL. FOR LARGER SPILLS, DIKE FAR AHEAD OF SPILL FOR LATER DISPOSAL. NO SMOKING, FLAMES OR FLARES IN HAZARD AREA. KEEP UNNECESSARY PEOPLE AWAY; ISOLATE HAZARD AREA AND RESTRICT ENTRY.

PROTECTIVE EQUIPMENT

VENTILATION: PROVIDE LOCAL EXHAUST OR PROCESS ENCLOSURE VENTILATION SYSTEM.

RESPIRATOR: THE FOLLOWING RESPIRATORS ARE RECOMMENDED BASED ON INFORMATION FOUND IN THE PHYSICAL DATA, TOXICITY AND HEALTH EFFECTS SECTIONS. THEY ARE RANKED IN ORDER FROM MINIMUM TO MAXIMUM RESPIRATORY PROTECTION. THE SPECIFIC RESPIRATOR SELECTED MUST BE BASED ON CONTAMINATION LEVELS FOUND IN THE WORK PLACE, MUST NOT EXCEED THE WORKING LIMITS OF THE RESPIRATOR AND BE JOINTLY APPROVED BY THE NATIONAL INSTITUTE FOR OCCUPATIONAL SAFETY AND HEALTH AND THE MINE SAFETY AND HEALTH ADMINISTRATION (NIOSH-MSHA).

TYPE 'C' SUPPLIED-AIR RESPIRATOR WITH A FULL FACEPIECE OPERATED IN PRESSURE-DEMAND OR OTHER POSITIVE PRESSURE MODE OR WITH A FULL FACEPIECE, HELMET OR HOOD OPERATED IN CONTINOUS-FLOW MODE.

SELF-CONTAINED BREATHING APPARATUS WITH A FULL FACEPIECE OPERATED IN PRESSURE-DEMAND OR OTHER POSITIVE PRESSURE MODE.

FOR FIREFIGHTING AND OTHER IMMEDIATELY DANGEROUS TO LIFE OR HEALTH CONDITIONS:

SELF-CONTAINED BREATHING APPARATUS WITH FULL FACEPIECE OPERATED IN PRESSURE-DEMAND OR OTHER POSITIVE PRESSURE MODE.

SUPPLIED-AIR RESPIRATOR WITH FULL FACEPIECE AND OPERATED IN PRESSURE-DEMAND OR OTHER POSITIVE PRESSURE MODE IN COMBINATION WITH AN AUXILIARY SELF-CONTAINED BREATHING APPARATUS OPERATED IN PRESSURE-DEMAND OR OTHER POSITIVE PRESSURE MODE.

CLOTHING: EMPLOYEE MUST WEAR APPROPRIATE PROTECTIVE (IMPERVIOUS) CLOTHING AND EQUIPMENT TO PREVENT REPEATED OR PROLONGED SKIN CONTACT WITH THIS SUBSTANCE.

GLOVES: EMPLOYEE MUST WEAR APPROPRIATE PROTECTIVE GLOVES TO PREVENT CONTACT WITH THIS SUBSTANCE.

EYE PROTECTION: EMPLOYEE MUST WEAR SPLASH-PROOF OR DUST-RESISTANT SAFETY GOGGLES TO PREVENT EYE CONTACT WITH THIS SUBSTANCE.

EMERGENCY EYE WASH: WHERE THERE IS ANY POSSIBILITY THAT AN EMPLOYEE'S EYES MAY BE EXPOSED TO THIS SUBSTANCE, THE EMPLOYER SHOULD PROVIDE AN EYE WASH FOUNTAIN WITHIN THE IMMEDIATE WORK AREA FOR EMERGENCY USE.

AUTHORIZED BY- OCCUPATIONAL HEALTH SERVICES, INC.
CREATION DATE: 10/04/89 ***REVISION DATE:*** 06/12/90

MATERIAL SAFETY DATA SHEET

OCCUPATIONAL HEALTH SERVICES, INC.
AGRICULTURE AND PESTICIDE DIVISION
450 SEVENTH AVENUE, SUITE 2407
NEW YORK, NEW YORK 10123
1-800-445-MSDS OR (212) 967-1100

EMERGENCY CONTACT:
JOHN S. BRANSFORD, JR. (615) 292-1180

SUBSTANCE IDENTIFICATION

CAS-NUMBER 94-09-7

SUBSTANCE: BENZOCAINE

TRADE NAMES/SYNONYMS: BENZOIC ACID, 4-AMINO-, ETHYL ESTER; 4-AMINOBENZOIC ACID, ETHYL ESTER; BENZOIC ACID, P-AMINO-, ETHYL ESTER; BENZOCAINE, USP; AMBEN ETHYL ESTER; P-CARBETHOXYANILINE; 4-CARBETHOXYANILINE; P-(ETHOXYCARBONYL)ANILINE; 4-(ETHOXYCARBONYL)ANILINE; P-ETHOXYCARBOXYLIC ANILINE; ETHYL P-AMINOBENZENECARBOXYLATE; ETHYL AMINOBENZOATE; ETHYL P-AMINOBENZOATE; ETHYL 4-AMINOBENZOATE; ETHYL P-AMINOPHENYLCARBOXYLATE; NORCAINE; ORTHESIN; ANESTHESINE; PARATHESINE; C9H11NO2; PST72267

CHEMICAL FAMILY: AMINE, AROMATIC

MOLECULAR FORMULA: H2-N-C6-H4-C-O2-C2-H5

MOLECULAR WEIGHT: 165.21

CERCLA RATINGS (SCALE 0-3): HEALTH=3 FIRE=1 REACTIVITY=0 PERSISTENCE=1

NFPA RATINGS (SCALE 0-4): HEALTH=3 FIRE=1 REACTIVITY=0

COMPONENTS AND CONTAMINANTS

COMPONENT: BENZOCAINE ***PERCENT:*** 100
CAS# 94-09-7

OTHER CONTAMINANTS: NONE

EXPOSURE LIMITS: NO OCCUPATIONAL EXPOSURE LIMITS ESTABLISHED BY OSHA, ACGIH, OR NIOSH.

PHYSICAL DATA

DESCRIPTION: ODORLESS, COLORLESS TO WHITE, SMALL RHOMBOHEDRA CRYSTALS OR CRYSTALLINE POWDER WITH A SLIGHT CHARACTERISTIC ODOR.

BOILING POINT: 590 F (310 C)

MELTING POINT: 190-194 F (88-90 C) ***VOLATILITY:*** <1.0%

SOLUBILITY IN WATER: 0.04%

SOLVENT SOLUBILITY: SOLUBLE IN ETHANOL, CARBON TETRACHLORIDE, CHLOROFORM, ETHER, DILUTE ACIDS; SPARINGLY SOLUBLE IN ALMOND OIL, OLIVE OIL

FIRE AND EXPLOSION DATA

FIRE AND EXPLOSION HAZARD: SLIGHT FIRE HAZARD WHEN EXPOSED TO HEAT OR FLAME.

FLASH POINT: >200 F (>93 C)

FIREFIGHTING MEDIA: DRY CHEMICAL, CARBON DIOXIDE, WATER SPRAY OR FOAM FOR LARGER FIRES, USE WATER SPRAY, FOG OR ALCOHOL FOAM

FIREFIGHTING: USE AGENTS SUITABLE FOR TYPE OF SURROUNDING FIRE. AVOID BREATHING HAZARDOUS VAPORS, KEEP UPWIND.

TOXICITY

BENZOCAINE: IRRITATION DATA: 2%/48 HOURS SKIN-GUINEA PIG MILD. TOXICITY DATA: 1150 MG/KG ORAL-RABBIT LDLO; 216 MG/KG INTRAPERITONEAL-MOUSE LD50; 12 MG/KG RECTAL-INFANT TDLO. CARCINOGEN STATUS: NONE. LOCAL EFFECTS: IRRITANT- SKIN. ACUTE TOXICITY LEVEL: INSUFFICIENT DATA. TARGET EFFECTS: SENSITIZER- SKIN. METHEMOGLOBIN FORMER. POISONING MAY AFFECT THE HEART, BLOOD, AND CENTRAL NERVOUS SYSTEM.

HEALTH EFFECTS AND FIRST AID

INHALATION: BENZOCAINE: **ACUTE EXPOSURE-** NO DATA AVAILABLE. MAY CAUSE IRRITATION. **CHRONIC EXPOSURE-** NO DATA AVAILABLE.

FIRST AID- REMOVE FROM EXPOSURE AREA TO FRESH AIR IMMEDIATELY. IF BREATHING HAS STOPPED, PERFORM ARTIFICIAL RESPIRATION. KEEP PERSON WARM AND AT REST. TREAT SYMPTOMATICALLY AND SUPPORTIVELY. GET MEDICAL ATTENTION IMMEDIATELY.

SKIN CONTACT: BENZOCAINE: IRRITANT/SENSITIZER/METHEMOGLOBIN FORMER. **ACUTE EXPOSURE-** DIRECT CONTACT MAY CAUSE IRRITATION WITH ITCHING, ERYTHEMA, EXCORIATION, URTICARIA, EDEMA, VESICULATION, OOZING, TINNITUS, AND CYANOSIS FROM METHEMOGLOBINEMIA. OTHER POSSIBLE METHEMOGLOBINEMIA SYMPTOMS MAY INCLUDE CHILLS, NAUSEA, VOMITING, DIZZINESS, HEADACHE, LETHARGY, STUPOR, FALL OF BLOOD PRESSURE, MUSCULAR TREMORS, CONVULSIONS, COMA, IRREGULAR AND WEAK BREATHING, CARDIAC STANDSTILL, AND BRONCHIAL SPASM. SENSITIZATION MAY OCCUR IN SUSCEPTIBLE INDIVIDUALS. ABSORPTION MAY OCCUR THROUGH INFLAMED OR BROKIN SKIN. APPLICATION OF A BENZOCAINE-CONTAINING OINTMENT TO AN INFANT WITH WEEPING DIAPER-RASH CAUSED IMMEDIATE CYANOSIS. **CHRONIC EXPOSURE-** REPEATED OR PROLONGED CONTACT MAY CAUSE ECZEMATOUS CONTACT DERMATITIS, SENSITIZATION, AND OTHER EFFECTS AS IN ACUTE EXPOSURE.

FIRST AID- REMOVE CONTAMINATED CLOTHING AND SHOES IMMEDIATELY. WASH AFFECTED AREA WITH SOAP OR MILD DETERGENT AND LARGE AMOUNTS OF WATER UNTIL NO EVIDENCE OF CHEMICAL REMAINS (APPROXIMATELY 15-20 MINUTES). GET MEDICAL ATTENTION IMMEDIATELY.

EYE CONTACT: BENZOCAINE: **ACUTE EXPOSURE-** NO DATA AVAILABLE. MAY CAUSE IRRITATION. **CHRONIC EXPOSURE-** NO DATA AVAILABLE.

FIRST AID- WASH EYES IMMEDIATELY WITH LARGE AMOUNTS OF WATER OR NORMAL SALINE, OCCASIONALLY LIFTING UPPER AND LOWER LIDS, UNTIL NO EVIDENCE OF CHEMICAL REMAINS (APPROXIMATELY 15-20 MINUTES). GET MEDICAL ATTENTION IMMEDIATELY.

INGESTION: BENZOCAINE: METHEMOGLOBIN FORMER. **ACUTE EXPOSURE-** METHEMOGLOBINEMIA MAY CAUSE CHILLS, NAUSEA, VOMITING, HEADACHE, DIZZINESS, LETHARGY, STUPOR, CYANOSIS, FALL OF BLOOD PRESSURE, TINNITUS, AGRANULOCYTOSIS, MUSCULAR TREMORS, CONVULSIONS, COMA, IRREGULAR AND WEAK BREATHING, CARDIAC STANDSTILL, AND BRONCHIAL SPASM. ORAL DOSES OF 150-300 MG PRODUCED CYANOSIS IN 4 ADULTS WITHIN 4 HOURS. INGESTION OF A LOZENGE CONTAINING BENZOCAINE AND TYROTHRICIN RESULTED IN IMMEDIATE ACUTE AND INCREASING RESPIRATORY DISTRESS AND DEATH WITHIN 20 MINUTES IN A 24-YEAR-OLD MAN. **CHRONIC EXPOSURE-** NO DATA AVAILABLE.

FIRST AID- REMOVE BY EMESIS. MAINTAIN BLOOD PRESSURE AND AIRWAY. GIVE OXYGEN IF RESPIRATION IS DEPRESSED. DO NOT INDUCE VOMITING IN AN UNCONSCIOUS PERSON. GET MEDICAL ATTENTION IMMEDIATELY. OXYGEN MUST BE ADMINISTERED BY QUALIFIED MEDICAL PERSONNEL. (DREISBACH, HANDBOOK OF POISONING, 11TH ED.)

ANTIDOTE: THE FOLLOWING ANTIDOTE HAS BEEN RECOMMENDED. HOWEVER, THE DECISION AS TO WHETHER THE SEVERITY OF POISONING REQUIRES ADMINISTRATION OF ANY ANTIDOTE AND ACTUAL DOSE REQUIRED SHOULD BE MADE BY QUALIFIED MEDICAL PERSONNEL.
METHEMOGLOBINEMIA: (WHEN METHEMOGLOBIN CONCENTRATION IS OVER 25-40% OR IN PRESENCE OF SYMPTOMS.) GIVE METHYLENE BLUE, 1% SOLUTION, 0.1 ML/KG INTRAVENOUSLY OVER A 10-MINUTE PERIOD. CYANOSIS MAY DISAPPEAR WITHIN MINUTES OR PERSIST LONGER DEPENDING ON DEGREE OF METHEMOGLOBINEMIA. INTRAVENOUS ADMINISTRATION OF THERAPEUTIC DOSES OF METHYLENE BLUE MAY CAUSE A RISE IN BLOOD PRESSURE, NAUSEA, AND DIZZINESS. LARGER DOSES (>500 MG) CAUSE VOMITING, DIARRHEA, CHEST PAIN, MENTAL CONFUSION, CYANOSIS, AND SWEATING. HEMOLYTIC ANEMIA HAS ALSO OCCURRED SEVERAL DAYS AFTER ADMINISTRATION. THESE EFFECTS ARE TEMPORARY, AND FATALITIES HAVE NOT BEEN REPORTED. IF METHYLENE BLUE IS NOT AVAILABLE, GIVE ASCORBIC ACID, 1 GRAM SLOWLY INTRAVENOUSLY. WITHOUT TREATMENT, METHEMOGLOBINEMIA LEVELS OF 20-30% REVERT TO NORMAL WITHIN 3 DAYS (DREISBACH, HANDBOOK OF POISONING, 12TH ED.). ANTIDOTE SHOULD BE ADMINISTERED BY QUALIFIED MEDICAL PERSONNEL.

REACTIVITY

REACTIVITY: STABLE UNDER NORMAL TEMPERATURES AND PRESSURES.

INCOMPATIBILITIES: BENZOCAINE: OXIDIZERS (STRONG): FIRE AND EXPLOSION HAZARD. SEE ALSO AMINES AND ESTERS.
AMINES: ACROLEIN: EXOTHERMIC POLYMERIZATION. CALCIUM HYPOCHLORITE: FORMATION OF EXPLOSIVE CHLOROAMINE. MALEIC ANHYDRIDE: EXPLOSIVE DECOMPOSITION. NITROSYL PERCHLORATE: EXPLOSIVE REACTION. SODIUM HYPOCHLORITE: FORMATION OF EXPLOSIVE CHLOROAMINE. TRI-ISO-BUTYL ALUMINUM: VIOLENT REACTION.
ESTERS: NITRATES: POSSIBLE EXPLOSIVE REACTION.

DECOMPOSITION: THERMAL DECOMPOSITION PRODUCTS MAY INCLUDE TOXIC OXIDES OF CARBON AND NITROGEN.

POLYMERIZATION: HAZARDOUS POLYMERIZATION HAS NOT BEEN REPORTED TO OCCUR UNDER NORMAL TEMPERATURES AND PRESSURES.

STORAGE AND DISPOSAL

OBSERVE ALL FEDERAL, STATE AND LOCAL REGULATIONS WHEN STORING OR DISPOSING OF THIS SUBSTANCE.

STORAGE

STORE IN ACCORDANCE WITH 29 CFR 1910.106.
BONDING AND GROUNDING: SUBSTANCES WITH LOW ELECTROCONDUCTIVITY, WHICH MAY BE IGNITED BY ELECTROSTATIC SPARKS, SHOULD BE STORED IN CONTAINERS WHICH MEET THE BONDING AND GROUNDING GUIDELINES SPECIFIED

IN NFPA 77-1983, RECOMMENDED PRACTICE ON STATIC ELECTRICITY.
STORE AWAY FROM INCOMPATIBLE SUBSTANCES.

****DISPOSAL****

DISPOSAL MUST BE IN ACCORDANCE WITH STANDARDS APPLICABLE TO GENERATORS OF HAZARDOUS WASTE, 40 CFR 262. EPA HAZARDOUS WASTE NUMBER D001

CONDITIONS TO AVOID

NONE REPORTED.

SPILL AND LEAK PROCEDURES

OCCUPATIONAL SPILL: NO SPECIAL PRECAUTIONS INDICATED.

PROTECTIVE EQUIPMENT

VENTILATION: PROVIDE LOCAL EXHAUST OR PROCESS ENCLOSURE VENTILATION. VENTILATION EQUIPMENT MUST BE EXPLOSION-PROOF.

RESPIRATOR: THE FOLLOWING RESPIRATORS ARE RECOMMENDED BASED ON INFORMATION FOUND IN THE PHYSICAL DATA, TOXICITY AND HEALTH EFFECTS SECTIONS. THEY ARE RANKED IN ORDER FROM MINIMUM TO MAXIMUM RESPIRATORY PROTECTION. THE SPECIFIC RESPIRATOR SELECTED MUST BE BASED ON CONTAMINATION LEVELS FOUND IN THE WORK PLACE, MUST NOT EXCEED THE WORKING LIMITS OF THE RESPIRATOR AND BE JOINTLY APPROVED BY THE NATIONAL INSTITUTE FOR OCCUPATIONAL SAFETY AND HEALTH AND THE MINE SAFETY AND HEALTH ADMINISTRATION (NIOSH-MSHA).
CHEMICAL CARTRIDGE RESPIRATOR WITH AN ORGANIC VAPOR CARTRIDGE(S) WITH A FULL FACEPIECE.
GAS MASK WITH ORGANIC VAPOR CANISTER (CHIN-STYLE OR FRONT- OR BACK-MOUNTED CANISTER) WITH A FULL FACEPIECE.
TYPE 'C' SUPPLIED-AIR RESPIRATOR WITH A FULL FACEPIECE OPERATED IN PRESSURE-DEMAND OR OTHER POSITIVE PRESSURE MODE OR WITH A FULL FACEPIECE, HELMET OR HOOD OPERATED IN CONTINUOUS-FLOW MODE.
SELF-CONTAINED BREATHING APPARATUS WITH A FULL FACEPIECE OPERATED IN PRESSURE-DEMAND OR OTHER POSITIVE PRESSURE MODE.
FOR FIREFIGHTING AND OTHER IMMEDIATELY DANGEROUS TO LIFE OR HEALTH CONDITIONS:
SELF-CONTAINED BREATHING APPARATUS WITH FULL FACEPIECE OPERATED IN PRESSURE-DEMAND OR OTHER POSITIVE PRESSURE MODE.
SUPPLIED-AIR RESPIRATOR WITH FULL FACEPIECE AND OPERATED IN PRESSURE-DEMAND OR OTHER POSITIVE PRESSURE MODE IN COMBINATION WITH AN AUXILIARY SELF-CONTAINED BREATHING APPARATUS OPERATED IN PRESSURE-DEMAND OR OTHER POSITIVE PRESSURE MODE.

CLOTHING: EMPLOYEE MUST WEAR APPROPRIATE PROTECTIVE (IMPERVIOUS) CLOTHING AND EQUIPMENT TO PREVENT REPEATED OR PROLONGED SKIN CONTACT WITH THIS SUBSTANCE.

GLOVES: EMPLOYEE MUST WEAR APPROPRIATE PROTECTIVE GLOVES TO PREVENT CONTACT WITH THIS SUBSTANCE.

EYE PROTECTION: EMPLOYEE MUST WEAR SPLASH-PROOF OR DUST-RESISTANT SAFETY GOGGLES TO PREVENT EYE CONTACT WITH THIS SUBSTANCE.
EMERGENCY EYE WASH: WHERE THERE IS ANY POSSIBILITY THAT AN EMPLOYEE'S EYES MAY BE EXPOSED TO THIS SUBSTANCE, THE EMPLOYER SHOULD PROVIDE AN EYE WASH FOUNTAIN WITHIN THE IMMEDIATE WORK AREA FOR EMERGENCY USE.

AUTHORIZED BY- OCCUPATIONAL HEALTH SERVICES, INC.
CREATION DATE: 11/15/89 ***REVISION DATE:*** 05/18/90

MATERIAL SAFETY DATA SHEET

OCCUPATIONAL HEALTH SERVICES, INC.	EMERGENCY CONTACT:
AGRICULTURE AND PESTICIDE DIVISION	JOHN S. BRANSFORD, JR. (615) 292-1180
450 SEVENTH AVENUE, SUITE 2407	
NEW YORK, NEW YORK 10123	
1-800-445-MSDS OR (212) 967-1100	

SUBSTANCE IDENTIFICATION

CAS-NUMBER 136-47-0

SUBSTANCE: TETRACAINE HYDROCHLORIDE

TRADE NAMES/SYNONYMS: BENZOIC ACID, 4-(BUTYLAMINO)-, 2-(DIMETHYLAMINO)ETHYL ESTER, MONOHYDROCHLORIDE; 4-BUTYLAMINOBENZOIC ACID, 2-(DIMETHYLAMINO)ETHYL ESTER, MONOHYDROCHLORIDE; BENZOIC ACID, P-(BUTYLAMINO)-, 2-(DIMETHYLAMINO)ETHYL ESTER, MONOHYDROCHLORIDE; P-(BUTYLAMINO)BENZOIC ACID, 2-(DIMETHYLAMINO)ETHYL ESTER, MONOHYDROCHLORIDE; AMETHOCAINE HYDROCHLORIDE; ANACEL; BUTETHENOL; CURTACAIN; PANTOCAIN; PONTOCAINE HYDROCHLORIDE; TETRACAINE MONOHYDROCHLORIDE; 2-(DIMETHYLAMINO)ETHYL-P-(BUTYLAMINO) BENZOATE MONOHYDROCHLORIDE; P-BUTYLAMINOBENZOYL-2-DIMETHYLAMINOETHANOL HYDROCHLORIDE; ANESTARON; TONEXOL; C15H25CLN2O2; PST72269

CHEMICAL FAMILY: AMINE, ALKYL-ARYL

MOLECULAR FORMULA: C15-H24-N2-O2.H-CL

MOLECULAR WEIGHT: 300.83

CERCLA RATINGS (SCALE 0-3): HEALTH=3 FIRE=1 REACTIVITY=0 PERSISTENCE=2

NFPA RATINGS (SCALE 0-4): HEALTH=3 FIRE=1 REACTIVITY=0

COMPONENTS AND CONTAMINANTS

COMPONENT: TETRACAINE HYDROCHLORIDE ***PERCENT:*** 100
CAS# 136-47-0

OTHER CONTAMINANTS: NONE

EXPOSURE LIMITS: NO OCCUPATIONAL EXPOSURE LIMITS ESTABLISHED BY OSHA, ACGIH, OR NIOSH.

PHYSICAL DATA

DESCRIPTION: ODORLESS WHITE CRYSTALLINE POWDER WITH A SLIGHTLY BITTER, NUMBING TASTE ***MELTING POINT:*** 297-302 F (147-150 C)

SPECIFIC GRAVITY: NOT AVAILABLE ***PH:*** NEUTRAL IN SOLN.

SOLUBILITY IN WATER: SOLUBLE

SOLVENT SOLUBILITY: SOLUBLE IN ALCOHOL; INSOLUBLE IN ETHER, BENZENE.

FIRE AND EXPLOSION DATA

FIRE AND EXPLOSION HAZARD: SLIGHT FIRE HAZARD WHEN EXPOSED TO HEAT OR FLAME.

FIREFIGHTING MEDIA: DRY CHEMICAL, CARBON DIOXIDE, HALON, WATER SPRAY OR STANDARD FOAM (1987 EMERGENCY RESPONSE GUIDEBOOK, DOT P 5800.4).
FOR LARGER FIRES, USE WATER SPRAY, FOG OR STANDARD FOAM (1987 EMERGENCY RESPONSE GUIDEBOOK, DOT P 5800.4).

FIREFIGHTING: MOVE CONTAINER FROM FIRE AREA IF POSSIBLE. DO NOT SCATTER SPILLED MATERIAL WITH HIGH PRESSURE WATER STREAMS. DIKE FIRE CONTROL WATER FOR LATER DISPOSAL (1987 EMERGENCY RESPONSE GUIDEBOOK, DOT P 5800.4, GUIDE PAGE 31).
USE AGENTS SUITABLE FOR TYPE OF SURROUNDING FIRE. AVOID BREATHING HAZARDOUS VAPORS, KEEP UPWIND.

TOXICITY

TETRACAINE HYDROCHLORIDE: IRRITATION DATA: 2% EYE-RABBIT MODERATE. TOXICITY DATA: 160 MG/KG ORAL-MOUSE LD50; 23,500 UG/KG INTRAPERITONEAL-RAT LD50; 23 MG/KG INTRAPERITONEAL-MOUSE LD50; 5 MG/KG INTRASPINAL-RABBIT LDLO; 4500 UG/KG INTRAVENOUS-RAT LD50; 6600 UG/KG INTRAVENOUS-MOUSE LD50; 4 MG/KG INTRAVENOUS-GUINEA PIG LD50; 2150 UG/KG INTRAVENOUS-RABBIT LD50; 24 MG/KG SUBCUTANEOUS-RAT LD50; 25 MG/KG SUBCUTANEOUS-MOUSE LD50; 19,500 UG/KG SUBCUTANEOUS-GUINEA PIG LD50; 15 MG/KG SUBCUTANEOUS-RABBIT LD50. CARCINOGEN STATUS: NONE. ACUTE TOXICITY LEVEL: TOXIC BY INGESTION. TARGET EFFECTS: SENSITIZER. POISONING MAY AFFECT THE CENTRAL NERVOUS SYSTEM AND THE CARDIOVASCULAR SYSTEM. AT INCREASED RISK FROM EXPOSURE: PERSONS WITH HYPERSENSITIVITY TO BENZOCAINE, ESTER-TYPE LOCAL ANESTHETICS, PARA-AMINOBENZOIC ACID OR ITS DERIVATIVES; ABNORMAL OR REDUCED LEVELS OF PLASMA ESTERASES; KNOWN ALLERGIES; CARDIAC DISEASE; HYPERTHYROIDISM; SECONDARY BACTERIAL INFECTION OF THE EYE; SEVERELY TRAUMATIZED MUCOSA AND SEPTIS; HEPATIC DAMAGE; DRUG ADDICTION. ADDITIONAL DATA: MAY CROSS THE PLACENTA. INTERACTIONS WITH MEDICATIONS HAVE BEEN REPORTED.

HEALTH EFFECTS AND FIRST AID

INHALATION: TETRACAINE HYDROCHLORIDE: SENSITIZER. ACUTE EXPOSURE- INHALATION OF DUSTS MAY CAUSE A LOCAL ANESTHETIC ACTION ON THE MUCOUS MEMBRANES. IN ADDITION, LOCAL ANESTHETICS MAY CAUSE BURNING, STINGING, TENDERNESS, SWELLING, TISSUE IRRITATION, SLOUGHING AND TISSUE NECROSIS. APPLICATION OF 2% TETRACAINE HYDROCHLORIDE TO THE MUCOUS MEMBRANES PRODUCED AN IMMEDIATE AND COMPLETE CESSATION OF CILIARY ACTION AND FLOW OF MUCOUS. A 48 YEAR-OLD WOMAN RECEIVED 3 ML OF 2% TETRACAINE HYDROCHLORIDE (60 MG) THROUGH A NASAL CATHETER. SHE QUICKLY BECAME COMATOSE, CONVULSED REPEATEDLY AND DIED 30 MINUTES LATER. TOPICAL APPLICATION OF LOCAL ANESTHETICS TO THE RESPIRATORY TRACT MAY CAUSE SYSTEMIC POISONING WITH LIGHTHEADEDNESS, NERVOUSNESS, APPREHENSION, EUPHORIA, CONFUSION, DIZZINESS, DROWSINESS, TINNITUS, BLURRED OR DOUBLE VISION, VOMITING, SENSATIONS OF HEAT, COLD OR NUMBNESS, TWITCHING, TREMORS, CONVULSIONS,

UNCONSCIOUSNESS AND RESPIRATORY DEPRESSION AND ARREST. MYOCARDIAL DEPRESSION, BRADYCARDIA, HYPOTENSION, AND CARDIOVASCULAR COLLAPSE WHICH MAY LEAD TO CARDIAC ARREST MAY OCCUR. SENSITIZATION REACTIONS MAY OCCUR IN PREVIOUSLY EXPOSED INDIVIDUALS. **CHRONIC EXPOSURE-** REPEATED OR PROLONGED APPLICATION OF LOCAL ANESTHETICS TO THE MUCOUS MEMBRANES MAY CAUSE ACCUMULATION TO TOXIC CONCENTRATIONS IN THE BLOOD AND CAUSE SYSTEMIC POISONING AS DETAILED IN ACUTE EXPOSURE. REPEATED EXPOSURE MAY RESULT IN SENSITIZATION. SYMPTOMS MAY INCLUDE CUTANEOUS LESIONS, URTICARIA, EDEMA OR POSSIBLY FATAL ANAPHYLACTOID REACTIONS.

FIRST AID- REMOVE FROM EXPOSURE AREA TO FRESH AIR IMMEDIATELY. IF BREATHING HAS STOPPED, PERFORM ARTIFICIAL RESPIRATION. KEEP PERSON WARM AND AT REST. TREAT SYMPTOMATICALLY AND SUPPORTIVELY. GET MEDICAL ATTENTION IMMEDIATELY.

SKIN CONTACT: TETRACAINE HYDROCHLORIDE: SENSITIZER. **ACUTE EXPOSURE-** TOPICAL APPLICATION MAY PRODUCE ANESTHESIA OF THE SKIN AND BURNING, STINGING, TENDERNESS, ERYTHEMA, EXCORIATION, VESICULATION, SLOUGHING AND TISSUE NECROSIS. SYSTEMIC POISONING DUE TO LOCAL ANESTHETICS MAY OCCUR WITH LIGHTHEADEDNESS, NERVOUSNESS, APPREHENSION, EUPHORIA, CONFUSION, DIZZINESS, DROWSINESS, TINNITUS, BLURRED OR DOUBLE VISION, VOMITING, SENSATIONS OF HEAT, COLD OR NUMBNESS, TWITCHING, TREMORS, CONVULSIONS, UNCONSCIOUSNESS, AND RESPIRATORY DEPRESSION AND ARREST. MYOCARDIAL DEPRESSION, BRADYCARDIA, HYPOTENSION, AND CARDIOVASCULAR COLLAPSE WHICH MAY LEAD TO CARDIAC ARREST MAY OCCUR. RARELY AN ALLERGIC REACTION MAY OCCUR IN PERSONS PREVIOUSLY EXPOSED. **CHRONIC EXPOSURE-** REPEATED OR PROLONGED EXPOSURE MAY CAUSE DEHYDRATION OF THE EPITHELIUM OR AN ESCHAROTIC EFFECT AND A DELAY IN WOUND HEALING. REPEATED APPLICATION MAY CAUSE SYSTEMIC POISONING AS DETAILED IN ACUTE EXPOSURE. REPEATED EXPOSURE MAY RESULT IN SENSITIZATION. SYMPTOMS OF HYPERSENSITIVITY DUE TO LOCAL ANESTHETICS MAY INCLUDE: ITCHING, PAIN, SKIN DISCOLORATION, ECZEMATOID DERMATITIS CHARACTERIZED BY ERYTHEMA AND PRURITUS WHICH PROCEEDS TO INFLAMMATION, SWELLING, EXCORIATION, VESICULATION AND OOZING, CUTANEOUS LESIONS, URTICARIA, NEURITIS, SLOUGHING AND TISSUE NECROSIS, ASTHMATIC ATTACK AND POSSIBLY FATAL ANAPHYLACTOID REACTIONS.

FIRST AID- REMOVE CONTAMINATED CLOTHING AND SHOES IMMEDIATELY. WASH AFFECTED AREA WITH SOAP OR MILD DETERGENT AND LARGE AMOUNTS OF WATER UNTIL NO EVIDENCE OF CHEMICAL REMAINS (APPROXIMATELY 15-20 MINUTES). GET MEDICAL ATTENTION IMMEDIATELY.

EYE CONTACT: TETRACAINE HYDROCHLORIDE: **ACUTE EXPOSURE-** APPLICATION OF TETRACAINE IN CONCENTRATIONS GREATER THAN 0.5% MAY CAUSE TRANSIENT STINGING OF THE EYE. A TRANSIENT INJURY OF A PERSONS CORNEA FROM THE ACCIDENTAL CONTACT WITH A CRYSTAL OF TETRACAINE HAS BEEN REPORTED. CONTACT WITH LOCAL ANESTHETICS MAY CAUSE ANESTHESIA OF THE EYE AND AN INCREASED RISK OF DAMAGE FROM IRRITATING CHEMICALS, FOREIGN BODIES AND MECHANICAL INJURY. IN ADDITION, THEY MAY CAUSE ABNORMAL DRYING OF THE CORNEA, OCCASIONALLY TEMPORARY BURNING, LACRIMATION, PHOTOPHOBIA, CHEMOSIS, INCREASED WINKING AND CONJUNCTIVAL REDNESS. SYSTEMIC TOXICITY MAY OCCUR DUE TO TETRACAINE AND BE MANIFESTED BY CENTRAL NERVOUS SYSTEM STIMULATION FOLLOWED BY CENTRAL NERVOUS SYSTEM AND CARDIOVASCULAR DEPRESSION AS DETAILED IN ACUTE INGESTION. SENSITIZATION REACTIONS HAVE BEEN REPORTED IN PERSONS PREVIOUSLY EXPOSED. **CHRONIC EXPOSURE-** APPLICATION OF 1% TETRACAINE HYDROCHLORIDE EYEDROPS REPEATEDLY EXTERNALLY TO RABBITS' EYES GAVE NO INDICATION OF INJURY TO THE CORNEAL ENDOTHELIUM OR INTERFERENCE IN REGENERATION AFTER STANDARD ABRASIONS OF THE ENDOTHELIUM. HOWEVER, PROLONGED USE OF LOCAL ANESTHETICS MAY CAUSE SYSTEMIC EFFECTS AS DETAILED IN ACUTE EXPOSURE, DIMINISHED DURATION OF ANESTHESIA, RETARDED WOUND HEALING AND CORNEAL EPITHELIAL EROSIONS. PERMANENT CORNEAL OPACIFICATION WITH ACCOMPANYING VISUAL LOSS, SEVERE KERATITIS, SCARRING OR CORNEAL PERFORATION MAY OCCUR. SENSITIZATION DUE TO LOCAL ANESTHETICS HAS BEEN REPORTED. SYMPTOMS MAY INCLUDE CUTANEOUS LESIONS, URTICARIA, EDEMA, CONTACT DERMATITIS, OR POSSIBLY FATAL ANAPHYLACTOID REACTIONS.

FIRST AID- WASH EYES IMMEDIATELY WITH LARGE AMOUNTS OF WATER OR NORMAL SALINE, OCCASIONALLY LIFTING UPPER AND LOWER LIDS, UNTIL NO EVIDENCE OF CHEMICAL REMAINS (APPROXIMATELY 15-20 MINUTES). GET MEDICAL ATTENTION IMMEDIATELY.

INGESTION: TETRACAINE HYDROCHLORIDE: SENSITIZER/TOXIC. **ACUTE EXPOSURE-** APPLICATION TO THE MUCOUS MEMBRANES MAY PRODUCE AN ANESTHETIC ACTION WITH NUMBNESS OF THE TONGUE AND BUCCAL MUCOSA. ADDITIONAL SYMPTOMS MAY INCLUDE BURNING, STINGING, TENDERNESS, ERYTHEMA, EXCORIATION, VESICULATION, SLOUGHING AND TISSUE NECROSIS. TOPICAL LOCAL ANESTHETICS MAY IMPAIR SWALLOWING AND THUS ENHANCE THE DANGER OF ASPIRATION. A 63 YEAR OLD MAN EXPERIENCED CONVULSIONS FOLLOWING A PHARYNGEAL-LARYNGEAL SPRAYING WITH 20 ML OF 5% TETRACAINE HYDROCHLORIDE (1000 MG). INGESTION OF LOCAL ANESTHETICS MAY CAUSE SYSTEMIC POISONING TO OCCUR. SYMPTOMS MAY INCLUDE LIGHTHEADEDNESS, NERVOUSNESS, APPREHENSION, EUPHORIA, DIZZINESS, DROWSINESS, TINNITUS, BLURRED OR DOUBLE VISION, CHILLS, PUPIL CONTRACTION, SENSATIONS OF HEAT, COLD OR NUMBNESS, TWITCHING, TREMORS, CLONIC CONVULSIONS, UNCONSCIOUSNESS, RESPIRATORY DEPRESSION WITH WEAK AND IRREGULAR BREATHING AND BRONCHIAL SPASM OR RESPIRATORY ARREST. MYOCARDIAL DEPRESSION, SHOCK, COMA, BRADYCARDIA, HYPOTENSION AND CARDIOVASCULAR COLLAPSE WHICH MAY LEAD TO CARDIAC ARREST MAY OCCUR. METHEMOGLOBINEMIA CHARACTERIZED BY CYANOSIS HAS BEEN REPORTED FOLLOWING EXCESSIVE APPLICATION TO MUCOUS MEMBRANES. HYPERSENSITIVITY REACTIONS MAY OCCUR IN PERSONS PREVIOUSLY EXPOSED. **CHRONIC EXPOSURE-** REPEATED OR PROLONGED EXPOSURE TO TETRACAINE MAY RESULT IN ACCUMULATION TO TOXIC CONCENTRATIONS IN THE BLOOD AND CAUSE SYSTEMIC POISONING DUE TO ABSORPTION FROM THE MUCOUS MEMBRANES OF THE MOUTH, PHARYNX AND ESOPHAGUS AS DETAILED IN ACUTE INGESTION. REPEATED EXPOSURE MAY RESULT IN SENSITIZATION CHARACTERIZED BY CUTANEOUS LESIONS, URTICARIA, EDEMA, CONTACT DERMATITIS, EXCORIATION, VESICULATION, ASTHMA OR POSSIBLY FATAL ANAPHYLACTOID REACTIONS.

FIRST AID- REMOVE INGESTED DRUG BY INDUCED EMESIS FOLLOWED BY ACTIVATED CHARCOAL. MAINTAIN AIRWAY AND GIVE ARTIFICIAL RESPIRATION WITH OXYGEN UNTIL CONVULSIONS OR DEPRESSION IS CONTROLLED AND BLOOD PRESSURE AND PULSE RETURN TO NORMAL. GET MEDICAL ATTENTION IMMEDIATELY. TREATMENT SHOULD BE ADMINISTERED BY QUALIFIED MEDICAL PERSONNEL. (DREISBACH, HANDBOOK OF POISONING, 11TH ED.).

ANTIDOTE: NO SPECIFIC ANTIDOTE. TREAT SYMPTOMATICALLY AND SUPPORTIVELY.

REACTIVITY

REACTIVITY: STABLE UNDER NORMAL TEMPERATURES AND PRESSURES.

INCOMPATIBILITIES: TETRACAINE HYDROCHLORIDE: NO DATA AVAILABLE.

DECOMPOSITION: THERMAL DECOMPOSITION PRODUCTS MAY INCLUDE TOXIC AND CORROSIVE FUMES OF CHLORIDES AND TOXIC OXIDES OF NITROGEN.

POLYMERIZATION: HAZARDOUS POLYMERIZATION HAS NOT BEEN REPORTED TO OCCUR UNDER NORMAL TEMPERATURES AND PRESSURES.

STORAGE AND DISPOSAL

OBSERVE ALL FEDERAL, STATE AND LOCAL REGULATIONS WHEN STORING OR DISPOSING OF THIS SUBSTANCE. FOR ASSISTANCE, CONTACT THE DISTRICT DIRECTOR OF THE ENVIRONMENTAL PROTECTION AGENCY.

STORAGE

STORE IN A COOL PLACE PROTECTED FROM LIGHT.

CONDITIONS TO AVOID

MAY BURN BUT DOES NOT IGNITE READILY. AVOID CONTACT WITH STRONG OXIDIZERS, EXCESSIVE HEAT, SPARKS, OR OPEN FLAME.

SPILL AND LEAK PROCEDURES

OCCUPATIONAL SPILL: SWEEP UP AND PLACE IN SUITABLE CLEAN, DRY CONTAINERS FOR RECLAMATION OR LATER DISPOSAL. DO NOT FLUSH SPILLED MATERIAL INTO SEWER. KEEP UNNECESSARY PEOPLE AWAY.

PROTECTIVE EQUIPMENT

VENTILATION: PROVIDE LOCAL EXHAUST OR PROCESS ENCLOSURE VENTILATION SYSTEM.

RESPIRATOR: THE FOLLOWING RESPIRATORS ARE RECOMMENDED BASED ON INFORMATION FOUND IN THE PHYSICAL DATA, TOXICITY AND HEALTH EFFECTS SECTIONS. THEY ARE RANKED IN ORDER FROM MINIMUM TO MAXIMUM RESPIRATORY PROTECTION. THE SPECIFIC RESPIRATOR SELECTED MUST BE BASED ON CONTAMINATION LEVELS FOUND IN THE WORK PLACE, MUST NOT EXCEED THE WORKING LIMITS OF THE RESPIRATOR AND BE JOINTLY APPROVED BY THE NATIONAL INSTITUTE FOR OCCUPATIONAL SAFETY AND HEALTH AND THE MINE SAFETY AND HEALTH ADMINISTRATION (NIOSH-MSHA).

TYPE 'C' SUPPLIED-AIR RESPIRATOR WITH A FULL FACEPIECE OPERATED IN PRESSURE-DEMAND OR OTHER POSITIVE PRESSURE MODE OR WITH A FULL FACEPIECE, HELMET OR HOOD OPERATED IN CONTINOUS-FLOW MODE.

SELF-CONTAINED BREATHING APPARATUS WITH A FULL FACEPIECE OPERATED IN PRESSURE-DEMAND OR OTHER POSITIVE PRESSURE MODE.

FOR FIREFIGHTING AND OTHER IMMEDIATELY DANGEROUS TO LIFE OR HEALTH CONDITIONS:

SELF-CONTAINED BREATHING APPARATUS WITH FULL FACEPIECE OPERATED IN PRESSURE-DEMAND OR OTHER POSITIVE PRESSURE MODE.

SUPPLIED-AIR RESPIRATOR WITH FULL FACEPIECE AND OPERATED IN PRESSURE-

DEMAND OR OTHER POSITIVE PRESSURE MODE IN COMBINATION WITH AN AUXILIARY SELF-CONTAINED BREATHING APPARATUS OPERATED IN PRESSURE-DEMAND OR OTHER POSITIVE PRESSURE MODE.

CLOTHING: EMPLOYEE MUST WEAR APPROPRIATE PROTECTIVE (IMPERVIOUS) CLOTHING AND EQUIPMENT TO PREVENT REPEATED OR PROLONGED SKIN CONTACT WITH THIS SUBSTANCE.

GLOVES: EMPLOYEE MUST WEAR APPROPRIATE PROTECTIVE GLOVES TO PREVENT CONTACT WITH THIS SUBSTANCE.

EYE PROTECTION: EMPLOYEE MUST WEAR SPLASH-PROOF OR DUST-RESISTANT SAFETY GOGGLES AND A FACESHIELD TO PREVENT CONTACT WITH THIS SUBSTANCE.

EMERGENCY WASH FACILITIES: WHERE THERE IS ANY POSSIBILITY THAT AN EMPLOYEE'S EYES AND/OR SKIN MAY BE EXPOSED TO THIS SUBSTANCE, THE EMPLOYER SHOULD PROVIDE AN EYE WASH FOUNTAIN AND QUICK DRENCH SHOWER WITHIN THE IMMEDIATE WORK AREA FOR EMERGENCY USE.

AUTHORIZED BY- OCCUPATIONAL HEALTH SERVICES, INC.

CREATION DATE: 10/05/89 ***REVISION DATE:*** 05/31/90

MATERIAL SAFETY DATA SHEET

OCCUPATIONAL HEALTH SERVICES, INC.
AGRICULTURE AND PESTICIDE DIVISION
450 SEVENTH AVENUE, SUITE 2407
NEW YORK, NEW YORK 10123
1-800-445-MSDS OR (212) 967-1100

EMERGENCY CONTACT:
JOHN S. BRANSFORD, JR. (615) 292-1180

SUBSTANCE IDENTIFICATION

CAS-NUMBER 4849-32-5

SUBSTANCE: KARBUTILATE

TRADE NAMES/SYNONYMS: CARBAMIC ACID, (1,1-DIMETHYLETHYL)-, 3-(((DIMETHYLAMINO)CARBONYL) AMINO)PHENYL ESTER; CARBAMIC ACID, TERT-BUTYL-, ESTER WITH 3-(M-HYDROXYPHENYL) -1,1-DIMETHYLUREA; TERT-BUTYLCARBAMIC ACID ESTER WITH 3-(M-HYDROXYPHENYL) -1,1-DIMETHYLUREA; (1,1-DIMETHYLETHYL)CARBAMIC ACID-3-(((DIMETHYLAMINO)CARBONYL)AMINO) PHENYL ESTER; 3-(3,3-DIMETHYLUREIDO)PHENYL TERT-BUTYLCARBAMATE; 3-(((DIMETHYLAMINO)CARBONYL)AMINO)PHENYL (1,1-DIMETHYLETHYL)CARBAMATE; M-(3,3-DIMETHYLUREIDO)PHENYL-TERT-BUTYLCARBAMATE; CARBUTILATE; NIA 11092; FMC 11092; TANDEX; C14H21N3O3; PST72271

CHEMICAL FAMILY: SUBSTITUTED UREA

MOLECULAR FORMULA: C14-H21-N3-O3

MOLECULAR WEIGHT: 279.38

CERCLA RATINGS (SCALE 0-3): HEALTH=2 FIRE=1 REACTIVITY=0 PERSISTENCE=0

NFPA RATINGS (SCALE 0-4): HEALTH=2 FIRE=1 REACTIVITY=0

COMPONENTS AND CONTAMINANTS

COMPONENT: KARBUTILATE ***PERCENT:*** 100
CAS# 4849-32-5

OTHER CONTAMINANTS: NONE

EXPOSURE LIMITS: NO OCCUPATIONAL EXPOSURE LIMITS ESTABLISHED BY OSHA, ACGIH, OR NIOSH.

PHYSICAL DATA

DESCRIPTION: ALMOST ODORLESS WHITE CRYSTALLINE SOLID.

MELTING POINT: 349-351 F (176-177 C) ***SPECIFIC GRAVITY:*** 1.175

VAPOR PRESSURE: NEGLIGIBLE ***SOLUBILITY IN WATER:*** 0.035% @ 20 C

SOLVENT SOLUBILITY: SOLUBLE IN DIMETHYLFORMAMIDE AND DIMETHYLSULFOXIDE; SLIGHTLY SOLUBLE IN ACETONE, ISOPHORONE, ISOPROPANOL, AND XYLENE.

FIRE AND EXPLOSION DATA

FIRE AND EXPLOSION HAZARD: SLIGHT FIRE HAZARD WHEN EXPOSED TO HEAT OR FLAME.

FIREFIGHTING MEDIA: DRY CHEMICAL, CARBON DIOXIDE, HALON, WATER SPRAY OR STANDARD FOAM (1987 EMERGENCY RESPONSE GUIDEBOOK, DOT P 5800.4). FOR LARGER FIRES, USE WATER SPRAY, FOG OR STANDARD FOAM (1987 EMERGENCY RESPONSE GUIDEBOOK, DOT P 5800.4).

FIREFIGHTING: MOVE CONTAINERS FROM FIRE AREA IF POSSIBLE. FIGHT FIRE FROM MAXIMUM DISTANCE. STAY AWAY FROM STORAGE TANK ENDS. DIKE FIRE CONTROL WATER FOR LATER DISPOSAL. DO NOT SCATTER MATERIAL (1987 EMERGENCY RESPONSE GUIDEBOOK, DOT P 5800.4, GUIDE PAGE 55).

EXTINGUISH USING AGENT SUITABLE FOR TYPE OF SURROUNDING FIRE. USE WATER IN FLOODING QUANTITIES AS FOG. KEEP SPARKS, FLAMES AND OTHER SOURCES OF IGNITION AWAY. KEEP MATERIAL OUT OF WATER SOURCES AND SEWERS. DO NOT TOUCH MATERIAL AND AVOID BREATHING DUSTS AND FUMES FROM BURNING MATERIAL. KEEP UPWIND.

TOXICITY

KARBUTILATE: TOXICITY DATA: 3000 MG/KG ORAL-RAT LD50; 320 MG/KG INTRAVENOUS-MOUSE LD50. CARCINOGEN STATUS: NONE. ACUTE TOXICITY LEVEL: MODERATELY TOXIC BY INGESTION. TARGET EFFECTS: NO DATA AVAILABLE.

HEALTH EFFECTS AND FIRST AID

INHALATION: KARBUTILATE: **ACUTE EXPOSURE-** A LETHAL CONCENTRATION IN RATS WAS GREATER THAN 3700 MG/M3. **CHRONIC EXPOSURE-** NO DATA AVAILABLE.

FIRST AID- REMOVE FROM EXPOSURE AREA TO FRESH AIR IMMEDIATELY. IF BREATHING HAS STOPPED, PERFORM ARTIFICIAL RESPIRATION. KEEP PERSON WARM AND AT REST. TREAT SYMPTOMATICALLY AND SUPPORTIVELY. GET MEDICAL ATTENTION IMMEDIATELY.

SKIN CONTACT: KARBUTILATE: **ACUTE EXPOSURE-** THIS MATERIAL WAS NOT IRRITATING TO RABBIT SKIN. NO OBSERVABLE EFFECTS WERE NOTED IN RABBITS TREATED WITH A 50% AQUEOUS PASTE OF KARBUTILATE. **CHRONIC EXPOSURE-** NO DATA AVAILABLE.

FIRST AID- REMOVE CONTAMINATED CLOTHING AND SHOES IMMEDIATELY. WASH AFFECTED AREA WITH SOAP OR MILD DETERGENT AND LARGE AMOUNTS OF WATER UNTIL NO EVIDENCE OF CHEMICAL REMAINS (APPROXIMATELY 15-20 MINUTES). GET MEDICAL ATTENTION IMMEDIATELY.

EYE CONTACT: KARBUTILATE: **ACUTE EXPOSURE-** THIS MATERIAL WAS SLIGHTLY IRRITATING TO RABBIT EYES. **CHRONIC EXPOSURE-** NO DATA AVAILABLE.

FIRST AID- WASH EYES IMMEDIATELY WITH LARGE AMOUNTS OF WATER OR NORMAL SALINE, OCCASIONALLY LIFTING UPPER AND LOWER LIDS, UNTIL NO EVIDENCE OF CHEMICAL REMAINS (APPROXIMATELY 15-20 MINUTES). GET MEDICAL ATTENTION IMMEDIATELY.

INGESTION: KARBUTILATE: **ACUTE EXPOSURE-** A LETHAL DOSE IN RATS WAS 3000 MG/KG; SYMPTOMS WERE NOT REPORTED. **CHRONIC EXPOSURE-** NO OBSERVABLE EFFECTS WERE NOTED IN A 90-DAY STUDY OF RATS FED 70 MG/KG/DAY AND DOGS FED 15 MG/KG/DAY.

FIRST AID- TREAT SYMPTOMATICALLY AND SUPPORTIVELY. GET MEDICAL ATTENTION IMMEDIATELY. IF VOMITING OCCURS, KEEP HEAD LOWER THAN HIPS TO PREVENT ASPIRATION.

ANTIDOTE: NO SPECIFIC ANTIDOTE. TREAT SYMPTOMATICALLY AND SUPPORTIVELY.

REACTIVITY

REACTIVITY: STABLE UNDER NORMAL TEMPERATURES AND PRESSURES.

INCOMPATIBILITIES: KARBUTILATE: OXIDIZERS (STRONG): FIRE AND EXPLOSION HAZARD.

DECOMPOSITION: THERMAL DECOMPOSITION PRODUCTS MAY INCLUDE TOXIC OXIDES OF CARBON AND NITROGEN.

POLYMERIZATION: HAZARDOUS POLYMERIZATION HAS NOT BEEN REPORTED TO OCCUR UNDER NORMAL TEMPERATURES AND PRESSURES.

STORAGE AND DISPOSAL

OBSERVE ALL FEDERAL, STATE AND LOCAL REGULATIONS WHEN STORING OR DISPOSING OF THIS SUBSTANCE. FOR ASSISTANCE, CONTACT THE DISTRICT DIRECTOR OF THE ENVIRONMENTAL PROTECTION AGENCY.

STORAGE

STORE IN ACCORDANCE WITH 40 CFR 165 RECOMMENDED PROCEDURES FOR THE DISPOSAL AND STORAGE OF PESTICIDES AND PESTICIDE CONTAINERS. STORE AWAY FROM INCOMPATIBLE SUBSTANCES.

DISPOSAL

DISPOSAL MUST BE IN ACCORDANCE WITH 40 CFR 165 RECOMMENDED PROCEDURES FOR THE DISPOSAL AND STORAGE OF PESTICIDES AND PESTICIDE CONTAINERS.

CONDITIONS TO AVOID

MAY BURN BUT DOES NOT IGNITE READILY. CONTAINERS MAY EXPLODE IN HEAT OF FIRE.

SPILL AND LEAK PROCEDURES

OCCUPATIONAL SPILL: DO NOT TOUCH SPILLED MATERIAL. STOP LEAK IF YOU CAN DO IT WITHOUT RISK. USE WATER SPRAY TO REDUCE VAPORS. FOR SMALL SPILLS, TAKE UP WITH SAND OR OTHER ABSORBENT MATERIAL AND PLACE INTO CONTAINERS FOR LATER DISPOSAL. FOR SMALL DRY SPILLS, WITH A CLEAN

SHOVEL PLACE MATERIAL INTO CLEAN, DRY CONTAINERS AND COVER. MOVE CONTAINERS FROM SPILL AREA. FOR LARGER SPILLS, DIKE FAR AHEAD OF SPILL FOR LATER DISPOSAL. KEEP UNNECESSARY PEOPLE AWAY. ISOLATE HAZARD AREA AND DENY ENTRY. VENTILATE CLOSED SPACES BEFORE ENTERING.

PROTECTIVE EQUIPMENT

VENTILATION: PROVIDE LOCAL EXHAUST OR GENERAL DILUTION VENTILATION SYSTEM.

RESPIRATOR: THE FOLLOWING RESPIRATORS ARE RECOMMENDED BASED ON INFORMATION FOUND IN THE PHYSICAL DATA, TOXICITY AND HEALTH EFFECTS SECTIONS. THEY ARE RANKED IN ORDER FROM MINIMUM TO MAXIMUM RESPIRATORY PROTECTION. THE SPECIFIC RESPIRATOR SELECTED MUST BE BASED ON CONTAMINATION LEVELS FOUND IN THE WORK PLACE, MUST NOT EXCEED THE WORKING LIMITS OF THE RESPIRATOR AND BE JOINTLY APPROVED BY THE NATIONAL INSTITUTE FOR OCCUPATIONAL SAFETY AND HEALTH AND THE MINE SAFETY AND HEALTH ADMINISTRATION (NIOSH-MSHA).

CHEMICAL CARTRIDGE RESPIRATOR WITH AN ORGANIC VAPOR CARTRIDGE(S) IN COMBINATION WITH A DUST AND MIST FILTER.

GAS MASK WITH ORGANIC VAPOR CANISTER (CHIN-STYLE OR FRONT- OR BACK-MOUNTED CANISTER) WITH A DUST AND MIST FILTER.

GAS MASK WITH ORGANIC VAPOR CANISTER (CHIN-STYLE OR FRONT- OR BACK-MOUNTED CANISTER) WITH A PARTICULATE FILTER.

POWERED AIR-PURIFYING RESPIRATOR WITH A HIGH-EFFICIENCY FILTER.

TYPE 'C' SUPPLIED-AIR RESPIRATOR WITH A FULL FACEPIECE OPERATED IN A PRESSURE-DEMAND OR OTHER POSITIVE PRESSURE MODE.

SELF-CONTAINED BREATHING APPARATUS WITH A FULL FACEPIECE OPERATED IN PRESSURE-DEMAND OR OTHER POSITIVE PRESSURE MODE.

FOR FIREFIGHTING AND OTHER IMMEDIATELY DANGEROUS TO LIFE OR HEALTH CONDITIONS:

SELF-CONTAINED BREATHING APPARATUS WITH FULL FACEPIECE OPERATED IN PRESSURE-DEMAND OR OTHER POSITIVE PRESSURE MODE.

SUPPLIED-AIR RESPIRATOR WITH FULL FACEPIECE AND OPERATED IN PRESSURE-DEMAND OR OTHER POSITIVE PRESSURE MODE IN COMBINATION WITH AN AUXILIARY SELF-CONTAINED BREATHING APPARATUS OPERATED IN PRESSURE-DEMAND OR OTHER POSITIVE PRESSURE MODE.

CLOTHING: EMPLOYEE MUST WEAR APPROPRIATE PROTECTIVE (IMPERVIOUS) CLOTHING AND EQUIPMENT TO PREVENT REPEATED OR PROLONGED SKIN CONTACT WITH THIS SUBSTANCE.

GLOVES: EMPLOYEE MUST WEAR APPROPRIATE PROTECTIVE GLOVES TO PREVENT CONTACT WITH THIS SUBSTANCE.

EYE PROTECTION: EMPLOYEE MUST WEAR SPLASH-PROOF OR DUST-RESISTANT SAFETY GOGGLES TO PREVENT EYE CONTACT WITH THIS SUBSTANCE.

EMERGENCY EYE WASH: WHERE THERE IS ANY POSSIBILITY THAT AN EMPLOYEE'S EYES MAY BE EXPOSED TO THIS SUBSTANCE, THE EMPLOYER SHOULD PROVIDE AN EYE WASH FOUNTAIN WITHIN THE IMMEDIATE WORK AREA FOR EMERGENCY USE.

AUTHORIZED BY- OCCUPATIONAL HEALTH SERVICES, INC.

CREATION DATE: 10/04/89 ***REVISION DATE:*** 05/11/90

MATERIAL SAFETY DATA SHEET

OCCUPATIONAL HEALTH SERVICES, INC.
AGRICULTURE AND PESTICIDE DIVISION
450 SEVENTH AVENUE, SUITE 2407
NEW YORK, NEW YORK 10123
1-800-445-MSDS OR (212) 967-1100

EMERGENCY CONTACT:
JOHN S. BRANSFORD, JR. (615) 292-1180

SUBSTANCE IDENTIFICATION

CAS-NUMBER 13684-63-4

SUBSTANCE: **PHENMEDIPHAM**

TRADE NAMES/SYNONYMS: CARBAMIC ACID, (3-METHYLPHENYL)-, 3-((METHOXYCARBONYL)AMINO)PHENYL ESTER; CARBANILIC ACID, M-HYDROXY-, METHYL ESTER, M-METHYLCARBANILATE (ESTER); (3-METHYLPHENYL)CARBAMIC ACID, 3-((METHOXYCARBONYL)AMINO)PHENYL ESTER; M-HYDROXYCARBANILIC ACID, METHYL ESTER, M-METHYLCARBANILATE (ESTER); METHYL 3-(M-TOLYLCARBAMOYLOXY)PHENYLCARBAMATE; METHYL 3-(3-METHYLCARBANILOYLOXY)CARBANILATE; 3-METHOXYCARBONY LAMINOPHENYL 3'-METHYLCARBANILATE; 3-((METHOXYCARBONYL)AMINO)PHENYL (3-METHYLPHENYL)CARBAMATE; METHYL M-HYDROXYCARBANILATE M-METHYLCARBANILATE (ESTER); BETANAL; FENMEDIFAM; SN 38584; SPIN-AID; C16H16N2O4; PST72282

CHEMICAL FAMILY: CARBAMATE

MOLECULAR FORMULA: C16-H16-N2-O4

MOLECULAR WEIGHT: 300.32

CERCLA RATINGS (SCALE 0-3): HEALTH = 2 FIRE = 1 REACTIVITY = 0 PERSISTENCE = 1

NFPA RATINGS (SCALE 0-4): HEALTH = U FIRE = 1 REACTIVITY = 0

COMPONENTS AND CONTAMINANTS

COMPONENT: PHENMEDIPHAM ***PERCENT:*** 100.0
CAS# 13684-63-4

EXPOSURE LIMITS: NO OCCUPATIONAL EXPOSURE LIMITS ESTABLISHED BY OSHA, ACGIH, OR NIOSH.

PHYSICAL DATA

DESCRIPTION: COLORLESS, CRYSTALLINE SOLID

MELTING POINT: 289-291 F (143-144 C)

SPECIFIC GRAVITY: 0.25-0.30 ***VAPOR PRESSURE:*** NEGLIGIBLE

SOLUBILITY IN WATER: 5 PPM

SOLVENT SOLUBILITY: SOLUBLE IN ACETONE, CYCLOHEXANONE, AND POLAR ORGANIC SOLVENTS; MODERATELY SOLUBLE IN METHANOL, CHLOROFORM; VERY SLIGHTLY SOLUBLE IN BENZENE AND HEXANE.

FIRE AND EXPLOSION DATA

FIRE AND EXPLOSION HAZARD: SLIGHT FIRE HAZARD WHEN EXPOSED TO HEAT OR FLAME.

FIREFIGHTING MEDIA: DRY CHEMICAL, CARBON DIOXIDE, HALON, WATER SPRAY OR STANDARD FOAM (1987 EMERGENCY RESPONSE GUIDEBOOK, DOT P 5800.4).
FOR LARGER FIRES, USE WATER SPRAY, FOG OR STANDARD FOAM (1987 EMERGENCY RESPONSE GUIDEBOOK, DOT P 5800.4).

FIREFIGHTING: MOVE CONTAINER FROM FIRE AREA IF POSSIBLE. DO NOT SCATTER SPILLED MATERIAL WITH HIGH PRESSURE WATER STREAMS. DIKE FIRE CONTROL WATER FOR LATER DISPOSAL (1987 EMERGENCY RESPONSE GUIDEBOOK, DOT P 5800.4, GUIDE PAGE 31).
USE AGENTS SUITABLE FOR TYPE OF SURROUNDING FIRE. AVOID BREATHING HAZARDOUS VAPORS, KEEP UPWIND.

TOXICITY

PHENMEDIPHAM: TOXICITY DATA: >4000 MG/KG SKIN-RAT LD50 (PEMNDP); 4 GM/KG ORAL-RAT LD50; 800 MG/KG UNREPORTED-RAT LD50; 3000 MG/KG UNREPORTED-MAMMAL LD50; MUTAGENIC DATA (RTECS); REPRODUCTIVE EFFECTS DATA (RTECS). CARCINOGEN STATUS: NONE. ACUTE TOXICITY: MODERATELY TOXIC BY INGESTION; SLIGHTLY TOXIC BY DERMAL ABSORPTION. TARGET EFFECTS: NO DATA AVAILABLE.

HEALTH EFFECTS AND FIRST AID

INHALATION: PHENMEDIPHAM: **ACUTE EXPOSURE**- NO DATA AVAILABLE. **CHRONIC EXPOSURE**- EMBRYOTOXIC AND TERATOGENIC EFFECTS WERE OBSERVED IN A STUDY OF RATS REPEATEDLY EXPOSED TO PHENMEDIPHAM.

FIRST AID- REMOVE FROM EXPOSURE AREA TO FRESH AIR IMMEDIATELY. IF BREATHING HAS STOPPED, PERFORM ARTIFICIAL RESPIRATION. KEEP PERSON WARM AND AT REST. TREAT SYMPTOMATICALLY AND SUPPORTIVELY. GET MEDICAL ATTENTION IMMEDIATELY.

SKIN CONTACT: PHENMEDIPHAM: **ACUTE EXPOSURE**- SENSITIZATION MAY OCCUR AMONG PREVIOUSLY EXPOSED INDIVIDUALS. **CHRONIC EXPOSURE**- PROLONGED OR REPEATED EXPOSURE MAY CAUSE SENSITIZATION DERMATITIS.

FIRST AID- REMOVE CONTAMINATED CLOTHING AND SHOES IMMEDIATELY. WASH AFFECTED AREA WITH SOAP OR MILD DETERGENT AND LARGE AMOUNTS OF WATER UNTIL NO EVIDENCE OF CHEMICAL REMAINS (APPROXIMATELY 15-20 MINUTES). GET MEDICAL ATTENTION IMMEDIATELY.

EYE CONTACT: PHENMEDIPHAM: **ACUTE EXPOSURE**- NO DATA AVAILABLE. **CHRONIC EXPOSURE**- NO DATA AVAILABLE.

FIRST AID- WASH EYES IMMEDIATELY WITH LARGE AMOUNTS OF WATER OR NORMAL SALINE, OCCASIONALLY LIFTING UPPER AND LOWER LIDS, UNTIL NO EVIDENCE OF CHEMICAL REMAINS (APPROXIMATELY 15-20 MINUTES). GET MEDICAL ATTENTION IMMEDIATELY.

INGESTION: PHENMEDIPHAM: **ACUTE EXPOSURE**- EMBRYOTOXIC AND TERATOGENIC EFFECTS WERE OBSERVED IN A STUDY OF PREGNANT RATS RECEIVING A SINGLE DOSE. **CHRONIC EXPOSURE**- NO REPORTED DEATHS OCCURRED AMONG RATS REPEATEDLY RECEIVING UP TO 500 MG/KG/DAY. INTRAGASTRIC ADMINISTRATION PRODUCED MUTAGENIC EFFECTS ON BONE MARROW CELLS IN MICE. REPRODUCTIVE EFFECTS HAVE BEEN REPORTED IN ANIMALS.

FIRST AID- IF THE PERSON IS CONSCIOUS AND NOT CONVULSING, REMOVE BY GASTRIC LAVAGE AND FOLLOW WITH A CATHARTIC (DREISBACH, HANDBOOK OF POISONING, 12TH ED.). TREAT SYMPTOMATICALLY AND SUPPORTIVELY. GASTRIC LAVAGE SHOULD BE PERFORMED BY QUALIFIED MEDICAL PERSONNEL. GET MEDICAL ATTENTION IMMEDIATELY.

ANTIDOTE: NO SPECIFIC ANTIDOTE. TREAT SYMPTOMATICALLY AND SUPPORTIVELY.

REACTIVITY

REACTIVITY: STABLE UNDER NORMAL TEMPERATURES AND PRESSURES.

INCOMPATIBILITIES: PHENMEDIPHAM: OXIDIZERS (STRONG): FIRE AND EXPLOSION HAZARD.

DECOMPOSITION: THERMAL DECOMPOSITION PRODUCTS MAY INCLUDE TOXIC OXIDES OF CARBON AND NITROGEN.

POLYMERIZATION: HAZARDOUS POLYMERIZATION HAS NOT BEEN REPORTED TO OCCUR UNDER NORMAL TEMPERATURES AND PRESSURES.

STORAGE AND DISPOSAL

OBSERVE ALL FEDERAL, STATE AND LOCAL REGULATIONS WHEN STORING OR DISPOSING OF THIS SUBSTANCE. FOR ASSISTANCE, CONTACT THE DISTRICT DIRECTOR OF THE ENVIRONMENTAL PROTECTION AGENCY.

STORAGE

STORE IN ACCORDANCE WITH 40 CFR 165 RECOMMENDED PROCEDURES FOR THE DISPOSAL AND STORAGE OF PESTICIDES AND PESTICIDE CONTAINERS.

STORE AWAY FROM INCOMPATIBLE SUBSTANCES.

DISPOSAL

DISPOSAL MUST BE IN ACCORDANCE WITH 40 CFR 165 RECOMMENDED PROCEDURES FOR THE DISPOSAL AND STORAGE OF PESTICIDES AND PESTICIDE CONTAINERS.

CONDITIONS TO AVOID

MAY BURN BUT DOES NOT IGNITE READILY. AVOID CONTACT WITH STRONG OXIDIZERS, EXCESSIVE HEAT, SPARKS, OR OPEN FLAME.

SPILL AND LEAK PROCEDURES

OCCUPATIONAL SPILL: SWEEP UP AND PLACE IN SUITABLE CLEAN, DRY CONTAINERS FOR RECLAMATION OR LATER DISPOSAL. DO NOT FLUSH SPILLED MATERIAL INTO SEWER. KEEP UNNECESSARY PEOPLE AWAY.

PROTECTIVE EQUIPMENT

VENTILATION: PROVIDE LOCAL EXHAUST OR GENERAL DILUTION VENTILATION SYSTEM.

RESPIRATOR: THE FOLLOWING RESPIRATORS ARE RECOMMENDED BASED ON INFORMATION FOUND IN THE PHYSICAL DATA, TOXICITY AND HEALTH EFFECTS SECTIONS. THEY ARE RANKED IN ORDER FROM MINIMUM TO MAXIMUM RESPIRATORY PROTECTION. THE SPECIFIC RESPIRATOR SELECTED MUST BE BASED ON CONTAMINATION LEVELS FOUND IN THE WORK PLACE, MUST NOT EXCEED THE WORKING LIMITS OF THE RESPIRATOR AND BE JOINTLY APPROVED BY THE NATIONAL INSTITUTE FOR OCCUPATIONAL SAFETY AND HEALTH AND THE MINE SAFETY AND HEALTH ADMINISTRATION (NIOSH-MSHA).

CHEMICAL CARTRIDGE RESPIRATOR WITH AN ORGANIC VAPOR CARTRIDGE(S) IN COMBINATION WITH A DUST AND MIST FILTER.

GAS MASK WITH ORGANIC VAPOR CANISTER (CHIN-STYLE OR FRONT- OR BACK-MOUNTED CANISTER) WITH A DUST AND MIST FILTER.

GAS MASK WITH ORGANIC VAPOR CANISTER (CHIN-STYLE OR FRONT- OR BACK-MOUNTED CANISTER) WITH A PARTICULATE FILTER.

POWERED AIR-PURIFYING RESPIRATOR WITH A HIGH-EFFICIENCY FILTER.

TYPE 'C' SUPPLIED-AIR RESPIRATOR WITH A FULL FACEPIECE OPERATED IN A PRESSURE-DEMAND OR OTHER POSITIVE PRESSURE MODE.

SELF-CONTAINED BREATHING APPARATUS WITH A FULL FACEPIECE OPERATED IN PRESSURE-DEMAND OR OTHER POSITIVE PRESSURE MODE.

FOR FIREFIGHTING AND OTHER IMMEDIATELY DANGEROUS TO LIFE OR HEALTH CONDITIONS:

SELF-CONTAINED BREATHING APPARATUS WITH FULL FACEPIECE OPERATED IN PRESSURE-DEMAND OR OTHER POSITIVE PRESSURE MODE.

SUPPLIED-AIR RESPIRATOR WITH FULL FACEPIECE AND OPERATED IN PRESSURE-DEMAND OR OTHER POSITIVE PRESSURE MODE IN COMBINATION WITH AN AUXILIARY SELF-CONTAINED BREATHING APPARATUS OPERATED IN PRESSURE-DEMAND OR OTHER POSITIVE PRESSURE MODE.

CLOTHING: EMPLOYEE MUST WEAR APPROPRIATE PROTECTIVE (IMPERVIOUS) CLOTHING AND EQUIPMENT TO PREVENT REPEATED OR PROLONGED SKIN CONTACT WITH THIS SUBSTANCE.

GLOVES: EMPLOYEE MUST WEAR APPROPRIATE PROTECTIVE GLOVES TO PREVENT CONTACT WITH THIS SUBSTANCE.

EYE PROTECTION: EMPLOYEE MUST WEAR SPLASH-PROOF OR DUST-RESISTANT SAFETY GOGGLES TO PREVENT EYE CONTACT WITH THIS SUBSTANCE.

EMERGENCY EYE WASH: WHERE THERE IS ANY POSSIBILITY THAT AN EMPLOYEE'S EYES MAY BE EXPOSED TO THIS SUBSTANCE, THE EMPLOYER SHOULD PROVIDE AN EYE WASH FOUNTAIN WITHIN THE IMMEDIATE WORK AREA FOR EMERGENCY USE.

AUTHORIZED BY- OCCUPATIONAL HEALTH SERVICES, INC.

CREATION DATE: 10/24/89 ***REVISION DATE:*** 05/31/90

MATERIAL SAFETY DATA SHEET

OCCUPATIONAL HEALTH SERVICES, INC.
AGRICULTURE AND PESTICIDE DIVISION
450 SEVENTH AVENUE, SUITE 2407
NEW YORK, NEW YORK 10123
1-800-445-MSDS OR (212) 967-1100

EMERGENCY CONTACT:
JOHN S. BRANSFORD, JR. (615) 292-1180

SUBSTANCE IDENTIFICATION

CAS-NUMBER 2536-31-4

SUBSTANCE: **CHLORFLURENOL METHYL ESTER**

TRADE NAMES/SYNONYMS: 9H-FLUORENE-9-CARBOXYLIC ACID, 2-CHLORO-9-HYDROXY-, METHYL ESTER; 2-CHLORO-9-HYDROXY-9H-FLUORENE-9-CARBOXYLIC ACID METHYL ESTER; FLUORENE-9-CARBOXYLIC ACID, 2-CHLORO-9-HYDROXY-, METHYL ESTER; 2-CHLORO-9-HYDROXY-FLUORENE-9-CARBOXYLIC ACID METHYL ESTER; METHYL 2-CHLORO-9-HYDROXY-9H-FLUORENE-9-CARBOXYLATE; CHLORFLURECOL; CHLORFLURENOL; CHLORFLURECOL-METHYL; CHLORFLURENOL-METHYL; CHLORFLURECOL METHYL ESTER; CURBISET; IT 3456; MAINTAIN; MORPHACTIN; MULTIPROP; C15H11CLO3; PST72283

CHEMICAL FAMILY: FLUORENE

MOLECULAR FORMULA: C15-H11-CL-O3

MOLECULAR WEIGHT: 274.71

CERCLA RATINGS (SCALE 0-3): HEALTH=2 FIRE=1 REACTIVITY=0 PERSISTENCE=1

NFPA RATINGS (SCALE 0-4): HEALTH=U FIRE=1 REACTIVITY=0

COMPONENTS AND CONTAMINANTS

COMPONENT: CHLORFURENOL METHYL ESTER ***PERCENT:*** 100.0

CAS# 2536-31-4

EXPOSURE LIMITS: NO OCCUPATIONAL EXPOSURE LIMITS ESTABLISHED BY OSHA, ACGIH, OR NIOSH.

PHYSICAL DATA

DESCRIPTION: COLORLESS TO CREAM-COLORED CRYSTALS.

MELTING POINT: 306 F (152 C)

SPECIFIC GRAVITY: 1.496 @ 20 C ***VAPOR PRESSURE:*** NEGLIGIBLE

SOLUBILITY IN WATER: 18 PPM

SOLVENT SOLUBILITY: SOLUBLE IN ACETONE AND METHANOL; MODERATELY SOLUBLE IN ETHANOL, BENZENE, ISOPROPANOL, CARBON TETRACHLORIDE; SLIGHTLY SOLUBLE IN CYCLOHEXANE.

FIRE AND EXPLOSION DATA

FIRE AND EXPLOSION HAZARD: SLIGHT FIRE HAZARD WHEN EXPOSED TO HEAT OR FLAME.

DUST-AIR MIXTURES MAY IGNITE OR EXPLODE.

FIREFIGHTING MEDIA: DRY CHEMICAL, CARBON DIOXIDE, HALON, WATER SPRAY OR STANDARD FOAM (1987 EMERGENCY RESPONSE GUIDEBOOK, DOT P 5800.4).

FOR LARGER FIRES, USE WATER SPRAY, FOG OR STANDARD FOAM (1987 EMERGENCY RESPONSE GUIDEBOOK, DOT P 5800.4).

FIREFIGHTING: MOVE CONTAINER FROM FIRE AREA IF POSSIBLE. DO NOT SCATTER SPILLED MATERIAL WITH HIGH PRESSURE WATER STREAMS. DIKE FIRE CONTROL WATER FOR LATER DISPOSAL (1987 EMERGENCY RESPONSE GUIDEBOOK, DOT P 5800.4, GUIDE PAGE 31).

USE AGENTS SUITABLE FOR TYPE OF SURROUNDING FIRE. AVOID BREATHING HAZARDOUS VAPORS, KEEP UPWIND.

TOXICITY

CHLORFLURENOL METHYL ESTER: TOXICITY DATA: >10,000 MG/KG SKIN-RAT LD50 (85JFAN); 3100 MG/KG ORAL-RAT LD50; 1417 MG/KG INTRAPERITONEAL-RAT LD50; 1670 MG/KG INTRAPERITONEAL-MOUSE LD50. CARCINOGEN STATUS: NONE. ACUTE TOXICITY LEVEL: MODERATELY TOXIC BY INGESTION; SLIGHTLY TOXIC BY DERMAL ABSORPTION. TARGET EFFECTS: NO DATA AVAILABLE.

HEALTH EFFECTS AND FIRST AID

INHALATION: CHLORFLURENOL METHYL ESTER: **ACUTE EXPOSURE-** NO DATA AVAILABLE. **CHRONIC EXPOSURE-** NO DATA AVAILABLE.

FIRST AID- REMOVE FROM EXPOSURE AREA TO FRESH AIR IMMEDIATELY. IF BREATHING HAS STOPPED, PERFORM ARTIFICIAL RESPIRATION. KEEP PERSON WARM AND AT REST. TREAT SYMPTOMATICALLY AND SUPPORTIVELY. GET MEDICAL ATTENTION IMMEDIATELY.

SKIN CONTACT: CHLORFLURENOL-METHYL: **ACUTE EXPOSURE-** MAY CAUSE IRRITATION. **CHRONIC EXPOSURE-** NO DATA AVAILABLE.

FIRST AID- REMOVE CONTAMINATED CLOTHING AND SHOES IMMEDIATELY. WASH AFFECTED AREA WITH SOAP OR MILD DETERGENT AND LARGE AMOUNTS OF WATER UNTIL NO EVIDENCE OF CHEMICAL REMAINS (APPROXIMATELY 15-20 MINUTES). GET MEDICAL ATTENTION IMMEDIATELY.

EYE CONTACT: CHLORFLURENOL METHYL ESTER: **ACUTE EXPOSURE-** MAY CAUSE IRRITATION. **CHRONIC EXPOSURE-** NO DATA AVAILABLE.

FIRST AID- WASH EYES IMMEDIATELY WITH LARGE AMOUNTS OF WATER OR NORMAL SALINE, OCCASIONALLY LIFTING UPPER AND LOWER LIDS, UNTIL NO EVIDENCE OF CHEMICAL REMAINS (APPROXIMATELY 15-20 MINUTES). GET MEDICAL ATTENTION IMMEDIATELY.

INGESTION: CHLORFLURENOL METHYL ESTER: **ACUTE EXPOSURE-** A LETHAL DOSE REPORTED IN RATS WAS 3100 MG/KG; SYMPTOMS WERE NOT REPORTED. **CHRONIC EXPOSURE-** NO OBSERVABLE EFFECTS WERE NOTED IN 2-YEAR STUDIES OF RATS RECEIVING A 3000 MG/KG DIET AND DOGS RECEIVING A 300 MG/KG DIET.

FIRST AID- IF THE PERSON IS CONSCIOUS AND NOT CONVULSING, REMOVE BY GIVING SYRUP OF IPECAC (IF VOMITING OCCURS, KEEP THE HEAD BELOW THE HIPS TO PREVENT ASPIRATION). GIVE ACTIVATED CHARCOAL FOLLOWED BY GASTRIC LAVAGE. FOLLOW WITH A SALINE CATHARTIC. DO NOT GIVE FATS OR OILS. INTESTINAL LAVAGE WITH 20% MANNITOL (200 ML) BY STOMACH TUBE IS ALSO USEFUL. GIVE ARTIFICIAL RESPIRATION WITH OXYGEN IF RESPIRATION IS DEPRESSED (DREISBACH, HANDBOOK OF POISONING, 12TH ED.). TREAT SYMPTOMATICALLY AND SUPPORTIVELY. LAVAGE AND ADMINISTRATION OF OXYGEN SHOULD BE PERFORMED BY QUALIFIED MEDICAL PERSONNEL. GET MEDICAL ATTENTION IMMEDIATELY.

ANTIDOTE: NO SPECIFIC ANTIDOTE. TREAT SYMPTOMATICALLY AND SUPPORTIVELY.

REACTIVITY

REACTIVITY: STABLE UNDER NORMAL TEMPERATURES AND PRESSURES.

INCOMPATIBILITIES: CHLORFLURENOL METHYL ESTER: OXIDIZERS (STRONG): FIRE AND EXPLOSION HAZARD.

DECOMPOSITION: THERMAL DECOMPOSITION PRODUCTS MAY INCLUDE TOXIC AND CORROSIVE FUMES OF CHLORIDES AND TOXIC OXIDES OF CARBON.

POLYMERIZATION: HAZARDOUS POLYMERIZATION HAS NOT BEEN REPORTED TO OCCUR UNDER NORMAL TEMPERATURES AND PRESSURES.

STORAGE AND DISPOSAL

OBSERVE ALL FEDERAL, STATE AND LOCAL REGULATIONS WHEN STORING OR DISPOSING OF THIS SUBSTANCE. FOR ASSISTANCE, CONTACT THE DISTRICT DIRECTOR OF THE ENVIRONMENTAL PROTECTION AGENCY.

STORAGE

STORE IN ACCORDANCE WITH 40 CFR 165 RECOMMENDED PROCEDURES FOR THE DISPOSAL AND STORAGE OF PESTICIDES AND PESTICIDE CONTAINERS.
STORE AWAY FROM INCOMPATIBLE SUBSTANCES.

DISPOSAL

DISPOSAL MUST BE IN ACCORDANCE WITH 40 CFR 165 RECOMMENDED PROCEDURES FOR THE DISPOSAL AND STORAGE OF PESTICIDES AND PESTICIDE CONTAINERS.

CONDITIONS TO AVOID

MAY BURN BUT DOES NOT IGNITE READILY. AVOID CONTACT WITH STRONG OXIDIZERS, EXCESSIVE HEAT, SPARKS, OR OPEN FLAME.

SPILL AND LEAK PROCEDURES

OCCUPATIONAL SPILL: SWEEP UP AND PLACE IN SUITABLE CLEAN, DRY CONTAINERS FOR RECLAMATION OR LATER DISPOSAL. DO NOT FLUSH SPILLED MATERIAL INTO SEWER. KEEP UNNECESSARY PEOPLE AWAY.

PROTECTIVE EQUIPMENT

VENTILATION: PROVIDE LOCAL EXHAUST OR GENERAL DILUTION VENTILATION SYSTEM.

RESPIRATOR: THE FOLLOWING RESPIRATORS ARE RECOMMENDED BASED ON INFORMATION FOUND IN THE PHYSICAL DATA, TOXICITY AND HEALTH EFFECTS SECTIONS. THEY ARE RANKED IN ORDER FROM MINIMUM TO MAXIMUM RESPIRATORY PROTECTION. THE SPECIFIC RESPIRATOR SELECTED MUST BE BASED ON CONTAMINATION LEVELS FOUND IN THE WORK PLACE, MUST NOT EXCEED THE WORKING LIMITS OF THE RESPIRATOR AND BE JOINTLY APPROVED BY THE NATIONAL INSTITUTE FOR OCCUPATIONAL SAFETY AND HEALTH AND THE MINE SAFETY AND HEALTH ADMINISTRATION (NIOSH-MSHA).

CHEMICAL CARTRIDGE RESPIRATOR WITH AN ORGANIC VAPOR CARTRIDGE(S) IN COMBINATION WITH A DUST AND MIST FILTER.
GAS MASK WITH ORGANIC VAPOR CANISTER (CHIN-STYLE OR FRONT- OR BACK-MOUNTED CANISTER) WITH A DUST AND MIST FILTER.
GAS MASK WITH ORGANIC VAPOR CANISTER (CHIN-STYLE OR FRONT- OR BACK-MOUNTED CANISTER) WITH A PARTICULATE FILTER.
POWERED AIR-PURIFYING RESPIRATOR WITH A HIGH-EFFICIENCY FILTER.
TYPE 'C' SUPPLIED-AIR RESPIRATOR WITH A FULL FACEPIECE OPERATED IN A PRESSURE-DEMAND OR OTHER POSITIVE PRESSURE MODE.
SELF-CONTAINED BREATHING APPARATUS WITH A FULL FACEPIECE OPERATED IN PRESSURE-DEMAND OR OTHER POSITIVE PRESSURE MODE.
FOR FIREFIGHTING AND OTHER IMMEDIATELY DANGEROUS TO LIFE OR HEALTH CONDITIONS:
SELF-CONTAINED BREATHING APPARATUS WITH FULL FACEPIECE OPERATED IN PRESSURE-DEMAND OR OTHER POSITIVE PRESSURE MODE.
SUPPLIED-AIR RESPIRATOR WITH FULL FACEPIECE AND OPERATED IN PRESSURE-DEMAND OR OTHER POSITIVE PRESSURE MODE IN COMBINATION WITH AN AUXILIARY SELF-CONTAINED BREATHING APPARATUS OPERATED IN PRESSURE-DEMAND OR OTHER POSITIVE PRESSURE MODE.

CLOTHING: EMPLOYEE MUST WEAR APPROPRIATE PROTECTIVE (IMPERVIOUS) CLOTHING AND EQUIPMENT TO PREVENT REPEATED OR PROLONGED SKIN CONTACT WITH THIS SUBSTANCE.

GLOVES: EMPLOYEE MUST WEAR APPROPRIATE PROTECTIVE GLOVES TO PREVENT CONTACT WITH THIS SUBSTANCE.

EYE PROTECTION: EMPLOYEE MUST WEAR SPLASH-PROOF OR DUST-RESISTANT SAFETY GOGGLES TO PREVENT EYE CONTACT WITH THIS SUBSTANCE.
EMERGENCY EYE WASH: WHERE THERE IS ANY POSSIBILITY THAT AN EMPLOYEE'S EYES MAY BE EXPOSED TO THIS SUBSTANCE, THE EMPLOYER SHOULD PROVIDE AN EYE WASH FOUNTAIN WITHIN THE IMMEDIATE WORK AREA FOR EMERGENCY USE.

AUTHORIZED BY- OCCUPATIONAL HEALTH SERVICES, INC.
CREATION DATE: 04/13/90 ***REVISION DATE:*** 05/31/90

MATERIAL SAFETY DATA SHEET

OCCUPATIONAL HEALTH SERVICES, INC.
AGRICULTURE AND PESTICIDE DIVISION
450 SEVENTH AVENUE, SUITE 2407
NEW YORK, NEW YORK 10123
1-800-445-MSDS OR (212) 967-1100

EMERGENCY CONTACT:
JOHN S. BRANSFORD, JR. (615) 292-1180

SUBSTANCE IDENTIFICATION

CAS-NUMBER 34375-28-5

SUBSTANCE: 2-((HYDROXYMETHYL)AMINO)ETHANOL

TRADE NAMES/SYNONYMS: ETHANOL, 2-(HYDROXYMETHYLAMINE)-; C3H9NO2; PST72288

CHEMICAL FAMILY: ALCOHOL, ALIPHATIC

MOLECULAR FORMULA: C3-H9-N-O2

MOLECULAR WEIGHT: 91.11

CERCLA RATINGS (SCALE 0-3): HEALTH=U FIRE=U REACTIVITY=0 PERSISTENCE=0

NFPA RATINGS (SCALE 0-4): HEALTH=U FIRE=U REACTIVITY=0

COMPONENTS AND CONTAMINANTS

COMPONENT: 2-((HYDROXYMETHYL)AMINO)ETHANOL ***PERCENT:*** 100.0
CAS# 34375-28-5

EXPOSURE LIMITS: NO OCCUPATIONAL EXPOSURE LIMITS ESTABLISHED BY OSHA, ACGIH, OR NIOSH.

PHYSICAL DATA

DESCRIPTION: UNKNOWN ***MELTING POINT:*** NOT AVAILABLE

SPECIFIC GRAVITY: NOT AVAILABLE ***SOLUBILITY IN WATER:*** NOT AVAILABLE

FIRE AND EXPLOSION DATA

FIRE AND EXPLOSION HAZARD: UNKNOWN FIRE AND EXPLOSION HAZARD.

FIREFIGHTING MEDIA: DRY CHEMICAL, CARBON DIOXIDE, HALON, WATER SPRAY OR ALCOHOL FOAM (1987 EMERGENCY RESPONSE GUIDEBOOK, DOT P 5800.4). FOR LARGER FIRES, USE WATER SPRAY, FOG OR ALCOHOL FOAM (1987 EMERGENCY RESPONSE GUIDEBOOK, DOT P 5800.4).

FIREFIGHTING: MOVE CONTAINER FROM FIRE AREA IF POSSIBLE. COOL FIRE-EXPOSED CONTAINERS WITH WATER FROM SIDE UNTIL WELL AFTER FIRE IS OUT. STAY AWAY FROM STORAGE TANK ENDS. FOR MASSIVE FIRE IN STORAGE AREA, USE UNMANNED HOSE HOLDER OR MONITOR NOZZLES, ELSE WITHDRAW FROM AREA AND LET FIRE BURN. WITHDRAW IMMEDIATELY IN CASE OF RISING SOUND FROM VENTING SAFETY DEVICE OR ANY DISCOLORATION OF STORAGE TANK DUE TO FIRE (1987 EMERGENCY RESPONSE GUIDEBOOK, DOT P 5800.4, GUIDE PAGE 26). EXTINGUISH ONLY IF FLOW CAN BE STOPPED. USE FLOODING AMOUNTS OF WATER AS FOG; SOLID STREAMS MAY BE INEFFECTIVE. COOL CONTAINERS WITH FLOODING AMOUNTS OF WATER FROM AS FAR A DISTANCE AS POSSIBLE. AVOID BREATHING VAPORS; KEEP UPWIND.

TOXICITY

2-(HYDROXYMETHYLAMINE)ETHANOL: CARCINGEN STATUS: NONE. ACUTE TOXICITY LEVEL: NO DATA AVAILABLE. TARGET EFFECTS: NO DATA AVAILABLE.

HEALTH EFFECTS AND FIRST AID

INHALATION: 2-(HYDROXYMETHYLAMINE)ETHANOL: **ACUTE EXPOSURE-** NO DATA AVAILABLE, MAY BE IRRITATING TO THE MUCOUS MEMBRANES. **CHRONIC EXPOSURE-** NO DATA AVAILABLE.

FIRST AID- REMOVE FROM EXPOSURE AREA TO FRESH AIR IMMEDIATELY. IF BREATHING HAS STOPPED, PERFORM ARTIFICIAL RESPIRATION. KEEP PERSON WARM AND AT REST. TREAT SYMPTOMATICALLY AND SUPPORTIVELY. GET MEDICAL ATTENTION IMMEDIATELY.

SKIN CONTACT: 2-(HYDROXYMETHYLAMINE)ETHANOL: **ACUTE EXPOSURE-** MAY CAUSE SENSITIZATION DERMATITIS. AT LEAST ONE PERSON RESPONDED POSITIVELY TO A PATCH TEST GIVEN TO WORKERS WITH WORK-RELATED DERMATITIS. **CHRONIC EXPOSURE-** SENSITIZATION DERMATITIS MAY OCCUR IN PREVIOUSLY EXPOSED INDIVIDUALS.

FIRST AID- REMOVE CONTAMINATED CLOTHING AND SHOES IMMEDIATELY. WASH AFFECTED AREA WITH SOAP OR MILD DETERGENT AND LARGE AMOUNTS OF WATER UNTIL NO EVIDENCE OF CHEMICAL REMAINS (APPROXIMATELY 15-20 MINUTES). GET MEDICAL ATTENTION IMMEDIATELY.

EYE CONTACT: 2-(HYDROXYMETHYLAMINE)ETHANOL: **ACUTE EXPOSURE-** NO DATA AVAILABLE, MAY BE IRRITATING. **CHRONIC EXPOSURE-** NO DATA AVAILABLE.

FIRST AID- WASH EYES IMMEDIATELY WITH LARGE AMOUNTS OF WATER OR NORMAL SALINE, OCCASIONALLY LIFTING UPPER AND LOWER LIDS, UNTIL NO EVIDENCE OF CHEMICAL REMAINS (APPROXIMATELY 15-20 MINUTES). GET MEDICAL ATTENTION IMMEDIATELY.

INGESTION: 2-(HYDROXYMETHYLAMINE)ETHANOL: **ACUTE EXPOSURE-** NO DATA AVAILABLE. **CHRONIC EXPOSURE-** NO DATA AVAILABLE.

FIRST AID- TREAT SYMPTOMATICALLY AND SUPPORTIVELY. GET MEDICAL ATTENTION IMMEDIATELY. IF VOMITING OCCURS, KEEP HEAD LOWER THAN HIPS TO PREVENT ASPIRATION.

REACTIVITY

REACTIVITY: STABLE UNDER NORMAL TEMPERATURES AND PRESSURES.

INCOMPATIBILITIES: 2-(HYDROXYMETHYLAMINE)ETHANOL: OXIDIZERS (STRONG): FIRE AND EXPLOSION HAZARD. SEE ALSO ALCOHOLS.
ALCOHOLS: ACETALDEHYDE: VIOLENT CONDENSATION REACTION. BARIUM PERCHLORATE: FORMATION OF HIGHLY EXPLOSIVE PERCHLORIC ESTER ON REFLUXING. CHLORINE: FORMATION OF HIGHLY EXPLOSIVE ALKYL HYPOCHLORITES. DIETHYL ALUMINUM BROMIDE: SPONTANEOUS IGNITION. ETHYLENE OXIDE: POSSIBLE EXPLOSION. HEXAMETHYLENE DIISOCYANATE: POSSIBLE EXPLOSION IN ABSENCE OF SOLVENT. HYDROGEN PEROXIDE + SULFURIC ACID: POSSIBLE EXPLOSION. HYPOCHLOROUS ACID: FORMATION OF HIGHLY EXPLOSIVE ALKYL HYPOCHLORITES. ISOCYANATES: POSSIBLE EXPLOSION IN ABSENCE OF SOLVENT. LITHIUM ALUMINUM HYDRIDE: VIGOROUS REACTION. NITROGEN TETROXIDE: POSSIBLE EXPLOSION. PERCHLORIC ACID (HOT): DANGEROUS INTERACTION. PERMONOSULFURIC ACID: POSSIBLE EXPLOSION ON CONTACT WITH PRIMARY OR SECONDARY ALCOHOLS. TRI-ISO-BUTYL ALUMINUM: VIOLENT REACTION.

DECOMPOSITION: THERMAL DECOMPOSITION PRODUCTS MAY INCLUDE TOXIC OXIDES OF CARBON AND NITROGEN.

POLYMERIZATION: HAZARDOUS POLYMERIZATION HAS NOT BEEN REPORTED TO OCCUR UNDER NORMAL TEMPERATURES AND PRESSURES.

STORAGE AND DISPOSAL

OBSERVE ALL FEDERAL, STATE AND LOCAL REGULATIONS WHEN STORING OR DISPOSING OF THIS SUBSTANCE. FOR ASSISTANCE, CONTACT THE DISTRICT DIRECTOR OF THE ENVIRONMENTAL PROTECTION AGENCY.

STORAGE

STORE AWAY FROM INCOMPATIBLE SUBSTANCES.

CONDITIONS TO AVOID

AVOID CONTACT WITH HEAT, SPARKS, FLAMES, OR OTHER SOURCES OF IGNITION. VAPORS MAY BE EXPLOSIVE AND POISONOUS; DO NOT ALLOW UNNECESSARY PERSONNEL IN AREA. DO NOT OVERHEAT CONTAINERS; CONTAINERS MAY VIOLENTLY RUPTURE AND TRAVEL A CONSIDERABLE DISTANCE IN HEAT OF FIRE.

SPILL AND LEAK PROCEDURES

OCCUPATIONAL SPILL: SHUT OFF IGNITION SOURCES. STOP LEAK IF YOU CAN DO IT WITHOUT RISK. USE WATER SPRAY TO REDUCE VAPORS. FOR SMALL SPILLS, TAKE UP WITH SAND OR OTHER ABSORBENT MATERIAL AND PLACE INTO CONTAINERS FOR LATER DISPOSAL. FOR LARGER SPILLS, DIKE FAR AHEAD OF SPILL FOR LATER DISPOSAL. NO SMOKING, FLAMES OR FLARES IN HAZARD AREA. KEEP UNNECESSARY PEOPLE AWAY; ISOLATE HAZARD AREA AND DENY ENTRY.

PROTECTIVE EQUIPMENT

VENTILATION: PROVIDE LOCAL EXHAUST OR PROCESS ENCLOSURE VENTILATION. VENTILATION EQUIPMENT MUST BE EXPLOSION-PROOF.

RESPIRATOR: THE FOLLOWING RESPIRATORS ARE RECOMMENDED BASED ON INFORMATION FOUND IN THE PHYSICAL DATA, TOXICITY AND HEALTH EFFECTS SECTIONS. THEY ARE RANKED IN ORDER FROM MINIMUM TO MAXIMUM RESPIRATORY PROTECTION. THE SPECIFIC RESPIRATOR SELECTED MUST BE BASED ON CONTAMINATION LEVELS FOUND IN THE WORK PLACE, MUST NOT EXCEED THE WORKING LIMITS OF THE RESPIRATOR AND BE JOINTLY APPROVED BY THE NATIONAL INSTITUTE FOR OCCUPATIONAL SAFETY AND HEALTH AND THE MINE SAFETY AND HEALTH ADMINISTRATION (NIOSH-MSHA).
DUST AND MIST RESPIRATOR WITH A FULL FACEPIECE.
AIR-PURIFYING FULL FACEPIECE RESPIRATOR WITH A HIGH-EFFICIENCY PARTICULATE FILTER.
POWERED AIR-PURIFYING RESPIRATOR WITH A TIGHT-FITTING FACEPIECE AND HIGH-EFFICIENCY PARTICULATE FILTER.
TYPE 'C' SUPPLIED-AIR RESPIRATOR WITH A FULL FACEPIECE OPERATED IN PRESSURE-DEMAND OR OTHER POSITIVE PRESSURE MODE OR WITH A FULL FACEPIECE, HELMET OR HOOD OPERATED IN CONTINUOUS-FLOW MODE.
SELF-CONTAINED BREATHING APPARATUS WITH A FULL FACEPIECE OPERATED IN PRESSURE-DEMAND OR OTHER POSITIVE PRESSURE MODE.
FOR FIREFIGHTING AND OTHER IMMEDIATELY DANGEROUS TO LIFE OR HEALTH CONDITIONS:
SELF-CONTAINED BREATHING APPARATUS WITH FULL FACEPIECE OPERATED IN PRESSURE-DEMAND OR OTHER POSITIVE PRESSURE MODE.
SUPPLIED-AIR RESPIRATOR WITH FULL FACEPIECE AND OPERATED IN PRESSURE-DEMAND OR OTHER POSITIVE PRESSURE MODE IN COMBINATION WITH AN AUXILIARY SELF-CONTAINED BREATHING APPARATUS OPERATED IN PRESSURE-DEMAND OR OTHER POSITIVE PRESSURE MODE.

CLOTHING: EMPLOYEE MUST WEAR APPROPRIATE PROTECTIVE (IMPERVIOUS) CLOTHING AND EQUIPMENT TO PREVENT REPEATED OR PROLONGED SKIN CONTACT WITH THIS SUBSTANCE.

GLOVES: EMPLOYEE MUST WEAR APPROPRIATE PROTECTIVE GLOVES TO PREVENT CONTACT WITH THIS SUBSTANCE.

EYE PROTECTION: EMPLOYEE MUST WEAR SPLASH-PROOF OR DUST-RESISTANT SAFETY GOGGLES TO PREVENT EYE CONTACT WITH THIS SUBSTANCE.
EMERGENCY EYE WASH: WHERE THERE IS ANY POSSIBILITY THAT AN EMPLOYEE'S EYES MAY BE EXPOSED TO THIS SUBSTANCE, THE EMPLOYER SHOULD PROVIDE AN EYE WASH FOUNTAIN WITHIN THE IMMEDIATE WORK AREA FOR EMERGENCY USE.

AUTHORIZED BY- OCCUPATIONAL HEALTH SERVICES, INC.
CREATION DATE: 10/05/89 ***REVISION DATE:*** 05/29/90

MATERIAL SAFETY DATA SHEET

OCCUPATIONAL HEALTH SERVICES, INC.
AGRICULTURE AND PESTICIDE DIVISION
450 SEVENTH AVENUE, SUITE 2407
NEW YORK, NEW YORK 10123
1-800-445-MSDS OR (212) 967-1100

EMERGENCY CONTACT:
JOHN S. BRANSFORD, JR. (615) 292-1180

SUBSTANCE IDENTIFICATION

CAS-NUMBER 3347-22-6

SUBSTANCE: **DITHIANON**

TRADE NAMES/SYNONYMS: NAPHTHO(2,3-B)-1,4-DITHIIN-2,3-DICARBONITRILE, 5,10-DIHYDRO-5, 10-DIOXO-; 5,10-DIHYDRO-5,10-DIOXONAPHTHO(2,3-B)-1,4-DITHIIN-2,3-DICARBONITRILE; NAPHTHO(2,3-B)-P-DITHIIN-2,3-DICARBONITRILE, 5,10-DIHYDRO-5,10-DIOXO-; 5,10-DIHYDRO-5,10-DIOXONAPHTHO(2,3-B)-P-DITHIIN-2,3-DICARBONITRILE; 1,4-DITHIAANTHRAQUINONE-2,3-DICARBONITRILE; 2,3-DICYANO-1,4-DITHIAANTHRAQUINONE; DELAN; DELAN-COL; DITHIANONE; MV 119A; IT-931; C14H4N2O2S2; PST72290

CHEMICAL FAMILY: NITRILE, ALICYCLIC HETEROCYCLIC SULFUR

MOLECULAR FORMULA: C14-H4-N2-O2-S2

MOLECULAR WEIGHT: 296.32

CERCLA RATINGS (SCALE 0-3): HEALTH=3 FIRE=1 REACTIVITY=0 PERSISTENCE=3

NFPA RATINGS (SCALE 0-4): HEALTH=3 FIRE=1 REACTIVITY=0

COMPONENTS AND CONTAMINANTS

COMPONENT: DITHIANON ***PERCENT:*** 100
CAS# 3347-22-6

OTHER CONTAMINANTS: NONE

EXPOSURE LIMITS: NO OCCUPATIONAL EXPOSURE LIMITS ESTABLISHED BY OSHA, ACGIH, OR NIOSH.

PHYSICAL DATA

DESCRIPTION: GRAY-BROWN NEEDLES OR CRYSTALS.

MELTING POINT: 428 F (220 C)

SPECIFIC GRAVITY: NOT AVAILABLE ***VAPOR PRESSURE:*** NEGLIGIBLE

SOLUBILITY IN WATER: 0.05 PPM @ 25 C

SOLVENT SOLUBILITY: SOLUBLE IN DIOXANE, CHLOROFORM, ACETONE, BENZENE, ACETONITRILE, CHLOROBENZENE.

FIRE AND EXPLOSION DATA

FIRE AND EXPLOSION HAZARD: SLIGHT FIRE HAZARD WHEN EXPOSED TO HEAT OR FLAME.

FIREFIGHTING MEDIA: DRY CHEMICAL, CARBON DIOXIDE, HALON, WATER SPRAY OR STANDARD FOAM (1987 EMERGENCY RESPONSE GUIDEBOOK, DOT P 5800.4).
FOR LARGER FIRES, USE WATER SPRAY, FOG OR STANDARD FOAM (1987 EMERGENCY RESPONSE GUIDEBOOK, DOT P 5800.4).

FIREFIGHTING: MOVE CONTAINERS FROM FIRE AREA IF POSSIBLE (1987 EMERGENCY RESPONSE GUIDEBOOK, DOT P 5800.4, GUIDE PAGE 53).
EXTINGUISH FIRE USING AGENTS SUITABLE FOR TYPE OF SURROUNDING FIRE. USE WATER IN FLOODING AMOUNTS AS A FOG. AVOID BREATHING DUSTS AND FUMES FROM BURNING MATERIAL; KEEP UPWIND.

TOXICITY

DITHIANON: TOXICITY DATA: 638 MG/KG ORAL-RAT LD50; 1140 MG/KG ORAL-MOUSE LD50; 110 MG/KG ORAL-GUINEA PIG LD50; 1015 MG/KG UNREPORTED-RAT LD50. CARCINOGEN STATUS: NONE. ACUTE TOXICITY LEVEL: MODERATELY TOXIC BY INGESTION. TARGET EFFECTS: NO DATA AVAILABLE.

HEALTH EFFECTS AND FIRST AID

INHALATION: DITHIANON: **ACUTE EXPOSURE-** NO DATA AVAILABLE. **CHRONIC EXPOSURE-** NO DATA AVAILABLE.

FIRST AID- REMOVE FROM EXPOSURE AREA TO FRESH AIR IMMEDIATELY. IF BREATHING HAS STOPPED, PERFORM ARTIFICIAL RESPIRATION. KEEP PERSON WARM AND AT REST. TREAT SYMPTOMATICALLY AND SUPPORTIVELY. GET MEDICAL ATTENTION IMMEDIATELY.

SKIN CONTACT: DITHIANON: **ACUTE EXPOSURE-** NO DATA AVAILABLE. **CHRONIC EXPOSURE-** NO DATA AVAILABLE.

FIRST AID- REMOVE CONTAMINATED CLOTHING AND SHOES IMMEDIATELY. WASH AFFECTED AREA WITH SOAP OR MILD DETERGENT AND LARGE AMOUNTS OF WATER UNTIL NO EVIDENCE OF CHEMICAL REMAINS (APPROXIMATELY 15-20 MINUTES). GET MEDICAL ATTENTION IMMEDIATELY.

EYE CONTACT: DITHIANON: **ACUTE EXPOSURE-** NO DATA AVAILABLE. **CHRONIC EXPOSURE-** NO DATA AVAILABLE.

FIRST AID- WASH EYES IMMEDIATELY WITH LARGE AMOUNTS OF WATER OR NORMAL SALINE, OCCASIONALLY LIFTING UPPER AND LOWER LIDS, UNTIL NO EVIDENCE OF CHEMICAL REMAINS (APPROXIMATELY 15-20 MINUTES). GET MEDICAL ATTENTION IMMEDIATELY.

INGESTION: DITHIANON: **ACUTE EXPOSURE-** A LETHAL DOSE IN RATS WAS 638 MG/KG. **CHRONIC EXPOSURE-** IN 2-YEAR FEEDING STUDIES, NO ADVERSE EFFECTS WERE OBSERVED IN RATS AT 20 MG/KG AND DOGS AT 40 MG/KG.

FIRST AID- REMOVE BY GASTRIC LAVAGE AND CATHARSIS. MAINTAIN BLOOD PRESSURE AND AIRWAY. GIVE OXYGEN IF RESPIRATION IS DEPRESSED. DO NOT PERFORM GASTRIC LAVAGE IF VICTIM IS UNCONSCIOUS. GET MEDICAL ATTENTION IMMEDIATELY (DREISBACH, HANDBOOK OF POISONING, 12TH ED.).
ADMINISTRATION OF LAVAGE OR OXYGEN SHOULD BE PERFORMED BY QUALIFIED MEDICAL PERSONNEL.

ANTIDOTE: NO SPECIFIC ANTIDOTE. TREAT SYMPTOMATICALLY AND SUPPORTIVELY.

REACTIVITY

REACTIVITY: STABLE UNDER NORMAL TEMPERATURES AND PRESSURES.

INCOMPATIBILITIES: DITHIANON: OIL MISTS: INCOMPATIBLE.

DECOMPOSITION: THERMAL DECOMPOSITION PRODUCTS MAY INCLUDE HIGHLY TOXIC FUMES OF HYDROGEN CYANIDE, HYDROGEN SULFIDE AND TOXIC OXIDES OF NITROGEN, SULFUR, AND CARBON.

POLYMERIZATION: HAZARDOUS POLYMERIZATION HAS NOT BEEN REPORTED TO OCCUR UNDER NORMAL TEMPERATURES AND PRESSURES.

STORAGE AND DISPOSAL

OBSERVE ALL FEDERAL, STATE AND LOCAL REGULATIONS WHEN STORING OR DISPOSING OF THIS SUBSTANCE. FOR ASSISTANCE, CONTACT THE DISTRICT DIRECTOR OF THE ENVIRONMENTAL PROTECTION AGENCY.

STORAGE

STORE IN ACCORDANCE WITH 40 CFR 165 RECOMMENDED PROCEDURES FOR THE DISPOSAL AND STORAGE OF PESTICIDES AND PESTICIDE CONTAINERS.

DISPOSAL

DISPOSAL MUST BE IN ACCORDANCE WITH 40 CFR 165 RECOMMENDED PROCEDURES FOR THE DISPOSAL AND STORAGE OF PESTICIDES AND PESTICIDE CONTAINERS.

CONDITIONS TO AVOID

MAY BURN BUT DOES NOT IGNITE READILY.

SPILL AND LEAK PROCEDURES

OCCUPATIONAL SPILL: DO NOT TOUCH SPILLED MATERIAL. STOP LEAK IF YOU CAN DO IT WITHOUT RISK. FOR SMALL SPILLS, TAKE UP WITH SAND OR OTHER ABSORBENT MATERIAL AND PLACE INTO CONTAINERS FOR LATER DISPOSAL. FOR SMALL DRY SPILLS, WITH A CLEAN SHOVEL PLACE MATERIAL INTO CLEAN, DRY CONTAINER AND COVER. MOVE CONTAINERS FROM SPILL AREA. FOR LARGER SPILLS, DIKE FAR AHEAD OF SPILL FOR LATER DISPOSAL. KEEP UNNECESSARY PEOPLE AWAY. ISOLATE HAZARD AREA AND DENY ENTRY.

PROTECTIVE EQUIPMENT

VENTILATION: PROVIDE LOCAL EXHAUST OR GENERAL DILUTION VENTILATION SYSTEM.

RESPIRATOR: THE FOLLOWING RESPIRATORS ARE RECOMMENDED BASED ON INFORMATION FOUND IN THE PHYSICAL DATA, TOXICITY AND HEALTH EFFECTS SECTIONS. THEY ARE RANKED IN ORDER FROM MINIMUM TO MAXIMUM RESPIRATORY PROTECTION. THE SPECIFIC RESPIRATOR SELECTED MUST BE BASED ON CONTAMINATION LEVELS FOUND IN THE WORK PLACE, MUST NOT EXCEED THE WORKING LIMITS OF THE RESPIRATOR AND BE JOINTLY APPROVED BY THE NATIONAL INSTITUTE FOR OCCUPATIONAL SAFETY AND HEALTH AND THE MINE SAFETY AND HEALTH ADMINISTRATION (NIOSH-MSHA).
CHEMICAL CARTRIDGE RESPIRATOR WITH AN ORGANIC VAPOR CARTRIDGE(S) WITH A FULL FACEPIECE AND ORGANIC VAPOR CARTRIDGE(S) IN COMBINATION WITH A DUST AND MIST FILTER.
POWERED AIR-PURIFYING RESPIRATOR WITH A TIGHT-FITTING FACEPIECE AND ORGANIC VAPOR CARTRIDGE(S) IN COMBINATION WITH A HIGH-EFFICIENCY PARTICULATE FILTER.
TYPE 'C' SUPPLIED-AIR RESPIRATOR WITH A FULL FACEPIECE OPERATED IN A PRESSURE-DEMAND OR OTHER POSITIVE PRESSURE MODE.
SELF-CONTAINED BREATHING APPARATUS WITH A FULL FACEPIECE OPERATED IN PRESSURE-DEMAND OR OTHER POSITIVE PRESSURE MODE.
FOR FIREFIGHTING AND OTHER IMMEDIATELY DANGEROUS TO LIFE OR HEALTH CONDITIONS:
SELF-CONTAINED BREATHING APPARATUS WITH FULL FACEPIECE OPERATED IN PRESSURE-DEMAND OR OTHER POSITIVE PRESSURE MODE.
SUPPLIED-AIR RESPIRATOR WITH FULL FACEPIECE AND OPERATED IN PRESSURE-DEMAND OR OTHER POSITIVE PRESSURE MODE IN COMBINATION WITH AN AUXILIARY SELF-CONTAINED BREATHING APPARATUS OPERATED IN PRESSURE-DEMAND OR OTHER POSITIVE PRESSURE MODE.

CLOTHING: EMPLOYEE MUST WEAR APPROPRIATE PROTECTIVE (IMPERVIOUS) CLOTHING AND EQUIPMENT TO PREVENT REPEATED OR PROLONGED SKIN CONTACT WITH THIS SUBSTANCE.

GLOVES: EMPLOYEE MUST WEAR APPROPRIATE PROTECTIVE GLOVES TO PREVENT CONTACT WITH THIS SUBSTANCE.

EYE PROTECTION: EMPLOYEE MUST WEAR SPLASH-PROOF OR DUST-RESISTANT SAFETY GOGGLES TO PREVENT EYE CONTACT WITH THIS SUBSTANCE. EMERGENCY EYE WASH: WHERE THERE IS ANY POSSIBILITY THAT AN EMPLOYEE'S EYES MAY BE EXPOSED TO THIS SUBSTANCE, THE EMPLOYER SHOULD PROVIDE AN EYE WASH FOUNTAIN WITHIN THE IMMEDIATE WORK AREA FOR EMERGENCY USE.

AUTHORIZED BY- OCCUPATIONAL HEALTH SERVICES, INC.
CREATION DATE: 10/04/89 ***REVISION DATE:*** 05/11/90

MATERIAL SAFETY DATA SHEET

OCCUPATIONAL HEALTH SERVICES, INC.
AGRICULTURE AND PESTICIDE DIVISION
450 SEVENTH AVENUE, SUITE 2407
NEW YORK, NEW YORK 10123
1-800-445-MSDS OR (212) 967-1100

EMERGENCY CONTACT:
JOHN S. BRANSFORD, JR. (615) 292-1180

SUBSTANCE IDENTIFICATION

CAS-NUMBER 16672-87-0

SUBSTANCE: **ETHEPHON**

TRADE NAMES/SYNONYMS: PHOSPHONIC ACID, (2-CHLOROETHYL)-; (2-CHLOROETHYL)PHOSPHONIC ACID; 2-CHLORETHANEPHOSPHONIC ACID; CHLOROETHYLPHOSPHONIC ACID; 2-CHLOROETHYLPHOSPHONIC ACID; BETA-CHLOROETHYLPHOSPHONIC ACID; CAMPOSAN; CEPA; CHLORETHEPHON; ETHEFON; ETHREL; FLORDIMEX; FLOREL; C2H6CLO3; PST72293

CHEMICAL FAMILY: HALOGEN INORGANIC ACID

MOLECULAR FORMULA: CL-C-H2-C-H2-P-(O)-(O-H)2

MOLECULAR WEIGHT: 144.49

CERCLA RATINGS (SCALE 0-3): HEALTH=3 FIRE=1 REACTIVITY=1 PERSISTENCE=3

NFPA RATINGS (SCALE 0-4): HEALTH=4 FIRE=1 REACTIVITY=1

COMPONENTS AND CONTAMINANTS

COMPONENT: ETHEPHON ***PERCENT:*** 100.0
CAS# 16672-87-0

OTHER CONTAMINANTS: NONE

EXPOSURE LIMITS: NO OCCUPATIONAL EXPOSURE LIMITS ESTABLISHED BY OSHA, ACGIH, OR NIOSH.

PHYSICAL DATA

DESCRIPTION: WHITE HYGROSCOPIC CRYSTALS OR WAXY SOLID.

MELTING POINT: 165-167 F (74-75 C) ***SPECIFIC GRAVITY:*** 1.58

SOLUBILITY IN WATER: 100%

SOLVENT SOLUBILITY: SOLUBLE IN METHANOL, ACETONE, ETHYLENE GLYCOL, AND PROPYLENE GLYCOL; SLIGHTLY SOLUBLE IN BENZENE AND TOLUENE; ALMOST INSOLUBLE IN PETROLEUM ETHER; INSOLUBLE IN KEROSENE AND DIESEL OIL.

FIRE AND EXPLOSION DATA

FIRE AND EXPLOSION HAZARD: SLIGHT FIRE HAZARD WHEN EXPOSED TO HEAT OR FLAME.

FIREFIGHTING MEDIA: DRY CHEMICAL, CARBON DIOXIDE, HALON, WATER SPRAY OR STANDARD FOAM (1987 EMERGENCY RESPONSE GUIDEBOOK, DOT P 5800.4). FOR LARGER FIRES, USE WATER SPRAY, FOG OR STANDARD FOAM (1987 EMERGENCY RESPONSE GUIDEBOOK, DOT P 5800.4).

FIREFIGHTING: MOVE CONTAINERS FROM FIRE AREA IF POSSIBLE. FIGHT FIRE FROM MAXIMUM DISTANCE. STAY AWAY FROM STORAGE TANK ENDS. DIKE FIRE CONTROL WATER FOR LATER DISPOSAL. DO NOT SCATTER MATERIAL (1987 EMERGENCY RESPONSE GUIDEBOOK, DOT P 5800.4, GUIDE PAGE 55). EXTINGUISH ONLY IF FLOW CAN BE STOPPED; USE FLOODING AMOUNTS OF WATER AS FOG, SOLID STREAMS MAY BE INEFFECTIVE. COOL CONTAINERS WITH FLOODING AMOUNTS OF WATER FROM AS FAR A DISTANCE AS POSSIBLE. USE WATER SPRAY TO ABSORB TOXIC VAPORS. AVOID BREATHING TOXIC VAPORS; KEEP UPWIND. CONSIDER EVACUATION OF DOWNWIND AREA IF MATERIAL IS LEAKING.

TRANSPORTATION DATA

DEPARTMENT OF TRANSPORTATION HAZARD CLASSIFICATION 49 CFR 172.101: POISON B
DEPARTMENT OF TRANSPORTATION LABELING REQUIREMENTS 49 CFR 172.101 AND SUBPART E: POISON
DEPARTMENT OF TRANSPORTATION PACKAGING REQUIREMENTS: 49 CFR 173.365
EXCEPTIONS: 49 CFR 173.364

TOXICITY

ETHEPHON: TOXICITY DATA: 90 MG/M3/4 HOURS INHALATION-RAT LC50; 5730 MG/KG SKIN-RABBIT LD50; 3400 MG/KG ORAL-RAT LD50; 2850 MG/KG ORAL-MOUSE LD50; 5000 MG/KG ORAL-RABBIT LD50; 4200 MG/KG ORAL-GUINEA PIG LD50; 4200 MG/KG UNREPORTED-MAMMAL LD50. CARCINOGEN STATUS: NONE. ACUTE TOXICITY: HIGHLY TOXIC BY INHALATION; MODERATELY TOXIC BY INGESTION; SLIGHTLY TOXIC BY DERMAL ABSORPTION. TARGET EFFECTS: NO DATA AVAILABLE.

HEALTH EFFECTS AND FIRST AID

INHALATION: ETHEPHON: HIGHLY TOXIC. **ACUTE EXPOSURE-** MAY CAUSE MUCOUS MEMBRANE IRRITATION. A LETHAL CONCENTRATION IN RATS WAS 90 MG/M3/4 HOURS. **CHRONIC EXPOSURE-** NO DATA AVAILABLE.

FIRST AID- REMOVE FROM EXPOSURE AREA TO FRESH AIR IMMEDIATELY. IF BREATHING HAS STOPPED, PERFORM ARTIFICIAL RESPIRATION. KEEP PERSON WARM AND AT REST. TREAT SYMPTOMATICALLY AND SUPPORTIVELY. GET MEDICAL ATTENTION IMMEDIATELY.

SKIN CONTACT: ETHEPHON: **ACUTE EXPOSURE-** MAY CAUSE IRRITATION. **CHRONIC EXPOSURE-** NO DATA AVAILABLE.

FIRST AID- REMOVE CONTAMINATED CLOTHING AND SHOES IMMEDIATELY. WASH AFFECTED AREA WITH SOAP OR MILD DETERGENT AND LARGE AMOUNTS OF WATER UNTIL NO EVIDENCE OF CHEMICAL REMAINS (APPROXIMATELY 15-20 MINUTES). GET MEDICAL ATTENTION IMMEDIATELY.

EYE CONTACT: ETHEPHON: **ACUTE EXPOSURE-** MAY CAUSE IRRITATION. **CHRONIC EXPOSURE-** NO DATA AVAILABLE.

FIRST AID- WASH EYES IMMEDIATELY WITH LARGE AMOUNTS OF WATER OR NORMAL SALINE, OCCASIONALLY LIFTING UPPER AND LOWER LIDS, UNTIL NO EVIDENCE OF CHEMICAL REMAINS (APPROXIMATELY 15-20 MINUTES). GET MEDICAL ATTENTION IMMEDIATELY.

INGESTION: ETHEPHON: **ACUTE EXPOSURE-** A LETHAL DOSE IN RATS WAS 3400 MG/KG; SYMPTOMS WERE NOT REPORTED. **CHRONIC EXPOSURE-** NO DATA AVAILABLE.

FIRST AID- IF THE PERSON IS CONSCIOUS AND NOT CONVULSING, REMOVE BY GASTRIC LAVAGE AND FOLLOW WITH A CATHARTIC (DREISBACH, HANDBOOK OF POISONING, 12TH ED.). TREAT SYMPTOMATICALLY AND SUPPORTIVELY. GASTRIC LAVAGE SHOULD BE PERFORMED BY QUALIFIED MEDICAL PERSONNEL. GET MEDICAL ATTENTION IMMEDIATELY.

ANTIDOTE: NO SPECIFIC ANTIDOTE. TREAT SYMPTOMATICALLY AND SUPPORTIVELY.

REACTIVITY

REACTIVITY: DECOMPOSES IN SOLUTION ABOVE PH 3.5 LIBERATING ETHYLENE GAS.

INCOMPATIBILITIES: ETHEPHON: OXIDIZERS (STRONG): FIRE AND EXPLOSION HAZARD.

DECOMPOSITION: THERMAL DECOMPOSITION PRODUCTS MAY INCLUDE TOXIC ANC CORROSIVE FUMES OF CHLORIDES AND TOXIC OXIDES OF PHOSPHORUS.

POLYMERIZATION: HAZARDOUS POLYMERIZATION HAS NOT BEEN REPORTED TO OCCUR UNDER NORMAL TEMPERATURES AND PRESSURES.

STORAGE AND DISPOSAL

OBSERVE ALL FEDERAL, STATE AND LOCAL REGULATIONS WHEN STORING OR DISPOSING OF THIS SUBSTANCE. FOR ASSISTANCE, CONTACT THE DISTRICT DIRECTOR OF THE ENVIRONMENTAL PROTECTION AGENCY.

****STORAGE****

STORE IN ACCORDANCE WITH 40 CFR 165 RECOMMENDED PROCEDURES FOR THE DISPOSAL AND STORAGE OF PESTICIDES AND PESTICIDE CONTAINERS. STORE AWAY FROM INCOMPATIBLE SUBSTANCES.

****DISPOSAL****

DISPOSAL MUST BE IN ACCORDANCE WITH 40 CFR 165 RECOMMENDED PROCEDURES FOR THE DISPOSAL AND STORAGE OF PESTICIDES AND PESTICIDE CONTAINERS.

CONDITIONS TO AVOID

MAY BURN BUT DOES NOT IGNITE READILY. CONTAINERS MAY EXPLODE IN HEAT OF FIRE.

SPILL AND LEAK PROCEDURES

OCCUPATIONAL SPILL: DO NOT TOUCH SPILLED MATERIAL. STOP LEAK IF YOU CAN DO IT WITHOUT RISK. USE WATER SPRAY TO REDUCE VAPORS. FOR SMALL SPILLS, TAKE UP WITH SAND OR OTHER ABSORBENT MATERIAL AND PLACE INTO CONTAINERS FOR LATER DISPOSAL. FOR SMALL DRY SPILLS, WITH A CLEAN SHOVEL PLACE MATERIAL INTO CLEAN, DRY CONTAINERS AND COVER. MOVE CONTAINERS FROM SPILL AREA. FOR LARGER SPILLS, DIKE FAR AHEAD OF SPILL FOR LATER DISPOSAL. KEEP UNNECESSARY PEOPLE AWAY. ISOLATE HAZARD AREA AND DENY ENTRY. VENTILATE CLOSED SPACES BEFORE ENTERING.

PROTECTIVE EQUIPMENT

VENTILATION: PROVIDE LOCAL EXHAUST VENTILATION SYSTEM.

RESPIRATOR: THE FOLLOWING RESPIRATORS ARE RECOMMENDED BASED ON INFORMATION FOUND IN THE PHYSICAL DATA, TOXICITY AND HEALTH EFFECTS SECTIONS. THEY ARE RANKED IN ORDER FROM MINIMUM TO MAXIMUM RESPIRATORY PROTECTION. THE SPECIFIC RESPIRATOR SELECTED MUST BE BASED ON CONTAMINATION LEVELS FOUND IN THE WORK PLACE, MUST NOT EXCEED THE WORKING LIMITS OF THE RESPIRATOR AND BE JOINTLY APPROVED BY THE NATIONAL INSTITUTE FOR OCCUPATIONAL SAFETY AND HEALTH AND THE MINE SAFETY AND HEALTH ADMINISTRATION (NIOSH-MSHA).

TYPE 'C' SUPPLIED-AIR RESPIRATOR WITH A FULL FACEPIECE OPERATED IN PRESSURE-DEMAND OR OTHER POSITIVE PRESSURE MODE OR WITH A FULL FACEPIECE, HELMET OR HOOD OPERATED IN CONTINOUS-FLOW MODE.

SELF-CONTAINED BREATHING APPARATUS WITH A FULL FACEPIECE OPERATED IN PRESSURE-DEMAND OR OTHER POSITIVE PRESSURE MODE.

FOR FIREFIGHTING AND OTHER IMMEDIATELY DANGEROUS TO LIFE OR HEALTH CONDITIONS:

SELF-CONTAINED BREATHING APPARATUS WITH FULL FACEPIECE OPERATED IN PRESSURE-DEMAND OR OTHER POSITIVE PRESSURE MODE.

SUPPLIED-AIR RESPIRATOR WITH FULL FACEPIECE AND OPERATED IN PRESSURE-DEMAND OR OTHER POSITIVE PRESSURE MODE IN COMBINATION WITH AN AUXILIARY SELF-CONTAINED BREATHING APPARATUS OPERATED IN PRESSURE-DEMAND OR OTHER POSITIVE PRESSURE MODE.

CLOTHING: EMPLOYEE MUST WEAR APPROPRIATE PROTECTIVE (IMPERVIOUS) CLOTHING AND EQUIPMENT TO PREVENT ANY POSSIBILITY OF SKIN CONTACT WITH THIS SUBSTANCE.

GLOVES: EMPLOYEE MUST WEAR APPROPRIATE PROTECTIVE GLOVES TO PREVENT CONTACT WITH THIS SUBSTANCE.

EYE PROTECTION: EMPLOYEE MUST WEAR SPLASH-PROOF OR DUST-RESISTANT SAFETY GOGGLES WITH OR WITHOUT A FACESHIELD TO PREVENT CONTACT WITH THIS SUBSTANCE.

EMERGENCY EYE WASH: WHERE THERE IS ANY POSSIBILITY THAT AN EMPLOYEE'S EYES MAY BE EXPOSED TO THIS SUBSTANCE, THE EMPLOYER SHOULD PROVIDE AN EYE WASH FOUNTAIN WITHIN THE IMMEDIATE WORK AREA FOR EMERGENCY USE.

AUTHORIZED BY- OCCUPATIONAL HEALTH SERVICES, INC.
CREATION DATE: 10/04/89 ***REVISION DATE:*** 05/08/90

MATERIAL SAFETY DATA SHEET

OCCUPATIONAL HEALTH SERVICES, INC.
AGRICULTURE AND PESTICIDE DIVISION
450 SEVENTH AVENUE, SUITE 2407
NEW YORK, NEW YORK 10123
1-800-445-MSDS OR (212) 967-1100

EMERGENCY CONTACT:
JOHN S. BRANSFORD, JR. (615) 292-1180

SUBSTANCE IDENTIFICATION

CAS-NUMBER 26530-20-1

SUBSTANCE: **2-N-OCTYL-4-ISOTHIAZOLIN-3-ONE**

TRADE NAMES/SYNONYMS: 3(2H)-ISOTHIAZOLONE, 2-OCTYL-; 2-OCTYL-3(2H)-ISOTHIAZOLONE; 4-ISOTHIAZOLIN-3-ONE, 2-OCTYL-; 2-OCTYL-4-ISOTHIAZOLIN-3-ONE; 4-ISOTHIAZOLIN-3-ONE, 2-N-OCTYL-; MICRO-CHEK 11; OCTHILINONE; C11H19NOS; PST72294

CHEMICAL FAMILY: ISOTHIAZOLONE

MOLECULAR FORMULA: C11-H19-N-O-S

MOLECULAR WEIGHT: 213.34

CERCLA RATINGS (SCALE 0-3): HEALTH=3 FIRE=U REACTIVITY=0 PERSISTENCE=1

NFPA RATINGS (SCALE 0-4): HEALTH=U FIRE=U REACTIVITY=0

COMPONENTS AND CONTAMINANTS

COMPONENT: 2-N-OCTYL-4-ISOTHIAZOLIN-3-ONE ***PERCENT:*** 100.0
CAS# 26530-20-1

OTHER CONTAMINANTS: NONE

EXPOSURE LIMITS: NO OCCUPATIONAL EXPOSURE LIMITS ESTABLISHED BY OSHA, ACGIH, OR NIOSH.

PHYSICAL DATA

DESCRIPTION: LIQUID. ***BOILING POINT:*** 248 F (120 C) @ 0.01 MMHG

SPECIFIC GRAVITY: NOT AVAILABLE ***SOLUBILITY IN WATER:*** NOT AVAILABLE

FIRE AND EXPLOSION DATA

FIRE AND EXPLOSION HAZARD: SLIGHT FIRE HAZARD WHEN EXPOSED TO HEAT OR FLAME.

FLASH POINT: NOT AVAILABLE

FIREFIGHTING MEDIA: DRY CHEMICAL, CARBON DIOXIDE, HALON, WATER SPRAY OR ALCOHOL FOAM (1987 EMERGENCY RESPONSE GUIDEBOOK, DOT P 5800.4). FOR LARGER FIRES, USE WATER SPRAY, FOG OR ALCOHOL FOAM (1987 EMERGENCY RESPONSE GUIDEBOOK, DOT P 5800.4).

FIREFIGHTING: MOVE CONTAINER FROM FIRE AREA IF POSSIBLE. COOL FIRE-EXPOSED CONTAINERS WITH WATER FROM SIDE UNTIL WELL AFTER FIRE IS OUT. STAY AWAY FROM STORAGE TANK ENDS. FOR MASSIVE FIRE IN STORAGE AREA, USE UNMANNED HOSE HOLDER OR MONITOR NOZZLES, ELSE WITHDRAW FROM AREA AND LET FIRE BURN. WITHDRAW IMMEDIATELY IN CASE OF RISING SOUND FROM VENTING SAFETY DEVICE OR ANY DISCOLORATION OF STORAGE TANK DUE TO FIRE (1987 EMERGENCY RESPONSE GUIDEBOOK, DOT P 5800.4, GUIDE PAGE 26). EXTINGUISH ONLY IF FLOW CAN BE STOPPED. USE FLOODING AMOUNTS OF WATER AS A FOG; SOLID STREAMS MAY BE INEFFECTIVE. COOL CONTAINERS WITH FLOODING AMOUNTS OF WATER, APPLY FROM AS FAR A DISTANCE AS POSSIBLE. AVOID BREATHING HAZARDOUS VAPORS, KEEP UPWIND.

TOXICITY

2-N-OCTYL-4-ISOTHIAZOLIN-3-ONE: IRRITATION DATA: 500 MG/24 HOURS SKIN-RABBIT; 100 MG EYE-RABBIT SEVERE. TOXICITY DATA: 690 MG/KG SKIN-RABBIT LD50; 550 MG/KG ORAL-RAT LD50. CARCINOGEN STATUS: NONE. LOCAL EFFECTS: IRRITANT- SKIN, EYES. ACUTE TOXICITY LEVEL: TOXIC BY DERMAL ABSORPTION; MODERATELY TOXIC BY INGESTION. TARGET EFFECTS: NO DATA AVAILABLE.

HEALTH EFFECTS AND FIRST AID

INHALATION: 2-N-OCTYL-4-ISOTHIAZOLIN-3-ONE: **ACUTE EXPOSURE**- NO DATA AVAILABLE. **CHRONIC EXPOSURE**- NO DATA AVAILABLE.

FIRST AID- REMOVE FROM EXPOSURE AREA TO FRESH AIR IMMEDIATELY. IF BREATHING HAS STOPPED, PERFORM ARTIFICIAL RESPIRATION. KEEP PERSON WARM AND AT REST. TREAT SYMPTOMATICALLY AND SUPPORTIVELY. GET MEDICAL ATTENTION IMMEDIATELY.

SKIN CONTACT: 2-N-OCTYL-4-ISOTHIAZOLIN-3-ONE: IRRITANT/TOXIC. **ACUTE EXPOSURE**- CONTACT PRODUCED IRRITATION IN RABBIT SKIN. DEATH OCCURRED DUE TO SKIN ABSORPTION IN RABBITS. **CHRONIC EXPOSURE**- REPEATED OR PROLONGED EXPOSURE TO IRRITANTS MAY CAUSE DERMATITIS.

FIRST AID- REMOVE CONTAMINATED CLOTHING AND SHOES IMMEDIATELY. WASH AFFECTED AREA WITH SOAP OR MILD DETERGENT AND LARGE AMOUNTS OF WATER UNTIL NO EVIDENCE OF CHEMICAL REMAINS (APPROXIMATELY 15-20 MINUTES). GET MEDICAL ATTENTION IMMEDIATELY.

EYE CONTACT: 2-N-OCTYL-4-ISOTHIAZOLIN-3-ONE: IRRITANT. **ACUTE EXPOSURE**- CONTACT WITH RABBIT EYES PRODUCED SEVERE IRRITATION. **CHRONIC EXPOSURE**- REPEATED OR PROLONGED EXPOSURE TO IRRITANTS MAY CAUSE CONJUNCTIVITIS.

FIRST AID- WASH EYES IMMEDIATELY WITH LARGE AMOUNTS OF WATER OR NORMAL SALINE, OCCASIONALLY LIFTING UPPER AND LOWER LIDS, UNTIL NO EVIDENCE OF CHEMICAL REMAINS (APPROXIMATELY 15-20 MINUTES). GET MEDICAL ATTENTION IMMEDIATELY.

INGESTION: 2-N-OCTYL-4-ISOTHIAZOLIN-3-ONE: **ACUTE EXPOSURE**- NO DATA AVAILABLE. **CHRONIC EXPOSURE**- NO DATA AVAILABLE.

FIRST AID- IF EXTENSIVE VOMITING HAS NOT OCCURRED, THE SUBSTANCE SHOULD BE REMOVED BY EMESIS OR GASTRIC LAVAGE PROVIDED THAT THE PATIENT IS CONSCIOUS AND CONVULSIONS ARE NOT PRESENT. KEEP HEAD BELOW HIPS DURING VOMITING TO PREVENT ASPIRATION. DO NOT ATTEMPT TO MAKE AN UNCONSCIOUS PERSON VOMIT. TREAT SYMPTOMATICALLY AND SUPPORTIVELY. GET MEDICAL ATTENTION IMMEDIATELY (DREISBACH, HANDBOOK OF POISONING, 12TH ED.). TREATMENT SHOULD BE PERFORMED BY QUALIFIED MEDICAL PERSONNEL.

AUTHORIZED BY- OCCUPATIONAL HEALTH SERVICES, INC.
CREATION DATE: 10/05/89 ***REVISION DATE:*** 05/10/90

MATERIAL SAFETY DATA SHEET

OCCUPATIONAL HEALTH SERVICES, INC.
AGRICULTURE AND PESTICIDE DIVISION
450 SEVENTH AVENUE, SUITE 2407
NEW YORK, NEW YORK 10123
1-800-445-MSDS OR (212) 967-1100

EMERGENCY CONTACT:
JOHN S. BRANSFORD, JR. (615) 292-1180

SUBSTANCE IDENTIFICATION

CAS-NUMBER 22936-86-3
SUBSTANCE: CYPRAZINE
TRADE NAMES/SYNONYMS: 1,3,5-TRIAZINE-2,4-DIAMINE, 6-CHLORO-N-CYCLOPROPYL-N'-(1-METHYLETHYL)-; S-TRIAZINE, 2-CHLORO-4-(CYCLOPROPYLAMINO)-6-(ISOPROPYLAMINO)-; 6-CHLORO-N-CYCLOPROPYL-N'-(1-METHYLETHYL)-1,3,5-TRIAZINE-2,4-DIAMINE;
2-CHLORO-4-(CYCLOPROPYLAMINO)-6-(ISOPROPYLAMINO)-S-TRIAZINE;
2-CHLORO-4-CYCLOPROPYLAMINO-6-ISOPROPYLAMINO-1,3,5-TRIAZINE;
CYPROZINE; K 6295; OUTFOX; S 6115; C9H14CLN5; PST72296
CHEMICAL FAMILY: S-TRIAZINE
MOLECULAR FORMULA: C9-H14-CL-N5
MOLECULAR WEIGHT: 227.73
CERCLA RATINGS (SCALE 0-3): HEALTH=2 FIRE=1 REACTIVITY=0 PERSISTENCE=3
NFPA RATINGS (SCALE 0-4): HEALTH=2 FIRE=1 REACTIVITY=0

COMPONENTS AND CONTAMINANTS

COMPONENT: CYPRAZINE ***PERCENT:*** 100.0
CAS# 22936-86-3
OTHER CONTAMINANTS: NONE
EXPOSURE LIMITS: NO OCCUPATIONAL EXPOSURE LIMITS ESTABLISHED BY OSHA, ACGIH, OR NIOSH.

PHYSICAL DATA

DESCRIPTION: WHITE CRYSTALLINE SOLID ***MELTING POINT:*** 333-334 F (167-168 C)
SPECIFIC GRAVITY: NOT AVAILABLE ***SOLUBILITY IN WATER:*** 6.9 PPM @ 25 C
SOLVENT SOLUBILITY: SOLUBLE IN ACETIC ACID, ACETONE, DIMETHYLFORMAMIDE, CHLOROFORM, ETHANOL, METHANOL, ETHYL ACETATE, TOLUENE, ACRYLONITRILE, BENZENE, CARBON TETRACHLORIDE; ALMOST INSOLUBLE IN HEXANE.

FIRE AND EXPLOSION DATA

FIRE AND EXPLOSION HAZARD: SLIGHT FIRE HAZARD WHEN EXPOSED TO HEAT OR FLAME.
FIREFIGHTING MEDIA: DRY CHEMICAL, CARBON DIOXIDE, HALON, WATER SPRAY OR STANDARD FOAM (1987 EMERGENCY RESPONSE GUIDEBOOK, DOT P 5800.4).
FOR LARGER FIRES, USE WATER SPRAY, FOG OR STANDARD FOAM (1987 EMERGENCY RESPONSE GUIDEBOOK, DOT P 5800.4).
FIREFIGHTING: MOVE CONTAINERS FROM FIRE AREA IF POSSIBLE (1987 EMERGENCY RESPONSE GUIDEBOOK, DOT P 5800.4, GUIDE PAGE 53).
EXTINGUISH USING AGENTS SUITABLE FOR SURROUNDING FIRE. USE FLOODING QUANTITIES OF WATER AS A FOG. KEEP MATERIAL OUT OF SEWERS AND WATER SOURCES. DO NOT TOUCH SPILLED MATERIAL. AVOID BREATHING HAZARDOUS FUMES; KEEP UPWIND.

TOXICITY

CYPRAZINE: TOXICITY DATA: 7500 MG/KG SKIN-RABBIT LD50; 1200 MG/KG ORAL-RAT LD50. CARCINOGEN STATUS: NONE. ACUTE TOXICITY LEVEL: MODERATELY TOXIC BY INGESTION AND SLIGHTLY TOXIC BY DERMAL ABSORPTION. TARGET EFFECTS: NO DATA AVAILABLE.

HEALTH EFFECTS AND FIRST AID

INHALATION: CYPRAZINE: ACUTE EXPOSURE- SOME TRIAZINES ARE MILDLY IRRITATING TO THE UPPER RESPIRATORY TRACT. CHRONIC EXPOSURE- NO DATA AVAILABLE.
FIRST AID- REMOVE FROM EXPOSURE AREA TO FRESH AIR IMMEDIATELY. IF BREATHING HAS STOPPED, PERFORM ARTIFICIAL RESPIRATION. KEEP PERSON WARM AND AT REST. TREAT SYMPTOMATICALLY AND SUPPORTIVELY. GET MEDICAL ATTENTION IMMEDIATELY.

REACTIVITY

REACTIVITY: STABLE UNDER NORMAL TEMPERATURES AND PRESSURES.
INCOMPATIBILITIES: 2-N-OCTYL-4-ISOTHIAZOLIN-3-ONE: OXIDIZERS (STRONG): FIRE AND EXPLOSION HAZARD. SEE ALSO KETONES.
KETONES: ACETALDEHYDE: VIOLENT CONDENSATION REACTION. NITRIC ACID + HYDROGEN PEROXIDE: FORMATION OF EXPLOSIVE PRODUCT. PERCHLORIC ACID: VIOLENT DECOMPOSITION.
DECOMPOSITION: THERMAL DECOMPOSITION MAY RELEASE TOXIC OXIDES OF NITROGEN AND SULFUR.
POLYMERIZATION: HAZARDOUS POLYMERIZATION HAS NOT BEEN REPORTED TO OCCUR UNDER NORMAL TEMPERATURES AND PRESSURES.

STORAGE AND DISPOSAL

OBSERVE ALL FEDERAL, STATE AND LOCAL REGULATIONS WHEN STORING OR DISPOSING OF THIS SUBSTANCE. FOR ASSISTANCE, CONTACT THE DISTRICT DIRECTOR OF THE ENVIRONMENTAL PROTECTION AGENCY.

STORAGE

STORE IN ACCORDANCE WITH 40 CFR 165 RECOMMENDED PROCEDURES FOR THE DISPOSAL AND STORAGE OF PESTICIDES AND PESTICIDE CONTAINERS.
STORE AWAY FROM INCOMPATIBLE SUBSTANCES.

DISPOSAL

DISPOSAL MUST BE IN ACCORDANCE WITH 40 CFR 165 RECOMMENDED PROCEDURES FOR THE DISPOSAL AND STORAGE OF PESTICIDES AND PESTICIDE CONTAINERS.

CONDITIONS TO AVOID

AVOID CONTACT WITH HEAT, SPARKS, FLAMES, OR OTHER SOURCES OF IGNITION. VAPORS MAY BE EXPLOSIVE AND POISONOUS; DO NOT ALLOW UNNECESSARY PERSONNEL IN AREA. DO NOT OVERHEAT CONTAINERS; CONTAINERS MAY VIOLENTLY RUPTURE AND TRAVEL A CONSIDERABLE DISTANCE IN HEAT OF FIRE.

SPILL AND LEAK PROCEDURES

OCCUPATIONAL SPILL: SHUT OFF IGNITION SOURCES. STOP LEAK IF YOU CAN DO IT WITHOUT RISK. USE WATER SPRAY TO REDUCE VAPORS. FOR SMALL SPILLS, TAKE UP WITH SAND OR OTHER ABSORBENT MATERIAL AND PLACE INTO CONTAINERS FOR LATER DISPOSAL. FOR LARGER SPILLS, DIKE FAR AHEAD OF SPILL FOR LATER DISPOSAL. NO SMOKING, FLAMES OR FLARES IN HAZARD AREA. KEEP UNNECESSARY PEOPLE AWAY; ISOLATE HAZARD AREA AND DENY ENTRY.

PROTECTIVE EQUIPMENT

VENTILATION: PROVIDE LOCAL EXHAUST OR PROCESS ENCLOSURE VENTILATION. VENTILATION EQUIPMENT MUST BE EXPLOSION-PROOF.
RESPIRATOR: THE FOLLOWING RESPIRATORS ARE RECOMMENDED BASED ON INFORMATION FOUND IN THE PHYSICAL DATA, TOXICITY AND HEALTH EFFECTS SECTIONS. THEY ARE RANKED IN ORDER FROM MINIMUM TO MAXIMUM RESPIRATORY PROTECTION. THE SPECIFIC RESPIRATOR SELECTED MUST BE BASED ON CONTAMINATION LEVELS FOUND IN THE WORK PLACE, MUST NOT EXCEED THE WORKING LIMITS OF THE RESPIRATOR AND BE JOINTLY APPROVED BY THE NATIONAL INSTITUTE FOR OCCUPATIONAL SAFETY AND HEALTH AND THE MINE SAFETY AND HEALTH ADMINISTRATION (NIOSH-MSHA).
TYPE 'C' SUPPLIED-AIR RESPIRATOR WITH A FULL FACEPIECE OPERATED IN PRESSURE-DEMAND OR OTHER POSITIVE PRESSURE MODE OR WITH A FULL FACEPIECE, HELMET OR HOOD OPERATED IN CONTINOUS-FLOW MODE.
SELF-CONTAINED BREATHING APPARATUS WITH A FULL FACEPIECE OPERATED IN PRESSURE-DEMAND OR OTHER POSITIVE PRESSURE MODE.
FOR FIREFIGHTING AND OTHER IMMEDIATELY DANGEROUS TO LIFE OR HEALTH CONDITIONS:
SELF-CONTAINED BREATHING APPARATUS WITH FULL FACEPIECE OPERATED IN PRESSURE-DEMAND OR OTHER POSITIVE PRESSURE MODE.
SUPPLIED-AIR RESPIRATOR WITH FULL FACEPIECE AND OPERATED IN PRESSURE-DEMAND OR OTHER POSITIVE PRESSURE MODE IN COMBINATION WITH AN AUXILIARY SELF-CONTAINED BREATHING APPARATUS OPERATED IN PRESSURE-DEMAND OR OTHER POSITIVE PRESSURE MODE.
CLOTHING: EMPLOYEE MUST WEAR APPROPRIATE PROTECTIVE (IMPERVIOUS) CLOTHING AND EQUIPMENT TO PREVENT ANY POSSIBILITY OF SKIN CONTACT WITH THIS SUBSTANCE.
GLOVES: EMPLOYEE MUST WEAR APPROPRIATE PROTECTIVE GLOVES TO PREVENT CONTACT WITH THIS SUBSTANCE.
EYE PROTECTION: EMPLOYEE MUST WEAR SPLASH-PROOF OR DUST-RESISTANT SAFETY GOGGLES AND A FACESHIELD TO PREVENT CONTACT WITH THIS SUBSTANCE.
EMERGENCY WASH FACILITIES: WHERE THERE IS ANY POSSIBILITY THAT AN EMPLOYEE'S EYES AND/OR SKIN MAY BE EXPOSED TO THIS SUBSTANCE, THE EMPLOYER SHOULD PROVIDE AN EYE WASH FOUNTAIN AND QUICK DRENCH SHOWER WITHIN THE IMMEDIATE WORK AREA FOR EMERGENCY USE.

SKIN CONTACT: CYPRAZINE: **ACUTE EXPOSURE**- THIS MATERIAL IS NOT EXPECTED TO BE IRRITATING TO THE SKIN. **CHRONIC EXPOSURE**- NO DATA AVAILABLE.

FIRST AID- REMOVE CONTAMINATED CLOTHING AND SHOES IMMEDIATELY. WASH AFFECTED AREA WITH SOAP OR MILD DETERGENT AND LARGE AMOUNTS OF WATER UNTIL NO EVIDENCE OF CHEMICAL REMAINS (APPROXIMATELY 15-20 MINUTES). GET MEDICAL ATTENTION IMMEDIATELY.

EYE CONTACT: CYPRAZINE: **ACUTE EXPOSURE**- SOME TRIAZINES ARE MILDLY IRRITATING TO THE EYES. **CHRONIC EXPOSURE**- NO DATA AVAILABLE.

FIRST AID- WASH EYES IMMEDIATELY WITH LARGE AMOUNTS OF WATER OR NORMAL SALINE, OCCASIONALLY LIFTING UPPER AND LOWER LIDS, UNTIL NO EVIDENCE OF CHEMICAL REMAINS (APPROXIMATELY 15-20 MINUTES). GET MEDICAL ATTENTION IMMEDIATELY.

INGESTION: CYPRAZINE: **ACUTE EXPOSURE**- A LETHAL DOSE IN RATS WAS 1200 MG/KG; NO SYMPTOMS WERE REPORTED. **CHRONIC EXPOSURE**- NO DATA AVAILABLE.

FIRST AID- REMOVE BY GASTRIC LAVAGE AND CATHARSIS. MAINTAIN BLOOD PRESSURE AND AIRWAY. GIVE OXYGEN IF RESPIRATION IS DEPRESSED. DO NOT PERFORM GASTRIC LAVAGE IF VICTIM IS UNCONSCIOUS. GET MEDICAL ATTENTION IMMEDIATELY (DREISBACH, HANDBOOK OF POISONING, 12TH ED.).
ADMINISTRATION OF LAVAGE OR OXYGEN SHOULD BE PERFORMED BY QUALIFIED MEDICAL PERSONNEL.

ANTIDOTE: NO SPECIFIC ANTIDOTE. TREAT SYMPTOMATICALLY AND SUPPORTIVELY.

REACTIVITY

REACTIVITY: STABLE UNDER NORMAL TEMPERATURES AND PRESSURES.

INCOMPATIBILITIES: CYPRAZINE: NO DATA AVAILABLE.

DECOMPOSITION: THERMAL DECOMPOSITION MAY YIELD CHLORIDE FUMES AND TOXIC OXIDES OF NITROGEN.

POLYMERIZATION: HAZARDOUS POLYMERIZATION HAS NOT BEEN REPORTED TO OCCUR UNDER NORMAL TEMPERATURES AND PRESSURES.

STORAGE AND DISPOSAL

OBSERVE ALL FEDERAL, STATE AND LOCAL REGULATIONS WHEN STORING OR DISPOSING OF THIS SUBSTANCE. FOR ASSISTANCE, CONTACT THE DISTRICT DIRECTOR OF THE ENVIRONMENTAL PROTECTION AGENCY.

****STORAGE****

STORE IN ACCORDANCE WITH 40 CFR 165 RECOMMENDED PROCEDURES FOR THE DISPOSAL AND STORAGE OF PESTICIDES AND PESTICIDE CONTAINERS.

****DISPOSAL****

DISPOSAL MUST BE IN ACCORDANCE WITH 40 CFR 165 RECOMMENDED PROCEDURES FOR THE DISPOSAL AND STORAGE OF PESTICIDES AND PESTICIDE CONTAINERS.

CONDITIONS TO AVOID

MAY BURN BUT DOES NOT IGNITE READILY.

SPILL AND LEAK PROCEDURES

OCCUPATIONAL SPILL: DO NOT TOUCH SPILLED MATERIAL. STOP LEAK IF YOU CAN DO IT WITHOUT RISK. FOR SMALL SPILLS, TAKE UP WITH SAND OR OTHER ABSORBENT MATERIAL AND PLACE INTO CONTAINERS FOR LATER DISPOSAL. FOR SMALL DRY SPILLS, WITH A CLEAN SHOVEL PLACE MATERIAL INTO CLEAN, DRY CONTAINER AND COVER. MOVE CONTAINERS FROM SPILL AREA. FOR LARGER SPILLS, DIKE FAR AHEAD OF SPILL FOR LATER DISPOSAL. KEEP UNNECESSARY PEOPLE AWAY. ISOLATE HAZARD AREA AND DENY ENTRY.

PROTECTIVE EQUIPMENT

VENTILATION: PROVIDE LOCAL EXHAUST OR GENERAL DILUTION VENTILATION SYSTEM.

RESPIRATOR: THE FOLLOWING RESPIRATORS ARE RECOMMENDED BASED ON INFORMATION FOUND IN THE PHYSICAL DATA, TOXICITY AND HEALTH EFFECTS SECTIONS. THEY ARE RANKED IN ORDER FROM MINIMUM TO MAXIMUM RESPIRATORY PROTECTION. THE SPECIFIC RESPIRATOR SELECTED MUST BE BASED ON CONTAMINATION LEVELS FOUND IN THE WORK PLACE, MUST NOT EXCEED THE WORKING LIMITS OF THE RESPIRATOR AND BE JOINTLY APPROVED BY THE NATIONAL INSTITUTE FOR OCCUPATIONAL SAFETY AND HEALTH AND THE MINE SAFETY AND HEALTH ADMINISTRATION (NIOSH-MSHA).
CHEMICAL CARTRIDGE RESPIRATOR WITH AN ORGANIC VAPOR CARTRIDGE(S) IN COMBINATION WITH A DUST AND MIST FILTER.
GAS MASK WITH ORGANIC VAPOR CANISTER (CHIN-STYLE OR FRONT- OR BACK-MOUNTED CANISTER) WITH A DUST AND MIST FILTER.
GAS MASK WITH ORGANIC VAPOR CANISTER (CHIN-STYLE OR FRONT- OR BACK-MOUNTED CANISTER) WITH A PARTICULATE FILTER.
POWERED AIR-PURIFYING RESPIRATOR WITH A HIGH-EFFICIENCY FILTER.
TYPE 'C' SUPPLIED-AIR RESPIRATOR WITH A FULL FACEPIECE OPERATED IN A PRESSURE-DEMAND OR OTHER POSITIVE PRESSURE MODE.
SELF-CONTAINED BREATHING APPARATUS WITH A FULL FACEPIECE OPERATED IN PRESSURE-DEMAND OR OTHER POSITIVE PRESSURE MODE.
FOR FIREFIGHTING AND OTHER IMMEDIATELY DANGEROUS TO LIFE OR HEALTH CONDITIONS:
SELF-CONTAINED BREATHING APPARATUS WITH FULL FACEPIECE OPERATED IN PRESSURE-DEMAND OR OTHER POSITIVE PRESSURE MODE.
SUPPLIED-AIR RESPIRATOR WITH FULL FACEPIECE AND OPERATED IN PRESSURE-DEMAND OR OTHER POSITIVE PRESSURE MODE IN COMBINATION WITH AN AUXILIARY SELF-CONTAINED BREATHING APPARATUS OPERATED IN PRESSURE-DEMAND OR OTHER POSITIVE PRESSURE MODE.

CLOTHING: EMPLOYEE MUST WEAR APPROPRIATE PROTECTIVE (IMPERVIOUS) CLOTHING AND EQUIPMENT TO PREVENT REPEATED OR PROLONGED SKIN CONTACT WITH THIS SUBSTANCE.

GLOVES: EMPLOYEE MUST WEAR APPROPRIATE PROTECTIVE GLOVES TO PREVENT CONTACT WITH THIS SUBSTANCE.

EYE PROTECTION: EMPLOYEE MUST WEAR SPLASH-PROOF OR DUST-RESISTANT SAFETY GOGGLES TO PREVENT EYE CONTACT WITH THIS SUBSTANCE.
EMERGENCY EYE WASH: WHERE THERE IS ANY POSSIBILITY THAT AN EMPLOYEE'S EYES MAY BE EXPOSED TO THIS SUBSTANCE, THE EMPLOYER SHOULD PROVIDE AN EYE WASH FOUNTAIN WITHIN THE IMMEDIATE WORK AREA FOR EMERGENCY USE.

AUTHORIZED BY- OCCUPATIONAL HEALTH SERVICES, INC.
CREATION DATE: 10/04/89 ***REVISION DATE:*** 05/10/90

MATERIAL SAFETY DATA SHEET

OCCUPATIONAL HEALTH SERVICES, INC.
AGRICULTURE AND PESTICIDE DIVISION
450 SEVENTH AVENUE, SUITE 2407
NEW YORK, NEW YORK 10123
1-800-445-MSDS OR (212) 967-1100

EMERGENCY CONTACT:
JOHN S. BRANSFORD, JR. (615) 292-1180

SUBSTANCE IDENTIFICATION

CAS-NUMBER 23564-05-8

SUBSTANCE: **THIOPHANATE-METHYL**

TRADE NAMES/SYNONYMS: 1,2-BIS(3-METHOXYCARBONYL-2-THIOUREIDO)BENZENE; DIMETHYL 4,4'-O-PHENYLENE-BIS(3-THIOALLOPHANATE); 1,2-DI(3-METHOXYCARBONYL-2-THIOUREIDO)BENZENE; CARBAMIC ACID, (1,2-PHENYLENEBIS(IMINOCARBONOTHIOYL))BIS-, DIMETHYL ESTER; (1,2-PHENYLENEBIS(IMINOCARBONOTHIOYL))BISCARBAMIC ACID DIMETHYL ESTER; ALLOPHANIC ACID, 4,4'-O-PHENYLENEBIS(3-THIO-, DIMETHYL ESTER; 4,4'-O-PHENYLENEBIS(3-THIOALLOPHANIC ACID) DIMETHYL ESTER; 1,2-DI-(3-METHOXYCARBONYL-2-THIOUREIDO)BENZENE; DIMETHYL (1,2-PHENYLENEBIS(IMINOCARBONOTHIOYL))BIS(CARBAMATE); CERCOBIN M; CERCOBIN METHYL; CYCOSIN; METHYLTHIOFANATE; METHYLTHIOPHANATE; MILDOTHANE; NF 44; TOPSIN M; TOPSIN METHYL; C12H14N4O4S2; PST72308

CHEMICAL FAMILY: THIOCARBAMATE

MOLECULAR FORMULA: C6-H4(N-H-C-S-N-H-C-O2-C-H3)2

MOLECULAR WEIGHT: 342.42

CERCLA RATINGS (SCALE 0-3): HEALTH=1 FIRE=1 REACTIVITY=0 PERSISTENCE=2

NFPA RATINGS (SCALE 0-4): HEALTH=1 FIRE=1 REACTIVITY=0

COMPONENTS AND CONTAMINANTS

COMPONENT: THIOPHANATE-METHYL ***PERCENT:*** 100
CAS# 23564-05-8

EXPOSURE LIMITS: NO OCCUPATIONAL EXPOSURE LIMITS ESTABLISHED BY OSHA, ACGIH, OR NIOSH.

PHYSICAL DATA

DESCRIPTION: COLORLESS, CRYSTALLINE SOLID.

MELTING POINT: 351-354 F (177-179 C) (DECOMPOSES)

SPECIFIC GRAVITY: NOT AVAILABLE ***VAPOR PRESSURE:*** NEGLIGIBLE

SOLUBILITY IN WATER: 3.5 PPM

SOLVENT SOLUBILITY: SLIGHTLY SOLUBLE IN ACETONE, METHANOL, CHLOROFORM, ACETONITRILE; SLIGHTLY SOLUBLE IN OTHER ORGANIC SOLVENTS

FIRE AND EXPLOSION DATA

FIRE AND EXPLOSION HAZARD: SLIGHT FIRE HAZARD WHEN EXPOSED TO HEAT OR FLAME.

FIREFIGHTING MEDIA: DRY CHEMICAL, CARBON DIOXIDE, HALON, WATER SPRAY OR STANDARD FOAM (1987 EMERGENCY RESPONSE GUIDEBOOK, DOT P 5800.4). FOR LARGER FIRES, USE WATER SPRAY, FOG OR STANDARD FOAM (1987 EMERGENCY RESPONSE GUIDEBOOK, DOT P 5800.4).

FIREFIGHTING: MOVE CONTAINERS FROM FIRE AREA IF POSSIBLE. FIGHT FIRE FROM MAXIMUM DISTANCE. STAY AWAY FROM STORAGE TANK ENDS. DIKE FIRE CONTROL WATER FOR LATER DISPOSAL. DO NOT SCATTER MATERIAL (1987 EMERGENCY RESPONSE GUIDEBOOK, DOT P 5800.4, GUIDE PAGE 55). EXTINGUISH FIRE USING AGENTS SUITABLE FOR TYPE OF SURROUNDING FIRE. USE WATER IN FLOODING AMOUNTS AS FOG. USE ALCOHOL FOAM, CARBON DIOXIDE OR DRY CHEMICAL. AVOID BREATHING TOXIC VAPORS, KEEP UPWIND.

TOXICITY

THIOPHANATE-METHYL: TOXICITY DATA: 6640 MG/KG ORAL-RAT LD50; 3400 MG/KG ORAL-MOUSE LD50; 2270 MG/KG ORAL-RABBIT LD50; 3640 MG/KG ORAL-GUINEA PIG LD50; 4000 MG/KG ORAL-DOG LDLO; 1140 MG/KG INTRAPERITONEAL-RAT LD50; 790 MG/KG INTRAPERITONEAL-MOUSE LD50; MUTAGENIC DATA (RTECS); REPRODUCTIVE EFFECTS DATA (RTECS). CARCINOGEN STATUS: NONE. AN EPA REPORT BY THE OFFICE OF PESTICIDES AND TOXIC SUBSTANCES INDICATED THAT A METABOLITE OF THIOPHANATE-METHYL, METHYL 2-BENZIMIDAZOLE CARBAMATE (MBC), IS AN HEPATOCARCINOGEN IN MICE BY INGESTION. ACUTE TOXICITY LEVEL: SLIGHTLY TOXIC BY INGESTION. TARGET EFFECTS: NO DATA AVAILABLE. ADDITIONAL DATA: EXPOSURE TO HIGH LEVELS OF A METABOLITE OF THIOPHANATE-METHYL, METHYL 2-BENZIMIDAZOLE CARBAMATE (MBC), MAY CAUSE AN INCREASE MUTAGENIC RISK IN THE FORM OF HERITABLE SPINDLE EFFECTS.

HEALTH EFFECTS AND FIRST AID

INHALATION: THIOPHANATE-METHYL: **ACUTE EXPOSURE-** MICE EXPOSED TO A CONCENTRATION OF 100,000 MG/M3 FOR 30, 60, OR 120 MINUTES, DEVELOPED LACRIMATION, SALIVATION, AND NASAL EXUDATION WITHIN 5 TO 6 MINUTES AFTER EXPOSURE BEGAN; NO FATALITIES WERE REPORTED. AFTER A FEW DAYS OF WHEEZING AND A CRUST FORMING AROUND THEIR EYES, THE MICE COMPLETELY RECOVERED WITH NO CHANGE IN GROWTH COMPARED TO CONTROLS. **CHRONIC EXPOSURE-** NO DATA AVAILABLE.

FIRST AID- REMOVE FROM EXPOSURE AREA TO FRESH AIR IMMEDIATELY. IF BREATHING HAS STOPPED, PERFORM ARTIFICIAL RESPIRATION. KEEP PERSON WARM AND AT REST. TREAT SYMPTOMATICALLY AND SUPPORTIVELY. GET MEDICAL ATTENTION IMMEDIATELY.

SKIN CONTACT: THIOPHANATE-METHYL: **ACUTE EXPOSURE-** THIS MATERIAL WAS MILDLY IRRITATING TO THE SKIN OF RABBITS. IT MAY CAUSE SENSITIZATION DERMATITIS IN PREVIOUSLY EXPOSED PERSONS. **CHRONIC EXPOSURE-** SYMPTOMS OF ITCHING, REDNESS, SWELLING, DRYNESS, AND SOMETIMES SENSITIZED DERMATITIS WERE REPORTED IN ONE CASE OF WORKERS EXPOSED TO THIOPHANATE-METHYL. SOME ABNORMALITIES OF HEMOGLOBIN WERE ALSO REPORTED. APPLICATION OF A 10% CONCENTRATION TO THE SKIN OF RABBITS PRODUCED A SLIGHT ERYTHEMA THAT DISAPPEARED WITHIN A FEW DAYS.

FIRST AID- REMOVE CONTAMINATED CLOTHING AND SHOES IMMEDIATELY. WASH AFFECTED AREA WITH SOAP OR MILD DETERGENT AND LARGE AMOUNTS OF WATER UNTIL NO EVIDENCE OF CHEMICAL REMAINS (APPROXIMATELY 15-20 MINUTES). GET MEDICAL ATTENTION IMMEDIATELY.

EYE CONTACT: THIOPHANATE-METHYL: **ACUTE EXPOSURE-** A 10% CONCENTRATION OF THIOPHANATE-METHYL APPLIED TO THE EYES OF RABBITS WAS NOT IRRITATING. **CHRONIC EXPOSURE-** NO DATA AVAILABLE.

FIRST AID- WASH EYES IMMEDIATELY WITH LARGE AMOUNTS OF WATER OR NORMAL SALINE, OCCASIONALLY LIFTING UPPER AND LOWER LIDS, UNTIL NO EVIDENCE OF CHEMICAL REMAINS (APPROXIMATELY 15-20 MINUTES). GET MEDICAL ATTENTION IMMEDIATELY.

INGESTION: THIOPHANATE-METHYL: **ACUTE EXPOSURE-** HIGH DOSES OF THIOPHANATE-METHYL PRODUCED TREMORS LEADING TO TONIC OR CLONIC CONVULSIONS, NOSE BLEEDING AND LACRIMATION IN RATS. IN RABBITS AND DOGS, THIOPHANATE-METHYL CAUSED DECREASED RESPIRATORY RATE, LETHARGY, LOSS OF TONE OF THE ABDOMINAL MUSCLES, DISCHARGE FROM THE EYES, AND MYDRIASIS PRIOR TO DEATH. **CHRONIC EXPOSURE-** A TWO-YEAR STUDY IN RATS AT A DIETARY LEVEL OF 640 PPM REPORTED A SLIGHT REDUCTION IN GROWTH IN BOTH MALE AND FEMALE RATS AND A SLIGHT ENLARGEMENT IN THE RELATIVE WEIGHT OF THE KIDNEYS IN MALE RATS; SOME ENLARGEMENT OF THYROID EPITHELIAL CELLS WAS OBSERVED AT THE END OF TWO YEARS. IN ANOTHER STUDY OF SHORTER DURATION AND AT HIGHER DOSES, A SLIGHT ENLARGEMENT OF THE LIVER WITH ENLARGEMENT OF SOME LIVER CELLS WAS OBSERVED IN RATS AND MICE. A SLIGHT BUT SIGNIFICANT REDUCTION IN THE NUMBER OF LIVE FETUSES WAS OBSERVED IN A STUDY OF PREGNANT MICE FED 1000 MG/KG/DAY. MATERNAL AND PATERNAL REPRODUCTIVE EFFECTS WERE REPORTED IN RATS FOLLOWING REPEATED ADMINISTRATION PRIOR TO MATING.

FIRST AID- REMOVE BY GASTRIC LAVAGE AND CATHARSIS. MAINTAIN BLOOD PRESSURE AND AIRWAY. GIVE OXYGEN IF RESPIRATION IS DEPRESSED. DO NOT PERFORM GASTRIC LAVAGE IF VICTIM IS UNCONSCIOUS. GET MEDICAL ATTENTION IMMEDIATELY (DREISBACH, HANDBOOK OF POISONING, 12TH ED.). ADMINISTRATION OF LAVAGE OR OXYGEN SHOULD BE PERFORMED BY QUALIFIED MEDICAL PERSONNEL.

ANTIDOTE: NO SPECIFIC ANTIDOTE. TREAT SYMPTOMATICALLY AND SUPPORTIVELY.

REACTIVITY

REACTIVITY: STABLE UNDER NORMAL TEMPERATURES AND PRESSURES; CONTACT WITH MOISTURE MAY CAUSE CONVERSION TO METHYL 2-BENZIMIDAZOLE CARBAMATE (MBC).

INCOMPATIBILITIES: THIOPHANATE-METHYL: ALKALINE SOLUTIONS: UNSTABLE.

DECOMPOSITION: THERMAL DECOMPOSITION MAY RELEASE TOXIC OXIDES OF NITROGEN AND SULFUR.

POLYMERIZATION: HAZARDOUS POLYMERIZATION HAS NOT BEEN REPORTED TO OCCUR UNDER NORMAL TEMPERATURES AND PRESSURES.

STORAGE AND DISPOSAL

OBSERVE ALL FEDERAL, STATE AND LOCAL REGULATIONS WHEN STORING OR DISPOSING OF THIS SUBSTANCE. FOR ASSISTANCE, CONTACT THE DISTRICT DIRECTOR OF THE ENVIRONMENTAL PROTECTION AGENCY.

STORAGE

STORE IN ACCORDANCE WITH 40 CFR 165 RECOMMENDED PROCEDURES FOR THE DISPOSAL AND STORAGE OF PESTICIDES AND PESTICIDE CONTAINERS. STORE AWAY FROM INCOMPATIBLE SUBSTANCES.

DISPOSAL

DISPOSAL MUST BE IN ACCORDANCE WITH 40 CFR 165 RECOMMENDED PROCEDURES FOR THE DISPOSAL AND STORAGE OF PESTICIDES AND PESTICIDE CONTAINERS.

CONDITIONS TO AVOID

MAY BURN BUT DOES NOT IGNITE READILY. CONTAINERS MAY EXPLODE IN HEAT OF FIRE.

SPILL AND LEAK PROCEDURES

OCCUPATIONAL SPILL: DO NOT TOUCH SPILLED MATERIAL. STOP LEAK IF YOU CAN DO IT WITHOUT RISK. USE WATER SPRAY TO REDUCE VAPORS. FOR SMALL SPILLS, TAKE UP WITH SAND OR OTHER ABSORBENT MATERIAL AND PLACE INTO CONTAINERS FOR LATER DISPOSAL. FOR SMALL DRY SPILLS, WITH A CLEAN SHOVEL PLACE MATERIAL INTO CLEAN, DRY CONTAINERS AND COVER. MOVE CONTAINERS FROM SPILL AREA. FOR LARGER SPILLS, DIKE FAR AHEAD OF SPILL FOR LATER DISPOSAL. KEEP UNNECESSARY PEOPLE AWAY. ISOLATE HAZARD AREA AND DENY ENTRY. VENTILATE CLOSED SPACES BEFORE ENTERING.

PROTECTIVE EQUIPMENT

VENTILATION: PROVIDE GENERAL DILUTION VENTILATION.

RESPIRATOR: THE FOLLOWING RESPIRATORS ARE RECOMMENDED BASED ON INFORMATION FOUND IN THE PHYSICAL DATA, TOXICITY AND HEALTH EFFECTS SECTIONS. THEY ARE RANKED IN ORDER FROM MINIMUM TO MAXIMUM RESPIRATORY PROTECTION. THE SPECIFIC RESPIRATOR SELECTED MUST BE BASED ON CONTAMINATION LEVELS FOUND IN THE WORK PLACE, MUST NOT EXCEED THE WORKING LIMITS OF THE RESPIRATOR AND BE JOINTLY APPROVED BY THE NATIONAL INSTITUTE FOR OCCUPATIONAL SAFETY AND HEALTH AND THE MINE SAFETY AND HEALTH ADMINISTRATION (NIOSH-MSHA).

CHEMICAL CARTRIDGE RESPIRATOR WITH AN ORGANIC VAPOR CARTRIDGE(S) WITH A FULL FACEPIECE AND ORGANIC VAPOR CARTRIDGE(S) IN COMBINATION WITH A DUST AND MIST FILTER.

POWERED AIR-PURIFYING RESPIRATOR WITH A TIGHT-FITTING FACEPIECE AND ORGANIC VAPOR CARTRIDGE(S) IN COMBINATION WITH A HIGH-EFFICIENCY PARTICULATE FILTER.

TYPE 'C' SUPPLIED-AIR RESPIRATOR WITH A FULL FACEPIECE OPERATED IN A PRESSURE-DEMAND OR OTHER POSITIVE PRESSURE MODE.

SELF-CONTAINED BREATHING APPARATUS WITH A FULL FACEPIECE OPERATED IN PRESSURE-DEMAND OR OTHER POSITIVE PRESSURE MODE.

FOR FIREFIGHTING AND OTHER IMMEDIATELY DANGEROUS TO LIFE OR HEALTH CONDITIONS:

SELF-CONTAINED BREATHING APPARATUS WITH FULL FACEPIECE OPERATED IN PRESSURE-DEMAND OR OTHER POSITIVE PRESSURE MODE.

SUPPLIED-AIR RESPIRATOR WITH FULL FACEPIECE AND OPERATED IN PRESSURE-DEMAND OR OTHER POSITIVE PRESSURE MODE IN COMBINATION WITH AN

AUXILIARY SELF-CONTAINED BREATHING APPARATUS OPERATED IN PRESSURE-DEMAND OR OTHER POSITIVE PRESSURE MODE.

CLOTHING: EMPLOYEE MUST WEAR APPROPRIATE PROTECTIVE (IMPERVIOUS) CLOTHING AND EQUIPMENT TO PREVENT REPEATED OR PROLONGED SKIN CONTACT WITH THIS SUBSTANCE.

GLOVES: EMPLOYEE MUST WEAR APPROPRIATE PROTECTIVE GLOVES TO PREVENT CONTACT WITH THIS SUBSTANCE.

EYE PROTECTION: EMPLOYEE MUST WEAR SPLASH-PROOF OR DUST-RESISTANT SAFETY GOGGLES TO PREVENT EYE CONTACT WITH THIS SUBSTANCE. EMERGENCY EYE WASH: WHERE THERE IS ANY POSSIBILITY THAT AN EMPLOYEE'S EYES MAY BE EXPOSED TO THIS SUBSTANCE, THE EMPLOYER SHOULD PROVIDE AN EYE WASH FOUNTAIN WITHIN THE IMMEDIATE WORK AREA FOR EMERGENCY USE.

AUTHORIZED BY- OCCUPATIONAL HEALTH SERVICES, INC.
CREATION DATE: 10/05/89 ***REVISION DATE:*** 05/11/90

MATERIAL SAFETY DATA SHEET

OCCUPATIONAL HEALTH SERVICES, INC.
AGRICULTURE AND PESTICIDE DIVISION
450 SEVENTH AVENUE, SUITE 2407
NEW YORK, NEW YORK 10123
1-800-445-MSDS OR (212) 967-1100

EMERGENCY CONTACT:
JOHN S. BRANSFORD, JR. (615) 292-1180

SUBSTANCE IDENTIFICATION

CAS-NUMBER 1754-58-1

SUBSTANCE: DIAMIDOFOS

TRADE NAMES/SYNONYMS: PHOSPHORODIAMIDIC ACID, N,N'-DIMETHYL-, PHENYL ESTER; PHENYL N,N'-DIMETHYL PHOSPHOROMIADATE; DIAMIDAFOS; DIAMIDAPHOS; DIAMIDFOS; DIAMIDOPHOS; DOWCO 169; NELLITE; C8-H13-N2-O2-P; PST72310

CHEMICAL FAMILY: ORGANOPHOSPHATE ESTER

MOLECULAR FORMULA: C8-H13-N2-O2-P

MOLECULAR WEIGHT: 200.20

CERCLA RATINGS (SCALE 0-3): HEALTH=3 FIRE=1 REACTIVITY=0 PERSISTENCE=2

NFPA RATINGS (SCALE 0-4): HEALTH=4 FIRE=1 REACTIVITY=0

COMPONENTS AND CONTAMINANTS

COMPONENT: DIAMIDOFOS ***PERCENT:*** 100.0
CAS# 1754-58-1

OTHER CONTAMINANTS: NONE

EXPOSURE LIMITS: NO OCCUPATIONAL EXPOSURE LIMITS ESTABLISHED BY OSHA, ACGIH, OR NIOSH.

PHYSICAL DATA

DESCRIPTION: WHITE CRYSTALLINE SOLID.

BOILING POINT: 324 F (162 C) @ 0.5 MMHG

MELTING POINT: 221-223 F (105-106 C) ***SPECIFIC GRAVITY:*** NOT AVAILABLE

VAPOR PRESSURE: NIL ***SOLUBILITY IN WATER:*** 12% @ 25 C

SOLVENT SOLUBILITY: SOLUBLE IN ACETONE, CHLOROFORM, METHANOL, AND METHYLENE CHLORIDE.

FIRE AND EXPLOSION DATA

FIRE AND EXPLOSION HAZARD: SLIGHT FIRE HAZARD WHEN EXPOSED TO HEAT OR FLAME.

FIREFIGHTING MEDIA: DRY CHEMICAL, CARBON DIOXIDE, HALON, WATER SPRAY OR STANDARD FOAM (1987 EMERGENCY RESPONSE GUIDEBOOK, DOT P 5800.4). FOR LARGER FIRES, USE WATER SPRAY, FOG OR STANDARD FOAM (1987 EMERGENCY RESPONSE GUIDEBOOK, DOT P 5800.4).

FIREFIGHTING: MOVE CONTAINERS FROM FIRE AREA IF POSSIBLE. FIGHT FIRE FROM MAXIMUM DISTANCE. STAY AWAY FROM STORAGE TANK ENDS. DIKE FIRE CONTROL WATER FOR LATER DISPOSAL. DO NOT SCATTER MATERIAL (1987 EMERGENCY RESPONSE GUIDEBOOK, DOT P 5800.4, GUIDE PAGE 55). EXTINGUISH ONLY IF FLOW CAN BE STOPPED; USE FLOODING AMOUNTS OF WATER AS FOG, SOLID STREAMS MAY BE INEFFECTIVE. COOL CONTAINERS WITH FLOODING AMOUNTS OF WATER FROM AS FAR A DISTANCE AS POSSIBLE. USE WATER SPRAY TO ABSORB TOXIC VAPORS. AVOID BREATHING TOXIC VAPORS; KEEP UPWIND. CONSIDER EVACUATION OF DOWNWIND AREA IF MATERIAL IS LEAKING.

TOXICITY

DIAMIDOFOS: TOXICITY DATA: 100 MG/KG SKIN-RABBIT LD50; 140 MG/KG ORAL-RAT LD50; 63 MG/KG ORAL-RABBIT LD50. CARCINOGEN STATUS: NONE. ACUTE TOXICITY LEVEL: HIGHLY TOXIC BY SKIN ABSORPTION; TOXIC BY INGESTION. TARGET EFFECTS: CHOLINESTERASE INHIBITOR. POISONING MAY AFFECT THE NERVOUS SYSTEM.* AT INCREASED RISK FROM EXPOSURE: PERSONS WITH RESPIRATORY AILMENTS, RECENT EXPOSURE TO CHOLINESTERASE INHIBITORS OR IMPAIRED CHOLINESTERASE PRODUCTION, OR LIVER MALFUNCTION.* ADDITIONAL DATA: MAY CROSS THE PLACENTA. HIGH ENVIRONMENTAL TEMPERATURES OR EXPOSURE OF THE CHEMICAL TO VISIBLE OR ULTRAVIOLET LIGHT MAY ENHANCE THE TOXICITY. INTERACTIONS WITH MEDICATIONS MAY OCCUR.*

* MAY BE BASED ON GENERAL INFORMATION ON ORGANOPHOSPHATES.

HEALTH EFFECTS AND FIRST AID

INHALATION: DIAMIDOFOS: SEE INFORMATION ON ORGANOPHOSPHATES. ORGANOPHOSPHATES: CHOLINESTERASE INHIBITOR. **ACUTE EXPOSURE-** WHEN INHALED, THE FIRST EFFECTS OF CHOLINESTERASE INHIBITORS ARE USUALLY RESPIRATORY AND MAY INCLUDE NASAL HYPEREMIA AND WATERY DISCHARGE, COUGH, CHEST DISCOMFORT, DYSPNEA, AND WHEEZING DUE TO INCREASED BRONCHIAL SECRETIONS AND BRONCHOCONSTRICTION. IF SUFFICIENT AMOUNTS ARE ABSORBED, OTHER SYSTEMIC EFFECTS MAY BEGIN WITHIN A FEW MINUTES OR BE DELAYED FOR UP TO 12 HOURS. SYMPTOMS MAY INCLUDE PALLOR, NAUSEA, VOMITING, DIARRHEA, ABDOMINAL CRAMPS, HEADACHE, DIZZINESS, OCULAR PAIN, BLURRED VISION, MIOSIS OR IN SOME CASES, ESPECIALLY INITIALLY, MYDRIASIS, LACRIMATION, SALIVATION, SWEATING, AND CONFUSION. OTHER REPORTED CENTRAL NERVOUS SYSTEM OR NEUROMUSCULAR EFFECTS MAY INCLUDE ATAXIA, SLURRED SPEECH, AREFLEXIA, WEAKNESS, FATIGUE, FASCICULATIONS, TWITCHING, TREMORS POSSIBLY OF THE TONGUE AND EYELIDS, AND EVENTUALLY PARALYSIS OF THE EXTREMITIES AND POSSIBLY OF THE RESPIRATORY MUSCLES. IN SEVERE CASES THERE MAY ALSO BE INVOLUNTARY DEFECATION AND URINATION, CYANOSIS, PSYCHOSIS, HYPERGLYCEMIA, ACUTE PANCREATITIS, CARDIAC IRREGULARITIES, PULMONARY EDEMA, UNCONSCIOUSNESS, CONVULSIONS, AND COMA. DEATH IS PRIMARILY DUE TO RESPIRATORY FAILURE, ALTHOUGH CARDIOVASCULAR EFFECTS INCLUDING CARDIAC ARREST MAY ALSO BE IMPLICATED. LONG TERM SEQUELAE ARE RARE BUT MAY INCLUDE NEUROPSYCHIATRIC DISORDERS AND MYOPATHY WITH MUSCLE TENDERNESS. SOME ORGANOPHOSPHATES MAY CAUSE A DELAYED NEUROPATHY BEGINNING 1-4 WEEKS AFTER AN ACUTE EXPOSURE WHICH MAY OR MAY NOT HAVE CAUSED ACUTE CHOLINERGIC EFFECTS. NUMBNESS, TINGLING, WEAKNESS AND CRAMPING BEGINNING SYMMETRICALLY IN THE LOWER LIMBS MAY PROGRESS TO ATAXIA AND PARALYSIS. IN SEVERE CASES, UPPER LIMB INVOLVEMENT IS POSSIBLE AND FLACCID PARALYSIS MAY PROGRESS TO SPASTIC PARALYSIS WITH EXAGGERATED REFLEXES. IMPROVEMENT MAY OCCUR OVER MONTHS TO YEARS, BUT SOME RESIDUAL IMPAIRMENT USUALLY REMAINS. **CHRONIC EXPOSURE-** REPEATED OR PROLONGED EXPOSURE MAY RESULT IN THE EFFECTS OF ACUTE EXPOSURE INCLUDING THE DELAYED NEUROPATHY. OTHER EFFECTS REPORTED IN WORKERS REPEATEDLY EXPOSED INCLUDE IMPAIRED MEMORY AND CONCENTRATION, ACUTE PSYCHOSIS, SEVERE DEPRESSIONS, IRRITABILTY, CONFUSION, APATHY, EMOTIONAL LABILITY, SOCIAL WITHDRAWAL, CONFUSION, HEADACHE, SPEECH DIFFICULTIES, DELAYED REACTION TIMES, SPATIAL DISORIENTATION, NIGHTMARES, SLEEPWALKING, AND DROWSINESS OR INSOMNIA. AN INFLUENZA-LIKE CONDITION WITH HEADACHE, NAUSEA, WEAKNESS, ANOREXIA AND MALAISE HAS ALSO BEEN REPORTED.

FIRST AID- REMOVE FROM EXPOSURE AREA TO FRESH AIR IMMEDIATELY. IF BREATHING HAS STOPPED, GIVE ARTIFICIAL RESPIRATION. MAINTAIN AIRWAY AND BLOOD PRESSURE AND ADMINISTER OXYGEN IF AVAILABLE. KEEP AFFECTED PERSON WARM AND AT REST. TREAT SYMPTOMATICALLY AND SUPPORTIVELY. ADMINISTRATION OF OXYGEN SHOULD BE PERFORMED BY QUALIFIED PERSONNEL. GET MEDICAL ATTENTION IMMEDIATELY.

SKIN CONTACT: DIAMIDOFOS: HIGHLY TOXIC. THIS MATERIAL MAY BE SLIGHTLY IRRITATING. SEE INFORMATION ON ORGANOPHOSPHATES. ORGANOPHOSPHATES: CHOLINESTERASE INHIBITOR. **ACUTE EXPOSURE-** LOCALIZED SWEATING AND FASCICULATIONS MAY OCCUR AT THE SITE OF CONTACT. IF SUFFICIENT AMOUNTS ARE ABSORBED, OTHER EFFECTS OF CHOLINESTERASE INHIBITION AS DESCRIBED IN ACUTE INHALATION MAY OCCUR. SYMPTOMS MAY BE DELAYED 2-3 HOURS, BUT USUALLY NO MORE THAN 12 HOURS. THE RATE OF ABSORPTION IS INCREASED BY THE PRESENCE OF DERMATITIS OR HIGH AMBIENT TEMPERATURES. DELAYED NEUROPATHY IS ALSO POSSIBLE. **CHRONIC EXPOSURE-** REPEATED OR PROLONGED EXPOSURE MAY CAUSE EFFECTS AS DESCRIBED IN ACUTE EXPOSURE. SOME ORGANOPHOSPHATES MAY CAUSE SENSITIZATION.

FIRST AID- REMOVE CONTAMINATED CLOTHING IMMEDIATELY. WASH CONTAMINATED AREAS WITH SOAP AND WATER FOLLOWED BY ALCOHOL (ARENA,

POISONING, 4TH ED.). EMERGENCY PERSONNEL SHOULD WEAR GLOVES AND AVOID CONTAMINATION. TREAT RESPIRATORY DIFFICULTY WITH ARTIFICIAL RESPIRATION. GET MEDICAL ATTENTION IMMEDIATELY.

EYE CONTACT: DIAMIDOFOS: SEE INFORMATION ON ORGANOPHOSPHATES.
ORGANOPHOSPHATES: CHOLINESTERASE INHIBITOR. **ACUTE EXPOSURE-** DIRECT CONTACT MAY CAUSE PAIN, HYPEREMIA, LACRIMATION, TWITCHING OF THE EYELIDS, MIOSIS, AND CILIARY MUSCLE SPASM WITH LOSS OF ACCOMODATION, BLURRED OR DIMMED VISION AND BROWACHE. SOMETIMES MYDRIASIS MAY OCCUR INSTEAD OF MIOSIS. WITH SUFFICIENT EXPOSURE, OTHER SYMPTOMS OF CHOLINESTERASE INHIBITION AS DESCRIBED IN ACUTE INHALATION MAY OCCUR. **CHRONIC EXPOSURE-** REPEATED OR PROLONGED EXPOSURE MAY CAUSE EFFECTS AS DESCRIBED IN ACUTE EXPOSURE. SOME COMPOUNDS HAVE CAUSED TOXIC EFFECTS ON THE CRYSTALLINE LENS, CONJUNCTIVAL THICKENING AND OBSTRUCTION OF THE NASOLACRIMAL CANALS WHEN USED AS MIOTIC EYEDROPS.

FIRST AID- IRRIGATE EYES WITH WATER OR SALINE SOLUTION. IF SYMPTOMS OF POISONING OCCUR, TREAT RESPIRATORY DIFFICULTY WITH ARTIFICIAL RESPIRATION AND OXYGEN. OBSERVE PATIENT FOR AT LEAST 24-36 HOURS (GOSSELIN, CLINICAL TOXICOLOGY OF COMMERCIAL PRODUCTS, 5TH ED.). GET MEDICAL ATTENTION IMMEDIATELY. OXYGEN SHOULD BE ADMINISTERED BY QUALIFIED MEDICAL PERSONNEL.

INGESTION: DIAMIDOFOS: TOXIC. CHOLINESTERASE INHIBITION WAS OBSERVED IN ANIMALS GIVEN 100 PPM IN FOOD FOR 90 DAYS. SEE INFORMATION ON ORGANOPHOSPHATES.
ORGANOPHOSPHATES: CHOLINESTERASE INHIBITOR. **ACUTE EXPOSURE-** WHEN INGESTED, THE FIRST EFFECTS MAY BE NAUSEA, VOMITING, ANOREXIA, ABDOMINAL CRAMPS AND DIARRHEA. GASTROINTESTINAL ABSORPTION MAY CAUSE SYMPTOMS OF CHOLINESTERASE INHIBITION AS DESCRIBED IN ACUTE INHALATION. SYMPTOMS MAY BEGIN WITHIN MINUTES OR BE DELAYED FOR HOURS. DELAYED EFFECTS INCLUDING NEUROPATHY MAY ALSO OCCUR. **CHRONIC EXPOSURE-** REPEATED INGESTION MAY CAUSE EFFECTS AS DESCRIBED IN ACUTE EXPOSURE.

FIRST AID- IF PERSON IS ALERT AND RESPIRATION IS NOT DEPRESSED, GIVE SYRUP OF IPECAC FOLLOWED BY WATER (IF VOMITING OCCURS, KEEP HEAD BELOW HIPS TO PREVENT ASPIRATION). IF CONSCIOUSNESS LEVEL DECLINES OR VOMITING HAS NOT OCCURRED IN 15 MINUTES EMPTY STOMACH BY GASTRIC LAVAGE WITH THE AID OF CUFFED ENDOTRACHEAL TUBE USING ISOTONIC SALINE OR 5% SODIUM BICARBONATE FOLLOW WITH ACTIVATED CHARCOAL. ESTABLISH AND MAINTAIN AIRWAY. TREAT RESPIRATORY DIFFICULTY WITH ARTIFICIAL RESPIRATION AND OXYGEN. DO NOT GIVE MORPHINE, AMINOPHYLLINE, PHENOTHIAZINES, RESERPINE, FUROSEMIDE, OR ETHACRYNIC ACID (MORGAN, RECOGNITION AND MANAGEMENT OF PESTICIDE POISONINGS, 3RD ED.). TREAT SYMPTOMATICALLY AND SUPPORTIVELY. ADMINISTRATION OF OXYGEN AND LAVAGE MUST BE PERFORMED BY QUALIFIED MEDICAL PERSONNEL. GET MEDICAL ATTENTION IMMEDIATELY.

ANTIDOTE: THE FOLLOWING ANTIDOTE(S) HAVE BEEN RECOMMENDED. HOWEVER, THE DECISION AS TO WHETHER THE SEVERITY OF POISONING REQUIRES ADMINISTRATION OF ANY ANTIDOTE AND ACTUAL DOSE REQUIRED SHOULD BE MADE BY QUALIFIED MEDICAL PERSONNEL. FOR CHOLINESTERASE INHIBITORS: ESTABLISH CLEAR AIRWAY AND TISSUE OXYGENATION BY ASPIRATION OF SECRETIONS, AND IF NECESSARY, BY ASSISTED PULMONARY VENTILATION WITH OXYGEN. IMPROVE TISSUE OXYGENATION AS MUCH AS POSSIBLE BEFORE ADMINISTERING ATROPINE TO MINIMIZE THE RISK OF VENTRICULAR FIBRILLATION. ADMINISTER ATROPINE SULFATE INTRAVENOUSLY, OR INTRAMUSCULARLY IF IV INJECTION IS NOT POSSIBLE. IN MODERATELY SEVERE POISONING ADMINISTER ATROPINE SULFATE, 0.4-2.0 MG REPEATED EVERY 15 MINUTES UNTIL ATROPINIZATION IS ACHIEVED (TACHYCARDIA, FLUSHING, DRY MOUTH, MYDRIASIS). MAINTAIN ATROPINIZATION BY REPEATED DOSES FOR 2-12 HOURS, OR LONGER, DEPENDING ON THE SEVERITY OF POISONING. THE APPEARANCE OF RALES IN THE LUNG BASES, MIOSIS, SALIVATION, NAUSEA, BRADYCARDIA, ARE ALL INDICATIONS OF INADEQUATE ATROPINIZATION. SEVERELY POISONED INDIVIDUALS MAY EXHIBIT REMARKABLE TOLERANCE TO ATROPINE; TWO OR MORE TIMES THE DOSAGES SUGGESTED ABOVE MAY BE NEEDED. PERSONS NOT POISONED OR ONLY SLIGHTLY POISONED, HOWEVER, MAY DEVELOP SIGNS OF ATROPINE TOXICITY FROM SUCH LARGE DOSAGES: FEVER, MUSCLE FIBRILLATIONS, AND DELIRIUM ARE THE MAIN SIGNS OF ATROPINE TOXICITY. IF THESE SIGNS APPEAR WHILE THE PATIENT IS FULLY ATROPINIZED, ATROPINE ADMINISTRATION SHOULD BE DISCONTINUED, AT LEAST TEMPORARILY. OBSERVE TREATED PATIENTS CLOSELY AT LEAST 24 HOURS TO INSURE THAT SYMPTOMS (POSSIBLY PULMONARY EDEMA) DO NOT RECUR AS ATROPINIZATION WEARS OFF. IN VERY SEVERE POISONINGS, METABOLIC DISPOSITION OF TOXICANT MAY REQUIRE SEVERAL HOURS OR DAYS DURING WHICH ATROPINIZATION MUST BE MAINTAINED. MARKEDLY LOWER LEVELS OF URINARY METABOLITES INDICATE THAT ATROPINE DOSAGE CAN BE TAPERED OFF. AS DOSAGE IS REDUCED, CHECK THE LUNG BASES FREQUENTLY FOR RALES. IF RALES ARE HEARD OR OTHER SYMPTOMS RETURN, RE-ESTABLISH ATROPINIZATION PROMPTLY (MORGAN, RECOGNITION AND MANAGEMENT OF PESTICIDE POISONINGS, 3RD ED.). ADMINISTRATION OF ANTIDOTE MUST BE PERFORMED BY QUALIFIED MEDICAL PERSONNEL.
IN CASES OF SEVERE POISONING BY ORGANOPHOSPHATE PESTICIDES IN WHICH RESPIRATORY DEPRESSION, MUSCLE WEAKNESS AND TWITCHINGS ARE SEVERE, GIVE PRALIDOXIME (PROTOPAM-AYERST, 2-PAM), 1.0 GRAM INTRAVENOUSLY AT NO MORE THAN 0.5 GRAM PER MINUTE. DOSAGE OF PRALIDOXIME MAY BE REPEATED IN 1-2 HOURS, THEN AT 10-12 HOUR INTERVALS IF NEEDED. IN VERY SEVERE POISONINGS, DOSAGE RATES MAY BE DOUBLED. TREATMENT WITH PRALIDOXIME WILL BE MOST EFFECTIVE IF GIVEN WITHIN THIRTY-SIX HOURS AFTER POISONING (MORGAN, RECOGNITION AND MANAGEMENT OF PESTICIDE POISONINGS, 3RD ED.). ANTIDOTE SHOULD BE ADMINISTERED BY QUALIFIED MEDICAL PERSONNEL.

REACTIVITY

REACTIVITY: STABLE UNDER NORMAL TEMPERATURES AND PRESSURES.
INCOMPATIBILITIES: DIAMIDOFOS: OXIDIZERS (STRONG): FIRE AND EXPLOSION HAZARD.
DECOMPOSITION: THERMAL DECOMPOSITION MAY RELEASE TOXIC OXIDES OF NITROGEN, PHOSPHORUS AND CARBON.
POLYMERIZATION: HAZARDOUS POLYMERIZATION HAS NOT BEEN REPORTED TO OCCUR UNDER NORMAL TEMPERATURES AND PRESSURES.

STORAGE AND DISPOSAL

OBSERVE ALL FEDERAL, STATE AND LOCAL REGULATIONS WHEN STORING OR DISPOSING OF THIS SUBSTANCE. FOR ASSISTANCE, CONTACT THE DISTRICT DIRECTOR OF THE ENVIRONMENTAL PROTECTION AGENCY.

****STORAGE****

STORE IN ACCORDANCE WITH 40 CFR 165 RECOMMENDED PROCEDURES FOR THE DISPOSAL AND STORAGE OF PESTICIDES AND PESTICIDE CONTAINERS.
STORE AWAY FROM INCOMPATIBLE SUBSTANCES.

****DISPOSAL****

DISPOSAL MUST BE IN ACCORDANCE WITH 40 CFR 165 RECOMMENDED PROCEDURES FOR THE DISPOSAL AND STORAGE OF PESTICIDES AND PESTICIDE CONTAINERS.

CONDITIONS TO AVOID

MAY BURN BUT DOES NOT IGNITE READILY. CONTAINERS MAY EXPLODE IN HEAT OF FIRE.

SPILL AND LEAK PROCEDURES

OCCUPATIONAL SPILL: DO NOT TOUCH SPILLED MATERIAL. STOP LEAK IF YOU CAN DO IT WITHOUT RISK. USE WATER SPRAY TO REDUCE VAPORS. FOR SMALL SPILLS, TAKE UP WITH SAND OR OTHER ABSORBENT MATERIAL AND PLACE INTO CONTAINERS FOR LATER DISPOSAL. FOR SMALL DRY SPILLS, WITH A CLEAN SHOVEL PLACE MATERIAL INTO CLEAN, DRY CONTAINERS AND COVER. MOVE CONTAINERS FROM SPILL AREA. FOR LARGER SPILLS, DIKE FAR AHEAD OF SPILL FOR LATER DISPOSAL. KEEP UNNECESSARY PEOPLE AWAY. ISOLATE HAZARD AREA AND DENY ENTRY. VENTILATE CLOSED SPACES BEFORE ENTERING.

PROTECTIVE EQUIPMENT

VENTILATION: PROCESS ENCLOSURE RECOMMENDED.
RESPIRATOR: THE FOLLOWING RESPIRATORS ARE RECOMMENDED BASED ON INFORMATION FOUND IN THE PHYSICAL DATA, TOXICITY AND HEALTH EFFECTS SECTIONS. THEY ARE RANKED IN ORDER FROM MINIMUM TO MAXIMUM RESPIRATORY PROTECTION. THE SPECIFIC RESPIRATOR SELECTED MUST BE BASED ON CONTAMINATION LEVELS FOUND IN THE WORK PLACE, MUST NOT EXCEED THE WORKING LIMITS OF THE RESPIRATOR AND BE JOINTLY APPROVED BY THE NATIONAL INSTITUTE FOR OCCUPATIONAL SAFETY AND HEALTH AND THE MINE SAFETY AND HEALTH ADMINISTRATION (NIOSH-MSHA).
TYPE 'C' SUPPLIED-AIR RESPIRATOR WITH A FULL FACEPIECE OPERATED IN PRESSURE-DEMAND OR OTHER POSITIVE PRESSURE MODE OR WITH A FULL FACEPIECE, HELMET OR HOOD OPERATED IN CONTINOUS-FLOW MODE.
SELF-CONTAINED BREATHING APPARATUS WITH A FULL FACEPIECE OPERATED IN PRESSURE-DEMAND OR OTHER POSITIVE PRESSURE MODE.
FOR FIREFIGHTING AND OTHER IMMEDIATELY DANGEROUS TO LIFE OR HEALTH CONDITIONS:
SELF-CONTAINED BREATHING APPARATUS WITH FULL FACEPIECE OPERATED IN PRESSURE-DEMAND OR OTHER POSITIVE PRESSURE MODE.
SUPPLIED-AIR RESPIRATOR WITH FULL FACEPIECE AND OPERATED IN PRESSURE-DEMAND OR OTHER POSITIVE PRESSURE MODE IN COMBINATION WITH AN AUXILIARY SELF-CONTAINED BREATHING APPARATUS OPERATED IN PRESSURE-DEMAND OR OTHER POSITIVE PRESSURE MODE.

CLOTHING: EMPLOYEE MUST WEAR APPROPRIATE PROTECTIVE (IMPERVIOUS) CLOTHING AND EQUIPMENT TO PREVENT ANY POSSIBILITY OF SKIN CONTACT WITH THIS SUBSTANCE.
GLOVES: EMPLOYEE MUST WEAR APPROPRIATE PROTECTIVE GLOVES TO PREVENT CONTACT WITH THIS SUBSTANCE.
EYE PROTECTION: EMPLOYEE MUST WEAR SPLASH-PROOF OR DUST-RESISTANT SAFETY GOGGLES WITH OR WITHOUT A FACESHIELD TO PREVENT CONTACT WITH THIS SUBSTANCE.
EMERGENCY EYE WASH: WHERE THERE IS ANY POSSIBILITY THAT AN EMPLOYEE'S EYES MAY BE EXPOSED TO THIS SUBSTANCE, THE EMPLOYER SHOULD PROVIDE AN EYE WASH FOUNTAIN WITHIN THE IMMEDIATE WORK AREA FOR EMERGENCY USE.

AUTHORIZED BY- OCCUPATIONAL HEALTH SERVICES, INC.
CREATION DATE: 10/04/89 ***REVISION DATE:*** 05/03/90

MATERIAL SAFETY DATA SHEET

OCCUPATIONAL HEALTH SERVICES, INC.
AGRICULTURE AND PESTICIDE DIVISION
450 SEVENTH AVENUE, SUITE 2407
NEW YORK, NEW YORK 10123
1-800-445-MSDS OR (212) 967-1100

EMERGENCY CONTACT:
JOHN S. BRANSFORD, JR. (615) 292-1180

SUBSTANCE IDENTIFICATION

CAS-NUMBER 122-70-3
SUBSTANCE: 2-PHENYLETHYL PROPIONATE
TRADE NAMES/SYNONYMS: PROPANOIC ACID, 2-PHENYLETHYL ESTER; 2-PHENYLETHYL PROPANOIC ACID ESTER; PROPANOIC ACID, PHENETHYL ESTER; PHENETHYL PROPANOIC ACID ESTER; BENZYLCARBINYL PROPIONATE; PHENETHYL ALCOHOL PROPIONATE; PHENETHYL PROPANOATE; PHENETHYL PROPIONATE; 2-PHENETHYL PROPIONATE; 2-PHENYLETHYL PROPANOATE; PHENYLETHYL PROPIONATE; BETA-PHENYLETHYL PROPIONATE; C11H14O2; PST72314
CHEMICAL FAMILY: ESTER, CARBOXYLIC, ALIPHATIC
MOLECULAR FORMULA: C2-H5-C-O-O-C2-H4-C6-H6
MOLECULAR WEIGHT: 177.27
CERCLA RATINGS (SCALE 0-3): HEALTH=U FIRE=1 REACTIVITY=0 PERSISTENCE=1
NFPA RATINGS (SCALE 0-4): HEALTH=U FIRE=1 REACTIVITY=0

COMPONENTS AND CONTAMINANTS

COMPONENT: 2-PHENYLETHYL PROPIONATE ***PERCENT:*** 100.0
CAS# 122-70-3
OTHER CONTAMINANTS: NONE
EXPOSURE LIMITS: NO OCCUPATIONAL EXPOSURE LIMITS ESTABLISHED BY OSHA, ACGIH, OR NIOSH.

PHYSICAL DATA

DESCRIPTION: CLEAR, COLORLESS LIQUID WITH A FRUITY-FLORAL ODOR.
BOILING POINT: 164-166 F (91-92 C) @ 5 MMHG ***SPECIFIC GRAVITY:*** 1.012 @ 25 C
SOLUBILITY IN WATER: NOT AVAILABLE
SOLVENT SOLUBILITY: SOLUBLE IN ALCOHOLS AND ETHER.

FIRE AND EXPLOSION DATA

FIRE AND EXPLOSION HAZARD: SLIGHT FIRE HAZARD WHEN EXPOSED TO HEAT OR FLAME.
FLASH POINT: 202 F (94 C) ***FLAMMABILITY CLASS(OSHA):*** IIIB
FIREFIGHTING MEDIA: DRY CHEMICAL, CARBON DIOXIDE, HALON, WATER SPRAY OR STANDARD FOAM (1987 EMERGENCY RESPONSE GUIDEBOOK, DOT P 5800.4).
FOR LARGER FIRES, USE WATER SPRAY, FOG OR STANDARD FOAM (1987 EMERGENCY RESPONSE GUIDEBOOK, DOT P 5800.4).
FIREFIGHTING: MOVE CONTAINER FROM FIRE AREA IF POSSIBLE. DO NOT SCATTER SPILLED MATERIAL WITH HIGH PRESSURE WATER STREAMS. DIKE FIRE CONTROL WATER FOR LATER DISPOSAL (1987 EMERGENCY RESPONSE GUIDEBOOK, DOT P 5800.4, GUIDE PAGE 31).
USE AGENTS SUITABLE FOR TYPE OF SURROUNDING FIRE. AVOID BREATHING HAZARDOUS VAPORS, KEEP UPWIND.

TOXICITY

2-PHENYLETHYL PROPIONATE: TOXICITY DATA: 4000 MG/KG ORAL-RAT LD50. CARCINOGEN STATUS: NONE. ACUTE TOXICITY LEVEL: MODERATELY TOXIC BY INGESTION. TARGET EFFECTS: NO DATA AVAILABLE.

HEALTH EFFECTS AND FIRST AID

INHALATION: 2-PHENYLETHYL PROPIONATE: **ACUTE EXPOSURE-** NO DATA AVAILABLE. **CHRONIC EXPOSURE-** NO DATA AVAILABLE.
FIRST AID- REMOVE FROM EXPOSURE AREA TO FRESH AIR IMMEDIATELY. IF BREATHING HAS STOPPED, PERFORM ARTIFICIAL RESPIRATION. KEEP PERSON WARM AND AT REST. TREAT SYMPTOMATICALLY AND SUPPORTIVELY. GET MEDICAL ATTENTION IMMEDIATELY.

SKIN CONTACT: 2-PHENYLETHYL PROPIONATE: **ACUTE EXPOSURE-** NO DATA AVAILABLE. **CHRONIC EXPOSURE-** NO DATA AVAILABLE.
FIRST AID- REMOVE CONTAMINATED CLOTHING AND SHOES IMMEDIATELY. WASH AFFECTED AREA WITH SOAP OR MILD DETERGENT AND LARGE AMOUNTS OF WATER UNTIL NO EVIDENCE OF CHEMICAL REMAINS (APPROXIMATELY 15-20 MINUTES). GET MEDICAL ATTENTION IMMEDIATELY.

EYE CONTACT: 2-PHENYLETHYL PROPIONATE: **ACUTE EXPOSURE-** NO DATA AVAILABLE. **CHRONIC EXPOSURE-** NO DATA AVAILABLE.
FIRST AID- WASH EYES IMMEDIATELY WITH LARGE AMOUNTS OF WATER OR NORMAL SALINE, OCCASIONALLY LIFTING UPPER AND LOWER LIDS, UNTIL NO EVIDENCE OF CHEMICAL REMAINS (APPROXIMATELY 15-20 MINUTES). GET MEDICAL ATTENTION IMMEDIATELY.

INGESTION: 2-PHENYLETHYL PROPIONATE: **ACUTE EXPOSURE-** INGESTION OF 4000 MG/KG WAS LETHAL TO RATS. **CHRONIC EXPOSURE-** NO DATA AVAILABLE.
FIRST AID- TREAT SYMPTOMATICALLY AND SUPPORTIVELY. GET MEDICAL ATTENTION IMMEDIATELY. IF VOMITING OCCURS, KEEP HEAD LOWER THAN HIPS TO PREVENT ASPIRATION.
ANTIDOTE: NO SPECIFIC ANTIDOTE. TREAT SYMPTOMATICALLY AND SUPPORTIVELY.

REACTIVITY

REACTIVITY: STABLE UNDER NORMAL TEMPERATURES AND PRESSURES.
INCOMPATIBILITIES: 2-PHENYLETHYL PROPIONATE: OXIDIZERS (STRONG): FIRE AND EXPLOSION HAZARD. SEE ALSO ESTERS.
ESTERS: NITRATES: POSSIBLE EXPLOSIVE REACTION.
DECOMPOSITION: THERMAL DECOMPOSITION PRODUCTS MAY INCLUDE TOXIC OXIDES OF CARBON.
POLYMERIZATION: HAZARDOUS POLYMERIZATION HAS NOT BEEN REPORTED TO OCCUR UNDER NORMAL TEMPERATURES AND PRESSURES.

STORAGE AND DISPOSAL

OBSERVE ALL FEDERAL, STATE AND LOCAL REGULATIONS WHEN STORING OR DISPOSING OF THIS SUBSTANCE. FOR ASSISTANCE, CONTACT THE DISTRICT DIRECTOR OF THE ENVIRONMENTAL PROTECTION AGENCY.

****STORAGE****

STORE IN ACCORDANCE WITH 40 CFR 165 RECOMMENDED PROCEDURES FOR THE DISPOSAL AND STORAGE OF PESTICIDES AND PESTICIDE CONTAINERS.
STORE AWAY FROM INCOMPATIBLE SUBSTANCES.

****DISPOSAL****

DISPOSAL MUST BE IN ACCORDANCE WITH 40 CFR 165 RECOMMENDED PROCEDURES FOR THE DISPOSAL AND STORAGE OF PESTICIDES AND PESTICIDE CONTAINERS.

CONDITIONS TO AVOID

MAY BURN BUT DOES NOT IGNITE READILY. AVOID CONTACT WITH STRONG OXIDIZERS, EXCESSIVE HEAT, SPARKS, OR OPEN FLAME.

SPILL AND LEAK PROCEDURES

OCCUPATIONAL SPILL: STOP LEAK IF YOU CAN DO IT WITHOUT RISK. FOR SMALL SPILLS, TAKE UP WITH SAND OR OTHER ABSORBENT MATERIAL AND PLACE INTO CLEAN, DRY CONTAINERS FOR LATER DISPOSAL. KEEP UNNECESSARY PEOPLE AWAY. ISOLATE HAZARD AREA AND DENY ENTRY.

PROTECTIVE EQUIPMENT

VENTILATION: PROVIDE LOCAL EXHAUST OR GENERAL DILUTION VENTILATION SYSTEM.
RESPIRATOR: THE FOLLOWING RESPIRATORS ARE RECOMMENDED BASED ON INFORMATION FOUND IN THE PHYSICAL DATA, TOXICITY AND HEALTH EFFECTS SECTIONS. THEY ARE RANKED IN ORDER FROM MINIMUM TO MAXIMUM RESPIRATORY PROTECTION. THE SPECIFIC RESPIRATOR SELECTED MUST BE BASED ON CONTAMINATION LEVELS FOUND IN THE WORK PLACE, MUST NOT EXCEED THE WORKING LIMITS OF THE RESPIRATOR AND BE JOINTLY APPROVED BY THE NATIONAL INSTITUTE FOR OCCUPATIONAL SAFETY AND HEALTH AND THE MINE SAFETY AND HEALTH ADMINISTRATION (NIOSH-MSHA).

CHEMICAL CARTRIDGE RESPIRATOR WITH FULL FACEPIECE AND PESTICIDE CARTRIDGE.
TYPE 'C' SUPPLIED-AIR RESPIRATOR WITH A FULL FACEPIECE OPERATED IN PRESSURE-DEMAND OR OTHER POSITIVE PRESSURE MODE OR WITH A FULL FACEPIECE, HELMET OR HOOD OPERATED IN CONTINUOUS-FLOW MODE.
SELF-CONTAINED BREATHING APPARATUS OPERATED IN PRESSURE-DEMAND OR OTHER POSITIVE PRESSURE MODE.
FOR FIREFIGHTING AND OTHER IMMEDIATELY DANGEROUS TO LIFE OR HEALTH CONDITIONS:
SELF-CONTAINED BREATHING APPARATUS WITH FULL FACEPIECE OPERATED IN PRESSURE-DEMAND OR OTHER POSITIVE PRESSURE MODE.
SUPPLIED-AIR RESPIRATOR WITH FULL FACEPIECE AND OPERATED IN PRESSURE-DEMAND OR OTHER POSITIVE PRESSURE MODE IN COMBINATION WITH AN AUXILIARY SELF-CONTAINED BREATHING APPARATUS OPERATED IN PRESSURE-DEMAND OR OTHER POSITIVE PRESSURE MODE.

CLOTHING: EMPLOYEE MUST WEAR APPROPRIATE PROTECTIVE (IMPERVIOUS) CLOTHING AND EQUIPMENT TO PREVENT REPEATED OR PROLONGED SKIN CONTACT WITH THIS SUBSTANCE.

GLOVES: EMPLOYEE MUST WEAR APPROPRIATE PROTECTIVE GLOVES TO PREVENT CONTACT WITH THIS SUBSTANCE.

EYE PROTECTION: EMPLOYEE MUST WEAR SPLASH-PROOF OR DUST-RESISTANT SAFETY GOGGLES TO PREVENT EYE CONTACT WITH THIS SUBSTANCE.
EMERGENCY EYE WASH: WHERE THERE IS ANY POSSIBILITY THAT AN EMPLOYEE'S EYES MAY BE EXPOSED TO THIS SUBSTANCE, THE EMPLOYER SHOULD PROVIDE AN EYE WASH FOUNTAIN WITHIN THE IMMEDIATE WORK AREA FOR EMERGENCY USE.

AUTHORIZED BY- OCCUPATIONAL HEALTH SERVICES, INC.
CREATION DATE: 10/05/89 ***REVISION DATE:*** 10/31/89

MATERIAL SAFETY DATA SHEET

OCCUPATIONAL HEALTH SERVICES, INC.
AGRICULTURE AND PESTICIDE DIVISION
450 SEVENTH AVENUE, SUITE 2407
NEW YORK, NEW YORK 10123
1-800-445-MSDS OR (212) 967-1100

EMERGENCY CONTACT:
JOHN S. BRANSFORD, JR. (615) 292-1180

SUBSTANCE IDENTIFICATION

CAS-NUMBER 15299-99-7

SUBSTANCE: **NAPROPAMIDE**

TRADE NAMES/SYNONYMS: PROPANAMIDE, N,N-DIETHYL-2-(1-NAPHTHALENYLOXY)-; PROPIONAMIDE, N,N-DIETHYL-2-(1-NAPHTHYLOXY)-; N,N-DIETHYL-2-(1-NAPHTHALENYLOXY)PROPANAMIDE; N,N-DIETHYL-2-(1-NAPHTHYLOXY)PROPIONAMIDE; 2-(ALPHA-NAPHTHOXY)-N,N-DIETHYLPROPIONAMIDE; DEVRINOL; R 7465; C17H21NO2; PST72319

CHEMICAL FAMILY: NAPHTHALENE
AMIDE

MOLECULAR FORMULA: C17-H21-N-O2

MOLECULAR WEIGHT: 271.37

CERCLA RATINGS (SCALE 0-3): HEALTH=2 FIRE=1 REACTIVITY=0 PERSISTENCE=2

NFPA RATINGS (SCALE 0-4): HEALTH=U FIRE=1 REACTIVITY=0

COMPONENTS AND CONTAMINANTS

COMPONENT: NAPROPAMIDE ***PERCENT:*** 100.0
CAS# 15299-99-7

OTHER CONTAMINANTS: NONE

EXPOSURE LIMITS: NO OCCUPATIONAL EXPOSURE LIMITS ESTABLISHED BY OSHA, ACGIH, OR NIOSH.

PHYSICAL DATA

DESCRIPTION: WHITE TO LIGHT BROWN CRYSTALLINE SOLID.

MELTING POINT: 167 F (75 C) ***SPECIFIC GRAVITY:*** NOT AVAILABLE

VAPOR PRESSURE: NEGLIGIBLE ***SOLUBILITY IN WATER:*** 0.0073% @ 20 C

SOLVENT SOLUBILITY: SOLUBLE IN XYLENE, ACETONE, ETHANOL, METHYLPENTANONE, BENZENE, CHLOROFORM, METHYL ISOBUTYL KETONE, TOLUENE, DICHLOROMETHANE, METHANOL; MODERATELY SOLUBLE IN KEROSENE; SLIGHTLY SOLUBLE IN HEXANE.

FIRE AND EXPLOSION DATA

FIRE AND EXPLOSION HAZARD: SLIGHT FIRE HAZARD WHEN EXPOSED TO HEAT OR FLAME.

FIREFIGHTING MEDIA: DRY CHEMICAL, CARBON DIOXIDE, HALON, WATER SPRAY OR STANDARD FOAM (1987 EMERGENCY RESPONSE GUIDEBOOK, DOT P 5800.4).
FOR LARGER FIRES, USE WATER SPRAY, FOG OR STANDARD FOAM (1987 EMERGENCY RESPONSE GUIDEBOOK, DOT P 5800.4).

FIREFIGHTING: MOVE CONTAINER FROM FIRE AREA IF POSSIBLE. DO NOT SCATTER SPILLED MATERIAL WITH HIGH PRESSURE WATER STREAMS. DIKE FIRE CONTROL WATER FOR LATER DISPOSAL (1987 EMERGENCY RESPONSE GUIDEBOOK, DOT P 5800.4, GUIDE PAGE 31).
USE AGENTS SUITABLE FOR TYPE OF SURROUNDING FIRE. AVOID BREATHING HAZARDOUS VAPORS, KEEP UPWIND.

TOXICITY

NAPROPAMIDE: TOXICITY DATA: 4640 MG/KG SKIN-RABBIT LD50; 5000 MG/KG ORAL-RAT LD50. CARCINOGEN STATUS: NONE. ACUTE TOXICITY LEVEL: MODERATELY TOXIC BY INGESTION; SLIGHTLY TOXIC BY DERMAL ABSORPTION. TARGET EFFECTS: NO DATA AVAILABLE.

HEALTH EFFECTS AND FIRST AID

INHALATION: NAPROPAMIDE: **ACUTE EXPOSURE-** NO DATA AVAILABLE. **CHRONIC EXPOSURE-** NO DATA AVAILABLE.

FIRST AID- REMOVE FROM EXPOSURE AREA TO FRESH AIR IMMEDIATELY. IF BREATHING HAS STOPPED, PERFORM ARTIFICIAL RESPIRATION. KEEP PERSON WARM AND AT REST. TREAT SYMPTOMATICALLY AND SUPPORTIVELY. GET MEDICAL ATTENTION IMMEDIATELY.

SKIN CONTACT: NAPROPAMIDE: **ACUTE EXPOSURE-** THIS MATERIAL WAS REPORTED TO BE NONIRRITATING TO THE SKIN. **CHRONIC EXPOSURE-** NO DATA AVAILABLE.

FIRST AID- REMOVE CONTAMINATED CLOTHING AND SHOES IMMEDIATELY. WASH AFFECTED AREA WITH SOAP OR MILD DETERGENT AND LARGE AMOUNTS OF WATER UNTIL NO EVIDENCE OF CHEMICAL REMAINS (APPROXIMATELY 15-20 MINUTES). GET MEDICAL ATTENTION IMMEDIATELY.

EYE CONTACT: NAPROPAMIDE: **ACUTE EXPOSURE-** THIS MATERIAL WAS REPORTED TO BE NONIRRITATING. **CHRONIC EXPOSURE-** NO DATA AVAILABLE.

FIRST AID- WASH EYES IMMEDIATELY WITH LARGE AMOUNTS OF WATER OR NORMAL SALINE, OCCASIONALLY LIFTING UPPER AND LOWER LIDS, UNTIL NO EVIDENCE OF CHEMICAL REMAINS (APPROXIMATELY 15-20 MINUTES). GET MEDICAL ATTENTION IMMEDIATELY.

INGESTION: NAPROPAMIDE: **ACUTE EXPOSURE-** A LETHAL DOSE IN RATS WAS 5000 MG/KG; SYMPTOMS WERE NOT REPORTED. **CHRONIC EXPOSURE-** IN CHRONIC FEEDING EXPERIMENTS WITH RATS, HISTOLOGICAL CHANGES IN LIVER AND KIDNEY WERE OBSERVED AT THE 2000 PPM LEVEL AND INCREASED ALKALINE PHOSPHATASE LEVELS IN LIVER AND KIDNEY AT THE 7000 PPM LEVEL. INCREASED LIVER WEIGHTS, DECREASED BODY WEIGHT, INCREASED SAP, AND DECREASED HEMOGLOBIN AND HEMATOCRIT WERE OBSERVED IN A 13-WEEK STUDY OF DOGS FED 100 MG/KG/DAY. DECREASED PUP WEIGHT GAIN AND DECREASED PARENTAL WEIGHT GAIN WAS NOTED IN A 3-GENERATION STUDY OF RATS FED 100 MG/KG/DAY.

FIRST AID- REMOVE BY GASTRIC LAVAGE AND CATHARSIS. MAINTAIN BLOOD PRESSURE AND AIRWAY. GIVE OXYGEN IF RESPIRATION IS DEPRESSED. DO NOT PERFORM GASTRIC LAVAGE IF VICTIM IS UNCONSCIOUS. GET MEDICAL ATTENTION IMMEDIATELY (DREISBACH, HANDBOOK OF POISONING, 12TH ED.).
ADMINISTRATION OF LAVAGE OR OXYGEN SHOULD BE PERFORMED BY QUALIFIED MEDICAL PERSONNEL.

ANTIDOTE: NO SPECIFIC ANTIDOTE. TREAT SYMPTOMATICALLY AND SUPPORTIVELY.

REACTIVITY

REACTIVITY: STABLE UNDER NORMAL TEMPERATURES AND PRESSURES.

INCOMPATIBILITIES: NAPROPAMIDE: OXIDIZERS (STRONG): FIRE AND EXPLOSION HAZARD.

DECOMPOSITION: THERMAL DECOMPOSITION PRODUCTS MAY INCLUDE TOXIC OXIDES OF CARBON AND NITROGEN.

POLYMERIZATION: HAZARDOUS POLYMERIZATION HAS NOT BEEN REPORTED TO OCCUR UNDER NORMAL TEMPERATURES AND PRESSURES.

STORAGE AND DISPOSAL

OBSERVE ALL FEDERAL, STATE AND LOCAL REGULATIONS WHEN STORING OR DISPOSING OF THIS SUBSTANCE. FOR ASSISTANCE, CONTACT THE DISTRICT DIRECTOR OF THE ENVIRONMENTAL PROTECTION AGENCY.

STORAGE

STORE IN ACCORDANCE WITH 40 CFR 165 RECOMMENDED PROCEDURES FOR THE DISPOSAL AND STORAGE OF PESTICIDES AND PESTICIDE CONTAINERS.
STORE AWAY FROM INCOMPATIBLE SUBSTANCES.

****DISPOSAL****

DISPOSAL MUST BE IN ACCORDANCE WITH 40 CFR 165 RECOMMENDED PROCEDURES FOR THE DISPOSAL AND STORAGE OF PESTICIDES AND PESTICIDE CONTAINERS.

CONDITIONS TO AVOID

MAY BURN BUT DOES NOT IGNITE READILY. AVOID CONTACT WITH STRONG OXIDIZERS, EXCESSIVE HEAT, SPARKS, OR OPEN FLAME.

SPILL AND LEAK PROCEDURES

OCCUPATIONAL SPILL: SWEEP UP AND PLACE IN SUITABLE CLEAN, DRY CONTAINERS FOR RECLAMATION OR LATER DISPOSAL. DO NOT FLUSH SPILLED MATERIAL INTO SEWER. KEEP UNNECESSARY PEOPLE AWAY.

PROTECTIVE EQUIPMENT

VENTILATION: PROVIDE LOCAL EXHAUST OR GENERAL DILUTION VENTILATION SYSTEM.

RESPIRATOR: THE FOLLOWING RESPIRATORS ARE RECOMMENDED BASED ON INFORMATION FOUND IN THE PHYSICAL DATA, TOXICITY AND HEALTH EFFECTS SECTIONS. THEY ARE RANKED IN ORDER FROM MINIMUM TO MAXIMUM RESPIRATORY PROTECTION. THE SPECIFIC RESPIRATOR SELECTED MUST BE BASED ON CONTAMINATION LEVELS FOUND IN THE WORK PLACE, MUST NOT EXCEED THE WORKING LIMITS OF THE RESPIRATOR AND BE JOINTLY APPROVED BY THE NATIONAL INSTITUTE FOR OCCUPATIONAL SAFETY AND HEALTH AND THE MINE SAFETY AND HEALTH ADMINISTRATION (NIOSH-MSHA).

CHEMICAL CARTRIDGE RESPIRATOR WITH AN ORGANIC VAPOR CARTRIDGE(S) IN COMBINATION WITH A DUST AND MIST FILTER.

GAS MASK WITH ORGANIC VAPOR CANISTER (CHIN-STYLE OR FRONT- OR BACK-MOUNTED CANISTER) WITH A DUST AND MIST FILTER.

GAS MASK WITH ORGANIC VAPOR CANISTER (CHIN-STYLE OR FRONT- OR BACK-MOUNTED CANISTER) WITH A PARTICULATE FILTER.

POWERED AIR-PURIFYING RESPIRATOR WITH A HIGH-EFFICIENCY FILTER.

TYPE 'C' SUPPLIED-AIR RESPIRATOR WITH A FULL FACEPIECE OPERATED IN A PRESSURE-DEMAND OR OTHER POSITIVE PRESSURE MODE.

SELF-CONTAINED BREATHING APPARATUS WITH A FULL FACEPIECE OPERATED IN PRESSURE-DEMAND OR OTHER POSITIVE PRESSURE MODE.

FOR FIREFIGHTING AND OTHER IMMEDIATELY DANGEROUS TO LIFE OR HEALTH CONDITIONS: SELF-CONTAINED BREATHING APPARATUS WITH FULL FACEPIECE OPERATED IN PRESSURE-DEMAND OR OTHER POSITIVE PRESSURE MODE.

SUPPLIED-AIR RESPIRATOR WITH FULL FACEPIECE AND OPERATED IN PRESSURE-DEMAND OR OTHER POSITIVE PRESSURE MODE IN COMBINATION WITH AN AUXILIARY SELF-CONTAINED BREATHING APPARATUS OPERATED IN PRESSURE-DEMAND OR OTHER POSITIVE PRESSURE MODE.

CLOTHING: EMPLOYEE MUST WEAR APPROPRIATE PROTECTIVE (IMPERVIOUS) CLOTHING AND EQUIPMENT TO PREVENT REPEATED OR PROLONGED SKIN CONTACT WITH THIS SUBSTANCE.

GLOVES: EMPLOYEE MUST WEAR APPROPRIATE PROTECTIVE GLOVES TO PREVENT CONTACT WITH THIS SUBSTANCE.

EYE PROTECTION: EMPLOYEE MUST WEAR SPLASH-PROOF OR DUST-RESISTANT SAFETY GOGGLES TO PREVENT EYE CONTACT WITH THIS SUBSTANCE.

EMERGENCY EYE WASH: WHERE THERE IS ANY POSSIBILITY THAT AN EMPLOYEE'S EYES MAY BE EXPOSED TO THIS SUBSTANCE, THE EMPLOYER SHOULD PROVIDE AN EYE WASH FOUNTAIN WITHIN THE IMMEDIATE WORK AREA FOR EMERGENCY USE.

AUTHORIZED BY- OCCUPATIONAL HEALTH SERVICES, INC.

CREATION DATE: 10/04/89 ***REVISION DATE:*** 05/31/90

MATERIAL SAFETY DATA SHEET

OCCUPATIONAL HEALTH SERVICES, INC.
AGRICULTURE AND PESTICIDE DIVISION
450 SEVENTH AVENUE, SUITE 2407
NEW YORK, NEW YORK 10123
1-800-445-MSDS OR (212) 967-1100

EMERGENCY CONTACT:
JOHN S. BRANSFORD, JR. (615) 292-1180

SUBSTANCE IDENTIFICATION

CAS-NUMBER 23564-06-9

SUBSTANCE: <u>THIOPHANATE</u>

TRADE NAMES/SYNONYMS: 1,2-BIS(3-ETHOXYCARBONYL-2-THIOUREIDO)BENZENE; DIETHYL 4,4'-O-PHENYLENE-BIS(3-THIOALLOPHANATE); 1,2-DI(3-ETHOXYCARBONYL-2-THIOUREIDO)BENZENE; CARBAMIC ACID, (1,2-PHENYLENEBIS(IMINOCARBONOTHIOYL))BIS-, DIETHYL ESTER; (1,2-PHENYLENEBIS(IMINOCARBONOTHIOYL))BIS-CARBAMIC ACID DIETHYL ESTER; ALLOPHANIC ACID, 4,4'-O-PHENYLENEBIS(3-THIO-, DIETHYL ESTER; 4,4'-O-PHENYLENEBIS(3-THIO-ALLOPHANIC ACID) DIETHYL ESTER; DIETHYL 4,4'-(O-PHENYLENE)BIS(3-THIOALLOPHANATE); DIETHYL (1,2-PHENYLENEBIS(IMINOCARBONOTHIOYL)BIS(CARBAMATE); CERCOBIN; ENOVIT; ETHYL THIOPHANATE; NF 35; NEMAFAX; PELT; THIOFANATE; THIOPHANATE-ETHYL; TOPSIN; C14H18N4O4S2; PST72322

CHEMICAL FAMILY: THIOCARBAMATE

MOLECULAR FORMULA: C6-H4(N-H-C-S-N-H-C-O2-C2-H5)2

MOLECULAR WEIGHT: 370.44

CERCLA RATINGS (SCALE 0-3): HEALTH=1 FIRE=1 REACTIVITY=0 PERSISTENCE=2

NFPA RATINGS (SCALE 0-4): HEALTH=U FIRE=1 REACTIVITY=0

COMPONENTS AND CONTAMINANTS

COMPONENT: THIOPHANATE ***PERCENT:*** 100
CAS# 23564-06-9

EXPOSURE LIMITS: NO OCCUPATIONAL EXPOSURE LIMITS ESTABLISHED BY OSHA, ACGIH, OR NIOSH.

PHYSICAL DATA

DESCRIPTION: COLORLESS, CRYSTALLINE SOLID

MELTING POINT: 383 F (195 C) (DECOMPOSES) ***SPECIFIC GRAVITY:*** NOT AVAILABLE

SOLUBILITY IN WATER: ALMOST INSOLUBLE

SOLVENT SOLUBILITY: SPARINGLY SOLUBLE IN MOST ORGANIC SOLVENTS

FIRE AND EXPLOSION DATA

FIRE AND EXPLOSION HAZARD: SLIGHT FIRE HAZARD WHEN EXPOSED TO HEAT OR FLAME.

FIREFIGHTING MEDIA: DRY CHEMICAL, CARBON DIOXIDE, HALON, WATER SPRAY OR STANDARD FOAM (1987 EMERGENCY RESPONSE GUIDEBOOK, DOT P 5800.4). FOR LARGER FIRES, USE WATER SPRAY, FOG OR STANDARD FOAM (1987 EMERGENCY RESPONSE GUIDEBOOK, DOT P 5800.4).

FIREFIGHTING: MOVE CONTAINERS FROM FIRE AREA IF POSSIBLE. FIGHT FIRE FROM MAXIMUM DISTANCE. STAY AWAY FROM STORAGE TANK ENDS. DIKE FIRE CONTROL WATER FOR LATER DISPOSAL. DO NOT SCATTER MATERIAL (1987 EMERGENCY RESPONSE GUIDEBOOK, DOT P 5800.4, GUIDE PAGE 55). EXTINGUISH FIRE USING AGENTS SUITABLE FOR TYPE OF SURROUNDING FIRE. USE WATER IN FLOODING AMOUNTS AS FOG. USE ALCOHOL FOAM, CARBON DIOXIDE OR DRY CHEMICAL. AVOID BREATHING TOXIC VAPORS, KEEP UPWIND.

TOXICITY

THIOPHANATE: TOXICITY DATA: >15,000 MG/KG SKIN-RAT LD50 (PENNWALT CORP.); >15,000 MG/KG ORAL-RAT LD50 (PENNWALT CORP.); 2400 MG/KG INTRAPERITONEAL-RAT LD50; 3750 MG/KG INTRAPERITONEAL-MOUSE LD50; MUTAGENIC DATA (RTECS); REPRODUCTIVE EFFECTS DATA (RTECS). CARCINOGEN STATUS: NONE. ACUTE TOXICITY LEVEL: SLIGHTLY TOXIC BY DERMAL ABSORPTION; RELATIVELY NONTOXIC BY INGESTION. TARGET EFFECTS: SENSITIZER-SKIN. ADDITIONAL DATA: CONSUMPTION OF ALCOHOLIC BEVERAGES MAY ENHANCE THE TOXIC EFFECTS.

HEALTH EFFECTS AND FIRST AID

INHALATION: THIOPHANATE: **<u>ACUTE EXPOSURE</u>-** MICE EXPOSED TO 100,000 MG/M3 OF THIOPHANATE-METHYL FOR 30, 60, 120 MINUTES, DEVELOPED LACRIMATION, SALIVATION, AND NASAL EXUDATION WITHIN 5 TO 6 MINUTES AFTER EXPOSURE BEGAN; NO FATALITIES WERE REPORTED. **<u>CHRONIC EXPOSURE</u>-** NO DATA AVAILABLE.

FIRST AID- REMOVE FROM EXPOSURE AREA TO FRESH AIR IMMEDIATELY. IF BREATHING HAS STOPPED, PERFORM ARTIFICIAL RESPIRATION. KEEP PERSON WARM AND AT REST. TREAT SYMPTOMATICALLY AND SUPPORTIVELY. GET MEDICAL ATTENTION IMMEDIATELY.

SKIN CONTACT: THIOPHANATE: SENSITIZER. **<u>ACUTE EXPOSURE</u>-** SKIN SENSITIZATION MAY OCCUR IN PERSONS PREVIOUSLY EXPOSED. A LETHAL DOSE IN RATS BY DERMAL ABSORPTION WAS GREATER THAN 15,000 MG/KG. **<u>CHRONIC EXPOSURE</u>-** PROLONGED OR REPEATED EXPOSURE MAY CAUSE SENSITIZATION DERMATITIS.

FIRST AID- REMOVE CONTAMINATED CLOTHING AND SHOES IMMEDIATELY. WASH AFFECTED AREA WITH SOAP OR MILD DETERGENT AND LARGE AMOUNTS OF WATER UNTIL NO EVIDENCE OF CHEMICAL REMAINS (APPROXIMATELY 15-20 MINUTES). GET MEDICAL ATTENTION IMMEDIATELY.

EYE CONTACT: THIOPHANATE: **<u>ACUTE EXPOSURE</u>-** A 10% CONCENTRATION OF THIOPHANATE-METHYL APPLIED TO THE EYES OF RABBITS WAS NOT IRRITATING. **<u>CHRONIC EXPOSURE</u>-** NO DATA AVAILABLE.

FIRST AID- WASH EYES IMMEDIATELY WITH LARGE AMOUNTS OF WATER OR NORMAL SALINE, OCCASIONALLY LIFTING UPPER AND LOWER LIDS, UNTIL NO EVIDENCE OF CHEMICAL REMAINS (APPROXIMATELY 15-20 MINUTES). GET MEDICAL ATTENTION IMMEDIATELY.

INGESTION: THIOPHANATE: **ACUTE EXPOSURE**- A LETHAL DOSE OF THIOPHANATE IN RATS WAS GREATER THAN 15,000 MG/KG. HIGH DOSES OF THIOPHANATE-METHYL PRODUCED TREMORS LEADING TO TONIC OR CLONIC CONVULSIONS, NOSE BLEEDING AND LACRIMATION IN RATS. IN RABBITS AND AND DOGS, THIS MATERIAL CAUSED DECREASED RESPIRATORY RATE, LETHARGY, LOSS OF TONE OF THE ABDOMINAL MUSCLES, DISCHARGE FROM THE EYES, AND MYDRIASIS PRIOR TO DEATH. **CHRONIC EXPOSURE**- SOME PATHOLOGICAL CHANGES IN THE THYROID WERE OBSERVED IN RATS AND DOGS REPEATEDLY FED THIS MATERIAL. REPRODUCTIVE EFFECTS HAVE BEEN REPORTED IN ANIMALS.

FIRST AID- REMOVE BY GASTRIC LAVAGE AND CATHARSIS. MAINTAIN BLOOD PRESSURE AND AIRWAY. GIVE OXYGEN IF RESPIRATION IS DEPRESSED. DO NOT PERFORM GASTRIC LAVAGE IF VICTIM IS UNCONSCIOUS. GET MEDICAL ATTENTION IMMEDIATELY (DREISBACH, HANDBOOK OF POISONING, 12TH ED.).
ADMINISTRATION OF LAVAGE OR OXYGEN SHOULD BE PERFORMED BY QUALIFIED MEDICAL PERSONNEL.

ANTIDOTE: NO SPECIFIC ANTIDOTE. TREAT SYMPTOMATICALLY AND SUPPORTIVELY.

REACTIVITY

REACTIVITY: STABLE UNDER NORMAL TEMPERATURES AND PRESSURES.
INCOMPATIBILITIES: THIOPHANATE: ALKALINE SOLUTIONS: UNSTABLE.
DECOMPOSITION: THERMAL DECOMPOSITION MAY RELEASE TOXIC OXIDES OF NITROGEN AND SULFUR.
POLYMERIZATION: HAZARDOUS POLYMERIZATION HAS NOT BEEN REPORTED TO OCCUR UNDER NORMAL TEMPERATURES AND PRESSURES.

STORAGE AND DISPOSAL

OBSERVE ALL FEDERAL, STATE AND LOCAL REGULATIONS WHEN STORING OR DISPOSING OF THIS SUBSTANCE. FOR ASSISTANCE, CONTACT THE DISTRICT DIRECTOR OF THE ENVIRONMENTAL PROTECTION AGENCY.

STORAGE

STORE IN ACCORDANCE WITH 40 CFR 165 RECOMMENDED PROCEDURES FOR THE DISPOSAL AND STORAGE OF PESTICIDES AND PESTICIDE CONTAINERS.
STORE AWAY FROM INCOMPATIBLE SUBSTANCES.

DISPOSAL

DISPOSAL MUST BE IN ACCORDANCE WITH 40 CFR 165 RECOMMENDED PROCEDURES FOR THE DISPOSAL AND STORAGE OF PESTICIDES AND PESTICIDE CONTAINERS.

CONDITIONS TO AVOID

MAY BURN BUT DOES NOT IGNITE READILY. CONTAINERS MAY EXPLODE IN HEAT OF FIRE.

SPILL AND LEAK PROCEDURES

OCCUPATIONAL SPILL: DO NOT TOUCH SPILLED MATERIAL. STOP LEAK IF YOU CAN DO IT WITHOUT RISK. USE WATER SPRAY TO REDUCE VAPORS. FOR SMALL SPILLS, TAKE UP WITH SAND OR OTHER ABSORBENT MATERIAL AND PLACE INTO CONTAINERS FOR LATER DISPOSAL. FOR SMALL DRY SPILLS, WITH A CLEAN SHOVEL PLACE MATERIAL INTO CLEAN, DRY CONTAINERS AND COVER. MOVE CONTAINERS FROM SPILL AREA. FOR LARGER SPILLS, DIKE FAR AHEAD OF SPILL FOR LATER DISPOSAL. KEEP UNNECESSARY PEOPLE AWAY. ISOLATE HAZARD AREA AND DENY ENTRY. VENTILATE CLOSED SPACES BEFORE ENTERING.

PROTECTIVE EQUIPMENT

VENTILATION: PROVIDE LOCAL EXHAUST OR GENERAL DILUTION VENTILATION SYSTEM.

RESPIRATOR: THE FOLLOWING RESPIRATORS ARE RECOMMENDED BASED ON INFORMATION FOUND IN THE PHYSICAL DATA, TOXICITY AND HEALTH EFFECTS SECTIONS. THEY ARE RANKED IN ORDER FROM MINIMUM TO MAXIMUM RESPIRATORY PROTECTION. THE SPECIFIC RESPIRATOR SELECTED MUST BE BASED ON CONTAMINATION LEVELS FOUND IN THE WORK PLACE, MUST NOT EXCEED THE WORKING LIMITS OF THE RESPIRATOR AND BE JOINTLY APPROVED BY THE NATIONAL INSTITUTE FOR OCCUPATIONAL SAFETY AND HEALTH AND THE MINE SAFETY AND HEALTH ADMINISTRATION (NIOSH-MSHA).
CHEMICAL CARTRIDGE RESPIRATOR WITH AN ORGANIC VAPOR CARTRIDGE(S) WITH A FULL FACEPIECE AND ORGANIC VAPOR CARTRIDGE(S) IN COMBINATION WITH A DUST AND MIST FILTER. POWERED AIR-PURIFYING RESPIRATOR WITH A TIGHT-FITTING FACEPIECE AND ORGANIC VAPOR CARTRIDGE(S) IN COMBINATION WITH A HIGH-EFFICIENCY PARTICULATE FILTER.
TYPE 'C' SUPPLIED-AIR RESPIRATOR WITH A FULL FACEPIECE OPERATED IN A PRESSURE-DEMAND OR OTHER POSITIVE PRESSURE MODE.
SELF-CONTAINED BREATHING APPARATUS WITH A FULL FACEPIECE OPERATED IN PRESSURE-DEMAND OR OTHER POSITIVE PRESSURE MODE.
FOR FIREFIGHTING AND OTHER IMMEDIATELY DANGEROUS TO LIFE OR HEALTH CONDITIONS:
SELF-CONTAINED BREATHING APPARATUS WITH FULL FACEPIECE OPERATED IN PRESSURE-DEMAND OR OTHER POSITIVE PRESSURE MODE.
SUPPLIED-AIR RESPIRATOR WITH FULL FACEPIECE AND OPERATED IN PRESSURE-DEMAND OR OTHER POSITIVE PRESSURE MODE IN COMBINATION WITH AN AUXILIARY SELF-CONTAINED BREATHING APPARATUS OPERATED IN PRESSURE-DEMAND OR OTHER POSITIVE PRESSURE MODE.

CLOTHING: EMPLOYEE MUST WEAR APPROPRIATE PROTECTIVE (IMPERVIOUS) CLOTHING AND EQUIPMENT TO PREVENT REPEATED OR PROLONGED SKIN CONTACT WITH THIS SUBSTANCE.

GLOVES: EMPLOYEE MUST WEAR APPROPRIATE PROTECTIVE GLOVES TO PREVENT CONTACT WITH THIS SUBSTANCE.

EYE PROTECTION: EMPLOYEE MUST WEAR SPLASH-PROOF OR DUST-RESISTANT SAFETY GOGGLES TO PREVENT EYE CONTACT WITH THIS SUBSTANCE.
EMERGENCY EYE WASH: WHERE THERE IS ANY POSSIBILITY THAT AN EMPLOYEE'S EYES MAY BE EXPOSED TO THIS SUBSTANCE, THE EMPLOYER SHOULD PROVIDE AN EYE WASH FOUNTAIN WITHIN THE IMMEDIATE WORK AREA FOR EMERGENCY USE.

AUTHORIZED BY- OCCUPATIONAL HEALTH SERVICES, INC.
CREATION DATE: 10/05/89 ***REVISION DATE:*** 05/10/90

MATERIAL SAFETY DATA SHEET

OCCUPATIONAL HEALTH SERVICES, INC.
AGRICULTURE AND PESTICIDE DIVISION
450 SEVENTH AVENUE, SUITE 2407
NEW YORK, NEW YORK 10123
1-800-445-MSDS OR (212) 967-1100

EMERGENCY CONTACT:
JOHN S. BRANSFORD, JR. (615) 292-1180

SUBSTANCE IDENTIFICATION

CAS-NUMBER 2941-55-1
***SUBSTANCE:* ETHIOLATE**
TRADE NAMES/SYNONYMS: CARBAMOTHIOIC ACID, DIETHYL-, S-ETHYL ESTER; DIETHYL-CARBAMOETHIOIC ACID S-ETHYL ESTER; CARBAMIC ACID, DIETHYLTHIO-, S-ETHYL ESTER; DIETHYLTHIO-CARBAMIC ACID S-ETHYL ESTER; ETIROX; ETHIOLAT; S-ETHYL DIETHYLCARBAMOTHIOATE; S-ETHYL DIETHYLTHIOCARBAMATE; C7H15NOS; PST72327
CHEMICAL FAMILY: THIOCARBAMATE
MOLECULAR FORMULA: (C2-H5)2-N-C-O-S-C2-H5
MOLECULAR WEIGHT: 161.27
CERCLA RATINGS (SCALE 0-3): HEALTH=3 FIRE=1 REACTIVITY=0 PERSISTENCE=0
NFPA RATINGS (SCALE 0-4): HEALTH=3 FIRE=1 REACTIVITY=0

COMPONENTS AND CONTAMINANTS

COMPONENT: ETHIOLATE ***PERCENT:*** 100
CAS# 2941-55-1
OTHER CONTAMINANTS: NONE
EXPOSURE LIMITS: NO OCCUPATIONAL EXPOSURE LIMITS ESTABLISHED BY OSHA, ACGIH, OR NIOSH.

PHYSICAL DATA

DESCRIPTION: LIGHT YELLOW LIQUID. ***BOILING POINT:*** 403 F (206 C)
MELTING POINT: -103 F (-75 C) ***SPECIFIC GRAVITY:*** NOT AVAILABLE
EVAPORATION RATE: NOT AVAILABLE ***SOLUBILITY IN WATER:*** SLIGHT
SOLVENT SOLUBILITY: SOLUBLE IN ACETONITRILE, MOST ORGANIC SOLVENTS.

FIRE AND EXPLOSION DATA

FIRE AND EXPLOSION HAZARD: SLIGHT FIRE HAZARD WHEN EXPOSED TO HEAT OR FLAME.
FIREFIGHTING MEDIA: DRY CHEMICAL, CARBON DIOXIDE, HALON, WATER SPRAY OR STANDARD FOAM (1987 EMERGENCY RESPONSE GUIDEBOOK, DOT P 5800.4).
FOR LARGER FIRES, USE WATER SPRAY, FOG OR STANDARD FOAM (1987 EMERGENCY RESPONSE GUIDEBOOK, DOT P 5800.4).
FIREFIGHTING: MOVE CONTAINERS FROM FIRE AREA IF POSSIBLE. FIGHT FIRE FROM MAXIMUM DISTANCE. STAY AWAY FROM STORAGE TANK ENDS. DIKE FIRE CONTROL WATER FOR LATER DISPOSAL. DO NOT SCATTER MATERIAL (1987 EMERGENCY RESPONSE GUIDEBOOK, DOT P 5800.4, GUIDE PAGE 55).

EXTINGUISH ONLY IF FLOW CAN BE STOPPED; USE FLOODING AMOUNTS OF WATER AS FOG, SOLID STREAMS MAY BE INEFFECTIVE. COOL CONTAINERS WITH FLOODING AMOUNTS OF WATER, APPLY FROM AS FAR A DISTANCE AS POSSIBLE. USE ALCOHOL FOAM, CARBON DIOXIDE OR DRY CHEMICAL. AVOID BREATHING TOXIC VAPORS, KEEP UPWIND.

TOXICITY

ETHIOLATE: 400 MG/KG ORAL-RAT LD50; CARCINOGEN STATUS: NONE. ETHIOLATE IS TOXIC AND MAY CAUSE EYE, SKIN AND MUCOUS MEMBRANE IRRITATION. ANIMAL STUDIES INDICATE THAT SOME THIOCARBAMATES ARE WEAK CHOLINESTERASE INHIBITOR.

HEALTH EFFECTS AND FIRST AID

INHALATION: ETHIOLATE: **ACUTE EXPOSURE-** INHALATION OF EXCESSIVE AMOUNTS OF SOME THIOCARBAMATES CAUSES SCRATCHY THROAT, SNEEZING, AND COUGHING. ANIMAL STUDIES INDICATE THAT SOME THIOCARBAMATES ARE CHOLINESTERASE INHIBITORS. EARLY SYMPTOMS OF CHOLINESTERASE INHIBITION ARE BLURRED VISION, FATIGUE, HEADACHE, VERTIGO, NAUSEA, MIOSIS, ABDOMINAL CRAMPS AND DIARRHEA. SEVERE INHIBITION OF CHOLINESTERASE MAY CAUSE EXCESSIVE SWEATING, TEARING, BRADYCARDIA, GIDDINESS, SLURRED SPEECH, CONFUSION, PULMONARY EDEMA, CONVULSIONS, AND COMA. **CHRONIC EXPOSURE-** NO DATA AVAILABLE.

FIRST AID- REMOVE FROM EXPOSURE AREA TO FRESH AIR IMMEDIATELY. IF BREATHING HAS STOPPED, PERFORM ARTIFICIAL RESPIRATION. KEEP PERSON WARM AND AT REST. TREAT SYMPTOMATICALLY AND SUPPORTIVELY. GET MEDICAL ATTENTION IMMEDIATELY.

SKIN CONTACT: ETHIOLATE: **ACUTE EXPOSURE-** MAY CAUSE IRRITATION. ANIMAL STUDIES INDICATE THAT SOME THIOCARBAMATES ARE WEAK CHOLINESTERASE INHIBITORS. **CHRONIC EXPOSURE-** NO DATA AVAILABLE.

FIRST AID- REMOVE CONTAMINATED CLOTHING AND SHOES IMMEDIATELY. WASH AFFECTED AREA WITH SOAP OR MILD DETERGENT AND LARGE AMOUNTS OF WATER UNTIL NO EVIDENCE OF CHEMICAL REMAINS (APPROXIMATELY 15-20 MINUTES). GET MEDICAL ATTENTION IMMEDIATELY.

EYE CONTACT: ETHIOLATE: **ACUTE EXPOSURE-** MAY CAUSE IRRITATION. **CHRONIC EXPOSURE-** PROLONGED OR REPEATED EXPOSURE MAY CAUSE IRRITATION.

FIRST AID- WASH EYES IMMEDIATELY WITH LARGE AMOUNTS OF WATER OR NORMAL SALINE, OCCASIONALLY LIFTING UPPER AND LOWER LIDS, UNTIL NO EVIDENCE OF CHEMICAL REMAINS (APPROXIMATELY 15-20 MINUTES). GET MEDICAL ATTENTION IMMEDIATELY.

INGESTION: ETHIOLATE: TOXIC. **ACUTE EXPOSURE-** A LETHAL DOSE IN RATS WAS 400 MG/KG. ANIMAL STUDIES INDICATE THAT SOME THIOCARBAMATES ARE WEAK CHOLINESTERASE INHIBITORS. **CHRONIC EXPOSURE-** NO DATA AVAILABLE.

FIRST AID- GIVE SYRUP OF IPECAC, FOLLOWED BY 1-2 GLASSES OF WATER, TO INDUCE VOMITING (ADULTS: 30 ML). FOLLOWING EMESIS, ADMINISTER 30-50 GRAMS ACTIVATED CHARCOAL. FOLLOW CHARCOAL WITH SODIUM OR MAGNESIUM SULFATE, 250 MG/KG, TO REMOVE TOXICANT FROM THE GUT BY CATHARSIS (EPA, RECOGNITION AND MANAGEMENT OF PESTICIDE POISONINGS, 3RD ED.). FIRST AID SHOULD BE ADMINISTERED UNDER THE DIRECTION OF QUALIFIED MEDICAL PERSONNEL. GET MEDICAL ATTENTION.

ANTIDOTE: NO SPECIFIC ANTIDOTE. TREAT SYMPTOMATICALLY AND SUPPORTIVELY.

REACTIVITY

REACTIVITY: STABLE UNDER NORMAL TEMPERATURES AND PRESSURES.

INCOMPATIBILITIES: ETHIOLATE: NO DATA AVAILABLE.

DECOMPOSITION: THERMAL DECOMPOSITION PRODUCTS MAY INCLUDE TOXIC OXIDES OF CARBON, NITROGEN, AND SULFUR.

POLYMERIZATION: HAZARDOUS POLYMERIZATION HAS NOT BEEN REPORTED TO OCCUR UNDER NORMAL TEMPERATURES AND PRESSURES.

STORAGE AND DISPOSAL

OBSERVE ALL FEDERAL, STATE AND LOCAL REGULATIONS WHEN STORING OR DISPOSING OF THIS SUBSTANCE. FOR ASSISTANCE, CONTACT THE DISTRICT DIRECTOR OF THE ENVIRONMENTAL PROTECTION AGENCY.

STORAGE

STORE IN ACCORDANCE WITH 40 CFR 165 RECOMMENDED PROCEDURES FOR THE DISPOSAL AND STORAGE OF PESTICIDES AND PESTICIDE CONTAINERS.

DISPOSAL

DISPOSAL MUST BE IN ACCORDANCE WITH 40 CFR 165 RECOMMENDED PROCEDURES FOR THE DISPOSAL AND STORAGE OF PESTICIDES AND PESTICIDE CONTAINERS.

CONDITIONS TO AVOID

MAY BURN BUT DOES NOT IGNITE READILY. CONTAINERS MAY EXPLODE IN HEAT OF FIRE.

SPILL AND LEAK PROCEDURES

OCCUPATIONAL SPILL: DO NOT TOUCH SPILLED MATERIAL. STOP LEAK IF YOU CAN DO IT WITHOUT RISK. USE WATER SPRAY TO REDUCE VAPORS. FOR SMALL SPILLS, TAKE UP WITH SAND OR OTHER ABSORBENT MATERIAL AND PLACE INTO CONTAINERS FOR LATER DISPOSAL. FOR SMALL DRY SPILLS, WITH A CLEAN SHOVEL PLACE MATERIAL INTO CLEAN, DRY CONTAINERS AND COVER. MOVE CONTAINERS FROM SPILL AREA. FOR LARGER SPILLS, DIKE FAR AHEAD OF SPILL FOR LATER DISPOSAL. KEEP UNNECESSARY PEOPLE AWAY. ISOLATE HAZARD AREA AND DENY ENTRY. VENTILATE CLOSED SPACES BEFORE ENTERING.

PROTECTIVE EQUIPMENT

VENTILATION: PROVIDE LOCAL EXHAUST OR PROCESS ENCLOSURE VENTILATION SYSTEM.

RESPIRATOR: THE FOLLOWING RESPIRATORS ARE RECOMMENDED BASED ON INFORMATION FOUND IN THE PHYSICAL DATA, TOXICITY AND HEALTH EFFECTS SECTIONS. THEY ARE RANKED IN ORDER FROM MINIMUM TO MAXIMUM RESPIRATORY PROTECTION. THE SPECIFIC RESPIRATOR SELECTED MUST BE BASED ON CONTAMINATION LEVELS FOUND IN THE WORK PLACE, MUST NOT EXCEED THE WORKING LIMITS OF THE RESPIRATOR AND BE JOINTLY APPROVED BY THE NATIONAL INSTITUTE FOR OCCUPATIONAL SAFETY AND HEALTH AND THE MINE SAFETY AND HEALTH ADMINISTRATION (NIOSH-MSHA).

CHEMICAL CARTRIDGE RESPIRATOR WITH AN ORGANIC VAPOR CARTRIDGE(S) WITH A FULL FACEPIECE AND ORGANIC VAPOR CARTRIDGE(S) IN COMBINATION WITH A DUST AND MIST FILTER.

POWERED AIR-PURIFYING RESPIRATOR WITH A TIGHT-FITTING FACEPIECE AND ORGANIC VAPOR CARTRIDGE(S) IN COMBINATION WITH A HIGH-EFFICIENCY PARTICULATE FILTER.

TYPE 'C' SUPPLIED-AIR RESPIRATOR WITH A FULL FACEPIECE OPERATED IN A PRESSURE-DEMAND OR OTHER POSITIVE PRESSURE MODE.

SELF-CONTAINED BREATHING APPARATUS WITH A FULL FACEPIECE OPERATED IN PRESSURE-DEMAND OR OTHER POSITIVE PRESSURE MODE.

FOR FIREFIGHTING AND OTHER IMMEDIATELY DANGEROUS TO LIFE OR HEALTH CONDITIONS: SELF-CONTAINED BREATHING APPARATUS WITH FULL FACEPIECE OPERATED IN PRESSURE-DEMAND OR OTHER POSITIVE PRESSURE MODE.

SUPPLIED-AIR RESPIRATOR WITH FULL FACEPIECE AND OPERATED IN PRESSURE-DEMAND OR OTHER POSITIVE PRESSURE MODE IN COMBINATION WITH AN AUXILIARY SELF-CONTAINED BREATHING APPARATUS OPERATED IN PRESSURE-DEMAND OR OTHER POSITIVE PRESSURE MODE.

CLOTHING: EMPLOYEE MUST WEAR APPROPRIATE PROTECTIVE (IMPERVIOUS) CLOTHING AND EQUIPMENT TO PREVENT ANY POSSIBILITY OF SKIN CONTACT WITH THIS SUBSTANCE.

GLOVES: EMPLOYEE MUST WEAR APPROPRIATE PROTECTIVE GLOVES TO PREVENT CONTACT WITH THIS SUBSTANCE.

EYE PROTECTION: EMPLOYEE MUST WEAR SPLASH-PROOF OR DUST-RESISTANT SAFETY GOGGLES AND A FACESHIELD TO PREVENT CONTACT WITH THIS SUBSTANCE.

EMERGENCY WASH FACILITIES: WHERE THERE IS ANY POSSIBILITY THAT AN EMPLOYEE'S EYES AND/OR SKIN MAY BE EXPOSED TO THIS SUBSTANCE, THE EMPLOYER SHOULD PROVIDE AN EYE WASH FOUNTAIN AND QUICK DRENCH SHOWER WITHIN THE IMMEDIATE WORK AREA FOR EMERGENCY USE.

AUTHORIZED BY- OCCUPATIONAL HEALTH SERVICES, INC.

CREATION DATE: 10/04/89 ***REVISION DATE:*** 05/07/90

MATERIAL SAFETY DATA SHEET

OCCUPATIONAL HEALTH SERVICES, INC.
AGRICULTURE AND PESTICIDE DIVISION
450 SEVENTH AVENUE, SUITE 2407
NEW YORK, NEW YORK 10123
1-800-445-MSDS OR (212) 967-1100

EMERGENCY CONTACT:
JOHN S. BRANSFORD, JR. (615) 292-1180

SUBSTANCE IDENTIFICATION

CAS-NUMBER 42576-02-3

SUBSTANCE: **BIFENOX**

TRADE NAMES/SYNONYMS: BENZOIC ACID, 5-(2,4-DICHLOROPHENOXY)-2-NITRO-, METHYL ESTER; METHYL 5-(2,4-DICHLOROPHENOXY)-2-NITROBENZOATE; 2,4-DICHLOROPHENYL 3'-METHOXYCARBONYL-4'-NITROPHENYL ETHER; 5-(2,4-

DICHLOROPHENOXY)-2-NITROBENZOIC ACID METHYL ESTER; BIPHENOX; MC 4379; MODOWN; C14H9CL2NO5; PST72332

CHEMICAL FAMILY: ETHER, AROMATIC
HALOGEN
NITRO

MOLECULAR FORMULA: (CL)2-C6-H3-O-C6-H3-(N-O2)-(C-O2-C-H3)

MOLECULAR WEIGHT: 342.14

CERCLA RATINGS (SCALE 0-3): HEALTH=U FIRE=1 REACTIVITY=0 PERSISTENCE=2

NFPA RATINGS (SCALE 0-4): HEALTH=U FIRE=1 REACTIVITY=0

COMPONENTS AND CONTAMINANTS

COMPONENT: BIFENOX ***PERCENT:*** 100.0
CAS# 42576-02-3

OTHER CONTAMINANTS: NONE

EXPOSURE LIMITS: NO OCCUPATIONAL EXPOSURE LIMITS ESTABLISHED BY OSHA, ACGIH, OR NIOSH.

PHYSICAL DATA

DESCRIPTION: PALE YELLOW TO TAN CRYSTALLINE SOLID WITH A SLIGHTLY AROMATIC ODOR.

BOILING POINT: >554 F (>290 C) (DECOMPOSES)

MELTING POINT: 183-187 F (84-86 C)

SPECIFIC GRAVITY: 1.155 ***VAPOR PRESSURE:*** NEGLIGIBLE @ 30 C

SOLUBILITY IN WATER: .35 PPM @ 25 C

SOLVENT SOLUBILITY: SOLUBLE IN ACETONE, CHLOROBENZENE, XYLENE, ISOPHORONE, METHYL ISOAMYL KETONE, METHYL CHLORIDE, ETHYLENE DICHLORIDE, MESITYL OXIDE, METHYL METHACRYLATE, CYCLOHEXANONE, DIACETONE ALCOHOL, 1,4-DIOXANE;
MODERATELY SOLUBLE IN CORN OIL, METHANOL, PINE OIL; SLIGHTLY SOLUBLE IN KEROSENE AND ALIPHATIC HYDROCARBONS.

FIRE AND EXPLOSION DATA

FIRE AND EXPLOSION HAZARD: SLIGHT FIRE HAZARD WHEN EXPOSED TO HEAT OR FLAME.
DUST-AIR MIXTURES MAY IGNITE OR EXPLODE.

FIREFIGHTING MEDIA: DRY CHEMICAL, CARBON DIOXIDE, HALON, WATER SPRAY OR STANDARD FOAM (1987 EMERGENCY RESPONSE GUIDEBOOK, DOT P 5800.4).
FOR LARGER FIRES, USE WATER SPRAY, FOG OR STANDARD FOAM (1987 EMERGENCY RESPONSE GUIDEBOOK, DOT P 5800.4).

FIREFIGHTING: MOVE CONTAINER FROM FIRE AREA IF POSSIBLE. DO NOT SCATTER SPILLED MATERIAL WITH HIGH PRESSURE WATER STREAMS. DIKE FIRE CONTROL WATER FOR LATER DISPOSAL (1987 EMERGENCY RESPONSE GUIDEBOOK, DOT P 5800.4, GUIDE PAGE 31).
USE AGENTS SUITABLE FOR TYPE OF SURROUNDING FIRE. AVOID BREATHING HAZARDOUS VAPORS, KEEP UPWIND.

TOXICITY

BIFENOX: TOXICITY DATA: >200000 MG/M3 INHALATION-RAT LC50 (85JFAN); >20,000 MG/KG SKIN-RABBIT LD50 (85JFAN). 6400 MG/KG ORAL-RAT LD50; 4556 MG/KG ORAL-MOUSE LD50. CARCINOGEN STATUS: NONE. ACUTE TOXICITY LEVEL: SLIGHTLY TOXIC BY DERMAL ABSORPTION AND INGESTION. RELATIVELY NON-TOXIC BY INHALATION. TARGET EFFECTS: NO DATA AVAILABLE. ADDITIONAL DATA: REPEATED ABSORPTION OF CHLORINATED DIPHENYL ETHERS HAS RESULTED IN LIVER DAMAGE IN ANIMALS.

HEALTH EFFECTS AND FIRST AID

INHALATION: BIFENOX: **ACUTE EXPOSURE-** A LETHAL CONCENTRATION IN RATS WAS GREATER THAN 200,000 MG/M3. **CHRONIC EXPOSURE-** NO DATA AVAILABLE.

FIRST AID- REMOVE FROM EXPOSURE AREA TO FRESH AIR IMMEDIATELY. IF BREATHING HAS STOPPED, PERFORM ARTIFICIAL RESPIRATION. KEEP PERSON WARM AND AT REST. TREAT SYMPTOMATICALLY AND SUPPORTIVELY. GET MEDICAL ATTENTION IMMEDIATELY.

SKIN CONTACT: BIFENOX: **ACUTE EXPOSURE-** THIS MATERIAL WAS NOT IRRITATING TO THE SKIN. **CHRONIC EXPOSURE-** NO DATA AVAILABLE.

FIRST AID- REMOVE CONTAMINATED CLOTHING AND SHOES IMMEDIATELY. WASH AFFECTED AREA WITH SOAP OR MILD DETERGENT AND LARGE AMOUNTS OF WATER UNTIL NO EVIDENCE OF CHEMICAL REMAINS (APPROXIMATELY 15-20 MINUTES). GET MEDICAL ATTENTION IMMEDIATELY.

EYE CONTACT: BIFENOX: **ACUTE EXPOSURE-** THIS MATERIAL WAS NOT IRRITATING TO RABBIT EYES. **CHRONIC EXPOSURE-** NO DATA AVAILABLE.

FIRST AID- WASH EYES IMMEDIATELY WITH LARGE AMOUNTS OF WATER OR NORMAL SALINE, OCCASIONALLY LIFTING UPPER AND LOWER LIDS, UNTIL NO EVIDENCE OF CHEMICAL REMAINS (APPROXIMATELY 15-20 MINUTES). GET MEDICAL ATTENTION IMMEDIATELY.

INGESTION: BIFENOX: **ACUTE EXPOSURE-** A LETHAL DOSE IN RATS WAS 6400 MG/KG. THE SYMPTOMS WERE NOT REPORTED. **CHRONIC EXPOSURE-** NO OBSERVABLE EFFECTS WERE NOTED IN 2-YEAR STUDIES OF RATS AND DOGS FED A 600 MG/KG DIET OR MICE FED A 50 MG/KG DIET. AN INCREASED INCIDENCE OF BLOODY TEARS WERE REPORTED IN LITTERS OF RATS GIVING BIFENOX DURING PREGNANCY.

FIRST AID- TREAT SYMPTOMATICALLY AND SUPPORTIVELY. GET MEDICAL ATTENTION IMMEDIATELY. IF VOMITING OCCURS, KEEP HEAD LOWER THAN HIPS TO PREVENT ASPIRATION.

ANTIDOTE: NO SPECIFIC ANTIDOTE. TREAT SYMPTOMATICALLY AND SUPPORTIVELY.

REACTIVITY

REACTIVITY: STABLE UNDER NORMAL TEMPERATURES AND PRESSURES.

INCOMPATIBILITIES: BIFENOX: ALUMINUM: MAY BE CORROSIVE. OXIDIZERS (STRONG): FIRE AND EXPLOSION HAZARD.

DECOMPOSITION: THERMAL DECOMPOSITION PRODUCTS MAY INCLUDE TOXIC OXIDES OF NITROGEN AND CARBON AND TOXIC AND CORROSIVE FUMES OF CHLORIDES.

POLYMERIZATION: HAZARDOUS POLYMERIZATION HAS NOT BEEN REPORTED TO OCCUR UNDER NORMAL TEMPERATURES AND PRESSURES.

STORAGE AND DISPOSAL

OBSERVE ALL FEDERAL, STATE AND LOCAL REGULATIONS WHEN STORING OR DISPOSING OF THIS SUBSTANCE. FOR ASSISTANCE, CONTACT THE DISTRICT DIRECTOR OF THE ENVIRONMENTAL PROTECTION AGENCY.

STORAGE

STORE IN ACCORDANCE WITH 40 CFR 165 RECOMMENDED PROCEDURES FOR THE DISPOSAL AND STORAGE OF PESTICIDES AND PESTICIDE CONTAINERS.
STORE AWAY FROM INCOMPATIBLE SUBSTANCES.

DISPOSAL

DISPOSAL MUST BE IN ACCORDANCE WITH 40 CFR 165 RECOMMENDED PROCEDURES FOR THE DISPOSAL AND STORAGE OF PESTICIDES AND PESTICIDE CONTAINERS.

CONDITIONS TO AVOID

MAY BURN BUT DOES NOT IGNITE READILY. AVOID CONTACT WITH STRONG OXIDIZERS, EXCESSIVE HEAT, SPARKS, OR OPEN FLAME.

SPILL AND LEAK PROCEDURES

OCCUPATIONAL SPILL: SWEEP UP AND PLACE IN SUITABLE CLEAN, DRY CONTAINERS FOR RECLAMATION OR LATER DISPOSAL. DO NOT FLUSH SPILLED MATERIAL INTO SEWER. KEEP UNNECESSARY PEOPLE AWAY.

PROTECTIVE EQUIPMENT

VENTILATION: PROVIDE LOCAL EXHAUST OR GENERAL DILUTION VENTILATION SYSTEM.

RESPIRATOR: THE FOLLOWING RESPIRATORS ARE RECOMMENDED BASED ON INFORMATION FOUND IN THE PHYSICAL DATA, TOXICITY AND HEALTH EFFECTS SECTIONS. THEY ARE RANKED IN ORDER FROM MINIMUM TO MAXIMUM RESPIRATORY PROTECTION. THE SPECIFIC RESPIRATOR SELECTED MUST BE BASED ON CONTAMINATION LEVELS FOUND IN THE WORK PLACE, MUST NOT EXCEED THE WORKING LIMITS OF THE RESPIRATOR AND BE JOINTLY APPROVED BY THE NATIONAL INSTITUTE FOR OCCUPATIONAL SAFETY AND HEALTH AND THE MINE SAFETY AND HEALTH ADMINISTRATION (NIOSH-MSHA).
CHEMICAL CARTRIDGE RESPIRATOR WITH AN ORGANIC VAPOR CARTRIDGE(S) IN COMBINATION WITH A DUST AND MIST FILTER.
GAS MASK WITH ORGANIC VAPOR CANISTER (CHIN-STYLE OR FRONT- OR BACK-MOUNTED CANISTER) WITH A DUST AND MIST FILTER.
GAS MASK WITH ORGANIC VAPOR CANISTER (CHIN-STYLE OR FRONT- OR BACK-MOUNTED CANISTER) WITH A PARTICULATE FILTER.
POWERED AIR-PURIFYING RESPIRATOR WITH A HIGH-EFFICIENCY FILTER.
TYPE 'C' SUPPLIED-AIR RESPIRATOR WITH A FULL FACEPIECE OPERATED IN A PRESSURE-DEMAND OR OTHER POSITIVE PRESSURE MODE.
SELF-CONTAINED BREATHING APPARATUS WITH A FULL FACEPIECE OPERATED IN PRESSURE-DEMAND OR OTHER POSITIVE PRESSURE MODE.
FOR FIREFIGHTING AND OTHER IMMEDIATELY DANGEROUS TO LIFE OR HEALTH CONDITIONS:
SELF-CONTAINED BREATHING APPARATUS WITH FULL FACEPIECE OPERATED IN PRESSURE-DEMAND OR OTHER POSITIVE PRESSURE MODE.
SUPPLIED-AIR RESPIRATOR WITH FULL FACEPIECE AND OPERATED IN PRESSURE-DEMAND OR OTHER POSITIVE PRESSURE MODE IN COMBINATION WITH AN AUXILIARY SELF-CONTAINED BREATHING APPARATUS OPERATED IN PRESSURE-DEMAND OR OTHER POSITIVE PRESSURE MODE.

CLOTHING: EMPLOYEE MUST WEAR APPROPRIATE PROTECTIVE (IMPERVIOUS) CLOTHING AND EQUIPMENT TO PREVENT REPEATED OR PROLONGED SKIN CONTACT WITH THIS SUBSTANCE.
GLOVES: EMPLOYEE MUST WEAR APPROPRIATE PROTECTIVE GLOVES TO PREVENT CONTACT WITH THIS SUBSTANCE.
EYE PROTECTION: EMPLOYEE MUST WEAR SPLASH-PROOF OR DUST-RESISTANT SAFETY GOGGLES TO PREVENT EYE CONTACT WITH THIS SUBSTANCE.
EMERGENCY EYE WASH: WHERE THERE IS ANY POSSIBILITY THAT AN EMPLOYEE'S EYES MAY BE EXPOSED TO THIS SUBSTANCE, THE EMPLOYER SHOULD PROVIDE AN EYE WASH FOUNTAIN WITHIN THE IMMEDIATE WORK AREA FOR EMERGENCY USE.

AUTHORIZED BY- OCCUPATIONAL HEALTH SERVICES, INC.
CREATION DATE: 05/22/90 ***REVISION DATE:*** 05/31/90

MATERIAL SAFETY DATA SHEET

OCCUPATIONAL HEALTH SERVICES, INC.
AGRICULTURE AND PESTICIDE DIVISION
450 SEVENTH AVENUE, SUITE 2407
NEW YORK, NEW YORK 10123
1-800-445-MSDS OR (212) 967-1100

EMERGENCY CONTACT:
JOHN S. BRANSFORD, JR. (615) 292-1180

SUBSTANCE IDENTIFICATION

CAS-NUMBER 4147-51-7
SUBSTANCE: DIPROPETRYN
TRADE NAMES/SYNONYMS: 1,3,5-TRIAZINE-2,4-DIAMINE, 6-(ETHYLTHIO)-N,N'-BIS(1-METHYLETHYL)-; 6-(ETHYLTHIO)-N,N'-BIS(1-METHYLETHYL)-1,3,5-TRIAZINE-2,4-DIAMINE; S-TRIAZINE, 2-(ETHYLTHIO)-4,6-BIS(ISOPROPYLAMINO)-; 2-(ETHYLTHIO)-4,6-BIS(ISOPROPYLAMINO)-S-TRIAZINE; 2-(ETHYLTHIO)-4,6-BIS(ISOPROPYLAMINO)-1,3,5-TRIAZINE; 6-ETHYLTHIO-N,N-DI-ISOPROPYL-1,3,5-TRIAZINE-2,4-DIAMINE; COTOFOR; GS 16068; SANCAP; C11H21N5S; PST72333
CHEMICAL FAMILY: TRIAZINE
MOLECULAR FORMULA: C11-H21-N5-S
MOLECULAR WEIGHT: 255.39
CERCLA RATINGS (SCALE 0-3): HEALTH=2 FIRE=1 REACTIVITY=0 PERSISTENCE=2
NFPA RATINGS (SCALE 0-4): HEALTH=2 FIRE=1 REACTIVITY=0

COMPONENTS AND CONTAMINANTS

COMPONENT: DIPROPETRYN ***PERCENT:*** 100
CAS# 4147-51-7
OTHER CONTAMINANTS: NONE
EXPOSURE LIMITS: NO OCCUPATIONAL EXPOSURE LIMITS ESTABLISHED BY OSHA, ACGIH, OR NIOSH.

PHYSICAL DATA

DESCRIPTION: COLORLESS POWDER ***MELTING POINT:*** 219-223 F (104-106 C)
SPECIFIC GRAVITY: 1.120 ***VAPOR PRESSURE:*** NEGLIGIBLE
SOLUBILITY IN WATER: 16 PPM @ 20 C
SOLVENT SOLUBILITY: SOLUBLE IN ACETONE, METHYLENE CHLORIDE, METHANOL, OCTANOL, TOLUENE, ETHANOL; SLIGHTLY SOLUBLE IN HEXANE.

FIRE AND EXPLOSION DATA

FIRE AND EXPLOSION HAZARD: SLIGHT FIRE HAZARD WHEN EXPOSED TO HEAT OR FLAME.
FIREFIGHTING MEDIA: DRY CHEMICAL, CARBON DIOXIDE, HALON, WATER SPRAY OR STANDARD FOAM (1987 EMERGENCY RESPONSE GUIDEBOOK, DOT P 5800.4).
FOR LARGER FIRES, USE WATER SPRAY, FOG OR STANDARD FOAM (1987 EMERGENCY RESPONSE GUIDEBOOK, DOT P 5800.4).
FIREFIGHTING: MOVE CONTAINERS FROM FIRE AREA IF POSSIBLE (1987 EMERGENCY RESPONSE GUIDEBOOK, DOT P 5800.4, GUIDE PAGE 53).
EXTINGUISH USING AGENTS SUITABLE FOR SURROUNDING FIRE. USE FLOODING QUANTITIES OF WATER AS A FOG. KEEP MATERIAL OUT OF SEWERS AND WATER SOURCES. DO NOT TOUCH SPILLED MATERIAL. AVOID BREATHING HAZARDOUS FUMES; KEEP UPWIND.

TOXICITY

DIPROPETRYN: TOXICITY DATA: 10 GM/KG SKIN-RABBIT LD50; 3900 MG/KG ORAL-RAT LD50. CARCINOGEN STATUS: NONE. ACUTE TOXICITY LEVEL: MODERATELY TOXIC BY INGESTION; SLIGHTLY TOXIC BY DERMAL ABSORPTION. TARGET EFFECTS: NO DATA AVAILABLE.

HEALTH EFFECTS AND FIRST AID

INHALATION: DIPROPETRYN: **ACUTE EXPOSURE-** NO DATA AVAILABLE. **CHRONIC EXPOSURE-** NO DATA AVAILABLE.
FIRST AID- REMOVE FROM EXPOSURE AREA TO FRESH AIR IMMEDIATELY. IF BREATHING HAS STOPPED, PERFORM ARTIFICIAL RESPIRATION. KEEP PERSON WARM AND AT REST. TREAT SYMPTOMATICALLY AND SUPPORTIVELY. GET MEDICAL ATTENTION IMMEDIATELY.

SKIN CONTACT: DIPROPETRYN: **ACUTE EXPOSURE-** THIS MATERIAL WAS MILDLY IRRITATING TO RABBIT SKIN. **CHRONIC EXPOSURE-** NO DATA AVAILABLE.
FIRST AID- REMOVE CONTAMINATED CLOTHING AND SHOES IMMEDIATELY. WASH AFFECTED AREA WITH SOAP OR MILD DETERGENT AND LARGE AMOUNTS OF WATER UNTIL NO EVIDENCE OF CHEMICAL REMAINS (APPROXIMATELY 15-20 MINUTES). GET MEDICAL ATTENTION IMMEDIATELY.

EYE CONTACT: DIPROPETRYN: **ACUTE EXPOSURE-** THIS MATERIAL WAS NOT AN IRRITANT IN RABBIT EYES. **CHRONIC EXPOSURE-** NO DATA AVAILABLE.
FIRST AID- WASH EYES IMMEDIATELY WITH LARGE AMOUNTS OF WATER OR NORMAL SALINE, OCCASIONALLY LIFTING UPPER AND LOWER LIDS, UNTIL NO EVIDENCE OF CHEMICAL REMAINS (APPROXIMATELY 15-20 MINUTES). GET MEDICAL ATTENTION IMMEDIATELY.

INGESTION: DIPROPETRYN: **ACUTE EXPOSURE-** A LETHAL DOSE IN RATS WAS 3900 MG/KG. **CHRONIC EXPOSURE-** NO ADVERSE EFFECTS WERE OBSERVED IN RATS FED 27 MG/KG/DAY OR IN DOGS FED 13 MG/KG/DAY.
FIRST AID- REMOVE BY GASTRIC LAVAGE AND CATHARSIS. MAINTAIN BLOOD PRESSURE AND AIRWAY. GIVE OXYGEN IF RESPIRATION IS DEPRESSED. DO NOT PERFORM GASTRIC LAVAGE IF VICTIM IS UNCONSCIOUS. GET MEDICAL ATTENTION IMMEDIATELY (DREISBACH, HANDBOOK OF POISONING, 12TH ED.).
ADMINISTRATION OF LAVAGE OR OXYGEN SHOULD BE PERFORMED BY QUALIFIED MEDICAL PERSONNEL.
ANTIDOTE: NO SPECIFIC ANTIDOTE. TREAT SYMPTOMATICALLY AND SUPPORTIVELY.

REACTIVITY

REACTIVITY: STABLE UNDER NORMAL TEMPERATURES AND PRESSURES.
INCOMPATIBILITIES: DIPROPETRYN: NO DATA AVAILABLE.
DECOMPOSITION: THERMAL DECOMPOSITION PRODUCTS MAY INCLUDE TOXIC OXIDES OF CARBON AND NITROGEN.
POLYMERIZATION: HAZARDOUS POLYMERIZATION HAS NOT BEEN REPORTED TO OCCUR UNDER NORMAL TEMPERATURES AND PRESSURES.

STORAGE AND DISPOSAL

OBSERVE ALL FEDERAL, STATE AND LOCAL REGULATIONS WHEN STORING OR DISPOSING OF THIS SUBSTANCE. FOR ASSISTANCE, CONTACT THE DISTRICT DIRECTOR OF THE ENVIRONMENTAL PROTECTION AGENCY.

****STORAGE****

STORE IN ACCORDANCE WITH 40 CFR 165 RECOMMENDED PROCEDURES FOR THE DISPOSAL AND STORAGE OF PESTICIDES AND PESTICIDE CONTAINERS.

****DISPOSAL****

DISPOSAL MUST BE IN ACCORDANCE WITH 40 CFR 165 RECOMMENDED PROCEDURES FOR THE DISPOSAL AND STORAGE OF PESTICIDES AND PESTICIDE CONTAINERS.

CONDITIONS TO AVOID

MAY BURN BUT DOES NOT IGNITE READILY.

SPILL AND LEAK PROCEDURES

OCCUPATIONAL SPILL: DO NOT TOUCH SPILLED MATERIAL. STOP LEAK IF YOU CAN DO IT WITHOUT RISK. FOR SMALL SPILLS, TAKE UP WITH SAND OR OTHER ABSORBENT MATERIAL AND PLACE INTO CONTAINERS FOR LATER DISPOSAL. FOR SMALL DRY SPILLS, WITH A CLEAN SHOVEL PLACE MATERIAL INTO CLEAN, DRY CONTAINER AND COVER. MOVE CONTAINERS FROM SPILL AREA. FOR LARGER SPILLS, DIKE FAR AHEAD OF SPILL FOR LATER DISPOSAL. KEEP UNNECESSARY PEOPLE AWAY. ISOLATE HAZARD AREA AND DENY ENTRY.

PROTECTIVE EQUIPMENT

VENTILATION: PROVIDE LOCAL EXHAUST OR GENERAL DILUTION VENTILATION SYSTEM.
RESPIRATOR: THE FOLLOWING RESPIRATORS ARE RECOMMENDED BASED ON INFORMATION FOUND IN THE PHYSICAL DATA, TOXICITY AND HEALTH EFFECTS SECTIONS. THEY ARE RANKED IN ORDER FROM MINIMUM TO MAXIMUM RESPIRATORY PROTECTION. THE SPECIFIC RESPIRATOR SELECTED MUST BE BASED ON CONTAMINATION LEVELS FOUND IN THE WORK PLACE, MUST NOT EXCEED THE WORKING LIMITS OF THE RESPIRATOR AND BE JOINTLY APPROVED BY THE

NATIONAL INSTITUTE FOR OCCUPATIONAL SAFETY AND HEALTH AND THE MINE SAFETY AND HEALTH ADMINISTRATION (NIOSH-MSHA).
CHEMICAL CARTRIDGE RESPIRATOR WITH AN ORGANIC VAPOR CARTRIDGE(S) WITH A FULL FACEPIECE AND ORGANIC VAPOR CARTRIDGE(S) IN COMBINATION WITH A DUST AND MIST FILTER.
POWERED AIR-PURIFYING RESPIRATOR WITH A TIGHT-FITTING FACEPIECE AND ORGANIC VAPOR CARTRIDGE(S) IN COMBINATION WITH A HIGH-EFFICIENCY PARTICULATE FILTER.
TYPE 'C' SUPPLIED-AIR RESPIRATOR WITH A FULL FACEPIECE OPERATED IN A PRESSURE-DEMAND OR OTHER POSITIVE PRESSURE MODE.
SELF-CONTAINED BREATHING APPARATUS WITH A FULL FACEPIECE OPERATED IN PRESSURE-DEMAND OR OTHER POSITIVE PRESSURE MODE.
FOR FIREFIGHTING AND OTHER IMMEDIATELY DANGEROUS TO LIFE OR HEALTH CONDITIONS:
SELF-CONTAINED BREATHING APPARATUS WITH FULL FACEPIECE OPERATED IN PRESSURE-DEMAND OR OTHER POSITIVE PRESSURE MODE.
SUPPLIED-AIR RESPIRATOR WITH FULL FACEPIECE AND OPERATED IN PRESSURE-DEMAND OR OTHER POSITIVE PRESSURE MODE IN COMBINATION WITH AN AUXILIARY SELF-CONTAINED BREATHING APPARATUS OPERATED IN PRESSURE-DEMAND OR OTHER POSITIVE PRESSURE MODE.

CLOTHING: EMPLOYEE MUST WEAR APPROPRIATE PROTECTIVE (IMPERVIOUS) CLOTHING AND EQUIPMENT TO PREVENT REPEATED OR PROLONGED SKIN CONTACT WITH THIS SUBSTANCE.

GLOVES: EMPLOYEE MUST WEAR APPROPRIATE PROTECTIVE GLOVES TO PREVENT CONTACT WITH THIS SUBSTANCE.

EYE PROTECTION: EMPLOYEE MUST WEAR SPLASH-PROOF OR DUST-RESISTANT SAFETY GOGGLES TO PREVENT EYE CONTACT WITH THIS SUBSTANCE.
EMERGENCY EYE WASH: WHERE THERE IS ANY POSSIBILITY THAT AN EMPLOYEE'S EYES MAY BE EXPOSED TO THIS SUBSTANCE, THE EMPLOYER SHOULD PROVIDE AN EYE WASH FOUNTAIN WITHIN THE IMMEDIATE WORK AREA FOR EMERGENCY USE.

AUTHORIZED BY- OCCUPATIONAL HEALTH SERVICES, INC.
CREATION DATE: 10/04/89 ***REVISION DATE:*** 05/11/90

MATERIAL SAFETY DATA SHEET

OCCUPATIONAL HEALTH SERVICES, INC.
AGRICULTURE AND PESTICIDE DIVISION
450 SEVENTH AVENUE, SUITE 2407
NEW YORK, NEW YORK 10123
1-800-445-MSDS OR (212) 967-1100

EMERGENCY CONTACT:
JOHN S. BRANSFORD, JR. (615) 292-1180

SUBSTANCE IDENTIFICATION

CAS-NUMBER 53558-25-1

SUBSTANCE: PYRIMINIL

TRADE NAMES/SYNONYMS: N-(NITROPHENYL)-N'-(3-PYRIDINYLMETHYL)UREA; PYRIDYLMETHYL-N'-PARA-NITROPHENYL UREA; 1-(4-NITROPHENYL)-3-(3-PYRIDYLMETHYL)UREA; N-3-PYRIDYLMETHYL-N'-PARA-NITROPHENYLUREA; 1-(3-PYRIDYLMETHYL)-3-(4-NITROPHENYL)UREA; UREA, N-(4-NITROPHENYL)-N'-(3-PYRIDINYLMETHYL)-; PYRIMINYL; PYRINURON; RH 787; VACOR; C13H12N4O3; PST72334

CHEMICAL FAMILY: PYRIDINE

MOLECULAR FORMULA: C13-H12-N4-O3

MOLECULAR WEIGHT: 272.29

CERCLA RATINGS (SCALE 0-3): HEALTH=3 FIRE=U REACTIVITY=U PERSISTENCE=2

NFPA RATINGS (SCALE 0-4): HEALTH=3 FIRE=U REACTIVITY=U

COMPONENTS AND CONTAMINANTS

COMPONENT: PYRIMINIL ***PERCENT:*** 100.0
CAS# 53558-25-1

OTHER CONTAMINANTS: NONE

EXPOSURE LIMITS: PYRIMINIL: 100/10,000 POUNDS SARA SECTION 302 THRESHOLD PLANNING QUANTITY 1 POUND SARA SECTION 304 REPORTABLE QUANTITY

PHYSICAL DATA

DESCRIPTION: YELLOW, RESEMBLING CORN MEAL

MELTING POINT: 443 F (223 C) DECOMPOSES ***SPECIFIC GRAVITY:*** NOT AVAILABLE

SOLUBILITY IN WATER: NOT AVAILABLE

FIRE AND EXPLOSION DATA

FIRE AND EXPLOSION HAZARD: UNKNOWN FIRE AND EXPLOSION HAZARD.

FIREFIGHTING MEDIA: DRY CHEMICAL, CARBON DIOXIDE, HALON, WATER SPRAY OR STANDARD FOAM (1987 EMERGENCY RESPONSE GUIDEBOOK, DOT P 5800.4).
FOR LARGER FIRES, USE WATER SPRAY, FOG OR STANDARD FOAM (1987 EMERGENCY RESPONSE GUIDEBOOK, DOT P 5800.4).

FIREFIGHTING: MOVE CONTAINERS FROM FIRE AREA IF POSSIBLE (1987 EMERGENCY RESPONSE GUIDEBOOK, DOT P 5800.4, GUIDE PAGE 53).
EXTINGUISH USING AGENT SUITABLE FOR TYPE OF SURROUNDING FIRE. AVOID BREATHING VAPORS AND DUSTS. KEEP UPWIND.

TRANSPORTATION DATA

DEPARTMENT OF TRANSPORTATION HAZARD CLASSIFICATION 49 CFR 172.101: POISON B
DEPARTMENT OF TRANSPORTATION LABELING REQUIREMENTS 49 CFR 172.101 AND SUBPART E: POISON
DEPARTMENT OF TRANSPORTATION PACKAGING REQUIREMENTS: 49 CFR 173.365 EXCEPTIONS: 49 CFR 173.364

TOXICITY

PYRIMINIL: TOXICITY DATA: 5571 UG/KG ORAL-MAN TDLO; 22286 UG/KG ORAL-MAN LDLO; 6200 UG/KG ORAL-RAT LD50; 56500 UG/KG ORAL-MOUSE LD50; 700 MG/KG ORAL-DOG LD50; 12800 UG/KG UNREPORTED-RAT LD50; 17200 UG/KG UNREPORTED-MOUSE LD50. CARCINOGEN STATUS: NONE. ACUTE TOXICITY LEVEL: HIGHLY TOXIC BY INGESTION. TARGET EFFECTS: NEUROTOXIN. POISONING MAY AFFECT THE HEART.

HEALTH EFFECTS AND FIRST AID

INHALATION: PYRIMINIL: **ACUTE EXPOSURE-** NO DATA AVAILABLE. **CHRONIC EXPOSURE-** NO DATA AVAILABLE.

FIRST AID- REMOVE FROM EXPOSURE AREA TO FRESH AIR IMMEDIATELY. IF BREATHING HAS STOPPED, PERFORM ARTIFICIAL RESPIRATION. KEEP PERSON WARM AND AT REST. TREAT SYMPTOMATICALLY AND SUPPORTIVELY. GET MEDICAL ATTENTION IMMEDIATELY.

SKIN CONTACT: PYRIMINIL: **ACUTE EXPOSURE-** NO DATA AVAILABLE. **CHRONIC EXPOSURE-** NO DATA AVAILABLE.

FIRST AID- REMOVE CONTAMINATED CLOTHING AND SHOES IMMEDIATELY. WASH AFFECTED AREA WITH SOAP OR MILD DETERGENT AND LARGE AMOUNTS OF WATER UNTIL NO EVIDENCE OF CHEMICAL REMAINS (APPROXIMATELY 15-20 MINUTES). GET MEDICAL ATTENTION IMMEDIATELY.

EYE CONTACT: PYRIMINIL: **ACUTE EXPOSURE-** NO DATA AVAILABLE. **CHRONIC EXPOSURE-** NO DATA AVAILABLE.

FIRST AID- WASH EYES IMMEDIATELY WITH LARGE AMOUNTS OF WATER OR NORMAL SALINE, OCCASIONALLY LIFTING UPPER AND LOWER LIDS, UNTIL NO EVIDENCE OF CHEMICAL REMAINS (APPROXIMATELY 15-20 MINUTES). GET MEDICAL ATTENTION IMMEDIATELY.

INGESTION: PYRIMINIL: NEUROTOXIN/HIGHLY TOXIC. **ACUTE EXPOSURE-** SYMPTOMS MAY NOT APPEAR FOR 4 TO 48 HOURS AFTER INGESTION. THE INITIAL SYMPTOMS ARE USUALLY NAUSEA, VOMITING, ABDOMINAL CRAMPS, CHILLS, AND CONFUSION. LATER MANIFESTATIONS ARE ACHING AND FINE TREMORS OF THE EXTREMITIES, DILATED PUPILS, PLANTAR HYPERESTHESIA, MUSCLE WEAKNESS, DYSPHAGIA, CHEST PAIN, POSTURAL HYPOTENSION, ANOREXIA, DIARRHEA, URINARY RETENTION, HYPOTHERMIA, AND COMA. DEATH MAY RESULT FORM RESPIRATORY FAILURE, CARDIOVASCULAR COLLAPSE, OR KETOACIDOSIS. SURVIVORS OF THE ACUTE PHASE OF POISONING ARE OFTEN LEFT WITH PERMANENT SEQUELAE: POSTURAL HYPOTENSION, DIABETES MELLITUS, BLADDER DYSTONIA, BOWEL DYSTONIA, AND PERIPHERAL NEUROPATHY. DIABETES MELLITUS MAY APPEAR UP TO SIX MONTHS AFTER POISONING. **CHRONIC EXPOSURE-** NO DATA AVAILABLE.

FIRST AID- IF TOXICANT WAS INGESTED RECENTLY, EVACUATE THE STOMACH BY INTUBATION, ASPIRATION, AND LAVAGE WITH 2-3 LITERS ISOTONIC SALINE. BEFORE WITHDRAWING STOMACH TUBE, INSTILL 30-50 GM OF ACTIVATED CHARCOAL AS A SLURRY IN 3-4 OUNCES OF WATER, TO LIMIT ABSORPTION OF REMAINING TOXICANT. AS SOON AS PATIENT CAN TOLERATE ORAL FLUIDS AFTER WITHDRAWAL OF STOMACH TUBE, GIVE SODIUM OR MAGNESIUM SULFATE, 0.25 GM/KG BODY WEIGHT IN 1-6 OUNCES OF WATER TO INDUCE CATHARSIS. REPEAT DOSE IN 4 HOURS IF PATIENT HAS HAD NO BOWEL MOVEMENT. (MORGAN, RECOGNITION AND MANAGEMENT OF PESTICIDE POSIONINGS, THIRD EDITION.)

ANTIDOTE: THE FOLLOWING ANTIDOTE HAS BEEN RECOMMENDED. HOWEVER, THE DECISION AS TO WHETHER THE SEVERITY OF POISONING REQUIRES ADMINISTRATION OF ANY ANTIDOTE AND ACTUAL DOSE REQUIRED SHOULD BE MADE BY QUALIFIED MEDICAL PERSONNEL.
ADMINISTER NICOTINAMIDE (NIACINAMIDE) INTRAVENOUSLY, SLOWLY, OR

INTRAMUSCULARLY. FOR ADULTS, GIVE 500 MG IMMEDIATELY, THEN REPEAT INJECTIONS OF 200-400 MG EVERY 4 HOURS FOR 10-12 DOSES. WITHIN THIS RANGE, SELECT THE DOSE ON THE BASIS OF BODY WEIGHT AND AND THE ESTIMATED QUANTITY OF POISONING INGESTED. IF MANIFESTATIONS OF POISONING APPEAR, GIVE NICOTINAMIDE BY CONTINUOUS IV INFUSION AT ABOUT 100 MG PER HOUR. THERE IS PROBABLY NO ADVANTAGE IN GIVING MORE THAN 3000 MG PER DAY OF NICOTINAMIDE. AFTER 2-3 DAYS OF PARENTERAL THERAPY, GIVE NICOTINAMIDE BY MOUTH, 100 MG FOUR TIMES DAILY, FOR 2 WEEKS. (MORGAN, RECOGNITION AND MANAGEMENT OF PESTICIDE POISONINGS, THIRD EDITION.) ANTIDOTE SHOULD BE ADMINISTERED BY A QUALIFIED MEDICAL PERSONNEL.

REACTIVITY

REACTIVITY: NO DATA AVAILABLE.

INCOMPATIBILITIES: PYRIMINIL: OXIDIZERS (STRONG): FIRE AND EXPLOSION HAZARD.

DECOMPOSITION: THERMAL DECOMPOSITION PRODUCTS MAY INCLUDE TOXIC OXIDES OF NITROGEN.

POLYMERIZATION: HAZARDOUS POLYMERIZATION HAS NOT BEEN REPORTED TO OCCUR UNDER NORMAL TEMPERATURES AND PRESSURES.

STORAGE AND DISPOSAL

OBSERVE ALL FEDERAL, STATE AND LOCAL REGULATIONS WHEN STORING OR DISPOSING OF THIS SUBSTANCE. FOR ASSISTANCE, CONTACT THE DISTRICT DIRECTOR OF THE ENVIRONMENTAL PROTECTION AGENCY.

****STORAGE****

STORE IN ACCORDANCE WITH 40 CFR 165 RECOMMENDED PROCEDURES FOR THE DISPOSAL AND STORAGE OF PESTICIDES AND PESTICIDE CONTAINERS.

THRESHOLD PLANNING QUANTITY (TPQ): THE SUPERFUND AMENDMENTS AND REAUTHORIZATION ACT (SARA) SECTION 302 REQUIRES THAT EACH FACILITY WHERE ANY EXTREMELY HAZARDOUS SUBSTANCE IS PRESENT IN A QUANTITY EQUAL TO OR GREATER THAN THE TPQ ESTABLISHED FOR THAT SUBSTANCE NOTIFY THE STATE EMERGENCY RESPONSE COMMISSION FOR THE STATE IN WHICH IT IS LOCATED. SECTION 303 OF SARA REQUIRES THESE FACILITIES TO PARTICIPATE IN LOCAL EMERGENCY RESPONSE PLANNING (40 CFR 355.30).

****DISPOSAL****

DISPOSAL MUST BE IN ACCORDANCE WITH 40 CFR 165 RECOMMENDED PROCEDURES FOR THE DISPOSAL AND STORAGE OF PESTICIDES AND PESTICIDE CONTAINERS.

CONDITIONS TO AVOID

NONE REPORTED.

SPILL AND LEAK PROCEDURES

OCCUPATIONAL SPILL: DO NOT TOUCH SPILLED MATERIAL. STOP LEAK IF YOU CAN DO IT WITHOUT RISK. FOR SMALL SPILLS, TAKE UP WITH SAND OR OTHER ABSORBENT MATERIAL AND PLACE INTO CONTAINERS FOR LATER DISPOSAL. FOR SMALL DRY SPILLS, WITH A CLEAN SHOVEL PLACE MATERIAL INTO CLEAN, DRY CONTAINER AND COVER. MOVE CONTAINERS FROM SPILL AREA. FOR LARGER SPILLS, DIKE FAR AHEAD OF SPILL FOR LATER DISPOSAL. KEEP UNNECESSARY PEOPLE AWAY. ISOLATE HAZARD AREA AND DENY ENTRY.

REPORTABLE QUANTITY (RQ): 1 POUND THE SUPERFUND AMENDMENTS AND REAUTHORIZATION ACT (SARA) SECTION 304 REQUIRES THAT A RELEASE EQUAL TO OR GREATER THAN THE REPORTABLE QUANTITY FOR THIS SUBSTANCE BE IMMEDIATELY REPORTED TO THE LOCAL EMERGENCY PLANNING COMMITTEE AND THE STATE EMERGENCY RESPONSE COMMISSION (40 CFR 355.40). IF THE RELEASE OF THIS SUBSTANCE IS REPORTABLE UNDER CERCLA SECTION 103, THE NATIONAL RESPONSE CENTER MUST BE NOTIFIED IMMEDIATELY AT (800) 424-8802 OR (202) 426-2675 IN THE METROPOLITAN WASHINGTON, D.C. AREA (40 CFR 302.6).

PROTECTIVE EQUIPMENT

VENTILATION: PROCESS ENCLOSURE RECOMMENDED.

RESPIRATOR: THE FOLLOWING RESPIRATORS ARE RECOMMENDED BASED ON INFORMATION FOUND IN THE PHYSICAL DATA, TOXICITY AND HEALTH EFFECTS SECTIONS. THEY ARE RANKED IN ORDER FROM MINIMUM TO MAXIMUM RESPIRATORY PROTECTION. THE SPECIFIC RESPIRATOR SELECTED MUST BE BASED ON CONTAMINATION LEVELS FOUND IN THE WORK PLACE, MUST NOT EXCEED THE WORKING LIMITS OF THE RESPIRATOR AND BE JOINTLY APPROVED BY THE NATIONAL INSTITUTE FOR OCCUPATIONAL SAFETY AND HEALTH AND THE MINE SAFETY AND HEALTH ADMINISTRATION (NIOSH-MSHA).

TYPE 'C' SUPPLIED-AIR RESPIRATOR WITH A FULL FACEPIECE OPERATED IN PRESSURE-DEMAND OR OTHER POSITIVE PRESSURE MODE OR WITH A FULL FACEPIECE, HELMET OR HOOD OPERATED IN CONTINOUS-FLOW MODE.

SELF-CONTAINED BREATHING APPARATUS WITH A FULL FACEPIECE OPERATED IN PRESSURE-DEMAND OR OTHER POSITIVE PRESSURE MODE.

FOR FIREFIGHTING AND OTHER IMMEDIATELY DANGEROUS TO LIFE OR HEALTH CONDITIONS:

SELF-CONTAINED BREATHING APPARATUS WITH FULL FACEPIECE OPERATED IN PRESSURE-DEMAND OR OTHER POSITIVE PRESSURE MODE.

SUPPLIED-AIR RESPIRATOR WITH FULL FACEPIECE AND OPERATED IN PRESSURE-DEMAND OR OTHER POSITIVE PRESSURE MODE IN COMBINATION WITH AN AUXILIARY SELF-CONTAINED BREATHING APPARATUS OPERATED IN PRESSURE-DEMAND OR OTHER POSITIVE PRESSURE MODE.

CLOTHING: EMPLOYEE MUST WEAR APPROPRIATE PROTECTIVE (IMPERVIOUS) CLOTHING AND EQUIPMENT TO PREVENT ANY POSSIBILITY OF SKIN CONTACT WITH THIS SUBSTANCE.

GLOVES: EMPLOYEE MUST WEAR APPROPRIATE PROTECTIVE GLOVES TO PREVENT CONTACT WITH THIS SUBSTANCE.

EYE PROTECTION: EMPLOYEE MUST WEAR SPLASH-PROOF OR DUST-RESISTANT SAFETY GOGGLES WITH OR WITHOUT A FACESHIELD TO PREVENT CONTACT WITH THIS SUBSTANCE.

EMERGENCY EYE WASH: WHERE THERE IS ANY POSSIBILITY THAT AN EMPLOYEE'S EYES MAY BE EXPOSED TO THIS SUBSTANCE, THE EMPLOYER SHOULD PROVIDE AN EYE WASH FOUNTAIN WITHIN THE IMMEDIATE WORK AREA FOR EMERGENCY USE.

AUTHORIZED BY- OCCUPATIONAL HEALTH SERVICES, INC.

CREATION DATE: 10/04/89 ***REVISION DATE:*** 05/15/90

MATERIAL SAFETY DATA SHEET

OCCUPATIONAL HEALTH SERVICES, INC.
AGRICULTURE AND PESTICIDE DIVISION
450 SEVENTH AVENUE, SUITE 2407
NEW YORK, NEW YORK 10123
1-800-445-MSDS OR (212) 967-1100

EMERGENCY CONTACT:
JOHN S. BRANSFORD, JR. (615) 292-1180

SUBSTANCE IDENTIFICATION

CAS-NUMBER 13684-56-5

SUBSTANCE: DESMEDIPHAM

TRADE NAMES/SYNONYMS: CARBAMIC ACID, (3-(((PHENYLAMINO)CARBONYL)OXY)PHENYL)-, ETHYL ESTER; CARBANILIC ACID, M-HYDROXY-, ETHYL ESTER, CARBANILATE (ESTER); (3-(((PHENYLAMINO)CARBONYL)OXY)PHENYL)CARBAMIC ACID ETHYL ESTER; M-HYDROXYCARBANILIC ACID, ETHYL ESTER, CARBANILATE (ESTER); ETHYL 3'-PHENYLCARBAMOYLOXYCARBANILATE; ETHYL 3-PHENYLCARBAMOYLOXYPHENYLCARBAMATE; 3-ETHOXYCARBONYLAMINOPHENYL PHENYLCARBAMATE; ETHYL (3-(((PHENYLAMINO)CARBONYL)OXY)PHENYL)CARBAMATE; ETHYL M-HYDROXYCARBANILATE CARBANILATE (ESTER); BETANEX; EP 475; C16H16N2O4; PST72336

CHEMICAL FAMILY: CARBAMATE

MOLECULAR FORMULA: C16-H16-N2-O4

MOLECULAR WEIGHT: 300.34

CERCLA RATINGS (SCALE 0-3): HEALTH=2 FIRE=1 REACTIVITY=0 PERSISTENCE=1

NFPA RATINGS (SCALE 0-4): HEALTH=U FIRE=1 REACTIVITY=0

COMPONENTS AND CONTAMINANTS

COMPONENT: DESMEDIPHAM ***PERCENT:*** 100.0

CAS# 13684-56-5

EXPOSURE LIMITS: NO OCCUPATIONAL EXPOSURE LIMITS ESTABLISHED BY OSHA, ACGIH, OR NIOSH.

PHYSICAL DATA

DESCRIPTION: COLORLESS OR LIGHT YELLOW, CRYSTALLINE SOLID.

MELTING POINT: 248 F (120 C) ***SPECIFIC GRAVITY:*** NOT AVAILABLE

VAPOR PRESSURE: NEGLIGIBLE ***SOLUBILITY IN WATER:*** 7 PPM

SOLVENT SOLUBILITY: SOLUBLE IN ACETONE, ISOPHORONE, METHANOL, AND POLAR ORGANIC SOLVENTS; MODERATELY SOLUBLE IN CHLOROFORM; VERY SLIGHTLY SOLUBLE IN BENZENE AND HEXANE.

FIRE AND EXPLOSION DATA

FIRE AND EXPLOSION HAZARD: SLIGHT FIRE HAZARD WHEN EXPOSED TO HEAT OR FLAME.

FIREFIGHTING MEDIA: DRY CHEMICAL, CARBON DIOXIDE, HALON, WATER SPRAY OR STANDARD FOAM (1987 EMERGENCY RESPONSE GUIDEBOOK, DOT P 5800.4).

FOR LARGER FIRES, USE WATER SPRAY, FOG OR STANDARD FOAM (1987 EMERGENCY RESPONSE GUIDEBOOK, DOT P 5800.4).

FIREFIGHTING: MOVE CONTAINER FROM FIRE AREA IF POSSIBLE. DO NOT SCATTER SPILLED MATERIAL WITH HIGH PRESSURE WATER STREAMS. DIKE FIRE CONTROL WATER FOR LATER DISPOSAL (1987 EMERGENCY RESPONSE GUIDEBOOK, DOT P 5800.4, GUIDE PAGE 31).

USE AGENTS SUITABLE FOR TYPE OF SURROUNDING FIRE. AVOID BREATHING HAZARDOUS VAPORS, KEEP UPWIND.

TOXICITY

DESMEDIPHAM: TOXICITY DATA: 10 GM/KG SKIN-RABBIT LD50; 9600 MG/KG ORAL-RAT LD50. CARCINOGEN STATUS: NONE. ACUTE TOXICITY: SLIGHTLY TOXIC BY DERMAL ABSORPTION AND INGESTION. TARGET EFFECTS: NO DATA AVAILABLE. ADDITIONAL DATA: MAY BE EXCRETED IN BREAST MILK. MAY PRODUCE CHOLINESTERASE INHIBITION IN ANIMALS.

HEALTH EFFECTS AND FIRST AID

INHALATION: DESMEDIPHAM: **ACUTE EXPOSURE**- SIGNS OF POISONING IN LABORATORY ANIMALS MAY INCLUDE SALIVATION, NASAL DISCHARGE, MUSCULAR WEAKNESS AND LABORED BREATHING. **CHRONIC EXPOSURE**- NO DATA AVAILABLE.

FIRST AID- REMOVE FROM EXPOSURE AREA TO FRESH AIR IMMEDIATELY. IF BREATHING HAS STOPPED, PERFORM ARTIFICIAL RESPIRATION. KEEP PERSON WARM AND AT REST. TREAT SYMPTOMATICALLY AND SUPPORTIVELY. GET MEDICAL ATTENTION IMMEDIATELY.

SKIN CONTACT: DESMEDIPHAM: **ACUTE EXPOSURE**- MAY CAUSE IRRITATION. **CHRONIC EXPOSURE**- NO DATA AVAILABLE.

FIRST AID- REMOVE CONTAMINATED CLOTHING AND SHOES IMMEDIATELY. WASH AFFECTED AREA WITH SOAP OR MILD DETERGENT AND LARGE AMOUNTS OF WATER UNTIL NO EVIDENCE OF CHEMICAL REMAINS (APPROXIMATELY 15-20 MINUTES). GET MEDICAL ATTENTION IMMEDIATELY.

EYE CONTACT: DESMEDIPHAM: **ACUTE EXPOSURE**- MAY CAUSE EYE IRRITATION. **CHRONIC EXPOSURE**- NO DATA AVAILABLE.

FIRST AID- WASH EYES IMMEDIATELY WITH LARGE AMOUNTS OF WATER OR NORMAL SALINE, OCCASIONALLY LIFTING UPPER AND LOWER LIDS, UNTIL NO EVIDENCE OF CHEMICAL REMAINS (APPROXIMATELY 15-20 MINUTES). GET MEDICAL ATTENTION IMMEDIATELY.

INGESTION: DESMEDIPHAM: **ACUTE EXPOSURE**- SIGNS OF POISONING BY LABORATORY ANIMALS INCLUDED HYPOACTIVITY, SALIVATION AND MUSCLE WEAKNESS. **CHRONIC EXPOSURE**- NO DATA AVAILABLE.

FIRST AID- TREAT SYMPTOMATICALLY AND SUPPORTIVELY. GET MEDICAL ATTENTION IMMEDIATELY. IF VOMITING OCCURS, KEEP HEAD LOWER THAN HIPS TO PREVENT ASPIRATION.

ANTIDOTE: NO SPECIFIC ANTIDOTE. TREAT SYMPTOMATICALLY AND SUPPORTIVELY.

REACTIVITY

REACTIVITY: STABLE UNDER NORMAL TEMPERATURES AND PRESSURES.

INCOMPATIBILITIES: DESMEDIPHAM: OXIDIZERS (STRONG): FIRE AND EXPLOSION HAZARD.

DECOMPOSITION: THERMAL DECOMPOSITION PRODUCTS MAY INCLUDE TOXIC OXIDES OF CARBON AND NITROGEN.

POLYMERIZATION: HAZARDOUS POLYMERIZATION HAS NOT BEEN REPORTED TO OCCUR UNDER NORMAL TEMPERATURES AND PRESSURES.

STORAGE AND DISPOSAL

OBSERVE ALL FEDERAL, STATE AND LOCAL REGULATIONS WHEN STORING OR DISPOSING OF THIS SUBSTANCE. FOR ASSISTANCE, CONTACT THE DISTRICT DIRECTOR OF THE ENVIRONMENTAL PROTECTION AGENCY.

****STORAGE****

STORE IN ACCORDANCE WITH 40 CFR 165 RECOMMENDED PROCEDURES FOR THE DISPOSAL AND STORAGE OF PESTICIDES AND PESTICIDE CONTAINERS.

STORE AWAY FROM INCOMPATIBLE SUBSTANCES.

****DISPOSAL****

DISPOSAL MUST BE IN ACCORDANCE WITH 40 CFR 165 RECOMMENDED PROCEDURES FOR THE DISPOSAL AND STORAGE OF PESTICIDES AND PESTICIDE CONTAINERS.

CONDITIONS TO AVOID

MAY BURN BUT DOES NOT IGNITE READILY. AVOID CONTACT WITH STRONG OXIDIZERS, EXCESSIVE HEAT, SPARKS, OR OPEN FLAME.

SPILL AND LEAK PROCEDURES

OCCUPATIONAL SPILL: SWEEP UP AND PLACE IN SUITABLE CLEAN, DRY CONTAINERS FOR RECLAMATION OR LATER DISPOSAL. DO NOT FLUSH SPILLED MATERIAL INTO SEWER. KEEP UNNECESSARY PEOPLE AWAY.

PROTECTIVE EQUIPMENT

VENTILATION: PROVIDE GENERAL DILUTION VENTILATION.

RESPIRATOR: THE FOLLOWING RESPIRATORS ARE RECOMMENDED BASED ON INFORMATION FOUND IN THE PHYSICAL DATA, TOXICITY AND HEALTH EFFECTS SECTIONS. THEY ARE RANKED IN ORDER FROM MINIMUM TO MAXIMUM RESPIRATORY PROTECTION. THE SPECIFIC RESPIRATOR SELECTED MUST BE BASED ON CONTAMINATION LEVELS FOUND IN THE WORK PLACE, MUST NOT EXCEED THE WORKING LIMITS OF THE RESPIRATOR AND BE JOINTLY APPROVED BY THE NATIONAL INSTITUTE FOR OCCUPATIONAL SAFETY AND HEALTH AND THE MINE SAFETY AND HEALTH ADMINISTRATION (NIOSH-MSHA).

CHEMICAL CARTRIDGE RESPIRATOR WITH AN ORGANIC VAPOR CARTRIDGE(S) IN COMBINATION WITH A DUST AND MIST FILTER.

GAS MASK WITH ORGANIC VAPOR CANISTER (CHIN-STYLE OR FRONT- OR BACK-MOUNTED CANISTER) WITH A DUST AND MIST FILTER.

GAS MASK WITH ORGANIC VAPOR CANISTER (CHIN-STYLE OR FRONT- OR BACK-MOUNTED CANISTER) WITH A PARTICULATE FILTER.

POWERED AIR-PURIFYING RESPIRATOR WITH A HIGH-EFFICIENCY FILTER.

TYPE 'C' SUPPLIED-AIR RESPIRATOR WITH A FULL FACEPIECE OPERATED IN A PRESSURE-DEMAND OR OTHER POSITIVE PRESSURE MODE.

SELF-CONTAINED BREATHING APPARATUS WITH A FULL FACEPIECE OPERATED IN PRESSURE-DEMAND OR OTHER POSITIVE PRESSURE MODE.

FOR FIREFIGHTING AND OTHER IMMEDIATELY DANGEROUS TO LIFE OR HEALTH CONDITIONS:

SELF-CONTAINED BREATHING APPARATUS WITH FULL FACEPIECE OPERATED IN PRESSURE-DEMAND OR OTHER POSITIVE PRESSURE MODE.

SUPPLIED-AIR RESPIRATOR WITH FULL FACEPIECE AND OPERATED IN PRESSURE-DEMAND OR OTHER POSITIVE PRESSURE MODE IN COMBINATION WITH AN AUXILIARY SELF-CONTAINED BREATHING APPARATUS OPERATED IN PRESSURE-DEMAND OR OTHER POSITIVE PRESSURE MODE.

CLOTHING: EMPLOYEE MUST WEAR APPROPRIATE PROTECTIVE (IMPERVIOUS) CLOTHING AND EQUIPMENT TO PREVENT REPEATED OR PROLONGED SKIN CONTACT WITH THIS SUBSTANCE.

GLOVES: EMPLOYEE MUST WEAR APPROPRIATE PROTECTIVE GLOVES TO PREVENT CONTACT WITH THIS SUBSTANCE.

EYE PROTECTION: EMPLOYEE MUST WEAR SPLASH-PROOF OR DUST-RESISTANT SAFETY GOGGLES TO PREVENT EYE CONTACT WITH THIS SUBSTANCE.

EMERGENCY EYE WASH: WHERE THERE IS ANY POSSIBILITY THAT AN EMPLOYEE'S EYES MAY BE EXPOSED TO THIS SUBSTANCE, THE EMPLOYER SHOULD PROVIDE AN EYE WASH FOUNTAIN WITHIN THE IMMEDIATE WORK AREA FOR EMERGENCY USE.

AUTHORIZED BY- OCCUPATIONAL HEALTH SERVICES, INC.

CREATION DATE: 10/24/89 ***REVISION DATE:*** 05/31/90

MATERIAL SAFETY DATA SHEET

OCCUPATIONAL HEALTH SERVICES, INC.
AGRICULTURE AND PESTICIDE DIVISION
450 SEVENTH AVENUE, SUITE 2407
NEW YORK, NEW YORK 10123
1-800-445-MSDS OR (212) 967-1100

EMERGENCY CONTACT:
JOHN S. BRANSFORD, JR. (615) 292-1180

SUBSTANCE IDENTIFICATION

CAS-NUMBER 2597-03-7

SUBSTANCE: **PHENTHOATE**

TRADE NAMES/SYNONYMS: BENZENEACETIC ACID, ALPHA-((DIMETHOXYPHOSPHINOTHIOYL)THIO)-, ETHYL ESTER; ALPHA-((DIMETHOXYPHOSPHINOTHIOYL)THIO)BENZENEACETIC ACID, ETHYL ESTER; ACETIC ACID, MERCAPTOPHENYL-, ETHYL ESTER, S-ESTER WITH O,O-DIMETHYLPHOSPHORODITHIOATE; MERCAPTOPHENYLACETIC ACID, ETHYL ESTER , S-ESTER WITH O,O-DIMETHYL PHOSPHORODITHIOATE; ETHYL MERCAPTOPHENYLACETATE, S-ESTER WITH O,O-DIMETHYL PHOSPHORODITHIOATE; S-ALPHA-ETHOXYCARBONYLBENZYL O,O-DIMETHYL PHOSPHORODITHIOATE; ALPHA-((DIMETHOXYPHOSPHINOTHIOYL)THIO)BENZENEACETATE; O,O-DIMETHYL S-ALPHA-ETHOXYCARBONYLBENZYLPHOSPHORODITHIOATE; ETHYL ALPHA-((DIMETHOXYPHOSPHINOTHIOYL)THIO) BENZENEACETATE; CIDIAL;

DIMEPHENTHOATE; ELSAN; PAPTHION; OMS 1075; ENT 27386; C12H17O4PS2; PST72337

CHEMICAL FAMILY: PHOSPHOROTHIOATE

MOLECULAR FORMULA: C12-H17-O4-P-S2

MOLECULAR WEIGHT: 320.38

CERCLA RATINGS (SCALE 0-3): HEALTH=3 FIRE=U REACTIVITY=0 PERSISTENCE=1

NFPA RATINGS (SCALE 0-4): HEALTH=3 FIRE=U REACTIVITY=0

COMPONENTS AND CONTAMINANTS

COMPONENT: PHENTHOATE ***PERCENT:*** 100.0
CAS# 2597-03-7

OTHER CONTAMINANTS: NONE

EXPOSURE LIMITS: NO OCCUPATIONAL EXPOSURE LIMITS ESTABLISHED BY OSHA, ACGIH, OR NIOSH.

PHYSICAL DATA

DESCRIPTION: REDDISH-YELLOW OIL. ***BOILING POINT:*** NOT AVAILABLE

MELTING POINT: 63-64 F (17-18 C) ***SPECIFIC GRAVITY:*** 1.226

VAPOR PRESSURE: NOT AVAILABLE ***SOLUBILITY IN WATER:*** 0.02% @ 20 C

SOLVENT SOLUBILITY: SOLUBLE IN METHANOL, ETHANOL, BENZENE, XYLENE, ACETONE, CYCLOHEXANONE, METHYLCELLOSOLVE, CARBON TETRACHLORIDE, CARBON DISULFIDE, ETHER, DIOXANE, CYCLOHEXANE, N-HEXANE, LIGROIN, AND DIETHYLENEGLYCOL.

FIRE AND EXPLOSION DATA

FIRE AND EXPLOSION HAZARD: UNKNOWN FIRE AND EXPLOSION HAZARD.

FIREFIGHTING MEDIA: DRY CHEMICAL, CARBON DIOXIDE, HALON, WATER SPRAY OR STANDARD FOAM (1987 EMERGENCY RESPONSE GUIDEBOOK, DOT P 5800.4). FOR LARGER FIRES, USE WATER SPRAY, FOG OR STANDARD FOAM (1987 EMERGENCY RESPONSE GUIDEBOOK, DOT P 5800.4).

FIREFIGHTING: MOVE CONTAINER FROM FIRE AREA IF POSSIBLE. DIKE FIRE CONTROL WATER FOR LATER DISPOSAL; DO NOT SCATTER THE MATERIAL. COOL FIRE-EXPOSED CONTAINERS WITH WATER FROM SIDE UNTIL WELL AFTER FIRE IS OUT. STAY AWAY FROM STORAGE TANK ENDS. WITHDRAW IMMEDIATELY IN CASE OF RISING SOUND FROM VENTING SAFETY DEVICE OR ANY DISCOLORATION OF STORAGE TANK DUE TO FIRE (1987 EMERGENCY RESPONSE GUIDEBOOK, DOT P 5800.4, GUIDE PAGE 28).
EXTINGUISH ONLY IF FLOW CAN BE STOPPED. USE FLOODING AMOUNTS OF WATER AS A FOG; SOLID STREAMS MAY BE INEFFECTIVE. COOL CONTAINERS WITH FLOODING AMOUNTS OF WATER FROM AS FAR A DISTANCE AS POSSIBLE. AVOID BREATHING POISONOUS VAPORS, KEEP UPWIND.

TOXICITY

PHENTHOATE: TOXICITY DATA: 59 MG/M3/4H INHALATION-RAT LC50 700 MG/KG SKIN-RAT LD50; 2620 MG/KG SKIN-MOUSE LD50; 116 MG/KG ORAL-RAT LD50; 138 MG/KG ORAL-MOUSE LD50; 72 MG/KG ORAL-RABBIT; 500 MG/KG ORAL-DOG LD50; 377 MG/KG ORAL-GUINEA PIG LD50; 250 MG/KG UNREPORTED-RAT LD50. CARCINOGEN STATUS: NONE. ACUTE TOXICITY LEVEL: HIGHLY TOXIC BY INHALATION AND TOXIC BY DERMAL ABSORPTION AND INGESTION. TARGET EFFECTS: CHOLINESTERASE INHIBITOR. POISONING MAY AFFECT THE NERVOUS SYSTEM.* AT INCREASED RISK FROM EXPOSURE: PERSONS WITH RESPIRATORY AILMENTS, RECENT EXPOSURE TO CHOLINESTERASE INHIBITORS OR IMPAIRED CHOLINESTERASE PRODUCTION, OR LIVER MALFUNCTION.* ADDITIONAL DATA: MAY CROSS THE PLACENTA. HIGH ENVIRONMENTAL TEMPERATURES OR EXPOSURE OF THE CHEMICAL TO VISIBLE OR ULTRAVIOLET LIGHT MAY ENHANCE THE TOXICITY. INTERACTIONS WITH MEDICATIONS MAY OCCUR.*
* MAY BE BASED ON GENERAL INFORMATION ON ORGANOPHOSPHATES.

HEALTH EFFECTS AND FIRST AID

INHALATION: PHENTHOATE: SEE INFORMATION ON ORGANOPHOSPHATES. ORGANOPHOSPHATES: CHOLINESTERASE INHIBITOR. **ACUTE EXPOSURE-** WHEN INHALED, THE FIRST EFFECTS OF CHOLINESTERASE INHIBITORS ARE USUALLY RESPIRATORY AND MAY INCLUDE NASAL HYPEREMIA AND WATERY DISCHARGE, COUGH, CHEST DISCOMFORT, DYSPNEA, AND WHEEZING DUE TO INCREASED BRONCHIAL SECRETIONS AND BRONCHOCONSTRICTION. IF SUFFICIENT AMOUNTS ARE ABSORBED, OTHER SYSTEMIC EFFECTS MAY BEGIN WITHIN A FEW MINUTES OR BE DELAYED FOR UP TO 12 HOURS. SYMPTOMS MAY INCLUDE PALLOR, NAUSEA, VOMITING, DIARRHEA, ABDOMINAL CRAMPS, HEADACHE, DIZZINESS, OCULAR PAIN, BLURRED VISION, MIOSIS OR IN SOME CASES, ESPECIALLY INITIALLY, MYDRIASIS, LACRIMATION, SALIVATION, SWEATING, AND CONFUSION. OTHER REPORTED CENTRAL NERVOUS SYSTEM OR NEUROMUSCULAR EFFECTS MAY INCLUDE ATAXIA, SLURRED SPEECH, AREFLEXIA, WEAKNESS, FATIGUE, FASCICULATIONS, TWITCHING, TREMORS POSSIBLY OF THE TONGUE AND EYELIDS, AND EVENTUALLY PARALYSIS OF THE EXTREMITIES AND POSSIBLY OF THE RESPIRATORY MUSCLES. IN SEVERE CASES THERE MAY ALSO BE INVOLUNTARY DEFECATION AND URINATION, CYANOSIS, PSYCHOSIS, HYPERGLYCEMIA, ACUTE PANCREATITIS, CARDIAC IRREGULARITIES, PULMONARY EDEMA, UNCONSCIOUSNESS, CONVULSIONS, AND COMA. DEATH IS PRIMARILY DUE TO RESPIRATORY FAILURE, ALTHOUGH CARDIOVASCULAR EFFECTS INCLUDING CARDIAC ARREST MAY ALSO BE IMPLICATED. LONG TERM SEQUELAE ARE RARE BUT MAY INCLUDE NEUROPSYCHIATRIC DISORDERS AND MYOPATHY WITH MUSCLE TENDERNESS. SOME ORGANOPHOSPHATES MAY CAUSE A DELAYED NEUROPATHY BEGINNING 1-4 WEEKS AFTER AN ACUTE EXPOSURE WHICH MAY OR MAY NOT HAVE CAUSED ACUTE CHOLINERGIC EFFECTS. NUMBNESS, TINGLING, WEAKNESS AND CRAMPING BEGINNING SYMMETRICALLY IN THE LOWER LIMBS MAY PROGRESS TO ATAXIA AND PARALYSIS. IN SEVERE CASES, UPPER LIMB INVOLVEMENT IS POSSIBLE AND FLACCID PARALYSIS MAY PROGRESS TO SPASTIC PARALYSIS WITH EXAGGERATED REFLEXES. IMPROVEMENT MAY OCCUR OVER MONTHS TO YEARS, BUT SOME RESIDUAL IMPAIRMENT USUALLY REMAINS. **CHRONIC EXPOSURE-** REPEATED OR PROLONGED EXPOSURE MAY RESULT IN THE EFFECTS OF ACUTE EXPOSURE INCLUDING THE DELAYED NEUROPATHY. OTHER EFFECTS REPORTED IN WORKERS REPEATEDLY EXPOSED INCLUDE IMPAIRED MEMORY AND CONCENTRATION, ACUTE PSYCHOSIS, SEVERE DEPRESSIONS, IRRITABILTY, CONFUSION, APATHY, EMOTIONAL LABILITY, SOCIAL WITHDRAWAL, CONFUSION, HEADACHE, SPEECH DIFFICULTIES, DELAYED REACTION TIMES, SPATIAL DISORIENTATION, NIGHTMARES, SLEEPWALKING, AND DROWSINESS OR INSOMNIA. AN INFLUENZA-LIKE CONDITION WITH HEADACHE, NAUSEA, WEAKNESS, ANOREXIA AND MALAISE HAS ALSO BEEN REPORTED.

FIRST AID- REMOVE FROM EXPOSURE AREA TO FRESH AIR IMMEDIATELY. IF BREATHING HAS STOPPED, GIVE ARTIFICIAL RESPIRATION. MAINTAIN AIRWAY AND BLOOD PRESSURE AND ADMINISTER OXYGEN IF AVAILABLE. KEEP AFFECTED PERSON WARM AND AT REST. TREAT SYMPTOMATICALLY AND SUPPORTIVELY. ADMINISTRATION OF OXYGEN SHOULD BE PERFORMED BY QUALIFIED PERSONNEL. GET MEDICAL ATTENTION IMMEDIATELY.

SKIN CONTACT: PHENTHOATE: TOXIC. SEE INFORMATION ON ORGANOPHOSPHATES. ORGANOPHOSPHATES: CHOLINESTERASE INHIBITOR. **ACUTE EXPOSURE-** LOCALIZED SWEATING AND FASCICULATIONS MAY OCCUR AT THE SITE OF CONTACT. IF SUFFICIENT AMOUNTS ARE ABSORBED, OTHER EFFECTS OF CHOLINESTERASE INHIBITION AS DESCRIBED IN ACUTE INHALATION MAY OCCUR. SYMPTOMS MAY BE DELAYED 2-3 HOURS, BUT USUALLY NO MORE THAN 12 HOURS. THE RATE OF ABSORPTION IS INCREASED BY THE PRESENCE OF DERMATITIS OR HIGH AMBIENT TEMPERATURES. DELAYED NEUROPATHY IS ALSO POSSIBLE. **CHRONIC EXPOSURE-** REPEATED OR PROLONGED EXPOSURE MAY CAUSE EFFECTS AS DESCRIBED IN ACUTE EXPOSURE. SOME ORGANOPHOSPHATES MAY CAUSE SENSITIZATION.

FIRST AID- REMOVE CONTAMINATED CLOTHING IMMEDIATELY. WASH CONTAMINATED AREAS WITH SOAP AND WATER FOLLOWED BY ALCOHOL (ARENA, POISONING, 4TH ED.). EMERGENCY PERSONNEL SHOULD WEAR GLOVES AND AVOID CONTAMINATION. TREAT RESPIRATORY DIFFICULTY WITH ARTIFICIAL RESPIRATION. GET MEDICAL ATTENTION IMMEDIATELY.

EYE CONTACT: PHENTHOATE: SEE INFORMATION ON ORGANOPHOSPHATES. ORGANOPHOSPHATES: CHOLINESTERASE INHIBITOR. **ACUTE EXPOSURE-** DIRECT CONTACT MAY CAUSE PAIN, HYPEREMIA, LACRIMATION, TWITCHING OF THE EYELIDS, MIOSIS, AND CILIARY MUSCLE SPASM WITH LOSS OF ACCOMODATION, BLURRED OR DIMMED VISION AND BROWACHE. SOMETIMES MYDRIASIS MAY OCCUR INSTEAD OF MIOSIS. WITH SUFFICIENT EXPOSURE, OTHER SYMPTOMS OF CHOLINESTERASE INHIBITION AS DESCRIBED IN ACUTE INHALATION MAY OCCUR. **CHRONIC EXPOSURE-** REPEATED OR PROLONGED EXPOSURE MAY CAUSE EFFECTS AS DESCRIBED IN ACUTE EXPOSURE. SOME COMPOUNDS HAVE CAUSED TOXIC EFFECTS ON THE CRYSTALLINE LENS, CONJUNCTIVAL THICKENING AND OBSTRUCTION OF THE NASOLACRIMAL CANALS WHEN USED AS MIOTIC EYEDROPS.

FIRST AID- IRRIGATE EYES WITH WATER OR SALINE SOLUTION. IF SYMPTOMS OF POISONING OCCUR, TREAT RESPIRATORY DIFFICULTY WITH ARTIFICIAL RESPIRATION AND OXYGEN. OBSERVE PATIENT FOR AT LEAST 24-36 HOURS (GOSSELIN, CLINICAL TOXICOLOGY OF COMMERCIAL PRODUCTS, 5TH ED.). GET MEDICAL ATTENTION IMMEDIATELY. OXYGEN SHOULD BE ADMINISTERED BY QUALIFIED MEDICAL PERSONNEL.

INGESTION: PHENTHOATE: TOXIC. SEE INFORMATION ON ORGANOPHOSPHATES. ORGANOPHOSPHATES: CHOLINESTERASE INHIBITOR. **ACUTE EXPOSURE-** WHEN INGESTED, THE FIRST EFFECTS MAY BE NAUSEA, VOMITING, ANOREXIA, ABDOMINAL CRAMPS AND DIARRHEA. GASTROINTESTINAL ABSORPTION MAY CAUSE SYMPTOMS OF CHOLINESTERASE INHIBITION AS DESCRIBED IN ACUTE INHALATION. SYMPTOMS MAY BEGIN WITHIN MINUTES OR BE DELAYED FOR HOURS. DELAYED EFFECTS INCLUDING NEUROPATHY MAY ALSO OCCUR. **CHRONIC EXPOSURE-** REPEATED INGESTION MAY CAUSE EFFECTS AS DESCRIBED IN ACUTE EXPOSURE.

FIRST AID- IF PERSON IS ALERT AND RESPIRATION IS NOT DEPRESSED, GIVE SYRUP OF IPECAC FOLLOWED BY WATER (IF VOMITING OCCURS, KEEP HEAD BELOW HIPS TO PREVENT ASPIRATION). IF CONSCIOUSNESS LEVEL DECLINES OR VOMITING HAS NOT OCCURRED IN 15 MINUTES EMPTY STOMACH BY GASTRIC LAVAGE WITH THE AID OF CUFFED ENDOTRACHEAL TUBE USING ISOTONIC SALINE OR 5% SODIUM BICARBONATE FOLLOW WITH ACTIVATED CHARCOAL. ESTABLISH AND MAINTAIN AIRWAY. TREAT RESPIRATORY DIFFICULTY WITH ARTIFICIAL RESPIRATION AND OXYGEN. DO NOT GIVE MORPHINE, AMINOPHYLLINE, PHENOTHIAZINES, RESERPINE, FUROSEMIDE, OR ETHACRYNIC ACID (MORGAN, RECOGNITION AND MANAGEMENT OF PESTICIDE POISONINGS, 3RD ED.). TREAT SYMPTOMATICALLY AND SUPPORTIVELY. ADMINISTRATION OF OXYGEN AND LAVAGE MUST BE PERFORMED BY QUALIFIED MEDICAL PERSONNEL. GET MEDICAL ATTENTION IMMEDIATELY.

ANTIDOTE: THE FOLLOWING ANTIDOTE(S) HAVE BEEN RECOMMENDED. HOWEVER, THE DECISION AS TO WHETHER THE SEVERITY OF POISONING REQUIRES ADMINISTRATION OF ANY ANTIDOTE AND ACTUAL DOSE REQUIRED SHOULD BE MADE BY QUALIFIED MEDICAL PERSONNEL.

FOR CHOLINESTERASE INHIBITORS: ESTABLISH CLEAR AIRWAY AND TISSUE OXYGENATION BY ASPIRATION OF SECRETIONS, AND IF NECESSARY, BY ASSISTED PULMONARY VENTILATION WITH OXYGEN. IMPROVE TISSUE OXYGENATION AS MUCH AS POSSIBLE BEFORE ADMINISTERING ATROPINE TO MINIMIZE THE RISK OF VENTRICULAR FIBRILLATION. ADMINISTER ATROPINE SULFATE INTRAVENOUSLY, OR INTRAMUSCULARLY IF IV INJECTION IS NOT POSSIBLE. IN MODERATELY SEVERE POISONING ADMINISTER ATROPINE SULFATE, 0.4-2.0 MG REPEATED EVERY 15 MINUTES UNTIL ATROPINIZATION IS ACHIEVED (TACHYCARDIA, FLUSHING, DRY MOUTH, MYDRIASIS). MAINTAIN ATROPINIZATION BY REPEATED DOSES FOR 2-12 HOURS, OR LONGER, DEPENDING ON THE SEVERITY OF POISONING. THE APPEARANCE OF RALES IN THE LUNG BASES, MIOSIS, SALIVATION, NAUSEA, BRADYCARDIA, ARE ALL INDICATIONS OF INADEQUATE ATROPINIZATION. SEVERELY POISONED INDIVIDUALS MAY EXHIBIT REMARKABLE TOLERANCE TO ATROPINE; TWO OR MORE TIMES THE DOSAGES SUGGESTED ABOVE MAY BE NEEDED. PERSONS NOT POISONED OR ONLY SLIGHTLY POISONED, HOWEVER, MAY DEVELOP SIGNS OF ATROPINE TOXICITY FROM SUCH LARGE DOSAGES: FEVER, MUSCLE FIBRILLATIONS, AND DELIRIUM ARE THE MAIN SIGNS OF ATROPINE TOXICITY. IF THESE SIGNS APPEAR WHILE THE PATIENT IS FULLY ATROPINIZED, ATROPINE ADMINISTRATION SHOULD BE DISCONTINUED, AT LEAST TEMPORARILY. OBSERVE TREATED PATIENTS CLOSELY AT LEAST 24 HOURS TO INSURE THAT SYMPTOMS (POSSIBLY PULMONARY EDEMA) DO NOT RECUR AS ATROPINIZATION WEARS OFF. IN VERY SEVERE POISONINGS, METABOLIC DISPOSITION OF TOXICANT MAY REQUIRE SEVERAL HOURS OR DAYS DURING WHICH ATROPINIZATION MUST BE MAINTAINED. MARKEDLY LOWER LEVELS OF URINARY METABOLITES INDICATE THAT ATROPINE DOSAGE CAN BE TAPERED OFF. AS DOSAGE IS REDUCED, CHECK THE LUNG BASES FREQUENTLY FOR RALES. IF RALES ARE HEARD OR OTHER SYMPTOMS RETURN, RE-ESTABLISH ATROPINIZATION PROMPTLY (MORGAN, RECOGNITION AND MANAGEMENT OF PESTICIDE POISONINGS, 3RD ED.). ADMINISTRATION OF ANTIDOTE MUST BE PERFORMED BY QUALIFIED MEDICAL PERSONNEL.

IN CASES OF SEVERE POISONING BY ORGANOPHOSPHATE PESTICIDES IN WHICH RESPIRATORY DEPRESSION, MUSCLE WEAKNESS AND TWITCHINGS ARE SEVERE, GIVE PRALIDOXIME (PROTOPAM-AYERST, 2-PAM), 1.0 GRAM INTRAVENOUSLY AT NO MORE THAN 0.5 GRAM PER MINUTE. DOSAGE OF PRALIDOXIME MAY BE REPEATED IN 1-2 HOURS, THEN AT 10-12 HOUR INTERVALS IF NEEDED. IN VERY SEVERE POISONINGS, DOSAGE RATES MAY BE DOUBLED. TREATMENT WITH PRALIDOXIME WILL BE MOST EFFECTIVE IF GIVEN WITHIN THIRTY-SIX HOURS AFTER POISONING (MORGAN, RECOGNITION AND MANAGEMENT OF PESTICIDE POISONINGS, 3RD ED.). ANTIDOTE SHOULD BE ADMINISTERED BY QUALIFIED MEDICAL PERSONNEL.

REACTIVITY

REACTIVITY: STABLE UNDER NORMAL TEMPERATURES AND PRESSURES.

INCOMPATIBILITIES: PHENTHOATE: ALKALIES: INCOMPATIBLE. OXIDIZERS (STRONG): FIRE AND EXPLOSION HAZARD

DECOMPOSITION: THERMAL DECOMPOSITION PRODUCTS MAY INCLUDE TOXIC OXIDES OF CARBON, SULFUR, AND PHOSPHORUS.

POLYMERIZATION: HAZARDOUS POLYMERIZATION HAS NOT BEEN REPORTED TO OCCUR UNDER NORMAL TEMPERATURES AND PRESSURES.

STORAGE AND DISPOSAL

OBSERVE ALL FEDERAL, STATE AND LOCAL REGULATIONS WHEN STORING OR DISPOSING OF THIS SUBSTANCE. FOR ASSISTANCE, CONTACT THE DISTRICT DIRECTOR OF THE ENVIRONMENTAL PROTECTION AGENCY.

****STORAGE****

STORE IN ACCORDANCE WITH 40 CFR 165 RECOMMENDED PROCEDURES FOR THE DISPOSAL AND STORAGE OF PESTICIDES AND PESTICIDE CONTAINERS.

STORE IN A COOL, DRY PLACE; KEEP CONTAINER TIGHTLY CLOSED WHEN NOT IN USE.

STORE AWAY FROM INCOMPATIBLE SUBSTANCES.

****DISPOSAL****

DISPOSAL MUST BE IN ACCORDANCE WITH 40 CFR 165 RECOMMENDED PROCEDURES FOR THE DISPOSAL AND STORAGE OF PESTICIDES AND PESTICIDE CONTAINERS.

CONDITIONS TO AVOID

AVOID CONTACT WITH HEAT, SPARKS, FLAMES OR OTHER IGNITION SOURCES. VAPORS MAY BE EXPLOSIVE. MATERIAL IS POISONOUS; AVOID INHALATION OF VAPORS OR CONTACT WITH SKIN. DO NOT ALLOW MATERIAL TO CONTAMINATE WATER SOURCES.

SPILL AND LEAK PROCEDURES

OCCUPATIONAL SPILL: SHUT OFF IGNITION SOURCES. DO NOT TOUCH SPILLED MATERIAL. STOP LEAK IF YOU CAN DO IT WITHOUT RISK. USE WATER SPRAY TO REDUCE VAPORS. FOR SMALL SPILLS, TAKE UP WITH SAND OR OTHER ABSORBENT MATERIAL AND PLACE INTO CONTAINERS FOR LATER DISPOSAL. FOR LARGER SPILLS, DIKE FAR AHEAD OF SPILL FOR LATER DISPOSAL. NO SMOKING, FLAMES OR FLARES IN HAZARD AREA! KEEP UNNECESSARY PEOPLE AWAY; ISOLATE HAZARD AREA AND DENY ENTRY.

PROTECTIVE EQUIPMENT

VENTILATION: PROVIDE LOCAL EXHAUST OR PROCESS ENCLOSURE VENTILATION SYSTEM.

RESPIRATOR: THE FOLLOWING RESPIRATORS ARE RECOMMENDED BASED ON INFORMATION FOUND IN THE PHYSICAL DATA, TOXICITY AND HEALTH EFFECTS SECTIONS. THEY ARE RANKED IN ORDER FROM MINIMUM TO MAXIMUM RESPIRATORY PROTECTION. THE SPECIFIC RESPIRATOR SELECTED MUST BE BASED ON CONTAMINATION LEVELS FOUND IN THE WORK PLACE, MUST NOT EXCEED THE WORKING LIMITS OF THE RESPIRATOR AND BE JOINTLY APPROVED BY THE NATIONAL INSTITUTE FOR OCCUPATIONAL SAFETY AND HEALTH AND THE MINE SAFETY AND HEALTH ADMINISTRATION (NIOSH-MSHA).

TYPE 'C' SUPPLIED-AIR RESPIRATOR WITH A FULL FACEPIECE OPERATED IN PRESSURE-DEMAND OR OTHER POSITIVE PRESSURE MODE OR WITH A FULL FACEPIECE, HELMET OR HOOD OPERATED IN CONTINOUS-FLOW MODE.

SELF-CONTAINED BREATHING APPARATUS WITH A FULL FACEPIECE OPERATED IN PRESSURE-DEMAND OR OTHER POSITIVE PRESSURE MODE.

FOR FIREFIGHTING AND OTHER IMMEDIATELY DANGEROUS TO LIFE OR HEALTH CONDITIONS:

SELF-CONTAINED BREATHING APPARATUS WITH FULL FACEPIECE OPERATED IN PRESSURE-DEMAND OR OTHER POSITIVE PRESSURE MODE.

SUPPLIED-AIR RESPIRATOR WITH FULL FACEPIECE AND OPERATED IN PRESSURE-DEMAND OR OTHER POSITIVE PRESSURE MODE IN COMBINATION WITH AN AUXILIARY SELF-CONTAINED BREATHING APPARATUS OPERATED IN PRESSURE-DEMAND OR OTHER POSITIVE PRESSURE MODE.

CLOTHING: EMPLOYEE MUST WEAR APPROPRIATE PROTECTIVE (IMPERVIOUS) CLOTHING AND EQUIPMENT TO PREVENT ANY POSSIBILITY OF SKIN CONTACT WITH THIS SUBSTANCE.

GLOVES: EMPLOYEE MUST WEAR APPROPRIATE PROTECTIVE GLOVES TO PREVENT CONTACT WITH THIS SUBSTANCE.

EYE PROTECTION: EMPLOYEE MUST WEAR SPLASH-PROOF OR DUST-RESISTANT SAFETY GOGGLES WITH OR WITHOUT A FACESHIELD TO PREVENT CONTACT WITH THIS SUBSTANCE.

EMERGENCY EYE WASH: WHERE THERE IS ANY POSSIBILITY THAT AN EMPLOYEE'S EYES MAY BE EXPOSED TO THIS SUBSTANCE, THE EMPLOYER SHOULD PROVIDE AN EYE WASH FOUNTAIN WITHIN THE IMMEDIATE WORK AREA FOR EMERGENCY USE.

AUTHORIZED BY- OCCUPATIONAL HEALTH SERVICES, INC.

CREATION DATE: 10/04/89 ***REVISION DATE:*** 04/26/90

MATERIAL SAFETY DATA SHEET

OCCUPATIONAL HEALTH SERVICES, INC.
AGRICULTURE AND PESTICIDE DIVISION
450 SEVENTH AVENUE, SUITE 2407
NEW YORK, NEW YORK 10123
1-800-445-MSDS OR (212) 967-1100

EMERGENCY CONTACT:
JOHN S. BRANSFORD, JR. (615) 292-1180

SUBSTANCE IDENTIFICATION

CAS-NUMBER 34014-18-1

SUBSTANCE: TEBUTHIURON

TRADE NAMES/SYNONYMS: UREA, N-(5-(1,1-DIMETHYLETHYL)-1,3,4-THIADIAZOL-2-YL)-N,N'-DIMETHYL-; UREA, 1-(5-TERT-BUTYL-1,3,4-THIADIAZOL-2-YL)-1,3-DIMETHYL-; N-(5-(1,1-DIMETHYLETHYL)-1,3,4-THIADIAZOL-2-YL)-N,N'-DIMETHYLUREA; 1-(5-TERT-BUTYL-1,3,4-THIADIAZOL-2-YL)-1,3-DIMETHYLUREA; EL 103; GRASLAN; PERFLAN; SPIKE; C9H16N4OS; PST72340

CHEMICAL FAMILY: SUBSTITUTED UREA

MOLECULAR FORMULA: C9-H16-N4-O-S

MOLECULAR WEIGHT: 228.35

CERCLA RATINGS (SCALE 0-3): HEALTH=3 FIRE=1 REACTIVITY=0 PERSISTENCE=1

NFPA RATINGS (SCALE 0-4): HEALTH=3 FIRE=1 REACTIVITY=0

COMPONENTS AND CONTAMINANTS

COMPONENT: TEBUTHIURON ***PERCENT:*** 100.0
CAS# 34014-18-1

OTHER CONTAMINANTS: NONE

EXPOSURE LIMITS: NO OCCUPATIONAL EXPOSURE LIMITS ESTABLISHED BY OSHA, ACGIH, OR NIOSH.

PHYSICAL DATA

DESCRIPTION: ODORLESS, COLORLESS CRYSTALLINE SOLID.

MELTING POINT: 324-327 F (162-164 C) ***VAPOR PRESSURE:*** NEGLIGIBLE

SOLUBILITY IN WATER: 0.25% @ 25 C

SOLVENT SOLUBILITY: SOLUBLE IN ACETONE, ACETONITRILE, HEXANE, METHANOL AND 2-METHOXYETHANOL; MODERATELY SOLUBLE IN CHLOROFORM.

FIRE AND EXPLOSION DATA

FIRE AND EXPLOSION HAZARD: SLIGHT FIRE HAZARD WHEN EXPOSED TO HEAT OR FLAME.

FIREFIGHTING MEDIA: DRY CHEMICAL, CARBON DIOXIDE, HALON, WATER SPRAY OR STANDARD FOAM (1987 EMERGENCY RESPONSE GUIDEBOOK, DOT P 5800.4). FOR LARGER FIRES, USE WATER SPRAY, FOG OR STANDARD FOAM (1987 EMERGENCY RESPONSE GUIDEBOOK, DOT P 5800.4).

FIREFIGHTING: MOVE CONTAINERS FROM FIRE AREA IF POSSIBLE. FIGHT FIRE FROM MAXIMUM DISTANCE. STAY AWAY FROM STORAGE TANK ENDS. DIKE FIRE CONTROL WATER FOR LATER DISPOSAL. DO NOT SCATTER MATERIAL (1987 EMERGENCY RESPONSE GUIDEBOOK, DOT P 5800.4, GUIDE PAGE 55). EXTINGUISH USING AGENT SUITABLE FOR TYPE OF SURROUNDING FIRE. USE WATER IN FLOODING QUANTITIES AS FOG. KEEP SPARKS, FLAMES AND OTHER SOURCES OF IGNITION AWAY. KEEP MATERIAL OUT OF WATER SOURCES AND SEWERS. DO NOT TOUCH MATERIAL AND AVOID BREATHING DUSTS AND FUMES FROM BURNING MATERIAL. KEEP UPWIND.

TOXICITY

TEBUTHIURON: TOXICITY DATA: 644 MG/KG ORAL-RAT LD50; 579 MG/KG ORAL-MOUSE LD50; 286 MG/KG ORAL-RABBIT LD50. CARCINOGEN STATUS: NONE. ACUTE TOXICITY LEVEL: MODERATELY TOXIC BY INGESTION. TARGET EFFECTS: NO DATA AVAILABLE.

HEALTH EFFECTS AND FIRST AID

INHALATION: TEBUTHIURON: **ACUTE EXPOSURE-** MANY SUBSTITUTED UREA HERBICIDES ARE MODERATELY IRRITATING TO THE MUCOUS MEMBRANES. **CHRONIC EXPOSURE-** NO DATA AVAILABLE.

FIRST AID- REMOVE FROM EXPOSURE AREA TO FRESH AIR IMMEDIATELY. IF BREATHING HAS STOPPED, PERFORM ARTIFICIAL RESPIRATION. KEEP PERSON WARM AND AT REST. TREAT SYMPTOMATICALLY AND SUPPORTIVELY. GET MEDICAL ATTENTION IMMEDIATELY.

SKIN CONTACT: TEBUTHIURON: **ACUTE EXPOSURE-** 200 MG APPLIED TO RABBIT SKIN DID NOT PRODUCED IRRITATION OR SYSTEMIC INTOXICATION. **CHRONIC EXPOSURE-** NO DATA AVAILABLE.

FIRST AID- REMOVE CONTAMINATED CLOTHING AND SHOES IMMEDIATELY. WASH AFFECTED AREA WITH SOAP OR MILD DETERGENT AND LARGE AMOUNTS OF WATER UNTIL NO EVIDENCE OF CHEMICAL REMAINS (APPROXIMATELY 15-20 MINUTES). GET MEDICAL ATTENTION IMMEDIATELY.

EYE CONTACT: TEBUTHIURON: **ACUTE EXPOSURE-** 71 MG APPLIED TO RABBIT EYES WAS NOT IRRITATING. **CHRONIC EXPOSURE-** NO DATA AVAILABLE.

FIRST AID- WASH EYES IMMEDIATELY WITH LARGE AMOUNTS OF WATER OR NORMAL SALINE, OCCASIONALLY LIFTING UPPER AND LOWER LIDS, UNTIL NO EVIDENCE OF CHEMICAL REMAINS (APPROXIMATELY 15-20 MINUTES). GET MEDICAL ATTENTION IMMEDIATELY.

INGESTION: TEBUTHIURON: **ACUTE EXPOSURE-** A LETHAL DOSE IN RATS WAS 644 MG/KG. IN RODENTS, INGESTION PRODUCED HYPOACTIVITY, ANOREXIA, ATAXIA AND DEATH. EMESIS OCCURRED IN CATS AND DOGS. **CHRONIC EXPOSURE-** DECREASED WEIGHT GAIN WAS OBSERVED IN RATS FED 2500 PPM FOR 3 MONTHS. THE OCCURRENCE OF DIFFUSE VACUOLIZATION OF PANCREATIC ACINAR CELLS, ACCOMPANIED BY A DECREASE IN ZYMOGEN GRANULES, WAS ATTRIBUTED TO AN INHIBITION OF PROTEIN SYNTHESIS IN THESE CELLS.

FIRST AID- REMOVE BY GASTRIC LAVAGE AND CATHARSIS. MAINTAIN BLOOD PRESSURE AND AIRWAY. GIVE OXYGEN IF RESPIRATION IS DEPRESSED. DO NOT PERFORM GASTRIC LAVAGE IF VICTIM IS UNCONSCIOUS. GET MEDICAL ATTENTION IMMEDIATELY (DREISBACH, HANDBOOK OF POISONING, 12TH ED.). ADMINISTRATION OF LAVAGE OR OXYGEN SHOULD BE PERFORMED BY QUALIFIED MEDICAL PERSONNEL.

ANTIDOTE: NO SPECIFIC ANTIDOTE. TREAT SYMPTOMATICALLY AND SUPPORTIVELY.

REACTIVITY

REACTIVITY: STABLE UNDER NORMAL TEMPERATURES AND PRESSURES.

INCOMPATIBILITIES: TEBUTHIURON: OXIDIZERS (STRONG): FIRE AND EXPLOSION HAZARD.

DECOMPOSITION: THERMAL DECOMPOSITION PRODUCTS MAY INCLUDE TOXIC OXIDES OF CARBON, NITROGEN, AND SULFUR.

POLYMERIZATION: HAZARDOUS POLYMERIZATION HAS NOT BEEN REPORTED TO OCCUR UNDER NORMAL TEMPERATURES AND PRESSURES.

STORAGE AND DISPOSAL

OBSERVE ALL FEDERAL, STATE AND LOCAL REGULATIONS WHEN STORING OR DISPOSING OF THIS SUBSTANCE. FOR ASSISTANCE, CONTACT THE DISTRICT DIRECTOR OF THE ENVIRONMENTAL PROTECTION AGENCY.

****STORAGE****

STORE IN ACCORDANCE WITH 40 CFR 165 RECOMMENDED PROCEDURES FOR THE DISPOSAL AND STORAGE OF PESTICIDES AND PESTICIDE CONTAINERS. STORE AWAY FROM INCOMPATIBLE SUBSTANCES.

****DISPOSAL****

DISPOSAL MUST BE IN ACCORDANCE WITH 40 CFR 165 RECOMMENDED PROCEDURES FOR THE DISPOSAL AND STORAGE OF PESTICIDES AND PESTICIDE CONTAINERS.

CONDITIONS TO AVOID

MAY BURN BUT DOES NOT IGNITE READILY. CONTAINERS MAY EXPLODE IN HEAT OF FIRE.

SPILL AND LEAK PROCEDURES

OCCUPATIONAL SPILL: DO NOT TOUCH SPILLED MATERIAL. STOP LEAK IF YOU CAN DO IT WITHOUT RISK. USE WATER SPRAY TO REDUCE VAPORS. FOR SMALL SPILLS, TAKE UP WITH SAND OR OTHER ABSORBENT MATERIAL AND PLACE INTO CONTAINERS FOR LATER DISPOSAL. FOR SMALL DRY SPILLS, WITH A CLEAN SHOVEL PLACE MATERIAL INTO CLEAN, DRY CONTAINERS AND COVER. MOVE CONTAINERS FROM SPILL AREA. FOR LARGER SPILLS, DIKE FAR AHEAD OF SPILL FOR LATER DISPOSAL. KEEP UNNECESSARY PEOPLE AWAY. ISOLATE HAZARD AREA AND DENY ENTRY. VENTILATE CLOSED SPACES BEFORE ENTERING.

PROTECTIVE EQUIPMENT

VENTILATION: PROVIDE LOCAL EXHAUST OR PROCESS ENCLOSURE VENTILATION SYSTEM.

RESPIRATOR: THE FOLLOWING RESPIRATORS ARE RECOMMENDED BASED ON INFORMATION FOUND IN THE PHYSICAL DATA, TOXICITY AND HEALTH EFFECTS SECTIONS. THEY ARE RANKED IN ORDER FROM MINIMUM TO MAXIMUM RESPIRATORY PROTECTION. THE SPECIFIC RESPIRATOR SELECTED MUST BE BASED ON CONTAMINATION LEVELS FOUND IN THE WORK PLACE, MUST NOT EXCEED THE WORKING LIMITS OF THE RESPIRATOR AND BE JOINTLY APPROVED BY THE NATIONAL INSTITUTE FOR OCCUPATIONAL SAFETY AND HEALTH AND THE MINE SAFETY AND HEALTH ADMINISTRATION (NIOSH-MSHA).

CHEMICAL CARTRIDGE RESPIRATOR WITH AN ORGANIC VAPOR CARTRIDGE(S) IN COMBINATION WITH A DUST AND MIST FILTER.

GAS MASK WITH ORGANIC VAPOR CANISTER (CHIN-STYLE OR FRONT- OR BACK-MOUNTED CANISTER) WITH A DUST AND MIST FILTER.

GAS MASK WITH ORGANIC VAPOR CANISTER (CHIN-STYLE OR FRONT- OR BACK-MOUNTED CANISTER) WITH A PARTICULATE FILTER.

POWERED AIR-PURIFYING RESPIRATOR WITH A HIGH-EFFICIENCY FILTER.

TYPE 'C' SUPPLIED-AIR RESPIRATOR WITH A FULL FACEPIECE OPERATED IN A PRESSURE-DEMAND OR OTHER POSITIVE PRESSURE MODE.

SELF-CONTAINED BREATHING APPARATUS WITH A FULL FACEPIECE OPERATED IN PRESSURE-DEMAND OR OTHER POSITIVE PRESSURE MODE.

FOR FIREFIGHTING AND OTHER IMMEDIATELY DANGEROUS TO LIFE OR HEALTH CONDITIONS: SELF-CONTAINED BREATHING APPARATUS WITH FULL FACEPIECE OPERATED IN PRESSURE-DEMAND OR OTHER POSITIVE PRESSURE MODE. SUPPLIED-AIR RESPIRATOR WITH FULL FACEPIECE AND OPERATED IN PRESSURE-DEMAND OR OTHER POSITIVE PRESSURE MODE IN COMBINATION WITH AN

AUXILIARY SELF-CONTAINED BREATHING APPARATUS OPERATED IN PRESSURE-DEMAND OR OTHER POSITIVE PRESSURE MODE.

CLOTHING: EMPLOYEE MUST WEAR APPROPRIATE PROTECTIVE (IMPERVIOUS) CLOTHING AND EQUIPMENT TO PREVENT REPEATED OR PROLONGED SKIN CONTACT WITH THIS SUBSTANCE.

GLOVES: EMPLOYEE MUST WEAR APPROPRIATE PROTECTIVE GLOVES TO PREVENT CONTACT WITH THIS SUBSTANCE.

EYE PROTECTION: EMPLOYEE MUST WEAR SPLASH-PROOF OR DUST-RESISTANT SAFETY GOGGLES TO PREVENT EYE CONTACT WITH THIS SUBSTANCE. EMERGENCY EYE WASH: WHERE THERE IS ANY POSSIBILITY THAT AN EMPLOYEE'S EYES MAY BE EXPOSED TO THIS SUBSTANCE, THE EMPLOYER SHOULD PROVIDE AN EYE WASH FOUNTAIN WITHIN THE IMMEDIATE WORK AREA FOR EMERGENCY USE.

AUTHORIZED BY- OCCUPATIONAL HEALTH SERVICES, INC.
CREATION DATE: 10/05/89 ***REVISION DATE:*** 05/11/90

MATERIAL SAFETY DATA SHEET

OCCUPATIONAL HEALTH SERVICES, INC.
AGRICULTURE AND PESTICIDE DIVISION
450 SEVENTH AVENUE, SUITE 2407
NEW YORK, NEW YORK 10123
1-800-445-MSDS OR (212) 967-1100

EMERGENCY CONTACT:
JOHN S. BRANSFORD, JR. (615) 292-1180

SUBSTANCE IDENTIFICATION

CAS-NUMBER 27314-13-2

SUBSTANCE: **NORFLURAZON**

TRADE NAMES/SYNONYMS: 3(2H)-PYRIDAZINONE, 4-CHLORO-5-(METHYLAMINO)-2-(3-(TRIFLUOROMETHYL) PHENYL)-; 3(2H)-PYRIDAZINONE, 4-CHLORO-5-(METHYLAMINO)-2-(ALPHA,ALPHA,ALPHA,- TRIFLUORO-M-TOLYL)-; 4-CHLORO-5-(METHYLAMINO)-2-(3-(TRIFLUOROMETHYL)PHENYL-3(2H)- PYRIDAZINONE; 4-CHLORO-5-(METHYLAMINO)-2-(ALPHA,ALPHA,ALPHA-TRIFLUORO-M-TOLYL)- 3(2H)-PYRIDAZINONE;
4-CHLORO-5-METHYLAMINO-2-(ALPHA,ALPHA,ALPHA-TRIFLUORO-M-TOLYL)-PYRIDAZIN-3(2H)-ONE; 4-CHLORO-5-METHYLAMINO-2-(3-TRIFLUOROMETHYLPHENYL)PYRIDAZIN-3-ONE; EVITAL; H 9789; NORFLURAZONE; SOLICAM; TELOK; ZORIAL; C12H9CLF3N3O; PST72343

CHEMICAL FAMILY: PYRIDAZINE
KETONE
HALOGEN

MOLECULAR FORMULA: C12-H9-CL-F3-N3-O

MOLECULAR WEIGHT: 303.69

CERCLA RATINGS (SCALE 0-3): HEALTH=U FIRE=1 REACTIVITY=0 PERSISTENCE=3

NFPA RATINGS (SCALE 0-4): HEALTH=U FIRE=1 REACTIVITY=0

COMPONENTS AND CONTAMINANTS

COMPONENT: NORFLURAZON ***PERCENT:*** 100.0
CAS# 27314-13-2

EXPOSURE LIMITS: NO OCCUPATIONAL EXPOSURE LIMITS ESTABLISHED BY OSHA, ACGIH, OR NIOSH.

PHYSICAL DATA

DESCRIPTION: ODORLESS, COLORLESS TO BROWNISH-GRAY CRYSTALLINE SOLID.

MELTING POINT: 345-356 F (174-180 C) ***SPECIFIC GRAVITY:*** NOT AVAILABLE

VAPOR PRESSURE: NEGLIGIBLE ***SOLUBILITY IN WATER:*** 28 PPM

SOLVENT SOLUBILITY: SOLUBLE IN ETHANOL; MODERATELY SOLUBLE IN ACETONE; SLIGHTLY SOLUBLE IN XYLENE, HYDROCARBONS, XYLOL; INSOLUBLE IN CARBON DISULFIDE.

FIRE AND EXPLOSION DATA

FIRE AND EXPLOSION HAZARD: SLIGHT FIRE HAZARD WHEN EXPOSED TO HEAT OR FLAME.

FIREFIGHTING MEDIA: DRY CHEMICAL, CARBON DIOXIDE, HALON, WATER SPRAY OR STANDARD FOAM (1987 EMERGENCY RESPONSE GUIDEBOOK, DOT P 5800.4).
FOR LARGER FIRES, USE WATER SPRAY, FOG OR STANDARD FOAM (1987 EMERGENCY RESPONSE GUIDEBOOK, DOT P 5800.4).

FIREFIGHTING: MOVE CONTAINER FROM FIRE AREA IF POSSIBLE. DO NOT SCATTER SPILLED MATERIAL WITH HIGH PRESSURE WATER STREAMS. DIKE FIRE CONTROL WATER FOR LATER DISPOSAL (1987 EMERGENCY RESPONSE GUIDEBOOK, DOT P 5800.4, GUIDE PAGE 31).
USE AGENTS SUITABLE FOR TYPE OF SURROUNDING FIRE. AVOID BREATHING HAZARDOUS VAPORS, KEEP UPWIND.

TOXICITY

NORFLURAZON: TOXICITY DATA: >20,000 MG/KG SKIN-RABBIT LD50 (85JFAN); >5,000 MG/KG SKIN-RAT LD50 (85JFAN); 8000 MG/KG ORAL-RAT LD50. CARCINOGEN STATUS: NONE. ACUTE TOXICITY LEVEL: SLIGHTLY TOXIC BY INGESTION; RELATIVELY NONTOXIC BY DERMAL ABSORPTION. TARGET EFFECTS: NO DATA AVAILABLE.

HEALTH EFFECTS AND FIRST AID

INHALATION: NORFLURAZON: **ACUTE EXPOSURE-** THE LC50 OF 80% WETTABLE POWDER IN RATS WAS GREATER THAN 200 MG/L/1 HOUR. **CHRONIC EXPOSURE-** NO OBSERVABLE EFFECTS WERE NOTED IN A 14-DAY STUDY OF RATS EXPOSED TO 10 MG/L.

FIRST AID- REMOVE FROM EXPOSURE AREA TO FRESH AIR IMMEDIATELY. IF BREATHING HAS STOPPED, PERFORM ARTIFICIAL RESPIRATION. KEEP PERSON WARM AND AT REST. TREAT SYMPTOMATICALLY AND SUPPORTIVELY. GET MEDICAL ATTENTION IMMEDIATELY.

SKIN CONTACT: NORFLURAZON: **ACUTE EXPOSURE-** THIS MATERIAL WAS NOT AN IRRITANT OR SENSITIZER OF ANIMAL SKIN. **CHRONIC EXPOSURE-** NO OBSERVABLE EFFECTS WERE NOTED IN A 21-DAY STUDY OF RABBITS RECEIVING AN APPLICATION OF 2000 MG/KG/DAY.

FIRST AID- REMOVE CONTAMINATED CLOTHING AND SHOES IMMEDIATELY. WASH AFFECTED AREA WITH SOAP OR MILD DETERGENT AND LARGE AMOUNTS OF WATER UNTIL NO EVIDENCE OF CHEMICAL REMAINS (APPROXIMATELY 15-20 MINUTES). GET MEDICAL ATTENTION IMMEDIATELY.

EYE CONTACT: NORFLURAZON: **ACUTE EXPOSURE-** THIS MATERIAL WAS NOT AN IRRITANT OF ANIMAL EYES. **CHRONIC EXPOSURE-** NO DATA AVAILABLE.

FIRST AID- WASH EYES IMMEDIATELY WITH LARGE AMOUNTS OF WATER OR NORMAL SALINE, OCCASIONALLY LIFTING UPPER AND LOWER LIDS, UNTIL NO EVIDENCE OF CHEMICAL REMAINS (APPROXIMATELY 15-20 MINUTES). GET MEDICAL ATTENTION IMMEDIATELY.

INGESTION: NORFLURAZON: **ACUTE EXPOSURE-** THE LETHAL DOSE REPORTED IN RATS WAS 8000 MG/KG; SYMPTOMS WERE NOT REPORTED. **CHRONIC EXPOSURE-** PATHOLOGICAL CHANGES IN THE LIVER, KIDNEYS, THYROID, PITUITARY, ADRENALS, OVARIES, AND UTERUS WERE OBSERVED IN STUDIES OF LABORATORY ANIMALS. EFFECTS OF REDUCED FERTILITY, GESTATION AND VIABILITY INDICES WERE OBSERVED IN A 3-GENERATION STUDY OF RATS RECEIVING A DIETARY LEVEL OF 1025 PPM. FETOTOXIC EFFECTS WERE NOTED IN A STUDY OF PREGNANT RABBITS AT LEVELS OF 30 AND 60 MG/KG/DAY.

FIRST AID- IF THE PERSON IS CONSCIOUS AND NOT CONVULSING, REMOVE BY GASTRIC LAVAGE AND FOLLOW WITH A CATHARTIC (DREISBACH, HANDBOOK OF POISONING, 12TH ED.). TREAT SYMPTOMATICALLY AND SUPPORTIVELY. GASTRIC LAVAGE SHOULD BE PERFORMED BY QUALIFIED MEDICAL PERSONNEL. GET MEDICAL ATTENTION IMMEDIATELY.

ANTIDOTE: NO SPECIFIC ANTIDOTE. TREAT SYMPTOMATICALLY AND SUPPORTIVELY.

REACTIVITY

REACTIVITY: STABLE UNDER NORMAL TEMPERATURES AND PRESSURES.

INCOMPATIBILITIES: NORFLURAZON: OXIDIZERS (STRONG): FIRE AND EXPLOSION HAZARD.

DECOMPOSITION: THERMAL DECOMPOSITION PRODUCTS MAY INCLUDE HIGHLY TOXIC FUMES OF FLUORIDES AND CHLORIDES AND TOXIC OXIDES OF NITROGEN AND CARBON.

POLYMERIZATION: HAZARDOUS POLYMERIZATION HAS NOT BEEN REPORTED TO OCCUR UNDER NORMAL TEMPERATURES AND PRESSURES.

STORAGE AND DISPOSAL

OBSERVE ALL FEDERAL, STATE AND LOCAL REGULATIONS WHEN STORING OR DISPOSING OF THIS SUBSTANCE. FOR ASSISTANCE, CONTACT THE DISTRICT DIRECTOR OF THE ENVIRONMENTAL PROTECTION AGENCY.

STORAGE

STORE IN ACCORDANCE WITH 40 CFR 165 RECOMMENDED PROCEDURES FOR THE DISPOSAL AND STORAGE OF PESTICIDES AND PESTICIDE CONTAINERS.
STORE AWAY FROM INCOMPATIBLE SUBSTANCES.

DISPOSAL

DISPOSAL MUST BE IN ACCORDANCE WITH 40 CFR 165 RECOMMENDED PROCEDURES FOR THE DISPOSAL AND STORAGE OF PESTICIDES AND PESTICIDE CONTAINERS.

CONDITIONS TO AVOID

MAY BURN BUT DOES NOT IGNITE READILY. AVOID CONTACT WITH STRONG OXIDIZERS, EXCESSIVE HEAT, SPARKS, OR OPEN FLAME.

SPILL AND LEAK PROCEDURES

OCCUPATIONAL SPILL: SWEEP UP AND PLACE IN SUITABLE CLEAN, DRY CONTAINERS FOR RECLAMATION OR LATER DISPOSAL. DO NOT FLUSH SPILLED MATERIAL INTO SEWER. KEEP UNNECESSARY PEOPLE AWAY.

PROTECTIVE EQUIPMENT

VENTILATION: PROVIDE GENERAL DILUTION VENTILATION.

RESPIRATOR: THE FOLLOWING RESPIRATORS ARE RECOMMENDED BASED ON INFORMATION FOUND IN THE PHYSICAL DATA, TOXICITY AND HEALTH EFFECTS SECTIONS. THEY ARE RANKED IN ORDER FROM MINIMUM TO MAXIMUM RESPIRATORY PROTECTION. THE SPECIFIC RESPIRATOR SELECTED MUST BE BASED ON CONTAMINATION LEVELS FOUND IN THE WORK PLACE, MUST NOT EXCEED THE WORKING LIMITS OF THE RESPIRATOR AND BE JOINTLY APPROVED BY THE NATIONAL INSTITUTE FOR OCCUPATIONAL SAFETY AND HEALTH AND THE MINE SAFETY AND HEALTH ADMINISTRATION (NIOSH-MSHA).

CHEMICAL CARTRIDGE RESPIRATOR WITH AN ORGANIC VAPOR CARTRIDGE(S) IN COMBINATION WITH A DUST AND MIST FILTER.

GAS MASK WITH ORGANIC VAPOR CANISTER (CHIN-STYLE OR FRONT- OR BACK-MOUNTED CANISTER) WITH A DUST AND MIST FILTER.

GAS MASK WITH ORGANIC VAPOR CANISTER (CHIN-STYLE OR FRONT- OR BACK-MOUNTED CANISTER) WITH A PARTICULATE FILTER.

POWERED AIR-PURIFYING RESPIRATOR WITH A HIGH-EFFICIENCY FILTER.

TYPE 'C' SUPPLIED-AIR RESPIRATOR WITH A FULL FACEPIECE OPERATED IN A PRESSURE-DEMAND OR OTHER POSITIVE PRESSURE MODE.

SELF-CONTAINED BREATHING APPARATUS WITH A FULL FACEPIECE OPERATED IN PRESSURE-DEMAND OR OTHER POSITIVE PRESSURE MODE.

FOR FIREFIGHTING AND OTHER IMMEDIATELY DANGEROUS TO LIFE OR HEALTH CONDITIONS:

SELF-CONTAINED BREATHING APPARATUS WITH FULL FACEPIECE OPERATED IN PRESSURE-DEMAND OR OTHER POSITIVE PRESSURE MODE.

SUPPLIED-AIR RESPIRATOR WITH FULL FACEPIECE AND OPERATED IN PRESSURE-DEMAND OR OTHER POSITIVE PRESSURE MODE IN COMBINATION WITH AN AUXILIARY SELF-CONTAINED BREATHING APPARATUS OPERATED IN PRESSURE-DEMAND OR OTHER POSITIVE PRESSURE MODE.

CLOTHING: EMPLOYEE MUST WEAR APPROPRIATE PROTECTIVE (IMPERVIOUS) CLOTHING AND EQUIPMENT TO PREVENT REPEATED OR PROLONGED SKIN CONTACT WITH THIS SUBSTANCE.

GLOVES: EMPLOYEE MUST WEAR APPROPRIATE PROTECTIVE GLOVES TO PREVENT CONTACT WITH THIS SUBSTANCE.

EYE PROTECTION: EMPLOYEE MUST WEAR SPLASH-PROOF OR DUST-RESISTANT SAFETY GOGGLES TO PREVENT EYE CONTACT WITH THIS SUBSTANCE.

EMERGENCY EYE WASH: WHERE THERE IS ANY POSSIBILITY THAT AN EMPLOYEE'S EYES MAY BE EXPOSED TO THIS SUBSTANCE, THE EMPLOYER SHOULD PROVIDE AN EYE WASH FOUNTAIN WITHIN THE IMMEDIATE WORK AREA FOR EMERGENCY USE.

AUTHORIZED BY- OCCUPATIONAL HEALTH SERVICES, INC.
CREATION DATE: 04/20/90 ***REVISION DATE:*** 05/31/90

MATERIAL SAFETY DATA SHEET

OCCUPATIONAL HEALTH SERVICES, INC.
AGRICULTURE AND PESTICIDE DIVISION
450 SEVENTH AVENUE, SUITE 2407
NEW YORK, NEW YORK 10123
1-800-445-MSDS OR (212) 967-1100

EMERGENCY CONTACT:
JOHN S. BRANSFORD, JR. (615) 292-1180

SUBSTANCE IDENTIFICATION

CAS-NUMBER 20354-26-1

SUBSTANCE: **METHAZOLE**

TRADE NAMES/SYNONYMS: 1,2,4-OXADIAZOLIDINE-3,5-DIONE, 2-(3,4-DICHLOROPHENYL)-4-METHYL-; 2-(3,4-DICHLOROPHENYL)-4-METHYL-1,2,4-OXADIAZOLIDINE-3,5-DIONE; BIOXONE; CHLORMETHAZOLE; METAZOL; METAZOLE; PROBE; MEZOPUR; TUNIC; TUNIC (PESTICIDE); VCS 438; PAXILON; OXYDIAZOL; C9H6CL2N2O3; PST72344

CHEMICAL FAMILY: HETEROCYCLIC NITROGEN

MOLECULAR FORMULA: C9-H6-CL2-N2-O3

MOLECULAR WEIGHT: 261.07

CERCLA RATINGS (SCALE 0-3): HEALTH=2 FIRE=1 REACTIVITY=0 PERSISTENCE=3

NFPA RATINGS (SCALE 0-4): HEALTH=2 FIRE=1 REACTIVITY=0

COMPONENTS AND CONTAMINANTS

COMPONENT: METHAZOLE ***PERCENT:*** 100
CAS# 20354-26-1

OTHER CONTAMINANTS: MAY CONTAIN TRACES OF TCAB AND TCAOB

EXPOSURE LIMITS: NO OCCUPATIONAL EXPOSURE LIMITS ESTABLISHED BY OSHA, ACGIH, OR NIOSH.

PHYSICAL DATA

DESCRIPTION: LIGHT TAN SOLID. ***MELTING POINT:*** 253-255 F (123-124 C)

SPECIFIC GRAVITY: 1.24 ***VAPOR PRESSURE:*** NEGLIGIBLE

SOLUBILITY IN WATER: 1.5 PPM

SOLVENT SOLUBILITY: SOLUBLE IN XYLENE, ACETONE, METHANOL.

FIRE AND EXPLOSION DATA

FIRE AND EXPLOSION HAZARD: SLIGHT FIRE HAZARD WHEN EXPOSED TO HEAT OR FLAME.

FIREFIGHTING MEDIA: DRY CHEMICAL, CARBON DIOXIDE, HALON, WATER SPRAY OR STANDARD FOAM (1987 EMERGENCY RESPONSE GUIDEBOOK, DOT P 5800.4).
FOR LARGER FIRES, USE WATER SPRAY, FOG OR STANDARD FOAM (1987 EMERGENCY RESPONSE GUIDEBOOK, DOT P 5800.4).

FIREFIGHTING: MOVE CONTAINERS FROM FIRE AREA IF POSSIBLE (1987 EMERGENCY RESPONSE GUIDEBOOK, DOT P 5800.4, GUIDE PAGE 53).
EXTINGUISH FIRE USING AGENTS SUITABLE FOR TYPE OF SURROUNDING FIRE. USE WATER IN FLOODING AMOUNTS AS A FOG. AVOID BREATHING DUSTS AND FUMES FROM BURNING MATERIAL; KEEP UPWIND.

TOXICITY

METHAZOLE: TOXICITY DATA: 10200 MG/KG SKIN-RAT LD50; 777 MG/KG ORAL-RAT LD50; 600 MG/KG INTRAPERITONEAL-MOUSE LD50. CARCINOGEN STATUS: NONE. ACUTE TOXICITY LEVEL: MODERATELY TOXIC BY INGESTION AND SLIGHTLY TOXIC BY DERMAL ABSORPTION. TARGET EFFECTS: NO DATA AVAILABLE.

HEALTH EFFECTS AND FIRST AID

INHALATION: METHAZOLE: **ACUTE EXPOSURE**- A LETHAL CONCENTRATION IN RATS IS GREATER THAN 200,000 MG/M3. **CHRONIC EXPOSURE**- NO DATA AVAILABLE.

FIRST AID- REMOVE FROM EXPOSURE AREA TO FRESH AIR IMMEDIATELY. IF BREATHING HAS STOPPED, PERFORM ARTIFICIAL RESPIRATION. KEEP PERSON WARM AND AT REST. TREAT SYMPTOMATICALLY AND SUPPORTIVELY. GET MEDICAL ATTENTION IMMEDIATELY.

SKIN CONTACT: METHAZOLE: **ACUTE EXPOSURE**- THIS MATERIAL WAS MILDLY IRRITATING TO RABBIT SKIN. CHLOROACNE WAS OBSERVED AMONG OCCUPATIONALLY EXPOSED WORKERS; IMPURITIES OF METHAZOLE, TCAB AND TCAOB, ARE THOUGHT RESPONSIBLE FOR APPEARANCE OF CHLOROACNE. **CHRONIC EXPOSURE**- NO DATA AVAILABLE.

FIRST AID- REMOVE CONTAMINATED CLOTHING AND SHOES IMMEDIATELY. WASH AFFECTED AREA WITH SOAP OR MILD DETERGENT AND LARGE AMOUNTS OF WATER UNTIL NO EVIDENCE OF CHEMICAL REMAINS (APPROXIMATELY 15-20 MINUTES). GET MEDICAL ATTENTION IMMEDIATELY.

EYE CONTACT: METHAZOLE: **ACUTE EXPOSURE**- THIS MATERIAL WAS MILDLY IRRITATING TO RABBIT EYES. **CHRONIC EXPOSURE**- NO DATA AVAILABLE.

FIRST AID- WASH EYES IMMEDIATELY WITH LARGE AMOUNTS OF WATER OR NORMAL SALINE, OCCASIONALLY LIFTING UPPER AND LOWER LIDS, UNTIL NO EVIDENCE OF CHEMICAL REMAINS (APPROXIMATELY 15-20 MINUTES). GET MEDICAL ATTENTION IMMEDIATELY.

INGESTION: METHAZOLE: **ACUTE EXPOSURE**- A LETHAL DOSE IN RATS WAS 777 MG/KG. **CHRONIC EXPOSURE**- EMBRYOLETHALITY WAS OBSERVED AT A DIETARY LEVEL OF 30 PPM IN ONE TERATOLOGY STUDY WITH RABBITS. REPEATED ADMINISTRATION PRODUCED A YELLOW-BROWN PIGMENT IN THE SPLEEN OR LIVER OF RATS, MICE, AND DOGS; CATARACTS WERE PRODUCED IN RATS.

FIRST AID- TREAT SYMPTOMATICALLY AND SUPPORTIVELY. GET MEDICAL ATTENTION IMMEDIATELY. IF VOMITING OCCURS, KEEP HEAD LOWER THAN HIPS TO PREVENT ASPIRATION.

ANTIDOTE: NO SPECIFIC ANTIDOTE. TREAT SYMPTOMATICALLY AND SUPPORTIVELY.

MATERIAL SAFETY DATA SHEET

OCCUPATIONAL HEALTH SERVICES, INC.
AGRICULTURE AND PESTICIDE DIVISION
450 SEVENTH AVENUE, SUITE 2407
NEW YORK, NEW YORK 10123
1-800-445-MSDS OR (212) 967-1100

EMERGENCY CONTACT:
JOHN S. BRANSFORD, JR. (615) 292-1180

SUBSTANCE IDENTIFICATION

CAS-NUMBER 23103-98-2

SUBSTANCE: **PIRIMICARB**

TRADE NAMES/SYNONYMS: CARBAMIC ACID, DIMETHYL-, 2-(DIMETHYLAMINO)-5,6-DIMETHYL-4-PYRIMIDINYL ESTER; DIMETHYLCARBAMIC ACID 2-(DIMETHYLAMINO)-5,6-DIMETHYL-4-PYRIMIDINYL ESTER; 2-(DIMETHYLAMINO)-5,6-DIMETHYL-4-PYRIMIDINYL DIMETHYLCARBAMATE; 5,6-DIMETHYL-2-DIMETHYLAMINO-4-DIMETHYLCARBAMOYLOXYPYRIMIDINE; 2-DIMETHYLAMINO-5,6-DIMETHYLPYRIMIDIN-4-YL DIMETHYLCARBAMATE; APHOX; FERNOS; PIRIMOR; PP 062; PYRIMOR; ENT 27766; C11H18N4O2; PST72345

CHEMICAL FAMILY: CARBAMATE

MOLECULAR FORMULA: C11-H18-N4-O2

MOLECULAR WEIGHT: 238.29

CERCLA RATINGS (SCALE 0-3): HEALTH=3 FIRE=1 REACTIVITY=0 PERSISTENCE=1

NFPA RATINGS (SCALE 0-4): HEALTH=U FIRE=1 REACTIVITY=0

COMPONENTS AND CONTAMINANTS

COMPONENT: PIRIMICARB ***PERCENT:*** 100.0
CAS# 23103-98-2

OTHER CONTAMINANTS: NONE

EXPOSURE LIMITS: NO OCCUPATIONAL EXPOSURE LIMITS ESTABLISHED BY OSHA, ACGIH, OR NIOSH.

PHYSICAL DATA

DESCRIPTION: COLORLESS, CRYSTALLINE SOLID.

MELTING POINT: 196-199 F (91-93 C)

SPECIFIC GRAVITY: NOT AVAILABLE ***VAPOR PRESSURE:*** 0.00003 MMHG @ 30 C

SOLUBILITY IN WATER: 0.27% @ 25 C

SOLVENT SOLUBILITY: SOLUBLE IN ACETONE, CHLOROFORM, ETHANOL, XYLENE, METHANOL, DICHLOROMETHANE, AND MOST ORGANIC SOLVENTS. DECOMPOSED BY PROLONGED BOILING WITH ACIDS OR ALKALI.

FIRE AND EXPLOSION DATA

FIRE AND EXPLOSION HAZARD: SLIGHT FIRE HAZARD WHEN EXPOSED TO HEAT OR FLAME.

FIREFIGHTING MEDIA: DRY CHEMICAL, CARBON DIOXIDE, HALON, WATER SPRAY OR STANDARD FOAM (1987 EMERGENCY RESPONSE GUIDEBOOK, DOT P 5800.4). FOR LARGER FIRES, USE WATER SPRAY, FOG OR STANDARD FOAM (1987 EMERGENCY RESPONSE GUIDEBOOK, DOT P 5800.4).

FIREFIGHTING: MOVE CONTAINERS FROM FIRE AREA IF POSSIBLE. FIGHT FIRE FROM MAXIMUM DISTANCE. STAY AWAY FROM STORAGE TANK ENDS. DIKE FIRE CONTROL WATER FOR LATER DISPOSAL. DO NOT SCATTER MATERIAL (1987 EMERGENCY RESPONSE GUIDEBOOK, DOT P 5800.4, GUIDE PAGE 55). EXTINGUISH USING AGENTS SUITABLE FOR TYPE OF SURROUNDING FIRE. USE FLOODING AMOUNTS OF WATER AS FOG. AVOID BREATHING TOXIC DUST AND FUMES FROM BURNING MATERIAL; KEEP UPWIND.

TOXICITY

PIRIMICARB: TOXICITY DATA: 100 MG/KG ORAL-RAT LD50; 107 MG/KG ORAL-MOUSE LD50; 100 MG/KG ORAL-DOG LD50; >500 MG/KG SKIN-RAT LD50 (FARM CHEMICAL HANDBOOK); 111 MG/KG UNREPORTED-RAT LD50; 68 MG/KG UNREPORTED-MOUSE LD50; MUTAGENIC DATA (RTECS). CARCINOGEN STATUS: NONE. ACUTE TOXICITY: TOXIC BY INGESTION. TARGET EFFECTS: CHOLINESTERASE INHIBITOR. AT INCREASED RISK FROM EXPOSURE: PERSONS WITH ASTHMA, DIABETES, CARDIOVASCULAR DISEASE, MECHANICAL OBSTRUCTION OF THE GASTROINTESTINAL OR UROGENITAL TRACT, AND THOSE IN VAGOTONIC STATES.*

* MAY BE BASED ON GENERAL INFORMATION ON CARBAMATES.

REACTIVITY

REACTIVITY: STABLE UNDER NORMAL TEMPERATURES AND PRESSURES.

INCOMPATIBILITIES: METHAZOLE: NO DATA AVAILABLE.

DECOMPOSITION: THERMAL DECOMPOSITION PRODUCTS MAY INCLUDE TOXIC OXIDES OF CARBON AND NITROGEN AND TOXIC FUMES OF CHLORINE AND PHOSGENE.

POLYMERIZATION: HAZARDOUS POLYMERIZATION HAS NOT BEEN REPORTED TO OCCUR UNDER NORMAL TEMPERATURES AND PRESSURES.

STORAGE AND DISPOSAL

OBSERVE ALL FEDERAL, STATE AND LOCAL REGULATIONS WHEN STORING OR DISPOSING OF THIS SUBSTANCE. FOR ASSISTANCE, CONTACT THE DISTRICT DIRECTOR OF THE ENVIRONMENTAL PROTECTION AGENCY.

STORAGE

STORE IN ACCORDANCE WITH 40 CFR 165 RECOMMENDED PROCEDURES FOR THE DISPOSAL AND STORAGE OF PESTICIDES AND PESTICIDE CONTAINERS.

DISPOSAL

DISPOSAL MUST BE IN ACCORDANCE WITH 40 CFR 165 RECOMMENDED PROCEDURES FOR THE DISPOSAL AND STORAGE OF PESTICIDES AND PESTICIDE CONTAINERS.

CONDITIONS TO AVOID

MAY BURN BUT DOES NOT IGNITE READILY.

SPILL AND LEAK PROCEDURES

OCCUPATIONAL SPILL: DO NOT TOUCH SPILLED MATERIAL. STOP LEAK IF YOU CAN DO IT WITHOUT RISK. FOR SMALL SPILLS, TAKE UP WITH SAND OR OTHER ABSORBENT MATERIAL AND PLACE INTO CONTAINERS FOR LATER DISPOSAL. FOR SMALL DRY SPILLS, WITH A CLEAN SHOVEL PLACE MATERIAL INTO CLEAN, DRY CONTAINER AND COVER. MOVE CONTAINERS FROM SPILL AREA. FOR LARGER SPILLS, DIKE FAR AHEAD OF SPILL FOR LATER DISPOSAL. KEEP UNNECESSARY PEOPLE AWAY. ISOLATE HAZARD AREA AND DENY ENTRY.

PROTECTIVE EQUIPMENT

VENTILATION: PROVIDE LOCAL EXHAUST OR GENERAL DILUTION VENTILATION SYSTEM.

RESPIRATOR: THE FOLLOWING RESPIRATORS ARE RECOMMENDED BASED ON INFORMATION FOUND IN THE PHYSICAL DATA, TOXICITY AND HEALTH EFFECTS SECTIONS. THEY ARE RANKED IN ORDER FROM MINIMUM TO MAXIMUM RESPIRATORY PROTECTION. THE SPECIFIC RESPIRATOR SELECTED MUST BE BASED ON CONTAMINATION LEVELS FOUND IN THE WORK PLACE, MUST NOT EXCEED THE WORKING LIMITS OF THE RESPIRATOR AND BE JOINTLY APPROVED BY THE NATIONAL INSTITUTE FOR OCCUPATIONAL SAFETY AND HEALTH AND THE MINE SAFETY AND HEALTH ADMINISTRATION (NIOSH-MSHA).

CHEMICAL CARTRIDGE RESPIRATOR WITH AN ORGANIC VAPOR CARTRIDGE(S) WITH A FULL FACEPIECE AND ORGANIC VAPOR CARTRIDGE(S) IN COMBINATION WITH A DUST AND MIST FILTER.

POWERED AIR-PURIFYING RESPIRATOR WITH A TIGHT-FITTING FACEPIECE AND ORGANIC VAPOR CARTRIDGE(S) IN COMBINATION WITH A HIGH-EFFICIENCY PARTICULATE FILTER.

TYPE 'C' SUPPLIED-AIR RESPIRATOR WITH A FULL FACEPIECE OPERATED IN A PRESSURE-DEMAND OR OTHER POSITIVE PRESSURE MODE.

SELF-CONTAINED BREATHING APPARATUS WITH A FULL FACEPIECE OPERATED IN PRESSURE-DEMAND OR OTHER POSITIVE PRESSURE MODE.

FOR FIREFIGHTING AND OTHER IMMEDIATELY DANGEROUS TO LIFE OR HEALTH CONDITIONS:

SELF-CONTAINED BREATHING APPARATUS WITH FULL FACEPIECE OPERATED IN PRESSURE-DEMAND OR OTHER POSITIVE PRESSURE MODE.

SUPPLIED-AIR RESPIRATOR WITH FULL FACEPIECE AND OPERATED IN PRESSURE-DEMAND OR OTHER POSITIVE PRESSURE MODE IN COMBINATION WITH AN AUXILIARY SELF-CONTAINED BREATHING APPARATUS OPERATED IN PRESSURE-DEMAND OR OTHER POSITIVE PRESSURE MODE.

CLOTHING: EMPLOYEE MUST WEAR APPROPRIATE PROTECTIVE (IMPERVIOUS) CLOTHING AND EQUIPMENT TO PREVENT REPEATED OR PROLONGED SKIN CONTACT WITH THIS SUBSTANCE.

GLOVES: EMPLOYEE MUST WEAR APPROPRIATE PROTECTIVE GLOVES TO PREVENT CONTACT WITH THIS SUBSTANCE.

EYE PROTECTION: EMPLOYEE MUST WEAR SPLASH-PROOF OR DUST-RESISTANT SAFETY GOGGLES TO PREVENT EYE CONTACT WITH THIS SUBSTANCE.

EMERGENCY EYE WASH: WHERE THERE IS ANY POSSIBILITY THAT AN EMPLOYEE'S EYES MAY BE EXPOSED TO THIS SUBSTANCE, THE EMPLOYER SHOULD PROVIDE AN EYE WASH FOUNTAIN WITHIN THE IMMEDIATE WORK AREA FOR EMERGENCY USE.

AUTHORIZED BY- OCCUPATIONAL HEALTH SERVICES, INC.
CREATION DATE: 10/04/89 ***REVISION DATE:*** 05/14/90

HEALTH EFFECTS AND FIRST AID

INHALATION: PIRIMICARB: SEE INFORMATION ON CARBAMATES. NO CHOLINESTERASE INHIBITION WAS OBSERVED IN RATS EXPOSED FOR 6 HOURS/DAY FOR 5 DAYS/WEEK/21 DAYS TO AIR WHICH HAD BEEN PASSED OVER TECHNICAL PIRIMICARB AT ROOM TEMPERATURE.
CARBAMATES: CHOLINESTERASE INHIBITOR. **ACUTE EXPOSURE-** WHEN INHALED, THE FIRST EFFECTS OF CHOLINESTERASE INHIBITION ARE USUALLY RESPIRATORY AND MAY INCLUDE NASAL HYPEREMIA AND WATERY DISCHARGE, CHEST DISCOMFORT, DYSPNEA, AND WHEEZING DUE TO INCREASED BRONCHIAL SECRETIONS AND BRONCHOCONSTRICTION. OTHER SYSTEMIC EFFECTS MAY BEGIN WITHIN A FEW MINUTES OR SEVERAL HOURS OF EXPOSURE. SYMPTOMS MAY INCLUDE NAUSEA, VOMITING, DIARRHEA, ABDOMINAL CRAMPS, HEADACHE, VERTIGO, OCULAR PAIN, CILIARY MUSCLE SPASM, BLURRING OR DIMNESS OF VISION, MIOSIS, OR IN SOME CASES MYDRIASIS, LACRIMATION, SALIVATION, SWEATING, AND CONFUSION. OTHER REPORTED CENTRAL NERVOUS SYSTEM OR NEUROMUSCULAR EFFECTS INCLUDE ATAXIA, SLURRED SPEECH, AREFLEXIA, WEAKNESS, FATIGUE, TWITCHING, FASCICULATION, TREMOR, AND EVENTUALLY PARALYSIS OF THE EXTREMITIES AND POSSIBLY OF THE RESPIRATORY MUSCLES. IN SEVERE CASES, THERE MAY ALSO BE INVOLUNTARY DEFECATION AND URINATION, BRADYCARDIA, HYPOTENSION, PULMONARY EDEMA, CONVULSIONS, COMA, AND DEATH FROM RESPIRATORY FAILURE OR CARDIAC ARREST. CARBAMATES GENERALLY DO NOT ACCUMULATE IN MAMMALIAN TISSUE AND THE CHOLINESTERASE INHIBITION REVERSES RATHER RAPIDLY. IN NON-FATAL CASES, THE ILLNESS GENERALLY LASTS LESS THAN 24 HOURS. **CHRONIC EXPOSURE-** PROLONGED OR REPEATED EXPOSURE MAY CAUSE EFFECTS AS DESCRIBED IN ACUTE EXPOSURE.
FIRST AID- REMOVE FROM EXPOSURE AREA TO FRESH AIR IMMEDIATELY. IF BREATHING HAS STOPPED, GIVE ARTIFICIAL RESPIRATION. MAINTAIN AIRWAY AND BLOOD PRESSURE AND ADMINISTER OXYGEN IF AVAILABLE. KEEP AFFECTED PERSON WARM AND AT REST. TREAT SYMPTOMATICALLY AND SUPPORTIVELY. ADMINISTRATION OF OXYGEN SHOULD BE PERFORMED BY QUALIFIED PERSONNEL. GET MEDICAL ATTENTION IMMEDIATELY.

SKIN CONTACT: PIRIMICARB: **ACUTE EXPOSURE-** A LETHAL DOSE IN RABBITS BY DERMAL ABSORPTION WAS GREATER THAN 500 MG/KG. **CHRONIC EXPOSURE-** NO ADVERSE EFFECTS WERE PRODUCED FROM DAILY APPLICATIONS OF 500 MG/KG TO RABBIT SKIN OVER A 14-DAY PERIOD.
FIRST AID- REMOVE CONTAMINATED CLOTHING IMMEDIATELY. WASH CONTAMINATED AREAS WITH SOAP AND WATER FOLLOWED BY ALCOHOL (ARENA, POISONING, 4TH ED.). EMERGENCY PERSONNEL SHOULD WEAR GLOVES AND AVOID CONTAMINATION. TREAT RESPIRATORY DIFFICULTY WITH ARTIFICIAL RESPIRATION. GET MEDICAL ATTENTION IMMEDIATELY.

EYE CONTACT: PIRIMICARB: SEE INFORMATION ON CARBAMATES.
CARBAMATES: CHOLINESTERASE INHIBITOR. **ACUTE EXPOSURE-** DIRECT CONTACT MAY CAUSE PAIN, HYPEREMIA, LACRIMATION, TWITCHING OF THE EYELIDS, MIOSIS, AND CILIARY MUSCLE SPASM WITH LOSS OF ACCOMODATION, BLURRED OR DIMMED VISION AND BROWACHE. SOMETIMES MYDRIASIS MAY OCCUR INSTEAD OF MIOSIS. WITH SUFFICIENT EXPOSURE, OTHER SYMPTOMS OF CHOLINESTERASE INHIBITION MAY OCCUR AS DESCRIBED IN ACUTE INHALATION. **CHRONIC EXPOSURE-** PROLONGED EXPOSURE MAY CAUSE EFFECTS AS DESCRIBED IN ACUTE EXPOSURE. SOME COMPOUNDS HAVE CAUSED TOXIC EFFECTS ON THE CRYSTALLINE LENS, CONJUNCTIVAL THICKENING AND OBSTRUCTION OF NASOLACRIMAL CANALS WHEN USED AS MIOTIC EYE DROPS.
FIRST AID- IRRIGATE EYES WITH WATER OR SALINE SOLUTION. IF SYMPTOMS OF POISONING OCCUR, TREAT RESPIRATORY DIFFICULTY WITH ARTIFICIAL RESPIRATION AND OXYGEN. OBSERVE PATIENT FOR AT LEAST 24-36 HOURS (GOSSELIN, CLINICAL TOXICOLOGY OF COMMERCIAL PRODUCTS, 5TH ED.). GET MEDICAL ATTENTION IMMEDIATELY. OXYGEN SHOULD BE ADMINISTERED BY QUALIFIED MEDICAL PERSONNEL.

INGESTION: PIRIMICARB: TOXIC. SEE INFORMATION ON CARBAMATES. ADMINISTRATION OF HIGH LEVELS OF PIRIMICARB IN THE DIET PRODUCED HEMOLYTIC ANEMIA IN DOGS, BUT NOT IN MONKEYS.
CARBAMATES: CHOLINESTERASE INHIBITOR. **ACUTE EXPOSURE-** WHEN INGESTED, THE FIRST EFFECTS MAY BE NAUSEA, VOMITING, ANOREXIA, ABDOMINAL CRAMPS, AND DIARRHEA. WITH ABSORPTION FROM THE GASTROINTESTINAL TRACT, THE OTHER EFFECTS OF CHOLINESTERASE INHIBITION AS DESCRIBED IN ACUTE INHALATION MAY OCCUR; SYMPTOMS MAY BEGIN WITHIN MINUTES OR BE DELAYED SEVERAL HOURS. **CHRONIC EXPOSURE-** REPEATED INGESTION MAY CAUSE EFFECTS AS DESCRIBED IN ACUTE EXPOSURE.
FIRST AID- IF PERSON IS ALERT AND RESPIRATION IS NOT DEPRESSED, GIVE SYRUP OF IPECAC FOLLOWED BY WATER (IF VOMITING OCCURS, KEEP HEAD BELOW HIPS TO PREVENT ASPIRATION). IF CONSCIOUSNESS LEVEL DECLINES OR VOMITING HAS NOT OCCURRED IN 15 MINUTES EMPTY STOMACH BY GASTRIC LAVAGE WITH THE AID OF CUFFED ENDOTRACHEAL TUBE USING ISOTONIC SALINE OR 5% SODIUM BICARBONATE FOLLOW WITH ACTIVATED CHARCOAL. ESTABLISH AND MAINTAIN AIRWAY. TREAT RESPIRATORY DIFFICULTY WITH ARTIFICIAL RESPIRATION AND OXYGEN. DO NOT GIVE MORPHINE, AMINOPHYLLINE, PHENOTHIAZINES, RESERPINE, FUROSEMIDE, OR ETHACRYNIC ACID (MORGAN, RECOGNITION AND MANAGEMENT OF PESTICIDE POISONINGS, 3RD ED.). TREAT SYMPTOMATICALLY AND SUPPORTIVELY. ADMINISTRATION OF OXYGEN AND LAVAGE MUST BE PERFORMED BY QUALIFIED MEDICAL PERSONNEL. GET MEDICAL ATTENTION IMMEDIATELY.

ANTIDOTE: THE FOLLOWING ANTIDOTE(S) HAVE BEEN RECOMMENDED. HOWEVER, THE DECISION AS TO WHETHER THE SEVERITY OF POISONING REQUIRES ADMINISTRATION OF ANY ANTIDOTE AND ACTUAL DOSE REQUIRED SHOULD BE MADE BY QUALIFIED MEDICAL PERSONNEL.
FOR CHOLINESTERASE INHIBITORS: ESTABLISH CLEAR AIRWAY AND TISSUE OXYGENATION BY ASPIRATION OF SECRETIONS, AND IF NECESSARY, BY ASSISTED PULMONARY VENTILATION WITH OXYGEN. IMPROVE TISSUE OXYGENATION AS MUCH AS POSSIBLE BEFORE ADMINISTERING ATROPINE TO MINIMIZE THE RISK OF VENTRICULAR FIBRILLATION. ADMINISTER ATROPINE SULFATE INTRAVENOUSLY, OR INTRAMUSCULARLY IF IV INJECTION IS NOT POSSIBLE. IN MODERATELY SEVERE POISONING ADMINISTER ATROPINE SULFATE, 0.4-2.0 MG REPEATED EVERY 15 MINUTES UNTIL ATROPINIZATION IS ACHIEVED (TACHYCARDIA, FLUSHING, DRY MOUTH, MYDRIASIS). MAINTAIN ATROPINIZATION BY REPEATED DOSES FOR 2-12 HOURS, OR LONGER, DEPENDING ON THE SEVERITY OF POISONING. THE APPEARANCE OF RALES IN THE LUNG BASES, MIOSIS, SALIVATION, NAUSEA, BRADYCARDIA, ARE ALL INDICATIONS OF INADEQUATE ATROPINIZATION. SEVERELY POISONED INDIVIDUALS MAY EXHIBIT REMARKABLE TOLERANCE TO ATROPINE; TWO OR MORE TIMES THE DOSAGES SUGGESTED ABOVE MAY BE NEEDED. PERSONS NOT POISONED OR ONLY SLIGHTLY POISONED, HOWEVER, MAY DEVELOP SIGNS OF ATROPINE TOXICITY FROM SUCH LARGE DOSAGES: FEVER, MUSCLE FIBRILLATIONS, AND DELIRIUM ARE THE MAIN SIGNS OF ATROPINE TOXICITY. IF THESE SIGNS APPEAR WHILE THE PATIENT IS FULLY ATROPINIZED, ATROPINE ADMINISTRATION SHOULD BE DISCONTINUED, AT LEAST TEMPORARILY. OBSERVE TREATED PATIENTS CLOSELY AT LEAST 24 HOURS TO INSURE THAT SYMPTOMS (POSSIBLY PULMONARY EDEMA) DO NOT RECUR AS ATROPINIZATION WEARS OFF. IN VERY SEVERE POISONINGS, METABOLIC DISPOSITION OF TOXICANT MAY REQUIRE SEVERAL HOURS OR DAYS DURING WHICH ATROPINIZATION MUST BE MAINTAINED. MARKEDLY LOWER LEVELS OF URINARY METABOLITES INDICATE THAT ATROPINE DOSAGE CAN BE TAPERED OFF. AS DOSAGE IS REDUCED, CHECK THE LUNG BASES FREQUENTLY FOR RALES. IF RALES ARE HEARD OR OTHER SYMPTOMS RETURN, RE-ESTABLISH ATROPINIZATION PROMPTLY (MORGAN, RECOGNITION AND MANAGEMENT OF PESTICIDE POISONINGS, 3RD ED.). ADMINISTRATION OF ANTIDOTE MUST BE PERFORMED BY QUALIFIED MEDICAL PERSONNEL.
PRALIDOXIME (PROTOPAM-AYERST, 2-PAM) IS OF DOUBTFUL VALUE IN POISONINGS BY CARBAMATE INHIBITORS OF CHOLINESTERASE. ATROPINE ALONE IS ALMOST ALWAYS AN ADEQUATE ANTIDOTE. PRALIDOXIME IS PROBABLY CONTRAINDICATED IN POISONING BY CARBARYL SPECIFICALLY, AND OTHER MONOMETHYLATED CARBAMATES. IF A VICTIM OF DIMETHYLCARBAMATE INSECTICIDE POISONING FAILS TO RESPOND PROMPTLY AND ADEQUATELY TO ATROPINE, OR IF POISONING INVOLVES A COMBINATION OF CARBAMATE AND ORGANOPHOSPHATE, A DILUTE SOLUTION OF PRALIDOXIME (TOTAL DOSE IN 250 ML 5% GLUCOSE SOLUTION) MAY BE GIVEN CAUTIOUSLY INTRAVENOUSLY. ADULT DOSAGE IS 1 GRAM (MORGAN, RECOGNITION AND MANAGEMENT OF PESTICIDE POISONINGS, THIRD EDITION; HAYES, PESTICIDES STUDIED IN MAN, 1982).

REACTIVITY

REACTIVITY: STABLE UNDER NORMAL TEMPERATURES AND PRESSURES.
INCOMPATIBILITIES: PIRIMICARB: OXIDIZERS (STRONG): FIRE AND EXPLOSION HAZARD.
DECOMPOSITION: THERMAL DECOMPOSITION PRODUCTS MAY INCLUDE TOXIC OXIDES OF CARBON AND NITROGEN.
POLYMERIZATION: HAZARDOUS POLYMERIZATION HAS NOT BEEN REPORTED TO OCCUR UNDER NORMAL TEMPERATURES AND PRESSURES.

STORAGE AND DISPOSAL

OBSERVE ALL FEDERAL, STATE AND LOCAL REGULATIONS WHEN STORING OR DISPOSING OF THIS SUBSTANCE. FOR ASSISTANCE, CONTACT THE DISTRICT DIRECTOR OF THE ENVIRONMENTAL PROTECTION AGENCY.

STORAGE

STORE IN ACCORDANCE WITH 40 CFR 165 RECOMMENDED PROCEDURES FOR THE DISPOSAL AND STORAGE OF PESTICIDES AND PESTICIDE CONTAINERS.
STORE AWAY FROM INCOMPATIBLE SUBSTANCES.

DISPOSAL

DISPOSAL MUST BE IN ACCORDANCE WITH 40 CFR 165 RECOMMENDED PROCEDURES FOR THE DISPOSAL AND STORAGE OF PESTICIDES AND PESTICIDE CONTAINERS.

CONDITIONS TO AVOID

MAY BURN BUT DOES NOT IGNITE READILY. CONTAINERS MAY EXPLODE IN HEAT OF FIRE.

SPILL AND LEAK PROCEDURES

OCCUPATIONAL SPILL: DO NOT TOUCH SPILLED MATERIAL. STOP LEAK IF YOU CAN DO IT WITHOUT RISK. USE WATER SPRAY TO REDUCE VAPORS. FOR SMALL SPILLS, TAKE UP WITH SAND OR OTHER ABSORBENT MATERIAL AND PLACE INTO CONTAINERS FOR LATER DISPOSAL. FOR SMALL DRY SPILLS, WITH A CLEAN SHOVEL PLACE MATERIAL INTO CLEAN, DRY CONTAINERS AND COVER. MOVE CONTAINERS FROM SPILL AREA. FOR LARGER SPILLS, DIKE FAR AHEAD OF SPILL FOR LATER DISPOSAL. KEEP UNNECESSARY PEOPLE AWAY. ISOLATE HAZARD AREA AND DENY ENTRY. VENTILATE CLOSED SPACES BEFORE ENTERING.

PROTECTIVE EQUIPMENT

VENTILATION: PROVIDE LOCAL EXHAUST OR GENERAL DILUTION VENTILATION SYSTEM.

RESPIRATOR: THE FOLLOWING RESPIRATORS ARE RECOMMENDED BASED ON INFORMATION FOUND IN THE PHYSICAL DATA, TOXICITY AND HEALTH EFFECTS SECTIONS. THEY ARE RANKED IN ORDER FROM MINIMUM TO MAXIMUM RESPIRATORY PROTECTION. THE SPECIFIC RESPIRATOR SELECTED MUST BE BASED ON CONTAMINATION LEVELS FOUND IN THE WORK PLACE, MUST NOT EXCEED THE WORKING LIMITS OF THE RESPIRATOR AND BE JOINTLY APPROVED BY THE NATIONAL INSTITUTE FOR OCCUPATIONAL SAFETY AND HEALTH AND THE MINE SAFETY AND HEALTH ADMINISTRATION (NIOSH-MSHA).

TYPE 'C' SUPPLIED-AIR RESPIRATOR WITH A FULL FACEPIECE OPERATED IN PRESSURE-DEMAND OR OTHER POSITIVE PRESSURE MODE OR WITH A FULL FACEPIECE, HELMET OR HOOD OPERATED IN CONTINOUS-FLOW MODE.

SELF-CONTAINED BREATHING APPARATUS WITH A FULL FACEPIECE OPERATED IN PRESSURE-DEMAND OR OTHER POSITIVE PRESSURE MODE.

FOR FIREFIGHTING AND OTHER IMMEDIATELY DANGEROUS TO LIFE OR HEALTH CONDITIONS:

SELF-CONTAINED BREATHING APPARATUS WITH FULL FACEPIECE OPERATED IN PRESSURE-DEMAND OR OTHER POSITIVE PRESSURE MODE.

SUPPLIED-AIR RESPIRATOR WITH FULL FACEPIECE AND OPERATED IN PRESSURE-DEMAND OR OTHER POSITIVE PRESSURE MODE IN COMBINATION WITH AN AUXILIARY SELF-CONTAINED BREATHING APPARATUS OPERATED IN PRESSURE-DEMAND OR OTHER POSITIVE PRESSURE MODE.

CLOTHING: EMPLOYEE MUST WEAR APPROPRIATE PROTECTIVE (IMPERVIOUS) CLOTHING AND EQUIPMENT TO PREVENT ANY POSSIBILITY OF SKIN CONTACT WITH THIS SUBSTANCE.

GLOVES: EMPLOYEE MUST WEAR APPROPRIATE PROTECTIVE GLOVES TO PREVENT CONTACT WITH THIS SUBSTANCE.

EYE PROTECTION: EMPLOYEE MUST WEAR SPLASH-PROOF OR DUST-RESISTANT SAFETY GOGGLES WITH OR WITHOUT A FACESHIELD TO PREVENT CONTACT WITH THIS SUBSTANCE. EMERGENCY EYE WASH: WHERE THERE IS ANY POSSIBILITY THAT AN EMPLOYEE'S EYES MAY BE EXPOSED TO THIS SUBSTANCE, THE EMPLOYER SHOULD PROVIDE AN EYE WASH FOUNTAIN WITHIN THE IMMEDIATE WORK AREA FOR EMERGENCY USE.

AUTHORIZED BY- OCCUPATIONAL HEALTH SERVICES, INC.
CREATION DATE: 10/04/89 ***REVISION DATE:*** 06/12/90

MATERIAL SAFETY DATA SHEET

OCCUPATIONAL HEALTH SERVICES, INC.
AGRICULTURE AND PESTICIDE DIVISION
450 SEVENTH AVENUE, SUITE 2407
NEW YORK, NEW YORK 10123
1-800-445-MSDS OR (212) 967-1100

EMERGENCY CONTACT:
JOHN S. BRANSFORD, JR. (615) 292-1180

SUBSTANCE IDENTIFICATION

CAS-NUMBER 5131-24-8

***SUBSTANCE:* <u>DITALIMFOS</u>**

TRADE NAMES/SYNONYMS: PHOSPHONOTHIOIC ACID, (1,3-DIHYDRO-1,3-DIOXO-2H-ISOINDOL-2-YL)-, O,O-DIETHYL ESTER; O,O-DIETHYL (1,3-DIHYDRO-1,3-DIOXO-2H-ISOINDOL-2-YL)PHOSPHONOTHIOATE; PHOSPHONOTHIOIC ACID, PHTHALIMIDO-, O,O-DIETHYL ESTER; PHTHALIMIDOPHOSPHONOTHIOIC ACID, O,O-DIETHYL ESTER; O,O-DIETHYL PHTHALIMIDOPHOSPHONOTHIOATE; N-DIETHOXYPHOSPHINOTHIOYLPHTHALIMIDE; DITALIMPHOS; DOWCO 199; MILLIE; PLONDREL; C12H14NO4PS; PST72347

CHEMICAL FAMILY: PHOSPHONOTHIOATE

MOLECULAR FORMULA: C12-H14-N-O4-P-S

MOLECULAR WEIGHT: 299.29

CERCLA RATINGS (SCALE 0-3): HEALTH=U FIRE=1 REACTIVITY=0 PERSISTENCE=3

NFPA RATINGS (SCALE 0-4): HEALTH=U FIRE=1 REACTIVITY=0

COMPONENTS AND CONTAMINANTS

COMPONENT: DITALIMFOS ***PERCENT:*** 100.0
CAS# 5131-24-8

OTHER CONTAMINANTS: NONE

EXPOSURE LIMITS: NO OCCUPATIONAL EXPOSURE LIMITS ESTABLISHED BY OSHA, ACGIH, OR NIOSH.

PHYSICAL DATA

DESCRIPTION: SOLID. ***MELTING POINT:*** 181-183 F (83-84 C)

SPECIFIC GRAVITY: NOT AVAILABLE ***VAPOR PRESSURE:*** NEGLIGIBLE

SOLUBILITY IN WATER: 133 PPM @ 20 C

SOLVENT SOLUBILITY: SOLUBLE IN ACETONE, ETHYL ACETATE, DICHLOROMETHANE, AND AROMATIC HYDROCARBONS; SLIGHTLY SOLUBLE IN ALIPHATIC HYDROCARBONS

FIRE AND EXPLOSION DATA

FIRE AND EXPLOSION HAZARD: SLIGHT FIRE HAZARD WHEN EXPOSED TO HEAT OR FLAME.

FIREFIGHTING MEDIA: DRY CHEMICAL, CARBON DIOXIDE, HALON, WATER SPRAY OR STANDARD FOAM (1987 EMERGENCY RESPONSE GUIDEBOOK, DOT P 5800.4). FOR LARGER FIRES, USE WATER SPRAY, FOG OR STANDARD FOAM (1987 EMERGENCY RESPONSE GUIDEBOOK, DOT P 5800.4).

FIREFIGHTING: MOVE CONTAINERS FROM FIRE AREA IF POSSIBLE. FIGHT FIRE FROM MAXIMUM DISTANCE. STAY AWAY FROM STORAGE TANK ENDS. DIKE FIRE CONTROL WATER FOR LATER DISPOSAL. DO NOT SCATTER MATERIAL (1987 EMERGENCY RESPONSE GUIDEBOOK, DOT P 5800.4, GUIDE PAGE 55). EXTINGUISH ONLY IF FLOW CAN BE STOPPED; USE FLOODING AMOUNTS OF WATER AS FOG, SOLID STREAMS MAY BE INEFFECTIVE. COOL CONTAINERS WITH FLOODING AMOUNTS OF WATER FROM AS FAR A DISTANCE AS POSSIBLE. USE WATER SPRAY TO ABSORB TOXIC VAPORS. AVOID BREATHING TOXIC VAPORS; KEEP UPWIND. CONSIDER EVACUATION OF DOWNWIND AREA IF MATERIAL IS LEAKING.

TOXICITY

DITALIMFOS: ACUTE TOXICITY: 4930 MG/KG ORAL-RAT LD50; 1000 MG/KG ORAL-RABBIT LD50; 5660 MG/KG ORAL-GUINEA PIG LD50. CARCINOGEN STATUS: NONE. ACUTE TOXICITY: MODERATELY TOXIC BY INGESTION. TARGET EFFECTS: NO DATA AVAILABLE.

HEALTH EFFECTS AND FIRST AID

INHALATION: DITALIMFOS: **<u>ACUTE EXPOSURE</u>-** NO DATA AVAILABLE. **<u>CHRONIC EXPOSURE</u>-** NO DATA AVAILABLE.

FIRST AID- REMOVE FROM EXPOSURE AREA TO FRESH AIR IMMEDIATELY. IF BREATHING HAS STOPPED, PERFORM ARTIFICIAL RESPIRATION. KEEP PERSON WARM AND AT REST. TREAT SYMPTOMATICALLY AND SUPPORTIVELY. GET MEDICAL ATTENTION IMMEDIATELY.

SKIN CONTACT: DITALIMFOS: **<u>ACUTE EXPOSURE</u>-** MAY CAUSE IRRITATION. SENSITIZATION REACTIONS MAY OCCUR IN PREVIOUSLY EXPOSED PERSONS. **<u>CHRONIC EXPOSURE</u>-** PROLONGED OR REPEATED EXPOSURE MAY RESULT IN SENSITIZATION DERMATITIS.

FIRST AID- REMOVE CONTAMINATED CLOTHING AND SHOES IMMEDIATELY. WASH AFFECTED AREA WITH SOAP OR MILD DETERGENT AND LARGE AMOUNTS OF WATER UNTIL NO EVIDENCE OF CHEMICAL REMAINS (APPROXIMATELY 15-20 MINUTES). GET MEDICAL ATTENTION IMMEDIATELY.

EYE CONTACT: DITALIMFOS: **<u>ACUTE EXPOSURE</u>-** MAY CAUSE IRRITATION. **<u>CHRONIC EXPOSURE</u>-** NO DATA AVAILABLE.

FIRST AID- WASH EYES IMMEDIATELY WITH LARGE AMOUNTS OF WATER OR NORMAL SALINE, OCCASIONALLY LIFTING UPPER AND LOWER LIDS, UNTIL NO EVIDENCE OF CHEMICAL REMAINS (APPROXIMATELY 15-20 MINUTES). GET MEDICAL ATTENTION IMMEDIATELY.

INGESTION: DITALIMFOS: **<u>ACUTE EXPOSURE</u>-** WEAK CHOLINESTERASE INHIBITION ACTIVITY HAS BEEN REPORTED IN ANIMALS. **<u>CHRONIC EXPOSURE</u>-** NO DATA AVAILABLE.

FIRST AID- TREAT SYMPTOMATICALLY AND SUPPORTIVELY. GET MEDICAL ATTENTION IMMEDIATELY. IF VOMITING OCCURS, KEEP HEAD LOWER THAN HIPS TO PREVENT ASPIRATION.

ANTIDOTE: NO SPECIFIC ANTIDOTE. TREAT SYMPTOMATICALLY AND SUPPORTIVELY.

REACTIVITY

REACTIVITY: STABLE UNDER NORMAL TEMPERATURES AND PRESSURES.
INCOMPATIBILITIES: DITALIMFOS: OXIDIZERS (STRONG): FIRE AND EXPLOSION HAZARD.
DECOMPOSITION: THERMAL DECOMPOSITION PRODUCTS MAY INCLUDE TOXIC OXIDES OF NITROGEN, CARBON, PHOSPHORUS, AND SULFUR.
POLYMERIZATION: HAZARDOUS POLYMERIZATION HAS NOT BEEN REPORTED TO OCCUR UNDER NORMAL TEMPERATURES AND PRESSURES.

STORAGE AND DISPOSAL

OBSERVE ALL FEDERAL, STATE AND LOCAL REGULATIONS WHEN STORING OR DISPOSING OF THIS SUBSTANCE. FOR ASSISTANCE, CONTACT THE DISTRICT DIRECTOR OF THE ENVIRONMENTAL PROTECTION AGENCY.

STORAGE

STORE IN ACCORDANCE WITH 40 CFR 165 RECOMMENDED PROCEDURES FOR THE DISPOSAL AND STORAGE OF PESTICIDES AND PESTICIDE CONTAINERS.
STORE AWAY FROM INCOMPATIBLE SUBSTANCES.

DISPOSAL

DISPOSAL MUST BE IN ACCORDANCE WITH 40 CFR 165 RECOMMENDED PROCEDURES FOR THE DISPOSAL AND STORAGE OF PESTICIDES AND PESTICIDE CONTAINERS.

CONDITIONS TO AVOID

MAY BURN BUT DOES NOT IGNITE READILY. CONTAINERS MAY EXPLODE IN HEAT OF FIRE.

SPILL AND LEAK PROCEDURES

OCCUPATIONAL SPILL: DO NOT TOUCH SPILLED MATERIAL. STOP LEAK IF YOU CAN DO IT WITHOUT RISK. USE WATER SPRAY TO REDUCE VAPORS. FOR SMALL SPILLS, TAKE UP WITH SAND OR OTHER ABSORBENT MATERIAL AND PLACE INTO CONTAINERS FOR LATER DISPOSAL. FOR SMALL DRY SPILLS, WITH A CLEAN SHOVEL PLACE MATERIAL INTO CLEAN, DRY CONTAINERS AND COVER. MOVE CONTAINERS FROM SPILL AREA. FOR LARGER SPILLS, DIKE FAR AHEAD OF SPILL FOR LATER DISPOSAL. KEEP UNNECESSARY PEOPLE AWAY. ISOLATE HAZARD AREA AND DENY ENTRY. VENTILATE CLOSED SPACES BEFORE ENTERING.

PROTECTIVE EQUIPMENT

VENTILATION: PROVIDE LOCAL EXHAUST OR GENERAL DILUTION VENTILATION SYSTEM.
RESPIRATOR: THE FOLLOWING RESPIRATORS ARE RECOMMENDED BASED ON INFORMATION FOUND IN THE PHYSICAL DATA, TOXICITY AND HEALTH EFFECTS SECTIONS. THEY ARE RANKED IN ORDER FROM MINIMUM TO MAXIMUM RESPIRATORY PROTECTION. THE SPECIFIC RESPIRATOR SELECTED MUST BE BASED ON CONTAMINATION LEVELS FOUND IN THE WORK PLACE, MUST NOT EXCEED THE WORKING LIMITS OF THE RESPIRATOR AND BE JOINTLY APPROVED BY THE NATIONAL INSTITUTE FOR OCCUPATIONAL SAFETY AND HEALTH AND THE MINE SAFETY AND HEALTH ADMINISTRATION (NIOSH-MSHA).
CHEMICAL CARTRIDGE RESPIRATOR WITH AN ORGANIC VAPOR CARTRIDGE(S) WITH A FULL FACEPIECE AND ORGANIC VAPOR CARTRIDGE(S) IN COMBINATION WITH A DUST AND MIST FILTER.
POWERED AIR-PURIFYING RESPIRATOR WITH A TIGHT-FITTING FACEPIECE AND ORGANIC VAPOR CARTRIDGE(S) IN COMBINATION WITH A HIGH-EFFICIENCY PARTICULATE FILTER.
TYPE 'C' SUPPLIED-AIR RESPIRATOR WITH A FULL FACEPIECE OPERATED IN A PRESSURE-DEMAND OR OTHER POSITIVE PRESSURE MODE.
SELF-CONTAINED BREATHING APPARATUS WITH A FULL FACEPIECE OPERATED IN PRESSURE-DEMAND OR OTHER POSITIVE PRESSURE MODE.
FOR FIREFIGHTING AND OTHER IMMEDIATELY DANGEROUS TO LIFE OR HEALTH CONDITIONS:
SELF-CONTAINED BREATHING APPARATUS WITH FULL FACEPIECE OPERATED IN PRESSURE-DEMAND OR OTHER POSITIVE PRESSURE MODE. SUPPLIED-AIR RESPIRATOR WITH FULL FACEPIECE AND OPERATED IN PRESSURE-DEMAND OR OTHER POSITIVE PRESSURE MODE IN COMBINATION WITH AN AUXILIARY SELF-CONTAINED BREATHING APPARATUS OPERATED IN PRESSURE-DEMAND OR OTHER POSITIVE PRESSURE MODE.
CLOTHING: EMPLOYEE MUST WEAR APPROPRIATE PROTECTIVE (IMPERVIOUS) CLOTHING AND EQUIPMENT TO PREVENT REPEATED OR PROLONGED SKIN CONTACT WITH THIS SUBSTANCE.
GLOVES: EMPLOYEE MUST WEAR APPROPRIATE PROTECTIVE GLOVES TO PREVENT CONTACT WITH THIS SUBSTANCE.
EYE PROTECTION: EMPLOYEE MUST WEAR SPLASH-PROOF OR DUST-RESISTANT SAFETY GOGGLES TO PREVENT EYE CONTACT WITH THIS SUBSTANCE.
EMERGENCY EYE WASH: WHERE THERE IS ANY POSSIBILITY THAT AN EMPLOYEE'S EYES MAY BE EXPOSED TO THIS SUBSTANCE, THE EMPLOYER SHOULD PROVIDE AN EYE WASH FOUNTAIN WITHIN THE IMMEDIATE WORK AREA FOR EMERGENCY USE.

AUTHORIZED BY- OCCUPATIONAL HEALTH SERVICES, INC.
CREATION DATE: 10/04/89 ***REVISION DATE:*** 05/07/90

MATERIAL SAFETY DATA SHEET

OCCUPATIONAL HEALTH SERVICES, INC.
AGRICULTURE AND PESTICIDE DIVISION
450 SEVENTH AVENUE, SUITE 2407
NEW YORK, NEW YORK 10123
1-800-445-MSDS OR (212) 967-1100

EMERGENCY CONTACT:
JOHN S. BRANSFORD, JR. (615) 292-1180

SUBSTANCE IDENTIFICATION

CAS-NUMBER 43222-48-6
SUBSTANCE: DIFENZOQUAT METHYL SULFATE
TRADE NAMES/SYNONYMS: 1H-PYRAZOLIUM, 1,2-DIMETHYL-3,5-DIPHENYL-, METHYL SULFATE; 1,2-DIMETHYL-3,5-DIPHENYL-1H-PYRAZOLIUM METHYL SULFATE; 1,2-DIMETHYL-3,5-DIPHENYLPYRAZOLIUM METHYL SULFATE; DIFENZOQUAT; AVENGE; AC 84777; FINAVEN; C18H20N2O4S; PST72348
CHEMICAL FAMILY: HETEROCYCLIC NITROGEN
MOLECULAR FORMULA: C17-H17-N2.C-H3-O4-S
MOLECULAR WEIGHT: 360.43
CERCLA RATINGS (SCALE 0-3): HEALTH=3 FIRE=1 REACTIVITY=0 PERSISTENCE=3
NFPA RATINGS (SCALE 0-4): HEALTH=3 FIRE=1 REACTIVITY=0

COMPONENTS AND CONTAMINANTS

COMPONENT: DIFENZOQUAT METHYL SULFATE ***PERCENT:*** 100
CAS# 43222-48-6
OTHER CONTAMINANTS: NONE
EXPOSURE LIMITS: NO OCCUPATIONAL EXPOSURE LIMITS ESTABLISHED BY OSHA, ACGIH, OR NIOSH.

PHYSICAL DATA

DESCRIPTION: COLORLESS HYGROSCOPIC SOLID
MELTING POINT: 311-315 F (155-157 C)
SPECIFIC GRAVITY: NOT AVAILABLE ***VAPOR PRESSURE:*** NEGLIGIBLE
SOLUBILITY IN WATER: 76% @ 25 C
SOLVENT SOLUBILITY: SOLUBLE IN METHANOL, METHYLENE CHLORIDE, PROPANOL, ACETONE, DICHLOROETHANE; SLIGHTLY SOLUBLE IN XYLENE.

FIRE AND EXPLOSION DATA

FIRE AND EXPLOSION HAZARD: SLIGHT FIRE HAZARD WHEN EXPOSED TO HEAT OR FLAME.
FIREFIGHTING MEDIA: DRY CHEMICAL, CARBON DIOXIDE, HALON, WATER SPRAY OR STANDARD FOAM (1987 EMERGENCY RESPONSE GUIDEBOOK, DOT P 5800.4).
FOR LARGER FIRES, USE WATER SPRAY, FOG OR STANDARD FOAM (1987 EMERGENCY RESPONSE GUIDEBOOK, DOT P 5800.4).
FIREFIGHTING: MOVE CONTAINERS FROM FIRE AREA IF POSSIBLE (1987 EMERGENCY RESPONSE GUIDEBOOK, DOT P 5800.4, GUIDE PAGE 53).
EXTINGUISH FIRE USING AGENTS SUITABLE FOR TYPE OF SURROUNDING FIRE. USE WATER IN FLOODING AMOUNTS AS A FOG. AVOID BREATHING DUSTS AND FUMES FROM BURNING MATERIAL; KEEP UPWIND.

TOXICITY

DIFENZOQUAT METHYL SULFATE: TOXICITY DATA: 3540 MG/KG SKIN-RABBIT LD50; 470 MG/KG ORAL-RAT LD50; 31 MG/KG ORAL-MOUSE LD50 (THE FDA SURVEILLANCE INDEX, SUPPLEMENT NO. 7, 1974); 470 MG/KG ORAL-RABBIT LD50 (THE FDA SURVEILLANCE INDEX, SUPPLEMENT NO.7, 1974). CARCINOGEN STATUS: NONE. ACUTE TOXICITY LEVEL: TOXIC BY INGESTION AND SLIGHTLY TOXIC BY DERMAL ABSORPTION. TARGET EFFECTS: NO DATA AVAILABLE.

HEALTH EFFECTS AND FIRST AID

INHALATION: DIFENZOQUAT METHYL SULFATE: **ACUTE EXPOSURE-** MAY CAUSE IRRITATION OF THE MUCOUS MEMBRANES. **CHRONIC EXPOSURE-** NO DATA AVAILABLE.
FIRST AID- REMOVE FROM EXPOSURE AREA TO FRESH AIR IMMEDIATELY. IF BREATHING HAS STOPPED, PERFORM ARTIFICIAL RESPIRATION. KEEP PERSON

WARM AND AT REST. TREAT SYMPTOMATICALLY AND SUPPORTIVELY. GET MEDICAL ATTENTION IMMEDIATELY.

SKIN CONTACT: DIFENZOQUAT METHYL SULFATE: **ACUTE EXPOSURE-** THIS MATERIAL WAS SLIGHTLY IRRITATING TO RABBIT SKIN. A LETHAL DOSE IN RABBITS BY DERMAL ABSORPTION WAS 3540 MG/KG. **CHRONIC EXPOSURE-** NO DATA AVAILABLE.

FIRST AID- REMOVE CONTAMINATED CLOTHING AND SHOES IMMEDIATELY. WASH AFFECTED AREA WITH SOAP OR MILD DETERGENT AND LARGE AMOUNTS OF WATER UNTIL NO EVIDENCE OF CHEMICAL REMAINS (APPROXIMATELY 15-20 MINUTES). GET MEDICAL ATTENTION IMMEDIATELY.

EYE CONTACT: DIFENZOQUAT METHYL SULFATE: **ACUTE EXPOSURE-** THIS MATERIAL WAS SLIGHTLY IRRITATING TO RABBIT EYES. **CHRONIC EXPOSURE-** NO DATA AVAILABLE.

FIRST AID- WASH EYES IMMEDIATELY WITH LARGE AMOUNTS OF WATER OR NORMAL SALINE, OCCASIONALLY LIFTING UPPER AND LOWER LIDS, UNTIL NO EVIDENCE OF CHEMICAL REMAINS (APPROXIMATELY 15-20 MINUTES). GET MEDICAL ATTENTION IMMEDIATELY.

INGESTION: DIFENZOQUAT METHYL SULFATE: TOXIC. **ACUTE EXPOSURE-** A LETHAL DOSE IN RATS WAS 270 MG/KG. **CHRONIC EXPOSURE-** DECREASED PUP WEIGHTS AT BIRTH AND AT WEANING WERE OBSERVED IN A 3-GENERATION STUDY WITH RATS FED A DIETARY LEVEL OF 2500 PPM.

FIRST AID- IF EXTENSIVE VOMITING HAS NOT OCCURRED, THE SUBSTANCE SHOULD BE REMOVED BY EMESIS OR GASTRIC LAVAGE PROVIDED THAT THE PATIENT IS CONSCIOUS AND CONVULSIONS ARE NOT PRESENT. KEEP HEAD BELOW HIPS DURING VOMITING TO PREVENT ASPIRATION. DO NOT ATTEMPT TO MAKE AN UNCONSCIOUS PERSON VOMIT. TREAT SYMPTOMATICALLY AND SUPPORTIVELY. GET MEDICAL ATTENTION IMMEDIATELY (DREISBACH, HANDBOOK OF POISONING, 12TH ED.). TREATMENT SHOULD BE PERFORMED BY QUALIFIED MEDICAL PERSONNEL.

ANTIDOTE: NO SPECIFIC ANTIDOTE. TREAT SYMPTOMATICALLY AND SUPPORTIVELY.

REACTIVITY

REACTIVITY: STABLE UNDER NORMAL TEMPERATURES AND PRESSURES.

INCOMPATIBILITIES: DIFENZOQUAT METHYL SULFATE: NO DATA AVAILABLE.

DECOMPOSITION: THERMAL DECOMPOSITION PRODUCTS MAY INCLUDE TOXIC OXIDES OF CARBON, NITROGEN, AND SULFUR.

POLYMERIZATION: HAZARDOUS POLYMERIZATION HAS NOT BEEN REPORTED TO OCCUR UNDER NORMAL TEMPERATURES AND PRESSURES.

STORAGE AND DISPOSAL

OBSERVE ALL FEDERAL, STATE AND LOCAL REGULATIONS WHEN STORING OR DISPOSING OF THIS SUBSTANCE. FOR ASSISTANCE, CONTACT THE DISTRICT DIRECTOR OF THE ENVIRONMENTAL PROTECTION AGENCY.

STORAGE

STORE IN ACCORDANCE WITH 40 CFR 165 RECOMMENDED PROCEDURES FOR THE DISPOSAL AND STORAGE OF PESTICIDES AND PESTICIDE CONTAINERS.

DISPOSAL

DISPOSAL MUST BE IN ACCORDANCE WITH 40 CFR 165 RECOMMENDED PROCEDURES FOR THE DISPOSAL AND STORAGE OF PESTICIDES AND PESTICIDE CONTAINERS.

CONDITIONS TO AVOID

MAY BURN BUT DOES NOT IGNITE READILY.

SPILL AND LEAK PROCEDURES

OCCUPATIONAL SPILL: DO NOT TOUCH SPILLED MATERIAL. STOP LEAK IF YOU CAN DO IT WITHOUT RISK. FOR SMALL SPILLS, TAKE UP WITH SAND OR OTHER ABSORBENT MATERIAL AND PLACE INTO CONTAINERS FOR LATER DISPOSAL. FOR SMALL DRY SPILLS, WITH A CLEAN SHOVEL PLACE MATERIAL INTO CLEAN, DRY CONTAINER AND COVER. MOVE CONTAINERS FROM SPILL AREA. FOR LARGER SPILLS, DIKE FAR AHEAD OF SPILL FOR LATER DISPOSAL. KEEP UNNECESSARY PEOPLE AWAY. ISOLATE HAZARD AREA AND DENY ENTRY.

PROTECTIVE EQUIPMENT

VENTILATION: PROVIDE LOCAL EXHAUST OR GENERAL DILUTION VENTILATION SYSTEM.

RESPIRATOR: THE FOLLOWING RESPIRATORS ARE RECOMMENDED BASED ON INFORMATION FOUND IN THE PHYSICAL DATA, TOXICITY AND HEALTH EFFECTS SECTIONS. THEY ARE RANKED IN ORDER FROM MINIMUM TO MAXIMUM RESPIRATORY PROTECTION. THE SPECIFIC RESPIRATOR SELECTED MUST BE BASED ON CONTAMINATION LEVELS FOUND IN THE WORK PLACE, MUST NOT EXCEED THE WORKING LIMITS OF THE RESPIRATOR AND BE JOINTLY APPROVED BY THE NATIONAL INSTITUTE FOR OCCUPATIONAL SAFETY AND HEALTH AND THE MINE SAFETY AND HEALTH ADMINISTRATION (NIOSH-MSHA).

CHEMICAL CARTRIDGE RESPIRATOR WITH AN ORGANIC VAPOR CARTRIDGE(S) WITH A FULL FACEPIECE AND ORGANIC VAPOR CARTRIDGE(S) IN COMBINATION WITH A DUST AND MIST FILTER.

POWERED AIR-PURIFYING RESPIRATOR WITH A TIGHT-FITTING FACEPIECE AND ORGANIC VAPOR CARTRIDGE(S) IN COMBINATION WITH A HIGH-EFFICIENCY PARTICULATE FILTER.

TYPE 'C' SUPPLIED-AIR RESPIRATOR WITH A FULL FACEPIECE OPERATED IN A PRESSURE-DEMAND OR OTHER POSITIVE PRESSURE MODE.

SELF-CONTAINED BREATHING APPARATUS WITH A FULL FACEPIECE OPERATED IN PRESSURE-DEMAND OR OTHER POSITIVE PRESSURE MODE.

FOR FIREFIGHTING AND OTHER IMMEDIATELY DANGEROUS TO LIFE OR HEALTH CONDITIONS:

SELF-CONTAINED BREATHING APPARATUS WITH FULL FACEPIECE OPERATED IN PRESSURE-DEMAND OR OTHER POSITIVE PRESSURE MODE.

SUPPLIED-AIR RESPIRATOR WITH FULL FACEPIECE AND OPERATED IN PRESSURE-DEMAND OR OTHER POSITIVE PRESSURE MODE IN COMBINATION WITH AN AUXILIARY SELF-CONTAINED BREATHING APPARATUS OPERATED IN PRESSURE-DEMAND OR OTHER POSITIVE PRESSURE MODE.

CLOTHING: EMPLOYEE MUST WEAR APPROPRIATE PROTECTIVE (IMPERVIOUS) CLOTHING AND EQUIPMENT TO PREVENT REPEATED OR PROLONGED SKIN CONTACT WITH THIS SUBSTANCE.

GLOVES: EMPLOYEE MUST WEAR APPROPRIATE PROTECTIVE GLOVES TO PREVENT CONTACT WITH THIS SUBSTANCE.

EYE PROTECTION: EMPLOYEE MUST WEAR SPLASH-PROOF OR DUST-RESISTANT SAFETY GOGGLES TO PREVENT EYE CONTACT WITH THIS SUBSTANCE.

EMERGENCY EYE WASH: WHERE THERE IS ANY POSSIBILITY THAT AN EMPLOYEE'S EYES MAY BE EXPOSED TO THIS SUBSTANCE, THE EMPLOYER SHOULD PROVIDE AN EYE WASH FOUNTAIN WITHIN THE IMMEDIATE WORK AREA FOR EMERGENCY USE.

AUTHORIZED BY- OCCUPATIONAL HEALTH SERVICES, INC.

CREATION DATE: 10/04/89 ***REVISION DATE:*** 05/14/90

MATERIAL SAFETY DATA SHEET

OCCUPATIONAL HEALTH SERVICES, INC.
AGRICULTURE AND PESTICIDE DIVISION
450 SEVENTH AVENUE, SUITE 2407
NEW YORK, NEW YORK 10123
1-800-445-MSDS OR (212) 967-1100

EMERGENCY CONTACT:
JOHN S. BRANSFORD, JR. (615) 292-1180

SUBSTANCE IDENTIFICATION

CAS-NUMBER 49866-87-7

SUBSTANCE: **DIFENZOQUAT ION**

TRADE NAMES/SYNONYMS: 1H-PYRAZOLIUM, 1,2-DIMETHYL-3,5-DIPHENYL-; 1,2-DIMETHYL-3,5-DIPHENYL-1H-PYRAZOLIUM; 1,2-DIMETHYL-3,5-DIPHENYLPYRAZOLIUM ION; DIFENZOQUAT; C17H17N2; PST72349

CHEMICAL FAMILY: HETEROCYCLIC NITROGEN

MOLECULAR FORMULA: C17-H17-N2

MOLECULAR WEIGHT: 249.3

CERCLA RATINGS (SCALE 0-3): HEALTH=U FIRE=1 REACTIVITY=0 PERSISTENCE=3

NFPA RATINGS (SCALE 0-4): HEALTH=U FIRE=1 REACTIVITY=0

COMPONENTS AND CONTAMINANTS

COMPONENT: DIFENZOQUAT ION ***PERCENT:*** 100
CAS# 49866-87-7

OTHER CONTAMINANTS: NONE

EXPOSURE LIMITS: NO OCCUPATIONAL EXPOSURE LIMITS ESTABLISHED BY OSHA, ACGIH, OR NIOSH.

PHYSICAL DATA

DESCRIPTION: SOLID ***MELTING POINT:*** NOT AVAILABLE

SPECIFIC GRAVITY: NOT AVAILABLE ***SOLUBILITY IN WATER:*** NOT AVAILABLE

FIRE AND EXPLOSION DATA

FIRE AND EXPLOSION HAZARD: SLIGHT FIRE HAZARD WHEN EXPOSED TO HEAT OR FLAME.

FIREFIGHTING MEDIA: DRY CHEMICAL, CARBON DIOXIDE, HALON, WATER SPRAY OR STANDARD FOAM (1987 EMERGENCY RESPONSE GUIDEBOOK, DOT P 5800.4).

FOR LARGER FIRES, USE WATER SPRAY, FOG OR STANDARD FOAM (1987 EMERGENCY RESPONSE GUIDEBOOK, DOT P 5800.4).

FIREFIGHTING: MOVE CONTAINERS FROM FIRE AREA IF POSSIBLE (1987 EMERGENCY RESPONSE GUIDEBOOK, DOT P 5800.4, GUIDE PAGE 53).
EXTINGUISH FIRE USING AGENTS SUITABLE FOR TYPE OF SURROUNDING FIRE. USE WATER IN FLOODING AMOUNTS AS A FOG. AVOID BREATHING DUSTS AND FUMES FROM BURNING MATERIAL; KEEP UPWIND.

TOXICITY

DIFENZOQUAT ION: CARCINOGEN STATUS: NONE. ACUTE TOXICITY LEVEL: NO DATA AVAILABLE. TARGET EFFECTS: NO DATA AVAILABLE.

HEALTH EFFECTS AND FIRST AID

INHALATION: DIFENZOQUAT ION: ACUTE EXPOSURE- NO DATA AVAILABLE. CHRONIC EXPOSURE- NO DATA AVAILABLE.

FIRST AID- REMOVE FROM EXPOSURE AREA TO FRESH AIR IMMEDIATELY. IF BREATHING HAS STOPPED, PERFORM ARTIFICIAL RESPIRATION. KEEP PERSON WARM AND AT REST. TREAT SYMPTOMATICALLY AND SUPPORTIVELY. GET MEDICAL ATTENTION IMMEDIATELY.

SKIN CONTACT: DIFENZOQUAT ION: ACUTE EXPOSURE- THE METHYL SULFATE SALT OF DIFENZOQUAT WAS SLIGHTLY IRRITATING TO RABBIT SKIN. A LETHAL DOSE IN RABBITS BY DERMAL ABSORPTION WAS 3540 MG/KG. CHRONIC EXPOSURE- NO DATA AVAILABLE.

FIRST AID- REMOVE CONTAMINATED CLOTHING AND SHOES IMMEDIATELY. WASH AFFECTED AREA WITH SOAP OR MILD DETERGENT AND LARGE AMOUNTS OF WATER UNTIL NO EVIDENCE OF CHEMICAL REMAINS (APPROXIMATELY 15-20 MINUTES). GET MEDICAL ATTENTION IMMEDIATELY.

EYE CONTACT: DIFENZOQUAT ION: ACUTE EXPOSURE- THE METHYL SULFATE SALT OF DIFENZOQUAT WAS SLIGHTLY IRRITATING TO RABBIT EYES. CHRONIC EXPOSURE- NO DATA AVAILABLE.

FIRST AID- WASH EYES IMMEDIATELY WITH LARGE AMOUNTS OF WATER OR NORMAL SALINE, OCCASIONALLY LIFTING UPPER AND LOWER LIDS, UNTIL NO EVIDENCE OF CHEMICAL REMAINS (APPROXIMATELY 15-20 MINUTES). GET MEDICAL ATTENTION IMMEDIATELY.

INGESTION: DIFENZOQUAT ION: ACUTE EXPOSURE- A LETHAL DOSE OF THE METHYL SULFATE SALT OF DIFENZOQUAT WAS 270 MG/KG IN RATS. CHRONIC EXPOSURE- NO DATA AVAILABLE.

FIRST AID- IF EXTENSIVE VOMITING HAS NOT OCCURRED, THE SUBSTANCE SHOULD BE REMOVED BY EMESIS OR GASTRIC LAVAGE PROVIDED THAT THE PATIENT IS CONSCIOUS AND CONVULSIONS ARE NOT PRESENT. KEEP HEAD BELOW HIPS DURING VOMITING TO PREVENT ASPIRATION. DO NOT ATTEMPT TO MAKE AN UNCONSCIOUS PERSON VOMIT. TREAT SYMPTOMATICALLY AND SUPPORTIVELY. GET MEDICAL ATTENTION IMMEDIATELY (DREISBACH, HANDBOOK OF POISONING, 12TH ED.). TREATMENT SHOULD BE PERFORMED BY QUALIFIED MEDICAL PERSONNEL.

ANTIDOTE: NO SPECIFIC ANTIDOTE. TREAT SYMPTOMATICALLY AND SUPPORTIVELY.

REACTIVITY

REACTIVITY: STABLE UNDER NORMAL TEMPERATURES AND PRESSURES.

INCOMPATIBILITIES: DIFENZOQUAT ION: NO DATA AVAILABLE.

DECOMPOSITION: THERMAL DECOMPOSITION PRODUCTS MAY INCLUDE TOXIC OXIDES OF CARBON, NITROGEN, AND SULFUR.

POLYMERIZATION: HAZARDOUS POLYMERIZATION HAS NOT BEEN REPORTED TO OCCUR UNDER NORMAL TEMPERATURES AND PRESSURES.

STORAGE AND DISPOSAL

OBSERVE ALL FEDERAL, STATE AND LOCAL REGULATIONS WHEN STORING OR DISPOSING OF THIS SUBSTANCE. FOR ASSISTANCE, CONTACT THE DISTRICT DIRECTOR OF THE ENVIRONMENTAL PROTECTION AGENCY.

STORAGE

STORE IN ACCORDANCE WITH 40 CFR 165 RECOMMENDED PROCEDURES FOR THE DISPOSAL AND STORAGE OF PESTICIDES AND PESTICIDE CONTAINERS.

DISPOSAL

DISPOSAL MUST BE IN ACCORDANCE WITH 40 CFR 165 RECOMMENDED PROCEDURES FOR THE DISPOSAL AND STORAGE OF PESTICIDES AND PESTICIDE CONTAINERS.

CONDITIONS TO AVOID

MAY BURN BUT DOES NOT IGNITE READILY.

SPILL AND LEAK PROCEDURES

OCCUPATIONAL SPILL: DO NOT TOUCH SPILLED MATERIAL. STOP LEAK IF YOU CAN DO IT WITHOUT RISK. FOR SMALL SPILLS, TAKE UP WITH SAND OR OTHER ABSORBENT MATERIAL AND PLACE INTO CONTAINERS FOR LATER DISPOSAL. FOR SMALL DRY SPILLS, WITH A CLEAN SHOVEL PLACE MATERIAL INTO CLEAN, DRY CONTAINER AND COVER. MOVE CONTAINERS FROM SPILL AREA. FOR LARGER SPILLS, DIKE FAR AHEAD OF SPILL FOR LATER DISPOSAL. KEEP UNNECESSARY PEOPLE AWAY. ISOLATE HAZARD AREA AND DENY ENTRY.

PROTECTIVE EQUIPMENT

VENTILATION: PROVIDE LOCAL EXHAUST OR GENERAL DILUTION VENTILATION SYSTEM.

RESPIRATOR: THE FOLLOWING RESPIRATORS ARE RECOMMENDED BASED ON INFORMATION FOUND IN THE PHYSICAL DATA, TOXICITY AND HEALTH EFFECTS SECTIONS. THEY ARE RANKED IN ORDER FROM MINIMUM TO MAXIMUM RESPIRATORY PROTECTION. THE SPECIFIC RESPIRATOR SELECTED MUST BE BASED ON CONTAMINATION LEVELS FOUND IN THE WORK PLACE, MUST NOT EXCEED THE WORKING LIMITS OF THE RESPIRATOR AND BE JOINTLY APPROVED BY THE NATIONAL INSTITUTE FOR OCCUPATIONAL SAFETY AND HEALTH AND THE MINE SAFETY AND HEALTH ADMINISTRATION (NIOSH-MSHA).
CHEMICAL CARTRIDGE RESPIRATOR WITH AN ORGANIC VAPOR CARTRIDGE(S) WITH A FULL FACEPIECE AND ORGANIC VAPOR CARTRIDGE(S) IN COMBINATION WITH A DUST AND MIST FILTER.
POWERED AIR-PURIFYING RESPIRATOR WITH A TIGHT-FITTING FACEPIECE AND ORGANIC VAPOR CARTRIDGE(S) IN COMBINATION WITH A HIGH-EFFICIENCY PARTICULATE FILTER.
TYPE 'C' SUPPLIED-AIR RESPIRATOR WITH A FULL FACEPIECE OPERATED IN A PRESSURE-DEMAND OR OTHER POSITIVE PRESSURE MODE.
SELF-CONTAINED BREATHING APPARATUS WITH A FULL FACEPIECE OPERATED IN PRESSURE-DEMAND OR OTHER POSITIVE PRESSURE MODE.
FOR FIREFIGHTING AND OTHER IMMEDIATELY DANGEROUS TO LIFE OR HEALTH CONDITIONS:
SELF-CONTAINED BREATHING APPARATUS WITH FULL FACEPIECE OPERATED IN PRESSURE-DEMAND OR OTHER POSITIVE PRESSURE MODE.
SUPPLIED-AIR RESPIRATOR WITH FULL FACEPIECE AND OPERATED IN PRESSURE-DEMAND OR OTHER POSITIVE PRESSURE MODE IN COMBINATION WITH AN AUXILIARY SELF-CONTAINED BREATHING APPARATUS OPERATED IN PRESSURE-DEMAND OR OTHER POSITIVE PRESSURE MODE.

CLOTHING: EMPLOYEE MUST WEAR APPROPRIATE PROTECTIVE (IMPERVIOUS) CLOTHING AND EQUIPMENT TO PREVENT REPEATED OR PROLONGED SKIN CONTACT WITH THIS SUBSTANCE.

GLOVES: EMPLOYEE MUST WEAR APPROPRIATE PROTECTIVE GLOVES TO PREVENT CONTACT WITH THIS SUBSTANCE.

EYE PROTECTION: EMPLOYEE MUST WEAR SPLASH-PROOF OR DUST-RESISTANT SAFETY GOGGLES TO PREVENT EYE CONTACT WITH THIS SUBSTANCE.
EMERGENCY EYE WASH: WHERE THERE IS ANY POSSIBILITY THAT AN EMPLOYEE'S EYES MAY BE EXPOSED TO THIS SUBSTANCE, THE EMPLOYER SHOULD PROVIDE AN EYE WASH FOUNTAIN WITHIN THE IMMEDIATE WORK AREA FOR EMERGENCY USE.

AUTHORIZED BY- OCCUPATIONAL HEALTH SERVICES, INC.
CREATION DATE: 10/04/89 ***REVISION DATE:*** 05/07/90

MATERIAL SAFETY DATA SHEET

OCCUPATIONAL HEALTH SERVICES, INC.
AGRICULTURE AND PESTICIDE DIVISION
450 SEVENTH AVENUE, SUITE 2407
NEW YORK, NEW YORK 10123
1-800-445-MSDS OR (212) 967-1100

EMERGENCY CONTACT:
JOHN S. BRANSFORD, JR. (615) 292-1180

SUBSTANCE IDENTIFICATION

CAS-NUMBER 3337-71-1

SUBSTANCE: **ASULAM**

TRADE NAMES/SYNONYMS: CARBAMIC ACID, ((4-AMINOPHENYL)SULFONYL)-, METHYL ESTER; CARBAMIC ACID, SULFANILYL-, METHYL ESTER; ((4-AMINOPHENYL)SULFONYL)CARBAMIC ACID, METHYL ESTER; SULFANILYLCARBAMIC ACID METHYL ESTER; METHYL ((4-AMINOPHENYL)SULFONYL)CARBAMATE; METHYL SULPHANILYLCARBAMATE; METHYL SULFANILYLCARBAMATE; METHYL 4-AMINOPHENYLSULPHONYLCARBAMATE; METHYL 4-AMINOBENZENESULPHONYLCARBAMATE; N1-METHOXYCARBONYLSULFANILAMIDE; ASULOX; ASUTOX; M AND B 9057; JONNIX; C8H10N2O4S; PST72352

CHEMICAL FAMILY: CARBAMATE

MOLECULAR FORMULA: C8-H10-N2-O4-S
MOLECULAR WEIGHT: 230.26
CERCLA RATINGS (SCALE 0-3): HEALTH=2 FIRE=1 REACTIVITY=0 PERSISTENCE=1
NFPA RATINGS (SCALE 0-4): HEALTH=U FIRE=1 REACTIVITY=0

COMPONENTS AND CONTAMINANTS

COMPONENT: ASULAM ***PERCENT:*** 100.0
CAS# 3337-71-1
EXPOSURE LIMITS: NO OCCUPATIONAL EXPOSURE LIMITS ESTABLISHED BY OSHA, ACGIH, OR NIOSH.

PHYSICAL DATA

DESCRIPTION: COLORLESS, CRYSTALLINE SOLID
MELTING POINT: 288-291 F (142-144 C) (DECOMPOSES)
SPECIFIC GRAVITY: NOT AVAILABLE ***VAPOR PRESSURE:*** NEGLIGIBLE
SOLUBILITY IN WATER: 0.4%
SOLVENT SOLUBILITY: SOLUBLE IN ACETONE, METHANOL, DIMETHYLFORMAMIDE, ETHANOL, METHYL ETHYL KETONE; MODERATELY SOLUBLE IN PETROLEUM OILS, HYDROCARBONS, CHLORINATED HYDROCARBONS, AND MANY ALCOHOLS.

FIRE AND EXPLOSION DATA

FIRE AND EXPLOSION HAZARD: SLIGHT FIRE HAZARD WHEN EXPOSED TO HEAT OR FLAME.
FIREFIGHTING MEDIA: DRY CHEMICAL, CARBON DIOXIDE, HALON, WATER SPRAY OR STANDARD FOAM (1987 EMERGENCY RESPONSE GUIDEBOOK, DOT P 5800.4).
FOR LARGER FIRES, USE WATER SPRAY, FOG OR STANDARD FOAM (1987 EMERGENCY RESPONSE GUIDEBOOK, DOT P 5800.4).
FIREFIGHTING: MOVE CONTAINER FROM FIRE AREA IF POSSIBLE. DO NOT SCATTER SPILLED MATERIAL WITH HIGH PRESSURE WATER STREAMS. DIKE FIRE CONTROL WATER FOR LATER DISPOSAL (1987 EMERGENCY RESPONSE GUIDEBOOK, DOT P 5800.4, GUIDE PAGE 31).
USE AGENTS SUITABLE FOR TYPE OF SURROUNDING FIRE. AVOID BREATHING HAZARDOUS VAPORS, KEEP UPWIND.

TOXICITY

ASULAM: TOXICITY DATA: >1800 MG/M3 INHALATION-RAT LC50 (85JFAN); >1200 MG/KG SKIN-RAT LD50 (85JFAN); 2000 MG/KG ORAL-RAT LD50; 5000 MG/KG UNREPORTED-MOUSE LD50. CARCINOGEN STATUS: NONE. ACUTE TOXICITY: MODERATELY TOXIC BY DERMAL ABSORPTION AND INGESTION. TARGET EFFECTS: NO DATA AVAILABLE.

HEALTH EFFECTS AND FIRST AID

INHALATION: ASULAM: **ACUTE EXPOSURE**- MAY BE MILDLY IRRITATING TO THE MUCOUS MEMBRANES. **CHRONIC EXPOSURE**- NO DATA AVAILABLE.
FIRST AID- REMOVE FROM EXPOSURE AREA TO FRESH AIR IMMEDIATELY. IF BREATHING HAS STOPPED, PERFORM ARTIFICIAL RESPIRATION. KEEP PERSON WARM AND AT REST. TREAT SYMPTOMATICALLY AND SUPPORTIVELY. GET MEDICAL ATTENTION IMMEDIATELY.

SKIN CONTACT: ASULAM: **ACUTE EXPOSURE**- MAY BE MILDLY IRRITATING. **CHRONIC EXPOSURE**- NO DATA AVAILABLE.
FIRST AID- REMOVE CONTAMINATED CLOTHING AND SHOES IMMEDIATELY. WASH AFFECTED AREA WITH SOAP OR MILD DETERGENT AND LARGE AMOUNTS OF WATER UNTIL NO EVIDENCE OF CHEMICAL REMAINS (APPROXIMATELY 15-20 MINUTES). GET MEDICAL ATTENTION IMMEDIATELY.

EYE CONTACT: ASULAM: **ACUTE EXPOSURE**- MAY BE MILDLY IRRITATING TO THE EYES. **CHRONIC EXPOSURE**- NO DATA AVAILABLE.
FIRST AID- WASH EYES IMMEDIATELY WITH LARGE AMOUNTS OF WATER OR NORMAL SALINE, OCCASIONALLY LIFTING UPPER AND LOWER LIDS, UNTIL NO EVIDENCE OF CHEMICAL REMAINS (APPROXIMATELY 15-20 MINUTES). GET MEDICAL ATTENTION IMMEDIATELY.

INGESTION: ASULAM: **ACUTE EXPOSURE**- A LETHAL DOSE IN RATS WAS 2000 MG/KG; SYMPTOMS WERE NOT REPORTED. **CHRONIC EXPOSURE**- NO ILL EFFECTS WERE OBSERVED IN DOGS RECEIVING DAILY DOSES OF 500 MG/KG FOR 13 WEEKS.
FIRST AID- IF THE PERSON IS CONSCIOUS AND NOT CONVULSING, REMOVE BY GASTRIC LAVAGE AND FOLLOW WITH A CATHARTIC (DREISBACH, HANDBOOK OF POISONING, 12TH ED.). TREAT SYMPTOMATICALLY AND SUPPORTIVELY. GASTRIC LAVAGE SHOULD BE PERFORMED BY QUALIFIED MEDICAL PERSONNEL. GET MEDICAL ATTENTION IMMEDIATELY.
ANTIDOTE: NO SPECIFIC ANTIDOTE. TREAT SYMPTOMATICALLY AND SUPPORTIVELY.

REACTIVITY

REACTIVITY: STABLE UNDER NORMAL TEMPERATURES AND PRESSURES.
INCOMPATIBILITIES: ASULAM: METALS: MAY BE CORRODED. OXIDIZERS (STRONG): FIRE AND EXPLOSION HAZARD.
DECOMPOSITION: THERMAL DECOMPOSITION PRODUCTS MAY INCLUDE TOXIC OXIDES OF CARBON, NITROGEN, AND SULFUR.
POLYMERIZATION: HAZARDOUS POLYMERIZATION HAS NOT BEEN REPORTED TO OCCUR UNDER NORMAL TEMPERATURES AND PRESSURES.

STORAGE AND DISPOSAL

OBSERVE ALL FEDERAL, STATE AND LOCAL REGULATIONS WHEN STORING OR DISPOSING OF THIS SUBSTANCE. FOR ASSISTANCE, CONTACT THE DISTRICT DIRECTOR OF THE ENVIRONMENTAL PROTECTION AGENCY.

STORAGE

STORE IN ACCORDANCE WITH 40 CFR 165 RECOMMENDED PROCEDURES FOR THE DISPOSAL AND STORAGE OF PESTICIDES AND PESTICIDE CONTAINERS.
STORE AWAY FROM INCOMPATIBLE SUBSTANCES.

DISPOSAL

DISPOSAL MUST BE IN ACCORDANCE WITH 40 CFR 165 RECOMMENDED PROCEDURES FOR THE DISPOSAL AND STORAGE OF PESTICIDES AND PESTICIDE CONTAINERS.

CONDITIONS TO AVOID

MAY BURN BUT DOES NOT IGNITE READILY. AVOID CONTACT WITH STRONG OXIDIZERS, EXCESSIVE HEAT, SPARKS, OR OPEN FLAME.

SPILL AND LEAK PROCEDURES

OCCUPATIONAL SPILL: SWEEP UP AND PLACE IN SUITABLE CLEAN, DRY CONTAINERS FOR RECLAMATION OR LATER DISPOSAL. DO NOT FLUSH SPILLED MATERIAL INTO SEWER. KEEP UNNECESSARY PEOPLE AWAY.

PROTECTIVE EQUIPMENT

VENTILATION: PROVIDE LOCAL EXHAUST OR GENERAL DILUTION VENTILATION SYSTEM.
RESPIRATOR: THE FOLLOWING RESPIRATORS ARE RECOMMENDED BASED ON INFORMATION FOUND IN THE PHYSICAL DATA, TOXICITY AND HEALTH EFFECTS SECTIONS. THEY ARE RANKED IN ORDER FROM MINIMUM TO MAXIMUM RESPIRATORY PROTECTION. THE SPECIFIC RESPIRATOR SELECTED MUST BE BASED ON CONTAMINATION LEVELS FOUND IN THE WORK PLACE, MUST NOT EXCEED THE WORKING LIMITS OF THE RESPIRATOR AND BE JOINTLY APPROVED BY THE NATIONAL INSTITUTE FOR OCCUPATIONAL SAFETY AND HEALTH AND THE MINE SAFETY AND HEALTH ADMINISTRATION (NIOSH-MSHA).
CHEMICAL CARTRIDGE RESPIRATOR WITH AN ORGANIC VAPOR CARTRIDGE(S) IN COMBINATION WITH A DUST AND MIST FILTER.
GAS MASK WITH ORGANIC VAPOR CANISTER (CHIN-STYLE OR FRONT- OR BACK-MOUNTED CANISTER) WITH A DUST AND MIST FILTER.
GAS MASK WITH ORGANIC VAPOR CANISTER (CHIN-STYLE OR FRONT- OR BACK-MOUNTED CANISTER) WITH A PARTICULATE FILTER.
POWERED AIR-PURIFYING RESPIRATOR WITH A HIGH-EFFICIENCY FILTER.
TYPE 'C' SUPPLIED-AIR RESPIRATOR WITH A FULL FACEPIECE OPERATED IN A PRESSURE-DEMAND OR OTHER POSITIVE PRESSURE MODE.
SELF-CONTAINED BREATHING APPARATUS WITH A FULL FACEPIECE OPERATED IN PRESSURE-DEMAND OR OTHER POSITIVE PRESSURE MODE.
FOR FIREFIGHTING AND OTHER IMMEDIATELY DANGEROUS TO LIFE OR HEALTH CONDITIONS:
SELF-CONTAINED BREATHING APPARATUS WITH FULL FACEPIECE OPERATED IN PRESSURE-DEMAND OR OTHER POSITIVE PRESSURE MODE.
SUPPLIED-AIR RESPIRATOR WITH FULL FACEPIECE AND OPERATED IN PRESSURE-DEMAND OR OTHER POSITIVE PRESSURE MODE IN COMBINATION WITH AN AUXILIARY SELF-CONTAINED BREATHING APPARATUS OPERATED IN PRESSURE-DEMAND OR OTHER POSITIVE PRESSURE MODE.
CLOTHING: EMPLOYEE MUST WEAR APPROPRIATE PROTECTIVE (IMPERVIOUS) CLOTHING AND EQUIPMENT TO PREVENT REPEATED OR PROLONGED SKIN CONTACT WITH THIS SUBSTANCE.
GLOVES: EMPLOYEE MUST WEAR APPROPRIATE PROTECTIVE GLOVES TO PREVENT CONTACT WITH THIS SUBSTANCE.
EYE PROTECTION: EMPLOYEE MUST WEAR SPLASH-PROOF OR DUST-RESISTANT SAFETY GOGGLES TO PREVENT EYE CONTACT WITH THIS SUBSTANCE.
EMERGENCY EYE WASH: WHERE THERE IS ANY POSSIBILITY THAT AN EMPLOYEE'S EYES MAY BE EXPOSED TO THIS SUBSTANCE, THE EMPLOYER SHOULD PROVIDE AN EYE WASH FOUNTAIN WITHIN THE IMMEDIATE WORK AREA FOR EMERGENCY USE.

AUTHORIZED BY- OCCUPATIONAL HEALTH SERVICES, INC.
CREATION DATE: 10/24/89 ***REVISION DATE:*** 05/31/90

MATERIAL SAFETY DATA SHEET

OCCUPATIONAL HEALTH SERVICES, INC.
AGRICULTURE AND PESTICIDE DIVISION
450 SEVENTH AVENUE, SUITE 2407
NEW YORK, NEW YORK 10123
1-800-445-MSDS OR (212) 967-1100

EMERGENCY CONTACT:
JOHN S. BRANSFORD, JR. (615) 292-1180

SUBSTANCE IDENTIFICATION

CAS-NUMBER 2682-20-4

SUBSTANCE: **2-METHYL-4-ISOTHIAZOLIN-3-ONE**

TRADE NAMES/SYNONYMS: 3(2H)-ISOTHIAZOLONE, 2-METHYL-; 2-METHYL-3(2)-ISOTHIAZOLONE; 4-ISOTHIAZOLIN-3-ONE, 2-METHYL-; KETHON CG 243; C4H5NOS; PST72362

CHEMICAL FAMILY: ISOTHIAZOLONE

MOLECULAR FORMULA: C4-H4-N-O-S

MOLECULAR WEIGHT: 114.14

CERCLA RATINGS (SCALE 0-3): HEALTH=U FIRE=U REACTIVITY=0 PERSISTENCE=1

NFPA RATINGS (SCALE 0-4): HEALTH=U FIRE=U REACTIVITY=0

COMPONENTS AND CONTAMINANTS

COMPONENT: 2-METHYL-4-ISOTHIAZOLIN-3-ONE ***PERCENT:*** 100.0
CAS# 2682-20-4

OTHER CONTAMINANTS: NONE

EXPOSURE LIMITS: NO OCCUPATIONAL EXPOSURE LIMITS ESTABLISHED BY OSHA, ACGIH, OR NIOSH.

PHYSICAL DATA

DESCRIPTION: UNKNOWN. ***MELTING POINT:*** NOT AVAILABLE

SPECIFIC GRAVITY: NOT AVAILABLE ***SOLUBILITY IN WATER:*** NOT AVAILABLE

FIRE AND EXPLOSION DATA

FIRE AND EXPLOSION HAZARD: UNKNOWN FIRE AND EXPLOSION HAZARD.

FIREFIGHTING MEDIA: DRY CHEMICAL, CARBON DIOXIDE, HALON, WATER SPRAY OR ALCOHOL FOAM (1987 EMERGENCY RESPONSE GUIDEBOOK, DOT P 5800.4). FOR LARGER FIRES, USE WATER SPRAY, FOG OR ALCOHOL FOAM (1987 EMERGENCY RESPONSE GUIDEBOOK, DOT P 5800.4).

FIREFIGHTING: MOVE CONTAINER FROM FIRE AREA IF POSSIBLE. COOL FIRE-EXPOSED CONTAINERS WITH WATER FROM SIDE UNTIL WELL AFTER FIRE IS OUT. STAY AWAY FROM STORAGE TANK ENDS. FOR MASSIVE FIRE IN STORAGE AREA, USE UNMANNED HOSE HOLDER OR MONITOR NOZZLES, ELSE WITHDRAW FROM AREA AND LET FIRE BURN. WITHDRAW IMMEDIATELY IN CASE OF RISING SOUND FROM VENTING SAFETY DEVICE OR ANY DISCOLORATION OF STORAGE TANK DUE TO FIRE (1987 EMERGENCY RESPONSE GUIDEBOOK, DOT P 5800.4, GUIDE PAGE 26). EXTINGUISH ONLY IF FLOW CAN BE STOPPED. USE FLOODING AMOUNTS OF WATER AS A FOG; SOLID STREAMS MAY BE INEFFECTIVE. COOL CONTAINERS WITH FLOODING AMOUNTS OF WATER, APPLY FROM AS FAR A DISTANCE AS POSSIBLE. AVOID BREATHING HAZARDOUS VAPORS, KEEP UPWIND.

TOXICITY

2-METHYL-4-ISOTHIAZOLIN-3-ONE: CARCINOGEN STATUS: NONE. ACUTE TOXICITY LEVEL: NO DATA AVAILABLE. TARGET EFFECTS: SENSITIZER- DERMAL.

HEALTH EFFECTS AND FIRST AID

INHALATION: 2-METHYL-4-ISOTHIAZOLIN-3-ONE: **ACUTE EXPOSURE-** NO DATA AVAILABLE. **CHRONIC EXPOSURE-** NO DATA AVAILABLE.

FIRST AID- REMOVE FROM EXPOSURE AREA TO FRESH AIR IMMEDIATELY. IF BREATHING HAS STOPPED, PERFORM ARTIFICIAL RESPIRATION. KEEP PERSON WARM AND AT REST. TREAT SYMPTOMATICALLY AND SUPPORTIVELY. GET MEDICAL ATTENTION IMMEDIATELY.

SKIN CONTACT: 2-METHYL-4-ISOTHIAZOLIN-3-ONE: SENSITIZER. **ACUTE EXPOSURE-** SENSITIZATION DERMATITIS MAY OCCUR IN PREVIOUSLY EXPOSED INDIVIDUALS. **CHRONIC EXPOSURE-** REPEATED OR PROLONGED CONTACT MAY LEAD TO SENSITIZATION DERMATITIS.

FIRST AID- REMOVE CONTAMINATED CLOTHING AND SHOES IMMEDIATELY. WASH AFFECTED AREA WITH SOAP OR MILD DETERGENT AND LARGE AMOUNTS OF WATER UNTIL NO EVIDENCE OF CHEMICAL REMAINS (APPROXIMATELY 15-20 MINUTES). GET MEDICAL ATTENTION IMMEDIATELY.

EYE CONTACT: 2-METHYL-4-ISOTHIAZOLIN-3-ONE: **ACUTE EXPOSURE-** NO DATA AVAILABLE. **CHRONIC EXPOSURE-** NO DATA AVAILABLE.

FIRST AID- WASH EYES IMMEDIATELY WITH LARGE AMOUNTS OF WATER OR NORMAL SALINE, OCCASIONALLY LIFTING UPPER AND LOWER LIDS, UNTIL NO EVIDENCE OF CHEMICAL REMAINS (APPROXIMATELY 15-20 MINUTES). GET MEDICAL ATTENTION IMMEDIATELY.

INGESTION: 2-METHYL-4-ISOTHIAZOLIN-3-ONE: **ACUTE EXPOSURE-** NO DATA AVAILABLE. **CHRONIC EXPOSURE-** NO DATA AVAILABLE.

FIRST AID- TREAT SYMPTOMATICALLY AND SUPPORTIVELY. GET MEDICAL ATTENTION IMMEDIATELY. IF VOMITING OCCURS, KEEP HEAD LOWER THAN HIPS TO PREVENT ASPIRATION.

REACTIVITY

REACTIVITY: STABLE UNDER NORMAL TEMPERATURES AND PRESSURES.

INCOMPATIBILITIES: 2-METHYL-4-ISOTHIAZOLIN-3-ONE: OXIDIZERS (STRONG): FIRE AND EXPLOSION HAZARD. SEE ALSO KETONES.
KETONES: ACETALDEHYDE: VIOLENT CONDENSATION REACTION. NITRIC ACID + HYDROGEN PEROXIDE: FORMATION OF EXPLOSIVE PRODUCT. PERCHLORIC ACID: VIOLENT DECOMPOSITION.

DECOMPOSITION: THERMAL DECOMPOSITION MAY RELEASE TOXIC AND/OR HAZARDOUS GASES.

POLYMERIZATION: HAZARDOUS POLYMERIZATION HAS NOT BEEN REPORTED TO OCCUR UNDER NORMAL TEMPERATURES AND PRESSURES.

STORAGE AND DISPOSAL

OBSERVE ALL FEDERAL, STATE AND LOCAL REGULATIONS WHEN STORING OR DISPOSING OF THIS SUBSTANCE. FOR ASSISTANCE, CONTACT THE DISTRICT DIRECTOR OF THE ENVIRONMENTAL PROTECTION AGENCY.

STORAGE

STORE IN ACCORDANCE WITH 40 CFR 165 RECOMMENDED PROCEDURES FOR THE DISPOSAL AND STORAGE OF PESTICIDES AND PESTICIDE CONTAINERS.
STORE AWAY FROM INCOMPATIBLE SUBSTANCES.

DISPOSAL

DISPOSAL MUST BE IN ACCORDANCE WITH 40 CFR 165 RECOMMENDED PROCEDURES FOR THE DISPOSAL AND STORAGE OF PESTICIDES AND PESTICIDE CONTAINERS.

CONDITIONS TO AVOID

AVOID CONTACT WITH HEAT, SPARKS, FLAMES, OR OTHER SOURCES OF IGNITION. VAPORS MAY BE EXPLOSIVE AND POISONOUS; DO NOT ALLOW UNNECESSARY PERSONNEL IN AREA. DO NOT OVERHEAT CONTAINERS; CONTAINERS MAY VIOLENTLY RUPTURE AND TRAVEL A CONSIDERABLE DISTANCE IN HEAT OF FIRE.

SPILL AND LEAK PROCEDURES

OCCUPATIONAL SPILL: SHUT OFF IGNITION SOURCES. STOP LEAK IF YOU CAN DO IT WITHOUT RISK. USE WATER SPRAY TO REDUCE VAPORS. FOR SMALL SPILLS, TAKE UP WITH SAND OR OTHER ABSORBENT MATERIAL AND PLACE INTO CONTAINERS FOR LATER DISPOSAL. FOR LARGER SPILLS, DIKE FAR AHEAD OF SPILL FOR LATER DISPOSAL. NO SMOKING, FLAMES OR FLARES IN HAZARD AREA. KEEP UNNECESSARY PEOPLE AWAY; ISOLATE HAZARD AREA AND DENY ENTRY.

PROTECTIVE EQUIPMENT

VENTILATION: PROVIDE LOCAL EXHAUST OR PROCESS ENCLOSURE VENTILATION. VENTILATION EQUIPMENT MUST BE EXPLOSION-PROOF.

RESPIRATOR: THE FOLLOWING RESPIRATORS ARE RECOMMENDED BASED ON INFORMATION FOUND IN THE PHYSICAL DATA, TOXICITY AND HEALTH EFFECTS SECTIONS. THEY ARE RANKED IN ORDER FROM MINIMUM TO MAXIMUM RESPIRATORY PROTECTION. THE SPECIFIC RESPIRATOR SELECTED MUST BE BASED ON CONTAMINATION LEVELS FOUND IN THE WORK PLACE, MUST NOT EXCEED THE WORKING LIMITS OF THE RESPIRATOR AND BE JOINTLY APPROVED BY THE NATIONAL INSTITUTE FOR OCCUPATIONAL SAFETY AND HEALTH AND THE MINE SAFETY AND HEALTH ADMINISTRATION (NIOSH-MSHA).
TYPE 'C' SUPPLIED-AIR RESPIRATOR WITH A FULL FACEPIECE OPERATED IN PRESSURE-DEMAND OR OTHER POSITIVE PRESSURE MODE OR WITH A FULL FACEPIECE, HELMET OR HOOD OPERATED IN CONTINOUS-FLOW MODE.
SELF-CONTAINED BREATHING APPARATUS WITH A FULL FACEPIECE OPERATED IN PRESSURE-DEMAND OR OTHER POSITIVE PRESSURE MODE.
FOR FIREFIGHTING AND OTHER IMMEDIATELY DANGEROUS TO LIFE OR HEALTH CONDITIONS:
SELF-CONTAINED BREATHING APPARATUS WITH FULL FACEPIECE OPERATED IN PRESSURE-DEMAND OR OTHER POSITIVE PRESSURE MODE.
SUPPLIED-AIR RESPIRATOR WITH FULL FACEPIECE AND OPERATED IN PRESSURE-DEMAND OR OTHER POSITIVE PRESSURE MODE IN COMBINATION WITH AN AUXILIARY SELF-CONTAINED BREATHING APPARATUS OPERATED IN PRESSURE-DEMAND OR OTHER POSITIVE PRESSURE MODE.

CLOTHING: EMPLOYEE MUST WEAR APPROPRIATE PROTECTIVE (IMPERVIOUS) CLOTHING AND EQUIPMENT TO PREVENT REPEATED OR PROLONGED SKIN CONTACT WITH THIS SUBSTANCE.

GLOVES: EMPLOYEE MUST WEAR APPROPRIATE PROTECTIVE GLOVES TO PREVENT CONTACT WITH THIS SUBSTANCE.

EYE PROTECTION: EMPLOYEE MUST WEAR SPLASH-PROOF OR DUST-RESISTANT SAFETY GOGGLES AND A FACESHIELD TO PREVENT CONTACT WITH THIS SUBSTANCE.

EMERGENCY WASH FACILITIES: WHERE THERE IS ANY POSSIBILITY THAT AN EMPLOYEE'S EYES AND/OR SKIN MAY BE EXPOSED TO THIS SUBSTANCE, THE EMPLOYER SHOULD PROVIDE AN EYE WASH FOUNTAIN AND QUICK DRENCH SHOWER WITHIN THE IMMEDIATE WORK AREA FOR EMERGENCY USE.

AUTHORIZED BY- OCCUPATIONAL HEALTH SERVICES, INC.

CREATION DATE: 10/05/89 ***REVISION DATE:*** 11/08/89

MATERIAL SAFETY DATA SHEET

OCCUPATIONAL HEALTH SERVICES, INC.
AGRICULTURE AND PESTICIDE DIVISION
450 SEVENTH AVENUE, SUITE 2407
NEW YORK, NEW YORK 10123
1-800-445-MSDS OR (212) 967-1100

EMERGENCY CONTACT:
JOHN S. BRANSFORD, JR. (615) 292-1180

SUBSTANCE IDENTIFICATION

CAS-NUMBER 27668-52-6

SUBSTANCE:
3-(TRIMETHOXYSILYL)PROPYLDIMETHYLOCTADECYLAMMONIUM CHLORIDE

TRADE NAMES/SYNONYMS: 1-OCTADECANAMINIUM, N,N-DIMETHYL-N-(3-(TRIMETHOXYSILYL)PROPYL)-, CHLORIDE; N,N-DIMETHYL-N-(3-(TRIMETHOXYSILYL)PROPYL)-1-OCTADECANAMINIUM CHLORIDE; AMMONIUM, DIMETHYLOCTADECYL(3-TRIMETHOXYSILYL)PROPYL)-, CHLORIDE; DIMETHYLOCTADECYL(3-TRIMETHOXYSILYL)PROPYL)AMMONIUM CHLORIDE; C26H58CLNO3SI; PST72370

CHEMICAL FAMILY: QUATERNARY AMMONIUM COMPOUND CATIONIC SURFACTANT

MOLECULAR FORMULA: C26-H58-N-O3-SI.CL

MOLECULAR WEIGHT: 496.29

CERCLA RATINGS (SCALE 0-3): HEALTH=U FIRE=1 REACTIVITY=0 PERSISTENCE=1

NFPA RATINGS (SCALE 0-4): HEALTH=U FIRE=1 REACTIVITY=0

COMPONENTS AND CONTAMINANTS

COMPONENT: ***PERCENT:*** 100.0
3-(TRIMETHOXYSILYL)PROPYLDIMETHYLOCTADECYLAMMONIUM CHLORIDE
CAS# 27668-52-6

OTHER CONTAMINANTS: NONE

EXPOSURE LIMITS: NO OCCUPATIONAL EXPOSURE LIMITS ESTABLISHED BY OSHA, ACGIH, OR NIOSH.

PHYSICAL DATA

DESCRIPTION: SOLID. ***MELTING POINT:*** NOT AVAILABLE

SPECIFIC GRAVITY: NOT AVAILABLE ***SOLUBILITY IN WATER:*** SOLUBLE

FIRE AND EXPLOSION DATA

FIRE AND EXPLOSION HAZARD: SLIGHT FIRE HAZARD WHEN EXPOSED TO HEAT OR FLAME.

FIREFIGHTING MEDIA: DRY CHEMICAL, CARBON DIOXIDE, HALON, WATER SPRAY OR STANDARD FOAM (1987 EMERGENCY RESPONSE GUIDEBOOK, DOT P 5800.4).
FOR LARGER FIRES, USE WATER SPRAY, FOG OR STANDARD FOAM (1987 EMERGENCY RESPONSE GUIDEBOOK, DOT P 5800.4).

FIREFIGHTING: MOVE CONTAINER FROM FIRE AREA IF POSSIBLE. DO NOT SCATTER SPILLED MATERIAL WITH HIGH PRESSURE WATER STREAMS. DIKE FIRE CONTROL WATER FOR LATER DISPOSAL (1987 EMERGENCY RESPONSE GUIDEBOOK, DOT P 5800.4, GUIDE PAGE 31).
USE AGENTS SUITABLE FOR TYPE OF SURROUNDING FIRE. AVOID BREATHING HAZARDOUS VAPORS, KEEP UPWIND.

TOXICITY

3-(TRIMETHYOXYSILYL)PROPYLDIMETHYLOCTADECYLAMMONIUM CHLORIDE: CARCINOGEN STATUS: NONE. ACUTE TOXICITY: NO DATA AVAILABLE. TARGET EFFECTS: NO DATA AVAILABLE.

HEALTH EFFECTS AND FIRST AID

INHALATION: 3-(TRIMETHOXYSILYL)PROPYLDIMETHYLOCTADECYLAMMONIUM CHLORIDE: SEE INFORMATION ON CATIONIC SURFACTANTS.
CATIONIC SURFACTANTS: **ACUTE EXPOSURE-** CONCENTRATIONS OF MANY CATIONIC SURFACTANTS AS LOW AS 0.1 TO 0.5% ARE IRRITATING TO THE MUCOUS MEMBRANES. 1% SOLUTIONS MAY PRODUCE SIGNIFICANT IRRITATION, AND CONCENTRATED SOLUTIONS (>10%), MAY HAVE CAUSTIC QUALITIES. **CHRONIC EXPOSURE-** NO DATA AVAILABLE.

FIRST AID- REMOVE FROM EXPOSURE AREA TO FRESH AIR IMMEDIATELY. IF BREATHING HAS STOPPED, GIVE ARTIFICIAL RESPIRATION. MAINTAIN AIRWAY AND BLOOD PRESSURE AND ADMINISTER OXYGEN IF AVAILABLE. KEEP AFFECTED PERSON WARM AND AT REST. TREAT SYMPTOMATICALLY AND SUPPORTIVELY. ADMINISTRATION OF OXYGEN SHOULD BE PERFORMED BY QUALIFIED PERSONNEL. GET MEDICAL ATTENTION IMMEDIATELY.

SKIN CONTACT: 3-(TRIMETHOXYSILYL)PROPYLDIMETHYLOCTADECYLAMMONIUM CHLORIDE: SEE INFORMATION ON CATIONIC SURFACTANTS.
CATIONIC SURFACTANTS: **ACUTE EXPOSURE-** 1% SOLUTIONS OF MANY CATIONIC SURFACTANTS PRODUCE IRRITATION AND CONCENTRATED SOLUTIONS (>10%), HAVE CAUSTIC QUALITIES. **CHRONIC EXPOSURE-** PROLONGED OR REPEATED EXPOSURE TO SOME CATIONIC SURFACTANTS HAS RESULTED IN ALLERGIC REACTIONS.

FIRST AID- REMOVE CONTAMINATED CLOTHING AND SHOES IMMEDIATELY. WASH AFFECTED AREA WITH SOAP OR MILD DETERGENT AND LARGE AMOUNTS OF WATER UNTIL NO EVIDENCE OF CHEMICAL REMAINS (AT LEAST 15-20 MINUTES). IN CASE OF CHEMICAL BURNS, COVER AREA WITH STERILE, DRY DRESSING. BANDAGE SECURELY, BUT NOT TOO TIGHTLY. GET MEDICAL ATTENTION IMMEDIATELY.

EYE CONTACT: 3-(TRIMETHOXYSILYL)PROPYLDIMETHYLOCTADECYLAMMONIUM CHLORIDE: SEE INFORMATION ON CATIONIC SURFACTANTS.
CATIONIC SURFACTANTS: **ACUTE EXPOSURE-** 1% SOLUTIONS, AND POSSIBLY AS LOW AS 0.1%, OF MANY CATIONIC SURFACTANTS PRODUCE SIGNIFICANT IRRITATION. HIGH CONCENTRATIONS (>10%), OF SOME CATIONIC SURFACTANTS CAUSE SEVERE BURNS WITH PERMANENT OPACITY AND VASCULARIZATION. **CHRONIC EXPOSURE-** NO DATA AVAILABLE.

FIRST AID- WASH EYES IMMEDIATELY WITH LARGE AMOUNTS OF WATER, OCCASIONALLY LIFTING UPPER AND LOWER LIDS, UNTIL NO EVIDENCE OF CHEMICAL REMAINS (AT LEAST 15-20 MINUTES). CONTINUE IRRIGATING WITH NORMAL SALINE UNTIL THE PH HAS RETURNED TO NORMAL (30-60 MINUTES). COVER WITH STERILE BANDAGES. GET MEDICAL ATTENTION IMMEDIATELY.

INGESTION: 3-(TRIMETHOXYSILYL)PROPYLDIMETHYLOCTADECYLAMMONIUM CHLORIDE. SEE INFORMATION ON CATIONIC SURFACTANTS.
CATIONIC SURFACTANTS: **ACUTE EXPOSURE-** CONCENTRATED SOLUTIONS (>10%), OF MANY CATIONIC SURFACTANTS, CAUSE CORROSIVE DAMAGE TO THE MUCOUS MEMBRANES AND ESOPHAGUS, NAUSEA, AND VOMITING. IF SUFFICIENT QUANTITIES ARE INGESTED OTHER SIGNS AND SYMPTOMS REFERABLE TO THE CENTRAL NERVOUS SYSTEM OR CIRCULATORY SHOCK MAY DEVELOP INCLUDING RESTLESSNESS, CONFUSION, HYPOTENSION, MUSCLE WEAKNESS, COLLAPSE, CONVULSIONS, RESPIRATORY PARALYSIS, CYANOSIS, AND COMA. DEATH MAY OCCUR WITHIN 1-4 HOURS. THE ESTIMATED FATAL HUMAN DOSE IS BETWEEN 1-3 GRAMS. **CHRONIC EXPOSURE-** NO DATA AVAILABLE.

FIRST AID- GIVE MILK OR ACTIVATED CHARCOAL AND REMOVE BY CATHARSIS WITH FLEET'S PHOSPHO-SODA, 15-60 ML DILUTED 1:4 WITH WATER. LAVAGE AND EMESIS ARE CONTRAINDICATED IN THE PRESENCE OF ESOPHAGEAL INJURY. GASTRIC LAVAGE SHOULD BE PERFORMED BY QUALIFIED MEDICAL PERSONNEL. GET MEDICAL ATTENTION IMMEDIATELY (DREISBACH, HANDBOOK OF POISONING, 12TH ED.). MAINTAIN AIRWAY, BLOOD PRESSURE AND RESPIRATION.

ANTIDOTE: NO SPECIFIC ANTIDOTE. TREAT SYMPTOMATICALLY AND SUPPORTIVELY.

REACTIVITY

REACTIVITY: STABLE UNDER NORMAL TEMPERATURES AND PRESSURES.

INCOMPATIBILITIES: 3-(TRIMETHOXYSILYL)PROPYLDIMETHYLOCTADECYLAMMONIUM CHLORIDE: OXIDIZERS (STRONG): FIRE AND EXPLOSION HAZARD.

DECOMPOSITION: THERMAL DECOMPOSITION MAY RELEASE TOXIC AND/OR HAZARDOUS GASES.

POLYMERIZATION: HAZARDOUS POLYMERIZATION HAS NOT BEEN REPORTED TO OCCUR UNDER NORMAL TEMPERATURES AND PRESSURES.

STORAGE AND DISPOSAL

OBSERVE ALL FEDERAL, STATE AND LOCAL REGULATIONS WHEN STORING OR DISPOSING OF THIS SUBSTANCE. FOR ASSISTANCE, CONTACT THE DISTRICT DIRECTOR OF THE ENVIRONMENTAL PROTECTION AGENCY.

STORAGE

STORE IN ACCORDANCE WITH 40 CFR 165 RECOMMENDED PROCEDURES FOR THE DISPOSAL AND STORAGE OF PESTICIDES AND PESTICIDE CONTAINERS.
STORE AWAY FROM INCOMPATIBLE SUBSTANCES.

DISPOSAL

DISPOSAL MUST BE IN ACCORDANCE WITH 40 CFR 165 RECOMMENDED PROCEDURES FOR THE DISPOSAL AND STORAGE OF PESTICIDES AND PESTICIDE CONTAINERS.

CONDITIONS TO AVOID

MAY BURN BUT DOES NOT IGNITE READILY. AVOID CONTACT WITH STRONG OXIDIZERS, EXCESSIVE HEAT, SPARKS, OR OPEN FLAME.

SPILL AND LEAK PROCEDURES

OCCUPATIONAL SPILL: SWEEP UP AND PLACE IN SUITABLE CLEAN, DRY CONTAINERS FOR RECLAMATION OR LATER DISPOSAL. DO NOT FLUSH SPILLED MATERIAL INTO SEWER. KEEP UNNECESSARY PEOPLE AWAY.

PROTECTIVE EQUIPMENT

VENTILATION: PROVIDE LOCAL EXHAUST OR GENERAL DILUTION VENTILATION SYSTEM.

RESPIRATOR: THE FOLLOWING RESPIRATORS ARE RECOMMENDED BASED ON INFORMATION FOUND IN THE PHYSICAL DATA, TOXICITY AND HEALTH EFFECTS SECTIONS. THEY ARE RANKED IN ORDER FROM MINIMUM TO MAXIMUM RESPIRATORY PROTECTION. THE SPECIFIC RESPIRATOR SELECTED MUST BE BASED ON CONTAMINATION LEVELS FOUND IN THE WORK PLACE, MUST NOT EXCEED THE WORKING LIMITS OF THE RESPIRATOR AND BE JOINTLY APPROVED BY THE NATIONAL INSTITUTE FOR OCCUPATIONAL SAFETY AND HEALTH AND THE MINE SAFETY AND HEALTH ADMINISTRATION (NIOSH-MSHA).
DUST AND MIST RESPIRATOR WITH A FULL FACEPIECE.
AIR-PURIFYING FULL FACEPIECE RESPIRATOR WITH A HIGH-EFFICIENCY PARTICULATE FILTER.
POWERED AIR-PURIFYING RESPIRATOR WITH A TIGHT-FITTING FACEPIECE AND HIGH-EFFICIENCY PARTICULATE FILTER.
TYPE 'C' SUPPLIED-AIR RESPIRATOR WITH A FULL FACEPIECE OPERATED IN PRESSURE-DEMAND OR OTHER POSITIVE PRESSURE MODE OR WITH A FULL FACEPIECE, HELMET OR HOOD OPERATED IN CONTINUOUS-FLOW MODE.
SELF-CONTAINED BREATHING APPARATUS WITH A FULL FACEPIECE OPERATED IN PRESSURE-DEMAND OR OTHER POSITIVE PRESSURE MODE.
FOR FIREFIGHTING AND OTHER IMMEDIATELY DANGEROUS TO LIFE OR HEALTH CONDITIONS:
SELF-CONTAINED BREATHING APPARATUS WITH FULL FACEPIECE OPERATED IN PRESSURE-DEMAND OR OTHER POSITIVE PRESSURE MODE.
SUPPLIED-AIR RESPIRATOR WITH FULL FACEPIECE AND OPERATED IN PRESSURE-DEMAND OR OTHER POSITIVE PRESSURE MODE IN COMBINATION WITH AN AUXILIARY SELF-CONTAINED BREATHING APPARATUS OPERATED IN PRESSURE-DEMAND OR OTHER POSITIVE PRESSURE MODE.

CLOTHING: EMPLOYEE MUST WEAR APPROPRIATE PROTECTIVE (IMPERVIOUS) CLOTHING AND EQUIPMENT TO PREVENT ANY POSSIBILITY OF SKIN CONTACT WITH THIS SUBSTANCE.

GLOVES: EMPLOYEE MUST WEAR APPROPRIATE PROTECTIVE GLOVES TO PREVENT CONTACT WITH THIS SUBSTANCE.

EYE PROTECTION: EMPLOYEE MUST WEAR SPLASH-PROOF OR DUST-RESISTANT SAFETY GOGGLES AND A FACESHIELD TO PREVENT CONTACT WITH THIS SUBSTANCE.
EMERGENCY WASH FACILITIES: WHERE THERE IS ANY POSSIBILITY THAT AN EMPLOYEE'S EYES AND/OR SKIN MAY BE EXPOSED TO THIS SUBSTANCE, THE EMPLOYER SHOULD PROVIDE AN EYE WASH FOUNTAIN AND QUICK DRENCH SHOWER WITHIN THE IMMEDIATE WORK AREA FOR EMERGENCY USE.

AUTHORIZED BY- OCCUPATIONAL HEALTH SERVICES, INC.
CREATION DATE: 10/06/89 ***REVISION DATE:*** 05/31/90

MATERIAL SAFETY DATA SHEET

OCCUPATIONAL HEALTH SERVICES, INC.
AGRICULTURE AND PESTICIDE DIVISION
450 SEVENTH AVENUE, SUITE 2407
NEW YORK, NEW YORK 10123
1-800-445-MSDS OR (212) 967-1100

EMERGENCY CONTACT:
JOHN S. BRANSFORD, JR. (615) 292-1180

SUBSTANCE IDENTIFICATION

CAS-NUMBER 37924-13-3
SUBSTANCE: PERFLUIDONE
TRADE NAMES/SYNONYMS: METHANESULFONAMIDE, 1,1,1-TRIFLUORO-N-(2-METHYL-4-(PHENYLSULFONYL) PHENYL)-; 1,1,1-TRIFLUORO-N-(2-METHYL-4-(PHENYLSULFONYL)PHENYL) METHANESULFONAMIDE; DESTUN; MBR 8251; C14H12F3NO4S2; PST72375
CHEMICAL FAMILY: SULFONAMIDE
MOLECULAR FORMULA: C14-H12-F3-N-O4-S2
MOLECULAR WEIGHT: 379.38
CERCLA RATINGS (SCALE 0-3): HEALTH=2 FIRE=1 REACTIVITY=0 PERSISTENCE=3
NFPA RATINGS (SCALE 0-4): HEALTH=U FIRE=1 REACTIVITY=0

COMPONENTS AND CONTAMINANTS

COMPONENT: PERFLUIDONE ***PERCENT:*** 100.0
CAS# 37924-13-3
OTHER CONTAMINANTS: NONE
EXPOSURE LIMITS: NO OCCUPATIONAL EXPOSURE LIMITS ESTABLISHED BY OSHA, ACGIH, OR NIOSH.

PHYSICAL DATA

DESCRIPTION: COLORLESS CRYSTALS. ***MELTING POINT:*** 288-291 F (142-144 C)
SPECIFIC GRAVITY: NOT AVAILABLE ***VAPOR PRESSURE:*** <1 MMHG @ 25 C
SOLUBILITY IN WATER: 0.006% @ 22 C
SOLVENT SOLUBILITY: SOLUBLE IN ACETONE, DICHLOROMETHANE AND METHANOL; SLIGHTLY SOLUBLE IN BENZENE.

FIRE AND EXPLOSION DATA

FIRE AND EXPLOSION HAZARD: SLIGHT FIRE HAZARD WHEN EXPOSED TO HEAT OR FLAME.

FIREFIGHTING MEDIA: DRY CHEMICAL, CARBON DIOXIDE, HALON, WATER SPRAY OR STANDARD FOAM (1987 EMERGENCY RESPONSE GUIDEBOOK, DOT P 5800.4).
FOR LARGER FIRES, USE WATER SPRAY, FOG OR STANDARD FOAM (1987 EMERGENCY RESPONSE GUIDEBOOK, DOT P 5800.4).

FIREFIGHTING: MOVE CONTAINER FROM FIRE AREA IF POSSIBLE. DO NOT SCATTER SPILLED MATERIAL WITH HIGH PRESSURE WATER STREAMS. DIKE FIRE CONTROL WATER FOR LATER DISPOSAL (1987 EMERGENCY RESPONSE GUIDEBOOK, DOT P 5800.4, GUIDE PAGE 31).
USE AGENTS SUITABLE FOR TYPE OF SURROUNDING FIRE. AVOID BREATHING HAZARDOUS VAPORS, KEEP UPWIND.

TOXICITY

PERFLUIDONE: TOXICITY DATA: >4000 MG/KG SKIN-RABBIT LD50 (FMCHA2); 633 MG/KG ORAL-RAT LD50; 920 MG/KG ORAL-MOUSE LD50. CARCINOGEN STATUS: NONE. ACUTE TOXICITY LEVEL: MODERATELY TOXIC BY INGESTION; SLIGHTLY TOXIC BY DERMAL ABSORPTION. TARGET EFFECTS: NO DATA AVAILABLE.

HEALTH EFFECTS AND FIRST AID

INHALATION: PERFLUIDONE: ACUTE EXPOSURE- NO DATA AVAILABLE. CHRONIC EXPOSURE- NO DATA AVAILABLE.
FIRST AID- REMOVE FROM EXPOSURE AREA TO FRESH AIR IMMEDIATELY. IF BREATHING HAS STOPPED, PERFORM ARTIFICIAL RESPIRATION. KEEP PERSON WARM AND AT REST. TREAT SYMPTOMATICALLY AND SUPPORTIVELY. GET MEDICAL ATTENTION IMMEDIATELY.

SKIN CONTACT: PERFLUIDONE: ACUTE EXPOSURE- MAY CAUSE MILD IRRITATION. THE LD50 FOR RABBITS WAS >4000 MG/KG. CHRONIC EXPOSURE- NO DATA AVAILABLE.
FIRST AID- REMOVE CONTAMINATED CLOTHING AND SHOES IMMEDIATELY. WASH AFFECTED AREA WITH SOAP OR MILD DETERGENT AND LARGE AMOUNTS OF WATER UNTIL NO EVIDENCE OF CHEMICAL REMAINS (APPROXIMATELY 15-20 MINUTES). GET MEDICAL ATTENTION IMMEDIATELY.

EYE CONTACT: PERFLUIDONE: ACUTE EXPOSURE- MAY CAUSE IRRITATION. CHRONIC EXPOSURE- NO DATA AVAILABLE.
FIRST AID- WASH EYES IMMEDIATELY WITH LARGE AMOUNTS OF WATER OR NORMAL SALINE, OCCASIONALLY LIFTING UPPER AND LOWER LIDS, UNTIL NO EVIDENCE OF CHEMICAL REMAINS (APPROXIMATELY 15-20 MINUTES). GET MEDICAL ATTENTION IMMEDIATELY.

INGESTION: PERFLUIDONE: **ACUTE EXPOSURE**- THE LETHAL DOSE REPORTED IN RATS WAS 633 MG/KG. THE SYMPTOMS WERE NOT REPORTED. **CHRONIC EXPOSURE**- NO DATA AVAILABLE.

FIRST AID- TREAT SYMPTOMATICALLY AND SUPPORTIVELY. GET MEDICAL ATTENTION IMMEDIATELY. IF VOMITING OCCURS, KEEP HEAD LOWER THAN HIPS TO PREVENT ASPIRATION.

ANTIDOTE: NO SPECIFIC ANTIDOTE. TREAT SYMPTOMATICALLY AND SUPPORTIVELY.

REACTIVITY

REACTIVITY: STABLE UNDER NORMAL TEMPERATURES AND PRESSURES.

INCOMPATIBILITIES: PERFLUIDONE: METALS: MAY CORRODE ON PROLONGED EXPOSURE TO AQUEOUS SOLUTIONS AND SUSPENSIONS. OXIDIZERS (STRONG): FIRE AND EXPLOSION HAZARD.

DECOMPOSITION: THERMAL DECOMPOSITION PRODUCTS MAY INCLUDE TOXIC AND CORROSIVE FUMES OF FLUORIDES AND TOXIC OXIDES OF NITROGEN AND SULFUR.

POLYMERIZATION: HAZARDOUS POLYMERIZATION HAS NOT BEEN REPORTED TO OCCUR UNDER NORMAL TEMPERATURES AND PRESSURES.

STORAGE AND DISPOSAL

OBSERVE ALL FEDERAL, STATE AND LOCAL REGULATIONS WHEN STORING OR DISPOSING OF THIS SUBSTANCE. FOR ASSISTANCE, CONTACT THE DISTRICT DIRECTOR OF THE ENVIRONMENTAL PROTECTION AGENCY.

****STORAGE****

STORE IN ACCORDANCE WITH 40 CFR 165 RECOMMENDED PROCEDURES FOR THE DISPOSAL AND STORAGE OF PESTICIDES AND PESTICIDE CONTAINERS.
STORE AWAY FROM INCOMPATIBLE SUBSTANCES.

****DISPOSAL****

DISPOSAL MUST BE IN ACCORDANCE WITH 40 CFR 165 RECOMMENDED PROCEDURES FOR THE DISPOSAL AND STORAGE OF PESTICIDES AND PESTICIDE CONTAINERS.

CONDITIONS TO AVOID

MAY BURN BUT DOES NOT IGNITE READILY. AVOID CONTACT WITH STRONG OXIDIZERS, EXCESSIVE HEAT, SPARKS, OR OPEN FLAME.

SPILL AND LEAK PROCEDURES

OCCUPATIONAL SPILL: STOP LEAK IF YOU CAN DO IT WITHOUT RISK. FOR SMALL SPILLS, TAKE UP WITH SAND OR OTHER ABSORBENT MATERIAL AND PLACE INTO CLEAN, DRY CONTAINERS FOR LATER DISPOSAL. KEEP UNNECESSARY PEOPLE AWAY. ISOLATE HAZARD AREA AND DENY ENTRY.

PROTECTIVE EQUIPMENT

VENTILATION: PROVIDE LOCAL EXHAUST OR GENERAL DILUTION VENTILATION SYSTEM.

RESPIRATOR: THE FOLLOWING RESPIRATORS ARE RECOMMENDED BASED ON INFORMATION FOUND IN THE PHYSICAL DATA, TOXICITY AND HEALTH EFFECTS SECTIONS. THEY ARE RANKED IN ORDER FROM MINIMUM TO MAXIMUM RESPIRATORY PROTECTION. THE SPECIFIC RESPIRATOR SELECTED MUST BE BASED ON CONTAMINATION LEVELS FOUND IN THE WORK PLACE, MUST NOT EXCEED THE WORKING LIMITS OF THE RESPIRATOR AND BE JOINTLY APPROVED BY THE NATIONAL INSTITUTE FOR OCCUPATIONAL SAFETY AND HEALTH AND THE MINE SAFETY AND HEALTH ADMINISTRATION (NIOSH-MSHA).
CHEMICAL CARTRIDGE RESPIRATOR WITH AN ORGANIC VAPOR CARTRIDGE(S) WITH A FULL FACEPIECE AND ORGANIC VAPOR CARTRIDGE(S) IN COMBINATION WITH A DUST AND MIST FILTER.
POWERED AIR-PURIFYING RESPIRATOR WITH A TIGHT-FITTING FACEPIECE AND ORGANIC VAPOR CARTRIDGE(S) IN COMBINATION WITH A HIGH-EFFICIENCY PARTICULATE FILTER.
TYPE 'C' SUPPLIED-AIR RESPIRATOR WITH A FULL FACEPIECE OPERATED IN A PRESSURE-DEMAND OR OTHER POSITIVE PRESSURE MODE.
SELF-CONTAINED BREATHING APPARATUS WITH A FULL FACEPIECE OPERATED IN PRESSURE-DEMAND OR OTHER POSITIVE PRESSURE MODE.
FOR FIREFIGHTING AND OTHER IMMEDIATELY DANGEROUS TO LIFE OR HEALTH CONDITIONS:
SELF-CONTAINED BREATHING APPARATUS WITH FULL FACEPIECE OPERATED IN PRESSURE-DEMAND OR OTHER POSITIVE PRESSURE MODE.
SUPPLIED-AIR RESPIRATOR WITH FULL FACEPIECE AND OPERATED IN PRESSURE-DEMAND OR OTHER POSITIVE PRESSURE MODE IN COMBINATION WITH AN AUXILIARY SELF-CONTAINED BREATHING APPARATUS OPERATED IN PRESSURE-DEMAND OR OTHER POSITIVE PRESSURE MODE.

CLOTHING: EMPLOYEE MUST WEAR APPROPRIATE PROTECTIVE (IMPERVIOUS) CLOTHING AND EQUIPMENT TO PREVENT REPEATED OR PROLONGED SKIN CONTACT WITH THIS SUBSTANCE.

GLOVES: EMPLOYEE MUST WEAR APPROPRIATE PROTECTIVE GLOVES TO PREVENT CONTACT WITH THIS SUBSTANCE.

EYE PROTECTION: EMPLOYEE MUST WEAR SPLASH-PROOF OR DUST-RESISTANT SAFETY GOGGLES TO PREVENT EYE CONTACT WITH THIS SUBSTANCE.
EMERGENCY EYE WASH: WHERE THERE IS ANY POSSIBILITY THAT AN EMPLOYEE'S EYES MAY BE EXPOSED TO THIS SUBSTANCE, THE EMPLOYER SHOULD PROVIDE AN EYE WASH FOUNTAIN WITHIN THE IMMEDIATE WORK AREA FOR EMERGENCY USE.

AUTHORIZED BY- OCCUPATIONAL HEALTH SERVICES, INC.
CREATION DATE: 10/04/89 ***REVISION DATE:*** 05/11/90

MATERIAL SAFETY DATA SHEET

OCCUPATIONAL HEALTH SERVICES, INC.
AGRICULTURE AND PESTICIDE DIVISION
450 SEVENTH AVENUE, SUITE 2407
NEW YORK, NEW YORK 10123
1-800-445-MSDS OR (212) 967-1100

EMERGENCY CONTACT:
JOHN S. BRANSFORD, JR. (615) 292-1180

SUBSTANCE IDENTIFICATION

CAS-NUMBER 23505-41-1

SUBSTANCE: **PIRIMIFOS-ETHYL**

TRADE NAMES/SYNONYMS: PHOSPHOROTHIOIC ACID, O-(2-(DIETHYLAMINO)-6-METHYL-4-PYRIMIDINYL) O,O-DIETHYL ESTER; O-O-DIETHYL-O-(2-DIETHYLAMINO-6-METHYL-4-PIRIMIDINYL)PHOSPHOROTHIOATE; DIETHYL 2-DIMETHYLAMINO-4-METHYLPYRIMIDIN-6-YL PHOSPHOROTHIONATE; ETHYL PIRIMIPHOS; FERNEX; PP 211; PRIMICID; R 42211; SOLGARD; PST72377

CHEMICAL FAMILY: PYRIMIDINE PHOSPHOROTHIOATE

MOLECULAR FORMULA: C13-H24-N3-O3-P-S

MOLECULAR WEIGHT: 333.43

CERCLA RATINGS (SCALE 0-3): HEALTH=3 FIRE=U REACTIVITY=0 PERSISTENCE=2

NFPA RATINGS (SCALE 0-4): HEALTH=3 FIRE=U REACTIVITY=0

COMPONENTS AND CONTAMINANTS

COMPONENT: PRIMIPHOS-ETHYL ***PERCENT:*** 100.0
CAS# 23505-41-1

OTHER CONTAMINANTS: NONE

EXPOSURE LIMITS: PIRIMIFOS-ETHYL: 1000 POUNDS SARA SECTION 302 THRESHOLD PLANNING QUANTITY 1 POUND SARA SECTION 304 REPORTABLE QUANTITY

PHYSICAL DATA

DESCRIPTION: STRAW COLORED LIQUID

BOILING POINT: DECOMPOSES ABOVE 266 F (130 C)

SPECIFIC GRAVITY: 1.14 @ 20 C ***VAPOR PRESSURE:*** 0.00029 MMHG @ 25 C

EVAPORATION RATE: NOT AVAILABLE ***SOLUBILITY IN WATER:*** <1 PPM

SOLVENT SOLUBILITY: MISCIBLE IN MOST ORGANIC SOLVENTS

FIRE AND EXPLOSION DATA

FIRE AND EXPLOSION HAZARD: UNKNOWN FIRE AND EXPLOSION HAZARD.

FIREFIGHTING MEDIA: DRY CHEMICAL, CARBON DIOXIDE, WATER SPRAY OR FOAM FOR LARGER FIRES, USE WATER SPRAY, FOG OR ALCOHOL FOAM

FIREFIGHTING: MOVE CONTAINER FROM FIRE AREA IF POSSIBLE. DO NOT SCATTER SPILLED MATERIAL WITH MORE WATER THAN NEEDED FOR FIRE CONTROL. DIKE FIRE CONTROL WATER FOR LATER DISPOSAL
USE AGENTS SUITABLE FOR TYPE OF SURROUNDING FIRE. AVOID BREATHING HAZARDOUS VAPORS, KEEP UPWIND.

TOXICITY

PIRIMIFOS-ETHYL: TOXICITY DATA: 1000 MG/KG SKIN-RAT LD50; 140 MG/KG ORAL-RAT LD50; 105 MG/KG ORAL-MOUSE LD50; 25 MG/KG ORAL-CAT LD50; 50 MG/KG ORAL-GUINEA PIG LD50; MUTAGENIC DATA (RTECS). CARCINOGEN STATUS: NONE. ACUTE TOXICITY LEVEL: TOXIC BY DERMAL ABSORPTION AND INGESTION. TARGET EFFECTS: CHOLINESTERASE INHIBITOR. POISONING MAY AFFECT THE NERVOUS SYSTEM.* AT INCREASED RISK FROM EXPOSURE: PERSONS WITH RESPIRATORY AILMENTS, RECENT EXPOSURE TO CHOLINESTERASE INHIBITORS OR IMPAIRED CHOLINESTERASE PRODUCTION, OR LIVER MALFUNCTION.* ADDITIONAL DATA: MAY CROSS THE PLACENTA. HIGH ENVIRONMENTAL TEMPERATURES OR EXPOSURE OF THE CHEMICAL TO VISIBLE OR ULTRAVIOLET LIGHT MAY ENHANCE THE TOXICITY. INTERACTIONS WITH MEDICATIONS MAY OCCUR.*
* MAY BE BASED ON GENERAL INFORMATION ON ORGANOPHOSPHATES.

HEALTH EFFECTS AND FIRST AID

INHALATION: PIRIMIFOS-ETHYL: SEE INFORMATION ON ORGANOPHOSPHATES.
ORGANOPHOSPHATES: CHOLINESTERASE INHIBITOR. **ACUTE EXPOSURE**- WHEN INHALED, THE FIRST EFFECTS OF CHOLINESTERASE INHIBITORS ARE USUALLY RESPIRATORY AND MAY INCLUDE NASAL HYPEREMIA AND WATERY DISCHARGE, COUGH, CHEST DISCOMFORT, DYSPNEA, AND WHEEZING DUE TO INCREASED BRONCHIAL SECRETIONS AND BRONCHOCONSTRICTION. IF SUFFICIENT AMOUNTS ARE ABSORBED, OTHER SYSTEMIC EFFECTS MAY BEGIN WITHIN A FEW MINUTES OR BE DELAYED FOR UP TO 12 HOURS. SYMPTOMS MAY INCLUDE PALLOR, NAUSEA, VOMITING, DIARRHEA, ABDOMINAL CRAMPS, HEADACHE, DIZZINESS, OCULAR PAIN, BLURRED VISION, MIOSIS OR IN SOME CASES, ESPECIALLY INITIALLY, MYDRIASIS, LACRIMATION, SALIVATION, SWEATING, AND CONFUSION. OTHER REPORTED CENTRAL NERVOUS SYSTEM OR NEUROMUSCULAR EFFECTS MAY INCLUDE ATAXIA, SLURRED SPEECH, AREFLEXIA, WEAKNESS, FATIGUE, FASCICULATIONS, TWITCHING, TREMORS POSSIBLY OF THE TONGUE AND EYELIDS, AND EVENTUALLY PARALYSIS OF THE EXTREMITIES AND POSSIBLY OF THE RESPIRATORY MUSCLES. IN SEVERE CASES THERE MAY ALSO BE INVOLUNTARY DEFECATION AND URINATION, CYANOSIS, PSYCHOSIS, HYPERGLYCEMIA, ACUTE PANCREATITIS, CARDIAC IRREGULARITIES, PULMONARY EDEMA, UNCONSCIOUSNESS, CONVULSIONS, AND COMA. DEATH IS PRIMARILY DUE TO RESPIRATORY FAILURE, ALTHOUGH CARDIOVASCULAR EFFECTS INCLUDING CARDIAC ARREST MAY ALSO BE IMPLICATED. LONG TERM SEQUELAE ARE RARE BUT MAY INCLUDE NEUROPSYCHIATRIC DISORDERS AND MYOPATHY WITH MUSCLE TENDERNESS. SOME ORGANOPHOSPHATES MAY CAUSE A DELAYED NEUROPATHY BEGINNING 1-4 WEEKS AFTER AN ACUTE EXPOSURE WHICH MAY OR MAY NOT HAVE CAUSED ACUTE CHOLINERGIC EFFECTS. NUMBNESS, TINGLING, WEAKNESS AND CRAMPING BEGINNING SYMMETRICALLY IN THE LOWER LIMBS MAY PROGRESS TO ATAXIA AND PARALYSIS. IN SEVERE CASES, UPPER LIMB INVOLVEMENT IS POSSIBLE AND FLACCID PARALYSIS MAY PROGRESS TO SPASTIC PARALYSIS WITH EXAGGERATED REFLEXES. IMPROVEMENT MAY OCCUR OVER MONTHS TO YEARS, BUT SOME RESIDUAL IMPAIRMENT USUALLY REMAINS.
CHRONIC EXPOSURE- REPEATED OR PROLONGED EXPOSURE MAY RESULT IN THE EFFECTS OF ACUTE EXPOSURE INCLUDING THE DELAYED NEUROPATHY. OTHER EFFECTS REPORTED IN WORKERS REPEATEDLY EXPOSED INCLUDE IMPAIRED MEMORY AND CONCENTRATION, ACUTE PSYCHOSIS, SEVERE DEPRESSIONS, IRRITABILTY, CONFUSION, APATHY, EMOTIONAL LABILITY, SOCIAL WITHDRAWAL, CONFUSION, HEADACHE, SPEECH DIFFICULTIES, DELAYED REACTION TIMES, SPATIAL DISORIENTATION, NIGHTMARES, SLEEPWALKING, AND DROWSINESS OR INSOMNIA. AN INFLUENZA-LIKE CONDITION WITH HEADACHE, NAUSEA, WEAKNESS, ANOREXIA AND MALAISE HAS ALSO BEEN REPORTED.

FIRST AID- REMOVE FROM EXPOSURE AREA TO FRESH AIR IMMEDIATELY. IF BREATHING HAS STOPPED, GIVE ARTIFICIAL RESPIRATION. MAINTAIN AIRWAY AND BLOOD PRESSURE AND ADMINISTER OXYGEN IF AVAILABLE. KEEP AFFECTED PERSON WARM AND AT REST. TREAT SYMPTOMATICALLY AND SUPPORTIVELY. ADMINISTRATION OF OXYGEN SHOULD BE PERFORMED BY QUALIFIED PERSONNEL. GET MEDICAL ATTENTION IMMEDIATELY.

SKIN CONTACT: PIRIMIFOS-ETHYL: TOXIC. SEE INFORMATION ON ORGANOPHOSPHATES.
ORGANOPHOSPHATES: CHOLINESTERASE INHIBITOR. **ACUTE EXPOSURE**- LOCALIZED SWEATING AND FASCICULATIONS MAY OCCUR AT THE SITE OF CONTACT. IF SUFFICIENT AMOUNTS ARE ABSORBED, OTHER EFFECTS OF CHOLINESTERASE INHIBITION AS DESCRIBED IN ACUTE INHALATION MAY OCCUR. SYMPTOMS MAY BE DELAYED 2-3 HOURS, BUT USUALLY NO MORE THAN 12 HOURS. THE RATE OF ABSORPTION IS INCREASED BY THE PRESENCE OF DERMATITIS OR HIGH AMBIENT TEMPERATURES. DELAYED NEUROPATHY IS ALSO POSSIBLE. **CHRONIC EXPOSURE**- REPEATED OR PROLONGED EXPOSURE MAY CAUSE EFFECTS AS DESCRIBED IN ACUTE EXPOSURE. SOME ORGANOPHOSPHATES MAY CAUSE SENSITIZATION.

FIRST AID- REMOVE CONTAMINATED CLOTHING IMMEDIATELY. WASH CONTAMINATED AREAS WITH SOAP AND WATER FOLLOWED BY ALCOHOL (ARENA, POISONING, 4TH ED.). EMERGENCY PERSONNEL SHOULD WEAR GLOVES AND AVOID CONTAMINATION. TREAT RESPIRATORY DIFFICULTY WITH ARTIFICIAL RESPIRATION. GET MEDICAL ATTENTION IMMEDIATELY.

EYE CONTACT: PIRIMIFOS-ETHYL: SEE INFORMATION ON ORGANOPHOPHATES.
ORGANOPHOSPHATES: CHOLINESTERASE INHIBITOR. **ACUTE EXPOSURE**- DIRECT CONTACT MAY CAUSE PAIN, HYPEREMIA, LACRIMATION, TWITCHING OF THE EYELIDS, MIOSIS, AND CILIARY MUSCLE SPASM WITH LOSS OF ACCOMODATION, BLURRED OR DIMMED VISION AND BROWACHE. SOMETIMES MYDRIASIS MAY OCCUR INSTEAD OF MIOSIS. WITH SUFFICIENT EXPOSURE, OTHER SYMPTOMS OF CHOLINESTERASE INHIBITION AS DESCRIBED IN ACUTE INHALATION MAY OCCUR.
CHRONIC EXPOSURE- REPEATED OR PROLONGED EXPOSURE MAY CAUSE EFFECTS AS DESCRIBED IN ACUTE EXPOSURE. SOME COMPOUNDS HAVE CAUSED TOXIC EFFECTS ON THE CRYSTALLINE LENS, CONJUNCTIVAL THICKENING AND OBSTRUCTION OF THE NASOLACRIMAL CANALS WHEN USED AS MIOTIC EYEDROPS.

FIRST AID- IRRIGATE EYES WITH WATER OR SALINE SOLUTION. IF SYMPTOMS OF POISONING OCCUR, TREAT RESPIRATORY DIFFICULTY WITH ARTIFICIAL RESPIRATION AND OXYGEN. OBSERVE PATIENT FOR AT LEAST 24-36 HOURS (GOSSELIN, CLINICAL TOXICOLOGY OF COMMERCIAL PRODUCTS, 5TH ED.). GET MEDICAL ATTENTION IMMEDIATELY. OXYGEN SHOULD BE ADMINISTERED BY QUALIFIED MEDICAL PERSONNEL.

INGESTION: PIRIMIFOS-ETHYL: TOXIC. SEE INFORMATION ON ORGANOPHOSPHATES.
ORGANOPHOSPHATES: CHOLINESTERASE INHIBITOR. **ACUTE EXPOSURE**- WHEN INGESTED, THE FIRST EFFECTS MAY BE NAUSEA, VOMITING, ANOREXIA, ABDOMINAL CRAMPS AND DIARRHEA. GASTROINTESTINAL ABSORPTION MAY CAUSE SYMPTOMS OF CHOLINESTERASE INHIBITION AS DESCRIBED IN ACUTE INHALATION. SYMPTOMS MAY BEGIN WITHIN MINUTES OR BE DELAYED FOR HOURS. DELAYED EFFECTS INCLUDING NEUROPATHY MAY ALSO OCCUR. **CHRONIC EXPOSURE**- REPEATED INGESTION MAY CAUSE EFFECTS AS DESCRIBED IN ACUTE EXPOSURE.

FIRST AID- IF PERSON IS ALERT AND RESPIRATION IS NOT DEPRESSED, GIVE SYRUP OF IPECAC FOLLOWED BY WATER (IF VOMITING OCCURS, KEEP HEAD BELOW HIPS TO PREVENT ASPIRATION). IF CONSCIOUSNESS LEVEL DECLINES OR VOMITING HAS NOT OCCURRED IN 15 MINUTES EMPTY STOMACH BY GASTRIC LAVAGE WITH THE AID OF CUFFED ENDOTRACHEAL TUBE USING ISOTONIC SALINE OR 5% SODIUM BICARBONATE FOLLOW WITH ACTIVATED CHARCOAL. ESTABLISH AND MAINTAIN AIRWAY. TREAT RESPIRATORY DIFFICULTY WITH ARTIFICIAL RESPIRATION AND OXYGEN. DO NOT GIVE MORPHINE, AMINOPHYLLINE, PHENOTHIAZINES, RESERPINE, FUROSEMIDE, OR ETHACRYNIC ACID (MORGAN, RECOGNITION AND MANAGEMENT OF PESTICIDE POISONINGS, 3RD ED.). TREAT SYMPTOMATICALLY AND SUPPORTIVELY. ADMINISTRATION OF OXYGEN AND LAVAGE MUST BE PERFORMED BY QUALIFIED MEDICAL PERSONNEL. GET MEDICAL ATTENTION IMMEDIATELY.

ANTIDOTE: THE FOLLOWING ANTIDOTE(S) HAVE BEEN RECOMMENDED. HOWEVER, THE DECISION AS TO WHETHER THE SEVERITY OF POISONING REQUIRES ADMINISTRATION OF ANY ANTIDOTE AND ACTUAL DOSE REQUIRED SHOULD BE MADE BY QUALIFIED MEDICAL PERSONNEL.
FOR CHOLINESTERASE INHIBITORS: ESTABLISH CLEAR AIRWAY AND TISSUE OXYGENATION BY ASPIRATION OF SECRETIONS, AND IF NECESSARY, BY ASSISTED PULMONARY VENTILATION WITH OXYGEN. IMPROVE TISSUE OXYGENATION AS MUCH AS POSSIBLE BEFORE ADMINISTERING ATROPINE TO MINIMIZE THE RISK OF VENTRICULAR FIBRILLATION. ADMINISTER ATROPINE SULFATE INTRAVENOUSLY, OR INTRAMUSCULARLY IF IV INJECTION IS NOT POSSIBLE. IN MODERATELY SEVERE POISONING ADMINISTER ATROPINE SULFATE, 0.4-2.0 MG REPEATED EVERY 15 MINUTES UNTIL ATROPINIZATION IS ACHIEVED (TACHYCARDIA, FLUSHING, DRY MOUTH, MYDRIASIS). MAINTAIN ATROPINIZATION BY REPEATED DOSES FOR 2-12 HOURS, OR LONGER, DEPENDING ON THE SEVERITY OF POISONING. THE APPEARANCE OF RALES IN THE LUNG BASES, MIOSIS, SALIVATION, NAUSEA, BRADYCARDIA, ARE ALL INDICATIONS OF INADEQUATE ATROPINIZATION. SEVERELY POISONED INDIVIDUALS MAY EXHIBIT REMARKABLE TOLERANCE TO ATROPINE; TWO OR MORE TIMES THE DOSAGES SUGGESTED ABOVE MAY BE NEEDED. PERSONS NOT POISONED OR ONLY SLIGHTLY POISONED, HOWEVER, MAY DEVELOP SIGNS OF ATROPINE TOXICITY FROM SUCH LARGE DOSAGES: FEVER, MUSCLE FIBRILLATIONS, AND DELIRIUM ARE THE MAIN SIGNS OF ATROPINE TOXICITY. IF THESE SIGNS APPEAR WHILE THE PATIENT IS FULLY ATROPINIZED, ATROPINE ADMINISTRATION SHOULD BE DISCONTINUED, AT LEAST TEMPORARILY. OBSERVE TREATED PATIENTS CLOSELY AT LEAST 24 HOURS TO INSURE THAT SYMPTOMS (POSSIBLY PULMONARY EDEMA) DO NOT RECUR AS ATROPINIZATION WEARS OFF. IN VERY SEVERE POISONINGS, METABOLIC DISPOSITION OF TOXICANT MAY REQUIRE SEVERAL HOURS OR DAYS DURING WHICH ATROPINIZATION MUST BE MAINTAINED. MARKEDLY LOWER LEVELS OF URINARY METABOLITES INDICATE THAT ATROPINE DOSAGE CAN BE TAPERED OFF. AS DOSAGE IS REDUCED, CHECK THE LUNG BASES FREQUENTLY FOR RALES. IF RALES ARE HEARD OR OTHER SYMPTOMS RETURN, RE-ESTABLISH ATROPINIZATION PROMPTLY (MORGAN, RECOGNITION AND MANAGEMENT OF PESTICIDE POISONINGS, 3RD ED.). ADMINISTRATION OF ANTIDOTE MUST BE PERFORMED BY QUALIFIED MEDICAL PERSONNEL.
IN CASES OF SEVERE POISONING BY ORGANOPHOSPHATE PESTICIDES IN WHICH RESPIRATORY DEPRESSION, MUSCLE WEAKNESS AND TWITCHINGS ARE SEVERE, GIVE PRALIDOXIME (PROTOPAM-AYERST, 2-PAM), 1.0 GRAM INTRAVENOUSLY AT NO MORE THAN 0.5 GRAM PER MINUTE. DOSAGE OF PRALIDOXIME MAY BE REPEATED IN 1-2 HOURS, THEN AT 10-12 HOUR INTERVALS IF NEEDED. IN VERY SEVERE POISONINGS, DOSAGE RATES MAY BE DOUBLED. TREATMENT WITH PRALIDOXIME WILL BE MOST EFFECTIVE IF GIVEN WITHIN THIRTY-SIX HOURS AFTER POISONING (MORGAN, RECOGNITION AND MANAGEMENT OF PESTICIDE POISONINGS, 3RD ED.). ANTIDOTE SHOULD BE ADMINISTERED BY QUALIFIED MEDICAL PERSONNEL.

REACTIVITY

REACTIVITY: STABLE AT ROOM TEMPERATURE BUT DECOMPOSES AT ELEVATED TEMPERATURES (WITHIN 5 DAYS AT 80 C). AT ROOM TEMPERATURE, UNSTABILIZED FORM REARRANGES TO FORM THE O,S-DIETHYL FORM.

INCOMPATIBILITIES: PIRIMIFOS-ETHYL: ACIDIC CONDITIONS: MAY BE HYDROLYZED. ALKALINE CONDITIONS: MAY BE HYDROLYZED. IRON: MAY BE CORROSIVE. OXIDIZERS (STRONG): FIRE AND EXPLOSION HAZARD. TINPLATE: MAY BE CORROSIVE.

DECOMPOSITION: THERMAL DECOMPOSITION PRODUCTS MAY INCLUDE TOXIC AND HAZARDOUS FUMES OF SULFUR, NITROGEN AND PHOSPHORUS.

POLYMERIZATION: HAZARDOUS POLYMERIZATION HAS NOT BEEN REPORTED TO OCCUR UNDER NORMAL TEMPERATURES AND PRESSURES.

STORAGE AND DISPOSAL

OBSERVE ALL FEDERAL, STATE AND LOCAL REGULATIONS WHEN STORING OR DISPOSING OF THIS SUBSTANCE. FOR ASSISTANCE, CONTACT THE DISTRICT DIRECTOR OF THE ENVIRONMENTAL PROTECTION AGENCY.

****STORAGE****

STORE IN ACCORDANCE WITH 40 CFR 165 RECOMMENDED PROCEDURES FOR THE DISPOSAL AND STORAGE OF PESTICIDES AND PESTICIDE CONTAINERS.
STORE AWAY FROM INCOMPATIBLE SUBSTANCES.
THRESHOLD PLANNING QUANTITY (TPQ): THE SUPERFUND AMENDMENTS AND REAUTHORIZATION ACT (SARA) SECTION 302 REQUIRES THAT EACH FACILITY WHERE ANY EXTREMELY HAZARDOUS SUBSTANCE IS PRESENT IN A QUANTITY EQUAL TO OR GREATER THAN THE TPQ ESTABLISHED FOR THAT SUBSTANCE NOTIFY THE STATE EMERGENCY RESPONSE COMMISSION FOR THE STATE IN WHICH IT IS LOCATED. SECTION 303 OF SARA REQUIRES THESE FACILITIES TO PARTICIPATE IN LOCAL EMERGENCY RESPONSE PLANNING (40 CFR 355.30).

****DISPOSAL****

DISPOSAL MUST BE IN ACCORDANCE WITH 40 CFR 165 RECOMMENDED PROCEDURES FOR THE DISPOSAL AND STORAGE OF PESTICIDES AND PESTICIDE CONTAINERS.

CONDITIONS TO AVOID

NONE REPORTED.

SPILL AND LEAK PROCEDURES

OCCUPATIONAL SPILL: STOP LEAK IF YOU CAN DO IT WITHOUT RISK. FOR SMALL SPILLS, TAKE UP WITH SAND OR OTHER ABSORBENT MATERIAL AND PLACE INTO CLEAN, DRY CONTAINERS FOR LATER DISPOSAL. KEEP UNNECESSARY PEOPLE AWAY. ISOLATE HAZARD AREA AND DENY ENTRY.
REPORTABLE QUANTITY (RQ): 1 POUND THE SUPERFUND AMENDMENTS AND REAUTHORIZATION ACT (SARA) SECTION 304 REQUIRES THAT A RELEASE EQUAL TO OR GREATER THAN THE REPORTABLE QUANTITY FOR THIS SUBSTANCE BE IMMEDIATELY REPORTED TO THE LOCAL EMERGENCY PLANNING COMMITTEE AND THE STATE EMERGENCY RESPONSE COMMISSION (40 CFR 355.40). IF THE RELEASE OF THIS SUBSTANCE IS REPORTABLE UNDER CERCLA SECTION 103, THE NATIONAL RESPONSE CENTER MUST BE NOTIFIED IMMEDIATELY AT (800) 424-8802 OR (202) 426-2675 IN THE METROPOLITAN WASHINGTON, D.C. AREA (40 CFR 302.6).

PROTECTIVE EQUIPMENT

VENTILATION: PROVIDE LOCAL EXHAUST OR PROCESS ENCLOSURE VENTILATION SYSTEM.

RESPIRATOR: THE FOLLOWING RESPIRATORS ARE RECOMMENDED BASED ON INFORMATION FOUND IN THE PHYSICAL DATA, TOXICITY AND HEALTH EFFECTS SECTIONS. THEY ARE RANKED IN ORDER FROM MINIMUM TO MAXIMUM RESPIRATORY PROTECTION. THE SPECIFIC RESPIRATOR SELECTED MUST BE BASED ON CONTAMINATION LEVELS FOUND IN THE WORK PLACE, MUST NOT EXCEED THE WORKING LIMITS OF THE RESPIRATOR AND BE JOINTLY APPROVED BY THE NATIONAL INSTITUTE FOR OCCUPATIONAL SAFETY AND HEALTH AND THE MINE SAFETY AND HEALTH ADMINISTRATION (NIOSH-MSHA).
TYPE 'C' SUPPLIED-AIR RESPIRATOR WITH A FULL FACEPIECE OPERATED IN PRESSURE-DEMAND OR OTHER POSITIVE PRESSURE MODE OR WITH A FULL FACEPIECE, HELMET OR HOOD OPERATED IN CONTINOUS-FLOW MODE.
SELF-CONTAINED BREATHING APPARATUS WITH A FULL FACEPIECE OPERATED IN PRESSURE-DEMAND OR OTHER POSITIVE PRESSURE MODE.
FOR FIREFIGHTING AND OTHER IMMEDIATELY DANGEROUS TO LIFE OR HEALTH CONDITIONS:
SELF-CONTAINED BREATHING APPARATUS WITH FULL FACEPIECE OPERATED IN PRESSURE-DEMAND OR OTHER POSITIVE PRESSURE MODE.
SUPPLIED-AIR RESPIRATOR WITH FULL FACEPIECE AND OPERATED IN PRESSURE-DEMAND OR OTHER POSITIVE PRESSURE MODE IN COMBINATION WITH AN AUXILIARY SELF-CONTAINED BREATHING APPARATUS OPERATED IN PRESSURE-DEMAND OR OTHER POSITIVE PRESSURE MODE.

CLOTHING: EMPLOYEE MUST WEAR APPROPRIATE PROTECTIVE (IMPERVIOUS) CLOTHING AND EQUIPMENT TO PREVENT ANY POSSIBILITY OF SKIN CONTACT WITH THIS SUBSTANCE.

GLOVES: EMPLOYEE MUST WEAR APPROPRIATE PROTECTIVE GLOVES TO PREVENT CONTACT WITH THIS SUBSTANCE.

EYE PROTECTION: EMPLOYEE MUST WEAR SPLASH-PROOF OR DUST-RESISTANT SAFETY GOGGLES AND A FACESHIELD TO PREVENT CONTACT WITH THIS SUBSTANCE.
EMERGENCY WASH FACILITIES: WHERE THERE IS ANY POSSIBILITY THAT AN EMPLOYEE'S EYES AND/OR SKIN MAY BE EXPOSED TO THIS SUBSTANCE, THE EMPLOYER SHOULD PROVIDE AN EYE WASH FOUNTAIN AND QUICK DRENCH SHOWER WITHIN THE IMMEDIATE WORK AREA FOR EMERGENCY USE.

AUTHORIZED BY- OCCUPATIONAL HEALTH SERVICES, INC.
CREATION DATE: 10/04/89 ***REVISION DATE:*** 04/30/90

MATERIAL SAFETY DATA SHEET

OCCUPATIONAL HEALTH SERVICES, INC.
AGRICULTURE AND PESTICIDE DIVISION
450 SEVENTH AVENUE, SUITE 2407
NEW YORK, NEW YORK 10123
1-800-445-MSDS OR (212) 967-1100

EMERGENCY CONTACT:
JOHN S. BRANSFORD, JR. (615) 292-1180

SUBSTANCE IDENTIFICATION

CAS-NUMBER 29232-93-7

SUBSTANCE: PIRIMIFOS-METHYL

TRADE NAMES/SYNONYMS: PHOSPHOROTHIOIC ACID, O-(2-(DIETHYLAMINO)-6-METHYL-4-PYRIMIDINYL) O,O-DIMETHYL ESTER; O-O-DIMETHYL-O-(2-DIETHYLAMINO-6-METHYL-4-PIRIMIDINYL)PHOSPHOROTHIOATE; DIMETHYL 2-DIETHYLAMINO-4-METHYLPYRIMIDIN-6-YL PHOSPHOROTHIONATE; ACETELLIC; ENT 27699GC; METHYLPIRIMIPHOS; METHYL PYRIMIPHOS; PIRIMIPHOS ME; PLANT PROTECTION PP511; PP 511; PYRIDIMINE PHOSPHATE; PYRIMIPHOS METHYL; PST72378

CHEMICAL FAMILY: PYRIMIDINE PHOSPHOROTHIOATE

MOLECULAR FORMULA: C11-H20-N3-O3-P-S

MOLECULAR WEIGHT: 305.37

CERCLA RATINGS (SCALE 0-3): HEALTH=2 FIRE=U REACTIVITY=0 PERSISTENCE=2

NFPA RATINGS (SCALE 0-4): HEALTH=2 FIRE=U REACTIVITY=0

COMPONENTS AND CONTAMINANTS

COMPONENT: PRIMIPHOS-METHYL ***PERCENT:*** 100.0
CAS# 29232-93-7

OTHER CONTAMINANTS: NONE

EXPOSURE LIMITS: NO OCCUPATIONAL EXPOSURE LIMITS ESTABLISHED BY OSHA, ACGIH, OR NIOSH.

PHYSICAL DATA

DESCRIPTION: STRAW COLORED LIQUID

BOILING POINT: DECOMPOSES ABOVE 212 F (100 C)

MELTING POINT: 59-64 F (15-18 C) ***SPECIFIC GRAVITY:*** 1.157 @ 30 C

VAPOR PRESSURE: 0.0001 MMHG @ 30 C ***EVAPORATION RATE:*** NOT AVAILABLE

SOLUBILITY IN WATER: 5 PPM

SOLVENT SOLUBILITY: MISCIBLE IN MOST ORGANIC SOLVENTS

FIRE AND EXPLOSION DATA

FIRE AND EXPLOSION HAZARD: UNKNOWN FIRE AND EXPLOSION HAZARD.

FIREFIGHTING MEDIA: DRY CHEMICAL, CARBON DIOXIDE, WATER SPRAY OR FOAM FOR LARGER FIRES, USE WATER SPRAY, FOG OR ALCOHOL FOAM

FIREFIGHTING: MOVE CONTAINER FROM FIRE AREA IF POSSIBLE. DO NOT SCATTER SPILLED MATERIAL WITH MORE WATER THAN NEEDED FOR FIRE CONTROL. DIKE FIRE CONTROL WATER FOR LATER DISPOSAL
USE AGENTS SUITABLE FOR TYPE OF SURROUNDING FIRE. AVOID BREATHING HAZARDOUS VAPORS, KEEP UPWIND.

TOXICITY

PIRIMIFOS-METHYL: TOXICITY DATA: 1250 MG/KG ORAL-RAT LD50; 1180 MG/KG ORAL-MOUSE LD50; 1150 MG/KG ORAL-RABBIT LD50; 1000 MG/KG ORAL-GUINEA PIG LD50; 1180 MG/KG UNREPORTED-MOUSE LD50; MUTAGENIC DATA (RTECS). CARCINOGEN STATUS: NONE. ACUTE TOXICITY LEVEL: MODERATELY TOXIC BY INGESTION. TARGET EFFECTS: CHOLINESTERASE INHIBITOR. POISONING MAY

AFFECT THE NERVOUS SYSTEM.* AT INCREASED RISK FROM EXPOSURE: PERSONS WITH RESPIRATORY AILMENTS, RECENT EXPOSURE TO CHOLINESTERASE INHIBITORS OR IMPAIRED CHOLINESTERASE PRODUCTION, OR LIVER MALFUNCTION.* ADDITIONAL DATA: MAY CROSS THE PLACENTA. HIGH ENVIRONMENTAL TEMPERATURES OR EXPOSURE OF THE CHEMICAL TO VISIBLE OR ULTRAVIOLET LIGHT MAY ENHANCE THE TOXICITY. INTERACTIONS WITH MEDICATIONS MAY OCCUR.*

* MAY BE BASED ON GENERAL INFORMATION ON ORGANOPHOSPHATES.

HEALTH EFFECTS AND FIRST AID

INHALATION: PIRIMIFOS-METHYL: SEE INFORMATION ON ORGANOPHOSPHATES. ORGANOPHOSPHATES: CHOLINESTERASE INHIBITOR. **ACUTE EXPOSURE**- WHEN INHALED, THE FIRST EFFECTS OF CHOLINESTERASE INHIBITORS ARE USUALLY RESPIRATORY AND MAY INCLUDE NASAL HYPEREMIA AND WATERY DISCHARGE, COUGH, CHEST DISCOMFORT, DYSPNEA, AND WHEEZING DUE TO INCREASED BRONCHIAL SECRETIONS AND BRONCHOCONSTRICTION. IF SUFFICIENT AMOUNTS ARE ABSORBED, OTHER SYSTEMIC EFFECTS MAY BEGIN WITHIN A FEW MINUTES OR BE DELAYED FOR UP TO 12 HOURS. SYMPTOMS MAY INCLUDE PALLOR, NAUSEA, VOMITING, DIARRHEA, ABDOMINAL CRAMPS, HEADACHE, DIZZINESS, OCULAR PAIN, BLURRED VISION, MIOSIS OR IN SOME CASES, ESPECIALLY INITIALLY, MYDRIASIS, LACRIMATION, SALIVATION, SWEATING, AND CONFUSION. OTHER REPORTED CENTRAL NERVOUS SYSTEM OR NEUROMUSCULAR EFFECTS MAY INCLUDE ATAXIA, SLURRED SPEECH, AREFLEXIA, WEAKNESS, FATIGUE, FASCICULATIONS, TWITCHING, TREMORS POSSIBLY OF THE TONGUE AND EYELIDS, AND EVENTUALLY PARALYSIS OF THE EXTREMITIES AND POSSIBLY OF THE RESPIRATORY MUSCLES. IN SEVERE CASES THERE MAY ALSO BE INVOLUNTARY DEFECATION AND URINATION, CYANOSIS, PSYCHOSIS, HYPERGLYCEMIA, ACUTE PANCREATITIS, CARDIAC IRREGULARITIES, PULMONARY EDEMA, UNCONSCIOUSNESS, CONVULSIONS, AND COMA. DEATH IS PRIMARILY DUE TO RESPIRATORY FAILURE, ALTHOUGH CARDIOVASCULAR EFFECTS INCLUDING CARDIAC ARREST MAY ALSO BE IMPLICATED. LONG TERM SEQUELAE ARE RARE BUT MAY INCLUDE NEUROPSYCHIATRIC DISORDERS AND MYOPATHY WITH MUSCLE TENDERNESS. SOME ORGANOPHOSPHATES MAY CAUSE A DELAYED NEUROPATHY BEGINNING 1-4 WEEKS AFTER AN ACUTE EXPOSURE WHICH MAY OR MAY NOT HAVE CAUSED ACUTE CHOLINERGIC EFFECTS. NUMBNESS, TINGLING, WEAKNESS AND CRAMPING BEGINNING SYMMETRICALLY IN THE LOWER LIMBS MAY PROGRESS TO ATAXIA AND PARALYSIS. IN SEVERE CASES, UPPER LIMB INVOLVEMENT IS POSSIBLE AND FLACCID PARALYSIS MAY PROGRESS TO SPASTIC PARALYSIS WITH EXAGGERATED REFLEXES. IMPROVEMENT MAY OCCUR OVER MONTHS TO YEARS, BUT SOME RESIDUAL IMPAIRMENT USUALLY REMAINS. **CHRONIC EXPOSURE**- REPEATED OR PROLONGED EXPOSURE MAY RESULT IN THE EFFECTS OF ACUTE EXPOSURE INCLUDING THE DELAYED NEUROPATHY. OTHER EFFECTS REPORTED IN WORKERS REPEATEDLY EXPOSED INCLUDE IMPAIRED MEMORY AND CONCENTRATION, ACUTE PSYCHOSIS, SEVERE DEPRESSIONS, IRRITABILTY, CONFUSION, APATHY, EMOTIONAL LABILITY, SOCIAL WITHDRAWAL, CONFUSION, HEADACHE, SPEECH DIFFICULTIES, DELAYED REACTION TIMES, SPATIAL DISORIENTATION, NIGHTMARES, SLEEPWALKING, AND DROWSINESS OR INSOMNIA. AN INFLUENZA-LIKE CONDITION WITH HEADACHE, NAUSEA, WEAKNESS, ANOREXIA AND MALAISE HAS ALSO BEEN REPORTED.

FIRST AID- REMOVE FROM EXPOSURE AREA TO FRESH AIR IMMEDIATELY. IF BREATHING HAS STOPPED, GIVE ARTIFICIAL RESPIRATION. MAINTAIN AIRWAY AND BLOOD PRESSURE AND ADMINISTER OXYGEN IF AVAILABLE. KEEP AFFECTED PERSON WARM AND AT REST. TREAT SYMPTOMATICALLY AND SUPPORTIVELY. ADMINISTRATION OF OXYGEN SHOULD BE PERFORMED BY QUALIFIED PERSONNEL. GET MEDICAL ATTENTION IMMEDIATELY.

SKIN CONTACT: PIRIMIFOS-METHYL:
THIS MATERIAL DID NOT PRODUCED IRRITATION OR SENSITIZATION IN RATS OR GUINEA PIGS. SEE INFORMATION ON ORGANOPHOSPHATES. ORGANOPHOSPHATES: CHOLINESTERASE INHIBITOR. **ACUTE EXPOSURE**- LOCALIZED SWEATING AND FASCICULATIONS MAY OCCUR AT THE SITE OF CONTACT. IF SUFFICIENT AMOUNTS ARE ABSORBED, OTHER EFFECTS OF CHOLINESTERASE INHIBITION AS DESCRIBED IN ACUTE INHALATION MAY OCCUR. SYMPTOMS MAY BE DELAYED 2-3 HOURS, BUT USUALLY NO MORE THAN 12 HOURS. THE RATE OF ABSORPTION IS INCREASED BY THE PRESENCE OF DERMATITIS OR HIGH AMBIENT TEMPERATURES. DELAYED NEUROPATHY IS ALSO POSSIBLE. **CHRONIC EXPOSURE**- REPEATED OR PROLONGED EXPOSURE MAY CAUSE EFFECTS AS DESCRIBED IN ACUTE EXPOSURE. SOME ORGANOPHOSPHATES MAY CAUSE SENSITIZATION.

FIRST AID- REMOVE CONTAMINATED CLOTHING IMMEDIATELY. WASH CONTAMINATED AREAS WITH SOAP AND WATER FOLLOWED BY ALCOHOL (ARENA, POISONING, 4TH ED.). EMERGENCY PERSONNEL SHOULD WEAR GLOVES AND AVOID CONTAMINATION. TREAT RESPIRATORY DIFFICULTY WITH ARTIFICIAL RESPIRATION. GET MEDICAL ATTENTION IMMEDIATELY.

EYE CONTACT: PIRIMIFOS-METHYL:
PIRIMIFOS-METHYL WAS NOT IRRITATING NOR DID IT CAUSE MIOSIS WHEN AN UNDILUTED DROP WAS PLACED IN THE CONJUNCTIVAL SAC OF RABBIT EYES. SEE INFORMATION ON ORGANOPHOSPHATES.
ORGANOPHOSPHATES: CHOLINESTERASE INHIBITOR. **ACUTE EXPOSURE**- DIRECT CONTACT MAY CAUSE PAIN, HYPEREMIA, LACRIMATION, TWITCHING OF THE EYELIDS, MIOSIS, AND CILIARY MUSCLE SPASM WITH LOSS OF ACCOMODATION, BLURRED OR DIMMED VISION AND BROWACHE. SOMETIMES MYDRIASIS MAY OCCUR INSTEAD OF MIOSIS. WITH SUFFICIENT EXPOSURE, OTHER SYMPTOMS OF CHOLINESTERASE INHIBITION AS DESCRIBED IN ACUTE INHALATION MAY OCCUR. **CHRONIC EXPOSURE**- REPEATED OR PROLONGED EXPOSURE MAY CAUSE EFFECTS AS DESCRIBED IN ACUTE EXPOSURE. SOME COMPOUNDS HAVE CAUSED TOXIC EFFECTS ON THE CRYSTALLINE LENS, CONJUNCTIVAL THICKENING AND OBSTRUCTION OF THE NASOLACRIMAL CANALS WHEN USED AS MIOTIC EYEDROPS.

FIRST AID- IRRIGATE EYES WITH WATER OR SALINE SOLUTION. IF SYMPTOMS OF POISONING OCCUR, TREAT RESPIRATORY DIFFICULTY WITH ARTIFICIAL RESPIRATION AND OXYGEN. OBSERVE PATIENT FOR AT LEAST 24-36 HOURS (GOSSELIN, CLINICAL TOXICOLOGY OF COMMERCIAL PRODUCTS, 5TH ED.). GET MEDICAL ATTENTION IMMEDIATELY. OXYGEN SHOULD BE ADMINISTERED BY QUALIFIED MEDICAL PERSONNEL.

INGESTION: PIRIMIFOS-METHYL: SEE INFORMATION ON ORGANOPHOSPHATES. ORGANOPHOSPHATES: CHOLINESTERASE INHIBITOR. **ACUTE EXPOSURE**- WHEN INGESTED, THE FIRST EFFECTS MAY BE NAUSEA, VOMITING, ANOREXIA, ABDOMINAL CRAMPS AND DIARRHEA. GASTROINTESTINAL ABSORPTION MAY CAUSE SYMPTOMS OF CHOLINESTERASE INHIBITION AS DESCRIBED IN ACUTE INHALATION. SYMPTOMS MAY BEGIN WITHIN MINUTES OR BE DELAYED FOR HOURS. DELAYED EFFECTS INCLUDING NEUROPATHY MAY ALSO OCCUR. **CHRONIC EXPOSURE**- REPEATED INGESTION MAY CAUSE EFFECTS AS DESCRIBED IN ACUTE EXPOSURE.

FIRST AID- IF PERSON IS ALERT AND RESPIRATION IS NOT DEPRESSED, GIVE SYRUP OF IPECAC FOLLOWED BY WATER (IF VOMITING OCCURS, KEEP HEAD BELOW HIPS TO PREVENT ASPIRATION). IF CONSCIOUSNESS LEVEL DECLINES OR VOMITING HAS NOT OCCURRED IN 15 MINUTES EMPTY STOMACH BY GASTRIC LAVAGE WITH THE AID OF CUFFED ENDOTRACHEAL TUBE USING ISOTONIC SALINE OR 5% SODIUM BICARBONATE FOLLOW WITH ACTIVATED CHARCOAL. ESTABLISH AND MAINTAIN AIRWAY. TREAT RESPIRATORY DIFFICULTY WITH ARTIFICIAL RESPIRATION AND OXYGEN. DO NOT GIVE MORPHINE, AMINOPHYLLINE, PHENOTHIAZINES, RESERPINE, FUROSEMIDE, OR ETHACRYNIC ACID (MORGAN, RECOGNITION AND MANAGEMENT OF PESTICIDE POISONINGS, 3RD ED.). TREAT SYMPTOMATICALLY AND SUPPORTIVELY. ADMINISTRATION OF OXYGEN AND LAVAGE MUST BE PERFORMED BY QUALIFIED MEDICAL PERSONNEL. GET MEDICAL ATTENTION IMMEDIATELY.

ANTIDOTE: THE FOLLOWING ANTIDOTE(S) HAVE BEEN RECOMMENDED. HOWEVER, THE DECISION AS TO WHETHER THE SEVERITY OF POISONING REQUIRES ADMINISTRATION OF ANY ANTIDOTE AND ACTUAL DOSE REQUIRED SHOULD BE MADE BY QUALIFIED MEDICAL PERSONNEL.
FOR CHOLINESTERASE INHIBITORS: ESTABLISH CLEAR AIRWAY AND TISSUE OXYGENATION BY ASPIRATION OF SECRETIONS, AND IF NECESSARY, BY ASSISTED PULMONARY VENTILATION WITH OXYGEN. IMPROVE TISSUE OXYGENATION AS MUCH AS POSSIBLE BEFORE ADMINISTERING ATROPINE TO MINIMIZE THE RISK OF VENTRICULAR FIBRILLATION. ADMINISTER ATROPINE SULFATE INTRAVENOUSLY, OR INTRAMUSCULARLY IF IV INJECTION IS NOT POSSIBLE. IN MODERATELY SEVERE POISONING ADMINISTER ATROPINE SULFATE, 0.4-2.0 MG REPEATED EVERY 15 MINUTES UNTIL ATROPINIZATION IS ACHIEVED (TACHYCARDIA, FLUSHING, DRY MOUTH, MYDRIASIS). MAINTAIN ATROPINIZATION BY REPEATED DOSES FOR 2-12 HOURS, OR LONGER, DEPENDING ON THE SEVERITY OF POISONING. THE APPEARANCE OF RALES IN THE LUNG BASES, MIOSIS, SALIVATION, NAUSEA, BRADYCARDIA, ARE ALL INDICATIONS OF INADEQUATE ATROPINIZATION. SEVERELY POISONED INDIVIDUALS MAY EXHIBIT REMARKABLE TOLERANCE TO ATROPINE; TWO OR MORE TIMES THE DOSAGES SUGGESTED ABOVE MAY BE NEEDED. PERSONS NOT POISONED OR ONLY SLIGHTLY POISONED, HOWEVER, MAY DEVELOP SIGNS OF ATROPINE TOXICITY FROM SUCH LARGE DOSAGES: FEVER, MUSCLE FIBRILLATIONS, AND DELIRIUM ARE THE MAIN SIGNS OF ATROPINE TOXICITY. IF THESE SIGNS APPEAR WHILE THE PATIENT IS FULLY ATROPINIZED, ATROPINE ADMINISTRATION SHOULD BE DISCONTINUED, AT LEAST TEMPORARILY. OBSERVE TREATED PATIENTS CLOSELY AT LEAST 24 HOURS TO INSURE THAT SYMPTOMS (POSSIBLY PULMONARY EDEMA) DO NOT RECUR AS ATROPINIZATION WEARS OFF. IN VERY SEVERE POISONINGS, METABOLIC DISPOSITION OF TOXICANT MAY REQUIRE SEVERAL HOURS OR DAYS DURING WHICH ATROPINIZATION MUST BE MAINTAINED. MARKEDLY LOWER LEVELS OF URINARY METABOLITES INDICATE THAT ATROPINE DOSAGE CAN BE TAPERED OFF. AS DOSAGE IS REDUCED, CHECK THE LUNG BASES FREQUENTLY FOR RALES. IF RALES ARE HEARD OR OTHER SYMPTOMS RETURN, RE-ESTABLISH ATROPINIZATION PROMPTLY (MORGAN, RECOGNITION AND MANAGEMENT OF PESTICIDE POISONINGS, 3RD ED.). ADMINISTRATION OF ANTIDOTE MUST BE PERFORMED BY QUALIFIED MEDICAL PERSONNEL.

IN CASES OF SEVERE POISONING BY ORGANOPHOSPHATE PESTICIDES IN WHICH RESPIRATORY DEPRESSION, MUSCLE WEAKNESS AND TWITCHINGS ARE SEVERE, GIVE PRALIDOXIME (PROTOPAM-AYERST, 2-PAM), 1.0 GRAM INTRAVENOUSLY AT NO MORE THAN 0.5 GRAM PER MINUTE. DOSAGE OF PRALIDOXIME MAY BE REPEATED IN 1-2 HOURS, THEN AT 10-12 HOUR INTERVALS IF NEEDED. IN VERY SEVERE POISONINGS, DOSAGE RATES MAY BE DOUBLED. TREATMENT WITH PRALIDOXIME WILL BE MOST EFFECTIVE IF GIVEN WITHIN THIRTY-SIX HOURS AFTER POISONING (MORGAN, RECOGNITION AND MANAGEMENT OF PESTICIDE POISONINGS, 3RD ED.). ANTIDOTE SHOULD BE ADMINISTERED BY QUALIFIED MEDICAL PERSONNEL.

REACTIVITY

REACTIVITY: STORAGE OF UNSTABILIZED PIRIMIPHOS-METHYL AT ELEVATED TEMPERATURES LEADS TO A VARIETY OF DEPHOSPHORYLATED PRODUCTS.

INCOMPATIBILITIES: PIRIMIFOS-METHYL: ACIDIC CONDITIONS: HYDROLYSIS. ALKALINE CONDITIONS: HYDROLYSIS. STEEL: CORROSIVE. UNPROTECTED TINPLATE: CORROSIVE.

DECOMPOSITION: THERMAL DECOMPOSITION PRODUCTS MAY INCLUDE TOXIC AND HAZARDOUS FUMES OF SULFUR, NITROGEN AND PHOSPHORUS.

POLYMERIZATION: HAZARDOUS POLYMERIZATION HAS NOT BEEN REPORTED TO OCCUR UNDER NORMAL TEMPERATURES AND PRESSURES.

STORAGE AND DISPOSAL

OBSERVE ALL FEDERAL, STATE AND LOCAL REGULATIONS WHEN STORING OR DISPOSING OF THIS SUBSTANCE. FOR ASSISTANCE, CONTACT THE DISTRICT DIRECTOR OF THE ENVIRONMENTAL PROTECTION AGENCY.

STORAGE

STORE IN ACCORDANCE WITH 40 CFR 165 RECOMMENDED PROCEDURES FOR THE DISPOSAL AND STORAGE OF PESTICIDES AND PESTICIDE CONTAINERS.
STORE AWAY FROM INCOMPATIBLE SUBSTANCES.

DISPOSAL

DISPOSAL MUST BE IN ACCORDANCE WITH 40 CFR 165 RECOMMENDED PROCEDURES FOR THE DISPOSAL AND STORAGE OF PESTICIDES AND PESTICIDE CONTAINERS.

CONDITIONS TO AVOID

NONE REPORTED.

SPILL AND LEAK PROCEDURES

OCCUPATIONAL SPILL: STOP LEAK IF YOU CAN DO IT WITHOUT RISK. FOR SMALL SPILLS, TAKE UP WITH SAND OR OTHER ABSORBENT MATERIAL AND PLACE INTO CLEAN, DRY CONTAINERS FOR LATER DISPOSAL. KEEP UNNECESSARY PEOPLE AWAY. ISOLATE HAZARD AREA AND DENY ENTRY.

PROTECTIVE EQUIPMENT

VENTILATION: PROVIDE LOCAL EXHAUST OR GENERAL DILUTION VENTILATION SYSTEM.

RESPIRATOR: THE FOLLOWING RESPIRATORS ARE RECOMMENDED BASED ON INFORMATION FOUND IN THE PHYSICAL DATA, TOXICITY AND HEALTH EFFECTS SECTIONS. THEY ARE RANKED IN ORDER FROM MINIMUM TO MAXIMUM RESPIRATORY PROTECTION. THE SPECIFIC RESPIRATOR SELECTED MUST BE BASED ON CONTAMINATION LEVELS FOUND IN THE WORK PLACE, MUST NOT EXCEED THE WORKING LIMITS OF THE RESPIRATOR AND BE JOINTLY APPROVED BY THE NATIONAL INSTITUTE FOR OCCUPATIONAL SAFETY AND HEALTH AND THE MINE SAFETY AND HEALTH ADMINISTRATION (NIOSH-MSHA).
CHEMICAL CARTRIDGE RESPIRATOR WITH PESTICIDE CARTRIDGE.
GAS MASK WITH A PESTICIDE CANISTER (CHIN-STYLE OR FRONT- OR BACK-MOUNTED CANISTER). TYPE 'C' SUPPLIED-AIR RESPIRATOR OPERATED IN THE PRESSURE-DEMAND OR OTHER POSITIVE PRESSURE OR CONTINUOUS-FLOW MODE.
SELF-CONTAINED BREATHING APPARATUS.
FOR FIREFIGHTING AND OTHER IMMEDIATELY DANGEROUS TO LIFE OR HEALTH CONDITIONS:
SELF-CONTAINED BREATHING APPARATUS WITH FULL FACEPIECE OPERATED IN PRESSURE-DEMAND OR OTHER POSITIVE PRESSURE MODE.
SUPPLIED-AIR RESPIRATOR WITH FULL FACEPIECE AND OPERATED IN PRESSURE-DEMAND OR OTHER POSITIVE PRESSURE MODE IN COMBINATION WITH AN AUXILIARY SELF-CONTAINED BREATHING APPARATUS OPERATED IN PRESSURE-DEMAND OR OTHER POSITIVE PRESSURE MODE.

CLOTHING: EMPLOYEE MUST WEAR APPROPRIATE PROTECTIVE (IMPERVIOUS) CLOTHING AND EQUIPMENT TO PREVENT REPEATED OR PROLONGED SKIN CONTACT WITH THIS SUBSTANCE.

GLOVES: EMPLOYEE MUST WEAR APPROPRIATE PROTECTIVE GLOVES TO PREVENT CONTACT WITH THIS SUBSTANCE.

EYE PROTECTION: EMPLOYEE MUST WEAR SPLASH-PROOF OR DUST-RESISTANT SAFETY GOGGLES TO PREVENT EYE CONTACT WITH THIS SUBSTANCE.
EMERGENCY EYE WASH: WHERE THERE IS ANY POSSIBILITY THAT AN EMPLOYEE'S EYES MAY BE EXPOSED TO THIS SUBSTANCE, THE EMPLOYER SHOULD PROVIDE AN EYE WASH FOUNTAIN WITHIN THE IMMEDIATE WORK AREA FOR EMERGENCY USE.

AUTHORIZED BY- OCCUPATIONAL HEALTH SERVICES, INC.
CREATION DATE: 10/04/89 ***REVISION DATE:*** 04/30/90

MATERIAL SAFETY DATA SHEET

OCCUPATIONAL HEALTH SERVICES, INC.
AGRICULTURE AND PESTICIDE DIVISION
450 SEVENTH AVENUE, SUITE 2407
NEW YORK, NEW YORK 10123
1-800-445-MSDS OR (212) 967-1100

EMERGENCY CONTACT:
JOHN S. BRANSFORD, JR. (615) 292-1180

SUBSTANCE IDENTIFICATION

CAS-NUMBER 28249-77-6

SUBSTANCE: **THIOBENCARB**

TRADE NAMES/SYNONYMS: CARBAMOTHIOIC ACID, DIETHYL-, S-((4-CHLOROPHENYL)METHYL) ESTER; DIETHYLCARBAMOTHIOIC ACID S-((4-CHLOROPHENYL)METHYL) ESTER; CARBAMIC ACID, DIETHYLTHIO-, S-(P-CHLOROBENZYL) ESTER; DIETHYLTHIOCARBAMIC ACID S-(P-CHLOROBENZYL)ESTER; S-4-CHLOROBENZYL DIETHYLTHIOCARBAMATE; S-4-CHLOROBENZYL DIETHYL(THIOCARBAMATE); S-((4-CHLOROPHENYL)METHYL) DIETHYLCARBAMOTHIOATE; S-(P-CHLOROBENZYL)DIETHYLTHIOCARBAMATE; S-(4-CHLOROPHENYL)METHYL DIETHYLCARBAMOTHIOATE; B 3015; BENTHIOCARB; BOLERO; IMC 3950; SATURN; PST72381

CHEMICAL FAMILY: THIOCARBAMATE

MOLECULAR FORMULA: C12-H16-CL-N-O-S

MOLECULAR WEIGHT: 257.8

CERCLA RATINGS (SCALE 0-3): HEALTH=2 FIRE=U REACTIVITY=0 PERSISTENCE=3

NFPA RATINGS (SCALE 0-4): HEALTH=2 FIRE=U REACTIVITY=0

COMPONENTS AND CONTAMINANTS

COMPONENT: THIOBENCARB ***PERCENT:*** 100
CAS# 28249-77-6

OTHER CONTAMINANTS: NONE

EXPOSURE LIMITS: NO OCCUPATIONAL EXPOSURE LIMITS ESTABLISHED BY OSHA, ACGIH, OR NIOSH.

PHYSICAL DATA

DESCRIPTION: PALE YELLOW LIQUID

BOILING POINT: 259-264 F (126-129 C) @ 0.008 MMHG ***MELTING POINT:*** 38 F (3 C)

SPECIFIC GRAVITY: 1.18 ***VAPOR PRESSURE:*** 0.0000015 MMHG @ 25

SOLUBILITY IN WATER: 0.003% @ 20 C

SOLVENT SOLUBILITY: ETHANOL, ACETONE, MOST ORGANIC SOLVENTS

FIRE AND EXPLOSION DATA

FIRE AND EXPLOSION HAZARD: UNKNOWN FIRE AND EXPLOSION HAZARD.

FIREFIGHTING MEDIA: DRY CHEMICAL, CARBON DIOXIDE, WATER SPRAY OR FOAM FOR LARGER FIRES, USE WATER SPRAY, FOG OR ALCOHOL FOAM

FIREFIGHTING: MOVE CONTAINER FROM FIRE AREA IF POSSIBLE. DO NOT SCATTER SPILLED MATERIAL WITH MORE WATER THAN NEEDED FOR FIRE CONTROL. DIKE FIRE CONTROL WATER FOR LATER DISPOSAL
USE AGENTS SUITABLE FOR TYPE OF SURROUNDING FIRE. AVOID BREATHING HAZARDOUS VAPORS, KEEP UPWIND.

TOXICITY

THIOBENCARB: TOXICITY DATA: 2900 MG/KG SKIN-RAT LD50; 1300 MG/KG ORAL-RAT LD50; 560 MG/KG ORAL-MOUSE LD50. CARCINOGEN STATUS: NONE. ACUTE TOXICITY LEVEL: MODERATELY TOXIC BY INGESTION AND SLIGHTLY TOXIC BY DERMAL ABSORPTION. TARGET EFFECTS: NO DATA AVAILABLE.

HEALTH EFFECTS AND FIRST AID

INHALATION: THIOBENCARB: **ACUTE EXPOSURE-** INHALATION OF EXCESSIVE AMOUNTS OF SOME THIOCARBAMATES CAUSES SCRATCHY THROAT, SNEEZING, AND COUGHING. **CHRONIC EXPOSURE-** NO DATA AVAILABLE.

FIRST AID- REMOVE FROM EXPOSURE AREA TO FRESH AIR IMMEDIATELY. IF BREATHING HAS STOPPED, PERFORM ARTIFICIAL RESPIRATION. KEEP PERSON

WARM AND AT REST. TREAT SYMPTOMATICALLY AND SUPPORTIVELY. GET MEDICAL ATTENTION IMMEDIATELY.

SKIN CONTACT: THIOBENCARB: **ACUTE EXPOSURE-** A LETHAL DOSE IN RATS BY DERMAL ABSORPTION IS GREATER THAN 2900 MG/KG. SOME THIOCARBAMATES ARE MODERATELY IRRITATING TO THE SKIN. **CHRONIC EXPOSURE-** NO DATA AVAILABLE.
FIRST AID- REMOVE CONTAMINATED CLOTHING AND SHOES IMMEDIATELY. WASH AFFECTED AREA WITH SOAP OR MILD DETERGENT AND LARGE AMOUNTS OF WATER UNTIL NO EVIDENCE OF CHEMICAL REMAINS (APPROXIMATELY 15-20 MINUTES). GET MEDICAL ATTENTION IMMEDIATELY.

EYE CONTACT: THIOBENCARB: **ACUTE EXPOSURE-** SOME THIOCARBAMATES ARE MODERATELY IRRITATING TO THE EYES. **CHRONIC EXPOSURE-** NO DATA AVAILABLE.
FIRST AID- WASH EYES IMMEDIATELY WITH LARGE AMOUNTS OF WATER OR NORMAL SALINE, OCCASIONALLY LIFTING UPPER AND LOWER LIDS, UNTIL NO EVIDENCE OF CHEMICAL REMAINS (APPROXIMATELY 15-20 MINUTES). GET MEDICAL ATTENTION IMMEDIATELY.

INGESTION: THIOBENCARB: **ACUTE EXPOSURE-** A LETHAL DOSE IN RATS WAS 1300 MG/KG. **CHRONIC EXPOSURE-** NO DATA AVAILABLE.
FIRST AID- GIVE SYRUP OF IPECAC, FOLLOWED BY 1-2 GLASSES OF WATER, TO INDUCE VOMITING (ADULTS: 30 ML). FOLLOWING EMESIS, ADMINISTER 30-50 GRAMS ACTIVATED CHARCOAL. FOLLOW CHARCOAL WITH SODIUM OR MAGNESIUM SULFATE, 250 MG/KG, TO REMOVE TOXICANT FROM THE GUT BY CATHARSIS (EPA, RECOGNITION AND MANAGEMENT OF PESTICIDE POISONINGS, 3RD ED.). FIRST AID SHOULD BE ADMINISTERED UNDER THE DIRECTION OF QUALIFIED MEDICAL PERSONNEL. GET MEDICAL ATTENTION.
ANTIDOTE: NO SPECIFIC ANTIDOTE. TREAT SYMPTOMATICALLY AND SUPPORTIVELY.

REACTIVITY

REACTIVITY: STABLE UNDER NORMAL TEMPERATURES AND PRESSURES.
INCOMPATIBILITIES: THIOBENCARB: NO DATA AVAILABLE.
DECOMPOSITION: THERMAL DECOMPOSITION PRODUCTS MAY INCLUDE TOXIC AND HAZARDOUS FUMES OF HYDROGEN CHLORIDE AND OXIDES OF SULFUR AND NITROGEN.
POLYMERIZATION: HAZARDOUS POLYMERIZATION HAS NOT BEEN REPORTED TO OCCUR UNDER NORMAL TEMPERATURES AND PRESSURES.

STORAGE AND DISPOSAL

OBSERVE ALL FEDERAL, STATE AND LOCAL REGULATIONS WHEN STORING OR DISPOSING OF THIS SUBSTANCE. FOR ASSISTANCE, CONTACT THE DISTRICT DIRECTOR OF THE ENVIRONMENTAL PROTECTION AGENCY.

****STORAGE****

STORE IN ACCORDANCE WITH 40 CFR 165 RECOMMENDED PROCEDURES FOR THE DISPOSAL AND STORAGE OF PESTICIDES AND PESTICIDE CONTAINERS.

****DISPOSAL****

DISPOSAL MUST BE IN ACCORDANCE WITH 40 CFR 165 RECOMMENDED PROCEDURES FOR THE DISPOSAL AND STORAGE OF PESTICIDES AND PESTICIDE CONTAINERS.

CONDITIONS TO AVOID

NONE REPORTED.

SPILL AND LEAK PROCEDURES

OCCUPATIONAL SPILL: STOP LEAK IF YOU CAN DO IT WITHOUT RISK. FOR SMALL SPILLS, TAKE UP WITH SAND OR OTHER ABSORBENT MATERIAL AND PLACE INTO CLEAN, DRY CONTAINERS FOR LATER DISPOSAL. KEEP UNNECESSARY PEOPLE AWAY. ISOLATE HAZARD AREA AND DENY ENTRY.

PROTECTIVE EQUIPMENT

VENTILATION: PROVIDE LOCAL EXHAUST VENTILATION SYSTEM.
RESPIRATOR: THE FOLLOWING RESPIRATORS ARE RECOMMENDED BASED ON INFORMATION FOUND IN THE PHYSICAL DATA, TOXICITY AND HEALTH EFFECTS SECTIONS. THEY ARE RANKED IN ORDER FROM MINIMUM TO MAXIMUM RESPIRATORY PROTECTION. THE SPECIFIC RESPIRATOR SELECTED MUST BE BASED ON CONTAMINATION LEVELS FOUND IN THE WORK PLACE, MUST NOT EXCEED THE WORKING LIMITS OF THE RESPIRATOR AND BE JOINTLY APPROVED BY THE NATIONAL INSTITUTE FOR OCCUPATIONAL SAFETY AND HEALTH AND THE MINE SAFETY AND HEALTH ADMINISTRATION (NIOSH-MSHA).
CHEMICAL CARTRIDGE RESPIRATOR WITH FULL FACEPIECE AND PESTICIDE CARTRIDGE.
TYPE 'C' SUPPLIED-AIR RESPIRATOR WITH A FULL FACEPIECE OPERATED IN PRESSURE-DEMAND OR OTHER POSITIVE PRESSURE MODE OR WITH A FULL FACEPIECE, HELMET OR HOOD OPERATED IN CONTINUOUS-FLOW MODE.
SELF-CONTAINED BREATHING APPARATUS OPERATED IN PRESSURE-DEMAND OR OTHER POSITIVE PRESSURE MODE.
FOR FIREFIGHTING AND OTHER IMMEDIATELY DANGEROUS TO LIFE OR HEALTH CONDITIONS:
SELF-CONTAINED BREATHING APPARATUS WITH FULL FACEPIECE OPERATED IN PRESSURE-DEMAND OR OTHER POSITIVE PRESSURE MODE.
SUPPLIED-AIR RESPIRATOR WITH FULL FACEPIECE AND OPERATED IN PRESSURE-DEMAND OR OTHER POSITIVE PRESSURE MODE IN COMBINATION WITH AN AUXILIARY SELF-CONTAINED BREATHING APPARATUS OPERATED IN PRESSURE-DEMAND OR OTHER POSITIVE PRESSURE MODE.
CLOTHING: EMPLOYEE MUST WEAR APPROPRIATE PROTECTIVE (IMPERVIOUS) CLOTHING AND EQUIPMENT TO PREVENT REPEATED OR PROLONGED SKIN CONTACT WITH THIS SUBSTANCE.
GLOVES: EMPLOYEE MUST WEAR APPROPRIATE PROTECTIVE GLOVES TO PREVENT CONTACT WITH THIS SUBSTANCE.
EYE PROTECTION: EMPLOYEE MUST WEAR SPLASH-PROOF OR DUST-RESISTANT SAFETY GOGGLES TO PREVENT EYE CONTACT WITH THIS SUBSTANCE.
EMERGENCY EYE WASH: WHERE THERE IS ANY POSSIBILITY THAT AN EMPLOYEE'S EYES MAY BE EXPOSED TO THIS SUBSTANCE, THE EMPLOYER SHOULD PROVIDE AN EYE WASH FOUNTAIN WITHIN THE IMMEDIATE WORK AREA FOR EMERGENCY USE.

AUTHORIZED BY- OCCUPATIONAL HEALTH SERVICES, INC.
CREATION DATE: 10/05/89 ***REVISION DATE:*** 05/11/90

MATERIAL SAFETY DATA SHEET

OCCUPATIONAL HEALTH SERVICES, INC.
AGRICULTURE AND PESTICIDE DIVISION
450 SEVENTH AVENUE, SUITE 2407
NEW YORK, NEW YORK 10123
1-800-445-MSDS OR (212) 967-1100

EMERGENCY CONTACT:
JOHN S. BRANSFORD, JR. (615) 292-1180

SUBSTANCE IDENTIFICATION

CAS-NUMBER 19666-30-9
SUBSTANCE: **OXADIAZON**
TRADE NAMES/SYNONYMS: 1,3,4-OXADIAZOL-2(3H)-ONE, 3-(2,4-DICHLORO-5-(1-METHYLETHOXY)PHENYL)- 5-(1,1-DIMETHYLETHYL)-; (DELTA)2-1,3,4-OXADIAZOLIN-5-ONE, 2-TERT-BUTYL-4-(2,4-DICHLORO-5- ISOPROPOXYPHENYL)-; 3-(2,4-DICHLORO-5-(1-METHYLETHOXY)PHENYL)-5-(1,1-DIMETHYLETHYL)- 1,3,4-OXADIAZOL-2(3H)-ONE; 2-TERT-BUTYL-4-(2,4-DICHLORO-5-ISOPROPOXYPHENYL)-(DELTA)2-1,3,4- OXADIAZOLIN-5-ONE; 5-TERT-BUTYL-3-(2,4-DICHLORO-5-ISOPROPOXYPHENYL)-1,3,4- OXADIAZOLIN-2-ONE; 5-TERT-BUTYL-3-(2,4-DICHLORO-5-ISOPROPOXYPHENYL)-1,3,4-OXADIAZOL- (2(3H)ONE; OXADIAZONE; RONSTAR; RP 17623; C15H18CL2N2O3; PST72385
CHEMICAL FAMILY: OXAZOLINONE
HALOGEN COMPOUND, AROMATIC
MOLECULAR FORMULA: C15-H18-CL2-N2-O
MOLECULAR WEIGHT: 345.22
CERCLA RATINGS (SCALE 0-3): HEALTH=U FIRE=1 REACTIVITY=0 PERSISTENCE=2
NFPA RATINGS (SCALE 0-4): HEALTH=U FIRE=1 REACTIVITY=0

COMPONENTS AND CONTAMINANTS

COMPONENT: OXADIAZON ***PERCENT:*** 100.0
CAS# 19666-30-9
EXPOSURE LIMITS: NO OCCUPATIONAL EXPOSURE LIMITS ESTABLISHED BY OSHA, ACGIH, OR NIOSH.

PHYSICAL DATA

DESCRIPTION: COLORLESS CRYSTALLINE SOLID.
MELTING POINT: 190-194 F (88-90 C)
SPECIFIC GRAVITY: NOT AVAILABLE ***VAPOR PRESSURE:*** <1 MMHG @ 20 C
SOLUBILITY IN WATER: 0.7 PPM
SOLVENT SOLUBILITY: SOLUBLE IN ACETONE, ACETOPHENONE, ANISOLE, BENZENE, CHLORFORM, TOLUENE, ETHANOL, METHANOL, AND CHLORINATED HYDROCARBONS.

FIRE AND EXPLOSION DATA

FIRE AND EXPLOSION HAZARD: SLIGHT FIRE HAZARD WHEN EXPOSED TO HEAT OR FLAME.

FIREFIGHTING MEDIA: DRY CHEMICAL, CARBON DIOXIDE, HALON, WATER SPRAY OR STANDARD FOAM (1987 EMERGENCY RESPONSE GUIDEBOOK, DOT P 5800.4). FOR LARGER FIRES, USE WATER SPRAY, FOG OR STANDARD FOAM (1987 EMERGENCY RESPONSE GUIDEBOOK, DOT P 5800.4).

FIREFIGHTING: MOVE CONTAINERS FROM FIRE AREA IF POSSIBLE (1987 EMERGENCY RESPONSE GUIDEBOOK, DOT P 5800.4, GUIDE PAGE 53).
EXTINGUISH FIRE USING AGENTS SUITABLE FOR TYPE OF SURROUNDING FIRE. USE WATER IN FLOODING AMOUNTS AS A FOG. AVOID BREATHING DUSTS AND FUMES FROM BURNING MATERIAL; KEEP UPWIND.

TOXICITY

OXADIAZON: TOXICITY DATA: 5200 MG/KG SKIN-RAT LD50; 3500 MG/KG ORAL-RAT LD50. CARCINOGEN STATUS: NONE. ACUTE TOXICITY LEVEL: MODERATELY TOXIC BY INGESTION; SLIGHTLY TOXIC BY DERMAL ABSORPTION. TARGET EFFECTS: NO DATA AVAILABLE.

HEALTH EFFECTS AND FIRST AID

INHALATION: OXADIAZON: **ACUTE EXPOSURE-** NO DATA AVAILABLE. **CHRONIC EXPOSURE-** NO DATA AVAILABLE.

FIRST AID- REMOVE FROM EXPOSURE AREA TO FRESH AIR IMMEDIATELY. IF BREATHING HAS STOPPED, PERFORM ARTIFICIAL RESPIRATION. KEEP PERSON WARM AND AT REST. TREAT SYMPTOMATICALLY AND SUPPORTIVELY. GET MEDICAL ATTENTION IMMEDIATELY.

SKIN CONTACT: OXADIAZON: **ACUTE EXPOSURE-** MAY CAUSE IRRITATION. **CHRONIC EXPOSURE-** NO DATA AVAILABLE.

FIRST AID- REMOVE CONTAMINATED CLOTHING AND SHOES IMMEDIATELY. WASH AFFECTED AREA WITH SOAP OR MILD DETERGENT AND LARGE AMOUNTS OF WATER UNTIL NO EVIDENCE OF CHEMICAL REMAINS (APPROXIMATELY 15-20 MINUTES). GET MEDICAL ATTENTION IMMEDIATELY.

EYE CONTACT: OXADIAZON: **ACUTE EXPOSURE-** MAY CAUSE IRRITATION. **CHRONIC EXPOSURE-** NO DATA AVAILABLE.

FIRST AID- WASH EYES IMMEDIATELY WITH LARGE AMOUNTS OF WATER OR NORMAL SALINE, OCCASIONALLY LIFTING UPPER AND LOWER LIDS, UNTIL NO EVIDENCE OF CHEMICAL REMAINS (APPROXIMATELY 15-20 MINUTES). GET MEDICAL ATTENTION IMMEDIATELY.

INGESTION: OXADIAZON: **ACUTE EXPOSURE-** A LETHAL DOSE IN RATS WAS 3500 MG/KG; SYMPTOMS WERE NOT REPORTED. **CHRONIC EXPOSURE-** NO OBSERVABLE EFFECTS WERE NOTED IN RATS AND DOGS RECEIVING 25 MG/KG/DAY.

FIRST AID- REMOVE BY GASTRIC LAVAGE AND CATHARSIS. MAINTAIN BLOOD PRESSURE AND AIRWAY. GIVE OXYGEN IF RESPIRATION IS DEPRESSED. DO NOT PERFORM GASTRIC LAVAGE IF VICTIM IS UNCONSCIOUS. GET MEDICAL ATTENTION IMMEDIATELY (DREISBACH, HANDBOOK OF POISONING, 12TH ED.).
ADMINISTRATION OF LAVAGE OR OXYGEN SHOULD BE PERFORMED BY QUALIFIED MEDICAL PERSONNEL.

ANTIDOTE: NO SPECIFIC ANTIDOTE. TREAT SYMPTOMATICALLY AND SUPPORTIVELY.

REACTIVITY

REACTIVITY: STABLE UNDER NORMAL TEMPERATURES AND PRESSURES.

INCOMPATIBILITIES: OXADIAZON: OXIDIZERS (STRONG): FIRE AND EXPLOSION HAZARD:

DECOMPOSITION: THERMAL DECOMPOSITION PRODUCTS MAY INCLUDE TOXIC OXIDES OF NITROGEN AND CARBON AND TOXIC AND CORROSIVE FUMES OF CHLORIDES.

POLYMERIZATION: HAZARDOUS POLYMERIZATION HAS NOT BEEN REPORTED TO OCCUR UNDER NORMAL TEMPERATURES AND PRESSURES.

STORAGE AND DISPOSAL

OBSERVE ALL FEDERAL, STATE AND LOCAL REGULATIONS WHEN STORING OR DISPOSING OF THIS SUBSTANCE. FOR ASSISTANCE, CONTACT THE DISTRICT DIRECTOR OF THE ENVIRONMENTAL PROTECTION AGENCY.

****STORAGE****

STORE IN ACCORDANCE WITH 40 CFR 165 RECOMMENDED PROCEDURES FOR THE DISPOSAL AND STORAGE OF PESTICIDES AND PESTICIDE CONTAINERS.
STORE AWAY FROM INCOMPATIBLE SUBSTANCES.

****DISPOSAL****

DISPOSAL MUST BE IN ACCORDANCE WITH 40 CFR 165 RECOMMENDED PROCEDURES FOR THE DISPOSAL AND STORAGE OF PESTICIDES AND PESTICIDE CONTAINERS.

CONDITIONS TO AVOID

MAY BURN BUT DOES NOT IGNITE READILY.

SPILL AND LEAK PROCEDURES

OCCUPATIONAL SPILL: DO NOT TOUCH SPILLED MATERIAL. STOP LEAK IF YOU CAN DO IT WITHOUT RISK. FOR SMALL SPILLS, TAKE UP WITH SAND OR OTHER ABSORBENT MATERIAL AND PLACE INTO CONTAINERS FOR LATER DISPOSAL. FOR SMALL DRY SPILLS, WITH A CLEAN SHOVEL PLACE MATERIAL INTO CLEAN, DRY CONTAINER AND COVER. MOVE CONTAINERS FROM SPILL AREA. FOR LARGER SPILLS, DIKE FAR AHEAD OF SPILL FOR LATER DISPOSAL. KEEP UNNECESSARY PEOPLE AWAY. ISOLATE HAZARD AREA AND DENY ENTRY.

PROTECTIVE EQUIPMENT

VENTILATION: PROVIDE GENERAL DILUTION VENTILATION.

RESPIRATOR: THE FOLLOWING RESPIRATORS ARE RECOMMENDED BASED ON INFORMATION FOUND IN THE PHYSICAL DATA, TOXICITY AND HEALTH EFFECTS SECTIONS. THEY ARE RANKED IN ORDER FROM MINIMUM TO MAXIMUM RESPIRATORY PROTECTION. THE SPECIFIC RESPIRATOR SELECTED MUST BE BASED ON CONTAMINATION LEVELS FOUND IN THE WORK PLACE, MUST NOT EXCEED THE WORKING LIMITS OF THE RESPIRATOR AND BE JOINTLY APPROVED BY THE NATIONAL INSTITUTE FOR OCCUPATIONAL SAFETY AND HEALTH AND THE MINE SAFETY AND HEALTH ADMINISTRATION (NIOSH-MSHA).
CHEMICAL CARTRIDGE RESPIRATOR WITH AN ORGANIC VAPOR CARTRIDGE(S) WITH A FULL FACEPIECE AND ORGANIC VAPOR CARTRIDGE(S) IN COMBINATION WITH A DUST AND MIST FILTER.
POWERED AIR-PURIFYING RESPIRATOR WITH A TIGHT-FITTING FACEPIECE AND ORGANIC VAPOR CARTRIDGE(S) IN COMBINATION WITH A HIGH-EFFICIENCY PARTICULATE FILTER.
TYPE 'C' SUPPLIED-AIR RESPIRATOR WITH A FULL FACEPIECE OPERATED IN A PRESSURE-DEMAND OR OTHER POSITIVE PRESSURE MODE.
SELF-CONTAINED BREATHING APPARATUS WITH A FULL FACEPIECE OPERATED IN PRESSURE-DEMAND OR OTHER POSITIVE PRESSURE MODE.
FOR FIREFIGHTING AND OTHER IMMEDIATELY DANGEROUS TO LIFE OR HEALTH CONDITIONS:
SELF-CONTAINED BREATHING APPARATUS WITH FULL FACEPIECE OPERATED IN PRESSURE-DEMAND OR OTHER POSITIVE PRESSURE MODE.
SUPPLIED-AIR RESPIRATOR WITH FULL FACEPIECE AND OPERATED IN PRESSURE-DEMAND OR OTHER POSITIVE PRESSURE MODE IN COMBINATION WITH AN AUXILIARY SELF-CONTAINED BREATHING APPARATUS OPERATED IN PRESSURE-DEMAND OR OTHER POSITIVE PRESSURE MODE.

CLOTHING: EMPLOYEE MUST WEAR APPROPRIATE PROTECTIVE (IMPERVIOUS) CLOTHING AND EQUIPMENT TO PREVENT REPEATED OR PROLONGED SKIN CONTACT WITH THIS SUBSTANCE.

GLOVES: EMPLOYEE MUST WEAR APPROPRIATE PROTECTIVE GLOVES TO PREVENT CONTACT WITH THIS SUBSTANCE.

EYE PROTECTION: EMPLOYEE MUST WEAR SPLASH-PROOF OR DUST-RESISTANT SAFETY GOGGLES WITH OR WITHOUT A FACESHIELD TO PREVENT CONTACT WITH THIS SUBSTANCE.
EMERGENCY EYE WASH: WHERE THERE IS ANY POSSIBILITY THAT AN EMPLOYEE'S EYES MAY BE EXPOSED TO THIS SUBSTANCE, THE EMPLOYER SHOULD PROVIDE AN EYE WASH FOUNTAIN WITHIN THE IMMEDIATE WORK AREA FOR EMERGENCY USE.

AUTHORIZED BY- OCCUPATIONAL HEALTH SERVICES, INC.
CREATION DATE: 10/04/89 ***REVISION DATE:*** 05/07/90

MATERIAL SAFETY DATA SHEET

OCCUPATIONAL HEALTH SERVICES, INC.
AGRICULTURE AND PESTICIDE DIVISION
450 SEVENTH AVENUE, SUITE 2407
NEW YORK, NEW YORK 10123
1-800-445-MSDS OR (212) 967-1100

EMERGENCY CONTACT:
JOHN S. BRANSFORD, JR. (615) 292-1180

SUBSTANCE IDENTIFICATION

CAS-NUMBER 24307-26-4

SUBSTANCE: **MEPIQUAT CHLORIDE**

TRADE NAMES/SYNONYMS: PIPERIDINIUM, 1,1-DIMETHYL-, CHLORIDE; 1,1-DIMETHYLPIPERIDINIUM CHLORIDE; N,N-DIMETHYLPIPERIDINIUM CHLORIDE; DIMETHYLPIPERIDIUM CHLORIDE; BAS 083; BAS 85559X; PIX; C7H16CLN; PST72386

CHEMICAL FAMILY: PIPERIDINE
QUATERNARY SALT

MOLECULAR FORMULA: C5-H10-N-(C-H3)2.CL

MOLECULAR WEIGHT: 149.67

CERCLA RATINGS (SCALE 0-3): HEALTH = U FIRE = 1 REACTIVITY = 0 PERSISTENCE = 3
NFPA RATINGS (SCALE 0-4): HEALTH = U FIRE = 1 REACTIVITY = 0

COMPONENTS AND CONTAMINANTS

COMPONENT: MEPIQUAT CHLORIDE ***PERCENT:*** 100.0
CAS# 24307-26-4
OTHER CONTAMINANTS: NONE
EXPOSURE LIMITS: NO OCCUPATIONAL EXPOSURE LIMITS ESTABLISHED BY OSHA, ACGIH, OR NIOSH.

PHYSICAL DATA

DESCRIPTION: ODORLESS, COLORLESS, HYGROSCOPIC CRYSTALS.
MELTING POINT: 545 F (285 C) (DECOMPOSES) ***SPECIFIC GRAVITY:*** NOT AVAILABLE
VAPOR PRESSURE: NEGLIGIBLE ***SOLUBILITY IN WATER:*** SOLUBLE
SOLVENT SOLUBILITY: SOLUBLE IN ETHANOL; MODERATELY SOLUBLE IN ACETONE AND CHLOROFORM; SPARINGLY SOLUBLE IN BENZENE, CYCLOHEXANE, ETHYL ACETATE, ETHER.

FIRE AND EXPLOSION DATA

FIRE AND EXPLOSION HAZARD: SLIGHT FIRE HAZARD WHEN EXPOSED TO HEAT OR FLAME.
FIREFIGHTING MEDIA: DRY CHEMICAL, CARBON DIOXIDE, HALON, WATER SPRAY OR STANDARD FOAM (1987 EMERGENCY RESPONSE GUIDEBOOK, DOT P 5800.4).
FOR LARGER FIRES, USE WATER SPRAY, FOG OR STANDARD FOAM (1987 EMERGENCY RESPONSE GUIDEBOOK, DOT P 5800.4).
FIREFIGHTING: MOVE CONTAINER FROM FIRE AREA IF POSSIBLE. DO NOT SCATTER SPILLED MATERIAL WITH HIGH PRESSURE WATER STREAMS. DIKE FIRE CONTROL WATER FOR LATER DISPOSAL (1987 EMERGENCY RESPONSE GUIDEBOOK, DOT P 5800.4, GUIDE PAGE 31).
USE AGENTS SUITABLE FOR TYPE OF SURROUNDING FIRE. AVOID BREATHING HAZARDOUS VAPORS, KEEP UPWIND.

TOXICITY

MEPIQUAT CHLORIDE: TOXICITY DATA: >3200 MG/M3/7 HOURS INHALATION-RAT LC50 (85JFAN); >7800 MG/KG SKIN-RAT LD50 (85JFAN); 1420 MG/KG ORAL-RAT LD50; APPROX. 1780 MG/KG ORAL-RABBIT LD50 (85JFAN). CARCINOGEN STATUS: NONE. ACUTE TOXICITY LEVEL: MODERATELY TOXIC BY INGESTION; SLIGHTLY TOXIC BY DERMAL ABSORPTION. TARGET EFFECTS: NO DATA AVAILABLE.

HEALTH EFFECTS AND FIRST AID

INHALATION: MEPIQUAT CHLORIDE: **ACUTE EXPOSURE-** A LETHAL CONCENTRATION IN RATS WAS GREATER THAN 3200 MG/M3/7 HOURS. **CHRONIC EXPOSURE-** NO DATA AVAILABLE.
FIRST AID- REMOVE FROM EXPOSURE AREA TO FRESH AIR IMMEDIATELY. IF BREATHING HAS STOPPED, PERFORM ARTIFICIAL RESPIRATION. KEEP PERSON WARM AND AT REST. TREAT SYMPTOMATICALLY AND SUPPORTIVELY. GET MEDICAL ATTENTION IMMEDIATELY.

SKIN CONTACT: MEPIQUAT CHLORIDE: **ACUTE EXPOSURE-** THIS MATERIAL WAS NOT IRRITATING TO RABBIT SKIN. **CHRONIC EXPOSURE-** NO DATA AVAILABLE.
FIRST AID- REMOVE CONTAMINATED CLOTHING AND SHOES IMMEDIATELY. WASH AFFECTED AREA WITH SOAP OR MILD DETERGENT AND LARGE AMOUNTS OF WATER UNTIL NO EVIDENCE OF CHEMICAL REMAINS (APPROXIMATELY 15-20 MINUTES). GET MEDICAL ATTENTION IMMEDIATELY.

EYE CONTACT: MEPIQUAT CHLORIDE: **ACUTE EXPOSURE-** THIS MATERIAL WAS NOT IRRITATING TO RABBIT EYES. **CHRONIC EXPOSURE-** NO DATA AVAILABLE.
FIRST AID- WASH EYES IMMEDIATELY WITH LARGE AMOUNTS OF WATER OR NORMAL SALINE, OCCASIONALLY LIFTING UPPER AND LOWER LIDS, UNTIL NO EVIDENCE OF CHEMICAL REMAINS (APPROXIMATELY 15-20 MINUTES). GET MEDICAL ATTENTION IMMEDIATELY.

INGESTION: MEPIQUAT CHLORIDE: **ACUTE EXPOSURE-** A LETHAL DOSE IN RATS WAS 1420 MG/KG. THE SYMPTOMS WERE NOT REPORTED. **CHRONIC EXPOSURE-** NO DATA AVAILABLE.
FIRST AID- TREAT SYMPTOMATICALLY AND SUPPORTIVELY. GET MEDICAL ATTENTION IMMEDIATELY. IF VOMITING OCCURS, KEEP HEAD LOWER THAN HIPS TO PREVENT ASPIRATION.
ANTIDOTE: NO SPECIFIC ANTIDOTE. TREAT SYMPTOMATICALLY AND SUPPORTIVELY.

REACTIVITY

REACTIVITY: STABLE UNDER NORMAL TEMPERATURES AND PRESSURES.
INCOMPATIBILITIES: MEPIQUAT CHLORIDE: ALUMINIUM: MAY CORRODE. IRON: MAY CORRODE. OXIDIZERS (STRONG): FIRE AND EXPLOSION HAZARD.
DECOMPOSITION: THERMAL DECOMPOSITION PRODUCTS MAY INCLUDE TOXIC OXIDES OF NITROGEN AND CARBON AND TOXIC AND CORROSIVE FUMES OF CHLORIDES.
POLYMERIZATION: HAZARDOUS POLYMERIZATION HAS NOT BEEN REPORTED TO OCCUR UNDER NORMAL TEMPERATURES AND PRESSURES.

STORAGE AND DISPOSAL

OBSERVE ALL FEDERAL, STATE AND LOCAL REGULATIONS WHEN STORING OR DISPOSING OF THIS SUBSTANCE. FOR ASSISTANCE, CONTACT THE DISTRICT DIRECTOR OF THE ENVIRONMENTAL PROTECTION AGENCY.

****STORAGE****

STORE IN ACCORDANCE WITH 40 CFR 165 RECOMMENDED PROCEDURES FOR THE DISPOSAL AND STORAGE OF PESTICIDES AND PESTICIDE CONTAINERS.
STORE AWAY FROM INCOMPATIBLE SUBSTANCES.

****DISPOSAL****

DISPOSAL MUST BE IN ACCORDANCE WITH 40 CFR 165 RECOMMENDED PROCEDURES FOR THE DISPOSAL AND STORAGE OF PESTICIDES AND PESTICIDE CONTAINERS.

CONDITIONS TO AVOID

MAY BURN BUT DOES NOT IGNITE READILY. AVOID CONTACT WITH STRONG OXIDIZERS, EXCESSIVE HEAT, SPARKS, OR OPEN FLAME.

SPILL AND LEAK PROCEDURES

OCCUPATIONAL SPILL: SWEEP UP AND PLACE IN SUITABLE CLEAN, DRY CONTAINERS FOR RECLAMATION OR LATER DISPOSAL. DO NOT FLUSH SPILLED MATERIAL INTO SEWER. KEEP UNNECESSARY PEOPLE AWAY.

PROTECTIVE EQUIPMENT

VENTILATION: PROVIDE LOCAL EXHAUST OR GENERAL DILUTION VENTILATION SYSTEM.
RESPIRATOR: THE FOLLOWING RESPIRATORS ARE RECOMMENDED BASED ON INFORMATION FOUND IN THE PHYSICAL DATA, TOXICITY AND HEALTH EFFECTS SECTIONS. THEY ARE RANKED IN ORDER FROM MINIMUM TO MAXIMUM RESPIRATORY PROTECTION. THE SPECIFIC RESPIRATOR SELECTED MUST BE BASED ON CONTAMINATION LEVELS FOUND IN THE WORK PLACE, MUST NOT EXCEED THE WORKING LIMITS OF THE RESPIRATOR AND BE JOINTLY APPROVED BY THE NATIONAL INSTITUTE FOR OCCUPATIONAL SAFETY AND HEALTH AND THE MINE SAFETY AND HEALTH ADMINISTRATION (NIOSH-MSHA).
CHEMICAL CARTRIDGE RESPIRATOR WITH AN ORGANIC VAPOR CARTRIDGE(S) IN COMBINATION WITH A DUST AND MIST FILTER.
GAS MASK WITH ORGANIC VAPOR CANISTER (CHIN-STYLE OR FRONT- OR BACK-MOUNTED CANISTER) WITH A DUST AND MIST FILTER.
GAS MASK WITH ORGANIC VAPOR CANISTER (CHIN-STYLE OR FRONT- OR BACK-MOUNTED CANISTER) WITH A PARTICULATE FILTER.
POWERED AIR-PURIFYING RESPIRATOR WITH A HIGH-EFFICIENCY FILTER.
TYPE 'C' SUPPLIED-AIR RESPIRATOR WITH A FULL FACEPIECE OPERATED IN A PRESSURE-DEMAND OR OTHER POSITIVE PRESSURE MODE.
SELF-CONTAINED BREATHING APPARATUS WITH A FULL FACEPIECE OPERATED IN PRESSURE-DEMAND OR OTHER POSITIVE PRESSURE MODE.
FOR FIREFIGHTING AND OTHER IMMEDIATELY DANGEROUS TO LIFE OR HEALTH CONDITIONS:
SELF-CONTAINED BREATHING APPARATUS WITH FULL FACEPIECE OPERATED IN PRESSURE-DEMAND OR OTHER POSITIVE PRESSURE MODE.
SUPPLIED-AIR RESPIRATOR WITH FULL FACEPIECE AND OPERATED IN PRESSURE-DEMAND OR OTHER POSITIVE PRESSURE MODE IN COMBINATION WITH AN AUXILIARY SELF-CONTAINED BREATHING APPARATUS OPERATED IN PRESSURE-DEMAND OR OTHER POSITIVE PRESSURE MODE.
CLOTHING: EMPLOYEE MUST WEAR APPROPRIATE PROTECTIVE (IMPERVIOUS) CLOTHING AND EQUIPMENT TO PREVENT REPEATED OR PROLONGED SKIN CONTACT WITH THIS SUBSTANCE.
GLOVES: EMPLOYEE MUST WEAR APPROPRIATE PROTECTIVE GLOVES TO PREVENT CONTACT WITH THIS SUBSTANCE.
EYE PROTECTION: EMPLOYEE MUST WEAR SPLASH-PROOF OR DUST-RESISTANT SAFETY GOGGLES TO PREVENT EYE CONTACT WITH THIS SUBSTANCE.
EMERGENCY EYE WASH: WHERE THERE IS ANY POSSIBILITY THAT AN EMPLOYEE'S EYES MAY BE EXPOSED TO THIS SUBSTANCE, THE EMPLOYER SHOULD PROVIDE AN EYE WASH FOUNTAIN WITHIN THE IMMEDIATE WORK AREA FOR EMERGENCY USE.

AUTHORIZED BY- OCCUPATIONAL HEALTH SERVICES, INC.
CREATION DATE: 10/18/89 ***REVISION DATE:*** 05/31/90

MATERIAL SAFETY DATA SHEET

OCCUPATIONAL HEALTH SERVICES, INC.
AGRICULTURE AND PESTICIDE DIVISION
450 SEVENTH AVENUE, SUITE 2407
NEW YORK, NEW YORK 10123
1-800-445-MSDS OR (212) 967-1100

EMERGENCY CONTACT:
JOHN S. BRANSFORD, JR. (615) 292-1180

SUBSTANCE IDENTIFICATION

CAS-NUMBER 52508-35-7

SUBSTANCE: **SODIUM DIKEGULAC**

TRADE NAMES/SYNONYMS: ALPHA-L-XYLO-2-HEXULOFURANOSONIC ACID, 2,3:4,6-BIS-O- (1-METHYLETHYLIDENE)-, SODIUM SALT; SODIUM 2,3:4,6-BIS-O-(1-METHYLETHYLIDENE)-A-L-XYOL -2-HEXULOFURANOSONATE; DIKEGULAC SODIUM; DIKEGULAC SODIUM SALT; ATRINAL; C12H17NAO7; PST72391

CHEMICAL FAMILY: SALT

MOLECULAR FORMULA: C12-H17-O7.NA

MOLECULAR WEIGHT: 296.3

CERCLA RATINGS (SCALE 0-3): HEALTH=1 FIRE=1 REACTIVITY=0 PERSISTENCE=1

NFPA RATINGS (SCALE 0-4): HEALTH=1 FIRE=1 REACTIVITY=0

COMPONENTS AND CONTAMINANTS

COMPONENT: SODIUM DIKEGULAC ***PERCENT:*** 100.0
CAS# 52508-35-7

OTHER CONTAMINANTS: NONE

EXPOSURE LIMITS: NO OCCUPATIONAL EXPOSURE LIMITS ESTABLISHED BY OSHA, ACGIH, OR NIOSH.

PHYSICAL DATA

DESCRIPTION: COLORLESS OR WHITE POWDER. ***MELTING POINT:*** >572 F (>300 C)

SPECIFIC GRAVITY: NOT AVAILABLE ***VAPOR PRESSURE:*** NEGLIGIBLE

SOLUBILITY IN WATER: 59%

SOLVENT SOLUBILITY: SOLUBLE IN ALCOHOL, CHLOROFORM; SLIGHTLY SOLUBLE IN ACETONE, HEXANE, CYCLOHEXANONE.

FIRE AND EXPLOSION DATA

FIRE AND EXPLOSION HAZARD: SLIGHT FIRE HAZARD WHEN EXPOSED TO HEAT OR FLAME.

FIREFIGHTING MEDIA: DRY CHEMICAL, CARBON DIOXIDE, HALON, WATER SPRAY OR STANDARD FOAM (1987 EMERGENCY RESPONSE GUIDEBOOK, DOT P 5800.4).
FOR LARGER FIRES, USE WATER SPRAY, FOG OR STANDARD FOAM (1987 EMERGENCY RESPONSE GUIDEBOOK, DOT P 5800.4).

FIREFIGHTING: MOVE CONTAINER FROM FIRE AREA IF POSSIBLE. DO NOT SCATTER SPILLED MATERIAL WITH HIGH PRESSURE WATER STREAMS. DIKE FIRE CONTROL WATER FOR LATER DISPOSAL (1987 EMERGENCY RESPONSE GUIDEBOOK, DOT P 5800.4, GUIDE PAGE 31).
USE AGENTS SUITABLE FOR TYPE OF SURROUNDING FIRE. AVOID BREATHING HAZARDOUS VAPORS, KEEP UPWIND.

TOXICITY

SODIUM DIKEGULAC: TOXICITY DATA: >1000 MG/KG SKIN-RABBIT LD50 (FMCHA2); 18,000 MG/KG ORAL-RAT LD50; 19,500 MG/KG ORAL-MOUSE LD50. CARCINOGEN STATUS: NONE. ACUTE TOXICITY LEVEL: MODERATELY TOXIC BY DERMAL ABSORPTION; RELATIVELY NONTOXIC BY INGESTION. TARGET EFFECTS: NO DATA AVAILABLE.

HEALTH EFFECTS AND FIRST AID

INHALATION: SODIUM DIKEGULAC: **ACUTE EXPOSURE-** NO DATA AVAILABLE.
CHRONIC EXPOSURE- NO DATA AVAILABLE.

FIRST AID- REMOVE FROM EXPOSURE AREA TO FRESH AIR IMMEDIATELY. IF BREATHING HAS STOPPED, PERFORM ARTIFICIAL RESPIRATION. KEEP PERSON WARM AND AT REST. TREAT SYMPTOMATICALLY AND SUPPORTIVELY. GET MEDICAL ATTENTION IMMEDIATELY.

SKIN CONTACT: SODIUM DIKEGULAC: **ACUTE EXPOSURE-** THE MEDIAN LETHAL DOSE IS GREATER THAN 1000 MG/KG. CONTACT WITH AQUEOUS SOLUTIONS OF DIKEGULAC (200 GM/L) CAUSED NO SKIN IRRITATION IN GUINEA PIGS. **CHRONIC EXPOSURE-** NO DATA AVAILABLE.

FIRST AID- REMOVE CONTAMINATED CLOTHING AND SHOES IMMEDIATELY. WASH AFFECTED AREA WITH SOAP OR MILD DETERGENT AND LARGE AMOUNTS OF WATER UNTIL NO EVIDENCE OF CHEMICAL REMAINS (APPROXIMATELY 15-20 MINUTES). GET MEDICAL ATTENTION IMMEDIATELY.

EYE CONTACT: SODIUM DIKEGULAC: **ACUTE EXPOSURE-** CONTACT WITH AQUEOUS SOLUTIONS OF DIKEGULAC (200 GM/L) CAUSED NO EYE IRRITATION IN RABBITS.
CHRONIC EXPOSURE- NO DATA AVAILABLE.

FIRST AID- WASH EYES IMMEDIATELY WITH LARGE AMOUNTS OF WATER OR NORMAL SALINE, OCCASIONALLY LIFTING UPPER AND LOWER LIDS, UNTIL NO EVIDENCE OF CHEMICAL REMAINS (APPROXIMATELY 15-20 MINUTES). GET MEDICAL ATTENTION IMMEDIATELY.

INGESTION: SODIUM DIKEGULAC: **ACUTE EXPOSURE-** THE MEDIAN LETHAL DOSE IN RATS WAS 18,000 MG/KG. **CHRONIC EXPOSURE-** IN A 90 DAY FEEDING STUDY WITH DIKEGULAC, NO SIGNIFICANT EFFECT WAS OBSERVED IN RATS RECEIVING 2000 MG/KG OR DOGS RECEIVING 3000 MG/KG DAILY.

FIRST AID- TREAT SYMPTOMATICALLY AND SUPPORTIVELY. GET MEDICAL ATTENTION IMMEDIATELY. IF VOMITING OCCURS, KEEP HEAD LOWER THAN HIPS TO PREVENT ASPIRATION.

ANTIDOTE: NO SPECIFIC ANTIDOTE. TREAT SYMPTOMATICALLY AND SUPPORTIVELY.

REACTIVITY

REACTIVITY: STABLE UNDER NORMAL TEMPERATURES AND PRESSURES.

INCOMPATIBILITIES: SODIUM DIKEGULAC: OXIDIZERS (STRONG): FIRE AND EXPLOSION HAZARD.

DECOMPOSITION: THERMAL DECOMPOSITION PRODUCTS MAY INCLUDE TOXIC OXIDES OF CARBON.

POLYMERIZATION: HAZARDOUS POLYMERIZATION HAS NOT BEEN REPORTED TO OCCUR UNDER NORMAL TEMPERATURES AND PRESSURES.

STORAGE AND DISPOSAL

OBSERVE ALL FEDERAL, STATE AND LOCAL REGULATIONS WHEN STORING OR DISPOSING OF THIS SUBSTANCE. FOR ASSISTANCE, CONTACT THE DISTRICT DIRECTOR OF THE ENVIRONMENTAL PROTECTION AGENCY.

STORAGE

STORE IN ACCORDANCE WITH 40 CFR 165 RECOMMENDED PROCEDURES FOR THE DISPOSAL AND STORAGE OF PESTICIDES AND PESTICIDE CONTAINERS.
STORE AWAY FROM INCOMPATIBLE SUBSTANCES.

DISPOSAL

DISPOSAL MUST BE IN ACCORDANCE WITH 40 CFR 165 RECOMMENDED PROCEDURES FOR THE DISPOSAL AND STORAGE OF PESTICIDES AND PESTICIDE CONTAINERS.

CONDITIONS TO AVOID

MAY BURN BUT DOES NOT IGNITE READILY. AVOID CONTACT WITH STRONG OXIDIZERS, EXCESSIVE HEAT, SPARKS, OR OPEN FLAME.

SPILL AND LEAK PROCEDURES

OCCUPATIONAL SPILL: SWEEP UP AND PLACE IN SUITABLE CLEAN, DRY CONTAINERS FOR RECLAMATION OR LATER DISPOSAL. DO NOT FLUSH SPILLED MATERIAL INTO SEWER. KEEP UNNECESSARY PEOPLE AWAY.

PROTECTIVE EQUIPMENT

VENTILATION: PROVIDE GENERAL DILUTION VENTILATION.

RESPIRATOR: THE FOLLOWING RESPIRATORS ARE RECOMMENDED BASED ON INFORMATION FOUND IN THE PHYSICAL DATA, TOXICITY AND HEALTH EFFECTS SECTIONS. THEY ARE RANKED IN ORDER FROM MINIMUM TO MAXIMUM RESPIRATORY PROTECTION. THE SPECIFIC RESPIRATOR SELECTED MUST BE BASED ON CONTAMINATION LEVELS FOUND IN THE WORK PLACE, MUST NOT EXCEED THE WORKING LIMITS OF THE RESPIRATOR AND BE JOINTLY APPROVED BY THE NATIONAL INSTITUTE FOR OCCUPATIONAL SAFETY AND HEALTH AND THE MINE SAFETY AND HEALTH ADMINISTRATION (NIOSH-MSHA).
CHEMICAL CARTRIDGE RESPIRATOR WITH AN ORGANIC VAPOR CARTRIDGE(S) WITH A FULL FACEPIECE AND ORGANIC VAPOR CARTRIDGE(S) IN COMBINATION WITH A DUST AND MIST FILTER.
POWERED AIR-PURIFYING RESPIRATOR WITH A TIGHT-FITTING FACEPIECE AND ORGANIC VAPOR CARTRIDGE(S) IN COMBINATION WITH A HIGH-EFFICIENCY PARTICULATE FILTER.
TYPE 'C' SUPPLIED-AIR RESPIRATOR WITH A FULL FACEPIECE OPERATED IN A PRESSURE-DEMAND OR OTHER POSITIVE PRESSURE MODE.
SELF-CONTAINED BREATHING APPARATUS WITH A FULL FACEPIECE OPERATED IN PRESSURE-DEMAND OR OTHER POSITIVE PRESSURE MODE.
FOR FIREFIGHTING AND OTHER IMMEDIATELY DANGEROUS TO LIFE OR HEALTH CONDITIONS:
SELF-CONTAINED BREATHING APPARATUS WITH FULL FACEPIECE OPERATED IN PRESSURE-DEMAND OR OTHER POSITIVE PRESSURE MODE.
SUPPLIED-AIR RESPIRATOR WITH FULL FACEPIECE AND OPERATED IN PRESSURE-DEMAND OR OTHER POSITIVE PRESSURE MODE IN COMBINATION WITH AN AUXILIARY SELF-CONTAINED BREATHING APPARATUS OPERATED IN PRESSURE-DEMAND OR OTHER POSITIVE PRESSURE MODE.

CLOTHING: EMPLOYEE MUST WEAR APPROPRIATE PROTECTIVE (IMPERVIOUS) CLOTHING AND EQUIPMENT TO PREVENT REPEATED OR PROLONGED SKIN CONTACT WITH THIS SUBSTANCE.

GLOVES: EMPLOYEE MUST WEAR APPROPRIATE PROTECTIVE GLOVES TO PREVENT CONTACT WITH THIS SUBSTANCE.

EYE PROTECTION: EMPLOYEE MUST WEAR SPLASH-PROOF OR DUST-RESISTANT SAFETY GOGGLES TO PREVENT EYE CONTACT WITH THIS SUBSTANCE.
EMERGENCY EYE WASH: WHERE THERE IS ANY POSSIBILITY THAT AN EMPLOYEE'S EYES MAY BE EXPOSED TO THIS SUBSTANCE, THE EMPLOYER SHOULD PROVIDE AN EYE WASH FOUNTAIN WITHIN THE IMMEDIATE WORK AREA FOR EMERGENCY USE.

AUTHORIZED BY- OCCUPATIONAL HEALTH SERVICES, INC.
CREATION DATE: 10/05/89 ***REVISION DATE:*** 05/31/90

MATERIAL SAFETY DATA SHEET

OCCUPATIONAL HEALTH SERVICES, INC.
AGRICULTURE AND PESTICIDE DIVISION
450 SEVENTH AVENUE, SUITE 2407
NEW YORK, NEW YORK 10123
1-800-445-MSDS OR (212) 967-1100

EMERGENCY CONTACT:
JOHN S. BRANSFORD, JR. (615) 292-1180

SUBSTANCE IDENTIFICATION

CAS-NUMBER 52315-07-8

SUBSTANCE: **CYPERMETHRIN**

TRADE NAMES/SYNONYMS: CYCLOPROPANECARBOXYLIC ACID, 3-(2,2-DICHLOROETHENYL)-2,2-DIMETHYL-, CYANO(3-PHENOXYPHENYL) METHYL ESTER; 3-(2,2-DICHLOROETHENYL)-2,2-DIMETHYLCYCLOPROPANECARBOXYLIC ACID CYANO(3-PHENOXYPHENYL) METHYL ESTER; (R,S)-ALPHA-CYANO-3-PHENOXYBENZYL (1R,S)-CIS,TRANS-3-(2,2- DICHLOROVINYL)-2,2-DIMETHYLCYCLOPROPANECARBOXYLATE; (+-)-ALPHA-CYANO-3-PHENOXYBENZYL-(+-)-CIS,TRANS-3-(2,2-DICHLOROVINYL)- 2,2-DIMETHYLCYCLOPROPANE CARBOXYLATE; ALPHA CYANO-3-PHENOXYBENZYL(+-)CIS,TRANS, 3-(,2-DICHLOROVINYL)-2,2- DIMETHYL CYCLOPROPANE CARBOXYLATE; AMMO; BARRICADE; CCN 52; CYMBUSH; CYPERKILL; FENDONA; FMC 30980; NRDC 149; RIPCORD; C22H19CL2NO3; PST72392

CHEMICAL FAMILY: PYRETHROID (SYNTHETIC)

MOLECULAR FORMULA: C22-H19-CL2-N-O3

MOLECULAR WEIGHT: 416.30

CERCLA RATINGS (SCALE 0-3): HEALTH=3 FIRE=1 REACTIVITY=0 PERSISTENCE=2

NFPA RATINGS (SCALE 0-4): HEALTH=3 FIRE=1 REACTIVITY=0

COMPONENTS AND CONTAMINANTS

COMPONENT: CYPERMETHRIN ***PERCENT:*** 100.0
CAS# 52315-07-8

EXPOSURE LIMITS: PYRETHROIDS: 1 POUND CERCLA SECTION 103 REPORTABLE QUANTITY

PHYSICAL DATA

DESCRIPTION: COLORLESS, CRYSTALLINE SOLID. ***MELTING POINT:*** 177 F (81 C)

SPECIFIC GRAVITY: 1.12 ***VOLATILITY:*** 0%

VAPOR PRESSURE: 0.0013 MMHG @ 20 C

EVAPORATION RATE: (BUTYL ACETATE=1) <1 ***SOLUBILITY IN WATER:*** 10 PPM

SOLVENT SOLUBILITY: SOLUBLE IN ACETONE, CYCLOHEXANONE, XYLENE, METHANOL, METHYLENE DICHLORIDE; MODERATELY SOLUBLE IN HEXANE. DECOMPOSES ABOVE 428 F (220 C)

FIRE AND EXPLOSION DATA

FIRE AND EXPLOSION HAZARD: SLIGHT FIRE HAZARD WHEN EXPOSED TO HEAT OR FLAME.

FLASH POINT: >572 F (>300 C)

FIREFIGHTING MEDIA: DRY CHEMICAL, CARBON DIOXIDE, HALON, WATER SPRAY OR STANDARD FOAM (1987 EMERGENCY RESPONSE GUIDEBOOK, DOT P 5800.4). FOR LARGER FIRES, USE WATER SPRAY, FOG OR STANDARD FOAM (1987 EMERGENCY RESPONSE GUIDEBOOK, DOT P 5800.4).

FIREFIGHTING: MOVE CONTAINER FROM FIRE AREA IF POSSIBLE. DO NOT SCATTER SPILLED MATERIAL WITH HIGH PRESSURE WATER STREAMS. DIKE FIRE CONTROL WATER FOR LATER DISPOSAL (1987 EMERGENCY RESPONSE GUIDEBOOK, DOT P 5800.4, GUIDE PAGE 31).
USE AGENTS SUITABLE FOR TYPE OF SURROUNDING FIRE. AVOID BREATHING HAZARDOUS VAPORS, KEEP UPWIND.

TOXICITY

CYPERMETHRIN: TOXICITY DATA: 1600 MG/KG SKIN-RAT LD50; 500 MG/KG SKIN-RAT LD50 (PEMNDP); 70 MG/KG ORAL-RAT LD50; 138 MG/KG ORAL-MOUSE LD50; 3 GM/KG ORAL-RABBIT LD50; 6 MG/KG INTRAVENOUS-RAT LDLO; 400 MG/KG UNREPORTED-RAT LD50; MUTAGENIC DATA (RTECS); REPRODUCTIVE EFFECTS DATA (RTECS). CARCINOGEN STATUS: NONE. ACUTE TOXICITY LEVEL: TOXIC BY DERMAL ABSORPTION AND INGESTION. TARGET EFFECTS: MAY AFFECT THE CENTRAL NERVOUS SYSTEM.*
* MAY BE BASED ON GROUP INFORMATION ON PYRETHROIDS.

HEALTH EFFECTS AND FIRST AID

INHALATION: CYPERMETHRIN: SEE INFORMATION ON PYRETHROIDS. INHALATION OF HIGH CONCENTRATIONS MAY BE FATAL.
PYRETHROIDS: **ACUTE EXPOSURE-** HEAVY EXPOSURE TO A MIST OF SOME PYRETHROIDS HAS PRODUCED HYPERSENSITIVIITY, ATAXIA, AND URINARY INCONTINENCE. CONVULSIONS MAY ALSO BE POSSIBLE. **CHRONIC EXPOSURE-** ANIMALS EXPOSED TO AEROSOLS OF SOME PYRETHROIDS FOR 3-4 HOURS/DAY FOR UP TO 4 WEEKS DID NOT EXHIBIT ANY SIGNIFICANT COMPOUND RELATED FINDINGS.

FIRST AID- REMOVE FROM EXPOSURE AREA TO FRESH AIR IMMEDIATELY. IF BREATHING HAS STOPPED, PERFORM ARTIFICIAL RESPIRATION. KEEP PERSON WARM AND AT REST. TREAT SYMPTOMATICALLY AND SUPPORTIVELY. GET MEDICAL ATTENTION IMMEDIATELY.

SKIN CONTACT: CYPERMETHRIN: TOXIC. SEE INFORMATION ON PYRETHROIDS. MAY CAUSE IRRITATION. A LETHAL DOSE IN RATS WAS 500 MG/KG. SYMPTOMS WERE NOT REPORTED.
PYRETHROIDS: **ACUTE EXPOSURE-** BASED ON ANIMAL AND HUMAN STUDIES AND HUMAN EXPERIENCES WITH SOME PYRETHROIDS, PRIMARY IRRITATION IS UNLIKELY. CUTANEOUS PARESTHESIAS MAY OCCUR INCLUDING NUMBNESS, ITCHING, BURNING, TINGLING AND WARMTH WITHOUT SIGNS OF IRRITATION. THESE EFFECTS MAY BE DELAYED FOR 30 MINUTES OR MORE AND LAST LESS THAN 24 HOURS. **CHRONIC EXPOSURE-** TESTS WITH SOME PYRETHROIDS ON HUMANS AND ANIMALS INDICATE SENSITIZATION IS UNLIKELY.

FIRST AID- REMOVE CONTAMINATED CLOTHING AND SHOES IMMEDIATELY. WASH AFFECTED AREA WITH SOAP OR MILD DETERGENT AND LARGE AMOUNTS OF WATER UNTIL NO EVIDENCE OF CHEMICAL REMAINS (APPROXIMATELY 15-20 MINUTES). GET MEDICAL ATTENTION IMMEDIATELY.

EYE CONTACT: CYPERMETHRIN: **ACUTE EXPOSURE-** THIS MATERIAL WAS MILDLY IRRITATING IN RABBIT EYES. EMULSIFIABLE CONCENTRATE FORMULATIONS WERE SEVERELY IRRITATING TO RABBIT EYES. **CHRONIC EXPOSURE-** NO DATA AVAILABLE.

FIRST AID- WASH EYES IMMEDIATELY WITH LARGE AMOUNTS OF WATER OR NORMAL SALINE, OCCASIONALLY LIFTING UPPER AND LOWER LIDS, UNTIL NO EVIDENCE OF CHEMICAL REMAINS (APPROXIMATELY 15-20 MINUTES). GET MEDICAL ATTENTION IMMEDIATELY.

INGESTION: CYPERMETHRIN: TOXIC. SEE INFORMATION ON PYRETHROIDS. A LETHAL DOSE IN RATS WAS 70 MG/KG. PATHOLOGICAL CHANGES IN THYMUS CORTEX, LIVER, ADRENAL GLANDS, LUNGS, AND SKIN WERE OBSERVED IN RABBITS REPEATEDLY FED THIS MATERIAL.
PYRETHROIDS: **ACUTE EXPOSURE-** SOME PYRETHROIDS HAVE PRODUCED HYPERSENSITIVITY, NERVOUS IRRITABILITY, TREMORS, ATAXIA, AND URINARY INCONTINENCE IN ANIMALS. CONVULSIONS MAY ALSO BE POSSIBLE. **CHRONIC EXPOSURE-** INCREASED KIDNEY AND LIVER WEIGHTS AND HEPATIC HISTOPATHOLOGICAL CHANGES WERE NOTED IN ANIMALS CHRONICALLY FED SOME PYRETHROIDS.

FIRST AID- REMOVE BY GASTRIC LAVAGE AND CATHARSIS. MAINTAIN BLOOD PRESSURE AND AIRWAY. GIVE OXYGEN IF RESPIRATION IS DEPRESSED. DO NOT PERFORM GASTRIC LAVAGE IF VICTIM IS UNCONSCIOUS. GET MEDICAL ATTENTION IMMEDIATELY (DREISBACH, HANDBOOK OF POISONING, 12TH ED.). ADMINISTRATION OF LAVAGE OR OXYGEN SHOULD BE PERFORMED BY QUALIFIED MEDICAL PERSONNEL.

ANTIDOTE: NO SPECIFIC ANTIDOTE. TREAT SYMPTOMATICALLY AND SUPPORTIVELY.

REACTIVITY

REACTIVITY: STABLE UNDER NORMAL TEMPERATURES AND PRESSURES.

INCOMPATIBILITIES: CYPERMETHRIN: OXIDIZERS (STRONG): FIRE AND EXPLOSION HAZARD.

DECOMPOSITION: THERMAL DECOMPOSITION MAY EMIT TOXIC FUMES OF HYDROGEN CYANIDE, CHLORINE, AND OXIDES OF NITROGEN AND CARBON.

POLYMERIZATION: HAZARDOUS POLYMERIZATION HAS NOT BEEN REPORTED TO OCCUR UNDER NORMAL TEMPERATURES AND PRESSURES.

STORAGE AND DISPOSAL

OBSERVE ALL FEDERAL, STATE AND LOCAL REGULATIONS WHEN STORING OR DISPOSING OF THIS SUBSTANCE. FOR ASSISTANCE, CONTACT THE DISTRICT DIRECTOR OF THE ENVIRONMENTAL PROTECTION AGENCY.

STORAGE

STORE IN ACCORDANCE WITH 40 CFR 165 RECOMMENDED PROCEDURES FOR THE DISPOSAL AND STORAGE OF PESTICIDES AND PESTICIDE CONTAINERS.
STORE AWAY FROM INCOMPATIBLE SUBSTANCES.

DISPOSAL

DISPOSAL MUST BE IN ACCORDANCE WITH 40 CFR 165 RECOMMENDED PROCEDURES FOR THE DISPOSAL AND STORAGE OF PESTICIDES AND PESTICIDE CONTAINERS.

CONDITIONS TO AVOID

MAY BURN BUT DOES NOT IGNITE READILY. AVOID CONTACT WITH STRONG OXIDIZERS, EXCESSIVE HEAT, SPARKS, OR OPEN FLAME.

SPILL AND LEAK PROCEDURES

SOIL SPILL: DIG HOLDING AREA SUCH AS LAGOON, POND OR PIT FOR CONTAINMENT. DIKE FLOW OF SPILLED MATERIAL USING SOIL OR SANDBAGS OR FOAMED BARRIERS SUCH AS POLYURETHANE OR CONCRETE.
USE CEMENT POWDER OR FLY ASH TO ABSORB LIQUID MASS.

WATER SPILL: USE ACTIVATED CARBON TO ABSORB SPILLED SUBSTANCE THAT IS DISSOLVED. USE MECHANICAL DREDGES OR LIFTS TO EXTRACT IMMOBILIZED MASSES OF POLLUTION AND PRECIPITATES.

OCCUPATIONAL SPILL: SWEEP UP AND PLACE IN SUITABLE CLEAN, DRY CONTAINERS FOR RECLAMATION OR LATER DISPOSAL. DO NOT FLUSH SPILLED MATERIAL INTO SEWER. KEEP UNNECESSARY PEOPLE AWAY.

PROTECTIVE EQUIPMENT

VENTILATION: PROVIDE LOCAL EXHAUST OR GENERAL DILUTION VENTILATION SYSTEM.

RESPIRATOR: THE FOLLOWING RESPIRATORS ARE RECOMMENDED BASED ON INFORMATION FOUND IN THE PHYSICAL DATA, TOXICITY AND HEALTH EFFECTS SECTIONS. THEY ARE RANKED IN ORDER FROM MINIMUM TO MAXIMUM RESPIRATORY PROTECTION. THE SPECIFIC RESPIRATOR SELECTED MUST BE BASED ON CONTAMINATION LEVELS FOUND IN THE WORK PLACE, MUST NOT EXCEED THE WORKING LIMITS OF THE RESPIRATOR AND BE JOINTLY APPROVED BY THE NATIONAL INSTITUTE FOR OCCUPATIONAL SAFETY AND HEALTH AND THE MINE SAFETY AND HEALTH ADMINISTRATION (NIOSH-MSHA).
CHEMICAL CARTRIDGE RESPIRATOR WITH AN ORGANIC VAPOR CARTRIDGE(S) IN COMBINATION WITH A DUST AND MIST FILTER.
GAS MASK WITH ORGANIC VAPOR CANISTER (CHIN-STYLE OR FRONT- OR BACK-MOUNTED CANISTER) WITH A DUST AND MIST FILTER.
GAS MASK WITH ORGANIC VAPOR CANISTER (CHIN-STYLE OR FRONT- OR BACK-MOUNTED CANISTER) WITH A PARTICULATE FILTER.
POWERED AIR-PURIFYING RESPIRATOR WITH A HIGH-EFFICIENCY FILTER.
TYPE 'C' SUPPLIED-AIR RESPIRATOR WITH A FULL FACEPIECE OPERATED IN A PRESSURE-DEMAND OR OTHER POSITIVE PRESSURE MODE.
SELF-CONTAINED BREATHING APPARATUS WITH A FULL FACEPIECE OPERATED IN PRESSURE-DEMAND OR OTHER POSITIVE PRESSURE MODE.
FOR FIREFIGHTING AND OTHER IMMEDIATELY DANGEROUS TO LIFE OR HEALTH CONDITIONS:
SELF-CONTAINED BREATHING APPARATUS WITH FULL FACEPIECE OPERATED IN PRESSURE-DEMAND OR OTHER POSITIVE PRESSURE MODE.
SUPPLIED-AIR RESPIRATOR WITH FULL FACEPIECE AND OPERATED IN PRESSURE-DEMAND OR OTHER POSITIVE PRESSURE MODE IN COMBINATION WITH AN AUXILIARY SELF-CONTAINED BREATHING APPARATUS OPERATED IN PRESSURE-DEMAND OR OTHER POSITIVE PRESSURE MODE.

CLOTHING: EMPLOYEE MUST WEAR APPROPRIATE PROTECTIVE (IMPERVIOUS) CLOTHING AND EQUIPMENT TO PREVENT REPEATED OR PROLONGED SKIN CONTACT WITH THIS SUBSTANCE.

GLOVES: EMPLOYEE MUST WEAR APPROPRIATE PROTECTIVE GLOVES TO PREVENT CONTACT WITH THIS SUBSTANCE.

EYE PROTECTION: EMPLOYEE MUST WEAR SPLASH-PROOF OR DUST-RESISTANT SAFETY GOGGLES AND A FACESHIELD TO PREVENT CONTACT WITH THIS SUBSTANCE.
EMERGENCY WASH FACILITIES: WHERE THERE IS ANY POSSIBILITY THAT AN EMPLOYEE'S EYES AND/OR SKIN MAY BE EXPOSED TO THIS SUBSTANCE, THE EMPLOYER SHOULD PROVIDE AN EYE WASH FOUNTAIN AND QUICK DRENCH SHOWER WITHIN THE IMMEDIATE WORK AREA FOR EMERGENCY USE.

AUTHORIZED BY- OCCUPATIONAL HEALTH SERVICES, INC.
CREATION DATE: 10/04/89 ***REVISION DATE:*** 05/31/90

MATERIAL SAFETY DATA SHEET

OCCUPATIONAL HEALTH SERVICES, INC.
AGRICULTURE AND PESTICIDE DIVISION
450 SEVENTH AVENUE, SUITE 2407
NEW YORK, NEW YORK 10123
1-800-445-MSDS OR (212) 967-1100

EMERGENCY CONTACT:
JOHN S. BRANSFORD, JR. (615) 292-1180

SUBSTANCE IDENTIFICATION

CAS-NUMBER 32889-48-8

SUBSTANCE: PROCYAZINE

TRADE NAMES/SYNONYMS: PROPANENITRILE, 2-((4-CHLORO-6-(CYCLOPROPYLAMINO)-1,3,5-TRIAZIN-2-YL) AMINO)-2-METHYL-; PROPIONITRILE, 2-((4-CHLORO-6-(CYCLOPROPYLAMINO)-S-TRIAZIN-2-YL) AMINO)-2-METHYL-; 2-((4-CHLORO-6-(CYCLOPROPYLAMINO)-1,3,5-TRIAZIN-2-YL)AMINO)-2-METHYL PROPANENITRILE; 2-((4-CHLORO-6-(CYCLOPROPYLAMINO)-S-TRIAZIN-2-YL)AMINO)-2-METHYL PROPIONITRILE; CYCLE; CGA-18762; C10H13CLN6; PST72398

CHEMICAL FAMILY: S-TRIAZINE

MOLECULAR FORMULA: C10-H13-CL-N6

MOLECULAR WEIGHT: 252.74

CERCLA RATINGS (SCALE 0-3): HEALTH=2 FIRE=1 REACTIVITY=0 PERSISTENCE=3

NFPA RATINGS (SCALE 0-4): HEALTH=2 FIRE=1 REACTIVITY=0

COMPONENTS AND CONTAMINANTS

COMPONENT: PROCYAZINE ***PERCENT:*** 100.0
CAS# 32889-48-8

OTHER CONTAMINANTS: NONE

EXPOSURE LIMITS: NO OCCUPATIONAL EXPOSURE LIMITS ESTABLISHED BY OSHA, ACGIH, OR NIOSH.

PHYSICAL DATA

DESCRIPTION: ODORLESS WHITE CRYSTALS. ***MELTING POINT:*** 334 F (168 C)

SPECIFIC GRAVITY: NOT AVAILABLE ***SOLUBILITY IN WATER:*** 300 PPM @ 20 C

SOLVENT SOLUBILITY: SOLUBLE IN METHYLENE CHLORIDE AND METHANOL; SLIGHTLY SOLUBLE IN HEXANE AND BENZENE.

FIRE AND EXPLOSION DATA

FIRE AND EXPLOSION HAZARD: SLIGHT FIRE HAZARD WHEN EXPOSED TO HEAT OR FLAME.

FIREFIGHTING MEDIA: DRY CHEMICAL, CARBON DIOXIDE, HALON, WATER SPRAY OR STANDARD FOAM (1987 EMERGENCY RESPONSE GUIDEBOOK, DOT P 5800.4).
FOR LARGER FIRES, USE WATER SPRAY, FOG OR STANDARD FOAM (1987 EMERGENCY RESPONSE GUIDEBOOK, DOT P 5800.4).

FIREFIGHTING: MOVE CONTAINERS FROM FIRE AREA IF POSSIBLE (1987 EMERGENCY RESPONSE GUIDEBOOK, DOT P 5800.4, GUIDE PAGE 53).
EXTINGUISH USING AGENTS SUITABLE FOR SURROUNDING FIRE. USE FLOODING QUANTITIES OF WATER AS A FOG. KEEP MATERIAL OUT OF SEWERS AND WATER SOURCES. DO NOT TOUCH SPILLED MATERIAL. AVOID BREATHING HAZARDOUS FUMES; KEEP UPWIND.

TOXICITY

PROCYAZINE: TOXICITY DATA: 290 MG/KG ORAL-RAT LD50; MUTAGENIC DATA (RTECS). CARCINOGEN STATUS: NONE. ACUTE TOXICITY LEVEL: TOXIC BY INGESTION. TARGET EFFECTS: NO DATA AVAILABLE.

HEALTH EFFECTS AND FIRST AID

INHALATION: PROCYAZINE: **ACUTE EXPOSURE-** SOME TRIAZINES ARE MILDLY IRRITATING TO THE UPPER RESPIRATORY TRACT. **CHRONIC EXPOSURE-** NO DATA AVAILABLE.

FIRST AID- REMOVE FROM EXPOSURE AREA TO FRESH AIR IMMEDIATELY. IF BREATHING HAS STOPPED, PERFORM ARTIFICIAL RESPIRATION. KEEP PERSON WARM AND AT REST. TREAT SYMPTOMATICALLY AND SUPPORTIVELY. GET MEDICAL ATTENTION IMMEDIATELY.

SKIN CONTACT: PROCYAZINE: **ACUTE EXPOSURE-** A LETHAL DOSE OF A 80% WETTABLE POWDER FORMULATION IN RATS WAS GREATER 3000 MG/KG. SOME TRIAZINES ARE MILDLY IRRITATING TO THE SKIN. **CHRONIC EXPOSURE-** NO DATA AVAILABLE.

FIRST AID- REMOVE CONTAMINATED CLOTHING AND SHOES IMMEDIATELY. WASH AFFECTED AREA WITH SOAP OR MILD DETERGENT AND LARGE AMOUNTS OF WATER UNTIL NO EVIDENCE OF CHEMICAL REMAINS (APPROXIMATELY 15-20 MINUTES). GET MEDICAL ATTENTION IMMEDIATELY.

EYE CONTACT: PROCYAZINE: **ACUTE EXPOSURE-** SOME TRIAZINES ARE MILDLY IRRITATING TO THE EYES. **CHRONIC EXPOSURE-** NO DATA AVAILABLE.

FIRST AID- WASH EYES IMMEDIATELY WITH LARGE AMOUNTS OF WATER OR NORMAL SALINE, OCCASIONALLY LIFTING UPPER AND LOWER LIDS, UNTIL NO EVIDENCE OF CHEMICAL REMAINS (APPROXIMATELY 15-20 MINUTES). GET MEDICAL ATTENTION IMMEDIATELY.

INGESTION: PROCYAZINE: TOXIC. **ACUTE EXPOSURE-** A LETHAL DOSE IN RATS WAS 290 MG/KG; SYMPTOMS WERE NOT REPORTED. **CHRONIC EXPOSURE-** NO DATA AVAILABLE.

FIRST AID- REMOVE BY GASTRIC LAVAGE AND CATHARSIS. MAINTAIN BLOOD PRESSURE AND AIRWAY. GIVE OXYGEN IF RESPIRATION IS DEPRESSED. DO NOT PERFORM GASTRIC LAVAGE IF VICTIM IS UNCONSCIOUS. GET MEDICAL ATTENTION IMMEDIATELY (DREISBACH, HANDBOOK OF POISONING, 12TH ED.).

ADMINISTRATION OF LAVAGE OR OXYGEN SHOULD BE PERFORMED BY QUALIFIED MEDICAL PERSONNEL.

ANTIDOTE: NO SPECIFIC ANTIDOTE. TREAT SYMPTOMATICALLY AND SUPPORTIVELY.

REACTIVITY

REACTIVITY: STABLE UNDER NORMAL TEMPERATURES AND PRESSURES.

INCOMPATIBILITIES: PROCYAZINE: NO DATA AVAILABLE.

DECOMPOSITION: THERMAL DECOMPOSITION PRODUCTS MAY INCLUDE TOXIC OXIDES OF NITROGEN AND CARBON AND TOXIC AND CORROSIVE FUMES OF CHLORIDES.

POLYMERIZATION: HAZARDOUS POLYMERIZATION HAS NOT BEEN REPORTED TO OCCUR UNDER NORMAL TEMPERATURES AND PRESSURES.

STORAGE AND DISPOSAL

OBSERVE ALL FEDERAL, STATE AND LOCAL REGULATIONS WHEN STORING OR DISPOSING OF THIS SUBSTANCE. FOR ASSISTANCE, CONTACT THE DISTRICT DIRECTOR OF THE ENVIRONMENTAL PROTECTION AGENCY.

****STORAGE****

STORE IN ACCORDANCE WITH 40 CFR 165 RECOMMENDED PROCEDURES FOR THE DISPOSAL AND STORAGE OF PESTICIDES AND PESTICIDE CONTAINERS.

****DISPOSAL****

DISPOSAL MUST BE IN ACCORDANCE WITH 40 CFR 165 RECOMMENDED PROCEDURES FOR THE DISPOSAL AND STORAGE OF PESTICIDES AND PESTICIDE CONTAINERS.

CONDITIONS TO AVOID

MAY BURN BUT DOES NOT IGNITE READILY.

SPILL AND LEAK PROCEDURES

OCCUPATIONAL SPILL: DO NOT TOUCH SPILLED MATERIAL. STOP LEAK IF YOU CAN DO IT WITHOUT RISK. FOR SMALL SPILLS, TAKE UP WITH SAND OR OTHER ABSORBENT MATERIAL AND PLACE INTO CONTAINERS FOR LATER DISPOSAL. FOR SMALL DRY SPILLS, WITH A CLEAN SHOVEL PLACE MATERIAL INTO CLEAN, DRY CONTAINER AND COVER. MOVE CONTAINERS FROM SPILL AREA. FOR LARGER SPILLS, DIKE FAR AHEAD OF SPILL FOR LATER DISPOSAL. KEEP UNNECESSARY PEOPLE AWAY. ISOLATE HAZARD AREA AND DENY ENTRY.

PROTECTIVE EQUIPMENT

VENTILATION: PROVIDE LOCAL EXHAUST OR GENERAL DILUTION VENTILATION SYSTEM.

RESPIRATOR: THE FOLLOWING RESPIRATORS ARE RECOMMENDED BASED ON INFORMATION FOUND IN THE PHYSICAL DATA, TOXICITY AND HEALTH EFFECTS SECTIONS. THEY ARE RANKED IN ORDER FROM MINIMUM TO MAXIMUM RESPIRATORY PROTECTION. THE SPECIFIC RESPIRATOR SELECTED MUST BE BASED ON CONTAMINATION LEVELS FOUND IN THE WORK PLACE, MUST NOT EXCEED THE WORKING LIMITS OF THE RESPIRATOR AND BE JOINTLY APPROVED BY THE NATIONAL INSTITUTE FOR OCCUPATIONAL SAFETY AND HEALTH AND THE MINE SAFETY AND HEALTH ADMINISTRATION (NIOSH-MSHA).

CHEMICAL CARTRIDGE RESPIRATOR WITH AN ORGANIC VAPOR CARTRIDGE(S) WITH A FULL FACEPIECE AND ORGANIC VAPOR CARTRIDGE(S) IN COMBINATION WITH A DUST AND MIST FILTER.

POWERED AIR-PURIFYING RESPIRATOR WITH A TIGHT-FITTING FACEPIECE AND ORGANIC VAPOR CARTRIDGE(S) IN COMBINATION WITH A HIGH-EFFICIENCY PARTICULATE FILTER.

TYPE 'C' SUPPLIED-AIR RESPIRATOR WITH A FULL FACEPIECE OPERATED IN A PRESSURE-DEMAND OR OTHER POSITIVE PRESSURE MODE.

SELF-CONTAINED BREATHING APPARATUS WITH A FULL FACEPIECE OPERATED IN PRESSURE-DEMAND OR OTHER POSITIVE PRESSURE MODE.

FOR FIREFIGHTING AND OTHER IMMEDIATELY DANGEROUS TO LIFE OR HEALTH CONDITIONS:

SELF-CONTAINED BREATHING APPARATUS WITH FULL FACEPIECE OPERATED IN PRESSURE-DEMAND OR OTHER POSITIVE PRESSURE MODE.

SUPPLIED-AIR RESPIRATOR WITH FULL FACEPIECE AND OPERATED IN PRESSURE-DEMAND OR OTHER POSITIVE PRESSURE MODE IN COMBINATION WITH AN AUXILIARY SELF-CONTAINED BREATHING APPARATUS OPERATED IN PRESSURE-DEMAND OR OTHER POSITIVE PRESSURE MODE.

CLOTHING: EMPLOYEE MUST WEAR APPROPRIATE PROTECTIVE (IMPERVIOUS) CLOTHING AND EQUIPMENT TO PREVENT REPEATED OR PROLONGED SKIN CONTACT WITH THIS SUBSTANCE.

GLOVES: EMPLOYEE MUST WEAR APPROPRIATE PROTECTIVE GLOVES TO PREVENT CONTACT WITH THIS SUBSTANCE.

EYE PROTECTION: EMPLOYEE MUST WEAR SPLASH-PROOF OR DUST-RESISTANT SAFETY GOGGLES TO PREVENT EYE CONTACT WITH THIS SUBSTANCE.

EMERGENCY EYE WASH: WHERE THERE IS ANY POSSIBILITY THAT AN EMPLOYEE'S EYES MAY BE EXPOSED TO THIS SUBSTANCE, THE EMPLOYER SHOULD PROVIDE AN EYE WASH FOUNTAIN WITHIN THE IMMEDIATE WORK AREA FOR EMERGENCY USE.

AUTHORIZED BY- OCCUPATIONAL HEALTH SERVICES, INC.

CREATION DATE: 10/04/89 ***REVISION DATE:*** 05/10/90

MATERIAL SAFETY DATA SHEET

OCCUPATIONAL HEALTH SERVICES, INC.
AGRICULTURE AND PESTICIDE DIVISION
450 SEVENTH AVENUE, SUITE 2407
NEW YORK, NEW YORK 10123
1-800-445-MSDS OR (212) 967-1100

EMERGENCY CONTACT:
JOHN S. BRANSFORD, JR. (615) 292-1180

SUBSTANCE IDENTIFICATION

CAS-NUMBER 26225-79-6

SUBSTANCE: **ETHOFUMESATE**

TRADE NAMES/SYNONYMS: 5-BENZOFURANOL, 2-ETHOXY-2,3-DIHYDRO-3,3-DIMETHYL-, METHANESULFONATE, (+,-)-; (+,-)-2-ETHOXY-2,3-DIHYDRO-3,3-DIMETHYL-5-BENZOFURANOL METHANESULFONATE; (+,-)-2-ETHOXY-2,3-DIHYDRO-3,3-DIMETHYLBENZOFURAN-5-YL-METHANE SULFONATE; (+,-)-2-ETHOXY-2,3-DIHYDRO-3,3-DIMETHYLBENZOFURAN-5-YL METHANESULPHONATE (+,-)-2-ETHOXY-2,3-DIHYDRO-3,3-DIMETHYLBENZOFURAN-5-YL METHANESULFONATE; (+,-)-2-ETHOXY-2,3-DIHYDRO-3,3-DIMETHYL-5-BENZOFURANYL METHANESULFONATE; 2-ETHOXY-2,3-DIHYDRO-3,3-DIMETHYL-5-BENZOFURANOL METHANESULFONATE; 2-ETHOXY-2,3-DIHYDRO-3,3-DIMETHYL-5-BENZOFURANYL METHANESULPHONATE; NC 8438; NORTON; TRAMAT; C13H18O5S; PST72404

CHEMICAL FAMILY: BENZOFURAN DERIVATIVE SULFONATE

MOLECULAR FORMULA: C13-H18-O5-S

MOLECULAR WEIGHT: 286.30

CERCLA RATINGS (SCALE 0-3): HEALTH=2 FIRE=1 REACTIVITY=0 PERSISTENCE=2

NFPA RATINGS (SCALE 0-4): HEALTH=2 FIRE=1 REACTIVITY=0

COMPONENTS AND CONTAMINANTS

COMPONENT: ETHOFUMESATE ***PERCENT:*** 100
CAS# 26225-79-6

OTHER CONTAMINANTS: NONE

EXPOSURE LIMITS: NO OCCUPATIONAL EXPOSURE LIMITS ESTABLISHED BY OSHA, ACGIH, OR NIOSH.

PHYSICAL DATA

DESCRIPTION: COLORLESS OR WHITE CRYSTALLINE SOLID.

MELTING POINT: 158-162 F (70-72 C) ***SPECIFIC GRAVITY:*** NOT AVAILABLE

VAPOR PRESSURE: NEGLIGIBLE ***SOLUBILITY IN WATER:*** 0.011%

SOLVENT SOLUBILITY: SOLUBLE IN ACETONE, BENZENE, CHLOROFORM, DIOXANE, ETHANOL, ACETONITRILE SOLUTIONS; SLIGHTLY SOLUBLE IN HEXANE.

FIRE AND EXPLOSION DATA

FIRE AND EXPLOSION HAZARD: SLIGHT FIRE HAZARD WHEN EXPOSED TO HEAT OR FLAME.

FIREFIGHTING MEDIA: DRY CHEMICAL, CARBON DIOXIDE, HALON, WATER SPRAY OR STANDARD FOAM (1987 EMERGENCY RESPONSE GUIDEBOOK, DOT P 5800.4). FOR LARGER FIRES, USE WATER SPRAY, FOG OR STANDARD FOAM (1987 EMERGENCY RESPONSE GUIDEBOOK, DOT P 5800.4).

FIREFIGHTING: MOVE CONTAINERS FROM FIRE AREA IF POSSIBLE (1987 EMERGENCY RESPONSE GUIDEBOOK, DOT P 5800.4, GUIDE PAGE 53). EXTINGUISH FIRE USING AGENTS SUITABLE FOR TYPE OF SURROUNDING FIRE. USE WATER IN FLOODING AMOUNTS AS A FOG. AVOID BREATHING DUSTS AND FUMES FROM BURNING MATERIAL; KEEP UPWIND.

TOXICITY

ETHOFUMESATE: TOXICITY DATA: 1440 MG/KG SKIN-RAT LD50; 1130 MG/KG ORAL-RAT LD50. CARCINOGEN STATUS: NONE. ACUTE TOXICITY LEVEL: MODERATELY TOXIC BY DERMAL ABSORPTION AND INGESTION. TARGET EFFECTS: NO DATA AVAILABLE.

HEALTH EFFECTS AND FIRST AID

INHALATION: ETHOFUMESATE: **ACUTE EXPOSURE-** NO DATA AVAILABLE. **CHRONIC EXPOSURE-** NO DATA AVAILABLE.

FIRST AID- REMOVE FROM EXPOSURE AREA TO FRESH AIR IMMEDIATELY. IF BREATHING HAS STOPPED, PERFORM ARTIFICIAL RESPIRATION. KEEP PERSON WARM AND AT REST. TREAT SYMPTOMATICALLY AND SUPPORTIVELY. GET MEDICAL ATTENTION IMMEDIATELY.

SKIN CONTACT: ETHOFUMESATE: **ACUTE EXPOSURE-** A LETHAL CONCENTRATION IN RATS BY DERMAL ABSORPTION IS GREATER THAN 1440 MG/KG. AN EMULSIFIABLE CONCENTRATE FORMULATION MAY CAUSE SKIN IRRITATION. **CHRONIC EXPOSURE-** NO DATA AVAILABLE.

FIRST AID- REMOVE CONTAMINATED CLOTHING AND SHOES IMMEDIATELY. WASH AFFECTED AREA WITH SOAP OR MILD DETERGENT AND LARGE AMOUNTS OF WATER UNTIL NO EVIDENCE OF CHEMICAL REMAINS (APPROXIMATELY 15-20 MINUTES). GET MEDICAL ATTENTION IMMEDIATELY.

EYE CONTACT: ETHOFUMESATE: **ACUTE EXPOSURE-** AN EMULSIFIABLE CONCENTRATE FORMULATION MAY CAUSE EYE IRRITATION. **CHRONIC EXPOSURE-** NO DATA AVAILABLE.

FIRST AID- WASH EYES IMMEDIATELY WITH LARGE AMOUNTS OF WATER OR NORMAL SALINE, OCCASIONALLY LIFTING UPPER AND LOWER LIDS, UNTIL NO EVIDENCE OF CHEMICAL REMAINS (APPROXIMATELY 15-20 MINUTES). GET MEDICAL ATTENTION IMMEDIATELY.

INGESTION: ETHOFUMESATE: **ACUTE EXPOSURE-** A LETHAL DOSE IN RATS WAS 1130 MG/KG. **CHRONIC EXPOSURE-** THE NO-EFFECT LEVEL FOR RATS WAS GREATER THAN A 1000 MG/KG DIET AS DETERMINE BY 2-YEAR STUDY.

FIRST AID- REMOVE BY GASTRIC LAVAGE AND CATHARSIS. MAINTAIN BLOOD PRESSURE AND AIRWAY. GIVE OXYGEN IF RESPIRATION IS DEPRESSED. DO NOT PERFORM GASTRIC LAVAGE IF VICTIM IS UNCONSCIOUS. GET MEDICAL ATTENTION IMMEDIATELY (DREISBACH, HANDBOOK OF POISONING, 12TH ED.). ADMINISTRATION OF LAVAGE OR OXYGEN SHOULD BE PERFORMED BY QUALIFIED MEDICAL PERSONNEL.

ANTIDOTE: NO SPECIFIC ANTIDOTE. TREAT SYMPTOMATICALLY AND SUPPORTIVELY.

REACTIVITY

REACTIVITY: STABLE UNDER NORMAL TEMPERATURES AND PRESSURES.

INCOMPATIBILITIES: ETHOFUMESATE: NO DATA AVAILABLE.

DECOMPOSITION: THERMAL DECOMPOSITION PRODUCTS MAY INCLUDE TOXIC OXIDES OF SULFUR AND CARBON.

POLYMERIZATION: HAZARDOUS POLYMERIZATION HAS NOT BEEN REPORTED TO OCCUR UNDER NORMAL TEMPERATURES AND PRESSURES.

STORAGE AND DISPOSAL

OBSERVE ALL FEDERAL, STATE AND LOCAL REGULATIONS WHEN STORING OR DISPOSING OF THIS SUBSTANCE. FOR ASSISTANCE, CONTACT THE DISTRICT DIRECTOR OF THE ENVIRONMENTAL PROTECTION AGENCY.

STORAGE

STORE IN ACCORDANCE WITH 40 CFR 165 RECOMMENDED PROCEDURES FOR THE DISPOSAL AND STORAGE OF PESTICIDES AND PESTICIDE CONTAINERS.

DISPOSAL

DISPOSAL MUST BE IN ACCORDANCE WITH 40 CFR 165 RECOMMENDED PROCEDURES FOR THE DISPOSAL AND STORAGE OF PESTICIDES AND PESTICIDE CONTAINERS.

CONDITIONS TO AVOID

MAY BURN BUT DOES NOT IGNITE READILY.

SPILL AND LEAK PROCEDURES

OCCUPATIONAL SPILL: DO NOT TOUCH SPILLED MATERIAL. STOP LEAK IF YOU CAN DO IT WITHOUT RISK. FOR SMALL SPILLS, TAKE UP WITH SAND OR OTHER ABSORBENT MATERIAL AND PLACE INTO CONTAINERS FOR LATER DISPOSAL. FOR SMALL DRY SPILLS, WITH A CLEAN SHOVEL PLACE MATERIAL INTO CLEAN, DRY CONTAINER AND COVER. MOVE CONTAINERS FROM SPILL AREA. FOR LARGER SPILLS, DIKE FAR AHEAD OF SPILL FOR LATER DISPOSAL. KEEP UNNECESSARY PEOPLE AWAY. ISOLATE HAZARD AREA AND DENY ENTRY.

PROTECTIVE EQUIPMENT

VENTILATION: PROVIDE LOCAL EXHAUST OR GENERAL DILUTION VENTILATION SYSTEM.

RESPIRATOR: THE FOLLOWING RESPIRATORS ARE RECOMMENDED BASED ON INFORMATION FOUND IN THE PHYSICAL DATA, TOXICITY AND HEALTH EFFECTS SECTIONS. THEY ARE RANKED IN ORDER FROM MINIMUM TO MAXIMUM RESPIRATORY PROTECTION. THE SPECIFIC RESPIRATOR SELECTED MUST BE BASED ON CONTAMINATION LEVELS FOUND IN THE WORK PLACE, MUST NOT EXCEED THE WORKING LIMITS OF THE RESPIRATOR AND BE JOINTLY APPROVED BY THE NATIONAL INSTITUTE FOR OCCUPATIONAL SAFETY AND HEALTH AND THE MINE SAFETY AND HEALTH ADMINISTRATION (NIOSH-MSHA).

CHEMICAL CARTRIDGE RESPIRATOR WITH AN ORGANIC VAPOR CARTRIDGE(S) WITH A FULL FACEPIECE AND ORGANIC VAPOR CARTRIDGE(S) IN COMBINATION WITH A DUST AND MIST FILTER.

POWERED AIR-PURIFYING RESPIRATOR WITH A TIGHT-FITTING FACEPIECE AND ORGANIC VAPOR CARTRIDGE(S) IN COMBINATION WITH A HIGH-EFFICIENCY PARTICULATE FILTER.

TYPE 'C' SUPPLIED-AIR RESPIRATOR WITH A FULL FACEPIECE OPERATED IN A PRESSURE-DEMAND OR OTHER POSITIVE PRESSURE MODE.

SELF-CONTAINED BREATHING APPARATUS WITH A FULL FACEPIECE OPERATED IN PRESSURE-DEMAND OR OTHER POSITIVE PRESSURE MODE.

FOR FIREFIGHTING AND OTHER IMMEDIATELY DANGEROUS TO LIFE OR HEALTH CONDITIONS:

SELF-CONTAINED BREATHING APPARATUS WITH FULL FACEPIECE OPERATED IN PRESSURE-DEMAND OR OTHER POSITIVE PRESSURE MODE.

SUPPLIED-AIR RESPIRATOR WITH FULL FACEPIECE AND OPERATED IN PRESSURE-DEMAND OR OTHER POSITIVE PRESSURE MODE IN COMBINATION WITH AN AUXILIARY SELF-CONTAINED BREATHING APPARATUS OPERATED IN PRESSURE-DEMAND OR OTHER POSITIVE PRESSURE MODE.

CLOTHING: EMPLOYEE MUST WEAR APPROPRIATE PROTECTIVE (IMPERVIOUS) CLOTHING AND EQUIPMENT TO PREVENT REPEATED OR PROLONGED SKIN CONTACT WITH THIS SUBSTANCE.

GLOVES: EMPLOYEE MUST WEAR APPROPRIATE PROTECTIVE GLOVES TO PREVENT CONTACT WITH THIS SUBSTANCE.

EYE PROTECTION: EMPLOYEE MUST WEAR SPLASH-PROOF OR DUST-RESISTANT SAFETY GOGGLES TO PREVENT EYE CONTACT WITH THIS SUBSTANCE. EMERGENCY EYE WASH: WHERE THERE IS ANY POSSIBILITY THAT AN EMPLOYEE'S EYES MAY BE EXPOSED TO THIS SUBSTANCE, THE EMPLOYER SHOULD PROVIDE AN EYE WASH FOUNTAIN WITHIN THE IMMEDIATE WORK AREA FOR EMERGENCY USE.

AUTHORIZED BY- OCCUPATIONAL HEALTH SERVICES, INC.

CREATION DATE: 10/04/89 ***REVISION DATE:*** 05/10/90

MATERIAL SAFETY DATA SHEET

OCCUPATIONAL HEALTH SERVICES, INC.
AGRICULTURE AND PESTICIDE DIVISION
450 SEVENTH AVENUE, SUITE 2407
NEW YORK, NEW YORK 10123
1-800-445-MSDS OR (212) 967-1100

EMERGENCY CONTACT:
JOHN S. BRANSFORD, JR. (615) 292-1180

SUBSTANCE IDENTIFICATION

CAS-NUMBER 36756-79-3

SUBSTANCE: TIOCABAZIL

TRADE NAMES/SYNONYMS: CARBAMOTHIOIC ACID, BIS(1-METHYLPROPYL)-, S-(PHENYLMETHYL) ESTER; BIS(1-METHYLPROPYL)CARBAMOTHIOIC ACID S-(PHENYLMETHYL) ESTER; S-BENZYL DI-SEC-BUTYLTHIOCARBAMATE; S-BENZYL DI-SEC-BUTYL(THIOCARBAMATE); S-(PHENYLMETHYL) BIS(1-

METHYLPROPYL)CARBAMOTHIOATE; S-BENZYL N,N-DI-SEC-BUTYLTHIOLCARBAMATE; N,N-DISECBUTYL-S-BENZYLTHIOLCARBAMATE; DREPAMON; M 3432; THIOCARBAZIL; PST72405

CHEMICAL FAMILY: THIOCARBAMATE

MOLECULAR FORMULA: C16-H25-N-O-S

MOLECULAR WEIGHT: 279.48

CERCLA RATINGS (SCALE 0-3): HEALTH=1 FIRE=U REACTIVITY=0 PERSISTENCE=1

NFPA RATINGS (SCALE 0-4): HEALTH=1 FIRE=U REACTIVITY=0

COMPONENTS AND CONTAMINANTS

COMPONENT: TIOCABAZIL ***PERCENT:*** 100

CAS# 36756-79-3

OTHER CONTAMINANTS: NONE

EXPOSURE LIMITS: NO OCCUPATIONAL EXPOSURE LIMITS ESTABLISHED BY OSHA, ACGIH, OR NIOSH.

PHYSICAL DATA

DESCRIPTION: COLORLESS LIQUID WITH A SLIGHTLY AROMATIC ODOR

BOILING POINT: 266-270 F (130-132 C) @ 0.1 MMHG

SPECIFIC GRAVITY: 1.023 20/4 C

VAPOR PRESSURE: 0.0007 MMHG @ 50 C ***SOLUBILITY IN WATER:*** 0.0025% AT 30 C

SOLVENT SOLUBILITY: SOLUBLE IN METHANOL, CYCLOHEXANONE, ACETONITRILE, BENZENE, N-HEPTANE, N-HEXANE, METHYLENE CHLORIDE, CHLOROFORM, AND MOST POLAR AND NONPOLAR SOLVENTS

FIRE AND EXPLOSION DATA

FIRE AND EXPLOSION HAZARD: UNKNOWN FIRE AND EXPLOSION HAZARD.

FIREFIGHTING MEDIA: DRY CHEMICAL, CARBON DIOXIDE, WATER SPRAY OR FOAM FOR LARGER FIRES, USE WATER SPRAY, FOG OR ALCOHOL FOAM

FIREFIGHTING: MOVE CONTAINER FROM FIRE AREA IF POSSIBLE. DO NOT SCATTER SPILLED MATERIAL WITH MORE WATER THAN NEEDED FOR FIRE CONTROL. DIKE FIRE CONTROL WATER FOR LATER DISPOSAL

USE AGENTS SUITABLE FOR TYPE OF SURROUNDING FIRE. AVOID BREATHING HAZARDOUS VAPORS, KEEP UPWIND.

TOXICITY

TIOCARBAZIL: TOXICITY DATA: 10000 MG/KG ORAL-RAT LD50; 8000 MG/KG ORAL-MICE LD50. CARCINOGEN STATUS: NONE. ACUTE TOXICITY LEVEL: SLIGHTLY TOXIC BY INGESTION. TARGET EFFECTS: NO DATA AVAILABLE.

HEALTH EFFECTS AND FIRST AID

INHALATION: TIOCARBAZIL: **ACUTE EXPOSURE-** INHALATION OF EXCESSIVE AMOUNTS OF SOME THIOCARBAMATES CAUSES SCRATCHY THROAT, SNEEZING, AND COUGHING. **CHRONIC EXPOSURE-** NO DATA AVAILABLE.

FIRST AID- REMOVE FROM EXPOSURE AREA TO FRESH AIR IMMEDIATELY. IF BREATHING HAS STOPPED, PERFORM ARTIFICIAL RESPIRATION. KEEP PERSON WARM AND AT REST. TREAT SYMPTOMATICALLY AND SUPPORTIVELY. GET MEDICAL ATTENTION IMMEDIATELY.

SKIN CONTACT: TIOCARBAZIL: **ACUTE EXPOSURE-** NO DEATHS WERE REPORTED IN RATS OR RABBITS FOLLOWING SKIN APPLICATION OF 1200 MG/KG. SOME THIOCARBAMATES ARE MODERATELY IRRITATING TO THE SKIN. **CHRONIC EXPOSURE-** NO DATA AVAILABLE.

FIRST AID- REMOVE CONTAMINATED CLOTHING AND SHOES IMMEDIATELY. WASH AFFECTED AREA WITH SOAP OR MILD DETERGENT AND LARGE AMOUNTS OF WATER UNTIL NO EVIDENCE OF CHEMICAL REMAINS (APPROXIMATELY 15-20 MINUTES). GET MEDICAL ATTENTION IMMEDIATELY.

EYE CONTACT: TIOCARBAZIL: **ACUTE EXPOSURE-** SOME THIOCARBAMATES ARE MODERATELY IRRITATING TO THE EYES. **CHRONIC EXPOSURE-** NO DATA AVAILABLE.

FIRST AID- WASH EYES IMMEDIATELY WITH LARGE AMOUNTS OF WATER OR NORMAL SALINE, OCCASIONALLY LIFTING UPPER AND LOWER LIDS, UNTIL NO EVIDENCE OF CHEMICAL REMAINS (APPROXIMATELY 15-20 MINUTES). GET MEDICAL ATTENTION IMMEDIATELY.

INGESTION: TIOCARBAZIL: **ACUTE EXPOSURE-** A LETHAL DOSE IN RATS WAS 10,000 MG/KG. **CHRONIC EXPOSURE-** IN A 2-YEAR STUDY OF DOGS AND RATS RECEIVING 1000 MG/KG DIET, NO ADVERSE EFFECTS EXCEPT FOR A SLIGHT WEIGHT LOSS IN DOGS WERE REPORTED. THERE WERE NO SIGNIFICANT DIFFERENCES BETWEEN CONTROLS AND ALBINO RATS RECEIVING 300 MG/KG DIET FOR 3 GENERATIONS.

FIRST AID- GIVE SYRUP OF IPECAC, FOLLOWED BY 1-2 GLASSES OF WATER, TO INDUCE VOMITING (ADULTS: 30 ML). FOLLOWING EMESIS, ADMINISTER 30-50 GRAMS ACTIVATED CHARCOAL. FOLLOW CHARCOAL WITH SODIUM OR MAGNESIUM SULFATE, 250 MG/KG, TO REMOVE TOXICANT FROM THE GUT BY CATHARSIS (EPA, RECOGNITION AND MANAGEMENT OF PESTICIDE POISONINGS, 3RD ED.). FIRST AID SHOULD BE ADMINISTERED UNDER THE DIRECTION OF QUALIFIED MEDICAL PERSONNEL. GET MEDICAL ATTENTION.

ANTIDOTE: NO SPECIFIC ANTIDOTE. TREAT SYMPTOMATICALLY AND SUPPORTIVELY.

REACTIVITY

REACTIVITY: STABLE UNDER NORMAL TEMPERATURES AND PRESSURES.

INCOMPATIBILITIES: TIOCARBAZIL: NO DATA AVAILABLE.

DECOMPOSITION: THERMAL DECOMPOSITION MAY RELEASE TOXIC AND/OR HAZARDOUS GASES.

POLYMERIZATION: HAZARDOUS POLYMERIZATION HAS NOT BEEN REPORTED TO OCCUR UNDER NORMAL TEMPERATURES AND PRESSURES.

STORAGE AND DISPOSAL

OBSERVE ALL FEDERAL, STATE AND LOCAL REGULATIONS WHEN STORING OR DISPOSING OF THIS SUBSTANCE. FOR ASSISTANCE, CONTACT THE DISTRICT DIRECTOR OF THE ENVIRONMENTAL PROTECTION AGENCY.

STORAGE

STORE IN ACCORDANCE WITH 40 CFR 165 RECOMMENDED PROCEDURES FOR THE DISPOSAL AND STORAGE OF PESTICIDES AND PESTICIDE CONTAINERS.

STORE IN SEALED ORIGINAL CONTAINERS, IN WELL-AIRED, FRESH, DRY AND SHADED AREA. THE TEMPERATURE OF THIS MATERIAL SHOULD NOT EXCEED 77-86 DEGREES F (25-30 DEGREES C). STORE AWAY FROM SOURCES OF HEAT, FREE FLAMES OR SPARK-GENERATING EQUIPMENT.

DISPOSAL

DISPOSAL MUST BE IN ACCORDANCE WITH 40 CFR 165 RECOMMENDED PROCEDURES FOR THE DISPOSAL AND STORAGE OF PESTICIDES AND PESTICIDE CONTAINERS.

CONDITIONS TO AVOID

NONE REPORTED.

SPILL AND LEAK PROCEDURES

OCCUPATIONAL SPILL: STOP LEAK IF YOU CAN DO IT WITHOUT RISK. FOR SMALL SPILLS, TAKE UP WITH SAND OR OTHER ABSORBENT MATERIAL AND PLACE INTO CLEAN, DRY CONTAINERS FOR LATER DISPOSAL. KEEP UNNECESSARY PEOPLE AWAY. ISOLATE HAZARD AREA AND DENY ENTRY.

PROTECTIVE EQUIPMENT

VENTILATION: PROVIDE LOCAL EXHAUST OR GENERAL DILUTION VENTILATION SYSTEM.

RESPIRATOR: THE FOLLOWING RESPIRATORS ARE RECOMMENDED BASED ON INFORMATION FOUND IN THE PHYSICAL DATA, TOXICITY AND HEALTH EFFECTS SECTIONS. THEY ARE RANKED IN ORDER FROM MINIMUM TO MAXIMUM RESPIRATORY PROTECTION. THE SPECIFIC RESPIRATOR SELECTED MUST BE BASED ON CONTAMINATION LEVELS FOUND IN THE WORK PLACE, MUST NOT EXCEED THE WORKING LIMITS OF THE RESPIRATOR AND BE JOINTLY APPROVED BY THE NATIONAL INSTITUTE FOR OCCUPATIONAL SAFETY AND HEALTH AND THE MINE SAFETY AND HEALTH ADMINISTRATION (NIOSH-MSHA).

CHEMICAL CARTRIDGE RESPIRATOR WITH FULL FACEPIECE AND PESTICIDE CARTRIDGE.

TYPE 'C' SUPPLIED-AIR RESPIRATOR WITH A FULL FACEPIECE OPERATED IN PRESSURE-DEMAND OR OTHER POSITIVE PRESSURE MODE OR WITH A FULL FACEPIECE, HELMET OR HOOD OPERATED IN CONTINUOUS-FLOW MODE.

SELF-CONTAINED BREATHING APPARATUS OPERATED IN PRESSURE-DEMAND OR OTHER POSITIVE PRESSURE MODE.

FOR FIREFIGHTING AND OTHER IMMEDIATELY DANGEROUS TO LIFE OR HEALTH CONDITIONS:

SELF-CONTAINED BREATHING APPARATUS WITH FULL FACEPIECE OPERATED IN PRESSURE-DEMAND OR OTHER POSITIVE PRESSURE MODE.

SUPPLIED-AIR RESPIRATOR WITH FULL FACEPIECE AND OPERATED IN PRESSURE-DEMAND OR OTHER POSITIVE PRESSURE MODE IN COMBINATION WITH AN AUXILIARY SELF-CONTAINED BREATHING APPARATUS OPERATED IN PRESSURE-DEMAND OR OTHER POSITIVE PRESSURE MODE.

CLOTHING: EMPLOYEE MUST WEAR APPROPRIATE PROTECTIVE (IMPERVIOUS) CLOTHING AND EQUIPMENT TO PREVENT REPEATED OR PROLONGED SKIN CONTACT WITH THIS SUBSTANCE.

GLOVES: EMPLOYEE MUST WEAR APPROPRIATE PROTECTIVE GLOVES TO PREVENT CONTACT WITH THIS SUBSTANCE.

EYE PROTECTION: EMPLOYEE MUST WEAR SPLASH-PROOF OR DUST-RESISTANT SAFETY GOGGLES TO PREVENT EYE CONTACT WITH THIS SUBSTANCE.

EMERGENCY EYE WASH: WHERE THERE IS ANY POSSIBILITY THAT AN EMPLOYEE'S EYES MAY BE EXPOSED TO THIS SUBSTANCE, THE EMPLOYER SHOULD PROVIDE AN EYE WASH FOUNTAIN WITHIN THE IMMEDIATE WORK AREA FOR EMERGENCY USE.

AUTHORIZED BY- OCCUPATIONAL HEALTH SERVICES, INC.
CREATION DATE: 10/05/89 ***REVISION DATE:*** 05/14/90

MATERIAL SAFETY DATA SHEET

OCCUPATIONAL HEALTH SERVICES, INC.
AGRICULTURE AND PESTICIDE DIVISION
450 SEVENTH AVENUE, SUITE 2407
NEW YORK, NEW YORK 10123
1-800-445-MSDS OR (212) 967-1100

EMERGENCY CONTACT:
JOHN S. BRANSFORD, JR. (615) 292-1180

SUBSTANCE IDENTIFICATION

CAS-NUMBER 1646-88-4

SUBSTANCE: **ALDOXYCARB**

TRADE NAMES/SYNONYMS: PROPANAL, 2-METHYL-2-(METHYLSULFONYL)-, O-((METHYLAMINO)CARBONYL)OXIME; PROPIONALDEHYDE, 2-METHYL-2-(METHYLSULFONYL)-, O-(METHYLCARBAMOYL) OXIME; 2-METHYL-2-(METHYLSULFONYL)PROPANAL O-((METHYLAMINO)CARBONYL)OXIME; 2-METHYL-2-(METHYLSULFONYL)PROPIONALDEHYDE O-(METHYLCARBAMOYL)OXIME; 2-MESYL-2-METHYLPROPIONALDEHYDE O-METHYLCARBAMOYLOXIME; 2-METHYL-2-METHYLSULPHONYLPROPIONALDEHYDE O-METHYLCARBAMOYLOXIME; ALDICARB SULFONE; STANDAK; SULFOCARB; UC 21865; ENT 29 261; C7H14N2O4S; PST72406

CHEMICAL FAMILY: CARBAMATE

MOLECULAR FORMULA: C7-H14-N2-O4-S

MOLECULAR WEIGHT: 222.29

CERCLA RATINGS (SCALE 0-3): HEALTH=3 FIRE=1 REACTIVITY=0 PERSISTENCE=1

NFPA RATINGS (SCALE 0-4): HEALTH=4 FIRE=1 REACTIVITY=0

COMPONENTS AND CONTAMINANTS

COMPONENT: ALDOXYCARB ***PERCENT:*** 100.0
CAS# 1646-88-4

OTHER CONTAMINANTS: NONE

EXPOSURE LIMITS: NO OCCUPATIONAL EXPOSURE LIMITS ESTABLISHED BY OSHA, ACGIH, OR NIOSH.

PHYSICAL DATA

DESCRIPTION: COLORLESS OR WHITE CRYSTALLINE SOLID.

MELTING POINT: 284-288 F (140-142 C) ***SPECIFIC GRAVITY:*** NOT AVAILABLE

VAPOR PRESSURE: 0.00009 MMHG @ 25 C ***SOLUBILITY IN WATER:*** 0.9% @ 25 C

SOLVENT SOLUBILITY: SOLUBLE IN ACETONE, ACETONITRILE, AND DICHLOROMETHANE.

FIRE AND EXPLOSION DATA

FIRE AND EXPLOSION HAZARD: SLIGHT FIRE HAZARD WHEN EXPOSED TO HEAT OR FLAME.

FIREFIGHTING MEDIA: DRY CHEMICAL, CARBON DIOXIDE, HALON, WATER SPRAY OR STANDARD FOAM (1987 EMERGENCY RESPONSE GUIDEBOOK, DOT P 5800.4). FOR LARGER FIRES, USE WATER SPRAY, FOG OR STANDARD FOAM (1987 EMERGENCY RESPONSE GUIDEBOOK, DOT P 5800.4).

FIREFIGHTING: MOVE CONTAINERS FROM FIRE AREA IF POSSIBLE. FIGHT FIRE FROM MAXIMUM DISTANCE. STAY AWAY FROM STORAGE TANK ENDS. DIKE FIRE CONTROL WATER FOR LATER DISPOSAL. DO NOT SCATTER MATERIAL (1987 EMERGENCY RESPONSE GUIDEBOOK, DOT P 5800.4, GUIDE PAGE 55). EXTINGUISH USING AGENTS SUITABLE FOR TYPE OF SURROUNDING FIRE. USE FLOODING AMOUNTS OF WATER AS FOG. AVOID BREATHING TOXIC DUST AND FUMES FROM BURNING MATERIAL; KEEP UPWIND.

TRANSPORTATION DATA

DEPARTMENT OF TRANSPORTATION HAZARD CLASSIFICATION 49 CFR 172.101: POISON B

DEPARTMENT OF TRANSPORTATION LABELING REQUIREMENTS 49 CFR 172.101 AND SUBPART E: POISON

DEPARTMENT OF TRANSPORTATION PACKAGING REQUIREMENTS: 49 CFR 173.365 EXCEPTIONS: 49 CFR 173.364

TOXICITY

ALDOXYCARB: TOXICITY DATA: 120 MG/M3/4 HOURS INHALATION-RAT LC50; 200 MG/KG SKIN-RABBIT LD50; 1000 MG/KG SKIN-RAT LD50; 25 MG/KG ORAL-RAT LD50. CARCINOGEN STATUS: NONE. ACUTE TOXICITY: HIGHLY TOXIC BY INHALATION, INGESTION, AND DERMAL ABSORPTION. TARGET EFFECTS: CHOLINESTERASE INHIBITOR. AT INCREASED RISK FROM EXPOSURE: PERSONS WITH ASTHMA, DIABETES. CARDIOVASCULAR DISEASE, MECHANICAL OBSTRUCTION OF THE GASTROINTESTINAL OR UROGENITAL TRACT, AND THOSE IN VAGOTONIC STATES.*

* MAY BE BASED ON GENERAL INFORMATION ON CARBAMATES.

HEALTH EFFECTS AND FIRST AID

INHALATION: ALDOXYCARB: HIGHLY TOXIC. SEE INFORMATION ON CARBAMATES.
CARBAMATES: CHOLINESTERASE INHIBITOR. **ACUTE EXPOSURE-** WHEN INHALED, THE FIRST EFFECTS OF CHOLINESTERASE INHIBITION ARE USUALLY RESPIRATORY AND MAY INCLUDE NASAL HYPEREMIA AND WATERY DISCHARGE, CHEST DISCOMFORT, DYSPNEA, AND WHEEZING DUE TO INCREASED BRONCHIAL SECRETIONS AND BRONCHOCONSTRICTION. OTHER SYSTEMIC EFFECTS MAY BEGIN WITHIN A FEW MINUTES OR SEVERAL HOURS OF EXPOSURE. SYMPTOMS MAY INCLUDE NAUSEA, VOMITING, DIARRHEA, ABDOMINAL CRAMPS, HEADACHE, VERTIGO, OCULAR PAIN, CILIARY MUSCLE SPASM, BLURRING OR DIMNESS OF VISION, MIOSIS, OR IN SOME CASES MYDRIASIS, LACRIMATION, SALIVATION, SWEATING, AND CONFUSION. OTHER REPORTED CENTRAL NERVOUS SYSTEM OR NEUROMUSCULAR EFFECTS INCLUDE ATAXIA, SLURRED SPEECH, AREFLEXIA, WEAKNESS, FATIGUE, TWITCHING, FASCICULATION, TREMOR, AND EVENTUALLY PARALYSIS OF THE EXTREMITIES AND POSSIBLY OF THE RESPIRATORY MUSCLES. IN SEVERE CASES, THERE MAY ALSO BE INVOLUNTARY DEFECATION AND URINATION, BRADYCARDIA, HYPOTENSION, PULMONARY EDEMA, CONVULSIONS, COMA, AND DEATH FROM RESPIRATORY FAILURE OR CARDIAC ARREST. CARBAMATES GENERALLY DO NOT ACCUMULATE IN MAMMALIAN TISSUE AND THE CHOLINESTERASE INHIBITION REVERSES RATHER RAPIDLY. IN NON-FATAL CASES, THE ILLNESS GENERALLY LASTS LESS THAN 24 HOURS. **CHRONIC EXPOSURE-** PROLONGED OR REPEATED EXPOSURE MAY CAUSE EFFECTS AS DESCRIBED IN ACUTE EXPOSURE.

FIRST AID- REMOVE FROM EXPOSURE AREA TO FRESH AIR IMMEDIATELY. IF BREATHING HAS STOPPED, GIVE ARTIFICIAL RESPIRATION. MAINTAIN AIRWAY AND BLOOD PRESSURE AND ADMINISTER OXYGEN IF AVAILABLE. KEEP AFFECTED PERSON WARM AND AT REST. TREAT SYMPTOMATICALLY AND SUPPORTIVELY. ADMINISTRATION OF OXYGEN SHOULD BE PERFORMED BY QUALIFIED PERSONNEL. GET MEDICAL ATTENTION IMMEDIATELY.

SKIN CONTACT: ALDOXYCARB: HIGHLY TOXIC. MAY CAUSE SLIGHT SKIN IRRITATION. SEE INFORMATION ON CARBAMATES.
CARBAMATES: CHOLINESTERASE INHIBITOR. **ACUTE EXPOSURE-** SOME COMPOUNDS MAY CAUSE IRRITATION. LOCALIZED SWEATING AND FASCICULATIONS MAY OCCUR AT THE SITE OF CONTACT. IF SUFFICIENT AMOUNTS ARE ABSORBED THROUGH THE SKIN, OTHER EFFECTS OF CHOLINESTERASE INHIBITION MAY OCCUR AS DESCRIBED IN ACUTE INHALATION; SYMPTOMS MAY BE DELAYED FOR 2-3 HOURS, USUALLY NO MORE THAN 8 HOURS. **CHRONIC EXPOSURE-** REPEATED OR PROLONGED EXPOSURE MAY CAUSE EFFECTS AS DESCRIBED IN ACUTE EXPOSURE.

FIRST AID- REMOVE CONTAMINATED CLOTHING IMMEDIATELY. WASH CONTAMINATED AREAS WITH SOAP AND WATER FOLLOWED BY ALCOHOL (ARENA, POISONING, 4TH ED.). EMERGENCY PERSONNEL SHOULD WEAR GLOVES AND AVOID CONTAMINATION. TREAT RESPIRATORY DIFFICULTY WITH ARTIFICIAL RESPIRATION. GET MEDICAL ATTENTION IMMEDIATELY.

EYE CONTACT: ALDOXYCARB: SEE INFORMATION ON CARBAMATES. CARBAMATES: CHOLINESTERASE INHIBITOR. **ACUTE EXPOSURE-** DIRECT CONTACT MAY CAUSE PAIN, HYPEREMIA, LACRIMATION, TWITCHING OF THE EYELIDS, MIOSIS, AND CILIARY MUSCLE SPASM WITH LOSS OF ACCOMODATION, BLURRED OR DIMMED VISION AND BROWACHE. SOMETIMES MYDRIASIS MAY OCCUR INSTEAD OF MIOSIS. WITH SUFFICIENT EXPOSURE, OTHER SYMPTOMS OF CHOLINESTERASE INHIBITION MAY OCCUR AS DESCRIBED IN ACUTE INHALATION. **CHRONIC EXPOSURE-** PROLONGED EXPOSURE MAY CAUSE EFFECTS AS DESCRIBED IN ACUTE EXPOSURE. SOME COMPOUNDS HAVE CAUSED TOXIC EFFECTS ON THE CRYSTALLINE LENS, CONJUNCTIVAL THICKENING AND OBSTRUCTION OF NASOLACRIMAL CANALS WHEN USED AS MIOTIC EYE DROPS.

FIRST AID- IRRIGATE EYES WITH WATER OR SALINE SOLUTION. IF SYMPTOMS OF POISONING OCCUR, TREAT RESPIRATORY DIFFICULTY WITH ARTIFICIAL RESPIRATION AND OXYGEN. OBSERVE PATIENT FOR AT LEAST 24-36 HOURS (GOSSELIN, CLINICAL TOXICOLOGY OF COMMERCIAL PRODUCTS, 5TH ED.). GET MEDICAL ATTENTION IMMEDIATELY. OXYGEN SHOULD BE ADMINISTERED BY QUALIFIED MEDICAL PERSONNEL.

INGESTION: ALDOXYCARB: HIGHLY TOXIC. IN LIFE-SPAN FEEDING STUDIES THE NO EFFECTS LEVEL WAS 9.6 MG/KG IN MICE AND 2.4 MG/KG IN RATS. TERATOLOGY, REPRODUCTION AND MUTAGENIC STUDIES WERE NEGATIVE. SEE INFORMATION ON CARBAMATES.

CARBAMATES: CHOLINESTERASE INHIBITOR. **ACUTE EXPOSURE**- WHEN INGESTED, THE FIRST EFFECTS MAY BE NAUSEA, VOMITING, ANOREXIA, ABDOMINAL CRAMPS, AND DIARRHEA. WITH ABSORPTION FROM THE GASTROINTESTINAL TRACT, THE OTHER EFFECTS OF CHOLINESTERASE INHIBITION AS DESCRIBED IN ACUTE INHALATION MAY OCCUR; SYMPTOMS MAY BEGIN WITHIN MINUTES OR BE DELAYED SEVERAL HOURS. **CHRONIC EXPOSURE**- REPEATED INGESTION MAY CAUSE EFFECTS AS DESCRIBED IN ACUTE EXPOSURE.

FIRST AID- IF PERSON IS ALERT AND RESPIRATION IS NOT DEPRESSED, GIVE SYRUP OF IPECAC FOLLOWED BY WATER (IF VOMITING OCCURS, KEEP HEAD BELOW HIPS TO PREVENT ASPIRATION). IF CONSCIOUSNESS LEVEL DECLINES OR VOMITING HAS NOT OCCURRED IN 15 MINUTES EMPTY STOMACH BY GASTRIC LAVAGE WITH THE AID OF CUFFED ENDOTRACHEAL TUBE USING ISOTONIC SALINE OR 5% SODIUM BICARBONATE FOLLOW WITH ACTIVATED CHARCOAL. ESTABLISH AND MAINTAIN AIRWAY. TREAT RESPIRATORY DIFFICULTY WITH ARTIFICIAL RESPIRATION AND OXYGEN. DO NOT GIVE MORPHINE, AMINOPHYLLINE, PHENOTHIAZINES, RESERPINE, FUROSEMIDE, OR ETHACRYNIC ACID (MORGAN, RECOGNITION AND MANAGEMENT OF PESTICIDE POISONINGS, 3RD ED.). TREAT SYMPTOMATICALLY AND SUPPORTIVELY. ADMINISTRATION OF OXYGEN AND LAVAGE MUST BE PERFORMED BY QUALIFIED MEDICAL PERSONNEL. GET MEDICAL ATTENTION IMMEDIATELY.

ANTIDOTE: THE FOLLOWING ANTIDOTE HAS BEEN RECOMMENDED. HOWEVER, THE DECISION AS TO WHETHER THE SEVERITY OF POISONING REQUIRES ADMINISTRATION OF ANY ANTIDOTE AND ACTUAL DOSE REQUIRED SHOULD BE MADE BY QUALIFIED MEDICAL PERSONNEL.

FOR CHOLINESTERASE INHIBITORS: ESTABLISH CLEAR AIRWAY AND TISSUE OXYGENATION BY ASPIRATION OF SECRETIONS, AND IF NECESSARY, BY ASSISTED PULMONARY VENTILATION WITH OXYGEN. IMPROVE TISSUE OXYGENATION AS MUCH AS POSSIBLE BEFORE ADMINISTERING ATROPINE TO MINIMIZE THE RISK OF VENTRICULAR FIBRILLATION. ADMINISTER ATROPINE SULFATE INTRAVENOUSLY, OR INTRAMUSCULARLY IF IV INJECTION IS NOT POSSIBLE. IN MODERATELY SEVERE POISONING ADMINISTER ATROPINE SULFATE, 0.4-2.0 MG REPEATED EVERY 15 MINUTES UNTIL ATROPINIZATION IS ACHIEVED (TACHYCARDIA, FLUSHING, DRY MOUTH, MYDRIASIS). MAINTAIN ATROPINIZATION BY REPEATED DOSES FOR 2-12 HOURS, OR LONGER, DEPENDING ON THE SEVERITY OF POISONING. THE APPEARANCE OF RALES IN THE LUNG BASES, MIOSIS, SALIVATION, NAUSEA, BRADYCARDIA, ARE ALL INDICATIONS OF INADEQUATE ATROPINIZATION. SEVERELY POISONED INDIVIDUALS MAY EXHIBIT REMARKABLE TOLERANCE TO ATROPINE; TWO OR MORE TIMES THE DOSAGES SUGGESTED ABOVE MAY BE NEEDED. PERSONS NOT POISONED OR ONLY SLIGHTLY POISONED, HOWEVER, MAY DEVELOP SIGNS OF ATROPINE TOXICITY FROM SUCH LARGE DOSAGES: FEVER, MUSCLE FIBRILLATIONS, AND DELIRIUM ARE THE MAIN SIGNS OF ATROPINE TOXICITY. IF THESE SIGNS APPEAR WHILE THE PATIENT IS FULLY ATROPINIZED, ATROPINE ADMINISTRATION SHOULD BE DISCONTINUED, AT LEAST TEMPORARILY. OBSERVE TREATED PATIENTS CLOSELY AT LEAST 24 HOURS TO INSURE THAT SYMPTOMS (POSSIBLY PULMONARY EDEMA) DO NOT RECUR AS ATROPINIZATION WEARS OFF. IN VERY SEVERE POISONINGS, METABOLIC DISPOSITION OF TOXICANT MAY REQUIRE SEVERAL HOURS OR DAYS DURING WHICH ATROPINIZATION MUST BE MAINTAINED. MARKEDLY LOWER LEVELS OF URINARY METABOLITES INDICATE THAT ATROPINE DOSAGE CAN BE TAPERED OFF. AS DOSAGE IS REDUCED, CHECK THE LUNG BASES FREQUENTLY FOR RALES. IF RALES ARE HEARD OR OTHER SYMPTOMS RETURN, RE-ESTABLISH ATROPINIZATION PROMPTLY (MORGAN, RECOGNITION AND MANAGEMENT OF PESTICIDE POISONINGS, 3RD ED.). ADMINISTRATION OF ANTIDOTE MUST BE PERFORMED BY QUALIFIED MEDICAL PERSONNEL.

REACTIVITY

REACTIVITY: STABLE UNDER NORMAL TEMPERATURES AND PRESSURES.

INCOMPATIBILITIES: ALDOXYCARB: ALKALIS (STRONG): DECOMPOSES. METAL ALLOYS: CORRODES. OXIDIZERS (STRONG): FIRE AND EXPLOSION HAZARD.

DECOMPOSITION: THERMAL DECOMPOSITION PRODUCTS MAY INCLUDE TOXIC OXIDES OF CARBON, NITROGEN, AND SULFUR.

POLYMERIZATION: HAZARDOUS POLYMERIZATION HAS NOT BEEN REPORTED TO OCCUR UNDER NORMAL TEMPERATURES AND PRESSURES.

STORAGE AND DISPOSAL

OBSERVE ALL FEDERAL, STATE AND LOCAL REGULATIONS WHEN STORING OR DISPOSING OF THIS SUBSTANCE. FOR ASSISTANCE, CONTACT THE DISTRICT DIRECTOR OF THE ENVIRONMENTAL PROTECTION AGENCY.

STORAGE

STORE IN ACCORDANCE WITH 40 CFR 165 RECOMMENDED PROCEDURES FOR THE DISPOSAL AND STORAGE OF PESTICIDES AND PESTICIDE CONTAINERS.
STORE AWAY FROM INCOMPATIBLE SUBSTANCES.

DISPOSAL

DISPOSAL MUST BE IN ACCORDANCE WITH 40 CFR 165 RECOMMENDED PROCEDURES FOR THE DISPOSAL AND STORAGE OF PESTICIDES AND PESTICIDE CONTAINERS.

CONDITIONS TO AVOID

MAY BURN BUT DOES NOT IGNITE READILY. CONTAINERS MAY EXPLODE IN HEAT OF FIRE.

SPILL AND LEAK PROCEDURES

OCCUPATIONAL SPILL: DO NOT TOUCH SPILLED MATERIAL. STOP LEAK IF YOU CAN DO IT WITHOUT RISK. USE WATER SPRAY TO REDUCE VAPORS. FOR SMALL SPILLS, TAKE UP WITH SAND OR OTHER ABSORBENT MATERIAL AND PLACE INTO CONTAINERS FOR LATER DISPOSAL. FOR SMALL DRY SPILLS, WITH A CLEAN SHOVEL PLACE MATERIAL INTO CLEAN, DRY CONTAINERS AND COVER. MOVE CONTAINERS FROM SPILL AREA. FOR LARGER SPILLS, DIKE FAR AHEAD OF SPILL FOR LATER DISPOSAL. KEEP UNNECESSARY PEOPLE AWAY. ISOLATE HAZARD AREA AND DENY ENTRY. VENTILATE CLOSED SPACES BEFORE ENTERING.

PROTECTIVE EQUIPMENT

VENTILATION: PROCESS ENCLOSURE RECOMMENDED.

RESPIRATOR: THE FOLLOWING RESPIRATORS ARE RECOMMENDED BASED ON INFORMATION FOUND IN THE PHYSICAL DATA, TOXICITY AND HEALTH EFFECTS SECTIONS. THEY ARE RANKED IN ORDER FROM MINIMUM TO MAXIMUM RESPIRATORY PROTECTION. THE SPECIFIC RESPIRATOR SELECTED MUST BE BASED ON CONTAMINATION LEVELS FOUND IN THE WORK PLACE, MUST NOT EXCEED THE WORKING LIMITS OF THE RESPIRATOR AND BE JOINTLY APPROVED BY THE NATIONAL INSTITUTE FOR OCCUPATIONAL SAFETY AND HEALTH AND THE MINE SAFETY AND HEALTH ADMINISTRATION (NIOSH-MSHA).

TYPE 'C' SUPPLIED-AIR RESPIRATOR WITH A FULL FACEPIECE OPERATED IN PRESSURE-DEMAND OR OTHER POSITIVE PRESSURE MODE OR WITH A FULL FACEPIECE, HELMET OR HOOD OPERATED IN CONTINOUS-FLOW MODE.

SELF-CONTAINED BREATHING APPARATUS WITH A FULL FACEPIECE OPERATED IN PRESSURE-DEMAND OR OTHER POSITIVE PRESSURE MODE.

FOR FIREFIGHTING AND OTHER IMMEDIATELY DANGEROUS TO LIFE OR HEALTH CONDITIONS:

SELF-CONTAINED BREATHING APPARATUS WITH FULL FACEPIECE OPERATED IN PRESSURE-DEMAND OR OTHER POSITIVE PRESSURE MODE.

SUPPLIED-AIR RESPIRATOR WITH FULL FACEPIECE AND OPERATED IN PRESSURE-DEMAND OR OTHER POSITIVE PRESSURE MODE IN COMBINATION WITH AN AUXILIARY SELF-CONTAINED BREATHING APPARATUS OPERATED IN PRESSURE-DEMAND OR OTHER POSITIVE PRESSURE MODE.

CLOTHING: EMPLOYEE MUST WEAR APPROPRIATE PROTECTIVE (IMPERVIOUS) CLOTHING AND EQUIPMENT TO PREVENT ANY POSSIBILITY OF SKIN CONTACT WITH THIS SUBSTANCE.

GLOVES: EMPLOYEE MUST WEAR APPROPRIATE PROTECTIVE GLOVES TO PREVENT CONTACT WITH THIS SUBSTANCE.

EYE PROTECTION: EMPLOYEE MUST WEAR SPLASH-PROOF OR DUST-RESISTANT SAFETY GOGGLES WITH OR WITHOUT A FACESHIELD TO PREVENT CONTACT WITH THIS SUBSTANCE.

EMERGENCY EYE WASH: WHERE THERE IS ANY POSSIBILITY THAT AN EMPLOYEE'S EYES MAY BE EXPOSED TO THIS SUBSTANCE, THE EMPLOYER SHOULD PROVIDE AN EYE WASH FOUNTAIN WITHIN THE IMMEDIATE WORK AREA FOR EMERGENCY USE.

AUTHORIZED BY- OCCUPATIONAL HEALTH SERVICES, INC.
CREATION DATE: 10/04/89 ***REVISION DATE:*** 06/12/90

MATERIAL SAFETY DATA SHEET

OCCUPATIONAL HEALTH SERVICES, INC.
AGRICULTURE AND PESTICIDE DIVISION
450 SEVENTH AVENUE, SUITE 2407
NEW YORK, NEW YORK 10123
1-800-445-MSDS OR (212) 967-1100

EMERGENCY CONTACT:
JOHN S. BRANSFORD, JR. (615) 292-1180

SUBSTANCE IDENTIFICATION

CAS-NUMBER 41198-08-7

SUBSTANCE: **PROFENOFOS**

TRADE NAMES/SYNONYMS: PHOSPHOROTHIOIC ACID, O-(4-BROMO-2-CHLOROPHENYL)O-ETHYL S-PROPYL ESTER; O-(4-BROMO-2-CHLOROPHENYL)O-ETHYL S-PROPYL PHOSPHOROTHIOATE; CGA 15324; CURACRON; POLYCRON; SELECRON; C11H15BRCLO3PS; PST72412

CHEMICAL FAMILY: PHOSPHOROTHIOATE

MOLECULAR FORMULA: C11-H15-BR-CL-O3-P-S

MOLECULAR WEIGHT: 373.65

CERCLA RATINGS (SCALE 0-3): HEALTH = 3 FIRE = U REACTIVITY = 0 PERSISTENCE = 1
NFPA RATINGS (SCALE 0-4): HEALTH = 4 FIRE = U REACTIVITY = 0

COMPONENTS AND CONTAMINANTS

COMPONENT: PROFENOFOS ***PERCENT:*** 100.0
CAS# 41198-08-7
OTHER CONTAMINANTS: NONE
EXPOSURE LIMITS: NO OCCUPATIONAL EXPOSURE LIMITS ESTABLISHED BY OSHA, ACGIH, OR NIOSH.

PHYSICAL DATA

DESCRIPTION: PALE YELLOW LIQUID. ***BOILING POINT:*** 230 F (110 C) @ 0.001 MMHG
SPECIFIC GRAVITY: 1.455 ***VAPOR PRESSURE:*** NEGLIGIBLE
SOLUBILITY IN WATER: 0.002% @ 20 C
SOLVENT SOLUBILITY: SOLUBLE IN METHANOL, ACETONE, ETHER, BENZENE, AND HEXANE.

FIRE AND EXPLOSION DATA

FIRE AND EXPLOSION HAZARD: UNKNOWN FIRE AND EXPLOSION HAZARD.
FIREFIGHTING MEDIA: DRY CHEMICAL, CARBON DIOXIDE, HALON, WATER SPRAY OR STANDARD FOAM (1987 EMERGENCY RESPONSE GUIDEBOOK, DOT P 5800.4). FOR LARGER FIRES, USE WATER SPRAY, FOG OR STANDARD FOAM (1987 EMERGENCY RESPONSE GUIDEBOOK, DOT P 5800.4).
FIREFIGHTING: MOVE CONTAINER FROM FIRE AREA IF POSSIBLE. DIKE FIRE CONTROL WATER FOR LATER DISPOSAL; DO NOT SCATTER THE MATERIAL. COOL FIRE-EXPOSED CONTAINERS WITH WATER FROM SIDE UNTIL WELL AFTER FIRE IS OUT. STAY AWAY FROM STORAGE TANK ENDS. WITHDRAW IMMEDIATELY IN CASE OF RISING SOUND FROM VENTING SAFETY DEVICE OR ANY DISCOLORATION OF STORAGE TANK DUE TO FIRE (1987 EMERGENCY RESPONSE GUIDEBOOK, DOT P 5800.4, GUIDE PAGE 28).
EXTINGUISH ONLY IF FLOW CAN BE STOPPED. USE FLOODING AMOUNTS OF WATER AS A FOG; SOLID STREAMS MAY BE INEFFECTIVE. COOL CONTAINERS WITH FLOODING AMOUNTS OF WATER FROM AS FAR A DISTANCE AS POSSIBLE. AVOID BREATHING POISONOUS VAPORS, KEEP UPWIND.

TRANSPORTATION DATA

DEPARTMENT OF TRANSPORTATION HAZARD CLASSIFICATION 49 CFR 172.101: POISON B
DEPARTMENT OF TRANSPORTATION LABELING REQUIREMENTS 49 CFR 172.101 AND SUBPART E: POISON
DEPARTMENT OF TRANSPORTATION PACKAGING REQUIREMENTS: 49 CFR 173.359 EXCEPTIONS: 49 CFR 173.359

TOXICITY

PROFENOFOS: TOXICITY DATA: 3 GM/M3/4 HOURS INHALATION-RAT LC50; 192 MG/KG SKIN-RABBIT LD50; 300 MG/KG SKIN-RAT LD50; 358 MG/KG ORAL-RAT LD50; 162 MG/KG ORAL-MOUSE LD50; 700 MG/KG ORAL-RABBIT LD50; MUTAGENIC DATA (RTECS). CARCINOGEN STATUS: NONE. ACUTE TOXICITY: HIGHLY TOXIC BY DERMAL ABSORPTION; TOXIC BY INHALATION AND INGESTION. TARGET EFFECTS: CHOLINESTERASE INHIBITOR. AT INCREASED RISK FROM EXPOSURE: PERSONS WITH RESPIRATORY AILMENTS, RECENT EXPOSURE TO CHOLINESTERASE INHIBITORS OR IMPAIRED CHOLINESTERASE PRODUCTION, OR LIVER MALFUNCTION.* ADDITIONAL DATA: MAY CROSS THE PLACENTA. HIGH ENVIRONMENTAL TEMPERATURES OR EXPOSURE OF THE CHEMICAL TO VISIBLE OR ULTRAVIOLET LIGHT MAY ENHANCE THE TOXICITY. INTERACTIONS WITH MEDICATIONS MAY OCCUR.*
* MAY BE BASED ON GENERAL INFORMATION ON ORGANOPHOSPHATES.

HEALTH EFFECTS AND FIRST AID

INHALATION: PROFENOFOS: TOXIC. SEE INFORMATION ON ORGANOPHOSPHATES.
ORGANOPHOSPHATES: CHOLINESTERASE INHIBITOR. **ACUTE EXPOSURE-** WHEN INHALED, THE FIRST EFFECTS OF CHOLINESTERASE INHIBITORS ARE USUALLY RESPIRATORY AND MAY INCLUDE NASAL HYPEREMIA AND WATERY DISCHARGE, COUGH, CHEST DISCOMFORT, DYSPNEA, AND WHEEZING DUE TO INCREASED BRONCHIAL SECRETIONS AND BRONCHOCONSTRICTION. IF SUFFICIENT AMOUNTS ARE ABSORBED, OTHER SYSTEMIC EFFECTS MAY BEGIN WITHIN A FEW MINUTES OR BE DELAYED FOR UP TO 12 HOURS. SYMPTOMS MAY INCLUDE PALLOR, NAUSEA, VOMITING, DIARRHEA, ABDOMINAL CRAMPS, HEADACHE, DIZZINESS, OCULAR PAIN, BLURRED VISION, MIOSIS OR IN SOME CASES, ESPECIALLY INITIALLY, MYDRIASIS, LACRIMATION, SALIVATION, SWEATING, AND CONFUSION. OTHER REPORTED CENTRAL NERVOUS SYSTEM OR NEUROMUSCULAR EFFECTS MAY INCLUDE ATAXIA, SLURRED SPEECH, AREFLEXIA, WEAKNESS, FATIGUE, FASCICULATIONS, TWITCHING, TREMORS POSSIBLY OF THE TONGUE AND EYELIDS, AND EVENTUALLY PARALYSIS OF THE EXTREMITIES AND POSSIBLY OF THE RESPIRATORY MUSCLES. IN SEVERE CASES THERE MAY ALSO BE INVOLUNTARY DEFECATION AND URINATION, CYANOSIS, PSYCHOSIS, HYPERGLYCEMIA, ACUTE PANCREATITIS, CARDIAC IRREGULARITIES, PULMONARY EDEMA, UNCONSCIOUSNESS, CONVULSIONS, AND COMA. DEATH IS PRIMARILY DUE TO RESPIRATORY FAILURE, ALTHOUGH CARDIOVASCULAR EFFECTS INCLUDING CARDIAC ARREST MAY ALSO BE IMPLICATED. LONG TERM SEQUELAE ARE RARE BUT MAY INCLUDE NEUROPSYCHIATRIC DISORDERS AND MYOPATHY WITH MUSCLE TENDERNESS. **CHRONIC EXPOSURE-** REPEATED OR PROLONGED EXPOSURE MAY RESULT IN THE EFFECTS OF ACUTE EXPOSURE. OTHER EFFECTS REPORTED IN WORKERS REPEATEDLY EXPOSED INCLUDE IMPAIRED MEMORY AND CONCENTRATION, ACUTE PSYCHOSIS, SEVERE DEPRESSIONS, IRRITABILTY, CONFUSION, APATHY, EMOTIONAL LABILITY, SOCIAL WITHDRAWAL, CONFUSION, HEADACHE, SPEECH DIFFICULTIES, DELAYED REACTION TIMES, SPATIAL DISORIENTATION, NIGHTMARES, SLEEPWALKING, AND DROWSINESS OR INSOMNIA. AN INFLUENZA-LIKE CONDITION WITH HEADACHE, NAUSEA, WEAKNESS, ANOREXIA AND MALAISE HAS ALSO BEEN REPORTED.
FIRST AID- REMOVE FROM EXPOSURE AREA TO FRESH AIR IMMEDIATELY. IF BREATHING HAS STOPPED, GIVE ARTIFICIAL RESPIRATION. MAINTAIN AIRWAY AND BLOOD PRESSURE AND ADMINISTER OXYGEN IF AVAILABLE. KEEP AFFECTED PERSON WARM AND AT REST. TREAT SYMPTOMATICALLY AND SUPPORTIVELY. ADMINISTRATION OF OXYGEN SHOULD BE PERFORMED BY QUALIFIED PERSONNEL. GET MEDICAL ATTENTION IMMEDIATELY.

SKIN CONTACT: PROFENOFOS: HIGHLY TOXIC. THIS MATERIAL WAS SLIGHLTLY IRRITATING TO RABBIT SKIN. SEE INFORMATION ON ORGANOPHOSPHATES.
ORGANOPHOSPHATES: CHOLINESTERASE INHIBITOR. **ACUTE EXPOSURE-** LOCALIZED SWEATING AND FASCICULATIONS MAY OCCUR AT THE SITE OF CONTACT. IF SUFFICIENT AMOUNTS ARE ABSORBED, OTHER EFFECTS OF CHOLINESTERASE INHIBITION AS DESCRIBED IN ACUTE INHALATION MAY OCCUR. SYMPTOMS MAY BE DELAYED 2-3 HOURS, BUT USUALLY NO MORE THAN 12 HOURS. THE RATE OF ABSORPTION IS INCREASED BY THE PRESENCE OF DERMATITIS OR HIGH AMBIENT TEMPERATURES. **CHRONIC EXPOSURE-** REPEATED OR PROLONGED EXPOSURE MAY CAUSE EFFECTS AS DESCRIBED IN ACUTE EXPOSURE. SOME ORGANOPHOSPHATES MAY CAUSE SENSITIZATION.
FIRST AID- REMOVE CONTAMINATED CLOTHING IMMEDIATELY. WASH CONTAMINATED AREAS WITH SOAP AND WATER FOLLOWED BY ALCOHOL (ARENA, POISONING, 4TH ED.). EMERGENCY PERSONNEL SHOULD WEAR GLOVES AND AVOID CONTAMINATION. TREAT RESPIRATORY DIFFICULTY WITH ARTIFICIAL RESPIRATION. GET MEDICAL ATTENTION IMMEDIATELY.

EYE CONTACT: PROFENOFOS: THIS MATERIAL WAS SLIGHTLY TO MODERATELY IRRITATING TO RABBIT EYES. SEE INFORMATION ON ORGANOPHOSPHATES.
ORGANOPHOSPHATES: CHOLINESTERASE INHIBITOR. **ACUTE EXPOSURE-** DIRECT CONTACT MAY CAUSE PAIN, HYPEREMIA, LACRIMATION, TWITCHING OF THE EYELIDS, MIOSIS, AND CILIARY MUSCLE SPASM WITH LOSS OF ACCOMODATION, BLURRED OR DIMMED VISION AND BROWACHE. SOMETIMES MYDRIASIS MAY OCCUR INSTEAD OF MIOSIS. WITH SUFFICIENT EXPOSURE, OTHER SYMPTOMS OF CHOLINESTERASE INHIBITION AS DESCRIBED IN ACUTE INHALATION MAY OCCUR. **CHRONIC EXPOSURE-** REPEATED OR PROLONGED EXPOSURE MAY CAUSE EFFECTS AS DESCRIBED IN ACUTE EXPOSURE. SOME COMPOUNDS HAVE CAUSED TOXIC EFFECTS ON THE CRYSTALLINE LENS, CONJUNCTIVAL THICKENING AND OBSTRUCTION OF THE NASOLACRIMAL CANALS WHEN USED AS MIOTIC EYEDROPS.
FIRST AID- IRRIGATE EYES WITH WATER OR SALINE SOLUTION. IF SYMPTOMS OF POISONING OCCUR, TREAT RESPIRATORY DIFFICULTY WITH ARTIFICIAL RESPIRATION AND OXYGEN. OBSERVE PATIENT FOR AT LEAST 24-36 HOURS (GOSSELIN, CLINICAL TOXICOLOGY OF COMMERCIAL PRODUCTS, 5TH ED.). GET MEDICAL ATTENTION IMMEDIATELY. OXYGEN SHOULD BE ADMINISTERED BY QUALIFIED MEDICAL PERSONNEL.

INGESTION: PROFENOFOS: TOXIC. AN ACUTE DELAYED NEUROTOXICITY TEST, USING HENS, WAS NEGATIVE. CHOLINESTERASE INHIBITION WAS OBSERVED IN A 2-YEAR STUDY OF RATS RECEIVING 10 PPM IN THE DIET. SEE INFORMATION ON ORGANOPHOSPHATES.
ORGANOPHOSPHATES: CHOLINESTERASE INHIBITOR. **ACUTE EXPOSURE-** WHEN INGESTED, THE FIRST EFFECTS MAY BE NAUSEA, VOMITING, ANOREXIA, ABDOMINAL CRAMPS AND DIARRHEA. GASTROINTESTINAL ABSORPTION MAY CAUSE THE SYMPTOMS OF CHOLINESTERASE INHIBITION AS DESCRIBED IN ACUTE INHALATION. SYMPTOMS MAY BEGIN WITHIN MINUTES OR BE DELAYED. **CHRONIC EXPOSURE-** REPEATED INGESTION MAY CAUSE EFFECTS AS DESCRIBED IN ACUTE EXPOSURE.
FIRST AID- IF PERSON IS ALERT AND RESPIRATION IS NOT DEPRESSED, GIVE SYRUP OF IPECAC FOLLOWED BY WATER (IF VOMITING OCCURS, KEEP HEAD BELOW HIPS TO PREVENT ASPIRATION). IF CONSCIOUSNESS LEVEL DECLINES OR VOMITING HAS NOT OCCURRED IN 15 MINUTES EMPTY STOMACH BY GASTRIC LAVAGE WITH THE AID OF CUFFED ENDOTRACHEAL TUBE USING ISOTONIC SALINE OR 5% SODIUM BICARBONATE FOLLOW WITH ACTIVATED CHARCOAL. ESTABLISH AND MAINTAIN

AIRWAY. TREAT RESPIRATORY DIFFICULTY WITH ARTIFICIAL RESPIRATION AND OXYGEN. DO NOT GIVE MORPHINE, AMINOPHYLLINE, PHENOTHIAZINES, RESERPINE, FUROSEMIDE, OR ETHACRYNIC ACID (MORGAN, RECOGNITION AND MANAGEMENT OF PESTICIDE POISONINGS, 3RD ED.). TREAT SYMPTOMATICALLY AND SUPPORTIVELY. ADMINISTRATION OF OXYGEN AND LAVAGE MUST BE PERFORMED BY QUALIFIED MEDICAL PERSONNEL. GET MEDICAL ATTENTION IMMEDIATELY.

ANTIDOTE: THE FOLLOWING ANTIDOTE(S) HAVE BEEN RECOMMENDED. HOWEVER, THE DECISION AS TO WHETHER THE SEVERITY OF POISONING REQUIRES ADMINISTRATION OF ANY ANTIDOTE AND ACTUAL DOSE REQUIRED SHOULD BE MADE BY QUALIFIED MEDICAL PERSONNEL.

FOR CHOLINESTERASE INHIBITORS: ESTABLISH CLEAR AIRWAY AND TISSUE OXYGENATION BY ASPIRATION OF SECRETIONS, AND IF NECESSARY, BY ASSISTED PULMONARY VENTILATION WITH OXYGEN. IMPROVE TISSUE OXYGENATION AS MUCH AS POSSIBLE BEFORE ADMINISTERING ATROPINE TO MINIMIZE THE RISK OF VENTRICULAR FIBRILLATION. ADMINISTER ATROPINE SULFATE INTRAVENOUSLY, OR INTRAMUSCULARLY IF IV INJECTION IS NOT POSSIBLE. IN MODERATELY SEVERE POISONING ADMINISTER ATROPINE SULFATE, 0.4-2.0 MG REPEATED EVERY 15 MINUTES UNTIL ATROPINIZATION IS ACHIEVED (TACHYCARDIA, FLUSHING, DRY MOUTH, MYDRIASIS). MAINTAIN ATROPINIZATION BY REPEATED DOSES FOR 2-12 HOURS, OR LONGER, DEPENDING ON THE SEVERITY OF POISONING. THE APPEARANCE OF RALES IN THE LUNG BASES, MIOSIS, SALIVATION, NAUSEA, BRADYCARDIA, ARE ALL INDICATIONS OF INADEQUATE ATROPINIZATION. SEVERELY POISONED INDIVIDUALS MAY EXHIBIT REMARKABLE TOLERANCE TO ATROPINE; TWO OR MORE TIMES THE DOSAGES SUGGESTED ABOVE MAY BE NEEDED. PERSONS NOT POISONED OR ONLY SLIGHTLY POISONED, HOWEVER, MAY DEVELOP SIGNS OF ATROPINE TOXICITY FROM SUCH LARGE DOSAGES: FEVER, MUSCLE FIBRILLATIONS, AND DELIRIUM ARE THE MAIN SIGNS OF ATROPINE TOXICITY. IF THESE SIGNS APPEAR WHILE THE PATIENT IS FULLY ATROPINIZED, ATROPINE ADMINISTRATION SHOULD BE DISCONTINUED, AT LEAST TEMPORARILY. OBSERVE TREATED PATIENTS CLOSELY AT LEAST 24 HOURS TO INSURE THAT SYMPTOMS (POSSIBLY PULMONARY EDEMA) DO NOT RECUR AS ATROPINIZATION WEARS OFF. IN VERY SEVERE POISONINGS, METABOLIC DISPOSITION OF TOXICANT MAY REQUIRE SEVERAL HOURS OR DAYS DURING WHICH ATROPINIZATION MUST BE MAINTAINED. MARKEDLY LOWER LEVELS OF URINARY METABOLITES INDICATE THAT ATROPINE DOSAGE CAN BE TAPERED OFF. AS DOSAGE IS REDUCED, CHECK THE LUNG BASES FREQUENTLY FOR RALES. IF RALES ARE HEARD OR OTHER SYMPTOMS RETURN, RE-ESTABLISH ATROPINIZATION PROMPTLY (MORGAN, RECOGNITION AND MANAGEMENT OF PESTICIDE POISONINGS, 3RD ED.). ADMINISTRATION OF ANTIDOTE MUST BE PERFORMED BY QUALIFIED MEDICAL PERSONNEL.

IN CASES OF SEVERE POISONING BY ORGANOPHOSPHATE PESTICIDES IN WHICH RESPIRATORY DEPRESSION, MUSCLE WEAKNESS AND TWITCHINGS ARE SEVERE, GIVE PRALIDOXIME (PROTOPAM-AYERST, 2-PAM), 1.0 GRAM INTRAVENOUSLY AT NO MORE THAN 0.5 GRAM PER MINUTE. DOSAGE OF PRALIDOXIME MAY BE REPEATED IN 1-2 HOURS, THEN AT 10-12 HOUR INTERVALS IF NEEDED. IN VERY SEVERE POISONINGS, DOSAGE RATES MAY BE DOUBLED. TREATMENT WITH PRALIDOXIME WILL BE MOST EFFECTIVE IF GIVEN WITHIN THIRTY-SIX HOURS AFTER POISONING (MORGAN, RECOGNITION AND MANAGEMENT OF PESTICIDE POISONINGS, 3RD ED.). ANTIDOTE SHOULD BE ADMINISTERED BY QUALIFIED MEDICAL PERSONNEL.

REACTIVITY

REACTIVITY: STABLE UNDER NORMAL TEMPERATURES AND PRESSURES.

INCOMPATIBILITIES: PROFENOFOS: ALKALIS: MAY DECOMPOSE. OXIDIZERS (STRONG): FIRE AND EXPLOSION HAZARD.

DECOMPOSITION: THERMAL DECOMPOSITION PRODUCTS MAY INCLUDE TOXIC AND CORROSIVE FUMES OF BROMIDES AND CHLORIDES, AND TOXIC OXIDES OF PHOSPHORUS AND SULFUR.

POLYMERIZATION: HAZARDOUS POLYMERIZATION HAS NOT BEEN REPORTED TO OCCUR UNDER NORMAL TEMPERATURES AND PRESSURES.

STORAGE AND DISPOSAL

OBSERVE ALL FEDERAL, STATE AND LOCAL REGULATIONS WHEN STORING OR DISPOSING OF THIS SUBSTANCE. FOR ASSISTANCE, CONTACT THE DISTRICT DIRECTOR OF THE ENVIRONMENTAL PROTECTION AGENCY.

STORAGE

STORE IN ACCORDANCE WITH 40 CFR 165 RECOMMENDED PROCEDURES FOR THE DISPOSAL AND STORAGE OF PESTICIDES AND PESTICIDE CONTAINERS.

STORE AWAY FROM INCOMPATIBLE SUBSTANCES.

DISPOSAL

DISPOSAL MUST BE IN ACCORDANCE WITH 40 CFR 165 RECOMMENDED PROCEDURES FOR THE DISPOSAL AND STORAGE OF PESTICIDES AND PESTICIDE CONTAINERS.

CONDITIONS TO AVOID

AVOID CONTACT WITH HEAT, SPARKS, FLAMES OR OTHER IGNITION SOURCES. VAPORS MAY BE EXPLOSIVE. MATERIAL IS POISONOUS; AVOID INHALATION OF VAPORS OR CONTACT WITH SKIN. DO NOT ALLOW MATERIAL TO CONTAMINATE WATER SOURCES.

SPILL AND LEAK PROCEDURES

OCCUPATIONAL SPILL: SHUT OFF IGNITION SOURCES. DO NOT TOUCH SPILLED MATERIAL. STOP LEAK IF YOU CAN DO IT WITHOUT RISK. USE WATER SPRAY TO REDUCE VAPORS. FOR SMALL SPILLS, TAKE UP WITH SAND OR OTHER ABSORBENT MATERIAL AND PLACE INTO CONTAINERS FOR LATER DISPOSAL. FOR LARGER SPILLS, DIKE FAR AHEAD OF SPILL FOR LATER DISPOSAL. NO SMOKING, FLAMES OR FLARES IN HAZARD AREA! KEEP UNNECESSARY PEOPLE AWAY; ISOLATE HAZARD AREA AND DENY ENTRY.

PROTECTIVE EQUIPMENT

VENTILATION: PROCESS ENCLOSURE RECOMMENDED.

RESPIRATOR: THE FOLLOWING RESPIRATORS ARE RECOMMENDED BASED ON INFORMATION FOUND IN THE PHYSICAL DATA, TOXICITY AND HEALTH EFFECTS SECTIONS. THEY ARE RANKED IN ORDER FROM MINIMUM TO MAXIMUM RESPIRATORY PROTECTION. THE SPECIFIC RESPIRATOR SELECTED MUST BE BASED ON CONTAMINATION LEVELS FOUND IN THE WORK PLACE, MUST NOT EXCEED THE WORKING LIMITS OF THE RESPIRATOR AND BE JOINTLY APPROVED BY THE NATIONAL INSTITUTE FOR OCCUPATIONAL SAFETY AND HEALTH AND THE MINE SAFETY AND HEALTH ADMINISTRATION (NIOSH-MSHA).

TYPE 'C' SUPPLIED-AIR RESPIRATOR WITH A FULL FACEPIECE OPERATED IN PRESSURE-DEMAND OR OTHER POSITIVE PRESSURE MODE OR WITH A FULL FACEPIECE, HELMET OR HOOD OPERATED IN CONTINOUS-FLOW MODE.

SELF-CONTAINED BREATHING APPARATUS WITH A FULL FACEPIECE OPERATED IN PRESSURE-DEMAND OR OTHER POSITIVE PRESSURE MODE.

FOR FIREFIGHTING AND OTHER IMMEDIATELY DANGEROUS TO LIFE OR HEALTH CONDITIONS:

SELF-CONTAINED BREATHING APPARATUS WITH FULL FACEPIECE OPERATED IN PRESSURE-DEMAND OR OTHER POSITIVE PRESSURE MODE.

SUPPLIED-AIR RESPIRATOR WITH FULL FACEPIECE AND OPERATED IN PRESSURE-DEMAND OR OTHER POSITIVE PRESSURE MODE IN COMBINATION WITH AN AUXILIARY SELF-CONTAINED BREATHING APPARATUS OPERATED IN PRESSURE-DEMAND OR OTHER POSITIVE PRESSURE MODE.

CLOTHING: EMPLOYEE MUST WEAR APPROPRIATE PROTECTIVE (IMPERVIOUS) CLOTHING AND EQUIPMENT TO PREVENT ANY POSSIBILITY OF SKIN CONTACT WITH THIS SUBSTANCE.

GLOVES: EMPLOYEE MUST WEAR APPROPRIATE PROTECTIVE GLOVES TO PREVENT CONTACT WITH THIS SUBSTANCE.

EYE PROTECTION: EMPLOYEE MUST WEAR SPLASH-PROOF OR DUST-RESISTANT SAFETY GOGGLES WITH OR WITHOUT A FACESHIELD TO PREVENT CONTACT WITH THIS SUBSTANCE.

EMERGENCY EYE WASH: WHERE THERE IS ANY POSSIBILITY THAT AN EMPLOYEE'S EYES MAY BE EXPOSED TO THIS SUBSTANCE, THE EMPLOYER SHOULD PROVIDE AN EYE WASH FOUNTAIN WITHIN THE IMMEDIATE WORK AREA FOR EMERGENCY USE.

AUTHORIZED BY- OCCUPATIONAL HEALTH SERVICES, INC.

CREATION DATE: 10/04/89 ***REVISION DATE:*** 06/20/90

MATERIAL SAFETY DATA SHEET

OCCUPATIONAL HEALTH SERVICES, INC.
AGRICULTURE AND PESTICIDE DIVISION
450 SEVENTH AVENUE, SUITE 2407
NEW YORK, NEW YORK 10123
1-800-445-MSDS OR (212) 967-1100

EMERGENCY CONTACT:
JOHN S. BRANSFORD, JR. (615) 292-1180

SUBSTANCE IDENTIFICATION

CAS-NUMBER 42874-03-3

SUBSTANCE: OXYFLUORFEN

TRADE NAMES/SYNONYMS: BENZENE, 2-CHLORO-1-(3-ETHOXY-4-NITROPHENOXY)-4-(TRIFLUOROMETHYL)-; 2-CHLORO-1-(3-ETHOXY-4-NITROPHENOXY)-4-(TRIFLUOROMETHYL)BENZENE; 2-CHLORO-ALPHA,ALPHA,ALPHA-TRIFLUORO-P-TOLYL-3-ETHOXY-4-NITROPHENYL ETHER; 2-CHLORO-4-TRIFLUOROMETHYLPHENYL 3-ETHOXY-4-NITROPHENYL ETHER; GOAL; KOLTAR; OXYFLUORFENE; RH 2915; C15H11CLF3NO4; PST72413

CHEMICAL FAMILY: ETHER, AROMATIC
HALOGEN
NITRO
MOLECULAR FORMULA: (C-F3)-CL-C6-H3-O-C6-H3-N-O2-(O-C2-H5)
MOLECULAR WEIGHT: 361.72
CERCLA RATINGS (SCALE 0-3): HEALTH=U FIRE=1 REACTIVITY=0 PERSISTENCE=2
NFPA RATINGS (SCALE 0-4): HEALTH=U FIRE=1 REACTIVITY=0

COMPONENTS AND CONTAMINANTS

COMPONENT: OXYFLUORFEN ***PERCENT:*** 100.0
CAS# 42874-03-3
OTHER CONTAMINANTS: MAY CONTAIN 6 PPM PERCHLOROETHYLENE
EXPOSURE LIMITS: NO OCCUPATIONAL EXPOSURE LIMITS ESTABLISHED BY OSHA, ACGIH, OR NIOSH.
OXYFLUORFEN: 0.2 MG/M3 ROHM AND HAAS RECOMMENDED TWA 1.6 MG/M3 ROHM AND HAAS RECOMMENDED STEL

PHYSICAL DATA

DESCRIPTION: WHITE TO ORANGE CRYSTALLINE SOLID WITH SMOKEY ODOR; MAY DECOMPOSE ON EXPOSURE TO UV LIGHT.
BOILING POINT: >464 F (>240 C) DECOMPOSES
MELTING POINT: 181-183 F (83-84 C) ***SPECIFIC GRAVITY:*** 1.35 @ 73 C
VISCOSITY: 10 CPS @ 90 C ***VAPOR PRESSURE:*** NEGLIGIBLE @ 25 C
EVAPORATION RATE: (BUTYL ACETATE=1) <1 ***SOLUBILITY IN WATER:*** 0.1 PPM
VAPOR DENSITY: >12
SOLVENT SOLUBILITY: SOLUBLE IN ACETONE, CYCLOHEXANONE, ISOPHORANE, DIMETHYLFORMAMIDE, CHLOROFORM, MESITYL OXIDE, AND MOST ORGANIC SOLVENTS.

FIRE AND EXPLOSION DATA

FIRE AND EXPLOSION HAZARD: SLIGHT FIRE HAZARD WHEN EXPOSED TO HEAT OR FLAME.
DUST-AIR MIXTURES MAY IGNITE OR EXPLODE.
FLASH POINT: >200 F (>93 C) (CC)
FIREFIGHTING MEDIA: DRY CHEMICAL, CARBON DIOXIDE, HALON, WATER SPRAY OR STANDARD FOAM (1987 EMERGENCY RESPONSE GUIDEBOOK, DOT P 5800.4).
FOR LARGER FIRES, USE WATER SPRAY, FOG OR STANDARD FOAM (1987 EMERGENCY RESPONSE GUIDEBOOK, DOT P 5800.4).
FIREFIGHTING: MOVE CONTAINER FROM FIRE AREA IF POSSIBLE. DO NOT SCATTER SPILLED MATERIAL WITH HIGH PRESSURE WATER STREAMS. DIKE FIRE CONTROL WATER FOR LATER DISPOSAL (1987 EMERGENCY RESPONSE GUIDEBOOK, DOT P 5800.4, GUIDE PAGE 31).
USE AGENTS SUITABLE FOR TYPE OF SURROUNDING FIRE. AVOID BREATHING HAZARDOUS VAPORS, KEEP UPWIND.

TOXICITY

OXYFLUORFEN: ACUTE TOXICITY: >10,000 MG/KG SKIN-RABBIT LD50 (85JFAN); 5000 MG/KG ORAL-RAT LD50; >5000 MG/KG ORAL-DOG LD50 (85JFAN). CARCINOGEN STATUS: NONE. ACUTE TOXICITY LEVEL: MODERATELY TOXIC BY INGESTION; SLIGHTLY TOXIC BY DERMAL ABSORPTION. TARGET EFFECTS: NO DATA AVAILABLE.

HEALTH EFFECTS AND FIRST AID

INHALATION: OXYFLUORFEN: **ACUTE EXPOSURE-** VAPORS CAN CAUSE IRRITATION OF NOSE AND THROAT. **CHRONIC EXPOSURE-** NO DATA AVAILABLE.
FIRST AID- REMOVE FROM EXPOSURE AREA TO FRESH AIR IMMEDIATELY. IF BREATHING HAS STOPPED, PERFORM ARTIFICIAL RESPIRATION. KEEP PERSON WARM AND AT REST. TREAT SYMPTOMATICALLY AND SUPPORTIVELY. GET MEDICAL ATTENTION IMMEDIATELY.

SKIN CONTACT: OXYFLUORFEN: **ACUTE EXPOSURE-** MAY CAUSE IRRITATION. **CHRONIC EXPOSURE-** PROLONGED OR REPEATED EXPOSURE MAY CAUSE IRRITATION.
FIRST AID- REMOVE CONTAMINATED CLOTHING AND SHOES IMMEDIATELY. WASH AFFECTED AREA WITH SOAP OR MILD DETERGENT AND LARGE AMOUNTS OF WATER UNTIL NO EVIDENCE OF CHEMICAL REMAINS (APPROXIMATELY 15-20 MINUTES). GET MEDICAL ATTENTION IMMEDIATELY.

EYE CONTACT: OXYFLUORFEN: **ACUTE EXPOSURE-** THIS MATERIAL WAS MILDLY TO MODERATELY IRRITATING TO RABBIT EYES. **CHRONIC EXPOSURE-** NO DATA AVAILABLE.
FIRST AID- WASH EYES IMMEDIATELY WITH LARGE AMOUNTS OF WATER OR NORMAL SALINE, OCCASIONALLY LIFTING UPPER AND LOWER LIDS, UNTIL NO EVIDENCE OF CHEMICAL REMAINS (APPROXIMATELY 15-20 MINUTES). GET MEDICAL ATTENTION IMMEDIATELY.

INGESTION: OXYFLUORFEN: **ACUTE EXPOSURE-** A LETHAL DOSE IN RATS WAS 5000 MG/KG; SYMPTOMS WERE NOT REPORTED. **CHRONIC EXPOSURE-** EFFECTS ON THE LIVER WERE OBSERVED IN LONG-TERM FEEDING STUDIES OF MICE, RATS, AND DOGS.
FIRST AID- IF THE PERSON IS CONSCIOUS AND NOT CONVULSING, REMOVE BY GASTRIC LAVAGE AND FOLLOW WITH A CATHARTIC (DREISBACH, HANDBOOK OF POISONING, 12TH ED.). TREAT SYMPTOMATICALLY AND SUPPORTIVELY. GASTRIC LAVAGE SHOULD BE PERFORMED BY QUALIFIED MEDICAL PERSONNEL. GET MEDICAL ATTENTION IMMEDIATELY.
ANTIDOTE: NO SPECIFIC ANTIDOTE. TREAT SYMPTOMATICALLY AND SUPPORTIVELY.

REACTIVITY

REACTIVITY: STABLE UNDER NORMAL TEMPERATURES AND PRESSURES.
INCOMPATIBILITIES: OXYFLUORFEN: OXIDIZERS (STRONG): FIRE AND EXPLOSION HAZARD.
DECOMPOSITION: THERMAL DECOMPOSITION PRODUCTS MAY INCLUDE HIGHLY TOXIC FUMES OF FLUORIDES AND CHLORIDES AND TOXIC OXIDES OF NITROGEN AND CARBON.
POLYMERIZATION: HAZARDOUS POLYMERIZATION HAS NOT BEEN REPORTED TO OCCUR UNDER NORMAL TEMPERATURES AND PRESSURES.

STORAGE AND DISPOSAL

OBSERVE ALL FEDERAL, STATE AND LOCAL REGULATIONS WHEN STORING OR DISPOSING OF THIS SUBSTANCE. FOR ASSISTANCE, CONTACT THE DISTRICT DIRECTOR OF THE ENVIRONMENTAL PROTECTION AGENCY.

STORAGE

STORE IN ACCORDANCE WITH 40 CFR 165 RECOMMENDED PROCEDURES FOR THE DISPOSAL AND STORAGE OF PESTICIDES AND PESTICIDE CONTAINERS.
KEEP CONTAINER TIGHTLY CLOSED. PROTECT FROM EXPOSURE TO AIR OR LIGHT. STORE AWAY FROM INCOMPATIBLE SUBSTANCES.

DISPOSAL

DISPOSAL MUST BE IN ACCORDANCE WITH 40 CFR 165 RECOMMENDED PROCEDURES FOR THE DISPOSAL AND STORAGE OF PESTICIDES AND PESTICIDE CONTAINERS.

CONDITIONS TO AVOID

MAY BURN BUT DOES NOT IGNITE READILY. AVOID CONTACT WITH STRONG OXIDIZERS, EXCESSIVE HEAT, SPARKS, OR OPEN FLAME.

SPILL AND LEAK PROCEDURES

OCCUPATIONAL SPILL: SWEEP UP AND PLACE IN SUITABLE CLEAN, DRY CONTAINERS FOR RECLAMATION OR LATER DISPOSAL. DO NOT FLUSH SPILLED MATERIAL INTO SEWER. KEEP UNNECESSARY PEOPLE AWAY.

PROTECTIVE EQUIPMENT

VENTILATION: PROVIDE LOCAL EXHAUST OR GENERAL DILUTION VENTILATION SYSTEM.
RESPIRATOR: THE FOLLOWING RESPIRATORS ARE RECOMMENDED BASED ON INFORMATION FOUND IN THE PHYSICAL DATA, TOXICITY AND HEALTH EFFECTS SECTIONS. THEY ARE RANKED IN ORDER FROM MINIMUM TO MAXIMUM RESPIRATORY PROTECTION. THE SPECIFIC RESPIRATOR SELECTED MUST BE BASED ON CONTAMINATION LEVELS FOUND IN THE WORK PLACE, MUST NOT EXCEED THE WORKING LIMITS OF THE RESPIRATOR AND BE JOINTLY APPROVED BY THE NATIONAL INSTITUTE FOR OCCUPATIONAL SAFETY AND HEALTH AND THE MINE SAFETY AND HEALTH ADMINISTRATION (NIOSH-MSHA).
CHEMICAL CARTRIDGE RESPIRATOR WITH AN ORGANIC VAPOR CARTRIDGE(S) IN COMBINATION WITH A DUST AND MIST FILTER.
GAS MASK WITH ORGANIC VAPOR CANISTER (CHIN-STYLE OR FRONT- OR BACK-MOUNTED CANISTER) WITH A DUST AND MIST FILTER.
GAS MASK WITH ORGANIC VAPOR CANISTER (CHIN-STYLE OR FRONT- OR BACK-MOUNTED CANISTER) WITH A PARTICULATE FILTER.
POWERED AIR-PURIFYING RESPIRATOR WITH A HIGH-EFFICIENCY FILTER. TYPE 'C' SUPPLIED-AIR RESPIRATOR WITH A FULL FACEPIECE OPERATED IN A PRESSURE-DEMAND OR OTHER POSITIVE PRESSURE MODE.
SELF-CONTAINED BREATHING APPARATUS WITH A FULL FACEPIECE OPERATED IN PRESSURE-DEMAND OR OTHER POSITIVE PRESSURE MODE.
FOR FIREFIGHTING AND OTHER IMMEDIATELY DANGEROUS TO LIFE OR HEALTH CONDITIONS:
SELF-CONTAINED BREATHING APPARATUS WITH FULL FACEPIECE OPERATED IN PRESSURE-DEMAND OR OTHER POSITIVE PRESSURE MODE.
SUPPLIED-AIR RESPIRATOR WITH FULL FACEPIECE AND OPERATED IN PRESSURE-DEMAND OR OTHER POSITIVE PRESSURE MODE IN COMBINATION WITH AN AUXILIARY SELF-CONTAINED BREATHING APPARATUS OPERATED IN PRESSURE-DEMAND OR OTHER POSITIVE PRESSURE MODE.

CLOTHING: EMPLOYEE MUST WEAR APPROPRIATE PROTECTIVE (IMPERVIOUS) CLOTHING AND EQUIPMENT TO PREVENT REPEATED OR PROLONGED SKIN CONTACT WITH THIS SUBSTANCE.

GLOVES: EMPLOYEE MUST WEAR APPROPRIATE PROTECTIVE GLOVES TO PREVENT CONTACT WITH THIS SUBSTANCE.

EYE PROTECTION: EMPLOYEE MUST WEAR SPLASH-PROOF OR DUST-RESISTANT SAFETY GOGGLES TO PREVENT EYE CONTACT WITH THIS SUBSTANCE. EMERGENCY EYE WASH: WHERE THERE IS ANY POSSIBILITY THAT AN EMPLOYEE'S EYES MAY BE EXPOSED TO THIS SUBSTANCE, THE EMPLOYER SHOULD PROVIDE AN EYE WASH FOUNTAIN WITHIN THE IMMEDIATE WORK AREA FOR EMERGENCY USE.

AUTHORIZED BY- OCCUPATIONAL HEALTH SERVICES, INC.
CREATION DATE: 05/22/90 ***REVISION DATE:*** 05/31/90

MATERIAL SAFETY DATA SHEET

OCCUPATIONAL HEALTH SERVICES, INC.
AGRICULTURE AND PESTICIDE DIVISION
450 SEVENTH AVENUE, SUITE 2407
NEW YORK, NEW YORK 10123
1-800-445-MSDS OR (212) 967-1100

EMERGENCY CONTACT:
JOHN S. BRANSFORD, JR. (615) 292-1180

SUBSTANCE IDENTIFICATION

CAS-NUMBER 29973-13-5

SUBSTANCE: **ETHIOFENCARB**

TRADE NAMES/SYNONYMS: PHENOL, 2-((ETHYLTHIO)METHYL)-, METHYLCARBAMATE; METHYLCARBAMIC ACID, ALPHA-(ETHYLTHIO)-O-TOLYL ESTER; ALPHA-(ETHYLTHIO)-O-TOLYL METHYLCARBAMATE; 2-((ETHYLTHIO)METHYL)PHENOL METHYLCARBAMATE; 2-ETHYLTHIOMETHYLPHENYL METHYLCARBAMATE; 2-((ETHYLTHIO)METHYL)PHENYL METHYLCARBAMATE; CARBAMIC ACID, METHYL-, ALPHA-(ETHYLTHIO)-O-TOLYL ESTER; ALPHA-ETHYLTHIO-O-TOLYL METHYLCARBAMATE; BAY HOX 1901; CRONETON; HOX 1901; C11H15NO2S; PST72421

CHEMICAL FAMILY: CARBAMATE

MOLECULAR FORMULA: (C2-H5-S-C-H2)-C6-H4-O2-C-N-(H)-C-H3

MOLECULAR WEIGHT: 225.33

CERCLA RATINGS (SCALE 0-3): HEALTH=3 FIRE=U REACTIVITY=0 PERSISTENCE=1

NFPA RATINGS (SCALE 0-4): HEALTH=U FIRE=U REACTIVITY=0

COMPONENTS AND CONTAMINANTS

COMPONENT: ETHIOFENCARB ***PERCENT:*** 100.0
CAS# 29973-13-5

OTHER CONTAMINANTS: NONE

EXPOSURE LIMITS: NO OCCUPATIONAL EXPOSURE LIMITS ESTABLISHED BY OSHA, ACGIH, OR NIOSH.

PHYSICAL DATA

DESCRIPTION: YELLOW, OILY LIQUID. ***BOILING POINT:*** 221 F (105 C) @ 5 MMHG
MELTING POINT: 88-93 F (31-34 C) ***SPECIFIC GRAVITY:*** 1.147
VAPOR PRESSURE: NEGLIGIBLE ***SOLUBILITY IN WATER:*** 0.182% @ 20 C
SOLVENT SOLUBILITY: SOLUBLE IN DICHLOROMETHANE, PROPANOL, TOLUENE, AND ISOPROPANOL.

FIRE AND EXPLOSION DATA

FIRE AND EXPLOSION HAZARD: UNKNOWN FIRE AND EXPLOSION HAZARD.

FLASH POINT: NOT AVAILABLE

FIREFIGHTING MEDIA: DRY CHEMICAL, CARBON DIOXIDE, HALON, WATER SPRAY OR STANDARD FOAM (1987 EMERGENCY RESPONSE GUIDEBOOK, DOT P 5800.4). FOR LARGER FIRES, USE WATER SPRAY, FOG OR STANDARD FOAM (1987 EMERGENCY RESPONSE GUIDEBOOK, DOT P 5800.4).

FIREFIGHTING: MOVE CONTAINER FROM FIRE AREA IF POSSIBLE. DIKE FIRE CONTROL WATER FOR LATER DISPOSAL; DO NOT SCATTER THE MATERIAL. COOL FIRE-EXPOSED CONTAINERS WITH WATER FROM SIDE UNTIL WELL AFTER FIRE IS OUT. STAY AWAY FROM STORAGE TANK ENDS. WITHDRAW IMMEDIATELY IN CASE OF RISING SOUND FROM VENTING SAFETY DEVICE OR ANY DISCOLORATION OF STORAGE TANK DUE TO FIRE (1987 EMERGENCY RESPONSE GUIDEBOOK, DOT P 5800.4, GUIDE PAGE 28).
DO NOT EXTINGUISH UNLESS FLOW CAN BE STOPPED. USE WATER IN FLOODING QUANTITIES AS FOG AS SOLID STREAMS MAY BE INEFFECTIVE. COOL CONTAINERS WITH FLOODING QUANTITIES OF WATER FROM AS FAR A DISTANCE AS POSSIBLE. AVOID CONTAMINATION OF WATER SOURCES AND SEWERS. AVOID BREATHING VAPORS AND KEEP UPWIND.

TOXICITY

ETHIOFENCARB: TOXICITY DATA: 97 MG/M3 INHALATION-RAT LCLO; 97 MG/K3 INHALATION-CAT LCLO; 2500 MG/KG SKIN-RABBIT LD50; 200 MG/KG ORAL-RAT LD50; 71 MG/KG ORAL-MOUSE LD50; 113 MG/KG ORAL-GUINEA PIG LD50; 113 MG/KG ORAL-GERBIL LD50; 400 MG/KG UNREPORTED-RAT LD50; 63 MG/KG UNREPORTED-MOUSE LD50; 118 MG/KG UNREPORTED-RABBIT LD50. CARCINOGEN STATUS: NONE. ACUTE TOXICITY: TOXIC BY INGESTION; SLIGHTLY TOXIC BY DERMAL ABSORPTION. TARGET EFFECTS: CHOLINESTERASE INHIBITOR. AT INCREASED RISK FROM EXPOSURE: PERSONS WITH ASTHMA, DIABETES, CARDIOVASCULAR DISEASE, MECHANICAL OBSTRUCTION OF THE GASTROINTESTINAL OR UROGENITAL TRACT, AND THOSE IN VAGOTONIC STATES.*
* MAY BE BASED ON GENERAL INFORMATION ON CARBAMATES.

HEALTH EFFECTS AND FIRST AID

INHALATION: ETHIOFENCARB: SEE INFORMATION ON CARBAMATES.
CARBAMATES: CHOLINESTERASE INHIBITOR. **ACUTE EXPOSURE-** WHEN INHALED, THE FIRST EFFECTS OF CHOLINESTERASE INHIBITION ARE USUALLY RESPIRATORY AND MAY INCLUDE NASAL HYPEREMIA AND WATERY DISCHARGE, CHEST DISCOMFORT, DYSPNEA, AND WHEEZING DUE TO INCREASED BRONCHIAL SECRETIONS AND BRONCHOCONSTRICTION. OTHER SYSTEMIC EFFECTS MAY BEGIN WITHIN A FEW MINUTES OR SEVERAL HOURS OF EXPOSURE. SYMPTOMS MAY INCLUDE NAUSEA, VOMITING, DIARRHEA, ABDOMINAL CRAMPS, HEADACHE, VERTIGO, OCULAR PAIN, CILIARY MUSCLE SPASM, BLURRING OR DIMNESS OF VISION, MIOSIS, OR IN SOME CASES MYDRIASIS, LACRIMATION, SALIVATION, SWEATING, AND CONFUSION. OTHER REPORTED CENTRAL NERVOUS SYSTEM OR NEUROMUSCULAR EFFECTS INCLUDE ATAXIA, SLURRED SPEECH, AREFLEXIA, WEAKNESS, FATIGUE, TWITCHING, FASCICULATION, TREMOR, AND EVENTUALLY PARALYSIS OF THE EXTREMITIES AND POSSIBLY OF THE RESPIRATORY MUSCLES. IN SEVERE CASES, THERE MAY ALSO BE INVOLUNTARY DEFECATION AND URINATION, BRADYCARDIA, HYPOTENSION, PULMONARY EDEMA, CONVULSIONS, COMA, AND DEATH FROM RESPIRATORY FAILURE OR CARDIAC ARREST. CARBAMATES GENERALLY DO NOT ACCUMULATE IN MAMMALIAN TISSUE AND THE CHOLINESTERASE INHIBITION REVERSES RATHER RAPIDLY. IN NON-FATAL CASES, THE ILLNESS GENERALLY LASTS LESS THAN 24 HOURS. **CHRONIC EXPOSURE-** PROLONGED OR REPEATED EXPOSURE MAY CAUSE EFFECTS AS DESCRIBED IN ACUTE EXPOSURE.

FIRST AID- REMOVE FROM EXPOSURE AREA TO FRESH AIR IMMEDIATELY. IF BREATHING HAS STOPPED, GIVE ARTIFICIAL RESPIRATION. MAINTAIN AIRWAY AND BLOOD PRESSURE AND ADMINISTER OXYGEN IF AVAILABLE. KEEP AFFECTED PERSON WARM AND AT REST. TREAT SYMPTOMATICALLY AND SUPPORTIVELY. ADMINISTRATION OF OXYGEN SHOULD BE PERFORMED BY QUALIFIED PERSONNEL. GET MEDICAL ATTENTION IMMEDIATELY.

SKIN CONTACT: ETHIOFENCARB: SEE INFORMATION ON CARBAMATES.
CARBAMATES: CHOLINESTERASE INHIBITOR. **ACUTE EXPOSURE-** SOME COMPOUNDS MAY CAUSE IRRITATION. LOCALIZED SWEATING AND FASCICULATIONS MAY OCCUR AT THE SITE OF CONTACT. IF SUFFICIENT AMOUNTS ARE ABSORBED THROUGH THE SKIN, OTHER EFFECTS OF CHOLINESTERASE INHIBITION MAY OCCUR AS DESCRIBED IN ACUTE INHALATION; SYMPTOMS MAY BE DELAYED FOR 2-3 HOURS, USUALLY NO MORE THAN 8 HOURS. **CHRONIC EXPOSURE-** REPEATED OR PROLONGED EXPOSURE MAY CAUSE EFFECTS AS DESCRIBED IN ACUTE EXPOSURE.

FIRST AID- REMOVE CONTAMINATED CLOTHING IMMEDIATELY. WASH CONTAMINATED AREAS WITH SOAP AND WATER FOLLOWED BY ALCOHOL (ARENA, POISONING, 4TH ED.). EMERGENCY PERSONNEL SHOULD WEAR GLOVES AND AVOID CONTAMINATION. TREAT RESPIRATORY DIFFICULTY WITH ARTIFICIAL RESPIRATION. GET MEDICAL ATTENTION IMMEDIATELY.

EYE CONTACT: ETHIOFENCARB: SEE INFORMATION ON CARBAMATES.
CARBAMATES: CHOLINESTERASE INHIBITOR. **ACUTE EXPOSURE-** DIRECT CONTACT MAY CAUSE PAIN, HYPEREMIA, LACRIMATION, TWITCHING OF THE EYELIDS, MIOSIS, AND CILIARY MUSCLE SPASM WITH LOSS OF ACCOMODATION, BLURRED OR DIMMED VISION AND BROWACHE. SOMETIMES MYDRIASIS MAY OCCUR INSTEAD OF MIOSIS. WITH SUFFICIENT EXPOSURE, OTHER SYMPTOMS OF CHOLINESTERASE INHIBITION MAY OCCUR AS DESCRIBED IN ACUTE INHALATION. **CHRONIC EXPOSURE-** PROLONGED EXPOSURE MAY CAUSE EFFECTS AS DESCRIBED IN ACUTE EXPOSURE. SOME COMPOUNDS HAVE CAUSED TOXIC EFFECTS ON THE CRYSTALLINE LENS, CONJUNCTIVAL THICKENING AND OBSTRUCTION OF NASOLACRIMAL CANALS WHEN USED AS MIOTIC EYE DROPS.

FIRST AID- IRRIGATE EYES WITH WATER OR SALINE SOLUTION. IF SYMPTOMS OF POISONING OCCUR, TREAT RESPIRATORY DIFFICULTY WITH ARTIFICIAL

RESPIRATION AND OXYGEN. OBSERVE PATIENT FOR AT LEAST 24-36 HOURS (GOSSELIN, CLINICAL TOXICOLOGY OF COMMERCIAL PRODUCTS, 5TH ED.). GET MEDICAL ATTENTION IMMEDIATELY. OXYGEN SHOULD BE ADMINISTERED BY QUALIFIED MEDICAL PERSONNEL.

INGESTION: ETHIOFENCARB: TOXIC. SEE INFORMATION ON CARBAMATES. CARBAMATES: CHOLINESTERASE INHIBITOR. **ACUTE EXPOSURE**- WHEN INGESTED, THE FIRST EFFECTS MAY BE NAUSEA, VOMITING, ANOREXIA, ABDOMINAL CRAMPS, AND DIARRHEA. WITH ABSORPTION FROM THE GASTROINTESTINAL TRACT, THE OTHER EFFECTS OF CHOLINESTERASE INHIBITION AS DESCRIBED IN ACUTE INHALATION MAY OCCUR; SYMPTOMS MAY BEGIN WITHIN MINUTES OR BE DELAYED SEVERAL HOURS. **CHRONIC EXPOSURE**- REPEATED INGESTION MAY CAUSE EFFECTS AS DESCRIBED IN ACUTE EXPOSURE.

FIRST AID- IF PERSON IS ALERT AND RESPIRATION IS NOT DEPRESSED, GIVE SYRUP OF IPECAC FOLLOWED BY WATER (IF VOMITING OCCURS, KEEP HEAD BELOW HIPS TO PREVENT ASPIRATION). IF CONSCIOUSNESS LEVEL DECLINES OR VOMITING HAS NOT OCCURRED IN 15 MINUTES EMPTY STOMACH BY GASTRIC LAVAGE WITH THE AID OF CUFFED ENDOTRACHEAL TUBE USING ISOTONIC SALINE OR 5% SODIUM BICARBONATE FOLLOW WITH ACTIVATED CHARCOAL. ESTABLISH AND MAINTAIN AIRWAY. TREAT RESPIRATORY DIFFICULTY WITH ARTIFICIAL RESPIRATION AND OXYGEN. DO NOT GIVE MORPHINE, AMINOPHYLLINE, PHENOTHIAZINES, RESERPINE, FUROSEMIDE, OR ETHACRYNIC ACID (MORGAN, RECOGNITION AND MANAGEMENT OF PESTICIDE POISONINGS, 3RD ED.). TREAT SYMPTOMATICALLY AND SUPPORTIVELY. ADMINISTRATION OF OXYGEN AND LAVAGE MUST BE PERFORMED BY QUALIFIED MEDICAL PERSONNEL. GET MEDICAL ATTENTION IMMEDIATELY.

ANTIDOTE: THE FOLLOWING ANTIDOTE HAS BEEN RECOMMENDED. HOWEVER, THE DECISION AS TO WHETHER THE SEVERITY OF POISONING REQUIRES ADMINISTRATION OF ANY ANTIDOTE AND ACTUAL DOSE REQUIRED SHOULD BE MADE BY QUALIFIED MEDICAL PERSONNEL.

FOR CHOLINESTERASE INHIBITORS: ESTABLISH CLEAR AIRWAY AND TISSUE OXYGENATION BY ASPIRATION OF SECRETIONS, AND IF NECESSARY, BY ASSISTED PULMONARY VENTILATION WITH OXYGEN. IMPROVE TISSUE OXYGENATION AS MUCH AS POSSIBLE BEFORE ADMINISTERING ATROPINE TO MINIMIZE THE RISK OF VENTRICULAR FIBRILLATION. ADMINISTER ATROPINE SULFATE INTRAVENOUSLY, OR INTRAMUSCULARLY IF IV INJECTION IS NOT POSSIBLE. IN MODERATELY SEVERE POISONING ADMINISTER ATROPINE SULFATE, 0.4-2.0 MG REPEATED EVERY 15 MINUTES UNTIL ATROPINIZATION IS ACHIEVED (TACHYCARDIA, FLUSHING, DRY MOUTH, MYDRIASIS). MAINTAIN ATROPINIZATION BY REPEATED DOSES FOR 2-12 HOURS, OR LONGER, DEPENDING ON THE SEVERITY OF POISONING. THE APPEARANCE OF RALES IN THE LUNG BASES, MIOSIS, SALIVATION, NAUSEA, BRADYCARDIA, ARE ALL INDICATIONS OF INADEQUATE ATROPINIZATION. SEVERELY POISONED INDIVIDUALS MAY EXHIBIT REMARKABLE TOLERANCE TO ATROPINE; TWO OR MORE TIMES THE DOSAGES SUGGESTED ABOVE MAY BE NEEDED. PERSONS NOT POISONED OR ONLY SLIGHTLY POISONED, HOWEVER, MAY DEVELOP SIGNS OF ATROPINE TOXICITY FROM SUCH LARGE DOSAGES: FEVER, MUSCLE FIBRILLATIONS, AND DELIRIUM ARE THE MAIN SIGNS OF ATROPINE TOXICITY. IF THESE SIGNS APPEAR WHILE THE PATIENT IS FULLY ATROPINIZED, ATROPINE ADMINISTRATION SHOULD BE DISCONTINUED, AT LEAST TEMPORARILY. OBSERVE TREATED PATIENTS CLOSELY AT LEAST 24 HOURS TO INSURE THAT SYMPTOMS (POSSIBLY PULMONARY EDEMA) DO NOT RECUR AS ATROPINIZATION WEARS OFF. IN VERY SEVERE POISONINGS, METABOLIC DISPOSITION OF TOXICANT MAY REQUIRE SEVERAL HOURS OR DAYS DURING WHICH ATROPINIZATION MUST BE MAINTAINED. MARKEDLY LOWER LEVELS OF URINARY METABOLITES INDICATE THAT ATROPINE DOSAGE CAN BE TAPERED OFF. AS DOSAGE IS REDUCED, CHECK THE LUNG BASES FREQUENTLY FOR RALES. IF RALES ARE HEARD OR OTHER SYMPTOMS RETURN, RE-ESTABLISH ATROPINIZATION PROMPTLY (MORGAN, RECOGNITION AND MANAGEMENT OF PESTICIDE POISONINGS, 3RD ED.). ADMINISTRATION OF ANTIDOTE MUST BE PERFORMED BY QUALIFIED MEDICAL PERSONNEL.

REACTIVITY

REACTIVITY: STABLE UNDER NORMAL TEMPERATURES AND PRESSURES.

INCOMPATIBILITIES: ETHIOFENCARB: OXIDIZERS (STRONG): FIRE AND EXPLOSION HAZARD.

DECOMPOSITION: THERMAL DECOMPOSITION PRODUCTS MAY INCLUDE TOXIC OXIDES OF CARBON, NITROGEN, AND SULFUR.

POLYMERIZATION: HAZARDOUS POLYMERIZATION HAS NOT BEEN REPORTED TO OCCUR UNDER NORMAL TEMPERATURES AND PRESSURES.

STORAGE AND DISPOSAL

OBSERVE ALL FEDERAL, STATE AND LOCAL REGULATIONS WHEN STORING OR DISPOSING OF THIS SUBSTANCE. FOR ASSISTANCE, CONTACT THE DISTRICT DIRECTOR OF THE ENVIRONMENTAL PROTECTION AGENCY.

STORAGE

STORE IN ACCORDANCE WITH 40 CFR 165 RECOMMENDED PROCEDURES FOR THE DISPOSAL AND STORAGE OF PESTICIDES AND PESTICIDE CONTAINERS.

STORE AWAY FROM INCOMPATIBLE SUBSTANCES.

PROTECT FROM LIGHT, STORE AT 4 C.

DISPOSAL

DISPOSAL MUST BE IN ACCORDANCE WITH 40 CFR 165 RECOMMENDED PROCEDURES FOR THE DISPOSAL AND STORAGE OF PESTICIDES AND PESTICIDE CONTAINERS.

CONDITIONS TO AVOID

AVOID CONTACT WITH HEAT, SPARKS, FLAMES OR OTHER IGNITION SOURCES. VAPORS MAY BE EXPLOSIVE. MATERIAL IS POISONOUS; AVOID INHALATION OF VAPORS OR CONTACT WITH SKIN. DO NOT ALLOW MATERIAL TO CONTAMINATE WATER SOURCES.

SPILL AND LEAK PROCEDURES

OCCUPATIONAL SPILL: SHUT OFF IGNITION SOURCES. DO NOT TOUCH SPILLED MATERIAL. STOP LEAK IF YOU CAN DO IT WITHOUT RISK. USE WATER SPRAY TO REDUCE VAPORS. FOR SMALL SPILLS, TAKE UP WITH SAND OR OTHER ABSORBENT MATERIAL AND PLACE INTO CONTAINERS FOR LATER DISPOSAL. FOR LARGER SPILLS, DIKE FAR AHEAD OF SPILL FOR LATER DISPOSAL. NO SMOKING, FLAMES OR FLARES IN HAZARD AREA! KEEP UNNECESSARY PEOPLE AWAY; ISOLATE HAZARD AREA AND DENY ENTRY.

PROTECTIVE EQUIPMENT

VENTILATION: PROVIDE LOCAL EXHAUST OR GENERAL DILUTION VENTILATION SYSTEM.

RESPIRATOR: THE FOLLOWING RESPIRATORS ARE RECOMMENDED BASED ON INFORMATION FOUND IN THE PHYSICAL DATA, TOXICITY AND HEALTH EFFECTS SECTIONS. THEY ARE RANKED IN ORDER FROM MINIMUM TO MAXIMUM RESPIRATORY PROTECTION. THE SPECIFIC RESPIRATOR SELECTED MUST BE BASED ON CONTAMINATION LEVELS FOUND IN THE WORK PLACE, MUST NOT EXCEED THE WORKING LIMITS OF THE RESPIRATOR AND BE JOINTLY APPROVED BY THE NATIONAL INSTITUTE FOR OCCUPATIONAL SAFETY AND HEALTH AND THE MINE SAFETY AND HEALTH ADMINISTRATION (NIOSH-MSHA).

CHEMICAL CARTRIDGE RESPIRATOR WITH PESTICIDE CARTRIDGE.

GAS MASK WITH A PESTICIDE CANISTER (CHIN-STYLE OR FRONT- OR BACK-MOUNTED CANISTER).

TYPE 'C' SUPPLIED-AIR RESPIRATOR OPERATED IN THE PRESSURE-DEMAND OR OTHER POSITIVE PRESSURE OR CONTINUOUS-FLOW MODE.

SELF-CONTAINED BREATHING APPARATUS.

FOR FIREFIGHTING AND OTHER IMMEDIATELY DANGEROUS TO LIFE OR HEALTH CONDITIONS:

SELF-CONTAINED BREATHING APPARATUS WITH FULL FACEPIECE OPERATED IN PRESSURE-DEMAND OR OTHER POSITIVE PRESSURE MODE.

SUPPLIED-AIR RESPIRATOR WITH FULL FACEPIECE AND OPERATED IN PRESSURE-DEMAND OR OTHER POSITIVE PRESSURE MODE IN COMBINATION WITH AN AUXILIARY SELF-CONTAINED BREATHING APPARATUS OPERATED IN PRESSURE-DEMAND OR OTHER POSITIVE PRESSURE MODE.

CLOTHING: EMPLOYEE MUST WEAR APPROPRIATE PROTECTIVE (IMPERVIOUS) CLOTHING AND EQUIPMENT TO PREVENT REPEATED OR PROLONGED SKIN CONTACT WITH THIS SUBSTANCE.

GLOVES: EMPLOYEE MUST WEAR APPROPRIATE PROTECTIVE GLOVES TO PREVENT CONTACT WITH THIS SUBSTANCE.

EYE PROTECTION: EMPLOYEE MUST WEAR SPLASH-PROOF OR DUST-RESISTANT SAFETY GOGGLES TO PREVENT EYE CONTACT WITH THIS SUBSTANCE.

EMERGENCY EYE WASH: WHERE THERE IS ANY POSSIBILITY THAT AN EMPLOYEE'S EYES MAY BE EXPOSED TO THIS SUBSTANCE, THE EMPLOYER SHOULD PROVIDE AN EYE WASH FOUNTAIN WITHIN THE IMMEDIATE WORK AREA FOR EMERGENCY USE.

AUTHORIZED BY- OCCUPATIONAL HEALTH SERVICES, INC.

CREATION DATE: 10/04/89 ***REVISION DATE:*** 06/12/90

MATERIAL SAFETY DATA SHEET

OCCUPATIONAL HEALTH SERVICES, INC.
AGRICULTURE AND PESTICIDE DIVISION
450 SEVENTH AVENUE, SUITE 2407
NEW YORK, NEW YORK 10123
1-800-445-MSDS OR (212) 967-1100

EMERGENCY CONTACT:
JOHN S. BRANSFORD, JR. (615) 292-1180

SUBSTANCE IDENTIFICATION

CAS-NUMBER 55635-13-7
SUBSTANCE: **SODIUM ALLOXYDIM**
TRADE NAMES/SYNONYMS: CYCLOHEXANECARBOXYLIC ACID, 2,2-DIMETHYL-4,6-DIOXO-5- (1-((2-PROPENYLOXY)IMINO)BUTYL)-, METHYL ESTER, ION(1-), SODIUM; 2,2-DIMETHYL-4,6-DIOXO-5-(1-((2-PROPENYOXY)IMINO)BUTYL)CYCLOHEXANECARBOXYLIC ACID METHYL ESTER; SODIUM(1-) ION; ALLOXYDIM SODIUM; ALLOXYDIMEDON SODIUM; C17H24NNAO5; PST72430
CHEMICAL FAMILY: SALT
MOLECULAR FORMULA: C17-H24-N-O5.NA
MOLECULAR WEIGHT: 345.4
CERCLA RATINGS (SCALE 0-3): HEALTH=U FIRE=1 REACTIVITY=0 PERSISTENCE=1
NFPA RATINGS (SCALE 0-4): HEALTH=U FIRE=1 REACTIVITY=0

COMPONENTS AND CONTAMINANTS

COMPONENT: SODIUM ALLOXYDIM ***PERCENT:*** 100.0
CAS# 55635-13-7
OTHER CONTAMINANTS: NONE
EXPOSURE LIMITS: NO OCCUPATIONAL EXPOSURE LIMITS ESTABLISHED BY OSHA, ACGIH, OR NIOSH.

PHYSICAL DATA

DESCRIPTION: WHITE OR COLORLESS HYGROSCOPIC CRYSTALLINE SOLID.
MELTING POINT: 367 F (186 C) (DECOMPOSES) ***SPECIFIC GRAVITY:*** NOT AVAILABLE
VAPOR PRESSURE: NEGLIGIBLE ***SOLUBILITY IN WATER:*** >200% @ 30 C
SOLVENT SOLUBILITY: SOLUBLE IN ACETONE, BUTANONE, CYCLOHEXANONE, ETHYL ACETATE, XYLENE, DIMETHYLFORMAMIDE, ALCOHOL.

FIRE AND EXPLOSION DATA

FIRE AND EXPLOSION HAZARD: SLIGHT FIRE HAZARD WHEN EXPOSED TO HEAT OR FLAME.
FIREFIGHTING MEDIA: DRY CHEMICAL, CARBON DIOXIDE, HALON, WATER SPRAY OR STANDARD FOAM (1987 EMERGENCY RESPONSE GUIDEBOOK, DOT P 5800.4).
FOR LARGER FIRES, USE WATER SPRAY, FOG OR STANDARD FOAM (1987 EMERGENCY RESPONSE GUIDEBOOK, DOT P 5800.4).
FIREFIGHTING: MOVE CONTAINER FROM FIRE AREA IF POSSIBLE. DO NOT SCATTER SPILLED MATERIAL WITH HIGH PRESSURE WATER STREAMS. DIKE FIRE CONTROL WATER FOR LATER DISPOSAL (1987 EMERGENCY RESPONSE GUIDEBOOK, DOT P 5800.4, GUIDE PAGE 31).
USE AGENTS SUITABLE FOR TYPE OF SURROUNDING FIRE. AVOID BREATHING HAZARDOUS VAPORS, KEEP UPWIND.

TOXICITY

SODIUM ALLOXYDIM: TOXICITY DATA: >2000 MG/KG SKIN-RABBIT LD50 (FMCHA2); 2260 MG/KG ORAL-RAT LD50; 3 GM/KG ORAL-MOUSE LD50; 1700 MG/KG INTRAPERITONEAL-RAT LD50. CARCINOGEN STATUS: NONE. ACUTE TOXICITY LEVEL: MODERATELY TOXIC BY INGESTION; SLIGHTLY TOXIC BY DERMAL ABSORPTION. TARGET EFFECTS: NO DATA AVAILABLE.

HEALTH EFFECTS AND FIRST AID

INHALATION: SODIUM ALLOXYDIM: **ACUTE EXPOSURE**- NO DATA AVAILABLE.
CHRONIC EXPOSURE- NO DATA AVAILABLE.
FIRST AID- REMOVE FROM EXPOSURE AREA TO FRESH AIR IMMEDIATELY. IF BREATHING HAS STOPPED, PERFORM ARTIFICIAL RESPIRATION. KEEP PERSON WARM AND AT REST. TREAT SYMPTOMATICALLY AND SUPPORTIVELY. GET MEDICAL ATTENTION IMMEDIATELY.

SKIN CONTACT: SODIUM ALLOXYDIM: **ACUTE EXPOSURE**- THE MEDIAN LETHAL DOSE IN RABBITS WAS GREATER THAN 2000 MG/KG. **CHRONIC EXPOSURE**- NO DATA AVAILABLE.
FIRST AID- REMOVE CONTAMINATED CLOTHING AND SHOES IMMEDIATELY. WASH AFFECTED AREA WITH SOAP OR MILD DETERGENT AND LARGE AMOUNTS OF WATER UNTIL NO EVIDENCE OF CHEMICAL REMAINS (APPROXIMATELY 15-20 MINUTES). GET MEDICAL ATTENTION IMMEDIATELY.

EYE CONTACT: SODIUM ALLOXYDIM: **ACUTE EXPOSURE**- NO DATA AVAILABLE.
CHRONIC EXPOSURE- NO DATA AVAILABLE.
FIRST AID- WASH EYES IMMEDIATELY WITH LARGE AMOUNTS OF WATER OR NORMAL SALINE, OCCASIONALLY LIFTING UPPER AND LOWER LIDS, UNTIL NO EVIDENCE OF CHEMICAL REMAINS (APPROXIMATELY 15-20 MINUTES). GET MEDICAL ATTENTION IMMEDIATELY.

INGESTION: SODIUM ALLOXYDIM: **ACUTE EXPOSURE**- THE MEDIAN LETHAL DOSE IN RATS WAS 2260 MG/KG. **CHRONIC EXPOSURE**- NO DATA AVAILABLE.
FIRST AID- TREAT SYMPTOMATICALLY AND SUPPORTIVELY. GET MEDICAL ATTENTION IMMEDIATELY. IF VOMITING OCCURS, KEEP HEAD LOWER THAN HIPS TO PREVENT ASPIRATION.
ANTIDOTE: NO SPECIFIC ANTIDOTE. TREAT SYMPTOMATICALLY AND SUPPORTIVELY.

REACTIVITY

REACTIVITY: STABLE UNDER NORMAL TEMPERATURES AND PRESSURES.
INCOMPATIBILITIES: SODIUM ALLOXYDIM: OXIDIZERS (STRONG): FIRE AND EXPLOSION HAZARD.
DECOMPOSITION: THERMAL DECOMPOSITION PRODUCTS MAY INCLUDE TOXIC OXIDES OF CARBON AND NITROGEN.
POLYMERIZATION: HAZARDOUS POLYMERIZATION HAS NOT BEEN REPORTED TO OCCUR UNDER NORMAL TEMPERATURES AND PRESSURES.

STORAGE AND DISPOSAL

OBSERVE ALL FEDERAL, STATE AND LOCAL REGULATIONS WHEN STORING OR DISPOSING OF THIS SUBSTANCE. FOR ASSISTANCE, CONTACT THE DISTRICT DIRECTOR OF THE ENVIRONMENTAL PROTECTION AGENCY.

STORAGE

STORE IN ACCORDANCE WITH 40 CFR 165 RECOMMENDED PROCEDURES FOR THE DISPOSAL AND STORAGE OF PESTICIDES AND PESTICIDE CONTAINERS.
STORE AWAY FROM INCOMPATIBLE SUBSTANCES.
STORE IN A COOL, DRY, WELL VENTILATED AREA

DISPOSAL

DISPOSAL MUST BE IN ACCORDANCE WITH 40 CFR 165 RECOMMENDED PROCEDURES FOR THE DISPOSAL AND STORAGE OF PESTICIDES AND PESTICIDE CONTAINERS.

CONDITIONS TO AVOID

MAY BURN BUT DOES NOT IGNITE READILY. AVOID CONTACT WITH STRONG OXIDIZERS, EXCESSIVE HEAT, SPARKS, OR OPEN FLAME.

SPILL AND LEAK PROCEDURES

OCCUPATIONAL SPILL: SWEEP UP AND PLACE IN SUITABLE CLEAN, DRY CONTAINERS FOR RECLAMATION OR LATER DISPOSAL. DO NOT FLUSH SPILLED MATERIAL INTO SEWER. KEEP UNNECESSARY PEOPLE AWAY.

PROTECTIVE EQUIPMENT

VENTILATION: PROVIDE LOCAL EXHAUST OR GENERAL DILUTION VENTILATION SYSTEM.
RESPIRATOR: THE FOLLOWING RESPIRATORS ARE RECOMMENDED BASED ON INFORMATION FOUND IN THE PHYSICAL DATA, TOXICITY AND HEALTH EFFECTS SECTIONS. THEY ARE RANKED IN ORDER FROM MINIMUM TO MAXIMUM RESPIRATORY PROTECTION. THE SPECIFIC RESPIRATOR SELECTED MUST BE BASED ON CONTAMINATION LEVELS FOUND IN THE WORK PLACE, MUST NOT EXCEED THE WORKING LIMITS OF THE RESPIRATOR AND BE JOINTLY APPROVED BY THE NATIONAL INSTITUTE FOR OCCUPATIONAL SAFETY AND HEALTH AND THE MINE SAFETY AND HEALTH ADMINISTRATION (NIOSH-MSHA).
CHEMICAL CARTRIDGE RESPIRATOR WITH AN ORGANIC VAPOR CARTRIDGE(S) WITH A FULL FACEPIECE AND ORGANIC VAPOR CARTRIDGE(S) IN COMBINATION WITH A DUST AND MIST FILTER.
POWERED AIR-PURIFYING RESPIRATOR WITH A TIGHT-FITTING FACEPIECE AND ORGANIC VAPOR CARTRIDGE(S) IN COMBINATION WITH A HIGH-EFFICIENCY PARTICULATE FILTER.
TYPE 'C' SUPPLIED-AIR RESPIRATOR WITH A FULL FACEPIECE OPERATED IN A PRESSURE-DEMAND OR OTHER POSITIVE PRESSURE MODE.
SELF-CONTAINED BREATHING APPARATUS WITH A FULL FACEPIECE OPERATED IN PRESSURE-DEMAND OR OTHER POSITIVE PRESSURE MODE.
FOR FIREFIGHTING AND OTHER IMMEDIATELY DANGEROUS TO LIFE OR HEALTH CONDITIONS:
SELF-CONTAINED BREATHING APPARATUS WITH FULL FACEPIECE OPERATED IN PRESSURE-DEMAND OR OTHER POSITIVE PRESSURE MODE.
SUPPLIED-AIR RESPIRATOR WITH FULL FACEPIECE AND OPERATED IN PRESSURE-DEMAND OR OTHER POSITIVE PRESSURE MODE IN COMBINATION WITH AN AUXILIARY SELF-CONTAINED BREATHING APPARATUS OPERATED IN PRESSURE-DEMAND OR OTHER POSITIVE PRESSURE MODE.
CLOTHING: EMPLOYEE MUST WEAR APPROPRIATE PROTECTIVE (IMPERVIOUS) CLOTHING AND EQUIPMENT TO PREVENT REPEATED OR PROLONGED SKIN CONTACT WITH THIS SUBSTANCE.
GLOVES: EMPLOYEE MUST WEAR APPROPRIATE PROTECTIVE GLOVES TO PREVENT CONTACT WITH THIS SUBSTANCE.
EYE PROTECTION: EMPLOYEE MUST WEAR SPLASH-PROOF OR DUST-RESISTANT SAFETY GOGGLES TO PREVENT EYE CONTACT WITH THIS SUBSTANCE.
EMERGENCY EYE WASH: WHERE THERE IS ANY POSSIBILITY THAT AN EMPLOYEE'S EYES MAY BE EXPOSED TO THIS SUBSTANCE, THE EMPLOYER SHOULD PROVIDE

AN EYE WASH FOUNTAIN WITHIN THE IMMEDIATE WORK AREA FOR EMERGENCY USE.

AUTHORIZED BY- OCCUPATIONAL HEALTH SERVICES, INC.
CREATION DATE: 10/05/89 ***REVISION DATE:*** 05/31/90

MATERIAL SAFETY DATA SHEET

OCCUPATIONAL HEALTH SERVICES, INC.
AGRICULTURE AND PESTICIDE DIVISION
450 SEVENTH AVENUE, SUITE 2407
NEW YORK, NEW YORK 10123
1-800-445-MSDS OR (212) 967-1100

EMERGENCY CONTACT:
JOHN S. BRANSFORD, JR. (615) 292-1180

SUBSTANCE IDENTIFICATION

CAS-NUMBER 34681-23-7
SUBSTANCE: BUTOXYCARBOXIM
TRADE NAMES/SYNONYMS: 2-BUTANONE, 3-(METHYLSULFONYL)-, O-((METHYLAMINO)CARBONYL)OXIME; 3-(METHYLSULFONYL)-2-BUTANONE O-((METHYLAMINO)CARBONYL)OXIME; 3-MESYLBUTANONE O-METHYLCARBAMOYLOXIME; 3-METHYLSULPHONYLBUTANONE O-METHYLCARBAMOYLOXIME; 3-METHYLSULFONYLBUTANONE O-METHYLCARBAMOYLOXIME; 3-(METHYLSULFONYL)-2-BUTANONE O-(METHYLCARBAMOYL)OXIME; BUTOXICARBOXIM; BUTOXYCARBOXIME; CO 859; PLANTPIN; C7H14N2O4S; PST72434
CHEMICAL FAMILY: CARBAMATE
MOLECULAR FORMULA: C7-H14-N2-O4-S
MOLECULAR WEIGHT: 222.29
CERCLA RATINGS (SCALE 0-3): HEALTH=3 FIRE=1 REACTIVITY=0 PERSISTENCE=0
NFPA RATINGS (SCALE 0-4): HEALTH=3 FIRE=1 REACTIVITY=0

COMPONENTS AND CONTAMINANTS

COMPONENT: BUTOXYCARBOXIM ***PERCENT:*** 100.0
CAS# 34681-23-7
OTHER CONTAMINANTS: NONE
EXPOSURE LIMITS: NO OCCUPATIONAL EXPOSURE LIMITS ESTABLISHED BY OSHA, ACGIH, OR NIOSH.

PHYSICAL DATA

DESCRIPTION: COLORLESS OR WHITE CRYSTALLINE SOLID.
MELTING POINT: 185-192 F (85-89 C) ***SPECIFIC GRAVITY:*** NOT AVAILABLE
VAPOR PRESSURE: NEGLIGIBLE ***SOLUBILITY IN WATER:*** 20.8%
SOLVENT SOLUBILITY: SOLUBLE IN CHLOROFORM, ACETONE, ALCOHOL, BENZENE, ISOPROPANOL, ETHYL ACETATE, AND ETHANOL; ALMOST INSOLUBLE IN PETROLEUM, PETROLEUM ETHER, CARBON TETRACHLORIDE, CYCLOHEXANE, AND TOLUENE.

FIRE AND EXPLOSION DATA

FIRE AND EXPLOSION HAZARD: SLIGHT FIRE HAZARD WHEN EXPOSED TO HEAT OR FLAME.
FIREFIGHTING MEDIA: DRY CHEMICAL, CARBON DIOXIDE, HALON, WATER SPRAY OR STANDARD FOAM (1987 EMERGENCY RESPONSE GUIDEBOOK, DOT P 5800.4). FOR LARGER FIRES, USE WATER SPRAY, FOG OR STANDARD FOAM (1987 EMERGENCY RESPONSE GUIDEBOOK, DOT P 5800.4).
FIREFIGHTING: MOVE CONTAINERS FROM FIRE AREA IF POSSIBLE. FIGHT FIRE FROM MAXIMUM DISTANCE. STAY AWAY FROM STORAGE TANK ENDS. DIKE FIRE CONTROL WATER FOR LATER DISPOSAL. DO NOT SCATTER MATERIAL (1987 EMERGENCY RESPONSE GUIDEBOOK, DOT P 5800.4, GUIDE PAGE 55). EXTINGUISH USING AGENTS SUITABLE FOR TYPE OF SURROUNDING FIRE. USE FLOODING AMOUNTS OF WATER AS FOG. AVOID BREATHING TOXIC DUST AND FUMES FROM BURNING MATERIAL; KEEP UPWIND.

TOXICITY

BUTOXYCARBOXIM: TOXICITY DATA: 458 MG/KG ORAL-RAT LD50; 275 MG/KG ORAL-RABBIT LD50; 288 MG/KG SUBCUTANEOUS-RAT LD50. CARCINOGEN STATUS: NONE. ACUTE TOXICITY LEVEL: TOXIC BY INGESTION. TARGET EFFECTS: CHOLINESTERASE INHIBITOR. AT INCREASED RISK FROM EXPOSURE: PERSONS WITH ASTHMA, DIABETES, CARDIOVASCULAR DISEASE, MECHANICAL OBSTRUCTION OF THE GASTROINTESTINAL OR UROGENITAL TRACT, AND THOSE IN VAGOTONIC STATES.*

* MAY BE BASED ON GENERAL INFORMATION ON CARBAMATES.

HEALTH EFFECTS AND FIRST AID

INHALATION: BUTOXYCARBOXIM: SEE INFORMATION ON CARBAMATES.
CARBAMATES: CHOLINESTERASE INHIBITOR. **ACUTE EXPOSURE-** WHEN INHALED, THE FIRST EFFECTS OF CHOLINESTERASE INHIBITION ARE USUALLY RESPIRATORY AND MAY INCLUDE NASAL HYPEREMIA AND WATERY DISCHARGE, CHEST DISCOMFORT, DYSPNEA, AND WHEEZING DUE TO INCREASED BRONCHIAL SECRETIONS AND BRONCHOCONSTRICTION. OTHER SYSTEMIC EFFECTS MAY BEGIN WITHIN A FEW MINUTES OR SEVERAL HOURS OF EXPOSURE. SYMPTOMS MAY INCLUDE NAUSEA, VOMITING, DIARRHEA, ABDOMINAL CRAMPS, HEADACHE, VERTIGO, OCULAR PAIN, CILIARY MUSCLE SPASM, BLURRING OR DIMNESS OF VISION, MIOSIS, OR IN SOME CASES MYDRIASIS, LACRIMATION, SALIVATION, SWEATING, AND CONFUSION. OTHER REPORTED CENTRAL NERVOUS SYSTEM OR NEUROMUSCULAR EFFECTS INCLUDE ATAXIA, SLURRED SPEECH, AREFLEXIA, WEAKNESS, FATIGUE, TWITCHING, FASCICULATION, TREMOR, AND EVENTUALLY PARALYSIS OF THE EXTREMITIES AND POSSIBLY OF THE RESPIRATORY MUSCLES. IN SEVERE CASES, THERE MAY ALSO BE INVOLUNTARY DEFECATION AND URINATION, BRADYCARDIA, HYPOTENSION, PULMONARY EDEMA, CONVULSIONS, COMA, AND DEATH FROM RESPIRATORY FAILURE OR CARDIAC ARREST. CARBAMATES GENERALLY DO NOT ACCUMULATE IN MAMMALIAN TISSUE AND THE CHOLINESTERASE INHIBITION REVERSES RATHER RAPIDLY. IN NON-FATAL CASES, THE ILLNESS GENERALLY LASTS LESS THAN 24 HOURS. **CHRONIC EXPOSURE-** PROLONGED OR REPEATED EXPOSURE MAY CAUSE EFFECTS AS DESCRIBED IN ACUTE EXPOSURE.
FIRST AID- REMOVE FROM EXPOSURE AREA TO FRESH AIR IMMEDIATELY. IF BREATHING HAS STOPPED, GIVE ARTIFICIAL RESPIRATION. MAINTAIN AIRWAY AND BLOOD PRESSURE AND ADMINISTER OXYGEN IF AVAILABLE. KEEP AFFECTED PERSON WARM AND AT REST. TREAT SYMPTOMATICALLY AND SUPPORTIVELY. ADMINISTRATION OF OXYGEN SHOULD BE PERFORMED BY QUALIFIED PERSONNEL. GET MEDICAL ATTENTION IMMEDIATELY.

SKIN CONTACT: BUTOXYCARBOXIM: SEE INFORMATION ON CARBAMATES.
CARBAMATES: CHOLINESTERASE INHIBITOR. **ACUTE EXPOSURE-** SOME COMPOUNDS MAY CAUSE IRRITATION. LOCALIZED SWEATING AND FASCICULATIONS MAY OCCUR AT THE SITE OF CONTACT. IF SUFFICIENT AMOUNTS ARE ABSORBED THROUGH THE SKIN, OTHER EFFECTS OF CHOLINESTERASE INHIBITION MAY OCCUR AS DESCRIBED IN ACUTE INHALATION; SYMPTOMS MAY BE DELAYED FOR 2-3 HOURS, USUALLY NO MORE THAN 8 HOURS. **CHRONIC EXPOSURE-** REPEATED OR PROLONGED EXPOSURE MAY CAUSE EFFECTS AS DESCRIBED IN ACUTE EXPOSURE.
FIRST AID- REMOVE CONTAMINATED CLOTHING IMMEDIATELY. WASH CONTAMINATED AREAS WITH SOAP AND WATER FOLLOWED BY ALCOHOL (ARENA, POISONING, 4TH ED.). EMERGENCY PERSONNEL SHOULD WEAR GLOVES AND AVOID CONTAMINATION. TREAT RESPIRATORY DIFFICULTY WITH ARTIFICIAL RESPIRATION. GET MEDICAL ATTENTION IMMEDIATELY.

EYE CONTACT: BUTOXYCARBOXIM: SEE INFORMATION ON CARBAMATES.
CARBAMATES: CHOLINESTERASE INHIBITOR. **ACUTE EXPOSURE-** DIRECT CONTACT MAY CAUSE PAIN, HYPEREMIA, LACRIMATION, TWITCHING OF THE EYELIDS, MIOSIS, AND CILIARY MUSCLE SPASM WITH LOSS OF ACCOMODATION, BLURRED OR DIMMED VISION AND BROWACHE. SOMETIMES MYDRIASIS MAY OCCUR INSTEAD OF MIOSIS. WITH SUFFICIENT EXPOSURE, OTHER SYMPTOMS OF CHOLINESTERASE INHIBITION MAY OCCUR AS DESCRIBED IN ACUTE INHALATION. **CHRONIC EXPOSURE-** PROLONGED EXPOSURE MAY CAUSE EFFECTS AS DESCRIBED IN ACUTE EXPOSURE. SOME COMPOUNDS HAVE CAUSED TOXIC EFFECTS ON THE CRYSTALLINE LENS, CONJUNCTIVAL THICKENING AND OBSTRUCTION OF NASOLACRIMAL CANALS WHEN USED AS MIOTIC EYE DROPS.
FIRST AID- IRRIGATE EYES WITH WATER OR SALINE SOLUTION. IF SYMPTOMS OF POISONING OCCUR, TREAT RESPIRATORY DIFFICULTY WITH ARTIFICIAL RESPIRATION AND OXYGEN. OBSERVE PATIENT FOR AT LEAST 24-36 HOURS (GOSSELIN, CLINICAL TOXICOLOGY OF COMMERCIAL PRODUCTS, 5TH ED.). GET MEDICAL ATTENTION IMMEDIATELY. OXYGEN SHOULD BE ADMINISTERED BY QUALIFIED MEDICAL PERSONNEL.

INGESTION: BUTOXYCARBOXIM: TOXIC. SEE INFORMATION ON CARBAMATES.
CARBAMATES: CHOLINESTERASE INHIBITOR. **ACUTE EXPOSURE-** WHEN INGESTED, THE FIRST EFFECTS MAY BE NAUSEA, VOMITING, ANOREXIA, ABDOMINAL CRAMPS, AND DIARRHEA. WITH ABSORPTION FROM THE GAST ROINTESTINAL TRACT, THE OTHER EFFECTS OF CHOLINESTERASE INHIBITION AS DESCRIBED IN ACUTE INHALATION MAY OCCUR; SYMPTOMS MAY BEGIN WITHIN MINUTES OR BE DELAYED SEVERAL HOURS. **CHRONIC EXPOSURE-** REPEATED INGESTION MAY CAUSE EFFECTS AS DESCRIBED IN ACUTE EXPOSURE.
FIRST AID- IF PERSON IS ALERT AND RESPIRATION IS NOT DEPRESSED, GIVE SYRUP OF IPECAC FOLLOWED BY WATER (IF VOMITING OCCURS, KEEP HEAD BELOW HIPS TO PREVENT ASPIRATION). IF CONSCIOUSNESS LEVEL DECLINES OR VOMITING HAS

NOT OCCURRED IN 15 MINUTES EMPTY STOMACH BY GASTRIC LAVAGE WITH THE AID OF CUFFED ENDOTRACHEAL TUBE USING ISOTONIC SALINE OR 5% SODIUM BICARBONATE FOLLOW WITH ACTIVATED CHARCOAL. ESTABLISH AND MAINTAIN AIRWAY. TREAT RESPIRATORY DIFFICULTY WITH ARTIFICIAL RESPIRATION AND OXYGEN. DO NOT GIVE MORPHINE, AMINOPHYLLINE, PHENOTHIAZINES, RESERPINE, FUROSEMIDE, OR ETHACRYNIC ACID (MORGAN, RECOGNITION AND MANAGEMENT OF PESTICIDE POISONINGS, 3RD ED.). TREAT SYMPTOMATICALLY AND SUPPORTIVELY. ADMINISTRATION OF OXYGEN AND LAVAGE MUST BE PERFORMED BY QUALIFIED MEDICAL PERSONNEL. GET MEDICAL ATTENTION IMMEDIATELY.

ANTIDOTE: THE FOLLOWING ANTIDOTE HAS BEEN RECOMMENDED. HOWEVER, THE DECISION AS TO WHETHER THE SEVERITY OF POISONING REQUIRES ADMINISTRATION OF ANY ANTIDOTE AND ACTUAL DOSE REQUIRED SHOULD BE MADE BY QUALIFIED MEDICAL PERSONNEL.

FOR CHOLINESTERASE INHIBITORS: ESTABLISH CLEAR AIRWAY AND TISSUE OXYGENATION BY ASPIRATION OF SECRETIONS, AND IF NECESSARY, BY ASSISTED PULMONARY VENTILATION WITH OXYGEN. IMPROVE TISSUE OXYGENATION AS MUCH AS POSSIBLE BEFORE ADMINISTERING ATROPINE TO MINIMIZE THE RISK OF VENTRICULAR FIBRILLATION. ADMINISTER ATROPINE SULFATE INTRAVENOUSLY, OR INTRAMUSCULARLY IF IV INJECTION IS NOT POSSIBLE. IN MODERATELY SEVERE POISONING ADMINISTER ATROPINE SULFATE, 0.4-2.0 MG REPEATED EVERY 15 MINUTES UNTIL ATROPINIZATION IS ACHIEVED (TACHYCARDIA, FLUSHING, DRY MOUTH, MYDRIASIS). MAINTAIN ATROPINIZATION BY REPEATED DOSES FOR 2-12 HOURS, OR LONGER, DEPENDING ON THE SEVERITY OF POISONING. THE APPEARANCE OF RALES IN THE LUNG BASES, MIOSIS, SALIVATION, NAUSEA, BRADYCARDIA, ARE ALL INDICATIONS OF INADEQUATE ATROPINIZATION. SEVERELY POISONED INDIVIDUALS MAY EXHIBIT REMARKABLE TOLERANCE TO ATROPINE; TWO OR MORE TIMES THE DOSAGES SUGGESTED ABOVE MAY BE NEEDED. PERSONS NOT POISONED OR ONLY SLIGHTLY POISONED, HOWEVER, MAY DEVELOP SIGNS OF ATROPINE TOXICITY FROM SUCH LARGE DOSAGES: FEVER, MUSCLE FIBRILLATIONS, AND DELIRIUM ARE THE MAIN SIGNS OF ATROPINE TOXICITY. IF THESE SIGNS APPEAR WHILE THE PATIENT IS FULLY ATROPINIZED, ATROPINE ADMINISTRATION SHOULD BE DISCONTINUED, AT LEAST TEMPORARILY. OBSERVE TREATED PATIENTS CLOSELY AT LEAST 24 HOURS TO INSURE THAT SYMPTOMS (POSSIBLY PULMONARY EDEMA) DO NOT RECUR AS ATROPINIZATION WEARS OFF. IN VERY SEVERE POISONINGS, METABOLIC DISPOSITION OF TOXICANT MAY REQUIRE SEVERAL HOURS OR DAYS DURING WHICH ATROPINIZATION MUST BE MAINTAINED. MARKEDLY LOWER LEVELS OF URINARY METABOLITES INDICATE THAT ATROPINE DOSAGE CAN BE TAPERED OFF. AS DOSAGE IS REDUCED, CHECK THE LUNG BASES FREQUENTLY FOR RALES. IF RALES ARE HEARD OR OTHER SYMPTOMS RETURN, RE-ESTABLISH ATROPINIZATION PROMPTLY (MORGAN, RECOGNITION AND MANAGEMENT OF PESTICIDE POISONINGS, 3RD ED.). ADMINISTRATION OF ANTIDOTE MUST BE PERFORMED BY QUALIFIED MEDICAL PERSONNEL.

REACTIVITY

REACTIVITY: STABLE UNDER NORMAL TEMPERATURES AND PRESSURES.

INCOMPATIBILITIES: BUTOXYCARBOXIM: OXIDIZERS (STRONG): FIRE AND EXPLOSION HAZARD.

DECOMPOSITION: THERMAL DECOMPOSITION PRODUCTS MAY INCLUDE TOXIC OXIDES OF CARBON, NITROGEN, AND SULFUR.

POLYMERIZATION: HAZARDOUS POLYMERIZATION HAS NOT BEEN REPORTED TO OCCUR UNDER NORMAL TEMPERATURES AND PRESSURES.

STORAGE AND DISPOSAL

OBSERVE ALL FEDERAL, STATE AND LOCAL REGULATIONS WHEN STORING OR DISPOSING OF THIS SUBSTANCE. FOR ASSISTANCE, CONTACT THE DISTRICT DIRECTOR OF THE ENVIRONMENTAL PROTECTION AGENCY.

STORAGE

STORE IN ACCORDANCE WITH 40 CFR 165 RECOMMENDED PROCEDURES FOR THE DISPOSAL AND STORAGE OF PESTICIDES AND PESTICIDE CONTAINERS.
STORE AWAY FROM INCOMPATIBLE SUBSTANCES.

DISPOSAL

DISPOSAL MUST BE IN ACCORDANCE WITH 40 CFR 165 RECOMMENDED PROCEDURES FOR THE DISPOSAL AND STORAGE OF PESTICIDES AND PESTICIDE CONTAINERS.

CONDITIONS TO AVOID

MAY BURN BUT DOES NOT IGNITE READILY. CONTAINERS MAY EXPLODE IN HEAT OF FIRE.

SPILL AND LEAK PROCEDURES

OCCUPATIONAL SPILL: DO NOT TOUCH SPILLED MATERIAL. STOP LEAK IF YOU CAN DO IT WITHOUT RISK. USE WATER SPRAY TO REDUCE VAPORS. FOR SMALL SPILLS, TAKE UP WITH SAND OR OTHER ABSORBENT MATERIAL AND PLACE INTO CONTAINERS FOR LATER DISPOSAL. FOR SMALL DRY SPILLS, WITH A CLEAN SHOVEL PLACE MATERIAL INTO CLEAN, DRY CONTAINERS AND COVER. MOVE CONTAINERS FROM SPILL AREA. FOR LARGER SPILLS, DIKE FAR AHEAD OF SPILL FOR LATER DISPOSAL. KEEP UNNECESSARY PEOPLE AWAY. ISOLATE HAZARD AREA AND DENY ENTRY. VENTILATE CLOSED SPACES BEFORE ENTERING.

PROTECTIVE EQUIPMENT

VENTILATION: PROVIDE LOCAL EXHAUST OR GENERAL DILUTION VENTILATION SYSTEM.

RESPIRATOR: THE FOLLOWING RESPIRATORS ARE RECOMMENDED BASED ON INFORMATION FOUND IN THE PHYSICAL DATA, TOXICITY AND HEALTH EFFECTS SECTIONS. THEY ARE RANKED IN ORDER FROM MINIMUM TO MAXIMUM RESPIRATORY PROTECTION. THE SPECIFIC RESPIRATOR SELECTED MUST BE BASED ON CONTAMINATION LEVELS FOUND IN THE WORK PLACE, MUST NOT EXCEED THE WORKING LIMITS OF THE RESPIRATOR AND BE JOINTLY APPROVED BY THE NATIONAL INSTITUTE FOR OCCUPATIONAL SAFETY AND HEALTH AND THE MINE SAFETY AND HEALTH ADMINISTRATION (NIOSH-MSHA).

CHEMICAL CARTRIDGE RESPIRATOR WITH AN ORGANIC VAPOR CARTRIDGE(S) WITH A FULL FACEPIECE AND ORGANIC VAPOR CARTRIDGE(S) IN COMBINATION WITH A DUST AND MIST FILTER.

POWERED AIR-PURIFYING RESPIRATOR WITH A TIGHT-FITTING FACEPIECE AND ORGANIC VAPOR CARTRIDGE(S) IN COMBINATION WITH A HIGH-EFFICIENCY PARTICULATE FILTER.

TYPE 'C' SUPPLIED-AIR RESPIRATOR WITH A FULL FACEPIECE OPERATED IN A PRESSURE-DEMAND OR OTHER POSITIVE PRESSURE MODE.

SELF-CONTAINED BREATHING APPARATUS WITH A FULL FACEPIECE OPERATED IN PRESSURE-DEMAND OR OTHER POSITIVE PRESSURE MODE.

FOR FIREFIGHTING AND OTHER IMMEDIATELY DANGEROUS TO LIFE OR HEALTH CONDITIONS:

SELF-CONTAINED BREATHING APPARATUS WITH FULL FACEPIECE OPERATED IN PRESSURE-DEMAND OR OTHER POSITIVE PRESSURE MODE.

SUPPLIED-AIR RESPIRATOR WITH FULL FACEPIECE AND OPERATED IN PRESSURE-DEMAND OR OTHER POSITIVE PRESSURE MODE IN COMBINATION WITH AN AUXILIARY SELF-CONTAINED BREATHING APPARATUS OPERATED IN PRESSURE-DEMAND OR OTHER POSITIVE PRESSURE MODE.

CLOTHING: EMPLOYEE MUST WEAR APPROPRIATE PROTECTIVE (IMPERVIOUS) CLOTHING AND EQUIPMENT TO PREVENT REPEATED OR PROLONGED SKIN CONTACT WITH THIS SUBSTANCE.

GLOVES: EMPLOYEE MUST WEAR APPROPRIATE PROTECTIVE GLOVES TO PREVENT CONTACT WITH THIS SUBSTANCE.

EYE PROTECTION: EMPLOYEE MUST WEAR SPLASH-PROOF OR DUST-RESISTANT SAFETY GOGGLES TO PREVENT EYE CONTACT WITH THIS SUBSTANCE.

EMERGENCY EYE WASH: WHERE THERE IS ANY POSSIBILITY THAT AN EMPLOYEE'S EYES MAY BE EXPOSED TO THIS SUBSTANCE, THE EMPLOYER SHOULD PROVIDE AN EYE WASH FOUNTAIN WITHIN THE IMMEDIATE WORK AREA FOR EMERGENCY USE.

AUTHORIZED BY- OCCUPATIONAL HEALTH SERVICES, INC.
CREATION DATE: 10/04/89 ***REVISION DATE:*** 06/12/90

MATERIAL SAFETY DATA SHEET

OCCUPATIONAL HEALTH SERVICES, INC.
AGRICULTURE AND PESTICIDE DIVISION
450 SEVENTH AVENUE, SUITE 2407
NEW YORK, NEW YORK 10123
1-800-445-MSDS OR (212) 967-1100

EMERGENCY CONTACT:
JOHN S. BRANSFORD, JR. (615) 292-1180

SUBSTANCE IDENTIFICATION

CAS-NUMBER 55283-68-6

SUBSTANCE: **ETHALFLURALIN**

TRADE NAMES/SYNONYMS: BENZENAMINE, N-ETHYL-N-(2-METHYL-2-PROPENYL)-2,6-DINITRO-4- (TRIFLUOROMETHYL)-; N-ETHYL-N-(2-METHYL-2-PROPENYL)-2,6-DINITRO-4-(TRIFLUOROMETHYL)- BENZENAMINE; N-ETHYL-ALPHA,ALPHA,ALPHA-TRIFLUORO-N-(2-METHYLALLYL)-2,6-DINITRO- P-TOLUIDINE; N-ETHYL-N-(2-METHYLALLYL)-2,6-DINITRO-4-TRIFLUOROMETHYLANILINE; EL 161; SONALAN; SONALEN; C13H14F3N3O4; PST72436

CHEMICAL FAMILY: ANILINE DERIVATIVE
NITRO
HALOGEN

MOLECULAR FORMULA: C13-H14-F3-N3-O4

MOLECULAR WEIGHT: 333.27

CERCLA RATINGS (SCALE 0-3): HEALTH = 1 FIRE = 1 REACTIVITY = 0 PERSISTENCE = 2
NFPA RATINGS (SCALE 0-4): HEALTH = 1 FIRE = 1 REACTIVITY = 0

COMPONENTS AND CONTAMINANTS

COMPONENT: ETHALFLURALIN ***PERCENT:*** 100.0
CAS# 55283-68-6
OTHER CONTAMINANTS: NONE
EXPOSURE LIMITS: NO OCCUPATIONAL EXPOSURE LIMITS ESTABLISHED BY OSHA, ACGIH, OR NIOSH.

PHYSICAL DATA

DESCRIPTION: YELLOW-ORANGE CRYSTALS WITH A FAINT AMINE ODOR.
MELTING POINT: 135-138 F (57-59 C) ***SPECIFIC GRAVITY:*** 1.32
VAPOR PRESSURE: NEGLIGIBLE @ 25 C ***SOLUBILITY IN WATER:*** 0.3 PPM @ 25 C
SOLVENT SOLUBILITY: SOLUBLE IN ACETONE, ACETRONITRILE, BENZENE, CHLOROFORM, DICHLOROMETHANE, XYLENE, METHANOL, ETHANOL, HEXANE, AND ORGANIC SOLVENTS.
DECOMPOSES AT 493 F (256 C).

FIRE AND EXPLOSION DATA

FIRE AND EXPLOSION HAZARD: NEGLIGIBLE FIRE HAZARD WHEN EXPOSED TO HEAT OR FLAME.
DUST-AIR MIXTURES MAY IGNITE OR EXPLODE.
FIREFIGHTING MEDIA: DRY CHEMICAL, CARBON DIOXIDE, HALON, WATER SPRAY OR STANDARD FOAM (1987 EMERGENCY RESPONSE GUIDEBOOK, DOT P 5800.4).
FOR LARGER FIRES, USE WATER SPRAY, FOG OR STANDARD FOAM (1987 EMERGENCY RESPONSE GUIDEBOOK, DOT P 5800.4).
FIREFIGHTING: MOVE CONTAINER FROM FIRE AREA IF POSSIBLE. DO NOT SCATTER SPILLED MATERIAL WITH HIGH PRESSURE WATER STREAMS. DIKE FIRE CONTROL WATER FOR LATER DISPOSAL (1987 EMERGENCY RESPONSE GUIDEBOOK, DOT P 5800.4, GUIDE PAGE 31).
USE AGENTS SUITABLE FOR TYPE OF SURROUNDING FIRE. AVOID BREATHING HAZARDOUS VAPORS, KEEP UPWIND.

TOXICITY

ETHALFLURALIN: TOXICITY DATA: >28 MG/M3/1 HOUR INHALATION-RAT LC50 (EPA); >2 GM/KG SKIN-RABBIT LD50 (EPA); 10,000 MG/KG ORAL-RAT LD50; >10,000 MG/KG ORAL-MOUSE LD50 (EPA); >200 MG/KG ORAL-DOG LD50 (EPA); >200 MG/KG ORAL-CAT LD50 (EPA). CARCINOGEN STATUS: NONE. ACUTE TOXICITY LEVEL: SLIGHTLY TOXIC BY DERMAL ABSORPTION AND INGESTION. TARGET EFFECTS: SENSTITIZER- SKIN.

HEALTH EFFECTS AND FIRST AID

INHALATION: ETHALFLURALIN: **ACUTE EXPOSURE-** A LETHAL CONCENTRATION IN RATS WAS GREATER THAN 28 MG/M3/HOUR. **CHRONIC EXPOSURE-** NO DATA AVAILABLE.
FIRST AID- REMOVE FROM EXPOSURE AREA TO FRESH AIR IMMEDIATELY. IF BREATHING HAS STOPPED, PERFORM ARTIFICIAL RESPIRATION. KEEP PERSON WARM AND AT REST. TREAT SYMPTOMATICALLY AND SUPPORTIVELY. GET MEDICAL ATTENTION IMMEDIATELY.

SKIN CONTACT: ETHALFLURALIN: SENSITIZER. **ACUTE EXPOSURE-** THIS MATERIAL WAS SLIGHTLY IRRITATING TO RABBIT SKIN. SENSITIZATION DERMATITIS MAY OCCUR IN PREVIOUSLY EXPOSED PERSONS. **CHRONIC EXPOSURE-** PROLONGED OR REPEATED EXPOSURE MAY PRODUCE SENSITIZATION DERMATITIS.
FIRST AID- REMOVE CONTAMINATED CLOTHING AND SHOES IMMEDIATELY. WASH AFFECTED AREA WITH SOAP OR MILD DETERGENT AND LARGE AMOUNTS OF WATER UNTIL NO EVIDENCE OF CHEMICAL REMAINS (APPROXIMATELY 15-20 MINUTES). GET MEDICAL ATTENTION IMMEDIATELY.

EYE CONTACT: ETHALFLURALIN: **ACUTE EXPOSURE-** THIS MATERIAL WAS SLIGHTLY IRRITATING TO RABBIT EYES. **CHRONIC EXPOSURE-** NO DATA AVAILABLE.
FIRST AID- WASH EYES IMMEDIATELY WITH LARGE AMOUNTS OF WATER OR NORMAL SALINE, OCCASIONALLY LIFTING UPPER AND LOWER LIDS, UNTIL NO EVIDENCE OF CHEMICAL REMAINS (APPROXIMATELY 15-20 MINUTES). GET MEDICAL ATTENTION IMMEDIATELY.

INGESTION: ETHALFLURALIN: **ACUTE EXPOSURE-** A LETHAL DOSE IN RATS WAS 10000 MG/KG; SYMPTOMS WERE NOT REPORTED. **CHRONIC EXPOSURE-** TERATOGENIC EFFECTS WERE REPORTED IN RABBITS, THE NO-OBSERVED-EFFECTS LEVEL WAS 75 MG/KG. MAMMARY GLAND FIBROADENOMAS (BENIGN) WERE OBSERVED IN FEMALE RATS AT 250 AND 750 PPM DOSE LEVELS.
FIRST AID- IF THE PERSON IS CONSCIOUS AND NOT CONVULSING, REMOVE BY GASTRIC LAVAGE AND FOLLOW WITH A CATHARTIC (DREISBACH, HANDBOOK OF POISONING, 12TH ED.). TREAT SYMPTOMATICALLY AND SUPPORTIVELY. GASTRIC LAVAGE SHOULD BE PERFORMED BY QUALIFIED MEDICAL PERSONNEL. GET MEDICAL ATTENTION IMMEDIATELY.
ANTIDOTE: NO SPECIFIC ANTIDOTE. TREAT SYMPTOMATICALLY AND SUPPORTIVELY.

REACTIVITY

REACTIVITY: ETHALFLURALIN: STABLE UNDER NORMAL TEMPERATURES AND PRESSURES. MAY DECOMPOSE ON EXPOSURE TO UV LIGHT OR TEMPERATURES GREATER THAN 493 F (256 C).
INCOMPATIBILITIES: ETHALFLURALIN: OXIDIZERS (STRONG): FIRE AND EXPLOSION HAZARD.
DECOMPOSITION: THERMAL DECOMPOSITION PRODUCTS MAY INCLUDE HIGHLY TOXIC FUMES OF FLUORIDES AND OXIDES OF NITROGEN AND CARBON.
POLYMERIZATION: HAZARDOUS POLYMERIZATION HAS NOT BEEN REPORTED TO OCCUR UNDER NORMAL TEMPERATURES AND PRESSURES.

STORAGE AND DISPOSAL

OBSERVE ALL FEDERAL, STATE AND LOCAL REGULATIONS WHEN STORING OR DISPOSING OF THIS SUBSTANCE. FOR ASSISTANCE, CONTACT THE DISTRICT DIRECTOR OF THE ENVIRONMENTAL PROTECTION AGENCY.

****STORAGE****

STORE IN ACCORDANCE WITH 40 CFR 165 RECOMMENDED PROCEDURES FOR THE DISPOSAL AND STORAGE OF PESTICIDES AND PESTICIDE CONTAINERS.
KEEP CONTAINER TIGHTLY CLOSED. PROTECT FROM EXPOSURE TO AIR OR LIGHT. STORE AWAY FROM INCOMPATIBLE SUBSTANCES.

****DISPOSAL****

DISPOSAL MUST BE IN ACCORDANCE WITH 40 CFR 165 RECOMMENDED PROCEDURES FOR THE DISPOSAL AND STORAGE OF PESTICIDES AND PESTICIDE CONTAINERS.

CONDITIONS TO AVOID

MAY BURN BUT DOES NOT IGNITE READILY. AVOID CONTACT WITH STRONG OXIDIZERS, EXCESSIVE HEAT, SPARKS, OR OPEN FLAME.

SPILL AND LEAK PROCEDURES

OCCUPATIONAL SPILL: SWEEP UP AND PLACE IN SUITABLE CLEAN, DRY CONTAINERS FOR RECLAMATION OR LATER DISPOSAL. DO NOT FLUSH SPILLED MATERIAL INTO SEWER. KEEP UNNECESSARY PEOPLE AWAY.

PROTECTIVE EQUIPMENT

VENTILATION: PROVIDE LOCAL EXHAUST OR GENERAL DILUTION VENTILATION SYSTEM.
RESPIRATOR: THE FOLLOWING RESPIRATORS ARE RECOMMENDED BASED ON INFORMATION FOUND IN THE PHYSICAL DATA, TOXICITY AND HEALTH EFFECTS SECTIONS. THEY ARE RANKED IN ORDER FROM MINIMUM TO MAXIMUM RESPIRATORY PROTECTION. THE SPECIFIC RESPIRATOR SELECTED MUST BE BASED ON CONTAMINATION LEVELS FOUND IN THE WORK PLACE, MUST NOT EXCEED THE WORKING LIMITS OF THE RESPIRATOR AND BE JOINTLY APPROVED BY THE NATIONAL INSTITUTE FOR OCCUPATIONAL SAFETY AND HEALTH AND THE MINE SAFETY AND HEALTH ADMINISTRATION (NIOSH-MSHA).
CHEMICAL CARTRIDGE RESPIRATOR WITH AN ORGANIC VAPOR CARTRIDGE(S) IN COMBINATION WITH A DUST AND MIST FILTER.
GAS MASK WITH ORGANIC VAPOR CANISTER (CHIN-STYLE OR FRONT- OR BACK-MOUNTED CANISTER) WITH A DUST AND MIST FILTER.
GAS MASK WITH ORGANIC VAPOR CANISTER (CHIN-STYLE OR FRONT- OR BACK-MOUNTED CANISTER) WITH A PARTICULATE FILTER.
POWERED AIR-PURIFYING RESPIRATOR WITH A HIGH-EFFICIENCY FILTER.
TYPE 'C' SUPPLIED-AIR RESPIRATOR WITH A FULL FACEPIECE OPERATED IN A PRESSURE-DEMAND OR OTHER POSITIVE PRESSURE MODE.
SELF-CONTAINED BREATHING APPARATUS WITH A FULL FACEPIECE OPERATED IN PRESSURE-DEMAND OR OTHER POSITIVE PRESSURE MODE.
FOR FIREFIGHTING AND OTHER IMMEDIATELY DANGEROUS TO LIFE OR HEALTH CONDITIONS:
SELF-CONTAINED BREATHING APPARATUS WITH FULL FACEPIECE OPERATED IN PRESSURE-DEMAND OR OTHER POSITIVE PRESSURE MODE.
SUPPLIED-AIR RESPIRATOR WITH FULL FACEPIECE AND OPERATED IN PRESSURE-DEMAND OR OTHER POSITIVE PRESSURE MODE IN COMBINATION WITH AN AUXILIARY SELF-CONTAINED BREATHING APPARATUS OPERATED IN PRESSURE-DEMAND OR OTHER POSITIVE PRESSURE MODE.
CLOTHING: EMPLOYEE MUST WEAR APPROPRIATE PROTECTIVE (IMPERVIOUS) CLOTHING AND EQUIPMENT TO PREVENT REPEATED OR PROLONGED SKIN CONTACT WITH THIS SUBSTANCE.
GLOVES: EMPLOYEE MUST WEAR APPROPRIATE PROTECTIVE GLOVES TO PREVENT CONTACT WITH THIS SUBSTANCE.
EYE PROTECTION: EMPLOYEE MUST WEAR SPLASH-PROOF OR DUST-RESISTANT SAFETY GOGGLES TO PREVENT EYE CONTACT WITH THIS SUBSTANCE.
EMERGENCY EYE WASH: WHERE THERE IS ANY POSSIBILITY THAT AN EMPLOYEE'S

EYES MAY BE EXPOSED TO THIS SUBSTANCE, THE EMPLOYER SHOULD PROVIDE AN EYE WASH FOUNTAIN WITHIN THE IMMEDIATE WORK AREA FOR EMERGENCY USE.

AUTHORIZED BY- OCCUPATIONAL HEALTH SERVICES, INC.
CREATION DATE: 06/26/90 ***REVISION DATE:*** 06/26/90

MATERIAL SAFETY DATA SHEET

OCCUPATIONAL HEALTH SERVICES, INC.
AGRICULTURE AND PESTICIDE DIVISION
450 SEVENTH AVENUE, SUITE 2407
NEW YORK, NEW YORK 10123
1-800-445-MSDS OR (212) 967-1100

EMERGENCY CONTACT:
JOHN S. BRANSFORD, JR. (615) 292-1180

SUBSTANCE IDENTIFICATION

CAS-NUMBER 31218-83-4

SUBSTANCE: **PROPETAMPHOS**

TRADE NAMES/SYNONYMS: 2-BUTENOIC ACID, 3-(((ETHYLAMINO)METHOXYPHOSPHINOTHIOYL)OXY)-, 1-METHYLETHYL ESTER, (E)-; (E)-3-(((ETHYLAMINO)METHOXYPHOSPHINOTHIOYL)OXY)-2-BUTENOIC ACID 1-METHYLETHYL ESTER; CROTONIC ACID, 3-HYDROXY-, ISOPROPYL ESTER, O-ESTER WITH O-METHYLETHYL -PHOSPHORAMIDOTHIOATE; (E)-3-HYDROXYCROTONIC ACID ISOPROPYL ESTER O-ESTER WITH O-METHYLETHYL -PHOSPHORAMIDOTHIOATE; (E)-1-METHYLETHYL 3-(((ETHYLAMINO)METHOXYPHOSPHINOTHIOYL)OXYL)-2-BUTENOATE; (E)-O-2-ISPROPROPOXYCARBONYL-1-METHYLVINYL O-METHYL ETHYL-PHOSPHORAMIDOTHIOATE; ISOPROPYL 3-(ETHYLAMINO(METHOXY)PHOSPHINOTHIOYLOXY)ISOCROTONATE; BLOTIC; SAN 322I; SAN 52 139I; SAFROTIN; OMS 1502; C10H20NO4PS; PST72440

CHEMICAL FAMILY: ORGANOPHOSPHATE ESTER

MOLECULAR FORMULA: C10-H20-N-O4-P-S

MOLECULAR WEIGHT: 281.31

CERCLA RATINGS (SCALE 0-3): HEALTH=3 FIRE=U REACTIVITY=0 PERSISTENCE=1

NFPA RATINGS (SCALE 0-4): HEALTH=3 FIRE=U REACTIVITY=0

COMPONENTS AND CONTAMINANTS

COMPONENT: PROPETAMPHOS ***PERCENT:*** 100.0
CAS# 31218-83-4

OTHER CONTAMINANTS: NONE

EXPOSURE LIMITS: NO OCCUPATIONAL EXPOSURE LIMITS ESTABLISHED BY OSHA, ACGIH, OR NIOSH.

PHYSICAL DATA

DESCRIPTION: COLORLESS TO YELLOW OILY LIQUID.

BOILING POINT: 189-192 F (87-89 C) @ 0.005 MMHG ***SPECIFIC GRAVITY:*** 1.1294

VAPOR PRESSURE: .000014 MMHG @ 20 C ***SOLUBILITY IN WATER:*** 0.011% @ 24 C

SOLVENT SOLUBILITY: SOLUBLE IN ACETONE, CHLOROFORM, ETHER, DIMETHYL SULFOXIDE, ETHANOL, HEXANE, METHANOL, AND XYLENE.

FIRE AND EXPLOSION DATA

FIRE AND EXPLOSION HAZARD: UNKNOWN FIRE AND EXPLOSION HAZARD.

FIREFIGHTING MEDIA: DRY CHEMICAL, CARBON DIOXIDE, HALON, WATER SPRAY OR STANDARD FOAM (1987 EMERGENCY RESPONSE GUIDEBOOK, DOT P 5800.4). FOR LARGER FIRES, USE WATER SPRAY, FOG OR STANDARD FOAM (1987 EMERGENCY RESPONSE GUIDEBOOK, DOT P 5800.4).

FIREFIGHTING: MOVE CONTAINER FROM FIRE AREA IF POSSIBLE. DIKE FIRE CONTROL WATER FOR LATER DISPOSAL; DO NOT SCATTER THE MATERIAL. COOL FIRE-EXPOSED CONTAINERS WITH WATER FROM SIDE UNTIL WELL AFTER FIRE IS OUT. STAY AWAY FROM STORAGE TANK ENDS. WITHDRAW IMMEDIATELY IN CASE OF RISING SOUND FROM VENTING SAFETY DEVICE OR ANY DISCOLORATION OF STORAGE TANK DUE TO FIRE (1987 EMERGENCY RESPONSE GUIDEBOOK, DOT P 5800.4, GUIDE PAGE 28).
EXTINGUISH ONLY IF FLOW CAN BE STOPPED. USE FLOODING AMOUNTS OF WATER AS A FOG; SOLID STREAMS MAY BE INEFFECTIVE. COOL CONTAINERS WITH FLOODING AMOUNTS OF WATER FROM AS FAR A DISTANCE AS POSSIBLE. AVOID BREATHING POISONOUS VAPORS, KEEP UPWIND.

TOXICITY

PROPETAMPHOS: TOXICITY DATA: 564 MG/KG SKIN-RAT LD50; 75 MG/KG ORAL-RAT LD50. CARCINOGEN STATUS: NONE. ACUTE TOXICITY: TOXIC BY DERMAL ABSORPTION AND INGESTION. TARGET EFFECTS: CHOLINESTERASE INHIBITOR. POISONING MAY AFFECT THE NERVOUS SYSTEM.* AT INCREASED RISK FROM EXPOSURE: PERSONS WITH RESPIRATORY AILMENTS, RECENT EXPOSURE TO CHOLINESTERASE INHIBITORS OR IMPAIRED CHOLINESTERASE PRODUCTION, OR LIVER MALFUNCTION.* ADDITIONAL DATA: MAY CROSS THE PLACENTA. HIGH ENVIRONMENTAL TEMPERATURES OR EXPOSURE OF THE CHEMICAL TO VISIBLE OR ULTRAVIOLET LIGHT MAY ENHANCE THE TOXICITY. INTERACTIONS WITH MEDICATIONS MAY OCCUR.*
* MAY BE BASED ON GENERAL INFORMATION ON ORGANOPHOSPHATES.

HEALTH EFFECTS AND FIRST AID

INHALATION: PROPETAMPHOS: SEE INFORMATION ON ORGANOPHOSPHATES.
ORGANOPHOSPHATES: CHOLINESTERASE INHIBITOR. **ACUTE EXPOSURE-** WHEN INHALED, THE FIRST EFFECTS OF CHOLINESTERASE INHIBITORS ARE USUALLY RESPIRATORY AND MAY INCLUDE NASAL HYPEREMIA AND WATERY DISCHARGE, COUGH, CHEST DISCOMFORT, DYSPNEA, AND WHEEZING DUE TO INCREASED BRONCHIAL SECRETIONS AND BRONCHOCONSTRICTION. IF SUFFICIENT AMOUNTS ARE ABSORBED, OTHER SYSTEMIC EFFECTS MAY BEGIN WITHIN A FEW MINUTES OR BE DELAYED FOR UP TO 12 HOURS. SYMPTOMS MAY INCLUDE PALLOR, NAUSEA, VOMITING, DIARRHEA, ABDOMINAL CRAMPS, HEADACHE, DIZZINESS, OCULAR PAIN, BLURRED VISION, MIOSIS OR IN SOME CASES, ESPECIALLY INITIALLY, MYDRIASIS, LACRIMATION, SALIVATION, SWEATING, AND CONFUSION. OTHER REPORTED CENTRAL NERVOUS SYSTEM OR NEUROMUSCULAR EFFECTS MAY INCLUDE ATAXIA, SLURRED SPEECH, AREFLEXIA, WEAKNESS, FATIGUE, FASCICULATIONS, TWITCHING, TREMORS POSSIBLY OF THE TONGUE AND EYELIDS, AND EVENTUALLY PARALYSIS OF THE EXTREMITIES AND POSSIBLY OF THE RESPIRATORY MUSCLES. IN SEVERE CASES THERE MAY ALSO BE INVOLUNTARY DEFECATION AND URINATION, CYANOSIS, PSYCHOSIS, HYPERGLYCEMIA, ACUTE PANCREATITIS, CARDIAC IRREGULARITIES, PULMONARY EDEMA, UNCONSCIOUSNESS, CONVULSIONS, AND COMA. DEATH IS PRIMARILY DUE TO RESPIRATORY FAILURE, ALTHOUGH CARDIOVASCULAR EFFECTS INCLUDING CARDIAC ARREST MAY ALSO BE IMPLICATED. LONG TERM SEQUELAE ARE RARE BUT MAY INCLUDE NEUROPSYCHIATRIC DISORDERS AND MYOPATHY WITH MUSCLE TENDERNESS. SOME ORGANOPHOSPHATES MAY CAUSE A DELAYED NEUROPATHY BEGINNING 1-4 WEEKS AFTER AN ACUTE EXPOSURE WHICH MAY OR MAY NOT HAVE CAUSED ACUTE CHOLINERGIC EFFECTS. NUMBNESS, TINGLING, WEAKNESS AND CRAMPING BEGINNING SYMMETRICALLY IN THE LOWER LIMBS MAY PROGRESS TO ATAXIA AND PARALYSIS. IN SEVERE CASES, UPPER LIMB INVOLVEMENT IS POSSIBLE AND FLACCID PARALYSIS MAY PROGRESS TO SPASTIC PARALYSIS WITH EXAGGERATED REFLEXES. IMPROVEMENT MAY OCCUR OVER MONTHS TO YEARS, BUT SOME RESIDUAL IMPAIRMENT USUALLY REMAINS.
CHRONIC EXPOSURE- REPEATED OR PROLONGED EXPOSURE MAY RESULT IN THE EFFECTS OF ACUTE EXPOSURE INCLUDING THE DELAYED NEUROPATHY. OTHER EFFECTS REPORTED IN WORKERS REPEATEDLY EXPOSED INCLUDE IMPAIRED MEMORY AND CONCENTRATION, ACUTE PSYCHOSIS, SEVERE DEPRESSIONS, IRRITABILTY, CONFUSION, APATHY, EMOTIONAL LABILITY, SOCIAL WITHDRAWAL, CONFUSION, HEADACHE, SPEECH DIFFICULTIES, DELAYED REACTION TIMES, SPATIAL DISORIENTATION, NIGHTMARES, SLEEPWALKING, AND DROWSINESS OR INSOMNIA. AN INFLUENZA-LIKE CONDITION WITH HEADACHE, NAUSEA, WEAKNESS, ANOREXIA AND MALAISE HAS ALSO BEEN REPORTED.

FIRST AID- REMOVE FROM EXPOSURE AREA TO FRESH AIR IMMEDIATELY. IF BREATHING HAS STOPPED, GIVE ARTIFICIAL RESPIRATION. MAINTAIN AIRWAY AND BLOOD PRESSURE AND ADMINISTER OXYGEN IF AVAILABLE. KEEP AFFECTED PERSON WARM AND AT REST. TREAT SYMPTOMATICALLY AND SUPPORTIVELY. ADMINISTRATION OF OXYGEN SHOULD BE PERFORMED BY QUALIFIED PERSONNEL. GET MEDICAL ATTENTION IMMEDIATELY.

SKIN CONTACT: PROPETAMPHOS: TOXIC. SEE INFORMATION ON ORGANOPHOSPHATES.
ORGANOPHOSPHATES: CHOLINESTERASE INHIBITOR. **ACUTE EXPOSURE-** LOCALIZED SWEATING AND FASCICULATIONS MAY OCCUR AT THE SITE OF CONTACT. IF SUFFICIENT AMOUNTS ARE ABSORBED, OTHER EFFECTS OF CHOLINESTERASE INHIBITION AS DESCRIBED IN ACUTE INHALATION MAY OCCUR. SYMPTOMS MAY BE DELAYED 2-3 HOURS, BUT USUALLY NO MORE THAN 12 HOURS. THE RATE OF ABSORPTION IS INCREASED BY THE PRESENCE OF DERMATITIS OR HIGH AMBIENT TEMPERATURES. DELAYED NEUROPATHY IS ALSO POSSIBLE. **CHRONIC EXPOSURE-** REPEATED OR PROLONGED EXPOSURE MAY CAUSE EFFECTS AS DESCRIBED IN ACUTE EXPOSURE. SOME ORGANOPHOSPHATES MAY CAUSE SENSITIZATION.

FIRST AID- REMOVE CONTAMINATED CLOTHING IMMEDIATELY. WASH CONTAMINATED AREAS WITH SOAP AND WATER FOLLOWED BY ALCOHOL (ARENA, POISONING, 4TH ED.). EMERGENCY PERSONNEL SHOULD WEAR GLOVES AND AVOID CONTAMINATION. TREAT RESPIRATORY DIFFICULTY WITH ARTIFICIAL RESPIRATION. GET MEDICAL ATTENTION IMMEDIATELY.

EYE CONTACT: PROPETAMPHOS: SEE INFORMATION ON ORGANOPHOSPHATES. ORGANOPHOSPHATES: CHOLINESTERASE INHIBITOR. **ACUTE EXPOSURE-** DIRECT CONTACT MAY CAUSE PAIN, HYPEREMIA, LACRIMATION, TWITCHING OF THE EYELIDS, MIOSIS, AND CILIARY MUSCLE SPASM WITH LOSS OF ACCOMODATION, BLURRED OR DIMMED VISION AND BROWACHE. SOMETIMES MYDRIASIS MAY OCCUR INSTEAD OF MIOSIS. WITH SUFFICIENT EXPOSURE, OTHER SYMPTOMS OF CHOLINESTERASE INHIBITION AS DESCRIBED IN ACUTE INHALATION MAY OCCUR. **CHRONIC EXPOSURE-** REPEATED OR PROLONGED EXPOSURE MAY CAUSE EFFECTS AS DESCRIBED IN ACUTE EXPOSURE. SOME COMPOUNDS HAVE CAUSED TOXIC EFFECTS ON THE CRYSTALLINE LENS, CONJUNCTIVAL THICKENING AND OBSTRUCTION OF THE NASOLACRIMAL CANALS WHEN USED AS MIOTIC EYEDROPS.

FIRST AID- IRRIGATE EYES WITH WATER OR SALINE SOLUTION. IF SYMPTOMS OF POISONING OCCUR, TREAT RESPIRATORY DIFFICULTY WITH ARTIFICIAL RESPIRATION AND OXYGEN. OBSERVE PATIENT FOR AT LEAST 24-36 HOURS (GOSSELIN, CLINICAL TOXICOLOGY OF COMMERCIAL PRODUCTS, 5TH ED.). GET MEDICAL ATTENTION IMMEDIATELY. OXYGEN SHOULD BE ADMINISTERED BY QUALIFIED MEDICAL PERSONNEL.

INGESTION: PROPETAMPHOS: TOXIC. SEE INFORMATION ON ORGANOPHOSPHATES. ORGANOPHOSPHATES: CHOLINESTERASE INHIBITOR. **ACUTE EXPOSURE-** WHEN INGESTED, THE FIRST EFFECTS MAY BE NAUSEA, VOMITING, ANOREXIA, ABDOMINAL CRAMPS AND DIARRHEA. GASTROINTESTINAL ABSORPTION MAY CAUSE SYMPTOMS OF CHOLINESTERASE INHIBITION AS DESCRIBED IN ACUTE INHALATION. SYMPTOMS MAY BEGIN WITHIN MINUTES OR BE DELAYED FOR HOURS. DELAYED EFFECTS INCLUDING NEUROPATHY MAY ALSO OCCUR. **CHRONIC EXPOSURE-** REPEATED INGESTION MAY CAUSE EFFECTS AS DESCRIBED IN ACUTE EXPOSURE.

FIRST AID- IF PERSON IS ALERT AND RESPIRATION IS NOT DEPRESSED, GIVE SYRUP OF IPECAC FOLLOWED BY WATER (IF VOMITING OCCURS, KEEP HEAD BELOW HIPS TO PREVENT ASPIRATION). IF CONSCIOUSNESS LEVEL DECLINES OR VOMITING HAS NOT OCCURRED IN 15 MINUTES EMPTY STOMACH BY GASTRIC LAVAGE WITH THE AID OF CUFFED ENDOTRACHEAL TUBE USING ISOTONIC SALINE OR 5% SODIUM BICARBONATE FOLLOW WITH ACTIVATED CHARCOAL. ESTABLISH AND MAINTAIN AIRWAY. TREAT RESPIRATORY DIFFICULTY WITH ARTIFICIAL RESPIRATION AND OXYGEN. DO NOT GIVE MORPHINE, AMINOPHYLLINE, PHENOTHIAZINES, RESERPINE, FUROSEMIDE, OR ETHACRYNIC ACID (MORGAN, RECOGNITION AND MANAGEMENT OF PESTICIDE POISONINGS, 3RD ED.). TREAT SYMPTOMATICALLY AND SUPPORTIVELY. ADMINISTRATION OF OXYGEN AND LAVAGE MUST BE PERFORMED BY QUALIFIED MEDICAL PERSONNEL. GET MEDICAL ATTENTION IMMEDIATELY.

ANTIDOTE: THE FOLLOWING ANTIDOTE(S) HAVE BEEN RECOMMENDED. HOWEVER, THE DECISION AS TO WHETHER THE SEVERITY OF POISONING REQUIRES ADMINISTRATION OF ANY ANTIDOTE AND ACTUAL DOSE REQUIRED SHOULD BE MADE BY QUALIFIED MEDICAL PERSONNEL.

FOR CHOLINESTERASE INHIBITORS: ESTABLISH CLEAR AIRWAY AND TISSUE OXYGENATION BY ASPIRATION OF SECRETIONS, AND IF NECESSARY, BY ASSISTED PULMONARY VENTILATION WITH OXYGEN. IMPROVE TISSUE OXYGENATION AS MUCH AS POSSIBLE BEFORE ADMINISTERING ATROPINE TO MINIMIZE THE RISK OF VENTRICULAR FIBRILLATION. ADMINISTER ATROPINE SULFATE INTRAVENOUSLY, OR INTRAMUSCULARLY IF IV INJECTION IS NOT POSSIBLE. IN MODERATELY SEVERE POISONING ADMINISTER ATROPINE SULFATE, 0.4-2.0 MG REPEATED EVERY 15 MINUTES UNTIL ATROPINIZATION IS ACHIEVED (TACHYCARDIA, FLUSHING, DRY MOUTH, MYDRIASIS). MAINTAIN ATROPINIZATION BY REPEATED DOSES FOR 2-12 HOURS, OR LONGER, DEPENDING ON THE SEVERITY OF POISONING. THE APPEARANCE OF RALES IN THE LUNG BASES, MIOSIS, SALIVATION, NAUSEA, BRADYCARDIA, ARE ALL INDICATIONS OF INADEQUATE ATROPINIZATION. SEVERELY POISONED INDIVIDUALS MAY EXHIBIT REMARKABLE TOLERANCE TO ATROPINE; TWO OR MORE TIMES THE DOSAGES SUGGESTED ABOVE MAY BE NEEDED. PERSONS NOT POISONED OR ONLY SLIGHTLY POISONED, HOWEVER, MAY DEVELOP SIGNS OF ATROPINE TOXICITY FROM SUCH LARGE DOSAGES: FEVER, MUSCLE FIBRILLATIONS, AND DELIRIUM ARE THE MAIN SIGNS OF ATROPINE TOXICITY. IF THESE SIGNS APPEAR WHILE THE PATIENT IS FULLY ATROPINIZED, ATROPINE ADMINISTRATION SHOULD BE DISCONTINUED, AT LEAST TEMPORARILY. OBSERVE TREATED PATIENTS CLOSELY AT LEAST 24 HOURS TO INSURE THAT SYMPTOMS (POSSIBLY PULMONARY EDEMA) DO NOT RECUR AS ATROPINIZATION WEARS OFF. IN VERY SEVERE POISONINGS, METABOLIC DISPOSITION OF TOXICANT MAY REQUIRE SEVERAL HOURS OR DAYS DURING WHICH ATROPINIZATION MUST BE MAINTAINED. MARKEDLY LOWER LEVELS OF URINARY METABOLITES INDICATE THAT ATROPINE DOSAGE CAN BE TAPERED OFF. AS DOSAGE IS REDUCED, CHECK THE LUNG BASES FREQUENTLY FOR RALES. IF RALES ARE HEARD OR OTHER SYMPTOMS RETURN, RE-ESTABLISH ATROPINIZATION PROMPTLY (MORGAN, RECOGNITION AND MANAGEMENT OF PESTICIDE POISONINGS, 3RD ED.). ADMINISTRATION OF ANTIDOTE MUST BE PERFORMED BY QUALIFIED MEDICAL PERSONNEL.

IN CASES OF SEVERE POISONING BY ORGANOPHOSPHATE PESTICIDES IN WHICH RESPIRATORY DEPRESSION, MUSCLE WEAKNESS AND TWITCHINGS ARE SEVERE, GIVE PRALIDOXIME (PROTOPAM-AYERST, 2-PAM), 1.0 GRAM INTRAVENOUSLY AT NO MORE THAN 0.5 GRAM PER MINUTE. DOSAGE OF PRALIDOXIME MAY BE REPEATED IN 1-2 HOURS, THEN AT 10-12 HOUR INTERVALS IF NEEDED. IN VERY SEVERE POISONINGS, DOSAGE RATES MAY BE DOUBLED. TREATMENT WITH PRALIDOXIME WILL BE MOST EFFECTIVE IF GIVEN WITHIN THIRTY-SIX HOURS AFTER POISONING (MORGAN, RECOGNITION AND MANAGEMENT OF PESTICIDE POISONINGS, 3RD ED.). ANTIDOTE SHOULD BE ADMINISTERED BY QUALIFIED MEDICAL PERSONNEL.

REACTIVITY

REACTIVITY: STABLE UNDER NORMAL TEMPERATURES AND PRESSURES.

INCOMPATIBILITIES: PROPETAMPHOS: OXIDIZERS (STRONG): FIRE AND EXPLOSION HAZARD.

DECOMPOSITION: THERMAL DECOMPOSITION PRODUCTS MAY INCLUDE TOXIC OXIDES OF NITROGEN, CARBON, PHOSPHORUS, AND SULFUR.

POLYMERIZATION: HAZARDOUS POLYMERIZATION HAS NOT BEEN REPORTED TO OCCUR UNDER NORMAL TEMPERATURES AND PRESSURES.

STORAGE AND DISPOSAL

OBSERVE ALL FEDERAL, STATE AND LOCAL REGULATIONS WHEN STORING OR DISPOSING OF THIS SUBSTANCE. FOR ASSISTANCE, CONTACT THE DISTRICT DIRECTOR OF THE ENVIRONMENTAL PROTECTION AGENCY.

****STORAGE****

STORE IN ACCORDANCE WITH 40 CFR 165 RECOMMENDED PROCEDURES FOR THE DISPOSAL AND STORAGE OF PESTICIDES AND PESTICIDE CONTAINERS.
STORE AWAY FROM INCOMPATIBLE SUBSTANCES.

****DISPOSAL****

DISPOSAL MUST BE IN ACCORDANCE WITH 40 CFR 165 RECOMMENDED PROCEDURES FOR THE DISPOSAL AND STORAGE OF PESTICIDES AND PESTICIDE CONTAINERS.

CONDITIONS TO AVOID

AVOID CONTACT WITH HEAT, SPARKS, FLAMES OR OTHER IGNITION SOURCES. VAPORS MAY BE EXPLOSIVE. MATERIAL IS POISONOUS; AVOID INHALATION OF VAPORS OR CONTACT WITH SKIN. DO NOT ALLOW MATERIAL TO CONTAMINATE WATER SOURCES.

SPILL AND LEAK PROCEDURES

OCCUPATIONAL SPILL: SHUT OFF IGNITION SOURCES. DO NOT TOUCH SPILLED MATERIAL. STOP LEAK IF YOU CAN DO IT WITHOUT RISK. USE WATER SPRAY TO REDUCE VAPORS. FOR SMALL SPILLS, TAKE UP WITH SAND OR OTHER ABSORBENT MATERIAL AND PLACE INTO CONTAINERS FOR LATER DISPOSAL. FOR LARGER SPILLS, DIKE FAR AHEAD OF SPILL FOR LATER DISPOSAL. NO SMOKING, FLAMES OR FLARES IN HAZARD AREA! KEEP UNNECESSARY PEOPLE AWAY; ISOLATE HAZARD AREA AND DENY ENTRY.

PROTECTIVE EQUIPMENT

VENTILATION: PROVIDE LOCAL EXHAUST OR PROCESS ENCLOSURE VENTILATION SYSTEM.

RESPIRATOR: THE FOLLOWING RESPIRATORS ARE RECOMMENDED BASED ON INFORMATION FOUND IN THE PHYSICAL DATA, TOXICITY AND HEALTH EFFECTS SECTIONS. THEY ARE RANKED IN ORDER FROM MINIMUM TO MAXIMUM RESPIRATORY PROTECTION. THE SPECIFIC RESPIRATOR SELECTED MUST BE BASED ON CONTAMINATION LEVELS FOUND IN THE WORK PLACE, MUST NOT EXCEED THE WORKING LIMITS OF THE RESPIRATOR AND BE JOINTLY APPROVED BY THE NATIONAL INSTITUTE FOR OCCUPATIONAL SAFETY AND HEALTH AND THE MINE SAFETY AND HEALTH ADMINISTRATION (NIOSH-MSHA).

TYPE 'C' SUPPLIED-AIR RESPIRATOR WITH A FULL FACEPIECE OPERATED IN PRESSURE-DEMAND OR OTHER POSITIVE PRESSURE MODE OR WITH A FULL FACEPIECE, HELMET OR HOOD OPERATED IN CONTINOUS-FLOW MODE.

SELF-CONTAINED BREATHING APPARATUS WITH A FULL FACEPIECE OPERATED IN PRESSURE-DEMAND OR OTHER POSITIVE PRESSURE MODE.

FOR FIREFIGHTING AND OTHER IMMEDIATELY DANGEROUS TO LIFE OR HEALTH CONDITIONS:

SELF-CONTAINED BREATHING APPARATUS WITH FULL FACEPIECE OPERATED IN PRESSURE-DEMAND OR OTHER POSITIVE PRESSURE MODE.

SUPPLIED-AIR RESPIRATOR WITH FULL FACEPIECE AND OPERATED IN PRESSURE-DEMAND OR OTHER POSITIVE PRESSURE MODE IN COMBINATION WITH AN AUXILIARY SELF-CONTAINED BREATHING APPARATUS OPERATED IN PRESSURE-DEMAND OR OTHER POSITIVE PRESSURE MODE.

CLOTHING: EMPLOYEE MUST WEAR APPROPRIATE PROTECTIVE (IMPERVIOUS) CLOTHING AND EQUIPMENT TO PREVENT ANY POSSIBILITY OF SKIN CONTACT WITH THIS SUBSTANCE.

GLOVES: EMPLOYEE MUST WEAR APPROPRIATE PROTECTIVE GLOVES TO PREVENT CONTACT WITH THIS SUBSTANCE.

EYE PROTECTION: EMPLOYEE MUST WEAR SPLASH-PROOF OR DUST-RESISTANT SAFETY GOGGLES WITH OR WITHOUT A FACESHIELD TO PREVENT CONTACT WITH THIS SUBSTANCE.
EMERGENCY EYE WASH: WHERE THERE IS ANY POSSIBILITY THAT AN EMPLOYEE'S EYES MAY BE EXPOSED TO THIS SUBSTANCE, THE EMPLOYER SHOULD PROVIDE AN EYE WASH FOUNTAIN WITHIN THE IMMEDIATE WORK AREA FOR EMERGENCY USE.

AUTHORIZED BY- OCCUPATIONAL HEALTH SERVICES, INC.
CREATION DATE: 10/04/89 ***REVISION DATE:*** 05/01/90

MATERIAL SAFETY DATA SHEET

OCCUPATIONAL HEALTH SERVICES, INC.
AGRICULTURE AND PESTICIDE DIVISION
450 SEVENTH AVENUE, SUITE 2407
NEW YORK, NEW YORK 10123
1-800-445-MSDS OR (212) 967-1100

EMERGENCY CONTACT:
JOHN S. BRANSFORD, JR. (615) 292-1180

SUBSTANCE IDENTIFICATION

CAS-NUMBER 53780-34-0
SUBSTANCE: MEFLUIDIDE
TRADE NAMES/SYNONYMS: ACETAMIDE, N-(2,4-DIMETHYL-5-(((TRIFLUOROMETHYL)SULFONYL) AMINO)PHENYL)-; N-(2,4-DIMETHYL-5-(((TRIFLUOROMETHYL)SULFONYL)AMINO)PHENYL)ACETAMIDE; 5'-(1,1,1-TRIFLUOROMETHANESULPHONAMIDO)ACET-2',4'-XYLIDIDE; 5'-(1,1,1-TRIFLUOROMETHANESULFONAMIDO)ACET-2',4'-XYLIDIDE; 5-ACETAMIDO-2,4-DIMETHYLTRIFLUOROMETHANESULFONANILIDE; 2',4'-DIMETHYL-5-((TRIFLUOROMETHYL)SULFONAMIDO)ACETANILIDE; METHAFLUORIDAMID; EMBARK; MBR 12325; VEL 3973; VISTAR; C11H13F3N2O3S; PST72444
CHEMICAL FAMILY: SULFONAMIDE
HALOGEN COMPOUND, AROMATIC
MOLECULAR FORMULA: C11-H13-F3-N2-O3-S
MOLECULAR WEIGHT: 310.29
CERCLA RATINGS (SCALE 0-3): HEALTH=2 FIRE=1 REACTIVITY=0 PERSISTENCE=2
NFPA RATINGS (SCALE 0-4): HEALTH=U FIRE=1 REACTIVITY=0

COMPONENTS AND CONTAMINANTS

COMPONENT: MEFLUIDIDE ***PERCENT:*** 100.0
CAS# 53780-34-0
OTHER CONTAMINANTS: NONE
EXPOSURE LIMITS: NO OCCUPATIONAL EXPOSURE LIMITS ESTABLISHED BY OSHA, ACGIH, OR NIOSH.

PHYSICAL DATA

DESCRIPTION: COLORLESS OR WHITE CRYSTALLINE SOLID.
MELTING POINT: 361-365 F (183-185 C) ***SPECIFIC GRAVITY:*** NOT AVAILABLE
VAPOR PRESSURE: NEGLIGIBLE ***SOLUBILITY IN WATER:*** 0.018% @ 25 C
SOLVENT SOLUBILITY: SOLUBLE IN METHANOL AND ACETONE; SLIGHTLY SOLUBLE IN BENZENE, DICHLOROMETHANE, AND OCTANOL. AQUEOUS SOLUTIONS DECOMPOSE ON EXPOSURE TO UV LIGHT.

FIRE AND EXPLOSION DATA

FIRE AND EXPLOSION HAZARD: SLIGHT FIRE HAZARD WHEN EXPOSED TO HEAT OR FLAME.
FIREFIGHTING MEDIA: DRY CHEMICAL, CARBON DIOXIDE, HALON, WATER SPRAY OR STANDARD FOAM (1987 EMERGENCY RESPONSE GUIDEBOOK, DOT P 5800.4).
FOR LARGER FIRES, USE WATER SPRAY, FOG OR STANDARD FOAM (1987 EMERGENCY RESPONSE GUIDEBOOK, DOT P 5800.4).
FIREFIGHTING: MOVE CONTAINER FROM FIRE AREA IF POSSIBLE. DO NOT SCATTER SPILLED MATERIAL WITH HIGH PRESSURE WATER STREAMS. DIKE FIRE CONTROL WATER FOR LATER DISPOSAL (1987 EMERGENCY RESPONSE GUIDEBOOK, DOT P 5800.4, GUIDE PAGE 31).
USE AGENTS SUITABLE FOR TYPE OF SURROUNDING FIRE. AVOID BREATHING HAZARDOUS VAPORS, KEEP UPWIND.

TOXICITY

MEFLUIDIDE: TOXICITY DATA: 4 GM/KG ORAL-RAT LD50. CARCINOGEN STATUS: NONE. ACUTE TOXICITY LEVEL: MODERATELY TOXIC BY INGESTION. TARGET EFFECTS: NO DATA AVAILABLE.

HEALTH EFFECTS AND FIRST AID

INHALATION: MEFLUIDIDE: **ACUTE EXPOSURE-** NO DATA AVAILABLE. **CHRONIC EXPOSURE-** NO DATA AVAILABLE.
FIRST AID- REMOVE FROM EXPOSURE AREA TO FRESH AIR IMMEDIATELY. IF BREATHING HAS STOPPED, PERFORM ARTIFICIAL RESPIRATION. KEEP PERSON WARM AND AT REST. TREAT SYMPTOMATICALLY AND SUPPORTIVELY. GET MEDICAL ATTENTION IMMEDIATELY.

SKIN CONTACT: MEFLUIDIDE: **ACUTE EXPOSURE-** A LETHAL DOSE IN RABBITS BY DERMAL ABSORPTION WAS GREATER THAN 4000 MG/KG. EXPOSURE TO SOME ACETAMIDE DERIVATIVE HERBICIDES RESULTS IN IRRITATION AND SENSITIZATION. **CHRONIC EXPOSURE-** NO DATA AVAILABLE.
FIRST AID- REMOVE CONTAMINATED CLOTHING AND SHOES IMMEDIATELY. WASH AFFECTED AREA WITH SOAP OR MILD DETERGENT AND LARGE AMOUNTS OF WATER UNTIL NO EVIDENCE OF CHEMICAL REMAINS (APPROXIMATELY 15-20 MINUTES). GET MEDICAL ATTENTION IMMEDIATELY.

EYE CONTACT: MEFLUIDIDE: **ACUTE EXPOSURE-** MAY CAUSE EYE IRRITATION. **CHRONIC EXPOSURE-** NO DATA AVAILABLE.
FIRST AID- WASH EYES IMMEDIATELY WITH LARGE AMOUNTS OF WATER OR NORMAL SALINE, OCCASIONALLY LIFTING UPPER AND LOWER LIDS, UNTIL NO EVIDENCE OF CHEMICAL REMAINS (APPROXIMATELY 15-20 MINUTES). GET MEDICAL ATTENTION IMMEDIATELY.

INGESTION: MEFLUIDIDE: **ACUTE EXPOSURE-** A LETHAL DOSE IN RATS WAS 4 GM/KG; SYMPTOMS WERE NOT REPORTED. **CHRONIC EXPOSURE-** NO DATA AVAILABLE.
FIRST AID- REMOVE BY GASTRIC LAVAGE AND CATHARSIS. MAINTAIN BLOOD PRESSURE AND AIRWAY. GIVE OXYGEN IF RESPIRATION IS DEPRESSED. DO NOT PERFORM GASTRIC LAVAGE IF VICTIM IS UNCONSCIOUS. GET MEDICAL ATTENTION IMMEDIATELY (DREISBACH, HANDBOOK OF POISONING, 12TH ED.). ADMINISTRATION OF LAVAGE OR OXYGEN SHOULD BE PERFORMED BY QUALIFIED MEDICAL PERSONNEL.
ANTIDOTE: NO SPECIFIC ANTIDOTE. TREAT SYMPTOMATICALLY AND SUPPORTIVELY.

REACTIVITY

REACTIVITY: STABLE UNDER NORMAL TEMPERATURES AND PRESSURES.
INCOMPATIBILITIES: MEFLUIDIDE: METALS: MAY CORRODE IN THE PRESENCE OF WATER. OXIDIZERS (STRONG): FIRE AND EXPLOSION HAZARD.
DECOMPOSITION: THERMAL DECOMPOSITION PRODUCTS MAY INCLUDE TOXIC AND HAZARDOUS FUMES OF FLUORINE AND OXIDES OF CARBON, NITROGEN AND SULFUR.
POLYMERIZATION: HAZARDOUS POLYMERIZATION HAS NOT BEEN REPORTED TO OCCUR UNDER NORMAL TEMPERATURES AND PRESSURES.

STORAGE AND DISPOSAL

OBSERVE ALL FEDERAL, STATE AND LOCAL REGULATIONS WHEN STORING OR DISPOSING OF THIS SUBSTANCE. FOR ASSISTANCE, CONTACT THE DISTRICT DIRECTOR OF THE ENVIRONMENTAL PROTECTION AGENCY.

STORAGE

STORE IN ACCORDANCE WITH 40 CFR 165 RECOMMENDED PROCEDURES FOR THE DISPOSAL AND STORAGE OF PESTICIDES AND PESTICIDE CONTAINERS.
STORE AWAY FROM INCOMPATIBLE SUBSTANCES.

DISPOSAL

DISPOSAL MUST BE IN ACCORDANCE WITH 40 CFR 165 RECOMMENDED PROCEDURES FOR THE DISPOSAL AND STORAGE OF PESTICIDES AND PESTICIDE CONTAINERS.

CONDITIONS TO AVOID

MAY BURN BUT DOES NOT IGNITE READILY. AVOID CONTACT WITH STRONG OXIDIZERS, EXCESSIVE HEAT, SPARKS, OR OPEN FLAME.

SPILL AND LEAK PROCEDURES

OCCUPATIONAL SPILL: SWEEP UP AND PLACE IN SUITABLE CLEAN, DRY CONTAINERS FOR RECLAMATION OR LATER DISPOSAL. DO NOT FLUSH SPILLED MATERIAL INTO SEWER. KEEP UNNECESSARY PEOPLE AWAY.

PROTECTIVE EQUIPMENT

VENTILATION: PROVIDE LOCAL EXHAUST OR GENERAL DILUTION VENTILATION SYSTEM.
RESPIRATOR: THE FOLLOWING RESPIRATORS ARE RECOMMENDED BASED ON INFORMATION FOUND IN THE PHYSICAL DATA, TOXICITY AND HEALTH EFFECTS SECTIONS. THEY ARE RANKED IN ORDER FROM MINIMUM TO MAXIMUM RESPIRATORY PROTECTION. THE SPECIFIC RESPIRATOR SELECTED MUST BE BASED ON CONTAMINATION LEVELS FOUND IN THE WORK PLACE, MUST NOT EXCEED THE WORKING LIMITS OF THE RESPIRATOR AND BE JOINTLY APPROVED BY THE

NATIONAL INSTITUTE FOR OCCUPATIONAL SAFETY AND HEALTH AND THE MINE SAFETY AND HEALTH ADMINISTRATION (NIOSH-MSHA).
CHEMICAL CARTRIDGE RESPIRATOR WITH AN ORGANIC VAPOR CARTRIDGE(S) WITH A FULL FACEPIECE AND ORGANIC VAPOR CARTRIDGE(S) IN COMBINATION WITH A DUST AND MIST FILTER.
POWERED AIR-PURIFYING RESPIRATOR WITH A TIGHT-FITTING FACEPIECE AND ORGANIC VAPOR CARTRIDGE(S) IN COMBINATION WITH A HIGH-EFFICIENCY PARTICULATE FILTER.
TYPE 'C' SUPPLIED-AIR RESPIRATOR WITH A FULL FACEPIECE OPERATED IN A PRESSURE-DEMAND OR OTHER POSITIVE PRESSURE MODE.
SELF-CONTAINED BREATHING APPARATUS WITH A FULL FACEPIECE OPERATED IN PRESSURE-DEMAND OR OTHER POSITIVE PRESSURE MODE.
FOR FIREFIGHTING AND OTHER IMMEDIATELY DANGEROUS TO LIFE OR HEALTH CONDITIONS:
SELF-CONTAINED BREATHING APPARATUS WITH FULL FACEPIECE OPERATED IN PRESSURE-DEMAND OR OTHER POSITIVE PRESSURE MODE.
SUPPLIED-AIR RESPIRATOR WITH FULL FACEPIECE AND OPERATED IN PRESSURE-DEMAND OR OTHER POSITIVE PRESSURE MODE IN COMBINATION WITH AN AUXILIARY SELF-CONTAINED BREATHING APPARATUS OPERATED IN PRESSURE-DEMAND OR OTHER POSITIVE PRESSURE MODE.

CLOTHING: EMPLOYEE MUST WEAR APPROPRIATE PROTECTIVE (IMPERVIOUS) CLOTHING AND EQUIPMENT TO PREVENT REPEATED OR PROLONGED SKIN CONTACT WITH THIS SUBSTANCE.

GLOVES: EMPLOYEE MUST WEAR APPROPRIATE PROTECTIVE GLOVES TO PREVENT CONTACT WITH THIS SUBSTANCE.

EYE PROTECTION: EMPLOYEE MUST WEAR SPLASH-PROOF OR DUST-RESISTANT SAFETY GOGGLES TO PREVENT EYE CONTACT WITH THIS SUBSTANCE.
EMERGENCY EYE WASH: WHERE THERE IS ANY POSSIBILITY THAT AN EMPLOYEE'S EYES MAY BE EXPOSED TO THIS SUBSTANCE, THE EMPLOYER SHOULD PROVIDE AN EYE WASH FOUNTAIN WITHIN THE IMMEDIATE WORK AREA FOR EMERGENCY USE.

AUTHORIZED BY- OCCUPATIONAL HEALTH SERVICES, INC.
CREATION DATE: 10/04/89 ***REVISION DATE:*** 05/31/90

MATERIAL SAFETY DATA SHEET

OCCUPATIONAL HEALTH SERVICES, INC.
AGRICULTURE AND PESTICIDE DIVISION
450 SEVENTH AVENUE, SUITE 2407
NEW YORK, NEW YORK 10123
1-800-445-MSDS OR (212) 967-1100

EMERGENCY CONTACT:
JOHN S. BRANSFORD, JR. (615) 292-1180

SUBSTANCE IDENTIFICATION

CAS-NUMBER 52207-99-5

SUBSTANCE: **(Z,Z)-7,11-HEXADECADIEN-1-OL ACETATE**

TRADE NAMES/SYNONYMS: 7,11-HEXADECADIEN-1-OL, ACETATE, (Z,Z)-; (Z,Z)-GOSSYPLURE; GOSSYPLURE; C18H32O2; PST72448

CHEMICAL FAMILY: ESTER, CARBOXYLIC, ALIPHATIC

MOLECULAR FORMULA: C18-H-32-O2

MOLECULAR WEIGHT: 280.46

CERCLA RATINGS (SCALE 0-3): HEALTH=U FIRE=2 REACTIVITY=0 PERSISTENCE=2

NFPA RATINGS (SCALE 0-4): HEALTH=U FIRE=2 REACTIVITY=0

COMPONENTS AND CONTAMINANTS

COMPONENT: (Z,Z)-7,11-HEXADECADIEN-1-OL ACETATE ***PERCENT:*** 100
CAS# 52207-99-5

OTHER CONTAMINANTS: NONE

EXPOSURE LIMITS: NO OCCUPATIONAL EXPOSURE LIMITS ESTABLISHED BY OSHA, ACGIH, OR NIOSH.

PHYSICAL DATA

DESCRIPTION: YELLOW LIQUID. ***BOILING POINT:*** 266-270 F (130-132 C)

SPECIFIC GRAVITY: NOT AVAILABLE ***VAPOR PRESSURE:*** NOT AVAILABLE

SOLUBILITY IN WATER: NOT AVAILABLE

SOLVENT SOLUBILITY: SOLUBLE IN MOST ORGANIC SOLVENTS.

FIRE AND EXPLOSION DATA

FIRE AND EXPLOSION HAZARD: MODERATE FIRE HAZARD WHEN EXPOSED TO HEAT OR FLAME.

FLASH POINT: 144 F (62 C) (CC)

FIREFIGHTING MEDIA: DRY CHEMICAL, CARBON DIOXIDE, HALON, WATER SPRAY OR ALCOHOL FOAM (1987 EMERGENCY RESPONSE GUIDEBOOK, DOT P 5800.4).
FOR LARGER FIRES, USE WATER SPRAY, FOG OR ALCOHOL FOAM (1987 EMERGENCY RESPONSE GUIDEBOOK, DOT P 5800.4).

FIREFIGHTING: MOVE CONTAINER FROM FIRE AREA IF POSSIBLE. COOL FIRE-EXPOSED CONTAINERS WITH WATER FROM SIDE UNTIL WELL AFTER FIRE IS OUT. STAY AWAY FROM STORAGE TANK ENDS. FOR MASSIVE FIRE IN STORAGE AREA, USE UNMANNED HOSE HOLDER OR MONITOR NOZZLES, ELSE WITHDRAW FROM AREA AND LET FIRE BURN. WITHDRAW IMMEDIATELY IN CASE OF RISING SOUND FROM VENTING SAFETY DEVICE OR ANY DISCOLORATION OF STORAGE TANK DUE TO FIRE (1987 EMERGENCY RESPONSE GUIDEBOOK, DOT P 5800.4, GUIDE PAGE 26).
EXTINGUISH ONLY IF FLOW CAN BE STOPPED. USE FLOODING AMOUNTS OF WATER AS FOG; SOLID STREAMS MAY BE INEFFECTIVE. COOL CONTAINERS WITH FLOODING AMOUNTS OF WATER FROM AS FAR A DISTANCE AS POSSIBLE. AVOID BREATHING VAPORS; KEEP UPWIND.

TRANSPORTATION DATA

DEPARTMENT OF TRANSPORTATION HAZARD CLASSIFICATION 49 CFR 172.101: COMBUSTIBLE LIQUID
DEPARTMENT OF TRANSPORTATION LABELING REQUIREMENTS 49 CFR 172.101 AND SUBPART E: NONE
DEPARTMENT OF TRANSPORTATION PACKAGING REQUIREMENTS: NONE
EXCEPTIONS: 49 CFR 173.118A

TOXICITY

(Z,Z)-7,11-HEXADECADIEN-1-OL ACETATE: CARCINOGEN STATUS: NONE. ACUTE TOXICITY LEVEL: NO DATA AVAILABLE. TARGET EFFECTS: NO DATA AVAILABLE.

HEALTH EFFECTS AND FIRST AID

INHALATION: (Z,Z)-7,11-HEXADECADIEN-1-OL ACETATE: **ACUTE EXPOSURE-** NO SPECIFIC DATA AVAILABLE. MAY BE IRRITATING. **CHRONIC EXPOSURE-** NO DATA AVAILABLE.

FIRST AID- REMOVE FROM EXPOSURE AREA TO FRESH AIR IMMEDIATELY. IF BREATHING HAS STOPPED, PERFORM ARTIFICIAL RESPIRATION. KEEP PERSON WARM AND AT REST. TREAT SYMPTOMATICALLY AND SUPPORTIVELY. GET MEDICAL ATTENTION IMMEDIATELY.

SKIN CONTACT: (Z,Z)-7,11-HEXADECADIEN-1-OL ACETATE: **ACUTE EXPOSURE-** NO SPECIFIC DATA AVAILABLE. MAY BE IRRITATING. **CHRONIC EXPOSURE-** NO DATA AVAILABLE.

FIRST AID- REMOVE CONTAMINATED CLOTHING AND SHOES IMMEDIATELY. WASH AFFECTED AREA WITH SOAP OR MILD DETERGENT AND LARGE AMOUNTS OF WATER UNTIL NO EVIDENCE OF CHEMICAL REMAINS (APPROXIMATELY 15-20 MINUTES). GET MEDICAL ATTENTION IMMEDIATELY.

EYE CONTACT: (Z,Z)-7,11-HEXADECADIEN-1-OL ACETATE: **ACUTE EXPOSURE-** NO SPECIFIC DATA AVAILABLE. MAY BE IRRITATING. **CHRONIC EXPOSURE-** NO DATA AVAILABLE.

FIRST AID- WASH EYES IMMEDIATELY WITH LARGE AMOUNTS OF WATER OR NORMAL SALINE, OCCASIONALLY LIFTING UPPER AND LOWER LIDS, UNTIL NO EVIDENCE OF CHEMICAL REMAINS (APPROXIMATELY 15-20 MINUTES). GET MEDICAL ATTENTION IMMEDIATELY.

INGESTION: (Z,Z)-7,11-HEXADECADIEN-1-OL ACETATE: **ACUTE EXPOSURE-** NO DATA AVAILABLE. **CHRONIC EXPOSURE-** NO DATA AVAILABLE.

FIRST AID- REMOVE BY GASTRIC LAVAGE AND CATHARSIS. MAINTAIN BLOOD PRESSURE AND AIRWAY. GIVE OXYGEN IF RESPIRATION IS DEPRESSED. DO NOT PERFORM GASTRIC LAVAGE IF VICTIM IS UNCONSCIOUS. GET MEDICAL ATTENTION IMMEDIATELY (DREISBACH, HANDBOOK OF POISONING, 12TH ED.).
ADMINISTRATION OF LAVAGE OR OXYGEN SHOULD BE PERFORMED BY QUALIFIED MEDICAL PERSONNEL.

ANTIDOTE: NO SPECIFIC ANTIDOTE. TREAT SYMPTOMATICALLY AND SUPPORTIVELY.

REACTIVITY

REACTIVITY: STABLE UNDER NORMAL TEMPERATURES AND PRESSURES.

INCOMPATIBILITIES: (Z,Z)-7,11-HEXADECADIEN-1-OL ACETATE: OXIDIZERS (STRONG): FIRE AND EXPLOSION HAZARD.

DECOMPOSITION: THERMAL DECOMPOSITION PRODUCTS MAY INCLUDE TOXIC OXIDES OF CARBON.

POLYMERIZATION: HAZARDOUS POLYMERIZATION HAS NOT BEEN REPORTED TO OCCUR UNDER NORMAL TEMPERATURES AND PRESSURES.

STORAGE AND DISPOSAL

OBSERVE ALL FEDERAL, STATE AND LOCAL REGULATIONS WHEN STORING OR DISPOSING OF THIS SUBSTANCE. FOR ASSISTANCE, CONTACT THE DISTRICT DIRECTOR OF THE ENVIRONMENTAL PROTECTION AGENCY.

STORAGE

STORE IN ACCORDANCE WITH 29 CFR 1910.106. STORE AWAY FROM INCOMPATIBLE SUBSTANCES.

CONDITIONS TO AVOID

AVOID CONTACT WITH HEAT, SPARKS, FLAMES, OR OTHER SOURCES OF IGNITION. VAPORS MAY BE EXPLOSIVE AND POISONOUS; DO NOT ALLOW UNNECESSARY PERSONNEL IN AREA. DO NOT OVERHEAT CONTAINERS; CONTAINERS MAY VIOLENTLY RUPTURE AND TRAVEL A CONSIDERABLE DISTANCE IN HEAT OF FIRE.

SPILL AND LEAK PROCEDURES

OCCUPATIONAL SPILL: SHUT OFF IGNITION SOURCES. STOP LEAK IF YOU CAN DO IT WITHOUT RISK. USE WATER SPRAY TO REDUCE VAPORS. FOR SMALL SPILLS, TAKE UP WITH SAND OR OTHER ABSORBENT MATERIAL AND PLACE INTO CONTAINERS FOR LATER DISPOSAL. FOR LARGER SPILLS, DIKE FAR AHEAD OF SPILL FOR LATER DISPOSAL. NO SMOKING, FLAMES OR FLARES IN HAZARD AREA. KEEP UNNECESSARY PEOPLE AWAY; ISOLATE HAZARD AREA AND DENY ENTRY.

PROTECTIVE EQUIPMENT

VENTILATION: PROVIDE LOCAL EXHAUST OR PROCESS ENCLOSURE VENTILATION SYSTEM.

RESPIRATOR: THE FOLLOWING RESPIRATORS ARE RECOMMENDED BASED ON INFORMATION FOUND IN THE PHYSICAL DATA, TOXICITY AND HEALTH EFFECTS SECTIONS. THEY ARE RANKED IN ORDER FROM MINIMUM TO MAXIMUM RESPIRATORY PROTECTION. THE SPECIFIC RESPIRATOR SELECTED MUST BE BASED ON CONTAMINATION LEVELS FOUND IN THE WORK PLACE, MUST NOT EXCEED THE WORKING LIMITS OF THE RESPIRATOR AND BE JOINTLY APPROVED BY THE NATIONAL INSTITUTE FOR OCCUPATIONAL SAFETY AND HEALTH AND THE MINE SAFETY AND HEALTH ADMINISTRATION (NIOSH-MSHA).

CHEMICAL CARTRIDGE RESPIRATOR WITH FULL FACEPIECE AND PESTICIDE CARTRIDGE.

TYPE 'C' SUPPLIED-AIR RESPIRATOR WITH A FULL FACEPIECE OPERATED IN PRESSURE-DEMAND OR OTHER POSITIVE PRESSURE MODE OR WITH A FULL FACEPIECE, HELMET OR HOOD OPERATED IN CONTINUOUS-FLOW MODE.

SELF-CONTAINED BREATHING APPARATUS OPERATED IN PRESSURE-DEMAND OR OTHER POSITIVE PRESSURE MODE.

FOR FIREFIGHTING AND OTHER IMMEDIATELY DANGEROUS TO LIFE OR HEALTH CONDITIONS:

SELF-CONTAINED BREATHING APPARATUS WITH FULL FACEPIECE OPERATED IN PRESSURE-DEMAND OR OTHER POSITIVE PRESSURE MODE.

SUPPLIED-AIR RESPIRATOR WITH FULL FACEPIECE AND OPERATED IN PRESSURE-DEMAND OR OTHER POSITIVE PRESSURE MODE IN COMBINATION WITH AN AUXILIARY SELF-CONTAINED BREATHING APPARATUS OPERATED IN PRESSURE-DEMAND OR OTHER POSITIVE PRESSURE MODE.

CLOTHING: EMPLOYEE MUST WEAR APPROPRIATE PROTECTIVE (IMPERVIOUS) CLOTHING AND EQUIPMENT TO PREVENT REPEATED OR PROLONGED SKIN CONTACT WITH THIS SUBSTANCE.

GLOVES: EMPLOYEE MUST WEAR APPROPRIATE PROTECTIVE GLOVES TO PREVENT CONTACT WITH THIS SUBSTANCE.

EYE PROTECTION: EMPLOYEE MUST WEAR SPLASH-PROOF OR DUST-RESISTANT SAFETY GOGGLES TO PREVENT EYE CONTACT WITH THIS SUBSTANCE.

EMERGENCY EYE WASH: WHERE THERE IS ANY POSSIBILITY THAT AN EMPLOYEE'S EYES MAY BE EXPOSED TO THIS SUBSTANCE, THE EMPLOYER SHOULD PROVIDE AN EYE WASH FOUNTAIN WITHIN THE IMMEDIATE WORK AREA FOR EMERGENCY USE.

AUTHORIZED BY- OCCUPATIONAL HEALTH SERVICES, INC.

CREATION DATE: 02/08/90 ***REVISION DATE:*** 05/18/90

MATERIAL SAFETY DATA SHEET

OCCUPATIONAL HEALTH SERVICES, INC.
AGRICULTURE AND PESTICIDE DIVISION
450 SEVENTH AVENUE, SUITE 2407
NEW YORK, NEW YORK 10123
1-800-445-MSDS OR (212) 967-1100

EMERGENCY CONTACT:
JOHN S. BRANSFORD, JR. (615) 292-1180

SUBSTANCE IDENTIFICATION

CAS-NUMBER 50594-66-6

SUBSTANCE: **ACIFLUORFEN**

TRADE NAMES/SYNONYMS: BENZOIC ACID, 5-(2-CHLORO-4-(TRIFLUOROMETHYL)PHENOXY)-2-NITRO-; 5-(2-CHLORO-4-(TRIFLUOROMETHYL)PHENOXY)-2-NITROBENZOIC ACID; C14H7CLF3NO5; PST72452

CHEMICAL FAMILY: ETHER, AROMATIC
HALOGEN
CARBOXYLIC ACID

MOLECULAR FORMULA: C-F3-(CL)-C6-H3-O-C6-H3-(N-O2)-C-O2-H

MOLECULAR WEIGHT: 361.66

CERCLA RATINGS (SCALE 0-3): HEALTH=U FIRE=1 REACTIVITY=0 PERSISTENCE=2

NFPA RATINGS (SCALE 0-4): HEALTH=U FIRE=1 REACTIVITY=0

COMPONENTS AND CONTAMINANTS

COMPONENT: ACIFLUORFEN ***PERCENT:*** 100.0
CAS# 50594-66-6

OTHER CONTAMINANTS: NONE

EXPOSURE LIMITS: NO OCCUPATIONAL EXPOSURE LIMITS ESTABLISHED BY OSHA, ACGIH, OR NIOSH.

ACIFLUORFEN: SUBJECT TO CALIFORNIA PROPOSITION 65 CANCER AND/OR REPRODUCTIVE TOXICITY WARNING AND RELEASE REQUIREMENTS- (JANUARY 1, 1990)

PHYSICAL DATA

DESCRIPTION: OFF-WHITE TO LIGHT BROWN SOLID.

MELTING POINT: 306-314 F (152-157 C) ***SPECIFIC GRAVITY:*** 1.546

VAPOR PRESSURE: NEGLIGIBLE ***SOLUBILITY IN WATER:*** 120 PPM

SOLVENT SOLUBILITY: SOLUBLE IN ETHANOL, METHANOL, ACETONE; MODERATELY SOLUBLE IN METHYLENE CHLORIDE; SLIGHTLY SOLUBLE IN KEROSENE, XYLENE. DECOMPOSES @ 455 F (235 C)

FIRE AND EXPLOSION DATA

FIRE AND EXPLOSION HAZARD: SLIGHT FIRE HAZARD WHEN EXPOSED TO HEAT OR FLAME.

FIREFIGHTING MEDIA: DRY CHEMICAL, CARBON DIOXIDE, HALON, WATER SPRAY OR STANDARD FOAM (1987 EMERGENCY RESPONSE GUIDEBOOK, DOT P 5800.4).

FOR LARGER FIRES, USE WATER SPRAY, FOG OR STANDARD FOAM (1987 EMERGENCY RESPONSE GUIDEBOOK, DOT P 5800.4).

FIREFIGHTING: MOVE CONTAINER FROM FIRE AREA IF POSSIBLE. DO NOT SCATTER SPILLED MATERIAL WITH HIGH PRESSURE WATER STREAMS. DIKE FIRE CONTROL WATER FOR LATER DISPOSAL (1987 EMERGENCY RESPONSE GUIDEBOOK, DOT P 5800.4, GUIDE PAGE 31).

USE AGENTS SUITABLE FOR TYPE OF SURROUNDING FIRE. AVOID BREATHING HAZARDOUS VAPORS, KEEP UPWIND.

TOXICITY

ACIFLUORFEN: CARCINOGEN STATUS: NONE. ACUTE TOXICITY LEVEL: NO DATA AVAILABLE. TARGET EFFECTS: NO DATA AVAILABLE. ADDITIONAL DATA: REPEATED ABSORPTION OF CHLORINATED DIPHENYL ETHERS HAS RESULTED IN LIVER DAMAGE IN ANIMALS.

HEALTH EFFECTS AND FIRST AID

INHALATION: ACIFLUORFEN: **ACUTE EXPOSURE-** NO DATA AVAILABLE. **CHRONIC EXPOSURE-** NO DATA AVAILABLE.

FIRST AID- REMOVE FROM EXPOSURE AREA TO FRESH AIR IMMEDIATELY. IF BREATHING HAS STOPPED, PERFORM ARTIFICIAL RESPIRATION. KEEP PERSON WARM AND AT REST. TREAT SYMPTOMATICALLY AND SUPPORTIVELY. GET MEDICAL ATTENTION IMMEDIATELY.

SKIN CONTACT: ACIFLUORFEN: **ACUTE EXPOSURE-** NO SPECIFIC DATA AVAILABLE. SOME FORMULATIONS HAVE CAUSED MODERATE IRRITATION TO RABBIT SKIN. **CHRONIC EXPOSURE-** NO DATA AVAILABLE.

FIRST AID- REMOVE CONTAMINATED CLOTHING AND SHOES IMMEDIATELY. WASH AFFECTED AREA WITH SOAP OR MILD DETERGENT AND LARGE AMOUNTS OF WATER UNTIL NO EVIDENCE OF CHEMICAL REMAINS (APPROXIMATELY 15-20 MINUTES). GET MEDICAL ATTENTION IMMEDIATELY.

EYE CONTACT: ACIFLUORFEN: **ACUTE EXPOSURE-** NO SPECIFIC DATA AVAILABLE. SOME FORMULATIONS HAVE CAUSED IRRITATION IN RABBIT EYES. **CHRONIC EXPOSURE-** NO DATA AVAILABLE.

FIRST AID- WASH EYES IMMEDIATELY WITH LARGE AMOUNTS OF WATER OR NORMAL SALINE, OCCASIONALLY LIFTING UPPER AND LOWER LIDS, UNTIL NO EVIDENCE OF CHEMICAL REMAINS (APPROXIMATELY 15-20 MINUTES). GET MEDICAL ATTENTION IMMEDIATELY.

INGESTION: ACIFLUORFEN: **ACUTE EXPOSURE**- NO DATA AVAILABLE. **CHRONIC EXPOSURE**- NO DATA AVAILABLE.

FIRST AID- TREAT SYMPTOMATICALLY AND SUPPORTIVELY. GET MEDICAL ATTENTION IMMEDIATELY. IF VOMITING OCCURS, KEEP HEAD LOWER THAN HIPS TO PREVENT ASPIRATION.

ANTIDOTE: NO SPECIFIC ANTIDOTE. TREAT SYMPTOMATICALLY AND SUPPORTIVELY.

REACTIVITY

REACTIVITY: STABLE UNDER NORMAL TEMPERATURES AND PRESSURES.

INCOMPATIBILITIES: ACIFLUORFEN: OXIDIZERS (STRONG): FIRE AND EXPLOSION HAZARD.

DECOMPOSITION: THERMAL DECOMPOSITION PRODUCTS MAY INCLUDE TOXIC OXIDES OF NITROGEN AND CARBON, AND TOXIC AND CORROSIVE FUMES OF CHLORIDES AND FLUORIDES.

POLYMERIZATION: HAZARDOUS POLYMERIZATION HAS NOT BEEN REPORTED TO OCCUR UNDER NORMAL TEMPERATURES AND PRESSURES.

STORAGE AND DISPOSAL

OBSERVE ALL FEDERAL, STATE AND LOCAL REGULATIONS WHEN STORING OR DISPOSING OF THIS SUBSTANCE. FOR ASSISTANCE, CONTACT THE DISTRICT DIRECTOR OF THE ENVIRONMENTAL PROTECTION AGENCY.

****STORAGE****

STORE IN ACCORDANCE WITH 40 CFR 165 RECOMMENDED PROCEDURES FOR THE DISPOSAL AND STORAGE OF PESTICIDES AND PESTICIDE CONTAINERS.
STORE AWAY FROM INCOMPATIBLE SUBSTANCES.

****DISPOSAL****

DISPOSAL MUST BE IN ACCORDANCE WITH 40 CFR 165 RECOMMENDED PROCEDURES FOR THE DISPOSAL AND STORAGE OF PESTICIDES AND PESTICIDE CONTAINERS.

CONDITIONS TO AVOID

MAY BURN BUT DOES NOT IGNITE READILY. AVOID CONTACT WITH STRONG OXIDIZERS, EXCESSIVE HEAT, SPARKS, OR OPEN FLAME.

SPILL AND LEAK PROCEDURES

WATER SPILL: THE CALIFORNIA SAFE DRINKING WATER AND TOXIC ENFORCEMENT ACT OF 1986 (PROPOSITION 65) PROHIBITS CONTAMINATING ANY KNOWN SOURCE OF DRINKING WATER WITH SUBSTANCES KNOWN TO CAUSE CANCER AND/OR REPRODUCTIVE TOXICITY.

OCCUPATIONAL SPILL: SWEEP UP AND PLACE IN SUITABLE CLEAN, DRY CONTAINERS FOR RECLAMATION OR LATER DISPOSAL. DO NOT FLUSH SPILLED MATERIAL INTO SEWER. KEEP UNNECESSARY PEOPLE AWAY.

PROTECTIVE EQUIPMENT

VENTILATION: PROVIDE LOCAL EXHAUST OR GENERAL DILUTION VENTILATION SYSTEM.

RESPIRATOR: THE FOLLOWING RESPIRATORS ARE RECOMMENDED BASED ON INFORMATION FOUND IN THE PHYSICAL DATA, TOXICITY AND HEALTH EFFECTS SECTIONS. THEY ARE RANKED IN ORDER FROM MINIMUM TO MAXIMUM RESPIRATORY PROTECTION. THE SPECIFIC RESPIRATOR SELECTED MUST BE BASED ON CONTAMINATION LEVELS FOUND IN THE WORK PLACE, MUST NOT EXCEED THE WORKING LIMITS OF THE RESPIRATOR AND BE JOINTLY APPROVED BY THE NATIONAL INSTITUTE FOR OCCUPATIONAL SAFETY AND HEALTH AND THE MINE SAFETY AND HEALTH ADMINISTRATION (NIOSH-MSHA).

CHEMICAL CARTRIDGE RESPIRATOR WITH AN ORGANIC VAPOR CARTRIDGE(S) WITH A FULL FACEPIECE AND ORGANIC VAPOR CARTRIDGE(S) IN COMBINATION WITH A DUST AND MIST FILTER.

POWERED AIR-PURIFYING RESPIRATOR WITH A TIGHT-FITTING FACEPIECE AND ORGANIC VAPOR CARTRIDGE(S) IN COMBINATION WITH A HIGH-EFFICIENCY PARTICULATE FILTER.

TYPE 'C' SUPPLIED-AIR RESPIRATOR WITH A FULL FACEPIECE OPERATED IN A PRESSURE-DEMAND OR OTHER POSITIVE PRESSURE MODE.

SELF-CONTAINED BREATHING APPARATUS WITH A FULL FACEPIECE OPERATED IN PRESSURE-DEMAND OR OTHER POSITIVE PRESSURE MODE.

FOR FIREFIGHTING AND OTHER IMMEDIATELY DANGEROUS TO LIFE OR HEALTH CONDITIONS:

SELF-CONTAINED BREATHING APPARATUS WITH FULL FACEPIECE OPERATED IN PRESSURE-DEMAND OR OTHER POSITIVE PRESSURE MODE. SUPPLIED-AIR RESPIRATOR WITH FULL FACEPIECE AND OPERATED IN PRESSURE-DEMAND OR OTHER POSITIVE PRESSURE MODE IN COMBINATION WITH AN AUXILIARY SELF-CONTAINED BREATHING APPARATUS OPERATED IN PRESSURE-DEMAND OR OTHER POSITIVE PRESSURE MODE.

CLOTHING: EMPLOYEE MUST WEAR APPROPRIATE PROTECTIVE (IMPERVIOUS) CLOTHING AND EQUIPMENT TO PREVENT REPEATED OR PROLONGED SKIN CONTACT WITH THIS SUBSTANCE.

GLOVES: EMPLOYEE MUST WEAR APPROPRIATE PROTECTIVE GLOVES TO PREVENT CONTACT WITH THIS SUBSTANCE.

EYE PROTECTION: EMPLOYEE MUST WEAR SPLASH-PROOF OR DUST-RESISTANT SAFETY GOGGLES TO PREVENT EYE CONTACT WITH THIS SUBSTANCE.
EMERGENCY EYE WASH: WHERE THERE IS ANY POSSIBILITY THAT AN EMPLOYEE'S EYES MAY BE EXPOSED TO THIS SUBSTANCE, THE EMPLOYER SHOULD PROVIDE AN EYE WASH FOUNTAIN WITHIN THE IMMEDIATE WORK AREA FOR EMERGENCY USE.

AUTHORIZED BY- OCCUPATIONAL HEALTH SERVICES, INC.
CREATION DATE: 10/04/89 ***REVISION DATE:*** 05/31/90

MATERIAL SAFETY DATA SHEET

OCCUPATIONAL HEALTH SERVICES, INC.
AGRICULTURE AND PESTICIDE DIVISION
450 SEVENTH AVENUE, SUITE 2407
NEW YORK, NEW YORK 10123
1-800-445-MSDS OR (212) 967-1100

EMERGENCY CONTACT:
JOHN S. BRANSFORD, JR. (615) 292-1180

SUBSTANCE IDENTIFICATION

CAS-NUMBER 62476-59-9

SUBSTANCE: **SODIUM ACIFLUORFEN**

TRADE NAMES/SYNONYMS: BENZOIC ACID, 5-(2-CHLORO-4-(TRIFLUOROMETHYL)PHENOXY)-2-NITRO-, SODIUM SALT; 5-(2-CHLORO-4-(TRIFLUOROMETHYL)PHENOXY)-2-NITROBENZOIC ACID SODIUM SALT; SODIUM 5-(2-CHLORO-4-(TRIFLUOROMETHYL)-PHENOXY)-2-NITROBENZOATE; ACIFLUORFEN SODIUM; ACIFLUORFEN SODIUM SALT; BLAZER; TACKLE; RH6201; C14H6CLF3NANO5; PST72453

CHEMICAL FAMILY: ETHER, AROMATIC
HALOGEN
CARBOXYLIC ACID

MOLECULAR FORMULA: C-F3-(CL)-C6-H3-O-C6-H3-(N-O2)-C-O2.NA

MOLECULAR WEIGHT: 383.6

CERCLA RATINGS (SCALE 0-3): HEALTH=U FIRE=1 REACTIVITY=0 PERSISTENCE=1

NFPA RATINGS (SCALE 0-4): HEALTH=U FIRE=1 REACTIVITY=0

COMPONENTS AND CONTAMINANTS

COMPONENT: SODIUM ACIFLUORFEN ***PERCENT:*** 100.0
CAS# 62476-59-9

OTHER CONTAMINANTS: NONE

EXPOSURE LIMITS: NO OCCUPATIONAL EXPOSURE LIMITS ESTABLISHED BY OSHA, ACGIH, OR NIOSH.

PHYSICAL DATA

DESCRIPTION: WHITE POWDER. ***MELTING POINT:*** 255-257 F (124-125 C)
SPECIFIC GRAVITY: NOT AVAILABLE ***SOLUBILITY IN WATER:*** >25%

FIRE AND EXPLOSION DATA

FIRE AND EXPLOSION HAZARD: SLIGHT FIRE HAZARD WHEN EXPOSED TO HEAT OR FLAME.

FIREFIGHTING MEDIA: DRY CHEMICAL, CARBON DIOXIDE, HALON, WATER SPRAY OR STANDARD FOAM (1987 EMERGENCY RESPONSE GUIDEBOOK, DOT P 5800.4).
FOR LARGER FIRES, USE WATER SPRAY, FOG OR STANDARD FOAM (1987 EMERGENCY RESPONSE GUIDEBOOK, DOT P 5800.4).

FIREFIGHTING: MOVE CONTAINER FROM FIRE AREA IF POSSIBLE. DO NOT SCATTER SPILLED MATERIAL WITH HIGH PRESSURE WATER STREAMS. DIKE FIRE CONTROL WATER FOR LATER DISPOSAL (1987 EMERGENCY RESPONSE GUIDEBOOK, DOT P 5800.4, GUIDE PAGE 31).

USE AGENTS SUITABLE FOR TYPE OF SURROUNDING FIRE. AVOID BREATHING HAZARDOUS VAPORS, KEEP UPWIND.

TOXICITY

SODIUM ACIFLUORFEN: TOXICITY DATA: 450 MG/KG SKIN-RABBIT LD50; 1300 MG/KG ORAL-RAT LD50 CARCINOGEN STATUS: NONE. ACUTE TOXICITY LEVEL: TOXIC BY DERMAL ABSORPTION; MODERATELY TOXIC BY INGESTION. TARGET EFFECTS: NO DATA AVAILABLE. ADDITIONAL DATA: REPEATED ABSORPTION OF CHLORINATED DIPHENYL ETHERS HAS RESULTED IN LIVER DAMAGE IN ANIMALS.

HEALTH EFFECTS AND FIRST AID

INHALATION: SODIUM ACIFLUORFEN: **ACUTE EXPOSURE-** NO DATA AVAILABLE. **CHRONIC EXPOSURE-** NO DATA AVAILABLE.

FIRST AID- REMOVE FROM EXPOSURE AREA TO FRESH AIR IMMEDIATELY. IF BREATHING HAS STOPPED, PERFORM ARTIFICIAL RESPIRATION. KEEP PERSON WARM AND AT REST. TREAT SYMPTOMATICALLY AND SUPPORTIVELY. GET MEDICAL ATTENTION IMMEDIATELY.

SKIN CONTACT: SODIUM ACIFLUORFEN: TOXIC. **ACUTE EXPOSURE-** NO DATA AVAILABLE. **CHRONIC EXPOSURE-** NO DATA AVAILABLE.

FIRST AID- REMOVE CONTAMINATED CLOTHING AND SHOES IMMEDIATELY. WASH AFFECTED AREA WITH SOAP OR MILD DETERGENT AND LARGE AMOUNTS OF WATER UNTIL NO EVIDENCE OF CHEMICAL REMAINS (APPROXIMATELY 15-20 MINUTES). GET MEDICAL ATTENTION IMMEDIATELY.

EYE CONTACT: ACIFLUORFEN: **ACUTE EXPOSURE-** NO DATA AVAILABLE. **CHRONIC EXPOSURE-** NO DATA AVAILABLE.

FIRST AID- WASH EYES IMMEDIATELY WITH LARGE AMOUNTS OF WATER OR NORMAL SALINE, OCCASIONALLY LIFTING UPPER AND LOWER LIDS, UNTIL NO EVIDENCE OF CHEMICAL REMAINS (APPROXIMATELY 15-20 MINUTES). GET MEDICAL ATTENTION IMMEDIATELY.

INGESTION: SODIUM ACIFLUORFEN: **ACUTE EXPOSURE-** NO DATA AVAILABLE. **CHRONIC EXPOSURE-** NO DATA AVAILABLE.

FIRST AID- TREAT SYMPTOMATICALLY AND SUPPORTIVELY. GET MEDICAL ATTENTION IMMEDIATELY. IF VOMITING OCCURS, KEEP HEAD LOWER THAN HIPS TO PREVENT ASPIRATION.

ANTIDOTE: NO SPECIFIC ANTIDOTE. TREAT SYMPTOMATICALLY AND SUPPORTIVELY.

REACTIVITY

REACTIVITY: STABLE UNDER NORMAL TEMPERATURES AND PRESSURES.

INCOMPATIBILITIES: SODIUM ACIFLUORFEN: OXIDIZERS (STRONG): FIRE AND EXPLOSION HAZARD.

DECOMPOSITION: THERMAL DECOMPOSITION PRODUCTS MAY INCLUDE TOXIC OXIDES OF NITROGEN AND CARBON, AND TOXIC AND CORROSIVE FUMES OF CHLORIDES AND FLUORIDES.

POLYMERIZATION: HAZARDOUS POLYMERIZATION HAS NOT BEEN REPORTED TO OCCUR UNDER NORMAL TEMPERATURES AND PRESSURES.

STORAGE AND DISPOSAL

OBSERVE ALL FEDERAL, STATE AND LOCAL REGULATIONS WHEN STORING OR DISPOSING OF THIS SUBSTANCE. FOR ASSISTANCE, CONTACT THE DISTRICT DIRECTOR OF THE ENVIRONMENTAL PROTECTION AGENCY.

****STORAGE****

STORE IN ACCORDANCE WITH 40 CFR 165 RECOMMENDED PROCEDURES FOR THE DISPOSAL AND STORAGE OF PESTICIDES AND PESTICIDE CONTAINERS.
STORE AWAY FROM INCOMPATIBLE SUBSTANCES.

****DISPOSAL****

DISPOSAL MUST BE IN ACCORDANCE WITH 40 CFR 165 RECOMMENDED PROCEDURES FOR THE DISPOSAL AND STORAGE OF PESTICIDES AND PESTICIDE CONTAINERS.

CONDITIONS TO AVOID

MAY BURN BUT DOES NOT IGNITE READILY. AVOID CONTACT WITH STRONG OXIDIZERS, EXCESSIVE HEAT, SPARKS, OR OPEN FLAME.

SPILL AND LEAK PROCEDURES

OCCUPATIONAL SPILL: SWEEP UP AND PLACE IN SUITABLE CLEAN, DRY CONTAINERS FOR RECLAMATION OR LATER DISPOSAL. DO NOT FLUSH SPILLED MATERIAL INTO SEWER. KEEP UNNECESSARY PEOPLE AWAY.

PROTECTIVE EQUIPMENT

VENTILATION: PROVIDE LOCAL EXHAUST OR GENERAL DILUTION VENTILATION SYSTEM.

RESPIRATOR: THE FOLLOWING RESPIRATORS ARE RECOMMENDED BASED ON INFORMATION FOUND IN THE PHYSICAL DATA, TOXICITY AND HEALTH EFFECTS SECTIONS. THEY ARE RANKED IN ORDER FROM MINIMUM TO MAXIMUM RESPIRATORY PROTECTION. THE SPECIFIC RESPIRATOR SELECTED MUST BE BASED ON CONTAMINATION LEVELS FOUND IN THE WORK PLACE, MUST NOT EXCEED THE WORKING LIMITS OF THE RESPIRATOR AND BE JOINTLY APPROVED BY THE NATIONAL INSTITUTE FOR OCCUPATIONAL SAFETY AND HEALTH AND THE MINE SAFETY AND HEALTH ADMINISTRATION (NIOSH-MSHA).

TYPE 'C' SUPPLIED-AIR RESPIRATOR WITH A FULL FACEPIECE OPERATED IN PRESSURE-DEMAND OR OTHER POSITIVE PRESSURE MODE OR WITH A FULL FACEPIECE, HELMET OR HOOD OPERATED IN CONTINOUS-FLOW MODE.

SELF-CONTAINED BREATHING APPARATUS WITH A FULL FACEPIECE OPERATED IN PRESSURE-DEMAND OR OTHER POSITIVE PRESSURE MODE.

FOR FIREFIGHTING AND OTHER IMMEDIATELY DANGEROUS TO LIFE OR HEALTH CONDITIONS:

SELF-CONTAINED BREATHING APPARATUS WITH FULL FACEPIECE OPERATED IN PRESSURE-DEMAND OR OTHER POSITIVE PRESSURE MODE.

SUPPLIED-AIR RESPIRATOR WITH FULL FACEPIECE AND OPERATED IN PRESSURE-DEMAND OR OTHER POSITIVE PRESSURE MODE IN COMBINATION WITH AN AUXILIARY SELF-CONTAINED BREATHING APPARATUS OPERATED IN PRESSURE-DEMAND OR OTHER POSITIVE PRESSURE MODE.

CLOTHING: EMPLOYEE MUST WEAR APPROPRIATE PROTECTIVE (IMPERVIOUS) CLOTHING AND EQUIPMENT TO PREVENT REPEATED OR PROLONGED SKIN CONTACT WITH THIS SUBSTANCE.

GLOVES: EMPLOYEE MUST WEAR APPROPRIATE PROTECTIVE GLOVES TO PREVENT CONTACT WITH THIS SUBSTANCE.

EYE PROTECTION: EMPLOYEE MUST WEAR SPLASH-PROOF OR DUST-RESISTANT SAFETY GOGGLES WITH OR WITHOUT A FACESHIELD TO PREVENT CONTACT WITH THIS SUBSTANCE.

EMERGENCY EYE WASH: WHERE THERE IS ANY POSSIBILITY THAT AN EMPLOYEE'S EYES MAY BE EXPOSED TO THIS SUBSTANCE, THE EMPLOYER SHOULD PROVIDE AN EYE WASH FOUNTAIN WITHIN THE IMMEDIATE WORK AREA FOR EMERGENCY USE.

AUTHORIZED BY- OCCUPATIONAL HEALTH SERVICES, INC.
CREATION DATE: 10/05/89 ***REVISION DATE:*** 05/31/90

MATERIAL SAFETY DATA SHEET

OCCUPATIONAL HEALTH SERVICES, INC.
AGRICULTURE AND PESTICIDE DIVISION
450 SEVENTH AVENUE, SUITE 2407
NEW YORK, NEW YORK 10123
1-800-445-MSDS OR (212) 967-1100

EMERGENCY CONTACT:
JOHN S. BRANSFORD, JR. (615) 292-1180

SUBSTANCE IDENTIFICATION

CAS-NUMBER 59669-26-0

SUBSTANCE: THIODICARB

TRADE NAMES/SYNONYMS: ETHANIMIDOTHIOIC ACID, N,N'-(THIOBIS((METHYLIMINO)CARBONYLOXY))BIS-, DIMETHYL ESTER; N,N-(THIOBIS((METHYLIMINO)CARBONYLOXY))BISETHANIMIDOTHIOIC ACID DIMETHYL ESTER; BIS-(O-1-METHYLTHIOETHYLIMINO)-N-METHYLCARBAMIC ACID)-N,N'-SULFIDE; 3,7,9,13-TETRAMETHYL-5,11-DIOXA-2,8,14-TRITHIA-4,7,9,12-TETRA-AZAPENTADECA-3,12-DIENE-6,10-DIONE; DIMETHYL N,N'-(THIOBIS((METHYLIMINO)CARBONYLOXY)) BISETHANIMIDOTHIOATE); CGA 45156; DICARBASULF; LARVIN; LEPICRON; UC 51762; C10H18N4O4S3; PST72456

CHEMICAL FAMILY: CARBAMATE

MOLECULAR FORMULA: C10-H18-N4-O4-S3

MOLECULAR WEIGHT: 354.46

CERCLA RATINGS (SCALE 0-3): HEALTH=3 FIRE=1 REACTIVITY=0 PERSISTENCE=0

NFPA RATINGS (SCALE 0-4): HEALTH=3 FIRE=1 REACTIVITY=0

COMPONENTS AND CONTAMINANTS

COMPONENT: THIODICARB ***PERCENT:*** 100.0
CAS# 59669-26-0

OTHER CONTAMINANTS: NONE

EXPOSURE LIMITS: NO OCCUPATIONAL EXPOSURE LIMITS ESTABLISHED BY OSHA, ACGIH, OR NIOSH.

PHYSICAL DATA

DESCRIPTION: WHITE TO LIGHT TAN CRYSTALLINE POWDER WITH A SLIGHTLY SULFUROUS ODOR.

MELTING POINT: 343-345 F (173-174 C) ***SPECIFIC GRAVITY:*** 1.4

VAPOR PRESSURE: 0.0000383 MMHG @ 20C

SOLUBILITY IN WATER: 0.0035% @ 25 C

SOLVENT SOLUBILITY: SOLUBLE IN DICHLOROMETHANE; SLIGHTLY SOLUBLE IN XYLENE, METHANOL, AND ACETONE.
SLOWLY HYDROLYZES AT 25 C AND PH 3.0; RAPIDLY HYDROLYZES AT PH > 9.0.

FIRE AND EXPLOSION DATA

FIRE AND EXPLOSION HAZARD: SLIGHT FIRE HAZARD WHEN EXPOSED TO HEAT OR FLAME.

FIREFIGHTING MEDIA: DRY CHEMICAL, CARBON DIOXIDE, HALON, WATER SPRAY OR STANDARD FOAM (1987 EMERGENCY RESPONSE GUIDEBOOK, DOT P 5800.4). FOR LARGER FIRES, USE WATER SPRAY, FOG OR STANDARD FOAM (1987 EMERGENCY RESPONSE GUIDEBOOK, DOT P 5800.4).

FIREFIGHTING: MOVE CONTAINERS FROM FIRE AREA IF POSSIBLE. FIGHT FIRE FROM MAXIMUM DISTANCE. STAY AWAY FROM STORAGE TANK ENDS. DIKE FIRE CONTROL WATER FOR LATER DISPOSAL. DO NOT SCATTER MATERIAL (1987 EMERGENCY RESPONSE GUIDEBOOK, DOT P 5800.4, GUIDE PAGE 55). EXTINGUISH USING AGENTS SUITABLE FOR TYPE OF SURROUNDING FIRE. USE FLOODING AMOUNTS OF WATER AS FOG. AVOID BREATHING TOXIC DUST AND FUMES FROM BURNING MATERIAL; KEEP UPWIND.

TOXICITY

THIODICARB: TOXICITY DATA: 520 MG/M3/4 HOURS INHALATION-RAT LC50; 160 MG/KG ORAL-RAT LD50; 800 MG/KG ORAL-DOG LD50. CARCINOGEN STATUS: NONE. ACUTE TOXICITY: HIGHLY TOXIC BY INHALATION; TOXIC BY INGESTION. TARGET EFFECTS: CHOLINESTERASE INHIBITOR. AT INCREASED RISK FROM EXPOSURE: PERSONS WITH ASTHMA, DIABETES, CARDIOVASCULAR DISEASE, MECHANICAL OBSTRUCTION OF THE GASTROINTESTINAL OR UROGENITAL TRACT, AND THOSE IN VAGOTONIC STATES.*

* MAY BE BASED ON GENERAL INFORMATION ON CARBAMATES.

HEALTH EFFECTS AND FIRST AID

INHALATION: THIODICARB: HIGHLY TOXIC. SEE INFORMATION ON CARBAMATES.
CARBAMATES: CHOLINESTERASE INHIBITOR. <u>**ACUTE EXPOSURE-**</u> WHEN INHALED, THE FIRST EFFECTS OF CHOLINESTERASE INHIBITION ARE USUALLY RESPIRATORY AND MAY INCLUDE NASAL HYPEREMIA AND WATERY DISCHARGE, CHEST DISCOMFORT, DYSPNEA, AND WHEEZING DUE TO INCREASED BRONCHIAL SECRETIONS AND BRONCHOCONSTRICTION. OTHER SYSTEMIC EFFECTS MAY BEGIN WITHIN A FEW MINUTES OR SEVERAL HOURS OF EXPOSURE. SYMPTOMS MAY INCLUDE NAUSEA, VOMITING, DIARRHEA, ABDOMINAL CRAMPS, HEADACHE, VERTIGO, OCULAR PAIN, CILIARY MUSCLE SPASM, BLURRING OR DIMNESS OF VISION, MIOSIS, OR IN SOME CASES MYDRIASIS, LACRIMATION, SALIVATION, SWEATING, AND CONFUSION. OTHER REPORTED CENTRAL NERVOUS SYSTEM OR NEUROMUSCULAR EFFECTS INCLUDE ATAXIA, SLURRED SPEECH, AREFLEXIA, WEAKNESS, FATIGUE, TWITCHING, FASCICULATION, TREMOR, AND EVENTUALLY PARALYSIS OF THE EXTREMITIES AND POSSIBLY OF THE RESPIRATORY MUSCLES. IN SEVERE CASES, THERE MAY ALSO BE INVOLUNTARY DEFECATION AND URINATION, BRADYCARDIA, HYPOTENSION, PULMONARY EDEMA, CONVULSIONS, COMA, AND DEATH FROM RESPIRATORY FAILURE OR CARDIAC ARREST. CARBAMATES GENERALLY DO NOT ACCUMULATE IN MAMMALIAN TISSUE AND THE CHOLINESTERASE INHIBITION REVERSES RATHER RAPIDLY. IN NON-FATAL CASES, THE ILLNESS GENERALLY LASTS LESS THAN 24 HOURS. <u>**CHRONIC EXPOSURE-**</u> PROLONGED OR REPEATED EXPOSURE MAY CAUSE EFFECTS AS DESCRIBED IN ACUTE EXPOSURE.

FIRST AID- REMOVE FROM EXPOSURE AREA TO FRESH AIR IMMEDIATELY. IF BREATHING HAS STOPPED, GIVE ARTIFICIAL RESPIRATION. MAINTAIN AIRWAY AND BLOOD PRESSURE AND ADMINISTER OXYGEN IF AVAILABLE. KEEP AFFECTED PERSON WARM AND AT REST. TREAT SYMPTOMATICALLY AND SUPPORTIVELY. ADMINISTRATION OF OXYGEN SHOULD BE PERFORMED BY QUALIFIED PERSONNEL. GET MEDICAL ATTENTION IMMEDIATELY.

SKIN CONTACT: THIODICARB: SEE INFORMATION ON CARBAMATES.
CARBAMATES: CHOLINESTERASE INHIBITOR. <u>**ACUTE EXPOSURE-**</u> SOME COMPOUNDS MAY CAUSE IRRITATION. LOCALIZED SWEATING AND FASCICULATIONS MAY OCCUR AT THE SITE OF CONTACT. IF SUFFICIENT AMOUNTS ARE ABSORBED THROUGH THE SKIN, OTHER EFFECTS OF CHOLINESTERASE INHIBITION MAY OCCUR AS DESCRIBED IN ACUTE INHALATION; SYMPTOMS MAY BE DELAYED FOR 2-3 HOURS, USUALLY NO MORE THAN 8 HOURS. <u>**CHRONIC EXPOSURE-**</u> REPEATED OR PROLONGED EXPOSURE MAY CAUSE EFFECTS AS DESCRIBED IN ACUTE EXPOSURE.

FIRST AID- REMOVE CONTAMINATED CLOTHING IMMEDIATELY. WASH CONTAMINATED AREAS WITH SOAP AND WATER FOLLOWED BY ALCOHOL (ARENA, POISONING, 4TH ED.). EMERGENCY PERSONNEL SHOULD WEAR GLOVES AND AVOID CONTAMINATION. TREAT RESPIRATORY DIFFICULTY WITH ARTIFICIAL RESPIRATION. GET MEDICAL ATTENTION IMMEDIATELY.

EYE CONTACT: THIODICARB: SEE INFORMATION ON CARBAMATES.
CARBAMATES: CHOLINESTERASE INHIBITOR. <u>**ACUTE EXPOSURE-**</u> DIRECT CONTACT MAY CAUSE PAIN, HYPEREMIA, LACRIMATION, TWITCHING OF THE EYELIDS, MIOSIS, AND CILIARY MUSCLE SPASM WITH LOSS OF ACCOMODATION, BLURRED OR DIMMED VISION AND BROWACHE. SOMETIMES MYDRIASIS MAY OCCUR INSTEAD OF MIOSIS. WITH SUFFICIENT EXPOSURE, OTHER SYMPTOMS OF CHOLINESTERASE INHIBITION MAY OCCUR AS DESCRIBED IN ACUTE INHALATION. <u>**CHRONIC EXPOSURE-**</u> PROLONGED EXPOSURE MAY CAUSE EFFECTS AS DESCRIBED IN ACUTE EXPOSURE. SOME COMPOUNDS HAVE CAUSED TOXIC EFFECTS ON THE CRYSTALLINE LENS, CONJUNCTIVAL THICKENING AND OBSTRUCTION OF NASOLACRIMAL CANALS WHEN USED AS MIOTIC EYE DROPS.

FIRST AID- IRRIGATE EYES WITH WATER OR SALINE SOLUTION. IF SYMPTOMS OF POISONING OCCUR, TREAT RESPIRATORY DIFFICULTY WITH ARTIFICIAL RESPIRATION AND OXYGEN. OBSERVE PATIENT FOR AT LEAST 24-36 HOURS (GOSSELIN, CLINICAL TOXICOLOGY OF COMMERCIAL PRODUCTS, 5TH ED.). GET MEDICAL ATTENTION IMMEDIATELY. OXYGEN SHOULD BE ADMINISTERED BY QUALIFIED MEDICAL PERSONNEL.

INGESTION: THIODICARB: TOXIC. AN INCREASED MORTALITY RATE WAS OBSERVED IN A 2-YEAR STUDY OF MICE FED 10 MG/KG/DAY. DECREASED BODY WEIGHTS WERE RECORDED IN RATS FED 10 MG/KG/DAY FOR 2 YEARS. AN INCREASED PERCENTAGE OF BILOBED VERTEBRAL CENTRA, DECREASED FETAL SIZE, AND MATERNAL EFFECTS WERE REPORTED IN A STUDY OF PREGNANT RATS FED 100 MG/KG/DAY. SEE INFORMATION ON CARBAMATES.
CARBAMATES: CHOLINESTERASE INHIBITOR. <u>**ACUTE EXPOSURE-**</u> WHEN INGESTED, THE FIRST EFFECTS MAY BE NAUSEA, VOMITING, ANOREXIA, ABDOMINAL CRAMPS, AND DIARRHEA. WITH ABSORPTION FROM THE GASTROINTESTINAL TRACT, THE OTHER EFFECTS OF CHOLINESTERASE INHIBITION AS DESCRIBED IN ACUTE INHALATION MAY OCCUR; SYMPTOMS MAY BEGIN WITHIN MINUTES OR BE DELAYED SEVERAL HOURS. <u>**CHRONIC EXPOSURE-**</u> REPEATED INGESTION MAY CAUSE EFFECTS AS DESCRIBED IN ACUTE EXPOSURE.

FIRST AID- IF PERSON IS ALERT AND RESPIRATION IS NOT DEPRESSED, GIVE SYRUP OF IPECAC FOLLOWED BY WATER (IF VOMITING OCCURS, KEEP HEAD BELOW HIPS TO PREVENT ASPIRATION). IF CONSCIOUSNESS LEVEL DECLINES OR VOMITING HAS NOT OCCURRED IN 15 MINUTES EMPTY STOMACH BY GASTRIC LAVAGE WITH THE AID OF CUFFED ENDOTRACHEAL TUBE USING ISOTONIC SALINE OR 5% SODIUM BICARBONATE FOLLOW WITH ACTIVATED CHARCOAL. ESTABLISH AND MAINTAIN AIRWAY. TREAT RESPIRATORY DIFFICULTY WITH ARTIFICIAL RESPIRATION AND OXYGEN. DO NOT GIVE MORPHINE, AMINOPHYLLINE, PHENOTHIAZINES, RESERPINE, FUROSEMIDE, OR ETHACRYNIC ACID (MORGAN, RECOGNITION AND MANAGEMENT OF PESTICIDE POISONINGS, 3RD ED.). TREAT SYMPTOMATICALLY AND SUPPORTIVELY. ADMINISTRATION OF OXYGEN AND LAVAGE MUST BE PERFORMED BY QUALIFIED MEDICAL PERSONNEL. GET MEDICAL ATTENTION IMMEDIATELY.

ANTIDOTE: THE FOLLOWING ANTIDOTE HAS BEEN RECOMMENDED. HOWEVER, THE DECISION AS TO WHETHER THE SEVERITY OF POISONING REQUIRES ADMINISTRATION OF ANY ANTIDOTE AND ACTUAL DOSE REQUIRED SHOULD BE MADE BY QUALIFIED MEDICAL PERSONNEL.
FOR CHOLINESTERASE INHIBITORS: ESTABLISH CLEAR AIRWAY AND TISSUE OXYGENATION BY ASPIRATION OF SECRETIONS, AND IF NECESSARY, BY ASSISTED PULMONARY VENTILATION WITH OXYGEN. IMPROVE TISSUE OXYGENATION AS MUCH AS POSSIBLE BEFORE ADMINISTERING ATROPINE TO MINIMIZE THE RISK OF VENTRICULAR FIBRILLATION. ADMINISTER ATROPINE SULFATE INTRAVENOUSLY, OR INTRAMUSCULARLY IF IV INJECTION IS NOT POSSIBLE. IN MODERATELY SEVERE POISONING ADMINISTER ATROPINE SULFATE, 0.4-2.0 MG REPEATED EVERY 15 MINUTES UNTIL ATROPINIZATION IS ACHIEVED (TACHYCARDIA, FLUSHING, DRY MOUTH, MYDRIASIS). MAINTAIN ATROPINIZATION BY REPEATED DOSES FOR 2-12 HOURS, OR LONGER, DEPENDING ON THE SEVERITY OF POISONING. THE APPEARANCE OF RALES IN THE LUNG BASES, MIOSIS, SALIVATION, NAUSEA, BRADYCARDIA, ARE ALL INDICATIONS OF INADEQUATE ATROPINIZATION. SEVERELY POISONED INDIVIDUALS MAY EXHIBIT REMARKABLE TOLERANCE TO ATROPINE; TWO OR MORE TIMES THE DOSAGES SUGGESTED ABOVE MAY BE NEEDED. PERSONS NOT POISONED OR ONLY SLIGHTLY POISONED, HOWEVER, MAY DEVELOP SIGNS OF ATROPINE TOXICITY FROM SUCH LARGE DOSAGES: FEVER, MUSCLE FIBRILLATIONS, AND DELIRIUM ARE THE MAIN SIGNS OF ATROPINE TOXICITY. IF THESE SIGNS APPEAR WHILE THE PATIENT IS FULLY ATROPINIZED, ATROPINE ADMINISTRATION SHOULD BE DISCONTINUED, AT LEAST TEMPORARILY. OBSERVE TREATED PATIENTS CLOSELY AT LEAST 24 HOURS TO INSURE THAT SYMPTOMS (POSSIBLY PULMONARY EDEMA) DO NOT RECUR AS ATROPINIZATION WEARS OFF. IN VERY SEVERE POISONINGS, METABOLIC DISPOSITION OF TOXICANT MAY REQUIRE SEVERAL HOURS OR DAYS DURING WHICH ATROPINIZATION MUST BE MAINTAINED. MARKEDLY LOWER LEVELS OF URINARY METABOLITES INDICATE THAT ATROPINE DOSAGE CAN BE TAPERED OFF. AS DOSAGE IS REDUCED, CHECK THE LUNG BASES FREQUENTLY FOR RALES. IF RALES ARE HEARD OR OTHER SYMPTOMS RETURN, RE-ESTABLISH ATROPINIZATION PROMPTLY (MORGAN, RECOGNITION AND MANAGEMENT OF PESTICIDE POISONINGS, 3RD ED.). ADMINISTRATION OF ANTIDOTE MUST BE PERFORMED BY QUALIFIED MEDICAL PERSONNEL.

REACTIVITY

REACTIVITY: STABLE UNDER NORMAL TEMPERATURES AND PRESSURES.

INCOMPATIBILITIES: THIODICARB: OXIDIZERS (STRONG): FIRE AND EXPLOSION HAZARD.

DECOMPOSITION: THERMAL DECOMPOSITION PRODUCTS MAY INCLUDE TOXIC OXIDES OF CARBON, NITROGEN, AND SULFUR.

POLYMERIZATION: HAZARDOUS POLYMERIZATION HAS NOT BEEN REPORTED TO OCCUR UNDER NORMAL TEMPERATURES AND PRESSURES.

STORAGE AND DISPOSAL

OBSERVE ALL FEDERAL, STATE AND LOCAL REGULATIONS WHEN STORING OR DISPOSING OF THIS SUBSTANCE. FOR ASSISTANCE, CONTACT THE DISTRICT DIRECTOR OF THE ENVIRONMENTAL PROTECTION AGENCY.

STORAGE

STORE IN ACCORDANCE WITH 40 CFR 165 RECOMMENDED PROCEDURES FOR THE DISPOSAL AND STORAGE OF PESTICIDES AND PESTICIDE CONTAINERS.
STORE AWAY FROM INCOMPATIBLE SUBSTANCES.
KEEP CONTAINER TIGHTLY CLOSED. PROTECT FROM EXPOSURE TO AIR OR LIGHT.

DISPOSAL

DISPOSAL MUST BE IN ACCORDANCE WITH 40 CFR 165 RECOMMENDED PROCEDURES FOR THE DISPOSAL AND STORAGE OF PESTICIDES AND PESTICIDE CONTAINERS.

CONDITIONS TO AVOID

MAY BURN BUT DOES NOT IGNITE READILY. CONTAINERS MAY EXPLODE IN HEAT OF FIRE.

SPILL AND LEAK PROCEDURES

OCCUPATIONAL SPILL: DO NOT TOUCH SPILLED MATERIAL. STOP LEAK IF YOU CAN DO IT WITHOUT RISK. USE WATER SPRAY TO REDUCE VAPORS. FOR SMALL SPILLS, TAKE UP WITH SAND OR OTHER ABSORBENT MATERIAL AND PLACE INTO CONTAINERS FOR LATER DISPOSAL. FOR SMALL DRY SPILLS, WITH A CLEAN SHOVEL PLACE MATERIAL INTO CLEAN, DRY CONTAINERS AND COVER. MOVE CONTAINERS FROM SPILL AREA. FOR LARGER SPILLS, DIKE FAR AHEAD OF SPILL FOR LATER DISPOSAL. KEEP UNNECESSARY PEOPLE AWAY. ISOLATE HAZARD AREA AND DENY ENTRY. VENTILATE CLOSED SPACES BEFORE ENTERING.

PROTECTIVE EQUIPMENT

VENTILATION: PROVIDE LOCAL EXHAUST OR GENERAL DILUTION VENTILATION SYSTEM.

RESPIRATOR: THE FOLLOWING RESPIRATORS ARE RECOMMENDED BASED ON INFORMATION FOUND IN THE PHYSICAL DATA, TOXICITY AND HEALTH EFFECTS SECTIONS. THEY ARE RANKED IN ORDER FROM MINIMUM TO MAXIMUM RESPIRATORY PROTECTION. THE SPECIFIC RESPIRATOR SELECTED MUST BE BASED ON CONTAMINATION LEVELS FOUND IN THE WORK PLACE, MUST NOT EXCEED THE WORKING LIMITS OF THE RESPIRATOR AND BE JOINTLY APPROVED BY THE NATIONAL INSTITUTE FOR OCCUPATIONAL SAFETY AND HEALTH AND THE MINE SAFETY AND HEALTH ADMINISTRATION (NIOSH-MSHA).
CHEMICAL CARTRIDGE RESPIRATOR WITH AN ORGANIC VAPOR CARTRIDGE(S) IN COMBINATION WITH A DUST AND MIST FILTER.
GAS MASK WITH ORGANIC VAPOR CANISTER (CHIN-STYLE OR FRONT- OR BACK-MOUNTED CANISTER) WITH A DUST AND MIST FILTER.
GAS MASK WITH ORGANIC VAPOR CANISTER (CHIN-STYLE OR FRONT- OR BACK-MOUNTED CANISTER) WITH A PARTICULATE FILTER.
POWERED AIR-PURIFYING RESPIRATOR WITH A HIGH-EFFICIENCY FILTER.
TYPE 'C' SUPPLIED-AIR RESPIRATOR WITH A FULL FACEPIECE OPERATED IN A PRESSURE-DEMAND OR OTHER POSITIVE PRESSURE MODE.
SELF-CONTAINED BREATHING APPARATUS WITH A FULL FACEPIECE OPERATED IN PRESSURE-DEMAND OR OTHER POSITIVE PRESSURE MODE.
FOR FIREFIGHTING AND OTHER IMMEDIATELY DANGEROUS TO LIFE OR HEALTH CONDITIONS:
SELF-CONTAINED BREATHING APPARATUS WITH FULL FACEPIECE OPERATED IN PRESSURE-DEMAND OR OTHER POSITIVE PRESSURE MODE.
SUPPLIED-AIR RESPIRATOR WITH FULL FACEPIECE AND OPERATED IN PRESSURE-DEMAND OR OTHER POSITIVE PRESSURE MODE IN COMBINATION WITH AN AUXILIARY SELF-CONTAINED BREATHING APPARATUS OPERATED IN PRESSURE-DEMAND OR OTHER POSITIVE PRESSURE MODE.

CLOTHING: EMPLOYEE MUST WEAR APPROPRIATE PROTECTIVE (IMPERVIOUS) CLOTHING AND EQUIPMENT TO PREVENT REPEATED OR PROLONGED SKIN CONTACT WITH THIS SUBSTANCE.

GLOVES: EMPLOYEE MUST WEAR APPROPRIATE PROTECTIVE GLOVES TO PREVENT CONTACT WITH THIS SUBSTANCE.

EYE PROTECTION: EMPLOYEE MUST WEAR SPLASH-PROOF OR DUST-RESISTANT SAFETY GOGGLES TO PREVENT EYE CONTACT WITH THIS SUBSTANCE.
EMERGENCY EYE WASH: WHERE THERE IS ANY POSSIBILITY THAT AN EMPLOYEE'S EYES MAY BE EXPOSED TO THIS SUBSTANCE, THE EMPLOYER SHOULD PROVIDE AN EYE WASH FOUNTAIN WITHIN THE IMMEDIATE WORK AREA FOR EMERGENCY USE.

AUTHORIZED BY- OCCUPATIONAL HEALTH SERVICES, INC.

CREATION DATE: 10/05/89 ***REVISION DATE:*** 06/12/90

MATERIAL SAFETY DATA SHEET

OCCUPATIONAL HEALTH SERVICES, INC.
AGRICULTURE AND PESTICIDE DIVISION
450 SEVENTH AVENUE, SUITE 2407
NEW YORK, NEW YORK 10123
1-800-445-MSDS OR (212) 967-1100

EMERGENCY CONTACT:
JOHN S. BRANSFORD, JR. (615) 292-1180

SUBSTANCE IDENTIFICATION

CAS-NUMBER 55335-06-3

SUBSTANCE: TRICLOPYR

TRADE NAMES/SYNONYMS: ACETIC ACID, ((3,5,6-TRICHLORO-2-PYRIDINYL)OXY)-; ACETIC ACID, ((3,5,6-TRICHLORO-2-PYRIDYL)OXY)-; ((3,5,6-TRICHLORO-2-PYRIDINYL)OXY)ACETIC ACID; ((3,5,6-TRICHLORO-2-PYRIDYL)OXY)ACETIC ACID; (3,5,6-TRICHLORO-2-PYRIDYLOXY)ACETIC ACID; 3,5,6-TRICHLORO-2-PYRIDYLOXYACETIC ACID; 3,5,6-TRICHLORO-2-PYRIDINYLOXYACETIC ACID; DOWCO 233; GARLON; C7H4CL3NO3; PST72472

CHEMICAL FAMILY: PYRIDINE
CARBOXYLIC ACID
HALOGEN

MOLECULAR FORMULA: CL3-(C5-N-H)-O-C-H2-C-O2-H

MOLECULAR WEIGHT: 256.46

CERCLA RATINGS (SCALE 0-3): HEALTH=2 FIRE=1 REACTIVITY=0 PERSISTENCE=3

NFPA RATINGS (SCALE 0-4): HEALTH=U FIRE=1 REACTIVITY=0

COMPONENTS AND CONTAMINANTS

COMPONENT: TRICLOPYR ***PERCENT:*** 100.0
CAS# 55335-06-3

OTHER CONTAMINANTS: NONE

EXPOSURE LIMITS: NO OCCUPATIONAL EXPOSURE LIMITS ESTABLISHED BY OSHA, ACGIH, OR NIOSH.

PHYSICAL DATA

DESCRIPTION: FLUFFY, COLORLESS SOLID. ***MELTING POINT:*** 298-302 F (148-150 C)

SPECIFIC GRAVITY: NOT AVAILABLE ***VAPOR PRESSURE:*** NEGLIGIBLE

SOLUBILITY IN WATER: 0.044% @ 25 C

SOLVENT SOLUBILITY: SOLUBLE IN ACETONE, 1-OCTANOL, AND CHLOROFORM; SLIGHTLY SOLUBLE IN HEXANE.
DECOMPOSES @ 554 F (290 C)

FIRE AND EXPLOSION DATA

FIRE AND EXPLOSION HAZARD: SLIGHT FIRE HAZARD WHEN EXPOSED TO HEAT OR FLAME.

FIREFIGHTING MEDIA: DRY CHEMICAL, CARBON DIOXIDE, HALON, WATER SPRAY OR STANDARD FOAM (1987 EMERGENCY RESPONSE GUIDEBOOK, DOT P 5800.4).
FOR LARGER FIRES, USE WATER SPRAY, FOG OR STANDARD FOAM (1987 EMERGENCY RESPONSE GUIDEBOOK, DOT P 5800.4).

FIREFIGHTING: MOVE CONTAINER FROM FIRE AREA IF POSSIBLE. DO NOT SCATTER SPILLED MATERIAL WITH HIGH PRESSURE WATER STREAMS. DIKE FIRE CONTROL WATER FOR LATER DISPOSAL (1987 EMERGENCY RESPONSE GUIDEBOOK, DOT P 5800.4, GUIDE PAGE 31).
USE AGENTS SUITABLE FOR TYPE OF SURROUNDING FIRE. AVOID BREATHING HAZARDOUS VAPORS, KEEP UPWIND.

TOXICITY

TRICLOPYR: TOXICITY DATA: 630 MG/KG ORAL-RAT LD50; 310 MG/KG ORAL-GUINEA PIG LD50; 550 MG/KG ORAL-RABBIT LD50; REPRODUCTIVE EFFECTS DATA (RTECS). CARCINOGEN STATUS: NONE. ACUTE TOXICITY LEVEL: MODERATELY TOXIC BY INGESTION. TARGET EFFECTS: NO DATA AVAILABLE.

HEALTH EFFECTS AND FIRST AID

INHALATION: TRICLOPYR: ACUTE EXPOSURE- NO DATA AVAILABLE. **CHRONIC EXPOSURE-** NO DATA AVAILABLE.

FIRST AID- REMOVE FROM EXPOSURE AREA TO FRESH AIR IMMEDIATELY. IF BREATHING HAS STOPPED, PERFORM ARTIFICIAL RESPIRATION. KEEP PERSON

WARM AND AT REST. TREAT SYMPTOMATICALLY AND SUPPORTIVELY. GET MEDICAL ATTENTION IMMEDIATELY.

SKIN CONTACT: TRICLOPYR: **ACUTE EXPOSURE-** THIS MATERIAL WAS ESSENTILLY NONIRRITATING TO RABBIT SKIN. A LETHAL DOSE IN RABBITS BY DERMAL ABSORPTION WAS GREATER THAN 2000 MG/KG. **CHRONIC EXPOSURE-** NO DATA AVAILABLE.

FIRST AID- REMOVE CONTAMINATED CLOTHING AND SHOES IMMEDIATELY. WASH AFFECTED AREA WITH SOAP OR MILD DETERGENT AND LARGE AMOUNTS OF WATER UNTIL NO EVIDENCE OF CHEMICAL REMAINS (APPROXIMATELY 15-20 MINUTES). GET MEDICAL ATTENTION IMMEDIATELY.

EYE CONTACT: TRICLOPYR: **ACUTE EXPOSURE-** THIS MATERIAL WAS MILDLY IRRITATING TO RABBIT EYES. **CHRONIC EXPOSURE-** NO DATA AVAILABLE.

FIRST AID- WASH EYES IMMEDIATELY WITH LARGE AMOUNTS OF WATER OR NORMAL SALINE, OCCASIONALLY LIFTING UPPER AND LOWER LIDS, UNTIL NO EVIDENCE OF CHEMICAL REMAINS (APPROXIMATELY 15-20 MINUTES). GET MEDICAL ATTENTION IMMEDIATELY.

INGESTION: TRICLOPYR: **ACUTE EXPOSURE-** A LETHAL DOSE IN RATS WAS 630 MG/KG; SYMPTOMS WERE NOT REPORTED. **CHRONIC EXPOSURE-** REPRODUCTIVE EFFECTS HAVE BEEN REPORTED IN ANIMALS.

FIRST AID- TREAT SYMPTOMATICALLY AND SUPPORTIVELY. GET MEDICAL ATTENTION IMMEDIATELY. IF VOMITING OCCURS, KEEP HEAD LOWER THAN HIPS TO PREVENT ASPIRATION.

ANTIDOTE: NO SPECIFIC ANTIDOTE. TREAT SYMPTOMATICALLY AND SUPPORTIVELY.

REACTIVITY

REACTIVITY: STABLE UNDER NORMAL TEMPERATURES AND PRESSURES IN A CLOSED CONTAINER. MAY DECOMPOSE ON EXPOSURE TO SUNLIGHT OR EXCESSIVE HEAT.

INCOMPATIBILITIES: TRICLOPYR: OXIDIZERS (STRONG): FIRE AND EXPLOSION HAZARD.

DECOMPOSITION: THERMAL DECOMPOSITION PRODUCTS MAY INCLUDE TOXIC OXIDES OF NITROGEN AND CARBON AND TOXIC AND CORROSIVE FUMES OF CHLORIDES.

POLYMERIZATION: HAZARDOUS POLYMERIZATION HAS NOT BEEN REPORTED TO OCCUR UNDER NORMAL TEMPERATURES AND PRESSURES.

STORAGE AND DISPOSAL

OBSERVE ALL FEDERAL, STATE AND LOCAL REGULATIONS WHEN STORING OR DISPOSING OF THIS SUBSTANCE. FOR ASSISTANCE, CONTACT THE DISTRICT DIRECTOR OF THE ENVIRONMENTAL PROTECTION AGENCY.

STORAGE

STORE IN ACCORDANCE WITH 40 CFR 165 RECOMMENDED PROCEDURES FOR THE DISPOSAL AND STORAGE OF PESTICIDES AND PESTICIDE CONTAINERS.
STORE AWAY FROM INCOMPATIBLE SUBSTANCES. KEEP CONTAINER TIGHTLY CLOSED. PROTECT FROM EXPOSURE TO AIR OR LIGHT.

DISPOSAL

DISPOSAL MUST BE IN ACCORDANCE WITH 40 CFR 165 RECOMMENDED PROCEDURES FOR THE DISPOSAL AND STORAGE OF PESTICIDES AND PESTICIDE CONTAINERS.

CONDITIONS TO AVOID

MAY BURN BUT DOES NOT IGNITE READILY. AVOID CONTACT WITH STRONG OXIDIZERS, EXCESSIVE HEAT, SPARKS, OR OPEN FLAME.

SPILL AND LEAK PROCEDURES

OCCUPATIONAL SPILL: SWEEP UP AND PLACE IN SUITABLE CLEAN, DRY CONTAINERS FOR RECLAMATION OR LATER DISPOSAL. DO NOT FLUSH SPILLED MATERIAL INTO SEWER. KEEP UNNECESSARY PEOPLE AWAY.

PROTECTIVE EQUIPMENT

VENTILATION: PROVIDE LOCAL EXHAUST OR GENERAL DILUTION VENTILATION SYSTEM.

RESPIRATOR: THE FOLLOWING RESPIRATORS ARE RECOMMENDED BASED ON INFORMATION FOUND IN THE PHYSICAL DATA, TOXICITY AND HEALTH EFFECTS SECTIONS. THEY ARE RANKED IN ORDER FROM MINIMUM TO MAXIMUM RESPIRATORY PROTECTION. THE SPECIFIC RESPIRATOR SELECTED MUST BE BASED ON CONTAMINATION LEVELS FOUND IN THE WORK PLACE, MUST NOT EXCEED THE WORKING LIMITS OF THE RESPIRATOR AND BE JOINTLY APPROVED BY THE NATIONAL INSTITUTE FOR OCCUPATIONAL SAFETY AND HEALTH AND THE MINE SAFETY AND HEALTH ADMINISTRATION (NIOSH-MSHA).
CHEMICAL CARTRIDGE RESPIRATOR WITH AN ORGANIC VAPOR CARTRIDGE(S) IN COMBINATION WITH A DUST AND MIST FILTER.
GAS MASK WITH ORGANIC VAPOR CANISTER (CHIN-STYLE OR FRONT- OR BACK-MOUNTED CANISTER) WITH A DUST AND MIST FILTER.
GAS MASK WITH ORGANIC VAPOR CANISTER (CHIN-STYLE OR FRONT- OR BACK-MOUNTED CANISTER) WITH A PARTICULATE FILTER.
POWERED AIR-PURIFYING RESPIRATOR WITH A HIGH-EFFICIENCY FILTER.
TYPE 'C' SUPPLIED-AIR RESPIRATOR WITH A FULL FACEPIECE OPERATED IN A PRESSURE-DEMAND OR OTHER POSITIVE PRESSURE MODE.
SELF-CONTAINED BREATHING APPARATUS WITH A FULL FACEPIECE OPERATED IN PRESSURE-DEMAND OR OTHER POSITIVE PRESSURE MODE.
FOR FIREFIGHTING AND OTHER IMMEDIATELY DANGEROUS TO LIFE OR HEALTH CONDITIONS:
SELF-CONTAINED BREATHING APPARATUS WITH FULL FACEPIECE OPERATED IN PRESSURE-DEMAND OR OTHER POSITIVE PRESSURE MODE.
SUPPLIED-AIR RESPIRATOR WITH FULL FACEPIECE AND OPERATED IN PRESSURE-DEMAND OR OTHER POSITIVE PRESSURE MODE IN COMBINATION WITH AN AUXILIARY SELF-CONTAINED BREATHING APPARATUS OPERATED IN PRESSURE-DEMAND OR OTHER POSITIVE PRESSURE MODE.

CLOTHING: EMPLOYEE MUST WEAR APPROPRIATE PROTECTIVE (IMPERVIOUS) CLOTHING AND EQUIPMENT TO PREVENT REPEATED OR PROLONGED SKIN CONTACT WITH THIS SUBSTANCE.

GLOVES: EMPLOYEE MUST WEAR APPROPRIATE PROTECTIVE GLOVES TO PREVENT CONTACT WITH THIS SUBSTANCE.

EYE PROTECTION: EMPLOYEE MUST WEAR SPLASH-PROOF OR DUST-RESISTANT SAFETY GOGGLES TO PREVENT EYE CONTACT WITH THIS SUBSTANCE.
EMERGENCY EYE WASH: WHERE THERE IS ANY POSSIBILITY THAT AN EMPLOYEE'S EYES MAY BE EXPOSED TO THIS SUBSTANCE, THE EMPLOYER SHOULD PROVIDE AN EYE WASH FOUNTAIN WITHIN THE IMMEDIATE WORK AREA FOR EMERGENCY USE.

AUTHORIZED BY- OCCUPATIONAL HEALTH SERVICES, INC.
CREATION DATE: 10/05/89 ***REVISION DATE:*** 05/31/90

MATERIAL SAFETY DATA SHEET

OCCUPATIONAL HEALTH SERVICES, INC.
AGRICULTURE AND PESTICIDE DIVISION
450 SEVENTH AVENUE, SUITE 2407
NEW YORK, NEW YORK 10123
1-800-445-MSDS OR (212) 967-1100

EMERGENCY CONTACT:
JOHN S. BRANSFORD, JR. (615) 292-1180

SUBSTANCE IDENTIFICATION

CAS-NUMBER 525-79-1

SUBSTANCE: **KINETIN**

TRADE NAMES/SYNONYMS: BP-942; 6-FURFURYLAMINO PURINE; N-(2-FURANYLMETHYL)1H-PURIN-6-AMINE; N-FURFURYLADENINE; FAP; 6-FURFURYLADENINE; PST72483

CHEMICAL FAMILY: PURINE

MOLECULAR FORMULA: C10-H9-N5-O

MOLECULAR WEIGHT: 215.21

CERCLA RATINGS (SCALE 0-3): HEALTH=U FIRE=U REACTIVITY=U PERSISTENCE=2

NFPA RATINGS (SCALE 0-4): HEALTH=U FIRE=U REACTIVITY=U

COMPONENTS AND CONTAMINANTS

COMPONENT: KINETIN ***PERCENT:*** 100
CAS# 525-79-1

OTHER CONTAMINANTS: NONE

EXPOSURE LIMITS: NO OCCUPATIONAL EXPOSURE LIMITS ESTABLISHED BY OSHA, ACGIH, OR NIOSH.

PHYSICAL DATA

DESCRIPTION: SOLID ***MELTING POINT:*** 428 F (220 C) SUBLIMES

SPECIFIC GRAVITY: NOT AVAILABLE ***SOLUBILITY IN WATER:*** SLIGHTLY SOLUBLE

SOLVENT SOLUBILITY: DILUTE HYDROCHLORIC ACID, DILUTE SODIUM HYDROXIDE

FIRE AND EXPLOSION DATA

FIRE AND EXPLOSION HAZARD: UNKNOWN FIRE AND EXPLOSION HAZARD.

FIREFIGHTING MEDIA: DRY CHEMICAL, CARBON DIOXIDE, WATER SPRAY OR FOAM FOR LARGER FIRES, USE WATER SPRAY, FOG OR ALCOHOL FOAM

FIREFIGHTING: MOVE CONTAINER FROM FIRE AREA IF POSSIBLE. DO NOT SCATTER SPILLED MATERIAL WITH MORE WATER THAN NEEDED FOR FIRE CONTROL. DIKE FIRE CONTROL WATER FOR LATER DISPOSAL

USE AGENTS SUITABLE FOR TYPE OF SURROUNDING FIRE. AVOID BREATHING HAZARDOUS VAPORS, KEEP UPWIND.

TOXICITY

KINETIN: TOXICITY DATA: 450 MG/KG INTRAPERITONEAL-MOUSE LD50; MUTAGENIC DATA (RTECS). CARCINOGEN STATUS: NONE. ACUTE TOXICITY LEVEL: INSUFFICIENT DATA. TARGET EFFECTS: NO DATA AVAILABLE.

HEALTH EFFECTS AND FIRST AID

INHALATION: KINETIN: **ACUTE EXPOSURE-** NO DATA AVAILABLE. **CHRONIC EXPOSURE-** NO DATA AVAILABLE.

FIRST AID- REMOVE FROM EXPOSURE AREA TO FRESH AIR IMMEDIATELY. IF BREATHING HAS STOPPED, PERFORM ARTIFICIAL RESPIRATION. KEEP PERSON WARM AND AT REST. TREAT SYMPTOMATICALLY AND SUPPORTIVELY. GET MEDICAL ATTENTION IMMEDIATELY.

SKIN CONTACT: KINETIN: **ACUTE EXPOSURE-** NO DATA AVAILABLE. **CHRONIC EXPOSURE-** NO DATA AVAILABLE.

FIRST AID- REMOVE CONTAMINATED CLOTHING AND SHOES IMMEDIATELY. WASH AFFECTED AREA WITH SOAP OR MILD DETERGENT AND LARGE AMOUNTS OF WATER UNTIL NO EVIDENCE OF CHEMICAL REMAINS (APPROXIMATELY 15-20 MINUTES). GET MEDICAL ATTENTION IMMEDIATELY.

EYE CONTACT: KINETIN: **ACUTE EXPOSURE-** NO DATA AVAILABLE. **CHRONIC EXPOSURE-** NO DATA AVAILABLE.

FIRST AID- WASH EYES IMMEDIATELY WITH LARGE AMOUNTS OF WATER OR NORMAL SALINE, OCCASIONALLY LIFTING UPPER AND LOWER LIDS, UNTIL NO EVIDENCE OF CHEMICAL REMAINS (APPROXIMATELY 15-20 MINUTES). GET MEDICAL ATTENTION IMMEDIATELY.

INGESTION: KINETIN: **ACUTE EXPOSURE-** NO DATA AVAILABLE. **CHRONIC EXPOSURE-** NO DATA AVAILABLE.

FIRST AID- TREAT SYMPTOMATICALLY AND SUPPORTIVELY. GET MEDICAL ATTENTION IMMEDIATELY. IF VOMITING OCCURS, KEEP HEAD LOWER THAN HIPS TO PREVENT ASPIRATION.

ANTIDOTE: NO SPECIFIC ANTIDOTE. TREAT SYMPTOMATICALLY AND SUPPORTIVELY.

REACTIVITY

REACTIVITY: NO DATA AVAILABLE.

INCOMPATIBILITIES: KINETIN: NO DATA AVAILABLE.

DECOMPOSITION: THERMAL DECOMPOSITION MAY RELEASE TOXIC AND/OR HAZARDOUS GASES.

POLYMERIZATION: HAZARDOUS POLYMERIZATION HAS NOT BEEN REPORTED TO OCCUR UNDER NORMAL TEMPERATURES AND PRESSURES.

CONDITIONS TO AVOID

NONE REPORTED.

SPILL AND LEAK PROCEDURES

OCCUPATIONAL SPILL: SWEEP UP AND PLACE IN SUITABLE CLEAN, DRY CONTAINERS FOR RECLAMATION OR LATER DISPOSAL. DO NOT FLUSH SPILLED MATERIAL INTO SEWER. KEEP UNNECESSARY PEOPLE AWAY.

PROTECTIVE EQUIPMENT

VENTILATION: PROVIDE LOCAL EXHAUST OR PROCESS ENCLOSURE VENTILATION SYSTEM.

RESPIRATOR: THE FOLLOWING RESPIRATORS ARE RECOMMENDED BASED ON INFORMATION FOUND IN THE PHYSICAL DATA, TOXICITY AND HEALTH EFFECTS SECTIONS. THEY ARE RANKED IN ORDER FROM MINIMUM TO MAXIMUM RESPIRATORY PROTECTION. THE SPECIFIC RESPIRATOR SELECTED MUST BE BASED ON CONTAMINATION LEVELS FOUND IN THE WORK PLACE, MUST NOT EXCEED THE WORKING LIMITS OF THE RESPIRATOR AND BE JOINTLY APPROVED BY THE NATIONAL INSTITUTE FOR OCCUPATIONAL SAFETY AND HEALTH AND THE MINE SAFETY AND HEALTH ADMINISTRATION (NIOSH-MSHA).

DUST AND MIST RESPIRATOR WITH A FULL FACEPIECE.

AIR-PURIFYING FULL FACEPIECE RESPIRATOR WITH A HIGH-EFFICIENCY PARTICULATE FILTER.

POWERED AIR-PURIFYING RESPIRATOR WITH A TIGHT-FITTING FACEPIECE AND HIGH-EFFICIENCY PARTICULATE FILTER.

TYPE 'C' SUPPLIED-AIR RESPIRATOR WITH A FULL FACEPIECE OPERATED IN PRESSURE-DEMAND OR OTHER POSITIVE PRESSURE MODE OR WITH A FULL FACEPIECE, HELMET OR HOOD OPERATED IN CONTINUOUS-FLOW MODE.

SELF-CONTAINED BREATHING APPARATUS WITH A FULL FACEPIECE OPERATED IN PRESSURE-DEMAND OR OTHER POSITIVE PRESSURE MODE.

FOR FIREFIGHTING AND OTHER IMMEDIATELY DANGEROUS TO LIFE OR HEALTH CONDITIONS:

SELF-CONTAINED BREATHING APPARATUS WITH FULL FACEPIECE OPERATED IN PRESSURE-DEMAND OR OTHER POSITIVE PRESSURE MODE.

SUPPLIED-AIR RESPIRATOR WITH FULL FACEPIECE AND OPERATED IN PRESSURE-DEMAND OR OTHER POSITIVE PRESSURE MODE IN COMBINATION WITH AN AUXILIARY SELF-CONTAINED BREATHING APPARATUS OPERATED IN PRESSURE-DEMAND OR OTHER POSITIVE PRESSURE MODE.

CLOTHING: EMPLOYEE MUST WEAR APPROPRIATE PROTECTIVE (IMPERVIOUS) CLOTHING AND EQUIPMENT TO PREVENT REPEATED OR PROLONGED SKIN CONTACT WITH THIS SUBSTANCE.

GLOVES: EMPLOYEE MUST WEAR APPROPRIATE PROTECTIVE GLOVES TO PREVENT CONTACT WITH THIS SUBSTANCE.

EYE PROTECTION: EMPLOYEE MUST WEAR SPLASH-PROOF OR DUST-RESISTANT SAFETY GOGGLES AND A FACESHIELD TO PREVENT CONTACT WITH THIS SUBSTANCE.

EMERGENCY WASH FACILITIES: WHERE THERE IS ANY POSSIBILITY THAT AN EMPLOYEE'S EYES AND/OR SKIN MAY BE EXPOSED TO THIS SUBSTANCE, THE EMPLOYER SHOULD PROVIDE AN EYE WASH FOUNTAIN AND QUICK DRENCH SHOWER WITHIN THE IMMEDIATE WORK AREA FOR EMERGENCY USE.

AUTHORIZED BY- OCCUPATIONAL HEALTH SERVICES, INC.
CREATION DATE: 02/08/90 ***REVISION DATE:*** 05/31/90

MATERIAL SAFETY DATA SHEET

OCCUPATIONAL HEALTH SERVICES, INC.
AGRICULTURE AND PESTICIDE DIVISION
450 SEVENTH AVENUE, SUITE 2407
NEW YORK, NEW YORK 10123
1-800-445-MSDS OR (212) 967-1100

EMERGENCY CONTACT:
JOHN S. BRANSFORD, JR. (615) 292-1180

SUBSTANCE IDENTIFICATION

CAS-NUMBER 64902-72-3

SUBSTANCE: **CHLORSULFURON**

TRADE NAMES/SYNONYMS: BENZENESULFONAMIDE, 2-CHLORO-N-(((4-METHOXY-6-METHYL-1,3,5- TRIAZIN-2-YL)AMINO)CARBONYL)-; 2-CHLORO-N-(((4-METHOXY-6-METHYL-1,3,5-TRIAZIN-2-YL)AMINO)CARBONYL) BENZENESULFONAMIDE; 1-(2-CHLOROPHENYLSULPHONYL)-3-(4-METHOXY-6-METHYL-1,3,5-TRIAZIN-2-YL)- UREA; 1-(2-CHLOROPHENYLSULFONYL)-3-(4-METHOXY-6-METHYL-1,3,5-TRIAZIN-2-YL)-UREA; DPX 4189; GLEAN; TELAR; C12H12CLN5O4S; PST72504

CHEMICAL FAMILY: SUBSTITUTED UREA
HALOGEN COMPOUND, AROMATIC

MOLECULAR FORMULA: C12-H12-CL-N5-O4-S

MOLECULAR WEIGHT: 357.78

CERCLA RATINGS (SCALE 0-3): HEALTH=2 FIRE=1 REACTIVITY=0 PERSISTENCE=0

NFPA RATINGS (SCALE 0-4): HEALTH=2 FIRE=1 REACTIVITY=0

COMPONENTS AND CONTAMINANTS

COMPONENT: CHLORSULFURON ***PERCENT:*** 100.0
CAS# 64902-72-3

OTHER CONTAMINANTS: NONE

EXPOSURE LIMITS: NO OCCUPATIONAL EXPOSURE LIMITS ESTABLISHED BY OSHA, ACGIH, OR NIOSH.

PHYSICAL DATA

DESCRIPTION: ODORLESS WHITE OR COLORLESS CRYSTALLINE SOLID.

MELTING POINT: 345-352 F (174-178 C) ***SPECIFIC GRAVITY:*** 1.52

VAPOR PRESSURE: NEGLIGIBLE ***PH:*** 4.1 (SAT SOLN)

SOLUBILITY IN WATER: 0.279% @ 22 C

SOLVENT SOLUBILITY: SOLUBLE IN METHYLENE CHLORIDE, ACETONE, METHANOL; SLIGHTLY SOLUBLE IN TOLUENE, ACETONITRILE; ALMOST INSOLUBLE IN HEXANE. DECOMPOSES ABOVE 378 F (192 C)

FIRE AND EXPLOSION DATA

FIRE AND EXPLOSION HAZARD: SLIGHT FIRE HAZARD WHEN EXPOSED TO HEAT OR FLAME.

FIREFIGHTING MEDIA: DRY CHEMICAL, CARBON DIOXIDE, HALON, WATER SPRAY OR STANDARD FOAM (1987 EMERGENCY RESPONSE GUIDEBOOK, DOT P 5800.4).

FOR LARGER FIRES, USE WATER SPRAY, FOG OR STANDARD FOAM (1987 EMERGENCY RESPONSE GUIDEBOOK, DOT P 5800.4).

FIREFIGHTING: MOVE CONTAINERS FROM FIRE AREA IF POSSIBLE. FIGHT FIRE FROM MAXIMUM DISTANCE. STAY AWAY FROM STORAGE TANK ENDS. DIKE FIRE CONTROL WATER FOR LATER DISPOSAL. DO NOT SCATTER MATERIAL (1987 EMERGENCY RESPONSE GUIDEBOOK, DOT P 5800.4, GUIDE PAGE 55). EXTINGUISH USING AGENT SUITABLE FOR TYPE OF SURROUNDING FIRE. USE WATER IN FLOODING QUANTITIES AS FOG. KEEP SPARKS, FLAMES AND OTHER SOURCES OF IGNITION AWAY. KEEP MATERIAL OUT OF WATER SOURCES AND SEWERS. DO NOT TOUCH MATERIAL AND AVOID BREATHING DUSTS AND FUMES FROM BURNING MATERIAL. KEEP UPWIND.

TOXICITY

CHLORSULFURON: TOXICITY DATA: 3400 MG/KG SKIN-RABBIT LD50; 5545 MG/KG ORAL-RAT LD50. CARCINOGEN STATUS: NONE. ACUTE TOXICITY LEVEL: SLIGHTLY TOXIC BY DERMAL ABSORPTION AND INGESTION. TARGET EFFECTS: NO DATA AVAILABLE.

HEALTH EFFECTS AND FIRST AID

INHALATION: CHLORSULFURON: **ACUTE EXPOSURE-** A LETHAL CONCENTRATION IN RATS WAS GREATER THAN 5900 MG/M3/4 HOURS. MANY SUBSTITUTED UREA HERBICIDES ARE MODERATELY IRRITATING TO THE MUCOUS MEMBRANES. **CHRONIC EXPOSURE-** NO DATA AVAILABLE.

FIRST AID- REMOVE FROM EXPOSURE AREA TO FRESH AIR IMMEDIATELY. IF BREATHING HAS STOPPED, PERFORM ARTIFICIAL RESPIRATION. KEEP PERSON WARM AND AT REST. TREAT SYMPTOMATICALLY AND SUPPORTIVELY. GET MEDICAL ATTENTION IMMEDIATELY.

SKIN CONTACT: CHLORSULFURON **ACUTE EXPOSURE-** THIS MATERIAL WAS SLIGHTLY IRRITATING TO RABBIT SKIN. **CHRONIC EXPOSURE-** NO DATA AVAILABLE.

FIRST AID- REMOVE CONTAMINATED CLOTHING AND SHOES IMMEDIATELY. WASH AFFECTED AREA WITH SOAP OR MILD DETERGENT AND LARGE AMOUNTS OF WATER UNTIL NO EVIDENCE OF CHEMICAL REMAINS (APPROXIMATELY 15-20 MINUTES). GET MEDICAL ATTENTION IMMEDIATELY.

EYE CONTACT: CHLORSULFURON: **ACUTE EXPOSURE-** THIS MATERIAL PRODUCED MILD CONJUNCTIVITIS AND SLIGHT CORNEAL CLOUDINESS IN RABBIT EYES; ALL EYES WERE NORMAL WITHIN 4 DAYS. **CHRONIC EXPOSURE-** NO DATA AVAILABLE.

FIRST AID- WASH EYES IMMEDIATELY WITH LARGE AMOUNTS OF WATER OR NORMAL SALINE, OCCASIONALLY LIFTING UPPER AND LOWER LIDS, UNTIL NO EVIDENCE OF CHEMICAL REMAINS (APPROXIMATELY 15-20 MINUTES). GET MEDICAL ATTENTION IMMEDIATELY.

INGESTION: CHLORSULFURON: **ACUTE EXPOSURE-** A LETHAL DOSE IN RATS WAS 5545 MG/KG. CLINICAL SIGNS OF POISONING INCLUDED WEIGHT LOSS, HUMPED POSTURE, LETHARGY, SALIVATION, DIARRHEA, AND HEMATURIA. GROSS PATHOLOGICAL CHANGES WERE NOTED IN LIVER, SPLEEN, KIDNEY, GASTROINTESTINAL TRACT, THYMUS, LUNGS, BRAIN, HEART, EYE, PANCREAS, TESTIS, SKIN, UTERUS, AND STOMACH. **CHRONIC EXPOSURE-** CLINICAL SIGNS OF DECREASED URINE PH, PLASMA CREATININE, MONOCYTE COUNTS, ERYTHROCYTE COUNTS AND INCREASED HEMATOCRITS WERE REPORTED IN A 90-DAY STUDY OF RATS FED AT A DIETARY LEVEL OF 500 OR 2500 PPM. EFFECTS OF DECREASED ERYTHROCYTE COUNTS AND INCREASED MEAN CORPUSCULAR VOLUMES AND MEAN CORPUSCULAR HEMOGLOBINS WERE OBSERVED IN MALE MICE FED AT A DIETARY LEVEL OF 5000 OR 7500 PPM; IN FEMALE MICE, DECREASED NEUTROPHILIC GRANULOCYTES AND INCREASED LYMPHOCYTES WERE NOTED AT THIS LEVEL. FETOTOXICITY WAS OBSERVED IN A STUDY OF PREGNANT RATS REPEATEDLY FED 75 MG/KG/DAY.

FIRST AID- TREAT SYMPTOMATICALLY AND SUPPORTIVELY. GET MEDICAL ATTENTION IMMEDIATELY. IF VOMITING OCCURS, KEEP HEAD LOWER THAN HIPS TO PREVENT ASPIRATION.

ANTIDOTE: NO SPECIFIC ANTIDOTE. TREAT SYMPTOMATICALLY AND SUPPORTIVELY.

REACTIVITY

REACTIVITY: STABLE UNDER NORMAL TEMPERATURES AND PRESSURES.

INCOMPATIBILITIES: CHLORSULFURON: ACIDIC CONDITIONS: MAY SLOWLY HYDROLYZE. OXIDIZERS (STRONG): FIRE AND EXPLOSION HAZARD.

DECOMPOSITION: THERMAL DECOMPOSITION PRODUCTS MAY INCLUDE TOXIC OXIDES OF NITROGEN, SULFUR, AND CARBON, AND TOXIC AND CORROSIVE FUMES OF CHLORIDES.

POLYMERIZATION: HAZARDOUS POLYMERIZATION HAS NOT BEEN REPORTED TO OCCUR UNDER NORMAL TEMPERATURES AND PRESSURES.

STORAGE AND DISPOSAL

OBSERVE ALL FEDERAL, STATE AND LOCAL REGULATIONS WHEN STORING OR DISPOSING OF THIS SUBSTANCE. FOR ASSISTANCE, CONTACT THE DISTRICT DIRECTOR OF THE ENVIRONMENTAL PROTECTION AGENCY.

****STORAGE****

STORE IN ACCORDANCE WITH 40 CFR 165 RECOMMENDED PROCEDURES FOR THE DISPOSAL AND STORAGE OF PESTICIDES AND PESTICIDE CONTAINERS. STORE AWAY FROM INCOMPATIBLE SUBSTANCES.

****DISPOSAL****

DISPOSAL MUST BE IN ACCORDANCE WITH 40 CFR 165 RECOMMENDED PROCEDURES FOR THE DISPOSAL AND STORAGE OF PESTICIDES AND PESTICIDE CONTAINERS.

CONDITIONS TO AVOID

MAY BURN BUT DOES NOT IGNITE READILY. CONTAINERS MAY EXPLODE IN HEAT OF FIRE.

SPILL AND LEAK PROCEDURES

OCCUPATIONAL SPILL: DO NOT TOUCH SPILLED MATERIAL. STOP LEAK IF YOU CAN DO IT WITHOUT RISK. USE WATER SPRAY TO REDUCE VAPORS. FOR SMALL SPILLS, TAKE UP WITH SAND OR OTHER ABSORBENT MATERIAL AND PLACE INTO CONTAINERS FOR LATER DISPOSAL. FOR SMALL DRY SPILLS, WITH A CLEAN SHOVEL PLACE MATERIAL INTO CLEAN, DRY CONTAINERS AND COVER. MOVE CONTAINERS FROM SPILL AREA. FOR LARGER SPILLS, DIKE FAR AHEAD OF SPILL FOR LATER DISPOSAL. KEEP UNNECESSARY PEOPLE AWAY. ISOLATE HAZARD AREA AND DENY ENTRY. VENTILATE CLOSED SPACES BEFORE ENTERING.

PROTECTIVE EQUIPMENT

VENTILATION: PROVIDE LOCAL EXHAUST OR GENERAL DILUTION VENTILATION SYSTEM.

RESPIRATOR: THE FOLLOWING RESPIRATORS ARE RECOMMENDED BASED ON INFORMATION FOUND IN THE PHYSICAL DATA, TOXICITY AND HEALTH EFFECTS SECTIONS. THEY ARE RANKED IN ORDER FROM MINIMUM TO MAXIMUM RESPIRATORY PROTECTION. THE SPECIFIC RESPIRATOR SELECTED MUST BE BASED ON CONTAMINATION LEVELS FOUND IN THE WORK PLACE, MUST NOT EXCEED THE WORKING LIMITS OF THE RESPIRATOR AND BE JOINTLY APPROVED BY THE NATIONAL INSTITUTE FOR OCCUPATIONAL SAFETY AND HEALTH AND THE MINE SAFETY AND HEALTH ADMINISTRATION (NIOSH-MSHA).

CHEMICAL CARTRIDGE RESPIRATOR WITH AN ORGANIC VAPOR CARTRIDGE(S) IN COMBINATION WITH A DUST AND MIST FILTER. GAS MASK WITH ORGANIC VAPOR CANISTER (CHIN-STYLE OR FRONT- OR BACK-MOUNTED CANISTER) WITH A DUST AND MIST FILTER.

GAS MASK WITH ORGANIC VAPOR CANISTER (CHIN-STYLE OR FRONT- OR BACK-MOUNTED CANISTER) WITH A PARTICULATE FILTER.

POWERED AIR-PURIFYING RESPIRATOR WITH A HIGH-EFFICIENCY FILTER.

TYPE 'C' SUPPLIED-AIR RESPIRATOR WITH A FULL FACEPIECE OPERATED IN A PRESSURE-DEMAND OR OTHER POSITIVE PRESSURE MODE.

SELF-CONTAINED BREATHING APPARATUS WITH A FULL FACEPIECE OPERATED IN PRESSURE-DEMAND OR OTHER POSITIVE PRESSURE MODE.

FOR FIREFIGHTING AND OTHER IMMEDIATELY DANGEROUS TO LIFE OR HEALTH CONDITIONS:

SELF-CONTAINED BREATHING APPARATUS WITH FULL FACEPIECE OPERATED IN PRESSURE-DEMAND OR OTHER POSITIVE PRESSURE MODE.

SUPPLIED-AIR RESPIRATOR WITH FULL FACEPIECE AND OPERATED IN PRESSURE-DEMAND OR OTHER POSITIVE PRESSURE MODE IN COMBINATION WITH AN AUXILIARY SELF-CONTAINED BREATHING APPARATUS OPERATED IN PRESSURE-DEMAND OR OTHER POSITIVE PRESSURE MODE.

CLOTHING: EMPLOYEE MUST WEAR APPROPRIATE PROTECTIVE (IMPERVIOUS) CLOTHING AND EQUIPMENT TO PREVENT REPEATED OR PROLONGED SKIN CONTACT WITH THIS SUBSTANCE.

GLOVES: EMPLOYEE MUST WEAR APPROPRIATE PROTECTIVE GLOVES TO PREVENT CONTACT WITH THIS SUBSTANCE.

EYE PROTECTION: EMPLOYEE MUST WEAR SPLASH-PROOF OR DUST-RESISTANT SAFETY GOGGLES TO PREVENT EYE CONTACT WITH THIS SUBSTANCE. EMERGENCY EYE WASH: WHERE THERE IS ANY POSSIBILITY THAT AN EMPLOYEE'S EYES MAY BE EXPOSED TO THIS SUBSTANCE, THE EMPLOYER SHOULD PROVIDE AN EYE WASH FOUNTAIN WITHIN THE IMMEDIATE WORK AREA FOR EMERGENCY USE.

AUTHORIZED BY- OCCUPATIONAL HEALTH SERVICES, INC.
CREATION DATE: 10/04/89 ***REVISION DATE:*** 05/15/90

MATERIAL SAFETY DATA SHEET

OCCUPATIONAL HEALTH SERVICES, INC.
AGRICULTURE AND PESTICIDE DIVISION

EMERGENCY CONTACT:
JOHN S. BRANSFORD, JR. (615) 292-1180

450 SEVENTH AVENUE, SUITE 2407
NEW YORK, NEW YORK 10123
1-800-445-MSDS OR (212) 967-1100

SUBSTANCE IDENTIFICATION

CAS-NUMBER 53939-28-9
SUBSTANCE: **(Z)-11-HEXADECENAL**
TRADE NAMES/SYNONYMS: 11-HEXADECENAL, (Z)-; CIS-11-HEXADECENAL; (Z)-11-HEXADECENYL ALDEHYDE; C16H30O; PST72519
CHEMICAL FAMILY: ALDEHYDE, ALIPHATIC
MOLECULAR FORMULA: C-H3-(C-H2)3-C-H-C-H-(C-H2)9-C-H-O
MOLECULAR WEIGHT: 238.42
CERCLA RATINGS (SCALE 0-3): HEALTH=U FIRE=2 REACTIVITY=0 PERSISTENCE=2
NFPA RATINGS (SCALE 0-4): HEALTH=U FIRE=2 REACTIVITY=0

COMPONENTS AND CONTAMINANTS

COMPONENT: (Z)-11-HEXADECENAL ***PERCENT:*** 100.0
CAS# 53939-28-9
OTHER CONTAMINANTS: NONE
EXPOSURE LIMITS: NO OCCUPATIONAL EXPOSURE LIMITS ESTABLISHED BY OSHA, ACGIH, OR NIOSH.

PHYSICAL DATA

DESCRIPTION: COLORLESS LIQUID. ***BOILING POINT:*** NOT AVAILABLE
SPECIFIC GRAVITY: NOT AVAILABLE ***EVAPORATION RATE:*** NOT AVAILABLE
SOLUBILITY IN WATER: NOT AVAILABLE

FIRE AND EXPLOSION DATA

FIRE AND EXPLOSION HAZARD: MODERATE FIRE HAZARD WHEN EXPOSED TO HEAT OR FLAME.
FLASH POINT: 142 F (61 C) (CC) ***FLAMMABILITY CLASS(OSHA):*** IIIA
FIREFIGHTING MEDIA: DRY CHEMICAL, CARBON DIOXIDE, HALON, WATER SPRAY OR ALCOHOL FOAM (1987 EMERGENCY RESPONSE GUIDEBOOK, DOT P 5800.4). FOR LARGER FIRES, USE WATER SPRAY, FOG OR ALCOHOL FOAM (1987 EMERGENCY RESPONSE GUIDEBOOK, DOT P 5800.4).
FIREFIGHTING: MOVE CONTAINER FROM FIRE AREA IF POSSIBLE. COOL FIRE-EXPOSED CONTAINERS WITH WATER FROM SIDE UNTIL WELL AFTER FIRE IS OUT. STAY AWAY FROM STORAGE TANK ENDS. FOR MASSIVE FIRE IN STORAGE AREA, USE UNMANNED HOSE HOLDER OR MONITOR NOZZLES, ELSE WITHDRAW FROM AREA AND LET FIRE BURN. WITHDRAW IMMEDIATELY IN CASE OF RISING SOUND FROM VENTING SAFETY DEVICE OR ANY DISCOLORATION OF STORAGE TANK DUE TO FIRE (1987 EMERGENCY RESPONSE GUIDEBOOK, DOT P 5800.4, GUIDE PAGE 26). EXTINGUISH ONLY IF FLOW CAN BE STOPPED. USE WATER IN FLOODING QUANTITIES AS A FOG; SOLID STREAMS MAY NOT BE EFFECTIVE. COOL CONTAINERS WITH FLOODING QUANTITIES OF WATER, APPLIED FROM AS FAR A DISTANCE AS POSSIBLE. AVOID BREATHING TOXIC VAPORS; KEEP UPWIND.

TOXICITY

(Z)-11-HEXADECENAL: CARCINOGEN STATUS: NONE. ACUTE TOXICITY DATA: NO DATA AVAILABLE. TARGET EFFECTS: NO DATA AVAILABLE.

HEALTH EFFECTS AND FIRST AID

INHALATION: (Z)-11-HEXADECENAL: **ACUTE EXPOSURE-** INHALATION OF ALDEHYDES MAY CAUSE IRRITATION. **CHRONIC EXPOSURE-** NO DATA AVAILABLE.
FIRST AID- REMOVE FROM EXPOSURE AREA TO FRESH AIR IMMEDIATELY. IF BREATHING HAS STOPPED, PERFORM ARTIFICIAL RESPIRATION. KEEP PERSON WARM AND AT REST. TREAT SYMPTOMATICALLY AND SUPPORTIVELY. GET MEDICAL ATTENTION IMMEDIATELY.

SKIN CONTACT: (Z)-11-HEXADECENAL: **ACUTE EXPOSURE-** CONTACT WITH ALDEHYDES MAY CAUSE IRRITATION. **CHRONIC EXPOSURE-** REPEATED OR PROLONGED CONTACT WITH IRRITANTS MAY CAUSE DERMATITIS.
FIRST AID- REMOVE CONTAMINATED CLOTHING AND SHOES IMMEDIATELY. WASH AFFECTED AREA WITH SOAP OR MILD DETERGENT AND LARGE AMOUNTS OF WATER UNTIL NO EVIDENCE OF CHEMICAL REMAINS (APPROXIMATELY 15-20 MINUTES). GET MEDICAL ATTENTION IMMEDIATELY.

EYE CONTACT: (Z)-11-HEXADECENAL: **ACUTE EXPOSURE-** CONTACT WITH ALDEHYDES MAY CAUSE IRRITATION. **CHRONIC EXPOSURE-** NO DATA AVAILABLE.
FIRST AID- WASH EYES IMMEDIATELY WITH LARGE AMOUNTS OF WATER OR NORMAL SALINE, OCCASIONALLY LIFTING UPPER AND LOWER LIDS, UNTIL NO EVIDENCE OF CHEMICAL REMAINS (APPROXIMATELY 15-20 MINUTES). GET MEDICAL ATTENTION IMMEDIATELY.

INGESTION: (Z)-11-HEXADECENAL: **ACUTE EXPOSURE-** NO DATA AVAILABLE. **CHRONIC EXPOSURE-** NO DATA AVAILABLE.
FIRST AID- TREAT SYMPTOMATICALLY AND SUPPORTIVELY. GET MEDICAL ATTENTION IMMEDIATELY. IF VOMITING OCCURS, KEEP HEAD LOWER THAN HIPS TO PREVENT ASPIRATION.
ANTIDOTE: NO SPECIFIC ANTIDOTE. TREAT SYMPTOMATICALLY AND SUPPORTIVELY.

REACTIVITY

REACTIVITY: STABLE UNDER NORMAL TEMPERATURES AND PRESSURES.
INCOMPATIBILITIES: (Z)-11-HEXADECENAL: OXIDIZERS (STRONG): FIRE AND EXPLOSION HAZARD.
DECOMPOSITION: THERMAL DECOMPOSITION PRODUCTS MAY INCLUDE TOXIC OXIDES OF CARBON.
POLYMERIZATION: HAZARDOUS POLYMERIZATION HAS NOT BEEN REPORTED TO OCCUR UNDER NORMAL TEMPERATURES AND PRESSURES.

STORAGE AND DISPOSAL

OBSERVE ALL FEDERAL, STATE AND LOCAL REGULATIONS WHEN STORING OR DISPOSING OF THIS SUBSTANCE. FOR ASSISTANCE, CONTACT THE DISTRICT DIRECTOR OF THE ENVIRONMENTAL PROTECTION AGENCY.

****STORAGE****

STORE AWAY FROM INCOMPATIBLE SUBSTANCES.
STORE IN ACCORDANCE WITH 29 CFR 1910.106.

CONDITIONS TO AVOID

AVOID CONTACT WITH HEAT, SPARKS, FLAMES, OR OTHER SOURCES OF IGNITION. VAPORS MAY BE EXPLOSIVE AND POISONOUS; DO NOT ALLOW UNNECESSARY PERSONNEL IN AREA. DO NOT OVERHEAT CONTAINERS; CONTAINERS MAY VIOLENTLY RUPTURE AND TRAVEL A CONSIDERABLE DISTANCE IN HEAT OF FIRE.

SPILL AND LEAK PROCEDURES

OCCUPATIONAL SPILL: SHUT OFF IGNITION SOURCES. STOP LEAK IF YOU CAN DO IT WITHOUT RISK. USE WATER SPRAY TO REDUCE VAPORS. FOR SMALL SPILLS, TAKE UP WITH SAND OR OTHER ABSORBENT MATERIAL AND PLACE INTO CONTAINERS FOR LATER DISPOSAL. FOR LARGER SPILLS, DIKE FAR AHEAD OF SPILL FOR LATER DISPOSAL. NO SMOKING, FLAMES OR FLARES IN HAZARD AREA. KEEP UNNECESSARY PEOPLE AWAY; ISOLATE HAZARD AREA AND DENY ENTRY.

PROTECTIVE EQUIPMENT

VENTILATION: PROVIDE LOCAL EXHAUST OR PROCESS ENCLOSURE VENTILATION SYSTEM.
RESPIRATOR: THE FOLLOWING RESPIRATORS ARE RECOMMENDED BASED ON INFORMATION FOUND IN THE PHYSICAL DATA, TOXICITY AND HEALTH EFFECTS SECTIONS. THEY ARE RANKED IN ORDER FROM MINIMUM TO MAXIMUM RESPIRATORY PROTECTION. THE SPECIFIC RESPIRATOR SELECTED MUST BE BASED ON CONTAMINATION LEVELS FOUND IN THE WORK PLACE, MUST NOT EXCEED THE WORKING LIMITS OF THE RESPIRATOR AND BE JOINTLY APPROVED BY THE NATIONAL INSTITUTE FOR OCCUPATIONAL SAFETY AND HEALTH AND THE MINE SAFETY AND HEALTH ADMINISTRATION (NIOSH-MSHA).
DUST AND MIST RESPIRATOR WITH A FULL FACEPIECE.
AIR-PURIFYING FULL FACEPIECE RESPIRATOR WITH A HIGH-EFFICIENCY PARTICULATE FILTER.
POWERED AIR-PURIFYING RESPIRATOR WITH A TIGHT-FITTING FACEPIECE AND HIGH-EFFICIENCY PARTICULATE FILTER.
TYPE 'C' SUPPLIED-AIR RESPIRATOR WITH A FULL FACEPIECE OPERATED IN PRESSURE-DEMAND OR OTHER POSITIVE PRESSURE MODE OR WITH A FULL FACEPIECE, HELMET OR HOOD OPERATED IN CONTINUOUS-FLOW MODE.
SELF-CONTAINED BREATHING APPARATUS WITH A FULL FACEPIECE OPERATED IN PRESSURE-DEMAND OR OTHER POSITIVE PRESSURE MODE.
FOR FIREFIGHTING AND OTHER IMMEDIATELY DANGEROUS TO LIFE OR HEALTH CONDITIONS:
SELF-CONTAINED BREATHING APPARATUS WITH FULL FACEPIECE OPERATED IN PRESSURE-DEMAND OR OTHER POSITIVE PRESSURE MODE.
SUPPLIED-AIR RESPIRATOR WITH FULL FACEPIECE AND OPERATED IN PRESSURE-DEMAND OR OTHER POSITIVE PRESSURE MODE IN COMBINATION WITH AN AUXILIARY SELF-CONTAINED BREATHING APPARATUS OPERATED IN PRESSURE-DEMAND OR OTHER POSITIVE PRESSURE MODE.
CLOTHING: EMPLOYEE MUST WEAR APPROPRIATE PROTECTIVE (IMPERVIOUS) CLOTHING AND EQUIPMENT TO PREVENT REPEATED OR PROLONGED SKIN CONTACT WITH THIS SUBSTANCE.
GLOVES: EMPLOYEE MUST WEAR APPROPRIATE PROTECTIVE GLOVES TO PREVENT CONTACT WITH THIS SUBSTANCE.
EYE PROTECTION: EMPLOYEE MUST WEAR SPLASH-PROOF OR DUST-RESISTANT SAFETY GOGGLES TO PREVENT EYE CONTACT WITH THIS SUBSTANCE.
EMERGENCY EYE WASH: WHERE THERE IS ANY POSSIBILITY THAT AN EMPLOYEE'S EYES MAY BE EXPOSED TO THIS SUBSTANCE, THE EMPLOYER SHOULD PROVIDE AN EYE WASH FOUNTAIN WITHIN THE IMMEDIATE WORK AREA FOR EMERGENCY USE.

AUTHORIZED BY- OCCUPATIONAL HEALTH SERVICES, INC.
CREATION DATE: 02/08/90 *REVISION DATE:* 05/25/90

MATERIAL SAFETY DATA SHEET

OCCUPATIONAL HEALTH SERVICES, INC.
AGRICULTURE AND PESTICIDE DIVISION
450 SEVENTH AVENUE, SUITE 2407
NEW YORK, NEW YORK 10123
1-800-445-MSDS OR (212) 967-1100

EMERGENCY CONTACT:
JOHN S. BRANSFORD, JR. (615) 292-1180

SUBSTANCE IDENTIFICATION

CAS-NUMBER 443-48-1
SUBSTANCE: **METRONIDAZOLE**
TRADE NAMES/SYNONYMS: 1H-IMIDAZOLE-1-ETHANOL, 2-METHYL-5-NITRO-; IMIDAZOLE-1-ETHANOL, 2-METHYL-5-NITRO-; 2-METHYL-5-NITRO-1H-IMIDAZOLE-1-ETHANOL; 2-METHYL-5-NITROIMIDAZOLE-1-ETHANOL; 1-(2-HYDROXYETHYL)-2-METHYL-5-NITROIMIDAZOLE; 1-(BETA-ETHYLOL)-2-METHYL-5-NITRO-3-AZAPYRROLE; 1-HYDROXYETHYL-2-METHYL-5-NITROIMIDAZOLE; 1-(BETA-HYDROXYETHYL)-2-METHYL-5-NITROIMIDAZOLE; 2-METHYL-5-NITRO-1-IMIDAZOLE-ETHANOL; METHYL-NITROIMIDAZOLE-1-ETHANOL; IMIDAZOLE, 1-(2-HYDROXYETHYL)-2-METHYL-5-NITRO; BAYER 5360; CLONT; FLAGYL; KLION; ORVAGIL; RP 8823; TRIVAZOL; VAGIMID; C6H9N3O3; PST72529
CHEMICAL FAMILY: IMIDAZOLE
NITRO
HYDROXYL, ALIPHATIC
MOLECULAR FORMULA: C6-H9-N3-O3
MOLECULAR WEIGHT: 171.16
CERCLA RATINGS (SCALE 0-3): HEALTH=3 FIRE=1 REACTIVITY=0 PERSISTENCE=2
NFPA RATINGS (SCALE 0-4): HEALTH=U FIRE=1 REACTIVITY=0

COMPONENTS AND CONTAMINANTS

COMPONENT: METRONIDAZOLE ***PERCENT:*** 100.0
CAS# 443-48-1
OTHER CONTAMINANTS: NONE
EXPOSURE LIMITS: NO OCCUPATIONAL EXPOSURE LIMITS ESTABLISHED BY OSHA, ACGIH, OR NIOSH.
METRONIDAZOLE: SUBJECT TO CALIFORNIA PROPOSITION 65 CANCER AND/OR REPRODUCTIVE TOXICITY WARNING AND RELEASE REQUIREMENTS (JANUARY 1, 1988)

PHYSICAL DATA

DESCRIPTION: WHITE TO PALE YELLOW CRYSTALLINE SOLID WITH A SLIGHT ODOR AND A BITTER, SLIGHTLY SALINE TASTE; DARKENS ON EXPOSURE TO LIGHT.
MELTING POINT: 320-322 F (160-161 C) ***SPECIFIC GRAVITY:*** NOT AVAILABLE
PH: 5.8 (SATD SOLN) ***SOLUBILITY IN WATER:*** 1.0%
SOLVENT SOLUBILITY: SOLUBLE IN DILUTE ACIDS; SLIGHTLY SOLUBLE IN ETHANOL; VERY SLIGHTLY SOLUBLE IN ETHER, CHLOROFORM, AND DIMETHYLFORMAMIDE.

FIRE AND EXPLOSION DATA

FIRE AND EXPLOSION HAZARD: SLIGHT FIRE HAZARD WHEN EXPOSED TO HEAT OR FLAME.
FIREFIGHTING MEDIA: DRY CHEMICAL, CARBON DIOXIDE, HALON, WATER SPRAY OR STANDARD FOAM (1987 EMERGENCY RESPONSE GUIDEBOOK, DOT P 5800.4).
FOR LARGER FIRES, USE WATER SPRAY, FOG OR STANDARD FOAM (1987 EMERGENCY RESPONSE GUIDEBOOK, DOT P 5800.4).
FIREFIGHTING: MOVE CONTAINER FROM FIRE AREA IF POSSIBLE. DO NOT SCATTER SPILLED MATERIAL WITH HIGH PRESSURE WATER STREAMS. DIKE FIRE CONTROL WATER FOR LATER DISPOSAL (1987 EMERGENCY RESPONSE GUIDEBOOK, DOT P 5800.4, GUIDE PAGE 31).
USE AGENTS SUITABLE FOR TYPE OF SURROUNDING FIRE. AVOID BREATHING HAZARDOUS VAPORS, KEEP UPWIND.

TOXICITY

METRONIDAZOLE: TOXICITY DATA: 3570 UG/KG/DAY ORAL-MAN TDLO; 1030 MG/KG/8 WEEKS ORAL-MAN TDLO; 40 MG/KG ORAL-WOMAN TDLO; 12 MG/KG-ORAL WOMAN TDLO; 3 GM/KG ORAL-RAT LD50; 3800 MG/KG ORAL-MOUSE LD50; 3640 MG/KG SUBCUTANEOUS-MOUSE LD50; 30 MG/KG/INTERMITTENT INTRAVENOUS-WOMAN TDLO; 2980 MG/KG INTRAPERITONEAL-MOUSE LD50; MUTAGENIC DATA (RTECS); REPRODUCTIVE EFFECTS DATA (RTECS); TUMORIGENIC DATA (RTECS). CARCINOGEN STATUS: ANTICIPATED HUMAN CARCINOGEN (NTP); HUMAN INADEQUATE EVIDENCE, ANIMAL SUFFICIENT EVIDENCE (IARC GROUP-2B). BY ORAL ADMINISTRATION, METRONIDAZOLE SIGNIFICANTLY INCREASED THE INCIDENCES OF LUNG TUMORS IN MICE OF EACH SEX, OF LYMPHOMAS IN FEMALE MICE, AND OF MAMMARY, PITUITARY, TESTICULAR AND LIVER TUMORS IN RATS. ACUTE TOXICITY LEVEL: MODERATELY TOXIC BY INGESTION. TARGET EFFECTS: POISONING MAY AFFECT THE PERIPHERAL AND CENTRAL NERVOUS SYSTEMS. AT INCREASED RISK FROM EXPOSURE: PERSONS WITH BLOOD DYSCRASIA AND HEPATIC AND CENTRAL NERVOUS SYSTEM DISEASES. ADDITIONAL DATA: MAY CROSS THE PLACENTA AND BE EXCRETED IN BREAST MILK. INTERACTIONS WITH ALCOHOL AND MEDICATIONS HAVE BEEN REPORTED.

HEALTH EFFECTS AND FIRST AID

INHALATION: METRONIDAZOLE: **ACUTE EXPOSURE-** NO DATA AVAILABLE. **CHRONIC EXPOSURE-** NO DATA AVAILABLE.
FIRST AID- REMOVE FROM EXPOSURE AREA TO FRESH AIR IMMEDIATELY. IF BREATHING HAS STOPPED, PERFORM ARTIFICIAL RESPIRATION. KEEP PERSON WARM AND AT REST. TREAT SYMPTOMATICALLY AND SUPPORTIVELY. GET MEDICAL ATTENTION IMMEDIATELY.

SKIN CONTACT: METRONIDAZOLE: **ACUTE EXPOSURE-** MAY CAUSE MILD DRYNESS, TRANSIENT REDNESS, BURNING AND IRRITATION. **CHRONIC EXPOSURE-** NO DATA AVAILABLE.
FIRST AID- REMOVE CONTAMINATED CLOTHING AND SHOES IMMEDIATELY. WASH AFFECTED AREA WITH SOAP OR MILD DETERGENT AND LARGE AMOUNTS OF WATER UNTIL NO EVIDENCE OF CHEMICAL REMAINS (APPROXIMATELY 15-20 MINUTES). GET MEDICAL ATTENTION IMMEDIATELY.

EYE CONTACT: METRONIDAZOLE: **ACUTE EXPOSURE-** MAY CAUSE REDNESS. **CHRONIC EXPOSURE-** NO DATA AVAILABLE.
FIRST AID- WASH EYES IMMEDIATELY WITH LARGE AMOUNTS OF WATER OR NORMAL SALINE, OCCASIONALLY LIFTING UPPER AND LOWER LIDS, UNTIL NO EVIDENCE OF CHEMICAL REMAINS (APPROXIMATELY 15-20 MINUTES). GET MEDICAL ATTENTION IMMEDIATELY.

INGESTION: METRONIDAZOLE: CARCINOGEN. **ACUTE EXPOSURE-** MAY CAUSE NAUSEA, VOMITING, ATAXIA, ANOREXIA, MALAISE, AND TRANSIENT DISORIENTATION. NO DEATHS OR PROLONGED MORBIDITY WERE REPORTED FROM DOSES OF 3.6 TO 19.5 GRAMS. **CHRONIC EXPOSURE-** IN ADDITION TO THE EFFECTS LISTED ABOVE, THERAPEUTIC USE OF METRONIDAZOLE HAS PRODUCED DIARRHEA, EPIGASTRIC DISTRESS, ABDOMINAL CRAMPING, CONSTIPATION, PROCTITIS, METALLIC TASTE, FURRY TONGUE, GLOSSITIS, AND STOMATITIS. OTHER EFFECTS MAY INCLUDE DYSURIA, POLYURIA, DARK COLORED URINE, INCONTINENCE, CYSTITIS, DYSPAREUNIA, SENSE OF PELVIC PRESSURE, DECREASED LIBIDO, GYNECOMASTIA, NUMBNESS, AND ENCEPHALOPATHY. JAUNDICE AND LIVER DYSFUNCTION ARE ALSO POSSIBLE. CENTRAL NERVOUS SYSTEM EFFECTS OF HEADACHE, DIZZINESS, INCOORDINATION, INSOMNIA, IRRITABILITY, DEPRESSION, WEAKNESS, SYNCOPE, AND CONVULSIONS MAY DEVELOP. PERIPHERAL NEUROPATHY AS CHARACTERIZED BY PARESTHESIA OF THE EXTREMITIES MAY OCCUR AND IN SOME CASES MAY NOT REVERSE ITSELF. HYPERSENSITIVE REACTIONS OF URTICARIA, ERYTHEMATOUS RASH, FLUSHING, FEVER, NASAL CONGESTION AND DRYNESS OF THE MOUTH (OR VAGINA OR VULVA) MAY APPEAR. EFFECTS INFREQUENTLY OBSERVED ARE REVERSIBLE NEUTROPENIA, PANCREATITIS, PSEUDOMEMBRANOUS COLITIS, REVERSIBLE THROMBOCYTOPENIA, FLEETING JOINT PAIN, AND AGRANULOCYTOSIS. BREAST AND COLON CANCER HAVE OCCURRED AMONG INDIVIDUALS WITH CROHN'S DISEASE TREATED WITH HIGH DOSES FOR EXTENDED PERIODS OF TIME. A CAUSE AND EFFECT RELATIONSHIP HAS NOT BEEN ESTABLISHED. SIGNIFICANT INCREASES IN THE INCIDENCES OF LUNG TUMORS IN MICE OF EACH SEX, OF LYMPHOMAS IN FEMALE MICE, AND OF MAMMARY, PITUITARY, TESTICULAR AND LIVER TUMORS IN RATS WERE REPORTED. HIGH DOSES PRODUCED INFERTILITY IN MALE RATS.
FIRST AID- TREAT SYMPTOMATICALLY AND SUPPORTIVELY. GET MEDICAL ATTENTION IMMEDIATELY. IF VOMITING OCCURS, KEEP HEAD LOWER THAN HIPS TO PREVENT ASPIRATION.
ANTIDOTE: NO SPECIFIC ANTIDOTE. TREAT SYMPTOMATICALLY AND SUPPORTIVELY.

REACTIVITY

REACTIVITY: STABLE UNDER NORMAL TEMPERATURES AND PRESSURES.
INCOMPATIBILITIES: METRONIDAZOLE: OXIDIZERS (STRONG): FIRE AND EXPLOSION HAZARD.
DECOMPOSITION: THERMAL DECOMPOSITION PRODUCTS MAY INCLUDE TOXIC OXIDES OF CARBON AND NITROGEN.
POLYMERIZATION: HAZARDOUS POLYMERIZATION HAS NOT BEEN REPORTED TO OCCUR UNDER NORMAL TEMPERATURES AND PRESSURES.

STORAGE AND DISPOSAL

OBSERVE ALL FEDERAL, STATE AND LOCAL REGULATIONS WHEN STORING OR DISPOSING OF THIS SUBSTANCE. FOR ASSISTANCE, CONTACT THE DISTRICT DIRECTOR OF THE ENVIRONMENTAL PROTECTION AGENCY.

STORAGE

STORE AWAY FROM INCOMPATIBLE SUBSTANCES.

CONDITIONS TO AVOID

MAY BURN BUT DOES NOT IGNITE READILY. AVOID CONTACT WITH STRONG OXIDIZERS, EXCESSIVE HEAT, SPARKS, OR OPEN FLAME.

SPILL AND LEAK PROCEDURES

WATER SPILL: THE CALIFORNIA SAFE DRINKING WATER AND TOXIC ENFORCEMENT ACT OF 1986 (PROPOSITION 65) PROHIBITS CONTAMINATING ANY KNOWN SOURCE OF DRINKING WATER WITH SUBSTANCES KNOWN TO CAUSE CANCER AND/OR REPRODUCTIVE TOXICITY.

OCCUPATIONAL SPILL: SWEEP UP AND PLACE IN SUITABLE CLEAN, DRY CONTAINERS FOR RECLAMATION OR LATER DISPOSAL. DO NOT FLUSH SPILLED MATERIAL INTO SEWER. KEEP UNNECESSARY PEOPLE AWAY.

PROTECTIVE EQUIPMENT

VENTILATION: PROVIDE LOCAL EXHAUST OR PROCESS ENCLOSURE VENTILATION SYSTEM.

RESPIRATOR: THE FOLLOWING RESPIRATORS ARE RECOMMENDED BASED ON INFORMATION FOUND IN THE PHYSICAL DATA, TOXICITY AND HEALTH EFFECTS SECTIONS. THEY ARE RANKED IN ORDER FROM MINIMUM TO MAXIMUM RESPIRATORY PROTECTION. THE SPECIFIC RESPIRATOR SELECTED MUST BE BASED ON CONTAMINATION LEVELS FOUND IN THE WORK PLACE, MUST NOT EXCEED THE WORKING LIMITS OF THE RESPIRATOR AND BE JOINTLY APPROVED BY THE NATIONAL INSTITUTE FOR OCCUPATIONAL SAFETY AND HEALTH AND THE MINE SAFETY AND HEALTH ADMINISTRATION (NIOSH-MSHA).

TYPE 'C' SUPPLIED-AIR RESPIRATOR WITH A FULL FACEPIECE OPERATED IN PRESSURE-DEMAND OR OTHER POSITIVE PRESSURE MODE OR WITH A FULL FACEPIECE, HELMET OR HOOD OPERATED IN CONTINOUS-FLOW MODE.

SELF-CONTAINED BREATHING APPARATUS WITH A FULL FACEPIECE OPERATED IN PRESSURE-DEMAND OR OTHER POSITIVE PRESSURE MODE.

FOR FIREFIGHTING AND OTHER IMMEDIATELY DANGEROUS TO LIFE OR HEALTH CONDITIONS:

SELF-CONTAINED BREATHING APPARATUS WITH FULL FACEPIECE OPERATED IN PRESSURE-DEMAND OR OTHER POSITIVE PRESSURE MODE.

SUPPLIED-AIR RESPIRATOR WITH FULL FACEPIECE AND OPERATED IN PRESSURE-DEMAND OR OTHER POSITIVE PRESSURE MODE IN COMBINATION WITH AN AUXILIARY SELF-CONTAINED BREATHING APPARATUS OPERATED IN PRESSURE-DEMAND OR OTHER POSITIVE PRESSURE MODE.

CLOTHING: EMPLOYEE MUST WEAR APPROPRIATE PROTECTIVE (IMPERVIOUS) CLOTHING AND EQUIPMENT TO PREVENT ANY POSSIBILITY OF SKIN CONTACT WITH THIS SUBSTANCE.

GLOVES: EMPLOYEE MUST WEAR APPROPRIATE PROTECTIVE GLOVES TO PREVENT CONTACT WITH THIS SUBSTANCE.

EYE PROTECTION: EMPLOYEE MUST WEAR SPLASH-PROOF OR DUST-RESISTANT SAFETY GOGGLES AND A FACESHIELD TO PREVENT CONTACT WITH THIS SUBSTANCE.

EMERGENCY WASH FACILITIES: WHERE THERE IS ANY POSSIBILITY THAT AN EMPLOYEE'S EYES AND/OR SKIN MAY BE EXPOSED TO THIS SUBSTANCE, THE EMPLOYER SHOULD PROVIDE AN EYE WASH FOUNTAIN AND QUICK DRENCH SHOWER WITHIN THE IMMEDIATE WORK AREA FOR EMERGENCY USE.

AUTHORIZED BY- OCCUPATIONAL HEALTH SERVICES, INC.

CREATION DATE: 02/21/90 ***REVISION DATE:*** 07/12/90

MATERIAL SAFETY DATA SHEET

OCCUPATIONAL HEALTH SERVICES, INC.
AGRICULTURE AND PESTICIDE DIVISION
450 SEVENTH AVENUE, SUITE 2407
NEW YORK, NEW YORK 10123
1-800-445-MSDS OR (212) 967-1100

EMERGENCY CONTACT:
JOHN S. BRANSFORD, JR. (615) 292-1180

SUBSTANCE IDENTIFICATION

CAS-NUMBER 66215-27-8

SUBSTANCE: **CYROMAZINE**

TRADE NAMES/SYNONYMS: 1,3,5-TRIAZINE-2,4,6-TRIAMINE, N-CYCLOPROPYL-; N-CYCLOPROPYL-1,3,5-TRIAZINE-2,4-6-TRIAMINE; 2-CYCLOPROPYLAMINO-4,6-DIAMINO-S-TRIAZINE; CGA 72662; CYCLOPROPYLMELAMINE; LARVADEX; TRIGARD; VETRAZIN; VETRAZINE; C6H10N6; PST72536

CHEMICAL FAMILY: S-TRIAZINE

MOLECULAR FORMULA: C6-H10-N6

MOLECULAR WEIGHT: 166.18

CERCLA RATINGS (SCALE 0-3): HEALTH=2 FIRE=1 REACTIVITY=0 PERSISTENCE=2

NFPA RATINGS (SCALE 0-4): HEALTH=2 FIRE=1 REACTIVITY=0

COMPONENTS AND CONTAMINANTS

COMPONENT: CYROMAZINE ***PERCENT:*** 100.0
CAS# 66215-27-8

OTHER CONTAMINANTS: NONE

EXPOSURE LIMITS: NO OCCUPATIONAL EXPOSURE LIMITS ESTABLISHED BY OSHA, ACGIH, OR NIOSH.

PHYSICAL DATA

DESCRIPTION: COLORLESS OR WHITE CRYSTALLINE SOLID.

MELTING POINT: 426-432 F (219-222 C) ***SPECIFIC GRAVITY:*** 1.35

VAPOR PRESSURE: NEGLIGIBLE ***SOLUBILITY IN WATER:*** 0.11 % @ 25 C

SOLVENT SOLUBILITY: SLIGHTLY SOLUBLE IN METHANOL

FIRE AND EXPLOSION DATA

FIRE AND EXPLOSION HAZARD: SLIGHT FIRE HAZARD WHEN EXPOSED TO HEAT OR FLAME.

FIREFIGHTING MEDIA: DRY CHEMICAL, CARBON DIOXIDE, HALON, WATER SPRAY OR STANDARD FOAM (1987 EMERGENCY RESPONSE GUIDEBOOK, DOT P 5800.4). FOR LARGER FIRES, USE WATER SPRAY, FOG OR STANDARD FOAM (1987 EMERGENCY RESPONSE GUIDEBOOK, DOT P 5800.4).

FIREFIGHTING: MOVE CONTAINERS FROM FIRE AREA IF POSSIBLE (1987 EMERGENCY RESPONSE GUIDEBOOK, DOT P 5800.4, GUIDE PAGE 53).

EXTINGUISH USING AGENTS SUITABLE FOR SURROUNDING FIRE. USE FLOODING QUANTITIES OF WATER AS A FOG. KEEP MATERIAL OUT OF SEWERS AND WATER SOURCES. DO NOT TOUCH SPILLED MATERIAL. AVOID BREATHING HAZARDOUS FUMES; KEEP UPWIND.

TOXICITY

CYROMAZINE: TOXICITY DATA: 3387 MG/KG ORAL-RAT LD50; CARCINOGEN STATUS: NONE. ACUTE TOXICITY LEVEL: MODERATELY TOXIC BY INGESTION. TARGET EFFECTS: NO DATA AVAILABLE.

HEALTH EFFECTS AND FIRST AID

INHALATION: CYROMAZINE: **ACUTE EXPOSURE-** A LETHAL CONCENTRATION IN RATS IS GREATER THAN 2720 MG/M3. SOME TRIAZINES ARE MILDLY IRRITATING TO THE UPPER RESPIRATORY TRACT. **CHRONIC EXPOSURE-** NO DATA AVAILABLE.

FIRST AID- REMOVE FROM EXPOSURE AREA TO FRESH AIR IMMEDIATELY. IF BREATHING HAS STOPPED, PERFORM ARTIFICIAL RESPIRATION. KEEP PERSON WARM AND AT REST. TREAT SYMPTOMATICALLY AND SUPPORTIVELY. GET MEDICAL ATTENTION IMMEDIATELY.

SKIN CONTACT: CYROMAZINE: **ACUTE EXPOSURE-** THIS MATERIAL WAS MILDLY IRRITATING TO RABBIT SKIN. A LETHAL DOSE BY DERMAL ABSORPTION IN RATS IS GREATER THAN 3100 MG/KG. **CHRONIC EXPOSURE-** NO DATA AVAILABLE.

FIRST AID- REMOVE CONTAMINATED CLOTHING AND SHOES IMMEDIATELY. WASH AFFECTED AREA WITH SOAP OR MILD DETERGENT AND LARGE AMOUNTS OF WATER UNTIL NO EVIDENCE OF CHEMICAL REMAINS (APPROXIMATELY 15-20 MINUTES). GET MEDICAL ATTENTION IMMEDIATELY.

EYE CONTACT: CYROMAZINE: **ACUTE EXPOSURE-** THIS MATERIAL WAS NOT IRRITATING TO RABBIT EYES. **CHRONIC EXPOSURE-** NO DATA AVAILABLE.

FIRST AID- WASH EYES IMMEDIATELY WITH LARGE AMOUNTS OF WATER OR NORMAL SALINE, OCCASIONALLY LIFTING UPPER AND LOWER LIDS, UNTIL NO EVIDENCE OF CHEMICAL REMAINS (APPROXIMATELY 15-20 MINUTES). GET MEDICAL ATTENTION IMMEDIATELY.

INGESTION: CYROMAZINE: **ACUTE EXPOSURE-** A LETHAL DOSE IN RATS WAS 3387 MG/KG; SYMPTOMS WERE NOT REPORTED. **CHRONIC EXPOSURE-** IN 2-YEAR FEEDING TRIALS THE NO EFFECTS LEVEL WAS 300 MG/KG DIET FOR RATS AND 1000 MG/KG DIET FOR MICE.

FIRST AID- TREAT SYMPTOMATICALLY AND SUPPORTIVELY. GET MEDICAL ATTENTION IMMEDIATELY. IF VOMITING OCCURS, KEEP HEAD LOWER THAN HIPS TO PREVENT ASPIRATION.

ANTIDOTE: NO SPECIFIC ANTIDOTE. TREAT SYMPTOMATICALLY AND SUPPORTIVELY.

CREATION DATE: 10/04/89 **REVISION DATE:** 05/15/90

MATERIAL SAFETY DATA SHEET

OCCUPATIONAL HEALTH SERVICES, INC.
AGRICULTURE AND PESTICIDE DIVISION
450 SEVENTH AVENUE, SUITE 2407
NEW YORK, NEW YORK 10123
1-800-445-MSDS OR (212) 967-1100

EMERGENCY CONTACT:
JOHN S. BRANSFORD, JR. (615) 292-1180

SUBSTANCE IDENTIFICATION

CAS-NUMBER 24602-86-6

SUBSTANCE: 2,6-DIMETHYL-4-TRIDECYLMORPHOLINE

TRADE NAMES/SYNONYMS: N-TRIDECYL-2,6-DIMETHYLMORPHOLINE; 2,6-DIMETHYL-4-TRIDECYLTETRAHYDRO-1,4-OXAZINE; TRIDEMORPH; CALIXIN (FORMULATION); C19H39NO; PST72537

CHEMICAL FAMILY: MORPHOLINE

MOLECULAR FORMULA: C-H3-(C-H2)12-N-C4-H6-O-(C-H3)2

MOLECULAR WEIGHT: 297.52

CERCLA RATINGS (SCALE 0-3): HEALTH=2 FIRE=1 REACTIVITY=0 PERSISTENCE=1

NFPA RATINGS (SCALE 0-4): HEALTH=U FIRE=1 REACTIVITY=0

COMPONENTS AND CONTAMINANTS

COMPONENT: 2,6-DIMETHYL-4-TRIDECYLMORPHOLINE **PERCENT:** 100.0
CAS# 24602-86-6

OTHER CONTAMINANTS: NONE

EXPOSURE LIMITS: NO OCCUPATIONAL EXPOSURE LIMITS ESTABLISHED BY OSHA, ACGIH, OR NIOSH.

PHYSICAL DATA

DESCRIPTION: YELLOW, OILY LIQUID WITH A SLIGHT AMINE-LIKE ODOR.

BOILING POINT: 266-271 F (130-133 C) @ 0.7 MMHG **MELTING POINT:** -4 F (-20 C)

SPECIFIC GRAVITY: NOT AVAILABLE **VISCOSITY:** <1 CPS @ 20 C

VAPOR PRESSURE: 0.0003 MMHG @ 20 C **EVAPORATION RATE:** NOT AVAILABLE

SOLUBILITY IN WATER: 0.01% @ 20 C

SOLVENT SOLUBILITY: SOLUBLE IN ACETONE, BENZENE, CHLOROFORM, CYCLOHEXANE, ETHANOL, OLIVE OIL, ETHYL ACETATE AND DIETHYL ETHER.

FIRE AND EXPLOSION DATA

FIRE AND EXPLOSION HAZARD: SLIGHT FIRE HAZARD WHEN EXPOSED TO HEAT OR FLAME.

FLASH POINT: 306 F (152 C) (APPROXIMATE) **FLAMMABILITY CLASS(OSHA):** IIIB

FIREFIGHTING MEDIA: DRY CHEMICAL, CARBON DIOXIDE, HALON, WATER SPRAY OR STANDARD FOAM (1987 EMERGENCY RESPONSE GUIDEBOOK, DOT P 5800.4). FOR LARGER FIRES, USE WATER SPRAY, FOG OR STANDARD FOAM (1987 EMERGENCY RESPONSE GUIDEBOOK, DOT P 5800.4).

FIREFIGHTING: MOVE CONTAINER FROM FIRE AREA IF POSSIBLE. DO NOT SCATTER SPILLED MATERIAL WITH HIGH PRESSURE WATER STREAMS. DIKE FIRE CONTROL WATER FOR LATER DISPOSAL (1987 EMERGENCY RESPONSE GUIDEBOOK, DOT P 5800.4, GUIDE PAGE 31).
USE AGENTS SUITABLE FOR TYPE OF SURROUNDING FIRE. AVOID BREATHING HAZARDOUS VAPORS, KEEP UPWIND.

TOXICITY

2,6-DIMETHYL-4-TRIDECYLMORPHOLINE: TOXICITY DATA: 650 MG/KG ORAL-RAT LD50; 1560 MG/KG ORAL-MOUSE LD50; 750 MG/KG ORAL-RABBIT LD50; 1 GM/KG ORAL-GUINEA PIG LD50; 540 MG/KG ORAL-CAT LD50; REPRODUCTIVE EFFECTS DATA (RTECS). CARCINOGEN STATUS: NONE. LOCAL EFFECTS: IRRITANT- SKIN AND EYE. ACUTE TOXICITY LEVEL: MODERATELY TOXIC BY INGESTION. TARGET EFFECTS: NO DATA AVAILABLE.

HEALTH EFFECTS AND FIRST AID

INHALATION: 2,6-DIMETHYL-4-TRIDECYLMORPHOLINE: ACUTE EXPOSURE- INHALATION OF VAPORS OR MIST MAY CAUSE ADVERSE HEALTH EFFECTS. RATS SURVIVED AN 8-HOUR EXPOSURE TO AIR SATURATED WITH THE VAPOR @ 20 C. CHRONIC EXPOSURE- NO DATA AVAILABLE.

FIRST AID- REMOVE FROM EXPOSURE AREA TO FRESH AIR IMMEDIATELY. IF BREATHING HAS STOPPED, PERFORM ARTIFICIAL RESPIRATION. KEEP PERSON WARM AND AT REST. TREAT SYMPTOMATICALLY AND SUPPORTIVELY. GET MEDICAL ATTENTION IMMEDIATELY.

REACTIVITY

REACTIVITY: STABLE UNDER NORMAL TEMPERATURES AND PRESSURES.

INCOMPATIBILITIES: CYROMAZINE: NO DATA AVAILABLE.

DECOMPOSITION: THERMAL DECOMPOSITION PRODUCTS MAY INCLUDE TOXIC OXIDES OF CARBON AND NITROGEN.

POLYMERIZATION: HAZARDOUS POLYMERIZATION HAS NOT BEEN REPORTED TO OCCUR UNDER NORMAL TEMPERATURES AND PRESSURES.

STORAGE AND DISPOSAL

OBSERVE ALL FEDERAL, STATE AND LOCAL REGULATIONS WHEN STORING OR DISPOSING OF THIS SUBSTANCE. FOR ASSISTANCE, CONTACT THE DISTRICT DIRECTOR OF THE ENVIRONMENTAL PROTECTION AGENCY.

STORAGE

STORE IN ACCORDANCE WITH 40 CFR 165 RECOMMENDED PROCEDURES FOR THE DISPOSAL AND STORAGE OF PESTICIDES AND PESTICIDE CONTAINERS.

DISPOSAL

DISPOSAL MUST BE IN ACCORDANCE WITH 40 CFR 165 RECOMMENDED PROCEDURES FOR THE DISPOSAL AND STORAGE OF PESTICIDES AND PESTICIDE CONTAINERS.

CONDITIONS TO AVOID

MAY BURN BUT DOES NOT IGNITE READILY.

SPILL AND LEAK PROCEDURES

OCCUPATIONAL SPILL: DO NOT TOUCH SPILLED MATERIAL. STOP LEAK IF YOU CAN DO IT WITHOUT RISK. FOR SMALL SPILLS, TAKE UP WITH SAND OR OTHER ABSORBENT MATERIAL AND PLACE INTO CONTAINERS FOR LATER DISPOSAL. FOR SMALL DRY SPILLS, WITH A CLEAN SHOVEL PLACE MATERIAL INTO CLEAN, DRY CONTAINER AND COVER. MOVE CONTAINERS FROM SPILL AREA. FOR LARGER SPILLS, DIKE FAR AHEAD OF SPILL FOR LATER DISPOSAL. KEEP UNNECESSARY PEOPLE AWAY. ISOLATE HAZARD AREA AND DENY ENTRY.

PROTECTIVE EQUIPMENT

VENTILATION: PROVIDE LOCAL EXHAUST OR GENERAL DILUTION VENTILATION SYSTEM.

RESPIRATOR: THE FOLLOWING RESPIRATORS ARE RECOMMENDED BASED ON INFORMATION FOUND IN THE PHYSICAL DATA, TOXICITY AND HEALTH EFFECTS SECTIONS. THEY ARE RANKED IN ORDER FROM MINIMUM TO MAXIMUM RESPIRATORY PROTECTION. THE SPECIFIC RESPIRATOR SELECTED MUST BE BASED ON CONTAMINATION LEVELS FOUND IN THE WORK PLACE, MUST NOT EXCEED THE WORKING LIMITS OF THE RESPIRATOR AND BE JOINTLY APPROVED BY THE NATIONAL INSTITUTE FOR OCCUPATIONAL SAFETY AND HEALTH AND THE MINE SAFETY AND HEALTH ADMINISTRATION (NIOSH-MSHA).
CHEMICAL CARTRIDGE RESPIRATOR WITH AN ORGANIC VAPOR CARTRIDGE(S) IN COMBINATION WITH A DUST AND MIST FILTER.
GAS MASK WITH ORGANIC VAPOR CANISTER (CHIN-STYLE OR FRONT- OR BACK-MOUNTED CANISTER) WITH A DUST AND MIST FILTER.
GAS MASK WITH ORGANIC VAPOR CANISTER (CHIN-STYLE OR FRONT- OR BACK-MOUNTED CANISTER) WITH A PARTICULATE FILTER.
POWERED AIR-PURIFYING RESPIRATOR WITH A HIGH-EFFICIENCY FILTER.
TYPE 'C' SUPPLIED-AIR RESPIRATOR WITH A FULL FACEPIECE OPERATED IN A PRESSURE-DEMAND OR OTHER POSITIVE PRESSURE MODE.
SELF-CONTAINED BREATHING APPARATUS WITH A FULL FACEPIECE OPERATED IN PRESSURE-DEMAND OR OTHER POSITIVE PRESSURE MODE.
FOR FIREFIGHTING AND OTHER IMMEDIATELY DANGEROUS TO LIFE OR HEALTH CONDITIONS:
SELF-CONTAINED BREATHING APPARATUS WITH FULL FACEPIECE OPERATED IN PRESSURE-DEMAND OR OTHER POSITIVE PRESSURE MODE.
SUPPLIED-AIR RESPIRATOR WITH FULL FACEPIECE AND OPERATED IN PRESSURE-DEMAND OR OTHER POSITIVE PRESSURE MODE IN COMBINATION WITH AN AUXILIARY SELF-CONTAINED BREATHING APPARATUS OPERATED IN PRESSURE-DEMAND OR OTHER POSITIVE PRESSURE MODE.

CLOTHING: EMPLOYEE MUST WEAR APPROPRIATE PROTECTIVE (IMPERVIOUS) CLOTHING AND EQUIPMENT TO PREVENT REPEATED OR PROLONGED SKIN CONTACT WITH THIS SUBSTANCE.

GLOVES: EMPLOYEE MUST WEAR APPROPRIATE PROTECTIVE GLOVES TO PREVENT CONTACT WITH THIS SUBSTANCE.

EYE PROTECTION: EMPLOYEE MUST WEAR SPLASH-PROOF OR DUST-RESISTANT SAFETY GOGGLES TO PREVENT EYE CONTACT WITH THIS SUBSTANCE.
EMERGENCY EYE WASH: WHERE THERE IS ANY POSSIBILITY THAT AN EMPLOYEE'S EYES MAY BE EXPOSED TO THIS SUBSTANCE, THE EMPLOYER SHOULD PROVIDE AN EYE WASH FOUNTAIN WITHIN THE IMMEDIATE WORK AREA FOR EMERGENCY USE.

AUTHORIZED BY- OCCUPATIONAL HEALTH SERVICES, INC.

SKIN CONTACT: 2,6-DIMETHYL-4-TRIDECYLMORPHOLINE: IRRITANT. **ACUTE EXPOSURE-** THIS MATERIAL WAS MODERATELY TO SEVERELY IRRITATING TO RABBIT SKIN. **CHRONIC EXPOSURE-** PROLONGED OR REPEATED EXPOSURE TO IRRITANTS MAY CAUSE DERMATITIS.

FIRST AID- REMOVE CONTAMINATED CLOTHING AND SHOES IMMEDIATELY. WASH AFFECTED AREA WITH SOAP OR MILD DETERGENT AND LARGE AMOUNTS OF WATER UNTIL NO EVIDENCE OF CHEMICAL REMAINS (APPROXIMATELY 15-20 MINUTES). GET MEDICAL ATTENTION IMMEDIATELY.

EYE CONTACT: 2,6-DIMETHYL-4-TRIDECYLMORPHOLINE: IRRITANT. **ACUTE EXPOSURE-** THIS MATERIAL WAS MODERATELY TO SEVERELY IRRITATING TO RABBIT EYES. **CHRONIC EXPOSURE-** PROLONGED OR REPEATED EXPOSURE TO IRRITANTS MAY CAUSE CONJUNCTIVITIS.

FIRST AID- WASH EYES IMMEDIATELY WITH LARGE AMOUNTS OF WATER OR NORMAL SALINE, OCCASIONALLY LIFTING UPPER AND LOWER LIDS, UNTIL NO EVIDENCE OF CHEMICAL REMAINS (APPROXIMATELY 15-20 MINUTES). GET MEDICAL ATTENTION IMMEDIATELY.

INGESTION: 2,6-DIMETHYL-4-TRIDECYLMORPHOLINE: **ACUTE EXPOSURE-** A LETHAL DOSE REPORTED IN RATS WAS 650 MG/KG; SYMPTOMS WERE NOT REPORTED. **CHRONIC EXPOSURE-** EMBRYOLETHALITY, CLEFT PALATE AND OTHER ANOMALIES, AND MATERNAL TOXICITY WERE REPORTED IN A STUDY OF PREGNANT RATS AND MICE.

FIRST AID- IF THE PERSON IS CONSCIOUS AND NOT CONVULSING, REMOVE BY GASTRIC LAVAGE AND FOLLOW WITH A CATHARTIC (DREISBACH, HANDBOOK OF POISONING, 12TH ED.). TREAT SYMPTOMATICALLY AND SUPPORTIVELY. GASTRIC LAVAGE SHOULD BE PERFORMED BY QUALIFIED MEDICAL PERSONNEL. GET MEDICAL ATTENTION IMMEDIATELY.

REACTIVITY

REACTIVITY: STABLE UNDER NORMAL TEMPERATURES AND PRESSURES.

INCOMPATIBILITIES: 2,6-DIMETHYL-4-TRIDECYLMORPHOLINE: OXIDIZERS (STRONG): FIRE AND EXPLOSION HAZARD.

DECOMPOSITION: THERMAL DECOMPOSITION PRODUCTS MAY INCLUDE TOXIC OXIDES OF CARBON AND NITROGEN.

POLYMERIZATION: HAZARDOUS POLYMERIZATION HAS NOT BEEN REPORTED TO OCCUR UNDER NORMAL TEMPERATURES AND PRESSURES.

STORAGE AND DISPOSAL

OBSERVE ALL FEDERAL, STATE AND LOCAL REGULATIONS WHEN STORING OR DISPOSING OF THIS SUBSTANCE. FOR ASSISTANCE, CONTACT THE DISTRICT DIRECTOR OF THE ENVIRONMENTAL PROTECTION AGENCY.

****STORAGE****

STORE IN ACCORDANCE WITH 40 CFR 165 RECOMMENDED PROCEDURES FOR THE DISPOSAL AND STORAGE OF PESTICIDES AND PESTICIDE CONTAINERS.

STORE AWAY FROM INCOMPATIBLE SUBSTANCES.

****DISPOSAL****

DISPOSAL MUST BE IN ACCORDANCE WITH 40 CFR 165 RECOMMENDED PROCEDURES FOR THE DISPOSAL AND STORAGE OF PESTICIDES AND PESTICIDE CONTAINERS.

CONDITIONS TO AVOID

MAY BURN BUT DOES NOT IGNITE READILY. AVOID CONTACT WITH STRONG OXIDIZERS, EXCESSIVE HEAT, SPARKS, OR OPEN FLAME.

SPILL AND LEAK PROCEDURES

OCCUPATIONAL SPILL: STOP LEAK IF YOU CAN DO IT WITHOUT RISK. FOR SMALL SPILLS, TAKE UP WITH SAND OR OTHER ABSORBENT MATERIAL AND PLACE INTO CLEAN, DRY CONTAINERS FOR LATER DISPOSAL. KEEP UNNECESSARY PEOPLE AWAY. ISOLATE HAZARD AREA AND DENY ENTRY.

PROTECTIVE EQUIPMENT

VENTILATION: PROVIDE LOCAL EXHAUST OR GENERAL DILUTION VENTILATION SYSTEM.

RESPIRATOR: THE FOLLOWING RESPIRATORS ARE RECOMMENDED BASED ON INFORMATION FOUND IN THE PHYSICAL DATA, TOXICITY AND HEALTH EFFECTS SECTIONS. THEY ARE RANKED IN ORDER FROM MINIMUM TO MAXIMUM RESPIRATORY PROTECTION. THE SPECIFIC RESPIRATOR SELECTED MUST BE BASED ON CONTAMINATION LEVELS FOUND IN THE WORK PLACE, MUST NOT EXCEED THE WORKING LIMITS OF THE RESPIRATOR AND BE JOINTLY APPROVED BY THE NATIONAL INSTITUTE FOR OCCUPATIONAL SAFETY AND HEALTH AND THE MINE SAFETY AND HEALTH ADMINISTRATION (NIOSH-MSHA).

CHEMICAL CARTRIDGE RESPIRATOR WITH FULL FACEPIECE AND PESTICIDE CARTRIDGE.

TYPE 'C' SUPPLIED-AIR RESPIRATOR WITH A FULL FACEPIECE OPERATED IN PRESSURE-DEMAND OR OTHER POSITIVE PRESSURE MODE OR WITH A FULL FACEPIECE, HELMET OR HOOD OPERATED IN CONTINUOUS-FLOW MODE.

SELF-CONTAINED BREATHING APPARATUS OPERATED IN PRESSURE-DEMAND OR OTHER POSITIVE PRESSURE MODE.

FOR FIREFIGHTING AND OTHER IMMEDIATELY DANGEROUS TO LIFE OR HEALTH CONDITIONS:

SELF-CONTAINED BREATHING APPARATUS WITH FULL FACEPIECE OPERATED IN PRESSURE-DEMAND OR OTHER POSITIVE PRESSURE MODE.

SUPPLIED-AIR RESPIRATOR WITH FULL FACEPIECE AND OPERATED IN PRESSURE-DEMAND OR OTHER POSITIVE PRESSURE MODE IN COMBINATION WITH AN AUXILIARY SELF-CONTAINED BREATHING APPARATUS OPERATED IN PRESSURE-DEMAND OR OTHER POSITIVE PRESSURE MODE.

CLOTHING: EMPLOYEE MUST WEAR APPROPRIATE PROTECTIVE (IMPERVIOUS) CLOTHING AND EQUIPMENT TO PREVENT REPEATED OR PROLONGED SKIN CONTACT WITH THIS SUBSTANCE.

GLOVES: EMPLOYEE MUST WEAR APPROPRIATE PROTECTIVE GLOVES TO PREVENT CONTACT WITH THIS SUBSTANCE.

EYE PROTECTION: EMPLOYEE MUST WEAR SPLASH-PROOF OR DUST-RESISTANT SAFETY GOGGLES TO PREVENT EYE CONTACT WITH THIS SUBSTANCE.

EMERGENCY EYE WASH: WHERE THERE IS ANY POSSIBILITY THAT AN EMPLOYEE'S EYES MAY BE EXPOSED TO THIS SUBSTANCE, THE EMPLOYER SHOULD PROVIDE AN EYE WASH FOUNTAIN WITHIN THE IMMEDIATE WORK AREA FOR EMERGENCY USE.

AUTHORIZED BY- OCCUPATIONAL HEALTH SERVICES, INC.

CREATION DATE: 03/22/90 ***REVISION DATE:*** 03/22/90

MATERIAL SAFETY DATA SHEET

OCCUPATIONAL HEALTH SERVICES, INC.
AGRICULTURE AND PESTICIDE DIVISION
450 SEVENTH AVENUE, SUITE 2407
NEW YORK, NEW YORK 10123
1-800-445-MSDS OR (212) 967-1100

EMERGENCY CONTACT:
JOHN S. BRANSFORD, JR. (615) 292-1180

SUBSTANCE IDENTIFICATION

CAS-NUMBER 66841-25-6

SUBSTANCE: TRALOMETHRIN

TRADE NAMES/SYNONYMS: CYCLOPROPANECARBOXYLIC ACID, 2,2-DIMETHYL-3-(1,2,2,2- TETRABROMOETHYL)-, CYANO(3-PHENOXYPHENYL)METHYL ESTER; 2,2-DIMETHYL-3-(1,2,2,2-TETRABROMOETHYL)CYCLOPROPANECARBOXYLIC ACID, CYANO(3-PHENOXYPHENYL)METHYL ESTER; SCOUT; C22H19BR4NO3; PST72538

CHEMICAL FAMILY: HYDROXYL, ALICYCLIC
ESTER
HALOGEN COMPOUND, ALIPHATIC

MOLECULAR FORMULA: C22-H19-BR4-N-O3

MOLECULAR WEIGHT: 665.0

CERCLA RATINGS (SCALE 0-3): HEALTH=3 FIRE=1 REACTIVITY=0 PERSISTENCE=3

NFPA RATINGS (SCALE 0-4): HEALTH=U FIRE=1 REACTIVITY=0

COMPONENTS AND CONTAMINANTS

COMPONENT: TRALOMETHRIN ***PERCENT:*** 100.0
CAS# 66841-25-6

OTHER CONTAMINANTS: NONE

EXPOSURE LIMITS: NO OCCUPATIONAL EXPOSURE LIMITS ESTABLISHED BY OSHA, ACGIH, OR NIOSH.

PHYSICAL DATA

DESCRIPTION: YELLOW-ORANGE RESINOUS SOLID. ***SPECIFIC GRAVITY:*** 1.700

SOLUBILITY IN WATER: 0.007%

SOLVENT SOLUBILITY: SOLUBLE IN MOST ORGANIC SOLVENTS.

FIRE AND EXPLOSION DATA

FIRE AND EXPLOSION HAZARD: SLIGHT FIRE HAZARD WHEN EXPOSED TO HEAT OR FLAME.

FIREFIGHTING MEDIA: DRY CHEMICAL, CARBON DIOXIDE, HALON, WATER SPRAY OR STANDARD FOAM (1987 EMERGENCY RESPONSE GUIDEBOOK, DOT P 5800.4).
FOR LARGER FIRES, USE WATER SPRAY, FOG OR STANDARD FOAM (1987 EMERGENCY RESPONSE GUIDEBOOK, DOT P 5800.4).

FIREFIGHTING: MOVE CONTAINER FROM FIRE AREA IF POSSIBLE. DO NOT SCATTER SPILLED MATERIAL WITH HIGH PRESSURE WATER STREAMS. DIKE FIRE CONTROL

WATER FOR LATER DISPOSAL (1987 EMERGENCY RESPONSE GUIDEBOOK, DOT P 5800.4, GUIDE PAGE 31).
USE AGENTS SUITABLE FOR TYPE OF SURROUNDING FIRE. AVOID BREATHING HAZARDOUS VAPORS, KEEP UPWIND.

TOXICITY

TRALOMETHRIN: TOXICITY DATA: 2700 MG/M3 INHALATION-RAT LC50; 99 MG/KG ORAL-RAT LD50. CARCINOGEN STATUS: NONE. ACUTE TOXICITY LEVEL: TOXIC BY INHALATION AND INGESTION. TARGET EFFECTS: NO DATA AVAILABLE.

HEALTH EFFECTS AND FIRST AID

INHALATION: TRALOMETHRIN: TOXIC. **ACUTE EXPOSURE-** THE LETHAL DOSE IN RATS IS GREATER THAN 0.286 MG/L. **CHRONIC EXPOSURE-** NO DATA AVAILABLE.
FIRST AID- REMOVE FROM EXPOSURE AREA TO FRESH AIR IMMEDIATELY. IF BREATHING HAS STOPPED, PERFORM ARTIFICIAL RESPIRATION. KEEP PERSON WARM AND AT REST. TREAT SYMPTOMATICALLY AND SUPPORTIVELY. GET MEDICAL ATTENTION IMMEDIATELY.

SKIN CONTACT: TRALOMETHRIN: **ACUTE EXPOSURE-** MAY CAUSE IRRITATION. THE LETHAL DOSE IN RABBITS IS GREATER THAN 2000 MG/KG. **CHRONIC EXPOSURE-** PROLONGED CONTACT WITH MIST MAY CAUSE IRRITATION.
FIRST AID- REMOVE CONTAMINATED CLOTHING AND SHOES IMMEDIATELY. WASH AFFECTED AREA WITH SOAP OR MILD DETERGENT AND LARGE AMOUNTS OF WATER UNTIL NO EVIDENCE OF CHEMICAL REMAINS (APPROXIMATELY 15-20 MINUTES). GET MEDICAL ATTENTION IMMEDIATELY.

EYE CONTACT: TRALOMETHRIN: **ACUTE EXPOSURE-** MAY CAUSE SLIGHT IRRITATION. **CHRONIC EXPOSURE-** NO DATA AVAILABLE.
FIRST AID- WASH EYES IMMEDIATELY WITH LARGE AMOUNTS OF WATER OR NORMAL SALINE, OCCASIONALLY LIFTING UPPER AND LOWER LIDS, UNTIL NO EVIDENCE OF CHEMICAL REMAINS (APPROXIMATELY 15-20 MINUTES). GET MEDICAL ATTENTION IMMEDIATELY.

INGESTION: TRALOMETHRIN: TOXIC. **ACUTE EXPOSURE-** INGESTION OF 99 MG/KG WAS LETHAL TO RATS. **CHRONIC EXPOSURE-** INGESTION OF 6 MG/KG/DAY AND 1 MG/KG/DAY FOR 90 DAYS RESULTED IN NO EFFECTS IN RATS AND DOGS, RESPECTIVELY.
FIRST AID- TREAT SYMPTOMATICALLY AND SUPPORTIVELY. GET MEDICAL ATTENTION IMMEDIATELY. IF VOMITING OCCURS, KEEP HEAD LOWER THAN HIPS TO PREVENT ASPIRATION.
ANTIDOTE: NO SPECIFIC ANTIDOTE. TREAT SYMPTOMATICALLY AND SUPPORTIVELY.

REACTIVITY

REACTIVITY: STABLE UNDER NORMAL TEMPERATURES AND PRESSURES.
INCOMPATIBILITIES: TRALOMETHRIN: OXIDIZERS (STRONG): FIRE AND EXPLOSION HAZARD. SEE ALSO ESTERS.
ESTERS: NITRATES: POSSIBLE EXPLOSIVE REACTION.
DECOMPOSITION: THERMAL DECOMPOSITION PRODUCTS MAY INCLUDE TOXIC AND CORROSIVE FUMES OF BROMIDES, AND TOXIC OXIDES OF CARBON AND NITROGEN.
POLYMERIZATION: HAZARDOUS POLYMERIZATION HAS NOT BEEN REPORTED TO OCCUR UNDER NORMAL TEMPERATURES AND PRESSURES.

STORAGE AND DISPOSAL

OBSERVE ALL FEDERAL, STATE AND LOCAL REGULATIONS WHEN STORING OR DISPOSING OF THIS SUBSTANCE. FOR ASSISTANCE, CONTACT THE DISTRICT DIRECTOR OF THE ENVIRONMENTAL PROTECTION AGENCY.

****STORAGE****

STORE IN ACCORDANCE WITH 40 CFR 165 RECOMMENDED PROCEDURES FOR THE DISPOSAL AND STORAGE OF PESTICIDES AND PESTICIDE CONTAINERS.
STORE AWAY FROM INCOMPATIBLE SUBSTANCES.

****DISPOSAL****

DISPOSAL MUST BE IN ACCORDANCE WITH 40 CFR 165 RECOMMENDED PROCEDURES FOR THE DISPOSAL AND STORAGE OF PESTICIDES AND PESTICIDE CONTAINERS.

CONDITIONS TO AVOID

MAY BURN BUT DOES NOT IGNITE READILY. AVOID CONTACT WITH STRONG OXIDIZERS, EXCESSIVE HEAT, SPARKS, OR OPEN FLAME.

SPILL AND LEAK PROCEDURES

OCCUPATIONAL SPILL: SWEEP UP AND PLACE IN SUITABLE CLEAN, DRY CONTAINERS FOR RECLAMATION OR LATER DISPOSAL. DO NOT FLUSH SPILLED MATERIAL INTO SEWER. KEEP UNNECESSARY PEOPLE AWAY.

PROTECTIVE EQUIPMENT

VENTILATION: PROVIDE LOCAL EXHAUST OR PROCESS ENCLOSURE VENTILATION SYSTEM.
RESPIRATOR: THE FOLLOWING RESPIRATORS ARE RECOMMENDED BASED ON INFORMATION FOUND IN THE PHYSICAL DATA, TOXICITY AND HEALTH EFFECTS SECTIONS. THEY ARE RANKED IN ORDER FROM MINIMUM TO MAXIMUM RESPIRATORY PROTECTION. THE SPECIFIC RESPIRATOR SELECTED MUST BE BASED ON CONTAMINATION LEVELS FOUND IN THE WORK PLACE, MUST NOT EXCEED THE WORKING LIMITS OF THE RESPIRATOR AND BE JOINTLY APPROVED BY THE NATIONAL INSTITUTE FOR OCCUPATIONAL SAFETY AND HEALTH AND THE MINE SAFETY AND HEALTH ADMINISTRATION (NIOSH-MSHA).
CHEMICAL CARTRIDGE RESPIRATOR WITH AN ORGANIC VAPOR CARTRIDGE(S) WITH A FULL FACEPIECE AND ORGANIC VAPOR CARTRIDGE(S) IN COMBINATION WITH A DUST AND MIST FILTER.
POWERED AIR-PURIFYING RESPIRATOR WITH A TIGHT-FITTING FACEPIECE AND ORGANIC VAPOR CARTRIDGE(S) IN COMBINATION WITH A HIGH-EFFICIENCY PARTICULATE FILTER.
TYPE 'C' SUPPLIED-AIR RESPIRATOR WITH A FULL FACEPIECE OPERATED IN A PRESSURE-DEMAND OR OTHER POSITIVE PRESSURE MODE.
SELF-CONTAINED BREATHING APPARATUS WITH A FULL FACEPIECE OPERATED IN PRESSURE-DEMAND OR OTHER POSITIVE PRESSURE MODE.
FOR FIREFIGHTING AND OTHER IMMEDIATELY DANGEROUS TO LIFE OR HEALTH CONDITIONS:
SELF-CONTAINED BREATHING APPARATUS WITH FULL FACEPIECE OPERATED IN PRESSURE-DEMAND OR OTHER POSITIVE PRESSURE MODE.
SUPPLIED-AIR RESPIRATOR WITH FULL FACEPIECE AND OPERATED IN PRESSURE-DEMAND OR OTHER POSITIVE PRESSURE MODE IN COMBINATION WITH AN AUXILIARY SELF-CONTAINED BREATHING APPARATUS OPERATED IN PRESSURE-DEMAND OR OTHER POSITIVE PRESSURE MODE.
CLOTHING: EMPLOYEE MUST WEAR APPROPRIATE PROTECTIVE (IMPERVIOUS) CLOTHING AND EQUIPMENT TO PREVENT REPEATED OR PROLONGED SKIN CONTACT WITH THIS SUBSTANCE.
GLOVES: EMPLOYEE MUST WEAR APPROPRIATE PROTECTIVE GLOVES TO PREVENT CONTACT WITH THIS SUBSTANCE.
EYE PROTECTION: EMPLOYEE MUST WEAR SPLASH-PROOF OR DUST-RESISTANT SAFETY GOGGLES TO PREVENT EYE CONTACT WITH THIS SUBSTANCE.
EMERGENCY EYE WASH: WHERE THERE IS ANY POSSIBILITY THAT AN EMPLOYEE'S EYES MAY BE EXPOSED TO THIS SUBSTANCE, THE EMPLOYER SHOULD PROVIDE AN EYE WASH FOUNTAIN WITHIN THE IMMEDIATE WORK AREA FOR EMERGENCY USE.

AUTHORIZED BY- OCCUPATIONAL HEALTH SERVICES, INC.
CREATION DATE: 10/05/89 ***REVISION DATE:*** 05/31/90

MATERIAL SAFETY DATA SHEET

OCCUPATIONAL HEALTH SERVICES, INC.
AGRICULTURE AND PESTICIDE DIVISION
450 SEVENTH AVENUE, SUITE 2407
NEW YORK, NEW YORK 10123
1-800-445-MSDS OR (212) 967-1100

EMERGENCY CONTACT:
JOHN S. BRANSFORD, JR. (615) 292-1180

SUBSTANCE IDENTIFICATION

CAS-NUMBER 34256-82-1
SUBSTANCE: **ACETOCHLOR**
TRADE NAMES/SYNONYMS: ACETAMIDE, 2-CHLORO-N-(ETHOXYMETHYL)-N-(2-ETHYL-6-METHYLPHENYL)-; O-ACETOTOLUIDIDE, 2-CHLORO-N-(ETHOXYMETHYL)-6'-ETHYL-; 2-CHLORO-N-(ETHOXYMETHYL)-N-(2-ETHYL-6-METHYLPHENYL)ACETAMIDE; 2-CHLORO-N-(ETHOXYMETHYL)-6'-ETHYL-O-ACETOTOLUIDIDE; 2-CHLORO-N-ETHOXYMETHYL-6'-ETHYLACET-O-TOLUIDIDE; 2-CHLORO-N-(ETHOXYMETHYL)-6'-ETHYLACET-O-TOLUIDIDE; HARNESS; MON 097; C14H20CLNO2; PST72539
CHEMICAL FAMILY: AMIDE, AROMATIC
HALOGEN COMPOUND, AROMATIC
MOLECULAR FORMULA: C14-H20-CL-N-O2
MOLECULAR WEIGHT: 269.80
CERCLA RATINGS (SCALE 0-3): HEALTH=2 FIRE=U REACTIVITY=0 PERSISTENCE=1
NFPA RATINGS (SCALE 0-4): HEALTH=U FIRE=U REACTIVITY=0

COMPONENTS AND CONTAMINANTS

COMPONENT: ACETOCHLOR ***PERCENT:*** 100.0
CAS# 34256-82-1

OTHER CONTAMINANTS: NONE

EXPOSURE LIMITS: NO OCCUPATIONAL EXPOSURE LIMITS ESTABLISHED BY OSHA, ACGIH, OR NIOSH.

ACETOCHLOR: SUBJECT TO CALIFORNIA PROPOSITION 65 CANCER AND/OR REPRODUCTIVE TOXICITY WARNING AND RELEASE REQUIREMENTS- (JANUARY 1, 1989)

PHYSICAL DATA

DESCRIPTION: BLUE TO PURPLE-COLORED OIL. ***BOILING POINT:*** NOT AVAILABLE

SPECIFIC GRAVITY: 1.1358 ***VAPOR PRESSURE:*** NEGLIGIBLE

SOLUBILITY IN WATER: 0.0223% @ 25 C

FIRE AND EXPLOSION DATA

FIRE AND EXPLOSION HAZARD: SLIGHT FIRE HAZARD WHEN EXPOSED TO HEAT OR FLAME.

FLASH POINT: NOT AVAILABLE

FIREFIGHTING MEDIA: DRY CHEMICAL, CARBON DIOXIDE, HALON, WATER SPRAY OR STANDARD FOAM (1987 EMERGENCY RESPONSE GUIDEBOOK, DOT P 5800.4). FOR LARGER FIRES, USE WATER SPRAY, FOG OR STANDARD FOAM (1987 EMERGENCY RESPONSE GUIDEBOOK, DOT P 5800.4).

FIREFIGHTING: MOVE CONTAINER FROM FIRE AREA IF POSSIBLE. COOL FIRE-EXPOSED CONTAINERS WITH WATER FROM SIDE UNTIL WELL AFTER FIRE IS OUT. STAY AWAY FROM STORAGE TANK ENDS. FOR MASSIVE FIRE IN STORAGE AREA, USE UNMANNED HOSE HOLDER OR MONITOR NOZZLES, ELSE WITHDRAW FROM AREA AND LET FIRE BURN. WITHDRAW IMMEDIATELY IN CASE OF RISING SOUND FROM VENTING SAFETY DEVICE OR ANY DISCOLORATION OF STORAGE TANK DUE TO FIRE (1987 EMERGENCY RESPONSE GUIDEBOOK, DOT P 5800.4, GUIDE PAGE 27). EXTINGUISH ONLY IF FLOW CAN BE STOPPED; USE FLOODING AMOUNTS OF WATER AS A FOG, SOLID STREAMS MAY BE INEFFECTIVE. COOL CONTAINERS WITH FLOODING AMOUNTS OF WATER, APPLY FROM AS FAR A DISTANCE AS POSSIBLE. AVOID BREATHING VAPORS, KEEP UPWIND.

TOXICITY

ACETOCHLOR: TOXICITY DATA: 2953 MG/KG ORAL-RAT LD50 (85ARAE). CARCINOGEN STATUS: NONE. ACUTE TOXICITY LEVEL: MODERATELY TOXIC BY INGESTION. TARGET EFFECTS: NO DATA AVAILABLE.

HEALTH EFFECTS AND FIRST AID

INHALATION: ACETOCHLOR: **ACUTE EXPOSURE-** NO DATA AVAILABLE. **CHRONIC EXPOSURE-** NO DATA AVAILABLE.

FIRST AID- REMOVE FROM EXPOSURE AREA TO FRESH AIR IMMEDIATELY. IF BREATHING HAS STOPPED, PERFORM ARTIFICIAL RESPIRATION. KEEP PERSON WARM AND AT REST. TREAT SYMPTOMATICALLY AND SUPPORTIVELY. GET MEDICAL ATTENTION IMMEDIATELY.

SKIN CONTACT: ACETOCHLOR: **ACUTE EXPOSURE-** NO DATA AVAILABLE. EXPOSURE TO SOME ACETANILIDE DERIVATIVE HERBICIDES RESULTS IN IRRITATION AND SENSITIZATION. **CHRONIC EXPOSURE-** NO DATA AVAILABLE.

FIRST AID- REMOVE CONTAMINATED CLOTHING AND SHOES IMMEDIATELY. WASH AFFECTED AREA WITH SOAP OR MILD DETERGENT AND LARGE AMOUNTS OF WATER UNTIL NO EVIDENCE OF CHEMICAL REMAINS (APPROXIMATELY 15-20 MINUTES). GET MEDICAL ATTENTION IMMEDIATELY.

EYE CONTACT: ACETOCHLOR: **ACUTE EXPOSURE-** MAY CAUSE IRRITATION. **CHRONIC EXPOSURE-** NO DATA AVAILABLE.

FIRST AID- WASH EYES IMMEDIATELY WITH LARGE AMOUNTS OF WATER OR NORMAL SALINE, OCCASIONALLY LIFTING UPPER AND LOWER LIDS, UNTIL NO EVIDENCE OF CHEMICAL REMAINS (APPROXIMATELY 15-20 MINUTES). GET MEDICAL ATTENTION IMMEDIATELY.

INGESTION: ACETOCHLOR: **ACUTE EXPOSURE-** A LETHAL DOSE IN RATS WAS 2953 MG/KG; SYMPTOMS WERE NOT REPORTED. **CHRONIC EXPOSURE-** NO DATA AVAILABLE.

FIRST AID- TREAT SYMPTOMATICALLY AND SUPPORTIVELY. GET MEDICAL ATTENTION IMMEDIATELY. IF VOMITING OCCURS, KEEP HEAD LOWER THAN HIPS TO PREVENT ASPIRATION.

ANTIDOTE: NO SPECIFIC ANTIDOTE. TREAT SYMPTOMATICALLY AND SUPPORTIVELY.

REACTIVITY

REACTIVITY: STABLE UNDER NORMAL TEMPERATURES AND PRESSURES.

INCOMPATIBILITIES: ACETOCHLOR: OXIDIZERS (STRONG): FIRE AND EXPLOSION HAZARD.

DECOMPOSITION: THERMAL DECOMPOSITION PRODUCTS MAY INCLUDE TOXIC OXIDES OF NITROGEN AND CARBON AND TOXIC AND CORROSIVE FUMES OF CHLORIDES.

POLYMERIZATION: HAZARDOUS POLYMERIZATION HAS NOT BEEN REPORTED TO OCCUR UNDER NORMAL TEMPERATURES AND PRESSURES.

STORAGE AND DISPOSAL

OBSERVE ALL FEDERAL, STATE AND LOCAL REGULATIONS WHEN STORING OR DISPOSING OF THIS SUBSTANCE. FOR ASSISTANCE, CONTACT THE DISTRICT DIRECTOR OF THE ENVIRONMENTAL PROTECTION AGENCY.

****STORAGE****

STORE IN ACCORDANCE WITH 40 CFR 165 RECOMMENDED PROCEDURES FOR THE DISPOSAL AND STORAGE OF PESTICIDES AND PESTICIDE CONTAINERS. STORE AWAY FROM INCOMPATIBLE SUBSTANCES.

****DISPOSAL****

DISPOSAL MUST BE IN ACCORDANCE WITH 40 CFR 165 RECOMMENDED PROCEDURES FOR THE DISPOSAL AND STORAGE OF PESTICIDES AND PESTICIDE CONTAINERS.

CONDITIONS TO AVOID

AVOID CONTACT WITH HEAT, SPARKS, FLAMES, OR OTHER SOURCES OF IGNITION. VAPORS MAY BE EXPLOSIVE. AVOID OVERHEATING OF CONTAINERS; CONTAINERS MAY VIOLENTLY RUPTURE IN HEAT OF FIRE. AVOID CONTAMINATION OF WATER SOURCES.

SPILL AND LEAK PROCEDURES

WATER SPILL: THE CALIFORNIA SAFE DRINKING WATER AND TOXIC ENFORCEMENT ACT OF 1986 (PROPOSITION 65) PROHIBITS CONTAMINATING ANY KNOWN SOURCE OF DRINKING WATER WITH SUBSTANCES KNOWN TO CAUSE CANCER AND/OR REPRODUCTIVE TOXICITY.

OCCUPATIONAL SPILL: SHUT OFF IGNITION SOURCES. STOP LEAK IF YOU CAN DO IT WITHOUT RISK. USE WATER SPRAY TO REDUCE VAPORS. FOR SMALL SPILLS, TAKE UP WITH SAND OR OTHER ABSORBENT MATERIAL AND PLACE INTO CONTAINERS FOR LATER DISPOSAL. FOR LARGER SPILLS, DIKE FAR AHEAD OF SPILL FOR LATER DISPOSAL. NO SMOKING, FLAMES OR FLARES IN HAZARD AREA. KEEP UNNECESSARY PEOPLE AWAY; ISOLATE HAZARD AREA AND RESTRICT ENTRY.

PROTECTIVE EQUIPMENT

VENTILATION: PROVIDE LOCAL EXHAUST OR GENERAL DILUTION VENTILATION SYSTEM.

RESPIRATOR: THE FOLLOWING RESPIRATORS ARE RECOMMENDED BASED ON INFORMATION FOUND IN THE PHYSICAL DATA, TOXICITY AND HEALTH EFFECTS SECTIONS. THEY ARE RANKED IN ORDER FROM MINIMUM TO MAXIMUM RESPIRATORY PROTECTION. THE SPECIFIC RESPIRATOR SELECTED MUST BE BASED ON CONTAMINATION LEVELS FOUND IN THE WORK PLACE, MUST NOT EXCEED THE WORKING LIMITS OF THE RESPIRATOR AND BE JOINTLY APPROVED BY THE NATIONAL INSTITUTE FOR OCCUPATIONAL SAFETY AND HEALTH AND THE MINE SAFETY AND HEALTH ADMINISTRATION (NIOSH-MSHA).

CHEMICAL CARTRIDGE RESPIRATOR WITH FULL FACEPIECE AND PESTICIDE CARTRIDGE.

TYPE 'C' SUPPLIED-AIR RESPIRATOR WITH A FULL FACEPIECE OPERATED IN PRESSURE-DEMAND OR OTHER POSITIVE PRESSURE MODE OR WITH A FULL FACEPIECE, HELMET OR HOOD OPERATED IN CONTINUOUS-FLOW MODE.

SELF-CONTAINED BREATHING APPARATUS OPERATED IN PRESSURE-DEMAND OR OTHER POSITIVE PRESSURE MODE.

FOR FIREFIGHTING AND OTHER IMMEDIATELY DANGEROUS TO LIFE OR HEALTH CONDITIONS:

SELF-CONTAINED BREATHING APPARATUS WITH FULL FACEPIECE OPERATED IN PRESSURE-DEMAND OR OTHER POSITIVE PRESSURE MODE.

SUPPLIED-AIR RESPIRATOR WITH FULL FACEPIECE AND OPERATED IN PRESSURE-DEMAND OR OTHER POSITIVE PRESSURE MODE IN COMBINATION WITH AN AUXILIARY SELF-CONTAINED BREATHING APPARATUS OPERATED IN PRESSURE-DEMAND OR OTHER POSITIVE PRESSURE MODE.

CLOTHING: EMPLOYEE MUST WEAR APPROPRIATE PROTECTIVE (IMPERVIOUS) CLOTHING AND EQUIPMENT TO PREVENT REPEATED OR PROLONGED SKIN CONTACT WITH THIS SUBSTANCE.

GLOVES: EMPLOYEE MUST WEAR APPROPRIATE PROTECTIVE GLOVES TO PREVENT CONTACT WITH THIS SUBSTANCE.

EYE PROTECTION: EMPLOYEE MUST WEAR SPLASH-PROOF OR DUST-RESISTANT SAFETY GOGGLES TO PREVENT EYE CONTACT WITH THIS SUBSTANCE.

EMERGENCY EYE WASH: WHERE THERE IS ANY POSSIBILITY THAT AN EMPLOYEE'S EYES MAY BE EXPOSED TO THIS SUBSTANCE, THE EMPLOYER SHOULD PROVIDE AN EYE WASH FOUNTAIN WITHIN THE IMMEDIATE WORK AREA FOR EMERGENCY USE.

AUTHORIZED BY- OCCUPATIONAL HEALTH SERVICES, INC.

CREATION DATE: 10/04/89 ***REVISION DATE:*** 10/31/89

MATERIAL SAFETY DATA SHEET

OCCUPATIONAL HEALTH SERVICES, INC.
AGRICULTURE AND PESTICIDE DIVISION
450 SEVENTH AVENUE, SUITE 2407
NEW YORK, NEW YORK 10123
1-800-445-MSDS OR (212) 967-1100

EMERGENCY CONTACT:
JOHN S. BRANSFORD, JR. (615) 292-1180

SUBSTANCE IDENTIFICATION

CAS-NUMBER 74222-97-2

SUBSTANCE: **SULFOMETURON-METHYL**

TRADE NAMES/SYNONYMS: BENZOIC ACID, 2-(((((4,6-DIMETHYL-2-PYRIMIDINYL)AMINO)CARBONYL)- AMINO)SULFONYL)-, METHYL ESTER; 2-((((4,6-DIMETHYL-2-PYRIMIDINYL)AMINO)CARBONYL)AMINO)SULFONYL)- BENZOIC ACID METHYL ESTER; METHYL 2-((((4,6-DIMETHYL-2-PYRIMIDINYL)AMINO)CARBONYL)AMINO)- SULFONYL)BENZOATE; METHYL 2-(3-(4,6-DIMETHYLPYRIMIDIN-2-YL)UREIDOSULPHONYL)BENZOATE; DXP 5648; OUST; C15H16N4O5S; PST72544

CHEMICAL FAMILY: UREIDE
PYRIMIDINE
SULFONYL

MOLECULAR FORMULA: C15-H16-N4-O5-S

MOLECULAR WEIGHT: 364.41

CERCLA RATINGS (SCALE 0-3): HEALTH=U FIRE=1 REACTIVITY=0 PERSISTENCE=2

NFPA RATINGS (SCALE 0-4): HEALTH=U FIRE=1 REACTIVITY=0

COMPONENTS AND CONTAMINANTS

COMPONENT: SULFOMETURON-METHYL ***PERCENT:*** 100.0
CAS# 74222-97-2

EXPOSURE LIMITS: NO OCCUPATIONAL EXPOSURE LIMITS ESTABLISHED BY OSHA, ACGIH, OR NIOSH.

PHYSICAL DATA

DESCRIPTION: ODORLESS, COLORLESS TO WHITE SOLID.

MELTING POINT: 397-401 F (203-205 C) ***SPECIFIC GRAVITY:*** 1.48

VAPOR PRESSURE: NEGLIGIBLE ***SOLUBILITY IN WATER:*** 10 PPM

SOLVENT SOLUBILITY: SOLUBLE IN ACETONE AND ACETONITRILE; SLIGHTLY SOLUBLE IN ETHANOL, ETHER AND XYLENE.

FIRE AND EXPLOSION DATA

FIRE AND EXPLOSION HAZARD: SLIGHT FIRE HAZARD WHEN EXPOSED TO HEAT OR FLAME.
DUST-AIR MIXTURES MAY IGNITE OR EXPLODE.

FIREFIGHTING MEDIA: DRY CHEMICAL, CARBON DIOXIDE, HALON, WATER SPRAY OR STANDARD FOAM (1987 EMERGENCY RESPONSE GUIDEBOOK, DOT P 5800.4).
FOR LARGER FIRES, USE WATER SPRAY, FOG OR STANDARD FOAM (1987 EMERGENCY RESPONSE GUIDEBOOK, DOT P 5800.4).

FIREFIGHTING: MOVE CONTAINER FROM FIRE AREA IF POSSIBLE. DO NOT SCATTER SPILLED MATERIAL WITH HIGH PRESSURE WATER STREAMS. DIKE FIRE CONTROL WATER FOR LATER DISPOSAL (1987 EMERGENCY RESPONSE GUIDEBOOK, DOT P 5800.4, GUIDE PAGE 31).
USE AGENTS SUITABLE FOR TYPE OF SURROUNDING FIRE. AVOID BREATHING HAZARDOUS VAPORS, KEEP UPWIND.

TOXICITY

SULFOMETURON-METHYL: IRRITATION DATA: 10 MG EYE-RABBIT MILD. TOXICITY DATA: >5000 MG/KG ORAL-RAT LD50 (85JFAN). CARCINOGEN STATUS: NONE. ACUTE TOXICITY LEVEL: SLIGHTLY TOXIC BY INGESTION. TARGET EFFECTS: NO DATA AVAILABLE.

HEALTH EFFECTS AND FIRST AID

INHALATION: SULFOMETURON-METHYL: **ACUTE EXPOSURE-** INHALATION OF DUST MAY IRRITATE THE NOSE AND THROAT AND CAUSE COUGHING AND CHEST DISCOMFORT. **CHRONIC EXPOSURE-** NO DATA AVAILABLE.

FIRST AID- REMOVE FROM EXPOSURE AREA TO FRESH AIR IMMEDIATELY. IF BREATHING HAS STOPPED, PERFORM ARTIFICIAL RESPIRATION. KEEP PERSON WARM AND AT REST. TREAT SYMPTOMATICALLY AND SUPPORTIVELY. GET MEDICAL ATTENTION IMMEDIATELY.

SKIN CONTACT: SULFOMETURON-METHYL: **ACUTE EXPOSURE-** THIS MATERIAL WAS SLIGHTLY IRRITATING TO RABBIT SKIN. IT DID NOT INDUCE SENSITIZATION IN GUINEA PIGS. **CHRONIC EXPOSURE-** PROLONGED OR REPEATED EXPOSURE MAY CAUSE IRRITATION.

FIRST AID- REMOVE CONTAMINATED CLOTHING AND SHOES IMMEDIATELY. WASH AFFECTED AREA WITH SOAP OR MILD DETERGENT AND LARGE AMOUNTS OF WATER UNTIL NO EVIDENCE OF CHEMICAL REMAINS (APPROXIMATELY 15-20 MINUTES). GET MEDICAL ATTENTION IMMEDIATELY.

EYE CONTACT: SULFOMETURON-METHYL: **ACUTE EXPOSURE-** THIS MATERIAL WAS MILDLY IRRITATING TO RABBIT EYES. **CHRONIC EXPOSURE-** NO DATA AVAILABLE.

FIRST AID- WASH EYES IMMEDIATELY WITH LARGE AMOUNTS OF WATER OR NORMAL SALINE, OCCASIONALLY LIFTING UPPER AND LOWER LIDS, UNTIL NO EVIDENCE OF CHEMICAL REMAINS (APPROXIMATELY 15-20 MINUTES). GET MEDICAL ATTENTION IMMEDIATELY.

INGESTION: SULFOMETURON-METHYL: **ACUTE EXPOSURE-** MAY CAUSE NAUSEA AND VOMITING. THE LD50 FOR RATS WAS GREATER THAN 5000 MG/KG. **CHRONIC EXPOSURE-** HEMOLYTIC EFFECTS AND DECREASED BRAIN AND BODY WEIGHTS WERE OBSERVED IN RATS RECEIVING A FORMULATION OF SULFOMETURON-METHYL AT LEVELS OF 5000 PPM.

FIRST AID- TREAT SYMPTOMATICALLY AND SUPPORTIVELY. GET MEDICAL ATTENTION IMMEDIATELY. IF VOMITING OCCURS, KEEP HEAD LOWER THAN HIPS TO PREVENT ASPIRATION.

ANTIDOTE: NO SPECIFIC ANTIDOTE. TREAT SYMPTOMATICALLY AND SUPPORTIVELY.

REACTIVITY

REACTIVITY: STABLE UNDER NORMAL TEMPERATURES AND PRESSURES.

INCOMPATIBILITIES: SULFOMETURON-METHYL: OXIDIZERS (STRONG): FIRE AND EXPLOSION HAZARD.

DECOMPOSITION: THERMAL DECOMPOSITION PRODUCTS MAY INCLUDE TOXIC OXIDES OF CARBON, NITROGEN, AND SULFUR.

POLYMERIZATION: HAZARDOUS POLYMERIZATION HAS NOT BEEN REPORTED TO OCCUR UNDER NORMAL TEMPERATURES AND PRESSURES.

STORAGE AND DISPOSAL

OBSERVE ALL FEDERAL, STATE AND LOCAL REGULATIONS WHEN STORING OR DISPOSING OF THIS SUBSTANCE. FOR ASSISTANCE, CONTACT THE DISTRICT DIRECTOR OF THE ENVIRONMENTAL PROTECTION AGENCY.

STORAGE

STORE IN ACCORDANCE WITH 40 CFR 165 RECOMMENDED PROCEDURES FOR THE DISPOSAL AND STORAGE OF PESTICIDES AND PESTICIDE CONTAINERS.
STORE AWAY FROM INCOMPATIBLE SUBSTANCES.

DISPOSAL

DISPOSAL MUST BE IN ACCORDANCE WITH 40 CFR 165 RECOMMENDED PROCEDURES FOR THE DISPOSAL AND STORAGE OF PESTICIDES AND PESTICIDE CONTAINERS.

CONDITIONS TO AVOID

MAY BURN BUT DOES NOT IGNITE READILY. AVOID CONTACT WITH STRONG OXIDIZERS, EXCESSIVE HEAT, SPARKS, OR OPEN FLAME.

SPILL AND LEAK PROCEDURES

OCCUPATIONAL SPILL: SWEEP UP AND PLACE IN SUITABLE CLEAN, DRY CONTAINERS FOR RECLAMATION OR LATER DISPOSAL. DO NOT FLUSH SPILLED MATERIAL INTO SEWER. KEEP UNNECESSARY PEOPLE AWAY.

PROTECTIVE EQUIPMENT

VENTILATION: PROVIDE LOCAL EXHAUST OR GENERAL DILUTION VENTILATION SYSTEM.

RESPIRATOR: THE FOLLOWING RESPIRATORS ARE RECOMMENDED BASED ON INFORMATION FOUND IN THE PHYSICAL DATA, TOXICITY AND HEALTH EFFECTS SECTIONS. THEY ARE RANKED IN ORDER FROM MINIMUM TO MAXIMUM RESPIRATORY PROTECTION. THE SPECIFIC RESPIRATOR SELECTED MUST BE BASED ON CONTAMINATION LEVELS FOUND IN THE WORK PLACE, MUST NOT EXCEED THE WORKING LIMITS OF THE RESPIRATOR AND BE JOINTLY APPROVED BY THE NATIONAL INSTITUTE FOR OCCUPATIONAL SAFETY AND HEALTH AND THE MINE SAFETY AND HEALTH ADMINISTRATION (NIOSH-MSHA).
CHEMICAL CARTRIDGE RESPIRATOR WITH AN ORGANIC VAPOR CARTRIDGE(S) IN COMBINATION WITH A DUST AND MIST FILTER.
GAS MASK WITH ORGANIC VAPOR CANISTER (CHIN-STYLE OR FRONT- OR BACK-MOUNTED CANISTER) WITH A DUST AND MIST FILTER.
GAS MASK WITH ORGANIC VAPOR CANISTER (CHIN-STYLE OR FRONT- OR BACK-MOUNTED CANISTER) WITH A PARTICULATE FILTER.
POWERED AIR-PURIFYING RESPIRATOR WITH A HIGH-EFFICIENCY FILTER.
TYPE 'C' SUPPLIED-AIR RESPIRATOR WITH A FULL FACEPIECE OPERATED IN A PRESSURE-DEMAND OR OTHER POSITIVE PRESSURE MODE.
SELF-CONTAINED BREATHING APPARATUS WITH A FULL FACEPIECE OPERATED IN

PRESSURE-DEMAND OR OTHER POSITIVE PRESSURE MODE.
FOR FIREFIGHTING AND OTHER IMMEDIATELY DANGEROUS TO LIFE OR HEALTH CONDITIONS:
SELF-CONTAINED BREATHING APPARATUS WITH FULL FACEPIECE OPERATED IN PRESSURE-DEMAND OR OTHER POSITIVE PRESSURE MODE. SUPPLIED-AIR RESPIRATOR WITH FULL FACEPIECE AND OPERATED IN PRESSURE-DEMAND OR OTHER POSITIVE PRESSURE MODE IN COMBINATION WITH AN AUXILIARY SELF-CONTAINED BREATHING APPARATUS OPERATED IN PRESSURE-DEMAND OR OTHER POSITIVE PRESSURE MODE.

CLOTHING: EMPLOYEE MUST WEAR APPROPRIATE PROTECTIVE (IMPERVIOUS) CLOTHING AND EQUIPMENT TO PREVENT REPEATED OR PROLONGED SKIN CONTACT WITH THIS SUBSTANCE.

GLOVES: EMPLOYEE MUST WEAR APPROPRIATE PROTECTIVE GLOVES TO PREVENT CONTACT WITH THIS SUBSTANCE.

EYE PROTECTION: EMPLOYEE MUST WEAR SPLASH-PROOF OR DUST-RESISTANT SAFETY GOGGLES TO PREVENT EYE CONTACT WITH THIS SUBSTANCE.
EMERGENCY EYE WASH: WHERE THERE IS ANY POSSIBILITY THAT AN EMPLOYEE'S EYES MAY BE EXPOSED TO THIS SUBSTANCE, THE EMPLOYER SHOULD PROVIDE AN EYE WASH FOUNTAIN WITHIN THE IMMEDIATE WORK AREA FOR EMERGENCY USE.

AUTHORIZED BY- OCCUPATIONAL HEALTH SERVICES, INC.
CREATION DATE: 05/22/90 ***REVISION DATE:*** 05/31/90

MATERIAL SAFETY DATA SHEET

OCCUPATIONAL HEALTH SERVICES, INC.
AGRICULTURE AND PESTICIDE DIVISION
450 SEVENTH AVENUE, SUITE 2407
NEW YORK, NEW YORK 10123
1-800-445-MSDS OR (212) 967-1100

EMERGENCY CONTACT:
JOHN S. BRANSFORD, JR. (615) 292-1180

SUBSTANCE IDENTIFICATION

CAS-NUMBER 74223-64-6

SUBSTANCE: METSULFURON-METHYL

TRADE NAMES/SYNONYMS: BENZOIC ACID, 2-((((4-METHOXY-6-METHYL-1,3,5-TRIAZIN-2-YL)AMINO) CARBONYL)AMINO)SULFONYL)-, METHYL ESTER; 2-(((((4-METHOXY-6-METHYL-1,3,5-TRIAZIN-2-YL)AMINO)CARBONYL)AMINO) SULFONYL)BENZOIC ACID, METHYL ESTER; METHYL-2-((((4-METHOXY-6-METHYL-1,3,5-TRIAZIN-2-YL)-AMINO)CARBONYL) AMINO)SULFONYL)BENZOATE; ALLIE; ALLY 20DF; DPD 63760H; DPX 6376; DPX-T 6376; ESCORT; GROPPER; METSULFURON METHYL; C14H15N5O6S; PST72546

CHEMICAL FAMILY: SUBSTITUTED UREA

MOLECULAR FORMULA: C14-H15-N5-O6-S

MOLECULAR WEIGHT: 381.4

CERCLA RATINGS (SCALE 0-3): HEALTH=2 FIRE=1 REACTIVITY=0 PERSISTENCE=0

NFPA RATINGS (SCALE 0-4): HEALTH=2 FIRE=1 REACTIVITY=0

COMPONENTS AND CONTAMINANTS

COMPONENT: METSULFURON-METHYL ***PERCENT:*** 100.0
CAS# 74223-64-6

OTHER CONTAMINANTS: NONE

EXPOSURE LIMITS: NO OCCUPATIONAL EXPOSURE LIMITS ESTABLISHED BY OSHA, ACGIH, OR NIOSH.

PHYSICAL DATA

DESCRIPTION: COLORLESS TO PALE YELLOW CRYSTALLINE SOLID.

MELTING POINT: 325-331 F (163-166 C) ***SPECIFIC GRAVITY:*** NOT AVAILABLE

VAPOR PRESSURE: NEGLIGIBLE ***SOLUBILITY IN WATER:*** 0.95% @ 20 C

SOLVENT SOLUBILITY: SOLUBLE IN ACETONE, DICHLOROMETHANE, ETHANOL, METHANOL, AND XYLENE; SLIGHTLY SOLUBLE IN HEXANE.

FIRE AND EXPLOSION DATA

FIRE AND EXPLOSION HAZARD: SLIGHT FIRE HAZARD WHEN EXPOSED TO HEAT OR FLAME.

FIREFIGHTING MEDIA: DRY CHEMICAL, CARBON DIOXIDE, HALON, WATER SPRAY OR STANDARD FOAM (1987 EMERGENCY RESPONSE GUIDEBOOK, DOT P 5800.4).
FOR LARGER FIRES, USE WATER SPRAY, FOG OR STANDARD FOAM (1987 EMERGENCY RESPONSE GUIDEBOOK, DOT P 5800.4).

FIREFIGHTING: MOVE CONTAINERS FROM FIRE AREA IF POSSIBLE. FIGHT FIRE FROM MAXIMUM DISTANCE. STAY AWAY FROM STORAGE TANK ENDS. DIKE FIRE CONTROL WATER FOR LATER DISPOSAL. DO NOT SCATTER MATERIAL (1987 EMERGENCY RESPONSE GUIDEBOOK, DOT P 5800.4, GUIDE PAGE 55).
EXTINGUISH USING AGENT SUITABLE FOR TYPE OF SURROUNDING FIRE. USE WATER IN FLOODING QUANTITIES AS FOG. KEEP SPARKS, FLAMES AND OTHER SOURCES OF IGNITION AWAY. KEEP MATERIAL OUT OF WATER SOURCES AND SEWERS. DO NOT TOUCH MATERIAL AND AVOID BREATHING DUSTS AND FUMES FROM BURNING MATERIAL. KEEP UPWIND.

TOXICITY

METSULFURON-METHYL: TOXICITY DATA: >2000 MG/KG SKIN-RABBIT LD50 (FMCHA2); >5000 MG/KG ORAL-RAT LD50 (FMCHA2). CARCINOGEN STATUS: NONE. ACUTE TOXICITY LEVEL: MODERATELY TOXIC BY DERMAL ABSORPTION AND INGESTION. TARGET EFFECTS: NO DATA AVAILABLE.

HEALTH EFFECTS AND FIRST AID

INHALATION: METSULFURON-METHYL: **ACUTE EXPOSURE-** MANY SUBSTITUTED UREA HERBICIDES ARE MODERATELY IRRITATING TO THE MUCOUS MEMBRANES.
CHRONIC EXPOSURE- NO DATA AVAILABLE.

FIRST AID- REMOVE FROM EXPOSURE AREA TO FRESH AIR IMMEDIATELY. IF BREATHING HAS STOPPED, PERFORM ARTIFICIAL RESPIRATION. KEEP PERSON WARM AND AT REST. TREAT SYMPTOMATICALLY AND SUPPORTIVELY. GET MEDICAL ATTENTION IMMEDIATELY.

SKIN CONTACT: METSULFURON-METHYL: **ACUTE EXPOSURE-** MANY SUBSTITUTED UREA HERBICIDES ARE MODERATELY IRRITATING TO THE SKIN. A LETHAL DOSE IN RABBITS BY DERMAL ABSORPTION IS GREATER THAN 2000 MG/KG. **CHRONIC EXPOSURE-** NO DATA AVAILABLE.

FIRST AID- REMOVE CONTAMINATED CLOTHING AND SHOES IMMEDIATELY. WASH AFFECTED AREA WITH SOAP OR MILD DETERGENT AND LARGE AMOUNTS OF WATER UNTIL NO EVIDENCE OF CHEMICAL REMAINS (APPROXIMATELY 15-20 MINUTES). GET MEDICAL ATTENTION IMMEDIATELY.

EYE CONTACT: METSULFURON-METHYL: **ACUTE EXPOSURE-** MANY SUBSTITUTED UREA HERBICIDES ARE MODERATELY IRRITATING TO THE EYES. **CHRONIC EXPOSURE-** NO DATA AVAILABLE.

FIRST AID- WASH EYES IMMEDIATELY WITH LARGE AMOUNTS OF WATER OR NORMAL SALINE, OCCASIONALLY LIFTING UPPER AND LOWER LIDS, UNTIL NO EVIDENCE OF CHEMICAL REMAINS (APPROXIMATELY 15-20 MINUTES). GET MEDICAL ATTENTION IMMEDIATELY.

INGESTION: METSULFURON-METHYL: **ACUTE EXPOSURE-** A LETHAL DOSE IN RATS WAS GREATER THAN 5000 MG/KG. **CHRONIC EXPOSURE-** NO DATA AVAILABLE.

FIRST AID- TREAT SYMPTOMATICALLY AND SUPPORTIVELY. GET MEDICAL ATTENTION IMMEDIATELY. IF VOMITING OCCURS, KEEP HEAD LOWER THAN HIPS TO PREVENT ASPIRATION.

ANTIDOTE: NO SPECIFIC ANTIDOTE. TREAT SYMPTOMATICALLY AND SUPPORTIVELY.

REACTIVITY

REACTIVITY: STABLE UNDER NORMAL TEMPERATURES AND PRESSURES.

INCOMPATIBILITIES: METSULFURON-METHYL: ACIDS: MAY HYDROLYZE. OXIDIZERS (STRONG): FIRE AND EXPLOSION HAZARD.

DECOMPOSITION: THERMAL DECOMPOSITION PRODUCTS MAY INCLUDE TOXIC OXIDES OF CARBON, NITROGEN, AND SULFUR.

POLYMERIZATION: HAZARDOUS POLYMERIZATION HAS NOT BEEN REPORTED TO OCCUR UNDER NORMAL TEMPERATURES AND PRESSURES.

STORAGE AND DISPOSAL

OBSERVE ALL FEDERAL, STATE AND LOCAL REGULATIONS WHEN STORING OR DISPOSING OF THIS SUBSTANCE. FOR ASSISTANCE, CONTACT THE DISTRICT DIRECTOR OF THE ENVIRONMENTAL PROTECTION AGENCY.

STORAGE

STORE IN ACCORDANCE WITH 40 CFR 165 RECOMMENDED PROCEDURES FOR THE DISPOSAL AND STORAGE OF PESTICIDES AND PESTICIDE CONTAINERS.
STORE AWAY FROM INCOMPATIBLE SUBSTANCES.

DISPOSAL

DISPOSAL MUST BE IN ACCORDANCE WITH 40 CFR 165 RECOMMENDED PROCEDURES FOR THE DISPOSAL AND STORAGE OF PESTICIDES AND PESTICIDE CONTAINERS.

CONDITIONS TO AVOID

MAY BURN BUT DOES NOT IGNITE READILY. CONTAINERS MAY EXPLODE IN HEAT OF FIRE.

SPILL AND LEAK PROCEDURES

OCCUPATIONAL SPILL: DO NOT TOUCH SPILLED MATERIAL. STOP LEAK IF YOU CAN DO IT WITHOUT RISK. USE WATER SPRAY TO REDUCE VAPORS. FOR SMALL SPILLS, TAKE UP WITH SAND OR OTHER ABSORBENT MATERIAL AND PLACE INTO CONTAINERS FOR LATER DISPOSAL. FOR SMALL DRY SPILLS, WITH A CLEAN SHOVEL PLACE MATERIAL INTO CLEAN, DRY CONTAINERS AND COVER. MOVE CONTAINERS FROM SPILL AREA. FOR LARGER SPILLS, DIKE FAR AHEAD OF SPILL FOR LATER DISPOSAL. KEEP UNNECESSARY PEOPLE AWAY. ISOLATE HAZARD AREA AND DENY ENTRY. VENTILATE CLOSED SPACES BEFORE ENTERING.

PROTECTIVE EQUIPMENT

VENTILATION: PROVIDE LOCAL EXHAUST OR GENERAL DILUTION VENTILATION SYSTEM.

RESPIRATOR: THE FOLLOWING RESPIRATORS ARE RECOMMENDED BASED ON INFORMATION FOUND IN THE PHYSICAL DATA, TOXICITY AND HEALTH EFFECTS SECTIONS. THEY ARE RANKED IN ORDER FROM MINIMUM TO MAXIMUM RESPIRATORY PROTECTION. THE SPECIFIC RESPIRATOR SELECTED MUST BE BASED ON CONTAMINATION LEVELS FOUND IN THE WORK PLACE, MUST NOT EXCEED THE WORKING LIMITS OF THE RESPIRATOR AND BE JOINTLY APPROVED BY THE NATIONAL INSTITUTE FOR OCCUPATIONAL SAFETY AND HEALTH AND THE MINE SAFETY AND HEALTH ADMINISTRATION (NIOSH-MSHA).

CHEMICAL CARTRIDGE RESPIRATOR WITH AN ORGANIC VAPOR CARTRIDGE(S) WITH A FULL FACEPIECE AND ORGANIC VAPOR CARTRIDGE(S) IN COMBINATION WITH A DUST AND MIST FILTER.

POWERED AIR-PURIFYING RESPIRATOR WITH A TIGHT-FITTING FACEPIECE AND ORGANIC VAPOR CARTRIDGE(S) IN COMBINATION WITH A HIGH-EFFICIENCY PARTICULATE FILTER.

TYPE 'C' SUPPLIED-AIR RESPIRATOR WITH A FULL FACEPIECE OPERATED IN A PRESSURE-DEMAND OR OTHER POSITIVE PRESSURE MODE.

SELF-CONTAINED BREATHING APPARATUS WITH A FULL FACEPIECE OPERATED IN PRESSURE-DEMAND OR OTHER POSITIVE PRESSURE MODE.

FOR FIREFIGHTING AND OTHER IMMEDIATELY DANGEROUS TO LIFE OR HEALTH CONDITIONS:

SELF-CONTAINED BREATHING APPARATUS WITH FULL FACEPIECE OPERATED IN PRESSURE-DEMAND OR OTHER POSITIVE PRESSURE MODE.

SUPPLIED-AIR RESPIRATOR WITH FULL FACEPIECE AND OPERATED IN PRESSURE-DEMAND OR OTHER POSITIVE PRESSURE MODE IN COMBINATION WITH AN AUXILIARY SELF-CONTAINED BREATHING APPARATUS OPERATED IN PRESSURE-DEMAND OR OTHER POSITIVE PRESSURE MODE.

CLOTHING: EMPLOYEE MUST WEAR APPROPRIATE PROTECTIVE (IMPERVIOUS) CLOTHING AND EQUIPMENT TO PREVENT REPEATED OR PROLONGED SKIN CONTACT WITH THIS SUBSTANCE.

GLOVES: EMPLOYEE MUST WEAR APPROPRIATE PROTECTIVE GLOVES TO PREVENT CONTACT WITH THIS SUBSTANCE.

EYE PROTECTION: EMPLOYEE MUST WEAR SPLASH-PROOF OR DUST-RESISTANT SAFETY GOGGLES TO PREVENT EYE CONTACT WITH THIS SUBSTANCE.

EMERGENCY EYE WASH: WHERE THERE IS ANY POSSIBILITY THAT AN EMPLOYEE'S EYES MAY BE EXPOSED TO THIS SUBSTANCE, THE EMPLOYER SHOULD PROVIDE AN EYE WASH FOUNTAIN WITHIN THE IMMEDIATE WORK AREA FOR EMERGENCY USE.

AUTHORIZED BY- OCCUPATIONAL HEALTH SERVICES, INC.

CREATION DATE: 10/04/89 ***REVISION DATE:*** 05/18/90

MATERIAL SAFETY DATA SHEET

OCCUPATIONAL HEALTH SERVICES, INC.
AGRICULTURE AND PESTICIDE DIVISION
450 SEVENTH AVENUE, SUITE 2407
NEW YORK, NEW YORK 10123
1-800-445-MSDS OR (212) 967-1100

EMERGENCY CONTACT:
JOHN S. BRANSFORD, JR. (615) 292-1180

SUBSTANCE IDENTIFICATION

CAS-NUMBER 30043-49-3

SUBSTANCE: **ETHIDIMURON**

TRADE NAMES/SYNONYMS: UREA, N-(5-(ETHYLSULFONYL)-1,3,4-THIADIAZOL-2-YL)-N,N'-DIMETHYL-; UREA, 1-(5-(ETHYLSULFONYL)-1,3,4-THIADIAZOL-2-YL)-1,3-DIMETHYL-; N-(5-(ETHYLSULFONYL)-1,3,4-THIADIAZOL-2-YL)-N,N'-DIMETHYLUREA; 1-(5-(ETHYLSULFONYL)-1,3,4-THIADIAZOL-2-YL)-1,3-DIMETHYLUREA; 1-(5-ETHYLSULPHONYL-1,3-4-THIADIAZOL-2-YL)-1,3-DIMETHYLUREA; BAY MET-1486; MET 1486; SULFODIAZOL; USTILAN; C7H12N4O3S2; PST72551

CHEMICAL FAMILY: SUBSTITUTED UREA

MOLECULAR FORMULA: C7-H12-N4-O3-S2

MOLECULAR WEIGHT: 264.35

CERCLA RATINGS (SCALE 0-3): HEALTH=2 FIRE=1 REACTIVITY=0 PERSISTENCE=3

NFPA RATINGS (SCALE 0-4): HEALTH=2 FIRE=1 REACTIVITY=0

COMPONENTS AND CONTAMINANTS

COMPONENT: ETHIDIMURON ***PERCENT:*** 100.0

CAS# 30043-49-3

OTHER CONTAMINANTS: NONE

EXPOSURE LIMITS: NO OCCUPATIONAL EXPOSURE LIMITS ESTABLISHED BY OSHA, ACGIH, OR NIOSH.

PHYSICAL DATA

DESCRIPTION: COLORLESS CRYSTALLINE SOLID. ***MELTING POINT:*** 313 F (156 C)

SPECIFIC GRAVITY: NOT AVAILABLE ***VAPOR PRESSURE:*** NEGLIGIBLE

SOLUBILITY IN WATER: 0.296%

SOLVENT SOLUBILITY: SOLUBLE IN DICHLOROMETHANE, 2-PROPANOL. DECOMPOSES ABOVE 423 F (217 C)

FIRE AND EXPLOSION DATA

FIRE AND EXPLOSION HAZARD: SLIGHT FIRE HAZARD WHEN EXPOSED TO HEAT OR FLAME.

FIREFIGHTING MEDIA: DRY CHEMICAL, CARBON DIOXIDE, HALON, WATER SPRAY OR STANDARD FOAM (1987 EMERGENCY RESPONSE GUIDEBOOK, DOT P 5800.4). FOR LARGER FIRES, USE WATER SPRAY, FOG OR STANDARD FOAM (1987 EMERGENCY RESPONSE GUIDEBOOK, DOT P 5800.4).

FIREFIGHTING: MOVE CONTAINERS FROM FIRE AREA IF POSSIBLE. FIGHT FIRE FROM MAXIMUM DISTANCE. STAY AWAY FROM STORAGE TANK ENDS. DIKE FIRE CONTROL WATER FOR LATER DISPOSAL. DO NOT SCATTER MATERIAL (1987 EMERGENCY RESPONSE GUIDEBOOK, DOT P 5800.4, GUIDE PAGE 55). EXTINGUISH USING AGENT SUITABLE FOR TYPE OF SURROUNDING FIRE. USE WATER IN FLOODING QUANTITIES AS FOG. KEEP SPARKS, FLAMES AND OTHER SOURCES OF IGNITION AWAY. KEEP MATERIAL OUT OF WATER SOURCES AND SEWERS. DO NOT TOUCH MATERIAL AND AVOID BREATHING DUSTS AND FUMES FROM BURNING MATERIAL. KEEP UPWIND.

TOXICITY

ETHIDIMURON: 5000 MG/KG ORAL-RAT LD50; 300 MG/KG ORAL-QUAIL LD50. CARCINOGEN STATUS: NONE. ETHIDIMURON MAY CAUSE EYE, SKIN AND MUCOUS MEMBRANE IRRITATION.

HEALTH EFFECTS AND FIRST AID

INHALATION: ETHIDIMURON: **ACUTE EXPOSURE-** MANY SUBSTITUTED UREA HERBICIDES ARE MODERATELY IRRITATING TO THE MUCOUS MEMBRANES. **CHRONIC EXPOSURE-** NO DATA AVAILABLE.

FIRST AID- REMOVE FROM EXPOSURE AREA TO FRESH AIR IMMEDIATELY. IF BREATHING HAS STOPPED, PERFORM ARTIFICIAL RESPIRATION. KEEP PERSON WARM AND AT REST. TREAT SYMPTOMATICALLY AND SUPPORTIVELY. GET MEDICAL ATTENTION IMMEDIATELY.

SKIN CONTACT: ETHIDIMURON: **ACUTE EXPOSURE-** MANY SUBSTITUTED UREA HERBICIDES ARE MODERATELY IRRITATING TO THE SKIN. A LETHAL DOSE IN RATS BY DERMAL ABSORPTION IS GREATER THAN 1000 MG/KG. **CHRONIC EXPOSURE-** NO DATA AVAILABLE.

FIRST AID- REMOVE CONTAMINATED CLOTHING AND SHOES IMMEDIATELY. WASH AFFECTED AREA WITH SOAP OR MILD DETERGENT AND LARGE AMOUNTS OF WATER UNTIL NO EVIDENCE OF CHEMICAL REMAINS (APPROXIMATELY 15-20 MINUTES). GET MEDICAL ATTENTION IMMEDIATELY.

EYE CONTACT: ETHIDIMURON: **ACUTE EXPOSURE-** MANY SUBSTITUTED UREA HERBICIDES ARE MODERATELY IRRITATING TO THE EYES. **CHRONIC EXPOSURE-** NO DATA AVAILABLE.

FIRST AID- WASH EYES IMMEDIATELY WITH LARGE AMOUNTS OF WATER OR NORMAL SALINE, OCCASIONALLY LIFTING UPPER AND LOWER LIDS, UNTIL NO EVIDENCE OF CHEMICAL REMAINS (APPROXIMATELY 15-20 MINUTES). GET MEDICAL ATTENTION IMMEDIATELY.

INGESTION: ETHIDIMURON: **ACUTE EXPOSURE-** A LETHAL DOSE IN RATS WAS 5000 MG/KG; SYMPTOMS WERE NOT REPORTED. **CHRONIC EXPOSURE-** NO OBSERVABLE EFFECTS WERE NOTED IN A 90-DAY STUDY OF RATS AT A DIETARY LEVEL OF 1000 MG/KG.

FIRST AID- TREAT SYMPTOMATICALLY AND SUPPORTIVELY. GET MEDICAL ATTENTION IMMEDIATELY. IF VOMITING OCCURS, KEEP HEAD LOWER THAN HIPS TO PREVENT ASPIRATION.

ANTIDOTE: NO SPECIFIC ANTIDOTE. TREAT SYMPTOMATICALLY AND SUPPORTIVELY.

REACTIVITY

REACTIVITY: STABLE UNDER NORMAL TEMPERATURES AND PRESSURES.
INCOMPATIBILITIES: ETHIDIMURON: ALKALI: HYDROLYZES OXIDIZERS (STRONG): FIRE AND EXPLOSION HAZARD.
DECOMPOSITION: THERMAL DECOMPOSITION PRODUCTS MAY INCLUDE TOXIC OXIDES OF CARBON, NITROGEN, AND SULFUR.
POLYMERIZATION: HAZARDOUS POLYMERIZATION HAS NOT BEEN REPORTED TO OCCUR UNDER NORMAL TEMPERATURES AND PRESSURES.

STORAGE AND DISPOSAL

OBSERVE ALL FEDERAL, STATE AND LOCAL REGULATIONS WHEN STORING OR DISPOSING OF THIS SUBSTANCE. FOR ASSISTANCE, CONTACT THE DISTRICT DIRECTOR OF THE ENVIRONMENTAL PROTECTION AGENCY.

STORAGE

STORE IN ACCORDANCE WITH 40 CFR 165 RECOMMENDED PROCEDURES FOR THE DISPOSAL AND STORAGE OF PESTICIDES AND PESTICIDE CONTAINERS.
STORE AWAY FROM INCOMPATIBLE SUBSTANCES.

DISPOSAL

DISPOSAL MUST BE IN ACCORDANCE WITH 40 CFR 165 RECOMMENDED PROCEDURES FOR THE DISPOSAL AND STORAGE OF PESTICIDES AND PESTICIDE CONTAINERS.

CONDITIONS TO AVOID

MAY BURN BUT DOES NOT IGNITE READILY. CONTAINERS MAY EXPLODE IN HEAT OF FIRE.

SPILL AND LEAK PROCEDURES

OCCUPATIONAL SPILL: DO NOT TOUCH SPILLED MATERIAL. STOP LEAK IF YOU CAN DO IT WITHOUT RISK. USE WATER SPRAY TO REDUCE VAPORS. FOR SMALL SPILLS, TAKE UP WITH SAND OR OTHER ABSORBENT MATERIAL AND PLACE INTO CONTAINERS FOR LATER DISPOSAL. FOR SMALL DRY SPILLS, WITH A CLEAN SHOVEL PLACE MATERIAL INTO CLEAN, DRY CONTAINERS AND COVER. MOVE CONTAINERS FROM SPILL AREA. FOR LARGER SPILLS, DIKE FAR AHEAD OF SPILL FOR LATER DISPOSAL. KEEP UNNECESSARY PEOPLE AWAY. ISOLATE HAZARD AREA AND DENY ENTRY. VENTILATE CLOSED SPACES BEFORE ENTERING.

PROTECTIVE EQUIPMENT

VENTILATION: PROVIDE LOCAL EXHAUST OR GENERAL DILUTION VENTILATION SYSTEM.
RESPIRATOR: THE FOLLOWING RESPIRATORS ARE RECOMMENDED BASED ON INFORMATION FOUND IN THE PHYSICAL DATA, TOXICITY AND HEALTH EFFECTS SECTIONS. THEY ARE RANKED IN ORDER FROM MINIMUM TO MAXIMUM RESPIRATORY PROTECTION. THE SPECIFIC RESPIRATOR SELECTED MUST BE BASED ON CONTAMINATION LEVELS FOUND IN THE WORK PLACE, MUST NOT EXCEED THE WORKING LIMITS OF THE RESPIRATOR AND BE JOINTLY APPROVED BY THE NATIONAL INSTITUTE FOR OCCUPATIONAL SAFETY AND HEALTH AND THE MINE SAFETY AND HEALTH ADMINISTRATION (NIOSH-MSHA).
CHEMICAL CARTRIDGE RESPIRATOR WITH AN ORGANIC VAPOR CARTRIDGE(S) WITH A FULL FACEPIECE AND ORGANIC VAPOR CARTRIDGE(S) IN COMBINATION WITH A DUST AND MIST FILTER.
POWERED AIR-PURIFYING RESPIRATOR WITH A TIGHT-FITTING FACEPIECE AND ORGANIC VAPOR CARTRIDGE(S) IN COMBINATION WITH A HIGH-EFFICIENCY PARTICULATE FILTER.
TYPE 'C' SUPPLIED-AIR RESPIRATOR WITH A FULL FACEPIECE OPERATED IN A PRESSURE-DEMAND OR OTHER POSITIVE PRESSURE MODE.
SELF-CONTAINED BREATHING APPARATUS WITH A FULL FACEPIECE OPERATED IN PRESSURE-DEMAND OR OTHER POSITIVE PRESSURE MODE.
FOR FIREFIGHTING AND OTHER IMMEDIATELY DANGEROUS TO LIFE OR HEALTH CONDITIONS:
SELF-CONTAINED BREATHING APPARATUS WITH FULL FACEPIECE OPERATED IN PRESSURE-DEMAND OR OTHER POSITIVE PRESSURE MODE.
SUPPLIED-AIR RESPIRATOR WITH FULL FACEPIECE AND OPERATED IN PRESSURE-DEMAND OR OTHER POSITIVE PRESSURE MODE IN COMBINATION WITH AN AUXILIARY SELF-CONTAINED BREATHING APPARATUS OPERATED IN PRESSURE-DEMAND OR OTHER POSITIVE PRESSURE MODE.
CLOTHING: EMPLOYEE MUST WEAR APPROPRIATE PROTECTIVE (IMPERVIOUS) CLOTHING AND EQUIPMENT TO PREVENT REPEATED OR PROLONGED SKIN CONTACT WITH THIS SUBSTANCE.
GLOVES: EMPLOYEE MUST WEAR APPROPRIATE PROTECTIVE GLOVES TO PREVENT CONTACT WITH THIS SUBSTANCE.
EYE PROTECTION: EMPLOYEE MUST WEAR SPLASH-PROOF OR DUST-RESISTANT SAFETY GOGGLES TO PREVENT EYE CONTACT WITH THIS SUBSTANCE.
EMERGENCY EYE WASH: WHERE THERE IS ANY POSSIBILITY THAT AN EMPLOYEE'S EYES MAY BE EXPOSED TO THIS SUBSTANCE, THE EMPLOYER SHOULD PROVIDE AN EYE WASH FOUNTAIN WITHIN THE IMMEDIATE WORK AREA FOR EMERGENCY USE.

AUTHORIZED BY- OCCUPATIONAL HEALTH SERVICES, INC.
CREATION DATE: 10/04/89 ***REVISION DATE:*** 05/07/90

MATERIAL SAFETY DATA SHEET

OCCUPATIONAL HEALTH SERVICES, INC.
AGRICULTURE AND PESTICIDE DIVISION
450 SEVENTH AVENUE, SUITE 2407
NEW YORK, NEW YORK 10123
1-800-445-MSDS OR (212) 967-1100

EMERGENCY CONTACT:
JOHN S. BRANSFORD, JR. (615) 292-1180

SUBSTANCE IDENTIFICATION

CAS-NUMBER 65195-55-3
SUBSTANCE: **AVERMECTIN B1A**
TRADE NAMES/SYNONYMS: AVERMECTIN A1A, 5-O-DEMETHYL-; 5-O-DEMETHYLAVERMECTIN A1A; ANTIBIOTIC C 076B1A; AVERMECTIN; C48H72O14; PST72553
CHEMICAL FAMILY: ANTIBIOTIC
MOLECULAR FORMULA: C48-H72-O14
MOLECULAR WEIGHT: 873.10
CERCLA RATINGS (SCALE 0-3): HEALTH=3 FIRE=1 REACTIVITY=0 PERSISTENCE=0
NFPA RATINGS (SCALE 0-4): HEALTH=3 FIRE=1 REACTIVITY=0

COMPONENTS AND CONTAMINANTS

COMPONENT: AVERMECTIN B1A ***PERCENT:*** 100.0
CAS# 65195-55-3
OTHER CONTAMINANTS: NONE
EXPOSURE LIMITS: NO OCCUPATIONAL EXPOSURE LIMITS ESTABLISHED BY OSHA, ACGIH, OR NIOSH.

PHYSICAL DATA

DESCRIPTION: SOLID. ***MELTING POINT:*** NOT AVAILABLE
SPECIFIC GRAVITY: NOT AVAILABLE ***SOLUBILITY IN WATER:*** NOT AVAILABLE

FIRE AND EXPLOSION DATA

FIRE AND EXPLOSION HAZARD: SLIGHT FIRE HAZARD WHEN EXPOSED TO HEAT OR FLAME.
FIREFIGHTING MEDIA: DRY CHEMICAL, CARBON DIOXIDE, HALON, WATER SPRAY OR STANDARD FOAM (1987 EMERGENCY RESPONSE GUIDEBOOK, DOT P 5800.4).
FOR LARGER FIRES, USE WATER SPRAY, FOG OR STANDARD FOAM (1987 EMERGENCY RESPONSE GUIDEBOOK, DOT P 5800.4).
FIREFIGHTING: MOVE CONTAINER FROM FIRE AREA IF POSSIBLE. DO NOT SCATTER SPILLED MATERIAL WITH HIGH PRESSURE WATER STREAMS. DIKE FIRE CONTROL WATER FOR LATER DISPOSAL (1987 EMERGENCY RESPONSE GUIDEBOOK, DOT P 5800.4, GUIDE PAGE 31).
USE AGENTS SUITABLE FOR TYPE OF SURROUNDING FIRE. AVOID BREATHING HAZARDOUS VAPORS, KEEP UPWIND.

TOXICITY

AVERMECTIN B1A: TOXICITY DATA: 400 MG/KG SKIN-RABBIT LD50; 400 MG/KG SKIN-RAT LD50; 10 MG/KG ORAL-RAT LD20; 10 MG/KG ORAL-MOUSE LD20. CARCINOGEN STATUS: NONE. ACUTE TOXICITY LEVEL: TOXIC BY DERMAL ABSORPTION. TARGET EFFECTS: NO DATA AVAILABLE.

HEALTH EFFECTS AND FIRST AID

INHALATION: AVERMECTIN B1A: **ACUTE EXPOSURE-** NO DATA AVAILABLE. **CHRONIC EXPOSURE-** NO DATA AVAILABLE.
FIRST AID- REMOVE FROM EXPOSURE AREA TO FRESH AIR IMMEDIATELY. IF BREATHING HAS STOPPED, PERFORM ARTIFICIAL RESPIRATION. KEEP PERSON WARM AND AT REST. TREAT SYMPTOMATICALLY AND SUPPORTIVELY. GET MEDICAL ATTENTION IMMEDIATELY.

SKIN CONTACT: AVERMECTIN B1A: TOXIC. **ACUTE EXPOSURE-**THE LETHAL DOSE REPORTED IN RABBITS WAS 400 MG/KG. THE SYMPTOMS WERE NOT REPORTED. **CHRONIC EXPOSURE-** NO DATA AVAILABLE.
FIRST AID- REMOVE CONTAMINATED CLOTHING AND SHOES IMMEDIATELY. WASH AFFECTED AREA WITH SOAP OR MILD DETERGENT AND LARGE AMOUNTS OF

WATER UNTIL NO EVIDENCE OF CHEMICAL REMAINS (APPROXIMATELY 15-20 MINUTES). GET MEDICAL ATTENTION IMMEDIATELY.

EYE CONTACT: AVERMECTIN B1A: **ACUTE EXPOSURE**- NO DATA AVAILABLE. **CHRONIC EXPOSURE**- NO DATA AVAILABLE.

FIRST AID- WASH EYES IMMEDIATELY WITH LARGE AMOUNTS OF WATER OR NORMAL SALINE, OCCASIONALLY LIFTING UPPER AND LOWER LIDS, UNTIL NO EVIDENCE OF CHEMICAL REMAINS (APPROXIMATELY 15-20 MINUTES). GET MEDICAL ATTENTION IMMEDIATELY.

INGESTION: AVERMECTIN B1A: **ACUTE EXPOSURE**- DOSES OF 10 MG/KG WERE LETHAL TO SOME RATS AND MICE. **CHRONIC EXPOSURE**- NO DATA AVAILABLE.

FIRST AID- TREAT SYMPTOMATICALLY AND SUPPORTIVELY. GET MEDICAL ATTENTION IMMEDIATELY. IF VOMITING OCCURS, KEEP HEAD LOWER THAN HIPS TO PREVENT ASPIRATION.

ANTIDOTE: NO SPECIFIC ANTIDOTE. TREAT SYMPTOMATICALLY AND SUPPORTIVELY.

REACTIVITY

REACTIVITY: STABLE UNDER NORMAL TEMPERATURES AND PRESSURES.

INCOMPATIBILITIES: AVERMECTIN B1A: OXIDIZERS (STRONG): FIRE AND EXPLOSION HAZARD.

DECOMPOSITION: THERMAL DECOMPOSITION PRODUCTS MAY INCLUDE TOXIC OXIDES OF CARBON.

POLYMERIZATION: HAZARDOUS POLYMERIZATION HAS NOT BEEN REPORTED TO OCCUR UNDER NORMAL TEMPERATURES AND PRESSURES.

STORAGE AND DISPOSAL

OBSERVE ALL FEDERAL, STATE AND LOCAL REGULATIONS WHEN STORING OR DISPOSING OF THIS SUBSTANCE. FOR ASSISTANCE, CONTACT THE DISTRICT DIRECTOR OF THE ENVIRONMENTAL PROTECTION AGENCY.

STORAGE

STORE AWAY FROM INCOMPATIBLE SUBSTANCES.

CONDITIONS TO AVOID

MAY BURN BUT DOES NOT IGNITE READILY. AVOID CONTACT WITH STRONG OXIDIZERS, EXCESSIVE HEAT, SPARKS, OR OPEN FLAME.

SPILL AND LEAK PROCEDURES

OCCUPATIONAL SPILL: SWEEP UP AND PLACE IN SUITABLE CLEAN, DRY CONTAINERS FOR RECLAMATION OR LATER DISPOSAL. DO NOT FLUSH SPILLED MATERIAL INTO SEWER. KEEP UNNECESSARY PEOPLE AWAY.

PROTECTIVE EQUIPMENT

VENTILATION: PROVIDE LOCAL EXHAUST OR PROCESS ENCLOSURE VENTILATION. VENTILATION EQUIPMENT MUST BE EXPLOSION-PROOF.

RESPIRATOR: THE FOLLOWING RESPIRATORS ARE RECOMMENDED BASED ON INFORMATION FOUND IN THE PHYSICAL DATA, TOXICITY AND HEALTH EFFECTS SECTIONS. THEY ARE RANKED IN ORDER FROM MINIMUM TO MAXIMUM RESPIRATORY PROTECTION. THE SPECIFIC RESPIRATOR SELECTED MUST BE BASED ON CONTAMINATION LEVELS FOUND IN THE WORK PLACE, MUST NOT EXCEED THE WORKING LIMITS OF THE RESPIRATOR AND BE JOINTLY APPROVED BY THE NATIONAL INSTITUTE FOR OCCUPATIONAL SAFETY AND HEALTH AND THE MINE SAFETY AND HEALTH ADMINISTRATION (NIOSH-MSHA).

TYPE 'C' SUPPLIED-AIR RESPIRATOR WITH A FULL FACEPIECE OPERATED IN PRESSURE-DEMAND OR OTHER POSITIVE PRESSURE MODE OR WITH A FULL FACEPIECE, HELMET OR HOOD OPERATED IN CONTINOUS-FLOW MODE.

SELF-CONTAINED BREATHING APPARATUS WITH A FULL FACEPIECE OPERATED IN PRESSURE-DEMAND OR OTHER POSITIVE PRESSURE MODE.

FOR FIREFIGHTING AND OTHER IMMEDIATELY DANGEROUS TO LIFE OR HEALTH CONDITIONS:

SELF-CONTAINED BREATHING APPARATUS WITH FULL FACEPIECE OPERATED IN PRESSURE-DEMAND OR OTHER POSITIVE PRESSURE MODE.

SUPPLIED-AIR RESPIRATOR WITH FULL FACEPIECE AND OPERATED IN PRESSURE-DEMAND OR OTHER POSITIVE PRESSURE MODE IN COMBINATION WITH AN AUXILIARY SELF-CONTAINED BREATHING APPARATUS OPERATED IN PRESSURE-DEMAND OR OTHER POSITIVE PRESSURE MODE.

CLOTHING: EMPLOYEE MUST WEAR APPROPRIATE PROTECTIVE (IMPERVIOUS) CLOTHING AND EQUIPMENT TO PREVENT REPEATED OR PROLONGED SKIN CONTACT WITH THIS SUBSTANCE.

GLOVES: EMPLOYEE MUST WEAR APPROPRIATE PROTECTIVE GLOVES TO PREVENT CONTACT WITH THIS SUBSTANCE.

EYE PROTECTION: EMPLOYEE MUST WEAR SPLASH-PROOF OR DUST-RESISTANT SAFETY GOGGLES TO PREVENT EYE CONTACT WITH THIS SUBSTANCE.

EMERGENCY EYE WASH: WHERE THERE IS ANY POSSIBILITY THAT AN EMPLOYEE'S EYES MAY BE EXPOSED TO THIS SUBSTANCE, THE EMPLOYER SHOULD PROVIDE AN EYE WASH FOUNTAIN WITHIN THE IMMEDIATE WORK AREA FOR EMERGENCY USE.

AUTHORIZED BY- OCCUPATIONAL HEALTH SERVICES, INC.
CREATION DATE: 11/17/89 ***REVISION DATE:*** 05/31/90

MATERIAL SAFETY DATA SHEET

OCCUPATIONAL HEALTH SERVICES, INC.
AGRICULTURE AND PESTICIDE DIVISION
450 SEVENTH AVENUE, SUITE 2407
NEW YORK, NEW YORK 10123
1-800-445-MSDS OR (212) 967-1100

EMERGENCY CONTACT:
JOHN S. BRANSFORD, JR. (615) 292-1180

SUBSTANCE IDENTIFICATION

CAS-NUMBER 69806-50-4

SUBSTANCE: **FLUAZIFOP-BUTYL**

TRADE NAMES/SYNONYMS: PROPANOIC ACID, 2-(4-((5-(TRIFLUOROMETHYL)-2-PYRIDINYL)OXY)PHENOXY)-, BUTYL ESTER; 2-(4-((5-(TRIFLUOROMETHYL)-2-PYRIDINYL)OXY)PHENOXY)PROPANOIC ACID BUTYL ESTER; BUTYL (RS)-2-(4-(5-TRIFLUOROMETHYL-2-PYRIDYLOXY)PHENOXY)PROPIONATE; BUTYL (+-)-2-(4-((5-(TRIFLUOROMETHYL)-2-PYRIDINYL)OXY) PHENOXY) PROPANOATE; BUTYL 2-(4-(5-TRIFLUOROMETHYL-2-PYRIDYLOXY)PHENOXY)PROPIONATE; BUTYL 2-(4-((5-(TRIFLUOROMETHYL)-2-PYRIDINYL)OXY)PHENOXY)PROPANOATE; FUSILADE; HACHE UNO SUPER; ONECIDE; PP 009; TF 1169; C19H20F3NO4; PST72554

CHEMICAL FAMILY: ESTER
ETHER
PYRIDINE

MOLECULAR FORMULA: C19-H20-F3-N-O4

MOLECULAR WEIGHT: 383.40

CERCLA RATINGS (SCALE 0-3): HEALTH=U FIRE=U REACTIVITY=0 PERSISTENCE=2

NFPA RATINGS (SCALE 0-4): HEALTH=U FIRE=U REACTIVITY=0

COMPONENTS AND CONTAMINANTS

COMPONENT: FLUAZIFOP-BUTYL ***PERCENT:*** 100.0
CAS# 69806-50-4

OTHER CONTAMINANTS: NONE

EXPOSURE LIMITS: NO OCCUPATIONAL EXPOSURE LIMITS ESTABLISHED BY OSHA, ACGIH, OR NIOSH.

PHYSICAL DATA

DESCRIPTION: PALE STRAW COLORED LIQUID.

BOILING POINT: 338 F (170 C) @ 0.5 MMHG

MELTING POINT: 55 F (13 C) ***SPECIFIC GRAVITY:*** 1.21 @ 20 C

VAPOR PRESSURE: NEGLIGIBLE @ 20 C ***SOLUBILITY IN WATER:*** 2 PPM

SOLVENT SOLUBILITY: SOLUBLE IN ACETONE, CYCLOHEXANONE, HEXANE, METHANOL, DICHLOROMETHANE, XYLENE, AND MOST ORGANIC SOLVENTS; MODERATELY SOLUBLE IN PROPYLENE GLYCOL.

FIRE AND EXPLOSION DATA

FIRE AND EXPLOSION HAZARD: UNKNOWN FIRE AND EXPLOSION HAZARD.

FLASH POINT: NOT AVAILABLE

FIREFIGHTING MEDIA: DRY CHEMICAL, CARBON DIOXIDE, HALON, WATER SPRAY OR STANDARD FOAM (1987 EMERGENCY RESPONSE GUIDEBOOK, DOT P 5800.4). FOR LARGER FIRES, USE WATER SPRAY, FOG OR STANDARD FOAM (1987 EMERGENCY RESPONSE GUIDEBOOK, DOT P 5800.4).

FIREFIGHTING: MOVE CONTAINER FROM FIRE AREA IF POSSIBLE. COOL FIRE-EXPOSED CONTAINERS WITH WATER FROM SIDE UNTIL WELL AFTER FIRE IS OUT. STAY AWAY FROM STORAGE TANK ENDS. FOR MASSIVE FIRE IN STORAGE AREA, USE UNMANNED HOSE HOLDER OR MONITOR NOZZLES, ELSE WITHDRAW FROM AREA AND LET FIRE BURN. WITHDRAW IMMEDIATELY IN CASE OF RISING SOUND FROM VENTING SAFETY DEVICE OR ANY DISCOLORATION OF STORAGE TANK DUE TO FIRE (1987 EMERGENCY RESPONSE GUIDEBOOK, DOT P 5800.4, GUIDE PAGE 27). EXTINGUISH ONLY IF FLOW CAN BE STOPPED; USE FLOODING AMOUNTS OF WATER AS A FOG, SOLID STREAMS MAY BE INEFFECTIVE. COOL CONTAINERS WITH FLOODING AMOUNTS OF WATER, APPLY FROM AS FAR A DISTANCE AS POSSIBLE. AVOID BREATHING VAPORS, KEEP UPWIND.

TOXICITY

FLUAZIFOP-BUTYL: TOXICITY DATA: >2420 MG/KG SKIN-RABBIT LD50 (85JFAN); >6050 MG/KG SKIN-RAT LD50 (85JFAN); 3328 MG/KG ORAL-RAT LD50; 621

MG/KG ORAL-RABBIT LD50; 1490 MG/KG ORAL-MOUSE LD50; 2659 MG/KG ORAL-GUINEA PIG LD50. CARCINOGEN STATUS: NONE. ACUTE TOXICITY LEVEL: MODERATELY TOXIC BY INGESTION; SLIGHTLY TOXIC BY DERMAL ABSORPTION. TARGET EFFECTS: NO DATA AVAILABLE.

HEALTH EFFECTS AND FIRST AID

INHALATION: FLUAZIFOP-BUTYL: **ACUTE EXPOSURE-** NO DATA AVAILABLE. **CHRONIC EXPOSURE-** NO DATA AVAILABLE.
FIRST AID- REMOVE FROM EXPOSURE AREA TO FRESH AIR IMMEDIATELY. IF BREATHING HAS STOPPED, PERFORM ARTIFICIAL RESPIRATION. KEEP PERSON WARM AND AT REST. TREAT SYMPTOMATICALLY AND SUPPORTIVELY. GET MEDICAL ATTENTION IMMEDIATELY.

SKIN CONTACT: FLUAZIFOP-BUTYL: **ACUTE EXPOSURE-** THIS MATERIAL WAS MILDLY IRRITATING TO RABBIT SKIN. **CHRONIC EXPOSURE-** NO DATA AVAILABLE.
FIRST AID- REMOVE CONTAMINATED CLOTHING AND SHOES IMMEDIATELY. WASH AFFECTED AREA WITH SOAP OR MILD DETERGENT AND LARGE AMOUNTS OF WATER UNTIL NO EVIDENCE OF CHEMICAL REMAINS (APPROXIMATELY 15-20 MINUTES). GET MEDICAL ATTENTION IMMEDIATELY.

EYE CONTACT: FLUAZIFOP-BUTYL: **ACUTE EXPOSURE-** MAY CAUSE IRRITATION. **CHRONIC EXPOSURE-** NO DATA AVAILABLE.
FIRST AID- WASH EYES IMMEDIATELY WITH LARGE AMOUNTS OF WATER OR NORMAL SALINE, OCCASIONALLY LIFTING UPPER AND LOWER LIDS, UNTIL NO EVIDENCE OF CHEMICAL REMAINS (APPROXIMATELY 15-20 MINUTES). GET MEDICAL ATTENTION IMMEDIATELY.

INGESTION: FLUAZIFOP-BUTYL: **ACUTE EXPOSURE-** A LETHAL DOSE REPORTED IN RATS WAS 3328 MG/KG; SYMPTOMS WERE NOT REPORTED. **CHRONIC EXPOSURE-** THIS MATERIAL INDUCED DIAPHRAGMATIC HERNIA IN RAT AT MODERATE DOSE LEVELS IN ORAL TERATOGENICITY STUDIES.
FIRST AID- IF THE PERSON IS CONSCIOUS AND NOT CONVULSING, REMOVE BY GASTRIC LAVAGE AND FOLLOW WITH A CATHARTIC (DREISBACH, HANDBOOK OF POISONING, 12TH ED.). TREAT SYMPTOMATICALLY AND SUPPORTIVELY. GASTRIC LAVAGE SHOULD BE PERFORMED BY QUALIFIED MEDICAL PERSONNEL. GET MEDICAL ATTENTION IMMEDIATELY.
ANTIDOTE: NO SPECIFIC ANTIDOTE. TREAT SYMPTOMATICALLY AND SUPPORTIVELY.

REACTIVITY

REACTIVITY: STABLE UNDER NORMAL TEMPERATURES AND PRESSURES.
INCOMPATIBILITIES: FLUAZIFOP-BUTYL: OXIDIZERS (STRONG): FIRE AND EXPLOSION HAZARD.
DECOMPOSITION: THERMAL DECOMPOSITION PRODUCTS MAY INCLUDE HIGHLY TOXIC FUMES OF FLUORIDES AND OXIDES OF NITROGEN AND CARBON.
POLYMERIZATION: HAZARDOUS POLYMERIZATION HAS NOT BEEN REPORTED TO OCCUR UNDER NORMAL TEMPERATURES AND PRESSURES.

STORAGE AND DISPOSAL

OBSERVE ALL FEDERAL, STATE AND LOCAL REGULATIONS WHEN STORING OR DISPOSING OF THIS SUBSTANCE. FOR ASSISTANCE, CONTACT THE DISTRICT DIRECTOR OF THE ENVIRONMENTAL PROTECTION AGENCY.

STORAGE

STORE IN ACCORDANCE WITH 40 CFR 165 RECOMMENDED PROCEDURES FOR THE DISPOSAL AND STORAGE OF PESTICIDES AND PESTICIDE CONTAINERS.
STORE AWAY FROM INCOMPATIBLE SUBSTANCES.

DISPOSAL

DISPOSAL MUST BE IN ACCORDANCE WITH 40 CFR 165 RECOMMENDED PROCEDURES FOR THE DISPOSAL AND STORAGE OF PESTICIDES AND PESTICIDE CONTAINERS.

CONDITIONS TO AVOID

AVOID CONTACT WITH HEAT, SPARKS, FLAMES, OR OTHER SOURCES OF IGNITION. VAPORS MAY BE EXPLOSIVE. AVOID OVERHEATING OF CONTAINERS; CONTAINERS MAY VIOLENTLY RUPTURE IN HEAT OF FIRE. AVOID CONTAMINATION OF WATER SOURCES.

SPILL AND LEAK PROCEDURES

OCCUPATIONAL SPILL: SHUT OFF IGNITION SOURCES. STOP LEAK IF YOU CAN DO IT WITHOUT RISK. USE WATER SPRAY TO REDUCE VAPORS. FOR SMALL SPILLS, TAKE UP WITH SAND OR OTHER ABSORBENT MATERIAL AND PLACE INTO CONTAINERS FOR LATER DISPOSAL. FOR LARGER SPILLS, DIKE FAR AHEAD OF SPILL FOR LATER DISPOSAL. NO SMOKING, FLAMES OR FLARES IN HAZARD AREA. KEEP UNNECESSARY PEOPLE AWAY; ISOLATE HAZARD AREA AND RESTRICT ENTRY.

PROTECTIVE EQUIPMENT

VENTILATION: PROVIDE LOCAL EXHAUST OR GENERAL DILUTION VENTILATION. VENTILATION EQUIPMENT MUST BE EXPLOSION-PROOF.
RESPIRATOR: THE FOLLOWING RESPIRATORS ARE RECOMMENDED BASED ON INFORMATION FOUND IN THE PHYSICAL DATA, TOXICITY AND HEALTH EFFECTS SECTIONS. THEY ARE RANKED IN ORDER FROM MINIMUM TO MAXIMUM RESPIRATORY PROTECTION. THE SPECIFIC RESPIRATOR SELECTED MUST BE BASED ON CONTAMINATION LEVELS FOUND IN THE WORK PLACE, MUST NOT EXCEED THE WORKING LIMITS OF THE RESPIRATOR AND BE JOINTLY APPROVED BY THE NATIONAL INSTITUTE FOR OCCUPATIONAL SAFETY AND HEALTH AND THE MINE SAFETY AND HEALTH ADMINISTRATION (NIOSH-MSHA).
CHEMICAL CARTRIDGE RESPIRATOR WITH PESTICIDE CARTRIDGE.
GAS MASK WITH A PESTICIDE CANISTER (CHIN-STYLE OR FRONT- OR BACK-MOUNTED CANISTER).
TYPE 'C' SUPPLIED-AIR RESPIRATOR OPERATED IN THE PRESSURE-DEMAND OR OTHER POSITIVE PRESSURE OR CONTINUOUS-FLOW MODE.
SELF-CONTAINED BREATHING APPARATUS.
FOR FIREFIGHTING AND OTHER IMMEDIATELY DANGEROUS TO LIFE OR HEALTH CONDITIONS:
SELF-CONTAINED BREATHING APPARATUS WITH FULL FACEPIECE OPERATED IN PRESSURE-DEMAND OR OTHER POSITIVE PRESSURE MODE.
SUPPLIED-AIR RESPIRATOR WITH FULL FACEPIECE AND OPERATED IN PRESSURE-DEMAND OR OTHER POSITIVE PRESSURE MODE IN COMBINATION WITH AN AUXILIARY SELF-CONTAINED BREATHING APPARATUS OPERATED IN PRESSURE-DEMAND OR OTHER POSITIVE PRESSURE MODE.
CLOTHING: EMPLOYEE MUST WEAR APPROPRIATE PROTECTIVE (IMPERVIOUS) CLOTHING AND EQUIPMENT TO PREVENT REPEATED OR PROLONGED SKIN CONTACT WITH THIS SUBSTANCE.
GLOVES: EMPLOYEE MUST WEAR APPROPRIATE PROTECTIVE GLOVES TO PREVENT CONTACT WITH THIS SUBSTANCE.
EYE PROTECTION: EMPLOYEE MUST WEAR SPLASH-PROOF OR DUST-RESISTANT SAFETY GOGGLES TO PREVENT EYE CONTACT WITH THIS SUBSTANCE.
EMERGENCY EYE WASH: WHERE THERE IS ANY POSSIBILITY THAT AN EMPLOYEE'S EYES MAY BE EXPOSED TO THIS SUBSTANCE, THE EMPLOYER SHOULD PROVIDE AN EYE WASH FOUNTAIN WITHIN THE IMMEDIATE WORK AREA FOR EMERGENCY USE.

AUTHORIZED BY- OCCUPATIONAL HEALTH SERVICES, INC.
CREATION DATE: 05/21/90 ***REVISION DATE:*** 05/21/90

MATERIAL SAFETY DATA SHEET

OCCUPATIONAL HEALTH SERVICES, INC.
AGRICULTURE AND PESTICIDE DIVISION
450 SEVENTH AVENUE, SUITE 2407
NEW YORK, NEW YORK 10123
1-800-445-MSDS OR (212) 967-1100

EMERGENCY CONTACT:
JOHN S. BRANSFORD, JR. (615) 292-1180

SUBSTANCE IDENTIFICATION

CAS-NUMBER 79241-46-6
SUBSTANCE: **FLUAZIFOP-P-BUTYL**
TRADE NAMES/SYNONYMS: PROPANOIC ACID, 2-(4-((5-TRIFLUOROMETHYL)-2-PYRIDINYL)OXY)PHENOXY)-, BUTYL ESTER, (R)-; (R)-2-(4-((5-(TRIFLUOROMETHYL)-2-PYRIDINYL)OXY)PHENOXY)PROPANOIC ACID BUTYL ESTER; BUTYL (R)-2-(4-(5-TRIFLUOROMETHYL-2-PYRIDYLOXY)PHENOXY)PROPIONATE; BUTYL (R)-2-(4-((5-(TRIFLUOROMETHYL)-2-PYRIDINYL)OXY)PHENOXY) PROPANOATE; FUSILADE 2000; FUSILADE 5 (FORMULATION); PP 005; C19H20F3NO4; PST72557
CHEMICAL FAMILY: ESTER
ETHER
PYRIDINE
MOLECULAR FORMULA: C19-H20-F3-N-O4
MOLECULAR WEIGHT: 383.40
CERCLA RATINGS (SCALE 0-3): HEALTH=U FIRE=U REACTIVITY=0 PERSISTENCE=2
NFPA RATINGS (SCALE 0-4): HEALTH=U FIRE=U REACTIVITY=0

COMPONENTS AND CONTAMINANTS

COMPONENT: FLUAZIFOP-P-BUTYL ***PERCENT:*** 100.0
CAS# 79241-46-6
EXPOSURE LIMITS: NO OCCUPATIONAL EXPOSURE LIMITS ESTABLISHED BY OSHA, ACGIH, OR NIOSH.

PHYSICAL DATA

DESCRIPTION: PALE LIQUID. ***BOILING POINT:*** NOT AVAILABLE
MELTING POINT: APPROXIMATELY 41 F (5 C) ***SPECIFIC GRAVITY:*** NOT AVAILABLE
VAPOR PRESSURE: NEGLIGIBLE @ 20 C ***SOLUBILITY IN WATER:*** 1 PPM
SOLVENT SOLUBILITY: SOLUBLE IN ACETONE, HEXANE, METHANOL, DICHLOROMETHANE, ETHYL ACETATE, TOLUENE, XYLENE, AND MOST ORGANIC SOLVENTS.

FIRE AND EXPLOSION DATA

FIRE AND EXPLOSION HAZARD: UNKNOWN FIRE AND EXPLOSION HAZARD.
FIREFIGHTING MEDIA: DRY CHEMICAL, CARBON DIOXIDE, HALON, WATER SPRAY OR STANDARD FOAM (1987 EMERGENCY RESPONSE GUIDEBOOK, DOT P 5800.4). FOR LARGER FIRES, USE WATER SPRAY, FOG OR STANDARD FOAM (1987 EMERGENCY RESPONSE GUIDEBOOK, DOT P 5800.4).
FIREFIGHTING: MOVE CONTAINER FROM FIRE AREA IF POSSIBLE. COOL FIRE-EXPOSED CONTAINERS WITH WATER FROM SIDE UNTIL WELL AFTER FIRE IS OUT. STAY AWAY FROM STORAGE TANK ENDS. FOR MASSIVE FIRE IN STORAGE AREA, USE UNMANNED HOSE HOLDER OR MONITOR NOZZLES, ELSE WITHDRAW FROM AREA AND LET FIRE BURN. WITHDRAW IMMEDIATELY IN CASE OF RISING SOUND FROM VENTING SAFETY DEVICE OR ANY DISCOLORATION OF STORAGE TANK DUE TO FIRE (1987 EMERGENCY RESPONSE GUIDEBOOK, DOT P 5800.4, GUIDE PAGE 27). EXTINGUISH ONLY IF FLOW CAN BE STOPPED; USE FLOODING AMOUNTS OF WATER AS A FOG, SOLID STREAMS MAY BE INEFFECTIVE. COOL CONTAINERS WITH FLOODING AMOUNTS OF WATER, APPLY FROM AS FAR A DISTANCE AS POSSIBLE. AVOID BREATHING VAPORS, KEEP UPWIND.

TOXICITY

FLUAZIFOP-P-BUTYL: TOXICITY DATA: >2400 MG/KG SKIN-RABBIT LD50 (85JFAN); 2451 MG/KG ORAL-RAT LD50. CARCINOGEN STATUS: NONE. ACUTE TOXICITY LEVEL: MODERATELY TOXIC BY INGESTION; SLIGHTLY TOXIC BY DERMAL ABSORPTION. TARGET EFFECTS: NO DATA AVAILABLE.

HEALTH EFFECTS AND FIRST AID

INHALATION: FLUAZIFOP-P-BUTYL: **ACUTE EXPOSURE**- NO DATA AVAILABLE. **CHRONIC EXPOSURE**- NO DATA AVAILABLE.
FIRST AID- REMOVE FROM EXPOSURE AREA TO FRESH AIR IMMEDIATELY. IF BREATHING HAS STOPPED, PERFORM ARTIFICIAL RESPIRATION. KEEP PERSON WARM AND AT REST. TREAT SYMPTOMATICALLY AND SUPPORTIVELY. GET MEDICAL ATTENTION IMMEDIATELY.

SKIN CONTACT: FLUAZIFOP-P-BUTYL: **ACUTE EXPOSURE**- THIS MATERIAL WAS MILDLY IRRITATING TO RABBIT SKIN. **CHRONIC EXPOSURE**- NO DATA AVAILABLE.
FIRST AID- REMOVE CONTAMINATED CLOTHING AND SHOES IMMEDIATELY. WASH AFFECTED AREA WITH SOAP OR MILD DETERGENT AND LARGE AMOUNTS OF WATER UNTIL NO EVIDENCE OF CHEMICAL REMAINS (APPROXIMATELY 15-20 MINUTES). GET MEDICAL ATTENTION IMMEDIATELY.

EYE CONTACT: FLUAZIFOP-P-BUTYL: **ACUTE EXPOSURE**- THIS MATERIAL WAS MILDLY IRRITATING TO RABBIT EYES. **CHRONIC EXPOSURE**- NO DATA AVAILABLE.
FIRST AID- WASH EYES IMMEDIATELY WITH LARGE AMOUNTS OF WATER OR NORMAL SALINE, OCCASIONALLY LIFTING UPPER AND LOWER LIDS, UNTIL NO EVIDENCE OF CHEMICAL REMAINS (APPROXIMATELY 15-20 MINUTES). GET MEDICAL ATTENTION IMMEDIATELY.

INGESTION: FLUAZIFOP-P-BUTYL: **ACUTE EXPOSURE**- THE LETHAL DOSE REPORTED IN RATS WAS 2721 MG/KG; SYMPTOMS WERE NOT REPORTED. **CHRONIC EXPOSURE**- NO DATA AVAILABLE.
FIRST AID- IF THE PERSON IS CONSCIOUS AND NOT CONVULSING, REMOVE BY GASTRIC LAVAGE AND FOLLOW WITH A CATHARTIC (DREISBACH, HANDBOOK OF POISONING, 12TH ED.). TREAT SYMPTOMATICALLY AND SUPPORTIVELY. GASTRIC LAVAGE SHOULD BE PERFORMED BY QUALIFIED MEDICAL PERSONNEL. GET MEDICAL ATTENTION IMMEDIATELY.
ANTIDOTE: NO SPECIFIC ANTIDOTE. TREAT SYMPTOMATICALLY AND SUPPORTIVELY.

REACTIVITY

REACTIVITY: STABLE UNDER NORMAL TEMPERATURES AND PRESSURES.
INCOMPATIBILITIES: FLUAZIFOP-P-BUTYL: OXIDIZERS (STRONG): FIRE AND EXPLOSION HAZARD.
DECOMPOSITION: THERMAL DECOMPOSITION PRODUCTS MAY INCLUDE HIGHLY TOXIC FUMES OF FLUORIDES AND OXIDES OF NITROGEN AND CARBON.
POLYMERIZATION: HAZARDOUS POLYMERIZATION HAS NOT BEEN REPORTED TO OCCUR UNDER NORMAL TEMPERATURES AND PRESSURES.

STORAGE AND DISPOSAL

OBSERVE ALL FEDERAL, STATE AND LOCAL REGULATIONS WHEN STORING OR DISPOSING OF THIS SUBSTANCE. FOR ASSISTANCE, CONTACT THE DISTRICT DIRECTOR OF THE ENVIRONMENTAL PROTECTION AGENCY.

****STORAGE****

STORE IN ACCORDANCE WITH 40 CFR 165 RECOMMENDED PROCEDURES FOR THE DISPOSAL AND STORAGE OF PESTICIDES AND PESTICIDE CONTAINERS. STORE AWAY FROM INCOMPATIBLE SUBSTANCES.

****DISPOSAL****

DISPOSAL MUST BE IN ACCORDANCE WITH 40 CFR 165 RECOMMENDED PROCEDURES FOR THE DISPOSAL AND STORAGE OF PESTICIDES AND PESTICIDE CONTAINERS.

CONDITIONS TO AVOID

AVOID CONTACT WITH HEAT, SPARKS, FLAMES, OR OTHER SOURCES OF IGNITION. VAPORS MAY BE EXPLOSIVE. AVOID OVERHEATING OF CONTAINERS; CONTAINERS MAY VIOLENTLY RUPTURE IN HEAT OF FIRE. AVOID CONTAMINATION OF WATER SOURCES.

SPILL AND LEAK PROCEDURES

OCCUPATIONAL SPILL: SHUT OFF IGNITION SOURCES. STOP LEAK IF YOU CAN DO IT WITHOUT RISK. USE WATER SPRAY TO REDUCE VAPORS. FOR SMALL SPILLS, TAKE UP WITH SAND OR OTHER ABSORBENT MATERIAL AND PLACE INTO CONTAINERS FOR LATER DISPOSAL. FOR LARGER SPILLS, DIKE FAR AHEAD OF SPILL FOR LATER DISPOSAL. NO SMOKING, FLAMES OR FLARES IN HAZARD AREA. KEEP UNNECESSARY PEOPLE AWAY; ISOLATE HAZARD AREA AND RESTRICT ENTRY.

PROTECTIVE EQUIPMENT

VENTILATION: PROVIDE LOCAL EXHAUST OR GENERAL DILUTION VENTILATION SYSTEM.
RESPIRATOR: THE FOLLOWING RESPIRATORS ARE RECOMMENDED BASED ON INFORMATION FOUND IN THE PHYSICAL DATA, TOXICITY AND HEALTH EFFECTS SECTIONS. THEY ARE RANKED IN ORDER FROM MINIMUM TO MAXIMUM RESPIRATORY PROTECTION. THE SPECIFIC RESPIRATOR SELECTED MUST BE BASED ON CONTAMINATION LEVELS FOUND IN THE WORK PLACE, MUST NOT EXCEED THE WORKING LIMITS OF THE RESPIRATOR AND BE JOINTLY APPROVED BY THE NATIONAL INSTITUTE FOR OCCUPATIONAL SAFETY AND HEALTH AND THE MINE SAFETY AND HEALTH ADMINISTRATION (NIOSH-MSHA).
CHEMICAL CARTRIDGE RESPIRATOR WITH PESTICIDE CARTRIDGE.
GAS MASK WITH A PESTICIDE CANISTER (CHIN-STYLE OR FRONT- OR BACK-MOUNTED CANISTER).
TYPE 'C' SUPPLIED-AIR RESPIRATOR OPERATED IN THE PRESSURE-DEMAND OR OTHER POSITIVE PRESSURE OR CONTINUOUS-FLOW MODE.
SELF-CONTAINED BREATHING APPARATUS.
FOR FIREFIGHTING AND OTHER IMMEDIATELY DANGEROUS TO LIFE OR HEALTH CONDITIONS:
SELF-CONTAINED BREATHING APPARATUS WITH FULL FACEPIECE OPERATED IN PRESSURE-DEMAND OR OTHER POSITIVE PRESSURE MODE.
SUPPLIED-AIR RESPIRATOR WITH FULL FACEPIECE AND OPERATED IN PRESSURE-DEMAND OR OTHER POSITIVE PRESSURE MODE IN COMBINATION WITH AN AUXILIARY SELF-CONTAINED BREATHING APPARATUS OPERATED IN PRESSURE-DEMAND OR OTHER POSITIVE PRESSURE MODE.
CLOTHING: EMPLOYEE MUST WEAR APPROPRIATE PROTECTIVE (IMPERVIOUS) CLOTHING AND EQUIPMENT TO PREVENT REPEATED OR PROLONGED SKIN CONTACT WITH THIS SUBSTANCE.
GLOVES: EMPLOYEE MUST WEAR APPROPRIATE PROTECTIVE GLOVES TO PREVENT CONTACT WITH THIS SUBSTANCE.
EYE PROTECTION: EMPLOYEE MUST WEAR SPLASH-PROOF OR DUST-RESISTANT SAFETY GOGGLES TO PREVENT EYE CONTACT WITH THIS SUBSTANCE.
EMERGENCY EYE WASH: WHERE THERE IS ANY POSSIBILITY THAT AN EMPLOYEE'S EYES MAY BE EXPOSED TO THIS SUBSTANCE, THE EMPLOYER SHOULD PROVIDE AN EYE WASH FOUNTAIN WITHIN THE IMMEDIATE WORK AREA FOR EMERGENCY USE.

AUTHORIZED BY- OCCUPATIONAL HEALTH SERVICES, INC.
CREATION DATE: 02/08/90 ***REVISION DATE:*** 05/17/90

MATERIAL SAFETY DATA SHEET

OCCUPATIONAL HEALTH SERVICES, INC.
AGRICULTURE AND PESTICIDE DIVISION
450 SEVENTH AVENUE, SUITE 2407
NEW YORK, NEW YORK 10123
1-800-445-MSDS OR (212) 967-1100

EMERGENCY CONTACT:
JOHN S. BRANSFORD, JR. (615) 292-1180

SUBSTANCE IDENTIFICATION

CAS-NUMBER 82560-54-1

***SUBSTANCE:* BENFURACARB**

TRADE NAMES/SYNONYMS: BETA-ALANINE, N-((((2,3-DIHYDRO-2,2-DIMETHYL-7-BENZOFURANYL)OXY) CARBONYL)METHYLAMINO)THIO)-N-(1-METHYLETHYL)-, ETHYL ESTER; N-((((2,3-DIHYDRO-2,2-DIMETHYL-7-BENZOFURANYL)OXY)CARBONYL) METHYLAMINO)THIO)-N-(1-METHYLETHYL)-BETA-ALANINE ETHYL ESTER; ETHYL-N-(2,3-DIHYDRO-2,2-DIMETHYLBENZOFURAN-7-YLOXYCARBONYL(METHYL) AMINOTHIO)-N-ISOPROPYL-BETA-ALANINATE; 2,3-DIHYDRO-2,2-DIMETHYL-7-BENZOFURANYL-2-METHYL-4-(1-METHYLETHYL)-7- OXO-8-OXA-3-THIA-2,4-DIAZADECANOATE; ETHYL N-((((2,3-DIHYDRO-2,2-DIMETHYL-7-BENZOFURANYL)OXY)CARBONYL) METHYLAMINO)THIO)-N-(1-METHYLETHYL)-BETA-ALANINATE; OK 174; ONCOL; C20H30N2O5S; PST72562

CHEMICAL FAMILY: CARBAMATE

MOLECULAR FORMULA: C20-H30-N2-O5-S

MOLECULAR WEIGHT: 410.58

CERCLA RATINGS (SCALE 0-3): HEALTH=3 FIRE=U REACTIVITY=0 PERSISTENCE=1

NFPA RATINGS (SCALE 0-4): HEALTH=3 FIRE=U REACTIVITY=0

COMPONENTS AND CONTAMINANTS

COMPONENT: BENFURACARB ***PERCENT:*** 100.0
CAS# 82560-54-1

OTHER CONTAMINANTS: NONE

EXPOSURE LIMITS: NO OCCUPATIONAL EXPOSURE LIMITS ESTABLISHED BY OSHA, ACGIH, OR NIOSH.

PHYSICAL DATA

DESCRIPTION: REDDISH-BROWN, VISCOUS LIQUID. ***BOILING POINT:*** NOT AVAILABLE

SPECIFIC GRAVITY: 1.171 ***VAPOR PRESSURE:*** NOT AVAILABLE

SOLUBILITY IN WATER: 0.008% @ 20 C

SOLVENT SOLUBILITY: SOLUBLE IN MOST ORGANIC SOLVENTS.

FIRE AND EXPLOSION DATA

FIRE AND EXPLOSION HAZARD: UNKNOWN FIRE AND EXPLOSION HAZARD.

FLASH POINT: NOT AVAILABLE

FIREFIGHTING MEDIA: DRY CHEMICAL, CARBON DIOXIDE, HALON, WATER SPRAY OR STANDARD FOAM (1987 EMERGENCY RESPONSE GUIDEBOOK, DOT P 5800.4). FOR LARGER FIRES, USE WATER SPRAY, FOG OR STANDARD FOAM (1987 EMERGENCY RESPONSE GUIDEBOOK, DOT P 5800.4).

FIREFIGHTING: MOVE CONTAINERS FROM FIRE AREA IF POSSIBLE. FIGHT FIRE FROM MAXIMUM DISTANCE. STAY AWAY FROM STORAGE TANK ENDS. DIKE FIRE CONTROL WATER FOR LATER DISPOSAL. DO NOT SCATTER MATERIAL (1987 EMERGENCY RESPONSE GUIDEBOOK, DOT P 5800.4, GUIDE PAGE 55). EXTINGUISH ONLY IF FLOW CAN BE STOPPED; USE FLOODING AMOUNTS OF WATER AS A FOG, SOLID STREAMS MAY BE INEFFECTIVE. COOL CONTAINERS WITH FLOODING AMOUNTS OF WATER, APPLY FROM AS FAR A DISTANCE AS POSSIBLE. AVOID BREATHING VAPORS, KEEP UPWIND.

TOXICITY

BENFURACARB: TOXICITY DATA: 138 MG/KG ORAL-RAT LD50; 175 MG/KG ORAL-MOUSE LD50; 300 MG/KG ORAL-DOG LD50. CARCINOGEN STATUS: NONE. ACUTE TOXICITY LEVEL: TOXIC BY INGESTION. TARGET EFFECTS: CHOLINESTERASE INHIBITOR. AT INCREASED RISK FROM EXPOSURE: PERSONS WITH ASTHMA, DIABETES, CARDIOVASCULAR DISEASE, MECHANICAL OBSTRUCTION OF THE GASTROINTESTINAL OR UROGENITAL TRACT, AND THOSE IN VAGOTONIC STATES.*

* MAY BE BASED ON GENERAL INFORMATION ON CARBAMATES.

HEALTH EFFECTS AND FIRST AID

INHALATION: BENFURACARB: SEE INFORMATION ON CARBAMATES.
CARBAMATES: CHOLINESTERASE INHIBITOR. **ACUTE EXPOSURE-** WHEN INHALED, THE FIRST EFFECTS OF CHOLINESTERASE INHIBITION ARE USUALLY RESPIRATORY AND MAY INCLUDE NASAL HYPEREMIA AND WATERY DISCHARGE, CHEST DISCOMFORT, DYSPNEA, AND WHEEZING DUE TO INCREASED BRONCHIAL SECRETIONS AND BRONCHOCONSTRICTION. OTHER SYSTEMIC EFFECTS MAY BEGIN WITHIN A FEW MINUTES OR SEVERAL HOURS OF EXPOSURE. SYMPTOMS MAY INCLUDE NAUSEA, VOMITING, DIARRHEA, ABDOMINAL CRAMPS, HEADACHE, VERTIGO, OCULAR PAIN, CILIARY MUSCLE SPASM, BLURRING OR DIMNESS OF VISION, MIOSIS, OR IN SOME CASES MYDRIASIS, LACRIMATION, SALIVATION, SWEATING, AND CONFUSION. OTHER REPORTED CENTRAL NERVOUS SYSTEM OR NEUROMUSCULAR EFFECTS INCLUDE ATAXIA, SLURRED SPEECH, AREFLEXIA, WEAKNESS, FATIGUE, TWITCHING, FASCICULATION, TREMOR, AND EVENTUALLY PARALYSIS OF THE EXTREMITIES AND POSSIBLY OF THE RESPIRATORY MUSCLES. IN SEVERE CASES, THERE MAY ALSO BE INVOLUNTARY DEFECATION AND URINATION, BRADYCARDIA, HYPOTENSION, PULMONARY EDEMA, CONVULSIONS, COMA, AND DEATH FROM RESPIRATORY FAILURE OR CARDIAC ARREST. CARBAMATES GENERALLY DO NOT ACCUMULATE IN MAMMALIAN TISSUE AND THE CHOLINESTERASE INHIBITION REVERSES RATHER RAPIDLY. IN NON-FATAL CASES, THE ILLNESS GENERALLY LASTS LESS THAN 24 HOURS. **CHRONIC EXPOSURE-** PROLONGED OR REPEATED EXPOSURE MAY CAUSE EFFECTS AS DESCRIBED IN ACUTE EXPOSURE.

FIRST AID- REMOVE FROM EXPOSURE AREA TO FRESH AIR IMMEDIATELY. IF BREATHING HAS STOPPED, GIVE ARTIFICIAL RESPIRATION. MAINTAIN AIRWAY AND BLOOD PRESSURE AND ADMINISTER OXYGEN IF AVAILABLE. KEEP AFFECTED PERSON WARM AND AT REST. TREAT SYMPTOMATICALLY AND SUPPORTIVELY. ADMINISTRATION OF OXYGEN SHOULD BE PERFORMED BY QUALIFIED PERSONNEL. GET MEDICAL ATTENTION IMMEDIATELY.

SKIN CONTACT: BENFURACARB: SEE INFORMATION ON CARBAMATES.
CARBAMATES: CHOLINESTERASE INHIBITOR. **ACUTE EXPOSURE-** SOME COMPOUNDS MAY CAUSE IRRITATION. LOCALIZED SWEATING AND FASCICULATIONS MAY OCCUR AT THE SITE OF CONTACT. IF SUFFICIENT AMOUNTS ARE ABSORBED THROUGH THE SKIN, OTHER EFFECTS OF CHOLINESTERASE INHIBITION MAY OCCUR AS DESCRIBED IN ACUTE INHALATION; SYMPTOMS MAY BE DELAYED FOR 2-3 HOURS, USUALLY NO MORE THAN 8 HOURS. **CHRONIC EXPOSURE-** REPEATED OR PROLONGED EXPOSURE MAY CAUSE EFFECTS AS DESCRIBED IN ACUTE EXPOSURE.

FIRST AID- REMOVE CONTAMINATED CLOTHING IMMEDIATELY. WASH CONTAMINATED AREAS WITH SOAP AND WATER FOLLOWED BY ALCOHOL (ARENA, POISONING, 4TH ED.). EMERGENCY PERSONNEL SHOULD WEAR GLOVES AND AVOID CONTAMINATION. TREAT RESPIRATORY DIFFICULTY WITH ARTIFICIAL RESPIRATION. GET MEDICAL ATTENTION IMMEDIATELY.

EYE CONTACT: BENFURACARB: SEE INFORMATION ON CARBAMATES.
CARBAMATES: CHOLINESTERASE INHIBITOR. **ACUTE EXPOSURE-** DIRECT CONTACT MAY CAUSE PAIN, HYPEREMIA, LACRIMATION, TWITCHING OF THE EYELIDS, MIOSIS, AND CILIARY MUSCLE SPASM WITH LOSS OF ACCOMODATION, BLURRED OR DIMMED VISION AND BROWACHE. SOMETIMES MYDRIASIS MAY OCCUR INSTEAD OF MIOSIS. WITH SUFFICIENT EXPOSURE, OTHER SYMPTOMS OF CHOLINESTERASE INHIBITION MAY OCCUR AS DESCRIBED IN ACUTE INHALATION. **CHRONIC EXPOSURE-** PROLONGED EXPOSURE MAY CAUSE EFFECTS AS DESCRIBED IN ACUTE EXPOSURE. SOME COMPOUNDS HAVE CAUSED TOXIC EFFECTS ON THE CRYSTALLINE LENS, CONJUNCTIVAL THICKENING AND OBSTRUCTION OF NASOLACRIMAL CANALS WHEN USED AS MIOTIC EYE DROPS.

FIRST AID- IRRIGATE EYES WITH WATER OR SALINE SOLUTION. IF SYMPTOMS OF POISONING OCCUR, TREAT RESPIRATORY DIFFICULTY WITH ARTIFICIAL RESPIRATION AND OXYGEN. OBSERVE PATIENT FOR AT LEAST 24-36 HOURS (GOSSELIN, CLINICAL TOXICOLOGY OF COMMERCIAL PRODUCTS, 5TH ED.). GET MEDICAL ATTENTION IMMEDIATELY. OXYGEN SHOULD BE ADMINISTERED BY QUALIFIED MEDICAL PERSONNEL.

INGESTION: BENFURACARB: TOXIC. SEE INFORMATION ON CARBAMATES.
CARBAMATES: CHOLINESTERASE INHIBITOR. **ACUTE EXPOSURE-** WHEN INGESTED, THE FIRST EFFECTS MAY BE NAUSEA, VOMITING, ANOREXIA, ABDOMINAL CRAMPS, AND DIARRHEA. WITH ABSORPTION FROM THE GASTROINTESTINAL TRACT, THE OTHER EFFECTS OF CHOLINESTERASE INHIBITION AS DESCRIBED IN ACUTE INHALATION MAY OCCUR; SYMPTOMS MAY BEGIN WITHIN MINUTES OR BE DELAYED SEVERAL HOURS. **CHRONIC EXPOSURE-** REPEATED INGESTION MAY CAUSE EFFECTS AS DESCRIBED IN ACUTE EXPOSURE.

FIRST AID- IF PERSON IS ALERT AND RESPIRATION IS NOT DEPRESSED, GIVE SYRUP OF IPECAC FOLLOWED BY WATER (IF VOMITING OCCURS, KEEP HEAD BELOW HIPS TO PREVENT ASPIRATION). IF CONSCIOUSNESS LEVEL DECLINES OR VOMITING HAS NOT OCCURRED IN 15 MINUTES EMPTY STOMACH BY GASTRIC LAVAGE WITH THE AID OF CUFFED ENDOTRACHEAL TUBE USING ISOTONIC SALINE OR 5% SODIUM BICARBONATE FOLLOW WITH ACTIVATED CHARCOAL. ESTABLISH AND MAINTAIN AIRWAY. TREAT RESPIRATORY DIFFICULTY WITH ARTIFICIAL RESPIRATION AND OXYGEN. DO NOT GIVE MORPHINE, AMINOPHYLLINE, PHENOTHIAZINES, RESERPINE, FUROSEMIDE, OR ETHACRYNIC ACID (MORGAN, RECOGNITION AND MANAGEMENT OF PESTICIDE POISONINGS, 3RD ED.). TREAT SYMPTOMATICALLY AND SUPPORTIVELY. ADMINISTRATION OF OXYGEN AND LAVAGE MUST BE PERFORMED BY QUALIFIED MEDICAL PERSONNEL. GET MEDICAL ATTENTION IMMEDIATELY.

ANTIDOTE: THE FOLLOWING ANTIDOTE HAS BEEN RECOMMENDED. HOWEVER, THE DECISION AS TO WHETHER THE SEVERITY OF POISONING REQUIRES ADMINISTRATION OF ANY ANTIDOTE AND ACTUAL DOSE REQUIRED SHOULD BE MADE BY QUALIFIED MEDICAL PERSONNEL.
FOR CHOLINESTERASE INHIBITORS: ESTABLISH CLEAR AIRWAY AND TISSUE OXYGENATION BY ASPIRATION OF SECRETIONS, AND IF NECESSARY, BY ASSISTED PULMONARY VENTILATION WITH OXYGEN. IMPROVE TISSUE OXYGENATION AS MUCH AS POSSIBLE BEFORE ADMINISTERING ATROPINE TO MINIMIZE THE RISK OF VENTRICULAR FIBRILLATION. ADMINISTER ATROPINE SULFATE INTRAVENOUSLY,

OR INTRAMUSCULARLY IF IV INJECTION IS NOT POSSIBLE. IN MODERATELY SEVERE POISONING ADMINISTER ATROPINE SULFATE, 0.4-2.0 MG REPEATED EVERY 15 MINUTES UNTIL ATROPINIZATION IS ACHIEVED (TACHYCARDIA, FLUSHING, DRY MOUTH, MYDRIASIS). MAINTAIN ATROPINIZATION BY REPEATED DOSES FOR 2-12 HOURS, OR LONGER, DEPENDING ON THE SEVERITY OF POISONING. THE APPEARANCE OF RALES IN THE LUNG BASES, MIOSIS, SALIVATION, NAUSEA, BRADYCARDIA, ARE ALL INDICATIONS OF INADEQUATE ATROPINIZATION. SEVERELY POISONED INDIVIDUALS MAY EXHIBIT REMARKABLE TOLERANCE TO ATROPINE; TWO OR MORE TIMES THE DOSAGES SUGGESTED ABOVE MAY BE NEEDED. PERSONS NOT POISONED OR ONLY SLIGHTLY POISONED, HOWEVER, MAY DEVELOP SIGNS OF ATROPINE TOXICITY FROM SUCH LARGE DOSAGES: FEVER, MUSCLE FIBRILLATIONS, AND DELIRIUM ARE THE MAIN SIGNS OF ATROPINE TOXICITY. IF THESE SIGNS APPEAR WHILE THE PATIENT IS FULLY ATROPINIZED, ATROPINE ADMINISTRATION SHOULD BE DISCONTINUED, AT LEAST TEMPORARILY. OBSERVE TREATED PATIENTS CLOSELY AT LEAST 24 HOURS TO INSURE THAT SYMPTOMS (POSSIBLY PULMONARY EDEMA) DO NOT RECUR AS ATROPINIZATION WEARS OFF. IN VERY SEVERE POISONINGS, METABOLIC DISPOSITION OF TOXICANT MAY REQUIRE SEVERAL HOURS OR DAYS DURING WHICH ATROPINIZATION MUST BE MAINTAINED. MARKEDLY LOWER LEVELS OF URINARY METABOLITES INDICATE THAT ATROPINE DOSAGE CAN BE TAPERED OFF. AS DOSAGE IS REDUCED, CHECK THE LUNG BASES FREQUENTLY FOR RALES. IF RALES ARE HEARD OR OTHER SYMPTOMS RETURN, RE-ESTABLISH ATROPINIZATION PROMPTLY (MORGAN, RECOGNITION AND MANAGEMENT OF PESTICIDE POISONINGS, 3RD ED.). ADMINISTRATION OF ANTIDOTE MUST BE PERFORMED BY QUALIFIED MEDICAL PERSONNEL.

REACTIVITY

REACTIVITY: STABLE UNDER NORMAL TEMPERATURES AND PRESSURES.

INCOMPATIBILITIES: BENFURACARB: OXIDIZERS (STRONG): FIRE AND EXPLOSION HAZARD.

DECOMPOSITION: THERMAL DECOMPOSITION PRODUCTS MAY INCLUDE TOXIC OXIDES OF CARBON, NITROGEN, AND SULFUR.

POLYMERIZATION: HAZARDOUS POLYMERIZATION HAS NOT BEEN REPORTED TO OCCUR UNDER NORMAL TEMPERATURES AND PRESSURES.

STORAGE AND DISPOSAL

OBSERVE ALL FEDERAL, STATE AND LOCAL REGULATIONS WHEN STORING OR DISPOSING OF THIS SUBSTANCE. FOR ASSISTANCE, CONTACT THE DISTRICT DIRECTOR OF THE ENVIRONMENTAL PROTECTION AGENCY.

****STORAGE****

STORE IN ACCORDANCE WITH 40 CFR 165 RECOMMENDED PROCEDURES FOR THE DISPOSAL AND STORAGE OF PESTICIDES AND PESTICIDE CONTAINERS.
STORE AWAY FROM INCOMPATIBLE SUBSTANCES.

****DISPOSAL****

DISPOSAL MUST BE IN ACCORDANCE WITH 40 CFR 165 RECOMMENDED PROCEDURES FOR THE DISPOSAL AND STORAGE OF PESTICIDES AND PESTICIDE CONTAINERS.

CONDITIONS TO AVOID

AVOID CONTACT WITH HEAT, SPARKS, FLAMES, OR OTHER SOURCES OF IGNITION. VAPORS MAY BE EXPLOSIVE. AVOID OVERHEATING OF CONTAINERS; CONTAINERS MAY VIOLENTLY RUPTURE IN HEAT OF FIRE. AVOID CONTAMINATION OF WATER SOURCES.

SPILL AND LEAK PROCEDURES

OCCUPATIONAL SPILL: SHUT OFF IGNITION SOURCES. STOP LEAK IF YOU CAN DO IT WITHOUT RISK. USE WATER SPRAY TO REDUCE VAPORS. FOR SMALL SPILLS, TAKE UP WITH SAND OR OTHER ABSORBENT MATERIAL AND PLACE INTO CONTAINERS FOR LATER DISPOSAL. FOR LARGER SPILLS, DIKE FAR AHEAD OF SPILL FOR LATER DISPOSAL. NO SMOKING, FLAMES OR FLARES IN HAZARD AREA. KEEP UNNECESSARY PEOPLE AWAY; ISOLATE HAZARD AREA AND RESTRICT ENTRY.

PROTECTIVE EQUIPMENT

VENTILATION: PROVIDE LOCAL EXHAUST OR PROCESS ENCLOSURE VENTILATION SYSTEM.

RESPIRATOR: THE FOLLOWING RESPIRATORS ARE RECOMMENDED BASED ON INFORMATION FOUND IN THE PHYSICAL DATA, TOXICITY AND HEALTH EFFECTS SECTIONS. THEY ARE RANKED IN ORDER FROM MINIMUM TO MAXIMUM RESPIRATORY PROTECTION. THE SPECIFIC RESPIRATOR SELECTED MUST BE BASED ON CONTAMINATION LEVELS FOUND IN THE WORK PLACE, MUST NOT EXCEED THE WORKING LIMITS OF THE RESPIRATOR AND BE JOINTLY APPROVED BY THE NATIONAL INSTITUTE FOR OCCUPATIONAL SAFETY AND HEALTH AND THE MINE SAFETY AND HEALTH ADMINISTRATION (NIOSH-MSHA).

TYPE 'C' SUPPLIED-AIR RESPIRATOR WITH A FULL FACEPIECE OPERATED IN PRESSURE-DEMAND OR OTHER POSITIVE PRESSURE MODE OR WITH A FULL FACEPIECE, HELMET OR HOOD OPERATED IN CONTINOUS-FLOW MODE.

SELF-CONTAINED BREATHING APPARATUS WITH A FULL FACEPIECE OPERATED IN PRESSURE-DEMAND OR OTHER POSITIVE PRESSURE MODE.

FOR FIREFIGHTING AND OTHER IMMEDIATELY DANGEROUS TO LIFE OR HEALTH CONDITIONS:

SELF-CONTAINED BREATHING APPARATUS WITH FULL FACEPIECE OPERATED IN PRESSURE-DEMAND OR OTHER POSITIVE PRESSURE MODE.

SUPPLIED-AIR RESPIRATOR WITH FULL FACEPIECE AND OPERATED IN PRESSURE-DEMAND OR OTHER POSITIVE PRESSURE MODE IN COMBINATION WITH AN AUXILIARY SELF-CONTAINED BREATHING APPARATUS OPERATED IN PRESSURE-DEMAND OR OTHER POSITIVE PRESSURE MODE.

CLOTHING: EMPLOYEE MUST WEAR APPROPRIATE PROTECTIVE (IMPERVIOUS) CLOTHING AND EQUIPMENT TO PREVENT ANY POSSIBILITY OF SKIN CONTACT WITH THIS SUBSTANCE.

GLOVES: EMPLOYEE MUST WEAR APPROPRIATE PROTECTIVE GLOVES TO PREVENT CONTACT WITH THIS SUBSTANCE.

EYE PROTECTION: EMPLOYEE MUST WEAR SPLASH-PROOF OR DUST-RESISTANT SAFETY GOGGLES WITH OR WITHOUT A FACESHIELD TO PREVENT CONTACT WITH THIS SUBSTANCE.

EMERGENCY EYE WASH: WHERE THERE IS ANY POSSIBILITY THAT AN EMPLOYEE'S EYES MAY BE EXPOSED TO THIS SUBSTANCE, THE EMPLOYER SHOULD PROVIDE AN EYE WASH FOUNTAIN WITHIN THE IMMEDIATE WORK AREA FOR EMERGENCY USE.

AUTHORIZED BY- OCCUPATIONAL HEALTH SERVICES, INC.
CREATION DATE: 10/04/89 ***REVISION DATE:*** 06/12/90

MATERIAL SAFETY DATA SHEET

OCCUPATIONAL HEALTH SERVICES, INC.
AGRICULTURE AND PESTICIDE DIVISION
450 SEVENTH AVENUE, SUITE 2407
NEW YORK, NEW YORK 10123
1-800-445-MSDS OR (212) 967-1100

EMERGENCY CONTACT:
JOHN S. BRANSFORD, JR. (615) 292-1180

SUBSTANCE IDENTIFICATION

CAS-NUMBER 39148-24-8

SUBSTANCE: FOSETYL AL

TRADE NAMES/SYNONYMS: PHOSPHONIC ACID, MONOETHYL ESTER, ALUMINUM SALT; ALUMINUM TRIS(ETHYL PHOSPHITE); ALUMINUM TRIS(O-ETHYLPHOSPHONATE); ALIETTE; EFOSITE AL; EPAL; EXP 1659; LS 74-783; PHOSETHYL AL; C6H18ALO9P3; PST72563

CHEMICAL FAMILY: ORGANOPHOSPHATE

MOLECULAR FORMULA: C6-H18-O9-P3.AL

MOLECULAR WEIGHT: 354.13

CERCLA RATINGS (SCALE 0-3): HEALTH=U FIRE=1 REACTIVITY=0 PERSISTENCE=1

NFPA RATINGS (SCALE 0-4): HEALTH=U FIRE=1 REACTIVITY=0

COMPONENTS AND CONTAMINANTS

COMPONENT: FOSETYL AL ***PERCENT:*** 100.0
CAS# 39148-24-8

EXPOSURE LIMITS: ALUMINUM, SOLUBLE SALTS, (AS AL): 2 MG/M3 OSHA TWA 2 MG/M3 ACGIH TWA

PHYSICAL DATA

DESCRIPTION: ODORLESS, WHITE CRYSTALLINE SOLID.

MELTING POINT: >392 F (>200 C) DECOMPOSES ***SPECIFIC GRAVITY:*** NOT AVAILABLE

VAPOR PRESSURE: NEGLIGIBLE ***SOLUBILITY IN WATER:*** 12.2%

SOLVENT SOLUBILITY: PRACTICALLY INSOLUBLE IN MOST ORGANIC SOLVENTS.

FIRE AND EXPLOSION DATA

FIRE AND EXPLOSION HAZARD: SLIGHT FIRE HAZARD WHEN EXPOSED TO HEAT OR FLAME.

FIREFIGHTING MEDIA: DRY CHEMICAL, CARBON DIOXIDE, HALON, WATER SPRAY OR STANDARD FOAM (1987 EMERGENCY RESPONSE GUIDEBOOK, DOT P 5800.4).

FOR LARGER FIRES, USE WATER SPRAY, FOG OR STANDARD FOAM (1987 EMERGENCY RESPONSE GUIDEBOOK, DOT P 5800.4).

FIREFIGHTING: MOVE CONTAINERS FROM FIRE AREA IF POSSIBLE (1987 EMERGENCY RESPONSE GUIDEBOOK, DOT P 5800.4, GUIDE PAGE 53).

EXTINGUISH FIRE USING AGENTS SUITABLE FOR TYPE OF SURROUNDING FIRE. USE WATER IN FLOODING AMOUNTS AS A FOG. AVOID BREATHING DUSTS AND FUMES FROM BURNING MATERIAL; KEEP UPWIND.

TOXICITY

FOSETYL AL: TOXICITY DATA: >3200 MG/KG SKIN-RAT LD50 (PEMNDP 8,438,87); 4600 MG/KG ORAL-RAT LD50; 3700 MG/KG ORAL-MOUSE LD50. CARCINOGEN STATUS: NONE. LOCAL EFFECTS: CORROSIVE- EYE. ACUTE TOXICITY LEVEL: MODERATELY TOXIC BY INGESTION; SLIGHTLY TOXIC BY DERMAL ABSORPTION. TARGET EFFECTS: NO DATA AVAILABLE.

HEALTH EFFECTS AND FIRST AID

INHALATION: FOSETYL AL: **ACUTE EXPOSURE-** NO DATA AVAILABLE. **CHRONIC EXPOSURE-** NO DATA AVAILABLE.

FIRST AID- REMOVE FROM EXPOSURE AREA TO FRESH AIR IMMEDIATELY. IF BREATHING HAS STOPPED, PERFORM ARTIFICIAL RESPIRATION. KEEP PERSON WARM AND AT REST. TREAT SYMPTOMATICALLY AND SUPPORTIVELY. GET MEDICAL ATTENTION IMMEDIATELY.

SKIN CONTACT: FOSETYL AL: **ACUTE EXPOSURE-** THIS MATERIAL WAS NOT AN IRRITANT OF RAT'S SKIN. **CHRONIC EXPOSURE-** NO DATA AVAILABLE.

FIRST AID- REMOVE CONTAMINATED CLOTHING AND SHOES IMMEDIATELY. WASH AFFECTED AREA WITH SOAP OR MILD DETERGENT AND LARGE AMOUNTS OF WATER UNTIL NO EVIDENCE OF CHEMICAL REMAINS (APPROXIMATELY 15-20 MINUTES). GET MEDICAL ATTENTION IMMEDIATELY.

EYE CONTACT: FOSETYL AL: CORROSIVE. **ACUTE EXPOSURE-** MAY CAUSE SEVERE IRRITATION AND DAMAGE TO THE EYE. **CHRONIC EXPOSURE-** EFFECTS DEPEND ON CONCENTRATION AND DURATION OF EXPOSURE. REPEATED OR PROLONGED CONTACT WITH CORROSIVE SUBSTANCES MAY RESULT IN CONJUNCTIVITIS OR EFFECTS AS IN ACUTE EXPOSURE.

FIRST AID- WASH EYES IMMEDIATELY WITH LARGE AMOUNTS OF WATER OR NORMAL SALINE, OCCASIONALLY LIFTING UPPER AND LOWER LIDS, UNTIL NO EVIDENCE OF CHEMICAL REMAINS (APPROXIMATELY 15-20 MINUTES). GET MEDICAL ATTENTION IMMEDIATELY.

INGESTION: FOSETYL AL: **ACUTE EXPOSURE-** A LETHAL DOSE IN RATS WAS 5400 MG/KG; SYMPTOMS WERE NOT REPORTED. **CHRONIC EXPOSURE-** IN A TWO YEAR FEEDING STUDY, ONCOGENIC EFFECTS WERE NOTED IN RATS.

FIRST AID- TREAT SYMPTOMATICALLY AND SUPPORTIVELY. GET MEDICAL ATTENTION IMMEDIATELY. IF VOMITING OCCURS, KEEP HEAD LOWER THAN HIPS TO PREVENT ASPIRATION.

ANTIDOTE: NO SPECIFIC ANTIDOTE. TREAT SYMPTOMATICALLY AND SUPPORTIVELY.

REACTIVITY

REACTIVITY: STABLE UNDER NORMAL TEMPERATURES AND PRESSURES.

INCOMPATIBILITIES: FOSETYL AL: ACID: INCOMPATIBLE. ALKALI: INCOMPATIBLE. OXIDIZERS (STRONG): FIRE AND EXPLOSION HAZARD.

DECOMPOSITION: THERMAL DECOMPOSITION PRODUCTS MAY INCLUDE TOXIC AND HAZARDOUS OXIDES OF PHOSPHORUS AND CARBON.

POLYMERIZATION: HAZARDOUS POLYMERIZATION HAS NOT BEEN REPORTED TO OCCUR UNDER NORMAL TEMPERATURES AND PRESSURES.

STORAGE AND DISPOSAL

OBSERVE ALL FEDERAL, STATE AND LOCAL REGULATIONS WHEN STORING OR DISPOSING OF THIS SUBSTANCE. FOR ASSISTANCE, CONTACT THE DISTRICT DIRECTOR OF THE ENVIRONMENTAL PROTECTION AGENCY.

****STORAGE****

STORE IN ACCORDANCE WITH 40 CFR 165 RECOMMENDED PROCEDURES FOR THE DISPOSAL AND STORAGE OF PESTICIDES AND PESTICIDE CONTAINERS.

STORE AWAY FROM INCOMPATIBLE SUBSTANCES.

****DISPOSAL****

DISPOSAL MUST BE IN ACCORDANCE WITH 40 CFR 165 RECOMMENDED PROCEDURES FOR THE DISPOSAL AND STORAGE OF PESTICIDES AND PESTICIDE CONTAINERS.

CONDITIONS TO AVOID

MAY BURN BUT DOES NOT IGNITE READILY.

SPILL AND LEAK PROCEDURES

OCCUPATIONAL SPILL: DO NOT TOUCH SPILLED MATERIAL. STOP LEAK IF YOU CAN DO IT WITHOUT RISK. FOR SMALL SPILLS, TAKE UP WITH SAND OR OTHER ABSORBENT MATERIAL AND PLACE INTO CONTAINERS FOR LATER DISPOSAL. FOR SMALL DRY SPILLS, WITH A CLEAN SHOVEL PLACE MATERIAL INTO CLEAN, DRY CONTAINER AND COVER. MOVE CONTAINERS FROM SPILL AREA. FOR LARGER SPILLS, DIKE FAR AHEAD OF SPILL FOR LATER DISPOSAL. KEEP UNNECESSARY PEOPLE AWAY. ISOLATE HAZARD AREA AND DENY ENTRY.

PROTECTIVE EQUIPMENT

VENTILATION: PROVIDE GENERAL DILUTION VENTILATION.

RESPIRATOR: THE FOLLOWING RESPIRATORS ARE RECOMMENDED BASED ON INFORMATION FOUND IN THE PHYSICAL DATA, TOXICITY AND HEALTH EFFECTS SECTIONS. THEY ARE RANKED IN ORDER FROM MINIMUM TO MAXIMUM RESPIRATORY PROTECTION. THE SPECIFIC RESPIRATOR SELECTED MUST BE BASED ON CONTAMINATION LEVELS FOUND IN THE WORK PLACE, MUST NOT EXCEED THE WORKING LIMITS OF THE RESPIRATOR AND BE JOINTLY APPROVED BY THE NATIONAL INSTITUTE FOR OCCUPATIONAL SAFETY AND HEALTH AND THE MINE SAFETY AND HEALTH ADMINISTRATION (NIOSH-MSHA).

CHEMICAL CARTRIDGE RESPIRATOR WITH AN ORGANIC VAPOR CARTRIDGE(S) WITH A FULL FACEPIECE AND ORGANIC VAPOR CARTRIDGE(S) IN COMBINATION WITH A DUST AND MIST FILTER.

POWERED AIR-PURIFYING RESPIRATOR WITH A TIGHT-FITTING FACEPIECE AND ORGANIC VAPOR CARTRIDGE(S) IN COMBINATION WITH A HIGH-EFFICIENCY PARTICULATE FILTER.

TYPE 'C' SUPPLIED-AIR RESPIRATOR WITH A FULL FACEPIECE OPERATED IN A PRESSURE-DEMAND OR OTHER POSITIVE PRESSURE MODE.

SELF-CONTAINED BREATHING APPARATUS WITH A FULL FACEPIECE OPERATED IN PRESSURE-DEMAND OR OTHER POSITIVE PRESSURE MODE.

FOR FIREFIGHTING AND OTHER IMMEDIATELY DANGEROUS TO LIFE OR HEALTH CONDITIONS:

SELF-CONTAINED BREATHING APPARATUS WITH FULL FACEPIECE OPERATED IN PRESSURE-DEMAND OR OTHER POSITIVE PRESSURE MODE.

SUPPLIED-AIR RESPIRATOR WITH FULL FACEPIECE AND OPERATED IN PRESSURE-DEMAND OR OTHER POSITIVE PRESSURE MODE IN COMBINATION WITH AN AUXILIARY SELF-CONTAINED BREATHING APPARATUS OPERATED IN PRESSURE-DEMAND OR OTHER POSITIVE PRESSURE MODE.

CLOTHING: EMPLOYEE MUST WEAR APPROPRIATE PROTECTIVE (IMPERVIOUS) CLOTHING AND EQUIPMENT TO PREVENT REPEATED OR PROLONGED SKIN CONTACT WITH THIS SUBSTANCE.

GLOVES: EMPLOYEE MUST WEAR APPROPRIATE PROTECTIVE GLOVES TO PREVENT CONTACT WITH THIS SUBSTANCE.

EYE PROTECTION: EMPLOYEE MUST WEAR SPLASH-PROOF OR DUST-RESISTANT SAFETY GOGGLES WITH OR WITHOUT A FACESHIELD TO PREVENT CONTACT WITH THIS SUBSTANCE.

EMERGENCY EYE WASH: WHERE THERE IS ANY POSSIBILITY THAT AN EMPLOYEE'S EYES MAY BE EXPOSED TO THIS SUBSTANCE, THE EMPLOYER SHOULD PROVIDE AN EYE WASH FOUNTAIN WITHIN THE IMMEDIATE WORK AREA FOR EMERGENCY USE.

AUTHORIZED BY- OCCUPATIONAL HEALTH SERVICES, INC.

CREATION DATE: 10/04/89 ***REVISION DATE:*** 05/11/90

MATERIAL SAFETY DATA SHEET

OCCUPATIONAL HEALTH SERVICES, INC.
AGRICULTURE AND PESTICIDE DIVISION
450 SEVENTH AVENUE, SUITE 2407
NEW YORK, NEW YORK 10123
1-800-445-MSDS OR (212) 967-1100

EMERGENCY CONTACT:
JOHN S. BRANSFORD, JR. (615) 292-1180

SUBSTANCE IDENTIFICATION

CAS-NUMBER 51487-69-5

SUBSTANCE: **CLOETHOCARB**

TRADE NAMES/SYNONYMS: PHENOL, 2-(2-CHLORO-1-METHOXYETHOXY)-, METHYLCARBAMATE; 2-(2-CHLORO-1-METHOXYETHOXY)PHENOL METHYLCARBAMATE; 2-(2-CHLORO-1-METHOXYETHOXY)PHENYL METHYLCARBAMATE; BAS 263; LANCE; C11H14CLNO4; PST72572

CHEMICAL FAMILY: CARBAMATE

MOLECULAR FORMULA: C11-H14-CL-N-O4

MOLECULAR WEIGHT: 259.71

CERCLA RATINGS (SCALE 0-3): HEALTH=3 FIRE=1 REACTIVITY=0 PERSISTENCE=2

NFPA RATINGS (SCALE 0-4): HEALTH=3 FIRE=1 REACTIVITY=0

COMPONENTS AND CONTAMINANTS

COMPONENT: CLOETHOCARB ***PERCENT:*** 100.0
CAS# 51487-69-5

OTHER CONTAMINANTS: NONE

EXPOSURE LIMITS: NO OCCUPATIONAL EXPOSURE LIMITS ESTABLISHED BY OSHA, ACGIH, OR NIOSH.

PHYSICAL DATA

DESCRIPTION: COLORLESS CRYSTALLINE SOLID. ***MELTING POINT:*** 176 F (80 C)
SPECIFIC GRAVITY: NOT AVAILABLE ***SOLUBILITY IN WATER:*** 0.13% @ 20 C
SOLVENT SOLUBILITY: SOLUBLE IN ACETONE, CHLOROFORM, AND ETHANOL.

FIRE AND EXPLOSION DATA

FIRE AND EXPLOSION HAZARD: SLIGHT FIRE HAZARD WHEN EXPOSED TO HEAT OR FLAME.

FIREFIGHTING MEDIA: DRY CHEMICAL, CARBON DIOXIDE, HALON, WATER SPRAY OR STANDARD FOAM (1987 EMERGENCY RESPONSE GUIDEBOOK, DOT P 5800.4). FOR LARGER FIRES, USE WATER SPRAY, FOG OR STANDARD FOAM (1987 EMERGENCY RESPONSE GUIDEBOOK, DOT P 5800.4).

FIREFIGHTING: MOVE CONTAINERS FROM FIRE AREA IF POSSIBLE. FIGHT FIRE FROM MAXIMUM DISTANCE. STAY AWAY FROM STORAGE TANK ENDS. DIKE FIRE CONTROL WATER FOR LATER DISPOSAL. DO NOT SCATTER MATERIAL (1987 EMERGENCY RESPONSE GUIDEBOOK, DOT P 5800.4, GUIDE PAGE 55). EXTINGUISH USING AGENTS SUITABLE FOR TYPE OF SURROUNDING FIRE. USE FLOODING AMOUNTS OF WATER AS FOG. AVOID BREATHING TOXIC DUST AND FUMES FROM BURNING MATERIAL; KEEP UPWIND.

TRANSPORTATION DATA

DEPARTMENT OF TRANSPORTATION HAZARD CLASSIFICATION 49 CFR 172.101: POISON B

DEPARTMENT OF TRANSPORTATION LABELING REQUIREMENTS 49 CFR 172.101 AND SUBPART E: POISON

DEPARTMENT OF TRANSPORTATION PACKAGING REQUIREMENTS: 49 CFR 173.365 EXCEPTIONS: 49 CFR 173.364

TOXICITY

CLOETHOCARB: TOXICITY DATA: 4 GM/KG SKIN-RABBIT LD50; 35400 UG/KG ORAL-RAT LD50. CARCINOGEN STATUS: NONE. ACUTE TOXICITY LEVEL: HIGHLY TOXIC BY INGESTION; SLIGHTLY TOXIC BY DERMAL ABSORPTION. TARGET EFFECTS: CHOLINESTERASE INHIBITOR. AT INCREASED RISK FROM EXPOSURE: PERSONS WITH ASTHMA, DIABETES, CARDIOVASCULAR DISEASE, MECHANICAL OBSTRUCTION OF THE GASTROINTESTINAL OR UROGENITAL TRACT, AND THOSE IN VAGOTONIC STATES.*

* MAY BE BASED ON GENERAL INFORMATION ON CARBAMATES.

HEALTH EFFECTS AND FIRST AID

INHALATION: CLOETHOCARB: SEE INFORMATION ON CARBAMATES.
CARBAMATES: CHOLINESTERASE INHIBITOR. **ACUTE EXPOSURE-** WHEN INHALED, THE FIRST EFFECTS OF CHOLINESTERASE INHIBITION ARE USUALLY RESPIRATORY AND MAY INCLUDE NASAL HYPEREMIA AND WATERY DISCHARGE, CHEST DISCOMFORT, DYSPNEA, AND WHEEZING DUE TO INCREASED BRONCHIAL SECRETIONS AND BRONCHOCONSTRICTION. OTHER SYSTEMIC EFFECTS MAY BEGIN WITHIN A FEW MINUTES OR SEVERAL HOURS OF EXPOSURE. SYMPTOMS MAY INCLUDE NAUSEA, VOMITING, DIARRHEA, ABDOMINAL CRAMPS, HEADACHE, VERTIGO, OCULAR PAIN, CILIARY MUSCLE SPASM, BLURRING OR DIMNESS OF VISION, MIOSIS, OR IN SOME CASES MYDRIASIS, LACRIMATION, SALIVATION, SWEATING, AND CONFUSION. OTHER REPORTED CENTRAL NERVOUS SYSTEM OR NEUROMUSCULAR EFFECTS INCLUDE ATAXIA, SLURRED SPEECH, AREFLEXIA, WEAKNESS, FATIGUE, TWITCHING, FASCICULATION, TREMOR, AND EVENTUALLY PARALYSIS OF THE EXTREMITIES AND POSSIBLY OF THE RESPIRATORY MUSCLES. IN SEVERE CASES, THERE MAY ALSO BE INVOLUNTARY DEFECATION AND URINATION, BRADYCARDIA, HYPOTENSION, PULMONARY EDEMA, CONVULSIONS, COMA, AND DEATH FROM RESPIRATORY FAILURE OR CARDIAC ARREST. CARBAMATES GENERALLY DO NOT ACCUMULATE IN MAMMALIAN TISSUE AND THE CHOLINESTERASE INHIBITION REVERSES RATHER RAPIDLY. IN NON-FATAL CASES, THE ILLNESS GENERALLY LASTS LESS THAN 24 HOURS. **CHRONIC EXPOSURE-** PROLONGED OR REPEATED EXPOSURE MAY CAUSE EFFECTS AS DESCRIBED IN ACUTE EXPOSURE.

FIRST AID- REMOVE FROM EXPOSURE AREA TO FRESH AIR IMMEDIATELY. IF BREATHING HAS STOPPED, GIVE ARTIFICIAL RESPIRATION. MAINTAIN AIRWAY AND BLOOD PRESSURE AND ADMINISTER OXYGEN IF AVAILABLE. KEEP AFFECTED PERSON WARM AND AT REST. TREAT SYMPTOMATICALLY AND SUPPORTIVELY. ADMINISTRATION OF OXYGEN SHOULD BE PERFORMED BY QUALIFIED PERSONNEL. GET MEDICAL ATTENTION IMMEDIATELY.

SKIN CONTACT: CLOETHOCARB: SEE INFORMATION ON CARBAMATES.
CARBAMATES: CHOLINESTERASE INHIBITOR. **ACUTE EXPOSURE-** SOME COMPOUNDS MAY CAUSE IRRITATION. LOCALIZED SWEATING AND FASCICULATIONS MAY OCCUR AT THE SITE OF CONTACT. IF SUFFICIENT AMOUNTS ARE ABSORBED THROUGH THE SKIN, OTHER EFFECTS OF CHOLINESTERASE INHIBITION MAY OCCUR AS DESCRIBED IN ACUTE INHALATION; SYMPTOMS MAY BE DELAYED FOR 2-3 HOURS, USUALLY NO MORE THAN 8 HOURS. **CHRONIC EXPOSURE-** REPEATED OR PROLONGED EXPOSURE MAY CAUSE EFFECTS AS DESCRIBED IN ACUTE EXPOSURE.

FIRST AID- REMOVE CONTAMINATED CLOTHING IMMEDIATELY. WASH CONTAMINATED AREAS WITH SOAP AND WATER FOLLOWED BY ALCOHOL (ARENA, POISONING, 4TH ED.). EMERGENCY PERSONNEL SHOULD WEAR GLOVES AND AVOID CONTAMINATION. TREAT RESPIRATORY DIFFICULTY WITH ARTIFICIAL RESPIRATION. GET MEDICAL ATTENTION IMMEDIATELY.

EYE CONTACT: CLOETHOCARB: SEE INFORMATION ON CARBAMATES.
CARBAMATES: CHOLINESTERASE INHIBITOR. **ACUTE EXPOSURE-** DIRECT CONTACT MAY CAUSE PAIN, HYPEREMIA, LACRIMATION, TWITCHING OF THE EYELIDS, MIOSIS, AND CILIARY MUSCLE SPASM WITH LOSS OF ACCOMODATION, BLURRED OR DIMMED VISION AND BROWACHE. SOMETIMES MYDRIASIS MAY OCCUR INSTEAD OF MIOSIS. WITH SUFFICIENT EXPOSURE, OTHER SYMPTOMS OF CHOLINESTERASE INHIBITION MAY OCCUR AS DESCRIBED IN ACUTE INHALATION. **CHRONIC EXPOSURE-** PROLONGED EXPOSURE MAY CAUSE EFFECTS AS DESCRIBED IN ACUTE EXPOSURE. SOME COMPOUNDS HAVE CAUSED TOXIC EFFECTS ON THE CRYSTALLINE LENS, CONJUNCTIVAL THICKENING AND OBSTRUCTION OF NASOLACRIMAL CANALS WHEN USED AS MIOTIC EYE DROPS.

FIRST AID- IRRIGATE EYES WITH WATER OR SALINE SOLUTION. IF SYMPTOMS OF POISONING OCCUR, TREAT RESPIRATORY DIFFICULTY WITH ARTIFICIAL RESPIRATION AND OXYGEN. OBSERVE PATIENT FOR AT LEAST 24-36 HOURS (GOSSELIN, CLINICAL TOXICOLOGY OF COMMERCIAL PRODUCTS, 5TH ED.). GET MEDICAL ATTENTION IMMEDIATELY. OXYGEN SHOULD BE ADMINISTERED BY QUALIFIED MEDICAL PERSONNEL.

INGESTION: CLOETHOCARB: HIGHLY TOXIC. SEE INFORMATION ON CARBAMATES.
CARBAMATES: CHOLINESTERASE INHIBITOR. **ACUTE EXPOSURE-** WHEN INGESTED, THE FIRST EFFECTS MAY BE NAUSEA, VOMITING, ANOREXIA, ABDOMINAL CRAMPS, AND DIARRHEA. WITH ABSORPTION FROM THE GASTROINTESTINAL TRACT, THE OTHER EFFECTS OF CHOLINESTERASE INHIBITION AS DESCRIBED IN ACUTE INHALATION MAY OCCUR; SYMPTOMS MAY BEGIN WITHIN MINUTES OR BE DELAYED SEVERAL HOURS. **CHRONIC EXPOSURE-** REPEATED INGESTION MAY CAUSE EFFECTS AS DESCRIBED IN ACUTE EXPOSURE.

FIRST AID- IF PERSON IS ALERT AND RESPIRATION IS NOT DEPRESSED, GIVE SYRUP OF IPECAC FOLLOWED BY WATER (IF VOMITING OCCURS, KEEP HEAD BELOW HIPS TO PREVENT ASPIRATION). IF CONSCIOUSNESS LEVEL DECLINES OR VOMITING HAS NOT OCCURRED IN 15 MINUTES EMPTY STOMACH BY GASTRIC LAVAGE WITH THE AID OF CUFFED ENDOTRACHEAL TUBE USING ISOTONIC SALINE OR 5% SODIUM BICARBONATE FOLLOW WITH ACTIVATED CHARCOAL. ESTABLISH AND MAINTAIN AIRWAY. TREAT RESPIRATORY DIFFICULTY WITH ARTIFICIAL RESPIRATION AND OXYGEN. DO NOT GIVE MORPHINE, AMINOPHYLLINE, PHENOTHIAZINES, RESERPINE, FUROSEMIDE, OR ETHACRYNIC ACID (MORGAN, RECOGNITION AND MANAGEMENT OF PESTICIDE POISONINGS, 3RD ED.). TREAT SYMPTOMATICALLY AND SUPPORTIVELY. ADMINISTRATION OF OXYGEN AND LAVAGE MUST BE PERFORMED BY QUALIFIED MEDICAL PERSONNEL. GET MEDICAL ATTENTION IMMEDIATELY.

ANTIDOTE: THE FOLLOWING ANTIDOTE HAS BEEN RECOMMENDED. HOWEVER, THE DECISION AS TO WHETHER THE SEVERITY OF POISONING REQUIRES ADMINISTRATION OF ANY ANTIDOTE AND ACTUAL DOSE REQUIRED SHOULD BE MADE BY QUALIFIED MEDICAL PERSONNEL.
FOR CHOLINESTERASE INHIBITORS: ESTABLISH CLEAR AIRWAY AND TISSUE OXYGENATION BY ASPIRATION OF SECRETIONS, AND IF NECESSARY, BY ASSISTED PULMONARY VENTILATION WITH OXYGEN. IMPROVE TISSUE OXYGENATION AS MUCH AS POSSIBLE BEFORE ADMINISTERING ATROPINE TO MINIMIZE THE RISK OF VENTRICULAR FIBRILLATION. ADMINISTER ATROPINE SULFATE INTRAVENOUSLY, OR INTRAMUSCULARLY IF IV INJECTION IS NOT POSSIBLE. IN MODERATELY SEVERE POISONING ADMINISTER ATROPINE SULFATE, 0.4-2.0 MG REPEATED EVERY 15 MINUTES UNTIL ATROPINIZATION IS ACHIEVED (TACHYCARDIA, FLUSHING, DRY MOUTH, MYDRIASIS). MAINTAIN ATROPINIZATION BY REPEATED DOSES FOR 2-12 HOURS, OR LONGER, DEPENDING ON THE SEVERITY OF POISONING. THE APPEARANCE OF RALES IN THE LUNG BASES, MIOSIS, SALIVATION, NAUSEA, BRADYCARDIA, ARE ALL INDICATIONS OF INADEQUATE ATROPINIZATION. SEVERELY POISONED INDIVIDUALS MAY EXHIBIT REMARKABLE TOLERANCE TO ATROPINE; TWO OR MORE TIMES THE DOSAGES SUGGESTED ABOVE MAY BE NEEDED. PERSONS NOT POISONED OR ONLY SLIGHTLY POISONED, HOWEVER, MAY DEVELOP SIGNS OF ATROPINE TOXICITY FROM SUCH LARGE DOSAGES: FEVER, MUSCLE FIBRILLATIONS, AND DELIRIUM ARE THE MAIN SIGNS OF ATROPINE TOXICITY. IF THESE SIGNS APPEAR WHILE THE PATIENT IS FULLY ATROPINIZED, ATROPINE ADMINISTRATION SHOULD BE DISCONTINUED, AT LEAST TEMPORARILY.

OBSERVE TREATED PATIENTS CLOSELY AT LEAST 24 HOURS TO INSURE THAT SYMPTOMS (POSSIBLY PULMONARY EDEMA) DO NOT RECUR AS ATROPINIZATION WEARS OFF. IN VERY SEVERE POISONINGS, METABOLIC DISPOSITION OF TOXICANT MAY REQUIRE SEVERAL HOURS OR DAYS DURING WHICH ATROPINIZATION MUST BE MAINTAINED. MARKEDLY LOWER LEVELS OF URINARY METABOLITES INDICATE THAT ATROPINE DOSAGE CAN BE TAPERED OFF. AS DOSAGE IS REDUCED, CHECK THE LUNG BASES FREQUENTLY FOR RALES. IF RALES ARE HEARD OR OTHER SYMPTOMS RETURN, RE-ESTABLISH ATROPINIZATION PROMPTLY (MORGAN, RECOGNITION AND MANAGEMENT OF PESTICIDE POISONINGS, 3RD ED.). ADMINISTRATION OF ANTIDOTE MUST BE PERFORMED BY QUALIFIED MEDICAL PERSONNEL.

REACTIVITY

REACTIVITY: STABLE UNDER NORMAL TEMPERATURES AND PRESSURES.

INCOMPATIBILITIES: CLOETHOCARB: OXIDIZERS (STRONG): FIRE AND EXPLOSION HAZARD.

DECOMPOSITION: THERMAL DECOMPOSITION PRODUCTS MAY INCLUDE TOXIC OXIDES OF NITROGEN AND CARBON AND TOXIC AND CORROSIVE FUMES OF CHLORIDES.

POLYMERIZATION: HAZARDOUS POLYMERIZATION HAS NOT BEEN REPORTED TO OCCUR UNDER NORMAL TEMPERATURES AND PRESSURES.

STORAGE AND DISPOSAL

OBSERVE ALL FEDERAL, STATE AND LOCAL REGULATIONS WHEN STORING OR DISPOSING OF THIS SUBSTANCE. FOR ASSISTANCE, CONTACT THE DISTRICT DIRECTOR OF THE ENVIRONMENTAL PROTECTION AGENCY.

STORAGE

STORE IN ACCORDANCE WITH 40 CFR 165 RECOMMENDED PROCEDURES FOR THE DISPOSAL AND STORAGE OF PESTICIDES AND PESTICIDE CONTAINERS.
STORE AWAY FROM INCOMPATIBLE SUBSTANCES.

DISPOSAL

DISPOSAL MUST BE IN ACCORDANCE WITH 40 CFR 165 RECOMMENDED PROCEDURES FOR THE DISPOSAL AND STORAGE OF PESTICIDES AND PESTICIDE CONTAINERS.

CONDITIONS TO AVOID

MAY BURN BUT DOES NOT IGNITE READILY. CONTAINERS MAY EXPLODE IN HEAT OF FIRE.

SPILL AND LEAK PROCEDURES

OCCUPATIONAL SPILL: DO NOT TOUCH SPILLED MATERIAL. STOP LEAK IF YOU CAN DO IT WITHOUT RISK. USE WATER SPRAY TO REDUCE VAPORS. FOR SMALL SPILLS, TAKE UP WITH SAND OR OTHER ABSORBENT MATERIAL AND PLACE INTO CONTAINERS FOR LATER DISPOSAL. FOR SMALL DRY SPILLS, WITH A CLEAN SHOVEL PLACE MATERIAL INTO CLEAN, DRY CONTAINERS AND COVER. MOVE CONTAINERS FROM SPILL AREA. FOR LARGER SPILLS, DIKE FAR AHEAD OF SPILL FOR LATER DISPOSAL. KEEP UNNECESSARY PEOPLE AWAY. ISOLATE HAZARD AREA AND DENY ENTRY. VENTILATE CLOSED SPACES BEFORE ENTERING.

PROTECTIVE EQUIPMENT

VENTILATION: PROVIDE LOCAL EXHAUST OR GENERAL DILUTION VENTILATION SYSTEM.

RESPIRATOR: THE FOLLOWING RESPIRATORS ARE RECOMMENDED BASED ON INFORMATION FOUND IN THE PHYSICAL DATA, TOXICITY AND HEALTH EFFECTS SECTIONS. THEY ARE RANKED IN ORDER FROM MINIMUM TO MAXIMUM RESPIRATORY PROTECTION. THE SPECIFIC RESPIRATOR SELECTED MUST BE BASED ON CONTAMINATION LEVELS FOUND IN THE WORK PLACE, MUST NOT EXCEED THE WORKING LIMITS OF THE RESPIRATOR AND BE JOINTLY APPROVED BY THE NATIONAL INSTITUTE FOR OCCUPATIONAL SAFETY AND HEALTH AND THE MINE SAFETY AND HEALTH ADMINISTRATION (NIOSH-MSHA).
CHEMICAL CARTRIDGE RESPIRATOR WITH AN ORGANIC VAPOR CARTRIDGE(S) IN COMBINATION WITH A DUST AND MIST FILTER.
GAS MASK WITH ORGANIC VAPOR CANISTER (CHIN-STYLE OR FRONT- OR BACK-MOUNTED CANISTER) WITH A DUST AND MIST FILTER.
GAS MASK WITH ORGANIC VAPOR CANISTER (CHIN-STYLE OR FRONT- OR BACK-MOUNTED CANISTER) WITH A PARTICULATE FILTER.
POWERED AIR-PURIFYING RESPIRATOR WITH A HIGH-EFFICIENCY FILTER.
TYPE 'C' SUPPLIED-AIR RESPIRATOR WITH A FULL FACEPIECE OPERATED IN A PRESSURE-DEMAND OR OTHER POSITIVE PRESSURE MODE.
SELF-CONTAINED BREATHING APPARATUS WITH A FULL FACEPIECE OPERATED IN PRESSURE-DEMAND OR OTHER POSITIVE PRESSURE MODE.
FOR FIREFIGHTING AND OTHER IMMEDIATELY DANGEROUS TO LIFE OR HEALTH CONDITIONS:
SELF-CONTAINED BREATHING APPARATUS WITH FULL FACEPIECE OPERATED IN PRESSURE-DEMAND OR OTHER POSITIVE PRESSURE MODE.
SUPPLIED-AIR RESPIRATOR WITH FULL FACEPIECE AND OPERATED IN PRESSURE-DEMAND OR OTHER POSITIVE PRESSURE MODE IN COMBINATION WITH AN AUXILIARY SELF-CONTAINED BREATHING APPARATUS OPERATED IN PRESSURE-DEMAND OR OTHER POSITIVE PRESSURE MODE.

CLOTHING: EMPLOYEE MUST WEAR APPROPRIATE PROTECTIVE (IMPERVIOUS) CLOTHING AND EQUIPMENT TO PREVENT REPEATED OR PROLONGED SKIN CONTACT WITH THIS SUBSTANCE.

GLOVES: EMPLOYEE MUST WEAR APPROPRIATE PROTECTIVE GLOVES TO PREVENT CONTACT WITH THIS SUBSTANCE.

EYE PROTECTION: EMPLOYEE MUST WEAR SPLASH-PROOF OR DUST-RESISTANT SAFETY GOGGLES TO PREVENT EYE CONTACT WITH THIS SUBSTANCE.
EMERGENCY EYE WASH: WHERE THERE IS ANY POSSIBILITY THAT AN EMPLOYEE'S EYES MAY BE EXPOSED TO THIS SUBSTANCE, THE EMPLOYER SHOULD PROVIDE AN EYE WASH FOUNTAIN WITHIN THE IMMEDIATE WORK AREA FOR EMERGENCY USE.

AUTHORIZED BY- OCCUPATIONAL HEALTH SERVICES, INC.
CREATION DATE: 10/04/89 ***REVISION DATE:*** 06/12/90

MATERIAL SAFETY DATA SHEET

OCCUPATIONAL HEALTH SERVICES, INC.
AGRICULTURE AND PESTICIDE DIVISION
450 SEVENTH AVENUE, SUITE 2407
NEW YORK, NEW YORK 10123
1-800-445-MSDS OR (212) 967-1100

EMERGENCY CONTACT:
JOHN S. BRANSFORD, JR. (615) 292-1180

SUBSTANCE IDENTIFICATION

CAS-NUMBER 69806-40-2

SUBSTANCE: HALOXYFOP-METHYL

TRADE NAMES/SYNONYMS: PROPANOIC ACID, 2-(4-((3-CHLORO-5-(TRIFLUOROMETHYL)-2-PYRIDINYL)OXY) PHENOXY)-, METHYL ESTER; 2-(4-((3-CHLORO-5-(TRIFLUOROMETHYL)-2-PYRIDINYL)OXY)PHENOXY)METHYL PROPANOATE; DOWCO 453ME; DOWCO 453 METHYL ESTER; DOWCO 453; VERDICT; C16H13F3CLNO4; PST72579

CHEMICAL FAMILY: ETHER, AROMATIC ESTER

MOLECULAR FORMULA: C16-H13-CL-F3-N-O4

MOLECULAR WEIGHT: 375.75

CERCLA RATINGS (SCALE 0-3): HEALTH=U FIRE=1 REACTIVITY=0 PERSISTENCE=0

NFPA RATINGS (SCALE 0-4): HEALTH=U FIRE=1 REACTIVITY=0

COMPONENTS AND CONTAMINANTS

COMPONENT: HALOXYFOP-METHYL ***PERCENT:*** 100.0
CAS# 69806-40-2

OTHER CONTAMINANTS: NONE

EXPOSURE LIMITS: NO OCCUPATIONAL EXPOSURE LIMITS ESTABLISHED BY OSHA, ACGIH, OR NIOSH.

PHYSICAL DATA

DESCRIPTION: COLORLESS CRYSTALS. ***MELTING POINT:*** 131-135 F (55-57 C)

SPECIFIC GRAVITY: NOT AVAILABLE ***VAPOR PRESSURE:*** NEGLIGIBLE

SOLUBILITY IN WATER: 9.3 PPM

SOLVENT SOLUBILITY: SOLUBLE IN ACETONE, ACETONITRILE, DICHLOROMETHANE AND XYLENE.

FIRE AND EXPLOSION DATA

FIRE AND EXPLOSION HAZARD: SLIGHT FIRE HAZARD WHEN EXPOSED TO HEAT OR FLAME.

FIREFIGHTING MEDIA: DRY CHEMICAL, CARBON DIOXIDE, HALON, WATER SPRAY OR STANDARD FOAM (1987 EMERGENCY RESPONSE GUIDEBOOK, DOT P 5800.4).
FOR LARGER FIRES, USE WATER SPRAY, FOG OR STANDARD FOAM (1987 EMERGENCY RESPONSE GUIDEBOOK, DOT P 5800.4).

FIREFIGHTING: MOVE CONTAINERS FROM FIRE AREA IF POSSIBLE (1987 EMERGENCY RESPONSE GUIDEBOOK, DOT P 5800.4, GUIDE PAGE 53).
EXTINGUISH USING AGENT SUITABLE FOR TYPE OF SURROUNDING FIRE. AVOID BREATHING VAPORS AND DUSTS. KEEP UPWIND.

TOXICITY

HALOXYFOP-METHYL: TOXICITY DATA: >5000 MG/KG SKIN-RABBIT LD50 (PEMNDP); 393 MG/KG ORAL-RAT LD50. CARCINOGEN STATUS: NONE. ACUTE

TOXICITY LEVEL: TOXIC BY INGESTION; SLIGHTLY TOXIC BY DERMAL ABSORPTION.
TARGET EFFECTS: NO DATA AVAILABLE.

HEALTH EFFECTS AND FIRST AID

INHALATION: HALOXYFOP-METHYL: **ACUTE EXPOSURE-** NO DATA AVAILABLE. **CHRONIC EXPOSURE-** NO SYSTEMIC EFFECTS HAVE BEEN REPORTED IN WORKERS EXPOSED TO CHLORINATED DIPHENYL ETHERS.

FIRST AID- REMOVE FROM EXPOSURE AREA TO FRESH AIR IMMEDIATELY. IF BREATHING HAS STOPPED, PERFORM ARTIFICIAL RESPIRATION. KEEP PERSON WARM AND AT REST. TREAT SYMPTOMATICALLY AND SUPPORTIVELY. GET MEDICAL ATTENTION IMMEDIATELY.

SKIN CONTACT: HALOXYFOP-METHYL: **ACUTE EXPOSURE-** IN ANIMALS STUDIES, THIS MATERIAL WAS NOT A SKIN IRRITANT OR SENSITIZER. **CHRONIC EXPOSURE-** PROLONGED CONTACT WITH CHLORINATED DIPHENYL ETHERS MAY CAUSE IRRITATION, WEIGHT LOSS, AND LIVER INJURY.

FIRST AID- REMOVE CONTAMINATED CLOTHING AND SHOES IMMEDIATELY. WASH AFFECTED AREA WITH SOAP OR MILD DETERGENT AND LARGE AMOUNTS OF WATER UNTIL NO EVIDENCE OF CHEMICAL REMAINS (APPROXIMATELY 15-20 MINUTES). GET MEDICAL ATTENTION IMMEDIATELY.

EYE CONTACT: HALOXYFOP-METHYL: **ACUTE EXPOSURE-** THIS MATERIAL WAS MODERATELY IRRITATING TO RABBIT EYES. **CHRONIC EXPOSURE-** NO DATA AVAILABLE.

FIRST AID- WASH EYES IMMEDIATELY WITH LARGE AMOUNTS OF WATER OR NORMAL SALINE, OCCASIONALLY LIFTING UPPER AND LOWER LIDS, UNTIL NO EVIDENCE OF CHEMICAL REMAINS (APPROXIMATELY 15-20 MINUTES). GET MEDICAL ATTENTION IMMEDIATELY.

INGESTION: HALOXYFOP-METHYL: TOXIC. **ACUTE EXPOSURE-** THE LETHAL DOSE REPORTED IN RATS WAS 393 MG/KG; SYMPTOMS WERE NOT REPORTED. **CHRONIC EXPOSURE-** ANIMALS FED CHLORINATED DIPHENYL ETHERS DEVELOPED LIVER DAMAGE WITH CONGESTION AND FATTY DEGENERATION.

FIRST AID- IF EXTENSIVE VOMITING HAS NOT OCCURRED, THE SUBSTANCE SHOULD BE REMOVED BY EMESIS OR GASTRIC LAVAGE PROVIDED THAT THE PATIENT IS CONSCIOUS AND CONVULSIONS ARE NOT PRESENT. KEEP HEAD BELOW HIPS DURING VOMITING TO PREVENT ASPIRATION. DO NOT ATTEMPT TO MAKE AN UNCONSCIOUS PERSON VOMIT. TREAT SYMPTOMATICALLY AND SUPPORTIVELY. GET MEDICAL ATTENTION IMMEDIATELY (DREISBACH, HANDBOOK OF POISONING, 12TH ED.). TREATMENT SHOULD BE PERFORMED BY QUALIFIED MEDICAL PERSONNEL.

ANTIDOTE: NO SPECIFIC ANTIDOTE. TREAT SYMPTOMATICALLY AND SUPPORTIVELY.

REACTIVITY

REACTIVITY: STABLE UNDER NORMAL TEMPERATURES AND PRESSURES.

INCOMPATIBILITIES: HALOXYFOP-METHYL: OXIDIZERS (STRONG): FIRE AND EXPLOSION HAZARD.

DECOMPOSITION: THERMAL DECOMPOSITION PRODUCTS MAY INCLUDE TOXIC OXIDES OF NITROGEN AND CARBON, AND TOXIC AND CORROSIVE FUMES OF CHLORIDES AND FLUORIDES.

POLYMERIZATION: HAZARDOUS POLYMERIZATION HAS NOT BEEN REPORTED TO OCCUR UNDER NORMAL TEMPERATURES AND PRESSURES.

STORAGE AND DISPOSAL

OBSERVE ALL FEDERAL, STATE AND LOCAL REGULATIONS WHEN STORING OR DISPOSING OF THIS SUBSTANCE. FOR ASSISTANCE, CONTACT THE DISTRICT DIRECTOR OF THE ENVIRONMENTAL PROTECTION AGENCY.

****STORAGE****

STORE IN ACCORDANCE WITH 40 CFR 165 RECOMMENDED PROCEDURES FOR THE DISPOSAL AND STORAGE OF PESTICIDES AND PESTICIDE CONTAINERS. STORE AWAY FROM INCOMPATIBLE SUBSTANCES.

****DISPOSAL****

DISPOSAL MUST BE IN ACCORDANCE WITH 40 CFR 165 RECOMMENDED PROCEDURES FOR THE DISPOSAL AND STORAGE OF PESTICIDES AND PESTICIDE CONTAINERS.

CONDITIONS TO AVOID

MAY BURN BUT DOES NOT IGNITE READILY.

SPILL AND LEAK PROCEDURES

OCCUPATIONAL SPILL: DO NOT TOUCH SPILLED MATERIAL. STOP LEAK IF YOU CAN DO IT WITHOUT RISK. FOR SMALL SPILLS, TAKE UP WITH SAND OR OTHER ABSORBENT MATERIAL AND PLACE INTO CONTAINERS FOR LATER DISPOSAL. FOR SMALL DRY SPILLS, WITH A CLEAN SHOVEL PLACE MATERIAL INTO CLEAN, DRY CONTAINER AND COVER. MOVE CONTAINERS FROM SPILL AREA. FOR LARGER SPILLS, DIKE FAR AHEAD OF SPILL FOR LATER DISPOSAL. KEEP UNNECESSARY PEOPLE AWAY. ISOLATE HAZARD AREA AND DENY ENTRY.

PROTECTIVE EQUIPMENT

VENTILATION: PROVIDE LOCAL EXHAUST OR GENERAL DILUTION VENTILATION SYSTEM.

RESPIRATOR: THE FOLLOWING RESPIRATORS ARE RECOMMENDED BASED ON INFORMATION FOUND IN THE PHYSICAL DATA, TOXICITY AND HEALTH EFFECTS SECTIONS. THEY ARE RANKED IN ORDER FROM MINIMUM TO MAXIMUM RESPIRATORY PROTECTION. THE SPECIFIC RESPIRATOR SELECTED MUST BE BASED ON CONTAMINATION LEVELS FOUND IN THE WORK PLACE, MUST NOT EXCEED THE WORKING LIMITS OF THE RESPIRATOR AND BE JOINTLY APPROVED BY THE NATIONAL INSTITUTE FOR OCCUPATIONAL SAFETY AND HEALTH AND THE MINE SAFETY AND HEALTH ADMINISTRATION (NIOSH-MSHA).

CHEMICAL CARTRIDGE RESPIRATOR WITH AN ORGANIC VAPOR CARTRIDGE(S) IN COMBINATION WITH A DUST AND MIST FILTER.

GAS MASK WITH ORGANIC VAPOR CANISTER (CHIN-STYLE OR FRONT- OR BACK-MOUNTED CANISTER) WITH A DUST AND MIST FILTER.

GAS MASK WITH ORGANIC VAPOR CANISTER (CHIN-STYLE OR FRONT- OR BACK-MOUNTED CANISTER) WITH A PARTICULATE FILTER.

POWERED AIR-PURIFYING RESPIRATOR WITH A HIGH-EFFICIENCY FILTER.

TYPE 'C' SUPPLIED-AIR RESPIRATOR WITH A FULL FACEPIECE OPERATED IN A PRESSURE-DEMAND OR OTHER POSITIVE PRESSURE MODE.

SELF-CONTAINED BREATHING APPARATUS WITH A FULL FACEPIECE OPERATED IN PRESSURE-DEMAND OR OTHER POSITIVE PRESSURE MODE.

FOR FIREFIGHTING AND OTHER IMMEDIATELY DANGEROUS TO LIFE OR HEALTH CONDITIONS:

SELF-CONTAINED BREATHING APPARATUS WITH FULL FACEPIECE OPERATED IN PRESSURE-DEMAND OR OTHER POSITIVE PRESSURE MODE.

SUPPLIED-AIR RESPIRATOR WITH FULL FACEPIECE AND OPERATED IN PRESSURE-DEMAND OR OTHER POSITIVE PRESSURE MODE IN COMBINATION WITH AN AUXILIARY SELF-CONTAINED BREATHING APPARATUS OPERATED IN PRESSURE-DEMAND OR OTHER POSITIVE PRESSURE MODE.

CLOTHING: EMPLOYEE MUST WEAR APPROPRIATE PROTECTIVE (IMPERVIOUS) CLOTHING AND EQUIPMENT TO PREVENT REPEATED OR PROLONGED SKIN CONTACT WITH THIS SUBSTANCE.

GLOVES: EMPLOYEE MUST WEAR APPROPRIATE PROTECTIVE GLOVES TO PREVENT CONTACT WITH THIS SUBSTANCE.

EYE PROTECTION: EMPLOYEE MUST WEAR SPLASH-PROOF OR DUST-RESISTANT SAFETY GOGGLES TO PREVENT EYE CONTACT WITH THIS SUBSTANCE.

EMERGENCY EYE WASH: WHERE THERE IS ANY POSSIBILITY THAT AN EMPLOYEE'S EYES MAY BE EXPOSED TO THIS SUBSTANCE, THE EMPLOYER SHOULD PROVIDE AN EYE WASH FOUNTAIN WITHIN THE IMMEDIATE WORK AREA FOR EMERGENCY USE.

AUTHORIZED BY- OCCUPATIONAL HEALTH SERVICES, INC.
CREATION DATE: 12/20/89 ***REVISION DATE:*** 05/07/90

MATERIAL SAFETY DATA SHEET

OCCUPATIONAL HEALTH SERVICES, INC.
AGRICULTURE AND PESTICIDE DIVISION
450 SEVENTH AVENUE, SUITE 2407
NEW YORK, NEW YORK 10123
1-800-445-MSDS OR (212) 967-1100

EMERGENCY CONTACT:
JOHN S. BRANSFORD, JR. (615) 292-1180

SUBSTANCE IDENTIFICATION

CAS-NUMBER 69806-34-4

SUBSTANCE: **HALOXYFOP**

TRADE NAMES/SYNONYMS: PROPANOIC ACID, 2-(4-((3-CHLORO-5-(TRIFLUOROMETHYL)-2-PYRIDINYL)OXY) PHENOXY)-; 2-(4-((3-CHLORO-5-(TRIFLUOROMETHYL)-2-PYRIDINYL)OXY)PHENOXY)PROPANOIC ACID; DOWCO 453; C15H11CLF3NO4; PST72580

CHEMICAL FAMILY: HALOGEN COMPOUND, AROMATIC ETHER, AROMATIC

MOLECULAR FORMULA: C15-H11-CL-F3-N-O4

MOLECULAR WEIGHT: 361.71

CERCLA RATINGS (SCALE 0-3): HEALTH=U FIRE=1 REACTIVITY=0 PERSISTENCE=1

NFPA RATINGS (SCALE 0-4): HEALTH=U FIRE=1 REACTIVITY=0

COMPONENTS AND CONTAMINANTS

COMPONENT: HALOXYFOP ***PERCENT:*** 100.0
CAS# 69806-34-4

OTHER CONTAMINANTS: NONE

EXPOSURE LIMITS: NO OCCUPATIONAL EXPOSURE LIMITS ESTABLISHED BY OSHA, ACGIH, OR NIOSH.

PHYSICAL DATA

DESCRIPTION: WHITE POWDER. ***MELTING POINT:*** NOT AVAILABLE
SPECIFIC GRAVITY: NOT AVAILABLE ***SOLUBILITY IN WATER:*** NOT AVAILABLE

FIRE AND EXPLOSION DATA

FIRE AND EXPLOSION HAZARD: SLIGHT FIRE HAZARD WHEN EXPOSED TO HEAT OR FLAME.

FIREFIGHTING MEDIA: DRY CHEMICAL, CARBON DIOXIDE, HALON, WATER SPRAY OR STANDARD FOAM (1987 EMERGENCY RESPONSE GUIDEBOOK, DOT P 5800.4). FOR LARGER FIRES, USE WATER SPRAY, FOG OR STANDARD FOAM (1987 EMERGENCY RESPONSE GUIDEBOOK, DOT P 5800.4).

FIREFIGHTING: MOVE CONTAINERS FROM FIRE AREA IF POSSIBLE (1987 EMERGENCY RESPONSE GUIDEBOOK, DOT P 5800.4, GUIDE PAGE 53).
EXTINGUISH USING AGENT SUITABLE FOR TYPE OF SURROUNDING FIRE. AVOID BREATHING VAPORS AND DUSTS. KEEP UPWIND.

TOXICITY

HALOXYFOP: CARCINOGEN STATUS: NONE. ACUTE TOXICITY LEVEL: NO DATA AVAILABLE. TARGET EFFECTS: NO DATA AVAILABLE.

HEALTH EFFECTS AND FIRST AID

INHALATION: HALOXYFOP: ACUTE EXPOSURE- NO DATA AVAILABLE. CHRONIC EXPOSURE- NO DATA AVAILABLE.

FIRST AID- REMOVE FROM EXPOSURE AREA TO FRESH AIR IMMEDIATELY. IF BREATHING HAS STOPPED, PERFORM ARTIFICIAL RESPIRATION. KEEP PERSON WARM AND AT REST. TREAT SYMPTOMATICALLY AND SUPPORTIVELY. GET MEDICAL ATTENTION IMMEDIATELY.

SKIN CONTACT: HALOXYFOP: ACUTE EXPOSURE- THIS MATERIAL WAS NOT A SKIN IRRITANT TO RABBITS OR A SKIN SENSITIZER TO GUINEA PIGS. CHRONIC EXPOSURE- NO DATA AVAILABLE.

FIRST AID- REMOVE CONTAMINATED CLOTHING AND SHOES IMMEDIATELY. WASH AFFECTED AREA WITH SOAP OR MILD DETERGENT AND LARGE AMOUNTS OF WATER UNTIL NO EVIDENCE OF CHEMICAL REMAINS (APPROXIMATELY 15-20 MINUTES). GET MEDICAL ATTENTION IMMEDIATELY.

EYE CONTACT: HALOXYFOP: ACUTE EXPOSURE- THIS MATERIAL WAS A MODERATE IRRITANT TO RABBITS. CHRONIC EXPOSURE- NO DATA AVAILABLE.

FIRST AID- WASH EYES IMMEDIATELY WITH LARGE AMOUNTS OF WATER OR NORMAL SALINE, OCCASIONALLY LIFTING UPPER AND LOWER LIDS, UNTIL NO EVIDENCE OF CHEMICAL REMAINS (APPROXIMATELY 15-20 MINUTES). GET MEDICAL ATTENTION IMMEDIATELY.

INGESTION: HALOXYFOP: ACUTE EXPOSURE- NO DATA AVAILABLE. CHRONIC EXPOSURE- NO DATA AVAILABLE.

FIRST AID- TREAT SYMPTOMATICALLY AND SUPPORTIVELY. GET MEDICAL ATTENTION IMMEDIATELY. IF VOMITING OCCURS, KEEP HEAD LOWER THAN HIPS TO PREVENT ASPIRATION.

ANTIDOTE: NO SPECIFIC ANTIDOTE. TREAT SYMPTOMATICALLY AND SUPPORTIVELY.

REACTIVITY

REACTIVITY: STABLE UNDER NORMAL TEMPERATURES AND PRESSURES.

INCOMPATIBILITIES: HALOXYFOP: OXIDIZERS (STRONG): FIRE AND EXPLOSION HAZARD.

DECOMPOSITION: THERMAL DECOMPOSITION PRODUCTS MAY INCLUDE TOXIC OXIDES OF NITROGEN AND CARBON, AND TOXIC AND CORROSIVE FUMES OF CHLORIDES AND FLUORIDES.

POLYMERIZATION: HAZARDOUS POLYMERIZATION HAS NOT BEEN REPORTED TO OCCUR UNDER NORMAL TEMPERATURES AND PRESSURES.

STORAGE AND DISPOSAL

OBSERVE ALL FEDERAL, STATE AND LOCAL REGULATIONS WHEN STORING OR DISPOSING OF THIS SUBSTANCE. FOR ASSISTANCE, CONTACT THE DISTRICT DIRECTOR OF THE ENVIRONMENTAL PROTECTION AGENCY.

STORAGE

STORE IN ACCORDANCE WITH 40 CFR 165 RECOMMENDED PROCEDURES FOR THE DISPOSAL AND STORAGE OF PESTICIDES AND PESTICIDE CONTAINERS.
STORE AWAY FROM INCOMPATIBLE SUBSTANCES.

DISPOSAL

DISPOSAL MUST BE IN ACCORDANCE WITH 40 CFR 165 RECOMMENDED PROCEDURES FOR THE DISPOSAL AND STORAGE OF PESTICIDES AND PESTICIDE CONTAINERS.

CONDITIONS TO AVOID

MAY BURN BUT DOES NOT IGNITE READILY.

SPILL AND LEAK PROCEDURES

OCCUPATIONAL SPILL: DO NOT TOUCH SPILLED MATERIAL. STOP LEAK IF YOU CAN DO IT WITHOUT RISK. FOR SMALL SPILLS, TAKE UP WITH SAND OR OTHER ABSORBENT MATERIAL AND PLACE INTO CONTAINERS FOR LATER DISPOSAL. FOR SMALL DRY SPILLS, WITH A CLEAN SHOVEL PLACE MATERIAL INTO CLEAN, DRY CONTAINER AND COVER. MOVE CONTAINERS FROM SPILL AREA. FOR LARGER SPILLS, DIKE FAR AHEAD OF SPILL FOR LATER DISPOSAL. KEEP UNNECESSARY PEOPLE AWAY. ISOLATE HAZARD AREA AND DENY ENTRY.

PROTECTIVE EQUIPMENT

VENTILATION: PROVIDE LOCAL EXHAUST OR PROCESS ENCLOSURE VENTILATION SYSTEM.

RESPIRATOR: THE FOLLOWING RESPIRATORS ARE RECOMMENDED BASED ON INFORMATION FOUND IN THE PHYSICAL DATA, TOXICITY AND HEALTH EFFECTS SECTIONS. THEY ARE RANKED IN ORDER FROM MINIMUM TO MAXIMUM RESPIRATORY PROTECTION. THE SPECIFIC RESPIRATOR SELECTED MUST BE BASED ON CONTAMINATION LEVELS FOUND IN THE WORK PLACE, MUST NOT EXCEED THE WORKING LIMITS OF THE RESPIRATOR AND BE JOINTLY APPROVED BY THE NATIONAL INSTITUTE FOR OCCUPATIONAL SAFETY AND HEALTH AND THE MINE SAFETY AND HEALTH ADMINISTRATION (NIOSH-MSHA).
CHEMICAL CARTRIDGE RESPIRATOR WITH AN ORGANIC VAPOR CARTRIDGE(S) IN COMBINATION WITH A DUST AND MIST FILTER.
GAS MASK WITH ORGANIC VAPOR CANISTER (CHIN-STYLE OR FRONT- OR BACK-MOUNTED CANISTER) WITH A DUST AND MIST FILTER.
GAS MASK WITH ORGANIC VAPOR CANISTER (CHIN-STYLE OR FRONT- OR BACK-MOUNTED CANISTER) WITH A PARTICULATE FILTER.
POWERED AIR-PURIFYING RESPIRATOR WITH A HIGH-EFFICIENCY FILTER.
TYPE 'C' SUPPLIED-AIR RESPIRATOR WITH A FULL FACEPIECE OPERATED IN A PRESSURE-DEMAND OR OTHER POSITIVE PRESSURE MODE.
SELF-CONTAINED BREATHING APPARATUS WITH A FULL FACEPIECE OPERATED IN PRESSURE-DEMAND OR OTHER POSITIVE PRESSURE MODE.
FOR FIREFIGHTING AND OTHER IMMEDIATELY DANGEROUS TO LIFE OR HEALTH CONDITIONS:
SELF-CONTAINED BREATHING APPARATUS WITH FULL FACEPIECE OPERATED IN PRESSURE-DEMAND OR OTHER POSITIVE PRESSURE MODE.
SUPPLIED-AIR RESPIRATOR WITH FULL FACEPIECE AND OPERATED IN PRESSURE-DEMAND OR OTHER POSITIVE PRESSURE MODE IN COMBINATION WITH AN AUXILIARY SELF-CONTAINED BREATHING APPARATUS OPERATED IN PRESSURE-DEMAND OR OTHER POSITIVE PRESSURE MODE.

CLOTHING: EMPLOYEE MUST WEAR APPROPRIATE PROTECTIVE (IMPERVIOUS) CLOTHING AND EQUIPMENT TO PREVENT REPEATED OR PROLONGED SKIN CONTACT WITH THIS SUBSTANCE.

GLOVES: EMPLOYEE MUST WEAR APPROPRIATE PROTECTIVE GLOVES TO PREVENT CONTACT WITH THIS SUBSTANCE.

EYE PROTECTION: EMPLOYEE MUST WEAR SPLASH-PROOF OR DUST-RESISTANT SAFETY GOGGLES TO PREVENT EYE CONTACT WITH THIS SUBSTANCE.
EMERGENCY EYE WASH: WHERE THERE IS ANY POSSIBILITY THAT AN EMPLOYEE'S EYES MAY BE EXPOSED TO THIS SUBSTANCE, THE EMPLOYER SHOULD PROVIDE AN EYE WASH FOUNTAIN WITHIN THE IMMEDIATE WORK AREA FOR EMERGENCY USE.

AUTHORIZED BY- OCCUPATIONAL HEALTH SERVICES, INC.
CREATION DATE: 10/18/89 ***REVISION DATE:*** 05/07/90

MATERIAL SAFETY DATA SHEET

OCCUPATIONAL HEALTH SERVICES, INC.
AGRICULTURE AND PESTICIDE DIVISION
450 SEVENTH AVENUE, SUITE 2407
NEW YORK, NEW YORK 10123
1-800-445-MSDS OR (212) 967-1100

EMERGENCY CONTACT:
JOHN S. BRANSFORD, JR. (615) 292-1180

SUBSTANCE IDENTIFICATION

CAS-NUMBER 55861-78-4

SUBSTANCE: **ISOURON**

TRADE NAMES/SYNONYMS: UREA, N'-(5-(1,1-DIMETHYLETHYL)-3-ISOXAZOLYL)-N,N-DIMETHYL-; N'-(5-(1,1-DIMETHYLETHYL)-3-ISOXAZOLYL)-N,N-DIMETHYLUREA; 3-(5-TERT-BUTYLISOXAZOL-3-YL)-1,1-DIMETHYLUREA; ISOXYL; C10H17N3O2; PST72586

CHEMICAL FAMILY: SUBSTITUTED UREA

MOLECULAR FORMULA: C10-H17-N3-O2

MOLECULAR WEIGHT: 211.3

CERCLA RATINGS (SCALE 0-3): HEALTH=2 FIRE=1 REACTIVITY=0 PERSISTENCE=0

NFPA RATINGS (SCALE 0-4): HEALTH=2 FIRE=1 REACTIVITY=0

COMPONENTS AND CONTAMINANTS

COMPONENT: ISOURON ***PERCENT:*** 100.0

CAS# 55861-78-4

OTHER CONTAMINANTS: NONE

EXPOSURE LIMITS: NO OCCUPATIONAL EXPOSURE LIMITS ESTABLISHED BY OSHA, ACGIH, OR NIOSH.

PHYSICAL DATA

DESCRIPTION: COLORLESS CRYSTALLINE SOLID.

MELTING POINT: 246-248 F (119-120 C)

SPECIFIC GRAVITY: NOT AVAILABLE ***VAPOR PRESSURE:*** NEGLIGIBLE

SOLUBILITY IN WATER: 0.079% @ 25 C

SOLVENT SOLUBILITY: SOLUBLE IN ACETONE, ETHANOL, O-XYLENE

FIRE AND EXPLOSION DATA

FIRE AND EXPLOSION HAZARD: SLIGHT FIRE HAZARD WHEN EXPOSED TO HEAT OR FLAME.

FIREFIGHTING MEDIA: DRY CHEMICAL, CARBON DIOXIDE, HALON, WATER SPRAY OR STANDARD FOAM (1987 EMERGENCY RESPONSE GUIDEBOOK, DOT P 5800.4). FOR LARGER FIRES, USE WATER SPRAY, FOG OR STANDARD FOAM (1987 EMERGENCY RESPONSE GUIDEBOOK, DOT P 5800.4).

FIREFIGHTING: MOVE CONTAINERS FROM FIRE AREA IF POSSIBLE. FIGHT FIRE FROM MAXIMUM DISTANCE. STAY AWAY FROM STORAGE TANK ENDS. DIKE FIRE CONTROL WATER FOR LATER DISPOSAL. DO NOT SCATTER MATERIAL (1987 EMERGENCY RESPONSE GUIDEBOOK, DOT P 5800.4, GUIDE PAGE 55). EXTINGUISH USING AGENT SUITABLE FOR TYPE OF SURROUNDING FIRE. USE WATER IN FLOODING QUANTITIES AS FOG. KEEP SPARKS, FLAMES AND OTHER SOURCES OF IGNITION AWAY. KEEP MATERIAL OUT OF WATER SOURCES AND SEWERS. DO NOT TOUCH MATERIAL AND AVOID BREATHING DUSTS AND FUMES FROM BURNING MATERIAL. KEEP UPWIND.

TOXICITY

ISOURON: TOXICITY DATA: 630 MG/KG ORAL-RAT LD50; 520 MG/KG ORAL-MOUSE LD50; 510 MG/KG SUBCUTANEOUS-RAT LD50; 550 MG/KG SUBCUTANEOUS-MOUSE LD50; 270 MG/KG INTRAPERITONEAL-RAT LD50; 390 MG/KG INTRAPERITONEAL-MOUSE LD50. CARCINOGEN STATUS: NONE. ACUTE TOXICITY DATA: MODERATELY TOXIC BY INGESTION. TARGET EFFECTS: NO DATA AVAILABLE.

HEALTH EFFECTS AND FIRST AID

INHALATION: ISOURON: **ACUTE EXPOSURE-** A LETHAL CONCENTRATION IN RATS IS GREATER THAN 415 MG/M3/8 HOURS. MANY SUBSTITUTED UREA HERBICIDES ARE MODERATELY IRRITATING TO THE MUCOUS MEMBRANES. **CHRONIC EXPOSURE-** NO DATA AVAILABLE.

FIRST AID- REMOVE FROM EXPOSURE AREA TO FRESH AIR IMMEDIATELY. IF BREATHING HAS STOPPED, PERFORM ARTIFICIAL RESPIRATION. KEEP PERSON WARM AND AT REST. TREAT SYMPTOMATICALLY AND SUPPORTIVELY. GET MEDICAL ATTENTION IMMEDIATELY.

SKIN CONTACT: ISOURON: **ACUTE EXPOSURE-** THIS MATERIAL IS NOT IRRITATING TO RABBIT SKIN. A LETHAL DOSE IN RATS BY DERMAL ABSORPTION IS GREATER THAN 5000 MG/KG. **CHRONIC EXPOSURE-** NO DATA AVAILABLE.

FIRST AID- REMOVE CONTAMINATED CLOTHING AND SHOES IMMEDIATELY. WASH AFFECTED AREA WITH SOAP OR MILD DETERGENT AND LARGE AMOUNTS OF WATER UNTIL NO EVIDENCE OF CHEMICAL REMAINS (APPROXIMATELY 15-20 MINUTES). GET MEDICAL ATTENTION IMMEDIATELY.

EYE CONTACT: ISOURON: **ACUTE EXPOSURE-** THIS MATERIAL IS NOT IRRITATING TO RABBIT EYES. **CHRONIC EXPOSURE-** NO DATA AVAILABLE.

FIRST AID- WASH EYES IMMEDIATELY WITH LARGE AMOUNTS OF WATER OR NORMAL SALINE, OCCASIONALLY LIFTING UPPER AND LOWER LIDS, UNTIL NO EVIDENCE OF CHEMICAL REMAINS (APPROXIMATELY 15-20 MINUTES). GET MEDICAL ATTENTION IMMEDIATELY.

INGESTION: ISOURON: **ACUTE EXPOSURE-** A LETHAL DOSE IN RATS IS 630 MG/KG; SYMPTOMS WERE NOT REPORTED. **CHRONIC EXPOSURE-** NO OBSERVABLE EFFECTS WERE NOTED IN A 90-DAY STUDY OF RATS FED 11.9-12.6 MG/KG/DAY AND MICE FED 118-127 MG/KG/DAY.

FIRST AID- TREAT SYMPTOMATICALLY AND SUPPORTIVELY. GET MEDICAL ATTENTION IMMEDIATELY. IF VOMITING OCCURS, KEEP HEAD LOWER THAN HIPS TO PREVENT ASPIRATION.

ANTIDOTE: NO SPECIFIC ANTIDOTE. TREAT SYMPTOMATICALLY AND SUPPORTIVELY.

REACTIVITY

REACTIVITY: STABLE UNDER NORMAL TEMPERATURES AND PRESSURES.

INCOMPATIBILITIES: ISOURON: OXIDIZERS (STRONG): FIRE AND EXPLOSION HAZARD.

DECOMPOSITION: THERMAL DECOMPOSITION PRODUCTS MAY INCLUDE TOXIC OXIDES OF CARBON AND NITROGEN.

POLYMERIZATION: HAZARDOUS POLYMERIZATION HAS NOT BEEN REPORTED TO OCCUR UNDER NORMAL TEMPERATURES AND PRESSURES.

STORAGE AND DISPOSAL

OBSERVE ALL FEDERAL, STATE AND LOCAL REGULATIONS WHEN STORING OR DISPOSING OF THIS SUBSTANCE. FOR ASSISTANCE, CONTACT THE DISTRICT DIRECTOR OF THE ENVIRONMENTAL PROTECTION AGENCY.

STORAGE

STORE IN ACCORDANCE WITH 40 CFR 165 RECOMMENDED PROCEDURES FOR THE DISPOSAL AND STORAGE OF PESTICIDES AND PESTICIDE CONTAINERS. STORE AWAY FROM INCOMPATIBLE SUBSTANCES.

DISPOSAL

DISPOSAL MUST BE IN ACCORDANCE WITH 40 CFR 165 RECOMMENDED PROCEDURES FOR THE DISPOSAL AND STORAGE OF PESTICIDES AND PESTICIDE CONTAINERS.

CONDITIONS TO AVOID

MAY BURN BUT DOES NOT IGNITE READILY. CONTAINERS MAY EXPLODE IN HEAT OF FIRE.

SPILL AND LEAK PROCEDURES

OCCUPATIONAL SPILL: DO NOT TOUCH SPILLED MATERIAL. STOP LEAK IF YOU CAN DO IT WITHOUT RISK. USE WATER SPRAY TO REDUCE VAPORS. FOR SMALL SPILLS, TAKE UP WITH SAND OR OTHER ABSORBENT MATERIAL AND PLACE INTO CONTAINERS FOR LATER DISPOSAL. FOR SMALL DRY SPILLS, WITH A CLEAN SHOVEL PLACE MATERIAL INTO CLEAN, DRY CONTAINERS AND COVER. MOVE CONTAINERS FROM SPILL AREA. FOR LARGER SPILLS, DIKE FAR AHEAD OF SPILL FOR LATER DISPOSAL. KEEP UNNECESSARY PEOPLE AWAY. ISOLATE HAZARD AREA AND DENY ENTRY. VENTILATE CLOSED SPACES BEFORE ENTERING.

PROTECTIVE EQUIPMENT

VENTILATION: PROVIDE LOCAL EXHAUST OR GENERAL DILUTION VENTILATION SYSTEM.

RESPIRATOR: THE FOLLOWING RESPIRATORS ARE RECOMMENDED BASED ON INFORMATION FOUND IN THE PHYSICAL DATA, TOXICITY AND HEALTH EFFECTS SECTIONS. THEY ARE RANKED IN ORDER FROM MINIMUM TO MAXIMUM RESPIRATORY PROTECTION. THE SPECIFIC RESPIRATOR SELECTED MUST BE BASED ON CONTAMINATION LEVELS FOUND IN THE WORK PLACE, MUST NOT EXCEED THE WORKING LIMITS OF THE RESPIRATOR AND BE JOINTLY APPROVED BY THE NATIONAL INSTITUTE FOR OCCUPATIONAL SAFETY AND HEALTH AND THE MINE SAFETY AND HEALTH ADMINISTRATION (NIOSH-MSHA).

CHEMICAL CARTRIDGE RESPIRATOR WITH AN ORGANIC VAPOR CARTRIDGE(S) IN COMBINATION WITH A DUST AND MIST FILTER.

GAS MASK WITH ORGANIC VAPOR CANISTER (CHIN-STYLE OR FRONT- OR BACK-MOUNTED CANISTER) WITH A DUST AND MIST FILTER.

GAS MASK WITH ORGANIC VAPOR CANISTER (CHIN-STYLE OR FRONT- OR BACK-MOUNTED CANISTER) WITH A PARTICULATE FILTER.

POWERED AIR-PURIFYING RESPIRATOR WITH A HIGH-EFFICIENCY FILTER.

TYPE 'C' SUPPLIED-AIR RESPIRATOR WITH A FULL FACEPIECE OPERATED IN A PRESSURE-DEMAND OR OTHER POSITIVE PRESSURE MODE.

SELF-CONTAINED BREATHING APPARATUS WITH A FULL FACEPIECE OPERATED IN PRESSURE-DEMAND OR OTHER POSITIVE PRESSURE MODE.

FOR FIREFIGHTING AND OTHER IMMEDIATELY DANGEROUS TO LIFE OR HEALTH CONDITIONS:

SELF-CONTAINED BREATHING APPARATUS WITH FULL FACEPIECE OPERATED IN PRESSURE-DEMAND OR OTHER POSITIVE PRESSURE MODE.

SUPPLIED-AIR RESPIRATOR WITH FULL FACEPIECE AND OPERATED IN PRESSURE-DEMAND OR OTHER POSITIVE PRESSURE MODE IN COMBINATION WITH AN AUXILIARY SELF-CONTAINED BREATHING APPARATUS OPERATED IN PRESSURE-DEMAND OR OTHER POSITIVE PRESSURE MODE.

CLOTHING: EMPLOYEE MUST WEAR APPROPRIATE PROTECTIVE (IMPERVIOUS) CLOTHING AND EQUIPMENT TO PREVENT REPEATED OR PROLONGED SKIN CONTACT WITH THIS SUBSTANCE.
GLOVES: EMPLOYEE MUST WEAR APPROPRIATE PROTECTIVE GLOVES TO PREVENT CONTACT WITH THIS SUBSTANCE.
EYE PROTECTION: EMPLOYEE MUST WEAR SPLASH-PROOF OR DUST-RESISTANT SAFETY GOGGLES TO PREVENT EYE CONTACT WITH THIS SUBSTANCE. EMERGENCY EYE WASH: WHERE THERE IS ANY POSSIBILITY THAT AN EMPLOYEE'S EYES MAY BE EXPOSED TO THIS SUBSTANCE, THE EMPLOYER SHOULD PROVIDE AN EYE WASH FOUNTAIN WITHIN THE IMMEDIATE WORK AREA FOR EMERGENCY USE.

AUTHORIZED BY- OCCUPATIONAL HEALTH SERVICES, INC.
CREATION DATE: 10/04/89 ***REVISION DATE:*** 05/14/90

MATERIAL SAFETY DATA SHEET

OCCUPATIONAL HEALTH SERVICES, INC.
AGRICULTURE AND PESTICIDE DIVISION
450 SEVENTH AVENUE, SUITE 2407
NEW YORK, NEW YORK 10123
1-800-445-MSDS OR (212) 967-1100

EMERGENCY CONTACT:
JOHN S. BRANSFORD, JR. (615) 292-1180

SUBSTANCE IDENTIFICATION

CAS-NUMBER 72490-01-8
SUBSTANCE: **FENOXYCARB**
TRADE NAMES/SYNONYMS: CARBAMIC ACID, (2-(4-PHENOXYPHENOXY)ETHYL)-, ETHYL ESTER; (2-(4-PHENOXYPHENOXY)ETHYL)CARBAMIC ACID ETHYL ESTER; ETHYL 2-(4-PHENOXYPHENOXY)ETHYLCARBAMATE; ETHYL (2-(4-PHENOXYPHENOXY)ETHYL)CARBAMATE; ETHYL (2-(P-PHENOXY)ETHYL)CARBAMATE; INSEGAR; LOGIC; RO 13-5223; C17H19NO4; PST72618
CHEMICAL FAMILY: CARBAMATE
MOLECULAR FORMULA: C17-H19-N-O4
MOLECULAR WEIGHT: 301.3
CERCLA RATINGS (SCALE 0-3): HEALTH=U FIRE=1 REACTIVITY=0 PERSISTENCE=1
NFPA RATINGS (SCALE 0-4): HEALTH=U FIRE=1 REACTIVITY=0

COMPONENTS AND CONTAMINANTS

COMPONENT: FENOXYCARB ***PERCENT:*** 100.0
CAS# 72490-01-8
OTHER CONTAMINANTS: NONE
EXPOSURE LIMITS: NO OCCUPATIONAL EXPOSURE LIMITS ESTABLISHED BY OSHA, ACGIH, OR NIOSH.

PHYSICAL DATA

DESCRIPTION: COLORLESS OR WHITE TO LIGHT BROWN CRYSTALLINE SOLID.
MELTING POINT: 127-129 F (53-54 C) ***SPECIFIC GRAVITY:*** NOT AVAILABLE
VAPOR PRESSURE: NEGLIGIBLE ***SOLUBILITY IN WATER:*** 6 PPM
SOLVENT SOLUBILITY: SOLUBLE IN ACETONE, CHLOROFORM, ETHER, ETHYL ACETATE, DIETHYL FORMAMIDE, METHANOL, TOLUENE, AND MOST ORGANIC SOLVENTS; SLIGHTLY SOLUBLE IN HEXANE.

FIRE AND EXPLOSION DATA

FIRE AND EXPLOSION HAZARD: SLIGHT FIRE HAZARD WHEN EXPOSED TO HEAT OR FLAME.
FLASH POINT: 435 F (224 C)
FIREFIGHTING MEDIA: DRY CHEMICAL, CARBON DIOXIDE, HALON, WATER SPRAY OR STANDARD FOAM (1987 EMERGENCY RESPONSE GUIDEBOOK, DOT P 5800.4). FOR LARGER FIRES, USE WATER SPRAY, FOG OR STANDARD FOAM (1987 EMERGENCY RESPONSE GUIDEBOOK, DOT P 5800.4).
FIREFIGHTING: MOVE CONTAINER FROM FIRE AREA IF POSSIBLE. DO NOT SCATTER SPILLED MATERIAL WITH HIGH PRESSURE WATER STREAMS. DIKE FIRE CONTROL WATER FOR LATER DISPOSAL (1987 EMERGENCY RESPONSE GUIDEBOOK, DOT P 5800.4, GUIDE PAGE 31).
USE AGENTS SUITABLE FOR TYPE OF SURROUNDING FIRE. AVOID BREATHING HAZARDOUS VAPORS, KEEP UPWIND.

TOXICITY

FENOXYCARB: TOXICITY DATA: >0.48 MG/L INHALATION-RAT LC50 (85JFAN); >2000 MG/KG SKIN-RAT LD50 (85JFAN); 16,800 MG/KG ORAL-RAT LD50. CARCINOGEN STATUS: NONE. ACUTE TOXICITY LEVEL: SLIGHTLY TOXIC BY DERMAL ABSORPTION; RELATIVELY NONTOXIC BY INGESTION. TARGET EFFECTS: NO DATA AVAILABLE.

HEALTH EFFECTS AND FIRST AID

INHALATION: FENOXYCARB: **ACUTE EXPOSURE-** THE LC50 IN RATS WAS GREATER THAN 0.48 MG/L. **CHRONIC EXPOSURE-** NO DATA AVAILABLE.
FIRST AID- REMOVE FROM EXPOSURE AREA TO FRESH AIR IMMEDIATELY. IF BREATHING HAS STOPPED, PERFORM ARTIFICIAL RESPIRATION. KEEP PERSON WARM AND AT REST. TREAT SYMPTOMATICALLY AND SUPPORTIVELY. GET MEDICAL ATTENTION IMMEDIATELY.

SKIN CONTACT: FENOXYCARB: **ACUTE EXPOSURE-** THIS MATERIAL WAS NOT IRRITATING OR SENSITIZING TO GUINEA PIG SKIN. APPLICATION TO RAT SKIN PRODUCED EFFECTS OF DYSPNEA, CURVED BODY POSITION, RUFFLED FUR, SEDATION AND DIARRHEA. **CHRONIC EXPOSURE-** REPEATED APPLICATION TO ANIMAL SKIN PRODUCED EFFECTS OF SLIGHT ERYTHEMA AND ELEVATED LIVER WEIGHT.
FIRST AID- REMOVE CONTAMINATED CLOTHING AND SHOES IMMEDIATELY. WASH AFFECTED AREA WITH SOAP OR MILD DETERGENT AND LARGE AMOUNTS OF WATER UNTIL NO EVIDENCE OF CHEMICAL REMAINS (APPROXIMATELY 15-20 MINUTES). GET MEDICAL ATTENTION IMMEDIATELY.

EYE CONTACT: FENOXYCARB: **ACUTE EXPOSURE-** THIS MATERIAL WAS MILDLY IRRITATING TO RABBIT EYES. **CHRONIC EXPOSURE-** NO DATA AVAILABLE.
FIRST AID- WASH EYES IMMEDIATELY WITH LARGE AMOUNTS OF WATER OR NORMAL SALINE, OCCASIONALLY LIFTING UPPER AND LOWER LIDS, UNTIL NO EVIDENCE OF CHEMICAL REMAINS (APPROXIMATELY 15-20 MINUTES). GET MEDICAL ATTENTION IMMEDIATELY.

INGESTION: FENOXYCARB: **ACUTE EXPOSURE-** A LETHAL DOSE IN RATS WAS 16,800 MG/KG; SYMPTOMS WERE NOT REPORTED. **CHRONIC EXPOSURE-** NO TERATOGENIC EFFECTS WERE OBSERVED IN ANIMALS RECEIVING 300 MG/KG/DAY.
FIRST AID- TREAT SYMPTOMATICALLY AND SUPPORTIVELY. GET MEDICAL ATTENTION IMMEDIATELY. IF VOMITING OCCURS, KEEP HEAD LOWER THAN HIPS TO PREVENT ASPIRATION.
ANTIDOTE: NO SPECIFIC ANTIDOTE. TREAT SYMPTOMATICALLY AND SUPPORTIVELY.

REACTIVITY

REACTIVITY: STABLE UNDER NORMAL TEMPERATURES AND PRESSURES.
INCOMPATIBILITIES: FENOXYCARB: OXIDIZERS (STRONG): FIRE AND EXPLOSION HAZARD.
DECOMPOSITION: THERMAL DECOMPOSITION PRODUCTS MAY INCLUDE TOXIC OXIDES OF CARBON AND NITROGEN.
POLYMERIZATION: HAZARDOUS POLYMERIZATION HAS NOT BEEN REPORTED TO OCCUR UNDER NORMAL TEMPERATURES AND PRESSURES.

STORAGE AND DISPOSAL

OBSERVE ALL FEDERAL, STATE AND LOCAL REGULATIONS WHEN STORING OR DISPOSING OF THIS SUBSTANCE. FOR ASSISTANCE, CONTACT THE DISTRICT DIRECTOR OF THE ENVIRONMENTAL PROTECTION AGENCY.

****STORAGE****

STORE IN ACCORDANCE WITH 40 CFR 165 RECOMMENDED PROCEDURES FOR THE DISPOSAL AND STORAGE OF PESTICIDES AND PESTICIDE CONTAINERS. STORE AWAY FROM INCOMPATIBLE SUBSTANCES.

****DISPOSAL****

DISPOSAL MUST BE IN ACCORDANCE WITH 40 CFR 165 RECOMMENDED PROCEDURES FOR THE DISPOSAL AND STORAGE OF PESTICIDES AND PESTICIDE CONTAINERS.

CONDITIONS TO AVOID

MAY BURN BUT DOES NOT IGNITE READILY. AVOID CONTACT WITH STRONG OXIDIZERS, EXCESSIVE HEAT, SPARKS, OR OPEN FLAME.

SPILL AND LEAK PROCEDURES

OCCUPATIONAL SPILL: SWEEP UP AND PLACE IN SUITABLE CLEAN, DRY CONTAINERS FOR RECLAMATION OR LATER DISPOSAL. DO NOT FLUSH SPILLED MATERIAL INTO SEWER. KEEP UNNECESSARY PEOPLE AWAY.

PROTECTIVE EQUIPMENT

VENTILATION: PROVIDE GENERAL DILUTION VENTILATION.
RESPIRATOR: THE FOLLOWING RESPIRATORS ARE RECOMMENDED BASED ON INFORMATION FOUND IN THE PHYSICAL DATA, TOXICITY AND HEALTH EFFECTS SECTIONS. THEY ARE RANKED IN ORDER FROM MINIMUM TO MAXIMUM

RESPIRATORY PROTECTION. THE SPECIFIC RESPIRATOR SELECTED MUST BE BASED ON CONTAMINATION LEVELS FOUND IN THE WORK PLACE, MUST NOT EXCEED THE WORKING LIMITS OF THE RESPIRATOR AND BE JOINTLY APPROVED BY THE NATIONAL INSTITUTE FOR OCCUPATIONAL SAFETY AND HEALTH AND THE MINE SAFETY AND HEALTH ADMINISTRATION (NIOSH-MSHA).
CHEMICAL CARTRIDGE RESPIRATOR WITH AN ORGANIC VAPOR CARTRIDGE(S) IN COMBINATION WITH A DUST AND MIST FILTER.
GAS MASK WITH ORGANIC VAPOR CANISTER (CHIN-STYLE OR FRONT- OR BACK-MOUNTED CANISTER) WITH A DUST AND MIST FILTER.
GAS MASK WITH ORGANIC VAPOR CANISTER (CHIN-STYLE OR FRONT- OR BACK-MOUNTED CANISTER) WITH A PARTICULATE FILTER.
POWERED AIR-PURIFYING RESPIRATOR WITH A HIGH-EFFICIENCY FILTER.
TYPE 'C' SUPPLIED-AIR RESPIRATOR WITH A FULL FACEPIECE OPERATED IN A PRESSURE-DEMAND OR OTHER POSITIVE PRESSURE MODE.
SELF-CONTAINED BREATHING APPARATUS WITH A FULL FACEPIECE OPERATED IN PRESSURE-DEMAND OR OTHER POSITIVE PRESSURE MODE.
FOR FIREFIGHTING AND OTHER IMMEDIATELY DANGEROUS TO LIFE OR HEALTH CONDITIONS:
SELF-CONTAINED BREATHING APPARATUS WITH FULL FACEPIECE OPERATED IN PRESSURE-DEMAND OR OTHER POSITIVE PRESSURE MODE.
SUPPLIED-AIR RESPIRATOR WITH FULL FACEPIECE AND OPERATED IN PRESSURE-DEMAND OR OTHER POSITIVE PRESSURE MODE IN COMBINATION WITH AN AUXILIARY SELF-CONTAINED BREATHING APPARATUS OPERATED IN PRESSURE-DEMAND OR OTHER POSITIVE PRESSURE MODE.

CLOTHING: EMPLOYEE MUST WEAR APPROPRIATE PROTECTIVE (IMPERVIOUS) CLOTHING AND EQUIPMENT TO PREVENT REPEATED OR PROLONGED SKIN CONTACT WITH THIS SUBSTANCE.

GLOVES: EMPLOYEE MUST WEAR APPROPRIATE PROTECTIVE GLOVES TO PREVENT CONTACT WITH THIS SUBSTANCE.

EYE PROTECTION: EMPLOYEE MUST WEAR SPLASH-PROOF OR DUST-RESISTANT SAFETY GOGGLES TO PREVENT EYE CONTACT WITH THIS SUBSTANCE.
EMERGENCY EYE WASH: WHERE THERE IS ANY POSSIBILITY THAT AN EMPLOYEE'S EYES MAY BE EXPOSED TO THIS SUBSTANCE, THE EMPLOYER SHOULD PROVIDE AN EYE WASH FOUNTAIN WITHIN THE IMMEDIATE WORK AREA FOR EMERGENCY USE.

AUTHORIZED BY- OCCUPATIONAL HEALTH SERVICES, INC.
CREATION DATE: 01/11/90 ***REVISION DATE:*** 05/31/90

MATERIAL SAFETY DATA SHEET

OCCUPATIONAL HEALTH SERVICES, INC.
AGRICULTURE AND PESTICIDE DIVISION
450 SEVENTH AVENUE, SUITE 2407
NEW YORK, NEW YORK 10123
1-800-445-MSDS OR (212) 967-1100

EMERGENCY CONTACT:
JOHN S. BRANSFORD, JR. (615) 292-1180

SUBSTANCE IDENTIFICATION

CAS-NUMBER 66063-05-6

SUBSTANCE: **PENCYCURON**

TRADE NAMES/SYNONYMS: UREA, N-((4-CHLOROPHENYL)METHYL-N-CYCLOPENTYL-N'-PENYL-; 1-(4-CHLOROBENZYL)-1-CYCLOPENTYL-3-PHENYLUREA; N-((4-CHLOROPHENYL)METHYL-N-CYCLOPENTYL-N'-PHENYLUREA; MONCEREN; NTN 19701; C19H21CLN2O; PST72622

CHEMICAL FAMILY: SUBSTITUTED UREA
HALOGEN COMPOUND, AROMATIC

MOLECULAR FORMULA: C19-H21-CL-N2-O

MOLECULAR WEIGHT: 328.8

CERCLA RATINGS (SCALE 0-3): HEALTH=2 FIRE=1 REACTIVITY=0 PERSISTENCE=1

NFPA RATINGS (SCALE 0-4): HEALTH=2 FIRE=1 REACTIVITY=0

COMPONENTS AND CONTAMINANTS

COMPONENT: PENCYCURON ***PERCENT:*** 100.0
CAS# 66063-05-6

OTHER CONTAMINANTS: NONE

EXPOSURE LIMITS: NO OCCUPATIONAL EXPOSURE LIMITS ESTABLISHED BY OSHA, ACGIH, OR NIOSH.

PHYSICAL DATA

DESCRIPTION: COLORLESS CRYSTALLINE SOLID. ***MELTING POINT:*** NOT AVAILABLE

SPECIFIC GRAVITY: NOT AVAILABLE ***VAPOR PRESSURE:*** NEGLIGIBLE

SOLUBILITY IN WATER: 0.00004% @ 20 C

SOLVENT SOLUBILITY: SOLUBLE IN DICHLOROMETHANE AND 2-PROPANOL.

FIRE AND EXPLOSION DATA

FIRE AND EXPLOSION HAZARD: SLIGHT FIRE HAZARD WHEN EXPOSED TO HEAT OR FLAME.

FIREFIGHTING MEDIA: DRY CHEMICAL, CARBON DIOXIDE, HALON, WATER SPRAY OR STANDARD FOAM (1987 EMERGENCY RESPONSE GUIDEBOOK, DOT P 5800.4). FOR LARGER FIRES, USE WATER SPRAY, FOG OR STANDARD FOAM (1987 EMERGENCY RESPONSE GUIDEBOOK, DOT P 5800.4).

FIREFIGHTING: MOVE CONTAINERS FROM FIRE AREA IF POSSIBLE. FIGHT FIRE FROM MAXIMUM DISTANCE. STAY AWAY FROM STORAGE TANK ENDS. DIKE FIRE CONTROL WATER FOR LATER DISPOSAL. DO NOT SCATTER MATERIAL (1987 EMERGENCY RESPONSE GUIDEBOOK, DOT P 5800.4, GUIDE PAGE 55). EXTINGUISH USING AGENT SUITABLE FOR TYPE OF SURROUNDING FIRE. USE WATER IN FLOODING QUANTITIES AS FOG. KEEP SPARKS, FLAMES AND OTHER SOURCES OF IGNITION AWAY. KEEP MATERIAL OUT OF WATER SOURCES AND SEWERS. DO NOT TOUCH MATERIAL AND AVOID BREATHING DUSTS AND FUMES FROM BURNING MATERIAL. KEEP UPWIND.

TOXICITY

PENCYCURON: TOXICITY DATA: >2000 MG/KG SKIN-RABBIT LD50 (FMCHA2); >5000 MG/KG ORAL-RAT LD50 (FMCHA2). CARCINOGEN STATUS: NONE. ACUTE TOXICITY LEVEL: MODERATELY TOXIC BY DERMAL ABSORPTION AND SLIGHTLY TOXIC BY INGESTION. TARGET EFFECTS: NO DATA AVAILABLE.

HEALTH EFFECTS AND FIRST AID

INHALATION: PENCYCURON: **ACUTE EXPOSURE-** MANY SUBSTITUTED UREA HERBICIDES ARE MODERATELY IRRITATING TO THE MUCOUS MEMBRANES. **CHRONIC EXPOSURE-** NO DATA AVAILABLE.

FIRST AID- REMOVE FROM EXPOSURE AREA TO FRESH AIR IMMEDIATELY. IF BREATHING HAS STOPPED, PERFORM ARTIFICIAL RESPIRATION. KEEP PERSON WARM AND AT REST. TREAT SYMPTOMATICALLY AND SUPPORTIVELY. GET MEDICAL ATTENTION IMMEDIATELY.

SKIN CONTACT: PENCYCURON: **ACUTE EXPOSURE-** MANY SUBSTITUTED UREA HERBICIDES ARE MODERATELY IRRITATING TO THE SKIN. A LETHAL DOSE IN RATS BY DERMAL ABSORPTION IS GREATER THAN 2000 MG/KG. **CHRONIC EXPOSURE-** NO DATA AVAILABLE.

FIRST AID- REMOVE CONTAMINATED CLOTHING AND SHOES IMMEDIATELY. WASH AFFECTED AREA WITH SOAP OR MILD DETERGENT AND LARGE AMOUNTS OF WATER UNTIL NO EVIDENCE OF CHEMICAL REMAINS (APPROXIMATELY 15-20 MINUTES). GET MEDICAL ATTENTION IMMEDIATELY.

EYE CONTACT: PENCYCURON: **ACUTE EXPOSURE-** MANY SUBSTITUTED UREA HERBICIDES ARE MODERATELY IRRITATING TO THE EYES. **CHRONIC EXPOSURE-** NO DATA AVAILABLE.

FIRST AID- WASH EYES IMMEDIATELY WITH LARGE AMOUNTS OF WATER OR NORMAL SALINE, OCCASIONALLY LIFTING UPPER AND LOWER LIDS, UNTIL NO EVIDENCE OF CHEMICAL REMAINS (APPROXIMATELY 15-20 MINUTES). GET MEDICAL ATTENTION IMMEDIATELY.

INGESTION: PENCYCURON: **ACUTE EXPOSURE-** A LETHAL DOSE IN RATS WAS GREATER THAN 2000 MG/KG. **CHRONIC EXPOSURE-** NO OBSERVABLE EFFECTS WERE NOTED IN 2-YEAR STUDIES OF MALE RATS FED 50 MG/KG DIET, FEMALE RATS FED 500 MG/KG DIET OR DOGS FED 1000 MG/KG DIET.

FIRST AID- TREAT SYMPTOMATICALLY AND SUPPORTIVELY. GET MEDICAL ATTENTION IMMEDIATELY. IF VOMITING OCCURS, KEEP HEAD LOWER THAN HIPS TO PREVENT ASPIRATION.

ANTIDOTE: NO SPECIFIC ANTIDOTE. TREAT SYMPTOMATICALLY AND SUPPORTIVELY.

REACTIVITY

REACTIVITY: STABLE UNDER NORMAL TEMPERATURES AND PRESSURES.

INCOMPATIBILITIES: PENCYCURON: OXIDIZERS (STRONG): FIRE AND EXPLOSION HAZARD.

DECOMPOSITION: THERMAL DECOMPOSITION PRODUCTS MAY INCLUDE TOXIC OXIDES OF NITROGEN AND CARBON AND TOXIC AND CORROSIVE FUMES OF CHLORIDES.

POLYMERIZATION: HAZARDOUS POLYMERIZATION HAS NOT BEEN REPORTED TO OCCUR UNDER NORMAL TEMPERATURES AND PRESSURES.

STORAGE AND DISPOSAL

OBSERVE ALL FEDERAL, STATE AND LOCAL REGULATIONS WHEN STORING OR DISPOSING OF THIS SUBSTANCE. FOR ASSISTANCE, CONTACT THE DISTRICT DIRECTOR OF THE ENVIRONMENTAL PROTECTION AGENCY.

STORAGE

STORE IN ACCORDANCE WITH 40 CFR 165 RECOMMENDED PROCEDURES FOR THE DISPOSAL AND STORAGE OF PESTICIDES AND PESTICIDE CONTAINERS.
STORE AWAY FROM INCOMPATIBLE SUBSTANCES.

DISPOSAL

DISPOSAL MUST BE IN ACCORDANCE WITH 40 CFR 165 RECOMMENDED PROCEDURES FOR THE DISPOSAL AND STORAGE OF PESTICIDES AND PESTICIDE CONTAINERS.

CONDITIONS TO AVOID

MAY BURN BUT DOES NOT IGNITE READILY. CONTAINERS MAY EXPLODE IN HEAT OF FIRE.

SPILL AND LEAK PROCEDURES

OCCUPATIONAL SPILL: DO NOT TOUCH SPILLED MATERIAL. STOP LEAK IF YOU CAN DO IT WITHOUT RISK. USE WATER SPRAY TO REDUCE VAPORS. FOR SMALL SPILLS, TAKE UP WITH SAND OR OTHER ABSORBENT MATERIAL AND PLACE INTO CONTAINERS FOR LATER DISPOSAL. FOR SMALL DRY SPILLS, WITH A CLEAN SHOVEL PLACE MATERIAL INTO CLEAN, DRY CONTAINERS AND COVER. MOVE CONTAINERS FROM SPILL AREA. FOR LARGER SPILLS, DIKE FAR AHEAD OF SPILL FOR LATER DISPOSAL. KEEP UNNECESSARY PEOPLE AWAY. ISOLATE HAZARD AREA AND DENY ENTRY. VENTILATE CLOSED SPACES BEFORE ENTERING.

PROTECTIVE EQUIPMENT

VENTILATION: PROVIDE LOCAL EXHAUST OR GENERAL DILUTION VENTILATION SYSTEM.

RESPIRATOR: THE FOLLOWING RESPIRATORS ARE RECOMMENDED BASED ON INFORMATION FOUND IN THE PHYSICAL DATA, TOXICITY AND HEALTH EFFECTS SECTIONS. THEY ARE RANKED IN ORDER FROM MINIMUM TO MAXIMUM RESPIRATORY PROTECTION. THE SPECIFIC RESPIRATOR SELECTED MUST BE BASED ON CONTAMINATION LEVELS FOUND IN THE WORK PLACE, MUST NOT EXCEED THE WORKING LIMITS OF THE RESPIRATOR AND BE JOINTLY APPROVED BY THE NATIONAL INSTITUTE FOR OCCUPATIONAL SAFETY AND HEALTH AND THE MINE SAFETY AND HEALTH ADMINISTRATION (NIOSH-MSHA).
CHEMICAL CARTRIDGE RESPIRATOR WITH AN ORGANIC VAPOR CARTRIDGE(S) WITH A FULL FACEPIECE AND ORGANIC VAPOR CARTRIDGE(S) IN COMBINATION WITH A DUST AND MIST FILTER.
POWERED AIR-PURIFYING RESPIRATOR WITH A TIGHT-FITTING FACEPIECE AND ORGANIC VAPOR CARTRIDGE(S) IN COMBINATION WITH A HIGH-EFFICIENCY PARTICULATE FILTER.
TYPE 'C' SUPPLIED-AIR RESPIRATOR WITH A FULL FACEPIECE OPERATED IN A PRESSURE-DEMAND OR OTHER POSITIVE PRESSURE MODE.
SELF-CONTAINED BREATHING APPARATUS WITH A FULL FACEPIECE OPERATED IN PRESSURE-DEMAND OR OTHER POSITIVE PRESSURE MODE.
FOR FIREFIGHTING AND OTHER IMMEDIATELY DANGEROUS TO LIFE OR HEALTH CONDITIONS:
SELF-CONTAINED BREATHING APPARATUS WITH FULL FACEPIECE OPERATED IN PRESSURE-DEMAND OR OTHER POSITIVE PRESSURE MODE.
SUPPLIED-AIR RESPIRATOR WITH FULL FACEPIECE AND OPERATED IN PRESSURE-DEMAND OR OTHER POSITIVE PRESSURE MODE IN COMBINATION WITH AN AUXILIARY SELF-CONTAINED BREATHING APPARATUS OPERATED IN PRESSURE-DEMAND OR OTHER POSITIVE PRESSURE MODE.

CLOTHING: EMPLOYEE MUST WEAR APPROPRIATE PROTECTIVE (IMPERVIOUS) CLOTHING AND EQUIPMENT TO PREVENT REPEATED OR PROLONGED SKIN CONTACT WITH THIS SUBSTANCE.

GLOVES: EMPLOYEE MUST WEAR APPROPRIATE PROTECTIVE GLOVES TO PREVENT CONTACT WITH THIS SUBSTANCE.

EYE PROTECTION: EMPLOYEE MUST WEAR SPLASH-PROOF OR DUST-RESISTANT SAFETY GOGGLES TO PREVENT EYE CONTACT WITH THIS SUBSTANCE.
EMERGENCY EYE WASH: WHERE THERE IS ANY POSSIBILITY THAT AN EMPLOYEE'S EYES MAY BE EXPOSED TO THIS SUBSTANCE, THE EMPLOYER SHOULD PROVIDE AN EYE WASH FOUNTAIN WITHIN THE IMMEDIATE WORK AREA FOR EMERGENCY USE.

AUTHORIZED BY- OCCUPATIONAL HEALTH SERVICES, INC.
CREATION DATE: 10/04/89 ***REVISION DATE:*** 05/18/90

MATERIAL SAFETY DATA SHEET

OCCUPATIONAL HEALTH SERVICES, INC.
AGRICULTURE AND PESTICIDE DIVISION
450 SEVENTH AVENUE, SUITE 2407
NEW YORK, NEW YORK 10123
1-800-445-MSDS OR (212) 967-1100

EMERGENCY CONTACT:
JOHN S. BRANSFORD, JR. (615) 292-1180

SUBSTANCE IDENTIFICATION

CAS-NUMBER 8000-78-0

SUBSTANCE: GARLIC OIL

TRADE NAMES/SYNONYMS: OILS, GARLIC; OIL OF GARLIC; ALLIUM SATIVUM; PST72626

CHEMICAL FAMILY: ESSENTIAL OIL

CERCLA RATINGS (SCALE 0-3): HEALTH=2 FIRE=U REACTIVITY=0 PERSISTENCE=1

NFPA RATINGS (SCALE 0-4): HEALTH=2 FIRE=U REACTIVITY=0

COMPONENTS AND CONTAMINANTS

COMPONENT: GARLIC OIL ***PERCENT:*** 100.0
CAS# 8000-78-0

OTHER CONTAMINANTS: NONE

EXPOSURE LIMITS: NO OCCUPATIONAL EXPOSURE LIMITS ESTABLISHED BY OSHA, ACGIH, OR NIOSH.

PHYSICAL DATA

DESCRIPTION: CLEAR, YELLOW TO REDDISH-ORANGE LIQUID WITH A STRONG GARLIC ODOR.

BOILING POINT: NOT AVAILABLE ***SPECIFIC GRAVITY:*** 1.046-1.057 @ 15 C

SOLUBILITY IN WATER: NOT AVAILABLE

SOLVENT SOLUBILITY: SOLUBLE IN MOST FIXED OILS AND MINERAL OIL; PARTIALLY SOLUBLE IN ALCOHOL; INSOLUBLE IN GLYCERIN AND PROPYLENE GLYCOL.

FIRE AND EXPLOSION DATA

FIRE AND EXPLOSION HAZARD: UNKNOWN FIRE AND EXPLOSION HAZARD.

FIREFIGHTING MEDIA: DRY CHEMICAL, CARBON DIOXIDE, HALON, WATER SPRAY OR STANDARD FOAM (1987 EMERGENCY RESPONSE GUIDEBOOK, DOT P 5800.4). FOR LARGER FIRES, USE WATER SPRAY, FOG OR STANDARD FOAM (1987 EMERGENCY RESPONSE GUIDEBOOK, DOT P 5800.4).

FIREFIGHTING: MOVE CONTAINER FROM FIRE AREA IF POSSIBLE. COOL FIRE-EXPOSED CONTAINERS WITH WATER FROM SIDE UNTIL WELL AFTER FIRE IS OUT. STAY AWAY FROM STORAGE TANK ENDS. FOR MASSIVE FIRE IN STORAGE AREA, USE UNMANNED HOSE HOLDER OR MONITOR NOZZLES, ELSE WITHDRAW FROM AREA AND LET FIRE BURN. WITHDRAW IMMEDIATELY IN CASE OF RISING SOUND FROM VENTING SAFETY DEVICE OR ANY DISCOLORATION OF STORAGE TANK DUE TO FIRE (1987 EMERGENCY RESPONSE GUIDEBOOK, DOT P 5800.4, GUIDE PAGE 27). EXTINGUISH ONLY IF FLOW CAN BE STOPPED; USE FLOODING AMOUNTS OF WATER AS A FOG, SOLID STREAMS MAY BE INEFFECTIVE. COOL CONTAINERS WITH FLOODING AMOUNTS OF WATER, APPLY FROM AS FAR A DISTANCE AS POSSIBLE. AVOID BREATHING VAPORS, KEEP UPWIND.

TOXICITY

GARLIC OIL: TOXICITY DATA: 1360 MG/KG ORAL-RAT LD50; 850 MG/KG ORAL-MOUSE LD50. CARCINOGEN STATUS: NONE. LOCAL EFFECTS: IRRITANT- SKIN. ACUTE TOXICITY LEVEL: MODERATELY TOXIC BY INGESTION. TARGET EFFECTS: NO DATA AVAILABLE.

HEALTH EFFECTS AND FIRST AID

INHALATION: GARLIC OIL: ACUTE EXPOSURE- INHALATION OF VOLATILE OILS MAY CAUSE DIZZINESS, RAPID, SHALLOW BREATHING, TACHYCARDIA, BRONCHIAL IRRITATION AND UNCONSCIOUSNESS OR CONVULSIONS. COMPLICATIONS MAY INCLUDE ANURIA, PULMONARY EDEMA, AND BRONCHIAL PNEUMONIA. CHRONIC EXPOSURE- NO DATA AVAILABLE.

FIRST AID- REMOVE FROM EXPOSURE AREA TO FRESH AIR IMMEDIATELY. IF BREATHING HAS STOPPED, PERFORM ARTIFICIAL RESPIRATION. KEEP PERSON WARM AND AT REST. TREAT SYMPTOMATICALLY AND SUPPORTIVELY. GET MEDICAL ATTENTION IMMEDIATELY.

SKIN CONTACT: GARLIC OIL: IRRITANT. ACUTE EXPOSURE- CONTACT WITH THE GARLIC CLOVE HAS PRODUCED IRRITATION AND ALLERGIC CONTACT DERMATITIS. BURNING AND BLISTERING OF THE SKIN WITH THE FORMATION OF INDOLENT ULCERS HAS ALSO BEEN REPORTED. CHRONIC EXPOSURE- REPEATED OR PROLONGED EXPOSURE TO IRRITANTS MAY CAUSE DERMATITIS.

FIRST AID- REMOVE CONTAMINATED CLOTHING AND SHOES IMMEDIATELY. WASH AFFECTED AREA WITH SOAP OR MILD DETERGENT AND LARGE AMOUNTS OF WATER UNTIL NO EVIDENCE OF CHEMICAL REMAINS (APPROXIMATELY 15-20 MINUTES). GET MEDICAL ATTENTION IMMEDIATELY.

EYE CONTACT: GARLIC OIL: ACUTE EXPOSURE- NO DATA AVAILABLE. CHRONIC EXPOSURE- NO DATA AVAILABLE.

FIRST AID- WASH EYES IMMEDIATELY WITH LARGE AMOUNTS OF WATER OR NORMAL SALINE, OCCASIONALLY LIFTING UPPER AND LOWER LIDS, UNTIL NO EVIDENCE OF CHEMICAL REMAINS (APPROXIMATELY 15-20 MINUTES). GET MEDICAL ATTENTION IMMEDIATELY.

INGESTION: GARLIC OIL: **ACUTE EXPOSURE**- INGESTION OF VOLATILE OILS MAY CAUSE ABDOMINAL BURNING, NAUSEA AND VOMITING, DIARRHEA, DYSURIA, HEMATURIA, UNCONSCIOUSNESS, SHALLOW RESPIRATION, AND CONVULSIONS. COMPLICATIONS MAY INCLUDE ANURIA, PULMONARY EDEMA, AND BRONCHIAL PNEUMONIA. PATHOLOGIC FINDINGS FROM INGESTION OF VOLATILE OILS INCLUDE RENAL DEGENERATIVE CHANGES AND INTENSE CONGESTION AND EDEMA IN THE LUNGS, BRAIN AND GASTRIC MUCOSA. **CHRONIC EXPOSURE**- NO DATA AVAILABLE.

FIRST AID- GIVE 120-240 ML OF MILK; THEN REMOVE BY GASTRIC LAVAGE OR EMESIS, TAKING CARE TO PREVENT ASPIRATION. FOLLOW THESE PROCEDURES BY ADMINISTERING 30-60 ML OF FLEET'S PHOSPHO-SODA DILUTED 1:4 IN WATER. PERFORM ARTIFICIAL RESPIRATION IF NECESSARY. GET MEDICAL ATTENTION (DREISBACH, HANDBOOK OF POISONING, 12TH ED.). FIRST AID SHOULD BE PERFORMED BY QUALIFIED MEDICAL PERSONNEL.

ANTIDOTE: NO SPECIFIC ANTIDOTE. TREAT SYMPTOMATICALLY AND SUPPORTIVELY.

REACTIVITY

REACTIVITY: STABLE UNDER NORMAL TEMPERATURES AND PRESSURES.

INCOMPATIBILITIES: GARLIC OIL: OXIDIZERS (STRONG): FIRE AND EXPLOSION HAZARD.

DECOMPOSITION: THERMAL DECOMPOSITION MAY RELEASE ACRID SMOKE AND IRRITATING FUMES.

POLYMERIZATION: HAZARDOUS POLYMERIZATION HAS NOT BEEN REPORTED TO OCCUR UNDER NORMAL TEMPERATURES AND PRESSURES.

STORAGE AND DISPOSAL

OBSERVE ALL FEDERAL, STATE AND LOCAL REGULATIONS WHEN STORING OR DISPOSING OF THIS SUBSTANCE. FOR ASSISTANCE, CONTACT THE DISTRICT DIRECTOR OF THE ENVIRONMENTAL PROTECTION AGENCY.

****STORAGE****

STORE AWAY FROM INCOMPATIBLE SUBSTANCES.

CONDITIONS TO AVOID

AVOID CONTACT WITH HEAT, SPARKS, FLAMES, OR OTHER SOURCES OF IGNITION. VAPORS MAY BE EXPLOSIVE. AVOID OVERHEATING OF CONTAINERS; CONTAINERS MAY VIOLENTLY RUPTURE IN HEAT OF FIRE. AVOID CONTAMINATION OF WATER SOURCES.

SPILL AND LEAK PROCEDURES

OCCUPATIONAL SPILL: SHUT OFF IGNITION SOURCES. STOP LEAK IF YOU CAN DO IT WITHOUT RISK. USE WATER SPRAY TO REDUCE VAPORS. FOR SMALL SPILLS, TAKE UP WITH SAND OR OTHER ABSORBENT MATERIAL AND PLACE INTO CONTAINERS FOR LATER DISPOSAL. FOR LARGER SPILLS, DIKE FAR AHEAD OF SPILL FOR LATER DISPOSAL. NO SMOKING, FLAMES OR FLARES IN HAZARD AREA. KEEP UNNECESSARY PEOPLE AWAY; ISOLATE HAZARD AREA AND RESTRICT ENTRY.

PROTECTIVE EQUIPMENT

VENTILATION: PROVIDE LOCAL EXHAUST OR GENERAL DILUTION VENTILATION. VENTILATION EQUIPMENT MUST BE EXPLOSION-PROOF.

RESPIRATOR: THE FOLLOWING RESPIRATORS ARE RECOMMENDED BASED ON INFORMATION FOUND IN THE PHYSICAL DATA, TOXICITY AND HEALTH EFFECTS SECTIONS. THEY ARE RANKED IN ORDER FROM MINIMUM TO MAXIMUM RESPIRATORY PROTECTION. THE SPECIFIC RESPIRATOR SELECTED MUST BE BASED ON CONTAMINATION LEVELS FOUND IN THE WORK PLACE, MUST NOT EXCEED THE WORKING LIMITS OF THE RESPIRATOR AND BE JOINTLY APPROVED BY THE NATIONAL INSTITUTE FOR OCCUPATIONAL SAFETY AND HEALTH AND THE MINE SAFETY AND HEALTH ADMINISTRATION (NIOSH-MSHA).

CHEMICAL CARTRIDGE RESPIRATOR WITH AN ORGANIC VAPOR CARTRIDGE(S) WITH A FULL FACEPIECE.

GAS MASK WITH ORGANIC VAPOR CANISTER (CHIN-STYLE OR FRONT- OR BACK-MOUNTED CANISTER) WITH A FULL FACEPIECE.

TYPE 'C' SUPPLIED-AIR RESPIRATOR WITH A FULL FACEPIECE OPERATED IN PRESSURE-DEMAND OR OTHER POSITIVE PRESSURE MODE OR WITH A FULL FACEPIECE, HELMET OR HOOD OPERATED IN CONTINUOUS-FLOW MODE.

SELF-CONTAINED BREATHING APPARATUS WITH A FULL FACEPIECE OPERATED IN PRESSURE-DEMAND OR OTHER POSITIVE PRESSURE MODE.

FOR FIREFIGHTING AND OTHER IMMEDIATELY DANGEROUS TO LIFE OR HEALTH CONDITIONS:

SELF-CONTAINED BREATHING APPARATUS WITH FULL FACEPIECE OPERATED IN PRESSURE-DEMAND OR OTHER POSITIVE PRESSURE MODE.

SUPPLIED-AIR RESPIRATOR WITH FULL FACEPIECE AND OPERATED IN PRESSURE-DEMAND OR OTHER POSITIVE PRESSURE MODE IN COMBINATION WITH AN AUXILIARY SELF-CONTAINED BREATHING APPARATUS OPERATED IN PRESSURE-DEMAND OR OTHER POSITIVE PRESSURE MODE.

CLOTHING: EMPLOYEE MUST WEAR APPROPRIATE PROTECTIVE (IMPERVIOUS) CLOTHING AND EQUIPMENT TO PREVENT REPEATED OR PROLONGED SKIN CONTACT WITH THIS SUBSTANCE.

GLOVES: EMPLOYEE MUST WEAR APPROPRIATE PROTECTIVE GLOVES TO PREVENT CONTACT WITH THIS SUBSTANCE.

EYE PROTECTION: EMPLOYEE MUST WEAR SPLASH-PROOF OR DUST-RESISTANT SAFETY GOGGLES TO PREVENT EYE CONTACT WITH THIS SUBSTANCE. EMERGENCY EYE WASH: WHERE THERE IS ANY POSSIBILITY THAT AN EMPLOYEE'S EYES MAY BE EXPOSED TO THIS SUBSTANCE, THE EMPLOYER SHOULD PROVIDE AN EYE WASH FOUNTAIN WITHIN THE IMMEDIATE WORK AREA FOR EMERGENCY USE.

AUTHORIZED BY- OCCUPATIONAL HEALTH SERVICES, INC.

CREATION DATE: 11/15/89 ***REVISION DATE:*** 05/18/90

MATERIAL SAFETY DATA SHEET

OCCUPATIONAL HEALTH SERVICES, INC.
AGRICULTURE AND PESTICIDE DIVISION
450 SEVENTH AVENUE, SUITE 2407
NEW YORK, NEW YORK 10123
1-800-445-MSDS OR (212) 967-1100

EMERGENCY CONTACT:
JOHN S. BRANSFORD, JR. (615) 292-1180

SUBSTANCE IDENTIFICATION

CAS-NUMBER 68359-37-5

SUBSTANCE: **CYFLUTHRIN**

TRADE NAMES/SYNONYMS: CYCLOPROPANECARBOXYLIC ACID, 3-(2,2-DICHLOROETHENYL)-2,2-DIMETHYL-, CYANO(4-FLUORO-3-PHENOXYPHENYL)METHYL ESTER; CYANO(4-FLUORO-3-PHENOXYPHENYL)METHYL-3-(2,2-DICHLOROETHENYL)2,2-DIMETHYLCYCLOPROPANECARBOXYLATE; (RS)-ALPHA-CYANO-4-FLUORO-3-PHENOXYBENZYL (1RS,3RS;1RS,3SR)-3- (2,2-DICHLOROVINYL)-2,2-DIMETHYLCYCLOPROPANECARBOXYLATE; (RS)-ALPHA-CYANO-4-FLUORO-3-PHENOXYBENZYL(1RS)-CIS-TRANS-3- (2,2-DICHLOROVINYL-2,2-DIMETHYLCYCLOPROPANECARBOXYLATE; BAY-FCR 1272; BAYTHROID; FCR 1272; C22H18CL2FNO3; PST72630

CHEMICAL FAMILY: PYRETHROID (SYNTHETIC)

MOLECULAR FORMULA: C22-H18-CL2-F-N-O3

MOLECULAR WEIGHT: 434.31

CERCLA RATINGS (SCALE 0-3): HEALTH=U FIRE=1 REACTIVITY=0 PERSISTENCE=2

NFPA RATINGS (SCALE 0-4): HEALTH=U FIRE=1 REACTIVITY=0

COMPONENTS AND CONTAMINANTS

COMPONENT: CYFLUTHRIN ***PERCENT:*** 100.0

CAS# 68359-37-5

EXPOSURE LIMITS: PYRETHROIDS: 1 POUND CERCLA SECTION 103 REPORTABLE QUANTITY

PHYSICAL DATA

DESCRIPTION: YELLOW PASTE. ***MELTING POINT:*** 140 F (60 C)

SPECIFIC GRAVITY: 1.27-1.28 ***VAPOR PRESSURE:*** NEGLIGIBLE

SOLUBILITY IN WATER: 20 PPM

SOLVENT SOLUBILITY: SOLUBLE IN DICHLOROMETHANE, TOLUENE; MODERATELY SOLUBLE IN HEXANE, ISOPROPANOL.

FIRE AND EXPLOSION DATA

FIRE AND EXPLOSION HAZARD: SLIGHT FIRE HAZARD WHEN EXPOSED TO HEAT OR FLAME.

FIREFIGHTING MEDIA: DRY CHEMICAL, CARBON DIOXIDE, HALON, WATER SPRAY OR STANDARD FOAM (1987 EMERGENCY RESPONSE GUIDEBOOK, DOT P 5800.4). FOR LARGER FIRES, USE WATER SPRAY, FOG OR STANDARD FOAM (1987 EMERGENCY RESPONSE GUIDEBOOK, DOT P 5800.4).

FIREFIGHTING: MOVE CONTAINER FROM FIRE AREA IF POSSIBLE. DO NOT SCATTER SPILLED MATERIAL WITH HIGH PRESSURE WATER STREAMS. DIKE FIRE CONTROL WATER FOR LATER DISPOSAL (1987 EMERGENCY RESPONSE GUIDEBOOK, DOT P 5800.4, GUIDE PAGE 31).

USE AGENTS SUITABLE FOR TYPE OF SURROUNDING FIRE. AVOID BREATHING HAZARDOUS VAPORS, KEEP UPWIND.

TOXICITY

CYFLUTHRIN: TOXICITY DATA: 469 GM/M3/4 HOURS INHALATION-RAT LC50; 600 MG/KG ORAL-RAT LD50; 590 MG/KG ORAL-RAT LD50 (FMCHA2). CARCINOGEN STATUS: NONE. LOCAL EFFECTS: IRRITANT- EYE. ACUTE TOXICITY LEVEL: MODERATELY TOXIC BY INGESTION; RELATIVELY NONTOXIC BY INHALATION. TARGET EFFECTS: MAY AFFECT THE CENTRAL NERVOUS SYSTEM.*
*MAY BE BASED ON GROUP INFORMATION ON PYRETHROIDS.

HEALTH EFFECTS AND FIRST AID

INHALATION: CYFLUTHRIN: SEE INFORMATION ON PYRETHROID.
PYRETHROIDS: **ACUTE EXPOSURE-** HEAVY EXPOSURE TO A MIST OF SOME PYRETHROIDS HAS PRODUCED HYPERSENSITIVIITY, ATAXIA, AND URINARY INCONTINENCE. CONVULSIONS MAY ALSO BE POSSIBLE. **CHRONIC EXPOSURE-** ANIMALS EXPOSED TO AEROSOLS OF SOME PYRETHROIDS FOR 3-4 HOURS/DAY FOR UP TO 4 WEEKS DID NOT EXHIBIT ANY SIGNIFICANT COMPOUND RELATED FINDINGS.
FIRST AID- REMOVE FROM EXPOSURE AREA TO FRESH AIR IMMEDIATELY. IF BREATHING HAS STOPPED, PERFORM ARTIFICIAL RESPIRATION. KEEP PERSON WARM AND AT REST. TREAT SYMPTOMATICALLY AND SUPPORTIVELY. GET MEDICAL ATTENTION IMMEDIATELY.

SKIN CONTACT: CYFLUTHRIN: SEE INFORMATION OF PYRETHROIDS. MAY CAUSE IRRITATION. ANIMAL STUDIES INDICATE SKIN ABSORPTION MAY OCCUR.
PYRETHROIDS: **ACUTE EXPOSURE-** BASED ON ANIMAL AND HUMAN STUDIES AND HUMAN EXPERIENCES WITH SOME PYRETHROIDS, PRIMARY IRRITATION IS UNLIKELY. CUTANEOUS PARESTHESIAS MAY OCCUR INCLUDING NUMBNESS, ITCHING, BURNING, TINGLING AND WARMTH WITHOUT SIGNS OF IRRITATION. THESE EFFECTS MAY BE DELAYED FOR 30 MINUTES OR MORE AND LAST LESS THAN 24 HOURS. **CHRONIC EXPOSURE-** TESTS WITH SOME PYRETHROIDS ON HUMANS AND ANIMALS INDICATE SENSITIZATION IS UNLIKELY.
FIRST AID- REMOVE CONTAMINATED CLOTHING AND SHOES IMMEDIATELY. WASH AFFECTED AREA WITH SOAP OR MILD DETERGENT AND LARGE AMOUNTS OF WATER UNTIL NO EVIDENCE OF CHEMICAL REMAINS (APPROXIMATELY 15-20 MINUTES). GET MEDICAL ATTENTION IMMEDIATELY.

EYE CONTACT: CYFLUTHRIN: IRRITANT. THIS MATERIAL WAS IRRITATING TO RABBIT EYES. SEE INFORMATION ON PYRETHROIDS.
PYRETHROIDS: **ACUTE EXPOSURE-** MASSIVE INSTILLATION OF SOME PYRETHROIDS INTO RABBIT EYES PRODUCED ONLY A SLIGHT, TRANSIENT CONGESTION OF THE CONJUNCTIVA OR LACRIMATION. **CHRONIC EXPOSURE-** NO DATA AVAILABLE.
FIRST AID- WASH EYES IMMEDIATELY WITH LARGE AMOUNTS OF WATER OR NORMAL SALINE, OCCASIONALLY LIFTING UPPER AND LOWER LIDS, UNTIL NO EVIDENCE OF CHEMICAL REMAINS (APPROXIMATELY 15-20 MINUTES). GET MEDICAL ATTENTION IMMEDIATELY.

INGESTION: CYFLUTHRIN: SEE INFORMATION ON PYRETHROIDS. NO OBSERVABLE EFFECTS WERE NOTED IN A 2-YEAR STUDY OF RATS AND MICE RECEIVING A 50 MG/KG AND 200 MG/KG DIET, RESPECTIVELY.
PYRETHROIDS: **ACUTE EXPOSURE-** SOME PYRETHROIDS HAVE PRODUCED HYPERSENSITIVITY, NERVOUS IRRITABILITY, TREMORS, ATAXIA, AND URINARY INCONTINENCE IN ANIMALS. CONVULSIONS MAY ALSO BE POSSIBLE. **CHRONIC EXPOSURE-** INCREASED KIDNEY AND LIVER WEIGHTS AND HEPATIC HISTOPATHOLOGICAL CHANGES WERE NOTED IN ANIMALS CHRONICALLY FED SOME PYRETHROIDS.
FIRST AID- REMOVE BY GASTRIC LAVAGE AND CATHARSIS. MAINTAIN BLOOD PRESSURE AND AIRWAY. GIVE OXYGEN IF RESPIRATION IS DEPRESSED. DO NOT PERFORM GASTRIC LAVAGE IF VICTIM IS UNCONSCIOUS. GET MEDICAL ATTENTION IMMEDIATELY (DREISBACH, HANDBOOK OF POISONING, 12TH ED.).
ADMINISTRATION OF LAVAGE OR OXYGEN SHOULD BE PERFORMED BY QUALIFIED MEDICAL PERSONNEL.
ANTIDOTE: NO SPECIFIC ANTIDOTE. TREAT SYMPTOMATICALLY AND SUPPORTIVELY.

REACTIVITY

REACTIVITY: STABLE UNDER NORMAL TEMPERATURES AND PRESSURES.
INCOMPATIBILITIES: CYFLUTHRIN: OXIDIZERS: FIRE AND EXPLOSION HAZARD.
DECOMPOSITION: THERMAL DECOMPOSITION PRODUCTS MAY INCLUDE TOXIC OXIDES OF NITROGEN AND CARBON, AND TOXIC AND CORROSIVE FUMES OF CHLORIDES AND FLUORIDES.
POLYMERIZATION: HAZARDOUS POLYMERIZATION HAS NOT BEEN REPORTED TO OCCUR UNDER NORMAL TEMPERATURES AND PRESSURES.

STORAGE AND DISPOSAL

OBSERVE ALL FEDERAL, STATE AND LOCAL REGULATIONS WHEN STORING OR DISPOSING OF THIS SUBSTANCE. FOR ASSISTANCE, CONTACT THE DISTRICT DIRECTOR OF THE ENVIRONMENTAL PROTECTION AGENCY.

STORAGE

STORE IN ACCORDANCE WITH 40 CFR 165 RECOMMENDED PROCEDURES FOR THE DISPOSAL AND STORAGE OF PESTICIDES AND PESTICIDE CONTAINERS.
STORE AWAY FROM INCOMPATIBLE SUBSTANCES.

DISPOSAL

DISPOSAL MUST BE IN ACCORDANCE WITH 40 CFR 165 RECOMMENDED PROCEDURES FOR THE DISPOSAL AND STORAGE OF PESTICIDES AND PESTICIDE CONTAINERS.

CONDITIONS TO AVOID

MAY BURN BUT DOES NOT IGNITE READILY. AVOID CONTACT WITH STRONG OXIDIZERS, EXCESSIVE HEAT, SPARKS, OR OPEN FLAME.

SPILL AND LEAK PROCEDURES

SOIL SPILL: DIG HOLDING AREA SUCH AS LAGOON, POND OR PIT FOR CONTAINMENT.
DIKE FLOW OF SPILLED MATERIAL USING SOIL OR SANDBAGS OR FOAMED BARRIERS SUCH AS POLYURETHANE OR CONCRETE.
USE CEMENT POWDER OR FLY ASH TO ABSORB LIQUID MASS.
WATER SPILL: USE ACTIVATED CARBON TO ABSORB SPILLED SUBSTANCE THAT IS DISSOLVED.
USE MECHANICAL DREDGES OR LIFTS TO EXTRACT IMMOBILIZED MASSES OF POLLUTION AND PRECIPITATES.
OCCUPATIONAL SPILL: SWEEP UP AND PLACE IN SUITABLE CLEAN, DRY CONTAINERS FOR RECLAMATION OR LATER DISPOSAL. DO NOT FLUSH SPILLED MATERIAL INTO SEWER. KEEP UNNECESSARY PEOPLE AWAY.

PROTECTIVE EQUIPMENT

VENTILATION: PROVIDE LOCAL EXHAUST OR GENERAL DILUTION VENTILATION SYSTEM.
RESPIRATOR: THE FOLLOWING RESPIRATORS ARE RECOMMENDED BASED ON INFORMATION FOUND IN THE PHYSICAL DATA, TOXICITY AND HEALTH EFFECTS SECTIONS. THEY ARE RANKED IN ORDER FROM MINIMUM TO MAXIMUM RESPIRATORY PROTECTION. THE SPECIFIC RESPIRATOR SELECTED MUST BE BASED ON CONTAMINATION LEVELS FOUND IN THE WORK PLACE, MUST NOT EXCEED THE WORKING LIMITS OF THE RESPIRATOR AND BE JOINTLY APPROVED BY THE NATIONAL INSTITUTE FOR OCCUPATIONAL SAFETY AND HEALTH AND THE MINE SAFETY AND HEALTH ADMINISTRATION (NIOSH-MSHA).
CHEMICAL CARTRIDGE RESPIRATOR WITH AN ORGANIC VAPOR CARTRIDGE(S) WITH A FULL FACEPIECE AND ORGANIC VAPOR CARTRIDGE(S) IN COMBINATION WITH A DUST AND MIST FILTER.
POWERED AIR-PURIFYING RESPIRATOR WITH A TIGHT-FITTING FACEPIECE AND ORGANIC VAPOR CARTRIDGE(S) IN COMBINATION WITH A HIGH-EFFICIENCY PARTICULATE FILTER.
TYPE 'C' SUPPLIED-AIR RESPIRATOR WITH A FULL FACEPIECE OPERATED IN A PRESSURE-DEMAND OR OTHER POSITIVE PRESSURE MODE.
SELF-CONTAINED BREATHING APPARATUS WITH A FULL FACEPIECE OPERATED IN PRESSURE-DEMAND OR OTHER POSITIVE PRESSURE MODE.
FOR FIREFIGHTING AND OTHER IMMEDIATELY DANGEROUS TO LIFE OR HEALTH CONDITIONS:
SELF-CONTAINED BREATHING APPARATUS WITH FULL FACEPIECE OPERATED IN PRESSURE-DEMAND OR OTHER POSITIVE PRESSURE MODE.
SUPPLIED-AIR RESPIRATOR WITH FULL FACEPIECE AND OPERATED IN PRESSURE-DEMAND OR OTHER POSITIVE PRESSURE MODE IN COMBINATION WITH AN AUXILIARY SELF-CONTAINED BREATHING APPARATUS OPERATED IN PRESSURE-DEMAND OR OTHER POSITIVE PRESSURE MODE.
CLOTHING: EMPLOYEE MUST WEAR APPROPRIATE PROTECTIVE (IMPERVIOUS) CLOTHING AND EQUIPMENT TO PREVENT REPEATED OR PROLONGED SKIN CONTACT WITH THIS SUBSTANCE.
GLOVES: EMPLOYEE MUST WEAR APPROPRIATE PROTECTIVE GLOVES TO PREVENT CONTACT WITH THIS SUBSTANCE.
EYE PROTECTION: EMPLOYEE MUST WEAR SPLASH-PROOF OR DUST-RESISTANT SAFETY GOGGLES TO PREVENT EYE CONTACT WITH THIS SUBSTANCE.
EMERGENCY EYE WASH: WHERE THERE IS ANY POSSIBILITY THAT AN EMPLOYEE'S EYES MAY BE EXPOSED TO THIS SUBSTANCE, THE EMPLOYER SHOULD PROVIDE AN EYE WASH FOUNTAIN WITHIN THE IMMEDIATE WORK AREA FOR EMERGENCY USE.

AUTHORIZED BY- OCCUPATIONAL HEALTH SERVICES, INC.
CREATION DATE: 10/04/89 ***REVISION DATE:*** 05/31/90

MATERIAL SAFETY DATA SHEET

OCCUPATIONAL HEALTH SERVICES, INC.
AGRICULTURE AND PESTICIDE DIVISION
450 SEVENTH AVENUE, SUITE 2407
NEW YORK, NEW YORK 10123
1-800-445-MSDS OR (212) 967-1100

EMERGENCY CONTACT:
JOHN S. BRANSFORD, JR. (615) 292-1180

SUBSTANCE IDENTIFICATION

CAS-NUMBER 77182-82-2

SUBSTANCE: **GLUFOSINATE-AMMONIUM**

TRADE NAMES/SYNONYMS: BUTANOIC ACID, 2-AMINO-4(HYDROXYMETHYLPHOSPHINYL), MONOAMMONIUM SALT; 2-AMINO-4(HYDROXYMETHYLPHOSPHINYL)BUTANOIC ACID, MONOAMMONIUM SALT; 4-(HYDROXYMETHYLPHOSPHINOYL)-DL-HOMOALANINE, MONOAMMONIUM SALT; DL-HOMOALANIN-4-YL(METHYL)PHOSPHINIC ACID, MONOAMMONIUM SALT; AMMONIUM-DL-HOMOALANIN-4-YL(METHYL)PHOSPHINATE; DL-HOMOALANIN-4-YL(METHYL)PHOSPHINIC ACID, AMMONIUM; HOE 39 866; BASTA; GLUFOSINATE; HOE-0066; TOTAL; C5H15N2O4P; PST72647

CHEMICAL FAMILY: AMINE SALT
AMINO ACID DERIVATIVE
PHOSPHATE

MOLECULAR FORMULA: (CH3-P-O2-C-H2-C-H2-C(NH2)-H-C-O2H).NH4

MOLECULAR WEIGHT: 198.15

CERCLA RATINGS (SCALE 0-3): HEALTH=2 FIRE=1 REACTIVITY=0 PERSISTENCE=0

NFPA RATINGS (SCALE 0-4): HEALTH=2 FIRE=1 REACTIVITY=0

COMPONENTS AND CONTAMINANTS

COMPONENT: GLUFOSINATE-AMMONIUM ***PERCENT:*** 100
CAS# 77182-82-2

OTHER CONTAMINANTS: NONE.

PHYSICAL DATA

DESCRIPTION: SOLID. ***MELTING POINT:*** 419 F (215 C)

SPECIFIC GRAVITY: NO DATA AVAILABLE. ***SOLUBILITY IN WATER:*** SOLUBLE.

FIRE AND EXPLOSION DATA

FIRE AND EXPLOSION HAZARD: SLIGHT FIRE HAZARD WHEN EXPOSED TO HEAT OR FLAME.

FIREFIGHTING MEDIA: DRY CHEMICAL, CARBON DIOXIDE, HALON, WATER SPRAY OR STANDARD FOAM (1987 EMERGENCY RESPONSE GUIDEBOOK, DOT P 5800.4). FOR LARGER FIRES, USE WATER SPRAY, FOG OR STANDARD FOAM (1987 EMERGENCY RESPONSE GUIDEBOOK, DOT P 5800.4).

FIREFIGHTING: MOVE CONTAINERS FROM FIRE AREA IF POSSIBLE (1987 EMERGENCY RESPONSE GUIDEBOOK, DOT P 5800.4, GUIDE PAGE 53).

TOXICITY

GLUFOSINATE-AMMONIUM: TOXICITY DATA: 1620 MG/KG ORAL-RAT LD50; 416 MG/KG ORAL-MOUSE LD50; 200 MG/KG ORAL-DOG LD50. CARCINOGEN STATUS: NONE. ACUTE TOXICITY DATA: MODERATELY TOXIC BY INGESTION. TARGET EFFECTS: NO DATA AVAILABLE.

HEALTH EFFECTS AND FIRST AID

INHALATION: GLUFOSINATE-AMMONIUM: **ACUTE EXPOSURE-** NO DATA AVAILABLE. **CHRONIC EXPOSURE-** NO DATA AVAILABLE.

FIRST AID- REMOVE FROM EXPOSURE AREA TO FRESH AIR IMMEDIATELY. IF BREATHING HAS STOPPED, PERFORM ARTIFICIAL RESPIRATION. KEEP PERSON WARM AND AT REST. TREAT SYMPTOMATICALLY AND SUPPORTIVELY. GET MEDICAL ATTENTION IMMEDIATELY.

SKIN CONTACT: GLUFOSINATE-AMMONIUM: **ACUTE EXPOSURE-** A LETHAL DOSE IN RATS BY DERMAL ABSORPTION IS GREATER THAN 2000 MG/KG. **CHRONIC EXPOSURE-** NO DATA AVAILABLE.

FIRST AID- REMOVE CONTAMINATED CLOTHING AND SHOES IMMEDIATELY. WASH AFFECTED AREA WITH SOAP OR MILD DETERGENT AND LARGE AMOUNTS OF WATER UNTIL NO EVIDENCE OF CHEMICAL REMAINS (APPROXIMATELY 15-20 MINUTES). GET MEDICAL ATTENTION IMMEDIATELY.

EYE CONTACT: GLUFOSINATE-AMMONIUM: **ACUTE EXPOSURE-** NO DATA AVAILABLE. **CHRONIC EXPOSURE-** NO DATA AVAILABLE.

FIRST AID- WASH EYES IMMEDIATELY WITH LARGE AMOUNTS OF WATER OR NORMAL SALINE, OCCASIONALLY LIFTING UPPER AND LOWER LIDS, UNTIL NO EVIDENCE OF CHEMICAL REMAINS (APPROXIMATELY 15-20 MINUTES). GET MEDICAL ATTENTION IMMEDIATELY.

INGESTION: GLUFOSINATE-AMMONIUM: **ACUTE EXPOSURE-** A LETHAL DOSE IN RATS WAS 1625 MG/KG. **CHRONIC EXPOSURE-** NO DATA AVAILABLE.

FIRST AID- TREAT SYMPTOMATICALLY AND SUPPORTIVELY. GET MEDICAL ATTENTION IMMEDIATELY. IF VOMITING OCCURS, KEEP HEAD LOWER THAN HIPS TO PREVENT ASPIRATION.

ANTIDOTE: NO SPECIFIC ANTIDOTE. TREAT SYMPTOMATICALLY AND SUPPORTIVELY.

REACTIVITY

REACTIVITY: STABLE UNDER NORMAL TEMPERATURES AND PRESSURES.

INCOMPATIBILITIES: GLUFOSINATE-AMMONIUM: NO DATA AVAILABLE.

DECOMPOSITION: THERMAL DECOMPOSITION MAY RELEASE AMMONIA FUMES, AND TOXIC OXIDES OF CARBON AND PHOSPHOROUS.

POLYMERIZATION: HAZARDOUS POLYMERIZATION HAS NOT BEEN REPORTED TO OCCUR UNDER NORMAL TEMPERATURES AND PRESSURES.

STORAGE AND DISPOSAL

OBSERVE ALL FEDERAL, STATE AND LOCAL REGULATIONS WHEN STORING OR DISPOSING OF THIS SUBSTANCE. FOR ASSISTANCE, CONTACT THE DISTRICT DIRECTOR OF THE ENVIRONMENTAL PROTECTION AGENCY.

****STORAGE****

STORE IN ACCORDANCE WITH 40 CFR 165 RECOMMENDED PROCEDURES FOR THE DISPOSAL AND STORAGE OF PESTICIDES AND PESTICIDE CONTAINERS.

****DISPOSAL****

DISPOSAL MUST BE IN ACCORDANCE WITH 40 CFR 165 RECOMMENDED PROCEDURES FOR THE DISPOSAL AND STORAGE OF PESTICIDES AND PESTICIDE CONTAINERS.

CONDITIONS TO AVOID

MAY BURN BUT DOES NOT IGNITE READILY.

SPILL AND LEAK PROCEDURES

OCCUPATIONAL SPILL: DO NOT TOUCH SPILLED MATERIAL. STOP LEAK IF YOU CAN DO IT WITHOUT RISK. FOR SMALL SPILLS, TAKE UP WITH SAND OR OTHER ABSORBENT MATERIAL AND PLACE INTO CONTAINERS FOR LATER DISPOSAL. FOR SMALL DRY SPILLS, WITH A CLEAN SHOVEL PLACE MATERIAL INTO CLEAN, DRY CONTAINER AND COVER. MOVE CONTAINERS FROM SPILL AREA. FOR LARGER SPILLS, DIKE FAR AHEAD OF SPILL FOR LATER DISPOSAL. KEEP UNNECESSARY PEOPLE AWAY. ISOLATE HAZARD AREA AND DENY ENTRY.

PROTECTIVE EQUIPMENT

VENTILATION: PROVIDE LOCAL EXHAUST OR GENERAL DILUTION VENTILATION SYSTEM.

RESPIRATOR: THE FOLLOWING RESPIRATORS ARE RECOMMENDED BASED ON INFORMATION FOUND IN THE PHYSICAL DATA, TOXICITY AND HEALTH EFFECTS SECTIONS. THEY ARE RANKED IN ORDER FROM MINIMUM TO MAXIMUM RESPIRATORY PROTECTION. THE SPECIFIC RESPIRATOR SELECTED MUST BE BASED ON CONTAMINATION LEVELS FOUND IN THE WORK PLACE, MUST NOT EXCEED THE WORKING LIMITS OF THE RESPIRATOR AND BE JOINTLY APPROVED BY THE NATIONAL INSTITUTE FOR OCCUPATIONAL SAFETY AND HEALTH AND THE MINE SAFETY AND HEALTH ADMINISTRATION (NIOSH-MSHA).

CHEMICAL CARTRIDGE RESPIRATOR WITH AN ORGANIC VAPOR CARTRIDGE(S) WITH A FULL FACEPIECE AND ORGANIC VAPOR CARTRIDGE(S) IN COMBINATION WITH A DUST AND MIST FILTER.

POWERED AIR-PURIFYING RESPIRATOR WITH A TIGHT-FITTING FACEPIECE AND ORGANIC VAPOR CARTRIDGE(S) IN COMBINATION WITH A HIGH-EFFICIENCY PARTICULATE FILTER.

TYPE 'C' SUPPLIED-AIR RESPIRATOR WITH A FULL FACEPIECE OPERATED IN A PRESSURE-DEMAND OR OTHER POSITIVE PRESSURE MODE.

SELF-CONTAINED BREATHING APPARATUS WITH A FULL FACEPIECE OPERATED IN PRESSURE-DEMAND OR OTHER POSITIVE PRESSURE MODE.

FOR FIREFIGHTING AND OTHER IMMEDIATELY DANGEROUS TO LIFE OR HEALTH CONDITIONS:

SELF-CONTAINED BREATHING APPARATUS WITH FULL FACEPIECE OPERATED IN PRESSURE-DEMAND OR OTHER POSITIVE PRESSURE MODE.

SUPPLIED-AIR RESPIRATOR WITH FULL FACEPIECE AND OPERATED IN PRESSURE-DEMAND OR OTHER POSITIVE PRESSURE MODE IN COMBINATION WITH AN AUXILIARY SELF-CONTAINED BREATHING APPARATUS OPERATED IN PRESSURE-DEMAND OR OTHER POSITIVE PRESSURE MODE.

CLOTHING: EMPLOYEE MUST WEAR APPROPRIATE PROTECTIVE (IMPERVIOUS) CLOTHING AND EQUIPMENT TO PREVENT REPEATED OR PROLONGED SKIN CONTACT WITH THIS SUBSTANCE.

GLOVES: EMPLOYEE MUST WEAR APPROPRIATE PROTECTIVE GLOVES TO PREVENT CONTACT WITH THIS SUBSTANCE.

EYE PROTECTION: EMPLOYEE MUST WEAR SPLASH-PROOF OR DUST-RESISTANT SAFETY GOGGLES TO PREVENT EYE CONTACT WITH THIS SUBSTANCE.

EMERGENCY EYE WASH: WHERE THERE IS ANY POSSIBILITY THAT AN EMPLOYEE'S

EYES MAY BE EXPOSED TO THIS SUBSTANCE, THE EMPLOYER SHOULD PROVIDE AN EYE WASH FOUNTAIN WITHIN THE IMMEDIATE WORK AREA FOR EMERGENCY USE.

AUTHORIZED BY- OCCUPATIONAL HEALTH SERVICES, INC.
CREATION DATE: 10/04/89 ***REVISION DATE:*** 05/18/90

MATERIAL SAFETY DATA SHEET

OCCUPATIONAL HEALTH SERVICES, INC.
AGRICULTURE AND PESTICIDE DIVISION
450 SEVENTH AVENUE, SUITE 2407
NEW YORK, NEW YORK 10123
1-800-445-MSDS OR (212) 967-1100

EMERGENCY CONTACT:
JOHN S. BRANSFORD, JR. (615) 292-1180

SUBSTANCE IDENTIFICATION

CAS-NUMBER 67747-09-5
SUBSTANCE: PROCHLORAZ
TRADE NAMES/SYNONYMS: 1H-IMIDAZOLE-1-CARBOXAMIDE, N-PROPYL-N-(2-(2,4,6-(TRICHLOROPHENOXY) ETHYL)-; SPORTAK; 1-(N-PROPYL.N-(2-(2,4,6-(TRICHLOROPHENOXY)ETHYL)CARBAMOYL)IMIDAZOLE; N-PROPYL-N-(2-(2,4,6-TRICHLOROPHENOXY)ETHYL)-1-IMIDAZOLE-1-CARBOXAMIDE; BTS 40542; C15H16CL3N3O2; PST72648
CHEMICAL FAMILY: AMIDE
IMIDAZOLE
MOLECULAR FORMULA: C15-H16-CL3-N3-O2
MOLECULAR WEIGHT: 376.67
CERCLA RATINGS (SCALE 0-3): HEALTH=U FIRE=1 REACTIVITY=0 PERSISTENCE=1
NFPA RATINGS (SCALE 0-4): HEALTH=U FIRE=1 REACTIVITY=0

COMPONENTS AND CONTAMINANTS

COMPONENT: PROCHLORAZ ***PERCENT:*** 100.0
CAS# 67747-09-5
OTHER CONTAMINANTS: NONE
EXPOSURE LIMITS: NO OCCUPATIONAL EXPOSURE LIMITS ESTABLISHED BY OSHA, ACGIH, OR NIOSH.

PHYSICAL DATA

DESCRIPTION: COLORLESS, ODORLESS, CRYSTALLINE SOLID.
MELTING POINT: 102-104 F (39-41 C) ***SPECIFIC GRAVITY:*** NOT AVAILABLE
VAPOR PRESSURE: NEGLIGIBLE ***SOLUBILITY IN WATER:*** 47.5 PPM
SOLVENT SOLUBILITY: MODERATELY SOLUBLE IN ACETONE, CHLOROFORM, DIETHYL ETHER, TOLUENE, AND XYLENE.

FIRE AND EXPLOSION DATA

FIRE AND EXPLOSION HAZARD: SLIGHT FIRE HAZARD WHEN EXPOSED TO HEAT OR FLAME.
FIREFIGHTING MEDIA: DRY CHEMICAL, CARBON DIOXIDE, HALON, WATER SPRAY OR STANDARD FOAM (1987 EMERGENCY RESPONSE GUIDEBOOK, DOT P 5800.4). FOR LARGER FIRES, USE WATER SPRAY, FOG OR STANDARD FOAM (1987 EMERGENCY RESPONSE GUIDEBOOK, DOT P 5800.4).
FIREFIGHTING: MOVE CONTAINER FROM FIRE AREA IF POSSIBLE. DO NOT SCATTER SPILLED MATERIAL WITH HIGH PRESSURE WATER STREAMS. DIKE FIRE CONTROL WATER FOR LATER DISPOSAL (1987 EMERGENCY RESPONSE GUIDEBOOK, DOT P 5800.4, GUIDE PAGE 31).
USE AGENTS SUITABLE FOR TYPE OF SURROUNDING FIRE. AVOID BREATHING HAZARDOUS VAPORS, KEEP UPWIND.

TOXICITY

PROCHLORAZ: TOXICITY DATA: >3000 MG/KG SKIN-RABBIT LD50 (85JFAN); >5000 MG/KG SKIN-RAT LD50 (PEMNDP); 1600 MG/KG ORAL-RAT LD50; 2400 MG/KG ORAL-MOUSE LD50. CARCINOGEN STATUS: NONE. ACUTE TOXICITY LEVEL: MODERATELY TOXIC BY INGESTION; SLIGHTLY TOXIC BY DERMAL ABSORPTION. TARGET EFFECTS: NO DATA AVAILABLE.

HEALTH EFFECTS AND FIRST AID

INHALATION: PROCHLORAZ: ACUTE EXPOSURE- NO DATA AVAILABLE. CHRONIC EXPOSURE- NO DATA AVAILABLE.
FIRST AID- REMOVE FROM EXPOSURE AREA TO FRESH AIR IMMEDIATELY. IF BREATHING HAS STOPPED, PERFORM ARTIFICIAL RESPIRATION. KEEP PERSON WARM AND AT REST. TREAT SYMPTOMATICALLY AND SUPPORTIVELY. GET MEDICAL ATTENTION IMMEDIATELY.

SKIN CONTACT: PROCHLORAZ: ACUTE EXPOSURE- MAY CAUSE IRRITATION. CHRONIC EXPOSURE- NO DATA AVAILABLE.
FIRST AID- REMOVE CONTAMINATED CLOTHING AND SHOES IMMEDIATELY. WASH AFFECTED AREA WITH SOAP OR MILD DETERGENT AND LARGE AMOUNTS OF WATER UNTIL NO EVIDENCE OF CHEMICAL REMAINS (APPROXIMATELY 15-20 MINUTES). GET MEDICAL ATTENTION IMMEDIATELY.

EYE CONTACT: PROCHLORAZ: ACUTE EXPOSURE- MAY CAUSE IRRITATION. CHRONIC EXPOSURE- NO DATA AVAILABLE.
FIRST AID- WASH EYES IMMEDIATELY WITH LARGE AMOUNTS OF WATER OR NORMAL SALINE, OCCASIONALLY LIFTING UPPER AND LOWER LIDS, UNTIL NO EVIDENCE OF CHEMICAL REMAINS (APPROXIMATELY 15-20 MINUTES). GET MEDICAL ATTENTION IMMEDIATELY.

INGESTION: PROCHLORAZ: ACUTE EXPOSURE- THE LETHAL DOSE REPORTED IN RATS WAS 1600 MG/KG. THE SYMPTOMS WERE NOT REPORTED. CHRONIC EXPOSURE- IN 2 YEAR FEEDING TRIALS, THE NO EFFECT LEVEL FOR DOGS WAS 30 MG/KG IN THE DIET.
FIRST AID- TREAT SYMPTOMATICALLY AND SUPPORTIVELY. GET MEDICAL ATTENTION IMMEDIATELY. IF VOMITING OCCURS, KEEP HEAD LOWER THAN HIPS TO PREVENT ASPIRATION.
ANTIDOTE: NO SPECIFIC ANTIDOTE. TREAT SYMPTOMATICALLY AND SUPPORTIVELY.

REACTIVITY

REACTIVITY: STABLE UNDER NORMAL TEMPERATURES AND PRESSURES.
INCOMPATIBILITIES: PROCHLORAZ: ACID (STRONG): INCOMPATABLE. ALKALI SOLUTIONS: INCOMPATABLE. OXIDIZERS (STRONG): FIRE AND EXPLOSION HAZARD.
DECOMPOSITION: THERMAL DECOMPOSITION PRODUCTS MAY INCLUDE TOXIC OXIDES OF NITROGEN AND CARBON AND TOXIC AND CORROSIVE FUMES OF CHLORIDES.
POLYMERIZATION: HAZARDOUS POLYMERIZATION HAS NOT BEEN REPORTED TO OCCUR UNDER NORMAL TEMPERATURES AND PRESSURES.

STORAGE AND DISPOSAL

OBSERVE ALL FEDERAL, STATE AND LOCAL REGULATIONS WHEN STORING OR DISPOSING OF THIS SUBSTANCE. FOR ASSISTANCE, CONTACT THE DISTRICT DIRECTOR OF THE ENVIRONMENTAL PROTECTION AGENCY.

STORAGE

STORE IN ACCORDANCE WITH 40 CFR 165 RECOMMENDED PROCEDURES FOR THE DISPOSAL AND STORAGE OF PESTICIDES AND PESTICIDE CONTAINERS.
STORE AWAY FROM INCOMPATIBLE SUBSTANCES.

DISPOSAL

DISPOSAL MUST BE IN ACCORDANCE WITH 40 CFR 165 RECOMMENDED PROCEDURES FOR THE DISPOSAL AND STORAGE OF PESTICIDES AND PESTICIDE CONTAINERS.

CONDITIONS TO AVOID

MAY BURN BUT DOES NOT IGNITE READILY. AVOID CONTACT WITH STRONG OXIDIZERS, EXCESSIVE HEAT, SPARKS, OR OPEN FLAME.

SPILL AND LEAK PROCEDURES

OCCUPATIONAL SPILL: SWEEP UP AND PLACE IN SUITABLE CLEAN, DRY CONTAINERS FOR RECLAMATION OR LATER DISPOSAL. DO NOT FLUSH SPILLED MATERIAL INTO SEWER. KEEP UNNECESSARY PEOPLE AWAY.

PROTECTIVE EQUIPMENT

VENTILATION: PROVIDE LOCAL EXHAUST OR GENERAL DILUTION VENTILATION SYSTEM.
RESPIRATOR: THE FOLLOWING RESPIRATORS ARE RECOMMENDED BASED ON INFORMATION FOUND IN THE PHYSICAL DATA, TOXICITY AND HEALTH EFFECTS SECTIONS. THEY ARE RANKED IN ORDER FROM MINIMUM TO MAXIMUM RESPIRATORY PROTECTION. THE SPECIFIC RESPIRATOR SELECTED MUST BE BASED ON CONTAMINATION LEVELS FOUND IN THE WORK PLACE, MUST NOT EXCEED THE WORKING LIMITS OF THE RESPIRATOR AND BE JOINTLY APPROVED BY THE NATIONAL INSTITUTE FOR OCCUPATIONAL SAFETY AND HEALTH AND THE MINE SAFETY AND HEALTH ADMINISTRATION (NIOSH-MSHA).
CHEMICAL CARTRIDGE RESPIRATOR WITH AN ORGANIC VAPOR CARTRIDGE(S) WITH A FULL FACEPIECE AND ORGANIC VAPOR CARTRIDGE(S) IN COMBINATION WITH A DUST AND MIST FILTER.
POWERED AIR-PURIFYING RESPIRATOR WITH A TIGHT-FITTING FACEPIECE AND ORGANIC VAPOR CARTRIDGE(S) IN COMBINATION WITH A HIGH-EFFICIENCY PARTICULATE FILTER.

TYPE 'C' SUPPLIED-AIR RESPIRATOR WITH A FULL FACEPIECE OPERATED IN A PRESSURE-DEMAND OR OTHER POSITIVE PRESSURE MODE.
SELF-CONTAINED BREATHING APPARATUS WITH A FULL FACEPIECE OPERATED IN PRESSURE-DEMAND OR OTHER POSITIVE PRESSURE MODE.
FOR FIREFIGHTING AND OTHER IMMEDIATELY DANGEROUS TO LIFE OR HEALTH CONDITIONS:
SELF-CONTAINED BREATHING APPARATUS WITH FULL FACEPIECE OPERATED IN PRESSURE-DEMAND OR OTHER POSITIVE PRESSURE MODE.
SUPPLIED-AIR RESPIRATOR WITH FULL FACEPIECE AND OPERATED IN PRESSURE-DEMAND OR OTHER POSITIVE PRESSURE MODE IN COMBINATION WITH AN AUXILIARY SELF-CONTAINED BREATHING APPARATUS OPERATED IN PRESSURE-DEMAND OR OTHER POSITIVE PRESSURE MODE.

CLOTHING: EMPLOYEE MUST WEAR APPROPRIATE PROTECTIVE (IMPERVIOUS) CLOTHING AND EQUIPMENT TO PREVENT REPEATED OR PROLONGED SKIN CONTACT WITH THIS SUBSTANCE.

GLOVES: EMPLOYEE MUST WEAR APPROPRIATE PROTECTIVE GLOVES TO PREVENT CONTACT WITH THIS SUBSTANCE.

EYE PROTECTION: EMPLOYEE MUST WEAR SPLASH-PROOF OR DUST-RESISTANT SAFETY GOGGLES TO PREVENT EYE CONTACT WITH THIS SUBSTANCE.
EMERGENCY EYE WASH: WHERE THERE IS ANY POSSIBILITY THAT AN EMPLOYEE'S EYES MAY BE EXPOSED TO THIS SUBSTANCE, THE EMPLOYER SHOULD PROVIDE AN EYE WASH FOUNTAIN WITHIN THE IMMEDIATE WORK AREA FOR EMERGENCY USE.

AUTHORIZED BY- OCCUPATIONAL HEALTH SERVICES, INC.
CREATION DATE: 10/20/89 ***REVISION DATE:*** 05/31/90

MATERIAL SAFETY DATA SHEET

OCCUPATIONAL HEALTH SERVICES, INC.
AGRICULTURE AND PESTICIDE DIVISION
450 SEVENTH AVENUE, SUITE 2407
NEW YORK, NEW YORK 10123
1-800-445-MSDS OR (212) 967-1100

EMERGENCY CONTACT:
JOHN S. BRANSFORD, JR. (615) 292-1180

SUBSTANCE IDENTIFICATION

CAS-NUMBER 34643-46-4
SUBSTANCE: **PROTHIOPHOS**
TRADE NAMES/SYNONYMS: PHOSPHORODITHIOIC ACID, O-(2,4-DICHLOROPHENYL) O-ETHYL-S-PROPYL ESTER; O-2,4-DICHLOROPHENYL O-ETHYL S-PROPYL PHOSPHORODITHIOATE; O-(2,4-DICHLOROPHENYL) O-ETHYL S-PROPYL PHOSPHORODITHIOATE; BAY NTN 8629; BIDERON; DICHLORPROPAPHOS; PROTHIOFOS; TOKUTHION; TOYODAN; TOYOTHION; C11H15CL2O2PS2; PST72655
CHEMICAL FAMILY: PHOSPHOROTHIOATE
MOLECULAR FORMULA: C11-H15-CL2-O2-P-S2
MOLECULAR WEIGHT: 345.25
CERCLA RATINGS (SCALE 0-3): HEALTH=2 FIRE=U REACTIVITY=0 PERSISTENCE=1
NFPA RATINGS (SCALE 0-4): HEALTH=2 FIRE=U REACTIVITY=0

COMPONENTS AND CONTAMINANTS

COMPONENT: PROTHIOPHOS ***PERCENT:*** 100.0
CAS# 34643-46-4
OTHER CONTAMINANTS: NONE
EXPOSURE LIMITS: NO OCCUPATIONAL EXPOSURE LIMITS ESTABLISHED BY OSHA, ACGIH, OR NIOSH.

PHYSICAL DATA

DESCRIPTION: COLORLESS LIQUID.
BOILING POINT: 257-262 F (125-128 C) @ 0.1 MMHG
SPECIFIC GRAVITY: 1.30 ***VAPOR PRESSURE:*** .0000075 MMHG @ 20 C
SOLUBILITY IN WATER: 0.00017% @ 20 C
SOLVENT SOLUBILITY: SOLUBLE IN CYCLOHEXANONE AND TOLUENE.

FIRE AND EXPLOSION DATA

FIRE AND EXPLOSION HAZARD: UNKNOWN FIRE AND EXPLOSION HAZARD.
FIREFIGHTING MEDIA: DRY CHEMICAL, CARBON DIOXIDE, HALON, WATER SPRAY OR STANDARD FOAM (1987 EMERGENCY RESPONSE GUIDEBOOK, DOT P 5800.4).
FOR LARGER FIRES, USE WATER SPRAY, FOG OR STANDARD FOAM (1987 EMERGENCY RESPONSE GUIDEBOOK, DOT P 5800.4).
FIREFIGHTING: MOVE CONTAINER FROM FIRE AREA IF POSSIBLE. DIKE FIRE CONTROL WATER FOR LATER DISPOSAL; DO NOT SCATTER THE MATERIAL. COOL FIRE-EXPOSED CONTAINERS WITH WATER FROM SIDE UNTIL WELL AFTER FIRE IS OUT. STAY AWAY FROM STORAGE TANK ENDS. WITHDRAW IMMEDIATELY IN CASE OF RISING SOUND FROM VENTING SAFETY DEVICE OR ANY DISCOLORATION OF STORAGE TANK DUE TO FIRE (1987 EMERGENCY RESPONSE GUIDEBOOK, DOT P 5800.4, GUIDE PAGE 28).
EXTINGUISH ONLY IF FLOW CAN BE STOPPED. USE FLOODING AMOUNTS OF WATER AS A FOG; SOLID STREAMS MAY BE INEFFECTIVE. COOL CONTAINERS WITH FLOODING AMOUNTS OF WATER FROM AS FAR A DISTANCE AS POSSIBLE. AVOID BREATHING POISONOUS VAPORS, KEEP UPWIND.

TOXICITY

PROTHIOPHOS: TOXICITY DATA: 3900 MG/KG SKIN-RAT LD50; 1600 MG/KG SKIN-MOUSE LD50;2 GM/KG SKIN-MAMMAL LD50; 875 MG/KG ORAL-RAT LD50; 570 MG/KG ORAL-MOUSE LD50. CARCINOGEN STATUS: NONE. ACUTE TOXICITY LEVEL: MODERATELY TOXIC BY INGESTION AND SLIGHTLY TOXIC BY DERMAL ABSORPTION. TARGET EFFECTS: CHOLINESTERASE INHIBITOR. POISONING MAY AFFECT THE NERVOUS SYSTEM.* AT INCREASED RISK FROM EXPOSURE: PERSONS WITH RESPIRATORY AILMENTS, RECENT EXPOSURE TO CHOLINESTERASE INHIBITORS OR IMPAIRED CHOLINESTERASE PRODUCTION, OR LIVER MALFUNCTION.* ADDITIONAL DATA: MAY CROSS THE PLACENTA. HIGH ENVIRONMENTAL TEMPERATURES OR EXPOSURE OF THE CHEMICAL TO VISIBLE OR ULTRAVIOLET LIGHT MAY ENHANCE THE TOXICITY. INTERACTIONS WITH MEDICATIONS MAY OCCUR.*
* MAY BE BASED ON GENERAL INFORMATION ON ORGANOPHOSPHATES.

HEALTH EFFECTS AND FIRST AID

INHALATION: PROTHIOPHOS: SEE INFORMATION ON ORGANOPHOSPHATES.
ORGANOPHOSPHATES: CHOLINESTERASE INHIBITOR. **ACUTE EXPOSURE**- WHEN INHALED, THE FIRST EFFECTS OF CHOLINESTERASE INHIBITORS ARE USUALLY RESPIRATORY AND MAY INCLUDE NASAL HYPEREMIA AND WATERY DISCHARGE, COUGH, CHEST DISCOMFORT, DYSPNEA, AND WHEEZING DUE TO INCREASED BRONCHIAL SECRETIONS AND BRONCHOCONSTRICTION. IF SUFFICIENT AMOUNTS ARE ABSORBED, OTHER SYSTEMIC EFFECTS MAY BEGIN WITHIN A FEW MINUTES OR BE DELAYED FOR UP TO 12 HOURS. SYMPTOMS MAY INCLUDE PALLOR, NAUSEA, VOMITING, DIARRHEA, ABDOMINAL CRAMPS, HEADACHE, DIZZINESS, OCULAR PAIN, BLURRED VISION, MIOSIS OR IN SOME CASES, ESPECIALLY INITIALLY, MYDRIASIS, LACRIMATION, SALIVATION, SWEATING, AND CONFUSION. OTHER REPORTED CENTRAL NERVOUS SYSTEM OR NEUROMUSCULAR EFFECTS MAY INCLUDE ATAXIA, SLURRED SPEECH, AREFLEXIA, WEAKNESS, FATIGUE, FASCICULATIONS, TWITCHING, TREMORS POSSIBLY OF THE TONGUE AND EYELIDS, AND EVENTUALLY PARALYSIS OF THE EXTREMITIES AND POSSIBLY OF THE RESPIRATORY MUSCLES. IN SEVERE CASES THERE MAY ALSO BE INVOLUNTARY DEFECATION AND URINATION, CYANOSIS, PSYCHOSIS, HYPERGLYCEMIA, ACUTE PANCREATITIS, CARDIAC IRREGULARITIES, PULMONARY EDEMA, UNCONSCIOUSNESS, CONVULSIONS, AND COMA. DEATH IS PRIMARILY DUE TO RESPIRATORY FAILURE, ALTHOUGH CARDIOVASCULAR EFFECTS INCLUDING CARDIAC ARREST MAY ALSO BE IMPLICATED. LONG TERM SEQUELAE ARE RARE BUT MAY INCLUDE NEUROPSYCHIATRIC DISORDERS AND MYOPATHY WITH MUSCLE TENDERNESS. SOME ORGANOPHOSPHATES MAY CAUSE A DELAYED NEUROPATHY BEGINNING 1-4 WEEKS AFTER AN ACUTE EXPOSURE WHICH MAY OR MAY NOT HAVE CAUSED ACUTE CHOLINERGIC EFFECTS. NUMBNESS, TINGLING, WEAKNESS AND CRAMPING BEGINNING SYMMETRICALLY IN THE LOWER LIMBS MAY PROGRESS TO ATAXIA AND PARALYSIS. IN SEVERE CASES, UPPER LIMB INVOLVEMENT IS POSSIBLE AND FLACCID PARALYSIS MAY PROGRESS TO SPASTIC PARALYSIS WITH EXAGGERATED REFLEXES. IMPROVEMENT MAY OCCUR OVER MONTHS TO YEARS, BUT SOME RESIDUAL IMPAIRMENT USUALLY REMAINS. **CHRONIC EXPOSURE**- REPEATED OR PROLONGED EXPOSURE MAY RESULT IN THE EFFECTS OF ACUTE EXPOSURE INCLUDING THE DELAYED NEUROPATHY. OTHER EFFECTS REPORTED IN WORKERS REPEATEDLY EXPOSED INCLUDE IMPAIRED MEMORY AND CONCENTRATION, ACUTE PSYCHOSIS, SEVERE DEPRESSIONS, IRRITABILTY, CONFUSION, APATHY, EMOTIONAL LABILITY, SOCIAL WITHDRAWAL, CONFUSION, HEADACHE, SPEECH DIFFICULTIES, DELAYED REACTION TIMES, SPATIAL DISORIENTATION, NIGHTMARES, SLEEPWALKING, AND DROWSINESS OR INSOMNIA. AN INFLUENZA-LIKE CONDITION WITH HEADACHE, NAUSEA, WEAKNESS, ANOREXIA AND MALAISE HAS ALSO BEEN REPORTED.

FIRST AID- REMOVE FROM EXPOSURE AREA TO FRESH AIR IMMEDIATELY. IF BREATHING HAS STOPPED, GIVE ARTIFICIAL RESPIRATION. MAINTAIN AIRWAY AND BLOOD PRESSURE AND ADMINISTER OXYGEN IF AVAILABLE. KEEP AFFECTED PERSON WARM AND AT REST. TREAT SYMPTOMATICALLY AND SUPPORTIVELY. ADMINISTRATION OF OXYGEN SHOULD BE PERFORMED BY QUALIFIED PERSONNEL. GET MEDICAL ATTENTION IMMEDIATELY.

SKIN CONTACT: PROTHIOPHOS: SEE INFORMATION ON ORGANOPHOSPHATES.
ORGANOPHOSPHATES: CHOLINESTERASE INHIBITOR. **ACUTE EXPOSURE**- LOCALIZED SWEATING AND FASCICULATIONS MAY OCCUR AT THE SITE OF

CONTACT. IF SUFFICIENT AMOUNTS ARE ABSORBED, OTHER EFFECTS OF CHOLINESTERASE INHIBITION AS DESCRIBED IN ACUTE INHALATION MAY OCCUR. SYMPTOMS MAY BE DELAYED 2-3 HOURS, BUT USUALLY NO MORE THAN 12 HOURS. THE RATE OF ABSORPTION IS INCREASED BY THE PRESENCE OF DERMATITIS OR HIGH AMBIENT TEMPERATURES. DELAYED NEUROPATHY IS ALSO POSSIBLE. **CHRONIC EXPOSURE-** REPEATED OR PROLONGED EXPOSURE MAY CAUSE EFFECTS AS DESCRIBED IN ACUTE EXPOSURE. SOME ORGANOPHOSPHATES MAY CAUSE SENSITIZATION.

FIRST AID- REMOVE CONTAMINATED CLOTHING IMMEDIATELY. WASH CONTAMINATED AREAS WITH SOAP AND WATER FOLLOWED BY ALCOHOL (ARENA, POISONING, 4TH ED.). EMERGENCY PERSONNEL SHOULD WEAR GLOVES AND AVOID CONTAMINATION. TREAT RESPIRATORY DIFFICULTY WITH ARTIFICIAL RESPIRATION. GET MEDICAL ATTENTION IMMEDIATELY.

EYE CONTACT: PROTHIOPHOS: SEE INFORMATION ON ORGANOPHOSPHATES. ORGANOPHOSPHATES: CHOLINESTERASE INHIBITOR. **ACUTE EXPOSURE-** DIRECT CONTACT MAY CAUSE PAIN, HYPEREMIA, LACRIMATION, TWITCHING OF THE EYELIDS, MIOSIS, AND CILIARY MUSCLE SPASM WITH LOSS OF ACCOMODATION, BLURRED OR DIMMED VISION AND BROWACHE. SOMETIMES MYDRIASIS MAY OCCUR INSTEAD OF MIOSIS. WITH SUFFICIENT EXPOSURE, OTHER SYMPTOMS OF CHOLINESTERASE INHIBITION AS DESCRIBED IN ACUTE INHALATION MAY OCCUR. **CHRONIC EXPOSURE-** REPEATED OR PROLONGED EXPOSURE MAY CAUSE EFFECTS AS DESCRIBED IN ACUTE EXPOSURE. SOME COMPOUNDS HAVE CAUSED TOXIC EFFECTS ON THE CRYSTALLINE LENS, CONJUNCTIVAL THICKENING AND OBSTRUCTION OF THE NASOLACRIMAL CANALS WHEN USED AS MIOTIC EYEDROPS.

FIRST AID- IRRIGATE EYES WITH WATER OR SALINE SOLUTION. IF SYMPTOMS OF POISONING OCCUR, TREAT RESPIRATORY DIFFICULTY WITH ARTIFICIAL RESPIRATION AND OXYGEN. OBSERVE PATIENT FOR AT LEAST 24-36 HOURS (GOSSELIN, CLINICAL TOXICOLOGY OF COMMERCIAL PRODUCTS, 5TH ED.). GET MEDICAL ATTENTION IMMEDIATELY. OXYGEN SHOULD BE ADMINISTERED BY QUALIFIED MEDICAL PERSONNEL.

INGESTION: PROTHIOPHOS: SEE INFORMATION ON ORGANOPHOSPHATES. ORGANOPHOSPHATES: CHOLINESTERASE INHIBITOR. **ACUTE EXPOSURE-** WHEN INGESTED, THE FIRST EFFECTS MAY BE NAUSEA, VOMITING, ANOREXIA, ABDOMINAL CRAMPS AND DIARRHEA. GASTROINTESTINAL ABSORPTION MAY CAUSE SYMPTOMS OF CHOLINESTERASE INHIBITION AS DESCRIBED IN ACUTE INHALATION. SYMPTOMS MAY BEGIN WITHIN MINUTES OR BE DELAYED FOR HOURS. DELAYED EFFECTS INCLUDING NEUROPATHY MAY ALSO OCCUR. **CHRONIC EXPOSURE-** REPEATED INGESTION MAY CAUSE EFFECTS AS DESCRIBED IN ACUTE EXPOSURE.

FIRST AID- IF PERSON IS ALERT AND RESPIRATION IS NOT DEPRESSED, GIVE SYRUP OF IPECAC FOLLOWED BY WATER (IF VOMITING OCCURS, KEEP HEAD BELOW HIPS TO PREVENT ASPIRATION). IF CONSCIOUSNESS LEVEL DECLINES OR VOMITING HAS NOT OCCURRED IN 15 MINUTES EMPTY STOMACH BY GASTRIC LAVAGE WITH THE AID OF CUFFED ENDOTRACHEAL TUBE USING ISOTONIC SALINE OR 5% SODIUM BICARBONATE FOLLOW WITH ACTIVATED CHARCOAL. ESTABLISH AND MAINTAIN AIRWAY. TREAT RESPIRATORY DIFFICULTY WITH ARTIFICIAL RESPIRATION AND OXYGEN. DO NOT GIVE MORPHINE, AMINOPHYLLINE, PHENOTHIAZINES, RESERPINE, FUROSEMIDE, OR ETHACRYNIC ACID (MORGAN, RECOGNITION AND MANAGEMENT OF PESTICIDE POISONINGS, 3RD ED.). TREAT SYMPTOMATICALLY AND SUPPORTIVELY. ADMINISTRATION OF OXYGEN AND LAVAGE MUST BE PERFORMED BY QUALIFIED MEDICAL PERSONNEL. GET MEDICAL ATTENTION IMMEDIATELY.

ANTIDOTE: THE FOLLOWING ANTIDOTE(S) HAVE BEEN RECOMMENDED. HOWEVER, THE DECISION AS TO WHETHER THE SEVERITY OF POISONING REQUIRES ADMINISTRATION OF ANY ANTIDOTE AND ACTUAL DOSE REQUIRED SHOULD BE MADE BY QUALIFIED MEDICAL PERSONNEL.

FOR CHOLINESTERASE INHIBITORS: ESTABLISH CLEAR AIRWAY AND TISSUE OXYGENATION BY ASPIRATION OF SECRETIONS, AND IF NECESSARY, BY ASSISTED PULMONARY VENTILATION WITH OXYGEN. IMPROVE TISSUE OXYGENATION AS MUCH AS POSSIBLE BEFORE ADMINISTERING ATROPINE TO MINIMIZE THE RISK OF VENTRICULAR FIBRILLATION. ADMINISTER ATROPINE SULFATE INTRAVENOUSLY, OR INTRAMUSCULARLY IF IV INJECTION IS NOT POSSIBLE. IN MODERATELY SEVERE POISONING ADMINISTER ATROPINE SULFATE, 0.4-2.0 MG REPEATED EVERY 15 MINUTES UNTIL ATROPINIZATION IS ACHIEVED (TACHYCARDIA, FLUSHING, DRY MOUTH, MYDRIASIS). MAINTAIN ATROPINIZATION BY REPEATED DOSES FOR 2-12 HOURS, OR LONGER, DEPENDING ON THE SEVERITY OF POISONING. THE APPEARANCE OF RALES IN THE LUNG BASES, MIOSIS, SALIVATION, NAUSEA, BRADYCARDIA, ARE ALL INDICATIONS OF INADEQUATE ATROPINIZATION. SEVERELY POISONED INDIVIDUALS MAY EXHIBIT REMARKABLE TOLERANCE TO ATROPINE; TWO OR MORE TIMES THE DOSAGES SUGGESTED ABOVE MAY BE NEEDED. PERSONS NOT POISONED OR ONLY SLIGHTLY POISONED, HOWEVER, MAY DEVELOP SIGNS OF ATROPINE TOXICITY FROM SUCH LARGE DOSAGES: FEVER, MUSCLE FIBRILLATIONS, AND DELIRIUM ARE THE MAIN SIGNS OF ATROPINE TOXICITY. IF THESE SIGNS APPEAR WHILE THE PATIENT IS FULLY ATROPINIZED, ATROPINE ADMINISTRATION SHOULD BE DISCONTINUED, AT LEAST TEMPORARILY. OBSERVE TREATED PATIENTS CLOSELY AT LEAST 24 HOURS TO INSURE THAT SYMPTOMS (POSSIBLY PULMONARY EDEMA) DO NOT RECUR AS ATROPINIZATION WEARS OFF. IN VERY SEVERE POISONINGS, METABOLIC DISPOSITION OF TOXICANT MAY REQUIRE SEVERAL HOURS OR DAYS DURING WHICH ATROPINIZATION MUST BE MAINTAINED. MARKEDLY LOWER LEVELS OF URINARY METABOLITES INDICATE THAT ATROPINE DOSAGE CAN BE TAPERED OFF. AS DOSAGE IS REDUCED, CHECK THE LUNG BASES FREQUENTLY FOR RALES. IF RALES ARE HEARD OR OTHER SYMPTOMS RETURN, RE-ESTABLISH ATROPINIZATION PROMPTLY (MORGAN, RECOGNITION AND MANAGEMENT OF PESTICIDE POISONINGS, 3RD ED.). ADMINISTRATION OF ANTIDOTE MUST BE PERFORMED BY QUALIFIED MEDICAL PERSONNEL.

IN CASES OF SEVERE POISONING BY ORGANOPHOSPHATE PESTICIDES IN WHICH RESPIRATORY DEPRESSION, MUSCLE WEAKNESS AND TWITCHINGS ARE SEVERE, GIVE PRALIDOXIME (PROTOPAM-AYERST, 2-PAM), 1.0 GRAM INTRAVENOUSLY AT NO MORE THAN 0.5 GRAM PER MINUTE. DOSAGE OF PRALIDOXIME MAY BE REPEATED IN 1-2 HOURS, THEN AT 10-12 HOUR INTERVALS IF NEEDED. IN VERY SEVERE POISONINGS, DOSAGE RATES MAY BE DOUBLED. TREATMENT WITH PRALIDOXIME WILL BE MOST EFFECTIVE IF GIVEN WITHIN THIRTY-SIX HOURS AFTER POISONING (MORGAN, RECOGNITION AND MANAGEMENT OF PESTICIDE POISONINGS, 3RD ED.). ANTIDOTE SHOULD BE ADMINISTERED BY QUALIFIED MEDICAL PERSONNEL.

REACTIVITY

REACTIVITY: STABLE UNDER NORMAL TEMPERATURES AND PRESSURES.

INCOMPATIBILITIES: PROTHIOPHOS: OXIDIZERS (STRONG): FIRE AND EXPLOSION HAZARD.

DECOMPOSITION: THERMAL DECOMPOSITION RELEASES CORROSIVE FUMES OF HYDROGEN CHLORIDE AND TOXIC OXIDES OF PHOSPHORUS AND SULFUR.

POLYMERIZATION: HAZARDOUS POLYMERIZATION HAS NOT BEEN REPORTED TO OCCUR UNDER NORMAL TEMPERATURES AND PRESSURES.

STORAGE AND DISPOSAL

OBSERVE ALL FEDERAL, STATE AND LOCAL REGULATIONS WHEN STORING OR DISPOSING OF THIS SUBSTANCE. FOR ASSISTANCE, CONTACT THE DISTRICT DIRECTOR OF THE ENVIRONMENTAL PROTECTION AGENCY.

****STORAGE****

STORE IN ACCORDANCE WITH 40 CFR 165 RECOMMENDED PROCEDURES FOR THE DISPOSAL AND STORAGE OF PESTICIDES AND PESTICIDE CONTAINERS.
STORE AWAY FROM INCOMPATIBLE SUBSTANCES.

****DISPOSAL****

DISPOSAL MUST BE IN ACCORDANCE WITH 40 CFR 165 RECOMMENDED PROCEDURES FOR THE DISPOSAL AND STORAGE OF PESTICIDES AND PESTICIDE CONTAINERS.

CONDITIONS TO AVOID

AVOID CONTACT WITH HEAT, SPARKS, FLAMES OR OTHER IGNITION SOURCES. VAPORS MAY BE EXPLOSIVE. MATERIAL IS POISONOUS; AVOID INHALATION OF VAPORS OR CONTACT WITH SKIN. DO NOT ALLOW MATERIAL TO CONTAMINATE WATER SOURCES.

SPILL AND LEAK PROCEDURES

OCCUPATIONAL SPILL: SHUT OFF IGNITION SOURCES. DO NOT TOUCH SPILLED MATERIAL. STOP LEAK IF YOU CAN DO IT WITHOUT RISK. USE WATER SPRAY TO REDUCE VAPORS. FOR SMALL SPILLS, TAKE UP WITH SAND OR OTHER ABSORBENT MATERIAL AND PLACE INTO CONTAINERS FOR LATER DISPOSAL. FOR LARGER SPILLS, DIKE FAR AHEAD OF SPILL FOR LATER DISPOSAL. NO SMOKING, FLAMES OR FLARES IN HAZARD AREA! KEEP UNNECESSARY PEOPLE AWAY; ISOLATE HAZARD AREA AND DENY ENTRY.

PROTECTIVE EQUIPMENT

VENTILATION: PROVIDE LOCAL EXHAUST OR GENERAL DILUTION VENTILATION SYSTEM.

RESPIRATOR: THE FOLLOWING RESPIRATORS ARE RECOMMENDED BASED ON INFORMATION FOUND IN THE PHYSICAL DATA, TOXICITY AND HEALTH EFFECTS SECTIONS. THEY ARE RANKED IN ORDER FROM MINIMUM TO MAXIMUM RESPIRATORY PROTECTION. THE SPECIFIC RESPIRATOR SELECTED MUST BE BASED ON CONTAMINATION LEVELS FOUND IN THE WORK PLACE, MUST NOT EXCEED THE WORKING LIMITS OF THE RESPIRATOR AND BE JOINTLY APPROVED BY THE NATIONAL INSTITUTE FOR OCCUPATIONAL SAFETY AND HEALTH AND THE MINE SAFETY AND HEALTH ADMINISTRATION (NIOSH-MSHA).

CHEMICAL CARTRIDGE RESPIRATOR WITH FULL FACEPIECE AND PESTICIDE CARTRIDGE.

TYPE 'C' SUPPLIED-AIR RESPIRATOR WITH A FULL FACEPIECE OPERATED IN PRESSURE-DEMAND OR OTHER POSITIVE PRESSURE MODE OR WITH A FULL FACEPIECE, HELMET OR HOOD OPERATED IN CONTINUOUS-FLOW MODE.

SELF-CONTAINED BREATHING APPARATUS OPERATED IN PRESSURE-DEMAND OR OTHER POSITIVE PRESSURE MODE.
FOR FIREFIGHTING AND OTHER IMMEDIATELY DANGEROUS TO LIFE OR HEALTH CONDITIONS:
SELF-CONTAINED BREATHING APPARATUS WITH FULL FACEPIECE OPERATED IN PRESSURE-DEMAND OR OTHER POSITIVE PRESSURE MODE.
SUPPLIED-AIR RESPIRATOR WITH FULL FACEPIECE AND OPERATED IN PRESSURE-DEMAND OR OTHER POSITIVE PRESSURE MODE IN COMBINATION WITH AN AUXILIARY SELF-CONTAINED BREATHING APPARATUS OPERATED IN PRESSURE-DEMAND OR OTHER POSITIVE PRESSURE MODE.

CLOTHING: EMPLOYEE MUST WEAR APPROPRIATE PROTECTIVE (IMPERVIOUS) CLOTHING AND EQUIPMENT TO PREVENT REPEATED OR PROLONGED SKIN CONTACT WITH THIS SUBSTANCE.

GLOVES: EMPLOYEE MUST WEAR APPROPRIATE PROTECTIVE GLOVES TO PREVENT CONTACT WITH THIS SUBSTANCE.

EYE PROTECTION: EMPLOYEE MUST WEAR SPLASH-PROOF OR DUST-RESISTANT SAFETY GOGGLES TO PREVENT EYE CONTACT WITH THIS SUBSTANCE.
EMERGENCY EYE WASH: WHERE THERE IS ANY POSSIBILITY THAT AN EMPLOYEE'S EYES MAY BE EXPOSED TO THIS SUBSTANCE, THE EMPLOYER SHOULD PROVIDE AN EYE WASH FOUNTAIN WITHIN THE IMMEDIATE WORK AREA FOR EMERGENCY USE.

AUTHORIZED BY- OCCUPATIONAL HEALTH SERVICES, INC.
CREATION DATE: 10/04/89 ***REVISION DATE:*** 05/01/90

MATERIAL SAFETY DATA SHEET

OCCUPATIONAL HEALTH SERVICES, INC.
AGRICULTURE AND PESTICIDE DIVISION
450 SEVENTH AVENUE, SUITE 2407
NEW YORK, NEW YORK 10123
1-800-445-MSDS OR (212) 967-1100

EMERGENCY CONTACT:
JOHN S. BRANSFORD, JR. (615) 292-1180

SUBSTANCE IDENTIFICATION

CAS-NUMBER 66441-23-4

SUBSTANCE: FENOXAPROP-ETHYL

TRADE NAMES/SYNONYMS: PROPANIC ACID, 2-(4-((6-CHLORO-2-BENZOXAZOLYL)OXY)PHENOXY)-, ETHYL ESTER, (+,-)-; (+,-)-ETHYL 2-(4-((6-CHLORO-2-BENZOXAZOLYL)OXY)PHENOXY)PROPANOATE; PHENOXAPROP-ETHYL; WHIP; HOE 33171; FURORE; C18H16CLNO5; PST72723

CHEMICAL FAMILY: ESTER
OXAZOLE

MOLECULAR FORMULA: C18-H16-CL-N-O5

MOLECULAR WEIGHT: 361.78

CERCLA RATINGS (SCALE 0-3): HEALTH=U FIRE=1 REACTIVITY=0 PERSISTENCE=1

NFPA RATINGS (SCALE 0-4): HEALTH=U FIRE=1 REACTIVITY=0

COMPONENTS AND CONTAMINANTS

COMPONENT: FENOXAPROP-ETHYL ***PERCENT:*** 100.0
CAS# 66441-23-4

OTHER CONTAMINANTS: NONE

EXPOSURE LIMITS: NO OCCUPATIONAL EXPOSURE LIMITS ESTABLISHED BY OSHA, ACGIH, OR NIOSH.

PHYSICAL DATA

DESCRIPTION: COLORLESS TO WHITE POWDER.

MELTING POINT: 183-184 F (84-85 C)

SPECIFIC GRAVITY: NOT AVAILABLE ***VAPOR PRESSURE:*** NEGLIGIBLE

SOLUBILITY IN WATER: 0.9 PPM

SOLVENT SOLUBILITY: SOLUBLE IN ACETONE, ETHYL ACETATE, AND TOLUENE; MODERATELY SOLUBLE IN CYCLOHEXANE, ETHANOL, AND OCTANOL.

FIRE AND EXPLOSION DATA

FIRE AND EXPLOSION HAZARD: SLIGHT FIRE HAZARD WHEN EXPOSED TO HEAT OR FLAME.

FIREFIGHTING MEDIA: DRY CHEMICAL, CARBON DIOXIDE, HALON, WATER SPRAY OR STANDARD FOAM (1987 EMERGENCY RESPONSE GUIDEBOOK, DOT P 5800.4).
FOR LARGER FIRES, USE WATER SPRAY, FOG OR STANDARD FOAM (1987 EMERGENCY RESPONSE GUIDEBOOK, DOT P 5800.4).

FIREFIGHTING: MOVE CONTAINER FROM FIRE AREA IF POSSIBLE. DO NOT SCATTER SPILLED MATERIAL WITH HIGH PRESSURE WATER STREAMS. DIKE FIRE CONTROL WATER FOR LATER DISPOSAL (1987 EMERGENCY RESPONSE GUIDEBOOK, DOT P 5800.4, GUIDE PAGE 31).
USE AGENTS SUITABLE FOR TYPE OF SURROUNDING FIRE. AVOID BREATHING HAZARDOUS VAPORS, KEEP UPWIND.

TOXICITY

FENOXAPROP-ETHYL: TOXICITY DATA: 3920 MG/M3/4 HOURS INHALATION-MAMMAL LC50; >1000 MG/KG SKIN-RABBIT LD50; >2000 MG/KG SKIN-RAT LD50; 2357 MG/KG ORAL-RAT LD50; 4670 MG/KG ORAL-MOUSE LD50. CARCINOGEN STATUS: NONE. ACUTE TOXICITY LEVEL: TOXIC BY INHALATION; MODERATELY TOXIC BY INGESTION. TARGET EFFECTS: NO DATA AVAILABLE.

HEALTH EFFECTS AND FIRST AID

INHALATION: FENOXAPROP-ETHYL: TOXIC. **ACUTE EXPOSURE-** NO DATA AVAILABLE. **CHRONIC EXPOSURE-** NO DATA AVAILABLE.

FIRST AID- REMOVE FROM EXPOSURE AREA TO FRESH AIR IMMEDIATELY. IF BREATHING HAS STOPPED, PERFORM ARTIFICIAL RESPIRATION. KEEP PERSON WARM AND AT REST. TREAT SYMPTOMATICALLY AND SUPPORTIVELY. GET MEDICAL ATTENTION IMMEDIATELY.

SKIN CONTACT: FENOXAPROP-ETHYL: **ACUTE EXPOSURE-** APPLICATION TO RABBIT SKIN CAUSED SLIGHT IRRITATION. **CHRONIC EXPOSURE-** NO DATA AVAILABLE.

FIRST AID- REMOVE CONTAMINATED CLOTHING AND SHOES IMMEDIATELY. WASH AFFECTED AREA WITH SOAP OR MILD DETERGENT AND LARGE AMOUNTS OF WATER UNTIL NO EVIDENCE OF CHEMICAL REMAINS (APPROXIMATELY 15-20 MINUTES). GET MEDICAL ATTENTION IMMEDIATELY.

EYE CONTACT: FENOXAPROP-ETHYL: **ACUTE EXPOSURE-**APPLICATION TO RABBIT EYES CAUSED SLIGHT IRRITATION. **CHRONIC EXPOSURE-** NO DATA AVAILABLE.

FIRST AID- WASH EYES IMMEDIATELY WITH LARGE AMOUNTS OF WATER OR NORMAL SALINE, OCCASIONALLY LIFTING UPPER AND LOWER LIDS, UNTIL NO EVIDENCE OF CHEMICAL REMAINS (APPROXIMATELY 15-20 MINUTES). GET MEDICAL ATTENTION IMMEDIATELY.

INGESTION: FENOXAPROP-ETHYL: **ACUTE EXPOSURE-** NO DATA AVAILABLE. **CHRONIC EXPOSURE-** NO TOXIC EFFECTS WERE NOTED IN RATS FED 1.5 MG/KG/DAY FOR 2 YEARS OR DOGS FED 1.9 MG/KG/DAY FOR 1 YEAR. IN RABBIT TERATOLOGY STUDIES, NO MATERNAL TOXICITY OCCURRED AT 12.5 MG/KG/DAY; 50 MG/KG/DAY DID NOT CAUSE DEVELOPMENTAL EFFECTS, BUT 200 MG/KG/DAY PRODUCED OFFSPRING WITH AN INCREASED INCIDENCE OF RIB ANOMALIES AND DIAPHRAGMATIC HERNIAS. NO ONCOGENIC POTENTIAL WAS OBSERVED IN RATS OR MICE FED 9 MG/KG/DAY FOR 28 MONTHS AND 6 MG/KG/DAY FOR 24 MONTHS RESPECTIVELY.

FIRST AID- TREAT SYMPTOMATICALLY AND SUPPORTIVELY. GET MEDICAL ATTENTION IMMEDIATELY. IF VOMITING OCCURS, KEEP HEAD LOWER THAN HIPS TO PREVENT ASPIRATION.

ANTIDOTE: NO SPECIFIC ANTIDOTE. TREAT SYMPTOMATICALLY AND SUPPORTIVELY.

REACTIVITY

REACTIVITY: STABLE UNDER NORMAL TEMPERATURES AND PRESSURES.

INCOMPATIBILITIES: PHENOXAPROP-ETHYL: OXIDIZERS (STRONG): FIRE AND EXPLOSION HAZARD.

DECOMPOSITION: THERMAL DECOMPOSITION PRODUCTS MAY INCLUDE TOXIC OXIDES OF NITROGEN AND CARBON AND TOXIC AND CORROSIVE FUMES OF CHLORIDES.

POLYMERIZATION: HAZARDOUS POLYMERIZATION HAS NOT BEEN REPORTED TO OCCUR UNDER NORMAL TEMPERATURES AND PRESSURES.

STORAGE AND DISPOSAL

OBSERVE ALL FEDERAL, STATE AND LOCAL REGULATIONS WHEN STORING OR DISPOSING OF THIS SUBSTANCE. FOR ASSISTANCE, CONTACT THE DISTRICT DIRECTOR OF THE ENVIRONMENTAL PROTECTION AGENCY.

STORAGE

STORE IN ACCORDANCE WITH 40 CFR 165 RECOMMENDED PROCEDURES FOR THE DISPOSAL AND STORAGE OF PESTICIDES AND PESTICIDE CONTAINERS.
STORE AWAY FROM INCOMPATIBLE SUBSTANCES.

DISPOSAL

DISPOSAL MUST BE IN ACCORDANCE WITH 40 CFR 165 RECOMMENDED PROCEDURES FOR THE DISPOSAL AND STORAGE OF PESTICIDES AND PESTICIDE CONTAINERS.

CONDITIONS TO AVOID

MAY BURN BUT DOES NOT IGNITE READILY. AVOID CONTACT WITH STRONG OXIDIZERS, EXCESSIVE HEAT, SPARKS, OR OPEN FLAME.

SPILL AND LEAK PROCEDURES

OCCUPATIONAL SPILL: SWEEP UP AND PLACE IN SUITABLE CLEAN, DRY CONTAINERS FOR RECLAMATION OR LATER DISPOSAL. DO NOT FLUSH SPILLED MATERIAL INTO SEWER. KEEP UNNECESSARY PEOPLE AWAY.

PROTECTIVE EQUIPMENT

VENTILATION: PROVIDE LOCAL EXHAUST OR GENERAL DILUTION VENTILATION SYSTEM.

RESPIRATOR: THE FOLLOWING RESPIRATORS ARE RECOMMENDED BASED ON INFORMATION FOUND IN THE PHYSICAL DATA, TOXICITY AND HEALTH EFFECTS SECTIONS. THEY ARE RANKED IN ORDER FROM MINIMUM TO MAXIMUM RESPIRATORY PROTECTION. THE SPECIFIC RESPIRATOR SELECTED MUST BE BASED ON CONTAMINATION LEVELS FOUND IN THE WORK PLACE, MUST NOT EXCEED THE WORKING LIMITS OF THE RESPIRATOR AND BE JOINTLY APPROVED BY THE NATIONAL INSTITUTE FOR OCCUPATIONAL SAFETY AND HEALTH AND THE MINE SAFETY AND HEALTH ADMINISTRATION (NIOSH-MSHA).

CHEMICAL CARTRIDGE RESPIRATOR WITH AN ORGANIC VAPOR CARTRIDGE(S) IN COMBINATION WITH A DUST AND MIST FILTER.

GAS MASK WITH ORGANIC VAPOR CANISTER (CHIN-STYLE OR FRONT- OR BACK-MOUNTED CANISTER) WITH A DUST AND MIST FILTER.

GAS MASK WITH ORGANIC VAPOR CANISTER (CHIN-STYLE OR FRONT- OR BACK-MOUNTED CANISTER) WITH A PARTICULATE FILTER.

POWERED AIR-PURIFYING RESPIRATOR WITH A HIGH-EFFICIENCY FILTER.

TYPE 'C' SUPPLIED-AIR RESPIRATOR WITH A FULL FACEPIECE OPERATED IN A PRESSURE-DEMAND OR OTHER POSITIVE PRESSURE MODE.

SELF-CONTAINED BREATHING APPARATUS WITH A FULL FACEPIECE OPERATED IN PRESSURE-DEMAND OR OTHER POSITIVE PRESSURE MODE.

FOR FIREFIGHTING AND OTHER IMMEDIATELY DANGEROUS TO LIFE OR HEALTH CONDITIONS:

SELF-CONTAINED BREATHING APPARATUS WITH FULL FACEPIECE OPERATED IN PRESSURE-DEMAND OR OTHER POSITIVE PRESSURE MODE.

SUPPLIED-AIR RESPIRATOR WITH FULL FACEPIECE AND OPERATED IN PRESSURE-DEMAND OR OTHER POSITIVE PRESSURE MODE IN COMBINATION WITH AN AUXILIARY SELF-CONTAINED BREATHING APPARATUS OPERATED IN PRESSURE-DEMAND OR OTHER POSITIVE PRESSURE MODE.

CLOTHING: EMPLOYEE MUST WEAR APPROPRIATE PROTECTIVE (IMPERVIOUS) CLOTHING AND EQUIPMENT TO PREVENT REPEATED OR PROLONGED SKIN CONTACT WITH THIS SUBSTANCE.

GLOVES: EMPLOYEE MUST WEAR APPROPRIATE PROTECTIVE GLOVES TO PREVENT CONTACT WITH THIS SUBSTANCE.

EYE PROTECTION: EMPLOYEE MUST WEAR SPLASH-PROOF OR DUST-RESISTANT SAFETY GOGGLES TO PREVENT EYE CONTACT WITH THIS SUBSTANCE.

EMERGENCY EYE WASH: WHERE THERE IS ANY POSSIBILITY THAT AN EMPLOYEE'S EYES MAY BE EXPOSED TO THIS SUBSTANCE, THE EMPLOYER SHOULD PROVIDE AN EYE WASH FOUNTAIN WITHIN THE IMMEDIATE WORK AREA FOR EMERGENCY USE.

AUTHORIZED BY- OCCUPATIONAL HEALTH SERVICES, INC.

CREATION DATE: 10/18/89 ***REVISION DATE:*** 05/31/90

MATERIAL SAFETY DATA SHEET

OCCUPATIONAL HEALTH SERVICES, INC.
AGRICULTURE AND PESTICIDE DIVISION
450 SEVENTH AVENUE, SUITE 2407
NEW YORK, NEW YORK 10123
1-800-445-MSDS OR (212) 967-1100

EMERGENCY CONTACT:
JOHN S. BRANSFORD, JR. (615) 292-1180

SUBSTANCE IDENTIFICATION

CAS-NUMBER 3813-05-6

SUBSTANCE: **BENAZOLIN**

TRADE NAMES/SYNONYMS: 3(2H)-BENZOTHIAZOLEACETIC ACID, 4-CHLORO-2-OXO'; 3-BENZOTHIAZOLINEACETIC ACID, 4-CHLORO-2-OXO'; BENAZOLINE; BENZAR; CORNOX CWK; LEY-CORNOX; 4-CHLORO-2-OXOBENZOTHIAZOLIN-3-YLACETIC ACID; 4-CHLORO-2,3-DIHYDRO-2-OXO-1,3-BENZOTHIAZOL-3-YLACETIC ACID; 4-CHLORO-2-OXO-3(2H)-BENZOTHIAZOLEACETIC ACID; 4-CHLORO-2-OXO-3-BENZOTHIAZOLINEACETIC ACID; C9H6CLNO3S; PST72725

CHEMICAL FAMILY: CARBOXYLIC ACID
THIAZOLE

MOLECULAR FORMULA: C9-H6-CL-N-O3-S

MOLECULAR WEIGHT: 243.66

CERCLA RATINGS (SCALE 0-3): HEALTH=U FIRE=1 REACTIVITY=0 PERSISTENCE=3

NFPA RATINGS (SCALE 0-4): HEALTH=U FIRE=1 REACTIVITY=0

COMPONENTS AND CONTAMINANTS

COMPONENT: BENAZOLIN ***PERCENT:*** 100.0
CAS# 3813-05-6

OTHER CONTAMINANTS: NONE

EXPOSURE LIMITS: NO OCCUPATIONAL EXPOSURE LIMITS ESTABLISHED BY OSHA, ACGIH, OR NIOSH.

PHYSICAL DATA

DESCRIPTION: WHITE, CRYSTALLINE SOLID. ***MELTING POINT:*** 379 F (193 C)

SPECIFIC GRAVITY: NOT AVAILABLE ***VAPOR PRESSURE:*** NEGLIGIBLE

SOLUBILITY IN WATER: 0.06%

FIRE AND EXPLOSION DATA

FIRE AND EXPLOSION HAZARD: SLIGHT FIRE HAZARD WHEN EXPOSED TO HEAT OR FLAME.

FIREFIGHTING MEDIA: DRY CHEMICAL, CARBON DIOXIDE, HALON, WATER SPRAY OR STANDARD FOAM (1987 EMERGENCY RESPONSE GUIDEBOOK, DOT P 5800.4).
FOR LARGER FIRES, USE WATER SPRAY, FOG OR STANDARD FOAM (1987 EMERGENCY RESPONSE GUIDEBOOK, DOT P 5800.4).

FIREFIGHTING: MOVE CONTAINER FROM FIRE AREA IF POSSIBLE. DO NOT SCATTER SPILLED MATERIAL WITH HIGH PRESSURE WATER STREAMS. DIKE FIRE CONTROL WATER FOR LATER DISPOSAL (1987 EMERGENCY RESPONSE GUIDEBOOK, DOT P 5800.4, GUIDE PAGE 31).
USE AGENTS SUITABLE FOR TYPE OF SURROUNDING FIRE. AVOID BREATHING HAZARDOUS VAPORS, KEEP UPWIND.

TOXICITY

BENAZOLIN: TOXICITY DATA: >5000 MG/KG SKIN-RAT LD50 (PESTICIDE MANUAL 8TH ED.); 3000 MG/KG ORAL-RAT LD50; 3200 MG/KG ORAL-MOUSE LD50. CARCINOGEN STATUS: NONE. ACUTE TOXICITY LEVEL: MODERATELY TOXIC BY INGESTION; SLIGHTLY TOXIC BY DERMAL ABSORPTION. TARGET EFFECTS: NO DATA AVAILABLE.

HEALTH EFFECTS AND FIRST AID

INHALATION: BENAZOLIN: **ACUTE EXPOSURE-** NO DATA AVAILABLE. **CHRONIC EXPOSURE-** NO DATA AVAILABLE.

FIRST AID- REMOVE FROM EXPOSURE AREA TO FRESH AIR IMMEDIATELY. IF BREATHING HAS STOPPED, PERFORM ARTIFICIAL RESPIRATION. KEEP PERSON WARM AND AT REST. TREAT SYMPTOMATICALLY AND SUPPORTIVELY. GET MEDICAL ATTENTION IMMEDIATELY.

SKIN CONTACT: BENAZOLIN: **ACUTE EXPOSURE-** A 30% SOLUTION OF BENAZOLIN-POTASSIUM CAUSED MILD IRRITATION TO THE SKIN OF RABBITS. **CHRONIC EXPOSURE-** NO DATA AVAILABLE.

FIRST AID- REMOVE CONTAMINATED CLOTHING AND SHOES IMMEDIATELY. WASH AFFECTED AREA WITH SOAP OR MILD DETERGENT AND LARGE AMOUNTS OF WATER UNTIL NO EVIDENCE OF CHEMICAL REMAINS (APPROXIMATELY 15-20 MINUTES). GET MEDICAL ATTENTION IMMEDIATELY.

EYE CONTACT: BENAZOLIN: **ACUTE EXPOSURE-** A 30% SOLUTION OF BENAZOLIN-POTASSIUM CAUSED MILD IRRITATION IN THE EYES OF RABBITS. **CHRONIC EXPOSURE-** NO DATA AVAILABLE.

FIRST AID- WASH EYES IMMEDIATELY WITH LARGE AMOUNTS OF WATER OR NORMAL SALINE, OCCASIONALLY LIFTING UPPER AND LOWER LIDS, UNTIL NO EVIDENCE OF CHEMICAL REMAINS (APPROXIMATELY 15-20 MINUTES). GET MEDICAL ATTENTION IMMEDIATELY.

INGESTION: BENAZOLIN: **ACUTE EXPOSURE-** THE LETHAL DOSE REPORTED IN RATS WAS 3000 MG/KG. THE SYMPTOMS WERE NOT REPORTED. **CHRONIC EXPOSURE-** IN 90 DAY FEEDING STUDIES OF 300 TO 1000 MG/KG/DAY TO RATS AND DOGS, NO TOXIC EFFECTS WERE PRODUCED.

FIRST AID- IF THE PERSON IS CONSCIOUS AND NOT CONVULSING, REMOVE BY GASTRIC LAVAGE AND FOLLOW WITH A CATHARTIC (DREISBACH, HANDBOOK OF POISONING, 12TH ED.). TREAT SYMPTOMATICALLY AND SUPPORTIVELY. GASTRIC LAVAGE SHOULD BE PERFORMED BY QUALIFIED MEDICAL PERSONNEL. GET MEDICAL ATTENTION IMMEDIATELY.

ANTIDOTE: NO SPECIFIC ANTIDOTE. TREAT SYMPTOMATICALLY AND SUPPORTIVELY.

REACTIVITY

REACTIVITY: STABLE UNDER NORMAL TEMPERATURES AND PRESSURES.

INCOMPATIBILITIES: BENAZOLIN: OXIDIZERS (STRONG); FIRE AND EXPLOSION HAZARD.

DECOMPOSITION: THERMAL DECOMPOSITION PRODUCTS MAY INCLUDE TOXIC AND CORROSIVE FUMES OF CHLORIDES, AND TOXIC OXIDES OF NITROGEN AND SULFUR.
POLYMERIZATION: HAZARDOUS POLYMERIZATION HAS NOT BEEN REPORTED TO OCCUR UNDER NORMAL TEMPERATURES AND PRESSURES.

STORAGE AND DISPOSAL

OBSERVE ALL FEDERAL, STATE AND LOCAL REGULATIONS WHEN STORING OR DISPOSING OF THIS SUBSTANCE. FOR ASSISTANCE, CONTACT THE DISTRICT DIRECTOR OF THE ENVIRONMENTAL PROTECTION AGENCY.

STORAGE

STORE IN ACCORDANCE WITH 40 CFR 165 RECOMMENDED PROCEDURES FOR THE DISPOSAL AND STORAGE OF PESTICIDES AND PESTICIDE CONTAINERS.
STORE AWAY FROM INCOMPATIBLE SUBSTANCES.

CONDITIONS TO AVOID

MAY BURN BUT DOES NOT IGNITE READILY. AVOID CONTACT WITH STRONG OXIDIZERS, EXCESSIVE HEAT, SPARKS, OR OPEN FLAME.

SPILL AND LEAK PROCEDURES

OCCUPATIONAL SPILL: SWEEP UP AND PLACE IN SUITABLE CLEAN, DRY CONTAINERS FOR RECLAMATION OR LATER DISPOSAL. DO NOT FLUSH SPILLED MATERIAL INTO SEWER. KEEP UNNECESSARY PEOPLE AWAY.

PROTECTIVE EQUIPMENT

VENTILATION: PROVIDE LOCAL EXHAUST OR GENERAL DILUTION VENTILATION SYSTEM.
RESPIRATOR: THE FOLLOWING RESPIRATORS ARE RECOMMENDED BASED ON INFORMATION FOUND IN THE PHYSICAL DATA, TOXICITY AND HEALTH EFFECTS SECTIONS. THEY ARE RANKED IN ORDER FROM MINIMUM TO MAXIMUM RESPIRATORY PROTECTION. THE SPECIFIC RESPIRATOR SELECTED MUST BE BASED ON CONTAMINATION LEVELS FOUND IN THE WORK PLACE, MUST NOT EXCEED THE WORKING LIMITS OF THE RESPIRATOR AND BE JOINTLY APPROVED BY THE NATIONAL INSTITUTE FOR OCCUPATIONAL SAFETY AND HEALTH AND THE MINE SAFETY AND HEALTH ADMINISTRATION (NIOSH-MSHA).
CHEMICAL CARTRIDGE RESPIRATOR WITH AN ORGANIC VAPOR CARTRIDGE(S) WITH A FULL FACEPIECE AND ORGANIC VAPOR CARTRIDGE(S) IN COMBINATION WITH A DUST AND MIST FILTER.
POWERED AIR-PURIFYING RESPIRATOR WITH A TIGHT-FITTING FACEPIECE AND ORGANIC VAPOR CARTRIDGE(S) IN COMBINATION WITH A HIGH-EFFICIENCY PARTICULATE FILTER.
TYPE 'C' SUPPLIED-AIR RESPIRATOR WITH A FULL FACEPIECE OPERATED IN A PRESSURE-DEMAND OR OTHER POSITIVE PRESSURE MODE.
SELF-CONTAINED BREATHING APPARATUS WITH A FULL FACEPIECE OPERATED IN PRESSURE-DEMAND OR OTHER POSITIVE PRESSURE MODE.
FOR FIREFIGHTING AND OTHER IMMEDIATELY DANGEROUS TO LIFE OR HEALTH CONDITIONS:
SELF-CONTAINED BREATHING APPARATUS WITH FULL FACEPIECE OPERATED IN PRESSURE-DEMAND OR OTHER POSITIVE PRESSURE MODE.
SUPPLIED-AIR RESPIRATOR WITH FULL FACEPIECE AND OPERATED IN PRESSURE-DEMAND OR OTHER POSITIVE PRESSURE MODE IN COMBINATION WITH AN AUXILIARY SELF-CONTAINED BREATHING APPARATUS OPERATED IN PRESSURE-DEMAND OR OTHER POSITIVE PRESSURE MODE.
CLOTHING: EMPLOYEE MUST WEAR APPROPRIATE PROTECTIVE (IMPERVIOUS) CLOTHING AND EQUIPMENT TO PREVENT REPEATED OR PROLONGED SKIN CONTACT WITH THIS SUBSTANCE.
GLOVES: EMPLOYEE MUST WEAR APPROPRIATE PROTECTIVE GLOVES TO PREVENT CONTACT WITH THIS SUBSTANCE.
EYE PROTECTION: EMPLOYEE MUST WEAR SPLASH-PROOF OR DUST-RESISTANT SAFETY GOGGLES TO PREVENT EYE CONTACT WITH THIS SUBSTANCE.
EMERGENCY EYE WASH: WHERE THERE IS ANY POSSIBILITY THAT AN EMPLOYEE'S EYES MAY BE EXPOSED TO THIS SUBSTANCE, THE EMPLOYER SHOULD PROVIDE AN EYE WASH FOUNTAIN WITHIN THE IMMEDIATE WORK AREA FOR EMERGENCY USE.

AUTHORIZED BY- OCCUPATIONAL HEALTH SERVICES, INC.
CREATION DATE: 02/08/90 ***REVISION DATE:*** 05/31/90

MATERIAL SAFETY DATA SHEET

OCCUPATIONAL HEALTH SERVICES, INC.
AGRICULTURE AND PESTICIDE DIVISION
450 SEVENTH AVENUE, SUITE 2407
NEW YORK, NEW YORK 10123
1-800-445-MSDS OR (212) 967-1100

EMERGENCY CONTACT:
JOHN S. BRANSFORD, JR. (615) 292-1180

SUBSTANCE IDENTIFICATION

CAS-NUMBER 1491-41-4
SUBSTANCE: NAPHTHALOPHOS
TRADE NAMES/SYNONYMS: 1-H-BENZ(DE)ISOQUINOLINE-1,3(2H)-DIONE, 2-((DIETHOXYPHOSPHINYL)OXY)-; 2-((DIETHOXYPHOSPHINYL)OXY)-1-H-BENZ(DE)ISOQUINOLINE-1,3(2H)-DIONE; NAPTHALIMIDE, N-HYDROXY-, DIETHYL PHOSPHATE; N-HYDROXYNAPTHALIMIDE DIETHYL PHOSPHATE; O,O-DIETHYL O-NAPHTHALOXIMIDE PHOSPHATE; BAY 9002; MARETIN; NAFTALOFOS; RAMETIN; ENT 25567; C16H16NO6P; PST72737
CHEMICAL FAMILY: ORGANOPHOSPHATE
MOLECULAR FORMULA: C16-H16-N-O6-P
MOLECULAR WEIGHT: 349.29
CERCLA RATINGS (SCALE 0-3): HEALTH=3 FIRE=1 REACTIVITY=0 PERSISTENCE=1
NFPA RATINGS (SCALE 0-4): HEALTH=4 FIRE=1 REACTIVITY=0

COMPONENTS AND CONTAMINANTS

COMPONENT: NAPHTHALOPHOS ***PERCENT:*** 100.0
CAS# 1491-41-4
OTHER CONTAMINANTS: NONE
EXPOSURE LIMITS: NO OCCUPATIONAL EXPOSURE LIMITS ESTABLISHED BY OSHA, ACGIH, OR NIOSH.

PHYSICAL DATA

DESCRIPTION: BROWN TO TAN MINUTE CRYSTALLINE SOLID.
MELTING POINT: 345-354 F (174-179 C) ***SPECIFIC GRAVITY:*** NOT AVAILABLE
SOLUBILITY IN WATER: ALMOST INSOLUBLE
SOLVENT SOLUBILITY: SOLUBLE IN METHYLENE CHLORIDE, SPARINGLY SOLUBLE IN OTHER ORGANIC SOLVENTS; ALMOST INSOLUBLE IN KEROSENE.

FIRE AND EXPLOSION DATA

FIRE AND EXPLOSION HAZARD: SLIGHT FIRE HAZARD WHEN EXPOSED TO HEAT OR FLAME.
FIREFIGHTING MEDIA: DRY CHEMICAL, CARBON DIOXIDE, HALON, WATER SPRAY OR STANDARD FOAM (1987 EMERGENCY RESPONSE GUIDEBOOK, DOT P 5800.4).
FOR LARGER FIRES, USE WATER SPRAY, FOG OR STANDARD FOAM (1987 EMERGENCY RESPONSE GUIDEBOOK, DOT P 5800.4).
FIREFIGHTING: MOVE CONTAINERS FROM FIRE AREA IF POSSIBLE. FIGHT FIRE FROM MAXIMUM DISTANCE. STAY AWAY FROM STORAGE TANK ENDS. DIKE FIRE CONTROL WATER FOR LATER DISPOSAL. DO NOT SCATTER MATERIAL (1987 EMERGENCY RESPONSE GUIDEBOOK, DOT P 5800.4, GUIDE PAGE 55).
EXTINGUISH ONLY IF FLOW CAN BE STOPPED; USE FLOODING AMOUNTS OF WATER AS FOG, SOLID STREAMS MAY BE INEFFECTIVE. COOL CONTAINERS WITH FLOODING AMOUNTS OF WATER FROM AS FAR A DISTANCE AS POSSIBLE. USE WATER SPRAY TO ABSORB TOXIC VAPORS. AVOID BREATHING TOXIC VAPORS; KEEP UPWIND. CONSIDER EVACUATION OF DOWNWIND AREA IF MATERIAL IS LEAKING.

TOXICITY

NAPHTHALOPHOS: TOXICITY DATA: 140 MG/KG SKIN-RAT LD50; 70 MG/KG ORAL-RAT LD50; 50 MG/KG ORAL-MOUSE LD50; 200 MG/KG ORAL-DOMESTIC ANIMAL LDLO. CARCINOGEN STATUS: NONE. ACUTE TOXICITY LEVEL: HIGHLY TOXIC BY DERMAL ABSORPTION; TOXIC BY INGESTION. TARGET EFFECTS: CHOLINESTERASE INHIBITOR. POISONING MAY AFFECT THE NERVOUS SYSTEM. AT INCREASED RISK FROM EXPOSURE: PERSONS WITH RESPIRATORY AILMENTS, RECENT EXPOSURE TO CHOLINESTERASE INHIBITORS OR IMPAIRED CHOLINESTERASE PRODUCTION, OR LIVER MALFUNCTION.* ADDITIONAL DATA: MAY CROSS THE PLACENTA. HIGH ENVIRONMENTAL TEMPERATURES OR EXPOSURE OF THE CHEMICAL TO VISIBLE OR ULTRAVIOLET LIGHT MAY ENHANCE THE TOXICITY. INTERACTIONS WITH MEDICATIONS MAY OCCUR.*
* MAY BE BASED ON GENERAL INFORMATION ON ORGANOPHOSPHATES.

HEALTH EFFECTS AND FIRST AID

INHALATION: NAPHTHALOPHOS: SEE INFORMATION ON ORGANOPHOSPHATES.
ORGANOPHOSPHATES: CHOLINESTERASE INHIBITOR. ACUTE EXPOSURE- WHEN INHALED, THE FIRST EFFECTS OF CHOLINESTERASE INHIBITORS ARE USUALLY RESPIRATORY AND MAY INCLUDE NASAL HYPEREMIA AND WATERY DISCHARGE, COUGH, CHEST DISCOMFORT, DYSPNEA, AND WHEEZING DUE TO INCREASED BRONCHIAL SECRETIONS AND BRONCHOCONSTRICTION. IF SUFFICIENT AMOUNTS ARE ABSORBED, OTHER SYSTEMIC EFFECTS MAY BEGIN WITHIN A FEW MINUTES OR BE DELAYED FOR UP TO 12 HOURS. SYMPTOMS MAY INCLUDE PALLOR,

NAUSEA, VOMITING, DIARRHEA, ABDOMINAL CRAMPS, HEADACHE, DIZZINESS, OCULAR PAIN, BLURRED VISION, MIOSIS OR IN SOME CASES, ESPECIALLY INITIALLY, MYDRIASIS, LACRIMATION, SALIVATION, SWEATING, AND CONFUSION. OTHER REPORTED CENTRAL NERVOUS SYSTEM OR NEUROMUSCULAR EFFECTS MAY INCLUDE ATAXIA, SLURRED SPEECH, AREFLEXIA, WEAKNESS, FATIGUE, FASCICULATIONS, TWITCHING, TREMORS POSSIBLY OF THE TONGUE AND EYELIDS, AND EVENTUALLY PARALYSIS OF THE EXTREMITIES AND POSSIBLY OF THE RESPIRATORY MUSCLES. IN SEVERE CASES THERE MAY ALSO BE INVOLUNTARY DEFECATION AND URINATION, CYANOSIS, PSYCHOSIS, HYPERGLYCEMIA, ACUTE PANCREATITIS, CARDIAC IRREGULARITIES, PULMONARY EDEMA, UNCONSCIOUSNESS, CONVULSIONS, AND COMA. DEATH IS PRIMARILY DUE TO RESPIRATORY FAILURE, ALTHOUGH CARDIOVASCULAR EFFECTS INCLUDING CARDIAC ARREST MAY ALSO BE IMPLICATED. LONG TERM SEQUELAE ARE RARE BUT MAY INCLUDE NEUROPSYCHIATRIC DISORDERS AND MYOPATHY WITH MUSCLE TENDERNESS. SOME ORGANOPHOSPHATES MAY CAUSE A DELAYED NEUROPATHY BEGINNING 1-4 WEEKS AFTER AN ACUTE EXPOSURE WHICH MAY OR MAY NOT HAVE CAUSED ACUTE CHOLINERGIC EFFECTS. NUMBNESS, TINGLING, WEAKNESS AND CRAMPING BEGINNING SYMMETRICALLY IN THE LOWER LIMBS MAY PROGRESS TO ATAXIA AND PARALYSIS. IN SEVERE CASES, UPPER LIMB INVOLVEMENT IS POSSIBLE AND FLACCID PARALYSIS MAY PROGRESS TO SPASTIC PARALYSIS WITH EXAGGERATED REFLEXES. IMPROVEMENT MAY OCCUR OVER MONTHS TO YEARS, BUT SOME RESIDUAL IMPAIRMENT USUALLY REMAINS. **CHRONIC EXPOSURE-** REPEATED OR PROLONGED EXPOSURE MAY RESULT IN THE EFFECTS OF ACUTE EXPOSURE INCLUDING THE DELAYED NEUROPATHY. OTHER EFFECTS REPORTED IN WORKERS REPEATEDLY EXPOSED INCLUDE IMPAIRED MEMORY AND CONCENTRATION, ACUTE PSYCHOSIS, SEVERE DEPRESSIONS, IRRITABILTY, CONFUSION, APATHY, EMOTIONAL LABILITY, SOCIAL WITHDRAWAL, CONFUSION, HEADACHE, SPEECH DIFFICULTIES, DELAYED REACTION TIMES, SPATIAL DISORIENTATION, NIGHTMARES, SLEEPWALKING, AND DROWSINESS OR INSOMNIA. AN INFLUENZA-LIKE CONDITION WITH HEADACHE, NAUSEA, WEAKNESS, ANOREXIA AND MALAISE HAS ALSO BEEN REPORTED.

FIRST AID- REMOVE FROM EXPOSURE AREA TO FRESH AIR IMMEDIATELY. IF BREATHING HAS STOPPED, GIVE ARTIFICIAL RESPIRATION. MAINTAIN AIRWAY AND BLOOD PRESSURE AND ADMINISTER OXYGEN IF AVAILABLE. KEEP AFFECTED PERSON WARM AND AT REST. TREAT SYMPTOMATICALLY AND SUPPORTIVELY. ADMINISTRATION OF OXYGEN SHOULD BE PERFORMED BY QUALIFIED PERSONNEL. GET MEDICAL ATTENTION IMMEDIATELY.

SKIN CONTACT: NAPHTHALOPHOS: HIGHLY TOXIC. SEE INFORMATION ON ORGANOPHOSPHATES.

ORGANOPHOSPHATES: CHOLINESTERASE INHIBITOR. **ACUTE EXPOSURE-** LOCALIZED SWEATING AND FASCICULATIONS MAY OCCUR AT THE SITE OF CONTACT. IF SUFFICIENT AMOUNTS ARE ABSORBED, OTHER EFFECTS OF CHOLINESTERASE INHIBITION AS DESCRIBED IN ACUTE INHALATION MAY OCCUR. SYMPTOMS MAY BE DELAYED 2-3 HOURS, BUT USUALLY NO MORE THAN 12 HOURS. THE RATE OF ABSORPTION IS INCREASED BY THE PRESENCE OF DERMATITIS OR HIGH AMBIENT TEMPERATURES. DELAYED NEUROPATHY IS ALSO POSSIBLE. **CHRONIC EXPOSURE-** REPEATED OR PROLONGED EXPOSURE MAY CAUSE EFFECTS AS DESCRIBED IN ACUTE EXPOSURE. SOME ORGANOPHOSPHATES MAY CAUSE SENSITIZATION.

FIRST AID- REMOVE CONTAMINATED CLOTHING IMMEDIATELY. WASH CONTAMINATED AREAS WITH SOAP AND WATER FOLLOWED BY ALCOHOL (ARENA, POISONING, 4TH ED.). EMERGENCY PERSONNEL SHOULD WEAR GLOVES AND AVOID CONTAMINATION. TREAT RESPIRATORY DIFFICULTY WITH ARTIFICIAL RESPIRATION. GET MEDICAL ATTENTION IMMEDIATELY.

EYE CONTACT: NAPHTHALOPHOS: SEE INFORMATION ON ORGANOPHOSPHATES.

ORGANOPHOSPHATES: CHOLINESTERASE INHIBITOR. **ACUTE EXPOSURE-** DIRECT CONTACT MAY CAUSE PAIN, HYPEREMIA, LACRIMATION, TWITCHING OF THE EYELIDS, MIOSIS, AND CILIARY MUSCLE SPASM WITH LOSS OF ACCOMODATION, BLURRED OR DIMMED VISION AND BROWACHE. SOMETIMES MYDRIASIS MAY OCCUR INSTEAD OF MIOSIS. WITH SUFFICIENT EXPOSURE, OTHER SYMPTOMS OF CHOLINESTERASE INHIBITION AS DESCRIBED IN ACUTE INHALATION MAY OCCUR. **CHRONIC EXPOSURE-** REPEATED OR PROLONGED EXPOSURE MAY CAUSE EFFECTS AS DESCRIBED IN ACUTE EXPOSURE. SOME COMPOUNDS HAVE CAUSED TOXIC EFFECTS ON THE CRYSTALLINE LENS, CONJUNCTIVAL THICKENING AND OBSTRUCTION OF THE NASOLACRIMAL CANALS WHEN USED AS MIOTIC EYEDROPS.

FIRST AID- IRRIGATE EYES WITH WATER OR SALINE SOLUTION. IF SYMPTOMS OF POISONING OCCUR, TREAT RESPIRATORY DIFFICULTY WITH ARTIFICIAL RESPIRATION AND OXYGEN. OBSERVE PATIENT FOR AT LEAST 24-36 HOURS (GOSSELIN, CLINICAL TOXICOLOGY OF COMMERCIAL PRODUCTS, 5TH ED.). GET MEDICAL ATTENTION IMMEDIATELY. OXYGEN SHOULD BE ADMINISTERED BY QUALIFIED MEDICAL PERSONNEL.

INGESTION: NAPHTHALOPHOS: TOXIC. SEE INFORMATION ON ORGANOPHOSPHATES.

ORGANOPHOSPHATES: CHOLINESTERASE INHIBITOR. **ACUTE EXPOSURE-** WHEN INGESTED, THE FIRST EFFECTS MAY BE NAUSEA, VOMITING, ANOREXIA, ABDOMINAL CRAMPS AND DIARRHEA. GASTROINTESTINAL ABSORPTION MAY CAUSE SYMPTOMS OF CHOLINESTERASE INHIBITION AS DESCRIBED IN ACUTE INHALATION. SYMPTOMS MAY BEGIN WITHIN MINUTES OR BE DELAYED FOR HOURS. DELAYED EFFECTS INCLUDING NEUROPATHY MAY ALSO OCCUR. **CHRONIC EXPOSURE-** REPEATED INGESTION MAY CAUSE EFFECTS AS DESCRIBED IN ACUTE EXPOSURE.

FIRST AID- IF PERSON IS ALERT AND RESPIRATION IS NOT DEPRESSED, GIVE SYRUP OF IPECAC FOLLOWED BY WATER (IF VOMITING OCCURS, KEEP HEAD BELOW HIPS TO PREVENT ASPIRATION). IF CONSCIOUSNESS LEVEL DECLINES OR VOMITING HAS NOT OCCURRED IN 15 MINUTES EMPTY STOMACH BY GASTRIC LAVAGE WITH THE AID OF CUFFED ENDOTRACHEAL TUBE USING ISOTONIC SALINE OR 5% SODIUM BICARBONATE FOLLOW WITH ACTIVATED CHARCOAL. ESTABLISH AND MAINTAIN AIRWAY. TREAT RESPIRATORY DIFFICULTY WITH ARTIFICIAL RESPIRATION AND OXYGEN. DO NOT GIVE MORPHINE, AMINOPHYLLINE, PHENOTHIAZINES, RESERPINE, FUROSEMIDE, OR ETHACRYNIC ACID (MORGAN, RECOGNITION AND MANAGEMENT OF PESTICIDE POISONINGS, 3RD ED.). TREAT SYMPTOMATICALLY AND SUPPORTIVELY. ADMINISTRATION OF OXYGEN AND LAVAGE MUST BE PERFORMED BY QUALIFIED MEDICAL PERSONNEL. GET MEDICAL ATTENTION IMMEDIATELY.

ANTIDOTE: THE FOLLOWING ANTIDOTE(S) HAVE BEEN RECOMMENDED. HOWEVER, THE DECISION AS TO WHETHER THE SEVERITY OF POISONING REQUIRES ADMINISTRATION OF ANY ANTIDOTE AND ACTUAL DOSE REQUIRED SHOULD BE MADE BY QUALIFIED MEDICAL PERSONNEL.

FOR CHOLINESTERASE INHIBITORS: ESTABLISH CLEAR AIRWAY AND TISSUE OXYGENATION BY ASPIRATION OF SECRETIONS, AND IF NECESSARY, BY ASSISTED PULMONARY VENTILATION WITH OXYGEN. IMPROVE TISSUE OXYGENATION AS MUCH AS POSSIBLE BEFORE ADMINISTERING ATROPINE TO MINIMIZE THE RISK OF VENTRICULAR FIBRILLATION. ADMINISTER ATROPINE SULFATE INTRAVENOUSLY, OR INTRAMUSCULARLY IF IV INJECTION IS NOT POSSIBLE. IN MODERATELY SEVERE POISONING ADMINISTER ATROPINE SULFATE, 0.4-2.0 MG REPEATED EVERY 15 MINUTES UNTIL ATROPINIZATION IS ACHIEVED (TACHYCARDIA, FLUSHING, DRY MOUTH, MYDRIASIS). MAINTAIN ATROPINIZATION BY REPEATED DOSES FOR 2-12 HOURS, OR LONGER, DEPENDING ON THE SEVERITY OF POISONING. THE APPEARANCE OF RALES IN THE LUNG BASES, MIOSIS, SALIVATION, NAUSEA, BRADYCARDIA, ARE ALL INDICATIONS OF INADEQUATE ATROPINIZATION. SEVERELY POISONED INDIVIDUALS MAY EXHIBIT REMARKABLE TOLERANCE TO ATROPINE; TWO OR MORE TIMES THE DOSAGES SUGGESTED ABOVE MAY BE NEEDED. PERSONS NOT POISONED OR ONLY SLIGHTLY POISONED, HOWEVER, MAY DEVELOP SIGNS OF ATROPINE TOXICITY FROM SUCH LARGE DOSAGES: FEVER, MUSCLE FIBRILLATIONS, AND DELIRIUM ARE THE MAIN SIGNS OF ATROPINE TOXICITY. IF THESE SIGNS APPEAR WHILE THE PATIENT IS FULLY ATROPINIZED, ATROPINE ADMINISTRATION SHOULD BE DISCONTINUED, AT LEAST TEMPORARILY. OBSERVE TREATED PATIENTS CLOSELY AT LEAST 24 HOURS TO INSURE THAT SYMPTOMS (POSSIBLY PULMONARY EDEMA) DO NOT RECUR AS ATROPINIZATION WEARS OFF. IN VERY SEVERE POISONINGS, METABOLIC DISPOSITION OF TOXICANT MAY REQUIRE SEVERAL HOURS OR DAYS DURING WHICH ATROPINIZATION MUST BE MAINTAINED. MARKEDLY LOWER LEVELS OF URINARY METABOLITES INDICATE THAT ATROPINE DOSAGE CAN BE TAPERED OFF. AS DOSAGE IS REDUCED, CHECK THE LUNG BASES FREQUENTLY FOR RALES. IF RALES ARE HEARD OR OTHER SYMPTOMS RETURN, RE-ESTABLISH ATROPINIZATION PROMPTLY (MORGAN, RECOGNITION AND MANAGEMENT OF PESTICIDE POISONINGS, 3RD ED.). ADMINISTRATION OF ANTIDOTE MUST BE PERFORMED BY QUALIFIED MEDICAL PERSONNEL.

IN CASES OF SEVERE POISONING BY ORGANOPHOSPHATE PESTICIDES IN WHICH RESPIRATORY DEPRESSION, MUSCLE WEAKNESS AND TWITCHINGS ARE SEVERE, GIVE PRALIDOXIME (PROTOPAM-AYERST, 2-PAM), 1.0 GRAM INTRAVENOUSLY AT NO MORE THAN 0.5 GRAM PER MINUTE. DOSAGE OF PRALIDOXIME MAY BE REPEATED IN 1-2 HOURS, THEN AT 10-12 HOUR INTERVALS IF NEEDED. IN VERY SEVERE POISONINGS, DOSAGE RATES MAY BE DOUBLED. TREATMENT WITH PRALIDOXIME WILL BE MOST EFFECTIVE IF GIVEN WITHIN THIRTY-SIX HOURS AFTER POISONING (MORGAN, RECOGNITION AND MANAGEMENT OF PESTICIDE POISONINGS, 3RD ED.). ANTIDOTE SHOULD BE ADMINISTERED BY QUALIFIED MEDICAL PERSONNEL.

REACTIVITY

REACTIVITY: STABLE UNDER NORMAL TEMPERATURES AND PRESSURES.

INCOMPATIBILITIES: NAPHTHALOPHOS: OXIDIZERS (STRONG): FIRE AND EXPLOSION HAZARD.

DECOMPOSITION: THERMAL DECOMPOSITION MAY RELEASE TOXIC OXIDES OF NITROGEN, PHOSPHORUS AND CARBON.

POLYMERIZATION: HAZARDOUS POLYMERIZATION HAS NOT BEEN REPORTED TO OCCUR UNDER NORMAL TEMPERATURES AND PRESSURES.

STORAGE AND DISPOSAL

OBSERVE ALL FEDERAL, STATE AND LOCAL REGULATIONS WHEN STORING OR DISPOSING OF THIS SUBSTANCE. FOR ASSISTANCE, CONTACT THE DISTRICT DIRECTOR OF THE ENVIRONMENTAL PROTECTION AGENCY.

STORAGE

STORE IN ACCORDANCE WITH 40 CFR 165 RECOMMENDED PROCEDURES FOR THE DISPOSAL AND STORAGE OF PESTICIDES AND PESTICIDE CONTAINERS. STORE AWAY FROM INCOMPATIBLE SUBSTANCES.

DISPOSAL

DISPOSAL MUST BE IN ACCORDANCE WITH 40 CFR 165 RECOMMENDED PROCEDURES FOR THE DISPOSAL AND STORAGE OF PESTICIDES AND PESTICIDE CONTAINERS.

CONDITIONS TO AVOID

MAY BURN BUT DOES NOT IGNITE READILY. CONTAINERS MAY EXPLODE IN HEAT OF FIRE.

SPILL AND LEAK PROCEDURES

OCCUPATIONAL SPILL: DO NOT TOUCH SPILLED MATERIAL. STOP LEAK IF YOU CAN DO IT WITHOUT RISK. USE WATER SPRAY TO REDUCE VAPORS. FOR SMALL SPILLS, TAKE UP WITH SAND OR OTHER ABSORBENT MATERIAL AND PLACE INTO CONTAINERS FOR LATER DISPOSAL. FOR SMALL DRY SPILLS, WITH A CLEAN SHOVEL PLACE MATERIAL INTO CLEAN, DRY CONTAINERS AND COVER. MOVE CONTAINERS FROM SPILL AREA. FOR LARGER SPILLS, DIKE FAR AHEAD OF SPILL FOR LATER DISPOSAL. KEEP UNNECESSARY PEOPLE AWAY. ISOLATE HAZARD AREA AND DENY ENTRY. VENTILATE CLOSED SPACES BEFORE ENTERING.

PROTECTIVE EQUIPMENT

VENTILATION: PROCESS ENCLOSURE RECOMMENDED.

RESPIRATOR: THE FOLLOWING RESPIRATORS ARE RECOMMENDED BASED ON INFORMATION FOUND IN THE PHYSICAL DATA, TOXICITY AND HEALTH EFFECTS SECTIONS. THEY ARE RANKED IN ORDER FROM MINIMUM TO MAXIMUM RESPIRATORY PROTECTION. THE SPECIFIC RESPIRATOR SELECTED MUST BE BASED ON CONTAMINATION LEVELS FOUND IN THE WORK PLACE, MUST NOT EXCEED THE WORKING LIMITS OF THE RESPIRATOR AND BE JOINTLY APPROVED BY THE NATIONAL INSTITUTE FOR OCCUPATIONAL SAFETY AND HEALTH AND THE MINE SAFETY AND HEALTH ADMINISTRATION (NIOSH-MSHA).

TYPE 'C' SUPPLIED-AIR RESPIRATOR WITH A FULL FACEPIECE OPERATED IN PRESSURE-DEMAND OR OTHER POSITIVE PRESSURE MODE OR WITH A FULL FACEPIECE, HELMET OR HOOD OPERATED IN CONTINOUS-FLOW MODE. SELF-CONTAINED BREATHING APPARATUS WITH A FULL FACEPIECE OPERATED IN PRESSURE-DEMAND OR OTHER POSITIVE PRESSURE MODE.

FOR FIREFIGHTING AND OTHER IMMEDIATELY DANGEROUS TO LIFE OR HEALTH CONDITIONS:

SELF-CONTAINED BREATHING APPARATUS WITH FULL FACEPIECE OPERATED IN PRESSURE-DEMAND OR OTHER POSITIVE PRESSURE MODE.

SUPPLIED-AIR RESPIRATOR WITH FULL FACEPIECE AND OPERATED IN PRESSURE-DEMAND OR OTHER POSITIVE PRESSURE MODE IN COMBINATION WITH AN AUXILIARY SELF-CONTAINED BREATHING APPARATUS OPERATED IN PRESSURE-DEMAND OR OTHER POSITIVE PRESSURE MODE.

CLOTHING: EMPLOYEE MUST WEAR APPROPRIATE PROTECTIVE (IMPERVIOUS) CLOTHING AND EQUIPMENT TO PREVENT ANY POSSIBILITY OF SKIN CONTACT WITH THIS SUBSTANCE.

GLOVES: EMPLOYEE MUST WEAR APPROPRIATE PROTECTIVE GLOVES TO PREVENT CONTACT WITH THIS SUBSTANCE.

EYE PROTECTION: EMPLOYEE MUST WEAR SPLASH-PROOF OR DUST-RESISTANT SAFETY GOGGLES WITH OR WITHOUT A FACESHIELD TO PREVENT CONTACT WITH THIS SUBSTANCE.

EMERGENCY EYE WASH: WHERE THERE IS ANY POSSIBILITY THAT AN EMPLOYEE'S EYES MAY BE EXPOSED TO THIS SUBSTANCE, THE EMPLOYER SHOULD PROVIDE AN EYE WASH FOUNTAIN WITHIN THE IMMEDIATE WORK AREA FOR EMERGENCY USE.

AUTHORIZED BY- OCCUPATIONAL HEALTH SERVICES, INC.

CREATION DATE: 10/04/89 ***REVISION DATE:*** 04/24/90

MATERIAL SAFETY DATA SHEET

OCCUPATIONAL HEALTH SERVICES, INC.
AGRICULTURE AND PESTICIDE DIVISION
450 SEVENTH AVENUE, SUITE 2407
NEW YORK, NEW YORK 10123
1-800-445-MSDS OR (212) 967-1100

EMERGENCY CONTACT:
JOHN S. BRANSFORD, JR. (615) 292-1180

SUBSTANCE IDENTIFICATION

CAS-NUMBER 3309-87-3

SUBSTANCE: **S-(4-CHLOROPHENYL) O,O-DIMETHYL PHOSPHOROTHIOATE**

TRADE NAMES/SYNONYMS: PHOSPHOROTHIOIC ACID, S-(4-CHLOROPHENYL) O,O-DIMETHYL ESTER; S-(4-CHLOROPHENYL) O,O-DIMETHYL PHOSPHOROTHIOIC ACID, ESTER; PHOSPHOROTHIOIC ACID, S-(P-CHLOROPHENYL) O,O-DIMETHYL ESTER; S-(P-CHLOROPHENYL) O,O-DIMETHYL PHOSPHOROTHIOIC ACID, ESTER; S-(P-CHLOROPHENYL) O,O-DIMETHYL PHOSPHOROTHIOATE; O,O-DIMETHYL-S-P-CHLOROPHENYL PHOSPHOROTHIOATE; DMCP; FUJITHION; ENT 25685; C8H10CLO3PS; PST72763

CHEMICAL FAMILY: PHOSPHOROTHIOATE

MOLECULAR FORMULA: (C-H3-O)2-P(O)-S-C6-H4-CL

MOLECULAR WEIGHT: 252.66

CERCLA RATINGS (SCALE 0-3): HEALTH=3 FIRE=U REACTIVITY=0 PERSISTENCE=1

NFPA RATINGS (SCALE 0-4): HEALTH=3 FIRE=U REACTIVITY=0

COMPONENTS AND CONTAMINANTS

COMPONENT: S-(4-CHLOROPHENYL) O,O-DIMETHYL PHOSPHOROTHIOATE ***PERCENT:*** 100.0

CAS# 3309-87-3

OTHER CONTAMINANTS: NONE

EXPOSURE LIMITS: NO OCCUPATIONAL EXPOSURE LIMITS ESTABLISHED BY OSHA, ACGIH, OR NIOSH.

PHYSICAL DATA

DESCRIPTION: YELLOWISH LIQUID.

BOILING POINT: 214-223 F (101-106 C) @ 0.006 MMHG ***SPECIFIC GRAVITY:*** 1.353

SOLUBILITY IN WATER: 0.24 % @ 21 C

SOLVENT SOLUBILITY: SOLUBLE IN ACETONE, CARBON TETRACHLORIDE, AND TOLUENE.

FIRE AND EXPLOSION DATA

FIRE AND EXPLOSION HAZARD: UNKNOWN FIRE AND EXPLOSION HAZARD.

FIREFIGHTING MEDIA: DRY CHEMICAL, CARBON DIOXIDE, HALON, WATER SPRAY OR STANDARD FOAM (1987 EMERGENCY RESPONSE GUIDEBOOK, DOT P 5800.4). FOR LARGER FIRES, USE WATER SPRAY, FOG OR STANDARD FOAM (1987 EMERGENCY RESPONSE GUIDEBOOK, DOT P 5800.4).

FIREFIGHTING: MOVE CONTAINERS FROM FIRE AREA IF POSSIBLE. FIGHT FIRE FROM MAXIMUM DISTANCE. STAY AWAY FROM STORAGE TANK ENDS. DIKE FIRE CONTROL WATER FOR LATER DISPOSAL. DO NOT SCATTER MATERIAL (1987 EMERGENCY RESPONSE GUIDEBOOK, DOT P 5800.4, GUIDE PAGE 55). EXTINGUISH ONLY IF FLOW CAN BE STOPPED; USE FLOODING AMOUNTS OF WATER AS FOG, SOLID STREAMS MAY BE INEFFECTIVE. COOL CONTAINERS WITH FLOODING AMOUNTS OF WATER FROM AS FAR A DISTANCE AS POSSIBLE. USE WATER SPRAY TO ABSORB TOXIC VAPORS. AVOID BREATHING TOXIC VAPORS; KEEP UPWIND. CONSIDER EVACUATION OF DOWNWIND AREA IF MATERIAL IS LEAKING.

TOXICITY

S-(4-CHLOROPHENYL) O,O-DIMETHYL PHOSPHOROTHIOATE: TOXICITY DATA: 920 MG/KG SKIN-MOUSE LD50; 94 MG/KG ORAL-MOUSE LD50. CARCINOGEN STATUS: NONE. ACUTE TOXICITY LEVEL: TOXIC BY DERMAL ABSORPTION AND INGESTION. TARGET EFFECTS: CHOLINESTERASE INHIBITOR. POISONING MAY AFFECT THE NERVOUS SYSTEM.* AT INCREASED RISK FROM EXPOSURE: PERSONS WITH RESPIRATORY AILMENTS, RECENT EXPOSURE TO CHOLINESTERASE INHIBITORS OR IMPAIRED CHOLINESTERASE PRODUCTION, OR LIVER MALFUNCTION.* ADDITIONAL DATA: MAY CROSS THE PLACENTA. HIGH ENVIRONMENTAL TEMPERATURES OR EXPOSURE OF THE CHEMICAL TO VISIBLE OR ULTRAVIOLET LIGHT MAY ENHANCE THE TOXICITY. INTERACTIONS WITH MEDICATIONS MAY OCCUR.*

* MAY BE BASED ON GENERAL INFORMATION ON ORGANOPHOSPHATES.

HEALTH EFFECTS AND FIRST AID

INHALATION: S-(4-CHLOROPHENYL) O,O-DIMETHYL PHOSPHOROTHIOATE: SEE INFORMATION ON ORGANOPHOSPHATES.

ORGANOPHOSPHATES: CHOLINESTERASE INHIBITOR. **ACUTE EXPOSURE**- WHEN INHALED, THE FIRST EFFECTS OF CHOLINESTERASE INHIBITORS ARE USUALLY RESPIRATORY AND MAY INCLUDE NASAL HYPEREMIA AND WATERY DISCHARGE, COUGH, CHEST DISCOMFORT, DYSPNEA, AND WHEEZING DUE TO INCREASED BRONCHIAL SECRETIONS AND BRONCHOCONSTRICTION. IF SUFFICIENT AMOUNTS ARE ABSORBED, OTHER SYSTEMIC EFFECTS MAY BEGIN WITHIN A FEW MINUTES OR BE DELAYED FOR UP TO 12 HOURS. SYMPTOMS MAY INCLUDE PALLOR,

NAUSEA, VOMITING, DIARRHEA, ABDOMINAL CRAMPS, HEADACHE, DIZZINESS, OCULAR PAIN, BLURRED VISION, MIOSIS OR IN SOME CASES, ESPECIALLY INITIALLY, MYDRIASIS, LACRIMATION, SALIVATION, SWEATING, AND CONFUSION. OTHER REPORTED CENTRAL NERVOUS SYSTEM OR NEUROMUSCULAR EFFECTS MAY INCLUDE ATAXIA, SLURRED SPEECH, AREFLEXIA, WEAKNESS, FATIGUE, FASCICULATIONS, TWITCHING, TREMORS POSSIBLY OF THE TONGUE AND EYELIDS, AND EVENTUALLY PARALYSIS OF THE EXTREMITIES AND POSSIBLY OF THE RESPIRATORY MUSCLES. IN SEVERE CASES THERE MAY ALSO BE INVOLUNTARY DEFECATION AND URINATION, CYANOSIS, PSYCHOSIS, HYPERGLYCEMIA, ACUTE PANCREATITIS, CARDIAC IRREGULARITIES, PULMONARY EDEMA, UNCONSCIOUSNESS, CONVULSIONS, AND COMA. DEATH IS PRIMARILY DUE TO RESPIRATORY FAILURE, ALTHOUGH CARDIOVASCULAR EFFECTS INCLUDING CARDIAC ARREST MAY ALSO BE IMPLICATED. LONG TERM SEQUELAE ARE RARE BUT MAY INCLUDE NEUROPSYCHIATRIC DISORDERS AND MYOPATHY WITH MUSCLE TENDERNESS. SOME ORGANOPHOSPHATES MAY CAUSE A DELAYED NEUROPATHY BEGINNING 1-4 WEEKS AFTER AN ACUTE EXPOSURE WHICH MAY OR MAY NOT HAVE CAUSED ACUTE CHOLINERGIC EFFECTS. NUMBNESS, TINGLING, WEAKNESS AND CRAMPING BEGINNING SYMMETRICALLY IN THE LOWER LIMBS MAY PROGRESS TO ATAXIA AND PARALYSIS. IN SEVERE CASES, UPPER LIMB INVOLVEMENT IS POSSIBLE AND FLACCID PARALYSIS MAY PROGRESS TO SPASTIC PARALYSIS WITH EXAGGERATED REFLEXES. IMPROVEMENT MAY OCCUR OVER MONTHS TO YEARS, BUT SOME RESIDUAL IMPAIRMENT USUALLY REMAINS. **CHRONIC EXPOSURE-** REPEATED OR PROLONGED EXPOSURE MAY RESULT IN THE EFFECTS OF ACUTE EXPOSURE INCLUDING THE DELAYED NEUROPATHY. OTHER EFFECTS REPORTED IN WORKERS REPEATEDLY EXPOSED INCLUDE IMPAIRED MEMORY AND CONCENTRATION, ACUTE PSYCHOSIS, SEVERE DEPRESSIONS, IRRITABILTY, CONFUSION, APATHY, EMOTIONAL LABILITY, SOCIAL WITHDRAWAL, CONFUSION, HEADACHE, SPEECH DIFFICULTIES, DELAYED REACTION TIMES, SPATIAL DISORIENTATION, NIGHTMARES, SLEEPWALKING, AND DROWSINESS OR INSOMNIA. AN INFLUENZA-LIKE CONDITION WITH HEADACHE, NAUSEA, WEAKNESS, ANOREXIA AND MALAISE HAS ALSO BEEN REPORTED.

FIRST AID- REMOVE FROM EXPOSURE AREA TO FRESH AIR IMMEDIATELY. IF BREATHING HAS STOPPED, GIVE ARTIFICIAL RESPIRATION. MAINTAIN AIRWAY AND BLOOD PRESSURE AND ADMINISTER OXYGEN IF AVAILABLE. KEEP AFFECTED PERSON WARM AND AT REST. TREAT SYMPTOMATICALLY AND SUPPORTIVELY. ADMINISTRATION OF OXYGEN SHOULD BE PERFORMED BY QUALIFIED PERSONNEL. GET MEDICAL ATTENTION IMMEDIATELY.

SKIN CONTACT: S-(4-CHLOROPHENYL) O,O-DIMETHYL PHOSPHOROTHIOATE: TOXIC. SEE INFORMATION ON ORGANOPHOSPHATES.

ORGANOPHOSPHATES: CHOLINESTERASE INHIBITOR. **ACUTE EXPOSURE-** LOCALIZED SWEATING AND FASCICULATIONS MAY OCCUR AT THE SITE OF CONTACT. IF SUFFICIENT AMOUNTS ARE ABSORBED, OTHER EFFECTS OF CHOLINESTERASE INHIBITION AS DESCRIBED IN ACUTE INHALATION MAY OCCUR. SYMPTOMS MAY BE DELAYED 2-3 HOURS, BUT USUALLY NO MORE THAN 12 HOURS. THE RATE OF ABSORPTION IS INCREASED BY THE PRESENCE OF DERMATITIS OR HIGH AMBIENT TEMPERATURES. DELAYED NEUROPATHY IS ALSO POSSIBLE. **CHRONIC EXPOSURE-** REPEATED OR PROLONGED EXPOSURE MAY CAUSE EFFECTS AS DESCRIBED IN ACUTE EXPOSURE. SOME ORGANOPHOSPHATES MAY CAUSE SENSITIZATION.

FIRST AID- REMOVE CONTAMINATED CLOTHING IMMEDIATELY. WASH CONTAMINATED AREAS WITH SOAP AND WATER FOLLOWED BY ALCOHOL (ARENA, POISONING, 4TH ED.). EMERGENCY PERSONNEL SHOULD WEAR GLOVES AND AVOID CONTAMINATION. TREAT RESPIRATORY DIFFICULTY WITH ARTIFICIAL RESPIRATION. GET MEDICAL ATTENTION IMMEDIATELY.

EYE CONTACT: S-(4-CHLOROPHENYL) O,O-DIMETHYL PHOSPHOROTHIOATE: SEE INFORMATION ON ORGANOPHOSPHATES.

ORGANOPHOSPHATES: CHOLINESTERASE INHIBITOR. **ACUTE EXPOSURE-** DIRECT CONTACT MAY CAUSE PAIN, HYPEREMIA, LACRIMATION, TWITCHING OF THE EYELIDS, MIOSIS, AND CILIARY MUSCLE SPASM WITH LOSS OF ACCOMODATION, BLURRED OR DIMMED VISION AND BROWACHE. SOMETIMES MYDRIASIS MAY OCCUR INSTEAD OF MIOSIS. WITH SUFFICIENT EXPOSURE, OTHER SYMPTOMS OF CHOLINESTERASE INHIBITION AS DESCRIBED IN ACUTE INHALATION MAY OCCUR. **CHRONIC EXPOSURE-** REPEATED OR PROLONGED EXPOSURE MAY CAUSE EFFECTS AS DESCRIBED IN ACUTE EXPOSURE. SOME COMPOUNDS HAVE CAUSED TOXIC EFFECTS ON THE CRYSTALLINE LENS, CONJUNCTIVAL THICKENING AND OBSTRUCTION OF THE NASOLACRIMAL CANALS WHEN USED AS MIOTIC EYEDROPS.

FIRST AID- IRRIGATE EYES WITH WATER OR SALINE SOLUTION. IF SYMPTOMS OF POISONING OCCUR, TREAT RESPIRATORY DIFFICULTY WITH ARTIFICIAL RESPIRATION AND OXYGEN. OBSERVE PATIENT FOR AT LEAST 24-36 HOURS (GOSSELIN, CLINICAL TOXICOLOGY OF COMMERCIAL PRODUCTS, 5TH ED.). GET MEDICAL ATTENTION IMMEDIATELY. OXYGEN SHOULD BE ADMINISTERED BY QUALIFIED MEDICAL PERSONNEL.

INGESTION: S-(4-CHLOROPHENYL) O,O-DIMETHYL PHOSPHOROTHIOATE: TOXIC. SEE INFORMATION ON ORGANOPHOSPHATES.

ORGANOPHOSPHATES: CHOLINESTERASE INHIBITOR. **ACUTE EXPOSURE-** WHEN INGESTED, THE FIRST EFFECTS MAY BE NAUSEA, VOMITING, ANOREXIA, ABDOMINAL CRAMPS AND DIARRHEA. GASTROINTESTINAL ABSORPTION MAY CAUSE SYMPTOMS OF CHOLINESTERASE INHIBITION AS DESCRIBED IN ACUTE INHALATION. SYMPTOMS MAY BEGIN WITHIN MINUTES OR BE DELAYED FOR HOURS. DELAYED EFFECTS INCLUDING NEUROPATHY MAY ALSO OCCUR. **CHRONIC EXPOSURE-** REPEATED INGESTION MAY CAUSE EFFECTS AS DESCRIBED IN ACUTE EXPOSURE.

FIRST AID- IF PERSON IS ALERT AND RESPIRATION IS NOT DEPRESSED, GIVE SYRUP OF IPECAC FOLLOWED BY WATER (IF VOMITING OCCURS, KEEP HEAD BELOW HIPS TO PREVENT ASPIRATION). IF CONSCIOUSNESS LEVEL DECLINES OR VOMITING HAS NOT OCCURRED IN 15 MINUTES EMPTY STOMACH BY GASTRIC LAVAGE WITH THE AID OF CUFFED ENDOTRACHEAL TUBE USING ISOTONIC SALINE OR 5% SODIUM BICARBONATE FOLLOW WITH ACTIVATED CHARCOAL. ESTABLISH AND MAINTAIN AIRWAY. TREAT RESPIRATORY DIFFICULTY WITH ARTIFICIAL RESPIRATION AND OXYGEN. DO NOT GIVE MORPHINE, AMINOPHYLLINE, PHENOTHIAZINES, RESERPINE, FUROSEMIDE, OR ETHACRYNIC ACID (MORGAN, RECOGNITION AND MANAGEMENT OF PESTICIDE POISONINGS, 3RD ED.). TREAT SYMPTOMATICALLY AND SUPPORTIVELY. ADMINISTRATION OF OXYGEN AND LAVAGE MUST BE PERFORMED BY QUALIFIED MEDICAL PERSONNEL. GET MEDICAL ATTENTION IMMEDIATELY.

ANTIDOTE: THE FOLLOWING ANTIDOTE(S) HAVE BEEN RECOMMENDED. HOWEVER, THE DECISION AS TO WHETHER THE SEVERITY OF POISONING REQUIRES ADMINISTRATION OF ANY ANTIDOTE AND ACTUAL DOSE REQUIRED SHOULD BE MADE BY QUALIFIED MEDICAL PERSONNEL.

FOR CHOLINESTERASE INHIBITORS: ESTABLISH CLEAR AIRWAY AND TISSUE OXYGENATION BY ASPIRATION OF SECRETIONS, AND IF NECESSARY, BY ASSISTED PULMONARY VENTILATION WITH OXYGEN. IMPROVE TISSUE OXYGENATION AS MUCH AS POSSIBLE BEFORE ADMINISTERING ATROPINE TO MINIMIZE THE RISK OF VENTRICULAR FIBRILLATION. ADMINISTER ATROPINE SULFATE INTRAVENOUSLY, OR INTRAMUSCULARLY IF IV INJECTION IS NOT POSSIBLE. IN MODERATELY SEVERE POISONING ADMINISTER ATROPINE SULFATE, 0.4-2.0 MG REPEATED EVERY 15 MINUTES UNTIL ATROPINIZATION IS ACHIEVED (TACHYCARDIA, FLUSHING, DRY MOUTH, MYDRIASIS). MAINTAIN ATROPINIZATION BY REPEATED DOSES FOR 2-12 HOURS, OR LONGER, DEPENDING ON THE SEVERITY OF POISONING. THE APPEARANCE OF RALES IN THE LUNG BASES, MIOSIS, SALIVATION, NAUSEA, BRADYCARDIA, ARE ALL INDICATIONS OF INADEQUATE ATROPINIZATION. SEVERELY POISONED INDIVIDUALS MAY EXHIBIT REMARKABLE TOLERANCE TO ATROPINE; TWO OR MORE TIMES THE DOSAGES SUGGESTED ABOVE MAY BE NEEDED. PERSONS NOT POISONED OR ONLY SLIGHTLY POISONED, HOWEVER, MAY DEVELOP SIGNS OF ATROPINE TOXICITY FROM SUCH LARGE DOSAGES: FEVER, MUSCLE FIBRILLATIONS, AND DELIRIUM ARE THE MAIN SIGNS OF ATROPINE TOXICITY. IF THESE SIGNS APPEAR WHILE THE PATIENT IS FULLY ATROPINIZED, ATROPINE ADMINISTRATION SHOULD BE DISCONTINUED, AT LEAST TEMPORARILY. OBSERVE TREATED PATIENTS CLOSELY AT LEAST 24 HOURS TO INSURE THAT SYMPTOMS (POSSIBLY PULMONARY EDEMA) DO NOT RECUR AS ATROPINIZATION WEARS OFF. IN VERY SEVERE POISONINGS, METABOLIC DISPOSITION OF TOXICANT MAY REQUIRE SEVERAL HOURS OR DAYS DURING WHICH ATROPINIZATION MUST BE MAINTAINED. MARKEDLY LOWER LEVELS OF URINARY METABOLITES INDICATE THAT ATROPINE DOSAGE CAN BE TAPERED OFF. AS DOSAGE IS REDUCED, CHECK THE LUNG BASES FREQUENTLY FOR RALES. IF RALES ARE HEARD OR OTHER SYMPTOMS RETURN, RE-ESTABLISH ATROPINIZATION PROMPTLY (MORGAN, RECOGNITION AND MANAGEMENT OF PESTICIDE POISONINGS, 3RD ED.). ADMINISTRATION OF ANTIDOTE MUST BE PERFORMED BY QUALIFIED MEDICAL PERSONNEL.

IN CASES OF SEVERE POISONING BY ORGANOPHOSPHATE PESTICIDES IN WHICH RESPIRATORY DEPRESSION, MUSCLE WEAKNESS AND TWITCHINGS ARE SEVERE, GIVE PRALIDOXIME (PROTOPAM-AYERST, 2-PAM), 1.0 GRAM INTRAVENOUSLY AT NO MORE THAN 0.5 GRAM PER MINUTE. DOSAGE OF PRALIDOXIME MAY BE REPEATED IN 1-2 HOURS, THEN AT 10-12 HOUR INTERVALS IF NEEDED. IN VERY SEVERE POISONINGS, DOSAGE RATES MAY BE DOUBLED. TREATMENT WITH PRALIDOXIME WILL BE MOST EFFECTIVE IF GIVEN WITHIN THIRTY-SIX HOURS AFTER POISONING (MORGAN, RECOGNITION AND MANAGEMENT OF PESTICIDE POISONINGS, 3RD ED.). ANTIDOTE SHOULD BE ADMINISTERED BY QUALIFIED MEDICAL PERSONNEL.

REACTIVITY

REACTIVITY: STABLE UNDER NORMAL TEMPERATURES AND PRESSURES.

INCOMPATIBILITIES: S-(4-CHLOROPHENYL) O,O-DIMETHYL PHOSPHOROTHIOATE: OXIDIZERS (STRONG): FIRE AND EXPLOSION HAZARD.

DECOMPOSITION: THERMAL DECOMPOSITION RELEASES CORROSIVE FUMES OF HYDROGEN CHLORIDE AND TOXIC OXIDES OF PHOSPHORUS AND SULFUR.

POLYMERIZATION: HAZARDOUS POLYMERIZATION HAS NOT BEEN REPORTED TO OCCUR UNDER NORMAL TEMPERATURES AND PRESSURES.

MATERIAL SAFETY DATA SHEET

OCCUPATIONAL HEALTH SERVICES, INC.
AGRICULTURE AND PESTICIDE DIVISION
450 SEVENTH AVENUE, SUITE 2407
NEW YORK, NEW YORK 10123
1-800-445-MSDS OR (212) 967-1100

EMERGENCY CONTACT:
JOHN S. BRANSFORD, JR. (615) 292-1180

SUBSTANCE IDENTIFICATION

CAS-NUMBER 3042-84-0

SUBSTANCE: **BROMPYRAZON**

TRADE NAMES/SYNONYMS: 3(2H)-PYRIDAZINONE, 5-AMINO-4-BROMO-2-PHENYL-; 5-AMINO-4-BROMO-2-PHENYL-3(2H)-PYRIDAZINONE; 5-AMINO-4-BROMO-2-PHENYLPYRIDAZIN-3(2H)-ONE; 5-AMINO-4-BROMO-2-PHENYLPYRIDAZINE-3-ONE; BROMPYRAZONE; C10H7BRN3O; PST72769

CHEMICAL FAMILY: PYRIDAZINE KETONE

MOLECULAR FORMULA: C6-H5-N2-C4-O-BR-N-H2

MOLECULAR WEIGHT: 266.10

CERCLA RATINGS (SCALE 0-3): HEALTH = 1 FIRE = 1 REACTIVITY = 0 PERSISTENCE = 3

NFPA RATINGS (SCALE 0-4): HEALTH = 1 FIRE = 1 REACTIVITY = 0

COMPONENTS AND CONTAMINANTS

COMPONENT: BROMPYRAZON ***PERCENT:*** 100
CAS# 3042-84-0

OTHER CONTAMINANTS: NONE

EXPOSURE LIMITS: NO OCCUPATIONAL EXPOSURE LIMITS ESTABLISHED BY OSHA, ACGIH, OR NIOSH.

PHYSICAL DATA

DESCRIPTION: SOLID ***MELTING POINT:*** 432-435 F (222-224 C)

SPECIFIC GRAVITY: NOT AVAILABLE ***SOLUBILITY IN WATER:*** NOT AVAILABLE

FIRE AND EXPLOSION DATA

FIRE AND EXPLOSION HAZARD: SLIGHT FIRE HAZARD WHEN EXPOSED TO HEAT OR FLAME.

FIREFIGHTING MEDIA: DRY CHEMICAL, CARBON DIOXIDE, HALON, WATER SPRAY OR STANDARD FOAM (1987 EMERGENCY RESPONSE GUIDEBOOK, DOT P 5800.4). FOR LARGER FIRES, USE WATER SPRAY, FOG OR STANDARD FOAM (1987 EMERGENCY RESPONSE GUIDEBOOK, DOT P 5800.4).

FIREFIGHTING: MOVE CONTAINERS FROM FIRE AREA IF POSSIBLE (1987 EMERGENCY RESPONSE GUIDEBOOK, DOT P 5800.4, GUIDE PAGE 53).
EXTINGUISH FIRE USING AGENTS SUITABLE FOR TYPE OF SURROUNDING FIRE. USE WATER IN FLOODING AMOUNTS AS A FOG. AVOID BREATHING DUSTS AND FUMES FROM BURNING MATERIAL; KEEP UPWIND.

TOXICITY

BROMPYRAZON: TOXICITY DATA: 8500 MG/KG ORAL-RAT LD50; 2 GM/KG ORAL-RABBIT LD50. CARCINOGEN STATUS: NONE. ACUTE TOXICITY LEVEL: SLIGHTLY TOXIC BY INGESTION. TARGET EFFECTS: NO DATA AVAILABLE.

HEALTH EFFECTS AND FIRST AID

INHALATION: BROMPYRAZON: **ACUTE EXPOSURE-** NO DATA AVAILABLE. **CHRONIC EXPOSURE-** NO DATA AVAILABLE.

FIRST AID- REMOVE FROM EXPOSURE AREA TO FRESH AIR IMMEDIATELY. IF BREATHING HAS STOPPED, PERFORM ARTIFICIAL RESPIRATION. KEEP PERSON WARM AND AT REST. TREAT SYMPTOMATICALLY AND SUPPORTIVELY. GET MEDICAL ATTENTION IMMEDIATELY.

SKIN CONTACT: BROMPYRAZON: **ACUTE EXPOSURE-** NO DATA AVAILABLE. **CHRONIC EXPOSURE-** NO DATA AVAILABLE.

FIRST AID- REMOVE CONTAMINATED CLOTHING AND SHOES IMMEDIATELY. WASH AFFECTED AREA WITH SOAP OR MILD DETERGENT AND LARGE AMOUNTS OF WATER UNTIL NO EVIDENCE OF CHEMICAL REMAINS (APPROXIMATELY 15-20 MINUTES). GET MEDICAL ATTENTION IMMEDIATELY.

EYE CONTACT: BROMPYRAZON: **ACUTE EXPOSURE-** NO DATA AVAILABLE. **CHRONIC EXPOSURE-** NO DATA AVAILABLE.

FIRST AID- WASH EYES IMMEDIATELY WITH LARGE AMOUNTS OF WATER OR NORMAL SALINE, OCCASIONALLY LIFTING UPPER AND LOWER LIDS, UNTIL NO EVIDENCE OF CHEMICAL REMAINS (APPROXIMATELY 15-20 MINUTES). GET MEDICAL ATTENTION IMMEDIATELY.

STORAGE AND DISPOSAL

OBSERVE ALL FEDERAL, STATE AND LOCAL REGULATIONS WHEN STORING OR DISPOSING OF THIS SUBSTANCE. FOR ASSISTANCE, CONTACT THE DISTRICT DIRECTOR OF THE ENVIRONMENTAL PROTECTION AGENCY.

STORAGE

STORE IN ACCORDANCE WITH 40 CFR 165 RECOMMENDED PROCEDURES FOR THE DISPOSAL AND STORAGE OF PESTICIDES AND PESTICIDE CONTAINERS.
STORE AWAY FROM INCOMPATIBLE SUBSTANCES.

DISPOSAL

DISPOSAL MUST BE IN ACCORDANCE WITH 40 CFR 165 RECOMMENDED PROCEDURES FOR THE DISPOSAL AND STORAGE OF PESTICIDES AND PESTICIDE CONTAINERS.

CONDITIONS TO AVOID

MAY BURN BUT DOES NOT IGNITE READILY. CONTAINERS MAY EXPLODE IN HEAT OF FIRE.

SPILL AND LEAK PROCEDURES

OCCUPATIONAL SPILL: DO NOT TOUCH SPILLED MATERIAL. STOP LEAK IF YOU CAN DO IT WITHOUT RISK. USE WATER SPRAY TO REDUCE VAPORS. FOR SMALL SPILLS, TAKE UP WITH SAND OR OTHER ABSORBENT MATERIAL AND PLACE INTO CONTAINERS FOR LATER DISPOSAL. FOR SMALL DRY SPILLS, WITH A CLEAN SHOVEL PLACE MATERIAL INTO CLEAN, DRY CONTAINERS AND COVER. MOVE CONTAINERS FROM SPILL AREA. FOR LARGER SPILLS, DIKE FAR AHEAD OF SPILL FOR LATER DISPOSAL. KEEP UNNECESSARY PEOPLE AWAY. ISOLATE HAZARD AREA AND DENY ENTRY. VENTILATE CLOSED SPACES BEFORE ENTERING.

PROTECTIVE EQUIPMENT

VENTILATION: PROVIDE LOCAL EXHAUST OR PROCESS ENCLOSURE VENTILATION SYSTEM.

RESPIRATOR: THE FOLLOWING RESPIRATORS ARE RECOMMENDED BASED ON INFORMATION FOUND IN THE PHYSICAL DATA, TOXICITY AND HEALTH EFFECTS SECTIONS. THEY ARE RANKED IN ORDER FROM MINIMUM TO MAXIMUM RESPIRATORY PROTECTION. THE SPECIFIC RESPIRATOR SELECTED MUST BE BASED ON CONTAMINATION LEVELS FOUND IN THE WORK PLACE, MUST NOT EXCEED THE WORKING LIMITS OF THE RESPIRATOR AND BE JOINTLY APPROVED BY THE NATIONAL INSTITUTE FOR OCCUPATIONAL SAFETY AND HEALTH AND THE MINE SAFETY AND HEALTH ADMINISTRATION (NIOSH-MSHA).
TYPE 'C' SUPPLIED-AIR RESPIRATOR WITH A FULL FACEPIECE OPERATED IN PRESSURE-DEMAND OR OTHER POSITIVE PRESSURE MODE OR WITH A FULL FACEPIECE, HELMET OR HOOD OPERATED IN CONTINOUS-FLOW MODE. SELF-CONTAINED BREATHING APPARATUS WITH A FULL FACEPIECE OPERATED IN PRESSURE-DEMAND OR OTHER POSITIVE PRESSURE MODE.
FOR FIREFIGHTING AND OTHER IMMEDIATELY DANGEROUS TO LIFE OR HEALTH CONDITIONS:
SELF-CONTAINED BREATHING APPARATUS WITH FULL FACEPIECE OPERATED IN PRESSURE-DEMAND OR OTHER POSITIVE PRESSURE MODE.
SUPPLIED-AIR RESPIRATOR WITH FULL FACEPIECE AND OPERATED IN PRESSURE-DEMAND OR OTHER POSITIVE PRESSURE MODE IN COMBINATION WITH AN AUXILIARY SELF-CONTAINED BREATHING APPARATUS OPERATED IN PRESSURE-DEMAND OR OTHER POSITIVE PRESSURE MODE.

CLOTHING: EMPLOYEE MUST WEAR APPROPRIATE PROTECTIVE (IMPERVIOUS) CLOTHING AND EQUIPMENT TO PREVENT ANY POSSIBILITY OF SKIN CONTACT WITH THIS SUBSTANCE.

GLOVES: EMPLOYEE MUST WEAR APPROPRIATE PROTECTIVE GLOVES TO PREVENT CONTACT WITH THIS SUBSTANCE.

EYE PROTECTION: EMPLOYEE MUST WEAR SPLASH-PROOF OR DUST-RESISTANT SAFETY GOGGLES WITH OR WITHOUT A FACESHIELD TO PREVENT CONTACT WITH THIS SUBSTANCE.
EMERGENCY EYE WASH: WHERE THERE IS ANY POSSIBILITY THAT AN EMPLOYEE'S EYES MAY BE EXPOSED TO THIS SUBSTANCE, THE EMPLOYER SHOULD PROVIDE AN EYE WASH FOUNTAIN WITHIN THE IMMEDIATE WORK AREA FOR EMERGENCY USE.

AUTHORIZED BY- OCCUPATIONAL HEALTH SERVICES, INC.
CREATION DATE: 10/05/89 ***REVISION DATE:*** 04/26/90

INGESTION: BROMPYRAZON: **ACUTE EXPOSURE-** A LETHAL DOSE IN RATS WAS 8500 MG/KG; NO SYMPTOMS WERE REPORTED. **CHRONIC EXPOSURE-** NO DATA AVAILABLE.

FIRST AID- TREAT SYMPTOMATICALLY AND SUPPORTIVELY. GET MEDICAL ATTENTION IMMEDIATELY. IF VOMITING OCCURS, KEEP HEAD LOWER THAN HIPS TO PREVENT ASPIRATION.

ANTIDOTE: NO SPECIFIC ANTIDOTE. TREAT SYMPTOMATICALLY AND SUPPORTIVELY.

REACTIVITY

REACTIVITY: STABLE UNDER NORMAL TEMPERATURES AND PRESSURES.

INCOMPATIBILITIES: BROMPYRAZON: NO SPECIFIC DATA AVAILABLE. SEE ALSO AMINES.

AMINES: ACROLEIN: EXOTHERMIC POLYMERIZATION. CALCIUM HYPOCHLORITE: FORMATION OF EXPLOSIVE CHLOROAMINE. MALEIC ANHYDRIDE: EXPLOSIVE DECOMPOSITION. NITROSYL PERCHLORATE: EXPLOSIVE REACTION. SODIUM HYPOCHLORITE: FORMATION OF EXPLOSIVE CHLOROAMINE. TRI-ISO-BUTYL ALUMINUM: VIOLENT REACTION.

DECOMPOSITION: THERMAL DECOMPOSITION PRODUCTS MAY INCLUDE TOXIC AND CORROSIVE FUMES OF BROMIDES, AND TOXIC OXIDES OF NITROGEN AND CARBON.

POLYMERIZATION: HAZARDOUS POLYMERIZATION HAS NOT BEEN REPORTED TO OCCUR UNDER NORMAL TEMPERATURES AND PRESSURES.

STORAGE AND DISPOSAL

OBSERVE ALL FEDERAL, STATE AND LOCAL REGULATIONS WHEN STORING OR DISPOSING OF THIS SUBSTANCE. FOR ASSISTANCE, CONTACT THE DISTRICT DIRECTOR OF THE ENVIRONMENTAL PROTECTION AGENCY.

STORAGE

STORE IN ACCORDANCE WITH 40 CFR 165 RECOMMENDED PROCEDURES FOR THE DISPOSAL AND STORAGE OF PESTICIDES AND PESTICIDE CONTAINERS.

DISPOSAL

DISPOSAL MUST BE IN ACCORDANCE WITH 40 CFR 165 RECOMMENDED PROCEDURES FOR THE DISPOSAL AND STORAGE OF PESTICIDES AND PESTICIDE CONTAINERS.

CONDITIONS TO AVOID

MAY BURN BUT DOES NOT IGNITE READILY.

SPILL AND LEAK PROCEDURES

OCCUPATIONAL SPILL: DO NOT TOUCH SPILLED MATERIAL. STOP LEAK IF YOU CAN DO IT WITHOUT RISK. FOR SMALL SPILLS, TAKE UP WITH SAND OR OTHER ABSORBENT MATERIAL AND PLACE INTO CONTAINERS FOR LATER DISPOSAL. FOR SMALL DRY SPILLS, WITH A CLEAN SHOVEL PLACE MATERIAL INTO CLEAN, DRY CONTAINER AND COVER. MOVE CONTAINERS FROM SPILL AREA. FOR LARGER SPILLS, DIKE FAR AHEAD OF SPILL FOR LATER DISPOSAL. KEEP UNNECESSARY PEOPLE AWAY. ISOLATE HAZARD AREA AND DENY ENTRY.

PROTECTIVE EQUIPMENT

VENTILATION: PROVIDE GENERAL DILUTION VENTILATION.

RESPIRATOR: THE FOLLOWING RESPIRATORS ARE RECOMMENDED BASED ON INFORMATION FOUND IN THE PHYSICAL DATA, TOXICITY AND HEALTH EFFECTS SECTIONS. THEY ARE RANKED IN ORDER FROM MINIMUM TO MAXIMUM RESPIRATORY PROTECTION. THE SPECIFIC RESPIRATOR SELECTED MUST BE BASED ON CONTAMINATION LEVELS FOUND IN THE WORK PLACE, MUST NOT EXCEED THE WORKING LIMITS OF THE RESPIRATOR AND BE JOINTLY APPROVED BY THE NATIONAL INSTITUTE FOR OCCUPATIONAL SAFETY AND HEALTH AND THE MINE SAFETY AND HEALTH ADMINISTRATION (NIOSH-MSHA).

CHEMICAL CARTRIDGE RESPIRATOR WITH AN ORGANIC VAPOR CARTRIDGE(S) WITH A FULL FACEPIECE AND ORGANIC VAPOR CARTRIDGE(S) IN COMBINATION WITH A DUST AND MIST FILTER.

POWERED AIR-PURIFYING RESPIRATOR WITH A TIGHT-FITTING FACEPIECE AND ORGANIC VAPOR CARTRIDGE(S) IN COMBINATION WITH A HIGH-EFFICIENCY PARTICULATE FILTER.

TYPE 'C' SUPPLIED-AIR RESPIRATOR WITH A FULL FACEPIECE OPERATED IN A PRESSURE-DEMAND OR OTHER POSITIVE PRESSURE MODE.

SELF-CONTAINED BREATHING APPARATUS WITH A FULL FACEPIECE OPERATED IN PRESSURE-DEMAND OR OTHER POSITIVE PRESSURE MODE.

FOR FIREFIGHTING AND OTHER IMMEDIATELY DANGEROUS TO LIFE OR HEALTH CONDITIONS:

SELF-CONTAINED BREATHING APPARATUS WITH FULL FACEPIECE OPERATED IN PRESSURE-DEMAND OR OTHER POSITIVE PRESSURE MODE.

SUPPLIED-AIR RESPIRATOR WITH FULL FACEPIECE AND OPERATED IN PRESSURE-DEMAND OR OTHER POSITIVE PRESSURE MODE IN COMBINATION WITH AN AUXILIARY SELF-CONTAINED BREATHING APPARATUS OPERATED IN PRESSURE-DEMAND OR OTHER POSITIVE PRESSURE MODE.

CLOTHING: EMPLOYEE MUST WEAR APPROPRIATE PROTECTIVE (IMPERVIOUS) CLOTHING AND EQUIPMENT TO PREVENT REPEATED OR PROLONGED SKIN CONTACT WITH THIS SUBSTANCE.

GLOVES: EMPLOYEE MUST WEAR APPROPRIATE PROTECTIVE GLOVES TO PREVENT CONTACT WITH THIS SUBSTANCE.

EYE PROTECTION: EMPLOYEE MUST WEAR SPLASH-PROOF OR DUST-RESISTANT SAFETY GOGGLES TO PREVENT EYE CONTACT WITH THIS SUBSTANCE.

EMERGENCY EYE WASH: WHERE THERE IS ANY POSSIBILITY THAT AN EMPLOYEE'S EYES MAY BE EXPOSED TO THIS SUBSTANCE, THE EMPLOYER SHOULD PROVIDE AN EYE WASH FOUNTAIN WITHIN THE IMMEDIATE WORK AREA FOR EMERGENCY USE.

AUTHORIZED BY- OCCUPATIONAL HEALTH SERVICES, INC.

CREATION DATE: 10/04/89 ***REVISION DATE:*** 06/11/90

MATERIAL SAFETY DATA SHEET

OCCUPATIONAL HEALTH SERVICES, INC.
AGRICULTURE AND PESTICIDE DIVISION
450 SEVENTH AVENUE, SUITE 2407
NEW YORK, NEW YORK 10123
1-800-445-MSDS OR (212) 967-1100

EMERGENCY CONTACT:
JOHN S. BRANSFORD, JR. (615) 292-1180

SUBSTANCE IDENTIFICATION

CAS-NUMBER 33693-04-8

SUBSTANCE: **TERBUMETON**

TRADE NAMES/SYNONYMS: 1,3,5-TRIAZINE-2,4-DIAMINE, N-(1,1-DIMETHYLETHYL)-N'-ETHYL-6-METHOXY-; S-TRIAZINE, 2-(TERT-BUTYLAMINO)-4-(ETHYLAMINO)-6-METHOXY-; N-(1,1-DIMETHYLETHYL)-N'-ETHYL-6-METHOXY-1,3,5-TRIAZINE-2,4-DIAMINE; 2-(TERT-BUTYLAMINO)-4-(ETHYLAMINO)-6-METHOXY-S-TRIAZINE; 2-TERT-BUTYLAMINO-4-ETHYLAMINO-6-METHOXY-1,3,5-TRIAZINE; A 2591; CARAGARD; GS 14259; MEBT; TERBUTHYLON; TERBUTONE; C10H19N5O; PST72770

CHEMICAL FAMILY: S-TRIAZINE

MOLECULAR FORMULA: C10-H19-N5-O

MOLECULAR WEIGHT: 225.34

CERCLA RATINGS (SCALE 0-3): HEALTH=2 FIRE=1 REACTIVITY=0 PERSISTENCE=2

NFPA RATINGS (SCALE 0-4): HEALTH=2 FIRE=1 REACTIVITY=0

COMPONENTS AND CONTAMINANTS

COMPONENT: TERBUMETON ***PERCENT:*** 100.0
CAS# 33693-04-8

OTHER CONTAMINANTS: NONE

EXPOSURE LIMITS: NO OCCUPATIONAL EXPOSURE LIMITS ESTABLISHED BY OSHA, ACGIH, OR NIOSH.

PHYSICAL DATA

DESCRIPTION: COLORLESS OR WHITE CRYSTALS.

MELTING POINT: 253-255 F (123-124 C)

SPECIFIC GRAVITY: 1.081 ***VAPOR PRESSURE:*** NEGLIGIBLE

SOLUBILITY IN WATER: 130 PPM @ 20 C

SOLVENT SOLUBILITY: SOLUBLE IN ACETONE, DICHLOROMETHANE, METHANOL, TOLUENE, OCTAN-1-OL AND ORGANIC SOLVENTS

FIRE AND EXPLOSION DATA

FIRE AND EXPLOSION HAZARD: SLIGHT FIRE HAZARD WHEN EXPOSED TO HEAT OR FLAME.

FIREFIGHTING MEDIA: DRY CHEMICAL, CARBON DIOXIDE, HALON, WATER SPRAY OR STANDARD FOAM (1987 EMERGENCY RESPONSE GUIDEBOOK, DOT P 5800.4). FOR LARGER FIRES, USE WATER SPRAY, FOG OR STANDARD FOAM (1987 EMERGENCY RESPONSE GUIDEBOOK, DOT P 5800.4).

FIREFIGHTING: MOVE CONTAINERS FROM FIRE AREA IF POSSIBLE (1987 EMERGENCY RESPONSE GUIDEBOOK, DOT P 5800.4, GUIDE PAGE 53).

EXTINGUISH USING AGENTS SUITABLE FOR SURROUNDING FIRE. USE FLOODING QUANTITIES OF WATER AS A FOG. KEEP MATERIAL OUT OF SEWERS AND WATER SOURCES. DO NOT TOUCH SPILLED MATERIAL. AVOID BREATHING HAZARDOUS FUMES; KEEP UPWIND.

TOXICITY

TERBUMETON: 482 MG/KG ORAL-RAT LD50. CARCINOGEN STATUS: NONE. TERBUMETON IS TOXIC AND MAY CAUSE EYE, SKIN, AND MUCOUS MEMBRANE IRRITATION.

HEALTH EFFECTS AND FIRST AID

INHALATION: TERBUMETON: **ACUTE EXPOSURE-** SOME TRIAZINES ARE MILDLY IRRITATING TO THE UPPER RESPIRATORY TRACT. **CHRONIC EXPOSURE-** NO DATA AVAILABLE.

FIRST AID- REMOVE FROM EXPOSURE AREA TO FRESH AIR IMMEDIATELY. IF BREATHING HAS STOPPED, PERFORM ARTIFICIAL RESPIRATION. KEEP PERSON WARM AND AT REST. TREAT SYMPTOMATICALLY AND SUPPORTIVELY. GET MEDICAL ATTENTION IMMEDIATELY.

SKIN CONTACT: TERBUMETON: **ACUTE EXPOSURE-** A LETHAL DOSE IN RATS BY DERMAL ABSORPTION WAS GREATER THAN 3170 MG/KG. SOME TRIAZINES ARE MILDLY IRRITATING TO THE SKIN. **CHRONIC EXPOSURE-** NO DATA AVAILABLE.

FIRST AID- REMOVE CONTAMINATED CLOTHING AND SHOES IMMEDIATELY. WASH AFFECTED AREA WITH SOAP OR MILD DETERGENT AND LARGE AMOUNTS OF WATER UNTIL NO EVIDENCE OF CHEMICAL REMAINS (APPROXIMATELY 15-20 MINUTES). GET MEDICAL ATTENTION IMMEDIATELY.

EYE CONTACT: TERBUMETON: **ACUTE EXPOSURE-** SOME TRIAZINES ARE MILDLY IRRITATING TO THE EYES. **CHRONIC EXPOSURE-** NO DATA AVAILABLE.

FIRST AID- WASH EYES IMMEDIATELY WITH LARGE AMOUNTS OF WATER OR NORMAL SALINE, OCCASIONALLY LIFTING UPPER AND LOWER LIDS, UNTIL NO EVIDENCE OF CHEMICAL REMAINS (APPROXIMATELY 15-20 MINUTES). GET MEDICAL ATTENTION IMMEDIATELY.

INGESTION: TERBUMETON: TOXIC. **ACUTE EXPOSURE-** A LETHAL DOSE IN RATS WAS 482 MG/KG; NO SYMPTOMS WERE REPORTED. **CHRONIC EXPOSURE-** NO ADVERSE EFFECTS WERE NOTED IN A 90-DAY STUDY OF RATS FED 10 MG/KG/DAY AND DOGS FED 25 MG/KG/DAY.

FIRST AID- REMOVE BY GASTRIC LAVAGE AND CATHARSIS. MAINTAIN BLOOD PRESSURE AND AIRWAY. GIVE OXYGEN IF RESPIRATION IS DEPRESSED. DO NOT PERFORM GASTRIC LAVAGE IF VICTIM IS UNCONSCIOUS. GET MEDICAL ATTENTION IMMEDIATELY (DREISBACH, HANDBOOK OF POISONING, 12TH ED.). ADMINISTRATION OF LAVAGE OR OXYGEN SHOULD BE PERFORMED BY QUALIFIED MEDICAL PERSONNEL.

ANTIDOTE: NO SPECIFIC ANTIDOTE. TREAT SYMPTOMATICALLY AND SUPPORTIVELY.

REACTIVITY

REACTIVITY: STABLE UNDER NORMAL TEMPERATURES AND PRESSURES.

INCOMPATIBILITIES: TERBUMETON: NO DATA AVAILABLE.

DECOMPOSITION: THERMAL DECOMPOSITION PRODUCTS MAY INCLUDE TOXIC OXIDES OF NITROGEN.

POLYMERIZATION: HAZARDOUS POLYMERIZATION HAS NOT BEEN REPORTED TO OCCUR UNDER NORMAL TEMPERATURES AND PRESSURES.

STORAGE AND DISPOSAL

OBSERVE ALL FEDERAL, STATE AND LOCAL REGULATIONS WHEN STORING OR DISPOSING OF THIS SUBSTANCE. FOR ASSISTANCE, CONTACT THE DISTRICT DIRECTOR OF THE ENVIRONMENTAL PROTECTION AGENCY.

****STORAGE****

STORE IN ACCORDANCE WITH 40 CFR 165 RECOMMENDED PROCEDURES FOR THE DISPOSAL AND STORAGE OF PESTICIDES AND PESTICIDE CONTAINERS.

****DISPOSAL****

DISPOSAL MUST BE IN ACCORDANCE WITH 40 CFR 165 RECOMMENDED PROCEDURES FOR THE DISPOSAL AND STORAGE OF PESTICIDES AND PESTICIDE CONTAINERS.

CONDITIONS TO AVOID

MAY BURN BUT DOES NOT IGNITE READILY.

SPILL AND LEAK PROCEDURES

OCCUPATIONAL SPILL: DO NOT TOUCH SPILLED MATERIAL. STOP LEAK IF YOU CAN DO IT WITHOUT RISK. FOR SMALL SPILLS, TAKE UP WITH SAND OR OTHER ABSORBENT MATERIAL AND PLACE INTO CONTAINERS FOR LATER DISPOSAL. FOR SMALL DRY SPILLS, WITH A CLEAN SHOVEL PLACE MATERIAL INTO CLEAN, DRY CONTAINER AND COVER. MOVE CONTAINERS FROM SPILL AREA. FOR LARGER SPILLS, DIKE FAR AHEAD OF SPILL FOR LATER DISPOSAL. KEEP UNNECESSARY PEOPLE AWAY. ISOLATE HAZARD AREA AND DENY ENTRY.

PROTECTIVE EQUIPMENT

VENTILATION: PROVIDE LOCAL EXHAUST OR GENERAL DILUTION VENTILATION SYSTEM.

RESPIRATOR: THE FOLLOWING RESPIRATORS ARE RECOMMENDED BASED ON INFORMATION FOUND IN THE PHYSICAL DATA, TOXICITY AND HEALTH EFFECTS SECTIONS. THEY ARE RANKED IN ORDER FROM MINIMUM TO MAXIMUM RESPIRATORY PROTECTION. THE SPECIFIC RESPIRATOR SELECTED MUST BE BASED ON CONTAMINATION LEVELS FOUND IN THE WORK PLACE, MUST NOT EXCEED THE WORKING LIMITS OF THE RESPIRATOR AND BE JOINTLY APPROVED BY THE NATIONAL INSTITUTE FOR OCCUPATIONAL SAFETY AND HEALTH AND THE MINE SAFETY AND HEALTH ADMINISTRATION (NIOSH-MSHA).

CHEMICAL CARTRIDGE RESPIRATOR WITH AN ORGANIC VAPOR CARTRIDGE(S) WITH A FULL FACEPIECE AND ORGANIC VAPOR CARTRIDGE(S) IN COMBINATION WITH A DUST AND MIST FILTER.

POWERED AIR-PURIFYING RESPIRATOR WITH A TIGHT-FITTING FACEPIECE AND ORGANIC VAPOR CARTRIDGE(S) IN COMBINATION WITH A HIGH-EFFICIENCY PARTICULATE FILTER.

TYPE 'C' SUPPLIED-AIR RESPIRATOR WITH A FULL FACEPIECE OPERATED IN A PRESSURE-DEMAND OR OTHER POSITIVE PRESSURE MODE.

SELF-CONTAINED BREATHING APPARATUS WITH A FULL FACEPIECE OPERATED IN PRESSURE-DEMAND OR OTHER POSITIVE PRESSURE MODE.

FOR FIREFIGHTING AND OTHER IMMEDIATELY DANGEROUS TO LIFE OR HEALTH CONDITIONS:

SELF-CONTAINED BREATHING APPARATUS WITH FULL FACEPIECE OPERATED IN PRESSURE-DEMAND OR OTHER POSITIVE PRESSURE MODE.

SUPPLIED-AIR RESPIRATOR WITH FULL FACEPIECE AND OPERATED IN PRESSURE-DEMAND OR OTHER POSITIVE PRESSURE MODE IN COMBINATION WITH AN AUXILIARY SELF-CONTAINED BREATHING APPARATUS OPERATED IN PRESSURE-DEMAND OR OTHER POSITIVE PRESSURE MODE.

CLOTHING: EMPLOYEE MUST WEAR APPROPRIATE PROTECTIVE (IMPERVIOUS) CLOTHING AND EQUIPMENT TO PREVENT REPEATED OR PROLONGED SKIN CONTACT WITH THIS SUBSTANCE.

GLOVES: EMPLOYEE MUST WEAR APPROPRIATE PROTECTIVE GLOVES TO PREVENT CONTACT WITH THIS SUBSTANCE.

EYE PROTECTION: EMPLOYEE MUST WEAR SPLASH-PROOF OR DUST-RESISTANT SAFETY GOGGLES TO PREVENT EYE CONTACT WITH THIS SUBSTANCE.

EMERGENCY EYE WASH: WHERE THERE IS ANY POSSIBILITY THAT AN EMPLOYEE'S EYES MAY BE EXPOSED TO THIS SUBSTANCE, THE EMPLOYER SHOULD PROVIDE AN EYE WASH FOUNTAIN WITHIN THE IMMEDIATE WORK AREA FOR EMERGENCY USE.

AUTHORIZED BY- OCCUPATIONAL HEALTH SERVICES, INC.

CREATION DATE: 10/05/89 ***REVISION DATE:*** 05/07/90

MATERIAL SAFETY DATA SHEET

OCCUPATIONAL HEALTH SERVICES, INC.
AGRICULTURE AND PESTICIDE DIVISION
450 SEVENTH AVENUE, SUITE 2407
NEW YORK, NEW YORK 10123
1-800-445-MSDS OR (212) 967-1100

EMERGENCY CONTACT:
JOHN S. BRANSFORD, JR. (615) 292-1180

SUBSTANCE IDENTIFICATION

CAS-NUMBER 52918-63-5

SUBSTANCE: **DELTAMETHRIN**

TRADE NAMES/SYNONYMS: CYCLOPROPANECARBOXYLIC ACID, 3-(2,2-DIBROMOETHENYL)-2,2-DIMETHYL-, CYANO(3-PHENOXYPHENYL)METHYL ESTER, (1R-(1 ALPHA(S*),3 ALPHA))-; 3-(2,2-DIBROMOETHENYL)-2,2-DIMETHYLCYCLOPROPANECARBOXYLIC ACID CYANO(3-PHENOXYPHENYL)METHYL ESTER; (1R-(1 ALPHA(S*),3 ALPHA))-3-(2,2-DIBROMOETHENYL)-2,2-DIMETHYLCYCLOPROPANECARBOXYLIC ACID CYANO(3-PHENOXYPHENYL)METHYL ESTER; DECAMETHRIN; DECIS; K-OTHRIN; (1R-(1 ALPHA(S*),3 ALPHA))-CYANO(3-PHENOXYPHENYL)METHYL-3-(2,2- DIBROMOVINYL)-2,2-DIMETHYLCYCLOPROPANECARBOXYLATE; DELTAMETHRINE; FMC 45498; NRDC 161; RU 22974; C22H19BR2NO3; PST72784

CHEMICAL FAMILY: PYRETHROID (SYNTHETIC)

MOLECULAR FORMULA: C22-H19-BR2-N-O3

MOLECULAR WEIGHT: 505.22

CERCLA RATINGS (SCALE 0-3): HEALTH=3 FIRE=1 REACTIVITY=0 PERSISTENCE=1

NFPA RATINGS (SCALE 0-4): HEALTH=4 FIRE=1 REACTIVITY=0

COMPONENTS AND CONTAMINANTS

COMPONENT: DELTAMETHRIN ***PERCENT:*** 100.0
CAS# 52918-63-5

OTHER CONTAMINANTS: NONE

EXPOSURE LIMITS: NO OCCUPATIONAL EXPOSURE LIMITS ESTABLISHED BY OSHA, ACGIH, OR NIOSH.
PYRETHROIDS: 1 POUND CERCLA SECTION 103 REPORTABLE QUANTITY

PHYSICAL DATA

DESCRIPTION: ODORLESS, COLORLESS, CRYSTALLINE SOLID.
MELTING POINT: 208-214 F (98-101 C) ***SPECIFIC GRAVITY:*** NOT AVAILABLE
VAPOR PRESSURE: NEGLIGIBLE ***SOLUBILITY IN WATER:*** 2 PPB
SOLVENT SOLUBILITY: SOLUBLE IN ACETONE, DIOXANE, BENZENE, CYCLOHEXANONE, DIMETHYLSULFOXIDE, XYLENE, TOLUENE; MODERATELY SOLUBLE IN ETHANOL; SLIGHTLY SOLUBLE IN KEROSENE

FIRE AND EXPLOSION DATA

FIRE AND EXPLOSION HAZARD: SLIGHT FIRE HAZARD WHEN EXPOSED TO HEAT OR FLAME.
FIREFIGHTING MEDIA: DRY CHEMICAL, CARBON DIOXIDE, HALON, WATER SPRAY OR STANDARD FOAM (1987 EMERGENCY RESPONSE GUIDEBOOK, DOT P 5800.4).
FOR LARGER FIRES, USE WATER SPRAY, FOG OR STANDARD FOAM (1987 EMERGENCY RESPONSE GUIDEBOOK, DOT P 5800.4).
FIREFIGHTING: MOVE CONTAINERS FROM FIRE AREA IF POSSIBLE (1987 EMERGENCY RESPONSE GUIDEBOOK, DOT P 5800.4, GUIDE PAGE 53).
EXTINGUISH ONLY IF FLOW CAN BE STOPPED. EXTINGUISH USING AGENT INDICATED. USE FLOODING AMOUNTS OF WATER AS A FOG. COOL CONTAINERS WITH FLOODING AMOUNTS OF WATER FROM AS FAR A DISTANCE AS POSSIBLE. AVOID BREATHING POISONOUS VAPORS, KEEP UPWIND. CONSIDER EVACUATION OF DOWNWIND AREA IF MATERIAL IS LEAKING.

TRANSPORTATION DATA

DEPARTMENT OF TRANSPORTATION HAZARD CLASSIFICATION 49 CFR 172.101: POISON B
DEPARTMENT OF TRANSPORTATION LABELING REQUIREMENTS 49 CFR 172.101 AND SUBPART E: POISON
DEPARTMENT OF TRANSPORTATION PACKAGING REQUIREMENTS: 49 CFR 173.365 EXCEPTIONS: 49 CFR 173.364

TOXICITY

DELTAMETHRIN: TOXICITY DATA: 785 MG/M3/2 HOURS INHALATION-RAT LC50; >2000 MG/KG SKIN-RAT LD50 (PEMNDP); 30 MG/KG ORAL-RAT LD50; 3450 MG/KG ORAL-MOUSE LD50; 3440 UG/KG INTRAVENOUS-DOG LD50; 2526 MG/KG INTRAVENOUS-RAT LD50; 26,100 UG/KG INTRACEREBRAL-MOUSE LD50; MUTAGENIC DATA (RTECS); REPRODUCTIVE EFFECTS DATA (RTECS). CARCINOGEN STATUS: NONE. ACUTE TOXICITY LEVEL: HIGHLY TOXIC BY INHALATION AND INGESTION; SLIGHTLY TOXIC BY DERMAL ABSORPTION. TARGET EFFECTS: MAY AFFECT THE CENTRAL NERVOUS SYSTEM.*
* MAY BE BASED ON GROUP INFORMATION ON PYRETHROIDS.

HEALTH EFFECTS AND FIRST AID

INHALATION: DELTAMETHRIN: HIGHLY TOXIC. SEE INFORMATION ON PYRETHROIDS. THE LETHAL CONCENTRATION IN RATS WAS 785 MG/M3/2 HOURS. SYMPTOMS WERE NOT REPORTED.
PYRETHROIDS: **ACUTE EXPOSURE-** HEAVY EXPOSURE TO A MIST OF SOME PYRETHROIDS HAS PRODUCED HYPERSENSITIVIITY, ATAXIA, AND URINARY INCONTINENCE. CONVULSIONS MAY ALSO BE POSSIBLE. **CHRONIC EXPOSURE-** ANIMALS EXPOSED TO AEROSOLS OF SOME PYRETHROIDS FOR 3-4 HOURS/DAY FOR UP TO 4 WEEKS DID NOT EXHIBIT ANY SIGNIFICANT COMPOUND RELATED FINDINGS.
FIRST AID- REMOVE FROM EXPOSURE AREA TO FRESH AIR IMMEDIATELY. IF BREATHING HAS STOPPED, PERFORM ARTIFICIAL RESPIRATION. KEEP PERSON WARM AND AT REST. TREAT SYMPTOMATICALLY AND SUPPORTIVELY. GET MEDICAL ATTENTION IMMEDIATELY.

SKIN CONTACT: DELTAMETHRIN: SEE INFORMATION ON PYRETHROIDS.
PYRETHROIDS: **ACUTE EXPOSURE-** BASED ON ANIMAL AND HUMAN STUDIES AND HUMAN EXPERIENCES WITH SOME PYRETHROIDS, PRIMARY IRRITATION IS UNLIKELY. CUTANEOUS PARESTHESIAS MAY OCCUR INCLUDING NUMBNESS, ITCHING, BURNING, TINGLING AND WARMTH WITHOUT SIGNS OF IRRITATION. THESE EFFECTS MAY BE DELAYED FOR 30 MINUTES OR MORE AND LAST LESS THAN 24 HOURS. **CHRONIC EXPOSURE-** TESTS WITH SOME PYRETHROIDS ON HUMANS AND ANIMALS INDICATE SENSITIZATION IS UNLIKELY.
FIRST AID- REMOVE CONTAMINATED CLOTHING AND SHOES IMMEDIATELY. WASH AFFECTED AREA WITH SOAP OR MILD DETERGENT AND LARGE AMOUNTS OF WATER UNTIL NO EVIDENCE OF CHEMICAL REMAINS (APPROXIMATELY 15-20 MINUTES). GET MEDICAL ATTENTION IMMEDIATELY.

EYE CONTACT: DELTAMETHRIN: **ACUTE EXPOSURE-** NO DATA AVAILABLE. **CHRONIC EXPOSURE-** NO DATA AVAILABLE.
FIRST AID- WASH EYES IMMEDIATELY WITH LARGE AMOUNTS OF WATER OR NORMAL SALINE, OCCASIONALLY LIFTING UPPER AND LOWER LIDS, UNTIL NO EVIDENCE OF CHEMICAL REMAINS (APPROXIMATELY 15-20 MINUTES). GET MEDICAL ATTENTION IMMEDIATELY.

INGESTION: DELTAMETHRIN: HIGHLY TOXIC. SEE INFORMATION ON PYRETHROIDS. THE LETHAL DOSE IN RATS WAS 30 MG/KG. SYMPTOMS WERE NOT REPORTED. REPRODUCTIVE EFFECTS HAVE BEEN REPORTED IN ANIMALS.
PYRETHROIDS: **ACUTE EXPOSURE-** SOME PYRETHROIDS HAVE PRODUCED HYPERSENSITIVITY, NERVOUS IRRITABILITY, TREMORS, ATAXIA, AND URINARY INCONTINENCE IN ANIMALS. CONVULSIONS MAY ALSO BE POSSIBLE. **CHRONIC EXPOSURE-** INCREASED KIDNEY AND LIVER WEIGHTS AND HEPATIC HISTOPATHOLOGICAL CHANGES WERE NOTED IN ANIMALS CHRONICALLY FED SOME PYRETHROIDS.
FIRST AID- REMOVE BY GASTRIC LAVAGE AND CATHARSIS. MAINTAIN BLOOD PRESSURE AND AIRWAY. GIVE OXYGEN IF RESPIRATION IS DEPRESSED. DO NOT PERFORM GASTRIC LAVAGE IF VICTIM IS UNCONSCIOUS. GET MEDICAL ATTENTION IMMEDIATELY (DREISBACH, HANDBOOK OF POISONING, 12TH ED.).
ADMINISTRATION OF LAVAGE OR OXYGEN SHOULD BE PERFORMED BY QUALIFIED MEDICAL PERSONNEL.
ANTIDOTE: NO SPECIFIC ANTIDOTE. TREAT SYMPTOMATICALLY AND SUPPORTIVELY.

REACTIVITY

REACTIVITY: STABLE UNDER NORMAL TEMPERATURES AND PRESSURES.
INCOMPATIBILITIES: DELTAMETHRIN: OXIDIZERS (STRONG): FIRE AND EXPLOSION HAZARD.
DECOMPOSITION: THERMAL DECOMPOSITION PRODUCTS MAY INCLUDE TOXIC AND CORROSIVE FUMES OF BROMIDES, AND TOXIC OXIDES OF CARBON AND NITROGEN.
POLYMERIZATION: HAZARDOUS POLYMERIZATION HAS NOT BEEN REPORTED TO OCCUR UNDER NORMAL TEMPERATURES AND PRESSURES.

STORAGE AND DISPOSAL

OBSERVE ALL FEDERAL, STATE AND LOCAL REGULATIONS WHEN STORING OR DISPOSING OF THIS SUBSTANCE. FOR ASSISTANCE, CONTACT THE DISTRICT DIRECTOR OF THE ENVIRONMENTAL PROTECTION AGENCY.

STORAGE

STORE IN ACCORDANCE WITH 40 CFR 165 RECOMMENDED PROCEDURES FOR THE DISPOSAL AND STORAGE OF PESTICIDES AND PESTICIDE CONTAINERS.
STORE AWAY FROM INCOMPATIBLE SUBSTANCES.

DISPOSAL

DISPOSAL MUST BE IN ACCORDANCE WITH 40 CFR 165 RECOMMENDED PROCEDURES FOR THE DISPOSAL AND STORAGE OF PESTICIDES AND PESTICIDE CONTAINERS.

CONDITIONS TO AVOID

MAY BURN BUT DOES NOT IGNITE READILY.

SPILL AND LEAK PROCEDURES

OCCUPATIONAL SPILL: DO NOT TOUCH SPILLED MATERIAL. STOP LEAK IF YOU CAN DO IT WITHOUT RISK. FOR SMALL SPILLS, TAKE UP WITH SAND OR OTHER ABSORBENT MATERIAL AND PLACE INTO CONTAINERS FOR LATER DISPOSAL. FOR SMALL DRY SPILLS, WITH A CLEAN SHOVEL PLACE MATERIAL INTO CLEAN, DRY CONTAINER AND COVER. MOVE CONTAINERS FROM SPILL AREA. FOR LARGER SPILLS, DIKE FAR AHEAD OF SPILL FOR LATER DISPOSAL. KEEP UNNECESSARY PEOPLE AWAY. ISOLATE HAZARD AREA AND DENY ENTRY.
REPORTABLE QUANTITY (RQ): 1 POUND THE SUPERFUND AMENDMENTS AND REAUTHORIZATION ACT (SARA) SECTION 304 REQUIRES THAT A RELEASE EQUAL TO OR GREATER THAN THE REPORTABLE QUANTITY FOR THIS SUBSTANCE BE IMMEDIATELY REPORTED TO THE LOCAL EMERGENCY PLANNING COMMITTEE AND THE STATE EMERGENCY RESPONSE COMMISSION (40 CFR 355.40). IF THE RELEASE OF THIS SUBSTANCE IS REPORTABLE UNDER CERCLA SECTION 103, THE NATIONAL RESPONSE CENTER MUST BE NOTIFIED IMMEDIATELY AT (800) 424-8802 OR (202) 426-2675 IN THE METROPOLITAN WASHINGTON, D.C. AREA (40 CFR 302.6).

PROTECTIVE EQUIPMENT

VENTILATION: PROVIDE LOCAL EXHAUST OR GENERAL DILUTION VENTILATION SYSTEM.
RESPIRATOR: THE FOLLOWING RESPIRATORS ARE RECOMMENDED BASED ON INFORMATION FOUND IN THE PHYSICAL DATA, TOXICITY AND HEALTH EFFECTS SECTIONS. THEY ARE RANKED IN ORDER FROM MINIMUM TO MAXIMUM RESPIRATORY PROTECTION. THE SPECIFIC RESPIRATOR SELECTED MUST BE BASED ON CONTAMINATION LEVELS FOUND IN THE WORK PLACE, MUST NOT EXCEED THE WORKING LIMITS OF THE RESPIRATOR AND BE JOINTLY APPROVED BY THE NATIONAL INSTITUTE FOR OCCUPATIONAL SAFETY AND HEALTH AND THE MINE SAFETY AND HEALTH ADMINISTRATION (NIOSH-MSHA).

TYPE 'C' SUPPLIED-AIR RESPIRATOR WITH A FULL FACEPIECE OPERATED IN PRESSURE-DEMAND OR OTHER POSITIVE PRESSURE MODE OR WITH A FULL FACEPIECE, HELMET OR HOOD OPERATED IN CONTINOUS-FLOW MODE.
SELF-CONTAINED BREATHING APPARATUS WITH A FULL FACEPIECE OPERATED IN PRESSURE-DEMAND OR OTHER POSITIVE PRESSURE MODE.
FOR FIREFIGHTING AND OTHER IMMEDIATELY DANGEROUS TO LIFE OR HEALTH CONDITIONS:
SELF-CONTAINED BREATHING APPARATUS WITH FULL FACEPIECE OPERATED IN PRESSURE-DEMAND OR OTHER POSITIVE PRESSURE MODE.
SUPPLIED-AIR RESPIRATOR WITH FULL FACEPIECE AND OPERATED IN PRESSURE-DEMAND OR OTHER POSITIVE PRESSURE MODE IN COMBINATION WITH AN AUXILIARY SELF-CONTAINED BREATHING APPARATUS OPERATED IN PRESSURE-DEMAND OR OTHER POSITIVE PRESSURE MODE.

CLOTHING: EMPLOYEE MUST WEAR APPROPRIATE PROTECTIVE (IMPERVIOUS) CLOTHING AND EQUIPMENT TO PREVENT REPEATED OR PROLONGED SKIN CONTACT WITH THIS SUBSTANCE.

GLOVES: EMPLOYEE MUST WEAR APPROPRIATE PROTECTIVE GLOVES TO PREVENT CONTACT WITH THIS SUBSTANCE.

EYE PROTECTION: EMPLOYEE MUST WEAR SPLASH-PROOF OR DUST-RESISTANT SAFETY GOGGLES TO PREVENT EYE CONTACT WITH THIS SUBSTANCE.
EMERGENCY EYE WASH: WHERE THERE IS ANY POSSIBILITY THAT AN EMPLOYEE'S EYES MAY BE EXPOSED TO THIS SUBSTANCE, THE EMPLOYER SHOULD PROVIDE AN EYE WASH FOUNTAIN WITHIN THE IMMEDIATE WORK AREA FOR EMERGENCY USE.

AUTHORIZED BY- OCCUPATIONAL HEALTH SERVICES, INC.
CREATION DATE: 10/04/89 ***REVISION DATE:*** 05/15/90

MATERIAL SAFETY DATA SHEET

OCCUPATIONAL HEALTH SERVICES, INC.
AGRICULTURE AND PESTICIDE DIVISION
450 SEVENTH AVENUE, SUITE 2407
NEW YORK, NEW YORK 10123
1-800-445-MSDS OR (212) 967-1100

EMERGENCY CONTACT:
JOHN S. BRANSFORD, JR. (615) 292-1180

SUBSTANCE IDENTIFICATION

CAS-NUMBER 17781-16-7

SUBSTANCE: **7-HYDROXY-2,2-DIMETHYL-3(2H)-BENZOFURANONE**

TRADE NAMES/SYNONYMS: 3(2H)-BENZOFURANONE, 7-HYDROXY-2,2-DIMETHYL-; 3-KETOCARBOFURAN PHENOL; CARBOFURAN-3-KETO-7-PHENOL; 2,3-DIHYDRO-2,2-DIMETHYL-3-KETO-7-HYDROXYBENZOFURAN; 2,3-DIHYDRO-2,2-DIMETHYL-3 OXO-7-BENZOFURANOL; 3-KETO-7-CARBOFURAN PHENOL; C10H10O3; PST72799

CHEMICAL FAMILY: BENZOFURAN DERIVATIVE

MOLECULAR FORMULA: C10-H10-O3

MOLECULAR WEIGHT: 178.11

CERCLA RATINGS (SCALE 0-3): HEALTH=U FIRE=1 REACTIVITY=0 PERSISTENCE=1

NFPA RATINGS (SCALE 0-4): HEALTH=U FIRE=1 REACTIVITY=0

COMPONENTS AND CONTAMINANTS

COMPONENT: 7-HYDROXY-2,2-DIMETHYL-3(2H)-BENZOFURANONE ***PERCENT:*** 100.0
CAS# 17781-16-7

OTHER CONTAMINANTS: NONE

EXPOSURE LIMITS: NO OCCUPATIONAL EXPOSURE LIMITS ESTABLISHED BY OSHA, ACGIH, OR NIOSH.

PHYSICAL DATA

DESCRIPTION: PALE YELLOW POWDER. ***MELTING POINT:*** 333-334 F (167-168 C)
SPECIFIC GRAVITY: NOT AVAILABLE ***SOLUBILITY IN WATER:*** NOT AVAILABLE

FIRE AND EXPLOSION DATA

FIRE AND EXPLOSION HAZARD: SLIGHT FIRE HAZARD WHEN EXPOSED TO HEAT OR FLAME.

FIREFIGHTING MEDIA: DRY CHEMICAL, CARBON DIOXIDE, HALON, WATER SPRAY OR STANDARD FOAM (1987 EMERGENCY RESPONSE GUIDEBOOK, DOT P 5800.4).
FOR LARGER FIRES, USE WATER SPRAY, FOG OR STANDARD FOAM (1987 EMERGENCY RESPONSE GUIDEBOOK, DOT P 5800.4).

FIREFIGHTING: MOVE CONTAINER FROM FIRE AREA IF POSSIBLE. DO NOT SCATTER SPILLED MATERIAL WITH HIGH PRESSURE WATER STREAMS. DIKE FIRE CONTROL WATER FOR LATER DISPOSAL (1987 EMERGENCY RESPONSE GUIDEBOOK, DOT P 5800.4, GUIDE PAGE 31).
USE AGENTS SUITABLE FOR TYPE OF SURROUNDING FIRE. AVOID BREATHING HAZARDOUS VAPORS, KEEP UPWIND.

TOXICITY

7-HYDROXY-2,2-DIMETHYL-3(2H)-BENZOFURANONE: TOXICITY DATA: 295 MG/KG ORAL-RAT LD50 (EPA). CARCINOGEN STATUS: NONE. ACUTE TOXCITY LEVEL: TOXIC BY INGESTION. TARGET EFFECTS: NO DATA AVAILABLE.

HEALTH EFFECTS AND FIRST AID

INHALATION: 7-HYDROXY-2,2-DIMETHYL-3(2H)-BENZOFURANONE: **ACUTE EXPOSURE-** NO DATA AVAILABLE. **CHRONIC EXPOSURE-** NO DATA AVAILABLE.

FIRST AID- REMOVE FROM EXPOSURE AREA TO FRESH AIR IMMEDIATELY. IF BREATHING HAS STOPPED, PERFORM ARTIFICIAL RESPIRATION. KEEP PERSON WARM AND AT REST. TREAT SYMPTOMATICALLY AND SUPPORTIVELY. GET MEDICAL ATTENTION IMMEDIATELY.

SKIN CONTACT: 7-HYDROXY-2,2-DIMETHYL-3(2H)-BENZOFURANONE: **ACUTE EXPOSURE-** NO DATA AVAILABLE. **CHRONIC EXPOSURE-** NO DATA AVAILABLE.

FIRST AID- REMOVE CONTAMINATED CLOTHING AND SHOES IMMEDIATELY. WASH AFFECTED AREA WITH SOAP OR MILD DETERGENT AND LARGE AMOUNTS OF WATER UNTIL NO EVIDENCE OF CHEMICAL REMAINS (APPROXIMATELY 15-20 MINUTES). GET MEDICAL ATTENTION IMMEDIATELY.

EYE CONTACT: 7-HYDROXY-2,2-DIMETHYL-3(2H)-BENZOFURANONE: **ACUTE EXPOSURE-** NO DATA AVAILABLE. **CHRONIC EXPOSURE-** NO DATA AVAILABLE.

FIRST AID- WASH EYES IMMEDIATELY WITH LARGE AMOUNTS OF WATER OR NORMAL SALINE, OCCASIONALLY LIFTING UPPER AND LOWER LIDS, UNTIL NO EVIDENCE OF CHEMICAL REMAINS (APPROXIMATELY 15-20 MINUTES). GET MEDICAL ATTENTION IMMEDIATELY.

INGESTION: 7-HYDROXY-2,2-DIMETHYL-3(2H)-BENZOFURANONE: TOXIC. **ACUTE EXPOSURE-** THE LETHAL DOSE REPORTED IN RATS WAS 295 MG/KG; SYMPTOMS WERE NOT REPORTED. **CHRONIC EXPOSURE-** NO DATA AVAILABLE.

FIRST AID- TREAT SYMPTOMATICALLY AND SUPPORTIVELY. GET MEDICAL ATTENTION IMMEDIATELY. IF VOMITING OCCURS, KEEP HEAD LOWER THAN HIPS TO PREVENT ASPIRATION.

ANTIDOTE: NO SPECIFIC ANTIDOTE. TREAT SYMPTOMATICALLY AND SUPPORTIVELY.

REACTIVITY

REACTIVITY: STABLE UNDER NORMAL TEMPERATURES AND PRESSURES.

INCOMPATIBILITIES: 7-HYDROXY-2,2-DIMETHYL-3(2H)-BENZOFURANONE: OXIDIZERS (STRONG): FIRE AND EXPLOSION HAZARD.

DECOMPOSITION: THERMAL DECOMPOSITION PRODUCTS MAY INCLUDE TOXIC OXIDES OF CARBON.

POLYMERIZATION: HAZARDOUS POLYMERIZATION HAS NOT BEEN REPORTED TO OCCUR UNDER NORMAL TEMPERATURES AND PRESSURES.

STORAGE AND DISPOSAL

OBSERVE ALL FEDERAL, STATE AND LOCAL REGULATIONS WHEN STORING OR DISPOSING OF THIS SUBSTANCE. FOR ASSISTANCE, CONTACT THE DISTRICT DIRECTOR OF THE ENVIRONMENTAL PROTECTION AGENCY.

STORAGE

STORE IN ACCORDANCE WITH 40 CFR 165 RECOMMENDED PROCEDURES FOR THE DISPOSAL AND STORAGE OF PESTICIDES AND PESTICIDE CONTAINERS.
STORE AWAY FROM INCOMPATIBLE SUBSTANCES.

DISPOSAL

DISPOSAL MUST BE IN ACCORDANCE WITH 40 CFR 165 RECOMMENDED PROCEDURES FOR THE DISPOSAL AND STORAGE OF PESTICIDES AND PESTICIDE CONTAINERS.

CONDITIONS TO AVOID

MAY BURN BUT DOES NOT IGNITE READILY. AVOID CONTACT WITH STRONG OXIDIZERS, EXCESSIVE HEAT, SPARKS, OR OPEN FLAME.

SPILL AND LEAK PROCEDURES

OCCUPATIONAL SPILL: SWEEP UP AND PLACE IN SUITABLE CLEAN, DRY CONTAINERS FOR RECLAMATION OR LATER DISPOSAL. DO NOT FLUSH SPILLED MATERIAL INTO SEWER. KEEP UNNECESSARY PEOPLE AWAY.

PROTECTIVE EQUIPMENT

VENTILATION: PROVIDE LOCAL EXHAUST OR PROCESS ENCLOSURE VENTILATION SYSTEM.

RESPIRATOR: THE FOLLOWING RESPIRATORS ARE RECOMMENDED BASED ON INFORMATION FOUND IN THE PHYSICAL DATA, TOXICITY AND HEALTH EFFECTS SECTIONS. THEY ARE RANKED IN ORDER FROM MINIMUM TO MAXIMUM

RESPIRATORY PROTECTION. THE SPECIFIC RESPIRATOR SELECTED MUST BE BASED ON CONTAMINATION LEVELS FOUND IN THE WORK PLACE, MUST NOT EXCEED THE WORKING LIMITS OF THE RESPIRATOR AND BE JOINTLY APPROVED BY THE NATIONAL INSTITUTE FOR OCCUPATIONAL SAFETY AND HEALTH AND THE MINE SAFETY AND HEALTH ADMINISTRATION (NIOSH-MSHA).

TYPE 'C' SUPPLIED-AIR RESPIRATOR WITH A FULL FACEPIECE OPERATED IN PRESSURE-DEMAND OR OTHER POSITIVE PRESSURE MODE OR WITH A FULL FACEPIECE, HELMET OR HOOD OPERATED IN CONTINOUS-FLOW MODE.

SELF-CONTAINED BREATHING APPARATUS WITH A FULL FACEPIECE OPERATED IN PRESSURE-DEMAND OR OTHER POSITIVE PRESSURE MODE.

FOR FIREFIGHTING AND OTHER IMMEDIATELY DANGEROUS TO LIFE OR HEALTH CONDITIONS:

SELF-CONTAINED BREATHING APPARATUS WITH FULL FACEPIECE OPERATED IN PRESSURE-DEMAND OR OTHER POSITIVE PRESSURE MODE.

SUPPLIED-AIR RESPIRATOR WITH FULL FACEPIECE AND OPERATED IN PRESSURE-DEMAND OR OTHER POSITIVE PRESSURE MODE IN COMBINATION WITH AN AUXILIARY SELF-CONTAINED BREATHING APPARATUS OPERATED IN PRESSURE-DEMAND OR OTHER POSITIVE PRESSURE MODE.

CLOTHING: EMPLOYEE MUST WEAR APPROPRIATE PROTECTIVE (IMPERVIOUS) CLOTHING AND EQUIPMENT TO PREVENT ANY POSSIBILITY OF SKIN CONTACT WITH THIS SUBSTANCE.

GLOVES: EMPLOYEE MUST WEAR APPROPRIATE PROTECTIVE GLOVES TO PREVENT CONTACT WITH THIS SUBSTANCE.

EYE PROTECTION: EMPLOYEE MUST WEAR SPLASH-PROOF OR DUST-RESISTANT SAFETY GOGGLES AND A FACESHIELD TO PREVENT CONTACT WITH THIS SUBSTANCE.

EMERGENCY WASH FACILITIES: WHERE THERE IS ANY POSSIBILITY THAT AN EMPLOYEE'S EYES AND/OR SKIN MAY BE EXPOSED TO THIS SUBSTANCE, THE EMPLOYER SHOULD PROVIDE AN EYE WASH FOUNTAIN AND QUICK DRENCH SHOWER WITHIN THE IMMEDIATE WORK AREA FOR EMERGENCY USE.

AUTHORIZED BY- OCCUPATIONAL HEALTH SERVICES, INC.
CREATION DATE: 12/14/89 ***REVISION DATE:*** 05/31/90

MATERIAL SAFETY DATA SHEET

OCCUPATIONAL HEALTH SERVICES, INC.
AGRICULTURE AND PESTICIDE DIVISION
450 SEVENTH AVENUE, SUITE 2407
NEW YORK, NEW YORK 10123
1-800-445-MSDS OR (212) 967-1100

EMERGENCY CONTACT:
JOHN S. BRANSFORD, JR. (615) 292-1180

SUBSTANCE IDENTIFICATION

CAS-NUMBER 16655-82-6

SUBSTANCE: 3-HYDROXYCARBOFURAN

TRADE NAMES/SYNONYMS: 3,7-BENZOFURANDIOL, 2,3-DIHYDRO-2,2-DIMETHYL-, 7-(METHYLCARBAMATE); 2,3-DIHYDRO-2,2-DIMETHYL-3,7-BENZOFURANDIOL-7-(METHYLCARBAMATE); CARBAMIC ACID, METHYL-, 2,3-DIHYDRO-3-HYDROXY-2,2-DIMETHYL-7- BENZOFURANYL ESTER; METHYLCARBAMIC ACID-2,3-DIHYDRO-3-HYDROXY-2,2-DIMETHYL-7-BENZOFURANYL ESTER; C12H15NO4; PST72800

CHEMICAL FAMILY: FURAN DERIVATIVE

MOLECULAR FORMULA: C12-H15-N-O4

MOLECULAR WEIGHT: 237.26

CERCLA RATINGS (SCALE 0-3): HEALTH=3 FIRE=1 REACTIVITY=0 PERSISTENCE=0

NFPA RATINGS (SCALE 0-4): HEALTH=3 FIRE=1 REACTIVITY=0

COMPONENTS AND CONTAMINANTS

COMPONENT: 3-HYDROXYCARBOFURAN ***PERCENT:*** 100.0
CAS# 16655-82-6

OTHER CONTAMINANTS: NONE

EXPOSURE LIMITS: NO OCCUPATIONAL EXPOSURE LIMITS ESTABLISHED BY OSHA, ACGIH, OR NIOSH.

PHYSICAL DATA

DESCRIPTION: SOLID. ***MELTING POINT:*** 397 F (147 C)

SPECIFIC GRAVITY: NOT AVAILABLE ***SOLUBILITY IN WATER:*** NOT AVAILABLE

SOLVENT SOLUBILITY: SOLUBLE IN N-HEXANE, ETHYL ACETATE.

FIRE AND EXPLOSION DATA

FIRE AND EXPLOSION HAZARD: SLIGHT FIRE HAZARD WHEN EXPOSED TO HEAT OR FLAME.

FIREFIGHTING MEDIA: DRY CHEMICAL, CARBON DIOXIDE, HALON, WATER SPRAY OR STANDARD FOAM (1987 EMERGENCY RESPONSE GUIDEBOOK, DOT P 5800.4).
FOR LARGER FIRES, USE WATER SPRAY, FOG OR STANDARD FOAM (1987 EMERGENCY RESPONSE GUIDEBOOK, DOT P 5800.4).

FIREFIGHTING: MOVE CONTAINERS FROM FIRE AREA IF POSSIBLE (1987 EMERGENCY RESPONSE GUIDEBOOK, DOT P 5800.4, GUIDE PAGE 53).
EXTINGUISH USING AGENT SUITABLE FOR TYPE OF SURROUNDING FIRE. AVOID BREATHING VAPORS AND DUSTS. KEEP UPWIND.

TRANSPORTATION DATA

DEPARTMENT OF TRANSPORTATION HAZARD CLASSIFICATION 49 CFR 172.101: POISON B

DEPARTMENT OF TRANSPORTATION LABELING REQUIREMENTS 49 CFR 172.101 AND SUBPART E: POISON

DEPARTMENT OF TRANSPORTATION PACKAGING REQUIREMENTS: 49 CFR 173.365 EXCEPTIONS: 49 CFR 173.364

TOXICITY

3-HYDROXYCARBOFURAN: TOXICITY DATA: 18 MG/KG ORAL-RAT LD50; 7 MG/KG ORAL-MOUSE LD50; MUTAGENIC DATA (RTECS). CARCINOGEN STATUS: NONE. ACUTE TOXICITY LEVEL: HIGHLY TOXIC BY INGESTION. TARGET EFFECTS: CHOLINESTERASE INHIBITOR. AT INCREASED RISK FROM EXPOSURE: PERSONS WITH ASTHMA, DIABETES, CARDIOVASCULAR DISEASE, MECHANICAL OBSTRUCTION OF THE GASTROINTESTINAL OR UROGENITAL TRACT, AND THOSE IN VAGOTONIC STATES.*

* MAY BE BASED ON GENERAL INFORMATION ON CARBAMATES.

HEALTH EFFECTS AND FIRST AID

INHALATION: 3-HYDROXYCARBOFURAN: SEE INFORMATION ON CARBAMATES.
CARBAMATES: CHOLINESTERASE INHIBITOR. **ACUTE EXPOSURE-** WHEN INHALED, THE FIRST EFFECTS OF CHOLINESTERASE INHIBITION ARE USUALLY RESPIRATORY AND MAY INCLUDE NASAL HYPEREMIA AND WATERY DISCHARGE, CHEST DISCOMFORT, DYSPNEA, AND WHEEZING DUE TO INCREASED BRONCHIAL SECRETIONS AND BRONCHOCONSTRICTION. OTHER SYSTEMIC EFFECTS MAY BEGIN WITHIN A FEW MINUTES OR SEVERAL HOURS OF EXPOSURE. SYMPTOMS MAY INCLUDE NAUSEA, VOMITING, DIARRHEA, ABDOMINAL CRAMPS, HEADACHE, VERTIGO, OCULAR PAIN, CILIARY MUSCLE SPASM, BLURRING OR DIMNESS OF VISION, MIOSIS, OR IN SOME CASES MYDRIASIS, LACRIMATION, SALIVATION, SWEATING, AND CONFUSION. OTHER REPORTED CENTRAL NERVOUS SYSTEM OR NEUROMUSCULAR EFFECTS INCLUDE ATAXIA, SLURRED SPEECH, AREFLEXIA, WEAKNESS, FATIGUE, TWITCHING, FASCICULATION, TREMOR, AND EVENTUALLY PARALYSIS OF THE EXTREMITIES AND POSSIBLY OF THE RESPIRATORY MUSCLES. IN SEVERE CASES, THERE MAY ALSO BE INVOLUNTARY DEFECATION AND URINATION, BRADYCARDIA, HYPOTENSION, PULMONARY EDEMA, CONVULSIONS, COMA, AND DEATH FROM RESPIRATORY FAILURE OR CARDIAC ARREST. CARBAMATES GENERALLY DO NOT ACCUMULATE IN MAMMALIAN TISSUE AND THE CHOLINESTERASE INHIBITION REVERSES RATHER RAPIDLY. IN NON-FATAL CASES, THE ILLNESS GENERALLY LASTS LESS THAN 24 HOURS.
CHRONIC EXPOSURE- PROLONGED OR REPEATED EXPOSURE MAY CAUSE EFFECTS AS DESCRIBED IN ACUTE EXPOSURE.

FIRST AID- REMOVE FROM EXPOSURE AREA TO FRESH AIR IMMEDIATELY. IF BREATHING HAS STOPPED, GIVE ARTIFICIAL RESPIRATION. MAINTAIN AIRWAY AND BLOOD PRESSURE AND ADMINISTER OXYGEN IF AVAILABLE. KEEP AFFECTED PERSON WARM AND AT REST. TREAT SYMPTOMATICALLY AND SUPPORTIVELY. ADMINISTRATION OF OXYGEN SHOULD BE PERFORMED BY QUALIFIED PERSONNEL. GET MEDICAL ATTENTION IMMEDIATELY.

SKIN CONTACT: 3-HYDROXYCARBOFURAN: SEE INFORMATION ON CARBAMATES.
CARBAMATES: CHOLINESTERASE INHIBITOR. **ACUTE EXPOSURE-** SOME COMPOUNDS MAY CAUSE IRRITATION. LOCALIZED SWEATING AND FASCICULATIONS MAY OCCUR AT THE SITE OF CONTACT. IF SUFFICIENT AMOUNTS ARE ABSORBED THROUGH THE SKIN, OTHER EFFECTS OF CHOLINESTERASE INHIBITION MAY OCCUR AS DESCRIBED IN ACUTE INHALATION; SYMPTOMS MAY BE DELAYED FOR 2-3 HOURS, USUALLY NO MORE THAN 8 HOURS. **CHRONIC EXPOSURE-** REPEATED OR PROLONGED EXPOSURE MAY CAUSE EFFECTS AS DESCRIBED IN ACUTE EXPOSURE.

FIRST AID- REMOVE CONTAMINATED CLOTHING IMMEDIATELY. WASH CONTAMINATED AREAS WITH SOAP AND WATER FOLLOWED BY ALCOHOL (ARENA, POISONING, 4TH ED.). EMERGENCY PERSONNEL SHOULD WEAR GLOVES AND AVOID CONTAMINATION. TREAT RESPIRATORY DIFFICULTY WITH ARTIFICIAL RESPIRATION. GET MEDICAL ATTENTION IMMEDIATELY.

EYE CONTACT: 3-HYDROXYCARBOFURAN: SEE INFORMATION ON CARBAMATES.
CARBAMATES: CHOLINESTERASE INHIBITOR. **ACUTE EXPOSURE-** DIRECT CONTACT MAY CAUSE PAIN, HYPEREMIA, LACRIMATION, TWITCHING OF THE EYELIDS,

MIOSIS, AND CILIARY MUSCLE SPASM WITH LOSS OF ACCOMODATION, BLURRED OR DIMMED VISION AND BROWACHE. SOMETIMES MYDRIASIS MAY OCCUR INSTEAD OF MIOSIS. WITH SUFFICIENT EXPOSURE, OTHER SYMPTOMS OF CHOLINESTERASE INHIBITION MAY OCCUR AS DESCRIBED IN ACUTE INHALATION. **CHRONIC EXPOSURE-** PROLONGED EXPOSURE MAY CAUSE EFFECTS AS DESCRIBED IN ACUTE EXPOSURE. SOME COMPOUNDS HAVE CAUSED TOXIC EFFECTS ON THE CRYSTALLINE LENS, CONJUNCTIVAL THICKENING AND OBSTRUCTION OF NASOLACRIMAL CANALS WHEN USED AS MIOTIC EYE DROPS.

FIRST AID- IRRIGATE EYES WITH WATER OR SALINE SOLUTION. IF SYMPTOMS OF POISONING OCCUR, TREAT RESPIRATORY DIFFICULTY WITH ARTIFICIAL RESPIRATION AND OXYGEN. OBSERVE PATIENT FOR AT LEAST 24-36 HOURS (GOSSELIN, CLINICAL TOXICOLOGY OF COMMERCIAL PRODUCTS, 5TH ED.). GET MEDICAL ATTENTION IMMEDIATELY. OXYGEN SHOULD BE ADMINISTERED BY QUALIFIED MEDICAL PERSONNEL.

INGESTION: 3-HYDROXYCARBOFURAN: HIGHLY TOXIC. SEE INFORMATION ON CARBAMATES.

CARBAMATES: CHOLINESTERASE INHIBITOR. **ACUTE EXPOSURE-** WHEN INGESTED, THE FIRST EFFECTS MAY BE NAUSEA, VOMITING, ANOREXIA, ABDOMINAL CRAMPS, AND DIARRHEA. WITH ABSORPTION FROM THE GASTROINTESTINAL TRACT, THE OTHER EFFECTS OF CHOLINESTERASE INHIBITION AS DESCRIBED IN ACUTE INHALATION MAY OCCUR; SYMPTOMS MAY BEGIN WITHIN MINUTES OR BE DELAYED SEVERAL HOURS. **CHRONIC EXPOSURE-** REPEATED INGESTION MAY CAUSE EFFECTS AS DESCRIBED IN ACUTE EXPOSURE.

FIRST AID- IF PERSON IS ALERT AND RESPIRATION IS NOT DEPRESSED, GIVE SYRUP OF IPECAC FOLLOWED BY WATER (IF VOMITING OCCURS, KEEP HEAD BELOW HIPS TO PREVENT ASPIRATION). IF CONSCIOUSNESS LEVEL DECLINES OR VOMITING HAS NOT OCCURRED IN 15 MINUTES EMPTY STOMACH BY GASTRIC LAVAGE WITH THE AID OF CUFFED ENDOTRACHEAL TUBE USING ISOTONIC SALINE OR 5% SODIUM BICARBONATE FOLLOW WITH ACTIVATED CHARCOAL. ESTABLISH AND MAINTAIN AIRWAY. TREAT RESPIRATORY DIFFICULTY WITH ARTIFICIAL RESPIRATION AND OXYGEN. DO NOT GIVE MORPHINE, AMINOPHYLLINE, PHENOTHIAZINES, RESERPINE, FUROSEMIDE, OR ETHACRYNIC ACID (MORGAN, RECOGNITION AND MANAGEMENT OF PESTICIDE POISONINGS, 3RD ED.). TREAT SYMPTOMATICALLY AND SUPPORTIVELY. ADMINISTRATION OF OXYGEN AND LAVAGE MUST BE PERFORMED BY QUALIFIED MEDICAL PERSONNEL. GET MEDICAL ATTENTION IMMEDIATELY.

ANTIDOTE: THE FOLLOWING ANTIDOTE(S) HAVE BEEN RECOMMENDED. HOWEVER, THE DECISION AS TO WHETHER THE SEVERITY OF POISONING REQUIRES ADMINISTRATION OF ANY ANTIDOTE AND ACTUAL DOSE REQUIRED SHOULD BE MADE BY QUALIFIED MEDICAL PERSONNEL.

FOR CHOLINESTERASE INHIBITORS: ESTABLISH CLEAR AIRWAY AND TISSUE OXYGENATION BY ASPIRATION OF SECRETIONS, AND IF NECESSARY, BY ASSISTED PULMONARY VENTILATION WITH OXYGEN. IMPROVE TISSUE OXYGENATION AS MUCH AS POSSIBLE BEFORE ADMINISTERING ATROPINE TO MINIMIZE THE RISK OF VENTRICULAR FIBRILLATION. ADMINISTER ATROPINE SULFATE INTRAVENOUSLY, OR INTRAMUSCULARLY IF IV INJECTION IS NOT POSSIBLE. IN MODERATELY SEVERE POISONING ADMINISTER ATROPINE SULFATE, 0.4-2.0 MG REPEATED EVERY 15 MINUTES UNTIL ATROPINIZATION IS ACHIEVED (TACHYCARDIA, FLUSHING, DRY MOUTH, MYDRIASIS). MAINTAIN ATROPINIZATION BY REPEATED DOSES FOR 2-12 HOURS, OR LONGER, DEPENDING ON THE SEVERITY OF POISONING. THE APPEARANCE OF RALES IN THE LUNG BASES, MIOSIS, SALIVATION, NAUSEA, BRADYCARDIA, ARE ALL INDICATIONS OF INADEQUATE ATROPINIZATION. SEVERELY POISONED INDIVIDUALS MAY EXHIBIT REMARKABLE TOLERANCE TO ATROPINE; TWO OR MORE TIMES THE DOSAGES SUGGESTED ABOVE MAY BE NEEDED. PERSONS NOT POISONED OR ONLY SLIGHTLY POISONED, HOWEVER, MAY DEVELOP SIGNS OF ATROPINE TOXICITY FROM SUCH LARGE DOSAGES: FEVER, MUSCLE FIBRILLATIONS, AND DELIRIUM ARE THE MAIN SIGNS OF ATROPINE TOXICITY. IF THESE SIGNS APPEAR WHILE THE PATIENT IS FULLY ATROPINIZED, ATROPINE ADMINISTRATION SHOULD BE DISCONTINUED, AT LEAST TEMPORARILY. OBSERVE TREATED PATIENTS CLOSELY AT LEAST 24 HOURS TO INSURE THAT SYMPTOMS (POSSIBLY PULMONARY EDEMA) DO NOT RECUR AS ATROPINIZATION WEARS OFF. IN VERY SEVERE POISONINGS, METABOLIC DISPOSITION OF TOXICANT MAY REQUIRE SEVERAL HOURS OR DAYS DURING WHICH ATROPINIZATION MUST BE MAINTAINED. MARKEDLY LOWER LEVELS OF URINARY METABOLITES INDICATE THAT ATROPINE DOSAGE CAN BE TAPERED OFF. AS DOSAGE IS REDUCED, CHECK THE LUNG BASES FREQUENTLY FOR RALES. IF RALES ARE HEARD OR OTHER SYMPTOMS RETURN, RE-ESTABLISH ATROPINIZATION PROMPTLY (MORGAN, RECOGNITION AND MANAGEMENT OF PESTICIDE POISONINGS, 3RD ED.). ADMINISTRATION OF ANTIDOTE MUST BE PERFORMED BY QUALIFIED MEDICAL PERSONNEL.

PRALIDOXIME (PROTOPAM-AYERST, 2-PAM) IS OF DOUBTFUL VALUE IN POISONINGS BY CARBAMATE INHIBITORS OF CHOLINESTERASE. ATROPINE ALONE IS ALMOST ALWAYS AN ADEQUATE ANTIDOTE. PRALIDOXIME IS PROBABLY CONTRAINDICATED IN POISONING BY CARBARYL SPECIFICALLY, AND OTHER MONOMETHYLATED CARBAMATES. IF A VICTIM OF DIMETHYLCARBAMATE INSECTICIDE POISONING FAILS TO RESPOND PROMPTLY AND ADEQUATELY TO ATROPINE, OR IF POISONING INVOLVES A COMBINATION OF CARBAMATE AND ORGANOPHOSPHATE, A DILUTE SOLUTION OF PRALIDOXIME (TOTAL DOSE IN 250 ML 5% GLUCOSE SOLUTION) MAY BE GIVEN CAUTIOUSLY INTRAVENOUSLY. ADULT DOSAGE IS 1 GRAM (MORGAN, RECOGNITION AND MANAGEMENT OF PESTICIDE POISONINGS, THIRD EDITION; HAYES, PESTICIDES STUDIED IN MAN, 1982).

REACTIVITY

REACTIVITY: STABLE UNDER NORMAL TEMPERATURES AND PRESSURES.

INCOMPATIBILITIES: 3-HYDROXYCARBOFURAN: OXIDIZERS (STRONG): FIRE AND EXPLOSION HAZARD.

DECOMPOSITION: THERMAL DECOMPOSITION PRODUCTS MAY INCLUDE TOXIC OXIDES OF CARBON AND NITROGEN.

POLYMERIZATION: HAZARDOUS POLYMERIZATION HAS NOT BEEN REPORTED TO OCCUR UNDER NORMAL TEMPERATURES AND PRESSURES.

STORAGE AND DISPOSAL

OBSERVE ALL FEDERAL, STATE AND LOCAL REGULATIONS WHEN STORING OR DISPOSING OF THIS SUBSTANCE. FOR ASSISTANCE, CONTACT THE DISTRICT DIRECTOR OF THE ENVIRONMENTAL PROTECTION AGENCY.

CONDITIONS TO AVOID

MAY BURN BUT DOES NOT IGNITE READILY.

SPILL AND LEAK PROCEDURES

OCCUPATIONAL SPILL: DO NOT TOUCH SPILLED MATERIAL. STOP LEAK IF YOU CAN DO IT WITHOUT RISK. FOR SMALL SPILLS, TAKE UP WITH SAND OR OTHER ABSORBENT MATERIAL AND PLACE INTO CONTAINERS FOR LATER DISPOSAL. FOR SMALL DRY SPILLS, WITH A CLEAN SHOVEL PLACE MATERIAL INTO CLEAN, DRY CONTAINER AND COVER. MOVE CONTAINERS FROM SPILL AREA. FOR LARGER SPILLS, DIKE FAR AHEAD OF SPILL FOR LATER DISPOSAL. KEEP UNNECESSARY PEOPLE AWAY. ISOLATE HAZARD AREA AND DENY ENTRY.

PROTECTIVE EQUIPMENT

VENTILATION: PROVIDE LOCAL EXHAUST OR PROCESS ENCLOSURE VENTILATION SYSTEM.

RESPIRATOR: THE FOLLOWING RESPIRATORS ARE RECOMMENDED BASED ON INFORMATION FOUND IN THE PHYSICAL DATA, TOXICITY AND HEALTH EFFECTS SECTIONS. THEY ARE RANKED IN ORDER FROM MINIMUM TO MAXIMUM RESPIRATORY PROTECTION. THE SPECIFIC RESPIRATOR SELECTED MUST BE BASED ON CONTAMINATION LEVELS FOUND IN THE WORK PLACE, MUST NOT EXCEED THE WORKING LIMITS OF THE RESPIRATOR AND BE JOINTLY APPROVED BY THE NATIONAL INSTITUTE FOR OCCUPATIONAL SAFETY AND HEALTH AND THE MINE SAFETY AND HEALTH ADMINISTRATION (NIOSH-MSHA).

TYPE 'C' SUPPLIED-AIR RESPIRATOR WITH A FULL FACEPIECE OPERATED IN PRESSURE-DEMAND OR OTHER POSITIVE PRESSURE MODE OR WITH A FULL FACEPIECE, HELMET OR HOOD OPERATED IN CONTINOUS-FLOW MODE.

SELF-CONTAINED BREATHING APPARATUS WITH A FULL FACEPIECE OPERATED IN PRESSURE-DEMAND OR OTHER POSITIVE PRESSURE MODE.

FOR FIREFIGHTING AND OTHER IMMEDIATELY DANGEROUS TO LIFE OR HEALTH CONDITIONS:

SELF-CONTAINED BREATHING APPARATUS WITH FULL FACEPIECE OPERATED IN PRESSURE-DEMAND OR OTHER POSITIVE PRESSURE MODE.

SUPPLIED-AIR RESPIRATOR WITH FULL FACEPIECE AND OPERATED IN PRESSURE-DEMAND OR OTHER POSITIVE PRESSURE MODE IN COMBINATION WITH AN AUXILIARY SELF-CONTAINED BREATHING APPARATUS OPERATED IN PRESSURE-DEMAND OR OTHER POSITIVE PRESSURE MODE.

CLOTHING: EMPLOYEE MUST WEAR APPROPRIATE PROTECTIVE (IMPERVIOUS) CLOTHING AND EQUIPMENT TO PREVENT ANY POSSIBILITY OF SKIN CONTACT WITH THIS SUBSTANCE.

GLOVES: EMPLOYEE MUST WEAR APPROPRIATE PROTECTIVE GLOVES TO PREVENT CONTACT WITH THIS SUBSTANCE.

EYE PROTECTION: EMPLOYEE MUST WEAR SPLASH-PROOF OR DUST-RESISTANT SAFETY GOGGLES TO PREVENT EYE CONTACT WITH THIS SUBSTANCE.

EMERGENCY EYE WASH: WHERE THERE IS ANY POSSIBILITY THAT AN EMPLOYEE'S EYES MAY BE EXPOSED TO THIS SUBSTANCE, THE EMPLOYER SHOULD PROVIDE AN EYE WASH FOUNTAIN WITHIN THE IMMEDIATE WORK AREA FOR EMERGENCY USE.

AUTHORIZED BY- OCCUPATIONAL HEALTH SERVICES, INC.

CREATION DATE: 05/18/90 ***REVISION DATE:*** 06/12/90

MATERIAL SAFETY DATA SHEET

OCCUPATIONAL HEALTH SERVICES, INC.
AGRICULTURE AND PESTICIDE DIVISION
450 SEVENTH AVENUE, SUITE 2407
NEW YORK, NEW YORK 10123
1-800-445-MSDS OR (212) 967-1100

EMERGENCY CONTACT:
JOHN S. BRANSFORD, JR. (615) 292-1180

SUBSTANCE IDENTIFICATION

CAS-NUMBER 52-51-7

SUBSTANCE: **2-BROMO-2-NITROPROPANE-1,3-DIOL**

TRADE NAMES/SYNONYMS: 1,3-PROPANEDIOL, 2-BROMO-2-NITRO-; 2-BROMO-2-NITRO-1,3-PROPANEDIOL; BETA-BROMO-BETA-NITROTRIMETHYLENEGLYCOL; BRONOCOT; BRONOPOL; BRONOSOL; MYACIDE AS; ONYOXIDE 500; C3H6BRNO4; PST72832

CHEMICAL FAMILY: ALCOHOL, ALIPHATIC

MOLECULAR FORMULA: H-O-C-H2-C-(BR)-(N-O2)-C-H2-O-H

MOLECULAR WEIGHT: 199.99

CERCLA RATINGS (SCALE 0-3): HEALTH=3 FIRE=1 REACTIVITY=0 PERSISTENCE=3

NFPA RATINGS (SCALE 0-4): HEALTH=3 FIRE=1 REACTIVITY=0

COMPONENTS AND CONTAMINANTS

COMPONENT: 2-BROMO-2-NITROPROPANE-1,3-DIOL ***PERCENT:*** 100.0
CAS# 52-51-7

OTHER CONTAMINANTS: NONE

EXPOSURE LIMITS: NO OCCUPATIONAL EXPOSURE LIMITS ESTABLISHED BY OSHA, ACGIH, OR NIOSH.

PHYSICAL DATA

DESCRIPTION: ODORLESS, COLORLESS TO PALE BROWN-YELLOW CRYSTALS.

MELTING POINT: 266-271 F (130-133 C) ***SPECIFIC GRAVITY:*** NOT AVAILABLE

SOLUBILITY IN WATER: SOLUBLE

SOLVENT SOLUBILITY: SOLUBLE IN ALCOHOL AND ETHYL ACETATE; SLIGHTLY SOLUBLE IN CHLOROFORM, ACETONE, ETHER, AND BENZENE; INSOLUBLE IN LIGROIN.

FIRE AND EXPLOSION DATA

FIRE AND EXPLOSION HAZARD: SLIGHT FIRE HAZARD WHEN EXPOSED TO HEAT OR FLAME.

FIREFIGHTING MEDIA: DRY CHEMICAL, CARBON DIOXIDE, HALON, WATER SPRAY OR STANDARD FOAM (1987 EMERGENCY RESPONSE GUIDEBOOK, DOT P 5800.4). FOR LARGER FIRES, USE WATER SPRAY, FOG OR STANDARD FOAM (1987 EMERGENCY RESPONSE GUIDEBOOK, DOT P 5800.4).

FIREFIGHTING: MOVE CONTAINER FROM FIRE AREA IF POSSIBLE. DO NOT SCATTER SPILLED MATERIAL WITH HIGH PRESSURE WATER STREAMS. DIKE FIRE CONTROL WATER FOR LATER DISPOSAL (1987 EMERGENCY RESPONSE GUIDEBOOK, DOT P 5800.4, GUIDE PAGE 31).
USE AGENTS SUITABLE FOR TYPE OF SURROUNDING FIRE. AVOID BREATHING HAZARDOUS VAPORS, KEEP UPWIND.

TOXICITY

2-BROMO-2-NITROPROPANE-1,3-DIOL: IRRITATION DATA: 10 MG SKIN-HUMAN MODERATE; 500 MG/24 HOURS SKIN-RABBIT MILD; 80 MG SKIN-RABBIT MODERATE; 5 MG EYE-RABBIT. TOXICITY DATA: 1600 MG/KG SKIN-RAT LD50; 4750 MG/ SKIN-MOUSE LD50; 180 MG/KG ORAL-RAT LD50; 250 MG/KG ORAL-DOG LD50; 170 MG/KG SUBCUTANEOUS-RAT LD50; 116 MG/KG SUBCUTANEOUS-MOUSE LD50; 37,400 UG/KG INTRAVENOUS-RAT LD50; 48 MG/KG INTRAVENOUS-MOUSE LD50; 26 MG/KG INTRAPERITONEAL-RAT LD50; 15,500 UG/KG INTRAPERITONEAL-MOUSE LD50. CARCINOGEN STATUS: NONE. LOCAL EFFECTS: IRRITANT- SKIN AND EYES. ACUTE TOXICITY LEVEL: TOXIC BY INGESTION AND MODERATELY TOXIC BY DERMAL ABSORPTION. TARGET EFFECTS: NO DATA AVAILABLE. AT INCREASED RISK FROM EXPOSURE: PERSONS WITH PRE-EXISTING FORMALDEHYDE SENSITIZATION.

HEALTH EFFECTS AND FIRST AID

INHALATION: 2-BROMO-2-NITROPROPANE-1,3-DIOL: **ACUTE EXPOSURE-** NO DATA AVAILABLE. **CHRONIC EXPOSURE-** NO DATA AVAILABLE.

FIRST AID- REMOVE FROM EXPOSURE AREA TO FRESH AIR IMMEDIATELY. IF BREATHING HAS STOPPED, PERFORM ARTIFICIAL RESPIRATION. KEEP PERSON WARM AND AT REST. TREAT SYMPTOMATICALLY AND SUPPORTIVELY. GET MEDICAL ATTENTION IMMEDIATELY.

SKIN CONTACT: 2-BROMO-2-NITROPROPANE-1,3-DIOL: IRRITANT. **ACUTE EXPOSURE-** 10 MG ON HUMAN SKIN CAUSED MODERATE IRRITATION. **CHRONIC EXPOSURE-** REPEATED AND PROLONGED CONTACT WITH IRRITANTS MAY CAUSE DERMATITIS. 2-BROMO-2-NITROPROPANE-1,3-DIOL MAY PRODUCE ALLERGIC CONTACT DERMATITIS ON DERMATITIC SKIN.

FIRST AID- REMOVE CONTAMINATED CLOTHING AND SHOES IMMEDIATELY. WASH AFFECTED AREA WITH SOAP OR MILD DETERGENT AND LARGE AMOUNTS OF WATER UNTIL NO EVIDENCE OF CHEMICAL REMAINS (APPROXIMATELY 15-20 MINUTES). GET MEDICAL ATTENTION IMMEDIATELY.

EYE CONTACT: 2-BROMO-2-NITROPROPANE-1,3-DIOL: IRRITANT. **ACUTE EXPOSURE-** 5 MG CAUSED IRRITATION TO RABBIT EYES. **CHRONIC EXPOSURE-** REPEATED AND PROLONGED CONTACT WITH IRRITANTS MAY CAUSE CONJUNCTIVITIS.

FIRST AID- WASH EYES IMMEDIATELY WITH LARGE AMOUNTS OF WATER OR NORMAL SALINE, OCCASIONALLY LIFTING UPPER AND LOWER LIDS, UNTIL NO EVIDENCE OF CHEMICAL REMAINS (APPROXIMATELY 15-20 MINUTES). GET MEDICAL ATTENTION IMMEDIATELY.

INGESTION: 2-BROMO-2-NITROPROPANE-1,3-DIOL: TOXIC. **ACUTE EXPOSURE-** THE LETHAL DOSE IN RATS IS 180 MG/KG. **CHRONIC EXPOSURE-** NO DATA AVAILABLE.

FIRST AID- IF EXTENSIVE VOMITING HAS NOT OCCURRED, THE SUBSTANCE SHOULD BE REMOVED BY EMESIS OR GASTRIC LAVAGE PROVIDED THAT THE PATIENT IS CONSCIOUS AND CONVULSIONS ARE NOT PRESENT. KEEP HEAD BELOW HIPS DURING VOMITING TO PREVENT ASPIRATION. DO NOT ATTEMPT TO MAKE AN UNCONSCIOUS PERSON VOMIT. TREAT SYMPTOMATICALLY AND SUPPORTIVELY. GET MEDICAL ATTENTION IMMEDIATELY (DREISBACH, HANDBOOK OF POISONING, 12TH ED.). TREATMENT SHOULD BE PERFORMED BY QUALIFIED MEDICAL PERSONNEL.

ANTIDOTE: NO SPECIFIC ANTIDOTE. TREAT SYMPTOMATICALLY AND SUPPORTIVELY.

REACTIVITY

REACTIVITY: STABLE UNDER NORMAL TEMPERATURES AND PRESSURES.

INCOMPATIBILITIES: 2-BROMO-2-NITROPROPANE-1,3-DIOL: OXIDIZERS (STRONG): FIRE AND EXPLOSION HAZARD.

DECOMPOSITION: THERMAL DECOMPOSITION PRODUCTS MAY INCLUDE TOXIC AND CORROSIVE FUMES OF BROMIDES, AND TOXIC OXIDES OF NITROGEN AND CARBON.

POLYMERIZATION: HAZARDOUS POLYMERIZATION HAS NOT BEEN REPORTED TO OCCUR UNDER NORMAL TEMPERATURES AND PRESSURES.

STORAGE AND DISPOSAL

OBSERVE ALL FEDERAL, STATE AND LOCAL REGULATIONS WHEN STORING OR DISPOSING OF THIS SUBSTANCE. FOR ASSISTANCE, CONTACT THE DISTRICT DIRECTOR OF THE ENVIRONMENTAL PROTECTION AGENCY.

****STORAGE****

STORE AWAY FROM INCOMPATIBLE SUBSTANCES.

CONDITIONS TO AVOID

MAY BURN BUT DOES NOT IGNITE READILY. AVOID CONTACT WITH STRONG OXIDIZERS, EXCESSIVE HEAT, SPARKS, OR OPEN FLAME.

SPILL AND LEAK PROCEDURES

OCCUPATIONAL SPILL: STOP LEAK IF YOU CAN DO IT WITHOUT RISK. FOR SMALL SPILLS, TAKE UP WITH SAND OR OTHER ABSORBENT MATERIAL AND PLACE INTO CLEAN, DRY CONTAINERS FOR LATER DISPOSAL. KEEP UNNECESSARY PEOPLE AWAY. ISOLATE HAZARD AREA AND DENY ENTRY.

PROTECTIVE EQUIPMENT

VENTILATION: PROVIDE LOCAL EXHAUST OR PROCESS ENCLOSURE VENTILATION SYSTEM.

RESPIRATOR: THE FOLLOWING RESPIRATORS ARE RECOMMENDED BASED ON INFORMATION FOUND IN THE PHYSICAL DATA, TOXICITY AND HEALTH EFFECTS SECTIONS. THEY ARE RANKED IN ORDER FROM MINIMUM TO MAXIMUM RESPIRATORY PROTECTION. THE SPECIFIC RESPIRATOR SELECTED MUST BE BASED ON CONTAMINATION LEVELS FOUND IN THE WORK PLACE, MUST NOT EXCEED THE WORKING LIMITS OF THE RESPIRATOR AND BE JOINTLY APPROVED BY THE NATIONAL INSTITUTE FOR OCCUPATIONAL SAFETY AND HEALTH AND THE MINE SAFETY AND HEALTH ADMINISTRATION (NIOSH-MSHA).
DUST AND MIST RESPIRATOR WITH A FULL FACEPIECE.
AIR-PURIFYING FULL FACEPIECE RESPIRATOR WITH A HIGH-EFFICIENCY PARTICULATE FILTER.
POWERED AIR-PURIFYING RESPIRATOR WITH A TIGHT-FITTING FACEPIECE AND HIGH-EFFICIENCY PARTICULATE FILTER.
TYPE 'C' SUPPLIED-AIR RESPIRATOR WITH A FULL FACEPIECE OPERATED IN PRESSURE-DEMAND OR OTHER POSITIVE PRESSURE MODE OR WITH A FULL FACEPIECE, HELMET OR HOOD OPERATED IN CONTINUOUS-FLOW MODE.
SELF-CONTAINED BREATHING APPARATUS WITH A FULL FACEPIECE OPERATED IN PRESSURE-DEMAND OR OTHER POSITIVE PRESSURE MODE.

FOR FIREFIGHTING AND OTHER IMMEDIATELY DANGEROUS TO LIFE OR HEALTH CONDITIONS:
SELF-CONTAINED BREATHING APPARATUS WITH FULL FACEPIECE OPERATED IN PRESSURE-DEMAND OR OTHER POSITIVE PRESSURE MODE.
SUPPLIED-AIR RESPIRATOR WITH FULL FACEPIECE AND OPERATED IN PRESSURE-DEMAND OR OTHER POSITIVE PRESSURE MODE IN COMBINATION WITH AN AUXILIARY SELF-CONTAINED BREATHING APPARATUS OPERATED IN PRESSURE-DEMAND OR OTHER POSITIVE PRESSURE MODE.

CLOTHING: EMPLOYEE MUST WEAR APPROPRIATE PROTECTIVE (IMPERVIOUS) CLOTHING AND EQUIPMENT TO PREVENT REPEATED OR PROLONGED SKIN CONTACT WITH THIS SUBSTANCE.

GLOVES: EMPLOYEE MUST WEAR APPROPRIATE PROTECTIVE GLOVES TO PREVENT CONTACT WITH THIS SUBSTANCE.

EYE PROTECTION: EMPLOYEE MUST WEAR SPLASH-PROOF OR DUST-RESISTANT SAFETY GOGGLES TO PREVENT EYE CONTACT WITH THIS SUBSTANCE.
EMERGENCY EYE WASH: WHERE THERE IS ANY POSSIBILITY THAT AN EMPLOYEE'S EYES MAY BE EXPOSED TO THIS SUBSTANCE, THE EMPLOYER SHOULD PROVIDE AN EYE WASH FOUNTAIN WITHIN THE IMMEDIATE WORK AREA FOR EMERGENCY USE.

AUTHORIZED BY- OCCUPATIONAL HEALTH SERVICES, INC.
CREATION DATE: 02/08/90 ***REVISION DATE:*** 05/25/90

MATERIAL SAFETY DATA SHEET

OCCUPATIONAL HEALTH SERVICES, INC.
AGRICULTURE AND PESTICIDE DIVISION
450 SEVENTH AVENUE, SUITE 2407
NEW YORK, NEW YORK 10123
1-800-445-MSDS OR (212) 967-1100

EMERGENCY CONTACT:
JOHN S. BRANSFORD, JR. (615) 292-1180

SUBSTANCE IDENTIFICATION

CAS-NUMBER 35256-85-0

SUBSTANCE: TEBUTAM

TRADE NAMES/SYNONYMS: PROPANAMIDE, 2,2-DIMETHYL-N-(1-METHYLETHYL)-N-(PHENYLMETHYL)-; 2,2-DIMETHYL-N-(1-METHYLETHYL)-N-(PHENYLMETHYL)PROPANAMIDE; N-BENZYL-N-ISOPROPYLPIVALAMIDE; N-BENZYL-N-ISOPROPYL TRIMETHYLACETAMIDE; BUTAM; COMODOR; C15H23NO; PST72852

CHEMICAL FAMILY: AMIDE

MOLECULAR FORMULA: C15-H23-N-O

MOLECULAR WEIGHT: 233.39

CERCLA RATINGS (SCALE 0-3): HEALTH=U FIRE=U REACTIVITY=0 PERSISTENCE=1

NFPA RATINGS (SCALE 0-4): HEALTH=U FIRE=U REACTIVITY=0

COMPONENTS AND CONTAMINANTS

COMPONENT: TEBUTAM ***PERCENT:*** 100.0
CAS# 35256-85-0

EXPOSURE LIMITS: NO OCCUPATIONAL EXPOSURE LIMITS ESTABLISHED BY OSHA, ACGIH, OR NIOSH.

PHYSICAL DATA

DESCRIPTION: COLORLESS TO AMBER OIL WITH AN AROMATIC ODOR.

BOILING POINT: 203-208 F (95-98 C) @ 0.1 MMHG ***SPECIFIC GRAVITY:*** 0.973 @ 25 C

VAPOR PRESSURE: 0.0975 MMHG @ 20 C

SOLUBILITY IN WATER: ALMOST INSOLUBLE

SOLVENT SOLUBILITY: SOLUBLE IN BENZENE, ETHANOL, TOLUENE, METHANOL, ACETONE, HEXANE, CHLOROFORM AND ORGANIC SOLVENTS.

FIRE AND EXPLOSION DATA

FIRE AND EXPLOSION HAZARD: UNKNOWN FIRE AND EXPLOSION HAZARD.

FLASH POINT: NOT AVAILABLE

FIREFIGHTING MEDIA: DRY CHEMICAL, CARBON DIOXIDE, HALON, WATER SPRAY OR STANDARD FOAM (1987 EMERGENCY RESPONSE GUIDEBOOK, DOT P 5800.4).
FOR LARGER FIRES, USE WATER SPRAY, FOG OR STANDARD FOAM (1987 EMERGENCY RESPONSE GUIDEBOOK, DOT P 5800.4).

FIREFIGHTING: MOVE CONTAINER FROM FIRE AREA IF POSSIBLE. COOL FIRE-EXPOSED CONTAINERS WITH WATER FROM SIDE UNTIL WELL AFTER FIRE IS OUT. STAY AWAY FROM STORAGE TANK ENDS. FOR MASSIVE FIRE IN STORAGE AREA, USE UNMANNED HOSE HOLDER OR MONITOR NOZZLES, ELSE WITHDRAW FROM AREA AND LET FIRE BURN. WITHDRAW IMMEDIATELY IN CASE OF RISING SOUND FROM VENTING SAFETY DEVICE OR ANY DISCOLORATION OF STORAGE TANK DUE TO FIRE (1987 EMERGENCY RESPONSE GUIDEBOOK, DOT P 5800.4, GUIDE PAGE 27). EXTINGUISH ONLY IF FLOW CAN BE STOPPED; USE FLOODING AMOUNTS OF WATER AS A FOG, SOLID STREAMS MAY BE INEFFECTIVE. COOL CONTAINERS WITH FLOODING AMOUNTS OF WATER, APPLY FROM AS FAR A DISTANCE AS POSSIBLE. AVOID BREATHING VAPORS, KEEP UPWIND.

TOXICITY

TEBUTAM: TOXICITY DATA: >2000 MG/KG SKIN-RABBIT LD50 (PEMNDP 8,767,87); 6200 MG/KG ORAL-RAT LD50; 2025 MG/KG ORAL-GUINEA PIG LD50. CARCINOGEN STATUS: NONE. ACUTE TOXICITY: SLIGHTLY TOXIC BY DERMAL ABSORPTION AND INGESTION. TARGET EFFECTS: NO DATA AVAILABLE.

HEALTH EFFECTS AND FIRST AID

INHALATION: TEBUTAM: **ACUTE EXPOSURE-** THERE WAS NO ADVERSE EFFECT WHEN ALBINO RATS WERE EXPOSED TO AN AEROSOL CONTAINING TEBUTAM AND ACETONE. **CHRONIC EXPOSURE-** NO DATA AVAILABLE.

FIRST AID- REMOVE FROM EXPOSURE AREA TO FRESH AIR IMMEDIATELY. IF BREATHING HAS STOPPED, PERFORM ARTIFICIAL RESPIRATION. KEEP PERSON WARM AND AT REST. TREAT SYMPTOMATICALLY AND SUPPORTIVELY. GET MEDICAL ATTENTION IMMEDIATELY.

SKIN CONTACT: TEBUTAM: **ACUTE EXPOSURE-** MAY CAUSE IRRITATION. **CHRONIC EXPOSURE-** NO DATA AVAILABLE.

FIRST AID- REMOVE CONTAMINATED CLOTHING AND SHOES IMMEDIATELY. WASH AFFECTED AREA WITH SOAP OR MILD DETERGENT AND LARGE AMOUNTS OF WATER UNTIL NO EVIDENCE OF CHEMICAL REMAINS (APPROXIMATELY 15-20 MINUTES). GET MEDICAL ATTENTION IMMEDIATELY.

EYE CONTACT: TEBUTAM: **ACUTE EXPOSURE-** MAY CAUSE EYE IRRITATION. **CHRONIC EXPOSURE-** NO DATA AVAILABLE.

FIRST AID- WASH EYES IMMEDIATELY WITH LARGE AMOUNTS OF WATER OR NORMAL SALINE, OCCASIONALLY LIFTING UPPER AND LOWER LIDS, UNTIL NO EVIDENCE OF CHEMICAL REMAINS (APPROXIMATELY 15-20 MINUTES). GET MEDICAL ATTENTION IMMEDIATELY.

INGESTION: TEBUTAM: **ACUTE EXPOSURE-** A LETHAL DOSE IN RATS WAS 6200 MG/KG; SYMPTOMS WERE NOT REPORTED. **CHRONIC EXPOSURE-** NO DATA AVAILABLE.

FIRST AID- TREAT SYMPTOMATICALLY AND SUPPORTIVELY. GET MEDICAL ATTENTION IMMEDIATELY. IF VOMITING OCCURS, KEEP HEAD LOWER THAN HIPS TO PREVENT ASPIRATION.

ANTIDOTE: NO SPECIFIC ANTIDOTE. TREAT SYMPTOMATICALLY AND SUPPORTIVELY.

REACTIVITY

REACTIVITY: STABLE UNDER NORMAL TEMPERATURES AND PRESSURES.

INCOMPATIBILITIES: TEBUTAM: OXIDIZERS (STRONG): FIRE AND EXPLOSION HAZARD.

DECOMPOSITION: THERMAL DECOMPOSITION PRODUCTS MAY INCLUDE TOXIC OXIDES OF CARBON AND NITROGEN.

POLYMERIZATION: HAZARDOUS POLYMERIZATION HAS NOT BEEN REPORTED TO OCCUR UNDER NORMAL TEMPERATURES AND PRESSURES.

STORAGE AND DISPOSAL

OBSERVE ALL FEDERAL, STATE AND LOCAL REGULATIONS WHEN STORING OR DISPOSING OF THIS SUBSTANCE. FOR ASSISTANCE, CONTACT THE DISTRICT DIRECTOR OF THE ENVIRONMENTAL PROTECTION AGENCY.

****STORAGE****

STORE IN ACCORDANCE WITH 40 CFR 165 RECOMMENDED PROCEDURES FOR THE DISPOSAL AND STORAGE OF PESTICIDES AND PESTICIDE CONTAINERS.
STORE AWAY FROM INCOMPATIBLE SUBSTANCES.

****DISPOSAL****

DISPOSAL MUST BE IN ACCORDANCE WITH 40 CFR 165 RECOMMENDED PROCEDURES FOR THE DISPOSAL AND STORAGE OF PESTICIDES AND PESTICIDE CONTAINERS.

CONDITIONS TO AVOID

AVOID CONTACT WITH HEAT, SPARKS, FLAMES, OR OTHER SOURCES OF IGNITION. VAPORS MAY BE EXPLOSIVE. AVOID OVERHEATING OF CONTAINERS; CONTAINERS MAY VIOLENTLY RUPTURE IN HEAT OF FIRE. AVOID CONTAMINATION OF WATER SOURCES.

SPILL AND LEAK PROCEDURES

OCCUPATIONAL SPILL: SHUT OFF IGNITION SOURCES. STOP LEAK IF YOU CAN DO IT WITHOUT RISK. USE WATER SPRAY TO REDUCE VAPORS. FOR SMALL SPILLS, TAKE UP WITH SAND OR OTHER ABSORBENT MATERIAL AND PLACE INTO CONTAINERS FOR LATER DISPOSAL. FOR LARGER SPILLS, DIKE FAR AHEAD OF SPILL FOR LATER

DISPOSAL. NO SMOKING, FLAMES OR FLARES IN HAZARD AREA. KEEP UNNECESSARY PEOPLE AWAY; ISOLATE HAZARD AREA AND RESTRICT ENTRY.

PROTECTIVE EQUIPMENT

VENTILATION: PROVIDE LOCAL EXHAUST OR GENERAL DILUTION VENTILATION. VENTILATION EQUIPMENT MUST BE EXPLOSION-PROOF.

RESPIRATOR: THE FOLLOWING RESPIRATORS ARE RECOMMENDED BASED ON INFORMATION FOUND IN THE PHYSICAL DATA, TOXICITY AND HEALTH EFFECTS SECTIONS. THEY ARE RANKED IN ORDER FROM MINIMUM TO MAXIMUM RESPIRATORY PROTECTION. THE SPECIFIC RESPIRATOR SELECTED MUST BE BASED ON CONTAMINATION LEVELS FOUND IN THE WORK PLACE, MUST NOT EXCEED THE WORKING LIMITS OF THE RESPIRATOR AND BE JOINTLY APPROVED BY THE NATIONAL INSTITUTE FOR OCCUPATIONAL SAFETY AND HEALTH AND THE MINE SAFETY AND HEALTH ADMINISTRATION (NIOSH-MSHA).

CHEMICAL CARTRIDGE RESPIRATOR WITH PESTICIDE CARTRIDGE.

GAS MASK WITH A PESTICIDE CANISTER (CHIN-STYLE OR FRONT- OR BACK-MOUNTED CANISTER).

TYPE 'C' SUPPLIED-AIR RESPIRATOR OPERATED IN THE PRESSURE-DEMAND OR OTHER POSITIVE PRESSURE OR CONTINUOUS-FLOW MODE.

SELF-CONTAINED BREATHING APPARATUS.

FOR FIREFIGHTING AND OTHER IMMEDIATELY DANGEROUS TO LIFE OR HEALTH CONDITIONS:

SELF-CONTAINED BREATHING APPARATUS WITH FULL FACEPIECE OPERATED IN PRESSURE-DEMAND OR OTHER POSITIVE PRESSURE MODE.

SUPPLIED-AIR RESPIRATOR WITH FULL FACEPIECE AND OPERATED IN PRESSURE-DEMAND OR OTHER POSITIVE PRESSURE MODE IN COMBINATION WITH AN AUXILIARY SELF-CONTAINED BREATHING APPARATUS OPERATED IN PRESSURE-DEMAND OR OTHER POSITIVE PRESSURE MODE.

CLOTHING: EMPLOYEE MUST WEAR APPROPRIATE PROTECTIVE (IMPERVIOUS) CLOTHING AND EQUIPMENT TO PREVENT REPEATED OR PROLONGED SKIN CONTACT WITH THIS SUBSTANCE.

GLOVES: EMPLOYEE MUST WEAR APPROPRIATE PROTECTIVE GLOVES TO PREVENT CONTACT WITH THIS SUBSTANCE.

EYE PROTECTION: EMPLOYEE MUST WEAR SPLASH-PROOF OR DUST-RESISTANT SAFETY GOGGLES TO PREVENT EYE CONTACT WITH THIS SUBSTANCE.

EMERGENCY EYE WASH: WHERE THERE IS ANY POSSIBILITY THAT AN EMPLOYEE'S EYES MAY BE EXPOSED TO THIS SUBSTANCE, THE EMPLOYER SHOULD PROVIDE AN EYE WASH FOUNTAIN WITHIN THE IMMEDIATE WORK AREA FOR EMERGENCY USE.

AUTHORIZED BY- OCCUPATIONAL HEALTH SERVICES, INC.

CREATION DATE: 10/24/89 ***REVISION DATE:*** 05/10/90

MATERIAL SAFETY DATA SHEET

OCCUPATIONAL HEALTH SERVICES, INC.
AGRICULTURE AND PESTICIDE DIVISION
450 SEVENTH AVENUE, SUITE 2407
NEW YORK, NEW YORK 10123
1-800-445-MSDS OR (212) 967-1100

EMERGENCY CONTACT:
JOHN S. BRANSFORD, JR. (615) 292-1180

SUBSTANCE IDENTIFICATION

CAS-NUMBER 5221-53-4

SUBSTANCE: DIMETHIRIMOL

TRADE NAMES/SYNONYMS: 4(1H)-PYRIMIDINONE, 5-BUTYL-2-(DIMETHYLAMINO)-6-METHYL-; 5-BUTYL-2-(DIMETHYLAMINO)-6-METHYL-4(1H)-PYRIMIDINONE; 4-PYRIMIDINOL, 5-BUTYL-2-(DIMETHYLAMINO)-6-METHYL-; 5-BUTYL-2-(DIMETHYLAMINO)-6-METHYL-4-PYRIMIDINOL; DIMETHYRIMOL; METHYRIMOL; MILCURB; PP 675; C11H19N3O; PST72919

CHEMICAL FAMILY: PYRIMIDINE KETONE

MOLECULAR FORMULA: C11-H19-N3-O

MOLECULAR WEIGHT: 209.29

CERCLA RATINGS (SCALE 0-3): HEALTH=3 FIRE=1 REACTIVITY=0 PERSISTENCE=1

NFPA RATINGS (SCALE 0-4): HEALTH=U FIRE=1 REACTIVITY=0

COMPONENTS AND CONTAMINANTS

COMPONENT: DIMETHIRIMOL ***PERCENT:*** 100.0
CAS# 5221-53-4

OTHER CONTAMINANTS: NONE

EXPOSURE LIMITS: NO OCCUPATIONAL EXPOSURE LIMITS ESTABLISHED BY OSHA, ACGIH, OR NIOSH.

PHYSICAL DATA

DESCRIPTION: ODORLESS, COLORLESS NEEDLES. ***MELTING POINT:*** 216 F (102 C)

SPECIFIC GRAVITY: NOT AVAILABLE ***VAPOR PRESSURE:*** NEGLIGIBLE

SOLUBILITY IN WATER: 0.12% @ 25 C

SOLVENT SOLUBILITY: SOLUBLE IN CHLOROFORM, XYLENE AND ACIDIC SOLUTIONS; MODERATELY SOLUBLE IN ACETONE AND ETHANOL.

FIRE AND EXPLOSION DATA

FIRE AND EXPLOSION HAZARD: SLIGHT FIRE HAZARD WHEN EXPOSED TO HEAT OR FLAME.

FIREFIGHTING MEDIA: DRY CHEMICAL, CARBON DIOXIDE, HALON, WATER SPRAY OR STANDARD FOAM (1987 EMERGENCY RESPONSE GUIDEBOOK, DOT P 5800.4). FOR LARGER FIRES, USE WATER SPRAY, FOG OR STANDARD FOAM (1987 EMERGENCY RESPONSE GUIDEBOOK, DOT P 5800.4).

FIREFIGHTING: MOVE CONTAINER FROM FIRE AREA IF POSSIBLE. DO NOT SCATTER SPILLED MATERIAL WITH HIGH PRESSURE WATER STREAMS. DIKE FIRE CONTROL WATER FOR LATER DISPOSAL (1987 EMERGENCY RESPONSE GUIDEBOOK, DOT P 5800.4, GUIDE PAGE 31).

USE AGENTS SUITABLE FOR TYPE OF SURROUNDING FIRE. AVOID BREATHING HAZARDOUS VAPORS, KEEP UPWIND.

TOXICITY

DIMETHIRIMOL: TOXICITY DATA: 2350 MG/KG ORAL-RAT LD50; 800 MG/KG ORAL-MOUSE LD50; 500 MG/KG ORAL-GUINEA PIG LD50; 200 MG/KG INTRAPERITONEAL-RAT LDLO; 4000 MG/KG UNREPORTED-MAMMAL LD50. CARCINOGEN STATUS: NONE. ACUTE TOXICITY LEVEL: MODERATELY TOXIC BY INGESTION. TARGET EFFECTS: NO DATA AVAILABLE.

HEALTH EFFECTS AND FIRST AID

INHALATION: DIMETHIRIMOL: **ACUTE EXPOSURE-** NO DATA AVAILABLE. **CHRONIC EXPOSURE-** NO DATA AVAILABLE.

FIRST AID- REMOVE FROM EXPOSURE AREA TO FRESH AIR IMMEDIATELY. IF BREATHING HAS STOPPED, PERFORM ARTIFICIAL RESPIRATION. KEEP PERSON WARM AND AT REST. TREAT SYMPTOMATICALLY AND SUPPORTIVELY. GET MEDICAL ATTENTION IMMEDIATELY.

SKIN CONTACT: DIMETHIRIMOL: **ACUTE EXPOSURE-** NO DATA AVAILABLE. **CHRONIC EXPOSURE-** DAILY APPLICATION OF 500 MG/KG TO SHAVED RABBIT SKIN FOR 14 DAYS CAUSED NO EFFECTS.

FIRST AID- REMOVE CONTAMINATED CLOTHING AND SHOES IMMEDIATELY. WASH AFFECTED AREA WITH SOAP OR MILD DETERGENT AND LARGE AMOUNTS OF WATER UNTIL NO EVIDENCE OF CHEMICAL REMAINS (APPROXIMATELY 15-20 MINUTES). GET MEDICAL ATTENTION IMMEDIATELY.

EYE CONTACT: DIMETHIRIMOL: **ACUTE EXPOSURE-** NO DATA AVAILABLE. **CHRONIC EXPOSURE-** NO DATA AVAILABLE.

FIRST AID- WASH EYES IMMEDIATELY WITH LARGE AMOUNTS OF WATER OR NORMAL SALINE, OCCASIONALLY LIFTING UPPER AND LOWER LIDS, UNTIL NO EVIDENCE OF CHEMICAL REMAINS (APPROXIMATELY 15-20 MINUTES). GET MEDICAL ATTENTION IMMEDIATELY.

INGESTION: DIMETHIRIMOL: **ACUTE EXPOSURE-** THE LETHAL DOSE REPORTED IN RATS WAS 2350 MG/KG. **CHRONIC EXPOSURE-** RATS FED 24 AND 300 MG/KG/DAY FOR 2 YEARS SHOWED NO ILL EFFECTS.

FIRST AID- IF THE PERSON IS CONSCIOUS AND NOT CONVULSING, REMOVE BY GASTRIC LAVAGE AND FOLLOW WITH A CATHARTIC (DREISBACH, HANDBOOK OF POISONING, 12TH ED.). TREAT SYMPTOMATICALLY AND SUPPORTIVELY. GASTRIC LAVAGE SHOULD BE PERFORMED BY QUALIFIED MEDICAL PERSONNEL. GET MEDICAL ATTENTION IMMEDIATELY.

ANTIDOTE: NO SPECIFIC ANTIDOTE. TREAT SYMPTOMATICALLY AND SUPPORTIVELY.

REACTIVITY

REACTIVITY: STABLE UNDER NORMAL TEMPERATURES AND PRESSURES.

INCOMPATIBILITIES: DIMETHIRIMOL: OXIDIZERS (STRONG): FIRE AND EXPLOSION HAZARD.

DECOMPOSITION: THERMAL DECOMPOSITION PRODUCTS MAY INCLUDE TOXIC OXIDES OF NITROGEN.

POLYMERIZATION: HAZARDOUS POLYMERIZATION HAS NOT BEEN REPORTED TO OCCUR UNDER NORMAL TEMPERATURES AND PRESSURES.

STORAGE AND DISPOSAL

OBSERVE ALL FEDERAL, STATE AND LOCAL REGULATIONS WHEN STORING OR DISPOSING OF THIS SUBSTANCE. FOR ASSISTANCE, CONTACT THE DISTRICT DIRECTOR OF THE ENVIRONMENTAL PROTECTION AGENCY.

STORAGE

STORE IN ACCORDANCE WITH 40 CFR 165 RECOMMENDED PROCEDURES FOR THE DISPOSAL AND STORAGE OF PESTICIDES AND PESTICIDE CONTAINERS.
STORE AWAY FROM INCOMPATIBLE SUBSTANCES.

DISPOSAL

DISPOSAL MUST BE IN ACCORDANCE WITH 40 CFR 165 RECOMMENDED PROCEDURES FOR THE DISPOSAL AND STORAGE OF PESTICIDES AND PESTICIDE CONTAINERS.

CONDITIONS TO AVOID

MAY BURN BUT DOES NOT IGNITE READILY. AVOID CONTACT WITH STRONG OXIDIZERS, EXCESSIVE HEAT, SPARKS, OR OPEN FLAME.

SPILL AND LEAK PROCEDURES

OCCUPATIONAL SPILL: SWEEP UP AND PLACE IN SUITABLE CLEAN, DRY CONTAINERS FOR RECLAMATION OR LATER DISPOSAL. DO NOT FLUSH SPILLED MATERIAL INTO SEWER. KEEP UNNECESSARY PEOPLE AWAY.

PROTECTIVE EQUIPMENT

VENTILATION: PROVIDE LOCAL EXHAUST OR PROCESS ENCLOSURE VENTILATION SYSTEM.

RESPIRATOR: THE FOLLOWING RESPIRATORS ARE RECOMMENDED BASED ON INFORMATION FOUND IN THE PHYSICAL DATA, TOXICITY AND HEALTH EFFECTS SECTIONS. THEY ARE RANKED IN ORDER FROM MINIMUM TO MAXIMUM RESPIRATORY PROTECTION. THE SPECIFIC RESPIRATOR SELECTED MUST BE BASED ON CONTAMINATION LEVELS FOUND IN THE WORK PLACE, MUST NOT EXCEED THE WORKING LIMITS OF THE RESPIRATOR AND BE JOINTLY APPROVED BY THE NATIONAL INSTITUTE FOR OCCUPATIONAL SAFETY AND HEALTH AND THE MINE SAFETY AND HEALTH ADMINISTRATION (NIOSH-MSHA).

CHEMICAL CARTRIDGE RESPIRATOR WITH AN ORGANIC VAPOR CARTRIDGE(S) WITH A FULL FACEPIECE AND ORGANIC VAPOR CARTRIDGE(S) IN COMBINATION WITH A DUST AND MIST FILTER.

POWERED AIR-PURIFYING RESPIRATOR WITH A TIGHT-FITTING FACEPIECE AND ORGANIC VAPOR CARTRIDGE(S) IN COMBINATION WITH A HIGH-EFFICIENCY PARTICULATE FILTER.

TYPE 'C' SUPPLIED-AIR RESPIRATOR WITH A FULL FACEPIECE OPERATED IN A PRESSURE-DEMAND OR OTHER POSITIVE PRESSURE MODE.

SELF-CONTAINED BREATHING APPARATUS WITH A FULL FACEPIECE OPERATED IN PRESSURE-DEMAND OR OTHER POSITIVE PRESSURE MODE.

FOR FIREFIGHTING AND OTHER IMMEDIATELY DANGEROUS TO LIFE OR HEALTH CONDITIONS:

SELF-CONTAINED BREATHING APPARATUS WITH FULL FACEPIECE OPERATED IN PRESSURE-DEMAND OR OTHER POSITIVE PRESSURE MODE.

SUPPLIED-AIR RESPIRATOR WITH FULL FACEPIECE AND OPERATED IN PRESSURE-DEMAND OR OTHER POSITIVE PRESSURE MODE IN COMBINATION WITH AN AUXILIARY SELF-CONTAINED BREATHING APPARATUS OPERATED IN PRESSURE-DEMAND OR OTHER POSITIVE PRESSURE MODE.

CLOTHING: EMPLOYEE MUST WEAR APPROPRIATE PROTECTIVE (IMPERVIOUS) CLOTHING AND EQUIPMENT TO PREVENT REPEATED OR PROLONGED SKIN CONTACT WITH THIS SUBSTANCE.

GLOVES: EMPLOYEE MUST WEAR APPROPRIATE PROTECTIVE GLOVES TO PREVENT CONTACT WITH THIS SUBSTANCE.

EYE PROTECTION: EMPLOYEE MUST WEAR SPLASH-PROOF OR DUST-RESISTANT SAFETY GOGGLES TO PREVENT EYE CONTACT WITH THIS SUBSTANCE.

EMERGENCY EYE WASH: WHERE THERE IS ANY POSSIBILITY THAT AN EMPLOYEE'S EYES MAY BE EXPOSED TO THIS SUBSTANCE, THE EMPLOYER SHOULD PROVIDE AN EYE WASH FOUNTAIN WITHIN THE IMMEDIATE WORK AREA FOR EMERGENCY USE.

AUTHORIZED BY- OCCUPATIONAL HEALTH SERVICES, INC.
CREATION DATE: 10/04/89 ***REVISION DATE:*** 05/31/90

MATERIAL SAFETY DATA SHEET

OCCUPATIONAL HEALTH SERVICES, INC.
AGRICULTURE AND PESTICIDE DIVISION
450 SEVENTH AVENUE, SUITE 2407
NEW YORK, NEW YORK 10123
1-800-445-MSDS OR (212) 967-1100

EMERGENCY CONTACT:
JOHN S. BRANSFORD, JR. (615) 292-1180

SUBSTANCE IDENTIFICATION

CAS-NUMBER 1420-07-1

SUBSTANCE: <u>DINOTERB</u>

TRADE NAMES/SYNONYMS: PHENOL, 2-(1,1-DIMETHYLETHYL)-4,6-DINITRO-; PHENOL, 2-TERT-BUTYL-4,6-DINITRO-; 2-(1,1-DIMETHYLETHYL)-4,6-DINITROPHENOL; 2-TERT-BUTYL-4,6-DINITROPHENOL; DINOTERBE; DNTBP; HERBOGIL; C10H12N2O5; PST72921

CHEMICAL FAMILY: NITRO PHENOL

MOLECULAR FORMULA: C10-H12-N2-O5

MOLECULAR WEIGHT: 240.24

CERCLA RATINGS (SCALE 0-3): HEALTH=3 FIRE=1 REACTIVITY=0 PERSISTENCE=1

NFPA RATINGS (SCALE 0-4): HEALTH=4 FIRE=1 REACTIVITY=0

COMPONENTS AND CONTAMINANTS

COMPONENT: DINOTERB ***PERCENT:*** 100.0
CAS# 1420-07-1

EXPOSURE LIMITS: NO OCCUPATIONAL EXPOSURE LIMITS ESTABLISHED BY OSHA, ACGIH, OR NIOSH.

DINOTERB: 500/10,000 POUNDS SARA SECTION 302 THRESHOLD PLANNING QUANTITY 1 POUND SARA SECTION 304 REPORTABLE QUANTITY

PHYSICAL DATA

DESCRIPTION: YELLOW CRYSTALLINE SOLID WITH PHENOL-LIKE ODOR.

MELTING POINT: 259-261 F (126-127 C) ***SPECIFIC GRAVITY:*** NOT AVAILABLE

VAPOR PRESSURE: NEGLIGIBLE ***SOLUBILITY IN WATER:*** 45 PPM @ PH5

SOLVENT SOLUBILITY: SOLUBLE IN ETHYL ACETATE, CYCLOHEXANONE, ALCOHOL, DIMETHYL SULFOXIDE, GLYCOLS, AQUEOUS ALKALIS, AND ALIPHATIC HYDROCARBONS.

FIRE AND EXPLOSION DATA

FIRE AND EXPLOSION HAZARD: SLIGHT FIRE HAZARD WHEN EXPOSED TO HEAT OR FLAME.

FIREFIGHTING MEDIA: DRY CHEMICAL, CARBON DIOXIDE, HALON, WATER SPRAY OR STANDARD FOAM (1987 EMERGENCY RESPONSE GUIDEBOOK, DOT P 5800.4).
FOR LARGER FIRES, USE WATER SPRAY, FOG OR STANDARD FOAM (1987 EMERGENCY RESPONSE GUIDEBOOK, DOT P 5800.4).

FIREFIGHTING: MOVE CONTAINERS FROM FIRE AREA IF POSSIBLE (1987 EMERGENCY RESPONSE GUIDEBOOK, DOT P 5800.4, GUIDE PAGE 53).
EXTINGUISH USING AGENT SUITABLE FOR TYPE OF SURROUNDING FIRE. AVOID BREATHING VAPORS AND DUSTS. KEEP UPWIND.

TRANSPORTATION DATA

DEPARTMENT OF TRANSPORTATION HAZARD CLASSIFICATION 49 CFR 172.101: POISON B

DEPARTMENT OF TRANSPORTATION LABELING REQUIREMENTS 49 CFR 172.101 AND SUBPART E: POISON

DEPARTMENT OF TRANSPORTATION PACKAGING REQUIREMENTS: 49 CFR 173.365 EXCEPTIONS: 49 CFR 173.364

TOXICITY

DINOTERB: TOXICITY DATA: 150 MG/KG SKIN-GUINEA PIG LD50; 62 MG/KG ORAL-RAT LD50; 25 MG/KG ORAL-MOUSE LD50; 28300 UG/KG ORAL-RABBIT LD50. CARCINOGEN STATUS: NONE. ACUTE TOXICITY LEVEL: HIGHLY TOXIC BY DERMAL ABSORPTION; TOXIC BY INGESTION. TARGET EFFECTS: POISONING MAY INCREASE THE METABOLIC RATE AND AFFECT THE NERVOUS SYSTEM, LIVER, AND KIDNEYS.* AT INCREASED RISK FROM EXPOSURE: ALCOHOLICS AND PERSONS WITH RENAL OR HEPATIC DISEASES.* ADDITIONAL DATA: HOT ENVIRONMENTS MAY ENHANCE ABSORPTION AND THE TOXIC EFFECTS.*

* MAY BE BASED ON INFORMATION ON DINITROPHENOL DERIVATIVES.

HEALTH EFFECTS AND FIRST AID

INHALATION: DINOTERB: SEE INFORMATION ON DINITROPHENOL DERIVATIVES.
DINITROPHENOL DERIVATIVES: <u>ACUTE EXPOSURE</u>- MAY BE ABSORBED WITH SYMPTOMS OCCURRING SUDDENLY AND UP TO 2 DAYS AFTER CESSATION OF EXPOSURE. SYMPTOMS MAY INCLUDE FATIGUE, WEAKNESS, FEVER, THIRST, NAUSEA, VOMITING, HEADACHES, FLUSHED SKIN, PROSTRATION, EXCESSIVE PERSPIRATION, TACHYCARDIA, TACHYPNEA, AND DYSPNEA. APPREHENSION, RESTLESSNESS, ANXIETY, MANIC BEHAVIOR, OR UNCONSCIOUSNESS MAY INDICATE CEREBRAL INJURY. CONVULSIONS MAY OCCUR IN THE MOST SEVERE POISONINGS. ANOXIA WITH CYANOSIS, LIVIDITY AND METABOLIC ACIDOSIS, SEVERE HYPERPYREXIA, DEHYDRATION, AND MUSCULAR TREMORS MAY BE

FOLLOWED BY CIRCULATORY OR RESPIRATORY COLLAPSE AND COMA. DEGENERATIVE CHANGES IN THE HEART, RENAL TUBULES AND LIVER PARENCHYMA MAY OCCUR. THERE MAY BE ALBUMINURIA, PYURIA, HEMATURIA, JAUNDICE, AND INCREASED BUN. THE EFFECTS FROM POISONING ARE RAPID AND DEATH OR RECOVERY GENERALLY OCCURS WITHIN 24 TO 48 HOURS. FATAL DINITROPHENOL POISONING IS FOLLOWED BY INSTANTANEOUS RIGOR MORTIS. **CHRONIC EXPOSURE**- IN ADDITION TO THE SYMPTOMS OF ACUTE EXPOSURE, PROLONGED OR REPEATED EXPOSURE MAY CAUSE WEIGHT LOSS, CATARACT FORMATION, AND LIVER AND KIDNEY DAMAGE. YELLOW STAINING OF THE SCLERAE AND URINE INDICATES ABSORPTION OF POTENTIALLY TOXIC AMOUNTS.

FIRST AID- REMOVE FROM EXPOSURE AREA TO FRESH AIR IMMEDIATELY. IF BREATHING HAS STOPPED, PERFORM ARTIFICIAL RESPIRATION. ADMINISTER OXYGEN. TREAT SYMPTOMATICALLY AND SUPPORTIVELY. GET MEDICAL ATTENTION IMMEDIATELY.

SKIN CONTACT: DINOTERB: HIGHLY TOXIC. SEE INFORMATION ON DINITROPHENOL DERIVATIVES.

DINITROPHENOL DERIVATIVES: **ACUTE EXPOSURE**- MAY CAUSE IRRITATION. CONTACT MAY RESULT IN YELLOW STAINING OF THE SKIN AHD HAIR. SOME DERIVATIVES MAY BE ABSORBED THROUGH THE SKIN WITH SYMPTOMS OCCURRING SUDDENLY AND UP TO 2 DAYS AFTER CESSATION OF EXPOSURE AND PRODUCE EFFECTS ON THE METABOLIC RATE, CENTRAL NERVOUS SYSTEM AND LIVER AND KIDNEY RESULTING IN SIGNS AND SYMPTOMS AS DESCRIBED IN ACUTE INHALATION. **CHRONIC EXPOSURE**- REPEATED OR PROLONGED CONTACT MAY RESULT IN DERMATITIS DUE TO IRRITATION OR ALLERGIC SENSITIVITY. IN ADDITION TO THE SYMPTOMS OF ACUTE EXPOSURE, CHRONIC ABSORPTION MAY CAUSE FATIGUE, WEIGHT LOSS, CATARACT FORMATION AND LIVER AND KIDNEY DAMAGE. YELLOW STAINING OF THE SCLERAE AND URINE INDICATES ABSORPTION OF POTENTIALLY TOXIC AMOUNTS.

FIRST AID- REMOVE CONTAMINATED CLOTHING AND SHOES IMMEDIATELY. THEN REMOVE SKIN AND HAIR CONTAMINATION BY SCRUBBING WITH SOAP AND WATER. IF BODY TEMPERATURE IS ELEVATED, REDUCE TO 37 C BY SPONGE BATH, IMMERSION IN COOL WATER OR BY APPLYING COOLING BLANKET. IF BODY TEMPERATURE IS ABOVE 40 C, ICE WATER IS NECESSARY (DREISBACH, HANDBOOK OF POISONING, 12TH EDITION; MORGAN, EPA RECOGNITION AND MANAGEMENT OF PESTICIDE POISONINGS, 3RD EDITION). GET MEDICAL ATTENTION IMMEDIATELY.

EYE CONTACT: DINOTERB: **ACUTE EXPOSURE**- NO DATA AVAILABLE. **CHRONIC EXPOSURE**- NO DATA AVAILABLE.

FIRST AID- WASH EYES IMMEDIATELY WITH LARGE AMOUNTS OF WATER OR NORMAL SALINE, OCCASIONALLY LIFTING UPPER AND LOWER LIDS, UNTIL NO EVIDENCE OF CHEMICAL REMAINS (APPROXIMATELY 15-20 MINUTES). GET MEDICAL ATTENTION IMMEDIATELY.

INGESTION: DINOTERB: TOXIC. SEE INFORMATION ON DINITROPHENOL DERIVATIVES.

DINITROPHENOL DERIVATIVES: **ACUTE EXPOSURE**- MAY CAUSE EFFECTS ON THE METABOLIC RATE, CENTRAL NERVOUS SYSTEM AND LIVER AND KIDNEY RESULTING IN SIGNS AND SYMPTOMS AS DESCRIBED IN ACUTE INHALATION. **CHRONIC EXPOSURE**- IN ADDITION TO THE SYMPTOMS OF ACUTE EXPOSURE, REPEATED INGESTION MAY CAUSE AN INITIAL SENSE OF WELL-BEING THEN ANOREXIA, DIARRHEA, DIZZINESS, RESTLESSNESS, FATIGUE, WEIGHT LOSS, SKIN ERUPTIONS, PERIPHERAL NEURITIS, LIVER AND KIDNEY DAMAGE, CARDIOVASCULAR COMPLICATIONS, GRANULOCYTOPENIA, AND CATARACT FORMATION. YELLOW STAINING OF THE SCLERAE AND URINE INDICATES ABSORPTION OF POTENTIALLY TOXIC AMOUNTS.

FIRST AID- REMOVE INGESTED POISON BY THOROUGH GASTRIC LAVAGE WITH SATURATED BICARBONATE SOLUTION. IF GASTRIC LAVAGE CANNOT BE ACCOMPLISHED IMMEDIATELY, GIVE SYRUP OF IPECAC TO INDUCE EMESIS AND FOLLOW WITH SALINE CATHARTIC. IF BODY TEMPERATURE IS ELEVATED, REDUCE TO 37 C BY IMMERSION IN COOL WATER OR BY APPLYING COOLING BLANKET. IF BODY TEMPERATURE IS ABOVE 40 C, ICE WATER IS NECESSARY (DREISBACH, HANDBOOK OF POISONING, 12TH ED.). ADMINISTRATION OF GASTRIC LAVAGE SHOULD BE PERFORMED BY QUALIFIED MEDICAL PERSONNEL. GET MEDICAL ATTENTION IMMEDIATELY.

ANTIDOTE: NO SPECIFIC ANTIDOTE. TREAT SYMPTOMATICALLY AND SUPPORTIVELY.

REACTIVITY

REACTIVITY: STABLE UNDER NORMAL TEMPERATURES AND PRESSURES.

INCOMPATIBILITIES: DINOTERB: METALS: MAY BE CORRODED. OXIDIZERS (STRONG): FIRE AND EXPLOSION HAZARD.

DECOMPOSITION: THERMAL DECOMPOSITION PRODUCTS MAY INCLUDE TOXIC OXIDES OF CARBON AND NITROGEN.

POLYMERIZATION: HAZARDOUS POLYMERIZATION HAS NOT BEEN REPORTED TO OCCUR UNDER NORMAL TEMPERATURES AND PRESSURES.

STORAGE AND DISPOSAL

OBSERVE ALL FEDERAL, STATE AND LOCAL REGULATIONS WHEN STORING OR DISPOSING OF THIS SUBSTANCE. FOR ASSISTANCE, CONTACT THE DISTRICT DIRECTOR OF THE ENVIRONMENTAL PROTECTION AGENCY.

****STORAGE****

STORE IN ACCORDANCE WITH 40 CFR 165 RECOMMENDED PROCEDURES FOR THE DISPOSAL AND STORAGE OF PESTICIDES AND PESTICIDE CONTAINERS.
STORE AWAY FROM INCOMPATIBLE SUBSTANCES.
THRESHOLD PLANNING QUANTITY (TPQ): THE SUPERFUND AMENDMENTS AND REAUTHORIZATION ACT (SARA) SECTION 302 REQUIRES THAT EACH FACILITY WHERE ANY EXTREMELY HAZARDOUS SUBSTANCE IS PRESENT IN A QUANTITY EQUAL TO OR GREATER THAN THE TPQ ESTABLISHED FOR THAT SUBSTANCE NOTIFY THE STATE EMERGENCY RESPONSE COMMISSION FOR THE STATE IN WHICH IT IS LOCATED. SECTION 303 OF SARA REQUIRES THESE FACILITIES TO PARTICIPATE IN LOCAL EMERGENCY RESPONSE PLANNING (40 CFR 355.30).

****DISPOSAL****

DISPOSAL MUST BE IN ACCORDANCE WITH 40 CFR 165 RECOMMENDED PROCEDURES FOR THE DISPOSAL AND STORAGE OF PESTICIDES AND PESTICIDE CONTAINERS.

CONDITIONS TO AVOID

MAY BURN BUT DOES NOT IGNITE READILY.

SPILL AND LEAK PROCEDURES

OCCUPATIONAL SPILL: DO NOT TOUCH SPILLED MATERIAL. STOP LEAK IF YOU CAN DO IT WITHOUT RISK. FOR SMALL SPILLS, TAKE UP WITH SAND OR OTHER ABSORBENT MATERIAL AND PLACE INTO CONTAINERS FOR LATER DISPOSAL. FOR SMALL DRY SPILLS, WITH A CLEAN SHOVEL PLACE MATERIAL INTO CLEAN, DRY CONTAINER AND COVER. MOVE CONTAINERS FROM SPILL AREA. FOR LARGER SPILLS, DIKE FAR AHEAD OF SPILL FOR LATER DISPOSAL. KEEP UNNECESSARY PEOPLE AWAY. ISOLATE HAZARD AREA AND DENY ENTRY.

REPORTABLE QUANTITY (RQ): 1 POUND THE SUPERFUND AMENDMENTS AND REAUTHORIZATION ACT (SARA) SECTION 304 REQUIRES THAT A RELEASE EQUAL TO OR GREATER THAN THE REPORTABLE QUANTITY FOR THIS SUBSTANCE BE IMMEDIATELY REPORTED TO THE LOCAL EMERGENCY PLANNING COMMITTEE AND THE STATE EMERGENCY RESPONSE COMMISSION (40 CFR 355.40). IF THE RELEASE OF THIS SUBSTANCE IS REPORTABLE UNDER CERCLA SECTION 103, THE NATIONAL RESPONSE CENTER MUST BE NOTIFIED IMMEDIATELY AT (800) 424-8802 OR (202) 426-2675 IN THE METROPOLITAN WASHINGTON, D.C. AREA (40 CFR 302.6).

PROTECTIVE EQUIPMENT

VENTILATION: PROVIDE LOCAL EXHAUST OR PROCESS ENCLOSURE VENTILATION SYSTEM.

RESPIRATOR: THE FOLLOWING RESPIRATORS ARE RECOMMENDED BASED ON INFORMATION FOUND IN THE PHYSICAL DATA, TOXICITY AND HEALTH EFFECTS SECTIONS. THEY ARE RANKED IN ORDER FROM MINIMUM TO MAXIMUM RESPIRATORY PROTECTION. THE SPECIFIC RESPIRATOR SELECTED MUST BE BASED ON CONTAMINATION LEVELS FOUND IN THE WORK PLACE, MUST NOT EXCEED THE WORKING LIMITS OF THE RESPIRATOR AND BE JOINTLY APPROVED BY THE NATIONAL INSTITUTE FOR OCCUPATIONAL SAFETY AND HEALTH AND THE MINE SAFETY AND HEALTH ADMINISTRATION (NIOSH-MSHA).

TYPE 'C' SUPPLIED-AIR RESPIRATOR WITH A FULL FACEPIECE OPERATED IN PRESSURE-DEMAND OR OTHER POSITIVE PRESSURE MODE OR WITH A FULL FACEPIECE, HELMET OR HOOD OPERATED IN CONTINOUS-FLOW MODE.

SELF-CONTAINED BREATHING APPARATUS WITH A FULL FACEPIECE OPERATED IN PRESSURE-DEMAND OR OTHER POSITIVE PRESSURE MODE.

FOR FIREFIGHTING AND OTHER IMMEDIATELY DANGEROUS TO LIFE OR HEALTH CONDITIONS:

SELF-CONTAINED BREATHING APPARATUS WITH FULL FACEPIECE OPERATED IN PRESSURE-DEMAND OR OTHER POSITIVE PRESSURE MODE.

SUPPLIED-AIR RESPIRATOR WITH FULL FACEPIECE AND OPERATED IN PRESSURE-DEMAND OR OTHER POSITIVE PRESSURE MODE IN COMBINATION WITH AN AUXILIARY SELF-CONTAINED BREATHING APPARATUS OPERATED IN PRESSURE-DEMAND OR OTHER POSITIVE PRESSURE MODE.

CLOTHING: EMPLOYEE MUST WEAR APPROPRIATE PROTECTIVE (IMPERVIOUS) CLOTHING AND EQUIPMENT TO PREVENT ANY POSSIBILITY OF SKIN CONTACT WITH THIS SUBSTANCE.

GLOVES: EMPLOYEE MUST WEAR APPROPRIATE PROTECTIVE GLOVES TO PREVENT CONTACT WITH THIS SUBSTANCE.

EYE PROTECTION: EMPLOYEE MUST WEAR SPLASH-PROOF OR DUST-RESISTANT SAFETY GOGGLES AND A FACESHIELD TO PREVENT CONTACT WITH THIS SUBSTANCE.

EMERGENCY WASH FACILITIES: WHERE THERE IS ANY POSSIBILITY THAT AN EMPLOYEE'S EYES AND/OR SKIN MAY BE EXPOSED TO THIS SUBSTANCE, THE

EMPLOYER SHOULD PROVIDE AN EYE WASH FOUNTAIN AND QUICK DRENCH SHOWER WITHIN THE IMMEDIATE WORK AREA FOR EMERGENCY USE.

AUTHORIZED BY- OCCUPATIONAL HEALTH SERVICES, INC.
CREATION DATE: 10/04/89 ***REVISION DATE:*** 04/18/90

MATERIAL SAFETY DATA SHEET

OCCUPATIONAL HEALTH SERVICES, INC.
AGRICULTURE AND PESTICIDE DIVISION
450 SEVENTH AVENUE, SUITE 2407
NEW YORK, NEW YORK 10123
1-800-445-MSDS OR (212) 967-1100

EMERGENCY CONTACT:
JOHN S. BRANSFORD, JR. (615) 292-1180

SUBSTANCE IDENTIFICATION

CAS-NUMBER 1031-47-6
SUBSTANCE: TRIAMIPHOS
TRADE NAMES/SYNONYMS: PHOSPHONIC DIAMIDE, P-(5-AMINO-3-PHENYL-1H-1,2,4-TRIAZOL-1-YL)-N,N,N', N'-TETRAMETHYL; P-(5-AMINO-3-PHENYL-1H-1,2,4,-TRIAZOL-1-YL) N,N,N',N'-TETRAMETHYL PHOSPHONODIAMIDATE; 5-AMINO-1-(BIS(DIMETHYLAMINO)PHOSPHINYL)-3-PHENYL-1,2,4-TRIAZOLE; 5-AMINO-1-BIS(DIMETHYLAMIDO)PHOSPHORYL-3-PHENYL-1,2,4-TRIAZOLE; 5-AMINO-3-PHENYL-1,2,4-TRIAZOLE-1-YL-N,N,N',N' -TETRAMETHYLPHOSPHODIAMIDE; WEPSYN; WP 155; PST72937
CHEMICAL FAMILY: TRIAZOLE
AMINE, AROMATIC
PHOSPHINE
MOLECULAR FORMULA: C12-H19-N6-O-P
MOLECULAR WEIGHT: 294.34
CERCLA RATINGS (SCALE 0-3): HEALTH=3 FIRE=U REACTIVITY=U PERSISTENCE=2
NFPA RATINGS (SCALE 0-4): HEALTH=3 FIRE=U REACTIVITY=U

COMPONENTS AND CONTAMINANTS

COMPONENT: TRIAMIPHOS ***PERCENT:*** 100.0
CAS# 1031-47-6
OTHER CONTAMINANTS: NONE
EXPOSURE LIMITS: NO OCCUPATIONAL EXPOSURE LIMITS ESTABLISHED BY OSHA, ACGIH, OR NIOSH.
TRIAMIPHOS: 500/10,000 POUNDS SARA SECTION 302 THRESHOLD PLANNING QUANTITY 1 POUND SARA SECTION 304 REPORTABLE QUANTITY

PHYSICAL DATA

DESCRIPTION: SOLID ***SPECIFIC GRAVITY:*** NOT AVAILABLE
SOLUBILITY IN WATER: NOT AVAILABLE

FIRE AND EXPLOSION DATA

FIRE AND EXPLOSION HAZARD: UNKNOWN FIRE AND EXPLOSION HAZARD.
FIREFIGHTING MEDIA: DRY CHEMICAL, CARBON DIOXIDE, HALON, WATER SPRAY OR STANDARD FOAM (1987 EMERGENCY RESPONSE GUIDEBOOK, DOT P 5800.4).
FOR LARGER FIRES, USE WATER SPRAY, FOG OR STANDARD FOAM (1987 EMERGENCY RESPONSE GUIDEBOOK, DOT P 5800.4).
FIREFIGHTING: MOVE CONTAINERS FROM FIRE AREA IF POSSIBLE (1987 EMERGENCY RESPONSE GUIDEBOOK, DOT P 5800.4, GUIDE PAGE 53).
EXTINGUISH USING AGENT SUITABLE FOR TYPE OF SURROUNDING FIRE. AVOID BREATHING VAPORS AND DUSTS. KEEP UPWIND.

TRANSPORTATION DATA

DEPARTMENT OF TRANSPORTATION HAZARD CLASSIFICATION 49 CFR 172.101: POISON B
DEPARTMENT OF TRANSPORTATION LABELING REQUIREMENTS 49 CFR 172.101 AND SUBPART E: POISON
DEPARTMENT OF TRANSPORTATION PACKAGING REQUIREMENTS: 49 CFR 173.365 EXCEPTIONS: 49 CFR 173.364

TOXICITY

TRIAMIPHOS: TOXICITY DATA: 1500 MG/KG SKIN-RABBIT LD50; 48 MG/KG SKIN-RAT LD50; 20 MG/KG ORAL-RAT LD50; 10 MG/KG ORAL-MOUSE LD50; 15 MG/KG INTRAPERITONEAL-RAT LD50; 10 MG/KG UNREPORTED-RAT LD50; REPRODUCTIVE EFFECTS DATA (RTECS). CARCINOGEN STATUS: NONE. ACUTE TOXICITY LEVEL: HIGHLY TOXIC BY INGESTION; MODERATELY TOXIC BY DERMAL ABSORPTION.
TARGET EFFECTS: CHOLINESTERASE INHIBITOR. POISONING MAY AFFECT THE NERVOUS SYSTEM.* AT INCREASED RISK FROM EXPOSURE: PERSONS WITH RESPIRATORY AILMENTS, RECENT EXPOSURE TO CHOLINESTERASE INHIBITORS OR IMPAIRED CHOLINESTERASE PRODUCTION, OR LIVER MALFUNCTION.* ADDITIONAL DATA: MAY CROSS THE PLACENTA. HIGH ENVIRONMENTAL TEMPERATURES OR EXPOSURE OF THE CHEMICAL TO VISIBLE OR ULTRAVIOLET LIGHT MAY ENHANCE THE TOXICITY. INTERACTIONS WITH MEDICATIONS MAY OCCUR.*
* MAY BE BASED ON GENERAL INFORMATION ON ORGANOPHOSPHATES.

HEALTH EFFECTS AND FIRST AID

INHALATION: TRIAMIPHOS: SEE INFORMATION ON ORGANOPHOSPHATES.
ORGANOPHOSPHATES: CHOLINESTERASE INHIBITOR. **ACUTE EXPOSURE-** WHEN INHALED, THE FIRST EFFECTS OF CHOLINESTERASE INHIBITORS ARE USUALLY RESPIRATORY AND MAY INCLUDE NASAL HYPEREMIA AND WATERY DISCHARGE, COUGH, CHEST DISCOMFORT, DYSPNEA, AND WHEEZING DUE TO INCREASED BRONCHIAL SECRETIONS AND BRONCHOCONSTRICTION. IF SUFFICIENT AMOUNTS ARE ABSORBED, OTHER SYSTEMIC EFFECTS MAY BEGIN WITHIN A FEW MINUTES OR BE DELAYED FOR UP TO 12 HOURS. SYMPTOMS MAY INCLUDE PALLOR, NAUSEA, VOMITING, DIARRHEA, ABDOMINAL CRAMPS, HEADACHE, DIZZINESS, OCULAR PAIN, BLURRED VISION, MIOSIS OR IN SOME CASES, ESPECIALLY INITIALLY, MYDRIASIS, LACRIMATION, SALIVATION, SWEATING, AND CONFUSION. OTHER REPORTED CENTRAL NERVOUS SYSTEM OR NEUROMUSCULAR EFFECTS MAY INCLUDE ATAXIA, SLURRED SPEECH, AREFLEXIA, WEAKNESS, FATIGUE, FASCICULATIONS, TWITCHING, TREMORS POSSIBLY OF THE TONGUE AND EYELIDS, AND EVENTUALLY PARALYSIS OF THE EXTREMITIES AND POSSIBLY OF THE RESPIRATORY MUSCLES. IN SEVERE CASES THERE MAY ALSO BE INVOLUNTARY DEFECATION AND URINATION, CYANOSIS, PSYCHOSIS, HYPERGLYCEMIA, ACUTE PANCREATITIS, CARDIAC IRREGULARITIES, PULMONARY EDEMA, UNCONSCIOUSNESS, CONVULSIONS, AND COMA. DEATH IS PRIMARILY DUE TO RESPIRATORY FAILURE, ALTHOUGH CARDIOVASCULAR EFFECTS INCLUDING CARDIAC ARREST MAY ALSO BE IMPLICATED. LONG TERM SEQUELAE ARE RARE BUT MAY INCLUDE NEUROPSYCHIATRIC DISORDERS AND MYOPATHY WITH MUSCLE TENDERNESS. SOME ORGANOPHOSPHATES MAY CAUSE A DELAYED NEUROPATHY BEGINNING 1-4 WEEKS AFTER AN ACUTE EXPOSURE WHICH MAY OR MAY NOT HAVE CAUSED ACUTE CHOLINERGIC EFFECTS. NUMBNESS, TINGLING, WEAKNESS AND CRAMPING BEGINNING SYMMETRICALLY IN THE LOWER LIMBS MAY PROGRESS TO ATAXIA AND PARALYSIS. IN SEVERE CASES, UPPER LIMB INVOLVEMENT IS POSSIBLE AND FLACCID PARALYSIS MAY PROGRESS TO SPASTIC PARALYSIS WITH EXAGGERATED REFLEXES. IMPROVEMENT MAY OCCUR OVER MONTHS TO YEARS, BUT SOME RESIDUAL IMPAIRMENT USUALLY REMAINS.
CHRONIC EXPOSURE- REPEATED OR PROLONGED EXPOSURE MAY RESULT IN THE EFFECTS OF ACUTE EXPOSURE INCLUDING THE DELAYED NEUROPATHY. OTHER EFFECTS REPORTED IN WORKERS REPEATEDLY EXPOSED INCLUDE IMPAIRED MEMORY AND CONCENTRATION, ACUTE PSYCHOSIS, SEVERE DEPRESSIONS, IRRITABILTY, CONFUSION, APATHY, EMOTIONAL LABILITY, SOCIAL WITHDRAWAL, CONFUSION, HEADACHE, SPEECH DIFFICULTIES, DELAYED REACTION TIMES, SPATIAL DISORIENTATION, NIGHTMARES, SLEEPWALKING, AND DROWSINESS OR INSOMNIA. AN INFLUENZA-LIKE CONDITION WITH HEADACHE, NAUSEA, WEAKNESS, ANOREXIA AND MALAISE HAS ALSO BEEN REPORTED.
FIRST AID- REMOVE FROM EXPOSURE AREA TO FRESH AIR IMMEDIATELY. IF BREATHING HAS STOPPED, GIVE ARTIFICIAL RESPIRATION. MAINTAIN AIRWAY AND BLOOD PRESSURE AND ADMINISTER OXYGEN IF AVAILABLE. KEEP AFFECTED PERSON WARM AND AT REST. TREAT SYMPTOMATICALLY AND SUPPORTIVELY. ADMINISTRATION OF OXYGEN SHOULD BE PERFORMED BY QUALIFIED PERSONNEL. GET MEDICAL ATTENTION IMMEDIATELY.

SKIN CONTACT: TRIAMIPHOS: SEE INFORMATION ON ORGANOPHOSPHATES.
ORGANOPHOSPHATES: CHOLINESTERASE INHIBITOR. **ACUTE EXPOSURE-** LOCALIZED SWEATING AND FASCICULATIONS MAY OCCUR AT THE SITE OF CONTACT. IF SUFFICIENT AMOUNTS ARE ABSORBED, OTHER EFFECTS OF CHOLINESTERASE INHIBITION AS DESCRIBED IN ACUTE INHALATION MAY OCCUR. SYMPTOMS MAY BE DELAYED 2-3 HOURS, BUT USUALLY NO MORE THAN 12 HOURS. THE RATE OF ABSORPTION IS INCREASED BY THE PRESENCE OF DERMATITIS OR HIGH AMBIENT TEMPERATURES. DELAYED NEUROPATHY IS ALSO POSSIBLE. **CHRONIC EXPOSURE-** REPEATED OR PROLONGED EXPOSURE MAY CAUSE EFFECTS AS DESCRIBED IN ACUTE EXPOSURE. SOME ORGANOPHOSPHATES MAY CAUSE SENSITIZATION.
FIRST AID- REMOVE CONTAMINATED CLOTHING IMMEDIATELY. WASH CONTAMINATED AREAS WITH SOAP AND WATER FOLLOWED BY ALCOHOL (ARENA, POISONING, 4TH ED.). EMERGENCY PERSONNEL SHOULD WEAR GLOVES AND AVOID CONTAMINATION. TREAT RESPIRATORY DIFFICULTY WITH ARTIFICIAL RESPIRATION. GET MEDICAL ATTENTION IMMEDIATELY.

EYE CONTACT: TRIAMIPHOS: SEE INFORMATION ON ORGANOPHOSPHATES.
ORGANOPHOSPHATES: CHOLINESTERASE INHIBITOR. **ACUTE EXPOSURE-** DIRECT CONTACT MAY CAUSE PAIN, HYPEREMIA, LACRIMATION, TWITCHING OF THE

EYELIDS, MIOSIS, AND CILIARY MUSCLE SPASM WITH LOSS OF ACCOMODATION, BLURRED OR DIMMED VISION AND BROWACHE. SOMETIMES MYDRIASIS MAY OCCUR INSTEAD OF MIOSIS. WITH SUFFICIENT EXPOSURE, OTHER SYMPTOMS OF CHOLINESTERASE INHIBITION AS DESCRIBED IN ACUTE INHALATION MAY OCCUR. **CHRONIC EXPOSURE-** REPEATED OR PROLONGED EXPOSURE MAY CAUSE EFFECTS AS DESCRIBED IN ACUTE EXPOSURE. SOME COMPOUNDS HAVE CAUSED TOXIC EFFECTS ON THE CRYSTALLINE LENS, CONJUNCTIVAL THICKENING AND OBSTRUCTION OF THE NASOLACRIMAL CANALS WHEN USED AS MIOTIC EYEDROPS.

FIRST AID- IRRIGATE EYES WITH WATER OR SALINE SOLUTION. IF SYMPTOMS OF POISONING OCCUR, TREAT RESPIRATORY DIFFICULTY WITH ARTIFICIAL RESPIRATION AND OXYGEN. OBSERVE PATIENT FOR AT LEAST 24-36 HOURS (GOSSELIN, CLINICAL TOXICOLOGY OF COMMERCIAL PRODUCTS, 5TH ED.). GET MEDICAL ATTENTION IMMEDIATELY. OXYGEN SHOULD BE ADMINISTERED BY QUALIFIED MEDICAL PERSONNEL.

INGESTION: TRIAMIPHOS: HIGHLY TOXIC. CHRONIC INGESTION BY MULTIPLE GENERATIONS OF RATS RESULTED IN ADVERSE FETAL DEVELOPMENTAL ABNORMALITIES. SEE INFORMATION ON ORGANOPHOSPHATES.
ORGANOPHOSPHATES: CHOLINESTERASE INHIBITOR. **ACUTE EXPOSURE-** WHEN INGESTED, THE FIRST EFFECTS MAY BE NAUSEA, VOMITING, ANOREXIA, ABDOMINAL CRAMPS AND DIARRHEA. GASTROINTESTINAL ABSORPTION MAY CAUSE SYMPTOMS OF CHOLINESTERASE INHIBITION AS DESCRIBED IN ACUTE INHALATION. SYMPTOMS MAY BEGIN WITHIN MINUTES OR BE DELAYED FOR HOURS. DELAYED EFFECTS INCLUDING NEUROPATHY MAY ALSO OCCUR. **CHRONIC EXPOSURE-** REPEATED INGESTION MAY CAUSE EFFECTS AS DESCRIBED IN ACUTE EXPOSURE.

FIRST AID- IF PERSON IS ALERT AND RESPIRATION IS NOT DEPRESSED, GIVE SYRUP OF IPECAC FOLLOWED BY WATER (IF VOMITING OCCURS, KEEP HEAD BELOW HIPS TO PREVENT ASPIRATION). IF CONSCIOUSNESS LEVEL DECLINES OR VOMITING HAS NOT OCCURRED IN 15 MINUTES EMPTY STOMACH BY GASTRIC LAVAGE WITH THE AID OF CUFFED ENDOTRACHEAL TUBE USING ISOTONIC SALINE OR 5% SODIUM BICARBONATE FOLLOW WITH ACTIVATED CHARCOAL. ESTABLISH AND MAINTAIN AIRWAY. TREAT RESPIRATORY DIFFICULTY WITH ARTIFICIAL RESPIRATION AND OXYGEN. DO NOT GIVE MORPHINE, AMINOPHYLLINE, PHENOTHIAZINES, RESERPINE, FUROSEMIDE, OR ETHACRYNIC ACID (MORGAN, RECOGNITION AND MANAGEMENT OF PESTICIDE POISONINGS, 3RD ED.). TREAT SYMPTOMATICALLY AND SUPPORTIVELY. ADMINISTRATION OF OXYGEN AND LAVAGE MUST BE PERFORMED BY QUALIFIED MEDICAL PERSONNEL. GET MEDICAL ATTENTION IMMEDIATELY.

ANTIDOTE: THE FOLLOWING ANTIDOTE(S) HAVE BEEN RECOMMENDED. HOWEVER, THE DECISION AS TO WHETHER THE SEVERITY OF POISONING REQUIRES ADMINISTRATION OF ANY ANTIDOTE AND ACTUAL DOSE REQUIRED SHOULD BE MADE BY QUALIFIED MEDICAL PERSONNEL.
FOR CHOLINESTERASE INHIBITORS: ESTABLISH CLEAR AIRWAY AND TISSUE OXYGENATION BY ASPIRATION OF SECRETIONS, AND IF NECESSARY, BY ASSISTED PULMONARY VENTILATION WITH OXYGEN. IMPROVE TISSUE OXYGENATION AS MUCH AS POSSIBLE BEFORE ADMINISTERING ATROPINE TO MINIMIZE THE RISK OF VENTRICULAR FIBRILLATION. ADMINISTER ATROPINE SULFATE INTRAVENOUSLY, OR INTRAMUSCULARLY IF IV INJECTION IS NOT POSSIBLE. IN MODERATELY SEVERE POISONING ADMINISTER ATROPINE SULFATE, 0.4-2.0 MG REPEATED EVERY 15 MINUTES UNTIL ATROPINIZATION IS ACHIEVED (TACHYCARDIA, FLUSHING, DRY MOUTH, MYDRIASIS). MAINTAIN ATROPINIZATION BY REPEATED DOSES FOR 2-12 HOURS, OR LONGER, DEPENDING ON THE SEVERITY OF POISONING. THE APPEARANCE OF RALES IN THE LUNG BASES, MIOSIS, SALIVATION, NAUSEA, BRADYCARDIA, ARE ALL INDICATIONS OF INADEQUATE ATROPINIZATION. SEVERELY POISONED INDIVIDUALS MAY EXHIBIT REMARKABLE TOLERANCE TO ATROPINE; TWO OR MORE TIMES THE DOSAGES SUGGESTED ABOVE MAY BE NEEDED. PERSONS NOT POISONED OR ONLY SLIGHTLY POISONED, HOWEVER, MAY DEVELOP SIGNS OF ATROPINE TOXICITY FROM SUCH LARGE DOSAGES: FEVER, MUSCLE FIBRILLATIONS, AND DELIRIUM ARE THE MAIN SIGNS OF ATROPINE TOXICITY. IF THESE SIGNS APPEAR WHILE THE PATIENT IS FULLY ATROPINIZED, ATROPINE ADMINISTRATION SHOULD BE DISCONTINUED, AT LEAST TEMPORARILY. OBSERVE TREATED PATIENTS CLOSELY AT LEAST 24 HOURS TO INSURE THAT SYMPTOMS (POSSIBLY PULMONARY EDEMA) DO NOT RECUR AS ATROPINIZATION WEARS OFF. IN VERY SEVERE POISONINGS, METABOLIC DISPOSITION OF TOXICANT MAY REQUIRE SEVERAL HOURS OR DAYS DURING WHICH ATROPINIZATION MUST BE MAINTAINED. MARKEDLY LOWER LEVELS OF URINARY METABOLITES INDICATE THAT ATROPINE DOSAGE CAN BE TAPERED OFF. AS DOSAGE IS REDUCED, CHECK THE LUNG BASES FREQUENTLY FOR RALES. IF RALES ARE HEARD OR OTHER SYMPTOMS RETURN, RE-ESTABLISH ATROPINIZATION PROMPTLY (MORGAN, RECOGNITION AND MANAGEMENT OF PESTICIDE POISONINGS, 3RD ED.). ADMINISTRATION OF ANTIDOTE MUST BE PERFORMED BY QUALIFIED MEDICAL PERSONNEL.
IN CASES OF SEVERE POISONING BY ORGANOPHOSPHATE PESTICIDES IN WHICH RESPIRATORY DEPRESSION, MUSCLE WEAKNESS AND TWITCHINGS ARE SEVERE, GIVE PRALIDOXIME (PROTOPAM-AYERST, 2-PAM), 1.0 GRAM INTRAVENOUSLY AT NO MORE THAN 0.5 GRAM PER MINUTE. DOSAGE OF PRALIDOXIME MAY BE REPEATED IN 1-2 HOURS, THEN AT 10-12 HOUR INTERVALS IF NEEDED. IN VERY SEVERE POISONINGS, DOSAGE RATES MAY BE DOUBLED. TREATMENT WITH PRALIDOXIME WILL BE MOST EFFECTIVE IF GIVEN WITHIN THIRTY-SIX HOURS AFTER POISONING (MORGAN, RECOGNITION AND MANAGEMENT OF PESTICIDE POISONINGS, 3RD ED.). ANTIDOTE SHOULD BE ADMINISTERED BY QUALIFIED MEDICAL PERSONNEL.

REACTIVITY

REACTIVITY: NO DATA AVAILABLE.

INCOMPATIBILITIES: TRIAMIPHOS: OXIDIZERS (STRONG): FIRE AND EXPLOSION HAZARD.

DECOMPOSITION: THERMAL DECOMPOSITION MAY EMIT TOXIC OXIDES OF NITROGEN AND PHOSPHORUS.

POLYMERIZATION: HAZARDOUS POLYMERIZATION HAS NOT BEEN REPORTED TO OCCUR UNDER NORMAL TEMPERATURES AND PRESSURES.

STORAGE AND DISPOSAL

OBSERVE ALL FEDERAL, STATE AND LOCAL REGULATIONS WHEN STORING OR DISPOSING OF THIS SUBSTANCE. FOR ASSISTANCE, CONTACT THE DISTRICT DIRECTOR OF THE ENVIRONMENTAL PROTECTION AGENCY.

STORAGE

STORE IN ACCORDANCE WITH 40 CFR 165 RECOMMENDED PROCEDURES FOR THE DISPOSAL AND STORAGE OF PESTICIDES AND PESTICIDE CONTAINERS.
THRESHOLD PLANNING QUANTITY (TPQ): THE SUPERFUND AMENDMENTS AND REAUTHORIZATION ACT (SARA) SECTION 302 REQUIRES THAT EACH FACILITY WHERE ANY EXTREMELY HAZARDOUS SUBSTANCE IS PRESENT IN A QUANTITY EQUAL TO OR GREATER THAN THE TPQ ESTABLISHED FOR THAT SUBSTANCE NOTIFY THE STATE EMERGENCY RESPONSE COMMISSION FOR THE STATE IN WHICH IT IS LOCATED. SECTION 303 OF SARA REQUIRES THESE FACILITIES TO PARTICIPATE IN LOCAL EMERGENCY RESPONSE PLANNING (40 CFR 355.30).

DISPOSAL

DISPOSAL MUST BE IN ACCORDANCE WITH 40 CFR 165 RECOMMENDED PROCEDURES FOR THE DISPOSAL AND STORAGE OF PESTICIDES AND PESTICIDE CONTAINERS.

CONDITIONS TO AVOID

NONE REPORTED.

SPILL AND LEAK PROCEDURES

OCCUPATIONAL SPILL: DO NOT TOUCH SPILLED MATERIAL. STOP LEAK IF YOU CAN DO IT WITHOUT RISK. FOR SMALL SPILLS, TAKE UP WITH SAND OR OTHER ABSORBENT MATERIAL AND PLACE INTO CONTAINERS FOR LATER DISPOSAL. FOR SMALL DRY SPILLS, WITH A CLEAN SHOVEL PLACE MATERIAL INTO CLEAN, DRY CONTAINER AND COVER. MOVE CONTAINERS FROM SPILL AREA. FOR LARGER SPILLS, DIKE FAR AHEAD OF SPILL FOR LATER DISPOSAL. KEEP UNNECESSARY PEOPLE AWAY. ISOLATE HAZARD AREA AND DENY ENTRY.
REPORTABLE QUANTITY (RQ): 1 POUND THE SUPERFUND AMENDMENTS AND REAUTHORIZATION ACT (SARA) SECTION 304 REQUIRES THAT A RELEASE EQUAL TO OR GREATER THAN THE REPORTABLE QUANTITY FOR THIS SUBSTANCE BE IMMEDIATELY REPORTED TO THE LOCAL EMERGENCY PLANNING COMMITTEE AND THE STATE EMERGENCY RESPONSE COMMISSION (40 CFR 355.40). IF THE RELEASE OF THIS SUBSTANCE IS REPORTABLE UNDER CERCLA SECTION 103, THE NATIONAL RESPONSE CENTER MUST BE NOTIFIED IMMEDIATELY AT (800) 424-8802 OR (202) 426-2675 IN THE METROPOLITAN WASHINGTON, D.C. AREA (40 CFR 302.6).

PROTECTIVE EQUIPMENT

VENTILATION: PROVIDE LOCAL EXHAUST OR PROCESS ENCLOSURE VENTILATION SYSTEM.

RESPIRATOR: THE FOLLOWING RESPIRATORS ARE RECOMMENDED BASED ON INFORMATION FOUND IN THE PHYSICAL DATA, TOXICITY AND HEALTH EFFECTS SECTIONS. THEY ARE RANKED IN ORDER FROM MINIMUM TO MAXIMUM RESPIRATORY PROTECTION. THE SPECIFIC RESPIRATOR SELECTED MUST BE BASED ON CONTAMINATION LEVELS FOUND IN THE WORK PLACE, MUST NOT EXCEED THE WORKING LIMITS OF THE RESPIRATOR AND BE JOINTLY APPROVED BY THE NATIONAL INSTITUTE FOR OCCUPATIONAL SAFETY AND HEALTH AND THE MINE SAFETY AND HEALTH ADMINISTRATION (NIOSH-MSHA).
TYPE 'C' SUPPLIED-AIR RESPIRATOR WITH A FULL FACEPIECE OPERATED IN PRESSURE-DEMAND OR OTHER POSITIVE PRESSURE MODE OR WITH A FULL FACEPIECE, HELMET OR HOOD OPERATED IN CONTINOUS-FLOW MODE.
SELF-CONTAINED BREATHING APPARATUS WITH A FULL FACEPIECE OPERATED IN PRESSURE-DEMAND OR OTHER POSITIVE PRESSURE MODE.
FOR FIREFIGHTING AND OTHER IMMEDIATELY DANGEROUS TO LIFE OR HEALTH CONDITIONS:
SELF-CONTAINED BREATHING APPARATUS WITH FULL FACEPIECE OPERATED IN PRESSURE-DEMAND OR OTHER POSITIVE PRESSURE MODE.

SUPPLIED-AIR RESPIRATOR WITH FULL FACEPIECE AND OPERATED IN PRESSURE-DEMAND OR OTHER POSITIVE PRESSURE MODE IN COMBINATION WITH AN AUXILIARY SELF-CONTAINED BREATHING APPARATUS OPERATED IN PRESSURE-DEMAND OR OTHER POSITIVE PRESSURE MODE.

CLOTHING: EMPLOYEE MUST WEAR APPROPRIATE PROTECTIVE (IMPERVIOUS) CLOTHING AND EQUIPMENT TO PREVENT ANY POSSIBILITY OF SKIN CONTACT WITH THIS SUBSTANCE.

GLOVES: EMPLOYEE MUST WEAR APPROPRIATE PROTECTIVE GLOVES TO PREVENT CONTACT WITH THIS SUBSTANCE.

EYE PROTECTION: EMPLOYEE MUST WEAR SPLASH-PROOF OR DUST-RESISTANT SAFETY GOGGLES AND A FACESHIELD TO PREVENT CONTACT WITH THIS SUBSTANCE.

EMERGENCY WASH FACILITIES: WHERE THERE IS ANY POSSIBILITY THAT AN EMPLOYEE'S EYES AND/OR SKIN MAY BE EXPOSED TO THIS SUBSTANCE, THE EMPLOYER SHOULD PROVIDE AN EYE WASH FOUNTAIN AND QUICK DRENCH SHOWER WITHIN THE IMMEDIATE WORK AREA FOR EMERGENCY USE.

AUTHORIZED BY- OCCUPATIONAL HEALTH SERVICES, INC.
CREATION DATE: 10/05/89 ***REVISION DATE:*** 04/26/90

MATERIAL SAFETY DATA SHEET

OCCUPATIONAL HEALTH SERVICES, INC.
AGRICULTURE AND PESTICIDE DIVISION
450 SEVENTH AVENUE, SUITE 2407
NEW YORK, NEW YORK 10123
1-800-445-MSDS OR (212) 967-1100

EMERGENCY CONTACT:
JOHN S. BRANSFORD, JR. (615) 292-1180

SUBSTANCE IDENTIFICATION

CAS-NUMBER 16118-49-3

SUBSTANCE: **CARBETAMIDE**

TRADE NAMES/SYNONYMS: PROPANAMIDE, N-ETHYL-2-(((PHENYLAMINO)CARBONYL)OXY)-, (R)-; LACTAMIDE, N-ETHYL-, CARBANILATE (ESTER), D-; (R)-N-ETHYL-2-(((PHENYLAMINO)CARBONYL)OXY)PROPANAMIDE; D-N-ETHYLLACTAMIDE CARBANILATE (ESTER); (R)-1-(ETHYLCARBAMOYL)ETHYL CARBANILATE; (R)-1-(ETHYLCARBAMOYL)ETHYL PHENYLCARBAMATE; D-(-)-N-ETHYL-2-(PHENYLCARBAMOYLOXY)PROPIONAMIDE; (R)-(-)-1-(ETHYLCARBAMOYL)ETHYL PHENYLCARBAMATE; CARBETAMEX; CARBETHAMIDE; LEGURAME; RP 11561; C12H16N2O3; PST72941

CHEMICAL FAMILY: CARBAMATE

MOLECULAR FORMULA: C12-H16-N2-O3

MOLECULAR WEIGHT: 236.3

CERCLA RATINGS (SCALE 0-3): HEALTH=2 FIRE=1 REACTIVITY=0 PERSISTENCE=1

NFPA RATINGS (SCALE 0-4): HEALTH=U FIRE=1 REACTIVITY=0

COMPONENTS AND CONTAMINANTS

COMPONENT: CARBETAMIDE ***PERCENT:*** 100.0
CAS# 16118-49-3

EXPOSURE LIMITS: NO OCCUPATIONAL EXPOSURE LIMITS ESTABLISHED BY OSHA, ACGIH, OR NIOSH.

PHYSICAL DATA

DESCRIPTION: COLORLESS, CRYSTALLINE SOLID. ***MELTING POINT:*** 246 F (119 C)

SPECIFIC GRAVITY: NOT AVAILABLE ***VAPOR PRESSURE:*** NEGLIGIBLE

SOLUBILITY IN WATER: 0.35%

SOLVENT SOLUBILITY: SOLUBLE IN ACETONE, DICHLOROMETHANE, DIMETHYLFORMAMIDE, ETHANOL, AND METHANOL; SPARINGLY SOLUBLE IN CYCLOHEXANONE AND PETROLEUM ETHER.

FIRE AND EXPLOSION DATA

FIRE AND EXPLOSION HAZARD: SLIGHT FIRE HAZARD WHEN EXPOSED TO HEAT OR FLAME.

FIREFIGHTING MEDIA: DRY CHEMICAL, CARBON DIOXIDE, HALON, WATER SPRAY OR STANDARD FOAM (1987 EMERGENCY RESPONSE GUIDEBOOK, DOT P 5800.4). FOR LARGER FIRES, USE WATER SPRAY, FOG OR STANDARD FOAM (1987 EMERGENCY RESPONSE GUIDEBOOK, DOT P 5800.4).

FIREFIGHTING: MOVE CONTAINER FROM FIRE AREA IF POSSIBLE. DO NOT SCATTER SPILLED MATERIAL WITH HIGH PRESSURE WATER STREAMS. DIKE FIRE CONTROL WATER FOR LATER DISPOSAL (1987 EMERGENCY RESPONSE GUIDEBOOK, DOT P 5800.4, GUIDE PAGE 31).

USE AGENTS SUITABLE FOR TYPE OF SURROUNDING FIRE. AVOID BREATHING HAZARDOUS VAPORS, KEEP UPWIND.

TOXICITY

CARBETAMIDE: TOXICITY DATA: >130 MG/M3/4 HOURS INHALATION-RAT LC50 (85JFAN); >500 MG/KG SKIN-RABBIT LD50 (85JFAN); 11000 MG/KG ORAL-RAT LD50; 1200 MG/KG ORAL-MOUSE LD50; 900 MG/KG ORAL-DOG LD50. CARCINOGEN STATUS: NONE. ACUTE TOXICITY: SLIGHTLY TOXIC BY INGESTION. TARGET EFFECTS: NO DATA AVAILABLE.

HEALTH EFFECTS AND FIRST AID

INHALATION: CARBETAMIDE: **ACUTE EXPOSURE-** THE LC50 FOR RABBITS WAS GREATER THAN 130 MG/M3/4 HOURS. **CHRONIC EXPOSURE-** NO DATA AVAILABLE.

FIRST AID- REMOVE FROM EXPOSURE AREA TO FRESH AIR IMMEDIATELY. IF BREATHING HAS STOPPED, PERFORM ARTIFICIAL RESPIRATION. KEEP PERSON WARM AND AT REST. TREAT SYMPTOMATICALLY AND SUPPORTIVELY. GET MEDICAL ATTENTION IMMEDIATELY.

SKIN CONTACT: CARBETAMIDE: **ACUTE EXPOSURE-** NO SYSTEMIC EFFECTS WERE OBSERVED FROM APPLICATION OF 500 MG/KG TO RABBIT SKINS. **CHRONIC EXPOSURE-** NO DATA AVAILABLE.

FIRST AID- REMOVE CONTAMINATED CLOTHING AND SHOES IMMEDIATELY. WASH AFFECTED AREA WITH SOAP OR MILD DETERGENT AND LARGE AMOUNTS OF WATER UNTIL NO EVIDENCE OF CHEMICAL REMAINS (APPROXIMATELY 15-20 MINUTES). GET MEDICAL ATTENTION IMMEDIATELY.

EYE CONTACT: CARBETAMIDE: **ACUTE EXPOSURE-** THIS MATERIAL WAS NOT IRRITATING TO RABBIT EYES. **CHRONIC EXPOSURE-** NO DATA AVAILABLE.

FIRST AID- WASH EYES IMMEDIATELY WITH LARGE AMOUNTS OF WATER OR NORMAL SALINE, OCCASIONALLY LIFTING UPPER AND LOWER LIDS, UNTIL NO EVIDENCE OF CHEMICAL REMAINS (APPROXIMATELY 15-20 MINUTES). GET MEDICAL ATTENTION IMMEDIATELY.

INGESTION: CARBETAMIDE: **ACUTE EXPOSURE-** A LETHAL DOSE IN RATS WAS 11000 MG/KG; SYMPTOMS WERE NOT REPORTED. **CHRONIC EXPOSURE-** NO OBSERVABLE EFFECTS WERE NOTED IN 90-DAY STUDIES OF RATS RECEIVING 3200 MG/KG DIET AND DOGS RECEIVING 12,800 MG/KG.

FIRST AID- IF THE PERSON IS CONSCIOUS AND NOT CONVULSING, REMOVE BY GASTRIC LAVAGE AND FOLLOW WITH A CATHARTIC (DREISBACH, HANDBOOK OF POISONING, 12TH ED.). TREAT SYMPTOMATICALLY AND SUPPORTIVELY. GASTRIC LAVAGE SHOULD BE PERFORMED BY QUALIFIED MEDICAL PERSONNEL. GET MEDICAL ATTENTION IMMEDIATELY.

ANTIDOTE: NO SPECIFIC ANTIDOTE. TREAT SYMPTOMATICALLY AND SUPPORTIVELY.

REACTIVITY

REACTIVITY: STABLE UNDER NORMAL TEMPERATURES AND PRESSURES.

INCOMPATIBILITIES: CARBETAMIDE: OXIDIZERS (STRONG): FIRE AND EXPLOSION HAZARD.

DECOMPOSITION: THERMAL DECOMPOSITION PRODUCTS MAY INCLUDE TOXIC OXIDES OF CARBON AND NITROGEN.

POLYMERIZATION: HAZARDOUS POLYMERIZATION HAS NOT BEEN REPORTED TO OCCUR UNDER NORMAL TEMPERATURES AND PRESSURES.

STORAGE AND DISPOSAL

OBSERVE ALL FEDERAL, STATE AND LOCAL REGULATIONS WHEN STORING OR DISPOSING OF THIS SUBSTANCE. FOR ASSISTANCE, CONTACT THE DISTRICT DIRECTOR OF THE ENVIRONMENTAL PROTECTION AGENCY.

STORAGE

STORE IN ACCORDANCE WITH 40 CFR 165 RECOMMENDED PROCEDURES FOR THE DISPOSAL AND STORAGE OF PESTICIDES AND PESTICIDE CONTAINERS.
STORE AWAY FROM INCOMPATIBLE SUBSTANCES.

DISPOSAL

DISPOSAL MUST BE IN ACCORDANCE WITH 40 CFR 165 RECOMMENDED PROCEDURES FOR THE DISPOSAL AND STORAGE OF PESTICIDES AND PESTICIDE CONTAINERS.

CONDITIONS TO AVOID

MAY BURN BUT DOES NOT IGNITE READILY. AVOID CONTACT WITH STRONG OXIDIZERS, EXCESSIVE HEAT, SPARKS, OR OPEN FLAME.

SPILL AND LEAK PROCEDURES

OCCUPATIONAL SPILL: SWEEP UP AND PLACE IN SUITABLE CLEAN, DRY CONTAINERS FOR RECLAMATION OR LATER DISPOSAL. DO NOT FLUSH SPILLED MATERIAL INTO SEWER. KEEP UNNECESSARY PEOPLE AWAY.

PROTECTIVE EQUIPMENT

VENTILATION: PROVIDE GENERAL DILUTION VENTILATION.

RESPIRATOR: THE FOLLOWING RESPIRATORS ARE RECOMMENDED BASED ON INFORMATION FOUND IN THE PHYSICAL DATA, TOXICITY AND HEALTH EFFECTS SECTIONS. THEY ARE RANKED IN ORDER FROM MINIMUM TO MAXIMUM RESPIRATORY PROTECTION. THE SPECIFIC RESPIRATOR SELECTED MUST BE BASED ON CONTAMINATION LEVELS FOUND IN THE WORK PLACE, MUST NOT EXCEED THE WORKING LIMITS OF THE RESPIRATOR AND BE JOINTLY APPROVED BY THE NATIONAL INSTITUTE FOR OCCUPATIONAL SAFETY AND HEALTH AND THE MINE SAFETY AND HEALTH ADMINISTRATION (NIOSH-MSHA).

CHEMICAL CARTRIDGE RESPIRATOR WITH AN ORGANIC VAPOR CARTRIDGE(S) IN COMBINATION WITH A DUST AND MIST FILTER.

GAS MASK WITH ORGANIC VAPOR CANISTER (CHIN-STYLE OR FRONT- OR BACK-MOUNTED CANISTER) WITH A DUST AND MIST FILTER.

GAS MASK WITH ORGANIC VAPOR CANISTER (CHIN-STYLE OR FRONT- OR BACK-MOUNTED CANISTER) WITH A PARTICULATE FILTER.

POWERED AIR-PURIFYING RESPIRATOR WITH A HIGH-EFFICIENCY FILTER.

TYPE 'C' SUPPLIED-AIR RESPIRATOR WITH A FULL FACEPIECE OPERATED IN A PRESSURE-DEMAND OR OTHER POSITIVE PRESSURE MODE.

SELF-CONTAINED BREATHING APPARATUS WITH A FULL FACEPIECE OPERATED IN PRESSURE-DEMAND OR OTHER POSITIVE PRESSURE MODE.

FOR FIREFIGHTING AND OTHER IMMEDIATELY DANGEROUS TO LIFE OR HEALTH CONDITIONS:

SELF-CONTAINED BREATHING APPARATUS WITH FULL FACEPIECE OPERATED IN PRESSURE-DEMAND OR OTHER POSITIVE PRESSURE MODE.

SUPPLIED-AIR RESPIRATOR WITH FULL FACEPIECE AND OPERATED IN PRESSURE-DEMAND OR OTHER POSITIVE PRESSURE MODE IN COMBINATION WITH AN AUXILIARY SELF-CONTAINED BREATHING APPARATUS OPERATED IN PRESSURE-DEMAND OR OTHER POSITIVE PRESSURE MODE.

CLOTHING: EMPLOYEE MUST WEAR APPROPRIATE PROTECTIVE (IMPERVIOUS) CLOTHING AND EQUIPMENT TO PREVENT REPEATED OR PROLONGED SKIN CONTACT WITH THIS SUBSTANCE.

GLOVES: EMPLOYEE MUST WEAR APPROPRIATE PROTECTIVE GLOVES TO PREVENT CONTACT WITH THIS SUBSTANCE.

EYE PROTECTION: EMPLOYEE MUST WEAR SPLASH-PROOF OR DUST-RESISTANT SAFETY GOGGLES TO PREVENT EYE CONTACT WITH THIS SUBSTANCE.

EMERGENCY EYE WASH: WHERE THERE IS ANY POSSIBILITY THAT AN EMPLOYEE'S EYES MAY BE EXPOSED TO THIS SUBSTANCE, THE EMPLOYER SHOULD PROVIDE AN EYE WASH FOUNTAIN WITHIN THE IMMEDIATE WORK AREA FOR EMERGENCY USE.

AUTHORIZED BY- OCCUPATIONAL HEALTH SERVICES, INC.

CREATION DATE: 12/14/89 ***REVISION DATE:*** 05/31/90

MATERIAL SAFETY DATA SHEET

OCCUPATIONAL HEALTH SERVICES, INC.
AGRICULTURE AND PESTICIDE DIVISION
450 SEVENTH AVENUE, SUITE 2407
NEW YORK, NEW YORK 10123
1-800-445-MSDS OR (212) 967-1100

EMERGENCY CONTACT:
JOHN S. BRANSFORD, JR. (615) 292-1180

SUBSTANCE IDENTIFICATION

CAS-NUMBER 3734-95-0

SUBSTANCE: **CYANTHOATE**

TRADE NAMES/SYNONYMS: PHOSPHOROTHIOIC ACID, S-(2-((1-CYANO-1-METHYLETHYL)AMINO)-2-OXOETHYL) O,O-DIETHYL ESTER; PHOSPHOROTHIOIC ACID, O,O-DIETHYL ESTER, S-ESTER WITH N-(1-CYANO- 1-METHYLETHYL)-2-MERCAPTOACETAMIDE; S-(2-((1-CYANO-1-METHYLETHYL)AMINO)-2-OXOETHYL) O,O-DIETHYL PHOSPHOROTHIOATE; O,O-DIETHYL PHOSPHOROTHIOATE S-ESTER WITH N-(1-CYANO-1-METHYLETHYL)-2 -MERCAPTOACETAMIDE; S-(N-(1-CYANO-1-METHYLETHYL)CARBAMOYLMETHYL) O,O-DIETHYL PHOSPHOROTHIOATE; N-(1-CYANO-1-METHYLETHYL)-2-(DIETHOXYPHOSPHINOYLTHIO)ACETAMIDE; M 1568; TARTAN; C10H19N2O4PS; PST72949

CHEMICAL FAMILY: PHOSPHOROTHIOATE

MOLECULAR FORMULA: C10-H19-N2-O4-P-S

MOLECULAR WEIGHT: 294.34

CERCLA RATINGS (SCALE 0-3): HEALTH=3 FIRE=U REACTIVITY=0 PERSISTENCE=1

NFPA RATINGS (SCALE 0-4): HEALTH=4 FIRE=U REACTIVITY=0

COMPONENTS AND CONTAMINANTS

COMPONENT: CYANTHOATE ***PERCENT:*** 100.0
CAS# 3734-95-0

OTHER CONTAMINANTS: NONE

EXPOSURE LIMITS: NO OCCUPATIONAL EXPOSURE LIMITS ESTABLISHED BY OSHA, ACGIH, OR NIOSH.

PHYSICAL DATA

DESCRIPTION: LIGHT YELLOW LIQUID. ***BOILING POINT:*** NOT AVAILABLE.

SPECIFIC GRAVITY: 1.191 ***VAPOR PRESSURE:*** NOT AVAILABLE

SOLUBILITY IN WATER: 7% @ 20 C

SOLVENT SOLUBILITY: SOLUBLE IN ETHER, ETHANOL, BENZENE, ACETONE, CHLOROFORM AND ORGANIC SOLVENTS.

FIRE AND EXPLOSION DATA

FIRE AND EXPLOSION HAZARD: UNKNOWN FIRE AND EXPLOSION HAZARD.

FLASH POINT: NOT AVAILABLE

FIREFIGHTING MEDIA: DRY CHEMICAL, CARBON DIOXIDE, HALON, WATER SPRAY OR STANDARD FOAM (1987 EMERGENCY RESPONSE GUIDEBOOK, DOT P 5800.4). FOR LARGER FIRES, USE WATER SPRAY, FOG OR STANDARD FOAM (1987 EMERGENCY RESPONSE GUIDEBOOK, DOT P 5800.4).

FIREFIGHTING: MOVE CONTAINERS FROM FIRE AREA IF POSSIBLE. FIGHT FIRE FROM MAXIMUM DISTANCE. STAY AWAY FROM STORAGE TANK ENDS. DIKE FIRE CONTROL WATER FOR LATER DISPOSAL. DO NOT SCATTER MATERIAL (1987 EMERGENCY RESPONSE GUIDEBOOK, DOT P 5800.4, GUIDE PAGE 55). EXTINGUISH ONLY IF FLOW CAN BE STOPPED; USE FLOODING AMOUNTS OF WATER AS FOG, SOLID STREAMS MAY BE INEFFECTIVE. COOL CONTAINERS WITH FLOODING AMOUNTS OF WATER FROM AS FAR A DISTANCE AS POSSIBLE. USE WATER SPRAY TO ABSORB TOXIC VAPORS. AVOID BREATHING TOXIC VAPORS; KEEP UPWIND. CONSIDER EVACUATION OF DOWNWIND AREA IF MATERIAL IS LEAKING.

TRANSPORTATION DATA

DEPARTMENT OF TRANSPORTATION HAZARD CLASSIFICATION 49 CFR 172.101: POISON B

DEPARTMENT OF TRANSPORTATION LABELING REQUIREMENTS 49 CFR 172.101 AND SUBPART E: POISON

DEPARTMENT OF TRANSPORTATION PACKAGING REQUIREMENTS: 49 CFR 173.359 EXCEPTIONS: 49 CFR 173.359

TOXICITY

CYANTHOATE: TOXICITY DATA: 105 MG/KG SKIN-RAT LD50; 3500 UG/KG ORAL-RAT LD50; 12 MG/KG ORAL-MOUSE LD50; 8 MG/KG ORAL-RABBIT LD50; 13 MG/KG ORAL-GUINEA PIG LD50; 20 MG/KG ORAL-DOG LD50. CARCINOGEN STATUS: NONE. ACUTE TOXICITY: HIGHLY TOXIC BY DERMAL ABSORPTION AND INGESTION. TARGET EFFECTS: CHOLINESTERASE INHIBITOR. POISONING MAY AFFECT THE NERVOUS SYSTEM.* AT INCREASED RISK FROM EXPOSURE: PERSONS WITH RESPIRATORY AILMENTS, RECENT EXPOSURE TO CHOLINESTERASE INHIBITORS OR IMPAIRED CHOLINESTERASE PRODUCTION, OR LIVER MALFUNCTION.* ADDITIONAL DATA: MAY CROSS THE PLACENTA. HIGH ENVIRONMENTAL TEMPERATURES OR EXPOSURE OF THE CHEMICAL TO VISIBLE OR ULTRAVIOLET LIGHT MAY ENHANCE THE TOXICITY. INTERACTIONS WITH MEDICATIONS MAY OCCUR.*

* MAY BE BASED ON GENERAL INFORMATION ON ORGANOPHOSPHATES.

HEALTH EFFECTS AND FIRST AID

INHALATION: CYANTHOATE: SEE INFORMATION ON ORGANOPHOSPHATES.

ORGANOPHOSPHATES: CHOLINESTERASE INHIBITOR. **ACUTE EXPOSURE-** WHEN INHALED, THE FIRST EFFECTS OF CHOLINESTERASE INHIBITORS ARE USUALLY RESPIRATORY AND MAY INCLUDE NASAL HYPEREMIA AND WATERY DISCHARGE, COUGH, CHEST DISCOMFORT, DYSPNEA, AND WHEEZING DUE TO INCREASED BRONCHIAL SECRETIONS AND BRONCHOCONSTRICTION. IF SUFFICIENT AMOUNTS ARE ABSORBED, OTHER SYSTEMIC EFFECTS MAY BEGIN WITHIN A FEW MINUTES OR BE DELAYED FOR UP TO 12 HOURS. SYMPTOMS MAY INCLUDE PALLOR, NAUSEA, VOMITING, DIARRHEA, ABDOMINAL CRAMPS, HEADACHE, DIZZINESS, OCULAR PAIN, BLURRED VISION, MIOSIS OR IN SOME CASES, ESPECIALLY INITIALLY, MYDRIASIS, LACRIMATION, SALIVATION, SWEATING, AND CONFUSION. OTHER REPORTED CENTRAL NERVOUS SYSTEM OR NEUROMUSCULAR EFFECTS MAY INCLUDE ATAXIA, SLURRED SPEECH, AREFLEXIA, WEAKNESS, FATIGUE, FASCICULATIONS, TWITCHING, TREMORS POSSIBLY OF THE TONGUE AND EYELIDS, AND EVENTUALLY PARALYSIS OF THE EXTREMITIES AND POSSIBLY OF THE RESPIRATORY MUSCLES. IN SEVERE CASES THERE MAY ALSO BE INVOLUNTARY DEFECATION AND URINATION, CYANOSIS, PSYCHOSIS, HYPERGLYCEMIA, ACUTE PANCREATITIS, CARDIAC IRREGULARITIES, PULMONARY EDEMA, UNCONSCIOUSNESS, CONVULSIONS, AND COMA. DEATH IS PRIMARILY DUE TO RESPIRATORY FAILURE, ALTHOUGH CARDIOVASCULAR EFFECTS INCLUDING CARDIAC ARREST MAY ALSO BE IMPLICATED. LONG TERM SEQUELAE ARE RARE

BUT MAY INCLUDE NEUROPSYCHIATRIC DISORDERS AND MYOPATHY WITH MUSCLE TENDERNESS. SOME ORGANOPHOSPHATES MAY CAUSE A DELAYED NEUROPATHY BEGINNING 1-4 WEEKS AFTER AN ACUTE EXPOSURE WHICH MAY OR MAY NOT HAVE CAUSED ACUTE CHOLINERGIC EFFECTS. NUMBNESS, TINGLING, WEAKNESS AND CRAMPING BEGINNING SYMMETRICALLY IN THE LOWER LIMBS MAY PROGRESS TO ATAXIA AND PARALYSIS. IN SEVERE CASES, UPPER LIMB INVOLVEMENT IS POSSIBLE AND FLACCID PARALYSIS MAY PROGRESS TO SPASTIC PARALYSIS WITH EXAGGERATED REFLEXES. IMPROVEMENT MAY OCCUR OVER MONTHS TO YEARS, BUT SOME RESIDUAL IMPAIRMENT USUALLY REMAINS. **CHRONIC EXPOSURE-** REPEATED OR PROLONGED EXPOSURE MAY RESULT IN THE EFFECTS OF ACUTE EXPOSURE INCLUDING THE DELAYED NEUROPATHY. OTHER EFFECTS REPORTED IN WORKERS REPEATEDLY EXPOSED INCLUDE IMPAIRED MEMORY AND CONCENTRATION, ACUTE PSYCHOSIS, SEVERE DEPRESSIONS, IRRITABILTY, CONFUSION, APATHY, EMOTIONAL LABILITY, SOCIAL WITHDRAWAL, CONFUSION, HEADACHE, SPEECH DIFFICULTIES, DELAYED REACTION TIMES, SPATIAL DISORIENTATION, NIGHTMARES, SLEEPWALKING, AND DROWSINESS OR INSOMNIA. AN INFLUENZA-LIKE CONDITION WITH HEADACHE, NAUSEA, WEAKNESS, ANOREXIA AND MALAISE HAS ALSO BEEN REPORTED.

FIRST AID- REMOVE FROM EXPOSURE AREA TO FRESH AIR IMMEDIATELY. IF BREATHING HAS STOPPED, GIVE ARTIFICIAL RESPIRATION. MAINTAIN AIRWAY AND BLOOD PRESSURE AND ADMINISTER OXYGEN IF AVAILABLE. KEEP AFFECTED PERSON WARM AND AT REST. TREAT SYMPTOMATICALLY AND SUPPORTIVELY. ADMINISTRATION OF OXYGEN SHOULD BE PERFORMED BY QUALIFIED PERSONNEL. GET MEDICAL ATTENTION IMMEDIATELY.

SKIN CONTACT: CYANTHOATE: HIGHLY TOXIC. SEE INFORMATION ON ORGANOPHOSPHATES.

ORGANOPHOSPHATES: CHOLINESTERASE INHIBITOR. **ACUTE EXPOSURE-** LOCALIZED SWEATING AND FASCICULATIONS MAY OCCUR AT THE SITE OF CONTACT. IF SUFFICIENT AMOUNTS ARE ABSORBED, OTHER EFFECTS OF CHOLINESTERASE INHIBITION AS DESCRIBED IN ACUTE INHALATION MAY OCCUR. SYMPTOMS MAY BE DELAYED 2-3 HOURS, BUT USUALLY NO MORE THAN 12 HOURS. THE RATE OF ABSORPTION IS INCREASED BY THE PRESENCE OF DERMATITIS OR HIGH AMBIENT TEMPERATURES. DELAYED NEUROPATHY IS ALSO POSSIBLE. **CHRONIC EXPOSURE-** REPEATED OR PROLONGED EXPOSURE MAY CAUSE EFFECTS AS DESCRIBED IN ACUTE EXPOSURE. SOME ORGANOPHOSPHATES MAY CAUSE SENSITIZATION.

FIRST AID- REMOVE CONTAMINATED CLOTHING IMMEDIATELY. WASH CONTAMINATED AREAS WITH SOAP AND WATER FOLLOWED BY ALCOHOL (ARENA, POISONING, 4TH ED.). EMERGENCY PERSONNEL SHOULD WEAR GLOVES AND AVOID CONTAMINATION. TREAT RESPIRATORY DIFFICULTY WITH ARTIFICIAL RESPIRATION. GET MEDICAL ATTENTION IMMEDIATELY.

EYE CONTACT: CYANTHOATE: SEE INFORMATION ON ORGANOPHOSPHATES.

ORGANOPHOSPHATES: CHOLINESTERASE INHIBITOR. **ACUTE EXPOSURE-** DIRECT CONTACT MAY CAUSE PAIN, HYPEREMIA, LACRIMATION, TWITCHING OF THE EYELIDS, MIOSIS, AND CILIARY MUSCLE SPASM WITH LOSS OF ACCOMODATION, BLURRED OR DIMMED VISION AND BROWACHE. SOMETIMES MYDRIASIS MAY OCCUR INSTEAD OF MIOSIS. WITH SUFFICIENT EXPOSURE, OTHER SYMPTOMS OF CHOLINESTERASE INHIBITION AS DESCRIBED IN ACUTE INHALATION MAY OCCUR. **CHRONIC EXPOSURE-** REPEATED OR PROLONGED EXPOSURE MAY CAUSE EFFECTS AS DESCRIBED IN ACUTE EXPOSURE. SOME COMPOUNDS HAVE CAUSED TOXIC EFFECTS ON THE CRYSTALLINE LENS, CONJUNCTIVAL THICKENING AND OBSTRUCTION OF THE NASOLACRIMAL CANALS WHEN USED AS MIOTIC EYEDROPS.

FIRST AID- IRRIGATE EYES WITH WATER OR SALINE SOLUTION. IF SYMPTOMS OF POISONING OCCUR, TREAT RESPIRATORY DIFFICULTY WITH ARTIFICIAL RESPIRATION AND OXYGEN. OBSERVE PATIENT FOR AT LEAST 24-36 HOURS (GOSSELIN, CLINICAL TOXICOLOGY OF COMMERCIAL PRODUCTS, 5TH ED.). GET MEDICAL ATTENTION IMMEDIATELY. OXYGEN SHOULD BE ADMINISTERED BY QUALIFIED MEDICAL PERSONNEL.

INGESTION: CYANTHOATE: HIGHLY TOXIC. SEE INFORMATION ON ORGANOPHOSPHATES.

ORGANOPHOSPHATES: CHOLINESTERASE INHIBITOR. **ACUTE EXPOSURE-** WHEN INGESTED, THE FIRST EFFECTS MAY BE NAUSEA, VOMITING, ANOREXIA, ABDOMINAL CRAMPS AND DIARRHEA. GASTROINTESTINAL ABSORPTION MAY CAUSE SYMPTOMS OF CHOLINESTERASE INHIBITION AS DESCRIBED IN ACUTE INHALATION. SYMPTOMS MAY BEGIN WITHIN MINUTES OR BE DELAYED FOR HOURS. DELAYED EFFECTS INCLUDING NEUROPATHY MAY ALSO OCCUR. **CHRONIC EXPOSURE-** REPEATED INGESTION MAY CAUSE EFFECTS AS DESCRIBED IN ACUTE EXPOSURE.

FIRST AID- IF PERSON IS ALERT AND RESPIRATION IS NOT DEPRESSED, GIVE SYRUP OF IPECAC FOLLOWED BY WATER (IF VOMITING OCCURS, KEEP HEAD BELOW HIPS TO PREVENT ASPIRATION). IF CONSCIOUSNESS LEVEL DECLINES OR VOMITING HAS NOT OCCURRED IN 15 MINUTES EMPTY STOMACH BY GASTRIC LAVAGE WITH THE AID OF CUFFED ENDOTRACHEAL TUBE USING ISOTONIC SALINE OR 5% SODIUM BICARBONATE FOLLOW WITH ACTIVATED CHARCOAL. ESTABLISH AND MAINTAIN AIRWAY. TREAT RESPIRATORY DIFFICULTY WITH ARTIFICIAL RESPIRATION AND OXYGEN. DO NOT GIVE MORPHINE, AMINOPHYLLINE, PHENOTHIAZINES, RESERPINE, FUROSEMIDE, OR ETHACRYNIC ACID (MORGAN, RECOGNITION AND MANAGEMENT OF PESTICIDE POISONINGS, 3RD ED.). TREAT SYMPTOMATICALLY AND SUPPORTIVELY. ADMINISTRATION OF OXYGEN AND LAVAGE MUST BE PERFORMED BY QUALIFIED MEDICAL PERSONNEL. GET MEDICAL ATTENTION IMMEDIATELY.

ANTIDOTE: THE FOLLOWING ANTIDOTE(S) HAVE BEEN RECOMMENDED. HOWEVER, THE DECISION AS TO WHETHER THE SEVERITY OF POISONING REQUIRES ADMINISTRATION OF ANY ANTIDOTE AND ACTUAL DOSE REQUIRED SHOULD BE MADE BY QUALIFIED MEDICAL PERSONNEL.

FOR CHOLINESTERASE INHIBITORS: ESTABLISH CLEAR AIRWAY AND TISSUE OXYGENATION BY ASPIRATION OF SECRETIONS, AND IF NECESSARY, BY ASSISTED PULMONARY VENTILATION WITH OXYGEN. IMPROVE TISSUE OXYGENATION AS MUCH AS POSSIBLE BEFORE ADMINISTERING ATROPINE TO MINIMIZE THE RISK OF VENTRICULAR FIBRILLATION. ADMINISTER ATROPINE SULFATE INTRAVENOUSLY, OR INTRAMUSCULARLY IF IV INJECTION IS NOT POSSIBLE. IN MODERATELY SEVERE POISONING ADMINISTER ATROPINE SULFATE, 0.4-2.0 MG REPEATED EVERY 15 MINUTES UNTIL ATROPINIZATION IS ACHIEVED (TACHYCARDIA, FLUSHING, DRY MOUTH, MYDRIASIS). MAINTAIN ATROPINIZATION BY REPEATED DOSES FOR 2-12 HOURS, OR LONGER, DEPENDING ON THE SEVERITY OF POISONING. THE APPEARANCE OF RALES IN THE LUNG BASES, MIOSIS, SALIVATION, NAUSEA, BRADYCARDIA, ARE ALL INDICATIONS OF INADEQUATE ATROPINIZATION. SEVERELY POISONED INDIVIDUALS MAY EXHIBIT REMARKABLE TOLERANCE TO ATROPINE; TWO OR MORE TIMES THE DOSAGES SUGGESTED ABOVE MAY BE NEEDED. PERSONS NOT POISONED OR ONLY SLIGHTLY POISONED, HOWEVER, MAY DEVELOP SIGNS OF ATROPINE TOXICITY FROM SUCH LARGE DOSAGES: FEVER, MUSCLE FIBRILLATIONS, AND DELIRIUM ARE THE MAIN SIGNS OF ATROPINE TOXICITY. IF THESE SIGNS APPEAR WHILE THE PATIENT IS FULLY ATROPINIZED, ATROPINE ADMINISTRATION SHOULD BE DISCONTINUED, AT LEAST TEMPORARILY. OBSERVE TREATED PATIENTS CLOSELY AT LEAST 24 HOURS TO INSURE THAT SYMPTOMS (POSSIBLY PULMONARY EDEMA) DO NOT RECUR AS ATROPINIZATION WEARS OFF. IN VERY SEVERE POISONINGS, METABOLIC DISPOSITION OF TOXICANT MAY REQUIRE SEVERAL HOURS OR DAYS DURING WHICH ATROPINIZATION MUST BE MAINTAINED. MARKEDLY LOWER LEVELS OF URINARY METABOLITES INDICATE THAT ATROPINE DOSAGE CAN BE TAPERED OFF. AS DOSAGE IS REDUCED, CHECK THE LUNG BASES FREQUENTLY FOR RALES. IF RALES ARE HEARD OR OTHER SYMPTOMS RETURN, RE-ESTABLISH ATROPINIZATION PROMPTLY (MORGAN, RECOGNITION AND MANAGEMENT OF PESTICIDE POISONINGS, 3RD ED.). ADMINISTRATION OF ANTIDOTE MUST BE PERFORMED BY QUALIFIED MEDICAL PERSONNEL.

IN CASES OF SEVERE POISONING BY ORGANOPHOSPHATE PESTICIDES IN WHICH RESPIRATORY DEPRESSION, MUSCLE WEAKNESS AND TWITCHINGS ARE SEVERE, GIVE PRALIDOXIME (PROTOPAM-AYERST, 2-PAM), 1.0 GRAM INTRAVENOUSLY AT NO MORE THAN 0.5 GRAM PER MINUTE. DOSAGE OF PRALIDOXIME MAY BE REPEATED IN 1-2 HOURS, THEN AT 10-12 HOUR INTERVALS IF NEEDED. IN VERY SEVERE POISONINGS, DOSAGE RATES MAY BE DOUBLED. TREATMENT WITH PRALIDOXIME WILL BE MOST EFFECTIVE IF GIVEN WITHIN THIRTY-SIX HOURS AFTER POISONING (MORGAN, RECOGNITION AND MANAGEMENT OF PESTICIDE POISONINGS, 3RD ED.). ANTIDOTE SHOULD BE ADMINISTERED BY QUALIFIED MEDICAL PERSONNEL.

REACTIVITY

REACTIVITY: STABLE UNDER NORMAL TEMPERATURES AND PRESSURES.

INCOMPATIBILITIES: CYANTHOATE: OXIDIZERS (STRONG): FIRE AND EXPLOSION HAZARD.

DECOMPOSITION: THERMAL DECOMPOSITION PRODUCTS MAY INCLUDE TOXIC OXIDES OF NITROGEN, CARBON, PHOSPHORUS, AND SULFUR.

POLYMERIZATION: HAZARDOUS POLYMERIZATION HAS NOT BEEN REPORTED TO OCCUR UNDER NORMAL TEMPERATURES AND PRESSURES.

STORAGE AND DISPOSAL

OBSERVE ALL FEDERAL, STATE AND LOCAL REGULATIONS WHEN STORING OR DISPOSING OF THIS SUBSTANCE. FOR ASSISTANCE, CONTACT THE DISTRICT DIRECTOR OF THE ENVIRONMENTAL PROTECTION AGENCY.

****STORAGE****

STORE IN ACCORDANCE WITH 40 CFR 165 RECOMMENDED PROCEDURES FOR THE DISPOSAL AND STORAGE OF PESTICIDES AND PESTICIDE CONTAINERS.
STORE AWAY FROM INCOMPATIBLE SUBSTANCES.

****DISPOSAL****

DISPOSAL MUST BE IN ACCORDANCE WITH 40 CFR 165 RECOMMENDED PROCEDURES FOR THE DISPOSAL AND STORAGE OF PESTICIDES AND PESTICIDE CONTAINERS.

CONDITIONS TO AVOID

MAY BURN BUT DOES NOT IGNITE READILY. CONTAINERS MAY EXPLODE IN HEAT OF FIRE.

SPILL AND LEAK PROCEDURES

OCCUPATIONAL SPILL: DO NOT TOUCH SPILLED MATERIAL. STOP LEAK IF YOU CAN DO IT WITHOUT RISK. USE WATER SPRAY TO REDUCE VAPORS. FOR SMALL SPILLS, TAKE UP WITH SAND OR OTHER ABSORBENT MATERIAL AND PLACE INTO CONTAINERS FOR LATER DISPOSAL. FOR SMALL DRY SPILLS, WITH A CLEAN SHOVEL PLACE MATERIAL INTO CLEAN, DRY CONTAINERS AND COVER. MOVE CONTAINERS FROM SPILL AREA. FOR LARGER SPILLS, DIKE FAR AHEAD OF SPILL FOR LATER DISPOSAL. KEEP UNNECESSARY PEOPLE AWAY. ISOLATE HAZARD AREA AND DENY ENTRY. VENTILATE CLOSED SPACES BEFORE ENTERING.

PROTECTIVE EQUIPMENT

VENTILATION: PROCESS ENCLOSURE RECOMMENDED.

RESPIRATOR: THE FOLLOWING RESPIRATORS ARE RECOMMENDED BASED ON INFORMATION FOUND IN THE PHYSICAL DATA, TOXICITY AND HEALTH EFFECTS SECTIONS. THEY ARE RANKED IN ORDER FROM MINIMUM TO MAXIMUM RESPIRATORY PROTECTION. THE SPECIFIC RESPIRATOR SELECTED MUST BE BASED ON CONTAMINATION LEVELS FOUND IN THE WORK PLACE, MUST NOT EXCEED THE WORKING LIMITS OF THE RESPIRATOR AND BE JOINTLY APPROVED BY THE NATIONAL INSTITUTE FOR OCCUPATIONAL SAFETY AND HEALTH AND THE MINE SAFETY AND HEALTH ADMINISTRATION (NIOSH-MSHA).

TYPE 'C' SUPPLIED-AIR RESPIRATOR WITH A FULL FACEPIECE OPERATED IN PRESSURE-DEMAND OR OTHER POSITIVE PRESSURE MODE OR WITH A FULL FACEPIECE, HELMET OR HOOD OPERATED IN CONTINOUS-FLOW MODE.

SELF-CONTAINED BREATHING APPARATUS WITH A FULL FACEPIECE OPERATED IN PRESSURE-DEMAND OR OTHER POSITIVE PRESSURE MODE.

FOR FIREFIGHTING AND OTHER IMMEDIATELY DANGEROUS TO LIFE OR HEALTH CONDITIONS:

SELF-CONTAINED BREATHING APPARATUS WITH FULL FACEPIECE OPERATED IN PRESSURE-DEMAND OR OTHER POSITIVE PRESSURE MODE.

SUPPLIED-AIR RESPIRATOR WITH FULL FACEPIECE AND OPERATED IN PRESSURE-DEMAND OR OTHER POSITIVE PRESSURE MODE IN COMBINATION WITH AN AUXILIARY SELF-CONTAINED BREATHING APPARATUS OPERATED IN PRESSURE-DEMAND OR OTHER POSITIVE PRESSURE MODE.

CLOTHING: EMPLOYEE MUST WEAR APPROPRIATE PROTECTIVE (IMPERVIOUS) CLOTHING AND EQUIPMENT TO PREVENT ANY POSSIBILITY OF SKIN CONTACT WITH THIS SUBSTANCE.

GLOVES: EMPLOYEE MUST WEAR APPROPRIATE PROTECTIVE GLOVES TO PREVENT CONTACT WITH THIS SUBSTANCE.

EYE PROTECTION: EMPLOYEE MUST WEAR SPLASH-PROOF OR DUST-RESISTANT SAFETY GOGGLES WITH OR WITHOUT A FACESHIELD TO PREVENT CONTACT WITH THIS SUBSTANCE.

EMERGENCY EYE WASH: WHERE THERE IS ANY POSSIBILITY THAT AN EMPLOYEE'S EYES MAY BE EXPOSED TO THIS SUBSTANCE, THE EMPLOYER SHOULD PROVIDE AN EYE WASH FOUNTAIN WITHIN THE IMMEDIATE WORK AREA FOR EMERGENCY USE.

AUTHORIZED BY- OCCUPATIONAL HEALTH SERVICES, INC.

CREATION DATE: 10/04/89 ***REVISION DATE:*** 04/26/90

MATERIAL SAFETY DATA SHEET

OCCUPATIONAL HEALTH SERVICES, INC.
AGRICULTURE AND PESTICIDE DIVISION
450 SEVENTH AVENUE, SUITE 2407
NEW YORK, NEW YORK 10123
1-800-445-MSDS OR (212) 967-1100

EMERGENCY CONTACT:
JOHN S. BRANSFORD, JR. (615) 292-1180

SUBSTANCE IDENTIFICATION

CAS-NUMBER 2636-26-2

SUBSTANCE: CYANOPHOS

TRADE NAMES/SYNONYMS: PHOSPHOROTHIOIC ACID, O-(4-CYANOPHENYL) O,O-DIMETHYL ESTER; O-(4-CYANOPHENYL) O,O-DIMETHYL PHOSPHOROTHIOATE; PHOSPHOROTHIOIC ACID, O,O-DIMETHYL ESTER, O-ESTER WITH P-HYDROXYBENZONITRILE; O-P-CYANOPHENYL O,O-DIMETHYL PHOSPHOROTHIOATE; O,O-DIMETHYL-O-P-CYANOPHENOL PHOSPHOROTHIOATE; O,O-DIMETHYL-O-(4-CYANOPHENYL) PHOSPHOROTHIOATE; O,O-DIMETHYL-O,4-CYANOPHENYL THIOPHOSPHATE; O-4-CYANOPHENYL O,O-DIMETHYL PHOSPHOROTHIOATE; 4-(DIMETHOXYPHOSPHINOTHIOYLOXY)BENZONITRILE; CIAFOS; CYANOX; CYAP; S 4084; SUMITOMO S 4084; C9H10NO3PS; PST72950

CHEMICAL FAMILY: PHOSPHOROTHIOATE
NITRILE, AROMATIC

MOLECULAR FORMULA: (C-H3-O)2-P-(S)-O-C6-H4-C-N

MOLECULAR WEIGHT: 243.23

CERCLA RATINGS (SCALE 0-3): HEALTH=3 FIRE=U REACTIVITY=0 PERSISTENCE=2

NFPA RATINGS (SCALE 0-4): HEALTH=3 FIRE=U REACTIVITY=0

COMPONENTS AND CONTAMINANTS

COMPONENT: CYANOPHOS ***PERCENT:*** 100.0
CAS# 2636-26-2

OTHER CONTAMINANTS: NONE

EXPOSURE LIMITS: NO OCCUPATIONAL EXPOSURE LIMITS ESTABLISHED BY OSHA, ACGIH, OR NIOSH.

CYANOPHOS: 1000 POUNDS SARA SECTION 302 THRESHOLD PLANNING QUANTITY
1 POUND SARA SECTION 304 REPORTABLE QUANTITY

PHYSICAL DATA

DESCRIPTION: YELLOW TO REDDISH-YELLOW, TRANSPARENT LIQUID.

BOILING POINT: 246-248 F (119-120 C) @ 0.09 MMHG (DEC)

MELTING POINT: 57-59 F (14-15 C) ***SPECIFIC GRAVITY:*** 1.255-1.265 @ 25 C

VAPOR PRESSURE: 0.0008 MMHG @ 20 C ***SOLUBILITY IN WATER:*** .005% @ 30 C

SOLVENT SOLUBILITY: SOLUBLE IN ALCOHOLS, KETONES, BENZENE, TOLUENE, XYLENE, ACETONE AND CHLOROFORM; MODERATELY SOLUBLE IN N-HEXANE; SLIGHTLY SOLUBLE IN KEROSENE.

FIRE AND EXPLOSION DATA

FIRE AND EXPLOSION HAZARD: UNKNOWN FIRE AND EXPLOSION HAZARD.

FLASH POINT: NOT AVAILABLE

FIREFIGHTING MEDIA: DRY CHEMICAL, CARBON DIOXIDE, HALON, WATER SPRAY OR STANDARD FOAM (1987 EMERGENCY RESPONSE GUIDEBOOK, DOT P 5800.4). FOR LARGER FIRES, USE WATER SPRAY, FOG OR STANDARD FOAM (1987 EMERGENCY RESPONSE GUIDEBOOK, DOT P 5800.4).

FIREFIGHTING: MOVE CONTAINERS FROM FIRE AREA IF POSSIBLE. COOL CONTAINERS EXPOSED TO FLAMES WITH WATER FROM SIDE UNTIL WELL AFTER FIRE IS OUT. FIGHT FIRE FROM MAXIMUM DISTANCE. STAY AWAY FROM STORAGE TANK ENDS. DIKE FIRE CONTROL WATER FOR LATER DISPOSAL. DO NOT SCATTER MATERIAL. (1987 EMERGENCY RESPONSE GUIDEBOOK, DOT P 5800.4, GUIDE PAGE 57). EXTINGUISH ONLY IF FLOW CAN BE STOPPED. USE FLOODING AMOUNTS OF WATER AS A FOG; SOLID STREAMS MAY BE INEFFECTIVE. COOL CONTAINERS WITH FLOODING AMOUNTS OF WATER FROM AS FAR A DISTANCE AS POSSIBLE. AVOID BREATHING POISONOUS VAPORS, KEEP UPWIND.

TOXICITY

CYANOPHOS: TOXICITY DATA: 800 MG/KG SKIN-RAT LD50; 2010 MG/KG SKIN-MAMMAL LD50; 215 MG/KG ORAL-RAT LD50; 324 MG/KG ORAL-MOUSE LD50; 324 MG/KG ORAL-GUINEA PIG LD50; 1080 MG/KG SUBCUTANEOUS-MOUSE LD50; 350 MG/KG INTRAPERITONEAL-MOUSE LD50. CARCINOGEN STATUS: NONE. ACUTE TOXICITY LEVEL: TOXIC BY DERMAL ABSORPTION AND INGESTION. TARGRT EFFECTS: CHOLINESTERASE INHIBITOR. POISONING MAY AFFECT THE NERVOUS SYSTEM. AT INCREASED RISK FROM EXPOSURE: PERSONS WITH RESPIRATORY AILMENTS, RECENT EXPOSURE TO CHOLINESTERASE INHIBITORS OR IMPAIRED CHOLINESTERASE PRODUCTION OR LIVER MALFUNCTION.* ADDITIONAL DATA: MAY CROSS THE PLACENTA. HIGH ENVIRONMENTAL TEMPERATURES OR EXPOSURE OF THE CHEMICAL TO VISIBLE OR ULTRAVIOLET LIGHT MAY ENHANCE THE TOXICITY. INTERACTIONS WITH MEDICATIONS HAVE BEEN REPORTED.*

* MAY BE BASED ON GENERAL INFORMATION ON ORGANOPHOSPHATES.

HEALTH EFFECTS AND FIRST AID

INHALATION: CYANOPHOS: SEE INFORMATION ON ORGANOPHOSPHATES.
ORGANOPHOSPHATES: CHOLINESTERASE INHIBITOR. ACUTE EXPOSURE- WHEN INHALED, THE FIRST EFFECTS OF CHOLINESTERASE INHIBITORS ARE USUALLY RESPIRATORY AND MAY INCLUDE NASAL HYPEREMIA AND WATERY DISCHARGE, COUGH, CHEST DISCOMFORT, DYSPNEA, AND WHEEZING DUE TO INCREASED BRONCHIAL SECRETIONS AND BRONCHOCONSTRICTION. IF SUFFICIENT AMOUNTS ARE ABSORBED, OTHER SYSTEMIC EFFECTS MAY BEGIN WITHIN A FEW MINUTES OR BE DELAYED FOR UP TO 12 HOURS. SYMPTOMS MAY INCLUDE PALLOR, NAUSEA, VOMITING, DIARRHEA, ABDOMINAL CRAMPS, HEADACHE, DIZZINESS, OCULAR PAIN, BLURRED VISION, MIOSIS OR IN SOME CASES, ESPECIALLY INITIALLY, MYDRIASIS, LACRIMATION, SALIVATION, SWEATING, AND CONFUSION. OTHER REPORTED CENTRAL NERVOUS SYSTEM OR NEUROMUSCULAR EFFECTS MAY INCLUDE ATAXIA, SLURRED SPEECH, AREFLEXIA, WEAKNESS, FATIGUE, FASCICULATIONS, TWITCHING, TREMORS POSSIBLY OF THE TONGUE AND EYELIDS, AND EVENTUALLY PARALYSIS OF THE EXTREMITIES AND POSSIBLY OF THE

RESPIRATORY MUSCLES. IN SEVERE CASES THERE MAY ALSO BE INVOLUNTARY DEFECATION AND URINATION, CYANOSIS, PSYCHOSIS, HYPERGLYCEMIA, ACUTE PANCREATITIS, CARDIAC IRREGULARITIES, PULMONARY EDEMA, UNCONSCIOUSNESS, CONVULSIONS, AND COMA. DEATH IS PRIMARILY DUE TO RESPIRATORY FAILURE, ALTHOUGH CARDIOVASCULAR EFFECTS INCLUDING CARDIAC ARREST MAY ALSO BE IMPLICATED. LONG TERM SEQUELAE ARE RARE BUT MAY INCLUDE NEUROPSYCHIATRIC DISORDERS AND MYOPATHY WITH MUSCLE TENDERNESS. SOME ORGANOPHOSPHATES MAY CAUSE A DELAYED NEUROPATHY BEGINNING 1-4 WEEKS AFTER AN ACUTE EXPOSURE WHICH MAY OR MAY NOT HAVE CAUSED ACUTE CHOLINERGIC EFFECTS. NUMBNESS, TINGLING, WEAKNESS AND CRAMPING BEGINNING SYMMETRICALLY IN THE LOWER LIMBS MAY PROGRESS TO ATAXIA AND PARALYSIS. IN SEVERE CASES, UPPER LIMB INVOLVEMENT IS POSSIBLE AND FLACCID PARALYSIS MAY PROGRESS TO SPASTIC PARALYSIS WITH EXAGGERATED REFLEXES. IMPROVEMENT MAY OCCUR OVER MONTHS TO YEARS, BUT SOME RESIDUAL IMPAIRMENT USUALLY REMAINS. **CHRONIC EXPOSURE-** REPEATED OR PROLONGED EXPOSURE MAY RESULT IN THE EFFECTS OF ACUTE EXPOSURE INCLUDING THE DELAYED NEUROPATHY. OTHER EFFECTS REPORTED IN WORKERS REPEATEDLY EXPOSED INCLUDE IMPAIRED MEMORY AND CONCENTRATION, ACUTE PSYCHOSIS, SEVERE DEPRESSIONS, IRRITABILTY, CONFUSION, APATHY, EMOTIONAL LABILITY, SOCIAL WITHDRAWAL, CONFUSION, HEADACHE, SPEECH DIFFICULTIES, DELAYED REACTION TIMES, SPATIAL DISORIENTATION, NIGHTMARES, SLEEPWALKING, AND DROWSINESS OR INSOMNIA. AN INFLUENZA-LIKE CONDITION WITH HEADACHE, NAUSEA, WEAKNESS, ANOREXIA AND MALAISE HAS ALSO BEEN REPORTED.

FIRST AID- REMOVE FROM EXPOSURE AREA TO FRESH AIR IMMEDIATELY. IF BREATHING HAS STOPPED, GIVE ARTIFICIAL RESPIRATION. MAINTAIN AIRWAY AND BLOOD PRESSURE AND ADMINISTER OXYGEN IF AVAILABLE. KEEP AFFECTED PERSON WARM AND AT REST. TREAT SYMPTOMATICALLY AND SUPPORTIVELY. ADMINISTRATION OF OXYGEN SHOULD BE PERFORMED BY QUALIFIED PERSONNEL. GET MEDICAL ATTENTION IMMEDIATELY.

SKIN CONTACT: CYANOPHOS: TOXIC. SEE INFORMATION ON ORGANOPHOSPHATES. ORGANOPHOSPHATES: CHOLINESTERASE INHIBITOR. **ACUTE EXPOSURE-** LOCALIZED SWEATING AND FASCICULATIONS MAY OCCUR AT THE SITE OF CONTACT. IF SUFFICIENT AMOUNTS ARE ABSORBED, OTHER EFFECTS OF CHOLINESTERASE INHIBITION AS DESCRIBED IN ACUTE INHALATION MAY OCCUR. SYMPTOMS MAY BE DELAYED 2-3 HOURS, BUT USUALLY NO MORE THAN 12 HOURS. THE RATE OF ABSORPTION IS INCREASED BY THE PRESENCE OF DERMATITIS OR HIGH AMBIENT TEMPERATURES. DELAYED NEUROPATHY IS ALSO POSSIBLE. **CHRONIC EXPOSURE-** REPEATED OR PROLONGED EXPOSURE MAY CAUSE EFFECTS AS DESCRIBED IN ACUTE EXPOSURE. SOME ORGANOPHOSPHATES MAY CAUSE SENSITIZATION.

FIRST AID- REMOVE CONTAMINATED CLOTHING IMMEDIATELY. WASH CONTAMINATED AREAS WITH SOAP AND WATER FOLLOWED BY ALCOHOL (ARENA, POISONING, 4TH ED.). EMERGENCY PERSONNEL SHOULD WEAR GLOVES AND AVOID CONTAMINATION. TREAT RESPIRATORY DIFFICULTY WITH ARTIFICIAL RESPIRATION. GET MEDICAL ATTENTION IMMEDIATELY.

EYE CONTACT: CYANOPHOS: SEE INFORMATION ON ORGANOPHOSPHATES. ORGANOPHOSPHATES: CHOLINESTERASE INHIBITOR. **ACUTE EXPOSURE-** DIRECT CONTACT MAY CAUSE PAIN, HYPEREMIA, LACRIMATION, TWITCHING OF THE EYELIDS, MIOSIS, AND CILIARY MUSCLE SPASM WITH LOSS OF ACCOMODATION, BLURRED OR DIMMED VISION AND BROWACHE. SOMETIMES MYDRIASIS MAY OCCUR INSTEAD OF MIOSIS. WITH SUFFICIENT EXPOSURE, OTHER SYMPTOMS OF CHOLINESTERASE INHIBITION AS DESCRIBED IN ACUTE INHALATION MAY OCCUR. **CHRONIC EXPOSURE-** REPEATED OR PROLONGED EXPOSURE MAY CAUSE EFFECTS AS DESCRIBED IN ACUTE EXPOSURE. SOME COMPOUNDS HAVE CAUSED TOXIC EFFECTS ON THE CRYSTALLINE LENS, CONJUNCTIVAL THICKENING AND OBSTRUCTION OF THE NASOLACRIMAL CANALS WHEN USED AS MIOTIC EYEDROPS.

FIRST AID- IRRIGATE EYES WITH WATER OR SALINE SOLUTION. IF SYMPTOMS OF POISONING OCCUR, TREAT RESPIRATORY DIFFICULTY WITH ARTIFICIAL RESPIRATION AND OXYGEN. OBSERVE PATIENT FOR AT LEAST 24-36 HOURS (GOSSELIN, CLINICAL TOXICOLOGY OF COMMERCIAL PRODUCTS, 5TH ED.). GET MEDICAL ATTENTION IMMEDIATELY. OXYGEN SHOULD BE ADMINISTERED BY QUALIFIED MEDICAL PERSONNEL.

INGESTION: CYANOPHOS: TOXIC. SEE INFORMATION ON ORGANOPHOSPHATES. ORGANOPHOSPHATES: CHOLINESTERASE INHIBITOR. **ACUTE EXPOSURE-** WHEN INGESTED, THE FIRST EFFECTS MAY BE NAUSEA, VOMITING, ANOREXIA, ABDOMINAL CRAMPS AND DIARRHEA. GASTROINTESTINAL ABSORPTION MAY CAUSE SYMPTOMS OF CHOLINESTERASE INHIBITION AS DESCRIBED IN ACUTE INHALATION. SYMPTOMS MAY BEGIN WITHIN MINUTES OR BE DELAYED FOR HOURS. DELAYED EFFECTS INCLUDING NEUROPATHY MAY ALSO OCCUR. **CHRONIC EXPOSURE-** REPEATED INGESTION MAY CAUSE EFFECTS AS DESCRIBED IN ACUTE EXPOSURE.

FIRST AID- IF PERSON IS ALERT AND RESPIRATION IS NOT DEPRESSED, GIVE SYRUP OF IPECAC FOLLOWED BY WATER (IF VOMITING OCCURS, KEEP HEAD BELOW HIPS TO PREVENT ASPIRATION). IF CONSCIOUSNESS LEVEL DECLINES OR VOMITING HAS NOT OCCURRED IN 15 MINUTES EMPTY STOMACH BY GASTRIC LAVAGE WITH THE AID OF CUFFED ENDOTRACHEAL TUBE USING ISOTONIC SALINE OR 5% SODIUM BICARBONATE FOLLOW WITH ACTIVATED CHARCOAL. ESTABLISH AND MAINTAIN AIRWAY. TREAT RESPIRATORY DIFFICULTY WITH ARTIFICIAL RESPIRATION AND OXYGEN. DO NOT GIVE MORPHINE, AMINOPHYLLINE, PHENOTHIAZINES, RESERPINE, FUROSEMIDE, OR ETHACRYNIC ACID (MORGAN, RECOGNITION AND MANAGEMENT OF PESTICIDE POISONINGS, 3RD ED.). TREAT SYMPTOMATICALLY AND SUPPORTIVELY. ADMINISTRATION OF OXYGEN AND LAVAGE MUST BE PERFORMED BY QUALIFIED MEDICAL PERSONNEL. GET MEDICAL ATTENTION IMMEDIATELY.

ANTIDOTE: THE FOLLOWING ANTIDOTE(S) HAVE BEEN RECOMMENDED. HOWEVER, THE DECISION AS TO WHETHER THE SEVERITY OF POISONING REQUIRES ADMINISTRATION OF ANY ANTIDOTE AND ACTUAL DOSE REQUIRED SHOULD BE MADE BY QUALIFIED MEDICAL PERSONNEL.

FOR CHOLINESTERASE INHIBITORS: ESTABLISH CLEAR AIRWAY AND TISSUE OXYGENATION BY ASPIRATION OF SECRETIONS, AND IF NECESSARY, BY ASSISTED PULMONARY VENTILATION WITH OXYGEN. IMPROVE TISSUE OXYGENATION AS MUCH AS POSSIBLE BEFORE ADMINISTERING ATROPINE TO MINIMIZE THE RISK OF VENTRICULAR FIBRILLATION. ADMINISTER ATROPINE SULFATE INTRAVENOUSLY, OR INTRAMUSCULARLY IF IV INJECTION IS NOT POSSIBLE. IN MODERATELY SEVERE POISONING ADMINISTER ATROPINE SULFATE, 0.4-2.0 MG REPEATED EVERY 15 MINUTES UNTIL ATROPINIZATION IS ACHIEVED (TACHYCARDIA, FLUSHING, DRY MOUTH, MYDRIASIS). MAINTAIN ATROPINIZATION BY REPEATED DOSES FOR 2-12 HOURS, OR LONGER, DEPENDING ON THE SEVERITY OF POISONING. THE APPEARANCE OF RALES IN THE LUNG BASES, MIOSIS, SALIVATION, NAUSEA, BRADYCARDIA, ARE ALL INDICATIONS OF INADEQUATE ATROPINIZATION. SEVERELY POISONED INDIVIDUALS MAY EXHIBIT REMARKABLE TOLERANCE TO ATROPINE; TWO OR MORE TIMES THE DOSAGES SUGGESTED ABOVE MAY BE NEEDED. PERSONS NOT POISONED OR ONLY SLIGHTLY POISONED, HOWEVER, MAY DEVELOP SIGNS OF ATROPINE TOXICITY FROM SUCH LARGE DOSAGES: FEVER, MUSCLE FIBRILLATIONS, AND DELIRIUM ARE THE MAIN SIGNS OF ATROPINE TOXICITY. IF THESE SIGNS APPEAR WHILE THE PATIENT IS FULLY ATROPINIZED, ATROPINE ADMINISTRATION SHOULD BE DISCONTINUED, AT LEAST TEMPORARILY. OBSERVE TREATED PATIENTS CLOSELY AT LEAST 24 HOURS TO INSURE THAT SYMPTOMS (POSSIBLY PULMONARY EDEMA) DO NOT RECUR AS ATROPINIZATION WEARS OFF. IN VERY SEVERE POISONINGS, METABOLIC DISPOSITION OF TOXICANT MAY REQUIRE SEVERAL HOURS OR DAYS DURING WHICH ATROPINIZATION MUST BE MAINTAINED. MARKEDLY LOWER LEVELS OF URINARY METABOLITES INDICATE THAT ATROPINE DOSAGE CAN BE TAPERED OFF. AS DOSAGE IS REDUCED, CHECK THE LUNG BASES FREQUENTLY FOR RALES. IF RALES ARE HEARD OR OTHER SYMPTOMS RETURN, RE-ESTABLISH ATROPINIZATION PROMPTLY (MORGAN, RECOGNITION AND MANAGEMENT OF PESTICIDE POISONINGS, 3RD ED.). ADMINISTRATION OF ANTIDOTE MUST BE PERFORMED BY QUALIFIED MEDICAL PERSONNEL.

IN CASES OF SEVERE POISONING BY ORGANOPHOSPHATE PESTICIDES IN WHICH RESPIRATORY DEPRESSION, MUSCLE WEAKNESS AND TWITCHINGS ARE SEVERE, GIVE PRALIDOXIME (PROTOPAM-AYERST, 2-PAM), 1.0 GRAM INTRAVENOUSLY AT NO MORE THAN 0.5 GRAM PER MINUTE. DOSAGE OF PRALIDOXIME MAY BE REPEATED IN 1-2 HOURS, THEN AT 10-12 HOUR INTERVALS IF NEEDED. IN VERY SEVERE POISONINGS, DOSAGE RATES MAY BE DOUBLED. TREATMENT WITH PRALIDOXIME WILL BE MOST EFFECTIVE IF GIVEN WITHIN THIRTY-SIX HOURS AFTER POISONING (MORGAN, RECOGNITION AND MANAGEMENT OF PESTICIDE POISONINGS, 3RD ED.). ANTIDOTE SHOULD BE ADMINISTERED BY QUALIFIED MEDICAL PERSONNEL.

REACTIVITY

REACTIVITY: CYANOPHOS: STABLE UNDER NORMAL TEMPERATURES AND PRESSURES. MAY RAPIDLY DECOMPOSE UPON EXPOSURE TO LIGHT.

INCOMPATIBILITIES: CYANOPHOS: ALKALIS (STRONG): MAY DECOMPOSE. OXIDIZERS (STRONG): FIRE AND EXPLOSION HAZARD.

DECOMPOSITION: THERMAL DECOMPOSITION MAY RELEASE TOXIC FUMES OF CYANIDE AND OXIDES OF SULFUR, NITROGEN, CARBON AND POTASSIUM.

POLYMERIZATION: HAZARDOUS POLYMERIZATION HAS NOT BEEN REPORTED TO OCCUR UNDER NORMAL TEMPERATURES AND PRESSURES.

STORAGE AND DISPOSAL

OBSERVE ALL FEDERAL, STATE AND LOCAL REGULATIONS WHEN STORING OR DISPOSING OF THIS SUBSTANCE. FOR ASSISTANCE, CONTACT THE DISTRICT DIRECTOR OF THE ENVIRONMENTAL PROTECTION AGENCY.

STORAGE

STORE IN ACCORDANCE WITH 40 CFR 165 RECOMMENDED PROCEDURES FOR THE DISPOSAL AND STORAGE OF PESTICIDES AND PESTICIDE CONTAINERS.

STORE AWAY FROM INCOMPATIBLE SUBSTANCES.

THRESHOLD PLANNING QUANTITY (TPQ): THE SUPERFUND AMENDMENTS AND

REAUTHORIZATION ACT (SARA) SECTION 302 REQUIRES THAT EACH FACILITY WHERE ANY EXTREMELY HAZARDOUS SUBSTANCE IS PRESENT IN A QUANTITY EQUAL TO OR GREATER THAN THE TPQ ESTABLISHED FOR THAT SUBSTANCE NOTIFY THE STATE EMERGENCY RESPONSE COMMISSION FOR THE STATE IN WHICH IT IS LOCATED. SECTION 303 OF SARA REQUIRES THESE FACILITIES TO PARTICIPATE IN LOCAL EMERGENCY RESPONSE PLANNING (40 CFR 355.30).

KEEP CONTAINER TIGHTLY CLOSED. PROTECT FROM EXPOSURE TO AIR OR LIGHT.

DISPOSAL

DISPOSAL MUST BE IN ACCORDANCE WITH 40 CFR 165 RECOMMENDED PROCEDURES FOR THE DISPOSAL AND STORAGE OF PESTICIDES AND PESTICIDE CONTAINERS.

CONDITIONS TO AVOID

MAY BE IGNITED BY HEAT, SPARKS OR FLAMES. CONTAINER MAY EXPLODE IN HEAT OF FIRE. VAPOR EXPLOSION AND POISON HAZARD INDOORS, OUTDOORS OR IN SEWERS.

SPILL AND LEAK PROCEDURES

OCCUPATIONAL SPILL: SHUT OFF IGNITION SOURCES. DO NOT TOUCH SPILLED MATERIAL. STOP LEAK IF YOU CAN DO IT WITHOUT RISK. USE WATER SPRAY TO REDUCE VAPORS. FOR SMALL SPILLS, TAKE UP WITH SAND OR OTHER ABSORBENT MATERIAL AND PLACE INTO CONTAINERS FOR LATER DISPOSAL. FOR SMALL DRY SPILLS, WITH CLEAN SHOVEL PLACE MATERIAL INTO CLEAN, DRY CONTAINERS AND COVER. MOVE CONTAINERS FROM SPILL AREA. FOR LARGER SPILLS, DIKE FAR AHEAD OF SPILL FOR LATER DISPOSAL. NO SMOKING, FLAMES OR FLARES IN HAZARD AREA! KEEP UNNECESSARY PEOPLE AWAY. ISOLATE HAZARD AREA AND DENY ENTRY. VENTILATE CLOSED SPACES BEFORE ENTERING.

REPORTABLE QUANTITY (RQ): 1 POUND THE SUPERFUND AMENDMENTS AND REAUTHORIZATION ACT (SARA) SECTION 304 REQUIRES THAT A RELEASE EQUAL TO OR GREATER THAN THE REPORTABLE QUANTITY FOR THIS SUBSTANCE BE IMMEDIATELY REPORTED TO THE LOCAL EMERGENCY PLANNING COMMITTEE AND THE STATE EMERGENCY RESPONSE COMMISSION (40 CFR 355.40). IF THE RELEASE OF THIS SUBSTANCE IS REPORTABLE UNDER CERCLA SECTION 103, THE NATIONAL RESPONSE CENTER MUST BE NOTIFIED IMMEDIATELY AT (800) 424-8802 OR (202) 426-2675 IN THE METROPOLITAN WASHINGTON, D.C. AREA (40 CFR 302.6).

PROTECTIVE EQUIPMENT

VENTILATION: PROCESS ENCLOSURE RECOMMENDED.

RESPIRATOR: THE FOLLOWING RESPIRATORS ARE RECOMMENDED BASED ON INFORMATION FOUND IN THE PHYSICAL DATA, TOXICITY AND HEALTH EFFECTS SECTIONS. THEY ARE RANKED IN ORDER FROM MINIMUM TO MAXIMUM RESPIRATORY PROTECTION. THE SPECIFIC RESPIRATOR SELECTED MUST BE BASED ON CONTAMINATION LEVELS FOUND IN THE WORK PLACE, MUST NOT EXCEED THE WORKING LIMITS OF THE RESPIRATOR AND BE JOINTLY APPROVED BY THE NATIONAL INSTITUTE FOR OCCUPATIONAL SAFETY AND HEALTH AND THE MINE SAFETY AND HEALTH ADMINISTRATION (NIOSH-MSHA).

TYPE 'C' SUPPLIED-AIR RESPIRATOR WITH A FULL FACEPIECE OPERATED IN PRESSURE-DEMAND OR OTHER POSITIVE PRESSURE MODE OR WITH A FULL FACEPIECE, HELMET OR HOOD OPERATED IN CONTINOUS-FLOW MODE.

SELF-CONTAINED BREATHING APPARATUS WITH A FULL FACEPIECE OPERATED IN PRESSURE-DEMAND OR OTHER POSITIVE PRESSURE MODE.

FOR FIREFIGHTING AND OTHER IMMEDIATELY DANGEROUS TO LIFE OR HEALTH CONDITIONS:

SELF-CONTAINED BREATHING APPARATUS WITH FULL FACEPIECE OPERATED IN PRESSURE-DEMAND OR OTHER POSITIVE PRESSURE MODE.

SUPPLIED-AIR RESPIRATOR WITH FULL FACEPIECE AND OPERATED IN PRESSURE-DEMAND OR OTHER POSITIVE PRESSURE MODE IN COMBINATION WITH AN AUXILIARY SELF-CONTAINED BREATHING APPARATUS OPERATED IN PRESSURE-DEMAND OR OTHER POSITIVE PRESSURE MODE.

CLOTHING: EMPLOYEE MUST WEAR APPROPRIATE PROTECTIVE (IMPERVIOUS) CLOTHING AND EQUIPMENT TO PREVENT ANY POSSIBILITY OF SKIN CONTACT WITH THIS SUBSTANCE.

GLOVES: EMPLOYEE MUST WEAR APPROPRIATE PROTECTIVE GLOVES TO PREVENT CONTACT WITH THIS SUBSTANCE.

EYE PROTECTION: EMPLOYEE MUST WEAR SPLASH-PROOF OR DUST-RESISTANT SAFETY GOGGLES AND A FACESHIELD TO PREVENT CONTACT WITH THIS SUBSTANCE.

EMERGENCY WASH FACILITIES: WHERE THERE IS ANY POSSIBILITY THAT AN EMPLOYEE'S EYES AND/OR SKIN MAY BE EXPOSED TO THIS SUBSTANCE, THE EMPLOYER SHOULD PROVIDE AN EYE WASH FOUNTAIN AND QUICK DRENCH SHOWER WITHIN THE IMMEDIATE WORK AREA FOR EMERGENCY USE.

AUTHORIZED BY- OCCUPATIONAL HEALTH SERVICES, INC.

CREATION DATE: 10/04/89 ***REVISION DATE:*** 04/26/90

MATERIAL SAFETY DATA SHEET

OCCUPATIONAL HEALTH SERVICES, INC.
AGRICULTURE AND PESTICIDE DIVISION
450 SEVENTH AVENUE, SUITE 2407
NEW YORK, NEW YORK 10123
1-800-445-MSDS OR (212) 967-1100

EMERGENCY CONTACT:
JOHN S. BRANSFORD, JR. (615) 292-1180

SUBSTANCE IDENTIFICATION

CAS-NUMBER 2631-37-0

SUBSTANCE: PROMECARB

TRADE NAMES/SYNONYMS: PHENOL, 3-METHYL-5-(1-METHYLETHYL)-, METHYLCARBAMATE; 3-METHYL-5-(1-METHYLETHYL)PHENOL METHYLCARBAMATE; CARBAMIC ACID, METHYL-, M-CYM-5-YL ESTER; M-CYM-5-YL METHYLCARBAMATE; 3-METHYL-5-ISOPROPYL N-METHYLCARBAMATE; 5-METHYL M-CUMENYL METHYLCARBAMATE; 3-ISOPROPYLL-5-METHYLPHENYL-N-METHYLCARBAMATE; 5-ISOPROPYL-M-TOLYL METHYL-CARBAMATE; CARBAMIC ACID, (3-METHYL-5-(1-METHYLETHYL)PHENYL-, METHYL ESTER; CARBAMIC ACID, N-METHYL-, 3-METHYL-5-ISOPROPYLPHENYL ESTER; CARBANILIC ACID, 3-ISOPROPYL-5-METHYL-, METHYL ESTER; CARBAMULT; MINACIDE; SCHERING 34615; ENT 27300; METHYLCARBAMIC ACID M-CYM-5-YL ESTER; 3-ISOPROPYL-5-METHYLCARBAMIC ACID METHYL ESTER; N-METHYLCARBAMIC ACID 3-METHYL-5-ISOPROPYLPHENYL ESTER; 3-METHYL-5-(1-METHYLETHYL)PHENYL-CARBAMIC ACID METHYL ESTER; C12H17NO2; PST72957

CHEMICAL FAMILY: CARBAMATE
AROMATIC

MOLECULAR FORMULA: C6-H3-(C-H3)-C-H-(C-H3)2-C-O2-N-H-C-H3

MOLECULAR WEIGHT: 207.28

CERCLA RATINGS (SCALE 0-3): HEALTH=3 FIRE=1 REACTIVITY=0 PERSISTENCE=2

NFPA RATINGS (SCALE 0-4): HEALTH=3 FIRE=1 REACTIVITY=0

COMPONENTS AND CONTAMINANTS

COMPONENT: PROMECARB ***PERCENT:*** 100.0
CAS# 2631-37-0

OTHER CONTAMINANTS: NONE

EXPOSURE LIMITS: NO OCCUPATIONAL EXPOSURE LIMITS ESTABLISHED BY OSHA, ACGIH, OR NIOSH.

PROMECARB: 500/10,000 POUNDS SARA SECTION 302 THRESHOLD PLANNING QUANTITY 1 POUND SARA SECTION 304 REPORTABLE QUANTITY

PHYSICAL DATA

DESCRIPTION: ALMOST ODORLESS, COLORLESS CRYSTALLINE SOLID.

BOILING POINT: 243 F (117 C) @ 0.01 MMHG ***MELTING POINT:*** 189-190 F (87-88 C)

SPECIFIC GRAVITY: NOT AVAILABLE ***VAPOR PRESSURE:*** NEGLIGIBLE

SOLUBILITY IN WATER: 92 PPM

SOLVENT SOLUBILITY: SOLUBLE IN CARBON TETRACHLORIDE, XYLENE, CYCLOHEXANONE, ALCOHOL, ACETONE, DIMETHYL FORMAMIDE, ETHYLENE DICHLORIDE, CYCLOHEXANOL AND OTHER ORGANIC SOLVENTS.

FIRE AND EXPLOSION DATA

FIRE AND EXPLOSION HAZARD: SLIGHT FIRE HAZARD WHEN EXPOSED TO HEAT OR FLAME.

DUST-AIR MIXTURES MAY IGNITE OR EXPLODE.

FIREFIGHTING MEDIA: DRY CHEMICAL, CARBON DIOXIDE, HALON, WATER SPRAY OR STANDARD FOAM (1987 EMERGENCY RESPONSE GUIDEBOOK, DOT P 5800.4).

FOR LARGER FIRES, USE WATER SPRAY, FOG OR STANDARD FOAM (1987 EMERGENCY RESPONSE GUIDEBOOK, DOT P 5800.4).

FIREFIGHTING: MOVE CONTAINERS FROM FIRE AREA IF POSSIBLE (1987 EMERGENCY RESPONSE GUIDEBOOK, DOT P 5800.4, GUIDE PAGE 53).

EXTINGUISH USING AGENT SUITABLE FOR TYPE OF SURROUNDING FIRE. AVOID BREATHING VAPORS AND DUSTS. KEEP UPWIND.

TRANSPORTATION DATA

DEPARTMENT OF TRANSPORTATION HAZARD CLASSIFICATION 49 CFR 172.101: POISON B

DEPARTMENT OF TRANSPORTATION LABELING REQUIREMENTS 49 CFR 172.101 AND SUBPART E: POISON

DEPARTMENT OF TRANSPORTATION PACKAGING REQUIREMENTS: 49 CFR 173.365 EXCEPTIONS: 49 CFR 173.364

TOXICITY

PROMECARB: TOXICITY DATA: >0.16 MG/L/4 HOURS INHALATION-RAT LC50 (85JFAN); 450 MG/KG SKIN-RAT LD50; 35 MG/KG ORAL-RAT LD50; 16 MG/KG ORAL-MOUSE LD50; 25 MG/KG ORAL-GUINEA PIG LDLO; 25 MG/KG SUBCUTANEOUS-GUINEA PIG LDLO; 5 MG/KG INTRAVENOUS-RAT LD50; 27200 UG/KG INTRAPERITONEAL-RAT LD50; 44 MG/KG INTRAMUSCULAR-RAT LD50. CARCINOGEN STATUS: NONE. ACUTE TOXICITY LEVEL: HIGHLY TOXIC BY INHALATION, INGESTION; TOXIC BY DERMAL ABSORPTION. TARGET EFFECTS: CHOLINESTERASE INHIBITOR. POISONING MAY AFFECT THE RESPIRATORY AND CENTRAL NERVOUS SYSTEMS.

HEALTH EFFECTS AND FIRST AID

INHALATION: PROMECARB: HIGHLY TOXIC. SEE INFORMATION ON CARBAMATES. CARBAMATES: CHOLINESTERASE INHIBITOR. **ACUTE EXPOSURE-** WHEN INHALED, THE FIRST EFFECTS OF CHOLINESTERASE INHIBITION ARE USUALLY RESPIRATORY AND MAY INCLUDE NASAL HYPEREMIA AND WATERY DISCHARGE, CHEST DISCOMFORT, DYSPNEA, AND WHEEZING DUE TO INCREASED BRONCHIAL SECRETIONS AND BRONCHOCONSTRICTION. OTHER SYSTEMIC EFFECTS MAY BEGIN WITHIN A FEW MINUTES OR SEVERAL HOURS OF EXPOSURE. SYMPTOMS MAY INCLUDE NAUSEA, VOMITING, DIARRHEA, ABDOMINAL CRAMPS, HEADACHE, VERTIGO, OCULAR PAIN, CILIARY MUSCLE SPASM, BLURRING OR DIMNESS OF VISION, MIOSIS, OR IN SOME CASES MYDRIASIS, LACRIMATION, SALIVATION, SWEATING, AND CONFUSION. OTHER REPORTED CENTRAL NERVOUS SYSTEM OR NEUROMUSCULAR EFFECTS INCLUDE ATAXIA, SLURRED SPEECH, AREFLEXIA, WEAKNESS, FATIGUE, TWITCHING, FASCICULATION, TREMOR, AND EVENTUALLY PARALYSIS OF THE EXTREMITIES AND POSSIBLY OF THE RESPIRATORY MUSCLES. IN SEVERE CASES, THERE MAY ALSO BE INVOLUNTARY DEFECATION AND URINATION, BRADYCARDIA, HYPOTENSION, PULMONARY EDEMA, CONVULSIONS, COMA, AND DEATH FROM RESPIRATORY FAILURE OR CARDIAC ARREST. CARBAMATES GENERALLY DO NOT ACCUMULATE IN MAMMALIAN TISSUE AND THE CHOLINESTERASE INHIBITION REVERSES RATHER RAPIDLY. IN NON-FATAL CASES, THE ILLNESS GENERALLY LASTS LESS THAN 24 HOURS. **CHRONIC EXPOSURE-** PROLONGED OR REPEATED EXPOSURE MAY CAUSE EFFECTS AS DESCRIBED IN ACUTE EXPOSURE.

FIRST AID- REMOVE FROM EXPOSURE AREA TO FRESH AIR IMMEDIATELY. IF BREATHING HAS STOPPED, GIVE ARTIFICIAL RESPIRATION. MAINTAIN AIRWAY AND BLOOD PRESSURE AND ADMINISTER OXYGEN IF AVAILABLE. KEEP AFFECTED PERSON WARM AND AT REST. TREAT SYMPTOMATICALLY AND SUPPORTIVELY. ADMINISTRATION OF OXYGEN SHOULD BE PERFORMED BY QUALIFIED PERSONNEL. GET MEDICAL ATTENTION IMMEDIATELY.

SKIN CONTACT: PROMECARB: TOXIC. SEE INFORMATION ON CARBAMATES. CASES OF CONTACT DERMATITIS WITH MODERATE ITCHING HAVE BEEN REPORTED FOLLOWING SPRAYING WITH PROMECARB IN NIGERIA.
CARBAMATES: CHOLINESTERASE INHIBITOR. **ACUTE EXPOSURE-** SOME COMPOUNDS MAY CAUSE IRRITATION. LOCALIZED SWEATING AND FASCICULATIONS MAY OCCUR AT THE SITE OF CONTACT. IF SUFFICIENT AMOUNTS ARE ABSORBED THROUGH THE SKIN, OTHER EFFECTS OF CHOLINESTERASE INHIBITION MAY OCCUR AS DESCRIBED IN ACUTE INHALATION; SYMPTOMS MAY BE DELAYED FOR 2-3 HOURS, USUALLY NO MORE THAN 8 HOURS. **CHRONIC EXPOSURE-** REPEATED OR PROLONGED EXPOSURE MAY CAUSE EFFECTS AS DESCRIBED IN ACUTE EXPOSURE.

FIRST AID- REMOVE CONTAMINATED CLOTHING IMMEDIATELY. WASH CONTAMINATED AREAS WITH SOAP AND WATER FOLLOWED BY ALCOHOL (ARENA, POISONING, 4TH ED.). EMERGENCY PERSONNEL SHOULD WEAR GLOVES AND AVOID CONTAMINATION. TREAT RESPIRATORY DIFFICULTY WITH ARTIFICIAL RESPIRATION. GET MEDICAL ATTENTION IMMEDIATELY.

EYE CONTACT: PROMECARB: SEE INFORMATION ON CARBAMATES.
CARBAMATES: CHOLINESTERASE INHIBITOR. **ACUTE EXPOSURE-** DIRECT CONTACT MAY CAUSE PAIN, HYPEREMIA, LACRIMATION, TWITCHING OF THE EYELIDS, MIOSIS, AND CILIARY MUSCLE SPASM WITH LOSS OF ACCOMODATION, BLURRED OR DIMMED VISION AND BROWACHE. SOMETIMES MYDRIASIS MAY OCCUR INSTEAD OF MIOSIS. WITH SUFFICIENT EXPOSURE, OTHER SYMPTOMS OF CHOLINESTERASE INHIBITION MAY OCCUR AS DESCRIBED IN ACUTE INHALATION. **CHRONIC EXPOSURE-** PROLONGED EXPOSURE MAY CAUSE EFFECTS AS DESCRIBED IN ACUTE EXPOSURE. SOME COMPOUNDS HAVE CAUSED TOXIC EFFECTS ON THE CRYSTALLINE LENS, CONJUNCTIVAL THICKENING AND OBSTRUCTION OF NASOLACRIMAL CANALS WHEN USED AS MIOTIC EYE DROPS.

FIRST AID- IRRIGATE EYES WITH WATER OR SALINE SOLUTION. IF SYMPTOMS OF POISONING OCCUR, TREAT RESPIRATORY DIFFICULTY WITH ARTIFICIAL RESPIRATION AND OXYGEN. OBSERVE PATIENT FOR AT LEAST 24-36 HOURS (GOSSELIN, CLINICAL TOXICOLOGY OF COMMERCIAL PRODUCTS, 5TH ED.). GET MEDICAL ATTENTION IMMEDIATELY. OXYGEN SHOULD BE ADMINISTERED BY QUALIFIED MEDICAL PERSONNEL.

INGESTION: PROMECARB: HIGHLY TOXIC. SEE INFORMATION ON CARBAMATES. RATS AND MICE FED 22 AND8.9 MG/KG/DAY FOR 3 MONTHS EXHIBITED TOTAL SUPPRESSION OF PLASMA AND BRAIN CHOLINESTERASE ACTIVITY, AN INCREASE IN BLOOD SUGAR, AND SIGNIFICANT INCREASE IN MORTALITY; AT DOSES OF 50 AND 20 MG/KG/DAY THERE WERE EXTENSIVE HISTOLOGICAL CHANGES IN THE LIVER, KIDNEYS, LUNGS, AND BRAIN, AND MOST ANIMALS DIED.
CARBAMATES: CHOLINESTERASE INHIBITOR. **ACUTE EXPOSURE-** WHEN INGESTED, THE FIRST EFFECTS MAY BE NAUSEA, VOMITING, ANOREXIA, ABDOMINAL CRAMPS, AND DIARRHEA. WITH ABSORPTION FROM THE GASTROINTESTINAL TRACT, THE OTHER EFFECTS OF CHOLINESTERASE INHIBITION AS DESCRIBED IN ACUTE INHALATION MAY OCCUR; SYMPTOMS MAY BEGIN WITHIN MINUTES OR BE DELAYED SEVERAL HOURS. **CHRONIC EXPOSURE-** REPEATED INGESTION MAY CAUSE EFFECTS AS DESCRIBED IN ACUTE EXPOSURE.

FIRST AID- IF PERSON IS ALERT AND RESPIRATION IS NOT DEPRESSED, GIVE SYRUP OF IPECAC FOLLOWED BY WATER (IF VOMITING OCCURS, KEEP HEAD BELOW HIPS TO PREVENT ASPIRATION). IF CONSCIOUSNESS LEVEL DECLINES OR VOMITING HAS NOT OCCURRED IN 15 MINUTES EMPTY STOMACH BY GASTRIC LAVAGE WITH THE AID OF CUFFED ENDOTRACHEAL TUBE USING ISOTONIC SALINE OR 5% SODIUM BICARBONATE FOLLOW WITH ACTIVATED CHARCOAL. ESTABLISH AND MAINTAIN AIRWAY. TREAT RESPIRATORY DIFFICULTY WITH ARTIFICIAL RESPIRATION AND OXYGEN. DO NOT GIVE MORPHINE, AMINOPHYLLINE, PHENOTHIAZINES, RESERPINE, FUROSEMIDE, OR ETHACRYNIC ACID (MORGAN, RECOGNITION AND MANAGEMENT OF PESTICIDE POISONINGS, 3RD ED.). TREAT SYMPTOMATICALLY AND SUPPORTIVELY. ADMINISTRATION OF OXYGEN AND LAVAGE MUST BE PERFORMED BY QUALIFIED MEDICAL PERSONNEL. GET MEDICAL ATTENTION IMMEDIATELY.

ANTIDOTE: THE FOLLOWING ANTIDOTE HAS BEEN RECOMMENDED. HOWEVER, THE DECISION AS TO WHETHER THE SEVERITY OF POISONING REQUIRES ADMINISTRATION OF ANY ANTIDOTE AND ACTUAL DOSE REQUIRED SHOULD BE MADE BY QUALIFIED MEDICAL PERSONNEL.
FOR CHOLINESTERASE INHIBITORS: ESTABLISH CLEAR AIRWAY AND TISSUE OXYGENATION BY ASPIRATION OF SECRETIONS, AND IF NECESSARY, BY ASSISTED PULMONARY VENTILATION WITH OXYGEN. IMPROVE TISSUE OXYGENATION AS MUCH AS POSSIBLE BEFORE ADMINISTERING ATROPINE TO MINIMIZE THE RISK OF VENTRICULAR FIBRILLATION. ADMINISTER ATROPINE SULFATE INTRAVENOUSLY, OR INTRAMUSCULARLY IF IV INJECTION IS NOT POSSIBLE. IN MODERATELY SEVERE POISONING ADMINISTER ATROPINE SULFATE, 0.4-2.0 MG REPEATED EVERY 15 MINUTES UNTIL ATROPINIZATION IS ACHIEVED (TACHYCARDIA, FLUSHING, DRY MOUTH, MYDRIASIS). MAINTAIN ATROPINIZATION BY REPEATED DOSES FOR 2-12 HOURS, OR LONGER, DEPENDING ON THE SEVERITY OF POISONING. THE APPEARANCE OF RALES IN THE LUNG BASES, MIOSIS, SALIVATION, NAUSEA, BRADYCARDIA, ARE ALL INDICATIONS OF INADEQUATE ATROPINIZATION. SEVERELY POISONED INDIVIDUALS MAY EXHIBIT REMARKABLE TOLERANCE TO ATROPINE; TWO OR MORE TIMES THE DOSAGES SUGGESTED ABOVE MAY BE NEEDED. PERSONS NOT POISONED OR ONLY SLIGHTLY POISONED, HOWEVER, MAY DEVELOP SIGNS OF ATROPINE TOXICITY FROM SUCH LARGE DOSAGES: FEVER, MUSCLE FIBRILLATIONS, AND DELIRIUM ARE THE MAIN SIGNS OF ATROPINE TOXICITY. IF THESE SIGNS APPEAR WHILE THE PATIENT IS FULLY ATROPINIZED, ATROPINE ADMINISTRATION SHOULD BE DISCONTINUED, AT LEAST TEMPORARILY. OBSERVE TREATED PATIENTS CLOSELY AT LEAST 24 HOURS TO INSURE THAT SYMPTOMS (POSSIBLY PULMONARY EDEMA) DO NOT RECUR AS ATROPINIZATION WEARS OFF. IN VERY SEVERE POISONINGS, METABOLIC DISPOSITION OF TOXICANT MAY REQUIRE SEVERAL HOURS OR DAYS DURING WHICH ATROPINIZATION MUST BE MAINTAINED. MARKEDLY LOWER LEVELS OF URINARY METABOLITES INDICATE THAT ATROPINE DOSAGE CAN BE TAPERED OFF. AS DOSAGE IS REDUCED, CHECK THE LUNG BASES FREQUENTLY FOR RALES. IF RALES ARE HEARD OR OTHER SYMPTOMS RETURN, RE-ESTABLISH ATROPINIZATION PROMPTLY (MORGAN, RECOGNITION AND MANAGEMENT OF PESTICIDE POISONINGS, 3RD ED.). ADMINISTRATION OF ANTIDOTE MUST BE PERFORMED BY QUALIFIED MEDICAL PERSONNEL.

REACTIVITY

REACTIVITY: STABLE UNDER NORMAL TEMPERATURES AND PRESSURES.

INCOMPATIBILITIES: PROMECARB: OXIDIZERS (STRONG): FIRE AND EXPLOSION HAZARD.

DECOMPOSITION: THERMAL DECOMPOSITION PRODUCTS MAY INCLUDE TOXIC OXIDES OF CARBON AND NITROGEN.

POLYMERIZATION: HAZARDOUS POLYMERIZATION HAS NOT BEEN REPORTED TO OCCUR UNDER NORMAL TEMPERATURES AND PRESSURES.

STORAGE AND DISPOSAL

OBSERVE ALL FEDERAL, STATE AND LOCAL REGULATIONS WHEN STORING OR DISPOSING OF THIS SUBSTANCE. FOR ASSISTANCE, CONTACT THE DISTRICT DIRECTOR OF THE ENVIRONMENTAL PROTECTION AGENCY.

****STORAGE****

STORE IN ACCORDANCE WITH 40 CFR 165 RECOMMENDED PROCEDURES FOR THE DISPOSAL AND STORAGE OF PESTICIDES AND PESTICIDE CONTAINERS.

STORE AWAY FROM INCOMPATIBLE SUBSTANCES.
THRESHOLD PLANNING QUANTITY (TPQ): THE SUPERFUND AMENDMENTS AND REAUTHORIZATION ACT (SARA) SECTION 302 REQUIRES THAT EACH FACILITY WHERE ANY EXTREMELY HAZARDOUS SUBSTANCE IS PRESENT IN A QUANTITY EQUAL TO OR GREATER THAN THE TPQ ESTABLISHED FOR THAT SUBSTANCE NOTIFY THE STATE EMERGENCY RESPONSE COMMISSION FOR THE STATE IN WHICH IT IS LOCATED. SECTION 303 OF SARA REQUIRES THESE FACILITIES TO PARTICIPATE IN LOCAL EMERGENCY RESPONSE PLANNING (40 CFR 355.30).

DISPOSAL

DISPOSAL MUST BE IN ACCORDANCE WITH 40 CFR 165 RECOMMENDED PROCEDURES FOR THE DISPOSAL AND STORAGE OF PESTICIDES AND PESTICIDE CONTAINERS.

CONDITIONS TO AVOID

MAY BURN BUT DOES NOT IGNITE READILY.

SPILL AND LEAK PROCEDURES

OCCUPATIONAL SPILL: DO NOT TOUCH SPILLED MATERIAL. STOP LEAK IF YOU CAN DO IT WITHOUT RISK. FOR SMALL SPILLS, TAKE UP WITH SAND OR OTHER ABSORBENT MATERIAL AND PLACE INTO CONTAINERS FOR LATER DISPOSAL. FOR SMALL DRY SPILLS, WITH A CLEAN SHOVEL PLACE MATERIAL INTO CLEAN, DRY CONTAINER AND COVER. MOVE CONTAINERS FROM SPILL AREA. FOR LARGER SPILLS, DIKE FAR AHEAD OF SPILL FOR LATER DISPOSAL. KEEP UNNECESSARY PEOPLE AWAY. ISOLATE HAZARD AREA AND DENY ENTRY.
REPORTABLE QUANTITY (RQ): 1 POUND THE SUPERFUND AMENDMENTS AND REAUTHORIZATION ACT (SARA) SECTION 304 REQUIRES THAT A RELEASE EQUAL TO OR GREATER THAN THE REPORTABLE QUANTITY FOR THIS SUBSTANCE BE IMMEDIATELY REPORTED TO THE LOCAL EMERGENCY PLANNING COMMITTEE AND THE STATE EMERGENCY RESPONSE COMMISSION (40 CFR 355.40). IF THE RELEASE OF THIS SUBSTANCE IS REPORTABLE UNDER CERCLA SECTION 103, THE NATIONAL RESPONSE CENTER MUST BE NOTIFIED IMMEDIATELY AT (800) 424-8802 OR (202) 426-2675 IN THE METROPOLITAN WASHINGTON, D.C. AREA (40 CFR 302.6).

PROTECTIVE EQUIPMENT

VENTILATION: PROVIDE LOCAL EXHAUST OR PROCESS ENCLOSURE VENTILATION SYSTEM.
RESPIRATOR: THE FOLLOWING RESPIRATORS ARE RECOMMENDED BASED ON INFORMATION FOUND IN THE PHYSICAL DATA, TOXICITY AND HEALTH EFFECTS SECTIONS. THEY ARE RANKED IN ORDER FROM MINIMUM TO MAXIMUM RESPIRATORY PROTECTION. THE SPECIFIC RESPIRATOR SELECTED MUST BE BASED ON CONTAMINATION LEVELS FOUND IN THE WORK PLACE, MUST NOT EXCEED THE WORKING LIMITS OF THE RESPIRATOR AND BE JOINTLY APPROVED BY THE NATIONAL INSTITUTE FOR OCCUPATIONAL SAFETY AND HEALTH AND THE MINE SAFETY AND HEALTH ADMINISTRATION (NIOSH-MSHA).
TYPE 'C' SUPPLIED-AIR RESPIRATOR WITH A FULL FACEPIECE OPERATED IN PRESSURE-DEMAND OR OTHER POSITIVE PRESSURE MODE OR WITH A FULL FACEPIECE, HELMET OR HOOD OPERATED IN CONTINOUS-FLOW MODE.
SELF-CONTAINED BREATHING APPARATUS WITH A FULL FACEPIECE OPERATED IN PRESSURE-DEMAND OR OTHER POSITIVE PRESSURE MODE.
FOR FIREFIGHTING AND OTHER IMMEDIATELY DANGEROUS TO LIFE OR HEALTH CONDITIONS:
SELF-CONTAINED BREATHING APPARATUS WITH FULL FACEPIECE OPERATED IN PRESSURE-DEMAND OR OTHER POSITIVE PRESSURE MODE.
SUPPLIED-AIR RESPIRATOR WITH FULL FACEPIECE AND OPERATED IN PRESSURE-DEMAND OR OTHER POSITIVE PRESSURE MODE IN COMBINATION WITH AN AUXILIARY SELF-CONTAINED BREATHING APPARATUS OPERATED IN PRESSURE-DEMAND OR OTHER POSITIVE PRESSURE MODE.
CLOTHING: EMPLOYEE MUST WEAR APPROPRIATE PROTECTIVE (IMPERVIOUS) CLOTHING AND EQUIPMENT TO PREVENT ANY POSSIBILITY OF SKIN CONTACT WITH THIS SUBSTANCE.
GLOVES: EMPLOYEE MUST WEAR APPROPRIATE PROTECTIVE GLOVES TO PREVENT CONTACT WITH THIS SUBSTANCE.
EYE PROTECTION: EMPLOYEE MUST WEAR SPLASH-PROOF OR DUST-RESISTANT SAFETY GOGGLES AND A FACESHIELD TO PREVENT CONTACT WITH THIS SUBSTANCE.
EMERGENCY WASH FACILITIES: WHERE THERE IS ANY POSSIBILITY THAT AN EMPLOYEE'S EYES AND/OR SKIN MAY BE EXPOSED TO THIS SUBSTANCE, THE EMPLOYER SHOULD PROVIDE AN EYE WASH FOUNTAIN AND QUICK DRENCH SHOWER WITHIN THE IMMEDIATE WORK AREA FOR EMERGENCY USE.

AUTHORIZED BY- OCCUPATIONAL HEALTH SERVICES, INC.
CREATION DATE: 10/04/89 ***REVISION DATE:*** 06/12/90

MATERIAL SAFETY DATA SHEET

OCCUPATIONAL HEALTH SERVICES, INC.
AGRICULTURE AND PESTICIDE DIVISION
450 SEVENTH AVENUE, SUITE 2407
NEW YORK, NEW YORK 10123
1-800-445-MSDS OR (212) 967-1100

EMERGENCY CONTACT:
JOHN S. BRANSFORD, JR. (615) 292-1180

SUBSTANCE IDENTIFICATION

CAS-NUMBER 5251-93-4
SUBSTANCE: BENZADOX
TRADE NAMES/SYNONYMS: ACETIC ACID, ((BENZOYLAMINO)OXY)-; ACETIC ACID, (BENZAMIDOOXY)-; (BENZAMIDOOXY)ACETIC ACID; ((BENZOYLAMINO)OXY)ACETIC ACID; BENZAMIDO-OXYACETIC ACID; S 6173; C9H9NO4; PST72964
CHEMICAL FAMILY: AMIDE, AROMATIC
MOLECULAR FORMULA: C9-H9-N-O4
MOLECULAR WEIGHT: 195.20
CERCLA RATINGS (SCALE 0-3): HEALTH=1 FIRE=1 REACTIVITY=0 PERSISTENCE=1
NFPA RATINGS (SCALE 0-4): HEALTH=U FIRE=1 REACTIVITY=0

COMPONENTS AND CONTAMINANTS

COMPONENT: BENZADOX ***PERCENT:*** 100.0
CAS# 5251-93-4
OTHER CONTAMINANTS: NONE
EXPOSURE LIMITS: NO OCCUPATIONAL EXPOSURE LIMITS ESTABLISHED BY OSHA, ACGIH, OR NIOSH.

PHYSICAL DATA

DESCRIPTION: WHITE SOLID. ***MELTING POINT:*** 284 F (140 C)
SPECIFIC GRAVITY: NOT AVAILABLE ***SOLUBILITY IN WATER:*** 0.0016% @ 20 C
SOLVENT SOLUBILITY: SOLUBLE IN METHANOL AND ACETONE.

FIRE AND EXPLOSION DATA

FIRE AND EXPLOSION HAZARD: SLIGHT FIRE HAZARD WHEN EXPOSED TO HEAT OR FLAME.
FIREFIGHTING MEDIA: DRY CHEMICAL, CARBON DIOXIDE, HALON, WATER SPRAY OR STANDARD FOAM (1987 EMERGENCY RESPONSE GUIDEBOOK, DOT P 5800.4). FOR LARGER FIRES, USE WATER SPRAY, FOG OR STANDARD FOAM (1987 EMERGENCY RESPONSE GUIDEBOOK, DOT P 5800.4).
FIREFIGHTING: MOVE CONTAINER FROM FIRE AREA IF POSSIBLE. DO NOT SCATTER SPILLED MATERIAL WITH HIGH PRESSURE WATER STREAMS. DIKE FIRE CONTROL WATER FOR LATER DISPOSAL (1987 EMERGENCY RESPONSE GUIDEBOOK, DOT P 5800.4, GUIDE PAGE 31).
USE AGENTS SUITABLE FOR TYPE OF SURROUNDING FIRE. AVOID BREATHING HAZARDOUS VAPORS, KEEP UPWIND.

TOXICITY

BENZADOX: TOXICITY DATA: 5600 MG/KG ORAL-RAT LD50 (BUCHEL, CHEMISTRY OF PESTICIDES, 1983). CARCINOGEN STATUS: NONE. ACUTE TOXICITY LEVEL: SLIGHTLY TOXIC BY INGESTION. TARGET EFFECTS: NO DATA AVAILABLE.

HEALTH EFFECTS AND FIRST AID

INHALATION: BENZADOX: ACUTE EXPOSURE- NO DATA AVAILABLE. CHRONIC EXPOSURE- NO DATA AVAILABLE.
FIRST AID- REMOVE FROM EXPOSURE AREA TO FRESH AIR IMMEDIATELY. IF BREATHING HAS STOPPED, PERFORM ARTIFICIAL RESPIRATION. KEEP PERSON WARM AND AT REST. TREAT SYMPTOMATICALLY AND SUPPORTIVELY. GET MEDICAL ATTENTION IMMEDIATELY.

SKIN CONTACT: BENZADOX: ACUTE EXPOSURE- NO DATA AVAILABLE. CHRONIC EXPOSURE- NO DATA AVAILABLE.
FIRST AID- REMOVE CONTAMINATED CLOTHING AND SHOES IMMEDIATELY. WASH AFFECTED AREA WITH SOAP OR MILD DETERGENT AND LARGE AMOUNTS OF WATER UNTIL NO EVIDENCE OF CHEMICAL REMAINS (APPROXIMATELY 15-20 MINUTES). GET MEDICAL ATTENTION IMMEDIATELY.

EYE CONTACT: BENZADOX: ACUTE EXPOSURE- NO DATA AVAILABLE. CHRONIC EXPOSURE- NO DATA AVAILABLE.
FIRST AID- WASH EYES IMMEDIATELY WITH LARGE AMOUNTS OF WATER OR NORMAL SALINE, OCCASIONALLY LIFTING UPPER AND LOWER LIDS, UNTIL NO EVIDENCE OF CHEMICAL REMAINS (APPROXIMATELY 15-20 MINUTES). GET MEDICAL ATTENTION IMMEDIATELY.

INGESTION: BENZADOX: **ACUTE EXPOSURE-** A LETHAL DOSE IN RATS WAS 5600 MG/KG; SYMPTOMS WERE NOT REPORTED. **CHRONIC EXPOSURE-** NO DATA AVAILABLE.

FIRST AID- TREAT SYMPTOMATICALLY AND SUPPORTIVELY. GET MEDICAL ATTENTION IMMEDIATELY. IF VOMITING OCCURS, KEEP HEAD LOWER THAN HIPS TO PREVENT ASPIRATION.

ANTIDOTE: NO SPECIFIC ANTIDOTE. TREAT SYMPTOMATICALLY AND SUPPORTIVELY.

REACTIVITY

REACTIVITY: STABLE UNDER NORMAL TEMPERATURES AND PRESSURES.

INCOMPATIBILITIES: BENZADOX: OXIDIZERS (STRONG): FIRE AND EXPLOSION HAZARD.

DECOMPOSITION: THERMAL DECOMPOSITION PRODUCTS MAY INCLUDE TOXIC OXIDES OF CARBON AND NITROGEN.

POLYMERIZATION: HAZARDOUS POLYMERIZATION HAS NOT BEEN REPORTED TO OCCUR UNDER NORMAL TEMPERATURES AND PRESSURES.

STORAGE AND DISPOSAL

OBSERVE ALL FEDERAL, STATE AND LOCAL REGULATIONS WHEN STORING OR DISPOSING OF THIS SUBSTANCE. FOR ASSISTANCE, CONTACT THE DISTRICT DIRECTOR OF THE ENVIRONMENTAL PROTECTION AGENCY.

****STORAGE****

STORE IN ACCORDANCE WITH 40 CFR 165 RECOMMENDED PROCEDURES FOR THE DISPOSAL AND STORAGE OF PESTICIDES AND PESTICIDE CONTAINERS.
STORE AWAY FROM INCOMPATIBLE SUBSTANCES.

****DISPOSAL****

DISPOSAL MUST BE IN ACCORDANCE WITH 40 CFR 165 RECOMMENDED PROCEDURES FOR THE DISPOSAL AND STORAGE OF PESTICIDES AND PESTICIDE CONTAINERS.

CONDITIONS TO AVOID

MAY BURN BUT DOES NOT IGNITE READILY. AVOID CONTACT WITH STRONG OXIDIZERS, EXCESSIVE HEAT, SPARKS, OR OPEN FLAME.

SPILL AND LEAK PROCEDURES

OCCUPATIONAL SPILL: SWEEP UP AND PLACE IN SUITABLE CLEAN, DRY CONTAINERS FOR RECLAMATION OR LATER DISPOSAL. DO NOT FLUSH SPILLED MATERIAL INTO SEWER. KEEP UNNECESSARY PEOPLE AWAY.

PROTECTIVE EQUIPMENT

VENTILATION: PROVIDE GENERAL DILUTION VENTILATION.

RESPIRATOR: THE FOLLOWING RESPIRATORS ARE RECOMMENDED BASED ON INFORMATION FOUND IN THE PHYSICAL DATA, TOXICITY AND HEALTH EFFECTS SECTIONS. THEY ARE RANKED IN ORDER FROM MINIMUM TO MAXIMUM RESPIRATORY PROTECTION. THE SPECIFIC RESPIRATOR SELECTED MUST BE BASED ON CONTAMINATION LEVELS FOUND IN THE WORK PLACE, MUST NOT EXCEED THE WORKING LIMITS OF THE RESPIRATOR AND BE JOINTLY APPROVED BY THE NATIONAL INSTITUTE FOR OCCUPATIONAL SAFETY AND HEALTH AND THE MINE SAFETY AND HEALTH ADMINISTRATION (NIOSH-MSHA).
CHEMICAL CARTRIDGE RESPIRATOR WITH AN ORGANIC VAPOR CARTRIDGE(S) WITH A FULL FACEPIECE AND ORGANIC VAPOR CARTRIDGE(S) IN COMBINATION WITH A DUST AND MIST FILTER.
POWERED AIR-PURIFYING RESPIRATOR WITH A TIGHT-FITTING FACEPIECE AND ORGANIC VAPOR CARTRIDGE(S) IN COMBINATION WITH A HIGH-EFFICIENCY PARTICULATE FILTER.
TYPE 'C' SUPPLIED-AIR RESPIRATOR WITH A FULL FACEPIECE OPERATED IN A PRESSURE-DEMAND OR OTHER POSITIVE PRESSURE MODE.
SELF-CONTAINED BREATHING APPARATUS WITH A FULL FACEPIECE OPERATED IN PRESSURE-DEMAND OR OTHER POSITIVE PRESSURE MODE.
FOR FIREFIGHTING AND OTHER IMMEDIATELY DANGEROUS TO LIFE OR HEALTH CONDITIONS:
SELF-CONTAINED BREATHING APPARATUS WITH FULL FACEPIECE OPERATED IN PRESSURE-DEMAND OR OTHER POSITIVE PRESSURE MODE.
SUPPLIED-AIR RESPIRATOR WITH FULL FACEPIECE AND OPERATED IN PRESSURE-DEMAND OR OTHER POSITIVE PRESSURE MODE IN COMBINATION WITH AN AUXILIARY SELF-CONTAINED BREATHING APPARATUS OPERATED IN PRESSURE-DEMAND OR OTHER POSITIVE PRESSURE MODE.

CLOTHING: EMPLOYEE MUST WEAR APPROPRIATE PROTECTIVE (IMPERVIOUS) CLOTHING AND EQUIPMENT TO PREVENT REPEATED OR PROLONGED SKIN CONTACT WITH THIS SUBSTANCE.

GLOVES: EMPLOYEE MUST WEAR APPROPRIATE PROTECTIVE GLOVES TO PREVENT CONTACT WITH THIS SUBSTANCE.

EYE PROTECTION: EMPLOYEE MUST WEAR SPLASH-PROOF OR DUST-RESISTANT SAFETY GOGGLES TO PREVENT EYE CONTACT WITH THIS SUBSTANCE.
EMERGENCY EYE WASH: WHERE THERE IS ANY POSSIBILITY THAT AN EMPLOYEE'S EYES MAY BE EXPOSED TO THIS SUBSTANCE, THE EMPLOYER SHOULD PROVIDE AN EYE WASH FOUNTAIN WITHIN THE IMMEDIATE WORK AREA FOR EMERGENCY USE.

AUTHORIZED BY- OCCUPATIONAL HEALTH SERVICES, INC.
CREATION DATE: 10/04/89 ***REVISION DATE:*** 05/31/90

MATERIAL SAFETY DATA SHEET

OCCUPATIONAL HEALTH SERVICES, INC.
AGRICULTURE AND PESTICIDE DIVISION
450 SEVENTH AVENUE, SUITE 2407
NEW YORK, NEW YORK 10123
1-800-445-MSDS OR (212) 967-1100

EMERGENCY CONTACT:
JOHN S. BRANSFORD, JR. (615) 292-1180

SUBSTANCE IDENTIFICATION

CAS-NUMBER 38727-55-8

SUBSTANCE: **DIETHATYL-ETHYL**

TRADE NAMES/SYNONYMS: GLYCINE, N-(CHLOROACETYL)-N-(2,6-DIETHYLPHENYL)-, ETHYL ESTER; N-(CHLOROACETYL)-N-(2,6-DIETHYLPHENYL)GLYCINE ETHYL ESTER; ANTOR; HERCULES 22234; C16H22CLNO3; PST72968

CHEMICAL FAMILY: AMINO ACID DERIVATIVE
AROMATIC
AMIDE

MOLECULAR FORMULA: C16-H22-CL-N-O3

MOLECULAR WEIGHT: 311.84

CERCLA RATINGS (SCALE 0-3): HEALTH=U FIRE=1 REACTIVITY=0 PERSISTENCE=1

NFPA RATINGS (SCALE 0-4): HEALTH=U FIRE=1 REACTIVITY=0

COMPONENTS AND CONTAMINANTS

COMPONENT: DIETHATYL-ETHYL ***PERCENT:*** 100.0
CAS# 38727-55-8

EXPOSURE LIMITS: NO OCCUPATIONAL EXPOSURE LIMITS ESTABLISHED BY OSHA, ACGIH, OR NIOSH.

PHYSICAL DATA

DESCRIPTION: COLORLESS CRYSTALS. ***MELTING POINT:*** 120-122 F (49-50 C)

SPECIFIC GRAVITY: 1.38 @ 25 C ***VAPOR PRESSURE:*** NEGLIGIBLE @ 30 C

SOLUBILITY IN WATER: 0.01% @ 25 C

SOLVENT SOLUBILITY: SOLUBLE IN METHANOL, ETHANOL, ISOPROPANOL, ACETONE, XYLENE, METHYL ISOBUTYL KETONE, CHLOROFORM, KEROSENE, CHLOROBENZENE, CYCLOHEXANONE, 3,5,5-TRIMETHYLCYCLOHEX-2-ENONE AND COMMON ORGANIC SOLVENTS.

FIRE AND EXPLOSION DATA

FIRE AND EXPLOSION HAZARD: SLIGHT FIRE HAZARD WHEN EXPOSED TO HEAT OR FLAME.
DUST-AIR MIXTURES MAY IGNITE OR EXPLODE.

FIREFIGHTING MEDIA: DRY CHEMICAL, CARBON DIOXIDE, HALON, WATER SPRAY OR STANDARD FOAM (1987 EMERGENCY RESPONSE GUIDEBOOK, DOT P 5800.4).
FOR LARGER FIRES, USE WATER SPRAY, FOG OR STANDARD FOAM (1987 EMERGENCY RESPONSE GUIDEBOOK, DOT P 5800.4).

FIREFIGHTING: MOVE CONTAINER FROM FIRE AREA IF POSSIBLE. DO NOT SCATTER SPILLED MATERIAL WITH HIGH PRESSURE WATER STREAMS. DIKE FIRE CONTROL WATER FOR LATER DISPOSAL (1987 EMERGENCY RESPONSE GUIDEBOOK, DOT P 5800.4, GUIDE PAGE 31).
USE AGENTS SUITABLE FOR TYPE OF SURROUNDING FIRE. AVOID BREATHING HAZARDOUS VAPORS, KEEP UPWIND.

TOXICITY

DIETHATYL-ETHYL: TOXICITY DATA: 4 GM/KG SKIN-RABBIT LD50; 2300 MG/KG ORAL-RAT LD50; 1653 MG/KG ORAL-MOUSE LD50 (85JFAN). CARCINOGEN STATUS: NONE. ACUTE TOXICITY LEVEL: MODERATELY TOXIC BY INGESTION; SLIGHTLY TOXIC BY DERMAL ABSORPTION. TARGET EFFECTS: NO DATA AVAILABLE.

HEALTH EFFECTS AND FIRST AID

INHALATION: DIETHATYL-ETHYL: **ACUTE EXPOSURE-** NO DATA AVAILABLE. **CHRONIC EXPOSURE-** NO DATA AVAILABLE.

FIRST AID- REMOVE FROM EXPOSURE AREA TO FRESH AIR IMMEDIATELY. IF BREATHING HAS STOPPED, PERFORM ARTIFICIAL RESPIRATION. KEEP PERSON

WARM AND AT REST. TREAT SYMPTOMATICALLY AND SUPPORTIVELY. GET MEDICAL ATTENTION IMMEDIATELY.

SKIN CONTACT: DIETHATYL-ETHYL: **ACUTE EXPOSURE-** MAY CAUSE IRRITATION. **CHRONIC EXPOSURE-** NO DATA AVAILABLE.

FIRST AID- REMOVE CONTAMINATED CLOTHING AND SHOES IMMEDIATELY. WASH AFFECTED AREA WITH SOAP OR MILD DETERGENT AND LARGE AMOUNTS OF WATER UNTIL NO EVIDENCE OF CHEMICAL REMAINS (APPROXIMATELY 15-20 MINUTES). GET MEDICAL ATTENTION IMMEDIATELY.

EYE CONTACT: DIETHATYL-ETHYL: **ACUTE EXPOSURE-** MAY CAUSE IRRITATION. **CHRONIC EXPOSURE-** NO DATA AVAILABLE.

FIRST AID- WASH EYES IMMEDIATELY WITH LARGE AMOUNTS OF WATER OR NORMAL SALINE, OCCASIONALLY LIFTING UPPER AND LOWER LIDS, UNTIL NO EVIDENCE OF CHEMICAL REMAINS (APPROXIMATELY 15-20 MINUTES). GET MEDICAL ATTENTION IMMEDIATELY.

INGESTION: DIETHATYL-ETHYL: **ACUTE EXPOSURE-** A LETHAL DOSE REPORTED IN ANIMALS WAS 2300 MG/KG; SYMPTOMS WERE NOT REPORTED. **CHRONIC EXPOSURE-** NO ILL-EFFECTS WERE OBSERVED IN A 90-DAY STUDY OF RATS RECEIVING 2000 MG/KG.

FIRST AID- IF THE PERSON IS CONSCIOUS AND NOT CONVULSING, REMOVE BY GASTRIC LAVAGE AND FOLLOW WITH A CATHARTIC (DREISBACH, HANDBOOK OF POISONING, 12TH ED.). TREAT SYMPTOMATICALLY AND SUPPORTIVELY. GASTRIC LAVAGE SHOULD BE PERFORMED BY QUALIFIED MEDICAL PERSONNEL. GET MEDICAL ATTENTION IMMEDIATELY.

ANTIDOTE: NO SPECIFIC ANTIDOTE. TREAT SYMPTOMATICALLY AND SUPPORTIVELY.

REACTIVITY

REACTIVITY: STABLE UNDER NORMAL TEMPERATURES AND PRESSURES.

INCOMPATIBILITIES: DIETHATYL-ETHYL: OXIDIZERS (STRONG): FIRE AND EXPLOSION HAZARD.

DECOMPOSITION: THERMAL DECOMPOSITION PRODUCTS MAY INCLUDE TOXIC OXIDES OF NITROGEN AND CARBON AND TOXIC AND CORROSIVE FUMES OF CHLORIDES.

POLYMERIZATION: HAZARDOUS POLYMERIZATION HAS NOT BEEN REPORTED TO OCCUR UNDER NORMAL TEMPERATURES AND PRESSURES.

STORAGE AND DISPOSAL

OBSERVE ALL FEDERAL, STATE AND LOCAL REGULATIONS WHEN STORING OR DISPOSING OF THIS SUBSTANCE. FOR ASSISTANCE, CONTACT THE DISTRICT DIRECTOR OF THE ENVIRONMENTAL PROTECTION AGENCY.

****STORAGE****

STORE IN ACCORDANCE WITH 40 CFR 165 RECOMMENDED PROCEDURES FOR THE DISPOSAL AND STORAGE OF PESTICIDES AND PESTICIDE CONTAINERS. STORE AWAY FROM INCOMPATIBLE SUBSTANCES.

****DISPOSAL****

DISPOSAL MUST BE IN ACCORDANCE WITH 40 CFR 165 RECOMMENDED PROCEDURES FOR THE DISPOSAL AND STORAGE OF PESTICIDES AND PESTICIDE CONTAINERS.

CONDITIONS TO AVOID

MAY BURN BUT DOES NOT IGNITE READILY. AVOID CONTACT WITH STRONG OXIDIZERS, EXCESSIVE HEAT, SPARKS, OR OPEN FLAME.

SPILL AND LEAK PROCEDURES

OCCUPATIONAL SPILL: SWEEP UP AND PLACE IN SUITABLE CLEAN, DRY CONTAINERS FOR RECLAMATION OR LATER DISPOSAL. DO NOT FLUSH SPILLED MATERIAL INTO SEWER. KEEP UNNECESSARY PEOPLE AWAY.

PROTECTIVE EQUIPMENT

VENTILATION: PROVIDE LOCAL EXHAUST OR GENERAL DILUTION VENTILATION SYSTEM.

RESPIRATOR: THE FOLLOWING RESPIRATORS ARE RECOMMENDED BASED ON INFORMATION FOUND IN THE PHYSICAL DATA, TOXICITY AND HEALTH EFFECTS SECTIONS. THEY ARE RANKED IN ORDER FROM MINIMUM TO MAXIMUM RESPIRATORY PROTECTION. THE SPECIFIC RESPIRATOR SELECTED MUST BE BASED ON CONTAMINATION LEVELS FOUND IN THE WORK PLACE, MUST NOT EXCEED THE WORKING LIMITS OF THE RESPIRATOR AND BE JOINTLY APPROVED BY THE NATIONAL INSTITUTE FOR OCCUPATIONAL SAFETY AND HEALTH AND THE MINE SAFETY AND HEALTH ADMINISTRATION (NIOSH-MSHA).

CHEMICAL CARTRIDGE RESPIRATOR WITH AN ORGANIC VAPOR CARTRIDGE(S) WITH A FULL FACEPIECE AND ORGANIC VAPOR CARTRIDGE(S) IN COMBINATION WITH A DUST AND MIST FILTER.

POWERED AIR-PURIFYING RESPIRATOR WITH A TIGHT-FITTING FACEPIECE AND ORGANIC VAPOR CARTRIDGE(S) IN COMBINATION WITH A HIGH-EFFICIENCY PARTICULATE FILTER.

TYPE 'C' SUPPLIED-AIR RESPIRATOR WITH A FULL FACEPIECE OPERATED IN A PRESSURE-DEMAND OR OTHER POSITIVE PRESSURE MODE.

SELF-CONTAINED BREATHING APPARATUS WITH A FULL FACEPIECE OPERATED IN PRESSURE-DEMAND OR OTHER POSITIVE PRESSURE MODE.

FOR FIREFIGHTING AND OTHER IMMEDIATELY DANGEROUS TO LIFE OR HEALTH CONDITIONS:

SELF-CONTAINED BREATHING APPARATUS WITH FULL FACEPIECE OPERATED IN PRESSURE-DEMAND OR OTHER POSITIVE PRESSURE MODE.

SUPPLIED-AIR RESPIRATOR WITH FULL FACEPIECE AND OPERATED IN PRESSURE-DEMAND OR OTHER POSITIVE PRESSURE MODE IN COMBINATION WITH AN AUXILIARY SELF-CONTAINED BREATHING APPARATUS OPERATED IN PRESSURE-DEMAND OR OTHER POSITIVE PRESSURE MODE.

CLOTHING: EMPLOYEE MUST WEAR APPROPRIATE PROTECTIVE (IMPERVIOUS) CLOTHING AND EQUIPMENT TO PREVENT REPEATED OR PROLONGED SKIN CONTACT WITH THIS SUBSTANCE.

GLOVES: EMPLOYEE MUST WEAR APPROPRIATE PROTECTIVE GLOVES TO PREVENT CONTACT WITH THIS SUBSTANCE.

EYE PROTECTION: EMPLOYEE MUST WEAR SPLASH-PROOF OR DUST-RESISTANT SAFETY GOGGLES TO PREVENT EYE CONTACT WITH THIS SUBSTANCE.

EMERGENCY EYE WASH: WHERE THERE IS ANY POSSIBILITY THAT AN EMPLOYEE'S EYES MAY BE EXPOSED TO THIS SUBSTANCE, THE EMPLOYER SHOULD PROVIDE AN EYE WASH FOUNTAIN WITHIN THE IMMEDIATE WORK AREA FOR EMERGENCY USE.

AUTHORIZED BY- OCCUPATIONAL HEALTH SERVICES, INC.

CREATION DATE: 03/23/90 ***REVISION DATE:*** 05/31/90

MATERIAL SAFETY DATA SHEET

OCCUPATIONAL HEALTH SERVICES, INC.
AGRICULTURE AND PESTICIDE DIVISION
450 SEVENTH AVENUE, SUITE 2407
NEW YORK, NEW YORK 10123
1-800-445-MSDS OR (212) 967-1100

EMERGENCY CONTACT:
JOHN S. BRANSFORD, JR. (615) 292-1180

SUBSTANCE IDENTIFICATION

CAS-NUMBER 1929-88-0

SUBSTANCE: **BENZTHIAZURON**

TRADE NAMES/SYNONYMS: UREA, N-2-BENZOTHIAZOLYL-N'-METHYL-; UREA, 1-(2-BENZOTHIAZOLYL)-3-METHYL-; N-2-BENZOTHIAZOLYL-N'-METHYLUREA; 1-(2-BENZOTHIAZOLYL)-3-METHYLUREA; 1-(1,3-BENZOTHIAZOL-2-YL)-3-METHYLUREA; 1-BENZOTHIAZOL-2-YL-3-METHYLUREA; BAYER 60618; GATNON; C9H9N3OS; PST72971

CHEMICAL FAMILY: SUBSTITUTED UREA

MOLECULAR FORMULA: C9-H9-N3-O-S

MOLECULAR WEIGHT: 207.27

CERCLA RATINGS (SCALE 0-3): HEALTH=2 FIRE=1 REACTIVITY=0 PERSISTENCE=3

NFPA RATINGS (SCALE 0-4): HEALTH=2 FIRE=1 REACTIVITY=0

COMPONENTS AND CONTAMINANTS

COMPONENT: BENZTHIAZURON ***PERCENT:*** 100
CAS# 1929-88-0

OTHER CONTAMINANTS: NONE

EXPOSURE LIMITS: NO OCCUPATIONAL EXPOSURE LIMITS ESTABLISHED BY OSHA, ACGIH, OR NIOSH.

PHYSICAL DATA

DESCRIPTION: WHITE CRYSTALLINE SOLID.

MELTING POINT: 549 F (287 C) (DECOMPOSES)

SPECIFIC GRAVITY: NOT AVAILABLE ***VAPOR PRESSURE:*** NEGLIGIBLE

SOLUBILITY IN WATER: 0.0012%

SOLVENT SOLUBILITY: SLIGHTLY SOLUBLE IN ACETONE, CHLOROBENZENE AND XYLENE.

FIRE AND EXPLOSION DATA

FIRE AND EXPLOSION HAZARD: SLIGHT FIRE HAZARD WHEN EXPOSED TO HEAT OR FLAME.

FIREFIGHTING MEDIA: DRY CHEMICAL, CARBON DIOXIDE, HALON, WATER SPRAY OR STANDARD FOAM (1987 EMERGENCY RESPONSE GUIDEBOOK, DOT P 5800.4). FOR LARGER FIRES, USE WATER SPRAY, FOG OR STANDARD FOAM (1987 EMERGENCY RESPONSE GUIDEBOOK, DOT P 5800.4).

FIREFIGHTING: MOVE CONTAINERS FROM FIRE AREA IF POSSIBLE. FIGHT FIRE FROM MAXIMUM DISTANCE. STAY AWAY FROM STORAGE TANK ENDS. DIKE FIRE CONTROL WATER FOR LATER DISPOSAL. DO NOT SCATTER MATERIAL (1987 EMERGENCY RESPONSE GUIDEBOOK, DOT P 5800.4, GUIDE PAGE 55). EXTINGUISH USING AGENT SUITABLE FOR TYPE OF SURROUNDING FIRE. USE WATER IN FLOODING QUANTITIES AS FOG. KEEP SPARKS, FLAMES AND OTHER SOURCES OF IGNITION AWAY. KEEP MATERIAL OUT OF WATER SOURCES AND SEWERS. DO NOT TOUCH MATERIAL AND AVOID BREATHING DUSTS AND FUMES FROM BURNING MATERIAL. KEEP UPWIND.

TOXICITY

BENZTHIAZURON: TOXICITY DATA: 1280 MG/KG ORAL-RAT LD50; 1000 MG/KG UNREPORTED-MAMMAL LD50. CARCINOGEN STATUS: NONE. ACUTE TOXICITY LEVEL: MODERATELY TOXIC BY INGESTION. TARGET EFFECTS: NO DATA AVAILABLE.

HEALTH EFFECTS AND FIRST AID

INHALATION: BENZTHIAZURON: **ACUTE EXPOSURE**- MANY SUBSTITUTED UREA HERBICIDES ARE MODERATELY IRRITATING TO THE MUCOUS MEMBRANES. **CHRONIC EXPOSURE**- NO DATA AVAILABLE.

FIRST AID- REMOVE FROM EXPOSURE AREA TO FRESH AIR IMMEDIATELY. IF BREATHING HAS STOPPED, PERFORM ARTIFICIAL RESPIRATION. KEEP PERSON WARM AND AT REST. TREAT SYMPTOMATICALLY AND SUPPORTIVELY. GET MEDICAL ATTENTION IMMEDIATELY.

SKIN CONTACT: BENZTHIAZURON: **ACUTE EXPOSURE**- SOME SUBSTITUED UREAS HERBICIDES ARE MODERATELY IRRITATING TO THE SKIN. PERCUTANEOUS APPLICATIONS OF 500 MG/KG DID NOT PRODUCED ANY SYSTEMIC EFFECTS IN RATS. **CHRONIC EXPOSURE**- NO DATA AVAILABLE.

FIRST AID- REMOVE CONTAMINATED CLOTHING AND SHOES IMMEDIATELY. WASH AFFECTED AREA WITH SOAP OR MILD DETERGENT AND LARGE AMOUNTS OF WATER UNTIL NO EVIDENCE OF CHEMICAL REMAINS (APPROXIMATELY 15-20 MINUTES). GET MEDICAL ATTENTION IMMEDIATELY.

EYE CONTACT: BENZTHIAZURON: **ACUTE EXPOSURE**- MANY SUBSTITUTED UREA HERBICIDES ARE MODERATELY IRRITATING TO THE EYES. **CHRONIC EXPOSURE**- NO DATA AVAILABLE.

FIRST AID- WASH EYES IMMEDIATELY WITH LARGE AMOUNTS OF WATER OR NORMAL SALINE, OCCASIONALLY LIFTING UPPER AND LOWER LIDS, UNTIL NO EVIDENCE OF CHEMICAL REMAINS (APPROXIMATELY 15-20 MINUTES). GET MEDICAL ATTENTION IMMEDIATELY.

INGESTION: BENZTHIAZURON: **ACUTE EXPOSURE**- A LETHAL DOSE IN RATS WAS 1280 MG/KG; SYMPTOMS WERE NOT REPORTED. **CHRONIC EXPOSURE**- NO DEATHS WERE OBSERVED IN A 60-DAY STUDY OF RATS REPEATEDLY FED 130 MG/KG/DAY.

FIRST AID- REMOVE BY GASTRIC LAVAGE AND CATHARSIS. MAINTAIN BLOOD PRESSURE AND AIRWAY. GIVE OXYGEN IF RESPIRATION IS DEPRESSED. DO NOT PERFORM GASTRIC LAVAGE IF VICTIM IS UNCONSCIOUS. GET MEDICAL ATTENTION IMMEDIATELY (DREISBACH, HANDBOOK OF POISONING, 12TH ED.). ADMINISTRATION OF LAVAGE OR OXYGEN SHOULD BE PERFORMED BY QUALIFIED MEDICAL PERSONNEL.

ANTIDOTE: NO SPECIFIC ANTIDOTE. TREAT SYMPTOMATICALLY AND SUPPORTIVELY.

REACTIVITY

REACTIVITY: STABLE UNDER NORMAL TEMPERATURES AND PRESSURES.

INCOMPATIBILITIES: BENZTHIAZURON: OXIDIZERS (STRONG): FIRE AND EXPLOSION HAZARD.

DECOMPOSITION: THERMAL DECOMPOSITION PRODUCTS MAY INCLUDE TOXIC OXIDES OF CARBON, NITROGEN, AND SULFUR.

POLYMERIZATION: HAZARDOUS POLYMERIZATION HAS NOT BEEN REPORTED TO OCCUR UNDER NORMAL TEMPERATURES AND PRESSURES.

STORAGE AND DISPOSAL

OBSERVE ALL FEDERAL, STATE AND LOCAL REGULATIONS WHEN STORING OR DISPOSING OF THIS SUBSTANCE. FOR ASSISTANCE, CONTACT THE DISTRICT DIRECTOR OF THE ENVIRONMENTAL PROTECTION AGENCY.

****STORAGE****

STORE IN ACCORDANCE WITH 40 CFR 165 RECOMMENDED PROCEDURES FOR THE DISPOSAL AND STORAGE OF PESTICIDES AND PESTICIDE CONTAINERS.

****DISPOSAL****

DISPOSAL MUST BE IN ACCORDANCE WITH 40 CFR 165 RECOMMENDED PROCEDURES FOR THE DISPOSAL AND STORAGE OF PESTICIDES AND PESTICIDE CONTAINERS.

CONDITIONS TO AVOID

MAY BURN BUT DOES NOT IGNITE READILY. CONTAINERS MAY EXPLODE IN HEAT OF FIRE.

SPILL AND LEAK PROCEDURES

OCCUPATIONAL SPILL: DO NOT TOUCH SPILLED MATERIAL. STOP LEAK IF YOU CAN DO IT WITHOUT RISK. USE WATER SPRAY TO REDUCE VAPORS. FOR SMALL SPILLS, TAKE UP WITH SAND OR OTHER ABSORBENT MATERIAL AND PLACE INTO CONTAINERS FOR LATER DISPOSAL. FOR SMALL DRY SPILLS, WITH A CLEAN SHOVEL PLACE MATERIAL INTO CLEAN, DRY CONTAINERS AND COVER. MOVE CONTAINERS FROM SPILL AREA. FOR LARGER SPILLS, DIKE FAR AHEAD OF SPILL FOR LATER DISPOSAL. KEEP UNNECESSARY PEOPLE AWAY. ISOLATE HAZARD AREA AND DENY ENTRY. VENTILATE CLOSED SPACES BEFORE ENTERING.

PROTECTIVE EQUIPMENT

VENTILATION: PROVIDE LOCAL EXHAUST OR GENERAL DILUTION VENTILATION SYSTEM.

RESPIRATOR: THE FOLLOWING RESPIRATORS ARE RECOMMENDED BASED ON INFORMATION FOUND IN THE PHYSICAL DATA, TOXICITY AND HEALTH EFFECTS SECTIONS. THEY ARE RANKED IN ORDER FROM MINIMUM TO MAXIMUM RESPIRATORY PROTECTION. THE SPECIFIC RESPIRATOR SELECTED MUST BE BASED ON CONTAMINATION LEVELS FOUND IN THE WORK PLACE, MUST NOT EXCEED THE WORKING LIMITS OF THE RESPIRATOR AND BE JOINTLY APPROVED BY THE NATIONAL INSTITUTE FOR OCCUPATIONAL SAFETY AND HEALTH AND THE MINE SAFETY AND HEALTH ADMINISTRATION (NIOSH-MSHA).

CHEMICAL CARTRIDGE RESPIRATOR WITH AN ORGANIC VAPOR CARTRIDGE(S) IN COMBINATION WITH A DUST AND MIST FILTER.

GAS MASK WITH ORGANIC VAPOR CANISTER (CHIN-STYLE OR FRONT- OR BACK-MOUNTED CANISTER) WITH A DUST AND MIST FILTER.

GAS MASK WITH ORGANIC VAPOR CANISTER (CHIN-STYLE OR FRONT- OR BACK-MOUNTED CANISTER) WITH A PARTICULATE FILTER.

POWERED AIR-PURIFYING RESPIRATOR WITH A HIGH-EFFICIENCY FILTER.

TYPE 'C' SUPPLIED-AIR RESPIRATOR WITH A FULL FACEPIECE OPERATED IN A PRESSURE-DEMAND OR OTHER POSITIVE PRESSURE MODE.

SELF-CONTAINED BREATHING APPARATUS WITH A FULL FACEPIECE OPERATED IN PRESSURE-DEMAND OR OTHER POSITIVE PRESSURE MODE.

FOR FIREFIGHTING AND OTHER IMMEDIATELY DANGEROUS TO LIFE OR HEALTH CONDITIONS:

SELF-CONTAINED BREATHING APPARATUS WITH FULL FACEPIECE OPERATED IN PRESSURE-DEMAND OR OTHER POSITIVE PRESSURE MODE.

SUPPLIED-AIR RESPIRATOR WITH FULL FACEPIECE AND OPERATED IN PRESSURE-DEMAND OR OTHER POSITIVE PRESSURE MODE IN COMBINATION WITH AN AUXILIARY SELF-CONTAINED BREATHING APPARATUS OPERATED IN PRESSURE-DEMAND OR OTHER POSITIVE PRESSURE MODE.

CLOTHING: EMPLOYEE MUST WEAR APPROPRIATE PROTECTIVE (IMPERVIOUS) CLOTHING AND EQUIPMENT TO PREVENT REPEATED OR PROLONGED SKIN CONTACT WITH THIS SUBSTANCE.

GLOVES: EMPLOYEE MUST WEAR APPROPRIATE PROTECTIVE GLOVES TO PREVENT CONTACT WITH THIS SUBSTANCE.

EYE PROTECTION: EMPLOYEE MUST WEAR SPLASH-PROOF OR DUST-RESISTANT SAFETY GOGGLES TO PREVENT EYE CONTACT WITH THIS SUBSTANCE.

EMERGENCY EYE WASH: WHERE THERE IS ANY POSSIBILITY THAT AN EMPLOYEE'S EYES MAY BE EXPOSED TO THIS SUBSTANCE, THE EMPLOYER SHOULD PROVIDE AN EYE WASH FOUNTAIN WITHIN THE IMMEDIATE WORK AREA FOR EMERGENCY USE.

AUTHORIZED BY- OCCUPATIONAL HEALTH SERVICES, INC.

CREATION DATE: 10/04/89 ***REVISION DATE:*** 05/14/90

MATERIAL SAFETY DATA SHEET

OCCUPATIONAL HEALTH SERVICES, INC.
AGRICULTURE AND PESTICIDE DIVISION
450 SEVENTH AVENUE, SUITE 2407
NEW YORK, NEW YORK 10123
1-800-445-MSDS OR (212) 967-1100

EMERGENCY CONTACT:
JOHN S. BRANSFORD, JR. (615) 292-1180

SUBSTANCE IDENTIFICATION

CAS-NUMBER 3134-12-1

SUBSTANCE: **PHENOBENZURON**

TRADE NAMES/SYNONYMS: BENZAMIDE, N-(3,4-DICHLOROPHENYL)-N-((DIMETHYLAMINO)CARBONYL)-; UREA, 1-BENZOYL-1-(3,4-DICHLOROPHENYL)-3,3-DIMETHYL; 1-BENZOYL-1-(3,4-DICHLOROPHENYL)-3,3-DIMETHYLUREA; N-(3,4-DICHLOROPHENYL)-N-((DIMETHYLAMINO)CARBONYL)BENZAMIDE; N-BENZYL-N-(DICHLORO-3,4-PHENYL)-N',N'-DIMETHYLUREA; BENZOMARC; C16H14CL2N2O2; PST72972

CHEMICAL FAMILY: SUBSTITUTED UREA
HALOGEN COMPOUND, AROMATIC

MOLECULAR FORMULA: C16-H14-CL2-N2-O2

MOLECULAR WEIGHT: 337.22

CERCLA RATINGS (SCALE 0-3): HEALTH=2 FIRE=1 REACTIVITY=0 PERSISTENCE=1

NFPA RATINGS (SCALE 0-4): HEALTH=2 FIRE=1 REACTIVITY=0

COMPONENTS AND CONTAMINANTS

COMPONENT: PHENOBENZURON ***PERCENT:*** 100.0
CAS# 3134-12-1

OTHER CONTAMINANTS: NONE

EXPOSURE LIMITS: NO OCCUPATIONAL EXPOSURE LIMITS ESTABLISHED BY OSHA, ACGIH, OR NIOSH.

PHYSICAL DATA

DESCRIPTION: SOLID. ***MELTING POINT:*** NOT AVAILABLE

SPECIFIC GRAVITY: NOT AVAILABLE ***SOLUBILITY IN WATER:*** NOT AVAILABLE

FIRE AND EXPLOSION DATA

FIRE AND EXPLOSION HAZARD: SLIGHT FIRE HAZARD WHEN EXPOSED TO HEAT OR FLAME.

FIREFIGHTING MEDIA: DRY CHEMICAL, CARBON DIOXIDE, HALON, WATER SPRAY OR STANDARD FOAM (1987 EMERGENCY RESPONSE GUIDEBOOK, DOT P 5800.4). FOR LARGER FIRES, USE WATER SPRAY, FOG OR STANDARD FOAM (1987 EMERGENCY RESPONSE GUIDEBOOK, DOT P 5800.4).

FIREFIGHTING: MOVE CONTAINERS FROM FIRE AREA IF POSSIBLE. FIGHT FIRE FROM MAXIMUM DISTANCE. STAY AWAY FROM STORAGE TANK ENDS. DIKE FIRE CONTROL WATER FOR LATER DISPOSAL. DO NOT SCATTER MATERIAL (1987 EMERGENCY RESPONSE GUIDEBOOK, DOT P 5800.4, GUIDE PAGE 55). EXTINGUISH USING AGENT SUITABLE FOR TYPE OF SURROUNDING FIRE. USE WATER IN FLOODING QUANTITIES AS FOG. KEEP SPARKS, FLAMES AND OTHER SOURCES OF IGNITION AWAY. KEEP MATERIAL OUT OF WATER SOURCES AND SEWERS. DO NOT TOUCH MATERIAL AND AVOID BREATHING DUSTS AND FUMES FROM BURNING MATERIAL. KEEP UPWIND.

TOXICITY

PHENOBENZURON: TOXICITY DATA: 5000 MG/KG ORAL-RAT LD50. CARCINOGEN STATUS: NONE. ACUTE TOXICITY DATA: MODERATELY TOXIC BY INGESTION. TARGET EFFECTS: NO DATA AVAILABLE.

HEALTH EFFECTS AND FIRST AID

INHALATION: PHENOBENZURON: **ACUTE EXPOSURE-** MANY SUBSTITUTED UREA HERBICIDES ARE MODERATELY IRRITATING TO THE MUCOUS MEMBRANES. **CHRONIC EXPOSURE-** NO DATA AVAILABLE.

FIRST AID- REMOVE FROM EXPOSURE AREA TO FRESH AIR IMMEDIATELY. IF BREATHING HAS STOPPED, PERFORM ARTIFICIAL RESPIRATION. KEEP PERSON WARM AND AT REST. TREAT SYMPTOMATICALLY AND SUPPORTIVELY. GET MEDICAL ATTENTION IMMEDIATELY.

SKIN CONTACT: PHENOBENZURON: **ACUTE EXPOSURE-** MANY SUBSTITUTED UREA HERBICIDES ARE MODERATELY IRRITATING TO THE SKIN. **CHRONIC EXPOSURE-** NO DATA AVAILABLE.

FIRST AID- REMOVE CONTAMINATED CLOTHING AND SHOES IMMEDIATELY. WASH AFFECTED AREA WITH SOAP OR MILD DETERGENT AND LARGE AMOUNTS OF WATER UNTIL NO EVIDENCE OF CHEMICAL REMAINS (APPROXIMATELY 15-20 MINUTES). GET MEDICAL ATTENTION IMMEDIATELY.

EYE CONTACT: PHENOBENZURON: **ACUTE EXPOSURE-** MANY SUBSTITUTED UREA HERBICIDES ARE MODERATELY IRRITATING TO THE EYES. **CHRONIC EXPOSURE-** NO DATA AVAILABLE.

FIRST AID- WASH EYES IMMEDIATELY WITH LARGE AMOUNTS OF WATER OR NORMAL SALINE, OCCASIONALLY LIFTING UPPER AND LOWER LIDS, UNTIL NO EVIDENCE OF CHEMICAL REMAINS (APPROXIMATELY 15-20 MINUTES). GET MEDICAL ATTENTION IMMEDIATELY.

INGESTION: PHENOBENZURON: **ACUTE EXPOSURE-** A LETHAL DOSE IN RATS WAS 5000 MG/KG; SYMPTOMS WERE NOT REPORTED. **CHRONIC EXPOSURE-** NO DATA AVAILABLE.

FIRST AID- TREAT SYMPTOMATICALLY AND SUPPORTIVELY. GET MEDICAL ATTENTION IMMEDIATELY. IF VOMITING OCCURS, KEEP HEAD LOWER THAN HIPS TO PREVENT ASPIRATION.

ANTIDOTE: NO SPECIFIC ANTIDOTE. TREAT SYMPTOMATICALLY AND SUPPORTIVELY.

REACTIVITY

REACTIVITY: STABLE UNDER NORMAL TEMPERATURES AND PRESSURES.

INCOMPATIBILITIES: PHENOBENZURON: OXIDIZERS (STRONG): FIRE AND EXPLOSION HAZARD.

DECOMPOSITION: THERMAL DECOMPOSITION PRODUCTS MAY INCLUDE TOXIC OXIDES OF NITROGEN AND CARBON AND TOXIC AND CORROSIVE FUMES OF CHLORIDES.

POLYMERIZATION: HAZARDOUS POLYMERIZATION HAS NOT BEEN REPORTED TO OCCUR UNDER NORMAL TEMPERATURES AND PRESSURES.

STORAGE AND DISPOSAL

OBSERVE ALL FEDERAL, STATE AND LOCAL REGULATIONS WHEN STORING OR DISPOSING OF THIS SUBSTANCE. FOR ASSISTANCE, CONTACT THE DISTRICT DIRECTOR OF THE ENVIRONMENTAL PROTECTION AGENCY.

STORAGE

STORE IN ACCORDANCE WITH 40 CFR 165 RECOMMENDED PROCEDURES FOR THE DISPOSAL AND STORAGE OF PESTICIDES AND PESTICIDE CONTAINERS.
STORE AWAY FROM INCOMPATIBLE SUBSTANCES.

DISPOSAL

DISPOSAL MUST BE IN ACCORDANCE WITH 40 CFR 165 RECOMMENDED PROCEDURES FOR THE DISPOSAL AND STORAGE OF PESTICIDES AND PESTICIDE CONTAINERS.

CONDITIONS TO AVOID

MAY BURN BUT DOES NOT IGNITE READILY. CONTAINERS MAY EXPLODE IN HEAT OF FIRE.

SPILL AND LEAK PROCEDURES

OCCUPATIONAL SPILL: DO NOT TOUCH SPILLED MATERIAL. STOP LEAK IF YOU CAN DO IT WITHOUT RISK. USE WATER SPRAY TO REDUCE VAPORS. FOR SMALL SPILLS, TAKE UP WITH SAND OR OTHER ABSORBENT MATERIAL AND PLACE INTO CONTAINERS FOR LATER DISPOSAL. FOR SMALL DRY SPILLS, WITH A CLEAN SHOVEL PLACE MATERIAL INTO CLEAN, DRY CONTAINERS AND COVER. MOVE CONTAINERS FROM SPILL AREA. FOR LARGER SPILLS, DIKE FAR AHEAD OF SPILL FOR LATER DISPOSAL. KEEP UNNECESSARY PEOPLE AWAY. ISOLATE HAZARD AREA AND DENY ENTRY. VENTILATE CLOSED SPACES BEFORE ENTERING.

PROTECTIVE EQUIPMENT

VENTILATION: PROVIDE LOCAL EXHAUST OR GENERAL DILUTION VENTILATION SYSTEM.

RESPIRATOR: THE FOLLOWING RESPIRATORS ARE RECOMMENDED BASED ON INFORMATION FOUND IN THE PHYSICAL DATA, TOXICITY AND HEALTH EFFECTS SECTIONS. THEY ARE RANKED IN ORDER FROM MINIMUM TO MAXIMUM RESPIRATORY PROTECTION. THE SPECIFIC RESPIRATOR SELECTED MUST BE BASED ON CONTAMINATION LEVELS FOUND IN THE WORK PLACE, MUST NOT EXCEED THE WORKING LIMITS OF THE RESPIRATOR AND BE JOINTLY APPROVED BY THE NATIONAL INSTITUTE FOR OCCUPATIONAL SAFETY AND HEALTH AND THE MINE SAFETY AND HEALTH ADMINISTRATION (NIOSH-MSHA).

CHEMICAL CARTRIDGE RESPIRATOR WITH AN ORGANIC VAPOR CARTRIDGE(S) WITH A FULL FACEPIECE AND ORGANIC VAPOR CARTRIDGE(S) IN COMBINATION WITH A DUST AND MIST FILTER.

POWERED AIR-PURIFYING RESPIRATOR WITH A TIGHT-FITTING FACEPIECE AND ORGANIC VAPOR CARTRIDGE(S) IN COMBINATION WITH A HIGH-EFFICIENCY PARTICULATE FILTER.

TYPE 'C' SUPPLIED-AIR RESPIRATOR WITH A FULL FACEPIECE OPERATED IN A PRESSURE-DEMAND OR OTHER POSITIVE PRESSURE MODE.

SELF-CONTAINED BREATHING APPARATUS WITH A FULL FACEPIECE OPERATED IN PRESSURE-DEMAND OR OTHER POSITIVE PRESSURE MODE.

FOR FIREFIGHTING AND OTHER IMMEDIATELY DANGEROUS TO LIFE OR HEALTH CONDITIONS:

SELF-CONTAINED BREATHING APPARATUS WITH FULL FACEPIECE OPERATED IN PRESSURE-DEMAND OR OTHER POSITIVE PRESSURE MODE.

SUPPLIED-AIR RESPIRATOR WITH FULL FACEPIECE AND OPERATED IN PRESSURE-DEMAND OR OTHER POSITIVE PRESSURE MODE IN COMBINATION WITH AN AUXILIARY SELF-CONTAINED BREATHING APPARATUS OPERATED IN PRESSURE-DEMAND OR OTHER POSITIVE PRESSURE MODE.

CLOTHING: EMPLOYEE MUST WEAR APPROPRIATE PROTECTIVE (IMPERVIOUS) CLOTHING AND EQUIPMENT TO PREVENT REPEATED OR PROLONGED SKIN CONTACT WITH THIS SUBSTANCE.

GLOVES: EMPLOYEE MUST WEAR APPROPRIATE PROTECTIVE GLOVES TO PREVENT CONTACT WITH THIS SUBSTANCE.

EYE PROTECTION: EMPLOYEE MUST WEAR SPLASH-PROOF OR DUST-RESISTANT SAFETY GOGGLES TO PREVENT EYE CONTACT WITH THIS SUBSTANCE. EMERGENCY EYE WASH: WHERE THERE IS ANY POSSIBILITY THAT AN EMPLOYEE'S EYES MAY BE EXPOSED TO THIS SUBSTANCE, THE EMPLOYER SHOULD PROVIDE AN EYE WASH FOUNTAIN WITHIN THE IMMEDIATE WORK AREA FOR EMERGENCY USE.

AUTHORIZED BY- OCCUPATIONAL HEALTH SERVICES, INC.
CREATION DATE: 10/04/89 ***REVISION DATE:*** 05/11/90

MATERIAL SAFETY DATA SHEET

OCCUPATIONAL HEALTH SERVICES, INC.
AGRICULTURE AND PESTICIDE DIVISION
450 SEVENTH AVENUE, SUITE 2407
NEW YORK, NEW YORK 10123
1-800-445-MSDS OR (212) 967-1100

EMERGENCY CONTACT:
JOHN S. BRANSFORD, JR. (615) 292-1180

SUBSTANCE IDENTIFICATION

CAS-NUMBER 6392-46-7

SUBSTANCE: **ALLYXYCARB**

TRADE NAMES/SYNONYMS: PHENOL, 4-(DI-2-PROPENYLAMINO)-3,5-DIMETHYL-, METHYLCARBAMATE (ESTER); CARBAMIC ACID, METHYL-, 4-(DIALLYLAMINO)-3,5-XYLYL ESTER; 4-(DI-2-PROPENYLAMINO)-3,5-DIMETHYLPHENOL METHYLCARBAMATE (ESTER); METHYL CARBAMIC ACID 4-(DIALLYLAMINO)-3,5-XYLYL ESTER; 4-DIALLYLAMINO-3,5-XYLYL METHYLCARBAMATE; 4-(DI-2-PROPENYLAMINO)-3,5-DIMETHYLPHENYL METHYLCARBAMATE; APC; BAY 50282; HYDROL; OMS 773; C16H22N2O2; PST72977

CHEMICAL FAMILY: CARBAMATE

MOLECULAR FORMULA: C16-H22-N2-O2

MOLECULAR WEIGHT: 274.40

CERCLA RATINGS (SCALE 0-3): HEALTH=3 FIRE=1 REACTIVITY=0 PERSISTENCE=1

NFPA RATINGS (SCALE 0-4): HEALTH=3 FIRE=1 REACTIVITY=0

COMPONENTS AND CONTAMINANTS

COMPONENT: ALLYXYCARB ***PERCENT:*** 100.0
CAS# 6392-46-7

OTHER CONTAMINANTS: NONE

EXPOSURE LIMITS: NO OCCUPATIONAL EXPOSURE LIMITS ESTABLISHED BY OSHA, ACGIH, OR NIOSH.

PHYSICAL DATA

DESCRIPTION: POWDER. ***MELTING POINT:*** NOT AVAILABLE

SPECIFIC GRAVITY: NOT AVAILABLE ***SOLUBILITY IN WATER:*** INSOLUBLE

SOLVENT SOLUBILITY: SOLUBLE IN ALCOHOL AND BENZENE.

FIRE AND EXPLOSION DATA

FIRE AND EXPLOSION HAZARD: SLIGHT FIRE HAZARD WHEN EXPOSED TO HEAT OR FLAME.

FIREFIGHTING MEDIA: DRY CHEMICAL, CARBON DIOXIDE, HALON, WATER SPRAY OR STANDARD FOAM (1987 EMERGENCY RESPONSE GUIDEBOOK, DOT P 5800.4). FOR LARGER FIRES, USE WATER SPRAY, FOG OR STANDARD FOAM (1987 EMERGENCY RESPONSE GUIDEBOOK, DOT P 5800.4).

FIREFIGHTING: MOVE CONTAINERS FROM FIRE AREA IF POSSIBLE. FIGHT FIRE FROM MAXIMUM DISTANCE. STAY AWAY FROM STORAGE TANK ENDS. DIKE FIRE CONTROL WATER FOR LATER DISPOSAL. DO NOT SCATTER MATERIAL (1987 EMERGENCY RESPONSE GUIDEBOOK, DOT P 5800.4, GUIDE PAGE 55). EXTINGUISH USING AGENTS SUITABLE FOR TYPE OF SURROUNDING FIRE. USE FLOODING AMOUNTS OF WATER AS FOG. AVOID BREATHING TOXIC DUST AND FUMES FROM BURNING MATERIAL; KEEP UPWIND.

TOXICITY

ALLYXYCARB: TOXICITY DATA: 89 MG/KG ORAL-RAT LD50; 62 MG/KG ORAL-MOUSE LDLO; 48 MG/KG UNREPORTED-MOUSE LD50. CARCINOGEN STATUS: NONE. ACUTE TOXICITY: TOXIC BY INGESTION. TARGET EFFECTS: CHOLINESTERASE INHIBITOR. AT INCREASED RISK FROM EXPOSURE: PERSONS WITH ASTHMA, DIABETES, CARDIOVASCULAR DISEASE, MECHANICAL OBSTRUCTION OF THE GASTROINTESTINAL OR UROGENITAL TRACT, AND THOSE IN VAGOTONIC STATES.*

* MAY BE BASED ON GENERAL INFORMATION ON CARBAMATES.

HEALTH EFFECTS AND FIRST AID

INHALATION: ALLYXYCARB: SEE INFORMATION ON CARBAMATES.
CARBAMATES: CHOLINESTERASE INHIBITOR. **ACUTE EXPOSURE-** WHEN INHALED, THE FIRST EFFECTS OF CHOLINESTERASE INHIBITION ARE USUALLY RESPIRATORY AND MAY INCLUDE NASAL HYPEREMIA AND WATERY DISCHARGE, CHEST DISCOMFORT, DYSPNEA, AND WHEEZING DUE TO INCREASED BRONCHIAL SECRETIONS AND BRONCHOCONSTRICTION. OTHER SYSTEMIC EFFECTS MAY BEGIN WITHIN A FEW MINUTES OR SEVERAL HOURS OF EXPOSURE. SYMPTOMS MAY INCLUDE NAUSEA, VOMITING, DIARRHEA, ABDOMINAL CRAMPS, HEADACHE, VERTIGO, OCULAR PAIN, CILIARY MUSCLE SPASM, BLURRING OR DIMNESS OF VISION, MIOSIS, OR IN SOME CASES MYDRIASIS, LACRIMATION, SALIVATION, SWEATING, AND CONFUSION. OTHER REPORTED CENTRAL NERVOUS SYSTEM OR NEUROMUSCULAR EFFECTS INCLUDE ATAXIA, SLURRED SPEECH, AREFLEXIA, WEAKNESS, FATIGUE, TWITCHING, FASCICULATION, TREMOR, AND EVENTUALLY PARALYSIS OF THE EXTREMITIES AND POSSIBLY OF THE RESPIRATORY MUSCLES. IN SEVERE CASES, THERE MAY ALSO BE INVOLUNTARY DEFECATION AND URINATION, BRADYCARDIA, HYPOTENSION, PULMONARY EDEMA, CONVULSIONS, COMA, AND DEATH FROM RESPIRATORY FAILURE OR CARDIAC ARREST. CARBAMATES GENERALLY DO NOT ACCUMULATE IN MAMMALIAN TISSUE AND THE CHOLINESTERASE INHIBITION REVERSES RATHER RAPIDLY. IN NON-FATAL CASES, THE ILLNESS GENERALLY LASTS LESS THAN 24 HOURS. **CHRONIC EXPOSURE-** PROLONGED OR REPEATED EXPOSURE MAY CAUSE EFFECTS AS DESCRIBED IN ACUTE EXPOSURE.

FIRST AID- REMOVE FROM EXPOSURE AREA TO FRESH AIR IMMEDIATELY. IF BREATHING HAS STOPPED, GIVE ARTIFICIAL RESPIRATION. MAINTAIN AIRWAY AND BLOOD PRESSURE AND ADMINISTER OXYGEN IF AVAILABLE. KEEP AFFECTED PERSON WARM AND AT REST. TREAT SYMPTOMATICALLY AND SUPPORTIVELY. ADMINISTRATION OF OXYGEN SHOULD BE PERFORMED BY QUALIFIED PERSONNEL. GET MEDICAL ATTENTION IMMEDIATELY.

SKIN CONTACT: ALLYXYCARB: SEE INFORMATION ON CARBAMATES.
CARBAMATES: CHOLINESTERASE INHIBITOR. **ACUTE EXPOSURE-** SOME COMPOUNDS MAY CAUSE IRRITATION. LOCALIZED SWEATING AND FASCICULATIONS MAY OCCUR AT THE SITE OF CONTACT. IF SUFFICIENT AMOUNTS ARE ABSORBED THROUGH THE SKIN, OTHER EFFECTS OF CHOLINESTERASE INHIBITION MAY OCCUR AS DESCRIBED IN ACUTE INHALATION; SYMPTOMS MAY BE DELAYED FOR 2-3 HOURS, USUALLY NO MORE THAN 8 HOURS. **CHRONIC EXPOSURE-** REPEATED OR PROLONGED EXPOSURE MAY CAUSE EFFECTS AS DESCRIBED IN ACUTE EXPOSURE.

FIRST AID- REMOVE CONTAMINATED CLOTHING IMMEDIATELY. WASH CONTAMINATED AREAS WITH SOAP AND WATER FOLLOWED BY ALCOHOL (ARENA, POISONING, 4TH ED.). EMERGENCY PERSONNEL SHOULD WEAR GLOVES AND AVOID CONTAMINATION. TREAT RESPIRATORY DIFFICULTY WITH ARTIFICIAL RESPIRATION. GET MEDICAL ATTENTION IMMEDIATELY.

EYE CONTACT: ALLYXYCARB: SEE INFORMATION ON CARBAMATES.
CARBAMATES: CHOLINESTERASE INHIBITOR. **ACUTE EXPOSURE-** DIRECT CONTACT MAY CAUSE PAIN, HYPEREMIA, LACRIMATION, TWITCHING OF THE EYELIDS, MIOSIS, AND CILIARY MUSCLE SPASM WITH LOSS OF ACCOMODATION, BLURRED OR DIMMED VISION AND BROWACHE. SOMETIMES MYDRIASIS MAY OCCUR INSTEAD OF MIOSIS. WITH SUFFICIENT EXPOSURE, OTHER SYMPTOMS OF CHOLINESTERASE INHIBITION MAY OCCUR AS DESCRIBED IN ACUTE INHALATION. **CHRONIC EXPOSURE-** PROLONGED EXPOSURE MAY CAUSE EFFECTS AS DESCRIBED IN ACUTE EXPOSURE. SOME COMPOUNDS HAVE CAUSED TOXIC EFFECTS ON THE CRYSTALLINE LENS, CONJUNCTIVAL THICKENING AND OBSTRUCTION OF NASOLACRIMAL CANALS WHEN USED AS MIOTIC EYE DROPS.

FIRST AID- IRRIGATE EYES WITH WATER OR SALINE SOLUTION. IF SYMPTOMS OF POISONING OCCUR, TREAT RESPIRATORY DIFFICULTY WITH ARTIFICIAL RESPIRATION AND OXYGEN. OBSERVE PATIENT FOR AT LEAST 24-36 HOURS (GOSSELIN, CLINICAL TOXICOLOGY OF COMMERCIAL PRODUCTS, 5TH ED.). GET MEDICAL ATTENTION IMMEDIATELY. OXYGEN SHOULD BE ADMINISTERED BY QUALIFIED MEDICAL PERSONNEL.

INGESTION: ALLYXYCARB: TOXIC. SEE INFORMATION ON CARBAMATES.
CARBAMATES: CHOLINESTERASE INHIBITOR. **ACUTE EXPOSURE-** WHEN INGESTED, THE FIRST EFFECTS MAY BE NAUSEA, VOMITING, ANOREXIA, ABDOMINAL CRAMPS, AND DIARRHEA. WITH ABSORPTION FROM THE GASTROINTESTINAL TRACT, THE OTHER EFFECTS OF CHOLINESTERASE INHIBITION AS DESCRIBED IN ACUTE INHALATION MAY OCCUR; SYMPTOMS MAY BEGIN WITHIN MINUTES OR BE DELAYED SEVERAL HOURS. **CHRONIC EXPOSURE-** REPEATED INGESTION MAY CAUSE EFFECTS AS DESCRIBED IN ACUTE EXPOSURE.

FIRST AID- IF PERSON IS ALERT AND RESPIRATION IS NOT DEPRESSED, GIVE SYRUP OF IPECAC FOLLOWED BY WATER (IF VOMITING OCCURS, KEEP HEAD BELOW HIPS TO PREVENT ASPIRATION). IF CONSCIOUSNESS LEVEL DECLINES OR VOMITING HAS NOT OCCURRED IN 15 MINUTES EMPTY STOMACH BY GASTRIC LAVAGE WITH THE AID OF CUFFED ENDOTRACHEAL TUBE USING ISOTONIC SALINE OR 5% SODIUM BICARBONATE FOLLOW WITH ACTIVATED CHARCOAL. ESTABLISH AND MAINTAIN AIRWAY. TREAT RESPIRATORY DIFFICULTY WITH ARTIFICIAL RESPIRATION AND OXYGEN. DO NOT GIVE MORPHINE, AMINOPHYLLINE, PHENOTHIAZINES, RESERPINE, FUROSEMIDE, OR ETHACRYNIC ACID (MORGAN, RECOGNITION AND MANAGEMENT OF PESTICIDE POISONINGS, 3RD ED.). TREAT SYMPTOMATICALLY AND SUPPORTIVELY. ADMINISTRATION OF OXYGEN AND LAVAGE MUST BE PERFORMED BY QUALIFIED MEDICAL PERSONNEL. GET MEDICAL ATTENTION IMMEDIATELY.

ANTIDOTE: THE FOLLOWING ANTIDOTE HAS BEEN RECOMMENDED. HOWEVER, THE DECISION AS TO WHETHER THE SEVERITY OF POISONING REQUIRES ADMINISTRATION OF ANY ANTIDOTE AND ACTUAL DOSE REQUIRED SHOULD BE MADE BY QUALIFIED MEDICAL PERSONNEL.

FOR CHOLINESTERASE INHIBITORS: ESTABLISH CLEAR AIRWAY AND TISSUE OXYGENATION BY ASPIRATION OF SECRETIONS, AND IF NECESSARY, BY ASSISTED PULMONARY VENTILATION WITH OXYGEN. IMPROVE TISSUE OXYGENATION AS MUCH AS POSSIBLE BEFORE ADMINISTERING ATROPINE TO MINIMIZE THE RISK OF VENTRICULAR FIBRILLATION. ADMINISTER ATROPINE SULFATE INTRAVENOUSLY, OR INTRAMUSCULARLY IF IV INJECTION IS NOT POSSIBLE. IN MODERATELY SEVERE POISONING ADMINISTER ATROPINE SULFATE, 0.4-2.0 MG REPEATED EVERY 15 MINUTES UNTIL ATROPINIZATION IS ACHIEVED (TACHYCARDIA, FLUSHING, DRY MOUTH, MYDRIASIS). MAINTAIN ATROPINIZATION BY REPEATED DOSES FOR 2-12 HOURS, OR LONGER, DEPENDING ON THE SEVERITY OF POISONING. THE APPEARANCE OF RALES IN THE LUNG BASES, MIOSIS, SALIVATION, NAUSEA, BRADYCARDIA, ARE ALL INDICATIONS OF INADEQUATE ATROPINIZATION. SEVERELY POISONED INDIVIDUALS MAY EXHIBIT REMARKABLE TOLERANCE TO ATROPINE; TWO OR MORE TIMES THE DOSAGES SUGGESTED ABOVE MAY BE NEEDED. PERSONS NOT POISONED OR ONLY SLIGHTLY POISONED, HOWEVER, MAY DEVELOP SIGNS OF ATROPINE TOXICITY FROM SUCH LARGE DOSAGES: FEVER, MUSCLE FIBRILLATIONS, AND DELIRIUM ARE THE MAIN SIGNS OF ATROPINE TOXICITY. IF THESE SIGNS APPEAR WHILE THE PATIENT IS FULLY ATROPINIZED, ATROPINE ADMINISTRATION SHOULD BE DISCONTINUED, AT LEAST TEMPORARILY. OBSERVE TREATED PATIENTS CLOSELY AT LEAST 24 HOURS TO INSURE THAT SYMPTOMS (POSSIBLY PULMONARY EDEMA) DO NOT RECUR AS ATROPINIZATION WEARS OFF. IN VERY SEVERE POISONINGS, METABOLIC DISPOSITION OF TOXICANT MAY REQUIRE SEVERAL HOURS OR DAYS DURING WHICH ATROPINIZATION MUST BE MAINTAINED. MARKEDLY LOWER LEVELS OF URINARY METABOLITES INDICATE THAT ATROPINE DOSAGE CAN BE TAPERED OFF. AS DOSAGE IS REDUCED, CHECK THE LUNG BASES FREQUENTLY FOR RALES. IF RALES ARE HEARD OR OTHER SYMPTOMS RETURN, RE-ESTABLISH ATROPINIZATION PROMPTLY (MORGAN, RECOGNITION AND MANAGEMENT OF PESTICIDE POISONINGS, 3RD ED.). ADMINISTRATION OF ANTIDOTE MUST BE PERFORMED BY QUALIFIED MEDICAL PERSONNEL.

REACTIVITY

REACTIVITY: STABLE UNDER NORMAL TEMPERATURES AND PRESSURES.

INCOMPATIBILITIES: ALLYXYCARB: OXIDIZERS (STRONG): FIRE AND EXPLOSION HAZARD.

DECOMPOSITION: THERMAL DECOMPOSITION PRODUCTS MAY INCLUDE TOXIC OXIDES OF CARBON AND NITROGEN.

POLYMERIZATION: HAZARDOUS POLYMERIZATION HAS NOT BEEN REPORTED TO OCCUR UNDER NORMAL TEMPERATURES AND PRESSURES.

STORAGE AND DISPOSAL

OBSERVE ALL FEDERAL, STATE AND LOCAL REGULATIONS WHEN STORING OR DISPOSING OF THIS SUBSTANCE. FOR ASSISTANCE, CONTACT THE DISTRICT DIRECTOR OF THE ENVIRONMENTAL PROTECTION AGENCY.

****STORAGE****

STORE IN ACCORDANCE WITH 40 CFR 165 RECOMMENDED PROCEDURES FOR THE DISPOSAL AND STORAGE OF PESTICIDES AND PESTICIDE CONTAINERS. STORE AWAY FROM INCOMPATIBLE SUBSTANCES.

****DISPOSAL****

DISPOSAL MUST BE IN ACCORDANCE WITH 40 CFR 165 RECOMMENDED PROCEDURES FOR THE DISPOSAL AND STORAGE OF PESTICIDES AND PESTICIDE CONTAINERS.

CONDITIONS TO AVOID

MAY BURN BUT DOES NOT IGNITE READILY. CONTAINERS MAY EXPLODE IN HEAT OF FIRE.

SPILL AND LEAK PROCEDURES

OCCUPATIONAL SPILL: DO NOT TOUCH SPILLED MATERIAL. STOP LEAK IF YOU CAN DO IT WITHOUT RISK. USE WATER SPRAY TO REDUCE VAPORS. FOR SMALL SPILLS, TAKE UP WITH SAND OR OTHER ABSORBENT MATERIAL AND PLACE INTO CONTAINERS FOR LATER DISPOSAL. FOR SMALL DRY SPILLS, WITH A CLEAN SHOVEL PLACE MATERIAL INTO CLEAN, DRY CONTAINERS AND COVER. MOVE CONTAINERS FROM SPILL AREA. FOR LARGER SPILLS, DIKE FAR AHEAD OF SPILL FOR LATER DISPOSAL. KEEP UNNECESSARY PEOPLE AWAY. ISOLATE HAZARD AREA AND DENY ENTRY. VENTILATE CLOSED SPACES BEFORE ENTERING.

PROTECTIVE EQUIPMENT

VENTILATION: PROVIDE LOCAL EXHAUST OR PROCESS ENCLOSURE VENTILATION SYSTEM.

RESPIRATOR: THE FOLLOWING RESPIRATORS ARE RECOMMENDED BASED ON INFORMATION FOUND IN THE PHYSICAL DATA, TOXICITY AND HEALTH EFFECTS SECTIONS. THEY ARE RANKED IN ORDER FROM MINIMUM TO MAXIMUM RESPIRATORY PROTECTION. THE SPECIFIC RESPIRATOR SELECTED MUST BE BASED ON CONTAMINATION LEVELS FOUND IN THE WORK PLACE, MUST NOT EXCEED THE WORKING LIMITS OF THE RESPIRATOR AND BE JOINTLY APPROVED BY THE NATIONAL INSTITUTE FOR OCCUPATIONAL SAFETY AND HEALTH AND THE MINE SAFETY AND HEALTH ADMINISTRATION (NIOSH-MSHA).

TYPE 'C' SUPPLIED-AIR RESPIRATOR WITH A FULL FACEPIECE OPERATED IN PRESSURE-DEMAND OR OTHER POSITIVE PRESSURE MODE OR WITH A FULL FACEPIECE, HELMET OR HOOD OPERATED IN CONTINOUS-FLOW MODE.

SELF-CONTAINED BREATHING APPARATUS WITH A FULL FACEPIECE OPERATED IN PRESSURE-DEMAND OR OTHER POSITIVE PRESSURE MODE.

FOR FIREFIGHTING AND OTHER IMMEDIATELY DANGEROUS TO LIFE OR HEALTH CONDITIONS:

SELF-CONTAINED BREATHING APPARATUS WITH FULL FACEPIECE OPERATED IN PRESSURE-DEMAND OR OTHER POSITIVE PRESSURE MODE.

SUPPLIED-AIR RESPIRATOR WITH FULL FACEPIECE AND OPERATED IN PRESSURE-DEMAND OR OTHER POSITIVE PRESSURE MODE IN COMBINATION WITH AN AUXILIARY SELF-CONTAINED BREATHING APPARATUS OPERATED IN PRESSURE-DEMAND OR OTHER POSITIVE PRESSURE MODE.

CLOTHING: EMPLOYEE MUST WEAR APPROPRIATE PROTECTIVE (IMPERVIOUS) CLOTHING AND EQUIPMENT TO PREVENT ANY POSSIBILITY OF SKIN CONTACT WITH THIS SUBSTANCE.

GLOVES: EMPLOYEE MUST WEAR APPROPRIATE PROTECTIVE GLOVES TO PREVENT CONTACT WITH THIS SUBSTANCE.

EYE PROTECTION: EMPLOYEE MUST WEAR SPLASH-PROOF OR DUST-RESISTANT SAFETY GOGGLES WITH OR WITHOUT A FACESHIELD TO PREVENT CONTACT WITH THIS SUBSTANCE.

EMERGENCY EYE WASH: WHERE THERE IS ANY POSSIBILITY THAT AN EMPLOYEE'S EYES MAY BE EXPOSED TO THIS SUBSTANCE, THE EMPLOYER SHOULD PROVIDE AN EYE WASH FOUNTAIN WITHIN THE IMMEDIATE WORK AREA FOR EMERGENCY USE.

AUTHORIZED BY- OCCUPATIONAL HEALTH SERVICES, INC.

CREATION DATE: 10/04/89 ***REVISION DATE:*** 06/12/90

MATERIAL SAFETY DATA SHEET

OCCUPATIONAL HEALTH SERVICES, INC.
AGRICULTURE AND PESTICIDE DIVISION
450 SEVENTH AVENUE, SUITE 2407
NEW YORK, NEW YORK 10123
1-800-445-MSDS OR (212) 967-1100

EMERGENCY CONTACT:
JOHN S. BRANSFORD, JR. (615) 292-1180

SUBSTANCE IDENTIFICATION

CAS-NUMBER 78-57-9

SUBSTANCE: **MENAZON**

TRADE NAMES/SYNONYMS: PHOSPHOROTHIOIC ACID, S-((4,6-DIAMINO-1,3,5-TRIAZIN-2-YL)METHYL) O,O-DIMETHYL ESTER; S-((4,6-DIAMINO-1,3,5-TRIAZIN-2-YL)METHYL)PHOSPHORODITHIOIC ACID, O,O-DIMETHYL ESTER; PHOSPHOROTHIOIC ACID, S-((4,6-DIAMINO-S-TRIAZIN-2-YL)METHYL) O,O-DIMETHYL ESTER; S-((4,6-DIAMINO-S-TRIAZIN-2-YL)PHOSPHOROTHIOIC ACID,O,O-DIMETHYL ESTER; S-4,6-DIAMINO-1,3,5-TRIAZIN-2-YLMETHYL O,O-DIMETHYL PHOSPORODITHIOATE; S-(4,6-DIAMINO-1,3,5-TRIAZIN-2-YL)METHYL O,O-DIMETHYL PHOSPHORODITHIOATE; S-(4,6-DIAMINO-S-TRIAZIN-2-YL)METHYL) O,O-DIMETHYL PHOSPHORODITHIOATE; O,O-DIMETHYL S-((4,6-DIAMINO-S-TRIAZIN-2-YL)METHYL) PHOSPHORODITHIOATE; 2-DIMETHOXYPHOSPHINOTHIOYLTHIOMETHYL-4,6-DIAMINO-S-TRIAZINE; AZIDITHION; SAPHIZON; SAPHICOL; SAYPHOS; OMS 503; ENT 25760; C6H12N5O2PS2; PST72980

CHEMICAL FAMILY: PHOSPHOROTHIOATE

MOLECULAR FORMULA: C6-H12-N5-O2-P-S2
MOLECULAR WEIGHT: 281.32
CERCLA RATINGS (SCALE 0-3): HEALTH=2 FIRE=1 REACTIVITY=0 PERSISTENCE=1
NFPA RATINGS (SCALE 0-4): HEALTH=2 FIRE=1 REACTIVITY=0

COMPONENTS AND CONTAMINANTS

COMPONENT: MENAZON ***PERCENT:*** 100.0
CAS# 78-57-9
OTHER CONTAMINANTS: NONE
EXPOSURE LIMITS: NO OCCUPATIONAL EXPOSURE LIMITS ESTABLISHED BY OSHA, ACGIH, OR NIOSH.

PHYSICAL DATA

DESCRIPTION: COLORLESS CRYSTALLINE SOLID WITH A MERCAPTAN-LIKE ODOR.
MELTING POINT: 320-324 F (160-162 C) (DECOMPOSES)
SPECIFIC GRAVITY: NOT AVAILABLE ***VAPOR PRESSURE:*** 0.000001 MMHG @ 25 C
SOLUBILITY IN WATER: 0.1%
SOLVENT SOLUBILITY: MODERATELY SOLUBLE IN ETHYL-CELLOSOLVE AND TETRAFURFURYL ALCOHOL.

FIRE AND EXPLOSION DATA

FIRE AND EXPLOSION HAZARD: SLIGHT FIRE HAZARD WHEN EXPOSED TO HEAT OR FLAME.

FIREFIGHTING MEDIA: DRY CHEMICAL, CARBON DIOXIDE, HALON, WATER SPRAY OR STANDARD FOAM (1987 EMERGENCY RESPONSE GUIDEBOOK, DOT P 5800.4). FOR LARGER FIRES, USE WATER SPRAY, FOG OR STANDARD FOAM (1987 EMERGENCY RESPONSE GUIDEBOOK, DOT P 5800.4).

FIREFIGHTING: MOVE CONTAINERS FROM FIRE AREA IF POSSIBLE. FIGHT FIRE FROM MAXIMUM DISTANCE. STAY AWAY FROM STORAGE TANK ENDS. DIKE FIRE CONTROL WATER FOR LATER DISPOSAL. DO NOT SCATTER MATERIAL (1987 EMERGENCY RESPONSE GUIDEBOOK, DOT P 5800.4, GUIDE PAGE 55). EXTINGUISH ONLY IF FLOW CAN BE STOPPED; USE FLOODING AMOUNTS OF WATER AS FOG, SOLID STREAMS MAY BE INEFFECTIVE. COOL CONTAINERS WITH FLOODING AMOUNTS OF WATER FROM AS FAR A DISTANCE AS POSSIBLE. USE WATER SPRAY TO ABSORB TOXIC VAPORS. AVOID BREATHING TOXIC VAPORS; KEEP UPWIND. CONSIDER EVACUATION OF DOWNWIND AREA IF MATERIAL IS LEAKING.

TOXICITY

MENAZON: TOXICITY DATA: 890 MG/KG ORAL-RAT LD50; 427 MG/KG ORAL-MOUSE LD50; 900 MG/KG UNREPORTED-MAMMAL LD50; MUTAGENIC DATA (RTECS). CARCINOGEN STATUS: NONE. ACUTE TOXICITY LEVEL: MODERATELY TOXIC BY INGESTION. TARGET EFFECTS: CHOLINESTERASE INHIBITOR. POISONING MAY AFFECT THE NERVOUS SYSTEM.* AT INCREASED RISK FROM EXPOSURE: PERSONS WITH RESPIRATORY AILMENTS, RECENT EXPOSURE TO CHOLINESTERASE INHIBITORS OR IMPAIRED CHOLINESTERASE PRODUCTION, OR LIVER MALFUNCTION.* ADDITIONAL DATA: MAY CROSS THE PLACENTA. HIGH ENVIRONMENTAL TEMPERATURES OR EXPOSURE OF THE CHEMICAL TO VISIBLE OR ULTRAVIOLET LIGHT MAY ENHANCE THE TOXICITY. INTERACTIONS WITH MEDICATIONS MAY OCCUR.*

* MAY BE BASED ON GENERAL INFORMATION ON ORGANOPHOSPHATES.

HEALTH EFFECTS AND FIRST AID

INHALATION: MENAZON: SEE INFORMATION ON ORGANOPHOSPHATES.
ORGANOPHOSPHATES: CHOLINESTERASE INHIBITOR. **ACUTE EXPOSURE-** WHEN INHALED, THE FIRST EFFECTS OF CHOLINESTERASE INHIBITORS ARE USUALLY RESPIRATORY AND MAY INCLUDE NASAL HYPEREMIA AND WATERY DISCHARGE, COUGH, CHEST DISCOMFORT, DYSPNEA, AND WHEEZING DUE TO INCREASED BRONCHIAL SECRETIONS AND BRONCHOCONSTRICTION. IF SUFFICIENT AMOUNTS ARE ABSORBED, OTHER SYSTEMIC EFFECTS MAY BEGIN WITHIN A FEW MINUTES OR BE DELAYED FOR UP TO 12 HOURS. SYMPTOMS MAY INCLUDE PALLOR, NAUSEA, VOMITING, DIARRHEA, ABDOMINAL CRAMPS, HEADACHE, DIZZINESS, OCULAR PAIN, BLURRED VISION, MIOSIS OR IN SOME CASES, ESPECIALLY INITIALLY, MYDRIASIS, LACRIMATION, SALIVATION, SWEATING, AND CONFUSION. OTHER REPORTED CENTRAL NERVOUS SYSTEM OR NEUROMUSCULAR EFFECTS MAY INCLUDE ATAXIA, SLURRED SPEECH, AREFLEXIA, WEAKNESS, FATIGUE, FASCICULATIONS, TWITCHING, TREMORS POSSIBLY OF THE TONGUE AND EYELIDS, AND EVENTUALLY PARALYSIS OF THE EXTREMITIES AND POSSIBLY OF THE RESPIRATORY MUSCLES. IN SEVERE CASES THERE MAY ALSO BE INVOLUNTARY DEFECATION AND URINATION, CYANOSIS, PSYCHOSIS, HYPERGLYCEMIA, ACUTE PANCREATITIS, CARDIAC IRREGULARITIES, PULMONARY EDEMA, UNCONSCIOUSNESS, CONVULSIONS, AND COMA. DEATH IS PRIMARILY DUE TO RESPIRATORY FAILURE, ALTHOUGH CARDIOVASCULAR EFFECTS INCLUDING CARDIAC ARREST MAY ALSO BE IMPLICATED. LONG TERM SEQUELAE ARE RARE BUT MAY INCLUDE NEUROPSYCHIATRIC DISORDERS AND MYOPATHY WITH MUSCLE TENDERNESS. SOME ORGANOPHOSPHATES MAY CAUSE A DELAYED NEUROPATHY BEGINNING 1-4 WEEKS AFTER AN ACUTE EXPOSURE WHICH MAY OR MAY NOT HAVE CAUSED ACUTE CHOLINERGIC EFFECTS. NUMBNESS, TINGLING, WEAKNESS AND CRAMPING BEGINNING SYMMETRICALLY IN THE LOWER LIMBS MAY PROGRESS TO ATAXIA AND PARALYSIS. IN SEVERE CASES, UPPER LIMB INVOLVEMENT IS POSSIBLE AND FLACCID PARALYSIS MAY PROGRESS TO SPASTIC PARALYSIS WITH EXAGGERATED REFLEXES. IMPROVEMENT MAY OCCUR OVER MONTHS TO YEARS, BUT SOME RESIDUAL IMPAIRMENT USUALLY REMAINS. **CHRONIC EXPOSURE-** REPEATED OR PROLONGED EXPOSURE MAY RESULT IN THE EFFECTS OF ACUTE EXPOSURE INCLUDING THE DELAYED NEUROPATHY. OTHER EFFECTS REPORTED IN WORKERS REPEATEDLY EXPOSED INCLUDE IMPAIRED MEMORY AND CONCENTRATION, ACUTE PSYCHOSIS, SEVERE DEPRESSIONS, IRRITABILTY, CONFUSION, APATHY, EMOTIONAL LABILITY, SOCIAL WITHDRAWAL, CONFUSION, HEADACHE, SPEECH DIFFICULTIES, DELAYED REACTION TIMES, SPATIAL DISORIENTATION, NIGHTMARES, SLEEPWALKING, AND DROWSINESS OR INSOMNIA. AN INFLUENZA-LIKE CONDITION WITH HEADACHE, NAUSEA, WEAKNESS, ANOREXIA AND MALAISE HAS ALSO BEEN REPORTED.

FIRST AID- REMOVE FROM EXPOSURE AREA TO FRESH AIR IMMEDIATELY. IF BREATHING HAS STOPPED, GIVE ARTIFICIAL RESPIRATION. MAINTAIN AIRWAY AND BLOOD PRESSURE AND ADMINISTER OXYGEN IF AVAILABLE. KEEP AFFECTED PERSON WARM AND AT REST. TREAT SYMPTOMATICALLY AND SUPPORTIVELY. ADMINISTRATION OF OXYGEN SHOULD BE PERFORMED BY QUALIFIED PERSONNEL. GET MEDICAL ATTENTION IMMEDIATELY.

SKIN CONTACT: MENAZON: SEE INFORMATION ON ORGANOPHOSPHATES.
ORGANOPHOSPHATES: CHOLINESTERASE INHIBITOR. **ACUTE EXPOSURE-** LOCALIZED SWEATING AND FASCICULATIONS MAY OCCUR AT THE SITE OF CONTACT. IF SUFFICIENT AMOUNTS ARE ABSORBED, OTHER EFFECTS OF CHOLINESTERASE INHIBITION AS DESCRIBED IN ACUTE INHALATION MAY OCCUR. SYMPTOMS MAY BE DELAYED 2-3 HOURS, BUT USUALLY NO MORE THAN 12 HOURS. THE RATE OF ABSORPTION IS INCREASED BY THE PRESENCE OF DERMATITIS OR HIGH AMBIENT TEMPERATURES. DELAYED NEUROPATHY IS ALSO POSSIBLE. **CHRONIC EXPOSURE-** REPEATED OR PROLONGED EXPOSURE MAY CAUSE EFFECTS AS DESCRIBED IN ACUTE EXPOSURE. SOME ORGANOPHOSPHATES MAY CAUSE SENSITIZATION.

FIRST AID- REMOVE CONTAMINATED CLOTHING IMMEDIATELY. WASH CONTAMINATED AREAS WITH SOAP AND WATER FOLLOWED BY ALCOHOL (ARENA, POISONING, 4TH ED.). EMERGENCY PERSONNEL SHOULD WEAR GLOVES AND AVOID CONTAMINATION. TREAT RESPIRATORY DIFFICULTY WITH ARTIFICIAL RESPIRATION. GET MEDICAL ATTENTION IMMEDIATELY.

EYE CONTACT: MENAZON: SEE INFORMATION ON ORGANOPHOSPHATES.
ORGANOPHOSPHATES: CHOLINESTERASE INHIBITOR. **ACUTE EXPOSURE-** DIRECT CONTACT MAY CAUSE PAIN, HYPEREMIA, LACRIMATION, TWITCHING OF THE EYELIDS, MIOSIS, AND CILIARY MUSCLE SPASM WITH LOSS OF ACCOMODATION, BLURRED OR DIMMED VISION AND BROWACHE. SOMETIMES MYDRIASIS MAY OCCUR INSTEAD OF MIOSIS. WITH SUFFICIENT EXPOSURE, OTHER SYMPTOMS OF CHOLINESTERASE INHIBITION AS DESCRIBED IN ACUTE INHALATION MAY OCCUR. **CHRONIC EXPOSURE-** REPEATED OR PROLONGED EXPOSURE MAY CAUSE EFFECTS AS DESCRIBED IN ACUTE EXPOSURE. SOME COMPOUNDS HAVE CAUSED TOXIC EFFECTS ON THE CRYSTALLINE LENS, CONJUNCTIVAL THICKENING AND OBSTRUCTION OF THE NASOLACRIMAL CANALS WHEN USED AS MIOTIC EYEDROPS.

FIRST AID- IRRIGATE EYES WITH WATER OR SALINE SOLUTION. IF SYMPTOMS OF POISONING OCCUR, TREAT RESPIRATORY DIFFICULTY WITH ARTIFICIAL RESPIRATION AND OXYGEN. OBSERVE PATIENT FOR AT LEAST 24-36 HOURS (GOSSELIN, CLINICAL TOXICOLOGY OF COMMERCIAL PRODUCTS, 5TH ED.). GET MEDICAL ATTENTION IMMEDIATELY. OXYGEN SHOULD BE ADMINISTERED BY QUALIFIED MEDICAL PERSONNEL.

INGESTION: MENAZON: SEE INFORMATION ON ORGANOPHOSPHATES.
ORGANOPHOSPHATES: CHOLINESTERASE INHIBITOR. **ACUTE EXPOSURE-** WHEN INGESTED, THE FIRST EFFECTS MAY BE NAUSEA, VOMITING, ANOREXIA, ABDOMINAL CRAMPS AND DIARRHEA. GASTROINTESTINAL ABSORPTION MAY CAUSE SYMPTOMS OF CHOLINESTERASE INHIBITION AS DESCRIBED IN ACUTE INHALATION. SYMPTOMS MAY BEGIN WITHIN MINUTES OR BE DELAYED FOR HOURS. DELAYED EFFECTS INCLUDING NEUROPATHY MAY ALSO OCCUR. **CHRONIC EXPOSURE-** REPEATED INGESTION MAY CAUSE EFFECTS AS DESCRIBED IN ACUTE EXPOSURE.

FIRST AID- IF PERSON IS ALERT AND RESPIRATION IS NOT DEPRESSED, GIVE SYRUP OF IPECAC FOLLOWED BY WATER (IF VOMITING OCCURS, KEEP HEAD BELOW HIPS TO PREVENT ASPIRATION). IF CONSCIOUSNESS LEVEL DECLINES OR VOMITING HAS NOT OCCURRED IN 15 MINUTES EMPTY STOMACH BY GASTRIC LAVAGE WITH THE AID OF CUFFED ENDOTRACHEAL TUBE USING ISOTONIC SALINE OR 5% SODIUM BICARBONATE FOLLOW WITH ACTIVATED CHARCOAL. ESTABLISH AND MAINTAIN AIRWAY. TREAT RESPIRATORY DIFFICULTY WITH ARTIFICIAL RESPIRATION AND

OXYGEN. DO NOT GIVE MORPHINE, AMINOPHYLLINE, PHENOTHIAZINES, RESERPINE, FUROSEMIDE, OR ETHACRYNIC ACID (MORGAN, RECOGNITION AND MANAGEMENT OF PESTICIDE POISONINGS, 3RD ED.). TREAT SYMPTOMATICALLY AND SUPPORTIVELY. ADMINISTRATION OF OXYGEN AND LAVAGE MUST BE PERFORMED BY QUALIFIED MEDICAL PERSONNEL. GET MEDICAL ATTENTION IMMEDIATELY.

ANTIDOTE: THE FOLLOWING ANTIDOTE(S) HAVE BEEN RECOMMENDED. HOWEVER, THE DECISION AS TO WHETHER THE SEVERITY OF POISONING REQUIRES ADMINISTRATION OF ANY ANTIDOTE AND ACTUAL DOSE REQUIRED SHOULD BE MADE BY QUALIFIED MEDICAL PERSONNEL.

FOR CHOLINESTERASE INHIBITORS: ESTABLISH CLEAR AIRWAY AND TISSUE OXYGENATION BY ASPIRATION OF SECRETIONS, AND IF NECESSARY, BY ASSISTED PULMONARY VENTILATION WITH OXYGEN. IMPROVE TISSUE OXYGENATION AS MUCH AS POSSIBLE BEFORE ADMINISTERING ATROPINE TO MINIMIZE THE RISK OF VENTRICULAR FIBRILLATION. ADMINISTER ATROPINE SULFATE INTRAVENOUSLY, OR INTRAMUSCULARLY IF IV INJECTION IS NOT POSSIBLE. IN MODERATELY SEVERE POISONING ADMINISTER ATROPINE SULFATE, 0.4-2.0 MG REPEATED EVERY 15 MINUTES UNTIL ATROPINIZATION IS ACHIEVED (TACHYCARDIA, FLUSHING, DRY MOUTH, MYDRIASIS). MAINTAIN ATROPINIZATION BY REPEATED DOSES FOR 2-12 HOURS, OR LONGER, DEPENDING ON THE SEVERITY OF POISONING. THE APPEARANCE OF RALES IN THE LUNG BASES, MIOSIS, SALIVATION, NAUSEA, BRADYCARDIA, ARE ALL INDICATIONS OF INADEQUATE ATROPINIZATION. SEVERELY POISONED INDIVIDUALS MAY EXHIBIT REMARKABLE TOLERANCE TO ATROPINE; TWO OR MORE TIMES THE DOSAGES SUGGESTED ABOVE MAY BE NEEDED. PERSONS NOT POISONED OR ONLY SLIGHTLY POISONED, HOWEVER, MAY DEVELOP SIGNS OF ATROPINE TOXICITY FROM SUCH LARGE DOSAGES: FEVER, MUSCLE FIBRILLATIONS, AND DELIRIUM ARE THE MAIN SIGNS OF ATROPINE TOXICITY. IF THESE SIGNS APPEAR WHILE THE PATIENT IS FULLY ATROPINIZED, ATROPINE ADMINISTRATION SHOULD BE DISCONTINUED, AT LEAST TEMPORARILY. OBSERVE TREATED PATIENTS CLOSELY AT LEAST 24 HOURS TO INSURE THAT SYMPTOMS (POSSIBLY PULMONARY EDEMA) DO NOT RECUR AS ATROPINIZATION WEARS OFF. IN VERY SEVERE POISONINGS, METABOLIC DISPOSITION OF TOXICANT MAY REQUIRE SEVERAL HOURS OR DAYS DURING WHICH ATROPINIZATION MUST BE MAINTAINED. MARKEDLY LOWER LEVELS OF URINARY METABOLITES INDICATE THAT ATROPINE DOSAGE CAN BE TAPERED OFF. AS DOSAGE IS REDUCED, CHECK THE LUNG BASES FREQUENTLY FOR RALES. IF RALES ARE HEARD OR OTHER SYMPTOMS RETURN, RE-ESTABLISH ATROPINIZATION PROMPTLY (MORGAN, RECOGNITION AND MANAGEMENT OF PESTICIDE POISONINGS, 3RD ED.). ADMINISTRATION OF ANTIDOTE MUST BE PERFORMED BY QUALIFIED MEDICAL PERSONNEL.

IN CASES OF SEVERE POISONING BY ORGANOPHOSPHATE PESTICIDES IN WHICH RESPIRATORY DEPRESSION, MUSCLE WEAKNESS AND TWITCHINGS ARE SEVERE, GIVE PRALIDOXIME (PROTOPAM-AYERST, 2-PAM), 1.0 GRAM INTRAVENOUSLY AT NO MORE THAN 0.5 GRAM PER MINUTE. DOSAGE OF PRALIDOXIME MAY BE REPEATED IN 1-2 HOURS, THEN AT 10-12 HOUR INTERVALS IF NEEDED. IN VERY SEVERE POISONINGS, DOSAGE RATES MAY BE DOUBLED. TREATMENT WITH PRALIDOXIME WILL BE MOST EFFECTIVE IF GIVEN WITHIN THIRTY-SIX HOURS AFTER POISONING (MORGAN, RECOGNITION AND MANAGEMENT OF PESTICIDE POISONINGS, 3RD ED.). ANTIDOTE SHOULD BE ADMINISTERED BY QUALIFIED MEDICAL PERSONNEL.

REACTIVITY

REACTIVITY: STABLE UNDER NORMAL TEMPERATURES AND PRESSURES.

INCOMPATIBILITIES: MENAZON: ACIDIC CONDITIONS (STRONG): UNSTABLE. ALKALINE CONDITIONS (STRONG): UNSTABLE. OXIDIZERS (STRONG): FIRE AND EXPLOSION HAZARD.

DECOMPOSITION: THERMAL DECOMPOSITION PRODUCTS MAY INCLUDE TOXIC OXIDES OF NITROGEN, CARBON, PHOSPHORUS, AND SULFUR.

POLYMERIZATION: HAZARDOUS POLYMERIZATION HAS NOT BEEN REPORTED TO OCCUR UNDER NORMAL TEMPERATURES AND PRESSURES.

STORAGE AND DISPOSAL

OBSERVE ALL FEDERAL, STATE AND LOCAL REGULATIONS WHEN STORING OR DISPOSING OF THIS SUBSTANCE. FOR ASSISTANCE, CONTACT THE DISTRICT DIRECTOR OF THE ENVIRONMENTAL PROTECTION AGENCY.

STORAGE

STORE IN ACCORDANCE WITH 40 CFR 165 RECOMMENDED PROCEDURES FOR THE DISPOSAL AND STORAGE OF PESTICIDES AND PESTICIDE CONTAINERS.
STORE AWAY FROM INCOMPATIBLE SUBSTANCES.

DISPOSAL

DISPOSAL MUST BE IN ACCORDANCE WITH 40 CFR 165 RECOMMENDED PROCEDURES FOR THE DISPOSAL AND STORAGE OF PESTICIDES AND PESTICIDE CONTAINERS.

CONDITIONS TO AVOID

MAY BURN BUT DOES NOT IGNITE READILY. CONTAINERS MAY EXPLODE IN HEAT OF FIRE.

SPILL AND LEAK PROCEDURES

OCCUPATIONAL SPILL: DO NOT TOUCH SPILLED MATERIAL. STOP LEAK IF YOU CAN DO IT WITHOUT RISK. USE WATER SPRAY TO REDUCE VAPORS. FOR SMALL SPILLS, TAKE UP WITH SAND OR OTHER ABSORBENT MATERIAL AND PLACE INTO CONTAINERS FOR LATER DISPOSAL. FOR SMALL DRY SPILLS, WITH A CLEAN SHOVEL PLACE MATERIAL INTO CLEAN, DRY CONTAINERS AND COVER. MOVE CONTAINERS FROM SPILL AREA. FOR LARGER SPILLS, DIKE FAR AHEAD OF SPILL FOR LATER DISPOSAL. KEEP UNNECESSARY PEOPLE AWAY. ISOLATE HAZARD AREA AND DENY ENTRY. VENTILATE CLOSED SPACES BEFORE ENTERING.

PROTECTIVE EQUIPMENT

VENTILATION: PROVIDE LOCAL EXHAUST OR GENERAL DILUTION VENTILATION SYSTEM.

RESPIRATOR: THE FOLLOWING RESPIRATORS ARE RECOMMENDED BASED ON INFORMATION FOUND IN THE PHYSICAL DATA, TOXICITY AND HEALTH EFFECTS SECTIONS. THEY ARE RANKED IN ORDER FROM MINIMUM TO MAXIMUM RESPIRATORY PROTECTION. THE SPECIFIC RESPIRATOR SELECTED MUST BE BASED ON CONTAMINATION LEVELS FOUND IN THE WORK PLACE, MUST NOT EXCEED THE WORKING LIMITS OF THE RESPIRATOR AND BE JOINTLY APPROVED BY THE NATIONAL INSTITUTE FOR OCCUPATIONAL SAFETY AND HEALTH AND THE MINE SAFETY AND HEALTH ADMINISTRATION (NIOSH-MSHA).

CHEMICAL CARTRIDGE RESPIRATOR WITH AN ORGANIC VAPOR CARTRIDGE(S) IN COMBINATION WITH A DUST AND MIST FILTER.

GAS MASK WITH ORGANIC VAPOR CANISTER (CHIN-STYLE OR FRONT- OR BACK-MOUNTED CANISTER) WITH A DUST AND MIST FILTER.

GAS MASK WITH ORGANIC VAPOR CANISTER (CHIN-STYLE OR FRONT- OR BACK-MOUNTED CANISTER) WITH A PARTICULATE FILTER.

POWERED AIR-PURIFYING RESPIRATOR WITH A HIGH-EFFICIENCY FILTER.

TYPE 'C' SUPPLIED-AIR RESPIRATOR WITH A FULL FACEPIECE OPERATED IN A PRESSURE-DEMAND OR OTHER POSITIVE PRESSURE MODE.

SELF-CONTAINED BREATHING APPARATUS WITH A FULL FACEPIECE OPERATED IN PRESSURE-DEMAND OR OTHER POSITIVE PRESSURE MODE.

FOR FIREFIGHTING AND OTHER IMMEDIATELY DANGEROUS TO LIFE OR HEALTH CONDITIONS:

SELF-CONTAINED BREATHING APPARATUS WITH FULL FACEPIECE OPERATED IN PRESSURE-DEMAND OR OTHER POSITIVE PRESSURE MODE.

SUPPLIED-AIR RESPIRATOR WITH FULL FACEPIECE AND OPERATED IN PRESSURE-DEMAND OR OTHER POSITIVE PRESSURE MODE IN COMBINATION WITH AN AUXILIARY SELF-CONTAINED BREATHING APPARATUS OPERATED IN PRESSURE-DEMAND OR OTHER POSITIVE PRESSURE MODE.

CLOTHING: EMPLOYEE MUST WEAR APPROPRIATE PROTECTIVE (IMPERVIOUS) CLOTHING AND EQUIPMENT TO PREVENT REPEATED OR PROLONGED SKIN CONTACT WITH THIS SUBSTANCE.

GLOVES: EMPLOYEE MUST WEAR APPROPRIATE PROTECTIVE GLOVES TO PREVENT CONTACT WITH THIS SUBSTANCE.

EYE PROTECTION: EMPLOYEE MUST WEAR SPLASH-PROOF OR DUST-RESISTANT SAFETY GOGGLES TO PREVENT EYE CONTACT WITH THIS SUBSTANCE.

EMERGENCY EYE WASH: WHERE THERE IS ANY POSSIBILITY THAT AN EMPLOYEE'S EYES MAY BE EXPOSED TO THIS SUBSTANCE, THE EMPLOYER SHOULD PROVIDE AN EYE WASH FOUNTAIN WITHIN THE IMMEDIATE WORK AREA FOR EMERGENCY USE.

AUTHORIZED BY- OCCUPATIONAL HEALTH SERVICES, INC.
CREATION DATE: 10/04/89 ***REVISION DATE:*** 05/07/90

MATERIAL SAFETY DATA SHEET

OCCUPATIONAL HEALTH SERVICES, INC.
AGRICULTURE AND PESTICIDE DIVISION
450 SEVENTH AVENUE, SUITE 2407
NEW YORK, NEW YORK 10123
1-800-445-MSDS OR (212) 967-1100

EMERGENCY CONTACT:
JOHN S. BRANSFORD, JR. (615) 292-1180

SUBSTANCE IDENTIFICATION

CAS-NUMBER 7287-36-7

SUBSTANCE: MONALIDE

TRADE NAMES/SYNONYMS: PENTANAMIDE, N-(4-CHLOROPHENYL)-2,2-DIMETHYL-; VALERANILIDE, 4'-CHLORO-2,2-DIMETHYL-; N-(4-CHLOROPHENYL)-2,2-DIMETHYLPENTANAMIDE; 4'-CHLORO-2,2-DIMETHYLVALERANILIDE; 4'-CHLORO-

ALPHA,ALPHA-DIMETHYLVALERANILIDE; N-(4-CHLOROPHENYL)-2,2-DIMETHYLVALERAMIDE; POTABLAN; C13N18CLNO; PST72987

CHEMICAL FAMILY: AMIDE

HALOGEN COMPOUND, AROMATIC

MOLECULAR FORMULA: CL-(C6-H4)-N-H-C-O-C-(C-H3)2-C3-H7

MOLECULAR WEIGHT: 239.77

CERCLA RATINGS (SCALE 0-3): HEALTH=2 FIRE=1 REACTIVITY=0 PERSISTENCE=2

NFPA RATINGS (SCALE 0-4): HEALTH=U FIRE=1 REACTIVITY=0

COMPONENTS AND CONTAMINANTS

COMPONENT: MONALIDE ***PERCENT:*** 100.0

CAS# 7287-36-7

OTHER CONTAMINANTS: NONE

EXPOSURE LIMITS: NO OCCUPATIONAL EXPOSURE LIMITS ESTABLISHED BY OSHA, ACGIH, OR NIOSH.

PHYSICAL DATA

DESCRIPTION: COLORLESS, CRYSTALLINE SOLID.

MELTING POINT: 189-190 F (87-88 C)

SPECIFIC GRAVITY: NOT AVAILABLE ***VAPOR PRESSURE:*** 0.0000018 MMHG @ 25C

SOLUBILITY IN WATER: 0.00228% @ 23 C

SOLVENT SOLUBILITY: SOLUBLE IN ACETONE, CYCLOHEXANONE, AND XYLENE; SLIGHTLY SOLUBLE IN LIGHT PETROLEUM.

FIRE AND EXPLOSION DATA

FIRE AND EXPLOSION HAZARD: SLIGHT FIRE HAZARD WHEN EXPOSED TO HEAT OR FLAME.

FIREFIGHTING MEDIA: DRY CHEMICAL, CARBON DIOXIDE, HALON, WATER SPRAY OR STANDARD FOAM (1987 EMERGENCY RESPONSE GUIDEBOOK, DOT P 5800.4).

FOR LARGER FIRES, USE WATER SPRAY, FOG OR STANDARD FOAM (1987 EMERGENCY RESPONSE GUIDEBOOK, DOT P 5800.4).

FIREFIGHTING: MOVE CONTAINER FROM FIRE AREA IF POSSIBLE. DO NOT SCATTER SPILLED MATERIAL WITH HIGH PRESSURE WATER STREAMS. DIKE FIRE CONTROL WATER FOR LATER DISPOSAL (1987 EMERGENCY RESPONSE GUIDEBOOK, DOT P 5800.4, GUIDE PAGE 31).

USE AGENTS SUITABLE FOR TYPE OF SURROUNDING FIRE. AVOID BREATHING HAZARDOUS VAPORS, KEEP UPWIND.

TOXICITY

MONALIDE: TOXICITY DATA: 2600 MG/KG SKIN-RABBIT LD50; 2600 MG/KG ORAL-RAT LD50; 4000 MG/KG UNREPORTED-MAMMAL LD50. CARCINOGEN STATUS: NONE. ACUTE TOXICITY LEVEL: MODERATELY TOXIC BY INGESTION; SLIGHTLY TOXIC BY DERMAL ABSORPTION. TARGET EFFECTS: NO DATA AVAILABLE.

HEALTH EFFECTS AND FIRST AID

INHALATION: MONALIDE: **ACUTE EXPOSURE**- NO DATA AVAILABLE. **CHRONIC EXPOSURE**- NO DATA AVAILABLE.

FIRST AID- REMOVE FROM EXPOSURE AREA TO FRESH AIR IMMEDIATELY. IF BREATHING HAS STOPPED, PERFORM ARTIFICIAL RESPIRATION. KEEP PERSON WARM AND AT REST. TREAT SYMPTOMATICALLY AND SUPPORTIVELY. GET MEDICAL ATTENTION IMMEDIATELY.

SKIN CONTACT: MONALIDE: **ACUTE EXPOSURE**- A LETHAL DOSE IN RABBITS BY DERMAL ABSORPTION WAS 2600 MG/KG; NO SYMPTOMS WERE REPORTED. **CHRONIC EXPOSURE**- NO DATA AVAILABLE.

FIRST AID- REMOVE CONTAMINATED CLOTHING AND SHOES IMMEDIATELY. WASH AFFECTED AREA WITH SOAP OR MILD DETERGENT AND LARGE AMOUNTS OF WATER UNTIL NO EVIDENCE OF CHEMICAL REMAINS (APPROXIMATELY 15-20 MINUTES). GET MEDICAL ATTENTION IMMEDIATELY.

EYE CONTACT: MONALIDE: **ACUTE EXPOSURE**- NO DATA AVAILABLE. **CHRONIC EXPOSURE**- NO DATA AVAILABLE.

FIRST AID- WASH EYES IMMEDIATELY WITH LARGE AMOUNTS OF WATER OR NORMAL SALINE, OCCASIONALLY LIFTING UPPER AND LOWER LIDS, UNTIL NO EVIDENCE OF CHEMICAL REMAINS (APPROXIMATELY 15-20 MINUTES). GET MEDICAL ATTENTION IMMEDIATELY.

INGESTION: MONALIDE: **ACUTE EXPOSURE**- A LETHAL DOSE IN RATS WAS 2600 MG/KG; SYMPTOMS WERE NOT REPORTED. **CHRONIC EXPOSURE**- NO OBSERVABLE EFFECTS WERE NOTED IN A 28-DAY STUDY OF RATS FED 150 MG/KG/DAY.

FIRST AID- REMOVE BY GASTRIC LAVAGE AND CATHARSIS. MAINTAIN BLOOD PRESSURE AND AIRWAY. GIVE OXYGEN IF RESPIRATION IS DEPRESSED. DO NOT PERFORM GASTRIC LAVAGE IF VICTIM IS UNCONSCIOUS. GET MEDICAL ATTENTION IMMEDIATELY (DREISBACH, HANDBOOK OF POISONING, 12TH ED.).

ADMINISTRATION OF LAVAGE OR OXYGEN SHOULD BE PERFORMED BY QUALIFIED MEDICAL PERSONNEL.

ANTIDOTE: NO SPECIFIC ANTIDOTE. TREAT SYMPTOMATICALLY AND SUPPORTIVELY.

REACTIVITY

REACTIVITY: STABLE UNDER NORMAL TEMPERATURES AND PRESSURES.

INCOMPATIBILITIES: MONALIDE: OXIDIZERS (STRONG): FIRE AND EXPLOSION HAZARD.

DECOMPOSITION: THERMAL DECOMPOSITION PRODUCTS MAY INCLUDE TOXIC OXIDES OF NITROGEN AND CARBON AND TOXIC AND CORROSIVE FUMES OF CHLORIDES.

POLYMERIZATION: HAZARDOUS POLYMERIZATION HAS NOT BEEN REPORTED TO OCCUR UNDER NORMAL TEMPERATURES AND PRESSURES.

STORAGE AND DISPOSAL

OBSERVE ALL FEDERAL, STATE AND LOCAL REGULATIONS WHEN STORING OR DISPOSING OF THIS SUBSTANCE. FOR ASSISTANCE, CONTACT THE DISTRICT DIRECTOR OF THE ENVIRONMENTAL PROTECTION AGENCY.

STORAGE

STORE IN ACCORDANCE WITH 40 CFR 165 RECOMMENDED PROCEDURES FOR THE DISPOSAL AND STORAGE OF PESTICIDES AND PESTICIDE CONTAINERS.

STORE AWAY FROM INCOMPATIBLE SUBSTANCES.

DO NOT STORE BELOW 23 F (-5 C).

DISPOSAL

DISPOSAL MUST BE IN ACCORDANCE WITH 40 CFR 165 RECOMMENDED PROCEDURES FOR THE DISPOSAL AND STORAGE OF PESTICIDES AND PESTICIDE CONTAINERS.

CONDITIONS TO AVOID

MAY BURN BUT DOES NOT IGNITE READILY. AVOID CONTACT WITH STRONG OXIDIZERS, EXCESSIVE HEAT, SPARKS, OR OPEN FLAME.

SPILL AND LEAK PROCEDURES

OCCUPATIONAL SPILL: SWEEP UP AND PLACE IN SUITABLE CLEAN, DRY CONTAINERS FOR RECLAMATION OR LATER DISPOSAL. DO NOT FLUSH SPILLED MATERIAL INTO SEWER. KEEP UNNECESSARY PEOPLE AWAY.

PROTECTIVE EQUIPMENT

VENTILATION: PROVIDE LOCAL EXHAUST OR GENERAL DILUTION VENTILATION SYSTEM.

RESPIRATOR: THE FOLLOWING RESPIRATORS ARE RECOMMENDED BASED ON INFORMATION FOUND IN THE PHYSICAL DATA, TOXICITY AND HEALTH EFFECTS SECTIONS. THEY ARE RANKED IN ORDER FROM MINIMUM TO MAXIMUM RESPIRATORY PROTECTION. THE SPECIFIC RESPIRATOR SELECTED MUST BE BASED ON CONTAMINATION LEVELS FOUND IN THE WORK PLACE, MUST NOT EXCEED THE WORKING LIMITS OF THE RESPIRATOR AND BE JOINTLY APPROVED BY THE NATIONAL INSTITUTE FOR OCCUPATIONAL SAFETY AND HEALTH AND THE MINE SAFETY AND HEALTH ADMINISTRATION (NIOSH-MSHA).

CHEMICAL CARTRIDGE RESPIRATOR WITH AN ORGANIC VAPOR CARTRIDGE(S) WITH A FULL FACEPIECE AND ORGANIC VAPOR CARTRIDGE(S) IN COMBINATION WITH A DUST AND MIST FILTER.

POWERED AIR-PURIFYING RESPIRATOR WITH A TIGHT-FITTING FACEPIECE AND ORGANIC VAPOR CARTRIDGE(S) IN COMBINATION WITH A HIGH-EFFICIENCY PARTICULATE FILTER.

TYPE 'C' SUPPLIED-AIR RESPIRATOR WITH A FULL FACEPIECE OPERATED IN A PRESSURE-DEMAND OR OTHER POSITIVE PRESSURE MODE.

SELF-CONTAINED BREATHING APPARATUS WITH A FULL FACEPIECE OPERATED IN PRESSURE-DEMAND OR OTHER POSITIVE PRESSURE MODE.

FOR FIREFIGHTING AND OTHER IMMEDIATELY DANGEROUS TO LIFE OR HEALTH CONDITIONS:

SELF-CONTAINED BREATHING APPARATUS WITH FULL FACEPIECE OPERATED IN PRESSURE-DEMAND OR OTHER POSITIVE PRESSURE MODE.

SUPPLIED-AIR RESPIRATOR WITH FULL FACEPIECE AND OPERATED IN PRESSURE-DEMAND OR OTHER POSITIVE PRESSURE MODE IN COMBINATION WITH AN AUXILIARY SELF-CONTAINED BREATHING APPARATUS OPERATED IN PRESSURE-DEMAND OR OTHER POSITIVE PRESSURE MODE.

CLOTHING: EMPLOYEE MUST WEAR APPROPRIATE PROTECTIVE (IMPERVIOUS) CLOTHING AND EQUIPMENT TO PREVENT REPEATED OR PROLONGED SKIN CONTACT WITH THIS SUBSTANCE.

GLOVES: EMPLOYEE MUST WEAR APPROPRIATE PROTECTIVE GLOVES TO PREVENT CONTACT WITH THIS SUBSTANCE.

EYE PROTECTION: EMPLOYEE MUST WEAR SPLASH-PROOF OR DUST-RESISTANT SAFETY GOGGLES TO PREVENT EYE CONTACT WITH THIS SUBSTANCE.

EMERGENCY EYE WASH: WHERE THERE IS ANY POSSIBILITY THAT AN EMPLOYEE'S EYES MAY BE EXPOSED TO THIS SUBSTANCE, THE EMPLOYER SHOULD PROVIDE AN EYE WASH FOUNTAIN WITHIN THE IMMEDIATE WORK AREA FOR EMERGENCY USE.

AUTHORIZED BY- OCCUPATIONAL HEALTH SERVICES, INC.
CREATION DATE: 10/04/89 ***REVISION DATE:*** 05/31/90

MATERIAL SAFETY DATA SHEET

OCCUPATIONAL HEALTH SERVICES, INC.
AGRICULTURE AND PESTICIDE DIVISION
450 SEVENTH AVENUE, SUITE 2407
NEW YORK, NEW YORK 10123
1-800-445-MSDS OR (212) 967-1100

EMERGENCY CONTACT:
JOHN S. BRANSFORD, JR. (615) 292-1180

SUBSTANCE IDENTIFICATION

CAS-NUMBER 29104-30-1
SUBSTANCE: **BENZOXIMATE**
TRADE NAMES/SYNONYMS: BENZOIC ACID, ANHYDRIDE WITH 3-CHLORO-N-ETHOXY-2,6-DIMETHOXYBENZENE CARBOXIMIDIC ACID; BENZOIC ACID, ANHYDRIDE WITH 3-CHLORO-N-ETHOXY-2,6-DIMETHOXYBENZIMIDIC ACID; ETHYL-O-BENZOYL-3-CHLORO-2,6-DIMETHOXYBENZOHYDROXIMATE; 3-CHLORO-ALPHA-ETHOXYIMINO-2,6-DIMETHOXYBENZYL BENZOATE; AAZOMATE; BENZOMATE; CITRAZON; ARTABAN; C18H18CLNO5; PST72988
CHEMICAL FAMILY: ESTER
AROMATIC
IMIDE
MOLECULAR FORMULA: C18-H18-CL-N-O5
MOLECULAR WEIGHT: 364
CERCLA RATINGS (SCALE 0-3): HEALTH=1 FIRE=1 REACTIVITY=0 PERSISTENCE=3
NFPA RATINGS (SCALE 0-4): HEALTH=1 FIRE=1 REACTIVITY=0

COMPONENTS AND CONTAMINANTS

COMPONENT: BENZOXIMATE ***PERCENT:*** 100
CAS# 29104-30-1
OTHER CONTAMINANTS: NONE
EXPOSURE LIMITS: NO OCCUPATIONAL EXPOSURE LIMITS ESTABLISHED BY OSHA, ACGIH, OR NIOSH.

PHYSICAL DATA

DESCRIPTION: COLORLESS, CRYSTALLINE SOLID ***MELTING POINT:*** 163 F (73 C)
SPECIFIC GRAVITY: NOT AVAILABLE ***SOLUBILITY IN WATER:*** ALMOST INSOLUBLE
SOLVENT SOLUBILITY: SOLUBLE IN BENZENE, DIMETHYLFORMAMIDE, XYLENE, HEXANE.

FIRE AND EXPLOSION DATA

FIRE AND EXPLOSION HAZARD: SLIGHT FIRE HAZARD WHEN EXPOSED TO HEAT OR FLAME.
FIREFIGHTING MEDIA: DRY CHEMICAL, CARBON DIOXIDE, HALON, WATER SPRAY OR STANDARD FOAM (1987 EMERGENCY RESPONSE GUIDEBOOK, DOT P 5800.4).
FOR LARGER FIRES, USE WATER SPRAY, FOG OR STANDARD FOAM (1987 EMERGENCY RESPONSE GUIDEBOOK, DOT P 5800.4).
FIREFIGHTING: MOVE CONTAINERS FROM FIRE AREA IF POSSIBLE (1987 EMERGENCY RESPONSE GUIDEBOOK, DOT P 5800.4, GUIDE PAGE 53).
EXTINGUISH ONLY IF FLOW CAN BE STOPPED; USE FLOODING AMOUNTS OF WATER AS FOG, SOLID STREAMS MAY NOT BE EFFECTIVE. COOL CONTAINERS WITH FLOODING AMOUNTS OF WATER, APPLY FROM AS FAR A DISTANCE AS POSSIBLE. AVOID BREATHING POISONOUS VAPORS, KEEP UPWIND.

TOXICITY

BENZOXIMATE: TOXICITY DATA: >15,000 MG/KG SKIN-RAT LD50 (85JFAN); >15,000 MG/KG SKIN-MOUSE LD50 (85JFAN); 15,000 MG/KG ORAL-RAT LD50; 12 GM/KG ORAL-MOUSE LD50; 4217 MG/KG INTRAPERITONEAL-RAT LD50; 4264 MG/KG INTRAPERITONEAL-MOUSE LD50. CARCINOGEN STATUS: NONE. ACUTE TOXICITY LEVEL: SLIGHTLY TOXIC BY DERMAL ABSORPTION AND INGESTION. TARGET EFFECTS: NO DATA AVAILABLE.

HEALTH EFFECTS AND FIRST AID

INHALATION: BENZOXIMATE: **ACUTE EXPOSURE**- NO DATA AVAILABLE. **CHRONIC EXPOSURE**- NO DATA AVAILABLE.
FIRST AID- REMOVE FROM EXPOSURE AREA TO FRESH AIR IMMEDIATELY. IF BREATHING HAS STOPPED, PERFORM ARTIFICIAL RESPIRATION. KEEP PERSON WARM AND AT REST. TREAT SYMPTOMATICALLY AND SUPPORTIVELY. GET MEDICAL ATTENTION IMMEDIATELY.

SKIN CONTACT: BENZOXIMATE: **ACUTE EXPOSURE**- A LETHAL DOSE IN RATS AND MICE BY DERMAL ABSORPTION IS GREATER THAN 15,000 MG/KG. **CHRONIC EXPOSURE**- NO DATA AVAILABLE.
FIRST AID- REMOVE CONTAMINATED CLOTHING AND SHOES IMMEDIATELY. WASH AFFECTED AREA WITH SOAP OR MILD DETERGENT AND LARGE AMOUNTS OF WATER UNTIL NO EVIDENCE OF CHEMICAL REMAINS (APPROXIMATELY 15-20 MINUTES). GET MEDICAL ATTENTION IMMEDIATELY.

EYE CONTACT: BENZOXIMATE: **ACUTE EXPOSURE**- NO DATA AVAILABLE. **CHRONIC EXPOSURE**- NO DATA AVAILABLE.
FIRST AID- WASH EYES IMMEDIATELY WITH LARGE AMOUNTS OF WATER OR NORMAL SALINE, OCCASIONALLY LIFTING UPPER AND LOWER LIDS, UNTIL NO EVIDENCE OF CHEMICAL REMAINS (APPROXIMATELY 15-20 MINUTES). GET MEDICAL ATTENTION IMMEDIATELY.

INGESTION: BENZOXIMATE: **ACUTE EXPOSURE**- A LETHAL DOSE IN RATS WAS 15000 MG/KG; NO SYMPTOMS WERE REPORTED. **CHRONIC EXPOSURE**- NO ADVERSE EFFECTS WERE OBSERVED IN A TWO-YEAR STUDY OF RATS FED 400 MG/KG.
FIRST AID- TREAT SYMPTOMATICALLY AND SUPPORTIVELY. GET MEDICAL ATTENTION IMMEDIATELY. IF VOMITING OCCURS, KEEP HEAD LOWER THAN HIPS TO PREVENT ASPIRATION.
ANTIDOTE: NO SPECIFIC ANTIDOTE. TREAT SYMPTOMATICALLY AND SUPPORTIVELY.

REACTIVITY

REACTIVITY: STABLE UNDER NORMAL TEMPERATURES AND PRESSURES.
INCOMPATIBILITIES: BENZOXIMATE: OXIDIZERS (STRONG): FIRE AND EXPLOSION HAZARD.
DECOMPOSITION: THERMAL DECOMPOSITION PRODUCTS MAY INCLUDE TOXIC OXIDES OF NITROGEN.
POLYMERIZATION: HAZARDOUS POLYMERIZATION HAS NOT BEEN REPORTED TO OCCUR UNDER NORMAL TEMPERATURES AND PRESSURES.

STORAGE AND DISPOSAL

OBSERVE ALL FEDERAL, STATE AND LOCAL REGULATIONS WHEN STORING OR DISPOSING OF THIS SUBSTANCE. FOR ASSISTANCE, CONTACT THE DISTRICT DIRECTOR OF THE ENVIRONMENTAL PROTECTION AGENCY.

STORAGE

STORE IN ACCORDANCE WITH 40 CFR 165 RECOMMENDED PROCEDURES FOR THE DISPOSAL AND STORAGE OF PESTICIDES AND PESTICIDE CONTAINERS.
STORE AWAY FROM INCOMPATIBLE SUBSTANCES.

DISPOSAL

DISPOSAL MUST BE IN ACCORDANCE WITH 40 CFR 165 RECOMMENDED PROCEDURES FOR THE DISPOSAL AND STORAGE OF PESTICIDES AND PESTICIDE CONTAINERS.

CONDITIONS TO AVOID

MAY BURN BUT DOES NOT IGNITE READILY.

SPILL AND LEAK PROCEDURES

OCCUPATIONAL SPILL: DO NOT TOUCH SPILLED MATERIAL. STOP LEAK IF YOU CAN DO IT WITHOUT RISK. FOR SMALL SPILLS, TAKE UP WITH SAND OR OTHER ABSORBENT MATERIAL AND PLACE INTO CONTAINERS FOR LATER DISPOSAL. FOR SMALL DRY SPILLS, WITH A CLEAN SHOVEL PLACE MATERIAL INTO CLEAN, DRY CONTAINER AND COVER. MOVE CONTAINERS FROM SPILL AREA. FOR LARGER SPILLS, DIKE FAR AHEAD OF SPILL FOR LATER DISPOSAL. KEEP UNNECESSARY PEOPLE AWAY. ISOLATE HAZARD AREA AND DENY ENTRY.

PROTECTIVE EQUIPMENT

VENTILATION: PROVIDE GENERAL DILUTION VENTILATION.
RESPIRATOR: THE FOLLOWING RESPIRATORS ARE RECOMMENDED BASED ON INFORMATION FOUND IN THE PHYSICAL DATA, TOXICITY AND HEALTH EFFECTS SECTIONS. THEY ARE RANKED IN ORDER FROM MINIMUM TO MAXIMUM RESPIRATORY PROTECTION. THE SPECIFIC RESPIRATOR SELECTED MUST BE BASED ON CONTAMINATION LEVELS FOUND IN THE WORK PLACE, MUST NOT EXCEED THE WORKING LIMITS OF THE RESPIRATOR AND BE JOINTLY APPROVED BY THE NATIONAL INSTITUTE FOR OCCUPATIONAL SAFETY AND HEALTH AND THE MINE SAFETY AND HEALTH ADMINISTRATION (NIOSH-MSHA).
CHEMICAL CARTRIDGE RESPIRATOR WITH AN ORGANIC VAPOR CARTRIDGE(S) WITH A FULL FACEPIECE AND ORGANIC VAPOR CARTRIDGE(S) IN COMBINATION WITH A DUST AND MIST FILTER.
POWERED AIR-PURIFYING RESPIRATOR WITH A TIGHT-FITTING FACEPIECE AND ORGANIC VAPOR CARTRIDGE(S) IN COMBINATION WITH A HIGH-EFFICIENCY PARTICULATE FILTER.
TYPE 'C' SUPPLIED-AIR RESPIRATOR WITH A FULL FACEPIECE OPERATED IN A PRESSURE-DEMAND OR OTHER POSITIVE PRESSURE MODE.

SELF-CONTAINED BREATHING APPARATUS WITH A FULL FACEPIECE OPERATED IN PRESSURE-DEMAND OR OTHER POSITIVE PRESSURE MODE.
FOR FIREFIGHTING AND OTHER IMMEDIATELY DANGEROUS TO LIFE OR HEALTH CONDITIONS:
SELF-CONTAINED BREATHING APPARATUS WITH FULL FACEPIECE OPERATED IN PRESSURE-DEMAND OR OTHER POSITIVE PRESSURE MODE.
SUPPLIED-AIR RESPIRATOR WITH FULL FACEPIECE AND OPERATED IN PRESSURE-DEMAND OR OTHER POSITIVE PRESSURE MODE IN COMBINATION WITH AN AUXILIARY SELF-CONTAINED BREATHING APPARATUS OPERATED IN PRESSURE-DEMAND OR OTHER POSITIVE PRESSURE MODE.

CLOTHING: EMPLOYEE MUST WEAR APPROPRIATE PROTECTIVE (IMPERVIOUS) CLOTHING AND EQUIPMENT TO PREVENT REPEATED OR PROLONGED SKIN CONTACT WITH THIS SUBSTANCE.

GLOVES: EMPLOYEE MUST WEAR APPROPRIATE PROTECTIVE GLOVES TO PREVENT CONTACT WITH THIS SUBSTANCE.

EYE PROTECTION: EMPLOYEE MUST WEAR SPLASH-PROOF OR DUST-RESISTANT SAFETY GOGGLES TO PREVENT EYE CONTACT WITH THIS SUBSTANCE.
EMERGENCY EYE WASH: WHERE THERE IS ANY POSSIBILITY THAT AN EMPLOYEE'S EYES MAY BE EXPOSED TO THIS SUBSTANCE, THE EMPLOYER SHOULD PROVIDE AN EYE WASH FOUNTAIN WITHIN THE IMMEDIATE WORK AREA FOR EMERGENCY USE.

AUTHORIZED BY- OCCUPATIONAL HEALTH SERVICES, INC.
CREATION DATE: 02/08/90 ***REVISION DATE:*** 05/10/90

MATERIAL SAFETY DATA SHEET

OCCUPATIONAL HEALTH SERVICES, INC.
AGRICULTURE AND PESTICIDE DIVISION
450 SEVENTH AVENUE, SUITE 2407
NEW YORK, NEW YORK 10123
1-800-445-MSDS OR (212) 967-1100

EMERGENCY CONTACT:
JOHN S. BRANSFORD, JR. (615) 292-1180

SUBSTANCE IDENTIFICATION

CAS-NUMBER 2655-19-8

SUBSTANCE: **BUTACARB**

TRADE NAMES/SYNONYMS: PHENOL, 3,5-BIS(1,1-DIMETHYLETHYL)-, METHYLCARBAMATE; CARBAMIC ACID, METHYL-, 3,5-DI-TERT-BUTYLPHENYL ESTER; 3,5-BIS(1,1-DIMETHYLETHYL)PHENOL METHYLCARBAMATE; METHYLCARBAMIC ACID 3,5-DI-TERT-BUTYLPHENYL ESTER; 3,5-BIS(1,1-DIMETHYLETHYL)PHENYL METHYLCARBAMATE; 3,5-DI-TERT-BUTYLPHENYL METHYLCARBAMATE; BUTACARBE; RD 14639; C16H25NO2; PST72994

CHEMICAL FAMILY: CARBAMATE

MOLECULAR FORMULA: C16-H25-N-O2

MOLECULAR WEIGHT: 263.42

CERCLA RATINGS (SCALE 0-3): HEALTH=2 FIRE=1 REACTIVITY=0 PERSISTENCE=1

NFPA RATINGS (SCALE 0-4): HEALTH=U FIRE=1 REACTIVITY=0

COMPONENTS AND CONTAMINANTS

COMPONENT: BUTACARB ***PERCENT:*** 100.0
CAS# 2655-19-8

OTHER CONTAMINANTS: NONE

EXPOSURE LIMITS: NO OCCUPATIONAL EXPOSURE LIMITS ESTABLISHED BY OSHA, ACGIH, OR NIOSH.

PHYSICAL DATA

DESCRIPTION: WHITE CRYSTALLINE SOLID. ***MELTING POINT:*** 216-217 F (102-103 C)

SPECIFIC GRAVITY: NOT AVAILABLE ***SOLUBILITY IN WATER:*** NOT AVAILABLE

SOLVENT SOLUBILITY: SOLUBLE IN ORGANIC SOLVENTS.

FIRE AND EXPLOSION DATA

FIRE AND EXPLOSION HAZARD: SLIGHT FIRE HAZARD WHEN EXPOSED TO HEAT OR FLAME.

FIREFIGHTING MEDIA: DRY CHEMICAL, CARBON DIOXIDE, HALON, WATER SPRAY OR STANDARD FOAM (1987 EMERGENCY RESPONSE GUIDEBOOK, DOT P 5800.4).
FOR LARGER FIRES, USE WATER SPRAY, FOG OR STANDARD FOAM (1987 EMERGENCY RESPONSE GUIDEBOOK, DOT P 5800.4).

FIREFIGHTING: MOVE CONTAINERS FROM FIRE AREA IF POSSIBLE. FIGHT FIRE FROM MAXIMUM DISTANCE. STAY AWAY FROM STORAGE TANK ENDS. DIKE FIRE CONTROL WATER FOR LATER DISPOSAL. DO NOT SCATTER MATERIAL (1987 EMERGENCY RESPONSE GUIDEBOOK, DOT P 5800.4, GUIDE PAGE 55).
EXTINGUISH USING AGENTS SUITABLE FOR TYPE OF SURROUNDING FIRE. USE FLOODING AMOUNTS OF WATER AS FOG. AVOID BREATHING TOXIC DUST AND FUMES FROM BURNING MATERIAL; KEEP UPWIND.

TOXICITY

BUTACARB: TOXICITY DATA: 1800 MG/KG ORAL-RAT LD50; 3200 MG/KG ORAL-MOUSE LD50; 1000 MG/KG ORAL-DOG LD50. CARCINOGEN STATUS: NONE. ACUTE TOXICITY: MODERATELY TOXIC BY INGESTION. TARGET EFFECTS: CHOLINESTERASE INHIBITOR. AT INCREASED RISK FROM EXPOSURE: PERSONS WITH ASTHMA, DIABETES, CARDIOVASCULAR DISEASE, MECHANICAL OBSTRUCTION OF THE GASTROINTESTINAL OR UROGENITAL TRACT, AND THOSE IN VAGOTONIC STATES.*
* MAY BE BASED ON GENERAL INFORMATION ON CARBAMATES.

HEALTH EFFECTS AND FIRST AID

INHALATION: BUTACARB: SEE INFORMATION ON CARBAMATES.
CARBAMATES: CHOLINESTERASE INHIBITOR. **ACUTE EXPOSURE-** WHEN INHALED, THE FIRST EFFECTS OF CHOLINESTERASE INHIBITION ARE USUALLY RESPIRATORY AND MAY INCLUDE NASAL HYPEREMIA AND WATERY DISCHARGE, CHEST DISCOMFORT, DYSPNEA, AND WHEEZING DUE TO INCREASED BRONCHIAL SECRETIONS AND BRONCHOCONSTRICTION. OTHER SYSTEMIC EFFECTS MAY BEGIN WITHIN A FEW MINUTES OR SEVERAL HOURS OF EXPOSURE. SYMPTOMS MAY INCLUDE NAUSEA, VOMITING, DIARRHEA, ABDOMINAL CRAMPS, HEADACHE, VERTIGO, OCULAR PAIN, CILIARY MUSCLE SPASM, BLURRING OR DIMNESS OF VISION, MIOSIS, OR IN SOME CASES MYDRIASIS, LACRIMATION, SALIVATION, SWEATING, AND CONFUSION. OTHER REPORTED CENTRAL NERVOUS SYSTEM OR NEUROMUSCULAR EFFECTS INCLUDE ATAXIA, SLURRED SPEECH, AREFLEXIA, WEAKNESS, FATIGUE, TWITCHING, FASCICULATION, TREMOR, AND EVENTUALLY PARALYSIS OF THE EXTREMITIES AND POSSIBLY OF THE RESPIRATORY MUSCLES. IN SEVERE CASES, THERE MAY ALSO BE INVOLUNTARY DEFECATION AND URINATION, BRADYCARDIA, HYPOTENSION, PULMONARY EDEMA, CONVULSIONS, COMA, AND DEATH FROM RESPIRATORY FAILURE OR CARDIAC ARREST. CARBAMATES GENERALLY DO NOT ACCUMULATE IN MAMMALIAN TISSUE AND THE CHOLINESTERASE INHIBITION REVERSES RATHER RAPIDLY. IN NON-FATAL CASES, THE ILLNESS GENERALLY LASTS LESS THAN 24 HOURS. **CHRONIC EXPOSURE-** PROLONGED OR REPEATED EXPOSURE MAY CAUSE EFFECTS AS DESCRIBED IN ACUTE EXPOSURE.

FIRST AID- REMOVE FROM EXPOSURE AREA TO FRESH AIR IMMEDIATELY. IF BREATHING HAS STOPPED, GIVE ARTIFICIAL RESPIRATION. MAINTAIN AIRWAY AND BLOOD PRESSURE AND ADMINISTER OXYGEN IF AVAILABLE. KEEP AFFECTED PERSON WARM AND AT REST. TREAT SYMPTOMATICALLY AND SUPPORTIVELY. ADMINISTRATION OF OXYGEN SHOULD BE PERFORMED BY QUALIFIED PERSONNEL. GET MEDICAL ATTENTION IMMEDIATELY.

SKIN CONTACT: BUTACARB: SEE INFORMATION ON CARBAMATES.
CARBAMATES: CHOLINESTERASE INHIBITOR. **ACUTE EXPOSURE-** SOME COMPOUNDS MAY CAUSE IRRITATION. LOCALIZED SWEATING AND FASCICULATIONS MAY OCCUR AT THE SITE OF CONTACT. IF SUFFICIENT AMOUNTS ARE ABSORBED THROUGH THE SKIN, OTHER EFFECTS OF CHOLINESTERASE INHIBITION MAY OCCUR AS DESCRIBED IN ACUTE INHALATION; SYMPTOMS MAY BE DELAYED FOR 2-3 HOURS, USUALLY NO MORE THAN 8 HOURS. **CHRONIC EXPOSURE-** REPEATED OR PROLONGED EXPOSURE MAY CAUSE EFFECTS AS DESCRIBED IN ACUTE EXPOSURE.

FIRST AID- REMOVE CONTAMINATED CLOTHING IMMEDIATELY. WASH CONTAMINATED AREAS WITH SOAP AND WATER FOLLOWED BY ALCOHOL (ARENA, POISONING, 4TH ED.). EMERGENCY PERSONNEL SHOULD WEAR GLOVES AND AVOID CONTAMINATION. TREAT RESPIRATORY DIFFICULTY WITH ARTIFICIAL RESPIRATION. GET MEDICAL ATTENTION IMMEDIATELY.

EYE CONTACT: BUTACARB: SEE INFORMATION ON CARBAMATES.
CARBAMATES: CHOLINESTERASE INHIBITOR. **ACUTE EXPOSURE-** DIRECT CONTACT MAY CAUSE PAIN, HYPEREMIA, LACRIMATION, TWITCHING OF THE EYELIDS, MIOSIS, AND CILIARY MUSCLE SPASM WITH LOSS OF ACCOMODATION, BLURRED OR DIMMED VISION AND BROWACHE. SOMETIMES MYDRIASIS MAY OCCUR INSTEAD OF MIOSIS. WITH SUFFICIENT EXPOSURE, OTHER SYMPTOMS OF CHOLINESTERASE INHIBITION MAY OCCUR AS DESCRIBED IN ACUTE INHALATION. **CHRONIC EXPOSURE-** PROLONGED EXPOSURE MAY CAUSE EFFECTS AS DESCRIBED IN ACUTE EXPOSURE. SOME COMPOUNDS HAVE CAUSED TOXIC EFFECTS ON THE CRYSTALLINE LENS, CONJUNCTIVAL THICKENING AND OBSTRUCTION OF NASOLACRIMAL CANALS WHEN USED AS MIOTIC EYE DROPS.

FIRST AID- IRRIGATE EYES WITH WATER OR SALINE SOLUTION. IF SYMPTOMS OF POISONING OCCUR, TREAT RESPIRATORY DIFFICULTY WITH ARTIFICIAL RESPIRATION AND OXYGEN. OBSERVE PATIENT FOR AT LEAST 24-36 HOURS (GOSSELIN, CLINICAL TOXICOLOGY OF COMMERCIAL PRODUCTS, 5TH ED.). GET

MEDICAL ATTENTION IMMEDIATELY. OXYGEN SHOULD BE ADMINISTERED BY QUALIFIED MEDICAL PERSONNEL.

INGESTION: BUTACARB: NO OBSERVABLE EFFECTS WERE NOTED IN DOGS RECEIVING 160 MG/KG/DAY FOR 90 DAYS. SEE INFORMATION ON CARBAMATES.
CARBAMATES: CHOLINESTERASE INHIBITOR. **ACUTE EXPOSURE**- WHEN INGESTED, THE FIRST EFFECTS MAY BE NAUSEA, VOMITING, ANOREXIA, ABDOMINAL CRAMPS, AND DIARRHEA. WITH ABSORPTION FROM THE GASTROINTESTINAL TRACT, THE OTHER EFFECTS OF CHOLINESTERASE INHIBITION AS DESCRIBED IN ACUTE INHALATION MAY OCCUR; SYMPTOMS MAY BEGIN WITHIN MINUTES OR BE DELAYED SEVERAL HOURS. **CHRONIC EXPOSURE**- REPEATED INGESTION MAY CAUSE EFFECTS AS DESCRIBED IN ACUTE EXPOSURE.

FIRST AID- IF PERSON IS ALERT AND RESPIRATION IS NOT DEPRESSED, GIVE SYRUP OF IPECAC FOLLOWED BY WATER (IF VOMITING OCCURS, KEEP HEAD BELOW HIPS TO PREVENT ASPIRATION). IF CONSCIOUSNESS LEVEL DECLINES OR VOMITING HAS NOT OCCURRED IN 15 MINUTES EMPTY STOMACH BY GASTRIC LAVAGE WITH THE AID OF CUFFED ENDOTRACHEAL TUBE USING ISOTONIC SALINE OR 5% SODIUM BICARBONATE FOLLOW WITH ACTIVATED CHARCOAL. ESTABLISH AND MAINTAIN AIRWAY. TREAT RESPIRATORY DIFFICULTY WITH ARTIFICIAL RESPIRATION AND OXYGEN. DO NOT GIVE MORPHINE, AMINOPHYLLINE, PHENOTHIAZINES, RESERPINE, FUROSEMIDE, OR ETHACRYNIC ACID (MORGAN, RECOGNITION AND MANAGEMENT OF PESTICIDE POISONINGS, 3RD ED.). TREAT SYMPTOMATICALLY AND SUPPORTIVELY. ADMINISTRATION OF OXYGEN AND LAVAGE MUST BE PERFORMED BY QUALIFIED MEDICAL PERSONNEL. GET MEDICAL ATTENTION IMMEDIATELY.

ANTIDOTE: THE FOLLOWING ANTIDOTE HAS BEEN RECOMMENDED. HOWEVER, THE DECISION AS TO WHETHER THE SEVERITY OF POISONING REQUIRES ADMINISTRATION OF ANY ANTIDOTE AND ACTUAL DOSE REQUIRED SHOULD BE MADE BY QUALIFIED MEDICAL PERSONNEL.
FOR CHOLINESTERASE INHIBITORS: ESTABLISH CLEAR AIRWAY AND TISSUE OXYGENATION BY ASPIRATION OF SECRETIONS, AND IF NECESSARY, BY ASSISTED PULMONARY VENTILATION WITH OXYGEN. IMPROVE TISSUE OXYGENATION AS MUCH AS POSSIBLE BEFORE ADMINISTERING ATROPINE TO MINIMIZE THE RISK OF VENTRICULAR FIBRILLATION. ADMINISTER ATROPINE SULFATE INTRAVENOUSLY, OR INTRAMUSCULARLY IF IV INJECTION IS NOT POSSIBLE. IN MODERATELY SEVERE POISONING ADMINISTER ATROPINE SULFATE, 0.4-2.0 MG REPEATED EVERY 15 MINUTES UNTIL ATROPINIZATION IS ACHIEVED (TACHYCARDIA, FLUSHING, DRY MOUTH, MYDRIASIS). MAINTAIN ATROPINIZATION BY REPEATED DOSES FOR 2-12 HOURS, OR LONGER, DEPENDING ON THE SEVERITY OF POISONING. THE APPEARANCE OF RALES IN THE LUNG BASES, MIOSIS, SALIVATION, NAUSEA, BRADYCARDIA, ARE ALL INDICATIONS OF INADEQUATE ATROPINIZATION. SEVERELY POISONED INDIVIDUALS MAY EXHIBIT REMARKABLE TOLERANCE TO ATROPINE; TWO OR MORE TIMES THE DOSAGES SUGGESTED ABOVE MAY BE NEEDED. PERSONS NOT POISONED OR ONLY SLIGHTLY POISONED, HOWEVER, MAY DEVELOP SIGNS OF ATROPINE TOXICITY FROM SUCH LARGE DOSAGES: FEVER, MUSCLE FIBRILLATIONS, AND DELIRIUM ARE THE MAIN SIGNS OF ATROPINE TOXICITY. IF THESE SIGNS APPEAR WHILE THE PATIENT IS FULLY ATROPINIZED, ATROPINE ADMINISTRATION SHOULD BE DISCONTINUED, AT LEAST TEMPORARILY. OBSERVE TREATED PATIENTS CLOSELY AT LEAST 24 HOURS TO INSURE THAT SYMPTOMS (POSSIBLY PULMONARY EDEMA) DO NOT RECUR AS ATROPINIZATION WEARS OFF. IN VERY SEVERE POISONINGS, METABOLIC DISPOSITION OF TOXICANT MAY REQUIRE SEVERAL HOURS OR DAYS DURING WHICH ATROPINIZATION MUST BE MAINTAINED. MARKEDLY LOWER LEVELS OF URINARY METABOLITES INDICATE THAT ATROPINE DOSAGE CAN BE TAPERED OFF. AS DOSAGE IS REDUCED, CHECK THE LUNG BASES FREQUENTLY FOR RALES. IF RALES ARE HEARD OR OTHER SYMPTOMS RETURN, RE-ESTABLISH ATROPINIZATION PROMPTLY (MORGAN, RECOGNITION AND MANAGEMENT OF PESTICIDE POISONINGS, 3RD ED.). ADMINISTRATION OF ANTIDOTE MUST BE PERFORMED BY QUALIFIED MEDICAL PERSONNEL.

REACTIVITY

REACTIVITY: STABLE UNDER NORMAL TEMPERATURES AND PRESSURES.

INCOMPATIBILITIES: BUTACARB: ALKALIS: HYDROLYZES. OXIDIZERS (STRONG): FIRE AND EXPLOSION HAZARD.

DECOMPOSITION: THERMAL DECOMPOSITION PRODUCTS MAY INCLUDE TOXIC OXIDES OF CARBON AND NITROGEN.

POLYMERIZATION: HAZARDOUS POLYMERIZATION HAS NOT BEEN REPORTED TO OCCUR UNDER NORMAL TEMPERATURES AND PRESSURES.

STORAGE AND DISPOSAL

OBSERVE ALL FEDERAL, STATE AND LOCAL REGULATIONS WHEN STORING OR DISPOSING OF THIS SUBSTANCE. FOR ASSISTANCE, CONTACT THE DISTRICT DIRECTOR OF THE ENVIRONMENTAL PROTECTION AGENCY.

****STORAGE****

STORE IN ACCORDANCE WITH 40 CFR 165 RECOMMENDED PROCEDURES FOR THE DISPOSAL AND STORAGE OF PESTICIDES AND PESTICIDE CONTAINERS.
STORE AWAY FROM INCOMPATIBLE SUBSTANCES.

****DISPOSAL****

DISPOSAL MUST BE IN ACCORDANCE WITH 40 CFR 165 RECOMMENDED PROCEDURES FOR THE DISPOSAL AND STORAGE OF PESTICIDES AND PESTICIDE CONTAINERS.

CONDITIONS TO AVOID

MAY BURN BUT DOES NOT IGNITE READILY. CONTAINERS MAY EXPLODE IN HEAT OF FIRE.

SPILL AND LEAK PROCEDURES

OCCUPATIONAL SPILL: DO NOT TOUCH SPILLED MATERIAL. STOP LEAK IF YOU CAN DO IT WITHOUT RISK. USE WATER SPRAY TO REDUCE VAPORS. FOR SMALL SPILLS, TAKE UP WITH SAND OR OTHER ABSORBENT MATERIAL AND PLACE INTO CONTAINERS FOR LATER DISPOSAL. FOR SMALL DRY SPILLS, WITH A CLEAN SHOVEL PLACE MATERIAL INTO CLEAN, DRY CONTAINERS AND COVER. MOVE CONTAINERS FROM SPILL AREA. FOR LARGER SPILLS, DIKE FAR AHEAD OF SPILL FOR LATER DISPOSAL. KEEP UNNECESSARY PEOPLE AWAY. ISOLATE HAZARD AREA AND DENY ENTRY. VENTILATE CLOSED SPACES BEFORE ENTERING.

PROTECTIVE EQUIPMENT

VENTILATION: PROVIDE LOCAL EXHAUST OR GENERAL DILUTION VENTILATION SYSTEM.

RESPIRATOR: THE FOLLOWING RESPIRATORS ARE RECOMMENDED BASED ON INFORMATION FOUND IN THE PHYSICAL DATA, TOXICITY AND HEALTH EFFECTS SECTIONS. THEY ARE RANKED IN ORDER FROM MINIMUM TO MAXIMUM RESPIRATORY PROTECTION. THE SPECIFIC RESPIRATOR SELECTED MUST BE BASED ON CONTAMINATION LEVELS FOUND IN THE WORK PLACE, MUST NOT EXCEED THE WORKING LIMITS OF THE RESPIRATOR AND BE JOINTLY APPROVED BY THE NATIONAL INSTITUTE FOR OCCUPATIONAL SAFETY AND HEALTH AND THE MINE SAFETY AND HEALTH ADMINISTRATION (NIOSH-MSHA).
CHEMICAL CARTRIDGE RESPIRATOR WITH AN ORGANIC VAPOR CARTRIDGE(S) IN COMBINATION WITH A DUST AND MIST FILTER.
GAS MASK WITH ORGANIC VAPOR CANISTER (CHIN-STYLE OR FRONT- OR BACK-MOUNTED CANISTER) WITH A DUST AND MIST FILTER.
GAS MASK WITH ORGANIC VAPOR CANISTER (CHIN-STYLE OR FRONT- OR BACK-MOUNTED CANISTER) WITH A PARTICULATE FILTER.
POWERED AIR-PURIFYING RESPIRATOR WITH A HIGH-EFFICIENCY FILTER.
TYPE 'C' SUPPLIED-AIR RESPIRATOR WITH A FULL FACEPIECE OPERATED IN A PRESSURE-DEMAND OR OTHER POSITIVE PRESSURE MODE.
SELF-CONTAINED BREATHING APPARATUS WITH A FULL FACEPIECE OPERATED IN PRESSURE-DEMAND OR OTHER POSITIVE PRESSURE MODE.
FOR FIREFIGHTING AND OTHER IMMEDIATELY DANGEROUS TO LIFE OR HEALTH CONDITIONS:
SELF-CONTAINED BREATHING APPARATUS WITH FULL FACEPIECE OPERATED IN PRESSURE-DEMAND OR OTHER POSITIVE PRESSURE MODE.
SUPPLIED-AIR RESPIRATOR WITH FULL FACEPIECE AND OPERATED IN PRESSURE-DEMAND OR OTHER POSITIVE PRESSURE MODE IN COMBINATION WITH AN AUXILIARY SELF-CONTAINED BREATHING APPARATUS OPERATED IN PRESSURE-DEMAND OR OTHER POSITIVE PRESSURE MODE.

CLOTHING: EMPLOYEE MUST WEAR APPROPRIATE PROTECTIVE (IMPERVIOUS) CLOTHING AND EQUIPMENT TO PREVENT REPEATED OR PROLONGED SKIN CONTACT WITH THIS SUBSTANCE.

GLOVES: EMPLOYEE MUST WEAR APPROPRIATE PROTECTIVE GLOVES TO PREVENT CONTACT WITH THIS SUBSTANCE.

EYE PROTECTION: EMPLOYEE MUST WEAR SPLASH-PROOF OR DUST-RESISTANT SAFETY GOGGLES TO PREVENT EYE CONTACT WITH THIS SUBSTANCE.
EMERGENCY EYE WASH: WHERE THERE IS ANY POSSIBILITY THAT AN EMPLOYEE'S EYES MAY BE EXPOSED TO THIS SUBSTANCE, THE EMPLOYER SHOULD PROVIDE AN EYE WASH FOUNTAIN WITHIN THE IMMEDIATE WORK AREA FOR EMERGENCY USE.

AUTHORIZED BY- OCCUPATIONAL HEALTH SERVICES, INC.
CREATION DATE: 10/04/89 ***REVISION DATE:*** 06/12/90

MATERIAL SAFETY DATA SHEET

OCCUPATIONAL HEALTH SERVICES, INC.
AGRICULTURE AND PESTICIDE DIVISION
450 SEVENTH AVENUE, SUITE 2407
NEW YORK, NEW YORK 10123
1-800-445-MSDS OR (212) 967-1100

EMERGENCY CONTACT:
JOHN S. BRANSFORD, JR. (615) 292-1180

SUBSTANCE IDENTIFICATION

CAS-NUMBER 1085-98-9

SUBSTANCE: **DICHLOFLUANID**

TRADE NAMES/SYNONYMS: METHANESULFENAMIDE, 1,1-DICHLORO-N-((DIMETHYLAMINO)SULFONYL)-1-FLUORO- N-PHENYL-; 1,1-DICHLORO-N-((DIMETHYLAMINO)SULFONYL)-1-FLUORO-N- PHENYLMETHANESULFENAMIDE; SULFAMIDE, N-((DICHLOROFLUOROMETHYL)THIO)-N',N'-DIMETHYL-N-PHENYL-; N-((DICHLOROFLUOROMETHYL)THIO)-N',N'-DIMETHYL-N-PHENYLSULFAMIDE; N-DICHLOROFLUOROMETHYLTHIO-N',N'-DIMETHYL-N-PHENYLSULPHAMIDE; N-DICHLOROFLUOROMETHANESULPHENYL-N',N'-DIMETHYL-N-PHENYLSULPHAMIDE; BAY 47531; DICHLOFULANIDE; ELVARON; EUPAREN; PREVENTOL A 4; C9H11CL2FN2O2S2; PST73026

CHEMICAL FAMILY: SULFAMIDE
HALOGEN
AROMATIC

MOLECULAR FORMULA: (C-H3)2-N-S-(O)2-N-(C6-H5)-S-C-CL2-F

MOLECULAR WEIGHT: 333.21

CERCLA RATINGS (SCALE 0-3): HEALTH=3 FIRE=1 REACTIVITY=0 PERSISTENCE=1

NFPA RATINGS (SCALE 0-4): HEALTH=4 FIRE=1 REACTIVITY=0

COMPONENTS AND CONTAMINANTS

COMPONENT: DICHLOFLUANID ***PERCENT:*** 100.0
CAS# 1085-98-9

OTHER CONTAMINANTS: NONE

EXPOSURE LIMITS: NO OCCUPATIONAL EXPOSURE LIMITS ESTABLISHED BY OSHA, ACGIH, OR NIOSH.

PHYSICAL DATA

DESCRIPTION: WHITE TO PALE YELLOW, FLUFFY, POWDER WITH A CHARACTERISTIC ODOR; DISCOLORS ON EXPOSURE TO LIGHT.

MELTING POINT: 221-223 F (105-106 C)

SPECIFIC GRAVITY: NOT AVAILABLE ***VAPOR PRESSURE:*** NEGLIGIBLE

SOLUBILITY IN WATER: 2 PPM

SOLVENT SOLUBILITY: SOLUBLE IN ACETONE; MODERATELY SOLUBLE IN ISOPROPANOL, N-HEXANE, METHANOL, AND XYLENE.

FIRE AND EXPLOSION DATA

FIRE AND EXPLOSION HAZARD: SLIGHT FIRE HAZARD WHEN EXPOSED TO HEAT OR FLAME.
DUST-AIR MIXTURES MAY IGNITE OR EXPLODE.

FIREFIGHTING MEDIA: DRY CHEMICAL, CARBON DIOXIDE, HALON, WATER SPRAY OR STANDARD FOAM (1987 EMERGENCY RESPONSE GUIDEBOOK, DOT P 5800.4).
FOR LARGER FIRES, USE WATER SPRAY, FOG OR STANDARD FOAM (1987 EMERGENCY RESPONSE GUIDEBOOK, DOT P 5800.4).

FIREFIGHTING: MOVE CONTAINERS FROM FIRE AREA IF POSSIBLE (1987 EMERGENCY RESPONSE GUIDEBOOK, DOT P 5800.4, GUIDE PAGE 53).
EXTINGUISH USING AGENT SUITABLE FOR TYPE OF SURROUNDING FIRE. AVOID BREATHING VAPORS AND DUSTS. KEEP UPWIND.

TOXICITY

DICHLOFLUANID: TOXICITY DATA: 300 MG/M3/4 HOURS INHALATION-RAT LC50; 1000 MG/KG SKIN-RAT LD50; >2000 MG/KG SKIN-RABBIT LD50 (BAYER MSDS); 500 MG/KG ORAL-RAT LD50; 1250 MG/KG ORAL-MOUSE LD50; 3500 MG/KG ORAL-RABBIT LD50; 945 MG/KG ORAL-GUINEA PIG LD50; 1 GM/KG ORAL-CAT LD50; MUTAGENIC DATA (RTECS). CARCINOGEN STATUS: NONE. LOCAL EFFECTS: IRRITANT- EYES. ACUTE TOXICITY LEVEL: HIGHLY TOXIC BY INHALATION; TOXIC BY SKIN AND INGESTION. TARGET EFFECTS: NO DATA AVAILABLE. ADDITIONAL DATA: HISTOLOGICAL CHANGES IN LIVER, PROXIMAL TUBULES AND ADRENAL CORTEX AND REDUCTION OF LYMPHATIC TISSUE IN THE THE SPLEEN HAVE BEEN REPORTED IN ANIMAL STUDIES.

HEALTH EFFECTS AND FIRST AID

INHALATION: DICHLOFLUANID: HIGHLY TOXIC. **ACUTE EXPOSURE-** MAY CAUSE IRRITATION OF THE MUCOUS MEMBRANES. A LETHAL CONCENTRATION REPORTED IN RATS WAS 300 MG/M3/4 HOURS; SYMPTOMS WERE NOT REPORTED. **CHRONIC EXPOSURE-** NO DATA AVAILABLE.

FIRST AID- REMOVE FROM EXPOSURE AREA TO FRESH AIR IMMEDIATELY. IF BREATHING HAS STOPPED, PERFORM ARTIFICIAL RESPIRATION. KEEP PERSON WARM AND AT REST. TREAT SYMPTOMATICALLY AND SUPPORTIVELY. GET MEDICAL ATTENTION IMMEDIATELY.

SKIN CONTACT: DICHLOFLUANID: TOXIC. **ACUTE EXPOSURE-** MAY CAUSE IRRITATION. SENSITIZATION DERMATITIS MAY OCCUR IN PREVIOUSLY EXPOSED PERSONS. THE LETHAL DOSE REPORTED IN RATS WAS 1000 MG/KG; SYMPTOMS WERE NOT REPORTED. **CHRONIC EXPOSURE-** REPEATED EXPOSURE MAY CAUSE SENSITIZATION.

FIRST AID- REMOVE CONTAMINATED CLOTHING AND SHOES IMMEDIATELY. WASH AFFECTED AREA WITH SOAP OR MILD DETERGENT AND LARGE AMOUNTS OF WATER UNTIL NO EVIDENCE OF CHEMICAL REMAINS (APPROXIMATELY 15-20 MINUTES). GET MEDICAL ATTENTION IMMEDIATELY.

EYE CONTACT: DICHLOFLUANID: IRRITANT. **ACUTE EXPOSURE-** THIS MATERIAL WAS MODERATELY IRRITATING TO RABBIT EYES. **CHRONIC EXPOSURE-** PROLONGED OR REPEATED EXPOSURE TO IRRITANTS MAY CAUSE CONJUNCTIVITIS.

FIRST AID- WASH EYES IMMEDIATELY WITH LARGE AMOUNTS OF WATER OR NORMAL SALINE, OCCASIONALLY LIFTING UPPER AND LOWER LIDS, UNTIL NO EVIDENCE OF CHEMICAL REMAINS (APPROXIMATELY 15-20 MINUTES). GET MEDICAL ATTENTION IMMEDIATELY.

INGESTION: DICHLOFLUANID: TOXIC. **ACUTE EXPOSURE-** THE LETHAL DOSE REPORTED IN RATS WAS 500 MG/KG; THE SYMPTOMS WERE NOT REPORTED. **CHRONIC EXPOSURE-** NO OBSERVABLE EFFECTS WERE NOTED IN A 2-YEAR STUDY OF RATS RECEIVING A 1500 MG/KG DIET AND DOGS AND MICE RECEIVING A 1000 MG/KG DIET.

FIRST AID- IF THE PERSON IS CONSCIOUS AND NOT CONVULSING, REMOVE BY GASTRIC LAVAGE AND FOLLOW WITH A CATHARTIC (DREISBACH, HANDBOOK OF POISONING, 12TH ED.). TREAT SYMPTOMATICALLY AND SUPPORTIVELY. GASTRIC LAVAGE SHOULD BE PERFORMED BY QUALIFIED MEDICAL PERSONNEL. GET MEDICAL ATTENTION IMMEDIATELY.

ANTIDOTE: NO SPECIFIC ANTIDOTE. TREAT SYMPTOMATICALLY AND SUPPORTIVELY.

REACTIVITY

REACTIVITY: STABLE UNDER NORMAL TEMPERATURES AND PRESSURES.

INCOMPATIBILITIES: DICHLOFLUANID: OXIDIZERS (STRONG): FIRE AND EXPLOSION HAZARD.

DECOMPOSITION: THERMAL DECOMPOSITION PRODUCTS MAY INCLUDE TOXIC OXIDES OF CARBON, SULFUR, AND NITROGEN AND TOXIC FUMES OF CHLORIDES AND FLUORIDES.

POLYMERIZATION: HAZARDOUS POLYMERIZATION HAS NOT BEEN REPORTED TO OCCUR UNDER NORMAL TEMPERATURES AND PRESSURES.

STORAGE AND DISPOSAL

OBSERVE ALL FEDERAL, STATE AND LOCAL REGULATIONS WHEN STORING OR DISPOSING OF THIS SUBSTANCE. FOR ASSISTANCE, CONTACT THE DISTRICT DIRECTOR OF THE ENVIRONMENTAL PROTECTION AGENCY.

****STORAGE****

STORE IN ACCORDANCE WITH 40 CFR 165 RECOMMENDED PROCEDURES FOR THE DISPOSAL AND STORAGE OF PESTICIDES AND PESTICIDE CONTAINERS.
STORE AWAY FROM INCOMPATIBLE SUBSTANCES.

****DISPOSAL****

DISPOSAL MUST BE IN ACCORDANCE WITH 40 CFR 165 RECOMMENDED PROCEDURES FOR THE DISPOSAL AND STORAGE OF PESTICIDES AND PESTICIDE CONTAINERS.

CONDITIONS TO AVOID

MAY BURN BUT DOES NOT IGNITE READILY.

SPILL AND LEAK PROCEDURES

OCCUPATIONAL SPILL: DO NOT TOUCH SPILLED MATERIAL. STOP LEAK IF YOU CAN DO IT WITHOUT RISK. FOR SMALL SPILLS, TAKE UP WITH SAND OR OTHER ABSORBENT MATERIAL AND PLACE INTO CONTAINERS FOR LATER DISPOSAL. FOR SMALL DRY SPILLS, WITH A CLEAN SHOVEL PLACE MATERIAL INTO CLEAN, DRY CONTAINER AND COVER. MOVE CONTAINERS FROM SPILL AREA. FOR LARGER SPILLS, DIKE FAR AHEAD OF SPILL FOR LATER DISPOSAL. KEEP UNNECESSARY PEOPLE AWAY. ISOLATE HAZARD AREA AND DENY ENTRY.

PROTECTIVE EQUIPMENT

VENTILATION: PROCESS ENCLOSURE RECOMMENDED.

RESPIRATOR: THE FOLLOWING RESPIRATORS ARE RECOMMENDED BASED ON INFORMATION FOUND IN THE PHYSICAL DATA, TOXICITY AND HEALTH EFFECTS SECTIONS. THEY ARE RANKED IN ORDER FROM MINIMUM TO MAXIMUM RESPIRATORY PROTECTION. THE SPECIFIC RESPIRATOR SELECTED MUST BE BASED ON CONTAMINATION LEVELS FOUND IN THE WORK PLACE, MUST NOT EXCEED THE WORKING LIMITS OF THE RESPIRATOR AND BE JOINTLY APPROVED BY THE NATIONAL INSTITUTE FOR OCCUPATIONAL SAFETY AND HEALTH AND THE MINE SAFETY AND HEALTH ADMINISTRATION (NIOSH-MSHA).
TYPE 'C' SUPPLIED-AIR RESPIRATOR WITH A FULL FACEPIECE OPERATED IN PRESSURE-DEMAND OR OTHER POSITIVE PRESSURE MODE OR WITH A FULL FACEPIECE, HELMET OR HOOD OPERATED IN CONTINOUS-FLOW MODE.
SELF-CONTAINED BREATHING APPARATUS WITH A FULL FACEPIECE OPERATED IN

PRESSURE-DEMAND OR OTHER POSITIVE PRESSURE MODE.
FOR FIREFIGHTING AND OTHER IMMEDIATELY DANGEROUS TO LIFE OR HEALTH CONDITIONS:
SELF-CONTAINED BREATHING APPARATUS WITH FULL FACEPIECE OPERATED IN PRESSURE-DEMAND OR OTHER POSITIVE PRESSURE MODE.
SUPPLIED-AIR RESPIRATOR WITH FULL FACEPIECE AND OPERATED IN PRESSURE-DEMAND OR OTHER POSITIVE PRESSURE MODE IN COMBINATION WITH AN AUXILIARY SELF-CONTAINED BREATHING APPARATUS OPERATED IN PRESSURE-DEMAND OR OTHER POSITIVE PRESSURE MODE.

CLOTHING: EMPLOYEE MUST WEAR APPROPRIATE PROTECTIVE (IMPERVIOUS) CLOTHING AND EQUIPMENT TO PREVENT ANY POSSIBILITY OF SKIN CONTACT WITH THIS SUBSTANCE.

GLOVES: EMPLOYEE MUST WEAR APPROPRIATE PROTECTIVE GLOVES TO PREVENT CONTACT WITH THIS SUBSTANCE.

EYE PROTECTION: EMPLOYEE MUST WEAR SPLASH-PROOF OR DUST-RESISTANT SAFETY GOGGLES AND A FACESHIELD TO PREVENT CONTACT WITH THIS SUBSTANCE.
EMERGENCY WASH FACILITIES: WHERE THERE IS ANY POSSIBILITY THAT AN EMPLOYEE'S EYES AND/OR SKIN MAY BE EXPOSED TO THIS SUBSTANCE, THE EMPLOYER SHOULD PROVIDE AN EYE WASH FOUNTAIN AND QUICK DRENCH SHOWER WITHIN THE IMMEDIATE WORK AREA FOR EMERGENCY USE.

AUTHORIZED BY- OCCUPATIONAL HEALTH SERVICES, INC.
CREATION DATE: 06/21/90 ***REVISION DATE:*** 06/21/90

MATERIAL SAFETY DATA SHEET

OCCUPATIONAL HEALTH SERVICES, INC.
AGRICULTURE AND PESTICIDE DIVISION
450 SEVENTH AVENUE, SUITE 2407
NEW YORK, NEW YORK 10123
1-800-445-MSDS OR (212) 967-1100

EMERGENCY CONTACT:
JOHN S. BRANSFORD, JR. (615) 292-1180

SUBSTANCE IDENTIFICATION

CAS-NUMBER 731-27-1

SUBSTANCE: **TOLYLFLUANID**

TRADE NAMES/SYNONYMS: METHANESULFENAMIDE, 1,1-DICHLORO-N-((DIMETHYLAMINO)SULFONYL)-1-FLUORO -N-(4-METHYLPHENYL)-; 1,1-DICHLORO-N-((DIMETHYLAMINO)SULFONYL)-1-FLUORO-N-(4-METHYLPHENYL) -METHANESULFENAMIDE; SULFAMIDE, N-((DICHLOROFLUOROMETHYL)THIO)-N',N'-DIMETHYL-N-P-TOLYL-; N-((DICHLOROFLUOROMETHYL)THIO)-N',N'-DIMETHYL-N-P-TOLYLSULFAMIDE; BAY 5712; DICHLOFLUANID-M; EUPAREN M; TOLILFLUANIDE; C10H13CL2FN2O2S2; PST73030

CHEMICAL FAMILY: SULFENAMIDE

MOLECULAR FORMULA: C10-H13-CL2-F-N2-O2-S2

MOLECULAR WEIGHT: 347.2

CERCLA RATINGS (SCALE 0-3): HEALTH=3 FIRE=1 REACTIVITY=0 PERSISTENCE=1

NFPA RATINGS (SCALE 0-4): HEALTH=3 FIRE=1 REACTIVITY=0

COMPONENTS AND CONTAMINANTS

COMPONENT: TOLYLFLUANID ***PERCENT:*** 100.0
CAS# 731-27-1

OTHER CONTAMINANTS: NONE

EXPOSURE LIMITS: NO OCCUPATIONAL EXPOSURE LIMITS ESTABLISHED BY OSHA, ACGIH, OR NIOSH.

PHYSICAL DATA

DESCRIPTION: COLORLESS TO PALE YELLOW POWDER.

MELTING POINT: 203-207 F (95-97 C) ***SPECIFIC GRAVITY:*** NOT AVAILABLE

VAPOR PRESSURE: NEGLIGIBLE ***SOLUBILITY IN WATER:*** 0.4% @ 25 C

SOLVENT SOLUBILITY: SOLUBLE IN BENZENE AND XYLENE; MODERATELY SOLUBLE IN METHANOL.

FIRE AND EXPLOSION DATA

FIRE AND EXPLOSION HAZARD: SLIGHT FIRE HAZARD WHEN EXPOSED TO HEAT OR FLAME.

FIREFIGHTING MEDIA: DRY CHEMICAL, CARBON DIOXIDE, HALON, WATER SPRAY OR STANDARD FOAM (1987 EMERGENCY RESPONSE GUIDEBOOK, DOT P 5800.4).
FOR LARGER FIRES, USE WATER SPRAY, FOG OR STANDARD FOAM (1987 EMERGENCY RESPONSE GUIDEBOOK, DOT P 5800.4).

FIREFIGHTING: MOVE CONTAINER FROM FIRE AREA IF POSSIBLE. DO NOT SCATTER SPILLED MATERIAL WITH HIGH PRESSURE WATER STREAMS. DIKE FIRE CONTROL WATER FOR LATER DISPOSAL (1987 EMERGENCY RESPONSE GUIDEBOOK, DOT P 5800.4, GUIDE PAGE 31).
USE AGENTS SUITABLE FOR TYPE OF SURROUNDING FIRE. AVOID BREATHING HAZARDOUS VAPORS, KEEP UPWIND.

TOXICITY

TOLYLFLUANID: TOXICITY DATA: 500 MG/KG SKIN-RAT LD50; 1000 MG/KG ORAL-RAT LD50; 500 MG/KG ORAL-RABBIT LD50; 1 GM/KG ORAL-MOUSE LD50; 250 MG/KG ORAL-GUINEA PIG LD50; 500 MG/KG SUBCUTANEOUS-RAT LD50.
CARCINOGEN STATUS: NONE. ACUTE TOXICITY LEVEL: TOXIC BY DERMAL ABSORPTION; MODERATELY TOXIC BY INGESTION. TARGET EFFECTS: NO DATA AVAILABLE.

HEALTH EFFECTS AND FIRST AID

INHALATION: TOLYLFLUANID: **ACUTE EXPOSURE-** NO SPECIFIC DATA AVAILABLE. A SIMILAR COMPOUND, DICHLOFLUANID, MAY CAUSE MODERATE IRRITATION OF THE MUCOUS MEMBRANES. **CHRONIC EXPOSURE-** NO DATA AVAILABLE.

FIRST AID- REMOVE FROM EXPOSURE AREA TO FRESH AIR IMMEDIATELY. IF BREATHING HAS STOPPED, PERFORM ARTIFICIAL RESPIRATION. KEEP PERSON WARM AND AT REST. TREAT SYMPTOMATICALLY AND SUPPORTIVELY. GET MEDICAL ATTENTION IMMEDIATELY.

SKIN CONTACT: TOLYLFLUANID: TOXIC. **ACUTE EXPOSURE-** THE LETHAL DOSE REPORTED IN RATS WAS 500 MG/KG. THE SYMPTOMS WERE NOT REPORTED. A SIMILAR COMPOUND, DICHLOFLUANID, MAY CAUSE MODERATE SKIN IRRITATION. **CHRONIC EXPOSURE-** NO DATA AVAILABLE.

FIRST AID- REMOVE CONTAMINATED CLOTHING AND SHOES IMMEDIATELY. WASH AFFECTED AREA WITH SOAP OR MILD DETERGENT AND LARGE AMOUNTS OF WATER UNTIL NO EVIDENCE OF CHEMICAL REMAINS (APPROXIMATELY 15-20 MINUTES). GET MEDICAL ATTENTION IMMEDIATELY.

EYE CONTACT: TOLYLFLUANID: **ACUTE EXPOSURE-** NO DATA AVAILABLE. **CHRONIC EXPOSURE-** NO DATA AVAILABLE.

FIRST AID- WASH EYES IMMEDIATELY WITH LARGE AMOUNTS OF WATER OR NORMAL SALINE, OCCASIONALLY LIFTING UPPER AND LOWER LIDS, UNTIL NO EVIDENCE OF CHEMICAL REMAINS (APPROXIMATELY 15-20 MINUTES). GET MEDICAL ATTENTION IMMEDIATELY.

INGESTION: TOLYLFLUANID: **ACUTE EXPOSURE-** THE LETHAL DOSE REPORTED IN RATS WAS 1000 MG/KG. A SIMILAR COMPOUND, DICHLOFLUANID, HAS CAUSED CHANGES IN THE LIVER, KIDNEYS, AND SPLEEN IN ANIMALS. **CHRONIC EXPOSURE-** IN A 90 DAY FEEDING STUDY, RATS RECEIVING 1000 MG/KG SHOWED NO EFFECTS.

FIRST AID- IF THE PERSON IS CONSCIOUS AND NOT CONVULSING, REMOVE BY GASTRIC LAVAGE AND FOLLOW WITH A CATHARTIC (DREISBACH, HANDBOOK OF POISONING, 12TH ED.). TREAT SYMPTOMATICALLY AND SUPPORTIVELY. GASTRIC LAVAGE SHOULD BE PERFORMED BY QUALIFIED MEDICAL PERSONNEL. GET MEDICAL ATTENTION IMMEDIATELY.

ANTIDOTE: NO SPECIFIC ANTIDOTE. TREAT SYMPTOMATICALLY AND SUPPORTIVELY.

REACTIVITY

REACTIVITY: STABLE UNDER NORMAL TEMPERATURES AND PRESSURES.

INCOMPATIBILITIES: TOLYLFLUANID: OXIDIZERS (STRONG): FIRE AND EXPLOSION HAZARD.

DECOMPOSITION: THERMAL DECOMPOSITION PRODUCTS MAY INCLUDE TOXIC AND CORROSIVE FUMES OF FLUORIDES, AND TOXIC OXIDES OF SULFUR.
THERMAL DECOMPOSITION MAY YIELD CHLORIDE FUMES AND TOXIC OXIDES OF NITROGEN.

POLYMERIZATION: HAZARDOUS POLYMERIZATION HAS NOT BEEN REPORTED TO OCCUR UNDER NORMAL TEMPERATURES AND PRESSURES.

STORAGE AND DISPOSAL

OBSERVE ALL FEDERAL, STATE AND LOCAL REGULATIONS WHEN STORING OR DISPOSING OF THIS SUBSTANCE. FOR ASSISTANCE, CONTACT THE DISTRICT DIRECTOR OF THE ENVIRONMENTAL PROTECTION AGENCY.

STORAGE

STORE IN ACCORDANCE WITH 40 CFR 165 RECOMMENDED PROCEDURES FOR THE DISPOSAL AND STORAGE OF PESTICIDES AND PESTICIDE CONTAINERS.
STORE AWAY FROM INCOMPATIBLE SUBSTANCES.

DISPOSAL

DISPOSAL MUST BE IN ACCORDANCE WITH 40 CFR 165 RECOMMENDED PROCEDURES FOR THE DISPOSAL AND STORAGE OF PESTICIDES AND PESTICIDE CONTAINERS.

CONDITIONS TO AVOID

MAY BURN BUT DOES NOT IGNITE READILY. AVOID CONTACT WITH STRONG OXIDIZERS, EXCESSIVE HEAT, SPARKS, OR OPEN FLAME.

SPILL AND LEAK PROCEDURES

OCCUPATIONAL SPILL: SWEEP UP AND PLACE IN SUITABLE CLEAN, DRY CONTAINERS FOR RECLAMATION OR LATER DISPOSAL. DO NOT FLUSH SPILLED MATERIAL INTO SEWER. KEEP UNNECESSARY PEOPLE AWAY.

PROTECTIVE EQUIPMENT

VENTILATION: PROVIDE LOCAL EXHAUST OR PROCESS ENCLOSURE VENTILATION SYSTEM.

RESPIRATOR: THE FOLLOWING RESPIRATORS ARE RECOMMENDED BASED ON INFORMATION FOUND IN THE PHYSICAL DATA, TOXICITY AND HEALTH EFFECTS SECTIONS. THEY ARE RANKED IN ORDER FROM MINIMUM TO MAXIMUM RESPIRATORY PROTECTION. THE SPECIFIC RESPIRATOR SELECTED MUST BE BASED ON CONTAMINATION LEVELS FOUND IN THE WORK PLACE, MUST NOT EXCEED THE WORKING LIMITS OF THE RESPIRATOR AND BE JOINTLY APPROVED BY THE NATIONAL INSTITUTE FOR OCCUPATIONAL SAFETY AND HEALTH AND THE MINE SAFETY AND HEALTH ADMINISTRATION (NIOSH-MSHA).

CHEMICAL CARTRIDGE RESPIRATOR WITH AN ORGANIC VAPOR CARTRIDGE(S) WITH A FULL FACEPIECE AND ORGANIC VAPOR CARTRIDGE(S) IN COMBINATION WITH A DUST AND MIST FILTER.

POWERED AIR-PURIFYING RESPIRATOR WITH A TIGHT-FITTING FACEPIECE AND ORGANIC VAPOR CARTRIDGE(S) IN COMBINATION WITH A HIGH-EFFICIENCY PARTICULATE FILTER.

TYPE 'C' SUPPLIED-AIR RESPIRATOR WITH A FULL FACEPIECE OPERATED IN A PRESSURE-DEMAND OR OTHER POSITIVE PRESSURE MODE.

SELF-CONTAINED BREATHING APPARATUS WITH A FULL FACEPIECE OPERATED IN PRESSURE-DEMAND OR OTHER POSITIVE PRESSURE MODE.

FOR FIREFIGHTING AND OTHER IMMEDIATELY DANGEROUS TO LIFE OR HEALTH CONDITIONS:

SELF-CONTAINED BREATHING APPARATUS WITH FULL FACEPIECE OPERATED IN PRESSURE-DEMAND OR OTHER POSITIVE PRESSURE MODE.

SUPPLIED-AIR RESPIRATOR WITH FULL FACEPIECE AND OPERATED IN PRESSURE-DEMAND OR OTHER POSITIVE PRESSURE MODE IN COMBINATION WITH AN AUXILIARY SELF-CONTAINED BREATHING APPARATUS OPERATED IN PRESSURE-DEMAND OR OTHER POSITIVE PRESSURE MODE.

CLOTHING: EMPLOYEE MUST WEAR APPROPRIATE PROTECTIVE (IMPERVIOUS) CLOTHING AND EQUIPMENT TO PREVENT ANY POSSIBILITY OF SKIN CONTACT WITH THIS SUBSTANCE.

GLOVES: EMPLOYEE MUST WEAR APPROPRIATE PROTECTIVE GLOVES TO PREVENT CONTACT WITH THIS SUBSTANCE.

EYE PROTECTION: EMPLOYEE MUST WEAR SPLASH-PROOF OR DUST-RESISTANT SAFETY GOGGLES WITH OR WITHOUT A FACESHIELD TO PREVENT CONTACT WITH THIS SUBSTANCE.

EMERGENCY EYE WASH: WHERE THERE IS ANY POSSIBILITY THAT AN EMPLOYEE'S EYES MAY BE EXPOSED TO THIS SUBSTANCE, THE EMPLOYER SHOULD PROVIDE AN EYE WASH FOUNTAIN WITHIN THE IMMEDIATE WORK AREA FOR EMERGENCY USE.

AUTHORIZED BY- OCCUPATIONAL HEALTH SERVICES, INC.

CREATION DATE: 10/05/89 ***REVISION DATE:*** 05/31/90

MATERIAL SAFETY DATA SHEET

OCCUPATIONAL HEALTH SERVICES, INC.
AGRICULTURE AND PESTICIDE DIVISION
450 SEVENTH AVENUE, SUITE 2407
NEW YORK, NEW YORK 10123
1-800-445-MSDS OR (212) 967-1100

EMERGENCY CONTACT:
JOHN S. BRANSFORD, JR. (615) 292-1180

SUBSTANCE IDENTIFICATION

CAS-NUMBER 18181-70-9

SUBSTANCE: <u>IODOFENPHOS</u>

TRADE NAMES/SYNONYMS: PHOSPHOROTHIOIC ACID, O-(2,5-DICHLORO-4-IODOPHENYL) O,O-DIMETHYL ESTER; O-(2,5-DICHLORO-4-IODOPHENYL) O,O-DIMETHYL ESTER PHOSPHOROTHIOATE; O-2,5-DICHLORO-4-IODOPHENYL O,O-DIMETHYL ESTER PHSOPHOROTHIOATE; O,O-DIMETHYL O-(2,5-DICHLORO-4-IODOPHENYL)PHOSPHORTHIOATE; ALFACRON; C 9491; IODOFENFOS; IODOPHOS; JODFENPHOS; NUVANOL N; OMS 1211; C8H8CL2IO3PS; PST73035

CHEMICAL FAMILY: PHOSPHOROTHIOATE

MOLECULAR FORMULA: C8-H8-CL2-I-O3-P-S

MOLECULAR WEIGHT: 412.99

CERCLA RATINGS (SCALE 0-3): HEALTH=2 FIRE=1 REACTIVITY=0 PERSISTENCE=1

NFPA RATINGS (SCALE 0-4): HEALTH=2 FIRE=1 REACTIVITY=0

COMPONENTS AND CONTAMINANTS

COMPONENT: IODOFENPHOS ***PERCENT:*** 100.0
CAS# 18181-70-9

OTHER CONTAMINANTS: NONE

EXPOSURE LIMITS: NO OCCUPATIONAL EXPOSURE LIMITS ESTABLISHED BY OSHA, ACGIH, OR NIOSH.

PHYSICAL DATA

DESCRIPTION: COLORLESS OR WHITE CRYSTALLINE SOLID WITH A MILD ODOR.

MELTING POINT: 169 F (76 C) ***SPECIFIC GRAVITY:*** 2.0

VAPOR PRESSURE: NEGLIGIBLE ***SOLUBILITY IN WATER:*** <0.0002% @ 20 C

SOLVENT SOLUBILITY: SOLUBLE IN KEROSENE, DIMETHYLFORMAMIDE, ACETONE, XYLENE, TOLUENE, DICHLOROMETHANE, METHANOL, OCTAN-1-OL, BENZENE, ISOPROPANOL, AND HEXANE.

FIRE AND EXPLOSION DATA

FIRE AND EXPLOSION HAZARD: SLIGHT FIRE HAZARD WHEN EXPOSED TO HEAT OR FLAME.

FIREFIGHTING MEDIA: DRY CHEMICAL, CARBON DIOXIDE, HALON, WATER SPRAY OR STANDARD FOAM (1987 EMERGENCY RESPONSE GUIDEBOOK, DOT P 5800.4). FOR LARGER FIRES, USE WATER SPRAY, FOG OR STANDARD FOAM (1987 EMERGENCY RESPONSE GUIDEBOOK, DOT P 5800.4).

FIREFIGHTING: MOVE CONTAINERS FROM FIRE AREA IF POSSIBLE. FIGHT FIRE FROM MAXIMUM DISTANCE. STAY AWAY FROM STORAGE TANK ENDS. DIKE FIRE CONTROL WATER FOR LATER DISPOSAL. DO NOT SCATTER MATERIAL (1987 EMERGENCY RESPONSE GUIDEBOOK, DOT P 5800.4, GUIDE PAGE 55). EXTINGUISH ONLY IF FLOW CAN BE STOPPED; USE FLOODING AMOUNTS OF WATER AS FOG, SOLID STREAMS MAY BE INEFFECTIVE. COOL CONTAINERS WITH FLOODING AMOUNTS OF WATER FROM AS FAR A DISTANCE AS POSSIBLE. USE WATER SPRAY TO ABSORB TOXIC VAPORS. AVOID BREATHING TOXIC VAPORS; KEEP UPWIND. CONSIDER EVACUATION OF DOWNWIND AREA IF MATERIAL IS LEAKING.

TOXICITY

IODOFENPHOS: TOXICITY DATA: 500 MG/KG SKIN-RABBIT LD50; 2150 MG/KG SKIN-RAT LD50; 2330 MG/KG ORAL-RAT LD50; 3 GM/KG ORAL-MOUSE LD50; 2 GM/KG ORAL-RABBIT LD50; 3 GM/KG ORAL-DOG LD50; 2000 MG/KG UNREPORTED-RAT LD50. CARCINOGEN STATUS: NONE. ACUTE TOXICITY LEVEL: TOXIC BY DERMAL ABSORPTION AND MODERATELY TOXIC BY INGESTION. TARGET EFFECTS: CHOLINESTERASE INHIBITOR. POISONING MAY AFFECT THE NERVOUS SYSTEM.* AT INCREASED RISK FROM EXPOSURE: PERSONS WITH RESPIRATORY AILMENTS, RECENT EXPOSURE TO CHOLINESTERASE INHIBITORS OR IMPAIRED CHOLINESTERASE PRODUCTION, OR LIVER MALFUNCTION.* ADDITIONAL DATA: MAY CROSS THE PLACENTA. HIGH ENVIRONMENTAL TEMPERATURES OR EXPOSURE OF THE CHEMICAL TO VISIBLE OR ULTRAVIOLET LIGHT MAY ENHANCE THE TOXICITY. INTERACTIONS WITH MEDICATIONS MAY OCCUR.*

* MAY BE BASED ON GENERAL INFORMATION ON ORGANOPHOSPHATES.

HEALTH EFFECTS AND FIRST AID

INHALATION: IODOFENPHOS: SEE INFORMATION ON ORGANOPHOSPHATES.
ORGANOPHOSPHATES: CHOLINESTERASE INHIBITOR. <u>ACUTE EXPOSURE-</u> WHEN INHALED, THE FIRST EFFECTS OF CHOLINESTERASE INHIBITORS ARE USUALLY RESPIRATORY AND MAY INCLUDE NASAL HYPEREMIA AND WATERY DISCHARGE, COUGH, CHEST DISCOMFORT, DYSPNEA, AND WHEEZING DUE TO INCREASED BRONCHIAL SECRETIONS AND BRONCHOCONSTRICTION. IF SUFFICIENT AMOUNTS ARE ABSORBED, OTHER SYSTEMIC EFFECTS MAY BEGIN WITHIN A FEW MINUTES OR BE DELAYED FOR UP TO 12 HOURS. SYMPTOMS MAY INCLUDE PALLOR, NAUSEA, VOMITING, DIARRHEA, ABDOMINAL CRAMPS, HEADACHE, DIZZINESS, OCULAR PAIN, BLURRED VISION, MIOSIS OR IN SOME CASES, ESPECIALLY INITIALLY, MYDRIASIS, LACRIMATION, SALIVATION, SWEATING, AND CONFUSION. OTHER REPORTED CENTRAL NERVOUS SYSTEM OR NEUROMUSCULAR EFFECTS MAY INCLUDE ATAXIA, SLURRED SPEECH, AREFLEXIA, WEAKNESS, FATIGUE, FASCICULATIONS, TWITCHING, TREMORS POSSIBLY OF THE TONGUE AND EYELIDS, AND EVENTUALLY PARALYSIS OF THE EXTREMITIES AND POSSIBLY OF THE RESPIRATORY MUSCLES. IN SEVERE CASES THERE MAY ALSO BE INVOLUNTARY DEFECATION AND URINATION, CYANOSIS, PSYCHOSIS, HYPERGLYCEMIA, ACUTE PANCREATITIS, CARDIAC IRREGULARITIES, PULMONARY EDEMA, UNCONSCIOUSNESS, CONVULSIONS, AND COMA. DEATH IS PRIMARILY DUE TO RESPIRATORY FAILURE, ALTHOUGH CARDIOVASCULAR EFFECTS

INCLUDING CARDIAC ARREST MAY ALSO BE IMPLICATED. LONG TERM SEQUELAE ARE RARE BUT MAY INCLUDE NEUROPSYCHIATRIC DISORDERS AND MYOPATHY WITH MUSCLE TENDERNESS. SOME ORGANOPHOSPHATES MAY CAUSE A DELAYED NEUROPATHY BEGINNING 1-4 WEEKS AFTER AN ACUTE EXPOSURE WHICH MAY OR MAY NOT HAVE CAUSED ACUTE CHOLINERGIC EFFECTS. NUMBNESS, TINGLING, WEAKNESS AND CRAMPING BEGINNING SYMMETRICALLY IN THE LOWER LIMBS MAY PROGRESS TO ATAXIA AND PARALYSIS. IN SEVERE CASES, UPPER LIMB INVOLVEMENT IS POSSIBLE AND FLACCID PARALYSIS MAY PROGRESS TO SPASTIC PARALYSIS WITH EXAGGERATED REFLEXES. IMPROVEMENT MAY OCCUR OVER MONTHS TO YEARS, BUT SOME RESIDUAL IMPAIRMENT USUALLY REMAINS. **CHRONIC EXPOSURE**- REPEATED OR PROLONGED EXPOSURE MAY RESULT IN THE EFFECTS OF ACUTE EXPOSURE INCLUDING THE DELAYED NEUROPATHY. OTHER EFFECTS REPORTED IN WORKERS REPEATEDLY EXPOSED INCLUDE IMPAIRED MEMORY AND CONCENTRATION, ACUTE PSYCHOSIS, SEVERE DEPRESSIONS, IRRITABILTY, CONFUSION, APATHY, EMOTIONAL LABILITY, SOCIAL WITHDRAWAL, CONFUSION, HEADACHE, SPEECH DIFFICULTIES, DELAYED REACTION TIMES, SPATIAL DISORIENTATION, NIGHTMARES, SLEEPWALKING, AND DROWSINESS OR INSOMNIA. AN INFLUENZA-LIKE CONDITION WITH HEADACHE, NAUSEA, WEAKNESS, ANOREXIA AND MALAISE HAS ALSO BEEN REPORTED.

FIRST AID- REMOVE FROM EXPOSURE AREA TO FRESH AIR IMMEDIATELY. IF BREATHING HAS STOPPED, GIVE ARTIFICIAL RESPIRATION. MAINTAIN AIRWAY AND BLOOD PRESSURE AND ADMINISTER OXYGEN IF AVAILABLE. KEEP AFFECTED PERSON WARM AND AT REST. TREAT SYMPTOMATICALLY AND SUPPORTIVELY. ADMINISTRATION OF OXYGEN SHOULD BE PERFORMED BY QUALIFIED PERSONNEL. GET MEDICAL ATTENTION IMMEDIATELY.

SKIN CONTACT: IODOFENPHOS: TOXIC. THIS MATERIAL WAS SLIGHTLY IRRITATING TO RABBIT SKIN. SEE INFORMATION ON ORGANOPHOSPHATES.
ORGANOPHOSPHATES: CHOLINESTERASE INHIBITOR. **ACUTE EXPOSURE**- LOCALIZED SWEATING AND FASCICULATIONS MAY OCCUR AT THE SITE OF CONTACT. IF SUFFICIENT AMOUNTS ARE ABSORBED, OTHER EFFECTS OF CHOLINESTERASE INHIBITION AS DESCRIBED IN ACUTE INHALATION MAY OCCUR. SYMPTOMS MAY BE DELAYED 2-3 HOURS, BUT USUALLY NO MORE THAN 12 HOURS. THE RATE OF ABSORPTION IS INCREASED BY THE PRESENCE OF DERMATITIS OR HIGH AMBIENT TEMPERATURES. DELAYED NEUROPATHY IS ALSO POSSIBLE. **CHRONIC EXPOSURE**- REPEATED OR PROLONGED EXPOSURE MAY CAUSE EFFECTS AS DESCRIBED IN ACUTE EXPOSURE. SOME ORGANOPHOSPHATES MAY CAUSE SENSITIZATION.

FIRST AID- REMOVE CONTAMINATED CLOTHING IMMEDIATELY. WASH CONTAMINATED AREAS WITH SOAP AND WATER FOLLOWED BY ALCOHOL (ARENA, POISONING, 4TH ED.). EMERGENCY PERSONNEL SHOULD WEAR GLOVES AND AVOID CONTAMINATION. TREAT RESPIRATORY DIFFICULTY WITH ARTIFICIAL RESPIRATION. GET MEDICAL ATTENTION IMMEDIATELY.

EYE CONTACT: IODOFENPHOS: SEE INFORMATION ON ORGANOPHOSPHATES.
ORGANOPHOSPHATES: CHOLINESTERASE INHIBITOR. **ACUTE EXPOSURE**- DIRECT CONTACT MAY CAUSE PAIN, HYPEREMIA, LACRIMATION, TWITCHING OF THE EYELIDS, MIOSIS, AND CILIARY MUSCLE SPASM WITH LOSS OF ACCOMODATION, BLURRED OR DIMMED VISION AND BROWACHE. SOMETIMES MYDRIASIS MAY OCCUR INSTEAD OF MIOSIS. WITH SUFFICIENT EXPOSURE, OTHER SYMPTOMS OF CHOLINESTERASE INHIBITION AS DESCRIBED IN ACUTE INHALATION MAY OCCUR. **CHRONIC EXPOSURE**- REPEATED OR PROLONGED EXPOSURE MAY CAUSE EFFECTS AS DESCRIBED IN ACUTE EXPOSURE. SOME COMPOUNDS HAVE CAUSED TOXIC EFFECTS ON THE CRYSTALLINE LENS, CONJUNCTIVAL THICKENING AND OBSTRUCTION OF THE NASOLACRIMAL CANALS WHEN USED AS MIOTIC EYEDROPS.

FIRST AID- IRRIGATE EYES WITH WATER OR SALINE SOLUTION. IF SYMPTOMS OF POISONING OCCUR, TREAT RESPIRATORY DIFFICULTY WITH ARTIFICIAL RESPIRATION AND OXYGEN. OBSERVE PATIENT FOR AT LEAST 24-36 HOURS (GOSSELIN, CLINICAL TOXICOLOGY OF COMMERCIAL PRODUCTS, 5TH ED.). GET MEDICAL ATTENTION IMMEDIATELY. OXYGEN SHOULD BE ADMINISTERED BY QUALIFIED MEDICAL PERSONNEL.

INGESTION: IODOFENPHOS: NO OBSERVABLE EFFECTS WERE NOTED IN A 90-DAY STUDY OF RATS FED 0.38 MG/KG/DAY OR DOGS FED 0.45 MG/KG/DAY. SEE INFORMATION ON ORGANOPHOSPHATES.
ORGANOPHOSPHATES: CHOLINESTERASE INHIBITOR. **ACUTE EXPOSURE**- WHEN INGESTED, THE FIRST EFFECTS MAY BE NAUSEA, VOMITING, ANOREXIA, ABDOMINAL CRAMPS AND DIARRHEA. GASTROINTESTINAL ABSORPTION MAY CAUSE SYMPTOMS OF CHOLINESTERASE INHIBITION AS DESCRIBED IN ACUTE INHALATION. SYMPTOMS MAY BEGIN WITHIN MINUTES OR BE DELAYED FOR HOURS. DELAYED EFFECTS INCLUDING NEUROPATHY MAY ALSO OCCUR. **CHRONIC EXPOSURE**- REPEATED INGESTION MAY CAUSE EFFECTS AS DESCRIBED IN ACUTE EXPOSURE.

FIRST AID- IF PERSON IS ALERT AND RESPIRATION IS NOT DEPRESSED, GIVE SYRUP OF IPECAC FOLLOWED BY WATER (IF VOMITING OCCURS, KEEP HEAD BELOW HIPS TO PREVENT ASPIRATION). IF CONSCIOUSNESS LEVEL DECLINES OR VOMITING HAS NOT OCCURRED IN 15 MINUTES EMPTY STOMACH BY GASTRIC LAVAGE WITH THE AID OF CUFFED ENDOTRACHEAL TUBE USING ISOTONIC SALINE OR 5% SODIUM BICARBONATE FOLLOW WITH ACTIVATED CHARCOAL. ESTABLISH AND MAINTAIN AIRWAY. TREAT RESPIRATORY DIFFICULTY WITH ARTIFICIAL RESPIRATION AND OXYGEN. DO NOT GIVE MORPHINE, AMINOPHYLLINE, PHENOTHIAZINES, RESERPINE, FUROSEMIDE, OR ETHACRYNIC ACID (MORGAN, RECOGNITION AND MANAGEMENT OF PESTICIDE POISONINGS, 3RD ED.). TREAT SYMPTOMATICALLY AND SUPPORTIVELY. ADMINISTRATION OF OXYGEN AND LAVAGE MUST BE PERFORMED BY QUALIFIED MEDICAL PERSONNEL. GET MEDICAL ATTENTION IMMEDIATELY.

ANTIDOTE: THE FOLLOWING ANTIDOTE(S) HAVE BEEN RECOMMENDED. HOWEVER, THE DECISION AS TO WHETHER THE SEVERITY OF POISONING REQUIRES ADMINISTRATION OF ANY ANTIDOTE AND ACTUAL DOSE REQUIRED SHOULD BE MADE BY QUALIFIED MEDICAL PERSONNEL.
FOR CHOLINESTERASE INHIBITORS: ESTABLISH CLEAR AIRWAY AND TISSUE OXYGENATION BY ASPIRATION OF SECRETIONS, AND IF NECESSARY, BY ASSISTED PULMONARY VENTILATION WITH OXYGEN. IMPROVE TISSUE OXYGENATION AS MUCH AS POSSIBLE BEFORE ADMINISTERING ATROPINE TO MINIMIZE THE RISK OF VENTRICULAR FIBRILLATION. ADMINISTER ATROPINE SULFATE INTRAVENOUSLY, OR INTRAMUSCULARLY IF IV INJECTION IS NOT POSSIBLE. IN MODERATELY SEVERE POISONING ADMINISTER ATROPINE SULFATE, 0.4-2.0 MG REPEATED EVERY 15 MINUTES UNTIL ATROPINIZATION IS ACHIEVED (TACHYCARDIA, FLUSHING, DRY MOUTH, MYDRIASIS). MAINTAIN ATROPINIZATION BY REPEATED DOSES FOR 2-12 HOURS, OR LONGER, DEPENDING ON THE SEVERITY OF POISONING. THE APPEARANCE OF RALES IN THE LUNG BASES, MIOSIS, SALIVATION, NAUSEA, BRADYCARDIA, ARE ALL INDICATIONS OF INADEQUATE ATROPINIZATION. SEVERELY POISONED INDIVIDUALS MAY EXHIBIT REMARKABLE TOLERANCE TO ATROPINE; TWO OR MORE TIMES THE DOSAGES SUGGESTED ABOVE MAY BE NEEDED. PERSONS NOT POISONED OR ONLY SLIGHTLY POISONED, HOWEVER, MAY DEVELOP SIGNS OF ATROPINE TOXICITY FROM SUCH LARGE DOSAGES: FEVER, MUSCLE FIBRILLATIONS, AND DELIRIUM ARE THE MAIN SIGNS OF ATROPINE TOXICITY. IF THESE SIGNS APPEAR WHILE THE PATIENT IS FULLY ATROPINIZED, ATROPINE ADMINISTRATION SHOULD BE DISCONTINUED, AT LEAST TEMPORARILY. OBSERVE TREATED PATIENTS CLOSELY AT LEAST 24 HOURS TO INSURE THAT SYMPTOMS (POSSIBLY PULMONARY EDEMA) DO NOT RECUR AS ATROPINIZATION WEARS OFF. IN VERY SEVERE POISONINGS, METABOLIC DISPOSITION OF TOXICANT MAY REQUIRE SEVERAL HOURS OR DAYS DURING WHICH ATROPINIZATION MUST BE MAINTAINED. MARKEDLY LOWER LEVELS OF URINARY METABOLITES INDICATE THAT ATROPINE DOSAGE CAN BE TAPERED OFF. AS DOSAGE IS REDUCED, CHECK THE LUNG BASES FREQUENTLY FOR RALES. IF RALES ARE HEARD OR OTHER SYMPTOMS RETURN, RE-ESTABLISH ATROPINIZATION PROMPTLY (MORGAN, RECOGNITION AND MANAGEMENT OF PESTICIDE POISONINGS, 3RD ED.). ADMINISTRATION OF ANTIDOTE MUST BE PERFORMED BY QUALIFIED MEDICAL PERSONNEL.
IN CASES OF SEVERE POISONING BY ORGANOPHOSPHATE PESTICIDES IN WHICH RESPIRATORY DEPRESSION, MUSCLE WEAKNESS AND TWITCHINGS ARE SEVERE, GIVE PRALIDOXIME (PROTOPAM-AYERST, 2-PAM), 1.0 GRAM INTRAVENOUSLY AT NO MORE THAN 0.5 GRAM PER MINUTE. DOSAGE OF PRALIDOXIME MAY BE REPEATED IN 1-2 HOURS, THEN AT 10-12 HOUR INTERVALS IF NEEDED. IN VERY SEVERE POISONINGS, DOSAGE RATES MAY BE DOUBLED. TREATMENT WITH PRALIDOXIME WILL BE MOST EFFECTIVE IF GIVEN WITHIN THIRTY-SIX HOURS AFTER POISONING (MORGAN, RECOGNITION AND MANAGEMENT OF PESTICIDE POISONINGS, 3RD ED.). ANTIDOTE SHOULD BE ADMINISTERED BY QUALIFIED MEDICAL PERSONNEL.

REACTIVITY

REACTIVITY: STABLE UNDER NORMAL TEMPERATURES AND PRESSURES.

INCOMPATIBILITIES: IODOFENPHOS: ACIDS (CONCENTRATED): UNSTABLE. ALKALIES (CONCENTRATED): UNSTABLE. OXIDIZERS (STRONG): FIRE AND EXPLOSION HAZARD.

DECOMPOSITION: THERMAL DECOMPOSITION PRODUCTS MAY INCLUDE TOXIC AND CORROSIVE FUMES OF CHLORIDES AND IODIDES, AND TOXIC OXIDES OF PHOSPHORUS AND SULFUR.

POLYMERIZATION: HAZARDOUS POLYMERIZATION HAS NOT BEEN REPORTED TO OCCUR UNDER NORMAL TEMPERATURES AND PRESSURES.

STORAGE AND DISPOSAL

OBSERVE ALL FEDERAL, STATE AND LOCAL REGULATIONS WHEN STORING OR DISPOSING OF THIS SUBSTANCE. FOR ASSISTANCE, CONTACT THE DISTRICT DIRECTOR OF THE ENVIRONMENTAL PROTECTION AGENCY.

****STORAGE****

STORE IN ACCORDANCE WITH 40 CFR 165 RECOMMENDED PROCEDURES FOR THE DISPOSAL AND STORAGE OF PESTICIDES AND PESTICIDE CONTAINERS.
STORE AWAY FROM INCOMPATIBLE SUBSTANCES.

DISPOSAL

DISPOSAL MUST BE IN ACCORDANCE WITH 40 CFR 165 RECOMMENDED PROCEDURES FOR THE DISPOSAL AND STORAGE OF PESTICIDES AND PESTICIDE CONTAINERS.

CONDITIONS TO AVOID

MAY BURN BUT DOES NOT IGNITE READILY. CONTAINERS MAY EXPLODE IN HEAT OF FIRE.

SPILL AND LEAK PROCEDURES

OCCUPATIONAL SPILL: DO NOT TOUCH SPILLED MATERIAL. STOP LEAK IF YOU CAN DO IT WITHOUT RISK. USE WATER SPRAY TO REDUCE VAPORS. FOR SMALL SPILLS, TAKE UP WITH SAND OR OTHER ABSORBENT MATERIAL AND PLACE INTO CONTAINERS FOR LATER DISPOSAL. FOR SMALL DRY SPILLS, WITH A CLEAN SHOVEL PLACE MATERIAL INTO CLEAN, DRY CONTAINERS AND COVER. MOVE CONTAINERS FROM SPILL AREA. FOR LARGER SPILLS, DIKE FAR AHEAD OF SPILL FOR LATER DISPOSAL. KEEP UNNECESSARY PEOPLE AWAY. ISOLATE HAZARD AREA AND DENY ENTRY. VENTILATE CLOSED SPACES BEFORE ENTERING.

PROTECTIVE EQUIPMENT

VENTILATION: PROVIDE LOCAL EXHAUST OR GENERAL DILUTION VENTILATION SYSTEM.

RESPIRATOR: THE FOLLOWING RESPIRATORS ARE RECOMMENDED BASED ON INFORMATION FOUND IN THE PHYSICAL DATA, TOXICITY AND HEALTH EFFECTS SECTIONS. THEY ARE RANKED IN ORDER FROM MINIMUM TO MAXIMUM RESPIRATORY PROTECTION. THE SPECIFIC RESPIRATOR SELECTED MUST BE BASED ON CONTAMINATION LEVELS FOUND IN THE WORK PLACE, MUST NOT EXCEED THE WORKING LIMITS OF THE RESPIRATOR AND BE JOINTLY APPROVED BY THE NATIONAL INSTITUTE FOR OCCUPATIONAL SAFETY AND HEALTH AND THE MINE SAFETY AND HEALTH ADMINISTRATION (NIOSH-MSHA).

CHEMICAL CARTRIDGE RESPIRATOR WITH AN ORGANIC VAPOR CARTRIDGE(S) IN COMBINATION WITH A DUST AND MIST FILTER.

GAS MASK WITH ORGANIC VAPOR CANISTER (CHIN-STYLE OR FRONT- OR BACK-MOUNTED CANISTER) WITH A DUST AND MIST FILTER.

GAS MASK WITH ORGANIC VAPOR CANISTER (CHIN-STYLE OR FRONT- OR BACK-MOUNTED CANISTER) WITH A PARTICULATE FILTER.

POWERED AIR-PURIFYING RESPIRATOR WITH A HIGH-EFFICIENCY FILTER.

TYPE 'C' SUPPLIED-AIR RESPIRATOR WITH A FULL FACEPIECE OPERATED IN A PRESSURE-DEMAND OR OTHER POSITIVE PRESSURE MODE.

SELF-CONTAINED BREATHING APPARATUS WITH A FULL FACEPIECE OPERATED IN PRESSURE-DEMAND OR OTHER POSITIVE PRESSURE MODE.

FOR FIREFIGHTING AND OTHER IMMEDIATELY DANGEROUS TO LIFE OR HEALTH CONDITIONS:

SELF-CONTAINED BREATHING APPARATUS WITH FULL FACEPIECE OPERATED IN PRESSURE-DEMAND OR OTHER POSITIVE PRESSURE MODE.

SUPPLIED-AIR RESPIRATOR WITH FULL FACEPIECE AND OPERATED IN PRESSURE-DEMAND OR OTHER POSITIVE PRESSURE MODE IN COMBINATION WITH AN AUXILIARY SELF-CONTAINED BREATHING APPARATUS OPERATED IN PRESSURE-DEMAND OR OTHER POSITIVE PRESSURE MODE.

CLOTHING: EMPLOYEE MUST WEAR APPROPRIATE PROTECTIVE (IMPERVIOUS) CLOTHING AND EQUIPMENT TO PREVENT ANY POSSIBILITY OF SKIN CONTACT WITH THIS SUBSTANCE.

GLOVES: EMPLOYEE MUST WEAR APPROPRIATE PROTECTIVE GLOVES TO PREVENT CONTACT WITH THIS SUBSTANCE.

EYE PROTECTION: EMPLOYEE MUST WEAR SPLASH-PROOF OR DUST-RESISTANT SAFETY GOGGLES WITH OR WITHOUT A FACESHIELD TO PREVENT CONTACT WITH THIS SUBSTANCE.

EMERGENCY EYE WASH: WHERE THERE IS ANY POSSIBILITY THAT AN EMPLOYEE'S EYES MAY BE EXPOSED TO THIS SUBSTANCE, THE EMPLOYER SHOULD PROVIDE AN EYE WASH FOUNTAIN WITHIN THE IMMEDIATE WORK AREA FOR EMERGENCY USE.

AUTHORIZED BY- OCCUPATIONAL HEALTH SERVICES, INC.

CREATION DATE: 10/04/89 ***REVISION DATE:*** 05/07/90

MATERIAL SAFETY DATA SHEET

OCCUPATIONAL HEALTH SERVICES, INC.
AGRICULTURE AND PESTICIDE DIVISION
450 SEVENTH AVENUE, SUITE 2407
NEW YORK, NEW YORK 10123

EMERGENCY CONTACT:
JOHN S. BRANSFORD, JR. (615) 292-1180
1-800-445-MSDS OR (212) 967-1100

SUBSTANCE IDENTIFICATION

CAS-NUMBER 21267-72-1

SUBSTANCE: **PRYNACHLOR**

TRADE NAMES/SYNONYMS: ACETAMIDE, 2-CHLORO-N-(1-METHYL-2-PROPYNYL)-N-PHENYL-; ACETANILIDE, 2-CHLORO-N-(1-METHYL-2-PROPYNYL)-; 2-CHLORO-N-(1-METHYL-2-PROPYNYL)-N-PHENYLACETAMIDE; 2-CHLORO-N-(1-METHYL-2-PROPYNYL)ACETANILIDE; 2-CHLORO-N-(1-METHYLPROP-2-YNYL)ACETANILIDE; BASAMAIZE; BAS 290H; BUTISAN; C12H12CLNO; PST73038

MOLECULAR FORMULA: C12-H12-CL-N-O

MOLECULAR WEIGHT: 221.69

CERCLA RATINGS (SCALE 0-3): HEALTH=2 FIRE=1 REACTIVITY=0 PERSISTENCE=3

NFPA RATINGS (SCALE 0-4): HEALTH=2 FIRE=1 REACTIVITY=0

COMPONENTS AND CONTAMINANTS

COMPONENT: PRYNACHLOR ***PERCENT:*** 100
CAS# 21267-72-1

OTHER CONTAMINANTS: NONE

EXPOSURE LIMITS: NO OCCUPATIONAL EXPOSURE LIMITS ESTABLISHED BY OSHA, ACGIH, OR NIOSH.

PHYSICAL DATA

DESCRIPTION: WHITE CRYSTALLINE SOLID. ***MELTING POINT:*** 104-117 F (40-47 C)

SPECIFIC GRAVITY: NOT AVAILABLE ***SOLUBILITY IN WATER:*** 0.05 %

SOLVENT SOLUBILITY: SOLUBLE IN BENZENE, ETHANOL.

FIRE AND EXPLOSION DATA

FIRE AND EXPLOSION HAZARD: SLIGHT FIRE HAZARD WHEN EXPOSED TO HEAT OR FLAME.

FIREFIGHTING MEDIA: DRY CHEMICAL, CARBON DIOXIDE, HALON, WATER SPRAY OR STANDARD FOAM (1987 EMERGENCY RESPONSE GUIDEBOOK, DOT P 5800.4). FOR LARGER FIRES, USE WATER SPRAY, FOG OR STANDARD FOAM (1987 EMERGENCY RESPONSE GUIDEBOOK, DOT P 5800.4).

FIREFIGHTING: MOVE CONTAINERS FROM FIRE AREA IF POSSIBLE (1987 EMERGENCY RESPONSE GUIDEBOOK, DOT P 5800.4, GUIDE PAGE 53).

EXTINGUISH FIRE USING AGENTS SUITABLE FOR TYPE OF SURROUNDING FIRE. USE WATER IN FLOODING AMOUNTS AS A FOG. AVOID BREATHING DUSTS AND FUMES FROM BURNING MATERIAL; KEEP UPWIND.

TOXICITY

PRYNACHLOR: TOXICITY DATA: 1926 MG/KG SKIN-RABBIT LD50; 1170 MG/KG ORAL-RAT LD50; 150 MG/KG ORAL-MOUSE LD50. CARCINOGEN STATUS: NONE. ACUTE TOXICITY DATA: MODERATELY TOXIC BY DERMAL ABSORPTION AND INGESTION. TARGET EFFECTS: NO DATA AVAILABLE.

HEALTH EFFECTS AND FIRST AID

INHALATION: PRYNACHLOR: **ACUTE EXPOSURE-** NO DATA AVAILABLE. **CHRONIC EXPOSURE-** NO DATA AVAILABLE.

FIRST AID- REMOVE FROM EXPOSURE AREA TO FRESH AIR IMMEDIATELY. IF BREATHING HAS STOPPED, PERFORM ARTIFICIAL RESPIRATION. KEEP PERSON WARM AND AT REST. TREAT SYMPTOMATICALLY AND SUPPORTIVELY. GET MEDICAL ATTENTION IMMEDIATELY.

SKIN CONTACT: PRYNACHLOR: **ACUTE EXPOSURE-** A LETHAL DOSE IN RABBITS BY DERMAL ABSORPTION WAS 1926 MG/KG. **CHRONIC EXPOSURE-** NO DATA AVAILABLE.

FIRST AID- REMOVE CONTAMINATED CLOTHING AND SHOES IMMEDIATELY. WASH AFFECTED AREA WITH SOAP OR MILD DETERGENT AND LARGE AMOUNTS OF WATER UNTIL NO EVIDENCE OF CHEMICAL REMAINS (APPROXIMATELY 15-20 MINUTES). GET MEDICAL ATTENTION IMMEDIATELY.

EYE CONTACT: PRYNACHLOR: **ACUTE EXPOSURE-** NO DATA AVAILABLE. **CHRONIC EXPOSURE-** NO DATA AVAILABLE.

FIRST AID- WASH EYES IMMEDIATELY WITH LARGE AMOUNTS OF WATER OR NORMAL SALINE, OCCASIONALLY LIFTING UPPER AND LOWER LIDS, UNTIL NO EVIDENCE OF CHEMICAL REMAINS (APPROXIMATELY 15-20 MINUTES). GET MEDICAL ATTENTION IMMEDIATELY.

INGESTION: PRYNACHLOR: **ACUTE EXPOSURE-** A LETHAL DOSE IN RATS WAS 1170 MG/KG. **CHRONIC EXPOSURE-** NO DATA AVAILABLE.

FIRST AID- REMOVE BY GASTRIC LAVAGE AND CATHARSIS. MAINTAIN BLOOD PRESSURE AND AIRWAY. GIVE OXYGEN IF RESPIRATION IS DEPRESSED. DO NOT PERFORM GASTRIC LAVAGE IF VICTIM IS UNCONSCIOUS. GET MEDICAL ATTENTION IMMEDIATELY (DREISBACH, HANDBOOK OF POISONING, 12TH ED.).

ADMINISTRATION OF LAVAGE OR OXYGEN SHOULD BE PERFORMED BY QUALIFIED MEDICAL PERSONNEL.

ANTIDOTE: NO SPECIFIC ANTIDOTE. TREAT SYMPTOMATICALLY AND SUPPORTIVELY.

REACTIVITY

REACTIVITY: STABLE UNDER NORMAL TEMPERATURES AND PRESSURES.

INCOMPATIBILITIES: PRYNACHLOR: NO DATA AVAILABLE.

DECOMPOSITION: THERMAL DECOMPOSITION PRODUCTS MAY INCLUDE TOXIC OXIDES OF NITROGEN AND CARBON AND TOXIC AND CORROSIVE FUMES OF CHLORIDES.

POLYMERIZATION: HAZARDOUS POLYMERIZATION HAS NOT BEEN REPORTED TO OCCUR UNDER NORMAL TEMPERATURES AND PRESSURES.

STORAGE AND DISPOSAL

OBSERVE ALL FEDERAL, STATE AND LOCAL REGULATIONS WHEN STORING OR DISPOSING OF THIS SUBSTANCE. FOR ASSISTANCE, CONTACT THE DISTRICT DIRECTOR OF THE ENVIRONMENTAL PROTECTION AGENCY.

STORAGE

STORE IN ACCORDANCE WITH 40 CFR 165 RECOMMENDED PROCEDURES FOR THE DISPOSAL AND STORAGE OF PESTICIDES AND PESTICIDE CONTAINERS.

DISPOSAL

DISPOSAL MUST BE IN ACCORDANCE WITH 40 CFR 165 RECOMMENDED PROCEDURES FOR THE DISPOSAL AND STORAGE OF PESTICIDES AND PESTICIDE CONTAINERS.

CONDITIONS TO AVOID

MAY BURN BUT DOES NOT IGNITE READILY.

SPILL AND LEAK PROCEDURES

OCCUPATIONAL SPILL: DO NOT TOUCH SPILLED MATERIAL. STOP LEAK IF YOU CAN DO IT WITHOUT RISK. FOR SMALL SPILLS, TAKE UP WITH SAND OR OTHER ABSORBENT MATERIAL AND PLACE INTO CONTAINERS FOR LATER DISPOSAL. FOR SMALL DRY SPILLS, WITH A CLEAN SHOVEL PLACE MATERIAL INTO CLEAN, DRY CONTAINER AND COVER. MOVE CONTAINERS FROM SPILL AREA. FOR LARGER SPILLS, DIKE FAR AHEAD OF SPILL FOR LATER DISPOSAL. KEEP UNNECESSARY PEOPLE AWAY. ISOLATE HAZARD AREA AND DENY ENTRY.

PROTECTIVE EQUIPMENT

VENTILATION: PROVIDE LOCAL EXHAUST OR GENERAL DILUTION VENTILATION SYSTEM.

RESPIRATOR: THE FOLLOWING RESPIRATORS ARE RECOMMENDED BASED ON INFORMATION FOUND IN THE PHYSICAL DATA, TOXICITY AND HEALTH EFFECTS SECTIONS. THEY ARE RANKED IN ORDER FROM MINIMUM TO MAXIMUM RESPIRATORY PROTECTION. THE SPECIFIC RESPIRATOR SELECTED MUST BE BASED ON CONTAMINATION LEVELS FOUND IN THE WORK PLACE, MUST NOT EXCEED THE WORKING LIMITS OF THE RESPIRATOR AND BE JOINTLY APPROVED BY THE NATIONAL INSTITUTE FOR OCCUPATIONAL SAFETY AND HEALTH AND THE MINE SAFETY AND HEALTH ADMINISTRATION (NIOSH-MSHA).

CHEMICAL CARTRIDGE RESPIRATOR WITH AN ORGANIC VAPOR CARTRIDGE(S) WITH A FULL FACEPIECE AND ORGANIC VAPOR CARTRIDGE(S) IN COMBINATION WITH A DUST AND MIST FILTER.

POWERED AIR-PURIFYING RESPIRATOR WITH A TIGHT-FITTING FACEPIECE AND ORGANIC VAPOR CARTRIDGE(S) IN COMBINATION WITH A HIGH-EFFICIENCY PARTICULATE FILTER.

TYPE 'C' SUPPLIED-AIR RESPIRATOR WITH A FULL FACEPIECE OPERATED IN A PRESSURE-DEMAND OR OTHER POSITIVE PRESSURE MODE.

SELF-CONTAINED BREATHING APPARATUS WITH A FULL FACEPIECE OPERATED IN PRESSURE-DEMAND OR OTHER POSITIVE PRESSURE MODE.

FOR FIREFIGHTING AND OTHER IMMEDIATELY DANGEROUS TO LIFE OR HEALTH CONDITIONS:

SELF-CONTAINED BREATHING APPARATUS WITH FULL FACEPIECE OPERATED IN PRESSURE-DEMAND OR OTHER POSITIVE PRESSURE MODE.

SUPPLIED-AIR RESPIRATOR WITH FULL FACEPIECE AND OPERATED IN PRESSURE-DEMAND OR OTHER POSITIVE PRESSURE MODE IN COMBINATION WITH AN AUXILIARY SELF-CONTAINED BREATHING APPARATUS OPERATED IN PRESSURE-DEMAND OR OTHER POSITIVE PRESSURE MODE.

CLOTHING: EMPLOYEE MUST WEAR APPROPRIATE PROTECTIVE (IMPERVIOUS) CLOTHING AND EQUIPMENT TO PREVENT REPEATED OR PROLONGED SKIN CONTACT WITH THIS SUBSTANCE.

GLOVES: EMPLOYEE MUST WEAR APPROPRIATE PROTECTIVE GLOVES TO PREVENT CONTACT WITH THIS SUBSTANCE.

EYE PROTECTION: EMPLOYEE MUST WEAR SPLASH-PROOF OR DUST-RESISTANT SAFETY GOGGLES TO PREVENT EYE CONTACT WITH THIS SUBSTANCE.

EMERGENCY EYE WASH: WHERE THERE IS ANY POSSIBILITY THAT AN EMPLOYEE'S EYES MAY BE EXPOSED TO THIS SUBSTANCE, THE EMPLOYER SHOULD PROVIDE AN EYE WASH FOUNTAIN WITHIN THE IMMEDIATE WORK AREA FOR EMERGENCY USE.

AUTHORIZED BY- OCCUPATIONAL HEALTH SERVICES, INC.

CREATION DATE: 10/04/89 ***REVISION DATE:*** 05/11/90

MATERIAL SAFETY DATA SHEET

OCCUPATIONAL HEALTH SERVICES, INC.	EMERGENCY CONTACT:
AGRICULTURE AND PESTICIDE DIVISION	JOHN S. BRANSFORD, JR. (615) 292-1180
450 SEVENTH AVENUE, SUITE 2407	
NEW YORK, NEW YORK 10123	
1-800-445-MSDS OR (212) 967-1100	

SUBSTANCE IDENTIFICATION

CAS-NUMBER 1918-13-4

SUBSTANCE: CHLORTHIAMID

TRADE NAMES/SYNONYMS: BENZENECARBOTHIOAMIDE, 2,6-DICHLORO-; BENZAMIDE, 2,6-DICHLOROTHIO-; 2,6-DICHLOROTHIOBENZAMIDE; 2,6-DICHLOROBENZENECARBOTHIOAMIDE; 2,6-DICHLORO(THIOBENZAMIDE); CHLORTHIAMIDE; PREFIX; WL 5792; C7H5CL2NS; PST73046

CHEMICAL FAMILY: AMIDE

HALOGEN COMPOUND, AROMATIC

MOLECULAR FORMULA: C7-H5-CL2-N-S

MOLECULAR WEIGHT: 206.10

CERCLA RATINGS (SCALE 0-3): HEALTH=3 FIRE=1 REACTIVITY=0 PERSISTENCE=3

NFPA RATINGS (SCALE 0-4): HEALTH=U FIRE=1 REACTIVITY=0

COMPONENTS AND CONTAMINANTS

COMPONENT: CHLORTHIAMID ***PERCENT:*** 100.0

CAS# 1918-13-4

OTHER CONTAMINANTS: NONE

EXPOSURE LIMITS: NO OCCUPATIONAL EXPOSURE LIMITS ESTABLISHED BY OSHA, ACGIH, OR NIOSH.

PHYSICAL DATA

DESCRIPTION: OFF-WHITE SOLID. ***MELTING POINT:*** 304-306 F (151-152 C)

SPECIFIC GRAVITY: NOT AVAILABLE ***VAPOR PRESSURE:*** NEGLIGIBLE

SOLUBILITY IN WATER: 0.095% @ 21 C

SOLVENT SOLUBILITY: SOLUBLE IN CHLOROFORM AND AROMATIC AND CHLORINATED HYDROCARBONS.

FIRE AND EXPLOSION DATA

FIRE AND EXPLOSION HAZARD: SLIGHT FIRE HAZARD WHEN EXPOSED TO HEAT OR FLAME.

FIREFIGHTING MEDIA: DRY CHEMICAL, CARBON DIOXIDE, HALON, WATER SPRAY OR STANDARD FOAM (1987 EMERGENCY RESPONSE GUIDEBOOK, DOT P 5800.4).

FOR LARGER FIRES, USE WATER SPRAY, FOG OR STANDARD FOAM (1987 EMERGENCY RESPONSE GUIDEBOOK, DOT P 5800.4).

FIREFIGHTING: MOVE CONTAINER FROM FIRE AREA IF POSSIBLE. DO NOT SCATTER SPILLED MATERIAL WITH HIGH PRESSURE WATER STREAMS. DIKE FIRE CONTROL WATER FOR LATER DISPOSAL (1987 EMERGENCY RESPONSE GUIDEBOOK, DOT P 5800.4, GUIDE PAGE 31).

USE AGENTS SUITABLE FOR TYPE OF SURROUNDING FIRE. AVOID BREATHING HAZARDOUS VAPORS, KEEP UPWIND.

TOXICITY

CHLORTHIAMID: TOXICITY DATA: 1000 MG/KG SKIN-RAT LD50; 757 MG/KG ORAL-RAT LD50; 500 MG/KG ORAL-MOUSE LD50; 300 MG/KG ORAL-RABBIT LD50; 125 MG/KG ORAL-DOMESTIC ANIMAL LDLO; 242 MG/KG INTRAPERITONEAL-RAT LD50; MUTAGENIC DATA (RTECS). CARCINOGEN STATUS: NONE. ACUTE TOXICITY LEVEL: TOXIC BY DERMAL ABSORPTION; MODERATELY TOXIC BY INGESTION. TARGET EFFECTS: NO DATA AVAILABLE.

HEALTH EFFECTS AND FIRST AID

INHALATION: CHLORTHIAMID: **ACUTE EXPOSURE-** NO DATA AVAILABLE. **CHRONIC EXPOSURE-** NO DATA AVAILABLE.

FIRST AID- REMOVE FROM EXPOSURE AREA TO FRESH AIR IMMEDIATELY. IF BREATHING HAS STOPPED, PERFORM ARTIFICIAL RESPIRATION. KEEP PERSON WARM AND AT REST. TREAT SYMPTOMATICALLY AND SUPPORTIVELY. GET MEDICAL ATTENTION IMMEDIATELY.

SKIN CONTACT: CHLORTHIAMID: TOXIC. **ACUTE EXPOSURE-** THIS MATERIAL WAS REPORTED TO BE NONIRRITATING TO THE SKIN. EFFECTS OF SEDATION AND NARCOSIS WERE PRODUCED IN RATS FROM DERMAL ABSORPTION. **CHRONIC EXPOSURE-** NO DATA AVAILABLE.
FIRST AID- REMOVE CONTAMINATED CLOTHING AND SHOES IMMEDIATELY. WASH AFFECTED AREA WITH SOAP OR MILD DETERGENT AND LARGE AMOUNTS OF WATER UNTIL NO EVIDENCE OF CHEMICAL REMAINS (APPROXIMATELY 15-20 MINUTES). GET MEDICAL ATTENTION IMMEDIATELY.

EYE CONTACT: CHLORTHIAMID: **ACUTE EXPOSURE-** THIS MATERIAL WAS REPORTED TO BE NONIRRITATING TO THE EYES. **CHRONIC EXPOSURE-** NO DATA AVAILABLE.
FIRST AID- WASH EYES IMMEDIATELY WITH LARGE AMOUNTS OF WATER OR NORMAL SALINE, OCCASIONALLY LIFTING UPPER AND LOWER LIDS, UNTIL NO EVIDENCE OF CHEMICAL REMAINS (APPROXIMATELY 15-20 MINUTES). GET MEDICAL ATTENTION IMMEDIATELY.

INGESTION: CHLORTHIAMID: **ACUTE EXPOSURE-** EFFECTS OF SEDATION AND NARCOSIS WERE OBSERVED IN RATS FED CHLORTHIAMID. IN DOGS, LARGE ORAL DOSES CAUSED VOMITING. A SIGNIFICANT INCREASE IN THE FREQUENCY OF ABERRANT METAPHASES WAS INDUCED IN MICE AT DOSES OF 500 TO 1,000 MG/KG. **CHRONIC EXPOSURE-** IN RAT FEEDING EXPERIMENTS AT THE 100 PPM LEVEL, CHLORTHIAMID PRODUCED REVERSIBLE HEPATOCELLULAR ALTERATIONS.
FIRST AID- REMOVE BY GASTRIC LAVAGE AND CATHARSIS. MAINTAIN BLOOD PRESSURE AND AIRWAY. GIVE OXYGEN IF RESPIRATION IS DEPRESSED. DO NOT PERFORM GASTRIC LAVAGE IF VICTIM IS UNCONSCIOUS. GET MEDICAL ATTENTION IMMEDIATELY (DREISBACH, HANDBOOK OF POISONING, 12TH ED.).
ADMINISTRATION OF LAVAGE OR OXYGEN SHOULD BE PERFORMED BY QUALIFIED MEDICAL PERSONNEL.
ANTIDOTE: NO SPECIFIC ANTIDOTE. TREAT SYMPTOMATICALLY AND SUPPORTIVELY.

REACTIVITY

REACTIVITY: STABLE UNDER NORMAL TEMPERATURES AND PRESSURES.
INCOMPATIBILITIES: CHLORTHIAMID: OXIDIZERS (STRONG): FIRE AND EXPLOSION HAZARD.
DECOMPOSITION: THERMAL DECOMPOSITION PRODUCTS MAY INCLUDE TOXIC OXIDES OF NITROGEN, SULFUR, AND CARBON, AND TOXIC AND CORROSIVE FUMES OF CHLORIDES.
POLYMERIZATION: HAZARDOUS POLYMERIZATION HAS NOT BEEN REPORTED TO OCCUR UNDER NORMAL TEMPERATURES AND PRESSURES.

STORAGE AND DISPOSAL

OBSERVE ALL FEDERAL, STATE AND LOCAL REGULATIONS WHEN STORING OR DISPOSING OF THIS SUBSTANCE. FOR ASSISTANCE, CONTACT THE DISTRICT DIRECTOR OF THE ENVIRONMENTAL PROTECTION AGENCY.

STORAGE

STORE IN ACCORDANCE WITH 40 CFR 165 RECOMMENDED PROCEDURES FOR THE DISPOSAL AND STORAGE OF PESTICIDES AND PESTICIDE CONTAINERS.
STORE AWAY FROM INCOMPATIBLE SUBSTANCES.

DISPOSAL

DISPOSAL MUST BE IN ACCORDANCE WITH 40 CFR 165 RECOMMENDED PROCEDURES FOR THE DISPOSAL AND STORAGE OF PESTICIDES AND PESTICIDE CONTAINERS.

CONDITIONS TO AVOID

MAY BURN BUT DOES NOT IGNITE READILY. AVOID CONTACT WITH STRONG OXIDIZERS, EXCESSIVE HEAT, SPARKS, OR OPEN FLAME.

SPILL AND LEAK PROCEDURES

OCCUPATIONAL SPILL: SWEEP UP AND PLACE IN SUITABLE CLEAN, DRY CONTAINERS FOR RECLAMATION OR LATER DISPOSAL. DO NOT FLUSH SPILLED MATERIAL INTO SEWER. KEEP UNNECESSARY PEOPLE AWAY.

PROTECTIVE EQUIPMENT

VENTILATION: PROVIDE LOCAL EXHAUST OR GENERAL DILUTION VENTILATION SYSTEM.
RESPIRATOR: THE FOLLOWING RESPIRATORS ARE RECOMMENDED BASED ON INFORMATION FOUND IN THE PHYSICAL DATA, TOXICITY AND HEALTH EFFECTS SECTIONS. THEY ARE RANKED IN ORDER FROM MINIMUM TO MAXIMUM RESPIRATORY PROTECTION. THE SPECIFIC RESPIRATOR SELECTED MUST BE BASED ON CONTAMINATION LEVELS FOUND IN THE WORK PLACE, MUST NOT EXCEED THE WORKING LIMITS OF THE RESPIRATOR AND BE JOINTLY APPROVED BY THE NATIONAL INSTITUTE FOR OCCUPATIONAL SAFETY AND HEALTH AND THE MINE SAFETY AND HEALTH ADMINISTRATION (NIOSH-MSHA).
CHEMICAL CARTRIDGE RESPIRATOR WITH AN ORGANIC VAPOR CARTRIDGE(S) IN COMBINATION WITH A DUST AND MIST FILTER.
GAS MASK WITH ORGANIC VAPOR CANISTER (CHIN-STYLE OR FRONT- OR BACK-MOUNTED CANISTER) WITH A DUST AND MIST FILTER.
GAS MASK WITH ORGANIC VAPOR CANISTER (CHIN-STYLE OR FRONT- OR BACK-MOUNTED CANISTER) WITH A PARTICULATE FILTER.
POWERED AIR-PURIFYING RESPIRATOR WITH A HIGH-EFFICIENCY FILTER.
TYPE 'C' SUPPLIED-AIR RESPIRATOR WITH A FULL FACEPIECE OPERATED IN A PRESSURE-DEMAND OR OTHER POSITIVE PRESSURE MODE.
SELF-CONTAINED BREATHING APPARATUS WITH A FULL FACEPIECE OPERATED IN PRESSURE-DEMAND OR OTHER POSITIVE PRESSURE MODE.
FOR FIREFIGHTING AND OTHER IMMEDIATELY DANGEROUS TO LIFE OR HEALTH CONDITIONS:
SELF-CONTAINED BREATHING APPARATUS WITH FULL FACEPIECE OPERATED IN PRESSURE-DEMAND OR OTHER POSITIVE PRESSURE MODE.
SUPPLIED-AIR RESPIRATOR WITH FULL FACEPIECE AND OPERATED IN PRESSURE-DEMAND OR OTHER POSITIVE PRESSURE MODE IN COMBINATION WITH AN AUXILIARY SELF-CONTAINED BREATHING APPARATUS OPERATED IN PRESSURE-DEMAND OR OTHER POSITIVE PRESSURE MODE.
CLOTHING: EMPLOYEE MUST WEAR APPROPRIATE PROTECTIVE (IMPERVIOUS) CLOTHING AND EQUIPMENT TO PREVENT REPEATED OR PROLONGED SKIN CONTACT WITH THIS SUBSTANCE.
GLOVES: EMPLOYEE MUST WEAR APPROPRIATE PROTECTIVE GLOVES TO PREVENT CONTACT WITH THIS SUBSTANCE.
EYE PROTECTION: EMPLOYEE MUST WEAR SPLASH-PROOF OR DUST-RESISTANT SAFETY GOGGLES TO PREVENT EYE CONTACT WITH THIS SUBSTANCE.
EMERGENCY EYE WASH: WHERE THERE IS ANY POSSIBILITY THAT AN EMPLOYEE'S EYES MAY BE EXPOSED TO THIS SUBSTANCE, THE EMPLOYER SHOULD PROVIDE AN EYE WASH FOUNTAIN WITHIN THE IMMEDIATE WORK AREA FOR EMERGENCY USE.

AUTHORIZED BY- OCCUPATIONAL HEALTH SERVICES, INC.
CREATION DATE: 10/04/89 ***REVISION DATE:*** 05/31/90

MATERIAL SAFETY DATA SHEET

OCCUPATIONAL HEALTH SERVICES, INC.
AGRICULTURE AND PESTICIDE DIVISION
450 SEVENTH AVENUE, SUITE 2407
NEW YORK, NEW YORK 10123
1-800-445-MSDS OR (212) 967-1100

EMERGENCY CONTACT:
JOHN S. BRANSFORD, JR. (615) 292-1180

SUBSTANCE IDENTIFICATION

CAS-NUMBER 3615-21-2
SUBSTANCE: **CHLORFLURAZOLE**
TRADE NAMES/SYNONYMS: 4,5-DICHLORO-2-(TRIFLUOROMETHYL)-1H-BENZIMIDAZOLE; 4,5-DICHLORO-2-(TRIFLUOROMETHYL)BENZIMIDAZOLE; 4,5(OR 6,7)-DICHLORO-2-(TRIFLUOROMETHYL)BENZIMIDAZOLE; 4,5-DICHLORO-2-TRIFLUOROMETHYLBENZIMIDAZOLE; CHLOROFLURAZOLE; BENZIMIDAZOLE, 4,5-DICHLORO-2-(TRIFLUOROMETHYL)-; NC 3363; PST73047
CHEMICAL FAMILY: IMIDAZOLE
HALOGEN
MOLECULAR FORMULA: C8-H3-CL2-F3-N2
MOLECULAR WEIGHT: 255.03
CERCLA RATINGS (SCALE 0-3): HEALTH=3 FIRE=U REACTIVITY=U PERSISTENCE=3
NFPA RATINGS (SCALE 0-4): HEALTH=3 FIRE=U REACTIVITY=U

COMPONENTS AND CONTAMINANTS

COMPONENT: CHLORFLURAZOLE ***PERCENT:*** 100.0
CAS# 3615-21-2
OTHER CONTAMINANTS: NONE
EXPOSURE LIMITS: CHLORFLURAZOLE: NO OCCUPATIONAL EXPOSURE LIMITS ESTABLISHED BY OSHA, ACGIH, OR NIOSH.
500/10,000 POUNDS SARA SECTION 302 THRESHOLD PLANNING QUANTITY 1 POUND SARA SECTION 304 REPORTABLE QUANTITY

PHYSICAL DATA

DESCRIPTION: SOLID ***MELTING POINT:*** 417 F (214 C)
SPECIFIC GRAVITY: NOT AVAILABLE ***SOLUBILITY IN WATER:*** NOT AVAILABLE

FIRE AND EXPLOSION DATA

FIRE AND EXPLOSION HAZARD: UNKNOWN FIRE AND EXPLOSION HAZARD.

FIREFIGHTING MEDIA: DRY CHEMICAL, CARBON DIOXIDE, HALON, WATER SPRAY OR STANDARD FOAM (1987 EMERGENCY RESPONSE GUIDEBOOK, DOT P 5800.4). FOR LARGER FIRES, USE WATER SPRAY, FOG OR STANDARD FOAM (1987 EMERGENCY RESPONSE GUIDEBOOK, DOT P 5800.4).

FIREFIGHTING: MOVE CONTAINERS FROM FIRE AREA IF POSSIBLE (1987 EMERGENCY RESPONSE GUIDEBOOK, DOT P 5800.4, GUIDE PAGE 53).
EXTINGUISH ONLY IF FLOW CAN BE STOPPED. EXTINGUISH USING AGENT INDICATED. USE FLOODING AMOUNTS OF WATER AS A FOG. COOL CONTAINERS WITH FLOODING AMOUNTS OF WATER FROM AS FAR A DISTANCE AS POSSIBLE. AVOID BREATHING POISONOUS VAPORS, KEEP UPWIND. CONSIDER EVACUATION OF DOWNWIND AREA IF MATERIAL IS LEAKING.

TRANSPORTATION DATA

DEPARTMENT OF TRANSPORTATION HAZARD CLASSIFICATION 49 CFR 172.101: POISON B
DEPARTMENT OF TRANSPORTATION LABELING REQUIREMENTS 49 CFR 172.101 AND SUBPART E: POISON
DEPARTMENT OF TRANSPORTATION PACKAGING REQUIREMENTS: 49 CFR 173.365 EXCEPTIONS: 49 CFR 173.364

TOXICITY

CHLORFLURAZOLE: TOXICITY DATA: 13080 UG/KG ORAL-RAT LD50; 14 MG/KG INTRAPERITONEAL-MOUSE LD50. CARCINOGEN STATUS: NONE. ACUTE TOXICITY LEVEL: HIGHLY TOXIC BY INGESTION. TARGET EFFECTS: NO DATA AVAILABLE.

HEALTH EFFECTS AND FIRST AID

INHALATION: CHLORFLURAZOLE: **ACUTE EXPOSURE-** NO DATA AVAILABLE. **CHRONIC EXPOSURE-** NO DATA AVAILABLE.

FIRST AID- REMOVE FROM EXPOSURE AREA TO FRESH AIR IMMEDIATELY. IF BREATHING HAS STOPPED, PERFORM ARTIFICIAL RESPIRATION. KEEP PERSON WARM AND AT REST. TREAT SYMPTOMATICALLY AND SUPPORTIVELY. GET MEDICAL ATTENTION IMMEDIATELY.

SKIN CONTACT: CHLORFLURAZOLE: **ACUTE EXPOSURE-** NO DATA AVAILABLE. **CHRONIC EXPOSURE-** NO DATA AVAILABLE.

FIRST AID- REMOVE CONTAMINATED CLOTHING AND SHOES IMMEDIATELY. WASH AFFECTED AREA WITH SOAP OR MILD DETERGENT AND LARGE AMOUNTS OF WATER UNTIL NO EVIDENCE OF CHEMICAL REMAINS (APPROXIMATELY 15-20 MINUTES). GET MEDICAL ATTENTION IMMEDIATELY.

EYE CONTACT: CHLORFLURAZOLE: **ACUTE EXPOSURE-** NO DATA AVAILABLE. **CHRONIC EXPOSURE-** NO DATA AVAILABLE.

FIRST AID- WASH EYES IMMEDIATELY WITH LARGE AMOUNTS OF WATER OR NORMAL SALINE, OCCASIONALLY LIFTING UPPER AND LOWER LIDS, UNTIL NO EVIDENCE OF CHEMICAL REMAINS (APPROXIMATELY 15-20 MINUTES). GET MEDICAL ATTENTION IMMEDIATELY.

INGESTION: CHLORFLURAZOLE: HIGHLY TOXIC. **ACUTE EXPOSURE-** A VERY SMALL DOSE WAS LETHAL IN RATS; NO SYMPTOMS WERE REPORTED. **CHRONIC EXPOSURE-** NO DATA AVAILABLE.

FIRST AID- IF EXTENSIVE VOMITING HAS NOT OCCURRED, THE SUBSTANCE SHOULD BE REMOVED BY EMESIS OR GASTRIC LAVAGE PROVIDED THAT THE PATIENT IS CONSCIOUS AND CONVULSIONS ARE NOT PRESENT. KEEP HEAD BELOW HIPS DURING VOMITING TO PREVENT ASPIRATION. DO NOT ATTEMPT TO MAKE AN UNCONSCIOUS PERSON VOMIT. TREAT SYMPTOMATICALLY AND SUPPORTIVELY. GET MEDICAL ATTENTION IMMEDIATELY (DREISBACH, HANDBOOK OF POISONING, 12TH ED.). TREATMENT SHOULD BE PERFORMED BY QUALIFIED MEDICAL PERSONNEL.

ANTIDOTE: NO SPECIFIC ANTIDOTE. TREAT SYMPTOMATICALLY AND SUPPORTIVELY.

REACTIVITY

REACTIVITY: NO DATA AVAILABLE.

INCOMPATIBILITIES: CHLORFLURAZOLE: NO DATA AVAILABLE.

DECOMPOSITION: THERMAL DECOMPOSITION MAY RELEASE TOXIC AND/OR HAZARDOUS GASES.

POLYMERIZATION: HAZARDOUS POLYMERIZATION HAS NOT BEEN REPORTED TO OCCUR UNDER NORMAL TEMPERATURES AND PRESSURES.

STORAGE AND DISPOSAL

OBSERVE ALL FEDERAL, STATE AND LOCAL REGULATIONS WHEN STORING OR DISPOSING OF THIS SUBSTANCE. FOR ASSISTANCE, CONTACT THE DISTRICT DIRECTOR OF THE ENVIRONMENTAL PROTECTION AGENCY.

****STORAGE****

STORE IN ACCORDANCE WITH 40 CFR 165 RECOMMENDED PROCEDURES FOR THE DISPOSAL AND STORAGE OF PESTICIDES AND PESTICIDE CONTAINERS.
THRESHOLD PLANNING QUANTITY (TPQ): THE SUPERFUND AMENDMENTS AND REAUTHORIZATION ACT (SARA) SECTION 302 REQUIRES THAT EACH FACILITY WHERE ANY EXTREMELY HAZARDOUS SUBSTANCE IS PRESENT IN A QUANTITY EQUAL TO OR GREATER THAN THE TPQ ESTABLISHED FOR THAT SUBSTANCE NOTIFY THE STATE EMERGENCY RESPONSE COMMISSION FOR THE STATE IN WHICH IT IS LOCATED. SECTION 303 OF SARA REQUIRES THESE FACILITIES TO PARTICIPATE IN LOCAL EMERGENCY RESPONSE PLANNING (40 CFR 355.30).

****DISPOSAL****

DISPOSAL MUST BE IN ACCORDANCE WITH 40 CFR 165 RECOMMENDED PROCEDURES FOR THE DISPOSAL AND STORAGE OF PESTICIDES AND PESTICIDE CONTAINERS.

CONDITIONS TO AVOID

NONE REPORTED.

SPILL AND LEAK PROCEDURES

OCCUPATIONAL SPILL: DO NOT TOUCH SPILLED MATERIAL. STOP LEAK IF YOU CAN DO IT WITHOUT RISK. FOR SMALL SPILLS, TAKE UP WITH SAND OR OTHER ABSORBENT MATERIAL AND PLACE INTO CONTAINERS FOR LATER DISPOSAL. FOR SMALL DRY SPILLS, WITH A CLEAN SHOVEL PLACE MATERIAL INTO CLEAN, DRY CONTAINER AND COVER. MOVE CONTAINERS FROM SPILL AREA. FOR LARGER SPILLS, DIKE FAR AHEAD OF SPILL FOR LATER DISPOSAL. KEEP UNNECESSARY PEOPLE AWAY. ISOLATE HAZARD AREA AND DENY ENTRY.
REPORTABLE QUANTITY (RQ): 1 POUND THE SUPERFUND AMENDMENTS AND REAUTHORIZATION ACT (SARA) SECTION 304 REQUIRES THAT A RELEASE EQUAL TO OR GREATER THAN THE REPORTABLE QUANTITY FOR THIS SUBSTANCE BE IMMEDIATELY REPORTED TO THE LOCAL EMERGENCY PLANNING COMMITTEE AND THE STATE EMERGENCY RESPONSE COMMISSION (40 CFR 355.40). IF THE RELEASE OF THIS SUBSTANCE IS REPORTABLE UNDER CERCLA SECTION 103, THE NATIONAL RESPONSE CENTER MUST BE NOTIFIED IMMEDIATELY AT (800) 424-8802 OR (202) 426-2675 IN THE METROPOLITAN WASHINGTON, D.C. AREA (40 CFR 302.6).

PROTECTIVE EQUIPMENT

VENTILATION: PROCESS ENCLOSURE RECOMMENDED.

RESPIRATOR: THE FOLLOWING RESPIRATORS ARE RECOMMENDED BASED ON INFORMATION FOUND IN THE PHYSICAL DATA, TOXICITY AND HEALTH EFFECTS SECTIONS. THEY ARE RANKED IN ORDER FROM MINIMUM TO MAXIMUM RESPIRATORY PROTECTION. THE SPECIFIC RESPIRATOR SELECTED MUST BE BASED ON CONTAMINATION LEVELS FOUND IN THE WORK PLACE, MUST NOT EXCEED THE WORKING LIMITS OF THE RESPIRATOR AND BE JOINTLY APPROVED BY THE NATIONAL INSTITUTE FOR OCCUPATIONAL SAFETY AND HEALTH AND THE MINE SAFETY AND HEALTH ADMINISTRATION (NIOSH-MSHA).
TYPE 'C' SUPPLIED-AIR RESPIRATOR WITH A FULL FACEPIECE OPERATED IN PRESSURE-DEMAND OR OTHER POSITIVE PRESSURE MODE OR WITH A FULL FACEPIECE, HELMET OR HOOD OPERATED IN CONTINOUS-FLOW MODE.
SELF-CONTAINED BREATHING APPARATUS WITH A FULL FACEPIECE OPERATED IN PRESSURE-DEMAND OR OTHER POSITIVE PRESSURE MODE.
FOR FIREFIGHTING AND OTHER IMMEDIATELY DANGEROUS TO LIFE OR HEALTH CONDITIONS:
SELF-CONTAINED BREATHING APPARATUS WITH FULL FACEPIECE OPERATED IN PRESSURE-DEMAND OR OTHER POSITIVE PRESSURE MODE.
SUPPLIED-AIR RESPIRATOR WITH FULL FACEPIECE AND OPERATED IN PRESSURE-DEMAND OR OTHER POSITIVE PRESSURE MODE IN COMBINATION WITH AN AUXILIARY SELF-CONTAINED BREATHING APPARATUS OPERATED IN PRESSURE-DEMAND OR OTHER POSITIVE PRESSURE MODE.

CLOTHING: EMPLOYEE MUST WEAR APPROPRIATE PROTECTIVE (IMPERVIOUS) CLOTHING AND EQUIPMENT TO PREVENT REPEATED OR PROLONGED SKIN CONTACT WITH THIS SUBSTANCE.

GLOVES: EMPLOYEE MUST WEAR APPROPRIATE PROTECTIVE GLOVES TO PREVENT CONTACT WITH THIS SUBSTANCE.

EYE PROTECTION: EMPLOYEE MUST WEAR SPLASH-PROOF OR DUST-RESISTANT SAFETY GOGGLES TO PREVENT EYE CONTACT WITH THIS SUBSTANCE.
EMERGENCY EYE WASH: WHERE THERE IS ANY POSSIBILITY THAT AN EMPLOYEE'S EYES MAY BE EXPOSED TO THIS SUBSTANCE, THE EMPLOYER SHOULD PROVIDE AN EYE WASH FOUNTAIN WITHIN THE IMMEDIATE WORK AREA FOR EMERGENCY USE.

AUTHORIZED BY- OCCUPATIONAL HEALTH SERVICES, INC.
CREATION DATE: 10/04/89 ***REVISION DATE:*** 05/11/90

MATERIAL SAFETY DATA SHEET

OCCUPATIONAL HEALTH SERVICES, INC.
AGRICULTURE AND PESTICIDE DIVISION
450 SEVENTH AVENUE, SUITE 2407
NEW YORK, NEW YORK 10123
1-800-445-MSDS OR (212) 967-1100

EMERGENCY CONTACT:
JOHN S. BRANSFORD, JR. (615) 292-1180

SUBSTANCE IDENTIFICATION

CAS-NUMBER 26259-45-0

SUBSTANCE: **SECBUMETON**

TRADE NAMES/SYNONYMS: 1,3,5-TRIAZINE-2,4-DIAMINE, N-ETHYL-6-METHOXY-N'-(1-METHYLPROPYL)-; N-ETHYL-6-METHOXY-N'-(1-METHYLPROPYL)-1,3,5-TRIAZINE-2,4-DIAMINE; S-TRIAZINE, 2-(SEC-BUTYLAMINO)-4-(ETHYLAMINO)-6-METHOXY-; 2-(SEC-BUTYLAMINO)-4-(ETHYLAMINO)-6-METHOXY-S-TRIAZINE; N-SEC-BUTYL-N-ETHYL-6-METHOXY-1,3,5-TRIAZINE-2,6-DIAMINE; 2-SEC-BUTYLAMINO-4-ETHYLAMINO-6-METHOXY-1,3,5-TRIAZINE; 2-SEC-BUTYLAMINO-4-ETHYLAMINO-6-METHOXY-S-TRIAZINE; SEC-BUMETON; SEC-BUMETONE; ETAZIN; ETAZINE; EZITAN; GEIGY GS 14254; GS 14254; ISOBUMETONE; SUMITOL; C10H19N5O; PST73051

CHEMICAL FAMILY: TRIAZINE

MOLECULAR FORMULA: C10-H19-N5-O

MOLECULAR WEIGHT: 225.29

CERCLA RATINGS (SCALE 0-3): HEALTH=2 FIRE=1 REACTIVITY=0 PERSISTENCE=2

NFPA RATINGS (SCALE 0-4): HEALTH=2 FIRE=1 REACTIVITY=0

COMPONENTS AND CONTAMINANTS

COMPONENT: SECBUMETON ***PERCENT:*** 100
CAS# 26259-45-0

OTHER CONTAMINANTS: NONE

EXPOSURE LIMITS: NO OCCUPATIONAL EXPOSURE LIMITS ESTABLISHED BY OSHA, ACGIH, OR NIOSH.

PHYSICAL DATA

DESCRIPTION: COLORLESS CRYSTALS. ***MELTING POINT:*** 187-190 F (86-88 C)

SPECIFIC GRAVITY: 1.105 ***VAPOR PRESSURE:*** 0.000007 MMHG @ 20 C

PH: ACID IN SOLUTION ***SOLUBILITY IN WATER:*** 600 PPM

SOLVENT SOLUBILITY: SOLUBLE IN ACETONE, DICHLOROMETHANE, HEXANE, METHANOL, N-OCTANOL, TOLUENE, ETHANOL

FIRE AND EXPLOSION DATA

FIRE AND EXPLOSION HAZARD: SLIGHT FIRE HAZARD WHEN EXPOSED TO HEAT OR FLAME.

FIREFIGHTING MEDIA: DRY CHEMICAL, CARBON DIOXIDE, HALON, WATER SPRAY OR STANDARD FOAM (1987 EMERGENCY RESPONSE GUIDEBOOK, DOT P 5800.4).
FOR LARGER FIRES, USE WATER SPRAY, FOG OR STANDARD FOAM (1987 EMERGENCY RESPONSE GUIDEBOOK, DOT P 5800.4).

FIREFIGHTING: MOVE CONTAINERS FROM FIRE AREA IF POSSIBLE (1987 EMERGENCY RESPONSE GUIDEBOOK, DOT P 5800.4, GUIDE PAGE 53).
EXTINGUISH USING AGENTS SUITABLE FOR SURROUNDING FIRE. USE FLOODING QUANTITIES OF WATER AS A FOG. KEEP MATERIAL OUT OF SEWERS AND WATER SOURCES. DO NOT TOUCH SPILLED MATERIAL. AVOID BREATHING HAZARDOUS FUMES; KEEP UPWIND.

TOXICITY

SECBUMETON: IRRITATION DATA: 35 MG/KG EYE-RABBIT SEVERE. TOXICITY DATA: 1000 MG/KG ORAL-RAT LD50. CARCINOGEN STATUS: NONE. LOCAL EFFECTS: IRRITANT- INHALATION, SKIN, AND EYES. ACUTE TOXICITY LEVEL: MODERATELY TOXIC BY INGESTION. TARGET EFFECTS: NO DATA AVAILABLE.

HEALTH EFFECTS AND FIRST AID

INHALATION: SECBUMETON: IRRITANT. **ACUTE EXPOSURE-** MAY CAUSE IRRITATION OF THE MUCOUS MEMBRANES. **CHRONIC EXPOSURE-** PROLONGED OR REPEATED EXPOSURE MAY CAUSE IRRITATION.

FIRST AID- REMOVE FROM EXPOSURE AREA TO FRESH AIR IMMEDIATELY. IF BREATHING HAS STOPPED, PERFORM ARTIFICIAL RESPIRATION. KEEP PERSON WARM AND AT REST. TREAT SYMPTOMATICALLY AND SUPPORTIVELY. GET MEDICAL ATTENTION IMMEDIATELY.

SKIN CONTACT: SECBUMETON: IRRITANT. **ACUTE EXPOSURE-** MAY CAUSE IRRITATION. **CHRONIC EXPOSURE-** PROLONGED OR REPEATED EXPOSURE TO IRRITANTS MAY CAUSE IRRITATION.

FIRST AID- REMOVE CONTAMINATED CLOTHING AND SHOES IMMEDIATELY. WASH AFFECTED AREA WITH SOAP OR MILD DETERGENT AND LARGE AMOUNTS OF WATER UNTIL NO EVIDENCE OF CHEMICAL REMAINS (APPROXIMATELY 15-20 MINUTES). GET MEDICAL ATTENTION IMMEDIATELY.

EYE CONTACT: SECBUMETON: IRRITANT. **ACUTE EXPOSURE-** 35 MG APPLIED TO THE EYES OF RABBITS WAS SEVERELY IRRITATING. **CHRONIC EXPOSURE-** PROLONGED OR REPEATED EXPOSURE TO IRRITANTS MAY CAUSE DERMATITIS.

FIRST AID- WASH EYES IMMEDIATELY WITH LARGE AMOUNTS OF WATER OR NORMAL SALINE, OCCASIONALLY LIFTING UPPER AND LOWER LIDS, UNTIL NO EVIDENCE OF CHEMICAL REMAINS (APPROXIMATELY 15-20 MINUTES). GET MEDICAL ATTENTION IMMEDIATELY.

INGESTION: SECUBMETON: **ACUTE EXPOSURE-** A LETHAL DOSE IN RATS WAS 1000 MG/KG. **CHRONIC EXPOSURE-** IN A 90-DAY STUDY OF RATS, A DIETARY LEVEL OF 640 MG/KG PRODUCED NO OBSERVABLE EFFECTS.

FIRST AID- REMOVE BY GASTRIC LAVAGE AND CATHARSIS. MAINTAIN BLOOD PRESSURE AND AIRWAY. GIVE OXYGEN IF RESPIRATION IS DEPRESSED. DO NOT PERFORM GASTRIC LAVAGE IF VICTIM IS UNCONSCIOUS. GET MEDICAL ATTENTION IMMEDIATELY (DREISBACH, HANDBOOK OF POISONING, 12TH ED.).
ADMINISTRATION OF LAVAGE OR OXYGEN SHOULD BE PERFORMED BY QUALIFIED MEDICAL PERSONNEL.

ANTIDOTE: NO SPECIFIC ANTIDOTE. TREAT SYMPTOMATICALLY AND SUPPORTIVELY.

REACTIVITY

REACTIVITY: STABLE UNDER NORMAL TEMPERATURES AND PRESSURES.

INCOMPATIBILITIES: SECBUMETON: NO DATA AVAILABLE.

DECOMPOSITION: THERMAL DECOMPOSITION PRODUCTS MAY INCLUDE TOXIC OXIDES OF CARBON AND NITROGEN.

POLYMERIZATION: HAZARDOUS POLYMERIZATION HAS NOT BEEN REPORTED TO OCCUR UNDER NORMAL TEMPERATURES AND PRESSURES.

STORAGE AND DISPOSAL

OBSERVE ALL FEDERAL, STATE AND LOCAL REGULATIONS WHEN STORING OR DISPOSING OF THIS SUBSTANCE. FOR ASSISTANCE, CONTACT THE DISTRICT DIRECTOR OF THE ENVIRONMENTAL PROTECTION AGENCY.

****STORAGE****

STORE IN ACCORDANCE WITH 40 CFR 165 RECOMMENDED PROCEDURES FOR THE DISPOSAL AND STORAGE OF PESTICIDES AND PESTICIDE CONTAINERS.

****DISPOSAL****

DISPOSAL MUST BE IN ACCORDANCE WITH 40 CFR 165 RECOMMENDED PROCEDURES FOR THE DISPOSAL AND STORAGE OF PESTICIDES AND PESTICIDE CONTAINERS.

CONDITIONS TO AVOID

MAY BURN BUT DOES NOT IGNITE READILY.

SPILL AND LEAK PROCEDURES

OCCUPATIONAL SPILL: DO NOT TOUCH SPILLED MATERIAL. STOP LEAK IF YOU CAN DO IT WITHOUT RISK. FOR SMALL SPILLS, TAKE UP WITH SAND OR OTHER ABSORBENT MATERIAL AND PLACE INTO CONTAINERS FOR LATER DISPOSAL. FOR SMALL DRY SPILLS, WITH A CLEAN SHOVEL PLACE MATERIAL INTO CLEAN, DRY CONTAINER AND COVER. MOVE CONTAINERS FROM SPILL AREA. FOR LARGER SPILLS, DIKE FAR AHEAD OF SPILL FOR LATER DISPOSAL. KEEP UNNECESSARY PEOPLE AWAY. ISOLATE HAZARD AREA AND DENY ENTRY.

PROTECTIVE EQUIPMENT

VENTILATION: PROVIDE LOCAL EXHAUST OR GENERAL DILUTION VENTILATION SYSTEM.

RESPIRATOR: THE FOLLOWING RESPIRATORS ARE RECOMMENDED BASED ON INFORMATION FOUND IN THE PHYSICAL DATA, TOXICITY AND HEALTH EFFECTS SECTIONS. THEY ARE RANKED IN ORDER FROM MINIMUM TO MAXIMUM RESPIRATORY PROTECTION. THE SPECIFIC RESPIRATOR SELECTED MUST BE BASED ON CONTAMINATION LEVELS FOUND IN THE WORK PLACE, MUST NOT EXCEED THE WORKING LIMITS OF THE RESPIRATOR AND BE JOINTLY APPROVED BY THE NATIONAL INSTITUTE FOR OCCUPATIONAL SAFETY AND HEALTH AND THE MINE SAFETY AND HEALTH ADMINISTRATION (NIOSH-MSHA).
CHEMICAL CARTRIDGE RESPIRATOR WITH AN ORGANIC VAPOR CARTRIDGE(S) WITH A FULL FACEPIECE AND ORGANIC VAPOR CARTRIDGE(S) IN COMBINATION WITH A DUST AND MIST FILTER.
POWERED AIR-PURIFYING RESPIRATOR WITH A TIGHT-FITTING FACEPIECE AND ORGANIC VAPOR CARTRIDGE(S) IN COMBINATION WITH A HIGH-EFFICIENCY PARTICULATE FILTER.
TYPE 'C' SUPPLIED-AIR RESPIRATOR WITH A FULL FACEPIECE OPERATED IN A PRESSURE-DEMAND OR OTHER POSITIVE PRESSURE MODE.
SELF-CONTAINED BREATHING APPARATUS WITH A FULL FACEPIECE OPERATED IN PRESSURE-DEMAND OR OTHER POSITIVE PRESSURE MODE.
FOR FIREFIGHTING AND OTHER IMMEDIATELY DANGEROUS TO LIFE OR HEALTH CONDITIONS:
SELF-CONTAINED BREATHING APPARATUS WITH FULL FACEPIECE OPERATED IN PRESSURE-DEMAND OR OTHER POSITIVE PRESSURE MODE. SUPPLIED-AIR RESPIRATOR WITH FULL FACEPIECE AND OPERATED IN PRESSURE-DEMAND OR

OTHER POSITIVE PRESSURE MODE IN COMBINATION WITH AN AUXILIARY SELF-CONTAINED BREATHING APPARATUS OPERATED IN PRESSURE-DEMAND OR OTHER POSITIVE PRESSURE MODE.

CLOTHING: EMPLOYEE MUST WEAR APPROPRIATE PROTECTIVE (IMPERVIOUS) CLOTHING AND EQUIPMENT TO PREVENT REPEATED OR PROLONGED SKIN CONTACT WITH THIS SUBSTANCE.

GLOVES: EMPLOYEE MUST WEAR APPROPRIATE PROTECTIVE GLOVES TO PREVENT CONTACT WITH THIS SUBSTANCE.

EYE PROTECTION: EMPLOYEE MUST WEAR SPLASH-PROOF OR DUST-RESISTANT SAFETY GOGGLES TO PREVENT EYE CONTACT WITH THIS SUBSTANCE. EMERGENCY EYE WASH: WHERE THERE IS ANY POSSIBILITY THAT AN EMPLOYEE'S EYES MAY BE EXPOSED TO THIS SUBSTANCE, THE EMPLOYER SHOULD PROVIDE AN EYE WASH FOUNTAIN WITHIN THE IMMEDIATE WORK AREA FOR EMERGENCY USE.

AUTHORIZED BY- OCCUPATIONAL HEALTH SERVICES, INC.
CREATION DATE: 10/05/89 ***REVISION DATE:*** 05/10/90

MATERIAL SAFETY DATA SHEET

OCCUPATIONAL HEALTH SERVICES, INC.
AGRICULTURE AND PESTICIDE DIVISION
450 SEVENTH AVENUE, SUITE 2407
NEW YORK, NEW YORK 10123
1-800-445-MSDS OR (212) 967-1100

EMERGENCY CONTACT:
JOHN S. BRANSFORD, JR. (615) 292-1180

SUBSTANCE IDENTIFICATION

CAS-NUMBER 2425-25-4

SUBSTANCE: <u>ACETOXON</u>

TRADE NAMES/SYNONYMS: ACETIC ACID, ((DIETHOXYPHOSPHINYL)THIO)-, ETHYL ESTER; ((DIETHOXYPHOSPHINYL)THIO)ACETIC ACID, ETHYL ESTER; ACETIC ACID, MERCAPTO-, ETHYL ESTER, S-ESTER WITH O,O-DIETHYL -PHOSPHOROTHIOATE; MERCAPTOACETIC ACID ETHYL ESTER, S-ESTER WITH O,O-DIETHYL -PHOSPHOROTHIOATE; O,O-DIETHYL S-CARBOETHOXYMETHYL PHOSPHOROTHIOATE; DIETHYL S-ETHOXYCARBONYLMETHYL PHOSPHOROTHIOLATE; ETHYL((DIETHOXYPHOSPHINYL)THIO)ACETATE; ACETAPHOS; ACETOPHOS; ACETOFOS; C8H17O5PS; PST73057

CHEMICAL FAMILY: PHOSPHOROTHIOATE

MOLECULAR FORMULA: (C2-H5-O)2-P(O)-S-C-H2-C(O)-O-C2-H5

MOLECULAR WEIGHT: 256.28

CERCLA RATINGS (SCALE 0-3): HEALTH=3 FIRE=U REACTIVITY=0 PERSISTENCE=1

NFPA RATINGS (SCALE 0-4): HEALTH=3 FIRE=U REACTIVITY=0

COMPONENTS AND CONTAMINANTS

COMPONENT: ACETOXON ***PERCENT:*** 100.0
CAS# 2425-25-4

OTHER CONTAMINANTS: NONE

EXPOSURE LIMITS: NO OCCUPATIONAL EXPOSURE LIMITS ESTABLISHED BY OSHA, ACGIH, OR NIOSH.

PHYSICAL DATA

DESCRIPTION: LIQUID. ***BOILING POINT:*** 248 F (120 C) @ 0.15 MMHG

SPECIFIC GRAVITY: 1.1840 ***SOLUBILITY IN WATER:*** SOLUBLE

SOLVENT SOLUBILITY: SOLUBLE IN MOST ORGANIC SOLVENTS.

FIRE AND EXPLOSION DATA

FIRE AND EXPLOSION HAZARD: UNKNOWN FIRE AND EXPLOSION HAZARD.

FIREFIGHTING MEDIA: DRY CHEMICAL, CARBON DIOXIDE, HALON, WATER SPRAY OR STANDARD FOAM (1987 EMERGENCY RESPONSE GUIDEBOOK, DOT P 5800.4). FOR LARGER FIRES, USE WATER SPRAY, FOG OR STANDARD FOAM (1987 EMERGENCY RESPONSE GUIDEBOOK, DOT P 5800.4).

FIREFIGHTING: MOVE CONTAINER FROM FIRE AREA IF POSSIBLE. DIKE FIRE CONTROL WATER FOR LATER DISPOSAL; DO NOT SCATTER THE MATERIAL. COOL FIRE-EXPOSED CONTAINERS WITH WATER FROM SIDE UNTIL WELL AFTER FIRE IS OUT. STAY AWAY FROM STORAGE TANK ENDS. WITHDRAW IMMEDIATELY IN CASE OF RISING SOUND FROM VENTING SAFETY DEVICE OR ANY DISCOLORATION OF STORAGE TANK DUE TO FIRE (1987 EMERGENCY RESPONSE GUIDEBOOK, DOT P 5800.4, GUIDE PAGE 28).
EXTINGUISH ONLY IF FLOW CAN BE STOPPED. USE FLOODING AMOUNTS OF WATER AS A FOG; SOLID STREAMS MAY BE INEFFECTIVE. COOL CONTAINERS WITH FLOODING AMOUNTS OF WATER FROM AS FAR A DISTANCE AS POSSIBLE. AVOID BREATHING POISONOUS VAPORS, KEEP UPWIND.

TRANSPORTATION DATA

DEPARTMENT OF TRANSPORTATION HAZARD CLASSIFICATION 49 CFR 172.101: POISON B
DEPARTMENT OF TRANSPORTATION LABELING REQUIREMENTS 49 CFR 172.101 AND SUBPART E: POISON
DEPARTMENT OF TRANSPORTATION PACKAGING REQUIREMENTS: 49 CFR 173.359 EXCEPTIONS: 49 CFR 173.359

TOXICITY

ACETOXON: TOXICITY DATA: 45 MG/KG ORAL-RAT LD50; 214 MG/KG INTRAPERITONEAL-MOUSE LD50; 300 MG/KG UNREPORTED-MAMMAL LD50. CARCINOGEN STATUS: NONE. ACUTE TOXICITY LEVEL: HIGHLY TOXIC BY INGESTION. TARGET EFFECTS: CHOLINESTERASE INHIBITOR. POISONING MAY AFFECT THE NERVOUS SYSTEM.* AT INCREASED RISK FROM EXPOSURE: PERSONS WITH RESPIRATORY AILMENTS, RECENT EXPOSURE TO CHOLINESTERASE INHIBITORS OR IMPAIRED CHOLINESTERASE PRODUCTION, OR LIVER MALFUNCTION.* ADDITIONAL DATA: MAY CROSS THE PLACENTA. HIGH ENVIRONMENTAL TEMPERATURES OR EXPOSURE OF THE CHEMICAL TO VISIBLE OR ULTRAVIOLET LIGHT MAY ENHANCE THE TOXICITY. INTERACTIONS WITH MEDICATIONS MAY OCCUR.*
* MAY BE BASED ON GENERAL INFORMATION ON ORGANOPHOSPHATES.

HEALTH EFFECTS AND FIRST AID

INHALATION: ACETOXON: SEE INFORMATION ON ORGANOPHOSPHATES. ORGANOPHOSPHATES: CHOLINESTERASE INHIBITOR. **<u>ACUTE EXPOSURE</u>-** WHEN INHALED, THE FIRST EFFECTS OF CHOLINESTERASE INHIBITORS ARE USUALLY RESPIRATORY AND MAY INCLUDE NASAL HYPEREMIA AND WATERY DISCHARGE, COUGH, CHEST DISCOMFORT, DYSPNEA, AND WHEEZING DUE TO INCREASED BRONCHIAL SECRETIONS AND BRONCHOCONSTRICTION. IF SUFFICIENT AMOUNTS ARE ABSORBED, OTHER SYSTEMIC EFFECTS MAY BEGIN WITHIN A FEW MINUTES OR BE DELAYED FOR UP TO 12 HOURS. SYMPTOMS MAY INCLUDE PALLOR, NAUSEA, VOMITING, DIARRHEA, ABDOMINAL CRAMPS, HEADACHE, DIZZINESS, OCULAR PAIN, BLURRED VISION, MIOSIS OR IN SOME CASES, ESPECIALLY INITIALLY, MYDRIASIS, LACRIMATION, SALIVATION, SWEATING, AND CONFUSION. OTHER REPORTED CENTRAL NERVOUS SYSTEM OR NEUROMUSCULAR EFFECTS MAY INCLUDE ATAXIA, SLURRED SPEECH, AREFLEXIA, WEAKNESS, FATIGUE, FASCICULATIONS, TWITCHING, TREMORS POSSIBLY OF THE TONGUE AND EYELIDS, AND EVENTUALLY PARALYSIS OF THE EXTREMITIES AND POSSIBLY OF THE RESPIRATORY MUSCLES. IN SEVERE CASES THERE MAY ALSO BE INVOLUNTARY DEFECATION AND URINATION, CYANOSIS, PSYCHOSIS, HYPERGLYCEMIA, ACUTE PANCREATITIS, CARDIAC IRREGULARITIES, PULMONARY EDEMA, UNCONSCIOUSNESS, CONVULSIONS, AND COMA. DEATH IS PRIMARILY DUE TO RESPIRATORY FAILURE, ALTHOUGH CARDIOVASCULAR EFFECTS INCLUDING CARDIAC ARREST MAY ALSO BE IMPLICATED. LONG TERM SEQUELAE ARE RARE BUT MAY INCLUDE NEUROPSYCHIATRIC DISORDERS AND MYOPATHY WITH MUSCLE TENDERNESS. SOME ORGANOPHOSPHATES MAY CAUSE A DELAYED NEUROPATHY BEGINNING 1-4 WEEKS AFTER AN ACUTE EXPOSURE WHICH MAY OR MAY NOT HAVE CAUSED ACUTE CHOLINERGIC EFFECTS. NUMBNESS, TINGLING, WEAKNESS AND CRAMPING BEGINNING SYMMETRICALLY IN THE LOWER LIMBS MAY PROGRESS TO ATAXIA AND PARALYSIS. IN SEVERE CASES, UPPER LIMB INVOLVEMENT IS POSSIBLE AND FLACCID PARALYSIS MAY PROGRESS TO SPASTIC PARALYSIS WITH EXAGGERATED REFLEXES. IMPROVEMENT MAY OCCUR OVER MONTHS TO YEARS, BUT SOME RESIDUAL IMPAIRMENT USUALLY REMAINS.
<u>CHRONIC EXPOSURE</u>- REPEATED OR PROLONGED EXPOSURE MAY RESULT IN THE EFFECTS OF ACUTE EXPOSURE INCLUDING THE DELAYED NEUROPATHY. OTHER EFFECTS REPORTED IN WORKERS REPEATEDLY EXPOSED INCLUDE IMPAIRED MEMORY AND CONCENTRATION, ACUTE PSYCHOSIS, SEVERE DEPRESSIONS, IRRITABILTY, CONFUSION, APATHY, EMOTIONAL LABILITY, SOCIAL WITHDRAWAL, CONFUSION, HEADACHE, SPEECH DIFFICULTIES, DELAYED REACTION TIMES, SPATIAL DISORIENTATION, NIGHTMARES, SLEEPWALKING, AND DROWSINESS OR INSOMNIA. AN INFLUENZA-LIKE CONDITION WITH HEADACHE, NAUSEA, WEAKNESS, ANOREXIA AND MALAISE HAS ALSO BEEN REPORTED.

FIRST AID- REMOVE FROM EXPOSURE AREA TO FRESH AIR IMMEDIATELY. IF BREATHING HAS STOPPED, GIVE ARTIFICIAL RESPIRATION. MAINTAIN AIRWAY AND BLOOD PRESSURE AND ADMINISTER OXYGEN IF AVAILABLE. KEEP AFFECTED PERSON WARM AND AT REST. TREAT SYMPTOMATICALLY AND SUPPORTIVELY. ADMINISTRATION OF OXYGEN SHOULD BE PERFORMED BY QUALIFIED PERSONNEL. GET MEDICAL ATTENTION IMMEDIATELY.

SKIN CONTACT: ACETOXON: SEE INFORMATION ON ORGANOPHOSPHATES. ORGANOPHOSPHATES: CHOLINESTERASE INHIBITOR. **<u>ACUTE EXPOSURE</u>-** LOCALIZED SWEATING AND FASCICULATIONS MAY OCCUR AT THE SITE OF CONTACT. IF SUFFICIENT AMOUNTS ARE ABSORBED, OTHER EFFECTS OF

CHOLINESTERASE INHIBITION AS DESCRIBED IN ACUTE INHALATION MAY OCCUR. SYMPTOMS MAY BE DELAYED 2-3 HOURS, BUT USUALLY NO MORE THAN 12 HOURS. THE RATE OF ABSORPTION IS INCREASED BY THE PRESENCE OF DERMATITIS OR HIGH AMBIENT TEMPERATURES. DELAYED NEUROPATHY IS ALSO POSSIBLE. **CHRONIC EXPOSURE-** REPEATED OR PROLONGED EXPOSURE MAY CAUSE EFFECTS AS DESCRIBED IN ACUTE EXPOSURE. SOME ORGANOPHOSPHATES MAY CAUSE SENSITIZATION.

FIRST AID- REMOVE CONTAMINATED CLOTHING IMMEDIATELY. WASH CONTAMINATED AREAS WITH SOAP AND WATER FOLLOWED BY ALCOHOL (ARENA, POISONING, 4TH ED.). EMERGENCY PERSONNEL SHOULD WEAR GLOVES AND AVOID CONTAMINATION. TREAT RESPIRATORY DIFFICULTY WITH ARTIFICIAL RESPIRATION. GET MEDICAL ATTENTION IMMEDIATELY.

EYE CONTACT: ACETOXON: SEE INFORMATION ON ORGANOPHOSPHATES.
ORGANOPHOSPHATES: CHOLINESTERASE INHIBITOR. **ACUTE EXPOSURE-** DIRECT CONTACT MAY CAUSE PAIN, HYPEREMIA, LACRIMATION, TWITCHING OF THE EYELIDS, MIOSIS, AND CILIARY MUSCLE SPASM WITH LOSS OF ACCOMODATION, BLURRED OR DIMMED VISION AND BROWACHE. SOMETIMES MYDRIASIS MAY OCCUR INSTEAD OF MIOSIS. WITH SUFFICIENT EXPOSURE, OTHER SYMPTOMS OF CHOLINESTERASE INHIBITION AS DESCRIBED IN ACUTE INHALATION MAY OCCUR. **CHRONIC EXPOSURE-** REPEATED OR PROLONGED EXPOSURE MAY CAUSE EFFECTS AS DESCRIBED IN ACUTE EXPOSURE. SOME COMPOUNDS HAVE CAUSED TOXIC EFFECTS ON THE CRYSTALLINE LENS, CONJUNCTIVAL THICKENING AND OBSTRUCTION OF THE NASOLACRIMAL CANALS WHEN USED AS MIOTIC EYEDROPS.

FIRST AID- IRRIGATE EYES WITH WATER OR SALINE SOLUTION. IF SYMPTOMS OF POISONING OCCUR, TREAT RESPIRATORY DIFFICULTY WITH ARTIFICIAL RESPIRATION AND OXYGEN. OBSERVE PATIENT FOR AT LEAST 24-36 HOURS (GOSSELIN, CLINICAL TOXICOLOGY OF COMMERCIAL PRODUCTS, 5TH ED.). GET MEDICAL ATTENTION IMMEDIATELY. OXYGEN SHOULD BE ADMINISTERED BY QUALIFIED MEDICAL PERSONNEL.

INGESTION: ACETOXON: HIGHLY TOXIC. SEE INFORMATION ON ORGANOPHOSPHATES.
ORGANOPHOSPHATES: CHOLINESTERASE INHIBITOR. **ACUTE EXPOSURE-** WHEN INGESTED, THE FIRST EFFECTS MAY BE NAUSEA, VOMITING, ANOREXIA, ABDOMINAL CRAMPS AND DIARRHEA. GASTROINTESTINAL ABSORPTION MAY CAUSE SYMPTOMS OF CHOLINESTERASE INHIBITION AS DESCRIBED IN ACUTE INHALATION. SYMPTOMS MAY BEGIN WITHIN MINUTES OR BE DELAYED FOR HOURS. DELAYED EFFECTS INCLUDING NEUROPATHY MAY ALSO OCCUR. **CHRONIC EXPOSURE-** REPEATED INGESTION MAY CAUSE EFFECTS AS DESCRIBED IN ACUTE EXPOSURE.

FIRST AID- IF PERSON IS ALERT AND RESPIRATION IS NOT DEPRESSED, GIVE SYRUP OF IPECAC FOLLOWED BY WATER (IF VOMITING OCCURS, KEEP HEAD BELOW HIPS TO PREVENT ASPIRATION). IF CONSCIOUSNESS LEVEL DECLINES OR VOMITING HAS NOT OCCURRED IN 15 MINUTES EMPTY STOMACH BY GASTRIC LAVAGE WITH THE AID OF CUFFED ENDOTRACHEAL TUBE USING ISOTONIC SALINE OR 5% SODIUM BICARBONATE FOLLOW WITH ACTIVATED CHARCOAL. ESTABLISH AND MAINTAIN AIRWAY. TREAT RESPIRATORY DIFFICULTY WITH ARTIFICIAL RESPIRATION AND OXYGEN. DO NOT GIVE MORPHINE, AMINOPHYLLINE, PHENOTHIAZINES, RESERPINE, FUROSEMIDE, OR ETHACRYNIC ACID (MORGAN, RECOGNITION AND MANAGEMENT OF PESTICIDE POISONINGS, 3RD ED.). TREAT SYMPTOMATICALLY AND SUPPORTIVELY. ADMINISTRATION OF OXYGEN AND LAVAGE MUST BE PERFORMED BY QUALIFIED MEDICAL PERSONNEL. GET MEDICAL ATTENTION IMMEDIATELY.

ANTIDOTE: THE FOLLOWING ANTIDOTE(S) HAVE BEEN RECOMMENDED. HOWEVER, THE DECISION AS TO WHETHER THE SEVERITY OF POISONING REQUIRES ADMINISTRATION OF ANY ANTIDOTE AND ACTUAL DOSE REQUIRED SHOULD BE MADE BY QUALIFIED MEDICAL PERSONNEL.
FOR CHOLINESTERASE INHIBITORS: ESTABLISH CLEAR AIRWAY AND TISSUE OXYGENATION BY ASPIRATION OF SECRETIONS, AND IF NECESSARY, BY ASSISTED PULMONARY VENTILATION WITH OXYGEN. IMPROVE TISSUE OXYGENATION AS MUCH AS POSSIBLE BEFORE ADMINISTERING ATROPINE TO MINIMIZE THE RISK OF VENTRICULAR FIBRILLATION. ADMINISTER ATROPINE SULFATE INTRAVENOUSLY, OR INTRAMUSCULARLY IF IV INJECTION IS NOT POSSIBLE. IN MODERATELY SEVERE POISONING ADMINISTER ATROPINE SULFATE, 0.4-2.0 MG REPEATED EVERY 15 MINUTES UNTIL ATROPINIZATION IS ACHIEVED (TACHYCARDIA, FLUSHING, DRY MOUTH, MYDRIASIS). MAINTAIN ATROPINIZATION BY REPEATED DOSES FOR 2-12 HOURS, OR LONGER, DEPENDING ON THE SEVERITY OF POISONING. THE APPEARANCE OF RALES IN THE LUNG BASES, MIOSIS, SALIVATION, NAUSEA, BRADYCARDIA, ARE ALL INDICATIONS OF INADEQUATE ATROPINIZATION. SEVERELY POISONED INDIVIDUALS MAY EXHIBIT REMARKABLE TOLERANCE TO ATROPINE; TWO OR MORE TIMES THE DOSAGES SUGGESTED ABOVE MAY BE NEEDED. PERSONS NOT POISONED OR ONLY SLIGHTLY POISONED, HOWEVER, MAY DEVELOP SIGNS OF ATROPINE TOXICITY FROM SUCH LARGE DOSAGES: FEVER, MUSCLE FIBRILLATIONS, AND DELIRIUM ARE THE MAIN SIGNS OF ATROPINE TOXICITY. IF THESE SIGNS APPEAR WHILE THE PATIENT IS FULLY ATROPINIZED, ATROPINE ADMINISTRATION SHOULD BE DISCONTINUED, AT LEAST TEMPORARILY. OBSERVE TREATED PATIENTS CLOSELY AT LEAST 24 HOURS TO INSURE THAT SYMPTOMS (POSSIBLY PULMONARY EDEMA) DO NOT RECUR AS ATROPINIZATION WEARS OFF. IN VERY SEVERE POISONINGS, METABOLIC DISPOSITION OF TOXICANT MAY REQUIRE SEVERAL HOURS OR DAYS DURING WHICH ATROPINIZATION MUST BE MAINTAINED. MARKEDLY LOWER LEVELS OF URINARY METABOLITES INDICATE THAT ATROPINE DOSAGE CAN BE TAPERED OFF. AS DOSAGE IS REDUCED, CHECK THE LUNG BASES FREQUENTLY FOR RALES. IF RALES ARE HEARD OR OTHER SYMPTOMS RETURN, RE-ESTABLISH ATROPINIZATION PROMPTLY (MORGAN, RECOGNITION AND MANAGEMENT OF PESTICIDE POISONINGS, 3RD ED.). ADMINISTRATION OF ANTIDOTE MUST BE PERFORMED BY QUALIFIED MEDICAL PERSONNEL.
IN CASES OF SEVERE POISONING BY ORGANOPHOSPHATE PESTICIDES IN WHICH RESPIRATORY DEPRESSION, MUSCLE WEAKNESS AND TWITCHINGS ARE SEVERE, GIVE PRALIDOXIME (PROTOPAM-AYERST, 2-PAM), 1.0 GRAM INTRAVENOUSLY AT NO MORE THAN 0.5 GRAM PER MINUTE. DOSAGE OF PRALIDOXIME MAY BE REPEATED IN 1-2 HOURS, THEN AT 10-12 HOUR INTERVALS IF NEEDED. IN VERY SEVERE POISONINGS, DOSAGE RATES MAY BE DOUBLED. TREATMENT WITH PRALIDOXIME WILL BE MOST EFFECTIVE IF GIVEN WITHIN THIRTY-SIX HOURS AFTER POISONING (MORGAN, RECOGNITION AND MANAGEMENT OF PESTICIDE POISONINGS, 3RD ED.). ANTIDOTE SHOULD BE ADMINISTERED BY QUALIFIED MEDICAL PERSONNEL.

REACTIVITY

REACTIVITY: STABLE UNDER NORMAL TEMPERATURES AND PRESSURES.

INCOMPATIBILITIES: ACETOXON: OXIDIZERS (STRONG): FIRE AND EXPLOSION HAZARD.

DECOMPOSITION: THERMAL DECOMPOSITION PRODUCTS MAY INCLUDE TOXIC OXIDES OF CARBON, SULFUR, AND PHOSPHORUS.

POLYMERIZATION: HAZARDOUS POLYMERIZATION HAS NOT BEEN REPORTED TO OCCUR UNDER NORMAL TEMPERATURES AND PRESSURES.

STORAGE AND DISPOSAL

OBSERVE ALL FEDERAL, STATE AND LOCAL REGULATIONS WHEN STORING OR DISPOSING OF THIS SUBSTANCE. FOR ASSISTANCE, CONTACT THE DISTRICT DIRECTOR OF THE ENVIRONMENTAL PROTECTION AGENCY.

STORAGE

STORE IN ACCORDANCE WITH 40 CFR 165 RECOMMENDED PROCEDURES FOR THE DISPOSAL AND STORAGE OF PESTICIDES AND PESTICIDE CONTAINERS.
STORE AWAY FROM INCOMPATIBLE SUBSTANCES.

DISPOSAL

DISPOSAL MUST BE IN ACCORDANCE WITH 40 CFR 165 RECOMMENDED PROCEDURES FOR THE DISPOSAL AND STORAGE OF PESTICIDES AND PESTICIDE CONTAINERS.

CONDITIONS TO AVOID

AVOID CONTACT WITH HEAT, SPARKS, FLAMES OR OTHER IGNITION SOURCES. VAPORS MAY BE EXPLOSIVE. MATERIAL IS POISONOUS; AVOID INHALATION OF VAPORS OR CONTACT WITH SKIN. DO NOT ALLOW MATERIAL TO CONTAMINATE WATER SOURCES.

SPILL AND LEAK PROCEDURES

OCCUPATIONAL SPILL: SHUT OFF IGNITION SOURCES. DO NOT TOUCH SPILLED MATERIAL. STOP LEAK IF YOU CAN DO IT WITHOUT RISK. USE WATER SPRAY TO REDUCE VAPORS. FOR SMALL SPILLS, TAKE UP WITH SAND OR OTHER ABSORBENT MATERIAL AND PLACE INTO CONTAINERS FOR LATER DISPOSAL. FOR LARGER SPILLS, DIKE FAR AHEAD OF SPILL FOR LATER DISPOSAL. NO SMOKING, FLAMES OR FLARES IN HAZARD AREA! KEEP UNNECESSARY PEOPLE AWAY; ISOLATE HAZARD AREA AND DENY ENTRY.

PROTECTIVE EQUIPMENT

VENTILATION: PROVIDE LOCAL EXHAUST OR PROCESS ENCLOSURE VENTILATION SYSTEM.

RESPIRATOR: THE FOLLOWING RESPIRATORS ARE RECOMMENDED BASED ON INFORMATION FOUND IN THE PHYSICAL DATA, TOXICITY AND HEALTH EFFECTS SECTIONS. THEY ARE RANKED IN ORDER FROM MINIMUM TO MAXIMUM RESPIRATORY PROTECTION. THE SPECIFIC RESPIRATOR SELECTED MUST BE BASED ON CONTAMINATION LEVELS FOUND IN THE WORK PLACE, MUST NOT EXCEED THE WORKING LIMITS OF THE RESPIRATOR AND BE JOINTLY APPROVED BY THE NATIONAL INSTITUTE FOR OCCUPATIONAL SAFETY AND HEALTH AND THE MINE SAFETY AND HEALTH ADMINISTRATION (NIOSH-MSHA).
TYPE 'C' SUPPLIED-AIR RESPIRATOR WITH A FULL FACEPIECE OPERATED IN PRESSURE-DEMAND OR OTHER POSITIVE PRESSURE MODE OR WITH A FULL FACEPIECE, HELMET OR HOOD OPERATED IN CONTINOUS-FLOW MODE.
SELF-CONTAINED BREATHING APPARATUS WITH A FULL FACEPIECE OPERATED IN PRESSURE-DEMAND OR OTHER POSITIVE PRESSURE MODE.

FOR FIREFIGHTING AND OTHER IMMEDIATELY DANGEROUS TO LIFE OR HEALTH CONDITIONS:
SELF-CONTAINED BREATHING APPARATUS WITH FULL FACEPIECE OPERATED IN PRESSURE-DEMAND OR OTHER POSITIVE PRESSURE MODE.
SUPPLIED-AIR RESPIRATOR WITH FULL FACEPIECE AND OPERATED IN PRESSURE-DEMAND OR OTHER POSITIVE PRESSURE MODE IN COMBINATION WITH AN AUXILIARY SELF-CONTAINED BREATHING APPARATUS OPERATED IN PRESSURE-DEMAND OR OTHER POSITIVE PRESSURE MODE.

CLOTHING: EMPLOYEE MUST WEAR APPROPRIATE PROTECTIVE (IMPERVIOUS) CLOTHING AND EQUIPMENT TO PREVENT ANY POSSIBILITY OF SKIN CONTACT WITH THIS SUBSTANCE.

GLOVES: EMPLOYEE MUST WEAR APPROPRIATE PROTECTIVE GLOVES TO PREVENT CONTACT WITH THIS SUBSTANCE.

EYE PROTECTION: EMPLOYEE MUST WEAR SPLASH-PROOF OR DUST-RESISTANT SAFETY GOGGLES WITH OR WITHOUT A FACESHIELD TO PREVENT CONTACT WITH THIS SUBSTANCE.
EMERGENCY EYE WASH: WHERE THERE IS ANY POSSIBILITY THAT AN EMPLOYEE'S EYES MAY BE EXPOSED TO THIS SUBSTANCE, THE EMPLOYER SHOULD PROVIDE AN EYE WASH FOUNTAIN WITHIN THE IMMEDIATE WORK AREA FOR EMERGENCY USE.

AUTHORIZED BY- OCCUPATIONAL HEALTH SERVICES, INC.
CREATION DATE: 10/04/89 ***REVISION DATE:*** 04/24/90

MATERIAL SAFETY DATA SHEET

OCCUPATIONAL HEALTH SERVICES, INC.
AGRICULTURE AND PESTICIDE DIVISION
450 SEVENTH AVENUE, SUITE 2407
NEW YORK, NEW YORK 10123
1-800-445-MSDS OR (212) 967-1100

EMERGENCY CONTACT:
JOHN S. BRANSFORD, JR. (615) 292-1180

SUBSTANCE IDENTIFICATION

CAS-NUMBER 24017-47-8

SUBSTANCE: TRIAZOPHOS

TRADE NAMES/SYNONYMS: PHOSPHOROTHIOIC ACID, O,O-DIETHYL O-(1-PHENYL-1H-1,2,4-TRIAZOL-3-YL) ESTER; 1-PHENYL-1,2,4-TRIAZOLYL-3-(O,O-DIETHYLTHIONOPHOSPHATE);
1-PHENYL-3-(O,O-DIETHYL-THIONOPHOSPHATE)-1,2,4-TRIAZOLE; O,O-DIETHYL O-(1-PHENYL-1H-1,2,4-TRIAZOL-3-YL)PHOSPHOROTHIOATE; HOSTATHION; HOE 2960; HOSTATION; TRIAZOFOS; PST73068

CHEMICAL FAMILY: THIAZOLE PHOSPHOROTHIOATE

MOLECULAR FORMULA: C12-H16-N3-O3-P-S

MOLECULAR WEIGHT: 313.34

CERCLA RATINGS (SCALE 0-3): HEALTH=3 FIRE=U REACTIVITY=0 PERSISTENCE=2

NFPA RATINGS (SCALE 0-4): HEALTH=3 FIRE=U REACTIVITY=0

COMPONENTS AND CONTAMINANTS

COMPONENT: TRIAZOPHOS ***PERCENT:*** 100.0
CAS# 24017-47-8

OTHER CONTAMINANTS: NONE

EXPOSURE LIMITS: NO OCCUPATIONAL EXPOSURE LIMITS ESTABLISHED BY OSHA, ACGIH, OR NIOSH.
TRIAZOPHOS: 500 POUNDS SARA SECTION 302 THRESHOLD PLANNING QUANTITY
1 POUND SARA SECTION 304 REPORTABLE QUANTITY

PHYSICAL DATA

DESCRIPTION: YELLOWISH OIL ***BOILING POINT:*** DECOMPOSES
MELTING POINT: 32-41 F (0-5 C) ***SPECIFIC GRAVITY:*** 1.247 @ 20 C
VAPOR PRESSURE: 0.00001 MMHG ***EVAPORATION RATE:*** NOT AVAILABLE
SOLUBILITY IN WATER: 30-40 MG/L

FIRE AND EXPLOSION DATA

FIRE AND EXPLOSION HAZARD: UNKNOWN FIRE AND EXPLOSION HAZARD.

FIREFIGHTING MEDIA: DRY CHEMICAL, CARBON DIOXIDE, HALON, WATER SPRAY OR STANDARD FOAM (1987 EMERGENCY RESPONSE GUIDEBOOK, DOT P 5800.4).
FOR LARGER FIRES, USE WATER SPRAY, FOG OR STANDARD FOAM (1987 EMERGENCY RESPONSE GUIDEBOOK, DOT P 5800.4).

FIREFIGHTING: MOVE CONTAINERS FROM FIRE AREA IF POSSIBLE. FIGHT FIRE FROM MAXIMUM DISTANCE. STAY AWAY FROM STORAGE TANK ENDS. DIKE FIRE CONTROL WATER FOR LATER DISPOSAL. DO NOT SCATTER MATERIAL (1987 EMERGENCY RESPONSE GUIDEBOOK, DOT P 5800.4, GUIDE PAGE 55).
EXTINGUISH ONLY IF FLOW CAN BE STOPPED. EXTINGUISH USING AGENT INDICATED. USE FLOODING AMOUNTS OF WATER AS A FOG. COOL CONTAINERS WITH FLOODING AMOUNTS OF WATER FROM AS FAR A DISTANCE AS POSSIBLE. AVOID BREATHING POISONOUS VAPORS, KEEP UPWIND. CONSIDER EVACUATION OF DOWNWIND AREA IF MATERIAL IS LEAKING.

TOXICITY

TRIAZOFOS: TOXICITY DATA: 280 MG/M3/4 HOURS INHALATION-RAT LC50; 1100 MG/KG SKIN-RAT LD50; 64 MG/KG ORAL-RAT LD50; 320 MG/KG ORAL-DOG LD50; 107 MG/KG INTRAPERITONEAL-RAT LD50. CARCINOGEN STATUS: NONE. ACUTE TOXICITY LEVEL: HIGHLY TOXIC BY INHALATION; TOXIC BY INGESTION; MODERATELY TOXIC BY DERMAL ABSORPTION. TARGET EFFECTS: CHOLINESTERASE INHIBITOR. POISONING MAY AFFECT THE NERVOUS SYSTEM.* AT INCREASED RISK FROM EXPOSURE: PERSONS WITH RESPIRATORY AILMENTS, RECENT EXPOSURE TO CHOLINESTERASE INHIBITORS OR IMPAIRED CHOLINESTERASE PRODUCTION, OR LIVER MALFUNCTION.* ADDITIONAL DATA: MAY CROSS THE PLACENTA. HIGH ENVIRONMENTAL TEMPERATURES OR EXPOSURE OF THE CHEMICAL TO VISIBLE OR ULTRAVIOLET LIGHT MAY ENHANCE THE TOXICITY. INTERACTIONS WITH MEDICATIONS MAY OCCUR.*
* MAY BE BASED ON GENERAL INFORMATION ON ORGANOPHOSPHATES.

HEALTH EFFECTS AND FIRST AID

INHALATION: TRIAZOPHOS: HIGHLY TOXIC. SEE INFORMATION ON ORGANOPHOSPHATES.
ORGANOPHOSPHATES: CHOLINESTERASE INHIBITOR. **ACUTE EXPOSURE-** WHEN INHALED, THE FIRST EFFECTS OF CHOLINESTERASE INHIBITORS ARE USUALLY RESPIRATORY AND MAY INCLUDE NASAL HYPEREMIA AND WATERY DISCHARGE, COUGH, CHEST DISCOMFORT, DYSPNEA, AND WHEEZING DUE TO INCREASED BRONCHIAL SECRETIONS AND BRONCHOCONSTRICTION. IF SUFFICIENT AMOUNTS ARE ABSORBED, OTHER SYSTEMIC EFFECTS MAY BEGIN WITHIN A FEW MINUTES OR BE DELAYED FOR UP TO 12 HOURS. SYMPTOMS MAY INCLUDE PALLOR, NAUSEA, VOMITING, DIARRHEA, ABDOMINAL CRAMPS, HEADACHE, DIZZINESS, OCULAR PAIN, BLURRED VISION, MIOSIS OR IN SOME CASES, ESPECIALLY INITIALLY, MYDRIASIS, LACRIMATION, SALIVATION, SWEATING, AND CONFUSION. OTHER REPORTED CENTRAL NERVOUS SYSTEM OR NEUROMUSCULAR EFFECTS MAY INCLUDE ATAXIA, SLURRED SPEECH, AREFLEXIA, WEAKNESS, FATIGUE, FASCICULATIONS, TWITCHING, TREMORS POSSIBLY OF THE TONGUE AND EYELIDS, AND EVENTUALLY PARALYSIS OF THE EXTREMITIES AND POSSIBLY OF THE RESPIRATORY MUSCLES. IN SEVERE CASES THERE MAY ALSO BE INVOLUNTARY DEFECATION AND URINATION, CYANOSIS, PSYCHOSIS, HYPERGLYCEMIA, ACUTE PANCREATITIS, CARDIAC IRREGULARITIES, PULMONARY EDEMA, UNCONSCIOUSNESS, CONVULSIONS, AND COMA. DEATH IS PRIMARILY DUE TO RESPIRATORY FAILURE, ALTHOUGH CARDIOVASCULAR EFFECTS INCLUDING CARDIAC ARREST MAY ALSO BE IMPLICATED. LONG TERM SEQUELAE ARE RARE BUT MAY INCLUDE NEUROPSYCHIATRIC DISORDERS AND MYOPATHY WITH MUSCLE TENDERNESS. SOME ORGANOPHOSPHATES MAY CAUSE A DELAYED NEUROPATHY BEGINNING 1-4 WEEKS AFTER AN ACUTE EXPOSURE WHICH MAY OR MAY NOT HAVE CAUSED ACUTE CHOLINERGIC EFFECTS. NUMBNESS, TINGLING, WEAKNESS AND CRAMPING BEGINNING SYMMETRICALLY IN THE LOWER LIMBS MAY PROGRESS TO ATAXIA AND PARALYSIS. IN SEVERE CASES, UPPER LIMB INVOLVEMENT IS POSSIBLE AND FLACCID PARALYSIS MAY PROGRESS TO SPASTIC PARALYSIS WITH EXAGGERATED REFLEXES. IMPROVEMENT MAY OCCUR OVER MONTHS TO YEARS, BUT SOME RESIDUAL IMPAIRMENT USUALLY REMAINS.
CHRONIC EXPOSURE- REPEATED OR PROLONGED EXPOSURE MAY RESULT IN THE EFFECTS OF ACUTE EXPOSURE INCLUDING THE DELAYED NEUROPATHY. OTHER EFFECTS REPORTED IN WORKERS REPEATEDLY EXPOSED INCLUDE IMPAIRED MEMORY AND CONCENTRATION, ACUTE PSYCHOSIS, SEVERE DEPRESSIONS, IRRITABILTY, CONFUSION, APATHY, EMOTIONAL LABILITY, SOCIAL WITHDRAWAL, CONFUSION, HEADACHE, SPEECH DIFFICULTIES, DELAYED REACTION TIMES, SPATIAL DISORIENTATION, NIGHTMARES, SLEEPWALKING, AND DROWSINESS OR INSOMNIA. AN INFLUENZA-LIKE CONDITION WITH HEADACHE, NAUSEA, WEAKNESS, ANOREXIA AND MALAISE HAS ALSO BEEN REPORTED.

FIRST AID- REMOVE FROM EXPOSURE AREA TO FRESH AIR IMMEDIATELY. IF BREATHING HAS STOPPED, GIVE ARTIFICIAL RESPIRATION. MAINTAIN AIRWAY AND BLOOD PRESSURE AND ADMINISTER OXYGEN IF AVAILABLE. KEEP AFFECTED PERSON WARM AND AT REST. TREAT SYMPTOMATICALLY AND SUPPORTIVELY. ADMINISTRATION OF OXYGEN SHOULD BE PERFORMED BY QUALIFIED PERSONNEL. GET MEDICAL ATTENTION IMMEDIATELY.

SKIN CONTACT: TRIAZOPHOS: SEE INFORMATION ON ORGANOPHOSPHATES.
ORGANOPHOSPHATES: CHOLINESTERASE INHIBITOR. **ACUTE EXPOSURE-** LOCALIZED SWEATING AND FASCICULATIONS MAY OCCUR AT THE SITE OF CONTACT. IF SUFFICIENT AMOUNTS ARE ABSORBED, OTHER EFFECTS OF

CHOLINESTERASE INHIBITION AS DESCRIBED IN ACUTE INHALATION MAY OCCUR. SYMPTOMS MAY BE DELAYED 2-3 HOURS, BUT USUALLY NO MORE THAN 12 HOURS. THE RATE OF ABSORPTION IS INCREASED BY THE PRESENCE OF DERMATITIS OR HIGH AMBIENT TEMPERATURES. DELAYED NEUROPATHY IS ALSO POSSIBLE. **CHRONIC EXPOSURE-** REPEATED OR PROLONGED EXPOSURE MAY CAUSE EFFECTS AS DESCRIBED IN ACUTE EXPOSURE. SOME ORGANOPHOSPHATES MAY CAUSE SENSITIZATION.

FIRST AID- REMOVE CONTAMINATED CLOTHING IMMEDIATELY. WASH CONTAMINATED AREAS WITH SOAP AND WATER FOLLOWED BY ALCOHOL (ARENA, POISONING, 4TH ED.). EMERGENCY PERSONNEL SHOULD WEAR GLOVES AND AVOID CONTAMINATION. TREAT RESPIRATORY DIFFICULTY WITH ARTIFICIAL RESPIRATION. GET MEDICAL ATTENTION IMMEDIATELY.

EYE CONTACT: TRIAZOPHOS: SEE INFORMATION ON ORGANOPHOSPHATES. ORGANOPHOSPHATES: CHOLINESTERASE INHIBITOR. **ACUTE EXPOSURE-** DIRECT CONTACT MAY CAUSE PAIN, HYPEREMIA, LACRIMATION, TWITCHING OF THE EYELIDS, MIOSIS, AND CILIARY MUSCLE SPASM WITH LOSS OF ACCOMODATION, BLURRED OR DIMMED VISION AND BROWACHE. SOMETIMES MYDRIASIS MAY OCCUR INSTEAD OF MIOSIS. WITH SUFFICIENT EXPOSURE, OTHER SYMPTOMS OF CHOLINESTERASE INHIBITION AS DESCRIBED IN ACUTE INHALATION MAY OCCUR. **CHRONIC EXPOSURE-** REPEATED OR PROLONGED EXPOSURE MAY CAUSE EFFECTS AS DESCRIBED IN ACUTE EXPOSURE. SOME COMPOUNDS HAVE CAUSED TOXIC EFFECTS ON THE CRYSTALLINE LENS, CONJUNCTIVAL THICKENING AND OBSTRUCTION OF THE NASOLACRIMAL CANALS WHEN USED AS MIOTIC EYEDROPS.

FIRST AID- IRRIGATE EYES WITH WATER OR SALINE SOLUTION. IF SYMPTOMS OF POISONING OCCUR, TREAT RESPIRATORY DIFFICULTY WITH ARTIFICIAL RESPIRATION AND OXYGEN. OBSERVE PATIENT FOR AT LEAST 24-36 HOURS (GOSSELIN, CLINICAL TOXICOLOGY OF COMMERCIAL PRODUCTS, 5TH ED.). GET MEDICAL ATTENTION IMMEDIATELY. OXYGEN SHOULD BE ADMINISTERED BY QUALIFIED MEDICAL PERSONNEL.

INGESTION: TRIAZOPHOS: TOXIC. SEE INFORMATION ON ORGANOPHOSPHATES. ORGANOPHOSPHATES: CHOLINESTERASE INHIBITOR. **ACUTE EXPOSURE-** WHEN INGESTED, THE FIRST EFFECTS MAY BE NAUSEA, VOMITING, ANOREXIA, ABDOMINAL CRAMPS AND DIARRHEA. GASTROINTESTINAL ABSORPTION MAY CAUSE SYMPTOMS OF CHOLINESTERASE INHIBITION AS DESCRIBED IN ACUTE INHALATION. SYMPTOMS MAY BEGIN WITHIN MINUTES OR BE DELAYED FOR HOURS. DELAYED EFFECTS INCLUDING NEUROPATHY MAY ALSO OCCUR. **CHRONIC EXPOSURE-** REPEATED INGESTION MAY CAUSE EFFECTS AS DESCRIBED IN ACUTE EXPOSURE.

FIRST AID- IF PERSON IS ALERT AND RESPIRATION IS NOT DEPRESSED, GIVE SYRUP OF IPECAC FOLLOWED BY WATER (IF VOMITING OCCURS, KEEP HEAD BELOW HIPS TO PREVENT ASPIRATION). IF CONSCIOUSNESS LEVEL DECLINES OR VOMITING HAS NOT OCCURRED IN 15 MINUTES EMPTY STOMACH BY GASTRIC LAVAGE WITH THE AID OF CUFFED ENDOTRACHEAL TUBE USING ISOTONIC SALINE OR 5% SODIUM BICARBONATE FOLLOW WITH ACTIVATED CHARCOAL. ESTABLISH AND MAINTAIN AIRWAY. TREAT RESPIRATORY DIFFICULTY WITH ARTIFICIAL RESPIRATION AND OXYGEN. DO NOT GIVE MORPHINE, AMINOPHYLLINE, PHENOTHIAZINES, RESERPINE, FUROSEMIDE, OR ETHACRYNIC ACID (MORGAN, RECOGNITION AND MANAGEMENT OF PESTICIDE POISONINGS, 3RD ED.). TREAT SYMPTOMATICALLY AND SUPPORTIVELY. ADMINISTRATION OF OXYGEN AND LAVAGE MUST BE PERFORMED BY QUALIFIED MEDICAL PERSONNEL. GET MEDICAL ATTENTION IMMEDIATELY.

ANTIDOTE: THE FOLLOWING ANTIDOTE(S) HAVE BEEN RECOMMENDED. HOWEVER, THE DECISION AS TO WHETHER THE SEVERITY OF POISONING REQUIRES ADMINISTRATION OF ANY ANTIDOTE AND ACTUAL DOSE REQUIRED SHOULD BE MADE BY QUALIFIED MEDICAL PERSONNEL.

FOR CHOLINESTERASE INHIBITORS: ESTABLISH CLEAR AIRWAY AND TISSUE OXYGENATION BY ASPIRATION OF SECRETIONS, AND IF NECESSARY, BY ASSISTED PULMONARY VENTILATION WITH OXYGEN. IMPROVE TISSUE OXYGENATION AS MUCH AS POSSIBLE BEFORE ADMINISTERING ATROPINE TO MINIMIZE THE RISK OF VENTRICULAR FIBRILLATION. ADMINISTER ATROPINE SULFATE INTRAVENOUSLY, OR INTRAMUSCULARLY IF IV INJECTION IS NOT POSSIBLE. IN MODERATELY SEVERE POISONING ADMINISTER ATROPINE SULFATE, 0.4-2.0 MG REPEATED EVERY 15 MINUTES UNTIL ATROPINIZATION IS ACHIEVED (TACHYCARDIA, FLUSHING, DRY MOUTH, MYDRIASIS). MAINTAIN ATROPINIZATION BY REPEATED DOSES FOR 2-12 HOURS, OR LONGER, DEPENDING ON THE SEVERITY OF POISONING. THE APPEARANCE OF RALES IN THE LUNG BASES, MIOSIS, SALIVATION, NAUSEA, BRADYCARDIA, ARE ALL INDICATIONS OF INADEQUATE ATROPINIZATION. SEVERELY POISONED INDIVIDUALS MAY EXHIBIT REMARKABLE TOLERANCE TO ATROPINE; TWO OR MORE TIMES THE DOSAGES SUGGESTED ABOVE MAY BE NEEDED. PERSONS NOT POISONED OR ONLY SLIGHTLY POISONED, HOWEVER, MAY DEVELOP SIGNS OF ATROPINE TOXICITY FROM SUCH LARGE DOSAGES: FEVER, MUSCLE FIBRILLATIONS, AND DELIRIUM ARE THE MAIN SIGNS OF ATROPINE TOXICITY. IF THESE SIGNS APPEAR WHILE THE PATIENT IS FULLY ATROPINIZED, ATROPINE ADMINISTRATION SHOULD BE DISCONTINUED, AT LEAST TEMPORARILY. OBSERVE TREATED PATIENTS CLOSELY AT LEAST 24 HOURS TO INSURE THAT SYMPTOMS (POSSIBLY PULMONARY EDEMA) DO NOT RECUR AS ATROPINIZATION WEARS OFF. IN VERY SEVERE POISONINGS, METABOLIC DISPOSITION OF TOXICANT MAY REQUIRE SEVERAL HOURS OR DAYS DURING WHICH ATROPINIZATION MUST BE MAINTAINED. MARKEDLY LOWER LEVELS OF URINARY METABOLITES INDICATE THAT ATROPINE DOSAGE CAN BE TAPERED OFF. AS DOSAGE IS REDUCED, CHECK THE LUNG BASES FREQUENTLY FOR RALES. IF RALES ARE HEARD OR OTHER SYMPTOMS RETURN, RE-ESTABLISH ATROPINIZATION PROMPTLY (MORGAN, RECOGNITION AND MANAGEMENT OF PESTICIDE POISONINGS, 3RD ED.). ADMINISTRATION OF ANTIDOTE MUST BE PERFORMED BY QUALIFIED MEDICAL PERSONNEL.

IN CASES OF SEVERE POISONING BY ORGANOPHOSPHATE PESTICIDES IN WHICH RESPIRATORY DEPRESSION, MUSCLE WEAKNESS AND TWITCHINGS ARE SEVERE, GIVE PRALIDOXIME (PROTOPAM-AYERST, 2-PAM), 1.0 GRAM INTRAVENOUSLY AT NO MORE THAN 0.5 GRAM PER MINUTE. DOSAGE OF PRALIDOXIME MAY BE REPEATED IN 1-2 HOURS, THEN AT 10-12 HOUR INTERVALS IF NEEDED. IN VERY SEVERE POISONINGS, DOSAGE RATES MAY BE DOUBLED. TREATMENT WITH PRALIDOXIME WILL BE MOST EFFECTIVE IF GIVEN WITHIN THIRTY-SIX HOURS AFTER POISONING (MORGAN, RECOGNITION AND MANAGEMENT OF PESTICIDE POISONINGS, 3RD ED.). ANTIDOTE SHOULD BE ADMINISTERED BY QUALIFIED MEDICAL PERSONNEL.

REACTIVITY

REACTIVITY: STABLE UNDER NORMAL TEMPERATURES AND PRESSURES.

INCOMPATIBILITIES: TRIAZOPHOS: OXIDIZERS (STRONG): FIRE AND EXPLOSION HAZARD.

DECOMPOSITION: THERMAL DECOMPOSITION PRODUCTS MAY INCLUDE TOXIC AND HAZARDOUS FUMES OF SULFUR, NITROGEN AND PHOSPHORUS.

POLYMERIZATION: HAZARDOUS POLYMERIZATION HAS NOT BEEN REPORTED TO OCCUR UNDER NORMAL TEMPERATURES AND PRESSURES.

STORAGE AND DISPOSAL

OBSERVE ALL FEDERAL, STATE AND LOCAL REGULATIONS WHEN STORING OR DISPOSING OF THIS SUBSTANCE. FOR ASSISTANCE, CONTACT THE DISTRICT DIRECTOR OF THE ENVIRONMENTAL PROTECTION AGENCY.

STORAGE

STORE IN ACCORDANCE WITH 40 CFR 165 RECOMMENDED PROCEDURES FOR THE DISPOSAL AND STORAGE OF PESTICIDES AND PESTICIDE CONTAINERS.

STORE AWAY FROM INCOMPATIBLE SUBSTANCES.

THRESHOLD PLANNING QUANTITY (TPQ): THE SUPERFUND AMENDMENTS AND REAUTHORIZATION ACT (SARA) SECTION 302 REQUIRES THAT EACH FACILITY WHERE ANY EXTREMELY HAZARDOUS SUBSTANCE IS PRESENT IN A QUANTITY EQUAL TO OR GREATER THAN THE TPQ ESTABLISHED FOR THAT SUBSTANCE NOTIFY THE STATE EMERGENCY RESPONSE COMMISSION FOR THE STATE IN WHICH IT IS LOCATED. SECTION 303 OF SARA REQUIRES THESE FACILITIES TO PARTICIPATE IN LOCAL EMERGENCY RESPONSE PLANNING (40 CFR 355.30).

DISPOSAL

DISPOSAL MUST BE IN ACCORDANCE WITH 40 CFR 165 RECOMMENDED PROCEDURES FOR THE DISPOSAL AND STORAGE OF PESTICIDES AND PESTICIDE CONTAINERS.

CONDITIONS TO AVOID

NONE REPORTED.

SPILL AND LEAK PROCEDURES

OCCUPATIONAL SPILL: DO NOT TOUCH SPILLED MATERIAL. STOP LEAK IF YOU CAN DO IT WITHOUT RISK. USE WATER SPRAY TO REDUCE VAPORS. FOR SMALL SPILLS, TAKE UP WITH SAND OR OTHER ABSORBENT MATERIAL AND PLACE INTO CONTAINERS FOR LATER DISPOSAL. FOR SMALL DRY SPILLS, WITH A CLEAN SHOVEL PLACE MATERIAL INTO CLEAN, DRY CONTAINERS AND COVER. MOVE CONTAINERS FROM SPILL AREA. FOR LARGER SPILLS, DIKE FAR AHEAD OF SPILL FOR LATER DISPOSAL. KEEP UNNECESSARY PEOPLE AWAY. ISOLATE HAZARD AREA AND DENY ENTRY. VENTILATE CLOSED SPACES BEFORE ENTERING.

REPORTABLE QUANTITY (RQ): 1 POUND THE SUPERFUND AMENDMENTS AND REAUTHORIZATION ACT (SARA) SECTION 304 REQUIRES THAT A RELEASE EQUAL TO OR GREATER THAN THE REPORTABLE QUANTITY FOR THIS SUBSTANCE BE IMMEDIATELY REPORTED TO THE LOCAL EMERGENCY PLANNING COMMITTEE AND THE STATE EMERGENCY RESPONSE COMMISSION (40 CFR 355.40). IF THE RELEASE OF THIS SUBSTANCE IS REPORTABLE UNDER CERCLA SECTION 103, THE NATIONAL RESPONSE CENTER MUST BE NOTIFIED IMMEDIATELY AT (800) 424-8802 OR (202) 426-2675 IN THE METROPOLITAN WASHINGTON, D.C. AREA (40 CFR 302.6).

PROTECTIVE EQUIPMENT

VENTILATION: PROCESS ENCLOSURE RECOMMENDED.

RESPIRATOR: THE FOLLOWING RESPIRATORS ARE RECOMMENDED BASED ON INFORMATION FOUND IN THE PHYSICAL DATA, TOXICITY AND HEALTH EFFECTS

SECTIONS. THEY ARE RANKED IN ORDER FROM MINIMUM TO MAXIMUM RESPIRATORY PROTECTION. THE SPECIFIC RESPIRATOR SELECTED MUST BE BASED ON CONTAMINATION LEVELS FOUND IN THE WORK PLACE, MUST NOT EXCEED THE WORKING LIMITS OF THE RESPIRATOR AND BE JOINTLY APPROVED BY THE NATIONAL INSTITUTE FOR OCCUPATIONAL SAFETY AND HEALTH AND THE MINE SAFETY AND HEALTH ADMINISTRATION (NIOSH-MSHA).

TYPE 'C' SUPPLIED-AIR RESPIRATOR WITH A FULL FACEPIECE OPERATED IN PRESSURE-DEMAND OR OTHER POSITIVE PRESSURE MODE OR WITH A FULL FACEPIECE, HELMET OR HOOD OPERATED IN CONTINOUS-FLOW MODE.

SELF-CONTAINED BREATHING APPARATUS WITH A FULL FACEPIECE OPERATED IN PRESSURE-DEMAND OR OTHER POSITIVE PRESSURE MODE.

FOR FIREFIGHTING AND OTHER IMMEDIATELY DANGEROUS TO LIFE OR HEALTH CONDITIONS:

SELF-CONTAINED BREATHING APPARATUS WITH FULL FACEPIECE OPERATED IN PRESSURE-DEMAND OR OTHER POSITIVE PRESSURE MODE.

SUPPLIED-AIR RESPIRATOR WITH FULL FACEPIECE AND OPERATED IN PRESSURE-DEMAND OR OTHER POSITIVE PRESSURE MODE IN COMBINATION WITH AN AUXILIARY SELF-CONTAINED BREATHING APPARATUS OPERATED IN PRESSURE-DEMAND OR OTHER POSITIVE PRESSURE MODE.

CLOTHING: EMPLOYEE MUST WEAR APPROPRIATE PROTECTIVE (IMPERVIOUS) CLOTHING AND EQUIPMENT TO PREVENT ANY POSSIBILITY OF SKIN CONTACT WITH THIS SUBSTANCE.

GLOVES: EMPLOYEE MUST WEAR APPROPRIATE PROTECTIVE GLOVES TO PREVENT CONTACT WITH THIS SUBSTANCE.

EYE PROTECTION: EMPLOYEE MUST WEAR SPLASH-PROOF OR DUST-RESISTANT SAFETY GOGGLES AND A FACESHIELD TO PREVENT CONTACT WITH THIS SUBSTANCE.

EMERGENCY WASH FACILITIES: WHERE THERE IS ANY POSSIBILITY THAT AN EMPLOYEE'S EYES AND/OR SKIN MAY BE EXPOSED TO THIS SUBSTANCE, THE EMPLOYER SHOULD PROVIDE AN EYE WASH FOUNTAIN AND QUICK DRENCH SHOWER WITHIN THE IMMEDIATE WORK AREA FOR EMERGENCY USE.

AUTHORIZED BY- OCCUPATIONAL HEALTH SERVICES, INC.
CREATION DATE: 10/05/89 ***REVISION DATE:*** 04/30/90

MATERIAL SAFETY DATA SHEET

OCCUPATIONAL HEALTH SERVICES, INC.
AGRICULTURE AND PESTICIDE DIVISION
450 SEVENTH AVENUE, SUITE 2407
NEW YORK, NEW YORK 10123
1-800-445-MSDS OR (212) 967-1100

EMERGENCY CONTACT:
JOHN S. BRANSFORD, JR. (615) 292-1180

SUBSTANCE IDENTIFICATION

CAS-NUMBER 572-48-5

SUBSTANCE: **COUMITHOATE**

TRADE NAMES/SYNONYMS: PHOSPHOROTHIOIC ACID, O,O-DIETHYL O-(7,8,9,10-TETRAHYDRO-6-OXO-6H -DIBENZO(B,D)PYRAN-3-YL) ESTER; O,O-DIETHYL O-(7,8,9,10-TETRAHYDRO-6-OXO-6H-DIBENZO(B,D)PYRAN-3-YL) PHOSPHOROTHIOATE; PHOSPHOROTHIOIC ACID, O,O-DIETHYL ESTER, O-ESTER WITH 7,8,9,10 -TETRAHYDRO-3-HYDROXY-6H-DIBENZO(B,D)PYRAN-6-ONE; 1-CYCLOHEXENE-1-CARBOXYLIC ACID, 2-(2,4-DIHYDROXYPHENYL)-, DELTA -LACTONE, O-ESTER WITH O,O-DIETHYL PHOSPHOROTHIOATE; 2-(2,4-DIHYDROXYPHENYL)-1-CYCLOHEXENE-1-CARBOXYLIC ACID DELTA-LACTONE O-ESTER WITH O,O-DIETHYL PHOSPHOROTHIOATE; 2-(2,4-DIHYDROXYPHENYL)-1-CYCLOHENXENE-1-CARBOXYLIC ACID DELTA -LACTONE O,O-DIETHYLPHOSPHOROTHIOATE; O,O-DIETHYLTHIOPHOSPHORIC ESTER OF 3,4-TETRAMETHYLENEUMBELLIFERONE; O,O-DIETHYL O-7-HYDROXY-3,4-TETRAMETHYLENECOUMARINYL PHOSPHOROTHIOATE; DITHION; DITHIONE; DITION; C17H21O5PS; PST73073

CHEMICAL FAMILY: PHOSPHOROTHIOATE

MOLECULAR FORMULA: C17-H21-O5-P-S

MOLECULAR WEIGHT: 368.40

CERCLA RATINGS (SCALE 0-3): HEALTH=3 FIRE=1 REACTIVITY=0 PERSISTENCE=3

NFPA RATINGS (SCALE 0-4): HEALTH=3 FIRE=1 REACTIVITY=0

COMPONENTS AND CONTAMINANTS

COMPONENT: COUMITHOATE ***PERCENT:*** 100.0
CAS# 572-48-5

OTHER CONTAMINANTS: NONE

EXPOSURE LIMITS: NO OCCUPATIONAL EXPOSURE LIMITS ESTABLISHED BY OSHA, ACGIH, OR NIOSH.

PHYSICAL DATA

DESCRIPTION: NEEDLES. ***MELTING POINT:*** 190-192 F (88-89 C)

SPECIFIC GRAVITY: NOT AVAILABLE ***SOLUBILITY IN WATER:*** ALMOST INSOLUBLE

SOLVENT SOLUBILITY: SLIGHTLY SOLUBLE IN ORGANIC SOLVENTS.

FIRE AND EXPLOSION DATA

FIRE AND EXPLOSION HAZARD: SLIGHT FIRE HAZARD WHEN EXPOSED TO HEAT OR FLAME.

FIREFIGHTING MEDIA: DRY CHEMICAL, CARBON DIOXIDE, HALON, WATER SPRAY OR STANDARD FOAM (1987 EMERGENCY RESPONSE GUIDEBOOK, DOT P 5800.4). FOR LARGER FIRES, USE WATER SPRAY, FOG OR STANDARD FOAM (1987 EMERGENCY RESPONSE GUIDEBOOK, DOT P 5800.4).

FIREFIGHTING: MOVE CONTAINERS FROM FIRE AREA IF POSSIBLE. FIGHT FIRE FROM MAXIMUM DISTANCE. STAY AWAY FROM STORAGE TANK ENDS. DIKE FIRE CONTROL WATER FOR LATER DISPOSAL. DO NOT SCATTER MATERIAL (1987 EMERGENCY RESPONSE GUIDEBOOK, DOT P 5800.4, GUIDE PAGE 55). EXTINGUISH ONLY IF FLOW CAN BE STOPPED; USE FLOODING AMOUNTS OF WATER AS FOG, SOLID STREAMS MAY BE INEFFECTIVE. COOL CONTAINERS WITH FLOODING AMOUNTS OF WATER FROM AS FAR A DISTANCE AS POSSIBLE. USE WATER SPRAY TO ABSORB TOXIC VAPORS. AVOID BREATHING TOXIC VAPORS; KEEP UPWIND. CONSIDER EVACUATION OF DOWNWIND AREA IF MATERIAL IS LEAKING.

TOXICITY

COUMITHOATE: TOXICITY DATA: 67 MG/KG ORAL-RAT LD50; 3800 MG/KG ORAL-MOUSE LD50; 500 MG/KG ORAL-RABBIT LD50; 200 MG/KG ORAL-GUINEA PIG LD50; 400 MG/KG ORAL-DOG LD50; 150 MG/KG UNREPORTED-RAT LD50. CARCINOGEN STATUS: NONE. ACUTE TOXICITY: TOXIC BY INGESTION. TARGET EFFECTS: CHOLINESTERASE INHIBITOR. POISONING MAY AFFECT THE NERVOUS SYSTEM.* AT INCREASED RISK FROM EXPOSURE: PERSONS WITH RESPIRATORY AILMENTS, RECENT EXPOSURE TO CHOLINESTERASE INHIBITORS OR IMPAIRED CHOLINESTERASE PRODUCTION, OR LIVER MALFUNCTION.* ADDITIONAL DATA: MAY CROSS THE PLACENTA. HIGH ENVIRONMENTAL TEMPERATURES OR EXPOSURE OF THE CHEMICAL TO VISIBLE OR ULTRAVIOLET LIGHT MAY ENHANCE THE TOXICITY. INTERACTIONS WITH MEDICATIONS MAY OCCUR.*

* MAY BE BASED ON GENERAL INFORMATION ON ORGANOPHOSPHATES.

HEALTH EFFECTS AND FIRST AID

INHALATION: COUMITHOATE: SEE INFORMATION ON ORGANOPHOSPHATES. ORGANOPHOSPHATES: CHOLINESTERASE INHIBITOR. **ACUTE EXPOSURE**- WHEN INHALED, THE FIRST EFFECTS OF CHOLINESTERASE INHIBITORS ARE USUALLY RESPIRATORY AND MAY INCLUDE NASAL HYPEREMIA AND WATERY DISCHARGE, COUGH, CHEST DISCOMFORT, DYSPNEA, AND WHEEZING DUE TO INCREASED BRONCHIAL SECRETIONS AND BRONCHOCONSTRICTION. IF SUFFICIENT AMOUNTS ARE ABSORBED, OTHER SYSTEMIC EFFECTS MAY BEGIN WITHIN A FEW MINUTES OR BE DELAYED FOR UP TO 12 HOURS. SYMPTOMS MAY INCLUDE PALLOR, NAUSEA, VOMITING, DIARRHEA, ABDOMINAL CRAMPS, HEADACHE, DIZZINESS, OCULAR PAIN, BLURRED VISION, MIOSIS OR IN SOME CASES, ESPECIALLY INITIALLY, MYDRIASIS, LACRIMATION, SALIVATION, SWEATING, AND CONFUSION. OTHER REPORTED CENTRAL NERVOUS SYSTEM OR NEUROMUSCULAR EFFECTS MAY INCLUDE ATAXIA, SLURRED SPEECH, AREFLEXIA, WEAKNESS, FATIGUE, FASCICULATIONS, TWITCHING, TREMORS POSSIBLY OF THE TONGUE AND EYELIDS, AND EVENTUALLY PARALYSIS OF THE EXTREMITIES AND POSSIBLY OF THE RESPIRATORY MUSCLES. IN SEVERE CASES THERE MAY ALSO BE INVOLUNTARY DEFECATION AND URINATION, CYANOSIS, PSYCHOSIS, HYPERGLYCEMIA, ACUTE PANCREATITIS, CARDIAC IRREGULARITIES, PULMONARY EDEMA, UNCONSCIOUSNESS, CONVULSIONS, AND COMA. DEATH IS PRIMARILY DUE TO RESPIRATORY FAILURE, ALTHOUGH CARDIOVASCULAR EFFECTS INCLUDING CARDIAC ARREST MAY ALSO BE IMPLICATED. LONG TERM SEQUELAE ARE RARE BUT MAY INCLUDE NEUROPSYCHIATRIC DISORDERS AND MYOPATHY WITH MUSCLE TENDERNESS. SOME ORGANOPHOSPHATES MAY CAUSE A DELAYED NEUROPATHY BEGINNING 1-4 WEEKS AFTER AN ACUTE EXPOSURE WHICH MAY OR MAY NOT HAVE CAUSED ACUTE CHOLINERGIC EFFECTS. NUMBNESS, TINGLING, WEAKNESS AND CRAMPING BEGINNING SYMMETRICALLY IN THE LOWER LIMBS MAY PROGRESS TO ATAXIA AND PARALYSIS. IN SEVERE CASES, UPPER LIMB INVOLVEMENT IS POSSIBLE AND FLACCID PARALYSIS MAY PROGRESS TO SPASTIC PARALYSIS WITH EXAGGERATED REFLEXES. IMPROVEMENT MAY OCCUR OVER MONTHS TO YEARS, BUT SOME RESIDUAL IMPAIRMENT USUALLY REMAINS. **CHRONIC EXPOSURE**- REPEATED OR PROLONGED EXPOSURE MAY RESULT IN THE EFFECTS OF ACUTE EXPOSURE INCLUDING THE DELAYED NEUROPATHY. OTHER

EFFECTS REPORTED IN WORKERS REPEATEDLY EXPOSED INCLUDE IMPAIRED MEMORY AND CONCENTRATION, ACUTE PSYCHOSIS, SEVERE DEPRESSIONS, IRRITABILTY, CONFUSION, APATHY, EMOTIONAL LABILITY, SOCIAL WITHDRAWAL, CONFUSION, HEADACHE, SPEECH DIFFICULTIES, DELAYED REACTION TIMES, SPATIAL DISORIENTATION, NIGHTMARES, SLEEPWALKING, AND DROWSINESS OR INSOMNIA. AN INFLUENZA-LIKE CONDITION WITH HEADACHE, NAUSEA, WEAKNESS, ANOREXIA AND MALAISE HAS ALSO BEEN REPORTED.

FIRST AID- REMOVE FROM EXPOSURE AREA TO FRESH AIR IMMEDIATELY. IF BREATHING HAS STOPPED, GIVE ARTIFICIAL RESPIRATION. MAINTAIN AIRWAY AND BLOOD PRESSURE AND ADMINISTER OXYGEN IF AVAILABLE. KEEP AFFECTED PERSON WARM AND AT REST. TREAT SYMPTOMATICALLY AND SUPPORTIVELY. ADMINISTRATION OF OXYGEN SHOULD BE PERFORMED BY QUALIFIED PERSONNEL. GET MEDICAL ATTENTION IMMEDIATELY.

SKIN CONTACT: COUMITHOATE: SEE INFORMATION ON ORGANOPHOSPHATES. ORGANOPHOSPHATES: CHOLINESTERASE INHIBITOR. **ACUTE EXPOSURE**- LOCALIZED SWEATING AND FASCICULATIONS MAY OCCUR AT THE SITE OF CONTACT. IF SUFFICIENT AMOUNTS ARE ABSORBED, OTHER EFFECTS OF CHOLINESTERASE INHIBITION AS DESCRIBED IN ACUTE INHALATION MAY OCCUR. SYMPTOMS MAY BE DELAYED 2-3 HOURS, BUT USUALLY NO MORE THAN 12 HOURS. THE RATE OF ABSORPTION IS INCREASED BY THE PRESENCE OF DERMATITIS OR HIGH AMBIENT TEMPERATURES. DELAYED NEUROPATHY IS ALSO POSSIBLE. **CHRONIC EXPOSURE**- REPEATED OR PROLONGED EXPOSURE MAY CAUSE EFFECTS AS DESCRIBED IN ACUTE EXPOSURE. SOME ORGANOPHOSPHATES MAY CAUSE SENSITIZATION.

FIRST AID- REMOVE CONTAMINATED CLOTHING IMMEDIATELY. WASH CONTAMINATED AREAS WITH SOAP AND WATER FOLLOWED BY ALCOHOL (ARENA, POISONING, 4TH ED.). EMERGENCY PERSONNEL SHOULD WEAR GLOVES AND AVOID CONTAMINATION. TREAT RESPIRATORY DIFFICULTY WITH ARTIFICIAL RESPIRATION. GET MEDICAL ATTENTION IMMEDIATELY.

EYE CONTACT: COUMITHOATE: SEE INFORMATION ON ORGANOPHOSPHATES. ORGANOPHOSPHATES: CHOLINESTERASE INHIBITOR. **ACUTE EXPOSURE**- DIRECT CONTACT MAY CAUSE PAIN, HYPEREMIA, LACRIMATION, TWITCHING OF THE EYELIDS, MIOSIS, AND CILIARY MUSCLE SPASM WITH LOSS OF ACCOMODATION, BLURRED OR DIMMED VISION AND BROWACHE. SOMETIMES MYDRIASIS MAY OCCUR INSTEAD OF MIOSIS. WITH SUFFICIENT EXPOSURE, OTHER SYMPTOMS OF CHOLINESTERASE INHIBITION AS DESCRIBED IN ACUTE INHALATION MAY OCCUR. **CHRONIC EXPOSURE**- REPEATED OR PROLONGED EXPOSURE MAY CAUSE EFFECTS AS DESCRIBED IN ACUTE EXPOSURE. SOME COMPOUNDS HAVE CAUSED TOXIC EFFECTS ON THE CRYSTALLINE LENS, CONJUNCTIVAL THICKENING AND OBSTRUCTION OF THE NASOLACRIMAL CANALS WHEN USED AS MIOTIC EYEDROPS.

FIRST AID- IRRIGATE EYES WITH WATER OR SALINE SOLUTION. IF SYMPTOMS OF POISONING OCCUR, TREAT RESPIRATORY DIFFICULTY WITH ARTIFICIAL RESPIRATION AND OXYGEN. OBSERVE PATIENT FOR AT LEAST 24-36 HOURS (GOSSELIN, CLINICAL TOXICOLOGY OF COMMERCIAL PRODUCTS, 5TH ED.). GET MEDICAL ATTENTION IMMEDIATELY. OXYGEN SHOULD BE ADMINISTERED BY QUALIFIED MEDICAL PERSONNEL.

INGESTION: COUMITHOATE: TOXIC. SEE INFORMATION ON ORGANOPHOSPHATES. ORGANOPHOSPHATES: CHOLINESTERASE INHIBITOR. **ACUTE EXPOSURE**- WHEN INGESTED, THE FIRST EFFECTS MAY BE NAUSEA, VOMITING, ANOREXIA, ABDOMINAL CRAMPS AND DIARRHEA. GASTROINTESTINAL ABSORPTION MAY CAUSE SYMPTOMS OF CHOLINESTERASE INHIBITION AS DESCRIBED IN ACUTE INHALATION. SYMPTOMS MAY BEGIN WITHIN MINUTES OR BE DELAYED FOR HOURS. DELAYED EFFECTS INCLUDING NEUROPATHY MAY ALSO OCCUR. **CHRONIC EXPOSURE**- REPEATED INGESTION MAY CAUSE EFFECTS AS DESCRIBED IN ACUTE EXPOSURE.

FIRST AID- IF PERSON IS ALERT AND RESPIRATION IS NOT DEPRESSED, GIVE SYRUP OF IPECAC FOLLOWED BY WATER (IF VOMITING OCCURS, KEEP HEAD BELOW HIPS TO PREVENT ASPIRATION). IF CONSCIOUSNESS LEVEL DECLINES OR VOMITING HAS NOT OCCURRED IN 15 MINUTES EMPTY STOMACH BY GASTRIC LAVAGE WITH THE AID OF CUFFED ENDOTRACHEAL TUBE USING ISOTONIC SALINE OR 5% SODIUM BICARBONATE FOLLOW WITH ACTIVATED CHARCOAL. ESTABLISH AND MAINTAIN AIRWAY. TREAT RESPIRATORY DIFFICULTY WITH ARTIFICIAL RESPIRATION AND OXYGEN. DO NOT GIVE MORPHINE, AMINOPHYLLINE, PHENOTHIAZINES, RESERPINE, FUROSEMIDE, OR ETHACRYNIC ACID (MORGAN, RECOGNITION AND MANAGEMENT OF PESTICIDE POISONINGS, 3RD ED.). TREAT SYMPTOMATICALLY AND SUPPORTIVELY. ADMINISTRATION OF OXYGEN AND LAVAGE MUST BE PERFORMED BY QUALIFIED MEDICAL PERSONNEL. GET MEDICAL ATTENTION IMMEDIATELY.

ANTIDOTE: THE FOLLOWING ANTIDOTE(S) HAVE BEEN RECOMMENDED. HOWEVER, THE DECISION AS TO WHETHER THE SEVERITY OF POISONING REQUIRES ADMINISTRATION OF ANY ANTIDOTE AND ACTUAL DOSE REQUIRED SHOULD BE MADE BY QUALIFIED MEDICAL PERSONNEL.

FOR CHOLINESTERASE INHIBITORS: ESTABLISH CLEAR AIRWAY AND TISSUE OXYGENATION BY ASPIRATION OF SECRETIONS, AND IF NECESSARY, BY ASSISTED PULMONARY VENTILATION WITH OXYGEN. IMPROVE TISSUE OXYGENATION AS MUCH AS POSSIBLE BEFORE ADMINISTERING ATROPINE TO MINIMIZE THE RISK OF VENTRICULAR FIBRILLATION. ADMINISTER ATROPINE SULFATE INTRAVENOUSLY, OR INTRAMUSCULARLY IF IV INJECTION IS NOT POSSIBLE. IN MODERATELY SEVERE POISONING ADMINISTER ATROPINE SULFATE, 0.4-2.0 MG REPEATED EVERY 15 MINUTES UNTIL ATROPINIZATION IS ACHIEVED (TACHYCARDIA, FLUSHING, DRY MOUTH, MYDRIASIS). MAINTAIN ATROPINIZATION BY REPEATED DOSES FOR 2-12 HOURS, OR LONGER, DEPENDING ON THE SEVERITY OF POISONING. THE APPEARANCE OF RALES IN THE LUNG BASES, MIOSIS, SALIVATION, NAUSEA, BRADYCARDIA, ARE ALL INDICATIONS OF INADEQUATE ATROPINIZATION. SEVERELY POISONED INDIVIDUALS MAY EXHIBIT REMARKABLE TOLERANCE TO ATROPINE; TWO OR MORE TIMES THE DOSAGES SUGGESTED ABOVE MAY BE NEEDED. PERSONS NOT POISONED OR ONLY SLIGHTLY POISONED, HOWEVER, MAY DEVELOP SIGNS OF ATROPINE TOXICITY FROM SUCH LARGE DOSAGES: FEVER, MUSCLE FIBRILLATIONS, AND DELIRIUM ARE THE MAIN SIGNS OF ATROPINE TOXICITY. IF THESE SIGNS APPEAR WHILE THE PATIENT IS FULLY ATROPINIZED, ATROPINE ADMINISTRATION SHOULD BE DISCONTINUED, AT LEAST TEMPORARILY. OBSERVE TREATED PATIENTS CLOSELY AT LEAST 24 HOURS TO INSURE THAT SYMPTOMS (POSSIBLY PULMONARY EDEMA) DO NOT RECUR AS ATROPINIZATION WEARS OFF. IN VERY SEVERE POISONINGS, METABOLIC DISPOSITION OF TOXICANT MAY REQUIRE SEVERAL HOURS OR DAYS DURING WHICH ATROPINIZATION MUST BE MAINTAINED. MARKEDLY LOWER LEVELS OF URINARY METABOLITES INDICATE THAT ATROPINE DOSAGE CAN BE TAPERED OFF. AS DOSAGE IS REDUCED, CHECK THE LUNG BASES FREQUENTLY FOR RALES. IF RALES ARE HEARD OR OTHER SYMPTOMS RETURN, RE-ESTABLISH ATROPINIZATION PROMPTLY (MORGAN, RECOGNITION AND MANAGEMENT OF PESTICIDE POISONINGS, 3RD ED.). ADMINISTRATION OF ANTIDOTE MUST BE PERFORMED BY QUALIFIED MEDICAL PERSONNEL.

IN CASES OF SEVERE POISONING BY ORGANOPHOSPHATE PESTICIDES IN WHICH RESPIRATORY DEPRESSION, MUSCLE WEAKNESS AND TWITCHINGS ARE SEVERE, GIVE PRALIDOXIME (PROTOPAM-AYERST, 2-PAM), 1.0 GRAM INTRAVENOUSLY AT NO MORE THAN 0.5 GRAM PER MINUTE. DOSAGE OF PRALIDOXIME MAY BE REPEATED IN 1-2 HOURS, THEN AT 10-12 HOUR INTERVALS IF NEEDED. IN VERY SEVERE POISONINGS, DOSAGE RATES MAY BE DOUBLED. TREATMENT WITH PRALIDOXIME WILL BE MOST EFFECTIVE IF GIVEN WITHIN THIRTY-SIX HOURS AFTER POISONING (MORGAN, RECOGNITION AND MANAGEMENT OF PESTICIDE POISONINGS, 3RD ED.). ANTIDOTE SHOULD BE ADMINISTERED BY QUALIFIED MEDICAL PERSONNEL.

REACTIVITY

REACTIVITY: STABLE UNDER NORMAL TEMPERATURES AND PRESSURES.

INCOMPATIBILITIES: COUMITHOATE: OXIDIZERS (STRONG): FIRE AND EXPLOSION HAZARD.

DECOMPOSITION: THERMAL DECOMPOSITION PRODUCTS MAY INCLUDE TOXIC OXIDES OF CARBON, SULFUR, AND PHOSPHORUS.

POLYMERIZATION: HAZARDOUS POLYMERIZATION HAS NOT BEEN REPORTED TO OCCUR UNDER NORMAL TEMPERATURES AND PRESSURES.

STORAGE AND DISPOSAL

OBSERVE ALL FEDERAL, STATE AND LOCAL REGULATIONS WHEN STORING OR DISPOSING OF THIS SUBSTANCE. FOR ASSISTANCE, CONTACT THE DISTRICT DIRECTOR OF THE ENVIRONMENTAL PROTECTION AGENCY.

STORAGE

STORE IN ACCORDANCE WITH 40 CFR 165 RECOMMENDED PROCEDURES FOR THE DISPOSAL AND STORAGE OF PESTICIDES AND PESTICIDE CONTAINERS. STORE AWAY FROM INCOMPATIBLE SUBSTANCES.

DISPOSAL

DISPOSAL MUST BE IN ACCORDANCE WITH 40 CFR 165 RECOMMENDED PROCEDURES FOR THE DISPOSAL AND STORAGE OF PESTICIDES AND PESTICIDE CONTAINERS.

CONDITIONS TO AVOID

MAY BURN BUT DOES NOT IGNITE READILY. CONTAINERS MAY EXPLODE IN HEAT OF FIRE.

SPILL AND LEAK PROCEDURES

OCCUPATIONAL SPILL: DO NOT TOUCH SPILLED MATERIAL. STOP LEAK IF YOU CAN DO IT WITHOUT RISK. USE WATER SPRAY TO REDUCE VAPORS. FOR SMALL SPILLS, TAKE UP WITH SAND OR OTHER ABSORBENT MATERIAL AND PLACE INTO CONTAINERS FOR LATER DISPOSAL. FOR SMALL DRY SPILLS, WITH A CLEAN SHOVEL PLACE MATERIAL INTO CLEAN, DRY CONTAINERS AND COVER. MOVE CONTAINERS FROM SPILL AREA. FOR LARGER SPILLS, DIKE FAR AHEAD OF SPILL FOR LATER DISPOSAL. KEEP UNNECESSARY PEOPLE AWAY. ISOLATE HAZARD AREA AND DENY ENTRY. VENTILATE CLOSED SPACES BEFORE ENTERING.

PROTECTIVE EQUIPMENT

VENTILATION: PROVIDE LOCAL EXHAUST OR PROCESS ENCLOSURE VENTILATION SYSTEM.

RESPIRATOR: THE FOLLOWING RESPIRATORS ARE RECOMMENDED BASED ON INFORMATION FOUND IN THE PHYSICAL DATA, TOXICITY AND HEALTH EFFECTS SECTIONS. THEY ARE RANKED IN ORDER FROM MINIMUM TO MAXIMUM RESPIRATORY PROTECTION. THE SPECIFIC RESPIRATOR SELECTED MUST BE BASED ON CONTAMINATION LEVELS FOUND IN THE WORK PLACE, MUST NOT EXCEED THE WORKING LIMITS OF THE RESPIRATOR AND BE JOINTLY APPROVED BY THE NATIONAL INSTITUTE FOR OCCUPATIONAL SAFETY AND HEALTH AND THE MINE SAFETY AND HEALTH ADMINISTRATION (NIOSH-MSHA).

TYPE 'C' SUPPLIED-AIR RESPIRATOR WITH A FULL FACEPIECE OPERATED IN PRESSURE-DEMAND OR OTHER POSITIVE PRESSURE MODE OR WITH A FULL FACEPIECE, HELMET OR HOOD OPERATED IN CONTINOUS-FLOW MODE.

SELF-CONTAINED BREATHING APPARATUS WITH A FULL FACEPIECE OPERATED IN PRESSURE-DEMAND OR OTHER POSITIVE PRESSURE MODE.

FOR FIREFIGHTING AND OTHER IMMEDIATELY DANGEROUS TO LIFE OR HEALTH CONDITIONS:

SELF-CONTAINED BREATHING APPARATUS WITH FULL FACEPIECE OPERATED IN PRESSURE-DEMAND OR OTHER POSITIVE PRESSURE MODE.

SUPPLIED-AIR RESPIRATOR WITH FULL FACEPIECE AND OPERATED IN PRESSURE-DEMAND OR OTHER POSITIVE PRESSURE MODE IN COMBINATION WITH AN AUXILIARY SELF-CONTAINED BREATHING APPARATUS OPERATED IN PRESSURE-DEMAND OR OTHER POSITIVE PRESSURE MODE.

CLOTHING: EMPLOYEE MUST WEAR APPROPRIATE PROTECTIVE (IMPERVIOUS) CLOTHING AND EQUIPMENT TO PREVENT ANY POSSIBILITY OF SKIN CONTACT WITH THIS SUBSTANCE.

GLOVES: EMPLOYEE MUST WEAR APPROPRIATE PROTECTIVE GLOVES TO PREVENT CONTACT WITH THIS SUBSTANCE.

EYE PROTECTION: EMPLOYEE MUST WEAR SPLASH-PROOF OR DUST-RESISTANT SAFETY GOGGLES WITH OR WITHOUT A FACESHIELD TO PREVENT CONTACT WITH THIS SUBSTANCE.

EMERGENCY EYE WASH: WHERE THERE IS ANY POSSIBILITY THAT AN EMPLOYEE'S EYES MAY BE EXPOSED TO THIS SUBSTANCE, THE EMPLOYER SHOULD PROVIDE AN EYE WASH FOUNTAIN WITHIN THE IMMEDIATE WORK AREA FOR EMERGENCY USE.

AUTHORIZED BY- OCCUPATIONAL HEALTH SERVICES, INC.

CREATION DATE: 10/04/89 ***REVISION DATE:*** 04/24/90

MATERIAL SAFETY DATA SHEET

OCCUPATIONAL HEALTH SERVICES, INC.	EMERGENCY CONTACT:
AGRICULTURE AND PESTICIDE DIVISION	JOHN S. BRANSFORD, JR. (615) 292-1180
450 SEVENTH AVENUE, SUITE 2407	
NEW YORK, NEW YORK 10123	
1-800-445-MSDS OR (212) 967-1100	

SUBSTANCE IDENTIFICATION

CAS-NUMBER 2961-62-8

SUBSTANCE: **IOXYNIL SODIUM**

TRADE NAMES/SYNONYMS: BENZONITRILE, 4-HYDROXY-3,5-DIIODO-, SODIUM SALT; 4-HYDROXY-3,5-DIIODOBENZONITRILE, SODIUM SALT; SODIUM, (4-CYANO-2,6-DIIODOPHENOXY)-; (4-CYANO-2,6-DIIODOPHENOXY)SODIUM; C7H3I2NNAO; PST73074

CHEMICAL FAMILY: NITRILE, AROMATIC
HALOGEN
SALT

MOLECULAR FORMULA: (I2)-(C-N)-C6-H2-O.NA

MOLECULAR WEIGHT: 393.30

CERCLA RATINGS (SCALE 0-3): HEALTH=3 FIRE=1 REACTIVITY=0 PERSISTENCE=1

NFPA RATINGS (SCALE 0-4): HEALTH=3 FIRE=1 REACTIVITY=0

COMPONENTS AND CONTAMINANTS

COMPONENT: IOXYNIL SODIUM ***PERCENT:*** 100.0
CAS# 2961-62-8

OTHER CONTAMINANTS: NONE

EXPOSURE LIMITS: NO OCCUPATIONAL EXPOSURE LIMITS ESTABLISHED BY OSHA, ACGIH, OR NIOSH.

PHYSICAL DATA

DESCRIPTION: SOLID. ***MELTING POINT:*** 680 F (360 C) (APPROXIMATE)

SPECIFIC GRAVITY: NOT AVAILABLE ***SOLUBILITY IN WATER:*** 14% @ 20-25 C

SOLVENT SOLUBILITY: SOLUBLE IN ACETONE, TETRAHYDROFURFURYL ALCOHOL, AND METHYL CELLOSOLVE.

FIRE AND EXPLOSION DATA

FIRE AND EXPLOSION HAZARD: SLIGHT FIRE HAZARD WHEN EXPOSED TO HEAT OR FLAME.

DUST-AIR MIXTURES MAY IGNITE OR EXPLODE.

FIREFIGHTING MEDIA: DRY CHEMICAL, CARBON DIOXIDE, HALON, WATER SPRAY OR STANDARD FOAM (1987 EMERGENCY RESPONSE GUIDEBOOK, DOT P 5800.4).

FOR LARGER FIRES, USE WATER SPRAY, FOG OR STANDARD FOAM (1987 EMERGENCY RESPONSE GUIDEBOOK, DOT P 5800.4).

FIREFIGHTING: MOVE CONTAINERS FROM FIRE AREA IF POSSIBLE (1987 EMERGENCY RESPONSE GUIDEBOOK, DOT P 5800.4, GUIDE PAGE 53).

EXTINGUISH USING AGENT SUITABLE FOR TYPE OF SURROUNDING FIRE. AVOID BREATHING VAPORS AND DUSTS. KEEP UPWIND.

TOXICITY

IOXYNIL SODIUM: TOXICITY DATA: 210 MG/KG SKIN-RAT LD50; 112 MG/KG ORAL-RAT LD50; 190 MG/KG ORAL-MOUSE LD50. CARCINOGEN STATUS: NONE. ACUTE TOXICITY LEVEL: TOXIC BY DERMAL ABSORPTION AND INGESTION. TARGET EFFECTS: NO DATA AVAILABLE. ADDITIONAL DATA: SOME NITRILES RELEASE HIGHLY TOXIC CYANIDE IN THE BODY.

HEALTH EFFECTS AND FIRST AID

INHALATION: IOXYNIL SODIUM: **ACUTE EXPOSURE-** NO DATA AVAILABLE. **CHRONIC EXPOSURE-** EFFECTS OF INORDINANT SWEATING AND THIRST, FEVER, HEADACHE, DIZZINESS, VOMITING, ASTHENIA, WEIGHT LOSS, AND MYALGIA OF THE LEGS WERE REPORTED FROM A CASE OF OCCUPATIONAL EXPOSURE TO IOXYNIL AND BROMOXYNIL. THE ONSET OF THESE EFFECTS WERE INSIDIOUS. LABORATORY TESTS REVEALED TRANSITORY ELEVATION OF CREATININE PHOSPHOKINASE, LDH, ALDOLASE, AND SGOT. REMOVAL OF THE AFFECTED MEN FROM EXPOSURE RESULTED IN PROMPT RECOVERY.

FIRST AID- REMOVE FROM EXPOSURE. IF BREATHING HAS STOPPED OR IS DEPRESSED, GIVE ARTIFICIAL RESPIRATION. MAINTAIN AIRWAY AND ADMINISTER OXYGEN TO MAINTAIN HIGH BLOOD/OXYGEN TENSION. GET MEDICAL ATTENTION IMMEDIATELY. (DREISBACH, HANDBOOK OF POISONING, 11TH ED.).

SKIN CONTACT: IOXYNIL SODIUM: TOXIC. **ACUTE EXPOSURE-** A LETHAL DOSE IN RATS BY DERMAL ABSORPTION WAS 210 MG/KG. SOME NITRILES MAY CAUSE CYANIDE POISONING WITH DIZZINESS, RAPID RESPIRATION, VOMITING, FLUSHING, HEADACHE, DROWSINESS, DROP IN BLOOD PRESSURE, RAPID PULSE, CYANOSIS, UNCONSCIOUSNESS, CONVULSIONS, AND DEATH. **CHRONIC EXPOSURE-** EFFECTS OF INORDINANT SWEATING AND THIRST, FEVER, HEADACHE, DIZZINESS, VOMITING, ASTHENIA, WEIGHT LOSS, AND MYALGIA OF THE LEGS WERE REPORTED FROM A CASE OF OCCUPATIONAL EXPOSURE TO IOXYNIL AND BROMOXYNIL. THE ONSET OF THESE EFFECTS WERE INSIDIOUS. LABORATORY TESTS REVEALED TRANSITORY ELEVATION OF CREATININE PHOSPHOKINASE, LDH, ALDOLASE, AND SGOT. REMOVAL OF THE AFFECTED MEN FROM EXPOSURE RESULTED IN PROMPT RECOVERY.

FIRST AID- REMOVE CONTAMINATED CLOTHING AND SHOES AND WASH AFFECTED AREAS WITH SOAP OR MILD DETERGENT AND LARGE AMOUNTS OF WATER, TAKING CARE NOT TO CONTACT THE CHEMICAL. GET MEDICAL ATTENTION IMMEDIATELY. (CAIN, EMERGENCY TREATMENT AND MANAGEMENT, 7TH ED.).

EYE CONTACT: IOXYNIL SODIUM: **ACUTE EXPOSURE-** NO DATA AVAILABLE. **CHRONIC EXPOSURE-** NO DATA AVAILABLE.

FIRST AID- WASH EYES IMMEDIATELY WITH LARGE AMOUNTS OF WATER OR NORMAL SALINE, OCCASIONALLY LIFTING UPPER AND LOWER LIDS, UNTIL NO EVIDENCE OF CHEMICAL REMAINS (APPROXIMATELY 15-20 MINUTES). GET MEDICAL ATTENTION IMMEDIATELY.

INGESTION: IOXYNIL SODIUM: TOXIC. **ACUTE EXPOSURE-** A LETHAL DOSE IN RATS WAS 110 MG/KG; SYMPTOMS WERE NOT REPORTED. HYPEREMIA OF ALL ORGANS AND EDEMA OF THE LUNGS AND BRAIN WERE DETERMINED BY AN AUTOPSY OF A MAN WHO INGESTED APPROXIMATELY 43 MG/KG IOXYNIL IN COMBINATION WITH ALCOHOL. SOME NITRILES MAY CAUSE CYANIDE POISONING WITH DIZZINESS, RAPID BLOOD PRESSURE, RAPID PULSE, CYANOSIS, UNCONSCIOUSNESS, CONVULSIONS, AND DEATHS. **CHRONIC EXPOSURE-** NO OBSERVABLE EFFECTS WERE NOTED IN A 90-DAY STUDY OF RATS FED 5.5 MG/KG/DAY. REPEATED INGESTION OF SMALL AMOUNTS OF IODINE COMPOUNDS MAY CAUSE IODISM CHARACTERIZED BY ERYTHEMA, CONJUNCTIVITIS, STOMATITIS, CLEEPLESSNESS, AND NERVOUS SYSTEM.

FIRST AID- IF PATIENT IS ASYMPTOMATIC ADMINISTER SYRUP OF IPECAC AND/OR PERFORM GASTRIC LAVAGE, USING TAP WATER, DILUTE SODIUM BICARBONATE SOLUTION OR PREFERABLY, IF AVAILABLE, DILUTE POTASSIUM PERMANGANATE SOLUTION (1:5000). ACTIVATED CHARCOAL IS INEFFECTIVE. IF BREATHING HAS STOPPED, GIVE ARTIFICIAL RESPIRATION. MAINTAIN AIRWAY. OXYGEN THERAPY MAY BE OF VALUE IN COMBINATION WITH THE ANTIDOTE (GOSSELIN, CLINICAL TOXICOLOGY OF COMMERCIAL PRODUCTS, 5TH ED.). TREATMENT SHOULD BE PERFORMED BY QUALIFIED MEDICAL PERSONNEL. GET MEDICAL ATTENTION IMMEDIATELY.

ANTIDOTE: THE FOLLOWING ANTIDOTE HAS BEEN RECOMMENDED. HOWEVER, THE DECISION AS TO WHETHER THE SEVERITY OF POISONING REQUIRES ADMINISTRATION OF ANY ANTIDOTE AND ACTUAL DOSE REQUIRED SHOULD BE MADE BY QUALIFIED MEDICAL PERSONNEL.

FOR CYANIDE POISONING: IF SYMPTOMS OF CYANIDE POISONING ARE EVIDENT, ADMINISTER IMMEDIATELY BEFORE ANY OTHER FIRST AID MEASURES.

ADMINISTER AMYL NITRITE (AMYL NITRITE PERLES) BY INHALATION FOR 15 TO 30 SECONDS OF EVERY MINUTE, WHILE SODIUM NITRITE SOLUTION IS BEING PREPARED. DISCONTINUE AMYL NITRITE AND IMMEDIATELY INJECT 10 ML OF A 3% SOLUTION OF SODIUM NITRITE INTRAVENOUSLY OVER A PERIOD OF 2 TO 4 MINUTES. IF NECESSARY, INJECT A NON-STERILE SOLUTION. DO NOT REMOVE THE NEEDLE. CAUTION: APPROPRIATE ADJUSTMENTS IN THE DOSE SHOULD BE MADE ON A BODY WEIGHT BASIS. THROUGH THE SAME NEEDLE, INFUSE INTRAVENOUSLY 50 ML OF A 25% AQUEOUS SOLUTION OF SODIUM THIOSULFATE. THE INJECTION SHOULD TAKE ABOUT 10 MINUTES. OTHER CONCENTRATIONS (5 TO 50%) ARE PERMISSIBLE IF THE TOTAL DOSE IS HELD AT APPROXIMATELY 12 GRAMS.

OXYGEN THERAPY MAY BE OF VALUE IN COMBINATION WITH NITRITE AND SODIUM THIOSULFATE THERAPY. IF SYMPTOMS RECUR, THE INJECTIONS OF NITRITE AND THIOSULFATE MAY BE REPEATED AT HALF THE ABOVE DOSES. IN VERY SEVERE POISONINGS IT IS SAFER AND PERHAPS MORE EFFICIENT TO KEEP REPEATING THE THIOSULFATE INJECTIONS INSTEAD OF THE NITRITE (GOSSELIN, SMITH, HODGE, CLINICAL TOXICOLOGY OF COMMERCIAL PRODUCTS, 5TH ED.). ANTIDOTE SHOULD BE ADMINISTERED BY QUALIFIED MEDICAL PERSONNEL.

REACTIVITY

REACTIVITY: STABLE UNDER NORMAL TEMPERATURES AND PRESSURES.

INCOMPATIBILITIES: IOXYNIL SODIUM: OXIDIZERS (STRONG): FIRE AND EXPLOSION HAZARD.

DECOMPOSITION: THERMAL DECOMPOSITION PRODUCTS MAY INCLUDE TOXIC AND HAZARDOUS FUMES OF IODINE AND CYANIDE AND OXIDES OF CARBON AND NITROGEN.

POLYMERIZATION: HAZARDOUS POLYMERIZATION HAS NOT BEEN REPORTED TO OCCUR UNDER NORMAL TEMPERATURES AND PRESSURES.

STORAGE AND DISPOSAL

OBSERVE ALL FEDERAL, STATE AND LOCAL REGULATIONS WHEN STORING OR DISPOSING OF THIS SUBSTANCE. FOR ASSISTANCE, CONTACT THE DISTRICT DIRECTOR OF THE ENVIRONMENTAL PROTECTION AGENCY.

STORAGE

STORE IN ACCORDANCE WITH 40 CFR 165 RECOMMENDED PROCEDURES FOR THE DISPOSAL AND STORAGE OF PESTICIDES AND PESTICIDE CONTAINERS.

STORE AWAY FROM INCOMPATIBLE SUBSTANCES.

DISPOSAL

DISPOSAL MUST BE IN ACCORDANCE WITH 40 CFR 165 RECOMMENDED PROCEDURES FOR THE DISPOSAL AND STORAGE OF PESTICIDES AND PESTICIDE CONTAINERS.

CONDITIONS TO AVOID

MAY BURN BUT DOES NOT IGNITE READILY.

SPILL AND LEAK PROCEDURES

OCCUPATIONAL SPILL: DO NOT TOUCH SPILLED MATERIAL. STOP LEAK IF YOU CAN DO IT WITHOUT RISK. FOR SMALL SPILLS, TAKE UP WITH SAND OR OTHER ABSORBENT MATERIAL AND PLACE INTO CONTAINERS FOR LATER DISPOSAL. FOR SMALL DRY SPILLS, WITH A CLEAN SHOVEL PLACE MATERIAL INTO CLEAN, DRY CONTAINER AND COVER. MOVE CONTAINERS FROM SPILL AREA. FOR LARGER SPILLS, DIKE FAR AHEAD OF SPILL FOR LATER DISPOSAL. KEEP UNNECESSARY PEOPLE AWAY. ISOLATE HAZARD AREA AND DENY ENTRY.

PROTECTIVE EQUIPMENT

VENTILATION: PROVIDE LOCAL EXHAUST OR PROCESS ENCLOSURE VENTILATION SYSTEM.

RESPIRATOR: THE FOLLOWING RESPIRATORS ARE RECOMMENDED BASED ON INFORMATION FOUND IN THE PHYSICAL DATA, TOXICITY AND HEALTH EFFECTS SECTIONS. THEY ARE RANKED IN ORDER FROM MINIMUM TO MAXIMUM RESPIRATORY PROTECTION. THE SPECIFIC RESPIRATOR SELECTED MUST BE BASED ON CONTAMINATION LEVELS FOUND IN THE WORK PLACE, MUST NOT EXCEED THE WORKING LIMITS OF THE RESPIRATOR AND BE JOINTLY APPROVED BY THE NATIONAL INSTITUTE FOR OCCUPATIONAL SAFETY AND HEALTH AND THE MINE SAFETY AND HEALTH ADMINISTRATION (NIOSH-MSHA).

TYPE 'C' SUPPLIED-AIR RESPIRATOR WITH A FULL FACEPIECE OPERATED IN PRESSURE-DEMAND OR OTHER POSITIVE PRESSURE MODE OR WITH A FULL FACEPIECE, HELMET OR HOOD OPERATED IN CONTINOUS-FLOW MODE.

SELF-CONTAINED BREATHING APPARATUS WITH A FULL FACEPIECE OPERATED IN PRESSURE-DEMAND OR OTHER POSITIVE PRESSURE MODE.

FOR FIREFIGHTING AND OTHER IMMEDIATELY DANGEROUS TO LIFE OR HEALTH CONDITIONS:

SELF-CONTAINED BREATHING APPARATUS WITH FULL FACEPIECE OPERATED IN PRESSURE-DEMAND OR OTHER POSITIVE PRESSURE MODE.

SUPPLIED-AIR RESPIRATOR WITH FULL FACEPIECE AND OPERATED IN PRESSURE-DEMAND OR OTHER POSITIVE PRESSURE MODE IN COMBINATION WITH AN AUXILIARY SELF-CONTAINED BREATHING APPARATUS OPERATED IN PRESSURE-DEMAND OR OTHER POSITIVE PRESSURE MODE.

CLOTHING: EMPLOYEE MUST WEAR APPROPRIATE PROTECTIVE (IMPERVIOUS) CLOTHING AND EQUIPMENT TO PREVENT ANY POSSIBILITY OF SKIN CONTACT WITH THIS SUBSTANCE.

GLOVES: EMPLOYEE MUST WEAR APPROPRIATE PROTECTIVE GLOVES TO PREVENT CONTACT WITH THIS SUBSTANCE.

EYE PROTECTION: EMPLOYEE MUST WEAR SPLASH-PROOF OR DUST-RESISTANT SAFETY GOGGLES AND A FACESHIELD TO PREVENT CONTACT WITH THIS SUBSTANCE.

EMERGENCY WASH FACILITIES: WHERE THERE IS ANY POSSIBILITY THAT AN EMPLOYEE'S EYES AND/OR SKIN MAY BE EXPOSED TO THIS SUBSTANCE, THE EMPLOYER SHOULD PROVIDE AN EYE WASH FOUNTAIN AND QUICK DRENCH SHOWER WITHIN THE IMMEDIATE WORK AREA FOR EMERGENCY USE.

AUTHORIZED BY- OCCUPATIONAL HEALTH SERVICES, INC.

CREATION DATE: 05/23/90 ***REVISION DATE:*** 05/23/90

MATERIAL SAFETY DATA SHEET

OCCUPATIONAL HEALTH SERVICES, INC.
AGRICULTURE AND PESTICIDE DIVISION
450 SEVENTH AVENUE, SUITE 2407
NEW YORK, NEW YORK 10123
1-800-445-MSDS OR (212) 967-1100

EMERGENCY CONTACT:
JOHN S. BRANSFORD, JR. (615) 292-1180

SUBSTANCE IDENTIFICATION

CAS-NUMBER 3861-47-0

SUBSTANCE: IOXYNIL OCTANOATE

TRADE NAMES/SYNONYMS: OCTANOIC ACID, 4-CYANO-2,6-DIIODOPHENYL ESTER; OCTANOIC ACID, ESTER WITH 4-HYDROXY-3,5-DIIODOBENZONITRILE; 4-CYANO-2,6-DI-IODOPHENYL OCTANOATE; 4-CYANO-2,6-DIIODOPHENYL OCTANOATE; 3,5-DIIODO-4-HYDROXYBENZONITRILE OCTANOATE; 3,5-DIIODO-4-OCTANOYLOXYBENZONITRILE; MB 11641; TOTRIL; C15H17I2NO2; PST73075

CHEMICAL FAMILY: NITRILE, AROMATIC
HALOGEN
ESTER

MOLECULAR FORMULA: (I2)-(C-N)-C6-H2-O-C-(O)-C7-H15

MOLECULAR WEIGHT: 497.15

CERCLA RATINGS (SCALE 0-3): HEALTH=3 FIRE=1 REACTIVITY=0 PERSISTENCE=1

NFPA RATINGS (SCALE 0-4): HEALTH=U FIRE=1 REACTIVITY=0

COMPONENTS AND CONTAMINANTS

COMPONENT: IOXYNIL OCTANOATE ***PERCENT:*** 100.0
CAS# 3861-47-0

OTHER CONTAMINANTS: NONE

EXPOSURE LIMITS: NO OCCUPATIONAL EXPOSURE LIMITS ESTABLISHED BY OSHA, ACGIH, OR NIOSH.

PHYSICAL DATA

DESCRIPTION: WHITE, CREAMY, WAXY SOLID. ***MELTING POINT:*** 138-140 F (59-60 C)

SPECIFIC GRAVITY: NOT AVAILABLE ***VAPOR PRESSURE:*** NEGLIGIBLE @ 105 C

SOLUBILITY IN WATER: VERY SLIGHTLY SOLUBLE

SOLVENT SOLUBILITY: SOLUBLE IN ACETONE, BENZENE, CHLOROFORM, XYLENE, CYCLOHEXANONE, DICHLOROMETHANE, ETHANOL, N-PROPANOL, ETHYL ACETATE, NAPHTHA, DIMETHYLFORMAMIDE, AND CARBON TETRACHLORIDE.

FIRE AND EXPLOSION DATA

FIRE AND EXPLOSION HAZARD: SLIGHT FIRE HAZARD WHEN EXPOSED TO HEAT OR FLAME.
DUST-AIR MIXTURES MAY IGNITE OR EXPLODE.

FIREFIGHTING MEDIA: DRY CHEMICAL, CARBON DIOXIDE, HALON, WATER SPRAY OR STANDARD FOAM (1987 EMERGENCY RESPONSE GUIDEBOOK, DOT P 5800.4).
FOR LARGER FIRES, USE WATER SPRAY, FOG OR STANDARD FOAM (1987 EMERGENCY RESPONSE GUIDEBOOK, DOT P 5800.4).

FIREFIGHTING: MOVE CONTAINERS FROM FIRE AREA IF POSSIBLE (1987 EMERGENCY RESPONSE GUIDEBOOK, DOT P 5800.4, GUIDE PAGE 53).
EXTINGUISH USING AGENT SUITABLE FOR TYPE OF SURROUNDING FIRE. AVOID BREATHING VAPORS AND DUSTS. KEEP UPWIND.

TOXICITY

IOXYNIL OCTANOATE: TOXICITY DATA: >900 MG/KG SKIN-RAT LD50 (85JFAN); 1240 MG/KG SKIN-MOUSE LD50; 190 MG/KG ORAL-RAT LD50; 205 MG/KG ORAL-MOUSE LD50; MUTAGENIC DATA (RTECS). CARCINOGEN STATUS: NONE. ACUTE TOXICITY LEVEL: TOXIC BY INGESTION; MODERATELY TOXIC BY DERMAL ABSORPTION. TARGET EFFECTS: NO DATA AVAILABLE. ADDITIONAL DATA: SOME NITRILES RELEASE HIGHLY TOXIC CYANIDE IN THE BODY.

HEALTH EFFECTS AND FIRST AID

INHALATION: IOXYNIL OCTANOATE: **ACUTE EXPOSURE-** NO DATA AVAILABLE.
CHRONIC EXPOSURE- EFFECTS OF INORDINANT SWEATING AND THIRST, FEVER, HEADACHE, DIZZINESS, VOMITING, ASTHENIA, WEIGHT LOSS, AND MYALGIA OF THE LEGS WERE REPORTED FROM A CASE OF OCCUPATIONAL EXPOSURE TO IOXYNIL AND BROMOXYNIL. THE ONSET OF THESE EFFECTS WERE INSIDIOUS. LABORATORY TESTS REVEALED TRANSITORY ELEVATION OF CREATININE PHOSPHOKINASE, LDH, ALDOLASE, AND SGOT. REMOVAL OF THE AFFECTED MEN FROM EXPOSURE RESULTED IN PROMPT RECOVERY.

FIRST AID- REMOVE FROM EXPOSURE. IF BREATHING HAS STOPPED OR IS DEPRESSED, GIVE ARTIFICIAL RESPIRATION. MAINTAIN AIRWAY AND ADMINISTER OXYGEN TO MAINTAIN HIGH BLOOD/OXYGEN TENSION. GET MEDICAL ATTENTION IMMEDIATELY. (DREISBACH, HANDBOOK OF POISONING, 11TH ED.).

SKIN CONTACT: IOXYNIL OCTANOATE: **ACUTE EXPOSURE-** A LETHAL DOSE IN MICE BY DERMAL ABSORPTION WAS 1240 MG/KG. **CHRONIC EXPOSURE-** EFFECTS OF INORDINANT SWEATING AND THIRST, FEVER, HEADACHE, DIZZINESS, VOMITING, ASTHENIA, WEIGHT LOSS, AND MYALGIA OF THE LEGS WERE REPORTED FROM A CASE OF OCCUPATIONAL EXPOSURE TO IOXYNIL AND BROMOXYNIL THE ONSET OF THESE EFFECTS WERE INSIDIOUS. LABORATORY TESTS REVEALED TRANSITORY ELEVATION OF CREATININE PHOSPHOKINASE, LDH, ALDOLASE, AND SGOT. REMOVAL OF THE AFFECTED MEN FROM EXPOSURE RESULTED IN PROMPT RECOVERY.

FIRST AID- REMOVE CONTAMINATED CLOTHING AND SHOES AND WASH AFFECTED AREAS WITH SOAP OR MILD DETERGENT AND LARGE AMOUNTS OF WATER, TAKING CARE NOT TO CONTACT THE CHEMICAL. GET MEDICAL ATTENTION IMMEDIATELY. (CAIN, EMERGENCY TREATMENT AND MANAGEMENT, 7TH ED.).

EYE CONTACT: IOXYNIL OCTANOATE: **ACUTE EXPOSURE-** NO DATA AVAILABLE.
CHRONIC EXPOSURE- NO DATA AVAILABLE.

FIRST AID- WASH EYES IMMEDIATELY WITH LARGE AMOUNTS OF WATER OR NORMAL SALINE, OCCASIONALLY LIFTING UPPER AND LOWER LIDS, UNTIL NO EVIDENCE OF CHEMICAL REMAINS (APPROXIMATELY 15-20 MINUTES). GET MEDICAL ATTENTION IMMEDIATELY.

INGESTION: IOXYNIL OCTANOATE: TOXIC. **ACUTE EXPOSURE-** A LETHAL DOSE IN RATS WAS 190 MG/KG; SYMPTOMS WERE NOT REPORTED. HYPEREMIA OF ALL ORGANS AND EDEMA OF THE LUNGS AND BRAIN WERE DETERMINED BY AN AUTOPSY OF A MAN WHO INGESTED APPROXIMATELY 43 MG/KG IOXYNIL IN COMBINATION WITH ALCOHOL. SOME NITRILES MAY CAUSE CYANIDE POSIONING WITH DIZZINESS, RAPID RESPIRATION, VOMITING, FLUSHING, HEADACHE, DROWSINESS, DROP IN BLOOD PRESSURE. RAPID PULSE, CYANOSIS, UNCONSCIOUSNESS, CONVULSIONS, AND DEATH. **CHRONIC EXPOSURE-** NO OBSERVABLE EFFECTS WERE NOTED IN A 90-DAY STUDY OF RATS FED 4.0 MG/KG/DAY. REPEATED INGESTION OF SMALL AMOUNTS OF IODINE COMPOUNDS MAY CAUSE IODISM CHARACTERIZED BY ERYTHEMA, CONJUNCTIVITIS, STOMATITIS, SLEEPLESSNESS, AND NERVOUS SYMPTOMS.

FIRST AID- IF PATIENT IS ASYMPTOMATIC ADMINISTER SYRUP OF IPECAC AND/OR PERFORM GASTRIC LAVAGE, USING TAP WATER, DILUTE SODIUM BICARBONATE SOLUTION OR PREFERABLY, IF AVAILABLE, DILUTE POTASSIUM PERMANGANATE SOLUTION (1:5000). ACTIVATED CHARCOAL IS INEFFECTIVE. IF BREATHING HAS STOPPED, GIVE ARTIFICIAL RESPIRATION. MAINTAIN AIRWAY. OXYGEN THERAPY MAY BE OF VALUE IN COMBINATION WITH THE ANTIDOTE (GOSSELIN, CLINICAL TOXICOLOGY OF COMMERCIAL PRODUCTS, 5TH ED.). TREATMENT SHOULD BE PERFORMED BY QUALIFIED MEDICAL PERSONNEL. GET MEDICAL ATTENTION IMMEDIATELY.

ANTIDOTE: THE FOLLOWING ANTIDOTE HAS BEEN RECOMMENDED. HOWEVER, THE DECISION AS TO WHETHER THE SEVERITY OF POISONING REQUIRES ADMINISTRATION OF ANY ANTIDOTE AND ACTUAL DOSE REQUIRED SHOULD BE MADE BY QUALIFIED MEDICAL PERSONNEL.
FOR CYANIDE POISONING: IF SYMPTOMS OF CYANIDE POISONING ARE EVIDENT, ADMINISTER IMMEDIATELY BEFORE ANY OTHER FIRST AID MEASURES.
ADMINISTER AMYL NITRITE (AMYL NITRITE PERLES) BY INHALATION FOR 15 TO 30 SECONDS OF EVERY MINUTE, WHILE SODIUM NITRITE SOLUTION IS BEING PREPARED. DISCONTINUE AMYL NITRITE AND IMMEDIATELY INJECT 10 ML OF A 3% SOLUTION OF SODIUM NITRITE INTRAVENOUSLY OVER A PERIOD OF 2 TO 4 MINUTES. IF NECESSARY, INJECT A NON-STERILE SOLUTION. DO NOT REMOVE THE NEEDLE. CAUTION: APPROPRIATE ADJUSTMENTS IN THE DOSE SHOULD BE MADE ON A BODY WEIGHT BASIS. THROUGH THE SAME NEEDLE, INFUSE INTRAVENOUSLY 50 ML OF A 25% AQUEOUS SOLUTION OF SODIUM THIOSULFATE. THE INJECTION SHOULD TAKE ABOUT 10 MINUTES. OTHER CONCENTRATIONS (5 TO 50%) ARE PERMISSIBLE IF THE TOTAL DOSE IS HELD AT APPROXIMATELY 12 GRAMS.
OXYGEN THERAPY MAY BE OF VALUE IN COMBINATION WITH NITRITE AND SODIUM THIOSULFATE THERAPY. IF SYMPTOMS RECUR, THE INJECTIONS OF NITRITE AND THIOSULFATE MAY BE REPEATED AT HALF THE ABOVE DOSES. IN VERY SEVERE POISONINGS IT IS SAFER AND PERHAPS MORE EFFICIENT TO KEEP REPEATING THE THIOSULFATE INJECTIONS INSTEAD OF THE NITRITE (GOSSELIN, SMITH, HODGE, CLINICAL TOXICOLOGY OF COMMERCIAL PRODUCTS, 5TH ED.).
ANTIDOTE SHOULD BE ADMINISTERED BY QUALIFIED MEDICAL PERSONNEL.

REACTIVITY

REACTIVITY: STABLE UNDER NORMAL TEMPERATURES AND PRESSURES.

INCOMPATIBILITIES: IOXYNIL OCTANOATE: OXIDIZERS (STRONG): FIRE AND EXPLOSION HAZARD.

DECOMPOSITION: THERMAL DECOMPOSITION PRODUCTS MAY INCLUDE TOXIC AND HAZARDOUS FUMES OF IODINE AND CYANIDE AND OXIDES OF CARBON AND NITROGEN.

POLYMERIZATION: HAZARDOUS POLYMERIZATION HAS NOT BEEN REPORTED TO OCCUR UNDER NORMAL TEMPERATURES AND PRESSURES.

STORAGE AND DISPOSAL

OBSERVE ALL FEDERAL, STATE AND LOCAL REGULATIONS WHEN STORING OR DISPOSING OF THIS SUBSTANCE. FOR ASSISTANCE, CONTACT THE DISTRICT DIRECTOR OF THE ENVIRONMENTAL PROTECTION AGENCY.

STORAGE

STORE IN ACCORDANCE WITH 40 CFR 165 RECOMMENDED PROCEDURES FOR THE DISPOSAL AND STORAGE OF PESTICIDES AND PESTICIDE CONTAINERS.
STORE AWAY FROM INCOMPATIBLE SUBSTANCES.

DISPOSAL

DISPOSAL MUST BE IN ACCORDANCE WITH 40 CFR 165 RECOMMENDED PROCEDURES FOR THE DISPOSAL AND STORAGE OF PESTICIDES AND PESTICIDE CONTAINERS.

CONDITIONS TO AVOID

MAY BURN BUT DOES NOT IGNITE READILY.

SPILL AND LEAK PROCEDURES

OCCUPATIONAL SPILL: DO NOT TOUCH SPILLED MATERIAL. STOP LEAK IF YOU CAN DO IT WITHOUT RISK. FOR SMALL SPILLS, TAKE UP WITH SAND OR OTHER ABSORBENT MATERIAL AND PLACE INTO CONTAINERS FOR LATER DISPOSAL. FOR SMALL DRY SPILLS, WITH A CLEAN SHOVEL PLACE MATERIAL INTO CLEAN, DRY CONTAINER AND COVER. MOVE CONTAINERS FROM SPILL AREA. FOR LARGER SPILLS, DIKE FAR AHEAD OF SPILL FOR LATER DISPOSAL. KEEP UNNECESSARY PEOPLE AWAY. ISOLATE HAZARD AREA AND DENY ENTRY.

PROTECTIVE EQUIPMENT

VENTILATION: PROVIDE LOCAL EXHAUST OR GENERAL DILUTION VENTILATION SYSTEM.

RESPIRATOR: THE FOLLOWING RESPIRATORS ARE RECOMMENDED BASED ON INFORMATION FOUND IN THE PHYSICAL DATA, TOXICITY AND HEALTH EFFECTS SECTIONS. THEY ARE RANKED IN ORDER FROM MINIMUM TO MAXIMUM RESPIRATORY PROTECTION. THE SPECIFIC RESPIRATOR SELECTED MUST BE BASED ON CONTAMINATION LEVELS FOUND IN THE WORK PLACE, MUST NOT EXCEED THE WORKING LIMITS OF THE RESPIRATOR AND BE JOINTLY APPROVED BY THE NATIONAL INSTITUTE FOR OCCUPATIONAL SAFETY AND HEALTH AND THE MINE SAFETY AND HEALTH ADMINISTRATION (NIOSH-MSHA).
CHEMICAL CARTRIDGE RESPIRATOR WITH AN ORGANIC VAPOR CARTRIDGE(S) WITH A FULL FACEPIECE AND ORGANIC VAPOR CARTRIDGE(S) IN COMBINATION WITH A DUST AND MIST FILTER.
POWERED AIR-PURIFYING RESPIRATOR WITH A TIGHT-FITTING FACEPIECE AND

ORGANIC VAPOR CARTRIDGE(S) IN COMBINATION WITH A HIGH-EFFICIENCY PARTICULATE FILTER.
TYPE 'C' SUPPLIED-AIR RESPIRATOR WITH A FULL FACEPIECE OPERATED IN A PRESSURE-DEMAND OR OTHER POSITIVE PRESSURE MODE.
SELF-CONTAINED BREATHING APPARATUS WITH A FULL FACEPIECE OPERATED IN PRESSURE-DEMAND OR OTHER POSITIVE PRESSURE MODE.
FOR FIREFIGHTING AND OTHER IMMEDIATELY DANGEROUS TO LIFE OR HEALTH CONDITIONS:
SELF-CONTAINED BREATHING APPARATUS WITH FULL FACEPIECE OPERATED IN PRESSURE-DEMAND OR OTHER POSITIVE PRESSURE MODE.
SUPPLIED-AIR RESPIRATOR WITH FULL FACEPIECE AND OPERATED IN PRESSURE-DEMAND OR OTHER POSITIVE PRESSURE MODE IN COMBINATION WITH AN AUXILIARY SELF-CONTAINED BREATHING APPARATUS OPERATED IN PRESSURE-DEMAND OR OTHER POSITIVE PRESSURE MODE.

CLOTHING: EMPLOYEE MUST WEAR APPROPRIATE PROTECTIVE (IMPERVIOUS) CLOTHING AND EQUIPMENT TO PREVENT REPEATED OR PROLONGED SKIN CONTACT WITH THIS SUBSTANCE.

GLOVES: EMPLOYEE MUST WEAR APPROPRIATE PROTECTIVE GLOVES TO PREVENT CONTACT WITH THIS SUBSTANCE.

EYE PROTECTION: EMPLOYEE MUST WEAR SPLASH-PROOF OR DUST-RESISTANT SAFETY GOGGLES TO PREVENT EYE CONTACT WITH THIS SUBSTANCE.
EMERGENCY EYE WASH: WHERE THERE IS ANY POSSIBILITY THAT AN EMPLOYEE'S EYES MAY BE EXPOSED TO THIS SUBSTANCE, THE EMPLOYER SHOULD PROVIDE AN EYE WASH FOUNTAIN WITHIN THE IMMEDIATE WORK AREA FOR EMERGENCY USE.

AUTHORIZED BY- OCCUPATIONAL HEALTH SERVICES, INC.
CREATION DATE: 05/23/90 ***REVISION DATE:*** 05/23/90

MATERIAL SAFETY DATA SHEET

OCCUPATIONAL HEALTH SERVICES, INC.
AGRICULTURE AND PESTICIDE DIVISION
450 SEVENTH AVENUE, SUITE 2407
NEW YORK, NEW YORK 10123
1-800-445-MSDS OR (212) 967-1100

EMERGENCY CONTACT:
JOHN S. BRANSFORD, JR. (615) 292-1180

SUBSTANCE IDENTIFICATION

CAS-NUMBER 17702-57-7

SUBSTANCE: FORMPARANATE

TRADE NAMES/SYNONYMS: N,N-DIMETHYL-N'-(2-METHYL-4-(((METHYLAMINO)CARBONYL)OXY)PHENYL) METHANIMIDAMIDE; METHYLCARBAMIC ACID ESTER WITH N'-(4-HYDROXY-O-TOLYL)-N,N-DIMETHYL FORMAMIDINE; 4-(((DIMETHYLAMINO)METHYLENE)AMINO)-M-TOLYL ESTER, METHYLCARBAMIC ACID; METHANIMIDAMIDE, N,N-DIMETHYL-N'-(2-METHYL-4-((METHYLAMINO)CARBONYL) OXY)PHENYL)-; CARBAMIC ACID, METHYL-, ESTER WITH N'-(4-HYDROXY-O-TOLYL)-N,N- DIMETHYLFORMAMIDINE; CARBAMIC ACID, METHYL-,4-((DIMETHYLAMINO)METHYLENE)AMINO)-M-TOLYL ESTER; UC-2507405; UNION CARBIDE UC-25074; SCHERING 36103; ENT 27,305; C12H17N3O2; PST73082

CHEMICAL FAMILY: CARBAMATE
AMINE
AROMATIC

MOLECULAR FORMULA: C12-H17-N3-O2

MOLECULAR WEIGHT: 235.32

CERCLA RATINGS (SCALE 0-3): HEALTH=3 FIRE=U REACTIVITY=U PERSISTENCE=1

NFPA RATINGS (SCALE 0-4): HEALTH=3 FIRE=U REACTIVITY=U

COMPONENTS AND CONTAMINANTS

COMPONENT: FORMPARANATE ***PERCENT:*** 100
CAS# 17702-57-7

OTHER CONTAMINANTS: NONE

EXPOSURE LIMITS: NO OCCUPATIONAL EXPOSURE LIMITS ESTABLISHED BY OSHA, ACGIH, OR NIOSH.
FORMPARANATE: 100/10,000 POUNDS SARA SECTION 302 THRESHOLD PLANNING QUANTITY 1 POUND SARA SECTION 304 REPORTABLE QUANTITY

PHYSICAL DATA

DESCRIPTION: SOLID ***MELTING POINT:*** NOT AVAILABLE

SPECIFIC GRAVITY: NOT AVAILABLE ***SOLUBILITY IN WATER:*** NOT AVAILABLE

FIRE AND EXPLOSION DATA

FIRE AND EXPLOSION HAZARD: UNKNOWN FIRE AND EXPLOSION HAZARD.

FIREFIGHTING MEDIA: DRY CHEMICAL, CARBON DIOXIDE, HALON, WATER SPRAY OR STANDARD FOAM (1987 EMERGENCY RESPONSE GUIDEBOOK, DOT P 5800.4).
FOR LARGER FIRES, USE WATER SPRAY, FOG OR STANDARD FOAM (1987 EMERGENCY RESPONSE GUIDEBOOK, DOT P 5800.4).

FIREFIGHTING: MOVE CONTAINERS FROM FIRE AREA IF POSSIBLE (1987 EMERGENCY RESPONSE GUIDEBOOK, DOT P 5800.4, GUIDE PAGE 53).
EXTINGUISH USING AGENT SUITABLE FOR TYPE OF SURROUNDING FIRE. AVOID BREATHING VAPORS AND DUSTS. KEEP UPWIND.

TRANSPORTATION DATA

DEPARTMENT OF TRANSPORTATION HAZARD CLASSIFICATION 49 CFR 172.101: POISON B
DEPARTMENT OF TRANSPORTATION LABELING REQUIREMENTS 49 CFR 172.101 AND SUBPART E: POISON
DEPARTMENT OF TRANSPORTATION PACKAGING REQUIREMENTS: 49 CFR 173.365 EXCEPTIONS: 49 CFR 173.364

TOXICITY

FORMPARANATE: TOXICITY DATA: 7200 UG/KG ORAL-RAT LD50; 16600 UG/KG ORAL-MOUSE LD50. CARCINOGEN STATUS: NONE. ACUTE TOXICITY: HIGHLY TOXIC BY INGESTION. TARGET EFFECTS: CHOLINESTERASE INHIBITOR. AT INCREASED RISK FROM EXPOSURE: PERSONS WITH ASTHMA, DIABETES, CARDIOVASCULAR DISEASE, MECHANICAL OBSTRUCTION OF THE GASTROINTESTINAL OR UROGENITAL TRACT, AND THOSE IN VAGOTONIC STATES.*
* MAY BE BASED ON GENERAL INFORMATION ON CARBAMATES.

HEALTH EFFECTS AND FIRST AID

INHALATION: FORMPARANATE: SEE INFORMATION ON CARBAMATES.
CARBAMATES: CHOLINESTERASE INHIBITOR. **ACUTE EXPOSURE-** WHEN INHALED, THE FIRST EFFECTS OF CHOLINESTERASE INHIBITION ARE USUALLY RESPIRATORY AND MAY INCLUDE NASAL HYPEREMIA AND WATERY DISCHARGE, CHEST DISCOMFORT, DYSPNEA, AND WHEEZING DUE TO INCREASED BRONCHIAL SECRETIONS AND BRONCHOCONSTRICTION. OTHER SYSTEMIC EFFECTS MAY BEGIN WITHIN A FEW MINUTES OR SEVERAL HOURS OF EXPOSURE. SYMPTOMS MAY INCLUDE NAUSEA, VOMITING, DIARRHEA, ABDOMINAL CRAMPS, HEADACHE, VERTIGO, OCULAR PAIN, CILIARY MUSCLE SPASM, BLURRING OR DIMNESS OF VISION, MIOSIS, OR IN SOME CASES MYDRIASIS, LACRIMATION, SALIVATION, SWEATING, AND CONFUSION. OTHER REPORTED CENTRAL NERVOUS SYSTEM OR NEUROMUSCULAR EFFECTS INCLUDE ATAXIA, SLURRED SPEECH, AREFLEXIA, WEAKNESS, FATIGUE, TWITCHING, FASCICULATION, TREMOR, AND EVENTUALLY PARALYSIS OF THE EXTREMITIES AND POSSIBLY OF THE RESPIRATORY MUSCLES. IN SEVERE CASES, THERE MAY ALSO BE INVOLUNTARY DEFECATION AND URINATION, BRADYCARDIA, HYPOTENSION, PULMONARY EDEMA, CONVULSIONS, COMA, AND DEATH FROM RESPIRATORY FAILURE OR CARDIAC ARREST. CARBAMATES GENERALLY DO NOT ACCUMULATE IN MAMMALIAN TISSUE AND THE CHOLINESTERASE INHIBITION REVERSES RATHER RAPIDLY. IN NON-FATAL CASES, THE ILLNESS GENERALLY LASTS LESS THAN 24 HOURS. **CHRONIC EXPOSURE-** PROLONGED OR REPEATED EXPOSURE MAY CAUSE EFFECTS AS DESCRIBED IN ACUTE EXPOSURE.

FIRST AID- REMOVE FROM EXPOSURE AREA TO FRESH AIR IMMEDIATELY. IF BREATHING HAS STOPPED, GIVE ARTIFICIAL RESPIRATION. MAINTAIN AIRWAY AND BLOOD PRESSURE AND ADMINISTER OXYGEN IF AVAILABLE. KEEP AFFECTED PERSON WARM AND AT REST. TREAT SYMPTOMATICALLY AND SUPPORTIVELY. ADMINISTRATION OF OXYGEN SHOULD BE PERFORMED BY QUALIFIED PERSONNEL. GET MEDICAL ATTENTION IMMEDIATELY.

SKIN CONTACT: FORMPARANATE: SEE INFORMATION ON CARBAMATES.
CARBAMATES: CHOLINESTERASE INHIBITOR. **ACUTE EXPOSURE-** SOME COMPOUNDS MAY CAUSE IRRITATION. LOCALIZED SWEATING AND FASCICULATIONS MAY OCCUR AT THE SITE OF CONTACT. IF SUFFICIENT AMOUNTS ARE ABSORBED THROUGH THE SKIN, OTHER EFFECTS OF CHOLINESTERASE INHIBITION MAY OCCUR AS DESCRIBED IN ACUTE INHALATION; SYMPTOMS MAY BE DELAYED FOR 2-3 HOURS, USUALLY NO MORE THAN 8 HOURS. **CHRONIC EXPOSURE-** REPEATED OR PROLONGED EXPOSURE MAY CAUSE EFFECTS AS DESCRIBED IN ACUTE EXPOSURE.

FIRST AID- REMOVE CONTAMINATED CLOTHING IMMEDIATELY. WASH CONTAMINATED AREAS WITH SOAP AND WATER FOLLOWED BY ALCOHOL (ARENA, POISONING, 4TH ED.). EMERGENCY PERSONNEL SHOULD WEAR GLOVES AND AVOID CONTAMINATION. TREAT RESPIRATORY DIFFICULTY WITH ARTIFICIAL RESPIRATION. GET MEDICAL ATTENTION IMMEDIATELY.

EYE CONTACT: FORMPARANATE: SEE INFORMATION ON CARBAMATES.
CARBAMATES: CHOLINESTERASE INHIBITOR. **ACUTE EXPOSURE-** DIRECT CONTACT MAY CAUSE PAIN, HYPEREMIA, LACRIMATION, TWITCHING OF THE EYELIDS, MIOSIS, AND CILIARY MUSCLE SPASM WITH LOSS OF ACCOMODATION, BLURRED OR DIMMED VISION AND BROWACHE. SOMETIMES MYDRIASIS MAY OCCUR INSTEAD OF MIOSIS. WITH SUFFICIENT EXPOSURE, OTHER SYMPTOMS OF CHOLINESTERASE INHIBITION MAY OCCUR AS DESCRIBED IN ACUTE INHALATION. **CHRONIC EXPOSURE-** PROLONGED EXPOSURE MAY CAUSE EFFECTS AS DESCRIBED IN ACUTE EXPOSURE. SOME COMPOUNDS HAVE CAUSED TOXIC EFFECTS ON THE CRYSTALLINE LENS, CONJUNCTIVAL THICKENING AND OBSTRUCTION OF NASOLACRIMAL CANALS WHEN USED AS MIOTIC EYE DROPS.

FIRST AID- IRRIGATE EYES WITH WATER OR SALINE SOLUTION. IF SYMPTOMS OF POISONING OCCUR, TREAT RESPIRATORY DIFFICULTY WITH ARTIFICIAL RESPIRATION AND OXYGEN. OBSERVE PATIENT FOR AT LEAST 24-36 HOURS (GOSSELIN, CLINICAL TOXICOLOGY OF COMMERCIAL PRODUCTS, 5TH ED.). GET MEDICAL ATTENTION IMMEDIATELY. OXYGEN SHOULD BE ADMINISTERED BY QUALIFIED MEDICAL PERSONNEL.

INGESTION: FORMPARANATE: HIGHLY TOXIC. SEE INFORMATION ON CARBAMATES.
CARBAMATES: CHOLINESTERASE INHIBITOR. **ACUTE EXPOSURE-** WHEN INGESTED, THE FIRST EFFECTS MAY BE NAUSEA, VOMITING, ANOREXIA, ABDOMINAL CRAMPS, AND DIARRHEA. WITH ABSORPTION FROM THE GASTROINTESTINAL TRACT, THE OTHER EFFECTS OF CHOLINESTERASE INHIBITION AS DESCRIBED IN ACUTE INHALATION MAY OCCUR; SYMPTOMS MAY BEGIN WITHIN MINUTES OR BE DELAYED SEVERAL HOURS. **CHRONIC EXPOSURE-** REPEATED INGESTION MAY CAUSE EFFECTS AS DESCRIBED IN ACUTE EXPOSURE.

FIRST AID- IF PERSON IS ALERT AND RESPIRATION IS NOT DEPRESSED, GIVE SYRUP OF IPECAC FOLLOWED BY WATER (IF VOMITING OCCURS, KEEP HEAD BELOW HIPS TO PREVENT ASPIRATION). IF CONSCIOUSNESS LEVEL DECLINES OR VOMITING HAS NOT OCCURRED IN 15 MINUTES EMPTY STOMACH BY GASTRIC LAVAGE WITH THE AID OF CUFFED ENDOTRACHEAL TUBE USING ISOTONIC SALINE OR 5% SODIUM BICARBONATE FOLLOW WITH ACTIVATED CHARCOAL. ESTABLISH AND MAINTAIN AIRWAY. TREAT RESPIRATORY DIFFICULTY WITH ARTIFICIAL RESPIRATION AND OXYGEN. DO NOT GIVE MORPHINE, AMINOPHYLLINE, PHENOTHIAZINES, RESERPINE, FUROSEMIDE, OR ETHACRYNIC ACID (MORGAN, RECOGNITION AND MANAGEMENT OF PESTICIDE POISONINGS, 3RD ED.). TREAT SYMPTOMATICALLY AND SUPPORTIVELY. ADMINISTRATION OF OXYGEN AND LAVAGE MUST BE PERFORMED BY QUALIFIED MEDICAL PERSONNEL. GET MEDICAL ATTENTION IMMEDIATELY.

ANTIDOTE: THE FOLLOWING ANTIDOTE HAS BEEN RECOMMENDED. HOWEVER, THE DECISION AS TO WHETHER THE SEVERITY OF POISONING REQUIRES ADMINISTRATION OF ANY ANTIDOTE AND ACTUAL DOSE REQUIRED SHOULD BE MADE BY QUALIFIED MEDICAL PERSONNEL.
FOR CHOLINESTERASE INHIBITORS: ESTABLISH CLEAR AIRWAY AND TISSUE OXYGENATION BY ASPIRATION OF SECRETIONS, AND IF NECESSARY, BY ASSISTED PULMONARY VENTILATION WITH OXYGEN. IMPROVE TISSUE OXYGENATION AS MUCH AS POSSIBLE BEFORE ADMINISTERING ATROPINE TO MINIMIZE THE RISK OF VENTRICULAR FIBRILLATION. ADMINISTER ATROPINE SULFATE INTRAVENOUSLY, OR INTRAMUSCULARLY IF IV INJECTION IS NOT POSSIBLE. IN MODERATELY SEVERE POISONING ADMINISTER ATROPINE SULFATE, 0.4-2.0 MG REPEATED EVERY 15 MINUTES UNTIL ATROPINIZATION IS ACHIEVED (TACHYCARDIA, FLUSHING, DRY MOUTH, MYDRIASIS). MAINTAIN ATROPINIZATION BY REPEATED DOSES FOR 2-12 HOURS, OR LONGER, DEPENDING ON THE SEVERITY OF POISONING. THE APPEARANCE OF RALES IN THE LUNG BASES, MIOSIS, SALIVATION, NAUSEA, BRADYCARDIA, ARE ALL INDICATIONS OF INADEQUATE ATROPINIZATION. SEVERELY POISONED INDIVIDUALS MAY EXHIBIT REMARKABLE TOLERANCE TO ATROPINE; TWO OR MORE TIMES THE DOSAGES SUGGESTED ABOVE MAY BE NEEDED. PERSONS NOT POISONED OR ONLY SLIGHTLY POISONED, HOWEVER, MAY DEVELOP SIGNS OF ATROPINE TOXICITY FROM SUCH LARGE DOSAGES: FEVER, MUSCLE FIBRILLATIONS, AND DELIRIUM ARE THE MAIN SIGNS OF ATROPINE TOXICITY. IF THESE SIGNS APPEAR WHILE THE PATIENT IS FULLY ATROPINIZED, ATROPINE ADMINISTRATION SHOULD BE DISCONTINUED, AT LEAST TEMPORARILY. OBSERVE TREATED PATIENTS CLOSELY AT LEAST 24 HOURS TO INSURE THAT SYMPTOMS (POSSIBLY PULMONARY EDEMA) DO NOT RECUR AS ATROPINIZATION WEARS OFF. IN VERY SEVERE POISONINGS, METABOLIC DISPOSITION OF TOXICANT MAY REQUIRE SEVERAL HOURS OR DAYS DURING WHICH ATROPINIZATION MUST BE MAINTAINED. MARKEDLY LOWER LEVELS OF URINARY METABOLITES INDICATE THAT ATROPINE DOSAGE CAN BE TAPERED OFF. AS DOSAGE IS REDUCED, CHECK THE LUNG BASES FREQUENTLY FOR RALES. IF RALES ARE HEARD OR OTHER SYMPTOMS RETURN, RE-ESTABLISH ATROPINIZATION PROMPTLY (MORGAN, RECOGNITION AND MANAGEMENT OF PESTICIDE POISONINGS, 3RD ED.). ADMINISTRATION OF ANTIDOTE MUST BE PERFORMED BY QUALIFIED MEDICAL PERSONNEL.

REACTIVITY

REACTIVITY: NO DATA AVAILABLE.

INCOMPATIBILITIES: FORMPARANATE: OXIDIZERS (STRONG): FIRE AND EXPLOSION HAZARD.

DECOMPOSITION: THERMAL DECOMPOSITION MAY RELEASE TOXIC AND/OR HAZARDOUS GASES.

POLYMERIZATION: HAZARDOUS POLYMERIZATION HAS NOT BEEN REPORTED TO OCCUR UNDER NORMAL TEMPERATURES AND PRESSURES.

STORAGE AND DISPOSAL

OBSERVE ALL FEDERAL, STATE AND LOCAL REGULATIONS WHEN STORING OR DISPOSING OF THIS SUBSTANCE. FOR ASSISTANCE, CONTACT THE DISTRICT DIRECTOR OF THE ENVIRONMENTAL PROTECTION AGENCY.

****STORAGE****

STORE IN ACCORDANCE WITH 40 CFR 165 RECOMMENDED PROCEDURES FOR THE DISPOSAL AND STORAGE OF PESTICIDES AND PESTICIDE CONTAINERS.
THRESHOLD PLANNING QUANTITY (TPQ): THE SUPERFUND AMENDMENTS AND REAUTHORIZATION ACT (SARA) SECTION 302 REQUIRES THAT EACH FACILITY WHERE ANY EXTREMELY HAZARDOUS SUBSTANCE IS PRESENT IN A QUANTITY EQUAL TO OR GREATER THAN THE TPQ ESTABLISHED FOR THAT SUBSTANCE NOTIFY THE STATE EMERGENCY RESPONSE COMMISSION FOR THE STATE IN WHICH IT IS LOCATED. SECTION 303 OF SARA REQUIRES THESE FACILITIES TO PARTICIPATE IN LOCAL EMERGENCY RESPONSE PLANNING (40 CFR 355.30).

****DISPOSAL****

DISPOSAL MUST BE IN ACCORDANCE WITH 40 CFR 165 RECOMMENDED PROCEDURES FOR THE DISPOSAL AND STORAGE OF PESTICIDES AND PESTICIDE CONTAINERS.

CONDITIONS TO AVOID

NONE REPORTED.

SPILL AND LEAK PROCEDURES

OCCUPATIONAL SPILL: DO NOT TOUCH SPILLED MATERIAL. STOP LEAK IF YOU CAN DO IT WITHOUT RISK. FOR SMALL SPILLS, TAKE UP WITH SAND OR OTHER ABSORBENT MATERIAL AND PLACE INTO CONTAINERS FOR LATER DISPOSAL. FOR SMALL DRY SPILLS, WITH A CLEAN SHOVEL PLACE MATERIAL INTO CLEAN, DRY CONTAINER AND COVER. MOVE CONTAINERS FROM SPILL AREA. FOR LARGER SPILLS, DIKE FAR AHEAD OF SPILL FOR LATER DISPOSAL. KEEP UNNECESSARY PEOPLE AWAY. ISOLATE HAZARD AREA AND DENY ENTRY.
REPORTABLE QUANTITY (RQ): 1 POUND THE SUPERFUND AMENDMENTS AND REAUTHORIZATION ACT (SARA) SECTION 304 REQUIRES THAT A RELEASE EQUAL TO OR GREATER THAN THE REPORTABLE QUANTITY FOR THIS SUBSTANCE BE IMMEDIATELY REPORTED TO THE LOCAL EMERGENCY PLANNING COMMITTEE AND THE STATE EMERGENCY RESPONSE COMMISSION (40 CFR 355.40). IF THE RELEASE OF THIS SUBSTANCE IS REPORTABLE UNDER CERCLA SECTION 103, THE NATIONAL RESPONSE CENTER MUST BE NOTIFIED IMMEDIATELY AT (800) 424-8802 OR (202) 426-2675 IN THE METROPOLITAN WASHINGTON, D.C. AREA (40 CFR 302.6).

PROTECTIVE EQUIPMENT

VENTILATION: PROVIDE LOCAL EXHAUST OR PROCESS ENCLOSURE VENTILATION SYSTEM.

RESPIRATOR: THE FOLLOWING RESPIRATORS ARE RECOMMENDED BASED ON INFORMATION FOUND IN THE PHYSICAL DATA, TOXICITY AND HEALTH EFFECTS SECTIONS. THEY ARE RANKED IN ORDER FROM MINIMUM TO MAXIMUM RESPIRATORY PROTECTION. THE SPECIFIC RESPIRATOR SELECTED MUST BE BASED ON CONTAMINATION LEVELS FOUND IN THE WORK PLACE, MUST NOT EXCEED THE WORKING LIMITS OF THE RESPIRATOR AND BE JOINTLY APPROVED BY THE NATIONAL INSTITUTE FOR OCCUPATIONAL SAFETY AND HEALTH AND THE MINE SAFETY AND HEALTH ADMINISTRATION (NIOSH-MSHA).
TYPE 'C' SUPPLIED-AIR RESPIRATOR WITH A FULL FACEPIECE OPERATED IN PRESSURE-DEMAND OR OTHER POSITIVE PRESSURE MODE OR WITH A FULL FACEPIECE, HELMET OR HOOD OPERATED IN CONTINOUS-FLOW MODE.
SELF-CONTAINED BREATHING APPARATUS WITH A FULL FACEPIECE OPERATED IN PRESSURE-DEMAND OR OTHER POSITIVE PRESSURE MODE. FOR FIREFIGHTING AND OTHER IMMEDIATELY DANGEROUS TO LIFE OR HEALTH CONDITIONS:
SELF-CONTAINED BREATHING APPARATUS WITH FULL FACEPIECE OPERATED IN PRESSURE-DEMAND OR OTHER POSITIVE PRESSURE MODE.
SUPPLIED-AIR RESPIRATOR WITH FULL FACEPIECE AND OPERATED IN PRESSURE-DEMAND OR OTHER POSITIVE PRESSURE MODE IN COMBINATION WITH AN AUXILIARY SELF-CONTAINED BREATHING APPARATUS OPERATED IN PRESSURE-DEMAND OR OTHER POSITIVE PRESSURE MODE.

CLOTHING: EMPLOYEE MUST WEAR APPROPRIATE PROTECTIVE (IMPERVIOUS) CLOTHING AND EQUIPMENT TO PREVENT ANY POSSIBILITY OF SKIN CONTACT WITH THIS SUBSTANCE.

GLOVES: EMPLOYEE MUST WEAR APPROPRIATE PROTECTIVE GLOVES TO PREVENT CONTACT WITH THIS SUBSTANCE.

EYE PROTECTION: EMPLOYEE MUST WEAR SPLASH-PROOF OR DUST-RESISTANT SAFETY GOGGLES AND A FACESHIELD TO PREVENT CONTACT WITH THIS SUBSTANCE.

EMERGENCY WASH FACILITIES: WHERE THERE IS ANY POSSIBILITY THAT AN EMPLOYEE'S EYES AND/OR SKIN MAY BE EXPOSED TO THIS SUBSTANCE, THE EMPLOYER SHOULD PROVIDE AN EYE WASH FOUNTAIN AND QUICK DRENCH SHOWER WITHIN THE IMMEDIATE WORK AREA FOR EMERGENCY USE.

AUTHORIZED BY- OCCUPATIONAL HEALTH SERVICES, INC.
CREATION DATE: 10/04/89 ***REVISION DATE:*** 06/12/90

MATERIAL SAFETY DATA SHEET

OCCUPATIONAL HEALTH SERVICES, INC.
AGRICULTURE AND PESTICIDE DIVISION
450 SEVENTH AVENUE, SUITE 2407
NEW YORK, NEW YORK 10123
1-800-445-MSDS OR (212) 967-1100

EMERGENCY CONTACT:
JOHN S. BRANSFORD, JR. (615) 292-1180

SUBSTANCE IDENTIFICATION

CAS-NUMBER 140-56-7
SUBSTANCE: **FENAMINOSULF**
TRADE NAMES/SYNONYMS: DIAZENESULFONIC ACID, (4-(DIMETHYLAMINO)PHENYL)-, SODIUM SALT; (4-(DIMETHYLAMINO)PHENYL)DIAZENESULFONIC ACID SODIUM SALT; BENZENEDIAZOSULFONIC ACID, P-(DIMETHYLAMINO)-, SODIUM SALT; P-(DIMETHYLAMINO)BENZENEDIAZOSULFONIC ACID SODIUM SALT; BAYER 22555; DEKSONAL; DEXOXON; DEXON; PARA-DIMETHYLAMINOBENZENEDIAZO SODIUM SULPHONATE; C8H10N3NAO3S; PST73084
CHEMICAL FAMILY: INORGANIC SALT
MOLECULAR FORMULA: (C-H3)2-N-C6-H4-N-N-S-O3.NA
MOLECULAR WEIGHT: 251.2
CERCLA RATINGS (SCALE 0-3): HEALTH=U FIRE=1 REACTIVITY=0 PERSISTENCE=1
NFPA RATINGS (SCALE 0-4): HEALTH=U FIRE=1 REACTIVITY=0

COMPONENTS AND CONTAMINANTS

COMPONENT: FENAMINOSULF ***PERCENT:*** 100.0
CAS# 140-56-7
OTHER CONTAMINANTS: NONE
EXPOSURE LIMITS: NO OCCUPATIONAL EXPOSURE LIMITS ESTABLISHED BY OSHA, ACGIH, OR NIOSH.

PHYSICAL DATA

DESCRIPTION: ODORLESS YELLOWISH-BROWN CRYSTALLINE POWDER.
MELTING POINT: NOT AVAILABLE ***SPECIFIC GRAVITY:*** NOT AVAILABLE
SOLUBILITY IN WATER: 4% @ 20 C
SOLVENT SOLUBILITY: SOLUBLE IN DIMETHYLFORMAMIDE, ETHANOL; INSOLUBLE IN ETHER, PETROLEUM OILS, BENZENE.
DECOMPOSES ABOVE 392 F (200 C)

FIRE AND EXPLOSION DATA

FIRE AND EXPLOSION HAZARD: SLIGHT FIRE HAZARD WHEN EXPOSED TO HEAT OR FLAME.
FIREFIGHTING MEDIA: DRY CHEMICAL, CARBON DIOXIDE, HALON, WATER SPRAY OR STANDARD FOAM (1987 EMERGENCY RESPONSE GUIDEBOOK, DOT P 5800.4).
FOR LARGER FIRES, USE WATER SPRAY, FOG OR STANDARD FOAM (1987 EMERGENCY RESPONSE GUIDEBOOK, DOT P 5800.4).
FIREFIGHTING: MOVE CONTAINER FROM FIRE AREA IF POSSIBLE. DO NOT SCATTER SPILLED MATERIAL WITH HIGH PRESSURE WATER STREAMS. DIKE FIRE CONTROL WATER FOR LATER DISPOSAL (1987 EMERGENCY RESPONSE GUIDEBOOK, DOT P 5800.4, GUIDE PAGE 31).
USE AGENTS SUITABLE FOR TYPE OF SURROUNDING FIRE. AVOID BREATHING HAZARDOUS VAPORS, KEEP UPWIND.

TOXICITY

FENAMINOSULF: TOXICITY DATA: 60 MG/KG ORAL-RAT LD50; >100 MG/KG SKIN-RAT LD50 (FMCHA2); 140 MG/KG ORAL-MOUSE LDLO; 150 MG/KG ORAL-RABBIT LD50; 150 MG/KG ORAL-GUINEA PIG LD50; 56 MG/KG INTRAVENOUS-MOUSE LD50; 10,300 UG/KG INTRAPERITONEAL-RAT LD50; 60 MG/KG INTRAPERITONEAL-MOUSE LD50; 5 MG/KG INTRAPERITONEAL-DOG LDLO; 10 MG/KG INTRAPERITONEAL-RABBIT LDLO; 30 MG/KG INTRAPERITONEAL-GUINEA PIG LD50; 60 MG/KG UNREPORTED-MAMMAL LD50; MUTAGENIC DATA (RTECS); REPRODUCTIVE EFFECTS DATA (RTECS). CARCINOGEN STATUS: ANIMAL INADEQUATE EVIDENCE (IARC GROUP-3). ACUTE TOXICITY LEVEL: TOXIC BY INGESTION. TARGET EFFECTS: POISONING MAY AFFECT THE LIVER AND KIDNEYS.

HEALTH EFFECTS AND FIRST AID

INHALATION: FENAMINOSULF: **ACUTE EXPOSURE-** NO DATA AVAILABLE. **CHRONIC EXPOSURE-** NO DATA AVAILABLE.
FIRST AID- REMOVE FROM EXPOSURE AREA TO FRESH AIR IMMEDIATELY. IF BREATHING HAS STOPPED, PERFORM ARTIFICIAL RESPIRATION. KEEP PERSON WARM AND AT REST. TREAT SYMPTOMATICALLY AND SUPPORTIVELY. GET MEDICAL ATTENTION IMMEDIATELY.

SKIN CONTACT: FENAMINOSULF: **ACUTE EXPOSURE-** MAY BE ABSORBED THROUGH THE SKIN. THE MEDIAN LETHAL DOSE IN RATS WAS GREATER THAN 100 MG/KG. **CHRONIC EXPOSURE-** NO DATA AVAILABLE.
FIRST AID- REMOVE CONTAMINATED CLOTHING AND SHOES IMMEDIATELY. WASH AFFECTED AREA WITH SOAP OR MILD DETERGENT AND LARGE AMOUNTS OF WATER UNTIL NO EVIDENCE OF CHEMICAL REMAINS (APPROXIMATELY 15-20 MINUTES). GET MEDICAL ATTENTION IMMEDIATELY.

EYE CONTACT: FENAMINOSULF: **ACUTE EXPOSURE-** NO DATA AVAILABLE. **CHRONIC EXPOSURE-** NO DATA AVAILABLE.
FIRST AID- WASH EYES IMMEDIATELY WITH LARGE AMOUNTS OF WATER OR NORMAL SALINE, OCCASIONALLY LIFTING UPPER AND LOWER LIDS, UNTIL NO EVIDENCE OF CHEMICAL REMAINS (APPROXIMATELY 15-20 MINUTES). GET MEDICAL ATTENTION IMMEDIATELY.

INGESTION: FENAMINOSULF: TOXIC. **ACUTE EXPOSURE-** INGESTION OF TOXIC DOSES MAY CAUSE IMMEDIATE HYPERGLYCEMIA, AND LETHARGY FOLLOWED BY TREMORS, CONVULSIONS AND DEATH. PATHOLOGIC FINDINGS IN RATS INCLUDED KIDNEY TUBULAR DEGENERATION AND ACUTE PASSIVE HYPEREMIA OF THE LIVER. **CHRONIC EXPOSURE-** RATS FED 0.10% FENAMINOSULF FOR 12 MONTHS DEVELOPED KIDNEY NEPHROPATHY AND MINERALIZATION OF THE RENAL TUBULES, WITH A LOW INCIDENCE OF HEPATOMAS. REPRODUCTIVE EFFECTS HAVE BEEN REPORTED IN ANIMALS.
FIRST AID- REMOVE BY GASTRIC LAVAGE AND CATHARSIS. MAINTAIN BLOOD PRESSURE AND AIRWAY. GIVE OXYGEN IF RESPIRATION IS DEPRESSED. DO NOT PERFORM GASTRIC LAVAGE IF VICTIM IS UNCONSCIOUS. GET MEDICAL ATTENTION IMMEDIATELY (DREISBACH, HANDBOOK OF POISONING, 12TH ED.).
ADMINISTRATION OF LAVAGE OR OXYGEN SHOULD BE PERFORMED BY QUALIFIED MEDICAL PERSONNEL.
ANTIDOTE: NO SPECIFIC ANTIDOTE. TREAT SYMPTOMATICALLY AND SUPPORTIVELY.

REACTIVITY

REACTIVITY: STABLE UNDER NORMAL TEMPERATURES AND PRESSURES.
INCOMPATIBILITIES: FENAMINOSULF: OXIDIZERS (STRONG): FIRE AND EXPLOSION HAZARD.
DECOMPOSITION: THERMAL DECOMPOSITION PRODUCTS MAY INCLUDE TOXIC OXIDES OF CARBON AND NITROGEN.
POLYMERIZATION: HAZARDOUS POLYMERIZATION HAS NOT BEEN REPORTED TO OCCUR UNDER NORMAL TEMPERATURES AND PRESSURES.

STORAGE AND DISPOSAL

OBSERVE ALL FEDERAL, STATE AND LOCAL REGULATIONS WHEN STORING OR DISPOSING OF THIS SUBSTANCE. FOR ASSISTANCE, CONTACT THE DISTRICT DIRECTOR OF THE ENVIRONMENTAL PROTECTION AGENCY.

STORAGE

STORE IN ACCORDANCE WITH 40 CFR 165 RECOMMENDED PROCEDURES FOR THE DISPOSAL AND STORAGE OF PESTICIDES AND PESTICIDE CONTAINERS.
STORE AWAY FROM INCOMPATIBLE SUBSTANCES.

DISPOSAL

DISPOSAL MUST BE IN ACCORDANCE WITH 40 CFR 165 RECOMMENDED PROCEDURES FOR THE DISPOSAL AND STORAGE OF PESTICIDES AND PESTICIDE CONTAINERS.

CONDITIONS TO AVOID

MAY BURN BUT DOES NOT IGNITE READILY. AVOID CONTACT WITH STRONG OXIDIZERS, EXCESSIVE HEAT, SPARKS, OR OPEN FLAME.

SPILL AND LEAK PROCEDURES

OCCUPATIONAL SPILL: SWEEP UP AND PLACE IN SUITABLE CLEAN, DRY CONTAINERS FOR RECLAMATION OR LATER DISPOSAL. DO NOT FLUSH SPILLED MATERIAL INTO SEWER. KEEP UNNECESSARY PEOPLE AWAY.

PROTECTIVE EQUIPMENT

VENTILATION: PROVIDE LOCAL EXHAUST OR PROCESS ENCLOSURE VENTILATION SYSTEM.

RESPIRATOR: THE FOLLOWING RESPIRATORS ARE RECOMMENDED BASED ON INFORMATION FOUND IN THE PHYSICAL DATA, TOXICITY AND HEALTH EFFECTS SECTIONS. THEY ARE RANKED IN ORDER FROM MINIMUM TO MAXIMUM RESPIRATORY PROTECTION. THE SPECIFIC RESPIRATOR SELECTED MUST BE BASED ON CONTAMINATION LEVELS FOUND IN THE WORK PLACE, MUST NOT EXCEED THE WORKING LIMITS OF THE RESPIRATOR AND BE JOINTLY APPROVED BY THE NATIONAL INSTITUTE FOR OCCUPATIONAL SAFETY AND HEALTH AND THE MINE SAFETY AND HEALTH ADMINISTRATION (NIOSH-MSHA).
CHEMICAL CARTRIDGE RESPIRATOR WITH AN ORGANIC VAPOR CARTRIDGE(S) WITH A FULL FACEPIECE AND ORGANIC VAPOR CARTRIDGE(S) IN COMBINATION WITH A DUST AND MIST FILTER.
POWERED AIR-PURIFYING RESPIRATOR WITH A TIGHT-FITTING FACEPIECE AND ORGANIC VAPOR CARTRIDGE(S) IN COMBINATION WITH A HIGH-EFFICIENCY PARTICULATE FILTER.
TYPE 'C' SUPPLIED-AIR RESPIRATOR WITH A FULL FACEPIECE OPERATED IN A PRESSURE-DEMAND OR OTHER POSITIVE PRESSURE MODE.
SELF-CONTAINED BREATHING APPARATUS WITH A FULL FACEPIECE OPERATED IN PRESSURE-DEMAND OR OTHER POSITIVE PRESSURE MODE. FOR FIREFIGHTING AND OTHER IMMEDIATELY DANGEROUS TO LIFE OR HEALTH CONDITIONS:
SELF-CONTAINED BREATHING APPARATUS WITH FULL FACEPIECE OPERATED IN PRESSURE-DEMAND OR OTHER POSITIVE PRESSURE MODE.
SUPPLIED-AIR RESPIRATOR WITH FULL FACEPIECE AND OPERATED IN PRESSURE-DEMAND OR OTHER POSITIVE PRESSURE MODE IN COMBINATION WITH AN AUXILIARY SELF-CONTAINED BREATHING APPARATUS OPERATED IN PRESSURE-DEMAND OR OTHER POSITIVE PRESSURE MODE.

CLOTHING: EMPLOYEE MUST WEAR APPROPRIATE PROTECTIVE (IMPERVIOUS) CLOTHING AND EQUIPMENT TO PREVENT REPEATED OR PROLONGED SKIN CONTACT WITH THIS SUBSTANCE.

GLOVES: EMPLOYEE MUST WEAR APPROPRIATE PROTECTIVE GLOVES TO PREVENT CONTACT WITH THIS SUBSTANCE.

EYE PROTECTION: EMPLOYEE MUST WEAR SPLASH-PROOF OR DUST-RESISTANT SAFETY GOGGLES TO PREVENT EYE CONTACT WITH THIS SUBSTANCE.
EMERGENCY EYE WASH: WHERE THERE IS ANY POSSIBILITY THAT AN EMPLOYEE'S EYES MAY BE EXPOSED TO THIS SUBSTANCE, THE EMPLOYER SHOULD PROVIDE AN EYE WASH FOUNTAIN WITHIN THE IMMEDIATE WORK AREA FOR EMERGENCY USE.

AUTHORIZED BY- OCCUPATIONAL HEALTH SERVICES, INC.
CREATION DATE: 10/04/89 ***REVISION DATE:*** 07/12/90

MATERIAL SAFETY DATA SHEET

OCCUPATIONAL HEALTH SERVICES, INC.
AGRICULTURE AND PESTICIDE DIVISION
450 SEVENTH AVENUE, SUITE 2407
NEW YORK, NEW YORK 10123
1-800-445-MSDS OR (212) 967-1100

EMERGENCY CONTACT:
JOHN S. BRANSFORD, JR. (615) 292-1180

SUBSTANCE IDENTIFICATION

CAS-NUMBER 3735-23-7

SUBSTANCE: METHYL PHENCAPTON

TRADE NAMES/SYNONYMS: S-(((2,5-DICHLOROPHENYL)THIO)METHYL) O,O-DIMETHYL ESTER PHOSPHORODITHIOIC ACID; S-(2,5,-DICHLOROPHENYLTHIOMETHYL) DIMETHYL PHOSPHORODITHIOATE; O,O DIMETHYL S-(2,5-DICHLOROPHENYLTHIO)METHYL) PHOSPHORODITHIOATE; METHYL PHENKAPTON; G-30494; ENT 25,554-X; PST73085

CHEMICAL FAMILY: PHOSPHONOTHIOATE
HALOGEN COMPOUND, AROMATIC

MOLECULAR FORMULA: C9-H11-CL2-O2-P-S3

MOLECULAR WEIGHT: 349.25

CERCLA RATINGS (SCALE 0-3): HEALTH=3 FIRE=U REACTIVITY=U PERSISTENCE=3

NFPA RATINGS (SCALE 0-4): HEALTH=3 FIRE=U REACTIVITY=U

COMPONENTS AND CONTAMINANTS

COMPONENT: METHYL PHENCAPTAN ***PERCENT:*** 100
CAS# 3735-23-7

OTHER CONTAMINANTS: NONE

EXPOSURE LIMITS: NO OCCUPATIONAL EXPOSURE LIMITS ESTABLISHED BY OSHA, ACGIH, OR NIOSH.
METHYL PHENCAPTON: 500 POUNDS SARA SECTION 302 THRESHOLD PLANNING QUANTITY 1 POUND SARA SECTION 304 REPORTABLE QUANTITY

PHYSICAL DATA

DESCRIPTION: LIQUID ***BOILING POINT:*** NOT AVAILABLE
SPECIFIC GRAVITY: NOT AVAILABLE ***EVAPORATION RATE:*** NOT AVAILABLE
SOLUBILITY IN WATER: NOT AVAILABLE

FIRE AND EXPLOSION DATA

FIRE AND EXPLOSION HAZARD: UNKNOWN FIRE AND EXPLOSION HAZARD.

FIREFIGHTING MEDIA: DRY CHEMICAL, CARBON DIOXIDE, HALON, WATER SPRAY OR STANDARD FOAM (1987 EMERGENCY RESPONSE GUIDEBOOK, DOT P 5800.4). FOR LARGER FIRES, USE WATER SPRAY, FOG OR STANDARD FOAM (1987 EMERGENCY RESPONSE GUIDEBOOK, DOT P 5800.4).

FIREFIGHTING: MOVE CONTAINERS FROM FIRE AREA IF POSSIBLE. COOL FIRE-EXPOSED CONTAINERS WITH WATER FROM SIDE UNTIL WELL AFTER FIRE IS OUT. STAY AWAY FROM STORAGE TANK ENDS (1987 EMERGENCY RESPONSE GUIDEBOOK, DOT P 5800.4, GUIDE PAGE 65).
EXTINGUISH ONLY IF FLOW CAN BE STOPPED. EXTINGUISH USING AGENT INDICATED. USE FLOODING AMOUNTS OF WATER AS A FOG. COOL CONTAINERS WITH FLOODING AMOUNTS OF WATER FROM AS FAR A DISTANCE AS POSSIBLE. AVOID BREATHING POISONOUS VAPORS, KEEP UPWIND. CONSIDER EVACUATION OF DOWNWIND AREA IF MATERIAL IS LEAKING.

TOXICITY

METHYL PHENCAPTON: TOXICITY DATA: 220 MG/KG ORAL-RAT LD50; 11 MG/KG ORAL-MOUSE LD50. CARCINOGEN STATUS: NONE. ACUTE TOXICITY LEVEL: TOXIC BY INGESTION. TARGET EFFECTS: CHOLINESTERASE INHIBITOR. POISONING MAY AFFECT THE NERVOUS SYSTEM.* AT INCREASED RISK FROM EXPOSURE: PERSONS WITH RESPIRATORY AILMENTS, RECENT EXPOSURE TO CHOLINESTERASE INHIBITORS OR IMPAIRED CHOLINESTERASE PRODUCTION, OR LIVER MALFUNCTION.* ADDITIONAL DATA: MAY CROSS THE PLACENTA. HIGH ENVIRONMENTAL TEMPERATURES OR EXPOSURE OF THE CHEMICAL TO VISIBLE OR ULTRAVIOLET LIGHT MAY ENHANCE THE TOXICITY. INTERACTIONS WITH MEDICATIONS MAY OCCUR.*
* MAY BE BASED ON GENERAL INFORMATION ON ORGANOPHOSPHATES.

HEALTH EFFECTS AND FIRST AID

INHALATION: METHYL PHENCAPTON: SEE INFORMATION ON ORGANOPHOSPHATES.
ORGANOPHOSPHATES: CHOLINESTERASE INHIBITOR. ACUTE EXPOSURE- WHEN INHALED, THE FIRST EFFECTS OF CHOLINESTERASE INHIBITORS ARE USUALLY RESPIRATORY AND MAY INCLUDE NASAL HYPEREMIA AND WATERY DISCHARGE, COUGH, CHEST DISCOMFORT, DYSPNEA, AND WHEEZING DUE TO INCREASED BRONCHIAL SECRETIONS AND BRONCHOCONSTRICTION. IF SUFFICIENT AMOUNTS ARE ABSORBED, OTHER SYSTEMIC EFFECTS MAY BEGIN WITHIN A FEW MINUTES OR BE DELAYED FOR UP TO 12 HOURS. SYMPTOMS MAY INCLUDE PALLOR, NAUSEA, VOMITING, DIARRHEA, ABDOMINAL CRAMPS, HEADACHE, DIZZINESS, OCULAR PAIN, BLURRED VISION, MIOSIS OR IN SOME CASES, ESPECIALLY INITIALLY, MYDRIASIS, LACRIMATION, SALIVATION, SWEATING, AND CONFUSION. OTHER REPORTED CENTRAL NERVOUS SYSTEM OR NEUROMUSCULAR EFFECTS MAY INCLUDE ATAXIA, SLURRED SPEECH, AREFLEXIA, WEAKNESS, FATIGUE, FASCICULATIONS, TWITCHING, TREMORS POSSIBLY OF THE TONGUE AND EYELIDS, AND EVENTUALLY PARALYSIS OF THE EXTREMITIES AND POSSIBLY OF THE RESPIRATORY MUSCLES. IN SEVERE CASES THERE MAY ALSO BE INVOLUNTARY DEFECATION AND URINATION, CYANOSIS, PSYCHOSIS, HYPERGLYCEMIA, ACUTE PANCREATITIS, CARDIAC IRREGULARITIES, PULMONARY EDEMA, UNCONSCIOUSNESS, CONVULSIONS, AND COMA. DEATH IS PRIMARILY DUE TO RESPIRATORY FAILURE, ALTHOUGH CARDIOVASCULAR EFFECTS INCLUDING CARDIAC ARREST MAY ALSO BE IMPLICATED. LONG TERM SEQUELAE ARE RARE BUT MAY INCLUDE NEUROPSYCHIATRIC DISORDERS AND MYOPATHY WITH MUSCLE TENDERNESS. SOME ORGANOPHOSPHATES MAY CAUSE A DELAYED NEUROPATHY BEGINNING 1-4 WEEKS AFTER AN ACUTE EXPOSURE WHICH MAY OR MAY NOT HAVE CAUSED ACUTE CHOLINERGIC EFFECTS. NUMBNESS, TINGLING, WEAKNESS AND CRAMPING BEGINNING SYMMETRICALLY IN THE LOWER LIMBS MAY PROGRESS TO ATAXIA AND PARALYSIS. IN SEVERE CASES, UPPER LIMB INVOLVEMENT IS POSSIBLE AND FLACCID PARALYSIS MAY PROGRESS TO SPASTIC PARALYSIS WITH EXAGGERATED REFLEXES. IMPROVEMENT MAY OCCUR OVER MONTHS TO YEARS, BUT SOME RESIDUAL IMPAIRMENT USUALLY REMAINS.
CHRONIC EXPOSURE- REPEATED OR PROLONGED EXPOSURE MAY RESULT IN THE EFFECTS OF ACUTE EXPOSURE INCLUDING THE DELAYED NEUROPATHY. OTHER EFFECTS REPORTED IN WORKERS REPEATEDLY EXPOSED INCLUDE IMPAIRED MEMORY AND CONCENTRATION, ACUTE PSYCHOSIS, SEVERE DEPRESSIONS, IRRITABILTY, CONFUSION, APATHY, EMOTIONAL LABILITY, SOCIAL WITHDRAWAL, CONFUSION, HEADACHE, SPEECH DIFFICULTIES, DELAYED REACTION TIMES, SPATIAL DISORIENTATION, NIGHTMARES, SLEEPWALKING, AND DROWSINESS OR INSOMNIA. AN INFLUENZA-LIKE CONDITION WITH HEADACHE, NAUSEA, WEAKNESS, ANOREXIA AND MALAISE HAS ALSO BEEN REPORTED.

FIRST AID- REMOVE FROM EXPOSURE AREA TO FRESH AIR IMMEDIATELY. IF BREATHING HAS STOPPED, GIVE ARTIFICIAL RESPIRATION. MAINTAIN AIRWAY AND BLOOD PRESSURE AND ADMINISTER OXYGEN IF AVAILABLE. KEEP AFFECTED PERSON WARM AND AT REST. TREAT SYMPTOMATICALLY AND SUPPORTIVELY. ADMINISTRATION OF OXYGEN SHOULD BE PERFORMED BY QUALIFIED PERSONNEL. GET MEDICAL ATTENTION IMMEDIATELY.

SKIN CONTACT: METHYL PHENCAPTON: SEE INFORMATION ON ORGANOPHOSPHATES. ORGANOPHOSPHATES: CHOLINESTERASE INHIBITOR. **ACUTE EXPOSURE-** LOCALIZED SWEATING AND FASCICULATIONS MAY OCCUR AT THE SITE OF CONTACT. IF SUFFICIENT AMOUNTS ARE ABSORBED, OTHER EFFECTS OF CHOLINESTERASE INHIBITION AS DESCRIBED IN ACUTE INHALATION MAY OCCUR. SYMPTOMS MAY BE DELAYED 2-3 HOURS, BUT USUALLY NO MORE THAN 12 HOURS. THE RATE OF ABSORPTION IS INCREASED BY THE PRESENCE OF DERMATITIS OR HIGH AMBIENT TEMPERATURES. DELAYED NEUROPATHY IS ALSO POSSIBLE. **CHRONIC EXPOSURE-** REPEATED OR PROLONGED EXPOSURE MAY CAUSE EFFECTS AS DESCRIBED IN ACUTE EXPOSURE. SOME ORGANOPHOSPHATES MAY CAUSE SENSITIZATION.

FIRST AID- REMOVE CONTAMINATED CLOTHING IMMEDIATELY. WASH CONTAMINATED AREAS WITH SOAP AND WATER FOLLOWED BY ALCOHOL (ARENA, POISONING, 4TH ED.). EMERGENCY PERSONNEL SHOULD WEAR GLOVES AND AVOID CONTAMINATION. TREAT RESPIRATORY DIFFICULTY WITH ARTIFICIAL RESPIRATION. GET MEDICAL ATTENTION IMMEDIATELY.

EYE CONTACT: METHYL PHENCAPTON: SEE INFORMATION ON ORGANOPHOSPHATES. ORGANOPHOSPHATES: CHOLINESTERASE INHIBITOR. **ACUTE EXPOSURE-** DIRECT CONTACT MAY CAUSE PAIN, HYPEREMIA, LACRIMATION, TWITCHING OF THE EYELIDS, MIOSIS, AND CILIARY MUSCLE SPASM WITH LOSS OF ACCOMODATION, BLURRED OR DIMMED VISION AND BROWACHE. SOMETIMES MYDRIASIS MAY OCCUR INSTEAD OF MIOSIS. WITH SUFFICIENT EXPOSURE, OTHER SYMPTOMS OF CHOLINESTERASE INHIBITION AS DESCRIBED IN ACUTE INHALATION MAY OCCUR. **CHRONIC EXPOSURE-** REPEATED OR PROLONGED EXPOSURE MAY CAUSE EFFECTS AS DESCRIBED IN ACUTE EXPOSURE. SOME COMPOUNDS HAVE CAUSED TOXIC EFFECTS ON THE CRYSTALLINE LENS, CONJUNCTIVAL THICKENING AND OBSTRUCTION OF THE NASOLACRIMAL CANALS WHEN USED AS MIOTIC EYEDROPS.

FIRST AID- IRRIGATE EYES WITH WATER OR SALINE SOLUTION. IF SYMPTOMS OF POISONING OCCUR, TREAT RESPIRATORY DIFFICULTY WITH ARTIFICIAL RESPIRATION AND OXYGEN. OBSERVE PATIENT FOR AT LEAST 24-36 HOURS (GOSSELIN, CLINICAL TOXICOLOGY OF COMMERCIAL PRODUCTS, 5TH ED.). GET MEDICAL ATTENTION IMMEDIATELY. OXYGEN SHOULD BE ADMINISTERED BY QUALIFIED MEDICAL PERSONNEL.

INGESTION: METHYL PHENCAPTON: SEE INFORMATION ON ORGANPHOSPHATES. ORGANOPHOSPHATES: CHOLINESTERASE INHIBITOR. **ACUTE EXPOSURE-** WHEN INGESTED, THE FIRST EFFECTS MAY BE NAUSEA, VOMITING, ANOREXIA, ABDOMINAL CRAMPS AND DIARRHEA. GASTROINTESTINAL ABSORPTION MAY CAUSE SYMPTOMS OF CHOLINESTERASE INHIBITION AS DESCRIBED IN ACUTE INHALATION. SYMPTOMS MAY BEGIN WITHIN MINUTES OR BE DELAYED FOR HOURS. DELAYED EFFECTS INCLUDING NEUROPATHY MAY ALSO OCCUR. **CHRONIC EXPOSURE-** REPEATED INGESTION MAY CAUSE EFFECTS AS DESCRIBED IN ACUTE EXPOSURE.

FIRST AID- IF PERSON IS ALERT AND RESPIRATION IS NOT DEPRESSED, GIVE SYRUP OF IPECAC FOLLOWED BY WATER (IF VOMITING OCCURS, KEEP HEAD BELOW HIPS TO PREVENT ASPIRATION). IF CONSCIOUSNESS LEVEL DECLINES OR VOMITING HAS NOT OCCURRED IN 15 MINUTES EMPTY STOMACH BY GASTRIC LAVAGE WITH THE AID OF CUFFED ENDOTRACHEAL TUBE USING ISOTONIC SALINE OR 5% SODIUM BICARBONATE FOLLOW WITH ACTIVATED CHARCOAL. ESTABLISH AND MAINTAIN AIRWAY. TREAT RESPIRATORY DIFFICULTY WITH ARTIFICIAL RESPIRATION AND OXYGEN. DO NOT GIVE MORPHINE, AMINOPHYLLINE, PHENOTHIAZINES, RESERPINE, FUROSEMIDE, OR ETHACRYNIC ACID (MORGAN, RECOGNITION AND MANAGEMENT OF PESTICIDE POISONINGS, 3RD ED.). TREAT SYMPTOMATICALLY AND SUPPORTIVELY. ADMINISTRATION OF OXYGEN AND LAVAGE MUST BE PERFORMED BY QUALIFIED MEDICAL PERSONNEL. GET MEDICAL ATTENTION IMMEDIATELY.

ANTIDOTE: THE FOLLOWING ANTIDOTE(S) HAVE BEEN RECOMMENDED. HOWEVER, THE DECISION AS TO WHETHER THE SEVERITY OF POISONING REQUIRES ADMINISTRATION OF ANY ANTIDOTE AND ACTUAL DOSE REQUIRED SHOULD BE MADE BY QUALIFIED MEDICAL PERSONNEL.

FOR CHOLINESTERASE INHIBITORS: ESTABLISH CLEAR AIRWAY AND TISSUE OXYGENATION BY ASPIRATION OF SECRETIONS, AND IF NECESSARY, BY ASSISTED PULMONARY VENTILATION WITH OXYGEN. IMPROVE TISSUE OXYGENATION AS MUCH AS POSSIBLE BEFORE ADMINISTERING ATROPINE TO MINIMIZE THE RISK OF VENTRICULAR FIBRILLATION. ADMINISTER ATROPINE SULFATE INTRAVENOUSLY, OR INTRAMUSCULARLY IF IV INJECTION IS NOT POSSIBLE. IN MODERATELY SEVERE POISONING ADMINISTER ATROPINE SULFATE, 0.4-2.0 MG REPEATED EVERY 15 MINUTES UNTIL ATROPINIZATION IS ACHIEVED (TACHYCARDIA, FLUSHING, DRY MOUTH, MYDRIASIS). MAINTAIN ATROPINIZATION BY REPEATED DOSES FOR 2-12 HOURS, OR LONGER, DEPENDING ON THE SEVERITY OF POISONING. THE APPEARANCE OF RALES IN THE LUNG BASES, MIOSIS, SALIVATION, NAUSEA, BRADYCARDIA, ARE ALL INDICATIONS OF INADEQUATE ATROPINIZATION. SEVERELY POISONED INDIVIDUALS MAY EXHIBIT REMARKABLE TOLERANCE TO ATROPINE; TWO OR MORE TIMES THE DOSAGES SUGGESTED ABOVE MAY BE NEEDED. PERSONS NOT POISONED OR ONLY SLIGHTLY POISONED, HOWEVER, MAY DEVELOP SIGNS OF ATROPINE TOXICITY FROM SUCH LARGE DOSAGES: FEVER, MUSCLE FIBRILLATIONS, AND DELIRIUM ARE THE MAIN SIGNS OF ATROPINE TOXICITY. IF THESE SIGNS APPEAR WHILE THE PATIENT IS FULLY ATROPINIZED, ATROPINE ADMINISTRATION SHOULD BE DISCONTINUED, AT LEAST TEMPORARILY. OBSERVE TREATED PATIENTS CLOSELY AT LEAST 24 HOURS TO INSURE THAT SYMPTOMS (POSSIBLY PULMONARY EDEMA) DO NOT RECUR AS ATROPINIZATION WEARS OFF. IN VERY SEVERE POISONINGS, METABOLIC DISPOSITION OF TOXICANT MAY REQUIRE SEVERAL HOURS OR DAYS DURING WHICH ATROPINIZATION MUST BE MAINTAINED. MARKEDLY LOWER LEVELS OF URINARY METABOLITES INDICATE THAT ATROPINE DOSAGE CAN BE TAPERED OFF. AS DOSAGE IS REDUCED, CHECK THE LUNG BASES FREQUENTLY FOR RALES. IF RALES ARE HEARD OR OTHER SYMPTOMS RETURN, RE-ESTABLISH ATROPINIZATION PROMPTLY (MORGAN, RECOGNITION AND MANAGEMENT OF PESTICIDE POISONINGS, 3RD ED.). ADMINISTRATION OF ANTIDOTE MUST BE PERFORMED BY QUALIFIED MEDICAL PERSONNEL.

IN CASES OF SEVERE POISONING BY ORGANOPHOSPHATE PESTICIDES IN WHICH RESPIRATORY DEPRESSION, MUSCLE WEAKNESS AND TWITCHINGS ARE SEVERE, GIVE PRALIDOXIME (PROTOPAM-AYERST, 2-PAM), 1.0 GRAM INTRAVENOUSLY AT NO MORE THAN 0.5 GRAM PER MINUTE. DOSAGE OF PRALIDOXIME MAY BE REPEATED IN 1-2 HOURS, THEN AT 10-12 HOUR INTERVALS IF NEEDED. IN VERY SEVERE POISONINGS, DOSAGE RATES MAY BE DOUBLED. TREATMENT WITH PRALIDOXIME WILL BE MOST EFFECTIVE IF GIVEN WITHIN THIRTY-SIX HOURS AFTER POISONING (MORGAN, RECOGNITION AND MANAGEMENT OF PESTICIDE POISONINGS, 3RD ED.). ANTIDOTE SHOULD BE ADMINISTERED BY QUALIFIED MEDICAL PERSONNEL.

REACTIVITY

REACTIVITY: STABLE UNDER NORMAL TEMPERATURES AND PRESSURES.

INCOMPATIBILITIES: METHYL PHENCAPTON: OXIDIZERS (STRONG): FIRE AND EXPLOSION HAZARD.

DECOMPOSITION: THERMAL DECOMPOSITION PRODUCTS MAY INCLUDE TOXIC AND HAZARDOUS FUMES OF CHLORINE AND OXIDES OF OXIDES OF SULFUR AND PHOSPHORUS.

POLYMERIZATION: HAZARDOUS POLYMERIZATION HAS NOT BEEN REPORTED TO OCCUR UNDER NORMAL TEMPERATURES AND PRESSURES.

STORAGE AND DISPOSAL

OBSERVE ALL FEDERAL, STATE AND LOCAL REGULATIONS WHEN STORING OR DISPOSING OF THIS SUBSTANCE. FOR ASSISTANCE, CONTACT THE DISTRICT DIRECTOR OF THE ENVIRONMENTAL PROTECTION AGENCY.

****STORAGE****

STORE IN ACCORDANCE WITH 40 CFR 165 RECOMMENDED PROCEDURES FOR THE DISPOSAL AND STORAGE OF PESTICIDES AND PESTICIDE CONTAINERS. THRESHOLD PLANNING QUANTITY (TPQ): THE SUPERFUND AMENDMENTS AND REAUTHORIZATION ACT (SARA) SECTION 302 REQUIRES THAT EACH FACILITY WHERE ANY EXTREMELY HAZARDOUS SUBSTANCE IS PRESENT IN A QUANTITY EQUAL TO OR GREATER THAN THE TPQ ESTABLISHED FOR THAT SUBSTANCE NOTIFY THE STATE EMERGENCY RESPONSE COMMISSION FOR THE STATE IN WHICH IT IS LOCATED. SECTION 303 OF SARA REQUIRES THESE FACILITIES TO PARTICIPATE IN LOCAL EMERGENCY RESPONSE PLANNING (40 CFR 355.30).

****DISPOSAL****

DISPOSAL MUST BE IN ACCORDANCE WITH 40 CFR 165 RECOMMENDED PROCEDURES FOR THE DISPOSAL AND STORAGE OF PESTICIDES AND PESTICIDE CONTAINERS.

CONDITIONS TO AVOID

NONE REPORTED.

SPILL AND LEAK PROCEDURES

OCCUPATIONAL SPILL: DO NOT TOUCH SPILLED MATERIAL. STOP LEAK IF YOU CAN DO IT WITHOUT RISK. USE WATER SPRAY TO REDUCE VAPORS. FOR SMALL SPILLS, TAKE UP WITH SAND OR OTHER ABSORBENT MATERIAL AND PLACE INTO CONTAINERS FOR LATER DISPOSAL. FOR SMALL DRY SPILLS, WITH A CLEAN SHOVEL PLACE MATERIAL INTO CLEAN, DRY CONTAINERS AND COVER. MOVE CONTAINERS FROM SPILL AREA. FOR LARGER SPILLS, DIKE FAR AHEAD OF SPILL FOR LATER DISPOSAL. KEEP UNNECESSARY PEOPLE AWAY. ISOLATE HAZARD AREA AND DENY ENTRY. VENTILATE CLOSED SPACES BEFORE ENTERING. REPORTABLE QUANTITY (RQ): 1 POUND THE SUPERFUND AMENDMENTS AND REAUTHORIZATION ACT (SARA) SECTION 304 REQUIRES THAT A RELEASE EQUAL

TO OR GREATER THAN THE REPORTABLE QUANTITY FOR THIS SUBSTANCE BE IMMEDIATELY REPORTED TO THE LOCAL EMERGENCY PLANNING COMMITTEE AND THE STATE EMERGENCY RESPONSE COMMISSION (40 CFR 355.40). IF THE RELEASE OF THIS SUBSTANCE IS REPORTABLE UNDER CERCLA SECTION 103, THE NATIONAL RESPONSE CENTER MUST BE NOTIFIED IMMEDIATELY AT (800) 424-8802 OR (202) 426-2675 IN THE METROPOLITAN WASHINGTON, D.C. AREA (40 CFR 302.6).

PROTECTIVE EQUIPMENT

VENTILATION: PROVIDE LOCAL EXHAUST OR PROCESS ENCLOSURE VENTILATION SYSTEM.

RESPIRATOR: THE FOLLOWING RESPIRATORS ARE RECOMMENDED BASED ON INFORMATION FOUND IN THE PHYSICAL DATA, TOXICITY AND HEALTH EFFECTS SECTIONS. THEY ARE RANKED IN ORDER FROM MINIMUM TO MAXIMUM RESPIRATORY PROTECTION. THE SPECIFIC RESPIRATOR SELECTED MUST BE BASED ON CONTAMINATION LEVELS FOUND IN THE WORK PLACE, MUST NOT EXCEED THE WORKING LIMITS OF THE RESPIRATOR AND BE JOINTLY APPROVED BY THE NATIONAL INSTITUTE FOR OCCUPATIONAL SAFETY AND HEALTH AND THE MINE SAFETY AND HEALTH ADMINISTRATION (NIOSH-MSHA).

TYPE 'C' SUPPLIED-AIR RESPIRATOR WITH A FULL FACEPIECE OPERATED IN PRESSURE-DEMAND OR OTHER POSITIVE PRESSURE MODE OR WITH A FULL FACEPIECE, HELMET OR HOOD OPERATED IN CONTINOUS-FLOW MODE.

SELF-CONTAINED BREATHING APPARATUS WITH A FULL FACEPIECE OPERATED IN PRESSURE-DEMAND OR OTHER POSITIVE PRESSURE MODE.

FOR FIREFIGHTING AND OTHER IMMEDIATELY DANGEROUS TO LIFE OR HEALTH CONDITIONS:

SELF-CONTAINED BREATHING APPARATUS WITH FULL FACEPIECE OPERATED IN PRESSURE-DEMAND OR OTHER POSITIVE PRESSURE MODE.

SUPPLIED-AIR RESPIRATOR WITH FULL FACEPIECE AND OPERATED IN PRESSURE-DEMAND OR OTHER POSITIVE PRESSURE MODE IN COMBINATION WITH AN AUXILIARY SELF-CONTAINED BREATHING APPARATUS OPERATED IN PRESSURE-DEMAND OR OTHER POSITIVE PRESSURE MODE.

CLOTHING: EMPLOYEE MUST WEAR APPROPRIATE PROTECTIVE (IMPERVIOUS) CLOTHING AND EQUIPMENT TO PREVENT ANY POSSIBILITY OF SKIN CONTACT WITH THIS SUBSTANCE.

GLOVES: EMPLOYEE MUST WEAR APPROPRIATE PROTECTIVE GLOVES TO PREVENT CONTACT WITH THIS SUBSTANCE.

EYE PROTECTION: EMPLOYEE MUST WEAR SPLASH-PROOF OR DUST-RESISTANT SAFETY GOGGLES AND A FACESHIELD TO PREVENT CONTACT WITH THIS SUBSTANCE.

EMERGENCY WASH FACILITIES: WHERE THERE IS ANY POSSIBILITY THAT AN EMPLOYEE'S EYES AND/OR SKIN MAY BE EXPOSED TO THIS SUBSTANCE, THE EMPLOYER SHOULD PROVIDE AN EYE WASH FOUNTAIN AND QUICK DRENCH SHOWER WITHIN THE IMMEDIATE WORK AREA FOR EMERGENCY USE.

AUTHORIZED BY- OCCUPATIONAL HEALTH SERVICES, INC.
CREATION DATE: 10/04/88 ***REVISION DATE:*** 04/26/90

MATERIAL SAFETY DATA SHEET

OCCUPATIONAL HEALTH SERVICES, INC.
AGRICULTURE AND PESTICIDE DIVISION
450 SEVENTH AVENUE, SUITE 2407
NEW YORK, NEW YORK 10123
1-800-445-MSDS OR (212) 967-1100

EMERGENCY CONTACT:
JOHN S. BRANSFORD, JR. (615) 292-1180

SUBSTANCE IDENTIFICATION

CAS-NUMBER 26419-73-8

SUBSTANCE: **TIRPATE**

TRADE NAMES/SYNONYMS: 2,4-DIMETHYL-1,3-DITHIOLANE-2-CARBOXALDEHYDE O-((METHYLAMINO)CARBONYL) OXIME; METHYLCARBAMIC ACID, O((2,4-DIMETHYL-1,3-DITHIOLAN-2-YL)METHYLENE) AMINO); MBR 61686; 2,4-DIMETHYL-1,3-DITHOLANE-2-CARBOXALDEHYDE O-(METHYLCARBAMOYL)OXIME; ENT 27696; C8H14N2O2S2; PST73088

CHEMICAL FAMILY: CARBAMATE OXIME

MOLECULAR FORMULA: C8-H14-N2-O2-S2

MOLECULAR WEIGHT: 234.36

CERCLA RATINGS (SCALE 0-3): HEALTH=3 FIRE=U REACTIVITY=U PERSISTENCE=1

NFPA RATINGS (SCALE 0-4): HEALTH=3 FIRE=U REACTIVITY=U

COMPONENTS AND CONTAMINANTS

COMPONENT: TIRPATE ***PERCENT:*** 100
CAS# 26419-73-8

OTHER CONTAMINANTS: NONE

EXPOSURE LIMITS: NO OCCUPATIONAL EXPOSURE LIMITS ESTABLISHED BY OSHA, ACGIH, OR NIOSH.

TIRPATE: 100/10,000 POUNDS SARA SECTION 302 THRESHOLD PLANNING QUANTITY 1 POUND SARA SECTION 304 REPORTABLE QUANTITY

PHYSICAL DATA

DESCRIPTION: NOT AVAILABLE ***SPECIFIC GRAVITY:*** NOT AVAILABLE

SOLUBILITY IN WATER: NOT AVAILABLE

FIRE AND EXPLOSION DATA

FIRE AND EXPLOSION HAZARD: UNKNOWN FIRE AND EXPLOSION HAZARD.

FIREFIGHTING MEDIA: DRY CHEMICAL, CARBON DIOXIDE, HALON, WATER SPRAY OR STANDARD FOAM (1987 EMERGENCY RESPONSE GUIDEBOOK, DOT P 5800.4).

FOR LARGER FIRES, USE WATER SPRAY, FOG OR STANDARD FOAM (1987 EMERGENCY RESPONSE GUIDEBOOK, DOT P 5800.4).

FIREFIGHTING: MOVE CONTAINERS FROM FIRE AREA IF POSSIBLE (1987 EMERGENCY RESPONSE GUIDEBOOK, DOT P 5800.4, GUIDE PAGE 53).

EXTINGUISH USING AGENT SUITABLE FOR TYPE OF SURROUNDING FIRE. AVOID BREATHING VAPORS AND DUSTS. KEEP UPWIND.

TRANSPORTATION DATA

DEPARTMENT OF TRANSPORTATION HAZARD CLASSIFICATION 49 CFR 172.101: POISON B

DEPARTMENT OF TRANSPORTATION LABELING REQUIREMENTS 49 CFR 172.101 AND SUBPART E: POISON

FOR LIQUID FORMS: DEPARTMENT OF TRANSPORTATION PACKAGING REQUIREMENTS: 49CFR173.346 EXCEPTIONS: 49CFR173.345

FOR SOLID FORMS: DEPARTMENT OF TRANSPORTATION PACKAGING REQUIREMENTS: 49CFR173.365 EXCEPTIONS: 49CFR173.364

TOXICITY

TIRPATE: TOXICITY DATA: 300 MG/KG SKIN-RAT LD50; 1 MG/KG ORAL-RAT LD50. CARCINOGEN STATUS: NONE. ACUTE TOXICITY LEVEL: HIGHLY TOXIC BY INGESTION; TOXIC BY DERMAL ABSORPTION. TARGET EFFECTS: CHOLINESTERASE INHIBITOR. AT INCREASED RISK FROM EXPOSURE: PERSONS WITH ASTHMA, DIABETES, CARDIOVASCULAR DISEASE, MECHANICAL OBSTRUCTION OF THE GASTROINTESTINAL OR UROGENITAL TRACT, AND THOSE IN VAGOTONIC STATES.*

* MAY BE BASED ON GENERAL INFORMATION ON CARBAMATES.

HEALTH EFFECTS AND FIRST AID

INHALATION: TIRPATE: SEE INFORMATION ON CARBAMATES.

CARBAMATES: CHOLINESTERASE INHIBITOR. **ACUTE EXPOSURE-** WHEN INHALED, THE FIRST EFFECTS OF CHOLINESTERASE INHIBITION ARE USUALLY RESPIRATORY AND MAY INCLUDE NASAL HYPEREMIA AND WATERY DISCHARGE, CHEST DISCOMFORT, DYSPNEA, AND WHEEZING DUE TO INCREASED BRONCHIAL SECRETIONS AND BRONCHOCONSTRICTION. OTHER SYSTEMIC EFFECTS MAY BEGIN WITHIN A FEW MINUTES OR SEVERAL HOURS OF EXPOSURE. SYMPTOMS MAY INCLUDE NAUSEA, VOMITING, DIARRHEA, ABDOMINAL CRAMPS, HEADACHE, VERTIGO, OCULAR PAIN, CILIARY MUSCLE SPASM, BLURRING OR DIMNESS OF VISION, MIOSIS, OR IN SOME CASES MYDRIASIS, LACRIMATION, SALIVATION, SWEATING, AND CONFUSION. OTHER REPORTED CENTRAL NERVOUS SYSTEM OR NEUROMUSCULAR EFFECTS INCLUDE ATAXIA, SLURRED SPEECH, AREFLEXIA, WEAKNESS, FATIGUE, TWITCHING, FASCICULATION, TREMOR, AND EVENTUALLY PARALYSIS OF THE EXTREMITIES AND POSSIBLY OF THE RESPIRATORY MUSCLES. IN SEVERE CASES, THERE MAY ALSO BE INVOLUNTARY DEFECATION AND URINATION, BRADYCARDIA, HYPOTENSION, PULMONARY EDEMA, CONVULSIONS, COMA, AND DEATH FROM RESPIRATORY FAILURE OR CARDIAC ARREST. CARBAMATES GENERALLY DO NOT ACCUMULATE IN MAMMALIAN TISSUE AND THE CHOLINESTERASE INHIBITION REVERSES RATHER RAPIDLY. IN NON-FATAL CASES, THE ILLNESS GENERALLY LASTS LESS THAN 24 HOURS. **CHRONIC EXPOSURE-** PROLONGED OR REPEATED EXPOSURE MAY CAUSE EFFECTS AS DESCRIBED IN ACUTE EXPOSURE.

FIRST AID- REMOVE FROM EXPOSURE AREA TO FRESH AIR IMMEDIATELY. IF BREATHING HAS STOPPED, GIVE ARTIFICIAL RESPIRATION. MAINTAIN AIRWAY AND BLOOD PRESSURE AND ADMINISTER OXYGEN IF AVAILABLE. KEEP AFFECTED PERSON WARM AND AT REST. TREAT SYMPTOMATICALLY AND SUPPORTIVELY. ADMINISTRATION OF OXYGEN SHOULD BE PERFORMED BY QUALIFIED PERSONNEL. GET MEDICAL ATTENTION IMMEDIATELY.

SKIN CONTACT: TIRPATE: TOXIC. SEE INFORMATION ON CARBAMATES.

CARBAMATES: CHOLINESTERASE INHIBITOR. **ACUTE EXPOSURE-** SOME

COMPOUNDS MAY CAUSE IRRITATION. LOCALIZED SWEATING AND FASCICULATIONS MAY OCCUR AT THE SITE OF CONTACT. IF SUFFICIENT AMOUNTS ARE ABSORBED THROUGH THE SKIN, OTHER EFFECTS OF CHOLINESTERASE INHIBITION MAY OCCUR AS DESCRIBED IN ACUTE INHALATION; SYMPTOMS MAY BE DELAYED FOR 2-3 HOURS, USUALLY NO MORE THAN 8 HOURS. **CHRONIC EXPOSURE-** REPEATED OR PROLONGED EXPOSURE MAY CAUSE EFFECTS AS DESCRIBED IN ACUTE EXPOSURE.

FIRST AID- REMOVE CONTAMINATED CLOTHING IMMEDIATELY. WASH CONTAMINATED AREAS WITH SOAP AND WATER FOLLOWED BY ALCOHOL (ARENA, POISONING, 4TH ED.). EMERGENCY PERSONNEL SHOULD WEAR GLOVES AND AVOID CONTAMINATION. TREAT RESPIRATORY DIFFICULTY WITH ARTIFICIAL RESPIRATION. GET MEDICAL ATTENTION IMMEDIATELY.

EYE CONTACT: TIRPATE: SEE INFORMATION ON CARBAMATES.

CARBAMATES: CHOLINESTERASE INHIBITOR. **ACUTE EXPOSURE-** DIRECT CONTACT MAY CAUSE PAIN, HYPEREMIA, LACRIMATION, TWITCHING OF THE EYELIDS, MIOSIS, AND CILIARY MUSCLE SPASM WITH LOSS OF ACCOMODATION, BLURRED OR DIMMED VISION AND BROWACHE. SOMETIMES MYDRIASIS MAY OCCUR INSTEAD OF MIOSIS. WITH SUFFICIENT EXPOSURE, OTHER SYMPTOMS OF CHOLINESTERASE INHIBITION MAY OCCUR AS DESCRIBED IN ACUTE INHALATION. **CHRONIC EXPOSURE-** PROLONGED EXPOSURE MAY CAUSE EFFECTS AS DESCRIBED IN ACUTE EXPOSURE. SOME COMPOUNDS HAVE CAUSED TOXIC EFFECTS ON THE CRYSTALLINE LENS, CONJUNCTIVAL THICKENING AND OBSTRUCTION OF NASOLACRIMAL CANALS WHEN USED AS MIOTIC EYE DROPS.

FIRST AID- IRRIGATE EYES WITH WATER OR SALINE SOLUTION. IF SYMPTOMS OF POISONING OCCUR, TREAT RESPIRATORY DIFFICULTY WITH ARTIFICIAL RESPIRATION AND OXYGEN. OBSERVE PATIENT FOR AT LEAST 24-36 HOURS (GOSSELIN, CLINICAL TOXICOLOGY OF COMMERCIAL PRODUCTS, 5TH ED.). GET MEDICAL ATTENTION IMMEDIATELY. OXYGEN SHOULD BE ADMINISTERED BY QUALIFIED MEDICAL PERSONNEL.

INGESTION: TIRPATE: HIGHLY TOXIC. SEE INFORMATION ON CARBAMATES.

CARBAMATES: CHOLINESTERASE INHIBITOR. **ACUTE EXPOSURE-** WHEN INGESTED, THE FIRST EFFECTS MAY BE NAUSEA, VOMITING, ANOREXIA, ABDOMINAL CRAMPS, AND DIARRHEA. WITH ABSORPTION FROM THE GASTROINTESTINAL TRACT, THE OTHER EFFECTS OF CHOLINESTERASE INHIBITION AS DESCRIBED IN ACUTE INHALATION MAY OCCUR; SYMPTOMS MAY BEGIN WITHIN MINUTES OR BE DELAYED SEVERAL HOURS. **CHRONIC EXPOSURE-** REPEATED INGESTION MAY CAUSE EFFECTS AS DESCRIBED IN ACUTE EXPOSURE.

FIRST AID- IF PERSON IS ALERT AND RESPIRATION IS NOT DEPRESSED, GIVE SYRUP OF IPECAC FOLLOWED BY WATER (IF VOMITING OCCURS, KEEP HEAD BELOW HIPS TO PREVENT ASPIRATION). IF CONSCIOUSNESS LEVEL DECLINES OR VOMITING HAS NOT OCCURRED IN 15 MINUTES EMPTY STOMACH BY GASTRIC LAVAGE WITH THE AID OF CUFFED ENDOTRACHEAL TUBE USING ISOTONIC SALINE OR 5% SODIUM BICARBONATE FOLLOW WITH ACTIVATED CHARCOAL. ESTABLISH AND MAINTAIN AIRWAY. TREAT RESPIRATORY DIFFICULTY WITH ARTIFICIAL RESPIRATION AND OXYGEN. DO NOT GIVE MORPHINE, AMINOPHYLLINE, PHENOTHIAZINES, RESERPINE, FUROSEMIDE, OR ETHACRYNIC ACID (MORGAN, RECOGNITION AND MANAGEMENT OF PESTICIDE POISONINGS, 3RD ED.). TREAT SYMPTOMATICALLY AND SUPPORTIVELY. ADMINISTRATION OF OXYGEN AND LAVAGE MUST BE PERFORMED BY QUALIFIED MEDICAL PERSONNEL. GET MEDICAL ATTENTION IMMEDIATELY.

ANTIDOTE: THE FOLLOWING ANTIDOTE HAS BEEN RECOMMENDED. HOWEVER, THE DECISION AS TO WHETHER THE SEVERITY OF POISONING REQUIRES ADMINISTRATION OF ANY ANTIDOTE AND ACTUAL DOSE REQUIRED SHOULD BE MADE BY QUALIFIED MEDICAL PERSONNEL.

FOR CHOLINESTERASE INHIBITORS: ESTABLISH CLEAR AIRWAY AND TISSUE OXYGENATION BY ASPIRATION OF SECRETIONS, AND IF NECESSARY, BY ASSISTED PULMONARY VENTILATION WITH OXYGEN. IMPROVE TISSUE OXYGENATION AS MUCH AS POSSIBLE BEFORE ADMINISTERING ATROPINE TO MINIMIZE THE RISK OF VENTRICULAR FIBRILLATION. ADMINISTER ATROPINE SULFATE INTRAVENOUSLY, OR INTRAMUSCULARLY IF IV INJECTION IS NOT POSSIBLE. IN MODERATELY SEVERE POISONING ADMINISTER ATROPINE SULFATE, 0.4-2.0 MG REPEATED EVERY 15 MINUTES UNTIL ATROPINIZATION IS ACHIEVED (TACHYCARDIA, FLUSHING, DRY MOUTH, MYDRIASIS). MAINTAIN ATROPINIZATION BY REPEATED DOSES FOR 2-12 HOURS, OR LONGER, DEPENDING ON THE SEVERITY OF POISONING. THE APPEARANCE OF RALES IN THE LUNG BASES, MIOSIS, SALIVATION, NAUSEA, BRADYCARDIA, ARE ALL INDICATIONS OF INADEQUATE ATROPINIZATION. SEVERELY POISONED INDIVIDUALS MAY EXHIBIT REMARKABLE TOLERANCE TO ATROPINE; TWO OR MORE TIMES THE DOSAGES SUGGESTED ABOVE MAY BE NEEDED. PERSONS NOT POISONED OR ONLY SLIGHTLY POISONED, HOWEVER, MAY DEVELOP SIGNS OF ATROPINE TOXICITY FROM SUCH LARGE DOSAGES: FEVER, MUSCLE FIBRILLATIONS, AND DELIRIUM ARE THE MAIN SIGNS OF ATROPINE TOXICITY. IF THESE SIGNS APPEAR WHILE THE PATIENT IS FULLY ATROPINIZED, ATROPINE ADMINISTRATION SHOULD BE DISCONTINUED, AT LEAST TEMPORARILY. OBSERVE TREATED PATIENTS CLOSELY AT LEAST 24 HOURS TO INSURE THAT SYMPTOMS (POSSIBLY PULMONARY EDEMA) DO NOT RECUR AS ATROPINIZATION WEARS OFF. IN VERY SEVERE POISONINGS, METABOLIC DISPOSITION OF TOXICANT MAY REQUIRE SEVERAL HOURS OR DAYS DURING WHICH ATROPINIZATION MUST BE MAINTAINED. MARKEDLY LOWER LEVELS OF URINARY METABOLITES INDICATE THAT ATROPINE DOSAGE CAN BE TAPERED OFF. AS DOSAGE IS REDUCED, CHECK THE LUNG BASES FREQUENTLY FOR RALES. IF RALES ARE HEARD OR OTHER SYMPTOMS RETURN, RE-ESTABLISH ATROPINIZATION PROMPTLY (MORGAN, RECOGNITION AND MANAGEMENT OF PESTICIDE POISONINGS, 3RD ED.). ADMINISTRATION OF ANTIDOTE MUST BE PERFORMED BY QUALIFIED MEDICAL PERSONNEL.

REACTIVITY

REACTIVITY: NO DATA AVAILABLE.

INCOMPATIBILITIES: TIRPATE: OXIDIZERS (STRONG): FIRE AND EXPLOSION HAZARD.

DECOMPOSITION: THERMAL DECOMPOSITION MAY RELEASE TOXIC AND/OR HAZARDOUS GASES.

POLYMERIZATION: HAZARDOUS POLYMERIZATION HAS NOT BEEN REPORTED TO OCCUR UNDER NORMAL TEMPERATURES AND PRESSURES.

STORAGE AND DISPOSAL

OBSERVE ALL FEDERAL, STATE AND LOCAL REGULATIONS WHEN STORING OR DISPOSING OF THIS SUBSTANCE. FOR ASSISTANCE, CONTACT THE DISTRICT DIRECTOR OF THE ENVIRONMENTAL PROTECTION AGENCY.

STORAGE

STORE IN ACCORDANCE WITH 40 CFR 165 RECOMMENDED PROCEDURES FOR THE DISPOSAL AND STORAGE OF PESTICIDES AND PESTICIDE CONTAINERS.
THRESHOLD PLANNING QUANTITY (TPQ): THE SUPERFUND AMENDMENTS AND REAUTHORIZATION ACT (SARA) SECTION 302 REQUIRES THAT EACH FACILITY WHERE ANY EXTREMELY HAZARDOUS SUBSTANCE IS PRESENT IN A QUANTITY EQUAL TO OR GREATER THAN THE TPQ ESTABLISHED FOR THAT SUBSTANCE NOTIFY THE STATE EMERGENCY RESPONSE COMMISSION FOR THE STATE IN WHICH IT IS LOCATED. SECTION 303 OF SARA REQUIRES THESE FACILITIES TO PARTICIPATE IN LOCAL EMERGENCY RESPONSE PLANNING (40 CFR 355.30).
STORE AWAY FROM INCOMPATIBLE SUBSTANCES.

DISPOSAL

DISPOSAL MUST BE IN ACCORDANCE WITH 40 CFR 165 RECOMMENDED PROCEDURES FOR THE DISPOSAL AND STORAGE OF PESTICIDES AND PESTICIDE CONTAINERS.

CONDITIONS TO AVOID

NONE REPORTED.

SPILL AND LEAK PROCEDURES

OCCUPATIONAL SPILL: DO NOT TOUCH SPILLED MATERIAL. STOP LEAK IF YOU CAN DO IT WITHOUT RISK. FOR SMALL SPILLS, TAKE UP WITH SAND OR OTHER ABSORBENT MATERIAL AND PLACE INTO CONTAINERS FOR LATER DISPOSAL. FOR SMALL DRY SPILLS, WITH A CLEAN SHOVEL PLACE MATERIAL INTO CLEAN, DRY CONTAINER AND COVER. MOVE CONTAINERS FROM SPILL AREA. FOR LARGER SPILLS, DIKE FAR AHEAD OF SPILL FOR LATER DISPOSAL. KEEP UNNECESSARY PEOPLE AWAY. ISOLATE HAZARD AREA AND DENY ENTRY.
REPORTABLE QUANTITY (RQ): 1 POUND THE SUPERFUND AMENDMENTS AND REAUTHORIZATION ACT (SARA) SECTION 304 REQUIRES THAT A RELEASE EQUAL TO OR GREATER THAN THE REPORTABLE QUANTITY FOR THIS SUBSTANCE BE IMMEDIATELY REPORTED TO THE LOCAL EMERGENCY PLANNING COMMITTEE AND THE STATE EMERGENCY RESPONSE COMMISSION (40 CFR 355.40). IF THE RELEASE OF THIS SUBSTANCE IS REPORTABLE UNDER CERCLA SECTION 103, THE NATIONAL RESPONSE CENTER MUST BE NOTIFIED IMMEDIATELY AT (800) 424-8802 OR (202) 426-2675 IN THE METROPOLITAN WASHINGTON, D.C. AREA (40 CFR 302.6).

PROTECTIVE EQUIPMENT

VENTILATION: PROVIDE LOCAL EXHAUST OR PROCESS ENCLOSURE VENTILATION SYSTEM.

RESPIRATOR: THE FOLLOWING RESPIRATORS ARE RECOMMENDED BASED ON INFORMATION FOUND IN THE PHYSICAL DATA, TOXICITY AND HEALTH EFFECTS SECTIONS. THEY ARE RANKED IN ORDER FROM MINIMUM TO MAXIMUM RESPIRATORY PROTECTION. THE SPECIFIC RESPIRATOR SELECTED MUST BE BASED ON CONTAMINATION LEVELS FOUND IN THE WORK PLACE, MUST NOT EXCEED THE WORKING LIMITS OF THE RESPIRATOR AND BE JOINTLY APPROVED BY THE NATIONAL INSTITUTE FOR OCCUPATIONAL SAFETY AND HEALTH AND THE MINE SAFETY AND HEALTH ADMINISTRATION (NIOSH-MSHA).
TYPE 'C' SUPPLIED-AIR RESPIRATOR WITH A FULL FACEPIECE OPERATED IN PRESSURE-DEMAND OR OTHER POSITIVE PRESSURE MODE OR WITH A FULL FACEPIECE, HELMET OR HOOD OPERATED IN CONTINOUS-FLOW MODE.
SELF-CONTAINED BREATHING APPARATUS WITH A FULL FACEPIECE OPERATED IN PRESSURE-DEMAND OR OTHER POSITIVE PRESSURE MODE. FOR FIREFIGHTING AND OTHER IMMEDIATELY DANGEROUS TO LIFE OR HEALTH CONDITIONS:
SELF-CONTAINED BREATHING APPARATUS WITH FULL FACEPIECE OPERATED IN

PRESSURE-DEMAND OR OTHER POSITIVE PRESSURE MODE.
SUPPLIED-AIR RESPIRATOR WITH FULL FACEPIECE AND OPERATED IN PRESSURE-DEMAND OR OTHER POSITIVE PRESSURE MODE IN COMBINATION WITH AN AUXILIARY SELF-CONTAINED BREATHING APPARATUS OPERATED IN PRESSURE-DEMAND OR OTHER POSITIVE PRESSURE MODE.

CLOTHING: EMPLOYEE MUST WEAR APPROPRIATE PROTECTIVE (IMPERVIOUS) CLOTHING AND EQUIPMENT TO PREVENT ANY POSSIBILITY OF SKIN CONTACT WITH THIS SUBSTANCE.

GLOVES: EMPLOYEE MUST WEAR APPROPRIATE PROTECTIVE GLOVES TO PREVENT CONTACT WITH THIS SUBSTANCE.

EYE PROTECTION: EMPLOYEE MUST WEAR SPLASH-PROOF OR DUST-RESISTANT SAFETY GOGGLES AND A FACESHIELD TO PREVENT CONTACT WITH THIS SUBSTANCE.

EMERGENCY WASH FACILITIES: WHERE THERE IS ANY POSSIBILITY THAT AN EMPLOYEE'S EYES AND/OR SKIN MAY BE EXPOSED TO THIS SUBSTANCE, THE EMPLOYER SHOULD PROVIDE AN EYE WASH FOUNTAIN AND QUICK DRENCH SHOWER WITHIN THE IMMEDIATE WORK AREA FOR EMERGENCY USE.

AUTHORIZED BY- OCCUPATIONAL HEALTH SERVICES, INC.
CREATION DATE: 05/18/90 ***REVISION DATE:*** 06/12/90

MATERIAL SAFETY DATA SHEET

OCCUPATIONAL HEALTH SERVICES, INC.
AGRICULTURE AND PESTICIDE DIVISION
450 SEVENTH AVENUE, SUITE 2407
NEW YORK, NEW YORK 10123
1-800-445-MSDS OR (212) 967-1100

EMERGENCY CONTACT:
JOHN S. BRANSFORD, JR. (615) 292-1180

SUBSTANCE IDENTIFICATION

CAS-NUMBER 682-80-4
SUBSTANCE: DEMEPHION-O
TRADE NAMES/SYNONYMS: PHOSPHOROTHIOIC ACID, O,O-DIMETHYL O-(2(METHYLTHIO)ETHYL)ESTER; O,O-DIMETHYL O-2-METHYLTHIOETHYL PHOSPHOROTHIOATE; O,O-DIMETHYL O-(2-(METHYLTHIO)ETHYL)PHOSPHOROTHIOATE; PST73093
CHEMICAL FAMILY: PHOSPHOROTHIOATE
MOLECULAR FORMULA: C5-H13-O3-P-S2
MOLECULAR WEIGHT: 216.27
CERCLA RATINGS (SCALE 0-3): HEALTH=3 FIRE=U REACTIVITY=U PERSISTENCE=1
NFPA RATINGS (SCALE 0-4): HEALTH=3 FIRE=U REACTIVITY=U

COMPONENTS AND CONTAMINANTS

COMPONENT: DEMEPHION-O ***PERCENT:*** 100.0
CAS# 682-80-4
OTHER CONTAMINANTS: NONE
EXPOSURE LIMITS: NO OCCUPATIONAL EXPOSURE LIMITS ESTABLISHED BY OSHA, ACGIH, OR NIOSH.

PHYSICAL DATA

DESCRIPTION: LIQUID ***BOILING POINT:*** 225 F (107 C) @ 0.1 MMHG DECOMPOSES
SPECIFIC GRAVITY: 1.198 @ 20 C ***EVAPORATION RATE:*** NOT AVAILABLE
SOLUBILITY IN WATER: 300 PPM
SOLVENT SOLUBILITY: MISCIBLE WITH MANY ORGANIC SOLVENTS EXCEPT ALIPHATIC HYDROCARBONS

FIRE AND EXPLOSION DATA

FIRE AND EXPLOSION HAZARD: UNKNOWN FIRE AND EXPLOSION HAZARD.
FIREFIGHTING MEDIA: DRY CHEMICAL, CARBON DIOXIDE, HALON, WATER SPRAY OR STANDARD FOAM (1987 EMERGENCY RESPONSE GUIDEBOOK, DOT P 5800.4).
FOR LARGER FIRES, USE WATER SPRAY, FOG OR STANDARD FOAM (1987 EMERGENCY RESPONSE GUIDEBOOK, DOT P 5800.4).
FIREFIGHTING: MOVE CONTAINERS FROM FIRE AREA IF POSSIBLE. FIGHT FIRE FROM MAXIMUM DISTANCE. STAY AWAY FROM STORAGE TANK ENDS. DIKE FIRE CONTROL WATER FOR LATER DISPOSAL. DO NOT SCATTER MATERIAL (1987 EMERGENCY RESPONSE GUIDEBOOK, DOT P 5800.4, GUIDE PAGE 55).
EXTINGUISH ONLY IF FLOW CAN BE STOPPED. EXTINGUISH USING AGENT INDICATED. USE FLOODING AMOUNTS OF WATER AS A FOG. COOL CONTAINERS WITH FLOODING AMOUNTS OF WATER FROM AS FAR A DISTANCE AS POSSIBLE. AVOID BREATHING POISONOUS VAPORS, KEEP UPWIND. CONSIDER EVACUATION OF DOWNWIND AREA IF MATERIAL IS LEAKING.

TOXICITY

DEMEPHION-O: TOXICITY DATA: >50 MG/KG ORAL-RAT LD50 (85JDAH).
CARCINOGEN STATUS: NONE. ACUTE TOXICITY LEVEL: TOXIC BY INGESTION.
TARGET EFFECTS: CHOLINESTERASE INHIBITOR. POISONING MAY AFFECT THE NERVOUS SYSTEM.* AT INCREASED RISK FROM EXPOSURE: PERSONS WITH RESPIRATORY AILMENTS, RECENT EXPOSURE TO CHOLINESTERASE INHIBITORS OR IMPAIRED CHOLINESTERASE PRODUCTION, OR LIVER MALFUNCTION.* ADDITIONAL DATA: MAY CROSS THE PLACENTA. HIGH ENVIRONMENTAL TEMPERATURES OR EXPOSURE OF THE CHEMICAL TO VISIBLE OR ULTRAVIOLET LIGHT MAY ENHANCE THE TOXICITY. INTERACTIONS WITH MEDICATIONS MAY OCCUR.*
* MAY BE BASED ON GENERAL INFORMATION ON ORGANOPHOSPHATES.

HEALTH EFFECTS AND FIRST AID

INHALATION: DEMEPHION-O: SEE INFORMATION ON ORGANOPHOSPHATES.
ORGANOPHOSPHATES: CHOLINESTERASE INHIBITOR. **ACUTE EXPOSURE-** WHEN INHALED, THE FIRST EFFECTS OF CHOLINESTERASE INHIBITORS ARE USUALLY RESPIRATORY AND MAY INCLUDE NASAL HYPEREMIA AND WATERY DISCHARGE, COUGH, CHEST DISCOMFORT, DYSPNEA, AND WHEEZING DUE TO INCREASED BRONCHIAL SECRETIONS AND BRONCHOCONSTRICTION. IF SUFFICIENT AMOUNTS ARE ABSORBED, OTHER SYSTEMIC EFFECTS MAY BEGIN WITHIN A FEW MINUTES OR BE DELAYED FOR UP TO 12 HOURS. SYMPTOMS MAY INCLUDE PALLOR, NAUSEA, VOMITING, DIARRHEA, ABDOMINAL CRAMPS, HEADACHE, DIZZINESS, OCULAR PAIN, BLURRED VISION, MIOSIS OR IN SOME CASES, ESPECIALLY INITIALLY, MYDRIASIS, LACRIMATION, SALIVATION, SWEATING, AND CONFUSION. OTHER REPORTED CENTRAL NERVOUS SYSTEM OR NEUROMUSCULAR EFFECTS MAY INCLUDE ATAXIA, SLURRED SPEECH, AREFLEXIA, WEAKNESS, FATIGUE, FASCICULATIONS, TWITCHING, TREMORS POSSIBLY OF THE TONGUE AND EYELIDS, AND EVENTUALLY PARALYSIS OF THE EXTREMITIES AND POSSIBLY OF THE RESPIRATORY MUSCLES. IN SEVERE CASES THERE MAY ALSO BE INVOLUNTARY DEFECATION AND URINATION, CYANOSIS, PSYCHOSIS, HYPERGLYCEMIA, ACUTE PANCREATITIS, CARDIAC IRREGULARITIES, PULMONARY EDEMA, UNCONSCIOUSNESS, CONVULSIONS, AND COMA. DEATH IS PRIMARILY DUE TO RESPIRATORY FAILURE, ALTHOUGH CARDIOVASCULAR EFFECTS INCLUDING CARDIAC ARREST MAY ALSO BE IMPLICATED. LONG TERM SEQUELAE ARE RARE BUT MAY INCLUDE NEUROPSYCHIATRIC DISORDERS AND MYOPATHY WITH MUSCLE TENDERNESS. SOME ORGANOPHOSPHATES MAY CAUSE A DELAYED NEUROPATHY BEGINNING 1-4 WEEKS AFTER AN ACUTE EXPOSURE WHICH MAY OR MAY NOT HAVE CAUSED ACUTE CHOLINERGIC EFFECTS. NUMBNESS, TINGLING, WEAKNESS AND CRAMPING BEGINNING SYMMETRICALLY IN THE LOWER LIMBS MAY PROGRESS TO ATAXIA AND PARALYSIS. IN SEVERE CASES, UPPER LIMB INVOLVEMENT IS POSSIBLE AND FLACCID PARALYSIS MAY PROGRESS TO SPASTIC PARALYSIS WITH EXAGGERATED REFLEXES. IMPROVEMENT MAY OCCUR OVER MONTHS TO YEARS, BUT SOME RESIDUAL IMPAIRMENT USUALLY REMAINS.
CHRONIC EXPOSURE- REPEATED OR PROLONGED EXPOSURE MAY RESULT IN THE EFFECTS OF ACUTE EXPOSURE INCLUDING THE DELAYED NEUROPATHY. OTHER EFFECTS REPORTED IN WORKERS REPEATEDLY EXPOSED INCLUDE IMPAIRED MEMORY AND CONCENTRATION, ACUTE PSYCHOSIS, SEVERE DEPRESSIONS, IRRITABILTY, CONFUSION, APATHY, EMOTIONAL LABILITY, SOCIAL WITHDRAWAL, CONFUSION, HEADACHE, SPEECH DIFFICULTIES, DELAYED REACTION TIMES, SPATIAL DISORIENTATION, NIGHTMARES, SLEEPWALKING, AND DROWSINESS OR INSOMNIA. AN INFLUENZA-LIKE CONDITION WITH HEADACHE, NAUSEA, WEAKNESS, ANOREXIA AND MALAISE HAS ALSO BEEN REPORTED.

FIRST AID- REMOVE FROM EXPOSURE AREA TO FRESH AIR IMMEDIATELY. IF BREATHING HAS STOPPED, GIVE ARTIFICIAL RESPIRATION. MAINTAIN AIRWAY AND BLOOD PRESSURE AND ADMINISTER OXYGEN IF AVAILABLE. KEEP AFFECTED PERSON WARM AND AT REST. TREAT SYMPTOMATICALLY AND SUPPORTIVELY. ADMINISTRATION OF OXYGEN SHOULD BE PERFORMED BY QUALIFIED PERSONNEL. GET MEDICAL ATTENTION IMMEDIATELY.

SKIN CONTACT: DEMEPHION-O: SEE INFORMATION ON ORGANOPHOSPHATES.
ORGANOPHOSPHATES: CHOLINESTERASE INHIBITOR. **ACUTE EXPOSURE-** LOCALIZED SWEATING AND FASCICULATIONS MAY OCCUR AT THE SITE OF CONTACT. IF SUFFICIENT AMOUNTS ARE ABSORBED, OTHER EFFECTS OF CHOLINESTERASE INHIBITION AS DESCRIBED IN ACUTE INHALATION MAY OCCUR. SYMPTOMS MAY BE DELAYED 2-3 HOURS, BUT USUALLY NO MORE THAN 12 HOURS. THE RATE OF ABSORPTION IS INCREASED BY THE PRESENCE OF DERMATITIS OR HIGH AMBIENT TEMPERATURES. DELAYED NEUROPATHY IS ALSO POSSIBLE. **CHRONIC EXPOSURE-** REPEATED OR PROLONGED EXPOSURE MAY CAUSE EFFECTS AS DESCRIBED IN ACUTE EXPOSURE. SOME ORGANOPHOSPHATES MAY CAUSE SENSITIZATION.

FIRST AID- REMOVE CONTAMINATED CLOTHING IMMEDIATELY. WASH CONTAMINATED AREAS WITH SOAP AND WATER FOLLOWED BY ALCOHOL (ARENA, POISONING, 4TH ED.). EMERGENCY PERSONNEL SHOULD WEAR GLOVES AND

AVOID CONTAMINATION. TREAT RESPIRATORY DIFFICULTY WITH ARTIFICIAL RESPIRATION. GET MEDICAL ATTENTION IMMEDIATELY.

EYE CONTACT: DEMEPHION-O: SEE INFORMATION ON ORGANOPHOSPHATES. ORGANOPHOSPHATES: CHOLINESTERASE INHIBITOR. **ACUTE EXPOSURE-** DIRECT CONTACT MAY CAUSE PAIN, HYPEREMIA, LACRIMATION, TWITCHING OF THE EYELIDS, MIOSIS, AND CILIARY MUSCLE SPASM WITH LOSS OF ACCOMODATION, BLURRED OR DIMMED VISION AND BROWACHE. SOMETIMES MYDRIASIS MAY OCCUR INSTEAD OF MIOSIS. WITH SUFFICIENT EXPOSURE, OTHER SYMPTOMS OF CHOLINESTERASE INHIBITION AS DESCRIBED IN ACUTE INHALATION MAY OCCUR. **CHRONIC EXPOSURE-** REPEATED OR PROLONGED EXPOSURE MAY CAUSE EFFECTS AS DESCRIBED IN ACUTE EXPOSURE. SOME COMPOUNDS HAVE CAUSED TOXIC EFFECTS ON THE CRYSTALLINE LENS, CONJUNCTIVAL THICKENING AND OBSTRUCTION OF THE NASOLACRIMAL CANALS WHEN USED AS MIOTIC EYEDROPS.

FIRST AID- IRRIGATE EYES WITH WATER OR SALINE SOLUTION. IF SYMPTOMS OF POISONING OCCUR, TREAT RESPIRATORY DIFFICULTY WITH ARTIFICIAL RESPIRATION AND OXYGEN. OBSERVE PATIENT FOR AT LEAST 24-36 HOURS (GOSSELIN, CLINICAL TOXICOLOGY OF COMMERCIAL PRODUCTS, 5TH ED.). GET MEDICAL ATTENTION IMMEDIATELY. OXYGEN SHOULD BE ADMINISTERED BY QUALIFIED MEDICAL PERSONNEL.

INGESTION: DEMEPHION-O: TOXIC. SEE INFORMATION ON ORGANOPHOSPHATES. ORGANOPHOSPHATES: CHOLINESTERASE INHIBITOR. **ACUTE EXPOSURE-** WHEN INGESTED, THE FIRST EFFECTS MAY BE NAUSEA, VOMITING, ANOREXIA, ABDOMINAL CRAMPS AND DIARRHEA. GASTROINTESTINAL ABSORPTION MAY CAUSE SYMPTOMS OF CHOLINESTERASE INHIBITION AS DESCRIBED IN ACUTE INHALATION. SYMPTOMS MAY BEGIN WITHIN MINUTES OR BE DELAYED FOR HOURS. DELAYED EFFECTS INCLUDING NEUROPATHY MAY ALSO OCCUR. **CHRONIC EXPOSURE-** REPEATED INGESTION MAY CAUSE EFFECTS AS DESCRIBED IN ACUTE EXPOSURE.

FIRST AID- IF PERSON IS ALERT AND RESPIRATION IS NOT DEPRESSED, GIVE SYRUP OF IPECAC FOLLOWED BY WATER (IF VOMITING OCCURS, KEEP HEAD BELOW HIPS TO PREVENT ASPIRATION). IF CONSCIOUSNESS LEVEL DECLINES OR VOMITING HAS NOT OCCURRED IN 15 MINUTES EMPTY STOMACH BY GASTRIC LAVAGE WITH THE AID OF CUFFED ENDOTRACHEAL TUBE USING ISOTONIC SALINE OR 5% SODIUM BICARBONATE FOLLOW WITH ACTIVATED CHARCOAL. ESTABLISH AND MAINTAIN AIRWAY. TREAT RESPIRATORY DIFFICULTY WITH ARTIFICIAL RESPIRATION AND OXYGEN. DO NOT GIVE MORPHINE, AMINOPHYLLINE, PHENOTHIAZINES, RESERPINE, FUROSEMIDE, OR ETHACRYNIC ACID (MORGAN, RECOGNITION AND MANAGEMENT OF PESTICIDE POISONINGS, 3RD ED.). TREAT SYMPTOMATICALLY AND SUPPORTIVELY. ADMINISTRATION OF OXYGEN AND LAVAGE MUST BE PERFORMED BY QUALIFIED MEDICAL PERSONNEL. GET MEDICAL ATTENTION IMMEDIATELY.

ANTIDOTE: THE FOLLOWING ANTIDOTE(S) HAVE BEEN RECOMMENDED. HOWEVER, THE DECISION AS TO WHETHER THE SEVERITY OF POISONING REQUIRES ADMINISTRATION OF ANY ANTIDOTE AND ACTUAL DOSE REQUIRED SHOULD BE MADE BY QUALIFIED MEDICAL PERSONNEL.

FOR CHOLINESTERASE INHIBITORS: ESTABLISH CLEAR AIRWAY AND TISSUE OXYGENATION BY ASPIRATION OF SECRETIONS, AND IF NECESSARY, BY ASSISTED PULMONARY VENTILATION WITH OXYGEN. IMPROVE TISSUE OXYGENATION AS MUCH AS POSSIBLE BEFORE ADMINISTERING ATROPINE TO MINIMIZE THE RISK OF VENTRICULAR FIBRILLATION. ADMINISTER ATROPINE SULFATE INTRAVENOUSLY, OR INTRAMUSCULARLY IF IV INJECTION IS NOT POSSIBLE. IN MODERATELY SEVERE POISONING ADMINISTER ATROPINE SULFATE, 0.4-2.0 MG REPEATED EVERY 15 MINUTES UNTIL ATROPINIZATION IS ACHIEVED (TACHYCARDIA, FLUSHING, DRY MOUTH, MYDRIASIS). MAINTAIN ATROPINIZATION BY REPEATED DOSES FOR 2-12 HOURS, OR LONGER, DEPENDING ON THE SEVERITY OF POISONING. THE APPEARANCE OF RALES IN THE LUNG BASES, MIOSIS, SALIVATION, NAUSEA, BRADYCARDIA, ARE ALL INDICATIONS OF INADEQUATE ATROPINIZATION. SEVERELY POISONED INDIVIDUALS MAY EXHIBIT REMARKABLE TOLERANCE TO ATROPINE; TWO OR MORE TIMES THE DOSAGES SUGGESTED ABOVE MAY BE NEEDED. PERSONS NOT POISONED OR ONLY SLIGHTLY POISONED, HOWEVER, MAY DEVELOP SIGNS OF ATROPINE TOXICITY FROM SUCH LARGE DOSAGES: FEVER, MUSCLE FIBRILLATIONS, AND DELIRIUM ARE THE MAIN SIGNS OF ATROPINE TOXICITY. IF THESE SIGNS APPEAR WHILE THE PATIENT IS FULLY ATROPINIZED, ATROPINE ADMINISTRATION SHOULD BE DISCONTINUED, AT LEAST TEMPORARILY. OBSERVE TREATED PATIENTS CLOSELY AT LEAST 24 HOURS TO INSURE THAT SYMPTOMS (POSSIBLY PULMONARY EDEMA) DO NOT RECUR AS ATROPINIZATION WEARS OFF. IN VERY SEVERE POISONINGS, METABOLIC DISPOSITION OF TOXICANT MAY REQUIRE SEVERAL HOURS OR DAYS DURING WHICH ATROPINIZATION MUST BE MAINTAINED. MARKEDLY LOWER LEVELS OF URINARY METABOLITES INDICATE THAT ATROPINE DOSAGE CAN BE TAPERED OFF. AS DOSAGE IS REDUCED, CHECK THE LUNG BASES FREQUENTLY FOR RALES. IF RALES ARE HEARD OR OTHER SYMPTOMS RETURN, RE-ESTABLISH ATROPINIZATION PROMPTLY (MORGAN, RECOGNITION AND MANAGEMENT OF PESTICIDE POISONINGS, 3RD ED.). ADMINISTRATION OF ANTIDOTE MUST BE PERFORMED BY QUALIFIED MEDICAL PERSONNEL.

IN CASES OF SEVERE POISONING BY ORGANOPHOSPHATE PESTICIDES IN WHICH RESPIRATORY DEPRESSION, MUSCLE WEAKNESS AND TWITCHINGS ARE SEVERE, GIVE PRALIDOXIME (PROTOPAM-AYERST, 2-PAM), 1.0 GRAM INTRAVENOUSLY AT NO MORE THAN 0.5 GRAM PER MINUTE. DOSAGE OF PRALIDOXIME MAY BE REPEATED IN 1-2 HOURS, THEN AT 10-12 HOUR INTERVALS IF NEEDED. IN VERY SEVERE POISONINGS, DOSAGE RATES MAY BE DOUBLED. TREATMENT WITH PRALIDOXIME WILL BE MOST EFFECTIVE IF GIVEN WITHIN THIRTY-SIX HOURS AFTER POISONING (MORGAN, RECOGNITION AND MANAGEMENT OF PESTICIDE POISONINGS, 3RD ED.). ANTIDOTE SHOULD BE ADMINISTERED BY QUALIFIED MEDICAL PERSONNEL.

REACTIVITY

REACTIVITY: NO DATA AVAILABLE.

INCOMPATIBILITIES: DEMEPHION-O: NO DATA AVAILABLE.

DECOMPOSITION: THERMAL DECOMPOSITION MAY RELEASE TOXIC AND/OR HAZARDOUS GASES.

POLYMERIZATION: HAZARDOUS POLYMERIZATION HAS NOT BEEN REPORTED TO OCCUR UNDER NORMAL TEMPERATURES AND PRESSURES.

STORAGE AND DISPOSAL

OBSERVE ALL FEDERAL, STATE AND LOCAL REGULATIONS WHEN STORING OR DISPOSING OF THIS SUBSTANCE. FOR ASSISTANCE, CONTACT THE DISTRICT DIRECTOR OF THE ENVIRONMENTAL PROTECTION AGENCY.

STORAGE

STORE IN ACCORDANCE WITH 40 CFR 165 RECOMMENDED PROCEDURES FOR THE DISPOSAL AND STORAGE OF PESTICIDES AND PESTICIDE CONTAINERS.

DISPOSAL

DISPOSAL MUST BE IN ACCORDANCE WITH 40 CFR 165 RECOMMENDED PROCEDURES FOR THE DISPOSAL AND STORAGE OF PESTICIDES AND PESTICIDE CONTAINERS.

CONDITIONS TO AVOID

NONE REPORTED.

SPILL AND LEAK PROCEDURES

OCCUPATIONAL SPILL: DO NOT TOUCH SPILLED MATERIAL. STOP LEAK IF YOU CAN DO IT WITHOUT RISK. FOR SMALL SPILLS, TAKE UP WITH SAND OR OTHER ABSORBENT MATERIAL AND PLACE INTO CONTAINERS FOR LATER DISPOSAL. FOR SMALL DRY SPILLS, WITH A CLEAN SHOVEL PLACE MATERIAL INTO CLEAN, DRY CONTAINER AND COVER. MOVE CONTAINERS FROM SPILL AREA. FOR LARGER SPILLS, DIKE FAR AHEAD OF SPILL FOR LATER DISPOSAL. KEEP UNNECESSARY PEOPLE AWAY. ISOLATE HAZARD AREA AND DENY ENTRY.

PROTECTIVE EQUIPMENT

VENTILATION: PROCESS ENCLOSURE RECOMMENDED.

RESPIRATOR: THE FOLLOWING RESPIRATORS ARE RECOMMENDED BASED ON INFORMATION FOUND IN THE PHYSICAL DATA, TOXICITY AND HEALTH EFFECTS SECTIONS. THEY ARE RANKED IN ORDER FROM MINIMUM TO MAXIMUM RESPIRATORY PROTECTION. THE SPECIFIC RESPIRATOR SELECTED MUST BE BASED ON CONTAMINATION LEVELS FOUND IN THE WORK PLACE, MUST NOT EXCEED THE WORKING LIMITS OF THE RESPIRATOR AND BE JOINTLY APPROVED BY THE NATIONAL INSTITUTE FOR OCCUPATIONAL SAFETY AND HEALTH AND THE MINE SAFETY AND HEALTH ADMINISTRATION (NIOSH-MSHA).

TYPE 'C' SUPPLIED-AIR RESPIRATOR WITH A FULL FACEPIECE OPERATED IN PRESSURE-DEMAND OR OTHER POSITIVE PRESSURE MODE OR WITH A FULL FACEPIECE, HELMET OR HOOD OPERATED IN CONTINOUS-FLOW MODE.

SELF-CONTAINED BREATHING APPARATUS WITH A FULL FACEPIECE OPERATED IN PRESSURE-DEMAND OR OTHER POSITIVE PRESSURE MODE.

FOR FIREFIGHTING AND OTHER IMMEDIATELY DANGEROUS TO LIFE OR HEALTH CONDITIONS:

SELF-CONTAINED BREATHING APPARATUS WITH FULL FACEPIECE OPERATED IN PRESSURE-DEMAND OR OTHER POSITIVE PRESSURE MODE.

SUPPLIED-AIR RESPIRATOR WITH FULL FACEPIECE AND OPERATED IN PRESSURE-DEMAND OR OTHER POSITIVE PRESSURE MODE IN COMBINATION WITH AN AUXILIARY SELF-CONTAINED BREATHING APPARATUS OPERATED IN PRESSURE-DEMAND OR OTHER POSITIVE PRESSURE MODE.

CLOTHING: EMPLOYEE MUST WEAR APPROPRIATE PROTECTIVE (IMPERVIOUS) CLOTHING AND EQUIPMENT TO PREVENT ANY POSSIBILITY OF SKIN CONTACT WITH THIS SUBSTANCE.

GLOVES: EMPLOYEE MUST WEAR APPROPRIATE PROTECTIVE GLOVES TO PREVENT CONTACT WITH THIS SUBSTANCE.

EYE PROTECTION: EMPLOYEE MUST WEAR SPLASH-PROOF OR DUST-RESISTANT SAFETY GOGGLES AND A FACESHIELD TO PREVENT CONTACT WITH THIS SUBSTANCE.

EMERGENCY WASH FACILITIES: WHERE THERE IS ANY POSSIBILITY THAT AN

EMPLOYEE'S EYES AND/OR SKIN MAY BE EXPOSED TO THIS SUBSTANCE, THE EMPLOYER SHOULD PROVIDE AN EYE WASH FOUNTAIN AND QUICK DRENCH SHOWER WITHIN THE IMMEDIATE WORK AREA FOR EMERGENCY USE.

AUTHORIZED BY- OCCUPATIONAL HEALTH SERVICES, INC.
CREATION DATE: 10/04/89 ***REVISION DATE:*** 05/01/90

MATERIAL SAFETY DATA SHEET

OCCUPATIONAL HEALTH SERVICES, INC.
AGRICULTURE AND PESTICIDE DIVISION
450 SEVENTH AVENUE, SUITE 2407
NEW YORK, NEW YORK 10123
1-800-445-MSDS OR (212) 967-1100

EMERGENCY CONTACT:
JOHN S. BRANSFORD, JR. (615) 292-1180

SUBSTANCE IDENTIFICATION

CAS-NUMBER 2587-90-8
SUBSTANCE: DEMEPHION-S
TRADE NAMES/SYNONYMS: PHOSPHOROTHIOIC ACID, O,O-DIMETHYL S-(2(METHYLTHIO)ETHYL)ESTER; O,O-DIMETHYL S-2-METHYLTHIOETHYL PHOSPHOROTHIOATE; O,O-DIMETHYL S-(2-(METHYLTHIO)ETHYL)PHOSPHOROTHIOATE; ISOTINOX; PST73094
CHEMICAL FAMILY: PHOSPHOROTHIOATE
MOLECULAR FORMULA: C5-H13-O3-P-S2
MOLECULAR WEIGHT: 216.27
CERCLA RATINGS (SCALE 0-3): HEALTH=3 FIRE=U REACTIVITY=U PERSISTENCE=1
NFPA RATINGS (SCALE 0-4): HEALTH=4 FIRE=U REACTIVITY=U

COMPONENTS AND CONTAMINANTS

COMPONENT: DEMEPHION-S ***PERCENT:*** 100.0
CAS# 2587-90-8
OTHER CONTAMINANTS: NONE
EXPOSURE LIMITS: NO OCCUPATIONAL EXPOSURE LIMITS ESTABLISHED BY OSHA, ACGIH, OR NIOSH.
DEMEPHION-S: 500 POUNDS SARA SECTION 302 THRESHOLD PLANNING QUANTITY
1 POUND SARA SECTION 304 REPORTABLE QUANTITY

PHYSICAL DATA

DESCRIPTION: LIQUID ***BOILING POINT:*** 149 F (65 C) @ 0.1 MMHG DECOMPOSES
SPECIFIC GRAVITY: 1.218 @ 25 C ***EVAPORATION RATE:*** NOT AVAILABLE
SOLUBILITY IN WATER: 3000 PPM
SOLVENT SOLUBILITY: MISCIBLE WITH MANY ORGANIC SOLVENTS EXCEPT ALIPHATIC HYDROCARBONS

FIRE AND EXPLOSION DATA

FIRE AND EXPLOSION HAZARD: UNKNOWN FIRE AND EXPLOSION HAZARD.
FIREFIGHTING MEDIA: DRY CHEMICAL, CARBON DIOXIDE, HALON, WATER SPRAY OR STANDARD FOAM (1987 EMERGENCY RESPONSE GUIDEBOOK, DOT P 5800.4). FOR LARGER FIRES, USE WATER SPRAY, FOG OR STANDARD FOAM (1987 EMERGENCY RESPONSE GUIDEBOOK, DOT P 5800.4).
FIREFIGHTING: MOVE CONTAINERS FROM FIRE AREA IF POSSIBLE. FIGHT FIRE FROM MAXIMUM DISTANCE. STAY AWAY FROM STORAGE TANK ENDS. DIKE FIRE CONTROL WATER FOR LATER DISPOSAL. DO NOT SCATTER MATERIAL (1987 EMERGENCY RESPONSE GUIDEBOOK, DOT P 5800.4, GUIDE PAGE 55). EXTINGUISH ONLY IF FLOW CAN BE STOPPED. EXTINGUISH USING AGENT INDICATED. USE FLOODING AMOUNTS OF WATER AS A FOG. COOL CONTAINERS WITH FLOODING AMOUNTS OF WATER FROM AS FAR A DISTANCE AS POSSIBLE. AVOID BREATHING POISONOUS VAPORS, KEEP UPWIND. CONSIDER EVACUATION OF DOWNWIND AREA IF MATERIAL IS LEAKING.

TRANSPORTATION DATA

DEPARTMENT OF TRANSPORTATION HAZARD CLASSIFICATION 49 CFR 172.101: POISON B
DEPARTMENT OF TRANSPORTATION LABELING REQUIREMENTS 49 CFR 172.101 AND SUBPART E: POISON
DEPARTMENT OF TRANSPORTATION PACKAGING REQUIREMENTS: 49 CFR 173.346 EXCEPTIONS: 49 CFR 173.345

TOXICITY

DEMEPHION-S: TOXICITY DATA: 68 MG/KG SKIN-RAT LD50; 20 MG/KG ORAL-RAT LD50; 23 MG/KG ORAL-MOUSE LD50; 37 MG/KG ORAL-DOG LD50; 200 MG/KG SUBCUTANEOUS-MOUSE LDLO; MUTAGENIC DATA (RTECS). CARCINOGEN STATUS: NONE. ACUTE TOXICITY LEVEL: HIGHLY TOXIC BY INGESTION AND DERMAL ABSORPTION. TARGET EFFECTS: CHOLINESTERASE INHIBITOR. POISONING MAY AFFECT THE NERVOUS SYSTEM.* AT INCREASED RISK FROM EXPOSURE: PERSONS WITH RESPIRATORY AILMENTS, RECENT EXPOSURE TO CHOLINESTERASE INHIBITORS OR IMPAIRED CHOLINESTERASE PRODUCTION, OR LIVER MALFUNCTION.* ADDITIONAL DATA: MAY CROSS THE PLACENTA. HIGH ENVIRONMENTAL TEMPERATURES OR EXPOSURE OF THE CHEMICAL TO VISIBLE OR ULTRAVIOLET LIGHT MAY ENHANCE THE TOXICITY. INTERACTIONS WITH MEDICATIONS MAY OCCUR.*
* MAY BE BASED ON GENERAL INFORMATION ON ORGANOPHOSPHATES.

HEALTH EFFECTS AND FIRST AID

INHALATION: DEMEPHION-S: SEE INFORMATION ON ORGANOPHOSPHATES.
ORGANOPHOSPHATES: CHOLINESTERASE INHIBITOR. **ACUTE EXPOSURE-** WHEN INHALED, THE FIRST EFFECTS OF CHOLINESTERASE INHIBITORS ARE USUALLY RESPIRATORY AND MAY INCLUDE NASAL HYPEREMIA AND WATERY DISCHARGE, COUGH, CHEST DISCOMFORT, DYSPNEA, AND WHEEZING DUE TO INCREASED BRONCHIAL SECRETIONS AND BRONCHOCONSTRICTION. IF SUFFICIENT AMOUNTS ARE ABSORBED, OTHER SYSTEMIC EFFECTS MAY BEGIN WITHIN A FEW MINUTES OR BE DELAYED FOR UP TO 12 HOURS. SYMPTOMS MAY INCLUDE PALLOR, NAUSEA, VOMITING, DIARRHEA, ABDOMINAL CRAMPS, HEADACHE, DIZZINESS, OCULAR PAIN, BLURRED VISION, MIOSIS OR IN SOME CASES, ESPECIALLY INITIALLY, MYDRIASIS, LACRIMATION, SALIVATION, SWEATING, AND CONFUSION. OTHER REPORTED CENTRAL NERVOUS SYSTEM OR NEUROMUSCULAR EFFECTS MAY INCLUDE ATAXIA, SLURRED SPEECH, AREFLEXIA, WEAKNESS, FATIGUE, FASCICULATIONS, TWITCHING, TREMORS POSSIBLY OF THE TONGUE AND EYELIDS, AND EVENTUALLY PARALYSIS OF THE EXTREMITIES AND POSSIBLY OF THE RESPIRATORY MUSCLES. IN SEVERE CASES THERE MAY ALSO BE INVOLUNTARY DEFECATION AND URINATION, CYANOSIS, PSYCHOSIS, HYPERGLYCEMIA, ACUTE PANCREATITIS, CARDIAC IRREGULARITIES, PULMONARY EDEMA, UNCONSCIOUSNESS, CONVULSIONS, AND COMA. DEATH IS PRIMARILY DUE TO RESPIRATORY FAILURE, ALTHOUGH CARDIOVASCULAR EFFECTS INCLUDING CARDIAC ARREST MAY ALSO BE IMPLICATED. LONG TERM SEQUELAE ARE RARE BUT MAY INCLUDE NEUROPSYCHIATRIC DISORDERS AND MYOPATHY WITH MUSCLE TENDERNESS. SOME ORGANOPHOSPHATES MAY CAUSE A DELAYED NEUROPATHY BEGINNING 1-4 WEEKS AFTER AN ACUTE EXPOSURE WHICH MAY OR MAY NOT HAVE CAUSED ACUTE CHOLINERGIC EFFECTS. NUMBNESS, TINGLING, WEAKNESS AND CRAMPING BEGINNING SYMMETRICALLY IN THE LOWER LIMBS MAY PROGRESS TO ATAXIA AND PARALYSIS. IN SEVERE CASES, UPPER LIMB INVOLVEMENT IS POSSIBLE AND FLACCID PARALYSIS MAY PROGRESS TO SPASTIC PARALYSIS WITH EXAGGERATED REFLEXES. IMPROVEMENT MAY OCCUR OVER MONTHS TO YEARS, BUT SOME RESIDUAL IMPAIRMENT USUALLY REMAINS.
CHRONIC EXPOSURE- REPEATED OR PROLONGED EXPOSURE MAY RESULT IN THE EFFECTS OF ACUTE EXPOSURE INCLUDING THE DELAYED NEUROPATHY. OTHER EFFECTS REPORTED IN WORKERS REPEATEDLY EXPOSED INCLUDE IMPAIRED MEMORY AND CONCENTRATION, ACUTE PSYCHOSIS, SEVERE DEPRESSIONS, IRRITABILTY, CONFUSION, APATHY, EMOTIONAL LABILITY, SOCIAL WITHDRAWAL, CONFUSION, HEADACHE, SPEECH DIFFICULTIES, DELAYED REACTION TIMES, SPATIAL DISORIENTATION, NIGHTMARES, SLEEPWALKING, AND DROWSINESS OR INSOMNIA. AN INFLUENZA-LIKE CONDITION WITH HEADACHE, NAUSEA, WEAKNESS, ANOREXIA AND MALAISE HAS ALSO BEEN REPORTED.
FIRST AID- REMOVE FROM EXPOSURE AREA TO FRESH AIR IMMEDIATELY. IF BREATHING HAS STOPPED, GIVE ARTIFICIAL RESPIRATION. MAINTAIN AIRWAY AND BLOOD PRESSURE AND ADMINISTER OXYGEN IF AVAILABLE. KEEP AFFECTED PERSON WARM AND AT REST. TREAT SYMPTOMATICALLY AND SUPPORTIVELY. ADMINISTRATION OF OXYGEN SHOULD BE PERFORMED BY QUALIFIED PERSONNEL. GET MEDICAL ATTENTION IMMEDIATELY.

SKIN CONTACT: DEMEPHION-S: HIGHLY TOXIC. SEE INFORMATION ON ORGANOPHOSPHATES.
ORGANOPHOSPHATES: CHOLINESTERASE INHIBITOR. **ACUTE EXPOSURE-** LOCALIZED SWEATING AND FASCICULATIONS MAY OCCUR AT THE SITE OF CONTACT. IF SUFFICIENT AMOUNTS ARE ABSORBED, OTHER EFFECTS OF CHOLINESTERASE INHIBITION AS DESCRIBED IN ACUTE INHALATION MAY OCCUR. SYMPTOMS MAY BE DELAYED 2-3 HOURS, BUT USUALLY NO MORE THAN 12 HOURS. THE RATE OF ABSORPTION IS INCREASED BY THE PRESENCE OF DERMATITIS OR HIGH AMBIENT TEMPERATURES. DELAYED NEUROPATHY IS ALSO POSSIBLE. **CHRONIC EXPOSURE-** REPEATED OR PROLONGED EXPOSURE MAY CAUSE EFFECTS AS DESCRIBED IN ACUTE EXPOSURE. SOME ORGANOPHOSPHATES MAY CAUSE SENSITIZATION.
FIRST AID- REMOVE CONTAMINATED CLOTHING IMMEDIATELY. WASH CONTAMINATED AREAS WITH SOAP AND WATER FOLLOWED BY ALCOHOL (ARENA, POISONING, 4TH ED.). EMERGENCY PERSONNEL SHOULD WEAR GLOVES AND

AVOID CONTAMINATION. TREAT RESPIRATORY DIFFICULTY WITH ARTIFICIAL RESPIRATION. GET MEDICAL ATTENTION IMMEDIATELY.

EYE CONTACT: DEMEPHION-S: SEE INFORMATION ON ORGANOPHOSPHATES.
ORGANOPHOSPHATES: CHOLINESTERASE INHIBITOR. **ACUTE EXPOSURE-** DIRECT CONTACT MAY CAUSE PAIN, HYPEREMIA, LACRIMATION, TWITCHING OF THE EYELIDS, MIOSIS, AND CILIARY MUSCLE SPASM WITH LOSS OF ACCOMODATION, BLURRED OR DIMMED VISION AND BROWACHE. SOMETIMES MYDRIASIS MAY OCCUR INSTEAD OF MIOSIS. WITH SUFFICIENT EXPOSURE, OTHER SYMPTOMS OF CHOLINESTERASE INHIBITION AS DESCRIBED IN ACUTE INHALATION MAY OCCUR. **CHRONIC EXPOSURE-** REPEATED OR PROLONGED EXPOSURE MAY CAUSE EFFECTS AS DESCRIBED IN ACUTE EXPOSURE. SOME COMPOUNDS HAVE CAUSED TOXIC EFFECTS ON THE CRYSTALLINE LENS, CONJUNCTIVAL THICKENING AND OBSTRUCTION OF THE NASOLACRIMAL CANALS WHEN USED AS MIOTIC EYEDROPS.

FIRST AID- IRRIGATE EYES WITH WATER OR SALINE SOLUTION. IF SYMPTOMS OF POISONING OCCUR, TREAT RESPIRATORY DIFFICULTY WITH ARTIFICIAL RESPIRATION AND OXYGEN. OBSERVE PATIENT FOR AT LEAST 24-36 HOURS (GOSSELIN, CLINICAL TOXICOLOGY OF COMMERCIAL PRODUCTS, 5TH ED.). GET MEDICAL ATTENTION IMMEDIATELY. OXYGEN SHOULD BE ADMINISTERED BY QUALIFIED MEDICAL PERSONNEL.

INGESTION: DEMEPHION-S: HIGHLY TOXIC. SEE INFORMATION ON ORGANOPHOSPHATES.
ORGANOPHOSPHATES: CHOLINESTERASE INHIBITOR. **ACUTE EXPOSURE-** WHEN INGESTED, THE FIRST EFFECTS MAY BE NAUSEA, VOMITING, ANOREXIA, ABDOMINAL CRAMPS AND DIARRHEA. GASTROINTESTINAL ABSORPTION MAY CAUSE SYMPTOMS OF CHOLINESTERASE INHIBITION AS DESCRIBED IN ACUTE INHALATION. SYMPTOMS MAY BEGIN WITHIN MINUTES OR BE DELAYED FOR HOURS. DELAYED EFFECTS INCLUDING NEUROPATHY MAY ALSO OCCUR. **CHRONIC EXPOSURE-** REPEATED INGESTION MAY CAUSE EFFECTS AS DESCRIBED IN ACUTE EXPOSURE.

FIRST AID- IF PERSON IS ALERT AND RESPIRATION IS NOT DEPRESSED, GIVE SYRUP OF IPECAC FOLLOWED BY WATER (IF VOMITING OCCURS, KEEP HEAD BELOW HIPS TO PREVENT ASPIRATION). IF CONSCIOUSNESS LEVEL DECLINES OR VOMITING HAS NOT OCCURRED IN 15 MINUTES EMPTY STOMACH BY GASTRIC LAVAGE WITH THE AID OF CUFFED ENDOTRACHEAL TUBE USING ISOTONIC SALINE OR 5% SODIUM BICARBONATE FOLLOW WITH ACTIVATED CHARCOAL. ESTABLISH AND MAINTAIN AIRWAY. TREAT RESPIRATORY DIFFICULTY WITH ARTIFICIAL RESPIRATION AND OXYGEN. DO NOT GIVE MORPHINE, AMINOPHYLLINE, PHENOTHIAZINES, RESERPINE, FUROSEMIDE, OR ETHACRYNIC ACID (MORGAN, RECOGNITION AND MANAGEMENT OF PESTICIDE POISONINGS, 3RD ED.). TREAT SYMPTOMATICALLY AND SUPPORTIVELY. ADMINISTRATION OF OXYGEN AND LAVAGE MUST BE PERFORMED BY QUALIFIED MEDICAL PERSONNEL. GET MEDICAL ATTENTION IMMEDIATELY.

ANTIDOTE: THE FOLLOWING ANTIDOTE(S) HAVE BEEN RECOMMENDED. HOWEVER, THE DECISION AS TO WHETHER THE SEVERITY OF POISONING REQUIRES ADMINISTRATION OF ANY ANTIDOTE AND ACTUAL DOSE REQUIRED SHOULD BE MADE BY QUALIFIED MEDICAL PERSONNEL.
FOR CHOLINESTERASE INHIBITORS: ESTABLISH CLEAR AIRWAY AND TISSUE OXYGENATION BY ASPIRATION OF SECRETIONS, AND IF NECESSARY, BY ASSISTED PULMONARY VENTILATION WITH OXYGEN. IMPROVE TISSUE OXYGENATION AS MUCH AS POSSIBLE BEFORE ADMINISTERING ATROPINE TO MINIMIZE THE RISK OF VENTRICULAR FIBRILLATION. ADMINISTER ATROPINE SULFATE INTRAVENOUSLY, OR INTRAMUSCULARLY IF IV INJECTION IS NOT POSSIBLE. IN MODERATELY SEVERE POISONING ADMINISTER ATROPINE SULFATE, 0.4-2.0 MG REPEATED EVERY 15 MINUTES UNTIL ATROPINIZATION IS ACHIEVED (TACHYCARDIA, FLUSHING, DRY MOUTH, MYDRIASIS). MAINTAIN ATROPINIZATION BY REPEATED DOSES FOR 2-12 HOURS, OR LONGER, DEPENDING ON THE SEVERITY OF POISONING. THE APPEARANCE OF RALES IN THE LUNG BASES, MIOSIS, SALIVATION, NAUSEA, BRADYCARDIA, ARE ALL INDICATIONS OF INADEQUATE ATROPINIZATION. SEVERELY POISONED INDIVIDUALS MAY EXHIBIT REMARKABLE TOLERANCE TO ATROPINE; TWO OR MORE TIMES THE DOSAGES SUGGESTED ABOVE MAY BE NEEDED. PERSONS NOT POISONED OR ONLY SLIGHTLY POISONED, HOWEVER, MAY DEVELOP SIGNS OF ATROPINE TOXICITY FROM SUCH LARGE DOSAGES: FEVER, MUSCLE FIBRILLATIONS, AND DELIRIUM ARE THE MAIN SIGNS OF ATROPINE TOXICITY. IF THESE SIGNS APPEAR WHILE THE PATIENT IS FULLY ATROPINIZED, ATROPINE ADMINISTRATION SHOULD BE DISCONTINUED, AT LEAST TEMPORARILY. OBSERVE TREATED PATIENTS CLOSELY AT LEAST 24 HOURS TO INSURE THAT SYMPTOMS (POSSIBLY PULMONARY EDEMA) DO NOT RECUR AS ATROPINIZATION WEARS OFF. IN VERY SEVERE POISONINGS, METABOLIC DISPOSITION OF TOXICANT MAY REQUIRE SEVERAL HOURS OR DAYS DURING WHICH ATROPINIZATION MUST BE MAINTAINED. MARKEDLY LOWER LEVELS OF URINARY METABOLITES INDICATE THAT ATROPINE DOSAGE CAN BE TAPERED OFF. AS DOSAGE IS REDUCED, CHECK THE LUNG BASES FREQUENTLY FOR RALES. IF RALES ARE HEARD OR OTHER SYMPTOMS RETURN, RE-ESTABLISH ATROPINIZATION PROMPTLY (MORGAN, RECOGNITION AND MANAGEMENT OF PESTICIDE POISONINGS, 3RD ED.). ADMINISTRATION OF ANTIDOTE MUST BE PERFORMED BY QUALIFIED MEDICAL PERSONNEL.
IN CASES OF SEVERE POISONING BY ORGANOPHOSPHATE PESTICIDES IN WHICH RESPIRATORY DEPRESSION, MUSCLE WEAKNESS AND TWITCHINGS ARE SEVERE, GIVE PRALIDOXIME (PROTOPAM-AYERST, 2-PAM), 1.0 GRAM INTRAVENOUSLY AT NO MORE THAN 0.5 GRAM PER MINUTE. DOSAGE OF PRALIDOXIME MAY BE REPEATED IN 1-2 HOURS, THEN AT 10-12 HOUR INTERVALS IF NEEDED. IN VERY SEVERE POISONINGS, DOSAGE RATES MAY BE DOUBLED. TREATMENT WITH PRALIDOXIME WILL BE MOST EFFECTIVE IF GIVEN WITHIN THIRTY-SIX HOURS AFTER POISONING (MORGAN, RECOGNITION AND MANAGEMENT OF PESTICIDE POISONINGS, 3RD ED.). ANTIDOTE SHOULD BE ADMINISTERED BY QUALIFIED MEDICAL PERSONNEL.

REACTIVITY

REACTIVITY: NO DATA AVAILABLE.

INCOMPATIBILITIES: DEMEPHION-S: OXIDIZERS (STRONG): FIRE AND EXPLOSION HAZARD.

DECOMPOSITION: THERMAL DECOMPOSITION MAY RELEASE TOXIC AND/OR HAZARDOUS GASES.

POLYMERIZATION: HAZARDOUS POLYMERIZATION HAS NOT BEEN REPORTED TO OCCUR UNDER NORMAL TEMPERATURES AND PRESSURES.

STORAGE AND DISPOSAL

OBSERVE ALL FEDERAL, STATE AND LOCAL REGULATIONS WHEN STORING OR DISPOSING OF THIS SUBSTANCE. FOR ASSISTANCE, CONTACT THE DISTRICT DIRECTOR OF THE ENVIRONMENTAL PROTECTION AGENCY.

STORAGE

STORE IN ACCORDANCE WITH 40 CFR 165 RECOMMENDED PROCEDURES FOR THE DISPOSAL AND STORAGE OF PESTICIDES AND PESTICIDE CONTAINERS.
THRESHOLD PLANNING QUANTITY (TPQ): THE SUPERFUND AMENDMENTS AND REAUTHORIZATION ACT (SARA) SECTION 302 REQUIRES THAT EACH FACILITY WHERE ANY EXTREMELY HAZARDOUS SUBSTANCE IS PRESENT IN A QUANTITY EQUAL TO OR GREATER THAN THE TPQ ESTABLISHED FOR THAT SUBSTANCE NOTIFY THE STATE EMERGENCY RESPONSE COMMISSION FOR THE STATE IN WHICH IT IS LOCATED. SECTION 303 OF SARA REQUIRES THESE FACILITIES TO PARTICIPATE IN LOCAL EMERGENCY RESPONSE PLANNING (40 CFR 355.30).

DISPOSAL

DISPOSAL MUST BE IN ACCORDANCE WITH 40 CFR 165 RECOMMENDED PROCEDURES FOR THE DISPOSAL AND STORAGE OF PESTICIDES AND PESTICIDE CONTAINERS.

CONDITIONS TO AVOID

NONE REPORTED.

SPILL AND LEAK PROCEDURES

OCCUPATIONAL SPILL: DO NOT TOUCH SPILLED MATERIAL. STOP LEAK IF YOU CAN DO IT WITHOUT RISK. FOR SMALL SPILLS, TAKE UP WITH SAND OR OTHER ABSORBENT MATERIAL AND PLACE INTO CONTAINERS FOR LATER DISPOSAL. FOR SMALL DRY SPILLS, WITH A CLEAN SHOVEL PLACE MATERIAL INTO CLEAN, DRY CONTAINER AND COVER. MOVE CONTAINERS FROM SPILL AREA. FOR LARGER SPILLS, DIKE FAR AHEAD OF SPILL FOR LATER DISPOSAL. KEEP UNNECESSARY PEOPLE AWAY. ISOLATE HAZARD AREA AND DENY ENTRY.
REPORTABLE QUANTITY (RQ): 1 POUND THE SUPERFUND AMENDMENTS AND REAUTHORIZATION ACT (SARA) SECTION 304 REQUIRES THAT A RELEASE EQUAL TO OR GREATER THAN THE REPORTABLE QUANTITY FOR THIS SUBSTANCE BE IMMEDIATELY REPORTED TO THE LOCAL EMERGENCY PLANNING COMMITTEE AND THE STATE EMERGENCY RESPONSE COMMISSION (40 CFR 355.40). IF THE RELEASE OF THIS SUBSTANCE IS REPORTABLE UNDER CERCLA SECTION 103, THE NATIONAL RESPONSE CENTER MUST BE NOTIFIED IMMEDIATELY AT (800) 424-8802 OR (202) 426-2675 IN THE METROPOLITAN WASHINGTON, D.C. AREA (40 CFR 302.6).

PROTECTIVE EQUIPMENT

VENTILATION: PROCESS ENCLOSURE RECOMMENDED.

RESPIRATOR: THE FOLLOWING RESPIRATORS ARE RECOMMENDED BASED ON INFORMATION FOUND IN THE PHYSICAL DATA, TOXICITY AND HEALTH EFFECTS SECTIONS. THEY ARE RANKED IN ORDER FROM MINIMUM TO MAXIMUM RESPIRATORY PROTECTION. THE SPECIFIC RESPIRATOR SELECTED MUST BE BASED ON CONTAMINATION LEVELS FOUND IN THE WORK PLACE, MUST NOT EXCEED THE WORKING LIMITS OF THE RESPIRATOR AND BE JOINTLY APPROVED BY THE NATIONAL INSTITUTE FOR OCCUPATIONAL SAFETY AND HEALTH AND THE MINE SAFETY AND HEALTH ADMINISTRATION (NIOSH-MSHA).
TYPE 'C' SUPPLIED-AIR RESPIRATOR WITH A FULL FACEPIECE OPERATED IN PRESSURE-DEMAND OR OTHER POSITIVE PRESSURE MODE OR WITH A FULL FACEPIECE, HELMET OR HOOD OPERATED IN CONTINOUS-FLOW MODE.
SELF-CONTAINED BREATHING APPARATUS WITH A FULL FACEPIECE OPERATED IN PRESSURE-DEMAND OR OTHER POSITIVE PRESSURE MODE.

FOR FIREFIGHTING AND OTHER IMMEDIATELY DANGEROUS TO LIFE OR HEALTH CONDITIONS:
SELF-CONTAINED BREATHING APPARATUS WITH FULL FACEPIECE OPERATED IN PRESSURE-DEMAND OR OTHER POSITIVE PRESSURE MODE.
SUPPLIED-AIR RESPIRATOR WITH FULL FACEPIECE AND OPERATED IN PRESSURE-DEMAND OR OTHER POSITIVE PRESSURE MODE IN COMBINATION WITH AN AUXILIARY SELF-CONTAINED BREATHING APPARATUS OPERATED IN PRESSURE-DEMAND OR OTHER POSITIVE PRESSURE MODE.

CLOTHING: EMPLOYEE MUST WEAR APPROPRIATE PROTECTIVE (IMPERVIOUS) CLOTHING AND EQUIPMENT TO PREVENT ANY POSSIBILITY OF SKIN CONTACT WITH THIS SUBSTANCE.

GLOVES: EMPLOYEE MUST WEAR APPROPRIATE PROTECTIVE GLOVES TO PREVENT CONTACT WITH THIS SUBSTANCE.

EYE PROTECTION: EMPLOYEE MUST WEAR SPLASH-PROOF OR DUST-RESISTANT SAFETY GOGGLES AND A FACESHIELD TO PREVENT CONTACT WITH THIS SUBSTANCE.
EMERGENCY WASH FACILITIES: WHERE THERE IS ANY POSSIBILITY THAT AN EMPLOYEE'S EYES AND/OR SKIN MAY BE EXPOSED TO THIS SUBSTANCE, THE EMPLOYER SHOULD PROVIDE AN EYE WASH FOUNTAIN AND QUICK DRENCH SHOWER WITHIN THE IMMEDIATE WORK AREA FOR EMERGENCY USE.

AUTHORIZED BY- OCCUPATIONAL HEALTH SERVICES, INC.
CREATION DATE: 10/04/89 ***REVISION DATE:*** 04/27/90

MATERIAL SAFETY DATA SHEET

OCCUPATIONAL HEALTH SERVICES, INC.
AGRICULTURE AND PESTICIDE DIVISION
450 SEVENTH AVENUE, SUITE 2407
NEW YORK, NEW YORK 10123
1-800-445-MSDS OR (212) 967-1100

EMERGENCY CONTACT:
JOHN S. BRANSFORD, JR. (615) 292-1180

SUBSTANCE IDENTIFICATION

CAS-NUMBER 3254-63-5
SUBSTANCE: **DIMETHYL P-(METHYLTHIO)PHENYL PHOSPHATE**
TRADE NAMES/SYNONYMS: DIMETHYL 4-(METHYLTHIO)PHENYL ESTER PHOSPHORIC ACID; DIMETHYL P-(METHYLTHIO)PHENYL ESTER PHOSPHORIC ACID; O,O DIMETHYL O-(4-METHYLMERCAPTOPHENYL)PHOSPHATE; 4-METHYLTHIOPHENYLDIMETHYL PHOSPHATE; ALLIED GC 6506; ENT 25734; GC 6506; PHOSPHORIC ACID, DIMETHYL 4-(METHYLTHIO) PHENYL ESTER; PST73095
CHEMICAL FAMILY: THIOL (MERCAPTAN)
PHOSPHATE
AROMATIC
MOLECULAR FORMULA: C9-H13-O4-P-S3
MOLECULAR WEIGHT: 248.25
CERCLA RATINGS (SCALE 0-3): HEALTH=3 FIRE=U REACTIVITY=U PERSISTENCE=1
NFPA RATINGS (SCALE 0-4): HEALTH=4 FIRE=U REACTIVITY=U

COMPONENTS AND CONTAMINANTS

COMPONENT: DIMETHYL P-(METHYLTHIO)PHENYL PHOSPHATE ***PERCENT:*** 100.0
CAS# 3254-63-5
OTHER CONTAMINANTS: NONE
EXPOSURE LIMITS: NO OCCUPATIONAL EXPOSURE LIMITS ESTABLISHED BY OSHA, ACGIH, OR NIOSH.
DIMETHYL P-(METHYLTHIO)PHENYL PHOSPHATE: 500 POUNDS SARA SECTION 302 THRESHOLD PLANNING QUANTITY 1 POUND SARA SECTION 304 REPORTABLE QUANTITY

PHYSICAL DATA

DESCRIPTION: COLORLESS LIQUID ***BOILING POINT:*** NOT AVAILABLE
SPECIFIC GRAVITY: 1.273 @ 21.4 C ***EVAPORATION RATE:*** NOT AVAILABLE
SOLUBILITY IN WATER: .0098%

FIRE AND EXPLOSION DATA

FIRE AND EXPLOSION HAZARD: UNKNOWN FIRE AND EXPLOSION HAZARD.
FIREFIGHTING MEDIA: DRY CHEMICAL, CARBON DIOXIDE, HALON, WATER SPRAY OR STANDARD FOAM (1987 EMERGENCY RESPONSE GUIDEBOOK, DOT P 5800.4).
FOR LARGER FIRES, USE WATER SPRAY, FOG OR STANDARD FOAM (1987 EMERGENCY RESPONSE GUIDEBOOK, DOT P 5800.4).
FIREFIGHTING: MOVE CONTAINERS FROM FIRE AREA IF POSSIBLE. FIGHT FIRE FROM MAXIMUM DISTANCE. STAY AWAY FROM STORAGE TANK ENDS. DIKE FIRE CONTROL WATER FOR LATER DISPOSAL. DO NOT SCATTER MATERIAL (1987 EMERGENCY RESPONSE GUIDEBOOK, DOT P 5800.4, GUIDE PAGE 55).
EXTINGUISH ONLY IF FLOW CAN BE STOPPED. EXTINGUISH USING AGENT INDICATED. USE FLOODING AMOUNTS OF WATER AS A FOG. COOL CONTAINERS WITH FLOODING AMOUNTS OF WATER FROM AS FAR A DISTANCE AS POSSIBLE. AVOID BREATHING POISONOUS VAPORS, KEEP UPWIND. CONSIDER EVACUATION OF DOWNWIND AREA IF MATERIAL IS LEAKING.

TRANSPORTATION DATA

DEPARTMENT OF TRANSPORTATION HAZARD CLASSIFICATION 49 CFR 172.101: POISON B
DEPARTMENT OF TRANSPORTATION LABELING REQUIREMENTS 49 CFR 172.101 AND SUBPART E: POISON
DEPARTMENT OF TRANSPORTATION PACKAGING REQUIREMENTS: 49 CFR 173.346
EXCEPTIONS: 49 CFR 173.345

TOXICITY

DIMETHYL P-(METHYLTHIO)PHENYL PHOSPHATE: TOXICITY DATA: 7 MG/KG ORAL-RAT LD50; 18 MG/KG ORAL-MOUSE LD50; 48 MG/KG SKIN-RABBIT LD50. CARCINOGEN STATUS: NONE. ACUTE TOXICITY LEVEL: HIGHLY TOXIC BY DERMAL ABSORPTION AND INGESTION. TARGET EFFECTS: CHOLINESTERASE INHIBITOR. POISONING MAY AFFECT THE NERVOUS SYSTEM.* AT INCREASED RISK FROM EXPOSURE: PERSONS WITH RESPIRATORY AILMENTS, RECENT EXPOSURE TO CHOLINESTERASE INHIBITORS OR IMPAIRED CHOLINESTERASE PRODUCTION, OR LIVER MALFUNCTION.* ADDITIONAL DATA: MAY CROSS THE PLACENTA. HIGH ENVIRONMENTAL TEMPERATURES OR EXPOSURE OF THE CHEMICAL TO VISIBLE OR ULTRAVIOLET LIGHT MAY ENHANCE THE TOXICITY. INTERACTIONS WITH MEDICATIONS MAY OCCUR.* * MAY BE BASED ON GENERAL INFORMATION ON ORGANOPHOSPHATES.

HEALTH EFFECTS AND FIRST AID

INHALATION: DIMETHYL P-(METHYLTHIO)PHENYL PHOSPHATE: SEE INFORMATION ON ORGANOPHOSPHATES.
ORGANOPHOSPHATES: CHOLINESTERASE INHIBITOR. **ACUTE EXPOSURE-** WHEN INHALED, THE FIRST EFFECTS OF CHOLINESTERASE INHIBITORS ARE USUALLY RESPIRATORY AND MAY INCLUDE NASAL HYPEREMIA AND WATERY DISCHARGE, COUGH, CHEST DISCOMFORT, DYSPNEA, AND WHEEZING DUE TO INCREASED BRONCHIAL SECRETIONS AND BRONCHOCONSTRICTION. IF SUFFICIENT AMOUNTS ARE ABSORBED, OTHER SYSTEMIC EFFECTS MAY BEGIN WITHIN A FEW MINUTES OR BE DELAYED FOR UP TO 12 HOURS. SYMPTOMS MAY INCLUDE PALLOR, NAUSEA, VOMITING, DIARRHEA, ABDOMINAL CRAMPS, HEADACHE, DIZZINESS, OCULAR PAIN, BLURRED VISION, MIOSIS OR IN SOME CASES, ESPECIALLY INITIALLY, MYDRIASIS, LACRIMATION, SALIVATION, SWEATING, AND CONFUSION. OTHER REPORTED CENTRAL NERVOUS SYSTEM OR NEUROMUSCULAR EFFECTS MAY INCLUDE ATAXIA, SLURRED SPEECH, AREFLEXIA, WEAKNESS, FATIGUE, FASCICULATIONS, TWITCHING, TREMORS POSSIBLY OF THE TONGUE AND EYELIDS, AND EVENTUALLY PARALYSIS OF THE EXTREMITIES AND POSSIBLY OF THE RESPIRATORY MUSCLES. IN SEVERE CASES THERE MAY ALSO BE INVOLUNTARY DEFECATION AND URINATION, CYANOSIS, PSYCHOSIS, HYPERGLYCEMIA, ACUTE PANCREATITIS, CARDIAC IRREGULARITIES, PULMONARY EDEMA, UNCONSCIOUSNESS, CONVULSIONS, AND COMA. DEATH IS PRIMARILY DUE TO RESPIRATORY FAILURE, ALTHOUGH CARDIOVASCULAR EFFECTS INCLUDING CARDIAC ARREST MAY ALSO BE IMPLICATED. LONG TERM SEQUELAE ARE RARE BUT MAY INCLUDE NEUROPSYCHIATRIC DISORDERS AND MYOPATHY WITH MUSCLE TENDERNESS. SOME ORGANOPHOSPHATES MAY CAUSE A DELAYED NEUROPATHY BEGINNING 1-4 WEEKS AFTER AN ACUTE EXPOSURE WHICH MAY OR MAY NOT HAVE CAUSED ACUTE CHOLINERGIC EFFECTS. NUMBNESS, TINGLING, WEAKNESS AND CRAMPING BEGINNING SYMMETRICALLY IN THE LOWER LIMBS MAY PROGRESS TO ATAXIA AND PARALYSIS. IN SEVERE CASES, UPPER LIMB INVOLVEMENT IS POSSIBLE AND FLACCID PARALYSIS MAY PROGRESS TO SPASTIC PARALYSIS WITH EXAGGERATED REFLEXES. IMPROVEMENT MAY OCCUR OVER MONTHS TO YEARS, BUT SOME RESIDUAL IMPAIRMENT USUALLY REMAINS.
CHRONIC EXPOSURE- REPEATED OR PROLONGED EXPOSURE MAY RESULT IN THE EFFECTS OF ACUTE EXPOSURE INCLUDING THE DELAYED NEUROPATHY. OTHER EFFECTS REPORTED IN WORKERS REPEATEDLY EXPOSED INCLUDE IMPAIRED MEMORY AND CONCENTRATION, ACUTE PSYCHOSIS, SEVERE DEPRESSIONS, IRRITABILTY, CONFUSION, APATHY, EMOTIONAL LABILITY, SOCIAL WITHDRAWAL, CONFUSION, HEADACHE, SPEECH DIFFICULTIES, DELAYED REACTION TIMES, SPATIAL DISORIENTATION, NIGHTMARES, SLEEPWALKING, AND DROWSINESS OR INSOMNIA. AN INFLUENZA-LIKE CONDITION WITH HEADACHE, NAUSEA, WEAKNESS, ANOREXIA AND MALAISE HAS ALSO BEEN REPORTED.

FIRST AID- REMOVE FROM EXPOSURE AREA TO FRESH AIR IMMEDIATELY. IF BREATHING HAS STOPPED, GIVE ARTIFICIAL RESPIRATION. MAINTAIN AIRWAY AND BLOOD PRESSURE AND ADMINISTER OXYGEN IF AVAILABLE. KEEP AFFECTED PERSON WARM AND AT REST. TREAT SYMPTOMATICALLY AND SUPPORTIVELY.

ADMINISTRATION OF OXYGEN SHOULD BE PERFORMED BY QUALIFIED PERSONNEL. GET MEDICAL ATTENTION IMMEDIATELY.

SKIN CONTACT: DIMETHYL P-(METHYLTHIO)PHENYL PHOSPHATE: HIGHLY TOXIC. SEE INFORMATION ON ORGANOPHOSPHATES.
ORGANOPHOSPHATES: CHOLINESTERASE INHIBITOR. **ACUTE EXPOSURE-** LOCALIZED SWEATING AND FASCICULATIONS MAY OCCUR AT THE SITE OF CONTACT. IF SUFFICIENT AMOUNTS ARE ABSORBED, OTHER EFFECTS OF CHOLINESTERASE INHIBITION AS DESCRIBED IN ACUTE INHALATION MAY OCCUR. SYMPTOMS MAY BE DELAYED 2-3 HOURS, BUT USUALLY NO MORE THAN 12 HOURS. THE RATE OF ABSORPTION IS INCREASED BY THE PRESENCE OF DERMATITIS OR HIGH AMBIENT TEMPERATURES. DELAYED NEUROPATHY IS ALSO POSSIBLE. **CHRONIC EXPOSURE-** REPEATED OR PROLONGED EXPOSURE MAY CAUSE EFFECTS AS DESCRIBED IN ACUTE EXPOSURE. SOME ORGANOPHOSPHATES MAY CAUSE SENSITIZATION.
FIRST AID- REMOVE CONTAMINATED CLOTHING IMMEDIATELY. WASH CONTAMINATED AREAS WITH SOAP AND WATER FOLLOWED BY ALCOHOL (ARENA, POISONING, 4TH ED.). EMERGENCY PERSONNEL SHOULD WEAR GLOVES AND AVOID CONTAMINATION. TREAT RESPIRATORY DIFFICULTY WITH ARTIFICIAL RESPIRATION. GET MEDICAL ATTENTION IMMEDIATELY.

EYE CONTACT: DIMETHYL P-(METHYLTHIO)PHENYL PHOSPHATE: SEE INFORMATION ON ORGANOPHOSPHATES.
ORGANOPHOSPHATES: CHOLINESTERASE INHIBITOR. **ACUTE EXPOSURE-** DIRECT CONTACT MAY CAUSE PAIN, HYPEREMIA, LACRIMATION, TWITCHING OF THE EYELIDS, MIOSIS, AND CILIARY MUSCLE SPASM WITH LOSS OF ACCOMODATION, BLURRED OR DIMMED VISION AND BROWACHE. SOMETIMES MYDRIASIS MAY OCCUR INSTEAD OF MIOSIS. WITH SUFFICIENT EXPOSURE, OTHER SYMPTOMS OF CHOLINESTERASE INHIBITION AS DESCRIBED IN ACUTE INHALATION MAY OCCUR. **CHRONIC EXPOSURE-** REPEATED OR PROLONGED EXPOSURE MAY CAUSE EFFECTS AS DESCRIBED IN ACUTE EXPOSURE. SOME COMPOUNDS HAVE CAUSED TOXIC EFFECTS ON THE CRYSTALLINE LENS, CONJUNCTIVAL THICKENING AND OBSTRUCTION OF THE NASOLACRIMAL CANALS WHEN USED AS MIOTIC EYEDROPS.
FIRST AID- IRRIGATE EYES WITH WATER OR SALINE SOLUTION. IF SYMPTOMS OF POISONING OCCUR, TREAT RESPIRATORY DIFFICULTY WITH ARTIFICIAL RESPIRATION AND OXYGEN. OBSERVE PATIENT FOR AT LEAST 24-36 HOURS (GOSSELIN, CLINICAL TOXICOLOGY OF COMMERCIAL PRODUCTS, 5TH ED.). GET MEDICAL ATTENTION IMMEDIATELY. OXYGEN SHOULD BE ADMINISTERED BY QUALIFIED MEDICAL PERSONNEL.

INGESTION: DIMETHYL P-(METHYLTHIO)PHENYL PHOSPHATE: HIGHLY TOXIC. SEE INFORMATION ON ORGANOPHOSPHATES.
ORGANOPHOSPHATES: CHOLINESTERASE INHIBITOR. **ACUTE EXPOSURE-** WHEN INGESTED, THE FIRST EFFECTS MAY BE NAUSEA, VOMITING, ANOREXIA, ABDOMINAL CRAMPS AND DIARRHEA. GASTROINTESTINAL ABSORPTION MAY CAUSE SYMPTOMS OF CHOLINESTERASE INHIBITION AS DESCRIBED IN ACUTE INHALATION. SYMPTOMS MAY BEGIN WITHIN MINUTES OR BE DELAYED FOR HOURS. DELAYED EFFECTS INCLUDING NEUROPATHY MAY ALSO OCCUR. **CHRONIC EXPOSURE-** REPEATED INGESTION MAY CAUSE EFFECTS AS DESCRIBED IN ACUTE EXPOSURE.
FIRST AID- IF PERSON IS ALERT AND RESPIRATION IS NOT DEPRESSED, GIVE SYRUP OF IPECAC FOLLOWED BY WATER (IF VOMITING OCCURS, KEEP HEAD BELOW HIPS TO PREVENT ASPIRATION). IF CONSCIOUSNESS LEVEL DECLINES OR VOMITING HAS NOT OCCURRED IN 15 MINUTES EMPTY STOMACH BY GASTRIC LAVAGE WITH THE AID OF CUFFED ENDOTRACHEAL TUBE USING ISOTONIC SALINE OR 5% SODIUM BICARBONATE FOLLOW WITH ACTIVATED CHARCOAL. ESTABLISH AND MAINTAIN AIRWAY. TREAT RESPIRATORY DIFFICULTY WITH ARTIFICIAL RESPIRATION AND OXYGEN. DO NOT GIVE MORPHINE, AMINOPHYLLINE, PHENOTHIAZINES, RESERPINE, FUROSEMIDE, OR ETHACRYNIC ACID (MORGAN, RECOGNITION AND MANAGEMENT OF PESTICIDE POISONINGS, 3RD ED.). TREAT SYMPTOMATICALLY AND SUPPORTIVELY. ADMINISTRATION OF OXYGEN AND LAVAGE MUST BE PERFORMED BY QUALIFIED MEDICAL PERSONNEL. GET MEDICAL ATTENTION IMMEDIATELY.
ANTIDOTE: THE FOLLOWING ANTIDOTE(S) HAVE BEEN RECOMMENDED. HOWEVER, THE DECISION AS TO WHETHER THE SEVERITY OF POISONING REQUIRES ADMINISTRATION OF ANY ANTIDOTE AND ACTUAL DOSE REQUIRED SHOULD BE MADE BY QUALIFIED MEDICAL PERSONNEL.
FOR CHOLINESTERASE INHIBITORS: ESTABLISH CLEAR AIRWAY AND TISSUE OXYGENATION BY ASPIRATION OF SECRETIONS, AND IF NECESSARY, BY ASSISTED PULMONARY VENTILATION WITH OXYGEN. IMPROVE TISSUE OXYGENATION AS MUCH AS POSSIBLE BEFORE ADMINISTERING ATROPINE TO MINIMIZE THE RISK OF VENTRICULAR FIBRILLATION. ADMINISTER ATROPINE SULFATE INTRAVENOUSLY, OR INTRAMUSCULARLY IF IV INJECTION IS NOT POSSIBLE. IN MODERATELY SEVERE POISONING ADMINISTER ATROPINE SULFATE, 0.4-2.0 MG REPEATED EVERY 15 MINUTES UNTIL ATROPINIZATION IS ACHIEVED (TACHYCARDIA, FLUSHING, DRY MOUTH, MYDRIASIS). MAINTAIN ATROPINIZATION BY REPEATED DOSES FOR 2-12 HOURS, OR LONGER, DEPENDING ON THE SEVERITY OF POISONING. THE APPEARANCE OF RALES IN THE LUNG BASES, MIOSIS, SALIVATION, NAUSEA, BRADYCARDIA, ARE ALL INDICATIONS OF INADEQUATE ATROPINIZATION. SEVERELY POISONED INDIVIDUALS MAY EXHIBIT REMARKABLE TOLERANCE TO ATROPINE; TWO OR MORE TIMES THE DOSAGES SUGGESTED ABOVE MAY BE NEEDED. PERSONS NOT POISONED OR ONLY SLIGHTLY POISONED, HOWEVER, MAY DEVELOP SIGNS OF ATROPINE TOXICITY FROM SUCH LARGE DOSAGES: FEVER, MUSCLE FIBRILLATIONS, AND DELIRIUM ARE THE MAIN SIGNS OF ATROPINE TOXICITY. IF THESE SIGNS APPEAR WHILE THE PATIENT IS FULLY ATROPINIZED, ATROPINE ADMINISTRATION SHOULD BE DISCONTINUED, AT LEAST TEMPORARILY. OBSERVE TREATED PATIENTS CLOSELY AT LEAST 24 HOURS TO INSURE THAT SYMPTOMS (POSSIBLY PULMONARY EDEMA) DO NOT RECUR AS ATROPINIZATION WEARS OFF. IN VERY SEVERE POISONINGS, METABOLIC DISPOSITION OF TOXICANT MAY REQUIRE SEVERAL HOURS OR DAYS DURING WHICH ATROPINIZATION MUST BE MAINTAINED. MARKEDLY LOWER LEVELS OF URINARY METABOLITES INDICATE THAT ATROPINE DOSAGE CAN BE TAPERED OFF. AS DOSAGE IS REDUCED, CHECK THE LUNG BASES FREQUENTLY FOR RALES. IF RALES ARE HEARD OR OTHER SYMPTOMS RETURN, RE-ESTABLISH ATROPINIZATION PROMPTLY (MORGAN, RECOGNITION AND MANAGEMENT OF PESTICIDE POISONINGS, 3RD ED.). ADMINISTRATION OF ANTIDOTE MUST BE PERFORMED BY QUALIFIED MEDICAL PERSONNEL.
IN CASES OF SEVERE POISONING BY ORGANOPHOSPHATE PESTICIDES IN WHICH RESPIRATORY DEPRESSION, MUSCLE WEAKNESS AND TWITCHINGS ARE SEVERE, GIVE PRALIDOXIME (PROTOPAM-AYERST, 2-PAM), 1.0 GRAM INTRAVENOUSLY AT NO MORE THAN 0.5 GRAM PER MINUTE. DOSAGE OF PRALIDOXIME MAY BE REPEATED IN 1-2 HOURS, THEN AT 10-12 HOUR INTERVALS IF NEEDED. IN VERY SEVERE POISONINGS, DOSAGE RATES MAY BE DOUBLED. TREATMENT WITH PRALIDOXIME WILL BE MOST EFFECTIVE IF GIVEN WITHIN THIRTY-SIX HOURS AFTER POISONING (MORGAN, RECOGNITION AND MANAGEMENT OF PESTICIDE POISONINGS, 3RD ED.). ANTIDOTE SHOULD BE ADMINISTERED BY QUALIFIED MEDICAL PERSONNEL.

REACTIVITY

REACTIVITY: NO DATA AVAILABLE.
INCOMPATIBILITIES: DIMETHYL P-(METHYLTHIO)PHENYL PHOSPHATE: ALKALIES: MAY CAUSE HYDROLYSIS. OXIDIZERS (STRONG): FIRE AND EXPLOSION HAZARD.
DECOMPOSITION: THERMAL DECOMPOSITION MAY EMIT TOXIC OXIDES OF SULFUR AND POTASSIUM.
POLYMERIZATION: HAZARDOUS POLYMERIZATION HAS NOT BEEN REPORTED TO OCCUR UNDER NORMAL TEMPERATURES AND PRESSURES.

STORAGE AND DISPOSAL

OBSERVE ALL FEDERAL, STATE AND LOCAL REGULATIONS WHEN STORING OR DISPOSING OF THIS SUBSTANCE. FOR ASSISTANCE, CONTACT THE DISTRICT DIRECTOR OF THE ENVIRONMENTAL PROTECTION AGENCY.

STORAGE

STORE IN ACCORDANCE WITH 40 CFR 165 RECOMMENDED PROCEDURES FOR THE DISPOSAL AND STORAGE OF PESTICIDES AND PESTICIDE CONTAINERS.
STORE AWAY FROM INCOMPATIBLE SUBSTANCES.
THRESHOLD PLANNING QUANTITY (TPQ): THE SUPERFUND AMENDMENTS AND REAUTHORIZATION ACT (SARA) SECTION 302 REQUIRES THAT EACH FACILITY WHERE ANY EXTREMELY HAZARDOUS SUBSTANCE IS PRESENT IN A QUANTITY EQUAL TO OR GREATER THAN THE TPQ ESTABLISHED FOR THAT SUBSTANCE NOTIFY THE STATE EMERGENCY RESPONSE COMMISSION FOR THE STATE IN WHICH IT IS LOCATED. SECTION 303 OF SARA REQUIRES THESE FACILITIES TO PARTICIPATE IN LOCAL EMERGENCY RESPONSE PLANNING (40 CFR 355.30).

DISPOSAL

DISPOSAL MUST BE IN ACCORDANCE WITH 40 CFR 165 RECOMMENDED PROCEDURES FOR THE DISPOSAL AND STORAGE OF PESTICIDES AND PESTICIDE CONTAINERS.

CONDITIONS TO AVOID

NONE REPORTED.

SPILL AND LEAK PROCEDURES

OCCUPATIONAL SPILL: DO NOT TOUCH SPILLED MATERIAL. STOP LEAK IF YOU CAN DO IT WITHOUT RISK. USE WATER SPRAY TO REDUCE VAPORS. FOR SMALL SPILLS, TAKE UP WITH SAND OR OTHER ABSORBENT MATERIAL AND PLACE INTO CONTAINERS FOR LATER DISPOSAL. FOR SMALL DRY SPILLS, WITH A CLEAN SHOVEL PLACE MATERIAL INTO CLEAN, DRY CONTAINERS AND COVER. MOVE CONTAINERS FROM SPILL AREA. FOR LARGER SPILLS, DIKE FAR AHEAD OF SPILL FOR LATER DISPOSAL. KEEP UNNECESSARY PEOPLE AWAY. ISOLATE HAZARD AREA AND DENY ENTRY. VENTILATE CLOSED SPACES BEFORE ENTERING.
REPORTABLE QUANTITY (RQ): 1 POUND THE SUPERFUND AMENDMENTS AND REAUTHORIZATION ACT (SARA) SECTION 304 REQUIRES THAT A RELEASE EQUAL TO OR GREATER THAN THE REPORTABLE QUANTITY FOR THIS SUBSTANCE BE

IMMEDIATELY REPORTED TO THE LOCAL EMERGENCY PLANNING COMMITTEE AND THE STATE EMERGENCY RESPONSE COMMISSION (40 CFR 355.40). IF THE RELEASE OF THIS SUBSTANCE IS REPORTABLE UNDER CERCLA SECTION 103, THE NATIONAL RESPONSE CENTER MUST BE NOTIFIED IMMEDIATELY AT (800) 424-8802 OR (202) 426-2675 IN THE METROPOLITAN WASHINGTON, D.C. AREA (40 CFR 302.6).

PROTECTIVE EQUIPMENT

VENTILATION: PROVIDE LOCAL EXHAUST OR PROCESS ENCLOSURE VENTILATION SYSTEM.

RESPIRATOR: THE FOLLOWING RESPIRATORS ARE RECOMMENDED BASED ON INFORMATION FOUND IN THE PHYSICAL DATA, TOXICITY AND HEALTH EFFECTS SECTIONS. THEY ARE RANKED IN ORDER FROM MINIMUM TO MAXIMUM RESPIRATORY PROTECTION. THE SPECIFIC RESPIRATOR SELECTED MUST BE BASED ON CONTAMINATION LEVELS FOUND IN THE WORK PLACE, MUST NOT EXCEED THE WORKING LIMITS OF THE RESPIRATOR AND BE JOINTLY APPROVED BY THE NATIONAL INSTITUTE FOR OCCUPATIONAL SAFETY AND HEALTH AND THE MINE SAFETY AND HEALTH ADMINISTRATION (NIOSH-MSHA).

TYPE 'C' SUPPLIED-AIR RESPIRATOR WITH A FULL FACEPIECE OPERATED IN PRESSURE-DEMAND OR OTHER POSITIVE PRESSURE MODE OR WITH A FULL FACEPIECE, HELMET OR HOOD OPERATED IN CONTINOUS-FLOW MODE.

SELF-CONTAINED BREATHING APPARATUS WITH A FULL FACEPIECE OPERATED IN PRESSURE-DEMAND OR OTHER POSITIVE PRESSURE MODE.

FOR FIREFIGHTING AND OTHER IMMEDIATELY DANGEROUS TO LIFE OR HEALTH CONDITIONS:

SELF-CONTAINED BREATHING APPARATUS WITH FULL FACEPIECE OPERATED IN PRESSURE-DEMAND OR OTHER POSITIVE PRESSURE MODE.

SUPPLIED-AIR RESPIRATOR WITH FULL FACEPIECE AND OPERATED IN PRESSURE-DEMAND OR OTHER POSITIVE PRESSURE MODE IN COMBINATION WITH AN AUXILIARY SELF-CONTAINED BREATHING APPARATUS OPERATED IN PRESSURE-DEMAND OR OTHER POSITIVE PRESSURE MODE.

CLOTHING: EMPLOYEE MUST WEAR APPROPRIATE PROTECTIVE (IMPERVIOUS) CLOTHING AND EQUIPMENT TO PREVENT ANY POSSIBILITY OF SKIN CONTACT WITH THIS SUBSTANCE.

GLOVES: EMPLOYEE MUST WEAR APPROPRIATE PROTECTIVE GLOVES TO PREVENT CONTACT WITH THIS SUBSTANCE.

EYE PROTECTION: EMPLOYEE MUST WEAR SPLASH-PROOF OR DUST-RESISTANT SAFETY GOGGLES AND A FACESHIELD TO PREVENT CONTACT WITH THIS SUBSTANCE.

EMERGENCY WASH FACILITIES: WHERE THERE IS ANY POSSIBILITY THAT AN EMPLOYEE'S EYES AND/OR SKIN MAY BE EXPOSED TO THIS SUBSTANCE, THE EMPLOYER SHOULD PROVIDE AN EYE WASH FOUNTAIN AND QUICK DRENCH SHOWER WITHIN THE IMMEDIATE WORK AREA FOR EMERGENCY USE.

AUTHORIZED BY- OCCUPATIONAL HEALTH SERVICES, INC.

CREATION DATE: 05/18/90 ***REVISION DATE:*** 05/18/90

MATERIAL SAFETY DATA SHEET

OCCUPATIONAL HEALTH SERVICES, INC.
AGRICULTURE AND PESTICIDE DIVISION
450 SEVENTH AVENUE, SUITE 2407
NEW YORK, NEW YORK 10123
1-800-445-MSDS OR (212) 967-1100

EMERGENCY CONTACT:
JOHN S. BRANSFORD, JR. (615) 292-1180

SUBSTANCE IDENTIFICATION

CAS-NUMBER 144-41-2

SUBSTANCE: **MORPHOTHION**

TRADE NAMES/SYNONYMS: PHOSPHORODITHIOIC ACID, O,O-DIMETHYL S-(2-(4-MORPHOLINYL)-2-OXOETHYL) ESTER; PHOSPHORODITHIOIC ACID, O,O-DIMETHYL ESTER, S-ESTER WITH 4-(MERCAPTOACETYL)MORPHOLINE; PHOSPHORODITHIOIC ACID, O,O-DIMETHYL-S-(MORPHOLINOCARBONYLMETHYL) ESTER; O,O-DIMETHYL S-MORPHOLINOCARBONYLMETHYL PHOSPHORODITHIOATE; O,O-DIMETHYL S-(2-(4-MORPHOLINYL)-2-OXOETHYL)PHOSPHORODITHIOATE; O,O-DIMETHYL PHOSPHORODITHIOATE S-ESTER WITH 4-(MERCAPTOACETYL) MORPHOLINE; O,O-DIMETHYL S-(MORPHOLINOCARBONYLMETHYL)PHOSPHORODITHIOATE; DIMETHYL S-(MORPHOLINOCARBONYLMETHYL)PHOSPHOROTHIOLOTHIONATE; EKATIN F; EKATIN M; MORPHOTOX; C8H16NO4PS2; PST73096

CHEMICAL FAMILY: PHOSPHOROTHIOATE

MOLECULAR FORMULA: C8-H16-N-O4-P-S2

MOLECULAR WEIGHT: 285.34

CERCLA RATINGS (SCALE 0-3): HEALTH=3 FIRE=1 REACTIVITY=0 PERSISTENCE=1

NFPA RATINGS (SCALE 0-4): HEALTH=3 FIRE=1 REACTIVITY=0

COMPONENTS AND CONTAMINANTS

COMPONENT: MORPHOTHION ***PERCENT:*** 100.0
CAS# 144-41-2

OTHER CONTAMINANTS: NONE

EXPOSURE LIMITS: NO OCCUPATIONAL EXPOSURE LIMITS ESTABLISHED BY OSHA, ACGIH, OR NIOSH.

PHYSICAL DATA

DESCRIPTION: COLORLESS, CRYSTALLINE SOLID.

MELTING POINT: 145-147 F (63-64 C)

SPECIFIC GRAVITY: NOT AVAILABLE ***SOLUBILITY IN WATER:*** INSOLUBLE

SOLVENT SOLUBILITY: SOLUBLE IN ACETONE, DIOXANE, ACETONITRILE, AND POLAR ORGANIC SOLVENTS.

FIRE AND EXPLOSION DATA

FIRE AND EXPLOSION HAZARD: SLIGHT FIRE HAZARD WHEN EXPOSED TO HEAT OR FLAME.

FIREFIGHTING MEDIA: DRY CHEMICAL, CARBON DIOXIDE, HALON, WATER SPRAY OR STANDARD FOAM (1987 EMERGENCY RESPONSE GUIDEBOOK, DOT P 5800.4). FOR LARGER FIRES, USE WATER SPRAY, FOG OR STANDARD FOAM (1987 EMERGENCY RESPONSE GUIDEBOOK, DOT P 5800.4).

FIREFIGHTING: MOVE CONTAINERS FROM FIRE AREA IF POSSIBLE. FIGHT FIRE FROM MAXIMUM DISTANCE. STAY AWAY FROM STORAGE TANK ENDS. DIKE FIRE CONTROL WATER FOR LATER DISPOSAL. DO NOT SCATTER MATERIAL (1987 EMERGENCY RESPONSE GUIDEBOOK, DOT P 5800.4, GUIDE PAGE 55). EXTINGUISH ONLY IF FLOW CAN BE STOPPED; USE FLOODING AMOUNTS OF WATER AS FOG, SOLID STREAMS MAY BE INEFFECTIVE. COOL CONTAINERS WITH FLOODING AMOUNTS OF WATER FROM AS FAR A DISTANCE AS POSSIBLE. USE WATER SPRAY TO ABSORB TOXIC VAPORS. AVOID BREATHING TOXIC VAPORS; KEEP UPWIND. CONSIDER EVACUATION OF DOWNWIND AREA IF MATERIAL IS LEAKING.

TOXICITY

MORPHOTHION: TOXICITY DATA: 283 MG/KG SKIN-RAT LD50; 190 MG/KG ORAL-RAT LD50; 130 MG/KG ORAL-MOUSE LD50; 190 MG/KG ORAL-RABBIT LD50. CARCINOGEN STATUS: NONE. ACUTE TOXICITY LEVEL: TOXIC BY DERMAL ABSORPTION AND INGESTION. TARGET EFFECTS: CHOLINESTERASE INHIBITOR. POISONING MAY AFFECT THE NERVOUS SYSTEM.* AT INCREASED RISK FROM EXPOSURE: PERSONS WITH RESPIRATORY AILMENTS, RECENT EXPOSURE TO CHOLINESTERASE INHIBITORS OR IMPAIRED CHOLINESTERASE PRODUCTION, OR LIVER MALFUNCTION.* ADDITIONAL DATA: MAY CROSS THE PLACENTA. HIGH ENVIRONMENTAL TEMPERATURES OR EXPOSURE OF THE CHEMICAL TO VISIBLE OR ULTRAVIOLET LIGHT MAY ENHANCE THE TOXICITY. INTERACTIONS WITH MEDICATIONS MAY OCCUR.*

* MAY BE BASED ON GENERAL INFORMATION ON ORGANOPHOSPHATES.

HEALTH EFFECTS AND FIRST AID

INHALATION: MORPHOTHION: SEE INFORMATION ON ORGANOPHOSPHATES.
ORGANOPHOSPHATES: CHOLINESTERASE INHIBITOR. <u>ACUTE EXPOSURE-</u> WHEN INHALED, THE FIRST EFFECTS OF CHOLINESTERASE INHIBITORS ARE USUALLY RESPIRATORY AND MAY INCLUDE NASAL HYPEREMIA AND WATERY DISCHARGE, COUGH, CHEST DISCOMFORT, DYSPNEA, AND WHEEZING DUE TO INCREASED BRONCHIAL SECRETIONS AND BRONCHOCONSTRICTION. IF SUFFICIENT AMOUNTS ARE ABSORBED, OTHER SYSTEMIC EFFECTS MAY BEGIN WITHIN A FEW MINUTES OR BE DELAYED FOR UP TO 12 HOURS. SYMPTOMS MAY INCLUDE PALLOR, NAUSEA, VOMITING, DIARRHEA, ABDOMINAL CRAMPS, HEADACHE, DIZZINESS, OCULAR PAIN, BLURRED VISION, MIOSIS OR IN SOME CASES, ESPECIALLY INITIALLY, MYDRIASIS, LACRIMATION, SALIVATION, SWEATING, AND CONFUSION. OTHER REPORTED CENTRAL NERVOUS SYSTEM OR NEUROMUSCULAR EFFECTS MAY INCLUDE ATAXIA, SLURRED SPEECH, AREFLEXIA, WEAKNESS, FATIGUE, FASCICULATIONS, TWITCHING, TREMORS POSSIBLY OF THE TONGUE AND EYELIDS, AND EVENTUALLY PARALYSIS OF THE EXTREMITIES AND POSSIBLY OF THE RESPIRATORY MUSCLES. IN SEVERE CASES THERE MAY ALSO BE INVOLUNTARY DEFECATION AND URINATION, CYANOSIS, PSYCHOSIS, HYPERGLYCEMIA, ACUTE PANCREATITIS, CARDIAC IRREGULARITIES, PULMONARY EDEMA, UNCONSCIOUSNESS, CONVULSIONS, AND COMA. DEATH IS PRIMARILY DUE TO RESPIRATORY FAILURE, ALTHOUGH CARDIOVASCULAR EFFECTS INCLUDING CARDIAC ARREST MAY ALSO BE IMPLICATED. LONG TERM SEQUELAE ARE RARE BUT MAY INCLUDE NEUROPSYCHIATRIC DISORDERS AND MYOPATHY WITH MUSCLE TENDERNESS. SOME ORGANOPHOSPHATES MAY CAUSE A DELAYED NEUROPATHY BEGINNING 1-4 WEEKS AFTER AN ACUTE EXPOSURE WHICH MAY OR MAY NOT HAVE CAUSED ACUTE CHOLINERGIC EFFECTS. NUMBNESS, TINGLING, WEAKNESS AND CRAMPING BEGINNING SYMMETRICALLY IN THE LOWER LIMBS

MAY PROGRESS TO ATAXIA AND PARALYSIS. IN SEVERE CASES, UPPER LIMB INVOLVEMENT IS POSSIBLE AND FLACCID PARALYSIS MAY PROGRESS TO SPASTIC PARALYSIS WITH EXAGGERATED REFLEXES. IMPROVEMENT MAY OCCUR OVER MONTHS TO YEARS, BUT SOME RESIDUAL IMPAIRMENT USUALLY REMAINS. **CHRONIC EXPOSURE-** REPEATED OR PROLONGED EXPOSURE MAY RESULT IN THE EFFECTS OF ACUTE EXPOSURE INCLUDING THE DELAYED NEUROPATHY. OTHER EFFECTS REPORTED IN WORKERS REPEATEDLY EXPOSED INCLUDE IMPAIRED MEMORY AND CONCENTRATION, ACUTE PSYCHOSIS, SEVERE DEPRESSIONS, IRRITABILTY, CONFUSION, APATHY, EMOTIONAL LABILITY, SOCIAL WITHDRAWAL, CONFUSION, HEADACHE, SPEECH DIFFICULTIES, DELAYED REACTION TIMES, SPATIAL DISORIENTATION, NIGHTMARES, SLEEPWALKING, AND DROWSINESS OR INSOMNIA. AN INFLUENZA-LIKE CONDITION WITH HEADACHE, NAUSEA, WEAKNESS, ANOREXIA AND MALAISE HAS ALSO BEEN REPORTED.

FIRST AID- REMOVE FROM EXPOSURE AREA TO FRESH AIR IMMEDIATELY. IF BREATHING HAS STOPPED, GIVE ARTIFICIAL RESPIRATION. MAINTAIN AIRWAY AND BLOOD PRESSURE AND ADMINISTER OXYGEN IF AVAILABLE. KEEP AFFECTED PERSON WARM AND AT REST. TREAT SYMPTOMATICALLY AND SUPPORTIVELY. ADMINISTRATION OF OXYGEN SHOULD BE PERFORMED BY QUALIFIED PERSONNEL. GET MEDICAL ATTENTION IMMEDIATELY.

SKIN CONTACT: MORPHOTHION: TOXIC. SEE INFORMATION ON ORGANOPHOSPHATES.

ORGANOPHOSPHATES: CHOLINESTERASE INHIBITOR. **ACUTE EXPOSURE-** LOCALIZED SWEATING AND FASCICULATIONS MAY OCCUR AT THE SITE OF CONTACT. IF SUFFICIENT AMOUNTS ARE ABSORBED, OTHER EFFECTS OF CHOLINESTERASE INHIBITION AS DESCRIBED IN ACUTE INHALATION MAY OCCUR. SYMPTOMS MAY BE DELAYED 2-3 HOURS, BUT USUALLY NO MORE THAN 12 HOURS. THE RATE OF ABSORPTION IS INCREASED BY THE PRESENCE OF DERMATITIS OR HIGH AMBIENT TEMPERATURES. DELAYED NEUROPATHY IS ALSO POSSIBLE. **CHRONIC EXPOSURE-** REPEATED OR PROLONGED EXPOSURE MAY CAUSE EFFECTS AS DESCRIBED IN ACUTE EXPOSURE. SOME ORGANOPHOSPHATES MAY CAUSE SENSITIZATION.

FIRST AID- REMOVE CONTAMINATED CLOTHING IMMEDIATELY. WASH CONTAMINATED AREAS WITH SOAP AND WATER FOLLOWED BY ALCOHOL (ARENA, POISONING, 4TH ED.). EMERGENCY PERSONNEL SHOULD WEAR GLOVES AND AVOID CONTAMINATION. TREAT RESPIRATORY DIFFICULTY WITH ARTIFICIAL RESPIRATION. GET MEDICAL ATTENTION IMMEDIATELY.

EYE CONTACT: MORPHOTHION: SEE INFORMATION ON ORGANOPHOSPHATES.

ORGANOPHOSPHATES: CHOLINESTERASE INHIBITOR. **ACUTE EXPOSURE-** DIRECT CONTACT MAY CAUSE PAIN, HYPEREMIA, LACRIMATION, TWITCHING OF THE EYELIDS, MIOSIS, AND CILIARY MUSCLE SPASM WITH LOSS OF ACCOMODATION, BLURRED OR DIMMED VISION AND BROWACHE. SOMETIMES MYDRIASIS MAY OCCUR INSTEAD OF MIOSIS. WITH SUFFICIENT EXPOSURE, OTHER SYMPTOMS OF CHOLINESTERASE INHIBITION AS DESCRIBED IN ACUTE INHALATION MAY OCCUR. **CHRONIC EXPOSURE-** REPEATED OR PROLONGED EXPOSURE MAY CAUSE EFFECTS AS DESCRIBED IN ACUTE EXPOSURE. SOME COMPOUNDS HAVE CAUSED TOXIC EFFECTS ON THE CRYSTALLINE LENS, CONJUNCTIVAL THICKENING AND OBSTRUCTION OF THE NASOLACRIMAL CANALS WHEN USED AS MIOTIC EYEDROPS.

FIRST AID- IRRIGATE EYES WITH WATER OR SALINE SOLUTION. IF SYMPTOMS OF POISONING OCCUR, TREAT RESPIRATORY DIFFICULTY WITH ARTIFICIAL RESPIRATION AND OXYGEN. OBSERVE PATIENT FOR AT LEAST 24-36 HOURS (GOSSELIN, CLINICAL TOXICOLOGY OF COMMERCIAL PRODUCTS, 5TH ED.). GET MEDICAL ATTENTION IMMEDIATELY. OXYGEN SHOULD BE ADMINISTERED BY QUALIFIED MEDICAL PERSONNEL.

INGESTION: MORPHOTHION: TOXIC. SEE INFORMATION ON ORGANOPHOSPHATES.

ORGANOPHOSPHATES: CHOLINESTERASE INHIBITOR. **ACUTE EXPOSURE-** WHEN INGESTED, THE FIRST EFFECTS MAY BE NAUSEA, VOMITING, ANOREXIA, ABDOMINAL CRAMPS AND DIARRHEA. GASTROINTESTINAL ABSORPTION MAY CAUSE SYMPTOMS OF CHOLINESTERASE INHIBITION AS DESCRIBED IN ACUTE INHALATION. SYMPTOMS MAY BEGIN WITHIN MINUTES OR BE DELAYED FOR HOURS. DELAYED EFFECTS INCLUDING NEUROPATHY MAY ALSO OCCUR. **CHRONIC EXPOSURE-** REPEATED INGESTION MAY CAUSE EFFECTS AS DESCRIBED IN ACUTE EXPOSURE.

FIRST AID- IF PERSON IS ALERT AND RESPIRATION IS NOT DEPRESSED, GIVE SYRUP OF IPECAC FOLLOWED BY WATER (IF VOMITING OCCURS, KEEP HEAD BELOW HIPS TO PREVENT ASPIRATION). IF CONSCIOUSNESS LEVEL DECLINES OR VOMITING HAS NOT OCCURRED IN 15 MINUTES EMPTY STOMACH BY GASTRIC LAVAGE WITH THE AID OF CUFFED ENDOTRACHEAL TUBE USING ISOTONIC SALINE OR 5% SODIUM BICARBONATE FOLLOW WITH ACTIVATED CHARCOAL. ESTABLISH AND MAINTAIN AIRWAY. TREAT RESPIRATORY DIFFICULTY WITH ARTIFICIAL RESPIRATION AND OXYGEN. DO NOT GIVE MORPHINE, AMINOPHYLLINE, PHENOTHIAZINES, RESERPINE, FUROSEMIDE, OR ETHACRYNIC ACID (MORGAN, RECOGNITION AND MANAGEMENT OF PESTICIDE POISONINGS, 3RD ED.). TREAT SYMPTOMATICALLY AND SUPPORTIVELY. ADMINISTRATION OF OXYGEN AND LAVAGE MUST BE PERFORMED BY QUALIFIED MEDICAL PERSONNEL. GET MEDICAL ATTENTION IMMEDIATELY.

ANTIDOTE: THE FOLLOWING ANTIDOTE(S) HAVE BEEN RECOMMENDED. HOWEVER, THE DECISION AS TO WHETHER THE SEVERITY OF POISONING REQUIRES ADMINISTRATION OF ANY ANTIDOTE AND ACTUAL DOSE REQUIRED SHOULD BE MADE BY QUALIFIED MEDICAL PERSONNEL.

FOR CHOLINESTERASE INHIBITORS: ESTABLISH CLEAR AIRWAY AND TISSUE OXYGENATION BY ASPIRATION OF SECRETIONS, AND IF NECESSARY, BY ASSISTED PULMONARY VENTILATION WITH OXYGEN. IMPROVE TISSUE OXYGENATION AS MUCH AS POSSIBLE BEFORE ADMINISTERING ATROPINE TO MINIMIZE THE RISK OF VENTRICULAR FIBRILLATION. ADMINISTER ATROPINE SULFATE INTRAVENOUSLY, OR INTRAMUSCULARLY IF IV INJECTION IS NOT POSSIBLE. IN MODERATELY SEVERE POISONING ADMINISTER ATROPINE SULFATE, 0.4-2.0 MG REPEATED EVERY 15 MINUTES UNTIL ATROPINIZATION IS ACHIEVED (TACHYCARDIA, FLUSHING, DRY MOUTH, MYDRIASIS). MAINTAIN ATROPINIZATION BY REPEATED DOSES FOR 2-12 HOURS, OR LONGER, DEPENDING ON THE SEVERITY OF POISONING. THE APPEARANCE OF RALES IN THE LUNG BASES, MIOSIS, SALIVATION, NAUSEA, BRADYCARDIA, ARE ALL INDICATIONS OF INADEQUATE ATROPINIZATION. SEVERELY POISONED INDIVIDUALS MAY EXHIBIT REMARKABLE TOLERANCE TO ATROPINE; TWO OR MORE TIMES THE DOSAGES SUGGESTED ABOVE MAY BE NEEDED. PERSONS NOT POISONED OR ONLY SLIGHTLY POISONED, HOWEVER, MAY DEVELOP SIGNS OF ATROPINE TOXICITY FROM SUCH LARGE DOSAGES: FEVER, MUSCLE FIBRILLATIONS, AND DELIRIUM ARE THE MAIN SIGNS OF ATROPINE TOXICITY. IF THESE SIGNS APPEAR WHILE THE PATIENT IS FULLY ATROPINIZED, ATROPINE ADMINISTRATION SHOULD BE DISCONTINUED, AT LEAST TEMPORARILY. OBSERVE TREATED PATIENTS CLOSELY AT LEAST 24 HOURS TO INSURE THAT SYMPTOMS (POSSIBLY PULMONARY EDEMA) DO NOT RECUR AS ATROPINIZATION WEARS OFF. IN VERY SEVERE POISONINGS, METABOLIC DISPOSITION OF TOXICANT MAY REQUIRE SEVERAL HOURS OR DAYS DURING WHICH ATROPINIZATION MUST BE MAINTAINED. MARKEDLY LOWER LEVELS OF URINARY METABOLITES INDICATE THAT ATROPINE DOSAGE CAN BE TAPERED OFF. AS DOSAGE IS REDUCED, CHECK THE LUNG BASES FREQUENTLY FOR RALES. IF RALES ARE HEARD OR OTHER SYMPTOMS RETURN, RE-ESTABLISH ATROPINIZATION PROMPTLY (MORGAN, RECOGNITION AND MANAGEMENT OF PESTICIDE POISONINGS, 3RD ED.). ADMINISTRATION OF ANTIDOTE MUST BE PERFORMED BY QUALIFIED MEDICAL PERSONNEL.

IN CASES OF SEVERE POISONING BY ORGANOPHOSPHATE PESTICIDES IN WHICH RESPIRATORY DEPRESSION, MUSCLE WEAKNESS AND TWITCHINGS ARE SEVERE, GIVE PRALIDOXIME (PROTOPAM-AYERST, 2-PAM), 1.0 GRAM INTRAVENOUSLY AT NO MORE THAN 0.5 GRAM PER MINUTE. DOSAGE OF PRALIDOXIME MAY BE REPEATED IN 1-2 HOURS, THEN AT 10-12 HOUR INTERVALS IF NEEDED. IN VERY SEVERE POISONINGS, DOSAGE RATES MAY BE DOUBLED. TREATMENT WITH PRALIDOXIME WILL BE MOST EFFECTIVE IF GIVEN WITHIN THIRTY-SIX HOURS AFTER POISONING (MORGAN, RECOGNITION AND MANAGEMENT OF PESTICIDE POISONINGS, 3RD ED.). ANTIDOTE SHOULD BE ADMINISTERED BY QUALIFIED MEDICAL PERSONNEL.

REACTIVITY

REACTIVITY: STABLE UNDER NORMAL TEMPERATURES AND PRESSURES.

INCOMPATIBILITIES: MORPHOTHION: OXIDIZERS (STRONG): FIRE AND EXPLOSION HAZARD.

DECOMPOSITION: THERMAL DECOMPOSITION PRODUCTS MAY INCLUDE TOXIC OXIDES OF NITROGEN, CARBON, PHOSPHORUS, AND SULFUR.

POLYMERIZATION: HAZARDOUS POLYMERIZATION HAS NOT BEEN REPORTED TO OCCUR UNDER NORMAL TEMPERATURES AND PRESSURES.

STORAGE AND DISPOSAL

OBSERVE ALL FEDERAL, STATE AND LOCAL REGULATIONS WHEN STORING OR DISPOSING OF THIS SUBSTANCE. FOR ASSISTANCE, CONTACT THE DISTRICT DIRECTOR OF THE ENVIRONMENTAL PROTECTION AGENCY.

****STORAGE****

STORE IN ACCORDANCE WITH 40 CFR 165 RECOMMENDED PROCEDURES FOR THE DISPOSAL AND STORAGE OF PESTICIDES AND PESTICIDE CONTAINERS.
STORE AWAY FROM INCOMPATIBLE SUBSTANCES.

****DISPOSAL****

DISPOSAL MUST BE IN ACCORDANCE WITH 40 CFR 165 RECOMMENDED PROCEDURES FOR THE DISPOSAL AND STORAGE OF PESTICIDES AND PESTICIDE CONTAINERS.

CONDITIONS TO AVOID

MAY BURN BUT DOES NOT IGNITE READILY. CONTAINERS MAY EXPLODE IN HEAT OF FIRE.

SPILL AND LEAK PROCEDURES

OCCUPATIONAL SPILL: DO NOT TOUCH SPILLED MATERIAL. STOP LEAK IF YOU CAN DO IT WITHOUT RISK. USE WATER SPRAY TO REDUCE VAPORS. FOR SMALL SPILLS,

TAKE UP WITH SAND OR OTHER ABSORBENT MATERIAL AND PLACE INTO CONTAINERS FOR LATER DISPOSAL. FOR SMALL DRY SPILLS, WITH A CLEAN SHOVEL PLACE MATERIAL INTO CLEAN, DRY CONTAINERS AND COVER. MOVE CONTAINERS FROM SPILL AREA. FOR LARGER SPILLS, DIKE FAR AHEAD OF SPILL FOR LATER DISPOSAL. KEEP UNNECESSARY PEOPLE AWAY. ISOLATE HAZARD AREA AND DENY ENTRY. VENTILATE CLOSED SPACES BEFORE ENTERING.

PROTECTIVE EQUIPMENT

VENTILATION: PROVIDE LOCAL EXHAUST OR PROCESS ENCLOSURE VENTILATION SYSTEM.

RESPIRATOR: THE FOLLOWING RESPIRATORS ARE RECOMMENDED BASED ON INFORMATION FOUND IN THE PHYSICAL DATA, TOXICITY AND HEALTH EFFECTS SECTIONS. THEY ARE RANKED IN ORDER FROM MINIMUM TO MAXIMUM RESPIRATORY PROTECTION. THE SPECIFIC RESPIRATOR SELECTED MUST BE BASED ON CONTAMINATION LEVELS FOUND IN THE WORK PLACE, MUST NOT EXCEED THE WORKING LIMITS OF THE RESPIRATOR AND BE JOINTLY APPROVED BY THE NATIONAL INSTITUTE FOR OCCUPATIONAL SAFETY AND HEALTH AND THE MINE SAFETY AND HEALTH ADMINISTRATION (NIOSH-MSHA).

TYPE 'C' SUPPLIED-AIR RESPIRATOR WITH A FULL FACEPIECE OPERATED IN PRESSURE-DEMAND OR OTHER POSITIVE PRESSURE MODE OR WITH A FULL FACEPIECE, HELMET OR HOOD OPERATED IN CONTINOUS-FLOW MODE.

SELF-CONTAINED BREATHING APPARATUS WITH A FULL FACEPIECE OPERATED IN PRESSURE-DEMAND OR OTHER POSITIVE PRESSURE MODE.

FOR FIREFIGHTING AND OTHER IMMEDIATELY DANGEROUS TO LIFE OR HEALTH CONDITIONS:

SELF-CONTAINED BREATHING APPARATUS WITH FULL FACEPIECE OPERATED IN PRESSURE-DEMAND OR OTHER POSITIVE PRESSURE MODE.

SUPPLIED-AIR RESPIRATOR WITH FULL FACEPIECE AND OPERATED IN PRESSURE-DEMAND OR OTHER POSITIVE PRESSURE MODE IN COMBINATION WITH AN AUXILIARY SELF-CONTAINED BREATHING APPARATUS OPERATED IN PRESSURE-DEMAND OR OTHER POSITIVE PRESSURE MODE.

CLOTHING: EMPLOYEE MUST WEAR APPROPRIATE PROTECTIVE (IMPERVIOUS) CLOTHING AND EQUIPMENT TO PREVENT ANY POSSIBILITY OF SKIN CONTACT WITH THIS SUBSTANCE.

GLOVES: EMPLOYEE MUST WEAR APPROPRIATE PROTECTIVE GLOVES TO PREVENT CONTACT WITH THIS SUBSTANCE.

EYE PROTECTION: EMPLOYEE MUST WEAR SPLASH-PROOF OR DUST-RESISTANT SAFETY GOGGLES WITH OR WITHOUT A FACESHIELD TO PREVENT CONTACT WITH THIS SUBSTANCE.

EMERGENCY EYE WASH: WHERE THERE IS ANY POSSIBILITY THAT AN EMPLOYEE'S EYES MAY BE EXPOSED TO THIS SUBSTANCE, THE EMPLOYER SHOULD PROVIDE AN EYE WASH FOUNTAIN WITHIN THE IMMEDIATE WORK AREA FOR EMERGENCY USE.

AUTHORIZED BY- OCCUPATIONAL HEALTH SERVICES, INC.

CREATION DATE: 10/04/88 ***REVISION DATE:*** 04/26/90

MATERIAL SAFETY DATA SHEET

OCCUPATIONAL HEALTH SERVICES, INC.
AGRICULTURE AND PESTICIDE DIVISION
450 SEVENTH AVENUE, SUITE 2407
NEW YORK, NEW YORK 10123
1-800-445-MSDS OR (212) 967-1100

EMERGENCY CONTACT:
JOHN S. BRANSFORD, JR. (615) 292-1180

SUBSTANCE IDENTIFICATION

CAS-NUMBER 2275-23-2

SUBSTANCE: VAMIDOTHION

TRADE NAMES/SYNONYMS: PHOSPHOROTHIOIC ACID, O,O-DIMETHYL S-(2-((1-METHYL-2-(METHYLAMINO) -2-OXOETHYL)THIO)ETHYL)ESTER; PHOSPHOROTHIOIC ACID, O,O-DIMETHYL ESTER, S-ESTER WITH 2-((2 -MERCAPTOETHYL)THIO)-N-METHYLPROPIONAMIDE; O,O-DIMETHYL S-(2-(1-METHYLCARBAMOYLETHYLTHIO)ETHYL PHOSPHOROTHIOATE; 2-(2-DIMETHOXYPHOSPHINOYLTHIOETHYLTHIO)-N-METHYLPROPIONAMIDE; O,O-DIMETHYL S-(2-((1-METHYL-2-(METHYLAMINO)-2-OXOETHYL)THIO)ETHYL PHOSPHOROTHIOATE; O,O-DIMETHYL PHOSPHOROTHIOATE, S-ESTER WITH 2-((2-MERCAPTOETHYL)THIO) -N-METHYLPROPIONAMIDE; KILVAL; TRUCIDOR; VAMIDOATE; ENT 26613; C8H18NO4PS2; PST73108

CHEMICAL FAMILY: PHOSPHOROTHIOATE

MOLECULAR FORMULA: C8-H18-N-04-P-S2

MOLECULAR WEIGHT: 287.36

CERCLA RATINGS (SCALE 0-3): HEALTH=3 FIRE=1 REACTIVITY=0 PERSISTENCE=1

NFPA RATINGS (SCALE 0-4): HEALTH=4 FIRE=1 REACTIVITY=0

COMPONENTS AND CONTAMINANTS

COMPONENT: VAMIDOTHION ***PERCENT:*** 100.0
CAS# 2275-23-2

OTHER CONTAMINANTS: NONE

EXPOSURE LIMITS: NO OCCUPATIONAL EXPOSURE LIMITS ESTABLISHED BY OSHA, ACGIH, OR NIOSH.

PHYSICAL DATA

DESCRIPTION: COLORLESS NEEDLES. ***MELTING POINT:*** 115-118 F (46-48 C)

SPECIFIC GRAVITY: NOT AVAILABLE ***VAPOR PRESSURE:*** NEGLIGIBLE

SOLUBILITY IN WATER: 400%

SOLVENT SOLUBILITY: SOLUBLE IN ANISOLE, BUTANONE, ETHYL ACETATE, ACETONE, AND MOST ORGANIC SOLVENTS; PRACTICALLY INSOLUBLE IN CYCLOHEXANE AND LIGHT PETROLEUM.

FIRE AND EXPLOSION DATA

FIRE AND EXPLOSION HAZARD: SLIGHT FIRE HAZARD WHEN EXPOSED TO HEAT OR FLAME.

FIREFIGHTING MEDIA: DRY CHEMICAL, CARBON DIOXIDE, HALON, WATER SPRAY OR STANDARD FOAM (1987 EMERGENCY RESPONSE GUIDEBOOK, DOT P 5800.4). FOR LARGER FIRES, USE WATER SPRAY, FOG OR STANDARD FOAM (1987 EMERGENCY RESPONSE GUIDEBOOK, DOT P 5800.4).

FIREFIGHTING: MOVE CONTAINERS FROM FIRE AREA IF POSSIBLE. FIGHT FIRE FROM MAXIMUM DISTANCE. STAY AWAY FROM STORAGE TANK ENDS. DIKE FIRE CONTROL WATER FOR LATER DISPOSAL. DO NOT SCATTER MATERIAL (1987 EMERGENCY RESPONSE GUIDEBOOK, DOT P 5800.4, GUIDE PAGE 55). EXTINGUISH ONLY IF FLOW CAN BE STOPPED; USE FLOODING AMOUNTS OF WATER AS FOG, SOLID STREAMS MAY BE INEFFECTIVE. COOL CONTAINERS WITH FLOODING AMOUNTS OF WATER FROM AS FAR A DISTANCE AS POSSIBLE. USE WATER SPRAY TO ABSORB TOXIC VAPORS. AVOID BREATHING TOXIC VAPORS; KEEP UPWIND. CONSIDER EVACUATION OF DOWNWIND AREA IF MATERIAL IS LEAKING.

TRANSPORTATION DATA

DEPARTMENT OF TRANSPORTATION HAZARD CLASSIFICATION 49 CFR 172.101: POISON B

DEPARTMENT OF TRANSPORTATION LABELING REQUIREMENTS 49 CFR 172.101 AND SUBPART E: POISON

DEPARTMENT OF TRANSPORTATION PACKAGING REQUIREMENTS: 49 (CFR 173.377 EXCEPTIONS: 49 CFR 173.377

TOXICITY

VAMIDOTHION: TOXICITY DATA: 160 MG/KG SKIN-RABBIT LD50; 1500 MG/KG SKIN-MOUSE LD50; 64 MG/KG ORAL-RAT LD50; 40 MG/KG ORAL-MOUSE LD50; 85 MG/KG ORAL-GUINEA PIG LD50; 110 MG/KG ORAL-DOG LD50; 64 MG/KG UNREPORTED-RAT LD50; 43 MG/KG UNREPORTED-MOUSE LD50; 85 MG/KG UNREPORTED-GUINEA PIG LD50; MUTAGENIC DATA (RTECS). CARCINOGEN STATUS: NONE. ACUTE TOXICITY LEVEL: HIGHLY TOXIC BY DERMAL ABSORPTION; TOXIC BY INGESTION. TARGET EFFECTS: CHOLINESTERASE INHIBITOR. POISONING MAY AFFECT THE NERVOUS SYSTEM.* AT INCREASED RISK FROM EXPOSURE: PERSONS WITH RESPIRATORY AILMENTS, RECENT EXPOSURE TO CHOLINESTERASE INHIBITORS OR IMPAIRED CHOLINESTERASE PRODUCTION, OR LIVER MALFUNCTION.* ADDITIONAL DATA: MAY CROSS THE PLACENTA. HIGH ENVIRONMENTAL TEMPERATURES OR EXPOSURE OF THE CHEMICAL TO VISIBLE OR ULTRAVIOLET LIGHT MAY ENHANCE THE TOXICITY. INTERACTIONS WITH MEDICATIONS MAY OCCUR.*

* MAY BE BASED ON GENERAL INFORMATION ON ORGANOPHOSPHATES.

HEALTH EFFECTS AND FIRST AID

INHALATION: VAMIDOTHION: SEE INFORMATION ON ORGANOPHOSPHATES. ORGANOPHOSPHATES: CHOLINESTERASE INHIBITOR. **ACUTE EXPOSURE-** WHEN INHALED, THE FIRST EFFECTS OF CHOLINESTERASE INHIBITORS ARE USUALLY RESPIRATORY AND MAY INCLUDE NASAL HYPEREMIA AND WATERY DISCHARGE, COUGH, CHEST DISCOMFORT, DYSPNEA, AND WHEEZING DUE TO INCREASED BRONCHIAL SECRETIONS AND BRONCHOCONSTRICTION. IF SUFFICIENT AMOUNTS ARE ABSORBED, OTHER SYSTEMIC EFFECTS MAY BEGIN WITHIN A FEW MINUTES OR BE DELAYED FOR UP TO 12 HOURS. SYMPTOMS MAY INCLUDE PALLOR, NAUSEA, VOMITING, DIARRHEA, ABDOMINAL CRAMPS, HEADACHE, DIZZINESS, OCULAR PAIN, BLURRED VISION, MIOSIS OR IN SOME CASES, ESPECIALLY INITIALLY, MYDRIASIS, LACRIMATION, SALIVATION, SWEATING, AND CONFUSION. OTHER REPORTED CENTRAL NERVOUS SYSTEM OR NEUROMUSCULAR EFFECTS MAY INCLUDE ATAXIA, SLURRED SPEECH, AREFLEXIA, WEAKNESS, FATIGUE,

FASCICULATIONS, TWITCHING, TREMORS POSSIBLY OF THE TONGUE AND EYELIDS, AND EVENTUALLY PARALYSIS OF THE EXTREMITIES AND POSSIBLY OF THE RESPIRATORY MUSCLES. IN SEVERE CASES THERE MAY ALSO BE INVOLUNTARY DEFECATION AND URINATION, CYANOSIS, PSYCHOSIS, HYPERGLYCEMIA, ACUTE PANCREATITIS, CARDIAC IRREGULARITIES, PULMONARY EDEMA, UNCONSCIOUSNESS, CONVULSIONS, AND COMA. DEATH IS PRIMARILY DUE TO RESPIRATORY FAILURE, ALTHOUGH CARDIOVASCULAR EFFECTS INCLUDING CARDIAC ARREST MAY ALSO BE IMPLICATED. LONG TERM SEQUELAE ARE RARE BUT MAY INCLUDE NEUROPSYCHIATRIC DISORDERS AND MYOPATHY WITH MUSCLE TENDERNESS. SOME ORGANOPHOSPHATES MAY CAUSE A DELAYED NEUROPATHY BEGINNING 1-4 WEEKS AFTER AN ACUTE EXPOSURE WHICH MAY OR MAY NOT HAVE CAUSED ACUTE CHOLINERGIC EFFECTS. NUMBNESS, TINGLING, WEAKNESS AND CRAMPING BEGINNING SYMMETRICALLY IN THE LOWER LIMBS MAY PROGRESS TO ATAXIA AND PARALYSIS. IN SEVERE CASES, UPPER LIMB INVOLVEMENT IS POSSIBLE AND FLACCID PARALYSIS MAY PROGRESS TO SPASTIC PARALYSIS WITH EXAGGERATED REFLEXES. IMPROVEMENT MAY OCCUR OVER MONTHS TO YEARS, BUT SOME RESIDUAL IMPAIRMENT USUALLY REMAINS. **CHRONIC EXPOSURE-** REPEATED OR PROLONGED EXPOSURE MAY RESULT IN THE EFFECTS OF ACUTE EXPOSURE INCLUDING THE DELAYED NEUROPATHY. OTHER EFFECTS REPORTED IN WORKERS REPEATEDLY EXPOSED INCLUDE IMPAIRED MEMORY AND CONCENTRATION, ACUTE PSYCHOSIS, SEVERE DEPRESSIONS, IRRITABILTY, CONFUSION, APATHY, EMOTIONAL LABILITY, SOCIAL WITHDRAWAL, CONFUSION, HEADACHE, SPEECH DIFFICULTIES, DELAYED REACTION TIMES, SPATIAL DISORIENTATION, NIGHTMARES, SLEEPWALKING, AND DROWSINESS OR INSOMNIA. AN INFLUENZA-LIKE CONDITION WITH HEADACHE, NAUSEA, WEAKNESS, ANOREXIA AND MALAISE HAS ALSO BEEN REPORTED.

FIRST AID- REMOVE FROM EXPOSURE AREA TO FRESH AIR IMMEDIATELY. IF BREATHING HAS STOPPED, GIVE ARTIFICIAL RESPIRATION. MAINTAIN AIRWAY AND BLOOD PRESSURE AND ADMINISTER OXYGEN IF AVAILABLE. KEEP AFFECTED PERSON WARM AND AT REST. TREAT SYMPTOMATICALLY AND SUPPORTIVELY. ADMINISTRATION OF OXYGEN SHOULD BE PERFORMED BY QUALIFIED PERSONNEL. GET MEDICAL ATTENTION IMMEDIATELY.

SKIN CONTACT: VAMIDOTHION: HIGHLY TOXIC. SEE INFORMATION ON ORGANOPHOSPHATES.

ORGANOPHOSPHATES: CHOLINESTERASE INHIBITOR. **ACUTE EXPOSURE-** LOCALIZED SWEATING AND FASCICULATIONS MAY OCCUR AT THE SITE OF CONTACT. IF SUFFICIENT AMOUNTS ARE ABSORBED, OTHER EFFECTS OF CHOLINESTERASE INHIBITION AS DESCRIBED IN ACUTE INHALATION MAY OCCUR. SYMPTOMS MAY BE DELAYED 2-3 HOURS, BUT USUALLY NO MORE THAN 12 HOURS. THE RATE OF ABSORPTION IS INCREASED BY THE PRESENCE OF DERMATITIS OR HIGH AMBIENT TEMPERATURES. DELAYED NEUROPATHY IS ALSO POSSIBLE. **CHRONIC EXPOSURE-** REPEATED OR PROLONGED EXPOSURE MAY CAUSE EFFECTS AS DESCRIBED IN ACUTE EXPOSURE. SOME ORGANOPHOSPHATES MAY CAUSE SENSITIZATION.

FIRST AID- REMOVE CONTAMINATED CLOTHING IMMEDIATELY. WASH CONTAMINATED AREAS WITH SOAP AND WATER FOLLOWED BY ALCOHOL (ARENA, POISONING, 4TH ED.). EMERGENCY PERSONNEL SHOULD WEAR GLOVES AND AVOID CONTAMINATION. TREAT RESPIRATORY DIFFICULTY WITH ARTIFICIAL RESPIRATION. GET MEDICAL ATTENTION IMMEDIATELY.

EYE CONTACT: VAMIDOTHION: SEE INFORMATION ON ORGANOPHOSPHATES.

ORGANOPHOSPHATES: CHOLINESTERASE INHIBITOR. **ACUTE EXPOSURE-** DIRECT CONTACT MAY CAUSE PAIN, HYPEREMIA, LACRIMATION, TWITCHING OF THE EYELIDS, MIOSIS, AND CILIARY MUSCLE SPASM WITH LOSS OF ACCOMODATION, BLURRED OR DIMMED VISION AND BROWACHE. SOMETIMES MYDRIASIS MAY OCCUR INSTEAD OF MIOSIS. WITH SUFFICIENT EXPOSURE, OTHER SYMPTOMS OF CHOLINESTERASE INHIBITION AS DESCRIBED IN ACUTE INHALATION MAY OCCUR. **CHRONIC EXPOSURE-** REPEATED OR PROLONGED EXPOSURE MAY CAUSE EFFECTS AS DESCRIBED IN ACUTE EXPOSURE. SOME COMPOUNDS HAVE CAUSED TOXIC EFFECTS ON THE CRYSTALLINE LENS, CONJUNCTIVAL THICKENING AND OBSTRUCTION OF THE NASOLACRIMAL CANALS WHEN USED AS MIOTIC EYEDROPS.

FIRST AID- IRRIGATE EYES WITH WATER OR SALINE SOLUTION. IF SYMPTOMS OF POISONING OCCUR, TREAT RESPIRATORY DIFFICULTY WITH ARTIFICIAL RESPIRATION AND OXYGEN. OBSERVE PATIENT FOR AT LEAST 24-36 HOURS (GOSSELIN, CLINICAL TOXICOLOGY OF COMMERCIAL PRODUCTS, 5TH ED.). GET MEDICAL ATTENTION IMMEDIATELY. OXYGEN SHOULD BE ADMINISTERED BY QUALIFIED MEDICAL PERSONNEL.

INGESTION: VAMIDOTHION: TOXIC. THE AVERAGE DAILY INTAKE IN MAN AT WHICH NO ADVERSE EFFECTS IS EXPECTED TO BE PRODUCED IS JUST OVER 50 UG/KG. SEE INFORMATION ON ORGANOPHOSPHATES.

ORGANOPHOSPHATES: CHOLINESTERASE INHIBITOR. **ACUTE EXPOSURE-** WHEN INGESTED, THE FIRST EFFECTS MAY BE NAUSEA, VOMITING, ANOREXIA, ABDOMINAL CRAMPS AND DIARRHEA. GASTROINTESTINAL ABSORPTION MAY CAUSE SYMPTOMS OF CHOLINESTERASE INHIBITION AS DESCRIBED IN ACUTE INHALATION. SYMPTOMS MAY BEGIN WITHIN MINUTES OR BE DELAYED FOR HOURS. DELAYED EFFECTS INCLUDING NEUROPATHY MAY ALSO OCCUR. **CHRONIC EXPOSURE-** REPEATED INGESTION MAY CAUSE EFFECTS AS DESCRIBED IN ACUTE EXPOSURE.

FIRST AID- IF PERSON IS ALERT AND RESPIRATION IS NOT DEPRESSED, GIVE SYRUP OF IPECAC FOLLOWED BY WATER (IF VOMITING OCCURS, KEEP HEAD BELOW HIPS TO PREVENT ASPIRATION). IF CONSCIOUSNESS LEVEL DECLINES OR VOMITING HAS NOT OCCURRED IN 15 MINUTES EMPTY STOMACH BY GASTRIC LAVAGE WITH THE AID OF CUFFED ENDOTRACHEAL TUBE USING ISOTONIC SALINE OR 5% SODIUM BICARBONATE FOLLOW WITH ACTIVATED CHARCOAL. ESTABLISH AND MAINTAIN AIRWAY. TREAT RESPIRATORY DIFFICULTY WITH ARTIFICIAL RESPIRATION AND OXYGEN. DO NOT GIVE MORPHINE, AMINOPHYLLINE, PHENOTHIAZINES, RESERPINE, FUROSEMIDE, OR ETHACRYNIC ACID (MORGAN, RECOGNITION AND MANAGEMENT OF PESTICIDE POISONINGS, 3RD ED.). TREAT SYMPTOMATICALLY AND SUPPORTIVELY. ADMINISTRATION OF OXYGEN AND LAVAGE MUST BE PERFORMED BY QUALIFIED MEDICAL PERSONNEL. GET MEDICAL ATTENTION IMMEDIATELY.

ANTIDOTE: THE FOLLOWING ANTIDOTE(S) HAVE BEEN RECOMMENDED. HOWEVER, THE DECISION AS TO WHETHER THE SEVERITY OF POISONING REQUIRES ADMINISTRATION OF ANY ANTIDOTE AND ACTUAL DOSE REQUIRED SHOULD BE MADE BY QUALIFIED MEDICAL PERSONNEL.

FOR CHOLINESTERASE INHIBITORS: ESTABLISH CLEAR AIRWAY AND TISSUE OXYGENATION BY ASPIRATION OF SECRETIONS, AND IF NECESSARY, BY ASSISTED PULMONARY VENTILATION WITH OXYGEN. IMPROVE TISSUE OXYGENATION AS MUCH AS POSSIBLE BEFORE ADMINISTERING ATROPINE TO MINIMIZE THE RISK OF VENTRICULAR FIBRILLATION. ADMINISTER ATROPINE SULFATE INTRAVENOUSLY, OR INTRAMUSCULARLY IF IV INJECTION IS NOT POSSIBLE. IN MODERATELY SEVERE POISONING ADMINISTER ATROPINE SULFATE, 0.4-2.0 MG REPEATED EVERY 15 MINUTES UNTIL ATROPINIZATION IS ACHIEVED (TACHYCARDIA, FLUSHING, DRY MOUTH, MYDRIASIS). MAINTAIN ATROPINIZATION BY REPEATED DOSES FOR 2-12 HOURS, OR LONGER, DEPENDING ON THE SEVERITY OF POISONING. THE APPEARANCE OF RALES IN THE LUNG BASES, MIOSIS, SALIVATION, NAUSEA, BRADYCARDIA, ARE ALL INDICATIONS OF INADEQUATE ATROPINIZATION. SEVERELY POISONED INDIVIDUALS MAY EXHIBIT REMARKABLE TOLERANCE TO ATROPINE; TWO OR MORE TIMES THE DOSAGES SUGGESTED ABOVE MAY BE NEEDED. PERSONS NOT POISONED OR ONLY SLIGHTLY POISONED, HOWEVER, MAY DEVELOP SIGNS OF ATROPINE TOXICITY FROM SUCH LARGE DOSAGES: FEVER, MUSCLE FIBRILLATIONS, AND DELIRIUM ARE THE MAIN SIGNS OF ATROPINE TOXICITY. IF THESE SIGNS APPEAR WHILE THE PATIENT IS FULLY ATROPINIZED, ATROPINE ADMINISTRATION SHOULD BE DISCONTINUED, AT LEAST TEMPORARILY. OBSERVE TREATED PATIENTS CLOSELY AT LEAST 24 HOURS TO INSURE THAT SYMPTOMS (POSSIBLY PULMONARY EDEMA) DO NOT RECUR AS ATROPINIZATION WEARS OFF. IN VERY SEVERE POISONINGS, METABOLIC DISPOSITION OF TOXICANT MAY REQUIRE SEVERAL HOURS OR DAYS DURING WHICH ATROPINIZATION MUST BE MAINTAINED. MARKEDLY LOWER LEVELS OF URINARY METABOLITES INDICATE THAT ATROPINE DOSAGE CAN BE TAPERED OFF. AS DOSAGE IS REDUCED, CHECK THE LUNG BASES FREQUENTLY FOR RALES. IF RALES ARE HEARD OR OTHER SYMPTOMS RETURN, RE-ESTABLISH ATROPINIZATION PROMPTLY (MORGAN, RECOGNITION AND MANAGEMENT OF PESTICIDE POISONINGS, 3RD ED.). ADMINISTRATION OF ANTIDOTE MUST BE PERFORMED BY QUALIFIED MEDICAL PERSONNEL.

IN CASES OF SEVERE POISONING BY ORGANOPHOSPHATE PESTICIDES IN WHICH RESPIRATORY DEPRESSION, MUSCLE WEAKNESS AND TWITCHINGS ARE SEVERE, GIVE PRALIDOXIME (PROTOPAM-AYERST, 2-PAM), 1.0 GRAM INTRAVENOUSLY AT NO MORE THAN 0.5 GRAM PER MINUTE. DOSAGE OF PRALIDOXIME MAY BE REPEATED IN 1-2 HOURS, THEN AT 10-12 HOUR INTERVALS IF NEEDED. IN VERY SEVERE POISONINGS, DOSAGE RATES MAY BE DOUBLED. TREATMENT WITH PRALIDOXIME WILL BE MOST EFFECTIVE IF GIVEN WITHIN THIRTY-SIX HOURS AFTER POISONING (MORGAN, RECOGNITION AND MANAGEMENT OF PESTICIDE POISONINGS, 3RD ED.). ANTIDOTE SHOULD BE ADMINISTERED BY QUALIFIED MEDICAL PERSONNEL.

REACTIVITY

REACTIVITY: STABLE UNDER NORMAL TEMPERATURES AND PRESSURES.

INCOMPATIBILITIES: VAMIDOTHION: OXIDIZERS (STRONG): FIRE AND EXPLOSION HAZARD.

DECOMPOSITION: THERMAL DECOMPOSITION PRODUCTS MAY INCLUDE TOXIC OXIDES OF NITROGEN, CARBON, PHOSPHORUS, AND SULFUR.

POLYMERIZATION: HAZARDOUS POLYMERIZATION HAS NOT BEEN REPORTED TO OCCUR UNDER NORMAL TEMPERATURES AND PRESSURES.

STORAGE AND DISPOSAL

OBSERVE ALL FEDERAL, STATE AND LOCAL REGULATIONS WHEN STORING OR DISPOSING OF THIS SUBSTANCE. FOR ASSISTANCE, CONTACT THE DISTRICT DIRECTOR OF THE ENVIRONMENTAL PROTECTION AGENCY.

STORAGE

STORE IN ACCORDANCE WITH 40 CFR 165 RECOMMENDED PROCEDURES FOR THE DISPOSAL AND STORAGE OF PESTICIDES AND PESTICIDE CONTAINERS.
STORE AWAY FROM INCOMPATIBLE SUBSTANCES.

DISPOSAL

DISPOSAL MUST BE IN ACCORDANCE WITH 40 CFR 165 RECOMMENDED PROCEDURES FOR THE DISPOSAL AND STORAGE OF PESTICIDES AND PESTICIDE CONTAINERS.

CONDITIONS TO AVOID

MAY BURN BUT DOES NOT IGNITE READILY. CONTAINERS MAY EXPLODE IN HEAT OF FIRE.

SPILL AND LEAK PROCEDURES

OCCUPATIONAL SPILL: DO NOT TOUCH SPILLED MATERIAL. STOP LEAK IF YOU CAN DO IT WITHOUT RISK. USE WATER SPRAY TO REDUCE VAPORS. FOR SMALL SPILLS, TAKE UP WITH SAND OR OTHER ABSORBENT MATERIAL AND PLACE INTO CONTAINERS FOR LATER DISPOSAL. FOR SMALL DRY SPILLS, WITH A CLEAN SHOVEL PLACE MATERIAL INTO CLEAN, DRY CONTAINERS AND COVER. MOVE CONTAINERS FROM SPILL AREA. FOR LARGER SPILLS, DIKE FAR AHEAD OF SPILL FOR LATER DISPOSAL. KEEP UNNECESSARY PEOPLE AWAY. ISOLATE HAZARD AREA AND DENY ENTRY. VENTILATE CLOSED SPACES BEFORE ENTERING.

PROTECTIVE EQUIPMENT

VENTILATION: PROCESS ENCLOSURE RECOMMENDED.

RESPIRATOR: THE FOLLOWING RESPIRATORS ARE RECOMMENDED BASED ON INFORMATION FOUND IN THE PHYSICAL DATA, TOXICITY AND HEALTH EFFECTS SECTIONS. THEY ARE RANKED IN ORDER FROM MINIMUM TO MAXIMUM RESPIRATORY PROTECTION. THE SPECIFIC RESPIRATOR SELECTED MUST BE BASED ON CONTAMINATION LEVELS FOUND IN THE WORK PLACE, MUST NOT EXCEED THE WORKING LIMITS OF THE RESPIRATOR AND BE JOINTLY APPROVED BY THE NATIONAL INSTITUTE FOR OCCUPATIONAL SAFETY AND HEALTH AND THE MINE SAFETY AND HEALTH ADMINISTRATION (NIOSH-MSHA).
TYPE 'C' SUPPLIED-AIR RESPIRATOR WITH A FULL FACEPIECE OPERATED IN PRESSURE-DEMAND OR OTHER POSITIVE PRESSURE MODE OR WITH A FULL FACEPIECE, HELMET OR HOOD OPERATED IN CONTINOUS-FLOW MODE.
SELF-CONTAINED BREATHING APPARATUS WITH A FULL FACEPIECE OPERATED IN PRESSURE-DEMAND OR OTHER POSITIVE PRESSURE MODE.
FOR FIREFIGHTING AND OTHER IMMEDIATELY DANGEROUS TO LIFE OR HEALTH CONDITIONS:
SELF-CONTAINED BREATHING APPARATUS WITH FULL FACEPIECE OPERATED IN PRESSURE-DEMAND OR OTHER POSITIVE PRESSURE MODE.
SUPPLIED-AIR RESPIRATOR WITH FULL FACEPIECE AND OPERATED IN PRESSURE-DEMAND OR OTHER POSITIVE PRESSURE MODE IN COMBINATION WITH AN AUXILIARY SELF-CONTAINED BREATHING APPARATUS OPERATED IN PRESSURE-DEMAND OR OTHER POSITIVE PRESSURE MODE.

CLOTHING: EMPLOYEE MUST WEAR APPROPRIATE PROTECTIVE (IMPERVIOUS) CLOTHING AND EQUIPMENT TO PREVENT ANY POSSIBILITY OF SKIN CONTACT WITH THIS SUBSTANCE.

GLOVES: EMPLOYEE MUST WEAR APPROPRIATE PROTECTIVE GLOVES TO PREVENT CONTACT WITH THIS SUBSTANCE.

EYE PROTECTION: EMPLOYEE MUST WEAR SPLASH-PROOF OR DUST-RESISTANT SAFETY GOGGLES WITH OR WITHOUT A FACESHIELD TO PREVENT CONTACT WITH THIS SUBSTANCE.
EMERGENCY EYE WASH: WHERE THERE IS ANY POSSIBILITY THAT AN EMPLOYEE'S EYES MAY BE EXPOSED TO THIS SUBSTANCE, THE EMPLOYER SHOULD PROVIDE AN EYE WASH FOUNTAIN WITHIN THE IMMEDIATE WORK AREA FOR EMERGENCY USE.

AUTHORIZED BY- OCCUPATIONAL HEALTH SERVICES, INC.
CREATION DATE: 10/05/89 ***REVISION DATE:*** 04/26/90

MATERIAL SAFETY DATA SHEET

OCCUPATIONAL HEALTH SERVICES, INC.
AGRICULTURE AND PESTICIDE DIVISION
450 SEVENTH AVENUE, SUITE 2407
NEW YORK, NEW YORK 10123
1-800-445-MSDS OR (212) 967-1100

EMERGENCY CONTACT:
JOHN S. BRANSFORD, JR. (615) 292-1180

SUBSTANCE IDENTIFICATION

CAS-NUMBER 13593-03-8

SUBSTANCE: QUINALPHOS

TRADE NAMES/SYNONYMS: PHOSPHOROTHIOIC ACID, O,O-DIETHYL-O-2-QUINOXALINYL ESTER; O,O-DIETHYL O-2-QUINOXALINYL PHOSPHOROTHIOATE; O,O-DIETHYL O-QUINOXALIN-2-YL PHOSPHOROTHIOATE; BAY 77049; BAYER 77049; BAYRUSIL; CHINALPHOS; DIETHQUINALPHIONE; EKALUX; QUINALPHOS-ETHYL; SANDOZ 6538; SANDOZ 6626; C12H15N2O3PS; PST73112

CHEMICAL FAMILY: PHOSPHOROTHIOATE

MOLECULAR FORMULA: C12-H15-N2-O3-P-S

MOLECULAR WEIGHT: 298.32

CERCLA RATINGS (SCALE 0-3): HEALTH=3 FIRE=1 REACTIVITY=0 PERSISTENCE=1

NFPA RATINGS (SCALE 0-4): HEALTH=4 FIRE=1 REACTIVITY=0

COMPONENTS AND CONTAMINANTS

COMPONENT: QUINALPHOS ***PERCENT:*** 100.0
CAS# 13593-03-8

OTHER CONTAMINANTS: NONE

EXPOSURE LIMITS: NO OCCUPATIONAL EXPOSURE LIMITS ESTABLISHED BY OSHA, ACGIH, OR NIOSH.

PHYSICAL DATA

DESCRIPTION: COLORLESS CRYSTALLINE SOLID.

BOILING POINT: 288 F (142 C) @ 0.0003 MMHG (DECOMPOSES)

MELTING POINT: 88-90 F (31-32 C) ***SPECIFIC GRAVITY:*** 1.235

VAPOR PRESSURE: 0.002595 MMHG @ 20 C

SOLUBILITY IN WATER: 0.0022% @ 24 C

SOLVENT SOLUBILITY: SOLUBLE IN ACETONE, CHLOROFORM, ETHER, DIMETHYL SULFOXIDE, ACETONITRILE, ETHYL ACETATE, ETHANOL, METHANOL, XYLENE, HEXANE, TOLUENE, AND AROMATIC HYDROCARBONS; SLIGHTLY SOLUBLE IN LIGHT PETROLEUM.

FIRE AND EXPLOSION DATA

FIRE AND EXPLOSION HAZARD: SLIGHT FIRE HAZARD WHEN EXPOSED TO HEAT OR FLAME.

FIREFIGHTING MEDIA: DRY CHEMICAL, CARBON DIOXIDE, HALON, WATER SPRAY OR STANDARD FOAM (1987 EMERGENCY RESPONSE GUIDEBOOK, DOT P 5800.4).
FOR LARGER FIRES, USE WATER SPRAY, FOG OR STANDARD FOAM (1987 EMERGENCY RESPONSE GUIDEBOOK, DOT P 5800.4).

FIREFIGHTING: MOVE CONTAINERS FROM FIRE AREA IF POSSIBLE. FIGHT FIRE FROM MAXIMUM DISTANCE. STAY AWAY FROM STORAGE TANK ENDS. DIKE FIRE CONTROL WATER FOR LATER DISPOSAL. DO NOT SCATTER MATERIAL (1987 EMERGENCY RESPONSE GUIDEBOOK, DOT P 5800.4, GUIDE PAGE 55).
EXTINGUISH ONLY IF FLOW CAN BE STOPPED; USE FLOODING AMOUNTS OF WATER AS FOG. SOLID STREAMS MAY BE INEFFECTIVE. COOL CONTAINERS WITH FLOODING AMOUNTS OF WATER FROM AS FAR A DISTANCE AS POSSIBLE. USE WATER SPRAY TO ABSORB TOXIC VAPORS. AVOID BREATHING TOXIC VAPORS; KEEP UPWIND. CONSIDER EVACUATION OF DOWNWIND AREA IF MATERIAL IS LEAKING.

TRANSPORTATION DATA

DEPARTMENT OF TRANSPORTATION HAZARD CLASSIFICATION 49 CFR 172.101: POISON B
DEPARTMENT OF TRANSPORTATION LABELING REQUIREMENTS 49 CFR 172.101 AND SUBPART E: POISON
DEPARTMENT OF TRANSPORTATION PACKAGING REQUIREMENTS: 49 (CFR 173.377 EXCEPTIONS: 49 CFR 173.377

TOXICITY

QUINALPHOS: TOXICITY DATA: 175 MG/M3 INHALATION-RAT LC50; 300 MG/KG SKIN-RAT LD50; 26 MG/KG ORAL-RAT LD50; 107 MG/KG ORAL-MOUSE LD50; 8500 UG/KG ORAL-DOMESTIC ANIMAL LDLO; 100 MG/KG ORAL-DOG LD50; 11,910 UG/KG INTRAPERITONEAL-GERBIL LD50; 10,250 UG/KG PARENTERAL-CHICKEN LD50; 10,500 UG/KG PARENTERAL-PIGEON LD50; REPRODUCTIVE EFFECTS DATA (RTECS). CARCINOGEN STATUS: NONE. ACUTE TOXICITY: HIGHLY TOXIC BY INHALATION AND INGESTION; TOXIC BY DERMAL ABSORPTION. TARGET EFFECTS: CHOLINESTERASE INHIBITOR. POISONING MAY AFFECT THE NERVOUS SYSTEM.* AT INCREASED RISK FROM EXPOSURE: PERSONS WITH RESPIRATORY AILMENTS, RECENT EXPOSURE TO CHOLINESTERASE INHIBITORS OR IMPAIRED CHOLINESTERASE PRODUCTION, OR LIVER MALFUNCTION.* ADDITIONAL DATA: MAY CROSS THE PLACENTA. HIGH ENVIRONMENTAL TEMPERATURES OR EXPOSURE OF THE CHEMICAL TO VISIBLE OR ULTRAVIOLET LIGHT MAY ENHANCE THE TOXICITY. INTERACTIONS WITH MEDICATIONS MAY OCCUR.*
* MAY BE BASED ON GENERAL INFORMATION ON ORGANOPHOSPHATES.

HEALTH EFFECTS AND FIRST AID

INHALATION: QUINALPHOS: HIGHLY TOXIC. SEE INFORMATION ON ORGANOPHOSPHATES.

ORGANOPHOSPHATES: CHOLINESTERASE INHIBITOR. **ACUTE EXPOSURE-** WHEN INHALED, THE FIRST EFFECTS OF CHOLINESTERASE INHIBITORS ARE USUALLY RESPIRATORY AND MAY INCLUDE NASAL HYPEREMIA AND WATERY DISCHARGE, COUGH, CHEST DISCOMFORT, DYSPNEA, AND WHEEZING DUE TO INCREASED BRONCHIAL SECRETIONS AND BRONCHOCONSTRICTION. IF SUFFICIENT AMOUNTS ARE ABSORBED, OTHER SYSTEMIC EFFECTS MAY BEGIN WITHIN A FEW MINUTES OR BE DELAYED FOR UP TO 12 HOURS. SYMPTOMS MAY INCLUDE PALLOR, NAUSEA, VOMITING, DIARRHEA, ABDOMINAL CRAMPS, HEADACHE, DIZZINESS, OCULAR PAIN, BLURRED VISION, MIOSIS OR IN SOME CASES, ESPECIALLY INITIALLY, MYDRIASIS, LACRIMATION, SALIVATION, SWEATING, AND CONFUSION. OTHER REPORTED CENTRAL NERVOUS SYSTEM OR NEUROMUSCULAR EFFECTS MAY INCLUDE ATAXIA, SLURRED SPEECH, AREFLEXIA, WEAKNESS, FATIGUE, FASCICULATIONS, TWITCHING, TREMORS POSSIBLY OF THE TONGUE AND EYELIDS, AND EVENTUALLY PARALYSIS OF THE EXTREMITIES AND POSSIBLY OF THE RESPIRATORY MUSCLES. IN SEVERE CASES THERE MAY ALSO BE INVOLUNTARY DEFECATION AND URINATION, CYANOSIS, PSYCHOSIS, HYPERGLYCEMIA, ACUTE PANCREATITIS, CARDIAC IRREGULARITIES, PULMONARY EDEMA, UNCONSCIOUSNESS, CONVULSIONS, AND COMA. DEATH IS PRIMARILY DUE TO RESPIRATORY FAILURE, ALTHOUGH CARDIOVASCULAR EFFECTS INCLUDING CARDIAC ARREST MAY ALSO BE IMPLICATED. LONG TERM SEQUELAE ARE RARE BUT MAY INCLUDE NEUROPSYCHIATRIC DISORDERS AND MYOPATHY WITH MUSCLE TENDERNESS. SOME ORGANOPHOSPHATES MAY CAUSE A DELAYED NEUROPATHY BEGINNING 1-4 WEEKS AFTER AN ACUTE EXPOSURE WHICH MAY OR MAY NOT HAVE CAUSED ACUTE CHOLINERGIC EFFECTS. NUMBNESS, TINGLING, WEAKNESS AND CRAMPING BEGINNING SYMMETRICALLY IN THE LOWER LIMBS MAY PROGRESS TO ATAXIA AND PARALYSIS. IN SEVERE CASES, UPPER LIMB INVOLVEMENT IS POSSIBLE AND FLACCID PARALYSIS MAY PROGRESS TO SPASTIC PARALYSIS WITH EXAGGERATED REFLEXES. IMPROVEMENT MAY OCCUR OVER MONTHS TO YEARS, BUT SOME RESIDUAL IMPAIRMENT USUALLY REMAINS. **CHRONIC EXPOSURE-** REPEATED OR PROLONGED EXPOSURE MAY RESULT IN THE EFFECTS OF ACUTE EXPOSURE INCLUDING THE DELAYED NEUROPATHY. OTHER EFFECTS REPORTED IN WORKERS REPEATEDLY EXPOSED INCLUDE IMPAIRED MEMORY AND CONCENTRATION, ACUTE PSYCHOSIS, SEVERE DEPRESSIONS, IRRITABILTY, CONFUSION, APATHY, EMOTIONAL LABILITY, SOCIAL WITHDRAWAL, CONFUSION, HEADACHE, SPEECH DIFFICULTIES, DELAYED REACTION TIMES, SPATIAL DISORIENTATION, NIGHTMARES, SLEEPWALKING, AND DROWSINESS OR INSOMNIA. AN INFLUENZA-LIKE CONDITION WITH HEADACHE, NAUSEA, WEAKNESS, ANOREXIA AND MALAISE HAS ALSO BEEN REPORTED.

FIRST AID- REMOVE FROM EXPOSURE AREA TO FRESH AIR IMMEDIATELY. IF BREATHING HAS STOPPED, GIVE ARTIFICIAL RESPIRATION. MAINTAIN AIRWAY AND BLOOD PRESSURE AND ADMINISTER OXYGEN IF AVAILABLE. KEEP AFFECTED PERSON WARM AND AT REST. TREAT SYMPTOMATICALLY AND SUPPORTIVELY. ADMINISTRATION OF OXYGEN SHOULD BE PERFORMED BY QUALIFIED PERSONNEL. GET MEDICAL ATTENTION IMMEDIATELY.

SKIN CONTACT: QUINALPHOS: TOXIC. SEE INFORMATION ON ORGANOPHOSPHATES.

ORGANOPHOSPHATES: CHOLINESTERASE INHIBITOR. **ACUTE EXPOSURE-** LOCALIZED SWEATING AND FASCICULATIONS MAY OCCUR AT THE SITE OF CONTACT. IF SUFFICIENT AMOUNTS ARE ABSORBED, OTHER EFFECTS OF CHOLINESTERASE INHIBITION AS DESCRIBED IN ACUTE INHALATION MAY OCCUR. SYMPTOMS MAY BE DELAYED 2-3 HOURS, BUT USUALLY NO MORE THAN 12 HOURS. THE RATE OF ABSORPTION IS INCREASED BY THE PRESENCE OF DERMATITIS OR HIGH AMBIENT TEMPERATURES. DELAYED NEUROPATHY IS ALSO POSSIBLE. **CHRONIC EXPOSURE-** REPEATED OR PROLONGED EXPOSURE MAY CAUSE EFFECTS AS DESCRIBED IN ACUTE EXPOSURE. SOME ORGANOPHOSPHATES MAY CAUSE SENSITIZATION.

FIRST AID- REMOVE CONTAMINATED CLOTHING IMMEDIATELY. WASH CONTAMINATED AREAS WITH SOAP AND WATER FOLLOWED BY ALCOHOL (ARENA, POISONING, 4TH ED.). EMERGENCY PERSONNEL SHOULD WEAR GLOVES AND AVOID CONTAMINATION. TREAT RESPIRATORY DIFFICULTY WITH ARTIFICIAL RESPIRATION. GET MEDICAL ATTENTION IMMEDIATELY.

EYE CONTACT: QUINALPHOS: SEE INFORMATION ON ORGANOPHOSPHATES.

ORGANOPHOSPHATES: CHOLINESTERASE INHIBITOR. **ACUTE EXPOSURE-** DIRECT CONTACT MAY CAUSE PAIN, HYPEREMIA, LACRIMATION, TWITCHING OF THE EYELIDS, MIOSIS, AND CILIARY MUSCLE SPASM WITH LOSS OF ACCOMODATION, BLURRED OR DIMMED VISION AND BROWACHE. SOMETIMES MYDRIASIS MAY OCCUR INSTEAD OF MIOSIS. WITH SUFFICIENT EXPOSURE, OTHER SYMPTOMS OF CHOLINESTERASE INHIBITION AS DESCRIBED IN ACUTE INHALATION MAY OCCUR. **CHRONIC EXPOSURE-** REPEATED OR PROLONGED EXPOSURE MAY CAUSE EFFECTS AS DESCRIBED IN ACUTE EXPOSURE. SOME COMPOUNDS HAVE CAUSED TOXIC EFFECTS ON THE CRYSTALLINE LENS, CONJUNCTIVAL THICKENING AND OBSTRUCTION OF THE NASOLACRIMAL CANALS WHEN USED AS MIOTIC EYEDROPS.

FIRST AID- IRRIGATE EYES WITH WATER OR SALINE SOLUTION. IF SYMPTOMS OF POISONING OCCUR, TREAT RESPIRATORY DIFFICULTY WITH ARTIFICIAL RESPIRATION AND OXYGEN. OBSERVE PATIENT FOR AT LEAST 24-36 HOURS (GOSSELIN, CLINICAL TOXICOLOGY OF COMMERCIAL PRODUCTS, 5TH ED.). GET MEDICAL ATTENTION IMMEDIATELY. OXYGEN SHOULD BE ADMINISTERED BY QUALIFIED MEDICAL PERSONNEL.

INGESTION: QUINALPHOS: HIGHLY TOXIC. REPRODUCTIVE EFFECTS HAVE BEEN REPORTED IN ANIMALS. SEE INFORMATION ON ORGANOPHOSPHATES.

ORGANOPHOSPHATES: CHOLINESTERASE INHIBITOR. **ACUTE EXPOSURE-** WHEN INGESTED, THE FIRST EFFECTS MAY BE NAUSEA, VOMITING, ANOREXIA, ABDOMINAL CRAMPS AND DIARRHEA. GASTROINTESTINAL ABSORPTION MAY CAUSE SYMPTOMS OF CHOLINESTERASE INHIBITION AS DESCRIBED IN ACUTE INHALATION. SYMPTOMS MAY BEGIN WITHIN MINUTES OR BE DELAYED FOR HOURS. DELAYED EFFECTS INCLUDING NEUROPATHY MAY ALSO OCCUR. **CHRONIC EXPOSURE-** REPEATED INGESTION MAY CAUSE EFFECTS AS DESCRIBED IN ACUTE EXPOSURE.

FIRST AID- IF PERSON IS ALERT AND RESPIRATION IS NOT DEPRESSED, GIVE SYRUP OF IPECAC FOLLOWED BY WATER (IF VOMITING OCCURS, KEEP HEAD BELOW HIPS TO PREVENT ASPIRATION). IF CONSCIOUSNESS LEVEL DECLINES OR VOMITING HAS NOT OCCURRED IN 15 MINUTES EMPTY STOMACH BY GASTRIC LAVAGE WITH THE AID OF CUFFED ENDOTRACHEAL TUBE USING ISOTONIC SALINE OR 5% SODIUM BICARBONATE FOLLOW WITH ACTIVATED CHARCOAL. ESTABLISH AND MAINTAIN AIRWAY. TREAT RESPIRATORY DIFFICULTY WITH ARTIFICIAL RESPIRATION AND OXYGEN. DO NOT GIVE MORPHINE, AMINOPHYLLINE, PHENOTHIAZINES, RESERPINE, FUROSEMIDE, OR ETHACRYNIC ACID (MORGAN, RECOGNITION AND MANAGEMENT OF PESTICIDE POISONINGS, 3RD ED.). TREAT SYMPTOMATICALLY AND SUPPORTIVELY. ADMINISTRATION OF OXYGEN AND LAVAGE MUST BE PERFORMED BY QUALIFIED MEDICAL PERSONNEL. GET MEDICAL ATTENTION IMMEDIATELY.

ANTIDOTE: THE FOLLOWING ANTIDOTE(S) HAVE BEEN RECOMMENDED. HOWEVER, THE DECISION AS TO WHETHER THE SEVERITY OF POISONING REQUIRES ADMINISTRATION OF ANY ANTIDOTE AND ACTUAL DOSE REQUIRED SHOULD BE MADE BY QUALIFIED MEDICAL PERSONNEL.

FOR CHOLINESTERASE INHIBITORS: ESTABLISH CLEAR AIRWAY AND TISSUE OXYGENATION BY ASPIRATION OF SECRETIONS, AND IF NECESSARY, BY ASSISTED PULMONARY VENTILATION WITH OXYGEN. IMPROVE TISSUE OXYGENATION AS MUCH AS POSSIBLE BEFORE ADMINISTERING ATROPINE TO MINIMIZE THE RISK OF VENTRICULAR FIBRILLATION. ADMINISTER ATROPINE SULFATE INTRAVENOUSLY, OR INTRAMUSCULARLY IF IV INJECTION IS NOT POSSIBLE. IN MODERATELY SEVERE POISONING ADMINISTER ATROPINE SULFATE, 0.4-2.0 MG REPEATED EVERY 15 MINUTES UNTIL ATROPINIZATION IS ACHIEVED (TACHYCARDIA, FLUSHING, DRY MOUTH, MYDRIASIS). MAINTAIN ATROPINIZATION BY REPEATED DOSES FOR 2-12 HOURS, OR LONGER, DEPENDING ON THE SEVERITY OF POISONING. THE APPEARANCE OF RALES IN THE LUNG BASES, MIOSIS, SALIVATION, NAUSEA, BRADYCARDIA, ARE ALL INDICATIONS OF INADEQUATE ATROPINIZATION. SEVERELY POISONED INDIVIDUALS MAY EXHIBIT REMARKABLE TOLERANCE TO ATROPINE; TWO OR MORE TIMES THE DOSAGES SUGGESTED ABOVE MAY BE NEEDED. PERSONS NOT POISONED OR ONLY SLIGHTLY POISONED, HOWEVER, MAY DEVELOP SIGNS OF ATROPINE TOXICITY FROM SUCH LARGE DOSAGES: FEVER, MUSCLE FIBRILLATIONS, AND DELIRIUM ARE THE MAIN SIGNS OF ATROPINE TOXICITY. IF THESE SIGNS APPEAR WHILE THE PATIENT IS FULLY ATROPINIZED, ATROPINE ADMINISTRATION SHOULD BE DISCONTINUED, AT LEAST TEMPORARILY. OBSERVE TREATED PATIENTS CLOSELY AT LEAST 24 HOURS TO INSURE THAT SYMPTOMS (POSSIBLY PULMONARY EDEMA) DO NOT RECUR AS ATROPINIZATION WEARS OFF. IN VERY SEVERE POISONINGS, METABOLIC DISPOSITION OF TOXICANT MAY REQUIRE SEVERAL HOURS OR DAYS DURING WHICH ATROPINIZATION MUST BE MAINTAINED. MARKEDLY LOWER LEVELS OF URINARY METABOLITES INDICATE THAT ATROPINE DOSAGE CAN BE TAPERED OFF. AS DOSAGE IS REDUCED, CHECK THE LUNG BASES FREQUENTLY FOR RALES. IF RALES ARE HEARD OR OTHER SYMPTOMS RETURN, RE-ESTABLISH ATROPINIZATION PROMPTLY (MORGAN, RECOGNITION AND MANAGEMENT OF PESTICIDE POISONINGS, 3RD ED.). ADMINISTRATION OF ANTIDOTE MUST BE PERFORMED BY QUALIFIED MEDICAL PERSONNEL.

IN CASES OF SEVERE POISONING BY ORGANOPHOSPHATE PESTICIDES IN WHICH RESPIRATORY DEPRESSION, MUSCLE WEAKNESS AND TWITCHINGS ARE SEVERE, GIVE PRALIDOXIME (PROTOPAM-AYERST, 2-PAM), 1.0 GRAM INTRAVENOUSLY AT NO MORE THAN 0.5 GRAM PER MINUTE. DOSAGE OF PRALIDOXIME MAY BE REPEATED IN 1-2 HOURS, THEN AT 10-12 HOUR INTERVALS IF NEEDED. IN VERY SEVERE POISONINGS, DOSAGE RATES MAY BE DOUBLED. TREATMENT WITH PRALIDOXIME WILL BE MOST EFFECTIVE IF GIVEN WITHIN THIRTY-SIX HOURS AFTER POISONING (MORGAN, RECOGNITION AND MANAGEMENT OF PESTICIDE POISONINGS, 3RD ED.). ANTIDOTE SHOULD BE ADMINISTERED BY QUALIFIED MEDICAL PERSONNEL.

REACTIVITY

REACTIVITY: STABLE UNDER NORMAL TEMPERATURES AND PRESSURES.

INCOMPATIBILITIES: QUINALPHOS: OXIDIZERS (STRONG): FIRE AND EXPLOSION HAZARD.

DECOMPOSITION: THERMAL DECOMPOSITION PRODUCTS MAY INCLUDE TOXIC OXIDES OF NITROGEN, CARBON, PHOSPHORUS, AND SULFUR.

POLYMERIZATION: HAZARDOUS POLYMERIZATION HAS NOT BEEN REPORTED TO OCCUR UNDER NORMAL TEMPERATURES AND PRESSURES.

STORAGE AND DISPOSAL

OBSERVE ALL FEDERAL, STATE AND LOCAL REGULATIONS WHEN STORING OR DISPOSING OF THIS SUBSTANCE. FOR ASSISTANCE, CONTACT THE DISTRICT DIRECTOR OF THE ENVIRONMENTAL PROTECTION AGENCY.

STORAGE

STORE IN ACCORDANCE WITH 40 CFR 165 RECOMMENDED PROCEDURES FOR THE DISPOSAL AND STORAGE OF PESTICIDES AND PESTICIDE CONTAINERS.
STORE AWAY FROM INCOMPATIBLE SUBSTANCES.

DISPOSAL

DISPOSAL MUST BE IN ACCORDANCE WITH 40 CFR 165 RECOMMENDED PROCEDURES FOR THE DISPOSAL AND STORAGE OF PESTICIDES AND PESTICIDE CONTAINERS.

CONDITIONS TO AVOID

MAY BURN BUT DOES NOT IGNITE READILY. CONTAINERS MAY EXPLODE IN HEAT OF FIRE.

SPILL AND LEAK PROCEDURES

OCCUPATIONAL SPILL: DO NOT TOUCH SPILLED MATERIAL. STOP LEAK IF YOU CAN DO IT WITHOUT RISK. USE WATER SPRAY TO REDUCE VAPORS. FOR SMALL SPILLS, TAKE UP WITH SAND OR OTHER ABSORBENT MATERIAL AND PLACE INTO CONTAINERS FOR LATER DISPOSAL. FOR SMALL DRY SPILLS, WITH A CLEAN SHOVEL PLACE MATERIAL INTO CLEAN, DRY CONTAINERS AND COVER. MOVE CONTAINERS FROM SPILL AREA. FOR LARGER SPILLS, DIKE FAR AHEAD OF SPILL FOR LATER DISPOSAL. KEEP UNNECESSARY PEOPLE AWAY. ISOLATE HAZARD AREA AND DENY ENTRY. VENTILATE CLOSED SPACES BEFORE ENTERING.

PROTECTIVE EQUIPMENT

VENTILATION: PROCESS ENCLOSURE RECOMMENDED.

RESPIRATOR: THE FOLLOWING RESPIRATORS ARE RECOMMENDED BASED ON INFORMATION FOUND IN THE PHYSICAL DATA, TOXICITY AND HEALTH EFFECTS SECTIONS. THEY ARE RANKED IN ORDER FROM MINIMUM TO MAXIMUM RESPIRATORY PROTECTION. THE SPECIFIC RESPIRATOR SELECTED MUST BE BASED ON CONTAMINATION LEVELS FOUND IN THE WORK PLACE, MUST NOT EXCEED THE WORKING LIMITS OF THE RESPIRATOR AND BE JOINTLY APPROVED BY THE NATIONAL INSTITUTE FOR OCCUPATIONAL SAFETY AND HEALTH AND THE MINE SAFETY AND HEALTH ADMINISTRATION (NIOSH-MSHA).
TYPE 'C' SUPPLIED-AIR RESPIRATOR WITH A FULL FACEPIECE OPERATED IN PRESSURE-DEMAND OR OTHER POSITIVE PRESSURE MODE OR WITH A FULL FACEPIECE, HELMET OR HOOD OPERATED IN CONTINOUS-FLOW MODE.
SELF-CONTAINED BREATHING APPARATUS WITH A FULL FACEPIECE OPERATED IN PRESSURE-DEMAND OR OTHER POSITIVE PRESSURE MODE.
FOR FIREFIGHTING AND OTHER IMMEDIATELY DANGEROUS TO LIFE OR HEALTH CONDITIONS:
SELF-CONTAINED BREATHING APPARATUS WITH FULL FACEPIECE OPERATED IN PRESSURE-DEMAND OR OTHER POSITIVE PRESSURE MODE.
SUPPLIED-AIR RESPIRATOR WITH FULL FACEPIECE AND OPERATED IN PRESSURE-DEMAND OR OTHER POSITIVE PRESSURE MODE IN COMBINATION WITH AN AUXILIARY SELF-CONTAINED BREATHING APPARATUS OPERATED IN PRESSURE-DEMAND OR OTHER POSITIVE PRESSURE MODE.

CLOTHING: EMPLOYEE MUST WEAR APPROPRIATE PROTECTIVE (IMPERVIOUS) CLOTHING AND EQUIPMENT TO PREVENT ANY POSSIBILITY OF SKIN CONTACT WITH THIS SUBSTANCE.

GLOVES: EMPLOYEE MUST WEAR APPROPRIATE PROTECTIVE GLOVES TO PREVENT CONTACT WITH THIS SUBSTANCE.

EYE PROTECTION: EMPLOYEE MUST WEAR SPLASH-PROOF OR DUST-RESISTANT SAFETY GOGGLES WITH OR WITHOUT A FACESHIELD TO PREVENT CONTACT WITH THIS SUBSTANCE.
EMERGENCY EYE WASH: WHERE THERE IS ANY POSSIBILITY THAT AN EMPLOYEE'S EYES MAY BE EXPOSED TO THIS SUBSTANCE, THE EMPLOYER SHOULD PROVIDE AN EYE WASH FOUNTAIN WITHIN THE IMMEDIATE WORK AREA FOR EMERGENCY USE.

AUTHORIZED BY- OCCUPATIONAL HEALTH SERVICES, INC.
CREATION DATE: 10/04/89 ***REVISION DATE:*** 04/27/90

MATERIAL SAFETY DATA SHEET

OCCUPATIONAL HEALTH SERVICES, INC.
AGRICULTURE AND PESTICIDE DIVISION
450 SEVENTH AVENUE, SUITE 2407
NEW YORK, NEW YORK 10123
1-800-445-MSDS OR (212) 967-1100

EMERGENCY CONTACT:
JOHN S. BRANSFORD, JR. (615) 292-1180

SUBSTANCE IDENTIFICATION

CAS-NUMBER 6988-21-2

SUBSTANCE: **DIOXACARB**

TRADE NAMES/SYNONYMS: PHENOL, 2-(1,3-DIOXOLAN-2YL)-, METHYLCARBAMATE; CARBAMIC ACID, METHYL-, O-1,3-DIOXOLAN-2-YLPHENYL ESTER; 2-(1,3-DIOXOLAN-2YL)PHENOL METHYLCARBAMATE; METHYLCARBAMIC ACID O-1,3-DIOXOLAN-2-YLPHENYL ESTER; 2-(1,3-DIOXOLAN-2-YL)PHENYL METHYLCARBAMATE; O-1,3-DIOXOLAN-2-YLPHENYL METHYLCARBAMATE; 2-(1,3-DIOXOLAN-2-YL)PHENYL-N-METHYLCARBAMATE; C 8353; ELOCRON; FAMID; OMS 1102; ENT 27389; C11H13NO4; PST73123

CHEMICAL FAMILY: CARBAMATE

MOLECULAR FORMULA: C11-H13-N-O4

MOLECULAR WEIGHT: 223.25

CERCLA RATINGS (SCALE 0-3): HEALTH=3 FIRE=1 REACTIVITY=0 PERSISTENCE=1

NFPA RATINGS (SCALE 0-4): HEALTH=4 FIRE=1 REACTIVITY=0

COMPONENTS AND CONTAMINANTS

COMPONENT: DIOXACARB ***PERCENT:*** 100.0
CAS# 6988-21-2

OTHER CONTAMINANTS: NONE

EXPOSURE LIMITS: NO OCCUPATIONAL EXPOSURE LIMITS ESTABLISHED BY OSHA, ACGIH, OR NIOSH.

PHYSICAL DATA

DESCRIPTION: COLORLESS TO WHITE CRYSTALS WITH A SLIGHT ODOR.

MELTING POINT: 237-239 F (114-115 C) ***SPECIFIC GRAVITY:*** 1.46 @ 20 C

VAPOR PRESSURE: NEGLIGIBLE ***SOLUBILITY IN WATER:*** 0.6% @ 20 C

SOLVENT SOLUBILITY: SOLUBLE IN ACETONE, CYCLOHEXANONE, DIMETHYLFORMAMIDE, DICHLOROMETHANE, AND TOLUENE; MODERATELY SOLUBLE IN ETHANOL; SLIGHTLY SOLUBLE IN HEXANE, KEROSENE, AND XYLENE.

FIRE AND EXPLOSION DATA

FIRE AND EXPLOSION HAZARD: SLIGHT FIRE HAZARD WHEN EXPOSED TO HEAT OR FLAME.

FIREFIGHTING MEDIA: DRY CHEMICAL, CARBON DIOXIDE, HALON, WATER SPRAY OR STANDARD FOAM (1987 EMERGENCY RESPONSE GUIDEBOOK, DOT P 5800.4). FOR LARGER FIRES, USE WATER SPRAY, FOG OR STANDARD FOAM (1987 EMERGENCY RESPONSE GUIDEBOOK, DOT P 5800.4).

FIREFIGHTING: MOVE CONTAINERS FROM FIRE AREA IF POSSIBLE. FIGHT FIRE FROM MAXIMUM DISTANCE. STAY AWAY FROM STORAGE TANK ENDS. DIKE FIRE CONTROL WATER FOR LATER DISPOSAL. DO NOT SCATTER MATERIAL (1987 EMERGENCY RESPONSE GUIDEBOOK, DOT P 5800.4, GUIDE PAGE 55). EXTINGUISH USING AGENTS SUITABLE FOR TYPE OF SURROUNDING FIRE. USE FLOODING AMOUNTS OF WATER AS FOG. AVOID BREATHING TOXIC DUST AND FUMES FROM BURNING MATERIAL; KEEP UPWIND.

TRANSPORTATION DATA

DEPARTMENT OF TRANSPORTATION HAZARD CLASSIFICATION 49 CFR 172.101: POISON B
DEPARTMENT OF TRANSPORTATION LABELING REQUIREMENTS 49 CFR 172.101 AND SUBPART E: POISON
DEPARTMENT OF TRANSPORTATION PACKAGING REQUIREMENTS: 49 CFR 173.365 EXCEPTIONS: 49 CFR 173.364

TOXICITY

DIOXACARB: TOXICITY DATA: 160 MG/M3 INHALATION-RAT LC50; 1950 MG/KG SKIN-RABBIT LD50; 3000 MG/KG SKIN-RAT LD50; 1660 MG/KG SKIN-MOUSE LD50; 25 MG/KG ORAL-RAT LD50; 48 MG/KG ORAL-MOUSE LD50; 8300 UG/KG INTRAPERITONEAL-RAT LD50; 20 MG/KG INTRAPERITONEAL-MOUSE LD50; 120 MG/KG UNREPORTED-RAT LD50; 100 MG/KG UNREPORTED-MAMMAL LD50; MUTAGENIC DATA (RTECS). CARCINOGEN STATUS: NONE. ACUTE TOXICITY: HIGHLY TOXIC BY INHALATION AND INGESTION; MODERATELY TOXIC BY DERMAL ABSORPTION. TARGET EFFECTS: CHOLINESTERASE INHIBITOR. AT INCREASED RISK

FROM EXPOSURE: PERSONS WITH ASTHMA, DIABETES, CARDIOVASCULAR DISEASE, MECHANICAL OBSTRUCTION OF THE GASTROINTESTINAL OR UROGENITAL TRACT, AND THOSE IN VAGOTONIC STATES.*
* MAY BE BASED ON GENERAL INFORMATION ON CARBAMATES.

HEALTH EFFECTS AND FIRST AID

INHALATION: DIOXACARB: HIGHLY TOXIC. SEE INFORMATION ON CARBAMATES.
CARBAMATES: CHOLINESTERASE INHIBITOR. **ACUTE EXPOSURE-** WHEN INHALED, THE FIRST EFFECTS OF CHOLINESTERASE INHIBITION ARE USUALLY RESPIRATORY AND MAY INCLUDE NASAL HYPEREMIA AND WATERY DISCHARGE, CHEST DISCOMFORT, DYSPNEA, AND WHEEZING DUE TO INCREASED BRONCHIAL SECRETIONS AND BRONCHOCONSTRICTION. OTHER SYSTEMIC EFFECTS MAY BEGIN WITHIN A FEW MINUTES OR SEVERAL HOURS OF EXPOSURE. SYMPTOMS MAY INCLUDE NAUSEA, VOMITING, DIARRHEA, ABDOMINAL CRAMPS, HEADACHE, VERTIGO, OCULAR PAIN, CILIARY MUSCLE SPASM, BLURRING OR DIMNESS OF VISION, MIOSIS, OR IN SOME CASES MYDRIASIS, LACRIMATION, SALIVATION, SWEATING, AND CONFUSION. OTHER REPORTED CENTRAL NERVOUS SYSTEM OR NEUROMUSCULAR EFFECTS INCLUDE ATAXIA, SLURRED SPEECH, AREFLEXIA, WEAKNESS, FATIGUE, TWITCHING, FASCICULATION, TREMOR, AND EVENTUALLY PARALYSIS OF THE EXTREMITIES AND POSSIBLY OF THE RESPIRATORY MUSCLES. IN SEVERE CASES, THERE MAY ALSO BE INVOLUNTARY DEFECATION AND URINATION, BRADYCARDIA, HYPOTENSION, PULMONARY EDEMA, CONVULSIONS, COMA, AND DEATH FROM RESPIRATORY FAILURE OR CARDIAC ARREST. CARBAMATES GENERALLY DO NOT ACCUMULATE IN MAMMALIAN TISSUE AND THE CHOLINESTERASE INHIBITION REVERSES RATHER RAPIDLY. IN NON-FATAL CASES, THE ILLNESS GENERALLY LASTS LESS THAN 24 HOURS. **CHRONIC EXPOSURE-** PROLONGED OR REPEATED EXPOSURE MAY CAUSE EFFECTS AS DESCRIBED IN ACUTE EXPOSURE.

FIRST AID- REMOVE FROM EXPOSURE AREA TO FRESH AIR IMMEDIATELY. IF BREATHING HAS STOPPED, GIVE ARTIFICIAL RESPIRATION. MAINTAIN AIRWAY AND BLOOD PRESSURE AND ADMINISTER OXYGEN IF AVAILABLE. KEEP AFFECTED PERSON WARM AND AT REST. TREAT SYMPTOMATICALLY AND SUPPORTIVELY. ADMINISTRATION OF OXYGEN SHOULD BE PERFORMED BY QUALIFIED PERSONNEL. GET MEDICAL ATTENTION IMMEDIATELY.

SKIN CONTACT: DIOXACARB: THIS MATERIAL WAS SLIGHTLY IRRITATING TO RABBIT SKIN. SEE INFORMATION ON CARBAMATES.
CARBAMATES: CHOLINESTERASE INHIBITOR. **ACUTE EXPOSURE-** SOME COMPOUNDS MAY CAUSE IRRITATION. LOCALIZED SWEATING AND FASCICULATIONS MAY OCCUR AT THE SITE OF CONTACT. IF SUFFICIENT AMOUNTS ARE ABSORBED THROUGH THE SKIN, OTHER EFFECTS OF CHOLINESTERASE INHIBITION MAY OCCUR AS DESCRIBED IN ACUTE INHALATION; SYMPTOMS MAY BE DELAYED FOR 2-3 HOURS, USUALLY NO MORE THAN 8 HOURS. **CHRONIC EXPOSURE-** REPEATED OR PROLONGED EXPOSURE MAY CAUSE EFFECTS AS DESCRIBED IN ACUTE EXPOSURE.

FIRST AID- REMOVE CONTAMINATED CLOTHING IMMEDIATELY. WASH CONTAMINATED AREAS WITH SOAP AND WATER FOLLOWED BY ALCOHOL (ARENA, POISONING, 4TH ED.). EMERGENCY PERSONNEL SHOULD WEAR GLOVES AND AVOID CONTAMINATION. TREAT RESPIRATORY DIFFICULTY WITH ARTIFICIAL RESPIRATION. GET MEDICAL ATTENTION IMMEDIATELY.

EYE CONTACT: DIOXACARB: THIS MATERIAL WAS SLIGHTLY IRRITATING TO RABBIT EYES. SEE INFORMATION ON CARBAMATES.
CARBAMATES: CHOLINESTERASE INHIBITOR. **ACUTE EXPOSURE-** DIRECT CONTACT MAY CAUSE PAIN, HYPEREMIA, LACRIMATION, TWITCHING OF THE EYELIDS, MIOSIS, AND CILIARY MUSCLE SPASM WITH LOSS OF ACCOMODATION, BLURRED OR DIMMED VISION AND BROWACHE. SOMETIMES MYDRIASIS MAY OCCUR INSTEAD OF MIOSIS. WITH SUFFICIENT EXPOSURE, OTHER SYMPTOMS OF CHOLINESTERASE INHIBITION MAY OCCUR AS DESCRIBED IN ACUTE INHALATION. **CHRONIC EXPOSURE-** PROLONGED EXPOSURE MAY CAUSE EFFECTS AS DESCRIBED IN ACUTE EXPOSURE. SOME COMPOUNDS HAVE CAUSED TOXIC EFFECTS ON THE CRYSTALLINE LENS, CONJUNCTIVAL THICKENING AND OBSTRUCTION OF NASOLACRIMAL CANALS WHEN USED AS MIOTIC EYE DROPS.

FIRST AID- IRRIGATE EYES WITH WATER OR SALINE SOLUTION. IF SYMPTOMS OF POISONING OCCUR, TREAT RESPIRATORY DIFFICULTY WITH ARTIFICIAL RESPIRATION AND OXYGEN. OBSERVE PATIENT FOR AT LEAST 24-36 HOURS (GOSSELIN, CLINICAL TOXICOLOGY OF COMMERCIAL PRODUCTS, 5TH ED.). GET MEDICAL ATTENTION IMMEDIATELY. OXYGEN SHOULD BE ADMINISTERED BY QUALIFIED MEDICAL PERSONNEL.

INGESTION: DIOXACARB: HIGHLY TOXIC. PERIDONTAL DAMAGE AND DYSTROPHIC CHANGES IN THE ORAL MUCOSA, GASTROINTESTINAL TRACT, LIVER AND HEART WERE OBSERVED IN RATS FED 4 MG/KG/DAY FOR 90 DAYS. SEE INFORMATION ON CARBAMATES.
CARBAMATES: CHOLINESTERASE INHIBITOR. **ACUTE EXPOSURE-** WHEN INGESTED, THE FIRST EFFECTS MAY BE NAUSEA, VOMITING, ANOREXIA, ABDOMINAL CRAMPS, AND DIARRHEA. WITH ABSORPTION FROM THE GASTROINTESTINAL TRACT, THE OTHER EFFECTS OF CHOLINESTERASE INHIBITION AS DESCRIBED IN ACUTE INHALATION MAY OCCUR; SYMPTOMS MAY BEGIN WITHIN MINUTES OR BE DELAYED SEVERAL HOURS. **CHRONIC EXPOSURE-** REPEATED INGESTION MAY CAUSE EFFECTS AS DESCRIBED IN ACUTE EXPOSURE.

FIRST AID- IF PERSON IS ALERT AND RESPIRATION IS NOT DEPRESSED, GIVE SYRUP OF IPECAC FOLLOWED BY WATER (IF VOMITING OCCURS, KEEP HEAD BELOW HIPS TO PREVENT ASPIRATION). IF CONSCIOUSNESS LEVEL DECLINES OR VOMITING HAS NOT OCCURRED IN 15 MINUTES EMPTY STOMACH BY GASTRIC LAVAGE WITH THE AID OF CUFFED ENDOTRACHEAL TUBE USING ISOTONIC SALINE OR 5% SODIUM BICARBONATE FOLLOW WITH ACTIVATED CHARCOAL. ESTABLISH AND MAINTAIN AIRWAY. TREAT RESPIRATORY DIFFICULTY WITH ARTIFICIAL RESPIRATION AND OXYGEN. DO NOT GIVE MORPHINE, AMINOPHYLLINE, PHENOTHIAZINES, RESERPINE, FUROSEMIDE, OR ETHACRYNIC ACID (MORGAN, RECOGNITION AND MANAGEMENT OF PESTICIDE POISONINGS, 3RD ED.). TREAT SYMPTOMATICALLY AND SUPPORTIVELY. ADMINISTRATION OF OXYGEN AND LAVAGE MUST BE PERFORMED BY QUALIFIED MEDICAL PERSONNEL. GET MEDICAL ATTENTION IMMEDIATELY.

ANTIDOTE: THE FOLLOWING ANTIDOTE HAS BEEN RECOMMENDED. HOWEVER, THE DECISION AS TO WHETHER THE SEVERITY OF POISONING REQUIRES ADMINISTRATION OF ANY ANTIDOTE AND ACTUAL DOSE REQUIRED SHOULD BE MADE BY QUALIFIED MEDICAL PERSONNEL.
FOR CHOLINESTERASE INHIBITORS: ESTABLISH CLEAR AIRWAY AND TISSUE OXYGENATION BY ASPIRATION OF SECRETIONS, AND IF NECESSARY, BY ASSISTED PULMONARY VENTILATION WITH OXYGEN. IMPROVE TISSUE OXYGENATION AS MUCH AS POSSIBLE BEFORE ADMINISTERING ATROPINE TO MINIMIZE THE RISK OF VENTRICULAR FIBRILLATION. ADMINISTER ATROPINE SULFATE INTRAVENOUSLY, OR INTRAMUSCULARLY IF IV INJECTION IS NOT POSSIBLE. IN MODERATELY SEVERE POISONING ADMINISTER ATROPINE SULFATE, 0.4-2.0 MG REPEATED EVERY 15 MINUTES UNTIL ATROPINIZATION IS ACHIEVED (TACHYCARDIA, FLUSHING, DRY MOUTH, MYDRIASIS). MAINTAIN ATROPINIZATION BY REPEATED DOSES FOR 2-12 HOURS, OR LONGER, DEPENDING ON THE SEVERITY OF POISONING. THE APPEARANCE OF RALES IN THE LUNG BASES, MIOSIS, SALIVATION, NAUSEA, BRADYCARDIA, ARE ALL INDICATIONS OF INADEQUATE ATROPINIZATION. SEVERELY POISONED INDIVIDUALS MAY EXHIBIT REMARKABLE TOLERANCE TO ATROPINE; TWO OR MORE TIMES THE DOSAGES SUGGESTED ABOVE MAY BE NEEDED. PERSONS NOT POISONED OR ONLY SLIGHTLY POISONED, HOWEVER, MAY DEVELOP SIGNS OF ATROPINE TOXICITY FROM SUCH LARGE DOSAGES: FEVER, MUSCLE FIBRILLATIONS, AND DELIRIUM ARE THE MAIN SIGNS OF ATROPINE TOXICITY. IF THESE SIGNS APPEAR WHILE THE PATIENT IS FULLY ATROPINIZED, ATROPINE ADMINISTRATION SHOULD BE DISCONTINUED, AT LEAST TEMPORARILY. OBSERVE TREATED PATIENTS CLOSELY AT LEAST 24 HOURS TO INSURE THAT SYMPTOMS (POSSIBLY PULMONARY EDEMA) DO NOT RECUR AS ATROPINIZATION WEARS OFF. IN VERY SEVERE POISONINGS, METABOLIC DISPOSITION OF TOXICANT MAY REQUIRE SEVERAL HOURS OR DAYS DURING WHICH ATROPINIZATION MUST BE MAINTAINED. MARKEDLY LOWER LEVELS OF URINARY METABOLITES INDICATE THAT ATROPINE DOSAGE CAN BE TAPERED OFF. AS DOSAGE IS REDUCED, CHECK THE LUNG BASES FREQUENTLY FOR RALES. IF RALES ARE HEARD OR OTHER SYMPTOMS RETURN, RE-ESTABLISH ATROPINIZATION PROMPTLY (MORGAN, RECOGNITION AND MANAGEMENT OF PESTICIDE POISONINGS, 3RD ED.). ADMINISTRATION OF ANTIDOTE MUST BE PERFORMED BY QUALIFIED MEDICAL PERSONNEL.

REACTIVITY

REACTIVITY: STABLE UNDER NORMAL TEMPERATURES AND PRESSURES.
INCOMPATIBILITIES: DIOXACARB: OXIDIZERS (STRONG): FIRE AND EXPLOSION HAZARD.
DECOMPOSITION: THERMAL DECOMPOSITION PRODUCTS MAY INCLUDE TOXIC OXIDES OF CARBON AND NITROGEN.
POLYMERIZATION: HAZARDOUS POLYMERIZATION HAS NOT BEEN REPORTED TO OCCUR UNDER NORMAL TEMPERATURES AND PRESSURES.

STORAGE AND DISPOSAL

OBSERVE ALL FEDERAL, STATE AND LOCAL REGULATIONS WHEN STORING OR DISPOSING OF THIS SUBSTANCE. FOR ASSISTANCE, CONTACT THE DISTRICT DIRECTOR OF THE ENVIRONMENTAL PROTECTION AGENCY.

STORAGE

STORE IN ACCORDANCE WITH 40 CFR 165 RECOMMENDED PROCEDURES FOR THE DISPOSAL AND STORAGE OF PESTICIDES AND PESTICIDE CONTAINERS.
STORE AWAY FROM INCOMPATIBLE SUBSTANCES.

DISPOSAL

DISPOSAL MUST BE IN ACCORDANCE WITH 40 CFR 165 RECOMMENDED PROCEDURES FOR THE DISPOSAL AND STORAGE OF PESTICIDES AND PESTICIDE CONTAINERS.

CONDITIONS TO AVOID

MAY BURN BUT DOES NOT IGNITE READILY. CONTAINERS MAY EXPLODE IN HEAT OF FIRE.

SPILL AND LEAK PROCEDURES

OCCUPATIONAL SPILL: DO NOT TOUCH SPILLED MATERIAL. STOP LEAK IF YOU CAN DO IT WITHOUT RISK. USE WATER SPRAY TO REDUCE VAPORS. FOR SMALL SPILLS, TAKE UP WITH SAND OR OTHER ABSORBENT MATERIAL AND PLACE INTO CONTAINERS FOR LATER DISPOSAL. FOR SMALL DRY SPILLS, WITH A CLEAN SHOVEL PLACE MATERIAL INTO CLEAN, DRY CONTAINERS AND COVER. MOVE CONTAINERS FROM SPILL AREA. FOR LARGER SPILLS, DIKE FAR AHEAD OF SPILL FOR LATER DISPOSAL. KEEP UNNECESSARY PEOPLE AWAY. ISOLATE HAZARD AREA AND DENY ENTRY. VENTILATE CLOSED SPACES BEFORE ENTERING.

PROTECTIVE EQUIPMENT

VENTILATION: PROCESS ENCLOSURE RECOMMENDED.

RESPIRATOR: THE FOLLOWING RESPIRATORS ARE RECOMMENDED BASED ON INFORMATION FOUND IN THE PHYSICAL DATA, TOXICITY AND HEALTH EFFECTS SECTIONS. THEY ARE RANKED IN ORDER FROM MINIMUM TO MAXIMUM RESPIRATORY PROTECTION. THE SPECIFIC RESPIRATOR SELECTED MUST BE BASED ON CONTAMINATION LEVELS FOUND IN THE WORK PLACE, MUST NOT EXCEED THE WORKING LIMITS OF THE RESPIRATOR AND BE JOINTLY APPROVED BY THE NATIONAL INSTITUTE FOR OCCUPATIONAL SAFETY AND HEALTH AND THE MINE SAFETY AND HEALTH ADMINISTRATION (NIOSH-MSHA).

TYPE 'C' SUPPLIED-AIR RESPIRATOR WITH A FULL FACEPIECE OPERATED IN PRESSURE-DEMAND OR OTHER POSITIVE PRESSURE MODE OR WITH A FULL FACEPIECE, HELMET OR HOOD OPERATED IN CONTINOUS-FLOW MODE.

SELF-CONTAINED BREATHING APPARATUS WITH A FULL FACEPIECE OPERATED IN PRESSURE-DEMAND OR OTHER POSITIVE PRESSURE MODE.

FOR FIREFIGHTING AND OTHER IMMEDIATELY DANGEROUS TO LIFE OR HEALTH CONDITIONS:

SELF-CONTAINED BREATHING APPARATUS WITH FULL FACEPIECE OPERATED IN PRESSURE-DEMAND OR OTHER POSITIVE PRESSURE MODE.

SUPPLIED-AIR RESPIRATOR WITH FULL FACEPIECE AND OPERATED IN PRESSURE-DEMAND OR OTHER POSITIVE PRESSURE MODE IN COMBINATION WITH AN AUXILIARY SELF-CONTAINED BREATHING APPARATUS OPERATED IN PRESSURE-DEMAND OR OTHER POSITIVE PRESSURE MODE.

CLOTHING: EMPLOYEE MUST WEAR APPROPRIATE PROTECTIVE (IMPERVIOUS) CLOTHING AND EQUIPMENT TO PREVENT ANY POSSIBILITY OF SKIN CONTACT WITH THIS SUBSTANCE.

GLOVES: EMPLOYEE MUST WEAR APPROPRIATE PROTECTIVE GLOVES TO PREVENT CONTACT WITH THIS SUBSTANCE.

EYE PROTECTION: EMPLOYEE MUST WEAR SPLASH-PROOF OR DUST-RESISTANT SAFETY GOGGLES WITH OR WITHOUT A FACESHIELD TO PREVENT CONTACT WITH THIS SUBSTANCE.

EMERGENCY EYE WASH: WHERE THERE IS ANY POSSIBILITY THAT AN EMPLOYEE'S EYES MAY BE EXPOSED TO THIS SUBSTANCE, THE EMPLOYER SHOULD PROVIDE AN EYE WASH FOUNTAIN WITHIN THE IMMEDIATE WORK AREA FOR EMERGENCY USE.

AUTHORIZED BY- OCCUPATIONAL HEALTH SERVICES, INC.
CREATION DATE: 10/04/89 ***REVISION DATE:*** 06/12/90

MATERIAL SAFETY DATA SHEET

OCCUPATIONAL HEALTH SERVICES, INC.
AGRICULTURE AND PESTICIDE DIVISION
450 SEVENTH AVENUE, SUITE 2407
NEW YORK, NEW YORK 10123
1-800-445-MSDS OR (212) 967-1100

EMERGENCY CONTACT:
JOHN S. BRANSFORD, JR. (615) 292-1180

SUBSTANCE IDENTIFICATION

CAS-NUMBER 6597-78-0

SUBSTANCE: **DICAMBA METHYL ESTER**

TRADE NAMES/SYNONYMS: BENZOIC ACID, 3,6-DICHLORO-2-METHOXY-, METHYL ESTER; 3,6-DICHLORO-2-METHOXYBENZOIC ACID METHYL ESTER; O-ANISIC ACID, 3,6-DICHLORO-, METHYL ESTER; 3,6-DICHLORO-O-ANISIC ACID METHYL ESTER; METHYL-3,6-DICHLORO-O-ANISATE; METHYL-2-METHOXY-3,6-DICHLOROBENZOATE; 3,6-DICHLORO-2-METHOXY METHYL BENZOATE; BANVEL D METHYL ESTER; DISUGRAN; RACUSA; RACUZA; C9H8CL2O3; PST73131

CHEMICAL FAMILY: HALOGEN COMPOUND, AROMATIC ESTER

MOLECULAR FORMULA: (C-H3-O)-C6-H2-(CL)2-(C-O2-C-H3)

MOLECULAR WEIGHT: 235.07

CERCLA RATINGS (SCALE 0-3): HEALTH=U FIRE=1 REACTIVITY=0 PERSISTENCE=1

NFPA RATINGS (SCALE 0-4): HEALTH=U FIRE=1 REACTIVITY=0

COMPONENTS AND CONTAMINANTS

COMPONENT: DICAMBA METHYL ESTER ***PERCENT:*** 100.0
CAS# 6597-78-0

OTHER CONTAMINANTS: NONE

EXPOSURE LIMITS: NO OCCUPATIONAL EXPOSURE LIMITS ESTABLISHED BY OSHA, ACGIH, OR NIOSH.

PHYSICAL DATA

DESCRIPTION: WHITE POWDER. ***MELTING POINT:*** 90 F (32 C)

SPECIFIC GRAVITY: NOT AVAILABLE ***SOLUBILITY IN WATER:*** NOT AVAILABLE

FIRE AND EXPLOSION DATA

FIRE AND EXPLOSION HAZARD: SLIGHT FIRE HAZARD WHEN EXPOSED TO HEAT OR FLAME.

DUST-AIR MIXTURES MAY IGNITE OR EXPLODE.

FIREFIGHTING MEDIA: DRY CHEMICAL, CARBON DIOXIDE, HALON, WATER SPRAY OR STANDARD FOAM (1987 EMERGENCY RESPONSE GUIDEBOOK, DOT P 5800.4).

FOR LARGER FIRES, USE WATER SPRAY, FOG OR STANDARD FOAM (1987 EMERGENCY RESPONSE GUIDEBOOK, DOT P 5800.4).

FIREFIGHTING: MOVE CONTAINER FROM FIRE AREA IF POSSIBLE. DO NOT SCATTER SPILLED MATERIAL WITH HIGH PRESSURE WATER STREAMS. DIKE FIRE CONTROL WATER FOR LATER DISPOSAL (1987 EMERGENCY RESPONSE GUIDEBOOK, DOT P 5800.4, GUIDE PAGE 31).

USE AGENTS SUITABLE FOR TYPE OF SURROUNDING FIRE. AVOID BREATHING HAZARDOUS VAPORS, KEEP UPWIND.

TOXICITY

DICAMBA METHYL ESTER: TOXICITY DATA: 2700 MG/KG ORAL-RAT LD50 (EPA); CARCINOGEN STATUS: NONE. ACUTE TOXICITY LEVEL: MODERATELY TOXIC BY INGESTION. TARGET EFFECTS: NO DATA AVAILABLE.

HEALTH EFFECTS AND FIRST AID

INHALATION: DICAMBA METHYL ESTER: **ACUTE EXPOSURE-** NO SPECIFIC DATA AVAILABLE. DICAMBA HAS BEEN REPORTED TO IRRITATE THE MUCOUS MEMBRANES. **CHRONIC EXPOSURE-** NO SPECIFIC DATA AVAILABLE. EFFECTS OF MUSCLE CRAMPS, DYSPNEA, NAUSEA, VOMITING, SKIN RASHES, LOSS OF VOICE OR SWELLING OF CERVICAL GLAND WERE REPORTED AMONG WORKERS EXPOSED TO DICAMBA.

FIRST AID- REMOVE FROM EXPOSURE AREA TO FRESH AIR IMMEDIATELY. IF BREATHING HAS STOPPED, PERFORM ARTIFICIAL RESPIRATION. KEEP PERSON WARM AND AT REST. TREAT SYMPTOMATICALLY AND SUPPORTIVELY. GET MEDICAL ATTENTION IMMEDIATELY.

SKIN CONTACT: DICAMBA METHYL ESTER: **ACUTE EXPOSURE-** NO SPECIFIC DATA AVAILBLE. DICAMBA HAS PRODUCED SLIGHT TO MODERATE IRRITATION AND MODERATE SENSITIZATION IN GUINEA PIGS. **CHRONIC EXPOSURE-** NO SPECIFIC DATA AVAILABLE. EFFECTS OF MUSCLE CRAMPS, DYSPNEA, NAUSEA, VOMITING, SKIN RASHES, LOSS OF VOICE OR SWELLING OF CERVICAL GLANDS WERE OBSERVED AMONG WORKERS EXPOSED TO DICAMBA.

FIRST AID- REMOVE CONTAMINATED CLOTHING AND SHOES IMMEDIATELY. WASH AFFECTED AREA WITH SOAP OR MILD DETERGENT AND LARGE AMOUNTS OF WATER UNTIL NO EVIDENCE OF CHEMICAL REMAINS (APPROXIMATELY 15-20 MINUTES). GET MEDICAL ATTENTION IMMEDIATELY.

EYE CONTACT: DICAMBA METHYL ESTER: **ACUTE EXPOSURE-** NO SPECIFIC DATA AVAILABLE. DICAMBA HAS PRODUCED EXTREME IRRITATION AND CORROSIVE EFFECTS IN RABBIT EYES. **CHRONIC EXPOSURE-** NO DATA AVAILABLE.

FIRST AID- WASH EYES IMMEDIATELY WITH LARGE AMOUNTS OF WATER OR NORMAL SALINE, OCCASIONALLY LIFTING UPPER AND LOWER LIDS, UNTIL NO EVIDENCE OF CHEMICAL REMAINS (APPROXIMATELY 15-20 MINUTES). GET MEDICAL ATTENTION IMMEDIATELY.

INGESTION: DICAMBA METHYL ESTER: **ACUTE EXPOSURE-** NO SPECIFIC DATA AVAILABLE. IN ANIMALS, ACUTE DOSES OF PRODUCED MYOTONIC MUSCULAR SPASMS, EXHAUSTION, URINARY INCONTINENCE, DYSPNEA, CYANOSIS, AND SOME DEATHS. MINOR LUNG HEMORRHAGES WERE FOUND IN SOME ANIMALS. MOST SURVIVORS RECOVERED IN 2 TO 3 DAYS AND SHOWED NO MACROSCOPIC PATHOLOGY. **CHRONIC EXPOSURE-** NO DATA AVAILABLE.

FIRST AID- TREAT SYMPTOMATICALLY AND SUPPORTIVELY. GET MEDICAL ATTENTION IMMEDIATELY. IF VOMITING OCCURS, KEEP HEAD LOWER THAN HIPS TO PREVENT ASPIRATION.

ANTIDOTE: NO SPECIFIC ANTIDOTE. TREAT SYMPTOMATICALLY AND SUPPORTIVELY.

REACTIVITY

REACTIVITY: STABLE UNDER NORMAL TEMPERATURES AND PRESSURES.

INCOMPATIBILITIES: DICAMBA METHYL ESTER: OXIDIZERS (STRONG): FIRE AND EXPLOSION HAZARD.

DECOMPOSITION: THERMAL DECOMPOSITION PRODUCTS MAY INCLUDE TOXIC AND CORROSIVE FUMES OF CHLORIDES AND TOXIC OXIDES OF CARBON.

POLYMERIZATION: HAZARDOUS POLYMERIZATION HAS NOT BEEN REPORTED TO OCCUR UNDER NORMAL TEMPERATURES AND PRESSURES.

STORAGE AND DISPOSAL

OBSERVE ALL FEDERAL, STATE AND LOCAL REGULATIONS WHEN STORING OR DISPOSING OF THIS SUBSTANCE. FOR ASSISTANCE, CONTACT THE DISTRICT DIRECTOR OF THE ENVIRONMENTAL PROTECTION AGENCY.

****STORAGE****

STORE IN ACCORDANCE WITH 40 CFR 165 RECOMMENDED PROCEDURES FOR THE DISPOSAL AND STORAGE OF PESTICIDES AND PESTICIDE CONTAINERS.

STORE IN A COOL, DRY PLACE PROTECTED AGAINST LIGHT. STORE AWAY FROM INCOMPATIBLE SUBSTANCES.

****DISPOSAL****

DISPOSAL MUST BE IN ACCORDANCE WITH 40 CFR 165 RECOMMENDED PROCEDURES FOR THE DISPOSAL AND STORAGE OF PESTICIDES AND PESTICIDE CONTAINERS.

CONDITIONS TO AVOID

MAY BURN BUT DOES NOT IGNITE READILY. AVOID CONTACT WITH STRONG OXIDIZERS, EXCESSIVE HEAT, SPARKS, OR OPEN FLAME.

SPILL AND LEAK PROCEDURES

OCCUPATIONAL SPILL: SWEEP UP AND PLACE IN SUITABLE CLEAN, DRY CONTAINERS FOR RECLAMATION OR LATER DISPOSAL. DO NOT FLUSH SPILLED MATERIAL INTO SEWER. KEEP UNNECESSARY PEOPLE AWAY.

PROTECTIVE EQUIPMENT

VENTILATION: PROVIDE LOCAL EXHAUST OR GENERAL DILUTION VENTILATION SYSTEM.

RESPIRATOR: THE FOLLOWING RESPIRATORS ARE RECOMMENDED BASED ON INFORMATION FOUND IN THE PHYSICAL DATA, TOXICITY AND HEALTH EFFECTS SECTIONS. THEY ARE RANKED IN ORDER FROM MINIMUM TO MAXIMUM RESPIRATORY PROTECTION. THE SPECIFIC RESPIRATOR SELECTED MUST BE BASED ON CONTAMINATION LEVELS FOUND IN THE WORK PLACE, MUST NOT EXCEED THE WORKING LIMITS OF THE RESPIRATOR AND BE JOINTLY APPROVED BY THE NATIONAL INSTITUTE FOR OCCUPATIONAL SAFETY AND HEALTH AND THE MINE SAFETY AND HEALTH ADMINISTRATION (NIOSH-MSHA).

CHEMICAL CARTRIDGE RESPIRATOR WITH AN ORGANIC VAPOR CARTRIDGE(S) WITH A FULL FACEPIECE AND ORGANIC VAPOR CARTRIDGE(S) IN COMBINATION WITH A DUST AND MIST FILTER.

POWERED AIR-PURIFYING RESPIRATOR WITH A TIGHT-FITTING FACEPIECE AND ORGANIC VAPOR CARTRIDGE(S) IN COMBINATION WITH A HIGH-EFFICIENCY PARTICULATE FILTER.

TYPE 'C' SUPPLIED-AIR RESPIRATOR WITH A FULL FACEPIECE OPERATED IN A PRESSURE-DEMAND OR OTHER POSITIVE PRESSURE MODE.

SELF-CONTAINED BREATHING APPARATUS WITH A FULL FACEPIECE OPERATED IN PRESSURE-DEMAND OR OTHER POSITIVE PRESSURE MODE.

FOR FIREFIGHTING AND OTHER IMMEDIATELY DANGEROUS TO LIFE OR HEALTH CONDITIONS:

SELF-CONTAINED BREATHING APPARATUS WITH FULL FACEPIECE OPERATED IN PRESSURE-DEMAND OR OTHER POSITIVE PRESSURE MODE.

SUPPLIED-AIR RESPIRATOR WITH FULL FACEPIECE AND OPERATED IN PRESSURE-DEMAND OR OTHER POSITIVE PRESSURE MODE IN COMBINATION WITH AN AUXILIARY SELF-CONTAINED BREATHING APPARATUS OPERATED IN PRESSURE-DEMAND OR OTHER POSITIVE PRESSURE MODE.

CLOTHING: EMPLOYEE MUST WEAR APPROPRIATE PROTECTIVE (IMPERVIOUS) CLOTHING AND EQUIPMENT TO PREVENT REPEATED OR PROLONGED SKIN CONTACT WITH THIS SUBSTANCE.

GLOVES: EMPLOYEE MUST WEAR APPROPRIATE PROTECTIVE GLOVES TO PREVENT CONTACT WITH THIS SUBSTANCE.

EYE PROTECTION: EMPLOYEE MUST WEAR SPLASH-PROOF OR DUST-RESISTANT SAFETY GOGGLES TO PREVENT EYE CONTACT WITH THIS SUBSTANCE.

EMERGENCY EYE WASH: WHERE THERE IS ANY POSSIBILITY THAT AN EMPLOYEE'S EYES MAY BE EXPOSED TO THIS SUBSTANCE, THE EMPLOYER SHOULD PROVIDE AN EYE WASH FOUNTAIN WITHIN THE IMMEDIATE WORK AREA FOR EMERGENCY USE.

AUTHORIZED BY- OCCUPATIONAL HEALTH SERVICES, INC.

CREATION DATE: 05/08/90 ***REVISION DATE:*** 05/31/90

MATERIAL SAFETY DATA SHEET

OCCUPATIONAL HEALTH SERVICES, INC.
AGRICULTURE AND PESTICIDE DIVISION
450 SEVENTH AVENUE, SUITE 2407
NEW YORK, NEW YORK 10123
1-800-445-MSDS OR (212) 967-1100

EMERGENCY CONTACT:
JOHN S. BRANSFORD, JR. (615) 292-1180

SUBSTANCE IDENTIFICATION

CAS-NUMBER 2778-04-3

SUBSTANCE: ENDOTHION

TRADE NAMES/SYNONYMS: O,O-DIMETHYL S-(5-METHOXY-4-OXO-4H-PYRAN-2-YL)PHOSPHOROTHIOATE; O,O-DIMETHYL S-(5-METHOXYPYRONYL-2-METHYL)THIOPHOSPHATE; 5-METHOXY-2-(DIMETHOXYPHOSPHINYLTHIOETHYL)PYRONE-4; S-5-METHOXY-4-OXOPYRAN-2-YLMETHYL DIMETHYL PHOSPHOROTHIOATE; S-(5-METHOXY-4-PYRON-2-YLMETHYL) DIMETHYL PHOSPHOROTHIOLATE; PHOSPHOROTHIOIC ACID, S-((5-METHOXY-4-OXO-4H-PYRAN-2-YL)METHYL) O,O-DIMETHYL ESTER; PHOSPHOROTHIOIC ACID, O,O-DIMETHYL ESTER, S-ESTER WITH 2-(MERCAPTOMETHYL)-5-METHOXY-4H-PYRAN-4-ONE; AC-18737; ENDOCID; ENDOCIDE; NIAGARA 5767; ENT 24,653; NIA-5767; PST73139

CHEMICAL FAMILY: PHOSPHOROTHIOATE

MOLECULAR FORMULA: C9-H13-O6-P-S

MOLECULAR WEIGHT: 280.25

CERCLA RATINGS (SCALE 0-3): HEALTH=3 FIRE=U REACTIVITY=0 PERSISTENCE=2

NFPA RATINGS (SCALE 0-4): HEALTH=4 FIRE=U REACTIVITY=0

COMPONENTS AND CONTAMINANTS

COMPONENT: ENDOTHION ***PERCENT:*** 100.0

CAS# 2778-04-3

OTHER CONTAMINANTS: NONE

EXPOSURE LIMITS: ENDOTHION: NO OCCUPATIONAL EXPOSURE LIMITS ESTABLISHED BY OSHA, ACGIH, OR NIOSH.

500 POUNDS SARA SECTION 302 THRESHOLD PLANNING QUANTITY 1 POUND SARA SECTION 304 REPORTABLE QUANTITY

PHYSICAL DATA

DESCRIPTION: WHITE CRYSTALS WITH A SLIGHT ODOR

MELTING POINT: 194-205 F (90-96 C) ***SOLUBILITY IN WATER:*** VERY SOLUBLE

SOLVENT SOLUBILITY: SOLUBLE IN ACETONE, BENZENE, AND CHLORFORM; INSOLUBLE IN ETHER, CYCLOHEXANE, OR CARBON TETRACHLORIDE

FIRE AND EXPLOSION DATA

FIRE AND EXPLOSION HAZARD: UNKNOWN FIRE AND EXPLOSION HAZARD.

FIREFIGHTING MEDIA: DRY CHEMICAL, CARBON DIOXIDE, HALON, WATER SPRAY OR STANDARD FOAM (1987 EMERGENCY RESPONSE GUIDEBOOK, DOT P 5800.4).

FOR LARGER FIRES, USE WATER SPRAY, FOG OR STANDARD FOAM (1987 EMERGENCY RESPONSE GUIDEBOOK, DOT P 5800.4).

FIREFIGHTING: MOVE CONTAINERS FROM FIRE AREA IF POSSIBLE (1987 EMERGENCY RESPONSE GUIDEBOOK, DOT P 5800.4, GUIDE PAGE 53).

EXTINGUISH USING AGENT SUITABLE FOR TYPE OF SURROUNDING FIRE. AVOID BREATHING VAPORS AND DUSTS. KEEP UPWIND.

TRANSPORTATION DATA

DEPARTMENT OF TRANSPORTATION HAZARD CLASSIFICATION 49 CFR 172.101: POISON B

DEPARTMENT OF TRANSPORTATION LABELING REQUIREMENTS 49 CFR 172.101 AND SUBPART E: POISON

DEPARTMENT OF TRANSPORTATION PACKAGING REQUIREMENTS: 49 CFR 173.365 EXCEPTIONS: 49 CFR 173.364

TOXICITY

ENDOTHION: TOXICITY DATA: 130 MG/KG SKIN-RAT LD50; 23 MG/KG ORAL-RAT LD50; 17 MG/KG ORAL-MOUSE LD50; 60 MG/KG ORAL-GUINEA PIG LD50; 30 MG/KG UNREPORTED-RAT LD50. CARCINOGEN STATUS: NONE. ACUTE TOXICITY LEVEL:

HIGHLY TOXIC BY DERMAL ABSORPTION AND INGESTION. TARGET EFFECTS: CHOLINESTERASE INHIBITOR. POISONING MAY AFFECT THE NERVOUS SYSTEM.* AT INCREASED RISK FROM EXPOSURE: PERSONS WITH RESPIRATORY AILMENTS, RECENT EXPOSURE TO CHOLINESTERASE INHIBITORS OR IMPAIRED CHOLINESTERASE PRODUCTION, OR LIVER MALFUNCTION.* ADDITIONAL DATA: MAY CROSS THE PLACENTA. HIGH ENVIRONMENTAL TEMPERATURES OR EXPOSURE OF THE CHEMICAL TO VISIBLE OR ULTRAVIOLET LIGHT MAY ENHANCE THE TOXICITY. INTERACTIONS WITH MEDICATIONS MAY OCCUR.*
* MAY BE BASED ON GENERAL INFORMATION ON ORGANOPHOSPHATES.

HEALTH EFFECTS AND FIRST AID

INHALATION: ENDOTHION: SEE INFORMATION ON ORGANOPHOSPHATES. ORGANOPHOSPHATES: CHOLINESTERASE INHIBITOR. **ACUTE EXPOSURE-** WHEN INHALED, THE FIRST EFFECTS OF CHOLINESTERASE INHIBITORS ARE USUALLY RESPIRATORY AND MAY INCLUDE NASAL HYPEREMIA AND WATERY DISCHARGE, COUGH, CHEST DISCOMFORT, DYSPNEA, AND WHEEZING DUE TO INCREASED BRONCHIAL SECRETIONS AND BRONCHOCONSTRICTION. IF SUFFICIENT AMOUNTS ARE ABSORBED, OTHER SYSTEMIC EFFECTS MAY BEGIN WITHIN A FEW MINUTES OR BE DELAYED FOR UP TO 12 HOURS. SYMPTOMS MAY INCLUDE PALLOR, NAUSEA, VOMITING, DIARRHEA, ABDOMINAL CRAMPS, HEADACHE, DIZZINESS, OCULAR PAIN, BLURRED VISION, MIOSIS OR IN SOME CASES, ESPECIALLY INITIALLY, MYDRIASIS, LACRIMATION, SALIVATION, SWEATING, AND CONFUSION. OTHER REPORTED CENTRAL NERVOUS SYSTEM OR NEUROMUSCULAR EFFECTS MAY INCLUDE ATAXIA, SLURRED SPEECH, AREFLEXIA, WEAKNESS, FATIGUE, FASCICULATIONS, TWITCHING, TREMORS POSSIBLY OF THE TONGUE AND EYELIDS, AND EVENTUALLY PARALYSIS OF THE EXTREMITIES AND POSSIBLY OF THE RESPIRATORY MUSCLES. IN SEVERE CASES THERE MAY ALSO BE INVOLUNTARY DEFECATION AND URINATION, CYANOSIS, PSYCHOSIS, HYPERGLYCEMIA, ACUTE PANCREATITIS, CARDIAC IRREGULARITIES, PULMONARY EDEMA, UNCONSCIOUSNESS, CONVULSIONS, AND COMA. DEATH IS PRIMARILY DUE TO RESPIRATORY FAILURE, ALTHOUGH CARDIOVASCULAR EFFECTS INCLUDING CARDIAC ARREST MAY ALSO BE IMPLICATED. LONG TERM SEQUELAE ARE RARE BUT MAY INCLUDE NEUROPSYCHIATRIC DISORDERS AND MYOPATHY WITH MUSCLE TENDERNESS. SOME ORGANOPHOSPHATES MAY CAUSE A DELAYED NEUROPATHY BEGINNING 1-4 WEEKS AFTER AN ACUTE EXPOSURE WHICH MAY OR MAY NOT HAVE CAUSED ACUTE CHOLINERGIC EFFECTS. NUMBNESS, TINGLING, WEAKNESS AND CRAMPING BEGINNING SYMMETRICALLY IN THE LOWER LIMBS MAY PROGRESS TO ATAXIA AND PARALYSIS. IN SEVERE CASES, UPPER LIMB INVOLVEMENT IS POSSIBLE AND FLACCID PARALYSIS MAY PROGRESS TO SPASTIC PARALYSIS WITH EXAGGERATED REFLEXES. IMPROVEMENT MAY OCCUR OVER MONTHS TO YEARS, BUT SOME RESIDUAL IMPAIRMENT USUALLY REMAINS. **CHRONIC EXPOSURE-** REPEATED OR PROLONGED EXPOSURE MAY RESULT IN THE EFFECTS OF ACUTE EXPOSURE INCLUDING THE DELAYED NEUROPATHY. OTHER EFFECTS REPORTED IN WORKERS REPEATEDLY EXPOSED INCLUDE IMPAIRED MEMORY AND CONCENTRATION, ACUTE PSYCHOSIS, SEVERE DEPRESSIONS, IRRITABILTY, CONFUSION, APATHY, EMOTIONAL LABILITY, SOCIAL WITHDRAWAL, CONFUSION, HEADACHE, SPEECH DIFFICULTIES, DELAYED REACTION TIMES, SPATIAL DISORIENTATION, NIGHTMARES, SLEEPWALKING, AND DROWSINESS OR INSOMNIA. AN INFLUENZA-LIKE CONDITION WITH HEADACHE, NAUSEA, WEAKNESS, ANOREXIA AND MALAISE HAS ALSO BEEN REPORTED.

FIRST AID- REMOVE FROM EXPOSURE AREA TO FRESH AIR IMMEDIATELY. IF BREATHING HAS STOPPED, GIVE ARTIFICIAL RESPIRATION. MAINTAIN AIRWAY AND BLOOD PRESSURE AND ADMINISTER OXYGEN IF AVAILABLE. KEEP AFFECTED PERSON WARM AND AT REST. TREAT SYMPTOMATICALLY AND SUPPORTIVELY. ADMINISTRATION OF OXYGEN SHOULD BE PERFORMED BY QUALIFIED PERSONNEL. GET MEDICAL ATTENTION IMMEDIATELY.

SKIN CONTACT: ENDOTHION: HIGHLY TOXIC. SEE INFORMATION ON ORGANOPHOSPHATES. ORGANOPHOSPHATES: CHOLINESTERASE INHIBITOR. **ACUTE EXPOSURE-** LOCALIZED SWEATING AND FASCICULATIONS MAY OCCUR AT THE SITE OF CONTACT. IF SUFFICIENT AMOUNTS ARE ABSORBED, OTHER EFFECTS OF CHOLINESTERASE INHIBITION AS DESCRIBED IN ACUTE INHALATION MAY OCCUR. SYMPTOMS MAY BE DELAYED 2-3 HOURS, BUT USUALLY NO MORE THAN 12 HOURS. THE RATE OF ABSORPTION IS INCREASED BY THE PRESENCE OF DERMATITIS OR HIGH AMBIENT TEMPERATURES. DELAYED NEUROPATHY IS ALSO POSSIBLE. **CHRONIC EXPOSURE-** REPEATED OR PROLONGED EXPOSURE MAY CAUSE EFFECTS AS DESCRIBED IN ACUTE EXPOSURE. SOME ORGANOPHOSPHATES MAY CAUSE SENSITIZATION.

FIRST AID- REMOVE CONTAMINATED CLOTHING IMMEDIATELY. WASH CONTAMINATED AREAS WITH SOAP AND WATER FOLLOWED BY ALCOHOL (ARENA, POISONING, 4TH ED.). EMERGENCY PERSONNEL SHOULD WEAR GLOVES AND AVOID CONTAMINATION. TREAT RESPIRATORY DIFFICULTY WITH ARTIFICIAL RESPIRATION. GET MEDICAL ATTENTION IMMEDIATELY.

EYE CONTACT: ENDOTHION: SEE INFORMATION ON ORGANOPHOSPHATES. ORGANOPHOSPHATES: CHOLINESTERASE INHIBITOR. **ACUTE EXPOSURE-** DIRECT CONTACT MAY CAUSE PAIN, HYPEREMIA, LACRIMATION, TWITCHING OF THE EYELIDS, MIOSIS, AND CILIARY MUSCLE SPASM WITH LOSS OF ACCOMODATION, BLURRED OR DIMMED VISION AND BROWACHE. SOMETIMES MYDRIASIS MAY OCCUR INSTEAD OF MIOSIS. WITH SUFFICIENT EXPOSURE, OTHER SYMPTOMS OF CHOLINESTERASE INHIBITION AS DESCRIBED IN ACUTE INHALATION MAY OCCUR. **CHRONIC EXPOSURE-** REPEATED OR PROLONGED EXPOSURE MAY CAUSE EFFECTS AS DESCRIBED IN ACUTE EXPOSURE. SOME COMPOUNDS HAVE CAUSED TOXIC EFFECTS ON THE CRYSTALLINE LENS, CONJUNCTIVAL THICKENING AND OBSTRUCTION OF THE NASOLACRIMAL CANALS WHEN USED AS MIOTIC EYEDROPS.

FIRST AID- IRRIGATE EYES WITH WATER OR SALINE SOLUTION. IF SYMPTOMS OF POISONING OCCUR, TREAT RESPIRATORY DIFFICULTY WITH ARTIFICIAL RESPIRATION AND OXYGEN. OBSERVE PATIENT FOR AT LEAST 24-36 HOURS (GOSSELIN, CLINICAL TOXICOLOGY OF COMMERCIAL PRODUCTS, 5TH ED.). GET MEDICAL ATTENTION IMMEDIATELY. OXYGEN SHOULD BE ADMINISTERED BY QUALIFIED MEDICAL PERSONNEL.

INGESTION: ENDOTHION: HIGHLY TOXIC. SEE INFORMATION ON ORGANOPHOSPHATES.
ORGANOPHOSPHATES: CHOLINESTERASE INHIBITOR. **ACUTE EXPOSURE-** WHEN INGESTED, THE FIRST EFFECTS MAY BE NAUSEA, VOMITING, ANOREXIA, ABDOMINAL CRAMPS AND DIARRHEA. GASTROINTESTINAL ABSORPTION MAY CAUSE SYMPTOMS OF CHOLINESTERASE INHIBITION AS DESCRIBED IN ACUTE INHALATION. SYMPTOMS MAY BEGIN WITHIN MINUTES OR BE DELAYED FOR HOURS. DELAYED EFFECTS INCLUDING NEUROPATHY MAY ALSO OCCUR. **CHRONIC EXPOSURE-** REPEATED INGESTION MAY CAUSE EFFECTS AS DESCRIBED IN ACUTE EXPOSURE.

FIRST AID- IF PERSON IS ALERT AND RESPIRATION IS NOT DEPRESSED, GIVE SYRUP OF IPECAC FOLLOWED BY WATER (IF VOMITING OCCURS, KEEP HEAD BELOW HIPS TO PREVENT ASPIRATION). IF CONSCIOUSNESS LEVEL DECLINES OR VOMITING HAS NOT OCCURRED IN 15 MINUTES EMPTY STOMACH BY GASTRIC LAVAGE WITH THE AID OF CUFFED ENDOTRACHEAL TUBE USING ISOTONIC SALINE OR 5% SODIUM BICARBONATE FOLLOW WITH ACTIVATED CHARCOAL. ESTABLISH AND MAINTAIN AIRWAY. TREAT RESPIRATORY DIFFICULTY WITH ARTIFICIAL RESPIRATION AND OXYGEN. DO NOT GIVE MORPHINE, AMINOPHYLLINE, PHENOTHIAZINES, RESERPINE, FUROSEMIDE, OR ETHACRYNIC ACID (MORGAN, RECOGNITION AND MANAGEMENT OF PESTICIDE POISONINGS, 3RD ED.). TREAT SYMPTOMATICALLY AND SUPPORTIVELY. ADMINISTRATION OF OXYGEN AND LAVAGE MUST BE PERFORMED BY QUALIFIED MEDICAL PERSONNEL. GET MEDICAL ATTENTION IMMEDIATELY.

ANTIDOTE: THE FOLLOWING ANTIDOTE(S) HAVE BEEN RECOMMENDED. HOWEVER, THE DECISION AS TO WHETHER THE SEVERITY OF POISONING REQUIRES ADMINISTRATION OF ANY ANTIDOTE AND ACTUAL DOSE REQUIRED SHOULD BE MADE BY QUALIFIED MEDICAL PERSONNEL.
FOR CHOLINESTERASE INHIBITORS: ESTABLISH CLEAR AIRWAY AND TISSUE OXYGENATION BY ASPIRATION OF SECRETIONS, AND IF NECESSARY, BY ASSISTED PULMONARY VENTILATION WITH OXYGEN. IMPROVE TISSUE OXYGENATION AS MUCH AS POSSIBLE BEFORE ADMINISTERING ATROPINE TO MINIMIZE THE RISK OF VENTRICULAR FIBRILLATION. ADMINISTER ATROPINE SULFATE INTRAVENOUSLY, OR INTRAMUSCULARLY IF IV INJECTION IS NOT POSSIBLE. IN MODERATELY SEVERE POISONING ADMINISTER ATROPINE SULFATE, 0.4-2.0 MG REPEATED EVERY 15 MINUTES UNTIL ATROPINIZATION IS ACHIEVED (TACHYCARDIA, FLUSHING, DRY MOUTH, MYDRIASIS). MAINTAIN ATROPINIZATION BY REPEATED DOSES FOR 2-12 HOURS, OR LONGER, DEPENDING ON THE SEVERITY OF POISONING. THE APPEARANCE OF RALES IN THE LUNG BASES, MIOSIS, SALIVATION, NAUSEA, BRADYCARDIA, ARE ALL INDICATIONS OF INADEQUATE ATROPINIZATION. SEVERELY POISONED INDIVIDUALS MAY EXHIBIT REMARKABLE TOLERANCE TO ATROPINE; TWO OR MORE TIMES THE DOSAGES SUGGESTED ABOVE MAY BE NEEDED. PERSONS NOT POISONED OR ONLY SLIGHTLY POISONED, HOWEVER, MAY DEVELOP SIGNS OF ATROPINE TOXICITY FROM SUCH LARGE DOSAGES: FEVER, MUSCLE FIBRILLATIONS, AND DELIRIUM ARE THE MAIN SIGNS OF ATROPINE TOXICITY. IF THESE SIGNS APPEAR WHILE THE PATIENT IS FULLY ATROPINIZED, ATROPINE ADMINISTRATION SHOULD BE DISCONTINUED, AT LEAST TEMPORARILY. OBSERVE TREATED PATIENTS CLOSELY AT LEAST 24 HOURS TO INSURE THAT SYMPTOMS (POSSIBLY PULMONARY EDEMA) DO NOT RECUR AS ATROPINIZATION WEARS OFF. IN VERY SEVERE POISONINGS, METABOLIC DISPOSITION OF TOXICANT MAY REQUIRE SEVERAL HOURS OR DAYS DURING WHICH ATROPINIZATION MUST BE MAINTAINED. MARKEDLY LOWER LEVELS OF URINARY METABOLITES INDICATE THAT ATROPINE DOSAGE CAN BE TAPERED OFF. AS DOSAGE IS REDUCED, CHECK THE LUNG BASES FREQUENTLY FOR RALES. IF RALES ARE HEARD OR OTHER SYMPTOMS RETURN, RE-ESTABLISH ATROPINIZATION PROMPTLY (MORGAN, RECOGNITION AND MANAGEMENT OF PESTICIDE POISONINGS, 3RD ED.). ADMINISTRATION OF ANTIDOTE MUST BE PERFORMED BY QUALIFIED MEDICAL PERSONNEL.
IN CASES OF SEVERE POISONING BY ORGANOPHOSPHATE PESTICIDES IN WHICH RESPIRATORY DEPRESSION, MUSCLE WEAKNESS AND TWITCHINGS ARE SEVERE, GIVE PRALIDOXIME (PROTOPAM-AYERST, 2-PAM), 1.0 GRAM INTRAVENOUSLY AT

NO MORE THAN 0.5 GRAM PER MINUTE. DOSAGE OF PRALIDOXIME MAY BE REPEATED IN 1-2 HOURS, THEN AT 10-12 HOUR INTERVALS IF NEEDED. IN VERY SEVERE POISONINGS, DOSAGE RATES MAY BE DOUBLED. TREATMENT WITH PRALIDOXIME WILL BE MOST EFFECTIVE IF GIVEN WITHIN THIRTY-SIX HOURS AFTER POISONING (MORGAN, RECOGNITION AND MANAGEMENT OF PESTICIDE POISONINGS, 3RD ED.). ANTIDOTE SHOULD BE ADMINISTERED BY QUALIFIED MEDICAL PERSONNEL.

REACTIVITY

REACTIVITY: STABLE UNDER NORMAL TEMPERATURES AND PRESSURES.
INCOMPATIBILITIES: ENDOTHION: NO DATA AVAILABLE.
DECOMPOSITION: THERMAL DECOMPOSITION MAY RELEASE TOXIC OXIDES OF PHOSPHORUS AND SULFUR.
POLYMERIZATION: HAZARDOUS POLYMERIZATION HAS NOT BEEN REPORTED TO OCCUR UNDER NORMAL TEMPERATURES AND PRESSURES.

STORAGE AND DISPOSAL

OBSERVE ALL FEDERAL, STATE AND LOCAL REGULATIONS WHEN STORING OR DISPOSING OF THIS SUBSTANCE. FOR ASSISTANCE, CONTACT THE DISTRICT DIRECTOR OF THE ENVIRONMENTAL PROTECTION AGENCY.

STORAGE

STORE IN ACCORDANCE WITH 40 CFR 165 RECOMMENDED PROCEDURES FOR THE DISPOSAL AND STORAGE OF PESTICIDES AND PESTICIDE CONTAINERS.
THRESHOLD PLANNING QUANTITY (TPQ): THE SUPERFUND AMENDMENTS AND REAUTHORIZATION ACT (SARA) SECTION 302 REQUIRES THAT EACH FACILITY WHERE ANY EXTREMELY HAZARDOUS SUBSTANCE IS PRESENT IN A QUANTITY EQUAL TO OR GREATER THAN THE TPQ ESTABLISHED FOR THAT SUBSTANCE NOTIFY THE STATE EMERGENCY RESPONSE COMMISSION FOR THE STATE IN WHICH IT IS LOCATED. SECTION 303 OF SARA REQUIRES THESE FACILITIES TO PARTICIPATE IN LOCAL EMERGENCY RESPONSE PLANNING (40 CFR 355.30).

DISPOSAL

DISPOSAL MUST BE IN ACCORDANCE WITH 40 CFR 165 RECOMMENDED PROCEDURES FOR THE DISPOSAL AND STORAGE OF PESTICIDES AND PESTICIDE CONTAINERS.

CONDITIONS TO AVOID

NONE REPORTED.

SPILL AND LEAK PROCEDURES

OCCUPATIONAL SPILL: DO NOT TOUCH SPILLED MATERIAL. STOP LEAK IF YOU CAN DO IT WITHOUT RISK. FOR SMALL SPILLS, TAKE UP WITH SAND OR OTHER ABSORBENT MATERIAL AND PLACE INTO CONTAINERS FOR LATER DISPOSAL. FOR SMALL DRY SPILLS, WITH A CLEAN SHOVEL PLACE MATERIAL INTO CLEAN, DRY CONTAINER AND COVER. MOVE CONTAINERS FROM SPILL AREA. FOR LARGER SPILLS, DIKE FAR AHEAD OF SPILL FOR LATER DISPOSAL. KEEP UNNECESSARY PEOPLE AWAY. ISOLATE HAZARD AREA AND DENY ENTRY.
REPORTABLE QUANTITY (RQ): 1 POUND THE SUPERFUND AMENDMENTS AND REAUTHORIZATION ACT (SARA) SECTION 304 REQUIRES THAT A RELEASE EQUAL TO OR GREATER THAN THE REPORTABLE QUANTITY FOR THIS SUBSTANCE BE IMMEDIATELY REPORTED TO THE LOCAL EMERGENCY PLANNING COMMITTEE AND THE STATE EMERGENCY RESPONSE COMMISSION (40 CFR 355.40). IF THE RELEASE OF THIS SUBSTANCE IS REPORTABLE UNDER CERCLA SECTION 103, THE NATIONAL RESPONSE CENTER MUST BE NOTIFIED IMMEDIATELY AT (800) 424-8802 OR (202) 426-2675 IN THE METROPOLITAN WASHINGTON, D.C. AREA (40 CFR 302.6).

PROTECTIVE EQUIPMENT

VENTILATION: PROCESS ENCLOSURE RECOMMENDED.
RESPIRATOR: THE FOLLOWING RESPIRATORS ARE RECOMMENDED BASED ON INFORMATION FOUND IN THE PHYSICAL DATA, TOXICITY AND HEALTH EFFECTS SECTIONS. THEY ARE RANKED IN ORDER FROM MINIMUM TO MAXIMUM RESPIRATORY PROTECTION. THE SPECIFIC RESPIRATOR SELECTED MUST BE BASED ON CONTAMINATION LEVELS FOUND IN THE WORK PLACE, MUST NOT EXCEED THE WORKING LIMITS OF THE RESPIRATOR AND BE JOINTLY APPROVED BY THE NATIONAL INSTITUTE FOR OCCUPATIONAL SAFETY AND HEALTH AND THE MINE SAFETY AND HEALTH ADMINISTRATION (NIOSH-MSHA).
TYPE 'C' SUPPLIED-AIR RESPIRATOR WITH A FULL FACEPIECE OPERATED IN PRESSURE-DEMAND OR OTHER POSITIVE PRESSURE MODE OR WITH A FULL FACEPIECE, HELMET OR HOOD OPERATED IN CONTINOUS-FLOW MODE.
SELF-CONTAINED BREATHING APPARATUS WITH A FULL FACEPIECE OPERATED IN PRESSURE-DEMAND OR OTHER POSITIVE PRESSURE MODE.
FOR FIREFIGHTING AND OTHER IMMEDIATELY DANGEROUS TO LIFE OR HEALTH CONDITIONS:
SELF-CONTAINED BREATHING APPARATUS WITH FULL FACEPIECE OPERATED IN PRESSURE-DEMAND OR OTHER POSITIVE PRESSURE MODE.
SUPPLIED-AIR RESPIRATOR WITH FULL FACEPIECE AND OPERATED IN PRESSURE-DEMAND OR OTHER POSITIVE PRESSURE MODE IN COMBINATION WITH AN AUXILIARY SELF-CONTAINED BREATHING APPARATUS OPERATED IN PRESSURE-DEMAND OR OTHER POSITIVE PRESSURE MODE.
CLOTHING: EMPLOYEE MUST WEAR APPROPRIATE PROTECTIVE (IMPERVIOUS) CLOTHING AND EQUIPMENT TO PREVENT ANY POSSIBILITY OF SKIN CONTACT WITH THIS SUBSTANCE.
GLOVES: EMPLOYEE MUST WEAR APPROPRIATE PROTECTIVE GLOVES TO PREVENT CONTACT WITH THIS SUBSTANCE.
EYE PROTECTION: EMPLOYEE MUST WEAR SPLASH-PROOF OR DUST-RESISTANT SAFETY GOGGLES AND A FACESHIELD TO PREVENT CONTACT WITH THIS SUBSTANCE.
EMERGENCY WASH FACILITIES: WHERE THERE IS ANY POSSIBILITY THAT AN EMPLOYEE'S EYES AND/OR SKIN MAY BE EXPOSED TO THIS SUBSTANCE, THE EMPLOYER SHOULD PROVIDE AN EYE WASH FOUNTAIN AND QUICK DRENCH SHOWER WITHIN THE IMMEDIATE WORK AREA FOR EMERGENCY USE.

AUTHORIZED BY- OCCUPATIONAL HEALTH SERVICES, INC.
CREATION DATE: 10/04/89 ***REVISION DATE:*** 04/26/90

MATERIAL SAFETY DATA SHEET

OCCUPATIONAL HEALTH SERVICES, INC.
AGRICULTURE AND PESTICIDE DIVISION
450 SEVENTH AVENUE, SUITE 2407
NEW YORK, NEW YORK 10123
1-800-445-MSDS OR (212) 967-1100

EMERGENCY CONTACT:
JOHN S. BRANSFORD, JR. (615) 292-1180

SUBSTANCE IDENTIFICATION

CAS-NUMBER 557-30-2
SUBSTANCE: GLYOXIME
TRADE NAMES/SYNONYMS: ETHANEDIAL, DIOXIME; GLYOXAL, DIOXIME; ETHANEDIONE DIOXIME; PIK-OFF; C2H4N2O2; PST73143
CHEMICAL FAMILY: OXIME
MOLECULAR FORMULA: H-O-N-C-H-C-H-N-O-H
MOLECULAR WEIGHT: 88.07
CERCLA RATINGS (SCALE 0-3): HEALTH=3 FIRE=1 REACTIVITY=U PERSISTENCE=1
NFPA RATINGS (SCALE 0-4): HEALTH=4 FIRE=1 REACTIVITY=U

COMPONENTS AND CONTAMINANTS

COMPONENT: GLYOXIME ***PERCENT:*** 100.0
CAS# 557-30-2
OTHER CONTAMINANTS: NONE
EXPOSURE LIMITS: NO OCCUPATIONAL EXPOSURE LIMITS ESTABLISHED BY OSHA, ACGIH, OR NIOSH.

PHYSICAL DATA

DESCRIPTION: COLORLESS TO WHITE PRISMS.
MELTING POINT: 352 F (178 C) (DECOMPOSES) ***SPECIFIC GRAVITY:*** NOT AVAILABLE
SOLUBILITY IN WATER: SOLUBLE
SOLVENT SOLUBILITY: SOLUBLE IN ALCOHOL AND ETHER.

FIRE AND EXPLOSION DATA

FIRE AND EXPLOSION HAZARD: SLIGHT FIRE HAZARD WHEN EXPOSED TO HEAT OR FLAME.
DUST-AIR MIXTURES MAY IGNITE OR EXPLODE.
FIREFIGHTING MEDIA: DRY CHEMICAL, CARBON DIOXIDE, HALON, WATER SPRAY OR STANDARD FOAM (1987 EMERGENCY RESPONSE GUIDEBOOK, DOT P 5800.4).
FOR LARGER FIRES, USE WATER SPRAY, FOG OR STANDARD FOAM (1987 EMERGENCY RESPONSE GUIDEBOOK, DOT P 5800.4).
FIREFIGHTING: MOVE CONTAINERS FROM FIRE AREA IF POSSIBLE (1987 EMERGENCY RESPONSE GUIDEBOOK, DOT P 5800.4, GUIDE PAGE 53).
EXTINGUISH USING AGENT SUITABLE FOR TYPE OF SURROUNDING FIRE. AVOID BREATHING VAPORS AND DUSTS. KEEP UPWIND.

TRANSPORTATION DATA

DEPARTMENT OF TRANSPORTATION HAZARD CLASSIFICATION 49 CFR 172.101: POISON B

DEPARTMENT OF TRANSPORTATION LABELING REQUIREMENTS 49 CFR 172.101 AND SUBPART E: POISON
DEPARTMENT OF TRANSPORTATION PACKAGING REQUIREMENTS: 49 CFR 173.365
EXCEPTIONS: 49 CFR 173.364

TOXICITY

GLYOXIME: TOXICITY DATA: <0.030 MG/L/4 HOURS INHALATION-RAT LC50 (FMCHA2); 1580 MG/KG SKIN-RABBIT LD50; 119 MG/KG ORAL-RAT LD50; MUTAGENIC DATA (RTECS). CARCINOGEN STATUS: NONE. ACUTE TOXICITY LEVEL: HIGHLY TOXIC BY INHALATION; TOXIC BY INGESTION; MODERATELY TOXIC BY DERMAL ABSORPTION. TARGET EFFECTS: NO DATA AVAILABLE.

HEALTH EFFECTS AND FIRST AID

INHALATION: GLYOXIME: HIGHLY TOXIC. **ACUTE EXPOSURE-** THE LC50 REPORTED IN RATS IS LESS THAN 0.030 MG/L/4 HOURS. **CHRONIC EXPOSURE-** NO DATA AVAILABLE.
FIRST AID- REMOVE FROM EXPOSURE AREA TO FRESH AIR IMMEDIATELY. IF BREATHING HAS STOPPED, PERFORM ARTIFICIAL RESPIRATION. KEEP PERSON WARM AND AT REST. TREAT SYMPTOMATICALLY AND SUPPORTIVELY. GET MEDICAL ATTENTION IMMEDIATELY.

SKIN CONTACT: GLYOXIME: **ACUTE EXPOSURE-** THIS MATERIAL WAS NOT IRRITATING TO RABBIT SKIN. ANIMAL STUDIES INDICATE THAT DERMAL ABSORPTION MAY OCCUR. **CHRONIC EXPOSURE-** NO DATA AVAILABLE.
FIRST AID- REMOVE CONTAMINATED CLOTHING AND SHOES IMMEDIATELY. WASH AFFECTED AREA WITH SOAP OR MILD DETERGENT AND LARGE AMOUNTS OF WATER UNTIL NO EVIDENCE OF CHEMICAL REMAINS (APPROXIMATELY 15-20 MINUTES). GET MEDICAL ATTENTION IMMEDIATELY.

EYE CONTACT: GLYOXIME: **ACUTE EXPOSURE-** THIS MATERIAL WAS MILDLY IRRITATING TO RABBIT EYES. **CHRONIC EXPOSURE-** NO DATA AVAILABLE.
FIRST AID- WASH EYES IMMEDIATELY WITH LARGE AMOUNTS OF WATER OR NORMAL SALINE, OCCASIONALLY LIFTING UPPER AND LOWER LIDS, UNTIL NO EVIDENCE OF CHEMICAL REMAINS (APPROXIMATELY 15-20 MINUTES). GET MEDICAL ATTENTION IMMEDIATELY.

INGESTION: GLYOXIME: TOXIC. **ACUTE EXPOSURE-** THE LETHAL DOSE REPORTED IN RATS WAS 119 MG/KG; SYMPTOMS WERE NOT REPORTED. **CHRONIC EXPOSURE-** NO DATA AVAILABLE.
FIRST AID- IF THE PERSON IS CONSCIOUS AND NOT CONVULSING, REMOVE BY GASTRIC LAVAGE AND FOLLOW WITH A CATHARTIC (DREISBACH, HANDBOOK OF POISONING, 12TH ED.). TREAT SYMPTOMATICALLY AND SUPPORTIVELY. GASTRIC LAVAGE SHOULD BE PERFORMED BY QUALIFIED MEDICAL PERSONNEL. GET MEDICAL ATTENTION IMMEDIATELY.
ANTIDOTE: NO SPECIFIC ANTIDOTE. TREAT SYMPTOMATICALLY AND SUPPORTIVELY.

REACTIVITY

REACTIVITY: NO DATA AVAILABLE.
INCOMPATIBILITIES: GLYOXIME: OXIDIZERS (STRONG): FIRE AND EXPLOSION HAZARD.
DECOMPOSITION: THERMAL DECOMPOSITION PRODUCTS MAY INCLUDE TOXIC OXIDES OF CARBON AND NITROGEN.
POLYMERIZATION: HAZARDOUS POLYMERIZATION HAS NOT BEEN REPORTED TO OCCUR UNDER NORMAL TEMPERATURES AND PRESSURES.

STORAGE AND DISPOSAL

OBSERVE ALL FEDERAL, STATE AND LOCAL REGULATIONS WHEN STORING OR DISPOSING OF THIS SUBSTANCE. FOR ASSISTANCE, CONTACT THE DISTRICT DIRECTOR OF THE ENVIRONMENTAL PROTECTION AGENCY.

STORAGE

STORE IN ACCORDANCE WITH 40 CFR 165 RECOMMENDED PROCEDURES FOR THE DISPOSAL AND STORAGE OF PESTICIDES AND PESTICIDE CONTAINERS.
STORE AWAY FROM INCOMPATIBLE SUBSTANCES.

DISPOSAL

DISPOSAL MUST BE IN ACCORDANCE WITH 40 CFR 165 RECOMMENDED PROCEDURES FOR THE DISPOSAL AND STORAGE OF PESTICIDES AND PESTICIDE CONTAINERS.

CONDITIONS TO AVOID

MAY BURN BUT DOES NOT IGNITE READILY.

SPILL AND LEAK PROCEDURES

OCCUPATIONAL SPILL: DO NOT TOUCH SPILLED MATERIAL. STOP LEAK IF YOU CAN DO IT WITHOUT RISK. FOR SMALL SPILLS, TAKE UP WITH SAND OR OTHER ABSORBENT MATERIAL AND PLACE INTO CONTAINERS FOR LATER DISPOSAL. FOR SMALL DRY SPILLS, WITH A CLEAN SHOVEL PLACE MATERIAL INTO CLEAN, DRY CONTAINER AND COVER. MOVE CONTAINERS FROM SPILL AREA. FOR LARGER SPILLS, DIKE FAR AHEAD OF SPILL FOR LATER DISPOSAL. KEEP UNNECESSARY PEOPLE AWAY. ISOLATE HAZARD AREA AND DENY ENTRY.

PROTECTIVE EQUIPMENT

VENTILATION: PROVIDE LOCAL EXHAUST OR PROCESS ENCLOSURE VENTILATION SYSTEM.
RESPIRATOR: THE FOLLOWING RESPIRATORS ARE RECOMMENDED BASED ON INFORMATION FOUND IN THE PHYSICAL DATA, TOXICITY AND HEALTH EFFECTS SECTIONS. THEY ARE RANKED IN ORDER FROM MINIMUM TO MAXIMUM RESPIRATORY PROTECTION. THE SPECIFIC RESPIRATOR SELECTED MUST BE BASED ON CONTAMINATION LEVELS FOUND IN THE WORK PLACE, MUST NOT EXCEED THE WORKING LIMITS OF THE RESPIRATOR AND BE JOINTLY APPROVED BY THE NATIONAL INSTITUTE FOR OCCUPATIONAL SAFETY AND HEALTH AND THE MINE SAFETY AND HEALTH ADMINISTRATION (NIOSH-MSHA).
TYPE 'C' SUPPLIED-AIR RESPIRATOR WITH A FULL FACEPIECE OPERATED IN PRESSURE-DEMAND OR OTHER POSITIVE PRESSURE MODE OR WITH A FULL FACEPIECE, HELMET OR HOOD OPERATED IN CONTINOUS-FLOW MODE.
SELF-CONTAINED BREATHING APPARATUS WITH A FULL FACEPIECE OPERATED IN PRESSURE-DEMAND OR OTHER POSITIVE PRESSURE MODE.
FOR FIREFIGHTING AND OTHER IMMEDIATELY DANGEROUS TO LIFE OR HEALTH CONDITIONS:
SELF-CONTAINED BREATHING APPARATUS WITH FULL FACEPIECE OPERATED IN PRESSURE-DEMAND OR OTHER POSITIVE PRESSURE MODE.
SUPPLIED-AIR RESPIRATOR WITH FULL FACEPIECE AND OPERATED IN PRESSURE-DEMAND OR OTHER POSITIVE PRESSURE MODE IN COMBINATION WITH AN AUXILIARY SELF-CONTAINED BREATHING APPARATUS OPERATED IN PRESSURE-DEMAND OR OTHER POSITIVE PRESSURE MODE.
CLOTHING: EMPLOYEE MUST WEAR APPROPRIATE PROTECTIVE (IMPERVIOUS) CLOTHING AND EQUIPMENT TO PREVENT ANY POSSIBILITY OF SKIN CONTACT WITH THIS SUBSTANCE.
GLOVES: EMPLOYEE MUST WEAR APPROPRIATE PROTECTIVE GLOVES TO PREVENT CONTACT WITH THIS SUBSTANCE.
EYE PROTECTION: EMPLOYEE MUST WEAR SPLASH-PROOF OR DUST-RESISTANT SAFETY GOGGLES AND A FACESHIELD TO PREVENT CONTACT WITH THIS SUBSTANCE.
EMERGENCY WASH FACILITIES: WHERE THERE IS ANY POSSIBILITY THAT AN EMPLOYEE'S EYES AND/OR SKIN MAY BE EXPOSED TO THIS SUBSTANCE, THE EMPLOYER SHOULD PROVIDE AN EYE WASH FOUNTAIN AND QUICK DRENCH SHOWER WITHIN THE IMMEDIATE WORK AREA FOR EMERGENCY USE.

AUTHORIZED BY- OCCUPATIONAL HEALTH SERVICES, INC.
CREATION DATE: 02/01/90 ***REVISION DATE:*** 03/28/90

MATERIAL SAFETY DATA SHEET

OCCUPATIONAL HEALTH SERVICES, INC.
AGRICULTURE AND PESTICIDE DIVISION
450 SEVENTH AVENUE, SUITE 2407
NEW YORK, NEW YORK 10123
1-800-445-MSDS OR (212) 967-1100

EMERGENCY CONTACT:
JOHN S. BRANSFORD, JR. (615) 292-1180

SUBSTANCE IDENTIFICATION

CAS-NUMBER 2669-32-1
SUBSTANCE: **LYTHIDATION**
TRADE NAMES/SYNONYMS: PHOSPHORODITHIOIC ACID, S-((5-ETHOXY-2-OXO-1,3,4-THIADIAZOL-3(2H)-YL) METHYL) O,O-DIMETHYL ESTER; PHOSPHORODITHIOIC ACID, O,O-DIMETHYL ESTER, S-ESTER WITH 2-ETHOXY-4 -(MERCAPTOMETHYL)-DELTA2-1,3,4-THIADIZOLIN-5-ONE; O,O-DIMETHYL ESTER, S-ESTER WITH 2-ETHOXY-4-(MERCATOMETHYL)-DELTA2 -1,3,4-THIADIAZOLIN-5-ONE PHOSPHOROTHIOIC ACID; S-5-ETHOXY-2,3-DIHYDRO-2-OXO-1,3,4-THIADIAZOL-3-YLMETHYL O,O-DIMETHYL PHOSPHORODITHIOATE; 3-DIMETHOXYPHOSPHINOTHIOYLTHIOMETHYL-5-ETHOXY-1,3,4-THIADIAZOL -2(3H)-ONE; S-(5-ETHOXY-2-OXO-1,3,4-THIADIAZOL-3(2H)-YLMETHYL) O,O-DIMETHYL PHOSPHORODITHIOATE; GS 12968; O,O-DIMETHYL PHOSPHORODITHIOATE S-ESTER WITH 2-ETHOXY-4 -(MERCAPTOMETHYL)- DELTA2-1,3,4-THIADIAZOLIN-5-ONE; GEIGY 12968; GEIGY GS 12968; OMS 958; C7H13N2O4PS3; PST73147
CHEMICAL FAMILY: PHOSPHOROTHIOATE
MOLECULAR FORMULA: C7-H13-N2-O4-P-S3
MOLECULAR WEIGHT: 316.37

CERCLA RATINGS (SCALE 0-3): HEALTH=3 FIRE=1 REACTIVITY=0 PERSISTENCE=1
NFPA RATINGS (SCALE 0-4): HEALTH=3 FIRE=1 REACTIVITY=0

COMPONENTS AND CONTAMINANTS

COMPONENT: LYTHIDATHION ***PERCENT:*** 100.0
CAS# 2669-32-1
OTHER CONTAMINANTS: NONE
EXPOSURE LIMITS: NO OCCUPATIONAL EXPOSURE LIMITS ESTABLISHED BY OSHA, ACGIH, OR NIOSH.

PHYSICAL DATA

DESCRIPTION: SOLID. ***MELTING POINT:*** 120-122 F (49-50 C)
SPECIFIC GRAVITY: NOT AVAILABLE ***SOLUBILITY IN WATER:*** NOT AVAILABLE

FIRE AND EXPLOSION DATA

FIRE AND EXPLOSION HAZARD: SLIGHT FIRE HAZARD WHEN EXPOSED TO HEAT OR FLAME.

FIREFIGHTING MEDIA: DRY CHEMICAL, CARBON DIOXIDE, HALON, WATER SPRAY OR STANDARD FOAM (1987 EMERGENCY RESPONSE GUIDEBOOK, DOT P 5800.4). FOR LARGER FIRES, USE WATER SPRAY, FOG OR STANDARD FOAM (1987 EMERGENCY RESPONSE GUIDEBOOK, DOT P 5800.4).

FIREFIGHTING: MOVE CONTAINERS FROM FIRE AREA IF POSSIBLE. FIGHT FIRE FROM MAXIMUM DISTANCE. STAY AWAY FROM STORAGE TANK ENDS. DIKE FIRE CONTROL WATER FOR LATER DISPOSAL. DO NOT SCATTER MATERIAL (1987 EMERGENCY RESPONSE GUIDEBOOK, DOT P 5800.4, GUIDE PAGE 55). EXTINGUISH ONLY IF FLOW CAN BE STOPPED; USE FLOODING AMOUNTS OF WATER AS FOG, SOLID STREAMS MAY BE INEFFECTIVE. COOL CONTAINERS WITH FLOODING AMOUNTS OF WATER FROM AS FAR A DISTANCE AS POSSIBLE. USE WATER SPRAY TO ABSORB TOXIC VAPORS. AVOID BREATHING TOXIC VAPORS; KEEP UPWIND. CONSIDER EVACUATION OF DOWNWIND AREA IF MATERIAL IS LEAKING.

TOXICITY

LYTHIDATHION: TOXICITY DATA: 268 MG/KG ORAL-RAT LD50; 225 MG/KG UNREPORTED-MAMMAL LD50. CARCINOGEN STATUS: NONE. ACUTE TOXICITY LEVEL: TOXIC BY INGESTION. TARGET EFFECTS: CHOLINESTERASE INHIBITOR. POISONING MAY AFFECT THE NERVOUS SYSTEM.* AT INCREASED RISK FROM EXPOSURE: PERSONS WITH RESPIRATORY AILMENTS, RECENT EXPOSURE TO CHOLINESTERASE INHIBITORS OR IMPAIRED CHOLINESTERASE PRODUCTION, OR LIVER MALFUNCTION.* ADDITIONAL DATA: MAY CROSS THE PLACENTA. HIGH ENVIRONMENTAL TEMPERATURES OR EXPOSURE OF THE CHEMICAL TO VISIBLE OR ULTRAVIOLET LIGHT MAY ENHANCE THE TOXICITY. INTERACTIONS WITH MEDICATIONS MAY OCCUR.*

* MAY BE BASED ON GENERAL INFORMATION ON ORGANOPHOSPHATES.

HEALTH EFFECTS AND FIRST AID

INHALATION: LYTHIDATHION: SEE INFORMATION ON ORGANOPHOSPHATES. ORGANOPHOSPHATES: CHOLINESTERASE INHIBITOR. **ACUTE EXPOSURE-** WHEN INHALED, THE FIRST EFFECTS OF CHOLINESTERASE INHIBITORS ARE USUALLY RESPIRATORY AND MAY INCLUDE NASAL HYPEREMIA AND WATERY DISCHARGE, COUGH, CHEST DISCOMFORT, DYSPNEA, AND WHEEZING DUE TO INCREASED BRONCHIAL SECRETIONS AND BRONCHOCONSTRICTION. IF SUFFICIENT AMOUNTS ARE ABSORBED, OTHER SYSTEMIC EFFECTS MAY BEGIN WITHIN A FEW MINUTES OR BE DELAYED FOR UP TO 12 HOURS. SYMPTOMS MAY INCLUDE PALLOR, NAUSEA, VOMITING, DIARRHEA, ABDOMINAL CRAMPS, HEADACHE, DIZZINESS, OCULAR PAIN, BLURRED VISION, MIOSIS OR IN SOME CASES, ESPECIALLY INITIALLY, MYDRIASIS, LACRIMATION, SALIVATION, SWEATING, AND CONFUSION. OTHER REPORTED CENTRAL NERVOUS SYSTEM OR NEUROMUSCULAR EFFECTS MAY INCLUDE ATAXIA, SLURRED SPEECH, AREFLEXIA, WEAKNESS, FATIGUE, FASCICULATIONS, TWITCHING, TREMORS POSSIBLY OF THE TONGUE AND EYELIDS, AND EVENTUALLY PARALYSIS OF THE EXTREMITIES AND POSSIBLY OF THE RESPIRATORY MUSCLES. IN SEVERE CASES THERE MAY ALSO BE INVOLUNTARY DEFECATION AND URINATION, CYANOSIS, PSYCHOSIS, HYPERGLYCEMIA, ACUTE PANCREATITIS, CARDIAC IRREGULARITIES, PULMONARY EDEMA, UNCONSCIOUSNESS, CONVULSIONS, AND COMA. DEATH IS PRIMARILY DUE TO RESPIRATORY FAILURE, ALTHOUGH CARDIOVASCULAR EFFECTS INCLUDING CARDIAC ARREST MAY ALSO BE IMPLICATED. LONG TERM SEQUELAE ARE RARE BUT MAY INCLUDE NEUROPSYCHIATRIC DISORDERS AND MYOPATHY WITH MUSCLE TENDERNESS. SOME ORGANOPHOSPHATES MAY CAUSE A DELAYED NEUROPATHY BEGINNING 1-4 WEEKS AFTER AN ACUTE EXPOSURE WHICH MAY OR MAY NOT HAVE CAUSED ACUTE CHOLINERGIC EFFECTS. NUMBNESS, TINGLING, WEAKNESS AND CRAMPING BEGINNING SYMMETRICALLY IN THE LOWER LIMBS MAY PROGRESS TO ATAXIA AND PARALYSIS. IN SEVERE CASES, UPPER LIMB INVOLVEMENT IS POSSIBLE AND FLACCID PARALYSIS MAY PROGRESS TO SPASTIC PARALYSIS WITH EXAGGERATED REFLEXES. IMPROVEMENT MAY OCCUR OVER MONTHS TO YEARS, BUT SOME RESIDUAL IMPAIRMENT USUALLY REMAINS. **CHRONIC EXPOSURE-** REPEATED OR PROLONGED EXPOSURE MAY RESULT IN THE EFFECTS OF ACUTE EXPOSURE INCLUDING THE DELAYED NEUROPATHY. OTHER EFFECTS REPORTED IN WORKERS REPEATEDLY EXPOSED INCLUDE IMPAIRED MEMORY AND CONCENTRATION, ACUTE PSYCHOSIS, SEVERE DEPRESSIONS, IRRITABILTY, CONFUSION, APATHY, EMOTIONAL LABILITY, SOCIAL WITHDRAWAL, CONFUSION, HEADACHE, SPEECH DIFFICULTIES, DELAYED REACTION TIMES, SPATIAL DISORIENTATION, NIGHTMARES, SLEEPWALKING, AND DROWSINESS OR INSOMNIA. AN INFLUENZA-LIKE CONDITION WITH HEADACHE, NAUSEA, WEAKNESS, ANOREXIA AND MALAISE HAS ALSO BEEN REPORTED.

FIRST AID- REMOVE FROM EXPOSURE AREA TO FRESH AIR IMMEDIATELY. IF BREATHING HAS STOPPED, GIVE ARTIFICIAL RESPIRATION. MAINTAIN AIRWAY AND BLOOD PRESSURE AND ADMINISTER OXYGEN IF AVAILABLE. KEEP AFFECTED PERSON WARM AND AT REST. TREAT SYMPTOMATICALLY AND SUPPORTIVELY. ADMINISTRATION OF OXYGEN SHOULD BE PERFORMED BY QUALIFIED PERSONNEL. GET MEDICAL ATTENTION IMMEDIATELY.

SKIN CONTACT: LYTHIDATHION: SEE INFORMATION ON ORGANOPHOSPHATES. ORGANOPHOSPHATES: CHOLINESTERASE INHIBITOR. **ACUTE EXPOSURE-** LOCALIZED SWEATING AND FASCICULATIONS MAY OCCUR AT THE SITE OF CONTACT. IF SUFFICIENT AMOUNTS ARE ABSORBED, OTHER EFFECTS OF CHOLINESTERASE INHIBITION AS DESCRIBED IN ACUTE INHALATION MAY OCCUR. SYMPTOMS MAY BE DELAYED 2-3 HOURS, BUT USUALLY NO MORE THAN 12 HOURS. THE RATE OF ABSORPTION IS INCREASED BY THE PRESENCE OF DERMATITIS OR HIGH AMBIENT TEMPERATURES. DELAYED NEUROPATHY IS ALSO POSSIBLE. **CHRONIC EXPOSURE-** REPEATED OR PROLONGED EXPOSURE MAY CAUSE EFFECTS AS DESCRIBED IN ACUTE EXPOSURE. SOME ORGANOPHOSPHATES MAY CAUSE SENSITIZATION.

FIRST AID- REMOVE CONTAMINATED CLOTHING IMMEDIATELY. WASH CONTAMINATED AREAS WITH SOAP AND WATER FOLLOWED BY ALCOHOL (ARENA, POISONING, 4TH ED.). EMERGENCY PERSONNEL SHOULD WEAR GLOVES AND AVOID CONTAMINATION. TREAT RESPIRATORY DIFFICULTY WITH ARTIFICIAL RESPIRATION. GET MEDICAL ATTENTION IMMEDIATELY.

EYE CONTACT: LYTHIDATHION: SEE INFORMATION ON ORGANOPHOSPHATES. ORGANOPHOSPHATES: CHOLINESTERASE INHIBITOR. **ACUTE EXPOSURE-** DIRECT CONTACT MAY CAUSE PAIN, HYPEREMIA, LACRIMATION, TWITCHING OF THE EYELIDS, MIOSIS, AND CILIARY MUSCLE SPASM WITH LOSS OF ACCOMODATION, BLURRED OR DIMMED VISION AND BROWACHE. SOMETIMES MYDRIASIS MAY OCCUR INSTEAD OF MIOSIS. WITH SUFFICIENT EXPOSURE, OTHER SYMPTOMS OF CHOLINESTERASE INHIBITION AS DESCRIBED IN ACUTE INHALATION MAY OCCUR. **CHRONIC EXPOSURE-** REPEATED OR PROLONGED EXPOSURE MAY CAUSE EFFECTS AS DESCRIBED IN ACUTE EXPOSURE. SOME COMPOUNDS HAVE CAUSED TOXIC EFFECTS ON THE CRYSTALLINE LENS, CONJUNCTIVAL THICKENING AND OBSTRUCTION OF THE NASOLACRIMAL CANALS WHEN USED AS MIOTIC EYEDROPS.

FIRST AID- IRRIGATE EYES WITH WATER OR SALINE SOLUTION. IF SYMPTOMS OF POISONING OCCUR, TREAT RESPIRATORY DIFFICULTY WITH ARTIFICIAL RESPIRATION AND OXYGEN. OBSERVE PATIENT FOR AT LEAST 24-36 HOURS (GOSSELIN, CLINICAL TOXICOLOGY OF COMMERCIAL PRODUCTS, 5TH ED.). GET MEDICAL ATTENTION IMMEDIATELY. OXYGEN SHOULD BE ADMINISTERED BY QUALIFIED MEDICAL PERSONNEL.

INGESTION: LYTHIDATHION: TOXIC. SEE INFORMATION ON ORGANOPHOSPHATES. ORGANOPHOSPHATES: CHOLINESTERASE INHIBITOR. **ACUTE EXPOSURE-** WHEN INGESTED, THE FIRST EFFECTS MAY BE NAUSEA, VOMITING, ANOREXIA, ABDOMINAL CRAMPS AND DIARRHEA. GASTROINTESTINAL ABSORPTION MAY CAUSE SYMPTOMS OF CHOLINESTERASE INHIBITION AS DESCRIBED IN ACUTE INHALATION. SYMPTOMS MAY BEGIN WITHIN MINUTES OR BE DELAYED FOR HOURS. DELAYED EFFECTS INCLUDING NEUROPATHY MAY ALSO OCCUR. **CHRONIC EXPOSURE-** REPEATED INGESTION MAY CAUSE EFFECTS AS DESCRIBED IN ACUTE EXPOSURE.

FIRST AID- IF PERSON IS ALERT AND RESPIRATION IS NOT DEPRESSED, GIVE SYRUP OF IPECAC FOLLOWED BY WATER (IF VOMITING OCCURS, KEEP HEAD BELOW HIPS TO PREVENT ASPIRATION). IF CONSCIOUSNESS LEVEL DECLINES OR VOMITING HAS NOT OCCURRED IN 15 MINUTES EMPTY STOMACH BY GASTRIC LAVAGE WITH THE AID OF CUFFED ENDOTRACHEAL TUBE USING ISOTONIC SALINE OR 5% SODIUM BICARBONATE FOLLOW WITH ACTIVATED CHARCOAL. ESTABLISH AND MAINTAIN AIRWAY. TREAT RESPIRATORY DIFFICULTY WITH ARTIFICIAL RESPIRATION AND OXYGEN. DO NOT GIVE MORPHINE, AMINOPHYLLINE, PHENOTHIAZINES, RESERPINE, FUROSEMIDE, OR ETHACRYNIC ACID (MORGAN, RECOGNITION AND MANAGEMENT OF PESTICIDE POISONINGS, 3RD ED.). TREAT SYMPTOMATICALLY AND SUPPORTIVELY. ADMINISTRATION OF OXYGEN AND LAVAGE MUST BE PERFORMED BY QUALIFIED MEDICAL PERSONNEL. GET MEDICAL ATTENTION IMMEDIATELY.

ANTIDOTE: THE FOLLOWING ANTIDOTE(S) HAVE BEEN RECOMMENDED. HOWEVER, THE DECISION AS TO WHETHER THE SEVERITY OF POISONING REQUIRES

ADMINISTRATION OF ANY ANTIDOTE AND ACTUAL DOSE REQUIRED SHOULD BE MADE BY QUALIFIED MEDICAL PERSONNEL.
FOR CHOLINESTERASE INHIBITORS: ESTABLISH CLEAR AIRWAY AND TISSUE OXYGENATION BY ASPIRATION OF SECRETIONS, AND IF NECESSARY, BY ASSISTED PULMONARY VENTILATION WITH OXYGEN. IMPROVE TISSUE OXYGENATION AS MUCH AS POSSIBLE BEFORE ADMINISTERING ATROPINE TO MINIMIZE THE RISK OF VENTRICULAR FIBRILLATION. ADMINISTER ATROPINE SULFATE INTRAVENOUSLY, OR INTRAMUSCULARLY IF IV INJECTION IS NOT POSSIBLE. IN MODERATELY SEVERE POISONING ADMINISTER ATROPINE SULFATE, 0.4-2.0 MG REPEATED EVERY 15 MINUTES UNTIL ATROPINIZATION IS ACHIEVED (TACHYCARDIA, FLUSHING, DRY MOUTH, MYDRIASIS). MAINTAIN ATROPINIZATION BY REPEATED DOSES FOR 2-12 HOURS, OR LONGER, DEPENDING ON THE SEVERITY OF POISONING. THE APPEARANCE OF RALES IN THE LUNG BASES, MIOSIS, SALIVATION, NAUSEA, BRADYCARDIA, ARE ALL INDICATIONS OF INADEQUATE ATROPINIZATION.
SEVERELY POISONED INDIVIDUALS MAY EXHIBIT REMARKABLE TOLERANCE TO ATROPINE; TWO OR MORE TIMES THE DOSAGES SUGGESTED ABOVE MAY BE NEEDED. PERSONS NOT POISONED OR ONLY SLIGHTLY POISONED, HOWEVER, MAY DEVELOP SIGNS OF ATROPINE TOXICITY FROM SUCH LARGE DOSAGES: FEVER, MUSCLE FIBRILLATIONS, AND DELIRIUM ARE THE MAIN SIGNS OF ATROPINE TOXICITY. IF THESE SIGNS APPEAR WHILE THE PATIENT IS FULLY ATROPINIZED, ATROPINE ADMINISTRATION SHOULD BE DISCONTINUED, AT LEAST TEMPORARILY.
OBSERVE TREATED PATIENTS CLOSELY AT LEAST 24 HOURS TO INSURE THAT SYMPTOMS (POSSIBLY PULMONARY EDEMA) DO NOT RECUR AS ATROPINIZATION WEARS OFF. IN VERY SEVERE POISONINGS, METABOLIC DISPOSITION OF TOXICANT MAY REQUIRE SEVERAL HOURS OR DAYS DURING WHICH ATROPINIZATION MUST BE MAINTAINED. MARKEDLY LOWER LEVELS OF URINARY METABOLITES INDICATE THAT ATROPINE DOSAGE CAN BE TAPERED OFF. AS DOSAGE IS REDUCED, CHECK THE LUNG BASES FREQUENTLY FOR RALES. IF RALES ARE HEARD OR OTHER SYMPTOMS RETURN, RE-ESTABLISH ATROPINIZATION PROMPTLY (MORGAN, RECOGNITION AND MANAGEMENT OF PESTICIDE POISONINGS, 3RD ED.). ADMINISTRATION OF ANTIDOTE MUST BE PERFORMED BY QUALIFIED MEDICAL PERSONNEL.
IN CASES OF SEVERE POISONING BY ORGANOPHOSPHATE PESTICIDES IN WHICH RESPIRATORY DEPRESSION, MUSCLE WEAKNESS AND TWITCHINGS ARE SEVERE, GIVE PRALIDOXIME (PROTOPAM-AYERST, 2-PAM), 1.0 GRAM INTRAVENOUSLY AT NO MORE THAN 0.5 GRAM PER MINUTE. DOSAGE OF PRALIDOXIME MAY BE REPEATED IN 1-2 HOURS, THEN AT 10-12 HOUR INTERVALS IF NEEDED. IN VERY SEVERE POISONINGS, DOSAGE RATES MAY BE DOUBLED. TREATMENT WITH PRALIDOXIME WILL BE MOST EFFECTIVE IF GIVEN WITHIN THIRTY-SIX HOURS AFTER POISONING (MORGAN, RECOGNITION AND MANAGEMENT OF PESTICIDE POISONINGS, 3RD ED.). ANTIDOTE SHOULD BE ADMINISTERED BY QUALIFIED MEDICAL PERSONNEL.

REACTIVITY

REACTIVITY: STABLE UNDER NORMAL TEMPERATURES AND PRESSURES.
INCOMPATIBILITIES: LYTHIDATHION: OXIDIZERS (STRONG): FIRE AND EXPLOSION HAZARD.
DECOMPOSITION: THERMAL DECOMPOSITION PRODUCTS MAY INCLUDE TOXIC OXIDES OF NITROGEN, CARBON, PHOSPHORUS, AND SULFUR.
POLYMERIZATION: HAZARDOUS POLYMERIZATION HAS NOT BEEN REPORTED TO OCCUR UNDER NORMAL TEMPERATURES AND PRESSURES.

STORAGE AND DISPOSAL

OBSERVE ALL FEDERAL, STATE AND LOCAL REGULATIONS WHEN STORING OR DISPOSING OF THIS SUBSTANCE. FOR ASSISTANCE, CONTACT THE DISTRICT DIRECTOR OF THE ENVIRONMENTAL PROTECTION AGENCY.

STORAGE

STORE IN ACCORDANCE WITH 40 CFR 165 RECOMMENDED PROCEDURES FOR THE DISPOSAL AND STORAGE OF PESTICIDES AND PESTICIDE CONTAINERS.
STORE AWAY FROM INCOMPATIBLE SUBSTANCES.

DISPOSAL

DISPOSAL MUST BE IN ACCORDANCE WITH 40 CFR 165 RECOMMENDED PROCEDURES FOR THE DISPOSAL AND STORAGE OF PESTICIDES AND PESTICIDE CONTAINERS.

CONDITIONS TO AVOID

MAY BURN BUT DOES NOT IGNITE READILY. CONTAINERS MAY EXPLODE IN HEAT OF FIRE.

SPILL AND LEAK PROCEDURES

OCCUPATIONAL SPILL: DO NOT TOUCH SPILLED MATERIAL. STOP LEAK IF YOU CAN DO IT WITHOUT RISK. USE WATER SPRAY TO REDUCE VAPORS. FOR SMALL SPILLS, TAKE UP WITH SAND OR OTHER ABSORBENT MATERIAL AND PLACE INTO CONTAINERS FOR LATER DISPOSAL. FOR SMALL DRY SPILLS, WITH A CLEAN SHOVEL PLACE MATERIAL INTO CLEAN, DRY CONTAINERS AND COVER. MOVE CONTAINERS FROM SPILL AREA. FOR LARGER SPILLS, DIKE FAR AHEAD OF SPILL FOR LATER DISPOSAL. KEEP UNNECESSARY PEOPLE AWAY. ISOLATE HAZARD AREA AND DENY ENTRY. VENTILATE CLOSED SPACES BEFORE ENTERING.

PROTECTIVE EQUIPMENT

VENTILATION: PROVIDE LOCAL EXHAUST OR PROCESS ENCLOSURE VENTILATION SYSTEM.
RESPIRATOR: THE FOLLOWING RESPIRATORS ARE RECOMMENDED BASED ON INFORMATION FOUND IN THE PHYSICAL DATA, TOXICITY AND HEALTH EFFECTS SECTIONS. THEY ARE RANKED IN ORDER FROM MINIMUM TO MAXIMUM RESPIRATORY PROTECTION. THE SPECIFIC RESPIRATOR SELECTED MUST BE BASED ON CONTAMINATION LEVELS FOUND IN THE WORK PLACE, MUST NOT EXCEED THE WORKING LIMITS OF THE RESPIRATOR AND BE JOINTLY APPROVED BY THE NATIONAL INSTITUTE FOR OCCUPATIONAL SAFETY AND HEALTH AND THE MINE SAFETY AND HEALTH ADMINISTRATION (NIOSH-MSHA).
TYPE 'C' SUPPLIED-AIR RESPIRATOR WITH A FULL FACEPIECE OPERATED IN PRESSURE-DEMAND OR OTHER POSITIVE PRESSURE MODE OR WITH A FULL FACEPIECE, HELMET OR HOOD OPERATED IN CONTINOUS-FLOW MODE.
SELF-CONTAINED BREATHING APPARATUS WITH A FULL FACEPIECE OPERATED IN PRESSURE-DEMAND OR OTHER POSITIVE PRESSURE MODE.
FOR FIREFIGHTING AND OTHER IMMEDIATELY DANGEROUS TO LIFE OR HEALTH CONDITIONS:
SELF-CONTAINED BREATHING APPARATUS WITH FULL FACEPIECE OPERATED IN PRESSURE-DEMAND OR OTHER POSITIVE PRESSURE MODE.
SUPPLIED-AIR RESPIRATOR WITH FULL FACEPIECE AND OPERATED IN PRESSURE-DEMAND OR OTHER POSITIVE PRESSURE MODE IN COMBINATION WITH AN AUXILIARY SELF-CONTAINED BREATHING APPARATUS OPERATED IN PRESSURE-DEMAND OR OTHER POSITIVE PRESSURE MODE.
CLOTHING: EMPLOYEE MUST WEAR APPROPRIATE PROTECTIVE (IMPERVIOUS) CLOTHING AND EQUIPMENT TO PREVENT ANY POSSIBILITY OF SKIN CONTACT WITH THIS SUBSTANCE.
GLOVES: EMPLOYEE MUST WEAR APPROPRIATE PROTECTIVE GLOVES TO PREVENT CONTACT WITH THIS SUBSTANCE.
EYE PROTECTION: EMPLOYEE MUST WEAR SPLASH-PROOF OR DUST-RESISTANT SAFETY GOGGLES WITH OR WITHOUT A FACESHIELD TO PREVENT CONTACT WITH THIS SUBSTANCE.
EMERGENCY EYE WASH: WHERE THERE IS ANY POSSIBILITY THAT AN EMPLOYEE'S EYES MAY BE EXPOSED TO THIS SUBSTANCE, THE EMPLOYER SHOULD PROVIDE AN EYE WASH FOUNTAIN WITHIN THE IMMEDIATE WORK AREA FOR EMERGENCY USE.

AUTHORIZED BY- OCCUPATIONAL HEALTH SERVICES, INC.
CREATION DATE: 10/04/89 ***REVISION DATE:*** 04/26/90

MATERIAL SAFETY DATA SHEET

OCCUPATIONAL HEALTH SERVICES, INC.
AGRICULTURE AND PESTICIDE DIVISION
450 SEVENTH AVENUE, SUITE 2407
NEW YORK, NEW YORK 10123
1-800-445-MSDS OR (212) 967-1100

EMERGENCY CONTACT:
JOHN S. BRANSFORD, JR. (615) 292-1180

SUBSTANCE IDENTIFICATION

CAS-NUMBER 38260-54-7
SUBSTANCE: ETRIMFOS
TRADE NAMES/SYNONYMS: PHOSPHOROTHIOIC ACID, O-(6-ETHOXY-2-ETHYL-4-PYRIMIDINYL)-O,O-DIMETHYL ESTER; O-6-ETHOXY-2-ETHYLPYRIMIDIN-4-YL O,O-DIMETHYL PHOSPHOROTHIOATE; O-(6-ETHOXY-2-ETHYL-4-PYRIMIDINYL) O,O-DIMETHYL PHOSPHOROTHIOATE; O-(6-ETHOXY-2-ETHYL-4-PYRIMIDINYL) O,O-DIMETHYL-PHOSPHOROTHIOATE; EKAMET (FORMULATION); ETRIMPHOS; SATISFAR; SAN 197; C10H17N2O4PS; PST73148
CHEMICAL FAMILY: ORGANOPHOSPHATE
MOLECULAR FORMULA: C10-H17-N2-O4-P-S
MOLECULAR WEIGHT: 292.29
CERCLA RATINGS (SCALE 0-3): HEALTH=U FIRE=1 REACTIVITY=1 PERSISTENCE=2
NFPA RATINGS (SCALE 0-4): HEALTH=U FIRE=1 REACTIVITY=1

COMPONENTS AND CONTAMINANTS

COMPONENT: ETRIMFOS ***PERCENT:*** 100.0
CAS# 38260-54-7
OTHER CONTAMINANTS: NONE

EXPOSURE LIMITS: NO OCCUPATIONAL EXPOSURE LIMITS ESTABLISHED BY OSHA, ACGIH, OR NIOSH.

PHYSICAL DATA

DESCRIPTION: COLORLESS OIL WITH A SLIGHT ODOR.
BOILING POINT: NOT AVAILABLE
MELTING POINT: 26 F (-3 C) ***SPECIFIC GRAVITY:*** 1.195
VAPOR PRESSURE: NEGLIGIBLE ***SOLUBILITY IN WATER:*** 40 PPM
SOLVENT SOLUBILITY: SOLUBLE IN ACETONE, METHANOL, HEXANE, CHLOROFORM, DIMETHYL SULFOXIDE, ETHANOL, XYLENE, ETHYL ACETATE, ETHER, ACETONITRILE, TOLUENE AND KEROSENE.

FIRE AND EXPLOSION DATA

FIRE AND EXPLOSION HAZARD: SLIGHT FIRE HAZARD WHEN EXPOSED TO HEAT OR FLAME.
FLASH POINT: 212 F (100 C) ***FLAMMABILITY CLASS(OSHA):*** IIIB
FIREFIGHTING MEDIA: DRY CHEMICAL, CARBON DIOXIDE, HALON, WATER SPRAY OR STANDARD FOAM (1987 EMERGENCY RESPONSE GUIDEBOOK, DOT P 5800.4). FOR LARGER FIRES, USE WATER SPRAY, FOG OR STANDARD FOAM (1987 EMERGENCY RESPONSE GUIDEBOOK, DOT P 5800.4).
FIREFIGHTING: MOVE CONTAINERS FROM FIRE AREA IF POSSIBLE. FIGHT FIRE FROM MAXIMUM DISTANCE. STAY AWAY FROM STORAGE TANK ENDS. DIKE FIRE CONTROL WATER FOR LATER DISPOSAL. DO NOT SCATTER MATERIAL (1987 EMERGENCY RESPONSE GUIDEBOOK, DOT P 5800.4, GUIDE PAGE 55). EXTINGUISH ONLY IF FLOW CAN BE STOPPED. EXTINGUISH USING AGENT INDICATED. USE FLOODING AMOUNTS OF WATER AS A FOG. COOL CONTAINERS WITH FLOODING AMOUNTS OF WATER FROM AS FAR A DISTANCE AS POSSIBLE. AVOID BREATHING POISONOUS VAPORS, KEEP UPWIND. CONSIDER EVACUATION OF DOWNWIND AREA IF MATERIAL IS LEAKING.

TOXICITY

ETRIMFOS: TOXICITY DATA: >500 MG/KG SKIN-RABBIT LD50 (FMCHA2); >2000 MG/KG SKIN-RAT LD50 (FMCHA2); 1800 MG/KG ORAL-RAT LD50; 921 MG/KG ORAL-MOUSE LD50. CARCINOGEN STATUS: NONE ACUTE TOXICITY LEVEL: MODERATELY TOXIC BY INGESTION. TARGET EFFECTS: CHOLINESTERASE INHIBITOR. POISONING MAY AFFECT THE NERVOUS SYSTEM.* AT INCREASED RISK FROM EXPOSURE: PERSONS WITH RESPIRATORY AILMENTS, RECENT EXPOSURE TO CHOLINESTERASE INHIBITORS OR IMPAIRED CHOLINESTERASE PRODUCTION, OR LIVER MALFUNCTION.* ADDITIONAL DATA: MAY CROSS THE PLACENTA. HIGH ENVIRONMENTAL TEMPERATURES OR EXPOSURE OF THE CHEMICAL TO VISIBLE OR ULTRAVIOLET LIGHT MAY ENHANCE THE TOXICITY. INTERACTIONS WITH MEDICATIONS MAY OCCUR.*

* MAY BE BASED ON GENERAL INFORMATION ON ORGANOPHOSPHATES.

HEALTH EFFECTS AND FIRST AID

INHALATION: ETRIMFOS: SEE INFORMATION ON ORGANOPHOSPHATES. ORGANOPHOSPHATES: CHOLINESTERASE INHIBITOR. **ACUTE EXPOSURE-** WHEN INHALED, THE FIRST EFFECTS OF CHOLINESTERASE INHIBITORS ARE USUALLY RESPIRATORY AND MAY INCLUDE NASAL HYPEREMIA AND WATERY DISCHARGE, COUGH, CHEST DISCOMFORT, DYSPNEA, AND WHEEZING DUE TO INCREASED BRONCHIAL SECRETIONS AND BRONCHOCONSTRICTION. IF SUFFICIENT AMOUNTS ARE ABSORBED, OTHER SYSTEMIC EFFECTS MAY BEGIN WITHIN A FEW MINUTES OR BE DELAYED FOR UP TO 12 HOURS. SYMPTOMS MAY INCLUDE PALLOR, NAUSEA, VOMITING, DIARRHEA, ABDOMINAL CRAMPS, HEADACHE, DIZZINESS, OCULAR PAIN, BLURRED VISION, MIOSIS OR IN SOME CASES, ESPECIALLY INITIALLY, MYDRIASIS, LACRIMATION, SALIVATION, SWEATING, AND CONFUSION. OTHER REPORTED CENTRAL NERVOUS SYSTEM OR NEUROMUSCULAR EFFECTS MAY INCLUDE ATAXIA, SLURRED SPEECH, AREFLEXIA, WEAKNESS, FATIGUE, FASCICULATIONS, TWITCHING, TREMORS POSSIBLY OF THE TONGUE AND EYELIDS, AND EVENTUALLY PARALYSIS OF THE EXTREMITIES AND POSSIBLY OF THE RESPIRATORY MUSCLES. IN SEVERE CASES THERE MAY ALSO BE INVOLUNTARY DEFECATION AND URINATION, CYANOSIS, PSYCHOSIS, HYPERGLYCEMIA, ACUTE PANCREATITIS, CARDIAC IRREGULARITIES, PULMONARY EDEMA, UNCONSCIOUSNESS, CONVULSIONS, AND COMA. DEATH IS PRIMARILY DUE TO RESPIRATORY FAILURE, ALTHOUGH CARDIOVASCULAR EFFECTS INCLUDING CARDIAC ARREST MAY ALSO BE IMPLICATED. LONG TERM SEQUELAE ARE RARE BUT MAY INCLUDE NEUROPSYCHIATRIC DISORDERS AND MYOPATHY WITH MUSCLE TENDERNESS. SOME ORGANOPHOSPHATES MAY CAUSE A DELAYED NEUROPATHY BEGINNING 1-4 WEEKS AFTER AN ACUTE EXPOSURE WHICH MAY OR MAY NOT HAVE CAUSED ACUTE CHOLINERGIC EFFECTS. NUMBNESS, TINGLING, WEAKNESS AND CRAMPING BEGINNING SYMMETRICALLY IN THE LOWER LIMBS MAY PROGRESS TO ATAXIA AND PARALYSIS. IN SEVERE CASES, UPPER LIMB INVOLVEMENT IS POSSIBLE AND FLACCID PARALYSIS MAY PROGRESS TO SPASTIC PARALYSIS WITH EXAGGERATED REFLEXES. IMPROVEMENT MAY OCCUR OVER MONTHS TO YEARS, BUT SOME RESIDUAL IMPAIRMENT USUALLY REMAINS. **CHRONIC EXPOSURE-** REPEATED OR PROLONGED EXPOSURE MAY RESULT IN THE EFFECTS OF ACUTE EXPOSURE INCLUDING THE DELAYED NEUROPATHY. OTHER EFFECTS REPORTED IN WORKERS REPEATEDLY EXPOSED INCLUDE IMPAIRED MEMORY AND CONCENTRATION, ACUTE PSYCHOSIS, SEVERE DEPRESSIONS, IRRITABILTY, CONFUSION, APATHY, EMOTIONAL LABILITY, SOCIAL WITHDRAWAL, CONFUSION, HEADACHE, SPEECH DIFFICULTIES, DELAYED REACTION TIMES, SPATIAL DISORIENTATION, NIGHTMARES, SLEEPWALKING, AND DROWSINESS OR INSOMNIA. AN INFLUENZA-LIKE CONDITION WITH HEADACHE, NAUSEA, WEAKNESS, ANOREXIA AND MALAISE HAS ALSO BEEN REPORTED.
FIRST AID- REMOVE FROM EXPOSURE AREA TO FRESH AIR IMMEDIATELY. IF BREATHING HAS STOPPED, GIVE ARTIFICIAL RESPIRATION. MAINTAIN AIRWAY AND BLOOD PRESSURE AND ADMINISTER OXYGEN IF AVAILABLE. KEEP AFFECTED PERSON WARM AND AT REST. TREAT SYMPTOMATICALLY AND SUPPORTIVELY. ADMINISTRATION OF OXYGEN SHOULD BE PERFORMED BY QUALIFIED PERSONNEL. GET MEDICAL ATTENTION IMMEDIATELY.

SKIN CONTACT: ETRIMFOS: SEE INFORMATION ON ORGANOPHOSPHATES. ORGANOPHOSPHATES: CHOLINESTERASE INHIBITOR. **ACUTE EXPOSURE-** LOCALIZED SWEATING AND FASCICULATIONS MAY OCCUR AT THE SITE OF CONTACT. IF SUFFICIENT AMOUNTS ARE ABSORBED, OTHER EFFECTS OF CHOLINESTERASE INHIBITION AS DESCRIBED IN ACUTE INHALATION MAY OCCUR. SYMPTOMS MAY BE DELAYED 2-3 HOURS, BUT USUALLY NO MORE THAN 12 HOURS. THE RATE OF ABSORPTION IS INCREASED BY THE PRESENCE OF DERMATITIS OR HIGH AMBIENT TEMPERATURES. DELAYED NEUROPATHY IS ALSO POSSIBLE. **CHRONIC EXPOSURE-** REPEATED OR PROLONGED EXPOSURE MAY CAUSE EFFECTS AS DESCRIBED IN ACUTE EXPOSURE. SOME ORGANOPHOSPHATES MAY CAUSE SENSITIZATION.
FIRST AID- REMOVE CONTAMINATED CLOTHING IMMEDIATELY. WASH CONTAMINATED AREAS WITH SOAP AND WATER FOLLOWED BY ALCOHOL (ARENA, POISONING, 4TH ED.). EMERGENCY PERSONNEL SHOULD WEAR GLOVES AND AVOID CONTAMINATION. TREAT RESPIRATORY DIFFICULTY WITH ARTIFICIAL RESPIRATION. GET MEDICAL ATTENTION IMMEDIATELY.

EYE CONTACT: ETRIMFOS: SEE INFORMATION ON ORGANOPHOSPHATES. ORGANOPHOSPHATES: CHOLINESTERASE INHIBITOR. **ACUTE EXPOSURE-** DIRECT CONTACT MAY CAUSE PAIN, HYPEREMIA, LACRIMATION, TWITCHING OF THE EYELIDS, MIOSIS, AND CILIARY MUSCLE SPASM WITH LOSS OF A CCOMODATION, BLURRED OR DIMMED VISION AND BROWACHE. SOMETIMES MYDRIASIS MAY OCCUR INSTEAD OF MIOSIS. WITH SUFFICIENT EXPOSURE, OTHER SYMPTOMS OF CHOLINESTERASE INHIBITION AS DESCRIBED IN ACUTE INHALATION MAY OCCUR. **CHRONIC EXPOSURE-** REPEATED OR PROLONGED EXPOSURE MAY CAUSE EFFECTS AS DESCRIBED IN ACUTE EXPOSURE. SOME COMPOUNDS HAVE CAUSED TOXIC EFFECTS ON THE CRYSTALLINE LENS, CONJUNCTIVAL THICKENING AND OBSTRUCTION OF THE NASOLACRIMAL CANALS WHEN USED AS MIOTIC EYEDROPS.
FIRST AID- IRRIGATE EYES WITH WATER OR SALINE SOLUTION. IF SYMPTOMS OF POISONING OCCUR, TREAT RESPIRATORY DIFFICULTY WITH ARTIFICIAL RESPIRATION AND OXYGEN. OBSERVE PATIENT FOR AT LEAST 24-36 HOURS (GOSSELIN, CLINICAL TOXICOLOGY OF COMMERCIAL PRODUCTS, 5TH ED.). GET MEDICAL ATTENTION IMMEDIATELY. OXYGEN SHOULD BE ADMINISTERED BY QUALIFIED MEDICAL PERSONNEL.

INGESTION: ETRIMFOS: SEE INFORMATION ON ORGANOPHOSPHATES. ORGANOPHOSPHATES: CHOLINESTERASE INHIBITOR. **ACUTE EXPOSURE-** WHEN INGESTED, THE FIRST EFFECTS MAY BE NAUSEA, VOMITING, ANOREXIA, ABDOMINAL CRAMPS AND DIARRHEA. GASTROINTESTINAL ABSORPTION MAY CAUSE SYMPTOMS OF CHOLINESTERASE INHIBITION AS DESCRIBED IN ACUTE INHALATION. SYMPTOMS MAY BEGIN WITHIN MINUTES OR BE DELAYED FOR HOURS. DELAYED EFFECTS INCLUDING NEUROPATHY MAY ALSO OCCUR. **CHRONIC EXPOSURE-** REPEATED INGESTION MAY CAUSE EFFECTS AS DESCRIBED IN ACUTE EXPOSURE.
FIRST AID- IF PERSON IS ALERT AND RESPIRATION IS NOT DEPRESSED, GIVE SYRUP OF IPECAC FOLLOWED BY WATER (IF VOMITING OCCURS, KEEP HEAD BELOW HIPS TO PREVENT ASPIRATION). IF CONSCIOUSNESS LEVEL DECLINES OR VOMITING HAS NOT OCCURRED IN 15 MINUTES EMPTY STOMACH BY GASTRIC LAVAGE WITH THE AID OF CUFFED ENDOTRACHEAL TUBE USING ISOTONIC SALINE OR 5% SODIUM BICARBONATE FOLLOW WITH ACTIVATED CHARCOAL. ESTABLISH AND MAINTAIN AIRWAY. TREAT RESPIRATORY DIFFICULTY WITH ARTIFICIAL RESPIRATION AND OXYGEN. DO NOT GIVE MORPHINE, AMINOPHYLLINE, PHENOTHIAZINES, RESERPINE, FUROSEMIDE, OR ETHACRYNIC ACID (MORGAN, RECOGNITION AND MANAGEMENT OF PESTICIDE POISONINGS, 3RD ED.). TREAT SYMPTOMATICALLY AND SUPPORTIVELY. ADMINISTRATION OF OXYGEN AND LAVAGE MUST BE PERFORMED BY QUALIFIED MEDICAL PERSONNEL. GET MEDICAL ATTENTION IMMEDIATELY.
ANTIDOTE: THE FOLLOWING ANTIDOTE(S) HAVE BEEN RECOMMENDED. HOWEVER, THE DECISION AS TO WHETHER THE SEVERITY OF POISONING REQUIRES ADMINISTRATION OF ANY ANTIDOTE AND ACTUAL DOSE REQUIRED SHOULD BE MADE BY QUALIFIED MEDICAL PERSONNEL.

FOR CHOLINESTERASE INHIBITORS: ESTABLISH CLEAR AIRWAY AND TISSUE OXYGENATION BY ASPIRATION OF SECRETIONS, AND IF NECESSARY, BY ASSISTED PULMONARY VENTILATION WITH OXYGEN. IMPROVE TISSUE OXYGENATION AS MUCH AS POSSIBLE BEFORE ADMINISTERING ATROPINE TO MINIMIZE THE RISK OF VENTRICULAR FIBRILLATION. ADMINISTER ATROPINE SULFATE INTRAVENOUSLY, OR INTRAMUSCULARLY IF IV INJECTION IS NOT POSSIBLE. IN MODERATELY SEVERE POISONING ADMINISTER ATROPINE SULFATE, 0.4-2.0 MG REPEATED EVERY 15 MINUTES UNTIL ATROPINIZATION IS ACHIEVED (TACHYCARDIA, FLUSHING, DRY MOUTH, MYDRIASIS). MAINTAIN ATROPINIZATION BY REPEATED DOSES FOR 2-12 HOURS, OR LONGER, DEPENDING ON THE SEVERITY OF POISONING. THE APPEARANCE OF RALES IN THE LUNG BASES, MIOSIS, SALIVATION, NAUSEA, BRADYCARDIA, ARE ALL INDICATIONS OF INADEQUATE ATROPINIZATION. SEVERELY POISONED INDIVIDUALS MAY EXHIBIT REMARKABLE TOLERANCE TO ATROPINE; TWO OR MORE TIMES THE DOSAGES SUGGESTED ABOVE MAY BE NEEDED. PERSONS NOT POISONED OR ONLY SLIGHTLY POISONED, HOWEVER, MAY DEVELOP SIGNS OF ATROPINE TOXICITY FROM SUCH LARGE DOSAGES: FEVER, MUSCLE FIBRILLATIONS, AND DELIRIUM ARE THE MAIN SIGNS OF ATROPINE TOXICITY. IF THESE SIGNS APPEAR WHILE THE PATIENT IS FULLY ATROPINIZED, ATROPINE ADMINISTRATION SHOULD BE DISCONTINUED, AT LEAST TEMPORARILY. OBSERVE TREATED PATIENTS CLOSELY AT LEAST 24 HOURS TO INSURE THAT SYMPTOMS (POSSIBLY PULMONARY EDEMA) DO NOT RECUR AS ATROPINIZATION WEARS OFF. IN VERY SEVERE POISONINGS, METABOLIC DISPOSITION OF TOXICANT MAY REQUIRE SEVERAL HOURS OR DAYS DURING WHICH ATROPINIZATION MUST BE MAINTAINED. MARKEDLY LOWER LEVELS OF URINARY METABOLITES INDICATE THAT ATROPINE DOSAGE CAN BE TAPERED OFF. AS DOSAGE IS REDUCED, CHECK THE LUNG BASES FREQUENTLY FOR RALES. IF RALES ARE HEARD OR OTHER SYMPTOMS RETURN, RE-ESTABLISH ATROPINIZATION PROMPTLY (MORGAN, RECOGNITION AND MANAGEMENT OF PESTICIDE POISONINGS, 3RD ED.). ADMINISTRATION OF ANTIDOTE MUST BE PERFORMED BY QUALIFIED MEDICAL PERSONNEL.

IN CASES OF SEVERE POISONING BY ORGANOPHOSPHATE PESTICIDES IN WHICH RESPIRATORY DEPRESSION, MUSCLE WEAKNESS AND TWITCHINGS ARE SEVERE, GIVE PRALIDOXIME (PROTOPAM-AYERST, 2-PAM), 1.0 GRAM INTRAVENOUSLY AT NO MORE THAN 0.5 GRAM PER MINUTE. DOSAGE OF PRALIDOXIME MAY BE REPEATED IN 1-2 HOURS, THEN AT 10-12 HOUR INTERVALS IF NEEDED. IN VERY SEVERE POISONINGS, DOSAGE RATES MAY BE DOUBLED. TREATMENT WITH PRALIDOXIME WILL BE MOST EFFECTIVE IF GIVEN WITHIN THIRTY-SIX HOURS AFTER POISONING (MORGAN, RECOGNITION AND MANAGEMENT OF PESTICIDE POISONINGS, 3RD ED.). ANTIDOTE SHOULD BE ADMINISTERED BY QUALIFIED MEDICAL PERSONNEL.

REACTIVITY

REACTIVITY: THE PURE MATERIAL IS UNSTABLE, DECOMPOSING ABOVE 25 C. DILUTE SOLUTIONS IN NON-POLAR SOLVENTS AND FORMULATIONS ARE STABLE.

INCOMPATIBILITIES: ETRIMPHOS: OXIDIZERS (STRONG): FIRE AND EXPLOSION HAZARD.

DECOMPOSITION: THERMAL DECOMPOSITION PRODUCTS MAY INCLUDE TOXIC OXIDES OF NITROGEN, CARBON, PHOSPHORUS, AND SULFUR.

POLYMERIZATION: HAZARDOUS POLYMERIZATION HAS NOT BEEN REPORTED TO OCCUR UNDER NORMAL TEMPERATURES AND PRESSURES.

STORAGE AND DISPOSAL

OBSERVE ALL FEDERAL, STATE AND LOCAL REGULATIONS WHEN STORING OR DISPOSING OF THIS SUBSTANCE. FOR ASSISTANCE, CONTACT THE DISTRICT DIRECTOR OF THE ENVIRONMENTAL PROTECTION AGENCY.

STORAGE

STORE IN ACCORDANCE WITH 40 CFR 165 RECOMMENDED PROCEDURES FOR THE DISPOSAL AND STORAGE OF PESTICIDES AND PESTICIDE CONTAINERS.
STORE IN TIGHTLY CLOSED CONTAINERS BELOW 25 C.
STORE AWAY FROM INCOMPATIBLE SUBSTANCES.

DISPOSAL

DISPOSAL MUST BE IN ACCORDANCE WITH 40 CFR 165 RECOMMENDED PROCEDURES FOR THE DISPOSAL AND STORAGE OF PESTICIDES AND PESTICIDE CONTAINERS.

CONDITIONS TO AVOID

MAY BURN BUT DOES NOT IGNITE READILY. CONTAINERS MAY EXPLODE IN HEAT OF FIRE.

SPILL AND LEAK PROCEDURES

OCCUPATIONAL SPILL: DO NOT TOUCH SPILLED MATERIAL. STOP LEAK IF YOU CAN DO IT WITHOUT RISK. USE WATER SPRAY TO REDUCE VAPORS. FOR SMALL SPILLS, TAKE UP WITH SAND OR OTHER ABSORBENT MATERIAL AND PLACE INTO CONTAINERS FOR LATER DISPOSAL. FOR SMALL DRY SPILLS, WITH A CLEAN SHOVEL PLACE MATERIAL INTO CLEAN, DRY CONTAINERS AND COVER. MOVE CONTAINERS FROM SPILL AREA. FOR LARGER SPILLS, DIKE FAR AHEAD OF SPILL FOR LATER DISPOSAL. KEEP UNNECESSARY PEOPLE AWAY. ISOLATE HAZARD AREA AND DENY ENTRY. VENTILATE CLOSED SPACES BEFORE ENTERING.

PROTECTIVE EQUIPMENT

VENTILATION: PROVIDE LOCAL EXHAUST OR GENERAL DILUTION VENTILATION SYSTEM.

RESPIRATOR: THE FOLLOWING RESPIRATORS ARE RECOMMENDED BASED ON INFORMATION FOUND IN THE PHYSICAL DATA, TOXICITY AND HEALTH EFFECTS SECTIONS. THEY ARE RANKED IN ORDER FROM MINIMUM TO MAXIMUM RESPIRATORY PROTECTION. THE SPECIFIC RESPIRATOR SELECTED MUST BE BASED ON CONTAMINATION LEVELS FOUND IN THE WORK PLACE, MUST NOT EXCEED THE WORKING LIMITS OF THE RESPIRATOR AND BE JOINTLY APPROVED BY THE NATIONAL INSTITUTE FOR OCCUPATIONAL SAFETY AND HEALTH AND THE MINE SAFETY AND HEALTH ADMINISTRATION (NIOSH-MSHA).
CHEMICAL CARTRIDGE RESPIRATOR WITH FULL FACEPIECE AND PESTICIDE CARTRIDGE. TYPE 'C' SUPPLIED-AIR RESPIRATOR WITH A FULL FACEPIECE OPERATED IN PRESSURE-DEMAND OR OTHER POSITIVE PRESSURE MODE OR WITH A FULL FACEPIECE, HELMET OR HOOD OPERATED IN CONTINUOUS-FLOW MODE.
SELF-CONTAINED BREATHING APPARATUS OPERATED IN PRESSURE-DEMAND OR OTHER POSITIVE PRESSURE MODE.
FOR FIREFIGHTING AND OTHER IMMEDIATELY DANGEROUS TO LIFE OR HEALTH CONDITIONS:
SELF-CONTAINED BREATHING APPARATUS WITH FULL FACEPIECE OPERATED IN PRESSURE-DEMAND OR OTHER POSITIVE PRESSURE MODE.
SUPPLIED-AIR RESPIRATOR WITH FULL FACEPIECE AND OPERATED IN PRESSURE-DEMAND OR OTHER POSITIVE PRESSURE MODE IN COMBINATION WITH AN AUXILIARY SELF-CONTAINED BREATHING APPARATUS OPERATED IN PRESSURE-DEMAND OR OTHER POSITIVE PRESSURE MODE.

CLOTHING: EMPLOYEE MUST WEAR APPROPRIATE PROTECTIVE (IMPERVIOUS) CLOTHING AND EQUIPMENT TO PREVENT REPEATED OR PROLONGED SKIN CONTACT WITH THIS SUBSTANCE.

GLOVES: EMPLOYEE MUST WEAR APPROPRIATE PROTECTIVE GLOVES TO PREVENT CONTACT WITH THIS SUBSTANCE.

EYE PROTECTION: EMPLOYEE MUST WEAR SPLASH-PROOF OR DUST-RESISTANT SAFETY GOGGLES TO PREVENT EYE CONTACT WITH THIS SUBSTANCE.
EMERGENCY EYE WASH: WHERE THERE IS ANY POSSIBILITY THAT AN EMPLOYEE'S EYES MAY BE EXPOSED TO THIS SUBSTANCE, THE EMPLOYER SHOULD PROVIDE AN EYE WASH FOUNTAIN WITHIN THE IMMEDIATE WORK AREA FOR EMERGENCY USE.

AUTHORIZED BY- OCCUPATIONAL HEALTH SERVICES, INC.
CREATION DATE: 10/04/89 ***REVISION DATE:*** 05/02/90

MATERIAL SAFETY DATA SHEET

OCCUPATIONAL HEALTH SERVICES, INC.
AGRICULTURE AND PESTICIDE DIVISION
450 SEVENTH AVENUE, SUITE 2407
NEW YORK, NEW YORK 10123
1-800-445-MSDS OR (212) 967-1100

EMERGENCY CONTACT:
JOHN S. BRANSFORD, JR. (615) 292-1180

SUBSTANCE IDENTIFICATION

CAS-NUMBER 13457-18-6

SUBSTANCE: PYRAZOPHOS

TRADE NAMES/SYNONYMS: PYRAZOLO(1,5-A)PYRIMIDINE-6-CARBOXYLIC ACID, 2-((DIETHOXYPHOSPHINOTHIOYL)OXY)-5-METHYL-, ETHYL ESTER; 2((DIETHOXYPHOSPHINOTHIOYL)OXY)-5-METHYLPYRAZOLO(1,5-A) PYRIMIDINE-6-CARBOXYLIC ACID, ETHYL ESTER; PYRAZOLO(1,5-A)PYRIMIDINE-6-CARBOXYLIC ACID, 2-HYDROXY-5-METHYL, ETHYL ESTER, O-ESTER WITH O,O-DIETHYLPHOSPHOROTHIOATE; 2-HYDROXY-5-METHYLPYRAZOLO(1,5-A)PYRIMIDINE-6-CARBOXYLIC ACID, ETHYL ESTER, O-ESTER WITH O,O-DIETHYLPHOSPHOROTHIOATE; ETHYL 2-DIETHOXYPHOSPHINOTHIOYLOXY-5-METHYLPYRAZOLO(1,5-A)PYRIMIDINE-6 CARBOXYLATE; ETHYL 2-HYDROXY-5-METHYLPYRAZOLO(1,5-A)PYRIMIDINE-6-CARBOXYLATE O-ESTER WITH O,O-DIETHYL PHOSPHOROTHIOATE; AFUGAN; O,O-DIETHYL-O-(5-METHYL-6-ETHOXY CARBONYL-PYRAZOLO-(1,5-A)PYRIMID -2-YL)-THIONOPHOSPHATE; CURAMIL; HOE 2873; MISSILE; C14H20N3O5PS; PST73169

CHEMICAL FAMILY: PHOSPHOROTHIOATE

MOLECULAR FORMULA: C14-H20-N3-O5-P-S

MOLECULAR WEIGHT: 373.40

CERCLA RATINGS (SCALE 0-3): HEALTH = 3 FIRE = 1 REACTIVITY = 0 PERSISTENCE = 1
NFPA RATINGS (SCALE 0-4): HEALTH = U FIRE = 1 REACTIVITY = 0

COMPONENTS AND CONTAMINANTS

COMPONENT: PYRAZOPHOS ***PERCENT:*** 100.0
CAS# 13457-18-6
OTHER CONTAMINANTS: NONE
EXPOSURE LIMITS: NO OCCUPATIONAL EXPOSURE LIMITS ESTABLISHED BY OSHA, ACGIH, OR NIOSH.

PHYSICAL DATA

DESCRIPTION: COLORLESS CRYSTALS. ***MELTING POINT:*** 122-124 F (50-51 C)
SPECIFIC GRAVITY: NOT AVAILABLE ***VAPOR PRESSURE:*** 0.0000017 MMHG @ 50C
SOLUBILITY IN WATER: 0.00042% @ 20 C
SOLVENT SOLUBILITY: SOLUBLE IN ACETONE, ETHANOL, ETHYL ACETATE, TOLUENE, HEXANE, BENZENE, AND XYLENE.

FIRE AND EXPLOSION DATA

FIRE AND EXPLOSION HAZARD: SLIGHT FIRE HAZARD WHEN EXPOSED TO HEAT OR FLAME.
FIREFIGHTING MEDIA: DRY CHEMICAL, CARBON DIOXIDE, HALON, WATER SPRAY OR STANDARD FOAM (1987 EMERGENCY RESPONSE GUIDEBOOK, DOT P 5800.4). FOR LARGER FIRES, USE WATER SPRAY, FOG OR STANDARD FOAM (1987 EMERGENCY RESPONSE GUIDEBOOK, DOT P 5800.4).
FIREFIGHTING: MOVE CONTAINERS FROM FIRE AREA IF POSSIBLE. FIGHT FIRE FROM MAXIMUM DISTANCE. STAY AWAY FROM STORAGE TANK ENDS. DIKE FIRE CONTROL WATER FOR LATER DISPOSAL. DO NOT SCATTER MATERIAL (1987 EMERGENCY RESPONSE GUIDEBOOK, DOT P 5800.4, GUIDE PAGE 55). EXTINGUISH ONLY IF FLOW CAN BE STOPPED; USE FLOODING AMOUNTS OF WATER AS FOG, SOLID STREAMS MAY BE INEFFECTIVE. COOL CONTAINERS WITH FLOODING AMOUNTS OF WATER FROM AS FAR A DISTANCE AS POSSIBLE. USE WATER SPRAY TO ABSORB TOXIC VAPORS. AVOID BREATHING TOXIC VAPORS; KEEP UPWIND. CONSIDER EVACUATION OF DOWNWIND AREA IF MATERIAL IS LEAKING.

TOXICITY

PYRAZOPHOS: TOXICITY DATA: >2000 MG/KG SKIN-RAT LD50 (PEMNDP); 218 MG/KG ORAL-RAT LD50. CARCINOGEN STATUS: NONE. ACUTE TOXICITY LEVEL: TOXIC BY INGESTION; SLIGHTLY TOXIC BY DERMAL ABSORPTION. TARGET EFFECTS: CHOLINESTERASE INHIBITOR. POISONING MAY AFFECT THE NERVOUS SYSTEM.* AT INCREASED RISK FROM EXPOSURE: PERSONS WITH RESPIRATORY AILMENTS, RECENT EXPOSURE TO CHOLINESTERASE INHIBITORS OR IMPAIRED CHOLINESTERASE PRODUCTION, OR LIVER MALFUNCTION.* ADDITIONAL DATA: MAY CROSS THE PLACENTA. HIGH ENVIRONMENTAL TEMPERATURES OR EXPOSURE OF THE CHEMICAL TO VISIBLE OR ULTRAVIOLET LIGHT MAY ENHANCE THE TOXICITY. INTERACTIONS WITH MEDICATIONS MAY OCCUR.*
* MAY BE BASED ON GENERAL INFORMATION ON ORGANOPHOSPHATES.

HEALTH EFFECTS AND FIRST AID

INHALATION: PYRAZOPHOS: SEE INFORMATION ON ORGANOPHOSPHATES. ORGANOPHOSPHATES: CHOLINESTERASE INHIBITOR. **ACUTE EXPOSURE-** WHEN INHALED, THE FIRST EFFECTS OF CHOLINESTERASE INHIBITORS ARE USUALLY RESPIRATORY AND MAY INCLUDE NASAL HYPEREMIA AND WATERY DISCHARGE, COUGH, CHEST DISCOMFORT, DYSPNEA, AND WHEEZING DUE TO INCREASED BRONCHIAL SECRETIONS AND BRONCHOCONSTRICTION. IF SUFFICIENT AMOUNTS ARE ABSORBED, OTHER SYSTEMIC EFFECTS MAY BEGIN WITHIN A FEW MINUTES OR BE DELAYED FOR UP TO 12 HOURS. SYMPTOMS MAY INCLUDE PALLOR, NAUSEA, VOMITING, DIARRHEA, ABDOMINAL CRAMPS, HEADACHE, DIZZINESS, OCULAR PAIN, BLURRED VISION, MIOSIS OR IN SOME CASES, ESPECIALLY INITIALLY, MYDRIASIS, LACRIMATION, SALIVATION, SWEATING, AND CONFUSION. OTHER REPORTED CENTRAL NERVOUS SYSTEM OR NEUROMUSCULAR EFFECTS MAY INCLUDE ATAXIA, SLURRED SPEECH, AREFLEXIA, WEAKNESS, FATIGUE, FASCICULATIONS, TWITCHING, TREMORS POSSIBLY OF THE TONGUE AND EYELIDS, AND EVENTUALLY PARALYSIS OF THE EXTREMITIES AND POSSIBLY OF THE RESPIRATORY MUSCLES. IN SEVERE CASES THERE MAY ALSO BE INVOLUNTARY DEFECATION AND URINATION, CYANOSIS, PSYCHOSIS, HYPERGLYCEMIA, ACUTE PANCREATITIS, CARDIAC IRREGULARITIES, PULMONARY EDEMA, UNCONSCIOUSNESS, CONVULSIONS, AND COMA. DEATH IS PRIMARILY DUE TO RESPIRATORY FAILURE, ALTHOUGH CARDIOVASCULAR EFFECTS INCLUDING CARDIAC ARREST MAY ALSO BE IMPLICATED. LONG TERM SEQUELAE ARE RARE BUT MAY INCLUDE NEUROPSYCHIATRIC DISORDERS AND MYOPATHY WITH MUSCLE TENDERNESS. SOME ORGANOPHOSPHATES MAY CAUSE A DELAYED NEUROPATHY BEGINNING 1-4 WEEKS AFTER AN ACUTE EXPOSURE WHICH MAY OR MAY NOT HAVE CAUSED ACUTE CHOLINERGIC EFFECTS. NUMBNESS, TINGLING, WEAKNESS AND CRAMPING BEGINNING SYMMETRICALLY IN THE LOWER LIMBS MAY PROGRESS TO ATAXIA AND PARALYSIS. IN SEVERE CASES, UPPER LIMB INVOLVEMENT IS POSSIBLE AND FLACCID PARALYSIS MAY PROGRESS TO SPASTIC PARALYSIS WITH EXAGGERATED REFLEXES. IMPROVEMENT MAY OCCUR OVER MONTHS TO YEARS, BUT SOME RESIDUAL IMPAIRMENT USUALLY REMAINS. **CHRONIC EXPOSURE-** REPEATED OR PROLONGED EXPOSURE MAY RESULT IN THE EFFECTS OF ACUTE EXPOSURE INCLUDING THE DELAYED NEUROPATHY. OTHER EFFECTS REPORTED IN WORKERS REPEATEDLY EXPOSED INCLUDE IMPAIRED MEMORY AND CONCENTRATION, ACUTE PSYCHOSIS, SEVERE DEPRESSIONS, IRRITABILTY, CONFUSION, APATHY, EMOTIONAL LABILITY, SOCIAL WITHDRAWAL, CONFUSION, HEADACHE, SPEECH DIFFICULTIES, DELAYED REACTION TIMES, SPATIAL DISORIENTATION, NIGHTMARES, SLEEPWALKING, AND DROWSINESS OR INSOMNIA. AN INFLUENZA-LIKE CONDITION WITH HEADACHE, NAUSEA, WEAKNESS, ANOREXIA AND MALAISE HAS ALSO BEEN REPORTED.
FIRST AID- REMOVE FROM EXPOSURE AREA TO FRESH AIR IMMEDIATELY. IF BREATHING HAS STOPPED, GIVE ARTIFICIAL RESPIRATION. MAINTAIN AIRWAY AND BLOOD PRESSURE AND ADMINISTER OXYGEN IF AVAILABLE. KEEP AFFECTED PERSON WARM AND AT REST. TREAT SYMPTOMATICALLY AND SUPPORTIVELY. ADMINISTRATION OF OXYGEN SHOULD BE PERFORMED BY QUALIFIED PERSONNEL. GET MEDICAL ATTENTION IMMEDIATELY.

SKIN CONTACT: PYRAZOPHOS: SEE INFORMATION ON ORGANOPHOSPHATES. ORGANOPHOSPHATES: CHOLINESTERASE INHIBITOR. **ACUTE EXPOSURE-** LOCALIZED SWEATING AND FASCICULATIONS MAY OCCUR AT THE SITE OF CONTACT. IF SUFFICIENT AMOUNTS ARE ABSORBED, OTHER EFFECTS OF CHOLINESTERASE INHIBITION AS DESCRIBED IN ACUTE INHALATION MAY OCCUR. SYMPTOMS MAY BE DELAYED 2-3 HOURS, BUT USUALLY NO MORE THAN 12 HOURS. THE RATE OF ABSORPTION IS INCREASED BY THE PRESENCE OF DERMATITIS OR HIGH AMBIENT TEMPERATURES. DELAYED NEUROPATHY IS ALSO POSSIBLE. **CHRONIC EXPOSURE-** REPEATED OR PROLONGED EXPOSURE MAY CAUSE EFFECTS AS DESCRIBED IN ACUTE EXPOSURE. SOME ORGANOPHOSPHATES MAY CAUSE SENSITIZATION.
FIRST AID- REMOVE CONTAMINATED CLOTHING IMMEDIATELY. WASH CONTAMINATED AREAS WITH SOAP AND WATER FOLLOWED BY ALCOHOL (ARENA, POISONING, 4TH ED.). EMERGENCY PERSONNEL SHOULD WEAR GLOVES AND AVOID CONTAMINATION. TREAT RESPIRATORY DIFFICULTY WITH ARTIFICIAL RESPIRATION. GET MEDICAL ATTENTION IMMEDIATELY.

EYE CONTACT: PYRAZOPHOS: SEE INFORMATION ON ORGANOPHOSPHATES. ORGANOPHOSPHATES: CHOLINESTERASE INHIBITOR. **ACUTE EXPOSURE-** DIRECT CONTACT MAY CAUSE PAIN, HYPEREMIA, LACRIMATION, TWITCHING OF THE EYELIDS, MIOSIS, AND CILIARY MUSCLE SPASM WITH LOSS OF ACCOMODATION, BLURRED OR DIMMED VISION AND BROWACHE. SOMETIMES MYDRIASIS MAY OCCUR INSTEAD OF MIOSIS. WITH SUFFICIENT EXPOSURE, OTHER SYMPTOMS OF CHOLINESTERASE INHIBITION AS DESCRIBED IN ACUTE INHALATION MAY OCCUR. **CHRONIC EXPOSURE-** REPEATED OR PROLONGED EXPOSURE MAY CAUSE EFFECTS AS DESCRIBED IN ACUTE EXPOSURE. SOME COMPOUNDS HAVE CAUSED TOXIC EFFECTS ON THE CRYSTALLINE LENS, CONJUNCTIVAL THICKENING AND OBSTRUCTION OF THE NASOLACRIMAL CANALS WHEN USED AS MIOTIC EYEDROPS.
FIRST AID- IRRIGATE EYES WITH WATER OR SALINE SOLUTION. IF SYMPTOMS OF POISONING OCCUR, TREAT RESPIRATORY DIFFICULTY WITH ARTIFICIAL RESPIRATION AND OXYGEN. OBSERVE PATIENT FOR AT LEAST 24-36 HOURS (GOSSELIN, CLINICAL TOXICOLOGY OF COMMERCIAL PRODUCTS, 5TH ED.). GET MEDICAL ATTENTION IMMEDIATELY. OXYGEN SHOULD BE ADMINISTERED BY QUALIFIED MEDICAL PERSONNEL.

INGESTION: PYRAZOPHOS: TOXIC. SEE INFORMATION ON ORGANOPHOSPHATES. ORGANOPHOSPHATES: CHOLINESTERASE INHIBITOR. **ACUTE EXPOSURE-** WHEN INGESTED, THE FIRST EFFECTS MAY BE NAUSEA, VOMITING, ANOREXIA, ABDOMINAL CRAMPS AND DIARRHEA. GASTROINTESTINAL ABSORPTION MAY CAUSE SYMPTOMS OF CHOLINESTERASE INHIBITION AS DESCRIBED IN ACUTE INHALATION. SYMPTOMS MAY BEGIN WITHIN MINUTES OR BE DELAYED FOR HOURS. DELAYED EFFECTS INCLUDING NEUROPATHY MAY ALSO OCCUR. **CHRONIC EXPOSURE-** REPEATED INGESTION MAY CAUSE EFFECTS AS DESCRIBED IN ACUTE EXPOSURE.
FIRST AID- IF PERSON IS ALERT AND RESPIRATION IS NOT DEPRESSED, GIVE SYRUP OF IPECAC FOLLOWED BY WATER (IF VOMITING OCCURS, KEEP HEAD BELOW HIPS TO PREVENT ASPIRATION). IF CONSCIOUSNESS LEVEL DECLINES OR VOMITING HAS NOT OCCURRED IN 15 MINUTES EMPTY STOMACH BY GASTRIC LAVAGE WITH THE AID OF CUFFED ENDOTRACHEAL TUBE USING ISOTONIC SALINE OR 5% SODIUM BICARBONATE FOLLOW WITH ACTIVATED CHARCOAL. ESTABLISH AND MAINTAIN AIRWAY. TREAT RESPIRATORY DIFFICULTY WITH ARTIFICIAL RESPIRATION AND OXYGEN. DO NOT GIVE MORPHINE, AMINOPHYLLINE, PHENOTHIAZINES, RESERPINE, FUROSEMIDE, OR ETHACRYNIC ACID (MORGAN, RECOGNITION AND MANAGEMENT OF PESTICIDE POISONINGS, 3RD ED.). TREAT SYMPTOMATICALLY AND SUPPORTIVELY. ADMINISTRATION OF OXYGEN AND LAVAGE MUST BE PERFORMED

BY QUALIFIED MEDICAL PERSONNEL. GET MEDICAL ATTENTION IMMEDIATELY.

ANTIDOTE: THE FOLLOWING ANTIDOTE(S) HAVE BEEN RECOMMENDED. HOWEVER, THE DECISION AS TO WHETHER THE SEVERITY OF POISONING REQUIRES ADMINISTRATION OF ANY ANTIDOTE AND ACTUAL DOSE REQUIRED SHOULD BE MADE BY QUALIFIED MEDICAL PERSONNEL.

FOR CHOLINESTERASE INHIBITORS: ESTABLISH CLEAR AIRWAY AND TISSUE OXYGENATION BY ASPIRATION OF SECRETIONS, AND IF NECESSARY, BY ASSISTED PULMONARY VENTILATION WITH OXYGEN. IMPROVE TISSUE OXYGENATION AS MUCH AS POSSIBLE BEFORE ADMINISTERING ATROPINE TO MINIMIZE THE RISK OF VENTRICULAR FIBRILLATION. ADMINISTER ATROPINE SULFATE INTRAVENOUSLY, OR INTRAMUSCULARLY IF IV INJECTION IS NOT POSSIBLE. IN MODERATELY SEVERE POISONING ADMINISTER ATROPINE SULFATE, 0.4-2.0 MG REPEATED EVERY 15 MINUTES UNTIL ATROPINIZATION IS ACHIEVED (TACHYCARDIA, FLUSHING, DRY MOUTH, MYDRIASIS). MAINTAIN ATROPINIZATION BY REPEATED DOSES FOR 2-12 HOURS, OR LONGER, DEPENDING ON THE SEVERITY OF POISONING. THE APPEARANCE OF RALES IN THE LUNG BASES, MIOSIS, SALIVATION, NAUSEA, BRADYCARDIA, ARE ALL INDICATIONS OF INADEQUATE ATROPINIZATION. SEVERELY POISONED INDIVIDUALS MAY EXHIBIT REMARKABLE TOLERANCE TO ATROPINE; TWO OR MORE TIMES THE DOSAGES SUGGESTED ABOVE MAY BE NEEDED. PERSONS NOT POISONED OR ONLY SLIGHTLY POISONED, HOWEVER, MAY DEVELOP SIGNS OF ATROPINE TOXICITY FROM SUCH LARGE DOSAGES: FEVER, MUSCLE FIBRILLATIONS, AND DELIRIUM ARE THE MAIN SIGNS OF ATROPINE TOXICITY. IF THESE SIGNS APPEAR WHILE THE PATIENT IS FULLY ATROPINIZED, ATROPINE ADMINISTRATION SHOULD BE DISCONTINUED, AT LEAST TEMPORARILY. OBSERVE TREATED PATIENTS CLOSELY AT LEAST 24 HOURS TO INSURE THAT SYMPTOMS (POSSIBLY PULMONARY EDEMA) DO NOT RECUR AS ATROPINIZATION WEARS OFF. IN VERY SEVERE POISONINGS, METABOLIC DISPOSITION OF TOXICANT MAY REQUIRE SEVERAL HOURS OR DAYS DURING WHICH ATROPINIZATION MUST BE MAINTAINED. MARKEDLY LOWER LEVELS OF URINARY METABOLITES INDICATE THAT ATROPINE DOSAGE CAN BE TAPERED OFF. AS DOSAGE IS REDUCED, CHECK THE LUNG BASES FREQUENTLY FOR RALES. IF RALES ARE HEARD OR OTHER SYMPTOMS RETURN, RE-ESTABLISH ATROPINIZATION PROMPTLY (MORGAN, RECOGNITION AND MANAGEMENT OF PESTICIDE POISONINGS, 3RD ED.). ADMINISTRATION OF ANTIDOTE MUST BE PERFORMED BY QUALIFIED MEDICAL PERSONNEL.

IN CASES OF SEVERE POISONING BY ORGANOPHOSPHATE PESTICIDES IN WHICH RESPIRATORY DEPRESSION, MUSCLE WEAKNESS AND TWITCHINGS ARE SEVERE, GIVE PRALIDOXIME (PROTOPAM-AYERST, 2-PAM), 1.0 GRAM INTRAVENOUSLY AT NO MORE THAN 0.5 GRAM PER MINUTE. DOSAGE OF PRALIDOXIME MAY BE REPEATED IN 1-2 HOURS, THEN AT 10-12 HOUR INTERVALS IF NEEDED. IN VERY SEVERE POISONINGS, DOSAGE RATES MAY BE DOUBLED. TREATMENT WITH PRALIDOXIME WILL BE MOST EFFECTIVE IF GIVEN WITHIN THIRTY-SIX HOURS AFTER POISONING (MORGAN, RECOGNITION AND MANAGEMENT OF PESTICIDE POISONINGS, 3RD ED.). ANTIDOTE SHOULD BE ADMINISTERED BY QUALIFIED MEDICAL PERSONNEL.

REACTIVITY

REACTIVITY: STABLE UNDER NORMAL TEMPERATURES AND PRESSURES.

INCOMPATIBILITIES: PYRAZOPHOS: OXIDIZERS (STRONG): FIRE AND EXPLOSION HAZARD

DECOMPOSITION: THERMAL DECOMPOSITION PRODUCTS MAY INCLUDE TOXIC OXIDES OF NITROGEN, CARBON, PHOSPHORUS, AND SULFUR.

POLYMERIZATION: HAZARDOUS POLYMERIZATION HAS NOT BEEN REPORTED TO OCCUR UNDER NORMAL TEMPERATURES AND PRESSURES.

STORAGE AND DISPOSAL

OBSERVE ALL FEDERAL, STATE AND LOCAL REGULATIONS WHEN STORING OR DISPOSING OF THIS SUBSTANCE. FOR ASSISTANCE, CONTACT THE DISTRICT DIRECTOR OF THE ENVIRONMENTAL PROTECTION AGENCY.

STORAGE

STORE IN ACCORDANCE WITH 40 CFR 165 RECOMMENDED PROCEDURES FOR THE DISPOSAL AND STORAGE OF PESTICIDES AND PESTICIDE CONTAINERS.
STORE AWAY FROM INCOMPATIBLE SUBSTANCES.

DISPOSAL

DISPOSAL MUST BE IN ACCORDANCE WITH 40 CFR 165 RECOMMENDED PROCEDURES FOR THE DISPOSAL AND STORAGE OF PESTICIDES AND PESTICIDE CONTAINERS.

CONDITIONS TO AVOID

MAY BURN BUT DOES NOT IGNITE READILY. CONTAINERS MAY EXPLODE IN HEAT OF FIRE.

SPILL AND LEAK PROCEDURES

OCCUPATIONAL SPILL: DO NOT TOUCH SPILLED MATERIAL. STOP LEAK IF YOU CAN DO IT WITHOUT RISK. USE WATER SPRAY TO REDUCE VAPORS. FOR SMALL SPILLS, TAKE UP WITH SAND OR OTHER ABSORBENT MATERIAL AND PLACE INTO CONTAINERS FOR LATER DISPOSAL. FOR SMALL DRY SPILLS, WITH A CLEAN SHOVEL PLACE MATERIAL INTO CLEAN, DRY CONTAINERS AND COVER. MOVE CONTAINERS FROM SPILL AREA. FOR LARGER SPILLS, DIKE FAR AHEAD OF SPILL FOR LATER DISPOSAL. KEEP UNNECESSARY PEOPLE AWAY. ISOLATE HAZARD AREA AND DENY ENTRY. VENTILATE CLOSED SPACES BEFORE ENTERING.

PROTECTIVE EQUIPMENT

VENTILATION: PROVIDE LOCAL EXHAUST OR GENERAL DILUTION VENTILATION SYSTEM.

RESPIRATOR: THE FOLLOWING RESPIRATORS ARE RECOMMENDED BASED ON INFORMATION FOUND IN THE PHYSICAL DATA, TOXICITY AND HEALTH EFFECTS SECTIONS. THEY ARE RANKED IN ORDER FROM MINIMUM TO MAXIMUM RESPIRATORY PROTECTION. THE SPECIFIC RESPIRATOR SELECTED MUST BE BASED ON CONTAMINATION LEVELS FOUND IN THE WORK PLACE, MUST NOT EXCEED THE WORKING LIMITS OF THE RESPIRATOR AND BE JOINTLY APPROVED BY THE NATIONAL INSTITUTE FOR OCCUPATIONAL SAFETY AND HEALTH AND THE MINE SAFETY AND HEALTH ADMINISTRATION (NIOSH-MSHA).

TYPE 'C' SUPPLIED-AIR RESPIRATOR WITH A FULL FACEPIECE OPERATED IN PRESSURE-DEMAND OR OTHER POSITIVE PRESSURE MODE OR WITH A FULL FACEPIECE, HELMET OR HOOD OPERATED IN CONTINOUS-FLOW MODE.

SELF-CONTAINED BREATHING APPARATUS WITH A FULL FACEPIECE OPERATED IN PRESSURE-DEMAND OR OTHER POSITIVE PRESSURE MODE.

FOR FIREFIGHTING AND OTHER IMMEDIATELY DANGEROUS TO LIFE OR HEALTH CONDITIONS:

SELF-CONTAINED BREATHING APPARATUS WITH FULL FACEPIECE OPERATED IN PRESSURE-DEMAND OR OTHER POSITIVE PRESSURE MODE.

SUPPLIED-AIR RESPIRATOR WITH FULL FACEPIECE AND OPERATED IN PRESSURE-DEMAND OR OTHER POSITIVE PRESSURE MODE IN COMBINATION WITH AN AUXILIARY SELF-CONTAINED BREATHING APPARATUS OPERATED IN PRESSURE-DEMAND OR OTHER POSITIVE PRESSURE MODE.

CLOTHING: EMPLOYEE MUST WEAR APPROPRIATE PROTECTIVE (IMPERVIOUS) CLOTHING AND EQUIPMENT TO PREVENT REPEATED OR PROLONGED SKIN CONTACT WITH THIS SUBSTANCE.

GLOVES: EMPLOYEE MUST WEAR APPROPRIATE PROTECTIVE GLOVES TO PREVENT CONTACT WITH THIS SUBSTANCE.

EYE PROTECTION: EMPLOYEE MUST WEAR SPLASH-PROOF OR DUST-RESISTANT SAFETY GOGGLES TO PREVENT EYE CONTACT WITH THIS SUBSTANCE.

EMERGENCY EYE WASH: WHERE THERE IS ANY POSSIBILITY THAT AN EMPLOYEE'S EYES MAY BE EXPOSED TO THIS SUBSTANCE, THE EMPLOYER SHOULD PROVIDE AN EYE WASH FOUNTAIN WITHIN THE IMMEDIATE WORK AREA FOR EMERGENCY USE.

AUTHORIZED BY- OCCUPATIONAL HEALTH SERVICES, INC.
CREATION DATE: 10/04/89 ***REVISION DATE:*** 05/04/90

MATERIAL SAFETY DATA SHEET

OCCUPATIONAL HEALTH SERVICES, INC.
AGRICULTURE AND PESTICIDE DIVISION
450 SEVENTH AVENUE, SUITE 2407
NEW YORK, NEW YORK 10123
1-800-445-MSDS OR (212) 967-1100

EMERGENCY CONTACT:
JOHN S. BRANSFORD, JR. (615) 292-1180

SUBSTANCE IDENTIFICATION

CAS-NUMBER 15271-41-7

SUBSTANCE: **EXO-3-CHLORO-ENDO-6-CYANO-2-NORBORANONE O-(METHYLCARBAMOYL)OXIME**

TRADE NAMES/SYNONYMS: 5-CHLORO-6-((((METHYLAMINO)CARBONYL)OXY)IMINO)-BICYCLO(2.2.1)HEPTANE 2-CARBONITRILE, (1S-(1 ALPHA, 2 BETA, 4 ALPHA, 5 ALPHA, 6 EPSILON)); 5-CHLORO-6-OXO-2-NORBORNANECARBONITRILE O-(METHYLCARBAMOYL)OXIME, (E)-ENDO-2-, EXO-5-; TRANID; ENT 25,962; C10H12CLN3O2; PST73177

CHEMICAL FAMILY: CARBAMATE
BICYCLIC

MOLECULAR FORMULA: C10-H12-CL-N3-O2

MOLECULAR WEIGHT: 241.70

CERCLA RATINGS (SCALE 0-3): HEALTH=3 FIRE=U REACTIVITY=U PERSISTENCE=3

NFPA RATINGS (SCALE 0-4): HEALTH=3 FIRE=U REACTIVITY=U

COMPONENTS AND CONTAMINANTS

COMPONENT: EXO-3-CHLORO-ENDO-6-CYANO-2-NORBORNANONE O-METHYLCARBAMOYL)OXIME ***PERCENT:*** 100
CAS# 15271-41-7

OTHER CONTAMINANTS: NONE

EXPOSURE LIMITS: NO OCCUPATIONAL EXPOSURE LIMITS ESTABLISHED BY OSHA, ACGIH, OR NIOSH.
EXO-3-CHLORO-ENDO-6-CYANO-2-NORBORNANONE O-(METHYLCARBAMOYL)OXIME: 500/10,000 POUNDS SARA SECTION 302 THRESHOLD PLANNING QUANTITY 1 POUND SARA SECTION 304 REPORTABLE QUANTITY

PHYSICAL DATA

DESCRIPTION: SOLID ***MELTING POINT:*** 318-320 F (159-160 C)
SPECIFIC GRAVITY: NOT AVAILABLE ***SOLUBILITY IN WATER:*** NOT AVAILABLE

FIRE AND EXPLOSION DATA

FIRE AND EXPLOSION HAZARD: UNKNOWN FIRE AND EXPLOSION HAZARD.

FIREFIGHTING MEDIA: DRY CHEMICAL, CARBON DIOXIDE, HALON, WATER SPRAY OR STANDARD FOAM (1987 EMERGENCY RESPONSE GUIDEBOOK, DOT P 5800.4).
FOR LARGER FIRES, USE WATER SPRAY, FOG OR STANDARD FOAM (1987 EMERGENCY RESPONSE GUIDEBOOK, DOT P 5800.4).

FIREFIGHTING: MOVE CONTAINERS FROM FIRE AREA IF POSSIBLE (1987 EMERGENCY RESPONSE GUIDEBOOK, DOT P 5800.4, GUIDE PAGE 53).
EXTINGUISH USING AGENT SUITABLE FOR TYPE OF SURROUNDING FIRE. AVOID BREATHING VAPORS AND DUSTS. KEEP UPWIND.

TRANSPORTATION DATA

DEPARTMENT OF TRANSPORTATION HAZARD CLASSIFICATION 49 CFR 172.101: POISON B
DEPARTMENT OF TRANSPORTATION LABELING REQUIREMENTS 49 CFR 172.101 AND SUBPART E: POISON
DEPARTMENT OF TRANSPORTATION PACKAGING REQUIREMENTS: 49 CFR 173.365 EXCEPTIONS: 49 CFR 173.364

TOXICITY

EXO-3-CHLORO-ENDO-6-CYANO-2-NORBORNANONE O-(METHYLCARBAMOYL)OXIME: TOXICITY DATA: 303 MG/KG SKIN-RABBIT LDLO; 303 MG/KG SKIN-RAT LD50; 19 MG/KG ORAL-RAT LD50; 26 MG/KG UNREPORTED-RAT LD50. CARCINOGEN STATUS: NONE. ACUTE TOXICITY LEVEL: HIGHLY TOXIC BY INGESTION; TOXIC BY DERMAL ABSORPTION. TARGET EFFECTS: CHOLINESTERASE INHIBITOR. AT INCREASED RISK FROM EXPOSURE: PERSONS WITH ASTHMA, DIABETES, CARDIOVASCULAR DISEASE, MECHANICAL OBSTRUCTION OF THE GASTROINTESTINAL OR UROGENITAL TRACT, AND THOSE IN VAGOTONIC STATES.*
* MAY BE BASED ON GENERAL INFORMATION ON CARBAMATES.

HEALTH EFFECTS AND FIRST AID

INHALATION: EXO-3-CHLORO-ENDO-6-CYANO-2-NORBORNANONE O-(METHYLCARBAMOYL)OXIME: SEE INFORMATION ON CARBAMATES.
CARBAMATES: CHOLINESTERASE INHIBITOR. **ACUTE EXPOSURE**- WHEN INHALED, THE FIRST EFFECTS OF CHOLINESTERASE INHIBITION ARE USUALLY RESPIRATORY AND MAY INCLUDE NASAL HYPEREMIA AND WATERY DISCHARGE, CHEST DISCOMFORT, DYSPNEA, AND WHEEZING DUE TO INCREASED BRONCHIAL SECRETIONS AND BRONCHOCONSTRICTION. OTHER SYSTEMIC EFFECTS MAY BEGIN WITHIN A FEW MINUTES OR SEVERAL HOURS OF EXPOSURE. SYMPTOMS MAY INCLUDE NAUSEA, VOMITING, DIARRHEA, ABDOMINAL CRAMPS, HEADACHE, VERTIGO, OCULAR PAIN, CILIARY MUSCLE SPASM, BLURRING OR DIMNESS OF VISION, MIOSIS, OR IN SOME CASES MYDRIASIS, LACRIMATION, SALIVATION, SWEATING, AND CONFUSION. OTHER REPORTED CENTRAL NERVOUS SYSTEM OR NEUROMUSCULAR EFFECTS INCLUDE ATAXIA, SLURRED SPEECH, AREFLEXIA, WEAKNESS, FATIGUE, TWITCHING, FASCICULATION, TREMOR, AND EVENTUALLY PARALYSIS OF THE EXTREMITIES AND POSSIBLY OF THE RESPIRATORY MUSCLES. IN SEVERE CASES, THERE MAY ALSO BE INVOLUNTARY DEFECATION AND URINATION, BRADYCARDIA, HYPOTENSION, PULMONARY EDEMA, CONVULSIONS, COMA, AND DEATH FROM RESPIRATORY FAILURE OR CARDIAC ARREST. CARBAMATES GENERALLY DO NOT ACCUMULATE IN MAMMALIAN TISSUE AND THE CHOLINESTERASE INHIBITION REVERSES RATHER RAPIDLY. IN NON-FATAL CASES, THE ILLNESS GENERALLY LASTS LESS THAN 24 HOURS. **CHRONIC EXPOSURE**- PROLONGED OR REPEATED EXPOSURE MAY CAUSE EFFECTS AS DESCRIBED IN ACUTE EXPOSURE.

FIRST AID- REMOVE FROM EXPOSURE AREA TO FRESH AIR IMMEDIATELY. IF BREATHING HAS STOPPED, GIVE ARTIFICIAL RESPIRATION. MAINTAIN AIRWAY AND BLOOD PRESSURE AND ADMINISTER OXYGEN IF AVAILABLE. KEEP AFFECTED PERSON WARM AND AT REST. TREAT SYMPTOMATICALLY AND SUPPORTIVELY. ADMINISTRATION OF OXYGEN SHOULD BE PERFORMED BY QUALIFIED PERSONNEL. GET MEDICAL ATTENTION IMMEDIATELY.

SKIN CONTACT: EXO-3-CHLORO-ENDO-6-CYANO-2-NORBORNANONE O-(METHYLCARBAMOYL) OXIME: TOXIC. SEE INFORMATION ON CARBAMATES.
CARBAMATES: CHOLINESTERASE INHIBITOR. **ACUTE EXPOSURE**- SOME COMPOUNDS MAY CAUSE IRRITATION. LOCALIZED SWEATING AND FASCICULATIONS MAY OCCUR AT THE SITE OF CONTACT. IF SUFFICIENT AMOUNTS ARE ABSORBED THROUGH THE SKIN, OTHER EFFECTS OF CHOLINESTERASE INHIBITION MAY OCCUR AS DESCRIBED IN ACUTE INHALATION; SYMPTOMS MAY BE DELAYED FOR 2-3 HOURS, USUALLY NO MORE THAN 8 HOURS. **CHRONIC EXPOSURE**- REPEATED OR PROLONGED EXPOSURE MAY CAUSE EFFECTS AS DESCRIBED IN ACUTE EXPOSURE.

FIRST AID- REMOVE CONTAMINATED CLOTHING IMMEDIATELY. WASH CONTAMINATED AREAS WITH SOAP AND WATER FOLLOWED BY ALCOHOL (ARENA, POISONING, 4TH ED.). EMERGENCY PERSONNEL SHOULD WEAR GLOVES AND AVOID CONTAMINATION. TREAT RESPIRATORY DIFFICULTY WITH ARTIFICIAL RESPIRATION. GET MEDICAL ATTENTION IMMEDIATELY.

EYE CONTACT: EXO-3-CHLORO-ENDO-6-CYANO-2-NORBORNANONE O-(METHYLCARBAMOYL)OXIME: SEE INFORMATION ON CARBAMATES.
CARBAMATES: CHOLINESTERASE INHIBITOR. **ACUTE EXPOSURE**- DIRECT CONTACT MAY CAUSE PAIN, HYPEREMIA, LACRIMATION, TWITCHING OF THE EYELIDS, MIOSIS, AND CILIARY MUSCLE SPASM WITH LOSS OF ACCOMODATION, BLURRED OR DIMMED VISION AND BROWACHE. SOMETIMES MYDRIASIS MAY OCCUR INSTEAD OF MIOSIS. WITH SUFFICIENT EXPOSURE, OTHER SYMPTOMS OF CHOLINESTERASE INHIBITION MAY OCCUR AS DESCRIBED IN ACUTE INHALATION. **CHRONIC EXPOSURE**- PROLONGED EXPOSURE MAY CAUSE EFFECTS AS DESCRIBED IN ACUTE EXPOSURE. SOME COMPOUNDS HAVE CAUSED TOXIC EFFECTS ON THE CRYSTALLINE LENS, CONJUNCTIVAL THICKENING AND OBSTRUCTION OF NASOLACRIMAL CANALS WHEN USED AS MIOTIC EYE DROPS.

FIRST AID- IRRIGATE EYES WITH WATER OR SALINE SOLUTION. IF SYMPTOMS OF POISONING OCCUR, TREAT RESPIRATORY DIFFICULTY WITH ARTIFICIAL RESPIRATION AND OXYGEN. OBSERVE PATIENT FOR AT LEAST 24-36 HOURS (GOSSELIN, CLINICAL TOXICOLOGY OF COMMERCIAL PRODUCTS, 5TH ED.). GET MEDICAL ATTENTION IMMEDIATELY. OXYGEN SHOULD BE ADMINISTERED BY QUALIFIED MEDICAL PERSONNEL.

INGESTION: EXO-3-CHLORO-ENDO-6-CYANO-2-NORBORNANONE O-(METHYLCARBAMOYL)OXIME: HIGHLY TOXIC. SEE INFORMATION ON CARBAMATES.
CARBAMATES: CHOLINESTERASE INHIBITOR. **ACUTE EXPOSURE**- WHEN INGESTED, THE FIRST EFFECTS MAY BE NAUSEA, VOMITING, ANOREXIA, ABDOMINAL CRAMPS, AND DIARRHEA. WITH ABSORPTION FROM THE GASTROINTESTINAL TRACT, THE OTHER EFFECTS OF CHOLINESTERASE INHIBITION AS DESCRIBED IN ACUTE INHALATION MAY OCCUR; SYMPTOMS MAY BEGIN WITHIN MINUTES OR BE DELAYED SEVERAL HOURS. **CHRONIC EXPOSURE**- REPEATED INGESTION MAY CAUSE EFFECTS AS DESCRIBED IN ACUTE EXPOSURE.

FIRST AID- IF PERSON IS ALERT AND RESPIRATION IS NOT DEPRESSED, GIVE SYRUP OF IPECAC FOLLOWED BY WATER (IF VOMITING OCCURS, KEEP HEAD BELOW HIPS TO PREVENT ASPIRATION). IF CONSCIOUSNESS LEVEL DECLINES OR VOMITING HAS NOT OCCURRED IN 15 MINUTES EMPTY STOMACH BY GASTRIC LAVAGE WITH THE AID OF CUFFED ENDOTRACHEAL TUBE USING ISOTONIC SALINE OR 5% SODIUM BICARBONATE FOLLOW WITH ACTIVATED CHARCOAL. ESTABLISH AND MAINTAIN AIRWAY. TREAT RESPIRATORY DIFFICULTY WITH ARTIFICIAL RESPIRATION AND OXYGEN. DO NOT GIVE MORPHINE, AMINOPHYLLINE, PHENOTHIAZINES, RESERPINE, FUROSEMIDE, OR ETHACRYNIC ACID (MORGAN, RECOGNITION AND MANAGEMENT OF PESTICIDE POISONINGS, 3RD ED.). TREAT SYMPTOMATICALLY AND SUPPORTIVELY. ADMINISTRATION OF OXYGEN AND LAVAGE MUST BE PERFORMED BY QUALIFIED MEDICAL PERSONNEL. GET MEDICAL ATTENTION IMMEDIATELY.

ANTIDOTE: THE FOLLOWING ANTIDOTE HAS BEEN RECOMMENDED. HOWEVER, THE DECISION AS TO WHETHER THE SEVERITY OF POISONING REQUIRES ADMINISTRATION OF ANY ANTIDOTE AND ACTUAL DOSE REQUIRED SHOULD BE MADE BY QUALIFIED MEDICAL PERSONNEL.
FOR CHOLINESTERASE INHIBITORS: ESTABLISH CLEAR AIRWAY AND TISSUE OXYGENATION BY ASPIRATION OF SECRETIONS, AND IF NECESSARY, BY ASSISTED PULMONARY VENTILATION WITH OXYGEN. IMPROVE TISSUE OXYGENATION AS MUCH AS POSSIBLE BEFORE ADMINISTERING ATROPINE TO MINIMIZE THE RISK OF VENTRICULAR FIBRILLATION. ADMINISTER ATROPINE SULFATE INTRAVENOUSLY, OR INTRAMUSCULARLY IF IV INJECTION IS NOT POSSIBLE. IN MODERATELY SEVERE POISONING ADMINISTER ATROPINE SULFATE, 0.4-2.0 MG REPEATED EVERY 15 MINUTES UNTIL ATROPINIZATION IS ACHIEVED (TACHYCARDIA, FLUSHING, DRY MOUTH, MYDRIASIS). MAINTAIN ATROPINIZATION BY REPEATED DOSES FOR 2-12 HOURS, OR LONGER, DEPENDING ON THE SEVERITY OF POISONING. THE APPEARANCE OF RALES IN THE LUNG BASES, MIOSIS, SALIVATION, NAUSEA, BRADYCARDIA, ARE ALL INDICATIONS OF INADEQUATE ATROPINIZATION. SEVERELY POISONED INDIVIDUALS MAY EXHIBIT REMARKABLE TOLERANCE TO

ATROPINE; TWO OR MORE TIMES THE DOSAGES SUGGESTED ABOVE MAY BE NEEDED. PERSONS NOT POISONED OR ONLY SLIGHTLY POISONED, HOWEVER, MAY DEVELOP SIGNS OF ATROPINE TOXICITY FROM SUCH LARGE DOSAGES: FEVER, MUSCLE FIBRILLATIONS, AND DELIRIUM ARE THE MAIN SIGNS OF ATROPINE TOXICITY. IF THESE SIGNS APPEAR WHILE THE PATIENT IS FULLY ATROPINIZED, ATROPINE ADMINISTRATION SHOULD BE DISCONTINUED, AT LEAST TEMPORARILY. OBSERVE TREATED PATIENTS CLOSELY AT LEAST 24 HOURS TO INSURE THAT SYMPTOMS (POSSIBLY PULMONARY EDEMA) DO NOT RECUR AS ATROPINIZATION WEARS OFF. IN VERY SEVERE POISONINGS, METABOLIC DISPOSITION OF TOXICANT MAY REQUIRE SEVERAL HOURS OR DAYS DURING WHICH ATROPINIZATION MUST BE MAINTAINED. MARKEDLY LOWER LEVELS OF URINARY METABOLITES INDICATE THAT ATROPINE DOSAGE CAN BE TAPERED OFF. AS DOSAGE IS REDUCED, CHECK THE LUNG BASES FREQUENTLY FOR RALES. IF RALES ARE HEARD OR OTHER SYMPTOMS RETURN, RE-ESTABLISH ATROPINIZATION PROMPTLY (MORGAN, RECOGNITION AND MANAGEMENT OF PESTICIDE POISONINGS, 3RD ED.). ADMINISTRATION OF ANTIDOTE MUST BE PERFORMED BY QUALIFIED MEDICAL PERSONNEL.

REACTIVITY

REACTIVITY: STABLE UNDER NORMAL TEMPERATURES AND PRESSURES.

INCOMPATIBILITIES: EXO-3-CHLORO-ENDO-6-CYANO-2-NORBORNANONE O-(METHYLCARBAMOYL)OXIME: OXIDIZERS (STRONG): FIRE AND EXPLOSION HAZARD.

DECOMPOSITION: THERMAL DECOMPOSITION PRODUCTS MAY INCLUDE TOXIC AND CORROSIVE FUMES OF CHLORIDES AND TOXIC OXIDES OF NITROGEN.

POLYMERIZATION: HAZARDOUS POLYMERIZATION HAS NOT BEEN REPORTED TO OCCUR UNDER NORMAL TEMPERATURES AND PRESSURES.

STORAGE AND DISPOSAL

OBSERVE ALL FEDERAL, STATE AND LOCAL REGULATIONS WHEN STORING OR DISPOSING OF THIS SUBSTANCE. FOR ASSISTANCE, CONTACT THE DISTRICT DIRECTOR OF THE ENVIRONMENTAL PROTECTION AGENCY.

STORAGE

STORE IN ACCORDANCE WITH 40 CFR 165 RECOMMENDED PROCEDURES FOR THE DISPOSAL AND STORAGE OF PESTICIDES AND PESTICIDE CONTAINERS.

STORE AWAY FROM INCOMPATIBLE SUBSTANCES.

THRESHOLD PLANNING QUANTITY (TPQ): THE SUPERFUND AMENDMENTS AND REAUTHORIZATION ACT (SARA) SECTION 302 REQUIRES THAT EACH FACILITY WHERE ANY EXTREMELY HAZARDOUS SUBSTANCE IS PRESENT IN A QUANTITY EQUAL TO OR GREATER THAN THE TPQ ESTABLISHED FOR THAT SUBSTANCE NOTIFY THE STATE EMERGENCY RESPONSE COMMISSION FOR THE STATE IN WHICH IT IS LOCATED. SECTION 303 OF SARA REQUIRES THESE FACILITIES TO PARTICIPATE IN LOCAL EMERGENCY RESPONSE PLANNING (40 CFR 355.30).

DISPOSAL

DISPOSAL MUST BE IN ACCORDANCE WITH 40 CFR 165 RECOMMENDED PROCEDURES FOR THE DISPOSAL AND STORAGE OF PESTICIDES AND PESTICIDE CONTAINERS.

CONDITIONS TO AVOID

NONE REPORTED.

SPILL AND LEAK PROCEDURES

OCCUPATIONAL SPILL: SWEEP UP AND PLACE IN SUITABLE CLEAN, DRY CONTAINERS FOR RECLAMATION OR LATER DISPOSAL. DO NOT FLUSH SPILLED MATERIAL INTO SEWER. KEEP UNNECESSARY PEOPLE AWAY.

REPORTABLE QUANTITY (RQ): 1 POUND THE SUPERFUND AMENDMENTS AND REAUTHORIZATION ACT (SARA) SECTION 304 REQUIRES THAT A RELEASE EQUAL TO OR GREATER THAN THE REPORTABLE QUANTITY FOR THIS SUBSTANCE BE IMMEDIATELY REPORTED TO THE LOCAL EMERGENCY PLANNING COMMITTEE AND THE STATE EMERGENCY RESPONSE COMMISSION (40 CFR 355.40). IF THE RELEASE OF THIS SUBSTANCE IS REPORTABLE UNDER CERCLA SECTION 103, THE NATIONAL RESPONSE CENTER MUST BE NOTIFIED IMMEDIATELY AT (800) 424-8802 OR (202) 426-2675 IN THE METROPOLITAN WASHINGTON, D.C. AREA (40 CFR 302.6).

PROTECTIVE EQUIPMENT

VENTILATION: PROVIDE LOCAL EXHAUST OR PROCESS ENCLOSURE VENTILATION SYSTEM.

RESPIRATOR: THE FOLLOWING RESPIRATORS ARE RECOMMENDED BASED ON INFORMATION FOUND IN THE PHYSICAL DATA, TOXICITY AND HEALTH EFFECTS SECTIONS. THEY ARE RANKED IN ORDER FROM MINIMUM TO MAXIMUM RESPIRATORY PROTECTION. THE SPECIFIC RESPIRATOR SELECTED MUST BE BASED ON CONTAMINATION LEVELS FOUND IN THE WORK PLACE, MUST NOT EXCEED THE WORKING LIMITS OF THE RESPIRATOR AND BE JOINTLY APPROVED BY THE NATIONAL INSTITUTE FOR OCCUPATIONAL SAFETY AND HEALTH AND THE MINE SAFETY AND HEALTH ADMINISTRATION (NIOSH-MSHA).

TYPE 'C' SUPPLIED-AIR RESPIRATOR WITH A FULL FACEPIECE OPERATED IN PRESSURE-DEMAND OR OTHER POSITIVE PRESSURE MODE OR WITH A FULL FACEPIECE, HELMET OR HOOD OPERATED IN CONTINOUS-FLOW MODE.

SELF-CONTAINED BREATHING APPARATUS WITH A FULL FACEPIECE OPERATED IN PRESSURE-DEMAND OR OTHER POSITIVE PRESSURE MODE.

FOR FIREFIGHTING AND OTHER IMMEDIATELY DANGEROUS TO LIFE OR HEALTH CONDITIONS:

SELF-CONTAINED BREATHING APPARATUS WITH FULL FACEPIECE OPERATED IN PRESSURE-DEMAND OR OTHER POSITIVE PRESSURE MODE.

SUPPLIED-AIR RESPIRATOR WITH FULL FACEPIECE AND OPERATED IN PRESSURE-DEMAND OR OTHER POSITIVE PRESSURE MODE IN COMBINATION WITH AN AUXILIARY SELF-CONTAINED BREATHING APPARATUS OPERATED IN PRESSURE-DEMAND OR OTHER POSITIVE PRESSURE MODE.

CLOTHING: EMPLOYEE MUST WEAR APPROPRIATE PROTECTIVE (IMPERVIOUS) CLOTHING AND EQUIPMENT TO PREVENT ANY POSSIBILITY OF SKIN CONTACT WITH THIS SUBSTANCE.

GLOVES: EMPLOYEE MUST WEAR APPROPRIATE PROTECTIVE GLOVES TO PREVENT CONTACT WITH THIS SUBSTANCE.

EYE PROTECTION: EMPLOYEE MUST WEAR SPLASH-PROOF OR DUST-RESISTANT SAFETY GOGGLES AND A FACESHIELD TO PREVENT CONTACT WITH THIS SUBSTANCE.

EMERGENCY WASH FACILITIES: WHERE THERE IS ANY POSSIBILITY THAT AN EMPLOYEE'S EYES AND/OR SKIN MAY BE EXPOSED TO THIS SUBSTANCE, THE EMPLOYER SHOULD PROVIDE AN EYE WASH FOUNTAIN AND QUICK DRENCH SHOWER WITHIN THE IMMEDIATE WORK AREA FOR EMERGENCY USE.

AUTHORIZED BY- OCCUPATIONAL HEALTH SERVICES, INC.

CREATION DATE: 05/18/90 ***REVISION DATE:*** 06/12/90

MATERIAL SAFETY DATA SHEET

OCCUPATIONAL HEALTH SERVICES, INC.
AGRICULTURE AND PESTICIDE DIVISION
450 SEVENTH AVENUE, SUITE 2407
NEW YORK, NEW YORK 10123
1-800-445-MSDS OR (212) 967-1100

EMERGENCY CONTACT:
JOHN S. BRANSFORD, JR. (615) 292-1180

SUBSTANCE IDENTIFICATION

CAS-NUMBER 47000-92-0

SUBSTANCE: FLUORIDAMID

TRADE NAMES/SYNONYMS: ACETAMIDE, N-(4-METHYL-3-(((TRIFLUOROMETHYL)SULFONYL)AMINO)PHENYL)-; N-(4-METHYL-3-(((TRIFLUOROMETHYL)SULFONYL)AMINO)PHENYL)ACETAMIDE; N-4-METHYL-3-((((1,1,1-TRIFLUOROMETHYL)SULFONYL)AMINO)PHENYL)ACETAMIDE; SUSTAR; C10H11F3N2O3S; PST73184

CHEMICAL FAMILY: AMIDE, AROMATIC
SULFONYL
HALOGEN

MOLECULAR FORMULA: C10-H11-F-N2-O3-S

MOLECULAR WEIGHT: 296.27

CERCLA RATINGS (SCALE 0-3): HEALTH=2 FIRE=1 REACTIVITY=0 PERSISTENCE=1

NFPA RATINGS (SCALE 0-4): HEALTH=U FIRE=1 REACTIVITY=0

COMPONENTS AND CONTAMINANTS

COMPONENT: FLUORIDAMID ***PERCENT:*** 100.0
CAS# 47000-92-0

OTHER CONTAMINANTS: NONE

EXPOSURE LIMITS: NO OCCUPATIONAL EXPOSURE LIMITS ESTABLISHED BY OSHA, ACGIH, OR NIOSH.

PHYSICAL DATA

DESCRIPTION: WHITE POWDER. ***MELTING POINT:*** 347-351 F (175-177 C)

SPECIFIC GRAVITY: NOT AVAILABLE ***SOLUBILITY IN WATER:*** NOT AVAILABLE

FIRE AND EXPLOSION DATA

FIRE AND EXPLOSION HAZARD: SLIGHT FIRE HAZARD WHEN EXPOSED TO HEAT OR FLAME.

DUST-AIR MIXTURES MAY IGNITE OR EXPLODE.

FIREFIGHTING MEDIA: DRY CHEMICAL, CARBON DIOXIDE, HALON, WATER SPRAY OR STANDARD FOAM (1987 EMERGENCY RESPONSE GUIDEBOOK, DOT P 5800.4).

FOR LARGER FIRES, USE WATER SPRAY, FOG OR STANDARD FOAM (1987 EMERGENCY RESPONSE GUIDEBOOK, DOT P 5800.4).

FIREFIGHTING: MOVE CONTAINER FROM FIRE AREA IF POSSIBLE. DO NOT SCATTER SPILLED MATERIAL WITH HIGH PRESSURE WATER STREAMS. DIKE FIRE CONTROL WATER FOR LATER DISPOSAL (1987 EMERGENCY RESPONSE GUIDEBOOK, DOT P 5800.4, GUIDE PAGE 31).

USE AGENTS SUITABLE FOR TYPE OF SURROUNDING FIRE. AVOID BREATHING HAZARDOUS VAPORS, KEEP UPWIND.

TOXICITY

FLUORIDAMID: TOXICITY DATA: 2580 MG/KG ORAL-RAT LD50; 2600 MG/KG ORAL-MOUSE LD50. CARCINOGEN STATUS: NONE. ACUTE TOXICITY LEVEL: MODERATELY TOXIC BY INGESTION. TARGET ORGAN EFFECT: NO DATA AVAILABLE.

HEALTH EFFECTS AND FIRST AID

INHALATION: FLUORIDAMID: **ACUTE EXPOSURE-** NO DATA AVAILABLE. **CHRONIC EXPOSURE-** NO DATA AVAILABLE.

FIRST AID- REMOVE FROM EXPOSURE AREA TO FRESH AIR IMMEDIATELY. IF BREATHING HAS STOPPED, PERFORM ARTIFICIAL RESPIRATION. KEEP PERSON WARM AND AT REST. TREAT SYMPTOMATICALLY AND SUPPORTIVELY. GET MEDICAL ATTENTION IMMEDIATELY.

SKIN CONTACT: FLUORIDAMID: **ACUTE EXPOSURE-** NO DATA AVAILABLE. **CHRONIC EXPOSURE-** NO DATA AVAILABLE.

FIRST AID- REMOVE CONTAMINATED CLOTHING AND SHOES IMMEDIATELY. WASH AFFECTED AREA WITH SOAP OR MILD DETERGENT AND LARGE AMOUNTS OF WATER UNTIL NO EVIDENCE OF CHEMICAL REMAINS (APPROXIMATELY 15-20 MINUTES). GET MEDICAL ATTENTION IMMEDIATELY.

EYE CONTACT: FLUORIDAMID: **ACUTE EXPOSURE-** NO DATA AVAILABLE. **CHRONIC EXPOSURE-** NO DATA AVAILABLE.

FIRST AID- WASH EYES IMMEDIATELY WITH LARGE AMOUNTS OF WATER OR NORMAL SALINE, OCCASIONALLY LIFTING UPPER AND LOWER LIDS, UNTIL NO EVIDENCE OF CHEMICAL REMAINS (APPROXIMATELY 15-20 MINUTES). GET MEDICAL ATTENTION IMMEDIATELY.

INGESTION: FLUORIDAMID: **ACUTE EXPOSURE-** THE LETHAL DOSE REPORTED IN RATS WAS 2580 MG/KG; SYMPTOMS WERE NOT REPORTED. **CHRONIC EXPOSURE-** NO DATA AVAILABLE.

FIRST AID- TREAT SYMPTOMATICALLY AND SUPPORTIVELY. GET MEDICAL ATTENTION IMMEDIATELY. IF VOMITING OCCURS, KEEP HEAD LOWER THAN HIPS TO PREVENT ASPIRATION.

ANTIDOTE: NO SPECIFIC ANTIDOTE. TREAT SYMPTOMATICALLY AND SUPPORTIVELY.

REACTIVITY

REACTIVITY: STABLE UNDER NORMAL TEMPERATURES AND PRESSURES.

INCOMPATIBILITIES: FLUORIDAMID: OXIDIZERS (STRONG): FIRE AND EXPLOSION HAZARD.

DECOMPOSITION: THERMAL DECOMPOSITION PRODUCTS MAY INCLUDE TOXIC AND HAZARDOUS FUMES OF FLUORINE AND AMMONIA AND OXIDES OF NITROGEN, CARBON AND SULFUR.

POLYMERIZATION: HAZARDOUS POLYMERIZATION HAS NOT BEEN REPORTED TO OCCUR UNDER NORMAL TEMPERATURES AND PRESSURES.

STORAGE AND DISPOSAL

OBSERVE ALL FEDERAL, STATE AND LOCAL REGULATIONS WHEN STORING OR DISPOSING OF THIS SUBSTANCE. FOR ASSISTANCE, CONTACT THE DISTRICT DIRECTOR OF THE ENVIRONMENTAL PROTECTION AGENCY.

STORAGE

STORE IN ACCORDANCE WITH 40 CFR 165 RECOMMENDED PROCEDURES FOR THE DISPOSAL AND STORAGE OF PESTICIDES AND PESTICIDE CONTAINERS.

STORE AWAY FROM INCOMPATIBLE SUBSTANCES.

DISPOSAL

DISPOSAL MUST BE IN ACCORDANCE WITH 40 CFR 165 RECOMMENDED PROCEDURES FOR THE DISPOSAL AND STORAGE OF PESTICIDES AND PESTICIDE CONTAINERS.

CONDITIONS TO AVOID

MAY BURN BUT DOES NOT IGNITE READILY. AVOID CONTACT WITH STRONG OXIDIZERS, EXCESSIVE HEAT, SPARKS, OR OPEN FLAME.

SPILL AND LEAK PROCEDURES

OCCUPATIONAL SPILL: SWEEP UP AND PLACE IN SUITABLE CLEAN, DRY CONTAINERS FOR RECLAMATION OR LATER DISPOSAL. DO NOT FLUSH SPILLED MATERIAL INTO SEWER. KEEP UNNECESSARY PEOPLE AWAY.

PROTECTIVE EQUIPMENT

VENTILATION: PROVIDE LOCAL EXHAUST OR GENERAL DILUTION VENTILATION SYSTEM.

RESPIRATOR: THE FOLLOWING RESPIRATORS ARE RECOMMENDED BASED ON INFORMATION FOUND IN THE PHYSICAL DATA, TOXICITY AND HEALTH EFFECTS SECTIONS. THEY ARE RANKED IN ORDER FROM MINIMUM TO MAXIMUM RESPIRATORY PROTECTION. THE SPECIFIC RESPIRATOR SELECTED MUST BE BASED ON CONTAMINATION LEVELS FOUND IN THE WORK PLACE, MUST NOT EXCEED THE WORKING LIMITS OF THE RESPIRATOR AND BE JOINTLY APPROVED BY THE NATIONAL INSTITUTE FOR OCCUPATIONAL SAFETY AND HEALTH AND THE MINE SAFETY AND HEALTH ADMINISTRATION (NIOSH-MSHA).

CHEMICAL CARTRIDGE RESPIRATOR WITH AN ORGANIC VAPOR CARTRIDGE(S) WITH A FULL FACEPIECE AND ORGANIC VAPOR CARTRIDGE(S) IN COMBINATION WITH A DUST AND MIST FILTER.

POWERED AIR-PURIFYING RESPIRATOR WITH A TIGHT-FITTING FACEPIECE AND ORGANIC VAPOR CARTRIDGE(S) IN COMBINATION WITH A HIGH-EFFICIENCY PARTICULATE FILTER.

TYPE 'C' SUPPLIED-AIR RESPIRATOR WITH A FULL FACEPIECE OPERATED IN A PRESSURE-DEMAND OR OTHER POSITIVE PRESSURE MODE.

SELF-CONTAINED BREATHING APPARATUS WITH A FULL FACEPIECE OPERATED IN PRESSURE-DEMAND OR OTHER POSITIVE PRESSURE MODE.

FOR FIREFIGHTING AND OTHER IMMEDIATELY DANGEROUS TO LIFE OR HEALTH CONDITIONS:

SELF-CONTAINED BREATHING APPARATUS WITH FULL FACEPIECE OPERATED IN PRESSURE-DEMAND OR OTHER POSITIVE PRESSURE MODE.

SUPPLIED-AIR RESPIRATOR WITH FULL FACEPIECE AND OPERATED IN PRESSURE-DEMAND OR OTHER POSITIVE PRESSURE MODE IN COMBINATION WITH AN AUXILIARY SELF-CONTAINED BREATHING APPARATUS OPERATED IN PRESSURE-DEMAND OR OTHER POSITIVE PRESSURE MODE.

CLOTHING: EMPLOYEE MUST WEAR APPROPRIATE PROTECTIVE (IMPERVIOUS) CLOTHING AND EQUIPMENT TO PREVENT REPEATED OR PROLONGED SKIN CONTACT WITH THIS SUBSTANCE.

GLOVES: EMPLOYEE MUST WEAR APPROPRIATE PROTECTIVE GLOVES TO PREVENT CONTACT WITH THIS SUBSTANCE.

EYE PROTECTION: EMPLOYEE MUST WEAR SPLASH-PROOF OR DUST-RESISTANT SAFETY GOGGLES TO PREVENT EYE CONTACT WITH THIS SUBSTANCE.

EMERGENCY EYE WASH: WHERE THERE IS ANY POSSIBILITY THAT AN EMPLOYEE'S EYES MAY BE EXPOSED TO THIS SUBSTANCE, THE EMPLOYER SHOULD PROVIDE AN EYE WASH FOUNTAIN WITHIN THE IMMEDIATE WORK AREA FOR EMERGENCY USE.

AUTHORIZED BY- OCCUPATIONAL HEALTH SERVICES, INC.

CREATION DATE: 02/01/90 ***REVISION DATE:*** 05/31/90

MATERIAL SAFETY DATA SHEET

OCCUPATIONAL HEALTH SERVICES, INC.
AGRICULTURE AND PESTICIDE DIVISION
450 SEVENTH AVENUE, SUITE 2407
NEW YORK, NEW YORK 10123
1-800-445-MSDS OR (212) 967-1100

EMERGENCY CONTACT:
JOHN S. BRANSFORD, JR. (615) 292-1180

SUBSTANCE IDENTIFICATION

CAS-NUMBER 22259-30-9

SUBSTANCE: **FORMETANATE**

TRADE NAMES/SYNONYMS: METHANIMIDAMIDE, N,N-DIMETHYL-N'-(3-(((METHYLAMINO)CARBONYL) OXY)PHENYL)-; CARBAMIC ACID, METHYL-, ESTER WITH N'-(M-HYDROXYPHENYL)-N,N-DIMETHYL- FORMAMIDINE; CARBAMIC ACID, METHYL-, M-(((DIMETHYLAMINO)METHYLENE)AMINO)PHENYL ESTER; METHYLCARBAMIC ACID, ESTER WITH N'-(M-HYDROXYPHENYL)-N,N-DIMETHYL-FORMAMIDINE; METHYLCARBAMIC ACID, M-(((DIMETHYLAMINO)METHYLENE)AMINO)PHENYL ESTER; 3-DIMETHYLAMINOMETHYLENEAMINOPHENYL METHYLCARBAMATE; N,N-DIMETHYL-N'-(3-(((METHYLAMINO)CARBONYL)OXY)PHENYL)METHANIMIDAMIDE; N'-(M-HYDROXYPHENYL)-N,N-DIMETHYLFORMAMIDINE METHYLCARBAMATE ESTER; FORMETANAT; C11H15N3O2; PST73187

CHEMICAL FAMILY: CARBAMATE

MOLECULAR FORMULA: C11-H15-N3-O2

MOLECULAR WEIGHT: 221.29

CERCLA RATINGS (SCALE 0-3): HEALTH = 3 FIRE = U REACTIVITY = U PERSISTENCE = 2
NFPA RATINGS (SCALE 0-4): HEALTH = 3 FIRE = U REACTIVITY = U

COMPONENTS AND CONTAMINANTS

COMPONENT: FORMETANATE ***PERCENT:*** 100
CAS# 22259-30-9
OTHER CONTAMINANTS: NONE
EXPOSURE LIMITS: NO OCCUPATIONAL EXPOSURE LIMITS ESTABLISHED BY OSHA, ACGIH, OR NIOSH.

PHYSICAL DATA

DESCRIPTION: YELLOWISH CRYSTALLINE SOLID
MELTING POINT: 216-217 F (102-103 C)
SPECIFIC GRAVITY: NOT AVAILABLE ***VAPOR PRESSURE:*** NEGLIGIBLE
SOLUBILITY IN WATER: 0.63 %
SOLVENT SOLUBILITY: SOLUBLE IN ACETONE, CHLOROFORM, AND METHANOL

FIRE AND EXPLOSION DATA

FIRE AND EXPLOSION HAZARD: UNKNOWN FIRE AND EXPLOSION HAZARD.
FIREFIGHTING MEDIA: DRY CHEMICAL, CARBON DIOXIDE, HALON, WATER SPRAY OR STANDARD FOAM (1987 EMERGENCY RESPONSE GUIDEBOOK, DOT P 5800.4). FOR LARGER FIRES, USE WATER SPRAY, FOG OR STANDARD FOAM (1987 EMERGENCY RESPONSE GUIDEBOOK, DOT P 5800.4).
FIREFIGHTING: MOVE CONTAINERS FROM FIRE AREA IF POSSIBLE (1987 EMERGENCY RESPONSE GUIDEBOOK, DOT P 5800.4, GUIDE PAGE 53).
EXTINGUISH USING AGENT SUITABLE FOR TYPE OF SURROUNDING FIRE. AVOID BREATHING VAPORS AND DUSTS. KEEP UPWIND.

TRANSPORTATION DATA

DEPARTMENT OF TRANSPORTATION HAZARD CLASSIFICATION 49 CFR 172.101: POISON B
DEPARTMENT OF TRANSPORTATION LABELING REQUIREMENTS 49 CFR 172.101 AND SUBPART E: POISON
DEPARTMENT OF TRANSPORTATION PACKAGING REQUIREMENTS: 49 CFR 173.365 EXCEPTIONS: 49 CFR 173.364

TOXICITY

FORMETANATE: TOXICITY DATA: 20 MG/KG ORAL-RAT LD50; 18 MG/KG ORAL-MOUSE LD50; 19 MG/KG ORAL-DOG LD50. CARCINOGEN STATUS: NONE. ACUTE TOXICITY LEVEL: HIGHLY TOXIC BY INGESTION. TARGET EFFECTS: CHOLINESTERASE INHIBITOR. AT INCREASED RISK FROM EXPOSURE: PERSONS WITH ASTHMA, DIABETES, CARDIOVASCULAR DISEASE, MECHANICAL OBSTRUCTION OF THE GASTROINTESTINAL OR UROGENITAL TRACT, AND THOSE IN VAGOTONIC STATES.*
* MAY BE BASED ON GENERAL INFORMATION ON CARBAMATES.

HEALTH EFFECTS AND FIRST AID

INHALATION: FORMETANATE: SEE INFORMATION ON CARBAMATES.
CARBAMATES: CHOLINESTERASE INHIBITOR. **ACUTE EXPOSURE**- WHEN INHALED, THE FIRST EFFECTS OF CHOLINESTERASE INHIBITION ARE USUALLY RESPIRATORY AND MAY INCLUDE NASAL HYPEREMIA AND WATERY DISCHARGE, CHEST DISCOMFORT, DYSPNEA, AND WHEEZING DUE TO INCREASED BRONCHIAL SECRETIONS AND BRONCHOCONSTRICTION. OTHER SYSTEMIC EFFECTS MAY BEGIN WITHIN A FEW MINUTES OR SEVERAL HOURS OF EXPOSURE. SYMPTOMS MAY INCLUDE NAUSEA, VOMITING, DIARRHEA, ABDOMINAL CRAMPS, HEADACHE, VERTIGO, OCULAR PAIN, CILIARY MUSCLE SPASM, BLURRING OR DIMNESS OF VISION, MIOSIS, OR IN SOME CASES MYDRIASIS, LACRIMATION, SALIVATION, SWEATING, AND CONFUSION. OTHER REPORTED CENTRAL NERVOUS SYSTEM OR NEUROMUSCULAR EFFECTS INCLUDE ATAXIA, SLURRED SPEECH, AREFLEXIA, WEAKNESS, FATIGUE, TWITCHING, FASCICULATION, TREMOR, AND EVENTUALLY PARALYSIS OF THE EXTREMITIES AND POSSIBLY OF THE RESPIRATORY MUSCLES. IN SEVERE CASES, THERE MAY ALSO BE INVOLUNTARY DEFECATION AND URINATION, BRADYCARDIA, HYPOTENSION, PULMONARY EDEMA, CONVULSIONS, COMA, AND DEATH FROM RESPIRATORY FAILURE OR CARDIAC ARREST. CARBAMATES GENERALLY DO NOT ACCUMULATE IN MAMMALIAN TISSUE AND THE CHOLINESTERASE INHIBITION REVERSES RATHER RAPIDLY. IN NON-FATAL CASES, THE ILLNESS GENERALLY LASTS LESS THAN 24 HOURS. **CHRONIC EXPOSURE**- PROLONGED OR REPEATED EXPOSURE MAY CAUSE EFFECTS AS DESCRIBED IN ACUTE EXPOSURE.
FIRST AID- REMOVE FROM EXPOSURE AREA TO FRESH AIR IMMEDIATELY. IF BREATHING HAS STOPPED, GIVE ARTIFICIAL RESPIRATION. MAINTAIN AIRWAY AND BLOOD PRESSURE AND ADMINISTER OXYGEN IF AVAILABLE. KEEP AFFECTED PERSON WARM AND AT REST. TREAT SYMPTOMATICALLY AND SUPPORTIVELY. ADMINISTRATION OF OXYGEN SHOULD BE PERFORMED BY QUALIFIED PERSONNEL. GET MEDICAL ATTENTION IMMEDIATELY.

SKIN CONTACT: FORMETANATE: **ACUTE EXPOSURE**- NO DATA AVAILABLE. **CHRONIC EXPOSURE**- NO DATA AVAILABLE.
FIRST AID- REMOVE CONTAMINATED CLOTHING IMMEDIATELY. WASH CONTAMINATED AREAS WITH SOAP AND WATER FOLLOWED BY ALCOHOL (ARENA, POISONING, 4TH ED.). EMERGENCY PERSONNEL SHOULD WEAR GLOVES AND AVOID CONTAMINATION. TREAT RESPIRATORY DIFFICULTY WITH ARTIFICIAL RESPIRATION. GET MEDICAL ATTENTION IMMEDIATELY.

EYE CONTACT: FORMETANATE: SEE INFORMATION ON CARBAMATES.
CARBAMATES: CHOLINESTERASE INHIBITOR. **ACUTE EXPOSURE**- DIRECT CONTACT MAY CAUSE PAIN, HYPEREMIA, LACRIMATION, TWITCHING OF THE EYELIDS, MIOSIS, AND CILIARY MUSCLE SPASM WITH LOSS OF ACCOMODATION, BLURRED OR DIMMED VISION AND BROWACHE. SOMETIMES MYDRIASIS MAY OCCUR INSTEAD OF MIOSIS. WITH SUFFICIENT EXPOSURE, OTHER SYMPTOMS OF CHOLINESTERASE INHIBITION MAY OCCUR AS DESCRIBED IN ACUTE INHALATION. **CHRONIC EXPOSURE**- PROLONGED EXPOSURE MAY CAUSE EFFECTS AS DESCRIBED IN ACUTE EXPOSURE. SOME COMPOUNDS HAVE CAUSED TOXIC EFFECTS ON THE CRYSTALLINE LENS, CONJUNCTIVAL THICKENING AND OBSTRUCTION OF NASOLACRIMAL CANALS WHEN USED AS MIOTIC EYE DROPS.
FIRST AID- IRRIGATE EYES WITH WATER OR SALINE SOLUTION. IF SYMPTOMS OF POISONING OCCUR, TREAT RESPIRATORY DIFFICULTY WITH ARTIFICIAL RESPIRATION AND OXYGEN. OBSERVE PATIENT FOR AT LEAST 24-36 HOURS (GOSSELIN, CLINICAL TOXICOLOGY OF COMMERCIAL PRODUCTS, 5TH ED.). GET MEDICAL ATTENTION IMMEDIATELY. OXYGEN SHOULD BE ADMINISTERED BY QUALIFIED MEDICAL PERSONNEL.

INGESTION: FORMETANATE: HIGHLY TOXIC. IN RATS, CHRONIC ADMINISTRATION OF 20 MG/KG DAILY FOR 90 DAYS PRODUCED LIVER AND KIDNEY DAMAGE WITH SOME DEATHS. SEE INFORMATION ON CARBAMATES.
CARBAMATES: CHOLINESTERASE INHIBITOR. **ACUTE EXPOSURE**- WHEN INGESTED, THE FIRST EFFECTS MAY BE NAUSEA, VOMITING, ANOREXIA, ABDOMINAL CRAMPS, AND DIARRHEA. WITH ABSORPTION FROM THE GASTROINTESTINAL TRACT, THE OTHER EFFECTS OF CHOLINESTERASE INHIBITION AS DESCRIBED IN ACUTE INHALATION MAY OCCUR; SYMPTOMS MAY BEGIN WITHIN MINUTES OR BE DELAYED SEVERAL HOURS. **CHRONIC EXPOSURE**- REPEATED INGESTION MAY CAUSE EFFECTS AS DESCRIBED IN ACUTE EXPOSURE.
FIRST AID- IF PERSON IS ALERT AND RESPIRATION IS NOT DEPRESSED, GIVE SYRUP OF IPECAC FOLLOWED BY WATER (IF VOMITING OCCURS, KEEP HEAD BELOW HIPS TO PREVENT ASPIRATION). IF CONSCIOUSNESS LEVEL DECLINES OR VOMITING HAS NOT OCCURRED IN 15 MINUTES EMPTY STOMACH BY GASTRIC LAVAGE WITH THE AID OF CUFFED ENDOTRACHEAL TUBE USING ISOTONIC SALINE OR 5% SODIUM BICARBONATE FOLLOW WITH ACTIVATED CHARCOAL. ESTABLISH AND MAINTAIN AIRWAY. TREAT RESPIRATORY DIFFICULTY WITH ARTIFICIAL RESPIRATION AND OXYGEN. DO NOT GIVE MORPHINE, AMINOPHYLLINE, PHENOTHIAZINES, RESERPINE, FUROSEMIDE, OR ETHACRYNIC ACID (MORGAN, RECOGNITION AND MANAGEMENT OF PESTICIDE POISONINGS, 3RD ED.). TREAT SYMPTOMATICALLY AND SUPPORTIVELY. ADMINISTRATION OF OXYGEN AND LAVAGE MUST BE PERFORMED BY QUALIFIED MEDICAL PERSONNEL. GET MEDICAL ATTENTION IMMEDIATELY.
ANTIDOTE: THE FOLLOWING ANTIDOTE HAS BEEN RECOMMENDED. HOWEVER, THE DECISION AS TO WHETHER THE SEVERITY OF POISONING REQUIRES ADMINISTRATION OF ANY ANTIDOTE AND ACTUAL DOSE REQUIRED SHOULD BE MADE BY QUALIFIED MEDICAL PERSONNEL.
FOR CHOLINESTERASE INHIBITORS: ESTABLISH CLEAR AIRWAY AND TISSUE OXYGENATION BY ASPIRATION OF SECRETIONS, AND IF NECESSARY, BY ASSISTED PULMONARY VENTILATION WITH OXYGEN. IMPROVE TISSUE OXYGENATION AS MUCH AS POSSIBLE BEFORE ADMINISTERING ATROPINE TO MINIMIZE THE RISK OF VENTRICULAR FIBRILLATION. ADMINISTER ATROPINE SULFATE INTRAVENOUSLY, OR INTRAMUSCULARLY IF IV INJECTION IS NOT POSSIBLE. IN MODERATELY SEVERE POISONING ADMINISTER ATROPINE SULFATE, 0.4-2.0 MG REPEATED EVERY 15 MINUTES UNTIL ATROPINIZATION IS ACHIEVED (TACHYCARDIA, FLUSHING, DRY MOUTH, MYDRIASIS). MAINTAIN ATROPINIZATION BY REPEATED DOSES FOR 2-12 HOURS, OR LONGER, DEPENDING ON THE SEVERITY OF POISONING. THE APPEARANCE OF RALES IN THE LUNG BASES, MIOSIS, SALIVATION, NAUSEA, BRADYCARDIA, ARE ALL INDICATIONS OF INADEQUATE ATROPINIZATION. SEVERELY POISONED INDIVIDUALS MAY EXHIBIT REMARKABLE TOLERANCE TO ATROPINE; TWO OR MORE TIMES THE DOSAGES SUGGESTED ABOVE MAY BE NEEDED. PERSONS NOT POISONED OR ONLY SLIGHTLY POISONED, HOWEVER, MAY DEVELOP SIGNS OF ATROPINE TOXICITY FROM SUCH LARGE DOSAGES: FEVER, MUSCLE FIBRILLATIONS, AND DELIRIUM ARE THE MAIN SIGNS OF ATROPINE TOXICITY. IF THESE SIGNS APPEAR WHILE THE PATIENT IS FULLY ATROPINIZED, ATROPINE ADMINISTRATION SHOULD BE DISCONTINUED, AT LEAST TEMPORARILY. OBSERVE TREATED PATIENTS CLOSELY AT LEAST 24 HOURS TO INSURE THAT SYMPTOMS (POSSIBLY PULMONARY EDEMA) DO NOT RECUR AS ATROPINIZATION WEARS OFF. IN VERY SEVERE POISONINGS, METABOLIC DISPOSITION OF

TOXICANT MAY REQUIRE SEVERAL HOURS OR DAYS DURING WHICH ATROPINIZATION MUST BE MAINTAINED. MARKEDLY LOWER LEVELS OF URINARY METABOLITES INDICATE THAT ATROPINE DOSAGE CAN BE TAPERED OFF. AS DOSAGE IS REDUCED, CHECK THE LUNG BASES FREQUENTLY FOR RALES. IF RALES ARE HEARD OR OTHER SYMPTOMS RETURN, RE-ESTABLISH ATROPINIZATION PROMPTLY (MORGAN, RECOGNITION AND MANAGEMENT OF PESTICIDE POISONINGS, 3RD ED.). ADMINISTRATION OF ANTIDOTE MUST BE PERFORMED BY QUALIFIED MEDICAL PERSONNEL.

REACTIVITY

REACTIVITY: STABLE UNDER NORMAL TEMPERATURES AND PRESSURES.
INCOMPATIBILITIES: FORMETANATE: ALKALINE CONDITIONS: UNSTABLE.
DECOMPOSITION: THERMAL DECOMPOSITION MAY RELEASE TOXIC AND/OR HAZARDOUS GASES.
POLYMERIZATION: HAZARDOUS POLYMERIZATION HAS NOT BEEN REPORTED TO OCCUR UNDER NORMAL TEMPERATURES AND PRESSURES.

STORAGE AND DISPOSAL

OBSERVE ALL FEDERAL, STATE AND LOCAL REGULATIONS WHEN STORING OR DISPOSING OF THIS SUBSTANCE. FOR ASSISTANCE, CONTACT THE DISTRICT DIRECTOR OF THE ENVIRONMENTAL PROTECTION AGENCY.

STORAGE

STORE IN ACCORDANCE WITH 40 CFR 165 RECOMMENDED PROCEDURES FOR THE DISPOSAL AND STORAGE OF PESTICIDES AND PESTICIDE CONTAINERS.
STORE AWAY FROM INCOMPATIBLE SUBSTANCES.

DISPOSAL

DISPOSAL MUST BE IN ACCORDANCE WITH 40 CFR 165 RECOMMENDED PROCEDURES FOR THE DISPOSAL AND STORAGE OF PESTICIDES AND PESTICIDE CONTAINERS.

CONDITIONS TO AVOID

NONE REPORTED.

SPILL AND LEAK PROCEDURES

OCCUPATIONAL SPILL: DO NOT TOUCH SPILLED MATERIAL. STOP LEAK IF YOU CAN DO IT WITHOUT RISK. FOR SMALL SPILLS, TAKE UP WITH SAND OR OTHER ABSORBENT MATERIAL AND PLACE INTO CONTAINERS FOR LATER DISPOSAL. FOR SMALL DRY SPILLS, WITH A CLEAN SHOVEL PLACE MATERIAL INTO CLEAN, DRY CONTAINER AND COVER. MOVE CONTAINERS FROM SPILL AREA. FOR LARGER SPILLS, DIKE FAR AHEAD OF SPILL FOR LATER DISPOSAL. KEEP UNNECESSARY PEOPLE AWAY. ISOLATE HAZARD AREA AND DENY ENTRY.

PROTECTIVE EQUIPMENT

VENTILATION: PROVIDE LOCAL EXHAUST OR PROCESS ENCLOSURE VENTILATION SYSTEM.
RESPIRATOR: THE FOLLOWING RESPIRATORS ARE RECOMMENDED BASED ON INFORMATION FOUND IN THE PHYSICAL DATA, TOXICITY AND HEALTH EFFECTS SECTIONS. THEY ARE RANKED IN ORDER FROM MINIMUM TO MAXIMUM RESPIRATORY PROTECTION. THE SPECIFIC RESPIRATOR SELECTED MUST BE BASED ON CONTAMINATION LEVELS FOUND IN THE WORK PLACE, MUST NOT EXCEED THE WORKING LIMITS OF THE RESPIRATOR AND BE JOINTLY APPROVED BY THE NATIONAL INSTITUTE FOR OCCUPATIONAL SAFETY AND HEALTH AND THE MINE SAFETY AND HEALTH ADMINISTRATION (NIOSH-MSHA).
TYPE 'C' SUPPLIED-AIR RESPIRATOR WITH A FULL FACEPIECE OPERATED IN PRESSURE-DEMAND OR OTHER POSITIVE PRESSURE MODE OR WITH A FULL FACEPIECE, HELMET OR HOOD OPERATED IN CONTINOUS-FLOW MODE.
SELF-CONTAINED BREATHING APPARATUS WITH A FULL FACEPIECE OPERATED IN PRESSURE-DEMAND OR OTHER POSITIVE PRESSURE MODE.
FOR FIREFIGHTING AND OTHER IMMEDIATELY DANGEROUS TO LIFE OR HEALTH CONDITIONS:
SELF-CONTAINED BREATHING APPARATUS WITH FULL FACEPIECE OPERATED IN PRESSURE-DEMAND OR OTHER POSITIVE PRESSURE MODE.
SUPPLIED-AIR RESPIRATOR WITH FULL FACEPIECE AND OPERATED IN PRESSURE-DEMAND OR OTHER POSITIVE PRESSURE MODE IN COMBINATION WITH AN AUXILIARY SELF-CONTAINED BREATHING APPARATUS OPERATED IN PRESSURE-DEMAND OR OTHER POSITIVE PRESSURE MODE.
CLOTHING: EMPLOYEE MUST WEAR APPROPRIATE PROTECTIVE (IMPERVIOUS) CLOTHING AND EQUIPMENT TO PREVENT ANY POSSIBILITY OF SKIN CONTACT WITH THIS SUBSTANCE.
GLOVES: EMPLOYEE MUST WEAR APPROPRIATE PROTECTIVE GLOVES TO PREVENT CONTACT WITH THIS SUBSTANCE.
EYE PROTECTION: EMPLOYEE MUST WEAR SPLASH-PROOF OR DUST-RESISTANT SAFETY GOGGLES WITH OR WITHOUT A FACESHIELD TO PREVENT CONTACT WITH THIS SUBSTANCE.
EMERGENCY EYE WASH: WHERE THERE IS ANY POSSIBILITY THAT AN EMPLOYEE'S EYES MAY BE EXPOSED TO THIS SUBSTANCE, THE EMPLOYER SHOULD PROVIDE AN EYE WASH FOUNTAIN WITHIN THE IMMEDIATE WORK AREA FOR EMERGENCY USE.

AUTHORIZED BY- OCCUPATIONAL HEALTH SERVICES, INC.
CREATION DATE: 10/04/89 ***REVISION DATE:*** 06/12/90

MATERIAL SAFETY DATA SHEET

OCCUPATIONAL HEALTH SERVICES, INC.
AGRICULTURE AND PESTICIDE DIVISION
450 SEVENTH AVENUE, SUITE 2407
NEW YORK, NEW YORK 10123
1-800-445-MSDS OR (212) 967-1100

EMERGENCY CONTACT:
JOHN S. BRANSFORD, JR. (615) 292-1180

SUBSTANCE IDENTIFICATION

CAS-NUMBER 3878-19-1
SUBSTANCE: FUBERIDAZOLE
TRADE NAMES/SYNONYMS: 2-(2-FURANYL)-1H-BENZIMIDAZOLE; 2-(2-FURYL)BENZIMIDAZOLE; 2-(2'-FURYL)BENZIMIDAZOLE; B-33172; BAY 33172; BAYER 33172; FUBERIDAZOL; BURIDAZOL; FURIDAZOLE; PF 7402; PST73188
CHEMICAL FAMILY: BENZIMIDAZOLE
MOLECULAR FORMULA: C11-H8-N2-O
MOLECULAR WEIGHT: 184.21
CERCLA RATINGS (SCALE 0-3): HEALTH=3 FIRE=U REACTIVITY=U PERSISTENCE=2
NFPA RATINGS (SCALE 0-4): HEALTH=4 FIRE=U REACTIVITY=U

COMPONENTS AND CONTAMINANTS

COMPONENT: FUBERIDAZOLE ***PERCENT:*** 100.0
CAS# 3878-19-1
OTHER CONTAMINANTS: NONE
EXPOSURE LIMITS: FUBERIDAZOLE: NO OCCUPATIONAL EXPOSURE LIMITS ESTABLISHED BY OSHA, ACGIH, OR NIOSH.
100/10,000 POUNDS SARA SECTION 302 THRESHOLD PLANNING QUANTITY 1 POUND SARA SECTION 304 REPORTABLE QUANTITY

PHYSICAL DATA

DESCRIPTION: CRYSTALLINE POWDER ***MELTING POINT:*** 543-550 F (284-288 C)
SPECIFIC GRAVITY: NOT AVAILABLE
SOLUBILITY IN WATER: PRACTICALLY INSOLUBLE
SOLVENT SOLUBILITY: SOLUBLE IN ACETONE, METHANOL, ETHANOL
DECOMPOSITION BEGINS AT 280 C

FIRE AND EXPLOSION DATA

FIRE AND EXPLOSION HAZARD: UNKNOWN FIRE AND EXPLOSION HAZARD.
FIREFIGHTING MEDIA: DRY CHEMICAL, CARBON DIOXIDE, HALON, WATER SPRAY OR STANDARD FOAM (1987 EMERGENCY RESPONSE GUIDEBOOK, DOT P 5800.4).
FOR LARGER FIRES, USE WATER SPRAY, FOG OR STANDARD FOAM (1987 EMERGENCY RESPONSE GUIDEBOOK, DOT P 5800.4).
FIREFIGHTING: MOVE CONTAINERS FROM FIRE AREA IF POSSIBLE (1987 EMERGENCY RESPONSE GUIDEBOOK, DOT P 5800.4, GUIDE PAGE 53).
EXTINGUISH USING AGENT SUITABLE FOR TYPE OF SURROUNDING FIRE. AVOID BREATHING VAPORS AND DUSTS. KEEP UPWIND.

TRANSPORTATION DATA

DEPARTMENT OF TRANSPORTATION HAZARD CLASSIFICATION 49 CFR 172.101: POISON B
DEPARTMENT OF TRANSPORTATION LABELING REQUIREMENTS 49 CFR 172.101 AND SUBPART E: POISON
DEPARTMENT OF TRANSPORTATION PACKAGING REQUIREMENTS: 49 CFR 173.365 EXCEPTIONS: 49 CFR 173.364

TOXICITY

FUBERIDAZOLE: TOXICITY DATA: 330 MG/M3/4 HOURS INHALATION-RAT LC50; 500 MG/KG SKIN-RAT LD50; 600 MG/KG ORAL-RAT LD50; 825 MG/KG ORAL-MOUSE LD50; 100 MG/KG INTRAPERITONEAL-RAT LD50; MUTAGENIC DATA (RTECS). CARCINOGEN STATUS: NONE. ACUTE TOXICITY LEVEL: HIGHLY TOXIC BY INHALATION; TOXIC BY DERMAL ABSORPTION; MODERATELY TOXIC BY INGESTION. TARGET EFFECTS: NO DATA AVAILABLE.

HEALTH EFFECTS AND FIRST AID

INHALATION: FUBERIDAZOLE: HIGHLY TOXIC. **ACUTE EXPOSURE-** A VERY LOW CONCENTRATION WAS LETHAL IN RATS; NO SYMPTOMS WERE REPORTED. **CHRONIC EXPOSURE-** NO DATA AVAILABLE.

FIRST AID- REMOVE FROM EXPOSURE AREA TO FRESH AIR IMMEDIATELY. IF BREATHING HAS STOPPED, PERFORM ARTIFICIAL RESPIRATION. KEEP PERSON WARM AND AT REST. TREAT SYMPTOMATICALLY AND SUPPORTIVELY. GET MEDICAL ATTENTION IMMEDIATELY.

SKIN CONTACT: FUBERIDAZOLE: TOXIC. **ACUTE EXPOSURE-** A LOW DOSE WAS LETHAL IN RATS BY DERMAL ABSORPTION; NO SYMPTOMS WERE REPORTED. **CHRONIC EXPOSURE-** NO DATA AVAILABLE.

FIRST AID- REMOVE CONTAMINATED CLOTHING AND SHOES IMMEDIATELY. WASH AFFECTED AREA WITH SOAP OR MILD DETERGENT AND LARGE AMOUNTS OF WATER UNTIL NO EVIDENCE OF CHEMICAL REMAINS (APPROXIMATELY 15-20 MINUTES). GET MEDICAL ATTENTION IMMEDIATELY.

EYE CONTACT: FUBERIDAZOLE: **ACUTE EXPOSURE-** NO DATA AVAILABLE. **CHRONIC EXPOSURE-** NO DATA AVAILABLE.

FIRST AID- WASH EYES IMMEDIATELY WITH LARGE AMOUNTS OF WATER OR NORMAL SALINE, OCCASIONALLY LIFTING UPPER AND LOWER LIDS, UNTIL NO EVIDENCE OF CHEMICAL REMAINS (APPROXIMATELY 15-20 MINUTES). GET MEDICAL ATTENTION IMMEDIATELY.

INGESTION: FUBERIDAZOLE: **ACUTE EXPOSURE-** A MODERATE DOSE WAS LETHAL IN RATS AND MICE. IN ANIMALS, FUBERIDAZOLE PRODUCED VOMITING, WAS RAPIDLY ABSORBED FROM THE STOMACH, AND DETOXIFIED BY OXIDATION IN THE LIVER. **CHRONIC EXPOSURE-** NO DATA AVAILABLE.

FIRST AID- TREAT SYMPTOMATICALLY AND SUPPORTIVELY. GET MEDICAL ATTENTION IMMEDIATELY. IF VOMITING OCCURS, KEEP HEAD LOWER THAN HIPS TO PREVENT ASPIRATION.

ANTIDOTE: NO SPECIFIC ANTIDOTE. TREAT SYMPTOMATICALLY AND SUPPORTIVELY.

REACTIVITY

REACTIVITY: NO DATA AVAILABLE.

INCOMPATIBILITIES: FUBERIDAZOLE: INCOMPATIBLE.

DECOMPOSITION: THERMAL DECOMPOSITION PRODUCTS MAY INCLUDE TOXIC OXIDES OF NITROGEN.

POLYMERIZATION: HAZARDOUS POLYMERIZATION HAS NOT BEEN REPORTED TO OCCUR UNDER NORMAL TEMPERATURES AND PRESSURES.

STORAGE AND DISPOSAL

OBSERVE ALL FEDERAL, STATE AND LOCAL REGULATIONS WHEN STORING OR DISPOSING OF THIS SUBSTANCE. FOR ASSISTANCE, CONTACT THE DISTRICT DIRECTOR OF THE ENVIRONMENTAL PROTECTION AGENCY.

****STORAGE****

STORE IN ACCORDANCE WITH 40 CFR 165 RECOMMENDED PROCEDURES FOR THE DISPOSAL AND STORAGE OF PESTICIDES AND PESTICIDE CONTAINERS.

THRESHOLD PLANNING QUANTITY (TPQ): THE SUPERFUND AMENDMENTS AND REAUTHORIZATION ACT (SARA) SECTION 302 REQUIRES THAT EACH FACILITY WHERE ANY EXTREMELY HAZARDOUS SUBSTANCE IS PRESENT IN A QUANTITY EQUAL TO OR GREATER THAN THE TPQ ESTABLISHED FOR THAT SUBSTANCE NOTIFY THE STATE EMERGENCY RESPONSE COMMISSION FOR THE STATE IN WHICH IT IS LOCATED. SECTION 303 OF SARA REQUIRES THESE FACILITIES TO PARTICIPATE IN LOCAL EMERGENCY RESPONSE PLANNING (40 CFR 355.30).

****DISPOSAL****

DISPOSAL MUST BE IN ACCORDANCE WITH 40 CFR 165 RECOMMENDED PROCEDURES FOR THE DISPOSAL AND STORAGE OF PESTICIDES AND PESTICIDE CONTAINERS.

CONDITIONS TO AVOID

NONE REPORTED.

SPILL AND LEAK PROCEDURES

OCCUPATIONAL SPILL: DO NOT TOUCH SPILLED MATERIAL. STOP LEAK IF YOU CAN DO IT WITHOUT RISK. FOR SMALL SPILLS, TAKE UP WITH SAND OR OTHER ABSORBENT MATERIAL AND PLACE INTO CONTAINERS FOR LATER DISPOSAL. FOR SMALL DRY SPILLS, WITH A CLEAN SHOVEL PLACE MATERIAL INTO CLEAN, DRY CONTAINER AND COVER. MOVE CONTAINERS FROM SPILL AREA. FOR LARGER SPILLS, DIKE FAR AHEAD OF SPILL FOR LATER DISPOSAL. KEEP UNNECESSARY PEOPLE AWAY. ISOLATE HAZARD AREA AND DENY ENTRY.

REPORTABLE QUANTITY (RQ): 1 POUND THE SUPERFUND AMENDMENTS AND REAUTHORIZATION ACT (SARA) SECTION 304 REQUIRES THAT A RELEASE EQUAL TO OR GREATER THAN THE REPORTABLE QUANTITY FOR THIS SUBSTANCE BE IMMEDIATELY REPORTED TO THE LOCAL EMERGENCY PLANNING COMMITTEE AND THE STATE EMERGENCY RESPONSE COMMISSION (40 CFR 355.40). IF THE RELEASE OF THIS SUBSTANCE IS REPORTABLE UNDER CERCLA SECTION 103, THE NATIONAL RESPONSE CENTER MUST BE NOTIFIED IMMEDIATELY AT (800) 424-8802 OR (202) 426-2675 IN THE METROPOLITAN WASHINGTON, D.C. AREA (40 CFR 302.6).

PROTECTIVE EQUIPMENT

VENTILATION: PROCESS ENCLOSURE RECOMMENDED.

RESPIRATOR: THE FOLLOWING RESPIRATORS ARE RECOMMENDED BASED ON INFORMATION FOUND IN THE PHYSICAL DATA, TOXICITY AND HEALTH EFFECTS SECTIONS. THEY ARE RANKED IN ORDER FROM MINIMUM TO MAXIMUM RESPIRATORY PROTECTION. THE SPECIFIC RESPIRATOR SELECTED MUST BE BASED ON CONTAMINATION LEVELS FOUND IN THE WORK PLACE, MUST NOT EXCEED THE WORKING LIMITS OF THE RESPIRATOR AND BE JOINTLY APPROVED BY THE NATIONAL INSTITUTE FOR OCCUPATIONAL SAFETY AND HEALTH AND THE MINE SAFETY AND HEALTH ADMINISTRATION (NIOSH-MSHA).

TYPE 'C' SUPPLIED-AIR RESPIRATOR WITH A FULL FACEPIECE OPERATED IN PRESSURE-DEMAND OR OTHER POSITIVE PRESSURE MODE OR WITH A FULL FACEPIECE, HELMET OR HOOD OPERATED IN CONTINOUS-FLOW MODE.

SELF-CONTAINED BREATHING APPARATUS WITH A FULL FACEPIECE OPERATED IN PRESSURE-DEMAND OR OTHER POSITIVE PRESSURE MODE.

FOR FIREFIGHTING AND OTHER IMMEDIATELY DANGEROUS TO LIFE OR HEALTH CONDITIONS:

SELF-CONTAINED BREATHING APPARATUS WITH FULL FACEPIECE OPERATED IN PRESSURE-DEMAND OR OTHER POSITIVE PRESSURE MODE.

SUPPLIED-AIR RESPIRATOR WITH FULL FACEPIECE AND OPERATED IN PRESSURE-DEMAND OR OTHER POSITIVE PRESSURE MODE IN COMBINATION WITH AN AUXILIARY SELF-CONTAINED BREATHING APPARATUS OPERATED IN PRESSURE-DEMAND OR OTHER POSITIVE PRESSURE MODE.

CLOTHING: EMPLOYEE MUST WEAR APPROPRIATE PROTECTIVE (IMPERVIOUS) CLOTHING AND EQUIPMENT TO PREVENT ANY POSSIBILITY OF SKIN CONTACT WITH THIS SUBSTANCE.

GLOVES: EMPLOYEE MUST WEAR APPROPRIATE PROTECTIVE GLOVES TO PREVENT CONTACT WITH THIS SUBSTANCE.

EYE PROTECTION: EMPLOYEE MUST WEAR SPLASH-PROOF OR DUST-RESISTANT SAFETY GOGGLES AND A FACESHIELD TO PREVENT CONTACT WITH THIS SUBSTANCE.

EMERGENCY WASH FACILITIES: WHERE THERE IS ANY POSSIBILITY THAT AN EMPLOYEE'S EYES AND/OR SKIN MAY BE EXPOSED TO THIS SUBSTANCE, THE EMPLOYER SHOULD PROVIDE AN EYE WASH FOUNTAIN AND QUICK DRENCH SHOWER WITHIN THE IMMEDIATE WORK AREA FOR EMERGENCY USE.

AUTHORIZED BY- OCCUPATIONAL HEALTH SERVICES, INC.

CREATION DATE: 10/04/89 ***REVISION DATE:*** 05/11/90

MATERIAL SAFETY DATA SHEET

OCCUPATIONAL HEALTH SERVICES, INC.
AGRICULTURE AND PESTICIDE DIVISION
450 SEVENTH AVENUE, SUITE 2407
NEW YORK, NEW YORK 10123
1-800-445-MSDS OR (212) 967-1100

EMERGENCY CONTACT:
JOHN S. BRANSFORD, JR. (615) 292-1180

SUBSTANCE IDENTIFICATION

CAS-NUMBER 2550-75-6

SUBSTANCE: **CHLORBICYCLEN**

TRADE NAMES/SYNONYMS: BICYCLO(2.2.1)HEPT-2-ENE, 1,2,3,4,7,7-HEXACHLORO-5,6-BIS(CHLOROMETHYL); 2-NORBORNENE, 1,2,3,4,7,7-HEXACHLORO-5,6-BIS(CHLOROMETHYL)-; 1,2,3,4,7,7-HEXACHLORO-5,6-BIS(CHLOROMETHYL)-8,9,10-TRINORBORN-2-ENE; 1,2,3,4,7,7-HEXACHLORO-5,6-BIS(CHLOROMETHYL)-BICYCLO(2.2.1)HEPT-2-ENE; 1,2,3,4,7,7-HEXACHLORO-5,6-BIS(CHLOROMETHYL)-2-NORBORNENE; 1,2,3,4,7,7-HEXACHLORO-5,6-BIS-(CHLOROMETHYL)-2-NORBON-ENE; 5,6-BIS(CHLOROMETHYL)-1,2,3,4,7,7-HEXACHLORO-BICYCLO(2.2.1)HEPT-2-ENE; ALODAN; CYCLODAN; HERCULES 426; ENT 211; ENT 785; C9H6CL8; PST73193

CHEMICAL FAMILY: HALOGEN COMPOUND, AROMATIC NORBORNENE

MOLECULAR FORMULA: C7-H2-CL6-(C-H2-CL)2

MOLECULAR WEIGHT: 397.77

CERCLA RATINGS (SCALE 0-3): HEALTH=3 FIRE=0 REACTIVITY=0 PERSISTENCE=3

NFPA RATINGS (SCALE 0-4): HEALTH=4 FIRE=0 REACTIVITY=0

COMPONENTS AND CONTAMINANTS

COMPONENT: CHLORBICYCLEN ***PERCENT:*** 100
CAS# 2550-75-6

OTHER CONTAMINANTS: NONE

EXPOSURE LIMITS: NO OCCUPATIONAL EXPOSURE LIMITS ESTABLISHED BY OSHA, ACGIH, OR NIOSH.

PHYSICAL DATA

DESCRIPTION: SOLID ***MELTING POINT:*** 212-216 F (100-102 C)

SPECIFIC GRAVITY: NOT AVAILABLE ***SOLUBILITY IN WATER:*** NOT AVAILABLE

SOLVENT SOLUBILITY: SOLUBLE IN METHYLENE CHLORIDE

FIRE AND EXPLOSION DATA

FIRE AND EXPLOSION HAZARD: NEGLIGIBLE FIRE HAZARD WHEN EXPOSED TO HEAT OR FLAME.

FIREFIGHTING MEDIA: DRY CHEMICAL, CARBON DIOXIDE, HALON, WATER SPRAY OR STANDARD FOAM (1987 EMERGENCY RESPONSE GUIDEBOOK, DOT P 5800.4). FOR LARGER FIRES, USE WATER SPRAY, FOG OR STANDARD FOAM (1987 EMERGENCY RESPONSE GUIDEBOOK, DOT P 5800.4).

FIREFIGHTING: MOVE CONTAINERS FROM FIRE AREA IF POSSIBLE. FIGHT FIRE FROM MAXIMUM DISTANCE. STAY AWAY FROM STORAGE TANK ENDS. DIKE FIRE CONTROL WATER FOR LATER DISPOSAL. DO NOT SCATTER MATERIAL (1987 EMERGENCY RESPONSE GUIDEBOOK, DOT P 5800.4, GUIDE PAGE 55). USE AGENTS SUITABLE FOR TYPE OF FIRE. COOL CONTAINERS WITH FLOODING AMOUNTS OF WATER. AVOID BREATHING VAPORS OR DUSTS, KEEP UPWIND.

TOXICITY

CHLORBICYCLEN (ALODAN): TOXICITY DATA: 100 MG/M3/4 HOURS INHALATION-RAT LC50; 1 GM/KG SKIN-RAT LD50; 200 MG/KG ORAL-RAT LD50; 750 MG/KG ORAL-MOUSE LD50. CARCINOGEN STATUS: NONE. ACUTE TOXICITY LEVEL: HIGHLY TOXIC BY INHALATION; TOXIC BY DERMAL ABSORPTION AND INGESTION. TARGET EFFECTS: POISONING MAY AFFECT THE LIVER AND KIDNEYS. ADDITIONAL DATA: MAY BE STORED IN ADIPOSE TISSUE; INTENSE ACTIVITY AND STARVATION MAY MOBILIZE THE PESTICIDE RESULTING IN THE REAPPEARANCE OF TOXIC SYMPTOMS. MAY BE EXCRETED IN BREAST MILK. STIMULANTS SUCH AS EPINEPHRINE MAY INDUCE VENTRICULAR FIBRILLATION.

HEALTH EFFECTS AND FIRST AID

INHALATION: CHLORBICYCLEN (ALODAN): HIGHLY TOXIC. **ACUTE EXPOSURE-** CHLORBICYLEN IS A CHLORINATED HYDROCARBON PESTICIDE. THESE PESTICIDES MAY BE ABSORBED FROM THE LUNGS AND PRODUCE CENTRAL NERVOUS SYSTEM EFFECTS WITH SYMPTOMS OF MOTOR HYPEREXCITABILITY THAT INCLUDE MUSCLE TWITCHING, MYOCLONIC JERKING, AND CONVULSIVE SEIZURES. THE CONVULSIONS MAY OCCUR WITH PERIODS OF UNCONSCIOUSNESS. OTHER SYMPTOMS MAY INCLUDE HEADACHE, NAUSEA, VOMITING, MALAISE, AND DIZZINESS. IN CASES OF GROSS OVEREXPOSURE, CONVULSIONS MAY OCCUR WITHOUT ANY PRIOR SYMPTOMS. ABNORMAL EEG PATTERNS MAY BE OBSERVED; THESE CHANGES IN EEG PATTERNS MAY PERSIST FOR WEEKS OR MONTHS WHILE NO OTHER OBSERVABLE SIGNS OF POISONING MAY EXIST. **CHRONIC EXPOSURE-** PROLONGED OR REPEATED EXPOSURE TO CHLORINATED HYDROCARBON PESTICIDES MAY RESULT IN THE ACCUMULATION OF THE PESTICIDE IN THE BLOOD RESULTING IN A PROGRESSION OF THE SYMPTOMS LISTED ABOVE OR IN A SUDDEN ONSET OF SYMPTOMS AFTER AN ACUTE EXPOSURE. IN ADDITION TO SYMPTOMS LISTED ABOVE, HYPERIRRITABILITY, DROWSINESS, AND ANOREXIA MAY OCCUR.

FIRST AID- REMOVE FROM EXPOSURE AREA TO FRESH AIR IMMEDIATELY. IF BREATHING HAS STOPPED, PERFORM ARTIFICIAL RESPIRATION. KEEP PERSON WARM AND AT REST. TREAT SYMPTOMATICALLY AND SUPPORTIVELY. GET MEDICAL ATTENTION IMMEDIATELY.

SKIN CONTACT: CHLORBICYCLEN (ALODAN): TOXIC. **ACUTE EXPOSURE-** CHLORINATED HYDROCARBON PESTICIDES MAY BE ABSORBED FROM THE SKIN AND PRODUCE CENTRAL NERVOUS SYSTEM EFFECTS WITH SYMPTOMS OF MOTOR HYPEREXCITABILITY THAT MAY INCLUDE MUSCLE TWITCHING, MYOCLONIC JERKING AND CONVULSIVE SEIZURES. THE CONVULSIONS MAY OCCUR WITH PERIODS OF UNCONSCIOUSNESS. OTHER SYMPTOMS MAY INCLUDE HEADACHE, NAUSEA, VOMITING, MALAISE, AND DIZZINESS. IN CASES OF GROSS OVEREXPOSURE, CONVULSIONS MAY OCCUR WITHOUT ANY PRIOR SYMPTOMS. ABNORMAL EEG PATTERNS MAY BE OBSERVED; THESE CHANGES IN EEG PATERNS MAY PERSIST FOR WEEKS OR MONTHS WHILE NO OTHER OBSERVABLE SIGNS OF POISONING MAY EXIST. **CHRONIC EXPOSURE-** PROLONGED OR REPEATED EXPOSURE TO CHLORINATED HYDROCARBON PESTICIDES MAY RESULT IN THE ACCUMULATION OF THE PESTICIDE IN THE BLOOD RESULTING IN A PROGRESSION OF THE SYMPTOMS LISTED ABOVE OR IN A SUDDEN ONSET OF SYMPTOMS AFTER AN ACUTE EXPOSURE. IN ADDITION TO THE SYMPTOMS LISTED ABOVE HYPERIRRITABILITY, DROWSINESS, AND ANOREXIA MAY OCCUR.

FIRST AID- REMOVE CONTAMINATED CLOTHING AND SHOES IMMEDIATELY. WASH AFFECTED AREA WITH SOAP OR MILD DETERGENT AND LARGE AMOUNTS OF WATER UNTIL NO EVIDENCE OF CHEMICAL REMAINS (APPROXIMATELY 15-20 MINUTES). GET MEDICAL ATTENTION IMMEDIATELY.

EYE CONTACT: CHLORBICYCLEN (ALODAN); **ACUTE EXPOSURE-** NO DATA AVAILABLE. **CHRONIC EXPOSURE-** NO DATA AVAILABLE.

FIRST AID- WASH EYES IMMEDIATELY WITH LARGE AMOUNTS OF WATER OR NORMAL SALINE, OCCASIONALLY LIFTING UPPER AND LOWER LIDS, UNTIL NO EVIDENCE OF CHEMICAL REMAINS (APPROXIMATELY 15-20 MINUTES). GET MEDICAL ATTENTION IMMEDIATELY.

INGESTION: CHLOROBICYLEN (ALODAN): TOXIC. **ACUTE EXPOSURE-** A LETHAL DOSE IN RATS WAS 200 MG/KG. CHLORINATED HYDROCARBON PESTICIDES WILL PRODUCE CENTRAL NERVOUS SYSTEM EFFECTS WITH SYMPTOMS OF MOTOR HYPEREXCITABILITY THAT MAY INCLUDE MUSCLE TWITCHING, MYOCLONIC JERKING, AND CONVULSIVE SEIZURES. THE CONVULSIONS MAY OCCUR WITH PERIODS OF UNCONSCIOUSNESS. OTHER SYMPTOMS MAY INCLUDE HEADACHE, NAUSEA, VOMITING, MALAISE, AND DIZZINESS. IN CASES OF GROSS OVEREXPOSURE, CONVULSIONS MAY OCCUR WITHOUT ANY PRIOR SYMPTOMS. ABNORMAL EEG PATTERNS MAY BE OBSERVED; THESE CHANGES IN EEG PATTERNS MAY PERSIST FOR WEEKS OR MONTHS WHILE NO OTHER OBSERVABLE SIGNS OF POISONING MAY EXIST. **CHRONIC EXPOSURE-** PROLONGED OR REPEATED EXPOSURE TO CHLORINATED HYDROCARBON PESTICIDES MAY RESULT IN A PROGRESSION OF THE SYMPTOMS LISTED ABOVE OR IN A SUDDEN ONSET OF SYMPTOMS AFTER AN ACUTE EXPOSURE. IN ADDITION TO SYMPTOMS LISTED ABOVE, HYPERIRRITABILITY, DROWSINESS, AND ANOREXIA MAY OCCUR.

FIRST AID- IF THE PERSON IS CONSCIOUS AND NOT CONVULSING, REMOVE BY GIVING SYRUP OF IPECAC (IF VOMITING OCCURS, KEEP THE HEAD BELOW THE HIPS TO PREVENT ASPIRATION). GIVE ACTIVATED CHARCOAL FOLLOWED BY GASTRIC LAVAGE. FOLLOW WITH A SALINE CATHARTIC. DO NOT GIVE FATS OR OILS. INTESTINAL LAVAGE WITH 20% MANNITOL (200 ML) BY STOMACH TUBE IS ALSO USEFUL. GIVE ARTIFICIAL RESPIRATION WITH OXYGEN IF RESPIRATION IS DEPRESSED (DREISBACH, HANDBOOK OF POISONING, 12TH ED.). TREAT SYMPTOMATICALLY AND SUPPORTIVELY. LAVAGE AND ADMINISTRATION OF OXYGEN SHOULD BE PERFORMED BY QUALIFIED MEDICAL PERSONNEL. GET MEDICAL ATTENTION IMMEDIATELY.

ANTIDOTE: NO SPECIFIC ANTIDOTE. TREAT SYMPTOMATICALLY AND SUPPORTIVELY.

REACTIVITY

REACTIVITY: STABLE UNDER NORMAL TEMPERATURES AND PRESSURES.

INCOMPATIBILITIES: CHLORBICYCLEN (ALODAN): NO DATA AVAILABLE.

DECOMPOSITION: THERMAL DECOMPOSITION PRODUCTS MAY INCLUDE HIGHLY TOXIC FUMES OF PHOSGENE, TOXIC AND CORROSIVE FUMES OF CHLORIDES, AND OXIDES OF CARBON.

POLYMERIZATION: HAZARDOUS POLYMERIZATION HAS NOT BEEN REPORTED TO OCCUR UNDER NORMAL TEMPERATURES AND PRESSURES.

STORAGE AND DISPOSAL

OBSERVE ALL FEDERAL, STATE AND LOCAL REGULATIONS WHEN STORING OR DISPOSING OF THIS SUBSTANCE. FOR ASSISTANCE, CONTACT THE DISTRICT DIRECTOR OF THE ENVIRONMENTAL PROTECTION AGENCY.

STORAGE

STORE IN ACCORDANCE WITH 40 CFR 165 RECOMMENDED PROCEDURES FOR THE DISPOSAL AND STORAGE OF PESTICIDES AND PESTICIDE CONTAINERS.

DISPOSAL

DISPOSAL MUST BE IN ACCORDANCE WITH 40 CFR 165 RECOMMENDED PROCEDURES FOR THE DISPOSAL AND STORAGE OF PESTICIDES AND PESTICIDE CONTAINERS.

CONDITIONS TO AVOID

MAY BURN BUT DOES NOT IGNITE READILY. CONTAINERS MAY EXPLODE IN HEAT OF FIRE.

SPILL AND LEAK PROCEDURES

OCCUPATIONAL SPILL: DO NOT TOUCH SPILLED MATERIAL. STOP LEAK IF YOU CAN DO IT WITHOUT RISK. USE WATER SPRAY TO REDUCE VAPORS. FOR SMALL SPILLS, TAKE UP WITH SAND OR OTHER ABSORBENT MATERIAL AND PLACE INTO CONTAINERS FOR LATER DISPOSAL. FOR SMALL DRY SPILLS, WITH A CLEAN SHOVEL PLACE MATERIAL INTO CLEAN, DRY CONTAINERS AND COVER. MOVE CONTAINERS FROM SPILL AREA. FOR LARGER SPILLS, DIKE FAR AHEAD OF SPILL FOR LATER DISPOSAL. KEEP UNNECESSARY PEOPLE AWAY. ISOLATE HAZARD AREA AND DENY ENTRY. VENTILATE CLOSED SPACES BEFORE ENTERING.

PROTECTIVE EQUIPMENT

VENTILATION: PROVIDE GENERAL DILUTION VENTILATION.

RESPIRATOR: THE FOLLOWING RESPIRATORS ARE RECOMMENDED BASED ON INFORMATION FOUND IN THE PHYSICAL DATA, TOXICITY AND HEALTH EFFECTS SECTIONS. THEY ARE RANKED IN ORDER FROM MINIMUM TO MAXIMUM RESPIRATORY PROTECTION. THE SPECIFIC RESPIRATOR SELECTED MUST BE BASED ON CONTAMINATION LEVELS FOUND IN THE WORK PLACE, MUST NOT EXCEED THE WORKING LIMITS OF THE RESPIRATOR AND BE JOINTLY APPROVED BY THE NATIONAL INSTITUTE FOR OCCUPATIONAL SAFETY AND HEALTH AND THE MINE SAFETY AND HEALTH ADMINISTRATION (NIOSH-MSHA).

CHEMICAL CARTRIDGE RESPIRATOR WITH AN ORGANIC VAPOR CARTRIDGE(S) WITH A FULL FACEPIECE AND ORGANIC VAPOR CARTRIDGE(S) IN COMBINATION WITH A DUST AND MIST FILTER.

POWERED AIR-PURIFYING RESPIRATOR WITH A TIGHT-FITTING FACEPIECE AND ORGANIC VAPOR CARTRIDGE(S) IN COMBINATION WITH A HIGH-EFFICIENCY PARTICULATE FILTER.

TYPE 'C' SUPPLIED-AIR RESPIRATOR WITH A FULL FACEPIECE OPERATED IN A PRESSURE-DEMAND OR OTHER POSITIVE PRESSURE MODE.

SELF-CONTAINED BREATHING APPARATUS WITH A FULL FACEPIECE OPERATED IN PRESSURE-DEMAND OR OTHER POSITIVE PRESSURE MODE.

FOR FIREFIGHTING AND OTHER IMMEDIATELY DANGEROUS TO LIFE OR HEALTH CONDITIONS:

SELF-CONTAINED BREATHING APPARATUS WITH FULL FACEPIECE OPERATED IN PRESSURE-DEMAND OR OTHER POSITIVE PRESSURE MODE.

SUPPLIED-AIR RESPIRATOR WITH FULL FACEPIECE AND OPERATED IN PRESSURE-DEMAND OR OTHER POSITIVE PRESSURE MODE IN COMBINATION WITH AN AUXILIARY SELF-CONTAINED BREATHING APPARATUS OPERATED IN PRESSURE-DEMAND OR OTHER POSITIVE PRESSURE MODE.

CLOTHING: EMPLOYEE MUST WEAR APPROPRIATE PROTECTIVE (IMPERVIOUS) CLOTHING AND EQUIPMENT TO PREVENT REPEATED OR PROLONGED SKIN CONTACT WITH THIS SUBSTANCE.

GLOVES: EMPLOYEE MUST WEAR APPROPRIATE PROTECTIVE GLOVES TO PREVENT CONTACT WITH THIS SUBSTANCE.

EYE PROTECTION: EMPLOYEE MUST WEAR SPLASH-PROOF OR DUST-RESISTANT SAFETY GOGGLES TO PREVENT EYE CONTACT WITH THIS SUBSTANCE.

EMERGENCY EYE WASH: WHERE THERE IS ANY POSSIBILITY THAT AN EMPLOYEE'S EYES MAY BE EXPOSED TO THIS SUBSTANCE, THE EMPLOYER SHOULD PROVIDE AN EYE WASH FOUNTAIN WITHIN THE IMMEDIATE WORK AREA FOR EMERGENCY USE.

AUTHORIZED BY- OCCUPATIONAL HEALTH SERVICES, INC.

CREATION DATE: 10/04/89 ***REVISION DATE:*** 05/17/90

MATERIAL SAFETY DATA SHEET

OCCUPATIONAL HEALTH SERVICES, INC.
AGRICULTURE AND PESTICIDE DIVISION
450 SEVENTH AVENUE, SUITE 2407
NEW YORK, NEW YORK 10123
1-800-445-MSDS OR (212) 967-1100

EMERGENCY CONTACT:
JOHN S. BRANSFORD, JR. (615) 292-1180

SUBSTANCE IDENTIFICATION

CAS-NUMBER 28805-78-9

SUBSTANCE: **ISONORURON**

TRADE NAMES/SYNONYMS: UREA, N,N-DIMETHYL-N'-(OCTAHYDRO-4,7-METHANO-1H-INDEN-1(OR 2)-YL)-; UREA, 3-(HEXAHYDRO-4,7-METHANOINDAN-1(OR 2)-YL)-1,1-DIMETHYL-; N,N-DIMETHYL-N'-(OCTAHYDRO-4,7-METHANO-1H-INDEN-1(OR 2)-YL)UREA; 3-(HEXAHYDRO-4,7-METHANOINDAN-1(OR 2)-YL)-1,1-DIMETHYLUREA; 3-(1 OR 2-HEXAHYDRO-4,7-METHANOINDANLYL)-1,1-DIMETHYLUREA; 1,1-DIMETHYL-3-(PERHYDRO-4,7-METHANOINDEN-1-YL)UREA + 1,1-DIMETHYL-3-(PERHYDRO-4,7-METHANOINDEN-2-YL)UREA;
N,N-DIMETHYL-N'-(2,3,3A,4,5,6,7,7A-OCTAHYDRO-4,7-METHANO-1H-INDEN-1-YL UREA + N,N-DIMETHYL-N'-(2,3,3A,4,5,6,7,7A-OCTAHYDRO-4,7-METHANO-1H-INDEN-2-YL)UREA; N,N-DIMETHYL-N'-(OCTAHYDRO-4,7-METHANOINDEN-1(OR 2)-YL)UREA; 3-(HEXAHYDRO-4,7-METHANOINDAN-1-YL)-1,1-DIMETHYLUREA + 3-HEXAHYDRO-4,7-METHANOINDAN-2-YL)-1,1-DIMETHYLUREA; BAS 210311; TRICURON; C13H22N2O; PST73199

CHEMICAL FAMILY: SUBSTITUTED UREA

MOLECULAR FORMULA: C13-H22-N2-O

MOLECULAR WEIGHT: 222.33

CERCLA RATINGS (SCALE 0-3): HEALTH=2 FIRE=1 REACTIVITY=0 PERSISTENCE=1

NFPA RATINGS (SCALE 0-4): HEALTH=2 FIRE=1 REACTIVITY=0

COMPONENTS AND CONTAMINANTS

COMPONENT: ISONORURON ***PERCENT:*** 100

CAS# 28805-78-9

OTHER CONTAMINANTS: NONE

EXPOSURE LIMITS: NO OCCUPATIONAL EXPOSURE LIMITS ESTABLISHED BY OSHA, ACGIH, OR NIOSH.

PHYSICAL DATA

DESCRIPTION: SOLID. ***MELTING POINT:*** NOT AVAILABLE

SPECIFIC GRAVITY: NOT AVAILABLE ***SOLUBILITY IN WATER:*** NOT AVAILABLE

FIRE AND EXPLOSION DATA

FIRE AND EXPLOSION HAZARD: SLIGHT FIRE HAZARD WHEN EXPOSED TO HEAT OR FLAME.

FIREFIGHTING MEDIA: DRY CHEMICAL, CARBON DIOXIDE, HALON, WATER SPRAY OR STANDARD FOAM (1987 EMERGENCY RESPONSE GUIDEBOOK, DOT P 5800.4). FOR LARGER FIRES, USE WATER SPRAY, FOG OR STANDARD FOAM (1987 EMERGENCY RESPONSE GUIDEBOOK, DOT P 5800.4).

FIREFIGHTING: MOVE CONTAINERS FROM FIRE AREA IF POSSIBLE. FIGHT FIRE FROM MAXIMUM DISTANCE. STAY AWAY FROM STORAGE TANK ENDS. DIKE FIRE CONTROL WATER FOR LATER DISPOSAL. DO NOT SCATTER MATERIAL (1987 EMERGENCY RESPONSE GUIDEBOOK, DOT P 5800.4, GUIDE PAGE 55). EXTINGUISH USING AGENT SUITABLE FOR TYPE OF SURROUNDING FIRE. USE WATER IN FLOODING QUANTITIES AS FOG. KEEP SPARKS, FLAMES AND OTHER SOURCES OF IGNITION AWAY. KEEP MATERIAL OUT OF WATER SOURCES AND SEWERS. DO NOT TOUCH MATERIAL AND AVOID BREATHING DUSTS AND FUMES FROM BURNING MATERIAL. KEEP UPWIND.

TOXICITY

ISONORURON: TOXICITY DATA: 1600 MG/KG ORAL-RAT LD50. CARCINOGEN STATUS: NONE. ACUTE TOXICITY LEVEL: MODERATELY TOXIC BY INGESTION. TARGET EFFECTS: NO DATA AVAILABLE.

HEALTH EFFECTS AND FIRST AID

INHALATION: ISONORURON: **ACUTE EXPOSURE-** MANY SUBSTITUTED UREA HERBICIDES ARE MODERATELY IRRITATING TO THE MUCOUS MEMBRANES. **CHRONIC EXPOSURE-** NO DATA AVAILABLE.

FIRST AID- REMOVE FROM EXPOSURE AREA TO FRESH AIR IMMEDIATELY. IF BREATHING HAS STOPPED, PERFORM ARTIFICIAL RESPIRATION. KEEP PERSON WARM AND AT REST. TREAT SYMPTOMATICALLY AND SUPPORTIVELY. GET MEDICAL ATTENTION IMMEDIATELY.

SKIN CONTACT: ISONORURON: **ACUTE EXPOSURE-** MANY SUBSTITUTED UREA HERBICIDES ARE MODERATELY IRRITATING TO THE SKIN. **CHRONIC EXPOSURE-** NO DATA AVAILABLE.

FIRST AID- REMOVE CONTAMINATED CLOTHING AND SHOES IMMEDIATELY. WASH AFFECTED AREA WITH SOAP OR MILD DETERGENT AND LARGE AMOUNTS OF WATER UNTIL NO EVIDENCE OF CHEMICAL REMAINS (APPROXIMATELY 15-20 MINUTES). GET MEDICAL ATTENTION IMMEDIATELY.

EYE CONTACT: ISONORURON: **ACUTE EXPOSURE-** MANY SUBSTITUTED UREA HERBICIDES ARE MODERATELY IRRITATING TO THE EYES. **CHRONIC EXPOSURE-** NO DATA AVAILABLE.

FIRST AID- WASH EYES IMMEDIATELY WITH LARGE AMOUNTS OF WATER OR NORMAL SALINE, OCCASIONALLY LIFTING UPPER AND LOWER LIDS, UNTIL NO EVIDENCE OF CHEMICAL REMAINS (APPROXIMATELY 15-20 MINUTES). GET MEDICAL ATTENTION IMMEDIATELY.

INGESTION: ISONORURON: **ACUTE EXPOSURE-** A LETHAL DOSE IN RATS WAS 2000 MG/KG; SYMPTOMS WERE NOT REPORTED. **CHRONIC EXPOSURE-** NO DATA AVAILABLE.

FIRST AID- TREAT SYMPTOMATICALLY AND SUPPORTIVELY. GET MEDICAL ATTENTION IMMEDIATELY. IF VOMITING OCCURS, KEEP HEAD LOWER THAN HIPS TO PREVENT ASPIRATION.

ANTIDOTE: NO SPECIFIC ANTIDOTE. TREAT SYMPTOMATICALLY AND SUPPORTIVELY.

REACTIVITY

REACTIVITY: STABLE UNDER NORMAL TEMPERATURES AND PRESSURES.

INCOMPATIBILITIES: ISONORURON: OXIDIZERS (STRONG): FIRE AND EXPLOSION HAZARD.

DECOMPOSITION: THERMAL DECOMPOSITION PRODUCTS MAY INCLUDE TOXIC OXIDES OF CARBON AND NITROGEN.

POLYMERIZATION: HAZARDOUS POLYMERIZATION HAS NOT BEEN REPORTED TO OCCUR UNDER NORMAL TEMPERATURES AND PRESSURES.

STORAGE AND DISPOSAL

OBSERVE ALL FEDERAL, STATE AND LOCAL REGULATIONS WHEN STORING OR DISPOSING OF THIS SUBSTANCE. FOR ASSISTANCE, CONTACT THE DISTRICT DIRECTOR OF THE ENVIRONMENTAL PROTECTION AGENCY.

STORAGE

STORE IN ACCORDANCE WITH 40 CFR 165 RECOMMENDED PROCEDURES FOR THE DISPOSAL AND STORAGE OF PESTICIDES AND PESTICIDE CONTAINERS.
STORE AWAY FROM INCOMPATIBLE SUBSTANCES.

DISPOSAL

DISPOSAL MUST BE IN ACCORDANCE WITH 40 CFR 165 RECOMMENDED PROCEDURES FOR THE DISPOSAL AND STORAGE OF PESTICIDES AND PESTICIDE CONTAINERS.

CONDITIONS TO AVOID

MAY BURN BUT DOES NOT IGNITE READILY. CONTAINERS MAY EXPLODE IN HEAT OF FIRE.

SPILL AND LEAK PROCEDURES

OCCUPATIONAL SPILL: DO NOT TOUCH SPILLED MATERIAL. STOP LEAK IF YOU CAN DO IT WITHOUT RISK. USE WATER SPRAY TO REDUCE VAPORS. FOR SMALL SPILLS, TAKE UP WITH SAND OR OTHER ABSORBENT MATERIAL AND PLACE INTO CONTAINERS FOR LATER DISPOSAL. FOR SMALL DRY SPILLS, WITH A CLEAN SHOVEL PLACE MATERIAL INTO CLEAN, DRY CONTAINERS AND COVER. MOVE CONTAINERS FROM SPILL AREA. FOR LARGER SPILLS, DIKE FAR AHEAD OF SPILL FOR LATER DISPOSAL. KEEP UNNECESSARY PEOPLE AWAY. ISOLATE HAZARD AREA AND DENY ENTRY. VENTILATE CLOSED SPACES BEFORE ENTERING.

PROTECTIVE EQUIPMENT

VENTILATION: PROVIDE LOCAL EXHAUST OR GENERAL DILUTION VENTILATION SYSTEM.

RESPIRATOR: THE FOLLOWING RESPIRATORS ARE RECOMMENDED BASED ON INFORMATION FOUND IN THE PHYSICAL DATA, TOXICITY AND HEALTH EFFECTS SECTIONS. THEY ARE RANKED IN ORDER FROM MINIMUM TO MAXIMUM RESPIRATORY PROTECTION. THE SPECIFIC RESPIRATOR SELECTED MUST BE BASED ON CONTAMINATION LEVELS FOUND IN THE WORK PLACE, MUST NOT EXCEED THE WORKING LIMITS OF THE RESPIRATOR AND BE JOINTLY APPROVED BY THE NATIONAL INSTITUTE FOR OCCUPATIONAL SAFETY AND HEALTH AND THE MINE SAFETY AND HEALTH ADMINISTRATION (NIOSH-MSHA).
CHEMICAL CARTRIDGE RESPIRATOR WITH AN ORGANIC VAPOR CARTRIDGE(S) WITH A FULL FACEPIECE AND ORGANIC VAPOR CARTRIDGE(S) IN COMBINATION WITH A DUST AND MIST FILTER.
POWERED AIR-PURIFYING RESPIRATOR WITH A TIGHT-FITTING FACEPIECE AND ORGANIC VAPOR CARTRIDGE(S) IN COMBINATION WITH A HIGH-EFFICIENCY PARTICULATE FILTER.
TYPE 'C' SUPPLIED-AIR RESPIRATOR WITH A FULL FACEPIECE OPERATED IN A PRESSURE-DEMAND OR OTHER POSITIVE PRESSURE MODE.
SELF-CONTAINED BREATHING APPARATUS WITH A FULL FACEPIECE OPERATED IN PRESSURE-DEMAND OR OTHER POSITIVE PRESSURE MODE.
FOR FIREFIGHTING AND OTHER IMMEDIATELY DANGEROUS TO LIFE OR HEALTH CONDITIONS:
SELF-CONTAINED BREATHING APPARATUS WITH FULL FACEPIECE OPERATED IN PRESSURE-DEMAND OR OTHER POSITIVE PRESSURE MODE.
SUPPLIED-AIR RESPIRATOR WITH FULL FACEPIECE AND OPERATED IN PRESSURE-DEMAND OR OTHER POSITIVE PRESSURE MODE IN COMBINATION WITH AN AUXILIARY SELF-CONTAINED BREATHING APPARATUS OPERATED IN PRESSURE-DEMAND OR OTHER POSITIVE PRESSURE MODE.

CLOTHING: EMPLOYEE MUST WEAR APPROPRIATE PROTECTIVE (IMPERVIOUS) CLOTHING AND EQUIPMENT TO PREVENT REPEATED OR PROLONGED SKIN CONTACT WITH THIS SUBSTANCE.

GLOVES: EMPLOYEE MUST WEAR APPROPRIATE PROTECTIVE GLOVES TO PREVENT CONTACT WITH THIS SUBSTANCE.

EYE PROTECTION: EMPLOYEE MUST WEAR SPLASH-PROOF OR DUST-RESISTANT SAFETY GOGGLES TO PREVENT EYE CONTACT WITH THIS SUBSTANCE.
EMERGENCY EYE WASH: WHERE THERE IS ANY POSSIBILITY THAT AN EMPLOYEE'S EYES MAY BE EXPOSED TO THIS SUBSTANCE, THE EMPLOYER SHOULD PROVIDE AN EYE WASH FOUNTAIN WITHIN THE IMMEDIATE WORK AREA FOR EMERGENCY USE.

AUTHORIZED BY- OCCUPATIONAL HEALTH SERVICES, INC.
CREATION DATE: 10/04/89 ***REVISION DATE:*** 06/11/90

MATERIAL SAFETY DATA SHEET

OCCUPATIONAL HEALTH SERVICES, INC.
AGRICULTURE AND PESTICIDE DIVISION
450 SEVENTH AVENUE, SUITE 2407
NEW YORK, NEW YORK 10123
1-800-445-MSDS OR (212) 967-1100

EMERGENCY CONTACT:
JOHN S. BRANSFORD, JR. (615) 292-1180

SUBSTANCE IDENTIFICATION

CAS-NUMBER 93-80-1

SUBSTANCE: **4-(2,4,5-TRICHLOROPHENOXY) BUTYRIC ACID**

TRADE NAMES/SYNONYMS: BUTANOIC ACID, 4-(2,4,5-TRICHLOROPHENOXY)-; BUTYRIC ACID, 4-(2,4,5-TRICHLOROPHENOXY)-; 4-(2,4,5-TRICHLOROPHENOXY) BUTANOIC ACID; 2,4,5-TB; 2,4,5-TRICHLOROPHENOXYBUTYRIC ACID; 4-(2,4,5-TB); C10H9CL3O3; PST73203

CHEMICAL FAMILY: HALOGEN COMPOUND, AROMATIC
ETHER
CARBOXYLIC ACID

MOLECULAR FORMULA: C6-H2-CL3-O-(C-H2)3-C-O-O-H

MOLECULAR WEIGHT: 283.54

CERCLA RATINGS (SCALE 0-3): HEALTH=3 FIRE=1 REACTIVITY=0 PERSISTENCE=1

NFPA RATINGS (SCALE 0-4): HEALTH=U FIRE=1 REACTIVITY=0

COMPONENTS AND CONTAMINANTS

COMPONENT: 4-(2,4,5-TRICHLOROPHENOXY) BUTYRIC ACID ***PERCENT:*** 100.0
CAS# 93-80-1

OTHER CONTAMINANTS: NONE

EXPOSURE LIMITS: NO OCCUPATIONAL EXPOSURE LIMITS ESTABLISHED BY OSHA, ACGIH, OR NIOSH.

PHYSICAL DATA

DESCRIPTION: WHITE POWDER. ***MELTING POINT:*** NOT AVAILABLE
SPECIFIC GRAVITY: NOT AVAILABLE ***SOLUBILITY IN WATER:*** NOT AVAILABLE

FIRE AND EXPLOSION DATA

FIRE AND EXPLOSION HAZARD: SLIGHT FIRE HAZARD WHEN EXPOSED TO HEAT OR FLAME.
DUST-AIR MIXTURES MAY IGNITE OR EXPLODE.

FIREFIGHTING MEDIA: DRY CHEMICAL, CARBON DIOXIDE, HALON, WATER SPRAY OR STANDARD FOAM (1987 EMERGENCY RESPONSE GUIDEBOOK, DOT P 5800.4).
FOR LARGER FIRES, USE WATER SPRAY, FOG OR STANDARD FOAM (1987 EMERGENCY RESPONSE GUIDEBOOK, DOT P 5800.4).

FIREFIGHTING: MOVE CONTAINER FROM FIRE AREA IF POSSIBLE. DO NOT SCATTER SPILLED MATERIAL WITH HIGH PRESSURE WATER STREAMS. DIKE FIRE CONTROL WATER FOR LATER DISPOSAL (1987 EMERGENCY RESPONSE GUIDEBOOK, DOT P 5800.4, GUIDE PAGE 31).
USE AGENTS SUITABLE FOR TYPE OF SURROUNDING FIRE. AVOID BREATHING HAZARDOUS VAPORS, KEEP UPWIND.

TOXICITY

4-(2,4,5-TRICHLOROPHENOXY) BUTYRIC ACID: TOXICITY DATA: 650 MG/KG ORAL-RAT LD50 APPROX. (EPA); REPRODUCTIVE EFFECTS DATA (RTECS). CARCINOGEN STATUS: HUMAN LIMITED EVIDENCE (IARC GROUP-2B FOR CHLOROPHENOXY HERBICIDES). STUDIES REVEALED A SIGNIFICANT INCREASE IN SOFT-TISSUE SARCOMAS, MALIGNANT LYMPHOMAS AND BRONCHIAL CARCINOMAS IN WORKERS EXPOSED TO CHLOROPHENOXY HERBICIDES. ACUTE TOXICITY LEVEL: MODERATELY TOXIC BY INGESTION. TARGET EFFECTS: POISONING MAY AFFECT THE GASTROINTESTINAL TRACT AND CARDIOVASCULAR SYSTEM.* AT INCREASED RISK FROM EXPOSURE: PERSONS WITH PREEXISTING LIVER, GASTROINTESTINAL TRACT OR SKIN DISORDERS.* ADDITIONAL DATA: STIMULANTS SUCH AS EPINEPHRINE MAY INDUCE VENTRICULAR FIBRILLATION.*
* MAY BE BASED ON GENERAL INFORMATION ON 2,4,5-T AND DERIVATIVES.

HEALTH EFFECTS AND FIRST AID

INHALATION: 4-(2,4,5-TRICHLOROPHENOXY) BUTYRIC ACID: SEE INFORMATION ON 2,4,5-T AND DERIVATIVES.
2,4,5-T AND DERIVATIVES: ACUTE EXPOSURE- MAY CAUSE IRRITATION WITH SORE THROAT AND BURNING SENSATIONS IN THE NASOPHARYNX AND CHEST, COUGHING, LACRIMATION, RHINITIS, DULLNESS, DIZZINESS, AND ATAXIA. IF SUFFICIENT AMOUNTS ARE ABSORBED THROUGH THE LUNGS, EFFECTS AS

DESCRIBED IN ACUTE INGESTION MAY OCCUR. **CHRONIC EXPOSURE-** OCCUPATIONAL EXPOSURE TO 2,4,5-T AND ITS DERIVATIVES HAS PRODUCED HEADACHE, DECREASED AUDITORY ACUITY, GASTROINTESTINAL SYMPTOMS OF NAUSEA, VOMITING, DIARRHEA, ABDOMINAL PAINS, AND BLOOD IN THE STOOL, CHLORACNE, PORPHYRIA CUTANEA TARDIA, HYPERTRICHOSIS, HYPERPIGMENTATION, INCREASED SKIN FRAGILITY, LIVER DISORDERS, PERSONALITY CHANGES, AND PERIPHERAL NEUROPATHY. MANY OF THESE EFFECTS MAY BE DUE TO DIOXINS, ESPECIALLY TCDD, AS CONTAMINANTS. EPIDEMIOLOGICAL STUDIES HAVE INDICATED AN ASSOCIATION BETWEEN EXPOSURE TO 2,4,5-T COMPOUNDS AND AN INCREASED PREVALENCE OF REPORTED SEXUAL DYSFUNCTION AND DECREASED LIBIDO, ABNORMAL SENSORY FINDINGS, GASTROINTESTINAL TRACT ULCER, AND BIRTH MALFORMATIONS OF THE FEET. AN INCREASED PREVALENCE OF SLOWED NERVE CONDUCTION VELOCITY WITH NO ASSOCIATED SYMPTOMS WAS REPORTED IN A STUDY OF CHEMICAL WORKERS EMPLOYED IN THE PRODUCTION OF 2,4-D AND 2,4,5-T. EPIDEMIOLOGICAL STUDIES REVEALED A SIGNIFICANT INCREASE IN SOFT-TISSUE SARCOMAS, MALIGNANT LYMPHOMAS, AND BRONCHIAL CARCINOMAS IN WORKERS EXPOSED TO CHLOROPHENOXY HERBICIDES INCLUDING 2,4,5-T.

FIRST AID- REMOVE FROM EXPOSURE AREA TO FRESH AIR IMMEDIATELY. IF BREATHING HAS STOPPED, PERFORM ARTIFICIAL RESPIRATION. KEEP PERSON WARM AND AT REST. TREAT SYMPTOMATICALLY AND SUPPORTIVELY. GET MEDICAL ATTENTION IMMEDIATELY.

SKIN CONTACT: 4-(2,4,5-TRICHLOROPHENOXY) BUTYRIC ACID: SEE INFORMATION ON 2,4,5-T AND DERIVATIVES.

2,4,5-T AND DERIVATIVES: **ACUTE EXPOSURE-** MAY CAUSE IRRITATION. IF SUFFICIENT AMOUNTS ARE ABSORBED THROUGH THE SKIN, EFFECTS AS DESCRIBED IN ACUTE INGESTION MAY OCCUR. **CHRONIC EXPOSURE-** PROLONGED OR REPEATED EXPOSURE MAY CAUSE DERMATITIS AND EFFECTS AS DESCRIBED IN CHRONIC INHALATION.

FIRST AID- REMOVE CONTAMINATED CLOTHING AND SHOES IMMEDIATELY. WASH AFFECTED AREA WITH SOAP OR MILD DETERGENT AND LARGE AMOUNTS OF WATER UNTIL NO EVIDENCE OF CHEMICAL REMAINS (APPROXIMATELY 15-20 MINUTES). GET MEDICAL ATTENTION IMMEDIATELY.

EYE CONTACT: 4-(2,4,5-TRICHLOROPHENOXY) BUTYRIC ACID: SEE INFORMATION ON 2,4,5-T AND DERIVATIVES.

2,4,5-T AND DERIVATIVES: **ACUTE EXPOSURE-** MAY CAUSE IRRITATION. **CHRONIC EXPOSURE-** NO DATA AVAILABLE.

FIRST AID- WASH EYES IMMEDIATELY WITH LARGE AMOUNTS OF WATER OR NORMAL SALINE, OCCASIONALLY LIFTING UPPER AND LOWER LIDS, UNTIL NO EVIDENCE OF CHEMICAL REMAINS (APPROXIMATELY 15-20 MINUTES). GET MEDICAL ATTENTION IMMEDIATELY.

INGESTION: 4-(2,4,5-TRICHLOROPHENOXY) BUTYRIC ACID: REPRODUCTIVE EFFECTS HAVE BEEN REPORTED IN ANIMALS. SEE INFORMATION ON 2,4,5-T AND DERIVATIVES.

2,4,5-T AND DERIVATIVES: **ACUTE EXPOSURE-** MAY CAUSE IRRITATION OF THE MOUTH, THROAT, AND GASTROINTESTINAL TRACT, NAUSEA, VOMITING, CHEST AND ABDOMINAL PAIN, AND DIARRHEA. INGESTION OF VERY LARGE DOSES MAY PRODUCE METABOLIC ACIDOSIS, FEVER OR SUBNORMAL TEMPERATURES, HYPERVENTILATION, HYPOTENSION, VASODILATION, FLUSHING OF THE SKIN, SWEATING, CARDIAC ARRHYTHMIAS, TACHYCARDIA, LETHARGY, WEAKNESS, INTERCOSTAL PARALYSIS, RENAL AND HEPATIC DYSFUNCTION, MYOTONIA, COMA, AND CONVULSIONS. DAMAGE TO SKELETAL MUSCLE MAY BE MANIFEST BY MUSCLE TWITCHING AND ACHING WITH ELEVATED SERUM ENZYMES AND MYOGLOBIN IN THE BLOOD AND URINE. DEATH MAY BE DUE TO CIRCULATORY COLLAPSE. **CHRONIC EXPOSURE-** NO DATA AVAILABLE.

FIRST AID- IF THE PERSON IS CONSCIOUS AND NOT CONVULSING, INDUCE EMESIS BY GIVING SYRUP OF IPECAC (KEEPING THE HEAD BELOW THE HIPS TO PREVENT ASPIRATION) FOLLOWED BY WATER. REPEAT IN 20 MINUTES IF NOT EFFECTIVE INITIALLY. IN PATIENTS WITH DEPRESSED RESPIRATION OR IF EMESIS IS NOT PRODUCED, PERFORM GASTRIC LAVAGE WITH ACTIVATED CHARCOAL. FOLLOW WITH A SALINE CATHARTIC (DREISBACH, HANDBOOK OF POISONING, 12TH ED.). TREAT SYMPTOMATICALLY AND SUPPORTIVELY. GASTRIC LAVAGE SHOULD BE PERFORMED BY QUALIFIED MEDICAL PERSONNEL. GET MEDICAL ATTENTION IMMEDIATELY.

ANTIDOTE: NO SPECIFIC ANTIDOTE. TREAT SYMPTOMATICALLY AND SUPPORTIVELY.

REACTIVITY

REACTIVITY: STABLE UNDER NORMAL TEMPERATURES AND PRESSURES.

INCOMPATIBILITIES: 4-(2,4,5-TRICHLOROPHENOXY) BUTYRIC ACID: OXIDIZERS (STRONG): FIRE AND EXPLOSION HAZARD.

DECOMPOSITION: THERMAL DECOMPOSITION PRODUCTS MAY INCLUDE TOXIC AND CORROSIVE FUMES OF CHLORIDES AND TOXIC OXIDES OF CARBON.

POLYMERIZATION: HAZARDOUS POLYMERIZATION HAS NOT BEEN REPORTED TO OCCUR UNDER NORMAL TEMPERATURES AND PRESSURES.

STORAGE AND DISPOSAL

OBSERVE ALL FEDERAL, STATE AND LOCAL REGULATIONS WHEN STORING OR DISPOSING OF THIS SUBSTANCE. FOR ASSISTANCE, CONTACT THE DISTRICT DIRECTOR OF THE ENVIRONMENTAL PROTECTION AGENCY.

STORAGE

STORE IN ACCORDANCE WITH 40 CFR 165 RECOMMENDED PROCEDURES FOR THE DISPOSAL AND STORAGE OF PESTICIDES AND PESTICIDE CONTAINERS.
STORE AWAY FROM INCOMPATIBLE SUBSTANCES.

DISPOSAL

DISPOSAL MUST BE IN ACCORDANCE WITH 40 CFR 165 RECOMMENDED PROCEDURES FOR THE DISPOSAL AND STORAGE OF PESTICIDES AND PESTICIDE CONTAINERS.

CONDITIONS TO AVOID

MAY BURN BUT DOES NOT IGNITE READILY. AVOID CONTACT WITH STRONG OXIDIZERS, EXCESSIVE HEAT, SPARKS, OR OPEN FLAME.

SPILL AND LEAK PROCEDURES

OCCUPATIONAL SPILL: SWEEP UP AND PLACE IN SUITABLE CLEAN, DRY CONTAINERS FOR RECLAMATION OR LATER DISPOSAL. DO NOT FLUSH SPILLED MATERIAL INTO SEWER. KEEP UNNECESSARY PEOPLE AWAY.

PROTECTIVE EQUIPMENT

VENTILATION: PROVIDE LOCAL EXHAUST OR PROCESS ENCLOSURE VENTILATION SYSTEM.

RESPIRATOR: THE FOLLOWING RESPIRATORS ARE RECOMMENDED BASED ON INFORMATION FOUND IN THE PHYSICAL DATA, TOXICITY AND HEALTH EFFECTS SECTIONS. THEY ARE RANKED IN ORDER FROM MINIMUM TO MAXIMUM RESPIRATORY PROTECTION. THE SPECIFIC RESPIRATOR SELECTED MUST BE BASED ON CONTAMINATION LEVELS FOUND IN THE WORK PLACE, MUST NOT EXCEED THE WORKING LIMITS OF THE RESPIRATOR AND BE JOINTLY APPROVED BY THE NATIONAL INSTITUTE FOR OCCUPATIONAL SAFETY AND HEALTH AND THE MINE SAFETY AND HEALTH ADMINISTRATION (NIOSH-MSHA).

CHEMICAL CARTRIDGE RESPIRATOR WITH AN ORGANIC VAPOR CARTRIDGE(S) WITH A FULL FACEPIECE AND ORGANIC VAPOR CARTRIDGE(S) IN COMBINATION WITH A DUST AND MIST FILTER.

POWERED AIR-PURIFYING RESPIRATOR WITH A TIGHT-FITTING FACEPIECE AND ORGANIC VAPOR CARTRIDGE(S) IN COMBINATION WITH A HIGH-EFFICIENCY PARTICULATE FILTER.

TYPE 'C' SUPPLIED-AIR RESPIRATOR WITH A FULL FACEPIECE OPERATED IN A PRESSURE-DEMAND OR OTHER POSITIVE PRESSURE MODE.

SELF-CONTAINED BREATHING APPARATUS WITH A FULL FACEPIECE OPERATED IN PRESSURE-DEMAND OR OTHER POSITIVE PRESSURE MODE.

FOR FIREFIGHTING AND OTHER IMMEDIATELY DANGEROUS TO LIFE OR HEALTH CONDITIONS:

SELF-CONTAINED BREATHING APPARATUS WITH FULL FACEPIECE OPERATED IN PRESSURE-DEMAND OR OTHER POSITIVE PRESSURE MODE.

SUPPLIED-AIR RESPIRATOR WITH FULL FACEPIECE AND OPERATED IN PRESSURE-DEMAND OR OTHER POSITIVE PRESSURE MODE IN COMBINATION WITH AN AUXILIARY SELF-CONTAINED BREATHING APPARATUS OPERATED IN PRESSURE-DEMAND OR OTHER POSITIVE PRESSURE MODE.

CLOTHING: EMPLOYEE MUST WEAR APPROPRIATE PROTECTIVE (IMPERVIOUS) CLOTHING AND EQUIPMENT TO PREVENT REPEATED OR PROLONGED SKIN CONTACT WITH THIS SUBSTANCE.

GLOVES: EMPLOYEE MUST WEAR APPROPRIATE PROTECTIVE GLOVES TO PREVENT CONTACT WITH THIS SUBSTANCE.

EYE PROTECTION: EMPLOYEE MUST WEAR SPLASH-PROOF OR DUST-RESISTANT SAFETY GOGGLES TO PREVENT EYE CONTACT WITH THIS SUBSTANCE.

EMERGENCY EYE WASH: WHERE THERE IS ANY POSSIBILITY THAT AN EMPLOYEE'S EYES MAY BE EXPOSED TO THIS SUBSTANCE, THE EMPLOYER SHOULD PROVIDE AN EYE WASH FOUNTAIN WITHIN THE IMMEDIATE WORK AREA FOR EMERGENCY USE.

AUTHORIZED BY- OCCUPATIONAL HEALTH SERVICES, INC.
CREATION DATE: 03/23/90 ***REVISION DATE:*** 07/12/90

MATERIAL SAFETY DATA SHEET

OCCUPATIONAL HEALTH SERVICES, INC.
AGRICULTURE AND PESTICIDE DIVISION
450 SEVENTH AVENUE, SUITE 2407
NEW YORK, NEW YORK 10123
1-800-445-MSDS OR (212) 967-1100

EMERGENCY CONTACT:
JOHN S. BRANSFORD, JR. (615) 292-1180

SUBSTANCE IDENTIFICATION

CAS-NUMBER 2631-40-5
SUBSTANCE: **ISOPROCARB**
TRADE NAMES/SYNONYMS: PHENOL, 2-(1-METHYLETHYL)-, METHYLCARBAMATE; CARBAMIC ACID, METHYL-, O-CUMENYL ESTER; 2-(1-METHYLETHYL)PHENOL METHYLCARBAMATE; METHYLCARBAMIC ACID O-CUMENYL ESTER; O-CUMENYL METHYLCARBAMATE; O-ISOPROPYLPHENOL METHYLCARBAMATE; O-ISOPROPYLPHENYL METHYLCARBAMATE; 2-ISOPROPYLPHENYL METHYLCARBAMATE; 2-(1-METHYLETHYL)PHENYL METHYLCARBAMATE; ETROFOLAN; MIPC; MIPCIN; OMS 32; ENT 25670; C11H15NO2; PST73231
CHEMICAL FAMILY: CARBAMATE
MOLECULAR FORMULA: C11-H15-N-O2
MOLECULAR WEIGHT: 193.27
CERCLA RATINGS (SCALE 0-3): HEALTH=3 FIRE=1 REACTIVITY=0 PERSISTENCE=1
NFPA RATINGS (SCALE 0-4): HEALTH=3 FIRE=1 REACTIVITY=0

COMPONENTS AND CONTAMINANTS

COMPONENT: ISOPROCARB ***PERCENT:*** 100.0
CAS# 2631-40-5
OTHER CONTAMINANTS: NONE
EXPOSURE LIMITS: NO OCCUPATIONAL EXPOSURE LIMITS ESTABLISHED BY OSHA, ACGIH, OR NIOSH.

PHYSICAL DATA

DESCRIPTION: COLORLESS OR WHITE CRYSTALLINE SOLID.
MELTING POINT: 190-199 F (88-93 C) ***SPECIFIC GRAVITY:*** NOT AVAILABLE
SOLUBILITY IN WATER: INSOLUBLE
SOLVENT SOLUBILITY: SOLUBLE IN ACETONE AND METHANOL.

FIRE AND EXPLOSION DATA

FIRE AND EXPLOSION HAZARD: SLIGHT FIRE HAZARD WHEN EXPOSED TO HEAT OR FLAME.
FIREFIGHTING MEDIA: DRY CHEMICAL, CARBON DIOXIDE, HALON, WATER SPRAY OR STANDARD FOAM (1987 EMERGENCY RESPONSE GUIDEBOOK, DOT P 5800.4). FOR LARGER FIRES, USE WATER SPRAY, FOG OR STANDARD FOAM (1987 EMERGENCY RESPONSE GUIDEBOOK, DOT P 5800.4).
FIREFIGHTING: MOVE CONTAINERS FROM FIRE AREA IF POSSIBLE. FIGHT FIRE FROM MAXIMUM DISTANCE. STAY AWAY FROM STORAGE TANK ENDS. DIKE FIRE CONTROL WATER FOR LATER DISPOSAL. DO NOT SCATTER MATERIAL (1987 EMERGENCY RESPONSE GUIDEBOOK, DOT P 5800.4, GUIDE PAGE 55). EXTINGUISH USING AGENTS SUITABLE FOR TYPE OF SURROUNDING FIRE. USE FLOODING AMOUNTS OF WATER AS FOG. AVOID BREATHING TOXIC DUST AND FUMES FROM BURNING MATERIAL; KEEP UPWIND.

TOXICITY

ISOPROCARB: TOXICITY DATA: 1620 MG/KG SKIN-MOUSE LD50; 178 MG/KG ORAL-RAT LD50; 94 MG/KG ORAL-MOUSE LD50; 500 MG/KG ORAL-RABBIT LD50; 500 MG/KG ORAL-GUINEA PIG LD50; 142 MG/KG INTRAPERITONEAL-RAT LD50; 66 MG/KG INTRAVENOUS-RAT LD50. CARCINOGEN STATUS: NONE. ACUTE TOXICITY: TOXIC BY INGESTION; MODERATELY TOXIC BY DERMAL ABSORPTION. TARGET EFFECTS: CHOLINESTERASE INHIBITOR. AT INCREASED RISK FROM EXPOSURE: PERSONS WITH ASTHMA, DIABETES, CARDIOVASCULAR DISEASE, MECHANICAL OBSTRUCTION OF THE GASTROINTESTINAL OR UROGENITAL TRACT, AND THOSE IN VAGOTONIC STATES.*
* MAY BE BASED ON GENERAL INFORMATION ON CARBAMATES.

HEALTH EFFECTS AND FIRST AID

INHALATION: ISOPROCARB: SEE INFORMATION ON CARBAMATES.
CARBAMATES: CHOLINESTERASE INHIBITOR. **ACUTE EXPOSURE-** WHEN INHALED, THE FIRST EFFECTS OF CHOLINESTERASE INHIBITION ARE USUALLY RESPIRATORY AND MAY INCLUDE NASAL HYPEREMIA AND WATERY DISCHARGE, CHEST DISCOMFORT, DYSPNEA, AND WHEEZING DUE TO INCREASED BRONCHIAL SECRETIONS AND BRONCHOCONSTRICTION. OTHER SYSTEMIC EFFECTS MAY BEGIN WITHIN A FEW MINUTES OR SEVERAL HOURS OF EXPOSURE. SYMPTOMS MAY INCLUDE NAUSEA, VOMITING, DIARRHEA, ABDOMINAL CRAMPS, HEADACHE, VERTIGO, OCULAR PAIN, CILIARY MUSCLE SPASM, BLURRING OR DIMNESS OF VISION, MIOSIS, OR IN SOME CASES MYDRIASIS, LACRIMATION, SALIVATION, SWEATING, AND CONFUSION. OTHER REPORTED CENTRAL NERVOUS SYSTEM OR NEUROMUSCULAR EFFECTS INCLUDE ATAXIA, SLURRED SPEECH, AREFLEXIA, WEAKNESS, FATIGUE, TWITCHING, FASCICULATION, TREMOR, AND EVENTUALLY PARALYSIS OF THE EXTREMITIES AND POSSIBLY OF THE RESPIRATORY MUSCLES. IN SEVERE CASES, THERE MAY ALSO BE INVOLUNTARY DEFECATION AND URINATION, BRADYCARDIA, HYPOTENSION, PULMONARY EDEMA, CONVULSIONS, COMA, AND DEATH FROM RESPIRATORY FAILURE OR CARDIAC ARREST. CARBAMATES GENERALLY DO NOT ACCUMULATE IN MAMMALIAN TISSUE AND THE CHOLINESTERASE INHIBITION REVERSES RATHER RAPIDLY. IN NON-FATAL CASES, THE ILLNESS GENERALLY LASTS LESS THAN 24 HOURS. **CHRONIC EXPOSURE-** PROLONGED OR REPEATED EXPOSURE MAY CAUSE EFFECTS AS DESCRIBED IN ACUTE EXPOSURE.
FIRST AID- REMOVE FROM EXPOSURE AREA TO FRESH AIR IMMEDIATELY. IF BREATHING HAS STOPPED, GIVE ARTIFICIAL RESPIRATION. MAINTAIN AIRWAY AND BLOOD PRESSURE AND ADMINISTER OXYGEN IF AVAILABLE. KEEP AFFECTED PERSON WARM AND AT REST. TREAT SYMPTOMATICALLY AND SUPPORTIVELY. ADMINISTRATION OF OXYGEN SHOULD BE PERFORMED BY QUALIFIED PERSONNEL. GET MEDICAL ATTENTION IMMEDIATELY.

SKIN CONTACT: ISOPROCARB: SEE INFORMATION ON CARBAMATES.
CARBAMATES: CHOLINESTERASE INHIBITOR. **ACUTE EXPOSURE-** SOME COMPOUNDS MAY CAUSE IRRITATION. LOCALIZED SWEATING AND FASCICULATIONS MAY OCCUR AT THE SITE OF CONTACT. IF SUFFICIENT AMOUNTS ARE ABSORBED THROUGH THE SKIN, OTHER EFFECTS OF CHOLINESTERASE INHIBITION MAY OCCUR AS DESCRIBED IN ACUTE INHALATION; SYMPTOMS MAY BE DELAYED FOR 2-3 HOURS, USUALLY NO MORE THAN 8 HOURS. **CHRONIC EXPOSURE-** REPEATED OR PROLONGED EXPOSURE MAY CAUSE EFFECTS AS DESCRIBED IN ACUTE EXPOSURE.
FIRST AID- REMOVE CONTAMINATED CLOTHING IMMEDIATELY. WASH CONTAMINATED AREAS WITH SOAP AND WATER FOLLOWED BY ALCOHOL (ARENA, POISONING, 4TH ED.). EMERGENCY PERSONNEL SHOULD WEAR GLOVES AND AVOID CONTAMINATION. TREAT RESPIRATORY DIFFICULTY WITH ARTIFICIAL RESPIRATION. GET MEDICAL ATTENTION IMMEDIATELY.

EYE CONTACT: ISOPROCARB: SEE INFORMATION ON CARBAMATES.
CARBAMATES: CHOLINESTERASE INHIBITOR. **ACUTE EXPOSURE-** DIRECT CONTACT MAY CAUSE PAIN, HYPEREMIA, LACRIMATION, TWITCHING OF THE EYELIDS, MIOSIS, AND CILIARY MUSCLE SPASM WITH LOSS OF ACCOMODATION, BLURRED OR DIMMED VISION AND BROWACHE. SOMETIMES MYDRIASIS MAY OCCUR INSTEAD OF MIOSIS. WITH SUFFICIENT EXPOSURE, OTHER SYMPTOMS OF CHOLINESTERASE INHIBITION MAY OCCUR AS DESCRIBED IN ACUTE INHALATION. **CHRONIC EXPOSURE-** PROLONGED EXPOSURE MAY CAUSE EFFECTS AS DESCRIBED IN ACUTE EXPOSURE. SOME COMPOUNDS HAVE CAUSED TOXIC EFFECTS ON THE CRYSTALLINE LENS, CONJUNCTIVAL THICKENING AND OBSTRUCTION OF NASOLACRIMAL CANALS WHEN USED AS MIOTIC EYE DROPS.
FIRST AID- IRRIGATE EYES WITH WATER OR SALINE SOLUTION. IF SYMPTOMS OF POISONING OCCUR, TREAT RESPIRATORY DIFFICULTY WITH ARTIFICIAL RESPIRATION AND OXYGEN. OBSERVE PATIENT FOR AT LEAST 24-36 HOURS (GOSSELIN, CLINICAL TOXICOLOGY OF COMMERCIAL PRODUCTS, 5TH ED.). GET MEDICAL ATTENTION IMMEDIATELY. OXYGEN SHOULD BE ADMINISTERED BY QUALIFIED MEDICAL PERSONNEL.

INGESTION: ISOPROCARB: TOXIC. SEE INFORMATION ON CARBAMATES.
CARBAMATES: CHOLINESTERASE INHIBITOR. **ACUTE EXPOSURE-** WHEN INGESTED, THE FIRST EFFECTS MAY BE NAUSEA, VOMITING, ANOREXIA, ABDOMINAL CRAMPS, AND DIARRHEA. WITH ABSORPTION FROM THE GASTROINTESTINAL TRACT, THE OTHER EFFECTS OF CHOLINESTERASE INHIBITION AS DESCRIBED IN ACUTE INHALATION MAY OCCUR; SYMPTOMS MAY BEGIN WITHIN MINUTES OR BE DELAYED SEVERAL HOURS. **CHRONIC EXPOSURE-** REPEATED INGESTION MAY CAUSE EFFECTS AS DESCRIBED IN ACUTE EXPOSURE.
FIRST AID- IF PERSON IS ALERT AND RESPIRATION IS NOT DEPRESSED, GIVE SYRUP OF IPECAC FOLLOWED BY WATER (IF VOMITING OCCURS, KEEP HEAD BELOW HIPS TO PREVENT ASPIRATION). IF CONSCIOUSNESS LEVEL DECLINES OR VOMITING HAS NOT OCCURRED IN 15 MINUTES EMPTY STOMACH BY GASTRIC LAVAGE WITH THE AID OF CUFFED ENDOTRACHEAL TUBE USING ISOTONIC SALINE OR 5% SODIUM BICARBONATE FOLLOW WITH ACTIVATED CHARCOAL. ESTABLISH AND MAINTAIN AIRWAY. TREAT RESPIRATORY DIFFICULTY WITH ARTIFICIAL RESPIRATION AND OXYGEN. DO NOT GIVE MORPHINE, AMINOPHYLLINE, PHENOTHIAZINES, RESERPINE, FUROSEMIDE, OR ETHACRYNIC ACID (MORGAN, RECOGNITION AND MANAGEMENT OF PESTICIDE POISONINGS, 3RD ED.). TREAT SYMPTOMATICALLY AND SUPPORTIVELY. ADMINISTRATION OF OXYGEN AND LAVAGE MUST BE PERFORMED BY QUALIFIED MEDICAL PERSONNEL. GET MEDICAL ATTENTION IMMEDIATELY.
ANTIDOTE: THE FOLLOWING ANTIDOTE HAS BEEN RECOMMENDED. HOWEVER, THE DECISION AS TO WHETHER THE SEVERITY OF POISONING REQUIRES ADMINISTRATION OF ANY ANTIDOTE AND ACTUAL DOSE REQUIRED SHOULD BE MADE BY QUALIFIED MEDICAL PERSONNEL.
FOR CHOLINESTERASE INHIBITORS: ESTABLISH CLEAR AIRWAY AND TISSUE OXYGENATION BY ASPIRATION OF SECRETIONS, AND IF NECESSARY, BY ASSISTED

PULMONARY VENTILATION WITH OXYGEN. IMPROVE TISSUE OXYGENATION AS MUCH AS POSSIBLE BEFORE ADMINISTERING ATROPINE TO MINIMIZE THE RISK OF VENTRICULAR FIBRILLATION. ADMINISTER ATROPINE SULFATE INTRAVENOUSLY, OR INTRAMUSCULARLY IF IV INJECTION IS NOT POSSIBLE. IN MODERATELY SEVERE POISONING ADMINISTER ATROPINE SULFATE, 0.4-2.0 MG REPEATED EVERY 15 MINUTES UNTIL ATROPINIZATION IS ACHIEVED (TACHYCARDIA, FLUSHING, DRY MOUTH, MYDRIASIS). MAINTAIN ATROPINIZATION BY REPEATED DOSES FOR 2-12 HOURS, OR LONGER, DEPENDING ON THE SEVERITY OF POISONING. THE APPEARANCE OF RALES IN THE LUNG BASES, MIOSIS, SALIVATION, NAUSEA, BRADYCARDIA, ARE ALL INDICATIONS OF INADEQUATE ATROPINIZATION. SEVERELY POISONED INDIVIDUALS MAY EXHIBIT REMARKABLE TOLERANCE TO ATROPINE; TWO OR MORE TIMES THE DOSAGES SUGGESTED ABOVE MAY BE NEEDED. PERSONS NOT POISONED OR ONLY SLIGHTLY POISONED, HOWEVER, MAY DEVELOP SIGNS OF ATROPINE TOXICITY FROM SUCH LARGE DOSAGES: FEVER, MUSCLE FIBRILLATIONS, AND DELIRIUM ARE THE MAIN SIGNS OF ATROPINE TOXICITY. IF THESE SIGNS APPEAR WHILE THE PATIENT IS FULLY ATROPINIZED, ATROPINE ADMINISTRATION SHOULD BE DISCONTINUED, AT LEAST TEMPORARILY. OBSERVE TREATED PATIENTS CLOSELY AT LEAST 24 HOURS TO INSURE THAT SYMPTOMS (POSSIBLY PULMONARY EDEMA) DO NOT RECUR AS ATROPINIZATION WEARS OFF. IN VERY SEVERE POISONINGS, METABOLIC DISPOSITION OF TOXICANT MAY REQUIRE SEVERAL HOURS OR DAYS DURING WHICH ATROPINIZATION MUST BE MAINTAINED. MARKEDLY LOWER LEVELS OF URINARY METABOLITES INDICATE THAT ATROPINE DOSAGE CAN BE TAPERED OFF. AS DOSAGE IS REDUCED, CHECK THE LUNG BASES FREQUENTLY FOR RALES. IF RALES ARE HEARD OR OTHER SYMPTOMS RETURN, RE-ESTABLISH ATROPINIZATION PROMPTLY (MORGAN, RECOGNITION AND MANAGEMENT OF PESTICIDE POISONINGS, 3RD ED.). ADMINISTRATION OF ANTIDOTE MUST BE PERFORMED BY QUALIFIED MEDICAL PERSONNEL.

REACTIVITY

REACTIVITY: STABLE UNDER NORMAL TEMPERATURES AND PRESSURES.

INCOMPATIBILITIES: ISOPROCARB: ALKALINE MEDIUM: UNSTABLE. OXIDIZERS (STRONG): FIRE AND EXPLOSION HAZARD.

DECOMPOSITION: THERMAL DECOMPOSITION PRODUCTS MAY INCLUDE TOXIC OXIDES OF CARBON AND NITROGEN.

POLYMERIZATION: HAZARDOUS POLYMERIZATION HAS NOT BEEN REPORTED TO OCCUR UNDER NORMAL TEMPERATURES AND PRESSURES.

STORAGE AND DISPOSAL

OBSERVE ALL FEDERAL, STATE AND LOCAL REGULATIONS WHEN STORING OR DISPOSING OF THIS SUBSTANCE. FOR ASSISTANCE, CONTACT THE DISTRICT DIRECTOR OF THE ENVIRONMENTAL PROTECTION AGENCY.

****STORAGE****

STORE IN ACCORDANCE WITH 40 CFR 165 RECOMMENDED PROCEDURES FOR THE DISPOSAL AND STORAGE OF PESTICIDES AND PESTICIDE CONTAINERS.
STORE AWAY FROM INCOMPATIBLE SUBSTANCES.
KEEP COOL AND DRY.

****DISPOSAL****

DISPOSAL MUST BE IN ACCORDANCE WITH 40 CFR 165 RECOMMENDED PROCEDURES FOR THE DISPOSAL AND STORAGE OF PESTICIDES AND PESTICIDE CONTAINERS.

CONDITIONS TO AVOID

MAY BURN BUT DOES NOT IGNITE READILY. CONTAINERS MAY EXPLODE IN HEAT OF FIRE.

SPILL AND LEAK PROCEDURES

OCCUPATIONAL SPILL: DO NOT TOUCH SPILLED MATERIAL. STOP LEAK IF YOU CAN DO IT WITHOUT RISK. USE WATER SPRAY TO REDUCE VAPORS. FOR SMALL SPILLS, TAKE UP WITH SAND OR OTHER ABSORBENT MATERIAL AND PLACE INTO CONTAINERS FOR LATER DISPOSAL. FOR SMALL DRY SPILLS, WITH A CLEAN SHOVEL PLACE MATERIAL INTO CLEAN, DRY CONTAINERS AND COVER. MOVE CONTAINERS FROM SPILL AREA. FOR LARGER SPILLS, DIKE FAR AHEAD OF SPILL FOR LATER DISPOSAL. KEEP UNNECESSARY PEOPLE AWAY. ISOLATE HAZARD AREA AND DENY ENTRY. VENTILATE CLOSED SPACES BEFORE ENTERING.

PROTECTIVE EQUIPMENT

VENTILATION: PROVIDE LOCAL EXHAUST OR GENERAL DILUTION VENTILATION SYSTEM.

RESPIRATOR: THE FOLLOWING RESPIRATORS ARE RECOMMENDED BASED ON INFORMATION FOUND IN THE PHYSICAL DATA, TOXICITY AND HEALTH EFFECTS SECTIONS. THEY ARE RANKED IN ORDER FROM MINIMUM TO MAXIMUM RESPIRATORY PROTECTION. THE SPECIFIC RESPIRATOR SELECTED MUST BE BASED ON CONTAMINATION LEVELS FOUND IN THE WORK PLACE, MUST NOT EXCEED THE WORKING LIMITS OF THE RESPIRATOR AND BE JOINTLY APPROVED BY THE NATIONAL INSTITUTE FOR OCCUPATIONAL SAFETY AND HEALTH AND THE MINE SAFETY AND HEALTH ADMINISTRATION (NIOSH-MSHA).
CHEMICAL CARTRIDGE RESPIRATOR WITH AN ORGANIC VAPOR CARTRIDGE(S) IN COMBINATION WITH A DUST AND MIST FILTER.
GAS MASK WITH ORGANIC VAPOR CANISTER (CHIN-STYLE OR FRONT- OR BACK-MOUNTED CANISTER) WITH A DUST AND MIST FILTER.
GAS MASK WITH ORGANIC VAPOR CANISTER (CHIN-STYLE OR FRONT- OR BACK-MOUNTED CANISTER) WITH A PARTICULATE FILTER.
POWERED AIR-PURIFYING RESPIRATOR WITH A HIGH-EFFICIENCY FILTER.
TYPE 'C' SUPPLIED-AIR RESPIRATOR WITH A FULL FACEPIECE OPERATED IN A PRESSURE-DEMAND OR OTHER POSITIVE PRESSURE MODE.
SELF-CONTAINED BREATHING APPARATUS WITH A FULL FACEPIECE OPERATED IN PRESSURE-DEMAND OR OTHER POSITIVE PRESSURE MODE.
FOR FIREFIGHTING AND OTHER IMMEDIATELY DANGEROUS TO LIFE OR HEALTH CONDITIONS:
SELF-CONTAINED BREATHING APPARATUS WITH FULL FACEPIECE OPERATED IN PRESSURE-DEMAND OR OTHER POSITIVE PRESSURE MODE.
SUPPLIED-AIR RESPIRATOR WITH FULL FACEPIECE AND OPERATED IN PRESSURE-DEMAND OR OTHER POSITIVE PRESSURE MODE IN COMBINATION WITH AN AUXILIARY SELF-CONTAINED BREATHING APPARATUS OPERATED IN PRESSURE-DEMAND OR OTHER POSITIVE PRESSURE MODE.

CLOTHING: EMPLOYEE MUST WEAR APPROPRIATE PROTECTIVE (IMPERVIOUS) CLOTHING AND EQUIPMENT TO PREVENT REPEATED OR PROLONGED SKIN CONTACT WITH THIS SUBSTANCE.

GLOVES: EMPLOYEE MUST WEAR APPROPRIATE PROTECTIVE GLOVES TO PREVENT CONTACT WITH THIS SUBSTANCE.

EYE PROTECTION: EMPLOYEE MUST WEAR SPLASH-PROOF OR DUST-RESISTANT SAFETY GOGGLES TO PREVENT EYE CONTACT WITH THIS SUBSTANCE.
EMERGENCY EYE WASH: WHERE THERE IS ANY POSSIBILITY THAT AN EMPLOYEE'S EYES MAY BE EXPOSED TO THIS SUBSTANCE, THE EMPLOYER SHOULD PROVIDE AN EYE WASH FOUNTAIN WITHIN THE IMMEDIATE WORK AREA FOR EMERGENCY USE.

AUTHORIZED BY- OCCUPATIONAL HEALTH SERVICES, INC.
CREATION DATE: 10/04/89 ***REVISION DATE:*** 06/12/90

MATERIAL SAFETY DATA SHEET

OCCUPATIONAL HEALTH SERVICES, INC.
AGRICULTURE AND PESTICIDE DIVISION
450 SEVENTH AVENUE, SUITE 2407
NEW YORK, NEW YORK 10123
1-800-445-MSDS OR (212) 967-1100

EMERGENCY CONTACT:
JOHN S. BRANSFORD, JR. (615) 292-1180

SUBSTANCE IDENTIFICATION

CAS-NUMBER 2164-08-1

SUBSTANCE: **LENACIL**

TRADE NAMES/SYNONYMS: 1H-CYCLOPENTAPYRIMIDINE-2,4(3H,5H)-DIONE, 3-CYCLOHEXYL-6,7-DIHYDRO-; 3-CYCLOHEXYL-6,7-DIHYDRO-1H-CYCLOPENTAPYRIMIDINE-2,4(3H,5H)-DIONE; 3-CYCLOHEXYL-1,5,6,7-TETRAHYDRO-2H-CYCLOPENTAPYRIMIDINE-2,4(3H)-DIONE; 3-CYCLOHEXYL-1,5,6,7-TETRAHYDROCYCLOPENTAPYRIMIDINE-2,4(3H)-DIONE; 3-CYCLOHEXYL-5,6-TRIMETHYLENEURACIL; BAN-HOE; DU PONT 634; VENZAR; C13H18N2O2; PST73238

CHEMICAL FAMILY: HETEROCYCLIC NITROGEN

MOLECULAR FORMULA: C13-H18-N2-O2

MOLECULAR WEIGHT: 234.30

CERCLA RATINGS (SCALE 0-3): HEALTH=1 FIRE=1 REACTIVITY=0 PERSISTENCE=0

NFPA RATINGS (SCALE 0-4): HEALTH=1 FIRE=1 REACTIVITY=0

COMPONENTS AND CONTAMINANTS

COMPONENT: LENACIL ***PERCENT:*** 100.0
CAS# 2164-08-1

OTHER CONTAMINANTS: NONE

EXPOSURE LIMITS: NO OCCUPATIONAL EXPOSURE LIMITS ESTABLISHED BY OSHA, ACGIH, OR NIOSH.

PHYSICAL DATA

DESCRIPTION: ODORLESS, COLORLESS TO WHITE CRYSTALLINE SOLID.

MELTING POINT: 601-603 F (316-317 C) ***SPECIFIC GRAVITY:*** 1.32

SOLUBILITY IN WATER: 0.0006% @ 25 C

SOLVENT SOLUBILITY: SOLUBLE IN PYRIDINE; SLIGHTLY SOLUBLE IN DIMETHYLFORMAMIDE, DIMETHYLSULFOXIDE, CYCLOHEXANONE AND XYLENE.

FIRE AND EXPLOSION DATA

FIRE AND EXPLOSION HAZARD: SLIGHT FIRE HAZARD WHEN EXPOSED TO HEAT OR FLAME.

FIREFIGHTING MEDIA: DRY CHEMICAL, CARBON DIOXIDE, HALON, WATER SPRAY OR STANDARD FOAM (1987 EMERGENCY RESPONSE GUIDEBOOK, DOT P 5800.4). FOR LARGER FIRES, USE WATER SPRAY, FOG OR STANDARD FOAM (1987 EMERGENCY RESPONSE GUIDEBOOK, DOT P 5800.4).

FIREFIGHTING: MOVE CONTAINER FROM FIRE AREA IF POSSIBLE. DO NOT SCATTER SPILLED MATERIAL WITH HIGH PRESSURE WATER STREAMS. DIKE FIRE CONTROL WATER FOR LATER DISPOSAL (1987 EMERGENCY RESPONSE GUIDEBOOK, DOT P 5800.4, GUIDE PAGE 31).
USE AGENTS SUITABLE FOR TYPE OF SURROUNDING FIRE. AVOID BREATHING HAZARDOUS VAPORS, KEEP UPWIND.

TOXICITY

LENACIL: TOXICITY DATA: 11000 MG/KG ORAL-RAT LD50. CARCINOGEN STATUS: NONE. ACUTE TOXICITY LEVEL: SLIGHTLY TOXIC BY INGESTION. TARGET EFFECTS: NO DATA AVAILABLE.

HEALTH EFFECTS AND FIRST AID

INHALATION: LENACIL: **ACUTE EXPOSURE-** MAY CAUSE IRRITATION OF THE MUCOUS MEMBRANES. **CHRONIC EXPOSURE-** NO DATA AVAILABLE.

FIRST AID- REMOVE FROM EXPOSURE AREA TO FRESH AIR IMMEDIATELY. IF BREATHING HAS STOPPED, PERFORM ARTIFICIAL RESPIRATION. KEEP PERSON WARM AND AT REST. TREAT SYMPTOMATICALLY AND SUPPORTIVELY. GET MEDICAL ATTENTION IMMEDIATELY.

SKIN CONTACT: LENACIL: **ACUTE EXPOSURE-** THIS MATERIAL WAS MILDLY TO MODERATELY IRRITATING TO GUINEA PIG SKIN. NO SIGNS OF SYSTEMIC TOXICITY WAS PRODUCED IN RABBITS FROM DERMAL APPLICATION OF 5000 MG/KG. **CHRONIC EXPOSURE-** NO DATA AVAILABLE.

FIRST AID- REMOVE CONTAMINATED CLOTHING AND SHOES IMMEDIATELY. WASH AFFECTED AREA WITH SOAP OR MILD DETERGENT AND LARGE AMOUNTS OF WATER UNTIL NO EVIDENCE OF CHEMICAL REMAINS (APPROXIMATELY 15-20 MINUTES). GET MEDICAL ATTENTION IMMEDIATELY.

EYE CONTACT: LENACIL: **ACUTE EXPOSURE-** THIS MATERIAL WAS MILDLY IRRITATING TO RABBIT EYES. **CHRONIC EXPOSURE-** NO DATA AVAILABLE.

FIRST AID- WASH EYES IMMEDIATELY WITH LARGE AMOUNTS OF WATER OR NORMAL SALINE, OCCASIONALLY LIFTING UPPER AND LOWER LIDS, UNTIL NO EVIDENCE OF CHEMICAL REMAINS (APPROXIMATELY 15-20 MINUTES). GET MEDICAL ATTENTION IMMEDIATELY.

INGESTION: LENACIL: **ACUTE EXPOSURE-** NO SIGN OF TOXICITY OR DEATH WAS PRODUCED IN RATS FROM AN ORAL DOSE OF 11,000 MG/KG. **CHRONIC EXPOSURE-** NO ADVERSE EFFECTS WERE OBSERVED IN A 2-YEAR FEEDING STUDY OF RATS.

FIRST AID- REMOVE BY GASTRIC LAVAGE AND CATHARSIS. MAINTAIN BLOOD PRESSURE AND AIRWAY. GIVE OXYGEN IF RESPIRATION IS DEPRESSED. DO NOT PERFORM GASTRIC LAVAGE IF VICTIM IS UNCONSCIOUS. GET MEDICAL ATTENTION IMMEDIATELY (DREISBACH, HANDBOOK OF POISONING, 12TH ED.).
ADMINISTRATION OF LAVAGE OR OXYGEN SHOULD BE PERFORMED BY QUALIFIED MEDICAL PERSONNEL.

ANTIDOTE: NO SPECIFIC ANTIDOTE. TREAT SYMPTOMATICALLY AND SUPPORTIVELY.

REACTIVITY

REACTIVITY: STABLE UNDER NORMAL TEMPERATURES AND PRESSURES.

INCOMPATIBILITIES: LENACIL: ALKALI (HOT): DECOMPOSES. OXIDIZERS (STRONG): FIRE AND EXPLOSION HAZARD.

DECOMPOSITION: THERMAL DECOMPOSITION PRODUCTS MAY INCLUDE TOXIC OXIDES OF CARBON AND NITROGEN.

POLYMERIZATION: HAZARDOUS POLYMERIZATION HAS NOT BEEN REPORTED TO OCCUR UNDER NORMAL TEMPERATURES AND PRESSURES.

STORAGE AND DISPOSAL

OBSERVE ALL FEDERAL, STATE AND LOCAL REGULATIONS WHEN STORING OR DISPOSING OF THIS SUBSTANCE. FOR ASSISTANCE, CONTACT THE DISTRICT DIRECTOR OF THE ENVIRONMENTAL PROTECTION AGENCY.

****STORAGE****

STORE IN ACCORDANCE WITH 40 CFR 165 RECOMMENDED PROCEDURES FOR THE DISPOSAL AND STORAGE OF PESTICIDES AND PESTICIDE CONTAINERS.
STORE AWAY FROM INCOMPATIBLE SUBSTANCES.

****DISPOSAL****

DISPOSAL MUST BE IN ACCORDANCE WITH 40 CFR 165 RECOMMENDED PROCEDURES FOR THE DISPOSAL AND STORAGE OF PESTICIDES AND PESTICIDE CONTAINERS.

CONDITIONS TO AVOID

MAY BURN BUT DOES NOT IGNITE READILY. AVOID CONTACT WITH STRONG OXIDIZERS, EXCESSIVE HEAT, SPARKS, OR OPEN FLAME.

SPILL AND LEAK PROCEDURES

OCCUPATIONAL SPILL: STOP LEAK IF YOU CAN DO IT WITHOUT RISK. FOR SMALL SPILLS, TAKE UP WITH SAND OR OTHER ABSORBENT MATERIAL AND PLACE INTO CLEAN, DRY CONTAINERS FOR LATER DISPOSAL. KEEP UNNECESSARY PEOPLE AWAY. ISOLATE HAZARD AREA AND DENY ENTRY.

PROTECTIVE EQUIPMENT

VENTILATION: PROVIDE GENERAL DILUTION VENTILATION.

RESPIRATOR: THE FOLLOWING RESPIRATORS ARE RECOMMENDED BASED ON INFORMATION FOUND IN THE PHYSICAL DATA, TOXICITY AND HEALTH EFFECTS SECTIONS. THEY ARE RANKED IN ORDER FROM MINIMUM TO MAXIMUM RESPIRATORY PROTECTION. THE SPECIFIC RESPIRATOR SELECTED MUST BE BASED ON CONTAMINATION LEVELS FOUND IN THE WORK PLACE, MUST NOT EXCEED THE WORKING LIMITS OF THE RESPIRATOR AND BE JOINTLY APPROVED BY THE NATIONAL INSTITUTE FOR OCCUPATIONAL SAFETY AND HEALTH AND THE MINE SAFETY AND HEALTH ADMINISTRATION (NIOSH-MSHA).
CHEMICAL CARTRIDGE RESPIRATOR WITH AN ORGANIC VAPOR CARTRIDGE(S) IN COMBINATION WITH A DUST AND MIST FILTER.
GAS MASK WITH ORGANIC VAPOR CANISTER (CHIN-STYLE OR FRONT- OR BACK-MOUNTED CANISTER) WITH A DUST AND MIST FILTER.
GAS MASK WITH ORGANIC VAPOR CANISTER (CHIN-STYLE OR FRONT- OR BACK-MOUNTED CANISTER) WITH A PARTICULATE FILTER.
POWERED AIR-PURIFYING RESPIRATOR WITH A HIGH-EFFICIENCY FILTER.
TYPE 'C' SUPPLIED-AIR RESPIRATOR WITH A FULL FACEPIECE OPERATED IN A PRESSURE-DEMAND OR OTHER POSITIVE PRESSURE MODE.
SELF-CONTAINED BREATHING APPARATUS WITH A FULL FACEPIECE OPERATED IN PRESSURE-DEMAND OR OTHER POSITIVE PRESSURE MODE.
FOR FIREFIGHTING AND OTHER IMMEDIATELY DANGEROUS TO LIFE OR HEALTH CONDITIONS:
SELF-CONTAINED BREATHING APPARATUS WITH FULL FACEPIECE OPERATED IN PRESSURE-DEMAND OR OTHER POSITIVE PRESSURE MODE.
SUPPLIED-AIR RESPIRATOR WITH FULL FACEPIECE AND OPERATED IN PRESSURE-DEMAND OR OTHER POSITIVE PRESSURE MODE IN COMBINATION WITH AN AUXILIARY SELF-CONTAINED BREATHING APPARATUS OPERATED IN PRESSURE-DEMAND OR OTHER POSITIVE PRESSURE MODE.

CLOTHING: EMPLOYEE MUST WEAR APPROPRIATE PROTECTIVE (IMPERVIOUS) CLOTHING AND EQUIPMENT TO PREVENT REPEATED OR PROLONGED SKIN CONTACT WITH THIS SUBSTANCE.

GLOVES: EMPLOYEE MUST WEAR APPROPRIATE PROTECTIVE GLOVES TO PREVENT CONTACT WITH THIS SUBSTANCE.

EYE PROTECTION: EMPLOYEE MUST WEAR SPLASH-PROOF OR DUST-RESISTANT SAFETY GOGGLES TO PREVENT EYE CONTACT WITH THIS SUBSTANCE.
EMERGENCY EYE WASH: WHERE THERE IS ANY POSSIBILITY THAT AN EMPLOYEE'S EYES MAY BE EXPOSED TO THIS SUBSTANCE, THE EMPLOYER SHOULD PROVIDE AN EYE WASH FOUNTAIN WITHIN THE IMMEDIATE WORK AREA FOR EMERGENCY USE.

AUTHORIZED BY- OCCUPATIONAL HEALTH SERVICES, INC.
CREATION DATE: 10/04/89 ***REVISION DATE:*** 05/10/90

MATERIAL SAFETY DATA SHEET

OCCUPATIONAL HEALTH SERVICES, INC.
AGRICULTURE AND PESTICIDE DIVISION
450 SEVENTH AVENUE, SUITE 2407
NEW YORK, NEW YORK 10123
1-800-445-MSDS OR (212) 967-1100

EMERGENCY CONTACT:
JOHN S. BRANSFORD, JR. (615) 292-1180

SUBSTANCE IDENTIFICATION

CAS-NUMBER 3792-59-4

SUBSTANCE: **O-(2,4-DICHLOROPHENYL) O-ETHYL PHENYLPHOSPHONOTHIOATE**

TRADE NAMES/SYNONYMS: PHOSPHONOTHIOIC ACID, PHENYL-, O-(2,4-DICHLOROPHENYL)-O-ETHYL ESTER; PHENYLPHOSPHONOTHIOIC ACID, O-(2,4-

DICHLOROPHENYL)-O-ETHYL ESTER; O-2,4-DICHLOROPHENYL O-ETHYL PHENYLPHOSPHONOTHIOATE; EPBP; S-SEVEN; C14H13CL2O2PS; PST73239
CHEMICAL FAMILY: PHOSPHOROTHIOATE
MOLECULAR FORMULA: C14-H13-CL2-O2-P-S
MOLECULAR WEIGHT: 347.20
CERCLA RATINGS (SCALE 0-3): HEALTH=3 FIRE=U REACTIVITY=0 PERSISTENCE=1
NFPA RATINGS (SCALE 0-4): HEALTH=3 FIRE=U REACTIVITY=0

COMPONENTS AND CONTAMINANTS

COMPONENT: O-(2,4-DICHLOROPHENYL) O-ETHYL PHOSPHONOTHIOATE ***PERCENT:*** 100.0
CAS# 3792-59-4
OTHER CONTAMINANTS: NONE
EXPOSURE LIMITS: NO OCCUPATIONAL EXPOSURE LIMITS ESTABLISHED BY OSHA, ACGIH, OR NIOSH.

PHYSICAL DATA

DESCRIPTION: LIGHT BROWN OIL. ***BOILING POINT:*** 403 F (206 C) @ 5 MMHG
SPECIFIC GRAVITY: 1.312 @ 24 C ***VAPOR PRESSURE:*** 3.82 MMHG @ 200 C
SOLUBILITY IN WATER: INSOLUBLE
SOLVENT SOLUBILITY: SOLUBLE IN MOST ORGANIC SOLVENTS.

FIRE AND EXPLOSION DATA

FIRE AND EXPLOSION HAZARD: UNKNOWN FIRE AND EXPLOSION HAZARD.
FIREFIGHTING MEDIA: DRY CHEMICAL, CARBON DIOXIDE, HALON, WATER SPRAY OR STANDARD FOAM (1987 EMERGENCY RESPONSE GUIDEBOOK, DOT P 5800.4).
FOR LARGER FIRES, USE WATER SPRAY, FOG OR STANDARD FOAM (1987 EMERGENCY RESPONSE GUIDEBOOK, DOT P 5800.4).
FIREFIGHTING: MOVE CONTAINER FROM FIRE AREA IF POSSIBLE. DIKE FIRE CONTROL WATER FOR LATER DISPOSAL; DO NOT SCATTER THE MATERIAL. COOL FIRE-EXPOSED CONTAINERS WITH WATER FROM SIDE UNTIL WELL AFTER FIRE IS OUT. STAY AWAY FROM STORAGE TANK ENDS. WITHDRAW IMMEDIATELY IN CASE OF RISING SOUND FROM VENTING SAFETY DEVICE OR ANY DISCOLORATION OF STORAGE TANK DUE TO FIRE (1987 EMERGENCY RESPONSE GUIDEBOOK, DOT P 5800.4, GUIDE PAGE 28).
EXTINGUISH ONLY IF FLOW CAN BE STOPPED. USE FLOODING AMOUNTS OF WATER AS A FOG; SOLID STREAMS MAY BE INEFFECTIVE. COOL CONTAINERS WITH FLOODING AMOUNTS OF WATER FROM AS FAR A DISTANCE AS POSSIBLE. AVOID BREATHING POISONOUS VAPORS, KEEP UPWIND.

TOXICITY

O-(2,4-DICHLOROPHENYL) O-ETHYL PHENYLPHOSPHONOTHIOATE: TOXICITY DATA: 274 MG/KG ORAL-MOUSE LD50; 784 MG/KG SUBCUTANEOUS-MOUSE LD50. CARCINOGEN STATUS: NONE. ACUTE TOXICITY LEVEL: TOXIC BY INGESTION. TARGET EFFECTS: CHOLINESTERASE INHIBITOR. POISONING MAY AFFECT THE NERVOUS SYSTEM.* AT INCREASED RISK FROM EXPOSURE: PERSONS WITH RESPIRATORY AILMENTS, RECENT EXPOSURE TO CHOLINESTERASE INHIBITORS OR IMPAIRED CHOLINESTERASE PRODUCTION, OR LIVER MALFUNCTION.* ADDITIONAL DATA: MAY CROSS THE PLACENTA. HIGH ENVIRONMENTAL TEMPERATURES OR EXPOSURE OF THE CHEMICAL TO VISIBLE OR ULTRAVIOLET LIGHT MAY ENHANCE THE TOXICITY. INTERACTIONS WITH MEDICATIONS MAY OCCUR.*
* MAY BE BASED ON GENERAL INFORMATION ON ORGANOPHOSPHATES.

HEALTH EFFECTS AND FIRST AID

INHALATION: O-(2,4-DICHLOROPHENYL) O-ETHYL PHENYLPHOSPHONOTHIOATE: SEE INFORMATION ON ORGANOPHOSPHATES.
ORGANOPHOSPHATES: CHOLINESTERASE INHIBITOR. **ACUTE EXPOSURE-** WHEN INHALED, THE FIRST EFFECTS OF CHOLINESTERASE INHIBITORS ARE USUALLY RESPIRATORY AND MAY INCLUDE NASAL HYPEREMIA AND WATERY DISCHARGE, COUGH, CHEST DISCOMFORT, DYSPNEA, AND WHEEZING DUE TO INCREASED BRONCHIAL SECRETIONS AND BRONCHOCONSTRICTION. IF SUFFICIENT AMOUNTS ARE ABSORBED, OTHER SYSTEMIC EFFECTS MAY BEGIN WITHIN A FEW MINUTES OR BE DELAYED FOR UP TO 12 HOURS. SYMPTOMS MAY INCLUDE PALLOR, NAUSEA, VOMITING, DIARRHEA, ABDOMINAL CRAMPS, HEADACHE, DIZZINESS, OCULAR PAIN, BLURRED VISION, MIOSIS OR IN SOME CASES, ESPECIALLY INITIALLY, MYDRIASIS, LACRIMATION, SALIVATION, SWEATING, AND CONFUSION. OTHER REPORTED CENTRAL NERVOUS SYSTEM OR NEUROMUSCULAR EFFECTS MAY INCLUDE ATAXIA, SLURRED SPEECH, AREFLEXIA, WEAKNESS, FATIGUE, FASCICULATIONS, TWITCHING, TREMORS POSSIBLY OF THE TONGUE AND EYELIDS, AND EVENTUALLY PARALYSIS OF THE EXTREMITIES AND POSSIBLY OF THE RESPIRATORY MUSCLES. IN SEVERE CASES THERE MAY ALSO BE INVOLUNTARY DEFECATION AND URINATION, CYANOSIS, PSYCHOSIS, HYPERGLYCEMIA, ACUTE PANCREATITIS, CARDIAC IRREGULARITIES, PULMONARY EDEMA, UNCONSCIOUSNESS, CONVULSIONS, AND COMA. DEATH IS PRIMARILY DUE TO RESPIRATORY FAILURE, ALTHOUGH CARDIOVASCULAR EFFECTS INCLUDING CARDIAC ARREST MAY ALSO BE IMPLICATED. LONG TERM SEQUELAE ARE RARE BUT MAY INCLUDE NEUROPSYCHIATRIC DISORDERS AND MYOPATHY WITH MUSCLE TENDERNESS. SOME ORGANOPHOSPHATES MAY CAUSE A DELAYED NEUROPATHY BEGINNING 1-4 WEEKS AFTER AN ACUTE EXPOSURE WHICH MAY OR MAY NOT HAVE CAUSED ACUTE CHOLINERGIC EFFECTS. NUMBNESS, TINGLING, WEAKNESS AND CRAMPING BEGINNING SYMMETRICALLY IN THE LOWER LIMBS MAY PROGRESS TO ATAXIA AND PARALYSIS. IN SEVERE CASES, UPPER LIMB INVOLVEMENT IS POSSIBLE AND FLACCID PARALYSIS MAY PROGRESS TO SPASTIC PARALYSIS WITH EXAGGERATED REFLEXES. IMPROVEMENT MAY OCCUR OVER MONTHS TO YEARS, BUT SOME RESIDUAL IMPAIRMENT USUALLY REMAINS. **CHRONIC EXPOSURE-** REPEATED OR PROLONGED EXPOSURE MAY RESULT IN THE EFFECTS OF ACUTE EXPOSURE INCLUDING THE DELAYED NEUROPATHY. OTHER EFFECTS REPORTED IN WORKERS REPEATEDLY EXPOSED INCLUDE IMPAIRED MEMORY AND CONCENTRATION, ACUTE PSYCHOSIS, SEVERE DEPRESSIONS, IRRITABILTY, CONFUSION, APATHY, EMOTIONAL LABILITY, SOCIAL WITHDRAWAL, CONFUSION, HEADACHE, SPEECH DIFFICULTIES, DELAYED REACTION TIMES, SPATIAL DISORIENTATION, NIGHTMARES, SLEEPWALKING, AND DROWSINESS OR INSOMNIA. AN INFLUENZA-LIKE CONDITION WITH HEADACHE, NAUSEA, WEAKNESS, ANOREXIA AND MALAISE HAS ALSO BEEN REPORTED.
FIRST AID- REMOVE FROM EXPOSURE AREA TO FRESH AIR IMMEDIATELY. IF BREATHING HAS STOPPED, GIVE ARTIFICIAL RESPIRATION. MAINTAIN AIRWAY AND BLOOD PRESSURE AND ADMINISTER OXYGEN IF AVAILABLE. KEEP AFFECTED PERSON WARM AND AT REST. TREAT SYMPTOMATICALLY AND SUPPORTIVELY. ADMINISTRATION OF OXYGEN SHOULD BE PERFORMED BY QUALIFIED PERSONNEL. GET MEDICAL ATTENTION IMMEDIATELY.

SKIN CONTACT: O-(2,4-DICHLOROPHENYL) O-ETHYL PHENYLPHOSPHONOTHIOATE: SEE INFORMATION ON ORGANOPHOSPHATES.
ORGANOPHOSPHATES: CHOLINESTERASE INHIBITOR. **ACUTE EXPOSURE-** LOCALIZED SWEATING AND FASCICULATIONS MAY OCCUR AT THE SITE OF CONTACT. IF SUFFICIENT AMOUNTS ARE ABSORBED, OTHER EFFECTS OF CHOLINESTERASE INHIBITION AS DESCRIBED IN ACUTE INHALATION MAY OCCUR. SYMPTOMS MAY BE DELAYED 2-3 HOURS, BUT USUALLY NO MORE THAN 12 HOURS. THE RATE OF ABSORPTION IS INCREASED BY THE PRESENCE OF DERMATITIS OR HIGH AMBIENT TEMPERATURES. DELAYED NEUROPATHY IS ALSO POSSIBLE. **CHRONIC EXPOSURE-** REPEATED OR PROLONGED EXPOSURE MAY CAUSE EFFECTS AS DESCRIBED IN ACUTE EXPOSURE. SOME ORGANOPHOSPHATES MAY CAUSE SENSITIZATION.
FIRST AID- REMOVE CONTAMINATED CLOTHING IMMEDIATELY. WASH CONTAMINATED AREAS WITH SOAP AND WATER FOLLOWED BY ALCOHOL (ARENA, POISONING, 4TH ED.). EMERGENCY PERSONNEL SHOULD WEAR GLOVES AND AVOID CONTAMINATION. TREAT RESPIRATORY DIFFICULTY WITH ARTIFICIAL RESPIRATION. GET MEDICAL ATTENTION IMMEDIATELY.

EYE CONTACT: O-(2,4-DICHLOROPHENYL) O-ETHYL PHENYLPHOSPHONOTHIOATE: SEE INFORMATION ON ORGANOPHOSPHATES.
ORGANOPHOSPHATES: CHOLINESTERASE INHIBITOR. **ACUTE EXPOSURE-** DIRECT CONTACT MAY CAUSE PAIN, HYPEREMIA, LACRIMATION, TWITCHING OF THE EYELIDS, MIOSIS, AND CILIARY MUSCLE SPASM WITH LOSS OF ACCOMODATION, BLURRED OR DIMMED VISION AND BROWACHE. SOMETIMES MYDRIASIS MAY OCCUR INSTEAD OF MIOSIS. WITH SUFFICIENT EXPOSURE, OTHER SYMPTOMS OF CHOLINESTERASE INHIBITION AS DESCRIBED IN ACUTE INHALATION MAY OCCUR. **CHRONIC EXPOSURE-** REPEATED OR PROLONGED EXPOSURE MAY CAUSE EFFECTS AS DESCRIBED IN ACUTE EXPOSURE. SOME COMPOUNDS HAVE CAUSED TOXIC EFFECTS ON THE CRYSTALLINE LENS, CONJUNCTIVAL THICKENING AND OBSTRUCTION OF THE NASOLACRIMAL CANALS WHEN USED AS MIOTIC EYEDROPS.
FIRST AID- IRRIGATE EYES WITH WATER OR SALINE SOLUTION. IF SYMPTOMS OF POISONING OCCUR, TREAT RESPIRATORY DIFFICULTY WITH ARTIFICIAL RESPIRATION AND OXYGEN. OBSERVE PATIENT FOR AT LEAST 24-36 HOURS (GOSSELIN, CLINICAL TOXICOLOGY OF COMMERCIAL PRODUCTS, 5TH ED.). GET MEDICAL ATTENTION IMMEDIATELY. OXYGEN SHOULD BE ADMINISTERED BY QUALIFIED MEDICAL PERSONNEL.

INGESTION: O-(2,4-DICHLOROPHENYL) O-ETHYL PHENYLPHOSPHONOTHIOATE: TOXIC. SEE INFORMATION ON ORGANOPHOSPHATES.
ORGANOPHOSPHATES: CHOLINESTERASE INHIBITOR. **ACUTE EXPOSURE-** WHEN INGESTED, THE FIRST EFFECTS MAY BE NAUSEA, VOMITING, ANOREXIA, ABDOMINAL CRAMPS AND DIARRHEA. GASTROINTESTINAL ABSORPTION MAY CAUSE SYMPTOMS OF CHOLINESTERASE INHIBITION AS DESCRIBED IN ACUTE INHALATION. SYMPTOMS MAY BEGIN WITHIN MINUTES OR BE DELAYED FOR HOURS. DELAYED EFFECTS INCLUDING NEUROPATHY MAY ALSO OCCUR. **CHRONIC EXPOSURE-** REPEATED INGESTION MAY CAUSE EFFECTS AS DESCRIBED IN ACUTE EXPOSURE.
FIRST AID- IF PERSON IS ALERT AND RESPIRATION IS NOT DEPRESSED, GIVE SYRUP OF IPECAC FOLLOWED BY WATER (IF VOMITING OCCURS, KEEP HEAD BELOW HIPS

TO PREVENT ASPIRATION). IF CONSCIOUSNESS LEVEL DECLINES OR VOMITING HAS NOT OCCURRED IN 15 MINUTES EMPTY STOMACH BY GASTRIC LAVAGE WITH THE AID OF CUFFED ENDOTRACHEAL TUBE USING ISOTONIC SALINE OR 5% SODIUM BICARBONATE FOLLOW WITH ACTIVATED CHARCOAL. ESTABLISH AND MAINTAIN AIRWAY. TREAT RESPIRATORY DIFFICULTY WITH ARTIFICIAL RESPIRATION AND OXYGEN. DO NOT GIVE MORPHINE, AMINOPHYLLINE, PHENOTHIAZINES, RESERPINE, FUROSEMIDE, OR ETHACRYNIC ACID (MORGAN, RECOGNITION AND MANAGEMENT OF PESTICIDE POISONINGS, 3RD ED.). TREAT SYMPTOMATICALLY AND SUPPORTIVELY. ADMINISTRATION OF OXYGEN AND LAVAGE MUST BE PERFORMED BY QUALIFIED MEDICAL PERSONNEL. GET MEDICAL ATTENTION IMMEDIATELY.

ANTIDOTE: THE FOLLOWING ANTIDOTE(S) HAVE BEEN RECOMMENDED. HOWEVER, THE DECISION AS TO WHETHER THE SEVERITY OF POISONING REQUIRES ADMINISTRATION OF ANY ANTIDOTE AND ACTUAL DOSE REQUIRED SHOULD BE MADE BY QUALIFIED MEDICAL PERSONNEL.

FOR CHOLINESTERASE INHIBITORS: ESTABLISH CLEAR AIRWAY AND TISSUE OXYGENATION BY ASPIRATION OF SECRETIONS, AND IF NECESSARY, BY ASSISTED PULMONARY VENTILATION WITH OXYGEN. IMPROVE TISSUE OXYGENATION AS MUCH AS POSSIBLE BEFORE ADMINISTERING ATROPINE TO MINIMIZE THE RISK OF VENTRICULAR FIBRILLATION. ADMINISTER ATROPINE SULFATE INTRAVENOUSLY, OR INTRAMUSCULARLY IF IV INJECTION IS NOT POSSIBLE. IN MODERATELY SEVERE POISONING ADMINISTER ATROPINE SULFATE, 0.4-2.0 MG REPEATED EVERY 15 MINUTES UNTIL ATROPINIZATION IS ACHIEVED (TACHYCARDIA, FLUSHING, DRY MOUTH, MYDRIASIS). MAINTAIN ATROPINIZATION BY REPEATED DOSES FOR 2-12 HOURS, OR LONGER, DEPENDING ON THE SEVERITY OF POISONING. THE APPEARANCE OF RALES IN THE LUNG BASES, MIOSIS, SALIVATION, NAUSEA, BRADYCARDIA, ARE ALL INDICATIONS OF INADEQUATE ATROPINIZATION. SEVERELY POISONED INDIVIDUALS MAY EXHIBIT REMARKABLE TOLERANCE TO ATROPINE; TWO OR MORE TIMES THE DOSAGES SUGGESTED ABOVE MAY BE NEEDED. PERSONS NOT POISONED OR ONLY SLIGHTLY POISONED, HOWEVER, MAY DEVELOP SIGNS OF ATROPINE TOXICITY FROM SUCH LARGE DOSAGES: FEVER, MUSCLE FIBRILLATIONS, AND DELIRIUM ARE THE MAIN SIGNS OF ATROPINE TOXICITY. IF THESE SIGNS APPEAR WHILE THE PATIENT IS FULLY ATROPINIZED, ATROPINE ADMINISTRATION SHOULD BE DISCONTINUED, AT LEAST TEMPORARILY. OBSERVE TREATED PATIENTS CLOSELY AT LEAST 24 HOURS TO INSURE THAT SYMPTOMS (POSSIBLY PULMONARY EDEMA) DO NOT RECUR AS ATROPINIZATION WEARS OFF. IN VERY SEVERE POISONINGS, METABOLIC DISPOSITION OF TOXICANT MAY REQUIRE SEVERAL HOURS OR DAYS DURING WHICH ATROPINIZATION MUST BE MAINTAINED. MARKEDLY LOWER LEVELS OF URINARY METABOLITES INDICATE THAT ATROPINE DOSAGE CAN BE TAPERED OFF. AS DOSAGE IS REDUCED, CHECK THE LUNG BASES FREQUENTLY FOR RALES. IF RALES ARE HEARD OR OTHER SYMPTOMS RETURN, RE-ESTABLISH ATROPINIZATION PROMPTLY (MORGAN, RECOGNITION AND MANAGEMENT OF PESTICIDE POISONINGS, 3RD ED.). ADMINISTRATION OF ANTIDOTE MUST BE PERFORMED BY QUALIFIED MEDICAL PERSONNEL.

IN CASES OF SEVERE POISONING BY ORGANOPHOSPHATE PESTICIDES IN WHICH RESPIRATORY DEPRESSION, MUSCLE WEAKNESS AND TWITCHINGS ARE SEVERE, GIVE PRALIDOXIME (PROTOPAM-AYERST, 2-PAM), 1.0 GRAM INTRAVENOUSLY AT NO MORE THAN 0.5 GRAM PER MINUTE. DOSAGE OF PRALIDOXIME MAY BE REPEATED IN 1-2 HOURS, THEN AT 10-12 HOUR INTERVALS IF NEEDED. IN VERY SEVERE POISONINGS, DOSAGE RATES MAY BE DOUBLED. TREATMENT WITH PRALIDOXIME WILL BE MOST EFFECTIVE IF GIVEN WITHIN THIRTY-SIX HOURS AFTER POISONING (MORGAN, RECOGNITION AND MANAGEMENT OF PESTICIDE POISONINGS, 3RD ED.). ANTIDOTE SHOULD BE ADMINISTERED BY QUALIFIED MEDICAL PERSONNEL.

REACTIVITY

REACTIVITY: STABLE UNDER NORMAL TEMPERATURES AND PRESSURES.

INCOMPATIBILITIES: O-(2,4-DICHLOROPHENYL) O-ETHYLPHENYLPHOSPONOTHIOATE: OXIDIZERS (STRONG): FIRE AND EXPLOSION HAZARD.

DECOMPOSITION: THERMAL DECOMPOSITION RELEASES CORROSIVE FUMES OF HYDROGEN CHLORIDE AND TOXIC OXIDES OF PHOSPHORUS AND SULFUR.

POLYMERIZATION: HAZARDOUS POLYMERIZATION HAS NOT BEEN REPORTED TO OCCUR UNDER NORMAL TEMPERATURES AND PRESSURES.

STORAGE AND DISPOSAL

OBSERVE ALL FEDERAL, STATE AND LOCAL REGULATIONS WHEN STORING OR DISPOSING OF THIS SUBSTANCE. FOR ASSISTANCE, CONTACT THE DISTRICT DIRECTOR OF THE ENVIRONMENTAL PROTECTION AGENCY.

STORAGE

STORE IN ACCORDANCE WITH 40 CFR 165 RECOMMENDED PROCEDURES FOR THE DISPOSAL AND STORAGE OF PESTICIDES AND PESTICIDE CONTAINERS.

STORE AWAY FROM INCOMPATIBLE SUBSTANCES.

DISPOSAL

DISPOSAL MUST BE IN ACCORDANCE WITH 40 CFR 165 RECOMMENDED PROCEDURES FOR THE DISPOSAL AND STORAGE OF PESTICIDES AND PESTICIDE CONTAINERS.

CONDITIONS TO AVOID

AVOID CONTACT WITH HEAT, SPARKS, FLAMES OR OTHER IGNITION SOURCES. VAPORS MAY BE EXPLOSIVE. MATERIAL IS POISONOUS; AVOID INHALATION OF VAPORS OR CONTACT WITH SKIN. DO NOT ALLOW MATERIAL TO CONTAMINATE WATER SOURCES.

SPILL AND LEAK PROCEDURES

OCCUPATIONAL SPILL: SHUT OFF IGNITION SOURCES. DO NOT TOUCH SPILLED MATERIAL. STOP LEAK IF YOU CAN DO IT WITHOUT RISK. USE WATER SPRAY TO REDUCE VAPORS. FOR SMALL SPILLS, TAKE UP WITH SAND OR OTHER ABSORBENT MATERIAL AND PLACE INTO CONTAINERS FOR LATER DISPOSAL. FOR LARGER SPILLS, DIKE FAR AHEAD OF SPILL FOR LATER DISPOSAL. NO SMOKING, FLAMES OR FLARES IN HAZARD AREA! KEEP UNNECESSARY PEOPLE AWAY; ISOLATE HAZARD AREA AND DENY ENTRY.

PROTECTIVE EQUIPMENT

VENTILATION: PROVIDE LOCAL EXHAUST OR PROCESS ENCLOSURE VENTILATION SYSTEM.

RESPIRATOR: THE FOLLOWING RESPIRATORS ARE RECOMMENDED BASED ON INFORMATION FOUND IN THE PHYSICAL DATA, TOXICITY AND HEALTH EFFECTS SECTIONS. THEY ARE RANKED IN ORDER FROM MINIMUM TO MAXIMUM RESPIRATORY PROTECTION. THE SPECIFIC RESPIRATOR SELECTED MUST BE BASED ON CONTAMINATION LEVELS FOUND IN THE WORK PLACE, MUST NOT EXCEED THE WORKING LIMITS OF THE RESPIRATOR AND BE JOINTLY APPROVED BY THE NATIONAL INSTITUTE FOR OCCUPATIONAL SAFETY AND HEALTH AND THE MINE SAFETY AND HEALTH ADMINISTRATION (NIOSH-MSHA).

TYPE 'C' SUPPLIED-AIR RESPIRATOR WITH A FULL FACEPIECE OPERATED IN PRESSURE-DEMAND OR OTHER POSITIVE PRESSURE MODE OR WITH A FULL FACEPIECE, HELMET OR HOOD OPERATED IN CONTINOUS-FLOW MODE.

SELF-CONTAINED BREATHING APPARATUS WITH A FULL FACEPIECE OPERATED IN PRESSURE-DEMAND OR OTHER POSITIVE PRESSURE MODE.

FOR FIREFIGHTING AND OTHER IMMEDIATELY DANGEROUS TO LIFE OR HEALTH CONDITIONS:

SELF-CONTAINED BREATHING APPARATUS WITH FULL FACEPIECE OPERATED IN PRESSURE-DEMAND OR OTHER POSITIVE PRESSURE MODE.

SUPPLIED-AIR RESPIRATOR WITH FULL FACEPIECE AND OPERATED IN PRESSURE-DEMAND OR OTHER POSITIVE PRESSURE MODE IN COMBINATION WITH AN AUXILIARY SELF-CONTAINED BREATHING APPARATUS OPERATED IN PRESSURE-DEMAND OR OTHER POSITIVE PRESSURE MODE.

CLOTHING: EMPLOYEE MUST WEAR APPROPRIATE PROTECTIVE (IMPERVIOUS) CLOTHING AND EQUIPMENT TO PREVENT ANY POSSIBILITY OF SKIN CONTACT WITH THIS SUBSTANCE.

GLOVES: EMPLOYEE MUST WEAR APPROPRIATE PROTECTIVE GLOVES TO PREVENT CONTACT WITH THIS SUBSTANCE.

EYE PROTECTION: EMPLOYEE MUST WEAR SPLASH-PROOF OR DUST-RESISTANT SAFETY GOGGLES WITH OR WITHOUT A FACESHIELD TO PREVENT CONTACT WITH THIS SUBSTANCE.

EMERGENCY EYE WASH: WHERE THERE IS ANY POSSIBILITY THAT AN EMPLOYEE'S EYES MAY BE EXPOSED TO THIS SUBSTANCE, THE EMPLOYER SHOULD PROVIDE AN EYE WASH FOUNTAIN WITHIN THE IMMEDIATE WORK AREA FOR EMERGENCY USE.

AUTHORIZED BY- OCCUPATIONAL HEALTH SERVICES, INC.

CREATION DATE: 05/18/90 ***REVISION DATE:*** 05/18/90

MATERIAL SAFETY DATA SHEET

OCCUPATIONAL HEALTH SERVICES, INC.
AGRICULTURE AND PESTICIDE DIVISION
450 SEVENTH AVENUE, SUITE 2407
NEW YORK, NEW YORK 10123
1-800-445-MSDS OR (212) 967-1100

EMERGENCY CONTACT:
JOHN S. BRANSFORD, JR. (615) 292-1180

SUBSTANCE IDENTIFICATION

CAS-NUMBER 29173-31-7

SUBSTANCE: MECARPHON

TRADE NAMES/SYNONYMS: 2-OXA-4-THIA-7-AZA-3-PHOSPHAOCTAN-8-OIC ACID, 3,7-DIMETHYL-6-OXO-, METHYL ESTER, 3-SULFIDE; 3,7-DIMETHYL-6-OXO-2-OXA-4-THIA-7-AZA-3-PHOSPHAOCTAN-8-OIC ACID, 3-

SULFIDE, METHYL ESTER; CARBAMIC ACID, (MERCAPTOACETYL)METHYL-, METHYL ESTER, S-ESTER WITH O-METHYL METHYLPHOSPHONODITHIOATE; (MERCAPTOACETYL)METHYLCARBAMIC ACID, METHYL ESTER, S-ESTER WITH O-METHYLMETHYLPHOSPHONODITHIOATE; METHYL 3,7-DIMETHYL-6-OXO-2-OXA-4-THIA-7-AZA-3-PHOSPHAOCTAN-8-OATE 3-SULFIDE; METHYL ((METHOXY(METHYLPHOSPHINOTHIOYL)THIO)ACETYL)METHYLCARBAMATE; S-(N-METHOXYCARBONYL-N-METHYLCARBAMOYLMETHYL) O-METHYL METHYLPHOSPHONODITHIOATE; METHYL (MERCAPTOACETYL)METHYLCARBAMATE S-ESTER WITH O-METHYL METHYLPHOSPHONODITHIOATE; METHYL(METHOXY(METHYL)PHOSPHINOTHIOYLTHIO)ACETYL(METHYL)CARBAMATE; METHYL N-(METHOXY(METHYL)THIOPHOSPHORYLTHIOACETYL)-N-METHYLCARBAMATE; OMS 1478; C7H14NO4PS2; PST73246

CHEMICAL FAMILY: PHOSPHOROTHIOATE

MOLECULAR FORMULA: C7-H14-N-O4-P-S2

MOLECULAR WEIGHT: 271.31

CERCLA RATINGS (SCALE 0-3): HEALTH=3 FIRE=1 REACTIVITY=0 PERSISTENCE=1

NFPA RATINGS (SCALE 0-4): HEALTH=3 FIRE=1 REACTIVITY=0

COMPONENTS AND CONTAMINANTS

COMPONENT: MECARPHON ***PERCENT:*** 100.0
CAS# 29173-31-7

OTHER CONTAMINANTS: NONE

EXPOSURE LIMITS: NO OCCUPATIONAL EXPOSURE LIMITS ESTABLISHED BY OSHA, ACGIH, OR NIOSH.

PHYSICAL DATA

DESCRIPTION: SOLID. ***MELTING POINT:*** 97 F (36 C)

SPECIFIC GRAVITY: NOT AVAILABLE ***SOLUBILITY IN WATER:*** INSOLUBLE

SOLVENT SOLUBILITY: SOLUBLE IN ETHANOL AND BENZENE; INSOLUBLE IN HEXANE.

FIRE AND EXPLOSION DATA

FIRE AND EXPLOSION HAZARD: SLIGHT FIRE HAZARD WHEN EXPOSED TO HEAT OR FLAME.

FIREFIGHTING MEDIA: DRY CHEMICAL, CARBON DIOXIDE, HALON, WATER SPRAY OR STANDARD FOAM (1987 EMERGENCY RESPONSE GUIDEBOOK, DOT P 5800.4). FOR LARGER FIRES, USE WATER SPRAY, FOG OR STANDARD FOAM (1987 EMERGENCY RESPONSE GUIDEBOOK, DOT P 5800.4).

FIREFIGHTING: MOVE CONTAINERS FROM FIRE AREA IF POSSIBLE. FIGHT FIRE FROM MAXIMUM DISTANCE. STAY AWAY FROM STORAGE TANK ENDS. DIKE FIRE CONTROL WATER FOR LATER DISPOSAL. DO NOT SCATTER MATERIAL (1987 EMERGENCY RESPONSE GUIDEBOOK, DOT P 5800.4, GUIDE PAGE 55). EXTINGUISH ONLY IF FLOW CAN BE STOPPED; USE FLOODING AMOUNTS OF WATER AS FOG, SOLID STREAMS MAY BE INEFFECTIVE. COOL CONTAINERS WITH FLOODING AMOUNTS OF WATER FROM AS FAR A DISTANCE AS POSSIBLE. USE WATER SPRAY TO ABSORB TOXIC VAPORS. AVOID BREATHING TOXIC VAPORS; KEEP UPWIND. CONSIDER EVACUATION OF DOWNWIND AREA IF MATERIAL IS LEAKING.

TOXICITY

MECARPHON: TOXICITY DATA: 720 MG/KG SKIN-RAT LD50; 57 MG/KG ORAL-RAT LD50. CARCINOGEN STATUS: NONE. ACUTE TOXICITY LEVEL: TOXIC BY DERMAL ABSORPTION AND INGESTION. TARGET EFFECTS: CHOLINESTERASE INHIBITOR. POISONING MAY AFFECT THE NERVOUS SYSTEM.* AT INCREASED RISK FROM EXPOSURE: PERSONS WITH RESPIRATORY AILMENTS, RECENT EXPOSURE TO CHOLINESTERASE INHIBITORS OR IMPAIRED CHOLINESTERASE PRODUCTION, OR LIVER MALFUNCTION.* ADDITIONAL DATA: MAY CROSS THE PLACENTA. HIGH ENVIRONMENTAL TEMPERATURES OR EXPOSURE OF THE CHEMICAL TO VISIBLE OR ULTRAVIOLET LIGHT MAY ENHANCE THE TOXICITY. INTERACTIONS WITH MEDICATIONS MAY OCCUR.*

* MAY BE BASED ON GENERAL INFORMATION ON ORGANOPHOSPHATES.

HEALTH EFFECTS AND FIRST AID

INHALATION: MECARPHON: SEE INFORMATION ON ORGANOPHOSPHATES. ORGANOPHOSPHATES: CHOLINESTERASE INHIBITOR. **ACUTE EXPOSURE**- WHEN INHALED, THE FIRST EFFECTS OF CHOLINESTERASE INHIBITORS ARE USUALLY RESPIRATORY AND MAY INCLUDE NASAL HYPEREMIA AND WATERY DISCHARGE, COUGH, CHEST DISCOMFORT, DYSPNEA, AND WHEEZING DUE TO INCREASED BRONCHIAL SECRETIONS AND BRONCHOCONSTRICTION. IF SUFFICIENT AMOUNTS ARE ABSORBED, OTHER SYSTEMIC EFFECTS MAY BEGIN WITHIN A FEW MINUTES OR BE DELAYED FOR UP TO 12 HOURS. SYMPTOMS MAY INCLUDE PALLOR, NAUSEA, VOMITING, DIARRHEA, ABDOMINAL CRAMPS, HEADACHE, DIZZINESS, OCULAR PAIN, BLURRED VISION, MIOSIS OR IN SOME CASES, ESPECIALLY INITIALLY, MYDRIASIS, LACRIMATION, SALIVATION, SWEATING, AND CONFUSION. OTHER REPORTED CENTRAL NERVOUS SYSTEM OR NEUROMUSCULAR EFFECTS MAY INCLUDE ATAXIA, SLURRED SPEECH, AREFLEXIA, WEAKNESS, FATIGUE, FASCICULATIONS, TWITCHING, TREMORS POSSIBLY OF THE TONGUE AND EYELIDS, AND EVENTUALLY PARALYSIS OF THE EXTREMITIES AND POSSIBLY OF THE RESPIRATORY MUSCLES. IN SEVERE CASES THERE MAY ALSO BE INVOLUNTARY DEFECATION AND URINATION, CYANOSIS, PSYCHOSIS, HYPERGLYCEMIA, ACUTE PANCREATITIS, CARDIAC IRREGULARITIES, PULMONARY EDEMA, UNCONSCIOUSNESS, CONVULSIONS, AND COMA. DEATH IS PRIMARILY DUE TO RESPIRATORY FAILURE, ALTHOUGH CARDIOVASCULAR EFFECTS INCLUDING CARDIAC ARREST MAY ALSO BE IMPLICATED. LONG TERM SEQUELAE ARE RARE BUT MAY INCLUDE NEUROPSYCHIATRIC DISORDERS AND MYOPATHY WITH MUSCLE TENDERNESS. SOME ORGANOPHOSPHATES MAY CAUSE A DELAYED NEUROPATHY BEGINNING 1-4 WEEKS AFTER AN ACUTE EXPOSURE WHICH MAY OR MAY NOT HAVE CAUSED ACUTE CHOLINERGIC EFFECTS. NUMBNESS, TINGLING, WEAKNESS AND CRAMPING BEGINNING SYMMETRICALLY IN THE LOWER LIMBS MAY PROGRESS TO ATAXIA AND PARALYSIS. IN SEVERE CASES, UPPER LIMB INVOLVEMENT IS POSSIBLE AND FLACCID PARALYSIS MAY PROGRESS TO SPASTIC PARALYSIS WITH EXAGGERATED REFLEXES. IMPROVEMENT MAY OCCUR OVER MONTHS TO YEARS, BUT SOME RESIDUAL IMPAIRMENT USUALLY REMAINS. **CHRONIC EXPOSURE**- REPEATED OR PROLONGED EXPOSURE MAY RESULT IN THE EFFECTS OF ACUTE EXPOSURE INCLUDING THE DELAYED NEUROPATHY. OTHER EFFECTS REPORTED IN WORKERS REPEATEDLY EXPOSED INCLUDE IMPAIRED MEMORY AND CONCENTRATION, ACUTE PSYCHOSIS, SEVERE DEPRESSIONS, IRRITABILTY, CONFUSION, APATHY, EMOTIONAL LABILITY, SOCIAL WITHDRAWAL, CONFUSION, HEADACHE, SPEECH DIFFICULTIES, DELAYED REACTION TIMES, SPATIAL DISORIENTATION, NIGHTMARES, SLEEPWALKING, AND DROWSINESS OR INSOMNIA. AN INFLUENZA-LIKE CONDITION WITH HEADACHE, NAUSEA, WEAKNESS, ANOREXIA AND MALAISE HAS ALSO BEEN REPORTED.

FIRST AID- REMOVE FROM EXPOSURE AREA TO FRESH AIR IMMEDIATELY. IF BREATHING HAS STOPPED, GIVE ARTIFICIAL RESPIRATION. MAINTAIN AIRWAY AND BLOOD PRESSURE AND ADMINISTER OXYGEN IF AVAILABLE. KEEP AFFECTED PERSON WARM AND AT REST. TREAT SYMPTOMATICALLY AND SUPPORTIVELY. ADMINISTRATION OF OXYGEN SHOULD BE PERFORMED BY QUALIFIED PERSONNEL. GET MEDICAL ATTENTION IMMEDIATELY.

SKIN CONTACT: MECARPHON: TOXIC. SEE INFORMATION ON ORGANOPHOSPHATES. ORGANOPHOSPHATES: CHOLINESTERASE INHIBITOR. **ACUTE EXPOSURE**- LOCALIZED SWEATING AND FASCICULATIONS MAY OCCUR AT THE SITE OF CONTACT. IF SUFFICIENT AMOUNTS ARE ABSORBED, OTHER EFFECTS OF CHOLINESTERASE INHIBITION AS DESCRIBED IN ACUTE INHALATION MAY OCCUR. SYMPTOMS MAY BE DELAYED 2-3 HOURS, BUT USUALLY NO MORE THAN 12 HOURS. THE RATE OF ABSORPTION IS INCREASED BY THE PRESENCE OF DERMATITIS OR HIGH AMBIENT TEMPERATURES. DELAYED NEUROPATHY IS ALSO POSSIBLE. **CHRONIC EXPOSURE**- REPEATED OR PROLONGED EXPOSURE MAY CAUSE EFFECTS AS DESCRIBED IN ACUTE EXPOSURE. SOME ORGANOPHOSPHATES MAY CAUSE SENSITIZATION.

FIRST AID- REMOVE CONTAMINATED CLOTHING IMMEDIATELY. WASH CONTAMINATED AREAS WITH SOAP AND WATER FOLLOWED BY ALCOHOL (ARENA, POISONING, 4TH ED.). EMERGENCY PERSONNEL SHOULD WEAR GLOVES AND AVOID CONTAMINATION. TREAT RESPIRATORY DIFFICULTY WITH ARTIFICIAL RESPIRATION. GET MEDICAL ATTENTION IMMEDIATELY.

EYE CONTACT: MECARPHON: SEE INFORMATION ON ORGANOPHOSPHATES. ORGANOPHOSPHATES: CHOLINESTERASE INHIBITOR. **ACUTE EXPOSURE**- DIRECT CONTACT MAY CAUSE PAIN, HYPEREMIA, LACRIMATION, TWITCHING OF THE EYELIDS, MIOSIS, AND CILIARY MUSCLE SPASM WITH LOSS OF ACCOMODATION, BLURRED OR DIMMED VISION AND BROWACHE. SOMETIMES MYDRIASIS MAY OCCUR INSTEAD OF MIOSIS. WITH SUFFICIENT EXPOSURE, OTHER SYMPTOMS OF CHOLINESTERASE INHIBITION AS DESCRIBED IN ACUTE INHALATION MAY OCCUR. **CHRONIC EXPOSURE**- REPEATED OR PROLONGED EXPOSURE MAY CAUSE EFFECTS AS DESCRIBED IN ACUTE EXPOSURE. SOME COMPOUNDS HAVE CAUSED TOXIC EFFECTS ON THE CRYSTALLINE LENS, CONJUNCTIVAL THICKENING AND OBSTRUCTION OF THE NASOLACRIMAL CANALS WHEN USED AS MIOTIC EYEDROPS.

FIRST AID- IRRIGATE EYES WITH WATER OR SALINE SOLUTION. IF SYMPTOMS OF POISONING OCCUR, TREAT RESPIRATORY DIFFICULTY WITH ARTIFICIAL RESPIRATION AND OXYGEN. OBSERVE PATIENT FOR AT LEAST 24-36 HOURS (GOSSELIN, CLINICAL TOXICOLOGY OF COMMERCIAL PRODUCTS, 5TH ED.). GET MEDICAL ATTENTION IMMEDIATELY. OXYGEN SHOULD BE ADMINISTERED BY QUALIFIED MEDICAL PERSONNEL.

INGESTION: MECARPHON: TOXIC. SEE INFORMATION ON ORGANOPHOSPHATES. ORGANOPHOSPHATES: CHOLINESTERASE INHIBITOR. **ACUTE EXPOSURE**- WHEN INGESTED, THE FIRST EFFECTS MAY BE NAUSEA, VOMITING, ANOREXIA, ABDOMINAL CRAMPS AND DIARRHEA. GASTROINTESTINAL ABSORPTION MAY CAUSE SYMPTOMS OF CHOLINESTERASE INHIBITION AS DESCRIBED IN ACUTE INHALATION. SYMPTOMS MAY BEGIN WITHIN MINUTES OR BE DELAYED FOR

HOURS. DELAYED EFFECTS INCLUDING NEUROPATHY MAY ALSO OCCUR. **CHRONIC EXPOSURE-** REPEATED INGESTION MAY CAUSE EFFECTS AS DESCRIBED IN ACUTE EXPOSURE.

FIRST AID- IF PERSON IS ALERT AND RESPIRATION IS NOT DEPRESSED, GIVE SYRUP OF IPECAC FOLLOWED BY WATER (IF VOMITING OCCURS, KEEP HEAD BELOW HIPS TO PREVENT ASPIRATION). IF CONSCIOUSNESS LEVEL DECLINES OR VOMITING HAS NOT OCCURRED IN 15 MINUTES EMPTY STOMACH BY GASTRIC LAVAGE WITH THE AID OF CUFFED ENDOTRACHEAL TUBE USING ISOTONIC SALINE OR 5% SODIUM BICARBONATE FOLLOW WITH ACTIVATED CHARCOAL. ESTABLISH AND MAINTAIN AIRWAY. TREAT RESPIRATORY DIFFICULTY WITH ARTIFICIAL RESPIRATION AND OXYGEN. DO NOT GIVE MORPHINE, AMINOPHYLLINE, PHENOTHIAZINES, RESERPINE, FUROSEMIDE, OR ETHACRYNIC ACID (MORGAN, RECOGNITION AND MANAGEMENT OF PESTICIDE POISONINGS, 3RD ED.). TREAT SYMPTOMATICALLY AND SUPPORTIVELY. ADMINISTRATION OF OXYGEN AND LAVAGE MUST BE PERFORMED BY QUALIFIED MEDICAL PERSONNEL. GET MEDICAL ATTENTION IMMEDIATELY.

ANTIDOTE: THE FOLLOWING ANTIDOTE(S) HAVE BEEN RECOMMENDED. HOWEVER, THE DECISION AS TO WHETHER THE SEVERITY OF POISONING REQUIRES ADMINISTRATION OF ANY ANTIDOTE AND ACTUAL DOSE REQUIRED SHOULD BE MADE BY QUALIFIED MEDICAL PERSONNEL.

FOR CHOLINESTERASE INHIBITORS: ESTABLISH CLEAR AIRWAY AND TISSUE OXYGENATION BY ASPIRATION OF SECRETIONS, AND IF NECESSARY, BY ASSISTED PULMONARY VENTILATION WITH OXYGEN. IMPROVE TISSUE OXYGENATION AS MUCH AS POSSIBLE BEFORE ADMINISTERING ATROPINE TO MINIMIZE THE RISK OF VENTRICULAR FIBRILLATION. ADMINISTER ATROPINE SULFATE INTRAVENOUSLY, OR INTRAMUSCULARLY IF IV INJECTION IS NOT POSSIBLE. IN MODERATELY SEVERE POISONING ADMINISTER ATROPINE SULFATE, 0.4-2.0 MG REPEATED EVERY 15 MINUTES UNTIL ATROPINIZATION IS ACHIEVED (TACHYCARDIA, FLUSHING, DRY MOUTH, MYDRIASIS). MAINTAIN ATROPINIZATION BY REPEATED DOSES FOR 2-12 HOURS, OR LONGER, DEPENDING ON THE SEVERITY OF POISONING. THE APPEARANCE OF RALES IN THE LUNG BASES, MIOSIS, SALIVATION, NAUSEA, BRADYCARDIA, ARE ALL INDICATIONS OF INADEQUATE ATROPINIZATION. SEVERELY POISONED INDIVIDUALS MAY EXHIBIT REMARKABLE TOLERANCE TO ATROPINE; TWO OR MORE TIMES THE DOSAGES SUGGESTED ABOVE MAY BE NEEDED. PERSONS NOT POISONED OR ONLY SLIGHTLY POISONED, HOWEVER, MAY DEVELOP SIGNS OF ATROPINE TOXICITY FROM SUCH LARGE DOSAGES: FEVER, MUSCLE FIBRILLATIONS, AND DELIRIUM ARE THE MAIN SIGNS OF ATROPINE TOXICITY. IF THESE SIGNS APPEAR WHILE THE PATIENT IS FULLY ATROPINIZED, ATROPINE ADMINISTRATION SHOULD BE DISCONTINUED, AT LEAST TEMPORARILY. OBSERVE TREATED PATIENTS CLOSELY AT LEAST 24 HOURS TO INSURE THAT SYMPTOMS (POSSIBLY PULMONARY EDEMA) DO NOT RECUR AS ATROPINIZATION WEARS OFF. IN VERY SEVERE POISONINGS, METABOLIC DISPOSITION OF TOXICANT MAY REQUIRE SEVERAL HOURS OR DAYS DURING WHICH ATROPINIZATION MUST BE MAINTAINED. MARKEDLY LOWER LEVELS OF URINARY METABOLITES INDICATE THAT ATROPINE DOSAGE CAN BE TAPERED OFF. AS DOSAGE IS REDUCED, CHECK THE LUNG BASES FREQUENTLY FOR RALES. IF RALES ARE HEARD OR OTHER SYMPTOMS RETURN, RE-ESTABLISH ATROPINIZATION PROMPTLY (MORGAN, RECOGNITION AND MANAGEMENT OF PESTICIDE POISONINGS, 3RD ED.). ADMINISTRATION OF ANTIDOTE MUST BE PERFORMED BY QUALIFIED MEDICAL PERSONNEL.

IN CASES OF SEVERE POISONING BY ORGANOPHOSPHATE PESTICIDES IN WHICH RESPIRATORY DEPRESSION, MUSCLE WEAKNESS AND TWITCHINGS ARE SEVERE, GIVE PRALIDOXIME (PROTOPAM-AYERST, 2-PAM), 1.0 GRAM INTRAVENOUSLY AT NO MORE THAN 0.5 GRAM PER MINUTE. DOSAGE OF PRALIDOXIME MAY BE REPEATED IN 1-2 HOURS, THEN AT 10-12 HOUR INTERVALS IF NEEDED. IN VERY SEVERE POISONINGS, DOSAGE RATES MAY BE DOUBLED. TREATMENT WITH PRALIDOXIME WILL BE MOST EFFECTIVE IF GIVEN WITHIN THIRTY-SIX HOURS AFTER POISONING (MORGAN, RECOGNITION AND MANAGEMENT OF PESTICIDE POISONINGS, 3RD ED.). ANTIDOTE SHOULD BE ADMINISTERED BY QUALIFIED MEDICAL PERSONNEL.

REACTIVITY

REACTIVITY: STABLE UNDER NORMAL TEMPERATURES AND PRESSURES.

INCOMPATIBILITIES: MECARPHON: OXIDIZERS (STRONG): FIRE AND EXPLOSION HAZARD.

DECOMPOSITION: THERMAL DECOMPOSITION PRODUCTS MAY INCLUDE TOXIC OXIDES OF NITROGEN, CARBON, PHOSPHORUS, AND SULFUR.

POLYMERIZATION: HAZARDOUS POLYMERIZATION HAS NOT BEEN REPORTED TO OCCUR UNDER NORMAL TEMPERATURES AND PRESSURES.

STORAGE AND DISPOSAL

OBSERVE ALL FEDERAL, STATE AND LOCAL REGULATIONS WHEN STORING OR DISPOSING OF THIS SUBSTANCE. FOR ASSISTANCE, CONTACT THE DISTRICT DIRECTOR OF THE ENVIRONMENTAL PROTECTION AGENCY.

STORAGE

STORE IN ACCORDANCE WITH 40 CFR 165 RECOMMENDED PROCEDURES FOR THE DISPOSAL AND STORAGE OF PESTICIDES AND PESTICIDE CONTAINERS. STORE AWAY FROM INCOMPATIBLE SUBSTANCES.

DISPOSAL

DISPOSAL MUST BE IN ACCORDANCE WITH 40 CFR 165 RECOMMENDED PROCEDURES FOR THE DISPOSAL AND STORAGE OF PESTICIDES AND PESTICIDE CONTAINERS.

CONDITIONS TO AVOID

MAY BURN BUT DOES NOT IGNITE READILY. CONTAINERS MAY EXPLODE IN HEAT OF FIRE.

SPILL AND LEAK PROCEDURES

OCCUPATIONAL SPILL: DO NOT TOUCH SPILLED MATERIAL. STOP LEAK IF YOU CAN DO IT WITHOUT RISK. USE WATER SPRAY TO REDUCE VAPORS. FOR SMALL SPILLS, TAKE UP WITH SAND OR OTHER ABSORBENT MATERIAL AND PLACE INTO CONTAINERS FOR LATER DISPOSAL. FOR SMALL DRY SPILLS, WITH A CLEAN SHOVEL PLACE MATERIAL INTO CLEAN, DRY CONTAINERS AND COVER. MOVE CONTAINERS FROM SPILL AREA. FOR LARGER SPILLS, DIKE FAR AHEAD OF SPILL FOR LATER DISPOSAL. KEEP UNNECESSARY PEOPLE AWAY. ISOLATE HAZARD AREA AND DENY ENTRY. VENTILATE CLOSED SPACES BEFORE ENTERING.

PROTECTIVE EQUIPMENT

VENTILATION: PROVIDE LOCAL EXHAUST OR PROCESS ENCLOSURE VENTILATION SYSTEM.

RESPIRATOR: THE FOLLOWING RESPIRATORS ARE RECOMMENDED BASED ON INFORMATION FOUND IN THE PHYSICAL DATA, TOXICITY AND HEALTH EFFECTS SECTIONS. THEY ARE RANKED IN ORDER FROM MINIMUM TO MAXIMUM RESPIRATORY PROTECTION. THE SPECIFIC RESPIRATOR SELECTED MUST BE BASED ON CONTAMINATION LEVELS FOUND IN THE WORK PLACE, MUST NOT EXCEED THE WORKING LIMITS OF THE RESPIRATOR AND BE JOINTLY APPROVED BY THE NATIONAL INSTITUTE FOR OCCUPATIONAL SAFETY AND HEALTH AND THE MINE SAFETY AND HEALTH ADMINISTRATION (NIOSH-MSHA).

TYPE 'C' SUPPLIED-AIR RESPIRATOR WITH A FULL FACEPIECE OPERATED IN PRESSURE-DEMAND OR OTHER POSITIVE PRESSURE MODE OR WITH A FULL FACEPIECE, HELMET OR HOOD OPERATED IN CONTINOUS-FLOW MODE.

SELF-CONTAINED BREATHING APPARATUS WITH A FULL FACEPIECE OPERATED IN PRESSURE-DEMAND OR OTHER POSITIVE PRESSURE MODE.

FOR FIREFIGHTING AND OTHER IMMEDIATELY DANGEROUS TO LIFE OR HEALTH CONDITIONS:

SELF-CONTAINED BREATHING APPARATUS WITH FULL FACEPIECE OPERATED IN PRESSURE-DEMAND OR OTHER POSITIVE PRESSURE MODE.

SUPPLIED-AIR RESPIRATOR WITH FULL FACEPIECE AND OPERATED IN PRESSURE-DEMAND OR OTHER POSITIVE PRESSURE MODE IN COMBINATION WITH AN AUXILIARY SELF-CONTAINED BREATHING APPARATUS OPERATED IN PRESSURE-DEMAND OR OTHER POSITIVE PRESSURE MODE.

CLOTHING: EMPLOYEE MUST WEAR APPROPRIATE PROTECTIVE (IMPERVIOUS) CLOTHING AND EQUIPMENT TO PREVENT ANY POSSIBILITY OF SKIN CONTACT WITH THIS SUBSTANCE.

GLOVES: EMPLOYEE MUST WEAR APPROPRIATE PROTECTIVE GLOVES TO PREVENT CONTACT WITH THIS SUBSTANCE.

EYE PROTECTION: EMPLOYEE MUST WEAR SPLASH-PROOF OR DUST-RESISTANT SAFETY GOGGLES WITH OR WITHOUT A FACESHIELD TO PREVENT CONTACT WITH THIS SUBSTANCE.

EMERGENCY EYE WASH: WHERE THERE IS ANY POSSIBILITY THAT AN EMPLOYEE'S EYES MAY BE EXPOSED TO THIS SUBSTANCE, THE EMPLOYER SHOULD PROVIDE AN EYE WASH FOUNTAIN WITHIN THE IMMEDIATE WORK AREA FOR EMERGENCY USE.

AUTHORIZED BY- OCCUPATIONAL HEALTH SERVICES, INC.

CREATION DATE: 10/04/89 ***REVISION DATE:*** 04/30/90

MATERIAL SAFETY DATA SHEET

OCCUPATIONAL HEALTH SERVICES, INC.
AGRICULTURE AND PESTICIDE DIVISION
450 SEVENTH AVENUE, SUITE 2407
NEW YORK, NEW YORK 10123
1-800-445-MSDS OR (212) 967-1100

EMERGENCY CONTACT:
JOHN S. BRANSFORD, JR. (615) 292-1180

SUBSTANCE IDENTIFICATION

CAS-NUMBER 87-47-8

SUBSTANCE: PYROLAN

TRADE NAMES/SYNONYMS: CARBAMIC ACID, DIMETHYL-, 3-METHYL-1-PHENYL-1H-PYRAZOL-5-YL ESTER; CARBAMIC ACID, DIMETHYL-, 3-METHYL-1-PHENYLPYRAZOL-5-YL ESTER; DIMETHYLCARBAMIC ACID 3-METHYL-1-PHENYL-1H-PYRAZOL-5-YL ESTER; DIMETHYLCARBAMIC ACID 3-METHYL-1-PHENYLPYRAZOL-5-YL ESTER; 1-PHENYL-3-METHYL-5-PYRAZOLYL DIMETHYLCARBAMATE; 3-METHYL-1-PHENYL-5-PYRAZOLYL DIMETHYLCARBAMATE; 3-METHYL-1-PHENYLPYRAZOL-5-YL DIMETHYLCARBAMATE; 3-METHYL-1-PHENYL-1H-PYRAZOL-5-YL DIMETHYLCARBAMATE; G 22008; OMS 20; ENT 17588; C13H15N3O2; PST73263

CHEMICAL FAMILY: CARBAMATE

MOLECULAR FORMULA: C13-H15-N3-O2

MOLECULAR WEIGHT: 245.27

CERCLA RATINGS (SCALE 0-3): HEALTH=3 FIRE=1 REACTIVITY=0 PERSISTENCE=1

NFPA RATINGS (SCALE 0-4): HEALTH=3 FIRE=1 REACTIVITY=0

COMPONENTS AND CONTAMINANTS

COMPONENT: PYROLAN ***PERCENT:*** 100.0
CAS# 87-47-8

OTHER CONTAMINANTS: NONE

EXPOSURE LIMITS: NO OCCUPATIONAL EXPOSURE LIMITS ESTABLISHED BY OSHA, ACGIH, OR NIOSH.

PHYSICAL DATA

DESCRIPTION: COLORLESS, CRYSTALLINE SOLID.

BOILING POINT: 320-324 F (160-162 C) @ 0.2 MMHG

MELTING POINT: 118-122 F (48-50 C) ***SPECIFIC GRAVITY:*** NOT AVAILABLE

SOLUBILITY IN WATER: 0.1% @ 20 C

SOLVENT SOLUBILITY: SOLUBLE IN ALCOHOL, ACETONE, BENZENE, FATS, AND OILS; SLIGHTLY SOLUBLE IN KEROSENE.

FIRE AND EXPLOSION DATA

FIRE AND EXPLOSION HAZARD: SLIGHT FIRE HAZARD WHEN EXPOSED TO HEAT OR FLAME.

FIREFIGHTING MEDIA: DRY CHEMICAL, CARBON DIOXIDE, HALON, WATER SPRAY OR STANDARD FOAM (1987 EMERGENCY RESPONSE GUIDEBOOK, DOT P 5800.4). FOR LARGER FIRES, USE WATER SPRAY, FOG OR STANDARD FOAM (1987 EMERGENCY RESPONSE GUIDEBOOK, DOT P 5800.4).

FIREFIGHTING: MOVE CONTAINERS FROM FIRE AREA IF POSSIBLE. FIGHT FIRE FROM MAXIMUM DISTANCE. STAY AWAY FROM STORAGE TANK ENDS. DIKE FIRE CONTROL WATER FOR LATER DISPOSAL. DO NOT SCATTER MATERIAL (1987 EMERGENCY RESPONSE GUIDEBOOK, DOT P 5800.4, GUIDE PAGE 55). EXTINGUISH USING AGENTS SUITABLE FOR TYPE OF SURROUNDING FIRE. USE FLOODING AMOUNTS OF WATER AS FOG. AVOID BREATHING TOXIC DUST AND FUMES FROM BURNING MATERIAL; KEEP UPWIND.

TOXICITY

PYROLAN: TOXICITY DATA: 62 MG/KG ORAL-RAT LD50; 90 MG/KG ORAL-MOUSE LD50. CARCINOGEN STATUS: NONE. ACUTE TOXICITY LEVEL: TOXIC BY INGESTION. TARGET EFFECTS: CHOLINESTERASE INHIBITOR. AT INCREASED RISK FROM EXPOSURE: PERSONS WITH ASTHMA, DIABETES, CARDIOVASCULAR DISEASE, MECHANICAL OBSTRUCTION OF THE GASTROINTESTINAL OR UROGENITAL TRACT, AND THOSE IN VAGOTONIC STATES.*
* MAY BE BASED ON GENERAL INFORMATION ON CARBAMATES.

HEALTH EFFECTS AND FIRST AID

INHALATION: PYROLAN: SEE INFORMATION ON CARBAMATES.
CARBAMATES: CHOLINESTERASE INHIBITOR. **ACUTE EXPOSURE-** WHEN INHALED, THE FIRST EFFECTS OF CHOLINESTERASE INHIBITION ARE USUALLY RESPIRATORY AND MAY INCLUDE NASAL HYPEREMIA AND WATERY DISCHARGE, CHEST DISCOMFORT, DYSPNEA, AND WHEEZING DUE TO INCREASED BRONCHIAL SECRETIONS AND BRONCHOCONSTRICTION. OTHER SYSTEMIC EFFECTS MAY BEGIN WITHIN A FEW MINUTES OR SEVERAL HOURS OF EXPOSURE. SYMPTOMS MAY INCLUDE NAUSEA, VOMITING, DIARRHEA, ABDOMINAL CRAMPS, HEADACHE, VERTIGO, OCULAR PAIN, CILIARY MUSCLE SPASM, BLURRING OR DIMNESS OF VISION, MIOSIS, OR IN SOME CASES MYDRIASIS, LACRIMATION, SALIVATION, SWEATING, AND CONFUSION. OTHER REPORTED CENTRAL NERVOUS SYSTEM OR NEUROMUSCULAR EFFECTS INCLUDE ATAXIA, SLURRED SPEECH, AREFLEXIA, WEAKNESS, FATIGUE, TWITCHING, FASCICULATION, TREMOR, AND EVENTUALLY PARALYSIS OF THE EXTREMITIES AND POSSIBLY OF THE RESPIRATORY MUSCLES. IN SEVERE CASES, THERE MAY ALSO BE INVOLUNTARY DEFECATION AND URINATION, BRADYCARDIA, HYPOTENSION, PULMONARY EDEMA, CONVULSIONS, COMA, AND DEATH FROM RESPIRATORY FAILURE OR CARDIAC ARREST. CARBAMATES GENERALLY DO NOT ACCUMULATE IN MAMMALIAN TISSUE AND THE CHOLINESTERASE INHIBITION REVERSES RATHER RAPIDLY. IN NON-FATAL CASES, THE ILLNESS GENERALLY LASTS LESS THAN 24 HOURS. **CHRONIC EXPOSURE-** PROLONGED OR REPEATED EXPOSURE MAY CAUSE EFFECTS AS DESCRIBED IN ACUTE EXPOSURE.

FIRST AID- REMOVE FROM EXPOSURE AREA TO FRESH AIR IMMEDIATELY. IF BREATHING HAS STOPPED, GIVE ARTIFICIAL RESPIRATION. MAINTAIN AIRWAY AND BLOOD PRESSURE AND ADMINISTER OXYGEN IF AVAILABLE. KEEP AFFECTED PERSON WARM AND AT REST. TREAT SYMPTOMATICALLY AND SUPPORTIVELY. ADMINISTRATION OF OXYGEN SHOULD BE PERFORMED BY QUALIFIED PERSONNEL. GET MEDICAL ATTENTION IMMEDIATELY.

SKIN CONTACT: PYROLAN: SEE INFORMATION ON CARBAMATES.
CARBAMATES: CHOLINESTERASE INHIBITOR. **ACUTE EXPOSURE-** SOME COMPOUNDS MAY CAUSE IRRITATION. LOCALIZED SWEATING AND FASCICULATIONS MAY OCCUR AT THE SITE OF CONTACT. IF SUFFICIENT AMOUNTS ARE ABSORBED THROUGH THE SKIN, OTHER EFFECTS OF CHOLINESTERASE INHIBITION MAY OCCUR AS DESCRIBED IN ACUTE INHALATION; SYMPTOMS MAY BE DELAYED FOR 2-3 HOURS, USUALLY NO MORE THAN 8 HOURS. **CHRONIC EXPOSURE-** REPEATED OR PROLONGED EXPOSURE MAY CAUSE EFFECTS AS DESCRIBED IN ACUTE EXPOSURE.

FIRST AID- REMOVE CONTAMINATED CLOTHING IMMEDIATELY. WASH CONTAMINATED AREAS WITH SOAP AND WATER FOLLOWED BY ALCOHOL (ARENA, POISONING, 4TH ED.). EMERGENCY PERSONNEL SHOULD WEAR GLOVES AND AVOID CONTAMINATION. TREAT RESPIRATORY DIFFICULTY WITH ARTIFICIAL RESPIRATION. GET MEDICAL ATTENTION IMMEDIATELY.

EYE CONTACT: PYROLAN: SEE INFORMATION ON CARBAMATES.
CARBAMATES: CHOLINESTERASE INHIBITOR. **ACUTE EXPOSURE-** DIRECT CONTACT MAY CAUSE PAIN, HYPEREMIA, LACRIMATION, TWITCHING OF THE EYELIDS, MIOSIS, AND CILIARY MUSCLE SPASM WITH LOSS OF ACCOMODATION, BLURRED OR DIMMED VISION AND BROWACHE. SOMETIMES MYDRIASIS MAY OCCUR INSTEAD OF MIOSIS. WITH SUFFICIENT EXPOSURE, OTHER SYMPTOMS OF CHOLINESTERASE INHIBITION MAY OCCUR AS DESCRIBED IN ACUTE INHALATION. **CHRONIC EXPOSURE-** PROLONGED EXPOSURE MAY CAUSE EFFECTS AS DESCRIBED IN ACUTE EXPOSURE. SOME COMPOUNDS HAVE CAUSED TOXIC EFFECTS ON THE CRYSTALLINE LENS, CONJUNCTIVAL THICKENING AND OBSTRUCTION OF NASOLACRIMAL CANALS WHEN USED AS MIOTIC EYE DROPS.

FIRST AID- IRRIGATE EYES WITH WATER OR SALINE SOLUTION. IF SYMPTOMS OF POISONING OCCUR, TREAT RESPIRATORY DIFFICULTY WITH ARTIFICIAL RESPIRATION AND OXYGEN. OBSERVE PATIENT FOR AT LEAST 24-36 HOURS (GOSSELIN, CLINICAL TOXICOLOGY OF COMMERCIAL PRODUCTS, 5TH ED.). GET MEDICAL ATTENTION IMMEDIATELY. OXYGEN SHOULD BE ADMINISTERED BY QUALIFIED MEDICAL PERSONNEL.

INGESTION: PYROLAN: TOXIC. SEE INFORMATION ON CARBAMATES.
CARBAMATES: CHOLINESTERASE INHIBITOR. **ACUTE EXPOSURE-** WHEN INGESTED, THE FIRST EFFECTS MAY BE NAUSEA, VOMITING, ANOREXIA, ABDOMINAL CRAMPS, AND DIARRHEA. WITH ABSORPTION FROM THE GASTROINTESTINAL TRACT, THE OTHER EFFECTS OF CHOLINESTERASE INHIBITION AS DESCRIBED IN ACUTE INHALATION MAY OCCUR; SYMPTOMS MAY BEGIN WITHIN MINUTES OR BE DELAYED SEVERAL HOURS. **CHRONIC EXPOSURE-** REPEATED INGESTION MAY CAUSE EFFECTS AS DESCRIBED IN ACUTE EXPOSURE.

FIRST AID- IF PERSON IS ALERT AND RESPIRATION IS NOT DEPRESSED, GIVE SYRUP OF IPECAC FOLLOWED BY WATER (IF VOMITING OCCURS, KEEP HEAD BELOW HIPS TO PREVENT ASPIRATION). IF CONSCIOUSNESS LEVEL DECLINES OR VOMITING HAS NOT OCCURRED IN 15 MINUTES EMPTY STOMACH BY GASTRIC LAVAGE WITH THE AID OF CUFFED ENDOTRACHEAL TUBE USING ISOTONIC SALINE OR 5% SODIUM BICARBONATE FOLLOW WITH ACTIVATED CHARCOAL. ESTABLISH AND MAINTAIN AIRWAY. TREAT RESPIRATORY DIFFICULTY WITH ARTIFICIAL RESPIRATION AND OXYGEN. DO NOT GIVE MORPHINE, AMINOPHYLLINE, PHENOTHIAZINES, RESERPINE, FUROSEMIDE, OR ETHACRYNIC ACID (MORGAN, RECOGNITION AND MANAGEMENT OF PESTICIDE POISONINGS, 3RD ED.). TREAT SYMPTOMATICALLY AND SUPPORTIVELY. ADMINISTRATION OF OXYGEN AND LAVAGE MUST BE PERFORMED BY QUALIFIED MEDICAL PERSONNEL. GET MEDICAL ATTENTION IMMEDIATELY.

ANTIDOTE: THE FOLLOWING ANTIDOTE(S) HAVE BEEN RECOMMENDED. HOWEVER, THE DECISION AS TO WHETHER THE SEVERITY OF POISONING REQUIRES ADMINISTRATION OF ANY ANTIDOTE AND ACTUAL DOSE REQUIRED SHOULD BE MADE BY QUALIFIED MEDICAL PERSONNEL.
FOR CHOLINESTERASE INHIBITORS: ESTABLISH CLEAR AIRWAY AND TISSUE OXYGENATION BY ASPIRATION OF SECRETIONS, AND IF NECESSARY, BY ASSISTED PULMONARY VENTILATION WITH OXYGEN. IMPROVE TISSUE OXYGENATION AS MUCH AS POSSIBLE BEFORE ADMINISTERING ATROPINE TO MINIMIZE THE RISK OF VENTRICULAR FIBRILLATION. ADMINISTER ATROPINE SULFATE INTRAVENOUSLY, OR INTRAMUSCULARLY IF IV INJECTION IS NOT POSSIBLE. IN MODERATELY SEVERE POISONING ADMINISTER ATROPINE SULFATE, 0.4-2.0 MG REPEATED EVERY 15 MINUTES UNTIL ATROPINIZATION IS ACHIEVED (TACHYCARDIA, FLUSHING, DRY MOUTH, MYDRIASIS). MAINTAIN ATROPINIZATION BY REPEATED DOSES FOR 2-12 HOURS, OR LONGER, DEPENDING ON THE SEVERITY OF POISONING. THE APPEARANCE OF RALES IN THE LUNG BASES, MIOSIS, SALIVATION, NAUSEA,

BRADYCARDIA, ARE ALL INDICATIONS OF INADEQUATE ATROPINIZATION. SEVERELY POISONED INDIVIDUALS MAY EXHIBIT REMARKABLE TOLERANCE TO ATROPINE; TWO OR MORE TIMES THE DOSAGES SUGGESTED ABOVE MAY BE NEEDED. PERSONS NOT POISONED OR ONLY SLIGHTLY POISONED, HOWEVER, MAY DEVELOP SIGNS OF ATROPINE TOXICITY FROM SUCH LARGE DOSAGES: FEVER, MUSCLE FIBRILLATIONS, AND DELIRIUM ARE THE MAIN SIGNS OF ATROPINE TOXICITY. IF THESE SIGNS APPEAR WHILE THE PATIENT IS FULLY ATROPINIZED, ATROPINE ADMINISTRATION SHOULD BE DISCONTINUED, AT LEAST TEMPORARILY. OBSERVE TREATED PATIENTS CLOSELY AT LEAST 24 HOURS TO INSURE THAT SYMPTOMS (POSSIBLY PULMONARY EDEMA) DO NOT RECUR AS ATROPINIZATION WEARS OFF. IN VERY SEVERE POISONINGS, METABOLIC DISPOSITION OF TOXICANT MAY REQUIRE SEVERAL HOURS OR DAYS DURING WHICH ATROPINIZATION MUST BE MAINTAINED. MARKEDLY LOWER LEVELS OF URINARY METABOLITES INDICATE THAT ATROPINE DOSAGE CAN BE TAPERED OFF. AS DOSAGE IS REDUCED, CHECK THE LUNG BASES FREQUENTLY FOR RALES. IF RALES ARE HEARD OR OTHER SYMPTOMS RETURN, RE-ESTABLISH ATROPINIZATION PROMPTLY (MORGAN, RECOGNITION AND MANAGEMENT OF PESTICIDE POISONINGS, 3RD ED.). ADMINISTRATION OF ANTIDOTE MUST BE PERFORMED BY QUALIFIED MEDICAL PERSONNEL.

PRALIDOXIME (PROTOPAM-AYERST, 2-PAM) IS OF DOUBTFUL VALUE IN POISONINGS BY CARBAMATE INHIBITORS OF CHOLINESTERASE. ATROPINE ALONE IS ALMOST ALWAYS AN ADEQUATE ANTIDOTE. PRALIDOXIME IS PROBABLY CONTRAINDICATED IN POISONING BY CARBARYL SPECIFICALLY, AND OTHER MONOMETHYLATED CARBAMATES. IF A VICTIM OF DIMETHYLCARBAMATE INSECTICIDE POISONING FAILS TO RESPOND PROMPTLY AND ADEQUATELY TO ATROPINE, OR IF POISONING INVOLVES A COMBINATION OF CARBAMATE AND ORGANOPHOSPHATE, A DILUTE SOLUTION OF PRALIDOXIME (TOTAL DOSE IN 250 ML 5% GLUCOSE SOLUTION) MAY BE GIVEN CAUTIOUSLY INTRAVENOUSLY. ADULT DOSAGE IS 1 GRAM (MORGAN, RECOGNITION AND MANAGEMENT OF PESTICIDE POISONINGS, THIRD EDITION; HAYES, PESTICIDES STUDIED IN MAN, 1982).

REACTIVITY

REACTIVITY: STABLE UNDER NORMAL TEMPERATURES AND PRESSURES.

INCOMPATIBILITIES: PYROLAN: OXIDIZERS (STRONG): FIRE AND EXPLOSION HAZARD.

DECOMPOSITION: THERMAL DECOMPOSITION PRODUCTS MAY INCLUDE TOXIC OXIDES OF CARBON AND NITROGEN.

POLYMERIZATION: HAZARDOUS POLYMERIZATION HAS NOT BEEN REPORTED TO OCCUR UNDER NORMAL TEMPERATURES AND PRESSURES.

STORAGE AND DISPOSAL

OBSERVE ALL FEDERAL, STATE AND LOCAL REGULATIONS WHEN STORING OR DISPOSING OF THIS SUBSTANCE. FOR ASSISTANCE, CONTACT THE DISTRICT DIRECTOR OF THE ENVIRONMENTAL PROTECTION AGENCY.

STORAGE

STORE IN ACCORDANCE WITH 40 CFR 165 RECOMMENDED PROCEDURES FOR THE DISPOSAL AND STORAGE OF PESTICIDES AND PESTICIDE CONTAINERS.
STORE AWAY FROM INCOMPATIBLE SUBSTANCES.

DISPOSAL

DISPOSAL MUST BE IN ACCORDANCE WITH 40 CFR 165 RECOMMENDED PROCEDURES FOR THE DISPOSAL AND STORAGE OF PESTICIDES AND PESTICIDE CONTAINERS.

CONDITIONS TO AVOID

MAY BURN BUT DOES NOT IGNITE READILY. CONTAINERS MAY EXPLODE IN HEAT OF FIRE.

SPILL AND LEAK PROCEDURES

OCCUPATIONAL SPILL: DO NOT TOUCH SPILLED MATERIAL. STOP LEAK IF YOU CAN DO IT WITHOUT RISK. USE WATER SPRAY TO REDUCE VAPORS. FOR SMALL SPILLS, TAKE UP WITH SAND OR OTHER ABSORBENT MATERIAL AND PLACE INTO CONTAINERS FOR LATER DISPOSAL. FOR SMALL DRY SPILLS, WITH A CLEAN SHOVEL PLACE MATERIAL INTO CLEAN, DRY CONTAINERS AND COVER. MOVE CONTAINERS FROM SPILL AREA. FOR LARGER SPILLS, DIKE FAR AHEAD OF SPILL FOR LATER DISPOSAL. KEEP UNNECESSARY PEOPLE AWAY. ISOLATE HAZARD AREA AND DENY ENTRY. VENTILATE CLOSED SPACES BEFORE ENTERING.

PROTECTIVE EQUIPMENT

VENTILATION: PROVIDE LOCAL EXHAUST OR PROCESS ENCLOSURE VENTILATION SYSTEM.

RESPIRATOR: THE FOLLOWING RESPIRATORS ARE RECOMMENDED BASED ON INFORMATION FOUND IN THE PHYSICAL DATA, TOXICITY AND HEALTH EFFECTS SECTIONS. THEY ARE RANKED IN ORDER FROM MINIMUM TO MAXIMUM RESPIRATORY PROTECTION. THE SPECIFIC RESPIRATOR SELECTED MUST BE BASED ON CONTAMINATION LEVELS FOUND IN THE WORK PLACE, MUST NOT EXCEED THE WORKING LIMITS OF THE RESPIRATOR AND BE JOINTLY APPROVED BY THE NATIONAL INSTITUTE FOR OCCUPATIONAL SAFETY AND HEALTH AND THE MINE SAFETY AND HEALTH ADMINISTRATION (NIOSH-MSHA).

TYPE 'C' SUPPLIED-AIR RESPIRATOR WITH A FULL FACEPIECE OPERATED IN PRESSURE-DEMAND OR OTHER POSITIVE PRESSURE MODE OR WITH A FULL FACEPIECE, HELMET OR HOOD OPERATED IN CONTINOUS-FLOW MODE.

SELF-CONTAINED BREATHING APPARATUS WITH A FULL FACEPIECE OPERATED IN PRESSURE-DEMAND OR OTHER POSITIVE PRESSURE MODE.

FOR FIREFIGHTING AND OTHER IMMEDIATELY DANGEROUS TO LIFE OR HEALTH CONDITIONS:

SELF-CONTAINED BREATHING APPARATUS WITH FULL FACEPIECE OPERATED IN PRESSURE-DEMAND OR OTHER POSITIVE PRESSURE MODE.

SUPPLIED-AIR RESPIRATOR WITH FULL FACEPIECE AND OPERATED IN PRESSURE-DEMAND OR OTHER POSITIVE PRESSURE MODE IN COMBINATION WITH AN AUXILIARY SELF-CONTAINED BREATHING APPARATUS OPERATED IN PRESSURE-DEMAND OR OTHER POSITIVE PRESSURE MODE.

CLOTHING: EMPLOYEE MUST WEAR APPROPRIATE PROTECTIVE (IMPERVIOUS) CLOTHING AND EQUIPMENT TO PREVENT ANY POSSIBILITY OF SKIN CONTACT WITH THIS SUBSTANCE.

GLOVES: EMPLOYEE MUST WEAR APPROPRIATE PROTECTIVE GLOVES TO PREVENT CONTACT WITH THIS SUBSTANCE.

EYE PROTECTION: EMPLOYEE MUST WEAR SPLASH-PROOF OR DUST-RESISTANT SAFETY GOGGLES WITH OR WITHOUT A FACESHIELD TO PREVENT CONTACT WITH THIS SUBSTANCE.

EMERGENCY EYE WASH: WHERE THERE IS ANY POSSIBILITY THAT AN EMPLOYEE'S EYES MAY BE EXPOSED TO THIS SUBSTANCE, THE EMPLOYER SHOULD PROVIDE AN EYE WASH FOUNTAIN WITHIN THE IMMEDIATE WORK AREA FOR EMERGENCY USE.

AUTHORIZED BY- OCCUPATIONAL HEALTH SERVICES, INC.
CREATION DATE: 10/04/89 ***REVISION DATE:*** 06/12/90

MATERIAL SAFETY DATA SHEET

OCCUPATIONAL HEALTH SERVICES, INC.
AGRICULTURE AND PESTICIDE DIVISION
450 SEVENTH AVENUE, SUITE 2407
NEW YORK, NEW YORK 10123
1-800-445-MSDS OR (212) 967-1100

EMERGENCY CONTACT:
JOHN S. BRANSFORD, JR. (615) 292-1180

SUBSTANCE IDENTIFICATION

CAS-NUMBER 1967-16-4

SUBSTANCE: **CHLORBUFAM**

TRADE NAMES/SYNONYMS: CARBAMIC ACID, (3-CHLOROPHENYL)-, 1-METHYL-2-PROPYNYL ESTER; CARBANILIC ACID, M-CHLORO-, 1-METHYL-2-PROPYNYL ESTER; (3-CHLOROPHENYL)CARBAMIC ACID, 1-METHYL-2-PROPYNYL ESTER; M-CHLOROCARBANILIC ACID, 1-METHYL-2-PROPYNYL ESTER; 1-METHYLPROP-2-YNYL 3-CHLOROCARBANILATE; 1-METHYLPROP-2-YNYL 3-CHLOROPHENYLCARBAMATE; 1-METHYL-2-PROPYNYL (3-CHLOROPHENYL)CARBAMATE; 1-METHYL-2-PROPYNYL M-CHLOROCARBANILATE; BIPC; CHLORBUPHAM; CHLOROBUFAM; CHLORBUFAME; C11H10CLNO2; PST73265

CHEMICAL FAMILY: CARBAMATE

MOLECULAR FORMULA: C11-H10-CL-N-O2

MOLECULAR WEIGHT: 223.67

CERCLA RATINGS (SCALE 0-3): HEALTH=3 FIRE=1 REACTIVITY=0 PERSISTENCE=1

NFPA RATINGS (SCALE 0-4): HEALTH=U FIRE=1 REACTIVITY=0

COMPONENTS AND CONTAMINANTS

COMPONENT: CHLORBUFAM ***PERCENT:*** 100.0
CAS# 1967-16-4

EXPOSURE LIMITS: NO OCCUPATIONAL EXPOSURE LIMITS ESTABLISHED BY OSHA, ACGIH, OR NIOSH.

PHYSICAL DATA

DESCRIPTION: COLORLESS, CRYSTALLINE SOLID.

MELTING POINT: 102-104 F (39-40 C)

SPECIFIC GRAVITY: NOT AVAILABLE ***VAPOR PRESSURE:*** NEGLIGIBLE

SOLUBILITY IN WATER: 0.5%

SOLVENT SOLUBILITY: SOLUBLE IN ACETONE AND METHANOL; MODERATELY SOLUBLE IN ETHANOL.

FIRE AND EXPLOSION DATA

FIRE AND EXPLOSION HAZARD: SLIGHT FIRE HAZARD WHEN EXPOSED TO HEAT OR FLAME.

FIREFIGHTING MEDIA: DRY CHEMICAL, CARBON DIOXIDE, HALON, WATER SPRAY OR STANDARD FOAM (1987 EMERGENCY RESPONSE GUIDEBOOK, DOT P 5800.4).
FOR LARGER FIRES, USE WATER SPRAY, FOG OR STANDARD FOAM (1987 EMERGENCY RESPONSE GUIDEBOOK, DOT P 5800.4).

FIREFIGHTING: MOVE CONTAINERS FROM FIRE AREA IF POSSIBLE (1987 EMERGENCY RESPONSE GUIDEBOOK, DOT P 5800.4, GUIDE PAGE 53).
USE AGENTS SUITABLE FOR TYPE OF SURROUNDING FIRE. AVOID BREATHING HAZARDOUS VAPORS, KEEP UPWIND.

TOXICITY

CHLORBUFAM: TOXICITY DATA: 2500 MG/KG ORAL-RAT LD50; 250 MG/KG INTRAPERITONEAL-MOUSE LD50; 15500 UG/KG UNREPORTED-MOUSE LD50. CARCINOGEN STATUS: NONE. ACUTE TOXICITY: MODERATELY TOXIC BY INGESTION. TARGET EFFECTS: NO DATA AVAILABLE.

HEALTH EFFECTS AND FIRST AID

INHALATION: CHLORBUFAM: **ACUTE EXPOSURE-** NO DATA AVAILABLE. **CHRONIC EXPOSURE-** NO DATA AVAILABLE.

FIRST AID- REMOVE FROM EXPOSURE AREA TO FRESH AIR IMMEDIATELY. IF BREATHING HAS STOPPED, PERFORM ARTIFICIAL RESPIRATION. KEEP PERSON WARM AND AT REST. TREAT SYMPTOMATICALLY AND SUPPORTIVELY. GET MEDICAL ATTENTION IMMEDIATELY.

SKIN CONTACT: CHLORBUFAM: **ACUTE EXPOSURE-** CHLORBUFAM APPLIED TO THE BACKS OF RABBITS PRODUCED A SLIGHT TEMPORARY ERYTHEMA AFTER 15 MINUTES; THIS EFFECT WAS MORE SIGNIFICANT AFTER 20-HOUR APPLICATION. **CHRONIC EXPOSURE-** NO DATA AVAILABLE.

FIRST AID- REMOVE CONTAMINATED CLOTHING AND SHOES IMMEDIATELY. WASH AFFECTED AREA WITH SOAP OR MILD DETERGENT AND LARGE AMOUNTS OF WATER UNTIL NO EVIDENCE OF CHEMICAL REMAINS (APPROXIMATELY 15-20 MINUTES). GET MEDICAL ATTENTION IMMEDIATELY.

EYE CONTACT: CHLORBUFAM: **ACUTE EXPOSURE-** NO DATA AVAILABLE. **CHRONIC EXPOSURE-** NO DATA AVAILABLE.

FIRST AID- WASH EYES IMMEDIATELY WITH LARGE AMOUNTS OF WATER OR NORMAL SALINE, OCCASIONALLY LIFTING UPPER AND LOWER LIDS, UNTIL NO EVIDENCE OF CHEMICAL REMAINS (APPROXIMATELY 15-20 MINUTES). GET MEDICAL ATTENTION IMMEDIATELY.

INGESTION: CHLORBUFAM: **ACUTE EXPOSURE-** A LETHAL DOSE IN RATS WAS 2500 MG/KG; SYMPTOMS WERE NOT REPORTED. **CHRONIC EXPOSURE-** NO DATA AVAILABLE.

FIRST AID- TREAT SYMPTOMATICALLY AND SUPPORTIVELY. GET MEDICAL ATTENTION IMMEDIATELY. IF VOMITING OCCURS, KEEP HEAD LOWER THAN HIPS TO PREVENT ASPIRATION.

ANTIDOTE: NO SPECIFIC ANTIDOTE. TREAT SYMPTOMATICALLY AND SUPPORTIVELY.

REACTIVITY

REACTIVITY: STABLE UNDER NORMAL TEMPERATURES AND PRESSURES.

INCOMPATIBILITIES: CHLORBUFAM: OXIDIZERS (STRONG): FIRE AND EXPLOSION HAZARD.

DECOMPOSITION: THERMAL DECOMPOSITION PRODUCTS MAY INCLUDE TOXIC OXIDES OF NITROGEN AND CARBON AND TOXIC AND CORROSIVE FUMES OF CHLORIDES.

POLYMERIZATION: HAZARDOUS POLYMERIZATION HAS NOT BEEN REPORTED TO OCCUR UNDER NORMAL TEMPERATURES AND PRESSURES.

STORAGE AND DISPOSAL

OBSERVE ALL FEDERAL, STATE AND LOCAL REGULATIONS WHEN STORING OR DISPOSING OF THIS SUBSTANCE. FOR ASSISTANCE, CONTACT THE DISTRICT DIRECTOR OF THE ENVIRONMENTAL PROTECTION AGENCY.

****STORAGE****

STORE IN ACCORDANCE WITH 40 CFR 165 RECOMMENDED PROCEDURES FOR THE DISPOSAL AND STORAGE OF PESTICIDES AND PESTICIDE CONTAINERS.
STORE AWAY FROM INCOMPATIBLE SUBSTANCES.

****DISPOSAL****

DISPOSAL MUST BE IN ACCORDANCE WITH 40 CFR 165 RECOMMENDED PROCEDURES FOR THE DISPOSAL AND STORAGE OF PESTICIDES AND PESTICIDE CONTAINERS.

CONDITIONS TO AVOID

MAY BURN BUT DOES NOT IGNITE READILY. AVOID CONTACT WITH STRONG OXIDIZERS, EXCESSIVE HEAT, SPARKS, OR OPEN FLAME.

SPILL AND LEAK PROCEDURES

OCCUPATIONAL SPILL: SWEEP UP AND PLACE IN SUITABLE CLEAN, DRY CONTAINERS FOR RECLAMATION OR LATER DISPOSAL. DO NOT FLUSH SPILLED MATERIAL INTO SEWER. KEEP UNNECESSARY PEOPLE AWAY.

PROTECTIVE EQUIPMENT

VENTILATION: PROVIDE LOCAL EXHAUST OR GENERAL DILUTION VENTILATION SYSTEM.

RESPIRATOR: THE FOLLOWING RESPIRATORS ARE RECOMMENDED BASED ON INFORMATION FOUND IN THE PHYSICAL DATA, TOXICITY AND HEALTH EFFECTS SECTIONS. THEY ARE RANKED IN ORDER FROM MINIMUM TO MAXIMUM RESPIRATORY PROTECTION. THE SPECIFIC RESPIRATOR SELECTED MUST BE BASED ON CONTAMINATION LEVELS FOUND IN THE WORK PLACE, MUST NOT EXCEED THE WORKING LIMITS OF THE RESPIRATOR AND BE JOINTLY APPROVED BY THE NATIONAL INSTITUTE FOR OCCUPATIONAL SAFETY AND HEALTH AND THE MINE SAFETY AND HEALTH ADMINISTRATION (NIOSH-MSHA).
CHEMICAL CARTRIDGE RESPIRATOR WITH AN ORGANIC VAPOR CARTRIDGE(S) IN COMBINATION WITH A DUST AND MIST FILTER.
GAS MASK WITH ORGANIC VAPOR CANISTER (CHIN-STYLE OR FRONT- OR BACK-MOUNTED CANISTER) WITH A DUST AND MIST FILTER.
GAS MASK WITH ORGANIC VAPOR CANISTER (CHIN-STYLE OR FRONT- OR BACK-MOUNTED CANISTER) WITH A PARTICULATE FILTER.
POWERED AIR-PURIFYING RESPIRATOR WITH A HIGH-EFFICIENCY FILTER.
TYPE 'C' SUPPLIED-AIR RESPIRATOR WITH A FULL FACEPIECE OPERATED IN A PRESSURE-DEMAND OR OTHER POSITIVE PRESSURE MODE.
SELF-CONTAINED BREATHING APPARATUS WITH A FULL FACEPIECE OPERATED IN PRESSURE-DEMAND OR OTHER POSITIVE PRESSURE MODE.
FOR FIREFIGHTING AND OTHER IMMEDIATELY DANGEROUS TO LIFE OR HEALTH CONDITIONS:
SELF-CONTAINED BREATHING APPARATUS WITH FULL FACEPIECE OPERATED IN PRESSURE-DEMAND OR OTHER POSITIVE PRESSURE MODE.
SUPPLIED-AIR RESPIRATOR WITH FULL FACEPIECE AND OPERATED IN PRESSURE-DEMAND OR OTHER POSITIVE PRESSURE MODE IN COMBINATION WITH AN AUXILIARY SELF-CONTAINED BREATHING APPARATUS OPERATED IN PRESSURE-DEMAND OR OTHER POSITIVE PRESSURE MODE.

CLOTHING: EMPLOYEE MUST WEAR APPROPRIATE PROTECTIVE (IMPERVIOUS) CLOTHING AND EQUIPMENT TO PREVENT REPEATED OR PROLONGED SKIN CONTACT WITH THIS SUBSTANCE.

GLOVES: EMPLOYEE MUST WEAR APPROPRIATE PROTECTIVE GLOVES TO PREVENT CONTACT WITH THIS SUBSTANCE.

EYE PROTECTION: EMPLOYEE MUST WEAR SPLASH-PROOF OR DUST-RESISTANT SAFETY GOGGLES TO PREVENT EYE CONTACT WITH THIS SUBSTANCE.
EMERGENCY EYE WASH: WHERE THERE IS ANY POSSIBILITY THAT AN EMPLOYEE'S EYES MAY BE EXPOSED TO THIS SUBSTANCE, THE EMPLOYER SHOULD PROVIDE AN EYE WASH FOUNTAIN WITHIN THE IMMEDIATE WORK AREA FOR EMERGENCY USE.

AUTHORIZED BY- OCCUPATIONAL HEALTH SERVICES, INC.
CREATION DATE: 10/23/89 ***REVISION DATE:*** 05/31/90

MATERIAL SAFETY DATA SHEET

OCCUPATIONAL HEALTH SERVICES, INC.
AGRICULTURE AND PESTICIDE DIVISION
450 SEVENTH AVENUE, SUITE 2407
NEW YORK, NEW YORK 10123
1-800-445-MSDS OR (212) 967-1100

EMERGENCY CONTACT:
JOHN S. BRANSFORD, JR. (615) 292-1180

SUBSTANCE IDENTIFICATION

CAS-NUMBER 2532-49-2

SUBSTANCE: **PYRAMAT**

TRADE NAMES/SYNONYMS: CARBAMIC ACID, DIMETHYL-, 6-METHYL-2-PROPYL-4-PYRIMIDINYL ESTER; DIMETHYLCARBAMIC ACID 6-METHYL-2-PROPYL-4-PYRIMIDINYL ESTER; 6-METHYL-2-PROPYL-4-PYRIMIDINYL DIMETHYLCARBAMATE; 2-N-PROPYL-4-METHYLPYRIMIDYL-(6)-DIMETHYLCARBAMATE; C11H17N3O2; PST73266

CHEMICAL FAMILY: CARBAMATE
PYRIMIDINE
MOLECULAR FORMULA: C11-H17-N3-O2
MOLECULAR WEIGHT: 223.28
CERCLA RATINGS (SCALE 0-3): HEALTH=3 FIRE=U REACTIVITY=0
PERSISTENCE=1
NFPA RATINGS (SCALE 0-4): HEALTH=U FIRE=U REACTIVITY=0

COMPONENTS AND CONTAMINANTS

COMPONENT: PYRAMAT ***PERCENT:*** 100.0
CAS# 2532-49-2
OTHER CONTAMINANTS: NONE
EXPOSURE LIMITS: NO OCCUPATIONAL EXPOSURE LIMITS ESTABLISHED BY OSHA, ACGIH, OR NIOSH.

PHYSICAL DATA

DESCRIPTION: STRAW-COLORED VISCOUS LIQUID. ***BOILING POINT:*** NOT AVAILABLE
SPECIFIC GRAVITY: NOT AVAILABLE ***VAPOR PRESSURE:*** NOT AVAILABLE
EVAPORATION RATE: NOT AVAILABLE ***SOLUBILITY IN WATER:*** SOLUBLE
SOLVENT SOLUBILITY: SOLUBLE IN MOST ORGANIC SOLVENTS.

FIRE AND EXPLOSION DATA

FIRE AND EXPLOSION HAZARD: UNKNOWN FIRE AND EXPLOSION HAZARD.
FLASH POINT: NOT AVAILABLE
FIREFIGHTING MEDIA: DRY CHEMICAL, CARBON DIOXIDE, HALON, WATER SPRAY OR STANDARD FOAM (1987 EMERGENCY RESPONSE GUIDEBOOK, DOT P 5800.4).
FOR LARGER FIRES, USE WATER SPRAY, FOG OR STANDARD FOAM (1987 EMERGENCY RESPONSE GUIDEBOOK, DOT P 5800.4).
FIREFIGHTING: MOVE CONTAINER FROM FIRE AREA IF POSSIBLE. DIKE FIRE CONTROL WATER FOR LATER DISPOSAL; DO NOT SCATTER THE MATERIAL. COOL FIRE-EXPOSED CONTAINERS WITH WATER FROM SIDE UNTIL WELL AFTER FIRE IS OUT. STAY AWAY FROM STORAGE TANK ENDS. WITHDRAW IMMEDIATELY IN CASE OF RISING SOUND FROM VENTING SAFETY DEVICE OR ANY DISCOLORATION OF STORAGE TANK DUE TO FIRE (1987 EMERGENCY RESPONSE GUIDEBOOK, DOT P 5800.4, GUIDE PAGE 28).
EXTINGUISH ONLY IF FLOW CAN BE STOPPED. USE FLOODING AMOUNTS OF WATER AS A FOG; SOLID STREAMS MAY BE INEFFECTIVE. COOL CONTAINERS WITH FLOODING AMOUNTS OF WATER FROM AS FAR A DISTANCE AS POSSIBLE. AVOID BREATHING POISONOUS VAPORS, KEEP UPWIND.

TOXICITY

PYRAMAT: TOXICITY DATA: 200 MG/KG ORAL-RAT LD50; 225 MG/KG ORAL-MOUSE LD50; 96 MG/KG INTRAPERITONEAL-MOUSE LDLO. CARCINOGEN STATUS: NONE. ACUTE TOXICITY LEVEL: TOXIC BY INGESTION. TARGET EFFECTS: CHOLINESTERASE INHIBITOR. AT INCREASED RISK FROM EXPOSURE: PERSONS WITH ASTHMA, DIABETES, CARDIOVASCULAR DISEASE, MECHANICAL OBSTRUCTION OF THE GASTROINTESTINAL OR UROGENITAL TRACT, AND THOSE IN VAGOTONIC STATES.*
* MAY BE BASED ON GENERAL INFORMATION ON CARBAMATES.

HEALTH EFFECTS AND FIRST AID

INHALATION: PYRAMAT: SEE INFORMATION ON CARBAMATES.
CARBAMATES: CHOLINESTERASE INHIBITOR. **ACUTE EXPOSURE**- WHEN INHALED, THE FIRST EFFECTS OF CHOLINESTERASE INHIBITION ARE USUALLY RESPIRATORY AND MAY INCLUDE NASAL HYPEREMIA AND WATERY DISCHARGE, CHEST DISCOMFORT, DYSPNEA, AND WHEEZING DUE TO INCREASED BRONCHIAL SECRETIONS AND BRONCHOCONSTRICTION. OTHER SYSTEMIC EFFECTS MAY BEGIN WITHIN A FEW MINUTES OR SEVERAL HOURS OF EXPOSURE. SYMPTOMS MAY INCLUDE NAUSEA, VOMITING, DIARRHEA, ABDOMINAL CRAMPS, HEADACHE, VERTIGO, OCULAR PAIN, CILIARY MUSCLE SPASM, BLURRING OR DIMNESS OF VISION, MIOSIS, OR IN SOME CASES MYDRIASIS, LACRIMATION, SALIVATION, SWEATING, AND CONFUSION. OTHER REPORTED CENTRAL NERVOUS SYSTEM OR NEUROMUSCULAR EFFECTS INCLUDE ATAXIA, SLURRED SPEECH, AREFLEXIA, WEAKNESS, FATIGUE, TWITCHING, FASCICULATION, TREMOR, AND EVENTUALLY PARALYSIS OF THE EXTREMITIES AND POSSIBLY OF THE RESPIRATORY MUSCLES. IN SEVERE CASES, THERE MAY ALSO BE INVOLUNTARY DEFECATION AND URINATION, BRADYCARDIA, HYPOTENSION, PULMONARY EDEMA, CONVULSIONS, COMA, AND DEATH FROM RESPIRATORY FAILURE OR CARDIAC ARREST. CARBAMATES GENERALLY DO NOT ACCUMULATE IN MAMMALIAN TISSUE AND THE CHOLINESTERASE INHIBITION REVERSES RATHER RAPIDLY. IN NON-FATAL CASES, THE ILLNESS GENERALLY LASTS LESS THAN 24 HOURS. **CHRONIC EXPOSURE**- PROLONGED OR REPEATED EXPOSURE MAY CAUSE EFFECTS AS DESCRIBED IN ACUTE EXPOSURE.
FIRST AID- REMOVE FROM EXPOSURE AREA TO FRESH AIR IMMEDIATELY. IF BREATHING HAS STOPPED, GIVE ARTIFICIAL RESPIRATION. MAINTAIN AIRWAY AND BLOOD PRESSURE AND ADMINISTER OXYGEN IF AVAILABLE. KEEP AFFECTED PERSON WARM AND AT REST. TREAT SYMPTOMATICALLY AND SUPPORTIVELY. ADMINISTRATION OF OXYGEN SHOULD BE PERFORMED BY QUALIFIED PERSONNEL. GET MEDICAL ATTENTION IMMEDIATELY.

SKIN CONTACT: PYRAMAT: SEE INFORMATION ON CARBAMATES.
CARBAMATES: CHOLINESTERASE INHIBITOR. **ACUTE EXPOSURE**- SOME COMPOUNDS MAY CAUSE IRRITATION. LOCALIZED SWEATING AND FASCICULATIONS MAY OCCUR AT THE SITE OF CONTACT. IF SUFFICIENT AMOUNTS ARE ABSORBED THROUGH THE SKIN, OTHER EFFECTS OF CHOLINESTERASE INHIBITION MAY OCCUR AS DESCRIBED IN ACUTE INHALATION; SYMPTOMS MAY BE DELAYED FOR 2-3 HOURS, USUALLY NO MORE THAN 8 HOURS. **CHRONIC EXPOSURE**- REPEATED OR PROLONGED EXPOSURE MAY CAUSE EFFECTS AS DESCRIBED IN ACUTE EXPOSURE.
FIRST AID- REMOVE CONTAMINATED CLOTHING IMMEDIATELY. WASH CONTAMINATED AREAS WITH SOAP AND WATER FOLLOWED BY ALCOHOL (ARENA, POISONING, 4TH ED.). EMERGENCY PERSONNEL SHOULD WEAR GLOVES AND AVOID CONTAMINATION. TREAT RESPIRATORY DIFFICULTY WITH ARTIFICIAL RESPIRATION. GET MEDICAL ATTENTION IMMEDIATELY.

EYE CONTACT: PYRAMAT: SEE INFORMATION ON CARBAMATES.
CARBAMATES: CHOLINESTERASE INHIBITOR. **ACUTE EXPOSURE**- DIRECT CONTACT MAY CAUSE PAIN, HYPEREMIA, LACRIMATION, TWITCHING OF THE EYELIDS, MIOSIS, AND CILIARY MUSCLE SPASM WITH LOSS OF ACCOMODATION, BLURRED OR DIMMED VISION AND BROWACHE. SOMETIMES MYDRIASIS MAY OCCUR INSTEAD OF MIOSIS. WITH SUFFICIENT EXPOSURE, OTHER SYMPTOMS OF CHOLINESTERASE INHIBITION MAY OCCUR AS DESCRIBED IN ACUTE INHALATION. **CHRONIC EXPOSURE**- PROLONGED EXPOSURE MAY CAUSE EFFECTS AS DESCRIBED IN ACUTE EXPOSURE. SOME COMPOUNDS HAVE CAUSED TOXIC EFFECTS ON THE CRYSTALLINE LENS, CONJUNCTIVAL THICKENING AND OBSTRUCTION OF NASOLACRIMAL CANALS WHEN USED AS MIOTIC EYE DROPS.
FIRST AID- IRRIGATE EYES WITH WATER OR SALINE SOLUTION. IF SYMPTOMS OF POISONING OCCUR, TREAT RESPIRATORY DIFFICULTY WITH ARTIFICIAL RESPIRATION AND OXYGEN. OBSERVE PATIENT FOR AT LEAST 24-36 HOURS (GOSSELIN, CLINICAL TOXICOLOGY OF COMMERCIAL PRODUCTS, 5TH ED.). GET MEDICAL ATTENTION IMMEDIATELY. OXYGEN SHOULD BE ADMINISTERED BY QUALIFIED MEDICAL PERSONNEL.

INGESTION: PYRAMAT: TOXIC. SEE INFORMATION ON CARBAMATES.
CARBAMATES: CHOLINESTERASE INHIBITOR. **ACUTE EXPOSURE**- WHEN INGESTED, THE FIRST EFFECTS MAY BE NAUSEA, VOMITING, ANOREXIA, ABDOMINAL CRAMPS, AND DIARRHEA. WITH ABSORPTION FROM THE GASTROINTESTINAL TRACT, THE OTHER EFFECTS OF CHOLINESTERASE INHIBITION AS DESCRIBED IN ACUTE INHALATION MAY OCCUR; SYMPTOMS MAY BEGIN WITHIN MINUTES OR BE DELAYED SEVERAL HOURS. **CHRONIC EXPOSURE**- REPEATED INGESTION MAY CAUSE EFFECTS AS DESCRIBED IN ACUTE EXPOSURE.
FIRST AID- IF PERSON IS ALERT AND RESPIRATION IS NOT DEPRESSED, GIVE SYRUP OF IPECAC FOLLOWED BY WATER (IF VOMITING OCCURS, KEEP HEAD BELOW HIPS TO PREVENT ASPIRATION). IF CONSCIOUSNESS LEVEL DECLINES OR VOMITING HAS NOT OCCURRED IN 15 MINUTES EMPTY STOMACH BY GASTRIC LAVAGE WITH THE AID OF CUFFED ENDOTRACHEAL TUBE USING ISOTONIC SALINE OR 5% SODIUM BICARBONATE FOLLOW WITH ACTIVATED CHARCOAL. ESTABLISH AND MAINTAIN AIRWAY. TREAT RESPIRATORY DIFFICULTY WITH ARTIFICIAL RESPIRATION AND OXYGEN. DO NOT GIVE MORPHINE, AMINOPHYLLINE, PHENOTHIAZINES, RESERPINE, FUROSEMIDE, OR ETHACRYNIC ACID (MORGAN, RECOGNITION AND MANAGEMENT OF PESTICIDE POISONINGS, 3RD ED.). TREAT SYMPTOMATICALLY AND SUPPORTIVELY. ADMINISTRATION OF OXYGEN AND LAVAGE MUST BE PERFORMED BY QUALIFIED MEDICAL PERSONNEL. GET MEDICAL ATTENTION IMMEDIATELY.
ANTIDOTE: THE FOLLOWING ANTIDOTE(S) HAVE BEEN RECOMMENDED. HOWEVER, THE DECISION AS TO WHETHER THE SEVERITY OF POISONING REQUIRES ADMINISTRATION OF ANY ANTIDOTE AND ACTUAL DOSE REQUIRED SHOULD BE MADE BY QUALIFIED MEDICAL PERSONNEL.
FOR CHOLINESTERASE INHIBITORS: ESTABLISH CLEAR AIRWAY AND TISSUE OXYGENATION BY ASPIRATION OF SECRETIONS, AND IF NECESSARY, BY ASSISTED PULMONARY VENTILATION WITH OXYGEN. IMPROVE TISSUE OXYGENATION AS MUCH AS POSSIBLE BEFORE ADMINISTERING ATROPINE TO MINIMIZE THE RISK OF VENTRICULAR FIBRILLATION. ADMINISTER ATROPINE SULFATE INTRAVENOUSLY, OR INTRAMUSCULARLY IF IV INJECTION IS NOT POSSIBLE. IN MODERATELY SEVERE POISONING ADMINISTER ATROPINE SULFATE, 0.4-2.0 MG REPEATED EVERY 15 MINUTES UNTIL ATROPINIZATION IS ACHIEVED (TACHYCARDIA, FLUSHING, DRY MOUTH, MYDRIASIS). MAINTAIN ATROPINIZATION BY REPEATED DOSES FOR 2-12 HOURS, OR LONGER, DEPENDING ON THE SEVERITY OF POISONING. THE APPEARANCE OF RALES IN THE LUNG BASES, MIOSIS, SALIVATION, NAUSEA, BRADYCARDIA, ARE ALL INDICATIONS OF INADEQUATE ATROPINIZATION. SEVERELY POISONED INDIVIDUALS MAY EXHIBIT REMARKABLE TOLERANCE TO ATROPINE; TWO OR MORE TIMES THE DOSAGES SUGGESTED ABOVE MAY BE NEEDED. PERSONS NOT POISONED OR ONLY SLIGHTLY POISONED, HOWEVER, MAY

DEVELOP SIGNS OF ATROPINE TOXICITY FROM SUCH LARGE DOSAGES: FEVER, MUSCLE FIBRILLATIONS, AND DELIRIUM ARE THE MAIN SIGNS OF ATROPINE TOXICITY. IF THESE SIGNS APPEAR WHILE THE PATIENT IS FULLY ATROPINIZED, ATROPINE ADMINISTRATION SHOULD BE DISCONTINUED, AT LEAST TEMPORARILY. OBSERVE TREATED PATIENTS CLOSELY AT LEAST 24 HOURS TO INSURE THAT SYMPTOMS (POSSIBLY PULMONARY EDEMA) DO NOT RECUR AS ATROPINIZATION WEARS OFF. IN VERY SEVERE POISONINGS, METABOLIC DISPOSITION OF TOXICANT MAY REQUIRE SEVERAL HOURS OR DAYS DURING WHICH ATROPINIZATION MUST BE MAINTAINED. MARKEDLY LOWER LEVELS OF URINARY METABOLITES INDICATE THAT ATROPINE DOSAGE CAN BE TAPERED OFF. AS DOSAGE IS REDUCED, CHECK THE LUNG BASES FREQUENTLY FOR RALES. IF RALES ARE HEARD OR OTHER SYMPTOMS RETURN, RE-ESTABLISH ATROPINIZATION PROMPTLY (MORGAN, RECOGNITION AND MANAGEMENT OF PESTICIDE POISONINGS, 3RD ED.). ADMINISTRATION OF ANTIDOTE MUST BE PERFORMED BY QUALIFIED MEDICAL PERSONNEL.

PRALIDOXIME (PROTOPAM-AYERST, 2-PAM) IS OF DOUBTFUL VALUE IN POISONINGS BY CARBAMATE INHIBITORS OF CHOLINESTERASE. ATROPINE ALONE IS ALMOST ALWAYS AN ADEQUATE ANTIDOTE. PRALIDOXIME IS PROBABLY CONTRAINDICATED IN POISONING BY CARBARYL SPECIFICALLY, AND OTHER MONOMETHYLATED CARBAMATES. IF A VICTIM OF DIMETHYLCARBAMATE INSECTICIDE POISONING FAILS TO RESPOND PROMPTLY AND ADEQUATELY TO ATROPINE, OR IF POISONING INVOLVES A COMBINATION OF CARBAMATE AND ORGANOPHOSPHATE, A DILUTE SOLUTION OF PRALIDOXIME (TOTAL DOSE IN 250 ML 5% GLUCOSE SOLUTION) MAY BE GIVEN CAUTIOUSLY INTRAVENOUSLY. ADULT DOSAGE IS 1 GRAM (MORGAN, RECOGNITION AND MANAGEMENT OF PESTICIDE POISONINGS, THIRD EDITION; HAYES, PESTICIDES STUDIED IN MAN, 1982).

REACTIVITY

REACTIVITY: STABLE UNDER NORMAL TEMPERATURES AND PRESSURES.

INCOMPATIBILITIES: PYRAMAT: OXIDIZERS (STRONG): FIRE AND EXPLOSION HAZARD.

DECOMPOSITION: THERMAL DECOMPOSITION PRODUCTS MAY INCLUDE TOXIC OXIDES OF CARBON AND NITROGEN.

POLYMERIZATION: HAZARDOUS POLYMERIZATION HAS NOT BEEN REPORTED TO OCCUR UNDER NORMAL TEMPERATURES AND PRESSURES.

STORAGE AND DISPOSAL

OBSERVE ALL FEDERAL, STATE AND LOCAL REGULATIONS WHEN STORING OR DISPOSING OF THIS SUBSTANCE. FOR ASSISTANCE, CONTACT THE DISTRICT DIRECTOR OF THE ENVIRONMENTAL PROTECTION AGENCY.

****STORAGE****

STORE IN ACCORDANCE WITH 40 CFR 165 RECOMMENDED PROCEDURES FOR THE DISPOSAL AND STORAGE OF PESTICIDES AND PESTICIDE CONTAINERS.

STORE AWAY FROM INCOMPATIBLE SUBSTANCES.

****DISPOSAL****

DISPOSAL MUST BE IN ACCORDANCE WITH 40 CFR 165 RECOMMENDED PROCEDURES FOR THE DISPOSAL AND STORAGE OF PESTICIDES AND PESTICIDE CONTAINERS.

CONDITIONS TO AVOID

AVOID CONTACT WITH HEAT, SPARKS, FLAMES OR OTHER IGNITION SOURCES. VAPORS MAY BE EXPLOSIVE. MATERIAL IS POISONOUS; AVOID INHALATION OF VAPORS OR CONTACT WITH SKIN. DO NOT ALLOW MATERIAL TO CONTAMINATE WATER SOURCES.

SPILL AND LEAK PROCEDURES

OCCUPATIONAL SPILL: SHUT OFF IGNITION SOURCES. DO NOT TOUCH SPILLED MATERIAL. STOP LEAK IF YOU CAN DO IT WITHOUT RISK. USE WATER SPRAY TO REDUCE VAPORS. FOR SMALL SPILLS, TAKE UP WITH SAND OR OTHER ABSORBENT MATERIAL AND PLACE INTO CONTAINERS FOR LATER DISPOSAL. FOR LARGER SPILLS, DIKE FAR AHEAD OF SPILL FOR LATER DISPOSAL. NO SMOKING, FLAMES OR FLARES IN HAZARD AREA! KEEP UNNECESSARY PEOPLE AWAY; ISOLATE HAZARD AREA AND DENY ENTRY.

PROTECTIVE EQUIPMENT

VENTILATION: PROVIDE LOCAL EXHAUST OR PROCESS ENCLOSURE VENTILATION SYSTEM.

RESPIRATOR: THE FOLLOWING RESPIRATORS ARE RECOMMENDED BASED ON INFORMATION FOUND IN THE PHYSICAL DATA, TOXICITY AND HEALTH EFFECTS SECTIONS. THEY ARE RANKED IN ORDER FROM MINIMUM TO MAXIMUM RESPIRATORY PROTECTION. THE SPECIFIC RESPIRATOR SELECTED MUST BE BASED ON CONTAMINATION LEVELS FOUND IN THE WORK PLACE, MUST NOT EXCEED THE WORKING LIMITS OF THE RESPIRATOR AND BE JOINTLY APPROVED BY THE NATIONAL INSTITUTE FOR OCCUPATIONAL SAFETY AND HEALTH AND THE MINE SAFETY AND HEALTH ADMINISTRATION (NIOSH-MSHA).

TYPE 'C' SUPPLIED-AIR RESPIRATOR WITH A FULL FACEPIECE OPERATED IN PRESSURE-DEMAND OR OTHER POSITIVE PRESSURE MODE OR WITH A FULL FACEPIECE, HELMET OR HOOD OPERATED IN CONTINOUS-FLOW MODE.

SELF-CONTAINED BREATHING APPARATUS WITH A FULL FACEPIECE OPERATED IN PRESSURE-DEMAND OR OTHER POSITIVE PRESSURE MODE.

FOR FIREFIGHTING AND OTHER IMMEDIATELY DANGEROUS TO LIFE OR HEALTH CONDITIONS:

SELF-CONTAINED BREATHING APPARATUS WITH FULL FACEPIECE OPERATED IN PRESSURE-DEMAND OR OTHER POSITIVE PRESSURE MODE.

SUPPLIED-AIR RESPIRATOR WITH FULL FACEPIECE AND OPERATED IN PRESSURE-DEMAND OR OTHER POSITIVE PRESSURE MODE IN COMBINATION WITH AN AUXILIARY SELF-CONTAINED BREATHING APPARATUS OPERATED IN PRESSURE-DEMAND OR OTHER POSITIVE PRESSURE MODE.

CLOTHING: EMPLOYEE MUST WEAR APPROPRIATE PROTECTIVE (IMPERVIOUS) CLOTHING AND EQUIPMENT TO PREVENT ANY POSSIBILITY OF SKIN CONTACT WITH THIS SUBSTANCE.

GLOVES: EMPLOYEE MUST WEAR APPROPRIATE PROTECTIVE GLOVES TO PREVENT CONTACT WITH THIS SUBSTANCE.

EYE PROTECTION: EMPLOYEE MUST WEAR SPLASH-PROOF OR DUST-RESISTANT SAFETY GOGGLES AND A FACESHIELD TO PREVENT CONTACT WITH THIS SUBSTANCE.

EMERGENCY WASH FACILITIES: WHERE THERE IS ANY POSSIBILITY THAT AN EMPLOYEE'S EYES AND/OR SKIN MAY BE EXPOSED TO THIS SUBSTANCE, THE EMPLOYER SHOULD PROVIDE AN EYE WASH FOUNTAIN AND QUICK DRENCH SHOWER WITHIN THE IMMEDIATE WORK AREA FOR EMERGENCY USE.

AUTHORIZED BY- OCCUPATIONAL HEALTH SERVICES, INC.

CREATION DATE: 03/22/90 ***REVISION DATE:*** 06/12/90

MATERIAL SAFETY DATA SHEET

OCCUPATIONAL HEALTH SERVICES, INC.
AGRICULTURE AND PESTICIDE DIVISION
450 SEVENTH AVENUE, SUITE 2407
NEW YORK, NEW YORK 10123
1-800-445-MSDS OR (212) 967-1100

EMERGENCY CONTACT:
JOHN S. BRANSFORD, JR. (615) 292-1180

SUBSTANCE IDENTIFICATION

CAS-NUMBER 34681-10-2

SUBSTANCE: BUTOCARBOXIM

TRADE NAMES/SYNONYMS: 2-BUTANONE, 3-(METHYLTHIO)-, O-((METHYLAMINO)CARBONYL)OXIME; 3-(METHYLTHIO)-2-BUTANONE O-((METHYLAMINO)CARBONYL)OXIME; 3-(METHYLTHIO)BUTANONE O-METHYLCARBAMOYLOXIME; 3-(METHYLTHIO)-2-BUTANONE O-(METHYLCARBAMOYL)OXIME; CO 755; DRAWIN 755; C7H14N2O2S; PST73270

CHEMICAL FAMILY: CARBAMATE

MOLECULAR FORMULA: C7-H14-N2-O2-S

MOLECULAR WEIGHT: 190.29

CERCLA RATINGS (SCALE 0-3): HEALTH=3 FIRE=1 REACTIVITY=0 PERSISTENCE=1

NFPA RATINGS (SCALE 0-4): HEALTH=3 FIRE=1 REACTIVITY=0

COMPONENTS AND CONTAMINANTS

COMPONENT: BUTOCARBOXIM ***PERCENT:*** 100.0
CAS# 34681-10-2

OTHER CONTAMINANTS: NONE

EXPOSURE LIMITS: NO OCCUPATIONAL EXPOSURE LIMITS ESTABLISHED BY OSHA, ACGIH, OR NIOSH.

PHYSICAL DATA

DESCRIPTION: WHITE CRYSTALLINE SOLID. ***MELTING POINT:*** 90-99 F (32-37 C)

SPECIFIC GRAVITY: NOT AVAILABLE ***SOLUBILITY IN WATER:*** 3%

SOLVENT SOLUBILITY: SOLUBLE IN AROMATIC HYDROCARBONS, ESTERS, KETONES; POORLY SOLUBLE IN CARBON TETRACHLORIDE, ALIPHATIC HYDROCARBONS.

FIRE AND EXPLOSION DATA

FIRE AND EXPLOSION HAZARD: SLIGHT FIRE HAZARD WHEN EXPOSED TO HEAT OR FLAME.

FIREFIGHTING MEDIA: DRY CHEMICAL, CARBON DIOXIDE, HALON, WATER SPRAY OR STANDARD FOAM (1987 EMERGENCY RESPONSE GUIDEBOOK, DOT P 5800.4).

FOR LARGER FIRES, USE WATER SPRAY, FOG OR STANDARD FOAM (1987 EMERGENCY RESPONSE GUIDEBOOK, DOT P 5800.4).

FIREFIGHTING: MOVE CONTAINERS FROM FIRE AREA IF POSSIBLE. FIGHT FIRE FROM MAXIMUM DISTANCE. STAY AWAY FROM STORAGE TANK ENDS. DIKE FIRE CONTROL WATER FOR LATER DISPOSAL. DO NOT SCATTER MATERIAL (1987 EMERGENCY RESPONSE GUIDEBOOK, DOT P 5800.4, GUIDE PAGE 55). EXTINGUISH USING AGENTS SUITABLE FOR TYPE OF SURROUNDING FIRE. USE FLOODING AMOUNTS OF WATER AS FOG. AVOID BREATHING TOXIC DUST AND FUMES FROM BURNING MATERIAL; KEEP UPWIND.

TOXICITY

BUTOCARBOXIM: TOXICITY DATA: 360 MG/KG SKIN-RABBIT LD50; 153 MG/KG ORAL-RAT LD50; 188 MG/KG SUBCUTANEOUS-RAT LD50. CARCINOGEN STATUS: NONE. LOCAL EFFECTS: CORROSIVE- EYES. ACUTE TOXICITY LEVEL: TOXIC BY DERMAL ABSORPTION AND INGESTION. TARGET EFFECTS: CHOLINESTERASE INHIBITOR. AT INCREASED RISK FROM EXPOSURE: PERSONS WITH ASTHMA, DIABETES, CARDIOVASCULAR DISEASE, MECHANICAL OBSTRUCTION OF THE GASTROINTESTINAL OR UROGENITAL TRACT, AND THOSE IN VAGOTONIC STATES.*

* MAY BE BASED ON GENERAL INFORMATION ON CARBAMATES.

HEALTH EFFECTS AND FIRST AID

INHALATION: BUTOCARBOXIM: SEE INFORMATION ON CARBAMATES.
CARBAMATES: CHOLINESTERASE INHIBITOR. **ACUTE EXPOSURE-** WHEN INHALED, THE FIRST EFFECTS OF CHOLINESTERASE INHIBITION ARE USUALLY RESPIRATORY AND MAY INCLUDE NASAL HYPEREMIA AND WATERY DISCHARGE, CHEST DISCOMFORT, DYSPNEA, AND WHEEZING DUE TO INCREASED BRONCHIAL SECRETIONS AND BRONCHOCONSTRICTION. OTHER SYSTEMIC EFFECTS MAY BEGIN WITHIN A FEW MINUTES OR SEVERAL HOURS OF EXPOSURE. SYMPTOMS MAY INCLUDE NAUSEA, VOMITING, DIARRHEA, ABDOMINAL CRAMPS, HEADACHE, VERTIGO, OCULAR PAIN, CILIARY MUSCLE SPASM, BLURRING OR DIMNESS OF VISION, MIOSIS, OR IN SOME CASES MYDRIASIS, LACRIMATION, SALIVATION, SWEATING, AND CONFUSION. OTHER REPORTED CENTRAL NERVOUS SYSTEM OR NEUROMUSCULAR EFFECTS INCLUDE ATAXIA, SLURRED SPEECH, AREFLEXIA, WEAKNESS, FATIGUE, TWITCHING, FASCICULATION, TREMOR, AND EVENTUALLY PARALYSIS OF THE EXTREMITIES AND POSSIBLY OF THE RESPIRATORY MUSCLES. IN SEVERE CASES, THERE MAY ALSO BE INVOLUNTARY DEFECATION AND URINATION, BRADYCARDIA, HYPOTENSION, PULMONARY EDEMA, CONVULSIONS, COMA, AND DEATH FROM RESPIRATORY FAILURE OR CARDIAC ARREST. CARBAMATES GENERALLY DO NOT ACCUMULATE IN MAMMALIAN TISSUE AND THE CHOLINESTERASE INHIBITION REVERSES RATHER RAPIDLY. IN NON-FATAL CASES, THE ILLNESS GENERALLY LASTS LESS THAN 24 HOURS. **CHRONIC EXPOSURE-** PROLONGED OR REPEATED EXPOSURE MAY CAUSE EFFECTS AS DESCRIBED IN ACUTE EXPOSURE.

FIRST AID- REMOVE FROM EXPOSURE AREA TO FRESH AIR IMMEDIATELY. IF BREATHING HAS STOPPED, GIVE ARTIFICIAL RESPIRATION. MAINTAIN AIRWAY AND BLOOD PRESSURE AND ADMINISTER OXYGEN IF AVAILABLE. KEEP AFFECTED PERSON WARM AND AT REST. TREAT SYMPTOMATICALLY AND SUPPORTIVELY. ADMINISTRATION OF OXYGEN SHOULD BE PERFORMED BY QUALIFIED PERSONNEL. GET MEDICAL ATTENTION IMMEDIATELY.

SKIN CONTACT: BUTOCARBOXIM: TOXIC. SEE INFORMATION ON CARBAMATES.
CARBAMATES: CHOLINESTERASE INHIBITOR. **ACUTE EXPOSURE-** SOME COMPOUNDS MAY CAUSE IRRITATION. LOCALIZED SWEATING AND FASCICULATIONS MAY OCCUR AT THE SITE OF CONTACT. IF SUFFICIENT AMOUNTS ARE ABSORBED THROUGH THE SKIN, OTHER EFFECTS OF CHOLINESTERASE INHIBITION MAY OCCUR AS DESCRIBED IN ACUTE INHALATION; SYMPTOMS MAY BE DELAYED FOR 2-3 HOURS, USUALLY NO MORE THAN 8 HOURS. **CHRONIC EXPOSURE-** REPEATED OR PROLONGED EXPOSURE MAY CAUSE EFFECTS AS DESCRIBED IN ACUTE EXPOSURE.

FIRST AID- REMOVE CONTAMINATED CLOTHING IMMEDIATELY. WASH CONTAMINATED AREAS WITH SOAP AND WATER FOLLOWED BY ALCOHOL (ARENA, POISONING, 4TH ED.). EMERGENCY PERSONNEL SHOULD WEAR GLOVES AND AVOID CONTAMINATION. TREAT RESPIRATORY DIFFICULTY WITH ARTIFICIAL RESPIRATION. GET MEDICAL ATTENTION IMMEDIATELY.

EYE CONTACT: BUTOCARBOXIM: CORROSIVE. THIS MATERIAL WAS SEVERELY IRRITATING TO RABBIT EYES INDUCING CORNEAL LESIONS AND IRREVERSIBLE CONJUNCTIVITIS. SEE INFORMATION ON CARBAMATES.
CARBAMATES: CHOLINESTERASE INHIBITOR. **ACUTE EXPOSURE-** DIRECT CONTACT MAY CAUSE PAIN, HYPEREMIA, LACRIMATION, TWITCHING OF THE EYELIDS, MIOSIS, AND CILIARY MUSCLE SPASM WITH LOSS OF ACCOMODATION, BLURRED OR DIMMED VISION AND BROWACHE. SOMETIMES MYDRIASIS MAY OCCUR INSTEAD OF MIOSIS. WITH SUFFICIENT EXPOSURE, OTHER SYMPTOMS OF CHOLINESTERASE INHIBITION MAY OCCUR AS DESCRIBED IN ACUTE INHALATION. **CHRONIC EXPOSURE-** PROLONGED EXPOSURE MAY CAUSE EFFECTS AS DESCRIBED IN ACUTE EXPOSURE. SOME COMPOUNDS HAVE CAUSED TOXIC EFFECTS ON THE CRYSTALLINE LENS, CONJUNCTIVAL THICKENING AND OBSTRUCTION OF NASOLACRIMAL CANALS WHEN USED AS MIOTIC EYE DROPS.

FIRST AID- IRRIGATE EYES WITH WATER OR SALINE SOLUTION. IF SYMPTOMS OF POISONING OCCUR, TREAT RESPIRATORY DIFFICULTY WITH ARTIFICIAL RESPIRATION AND OXYGEN. OBSERVE PATIENT FOR AT LEAST 24-36 HOURS (GOSSELIN, CLINICAL TOXICOLOGY OF COMMERCIAL PRODUCTS, 5TH ED.). GET MEDICAL ATTENTION IMMEDIATELY. OXYGEN SHOULD BE ADMINISTERED BY QUALIFIED MEDICAL PERSONNEL.

INGESTION: BUTOCARBOXIM: TOXIC. SLIGHTLY DECREASED RED BLOOD CELL CHOLINESTERASE LEVELS AND SLIGHTLY INCREASED LIVER WEIGHT IN FEMALES WERE OBSERVED IN A 3-GENERATION REPRODUCTION STUDY OF RATS AT DIETARY LEVELS OF 300 PPM. SEE INFORMATION ON CARBAMATES.
CARBAMATES: CHOLINESTERASE INHIBITOR. **ACUTE EXPOSURE-** WHEN INGESTED, THE FIRST EFFECTS MAY BE NAUSEA, VOMITING, ANOREXIA, ABDOMINAL CRAMPS, AND DIARRHEA. WITH ABSORPTION FROM THE GASTROINTESTINAL TRACT, THE OTHER EFFECTS OF CHOLINESTERASE INHIBITION AS DESCRIBED IN ACUTE INHALATION MAY OCCUR; SYMPTOMS MAY BEGIN WITHIN MINUTES OR BE DELAYED SEVERAL HOURS. **CHRONIC EXPOSURE-** REPEATED INGESTION MAY CAUSE EFFECTS AS DESCRIBED IN ACUTE EXPOSURE.

FIRST AID- IF PERSON IS ALERT AND RESPIRATION IS NOT DEPRESSED, GIVE SYRUP OF IPECAC FOLLOWED BY WATER (IF VOMITING OCCURS, KEEP HEAD BELOW HIPS TO PREVENT ASPIRATION). IF CONSCIOUSNESS LEVEL DECLINES OR VOMITING HAS NOT OCCURRED IN 15 MINUTES EMPTY STOMACH BY GASTRIC LAVAGE WITH THE AID OF CUFFED ENDOTRACHEAL TUBE USING ISOTONIC SALINE OR 5% SODIUM BICARBONATE FOLLOW WITH ACTIVATED CHARCOAL. ESTABLISH AND MAINTAIN AIRWAY. TREAT RESPIRATORY DIFFICULTY WITH ARTIFICIAL RESPIRATION AND OXYGEN. DO NOT GIVE MORPHINE, AMINOPHYLLINE, PHENOTHIAZINES, RESERPINE, FUROSEMIDE, OR ETHACRYNIC ACID (MORGAN, RECOGNITION AND MANAGEMENT OF PESTICIDE POISONINGS, 3RD ED.). TREAT SYMPTOMATICALLY AND SUPPORTIVELY. ADMINISTRATION OF OXYGEN AND LAVAGE MUST BE PERFORMED BY QUALIFIED MEDICAL PERSONNEL. GET MEDICAL ATTENTION IMMEDIATELY.

ANTIDOTE: THE FOLLOWING ANTIDOTE HAS BEEN RECOMMENDED. HOWEVER, THE DECISION AS TO WHETHER THE SEVERITY OF POISONING REQUIRES ADMINISTRATION OF ANY ANTIDOTE AND ACTUAL DOSE REQUIRED SHOULD BE MADE BY QUALIFIED MEDICAL PERSONNEL.
FOR CHOLINESTERASE INHIBITORS: ESTABLISH CLEAR AIRWAY AND TISSUE OXYGENATION BY ASPIRATION OF SECRETIONS, AND IF NECESSARY, BY ASSISTED PULMONARY VENTILATION WITH OXYGEN. IMPROVE TISSUE OXYGENATION AS MUCH AS POSSIBLE BEFORE ADMINISTERING ATROPINE TO MINIMIZE THE RISK OF VENTRICULAR FIBRILLATION. ADMINISTER ATROPINE SULFATE INTRAVENOUSLY, OR INTRAMUSCULARLY IF IV INJECTION IS NOT POSSIBLE. IN MODERATELY SEVERE POISONING ADMINISTER ATROPINE SULFATE, 0.4-2.0 MG REPEATED EVERY 15 MINUTES UNTIL ATROPINIZATION IS ACHIEVED (TACHYCARDIA, FLUSHING, DRY MOUTH, MYDRIASIS). MAINTAIN ATROPINIZATION BY REPEATED DOSES FOR 2-12 HOURS, OR LONGER, DEPENDING ON THE SEVERITY OF POISONING. THE APPEARANCE OF RALES IN THE LUNG BASES, MIOSIS, SALIVATION, NAUSEA, BRADYCARDIA, ARE ALL INDICATIONS OF INADEQUATE ATROPINIZATION. SEVERELY POISONED INDIVIDUALS MAY EXHIBIT REMARKABLE TOLERANCE TO ATROPINE; TWO OR MORE TIMES THE DOSAGES SUGGESTED ABOVE MAY BE NEEDED. PERSONS NOT POISONED OR ONLY SLIGHTLY POISONED, HOWEVER, MAY DEVELOP SIGNS OF ATROPINE TOXICITY FROM SUCH LARGE DOSAGES: FEVER, MUSCLE FIBRILLATIONS, AND DELIRIUM ARE THE MAIN SIGNS OF ATROPINE TOXICITY. IF THESE SIGNS APPEAR WHILE THE PATIENT IS FULLY ATROPINIZED, ATROPINE ADMINISTRATION SHOULD BE DISCONTINUED, AT LEAST TEMPORARILY. OBSERVE TREATED PATIENTS CLOSELY AT LEAST 24 HOURS TO INSURE THAT SYMPTOMS (POSSIBLY PULMONARY EDEMA) DO NOT RECUR AS ATROPINIZATION WEARS OFF. IN VERY SEVERE POISONINGS, METABOLIC DISPOSITION OF TOXICANT MAY REQUIRE SEVERAL HOURS OR DAYS DURING WHICH ATROPINIZATION MUST BE MAINTAINED. MARKEDLY LOWER LEVELS OF URINARY METABOLITES INDICATE THAT ATROPINE DOSAGE CAN BE TAPERED OFF. AS DOSAGE IS REDUCED, CHECK THE LUNG BASES FREQUENTLY FOR RALES. IF RALES ARE HEARD OR OTHER SYMPTOMS RETURN, RE-ESTABLISH ATROPINIZATION PROMPTLY (MORGAN, RECOGNITION AND MANAGEMENT OF PESTICIDE POISONINGS, 3RD ED.). ADMINISTRATION OF ANTIDOTE MUST BE PERFORMED BY QUALIFIED MEDICAL PERSONNEL.

REACTIVITY

REACTIVITY: STABLE UNDER NORMAL TEMPERATURES AND PRESSURES.

INCOMPATIBILITIES: BUTOXCARBOXIM: OXIDIZERS (STRONG): FIRE AND EXPLOSION HAZARD.

DECOMPOSITION: THERMAL DECOMPOSITION PRODUCTS MAY INCLUDE TOXIC OXIDES OF CARBON, NITROGEN, AND SULFUR.

POLYMERIZATION: HAZARDOUS POLYMERIZATION HAS NOT BEEN REPORTED TO OCCUR UNDER NORMAL TEMPERATURES AND PRESSURES.

PA

STORAGE AND DISPOSAL

OBSERVE ALL FEDERAL, STATE AND LOCAL REGULATIONS WHEN STORING OR DISPOSING OF THIS SUBSTANCE. FOR ASSISTANCE, CONTACT THE DISTRICT DIRECTOR OF THE ENVIRONMENTAL PROTECTION AGENCY.

STORAGE

STORE IN ACCORDANCE WITH 40 CFR 165 RECOMMENDED PROCEDURES FOR THE DISPOSAL AND STORAGE OF PESTICIDES AND PESTICIDE CONTAINERS.
STORE AWAY FROM INCOMPATIBLE SUBSTANCES.

DISPOSAL

DISPOSAL MUST BE IN ACCORDANCE WITH 40 CFR 165 RECOMMENDED PROCEDURES FOR THE DISPOSAL AND STORAGE OF PESTICIDES AND PESTICIDE CONTAINERS.

CONDITIONS TO AVOID

MAY BURN BUT DOES NOT IGNITE READILY. CONTAINERS MAY EXPLODE IN HEAT OF FIRE.

SPILL AND LEAK PROCEDURES

OCCUPATIONAL SPILL: DO NOT TOUCH SPILLED MATERIAL. STOP LEAK IF YOU CAN DO IT WITHOUT RISK. USE WATER SPRAY TO REDUCE VAPORS. FOR SMALL SPILLS, TAKE UP WITH SAND OR OTHER ABSORBENT MATERIAL AND PLACE INTO CONTAINERS FOR LATER DISPOSAL. FOR SMALL DRY SPILLS, WITH A CLEAN SHOVEL PLACE MATERIAL INTO CLEAN, DRY CONTAINERS AND COVER. MOVE CONTAINERS FROM SPILL AREA. FOR LARGER SPILLS, DIKE FAR AHEAD OF SPILL FOR LATER DISPOSAL. KEEP UNNECESSARY PEOPLE AWAY. ISOLATE HAZARD AREA AND DENY ENTRY. VENTILATE CLOSED SPACES BEFORE ENTERING.

PROTECTIVE EQUIPMENT

VENTILATION: PROVIDE LOCAL EXHAUST OR PROCESS ENCLOSURE VENTILATION SYSTEM.

RESPIRATOR: THE FOLLOWING RESPIRATORS ARE RECOMMENDED BASED ON INFORMATION FOUND IN THE PHYSICAL DATA, TOXICITY AND HEALTH EFFECTS SECTIONS. THEY ARE RANKED IN ORDER FROM MINIMUM TO MAXIMUM RESPIRATORY PROTECTION. THE SPECIFIC RESPIRATOR SELECTED MUST BE BASED ON CONTAMINATION LEVELS FOUND IN THE WORK PLACE, MUST NOT EXCEED THE WORKING LIMITS OF THE RESPIRATOR AND BE JOINTLY APPROVED BY THE NATIONAL INSTITUTE FOR OCCUPATIONAL SAFETY AND HEALTH AND THE MINE SAFETY AND HEALTH ADMINISTRATION (NIOSH-MSHA).
TYPE 'C' SUPPLIED-AIR RESPIRATOR WITH A FULL FACEPIECE OPERATED IN PRESSURE-DEMAND OR OTHER POSITIVE PRESSURE MODE OR WITH A FULL FACEPIECE, HELMET OR HOOD OPERATED IN CONTINOUS-FLOW MODE.
SELF-CONTAINED BREATHING APPARATUS WITH A FULL FACEPIECE OPERATED IN PRESSURE-DEMAND OR OTHER POSITIVE PRESSURE MODE.
FOR FIREFIGHTING AND OTHER IMMEDIATELY DANGEROUS TO LIFE OR HEALTH CONDITIONS:
SELF-CONTAINED BREATHING APPARATUS WITH FULL FACEPIECE OPERATED IN PRESSURE-DEMAND OR OTHER POSITIVE PRESSURE MODE.
SUPPLIED-AIR RESPIRATOR WITH FULL FACEPIECE AND OPERATED IN PRESSURE-DEMAND OR OTHER POSITIVE PRESSURE MODE IN COMBINATION WITH AN AUXILIARY SELF-CONTAINED BREATHING APPARATUS OPERATED IN PRESSURE-DEMAND OR OTHER POSITIVE PRESSURE MODE.

CLOTHING: EMPLOYEE MUST WEAR APPROPRIATE PROTECTIVE (IMPERVIOUS) CLOTHING AND EQUIPMENT TO PREVENT ANY POSSIBILITY OF SKIN CONTACT WITH THIS SUBSTANCE.

GLOVES: EMPLOYEE MUST WEAR APPROPRIATE PROTECTIVE GLOVES TO PREVENT CONTACT WITH THIS SUBSTANCE.

EYE PROTECTION: EMPLOYEE MUST WEAR SPLASH-PROOF OR DUST-RESISTANT SAFETY GOGGLES WITH OR WITHOUT A FACESHIELD TO PREVENT CONTACT WITH THIS SUBSTANCE.
EMERGENCY EYE WASH: WHERE THERE IS ANY POSSIBILITY THAT AN EMPLOYEE'S EYES MAY BE EXPOSED TO THIS SUBSTANCE, THE EMPLOYER SHOULD PROVIDE AN EYE WASH FOUNTAIN WITHIN THE IMMEDIATE WORK AREA FOR EMERGENCY USE.

AUTHORIZED BY- OCCUPATIONAL HEALTH SERVICES, INC.
CREATION DATE: 10/04/89 ***REVISION DATE:*** 06/12/90

MATERIAL SAFETY DATA SHEET

OCCUPATIONAL HEALTH SERVICES, INC.
AGRICULTURE AND PESTICIDE DIVISION
450 SEVENTH AVENUE, SUITE 2407
NEW YORK, NEW YORK 10123
1-800-445-MSDS OR (212) 967-1100

EMERGENCY CONTACT:
JOHN S. BRANSFORD, JR. (615) 292-1180

SUBSTANCE IDENTIFICATION

CAS-NUMBER 2665-30-7

SUBSTANCE: **METHYLPHOSPHONOTHIOIC ACID, O-(4-NITROPHENYL) O-PHENYL ESTER**

TRADE NAMES/SYNONYMS: METHYLPHOSPHONOTHIOIC ACID, O-(PARA-NITROPHENYL) O-PHENYL ESTER; PARA-NITROPHENYL PHENYL METHYLPHOSPHONOTHIONATE; COLEP; CP 40294; ENT 25,613; PST73278

CHEMICAL FAMILY: ESTER, CARBOXYLIC, ALIPHATIC THIOPHOSPHATE

MOLECULAR FORMULA: C13-H12-N-O4-P-S

MOLECULAR WEIGHT: 309.29

CERCLA RATINGS (SCALE 0-3): HEALTH=3 FIRE=U REACTIVITY=U PERSISTENCE=2

NFPA RATINGS (SCALE 0-4): HEALTH=3 FIRE=U REACTIVITY=U

COMPONENTS AND CONTAMINANTS

COMPONENT: METHYLPHOSPHONOTHIOIC ACID, O-(4-NITROPHENYL)O-PHENYL ESTER ***PERCENT:*** 100.0
CAS# 2665-30-7

OTHER CONTAMINANTS: NONE

EXPOSURE LIMITS: NO OCCUPATIONAL EXPOSURE LIMITS ESTABLISHED BY OSHA, ACGIH, OR NIOSH.
METHYLPHOSPHONOTHIOIC ACID, O-(4-NITROPHENYL) O-PHENYL ESTER: 500 POUNDS SARA SECTION 302 THRESHOLD PLANNING QUANTITY 1 POUND SARA SECTION 304 REPORTABLE QUANTITY

PHYSICAL DATA

DESCRIPTION: NOT AVAILABLE ***MELTING POINT:*** NOT AVAILABLE
SPECIFIC GRAVITY: NOT AVAILABLE ***SOLUBILITY IN WATER:*** NOT AVAILABLE

FIRE AND EXPLOSION DATA

FIRE AND EXPLOSION HAZARD: UNKNOWN FIRE AND EXPLOSION HAZARD.

FIREFIGHTING MEDIA: DRY CHEMICAL, CARBON DIOXIDE, HALON, WATER SPRAY OR STANDARD FOAM (1987 EMERGENCY RESPONSE GUIDEBOOK, DOT P 5800.4).
FOR LARGER FIRES, USE WATER SPRAY, FOG OR STANDARD FOAM (1987 EMERGENCY RESPONSE GUIDEBOOK, DOT P 5800.4).

FIREFIGHTING: MOVE CONTAINERS FROM FIRE AREA IF POSSIBLE. FIGHT FIRE FROM MAXIMUM DISTANCE. STAY AWAY FROM STORAGE TANK ENDS. DIKE FIRE CONTROL WATER FOR LATER DISPOSAL. DO NOT SCATTER MATERIAL (1987 EMERGENCY RESPONSE GUIDEBOOK, DOT P 5800.4, GUIDE PAGE 55).
EXTINGUISH ONLY IF FLOW CAN BE STOPPED. EXTINGUISH USING AGENT INDICATED. USE FLOODING AMOUNTS OF WATER AS A FOG. COOL CONTAINERS WITH FLOODING AMOUNTS OF WATER FROM AS FAR A DISTANCE AS POSSIBLE. AVOID BREATHING POISONOUS VAPORS, KEEP UPWIND. CONSIDER EVACUATION OF DOWNWIND AREA IF MATERIAL IS LEAKING.

TRANSPORTATION DATA

DEPARTMENT OF TRANSPORTATION HAZARD CLASSIFICATION 49 CFR 172.101: POISON B
DEPARTMENT OF TRANSPORTATION LABELING REQUIREMENTS 49 CFR 172.101 AND SUBPART E: POISON
FOR LIQUID FORMS: DEPARTMENT OF TRANSPORTATION PACKAGING REQUIREMENTS: 49CFR173.346 EXCEPTIONS: 49CFR173.345
FOR SOLID FORMS: DEPARTMENT OF TRANSPORTATION PACKAGING REQUIREMENTS: 49CFR173.365 EXCEPTIONS: 49CFR173.364

TOXICITY

METHYLPHOSPHONOTHIOIC ACID, O-(4-NITROPHENYL) O-PHENYL ESTER: TOXICITY DATA: 8 MG/KG ORAL-RAT LD50. CARCINOGEN STATUS: NONE. ACUTE TOXICITY LEVEL: HIGHLY TOXIC BY INGESTION. TARGET EFFECTS: CHOLINESTERASE INHIBITOR. POISONING MAY AFFECT THE NERVOUS SYSTEM.* AT INCREASED RISK FROM EXPOSURE: PERSONS WITH RESPIRATORY AILMENTS, RECENT EXPOSURE TO CHOLINESTERASE INHIBITORS OR IMPAIRED CHOLINESTERASE PRODUCTION, OR LIVER MALFUNCTION.* ADDITIONAL DATA: MAY CROSS THE PLACENTA. HIGH ENVIRONMENTAL TEMPERATURES OR EXPOSURE OF THE CHEMICAL TO VISIBLE OR ULTRAVIOLET LIGHT MAY ENHANCE THE TOXICITY. INTERACTIONS WITH MEDICATIONS MAY OCCUR.*
* MAY BE BASED ON GENERAL INFORMATION ON ORGANOPHOSPHATES.

HEALTH EFFECTS AND FIRST AID

INHALATION: METHYLPHOSPHONOTHIOIC ACID, O-(4-NITROPHENYL) O-PHENYL ESTER: SEE INFORMATION ON ORGANOPHOSPHATES.

ORGANOPHOSPHATES: CHOLINESTERASE INHIBITOR. **ACUTE EXPOSURE**- WHEN INHALED, THE FIRST EFFECTS OF CHOLINESTERASE INHIBITORS ARE USUALLY RESPIRATORY AND MAY INCLUDE NASAL HYPEREMIA AND WATERY DISCHARGE, COUGH, CHEST DISCOMFORT, DYSPNEA, AND WHEEZING DUE TO INCREASED BRONCHIAL SECRETIONS AND BRONCHOCONSTRICTION. IF SUFFICIENT AMOUNTS ARE ABSORBED, OTHER SYSTEMIC EFFECTS MAY BEGIN WITHIN A FEW MINUTES OR BE DELAYED FOR UP TO 12 HOURS. SYMPTOMS MAY INCLUDE PALLOR, NAUSEA, VOMITING, DIARRHEA, ABDOMINAL CRAMPS, HEADACHE, DIZZINESS, OCULAR PAIN, BLURRED VISION, MIOSIS OR IN SOME CASES, ESPECIALLY INITIALLY, MYDRIASIS, LACRIMATION, SALIVATION, SWEATING, AND CONFUSION. OTHER REPORTED CENTRAL NERVOUS SYSTEM OR NEUROMUSCULAR EFFECTS MAY INCLUDE ATAXIA, SLURRED SPEECH, AREFLEXIA, WEAKNESS, FATIGUE, FASCICULATIONS, TWITCHING, TREMORS POSSIBLY OF THE TONGUE AND EYELIDS, AND EVENTUALLY PARALYSIS OF THE EXTREMITIES AND POSSIBLY OF THE RESPIRATORY MUSCLES. IN SEVERE CASES THERE MAY ALSO BE INVOLUNTARY DEFECATION AND URINATION, CYANOSIS, PSYCHOSIS, HYPERGLYCEMIA, ACUTE PANCREATITIS, CARDIAC IRREGULARITIES, PULMONARY EDEMA, UNCONSCIOUSNESS, CONVULSIONS, AND COMA. DEATH IS PRIMARILY DUE TO RESPIRATORY FAILURE, ALTHOUGH CARDIOVASCULAR EFFECTS INCLUDING CARDIAC ARREST MAY ALSO BE IMPLICATED. LONG TERM SEQUELAE ARE RARE BUT MAY INCLUDE NEUROPSYCHIATRIC DISORDERS AND MYOPATHY WITH MUSCLE TENDERNESS. SOME ORGANOPHOSPHATES MAY CAUSE A DELAYED NEUROPATHY BEGINNING 1-4 WEEKS AFTER AN ACUTE EXPOSURE WHICH MAY OR MAY NOT HAVE CAUSED ACUTE CHOLINERGIC EFFECTS. NUMBNESS, TINGLING, WEAKNESS AND CRAMPING BEGINNING SYMMETRICALLY IN THE LOWER LIMBS MAY PROGRESS TO ATAXIA AND PARALYSIS. IN SEVERE CASES, UPPER LIMB INVOLVEMENT IS POSSIBLE AND FLACCID PARALYSIS MAY PROGRESS TO SPASTIC PARALYSIS WITH EXAGGERATED REFLEXES. IMPROVEMENT MAY OCCUR OVER MONTHS TO YEARS, BUT SOME RESIDUAL IMPAIRMENT USUALLY REMAINS. **CHRONIC EXPOSURE**- REPEATED OR PROLONGED EXPOSURE MAY RESULT IN THE EFFECTS OF ACUTE EXPOSURE INCLUDING THE DELAYED NEUROPATHY. OTHER EFFECTS REPORTED IN WORKERS REPEATEDLY EXPOSED INCLUDE IMPAIRED MEMORY AND CONCENTRATION, ACUTE PSYCHOSIS, SEVERE DEPRESSIONS, IRRITABILTY, CONFUSION, APATHY, EMOTIONAL LABILITY, SOCIAL WITHDRAWAL, CONFUSION, HEADACHE, SPEECH DIFFICULTIES, DELAYED REACTION TIMES, SPATIAL DISORIENTATION, NIGHTMARES, SLEEPWALKING, AND DROWSINESS OR INSOMNIA. AN INFLUENZA-LIKE CONDITION WITH HEADACHE, NAUSEA, WEAKNESS, ANOREXIA AND MALAISE HAS ALSO BEEN REPORTED.

FIRST AID- REMOVE FROM EXPOSURE AREA TO FRESH AIR IMMEDIATELY. IF BREATHING HAS STOPPED, GIVE ARTIFICIAL RESPIRATION. MAINTAIN AIRWAY AND BLOOD PRESSURE AND ADMINISTER OXYGEN IF AVAILABLE. KEEP AFFECTED PERSON WARM AND AT REST. TREAT SYMPTOMATICALLY AND SUPPORTIVELY. ADMINISTRATION OF OXYGEN SHOULD BE PERFORMED BY QUALIFIED PERSONNEL. GET MEDICAL ATTENTION IMMEDIATELY.

SKIN CONTACT: METHYLPHOSPHONOTHIOIC ACID, O-(4-NITROPHENYL) O-PHENYL ESTER: SEE INFORMATION ON ORGANOPHOSPHATES.
ORGANOPHOSPHATES: CHOLINESTERASE INHIBITOR. **ACUTE EXPOSURE**- LOCALIZED SWEATING AND FASCICULATIONS MAY OCCUR AT THE SITE OF CONTACT. IF SUFFICIENT AMOUNTS ARE ABSORBED, OTHER EFFECTS OF CHOLINESTERASE INHIBITION AS DESCRIBED IN ACUTE INHALATION MAY OCCUR. SYMPTOMS MAY BE DELAYED 2-3 HOURS, BUT USUALLY NO MORE THAN 12 HOURS. THE RATE OF ABSORPTION IS INCREASED BY THE PRESENCE OF DERMATITIS OR HIGH AMBIENT TEMPERATURES. DELAYED NEUROPATHY IS ALSO POSSIBLE. **CHRONIC EXPOSURE**- REPEATED OR PROLONGED EXPOSURE MAY CAUSE EFFECTS AS DESCRIBED IN ACUTE EXPOSURE. SOME ORGANOPHOSPHATES MAY CAUSE SENSITIZATION.

FIRST AID- REMOVE CONTAMINATED CLOTHING IMMEDIATELY. WASH CONTAMINATED AREAS WITH SOAP AND WATER FOLLOWED BY ALCOHOL (ARENA, POISONING, 4TH ED.). EMERGENCY PERSONNEL SHOULD WEAR GLOVES AND AVOID CONTAMINATION. TREAT RESPIRATORY DIFFICULTY WITH ARTIFICIAL RESPIRATION. GET MEDICAL ATTENTION IMMEDIATELY.

EYE CONTACT: METHYLPHOSPHONOTHIOIC ACID, O-(4-NITROPHENYL)O-PHENYL ESTER: SEE INFORMATION ON ORGANOPHOSPHATES.
ORGANOPHOSPHATES: CHOLINESTERASE INHIBITOR. **ACUTE EXPOSURE**- DIRECT CONTACT MAY CAUSE PAIN, HYPEREMIA, LACRIMATION, TWITCHING OF THE EYELIDS, MIOSIS, AND CILIARY MUSCLE SPASM WITH LOSS OF ACCOMODATION, BLURRED OR DIMMED VISION AND BROWACHE. SOMETIMES MYDRIASIS MAY OCCUR INSTEAD OF MIOSIS. WITH SUFFICIENT EXPOSURE, OTHER SYMPTOMS OF CHOLINESTERASE INHIBITION AS DESCRIBED IN ACUTE INHALATION MAY OCCUR. **CHRONIC EXPOSURE**- REPEATED OR PROLONGED EXPOSURE MAY CAUSE EFFECTS AS DESCRIBED IN ACUTE EXPOSURE. SOME COMPOUNDS HAVE CAUSED TOXIC EFFECTS ON THE CRYSTALLINE LENS, CONJUNCTIVAL THICKENING AND OBSTRUCTION OF THE NASOLACRIMAL CANALS WHEN USED AS MIOTIC EYEDROPS.

FIRST AID- IRRIGATE EYES WITH WATER OR SALINE SOLUTION. IF SYMPTOMS OF POISONING OCCUR, TREAT RESPIRATORY DIFFICULTY WITH ARTIFICIAL RESPIRATION AND OXYGEN. OBSERVE PATIENT FOR AT LEAST 24-36 HOURS (GOSSELIN, CLINICAL TOXICOLOGY OF COMMERCIAL PRODUCTS, 5TH ED.). GET MEDICAL ATTENTION IMMEDIATELY. OXYGEN SHOULD BE ADMINISTERED BY QUALIFIED MEDICAL PERSONNEL.

INGESTION: METHYLPHOSPHONOTHIOIC ACID, O-(4-NITROPHENYL) O-PHENYL ESTER: HIGHLY TOXIC. SEE INFORMATION ON ORGANOPHOSPHATES.
ORGANOPHOSPHATES: CHOLINESTERASE INHIBITOR. **ACUTE EXPOSURE**- WHEN INGESTED, THE FIRST EFFECTS MAY BE NAUSEA, VOMITING, ANOREXIA, ABDOMINAL CRAMPS AND DIARRHEA. GASTROINTESTINAL ABSORPTION MAY CAUSE SYMPTOMS OF CHOLINESTERASE INHIBITION AS DESCRIBED IN ACUTE INHALATION. SYMPTOMS MAY BEGIN WITHIN MINUTES OR BE DELAYED FOR HOURS. DELAYED EFFECTS INCLUDING NEUROPATHY MAY ALSO OCCUR. **CHRONIC EXPOSURE**- REPEATED INGESTION MAY CAUSE EFFECTS AS DESCRIBED IN ACUTE EXPOSURE.

FIRST AID- IF PERSON IS ALERT AND RESPIRATION IS NOT DEPRESSED, GIVE SYRUP OF IPECAC FOLLOWED BY WATER (IF VOMITING OCCURS, KEEP HEAD BELOW HIPS TO PREVENT ASPIRATION). IF CONSCIOUSNESS LEVEL DECLINES OR VOMITING HAS NOT OCCURRED IN 15 MINUTES EMPTY STOMACH BY GASTRIC LAVAGE WITH THE AID OF CUFFED ENDOTRACHEAL TUBE USING ISOTONIC SALINE OR 5% SODIUM BICARBONATE FOLLOW WITH ACTIVATED CHARCOAL. ESTABLISH AND MAINTAIN AIRWAY. TREAT RESPIRATORY DIFFICULTY WITH ARTIFICIAL RESPIRATION AND OXYGEN. DO NOT GIVE MORPHINE, AMINOPHYLLINE, PHENOTHIAZINES, RESERPINE, FUROSEMIDE, OR ETHACRYNIC ACID (MORGAN, RECOGNITION AND MANAGEMENT OF PESTICIDE POISONINGS, 3RD ED.). TREAT SYMPTOMATICALLY AND SUPPORTIVELY. ADMINISTRATION OF OXYGEN AND LAVAGE MUST BE PERFORMED BY QUALIFIED MEDICAL PERSONNEL. GET MEDICAL ATTENTION IMMEDIATELY.

ANTIDOTE: THE FOLLOWING ANTIDOTE(S) HAVE BEEN RECOMMENDED. HOWEVER, THE DECISION AS TO WHETHER THE SEVERITY OF POISONING REQUIRES ADMINISTRATION OF ANY ANTIDOTE AND ACTUAL DOSE REQUIRED SHOULD BE MADE BY QUALIFIED MEDICAL PERSONNEL.
FOR CHOLINESTERASE INHIBITORS: ESTABLISH CLEAR AIRWAY AND TISSUE OXYGENATION BY ASPIRATION OF SECRETIONS, AND IF NECESSARY, BY ASSISTED PULMONARY VENTILATION WITH OXYGEN. IMPROVE TISSUE OXYGENATION AS MUCH AS POSSIBLE BEFORE ADMINISTERING ATROPINE TO MINIMIZE THE RISK OF VENTRICULAR FIBRILLATION. ADMINISTER ATROPINE SULFATE INTRAVENOUSLY, OR INTRAMUSCULARLY IF IV INJECTION IS NOT POSSIBLE. IN MODERATELY SEVERE POISONING ADMINISTER ATROPINE SULFATE, 0.4-2.0 MG REPEATED EVERY 15 MINUTES UNTIL ATROPINIZATION IS ACHIEVED (TACHYCARDIA, FLUSHING, DRY MOUTH, MYDRIASIS). MAINTAIN ATROPINIZATION BY REPEATED DOSES FOR 2-12 HOURS, OR LONGER, DEPENDING ON THE SEVERITY OF POISONING. THE APPEARANCE OF RALES IN THE LUNG BASES, MIOSIS, SALIVATION, NAUSEA, BRADYCARDIA, ARE ALL INDICATIONS OF INADEQUATE ATROPINIZATION. SEVERELY POISONED INDIVIDUALS MAY EXHIBIT REMARKABLE TOLERANCE TO ATROPINE; TWO OR MORE TIMES THE DOSAGES SUGGESTED ABOVE MAY BE NEEDED. PERSONS NOT POISONED OR ONLY SLIGHTLY POISONED, HOWEVER, MAY DEVELOP SIGNS OF ATROPINE TOXICITY FROM SUCH LARGE DOSAGES: FEVER, MUSCLE FIBRILLATIONS, AND DELIRIUM ARE THE MAIN SIGNS OF ATROPINE TOXICITY. IF THESE SIGNS APPEAR WHILE THE PATIENT IS FULLY ATROPINIZED, ATROPINE ADMINISTRATION SHOULD BE DISCONTINUED, AT LEAST TEMPORARILY. OBSERVE TREATED PATIENTS CLOSELY AT LEAST 24 HOURS TO INSURE THAT SYMPTOMS (POSSIBLY PULMONARY EDEMA) DO NOT RECUR AS ATROPINIZATION WEARS OFF. IN VERY SEVERE POISONINGS, METABOLIC DISPOSITION OF TOXICANT MAY REQUIRE SEVERAL HOURS OR DAYS DURING WHICH ATROPINIZATION MUST BE MAINTAINED. MARKEDLY LOWER LEVELS OF URINARY METABOLITES INDICATE THAT ATROPINE DOSAGE CAN BE TAPERED OFF. AS DOSAGE IS REDUCED, CHECK THE LUNG BASES FREQUENTLY FOR RALES. IF RALES ARE HEARD OR OTHER SYMPTOMS RETURN, RE-ESTABLISH ATROPINIZATION PROMPTLY (MORGAN, RECOGNITION AND MANAGEMENT OF PESTICIDE POISONINGS, 3RD ED.). ADMINISTRATION OF ANTIDOTE MUST BE PERFORMED BY QUALIFIED MEDICAL PERSONNEL.
IN CASES OF SEVERE POISONING BY ORGANOPHOSPHATE PESTICIDES IN WHICH RESPIRATORY DEPRESSION, MUSCLE WEAKNESS AND TWITCHINGS ARE SEVERE, GIVE PRALIDOXIME (PROTOPAM-AYERST, 2-PAM), 1.0 GRAM INTRAVENOUSLY AT NO MORE THAN 0.5 GRAM PER MINUTE. DOSAGE OF PRALIDOXIME MAY BE REPEATED IN 1-2 HOURS, THEN AT 10-12 HOUR INTERVALS IF NEEDED. IN VERY SEVERE POISONINGS, DOSAGE RATES MAY BE DOUBLED. TREATMENT WITH PRALIDOXIME WILL BE MOST EFFECTIVE IF GIVEN WITHIN THIRTY-SIX HOURS AFTER POISONING (MORGAN, RECOGNITION AND MANAGEMENT OF PESTICIDE POISONINGS, 3RD ED.). ANTIDOTE SHOULD BE ADMINISTERED BY QUALIFIED MEDICAL PERSONNEL.

REACTIVITY

REACTIVITY: NO DATA AVAILABLE.

INCOMPATIBILITIES: METHYLPHOSPHONOTHIOIC ACID, O-(4-NITROPHENYL) O-PHENYL ESTER: OXIDIZERS (STRONG): FIRE AND EXPLOSION HAZARD.

DECOMPOSITION: THERMAL DECOMPOSITION MAY RELEASE TOXIC AND/OR HAZARDOUS GASES.

POLYMERIZATION: HAZARDOUS POLYMERIZATION HAS NOT BEEN REPORTED TO OCCUR UNDER NORMAL TEMPERATURES AND PRESSURES.

STORAGE AND DISPOSAL

OBSERVE ALL FEDERAL, STATE AND LOCAL REGULATIONS WHEN STORING OR DISPOSING OF THIS SUBSTANCE. FOR ASSISTANCE, CONTACT THE DISTRICT DIRECTOR OF THE ENVIRONMENTAL PROTECTION AGENCY.

STORAGE

STORE IN ACCORDANCE WITH 40 CFR 165 RECOMMENDED PROCEDURES FOR THE DISPOSAL AND STORAGE OF PESTICIDES AND PESTICIDE CONTAINERS.

THRESHOLD PLANNING QUANTITY (TPQ): THE SUPERFUND AMENDMENTS AND REAUTHORIZATION ACT (SARA) SECTION 302 REQUIRES THAT EACH FACILITY WHERE ANY EXTREMELY HAZARDOUS SUBSTANCE IS PRESENT IN A QUANTITY EQUAL TO OR GREATER THAN THE TPQ ESTABLISHED FOR THAT SUBSTANCE NOTIFY THE STATE EMERGENCY RESPONSE COMMISSION FOR THE STATE IN WHICH IT IS LOCATED. SECTION 303 OF SARA REQUIRES THESE FACILITIES TO PARTICIPATE IN LOCAL EMERGENCY RESPONSE PLANNING (40 CFR 355.30).

DISPOSAL

DISPOSAL MUST BE IN ACCORDANCE WITH 40 CFR 165 RECOMMENDED PROCEDURES FOR THE DISPOSAL AND STORAGE OF PESTICIDES AND PESTICIDE CONTAINERS.

CONDITIONS TO AVOID

NONE REPORTED.

SPILL AND LEAK PROCEDURES

OCCUPATIONAL SPILL: DO NOT TOUCH SPILLED MATERIAL. STOP LEAK IF YOU CAN DO IT WITHOUT RISK. USE WATER SPRAY TO REDUCE VAPORS. FOR SMALL SPILLS, TAKE UP WITH SAND OR OTHER ABSORBENT MATERIAL AND PLACE INTO CONTAINERS FOR LATER DISPOSAL. FOR SMALL DRY SPILLS, WITH A CLEAN SHOVEL PLACE MATERIAL INTO CLEAN, DRY CONTAINERS AND COVER. MOVE CONTAINERS FROM SPILL AREA. FOR LARGER SPILLS, DIKE FAR AHEAD OF SPILL FOR LATER DISPOSAL. KEEP UNNECESSARY PEOPLE AWAY. ISOLATE HAZARD AREA AND DENY ENTRY. VENTILATE CLOSED SPACES BEFORE ENTERING.

REPORTABLE QUANTITY (RQ): 1 POUND THE SUPERFUND AMENDMENTS AND REAUTHORIZATION ACT (SARA) SECTION 304 REQUIRES THAT A RELEASE EQUAL TO OR GREATER THAN THE REPORTABLE QUANTITY FOR THIS SUBSTANCE BE IMMEDIATELY REPORTED TO THE LOCAL EMERGENCY PLANNING COMMITTEE AND THE STATE EMERGENCY RESPONSE COMMISSION (40 CFR 355.40). IF THE RELEASE OF THIS SUBSTANCE IS REPORTABLE UNDER CERCLA SECTION 103, THE NATIONAL RESPONSE CENTER MUST BE NOTIFIED IMMEDIATELY AT (800) 424-8802 OR (202) 426-2675 IN THE METROPOLITAN WASHINGTON, D.C. AREA (40 CFR 302.6).

PROTECTIVE EQUIPMENT

VENTILATION: PROVIDE LOCAL EXHAUST OR PROCESS ENCLOSURE VENTILATION SYSTEM.

RESPIRATOR: THE FOLLOWING RESPIRATORS ARE RECOMMENDED BASED ON INFORMATION FOUND IN THE PHYSICAL DATA, TOXICITY AND HEALTH EFFECTS SECTIONS. THEY ARE RANKED IN ORDER FROM MINIMUM TO MAXIMUM RESPIRATORY PROTECTION. THE SPECIFIC RESPIRATOR SELECTED MUST BE BASED ON CONTAMINATION LEVELS FOUND IN THE WORK PLACE, MUST NOT EXCEED THE WORKING LIMITS OF THE RESPIRATOR AND BE JOINTLY APPROVED BY THE NATIONAL INSTITUTE FOR OCCUPATIONAL SAFETY AND HEALTH AND THE MINE SAFETY AND HEALTH ADMINISTRATION (NIOSH-MSHA).

TYPE 'C' SUPPLIED-AIR RESPIRATOR WITH A FULL FACEPIECE OPERATED IN PRESSURE-DEMAND OR OTHER POSITIVE PRESSURE MODE OR WITH A FULL FACEPIECE, HELMET OR HOOD OPERATED IN CONTINOUS-FLOW MODE.

SELF-CONTAINED BREATHING APPARATUS WITH A FULL FACEPIECE OPERATED IN PRESSURE-DEMAND OR OTHER POSITIVE PRESSURE MODE.

FOR FIREFIGHTING AND OTHER IMMEDIATELY DANGEROUS TO LIFE OR HEALTH CONDITIONS:

SELF-CONTAINED BREATHING APPARATUS WITH FULL FACEPIECE OPERATED IN PRESSURE-DEMAND OR OTHER POSITIVE PRESSURE MODE.

SUPPLIED-AIR RESPIRATOR WITH FULL FACEPIECE AND OPERATED IN PRESSURE-DEMAND OR OTHER POSITIVE PRESSURE MODE IN COMBINATION WITH AN AUXILIARY SELF-CONTAINED BREATHING APPARATUS OPERATED IN PRESSURE-DEMAND OR OTHER POSITIVE PRESSURE MODE.

CLOTHING: EMPLOYEE MUST WEAR APPROPRIATE PROTECTIVE (IMPERVIOUS) CLOTHING AND EQUIPMENT TO PREVENT ANY POSSIBILITY OF SKIN CONTACT WITH THIS SUBSTANCE.

GLOVES: EMPLOYEE MUST WEAR APPROPRIATE PROTECTIVE GLOVES TO PREVENT CONTACT WITH THIS SUBSTANCE.

EYE PROTECTION: EMPLOYEE MUST WEAR SPLASH-PROOF OR DUST-RESISTANT SAFETY GOGGLES AND A FACESHIELD TO PREVENT CONTACT WITH THIS SUBSTANCE.

EMERGENCY WASH FACILITIES: WHERE THERE IS ANY POSSIBILITY THAT AN EMPLOYEE'S EYES AND/OR SKIN MAY BE EXPOSED TO THIS SUBSTANCE, THE EMPLOYER SHOULD PROVIDE AN EYE WASH FOUNTAIN AND QUICK DRENCH SHOWER WITHIN THE IMMEDIATE WORK AREA FOR EMERGENCY USE.

AUTHORIZED BY- OCCUPATIONAL HEALTH SERVICES, INC.

CREATION DATE: 05/18/90 ***REVISION DATE:*** 05/18/90

MATERIAL SAFETY DATA SHEET

OCCUPATIONAL HEALTH SERVICES, INC.
AGRICULTURE AND PESTICIDE DIVISION
450 SEVENTH AVENUE, SUITE 2407
NEW YORK, NEW YORK 10123
1-800-445-MSDS OR (212) 967-1100

EMERGENCY CONTACT:
JOHN S. BRANSFORD, JR. (615) 292-1180

SUBSTANCE IDENTIFICATION

CAS-NUMBER 8000-46-2

SUBSTANCE: OIL OF GERANIUM

TRADE NAMES/SYNONYMS: OILS, GERANIUM; GERANIUM OIL; GERANIUM OIL ALGERIAN; OIL OF PELARGONIUM; OIL OF ROSE GERANIUM; PELARGONIUM OIL; ROSE GERANIUM OIL ALGERIAN; PST73283

CHEMICAL FAMILY: ESSENTIAL OIL

CERCLA RATINGS (SCALE 0-3): HEALTH=U FIRE=1 REACTIVITY=0 PERSISTENCE=1

NFPA RATINGS (SCALE 0-4): HEALTH=U FIRE=1 REACTIVITY=0

COMPONENTS AND CONTAMINANTS

COMPONENT: OIL OF GERANIUM ***PERCENT:*** 100.0
CAS# 8000-46-2

OTHER CONTAMINANTS: NONE

EXPOSURE LIMITS: NO OCCUPATIONAL EXPOSURE LIMITS ESTABLISHED BY OSHA, ACGIH, OR NIOSH.

PHYSICAL DATA

DESCRIPTION: GREENISH OR PALE YELLOW TO BROWN LIQUID.

BOILING POINT: NOT AVAILABLE ***SPECIFIC GRAVITY:*** 0.894-0.905 @ 15 C

SOLUBILITY IN WATER: SLIGHTLY SOLUBLE

SOLVENT SOLUBILITY: SOLUBLE IN ALCOHOL, CHLOROFORM, ETHER, MINERAL OIL, PROPYLENE GLYCOL, AND MOST FIXED OILS; PRACTICALLY INSOLUBLE IN GLYCERINE.

FIRE AND EXPLOSION DATA

FIRE AND EXPLOSION HAZARD: SLIGHT FIRE HAZARD WHEN EXPOSED TO HEAT OR FLAME.

FIREFIGHTING MEDIA: DRY CHEMICAL, CARBON DIOXIDE, HALON, WATER SPRAY OR STANDARD FOAM (1987 EMERGENCY RESPONSE GUIDEBOOK, DOT P 5800.4). FOR LARGER FIRES, USE WATER SPRAY, FOG OR STANDARD FOAM (1987 EMERGENCY RESPONSE GUIDEBOOK, DOT P 5800.4).

FIREFIGHTING: MOVE CONTAINER FROM FIRE AREA IF POSSIBLE. DO NOT SCATTER SPILLED MATERIAL WITH HIGH PRESSURE WATER STREAMS. DIKE FIRE CONTROL WATER FOR LATER DISPOSAL (1987 EMERGENCY RESPONSE GUIDEBOOK, DOT P 5800.4, GUIDE PAGE 31).

USE AGENTS SUITABLE FOR TYPE OF SURROUNDING FIRE. AVOID BREATHING HAZARDOUS VAPORS, KEEP UPWIND.

TOXICITY

OIL OF GERANIUM: IRRITATION DATA: 500 MG/24 HOURS SKIN-RABBIT MILD; 100% SKIN-GUINEA PIG MILD. CARCINOGEN STATUS: NONE. ACUTE TOXICITY LEVEL: NO DATA AVAILABLE. TARGET EFFECTS: NO DATA AVAILABLE.

HEALTH EFFECTS AND FIRST AID

INHALATION: OIL OF GERANIUM: **ACUTE EXPOSURE-** INHALATION OF VOLATILE OILS MAY CAUSE DIZZINESS, RAPID, SHALLOW BREATHING, TACHYCARDIA, BRONCHIAL IRRITATION AND UNCONSCIOUSNESS OR CONVULSIONS. COMPLICATIONS MAY INCLUDE ANURIA, PULMONARY EDEMA, AND BRONCHIAL PNEUMONIA. **CHRONIC EXPOSURE-** NO DATA AVAILABLE.

FIRST AID- REMOVE FROM EXPOSURE AREA TO FRESH AIR IMMEDIATELY. IF BREATHING HAS STOPPED, PERFORM ARTIFICIAL RESPIRATION. KEEP PERSON WARM AND AT REST. TREAT SYMPTOMATICALLY AND SUPPORTIVELY. GET MEDICAL ATTENTION IMMEDIATELY.

SKIN CONTACT: OIL OF GERANIUM: **ACUTE EXPOSURE**- CONTACT WITH THE PURE OIL PRODUCED MILD IRRITATION IN GUINEA PIGS. **CHRONIC EXPOSURE**- NO DATA AVAILABLE.
FIRST AID- REMOVE CONTAMINATED CLOTHING AND SHOES IMMEDIATELY. WASH AFFECTED AREA WITH SOAP OR MILD DETERGENT AND LARGE AMOUNTS OF WATER UNTIL NO EVIDENCE OF CHEMICAL REMAINS (APPROXIMATELY 15-20 MINUTES). GET MEDICAL ATTENTION IMMEDIATELY.

EYE CONTACT: OIL OF GERANIUM: **ACUTE EXPOSURE**- DIRECT CONTACT WITH VOLATILE OILS MAY CAUSE IRRITATION. **CHRONIC EXPOSURE**- NO DATA AVAILABLE.
FIRST AID- WASH EYES IMMEDIATELY WITH LARGE AMOUNTS OF WATER OR NORMAL SALINE, OCCASIONALLY LIFTING UPPER AND LOWER LIDS, UNTIL NO EVIDENCE OF CHEMICAL REMAINS (APPROXIMATELY 15-20 MINUTES). GET MEDICAL ATTENTION IMMEDIATELY.

INGESTION: OIL OF GERANIUM: **ACUTE EXPOSURE**- INGESTION OF VOLATILE OILS MAY CAUSE ABDOMINAL BURNING, NAUSEA AND VOMITING, DIARRHEA, DYSURIA, HEMATURIA, UNCONSCIOUSNESS, SHALLOW RESPIRATION, AND CONVULSIONS. COMPLICATIONS MAY INCLUDE ANURIA, PULMONARY EDEMA, AND BRONCHIAL PNEUMONIA. PATHOLOGIC FINDINGS FROM INGESTION OF VOLATILE OILS INCLUDE RENAL DEGENERATIVE CHANGES AND INTENSE CONGESTION AND EDEMA IN THE LUNGS, BRAIN AND GASTRIC MUCOSA. **CHRONIC EXPOSURE**- NO DATA AVAILABLE.
FIRST AID- GIVE 120-240 ML OF MILK; THEN REMOVE BY GASTRIC LAVAGE OR EMESIS, TAKING CARE TO PREVENT ASPIRATION. FOLLOW THESE PROCEDURES BY ADMINISTERING 30-60 ML OF FLEET'S PHOSPHO-SODA DILUTED 1:4 IN WATER. PERFORM ARTIFICIAL RESPIRATION IF NECESSARY. GET MEDICAL ATTENTION (DREISBACH, HANDBOOK OF POISONING, 12TH ED.). FIRST AID SHOULD BE PERFORMED BY QUALIFIED MEDICAL PERSONNEL.
ANTIDOTE: NO SPECIFIC ANTIDOTE. TREAT SYMPTOMATICALLY AND SUPPORTIVELY.

REACTIVITY

REACTIVITY: STABLE UNDER NORMAL TEMPERATURES AND PRESSURES.
INCOMPATIBILITIES: OIL OF GERANIUM: OXIDIZERS (STRONG): FIRE AND EXPLOSION HAZARD.
DECOMPOSITION: THERMAL DECOMPOSITION MAY RELEASE ACRID SMOKE AND IRRITATING FUMES.
POLYMERIZATION: HAZARDOUS POLYMERIZATION HAS NOT BEEN REPORTED TO OCCUR UNDER NORMAL TEMPERATURES AND PRESSURES.

STORAGE AND DISPOSAL

OBSERVE ALL FEDERAL, STATE AND LOCAL REGULATIONS WHEN STORING OR DISPOSING OF THIS SUBSTANCE. FOR ASSISTANCE, CONTACT THE DISTRICT DIRECTOR OF THE ENVIRONMENTAL PROTECTION AGENCY.

STORAGE

STORE AWAY FROM INCOMPATIBLE SUBSTANCES.
STORE IN A COOL, DRY PLACE PROTECTED AGAINST LIGHT.

CONDITIONS TO AVOID

MAY BURN BUT DOES NOT IGNITE READILY. AVOID CONTACT WITH STRONG OXIDIZERS, EXCESSIVE HEAT, SPARKS, OR OPEN FLAME.

SPILL AND LEAK PROCEDURES

OCCUPATIONAL SPILL: STOP LEAK IF YOU CAN DO IT WITHOUT RISK. FOR SMALL SPILLS, TAKE UP WITH SAND OR OTHER ABSORBENT MATERIAL AND PLACE INTO CLEAN, DRY CONTAINERS FOR LATER DISPOSAL. KEEP UNNECESSARY PEOPLE AWAY. ISOLATE HAZARD AREA AND DENY ENTRY.

PROTECTIVE EQUIPMENT

VENTILATION: PROVIDE LOCAL EXHAUST OR PROCESS ENCLOSURE VENTILATION SYSTEM.
RESPIRATOR: THE FOLLOWING RESPIRATORS ARE RECOMMENDED BASED ON INFORMATION FOUND IN THE PHYSICAL DATA, TOXICITY AND HEALTH EFFECTS SECTIONS. THEY ARE RANKED IN ORDER FROM MINIMUM TO MAXIMUM RESPIRATORY PROTECTION. THE SPECIFIC RESPIRATOR SELECTED MUST BE BASED ON CONTAMINATION LEVELS FOUND IN THE WORK PLACE, MUST NOT EXCEED THE WORKING LIMITS OF THE RESPIRATOR AND BE JOINTLY APPROVED BY THE NATIONAL INSTITUTE FOR OCCUPATIONAL SAFETY AND HEALTH AND THE MINE SAFETY AND HEALTH ADMINISTRATION (NIOSH-MSHA).
CHEMICAL CARTRIDGE RESPIRATOR WITH AN ORGANIC VAPOR CARTRIDGE(S) WITH A FULL FACEPIECE.
GAS MASK WITH ORGANIC VAPOR CANISTER (CHIN-STYLE OR FRONT- OR BACK-MOUNTED CANISTER) WITH A FULL FACEPIECE.
TYPE 'C' SUPPLIED-AIR RESPIRATOR WITH A FULL FACEPIECE OPERATED IN PRESSURE-DEMAND OR OTHER POSITIVE PRESSURE MODE OR WITH A FULL FACEPIECE, HELMET OR HOOD OPERATED IN CONTINUOUS-FLOW MODE.
SELF-CONTAINED BREATHING APPARATUS WITH A FULL FACEPIECE OPERATED IN PRESSURE-DEMAND OR OTHER POSITIVE PRESSURE MODE.
FOR FIREFIGHTING AND OTHER IMMEDIATELY DANGEROUS TO LIFE OR HEALTH CONDITIONS:
SELF-CONTAINED BREATHING APPARATUS WITH FULL FACEPIECE OPERATED IN PRESSURE-DEMAND OR OTHER POSITIVE PRESSURE MODE.
SUPPLIED-AIR RESPIRATOR WITH FULL FACEPIECE AND OPERATED IN PRESSURE-DEMAND OR OTHER POSITIVE PRESSURE MODE IN COMBINATION WITH AN AUXILIARY SELF-CONTAINED BREATHING APPARATUS OPERATED IN PRESSURE-DEMAND OR OTHER POSITIVE PRESSURE MODE.
CLOTHING: EMPLOYEE MUST WEAR APPROPRIATE PROTECTIVE (IMPERVIOUS) CLOTHING AND EQUIPMENT TO PREVENT REPEATED OR PROLONGED SKIN CONTACT WITH THIS SUBSTANCE.
GLOVES: EMPLOYEE MUST WEAR APPROPRIATE PROTECTIVE GLOVES TO PREVENT CONTACT WITH THIS SUBSTANCE.
EYE PROTECTION: EMPLOYEE MUST WEAR SPLASH-PROOF OR DUST-RESISTANT SAFETY GOGGLES TO PREVENT EYE CONTACT WITH THIS SUBSTANCE.
EMERGENCY EYE WASH: WHERE THERE IS ANY POSSIBILITY THAT AN EMPLOYEE'S EYES MAY BE EXPOSED TO THIS SUBSTANCE, THE EMPLOYER SHOULD PROVIDE AN EYE WASH FOUNTAIN WITHIN THE IMMEDIATE WORK AREA FOR EMERGENCY USE.

AUTHORIZED BY- OCCUPATIONAL HEALTH SERVICES, INC.
CREATION DATE: 02/08/90 ***REVISION DATE:*** 05/18/90

MATERIAL SAFETY DATA SHEET

OCCUPATIONAL HEALTH SERVICES, INC.
AGRICULTURE AND PESTICIDE DIVISION
450 SEVENTH AVENUE, SUITE 2407
NEW YORK, NEW YORK 10123
1-800-445-MSDS OR (212) 967-1100

EMERGENCY CONTACT:
JOHN S. BRANSFORD, JR. (615) 292-1180

SUBSTANCE IDENTIFICATION

CAS-NUMBER 14816-18-3
SUBSTANCE: **PHOXIM**
TRADE NAMES/SYNONYMS: 3,5-DIOXA-6-AZA-4-PHOSPHAOCT-6-ENE-8-NITRILE, 4-ETHOXY-7-PHENYL-, 4-SULFIDE; 4-ETHOXY-7-PHENYL-3,5-DIOXA-6-AZA-4-PHOSPHAOCT-6-ENE-8-NITRILE -4-SULFIDE; GLYOXYLONITRILE, PHENYL-, OXIME O,O-DIETHYL PHOSPHOROTHIOATE; PHENYLGLYOXYLONITRILE OXIME O,O-DIETHYL PHOSPHOROTHIOATE; O,O-DIETHYL-PHENYLGLYOXYNITRITE OXIME PHOSPHOROTHIOATE; DIETHOXYPHOSPHINOTHIOYLOXYIMINO(PHENYL)ACETONITRILE; 2-(DIETHOXYPHOSPHINOTHIOYLOXYIMINO)-2-PHENYLACETONITRILE; O,O-DIETHYL ALPHA-CYANOBENZYLIDENEAMINO-OXYPHOSPHONOTHIOATE; ALPHA-(((DIETHOXYPHOSPHINOTHIOYL)OXY)IMINO)BENZENEACETONITRILE; BAY 5621; BAY 77488; BAYER 77488; BAYTHION; VALEXON; VOLATION; OMS 1170; C12H15N2O3PS; PST73292
CHEMICAL FAMILY: PHOSPHOROTHIOATE
MOLECULAR FORMULA: (C2-H5-O)2-P-(S)-O-N-C-(C-N)-C6-H5
MOLECULAR WEIGHT: 298.29
CERCLA RATINGS (SCALE 0-3): HEALTH=3 FIRE=U REACTIVITY=0 PERSISTENCE=2
NFPA RATINGS (SCALE 0-4): HEALTH=3 FIRE=U REACTIVITY=0

COMPONENTS AND CONTAMINANTS

COMPONENT: PHOXIM ***PERCENT:*** 100.0
CAS# 14816-18-3
OTHER CONTAMINANTS: NONE
EXPOSURE LIMITS: NO OCCUPATIONAL EXPOSURE LIMITS ESTABLISHED BY OSHA, ACGIH, OR NIOSH.

PHYSICAL DATA

DESCRIPTION: PALE YELLOW OILY LIQUID.
BOILING POINT: 216 F (102 C) @ 0.01 MMHG

MELTING POINT: 41-43 F (5-6 C) ***SPECIFIC GRAVITY:*** 1.176
VAPOR PRESSURE: 0.000075 MMHG @ 20 C
SOLUBILITY IN WATER: 0.0007% @ 20 C
SOLVENT SOLUBILITY: SOLUBLE IN ALCOHOL, ACETONE, AROMATIC HYDROCARBONS, DICHLOROMETHANE, KETONES, 2-PROPANOL, AND XYLENE; MODERATELY SOLUBLE IN LIGHT PETROLEUM.

FIRE AND EXPLOSION DATA

FIRE AND EXPLOSION HAZARD: UNKNOWN FIRE AND EXPLOSION HAZARD.
FIREFIGHTING MEDIA: DRY CHEMICAL, CARBON DIOXIDE, HALON, WATER SPRAY OR STANDARD FOAM (1987 EMERGENCY RESPONSE GUIDEBOOK, DOT P 5800.4). FOR LARGER FIRES, USE WATER SPRAY, FOG OR STANDARD FOAM (1987 EMERGENCY RESPONSE GUIDEBOOK, DOT P 5800.4).
FIREFIGHTING: MOVE CONTAINER FROM FIRE AREA IF POSSIBLE. DIKE FIRE CONTROL WATER FOR LATER DISPOSAL; DO NOT SCATTER THE MATERIAL. COOL FIRE-EXPOSED CONTAINERS WITH WATER FROM SIDE UNTIL WELL AFTER FIRE IS OUT. STAY AWAY FROM STORAGE TANK ENDS. WITHDRAW IMMEDIATELY IN CASE OF RISING SOUND FROM VENTING SAFETY DEVICE OR ANY DISCOLORATION OF STORAGE TANK DUE TO FIRE (1987 EMERGENCY RESPONSE GUIDEBOOK, DOT P 5800.4, GUIDE PAGE 28).
EXTINGUISH ONLY IF FLOW CAN BE STOPPED. USE FLOODING AMOUNTS OF WATER AS A FOG; SOLID STREAMS MAY BE INEFFECTIVE. COOL CONTAINERS WITH FLOODING AMOUNTS OF WATER FROM AS FAR A DISTANCE AS POSSIBLE. AVOID BREATHING POISONOUS VAPORS, KEEP UPWIND.

TOXICITY

PHOXIM: TOXICITY DATA: 1000 MG/KG SKIN-RAT LD50; 300 MG/KG ORAL-RAT LD50; 1050 MG/KG ORAL-MOUSE LD50; 250 MG/KG ORAL-RABBIT LD50; 600 MG/KG ORAL-GUINEA PIG LD50; 250 MG/KG ORAL-DOG LD50; 250 MG/KG ORAL-CAT LD50; REPRODUCTIVE EFFECTS DATA (RTECS). CARCINOGEN STATUS: NONE. ACUTE TOXICITY LEVEL: TOXIC BY INGESTION AND DERMAL ABSORPTION. TARGET EFFECTS: CHOLINESTERASE INHIBITOR. POISONING MAY AFFECT THE NERVOUS SYSTEM.* AT INCREASED RISK FROM EXPOSURE: PERSONS WITH RESPIRATORY AILMENTS, RECENT EXPOSURE TO CHOLINESTERASE INHIBITORS OR IMPAIRED CHOLINESTERASE PRODUCTION, OR LIVER MALFUNCTION.* ADDITIONAL DATA: MAY CROSS THE PLACENTA. HIGH ENVIRONMENTAL TEMPERATURES OR EXPOSURE OF THE CHEMICAL TO VISIBLE OR ULTRAVIOLET LIGHT MAY ENHANCE THE TOXICITY. INTERACTIONS WITH MEDICATIONS MAY OCCUR.*
* MAY BE BASED ON GENERAL INFORMATION ON ORGANOPHOSPHATES.

HEALTH EFFECTS AND FIRST AID

INHALATION: PHOXIM: SEE INFORMATION ON ORGANOPHOSPHATES.
ORGANOPHOSPHATES: CHOLINESTERASE INHIBITOR. **ACUTE EXPOSURE-** WHEN INHALED, THE FIRST EFFECTS OF CHOLINESTERASE INHIBITORS ARE USUALLY RESPIRATORY AND MAY INCLUDE NASAL HYPEREMIA AND WATERY DISCHARGE, COUGH, CHEST DISCOMFORT, DYSPNEA, AND WHEEZING DUE TO INCREASED BRONCHIAL SECRETIONS AND BRONCHOCONSTRICTION. IF SUFFICIENT AMOUNTS ARE ABSORBED, OTHER SYSTEMIC EFFECTS MAY BEGIN WITHIN A FEW MINUTES OR BE DELAYED FOR UP TO 12 HOURS. SYMPTOMS MAY INCLUDE PALLOR, NAUSEA, VOMITING, DIARRHEA, ABDOMINAL CRAMPS, HEADACHE, DIZZINESS, OCULAR PAIN, BLURRED VISION, MIOSIS OR IN SOME CASES, ESPECIALLY INITIALLY, MYDRIASIS, LACRIMATION, SALIVATION, SWEATING, AND CONFUSION. OTHER REPORTED CENTRAL NERVOUS SYSTEM OR NEUROMUSCULAR EFFECTS MAY INCLUDE ATAXIA, SLURRED SPEECH, AREFLEXIA, WEAKNESS, FATIGUE, FASCICULATIONS, TWITCHING, TREMORS POSSIBLY OF THE TONGUE AND EYELIDS, AND EVENTUALLY PARALYSIS OF THE EXTREMITIES AND POSSIBLY OF THE RESPIRATORY MUSCLES. IN SEVERE CASES THERE MAY ALSO BE INVOLUNTARY DEFECATION AND URINATION, CYANOSIS, PSYCHOSIS, HYPERGLYCEMIA, ACUTE PANCREATITIS, CARDIAC IRREGULARITIES, PULMONARY EDEMA, UNCONSCIOUSNESS, CONVULSIONS, AND COMA. DEATH IS PRIMARILY DUE TO RESPIRATORY FAILURE, ALTHOUGH CARDIOVASCULAR EFFECTS INCLUDING CARDIAC ARREST MAY ALSO BE IMPLICATED. LONG TERM SEQUELAE ARE RARE BUT MAY INCLUDE NEUROPSYCHIATRIC DISORDERS AND MYOPATHY WITH MUSCLE TENDERNESS. SOME ORGANOPHOSPHATES MAY CAUSE A DELAYED NEUROPATHY BEGINNING 1-4 WEEKS AFTER AN ACUTE EXPOSURE WHICH MAY OR MAY NOT HAVE CAUSED ACUTE CHOLINERGIC EFFECTS. NUMBNESS, TINGLING, WEAKNESS AND CRAMPING BEGINNING SYMMETRICALLY IN THE LOWER LIMBS MAY PROGRESS TO ATAXIA AND PARALYSIS. IN SEVERE CASES, UPPER LIMB INVOLVEMENT IS POSSIBLE AND FLACCID PARALYSIS MAY PROGRESS TO SPASTIC PARALYSIS WITH EXAGGERATED REFLEXES. IMPROVEMENT MAY OCCUR OVER MONTHS TO YEARS, BUT SOME RESIDUAL IMPAIRMENT USUALLY REMAINS.
CHRONIC EXPOSURE- REPEATED OR PROLONGED EXPOSURE MAY RESULT IN THE EFFECTS OF ACUTE EXPOSURE INCLUDING THE DELAYED NEUROPATHY. OTHER EFFECTS REPORTED IN WORKERS REPEATEDLY EXPOSED INCLUDE IMPAIRED MEMORY AND CONCENTRATION, ACUTE PSYCHOSIS, SEVERE DEPRESSIONS, IRRITABILTY, CONFUSION, APATHY, EMOTIONAL LABILITY, SOCIAL WITHDRAWAL, CONFUSION, HEADACHE, SPEECH DIFFICULTIES, DELAYED REACTION TIMES, SPATIAL DISORIENTATION, NIGHTMARES, SLEEPWALKING, AND DROWSINESS OR INSOMNIA. AN INFLUENZA-LIKE CONDITION WITH HEADACHE, NAUSEA, WEAKNESS, ANOREXIA AND MALAISE HAS ALSO BEEN REPORTED.
FIRST AID- REMOVE FROM EXPOSURE AREA TO FRESH AIR IMMEDIATELY. IF BREATHING HAS STOPPED, GIVE ARTIFICIAL RESPIRATION. MAINTAIN AIRWAY AND BLOOD PRESSURE AND ADMINISTER OXYGEN IF AVAILABLE. KEEP AFFECTED PERSON WARM AND AT REST. TREAT SYMPTOMATICALLY AND SUPPORTIVELY. ADMINISTRATION OF OXYGEN SHOULD BE PERFORMED BY QUALIFIED PERSONNEL. GET MEDICAL ATTENTION IMMEDIATELY.

SKIN CONTACT: PHOXIM: TOXIC. SEE INFORMATION ON ORGANOPHOSPHATES.
ORGANOPHOSPHATES: CHOLINESTERASE INHIBITOR. **ACUTE EXPOSURE-** LOCALIZED SWEATING AND FASCICULATIONS MAY OCCUR AT THE SITE OF CONTACT. IF SUFFICIENT AMOUNTS ARE ABSORBED, OTHER EFFECTS OF CHOLINESTERASE INHIBITION AS DESCRIBED IN ACUTE INHALATION MAY OCCUR. SYMPTOMS MAY BE DELAYED 2-3 HOURS, BUT USUALLY NO MORE THAN 12 HOURS. THE RATE OF ABSORPTION IS INCREASED BY THE PRESENCE OF DERMATITIS OR HIGH AMBIENT TEMPERATURES. DELAYED NEUROPATHY IS ALSO POSSIBLE. **CHRONIC EXPOSURE-** REPEATED OR PROLONGED EXPOSURE MAY CAUSE EFFECTS AS DESCRIBED IN ACUTE EXPOSURE. SOME ORGANOPHOSPHATES MAY CAUSE SENSITIZATION.
FIRST AID- REMOVE CONTAMINATED CLOTHING IMMEDIATELY. WASH CONTAMINATED AREAS WITH SOAP AND WATER FOLLOWED BY ALCOHOL (ARENA, POISONING, 4TH ED.). EMERGENCY PERSONNEL SHOULD WEAR GLOVES AND AVOID CONTAMINATION. TREAT RESPIRATORY DIFFICULTY WITH ARTIFICIAL RESPIRATION. GET MEDICAL ATTENTION IMMEDIATELY.

EYE CONTACT: PHOXIM: SEE INFORMATION ON ORGANOPHOSPHATES.
ORGANOPHOSPHATES: CHOLINESTERASE INHIBITOR. **ACUTE EXPOSURE-** DIRECT CONTACT MAY CAUSE PAIN, HYPEREMIA, LACRIMATION, TWITCHING OF THE EYELIDS, MIOSIS, AND CILIARY MUSCLE SPASM WITH LOSS OF ACCOMODATION, BLURRED OR DIMMED VISION AND BROWACHE. SOMETIMES MYDRIASIS MAY OCCUR INSTEAD OF MIOSIS. WITH SUFFICIENT EXPOSURE, OTHER SYMPTOMS OF CHOLINESTERASE INHIBITION AS DESCRIBED IN ACUTE INHALATION MAY OCCUR. **CHRONIC EXPOSURE-** REPEATED OR PROLONGED EXPOSURE MAY CAUSE EFFECTS AS DESCRIBED IN ACUTE EXPOSURE. SOME COMPOUNDS HAVE CAUSED TOXIC EFFECTS ON THE CRYSTALLINE LENS, CONJUNCTIVAL THICKENING AND OBSTRUCTION OF THE NASOLACRIMAL CANALS WHEN USED AS MIOTIC EYEDROPS.
FIRST AID- IRRIGATE EYES WITH WATER OR SALINE SOLUTION. IF SYMPTOMS OF POISONING OCCUR, TREAT RESPIRATORY DIFFICULTY WITH ARTIFICIAL RESPIRATION AND OXYGEN. OBSERVE PATIENT FOR AT LEAST 24-36 HOURS (GOSSELIN, CLINICAL TOXICOLOGY OF COMMERCIAL PRODUCTS, 5TH ED.). GET MEDICAL ATTENTION IMMEDIATELY. OXYGEN SHOULD BE ADMINISTERED BY QUALIFIED MEDICAL PERSONNEL.

INGESTION: PHOXIM: TOXIC. SEE INFORMATION ON ORGANOPHOSPHATES.
ORGANOPHOSPHATES: CHOLINESTERASE INHIBITOR. **ACUTE EXPOSURE-** WHEN INGESTED, THE FIRST EFFECTS MAY BE NAUSEA, VOMITING, ANOREXIA, ABDOMINAL CRAMPS AND DIARRHEA. GASTROINTESTINAL ABSORPTION MAY CAUSE SYMPTOMS OF CHOLINESTERASE INHIBITION AS DESCRIBED IN ACUTE INHALATION. SYMPTOMS MAY BEGIN WITHIN MINUTES OR BE DELAYED FOR HOURS. DELAYED EFFECTS INCLUDING NEUROPATHY MAY ALSO OCCUR. **CHRONIC EXPOSURE-** REPEATED INGESTION MAY CAUSE EFFECTS AS DESCRIBED IN ACUTE EXPOSURE.
FIRST AID- IF PERSON IS ALERT AND RESPIRATION IS NOT DEPRESSED, GIVE SYRUP OF IPECAC FOLLOWED BY WATER (IF VOMITING OCCURS, KEEP HEAD BELOW HIPS TO PREVENT ASPIRATION). IF CONSCIOUSNESS LEVEL DECLINES OR VOMITING HAS NOT OCCURRED IN 15 MINUTES EMPTY STOMACH BY GASTRIC LAVAGE WITH THE AID OF CUFFED ENDOTRACHEAL TUBE USING ISOTONIC SALINE OR 5% SODIUM BICARBONATE FOLLOW WITH ACTIVATED CHARCOAL. ESTABLISH AND MAINTAIN AIRWAY. TREAT RESPIRATORY DIFFICULTY WITH ARTIFICIAL RESPIRATION AND OXYGEN. DO NOT GIVE MORPHINE, AMINOPHYLLINE, PHENOTHIAZINES, RESERPINE, FUROSEMIDE, OR ETHACRYNIC ACID (MORGAN, RECOGNITION AND MANAGEMENT OF PESTICIDE POISONINGS, 3RD ED.). TREAT SYMPTOMATICALLY AND SUPPORTIVELY. ADMINISTRATION OF OXYGEN AND LAVAGE MUST BE PERFORMED BY QUALIFIED MEDICAL PERSONNEL. GET MEDICAL ATTENTION IMMEDIATELY.
ANTIDOTE: THE FOLLOWING ANTIDOTE(S) HAVE BEEN RECOMMENDED. HOWEVER, THE DECISION AS TO WHETHER THE SEVERITY OF POISONING REQUIRES ADMINISTRATION OF ANY ANTIDOTE AND ACTUAL DOSE REQUIRED SHOULD BE MADE BY QUALIFIED MEDICAL PERSONNEL.
FOR CHOLINESTERASE INHIBITORS: ESTABLISH CLEAR AIRWAY AND TISSUE OXYGENATION BY ASPIRATION OF SECRETIONS, AND IF NECESSARY, BY ASSISTED PULMONARY VENTILATION WITH OXYGEN. IMPROVE TISSUE OXYGENATION AS MUCH AS POSSIBLE BEFORE ADMINISTERING ATROPINE TO MINIMIZE THE RISK OF

VENTRICULAR FIBRILLATION. ADMINISTER ATROPINE SULFATE INTRAVENOUSLY, OR INTRAMUSCULARLY IF IV INJECTION IS NOT POSSIBLE. IN MODERATELY SEVERE POISONING ADMINISTER ATROPINE SULFATE, 0.4-2.0 MG REPEATED EVERY 15 MINUTES UNTIL ATROPINIZATION IS ACHIEVED (TACHYCARDIA, FLUSHING, DRY MOUTH, MYDRIASIS). MAINTAIN ATROPINIZATION BY REPEATED DOSES FOR 2-12 HOURS, OR LONGER, DEPENDING ON THE SEVERITY OF POISONING. THE APPEARANCE OF RALES IN THE LUNG BASES, MIOSIS, SALIVATION, NAUSEA, BRADYCARDIA, ARE ALL INDICATIONS OF INADEQUATE ATROPINIZATION. SEVERELY POISONED INDIVIDUALS MAY EXHIBIT REMARKABLE TOLERANCE TO ATROPINE; TWO OR MORE TIMES THE DOSAGES SUGGESTED ABOVE MAY BE NEEDED. PERSONS NOT POISONED OR ONLY SLIGHTLY POISONED, HOWEVER, MAY DEVELOP SIGNS OF ATROPINE TOXICITY FROM SUCH LARGE DOSAGES: FEVER, MUSCLE FIBRILLATIONS, AND DELIRIUM ARE THE MAIN SIGNS OF ATROPINE TOXICITY. IF THESE SIGNS APPEAR WHILE THE PATIENT IS FULLY ATROPINIZED, ATROPINE ADMINISTRATION SHOULD BE DISCONTINUED, AT LEAST TEMPORARILY. OBSERVE TREATED PATIENTS CLOSELY AT LEAST 24 HOURS TO INSURE THAT SYMPTOMS (POSSIBLY PULMONARY EDEMA) DO NOT RECUR AS ATROPINIZATION WEARS OFF. IN VERY SEVERE POISONINGS, METABOLIC DISPOSITION OF TOXICANT MAY REQUIRE SEVERAL HOURS OR DAYS DURING WHICH ATROPINIZATION MUST BE MAINTAINED. MARKEDLY LOWER LEVELS OF URINARY METABOLITES INDICATE THAT ATROPINE DOSAGE CAN BE TAPERED OFF. AS DOSAGE IS REDUCED, CHECK THE LUNG BASES FREQUENTLY FOR RALES. IF RALES ARE HEARD OR OTHER SYMPTOMS RETURN, RE-ESTABLISH ATROPINIZATION PROMPTLY (MORGAN, RECOGNITION AND MANAGEMENT OF PESTICIDE POISONINGS, 3RD ED.). ADMINISTRATION OF ANTIDOTE MUST BE PERFORMED BY QUALIFIED MEDICAL PERSONNEL.

IN CASES OF SEVERE POISONING BY ORGANOPHOSPHATE PESTICIDES IN WHICH RESPIRATORY DEPRESSION, MUSCLE WEAKNESS AND TWITCHINGS ARE SEVERE, GIVE PRALIDOXIME (PROTOPAM-AYERST, 2-PAM), 1.0 GRAM INTRAVENOUSLY AT NO MORE THAN 0.5 GRAM PER MINUTE. DOSAGE OF PRALIDOXIME MAY BE REPEATED IN 1-2 HOURS, THEN AT 10-12 HOUR INTERVALS IF NEEDED. IN VERY SEVERE POISONINGS, DOSAGE RATES MAY BE DOUBLED. TREATMENT WITH PRALIDOXIME WILL BE MOST EFFECTIVE IF GIVEN WITHIN THIRTY-SIX HOURS AFTER POISONING (MORGAN, RECOGNITION AND MANAGEMENT OF PESTICIDE POISONINGS, 3RD ED.). ANTIDOTE SHOULD BE ADMINISTERED BY QUALIFIED MEDICAL PERSONNEL.

REACTIVITY

REACTIVITY: STABLE UNDER NORMAL TEMPERATURES AND PRESSURES.

INCOMPATIBILITIES: PHOXIM: ALKALINE MATERIALS: INCOMPATIBLE. OXIDIZERS (STRONG): FIRE AND EXPLOSION HAZARD.

DECOMPOSITION: THERMAL DECOMPOSITION PRODUCTS MAY INCLUDE TOXIC OXIDES OF NITROGEN, CARBON, PHOSPHORUS, AND SULFUR.

POLYMERIZATION: HAZARDOUS POLYMERIZATION HAS NOT BEEN REPORTED TO OCCUR UNDER NORMAL TEMPERATURES AND PRESSURES.

STORAGE AND DISPOSAL

OBSERVE ALL FEDERAL, STATE AND LOCAL REGULATIONS WHEN STORING OR DISPOSING OF THIS SUBSTANCE. FOR ASSISTANCE, CONTACT THE DISTRICT DIRECTOR OF THE ENVIRONMENTAL PROTECTION AGENCY.

STORAGE

STORE IN ACCORDANCE WITH 40 CFR 165 RECOMMENDED PROCEDURES FOR THE DISPOSAL AND STORAGE OF PESTICIDES AND PESTICIDE CONTAINERS.
STORE AWAY FROM INCOMPATIBLE SUBSTANCES.
STORE AT 4 DEGREES C.

DISPOSAL

DISPOSAL MUST BE IN ACCORDANCE WITH 40 CFR 165 RECOMMENDED PROCEDURES FOR THE DISPOSAL AND STORAGE OF PESTICIDES AND PESTICIDE CONTAINERS.

CONDITIONS TO AVOID

AVOID CONTACT WITH HEAT, SPARKS, FLAMES OR OTHER IGNITION SOURCES. VAPORS MAY BE EXPLOSIVE. MATERIAL IS POISONOUS; AVOID INHALATION OF VAPORS OR CONTACT WITH SKIN. DO NOT ALLOW MATERIAL TO CONTAMINATE WATER SOURCES.

SPILL AND LEAK PROCEDURES

OCCUPATIONAL SPILL: SHUT OFF IGNITION SOURCES. DO NOT TOUCH SPILLED MATERIAL. STOP LEAK IF YOU CAN DO IT WITHOUT RISK. USE WATER SPRAY TO REDUCE VAPORS. FOR SMALL SPILLS, TAKE UP WITH SAND OR OTHER ABSORBENT MATERIAL AND PLACE INTO CONTAINERS FOR LATER DISPOSAL. FOR LARGER SPILLS, DIKE FAR AHEAD OF SPILL FOR LATER DISPOSAL. NO SMOKING, FLAMES OR FLARES IN HAZARD AREA! KEEP UNNECESSARY PEOPLE AWAY; ISOLATE HAZARD AREA AND DENY ENTRY.

PROTECTIVE EQUIPMENT

VENTILATION: PROVIDE LOCAL EXHAUST OR GENERAL DILUTION VENTILATION SYSTEM.

RESPIRATOR: THE FOLLOWING RESPIRATORS ARE RECOMMENDED BASED ON INFORMATION FOUND IN THE PHYSICAL DATA, TOXICITY AND HEALTH EFFECTS SECTIONS. THEY ARE RANKED IN ORDER FROM MINIMUM TO MAXIMUM RESPIRATORY PROTECTION. THE SPECIFIC RESPIRATOR SELECTED MUST BE BASED ON CONTAMINATION LEVELS FOUND IN THE WORK PLACE, MUST NOT EXCEED THE WORKING LIMITS OF THE RESPIRATOR AND BE JOINTLY APPROVED BY THE NATIONAL INSTITUTE FOR OCCUPATIONAL SAFETY AND HEALTH AND THE MINE SAFETY AND HEALTH ADMINISTRATION (NIOSH-MSHA).
TYPE 'C' SUPPLIED-AIR RESPIRATOR WITH A FULL FACEPIECE OPERATED IN PRESSURE-DEMAND OR OTHER POSITIVE PRESSURE MODE OR WITH A FULL FACEPIECE, HELMET OR HOOD OPERATED IN CONTINOUS-FLOW MODE.
SELF-CONTAINED BREATHING APPARATUS WITH A FULL FACEPIECE OPERATED IN PRESSURE-DEMAND OR OTHER POSITIVE PRESSURE MODE.
FOR FIREFIGHTING AND OTHER IMMEDIATELY DANGEROUS TO LIFE OR HEALTH CONDITIONS:
SELF-CONTAINED BREATHING APPARATUS WITH FULL FACEPIECE OPERATED IN PRESSURE-DEMAND OR OTHER POSITIVE PRESSURE MODE.
SUPPLIED-AIR RESPIRATOR WITH FULL FACEPIECE AND OPERATED IN PRESSURE-DEMAND OR OTHER POSITIVE PRESSURE MODE IN COMBINATION WITH AN AUXILIARY SELF-CONTAINED BREATHING APPARATUS OPERATED IN PRESSURE-DEMAND OR OTHER POSITIVE PRESSURE MODE.

CLOTHING: EMPLOYEE MUST WEAR APPROPRIATE PROTECTIVE (IMPERVIOUS) CLOTHING AND EQUIPMENT TO PREVENT REPEATED OR PROLONGED SKIN CONTACT WITH THIS SUBSTANCE.

GLOVES: EMPLOYEE MUST WEAR APPROPRIATE PROTECTIVE GLOVES TO PREVENT CONTACT WITH THIS SUBSTANCE.

EYE PROTECTION: EMPLOYEE MUST WEAR SPLASH-PROOF OR DUST-RESISTANT SAFETY GOGGLES TO PREVENT EYE CONTACT WITH THIS SUBSTANCE.
EMERGENCY EYE WASH: WHERE THERE IS ANY POSSIBILITY THAT AN EMPLOYEE'S EYES MAY BE EXPOSED TO THIS SUBSTANCE, THE EMPLOYER SHOULD PROVIDE AN EYE WASH FOUNTAIN WITHIN THE IMMEDIATE WORK AREA FOR EMERGENCY USE.

AUTHORIZED BY- OCCUPATIONAL HEALTH SERVICES, INC.
CREATION DATE: 10/04/89 ***REVISION DATE:*** 04/27/90

MATERIAL SAFETY DATA SHEET

OCCUPATIONAL HEALTH SERVICES, INC.
AGRICULTURE AND PESTICIDE DIVISION
450 SEVENTH AVENUE, SUITE 2407
NEW YORK, NEW YORK 10123
1-800-445-MSDS OR (212) 967-1100

EMERGENCY CONTACT:
JOHN S. BRANSFORD, JR. (615) 292-1180

SUBSTANCE IDENTIFICATION

CAS-NUMBER 650-51-1

SUBSTANCE: SODIUM TRICHLOROACETATE

TRADE NAMES/SYNONYMS: ACETIC ACID, TRICHLORO-, SODIUM SALT; TRICHLOROACETIC ACID SODIUM SALT; ANTIPERZ; ANTYPERZ; NATA; SODIUM TCA; TCA SODIUM; VARITOX; C2CL3NAO2; PST73307

CHEMICAL FAMILY: SALT

MOLECULAR FORMULA: C-CL3-C-O-O.NA

MOLECULAR WEIGHT: 185.37

CERCLA RATINGS (SCALE 0-3): HEALTH=U FIRE=1 REACTIVITY=0 PERSISTENCE=1

NFPA RATINGS (SCALE 0-4): HEALTH=U FIRE=1 REACTIVITY=0

COMPONENTS AND CONTAMINANTS

COMPONENT: SODIUM TRICHLOROACETATE ***PERCENT:*** 100.0
CAS# 650-51-1

OTHER CONTAMINANTS: NONE

EXPOSURE LIMITS: NO OCCUPATIONAL EXPOSURE LIMITS ESTABLISHED BY OSHA, ACGIH, OR NIOSH.

PHYSICAL DATA

DESCRIPTION: YELLOW DELIQUESCENT POWDER. ***MELTING POINT:*** >572 F (>300 C)

SPECIFIC GRAVITY: NOT AVAILABLE ***SOLUBILITY IN WATER:*** 120% @ 25 C

SOLVENT SOLUBILITY: SOLUBLE IN ETHANOL, ORGANIC SOLVENTS.

FIRE AND EXPLOSION DATA

FIRE AND EXPLOSION HAZARD: SLIGHT FIRE HAZARD WHEN EXPOSED TO HEAT OR FLAME.

FIREFIGHTING MEDIA: DRY CHEMICAL, CARBON DIOXIDE, HALON, WATER SPRAY OR STANDARD FOAM (1987 EMERGENCY RESPONSE GUIDEBOOK, DOT P 5800.4). FOR LARGER FIRES, USE WATER SPRAY, FOG OR STANDARD FOAM (1987 EMERGENCY RESPONSE GUIDEBOOK, DOT P 5800.4).

FIREFIGHTING: MOVE CONTAINER FROM FIRE AREA IF POSSIBLE. DO NOT SCATTER SPILLED MATERIAL WITH HIGH PRESSURE WATER STREAMS. DIKE FIRE CONTROL WATER FOR LATER DISPOSAL (1987 EMERGENCY RESPONSE GUIDEBOOK, DOT P 5800.4, GUIDE PAGE 31).
USE AGENTS SUITABLE FOR TYPE OF SURROUNDING FIRE. AVOID BREATHING HAZARDOUS VAPORS, KEEP UPWIND.

TOXICITY

SODIUM TRICHLOROACETATE: TOXICITY DATA: 3320 MG/KG ORAL-RAT LD50; 3600 MG/KG ORAL-MOUSE LD50; 3300 MG/KG UNREPORTED-MAMMAL LD50; MUTAGENIC DATA (RTECS). CARCINOGEN STATUS: NONE. LOCAL EFFECTS: CORROSIVE- EYE, SKIN AND MUCOUS MEMBRANES. ACUTE TOXICITY LEVEL: MODERATELY TOXIC BY INGESTION. TARGET EFFECTS: NO DATA AVAILABLE.

HEALTH EFFECTS AND FIRST AID

INHALATION: SODIUM TRICHLOROACETATE: CORROSIVE. **ACUTE EXPOSURE-** ON CONTACT WITH MOISTURE, THIS CHEMICAL RELEASES TRICHLOROACETIC ACID WHICH IS CORROSIVE. INHALATION OF ACIDIC SUBSTANCES MAY CAUSE SEVERE RESPIRATORY IRRITATION WITH COUGHING, CHOKING, AND POSSIBLY BURNS OF THE MUCOUS MEMBRANES. OTHER INITIAL SYMPTOMS MAY INCLUDE DIZZINESS, HEADACHE, NAUSEA, AND WEAKNESS. PULMONARY EDEMA MAY BE IMMEDIATE IN THE MOST SEVERE EXPOSURES, BUT MORE LIKELY WILL OCCUR AFTER A LATENT PERIOD OF 5-72 HOURS, AS A SLOWLY PROGRESSIVE, BUT MARKED INFLAMMATORY REACTION TAKES PLACE. THE SYMPTOMS MAY INCLUDE TIGHTNESS IN THE CHEST, DYSPNEA, DIZZINESS, FROTHY SPUTUM, AND CYANOSIS. PHYSICAL FINDINGS MAY INCLUDE HYPOTENSION, WEAK, RAPID PULSE, MOIST RALES, AND HEMOCONCENTRATION. IN NON-FATAL CASES, COMPLETE RECOVERY MAY OCCUR WITHIN A FEW DAYS OR WEEKS OR, CONVALESCENCE MAY BE PROLONGED WITH FREQUENT RELAPSES AND CONTINUED DYSPNEA AND OTHER SIGNS AND SYMPTOMS OF PULMONARY INSUFFICIENCY. IN SEVERE EXPOSURES, DEATH DUE TO ANOXIA MAY OCCUR WITHIN A FEW HOURS AFTER ONSET OF THE SYMPTOMS OF PULMONARY EDEMA OR FOLLOWING A RELAPSE. **CHRONIC EXPOSURE-** DEPENDING ON THE CONCENTRATION AND DURATION OF EXPOSURE, REPEATED OR PROLONGED EXPOSURE TO AN ACIDIC SUBSTANCE MAY CAUSE EROSION OF THE TEETH, INFLAMMATORY AND ULCERATIVE CHANGES IN THE MOUTH, AND POSSIBLY JAW NECROSIS. BRONCHIAL IRRITATION WITH COUGH AND FREQUENT ATTACKS OF BRONCHIAL PNEUMONIA MAY OCCUR. GASTROINTESTINAL DISTURBANCES ARE ALSO POSSIBLE.

FIRST AID- REMOVE FROM EXPOSURE AREA TO FRESH AIR IMMEDIATELY. IF BREATHING HAS STOPPED, PERFORM ARTIFICIAL RESPIRATION. KEEP PERSON WARM AND AT REST. TREAT SYMPTOMATICALLY AND SUPPORTIVELY. GET MEDICAL ATTENTION IMMEDIATELY.

SKIN CONTACT: SODIUM TRICHLOROACETATE: CORROSIVE. **ACUTE EXPOSURE-** CONTACT WITH THE POWDER MAY CAUSE IRRITATION AND SKIN ABSORPTION. ON CONTACT WITH MOISTURE, THIS CHEMICAL RELEASES TRICHLOROACETIC ACID WHICH IS CORROSIVE. DIRECT CONTACT WITH ACIDIC SUBSTANCES MAY CAUSE SEVERE PAIN, BURNS AND POSSIBLY BROWNISH OR YELLOWISH STAINS. BURNS MAY BE DEEP WITH SHARP EDGES AND HEAL SLOWLY WITH SCAR TISSUE FORMATION. **CHRONIC EXPOSURE-** EFFECTS DEPEND ON THE CONCENTRATION AND DURATION OF EXPOSURE. REPEATED OR PROLONGED CONTACT WITH ACIDIC SUBSTANCES MAY RESULT IN DERMATITIS OR EFFECTS SIMILAR TO ACUTE EXPOSURE.

FIRST AID- REMOVE CONTAMINATED CLOTHING AND SHOES IMMEDIATELY. WASH AFFECTED AREA WITH SOAP OR MILD DETERGENT AND LARGE AMOUNTS OF WATER UNTIL NO EVIDENCE OF CHEMICAL REMAINS (APPROXIMATELY 15-20 MINUTES). GET MEDICAL ATTENTION IMMEDIATELY.

EYE CONTACT: SODIUM TRICHLOROACETATE: CORROSIVE. **ACUTE EXPOSURE-** CONTACT WITH THE POWDER MAY CAUSE IRRITATION. ON CONTACT WITH MOISTURE, THIS CHEMICAL RELEASES TRICHLOROACETIC ACID WHICH IS CORROSIVE. DIRECT CONTACT WITH ACIDIC SUBSTANCES MAY CAUSE PAIN, LACRIMATION, PHOTOPHOBIA, AND BURNS, POSSIBLY SEVERE. THE DEGREE OF INJURY DEPENDS ON THE CONCENTRATION AND DURATION OF CONTACT. IN MILD BURNS, THE EPITHELIUM REGENERATES RAPIDLY AND THE EYE RECOVERS COMPLETELY. IN SEVERE CASES, THE EXTENT OF INJURY MAY NOT BE FULLY APPARENT FOR SEVERAL WEEKS. ULTIMATELY, THE WHOLE CORNEA MAY BECOME DEEPLY VASCULARIZED AND OPAQUE RESULTING IN BLINDNESS. IN THE WORST CASES, THE EYE MAY BE TOTALLY DESTROYED. **CHRONIC EXPOSURE-** EFFECTS DEPEND ON THE CONCENTRATION AND DURATION OF EXPOSURE. REPEATED OR PROLONGED EXPOSURE TO ACIDIC SUBSTANCES MAY CAUSE CONJUNCTIVITIS OR EFFECTS AS IN ACUTE EXPOSURE.

FIRST AID- WASH EYES IMMEDIATELY WITH LARGE AMOUNTS OF WATER OR NORMAL SALINE, OCCASIONALLY LIFTING UPPER AND LOWER LIDS, UNTIL NO EVIDENCE OF CHEMICAL REMAINS (APPROXIMATELY 15-20 MINUTES). GET MEDICAL ATTENTION IMMEDIATELY.

INGESTION: SODIUM TRICHLOROACETATE: CORROSIVE. **ACUTE EXPOSURE-** ANIMALS MAY QUICKLY BECOME COMATOSE AND RECOVER WITHIN 36 HOURS OR DIE IN COMA. ON CONTACT WITH MOISTURE, THIS CHEMICAL RELEASES TRICHLOROACETIC ACID WHICH IS CORROSIVE. ACIDIC SUBSTANCES MAY CAUSE CIRCUMORAL BURNS WITH DISCOLORATION AND CORROSION OF THE MUCOUS MEMBRANES OF THE MOUTH, THROAT AND ESOPHAGUS. THERE MAY BE IMMEDIATE PAIN AND DIFFICULTY OR INABILITY TO SWALLOW OR SPEAK. EPIGLOTTAL EDEMA MAY RESULT IN RESPIRATORY DISTRESS AND POSSIBLY ASPHYXIA. MARKED THIRST, EPIGASTRIC PAIN, NAUSEA, VOMITING AND DIARRHEA MAY OCCUR. DEPENDING ON THE DEGREE OF ESOPHAGEAL AND GASTRIC CORROSION, THE VOMITUS MAY CONTAIN FRESH OR DARK PRECIPITATED BLOOD AND LARGE SHREDS OF MUCOSA. SHOCK WITH MARKED HYPOTENSION, WEAK, RAPID PULSE, SHALLOW RESPIRATION, AND CLAMMY SKIN MAY OCCUR. CIRCULATORY COLLAPSE MAY ENSUE AND IF UNCORRECTED, LEAD TO RENAL FAILURE. IN SEVERE CASES, GASTRIC AND, TO A LESSER DEGREE, ESOPHAGEAL PERFORATION AND SUBSEQUENT PERITONITIS MAY OCCUR AND BE ACCOMPANIED BY FEVER AND ABDOMINAL RIGIDITY. ESOPHAGEAL, GASTRIC AND PYLORIC STRICTURE MAY OCCUR WITHIN A FEW WEEKS, BUT MAY BE DELAYED FOR MONTHS OR EVEN YEARS. DEATH MAY RESULT WITHIN A SHORT TIME FROM ASPHYXIA, CIRCULATORY COLLAPSE OR ASPIRATION OF EVEN MINUTE AMOUNTS. LATER DEATH MAY BE DUE TO PERITONITIS, SEVERE NEPHRITIS OR PNEUMONIA. COMA AND CONVULSIONS SOMETIMES OCCUR TERMINALLY. **CHRONIC EXPOSURE-** DEPENDING ON THE CONCENTRATION, REPEATED INGESTION OF ACIDIC SUBSTANCES MAY RESULT IN INFLAMMATORY AND ULCERATIVE CHANGES IN THE MUCOUS MEMBRANES OF THE MOUTH AND OTHER EFFECTS AS IN ACUTE INGESTION.

FIRST AID- TREAT SYMPTOMATICALLY AND SUPPORTIVELY. GET MEDICAL ATTENTION IMMEDIATELY. IF VOMITING OCCURS, KEEP HEAD LOWER THAN HIPS TO PREVENT ASPIRATION.

ANTIDOTE: NO SPECIFIC ANTIDOTE. TREAT SYMPTOMATICALLY AND SUPPORTIVELY.

REACTIVITY

REACTIVITY: STABLE UNDER NORMAL TEMPERATURES AND PRESSURES.

INCOMPATIBILITIES: SODIUM TRICHLOROACETATE: ALUMINUM: MAY CORRODE. IRON: MAY CORRODE. OXIDIZERS (STRONG): FIRE AND EXPLOSION HAZARD. ZINC: MAY CORRODE.

DECOMPOSITION: THERMAL DECOMPOSITION PRODUCTS MAY INCLUDE TOXIC AND CORROSIVE FUMES OF CHLORIDES AND TOXIC OXIDES OF CARBON.

POLYMERIZATION: HAZARDOUS POLYMERIZATION HAS NOT BEEN REPORTED TO OCCUR UNDER NORMAL TEMPERATURES AND PRESSURES.

STORAGE AND DISPOSAL

OBSERVE ALL FEDERAL, STATE AND LOCAL REGULATIONS WHEN STORING OR DISPOSING OF THIS SUBSTANCE. FOR ASSISTANCE, CONTACT THE DISTRICT DIRECTOR OF THE ENVIRONMENTAL PROTECTION AGENCY.

****STORAGE****

STORE IN ACCORDANCE WITH 40 CFR 165 RECOMMENDED PROCEDURES FOR THE DISPOSAL AND STORAGE OF PESTICIDES AND PESTICIDE CONTAINERS.
STORE AWAY FROM INCOMPATIBLE SUBSTANCES.

****DISPOSAL****

DISPOSAL MUST BE IN ACCORDANCE WITH 40 CFR 165 RECOMMENDED PROCEDURES FOR THE DISPOSAL AND STORAGE OF PESTICIDES AND PESTICIDE CONTAINERS.

CONDITIONS TO AVOID

MAY BURN BUT DOES NOT IGNITE READILY. AVOID CONTACT WITH STRONG OXIDIZERS, EXCESSIVE HEAT, SPARKS, OR OPEN FLAME.

SPILL AND LEAK PROCEDURES

OCCUPATIONAL SPILL: SWEEP UP AND PLACE IN SUITABLE CLEAN, DRY CONTAINERS FOR RECLAMATION OR LATER DISPOSAL. DO NOT FLUSH SPILLED MATERIAL INTO SEWER. KEEP UNNECESSARY PEOPLE AWAY.

PROTECTIVE EQUIPMENT

VENTILATION: PROVIDE LOCAL EXHAUST OR GENERAL DILUTION VENTILATION SYSTEM.

RESPIRATOR: THE FOLLOWING RESPIRATORS ARE RECOMMENDED BASED ON INFORMATION FOUND IN THE PHYSICAL DATA, TOXICITY AND HEALTH EFFECTS SECTIONS. THEY ARE RANKED IN ORDER FROM MINIMUM TO MAXIMUM RESPIRATORY PROTECTION. THE SPECIFIC RESPIRATOR SELECTED MUST BE BASED ON CONTAMINATION LEVELS FOUND IN THE WORK PLACE, MUST NOT EXCEED THE WORKING LIMITS OF THE RESPIRATOR AND BE JOINTLY APPROVED BY THE NATIONAL INSTITUTE FOR OCCUPATIONAL SAFETY AND HEALTH AND THE MINE SAFETY AND HEALTH ADMINISTRATION (NIOSH-MSHA).

CHEMICAL CARTRIDGE RESPIRATOR WITH AN ORGANIC VAPOR CARTRIDGE(S) WITH A FULL FACEPIECE AND ORGANIC VAPOR CARTRIDGE(S) IN COMBINATION WITH A DUST AND MIST FILTER.

POWERED AIR-PURIFYING RESPIRATOR WITH A TIGHT-FITTING FACEPIECE AND ORGANIC VAPOR CARTRIDGE(S) IN COMBINATION WITH A HIGH-EFFICIENCY PARTICULATE FILTER.

TYPE 'C' SUPPLIED-AIR RESPIRATOR WITH A FULL FACEPIECE OPERATED IN A PRESSURE-DEMAND OR OTHER POSITIVE PRESSURE MODE.

SELF-CONTAINED BREATHING APPARATUS WITH A FULL FACEPIECE OPERATED IN PRESSURE-DEMAND OR OTHER POSITIVE PRESSURE MODE.

FOR FIREFIGHTING AND OTHER IMMEDIATELY DANGEROUS TO LIFE OR HEALTH CONDITIONS:

SELF-CONTAINED BREATHING APPARATUS WITH FULL FACEPIECE OPERATED IN PRESSURE-DEMAND OR OTHER POSITIVE PRESSURE MODE.

SUPPLIED-AIR RESPIRATOR WITH FULL FACEPIECE AND OPERATED IN PRESSURE-DEMAND OR OTHER POSITIVE PRESSURE MODE IN COMBINATION WITH AN AUXILIARY SELF-CONTAINED BREATHING APPARATUS OPERATED IN PRESSURE-DEMAND OR OTHER POSITIVE PRESSURE MODE.

CLOTHING: EMPLOYEE MUST WEAR APPROPRIATE PROTECTIVE (IMPERVIOUS) CLOTHING AND EQUIPMENT TO PREVENT REPEATED OR PROLONGED SKIN CONTACT WITH THIS SUBSTANCE.

GLOVES: EMPLOYEE MUST WEAR APPROPRIATE PROTECTIVE GLOVES TO PREVENT CONTACT WITH THIS SUBSTANCE.

EYE PROTECTION: EMPLOYEE MUST WEAR SPLASH-PROOF OR DUST-RESISTANT SAFETY GOGGLES TO PREVENT EYE CONTACT WITH THIS SUBSTANCE.

EMERGENCY EYE WASH: WHERE THERE IS ANY POSSIBILITY THAT AN EMPLOYEE'S EYES MAY BE EXPOSED TO THIS SUBSTANCE, THE EMPLOYER SHOULD PROVIDE AN EYE WASH FOUNTAIN WITHIN THE IMMEDIATE WORK AREA FOR EMERGENCY USE.

AUTHORIZED BY- OCCUPATIONAL HEALTH SERVICES, INC.
CREATION DATE: 02/08/90 ***REVISION DATE:*** 05/31/90

MATERIAL SAFETY DATA SHEET

OCCUPATIONAL HEALTH SERVICES, INC.
AGRICULTURE AND PESTICIDE DIVISION
450 SEVENTH AVENUE, SUITE 2407
NEW YORK, NEW YORK 10123
1-800-445-MSDS OR (212) 967-1100

EMERGENCY CONTACT:
JOHN S. BRANSFORD, JR. (615) 292-1180

SUBSTANCE IDENTIFICATION

SUBSTANCE: **21 MALATHION 57E 05623441**

TRADE NAMES/SYNONYMS: PST75465

CERCLA RATINGS (SCALE 0-3): HEALTH=3 FIRE=2 REACTIVITY=0 PERSISTENCE=2

NFPA RATINGS (SCALE 0-4): HEALTH=3 FIRE=2 REACTIVITY=0

COMPONENTS AND CONTAMINANTS

COMPONENT: CYCLO SOL 53 ***PERCENT:*** 35.45

CAS# 64742-95-6 CONTAINS:
XYLENE (3-4%) CAS# 1330-20-7
ETHYL TOLUENES (22-28%) CAS# 25550-14-5
TRIMETHYL BENZENES (57-67%) CAS# 25551-13-7
AROMATICS (6-9%)
PARAFFINS (<1%)

COMPONENT: TOXIMUL MP (DODECYLBENZENE SULFONATE) ***PERCENT:*** 5.36

COMPONENT: CYTHION (MALATHION) ***PERCENT:*** 59.19

CAS# 121-75-5

EXPOSURE LIMITS: XYLENE: 100 PPM (435 MG/M3) OSHA TWA; 150 PPM (655 MG/M3) OSHA STEL 100 PPM (435 MG/M3) ACGIH TWA; 150 PPM (655 MG/M3) ACGIH STEL 100 PPM (435 MG/M3) NIOSH RECOMMENDED 10 HOUR TWA; 200 PPM (870 MG/M3) NIOSH RECOMMENDED 10 MINUTE CEILING

1000 POUNDS CERCLA SECTION 103 REPORTABLE QUANTITY SUBJECT TO SARA SECTION 313 ANNUAL TOXIC CHEMICAL RELEASE REPORTING

TRIMETHYL BENZENE: 25 PPM (125 MG/M3) OSHA TWA 25 PPM (125 MG/M3) ACGIH TWA

MALATHION: 10 MG/M3 OSHA TWA (TOTAL DUST) (SKIN) 10 MG/M3 ACGIH TWA (SKIN) 15 MG/M3 NIOSH RECOMMENDED 10 HOUR TWA

100 POUNDS CERCLA SECTION 103 REPORTABLE QUANTITY

PHYSICAL DATA

DESCRIPTION: CLEAR, BROWNISH LIQUID WITH A MERCAPTAN-LIKE ODOR.

BOILING POINT: NOT AVAILABLE ***SPECIFIC GRAVITY:*** 1.07

EVAPORATION RATE: NOT AVAILABLE ***SOLUBILITY IN WATER:*** EMULSIFIABLE

VAPOR DENSITY: >1

FIRE AND EXPLOSION DATA

FIRE AND EXPLOSION HAZARD: MODERATE FIRE HAZARD WHEN EXPOSED TO HEAT OR FLAME.

VAPORS ARE HEAVIER THAN AIR AND MAY TRAVEL A CONSIDERABLE DISTANCE TO A SOURCE OF IGNITION AND FLASH BACK.

VAPOR-AIR MIXTURES ARE EXPLOSIVE ABOVE FLASH POINT.

FLASH POINT: >100 F (>38 C) (CC) ***FLAMMABILITY CLASS(OSHA):*** II

FIREFIGHTING MEDIA: DRY CHEMICAL, CARBON DIOXIDE, HALON, WATER SPRAY OR STANDARD FOAM (1987 EMERGENCY RESPONSE GUIDEBOOK, DOT P 5800.4).

FOR LARGER FIRES, USE WATER SPRAY, FOG OR STANDARD FOAM (1987 EMERGENCY RESPONSE GUIDEBOOK, DOT P 5800.4).

FIREFIGHTING: MOVE CONTAINER FROM FIRE AREA IF POSSIBLE. COOL FIRE-EXPOSED CONTAINERS WITH WATER FROM SIDE UNTIL WELL AFTER FIRE IS OUT. STAY AWAY FROM STORAGE TANK ENDS. FOR MASSIVE FIRE IN STORAGE AREA, USE UNMANNED HOSE HOLDER OR MONITOR NOZZLES, ELSE WITHDRAW FROM AREA AND LET FIRE BURN. WITHDRAW IMMEDIATELY IN CASE OF RISING SOUND FROM VENTING SAFETY DEVICE OR ANY DISCOLORATION OF STORAGE TANK DUE TO FIRE (1987 EMERGENCY RESPONSE GUIDEBOOK, DOT P 5800.4, GUIDE PAGE 27).

EXTINGUISH ONLY IF FLOW CAN BE STOPPED; USE FLOODING AMOUNTS OF WATER AS A FOG, SOLID STREAMS MAY BE INEFFECTIVE. COOL CONTAINERS WITH FLOODING AMOUNTS OF WATER, APPLY FROM AS FAR A DISTANCE AS POSSIBLE. AVOID BREATHING VAPORS, KEEP UPWIND.

TRANSPORTATION DATA

DEPARTMENT OF TRANSPORTATION HAZARD CLASSIFICATION 49 CFR 172.101: COMBUSTIBLE LIQUID

DEPARTMENT OF TRANSPORTATION LABELING REQUIREMENTS 49 CFR 172.101 AND SUBPART E: NONE

DEPARTMENT OF TRANSPORTATION PACKAGING REQUIREMENTS: NONE EXCEPTIONS: 49 CFR 173.118A

TOXICITY

XYLENE: IRRITATION DATA: 200 PPM EYE-HUMAN; 87 MG EYE-RABBIT MILD; 5 MG/24 HOURS EYE-RABBIT SEVERE; 100% SKIN-RABBIT MODERATE; 500 MG/24 HOURS SKIN-RABBIT MODERATE. TOXICITY DATA: 10000 PPM/6 HOURS INHALATION-MAN LCLO; 200 PPM INHALATION-HUMAN TCLO; 5000 PPM/4 HOURS INHALATION-RAT LC50; 450 PPM INHALATION-GUINEA PIG LCLO; 50 MG/KG ORAL-HUMAN LDLO; 4300 MG/KG ORAL-RAT LD50; 1700 MG/KG SUBCUTANEOUS-RAT LD50; 129 MG/KG INTRAVENOUS-RABBIT LDLO; 2 GM/KG INTRAPERITONEAL-MAMMAL LDLO; 2459 MG/KG INTRAPERITONEAL-RAT LD50; 1548 MG/KG INTRAPERITONEAL-MOUSE LD50; 2000 MG/KG INTRAPERITONEAL-GUINEA PIG LDLO; REPRODUCTIVE EFFECTS DATA (RTECS). CARCINOGEN STATUS: NONE. LOCAL EFFECTS: IRRITANT- INHALATION, SKIN, EYE. ACUTE TOXICITY LEVEL: MODERATELY TOXIC BY INHALATION, INGESTION. TARGET EFFECTS: CENTRAL NERVOUS SYSTEM DEPRESSANT. POISONING MAY ALSO AFFECT THE NERVOUS SYSTEM, LIVER AND KIDNEYS. AT INCREASED RISK FROM EXPOSURE: PREGNANT WOMEN. ADDITIONAL INFORMATION: CONSUMPTION OF ALCOHOLIC BEVERAGES MAY ENHANCE THE TOXIC EFFECTS. STIMULANTS SUCH AS EPINEPHRINE OR EPHEDRINE MAY INDUCE VENTRICULAR FIBRILLATION.

ETHYL TOLUENES: CARCINOGEN STATUS: NONE. THERE IS INSUFFICIENT DATA TO QUANTIFY THE TOXICITY OF ETHYL TOLUENES. IT IS AN EYE, MUCOUS MEMBRANE AND SKIN IRRITANT AND A CENTRAL NERVOUS SYSTEM DEPRESSANT.

TRIMETHYL BENZENES: 1,3,5-TRIMETHYL BENZENE: 24 GM/M3/4 HOURS INHALATION-RAT LC50; 10 PPM INHALATION-HUMAN TCLO; MUTAGENIC DATA (RTEC); CARCINOGEN STATUS: NONE. 1,2,4-TRIMETHYL BENZENE: 5000 MG/KG ORAL-RAT LD50; 18 GM/M3/4 HOURS INHALATION-RAT LC50; CARCINOGEN STATUS: NONE. TRIMETHYL BENZENES ARE EYE, MUCOUS MEMBRANE AND SKIN IRRITANTS AND CENTRAL NERVOUS SYSTEM DEPRESSANTS.

AROMATICS: CARCINOGEN STATUS: NONE. LOCAL EFFECTS: IRRITANT-INHALATION, SKIN, EYE.* ACUTE TOXICITY LEVEL: THE TOXICITY WILL VARY DEPENDING ON THE SPECIFIC COMPOSITION. TARGET EFFECTS: CENTRAL NERVOUS SYSTEM DEPRESSANT* ADDITIONAL DATA: STIMULANTS SUCH AS

EPINEPHRINE MAY INDUCE VENTRICULAR FIBRILLATION.*
* BASED ON GENERAL AROMATICS INFORMATION.
DODECYLBENZENE SULFONATE: 650 MG/KG ORAL-RAT LD50; CARCINOGEN STATUS: NONE. THERE IS INSUFFICIENT DATA TO EVALUATE THE SYSTEMIC EFFECTS OF DODECYLBENZENE SULFONATE. IT MAY BE IRRITATING TO THE EYES, MUCOUS MEMBRANES AND SKIN.
MALATHION: TOXICITY DATA: 84,600 UG/M3/4 HOURS INHALATION-RAT LC50; 10 MG/M3/4 HOURS INHALATION-CAT LCLO; 4100 MG/KG SKIN-RABBIT LD50; 2330 MG/KG SKIN-MOUSE LD50; 4444 MG/KG SKIN-RAT LD50; 6700 MG/KG SKIN-GUINEA PIG LD50; 471 MG/KG ORAL-MAN LDLO; 246 MG/KG ORAL-WOMAN LDLO; 290 MG/KG ORAL-RAT LD50; 190 MG/KG ORAL-MOUSE LD50; 250 MG/KG ORAL-RABBIT LD50; 1200 MG/KG ORAL-RABBIT LDLO; 570 MG/KG ORAL-GUINEA PIG LD50; 500 MG/KG ORAL-DOMESTIC ANIMAL LD50; 53 MG/KG ORAL-CATTLE LD50; 1000 MG/KG SUBCUTANEOUS-RAT LD50; 221 MG/KG SUBCUTANEOUS-MOUSE LD50; 184 MG/KG INTRAVENOUS-MOUSE LD50; 50 MG/KG INTRAVENOUS-RAT LD50; 250 MG/KG INTRAPERITONEAL-RAT LD50; 193 MG/KG INTRAPERITONEAL-MOUSE LD50; 1857 MG/KG INTRAPERITONEAL-DOG LD50; 550 MG/KG INTRAPERITONEAL-GUINEA PIG LD50; 2400 MG/KG INTRAPERITONEAL-HAMSTER LD50; 1820 UG/KG INTRAARTERIAL-CAT LDLO; MUTAGENIC DATA (RTECS); REPRODUCTIVE EFFECTS DATA (RTECS). CARCINOGEN STATUS: ANIMAL INADEQUATE EVIDENCE (IARC GROUP-3). ACUTE TOXICITY LEVEL: HIGHLY TOXIC BY INHALATION; TOXIC BY INGESTION; SLIGHTLY TOXIC BY DERMAL ABSORPTION. TARGET EFFECTS: SENSITIZER- DERMAL; CHOLINESTERASE INHIBITOR. AT INCREASED RISK FROM EXPOSURE: PERSONS WITH RESPIRATORY AILMENTS, RECENT EXPOSURE TO CHOLINESTERASE INHIBITORS OR IMPAIRED CHOLINESTERASE PRODUCTION, OR LIVER MALFUNCTION.* ADDITIONAL DATA: EPN, TRICHLORFON AND TRI-O-TOLYL PHOSPHATES MAY POTENTIATE THE TOXICITY OF MALATHION. ANIMAL STUDIES INDICATE THAT MALATHION DOES NOT INDUCE DELAYED NEUROPATHY. MAY CROSS THE PLACENTA. HIGH ENVIRONMENTAL TEMPERATURES OR EXPOSURE OF THE CHEMICAL TO VISIBLE OR ULTRAVIOLET LIGHT MAY ENHANCE THE TOXICITY. INTERACTIONS WITH MEDICATIONS MAY OCCUR.*
* MAY BE BASED ON GENERAL INFORMATION ON ORGANOPHOSPHATES.

HEALTH EFFECTS AND FIRST AID

INHALATION: XYLENE: IRRITANT/NARCOTIC. 1000 PPM IMMEDIATELY DANGEROUS TO LIFE OR HEALTH. **ACUTE EXPOSURE-** IRRITATION OF THE UPPER RESPIRATORY TRACT MAY OCCUR AT 200 PPM. EXPOSURE TO HIGHER CONCENTRATIONS MAY CAUSE MORE SEVERE IRRITATION AND INITIAL CENTRAL NERVOUS SYSTEM EXCITATION FOLLOWED BY DEPRESSION. SIGNS AND SYMPTOMS MAY INCLUDE RESPIRATORY DIFFICULTY AND SUBSTERNAL PAIN, TRANSIENT EUPHORIA AND EMOTIONAL LABILITY, HEADACHE, NAUSEA, VOMITING, ANOREXIA, ABDOMINAL PAIN, DIZZINESS, DROWSINESS, ATAXIA, AND STAGGERING. THERE MAY BE SALIVATION, SLURRED SPEECH, BLURRED VISION, NYSTAGMUS, TINNITUS, TREMORS, CONFUSION, AND FLUSHING OF THE FACE AND A FEELING OF INCREASED BODY HEAT. IN SEVERE EXPOSURES, THERE MAY BE STUPOR, ANESTHESIA, UNCONSCIOUSNESS, AND COMA WHICH MAY BE PUNCTUATED BY EPISODES OF NEUROIRRITABILITY, BUT RARELY FRANK CONVULSIONS, EXCEPT IN TERMINAL ASPHYXIA. LIVER AND KIDNEY DAMAGE MAY OCCUR, BUT ARE USUALLY MILD AND TRANSIENT. A GROUP OF SUBJECTS WHO INHALED 12.3 UMOL/L OF XYLENE WHILE EXERCISING BECAME SIGNIFICANTLY IMPAIRED ON 3 NEUROPSYCHOLOGICAL TESTS. EXPOSURE OF 3 PAINTERS TO APPROXIMATELY 10,000 PPM FOR 18.5 HOURS RESULTED IN 1 DEATH FROM PULMONARY EDEMA AND PETECHIAL BRAIN HEMORRHAGE. BOTH SURVIVORS WERE UNCONSCIOUS FOR 19-24 HOURS AND EXPERIENCED RETROGRADE AMNESIA, HYPOTHERMIA, AND LUNG CONGESTION. RENAL AND HEPATIC IMPAIRMENT ALSO DEVELOPED. COMPLETE RECOVERY TOOK 15 DAYS. HIGH CONCENTRATIONS MAY CAUSE DEATH FROM SUDDEN VENTRICULAR FIBRILLATION, BUT MORE FREQUENTLY DEATH OCCURS FROM RESPIRATORY ARREST. **CHRONIC EXPOSURE-** REPEATED OR PROLONGED INHALATION OF VAPORS ABOVE 200 PPM MAY CAUSE NAUSEA, VOMITING, ABDOMINAL PAIN, AND ANOREXIA. OTHER COMMON COMPLAINTS INCLUDE HEADACHE, FATIGUE, LASSITUDE, IRRITABILITY, BREATHING DIFFICULTIES, AND FLATULENCE. EFFECTS ON THE NERVOUS SYSTEM MAY RESULT IN EXCITATION, FOLLOWED BY DEPRESSION, PARESTHESIAS, TREMORS, APPREHENSION, IMPAIRED MEMORY, INSOMNIA, VERTIGO, AND TINNITUS. EFFECTS ON REACTION TIME, MANUAL COORDINATION, BODY BALANCE AND EEG OCCURRED WITH REPEATED EXPOSURE TO 90 PPM OF M-XYLENE. SWEETISH TASTE IN THE MOUTH, DRY NOSE AND THROAT, STRONG THIRST, MUCOSAL HEMORRHAGE, AND ANEMIA HAVE BEEN REPORTED. EFFECTS ON THE LIVER, KIDNEY, CARDIOVASCULAR SYSTEM, AND THE BONE MARROW HAVE ALSO BEEN REPORTED, ALTHOUGH THE LATTER HAS BEEN QUESTIONED. EXPOSURE OF RABBITS TO 1150 PPM FOR 40-55 DAYS RESULTED IN A REVERSIBLE DECREASE IN THE RED AND WHITE CELL COUNTS AND AN INCREASE IN THE PLATELETS. ONE CASE OF AN APPARENT EPILEPTIFORM SEIZURE FOLLOWING A RELATIVELY BRIEF EXPOSURE HAS OCCURRED. WOMEN MAY DEVELOP MENSTRUAL DISORDERS, SUCH AS MENORRHAGIA OR METRORRHAGIA, INFERTILITY, AND PATHOLOGICAL PREGNANCY CONDITIONS INCLUDING TOXICOSIS, DANGER OF MISCARRIAGE, AND HEMORRHAGING DURING DELIVERY. REPEATED EXPOSURE OF PREGNANT MICE, RATS AND RABBITS TO THE INDIVIDUAL OR THE MIXED ISOMERS HAS RESULTED IN MATERNAL EFFECTS AND EFFECTS ON FERTILITY, ON THE EMBRYO OR FETUS, AND SPECIFIC DEVELOPMENTAL ABNORMALITIES. INCLUDED AMONG THESE EFFECTS ARE FETAL DEATH, FETOTOXICITY, PRE- AND POST-IMPLANTATION MORTALITY, ABORTION, CRANIOFACIAL AND MUSCULOSKELETAL ABNORMALITIES, AND EXTRA EMBRYONIC STRUCTURES.
ETHYL TOLUENES: IRRITANT/NARCOTIC. **ACUTE EXPOSURE-** VAPORS OF ETHYL TOLUENES MAY BE IRRITATING TO THE RESPIRATORY TRACT. IN GENERAL, ETHYL TOLUENES ARE OF A LOW ORDER OF TOXICITY BY INHALATION. SYSTEMIC EFFECTS HAVE NOT BEEN REPORTED BUT ARE SUSPECTED TO BE SIMILAR TO OTHER AROMATIC COMPOUNDS WITH 9 CARBONS SUCH AS NAUSEA, VOMITING, WEAKNESS, TIREDNESS, VERTIGO, OR IN SEVERE CASES, INEBRIATION OR UNCONSCIOUSNESS. **CHRONIC EXPOSURE-** NO DATA AVAILABLE.
TRIMETHYL BENZENES: IRRITANT/NARCOTIC. **ACUTE EXPOSURE-** TRIMETHYL BENZENES MAY CAUSE IRRITATION OF THE NOSE AND THROAT. DYSPNEA, COUGHING, NAUSEA, ASTHMATIC BRONCHITIS AND BRONCHIAL PNEUMONIA WITH FEVER MAY OCCUR. CENTRAL NERVOUS SYSTEM DEPRESSION WITH HEADACHE, FATIGUE, NERVOUSNESS, ANXIETY AND NARCOSIS MAY ALSO RESULT. 1,2,4-TRIMETHYL BENZENE AND 1,3,5-TRIMETHYL BENZENE BOTH MAY CAUSE CHEMICAL PNEUMONITIS AT THE SITE OF CONTACT AND HEMORRHAGIC INFLAMMATORY LESIONS OF THE MUCOUS MEMBRANES. **CHRONIC EXPOSURE-** REPEATED OR PROLONGED EXPOSURE TO TRIMETHYL BENZENES MAY CAUSE DIZZINESS, WEAKNESS, WEIGHT LOSS, ANEMIA, PERIPHERAL NUMBNESS, PARESTHESIAS, NERVOUSNESS, PAINS IN THE LIMBS, AND ASTHMATIC BRONCHITIS. 1,2,4-TRIMETHYL BENZENE MAY CAUSE BONE MARROW DAMAGE.
AROMATICS: IRRITANT/NARCOTIC. **ACUTE EXPOSURE-** THE DEGREE AND RANGE OF EFFECTS WILL VARY DEPENDING ON THE SPECIFIC HYDROCARBON COMPOSITION. HIGH VAPOR CONCENTRATIONS MAY CAUSE MUCOUS MEMBRANE IRRITATION, COUGH AND SUBSTERNAL PAIN; PULMONARY EDEMA IS POSSIBLE. THE CENTRAL NERVOUS SYSTEM MAY BE STIMULATED THEN DEPRESSED. SYMPTOMS MAY INCLUDE TRANSIENT EUPHORIA, NAUSEA, VOMITING, WEAKNESS, FATIGUE, VERTIGO, ATAXIA, AND IN MORE SEVERE CASES, STUPOR, ANESTHESIA, UNCONSCIOUSNESS, AND COMA. TREMORS AND CONVULSIONS ARE POSSIBLE. IN FATAL CASES, DEATH IS USUALLY DUE TO RESPIRATORY ARREST, ALTHOUGH SUDDEN DEATH MAY RESULT FROM VENTRICULAR FIBRILLATION. PATHOLOGICAL FINDINGS MAY INCLUDE HYPEREMIA, EDEMA AND GROSS AND PETECHIAL HEMORRHAGES IN THE INTERNAL ORGANS. **CHRONIC EXPOSURE-** REPEATED EXPOSURE TO SOME AROMATIC HYDROCARBONS MAY CAUSE HEADACHE, ANOREXIA, DROWSINESS, NERVOUSNESS, AND PALLOR. RECENT STUDIES ON WORKERS CHRONICALLY EXPOSED TO MIXTURES OF AROMATIC AND ALIPHATIC SUBSTANCES HAVE FOUND PSYCHOLOGICAL AND NEUROPHYSIOLOGICAL DIFFERENCES BETWEEN EXPOSED AND NON-EXPOSED WORKERS SUGGESTING THAT AROMATIC HYDROCARBONS MAY CAUSE SUBTLE, LONG LASTING NEUROLOGIC EFFECTS.
DODECYLBENZENE SULFONATE: **ACUTE EXPOSURE-** NO DATA AVAILABLE. MAY BE IRRITATING TO THE MUCOUS MEMBRANES. **CHRONIC EXPOSURE-** NO DATA AVAILABLE.
MALATHION: HIGHLY TOXIC. 5000 MG/M3 IMMEDIATELY DANGEROUS TO LIFE OR HEALTH. SEE INFORMATION ON ORGANOPHOSPHATES.
ORGANOPHOSPHATES: CHOLINESTERASE INHIBITOR. **ACUTE EXPOSURE-** WHEN INHALED, THE FIRST EFFECTS OF CHOLINESTERASE INHIBITORS ARE USUALLY RESPIRATORY AND MAY INCLUDE NASAL HYPEREMIA AND WATERY DISCHARGE, COUGH, CHEST DISCOMFORT, DYSPNEA, AND WHEEZING DUE TO INCREASED BRONCHIAL SECRETIONS AND BRONCHOCONSTRICTION. IF SUFFICIENT AMOUNTS ARE ABSORBED, OTHER SYSTEMIC EFFECTS MAY BEGIN WITHIN A FEW MINUTES OR BE DELAYED FOR UP TO 12 HOURS. SYMPTOMS MAY INCLUDE PALLOR, NAUSEA, VOMITING, DIARRHEA, ABDOMINAL CRAMPS, HEADACHE, DIZZINESS, OCULAR PAIN, BLURRED VISION, MIOSIS OR IN SOME CASES, ESPECIALLY INITIALLY, MYDRIASIS, LACRIMATION, SALIVATION, SWEATING, AND CONFUSION. OTHER REPORTED CENTRAL NERVOUS SYSTEM OR NEUROMUSCULAR EFFECTS MAY INCLUDE ATAXIA, SLURRED SPEECH, AREFLEXIA, WEAKNESS, FATIGUE, FASCICULATIONS, TWITCHING, TREMORS POSSIBLY OF THE TONGUE AND EYELIDS, AND EVENTUALLY PARALYSIS OF THE EXTREMITIES AND POSSIBLY OF THE RESPIRATORY MUSCLES. IN SEVERE CASES THERE MAY ALSO BE INVOLUNTARY DEFECATION AND URINATION, CYANOSIS, PSYCHOSIS, HYPERGLYCEMIA, ACUTE PANCREATITIS, CARDIAC IRREGULARITIES, PULMONARY EDEMA, UNCONSCIOUSNESS, CONVULSIONS, AND COMA. DEATH IS PRIMARILY DUE TO RESPIRATORY FAILURE, ALTHOUGH CARDIOVASCULAR EFFECTS INCLUDING CARDIAC ARREST MAY ALSO BE IMPLICATED. LONG TERM SEQUELAE ARE RARE BUT MAY INCLUDE NEUROPSYCHIATRIC DISORDERS AND MYOPATHY WITH MUSCLE TENDERNESS. SOME ORGANOPHOSPHATES MAY CAUSE A DELAYED NEUROPATHY BEGINNING 1-4 WEEKS AFTER AN ACUTE EXPOSURE WHICH MAY OR MAY NOT HAVE CAUSED ACUTE CHOLINERGIC EFFECTS. NUMBNESS, TINGLING, WEAKNESS AND CRAMPING BEGINNING SYMMETRICALLY IN THE LOWER LIMBS MAY PROGRESS TO ATAXIA AND PARALYSIS. IN SEVERE CASES, UPPER LIMB

INVOLVEMENT IS POSSIBLE AND FLACCID PARALYSIS MAY PROGRESS TO SPASTIC PARALYSIS WITH EXAGGERATED REFLEXES. IMPROVEMENT MAY OCCUR OVER MONTHS TO YEARS, BUT SOME RESIDUAL IMPAIRMENT USUALLY REMAINS. **CHRONIC EXPOSURE-** REPEATED OR PROLONGED EXPOSURE MAY RESULT IN THE EFFECTS OF ACUTE EXPOSURE INCLUDING THE DELAYED NEUROPATHY. OTHER EFFECTS REPORTED IN WORKERS REPEATEDLY EXPOSED INCLUDE IMPAIRED MEMORY AND CONCENTRATION, ACUTE PSYCHOSIS, SEVERE DEPRESSIONS, IRRITABILTY, CONFUSION, APATHY, EMOTIONAL LABILITY, SOCIAL WITHDRAWAL, CONFUSION, HEADACHE, SPEECH DIFFICULTIES, DELAYED REACTION TIMES, SPATIAL DISORIENTATION, NIGHTMARES, SLEEPWALKING, AND DROWSINESS OR INSOMNIA. AN INFLUENZA-LIKE CONDITION WITH HEADACHE, NAUSEA, WEAKNESS, ANOREXIA AND MALAISE HAS ALSO BEEN REPORTED.

FIRST AID- REMOVE FROM EXPOSURE AREA TO FRESH AIR IMMEDIATELY. IF BREATHING HAS STOPPED, GIVE ARTIFICIAL RESPIRATION. MAINTAIN AIRWAY AND BLOOD PRESSURE AND ADMINISTER OXYGEN IF AVAILABLE. KEEP AFFECTED PERSON WARM AND AT REST. TREAT SYMPTOMATICALLY AND SUPPORTIVELY. ADMINISTRATION OF OXYGEN SHOULD BE PERFORMED BY QUALIFIED PERSONNEL. GET MEDICAL ATTENTION IMMEDIATELY.

SKIN CONTACT: XYLENE: IRRITANT. **ACUTE EXPOSURE-** LIQUID XYLENE IS A DEFATTING AGENT AND MAY CAUSE A BURNING SENSATION, DRYING, VASODILATION, ERYTHEMA, AND POSSIBLY BLISTERING. THE LIQUID IS READILY ABSORBED THROUGH INTACT OR BROKEN SKIN AT A RATE OF APPROXIMATELY 4-10 MG/CM2/HOUR, BUT SYSTEMIC EFFECTS HAVE NOT BEEN REPORTED. **CHRONIC EXPOSURE-** REPEATED OR PROLONGED CONTACT MAY CAUSE DEFATTING OF THE SKIN WITH DRYING, ERYTHEMA, CRACKING, THICKENING AND BLISTERING. REPEATED APPLICATION OF 95% XYLENE TO RABBIT SKIN CAUSED MODERATE TO MARKED IRRITATION WITH ERYTHEMA AND MODERATE NECROSIS. ONE CASE OF ALLERGIC CONTACT URTICARIA HAS BEEN REPORTED.

ETHYL TOLUENES: IRRITANT. **ACUTE EXPOSURE-** MAY BE IRRITATING AND HAVE A DEFATTING ACTION ON THE SKIN. **CHRONIC EXPOSURE-** REPEATED OR PROLONGED EXPOSURE MAY CAUSE DERMATITIS.

TRIMETHYL BENZENES: IRRITANT/NARCOTIC. **ACUTE EXPOSURE-** MAY CAUSE IRRITATION, REDNESS, AND DEFATTING OF THE SKIN. **CHRONIC EXPOSURE-** MAY CAUSE DERMATITIS AND MAY BE SLOWLY ABSORBED AND CAUSE CENTRAL NERVOUS SYSTEM DEPRESSION WITH HEADACHE, FATIGUE, NERVOUSNESS, ANXIETY, AND NARCOSIS.

AROMATICS: IRRITANT. **ACUTE EXPOSURE-** DIRECT CONTACT WITH LIQUID AROMATIC HYDROCARBONS MAY CAUSE VASODILATION, ERYTHEMA AND IRRITATION. WITH PROLONGED CONTACT, BLISTERS MAY DEVELOP. ABSORPTION THROUGH THE SKIN IS GENERALLY SLOW. **CHRONIC EXPOSURE-** REPEATED AND PROLONGED CONTACT MAY CAUSE DERMATITIS WITH DRYING, SCALING AND FISSURING OF THE SKIN DUE TO THE DEFATTING ACTION OF THE LIQUID.

DODECYLBENZENE SULFONATE: **ACUTE EXPOSURE-** NO DATA AVAILABLE. MAY BE IRRITATING. **CHRONIC EXPOSURE-** NO DATA AVAILABLE.

MALATHION: SENSITIZER. PROLONGED OR REPEATED EXPOSURE MAY CAUSE SENSITIZATION DERMATITIS. SEE INFORMATION ON ORGANOPHOSPHATES.

ORGANOPHOSPHATES: CHOLINESTERASE INHIBITOR. **ACUTE EXPOSURE-** LOCALIZED SWEATING AND FASCICULATIONS MAY OCCUR AT THE SITE OF CONTACT. IF SUFFICIENT AMOUNTS ARE ABSORBED, OTHER EFFECTS OF CHOLINESTERASE INHIBITION AS DESCRIBED IN ACUTE INHALATION MAY OCCUR. SYMPTOMS MAY BE DELAYED 2-3 HOURS, BUT USUALLY NO MORE THAN 12 HOURS. THE RATE OF ABSORPTION IS INCREASED BY THE PRESENCE OF DERMATITIS OR HIGH AMBIENT TEMPERATURES. DELAYED NEUROPATHY IS ALSO POSSIBLE. **CHRONIC EXPOSURE-** REPEATED OR PROLONGED EXPOSURE MAY CAUSE EFFECTS AS DESCRIBED IN ACUTE EXPOSURE. SOME ORGANOPHOSPHATES MAY CAUSE SENSITIZATION.

FIRST AID- REMOVE CONTAMINATED CLOTHING AND SHOES IMMEDIATELY. WASH AFFECTED AREA WITH SOAP OR MILD DETERGENT AND LARGE AMOUNTS OF WATER UNTIL NO EVIDENCE OF CHEMICAL REMAINS (APPROXIMATELY 15-20 MINUTES). GET MEDICAL ATTENTION IMMEDIATELY.

EYE CONTACT: XYLENE: IRRITANT. **ACUTE EXPOSURE-** 200 PPM HAS CAUSED CONJUNCTIVAL IRRITATION IN HUMANS; AT HIGHER CONCENTRATIONS, IRRITATION MAY BE SEVERE. VAPOR EXPOSURE HAS ALSO CAUSED TEARING AND PHOTOPHOBIA. AN ACCIDENTAL SPLASH IN THE HUMAN EYE CAUSED TRANSIENT SUPERFICIAL DAMAGE WITH RAPID RECOVERY, ALTHOUGH REVERSIBLE CORNEAL BURNS HAVE ALSO BEEN REPORTED. **CHRONIC EXPOSURE-** REPEATED OR PROLONGED EXPOSURE TO HIGH VAPOR CONCENTRATIONS MAY CAUSE A BURNING SENSATION, CONJUNCTIVITIS AND BLURRED VISION; REVERSIBLE VACUOLAR, EPITHELIAL KERATOPATHY HAS BEEN REPORTED IN SOME WORKERS.

ETHYL TOLUENES: IRRITANT. **ACUTE EXPOSURE-** VAPORS MAY BE IRRITATING. **CHRONIC EXPOSURE-** REPEATED OR PROLONGED EXPOSURE MAY CAUSE CONJUNCTIVITIS.

TRIMETHYL BENZENES: IRRITANT. **ACUTE EXPOSURE-** MAY CAUSE REDNESS, PAIN, AND IRRITATION. **CHRONIC EXPOSURE-** REPEATED OR PROLONGED EXPOSURE MAY CAUSE CONJUNCTIVITIS.

AROMATICS: IRRITANT. **ACUTE EXPOSURE-** DIRECT CONTACT WITH SOME AROMATIC HYDROCARBONS MAY CAUSE ITCHING, LACRIMATION, AND IRRITATION. IF CONTACT IS SUFFICIENTLY PROLONGED TISSUE INJURY MAY RESULT. CONJUNCTIVITIS AND CORNEAL BURNS HAVE BEEN REPORTED FROM SOME AROMATICS. **CHRONIC EXPOSURE-** REPEATED OR PROLONGED EXPOSURE MAY CAUSE CONJUNCTIVITIS.

DODECYLBENZENE SULFONATE: **ACUTE EXPOSURE-** NO DATA AVAILABLE. SIMILAR COMPOUNDS ARE IRRITATING TO THE EYES. **CHRONIC EXPOSURE-** NO DATA AVAILABLE.

MALATHION: SEE INFORMATION ON ORGANOPHOSPHATES.

ORGANOPHOSPHATES: CHOLINESTERASE INHIBITOR. **ACUTE EXPOSURE-** DIRECT CONTACT MAY CAUSE PAIN, HYPEREMIA, LACRIMATION, TWITCHING OF THE EYELIDS, MIOSIS, AND CILIARY MUSCLE SPASM WITH LOSS OF ACCOMODATION, BLURRED OR DIMMED VISION AND BROWACHE. SOMETIMES MYDRIASIS MAY OCCUR INSTEAD OF MIOSIS. WITH SUFFICIENT EXPOSURE, OTHER SYMPTOMS OF CHOLINESTERASE INHIBITION AS DESCRIBED IN ACUTE INHALATION MAY OCCUR. **CHRONIC EXPOSURE-** REPEATED OR PROLONGED EXPOSURE MAY CAUSE EFFECTS AS DESCRIBED IN ACUTE EXPOSURE. SOME COMPOUNDS HAVE CAUSED TOXIC EFFECTS ON THE CRYSTALLINE LENS, CONJUNCTIVAL THICKENING AND OBSTRUCTION OF THE NASOLACRIMAL CANALS WHEN USED AS MIOTIC EYEDROPS.

FIRST AID- WASH EYES IMMEDIATELY WITH LARGE AMOUNTS OF WATER OR NORMAL SALINE, OCCASIONALLY LIFTING UPPER AND LOWER LIDS, UNTIL NO EVIDENCE OF CHEMICAL REMAINS (APPROXIMATELY 15-20 MINUTES). GET MEDICAL ATTENTION IMMEDIATELY.

INGESTION: XYLENE: NARCOTIC. **ACUTE EXPOSURE-** MAY CAUSE A BURNING SENSATION IN THE MOUTH AND STOMACH, SALIVATION, SEVERE GASTROINTESTINAL DISTRESS WITH NAUSEA AND VOMITING, POSSIBLY HEMATEMESIS, AND TOXIC EFFECTS INCLUDING SIGNS OF CENTRAL NERVOUS SYSTEM DEPRESSION AND OTHER SYMPTOMS AS IN ACUTE INHALATION, INCLUDING VENTRICULAR FIBRILLATION AND LIVER AND KIDNEY INJURY. INGESTION OF SMALL QUANTITIES OF 90% XYLENE PLUS TOLUENE PRODUCED URINARY DEXTROSE AND UROBILINOGEN EXCRETION WITH TOXIC HEPATITIS, WHICH WAS REVERSIBLE IN 20 DAYS. A DOSE OF 15-30 MILLILITERS (ABOUT 1/2-1 OUNCE) IS THE EXPECTED HUMAN LETHAL DOSE. WITH ASPIRATION OF EVEN A FEW MILLILITERS INTO THE LUNGS, SEVERE COUGHING, DISTRESS, CHEMICAL PNEUMONITIS, RAPIDLY DEVELOPING PULMONARY EDEMA, AND HEMORRHAGE MAY OCCUR. **CHRONIC EXPOSURE-** NO DATA AVAILABLE ON THE ORTHO-ISOMER. REPEATED INGESTION OF THE MIXED, META-, OR PARA-ISOMERS BY PREGNANT MICE RESULTED IN EFFECTS ON FERTILITY, ON THE EMBRYO OR FETUS, OR SPECIFIC DEVELOPMENTAL ABNORMALITIES. INCLUDED AMONG THESE EFFECTS WERE FETOTOXICITY, LITTER SIZE, CRANIOFACIAL AND MUSCULOSKELETAL SYSTEM ABNORMALITIES, AND POST-IMPLANTATION MORTALITY.

ETHYL TOLUENES: NARCOTIC. **ACUTE EXPOSURE-** ETHYL TOLUENES ARE BELIEVED TO BE OF A LOW ORDER ORAL TOXICITY. SYSTEMIC EFFECTS ARE SUSPECTED TO BE SIMILAR TO OTHER AROMATICS WITH 9 CARBONS SUCH AS NAUSEA, VOMITING, DIZZINESS, WEAKNESS, EUPHORIA, HEADACHE, TIGHTNESS IN THE CHEST AND STAGGERING. **CHRONIC EXPOSURE-** NO DATA AVAILABLE.

TRIMETHYL BENZENES: NARCOTIC. **ACUTE EXPOSURE-** TRIMETHYL BENZENES MAY CAUSE SORE THROAT, COUGHING, DYSPNEA, NAUSEA AND VOMITING. CENTRAL NERVOUS SYSTEM DEPRESSION WITH HEADACHE, WEAKNESS, DIZZINESS, NARCOSIS, UNCONSCIOUSNESS AND CONVULSIONS MAY OCCUR. **CHRONIC EXPOSURE-** NO DATA AVAILABLE.

AROMATICS: NARCOTIC. **ACUTE EXPOSURE-** THE GASTROINTESTINAL AND SYSTEMIC EFFECTS MAY VARY DEPENDING ON THE SPECIFIC COMPOSITION. THERE MAY BE A BLAND, OILY TASTE; A WARM, SHARP TINGLING, FOLLOWED BY NUMBNESS; OR A PAINFUL, BURNING SENSATION AND PROFUSE SALIVATION. NAUSEA, VOMITING, HEMATEMESIS AND SUBSTERNAL PAIN MAY OCCUR. ABSORPTION OF A SUFFICIENT AMOUNT MAY RESULT IN SYMPTOMS OF CENTRAL NERVOUS SYSTEM DEPRESSION AND OTHER SYSTEMIC AND PATHOLOGICAL EFFECTS AS DESCRIBED IN ACUTE INHALATION. THE GREATER HAZARD MAY BE FROM ASPIRATION WHICH MAY OCCUR DURING INGESTION OR SUBSEQUENT VOMITING. DEPENDING ON CERTAIN PHYSICAL FACTORS, INCLUDING VISCOSITY, ASPIRATION MAY RESULT IN DEATH WITHIN MINUTES DUE TO CARDIAC ARREST, RESPIRATORY PARALYSIS AND ASPHYXIA; IN DELAYED CHEMICAL PNEUMONITIS WITH PULMONARY EDEMA AND HEMORRHAGE; OR, IN THE CASE OF HIGHER MOLECULAR WEIGHT COMPOUNDS, MINIMAL EDEMA AND HEMORRHAGE. **CHRONIC EXPOSURE-** NO DATA AVAILABLE.

DODECYLBENZENE SULFONATE: **ACUTE EXPOSURE-** 650 MG/KG WAS REQUIRED TO KILL 50% OF THE RATS TESTED. **CHRONIC EXPOSURE-** NO DATA AVAILABLE.

MALATHION: TOXIC. CHROMOSOMAL ABERRATIONS WERE INCREASED IN THE PRIMARY SPERMATOCYTES OF MALE MICE AND BONE-MARROW CELLS OF RATS. EFFECTS OF DECREASED FETAL WEIGHTS, AN INCREASED INCIDENCE IN EXTERNAL HEMORRHAGIC SPOTS, INCREASED SUSCEPTIBILITY TO DISEASE, AND INCREASED

MORTALITY, ABSORPTIONS AND ANOMALIES SUCH AS MILD HYDRONEPHROSIS AND HYDROURETER WERE REPORTED IN STUDIES OF RATS. SEE INFORMATION ON ORGANOPHOSPHATES.
ORGANOPHOSPHATES: CHOLINESTERASE INHIBITOR. **ACUTE EXPOSURE**- WHEN INGESTED, THE FIRST EFFECTS MAY BE NAUSEA, VOMITING, ANOREXIA, ABDOMINAL CRAMPS AND DIARRHEA. GASTROINTESTINAL ABSORPTION MAY CAUSE SYMPTOMS OF CHOLINESTERASE INHIBITION AS DESCRIBED IN ACUTE INHALATION. SYMPTOMS MAY BEGIN WITHIN MINUTES OR BE DELAYED FOR HOURS. DELAYED EFFECTS INCLUDING NEUROPATHY MAY ALSO OCCUR. **CHRONIC EXPOSURE**- REPEATED INGESTION MAY CAUSE EFFECTS AS DESCRIBED IN ACUTE EXPOSURE.

FIRST AID- TREAT SYMPTOMATICALLY AND SUPPORTIVELY. GET MEDICAL ATTENTION AND ADVICE ON WHETHER TO USE GASTRIC LAVAGE. EXTREME CARE MUST BE TAKEN TO PREVENT ASPIRATION. A CUFFED ENDOTRACHEAL TUBE USED BY QUALIFIED MEDICAL PERSONNEL MIGHT BE ADVISABLE. KEEP HEAD LOWER THAN HIPS TO PREVENT ASPIRATION SHOULD VOMITING OCCUR.

REACTIVITY

REACTIVITY: STABLE UNDER NORMAL TEMPERATURES AND PRESSURES.

INCOMPATIBILITIES: XYLENE: NITRIC ACID: EXOTHERMIC REACTION. OXIDIZERS (STRONG): FIRE AND EXPLOSION HAZARD. PLASTICS, RUBBER, COATINGS: MAY BE ATTACKED. SULFURIC ACID: EXOTHERMIC REACTION.
ETHYL TOLUENES: NO DATA AVAILABLE.
TRIMETHYL BENZENES: NITRIC ACID: EXPLOSION HAZARD ON HEATING ABOVE 115 C.
AROMATICS: OXIDIZERS (STRONG): FIRE AND EXPLOSION HAZARD.
DODECYLBENZENE SULFONATE: NO DATA AVAILABLE.
MALATHION: COPPER: MAY CORRODE. IRON: MAY CORRODE. LEAD: MAY CORRODE. OXIDIZERS (STRONG): FIRE AND EXPLOSION HAZARD. PLASTICS, RUBBER AND COATINGS: MAY BE ATTACKED. STEEL: MAY CORRODE. TIN PLATE: MAY CORRODE.

DECOMPOSITION: THERMAL DECOMPOSITION MAY RELEASE TOXIC AND/OR HAZARDOUS GASES.

POLYMERIZATION: HAZARDOUS POLYMERIZATION HAS NOT BEEN REPORTED TO OCCUR UNDER NORMAL TEMPERATURES AND PRESSURES.

STORAGE AND DISPOSAL

OBSERVE ALL FEDERAL, STATE AND LOCAL REGULATIONS WHEN STORING OR DISPOSING OF THIS SUBSTANCE. FOR ASSISTANCE, CONTACT THE DISTRICT DIRECTOR OF THE ENVIRONMENTAL PROTECTION AGENCY.

STORAGE

STORE IN ACCORDANCE WITH 29 CFR 1910.106.
STORE IN ACCORDANCE WITH 40 CFR 165 RECOMMENDED PROCEDURES FOR THE DISPOSAL AND STORAGE OF PESTICIDES AND PESTICIDE CONTAINERS.
BONDING AND GROUNDING: SUBSTANCES WITH LOW ELECTROCONDUCTIVITY, WHICH MAY BE IGNITED BY ELECTROSTATIC SPARKS, SHOULD BE STORED IN CONTAINERS WHICH MEET THE BONDING AND GROUNDING GUIDELINES SPECIFIED IN NFPA 77-1983, RECOMMENDED PRACTICE ON STATIC ELECTRICITY.
STORE AWAY FROM INCOMPATIBLE SUBSTANCES.

DISPOSAL

DISPOSAL MUST BE IN ACCORDANCE WITH STANDARDS APPLICABLE TO GENERATORS OF HAZARDOUS WASTE, 40 CFR 262. EPA HAZARDOUS WASTE NUMBER D001. 100 POUND CERCLA SECTION 103 REPORTABLE QUANTITY.
DISPOSAL MUST BE IN ACCORDANCE WITH 40 CFR 165 RECOMMENDED PROCEDURES FOR THE DISPOSAL AND STORAGE OF PESTICIDES AND PESTICIDE CONTAINERS.

CONDITIONS TO AVOID

AVOID CONTACT WITH HEAT, SPARKS, FLAMES, OR OTHER SOURCES OF IGNITION. VAPORS MAY BE EXPLOSIVE. AVOID OVERHEATING OF CONTAINERS; CONTAINERS MAY VIOLENTLY RUPTURE IN HEAT OF FIRE. AVOID CONTAMINATION OF WATER SOURCES.

SPILL AND LEAK PROCEDURES

OCCUPATIONAL SPILL: SHUT OFF IGNITION SOURCES. STOP LEAK IF YOU CAN DO IT WITHOUT RISK. USE WATER SPRAY TO REDUCE VAPORS. FOR SMALL SPILLS, TAKE UP WITH SAND OR OTHER ABSORBENT MATERIAL AND PLACE INTO CONTAINERS FOR LATER DISPOSAL. FOR LARGER SPILLS, DIKE FAR AHEAD OF SPILL FOR LATER DISPOSAL. NO SMOKING, FLAMES OR FLARES IN HAZARD AREA. KEEP UNNECESSARY PEOPLE AWAY; ISOLATE HAZARD AREA AND RESTRICT ENTRY.

PROTECTIVE EQUIPMENT

VENTILATION: PROVIDE LOCAL EXHAUST OR PROCESS ENCLOSURE VENTILATION TO MEET PUBLISHED EXPOSURE LIMITS.

RESPIRATOR: THE FOLLOWING RESPIRATORS ARE RECOMMENDED BASED ON INFORMATION FOUND IN THE PHYSICAL DATA, TOXICITY AND HEALTH EFFECTS SECTIONS. THEY ARE RANKED IN ORDER FROM MINIMUM TO MAXIMUM RESPIRATORY PROTECTION. THE SPECIFIC RESPIRATOR SELECTED MUST BE BASED ON CONTAMINATION LEVELS FOUND IN THE WORK PLACE, MUST NOT EXCEED THE WORKING LIMITS OF THE RESPIRATOR AND BE JOINTLY APPROVED BY THE NATIONAL INSTITUTE FOR OCCUPATIONAL SAFETY AND HEALTH AND THE MINE SAFETY AND HEALTH ADMINISTRATION (NIOSH-MSHA).
TYPE 'C' SUPPLIED-AIR RESPIRATOR WITH A FULL FACEPIECE OPERATED IN PRESSURE-DEMAND OR OTHER POSITIVE PRESSURE MODE OR WITH A FULL FACEPIECE, HELMET OR HOOD OPERATED IN CONTINOUS-FLOW MODE.
SELF-CONTAINED BREATHING APPARATUS WITH A FULL FACEPIECE OPERATED IN PRESSURE-DEMAND OR OTHER POSITIVE PRESSURE MODE.
FOR FIREFIGHTING AND OTHER IMMEDIATELY DANGEROUS TO LIFE OR HEALTH CONDITIONS:
SELF-CONTAINED BREATHING APPARATUS WITH FULL FACEPIECE OPERATED IN PRESSURE-DEMAND OR OTHER POSITIVE PRESSURE MODE.
SUPPLIED-AIR RESPIRATOR WITH FULL FACEPIECE AND OPERATED IN PRESSURE-DEMAND OR OTHER POSITIVE PRESSURE MODE IN COMBINATION WITH AN AUXILIARY SELF-CONTAINED BREATHING APPARATUS OPERATED IN PRESSURE-DEMAND OR OTHER POSITIVE PRESSURE MODE.

CLOTHING: EMPLOYEE MUST WEAR APPROPRIATE PROTECTIVE (IMPERVIOUS) CLOTHING AND EQUIPMENT TO PREVENT ANY POSSIBILITY OF SKIN CONTACT WITH THIS SUBSTANCE.

GLOVES: EMPLOYEE MUST WEAR APPROPRIATE PROTECTIVE GLOVES TO PREVENT CONTACT WITH THIS SUBSTANCE.

EYE PROTECTION: EMPLOYEE MUST WEAR SPLASH-PROOF OR DUST-RESISTANT SAFETY GOGGLES AND A FACESHIELD TO PREVENT CONTACT WITH THIS SUBSTANCE.
EMERGENCY WASH FACILITIES: WHERE THERE IS ANY POSSIBILITY THAT AN EMPLOYEE'S EYES AND/OR SKIN MAY BE EXPOSED TO THIS SUBSTANCE, THE EMPLOYER SHOULD PROVIDE AN EYE WASH FOUNTAIN AND QUICK DRENCH SHOWER WITHIN THE IMMEDIATE WORK AREA FOR EMERGENCY USE.

AUTHORIZED BY- OCCUPATIONAL HEALTH SERVICES, INC.
CREATION DATE: 10/05/89 ***REVISION DATE:*** 07/12/90

MATERIAL SAFETY DATA SHEET

OCCUPATIONAL HEALTH SERVICES, INC.
AGRICULTURE AND PESTICIDE DIVISION
450 SEVENTH AVENUE, SUITE 2407
NEW YORK, NEW YORK 10123
1-800-445-MSDS OR (212) 967-1100

EMERGENCY CONTACT:
JOHN S. BRANSFORD, JR. (615) 292-1180

SUBSTANCE IDENTIFICATION

SUBSTANCE: 21 NAMTOX 05623598

TRADE NAMES/SYNONYMS: PST75467

CERCLA RATINGS (SCALE 0-3): HEALTH=3 FIRE=2 REACTIVITY=0 PERSISTENCE=1

NFPA RATINGS (SCALE 0-4): HEALTH=3 FIRE=2 REACTIVITY=0

COMPONENTS AND CONTAMINANTS

COMPONENT: CYCLO SOL 53 ***PERCENT:*** 3.20
CAS# 64742-95-6 CONTAINS:
XYLENE (3-4%) CAS# 1330-20-7
ETHYL TOLUENES (22-28%) CAS# 25550-14-5
TRIMETHYL BENZENES (57-67%) CAS# 25551-13-7
AROMATICS (6-9%)
PARAFFINS (<1.0%)

COMPONENT: PYRENONE O.T. 50-5 ***PERCENT:*** 1.36
CONTAINS:
PYRETHRUMS (5.3%) CAS# 8003-34-7
PIPERONLY BUTOXIDE, TECHNICAL (53.07%) CAS# 51-03-6
MIXED HYDROCARBONS (41.63%)

COMPONENT: DIAZINON MGB ***PERCENT:*** 0.58
CAS# 333-41-5

COMPONENT: LPA SOLVENT VISTA ***PERCENT:*** 93.63
CONTAINS:
PARAFFINS (100%)

COMPONENT: LETHANE ***PERCENT:*** 1.23

OTHER CONTAMINANTS: NONE

EXPOSURE LIMITS: TRIMETHYL BENZENE: 25 PPM (125 MG/M3) OSHA TWA 25 PPM (125 MG/M3) ACGIH TWA

LPA SOLVENT: REFINED PETROLEUM SOLVENTS: 350 MG/M3 NIOSH RECOMMENDED TWA 1800 MG/M3 NIOSH RECOMMENDED 15 MINUTE CEILING

PHYSICAL DATA

DESCRIPTION: CLEAR, BROWNISH LIQUID WITH A SLIGHT SULFUR-LIKE ODOR

BOILING POINT: NOT AVAILABLE ***SPECIFIC GRAVITY:*** 0.81

EVAPORATION RATE: NOT AVAILABLE ***SOLUBILITY IN WATER:*** SLIGHT

VAPOR DENSITY: >1

FIRE AND EXPLOSION DATA

FIRE AND EXPLOSION HAZARD: MODERATE FIRE HAZARD WHEN EXPOSED TO HEAT OR FLAME.

VAPORS ARE HEAVIER THAN AIR AND MAY TRAVEL A CONSIDERABLE DISTANCE TO A SOURCE OF IGNITION AND FLASH BACK.

VAPOR-AIR MIXTURES ARE EXPLOSIVE ABOVE FLASH POINT.

FLASH POINT: >100 F (>38 C) (CC) ***FLAMMABILITY CLASS(OSHA):*** II

FIREFIGHTING MEDIA: DRY CHEMICAL, CARBON DIOXIDE, HALON, WATER SPRAY OR STANDARD FOAM (1987 EMERGENCY RESPONSE GUIDEBOOK, DOT P 5800.4).

FOR LARGER FIRES, USE WATER SPRAY, FOG OR STANDARD FOAM (1987 EMERGENCY RESPONSE GUIDEBOOK, DOT P 5800.4).

FIREFIGHTING: MOVE CONTAINER FROM FIRE AREA IF POSSIBLE. COOL FIRE-EXPOSED CONTAINERS WITH WATER FROM SIDE UNTIL WELL AFTER FIRE IS OUT. STAY AWAY FROM STORAGE TANK ENDS. FOR MASSIVE FIRE IN STORAGE AREA, USE UNMANNED HOSE HOLDER OR MONITOR NOZZLES, ELSE WITHDRAW FROM AREA AND LET FIRE BURN. WITHDRAW IMMEDIATELY IN CASE OF RISING SOUND FROM VENTING SAFETY DEVICE OR ANY DISCOLORATION OF STORAGE TANK DUE TO FIRE (1987 EMERGENCY RESPONSE GUIDEBOOK, DOT P 5800.4, GUIDE PAGE 27). EXTINGUISH ONLY IF FLOW CAN BE STOPPED; USE FLOODING AMOUNTS OF WATER AS A FOG, SOLID STREAMS MAY BE INEFFECTIVE. COOL CONTAINERS WITH FLOODING AMOUNTS OF WATER, APPLY FROM AS FAR A DISTANCE AS POSSIBLE. AVOID BREATHING VAPORS, KEEP UPWIND.

TRANSPORTATION DATA

DEPARTMENT OF TRANSPORTATION HAZARD CLASSIFICATION 49 CFR 172.101: COMBUSTIBLE LIQUID

DEPARTMENT OF TRANSPORTATION LABELING REQUIREMENTS 49 CFR 172.101 AND SUBPART E: NONE

DEPARTMENT OF TRANSPORTATION PACKAGING REQUIREMENTS: NONE EXCEPTIONS: 49 CFR 173.118A

TOXICITY

TRIMETHYL BENZENES: 1,3,5-TRIMETHYL BENZENE: 24 GM/M3/4 HOURS INHALATION-RAT LC50; 10 PPM INHALATION-HUMAN TCLO; MUTAGENIC DATA (RTEC); CARCINOGEN STATUS: NONE. 1,2,4-TRIMETHYL BENZENE: 5000 MG/KG ORAL-RAT LD50; 18 GM/M3/4 HOURS INHALATION-RAT LC50; CARCINOGEN STATUS: NONE. TRIMETHYL BENZENES ARE EYE, MUCOUS MEMBRANE AND SKIN IRRITANTS AND CENTRAL NERVOUS SYSTEM DEPRESSANTS.

PYRENONE O.T. 50-5: 3038-4556 MG/KG ORAL-RAT LD50 (FAIRFIELD AMERICAN CORPORATION MSDS); >7.57 MG/L INHALATION-RAT LC50 (FAIRFIELD AMERICAN CORPORATION MSDS); >3000 MG/KG SKIN-RABBIT (FAIRFIELD AMERICAN CORPORATION MSDS); CARCINOGEN STATUS: NONE. PYRENONE O.T. 50-5 IS A MILD SKIN IRRITANT.

LPA SOLVENT: 2.0-4.0 GM/KG SKIN-RABBIT LD50 (VISTA MSDS); 39.9 GM/KG ORAL-RAT LD(0) (VISTA MSDS); 24.1 MG/L/1 HOUR INHALATION-RAT LC(0) (VISTA MSDS); CARCINOGEN STATUS: NONE. LPA SOLVENT IS AN EYE, MUCOUS MEMBRANE AND SKIN IRRITANT AND A CENTRAL NERVOUS SYSTEM DEPRESSANT.

PARAFFINS: CARCINOGEN STATUS: NONE. THE TOXICITY OF PARAFFINS WILL VARY DEPENDING ON THE SPECIFIC COMPOSITION. PARAFFINS ARE EYE, SKIN AND MUCUOUS MEMBRANE IRRITANTS AND CENTRAL NERVOUS SYSTEM DEPRESSANTS. STIMULANTS SUCH AS EPINEPHRINE MAY INDUCE VENTRICULAR FIBRILLATION.

LETHANE 384: TOXICITY DATA: 34 MG/KG SKIN-RABBIT LD50; 250 MG/KG SKIN-RAT LD50; 90 MG/KG ORAL-RAT LD50; 35 MG/KG ORAL-RABBIT LD50; 250 MG/KG ORAL-GUINEA PIG LD50; 30 MG/KG ORAL-DOG LD50; 200 MG/KG SUBCUTANEOUS-MOUSE LDLO; 550 MG/KG SUBCUTANEOUS-RAT LD50; 100 MG/KG SUBCUTANEOUS-RABBIT LD50; RABBIT 200 MG/KG SUBCUTANEOUS-DOG LD50; 450 MG/KG SUBCUTANEOUS-GUINEA PIG LD50; 56 MG/KG INTRAVENOUS-MOUSE LD50; 90 MG/KG INTRAPERITONEAL-RAT LD50; 80 MG/KG INTRAPERITONEAL-RABBIT LD50; 84 MG/KG INTRAPERITONEAL-GUINEA PIG LD50; 41 MG/KG INTRAPERITONEAL-MOUSE LD50; 550 MG/KG UNREPORTED-MAMMAL LD50. CARCINOGEN STATUS: NONE. LOCAL EFFECTS: IRRITANT- INHALATION, SKIN, AND EYES. ACUTE TOXICITY LEVEL: HIGHLY TOXIC BY DERMAL ABSORPTION AND TOXIC BY INGESTION. TARGET EFFECTS: CENTRAL NERVOUS SYSTEM DEPRESSANT. POISONING MAY AFFECT THE LIVER AND KIDNEYS.

HEALTH EFFECTS AND FIRST AID

INHALATION: TRIMETHYL BENZENES: IRRITANT/NARCOTIC. **ACUTE EXPOSURE-** TRIMETHYL BENZENES MAY CAUSE IRRITATION OF THE NOSE AND THROAT. DYSPNEA, COUGHING, NAUSEA, ASTHMATIC BRONCHITIS AND BRONCHIAL PNEUMONIA WITH FEVER MAY OCCUR. CENTRAL NERVOUS SYSTEM DEPRESSION WITH HEADACHE, FATIGUE, NERVOUSNESS, ANXIETY AND NARCOSIS MAY ALSO RESULT. 1,2,4-TRIMETHYL BENZENE AND 1,3,5-TRIMETHYL BENZENE BOTH MAY CAUSE CHEMICAL PNEUMONITIS AT THE SITE OF CONTACT AND HEMORRHAGIC INFLAMMATORY LESIONS OF THE MUCOUS MEMBRANES. **CHRONIC EXPOSURE-** REPEATED OR PROLONGED EXPOSURE TO TRIMETHYL BENZENES MAY CAUSE DIZZINESS, WEAKNESS, WEIGHT LOSS, ANEMIA, PERIPHERAL NUMBNESS, PARESTHESIAS, NERVOUSNESS, PAINS IN THE LIMBS, AND ASTHMATIC BRONCHITIS. 1,2,4-TRIMETHYL BENZENE MAY CAUSE BONE MARROW DAMAGE.

PYRENONE O.T. 50-5: **ACUTE EXPOSURE-** NO SPECIFIC DATA AVAILABLE, MAY BE IRRITATING. **CHRONIC EXPOSURE-** NO SPECIFIC DATA AVAILABLE, MAY BE IRRITATING.

LPA SOLVENT: IRRITANT/NARCOTIC. **ACUTE EXPOSURE-** VAPORS MAY BE IRRITATING. EXPOSURE TO HIGH CONCENTRATIONS MAY RESULT IN CENTRAL NERVOUS SYSTEM DEPRESSION WITH HEADACHE, STUPOR, NAUSEA AND VOMITING. ANIMAL STUDIES INDICATE INHALATION OF 24.1 MG/L FOR 1 HOUR CAUSED NO DEATHS. **CHRONIC EXPOSURE-** NO DATA AVAILABLE.

PARAFFINS: IRRITANT/NARCOTIC. **ACUTE EXPOSURE-** THE DEGREE AND RANGE OF EFFECTS WILL VARY DEPENDING ON THE SPECIFIC HYDROCARBON COMPOSITION. HIGH VAPOR CONCENTRATIONS MAY IRRITATE MUCOUS MEMBRANES AND CAUSE CENTRAL NERVOUS SYSTEM DEPRESSION. SYMPTOMS MAY INCLUDE EXHILARATION, HEADACHE, DIZZINESS, NAUSEA, ANOREXIA, CONFUSION, INCOORDINATION, AND IN MORE SEVERE CASES, STUPOR, ANESTHESIA, UNCONSCIOUSNESS AND COMA WITH INHIBITION OF DEEP TENDON REFLEXES. CONVULSIONS ARE POSSIBLE. IN FATAL CASES, DEATH IS USUALLY DUE TO RESPIRATORY ARREST, ALTHOUGH SUDDEN DEATH MAY RESULT FROM VENTRICULAR FIBRILLATION. VISCERAL DAMAGE MAY OCCUR. **CHRONIC EXPOSURE-** REPEATED OR PROLONGED EXPOSURE TO SOME MEMBERS OF THIS GROUP MAY RESULT IN NEUROLOGIC EFFECTS.

LETHANE 384: IRRITANT/NARCOTIC. **ACUTE EXPOSURE-** INHALATION MAY BE IRRITATING TO THE MUCOUS MEMBRANES, AND MAY CAUSE CENTRAL NERVOUS SYSTEM DEPRESSION WITH HEADACHE, DIZZINESS, AND A TRANSIENT PERIOD OF RESPIRATORY STIMULATION PROGRESSING PROMPTLY TO DEATH FROM RESPIRATORY FAILURE. **CHRONIC EXPOSURE-** REPEATED OR PROLONGED EXPOSURE MAY RESULT IN MUCOUS MEMBRANE IRRITATION.

FIRST AID- REMOVE FROM EXPOSURE AREA TO FRESH AIR IMMEDIATELY. IF BREATHING HAS STOPPED, PERFORM ARTIFICIAL RESPIRATION. KEEP PERSON WARM AND AT REST. TREAT SYMPTOMATICALLY AND SUPPORTIVELY. GET MEDICAL ATTENTION IMMEDIATELY.

SKIN CONTACT: TRIMETHYL BENZENES: IRRITANT/NARCOTIC. **ACUTE EXPOSURE-** MAY CAUSE IRRITATION, REDNESS, AND DEFATTING OF THE SKIN. **CHRONIC EXPOSURE-** MAY CAUSE DERMATITIS AND MAY BE SLOWLY ABSORBED AND CAUSE CENTRAL NERVOUS SYSTEM DEPRESSION WITH HEADACHE, FATIGUE, NERVOUSNESS, ANXIETY, AND NARCOSIS.

PYRENONE O.T. 50-5: IRRITANT. **ACUTE EXPOSURE-** MAY CAUSE MILD SKIN IRRITATION. **CHRONIC EXPOSURE-** REPEATED AND PROLONGED CONTACT MAY CAUSE DERMATITIS.

LPA SOLVENT: IRRITANT. **ACUTE EXPOSURE-** SKIN CONTACT MAY CAUSE IRRITATION WITH REDNESS. ANIMAL STUDIES INDICATE A MODERATE AMOUNT WAS ABSORBED THROUGH INTACT SKIN TO CAUSE DEATH. **CHRONIC EXPOSURE-** REPEATED OR PROLONGED EXPOSURE MAY CAUSE DERMATITIS.

PARAFFINS: IRRITANT. **ACUTE EXPOSURE-** DIRECT CONTACT WITH SOME PARAFFINIC HYDROCARBONS MAY CAUSE IRRITATION. **CHRONIC EXPOSURE-** REPEATED OR PROLONGED CONTACT WITH DEFATTING AGENTS MAY CAUSE DERMATITIS.

LETHANE 384: IRRITANT/NARCOTIC/TOXIC. **ACUTE EXPOSURE-** DIRECT CONTACT WITH THE LIQUID MAY BE IRRITATING TO THE SKIN. MAY BE ABSORBED TO CAUSE CENTRAL NERVOUS SYSTEM DEPRESSION WITH HEADACHE, DIZZINESS AND A TRANSIENT PERIOD OF RESPIRATORY STIMULATION PROGRESSING PROMPTLY TO DEATH FROM RESPIRATORY FAILURE. **CHRONIC EXPOSURE-** PROLONGED OR REPEATED EXPOSURE MAY CAUSE DERMATITIS. PROLONGED ABSORPTION MAY CAUSE SKIN ERUPTIONS, RUNNY NOSE, DIZZINESS, CRAMPS, NAUSEA AND VOMITING.

FIRST AID- REMOVE CONTAMINATED CLOTHING AND SHOES IMMEDIATELY. WASH AFFECTED AREA WITH SOAP OR MILD DETERGENT AND LARGE AMOUNTS OF WATER UNTIL NO EVIDENCE OF CHEMICAL REMAINS (APPROXIMATELY 15-20 MINUTES). GET MEDICAL ATTENTION IMMEDIATELY.

EYE CONTACT: TRIMETHYL BENZENES: IRRITANT. **ACUTE EXPOSURE-** MAY CAUSE REDNESS, PAIN, AND IRRITATION. **CHRONIC EXPOSURE-** REPEATED OR PROLONGED EXPOSURE MAY CAUSE CONJUNCTIVITIS.
PYRENONE O.T. 50-5: IRRITANT. **ACUTE EXPOSURE-** MAY CAUSE MILD IRRITATION. **CHRONIC EXPOSURE-** REPEATED AND PROLONGED CONTACT MAY CAUSE CONJUNCTIVITIS.
LPA SOLVENT: IRRITANT. **ACUTE EXPOSURE-** CONTACT WITH VAPORS OR LIQUID MAY CAUSE SLIGHT IRRITATION. **CHRONIC EXPOSURE-** REPEATED OR PROLONGED EXPOSURE MAY CAUSE CONJUNCTIVITIS.
PARAFFINS: IRRITANT. **ACUTE EXPOSURE-** DIRECT CONTACT WITH SOME PARAFFINIC HYDROCARBONS MAY CAUSE IRRITATION. HIGHER MOLECULAR WEIGHT MEMBERS MAY BE NON-IRRITATING. **CHRONIC EXPOSURE-** REPEATED OR PROLONGED CONTACT WITH IRRITANTS MAY CAUSE CONJUNCTIVITIS.
LETHANE 384: IRRITANT. **ACUTE EXPOSURE-** MAY BE IRRITATING TO THE EYES. **CHRONIC EXPOSURE-** REPEATED OR PROLONGED EXPOSURE MAY CAUSE CONJUNCTIVITIS.
FIRST AID- WASH EYES IMMEDIATELY WITH LARGE AMOUNTS OF WATER OR NORMAL SALINE, OCCASIONALLY LIFTING UPPER AND LOWER LIDS, UNTIL NO EVIDENCE OF CHEMICAL REMAINS (APPROXIMATELY 15-20 MINUTES). GET MEDICAL ATTENTION IMMEDIATELY.

INGESTION: TRIMETHYL BENZENES: NARCOTIC. **ACUTE EXPOSURE-** TRIMETHYL BENZENES MAY CAUSE SORE THROAT, COUGHING, DYSPNEA, NAUSEA AND VOMITING. CENTRAL NERVOUS SYSTEM DEPRESSION WITH HEADACHE, WEAKNESS, DIZZINESS, NARCOSIS, UNCONSCIOUSNESS AND CONVULSIONS MAY OCCUR. **CHRONIC EXPOSURE-** NO DATA AVAILABLE.
PYRENONE O.T. 50-5: **ACUTE EXPOSURE-** NO DATA AVAILABLE. **CHRONIC EXPOSURE-** NO DATA AVAILABLE.
LPA SOLVENT: **ACUTE EXPOSURE-** INGESTION MAY CAUSE IRRITATION OF THE STOMACH AND INTESTINES RESULTING IN NAUSEA AND VOMITING POSSIBLY POSING AN ASPIRATION HAZARD. ANIMAL STUDIES INDICATE A RELATIVELY LARGE AMOUNT WAS LETHAL. **CHRONIC EXPOSURE-** NO DATA AVAILABLE.
PARAFFINS: NARCOTIC. **ACUTE EXPOSURE-** THE GASTROINTESTINAL AND SYSTEMIC EFFECTS MAY VARY DEPENDING ON THE SPECIFIC COMPOSITION. THERE MAY BE A BURNING SENSATION AND LOCAL IRRITATION IN THE MOUTH, THROAT AND STOMACH, VOMITING AND DIARRHEA. ABSORPTION OF A SUFFICIENT AMOUNT MAY RESULT IN SYMPTOMS OF CENTRAL NERVOUS SYSTEM DEPRESSION AND OTHER SYSTEMIC AND PATHOLOGICAL EFFECTS AS DESCRIBED IN ACUTE INHALATION. THE GREATER HAZARD MAY BE FROM ASPIRATION WHICH MAY OCCUR DURING INGESTION OR SUBSEQUENT VOMITING. IN RATS, ASPIRATION OF PARAFFINS, CARBON RANGE 9-16 CAUSED CHEMICAL PNEUMONITIS, PULMONARY EDEMA, AND HEMORRHAGING. CARBON RANGE 6-8 CAUSED IMMEDIATE DEATH DUE TO CARDIAC ARREST, RESPIRATORY PARALYSIS, AND ASPHYXIA. **CHRONIC EXPOSURE-** NO DATA AVAILABLE.
LETHANE 384: NARCOTIC/TOXIC. **ACUTE EXPOSURE-** INGESTION MAY CAUSE CENTRAL NERVOUS SYSTEM DEPRESSION WITH HEADACHE, DIZZINESS, DROWSINESS, NAUSEA, VOMITING AND UNCONSCIOUSNESS. LETHANE 384 IS A RAPID ACTING POISON. TOXICITY IS PROBABLY DUE TO THE METABOLIC FORMATION OF CYANIDE. CENTRAL NERVOUS SYSTEM DEPRESSION, WHICH MAY BE INTERRUPTED BY PERIODS OF RESTLESSNESS, HYPERPNEA, AND TOXIC CONVULSIONS MAY LAST SEVERAL DAYS. TREMORS, PARALYSIS, SPASTICITY, AND EVEN OPISTHOTONOS HAVE OCCURRED IN RABBITS. THE ADULT LETHAL DOSE IS ESTIMATED TO BE 1 TEASPOON TO 1 OUNCE. LETHANE 384 MAY CONTAIN KEROSENE, OR SOME OTHER PETROLEUM DISTILLATE, WHICH MAY POSE AN ASPIRATION HAZARD IF VOMITING SHOULD OCCUR. ORGANIC THIOCYANATES, IN GENERAL, MAY CAUSE CENTRAL NERVOUS SYSTEM DEPRESSION, INTENSE DYSPNEA, CYANOSIS, AND SOMETIMES CONVULSIONS. LIVER AND KIDNEY DAMAGE MAY OCCUR. **CHRONIC EXPOSURE-** NO DATA AVAILABLE.
FIRST AID- TREAT SYMPTOMATICALLY AND SUPPORTIVELY. GET MEDICAL ATTENTION AND ADVICE ON WHETHER TO USE GASTRIC LAVAGE. EXTREME CARE MUST BE TAKEN TO PREVENT ASPIRATION. A CUFFED ENDOTRACHEAL TUBE USED BY QUALIFIED MEDICAL PERSONNEL MIGHT BE ADVISABLE. KEEP HEAD LOWER THAN HIPS TO PREVENT ASPIRATION SHOULD VOMITING OCCUR.

REACTIVITY

REACTIVITY: STABLE UNDER NORMAL TEMPERATURES AND PRESSURES.
INCOMPATIBILITIES: TRIMETHYL BENZENES: NITRIC ACID: EXPLOSION HAZARD ON HEATING ABOVE 115 C.
PYRENONE O.T. 50-5: NO DATA AVAILABLE.
LPA SOLVENT: STRONG OXIDIZERS: INCOMPATIBLE.
PARAFFINS: OXIDIZERS (STRONG): FIRE AND EXPLOSION HAZARD.
LETHANE 384: NO DATA AVAILABLE.
DECOMPOSITION: THERMAL DECOMPOSITION MAY RELEASE TOXIC AND/OR HAZARDOUS GASES.
POLYMERIZATION: HAZARDOUS POLYMERIZATION HAS NOT BEEN REPORTED TO OCCUR UNDER NORMAL TEMPERATURES AND PRESSURES.

CONDITIONS TO AVOID

AVOID CONTACT WITH HEAT, SPARKS, FLAMES, OR OTHER SOURCES OF IGNITION. VAPORS MAY BE EXPLOSIVE. AVOID OVERHEATING OF CONTAINERS; CONTAINERS MAY VIOLENTLY RUPTURE IN HEAT OF FIRE. AVOID CONTAMINATION OF WATER SOURCES.

SPILL AND LEAK PROCEDURES

OCCUPATIONAL SPILL: SHUT OFF IGNITION SOURCES. STOP LEAK IF YOU CAN DO IT WITHOUT RISK. USE WATER SPRAY TO REDUCE VAPORS. FOR SMALL SPILLS, TAKE UP WITH SAND OR OTHER ABSORBENT MATERIAL AND PLACE INTO CONTAINERS FOR LATER DISPOSAL. FOR LARGER SPILLS, DIKE FAR AHEAD OF SPILL FOR LATER DISPOSAL. NO SMOKING, FLAMES OR FLARES IN HAZARD AREA. KEEP UNNECESSARY PEOPLE AWAY; ISOLATE HAZARD AREA AND RESTRICT ENTRY.

PROTECTIVE EQUIPMENT

VENTILATION: PROVIDE LOCAL EXHAUST OR GENERAL DILUTION VENTILATION TO MEET PUBLISHED EXPOSURE LIMITS. VENTILATION EQUIPMENT MUST BE EXPLOSION-PROOF.
RESPIRATOR: THE FOLLOWING RESPIRATORS ARE RECOMMENDED BASED ON INFORMATION FOUND IN THE PHYSICAL DATA, TOXICITY AND HEALTH EFFECTS SECTIONS. THEY ARE RANKED IN ORDER FROM MINIMUM TO MAXIMUM RESPIRATORY PROTECTION. THE SPECIFIC RESPIRATOR SELECTED MUST BE BASED ON CONTAMINATION LEVELS FOUND IN THE WORK PLACE, MUST NOT EXCEED THE WORKING LIMITS OF THE RESPIRATOR AND BE JOINTLY APPROVED BY THE NATIONAL INSTITUTE FOR OCCUPATIONAL SAFETY AND HEALTH AND THE MINE SAFETY AND HEALTH ADMINISTRATION (NIOSH-MSHA).
CHEMICAL CARTRIDGE RESPIRATOR WITH AN ORGANIC VAPOR CARTRIDGE(S) WITH AN ACID GAS CARTRIDGE(S) AND A FULL FACEPIECE.
GAS MASK WITH ORGANIC VAPOR CANISTER (CHIN-STYLE OR FRONT- OR BACK-MOUNTED CANISTER), WITH A FULL FACEPIECE, PROVIDING PROTECTION AGAINST ACID GASES.
TYPE 'C' SUPPLIED-AIR RESPIRATOR WITH A FULL FACEPIECE OPERATED IN PRESSURE-DEMAND OR OTHER POSITIVE PRESSURE MODE OR WITH A FULL FACEPIECE, HELMET OR HOOD OPERATED IN CONTINUOUS-FLOW MODE.
SELF-CONTAINED BREATHING APPARATUS WITH A FULL FACEPIECE OPERATED IN PRESSURE-DEMAND OR OTHER POSITIVE PRESSURE MODE.
FOR FIREFIGHTING AND OTHER IMMEDIATELY DANGEROUS TO LIFE OR HEALTH CONDITIONS:
SELF-CONTAINED BREATHING APPARATUS WITH FULL FACEPIECE OPERATED IN PRESSURE-DEMAND OR OTHER POSITIVE PRESSURE MODE.
SUPPLIED-AIR RESPIRATOR WITH FULL FACEPIECE AND OPERATED IN PRESSURE-DEMAND OR OTHER POSITIVE PRESSURE MODE IN COMBINATION WITH AN AUXILIARY SELF-CONTAINED BREATHING APPARATUS OPERATED IN PRESSURE-DEMAND OR OTHER POSITIVE PRESSURE MODE.
CLOTHING: EMPLOYEE MUST WEAR APPROPRIATE PROTECTIVE (IMPERVIOUS) CLOTHING AND EQUIPMENT TO PREVENT REPEATED OR PROLONGED SKIN CONTACT WITH THIS SUBSTANCE.
GLOVES: EMPLOYEE MUST WEAR APPROPRIATE PROTECTIVE GLOVES TO PREVENT CONTACT WITH THIS SUBSTANCE.
EYE PROTECTION: EMPLOYEE MUST WEAR SPLASH-PROOF OR DUST-RESISTANT SAFETY GOGGLES TO PREVENT EYE CONTACT WITH THIS SUBSTANCE.
EMERGENCY EYE WASH: WHERE THERE IS ANY POSSIBILITY THAT AN EMPLOYEE'S EYES MAY BE EXPOSED TO THIS SUBSTANCE, THE EMPLOYER SHOULD PROVIDE AN EYE WASH FOUNTAIN WITHIN THE IMMEDIATE WORK AREA FOR EMERGENCY USE.

AUTHORIZED BY- OCCUPATIONAL HEALTH SERVICES, INC.
CREATION DATE: 10/05/89 ***REVISION DATE:*** 05/11/90

MATERIAL SAFETY DATA SHEET

OCCUPATIONAL HEALTH SERVICES, INC.
AGRICULTURE AND PESTICIDE DIVISION
450 SEVENTH AVENUE, SUITE 2407
NEW YORK, NEW YORK 10123
1-800-445-MSDS OR (212) 967-1100

EMERGENCY CONTACT:
JOHN S. BRANSFORD, JR. (615) 292-1180

SUBSTANCE IDENTIFICATION

SUBSTANCE: **21 DIAZINON 4E NAMCO 05628671**
TRADE NAMES/SYNONYMS: 21 DIAZINON 4S 05622664; PST75469

CERCLA RATINGS (SCALE 0-3): HEALTH = 3 FIRE = 2 REACTIVITY = 0
PERSISTENCE = 2
NFPA RATINGS (SCALE 0-4): HEALTH = 3 FIRE = 2 REACTIVITY = 0

COMPONENTS AND CONTAMINANTS

COMPONENT: CYCLO SOL 53 SHELL ***PERCENT:*** 39-50
CAS# 64742-95-6 CONTAINS:
XYLENE (3-4%) CAS# 1330-20-7
ETHYL TOLUENES (22-28%) CAS# 25550-14-5
TRIMETHYL BENZENES (57-67%) CAS# 25551-13-7
AROMATICS (C 9-12) (6-9%)
PARAFFINS (< 1%)
COMPONENT: ATLOX 3403F ***PERCENT:*** 0-10
CONTAINS:
METHYL ALCOHOL (13%) CAS# 67-56-1
AROMATIC PETROLEUM SOLVENT (XYLENE BASED) CAS# 1330-20-7
ALKYL ARYL SULFONATES (17%)
NONIONIC SURFACTANTS (55%)
COMPONENT: DIAZINON MG8 ***PERCENT:*** 50-55
CAS# 333-41-5
OTHER CONTAMINANTS: NONE
EXPOSURE LIMITS: XYLENE: 100 PPM (435 MG/M3) OSHA TWA; 150 PPM (655 MG/M3) OSHA STEL 100 PPM (435 MG/M3) ACGIH TWA; 150 PPM (655 MG/M3) ACGIH STEL 100 PPM (435 MG/M3) NIOSH RECOMMENDED 10 HOUR TWA; 200 PPM (870 MG/M3) NIOSH RECOMMENDED 10 MINUTE CEILING
1000 POUNDS CERCLA SECTION 103 REPORTABLE QUANTITY SUBJECT TO SARA SECTION 313 ANNUAL TOXIC CHEMICAL RELEASE REPORTING
TRIMETHYL BENZENE: 25 PPM (125 MG/M3) OSHA TWA 25 PPM (125 MG/M3) ACGIH TWA
METHYL ALCOHOL (METHANOL): 200 PPM (260 MG/M3) OSHA TWA (SKIN); 250 PPM (325 MG/M3) OSHA STEL 200 PPM (260 MG/M3) ACGIH TWA (SKIN); 250 PPM (310 MG/M3) ACGIH STEL 200 PPM NIOSH RECOMMENDED 10 HOUR TWA; 800 PPM NIOSH RECOMMENDED 15 MINUTE CEILING
5000 POUNDS CERCLA SECTION 103 REPORTABLE QUANTITY SUBJECT TO SARA SECTION 313 ANNUAL TOXIC CHEMICAL RELEASE REPORTING
DIAZINON: 0.1 MG/M3 OSHA TWA (SKIN) 0.1 MG/M3 ACGIH TWA (SKIN)
1 POUND CERCLA SECTION 103 REPORTABLE QUANTITY

PHYSICAL DATA

DESCRIPTION: CLEAR, BROWNISH LIQUID WITH A STRONG IRRITATING ODOR
BOILING POINT: NOT AVAILABLE ***SPECIFIC GRAVITY:*** 1.00
EVAPORATION RATE: NOT AVAILABLE ***SOLUBILITY IN WATER:*** SLIGHT
VAPOR DENSITY: > 1

FIRE AND EXPLOSION DATA

FIRE AND EXPLOSION HAZARD: MODERATE FIRE HAZARD WHEN EXPOSED TO HEAT OR FLAME.
VAPORS ARE HEAVIER THAN AIR AND MAY TRAVEL A CONSIDERABLE DISTANCE TO A SOURCE OF IGNITION AND FLASH BACK.
VAPOR-AIR MIXTURES ARE EXPLOSIVE ABOVE FLASH POINT.
FLASH POINT: > 100 F (> 38 C) (CC) ***FLAMMABILITY CLASS(OSHA):*** II
FIREFIGHTING MEDIA: DRY CHEMICAL, CARBON DIOXIDE, HALON, WATER SPRAY OR STANDARD FOAM (1987 EMERGENCY RESPONSE GUIDEBOOK, DOT P 5800.4).
FOR LARGER FIRES, USE WATER SPRAY, FOG OR STANDARD FOAM (1987 EMERGENCY RESPONSE GUIDEBOOK, DOT P 5800.4).
FIREFIGHTING: MOVE CONTAINER FROM FIRE AREA IF POSSIBLE. COOL FIRE-EXPOSED CONTAINERS WITH WATER FROM SIDE UNTIL WELL AFTER FIRE IS OUT. STAY AWAY FROM STORAGE TANK ENDS. FOR MASSIVE FIRE IN STORAGE AREA, USE UNMANNED HOSE HOLDER OR MONITOR NOZZLES, ELSE WITHDRAW FROM AREA AND LET FIRE BURN. WITHDRAW IMMEDIATELY IN CASE OF RISING SOUND FROM VENTING SAFETY DEVICE OR ANY DISCOLORATION OF STORAGE TANK DUE TO FIRE (1987 EMERGENCY RESPONSE GUIDEBOOK, DOT P 5800.4, GUIDE PAGE 27). EXTINGUISH ONLY IF FLOW CAN BE STOPPED; USE FLOODING AMOUNTS OF WATER AS A FOG, SOLID STREAMS MAY BE INEFFECTIVE. COOL CONTAINERS WITH FLOODING AMOUNTS OF WATER, APPLY FROM AS FAR A DISTANCE AS POSSIBLE. AVOID BREATHING VAPORS, KEEP UPWIND.

TRANSPORTATION DATA

DEPARTMENT OF TRANSPORTATION HAZARD CLASSIFICATION 49 CFR 172.101: COMBUSTIBLE LIQUID
DEPARTMENT OF TRANSPORTATION LABELING REQUIREMENTS 49 CFR 172.101 AND SUBPART E: NONE
DEPARTMENT OF TRANSPORTATION PACKAGING REQUIREMENTS: NONE
EXCEPTIONS: 49 CFR 173.118A

TOXICITY

CYCLO SOL 53: 4.7 GM/KG ORAL-RAT LD50 (SHELL MSDS); >4 ML/KG SKIN-RAT LD50 (SHELL MSDS); >3670 PPM/8 HOURS INHALATION-RAT LC50 (SHELL MSDS); CARCINOGEN STATUS: NONE. CYCLO SOL 53 IS AN EYE, MUCOUS MEMBRANE AND SKIN IRRITANT AND A CENTRAL NERVOUS SYSTEM DEPRESSANT.
XYLENE: IRRITATION DATA: 200 PPM EYE-HUMAN; 87 MG EYE-RABBIT MILD; 5 MG/24 HOURS EYE-RABBIT SEVERE; 100% SKIN-RABBIT MODERATE; 500 MG/24 HOURS SKIN-RABBIT MODERATE. TOXICITY DATA: 10000 PPM/6 HOURS INHALATION-MAN LCLO; 200 PPM INHALATION-HUMAN TCLO; 5000 PPM/4 HOURS INHALATION-RAT LC50; 450 PPM INHALATION-GUINEA PIG LCLO; 50 MG/KG ORAL-HUMAN LDLO; 4300 MG/KG ORAL-RAT LD50; 1700 MG/KG SUBCUTANEOUS-RAT LD50; 129 MG/KG INTRAVENOUS-RABBIT LDLO; 2 GM/KG INTRAPERITONEAL-MAMMAL LDLO; 2459 MG/KG INTRAPERITONEAL-RAT LD50; 1548 MG/KG INTRAPERITONEAL-MOUSE LD50; 2000 MG/KG INTRAPERITONEAL-GUINEA PIG LDLO; REPRODUCTIVE EFFECTS DATA (RTECS). CARCINOGEN STATUS: NONE. LOCAL EFFECTS: IRRITANT- INHALATION, SKIN, EYE. ACUTE TOXICITY LEVEL: MODERATELY TOXIC BY INHALATION, INGESTION. TARGET EFFECTS: CENTRAL NERVOUS SYSTEM DEPRESSANT. POISONING MAY ALSO AFFECT THE NERVOUS SYSTEM, LIVER AND KIDNEYS. AT INCREASED RISK FROM EXPOSURE: PREGNANT WOMEN. ADDITIONAL INFORMATION: CONSUMPTION OF ALCOHOLIC BEVERAGES MAY ENHANCE THE TOXIC EFFECTS. STIMULANTS SUCH AS EPINEPHRINE OR EPHEDRINE MAY INDUCE VENTRICULAR FIBRILLATION.
ETHYL TOLUENES: CARCINOGEN STATUS: NONE. THERE IS INSUFFICIENT DATA TO QUANTIFY THE TOXICITY OF ETHYL TOLUENES. IT IS AN EYE, MUCOUS MEMBRANE AND SKIN IRRITANT AND A CENTRAL NERVOUS SYSTEM DEPRESSANT.
TRIMETHYL BENZENES: 1,3,5-TRIMETHYL BENZENE: 24 GM/M3/4 HOURS INHALATION-RAT LC50; 10 PPM INHALATION-HUMAN TCLO; MUTAGENIC DATA (RTEC); CARCINOGEN STATUS: NONE. 1,2,4-TRIMETHYL BENZENE: 5000 MG/KG ORAL-RAT LD50; 18 GM/M3/4 HOURS INHALATION-RAT LC50; CARCINOGEN STATUS: NONE. TRIMETHYL BENZENES ARE EYE, MUCOUS MEMBRANE AND SKIN IRRITANTS AND CENTRAL NERVOUS SYSTEM DEPRESSANTS.
AROMATICS: CARCINOGEN STATUS: NONE. LOCAL EFFECTS: IRRITANT- INHALATION, SKIN, EYE.* ACUTE TOXICITY LEVEL: THE TOXICITY WILL VARY DEPENDING ON THE SPECIFIC COMPOSITION. TARGET EFFECTS: CENTRAL NERVOUS SYSTEM DEPRESSANT* ADDITIONAL DATA: STIMULANTS SUCH AS EPINEPHRINE MAY INDUCE VENTRICULAR FIBRILLATION.*
* BASED ON GENERAL AROMATICS INFORMATION.
METHYL ALCOHOL (METHANOL): IRRITATION DATA: 20 MG/24 HOURS SKIN-RABBIT MODERATE; 40 MG EYE-RABBIT MODERATE; 100 MG/24 HOURS EYE-RABBIT MODERATE. TOXICITY DATA: 86,000 MG/M3 INHALATION-HUMAN TCLO; 300 PPM INHALATION-HUMAN TCLO; 64,000 PPM/4 HOURS INHALATION-RAT LC50; 1000 PPM INHALATION-MONKEY LCLO; 50 GM/M3/2 HOURS INHALATION-MOUSE LCLO; 44,000 MG/M3/6 HOURS INHALATION-CAT LCLO; 15,800 MG/KG SKIN-RABBIT LD50; 393 MG/KG SKIN-MONKEY LDLO; 428 MG/KG ORAL-HUMAN LDLO; 143 MG/KG ORAL-HUMAN LDLO; 6422 MG/KG ORAL-MAN LDLO; 3429 MG/KG ORAL-MAN TDLO; 4 GM/KG ORAL-WOMAN TDLO; 7 GM/KG ORAL-MONKEY LD50; 5628 MG/KG ORAL-RAT LD50; 7300 MG/KG ORAL-MOUSE LD50; 14,200 MG/KG ORAL-RABBIT LD50; 7500 MG/KG ORAL-DOG LDLO; 9800 MG/KG SUBCUT ANEOUS-MOUSE LD50; 2131 MG/KG INTRAVENOUS-RAT LD50; 4710 MG/KG INTRAVENOUS-MOUSE LD50; 8907 MG/KG INTRAVENOUS-RABBIT LD50; 7529 MG/KG INTRAPERITONEAL-RAT LD50; 10,765 MG/KG INTRAPERITONEAL-MOUSE LD50; 1826 MG/KG INTRAPERITONEAL-RABBIT LD50; 868 MG/KG UNREPORTED-MAN LDLO; MUTAGENIC DATA (RTECS); REPRODUCTIVE EFFECTS DATA (RTECS). CARCINOGEN STATUS: NONE. LOCAL EFFECTS: IRRITANT- SKIN, EYE. ACUTE TOXICITY LEVEL: SLIGHTLY TOXIC BY INHALATION, DERMAL ABSORPTION, INGESTION. TARGET EFFECTS: NEUROTOXIN; CENTRAL NERVOUS SYSTEM DEPRESSANT. AT INCREASED RISK FROM EXPOSURE: PERSONS WITH KIDNEY, EYE OR SKIN DISORDERS.
ALKYL ARYL SULFONATES: CARCINOGEN STATUS: NONE. THERE IS INSUFFICIENT DATA TO QUANTIFY THE TOXICITY OF ALKYL ARLY SULFONATES.
NONIONIC SURFACTANTS: CARCINOGEN STATUS: NONE. NONIONIC SURFACTANTS ARE EYE, MUCOUS MEMBRANE AND SKIN IRRITANTS. THERE IS INSUFFICIENT DATA TO QUANTIFY THE TOXICITY.
DIAZINON: IRRITATION DATA: 100 MG EYE-RABBIT SEVERE; 500 MG OPEN SKIN-RABBIT MODERATE. TOXICITY DATA: 3500 MG/M3/4 HOURS INHALATION-RAT LC50; 1600 MG/M3/4 HOURS INHALATION-MOUSE LC50; 5500 MG/M3/4 HOURS INHALATION-GUINEA PIG LC50; 180 MG/KG SKIN-RABBIT LD50; 180 MG/KG SKIN-RAT LD50; 2750 MG/KG SKIN-MOUSE LD50; 633 MG/KG SKIN-PIG LD50; 214 MG/KG ORAL-HUMAN TDLO; 66 MG/KG ORAL-RAT LD50; 143 MG/KG ORAL-RABBIT LD50; 17 MG/KG ORAL-MOUSE LD50; 250 MG/KG ORAL-GUINEA PIG LD50; 320 MG/KG ORAL-PIG LD50; 58 MG/KG SUBCUTANEOUS-MOUSE LD50; 180 MG/KG INTRAVENOUS-MOUSE LD50; 65 MG/KG INTRAPERITONEAL-RAT LD50; 33 MG/KG INTRAPERITONEAL-MOUSE LD50; 76 MG/KG UNREPORTED-MAMMAL LD50; MUTAGENIC DATA (RTECS); REPRODUCTIVE EFFECTS DATA (RTECS). CARCINOGEN STATUS: NONE. LOCAL EFFECTS: IRRITANT- SKIN, EYE. ACUTE TOXICITY DATA: HIGHLY TOXIC BY DERMAL ABSORPTION; TOXIC BY INHALATION AND INGESTION. TARGET EFFECTS: CHOLINESTERASE INHIBITOR. POISONING MAY AFFECT THE

NERVOUS SYSTEM.* AT INCREASED RISK FROM EXPOSURE: PERSONS WITH RESPIRATORY AILMENTS, RECENT EXPOSURE TO CHOLINESTERASE INHIBITORS OR IMPAIRED CHOLINESTERASE PRODUCTION, OR LIVER MALFUNCTION.* ADDITIONAL DATA: MAY CROSS THE PLACENTA. HIGH ENVIRONMENTAL TEMPERATURES OR EXPOSURE OF THE CHEMICAL TO VISIBLE OR ULTRAVIOLET LIGHT MAY ENHANCE THE TOXICITIY. INTERACTIONS WITH MEDICATIONS MAY OCCUR.*
* MAY BE BASED ON GENERAL INFORMATION ON ORGANOPHOSPHATES.

HEALTH EFFECTS AND FIRST AID

INHALATION: CYCLO SOL 53: IRRITANT/NARCOTIC. **ACUTE EXPOSURE-** HIGH VAPOR CONCENTRATIONS MAY BE IRRITATING TO THE NOSE, THROAT, AND RESPIRATORY TRACT. MAY CAUSE CENTRAL NERVOUS SYSTEM DEPRESSION WITH GIDDINESS, HEADACHE, DIZZINESS AND NAUSEA. IN EXTREME CASES, UNCONSCIOUSNESS AND DEATH MAY OCCUR. **CHRONIC EXPOSURE-** REPEATED OR PROLONGED EXPOSURE MAY CAUSE RESPIRATORY IRRITATION. RATS EXPOSED FOR 4 MONTHS TO 1700 PPM OF A SIMILAR SOLVENT SHOWED EVIDENCE OF DAMAGE TO THE LIVER, LUNGS AND KIDNEYS.

XYLENE: IRRITANT/NARCOTIC. 1000 PPM IMMEDIATELY DANGEROUS TO LIFE OR HEALTH. **ACUTE EXPOSURE-** IRRITATION OF THE UPPER RESPIRATORY TRACT MAY OCCUR AT 200 PPM. EXPOSURE TO HIGHER CONCENTRATIONS MAY CAUSE MORE SEVERE IRRITATION AND INITIAL CENTRAL NERVOUS SYSTEM EXCITATION FOLLOWED BY DEPRESSION. SIGNS AND SYMPTOMS MAY INCLUDE RESPIRATORY DIFFICULTY AND SUBSTERNAL PAIN, TRANSIENT EUPHORIA AND EMOTIONAL LABILITY, HEADACHE, NAUSEA, VOMITING, ANOREXIA, ABDOMINAL PAIN, DIZZINESS, DROWSINESS, ATAXIA, AND STAGGERING. THERE MAY BE SALIVATION, SLURRED SPEECH, BLURRED VISION, NYSTAGMUS, TINNITUS, TREMORS, CONFUSION, AND FLUSHING OF THE FACE AND A FEELING OF INCREASED BODY HEAT. IN SEVERE EXPOSURES, THERE MAY BE STUPOR, ANESTHESIA, UNCONSCIOUSNESS, AND COMA WHICH MAY BE PUNCTUATED BY EPISODES OF NEUROIRRITABILITY, BUT RARELY FRANK CONVULSIONS, EXCEPT IN TERMINAL ASPHYXIA. LIVER AND KIDNEY DAMAGE MAY OCCUR, BUT ARE USUALLY MILD AND TRANSIENT. A GROUP OF SUBJECTS WHO INHALED 12.3 UMOL/L OF XYLENE WHILE EXERCISING BECAME SIGNIFICANTLY IMPAIRED ON 3 NEUROPSYCHOLOGICAL TESTS. EXPOSURE OF 3 PAINTERS TO APPROXIMATELY 10,000 PPM FOR 18.5 HOURS RESULTED IN 1 DEATH FROM PULMONARY EDEMA AND PETECHIAL BRAIN HEMORRHAGE. BOTH SURVIVORS WERE UNCONSCIOUS FOR 19-24 HOURS AND EXPERIENCED RETROGRADE AMNESIA, HYPOTHERMIA, AND LUNG CONGESTION. RENAL AND HEPATIC IMPAIRMENT ALSO DEVELOPED. COMPLETE RECOVERY TOOK 15 DAYS. HIGH CONCENTRATIONS MAY CAUSE DEATH FROM SUDDEN VENTRICULAR FIBRILLATION, BUT MORE FREQUENTLY DEATH OCCURS FROM RESPIRATORY ARREST. **CHRONIC EXPOSURE-** REPEATED OR PROLONGED INHALATION OF VAPORS ABOVE 200 PPM MAY CAUSE NAUSEA, VOMITING, ABDOMINAL PAIN, AND ANOREXIA. OTHER COMMON COMPLAINTS INCLUDE HEADACHE, FATIGUE, LASSITUDE, IRRITABILITY, BREATHING DIFFICULTIES, AND FLATULENCE. EFFECTS ON THE NERVOUS SYSTEM MAY RESULT IN EXCITATION, FOLLOWED BY DEPRESSION, PARESTHESIAS, TREMORS, APPREHENSION, IMPAIRED MEMORY, INSOMNIA, VERTIGO, AND TINNITUS. EFFECTS ON REACTION TIME, MANUAL COORDINATION, BODY BALANCE AND EEG OCCURRED WITH REPEATED EXPOSURE TO 90 PPM OF M-XYLENE. SWEETISH TASTE IN THE MOUTH, DRY NOSE AND THROAT, STRONG THIRST, MUCOSAL HEMORRHAGE, AND ANEMIA HAVE BEEN REPORTED. EFFECTS ON THE LIVER, KIDNEY, CARDIOVASCULAR SYSTEM, AND THE BONE MARROW HAVE ALSO BEEN REPORTED, ALTHOUGH THE LATTER HAS BEEN QUESTIONED. EXPOSURE OF RABBITS TO 1150 PPM FOR 40-55 DAYS RESULTED IN A REVERSIBLE DECREASE IN THE RED AND WHITE CELL COUNTS AND AN INCREASE IN THE PLATELETS. ONE CASE OF AN APPARENT EPILEPTIFORM SEIZURE FOLLOWING A RELATIVELY BRIEF EXPOSURE HAS OCCURRED. WOMEN MAY DEVELOP MENSTRUAL DISORDERS, SUCH AS MENORRHAGIA OR METRORRHAGIA, INFERTILITY, AND PATHOLOGICAL PREGNANCY CONDITIONS INCLUDING TOXICOSIS, DANGER OF MISCARRIAGE, AND HEMORRHAGING DURING DELIVERY. REPEATED EXPOSURE OF PREGNANT MICE, RATS AND RABBITS TO THE INDIVIDUAL OR THE MIXED ISOMERS HAS RESULTED IN MATERNAL EFFECTS AND EFFECTS ON FERTILITY, ON THE EMBRYO OR FETUS, AND SPECIFIC DEVELOPMENTAL ABNORMALITIES. INCLUDED AMONG THESE EFFECTS ARE FETAL DEATH, FETOTOXICITY, PRE- AND POST-IMPLANTATION MORTALITY, ABORTION, CRANIOFACIAL AND MUSCULOSKELETAL ABNORMALITIES, AND EXTRA EMBRYONIC STRUCTURES.

ETHYL TOLUENES: IRRITANT/NARCOTIC. **ACUTE EXPOSURE-** VAPORS OF ETHYL TOLUENES MAY BE IRRITATING TO THE RESPIRATORY TRACT. IN GENERAL, ETHYL TOLUENES ARE OF A LOW ORDER OF TOXICITY BY INHALATION. SYSTEMIC EFFECTS HAVE NOT BEEN REPORTED BUT ARE SUSPECTED TO BE SIMILAR TO OTHER AROMATIC COMPOUNDS WITH 9 CARBONS SUCH AS NAUSEA, VOMITING, WEAKNESS, TIREDNESS, VERTIGO, OR IN SEVERE CASES, INEBRIATION OR UNCONSCIOUSNESS. **CHRONIC EXPOSURE-** NO DATA AVAILABLE.

TRIMETHYL BENZENES: IRRITANT/NARCOTIC. **ACUTE EXPOSURE-** TRIMETHYL BENZENES MAY CAUSE IRRITATION OF THE NOSE AND THROAT. DYSPNEA, COUGHING, NAUSEA, ASTHMATIC BRONCHITIS AND BRONCHIAL PNEUMONIA WITH FEVER MAY OCCUR. CENTRAL NERVOUS SYSTEM DEPRESSION WITH HEADACHE, FATIGUE, NERVOUSNESS, ANXIETY AND NARCOSIS MAY ALSO RESULT. 1,2,4-TRIMETHYL BENZENE AND 1,3,5-TRIMETHYL BENZENE BOTH MAY CAUSE CHEMICAL PNEUMONITIS AT THE SITE OF CONTACT AND HEMORRHAGIC INFLAMMATORY LESIONS OF THE MUCOUS MEMBRANES. **CHRONIC EXPOSURE-** REPEATED OR PROLONGED EXPOSURE TO TRIMETHYL BENZENES MAY CAUSE DIZZINESS, WEAKNESS, WEIGHT LOSS, ANEMIA, PERIPHERAL NUMBNESS, PARESTHESIAS, NERVOUSNESS, PAINS IN THE LIMBS, AND ASTHMATIC BRONCHITIS. 1,2,4-TRIMETHYL BENZENE MAY CAUSE BONE MARROW DAMAGE.

AROMATICS: IRRITANT/NARCOTIC. **ACUTE EXPOSURE-** THE DEGREE AND RANGE OF EFFECTS WILL VARY DEPENDING ON THE SPECIFIC HYDROCARBON COMPOSITION. HIGH VAPOR CONCENTRATIONS MAY CAUSE MUCOUS MEMBRANE IRRITATION, COUGH AND SUBSTERNAL PAIN; PULMONARY EDEMA IS POSSIBLE. THE CENTRAL NERVOUS SYSTEM MAY BE STIMULATED THEN DEPRESSED. SYMPTOMS MAY INCLUDE TRANSIENT EUPHORIA, NAUSEA, VOMITING, WEAKNESS, FATIGUE, VERTIGO, ATAXIA, AND IN MORE SEVERE CASES, STUPOR, ANESTHESIA, UNCONSCIOUSNESS, AND COMA. TREMORS AND CONVULSIONS ARE POSSIBLE. IN FATAL CASES, DEATH IS USUALLY DUE TO RESPIRATORY ARREST, ALTHOUGH SUDDEN DEATH MAY RESULT FROM VENTRICULAR FIBRILLATION. PATHOLOGICAL FINDINGS MAY INCLUDE HYPEREMIA, EDEMA AND GROSS AND PETECHIAL HEMORRHAGES IN THE INTERNAL ORGANS. **CHRONIC EXPOSURE-** REPEATED EXPOSURE TO SOME AROMATIC HYDROCARBONS MAY CAUSE HEADACHE, ANOREXIA, DROWSINESS, NERVOUSNESS, AND PALLOR. RECENT STUDIES ON WORKERS CHRONICALLY EXPOSED TO MIXTURES OF AROMATIC AND ALIPHATIC SUBSTANCES HAVE FOUND PSYCHOLOGICAL AND NEUROPHYSIOLOGICAL DIFFERENCES BETWEEN EXPOSED AND NON-EXPOSED WORKERS SUGGESTING THAT AROMATIC HYDROCARBONS MAY CAUSE SUBTLE, LONG LASTING NEUROLOGIC EFFECTS.

METHYL ALCOHOL (METHANOL): NARCOTIC/NEUROTOXIN. 25,000 PPM IMMEDIATELY DANGEROUS TO LIFE OR HEALTH. **ACUTE EXPOSURE-** MAY CAUSE IRRITATION OF THE MUCOUS MEMBRANES, COUGHING, OPPRESSION IN THE CHEST, TRACHEITIS, BRONCHITIS, TINNITUS, UNSTEADY GAIT, TWITCHING, COLIC, CONSTIPATION, NYSTAGMUS, AND BLEPHAROSPASM. SYMPTOMS FROM OCCUPATIONAL EXPOSURE INCLUDE PARESTHESIAS, NUMBNESS AND SHOOTING PAINS IN THE HANDS AND FOREARMS. METABOLIC ACIDOSIS, AND EFFECTS ON THE EYES AND CENTRAL NERVOUS SYSTEM MAY OCCUR AS DETAILED IN ACUTE INGESTION. **CHRONIC EXPOSURE-** REPEATED OR PROLONGED EXPOSURE MAY CAUSE EFFECTS AS IN ACUTE INGESTION. REPEATED EXPOSURE TO 200-375 PPM CAUSED RECURRENT HEADACHES IN WORKERS. EXPOSURE FOR 4 YEARS TO 1200-8000 PPM RESULTED IN MARKED DIMINUTION OF VISION AND ENLARGEMENT OF THE LIVER IN A WORKMAN. REPRODUCTIVE EFFECTS HAVE BEEN REPORTED IN ANIMALS.

ALKYL ARYL SULFONATE: IRRITANT. **ACUTE EXPOSURE-** NO DATA AVAILABLE ON THIS SPECIFIC GROUP. HOWEVER, ANIONIC SURFACTANTS MAY CAUSE IRRITATION OF THE RESPIRATORY TRACT. THE AIRBORNE DUST OF SULFONATED SURFACTANTS MAY CAUSE RESPIRATORY ALLERGIES IN SOME INDIVIUALS. **CHRONIC EXPOSURE-** PROLONGED OR REPEATED EXPOSURE MAY CAUSE IRRITATION OF THE RESPIRATORY TRACT. PROLONGED OR REPEATED EXPOSURE MAY CAUSE RESPIRATORY ALLERGIES IN SOME INDIVIUALS.

NONIONIC SURFACTANTS: **ACUTE EXPOSURE-** EXPOSURE TO A LARGE CONCENTRATION MAY CAUSE IRRITATION OF THE MUCOUS MEMBRANES. **CHRONIC EXPOSURE-** PROLONGED OR REPEATED EXPOSURE TO A LARGE CONCENTRATION MAY CAUSE IRRITATION OF THE MUCOUS MEMBRANES.

DIAZINON: TOXIC. SEE INFORMATION ON ORGANOPHOSPHATES.

ORGANOPHOSPHATES: CHOLINESTERASE INHIBITOR. **ACUTE EXPOSURE-** WHEN INHALED, THE FIRST EFFECTS OF CHOLINESTERASE INHIBITORS ARE USUALLY RESPIRATORY AND MAY INCLUDE NASAL HYPEREMIA AND WATERY DISCHARGE, COUGH, CHEST DISCOMFORT, DYSPNEA, AND WHEEZING DUE TO INCREASED BRONCHIAL SECRETIONS AND BRONCHOCONSTRICTION. IF SUFFICIENT AMOUNTS ARE ABSORBED, OTHER SYSTEMIC EFFECTS MAY BEGIN WITHIN A FEW MINUTES OR BE DELAYED FOR UP TO 12 HOURS. SYMPTOMS MAY INCLUDE PALLOR, NAUSEA, VOMITING, DIARRHEA, ABDOMINAL CRAMPS, HEADACHE, DIZZINESS, OCULAR PAIN, BLURRED VISION, MIOSIS OR IN SOME CASES, ESPECIALLY INITIALLY, MYDRIASIS, LACRIMATION, SALIVATION, SWEATING, AND CONFUSION. OTHER REPORTED CENTRAL NERVOUS SYSTEM OR NEUROMUSCULAR EFFECTS MAY INCLUDE ATAXIA, SLURRED SPEECH, AREFLEXIA, WEAKNESS, FATIGUE, FASCICULATIONS, TWITCHING, TREMORS POSSIBLY OF THE TONGUE AND EYELIDS, AND EVENTUALLY PARALYSIS OF THE EXTREMITIES AND POSSIBLY OF THE RESPIRATORY MUSCLES. IN SEVERE CASES THERE MAY ALSO BE INVOLUNTARY DEFECATION AND URINATION, CYANOSIS, PSYCHOSIS, HYPERGLYCEMIA, ACUTE PANCREATITIS, CARDIAC IRREGULARITIES, PULMONARY EDEMA, UNCONSCIOUSNESS, CONVULSIONS, AND COMA. DEATH IS PRIMARILY DUE TO RESPIRATORY FAILURE, ALTHOUGH CARDIOVASCULAR EFFECTS INCLUDING CARDIAC ARREST MAY ALSO BE IMPLICATED. LONG TERM SEQUELAE ARE RARE BUT MAY INCLUDE NEUROPSYCHIATRIC DISORDERS AND MYOPATHY WITH MUSCLE TENDERNESS. SOME ORGANOPHOSPHATES MAY CAUSE A DELAYED

NEUROPATHY BEGINNING 1-4 WEEKS AFTER AN ACUTE EXPOSURE WHICH MAY OR MAY NOT HAVE CAUSED ACUTE CHOLINERGIC EFFECTS. NUMBNESS, TINGLING, WEAKNESS AND CRAMPING BEGINNING SYMMETRICALLY IN THE LOWER LIMBS MAY PROGRESS TO ATAXIA AND PARALYSIS. IN SEVERE CASES, UPPER LIMB INVOLVEMENT IS POSSIBLE AND FLACCID PARALYSIS MAY PROGRESS TO SPASTIC PARALYSIS WITH EXAGGERATED REFLEXES. IMPROVEMENT MAY OCCUR OVER MONTHS TO YEARS, BUT SOME RESIDUAL IMPAIRMENT USUALLY REMAINS. **CHRONIC EXPOSURE-** REPEATED OR PROLONGED EXPOSURE MAY RESULT IN THE EFFECTS OF ACUTE EXPOSURE INCLUDING THE DELAYED NEUROPATHY. OTHER EFFECTS REPORTED IN WORKERS REPEATEDLY EXPOSED INCLUDE IMPAIRED MEMORY AND CONCENTRATION, ACUTE PSYCHOSIS, SEVERE DEPRESSIONS, IRRITABILTY, CONFUSION, APATHY, EMOTIONAL LABILITY, SOCIAL WITHDRAWAL, CONFUSION, HEADACHE, SPEECH DIFFICULTIES, DELAYED REACTION TIMES, SPATIAL DISORIENTATION, NIGHTMARES, SLEEPWALKING, AND DROWSINESS OR INSOMNIA. AN INFLUENZA-LIKE CONDITION WITH HEADACHE, NAUSEA, WEAKNESS, ANOREXIA AND MALAISE HAS ALSO BEEN REPORTED.

FIRST AID- REMOVE FROM EXPOSURE AREA TO FRESH AIR IMMEDIATELY. IF BREATHING HAS STOPPED, GIVE ARTIFICIAL RESPIRATION. MAINTAIN AIRWAY AND BLOOD PRESSURE AND ADMINISTER OXYGEN IF AVAILABLE. KEEP AFFECTED PERSON WARM AND AT REST. TREAT SYMPTOMATICALLY AND SUPPORTIVELY. ADMINISTRATION OF OXYGEN SHOULD BE PERFORMED BY QUALIFIED PERSONNEL. GET MEDICAL ATTENTION IMMEDIATELY.

SKIN CONTACT: CYCLO SOL 53: IRRITANT. **ACUTE EXPOSURE-** LIQUID IS SLIGHTLY IRRITATING TO THE SKIN. **CHRONIC EXPOSURE-** REPEATED OR PROLONGED EXPOSURE MAY RESULT IN DEFATTING AND DRYING OF THE SKIN LEADING TO DERMATITIS.

XYLENE: IRRITANT. **ACUTE EXPOSURE-** LIQUID XYLENE IS A DEFATTING AGENT AND MAY CAUSE A BURNING SENSATION, DRYING, VASODILATION, ERYTHEMA, AND POSSIBLY BLISTERING. THE LIQUID IS READILY ABSORBED THROUGH INTACT OR BROKEN SKIN AT A RATE OF APPROXIMATELY 4-10 MG/CM2/HOUR, BUT SYSTEMIC EFFECTS HAVE NOT BEEN REPORTED. **CHRONIC EXPOSURE-** REPEATED OR PROLONGED CONTACT MAY CAUSE DEFATTING OF THE SKIN WITH DRYING, ERYTHEMA, CRACKING, THICKENING AND BLISTERING. REPEATED APPLICATION OF 95% XYLENE TO RABBIT SKIN CAUSED MODERATE TO MARKED IRRITATION WITH ERYTHEMA AND MODERATE NECROSIS. ONE CASE OF ALLERGIC CONTACT URTICARIA HAS BEEN REPORTED.

ETHYL TOLUENES: IRRITANT. **ACUTE EXPOSURE-** MAY BE IRRITATING AND HAVE A DEFATTING ACTION ON THE SKIN. **CHRONIC EXPOSURE-** REPEATED OR PROLONGED EXPOSURE MAY CAUSE DERMATITIS.

TRIMETHYL BENZENES: IRRITANT/NARCOTIC. **ACUTE EXPOSURE-** MAY CAUSE IRRITATION, REDNESS, AND DEFATTING OF THE SKIN. **CHRONIC EXPOSURE-** MAY CAUSE DERMATITIS AND MAY BE SLOWLY ABSORBED AND CAUSE CENTRAL NERVOUS SYSTEM DEPRESSION WITH HEADACHE, FATIGUE, NERVOUSNESS, ANXIETY, AND NARCOSIS.

AROMATICS: IRRITANT. **ACUTE EXPOSURE-** DIRECT CONTACT WITH LIQUID AROMATIC HYDROCARBONS MAY CAUSE VASODILATION, ERYTHEMA AND IRRITATION. WITH PROLONGED CONTACT, BLISTERS MAY DEVELOP. ABSORPTION THROUGH THE SKIN IS GENERALLY SLOW. **CHRONIC EXPOSURE-** REPEATED AND PROLONGED CONTACT MAY CAUSE DERMATITIS WITH DRYING, SCALING AND FISSURING OF THE SKIN DUE TO THE DEFATTING ACTION OF THE LIQUID.

METHYL ALCOHOL (METHANOL): IRRITANT/NARCOTIC/NEUROTOXIN. **ACUTE EXPOSURE-** CONTACT WITH LIQUID MAY CAUSE IRRITATION. SKIN ABSORPTION MAY OCCUR AND CAUSE METABOLIC ACIDOSIS AND EFFECTS ON THE EYES AND CENTRAL NERVOUS SYSTEM AS DETAILED IN ACUTE INGESTION. **CHRONIC EXPOSURE-** REPEATED OR PROLONGED CONTACT WITH THE LIQUID MAY CAUSE DEFATTING OF THE SKIN RESULTING IN ERYTHEMA, SCALING, AND ECZEMATOID DERMATITIS. CHRONIC ABSORPTION MAY RESULT METABOLIC ACIDOSIS AND EFFECTS AS DETAILED IN ACUTE INGESTION.

ALKYL ARYL SULFONATES: IRRITANT. **ACUTE EXPOSURE-** NO DATA AVAILABLE ON THIS SPECIFIC GROUP. HOWEVER ANIONIC SURFACTANTS MAY CAUSE IRRITATION OF THE SKIN BY REMOVING NATURAL OILS, CAUSING REDNESS, SORENESS, AND PAPULAR DERMATITIS. IN SENSITIVE PERSONS IT MAY ALSO CAUSE THICKENING OF THE SKIN WITH WEEPING, CRACKING, SCALING, AND BLISTERING. THE PRESENCE OF ENZYMES MAY CAUSE SENSITIZATION DERMATITIS IN SOME INDIVIUALS. **CHRONIC EXPOSURE-** REPEATED OR PROLONGED EXPOSURE MAY CAUSE DERMATITIS AND MAY CAUSE SENSITIZATION DERMATITIS IN SOME INDIVIUALS.

NONIONIC SURFACTANTS: **ACUTE EXPOSURE-** MAY CAUSE IRRITATION. CONCENTRATED NONIONIC SURFACTANTS ARE CAPABLE OF DEGREASING THE SKIN PRODUCING DRYING AND CRACKING. **CHRONIC EXPOSURE-** PROLONGED OR REPEATED EXPOSURE MAY CAUSE DERMATITIS.

DIAZINON: IRRITANT/HIGHLY TOXIC. 500 MG APPLIED TO OPEN RABBIT SKIN PRODUCED MODERATE IRRITATION. SEE INFORMATION ON ORGANOPHOSPHATES.

ORGANOPHOSPHATES: CHOLINESTERASE INHIBITOR. **ACUTE EXPOSURE-** LOCALIZED SWEATING AND FASCICULATIONS MAY OCCUR AT THE SITE OF CONTACT. IF SUFFICIENT AMOUNTS ARE ABSORBED, OTHER EFFECTS OF CHOLINESTERASE INHIBITION AS DESCRIBED IN ACUTE INHALATION MAY OCCUR. SYMPTOMS MAY BE DELAYED 2-3 HOURS, BUT USUALLY NO MORE THAN 12 HOURS. THE RATE OF ABSORPTION IS INCREASED BY THE PRESENCE OF DERMATITIS OR HIGH AMBIENT TEMPERATURES. DELAYED NEUROPATHY IS ALSO POSSIBLE. **CHRONIC EXPOSURE-** REPEATED OR PROLONGED EXPOSURE MAY CAUSE EFFECTS AS DESCRIBED IN ACUTE EXPOSURE. SOME ORGANOPHOSPHATES MAY CAUSE SENSITIZATION.

FIRST AID- REMOVE CONTAMINATED CLOTHING AND SHOES IMMEDIATELY. WASH AFFECTED AREA WITH SOAP OR MILD DETERGENT AND LARGE AMOUNTS OF WATER UNTIL NO EVIDENCE OF CHEMICAL REMAINS (APPROXIMATELY 15-20 MINUTES). GET MEDICAL ATTENTION IMMEDIATELY.

EYE CONTACT: CYCLO SOL 53: IRRITANT. **ACUTE EXPOSURE-** HIGH VAPOR CONCENTRATIONS MAY BE IRRITATING TO THE EYES. THE LIQUID IS SLIGHTLY IRRITATING. **CHRONIC EXPOSURE-** REPEATED OR PROLONGED EXPOSURE MAY CAUSE CONJUNCTIVITIS.

XYLENE: IRRITANT. **ACUTE EXPOSURE-** 200 PPM HAS CAUSED CONJUNCTIVAL IRRITATION IN HUMANS; AT HIGHER CONCENTRATIONS, IRRITATION MAY BE SEVERE. VAPOR EXPOSURE HAS ALSO CAUSED TEARING AND PHOTOPHOBIA. AN ACCIDENTAL SPLASH IN THE HUMAN EYE CAUSED TRANSIENT SUPERFICIAL DAMAGE WITH RAPID RECOVERY, ALTHOUGH REVERSIBLE CORNEAL BURNS HAVE ALSO BEEN REPORTED. **CHRONIC EXPOSURE-** REPEATED OR PROLONGED EXPOSURE TO HIGH VAPOR CONCENTRATIONS MAY CAUSE A BURNING SENSATION, CONJUNCTIVITIS AND BLURRED VISION; REVERSIBLE VACUOLAR, EPITHELIAL KERATOPATHY HAS BEEN REPORTED IN SOME WORKERS.

ETHYL TOLUENES: IRRITANT. **ACUTE EXPOSURE-** VAPORS MAY BE IRRITATING. **CHRONIC EXPOSURE-** REPEATED OR PROLONGED EXPOSURE MAY CAUSE CONJUNCTIVITIS.

TRIMETHYL BENZENES: IRRITANT. **ACUTE EXPOSURE-** MAY CAUSE REDNESS, PAIN, AND IRRITATION. **CHRONIC EXPOSURE-** REPEATED OR PROLONGED EXPOSURE MAY CAUSE CONJUNCTIVITIS.

AROMATICS: IRRITANT. **ACUTE EXPOSURE-** DIRECT CONTACT WITH SOME AROMATIC HYDROCARBONS MAY CAUSE ITCHING, LACRIMATION, AND IRRITATION. IF CONTACT IS SUFFICIENTLY PROLONGED TISSUE INJURY MAY RESULT. CONJUNCTIVITIS AND CORNEAL BURNS HAVE BEEN REPORTED FROM SOME AROMATICS. **CHRONIC EXPOSURE-** REPEATED OR PROLONGED EXPOSURE MAY CAUSE CONJUNCTIVITIS.

METHYL ALCOHOL (METHANOL): IRRITANT. **ACUTE EXPOSURE-** VAPORS MAY CAUSE IRRITATION. HIGH CONCENTRATIONS HAVE BEEN REPORTED TO CAUSE VIOLENT INFLAMMATION OF THE CONJUNCTIVA AND EPITHELIAL DEFECTS ON THE CORNEA. MILD IRRITATION MAY OCCUR WITH DILUTE SOLUTIONS; THE UNDILUTED LIQUID HAS PRODUCED MODERATE CORNEAL OPACITY AND CONJUNCTIVAL REDNESS IN RABBITS. APPLICATION OF A DROP OF METHANOL IN RABBIT EYES CAUSED A MILD REVERSIBLE REACTION, GRADED 3 ON A SCALE OF 1-10 AFTER 24 HOURS. **CHRONIC EXPOSURE-** REPEATED OR PROLONGED CONTACT MAY CAUSE CONJUNCTIVITIS.

ALKYL ARYL SULFONATES: IRRITANT. **ACUTE EXPOSURE-** NO DATA AVAILABLE ON THIS SPECIFIC GROUP. HOWEVER, ANIONIC SURFACTANTS MAY CAUSE SEVERE IRRITATION. DIRECT CONTACT WITH A CONCENTRATED FORM MAY CAUSE MODERATE TO SEVERE CORNEAL DAMAGE. IN HUMAN ACCIDENTS THE IMMEDIATE SEVERE PAIN LEADS TO RAPID WASHING OUT OF THE EYE, AND ONLY IN THE MOST EXTREME CIRCUMSTANCES WILL PERMANENT DAMAGE RESULT. **CHRONIC EXPOSURE-** REPEATED OR PROLONGED EXPOSURE MAY CAUSE CONJUNCTIVITIS.

NONIONIC SURFACTANTS: IRRITANT. **ACUTE EXPOSURE-** MAY CAUSE IRRITATION. THE SEVERITY OF IRRITATION VARIES AMONG THE DIFFERENT NONIONIC SURFACTANTS. SOME OF THE SURFACTANTS MAY CAUSE PAIN AND CORNEAL DAMAGE WHILE OTHERS CAUSE LITTLE OR NO DAMAGE. IN HUMAN ACCIDENTS THE IMMEDIATE SEVERE PAIN LEADS TO RAPID WASHING OUT OF EYE, AND ONLY IN THE MOST EXTREME CIRCUMSTANCES WILL PERMANENT DAMAGE RESULT. CERTAIN NONIONIC SURFACTANTS HAVE LOCAL ANESTHETIC EFFECTS ON THE CORNEA. IN FORMULATION WITH OTHER HAZARDOUS MATERIALS, THIS ANESTHETIC EFFECT MIGHT ELIMINATE THE PAIN WARNING AND ALLOW SEVERE DAMAGE TO OCCUR UPON EXPOSURE TO THE FORMULATION. **CHRONIC EXPOSURE-** NO DATA AVAILABLE.

DIAZINON: IRRITANT. 100 MG APPLIED TO THE EYES OF RABBITS PRODUCED SEVERE IRRITATION. SEE INFORMATION ON ORGANOPHOSPHATES.

ORGANOPHOSPHATES: CHOLINESTERASE INHIBITOR. **ACUTE EXPOSURE-** DIRECT CONTACT MAY CAUSE PAIN, HYPEREMIA, LACRIMATION, TWITCHING OF THE EYELIDS, MIOSIS, AND CILIARY MUSCLE SPASM WITH LOSS OF ACCOMODATION, BLURRED OR DIMMED VISION AND BROWACHE. SOMETIMES MYDRIASIS MAY OCCUR INSTEAD OF MIOSIS. WITH SUFFICIENT EXPOSURE, OTHER SYMPTOMS OF CHOLINESTERASE INHIBITION AS DESCRIBED IN ACUTE INHALATION MAY OCCUR. **CHRONIC EXPOSURE-** REPEATED OR PROLONGED EXPOSURE MAY CAUSE EFFECTS AS DESCRIBED IN ACUTE EXPOSURE. SOME COMPOUNDS HAVE CAUSED TOXIC EFFECTS ON THE CRYSTALLINE LENS, CONJUNCTIVAL THICKENING AND

OBSTRUCTION OF THE NASOLACRIMAL CANALS WHEN USED AS MIOTIC EYEDROPS.

FIRST AID- WASH EYES IMMEDIATELY WITH LARGE AMOUNTS OF WATER OR NORMAL SALINE, OCCASIONALLY LIFTING UPPER AND LOWER LIDS, UNTIL NO EVIDENCE OF CHEMICAL REMAINS (APPROXIMATELY 15-20 MINUTES). GET MEDICAL ATTENTION IMMEDIATELY.

INGESTION: CYCLO SOL 53: NARCOTIC. **ACUTE EXPOSURE**- INGESTION MAY RESULT IN CENTRAL NERVOUS SYSTEM DEPRESSION WITH GIDDINESS, HEADACHE, DIZZINESS, NAUSEA, AND VOMITING. ASPIRATION OF VOMITUS INTO THE LUNGS MUST BE AVOIDED AS EVEN SMALL QUANTITIES MAY RESULT IN ASPIRATION PNEUMONITIS EVIDENCED BY COUGHING, LABORED BREATHING, AND CYANOSIS. IN SEVERE CASES DEATH MAY OCCUR. **CHRONIC EXPOSURE**- NO DATA AVAILABLE.

XYLENE: NARCOTIC. **ACUTE EXPOSURE**- MAY CAUSE A BURNING SENSATION IN THE MOUTH AND STOMACH, SALIVATION, SEVERE GASTROINTESTINAL DISTRESS WITH NAUSEA AND VOMITING, POSSIBLY HEMATEMESIS, AND TOXIC EFFECTS INCLUDING SIGNS OF CENTRAL NERVOUS SYSTEM DEPRESSION AND OTHER SYMPTOMS AS IN ACUTE INHALATION, INCLUDING VENTRICULAR FIBRILLATION AND LIVER AND KIDNEY INJURY. INGESTION OF SMALL QUANTITIES OF 90% XYLENE PLUS TOLUENE PRODUCED URINARY DEXTROSE AND UROBILINOGEN EXCRETION WITH TOXIC HEPATITIS, WHICH WAS REVERSIBLE IN 20 DAYS. A DOSE OF 15-30 MILLILITERS (ABOUT 1/2-1 OUNCE) IS THE EXPECTED HUMAN LETHAL DOSE. WITH ASPIRATION OF EVEN A FEW MILLILITERS INTO THE LUNGS, SEVERE COUGHING, DISTRESS, CHEMICAL PNEUMONITIS, RAPIDLY DEVELOPING PULMONARY EDEMA, AND HEMORRHAGE MAY OCCUR. **CHRONIC EXPOSURE**- NO DATA AVAILABLE ON THE ORTHO-ISOMER. REPEATED INGESTION OF THE MIXED, META-, OR PARA-ISOMERS BY PREGNANT MICE RESULTED IN EFFECTS ON FERTILITY, ON THE EMBRYO OR FETUS, OR SPECIFIC DEVELOPMENTAL ABNORMALITIES. INCLUDED AMONG THESE EFFECTS WERE FETOTOXICITY, LITTER SIZE, CRANIOFACIAL AND MUSCULOSKELETAL SYSTEM ABNORMALITIES, AND POST-IMPLANTATION MORTALITY.

ETHYL TOLUENES: NARCOTIC. **ACUTE EXPOSURE**- ETHYL TOLUENES ARE BELIEVED TO BE OF A LOW ORDER ORAL TOXICITY. SYSTEMIC EFFECTS ARE SUSPECTED TO BE SIMILAR TO OTHER AROMATICS WITH 9 CARBONS SUCH AS NAUSEA, VOMITING, DIZZINESS, WEAKNESS, EUPHORIA, HEADACHE, TIGHTNESS IN THE CHEST AND STAGGERING. **CHRONIC EXPOSURE**- NO DATA AVAILABLE.

TRIMETHYL BENZENES: NARCOTIC. **ACUTE EXPOSURE**- TRIMETHYL BENZENES MAY CAUSE SORE THROAT, COUGHING, DYSPNEA, NAUSEA AND VOMITING. CENTRAL NERVOUS SYSTEM DEPRESSION WITH HEADACHE, WEAKNESS, DIZZINESS, NARCOSIS, UNCONSCIOUSNESS AND CONVULSIONS MAY OCCUR. **CHRONIC EXPOSURE**- NO DATA AVAILABLE.

AROMATICS: NARCOTIC. **ACUTE EXPOSURE**- THE GASTROINTESTINAL AND SYSTEMIC EFFECTS MAY VARY DEPENDING ON THE SPECIFIC COMPOSITION. THERE MAY BE A BLAND, OILY TASTE; A WARM, SHARP TINGLING, FOLLOWED BY NUMBNESS; OR A PAINFUL, BURNING SENSATION AND PROFUSE SALIVATION. NAUSEA, VOMITING, HEMATEMESIS AND SUBSTERNAL PAIN MAY OCCUR. ABSORPTION OF A SUFFICIENT AMOUNT MAY RESULT IN SYMPTOMS OF CENTRAL NERVOUS SYSTEM DEPRESSION AND OTHER SYSTEMIC AND PATHOLOGICAL EFFECTS AS DESCRIBED IN ACUTE INHALATION. THE GREATER HAZARD MAY BE FROM ASPIRATION WHICH MAY OCCUR DURING INGESTION OR SUBSEQUENT VOMITING. DEPENDING ON CERTAIN PHYSICAL FACTORS, INCLUDING VISCOSITY, ASPIRATION MAY RESULT IN DEATH WITHIN MINUTES DUE TO CARDIAC ARREST, RESPIRATORY PARALYSIS AND ASPHYXIA; IN DELAYED CHEMICAL PNEUMONITIS WITH PULMONARY EDEMA AND HEMORRHAGE; OR, IN THE CASE OF HIGHER MOLECULAR WEIGHT COMPOUNDS, MINIMAL EDEMA AND HEMORRHAGE. **CHRONIC EXPOSURE**- NO DATA AVAILABLE.

METHYL ALCOHOL (METHANOL): NARCOTIC/NEUROTOXIN. **ACUTE EXPOSURE**- MAY CAUSE MILD AND TRANSIENT INEBRIATION AND SUBSEQUENT DROWSINESS FOLLOWED BY AN ASYMPTOMATIC PERIOD LASTING 8-48 HOURS. FOLLOWING THE DELAY, COUGHING, DYSPNEA, HEADACHE, DULLNESS, WEAKNESS, VERTIGO OR DIZZINESS, NAUSEA, VOMITING, OCCASIONAL DIARRHEA, ANOREXIA, VIOLENT PAIN IN THE BACK, ABDOMEN, AND EXTREMITIES, RESTLESSNESS, APATHY OR DELIUIUM, AND RARELY, EXCITEMENT AND MANIA MAY OCCUR. RAPID, SHALLOW RESPIRATION DUE TO METABOLIC ACIDOSIS, COLD AND CLAMMY SKIN, HYPOTENSION, CYANOSIS, OPISTHOTONOS, CONVULSIONS, MILD TACHYCARDIA, CARDIAC DEPRESSION, PERIPHERAL NEURITIS, CEREBRAL AND PULMONARY EDEMA, UNCONSCIOUSNESS, AND COMA ARE POSSIBLE. EFFECTS ON THE EYE MAY INCLUDE OPTIC NEURITIS, BLURRED OR DIMMED VISION, DILATED, UNRESPONSIVE PUPILS, PTOSIS, EYE PAIN, CONCENTRIC CONSTRICTION OF VISUAL FIELDS, DIPLOPIA, CHANGE IN COLOR PERCEPTION, PHOTOPHOBIA, AND OPTIC NERVE ATROPHY. PARTIAL BLINDNESS OR POSSIBLY DELAYED TRANSIENT OR PERMANENT BLINDNESS MAY OCCUR. BILATERAL SENSORINEURAL DEAFNESS HAS BEEN REPORTED IN A SINGLE CASE. LIVER, KIDNEY, HEART, STOMACH, INTESTINAL AND PANCREATIC DAMAGE MAY ALSO OCCUR. DEATH MAY BE DUE TO RESPIRATORY FAILURE OR RARELY FROM CIRCULATORY COLLAPSE. AS LITTLE AS 15 ML HAS CAUSED BLINDNESS; THE USUAL FATAL DOSE IS 60-240 ML. PROLONGED ASTHENIA AND IRREVERSIBLE EFFECTS ON THE NERVOUS SYSTEM INCLUDING DIFFICULTY IN SPEECH, MOTOR DYSFUNCTION WITH RIGIDITY, SPASTICITY, AND HYPOKINESIS HAVE BEEN REPORTED. **CHRONIC EXPOSURE**- REPEATED INGESTION MAY CAUSE VISUAL IMPAIRMENT AND BLINDNESS AND OTHER SYSTEMIC EFFECTS AS DETAILED IN ACUTE INGESTION. REPRODUCTIVE EFFECTS HAVE BEEN REPORTED IN ANIMALS.

ALKYL ARYL SULFONATES: **ACUTE EXPOSURE**- NO DATA AVAILABLE IN THIS SPECIFIC GROUP. HOWVER, INGESTION OF A LARGE DOSE OF ANIONIC SURFANTANTS MAY CAUSE GASTROINTESTINAL IRRITATION, VOMITING, AND DIARRHEA. **CHRONIC EXPOSURE**- NO DATA AVAILABLE.

NONIONIC SURFACTANTS: **ACUTE EXPOSURE**- INGESTION OF A LARGE DOSE MAY CAUSE GASTROINTESTINAL IRRITATION, VOMITING, AND DIARRHEA. **CHRONIC EXPOSURE**- NO DATA AVAILABLE.

DIAZINON: TOXIC. A DOSE OF 63.5 MG/KG FED TO PREGNANT RATS PRODUCED ADVERSE EFFECTS ON FERTILITY. CHRONIC ADMINISTRATION TO PREGNANT RATS RESULTED IN FETAL DEVELOPMENTAL ABNORMALITIES. IN PREGNANT MICE, CHRONIC INGESTION PRODUCED ADVERSE EFFECTS ON FERTILITY AND THE NEWBORN AND FETAL DEVELOPMENTAL ABNORMALITIES. SEE INFORMATION ON ORGANOPHOSPHATES.

ORGANOPHOSPHATES: CHOLINESTERASE INHIBITOR. **ACUTE EXPOSURE**- WHEN INGESTED, THE FIRST EFFECTS MAY BE NAUSEA, VOMITING, ANOREXIA, ABDOMINAL CRAMPS AND DIARRHEA. GASTROINTESTINAL ABSORPTION MAY CAUSE SYMPTOMS OF CHOLINESTERASE INHIBITION AS DESCRIBED IN ACUTE INHALATION. SYMPTOMS MAY BEGIN WITHIN MINUTES OR BE DELAYED FOR HOURS. DELAYED EFFECTS INCLUDING NEUROPATHY MAY ALSO OCCUR. **CHRONIC EXPOSURE**- REPEATED INGESTION MAY CAUSE EFFECTS AS DESCRIBED IN ACUTE EXPOSURE.

FIRST AID- TREAT SYMPTOMATICALLY AND SUPPORTIVELY. GET MEDICAL ATTENTION AND ADVICE ON WHETHER TO USE GASTRIC LAVAGE. EXTREME CARE MUST BE TAKEN TO PREVENT ASPIRATION. A CUFFED ENDOTRACHEAL TUBE USED BY QUALIFIED MEDICAL PERSONNEL MIGHT BE ADVISABLE. KEEP HEAD LOWER THAN HIPS TO PREVENT ASPIRATION SHOULD VOMITING OCCUR.

REACTIVITY

REACTIVITY: STABLE UNDER NORMAL TEMPERATURES AND PRESSURES.

INCOMPATIBILITIES: CYCLO SOL 53: STRONG OXIDIZERS: INCOMPATIBLE.

XYLENE: NITRIC ACID: EXOTHERMIC REACTION. OXIDIZERS (STRONG): FIRE AND EXPLOSION HAZARD. PLASTICS, RUBBER, COATINGS: MAY BE ATTACKED. SULFURIC ACID: EXOTHERMIC REACTION.

ETHYL TOLUENES: NO DATA AVAILABLE.

TRIMETHYL BENZENES: NITRIC ACID: EXPLOSION HAZARD ON HEATING ABOVE 115 C.

AROMATICS: OXIDIZERS (STRONG): FIRE AND EXPLOSION HAZARD.

METHYL ALCOHOL (METHANOL): ACETYL BROMIDE: VIOLENT REACTION WITH FORMATION OF HYDROGEN BROMIDE. ALKYLALUMINUM SOLUTIONS: VIOLENT REACTION. ALUMINUM: EXPLOSION HAZARD. BARIUM PERCHLORATE: DISTILLATION YIELDS HIGHLY EXPLOSIVE ALKYL PERCHLORATE. BERYLLIUM HYDRIDE: VIOLENT REACTION, EVEN AT -196 C. BROMINE: VIGOROUSLY EXOTHERMIC REACTION. CALCIUM CARBIDE: VIOLENT REACTION. CHLORINE: POSSIBLE IGNITION AND EXPLOSION HAZARD. CHLOROFORM AND SODIUM HYDROXIDE: EXPLOSIVE REACTION. CHROMIUM TRIOXIDE (CHROMIC ANHYDRIDE): POSSIBLE IGNITION. CYANURIC CHLORIDE: VIOLENT REACTION. DICHLOROMETHANE: POSSIBLE IGNITION AND EXPLOSION. DIETHYL ZINC: POSSIBLE IGNITION AND EXPLOSION. HYDROGEN PEROXIDE + WATER: EXPLOSION HAZARD. IODINE + ETHANOL + MERCURIC OXIDE: EXPLOSION HAZARD. LEAD: CORRODES. LEAD PERCHLORATE: EXPLOSION HAZARD. MAGNESIUM: VIOLENT REACTION. MAGNESIUM (POWDERED): MIXTURES ARE CAPABLE OF DETONATION. NICKEL: POSSIBLE IGNITION IN THE PRESENCE OF NICKEL CATALYST. NITRIC ACID (CONCENTRATED): MIXTURES OF GREATER THAN 25% ACID MAY DECOMPOSE VIOLENTLY. OXIDIZERS (STRONG): FIRE AND EXPLOSION HAZARD. PERCHLORIC ACID: EXPLOSION HAZARD. PHOSPHOROUS TRIOXIDE: POSSIBLE VIOLENT REACTION AND IGNITION. POTASSIUM: POSSIBLE DANGEROUS REACTION. POTASSIUM HYDROXIDE + CHLOROFORM: EXOTHERMIC REACTION. POTASSIUM TERT-BUTOXIDE: FIRE AND EXPLOSION HAZARD. SODIUM + CHLOROFORM: POSSIBLE EXPLOSION. SODIUM HYPOCHLORITE: EXPLOSION HAZARD. SODIUM METHOXIDE + CHLOROFORM: POSSIBLE EXPLOSION. SULFURIC ACID: FIRE AND EXPLOSION HAZARD. ZINC: EXPLOSION HAZARD.

ALKYL ARLY SULFONATES: NO DATA AVAILABLE.

NONIONIC SURFACTANTS: NO DATA AVAILABLE.

DIAZINON: WATER: HYDROLYZE SLOWLY. ACIDS: HYDROLYZE SLOWLY. STRONG ALKALIES: HYDROLYZE.

DECOMPOSITION: THERMAL DECOMPOSITION MAY RELEASE TOXIC AND/OR HAZARDOUS GASES.

POLYMERIZATION: HAZARDOUS POLYMERIZATION HAS NOT BEEN REPORTED TO OCCUR UNDER NORMAL TEMPERATURES AND PRESSURES.

STORAGE AND DISPOSAL

OBSERVE ALL FEDERAL, STATE AND LOCAL REGULATIONS WHEN STORING OR DISPOSING OF THIS SUBSTANCE. FOR ASSISTANCE, CONTACT THE DISTRICT DIRECTOR OF THE ENVIRONMENTAL PROTECTION AGENCY.

STORAGE

STORE IN ACCORDANCE WITH 29 CFR 1910.106.
STORE IN ACCORDANCE WITH 40 CFR 165 RECOMMENDED PROCEDURES FOR THE DISPOSAL AND STORAGE OF PESTICIDES AND PESTICIDE CONTAINERS.
BONDING AND GROUNDING: SUBSTANCES WITH LOW ELECTROCONDUCTIVITY, WHICH MAY BE IGNITED BY ELECTROSTATIC SPARKS, SHOULD BE STORED IN CONTAINERS WHICH MEET THE BONDING AND GROUNDING GUIDELINES SPECIFIED IN NFPA 77-1983, RECOMMENDED PRACTICE ON STATIC ELECTRICITY.
STORE AWAY FROM INCOMPATIBLE SUBSTANCES.

DISPOSAL

DISPOSAL MUST BE IN ACCORDANCE WITH STANDARDS APPLICABLE TO GENERATORS OF HAZARDOUS WASTE, 40 CFR 262. EPA HAZARDOUS WASTE NUMBER D001. 100 POUND CERCLA SECTION 103 REPORTABLE QUANTITY.
DISPOSAL MUST BE IN ACCORDANCE WITH 40 CFR 165 RECOMMENDED PROCEDURES FOR THE DISPOSAL AND STORAGE OF PESTICIDES AND PESTICIDE CONTAINERS.

CONDITIONS TO AVOID

AVOID CONTACT WITH HEAT, SPARKS, FLAMES, OR OTHER SOURCES OF IGNITION. VAPORS MAY BE EXPLOSIVE. AVOID OVERHEATING OF CONTAINERS; CONTAINERS MAY VIOLENTLY RUPTURE IN HEAT OF FIRE. AVOID CONTAMINATION OF WATER SOURCES.

SPILL AND LEAK PROCEDURES

OCCUPATIONAL SPILL: SHUT OFF IGNITION SOURCES. STOP LEAK IF YOU CAN DO IT WITHOUT RISK. USE WATER SPRAY TO REDUCE VAPORS. FOR SMALL SPILLS, TAKE UP WITH SAND OR OTHER ABSORBENT MATERIAL AND PLACE INTO CONTAINERS FOR LATER DISPOSAL. FOR LARGER SPILLS, DIKE FAR AHEAD OF SPILL FOR LATER DISPOSAL. NO SMOKING, FLAMES OR FLARES IN HAZARD AREA. KEEP UNNECESSARY PEOPLE AWAY; ISOLATE HAZARD AREA AND RESTRICT ENTRY.

PROTECTIVE EQUIPMENT

VENTILATION: PROVIDE LOCAL EXHAUST OR PROCESS ENCLOSURE VENTILATION TO MEET PUBLISHED EXPOSURE LIMITS.

RESPIRATOR: THE FOLLOWING RESPIRATORS ARE RECOMMENDED BASED ON INFORMATION FOUND IN THE PHYSICAL DATA, TOXICITY AND HEALTH EFFECTS SECTIONS. THEY ARE RANKED IN ORDER FROM MINIMUM TO MAXIMUM RESPIRATORY PROTECTION. THE SPECIFIC RESPIRATOR SELECTED MUST BE BASED ON CONTAMINATION LEVELS FOUND IN THE WORK PLACE, MUST NOT EXCEED THE WORKING LIMITS OF THE RESPIRATOR AND BE JOINTLY APPROVED BY THE NATIONAL INSTITUTE FOR OCCUPATIONAL SAFETY AND HEALTH AND THE MINE SAFETY AND HEALTH ADMINISTRATION (NIOSH-MSHA).
CHEMICAL CARTRIDGE RESPIRATOR WITH AN ORGANIC VAPOR CARTRIDGE(S) WITH AN ACID GAS CARTRIDGE(S) AND A FULL FACEPIECE.
GAS MASK WITH ORGANIC VAPOR CANISTER (CHIN-STYLE OR FRONT- OR BACK-MOUNTED CANISTER), WITH A FULL FACEPIECE, PROVIDING PROTECTION AGAINST ACID GASES.
TYPE 'C' SUPPLIED-AIR RESPIRATOR WITH A FULL FACEPIECE OPERATED IN PRESSURE-DEMAND OR OTHER POSITIVE PRESSURE MODE OR WITH A FULL FACEPIECE, HELMET OR HOOD OPERATED IN CONTINUOUS-FLOW MODE.
SELF-CONTAINED BREATHING APPARATUS WITH A FULL FACEPIECE OPERATED IN PRESSURE-DEMAND OR OTHER POSITIVE PRESSURE MODE.
FOR FIREFIGHTING AND OTHER IMMEDIATELY DANGEROUS TO LIFE OR HEALTH CONDITIONS:
SELF-CONTAINED BREATHING APPARATUS WITH FULL FACEPIECE OPERATED IN PRESSURE-DEMAND OR OTHER POSITIVE PRESSURE MODE.
SUPPLIED-AIR RESPIRATOR WITH FULL FACEPIECE AND OPERATED IN PRESSURE-DEMAND OR OTHER POSITIVE PRESSURE MODE IN COMBINATION WITH AN AUXILIARY SELF-CONTAINED BREATHING APPARATUS OPERATED IN PRESSURE-DEMAND OR OTHER POSITIVE PRESSURE MODE.

CLOTHING: EMPLOYEE MUST WEAR APPROPRIATE PROTECTIVE (IMPERVIOUS) CLOTHING AND EQUIPMENT TO PREVENT REPEATED OR PROLONGED SKIN CONTACT WITH THIS SUBSTANCE.

GLOVES: EMPLOYEE MUST WEAR APPROPRIATE PROTECTIVE GLOVES TO PREVENT CONTACT WITH THIS SUBSTANCE.

EYE PROTECTION: EMPLOYEE MUST WEAR SPLASH-PROOF OR DUST-RESISTANT SAFETY GOGGLES TO PREVENT EYE CONTACT WITH THIS SUBSTANCE.
EMERGENCY EYE WASH: WHERE THERE IS ANY POSSIBILITY THAT AN EMPLOYEE'S EYES MAY BE EXPOSED TO THIS SUBSTANCE, THE EMPLOYER SHOULD PROVIDE AN EYE WASH FOUNTAIN WITHIN THE IMMEDIATE WORK AREA FOR EMERGENCY USE.

AUTHORIZED BY- OCCUPATIONAL HEALTH SERVICES, INC.
CREATION DATE: 10/05/89 ***REVISION DATE:*** 05/15/90

MATERIAL SAFETY DATA SHEET

OCCUPATIONAL HEALTH SERVICES, INC.
AGRICULTURE AND PESTICIDE DIVISION
450 SEVENTH AVENUE, SUITE 2407
NEW YORK, NEW YORK 10123
1-800-445-MSDS OR (212) 967-1100

EMERGENCY CONTACT:
JOHN S. BRANSFORD, JR. (615) 292-1180

SUBSTANCE IDENTIFICATION

SUBSTANCE: **21 NAMFUME 05001667**
TRADE NAMES/SYNONYMS: 21 PINTOFUME 05623736; UN 1062; PST75470
CERCLA RATINGS (SCALE 0-3): HEALTH=3 FIRE=1 REACTIVITY=1 PERSISTENCE=3
NFPA RATINGS (SCALE 0-4): HEALTH=4 FIRE=1 REACTIVITY=1

COMPONENTS AND CONTAMINANTS

COMPONENT: METHYL BROMIDE ***PERCENT:*** 98-99
CAS# 74-83-9
COMPONENT: CHLOROPICRIN 200 LB ***PERCENT:*** 0.5-2.0
CAS# 76-06-2
OTHER CONTAMINANTS: NONE
EXPOSURE LIMITS: METHYL BROMIDE: 5 PPM (20 MG/M3) OSHA TWA (SKIN) 5 PPM (20 MG/M3) ACGIH TWA (SKIN) LOWEST FEASIBLE LIMIT NIOSH RECOMMENDED EXPOSURE CRITERIA
1000 POUNDS SARA SECTION 302 THRESHOLD PLANNING QUANTITY 1000 POUNDS SARA SECTION 304 REPORTABLE QUANTITY 1000 POUNDS CERCLA SECTION 103 REPORTABLE QUANTITY SUBJECT TO SARA SECTION 313 ANNUAL TOXIC CHEMICAL RELEASE REPORTING

PHYSICAL DATA

DESCRIPTION: COLORLESS LIQUID WITH A STRONG IRRITATING TEAR-GAS ODOR
BOILING POINT: NOT AVAILABLE ***SPECIFIC GRAVITY:*** 1.66
EVAPORATION RATE: NOT AVAILABLE ***SOLUBILITY IN WATER:*** SLIGHT
VAPOR DENSITY: >3

FIRE AND EXPLOSION DATA

FIRE AND EXPLOSION HAZARD: SLIGHT FIRE HAZARD WHEN EXPOSED TO HEAT OR FLAME.

FIREFIGHTING MEDIA: DRY CHEMICAL, CARBON DIOXIDE, HALON, WATER SPRAY OR STANDARD FOAM (1987 EMERGENCY RESPONSE GUIDEBOOK, DOT P 5800.4).
FOR LARGER FIRES, USE WATER SPRAY, FOG OR STANDARD FOAM (1987 EMERGENCY RESPONSE GUIDEBOOK, DOT P 5800.4).

FIREFIGHTING: MOVE CONTAINERS FROM FIRE AREA IF POSSIBLE. FIGHT FIRE FROM MAXIMUM DISTANCE. STAY AWAY FROM STORAGE TANK ENDS. DIKE FIRE CONTROL WATER FOR LATER DISPOSAL. DO NOT SCATTER MATERIAL (1987 EMERGENCY RESPONSE GUIDEBOOK, DOT P 5800.4, GUIDE PAGE 55).
USE AGENTS SUITABLE FOR TYPE OF FIRE. USE WATER IN FLOODING AMOUNTS AS FOG. COOL CONTAINERS WITH FLOODING AMOUNTS OF WATER, APPLY FROM AS FAR A DISTANCE AS POSSIBLE. AVOID BREATHING POISONOUS VAPORS, KEEP UPWIND. CONSIDER EVACUATION OF DOWNWIND AREA IF MATERIAL IS LEAKING.

TRANSPORTATION DATA

DEPARTMENT OF TRANSPORTATION HAZARD CLASSIFICATION 49 CFR 172.101: POISON B
DEPARTMENT OF TRANSPORTATION LABELING REQUIREMENTS 49 CFR 172.101 AND SUBPART E: POISON
DEPARTMENT OF TRANSPORTATION PACKAGING REQUIREMENTS: 49 CFR 173.353 EXCEPTIONS: NONE

TOXICITY

METHYL BROMIDE: TOXICITY DATA: 1 GM/M3/2 HOURS INHALATION-CHILD LCLO; 35 PPM INHALATION-HUMAN TCLO; 60,000 PPM/2 HOURS INHALATION-MAN LCLO; 302 PPM/8 HOURS INHALATION-RAT LC50; 1540 MG/M3/2 HOURS INHALATION-MOUSE LCLO; 28,900 MG/M3/30 MINUTES INHALATION-RABBIT LC50; 300 PPM/9 HOURS INHALATION-GUINEA PIG LCLO; 35 GM/M3/40 MINUTES INTERMITTENT SKIN-HUMAN TDLO; 214 MG/KG ORAL-RAT LD50; 135 MG/KG SUBCUTANEOUS-RAT LD50; MUTAGENIC DATA (RTECS); TUMORIGENIC DATA (RTECS). CARCINOGEN

STATUS: ANIMAL LIMITED EVIDENCE (IARC GROUP-3). IN ONE 90 DAY STUDY BY ORAL ADMINISTRATION IN RATS, METHYL BROMIDE WAS REPORTED TO PRODUCE SQUAMOUS-CELL CARCINOMAS OF THE FORESTOMACH. LOCAL EFFECTS: IRRITANT- SKIN, EYE. ACUTE TOXICITY LEVEL: TOXIC BY INHALATION AND INGESTION. TARGET EFFECTS: CENTRAL NERVOUS SYSTEM DEPRESSANT. POISONING MAY AFFECT THE BRAIN, KIDNEYS, AND LIVER. ADDITIONAL INFORMATION: STIMULANTS SUCH AS EPINEPHINE MAY INDUCE VENTRICULAR FIBRILLATION.*

* BASED ON GENERAL INFORMATION ON HALOGENATED ALKANES.

CHLOROPICRIN: TOXICITY DATA: 2 MG/M3 INHALATION-HUMAN TCLO; 2000 MG/M3/10 MINUTES INHALATION-HUMAN LCLO; 66 MG/M3/4 HOURS INHALATION-MOUSE LC50; 800 MG/M3/20 MINUTES INHALATION-CAT LCLO; 800 MG/M3/20 MINUTES INHALATION-RABBIT LC50; 800 MG/M3/20 MINUTES INHALATION-GUINEA PIG LCLO; 250 MG/KG ORAL-RAT LD50; 4200 UG/KG INTRAVENOUS-GUINEA PIG LD50; 25 MG/KG INTRAPERITONEAL-MOUSE LD50; MUTAGENIC DATA (RTECS); TUMORIGENIC DATA (RTECS). CARCINOGEN STATUS: NONE. LOCAL EFFECTS: CORROSIVE- INHALATION, SKIN, AND EYES; LACRIMATOR. ACUTE TOXICITY LEVEL: HIGHLY TOXIC BY INHALATION; TOXIC BY INGESTION. TARGET EFFECTS: METHEMOGLOBIN FORMER. POISONING MAY AFFECT THE RESPIRATORY AND CARDIOVASCULAR SYSTEMS.

HEALTH EFFECTS AND FIRST AID

INHALATION: METHYL BROMIDE: NARCOTIC/TOXIC. **ACUTE EXPOSURE-** SYMPTOMS MAY BE DELAYED FROM 1-12 HOURS AFTER EXPOSURE TO HIGH CONCENTRATIONS; LOWER CONCENTRATIONS RESULT IN LESS SEVERE SYMPTOMS WITH A LATENT PERIOD OF 12 TO 24 HOURS. REPORTED EFFECTS INCLUDE HEADACHE, VISUAL DISTURBANCES, NAUSEA, VOMITING, ANOREXIA, ABDOMINAL PAIN, WEAKNESS, MALAISE, VERTIGO, PARESTHESIAS AND PARALYSIS OF THE EXTREMITIES, OLIGURIA OR ANURIA, DROWSINESS, CONFUSION, HYPERACTIVITY, HYPOTENSION, MANIA, HALLUCINATIONS, TREMORS OR TWITCHING, ATAXIA, AND CONVULSIONS. HIGH CONCENTRATIONS MAY CAUSE RAPID NARCOSIS AND DEATH FROM RESPIRATORY FAILURE. LESSER CONCENTRATIONS MAY CAUSE PULMONARY IRRITATION, COUGHING, CHEST PAIN, SHORTNESS OF BREATH, CONGESTION, EDEMA, AND DEVELOPMENT OF BRONCHITIS OR PNEUMONITIS. JAUNDICE AND CYANOSIS MAY ALSO RESULT. UNCONSCIOUSNESS, COMA, AND DEATH DUE TO RESPIRATORY OR CIRCULATORY COLLAPSE MAY OCCUR. TUBULAR DAMAGE IN THE KIDNEYS HAS BEEN OBSERVED IN FATAL CASES. SURVIVING INDIVIDUALS MAY HAVE PERSISTENT CENTRAL AND PERIPHERAL NERVOUS SYSTEM EFFECTS INCLUDING VERTIGO, DEPRESSION, HALLUCINATIONS, ANMESIA, ANXIETY, INABILITY TO CONCENTRATE, SENSORY DISTURBANCES, WEAKNESS, AND IRRITABILITY. **CHRONIC EXPOSURE-** REPEATED EXPOSURE MAY RESULT IN ADVERSE CENTRAL NERVOUS SYSTEM EFFECTS INCLUDING LETHARGY, MUSCULAR PAINS, VISUAL, SPEECH, AND SENSORY DISTURBANCES, MENTAL CONFUSION, BLURRED VISION, PAPILLEDEMA, HALLUCINATIONS, SOMNOLENCE, FAINTING ATTACKS, BRONCHOSPASMS, AND CENTRAL NERVOUS SYSTEM EDEMA. PERIPHERAL NEUROPATHY MAY BE INDICATED BY PARALYSIS OF THE EXTREMITIES, MYOCLONUS, POLYNEURITIS, AND CONVULSIONS. LIVER, KIDNEY AND PERMANENT BRAIN DAMAGE MAY OCCUR.

CHLOROPICRIN: CORROSIVE/METHEMOGLOBIN FORMER/HIGHLY TOXIC. 4 PPM IMMEDIATELY DANGEROUS TO LIFE OR HEALTH. **ACUTE EXPOSURE-** MAY CAUSE IRRITATION, SORE THROAT, COUGHING, LABORED BREATHING, DIZZINESS, NAUSEA, VOMITING, CYANOSIS, FAINTNESS, AND PULMONARY EDEMA. LOW METHEMOGLOBIN LEVELS MAY RESULT IN HEADACHE, WEAKNESS, AND DYSPNEA. HIGH METHEMOGLOBIN LEVELS MAY RESULT IN STUPOR, RESPIRATORY DEPRESSION, AND CHOCOLATE COLORED BLOOD FROM LACK OF OXYGENATION. **CHRONIC EXPOSURE-** PROLONGED AND REPEATED EXPOSURE MAY CAUSE HEART AND LUNG DAMAGE AND PULMONARY EDEMA WITH POSSIBLE COMA AND DEATH.

FIRST AID- REMOVE FROM EXPOSURE AREA TO FRESH AIR IMMEDIATELY. IF BREATHING HAS STOPPED, GIVE ARTIFICIAL RESPIRATION. MAINTAIN AIRWAY AND BLOOD PRESSURE AND ADMINISTER OXYGEN IF AVAILABLE. KEEP AFFECTED PERSON WARM AND AT REST. TREAT SYMPTOMATICALLY AND SUPPORTIVELY. ADMINISTRATION OF OXYGEN SHOULD BE PERFORMED BY QUALIFIED PERSONNEL. GET MEDICAL ATTENTION IMMEDIATELY.

SKIN CONTACT: METHYL BROMIDE: IRRITANT. **ACUTE EXPOSURE-** CONTACT WITH THE LIQUID MAY CAUSE IRRITATION, ERYTHEMA, EDEMA, SCALING, AND ITCHING DERMATITIS. THE LIQUID MAY BE ABSORBED THROUGH INTACT SKIN. **CHRONIC EXPOSURE-** REPEATED OR PROLONGED EXPOSURE MAY LEAD TO VESICULATION AND POSSIBLE DEEP BURNS.

CHLOROPICRIN: CORROSIVE/METHEMOGLOBIN FORMER. **ACUTE EXPOSURE-** MAY CAUSE IRRITATION, REDNESS, PAIN AND SKIN BURNS. IT IS ABSORBED THROUGH THE SKIN AND MAY RESULT IN METHEMOGLOBINEMIA. LOW METHEMOGLOBIN LEVELS MAY RESULT IN HEADACHE, WEAKNESS, AND DYSPNEA. HIGH METHEMOGLOBIN LEVELS MAY RESULT IN STUPOR, RESPIRATORY DEPRESSION, AND CHOCOLATE COLORED BLOOD FROM LACK OF OXYGENATION. **CHRONIC EXPOSURE-** PROLONGED AND REPEATED EXPOSURE MAY CAUSE DERMATITIS AND SKIN BURNS.

FIRST AID- REMOVE CONTAMINATED CLOTHING AND SHOES IMMEDIATELY. WASH AFFECTED AREA WITH SOAP OR MILD DETERGENT AND LARGE AMOUNTS OF WATER UNTIL NO EVIDENCE OF CHEMICAL REMAINS (AT LEAST 15-20 MINUTES). IN CASE OF CHEMICAL BURNS, COVER AREA WITH STERILE, DRY DRESSING. BANDAGE SECURELY, BUT NOT TOO TIGHTLY. GET MEDICAL ATTENTION IMMEDIATELY.

EYE CONTACT: METHYL BROMIDE: **ACUTE EXPOSURE-** VAPORS AND LIQUID MAY CAUSE TRANSIENT IRRITATION AND CONJUNCTIVITIS. RABBITS EXPOSED TO CONCENTRATED VAPORS FOR 1 MINUTE 30 SECONDS RESULTED IN LOSS OF EYE SURFACE LUSTER, LOSS OF CORNEAL EPITHELIUM, EDEMA OF THE CONJUNCTIVAE AND LIDS, AND TRANSIENT CORNEAL OPACITY. **CHRONIC EXPOSURE-** REPEATED OR PROLONGED EXPOSURE MAY CAUSE CONJUNCTIVITIS.

CHLOROPICRIN: CORROSIVE/LACRIMATOR. **ACUTE EXPOSURE-** MAY CAUSE IRRITATION, REDNESS, PAIN, LACRIMATION, BLURRED VISION AND CORNEAL DAMAGE. **CHRONIC EXPOSURE-** MAY CAUSE CORNEAL DAMAGE AND CONJUNCTIVITIS.

FIRST AID- WASH EYES IMMEDIATELY WITH LARGE AMOUNTS OF WATER, OCCASIONALLY LIFTING UPPER AND LOWER LIDS, UNTIL NO EVIDENCE OF CHEMICAL REMAINS (AT LEAST 15-20 MINUTES). CONTINUE IRRIGATING WITH NORMAL SALINE UNTIL THE PH HAS RETURNED TO NORMAL (30-60 MINUTES). COVER WITH STERILE BANDAGES. GET MEDICAL ATTENTION IMMEDIATELY.

INGESTION: METHYL BROMIDE: TOXIC/LIMITED ANIMAL CARCINOGEN. **ACUTE EXPOSURE-** INGESTION OF LIQUID MAY RESULT IN SYSTEMIC TOXICITY AS DETAILED IN ACUTE INHALATION. THE LETHAL DOSE REPORTED IN RATS WAS 214 MG/KG. THE SYMPTOMS WERE NOT REPORTED. **CHRONIC EXPOSURE-** DEGENERATION OF PERIPHERAL NERVES AND THE DORSAL COLUMNS OF THE SPINAL CORD HAS BEEN REPORTED IN RATS FED DIETS WITH METHYL BROMIDE. REPEATED ADMINISTRATION TO RATS BY ORAL GAVAGE INDUCED TUMORS OF THE FORESTOMACH.

CHLOROPICRIN: CORROSIVE/METHEMOGLOBIN FORMER/TOXIC. **ACUTE EXPOSURE-** MAY CAUSE IRRITATION, SORE THROAT, COUGHING, LABORED BREATHING, DIZZINESS, NAUSEA, VOMITING, CYANOSIS, AND FAINTNESS. INGESTION OF LIQUID CAN CAUSE SEVERE GASTROENTERITIS. LOW METHEMOGLOBIN LEVELS MAY RESULT IN HEADACHE, WEAKNESS, AND DYSPNEA. HIGH METHEMOGLOBIN LEVELS MAY RESULT IN STUPOR, RESPIRATORY DEPRESSION, AND CHOCOLATE COLORED BLOOD FROM LACK OF OXYGENATION. **CHRONIC EXPOSURE-** MAY CAUSE HEART AND LUNG DAMAGE.

FIRST AID- TREAT SYMPTOMATICALLY AND SUPPORTIVELY. GET MEDICAL ATTENTION IMMEDIATELY. IF VOMITING OCCURS, KEEP HEAD LOWER THAN HIPS TO PREVENT ASPIRATION.

REACTIVITY

REACTIVITY: CHLOROPICRIN: BULK CONTAINERS CAN BE SHOCK DETONATED.

INCOMPATIBILITIES: METHYL BROMIDE: ALUMINUM: SEVERE EXPLOSION HAZARD. MAGNESIUM: SEVERE EXPLOSION HAZARD. ZINC: SEVERE EXPLOSION HAZARD. DIMETHYL SULFOXIDE: DELAYED EXPLOSION HAZARD. STRONG OXIDIZERS: VIGOROUS REACTION. ETHYLENE OXIDE: VIGOROUS REACTION.

CHLOROPICRIN: ANILINE: VIOLENT REACTION. BROMO-2-PROPYNE: EXPLOSIVE, SHOCK- AND HEAT- SENSITIVE. SODIUM HYDROXIDE: REACTS VIOLENTLY SODIUM METHOXIDE: BELOW 50 C, NITRO COMPOUND WILL ACCUMULATE AND CAUSE A VIOLENT AND DANGEROUS EXOTHERMIC REACTION. STRONG OXIDIZERS: POSSIBLE VIOLENT REACTION.

DECOMPOSITION: THERMAL DECOMPOSITION MAY RELEASE TOXIC AND/OR HAZARDOUS GASES.

POLYMERIZATION: HAZARDOUS POLYMERIZATION HAS NOT BEEN REPORTED TO OCCUR UNDER NORMAL TEMPERATURES AND PRESSURES.

CONDITIONS TO AVOID

MAY BURN BUT DOES NOT IGNITE READILY. CONTAINERS MAY EXPLODE IN HEAT OF FIRE.

SPILL AND LEAK PROCEDURES

OCCUPATIONAL SPILL: DO NOT TOUCH SPILLED MATERIAL. STOP LEAK IF YOU CAN DO IT WITHOUT RISK. USE WATER SPRAY TO REDUCE VAPORS. FOR SMALL SPILLS, TAKE UP WITH SAND OR OTHER ABSORBENT MATERIAL AND PLACE INTO CONTAINERS FOR LATER DISPOSAL. FOR SMALL DRY SPILLS, WITH A CLEAN SHOVEL PLACE MATERIAL INTO CLEAN, DRY CONTAINERS AND COVER. MOVE CONTAINERS FROM SPILL AREA. FOR LARGER SPILLS, DIKE FAR AHEAD OF SPILL FOR LATER DISPOSAL. KEEP UNNECESSARY PEOPLE AWAY. ISOLATE HAZARD AREA AND DENY ENTRY. VENTILATE CLOSED SPACES BEFORE ENTERING.

PROTECTIVE EQUIPMENT

VENTILATION: PROCESS ENCLOSURE RECOMMENDED TO MEET PUBLISHED EXPOSURE LIMITS.

RESPIRATOR: THE FOLLOWING RESPIRATORS ARE RECOMMENDED BASED ON INFORMATION FOUND IN THE PHYSICAL DATA, TOXICITY AND HEALTH EFFECTS SECTIONS. THEY ARE RANKED IN ORDER FROM MINIMUM TO MAXIMUM RESPIRATORY PROTECTION. THE SPECIFIC RESPIRATOR SELECTED MUST BE BASED ON CONTAMINATION LEVELS FOUND IN THE WORK PLACE, MUST NOT EXCEED THE WORKING LIMITS OF THE RESPIRATOR AND BE JOINTLY APPROVED BY THE NATIONAL INSTITUTE FOR OCCUPATIONAL SAFETY AND HEALTH AND THE MINE SAFETY AND HEALTH ADMINISTRATION (NIOSH-MSHA).

TYPE 'C' SUPPLIED-AIR RESPIRATOR WITH A FULL FACEPIECE OPERATED IN PRESSURE-DEMAND OR OTHER POSITIVE PRESSURE MODE OR WITH A FULL FACEPIECE, HELMET OR HOOD OPERATED IN CONTINOUS-FLOW MODE.

SELF-CONTAINED BREATHING APPARATUS WITH A FULL FACEPIECE OPERATED IN PRESSURE-DEMAND OR OTHER POSITIVE PRESSURE MODE.

FOR FIREFIGHTING AND OTHER IMMEDIATELY DANGEROUS TO LIFE OR HEALTH CONDITIONS:

SELF-CONTAINED BREATHING APPARATUS WITH FULL FACEPIECE OPERATED IN PRESSURE-DEMAND OR OTHER POSITIVE PRESSURE MODE.

SUPPLIED-AIR RESPIRATOR WITH FULL FACEPIECE AND OPERATED IN PRESSURE-DEMAND OR OTHER POSITIVE PRESSURE MODE IN COMBINATION WITH AN AUXILIARY SELF-CONTAINED BREATHING APPARATUS OPERATED IN PRESSURE-DEMAND OR OTHER POSITIVE PRESSURE MODE.

CLOTHING: EMPLOYEE MUST WEAR APPROPRIATE PROTECTIVE (IMPERVIOUS) CLOTHING AND EQUIPMENT TO PREVENT ANY POSSIBILITY OF SKIN CONTACT WITH THIS SUBSTANCE.

GLOVES: EMPLOYEE MUST WEAR APPROPRIATE PROTECTIVE GLOVES TO PREVENT CONTACT WITH THIS SUBSTANCE.

EYE PROTECTION: EMPLOYEE MUST WEAR SPLASH-PROOF OR DUST-RESISTANT SAFETY GOGGLES AND A FACESHIELD TO PREVENT CONTACT WITH THIS SUBSTANCE.

EMERGENCY WASH FACILITIES: WHERE THERE IS ANY POSSIBILITY THAT AN EMPLOYEE'S EYES AND/OR SKIN MAY BE EXPOSED TO THIS SUBSTANCE, THE EMPLOYER SHOULD PROVIDE AN EYE WASH FOUNTAIN AND QUICK DRENCH SHOWER WITHIN THE IMMEDIATE WORK AREA FOR EMERGENCY USE.

AUTHORIZED BY- OCCUPATIONAL HEALTH SERVICES, INC.

CREATION DATE: 10/05/89 ***REVISION DATE:*** 07/13/90

MATERIAL SAFETY DATA SHEET

OCCUPATIONAL HEALTH SERVICES, INC.
AGRICULTURE AND PESTICIDE DIVISION
450 SEVENTH AVENUE, SUITE 2407
NEW YORK, NEW YORK 10123
1-800-445-MSDS OR (212) 967-1100

EMERGENCY CONTACT:
JOHN S. BRANSFORD, JR. (615) 292-1180

SUBSTANCE IDENTIFICATION

SUBSTANCE: 21 PATHOFUME 75-25 50 LB CYL 05131200

TRADE NAMES/SYNONYMS: 21 PATHOFUME B 67-33 05360954; 21 PATHOFUME 57-43 05224650; NA 1581; PST75471

CERCLA RATINGS (SCALE 0-3): HEALTH = 3 FIRE = 1 REACTIVITY = 1 PERSISTENCE = 3

NFPA RATINGS (SCALE 0-4): HEALTH = 4 FIRE = 1 REACTIVITY = 1

COMPONENTS AND CONTAMINANTS

COMPONENT: METHYL BROMIDE ***PERCENT:*** 57.0-75.0
CAS# 74-83-9

COMPONENT: CHLOROPICRIN 200 LB ***PERCENT:*** 25.0-43.0
CAS# 76-06-2

OTHER CONTAMINANTS: NONE

EXPOSURE LIMITS: METHYL BROMIDE: 5 PPM (20 MG/M3) OSHA TWA (SKIN) 5 PPM (20 MG/M3) ACGIH TWA (SKIN) LOWEST FEASIBLE LIMIT NIOSH RECOMMENDED EXPOSURE CRITERIA

1000 POUNDS SARA SECTION 302 THRESHOLD PLANNING QUANTITY 1000 POUNDS SARA SECTION 304 REPORTABLE QUANTITY 1000 POUNDS CERCLA SECTION 103 REPORTABLE QUANTITY SUBJECT TO SARA SECTION 313 ANNUAL TOXIC CHEMICAL RELEASE REPORTING

PHYSICAL DATA

DESCRIPTION: COLORLESS LIQUID WITH A STRONG IRRITATING TEAR-GAS ODOR

BOILING POINT: NOT AVAILABLE ***SPECIFIC GRAVITY:*** 1.66

EVAPORATION RATE: NOT AVAILABLE ***SOLUBILITY IN WATER:*** SLIGHT

VAPOR DENSITY: > 3

FIRE AND EXPLOSION DATA

FIRE AND EXPLOSION HAZARD: SLIGHT FIRE HAZARD WHEN EXPOSED TO HEAT OR FLAME.

FIREFIGHTING MEDIA: DRY CHEMICAL, CARBON DIOXIDE, HALON, WATER SPRAY OR STANDARD FOAM (1987 EMERGENCY RESPONSE GUIDEBOOK, DOT P 5800.4). FOR LARGER FIRES, USE WATER SPRAY, FOG OR STANDARD FOAM (1987 EMERGENCY RESPONSE GUIDEBOOK, DOT P 5800.4).

FIREFIGHTING: MOVE CONTAINERS FROM FIRE AREA IF POSSIBLE. FIGHT FIRE FROM MAXIMUM DISTANCE. STAY AWAY FROM STORAGE TANK ENDS. DIKE FIRE CONTROL WATER FOR LATER DISPOSAL. DO NOT SCATTER MATERIAL (1987 EMERGENCY RESPONSE GUIDEBOOK, DOT P 5800.4, GUIDE PAGE 55).

USE AGENTS SUITABLE FOR TYPE OF FIRE. USE WATER IN FLOODING AMOUNTS AS FOG. COOL CONTAINERS WITH FLOODING AMOUNTS OF WATER, APPLY FROM AS FAR A DISTANCE AS POSSIBLE. AVOID BREATHING POISONOUS VAPORS, KEEP UPWIND. CONSIDER EVACUATION OF DOWNWIND AREA IF MATERIAL IS LEAKING.

TRANSPORTATION DATA

DEPARTMENT OF TRANSPORTATION HAZARD CLASSIFICATION 49 CFR 172.101: POISON B

DEPARTMENT OF TRANSPORTATION LABELING REQUIREMENTS 49 CFR 172.101 AND SUBPART E: POISON

DEPARTMENT OF TRANSPORTATION PACKAGING REQUIREMENTS: 49 CFR 173.353 EXCEPTIONS: NONE

TOXICITY

METHYL BROMIDE: TOXICITY DATA: 1 GM/M3/2 HOURS INHALATION-CHILD LCLO; 35 PPM INHALATION-HUMAN TCLO; 60,000 PPM/2 HOURS INHALATION-MAN LCLO; 302 PPM/8 HOURS INHALATION-RAT LC50; 1540 MG/M3/2 HOURS INHALATION-MOUSE LCLO; 28,900 MG/M3/30 MINUTES INHALATION-RABBIT LC50; 300 PPM/9 HOURS INHALATION-GUINEA PIG LCLO; 35 GM/M3/40 MINUTES INTERMITTENT SKIN-HUMAN TDLO; 214 MG/KG ORAL-RAT LD50; 135 MG/KG SUBCUTANEOUS-RAT LD50; MUTAGENIC DATA (RTECS); TUMORIGENIC DATA (RTECS). CARCINOGEN STATUS: ANIMAL LIMITED EVIDENCE (IARC GROUP-3). IN ONE 90 DAY STUDY BY ORAL ADMINISTRATION IN RATS, METHYL BROMIDE WAS REPORTED TO PRODUCE SQUAMOUS-CELL CARCINOMAS OF THE FORESTOMACH. LOCAL EFFECTS: IRRITANT- SKIN, EYE. ACUTE TOXICITY LEVEL: TOXIC BY INHALATION AND INGESTION. TARGET EFFECTS: CENTRAL NERVOUS SYSTEM DEPRESSANT. POISONING MAY AFFECT THE BRAIN, KIDNEYS, AND LIVER. ADDITIONAL INFORMATION: STIMULANTS SUCH AS EPINEPHINE MAY INDUCE VENTRICULAR FIBRILLATION.*

* BASED ON GENERAL INFORMATION ON HALOGENATED ALKANES.

CHLOROPICRIN: TOXICITY DATA: 2 MG/M3 INHALATION-HUMAN TCLO; 2000 MG/M3/10 MINUTES INHALATION-HUMAN LCLO; 66 MG/M3/4 HOURS INHALATION-MOUSE LC50; 800 MG/M3/20 MINUTES INHALATION-CAT LCLO; 800 MG/M3/20 MINUTES INHALATION-RABBIT LC50; 800 MG/M3/20 MINUTES INHALATION-GUINEA PIG LCLO; 250 MG/KG ORAL-RAT LD50; 4200 UG/KG INTRAVENOUS-GUINEA PIG LD50; 25 MG/KG INTRAPERITONEAL-MOUSE LD50; MUTAGENIC DATA (RTECS); TUMORIGENIC DATA (RTECS). CARCINOGEN STATUS: NONE. LOCAL EFFECTS: CORROSIVE- INHALATION, SKIN, AND EYES; LACRIMATOR. ACUTE TOXICITY LEVEL: HIGHLY TOXIC BY INHALATION; TOXIC BY INGESTION. TARGET EFFECTS: METHEMOGLOBIN FORMER. POISONING MAY AFFECT THE RESPIRATORY AND CARDIOVASCULAR SYSTEMS.

HEALTH EFFECTS AND FIRST AID

INHALATION: METHYL BROMIDE: NARCOTIC/TOXIC. ACUTE EXPOSURE- SYMPTOMS MAY BE DELAYED FROM 1-12 HOURS AFTER EXPOSURE TO HIGH CONCENTRATIONS; LOWER CONCENTRATIONS RESULT IN LESS SEVERE SYMPTOMS WITH A LATENT PERIOD OF 12 TO 24 HOURS. REPORTED EFFECTS INCLUDE HEADACHE, VISUAL DISTURBANCES, NAUSEA, VOMITING, ANOREXIA, ABDOMINAL PAIN, WEAKNESS, MALAISE, VERTIGO, PARESTHESIAS AND PARALYSIS OF THE EXTREMITIES, OLIGURIA OR ANURIA, DROWSINESS, CONFUSION, HYPERACTIVITY, HYPOTENSION, MANIA, HALLUCINATIONS, TREMORS OR TWITCHING, ATAXIA, AND CONVULSIONS. HIGH CONCENTRATIONS MAY CAUSE RAPID NARCOSIS AND DEATH FROM RESPIRATORY FAILURE. LESSER CONCENTRATIONS MAY CAUSE PULMONARY IRRITATION, COUGHING, CHEST PAIN, SHORTNESS OF BREATH, CONGESTION, EDEMA, AND DEVELOPMENT OF BRONCHITIS OR PNEUMONITIS. JAUNDICE AND CYANOSIS MAY ALSO RESULT. UNCONSCIOUSNESS, COMA, AND DEATH DUE TO RESPIRATORY OR CIRCULATORY COLLAPSE MAY OCCUR. TUBULAR DAMAGE IN THE KIDNEYS HAS BEEN OBSERVED IN FATAL CASES. SURVIVING INDIVIDUALS MAY HAVE PERSISTENT CENTRAL AND PERIPHERAL NERVOUS SYSTEM EFFECTS INCLUDING VERTIGO, DEPRESSION,

HALLUCINATIONS, ANMESIA, ANXIETY, INABILITY TO CONCENTRATE, SENSORY DISTURBANCES, WEAKNESS, AND IRRITABILITY. **CHRONIC EXPOSURE-** REPEATED EXPOSURE MAY RESULT IN ADVERSE CENTRAL NERVOUS SYSTEM EFFECTS INCLUDING LETHARGY, MUSCULAR PAINS, VISUAL, SPEECH, AND SENSORY DISTURBANCES, MENTAL CONFUSION, BLURRED VISION, PAPILLEDEMA, HALLUCINATIONS, SOMNOLENCE, FAINTING ATTACKS, BRONCHOSPASMS, AND CENTRAL NERVOUS SYSTEM EDEMA. PERIPHERAL NEUROPATHY MAY BE INDICATED BY PARALYSIS OF THE EXTREMITIES, MYOCLONUS, POLYNEURITIS, AND CONVULSIONS. LIVER, KIDNEY AND PERMANENT BRAIN DAMAGE MAY OCCUR.

CHLOROPICRIN: CORROSIVE/METHEMOGLOBIN FORMER/HIGHLY TOXIC. 4 PPM IMMEDIATELY DANGEROUS TO LIFE OR HEALTH. **ACUTE EXPOSURE-** MAY CAUSE IRRITATION, SORE THROAT, COUGHING, LABORED BREATHING, DIZZINESS, NAUSEA, VOMITING, CYANOSIS, FAINTNESS, AND PULMONARY EDEMA. LOW METHEMOGLOBIN LEVELS MAY RESULT IN HEADACHE, WEAKNESS, AND DYSPNEA. HIGH METHEMOGLOBIN LEVELS MAY RESULT IN STUPOR, RESPIRATORY DEPRESSION, AND CHOCOLATE COLORED BLOOD FROM LACK OF OXYGENATION. **CHRONIC EXPOSURE-** PROLONGED AND REPEATED EXPOSURE MAY CAUSE HEART AND LUNG DAMAGE AND PULMONARY EDEMA WITH POSSIBLE COMA AND DEATH.

FIRST AID- REMOVE FROM EXPOSURE AREA TO FRESH AIR IMMEDIATELY. IF BREATHING HAS STOPPED, GIVE ARTIFICIAL RESPIRATION. MAINTAIN AIRWAY AND BLOOD PRESSURE AND ADMINISTER OXYGEN IF AVAILABLE. KEEP AFFECTED PERSON WARM AND AT REST. TREAT SYMPTOMATICALLY AND SUPPORTIVELY. ADMINISTRATION OF OXYGEN SHOULD BE PERFORMED BY QUALIFIED PERSONNEL. GET MEDICAL ATTENTION IMMEDIATELY.

SKIN CONTACT: METHYL BROMIDE: IRRITANT. **ACUTE EXPOSURE-** CONTACT WITH THE LIQUID MAY CAUSE IRRITATION, ERYTHEMA, EDEMA, SCALING, AND ITCHING DERMATITIS. THE LIQUID MAY BE ABSORBED THROUGH INTACT SKIN. **CHRONIC EXPOSURE-** REPEATED OR PROLONGED EXPOSURE MAY LEAD TO VESICULATION AND POSSIBLE DEEP BURNS.

CHLOROPICRIN: CORROSIVE/METHEMOGLOBIN FORMER. **ACUTE EXPOSURE-** MAY CAUSE IRRITATION, REDNESS, PAIN AND SKIN BURNS. IT IS ABSORBED THROUGH THE SKIN AND MAY RESULT IN METHEMOGLOBINEMIA. LOW METHEMOGLOBIN LEVELS MAY RESULT IN HEADACHE, WEAKNESS, AND DYSPNEA. HIGH METHEMOGLOBIN LEVELS MAY RESULT IN STUPOR, RESPIRATORY DEPRESSION, AND CHOCOLATE COLORED BLOOD FROM LACK OF OXYGENATION. **CHRONIC EXPOSURE-** PROLONGED AND REPEATED EXPOSURE MAY CAUSE DERMATITIS AND SKIN BURNS.

FIRST AID- REMOVE CONTAMINATED CLOTHING AND SHOES IMMEDIATELY. WASH AFFECTED AREA WITH SOAP OR MILD DETERGENT AND LARGE AMOUNTS OF WATER UNTIL NO EVIDENCE OF CHEMICAL REMAINS (AT LEAST 15-20 MINUTES). IN CASE OF CHEMICAL BURNS, COVER AREA WITH STERILE, DRY DRESSING. BANDAGE SECURELY, BUT NOT TOO TIGHTLY. GET MEDICAL ATTENTION IMMEDIATELY.

EYE CONTACT: METHYL BROMIDE: **ACUTE EXPOSURE-** VAPORS AND LIQUID MAY CAUSE TRANSIENT IRRITATION AND CONJUNCTIVITIS. RABBITS EXPOSED TO CONCENTRATED VAPORS FOR 1 MINUTE 30 SECONDS RESULTED IN LOSS OF EYE SURFACE LUSTER, LOSS OF CORNEAL EPITHELIUM, EDEMA OF THE CONJUNCTIVAE AND LIDS, AND TRANSIENT CORNEAL OPACITY. **CHRONIC EXPOSURE-** REPEATED OR PROLONGED EXPOSURE MAY CAUSE CONJUNCTIVITIS.

CHLOROPICRIN: CORROSIVE/LACRIMATOR. **ACUTE EXPOSURE-** MAY CAUSE IRRITATION, REDNESS, PAIN, LACRIMATION, BLURRED VISION AND CORNEAL DAMAGE. **CHRONIC EXPOSURE-** MAY CAUSE CORNEAL DAMAGE AND CONJUNCTIVITIS.

FIRST AID- WASH EYES IMMEDIATELY WITH LARGE AMOUNTS OF WATER, OCCASIONALLY LIFTING UPPER AND LOWER LIDS, UNTIL NO EVIDENCE OF CHEMICAL REMAINS (AT LEAST 15-20 MINUTES). CONTINUE IRRIGATING WITH NORMAL SALINE UNTIL THE PH HAS RETURNED TO NORMAL (30-60 MINUTES). COVER WITH STERILE BANDAGES. GET MEDICAL ATTENTION IMMEDIATELY.

INGESTION: METHYL BROMIDE: TOXIC/LIMITED ANIMAL CARCINOGEN. **ACUTE EXPOSURE-** INGESTION OF LIQUID MAY RESULT IN SYSTEMIC TOXICITY AS DETAILED IN ACUTE INHALATION. THE LETHAL DOSE REPORTED IN RATS WAS 214 MG/KG. THE SYMPTOMS WERE NOT REPORTED. **CHRONIC EXPOSURE-** DEGENERATION OF PERIPHERAL NERVES AND THE DORSAL COLUMNS OF THE SPINAL CORD HAS BEEN REPORTED IN RATS FED DIETS WITH METHYL BROMIDE. REPEATED ADMINISTRATION TO RATS BY ORAL GAVAGE INDUCED TUMORS OF THE FORESTOMACH.

CHLOROPICRIN: CORROSIVE/METHEMOGLOBIN FORMER/TOXIC. **ACUTE EXPOSURE-** MAY CAUSE IRRITATION, SORE THROAT, COUGHING, LABORED BREATHING, DIZZINESS, NAUSEA, VOMITING, CYANOSIS, AND FAINTNESS. INGESTION OF LIQUID CAN CAUSE SEVERE GASTROENTERITIS. LOW METHEMOGLOBIN LEVELS MAY RESULT IN HEADACHE, WEAKNESS, AND DYSPNEA. HIGH METHEMOGLOBIN LEVELS MAY RESULT IN STUPOR, RESPIRATORY DEPRESSION, AND CHOCOLATE COLORED BLOOD FROM LACK OF OXYGENATION. **CHRONIC EXPOSURE-** MAY CAUSE HEART AND LUNG DAMAGE.

FIRST AID- TREAT SYMPTOMATICALLY AND SUPPORTIVELY. GET MEDICAL ATTENTION IMMEDIATELY. IF VOMITING OCCURS, KEEP HEAD LOWER THAN HIPS TO PREVENT ASPIRATION.

REACTIVITY

REACTIVITY: CHLOROPICRIN: BULK CONTAINERS CAN BE SHOCK DETONATED.

INCOMPATIBILITIES: METHYL BROMIDE: ALUMINUM: SEVERE EXPLOSION HAZARD. MAGNESIUM: SEVERE EXPLOSION HAZARD. ZINC: SEVERE EXPLOSION HAZARD. DIMETHYL SULFOXIDE: DELAYED EXPLOSION HAZARD. STRONG OXIDIZERS: VIGOROUS REACTION. ETHYLENE OXIDE: VIGOROUS REACTION.

CHLOROPICRIN: ANILINE: VIOLENT REACTION. BROMO-2-PROPYNE: EXPLOSIVE, SHOCK- AND HEAT- SENSITIVE. SODIUM HYDROXIDE: REACTS VIOLENTLY SODIUM METHOXIDE: BELOW 50 C, NITRO COMPOUND WILL ACCUMULATE AND CAUSE A VIOLENT AND DANGEROUS EXOTHERMIC REACTION. STRONG OXIDIZERS: POSSIBLE VIOLENT REACTION.

DECOMPOSITION: THERMAL DECOMPOSITION MAY RELEASE TOXIC AND/OR HAZARDOUS GASES.

POLYMERIZATION: HAZARDOUS POLYMERIZATION HAS NOT BEEN REPORTED TO OCCUR UNDER NORMAL TEMPERATURES AND PRESSURES.

CONDITIONS TO AVOID

MAY BURN BUT DOES NOT IGNITE READILY. CONTAINERS MAY EXPLODE IN HEAT OF FIRE.

SPILL AND LEAK PROCEDURES

OCCUPATIONAL SPILL: DO NOT TOUCH SPILLED MATERIAL. STOP LEAK IF YOU CAN DO IT WITHOUT RISK. USE WATER SPRAY TO REDUCE VAPORS. FOR SMALL SPILLS, TAKE UP WITH SAND OR OTHER ABSORBENT MATERIAL AND PLACE INTO CONTAINERS FOR LATER DISPOSAL. FOR SMALL DRY SPILLS, WITH A CLEAN SHOVEL PLACE MATERIAL INTO CLEAN, DRY CONTAINERS AND COVER. MOVE CONTAINERS FROM SPILL AREA. FOR LARGER SPILLS, DIKE FAR AHEAD OF SPILL FOR LATER DISPOSAL. KEEP UNNECESSARY PEOPLE AWAY. ISOLATE HAZARD AREA AND DENY ENTRY. VENTILATE CLOSED SPACES BEFORE ENTERING.

PROTECTIVE EQUIPMENT

VENTILATION: PROCESS ENCLOSURE RECOMMENDED TO MEET PUBLISHED EXPOSURE LIMITS.

RESPIRATOR: THE FOLLOWING RESPIRATORS ARE RECOMMENDED BASED ON INFORMATION FOUND IN THE PHYSICAL DATA, TOXICITY AND HEALTH EFFECTS SECTIONS. THEY ARE RANKED IN ORDER FROM MINIMUM TO MAXIMUM RESPIRATORY PROTECTION. THE SPECIFIC RESPIRATOR SELECTED MUST BE BASED ON CONTAMINATION LEVELS FOUND IN THE WORK PLACE, MUST NOT EXCEED THE WORKING LIMITS OF THE RESPIRATOR AND BE JOINTLY APPROVED BY THE NATIONAL INSTITUTE FOR OCCUPATIONAL SAFETY AND HEALTH AND THE MINE SAFETY AND HEALTH ADMINISTRATION (NIOSH-MSHA).

TYPE 'C' SUPPLIED-AIR RESPIRATOR WITH A FULL FACEPIECE OPERATED IN PRESSURE-DEMAND OR OTHER POSITIVE PRESSURE MODE OR WITH A FULL FACEPIECE, HELMET OR HOOD OPERATED IN CONTINOUS-FLOW MODE.

SELF-CONTAINED BREATHING APPARATUS WITH A FULL FACEPIECE OPERATED IN PRESSURE-DEMAND OR OTHER POSITIVE PRESSURE MODE.

FOR FIREFIGHTING AND OTHER IMMEDIATELY DANGEROUS TO LIFE OR HEALTH CONDITIONS:

SELF-CONTAINED BREATHING APPARATUS WITH FULL FACEPIECE OPERATED IN PRESSURE-DEMAND OR OTHER POSITIVE PRESSURE MODE.

SUPPLIED-AIR RESPIRATOR WITH FULL FACEPIECE AND OPERATED IN PRESSURE-DEMAND OR OTHER POSITIVE PRESSURE MODE IN COMBINATION WITH AN AUXILIARY SELF-CONTAINED BREATHING APPARATUS OPERATED IN PRESSURE-DEMAND OR OTHER POSITIVE PRESSURE MODE.

CLOTHING: EMPLOYEE MUST WEAR APPROPRIATE PROTECTIVE (IMPERVIOUS) CLOTHING AND EQUIPMENT TO PREVENT ANY POSSIBILITY OF SKIN CONTACT WITH THIS SUBSTANCE.

GLOVES: EMPLOYEE MUST WEAR APPROPRIATE PROTECTIVE GLOVES TO PREVENT CONTACT WITH THIS SUBSTANCE.

EYE PROTECTION: EMPLOYEE MUST WEAR SPLASH-PROOF OR DUST-RESISTANT SAFETY GOGGLES AND A FACESHIELD TO PREVENT CONTACT WITH THIS SUBSTANCE.

EMERGENCY WASH FACILITIES: WHERE THERE IS ANY POSSIBILITY THAT AN EMPLOYEE'S EYES AND/OR SKIN MAY BE EXPOSED TO THIS SUBSTANCE, THE EMPLOYER SHOULD PROVIDE AN EYE WASH FOUNTAIN AND QUICK DRENCH SHOWER WITHIN THE IMMEDIATE WORK AREA FOR EMERGENCY USE.

AUTHORIZED BY- OCCUPATIONAL HEALTH SERVICES, INC.

CREATION DATE: 10/05/89 ***REVISION DATE:*** 07/13/90

MATERIAL SAFETY DATA SHEET

OCCUPATIONAL HEALTH SERVICES, INC.
AGRICULTURE AND PESTICIDE DIVISION
450 SEVENTH AVENUE, SUITE 2407
NEW YORK, NEW YORK 10123
1-800-445-MSDS OR (212) 967-1100

EMERGENCY CONTACT:
JOHN S. BRANSFORD, JR. (615) 292-1180

SUBSTANCE IDENTIFICATION

SUBSTANCE: **21 PYRENONE CONCENTRATE 05623838**

TRADE NAMES/SYNONYMS: 21 PYRENONE FOOD STORAGE SPRAY 05623871; PST75472

CERCLA RATINGS (SCALE 0-3): HEALTH = 3 FIRE = 2 REACTIVITY = 0 PERSISTENCE = 2

NFPA RATINGS (SCALE 0-4): HEALTH = 3 FIRE = 2 REACTIVITY = 0

COMPONENTS AND CONTAMINANTS

COMPONENT: LPA SOLVENT VISTA ***PERCENT:*** 68.0-98.0
CONTAINS:
PARAFFINS (100%)

COMPONENT: ATLOX 1045A ***PERCENT:*** 0.0-15.0
CONTAINS:
METHYL ALCOHOL (13.0%) CAS# 67-56-1
AROMATIC PETROLEUM SOLVENT (XYLENE BASED) (15%) CAS# 1330-20-7
ALKYL ARYL SULFONATES (17.0%)
NONIONIC SURFACTANTS (55.0%)

COMPONENT: PYRENONE O.T. 50-5 ***PERCENT:*** 1.70-18.0
CONTAINS:
PYRETHRUM (5.30%) CAS# 8003-34-7
PIPERONYL BUTOXIDE, TECHNICAL (53.07%) CAS# 51-03-6
MIXED HYDROCARBONS (41.63%)

OTHER CONTAMINANTS: NONE

EXPOSURE LIMITS: METHYL ALCOHOL (METHANOL): 200 PPM (260 MG/M3) OSHA TWA (SKIN); 250 PPM (325 MG/M3) OSHA STEL 200 PPM (260 MG/M3) ACGIH TWA (SKIN); 250 PPM (310 MG/M3) ACGIH STEL 200 PPM NIOSH RECOMMENDED 10 HOUR TWA; 800 PPM NIOSH RECOMMENDED 15 MINUTE CEILING 5000 POUNDS CERCLA SECTION 103 REPORTABLE QUANTITY SUBJECT TO SARA SECTION 313 ANNUAL TOXIC CHEMICAL RELEASE REPORTING

XYLENE: 100 PPM (435 MG/M3) OSHA TWA; 150 PPM (655 MG/M3) OSHA STEL 100 PPM (435 MG/M3) ACGIH TWA; 150 PPM (655 MG/M3) ACGIH STEL 100 PPM (435 MG/M3) NIOSH RECOMMENDED 10 HOUR TWA; 200 PPM (870 MG/M3) NIOSH RECOMMENDED 10 MINUTE CEILING

1000 POUNDS CERCLA SECTION 103 REPORTABLE QUANTITY SUBJECT TO SARA SECTION 313 ANNUAL TOXIC CHEMICAL RELEASE REPORTING

PHYSICAL DATA

DESCRIPTION: CLEAR, TAN TO BROWN LIQUID WITH A CHRYSANTHEMUM-LIKE ODOR

BOILING POINT: NOT AVAILABLE ***SPECIFIC GRAVITY:*** 0.81

EVAPORATION RATE: NOT AVAILABLE ***SOLUBILITY IN WATER:*** SLIGHT

VAPOR DENSITY: >1

FIRE AND EXPLOSION DATA

FIRE AND EXPLOSION HAZARD: MODERATE FIRE HAZARD WHEN EXPOSED TO HEAT OR FLAME.
VAPORS ARE HEAVIER THAN AIR AND MAY TRAVEL A CONSIDERABLE DISTANCE TO A SOURCE OF IGNITION AND FLASH BACK.
VAPOR-AIR MIXTURES ARE EXPLOSIVE ABOVE FLASH POINT.

FLASH POINT: >100 F (>38 C) (CC) ***FLAMMABILITY CLASS(OSHA):*** II

FIREFIGHTING MEDIA: DRY CHEMICAL, CARBON DIOXIDE, HALON, WATER SPRAY OR STANDARD FOAM (1987 EMERGENCY RESPONSE GUIDEBOOK, DOT P 5800.4).
FOR LARGER FIRES, USE WATER SPRAY, FOG OR STANDARD FOAM (1987 EMERGENCY RESPONSE GUIDEBOOK, DOT P 5800.4).

FIREFIGHTING: MOVE CONTAINER FROM FIRE AREA IF POSSIBLE. COOL FIRE-EXPOSED CONTAINERS WITH WATER FROM SIDE UNTIL WELL AFTER FIRE IS OUT. STAY AWAY FROM STORAGE TANK ENDS. FOR MASSIVE FIRE IN STORAGE AREA, USE UNMANNED HOSE HOLDER OR MONITOR NOZZLES, ELSE WITHDRAW FROM AREA AND LET FIRE BURN. WITHDRAW IMMEDIATELY IN CASE OF RISING SOUND FROM VENTING SAFETY DEVICE OR ANY DISCOLORATION OF STORAGE TANK DUE TO FIRE (1987 EMERGENCY RESPONSE GUIDEBOOK, DOT P 5800.4, GUIDE PAGE 27). EXTINGUISH ONLY IF FLOW CAN BE STOPPED; USE FLOODING AMOUNTS OF WATER AS A FOG, SOLID STREAMS MAY BE INEFFECTIVE. COOL CONTAINERS WITH FLOODING AMOUNTS OF WATER, APPLY FROM AS FAR A DISTANCE AS POSSIBLE. AVOID BREATHING VAPORS, KEEP UPWIND.

TOXICITY

LPA SOLVENT: 2.0-4.0 GM/KG SKIN-RABBIT LD50 (VISTA MSDS); 39.9 GM/KG ORAL-RAT LD(0) (VISTA MSDS); 24.1 MG/L/1 HOUR INHALATION-RAT LC(0) (VISTA MSDS); CARCINOGEN STATUS: NONE. LPA SOLVENT IS AN EYE, MUCOUS MEMBRANE AND SKIN IRRITANT AND A CENTRAL NERVOUS SYSTEM DEPRESSANT.
PARAFFINS: CARCINOGEN STATUS: NONE. THE TOXICITY OF PARAFFINS WILL VARY DEPENDING ON THE SPECIFIC COMPOSITION. PARAFFINS ARE EYE, SKIN AND MUCUOUS MEMBRANE IRRITANTS AND CENTRAL NERVOUS SYSTEM DEPRESSANTS. STIMULANTS SUCH AS EPINEPHRINE MAY INDUCE VENTRICULAR FIBRILLATION.
METHYL ALCOHOL (METHANOL): IRRITATION DATA: 20 MG/24 HOURS SKIN-RABBIT MODERATE; 40 MG EYE-RABBIT MODERATE; 100 MG/24 HOURS EYE-RABBIT MODERATE. TOXICITY DATA: 86,000 MG/M3 INHALATION-HUMAN TCLO; 300 PPM INHALATION-HUMAN TCLO; 64,000 PPM/4 HOURS INHALATION-RAT LC50; 1000 PPM INHALATION-MONKEY LCLO; 50 GM/M3/2 HOURS INHALATION-MOUSE LCLO; 44,000 MG/M3/6 HOURS INHALATION-CAT LCLO; 15,800 MG/KG SKIN-RABBIT LD50; 393 MG/KG SKIN-MONKEY LDLO; 428 MG/KG ORAL-HUMAN LDLO; 143 MG/KG ORAL-HUMAN LDLO; 6422 MG/KG ORAL-MAN LDLO; 3429 MG/KG ORAL-MAN TDLO; 4 GM/KG ORAL-WOMAN TDLO; 7 GM/KG ORAL-MONKEY LD50; 5628 MG/KG ORAL-RAT LD50; 7300 MG/KG ORAL-MOUSE LD50; 14,200 MG/KG ORAL-RABBIT LD50; 7500 MG/KG ORAL-DOG LDLO; 9800 MG/KG SUBCUTANEOUS-MOUSE LD50; 2131 MG/KG INTRAVENOUS-RAT LD50; 4710 MG/KG INTRAVENOUS-MOUSE LD50; 8907 MG/KG INTRAVENOUS-RABBIT LD50; 7529 MG/KG INTRAPERITONEAL-RAT LD50; 10,765 MG/KG INTRAPERITONEAL-MOUSE LD50; 1826 MG/KG INTRAPERITONEAL-RABBIT LD50; 868 MG/KG UNREPORTED-MAN LDLO; MUTAGENIC DATA (RTECS); REPRODUCTIVE EFFECTS DATA (RTECS). CARCINOGEN STATUS: NONE. LOCAL EFFECTS: IRRITANT- SKIN, EYE. ACUTE TOXICITY LEVEL: SLIGHTLY TOXIC BY INHALATION, DERMAL ABSORPTION, INGESTION. TARGET EFFECTS: NEUROTOXIN; CENTRAL NERVOUS SYSTEM DEPRESSANT. AT INCREASED RISK FROM EXPOSURE: PERSONS WITH KIDNEY, EYE OR SKIN DISORDERS.
XYLENE: IRRITATION DATA: 200 PPM EYE-HUMAN; 87 MG EYE-RABBIT MILD; 5 MG/24 HOURS EYE-RABBIT SEVERE; 100% SKIN-RABBIT MODERATE; 500 MG/24 HOURS SKIN-RABBIT MODERATE. TOXICITY DATA: 10000 PPM/6 HOURS INHALATION-MAN LCLO; 200 PPM INHALATION-HUMAN TCLO; 5000 PPM/4 HOURS INHALATION-RAT LC50; 450 PPM INHALATION-GUINEA PIG LCLO; 50 MG/KG ORAL-HUMAN LDLO; 4300 MG/KG ORAL-RAT LD50; 1700 MG/KG SUBCUTANEOUS-RAT LD50; 129 MG/KG INTRAVENOUS-RABBIT LDLO; 2 GM/KG INTRAPERITONEAL-MAMMAL LDLO; 2459 MG/KG INTRAPERITONEAL-RAT LD50; 1548 MG/KG INTRAPERITONEAL-MOUSE LD50; 2000 MG/KG INTRAPERITONEAL-GUINEA PIG LDLO; REPRODUCTIVE EFFECTS DATA (RTECS). CARCINOGEN STATUS: NONE. LOCAL EFFECTS: IRRITANT- INHALATION, SKIN, EYE. ACUTE TOXICITY LEVEL: MODERATELY TOXIC BY INHALATION, INGESTION. TARGET EFFECTS: CENTRAL NERVOUS SYSTEM DEPRESSANT. POISONING MAY ALSO AFFECT THE NERVOUS SYSTEM, LIVER AND KIDNEYS. AT INCREASED RISK FROM EXPOSURE: PREGNANT WOMEN. ADDITIONAL INFORMATION: CONSUMPTION OF ALCOHOLIC BEVERAGES MAY ENHANCE THE TOXIC EFFECTS. STIMULANTS SUCH AS EPINEPHRINE OR EPHEDRINE MAY INDUCE VENTRICULAR FIBRILLATION.
ALKYL ARYL SULFONATES: CARCINOGEN STATUS: NONE. THERE IS INSUFFICIENT DATA TO QUANTIFY THE TOXICITY OF ALKYL ARLY SULFONATES.
NONIONIC SURFACTANTS: CARCINOGEN STATUS: NONE. NONIONIC SURFACTANTS ARE EYE, MUCOUS MEMBRANE AND SKIN IRRITANTS. THERE IS INSUFFICIENT DATA TO QUANTIFY THE TOXICITY.
PYRENONE O.T. 50-5: 3038-4556 MG/KG ORAL-RAT LD50 (FAIRFIELD AMERICAN CORPORATION MSDS); >7.57 MG/L INHALATION-RAT LC50 (FAIRFIELD AMERICAN CORPORATION MSDS); >3000 MG/KG SKIN-RABBIT (FAIRFIELD AMERICAN CORPORATION MSDS); CARCINOGEN STATUS: NONE. PYRENONE O.T. 50-5 IS A MILD SKIN IRRITANT.
PIPERONYL BUTOXIDE: TOXICITY DATA: 200 MG/KG SKIN-RABBIT LD50; 6150 MG/KG ORAL-RAT LD50; 2600 MG/KG ORAL-MOUSE LD50; 2650 MG/KG ORAL-RABBIT LD50; 1000 MG/KG INTRAPERITONEAL-MOUSE LDLO; MUTAGENIC DATA (RTECS); REPRODUCTIVE EFFECTS DATA (RTECS); TUMORIGENIC DATA (RTECS); CARCINOGEN STATUS: ANIMAL INADEQUATE EVIDENCE (IARC GROUP-3). ACUTE TOXICITY LEVEL: HIGHLY TOXIC BY DERMAL ABSORPTION; SLIGHTLY TOXIC BY INGESTION. TARGET EFFECTS: POISONING MAY AFFECT THE LIVER. ADDITIONAL DATA: THIS MATERIAL MAY ENHANCE THE PHARMACOLOGIC EFFECT OF DRUGS AND POTENTIATE THE TOXICITY OF ENVIRONMENTAL AGENTS.
MIXED HYDROCARBONS: CARCINOGEN STATUS: NONE. THE TOXICITY OF MIXED HYDROCARBONS WILL VARY WITH THE SPECIFIC COMPOSITION. THEY ARE EYE, SKIN, AND MUCOUS MEMBRANE IRRITANTS AND CENTRAL NERVOUS SYSTEM DEPRESSANTS. STIMULANTS SUCH AS EPINEPHRINE MAY INDUCE VENTRICULAR FIBRILLATION.

HEALTH EFFECTS AND FIRST AID

INHALATION: LPA SOLVENT: IRRITANT/NARCOTIC. **ACUTE EXPOSURE-** VAPORS MAY BE IRRITATING. EXPOSURE TO HIGH CONCENTRATIONS MAY RESULT IN CENTRAL NERVOUS SYSTEM DEPRESSION WITH HEADACHE, STUPOR, NAUSEA AND VOMITING. ANIMAL STUDIES INDICATE INHALATION OF 24.1 MG/L FOR 1 HOUR CAUSED NO DEATHS. **CHRONIC EXPOSURE-** NO DATA AVAILABLE.

PARAFFINS: IRRITANT/NARCOTIC. **ACUTE EXPOSURE-** THE DEGREE AND RANGE OF EFFECTS WILL VARY DEPENDING ON THE SPECIFIC HYDROCARBON COMPOSITION. HIGH VAPOR CONCENTRATIONS MAY IRRITATE MUCOUS MEMBRANES AND CAUSE CENTRAL NERVOUS SYSTEM DEPRESSION. SYMPTOMS MAY INCLUDE EXHILARATION, HEADACHE, DIZZINESS, NAUSEA, ANOREXIA, CONFUSION, INCOORDINATION, AND IN MORE SEVERE CASES, STUPOR, ANESTHESIA, UNCONSCIOUSNESS AND COMA WITH INHIBITION OF DEEP TENDON REFLEXES. CONVULSIONS ARE POSSIBLE. IN FATAL CASES, DEATH IS USUALLY DUE TO RESPIRATORY ARREST, ALTHOUGH SUDDEN DEATH MAY RESULT FROM VENTRICULAR FIBRILLATION. VISCERAL DAMAGE MAY OCCUR. **CHRONIC EXPOSURE-** REPEATED OR PROLONGED EXPOSURE TO SOME MEMBERS OF THIS GROUP MAY RESULT IN NEUROLOGIC EFFECTS.

METHYL ALCOHOL (METHANOL): NARCOTIC/NEUROTOXIN. 25,000 PPM IMMEDIATELY DANGEROUS TO LIFE OR HEALTH. **ACUTE EXPOSURE-** MAY CAUSE IRRITATION OF THE MUCOUS MEMBRANES, COUGHING, OPPRESSION IN THE CHEST, TRACHEITIS, BRONCHITIS, TINNITUS, UNSTEADY GAIT, TWITCHING, COLIC, CONSTIPATION, NYSTAGMUS, AND BLEPHAROSPASM. SYMPTOMS FROM OCCUPATIONAL EXPOSURE INCLUDE PARESTHESIAS, NUMBNESS AND SHOOTING PAINS IN THE HANDS AND FOREARMS. METABOLIC ACIDOSIS, AND EFFECTS ON THE EYES AND CENTRAL NERVOUS SYSTEM MAY OCCUR AS DETAILED IN ACUTE INGESTION. **CHRONIC EXPOSURE-** REPEATED OR PROLONGED EXPOSURE MAY CAUSE EFFECTS AS IN ACUTE INGESTION. REPEATED EXPOSURE TO 200-375 PPM CAUSED RECURRENT HEADACHES IN WORKERS. EXPOSURE FOR 4 YEARS TO 1200-8000 PPM RESULTED IN MARKED DIMINUTION OF VISION AND ENLARGEMENT OF THE LIVER IN A WORKMAN. REPRODUCTIVE EFFECTS HAVE BEEN REPORTED IN ANIMALS.

XYLENE: IRRITANT/NARCOTIC. 1000 PPM IMMEDIATELY DANGEROUS TO LIFE OR HEALTH. **ACUTE EXPOSURE-** IRRITATION OF THE UPPER RESPIRATORY TRACT MAY OCCUR AT 200 PPM. EXPOSURE TO HIGHER CONCENTRATIONS MAY CAUSE MORE SEVERE IRRITATION AND INITIAL CENTRAL NERVOUS SYSTEM EXCITATION FOLLOWED BY DEPRESSION. SIGNS AND SYMPTOMS MAY INCLUDE RESPIRATORY DIFFICULTY AND SUBSTERNAL PAIN, TRANSIENT EUPHORIA AND EMOTIONAL LABILITY, HEADACHE, NAUSEA, VOMITING, ANOREXIA, ABDOMINAL PAIN, DIZZINESS, DROWSINESS, ATAXIA, AND STAGGERING. THERE MAY BE SALIVATION, SLURRED SPEECH, BLURRED VISION, NYSTAGMUS, TINNITUS, TREMORS, CONFUSION, AND FLUSHING OF THE FACE AND A FEELING OF INCREASED BODY HEAT. IN SEVERE EXPOSURES, THERE MAY BE STUPOR, ANESTHESIA, UNCONSCIOUSNESS, AND COMA WHICH MAY BE PUNCTUATED BY EPISODES OF NEUROIRRITABILITY, BUT RARELY FRANK CONVULSIONS, EXCEPT IN TERMINAL ASPHYXIA. LIVER AND KIDNEY DAMAGE MAY OCCUR, BUT ARE USUALLY MILD AND TRANSIENT. A GROUP OF SUBJECTS WHO INHALED 12.3 UMOL/L OF XYLENE WHILE EXERCISING BECAME SIGNIFICANTLY IMPAIRED ON 3 NEUROPSYCHOLOGICAL TESTS. EXPOSURE OF 3 PAINTERS TO APPROXIMATELY 10,000 PPM FOR 18.5 HOURS RESULTED IN 1 DEATH FROM PULMONARY EDEMA AND PETECHIAL BRAIN HEMORRHAGE. BOTH SURVIVORS WERE UNCONSCIOUS FOR 19-24 HOURS AND EXPERIENCED RETROGRADE AMNESIA, HYPOTHERMIA, AND LUNG CONGESTION. RENAL AND HEPATIC IMPAIRMENT ALSO DEVELOPED. COMPLETE RECOVERY TOOK 15 DAYS. HIGH CONCENTRATIONS MAY CAUSE DEATH FROM SUDDEN VENTRICULAR FIBRILLATION, BUT MORE FREQUENTLY DEATH OCCURS FROM RESPIRATORY ARREST. **CHRONIC EXPOSURE-** REPEATED OR PROLONGED INHALATION OF VAPORS ABOVE 200 PPM MAY CAUSE NAUSEA, VOMITING, ABDOMINAL PAIN, AND ANOREXIA. OTHER COMMON COMPLAINTS INCLUDE HEADACHE, FATIGUE, LASSITUDE, IRRITABILITY, BREATHING DIFFICULTIES, AND FLATULENCE. EFFECTS ON THE NERVOUS SYSTEM MAY RESULT IN EXCITATION, FOLLOWED BY DEPRESSION, PARESTHESIAS, TREMORS, APPREHENSION, IMPAIRED MEMORY, INSOMNIA, VERTIGO, AND TINNITUS. EFFECTS ON REACTION TIME, MANUAL COORDINATION, BODY BALANCE AND EEG OCCURRED WITH REPEATED EXPOSURE TO 90 PPM OF M-XYLENE. SWEETISH TASTE IN THE MOUTH, DRY NOSE AND THROAT, STRONG THIRST, MUCOSAL HEMORRHAGE, AND ANEMIA HAVE BEEN REPORTED. EFFECTS ON THE LIVER, KIDNEY, CARDIOVASCULAR SYSTEM, AND THE BONE MARROW HAVE ALSO BEEN REPORTED, ALTHOUGH THE LATTER HAS BEEN QUESTIONED. EXPOSURE OF RABBITS TO 1150 PPM FOR 40-55 DAYS RESULTED IN A REVERSIBLE DECREASE IN THE RED AND WHITE CELL COUNTS AND AN INCREASE IN THE PLATELETS. ONE CASE OF AN APPARENT EPILEPTIFORM SEIZURE FOLLOWING A RELATIVELY BRIEF EXPOSURE HAS OCCURRED. WOMEN MAY DEVELOP MENSTRUAL DISORDERS, SUCH AS MENORRHAGIA OR METRORRHAGIA, INFERTILITY, AND PATHOLOGICAL PREGNANCY CONDITIONS INCLUDING TOXICOSIS, DANGER OF MISCARRIAGE, AND HEMORRHAGING DURING DELIVERY. REPEATED EXPOSURE OF PREGNANT MICE, RATS AND RABBITS TO THE INDIVIDUAL OR THE MIXED ISOMERS HAS RESULTED IN MATERNAL EFFECTS AND EFFECTS ON FERTILITY, ON THE EMBRYO OR FETUS, AND SPECIFIC DEVELOPMENTAL ABNORMALITIES. INCLUDED AMONG THESE EFFECTS ARE FETAL DEATH, FETOTOXICITY, PRE- AND POST-IMPLANTATION MORTALITY, ABORTION, CRANIOFACIAL AND MUSCULOSKELETAL ABNORMALITIES, AND EXTRA EMBRYONIC STRUCTURES.

ALKYL ARYL SULFONATE: IRRITANT. **ACUTE EXPOSURE-** NO DATA AVAILABLE ON THIS SPECIFIC GROUP. HOWEVER, ANIONIC SURFACTANTS MAY CAUSE IRRITATION OF THE RESPIRATORY TRACT. THE AIRBORNE DUST OF SULFONATED SURFACTANTS MAY CAUSE RESPIRATORY ALLERGIES IN SOME INDIVIUALS. **CHRONIC EXPOSURE-** PROLONGED OR REPEATED EXPOSURE MAY CAUSE IRRITATION OF THE RESPIRATORY TRACT. PROLONGED OR REPEATED EXPOSURE MAY CAUSE RESPIRATORY ALLERGIES IN SOME INDIVIUALS.

NONIONIC SURFACTANTS: **ACUTE EXPOSURE-** EXPOSURE TO A LARGE CONCENTRATION MAY CAUSE IRRITATION OF THE MUCOUS MEMBRANES. **CHRONIC EXPOSURE-** PROLONGED OR REPEATED EXPOSURE TO A LARGE CONCENTRATION MAY CAUSE IRRITATION OF THE MUCOUS MEMBRANES.

PYRENONE O.T. 50-5: **ACUTE EXPOSURE-** NO SPECIFIC DATA AVAILABLE, MAY BE IRRITATING. **CHRONIC EXPOSURE-** NO SPECIFIC DATA AVAILABLE, MAY BE IRRITATING.

PIPERONYL BUTOXIDE: **ACUTE EXPOSURE-** MAY CAUSE IRRITATION OF THE MUCOUS MEMBRANES. **CHRONIC EXPOSURE-** TWO SISTERS WHO WERE EXPOSED DURING THE FIRST TRIMESTER OF PREGNANCY TO LARGE AMOUNTS OF INSECT REPELLENT AND INSECTICIDES THAT CONTAINED PIPERONYL BUTOXIDE EACH GAVE BIRTH TO AN INFANT WITH COARCTATION OF THE AORTA.

MIXED HYDROCARBONS: IRRITANT/NARCOTIC. **ACUTE EXPOSURE-** THE DEGREE AND RANGE OF EFFECTS WILL VARY DEPENDING ON THE SPECIFIC HYDROCARBON COMPOSITION. HIGH VAPOR CONCENTRATIONS MAY IRRITATE MUCOUS MEMBRANES AND CAUSE CENTRAL NERVOUS SYSTEM DEPRESSION. SYMPTOMS MAY INCLUDE NAUSEA, VOMITING, WEAKNESS, FATIGUE, VERTIGO, ATAXIA, AND, IN MORE SEVERE CASES, STUPOR, ANESTHESIA, UNCONSCIOUSNESS AND COMA. CONVULSIONS ARE POSSIBLE. IN FATAL CASES, DEATH IS USUALLY DUE TO RESPIRATORY ARREST, ALTHOUGH SUDDEN DEATH MAY RESULT FROM VENTRICULAR FIBRILLATION. VISCERAL DAMAGE MAY OCCUR. **CHRONIC EXPOSURE-** REPEATED OR PROLONGED EXPOSURE TO SOME HYDROCARBONS MAY RESULT IN NEUROLOGIC EFFECTS.

FIRST AID- REMOVE FROM EXPOSURE AREA TO FRESH AIR IMMEDIATELY. IF BREATHING HAS STOPPED, PERFORM ARTIFICIAL RESPIRATION. KEEP PERSON WARM AND AT REST. TREAT SYMPTOMATICALLY AND SUPPORTIVELY. GET MEDICAL ATTENTION IMMEDIATELY.

SKIN CONTACT: LPA SOLVENT: IRRITANT. **ACUTE EXPOSURE-** SKIN CONTACT MAY CAUSE IRRITATION WITH REDNESS. ANIMAL STUDIES INDICATE A MODERATE AMOUNT WAS ABSORBED THROUGH INTACT SKIN TO CAUSE DEATH. **CHRONIC EXPOSURE-** REPEATED OR PROLONGED EXPOSURE MAY CAUSE DERMATITIS.

PARAFFINS: IRRITANT. **ACUTE EXPOSURE-** DIRECT CONTACT WITH SOME PARAFFINIC HYDROCARBONS MAY CAUSE IRRITATION. **CHRONIC EXPOSURE-** REPEATED OR PROLONGED CONTACT WITH DEFATTING AGENTS MAY CAUSE DERMATITIS.

METHYL ALCOHOL (METHANOL): IRRITANT/NARCOTIC/NEUROTOXIN. **ACUTE EXPOSURE-** CONTACT WITH LIQUID MAY CAUSE IRRITATION. SKIN ABSORPTION MAY OCCUR AND CAUSE METABOLIC ACIDOSIS AND EFFECTS ON THE EYES AND CENTRAL NERVOUS SYSTEM AS DETAILED IN ACUTE INGESTION. **CHRONIC EXPOSURE-** REPEATED OR PROLONGED CONTACT WITH THE LIQUID MAY CAUSE DEFATTING OF THE SKIN RESULTING IN ERYTHEMA, SCALING, AND ECZEMATOID DERMATITIS. CHRONIC ABSORPTION MAY RESULT METABOLIC ACIDOSIS AND EFFECTS AS DETAILED IN ACUTE INGESTION.

XYLENE: IRRITANT. **ACUTE EXPOSURE-** LIQUID XYLENE IS A DEFATTING AGENT AND MAY CAUSE A BURNING SENSATION, DRYING, VASODILATION, ERYTHEMA, AND POSSIBLY BLISTERING. THE LIQUID IS READILY ABSORBED THROUGH INTACT OR BROKEN SKIN AT A RATE OF APPROXIMATELY 4-10 MG/CM2/HOUR, BUT SYSTEMIC EFFECTS HAVE NOT BEEN REPORTED. **CHRONIC EXPOSURE-** REPEATED OR PROLONGED CONTACT MAY CAUSE DEFATTING OF THE SKIN WITH DRYING, ERYTHEMA, CRACKING, THICKENING AND BLISTERING. REPEATED APPLICATION OF 95% XYLENE TO RABBIT SKIN CAUSED MODERATE TO MARKED IRRITATION WITH ERYTHEMA AND MODERATE NECROSIS. ONE CASE OF ALLERGIC CONTACT URTICARIA HAS BEEN REPORTED.

ALKYL ARYL SULFONATES: IRRITANT. **ACUTE EXPOSURE-** NO DATA AVAILABLE ON THIS SPECIFIC GROUP. HOWEVER ANIONIC SURFACTANTS MAY CAUSE IRRITATION OF THE SKIN BY REMOVING NATURAL OILS, CAUSING REDNESS, SORENESS, AND PAPULAR DERMATITIS. IN SENSITIVE PERSONS IT MAY ALSO CAUSE THICKENING OF THE SKIN WITH WEEPING, CRACKING, SCALING, AND BLISTERING. THE PRESENCE OF ENZYMES MAY CAUSE SENSITIZATION DERMATITIS IN SOME INDIVIUALS. **CHRONIC EXPOSURE-** REPEATED OR PROLONGED EXPOSURE MAY CAUSE DERMATITIS AND MAY CAUSE SENSITIZATION DERMATITIS IN SOME INDIVIUALS.

NONIONIC SURFACTANTS: ACUTE EXPOSURE- MAY CAUSE IRRITATION. CONCENTRATED NONIONIC SURFACTANTS ARE CAPABLE OF DEGREASING THE SKIN PRODUCING DRYING AND CRACKING. CHRONIC EXPOSURE- PROLONGED OR REPEATED EXPOSURE MAY CAUSE DERMATITIS.

PYRENONE O.T. 50-5: IRRITANT. ACUTE EXPOSURE- MAY CAUSE MILD SKIN IRRITATION. CHRONIC EXPOSURE- REPEATED AND PROLONGED CONTACT MAY CAUSE DERMATITIS.

PIPERONYL BUTOXIDE: HIGHLY TOXIC. ACUTE EXPOSURE- THIS MATERIAL WAS NOT DAMAGING TO THE SKIN OF RABBITS, RATS, CATS AND DOGS. A LETHAL DOSE IN RABBITS BY DERMAL ABSORPTION WAS 200 MG/KG. A DERMAL APPLICATION AT THE RATE OF 1,880 MG/KG AS A 20% SOLUTION IN DIMETHYL PHTHALATE PRODUCED EFFECTS OF HYPEREXCITIBILITY AND CONVULSIONS IN RABBITS WITH NO REPORTED IRRITATION. CHRONIC EXPOSURE- REPEATED APPLICATION OF UNDILUTED PIPERONYL BUTOXIDE WAS MILDLY IRRITATING TO RABBIT SKIN; NO SENSITIZATION WAS PRODUCED. A LETHAL DOSE IN RABBITS FROM REPEATED APPLICATION WAS 200 MG/KG AS DETERMINED IN A 90-DAY STUDY.

MIXED HYDROCARBONS: IRRITANT. ACUTE EXPOSURE- DIRECT CONTACT WITH SOME HYDROCARBONS MAY CAUSE IRRITATION. CHRONIC EXPOSURE- PROLONGED OR REPEATED CONTACT MAY RESULT IN DERMATITIS WITH DRYING, CRACKING AND SCALING DUE TO THE DEFATTING ACTION OF LIQUID HYDROCARBONS ON THE SKIN.

FIRST AID- REMOVE CONTAMINATED CLOTHING AND SHOES IMMEDIATELY. WASH AFFECTED AREA WITH SOAP OR MILD DETERGENT AND LARGE AMOUNTS OF WATER UNTIL NO EVIDENCE OF CHEMICAL REMAINS (APPROXIMATELY 15-20 MINUTES). GET MEDICAL ATTENTION IMMEDIATELY.

EYE CONTACT: LPA SOLVENT: IRRITANT. ACUTE EXPOSURE- CONTACT WITH VAPORS OR LIQUID MAY CAUSE SLIGHT IRRITATION. CHRONIC EXPOSURE- REPEATED OR PROLONGED EXPOSURE MAY CAUSE CONJUNCTIVITIS.

PARAFFINS: IRRITANT. ACUTE EXPOSURE- DIRECT CONTACT WITH SOME PARAFFINIC HYDROCARBONS MAY CAUSE IRRITATION. HIGHER MOLECULAR WEIGHT MEMBERS MAY BE NON-IRRITATING. CHRONIC EXPOSURE- REPEATED OR PROLONGED CONTACT WITH IRRITANTS MAY CAUSE CONJUNCTIVITIS.

METHYL ALCOHOL (METHANOL): IRRITANT. ACUTE EXPOSURE- VAPORS MAY CAUSE IRRITATION. HIGH CONCENTRATIONS HAVE BEEN REPORTED TO CAUSE VIOLENT INFLAMMATION OF THE CONJUNCTIVA AND EPITHELIAL DEFECTS ON THE CORNEA. MILD IRRITATION MAY OCCUR WITH DILUTE SOLUTIONS; THE UNDILUTED LIQUID HAS PRODUCED MODERATE CORNEAL OPACITY AND CONJUNCTIVAL REDNESS IN RABBITS. APPLICATION OF A DROP OF METHANOL IN RABBIT EYES CAUSED A MILD REVERSIBLE REACTION, GRADED 3 ON A SCALE OF 1-10 AFTER 24 HOURS. CHRONIC EXPOSURE- REPEATED OR PROLONGED CONTACT MAY CAUSE CONJUNCTIVITIS.

XYLENE: IRRITANT. ACUTE EXPOSURE- 200 PPM HAS CAUSED CONJUNCTIVAL IRRITATION IN HUMANS; AT HIGHER CONCENTRATIONS, IRRITATION MAY BE SEVERE. VAPOR EXPOSURE HAS ALSO CAUSED TEARING AND PHOTOPHOBIA. AN ACCIDENTAL SPLASH IN THE HUMAN EYE CAUSED TRANSIENT SUPERFICIAL DAMAGE WITH RAPID RECOVERY, ALTHOUGH REVERSIBLE CORNEAL BURNS HAVE ALSO BEEN REPORTED. CHRONIC EXPOSURE- REPEATED OR PROLONGED EXPOSURE TO HIGH VAPOR CONCENTRATIONS MAY CAUSE A BURNING SENSATION, CONJUNCTIVITIS AND BLURRED VISION; REVERSIBLE VACUOLAR, EPITHELIAL KERATOPATHY HAS BEEN REPORTED IN SOME WORKERS.

ALKYL ARYL SULFONATES: IRRITANT. ACUTE EXPOSURE- NO DATA AVAILABLE ON THIS SPECIFIC GROUP. HOWEVER, ANIONIC SURFACTANTS MAY CAUSE SEVERE IRRITATION. DIRECT CONTACT WITH A CONCENTRATED FORM MAY CAUSE MODERATE TO SEVERE CORNEAL DAMAGE. IN HUMAN ACCIDENTS THE IMMEDIATE SEVERE PAIN LEADS TO RAPID WASHING OUT OF THE EYE, AND ONLY IN THE MOST EXTREME CIRCUMSTANCES WILL PERMANENT DAMAGE RESULT. CHRONIC EXPOSURE- REPEATED OR PROLONGED EXPOSURE MAY CAUSE CONJUNCTIVITIS.

NONIONIC SURFACTANTS: IRRITANT. ACUTE EXPOSURE- MAY CAUSE IRRITATION. THE SEVERITY OF IRRITATION VARIES AMONG THE DIFFERENT NONIONIC SURFACTANTS. SOME OF THE SURFACTANTS MAY CAUSE PAIN AND CORNEAL DAMAGE WHILE OTHERS CAUSE LITTLE OR NO DAMAGE. IN HUMAN ACCIDENTS THE IMMEDIATE SEVERE PAIN LEADS TO RAPID WASHING OUT OF EYE, AND ONLY IN THE MOST EXTREME CIRCUMSTANCES WILL PERMANENT DAMAGE RESULT. CERTAIN NONIONIC SURFACTANTS HAVE LOCAL ANESTHETIC EFFECTS ON THE CORNEA. IN FORMULATION WITH OTHER HAZARDOUS MATERIALS, THIS ANESTHETIC EFFECT MIGHT ELIMINATE THE PAIN WARNING AND ALLOW SEVERE DAMAGE TO OCCUR UPON EXPOSURE TO THE FORMULATION. CHRONIC EXPOSURE- NO DATA AVAILABLE.

PYRENONE O.T. 50-5: IRRITANT. ACUTE EXPOSURE- MAY CAUSE MILD IRRITATION. CHRONIC EXPOSURE- REPEATED AND PROLONGED CONTACT MAY CAUSE CONJUNCTIVITIS.

PIPERONYL BUTOXIDE: ACUTE EXPOSURE- MAY CAUSE IRRITATION. THIS MATERIAL WAS NOT DAMAGING TO THE EYES OF RABBITS, RATS, CATS, AND DOGS. CHRONIC EXPOSURE- NO DATA AVAILABLE.

MIXED HYDROCARBONS: IRRITANT. ACUTE EXPOSURE- DIRECT CONTACT WITH SOME HYDROCARBONS MAY CAUSE IRRITATION. CHRONIC EXPOSURE- REPEATED OR PROLONGED CONTACT WITH IRRITANTS MAY CAUSE CONJUNCTIVITIS.

FIRST AID- WASH EYES IMMEDIATELY WITH LARGE AMOUNTS OF WATER OR NORMAL SALINE, OCCASIONALLY LIFTING UPPER AND LOWER LIDS, UNTIL NO EVIDENCE OF CHEMICAL REMAINS (APPROXIMATELY 15-20 MINUTES). GET MEDICAL ATTENTION IMMEDIATELY.

INGESTION: LPA SOLVENT: ACUTE EXPOSURE- INGESTION MAY CAUSE IRRITATION OF THE STOMACH AND INTESTINES RESULTING IN NAUSEA AND VOMITING POSSIBLY POSING AN ASPIRATION HAZARD. ANIMAL STUDIES INDICATE A RELATIVELY LARGE AMOUNT WAS LETHAL. CHRONIC EXPOSURE- NO DATA AVAILABLE.

PARAFFINS: NARCOTIC. ACUTE EXPOSURE- THE GASTROINTESTINAL AND SYSTEMIC EFFECTS MAY VARY DEPENDING ON THE SPECIFIC COMPOSITION. THERE MAY BE A BURNING SENSATION AND LOCAL IRRITATION IN THE MOUTH, THROAT AND STOMACH, VOMITING AND DIARRHEA. ABSORPTION OF A SUFFICIENT AMOUNT MAY RESULT IN SYMPTOMS OF CENTRAL NERVOUS SYSTEM DEPRESSION AND OTHER SYSTEMIC AND PATHOLOGICAL EFFECTS AS DESCRIBED IN ACUTE INHALATION. THE GREATER HAZARD MAY BE FROM ASPIRATION WHICH MAY OCCUR DURING INGESTION OR SUBSEQUENT VOMITING. IN RATS, ASPIRATION OF PARAFFINS, CARBON RANGE 9-16 CAUSED CHEMICAL PNEUMONITIS, PULMONARY EDEMA, AND HEMORRHAGING. CARBON RANGE 6-8 CAUSED IMMEDIATE DEATH DUE TO CARDIAC ARREST, RESPIRATORY PARALYSIS, AND ASPHYXIA. CHRONIC EXPOSURE- NO DATA AVAILABLE.

METHYL ALCOHOL (METHANOL): NARCOTIC/NEUROTOXIN. ACUTE EXPOSURE- MAY CAUSE MILD AND TRANSIENT INEBRIATION AND SUBSEQUENT DROWSINESS FOLLOWED BY AN ASYMPTOMATIC PERIOD LASTING 8-48 HOURS. FOLLOWING THE DELAY, COUGHING, DYSPNEA, HEADACHE, DULLNESS, WEAKNESS, VERTIGO OR DIZZINESS, NAUSEA, VOMITING, OCCASIONAL DIARRHEA, ANOREXIA, VIOLENT PAIN IN THE BACK, ABDOMEN, AND EXTREMITIES, RESTLESSNESS, APATHY OR DELIUIUM, AND RARELY, EXCITEMENT AND MANIA MAY OCCUR. RAPID, SHALLOW RESPIRATION DUE TO METABOLIC ACIDOSIS, COLD AND CLAMMY SKIN, HYPOTENSION, CYANOSIS, OPISTHOTONOS, CONVULSIONS, MILD TACHYCARDIA, CARDIAC DEPRESSION, PERIPHERAL NEURITIS, CEREBRAL AND PULMONARY EDEMA, UNCONSCIOUSNESS, AND COMA ARE POSSIBLE. EFFECTS ON THE EYE MAY INCLUDE OPTIC NEURITIS, BLURRED OR DIMMED VISION, DILATED, UNRESPONSIVE PUPILS, PTOSIS, EYE PAIN, CONCENTRIC CONSTRICTION OF VISUAL FIELDS, DIPLOPIA, CHANGE IN COLOR PERCEPTION, PHOTOPHOBIA, AND OPTIC NERVE ATROPHY. PARTIAL BLINDNESS OR POSSIBLY DELAYED TRANSIENT OR PERMANENT BLINDNESS MAY OCCUR. BILATERAL SENSORINEURAL DEAFNESS HAS BEEN REPORTED IN A SINGLE CASE. LIVER, KIDNEY, HEART, STOMACH, INTESTINAL AND PANCREATIC DAMAGE MAY ALSO OCCUR. DEATH MAY BE DUE TO RESPIRATORY FAILURE OR RARELY FROM CIRCULATORY COLLAPSE. AS LITTLE AS 15 ML HAS CAUSED BLINDNESS; THE USUAL FATAL DOSE IS 60-240 ML. PROLONGED ASTHENIA AND IRREVERSIBLE EFFECTS ON THE NERVOUS SYSTEM INCLUDING DIFFICULTY IN SPEECH, MOTOR DYSFUNCTION WITH RIGIDITY, SPASTICITY, AND HYPOKINESIS HAVE BEEN REPORTED. CHRONIC EXPOSURE- REPEATED INGESTION MAY CAUSE VISUAL IMPAIRMENT AND BLINDNESS AND OTHER SYSTEMIC EFFECTS AS DETAILED IN ACUTE INGESTION. REPRODUCTIVE EFFECTS HAVE BEEN REPORTED IN ANIMALS.

XYLENE: NARCOTIC. ACUTE EXPOSURE- MAY CAUSE A BURNING SENSATION IN THE MOUTH AND STOMACH, SALIVATION, SEVERE GASTROINTESTINAL DISTRESS WITH NAUSEA AND VOMITING, POSSIBLY HEMATEMESIS, AND TOXIC EFFECTS INCLUDING SIGNS OF CENTRAL NERVOUS SYSTEM DEPRESSION AND OTHER SYMPTOMS AS IN ACUTE INHALATION, INCLUDING VENTRICULAR FIBRILLATION AND LIVER AND KIDNEY INJURY. INGESTION OF SMALL QUANTITIES OF 90% XYLENE PLUS TOLUENE PRODUCED URINARY DEXTROSE AND UROBILINOGEN EXCRETION WITH TOXIC HEPATITIS, WHICH WAS REVERSIBLE IN 20 DAYS. A DOSE OF 15-30 MILLILITERS (ABOUT 1/2-1 OUNCE) IS THE EXPECTED HUMAN LETHAL DOSE. WITH ASPIRATION OF EVEN A FEW MILLILITERS INTO THE LUNGS, SEVERE COUGHING, DISTRESS, CHEMICAL PNEUMONITIS, RAPIDLY DEVELOPING PULMONARY EDEMA, AND HEMORRHAGE MAY OCCUR. CHRONIC EXPOSURE- NO DATA AVAILABLE ON THE ORTHO-ISOMER. REPEATED INGESTION OF THE MIXED, META-, OR PARA-ISOMERS BY PREGNANT MICE RESULTED IN EFFECTS ON FERTILITY, ON THE EMBRYO OR FETUS, OR SPECIFIC DEVELOPMENTAL ABNORMALITIES. INCLUDED AMONG THESE EFFECTS WERE FETOTOXICITY, LITTER SIZE, CRANIOFACIAL AND MUSCULOSKELETAL SYSTEM ABNORMALITIES, AND POST-IMPLANTATION MORTALITY.

ALKYL ARYL SULFONATES: ACUTE EXPOSURE- NO DATA AVAILABLE IN THIS SPECIFIC GROUP. HOWVER, INGESTION OF A LARGE DOSE OF ANIONIC SURFANTANTS MAY CAUSE GASTROINTESTINAL IRRITATION, VOMITING, AND DIARRHEA. CHRONIC EXPOSURE- NO DATA AVAILABLE.

NONIONIC SURFACTANTS: ACUTE EXPOSURE- INGESTION OF A LARGE DOSE MAY CAUSE GASTROINTESTINAL IRRITATION, VOMITING, AND DIARRHEA. CHRONIC EXPOSURE- NO DATA AVAILABLE.

PYRENONE O.T. 50-5: **ACUTE EXPOSURE-** NO DATA AVAILABLE. **CHRONIC EXPOSURE-** NO DATA AVAILABLE.

PIPERONYL BUTOXIDE: **ACUTE EXPOSURE-** LABORATORY ANIMALS EXPOSED TO A SINGLE, LARGE ORAL DOSE EXHIBITED ANOREXIA, VOMITING, DIARRHEA, UNSTEADINESS, ROUGH COAT, WATERY EYES, IRRITABILITY, PROSTRATION, HEMORRHAGIC ENTERITIS, INANITION, PULMONARY HEMORRHAGE, MILD CENTRAL NERVOUS SYSTEM DEPRESSION, BLOODY DISCHARGE FROM EYES AND NOSE, LIVER DAMAGE, COMA AND DEATH. ONSET MAY BE AS EARLY AS 20 MINUTES AFTER DOSING AND DEATH MAY BE DELAYED UP TO A WEEK. **CHRONIC EXPOSURE-** EFFECTS OF ANOREXIA, STUNTING, CACHEXIA, DECREASED TESTES WEIGHT, MORPHOLOGICAL CHANGES IN THE LIVER, AN INDUCTION OF ILEOCECAL ULCERS, AND AN INCREASED IN MORTALITY WERE OBSERVED IN RATS RECEIVING A DIETARY LEVEL OF 1-3%. THIS DIETARY LEVEL ADMINISTERED TO RATS FOR THREE GENERATIONS ALSO PRODUCED A REDUCTION IN THE NUMBER OF PREGNANCIES AND OFFSPRING. NO EFFECTS WERE OBSERVED AT LEVELS LESS THAN 0.1%. WEIGHT LOSS, MORPHOLOGICAL CHANGES IN THE LIVER, KIDNEY, AND ADRENAL GLAND WERE REPORTED IN DOGS FED DOSAGES OF 105 OR 315 MG/KG/DAY. THE 315 MG/KG/DAY LEVEL WAS LETHAL TO ALL DOGS WITHIN 4 TO 15 WEEKS DUE TO LIVER INJURY.

MIXED HYDROCARBONS: NARCOTIC. **ACUTE EXPOSURE-** THE GASTROINTESTINAL AND SYSTEMIC EFFECTS MAY VARY DEPENDING ON THE SPECIFIC COMPOSITION. THERE MAY BE IRRITATION OF THE MOUTH, THROAT AND STOMACH AND VOMITING AND DIARRHEA. ABSORPTION OF A SUFFICIENT AMOUNT MAY RESULT IN SYMPTOMS OF CENTRAL NERVOUS SYSTEM DEPRESSION AND OTHER SYSTEMIC AND PATHOLOGICAL EFFECTS AS DESCRIBED IN ACUTE INHALATION. THE GREATER HAZARD MAY BE FROM ASPIRATION WHICH MAY OCCUR DURING INGESTION OR SUBSEQUENT VOMITING. DEPENDING ON CERTAIN PHYSICAL FACTORS, INCLUDING VISCOSITY, ASPIRATION MAY RESULT IN DEATH WITHIN MINUTES DUE TO CARDIAC ARREST, RESPIRATORY PARALYSIS AND ASPHYXIA; IN DELAYED CHEMICAL PNEUMONITIS WITH PULMONARY EDEMA AND HEMORRHAGE; OR, IN THE CASE OF HIGHER MOLECULAR WEIGHT COMPOUNDS, MINIMAL EDEMA AND HEMORRHAGE. **CHRONIC EXPOSURE-** NO DATA AVAILABLE.

FIRST AID- TREAT SYMPTOMATICALLY AND SUPPORTIVELY. GET MEDICAL ATTENTION AND ADVICE ON WHETHER TO USE GASTRIC LAVAGE. EXTREME CARE MUST BE TAKEN TO PREVENT ASPIRATION. A CUFFED ENDOTRACHEAL TUBE USED BY QUALIFIED MEDICAL PERSONNEL MIGHT BE ADVISABLE. KEEP HEAD LOWER THAN HIPS TO PREVENT ASPIRATION SHOULD VOMITING OCCUR.

REACTIVITY

REACTIVITY: STABLE UNDER NORMAL TEMPERATURES AND PRESSURES.

INCOMPATIBILITIES: LPA SOLVENT: STRONG OXIDIZERS: INCOMPATIBLE.

PARAFFINS: OXIDIZERS (STRONG): FIRE AND EXPLOSION HAZARD.

METHYL ALCOHOL (METHANOL): ACETYL BROMIDE: VIOLENT REACTION WITH FORMATION OF HYDROGEN BROMIDE. ALKYLALUMINUM SOLUTIONS: VIOLENT REACTION. ALUMINUM: EXPLOSION HAZARD. BARIUM PERCHLORATE: DISTILLATION YIELDS HIGHLY EXPLOSIVE ALKYL PERCHLORATE. BERYLLIUM HYDRIDE: VIOLENT REACTION, EVEN AT -196 C. BROMINE: VIGOROUSLY EXOTHERMIC REACTION. CALCIUM CARBIDE: VIOLENT REACTION. CHLORINE: POSSIBLE IGNITION AND EXPLOSION HAZARD. CHLOROFORM AND SODIUM HYDROXIDE: EXPLOSIVE REACTION. CHROMIUM TRIOXIDE (CHROMIC ANHYDRIDE): POSSIBLE IGNITION. CYANURIC CHLORIDE: VIOLENT REACTION. DICHLOROMETHANE: POSSIBLE IGNITION AND EXPLOSION. DIETHYL ZINC: POSSIBLE IGNITION AND EXPLOSION. HYDROGEN PEROXIDE + WATER: EXPLOSION HAZARD. IODINE + ETHANOL + MERCURIC OXIDE: EXPLOSION HAZARD. LEAD: CORRODES. LEAD PERCHLORATE: EXPLOSION HAZARD. MAGNESIUM: VIOLENT REACTION. MAGNESIUM (POWDERED): MIXTURES ARE CAPABLE OF DETONATION. NICKEL: POSSIBLE IGNITION IN THE PRESENCE OF NICKEL CATALYST. NITRIC ACID (CONCENTRATED): MIXTURES OF GREATER THAN 25% ACID MAY DECOMPOSE VIOLENTLY. OXIDIZERS (STRONG): FIRE AND EXPLOSION HAZARD. PERCHLORIC ACID: EXPLOSION HAZARD. PHOSPHOROUS TRIOXIDE: POSSIBLE VIOLENT REACTION AND IGNITION. POTASSIUM: POSSIBLE DANGEROUS REACTION. POTASSIUM HYDROXIDE + CHLOROFORM: EXOTHERMIC REACTION. POTASSIUM TERT-BUTOXIDE: FIRE AND EXPLOSION HAZARD. SODIUM + CHLOROFORM: POSSIBLE EXPLOSION. SODIUM HYPOCHLORITE: EXPLOSION HAZARD. SODIUM METHOXIDE + CHLOROFORM: POSSIBLE EXPLOSION. SULFURIC ACID: FIRE AND EXPLOSION HAZARD. ZINC: EXPLOSION HAZARD.

XYLENE: NITRIC ACID: EXOTHERMIC REACTION. OXIDIZERS (STRONG): FIRE AND EXPLOSION HAZARD. PLASTICS, RUBBER, COATINGS: MAY BE ATTACKED. SULFURIC ACID: EXOTHERMIC REACTION.

ALKYL ARLY SULFONATES: NO DATA AVAILABLE.

NONIONIC SURFACTANTS: NO DATA AVAILABLE.

PYRENONE O.T. 50-5: NO DATA AVAILABLE.

PIPERONYL BUTOXIDE: ACIDS (STRONG): MAY CAUSE DECOMPOSITION.

MIXED HYDROCARBONS: OXIDIZERS (STRONG): FIRE AND EXPLOSION HAZARD.

DECOMPOSITION: THERMAL DECOMPOSITION MAY RELEASE TOXIC AND/OR HAZARDOUS GASES.

POLYMERIZATION: HAZARDOUS POLYMERIZATION HAS NOT BEEN REPORTED TO OCCUR UNDER NORMAL TEMPERATURES AND PRESSURES.

CONDITIONS TO AVOID

AVOID CONTACT WITH HEAT, SPARKS, FLAMES, OR OTHER SOURCES OF IGNITION. VAPORS MAY BE EXPLOSIVE. AVOID OVERHEATING OF CONTAINERS; CONTAINERS MAY VIOLENTLY RUPTURE IN HEAT OF FIRE. AVOID CONTAMINATION OF WATER SOURCES.

SPILL AND LEAK PROCEDURES

OCCUPATIONAL SPILL: SHUT OFF IGNITION SOURCES. STOP LEAK IF YOU CAN DO IT WITHOUT RISK. USE WATER SPRAY TO REDUCE VAPORS. FOR SMALL SPILLS, TAKE UP WITH SAND OR OTHER ABSORBENT MATERIAL AND PLACE INTO CONTAINERS FOR LATER DISPOSAL. FOR LARGER SPILLS, DIKE FAR AHEAD OF SPILL FOR LATER DISPOSAL. NO SMOKING, FLAMES OR FLARES IN HAZARD AREA. KEEP UNNECESSARY PEOPLE AWAY; ISOLATE HAZARD AREA AND RESTRICT ENTRY.

PROTECTIVE EQUIPMENT

VENTILATION: PROVIDE LOCAL EXHAUST OR GENERAL DILUTION VENTILATION TO MEET PUBLISHED EXPOSURE LIMITS. VENTILATION EQUIPMENT MUST BE EXPLOSION-PROOF.

RESPIRATOR: THE FOLLOWING RESPIRATORS ARE RECOMMENDED BASED ON INFORMATION FOUND IN THE PHYSICAL DATA, TOXICITY AND HEALTH EFFECTS SECTIONS. THEY ARE RANKED IN ORDER FROM MINIMUM TO MAXIMUM RESPIRATORY PROTECTION. THE SPECIFIC RESPIRATOR SELECTED MUST BE BASED ON CONTAMINATION LEVELS FOUND IN THE WORK PLACE, MUST NOT EXCEED THE WORKING LIMITS OF THE RESPIRATOR AND BE JOINTLY APPROVED BY THE NATIONAL INSTITUTE FOR OCCUPATIONAL SAFETY AND HEALTH AND THE MINE SAFETY AND HEALTH ADMINISTRATION (NIOSH-MSHA).

CHEMICAL CARTRIDGE RESPIRATOR WITH AN ORGANIC VAPOR CARTRIDGE(S) WITH AN ACID GAS CARTRIDGE(S) AND A FULL FACEPIECE.

GAS MASK WITH ORGANIC VAPOR CANISTER (CHIN-STYLE OR FRONT- OR BACK-MOUNTED CANISTER), WITH A FULL FACEPIECE, PROVIDING PROTECTION AGAINST ACID GASES.

TYPE 'C' SUPPLIED-AIR RESPIRATOR WITH A FULL FACEPIECE OPERATED IN PRESSURE-DEMAND OR OTHER POSITIVE PRESSURE MODE OR WITH A FULL FACEPIECE, HELMET OR HOOD OPERATED IN CONTINUOUS-FLOW MODE.

SELF-CONTAINED BREATHING APPARATUS WITH A FULL FACEPIECE OPERATED IN PRESSURE-DEMAND OR OTHER POSITIVE PRESSURE MODE.

FOR FIREFIGHTING AND OTHER IMMEDIATELY DANGEROUS TO LIFE OR HEALTH CONDITIONS: SELF-CONTAINED BREATHING APPARATUS WITH FULL FACEPIECE OPERATED IN PRESSURE-DEMAND OR OTHER POSITIVE PRESSURE MODE. SUPPLIED-AIR RESPIRATOR WITH FULL FACEPIECE AND OPERATED IN PRESSURE-DEMAND OR OTHER POSITIVE PRESSURE MODE IN COMBINATION WITH AN AUXILIARY SELF-CONTAINED BREATHING APPARATUS OPERATED IN PRESSURE-DEMAND OR OTHER POSITIVE PRESSURE MODE.

CLOTHING: EMPLOYEE MUST WEAR APPROPRIATE PROTECTIVE (IMPERVIOUS) CLOTHING AND EQUIPMENT TO PREVENT ANY POSSIBILITY OF SKIN CONTACT WITH THIS SUBSTANCE.

GLOVES: EMPLOYEE MUST WEAR APPROPRIATE PROTECTIVE GLOVES TO PREVENT CONTACT WITH THIS SUBSTANCE.

EYE PROTECTION: EMPLOYEE MUST WEAR SPLASH-PROOF OR DUST-RESISTANT SAFETY GOGGLES AND A FACESHIELD TO PREVENT CONTACT WITH THIS SUBSTANCE.

EMERGENCY WASH FACILITIES: WHERE THERE IS ANY POSSIBILITY THAT AN EMPLOYEE'S EYES AND/OR SKIN MAY BE EXPOSED TO THIS SUBSTANCE, THE EMPLOYER SHOULD PROVIDE AN EYE WASH FOUNTAIN AND QUICK DRENCH SHOWER WITHIN THE IMMEDIATE WORK AREA FOR EMERGENCY USE.

AUTHORIZED BY- OCCUPATIONAL HEALTH SERVICES, INC.

CREATION DATE: 10/05/89 ***REVISION DATE:*** 07/12/90

MATERIAL SAFETY DATA SHEET

OCCUPATIONAL HEALTH SERVICES, INC.
AGRICULTURE AND PESTICIDE DIVISION
450 SEVENTH AVENUE, SUITE 2407
NEW YORK, NEW YORK 10123
1-800-445-MSDS OR (212) 967-1100

EMERGENCY CONTACT:
JOHN S. BRANSFORD, JR. (615) 292-1180

SUBSTANCE IDENTIFICATION

SUBSTANCE: **21 PYROCIDE FOGGING CONC(0.5-1-1.67) NAMCO 05194935**

TRADE NAMES/SYNONYMS: 21 PYROCIDE FOGGING CONC 1-2-3 05141258; 21 PYROCIDE FOGGING CONC 3-6-10 05141622; PST75473

CERCLA RATINGS (SCALE 0-3): HEALTH=3 FIRE=2 REACTIVITY=0 PERSISTENCE=2

NFPA RATINGS (SCALE 0-4): HEALTH=3 FIRE=2 REACTIVITY=0

COMPONENTS AND CONTAMINANTS

COMPONENT: LPA SOLVENT VISTA ***PERCENT:*** 81.0-95.0
CONTAINS:
PARAFFINS (100%)

COMPONENT: PYROCIDE 175 ***PERCENT:*** 1.0-3.0
CONTAINS:
PYRETHRINS (PYRETHRUM) (20%) CAS# 8003-34-7
LPA SOLVENT (80%)

COMPONENT: PIPERONYL BUTOXIDE TECHNICAL ***PERCENT:*** 1.0-6.0
CAS# 51-03-6

COMPONENT: MGK 264 (N-OCTYL BICYCLOHEPTENE DICARBOXIMIDE) ***PERCENT:*** 1.7-10.0
CAS# 113-48-4

EXPOSURE LIMITS: LPA SOLVENT: REFINED PETROLEUM SOLVENTS: 350 MG/M3 NIOSH RECOMMENDED TWA 1800 MG/M3 NIOSH RECOMMENDED 15 MINUTE CEILING

PHYSICAL DATA

DESCRIPTION: CLEAR, TAN TO BROWN LIQUID WITH A CHRYSANTHEMUM ODOR.
BOILING POINT: NOT AVAILABLE ***SPECIFIC GRAVITY:*** 0.81
EVAPORATION RATE: NOT AVAILABLE ***SOLUBILITY IN WATER:*** SLIGHT
VAPOR DENSITY: >1

FIRE AND EXPLOSION DATA

FIRE AND EXPLOSION HAZARD: MODERATE FIRE HAZARD WHEN EXPOSED TO HEAT OR FLAME.
VAPORS ARE HEAVIER THAN AIR AND MAY TRAVEL A CONSIDERABLE DISTANCE TO A SOURCE OF IGNITION AND FLASH BACK.
VAPOR-AIR MIXTURES ARE EXPLOSIVE ABOVE FLASH POINT.

FLASH POINT: >100 F (>38 C) (CC) ***FLAMMABILITY CLASS(OSHA):*** II

FIREFIGHTING MEDIA: DRY CHEMICAL, CARBON DIOXIDE, HALON, WATER SPRAY OR STANDARD FOAM (1987 EMERGENCY RESPONSE GUIDEBOOK, DOT P 5800.4).
FOR LARGER FIRES, USE WATER SPRAY, FOG OR STANDARD FOAM (1987 EMERGENCY RESPONSE GUIDEBOOK, DOT P 5800.4).

FIREFIGHTING: MOVE CONTAINER FROM FIRE AREA IF POSSIBLE. COOL FIRE-EXPOSED CONTAINERS WITH WATER FROM SIDE UNTIL WELL AFTER FIRE IS OUT. STAY AWAY FROM STORAGE TANK ENDS. FOR MASSIVE FIRE IN STORAGE AREA, USE UNMANNED HOSE HOLDER OR MONITOR NOZZLES, ELSE WITHDRAW FROM AREA AND LET FIRE BURN. WITHDRAW IMMEDIATELY IN CASE OF RISING SOUND FROM VENTING SAFETY DEVICE OR ANY DISCOLORATION OF STORAGE TANK DUE TO FIRE (1987 EMERGENCY RESPONSE GUIDEBOOK, DOT P 5800.4, GUIDE PAGE 27). EXTINGUISH ONLY IF FLOW CAN BE STOPPED; USE FLOODING AMOUNTS OF WATER AS A FOG, SOLID STREAMS MAY BE INEFFECTIVE. COOL CONTAINERS WITH FLOODING AMOUNTS OF WATER, APPLY FROM AS FAR A DISTANCE AS POSSIBLE. AVOID BREATHING VAPORS, KEEP UPWIND.

TRANSPORTATION DATA

DEPARTMENT OF TRANSPORTATION HAZARD CLASSIFICATION 49 CFR 172.101: COMBUSTIBLE LIQUID
DEPARTMENT OF TRANSPORTATION LABELING REQUIREMENTS 49 CFR 172.101 AND SUBPART E: NONE
DEPARTMENT OF TRANSPORTATION PACKAGING REQUIREMENTS: NONE EXCEPTIONS: 49 CFR 173.118A

TOXICITY

LPA SOLVENT: 2.0-4.0 GM/KG SKIN-RABBIT LD50 (VISTA MSDS); 39.9 GM/KG ORAL-RAT LD(0) (VISTA MSDS); 24.1 MG/L/1 HOUR INHALATION-RAT LC(0) (VISTA MSDS); CARCINOGEN STATUS: NONE. LPA SOLVENT IS AN EYE, MUCOUS MEMBRANE AND SKIN IRRITANT AND A CENTRAL NERVOUS SYSTEM DEPRESSANT.
PARAFFINS: CARCINOGEN STATUS: NONE. THE TOXICITY OF PARAFFINS WILL VARY DEPENDING ON THE SPECIFIC COMPOSITION. PARAFFINS ARE EYE, SKIN AND MUCUOUS MEMBRANE IRRITANTS AND CENTRAL NERVOUS SYSTEM DEPRESSANTS. STIMULANTS SUCH AS EPINEPHRINE MAY INDUCE VENTRICULAR FIBRILLATION.
PIPERONYL BUTOXIDE: TOXICITY DATA: 200 MG/KG SKIN-RABBIT LD50; 6150 MG/KG ORAL-RAT LD50; 2600 MG/KG ORAL-MOUSE LD50; 2650 MG/KG ORAL-RABBIT LD50; 1000 MG/KG INTRAPERITONEAL-MOUSE LDLO; MUTAGENIC DATA (RTECS); REPRODUCTIVE EFFECTS DATA (RTECS); TUMORIGENIC DATA (RTECS); CARCINOGEN STATUS: ANIMAL INADEQUATE EVIDENCE (IARC GROUP-3). ACUTE TOXICITY LEVEL: HIGHLY TOXIC BY DERMAL ABSORPTION; SLIGHTLY TOXIC BY INGESTION. TARGET EFFECTS: POISONING MAY AFFECT THE LIVER. ADDITIONAL DATA: THIS MATERIAL MAY ENHANCE THE PHARMACOLOGIC EFFECT OF DRUGS AND POTENTIATE THE TOXICITY OF ENVIRONMENTAL AGENTS.
N-OCTYL BICYCLOHEPTENE DICARBOXIMIDE (MGK 264): TOXICITY DATA: 470 MG/KG SKIN-RABBIT LD50; 470 MG/KG SKIN-RAT LD50; 2800 MG/KG ORAL-RAT LD50; 1 GM/KG ORAL-MOUSE LD50; REPRODUCTIVE EFFECTS DATA (RTECS). CARCINOGEN STATUS: NONE. ACUTE TOXICITY LEVEL: TOXIC BY DERMAL ABSORPTION; MODERATELY TOXIC BY INGESTION. TARGET EFFECTS: POISONING MAY AFFECT THE CENTRAL NERVOUS SYSTEM.

HEALTH EFFECTS AND FIRST AID

INHALATION: LPA SOLVENT: IRRITANT/NARCOTIC. **ACUTE EXPOSURE-** VAPORS MAY BE IRRITATING. EXPOSURE TO HIGH CONCENTRATIONS MAY RESULT IN CENTRAL NERVOUS SYSTEM DEPRESSION WITH HEADACHE, STUPOR, NAUSEA AND VOMITING. ANIMAL STUDIES INDICATE INHALATION OF 24.1 MG/L FOR 1 HOUR CAUSED NO DEATHS. **CHRONIC EXPOSURE-** NO DATA AVAILABLE.
PARAFFINS: IRRITANT/NARCOTIC. **ACUTE EXPOSURE-** THE DEGREE AND RANGE OF EFFECTS WILL VARY DEPENDING ON THE SPECIFIC HYDROCARBON COMPOSITION. HIGH VAPOR CONCENTRATIONS MAY IRRITATE MUCOUS MEMBRANES AND CAUSE CENTRAL NERVOUS SYSTEM DEPRESSION. SYMPTOMS MAY INCLUDE EXHILARATION, HEADACHE, DIZZINESS, NAUSEA, ANOREXIA, CONFUSION, INCOORDINATION, AND IN MORE SEVERE CASES, STUPOR, ANESTHESIA, UNCONSCIOUSNESS AND COMA WITH INHIBITION OF DEEP TENDON REFLEXES. CONVULSIONS ARE POSSIBLE. IN FATAL CASES, DEATH IS USUALLY DUE TO RESPIRATORY ARREST, ALTHOUGH SUDDEN DEATH MAY RESULT FROM VENTRICULAR FIBRILLATION. VISCERAL DAMAGE MAY OCCUR. **CHRONIC EXPOSURE-** REPEATED OR PROLONGED EXPOSURE TO SOME MEMBERS OF THIS GROUP MAY RESULT IN NEUROLOGIC EFFECTS.
PIPERONYL BUTOXIDE: **ACUTE EXPOSURE-** MAY CAUSE IRRITATION OF THE MUCOUS MEMBRANES. **CHRONIC EXPOSURE-** TWO SISTERS WHO WERE EXPOSED DURING THE FIRST TRIMESTER OF PREGNANCY TO LARGE AMOUNTS OF INSECT REPELLENT AND INSECTICIDES THAT CONTAINED PIPERONYL BUTOXIDE EACH GAVE BIRTH TO AN INFANT WITH COARCTATION OF THE AORTA.
N-OCTYL BICYCLOHEPTENE CARBOXIMIDE (MGK 264): **ACUTE EXPOSURE-** NO DATA AVAILABLE. **CHRONIC EXPOSURE-** A HEMATOTOXICITY STUDY WAS DONE IN INTACT, TOTALLY AND SUBTOTALLY SPLENECTOMIZED DOGS BY FOGGING THEM FOR 5 MINUTE PERIODS ON 4 CONSECUTIVE DAYS WITH 1.5% N-OCTYL BICYCLOHEPTENE CARBOXIMIDE. NO HEMATALOGIC CHANGES WERE NOTED IN SUBSEQUENT BLOOD OR BONE MARROW SAMPLES.

FIRST AID- REMOVE FROM EXPOSURE AREA TO FRESH AIR IMMEDIATELY. IF BREATHING HAS STOPPED, PERFORM ARTIFICIAL RESPIRATION. KEEP PERSON WARM AND AT REST. TREAT SYMPTOMATICALLY AND SUPPORTIVELY. GET MEDICAL ATTENTION IMMEDIATELY.

SKIN CONTACT: LPA SOLVENT: IRRITANT. **ACUTE EXPOSURE-** SKIN CONTACT MAY CAUSE IRRITATION WITH REDNESS. ANIMAL STUDIES INDICATE A MODERATE AMOUNT WAS ABSORBED THROUGH INTACT SKIN TO CAUSE DEATH. **CHRONIC EXPOSURE-** REPEATED OR PROLONGED EXPOSURE MAY CAUSE DERMATITIS.
PARAFFINS: IRRITANT. **ACUTE EXPOSURE-** DIRECT CONTACT WITH SOME PARAFFINIC HYDROCARBONS MAY CAUSE IRRITATION. **CHRONIC EXPOSURE-** REPEATED OR PROLONGED CONTACT WITH DEFATTING AGENTS MAY CAUSE DERMATITIS.
PIPERONYL BUTOXIDE: HIGHLY TOXIC. **ACUTE EXPOSURE-** THIS MATERIAL WAS NOT DAMAGING TO THE SKIN OF RABBITS, RATS, CATS AND DOGS. A LETHAL DOSE IN RABBITS BY DERMAL ABSORPTION WAS 200 MG/KG. A DERMAL APPLICATION AT THE RATE OF 1,880 MG/KG AS A 20% SOLUTION IN DIMETHYL PHTHALATE PRODUCED EFFECTS OF HYPEREXCITIBILITY AND CONVULSIONS IN RABBITS WITH NO REPORTED IRRITATION. **CHRONIC EXPOSURE-** REPEATED APPLICATION OF UNDILUTED PIPERONYL BUTOXIDE WAS MILDLY IRRITATING TO RABBIT SKIN; NO SENSITIZATION WAS PRODUCED. A LETHAL DOSE IN RABBITS FROM REPEATED APPLICATION WAS 200 MG/KG AS DETERMINED IN A 90-DAY STUDY.
N-OCTYL BICYCLOHEPTENE CARBOXIMIDE (MGK 264): TOXIC. **ACUTE EXPOSURE-** NOT EXPECTED TO CAUSE IRRITATION. IN RABBITS THE LETHAL DOSE WAS 470 MG/KG. SYSTEMIC EFFECTS INCLUDE CENTRAL NERVOUS EXCITATION FOLLOWED BY DEPRESSION. **CHRONIC EXPOSURE-** NO DATA AVAILABLE.

FIRST AID- REMOVE CONTAMINATED CLOTHING AND SHOES IMMEDIATELY. WASH AFFECTED AREA WITH SOAP OR MILD DETERGENT AND LARGE AMOUNTS OF WATER UNTIL NO EVIDENCE OF CHEMICAL REMAINS (APPROXIMATELY 15-20 MINUTES). GET MEDICAL ATTENTION IMMEDIATELY.

EYE CONTACT: LPA SOLVENT: IRRITANT. **ACUTE EXPOSURE-** CONTACT WITH VAPORS OR LIQUID MAY CAUSE SLIGHT IRRITATION. **CHRONIC EXPOSURE-** REPEATED OR

PROLONGED EXPOSURE MAY CAUSE CONJUNCTIVITIS. PARAFFINS: IRRITANT. **ACUTE EXPOSURE-** DIRECT CONTACT WITH SOME PARAFFINIC HYDROCARBONS MAY CAUSE IRRITATION. HIGHER MOLECULAR WEIGHT MEMBERS MAY BE NON-IRRITATING. **CHRONIC EXPOSURE-** REPEATED OR PROLONGED CONTACT WITH IRRITANTS MAY CAUSE CONJUNCTIVITIS.

PIPERONYL BUTOXIDE: **ACUTE EXPOSURE-** MAY CAUSE IRRITATION. THIS MATERIAL WAS NOT DAMAGING TO THE EYES OF RABBITS, RATS, CATS, AND DOGS. **CHRONIC EXPOSURE-** NO DATA AVAILABLE.

N-OCTYL BICYCLOHEPTENE DICARBOXIMIDE (MGK 264): **ACUTE EXPOSURE-** NO DATA AVAILABLE. **CHRONIC EXPOSURE-** NO DATA AVAILABLE.

FIRST AID- WASH EYES IMMEDIATELY WITH LARGE AMOUNTS OF WATER OR NORMAL SALINE, OCCASIONALLY LIFTING UPPER AND LOWER LIDS, UNTIL NO EVIDENCE OF CHEMICAL REMAINS (APPROXIMATELY 15-20 MINUTES). GET MEDICAL ATTENTION IMMEDIATELY.

INGESTION: LPA SOLVENT: **ACUTE EXPOSURE-** INGESTION MAY CAUSE IRRITATION OF THE STOMACH AND INTESTINES RESULTING IN NAUSEA AND VOMITING POSSIBLY POSING AN ASPIRATION HAZARD. ANIMAL STUDIES INDICATE A RELATIVELY LARGE AMOUNT WAS LETHAL. **CHRONIC EXPOSURE-** NO DATA AVAILABLE.

PARAFFINS: NARCOTIC. **ACUTE EXPOSURE-** THE GASTROINTESTINAL AND SYSTEMIC EFFECTS MAY VARY DEPENDING ON THE SPECIFIC COMPOSITION. THERE MAY BE A BURNING SENSATION AND LOCAL IRRITATION IN THE MOUTH, THROAT AND STOMACH, VOMITING AND DIARRHEA. ABSORPTION OF A SUFFICIENT AMOUNT MAY RESULT IN SYMPTOMS OF CENTRAL NERVOUS SYSTEM DEPRESSION AND OTHER SYSTEMIC AND PATHOLOGICAL EFFECTS AS DESCRIBED IN ACUTE INHALATION. THE GREATER HAZARD MAY BE FROM ASPIRATION WHICH MAY OCCUR DURING INGESTION OR SUBSEQUENT VOMITING. IN RATS, ASPIRATION OF PARAFFINS, CARBON RANGE 9-16 CAUSED CHEMICAL PNEUMONITIS, PULMONARY EDEMA, AND HEMORRHAGING. CARBON RANGE 6-8 CAUSED IMMEDIATE DEATH DUE TO CARDIAC ARREST, RESPIRATORY PARALYSIS, AND ASPHYXIA. **CHRONIC EXPOSURE-** NO DATA AVAILABLE.

PIPERONYL BUTOXIDE: **ACUTE EXPOSURE-** LABORATORY ANIMALS EXPOSED TO A SINGLE, LARGE ORAL DOSE EXHIBITED ANOREXIA, VOMITING, DIARRHEA, UNSTEADINESS, ROUGH COAT, WATERY EYES, IRRITABILITY, PROSTRATION, HEMORRHAGIC ENTERITIS, INANITION, PULMONARY HEMORRHAGE, MILD CENTRAL NERVOUS SYSTEM DEPRESSION, BLOODY DISCHARGE FROM EYES AND NOSE, LIVER DAMAGE, COMA AND DEATH. ONSET MAY BE AS EARLY AS 20 MINUTES AFTER DOSING AND DEATH MAY BE DELAYED UP TO A WEEK. **CHRONIC EXPOSURE-** EFFECTS OF ANOREXIA, STUNTING, CACHEXIA, DECREASED TESTES WEIGHT, MORPHOLOGICAL CHANGES IN THE LIVER, AN INDUCTION OF ILEOCECAL ULCERS, AND AN INCREASED IN MORTALITY WERE OBSERVED IN RATS RECEIVING A DIETARY LEVEL OF 1-3%. THIS DIETARY LEVEL ADMINISTERED TO RATS FOR THREE GENERATIONS ALSO PRODUCED A REDUCTION IN THE NUMBER OF PREGNANCIES AND OFFSPRING. NO EFFECTS WERE OBSERVED AT LEVELS LESS THAN 0.1%. WEIGHT LOSS, MORPHOLOGICAL CHANGES IN THE LIVER, KIDNEY, AND ADRENAL GLAND WERE REPORTED IN DOGS FED DOSAGES OF 105 OR 315 MG/KG/DAY. THE 315 MG/KG/DAY LEVEL WAS LETHAL TO ALL DOGS WITHIN 4 TO 15 WEEKS DUE TO LIVER INJURY.

N-OCTYL BICYCLOHEPTENE DICARBOXIMIDE (MGK 264): **ACUTE EXPOSURE-** MAY CAUSE HEADACHE AND DIARRHEA. LARGE DOSES MAY CAUSE CENTRAL NERVOUS SYSTEM STIMULATION FOLLOWED BY DEPRESSION. **CHRONIC EXPOSURE-** A 2 YEAR FEEDING STUDY ON RATS AND SWINE PRODUCED NO TOXIC EFFECTS AT LEVELS OF 1000 MG/KG AND 300 MG/KG RESPECTIVELY. EFFECTS ON FEMALE FERTILITY, LITTER SIZE AND GROWTH RATIO HAVE BEEN REPORTED IN MULTIGENERATIONAL STUDIES WITH RATS.

FIRST AID- TREAT SYMPTOMATICALLY AND SUPPORTIVELY. GET MEDICAL ATTENTION AND ADVICE ON WHETHER TO USE GASTRIC LAVAGE. EXTREME CARE MUST BE TAKEN TO PREVENT ASPIRATION. A CUFFED ENDOTRACHEAL TUBE USED BY QUALIFIED MEDICAL PERSONNEL MIGHT BE ADVISABLE. KEEP HEAD LOWER THAN HIPS TO PREVENT ASPIRATION SHOULD VOMITING OCCUR.

REACTIVITY

REACTIVITY: STABLE UNDER NORMAL TEMPERATURES AND PRESSURES.

INCOMPATIBILITIES: LPA SOLVENT: STRONG OXIDIZERS: INCOMPATIBLE.
PARAFFINS: OXIDIZERS (STRONG): FIRE AND EXPLOSION HAZARD.
PIPERONYL BUTOXIDE: ACIDS (STRONG): MAY CAUSE DECOMPOSITION.
N-OCYTL BICYCLOHEPTENE DICARBOXIMIDE (MGK 264): ACIDS (STRONG): POSSIBLE REACTION. ALKALIS (STRONG): POSSIBLE REACTION.

DECOMPOSITION: THERMAL DECOMPOSITION MAY RELEASE TOXIC AND/OR HAZARDOUS GASES.

POLYMERIZATION: HAZARDOUS POLYMERIZATION HAS NOT BEEN REPORTED TO OCCUR UNDER NORMAL TEMPERATURES AND PRESSURES.

CONDITIONS TO AVOID

AVOID CONTACT WITH HEAT, SPARKS, FLAMES, OR OTHER SOURCES OF IGNITION. VAPORS MAY BE EXPLOSIVE. AVOID OVERHEATING OF CONTAINERS; CONTAINERS MAY VIOLENTLY RUPTURE IN HEAT OF FIRE. AVOID CONTAMINATION OF WATER SOURCES.

SPILL AND LEAK PROCEDURES

OCCUPATIONAL SPILL: SHUT OFF IGNITION SOURCES. STOP LEAK IF YOU CAN DO IT WITHOUT RISK. USE WATER SPRAY TO REDUCE VAPORS. FOR SMALL SPILLS, TAKE UP WITH SAND OR OTHER ABSORBENT MATERIAL AND PLACE INTO CONTAINERS FOR LATER DISPOSAL. FOR LARGER SPILLS, DIKE FAR AHEAD OF SPILL FOR LATER DISPOSAL. NO SMOKING, FLAMES OR FLARES IN HAZARD AREA. KEEP UNNECESSARY PEOPLE AWAY; ISOLATE HAZARD AREA AND RESTRICT ENTRY.

PROTECTIVE EQUIPMENT

VENTILATION: PROVIDE LOCAL EXHAUST OR PROCESS ENCLOSURE VENTILATION TO MEET PUBLISHED EXPOSURE LIMITS.

RESPIRATOR: THE FOLLOWING RESPIRATORS ARE RECOMMENDED BASED ON INFORMATION FOUND IN THE PHYSICAL DATA, TOXICITY AND HEALTH EFFECTS SECTIONS. THEY ARE RANKED IN ORDER FROM MINIMUM TO MAXIMUM RESPIRATORY PROTECTION. THE SPECIFIC RESPIRATOR SELECTED MUST BE BASED ON CONTAMINATION LEVELS FOUND IN THE WORK PLACE, MUST NOT EXCEED THE WORKING LIMITS OF THE RESPIRATOR AND BE JOINTLY APPROVED BY THE NATIONAL INSTITUTE FOR OCCUPATIONAL SAFETY AND HEALTH AND THE MINE SAFETY AND HEALTH ADMINISTRATION (NIOSH-MSHA).

TYPE 'C' SUPPLIED-AIR RESPIRATOR WITH A FULL FACEPIECE OPERATED IN PRESSURE-DEMAND OR OTHER POSITIVE PRESSURE MODE OR WITH A FULL FACEPIECE, HELMET OR HOOD OPERATED IN CONTINOUS-FLOW MODE.

SELF-CONTAINED BREATHING APPARATUS WITH A FULL FACEPIECE OPERATED IN PRESSURE-DEMAND OR OTHER POSITIVE PRESSURE MODE.

FOR FIREFIGHTING AND OTHER IMMEDIATELY DANGEROUS TO LIFE OR HEALTH CONDITIONS:

SELF-CONTAINED BREATHING APPARATUS WITH FULL FACEPIECE OPERATED IN PRESSURE-DEMAND OR OTHER POSITIVE PRESSURE MODE.

SUPPLIED-AIR RESPIRATOR WITH FULL FACEPIECE AND OPERATED IN PRESSURE-DEMAND OR OTHER POSITIVE PRESSURE MODE IN COMBINATION WITH AN AUXILIARY SELF-CONTAINED BREATHING APPARATUS OPERATED IN PRESSURE-DEMAND OR OTHER POSITIVE PRESSURE MODE.

CLOTHING: EMPLOYEE MUST WEAR APPROPRIATE PROTECTIVE (IMPERVIOUS) CLOTHING AND EQUIPMENT TO PREVENT ANY POSSIBILITY OF SKIN CONTACT WITH THIS SUBSTANCE.

GLOVES: EMPLOYEE MUST WEAR APPROPRIATE PROTECTIVE GLOVES TO PREVENT CONTACT WITH THIS SUBSTANCE.

EYE PROTECTION: EMPLOYEE MUST WEAR SPLASH-PROOF OR DUST-RESISTANT SAFETY GOGGLES AND A FACESHIELD TO PREVENT CONTACT WITH THIS SUBSTANCE.

EMERGENCY WASH FACILITIES: WHERE THERE IS ANY POSSIBILITY THAT AN EMPLOYEE'S EYES AND/OR SKIN MAY BE EXPOSED TO THIS SUBSTANCE, THE EMPLOYER SHOULD PROVIDE AN EYE WASH FOUNTAIN AND QUICK DRENCH SHOWER WITHIN THE IMMEDIATE WORK AREA FOR EMERGENCY USE.

AUTHORIZED BY- OCCUPATIONAL HEALTH SERVICES, INC.
CREATION DATE: 10/05/89 ***REVISION DATE:*** 07/12/90

MATERIAL SAFETY DATA SHEET

OCCUPATIONAL HEALTH SERVICES, INC.
AGRICULTURE AND PESTICIDE DIVISION
450 SEVENTH AVENUE, SUITE 2407
NEW YORK, NEW YORK 10123
1-800-445-MSDS OR (212) 967-1100

EMERGENCY CONTACT:
JOHN S. BRANSFORD, JR. (615) 292-1180

SUBSTANCE IDENTIFICATION

SUBSTANCE: 21 TRIFUME 2+2 05066709

TRADE NAMES/SYNONYMS: 21 TRIFUME 43-57 05066695; NA 1581; PST75474

CERCLA RATINGS (SCALE 0-3): HEALTH=3 FIRE=1 REACTIVITY=1 PERSISTENCE=3

NFPA RATINGS (SCALE 0-4): HEALTH=4 FIRE=1 REACTIVITY=1

COMPONENTS AND CONTAMINANTS

COMPONENT: METHYL BROMIDE ***PERCENT:*** 43.0-50.0
CAS# 74-83-9

COMPONENT: CHLOROPICRIN 200 LB ***PERCENT:*** 50.0-57.0
CAS# 76-06-2

OTHER CONTAMINANTS: NONE
EXPOSURE LIMITS: METHYL BROMIDE: 5 PPM (20 MG/M3) OSHA TWA (SKIN) 5 PPM (20 MG/M3) ACGIH TWA (SKIN) LOWEST FEASIBLE LIMIT NIOSH RECOMMENDED EXPOSURE CRITERIA
1000 POUNDS SARA SECTION 302 THRESHOLD PLANNING QUANTITY 1000 POUNDS SARA SECTION 304 REPORTABLE QUANTITY 1000 POUNDS CERCLA SECTION 103 REPORTABLE QUANTITY SUBJECT TO SARA SECTION 313 ANNUAL TOXIC CHEMICAL RELEASE REPORTING

PHYSICAL DATA

DESCRIPTION: COLORLESS LIQUID WITH A STRONG, IRRITATING TEAR-GAS ODOR.
BOILING POINT: NOT AVAILABLE ***SPECIFIC GRAVITY:*** 1.66
EVAPORATION RATE: NOT AVAILABLE ***SOLUBILITY IN WATER:*** SLIGHT
VAPOR DENSITY: >3

FIRE AND EXPLOSION DATA

FIRE AND EXPLOSION HAZARD: SLIGHT FIRE HAZARD WHEN EXPOSED TO HEAT OR FLAME.
VAPORS ARE HEAVIER THAN AIR AND MAY TRAVEL A CONSIDERABLE DISTANCE TO A SOURCE OF IGNITION AND FLASH BACK.
FIREFIGHTING MEDIA: DRY CHEMICAL, CARBON DIOXIDE, HALON, WATER SPRAY OR STANDARD FOAM (1987 EMERGENCY RESPONSE GUIDEBOOK, DOT P 5800.4).
FOR LARGER FIRES, USE WATER SPRAY, FOG OR STANDARD FOAM (1987 EMERGENCY RESPONSE GUIDEBOOK, DOT P 5800.4).
FIREFIGHTING: MOVE CONTAINERS FROM FIRE AREA IF POSSIBLE. FIGHT FIRE FROM MAXIMUM DISTANCE. STAY AWAY FROM STORAGE TANK ENDS. DIKE FIRE CONTROL WATER FOR LATER DISPOSAL. DO NOT SCATTER MATERIAL (1987 EMERGENCY RESPONSE GUIDEBOOK, DOT P 5800.4, GUIDE PAGE 55).
USE AGENTS SUITABLE FOR TYPE OF FIRE. USE WATER IN FLOODING AMOUNTS AS FOG. COOL CONTAINERS WITH FLOODING AMOUNTS OF WATER, APPLY FROM AS FAR A DISTANCE AS POSSIBLE. AVOID BREATHING POISONOUS VAPORS, KEEP UPWIND. CONSIDER EVACUATION OF DOWNWIND AREA IF MATERIAL IS LEAKING.

TRANSPORTATION DATA

DEPARTMENT OF TRANSPORTATION HAZARD CLASSIFICATION 49 CFR 172.101: POISON B
DEPARTMENT OF TRANSPORTATION LABELING REQUIREMENTS 49 CFR 172.101 AND SUBPART E: POISON
DEPARTMENT OF TRANSPORTATION PACKAGING REQUIREMENTS: 49 CFR 173.353 EXCEPTIONS: NONE

TOXICITY

METHYL BROMIDE: TOXICITY DATA: 1 GM/M3/2 HOURS INHALATION-CHILD LCLO; 35 PPM INHALATION-HUMAN TCLO; 60,000 PPM/2 HOURS INHALATION-MAN LCLO; 302 PPM/8 HOURS INHALATION-RAT LC50; 1540 MG/M3/2 HOURS INHALATION-MOUSE LCLO; 28,900 MG/M3/30 MINUTES INHALATION-RABBIT LC50; 300 PPM/9 HOURS INHALATION-GUINEA PIG LCLO; 35 GM/M3/40 MINUTES INTERMITTENT SKIN-HUMAN TDLO; 214 MG/KG ORAL-RAT LD50; 135 MG/KG SUBCUTANEOUS-RAT LD50; MUTAGENIC DATA (RTECS); TUMORIGENIC DATA (RTECS). CARCINOGEN STATUS: ANIMAL LIMITED EVIDENCE (IARC GROUP-3). IN ONE 90 DAY STUDY BY ORAL ADMINISTRATION IN RATS, METHYL BROMIDE WAS REPORTED TO PRODUCE SQUAMOUS-CELL CARCINOMAS OF THE FORESTOMACH. LOCAL EFFECTS: IRRITANT- SKIN, EYE. ACUTE TOXICITY LEVEL: TOXIC BY INHALATION AND INGESTION. TARGET EFFECTS: CENTRAL NERVOUS SYSTEM DEPRESSANT. POISONING MAY AFFECT THE BRAIN, KIDNEYS, AND LIVER. ADDITIONAL INFORMATION: STIMULANTS SUCH AS EPINEPHINE MAY INDUCE VENTRICULAR FIBRILLATION.*
* BASED ON GENERAL INFORMATION ON HALOGENATED ALKANES.
CHLOROPICRIN: TOXICITY DATA: 2 MG/M3 INHALATION-HUMAN TCLO; 2000 MG/M3/10 MINUTES INHALATION-HUMAN LCLO; 66 MG/M3/4 HOURS INHALATION-MOUSE LC50; 800 MG/M3/20 MINUTES INHALATION-CAT LCLO; 800 MG/M3/20 MINUTES INHALATION-RABBIT LC50; 800 MG/M3/20 MINUTES INHALATION-GUINEA PIG LCLO; 250 MG/KG ORAL-RAT LD50; 4200 UG/KG INTRAVENOUS-GUINEA PIG LD50; 25 MG/KG INTRAPERITONEAL-MOUSE LD50; MUTAGENIC DATA (RTECS); TUMORIGENIC DATA (RTECS). CARCINOGEN STATUS: NONE. LOCAL EFFECTS: CORROSIVE- INHALATION, SKIN, AND EYES; LACRIMATOR. ACUTE TOXICITY LEVEL: HIGHLY TOXIC BY INHALATION; TOXIC BY INGESTION. TARGET EFFECTS: METHEMOGLOBIN FORMER. POISONING MAY AFFECT THE RESPIRATORY AND CARDIOVASCULAR SYSTEMS.

HEALTH EFFECTS AND FIRST AID

INHALATION: METHYL BROMIDE: NARCOTIC/TOXIC. **ACUTE EXPOSURE-** SYMPTOMS MAY BE DELAYED FROM 1-12 HOURS AFTER EXPOSURE TO HIGH CONCENTRATIONS; LOWER CONCENTRATIONS RESULT IN LESS SEVERE SYMPTOMS WITH A LATENT PERIOD OF 12 TO 24 HOURS. REPORTED EFFECTS INCLUDE HEADACHE, VISUAL DISTURBANCES, NAUSEA, VOMITING, ANOREXIA, ABDOMINAL PAIN, WEAKNESS, MALAISE, VERTIGO, PARESTHESIAS AND PARALYSIS OF THE EXTREMITIES, OLIGURIA OR ANURIA, DROWSINESS, CONFUSION, HYPERACTIVITY, HYPOTENSION, MANIA, HALLUCINATIONS, TREMORS OR TWITCHING, ATAXIA, AND CONVULSIONS. HIGH CONCENTRATIONS MAY CAUSE RAPID NARCOSIS AND DEATH FROM RESPIRATORY FAILURE. LESSER CONCENTRATIONS MAY CAUSE PULMONARY IRRITATION, COUGHING, CHEST PAIN, SHORTNESS OF BREATH, CONGESTION, EDEMA, AND DEVELOPMENT OF BRONCHITIS OR PNEUMONITIS. JAUNDICE AND CYANOSIS MAY ALSO RESULT. UNCONSCIOUSNESS, COMA, AND DEATH DUE TO RESPIRATORY OR CIRCULATORY COLLAPSE MAY OCCUR. TUBULAR DAMAGE IN THE KIDNEYS HAS BEEN OBSERVED IN FATAL CASES. SURVIVING INDIVIDUALS MAY HAVE PERSISTENT CENTRAL AND PERIPHERAL NERVOUS SYSTEM EFFECTS INCLUDING VERTIGO, DEPRESSION, HALLUCINATIONS, ANMESIA, ANXIETY, INABILITY TO CONCENTRATE, SENSORY DISTURBANCES, WEAKNESS, AND IRRITABILITY. **CHRONIC EXPOSURE-** REPEATED EXPOSURE MAY RESULT IN ADVERSE CENTRAL NERVOUS SYSTEM EFFECTS INCLUDING LETHARGY, MUSCULAR PAINS, VISUAL, SPEECH, AND SENSORY DISTURBANCES, MENTAL CONFUSION, BLURRED VISION, PAPILLEDEMA, HALLUCINATIONS, SOMNOLENCE, FAINTING ATTACKS, BRONCHOSPASMS, AND CENTRAL NERVOUS SYSTEM EDEMA. PERIPHERAL NEUROPATHY MAY BE INDICATED BY PARALYSIS OF THE EXTREMITIES, MYOCLONUS, POLYNEURITIS, AND CONVULSIONS. LIVER, KIDNEY AND PERMANENT BRAIN DAMAGE MAY OCCUR.
CHLOROPICRIN: CORROSIVE/METHEMOGLOBIN FORMER/HIGHLY TOXIC. 4 PPM IMMEDIATELY DANGEROUS TO LIFE OR HEALTH. **ACUTE EXPOSURE-** MAY CAUSE IRRITATION, SORE THROAT, COUGHING, LABORED BREATHING, DIZZINESS, NAUSEA, VOMITING, CYANOSIS, FAINTNESS, AND PULMONARY EDEMA. LOW METHEMOGLOBIN LEVELS MAY RESULT IN HEADACHE, WEAKNESS, AND DYSPNEA. HIGH METHEMOGLOBIN LEVELS MAY RESULT IN STUPOR, RESPIRATORY DEPRESSION, AND CHOCOLATE COLORED BLOOD FROM LACK OF OXYGENATION. **CHRONIC EXPOSURE-** PROLONGED AND REPEATED EXPOSURE MAY CAUSE HEART AND LUNG DAMAGE AND PULMONARY EDEMA WITH POSSIBLE COMA AND DEATH.
FIRST AID- REMOVE FROM EXPOSURE AREA TO FRESH AIR IMMEDIATELY. IF BREATHING HAS STOPPED, GIVE ARTIFICIAL RESPIRATION. MAINTAIN AIRWAY AND BLOOD PRESSURE AND ADMINISTER OXYGEN IF AVAILABLE. KEEP AFFECTED PERSON WARM AND AT REST. TREAT SYMPTOMATICALLY AND SUPPORTIVELY. ADMINISTRATION OF OXYGEN SHOULD BE PERFORMED BY QUALIFIED PERSONNEL. GET MEDICAL ATTENTION IMMEDIATELY.

SKIN CONTACT: METHYL BROMIDE: IRRITANT. **ACUTE EXPOSURE-** CONTACT WITH THE LIQUID MAY CAUSE IRRITATION, ERYTHEMA, EDEMA, SCALING, AND ITCHING DERMATITIS. THE LIQUID MAY BE ABSORBED THROUGH INTACT SKIN. **CHRONIC EXPOSURE-** REPEATED OR PROLONGED EXPOSURE MAY LEAD TO VESICULATION AND POSSIBLE DEEP BURNS.
CHLOROPICRIN: CORROSIVE/METHEMOGLOBIN FORMER. **ACUTE EXPOSURE-** MAY CAUSE IRRITATION, REDNESS, PAIN AND SKIN BURNS. IT IS ABSORBED THROUGH THE SKIN AND MAY RESULT IN METHEMOGLOBINEMIA. LOW METHEMOGLOBIN LEVELS MAY RESULT IN HEADACHE, WEAKNESS, AND DYSPNEA. HIGH METHEMOGLOBIN LEVELS MAY RESULT IN STUPOR, RESPIRATORY DEPRESSION, AND CHOCOLATE COLORED BLOOD FROM LACK OF OXYGENATION. **CHRONIC EXPOSURE-** PROLONGED AND REPEATED EXPOSURE MAY CAUSE DERMATITIS AND SKIN BURNS.
FIRST AID- REMOVE CONTAMINATED CLOTHING AND SHOES IMMEDIATELY. WASH AFFECTED AREA WITH SOAP OR MILD DETERGENT AND LARGE AMOUNTS OF WATER UNTIL NO EVIDENCE OF CHEMICAL REMAINS (AT LEAST 15-20 MINUTES). IN CASE OF CHEMICAL BURNS, COVER AREA WITH STERILE, DRY DRESSING. BANDAGE SECURELY, BUT NOT TOO TIGHTLY. GET MEDICAL ATTENTION IMMEDIATELY.

EYE CONTACT: METHYL BROMIDE: **ACUTE EXPOSURE-** VAPORS AND LIQUID MAY CAUSE TRANSIENT IRRITATION AND CONJUNCTIVITIS. RABBITS EXPOSED TO CONCENTRATED VAPORS FOR 1 MINUTE 30 SECONDS RESULTED IN LOSS OF EYE SURFACE LUSTER, LOSS OF CORNEAL EPITHELIUM, EDEMA OF THE CONJUNCTIVAE AND LIDS, AND TRANSIENT CORNEAL OPACITY. **CHRONIC EXPOSURE-** REPEATED OR PROLONGED EXPOSURE MAY CAUSE CONJUNCTIVITIS.
CHLOROPICRIN: CORROSIVE/LACRIMATOR. **ACUTE EXPOSURE-** MAY CAUSE IRRITATION, REDNESS, PAIN, LACRIMATION, BLURRED VISION AND CORNEAL DAMAGE. **CHRONIC EXPOSURE-** MAY CAUSE CORNEAL DAMAGE AND CONJUNCTIVITIS.
FIRST AID- WASH EYES IMMEDIATELY WITH LARGE AMOUNTS OF WATER, OCCASIONALLY LIFTING UPPER AND LOWER LIDS, UNTIL NO EVIDENCE OF CHEMICAL REMAINS (AT LEAST 15-20 MINUTES). CONTINUE IRRIGATING WITH NORMAL SALINE UNTIL THE PH HAS RETURNED TO NORMAL (30-60 MINUTES). COVER WITH STERILE BANDAGES. GET MEDICAL ATTENTION IMMEDIATELY.

INGESTION: METHYL BROMIDE: TOXIC/LIMITED ANIMAL CARCINOGEN. **ACUTE EXPOSURE-** INGESTION OF LIQUID MAY RESULT IN SYSTEMIC TOXICITY AS

DETAILED IN ACUTE INHALATION. THE LETHAL DOSE REPORTED IN RATS WAS 214 MG/KG. THE SYMPTOMS WERE NOT REPORTED. **CHRONIC EXPOSURE**- DEGENERATION OF PERIPHERAL NERVES AND THE DORSAL COLUMNS OF THE SPINAL CORD HAS BEEN REPORTED IN RATS FED DIETS WITH METHYL BROMIDE. REPEATED ADMINISTRATION TO RATS BY ORAL GAVAGE INDUCED TUMORS OF THE FORESTOMACH.

CHLOROPICRIN: CORROSIVE/METHEMOGLOBIN FORMER/TOXIC. **ACUTE EXPOSURE**- MAY CAUSE IRRITATION, SORE THROAT, COUGHING, LABORED BREATHING, DIZZINESS, NAUSEA, VOMITING, CYANOSIS, AND FAINTNESS. INGESTION OF LIQUID CAN CAUSE SEVERE GASTROENTERITIS. LOW METHEMOGLOBIN LEVELS MAY RESULT IN HEADACHE, WEAKNESS, AND DYSPNEA. HIGH METHEMOGLOBIN LEVELS MAY RESULT IN STUPOR, RESPIRATORY DEPRESSION, AND CHOCOLATE COLORED BLOOD FROM LACK OF OXYGENATION. **CHRONIC EXPOSURE**- MAY CAUSE HEART AND LUNG DAMAGE.

FIRST AID- TREAT SYMPTOMATICALLY AND SUPPORTIVELY. GET MEDICAL ATTENTION IMMEDIATELY. IF VOMITING OCCURS, KEEP HEAD LOWER THAN HIPS TO PREVENT ASPIRATION.

REACTIVITY

REACTIVITY: CHLOROPICRIN: BULK CONTAINERS CAN BE SHOCK DETONATED.

INCOMPATIBILITIES: METHYL BROMIDE: ALUMINUM: SEVERE EXPLOSION HAZARD. MAGNESIUM: SEVERE EXPLOSION HAZARD. ZINC: SEVERE EXPLOSION HAZARD. DIMETHYL SULFOXIDE: DELAYED EXPLOSION HAZARD. STRONG OXIDIZERS: VIGOROUS REACTION. ETHYLENE OXIDE: VIGOROUS REACTION.

CHLOROPICRIN: ANILINE: VIOLENT REACTION. BROMO-2-PROPYNE: EXPLOSIVE, SHOCK- AND HEAT- SENSITIVE. SODIUM HYDROXIDE: REACTS VIOLENTLY SODIUM METHOXIDE: BELOW 50 C, NITRO COMPOUND WILL ACCUMULATE AND CAUSE A VIOLENT AND DANGEROUS EXOTHERMIC REACTION. STRONG OXIDIZERS: POSSIBLE VIOLENT REACTION.

DECOMPOSITION: THERMAL DECOMPOSITION MAY RELEASE TOXIC AND/OR HAZARDOUS GASES.

POLYMERIZATION: HAZARDOUS POLYMERIZATION HAS NOT BEEN REPORTED TO OCCUR UNDER NORMAL TEMPERATURES AND PRESSURES.

CONDITIONS TO AVOID

MAY BURN BUT DOES NOT IGNITE READILY. CONTAINERS MAY EXPLODE IN HEAT OF FIRE.

SPILL AND LEAK PROCEDURES

OCCUPATIONAL SPILL: DO NOT TOUCH SPILLED MATERIAL. STOP LEAK IF YOU CAN DO IT WITHOUT RISK. USE WATER SPRAY TO REDUCE VAPORS. FOR SMALL SPILLS, TAKE UP WITH SAND OR OTHER ABSORBENT MATERIAL AND PLACE INTO CONTAINERS FOR LATER DISPOSAL. FOR SMALL DRY SPILLS, WITH A CLEAN SHOVEL PLACE MATERIAL INTO CLEAN, DRY CONTAINERS AND COVER. MOVE CONTAINERS FROM SPILL AREA. FOR LARGER SPILLS, DIKE FAR AHEAD OF SPILL FOR LATER DISPOSAL. KEEP UNNECESSARY PEOPLE AWAY. ISOLATE HAZARD AREA AND DENY ENTRY. VENTILATE CLOSED SPACES BEFORE ENTERING.

PROTECTIVE EQUIPMENT

VENTILATION: PROCESS ENCLOSURE RECOMMENDED TO MEET PUBLISHED EXPOSURE LIMITS.

RESPIRATOR: THE FOLLOWING RESPIRATORS ARE RECOMMENDED BASED ON INFORMATION FOUND IN THE PHYSICAL DATA, TOXICITY AND HEALTH EFFECTS SECTIONS. THEY ARE RANKED IN ORDER FROM MINIMUM TO MAXIMUM RESPIRATORY PROTECTION. THE SPECIFIC RESPIRATOR SELECTED MUST BE BASED ON CONTAMINATION LEVELS FOUND IN THE WORK PLACE, MUST NOT EXCEED THE WORKING LIMITS OF THE RESPIRATOR AND BE JOINTLY APPROVED BY THE NATIONAL INSTITUTE FOR OCCUPATIONAL SAFETY AND HEALTH AND THE MINE SAFETY AND HEALTH ADMINISTRATION (NIOSH-MSHA).

TYPE 'C' SUPPLIED-AIR RESPIRATOR WITH A FULL FACEPIECE OPERATED IN PRESSURE-DEMAND OR OTHER POSITIVE PRESSURE MODE OR WITH A FULL FACEPIECE, HELMET OR HOOD OPERATED IN CONTINOUS-FLOW MODE.

SELF-CONTAINED BREATHING APPARATUS WITH A FULL FACEPIECE OPERATED IN PRESSURE-DEMAND OR OTHER POSITIVE PRESSURE MODE.

FOR FIREFIGHTING AND OTHER IMMEDIATELY DANGEROUS TO LIFE OR HEALTH CONDITIONS:

SELF-CONTAINED BREATHING APPARATUS WITH FULL FACEPIECE OPERATED IN PRESSURE-DEMAND OR OTHER POSITIVE PRESSURE MODE.

SUPPLIED-AIR RESPIRATOR WITH FULL FACEPIECE AND OPERATED IN PRESSURE-DEMAND OR OTHER POSITIVE PRESSURE MODE IN COMBINATION WITH AN AUXILIARY SELF-CONTAINED BREATHING APPARATUS OPERATED IN PRESSURE-DEMAND OR OTHER POSITIVE PRESSURE MODE.

CLOTHING: EMPLOYEE MUST WEAR APPROPRIATE PROTECTIVE (IMPERVIOUS) CLOTHING AND EQUIPMENT TO PREVENT ANY POSSIBILITY OF SKIN CONTACT WITH THIS SUBSTANCE.

GLOVES: EMPLOYEE MUST WEAR APPROPRIATE PROTECTIVE GLOVES TO PREVENT CONTACT WITH THIS SUBSTANCE.

EYE PROTECTION: EMPLOYEE MUST WEAR SPLASH-PROOF OR DUST-RESISTANT SAFETY GOGGLES AND A FACESHIELD TO PREVENT CONTACT WITH THIS SUBSTANCE.

EMERGENCY WASH FACILITIES: WHERE THERE IS ANY POSSIBILITY THAT AN EMPLOYEE'S EYES AND/OR SKIN MAY BE EXPOSED TO THIS SUBSTANCE, THE EMPLOYER SHOULD PROVIDE AN EYE WASH FOUNTAIN AND QUICK DRENCH SHOWER WITHIN THE IMMEDIATE WORK AREA FOR EMERGENCY USE.

AUTHORIZED BY- OCCUPATIONAL HEALTH SERVICES, INC.

CREATION DATE: 10/05/89 ***REVISION DATE:*** 07/13/90

MATERIAL SAFETY DATA SHEET

OCCUPATIONAL HEALTH SERVICES, INC.
AGRICULTURE AND PESTICIDE DIVISION
450 SEVENTH AVENUE, SUITE 2407
NEW YORK, NEW YORK 10123
1-800-445-MSDS OR (212) 967-1100

EMERGENCY CONTACT:
JOHN S. BRANSFORD, JR. (615) 292-1180

SUBSTANCE IDENTIFICATION

CAS-NUMBER 1300-72-7

SUBSTANCE: **SODIUM XYLENE SULFONATE**

TRADE NAMES/SYNONYMS: BENZENESULFONIC ACID, DIMETHYL-, SODIUM SALT; XYLENESULFONIC ACID, SODIUM SALT; CONCO SXS; CYCLOPHIL SXS 30; ELTESOL SX 30; NAXONATE; NAXONATE G; RICHONATE SXS; SODIUM DIMETHYLBENZENESULFONATE; SODIUM XYLENESULFONATE; STEPANATE X; SXS 40; ULTRAWET 40SX; C8H10NAO3S; PST75603

CHEMICAL FAMILY: SULFONATE

MOLECULAR FORMULA: C8-H10-O3-S-NA

CERCLA RATINGS (SCALE 0-3): HEALTH=U FIRE=0 REACTIVITY=0 PERSISTENCE=0

NFPA RATINGS (SCALE 0-4): HEALTH=U FIRE=0 REACTIVITY=0

COMPONENTS AND CONTAMINANTS

COMPONENT: SODIUM XYLENE SULFONATE ***PERCENT:*** 40-42
CAS# 1300-72-7

COMPONENT: WATER ***PERCENT:*** 55-60

EXPOSURE LIMITS: NO OCCUPATIONAL EXPOSURE LIMITS ESTABLISHED BY OSHA, ACGIH, OR NIOSH.

PHYSICAL DATA

DESCRIPTION: SOLUTION. ***BOILING POINT:*** 212 F (100 C)

VAPOR PRESSURE: 18 MMHG @ 20 C ***EVAPORATION RATE:*** (ETHER=1) <1.0

SOLVENT SOLUBILITY: SOLUBLE IN DIMETHYL SULFOXIDE

FIRE AND EXPLOSION DATA

FIRE AND EXPLOSION HAZARD: NEGLIGIBLE FIRE HAZARD WHEN EXPOSED TO HEAT OR FLAME.

FIREFIGHTING MEDIA: DRY CHEMICAL, CARBON DIOXIDE, HALON, WATER SPRAY OR STANDARD FOAM (1987 EMERGENCY RESPONSE GUIDEBOOK, DOT P 5800.4). FOR LARGER FIRES, USE WATER SPRAY, FOG OR STANDARD FOAM (1987 EMERGENCY RESPONSE GUIDEBOOK, DOT P 5800.4).

FIREFIGHTING: NO ACUTE HAZARD. MOVE CONTAINER FROM FIRE AREA IF POSSIBLE. AVOID BREATHING VAPORS OR DUSTS; KEEP UPWIND.

TOXICITY

SODIUM XYLENE SULFONATE: CARCINOGEN STATUS: NONE. ACUTE TOXICITY LEVEL: NO DATA AVAILABLE. TARGET EFFECTS: NO DATA AVAILABLE.

HEALTH EFFECTS AND FIRST AID

INHALATION: SODIUM XYLENE SULFONATE: **ACUTE EXPOSURE**- MAY CAUSE IRRITATION. **CHRONIC EXPOSURE**- NO DATA AVAILABLE.

FIRST AID- REMOVE FROM EXPOSURE AREA TO FRESH AIR IMMEDIATELY. IF BREATHING HAS STOPPED, PERFORM ARTIFICIAL RESPIRATION. KEEP PERSON WARM AND AT REST. TREAT SYMPTOMATICALLY AND SUPPORTIVELY. GET MEDICAL ATTENTION IMMEDIATELY.

SKIN CONTACT: SODIUM XYLENE SULFONATE: **ACUTE EXPOSURE**- MAY CAUSE IRRITATION. **CHRONIC EXPOSURE**- REPEATED OR PROLONGED CONTACT MAY CAUSE DERMATITIS.

FIRST AID- REMOVE CONTAMINATED CLOTHING AND SHOES IMMEDIATELY. WASH AFFECTED AREA WITH SOAP OR MILD DETERGENT AND LARGE AMOUNTS OF WATER UNTIL NO EVIDENCE OF CHEMICAL REMAINS (APPROXIMATELY 15-20 MINUTES). GET MEDICAL ATTENTION IMMEDIATELY.

EYE CONTACT: SODIUM XYLENE SULFONATE: **ACUTE EXPOSURE**- MAY CAUSE IRRITATION. **CHRONIC EXPOSURE**- REPEATED OR PROLONGED EXPOSURE MAY CAUSE CONJUNCTIVITIS.
FIRST AID- WASH EYES IMMEDIATELY WITH LARGE AMOUNTS OF WATER OR NORMAL SALINE, OCCASIONALLY LIFTING UPPER AND LOWER LIDS, UNTIL NO EVIDENCE OF CHEMICAL REMAINS (APPROXIMATELY 15-20 MINUTES). GET MEDICAL ATTENTION IMMEDIATELY.

INGESTION: SODIUM XYLENE SULFONATE: **ACUTE EXPOSURE**- NO DATA AVAILABLE. **CHRONIC EXPOSURE**- NO DATA AVAILABLE.
FIRST AID- TREAT SYMPTOMATICALLY AND SUPPORTIVELY. GET MEDICAL ATTENTION IMMEDIATELY. IF VOMITING OCCURS, KEEP HEAD LOWER THAN HIPS TO PREVENT ASPIRATION.

REACTIVITY

REACTIVITY: SODIUM XYLENE SULFONATE: SENSITIVE TO MOISTURE.
INCOMPATIBILITIES: SODIUM XYLENE SULFONATE: NO DATA AVAILABLE.
DECOMPOSITION: THERMAL DECOMPOSITION PRODUCTS MAY INCLUDE TOXIC OXIDES OF SULFUR AND CARBON.
POLYMERIZATION: HAZARDOUS POLYMERIZATION HAS NOT BEEN REPORTED TO OCCUR UNDER NORMAL TEMPERATURES AND PRESSURES.

STORAGE AND DISPOSAL

OBSERVE ALL FEDERAL, STATE AND LOCAL REGULATIONS WHEN STORING OR DISPOSING OF THIS SUBSTANCE. FOR ASSISTANCE, CONTACT THE DISTRICT DIRECTOR OF THE ENVIRONMENTAL PROTECTION AGENCY.

CONDITIONS TO AVOID

NONE REPORTED.

SPILL AND LEAK PROCEDURES

OCCUPATIONAL SPILL: NO SPECIAL PRECAUTIONS INDICATED.

PROTECTIVE EQUIPMENT

VENTILATION: PROVIDE LOCAL EXHAUST OR PROCESS ENCLOSURE VENTILATION TO MEET PUBLISHED EXPOSURE LIMITS.
RESPIRATOR: THE FOLLOWING RESPIRATORS ARE RECOMMENDED BASED ON INFORMATION FOUND IN THE PHYSICAL DATA, TOXICITY AND HEALTH EFFECTS SECTIONS. THEY ARE RANKED IN ORDER FROM MINIMUM TO MAXIMUM RESPIRATORY PROTECTION. THE SPECIFIC RESPIRATOR SELECTED MUST BE BASED ON CONTAMINATION LEVELS FOUND IN THE WORK PLACE, MUST NOT EXCEED THE WORKING LIMITS OF THE RESPIRATOR AND BE JOINTLY APPROVED BY THE NATIONAL INSTITUTE FOR OCCUPATIONAL SAFETY AND HEALTH AND THE MINE SAFETY AND HEALTH ADMINISTRATION (NIOSH-MSHA).
CHEMICAL CARTRIDGE RESPIRATOR WITH AN ORGANIC VAPOR CARTRIDGE(S) WITH A FULL FACEPIECE.
GAS MASK WITH ORGANIC VAPOR CANISTER (CHIN-STYLE OR FRONT- OR BACK-MOUNTED CANISTER) WITH A FULL FACEPIECE. TYPE 'C' SUPPLIED-AIR RESPIRATOR WITH A FULL FACEPIECE OPERATED IN PRESSURE-DEMAND OR OTHER POSITIVE PRESSURE MODE OR WITH A FULL FACEPIECE, HELMET OR HOOD OPERATED IN CONTINUOUS-FLOW MODE.
SELF-CONTAINED BREATHING APPARATUS WITH A FULL FACEPIECE OPERATED IN PRESSURE-DEMAND OR OTHER POSITIVE PRESSURE MODE.
FOR FIREFIGHTING AND OTHER IMMEDIATELY DANGEROUS TO LIFE OR HEALTH CONDITIONS:
SELF-CONTAINED BREATHING APPARATUS WITH FULL FACEPIECE OPERATED IN PRESSURE-DEMAND OR OTHER POSITIVE PRESSURE MODE.
SUPPLIED-AIR RESPIRATOR WITH FULL FACEPIECE AND OPERATED IN PRESSURE-DEMAND OR OTHER POSITIVE PRESSURE MODE IN COMBINATION WITH AN AUXILIARY SELF-CONTAINED BREATHING APPARATUS OPERATED IN PRESSURE-DEMAND OR OTHER POSITIVE PRESSURE MODE.
CLOTHING: EMPLOYEE MUST WEAR APPROPRIATE PROTECTIVE (IMPERVIOUS) CLOTHING AND EQUIPMENT TO PREVENT REPEATED OR PROLONGED SKIN CONTACT WITH THIS SUBSTANCE.
GLOVES: EMPLOYEE MUST WEAR APPROPRIATE PROTECTIVE GLOVES TO PREVENT CONTACT WITH THIS SUBSTANCE.
EYE PROTECTION: EMPLOYEE MUST WEAR SPLASH-PROOF OR DUST-RESISTANT SAFETY GOGGLES TO PREVENT EYE CONTACT WITH THIS SUBSTANCE.
EMERGENCY EYE WASH: WHERE THERE IS ANY POSSIBILITY THAT AN EMPLOYEE'S EYES MAY BE EXPOSED TO THIS SUBSTANCE, THE EMPLOYER SHOULD PROVIDE AN EYE WASH FOUNTAIN WITHIN THE IMMEDIATE WORK AREA FOR EMERGENCY USE.

AUTHORIZED BY- OCCUPATIONAL HEALTH SERVICES, INC.
CREATION DATE: 02/08/90 ***REVISION DATE:*** 05/09/90

MATERIAL SAFETY DATA SHEET

OCCUPATIONAL HEALTH SERVICES, INC.
AGRICULTURE AND PESTICIDE DIVISION
450 SEVENTH AVENUE, SUITE 2407
NEW YORK, NEW YORK 10123
1-800-445-MSDS OR (212) 967-1100

EMERGENCY CONTACT:
JOHN S. BRANSFORD, JR. (615) 292-1180

SUBSTANCE IDENTIFICATION

CAS-NUMBER 51-03-6
SUBSTANCE: PIPERONYL BUTOXIDE
TRADE NAMES/SYNONYMS: 1,3-BENZODIOXOLE, 5-((2-(2-BUTOXYETHOXY)ETHOXY)METHYL)-6-PROPYL-; TOLUENE, ALPHA-(2-(2-BUTOXYETHOXY)ETHOXY)-4,5-(METHYLENEDIOXY)- 2-PROPYL-; 5-((2-(2-BUTOXYETHOXY)ETHOXY)METHYL)-6-PROPYL-1,3-BENZODIOXOLE; ALPHA-(2-(2-BUTOXYETHYOXY)ETHOXY-4,5-METHYLENEDIOXY-2-PROPYLTOLUENE; (3,4-(METHYLENEDIOXY)-6-PROPYLBENZYL) BUTYL DIETHYLENEGLYCOL ETHER; BUTYLCARBITYL (6-PROPYLPIPERONYL) ETHER; 2-(2-BUTOXYETHOXY)ETHYL 6-PROPYLPIPERONYL ETHER; BUTACIDE; BUTOCIDE; BUTOXIDE; PYRENONE; NIA 5273; ENT 14,250; C19H3005; PST75640
CHEMICAL FAMILY: ETHER, AROMATIC
MOLECULAR FORMULA: C19-H30-O5
MOLECULAR WEIGHT: 338.43
CERCLA RATINGS (SCALE 0-3): HEALTH=3 FIRE=1 REACTIVITY=0 PERSISTENCE=2
NFPA RATINGS (SCALE 0-4): HEALTH=3 FIRE=1 REACTIVITY=0

COMPONENTS AND CONTAMINANTS

COMPONENT: PIPERONYL BUTOXIDE ***PERCENT:*** 100.0
CAS# 51-03-6
OTHER CONTAMINANTS: NONE
EXPOSURE LIMITS: NO OCCUPATIONAL EXPOSURE LIMITS ESTABLISHED BY OSHA, ACGIH, OR NIOSH.

PHYSICAL DATA

DESCRIPTION: A PALE YELLOW OIL WITH A FAINT BITTER TASTE.
BOILING POINT: 180 F (82 C) ***SPECIFIC GRAVITY:*** 1.04 TO 1.07
EVAPORATION RATE: NOT AVAILABLE ***SOLUBILITY IN WATER:*** INSOLUBLE
SOLVENT SOLUBILITY: SOLUBLE IN METHANOL, ETHANOL, BENZENE, FREONS, GEONS, DICHLOROFLUOROMETHANE, ISOPROPANOL, PETROLEUM OILS, AND ORGANIC SOLVENTS.

FIRE AND EXPLOSION DATA

FIRE AND EXPLOSION HAZARD: SLIGHT FIRE HAZARD WHEN EXPOSED TO HEAT OR FLAME.
FLASH POINT: 340 F (171 C) (CC) ***FLAMMABILITY CLASS(OSHA):*** IIIB
FIREFIGHTING MEDIA: DRY CHEMICAL, CARBON DIOXIDE, HALON, WATER SPRAY OR STANDARD FOAM (1987 EMERGENCY RESPONSE GUIDEBOOK, DOT P 5800.4). FOR LARGER FIRES, USE WATER SPRAY, FOG OR STANDARD FOAM (1987 EMERGENCY RESPONSE GUIDEBOOK, DOT P 5800.4).
FIREFIGHTING: MOVE CONTAINER FROM FIRE AREA IF POSSIBLE. DO NOT SCATTER SPILLED MATERIAL WITH HIGH PRESSURE WATER STREAMS. DIKE FIRE CONTROL WATER FOR LATER DISPOSAL (1987 EMERGENCY RESPONSE GUIDEBOOK, DOT P 5800.4, GUIDE PAGE 31).
USE AGENTS SUITABLE FOR TYPE OF SURROUNDING FIRE. AVOID BREATHING HAZARDOUS VAPORS, KEEP UPWIND.

TOXICITY

PIPERONYL BUTOXIDE: TOXICITY DATA: 200 MG/KG SKIN-RABBIT LD50; 6150 MG/KG ORAL-RAT LD50; 2600 MG/KG ORAL-MOUSE LD50; 2650 MG/KG ORAL-RABBIT LD50; 1000 MG/KG INTRAPERITONEAL-MOUSE LDLO; MUTAGENIC DATA (RTECS); REPRODUCTIVE EFFECTS DATA (RTECS); TUMORIGENIC DATA (RTECS);

CARCINOGEN STATUS: ANIMAL INADEQUATE EVIDENCE (IARC GROUP-3). ACUTE TOXICITY LEVEL: HIGHLY TOXIC BY DERMAL ABSORPTION; SLIGHTLY TOXIC BY INGESTION. TARGET EFFECTS: POISONING MAY AFFECT THE LIVER. ADDITIONAL DATA: THIS MATERIAL MAY ENHANCE THE PHARMACOLOGIC EFFECT OF DRUGS AND POTENTIATE THE TOXICITY OF ENVIRONMENTAL AGENTS.

HEALTH EFFECTS AND FIRST AID

INHALATION: PIPERONYL BUTOXIDE: **ACUTE EXPOSURE-** MAY CAUSE IRRITATION OF THE MUCOUS MEMBRANES. **CHRONIC EXPOSURE-** TWO SISTERS WHO WERE EXPOSED DURING THE FIRST TRIMESTER OF PREGNANCY TO LARGE AMOUNTS OF INSECT REPELLENT AND INSECTICIDES THAT CONTAINED PIPERONYL BUTOXIDE EACH GAVE BIRTH TO AN INFANT WITH COARCTATION OF THE AORTA.

FIRST AID- REMOVE FROM EXPOSURE AREA TO FRESH AIR IMMEDIATELY. IF BREATHING HAS STOPPED, PERFORM ARTIFICIAL RESPIRATION. KEEP PERSON WARM AND AT REST. TREAT SYMPTOMATICALLY AND SUPPORTIVELY. GET MEDICAL ATTENTION IMMEDIATELY.

SKIN CONTACT: PIPERONYL BUTOXIDE: HIGHLY TOXIC. **ACUTE EXPOSURE-** THIS MATERIAL WAS NOT DAMAGING TO THE SKIN OF RABBITS, RATS, CATS AND DOGS. A LETHAL DOSE IN RABBITS BY DERMAL ABSORPTION WAS 200 MG/KG. A DERMAL APPLICATION AT THE RATE OF 1,880 MG/KG AS A 20% SOLUTION IN DIMETHYL PHTHALATE PRODUCED EFFECTS OF HYPEREXCITIBILITY AND CONVULSIONS IN RABBITS WITH NO REPORTED IRRITATION. **CHRONIC EXPOSURE-** REPEATED APPLICATION OF UNDILUTED PIPERONYL BUTOXIDE WAS MILDLY IRRITATING TO RABBIT SKIN; NO SENSITIZATION WAS PRODUCED. A LETHAL DOSE IN RABBITS FROM REPEATED APPLICATION WAS 200 MG/KG AS DETERMINED IN A 90-DAY STUDY.

FIRST AID- REMOVE CONTAMINATED CLOTHING AND SHOES IMMEDIATELY. WASH AFFECTED AREA WITH SOAP OR MILD DETERGENT AND LARGE AMOUNTS OF WATER UNTIL NO EVIDENCE OF CHEMICAL REMAINS (APPROXIMATELY 15-20 MINUTES). GET MEDICAL ATTENTION IMMEDIATELY.

EYE CONTACT: PIPERONYL BUTOXIDE: **ACUTE EXPOSURE-** MAY CAUSE IRRITATION. THIS MATERIAL WAS NOT DAMAGING TO THE EYES OF RABBITS, RATS, CATS, AND DOGS. **CHRONIC EXPOSURE-** NO DATA AVAILABLE.

FIRST AID- WASH EYES IMMEDIATELY WITH LARGE AMOUNTS OF WATER OR NORMAL SALINE, OCCASIONALLY LIFTING UPPER AND LOWER LIDS, UNTIL NO EVIDENCE OF CHEMICAL REMAINS (APPROXIMATELY 15-20 MINUTES). GET MEDICAL ATTENTION IMMEDIATELY.

INGESTION: PIPERONYL BUTOXIDE: **ACUTE EXPOSURE-** LABORATORY ANIMALS EXPOSED TO A SINGLE, LARGE ORAL DOSE EXHIBITED ANOREXIA, VOMITING, DIARRHEA, UNSTEADINESS, ROUGH COAT, WATERY EYES, IRRITABILITY, PROSTRATION, HEMORRHAGIC ENTERITIS, INANITION, PULMONARY HEMORRHAGE, MILD CENTRAL NERVOUS SYSTEM DEPRESSION, BLOODY DISCHARGE FROM EYES AND NOSE, LIVER DAMAGE, COMA AND DEATH. ONSET MAY BE AS EARLY AS 20 MINUTES AFTER DOSING AND DEATH MAY BE DELAYED UP TO A WEEK. **CHRONIC EXPOSURE-** EFFECTS OF ANOREXIA, STUNTING, CACHEXIA, DECREASED TESTES WEIGHT, MORPHOLOGICAL CHANGES IN THE LIVER, AN INDUCTION OF ILEOCECAL ULCERS, AND AN INCREASED IN MORTALITY WERE OBSERVED IN RATS RECEIVING A DIETARY LEVEL OF 1-3%. THIS DIETARY LEVEL ADMINISTERED TO RATS FOR THREE GENERATIONS ALSO PRODUCED A REDUCTION IN THE NUMBER OF PREGNANCIES AND OFFSPRING. NO EFFECTS WERE OBSERVED AT LEVELS LESS THAN 0.1%. WEIGHT LOSS, MORPHOLOGICAL CHANGES IN THE LIVER, KIDNEY, AND ADRENAL GLAND WERE REPORTED IN DOGS FED DOSAGES OF 105 OR 315 MG/KG/DAY. THE 315 MG/KG/DAY LEVEL WAS LETHAL TO ALL DOGS WITHIN 4 TO 15 WEEKS DUE TO LIVER INJURY.

FIRST AID- REMOVE BY GASTRIC LAVAGE AND CATHARSIS. MAINTAIN BLOOD PRESSURE AND AIRWAY. GIVE OXYGEN IF RESPIRATION IS DEPRESSED. DO NOT PERFORM GASTRIC LAVAGE IF VICTIM IS UNCONSCIOUS. GET MEDICAL ATTENTION IMMEDIATELY (DREISBACH, HANDBOOK OF POISONING, 12TH ED.). ADMINISTRATION OF LAVAGE OR OXYGEN SHOULD BE PERFORMED BY QUALIFIED MEDICAL PERSONNEL.

ANTIDOTE: NO SPECIFIC ANTIDOTE. TREAT SYMPTOMATICALLY AND SUPPORTIVELY.

REACTIVITY

REACTIVITY: STABLE UNDER NORMAL TEMPERATURES AND PRESSURES.

INCOMPATIBILITIES: PIPERONYL BUTOXIDE: ACIDS (STRONG): MAY CAUSE DECOMPOSITION.

DECOMPOSITION: THERMAL DECOMPOSITION PRODUCTS MAY INCLUDE TOXIC OXIDES OF CARBON.

POLYMERIZATION: HAZARDOUS POLYMERIZATION HAS NOT BEEN REPORTED TO OCCUR UNDER NORMAL TEMPERATURES AND PRESSURES.

STORAGE AND DISPOSAL

OBSERVE ALL FEDERAL, STATE AND LOCAL REGULATIONS WHEN STORING OR DISPOSING OF THIS SUBSTANCE. FOR ASSISTANCE, CONTACT THE DISTRICT DIRECTOR OF THE ENVIRONMENTAL PROTECTION AGENCY.

****STORAGE****

STORE AWAY FROM INCOMPATIBLE SUBSTANCES.

CONDITIONS TO AVOID

MAY BURN BUT DOES NOT IGNITE READILY. AVOID CONTACT WITH STRONG OXIDIZERS, EXCESSIVE HEAT, SPARKS, OR OPEN FLAME.

SPILL AND LEAK PROCEDURES

OCCUPATIONAL SPILL: STOP LEAK IF YOU CAN DO IT WITHOUT RISK. FOR SMALL SPILLS, TAKE UP WITH SAND OR OTHER ABSORBENT MATERIAL AND PLACE INTO CLEAN, DRY CONTAINERS FOR LATER DISPOSAL. KEEP UNNECESSARY PEOPLE AWAY. ISOLATE HAZARD AREA AND DENY ENTRY.

PROTECTIVE EQUIPMENT

VENTILATION: PROVIDE LOCAL EXHAUST OR PROCESS ENCLOSURE VENTILATION SYSTEM.

RESPIRATOR: THE FOLLOWING RESPIRATORS ARE RECOMMENDED BASED ON INFORMATION FOUND IN THE PHYSICAL DATA, TOXICITY AND HEALTH EFFECTS SECTIONS. THEY ARE RANKED IN ORDER FROM MINIMUM TO MAXIMUM RESPIRATORY PROTECTION. THE SPECIFIC RESPIRATOR SELECTED MUST BE BASED ON CONTAMINATION LEVELS FOUND IN THE WORK PLACE, MUST NOT EXCEED THE WORKING LIMITS OF THE RESPIRATOR AND BE JOINTLY APPROVED BY THE NATIONAL INSTITUTE FOR OCCUPATIONAL SAFETY AND HEALTH AND THE MINE SAFETY AND HEALTH ADMINISTRATION (NIOSH-MSHA).

CHEMICAL CARTRIDGE RESPIRATOR WITH AN ORGANIC VAPOR CARTRIDGE(S)

GAS MASK WITH ORGANIC VAPOR CANISTER (CHIN-STYLE OR FRONT- OR BACK-MOUNTED CANISTER).

TYPE 'C' SUPPLIED-AIR RESPIRATOR OPERATED IN THE PRESSURE-DEMAND OR OTHER POSITIVE PRESSURE OR CONTINUOUS-FLOW MODE.

SELF-CONTAINED BREATHING APPARATUS.

FOR FIREFIGHTING AND OTHER IMMEDIATELY DANGEROUS TO LIFE OR HEALTH CONDITIONS:

SELF-CONTAINED BREATHING APPARATUS WITH FULL FACEPIECE OPERATED IN PRESSURE-DEMAND OR OTHER POSITIVE PRESSURE MODE.

SUPPLIED-AIR RESPIRATOR WITH FULL FACEPIECE AND OPERATED IN PRESSURE-DEMAND OR OTHER POSITIVE PRESSURE MODE IN COMBINATION WITH AN AUXILIARY SELF-CONTAINED BREATHING APPARATUS OPERATED IN PRESSURE-DEMAND OR OTHER POSITIVE PRESSURE MODE.

CLOTHING: EMPLOYEE MUST WEAR APPROPRIATE PROTECTIVE (IMPERVIOUS) CLOTHING AND EQUIPMENT TO PREVENT ANY POSSIBILITY OF SKIN CONTACT WITH THIS SUBSTANCE.

GLOVES: EMPLOYEE MUST WEAR APPROPRIATE PROTECTIVE GLOVES TO PREVENT CONTACT WITH THIS SUBSTANCE.

EYE PROTECTION: EMPLOYEE MUST WEAR SPLASH-PROOF OR DUST-RESISTANT SAFETY GOGGLES WITH OR WITHOUT A FACESHIELD TO PREVENT CONTACT WITH THIS SUBSTANCE.

EMERGENCY EYE WASH: WHERE THERE IS ANY POSSIBILITY THAT AN EMPLOYEE'S EYES MAY BE EXPOSED TO THIS SUBSTANCE, THE EMPLOYER SHOULD PROVIDE AN EYE WASH FOUNTAIN WITHIN THE IMMEDIATE WORK AREA FOR EMERGENCY USE.

AUTHORIZED BY- OCCUPATIONAL HEALTH SERVICES, INC.

CREATION DATE: 10/04/89 ***REVISION DATE:*** 07/12/90

MATERIAL SAFETY DATA SHEET

OCCUPATIONAL HEALTH SERVICES, INC.
AGRICULTURE AND PESTICIDE DIVISION
450 SEVENTH AVENUE, SUITE 2407
NEW YORK, NEW YORK 10123
1-800-445-MSDS OR (212) 967-1100

EMERGENCY CONTACT:
JOHN S. BRANSFORD, JR. (615) 292-1180

SUBSTANCE IDENTIFICATION

CAS-NUMBER 112-56-1

SUBSTANCE: **LETHANE 384**

TRADE NAMES/SYNONYMS: 2-(2-BUTYOXYETHOXY)ETHYL ESTER THIOCYANIC ACID; 2-(2-BUTYOXYETHOXY)ETHYL THIOCYANATE; 2-(2-(BUTOXY)ETHOXY)ETHYL THIOCYANIC ACID ESTER; BUTOXYRHODANODIETHYL ETHER; BETA-BUTOXY-BETA'-THIOCYANODIETHYL ETHER; 1-BUTOXY-ALPHA-(2-THIOCYANOETHOXY)ETHANE;

BUTYL CARBITOL RHODANATE; BUTYL CARBITOL THIOCYANATE; ENT 6; 2-(2-BUTYOXYETHOXY)-ETHANOL THIOCYANATE; LETHANE; LETHANE 384 REGULAR; C9H17NO2S; PST75661

CHEMICAL FAMILY: ESTER

MOLECULAR FORMULA: C9-H17-N-O2-S

MOLECULAR WEIGHT: 203.33

CERCLA RATINGS (SCALE 0-3): HEALTH=3 FIRE=2 REACTIVITY=0 PERSISTENCE=1

NFPA RATINGS (SCALE 0-4): HEALTH=3 FIRE=2 REACTIVITY=0

COMPONENTS AND CONTAMINANTS

COMPONENT: LETHANE 384 ***PERCENT:*** 100
CAS# 112-56-1

EXPOSURE LIMITS: NO OCCUPATIONAL EXPOSURE LIMITS ESTABLISHED BY OSHA, ACGIH, OR NIOSH.

PHYSICAL DATA

DESCRIPTION: BROWNISH OIL. ***BOILING POINT:*** NOT AVAILABLE

SPECIFIC GRAVITY: 0.915-0.930 ***EVAPORATION RATE:*** NOT AVAILABLE

SOLUBILITY IN WATER: NOT AVAILABLE

SOLVENT SOLUBILITY: MOST ORGANIC SOLVENTS, HYDROCARBONS

FIRE AND EXPLOSION DATA

FIRE AND EXPLOSION HAZARD: MODERATE FIRE HAZARD WHEN EXPOSED TO HEAT OR FLAME.

FLASH POINT: 130 F (54 C) (CC) ***FLAMMABILITY CLASS(OSHA):*** II

FIREFIGHTING MEDIA: DRY CHEMICAL, CARBON DIOXIDE, HALON, WATER SPRAY OR STANDARD FOAM (1987 EMERGENCY RESPONSE GUIDEBOOK, DOT P 5800.4). FOR LARGER FIRES, USE WATER SPRAY, FOG OR STANDARD FOAM (1987 EMERGENCY RESPONSE GUIDEBOOK, DOT P 5800.4).

FIREFIGHTING: FLAMMABLE LIQUID. WEAR PERSONAL PROTECTIVE EQUIPMENT. USE FLOODING QUANTITIES OF WATER AS A FOG AND TO COOL ALL CONTAINERS INVOLVED IN FIRE. APPLY WATER TO MATERIAL FROM AS FAR A DISTANCE AS POSSIBLE. APPLICATION OF SOLID STREAMS OF WATER MAY SPREAD FIRE. EXTINGUISH ONLY IF FLOW CAN BE STOPPED; USE FLOODING AMOUNTS OF WATER AS A FOG, SOLID STREAMS MAY BE INEFFECTIVE. COOL CONTAINERS WITH FLOODING AMOUNTS OF WATER, APPLY FROM AS FAR A DISTANCE AS POSSIBLE. AVOID BREATHING VAPORS, KEEP UPWIND.

TRANSPORTATION DATA

DEPARTMENT OF TRANSPORTATION HAZARD CLASSIFICATION 49 CFR 172.101: COMBUSTIBLE LIQUID

DEPARTMENT OF TRANSPORTATION LABELING REQUIREMENTS 49 CFR 172.101 AND SUBPART E: NONE

DEPARTMENT OF TRANSPORTATION PACKAGING REQUIREMENTS: NONE EXCEPTIONS: 49 CFR 173.118A

TOXICITY

LETHANE 384: TOXICITY DATA: 34 MG/KG SKIN-RABBIT LD50; 250 MG/KG SKIN-RAT LD50; 90 MG/KG ORAL-RAT LD50; 35 MG/KG ORAL-RABBIT LD50; 250 MG/KG ORAL-GUINEA PIG LD50; 30 MG/KG ORAL-DOG LD50; 200 MG/KG SUBCUTANEOUS-MOUSE LDLO; 550 MG/KG SUBCUTANEOUS-RAT LD50; 100 MG/KG SUBCUTANEOUS-RABBIT LD50; RABBIT 200 MG/KG SUBCUTANEOUS-DOG LD50; 450 MG/KG SUBCUTANEOUS-GUINEA PIG LD50; 56 MG/KG INTRAVENOUS-MOUSE LD50; 90 MG/KG INTRAPERITONEAL-RAT LD50; 80 MG/KG INTRAPERITONEAL-RABBIT LD50; 84 MG/KG INTRAPERITONEAL-GUINEA PIG LD50; 41 MG/KG INTRAPERITONEAL-MOUSE LD50; 550 MG/KG UNREPORTED-MAMMAL LD50. CARCINOGEN STATUS: NONE. LOCAL EFFECTS: IRRITANT- INHALATION, SKIN, AND EYES. ACUTE TOXICITY LEVEL: HIGHLY TOXIC BY DERMAL ABSORPTION AND TOXIC BY INGESTION. TARGET EFFECTS: CENTRAL NERVOUS SYSTEM DEPRESSANT. POISONING MAY AFFECT THE LIVER AND KIDNEYS.

HEALTH EFFECTS AND FIRST AID

INHALATION: LETHANE 384: IRRITANT/NARCOTIC. **ACUTE EXPOSURE-** INHALATION MAY BE IRRITATING TO THE MUCOUS MEMBRANES, AND MAY CAUSE CENTRAL NERVOUS SYSTEM DEPRESSION WITH HEADACHE, DIZZINESS, AND A TRANSIENT PERIOD OF RESPIRATORY STIMULATION PROGRESSING PROMPTLY TO DEATH FROM RESPIRATORY FAILURE. **CHRONIC EXPOSURE-** REPEATED OR PROLONGED EXPOSURE MAY RESULT IN MUCOUS MEMBRANE IRRITATION.

FIRST AID- REMOVE FROM EXPOSURE AREA TO FRESH AIR IMMEDIATELY. IF BREATHING HAS STOPPED, PERFORM ARTIFICIAL RESPIRATION. KEEP PERSON WARM AND AT REST. TREAT SYMPTOMATICALLY AND SUPPORTIVELY. GET MEDICAL ATTENTION IMMEDIATELY.

SKIN CONTACT: LETHANE 384: IRRITANT/NARCOTIC/TOXIC. **ACUTE EXPOSURE-** DIRECT CONTACT WITH THE LIQUID MAY BE IRRITATING TO THE SKIN. MAY BE ABSORBED TO CAUSE CENTRAL NERVOUS SYSTEM DEPRESSION WITH HEADACHE, DIZZINESS AND A TRANSIENT PERIOD OF RESPIRATORY STIMULATION PROGRESSING PROMPTLY TO DEATH FROM RESPIRATORY FAILURE. **CHRONIC EXPOSURE-** PROLONGED OR REPEATED EXPOSURE MAY CAUSE DERMATITIS. PROLONGED ABSORPTION MAY CAUSE SKIN ERUPTIONS, RUNNY NOSE, DIZZINESS, CRAMPS, NAUSEA AND VOMITING.

FIRST AID- REMOVE CONTAMINATED CLOTHING AND SHOES IMMEDIATELY. WASH AFFECTED AREA WITH SOAP OR MILD DETERGENT AND LARGE AMOUNTS OF WATER UNTIL NO EVIDENCE OF CHEMICAL REMAINS (APPROXIMATELY 15-20 MINUTES). GET MEDICAL ATTENTION IMMEDIATELY.

EYE CONTACT: LETHANE 384: IRRITANT. **ACUTE EXPOSURE-** MAY BE IRRITATING TO THE EYES. **CHRONIC EXPOSURE-** REPEATED OR PROLONGED EXPOSURE MAY CAUSE CONJUNCTIVITIS.

FIRST AID- WASH EYES IMMEDIATELY WITH LARGE AMOUNTS OF WATER OR NORMAL SALINE, OCCASIONALLY LIFTING UPPER AND LOWER LIDS, UNTIL NO EVIDENCE OF CHEMICAL REMAINS (APPROXIMATELY 15-20 MINUTES). GET MEDICAL ATTENTION IMMEDIATELY.

INGESTION: LETHANE 384: NARCOTIC/TOXIC. **ACUTE EXPOSURE-** INGESTION MAY CAUSE CENTRAL NERVOUS SYSTEM DEPRESSION WITH HEADACHE, DIZZINESS, DROWSINESS, NAUSEA, VOMITING AND UNCONSCIOUSNESS. LETHANE 384 IS A RAPID ACTING POISON. TOXICITY IS PROBABLY DUE TO THE METABOLIC FORMATION OF CYANIDE. CENTRAL NERVOUS SYSTEM DEPRESSION, WHICH MAY BE INTERRUPTED BY PERIODS OF RESTLESSNESS, HYPERPNEA, AND TOXIC CONVULSIONS MAY LAST SEVERAL DAYS. TREMORS, PARALYSIS, SPASTICITY, AND EVEN OPISTHOTONOS HAVE OCCURRED IN RABBITS. THE ADULT LETHAL DOSE IS ESTIMATED TO BE 1 TEASPOON TO 1 OUNCE. LETHANE 384 MAY CONTAIN KEROSENE, OR SOME OTHER PETROLEUM DISTILLATE, WHICH MAY POSE AN ASPIRATION HAZARD IF VOMITING SHOULD OCCUR. ORGANIC THIOCYANATES, IN GENERAL, MAY CAUSE CENTRAL NERVOUS SYSTEM DEPRESSION, INTENSE DYSPNEA, CYANOSIS, AND SOMETIMES CONVULSIONS. LIVER AND KIDNEY DAMAGE MAY OCCUR. **CHRONIC EXPOSURE-** NO DATA AVAILABLE.

FIRST AID- REMOVE SWALLOWED POISON BY THOROUGH GASTRIC LAVAGE WITH TAP WATER. IF GASTRIC LAVAGE CANNOT BE ACCOMPLISHED IMMEDIATELY, GIVE SYRUP OF IPECAC, 15 ML, AND 250 ML OF TAP WATER OF MILK. MAINTAIN ARTIFICIAL DURING CONVULSIONS OR RESPIRATORY DIFFICULTY (DREISBACH, HANDBOOK OF POISONING, 12TH ED.) GET MEDICAL ATTENTION IMMEDIATELY. TREAMENT SHOULD BE ADMINISTERED ONLY BY QUALIFIED MEDICAL PERSONNEL.

ANTIDOTE: THE FOLLOWING ANTIDOTE HAS BEEN RECOMMENDED. HOWEVER, THE DECISION AS TO WHETHER THE SEVERITY OF POISONING REQUIRES ADMINISTRATION OF ANY ANTIDOTE AND ACTUAL DOSE REQUIRED SHOULD BE MADE BY QUALIFIED MEDICAL PERSONNEL.
FOR CYANIDE POISONING: IF SYMPTOMS OF CYANIDE POISONING ARE EVIDENT, ADMINISTER IMMEDIATELY BEFORE ANY OTHER FIRST AID MEASURES. ADMINISTER AMYL NITRITE (AMYL NITRITE PERLES) BY INHALATION FOR 15 TO 30 SECONDS OF EVERY MINUTE, WHILE SODIUM NITRITE SOLUTION IS BEING PREPARED. DISCONTINUE AMYL NITRITE AND IMMEDIATELY INJECT 10 ML OF A 3% SOLUTION OF SODIUM NITRITE INTRAVENOUSLY OVER A PERIOD OF 2 TO 4 MINUTES. IF NECESSARY, INJECT A NON-STERILE SOLUTION. DO NOT REMOVE THE NEEDLE. CAUTION: APPROPRIATE ADJUSTMENTS IN THE DOSE SHOULD BE MADE ON A BODY WEIGHT BASIS. THROUGH THE SAME NEEDLE, INFUSE INTRAVENOUSLY 50 ML OF A 25% AQUEOUS SOLUTION OF SODIUM THIOSULFATE. THE INJECTION SHOULD TAKE ABOUT 10 MINUTES. OTHER CONCENTRATIONS (5 TO 50%) ARE PERMISSIBLE IF THE TOTAL DOSE IS HELD AT APPROXIMATELY 12 GRAMS. OXYGEN THERAPY MAY BE OF VALUE IN COMBINATION WITH NITRITE AND SODIUM THIOSULFATE THERAPY. IF SYMPTOMS RECUR, THE INJECTIONS OF NITRITE AND THIOSULFATE MAY BE REPEATED AT HALF THE ABOVE DOSES. IN VERY SEVERE POISONINGS IT IS SAFER AND PERHAPS MORE EFFICIENT TO KEEP REPEATING THE THIOSULFATE INJECTIONS INSTEAD OF THE NITRITE (GOSSELIN, SMITH, HODGE, CLINICAL TOXICOLOGY OF COMMERCIAL PRODUCTS, 5TH ED.). ANTIDOTE SHOULD BE ADMINISTERED BY QUALIFIED MEDICAL PERSONNEL.

REACTIVITY

REACTIVITY: STABLE UNDER NORMAL TEMPERATURES AND PRESSURES.

INCOMPATIBILITIES: LETHANE 384: NO DATA AVAILABLE.

DECOMPOSITION: THERMAL DECOMPOSITION MAY RELEASE CYANIDE AND TOXIC OXIDES OF SULFUR AND NITROGEN.

POLYMERIZATION: HAZARDOUS POLYMERIZATION HAS NOT BEEN REPORTED TO OCCUR UNDER NORMAL TEMPERATURES AND PRESSURES.

CONDITIONS TO AVOID

AVOID CONTACT WITH HEAT, SPARKS, FLAMES, OR OTHER SOURCES OF IGNITION. VAPORS MAY BE EXPLOSIVE. AVOID OVERHEATING OF CONTAINERS; CONTAINERS MAY VIOLENTLY RUPTURE IN HEAT OF FIRE. AVOID CONTAMINATION OF WATER SOURCES.

SPILL AND LEAK PROCEDURES

OCCUPATIONAL SPILL: SHUT OFF IGNITION SOURCES. STOP LEAK IF YOU CAN DO IT WITHOUT RISK. USE WATER SPRAY TO REDUCE VAPORS. FOR SMALL SPILLS, TAKE UP WITH SAND OR OTHER ABSORBENT MATERIAL AND PLACE INTO CONTAINERS FOR LATER DISPOSAL. FOR LARGER SPILLS, DIKE FAR AHEAD OF SPILL FOR LATER DISPOSAL. NO SMOKING, FLAMES OR FLARES IN HAZARD AREA. KEEP UNNECESSARY PEOPLE AWAY; ISOLATE HAZARD AREA AND RESTRICT ENTRY.

PROTECTIVE EQUIPMENT

VENTILATION: PROVIDE LOCAL EXHAUST OR PROCESS ENCLOSURE VENTILATION TO MEET PUBLISHED EXPOSURE LIMITS.

RESPIRATOR: THE FOLLOWING RESPIRATORS ARE RECOMMENDED BASED ON INFORMATION FOUND IN THE PHYSICAL DATA, TOXICITY AND HEALTH EFFECTS SECTIONS. THEY ARE RANKED IN ORDER FROM MINIMUM TO MAXIMUM RESPIRATORY PROTECTION. THE SPECIFIC RESPIRATOR SELECTED MUST BE BASED ON CONTAMINATION LEVELS FOUND IN THE WORK PLACE, MUST NOT EXCEED THE WORKING LIMITS OF THE RESPIRATOR AND BE JOINTLY APPROVED BY THE NATIONAL INSTITUTE FOR OCCUPATIONAL SAFETY AND HEALTH AND THE MINE SAFETY AND HEALTH ADMINISTRATION (NIOSH-MSHA).

TYPE 'C' SUPPLIED-AIR RESPIRATOR WITH A FULL FACEPIECE OPERATED IN PRESSURE-DEMAND OR OTHER POSITIVE PRESSURE MODE OR WITH A FULL FACEPIECE, HELMET OR HOOD OPERATED IN CONTINOUS-FLOW MODE.

SELF-CONTAINED BREATHING APPARATUS WITH A FULL FACEPIECE OPERATED IN PRESSURE-DEMAND OR OTHER POSITIVE PRESSURE MODE.

FOR FIREFIGHTING AND OTHER IMMEDIATELY DANGEROUS TO LIFE OR HEALTH CONDITIONS:

SELF-CONTAINED BREATHING APPARATUS WITH FULL FACEPIECE OPERATED IN PRESSURE-DEMAND OR OTHER POSITIVE PRESSURE MODE.

SUPPLIED-AIR RESPIRATOR WITH FULL FACEPIECE AND OPERATED IN PRESSURE-DEMAND OR OTHER POSITIVE PRESSURE MODE IN COMBINATION WITH AN AUXILIARY SELF-CONTAINED BREATHING APPARATUS OPERATED IN PRESSURE-DEMAND OR OTHER POSITIVE PRESSURE MODE.

CLOTHING: EMPLOYEE MUST WEAR APPROPRIATE PROTECTIVE (IMPERVIOUS) CLOTHING AND EQUIPMENT TO PREVENT ANY POSSIBILITY OF SKIN CONTACT WITH THIS SUBSTANCE.

GLOVES: EMPLOYEE MUST WEAR APPROPRIATE PROTECTIVE GLOVES TO PREVENT CONTACT WITH THIS SUBSTANCE.

EYE PROTECTION: EMPLOYEE MUST WEAR SPLASH-PROOF OR DUST-RESISTANT SAFETY GOGGLES AND A FACESHIELD TO PREVENT CONTACT WITH THIS SUBSTANCE.

EMERGENCY WASH FACILITIES: WHERE THERE IS ANY POSSIBILITY THAT AN EMPLOYEE'S EYES AND/OR SKIN MAY BE EXPOSED TO THIS SUBSTANCE, THE EMPLOYER SHOULD PROVIDE AN EYE WASH FOUNTAIN AND QUICK DRENCH SHOWER WITHIN THE IMMEDIATE WORK AREA FOR EMERGENCY USE.

AUTHORIZED BY- OCCUPATIONAL HEALTH SERVICES, INC.
CREATION DATE: 10/04/89 ***REVISION DATE:*** 05/11/90

MATERIAL SAFETY DATA SHEET

OCCUPATIONAL HEALTH SERVICES, INC.
AGRICULTURE AND PESTICIDE DIVISION
450 SEVENTH AVENUE, SUITE 2407
NEW YORK, NEW YORK 10123
1-800-445-MSDS OR (212) 967-1100

EMERGENCY CONTACT:
JOHN S. BRANSFORD, JR. (615) 292-1180

SUBSTANCE IDENTIFICATION

CAS-NUMBER 9003-29-6

SUBSTANCE: POLYBUTENE

TRADE NAMES/SYNONYMS: INDOPOL L-50; PST75671

CHEMICAL FAMILY: POLYMER
HYDROCARBON, ALIPHATIC

CERCLA RATINGS (SCALE 0-3): HEALTH=2 FIRE=1 REACTIVITY=0 PERSISTENCE=1

NFPA RATINGS (SCALE 0-4): HEALTH=2 FIRE=1 REACTIVITY=0

COMPONENTS AND CONTAMINANTS

COMPONENT: POLYBUTENE ***PERCENT:*** 100
CAS# 9003-29-6

EXPOSURE LIMITS: NO OCCUPATIONAL EXPOSURE LIMITS ESTABLISHED BY OSHA, ACGIH, OR NIOSH.

PHYSICAL DATA

DESCRIPTION: CLEAR LIQUID. ***BOILING POINT:*** >95 F (>35 C)
MELTING POINT: >-40 F (>-40 C) ***SPECIFIC GRAVITY:*** 0.85
VISCOSITY: 106-112 CST @ 38 C ***EVAPORATION RATE:*** NOT AVAILABLE
SOLUBILITY IN WATER: <0.1%

FIRE AND EXPLOSION DATA

FIRE AND EXPLOSION HAZARD: SLIGHT FIRE HAZARD WHEN EXPOSED TO HEAT OR FLAME.

FLASH POINT: 280 F (138 C) (CC) ***FLAMMABILITY CLASS(OSHA):*** IIIB

FIREFIGHTING MEDIA: DRY CHEMICAL, CARBON DIOXIDE, WATER SPRAY OR FOAM FOR LARGER FIRES, USE WATER SPRAY, FOG OR ALCOHOL FOAM

FIREFIGHTING: MOVE CONTAINER FROM FIRE AREA IF POSSIBLE. DO NOT SCATTER SPILLED MATERIAL WITH MORE WATER THAN NEEDED FOR FIRE CONTROL. DIKE FIRE CONTROL WATER FOR LATER DISPOSAL

USE AGENTS SUITABLE FOR TYPE OF SURROUNDING FIRE. AVOID BREATHING HAZARDOUS VAPORS, KEEP UPWIND.

TOXICITY

INDOPOL L-50: TOXICITY DATA: 17.3 MG/L/4 HOURS INHALATION-RAT LC50; >10.25 GM/KG SKIN-RABBIT LD50 (AMOCO MSDS); >34.6 GM/KG ORAL-RAT LD50 (AMOCO MSDS). CARCINOGEN STATUS: NONE. ACUTE TOXICITY LEVEL: TOXIC BY INHALATION, SLIGHTLY TOXIC BY DERMAL ABSORPTION, AND RELATIVELY NON-TOXIC BY INGESTION. TARGET EFFECTS: NO DATA AVAILABLE.

HEALTH EFFECTS AND FIRST AID

INHALATION: INDOPOL L-50: **ACUTE EXPOSURE-** A RELATIVELY LARGE DOSE PRODUCE NO DEATHS OR UNTOWARD BEHAVIORAL REACTIONS IN RATS. **CHRONIC EXPOSURE-** NO DATA AVAILABLE.

FIRST AID- REMOVE FROM EXPOSURE AREA TO FRESH AIR IMMEDIATELY. IF BREATHING HAS STOPPED, PERFORM ARTIFICIAL RESPIRATION. KEEP PERSON WARM AND AT REST. TREAT SYMPTOMATICALLY AND SUPPORTIVELY. GET MEDICAL ATTENTION IMMEDIATELY.

SKIN CONTACT: INDOPOL L-50: **ACUTE EXPOSURE-** NO SIGNIFICANT IRRITATION EXPECTED. ANIMAL STUDIES INDICATE A RELATIVELY LARGE DOSE WAS LETHAL. **CHRONIC EXPOSURE-** NO DATA AVAILABLE.

FIRST AID- REMOVE CONTAMINATED CLOTHING AND SHOES IMMEDIATELY. WASH AFFECTED AREA WITH SOAP OR MILD DETERGENT AND LARGE AMOUNTS OF WATER UNTIL NO EVIDENCE OF CHEMICAL REMAINS (APPROXIMATELY 15-20 MINUTES). GET MEDICAL ATTENTION IMMEDIATELY.

EYE CONTACT: INDOPOL L-50: **ACUTE EXPOSURE-** NO SIGNIFICANT IRRITATION EXPECTED. **CHRONIC EXPOSURE-** NO DATA AVAILABLE.

FIRST AID- WASH EYES IMMEDIATELY WITH LARGE AMOUNTS OF WATER OR NORMAL SALINE, OCCASIONALLY LIFTING UPPER AND LOWER LIDS, UNTIL NO EVIDENCE OF CHEMICAL REMAINS (APPROXIMATELY 15-20 MINUTES). GET MEDICAL ATTENTION IMMEDIATELY.

INGESTION: INDOPOL L-50: **ACUTE EXPOSURE-** A RELATIVELY LARGE DOSE WAS LETHAL TO RATS TESTED. **CHRONIC EXPOSURE-** RATS FED A DIET CONTAINING 10% POLYBUTENE POWDER FOR 6 MONTHS SHOWED NO EVIDENCE OF TOXICITY.

FIRST AID- TREAT SYMPTOMATICALLY AND SUPPORTIVELY. GET MEDICAL ATTENTION IMMEDIATELY. IF VOMITING OCCURS, KEEP HEAD LOWER THAN HIPS TO PREVENT ASPIRATION.

ANTIDOTE: NO SPECIFIC ANTIDOTE. TREAT SYMPTOMATICALLY AND SUPPORTIVELY.

REACTIVITY

REACTIVITY: STABLE UNDER NORMAL TEMPERATURES AND PRESSURES.

INCOMPATIBILITIES: INDOPOL L-50: NO DATA AVAILABLE.

DECOMPOSITION: THERMAL DECOMPOSITION PRODUCTS MAY INCLUDE TOXIC OXIDES OF CARBON.

POLYMERIZATION: HAZARDOUS POLYMERIZATION HAS NOT BEEN REPORTED TO OCCUR UNDER NORMAL TEMPERATURES AND PRESSURES.

CONDITIONS TO AVOID

MAY BURN BUT DOES NOT IGNITE READILY. AVOID CONTACT WITH STRONG OXIDIZERS, EXCESSIVE HEAT, SPARKS, OR OPEN FLAME.

SPILL AND LEAK PROCEDURES

OCCUPATIONAL SPILL: STOP LEAK IF YOU CAN DO IT WITHOUT RISK. FOR SMALL SPILLS, TAKE UP WITH SAND OR OTHER ABSORBENT MATERIAL AND PLACE INTO CLEAN, DRY CONTAINERS FOR LATER DISPOSAL. KEEP UNNECESSARY PEOPLE AWAY. ISOLATE HAZARD AREA AND DENY ENTRY.

PROTECTIVE EQUIPMENT

VENTILATION: PROVIDE GENERAL DILUTION VENTILATION.

RESPIRATOR: THE FOLLOWING RESPIRATORS ARE RECOMMENDED BASED ON INFORMATION FOUND IN THE PHYSICAL DATA, TOXICITY AND HEALTH EFFECTS SECTIONS. THEY ARE RANKED IN ORDER FROM MINIMUM TO MAXIMUM RESPIRATORY PROTECTION. THE SPECIFIC RESPIRATOR SELECTED MUST BE BASED ON CONTAMINATION LEVELS FOUND IN THE WORK PLACE, MUST NOT EXCEED THE WORKING LIMITS OF THE RESPIRATOR AND BE JOINTLY APPROVED BY THE NATIONAL INSTITUTE FOR OCCUPATIONAL SAFETY AND HEALTH AND THE MINE SAFETY AND HEALTH ADMINISTRATION (NIOSH-MSHA).

CHEMICAL CARTRIDGE RESPIRATOR WITH AN ORGANIC VAPOR CARTRIDGE(S)

GAS MASK WITH ORGANIC VAPOR CANISTER (CHIN-STYLE OR FRONT- OR BACK-MOUNTED CANISTER). TYPE 'C' SUPPLIED-AIR RESPIRATOR OPERATED IN THE PRESSURE-DEMAND OR OTHER POSITIVE PRESSURE OR CONTINUOUS-FLOW MODE.

SELF-CONTAINED BREATHING APPARATUS.

FOR FIREFIGHTING AND OTHER IMMEDIATELY DANGEROUS TO LIFE OR HEALTH CONDITIONS:

SELF-CONTAINED BREATHING APPARATUS WITH FULL FACEPIECE OPERATED IN PRESSURE-DEMAND OR OTHER POSITIVE PRESSURE MODE.

SUPPLIED-AIR RESPIRATOR WITH FULL FACEPIECE AND OPERATED IN PRESSURE-DEMAND OR OTHER POSITIVE PRESSURE MODE IN COMBINATION WITH AN AUXILIARY SELF-CONTAINED BREATHING APPARATUS OPERATED IN PRESSURE-DEMAND OR OTHER POSITIVE PRESSURE MODE.

CLOTHING: PROTECTIVE CLOTHING NOT REQUIRED. AVOID REPEATED OR PROLONGED CONTACT WITH THIS SUBSTANCE.

GLOVES: PROTECTIVE GLOVES ARE NOT REQUIRED BUT RECOMMENDED.

EYE PROTECTION: EYE PROTECTION NOT REQUIRED, BUT ADVISABLE.

AUTHORIZED BY- OCCUPATIONAL HEALTH SERVICES, INC.

CREATION DATE: 11/17/89 ***REVISION DATE:*** 05/18/90

MATERIAL SAFETY DATA SHEET

OCCUPATIONAL HEALTH SERVICES, INC.
AGRICULTURE AND PESTICIDE DIVISION
450 SEVENTH AVENUE, SUITE 2407
NEW YORK, NEW YORK 10123
1-800-445-MSDS OR (212) 967-1100

EMERGENCY CONTACT:
JOHN S. BRANSFORD, JR. (615) 292-1180

SUBSTANCE IDENTIFICATION

CAS-NUMBER 9005-64-5

SUBSTANCE: **POLYOXYETHYLENE (20) SORBITAN MONOLAURATE**

TRADE NAMES/SYNONYMS: OXYETHYLATED SORBITAN MONOLAURATE; POLY(OXYETHYLENE SORBITAN LAURATE); SORBITAN POLYETHOXY MONOLAURATE; ETHOXYLATED SORBITAN MONOOLAURATE; SORBITAN, MONODODECANOTE, POLY(OXY-1,2-ETHANEDIYL) DERIVATIVES; POLYSORBATE 20; TWEEN 20; PST80107

CHEMICAL FAMILY: SORBITAN FATTY ACID ESTER
ETHOXYLATED FATTY ACID

CERCLA RATINGS (SCALE 0-3): HEALTH=2 FIRE=1 REACTIVITY=0 PERSISTENCE=1

NFPA RATINGS (SCALE 0-4): HEALTH=2 FIRE=1 REACTIVITY=0

COMPONENTS AND CONTAMINANTS

COMPONENT: POLYOXYETHYLENE (20) SORBITAN MONOLAURATE ***PERCENT:*** 97-98
CAS# 9005-64-5

COMPONENT: WATER ***PERCENT:*** 2-3

EXPOSURE LIMITS: NO OCCUPATIONAL EXPOSURE LIMITS ESTABLISHED BY OSHA, ACGIH, OR NIOSH.

PHYSICAL DATA

DESCRIPTION: LEMON YELLOW TO AMBER COLORED, OILY LIQUID WITH A FAINT CHARACTERISTIC ODOR AND WARM, BITTER TASTE. ***BOILING POINT:*** >212 F (>100 C)

MELTING POINT: 14 F (-10 C) ***SPECIFIC GRAVITY:*** 1.084 @ 45 C

VISCOSITY: 400 CPS ***VOLATILITY:*** 2-3% ***VAPOR PRESSURE:*** <1.0 MMHG @ 20 C

SOLUBILITY IN WATER: SOLUBLE ***VAPOR DENSITY:*** >1

SOLVENT SOLUBILITY: SOLUBLE IN METHANOL, ETHANOL, ISOPROPANOL, PROPYLENE GLYCOL, ETHYLENE GLYCOL, ETHYL ACETATE, DIOXANE, COTTONSEED OIL; INSOLUBLE IN MINERAL OIL, MINERAL SPIRITS

FIRE AND EXPLOSION DATA

FIRE AND EXPLOSION HAZARD: SLIGHT FIRE HAZARD WHEN EXPOSED TO HEAT OR FLAME.

FLASH POINT: >300 F (>149 C) (OC) ***FLAMMABILITY CLASS(OSHA):*** IIIB

FIREFIGHTING MEDIA: DRY CHEMICAL, CARBON DIOXIDE, HALON, WATER SPRAY OR STANDARD FOAM (1987 EMERGENCY RESPONSE GUIDEBOOK, DOT P 5800.4).
FOR LARGER FIRES, USE WATER SPRAY, FOG OR STANDARD FOAM (1987 EMERGENCY RESPONSE GUIDEBOOK, DOT P 5800.4).

FIREFIGHTING: MOVE CONTAINER FROM FIRE AREA IF POSSIBLE. DO NOT SCATTER SPILLED MATERIAL WITH HIGH PRESSURE WATER STREAMS. DIKE FIRE CONTROL WATER FOR LATER DISPOSAL (1987 EMERGENCY RESPONSE GUIDEBOOK, DOT P 5800.4, GUIDE PAGE 31).
USE AGENTS SUITABLE FOR TYPE OF SURROUNDING FIRE. AVOID BREATHING HAZARDOUS VAPORS, KEEP UPWIND.

TOXICITY

POLYOXYETHYLENE (20) SORBITAN MONOLAURATE (ETHOXYLATED SORBITAN MONOLAURATE): IRRITATION DATA: 15 MG/3 DAYS SKIN-HUMAN MILD. TOXICITY DATA: 37 MG/KG ORAL-RAT LD50; 18 MG/KG ORAL-HAMSTER LD50; 1420 MG/KG INTRAVENOUS-MOUSE LD50. CARCINOGEN STATUS: NONE. ACUTE TOXICITY LEVEL: RELATIVELY NONTOXIC BY INGESTION. TARGET EFFECTS: NO DATA AVAILABLE.

HEALTH EFFECTS AND FIRST AID

INHALATION: POLYOXYETHYLENE (20) SORBITAN MONOLAURATE (ETHOXYLATED SORBITAN MONOLAUREATE): **ACUTE EXPOSURE-** DUE TO THE LOW VAPOR PRESSURE, NO SIGNIFICANT HEALTH HAZARD FROM INHALATION IS LIKELY TO OCCUR AT NORMAL ROOM TEMPERATURES. INHALATION OF GENERATED MIST OR VAPORS PRODUCED FROM ELEVATED TEMPERATURES MAY CAUSE IRRITATION OF THE MUCOUS MEMBRANES. INHALATION OF HIGH LEVELS OF SOME POLYSORBATES MAY CAUSE A CHEMICAL PNEUMONITIS. **CHRONIC EXPOSURE-** NO DATA AVAILABLE.

FIRST AID- REMOVE FROM EXPOSURE AREA TO FRESH AIR IMMEDIATELY. IF BREATHING HAS STOPPED, PERFORM ARTIFICIAL RESPIRATION. KEEP PERSON WARM AND AT REST. TREAT SYMPTOMATICALLY AND SUPPORTIVELY. GET MEDICAL ATTENTION IMMEDIATELY.

SKIN CONTACT: POLYOXYETHYLENE (20) SORBITAN MONOLAURATE (ETHOXYLATED SORBITAN MONOLAURATE): **ACUTE EXPOSURE-** THIS MATERIAL WAS NONIRRITATING ON HUMAN SUBJECT PATCH TESTS. THE PRIMARY INDEX OF THE UNDILUTED MATERIAL WAS FOUND TO BE 0.34 TO 0.96 FOLLOWING A 24-HOUR APPLICATION TO INTACT AND ABRADED SKIN OF RABBITS. **CHRONIC EXPOSURE-** PROLONGED OR REPEATED EXPOSURE MAY CAUSE IRRITATION OF THE SKIN BY REMOVING NATURAL OILS, CAUSING REDNESS, SORENESS, AND PAPULAR DERMATITIS.

FIRST AID- REMOVE CONTAMINATED CLOTHING AND SHOES IMMEDIATELY. WASH AFFECTED AREA WITH SOAP OR MILD DETERGENT AND LARGE AMOUNTS OF WATER UNTIL NO EVIDENCE OF CHEMICAL REMAINS (APPROXIMATELY 15-20 MINUTES). GET MEDICAL ATTENTION IMMEDIATELY.

EYE CONTACT: POLYOXYETHYLENE (20) SORBITAN MONOLAURATE (ETHOXYLATED SORBITAN MONOLAUREATE): **ACUTE EXPOSURE-** APPLICATION OF THE UNDILUTED MATERIAL IN RABBITS' EYES RESULTED IN MINIMAL TO MODERATE CONJUNCTIVAL IRRITATION. RINSING WITHIN 4 SECONDS OF EXPOSURE RESULTED IN LITTLE CHANGE TO COMPLETE PREVENTION. DRAIZE EYE IRRITATION SCORE WAS 5.3 OUT OF A POSSIBLE 110. **CHRONIC EXPOSURE-** NO DATA AVAILABLE.

FIRST AID- WASH EYES IMMEDIATELY WITH LARGE AMOUNTS OF WATER OR NORMAL SALINE, OCCASIONALLY LIFTING UPPER AND LOWER LIDS, UNTIL NO EVIDENCE OF CHEMICAL REMAINS (APPROXIMATELY 15-20 MINUTES). GET MEDICAL ATTENTION IMMEDIATELY.

INGESTION: POLYOXYETHYLENE (20) SORBITAN MONOLAURATE (ETHOXYLATED SORBITAN MONOLAUREATE): **ACUTE EXPOSURE-** INGESTION OF HIGH LEVELS CAUSED DIARRHEA AND OTHER EFFECTS SECONDARY TO LAXATION. INGESTION OF >33 CC/KG WAS LETHAL TO RATS. INGESTION OF HIGH LEVELS OF SOME POLYSORBATES MAY CAUSE INTESTINAL OBSTRUCTION. **CHRONIC EXPOSURE-** REPEATED OR PROLONGED INGESTION OF HIGH CONCENTRATIONS OF THIS MATERIAL CAUSED DIARRHEA AND OTHER EFFECTS SECONDARY TO LAXATION IN RATS AND HAMSTERS.

FIRST AID- TREAT SYMPTOMATICALLY AND SUPPORTIVELY. GET MEDICAL ATTENTION IMMEDIATELY. IF VOMITING OCCURS, KEEP HEAD LOWER THAN HIPS TO PREVENT ASPIRATION.

ANTIDOTE: NO SPECIFIC ANTIDOTE. TREAT SYMPTOMATICALLY AND SUPPORTIVELY.

REACTIVITY

REACTIVITY: STABLE UNDER NORMAL TEMPERATURES AND PRESSURES.

INCOMPATIBILITIES: POLYOXYETHYLENE (20) SORBITAN MONOLAURATE (ETHOXYLATED SORBITAN MONOLAUREATE): OXIDIZING MATERIALS: INCOMPATIBLE.

DECOMPOSITION: THERMAL DECOMPOSITION PRODUCTS MAY INCLUDE TOXIC OXIDES OF CARBON.

POLYMERIZATION: HAZARDOUS POLYMERIZATION HAS NOT BEEN REPORTED TO OCCUR UNDER NORMAL TEMPERATURES AND PRESSURES.

STORAGE AND DISPOSAL

OBSERVE ALL FEDERAL, STATE AND LOCAL REGULATIONS WHEN STORING OR DISPOSING OF THIS SUBSTANCE. FOR ASSISTANCE, CONTACT THE DISTRICT DIRECTOR OF THE ENVIRONMENTAL PROTECTION AGENCY.

STORAGE

STORE AWAY FROM INCOMPATIBLE SUBSTANCES.

CONDITIONS TO AVOID

MAY BURN BUT DOES NOT IGNITE READILY. AVOID CONTACT WITH STRONG OXIDIZERS, EXCESSIVE HEAT, SPARKS, OR OPEN FLAME.

SPILL AND LEAK PROCEDURES

OCCUPATIONAL SPILL: STOP LEAK IF YOU CAN DO IT WITHOUT RISK. FOR SMALL SPILLS, TAKE UP WITH SAND OR OTHER ABSORBENT MATERIAL AND PLACE INTO CLEAN, DRY CONTAINERS FOR LATER DISPOSAL. KEEP UNNECESSARY PEOPLE AWAY. ISOLATE HAZARD AREA AND DENY ENTRY.

PROTECTIVE EQUIPMENT

VENTILATION: PROVIDE LOCAL EXHAUST OR GENERAL DILUTION VENTILATION SYSTEM.

RESPIRATOR: THE FOLLOWING RESPIRATORS ARE RECOMMENDED BASED ON INFORMATION FOUND IN THE PHYSICAL DATA, TOXICITY AND HEALTH EFFECTS SECTIONS. THEY ARE RANKED IN ORDER FROM MINIMUM TO MAXIMUM RESPIRATORY PROTECTION. THE SPECIFIC RESPIRATOR SELECTED MUST BE BASED ON CONTAMINATION LEVELS FOUND IN THE WORK PLACE, MUST NOT EXCEED THE WORKING LIMITS OF THE RESPIRATOR AND BE JOINTLY APPROVED BY THE NATIONAL INSTITUTE FOR OCCUPATIONAL SAFETY AND HEALTH AND THE MINE SAFETY AND HEALTH ADMINISTRATION (NIOSH-MSHA).

CHEMICAL CARTRIDGE RESPIRATOR WITH AN ORGANIC VAPOR CARTRIDGE(S) WITH A FULL FACEPIECE.

GAS MASK WITH ORGANIC VAPOR CANISTER (CHIN-STYLE OR FRONT- OR BACK-MOUNTED CANISTER) WITH A FULL FACEPIECE.

TYPE 'C' SUPPLIED-AIR RESPIRATOR WITH A FULL FACEPIECE OPERATED IN PRESSURE-DEMAND OR OTHER POSITIVE PRESSURE MODE OR WITH A FULL FACEPIECE, HELMET OR HOOD OPERATED IN CONTINUOUS-FLOW MODE.

SELF-CONTAINED BREATHING APPARATUS WITH A FULL FACEPIECE OPERATED IN PRESSURE-DEMAND OR OTHER POSITIVE PRESSURE MODE.

FOR FIREFIGHTING AND OTHER IMMEDIATELY DANGEROUS TO LIFE OR HEALTH CONDITIONS:

SELF-CONTAINED BREATHING APPARATUS WITH FULL FACEPIECE OPERATED IN PRESSURE-DEMAND OR OTHER POSITIVE PRESSURE MODE.

SUPPLIED-AIR RESPIRATOR WITH FULL FACEPIECE AND OPERATED IN PRESSURE-DEMAND OR OTHER POSITIVE PRESSURE MODE IN COMBINATION WITH AN AUXILIARY SELF-CONTAINED BREATHING APPARATUS OPERATED IN PRESSURE-DEMAND OR OTHER POSITIVE PRESSURE MODE.

CLOTHING: EMPLOYEE MUST WEAR APPROPRIATE PROTECTIVE (IMPERVIOUS) CLOTHING AND EQUIPMENT TO PREVENT REPEATED OR PROLONGED SKIN CONTACT WITH THIS SUBSTANCE.

GLOVES: EMPLOYEE MUST WEAR APPROPRIATE PROTECTIVE GLOVES TO PREVENT CONTACT WITH THIS SUBSTANCE.

EYE PROTECTION: EMPLOYEE MUST WEAR SPLASH-PROOF OR DUST-RESISTANT SAFETY GOGGLES TO PREVENT EYE CONTACT WITH THIS SUBSTANCE.

EMERGENCY EYE WASH: WHERE THERE IS ANY POSSIBILITY THAT AN EMPLOYEE'S EYES MAY BE EXPOSED TO THIS SUBSTANCE, THE EMPLOYER SHOULD PROVIDE AN EYE WASH FOUNTAIN WITHIN THE IMMEDIATE WORK AREA FOR EMERGENCY USE.

AUTHORIZED BY- OCCUPATIONAL HEALTH SERVICES, INC.

CREATION DATE: 10/04/89 ***REVISION DATE:*** 05/16/90

MATERIAL SAFETY DATA SHEET

OCCUPATIONAL HEALTH SERVICES, INC.
AGRICULTURE AND PESTICIDE DIVISION
450 SEVENTH AVENUE, SUITE 2407
NEW YORK, NEW YORK 10123
1-800-445-MSDS OR (212) 967-1100

EMERGENCY CONTACT:
JOHN S. BRANSFORD, JR. (615) 292-1180

SUBSTANCE IDENTIFICATION

CAS-NUMBER 7673-09-8

SUBSTANCE: **TRICHLOROMELAMINE**

TRADE NAMES/SYNONYMS: TCM; N,N',N''-TRICHLORO-2,4,6-TRIAMINE-4,3,5-TRIAZINE; CHLOROMELAMINE; DECCO SALT NO 5; 2,4,6-TRIS(CHLOROAMINE) TRIAZINE; 1,3,5-TRIAZINE, N,N',N''-TRICHLORO-2,4,6 TRIAMINO; PST80113

CHEMICAL FAMILY: HALOGEN COMPOUND, ALIPHATIC AMINE

MOLECULAR FORMULA: C3-H3-N6-CL3

MOLECULAR WEIGHT: 229.47

CERCLA RATINGS (SCALE 0-3): HEALTH=3 FIRE=0 REACTIVITY=3 PERSISTENCE=2

NFPA RATINGS (SCALE 0-4): HEALTH=3 FIRE=0 REACTIVITY=3

COMPONENTS AND CONTAMINANTS

COMPONENT: TRICHLOROMELAMINE ***PERCENT:*** 100
CAS# 7673-09-8

OTHER CONTAMINANTS: NONE

EXPOSURE LIMITS: NO OCCUPATIONAL EXPOSURE LIMITS ESTABLISHED BY OSHA, ACGIH, OR NIOSH.

PHYSICAL DATA

DESCRIPTION: FINE WHITE POWDER ***MELTING POINT:*** >572 F (>300 C)

SOLUBILITY IN WATER: SOLUBLE 0.34%

SOLVENT SOLUBILITY: GLACIAL ACETIC ACID, INSOL.> BENZENE, CCL4

FIRE AND EXPLOSION DATA

FIRE AND EXPLOSION HAZARD: NEGLIGIBLE FIRE HAZARD WHEN EXPOSED TO HEAT OR FLAME.

AUTOIGNITION TEMP.: 320 F (160 C)

FIREFIGHTING MEDIA: DRY CHEMICAL, CARBON DIOXIDE, HALON OR WATER SPRAY (1987 EMERGENCY RESPONSE GUIDEBOOK, DOT P 5800.4).

FOR LARGER FIRES, USE WATER SPRAY OR FOG (1987 EMERGENCY RESPONSE GUIDEBOOK, DOT P 5800.4).

FIREFIGHTING: MOVE CONTAINERS FROM FIRE AREA IF POSSIBLE. COOL CONTAINERS EXPOSED TO FLAMES WITH WATER FROM SIDE UNTIL WELL AFTER FIRE IS OUT. STAY AWAY FROM STORAGE TANK ENDS. FOR MASSIVE FIRE IN STORAGE AREA, USE UNMANNED HOSE HOLDER OR MONITOR NOZZLES; ELSE WITHDRAW FROM AREA AND LET FIRE BURN (1987 EMERGENCY RESPONSE GUIDEBOOK, DOT P 5800.4, GUIDE PAGE 35)

FLOOD WITH WATER. COOL CONTAINERS WITH FLOODING AMOUNTS OF WATER FROM AS FAR A DISTANCE AS POSSIBLE. AVOID BREATHING VAPORS OR DUSTS. EVACUATE TO A RADIUS OF 2500 FEET FOR UNCONTROLLABLE FIRES.

TRANSPORTATION DATA

DEPARTMENT OF TRANSPORTATION HAZARD CLASSIFICATION 49 CFR 172.101: OXIDIZER

DEPARTMENT OF TRANSPORTATION LABELING REQUIREMENTS 49 CFR 172.101 AND SUBPART E: OXIDIZER

DEPARTMENT OF TRANSPORTATION PACKAGING REQUIREMENTS: 49 CFR 173.154 EXCEPTIONS: 49 CFR 173.153

TOXICITY

TRICHLOROMELAMINE: TOXICITY DATA: 490 MG/KG ORAL-MOUSE LD50. CARCINOGEN STATUS: NONE. LOCAL EFFECTS: IRRITANT- INHALATION, SKIN, AND EYES. ACUTE TOXICITY LEVEL: TOXIC BY INGESTION. TARGET EFFECTS: NO DATA AVAILABLE.

HEALTH EFFECTS AND FIRST AID

INHALATION: TRICHLOROMELAMINE: IRRITANT. **ACUTE EXPOSURE-** MAY IRRITATE THE MUCOUS MEMBRANES WITH SYMPTOMS OF A HEADACHE AND SHORTNESS OF BREATH. **CHRONIC EXPOSURE-** NO DATA AVAILABLE.

FIRST AID- REMOVE FROM EXPOSURE AREA TO FRESH AIR IMMEDIATELY. IF BREATHING HAS STOPPED, PERFORM ARTIFICIAL RESPIRATION. KEEP PERSON WARM AND AT REST. TREAT SYMPTOMATICALLY AND SUPPORTIVELY. GET MEDICAL ATTENTION IMMEDIATELY.

SKIN CONTACT: TRICHLOROMELAMINE: IRRITANT. **ACUTE EXPOSURE-** MAY BE AN IRRITANT OF THE SKIN WITH SYMPTOMS OF REDNESS AND ITCHING. **CHRONIC EXPOSURE-** PROLONGED OR REPEATED EXPOSURE MAY PRODUCE DERMATITIS.
FIRST AID- REMOVE CONTAMINATED CLOTHING AND SHOES IMMEDIATELY. WASH AFFECTED AREA WITH SOAP OR MILD DETERGENT AND LARGE AMOUNTS OF WATER UNTIL NO EVIDENCE OF CHEMICAL REMAINS (APPROXIMATELY 15-20 MINUTES). GET MEDICAL ATTENTION IMMEDIATELY.

EYE CONTACT: TRICHLOROMELAMINE: IRRITANT: **ACUTE EXPOSURE-** MAY BE IRRITATING TO THE EYES WITH SYMPTOMS OF REDNESS AND BURNING SENSATION. **CHRONIC EXPOSURE-** MAY CAUSE CONJUNCTIVITIS.
FIRST AID- WASH EYES IMMEDIATELY WITH LARGE AMOUNTS OF WATER OR NORMAL SALINE, OCCASIONALLY LIFTING UPPER AND LOWER LIDS, UNTIL NO EVIDENCE OF CHEMICAL REMAINS (APPROXIMATELY 15-20 MINUTES). GET MEDICAL ATTENTION IMMEDIATELY.

INGESTION: TRICHLOROMELAMINE: TOXIC. **ACUTE EXPOSURE-** MAY IRRITATE THE MOUTH, THROAT, STOMACH AND OTHER PARTS OF THE ALIMENTARY SYSTEM WITH SYMPTOMS OF SORE THROAT, ABDOMINAL PAIN, NAUSEA, VOMITING AND DIARRHEA. **CHRONIC EXPOSURE-** NO DATA AVAILABLE.
FIRST AID- IF VICTIM IS CONSCIOUS, IMMEDIATELY GIVE 2 TO 4 GLASSES OF WATER, AND INDUCE VOMITING BY TOUCHING FINGER TO BACK OF THROAT. GET MEDICAL ATTENTION IMMEDIATELY.
ANTIDOTE: NO SPECIFIC ANTIDOTE. TREAT SYMPTOMATICALLY AND SUPPORTIVELY.

REACTIVITY

REACTIVITY: IS SENSITIVE TO AIR. IS AN OXIDIZING AGENT AND MAY REACT VIOLENTLY ON CONTACT WITH REDUCING AGENTS AND ORGANIC MATERIALS. MAY BE IGNITED WITH A SPARK.
INCOMPATIBILITIES: TRICHLOROMELAMINE: ACETONE: REACTS VIGOROUSLY AMMONIA: REACTS VIGOROUSLY ANILINE: REACTS VIGOROUSLY DIPHENYLAMINE: REACTS VIGOROUSLY TURPENTINE: REACTS VIGOROUSLY REDUCING AGENTS: REACTS VIOLENTLY ORGANIC MATERIALS: CAN REACT SPONTANEOUSLY ON CONTACT
DECOMPOSITION: THERMAL DECOMPOSITION MAY EMIT TOXIC FUMES OF CHLORIDE AND OXIDES OF NITROGEN AND CARBON.
POLYMERIZATION: HAZARDOUS POLYMERIZATION HAS NOT BEEN REPORTED TO OCCUR UNDER NORMAL TEMPERATURES AND PRESSURES.

CONDITIONS TO AVOID

AVOID CONTACT WITH COMBUSTIBLE MATERIALS (WOOD, PAPER, FUEL, OILS, ETC); IGNITION OR EXPLOSION MAY RESULT. AVOID CONTAMINATION OF WATER SOURCES.

SPILL AND LEAK PROCEDURES

OCCUPATIONAL SPILL: KEEP COMBUSTIBLES (WOOD, PAPER, OIL, ETC) AWAY FROM SPILLED MATERIAL. DO NOT TOUCH SPILLED MATERIAL. FOR SMALL DRY SPILLS, WITH CLEAN SHOVEL PLACE MATERIAL INTO CLEAN, DRY CONTAINER AND COVER; MOVE CONTAINERS FROM SPILL AREA. FOR SMALL LIQUID SPILLS, TAKE UP WITH SAND, EARTH OR OTHER ABSORBENT MATERIAL AND PLACE INTO CONTAINERS FOR LATER DISPOSAL. FOR LARGER SPILLS, DIKE FAR AHEAD OF SPILL FOR LATER DISPOSAL. KEEP UNNECESSARY PEOPLE AWAY. ISOLATE HAZARD AREA AND DENY ENTRY.

PROTECTIVE EQUIPMENT

VENTILATION: PROVIDE LOCAL EXHAUST OR PROCESS ENCLOSURE VENTILATION SYSTEM.
RESPIRATOR: THE FOLLOWING RESPIRATORS ARE RECOMMENDED BASED ON INFORMATION FOUND IN THE PHYSICAL DATA, TOXICITY AND HEALTH EFFECTS SECTIONS. THEY ARE RANKED IN ORDER FROM MINIMUM TO MAXIMUM RESPIRATORY PROTECTION. THE SPECIFIC RESPIRATOR SELECTED MUST BE BASED ON CONTAMINATION LEVELS FOUND IN THE WORK PLACE, MUST NOT EXCEED THE WORKING LIMITS OF THE RESPIRATOR AND BE JOINTLY APPROVED BY THE NATIONAL INSTITUTE FOR OCCUPATIONAL SAFETY AND HEALTH AND THE MINE SAFETY AND HEALTH ADMINISTRATION (NIOSH-MSHA).
HIGH LEVELS- SUPPLIED-AIR RESPIRATOR. SELF-CONTAINED BREATHING APPARATUS.
FIREFIGHTING- SELF-CONTAINED BREATHING APPARATUS WITH A FULL FACEPIECE OPERATED IN PRESSURE-DEMAND OR OTHER POSITIVE PRESSURE MODE.
FOR FIREFIGHTING AND OTHER IMMEDIATELY DANGEROUS TO LIFE OR HEALTH CONDITIONS:
SELF-CONTAINED BREATHING APPARATUS WITH FULL FACEPIECE OPERATED IN PRESSURE-DEMAND OR OTHER POSITIVE PRESSURE MODE.
SUPPLIED-AIR RESPIRATOR WITH FULL FACEPIECE AND OPERATED IN PRESSURE-DEMAND OR OTHER POSITIVE PRESSURE MODE IN COMBINATION WITH AN AUXILIARY SELF-CONTAINED BREATHING APPARATUS OPERATED IN PRESSURE-DEMAND OR OTHER POSITIVE PRESSURE MODE.
CLOTHING: EMPLOYEE MUST WEAR APPROPRIATE PROTECTIVE (IMPERVIOUS) CLOTHING AND EQUIPMENT TO PREVENT REPEATED OR PROLONGED SKIN CONTACT WITH THIS SUBSTANCE.
GLOVES: EMPLOYEE MUST WEAR APPROPRIATE PROTECTIVE GLOVES TO PREVENT CONTACT WITH THIS SUBSTANCE.
EYE PROTECTION: EMPLOYEE MUST WEAR SPLASH-PROOF OR DUST-RESISTANT SAFETY GOGGLES TO PREVENT EYE CONTACT WITH THIS SUBSTANCE.
EMERGENCY EYE WASH: WHERE THERE IS ANY POSSIBILITY THAT AN EMPLOYEE'S EYES MAY BE EXPOSED TO THIS SUBSTANCE, THE EMPLOYER SHOULD PROVIDE AN EYE WASH FOUNTAIN WITHIN THE IMMEDIATE WORK AREA FOR EMERGENCY USE.

AUTHORIZED BY- OCCUPATIONAL HEALTH SERVICES, INC.
CREATION DATE: 10/05/89 ***REVISION DATE:*** 05/16/90

MATERIAL SAFETY DATA SHEET

OCCUPATIONAL HEALTH SERVICES, INC.
AGRICULTURE AND PESTICIDE DIVISION
450 SEVENTH AVENUE, SUITE 2407
NEW YORK, NEW YORK 10123
1-800-445-MSDS OR (212) 967-1100

EMERGENCY CONTACT:
JOHN S. BRANSFORD, JR. (615) 292-1180

SUBSTANCE IDENTIFICATION

CAS-NUMBER 56802-99-4
SUBSTANCE: CHLORINATED TRISODIUM PHOSPHATE
TRADE NAMES/SYNONYMS: SODIUM HYPOCHLORITE, PHOSPHATE; PHOSPHORIC ACID, TRISODIUM SALT (CHLORINATED); PST80117
CHEMICAL FAMILY: INORGANIC SALT
MOLECULAR FORMULA: (NA3-PO4.12H2-O)4.NA-O-CL
CERCLA RATINGS (SCALE 0-3): HEALTH=U FIRE=0 REACTIVITY=0 PERSISTENCE=0
NFPA RATINGS (SCALE 0-4): HEALTH=U FIRE=0 REACTIVITY=0

COMPONENTS AND CONTAMINANTS

COMPONENT: TRISODIUM PHOSPHATE DODECAHYDRATE ***PERCENT:*** 91.75
CAS# 10101-89-0
COMPONENT: SODIUM HYPOCHLORITE ***PERCENT:*** 3.25
CAS# 7681-52-9
COMPONENT: SODIUM CHLORIDE ***PERCENT:*** <5.0
CAS# 7647-14-5
OTHER CONTAMINANTS: NONE
EXPOSURE LIMITS: NO OCCUPATIONAL EXPOSURE LIMITS ESTABLISHED BY OSHA, ACGIH, OR NIOSH.

PHYSICAL DATA

DESCRIPTION: WHITE CRYSTALLINE SOLID ***SPECIFIC GRAVITY:*** NOT AVAILABLE
PH: ALKALINE ***SOLUBILITY IN WATER:*** SOLUBLE

FIRE AND EXPLOSION DATA

FIRE AND EXPLOSION HAZARD: NEGLIGIBLE FIRE HAZARD WHEN EXPOSED TO HEAT OR FLAME.
FIREFIGHTING MEDIA: DRY CHEMICAL, CARBON DIOXIDE, HALON, WATER SPRAY OR STANDARD FOAM (1987 EMERGENCY RESPONSE GUIDEBOOK, DOT P 5800.4).
FOR LARGER FIRES, USE WATER SPRAY, FOG OR STANDARD FOAM (1987 EMERGENCY RESPONSE GUIDEBOOK, DOT P 5800.4).
FIREFIGHTING: MOVE CONTAINERS FROM FIRE AREA IF POSSIBLE. COOL CONTAINERS EXPOSED TO FLAMES WITH WATER FROM SIDE UNTIL WELL AFTER FIRE IS OUT. STAY AWAY FROM STORAGE TANK ENDS (1987 EMERGENCY RESPONSE GUIDEBOOK, DOT P 5800.4, GUIDE PAGE 60).
EXTINGUISH USING AGENT INDICATED; DO NOT USE WATER DIRECTLY ON MATERIAL. IF LARGE AMOUNTS OF COMBUSTIBLE MATERIALS ARE INVOLVED, USE WATER SPRAY OR FOG IN FLOODING AMOUNTS. AVOID BREATHING CORROSIVE DUSTS AND FUMES FROM BURNING MATERIAL, KEEP UPWIND.

TOXICITY

TRISODIUM PHOSPHATE (SODIUM PHOSPHATE, TRIBASIC): TOXICITY DATA: ANHYDROUS: 1580 MG/KG INTRAVENOUS-RABBIT LDLO; MUTAGENIC DATA (RTEC). DODECAHYDRATE: 430 MG/KG INTRAPERITONEAL-MOUSE LD50; 7400 MG/KG ORAL-RAT LD50. CARCINOGEN STATUS: NONE. LOCAL EFFECTS:

CORROSIVE: INHALATION, SKIN, AND EYES. ACUTE TOXICITY LEVEL: SLIGHTLY TOXIC BY INGESTION. TARGET EFFECTS: POISONING MAY AFFECT THE SERUM CALCIUM LEVEL.

SODIUM HYPOCHLORITE: IRRITATION DATA: SODIUM HYPOCHLORITE: 10 MG/KG EYE-RABBIT MODERATE. PENTAHYDRATE: 500 MG/24 HOURS SKIN-RABBIT MODERATE; 100 MG EYE-RABBIT MODERATE. TOXICITY DATA: SODIUM HYPOCHLORITE: 8910 MG/KG ORAL-RAT LD50 (BIOFX*); 1 GM/KG ORAL-WOMAN TCLO; >10.5 MG/L INHALATION-RAT LCLO; >10,000 MG/KG SKIN-RABBIT LDLO; MUTAGENIC DATA (RTECS). PENTAHYDRATE: 8910 MG/KG ORAL-RAT LD50. CARCINOGEN STATUS: NONE. LOCAL EFFECTS: CORROSIVE- INHALATION, SKIN, EYE. ACUTE TOXICITY LEVEL: SLIGHTLY TOXIC BY INGESTION. TARGET EFFECTS: SENSITIZER- DERMAL.

SODIUM CHLORIDE: IRRITATION DATA: 50 MG/24 HOURS SKIN-RABBIT MILD; 500 MG/24 HOURS SKIN-RABBIT MILD; 100 MG EYE-RABBIT MILD; 100 MG/24 HOURS EYE-RABBIT MODERATE; 10 MG EYE-RABBIT MODERATE. TOXICITY DATA: 12,357 MG/KG/23 DAYS CONTINUOUS ORAL-HUMAN TDLO; 3000 MG/KG ORAL-RAT LD50; 4000 MG/KG ORAL-MOUSE LD50; 8 GM/KG ORAL-RABBIT LDLO; 3500 MG/KG SUBCUTANEOUS-RAT LDLO; 3 GM/KG SUBCUTANEOUS-MOUSE LD50; 2160 MG/KG SUBCUTANEOUS-GUINEA PIG LDLO; 645 MG/KG INTRAVENOUS-MOUSE LD50; 2 GM/KG INTRAVENOUS-DOG LDLO; 1100 MG/KG INTRAVENOUS-RABBIT LDLO; 300 MG/KG INTRAVENOUS-GUINEA PIG LDLO; 6614 MG/KG INTRAPERITONEAL-MOUSE LD50; 364 MG/KG INTRAPERITONEAL-DOG LDLO; 131 MG/KG INTRACERVICAL-MOUSE LD50; 300 MG/KG INTRAARTERIAL-GUINEA PIG LDLO; MUTAGENIC DATA (RTECS); REPRODUCTIVE EFFECTS DATA (RTECS). CARCINOGEN STATUS: NONE. LOCAL EFFECTS: IRRITANT- EYE. ACUTE TOXICITY LEVEL: MODERATELY TOXIC BY INGESTION. TARGET EFFECTS: POISONING MAY AFFECT THE CENTRAL NERVOUS SYSTEM.

HEALTH EFFECTS AND FIRST AID

INHALATION: TRISODIUM PHOSPHATE (SODIUM PHOSPHATE, TRIBASIC): CORROSIVE. **ACUTE EXPOSURE-** MAY CAUSE SEVERE IRRITATION AND POSSIBLY CORROSIVE EFFECTS. IF SUFFICIENT QUANTITIES OF A CORROSIVE SUBSTANCE ARE INHALED, PULMONARY EDEMA MAY DEVELOP, OFTEN WITH A LATENCY PERIOD OF 48-72 HOURS. **CHRONIC EXPOSURE-** DEPENDING ON CONCENTRATION AND DURATION OF CONTACT, EFFECTS AS IN ACUTE EXPOSURE MAY OCCUR WITH REPEATED OR PROLONGED EXPOSURE.

SODIUM HYPOCHLORITE: CORROSIVE. **ACUTE EXPOSURE-** MAY CAUSE SEVERE BRONCHIAL IRRITATION, SORE THROAT WITH POSSIBLE BLISTERING, COUGHING, STOMATITIS, NAUSEA, LABORED BREATHING, SHORTNESS OF BREATH AND PULMONARY EDEMA. 10-20 MG/M3 CAUSES BURNING OF THE NOSE AND THROAT; 40-60 MG/M3 MAY BE FATAL. IF SUFFICIENT AMOUNTS ARE ABSORBED, MAY CAUSE EFFECTS AS DETAILED IN ACUTE INGESTION. **CHRONIC EXPOSURE-** NO DATA AVAILABLE.

SODIUM CHLORIDE: **ACUTE EXPOSURE-** INHALATION OF DUST MAY LEAVE A SALTY TASTE AND CAUSE IRRITATION TO THE NOSE AND THROAT. SYMPTOMS MAY INCLUDE COUGHING, DRYNESS, AND SORE THROAT. **CHRONIC EXPOSURE-** NO DATA AVAILABLE.

FIRST AID- REMOVE FROM EXPOSURE AREA TO FRESH AIR IMMEDIATELY. IF BREATHING HAS STOPPED, GIVE ARTIFICIAL RESPIRATION. MAINTAIN AIRWAY AND BLOOD PRESSURE AND ADMINISTER OXYGEN IF AVAILABLE. KEEP AFFECTED PERSON WARM AND AT REST. TREAT SYMPTOMATICALLY AND SUPPORTIVELY. ADMINISTRATION OF OXYGEN SHOULD BE PERFORMED BY QUALIFIED PERSONNEL. GET MEDICAL ATTENTION IMMEDIATELY.

SKIN CONTACT: TRISODIUM PHOSPHATE (SODIUM PHOSPHATE, TRIBASIC): CORROSIVE. **ACUTE EXPOSURE-** CONTACT MAY PRODUCE STRONG IRRITATION, ERYTHEMA, PAIN AND BLISTERING. SOLUTIONS MAY CAUSE CAUSTIC BURNS. **CHRONIC EXPOSURE-** DEPENDING ON CONCENTRATION AND DURATION OF CONTACT, EFFECTS AS IN ACUTE EXPOSURE MAY OCCUR WITH REPEATED OR PROLONGED EXPOSURE.

SODIUM HYPOCHLORITE: CORROSIVE. **ACUTE EXPOSURE-** EXTENT OF DAMAGE DEPENDS ON CONCENTRATION, PH, VOLUME OF SOLUTION AND DURATION OF CONTACT. MAY CAUSE REDNESS, PAIN, BLISTERING, ITCHY ECZEMA AND CHEMICAL BURNS. SENSITIZATION REACTIONS ARE POSSIBLE IN PREVIOUSLY EXPOSED PERSONS. **CHRONIC EXPOSURE-** EFFECTS DEPEND ON CONCENTRATION AND DURATION OF EXPOSURE. REPEATED OR PROLONGED CONTACT WITH CORROSIVE SUBSTANCES MAY RESULT IN DERMATITIS OR EFFECTS SIMILAR TO ACUTE EXPOSURE.

SODIUM CHLORIDE: **ACUTE EXPOSURE-** MAY CAUSE MILD IRRITATION UNLESS THE CONTACT IS INTENSIVE WHICH MAY RESULT IN DERMATITIS. **CHRONIC EXPOSURE-** PRIMARY IRRITANT DERMATITIS MAY RESULT FROM SODIUM CHLORIDE BEING TRAPPED BETWEEN THE SKIN AND JEWELRY SINCE SOME METAL ALLOYS MAY BE CORRODED AND DISCOLORED BY SUCH CONTACT.

FIRST AID- REMOVE CONTAMINATED CLOTHING AND SHOES IMMEDIATELY. WASH AFFECTED AREA WITH SOAP OR MILD DETERGENT AND LARGE AMOUNTS OF WATER UNTIL NO EVIDENCE OF CHEMICAL REMAINS (AT LEAST 15-20 MINUTES). IN CASE OF CHEMICAL BURNS, COVER AREA WITH STERILE, DRY DRESSING. BANDAGE SECURELY, BUT NOT TOO TIGHTLY. GET MEDICAL ATTENTION IMMEDIATELY.

EYE CONTACT: TRISODIUM PHOSPHATE (SODIUM PHOSPHATE, TRIBASIC): CORROSIVE. **ACUTE EXPOSURE-** DIRECT CONTACT MAY CAUSE IRRITATION, PAIN, AND POSSIBLY CORNEAL INJURY. SOLUTIONS MAY CAUSE CORNEAL DAMAGE. A SPLASH OF AQUEOUS SOLUTION IN HUMAN EYES HAS CAUSED SLIGHT TRANSIENT INJURY IN ONE CASE AND MODERATE PERMANENT CORNEAL OPACIFICATION AND VASCULARIZATION IN TWO CASES. **CHRONIC EXPOSURE-** DEPENDING ON CONCENTRATION AND DURATION OF CONTACT, EFFECTS AS IN ACUTE EXPOSURE MAY OCCUR WITH REPEATED OR PROLONGED EXPOSURE.

SODIUM HYPOCHLORITE: CORROSIVE. **ACUTE EXPOSURE-** MAY CAUSE REDNESS, PAIN, AND BLURRED VISION. SOLUTIONS OF 5% SPLASHED IN HUMAN EYES HAVE CAUSED A BURNING SENSATION AND LATER ONLY SLIGHT SUPERFICIAL DISTURBANCE OF THE CORNEAL EPITHELIUM WHICH CLEARED COMPLETELY IN THE NEXT DAY OR TWO WITHOUT SPECIAL TREATMENT. HOWEVER, ONE ANIMAL STUDY REPORTS A 5% SOLUTION CAUSING ONLY MODERATE IRRITATION WITH CLEARING WITHIN 7 DAYS. A HIGHER CONCENTRATION OF 15% TESTED ON RABBIT EYES CAUSED IMMEDIATE SEVERE PAIN, HEMORRHAGES, RAPID ONSET OF GROUND-GLASS APPEARANCE OF THE CORNEAL EPITHELIUM, MODERATE BLUISH EDEMA OF THE WHOLE CORNEA, CHEMOSIS AND DISCHARGE FOR SEVERAL DAYS. SUCH EYES HAVE SOMETIMES HEALED IN 2-3 WEEKS WITH SLIGHT OR NO RESIDUAL CORNEAL DAMAGE BUT THEY HAD NEOVASCULARIZATION OF THE CONJUNCTIVA AND DISTORTION OF THE NICTITATING MEMBRANE BY SCARRING. **CHRONIC EXPOSURE-** DEPENDING ON CONCENTRATION AND DURATION OF EXPOSURE, SYMPTOMS MAY BE AS THOSE OF ACUTE EXPOSURE.

SODIUM CHLORIDE: IRRITANT. **ACUTE EXPOSURE-** SOLID PARTICLES OR HYPERTONIC SOLUTIONS MAY CAUSE REDNESS, PAIN, IRRITATION AND A STINGING SENSATION ON CONTACT. SOLUTIONS MORE DILUTE THAN 0.9% SODIUM CHLORIDE CAUSE INCREASED PERMEABILITY OF THE CORNEAL EPITHELIUM. **CHRONIC EXPOSURE-** REPEATED AND PROLONGED CONTACT WITH IRRITANTS MAY CAUSE CONJUNCTIVITIS.

FIRST AID- WASH EYES IMMEDIATELY WITH LARGE AMOUNTS OF WATER, OCCASIONALLY LIFTING UPPER AND LOWER LIDS, UNTIL NO EVIDENCE OF CHEMICAL REMAINS (AT LEAST 15-20 MINUTES). CONTINUE IRRIGATING WITH NORMAL SALINE UNTIL THE PH HAS RETURNED TO NORMAL (30-60 MINUTES). COVER WITH STERILE BANDAGES. GET MEDICAL ATTENTION IMMEDIATELY.

INGESTION: TRISODIUM PHOSPHATE (SODIUM PHOSPHATE, TRIBASIC): CORROSIVE. **ACUTE EXPOSURE-** A VERY LARGE DOSE OF TRISODIUM PHOSPHATE, DODECAHYDRATE WAS LETHAL IN RATS. INGESTION OF STRONG ALKALIES MAY CAUSE SEVERE PAIN, VOMITING, DIARRHEA, AND COLLAPSE. GASTRIC OR ESOPAGEAL PERFORATION MAY BE DELAYED FOR 2-4 DAYS, AND MAY BE INDICATED BY SUDDEN ONSET OF SEVERE ABDOMINAL PAIN, BOARDLIKE ABDOMINAL RIGIDITY AND RAPID HYPOTENSION. ESOPHAGEAL STRICTURE MAY BE DELAYED SEVERAL WEEKS, MONTHS, OR YEARS AFTER INITIAL RECOVERY. **CHRONIC EXPOSURE-** TRISODIUM PHOSPHATE IS USED AS A FOOD ADDITIVE, NUTRIENT, SEQUESTRANT, AND DIETARY SUPPLEMENT.

SODIUM HYPOCHLORITE: CORROSIVE. **ACUTE EXPOSURE-** MAY CAUSE IRRITATION AND EROSION OF THE MUCOUS MEMBRANES, VOMITING (POSSIBLY BLOODY) AND ABDOMINAL PAIN AND SPASMS. A DROP IN BLOOD PRESSURE, SHALLOW RESPIRATION, EDEMA (POSSIBLY SEVERE) OF PHARYNX, LARYNX, AND GLOTTIS, CONFUSION, CONVULSIONS, DELIRIUM AND COMA MAY OCCUR. CYANOSIS AND CIRCULATORY COLLAPSE ARE POSSIBLE. ESOPHAGEAL OR GASTRIC PERFORATION AND STRICTURES ARE RARE. DEATH MAY OCCUR, USUALLY DUE TO COMPLICATIONS OF SEVERE LOCAL INJURY SUCH AS: TOXEMIA, SHOCK, PERFORATIONS, HEMORRHAGE, INFECTION AND OBSTRUCTION. MASSIVE INGESTIONS MAY PRODUCE FATAL HYPERCHLOREMIC METABOLIC ACIDOSIS OR ASPIRATION PNEUMONITIS. **CHRONIC EXPOSURE-** SENSITIZATION REACTIONS ARE REPORTED IN INDIVIDUALS WHO ARE EXPOSED IN SMALL AMOUNTS THROUGH THEIR WATER SUPPLY. HIGH DOSES HAVE CAUSED SPERM ABNORMALITY IN MICE.

SODIUM CHLORIDE: **ACUTE EXPOSURE-** INGESTION OF VERY LARGE DOSES OF HYPERTONIC SOLUTIONS MAY CAUSE DRYNESS OF MUCOUS MEMBRANES AND A VIOLENT INFLAMMATORY REACTION IN THE GASTROINTESTINAL TRACT; ULCERATION MAY OCCUR. SYMPTOMS MAY INCLUDE NAUSEA, VOMITING, DIARRHEA, ANOREXIA, THIRST, FEVER, MUSCULAR TWITCHING, RIGIDITY, CONVULSIONS, HYPERNEA AND PROSTRATION. DEHYDRATION AND CONGESTION MAY OCCUR IN MOST INTERNAL ORGANS, PARTICULARLY THE MENINGES AND BRAIN. CENTRAL NERVOUS SYSTEM DISTURBANCES SUCH AS CONFUSION AND COMA MAY RESULT. GENERALIZED AND PULMONARY EDEMA ARE POSSIBLE. DEATH MAY OCCUR FROM RESPIRATORY FAILURE SECONDARY TO AN ACUTE ENCEPHALOPATHY. **CHRONIC EXPOSURE-** DIETS HIGH IN SODIUM CHLORIDE MAY CAUSE ELEVATED BLOOD PRESSURE, ESPECIALLY IN PREDISPOSED INDIVIDUALS. REPRODUCTIVE EFFECTS HAVE BEEN REPORTED IN ANIMALS.

FIRST AID- TREAT SYMPTOMATICALLY AND SUPPORTIVELY. IF PERSON IS CONSCIOUS AND ABLE TO SWALLOW, GIVE LARGE AMOUNTS OF WATER OR MILK TO DILUTE SUBSTANCE. GET MEDICAL ATTENTION IMMEDIATELY. GASTRIC LAVAGE PERFORMED BY QUALIFIED MEDICAL PERSONNEL MIGHT BE ADVISABLE IF THERE ARE NO SIGNS OF PERFORATION FROM THE INGESTION OF A CORROSIVE SUBSTANCE. IF VOMITING OCCURS, KEEP HEAD BELOW HIPS TO HELP PREVENT ASPIRATION.

REACTIVITY

REACTIVITY: STABLE UNDER NORMAL TEMPERATURES AND PRESSURES.

INCOMPATIBILITIES: TRISODIUM PHOSPHATE (SODIUM PHOSPHATE, TRIBASIC): ACIDS (STRONG): VIOLENT REACTION. MAGNESIUM: VIOLENT REACTION. METALS: CORROSIVE WITH RELEASE OF HYDDROGEN GAS. OXIDIZERS (STRONG): FIRE AND EXPLOSION HAZARD.

SODIUM HYPOCHLORITE: ACIDS: VIOLENT REACTION. ALUMINUM: CORROSIVE ACTION. AMINES: FORM EXPLOSIVE CHLOROAMINES. AMMONIUM SALTS: MAY FORM EXPLOSIVE PRODUCT. BENZYL CYANIDE (ACIDIFIED): EXPLOSIVE REACTION. CELLOLOSE: VIOLENT REACTION. ETHYLENEIMINE: FORMS EXPLOSIVE 1-CHLOROETHYLENEIMINE. FORMIC ACID: EXPLOSIVE MIXTURE. METHANOL: MAY FORM EXPLOSIVE COMPOUND. NITROGEN COMPOUNDS: FORMS EXPLOSIVE N-CHLORO COMPOUNDS. ORGANIC AND COMBUSTIBLE MATERIALS: FIRE AND EXPLOSION HAZARD. OXALIC ACID: INTENSE REACTION. REDUCING AGENTS: FIRE AND EXPLOSION HAZARD. ZINC: CORROSIVE.

SODIUM CHLORIDE: BROMINE TRIFLUORIDE: POSSIBLE VIOLENT REACTION. BUILDING MATERIALS: MAY BE ATTACKED. DICHLOROMALEIC ANHYDRIDE + UREA: EXPLOSIVE REACTION ABOVE 118 C. LITHIUM (BURNING): RELEASES VIOLENTLY FLAMMABLE SODIUM. METALS: MAY BE ATTACKED. NITROGEN COMPOUNDS: MAY FORM EXPLOSIVE COMPOUNDS UNDER ELECTROLYSIS CONDITIONS.

DECOMPOSITION: THERMAL DECOMPOSITION MAY RELEASE CORROSIVE FUMES OF HYDROGEN CHLORIDE OR TOXIC CHLORINE GAS, AND TOXIC OXIDES OF CARBON AND PHOSPHORUS.

POLYMERIZATION: HAZARDOUS POLYMERIZATION HAS NOT BEEN REPORTED TO OCCUR UNDER NORMAL TEMPERATURES AND PRESSURES.

CONDITIONS TO AVOID

MAY BURN BUT DOES NOT IGNITE READILY. FLAMMABLE, POISONOUS GASES MAY ACCUMULATE IN TANKS AND HOPPER CARS. MAY IGNITE COMBUSTIBLES (WOOD, PAPER, OIL, ETC.).

SPILL AND LEAK PROCEDURES

OCCUPATIONAL SPILL: DO NOT TOUCH SPILLED MATERIAL. STOP LEAK IF YOU CAN DO IT WITHOUT RISK. FOR SMALL SPILLS, TAKE UP WITH SAND OR OTHER ABSORBENT MATERIAL AND PLACE INTO CONTAINERS FOR LATER DISPOSAL. FOR SMALL DRY SPILLS, WITH CLEAN SHOVEL PLACE MATERIAL INTO CLEAN, DRY CONTAINER AND COVER. MOVE CONTAINERS FROM SPILL AREA. FOR LARGER SPILLS, DIKE FAR AHEAD OF SPILL FOR LATER DISPOSAL. KEEP UNNECESSARY PEOPLE AWAY. ISOLATE HAZARD AREA AND DENY ENTRY.

PROTECTIVE EQUIPMENT

VENTILATION: PROVIDE LOCAL EXHAUST OR PROCESS ENCLOSURE VENTILATION SYSTEM.

RESPIRATOR: THE FOLLOWING RESPIRATORS ARE RECOMMENDED BASED ON INFORMATION FOUND IN THE PHYSICAL DATA, TOXICITY AND HEALTH EFFECTS SECTIONS. THEY ARE RANKED IN ORDER FROM MINIMUM TO MAXIMUM RESPIRATORY PROTECTION. THE SPECIFIC RESPIRATOR SELECTED MUST BE BASED ON CONTAMINATION LEVELS FOUND IN THE WORK PLACE, MUST NOT EXCEED THE WORKING LIMITS OF THE RESPIRATOR AND BE JOINTLY APPROVED BY THE NATIONAL INSTITUTE FOR OCCUPATIONAL SAFETY AND HEALTH AND THE MINE SAFETY AND HEALTH ADMINISTRATION (NIOSH-MSHA).

DUST AND MIST RESPIRATOR WITH A FULL FACEPIECE.

AIR-PURIFYING FULL FACEPIECE RESPIRATOR WITH A HIGH-EFFICIENCY PARTICULATE FILTER.

POWERED AIR-PURIFYING RESPIRATOR WITH A TIGHT-FITTING FACEPIECE AND HIGH-EFFICIENCY PARTICULATE FILTER.

TYPE 'C' SUPPLIED-AIR RESPIRATOR WITH A FULL FACEPIECE OPERATED IN PRESSURE-DEMAND OR OTHER POSITIVE PRESSURE MODE OR WITH A FULL FACEPIECE, HELMET OR HOOD OPERATED IN CONTINUOUS-FLOW MODE.

SELF-CONTAINED BREATHING APPARATUS WITH A FULL FACEPIECE OPERATED IN PRESSURE-DEMAND OR OTHER POSITIVE PRESSURE MODE.

FOR FIREFIGHTING AND OTHER IMMEDIATELY DANGEROUS TO LIFE OR HEALTH CONDITIONS:

SELF-CONTAINED BREATHING APPARATUS WITH FULL FACEPIECE OPERATED IN PRESSURE-DEMAND OR OTHER POSITIVE PRESSURE MODE.

SUPPLIED-AIR RESPIRATOR WITH FULL FACEPIECE AND OPERATED IN PRESSURE-DEMAND OR OTHER POSITIVE PRESSURE MODE IN COMBINATION WITH AN AUXILIARY SELF-CONTAINED BREATHING APPARATUS OPERATED IN PRESSURE-DEMAND OR OTHER POSITIVE PRESSURE MODE.

CLOTHING: EMPLOYEE MUST WEAR APPROPRIATE PROTECTIVE (IMPERVIOUS) CLOTHING AND EQUIPMENT TO PREVENT ANY POSSIBILITY OF SKIN CONTACT WITH THIS SUBSTANCE.

GLOVES: EMPLOYEE MUST WEAR APPROPRIATE PROTECTIVE GLOVES TO PREVENT CONTACT WITH THIS SUBSTANCE.

EYE PROTECTION: EMPLOYEE MUST WEAR SPLASH-PROOF OR DUST-RESISTANT SAFETY GOGGLES AND A FACESHIELD TO PREVENT CONTACT WITH THIS SUBSTANCE.

EMERGENCY WASH FACILITIES: WHERE THERE IS ANY POSSIBILITY THAT AN EMPLOYEE'S EYES AND/OR SKIN MAY BE EXPOSED TO THIS SUBSTANCE, THE EMPLOYER SHOULD PROVIDE AN EYE WASH FOUNTAIN AND QUICK DRENCH SHOWER WITHIN THE IMMEDIATE WORK AREA FOR EMERGENCY USE.

AUTHORIZED BY- OCCUPATIONAL HEALTH SERVICES, INC.

CREATION DATE: 11/15/89 ***REVISION DATE:*** 05/18/90

MATERIAL SAFETY DATA SHEET

OCCUPATIONAL HEALTH SERVICES, INC.
AGRICULTURE AND PESTICIDE DIVISION
450 SEVENTH AVENUE, SUITE 2407
NEW YORK, NEW YORK 10123
1-800-445-MSDS OR (212) 967-1100

EMERGENCY CONTACT:
JOHN S. BRANSFORD, JR. (615) 292-1180

SUBSTANCE IDENTIFICATION

CAS-NUMBER 78-53-5

SUBSTANCE: AMITON

TRADE NAMES/SYNONYMS: S-(2-(DIETHYLAMINO)ETHYL) O,O-DIETHYL ESTER PHOSPHOROTHIOIC ACID; S-(DIETHYLAMINOETHYL) O,O-DIETHYL PHOSPHOROTHIOATE; S-(2-(DIETHYLAMINO)ETHYL)PHOSPHOROTHIOIC ACID O,O-DIETHYL ESTER; DIETHYL S-2-DIETHYLAMINOETHYL PHOSPHOROTHIOATE; (2-DIETHYLAMINO)ETHYLPHOSPHOROTHIOIC ACID O,O-DIETHYL ESTER; O,O-DIETHYL S-(BETA-DIETHYLAMINO)ETHYL PHOSPHOROTHIOLATE; O,O-DIETHYL S-2-DIETHYLAMINOETHYL PHOSPHOROTHIOATE; O,O-DIETHYL S-DIETHYLAMINOETHYL PHOSPHOROTHIOLATE; O,O-DIETHYL S-2-DIETHYLAMINOETHYL PHOSPHOROTHIOLATE; O,O-DIETHYL S-(2-DIETHYLAMINOETHYL) THIOPHOSPHATE; DSDP; INFERNO; METRAMAC; R 5153; ENT 24, 980; PST83006

CHEMICAL FAMILY: THIOPHOSPHATE
AMINE

MOLECULAR FORMULA: C10-H24-N-O3-P-S

MOLECULAR WEIGHT: 269.38

CERCLA RATINGS (SCALE 0-3): HEALTH=3 FIRE=U REACTIVITY=0 PERSISTENCE=1

NFPA RATINGS (SCALE 0-4): HEALTH=3 FIRE=U REACTIVITY=0

COMPONENTS AND CONTAMINANTS

COMPONENT: AMITON ***PERCENT:*** 100.0
CAS# 78-53-5

OTHER CONTAMINANTS: NONE

EXPOSURE LIMITS: NO OCCUPATIONAL EXPOSURE LIMITS ESTABLISHED BY OSHA, ACGIH, OR NIOSH.

AMITON: 500 POUNDS SARA SECTION 302 THRESHOLD PLANNING QUANTITY 1 POUND SARA SECTION 304 REPORTABLE QUANTITY

PHYSICAL DATA

DESCRIPTION: COLORLESS LIQUID ***BOILING POINT:*** 230 F (110 C) @ 0.2 MMHG

SPECIFIC GRAVITY: NOT AVAILABLE ***EVAPORATION RATE:*** NOT AVAILABLE

SOLUBILITY IN WATER: SOLUBLE

SOLVENT SOLUBILITY: MOST ORGANIC SOLVENTS

FIRE AND EXPLOSION DATA

FIRE AND EXPLOSION HAZARD: UNKNOWN FIRE AND EXPLOSION HAZARD.

FIREFIGHTING MEDIA: DRY CHEMICAL, CARBON DIOXIDE, HALON, WATER SPRAY OR STANDARD FOAM (1987 EMERGENCY RESPONSE GUIDEBOOK, DOT P 5800.4).

FOR LARGER FIRES, USE WATER SPRAY, FOG OR STANDARD FOAM (1987 EMERGENCY RESPONSE GUIDEBOOK, DOT P 5800.4).

FIREFIGHTING: MOVE CONTAINERS FROM FIRE AREA IF POSSIBLE. FIGHT FIRE FROM MAXIMUM DISTANCE. STAY AWAY FROM STORAGE TANK ENDS. DIKE FIRE CONTROL WATER FOR LATER DISPOSAL. DO NOT SCATTER MATERIAL (1987

EMERGENCY RESPONSE GUIDEBOOK, DOT P 5800.4, GUIDE PAGE 55). EXTINGUISH ONLY IF FLOW CAN BE STOPPED. EXTINGUISH USING AGENT INDICATED. USE FLOODING AMOUNTS OF WATER AS A FOG. COOL CONTAINERS WITH FLOODING AMOUNTS OF WATER FROM AS FAR A DISTANCE AS POSSIBLE. AVOID BREATHING POISONOUS VAPORS, KEEP UPWIND. CONSIDER EVACUATION OF DOWNWIND AREA IF MATERIAL IS LEAKING.

TRANSPORTATION DATA

DEPARTMENT OF TRANSPORTATION HAZARD CLASSIFICATION 49 CFR 172.101: POISON B

DEPARTMENT OF TRANSPORTATION LABELING REQUIREMENTS 49 CFR 172.101 AND SUBPART E: POISON

DEPARTMENT OF TRANSPORTATION PACKAGING REQUIREMENTS: 49 CFR 173.346 EXCEPTIONS: 49 CFR 173.345

TOXICITY

AMITON: TOXICITY DATA: 3300 UG/KG ORAL-RAT LD50; 150 UG/KG SUBCUTANEOUS-RAT LD50; 190 UG/KG SUBCUTANEOUS-MOUSE LD50; 125 UG/KG SUBCUTANEOUS-RABBIT LD50; 80 UG/KG SUBCUTANEOUS-GUINEA PIG LD50; 210 UG/KG SUBCUTANEOUS-HAMSTER LD50; 600 UG/KG INTRAPERITONEAL-RAT LD50; 300 UG/KG INTRAPERITONEAL-MOUSE LD50. CARCINOGEN STATUS: NONE. ACUTE TOXICITY LEVEL: HIGHLY TOXIC BY INGESTION. TARGET EFFECTS: CHOLINESTERASE INHIBITOR. POISONING MAY AFFECT THE NERVOUS SYSTEM.* AT INCREASED RISK FROM EXPOSURE: PERSONS WITH RESPIRATORY AILMENTS, RECENT EXPOSURE TO CHOLINESTERASE INHIBITORS OR IMPAIRED CHOLINESTERASE PRODUCTION, OR LIVER MALFUNCTION.* ADDITIONAL DATA: MAY CROSS THE PLACENTA. HIGH ENVIRONMENTAL TEMPERATURES OR EXPOSURE OF THE CHEMICAL TO VISIBLE OR ULTRAVIOLET LIGHT MAY ENHANCE THE TOXICITY. INTERACTIONS WITH MEDICATIONS MAY OCCUR.*

* MAY BE BASED ON GENERAL INFORMATION ON ORGANOPHOSPHATES.

HEALTH EFFECTS AND FIRST AID

INHALATION: AMITON: SEE INFORMATION ON ORGANOPHOSPHATES. ORGANOPHOSPHATES: CHOLINESTERASE INHIBITOR. **ACUTE EXPOSURE-** WHEN INHALED, THE FIRST EFFECTS OF CHOLINESTERASE INHIBITORS ARE USUALLY RESPIRATORY AND MAY INCLUDE NASAL HYPEREMIA AND WATERY DISCHARGE, COUGH, CHEST DISCOMFORT, DYSPNEA, AND WHEEZING DUE TO INCREASED BRONCHIAL SECRETIONS AND BRONCHOCONSTRICTION. IF SUFFICIENT AMOUNTS ARE ABSORBED, OTHER SYSTEMIC EFFECTS MAY BEGIN WITHIN A FEW MINUTES OR BE DELAYED FOR UP TO 12 HOURS. SYMPTOMS MAY INCLUDE PALLOR, NAUSEA, VOMITING, DIARRHEA, ABDOMINAL CRAMPS, HEADACHE, DIZZINESS, OCULAR PAIN, BLURRED VISION, MIOSIS OR IN SOME CASES, ESPECIALLY INITIALLY, MYDRIASIS, LACRIMATION, SALIVATION, SWEATING, AND CONFUSION. OTHER REPORTED CENTRAL NERVOUS SYSTEM OR NEUROMUSCULAR EFFECTS MAY INCLUDE ATAXIA, SLURRED SPEECH, AREFLEXIA, WEAKNESS, FATIGUE, FASCICULATIONS, TWITCHING, TREMORS POSSIBLY OF THE TONGUE AND EYELIDS, AND EVENTUALLY PARALYSIS OF THE EXTREMITIES AND POSSIBLY OF THE RESPIRATORY MUSCLES. IN SEVERE CASES THERE MAY ALSO BE INVOLUNTARY DEFECATION AND URINATION, CYANOSIS, PSYCHOSIS, HYPERGLYCEMIA, ACUTE PANCREATITIS, CARDIAC IRREGULARITIES, PULMONARY EDEMA, UNCONSCIOUSNESS, CONVULSIONS, AND COMA. DEATH IS PRIMARILY DUE TO RESPIRATORY FAILURE, ALTHOUGH CARDIOVASCULAR EFFECTS INCLUDING CARDIAC ARREST MAY ALSO BE IMPLICATED. LONG TERM SEQUELAE ARE RARE BUT MAY INCLUDE NEUROPSYCHIATRIC DISORDERS AND MYOPATHY WITH MUSCLE TENDERNESS. SOME ORGANOPHOSPHATES MAY CAUSE A DELAYED NEUROPATHY BEGINNING 1-4 WEEKS AFTER AN ACUTE EXPOSURE WHICH MAY OR MAY NOT HAVE CAUSED ACUTE CHOLINERGIC EFFECTS. NUMBNESS, TINGLING, WEAKNESS AND CRAMPING BEGINNING SYMMETRICALLY IN THE LOWER LIMBS MAY PROGRESS TO ATAXIA AND PARALYSIS. IN SEVERE CASES, UPPER LIMB INVOLVEMENT IS POSSIBLE AND FLACCID PARALYSIS MAY PROGRESS TO SPASTIC PARALYSIS WITH EXAGGERATED REFLEXES. IMPROVEMENT MAY OCCUR OVER MONTHS TO YEARS, BUT SOME RESIDUAL IMPAIRMENT USUALLY REMAINS. **CHRONIC EXPOSURE-** REPEATED OR PROLONGED EXPOSURE MAY RESULT IN THE EFFECTS OF ACUTE EXPOSURE INCLUDING THE DELAYED NEUROPATHY. OTHER EFFECTS REPORTED IN WORKERS REPEATEDLY EXPOSED INCLUDE IMPAIRED MEMORY AND CONCENTRATION, ACUTE PSYCHOSIS, SEVERE DEPRESSIONS, IRRITABILTY, CONFUSION, APATHY, EMOTIONAL LABILITY, SOCIAL WITHDRAWAL, CONFUSION, HEADACHE, SPEECH DIFFICULTIES, DELAYED REACTION TIMES, SPATIAL DISORIENTATION, NIGHTMARES, SLEEPWALKING, AND DROWSINESS OR INSOMNIA. AN INFLUENZA-LIKE CONDITION WITH HEADACHE, NAUSEA, WEAKNESS, ANOREXIA AND MALAISE HAS ALSO BEEN REPORTED.

FIRST AID- REMOVE FROM EXPOSURE AREA TO FRESH AIR IMMEDIATELY. IF BREATHING HAS STOPPED, GIVE ARTIFICIAL RESPIRATION. MAINTAIN AIRWAY AND BLOOD PRESSURE AND ADMINISTER OXYGEN IF AVAILABLE. KEEP AFFECTED PERSON WARM AND AT REST. TREAT SYMPTOMATICALLY AND SUPPORTIVELY. ADMINISTRATION OF OXYGEN SHOULD BE PERFORMED BY QUALIFIED PERSONNEL. GET MEDICAL ATTENTION IMMEDIATELY.

SKIN CONTACT: AMITON: SEE INFORMATION ON ORGANOPHOSPHATES. ORGANOPHOSPHATES: CHOLINESTERASE INHIBITOR. **ACUTE EXPOSURE-** LOCALIZED SWEATING AND FASCICULATIONS MAY OCCUR AT THE SITE OF CONTACT. IF SUFFICIENT AMOUNTS ARE ABSORBED, OTHER EFFECTS OF CHOLINESTERASE INHIBITION AS DESCRIBED IN ACUTE INHALATION MAY OCCUR. SYMPTOMS MAY BE DELAYED 2-3 HOURS, BUT USUALLY NO MORE THAN 12 HOURS. THE RATE OF ABSORPTION IS INCREASED BY THE PRESENCE OF DERMATITIS OR HIGH AMBIENT TEMPERATURES. DELAYED NEUROPATHY IS ALSO POSSIBLE. **CHRONIC EXPOSURE-** REPEATED OR PROLONGED EXPOSURE MAY CAUSE EFFECTS AS DESCRIBED IN ACUTE EXPOSURE. SOME ORGANOPHOSPHATES MAY CAUSE SENSITIZATION.

FIRST AID- REMOVE CONTAMINATED CLOTHING IMMEDIATELY. WASH CONTAMINATED AREAS WITH SOAP AND WATER FOLLOWED BY ALCOHOL (ARENA, POISONING, 4TH ED.). EMERGENCY PERSONNEL SHOULD WEAR GLOVES AND AVOID CONTAMINATION. TREAT RESPIRATORY DIFFICULTY WITH ARTIFICIAL RESPIRATION. GET MEDICAL ATTENTION IMMEDIATELY.

EYE CONTACT: AMITON: SEE INFORMATION ON ORGANOPHOSPHATES. ORGANOPHOSPHATES: CHOLINESTERASE INHIBITOR. **ACUTE EXPOSURE-** DIRECT CONTACT MAY CAUSE PAIN, HYPEREMIA, LACRIMATION, TWITCHING OF THE EYELIDS, MIOSIS, AND CILIARY MUSCLE SPASM WITH LOSS OF ACCOMODATION, BLURRED OR DIMMED VISION AND BROWACHE. SOMETIMES MYDRIASIS MAY OCCUR INSTEAD OF MIOSIS. WITH SUFFICIENT EXPOSURE, OTHER SYMPTOMS OF CHOLINESTERASE INHIBITION AS DESCRIBED IN ACUTE INHALATION MAY OCCUR. **CHRONIC EXPOSURE-** REPEATED OR PROLONGED EXPOSURE MAY CAUSE EFFECTS AS DESCRIBED IN ACUTE EXPOSURE. SOME COMPOUNDS HAVE CAUSED TOXIC EFFECTS ON THE CRYSTALLINE LENS, CONJUNCTIVAL THICKENING AND OBSTRUCTION OF THE NASOLACRIMAL CANALS WHEN USED AS MIOTIC EYEDROPS.

FIRST AID- IRRIGATE EYES WITH WATER OR SALINE SOLUTION. IF SYMPTOMS OF POISONING OCCUR, TREAT RESPIRATORY DIFFICULTY WITH ARTIFICIAL RESPIRATION AND OXYGEN. OBSERVE PATIENT FOR AT LEAST 24-36 HOURS (GOSSELIN, CLINICAL TOXICOLOGY OF COMMERCIAL PRODUCTS, 5TH ED.). GET MEDICAL ATTENTION IMMEDIATELY. OXYGEN SHOULD BE ADMINISTERED BY QUALIFIED MEDICAL PERSONNEL.

INGESTION: AMITON: HIGHLY TOXIC. SEE INFORMATION ON ORGANOPHOSPHATES. ORGANOPHOSPHATES: CHOLINESTERASE INHIBITOR. **ACUTE EXPOSURE-** WHEN INGESTED, THE FIRST EFFECTS MAY BE NAUSEA, VOMITING, ANOREXIA, ABDOMINAL CRAMPS AND DIARRHEA. GASTROINTESTINAL ABSORPTION MAY CAUSE SYMPTOMS OF CHOLINESTERASE INHIBITION AS DESCRIBED IN ACUTE INHALATION. SYMPTOMS MAY BEGIN WITHIN MINUTES OR BE DELAYED FOR HOURS. DELAYED EFFECTS INCLUDING NEUROPATHY MAY ALSO OCCUR. **CHRONIC EXPOSURE-** REPEATED INGESTION MAY CAUSE EFFECTS AS DESCRIBED IN ACUTE EXPOSURE.

FIRST AID- IF PERSON IS ALERT AND RESPIRATION IS NOT DEPRESSED, GIVE SYRUP OF IPECAC FOLLOWED BY WATER (IF VOMITING OCCURS, KEEP HEAD BELOW HIPS TO PREVENT ASPIRATION). IF CONSCIOUSNESS LEVEL DECLINES OR VOMITING HAS NOT OCCURRED IN 15 MINUTES EMPTY STOMACH BY GASTRIC LAVAGE WITH THE AID OF CUFFED ENDOTRACHEAL TUBE USING ISOTONIC SALINE OR 5% SODIUM BICARBONATE FOLLOW WITH ACTIVATED CHARCOAL. ESTABLISH AND MAINTAIN AIRWAY. TREAT RESPIRATORY DIFFICULTY WITH ARTIFICIAL RESPIRATION AND OXYGEN. DO NOT GIVE MORPHINE, AMINOPHYLLINE, PHENOTHIAZINES, RESERPINE, FUROSEMIDE, OR ETHACRYNIC ACID (MORGAN, RECOGNITION AND MANAGEMENT OF PESTICIDE POISONINGS, 3RD ED.). TREAT SYMPTOMATICALLY AND SUPPORTIVELY. ADMINISTRATION OF OXYGEN AND LAVAGE MUST BE PERFORMED BY QUALIFIED MEDICAL PERSONNEL. GET MEDICAL ATTENTION IMMEDIATELY.

ANTIDOTE: THE FOLLOWING ANTIDOTE(S) HAVE BEEN RECOMMENDED. HOWEVER, THE DECISION AS TO WHETHER THE SEVERITY OF POISONING REQUIRES ADMINISTRATION OF ANY ANTIDOTE AND ACTUAL DOSE REQUIRED SHOULD BE MADE BY QUALIFIED MEDICAL PERSONNEL.

FOR CHOLINESTERASE INHIBITORS: ESTABLISH CLEAR AIRWAY AND TISSUE OXYGENATION BY ASPIRATION OF SECRETIONS, AND IF NECESSARY, BY ASSISTED PULMONARY VENTILATION WITH OXYGEN. IMPROVE TISSUE OXYGENATION AS MUCH AS POSSIBLE BEFORE ADMINISTERING ATROPINE TO MINIMIZE THE RISK OF VENTRICULAR FIBRILLATION. ADMINISTER ATROPINE SULFATE INTRAVENOUSLY, OR INTRAMUSCULARLY IF IV INJECTION IS NOT POSSIBLE. IN MODERATELY SEVERE POISONING ADMINISTER ATROPINE SULFATE, 0.4-2.0 MG REPEATED EVERY 15 MINUTES UNTIL ATROPINIZATION IS ACHIEVED (TACHYCARDIA, FLUSHING, DRY MOUTH, MYDRIASIS). MAINTAIN ATROPINIZATION BY REPEATED DOSES FOR 2-12 HOURS, OR LONGER, DEPENDING ON THE SEVERITY OF POISONING. THE APPEARANCE OF RALES IN THE LUNG BASES, MIOSIS, SALIVATION, NAUSEA, BRADYCARDIA, ARE ALL INDICATIONS OF INADEQUATE ATROPINIZATION. SEVERELY POISONED INDIVIDUALS MAY EXHIBIT REMARKABLE TOLERANCE TO

ATROPINE; TWO OR MORE TIMES THE DOSAGES SUGGESTED ABOVE MAY BE NEEDED. PERSONS NOT POISONED OR ONLY SLIGHTLY POISONED, HOWEVER, MAY DEVELOP SIGNS OF ATROPINE TOXICITY FROM SUCH LARGE DOSAGES: FEVER, MUSCLE FIBRILLATIONS, AND DELIRIUM ARE THE MAIN SIGNS OF ATROPINE TOXICITY. IF THESE SIGNS APPEAR WHILE THE PATIENT IS FULLY ATROPINIZED, ATROPINE ADMINISTRATION SHOULD BE DISCONTINUED, AT LEAST TEMPORARILY. OBSERVE TREATED PATIENTS CLOSELY AT LEAST 24 HOURS TO INSURE THAT SYMPTOMS (POSSIBLY PULMONARY EDEMA) DO NOT RECUR AS ATROPINIZATION WEARS OFF. IN VERY SEVERE POISONINGS, METABOLIC DISPOSITION OF TOXICANT MAY REQUIRE SEVERAL HOURS OR DAYS DURING WHICH ATROPINIZATION MUST BE MAINTAINED. MARKEDLY LOWER LEVELS OF URINARY METABOLITES INDICATE THAT ATROPINE DOSAGE CAN BE TAPERED OFF. AS DOSAGE IS REDUCED, CHECK THE LUNG BASES FREQUENTLY FOR RALES. IF RALES ARE HEARD OR OTHER SYMPTOMS RETURN, RE-ESTABLISH ATROPINIZATION PROMPTLY (MORGAN, RECOGNITION AND MANAGEMENT OF PESTICIDE POISONINGS, 3RD ED.). ADMINISTRATION OF ANTIDOTE MUST BE PERFORMED BY QUALIFIED MEDICAL PERSONNEL.

IN CASES OF SEVERE POISONING BY ORGANOPHOSPHATE PESTICIDES IN WHICH RESPIRATORY DEPRESSION, MUSCLE WEAKNESS AND TWITCHINGS ARE SEVERE, GIVE PRALIDOXIME (PROTOPAM-AYERST, 2-PAM), 1.0 GRAM INTRAVENOUSLY AT NO MORE THAN 0.5 GRAM PER MINUTE. DOSAGE OF PRALIDOXIME MAY BE REPEATED IN 1-2 HOURS, THEN AT 10-12 HOUR INTERVALS IF NEEDED. IN VERY SEVERE POISONINGS, DOSAGE RATES MAY BE DOUBLED. TREATMENT WITH PRALIDOXIME WILL BE MOST EFFECTIVE IF GIVEN WITHIN THIRTY-SIX HOURS AFTER POISONING (MORGAN, RECOGNITION AND MANAGEMENT OF PESTICIDE POISONINGS, 3RD ED.). ANTIDOTE SHOULD BE ADMINISTERED BY QUALIFIED MEDICAL PERSONNEL.

REACTIVITY

REACTIVITY: STABLE UNDER NORMAL TEMPERATURES AND PRESSURES.

INCOMPATIBILITIES: AMITON: NO DATA AVAILABLE.

DECOMPOSITION: THERMAL DECOMPOSITION PRODUCTS MAY INCLUDE TOXIC AND HAZARDOUS FUMES OF SULFUR, NITROGEN AND PHOSPHORUS.

POLYMERIZATION: HAZARDOUS POLYMERIZATION HAS NOT BEEN REPORTED TO OCCUR UNDER NORMAL TEMPERATURES AND PRESSURES.

STORAGE AND DISPOSAL

OBSERVE ALL FEDERAL, STATE AND LOCAL REGULATIONS WHEN STORING OR DISPOSING OF THIS SUBSTANCE. FOR ASSISTANCE, CONTACT THE DISTRICT DIRECTOR OF THE ENVIRONMENTAL PROTECTION AGENCY.

STORAGE

STORE IN ACCORDANCE WITH 40 CFR 165 RECOMMENDED PROCEDURES FOR THE DISPOSAL AND STORAGE OF PESTICIDES AND PESTICIDE CONTAINERS.

THRESHOLD PLANNING QUANTITY (TPQ): THE SUPERFUND AMENDMENTS AND REAUTHORIZATION ACT (SARA) SECTION 302 REQUIRES THAT EACH FACILITY WHERE ANY EXTREMELY HAZARDOUS SUBSTANCE IS PRESENT IN A QUANTITY EQUAL TO OR GREATER THAN THE TPQ ESTABLISHED FOR THAT SUBSTANCE NOTIFY THE STATE EMERGENCY RESPONSE COMMISSION FOR THE STATE IN WHICH IT IS LOCATED. SECTION 303 OF SARA REQUIRES THESE FACILITIES TO PARTICIPATE IN LOCAL EMERGENCY RESPONSE PLANNING (40 CFR 355.30).

DISPOSAL

DISPOSAL MUST BE IN ACCORDANCE WITH 40 CFR 165 RECOMMENDED PROCEDURES FOR THE DISPOSAL AND STORAGE OF PESTICIDES AND PESTICIDE CONTAINERS.

CONDITIONS TO AVOID

NONE REPORTED.

SPILL AND LEAK PROCEDURES

OCCUPATIONAL SPILL: DO NOT TOUCH SPILLED MATERIAL. STOP LEAK IF YOU CAN DO IT WITHOUT RISK. USE WATER SPRAY TO REDUCE VAPORS. FOR SMALL SPILLS, TAKE UP WITH SAND OR OTHER ABSORBENT MATERIAL AND PLACE INTO CONTAINERS FOR LATER DISPOSAL. FOR SMALL DRY SPILLS, WITH A CLEAN SHOVEL PLACE MATERIAL INTO CLEAN, DRY CONTAINERS AND COVER. MOVE CONTAINERS FROM SPILL AREA. FOR LARGER SPILLS, DIKE FAR AHEAD OF SPILL FOR LATER DISPOSAL. KEEP UNNECESSARY PEOPLE AWAY. ISOLATE HAZARD AREA AND DENY ENTRY. VENTILATE CLOSED SPACES BEFORE ENTERING.

REPORTABLE QUANTITY (RQ): 1 POUND THE SUPERFUND AMENDMENTS AND REAUTHORIZATION ACT (SARA) SECTION 304 REQUIRES THAT A RELEASE EQUAL TO OR GREATER THAN THE REPORTABLE QUANTITY FOR THIS SUBSTANCE BE IMMEDIATELY REPORTED TO THE LOCAL EMERGENCY PLANNING COMMITTEE AND THE STATE EMERGENCY RESPONSE COMMISSION (40 CFR 355.40). IF THE RELEASE OF THIS SUBSTANCE IS REPORTABLE UNDER CERCLA SECTION 103, THE NATIONAL RESPONSE CENTER MUST BE NOTIFIED IMMEDIATELY AT (800) 424-8802 OR (202) 426-2675 IN THE METROPOLITAN WASHINGTON, D.C. AREA (40 CFR 302.6).

PROTECTIVE EQUIPMENT

VENTILATION: PROVIDE LOCAL EXHAUST OR PROCESS ENCLOSURE VENTILATION SYSTEM.

RESPIRATOR: THE FOLLOWING RESPIRATORS ARE RECOMMENDED BASED ON INFORMATION FOUND IN THE PHYSICAL DATA, TOXICITY AND HEALTH EFFECTS SECTIONS. THEY ARE RANKED IN ORDER FROM MINIMUM TO MAXIMUM RESPIRATORY PROTECTION. THE SPECIFIC RESPIRATOR SELECTED MUST BE BASED ON CONTAMINATION LEVELS FOUND IN THE WORK PLACE, MUST NOT EXCEED THE WORKING LIMITS OF THE RESPIRATOR AND BE JOINTLY APPROVED BY THE NATIONAL INSTITUTE FOR OCCUPATIONAL SAFETY AND HEALTH AND THE MINE SAFETY AND HEALTH ADMINISTRATION (NIOSH-MSHA).

TYPE 'C' SUPPLIED-AIR RESPIRATOR WITH A FULL FACEPIECE OPERATED IN PRESSURE-DEMAND OR OTHER POSITIVE PRESSURE MODE OR WITH A FULL FACEPIECE, HELMET OR HOOD OPERATED IN CONTINOUS-FLOW MODE.

SELF-CONTAINED BREATHING APPARATUS WITH A FULL FACEPIECE OPERATED IN PRESSURE-DEMAND OR OTHER POSITIVE PRESSURE MODE.

FOR FIREFIGHTING AND OTHER IMMEDIATELY DANGEROUS TO LIFE OR HEALTH CONDITIONS:

SELF-CONTAINED BREATHING APPARATUS WITH FULL FACEPIECE OPERATED IN PRESSURE-DEMAND OR OTHER POSITIVE PRESSURE MODE.

SUPPLIED-AIR RESPIRATOR WITH FULL FACEPIECE AND OPERATED IN PRESSURE-DEMAND OR OTHER POSITIVE PRESSURE MODE IN COMBINATION WITH AN AUXILIARY SELF-CONTAINED BREATHING APPARATUS OPERATED IN PRESSURE-DEMAND OR OTHER POSITIVE PRESSURE MODE.

CLOTHING: EMPLOYEE MUST WEAR APPROPRIATE PROTECTIVE (IMPERVIOUS) CLOTHING AND EQUIPMENT TO PREVENT ANY POSSIBILITY OF SKIN CONTACT WITH THIS SUBSTANCE.

GLOVES: EMPLOYEE MUST WEAR APPROPRIATE PROTECTIVE GLOVES TO PREVENT CONTACT WITH THIS SUBSTANCE.

EYE PROTECTION: EMPLOYEE MUST WEAR SPLASH-PROOF OR DUST-RESISTANT SAFETY GOGGLES AND A FACESHIELD TO PREVENT CONTACT WITH THIS SUBSTANCE.

EMERGENCY WASH FACILITIES: WHERE THERE IS ANY POSSIBILITY THAT AN EMPLOYEE'S EYES AND/OR SKIN MAY BE EXPOSED TO THIS SUBSTANCE, THE EMPLOYER SHOULD PROVIDE AN EYE WASH FOUNTAIN AND QUICK DRENCH SHOWER WITHIN THE IMMEDIATE WORK AREA FOR EMERGENCY USE.

AUTHORIZED BY- OCCUPATIONAL HEALTH SERVICES, INC.

CREATION DATE: 10/04/89 ***REVISION DATE:*** 05/16/90

MATERIAL SAFETY DATA SHEET

OCCUPATIONAL HEALTH SERVICES, INC.
AGRICULTURE AND PESTICIDE DIVISION
450 SEVENTH AVENUE, SUITE 2407
NEW YORK, NEW YORK 10123
1-800-445-MSDS OR (212) 967-1100

EMERGENCY CONTACT:
JOHN S. BRANSFORD, JR. (615) 292-1180

SUBSTANCE IDENTIFICATION

CAS-NUMBER 129-06-6

SUBSTANCE: WARFARIN SODIUM

TRADE NAMES/SYNONYMS: 3-(ALPHA-ACETONYLBENZYL)-4-HYDROXYCOUMARIN, SODIUM SALT; 4-HYDROXY-3-(3-OXO-1-PHENYLBUTYL)-2H-1-BENZOPYRAN-2-ONE, SODIUM SALT; 2H-1-BENZOPYRAN-2-ONE, 4-HYDROXY-3-(3-OXO-1-PHENYLBUTYL)-, SODIUM SALT; COUMARIN, 3-(ALPHA-ACETONYLBENZYL)-4-HDYROXY-, SODIUM SALT; ATHROMBIN; COUMADIN; COUMAFENE SODIUM; MAREVAN; PANWARFIN; PROTHROMADIN; RATSUL SOLUBLE; SODIUM COUMADIN; SODIUM WARFARIN; TINTORANE; VARFINE; WARAN; WARFARIN SODIUM SALT; WARFILONE SODIUM SALT; RCRA P001; C19H15NAO4; PST83008

CHEMICAL FAMILY: COUMARIN

MOLECULAR FORMULA: C19-H15-O4.NA

MOLECULAR WEIGHT: 330.33

CERCLA RATINGS (SCALE 0-3): HEALTH=3 FIRE=1 REACTIVITY=0 PERSISTENCE=2

NFPA RATINGS (SCALE 0-4): HEALTH=3 FIRE=1 REACTIVITY=0

COMPONENTS AND CONTAMINANTS

COMPONENT: WARFARIN SODIUM ***PERCENT:*** 100.00

CAS# 129-06-6

EXPOSURE LIMITS: WARFARIN SODIUM: 100/10,000 POUNDS SARA SECTION 302 THRESHOLD PLANNING QUANTITY 1 POUND SARA SECTION 304 REPORTABLE

QUANTITY
WARFARIN: 0.1 MG/M3 OSHA TWA 0.1 MG/M3 ACGIH TWA
500/10,000 POUNDS SARA SECTION 302 THRESHOLD PLANNING QUANTITY 100 POUNDS SARA SECTION 304 REPORTABLE QUANTITY 100 POUNDS CERCLA SECTION 103 REPORTABLE QUANTITY SUBJECT TO CALIFORNIA PROPOSITION 65 CANCER AND/OR REPRODUCTIVE TOXICITY WARNING AND RELEASE REQUIREMENTS- (JULY 1, 1987)

PHYSICAL DATA

DESCRIPTION: WHITE, CRYSTALLINE POWDER WITH A SLIGHTLY BITTER TASTE.

MELTING POINT: 324 F (162 C) ***SPECIFIC GRAVITY:*** NOT AVAILABLE

SOLUBILITY IN WATER: SOLUBLE

SOLVENT SOLUBILITY: SOLUBLE IN ALCOHOL; VERY SLIGHTLY SOLUBLE IN CHLOROFORM AND ETHER.

FIRE AND EXPLOSION DATA

FIRE AND EXPLOSION HAZARD: SLIGHT FIRE HAZARD WHEN EXPOSED TO HEAT OR FLAME.

FIREFIGHTING MEDIA: DRY CHEMICAL, CARBON DIOXIDE, HALON, WATER SPRAY OR STANDARD FOAM (1987 EMERGENCY RESPONSE GUIDEBOOK, DOT P 5800.4).
FOR LARGER FIRES, USE WATER SPRAY, FOG OR STANDARD FOAM (1987 EMERGENCY RESPONSE GUIDEBOOK, DOT P 5800.4).

FIREFIGHTING: MOVE CONTAINERS FROM FIRE AREA IF POSSIBLE. FIGHT FIRE FROM MAXIMUM DISTANCE. STAY AWAY FROM STORAGE TANK ENDS. DIKE FIRE CONTROL WATER FOR LATER DISPOSAL. DO NOT SCATTER MATERIAL (1987 EMERGENCY RESPONSE GUIDEBOOK, DOT P 5800.4, GUIDE PAGE 55).
EXTINGUISH USING AGENT SUITABLE FOR TYPE OF SURROUNDING FIRE. AVOID BREATHING VAPORS AND DUSTS. KEEP UPWIND.

TRANSPORTATION DATA

DEPARTMENT OF TRANSPORTATION HAZARD CLASSIFICATION 49 CFR 172.101: POISON B
DEPARTMENT OF TRANSPORTATION LABELING REQUIREMENTS 49 CFR 172.101 AND SUBPART E: POISON
DEPARTMENT OF TRANSPORTATION PACKAGING REQUIREMENTS: 49 CFR 173.365 EXCEPTIONS: 49 CFR 173.364

TOXICITY

WARFARIN SODIUM: TOXICITY DATA: 300 UG/KG/2 DAYS ORAL-WOMAN TDLO; 8700 UG/KG ORAL-RAT LD50; 200 MG/KG ORAL-DOG LD50; 800 MG/KG ORAL-RABBIT LD50; 182 MG/KG ORAL-GUINEA PIG LD50; 374 MG/KG ORAL-MOUSE LD50; 25 MG/KG INTRAVENOUS-RAT LD50; 100 MG/KG INTRAVENOUS-RABBIT LD50; 200 MG/KG INTRAVENOUS-DOG LD50; 160 MG/KG INTRAVENOUS-MOUSE LD50; 543 MG/KG INTRAVENOUS-GUINEA PIG LDLO; MUTAGENIC DATA (RTECS); REPRODUCTIVE EFFECTS DATA (RTECS). CARCINOGEN STATUS: NONE. ACUTE TOXICITY LEVEL: HIGHLY TOXIC BY INGESTION. TARGET EFFECTS: HEMORRHAGIC AGENT; TERATOGEN. AT INCREASED RISK FROM EXPOSURE: PERSONS WITH BLOOD DYSCRASIAS, BLEEDING TENDENCIES, LIVER OR KIDNEY DISEASE, ULCERS OF THE GASTROINTESTINAL TRACT, OR HYPERTENSION.* ADDITIONAL DATA: INTERACTIONS WITH MEDICATIONS HAVE BEEN REPORTED.*
* MAY BE BASED ON GENERAL INFORMATION ON COUMARIN DERIVATIVES.

HEALTH EFFECTS AND FIRST AID

INHALATION: WARFARIN SODIUM: SEE INFORMATION ON COUMARIN DERIVATIVES.
COUMARIN DERIVATIVES: HEMORRHAGIC AGENT. **ACUTE EXPOSURE-** ABSORPTION BY THE LUNGS MAY RESULT IN HEMORRHAGIC EFFECTS AS DESCRIBED IN CHRONIC EXPOSURE. SEVERE CASES MAY BE FATAL. **CHRONIC EXPOSURE-** REPEATED ABSORPTION MAY CAUSE THE INHIBITION OF PROTHROMBIN SYNTHESIS AND DAMAGE TO CAPILLARY PERMEABILITY RESULTING IN WIDESPREAD INTERNAL HEMORRHAGE WITH ASSOCIATED EFFECTS OF NOSEBLEED, HEMATOMA, HEMATURIA, WIDESPREAD BRUISING, AND ANEMIA.

FIRST AID- REMOVE FROM EXPOSURE AREA TO FRESH AIR IMMEDIATELY. IF BREATHING HAS STOPPED, PERFORM ARTIFICIAL RESPIRATION. KEEP PERSON WARM AND AT REST. TREAT SYMPTOMATICALLY AND SUPPORTIVELY. GET MEDICAL ATTENTION IMMEDIATELY.

SKIN CONTACT: WARFARIN SODIUM: SEE INFORMATION ON COUMARIN DERIVATIVES.
COUMARIN DERIVATIVES: HEMORRHAGIC AGENT. **ACUTE EXPOSURE-** ABSORPTION THROUGH THE SKIN MAY RESULT IN HEMORRHAGIC EFFECTS AS DESCRIBED IN CHRONIC EXPOSURE. SEVERE CASES MAY BE FATAL. **CHRONIC EXPOSURE-** REPEATED ABSORPTION MAY CAUSE THE INHIBITION OF PROTHROMBIN SYNTHESIS AND DAMAGE TO CAPILLARY PERMEABILITY RESULTING IN WIDESPREAD INTERNAL HEMORRHAGE WITH ASSOCIATED EFFECTS OF NOSEBLEED, HEMATOMA, HEMATURIA, WIDESPREAD BRUISING, AND ANEMIA.

FIRST AID- REMOVE CONTAMINATED CLOTHING AND SHOES IMMEDIATELY. WASH AFFECTED AREA WITH SOAP OR MILD DETERGENT AND LARGE AMOUNTS OF WATER UNTIL NO EVIDENCE OF CHEMICAL REMAINS (APPROXIMATELY 15-20 MINUTES). GET MEDICAL ATTENTION IMMEDIATELY.

EYE CONTACT: WARFARIN SODIUM: **ACUTE EXPOSURE-** NO DATA AVAILABLE. **CHRONIC EXPOSURE-** NO DATA AVAILABLE.

FIRST AID- WASH EYES IMMEDIATELY WITH LARGE AMOUNTS OF WATER OR NORMAL SALINE, OCCASIONALLY LIFTING UPPER AND LOWER LIDS, UNTIL NO EVIDENCE OF CHEMICAL REMAINS (APPROXIMATELY 15-20 MINUTES). GET MEDICAL ATTENTION IMMEDIATELY.

INGESTION: WARFARIN SODIUM: TETRATOGEN/HIGHLY TOXIC. SEE INFORMATION ON COUMARIN DERIVATIVES. THERAPEUTIC USE BY PREGNANT WOMEN HAS RESULTED IN FATAL HEMORRHAGING OF THE FETUS AND MALFORMATIONS AND MENTAL RETARDATION IN INFANTS.
COUMARIN DERIVATIVES: HEMORRHAGIC AGENT. **ACUTE EXPOSURE-** MAY BE READILY ABSORBED FROM THE GASTROINTESTINAL TRACT AND CAUSE THE INHIBITION OF PROTHROMBIN SYNTHESIS AND DAMAGE TO CAPILLARY PERMEABILITY RESULTING IN WIDESPREAD INTERNAL HEMORRHAGE ACCOMPANIED BY THE HEMORRHAGIC SYMPTOMS AS DESCRIBED IN CHRONIC EXPOSURE. SEVERE CASES MAY BE FATAL. **CHRONIC EXPOSURE-** REPEATED INGESTION MAY CAUSE NOSEBLEED, BLEEDING GUMS AND PHARYNX, PETECHIAL RASH, WIDESPREAD BRUISING, HEMATOMA, HEMOPTYSIS, HEMATEMESIS, HEMATURIA, BLOODY STOOLS, BLEEDING INTO THE ORGANS, GASTROINTESTINAL TRACT, JOINTS, ABDOMINAL OR RETROPERITONEAL AREA WITH ABDOMINAL, BACK, JOINT AND LIMB PAIN AND CEREBROVASCULAR ACCIDENT. ANEMIA ACCOMPANIED BY WEAKNESS, PALLOR, AND SHOCK MAY OCCUR. SEVERE HEMORRHAGING MAY CAUSE DEATH. THERAPEUTIC USE OF SOME COUMARIN DERIVATIVES HAS INFREQUENTLY PRODUCED GASTROINTESTINAL DISTURBANCES, ELEVATED TRANSAMINASE, URTICARIA, DERMATITIS, LEUKOPENIA, ALOPECIA, FEVER, HYPERSENSITIVITY REACTIONS, AND RARELY SKIN NECROSIS.

FIRST AID- IF ONLY A FEW GRAINS OF ANTICOAGULANT BAIT HAVE BEEN INGESTED BY AN ADULT OR CHILD HAVING NO ANTECEDENT LIVER OR BLOOD CLOTTING DISEASE, TREATMENT IS PROBABLY UNNECESSARY. IF LARGE AMOUNTS OF ANTICOAGULANT WERE INGESTED IN THE PRECEDING 2-3 HOURS, INDUCE VOMITING WITH SYRUP OF IPECAC, FOLLOWED BY 1-2 GLASSES OF WATER. FOLLOWING EMESIS, GIVE ACTIVATED CHARCOAL IN 4-6 OUNCES OF WATER TO LIMIT ABSORPTION OF ANTICOAGULANT REMAINING IN THE GUT. OBSERVE PATIENT 4-5 DAYS AFTER INGESTION. (MORGAN, RECOGNITION AND MANAGEMENT OF PESTICIDE POISONINGS, THIRD EDITION). GET MEDICAL ATTENTION.

ANTIDOTE: THE FOLLOWING ANTIDOTE HAS BEEN RECOMMENDED. HOWEVER, THE DECISION AS TO WHETHER THE SEVERITY OF POISONING REQUIRES ADMINISTRATION OF ANY ANTIDOTE AND ACTUAL DOSE REQUIRED SHOULD BE MADE BY QUALIFIED MEDICAL PERSONNEL.
OVERDOSE OF ANTICOAGULANTS: VITAMIN K IS A SPECIFIC ANTIDOTE. VITAMIN K1 EMULSION IS THE PREFERRED FORM. THE INITIAL SUBCUTANEOUS OR INTRAMUSCULAR DOSE IN ADULTS IS 5 TO 10 MG (UP TO 25 MG), REPEATED ONCE IF NECESSARY. ONLY IN VICTIMS WHO ARE BLEEDING SEVERLY OR OTHERWISE IN SERIOUS DISTRESS SHOULD THE DRUG BE GIVEN INTRAVENOUSLY AND THEN AT A RATE NO FASTER THAN 1 MG/MINUTE. IF NECESSARY, ON SUBSEQUENT DAYS, VITAMIN K1 SHOULD BE CONTINUED AT A REDUCED LEVEL UNTIL THE PROTHROMBIN TIME RETURNS TO NORMAL. VITAMIN K1 IS PREFERABLE TO K1 OXIDE (DOSE 0.5-2.5) AND CERTAINLY PREFERABLE TO MENADIONE OR MENADIONE SODIUM BISULFITE (GOSSELIN, CLINICAL TOXICOLOGY OF COMMERCIAL PRODUCTS, 5TH ED.). ANTIDOTE SHOULD BE ADMINISTERED BY QUALIFIED MEDICAL PERSONNEL.

REACTIVITY

REACTIVITY: STABLE UNDER NORMAL TEMPERATURES AND PRESSURES.

INCOMPATIBILITIES: WARFARIN SODIUM: OXIDIZERS (STRONG): FIRE AND EXPLOSION HAZARD.

DECOMPOSITION: THERMAL DECOMPOSITION PRODUCTS MAY INCLUDE TOXIC FUMES OF SODIUM OXIDE.

POLYMERIZATION: HAZARDOUS POLYMERIZATION HAS NOT BEEN REPORTED TO OCCUR UNDER NORMAL TEMPERATURES AND PRESSURES.

STORAGE AND DISPOSAL

OBSERVE ALL FEDERAL, STATE AND LOCAL REGULATIONS WHEN STORING OR DISPOSING OF THIS SUBSTANCE. FOR ASSISTANCE, CONTACT THE DISTRICT DIRECTOR OF THE ENVIRONMENTAL PROTECTION AGENCY.

STORAGE

STORE AWAY FROM INCOMPATIBLE SUBSTANCES.
THRESHOLD PLANNING QUANTITY (TPQ): THE SUPERFUND AMENDMENTS AND REAUTHORIZATION ACT (SARA) SECTION 302 REQUIRES THAT EACH FACILITY WHERE ANY EXTREMELY HAZARDOUS SUBSTANCE IS PRESENT IN A QUANTITY EQUAL TO OR GREATER THAN THE TPQ ESTABLISHED FOR THAT SUBSTANCE

NOTIFY THE STATE EMERGENCY RESPONSE COMMISSION FOR THE STATE IN WHICH IT IS LOCATED. SECTION 303 OF SARA REQUIRES THESE FACILITIES TO PARTICIPATE IN LOCAL EMERGENCY RESPONSE PLANNING (40 CFR 355.30).

DISPOSAL

DISPOSAL MUST BE IN ACCORDANCE WITH STANDARDS APPLICABLE TO GENERATORS OF HAZARDOUS WASTE, 40CFR 262. EPA HAZARDOUS WASTE NUMBER P001.

CONDITIONS TO AVOID

MAY BURN BUT DOES NOT IGNITE READILY. CONTAINERS MAY EXPLODE IN HEAT OF FIRE.

SPILL AND LEAK PROCEDURES

OCCUPATIONAL SPILL: DO NOT TOUCH SPILLED MATERIAL. STOP LEAK IF YOU CAN DO IT WITHOUT RISK. USE WATER SPRAY TO REDUCE VAPORS. FOR SMALL SPILLS, TAKE UP WITH SAND OR OTHER ABSORBENT MATERIAL AND PLACE INTO CONTAINERS FOR LATER DISPOSAL. FOR SMALL DRY SPILLS, WITH A CLEAN SHOVEL PLACE MATERIAL INTO CLEAN, DRY CONTAINERS AND COVER. MOVE CONTAINERS FROM SPILL AREA. FOR LARGER SPILLS, DIKE FAR AHEAD OF SPILL FOR LATER DISPOSAL. KEEP UNNECESSARY PEOPLE AWAY. ISOLATE HAZARD AREA AND DENY ENTRY. VENTILATE CLOSED SPACES BEFORE ENTERING. REPORTABLE QUANTITY (RQ): 1 POUND THE SUPERFUND AMENDMENTS AND REAUTHORIZATION ACT (SARA) SECTION 304 REQUIRES THAT A RELEASE EQUAL TO OR GREATER THAN THE REPORTABLE QUANTITY FOR THIS SUBSTANCE BE IMMEDIATELY REPORTED TO THE LOCAL EMERGENCY PLANNING COMMITTEE AND THE STATE EMERGENCY RESPONSE COMMISSION (40 CFR 355.40). IF THE RELEASE OF THIS SUBSTANCE IS REPORTABLE UNDER CERCLA SECTION 103, THE NATIONAL RESPONSE CENTER MUST BE NOTIFIED IMMEDIATELY AT (800) 424-8802 OR (202) 426-2675 IN THE METROPOLITAN WASHINGTON, D.C. AREA (40 CFR 302.6).

PROTECTIVE EQUIPMENT

VENTILATION: PROCESS ENCLOSURE RECOMMENDED.

RESPIRATOR: THE FOLLOWING RESPIRATORS AND MAXIMUM USE CONCENTRATIONS ARE RECOMMENDATIONS BY THE U.S. DEPARTMENT OF HEALTH AND HUMAN SERVICES, NIOSH POCKET GUIDE TO CHEMICAL HAZARDS; NIOSH CRITERIA DOCUMENTS OR BY THE U.S. DEPARTMENT OF LABOR, 29 CFR 1910 SUBPART Z. THE SPECIFIC RESPIRATOR SELECTED MUST BE BASED ON CONTAMINATION LEVELS FOUND IN THE WORK PLACE, MUST NOT EXCEED THE WORKING LIMITS OF THE RESPIRATOR AND BE JOINTLY APPROVED BY THE NATIONAL INSTITUTE FOR OCCUPATIONAL SAFETY AND HEALTH AND THE MINE SAFETY AND HEALTH ADMINISTRATION (NIOSH-MSHA).

WARFARIN: 0.5 MG/M3- ANY DUST AND MIST RESPIRATOR EXCEPT SINGLE-USE RESPIRATORS.

1.0 MG/M3- ANY DUST AND MIST RESPIRATOR, EXCEPT SINGLE-USE AND QUARTER-MASK RESPIRATORS. ANY SUPPLIED-AIR RESPIRATOR. ANY SELF-CONTAINED BREATHING APPARATUS.

2.5 MG/M3- ANY POWERED AIR-PURIFYING RESPIRATOR WITH A DUST AND MIST FILTER. ANY SUPPLIED-AIR RESPIRATOR OPERATED IN A CONTINUOUS FLOW MODE.

5.0 MG/M3- ANY AIR-PURIFYING FULL FACEPIECE RESPIRATOR WITH A HIGH-EFFICIENCY PARTICULATE FILTER. ANY POWERED AIR-PURIFYING RESPIRATOR WITH A TIGHT-FITTING FACEPIECE AND A HIGH-EFFICIENCY PARTICULATE FILTER. ANY SELF-CONTAINED BREATHING APPARATUS WITH A FULL FACEPIECE. ANY SUPPLIED-AIR RESPIRATOR WITH A FULL FACEPIECE. ANY SUPPLIED-AIR RESPIRATOR WITH A TIGHT-FITTING FACEPIECE OPERATED IN A CONTINUOUS FLOW MODE.

100 MG/M3- ANY SUPPLIED-AIR RESPIRATOR WITH A HALF-MASK AND OPERATED IN A PRESSURE-DEMAND OR OTHER POSITIVE PRESSURE MODE.

200 MG/M3- ANY SUPPLIED-AIR RESPIRATOR WITH A FULL FACEPIECE AND OPERATED IN A PRESSURE-DEMAND OR OTHER POSITIVE PRESSURE MODE.

ESCAPE- ANY AIR-PURIFYING FULL FACEPIECE RESPIRATOR WITH A HIGH-EFFICIENCY PARTICULATE FILTER. ANY APPROPRIATE ESCAPE-TYPE SELF-CONTAINED BREATHING APPARATUS.

FOR FIREFIGHTING AND OTHER IMMEDIATELY DANGEROUS TO LIFE OR HEALTH CONDITIONS:

SELF-CONTAINED BREATHING APPARATUS WITH FULL FACEPIECE OPERATED IN PRESSURE-DEMAND OR OTHER POSITIVE PRESSURE MODE.

SUPPLIED-AIR RESPIRATOR WITH FULL FACEPIECE AND OPERATED IN PRESSURE-DEMAND OR OTHER POSITIVE PRESSURE MODE IN COMBINATION WITH AN AUXILIARY SELF-CONTAINED BREATHING APPARATUS OPERATED IN PRESSURE-DEMAND OR OTHER POSITIVE PRESSURE MODE.

CLOTHING: EMPLOYEE MUST WEAR APPROPRIATE PROTECTIVE (IMPERVIOUS) CLOTHING AND EQUIPMENT TO PREVENT ANY POSSIBILITY OF SKIN CONTACT WITH THIS SUBSTANCE.

GLOVES: EMPLOYEE MUST WEAR APPROPRIATE PROTECTIVE GLOVES TO PREVENT CONTACT WITH THIS SUBSTANCE.

EYE PROTECTION: EMPLOYEE MUST WEAR SPLASH-PROOF OR DUST-RESISTANT SAFETY GOGGLES WITH OR WITHOUT A FACESHIELD TO PREVENT CONTACT WITH THIS SUBSTANCE.

EMERGENCY EYE WASH: WHERE THERE IS ANY POSSIBILITY THAT AN EMPLOYEE'S EYES MAY BE EXPOSED TO THIS SUBSTANCE, THE EMPLOYER SHOULD PROVIDE AN EYE WASH FOUNTAIN WITHIN THE IMMEDIATE WORK AREA FOR EMERGENCY USE.

AUTHORIZED BY- OCCUPATIONAL HEALTH SERVICES, INC.

CREATION DATE: 10/05/89 ***REVISION DATE:*** 05/09/90

MATERIAL SAFETY DATA SHEET

OCCUPATIONAL HEALTH SERVICES, INC.
AGRICULTURE AND PESTICIDE DIVISION
450 SEVENTH AVENUE, SUITE 2407
NEW YORK, NEW YORK 10123
1-800-445-MSDS OR (212) 967-1100

EMERGENCY CONTACT:
JOHN S. BRANSFORD, JR. (615) 292-1180

SUBSTANCE IDENTIFICATION

CAS-NUMBER 119-38-0

SUBSTANCE: ISOLAN

TRADE NAMES/SYNONYMS: CARBAMIC ACID, DIMETHYL-, 3-METHYL-1-(1-METHYLETHYL)-1H-PYRAZOL-5-YL ESTER; 3-METHYL-1-(1-METHYLETHYL)-1H-PYRAZOL-5-YL DIMETHYLCARBAMATE; CARBAMIC ACID, DIMETHYL-, 1-ISOPROPYL-3-METHYLPYRAZOL-5-YL ESTER; 1-ISOPROPYL-3-METHYLPYRAZOL-5-YL DIMETHYLCARBAMATETE; DIMETHYLCARBAMIC ACID 3-METHYL-1-(1-METHYLETHYL)-1H-PYRAZOL-5-YL ESTER; ISOPROPYLMETHYLPYRAZOLYL DIMETHYLCARBAMATE; DIMETHYL-5-(1-ISOPROPYL-3-METHYLPYRAZOLYL)CARBAMATEE; ENT 19,060 G 23611; SAOLAN; PRIMIN; C10H17N3O2; PST83027

CHEMICAL FAMILY: PYRAZOLE CARBAMATE

MOLECULAR FORMULA: C10-H17-N3-O2

MOLECULAR WEIGHT: 211.27

CERCLA RATINGS (SCALE 0-3): HEALTH=3 FIRE=U REACTIVITY=0 PERSISTENCE=2

NFPA RATINGS (SCALE 0-4): HEALTH=4 FIRE=U REACTIVITY=0

COMPONENTS AND CONTAMINANTS

COMPONENT: ISOLAN ***PERCENT:*** 100.0

CAS# 119-38-0

OTHER CONTAMINANTS: NONE

EXPOSURE LIMITS: NO OCCUPATIONAL EXPOSURE LIMITS ESTABLISHED BY OSHA, ACGIH, OR NIOSH.

ISOLAN: 500 POUNDS SARA SECTION 302 THRESHOLD PLANNING QUANTITY 1 POUND SARA SECTION 304 REPORTABLE QUANTITY

PHYSICAL DATA

DESCRIPTION: COLORLESS LIQUID ***BOILING POINT:*** 217 F (103 C) @ 0.7 MMHG

SPECIFIC GRAVITY: 1.07 ***VAPOR PRESSURE:*** 0.001 MMHG @ 20 C

SOLUBILITY IN WATER: SOLUBLE

SOLVENT SOLUBILITY: SOLUBLE IN ALCOHOL, ACETONE AND XYLENE.

FIRE AND EXPLOSION DATA

FIRE AND EXPLOSION HAZARD: UNKNOWN FIRE AND EXPLOSION HAZARD.

FIREFIGHTING MEDIA: DRY CHEMICAL, CARBON DIOXIDE, HALON, WATER SPRAY OR STANDARD FOAM (1987 EMERGENCY RESPONSE GUIDEBOOK, DOT P 5800.4).

FOR LARGER FIRES, USE WATER SPRAY, FOG OR STANDARD FOAM (1987 EMERGENCY RESPONSE GUIDEBOOK, DOT P 5800.4).

FIREFIGHTING: MOVE CONTAINERS FROM FIRE AREA IF POSSIBLE (1987 EMERGENCY RESPONSE GUIDEBOOK, DOT P 5800.4, GUIDE PAGE 53).

EXTINGUISH USING AGENT SUITABLE FOR TYPE OF SURROUNDING FIRE. AVOID BREATHING VAPORS AND DUSTS. KEEP UPWIND.

TRANSPORTATION DATA

DEPARTMENT OF TRANSPORTATION HAZARD CLASSIFICATION 49 CFR 172.101: POISON B

DEPARTMENT OF TRANSPORTATION LABELING REQUIREMENTS 49 CFR 172.101 AND SUBPART E: POISON

DEPARTMENT OF TRANSPORTATION PACKAGING REQUIREMENTS: 49 CFR 173.365
EXCEPTIONS: 49 CFR 173.364

TOXICITY

ISOLAN: TOXICITY DATA: 5600 UG/KG SKIN-RAT LD50; 10,800 UG/KG ORAL-RAT LD50; 9800 UG/KG ORAL-MOUSE LD50; 2150 UG/KG INTRAPERITONEAL-RAT LD50; 1 MG/KG INTRAPERITONEAL-MOUSE LD50; 11 MG/KG UNREPORTED-MAMMAL LD50; MUTAGENIC DATA (RTECS); TUMORIGENIC DATA (RTECS). CARCINOGEN STATUS: NONE. ACUTE TOXICITY LEVEL: HIGHLY TOXIC BY DERMAL ABSORPTION AND INGESTION. TARGET EFFECTS: CHOLINESTERASE INHIBITOR. AT INCREASED RISK FROM EXPOSURE: PERSONS WITH ASTHMA, DIABETES, CARDIOVASCULAR DISEASE, MECHANICAL OBSTRUCTION OF THE GASTROINTESTINAL OR UROGENITAL TRACT, AND THOSE IN VAGOTONIC STATES.*

* MAY BE BASED ON GENERAL INFORMATION ON CARBAMATES.

HEALTH EFFECTS AND FIRST AID

INHALATION: ISOLAN: IN SEVERAL CASES OF NONFATAL POISONING, LIVER DAMAGE WAS REPORTED WITH OTHER SYMPTOMS OF CHOLINESTERASE INHIBITION. THE LIVER DAMAGE INDICATED BY ABNORMAL LIVER FUNCTION TEST WAS TRANSIENT WITH RECOVERY IN 2 TO 9 DAYS. SEE INFORMATION ON CARBAMATES.

CARBAMATES: CHOLINESTERASE INHIBITOR. **ACUTE EXPOSURE-** WHEN INHALED, THE FIRST EFFECTS OF CHOLINESTERASE INHIBITION ARE USUALLY RESPIRATORY AND MAY INCLUDE NASAL HYPEREMIA AND WATERY DISCHARGE, CHEST DISCOMFORT, DYSPNEA, AND WHEEZING DUE TO INCREASED BRONCHIAL SECRETIONS AND BRONCHOCONSTRICTION. OTHER SYSTEMIC EFFECTS MAY BEGIN WITHIN A FEW MINUTES OR SEVERAL HOURS OF EXPOSURE. SYMPTOMS MAY INCLUDE NAUSEA, VOMITING, DIARRHEA, ABDOMINAL CRAMPS, HEADACHE, VERTIGO, OCULAR PAIN, CILIARY MUSCLE SPASM, BLURRING OR DIMNESS OF VISION, MIOSIS, OR IN SOME CASES MYDRIASIS, LACRIMATION, SALIVATION, SWEATING, AND CONFUSION. OTHER REPORTED CENTRAL NERVOUS SYSTEM OR NEUROMUSCULAR EFFECTS INCLUDE ATAXIA, SLURRED SPEECH, AREFLEXIA, WEAKNESS, FATIGUE, TWITCHING, FASCICULATION, TREMOR, AND EVENTUALLY PARALYSIS OF THE EXTREMITIES AND POSSIBLY OF THE RESPIRATORY MUSCLES. IN SEVERE CASES, THERE MAY ALSO BE INVOLUNTARY DEFECATION AND URINATION, BRADYCARDIA, HYPOTENSION, PULMONARY EDEMA, CONVULSIONS, COMA, AND DEATH FROM RESPIRATORY FAILURE OR CARDIAC ARREST. CARBAMATES GENERALLY DO NOT ACCUMULATE IN MAMMALIAN TISSUE AND THE CHOLINESTERASE INHIBITION REVERSES RATHER RAPIDLY. IN NON-FATAL CASES, THE ILLNESS GENERALLY LASTS LESS THAN 24 HOURS. **CHRONIC EXPOSURE-** PROLONGED OR REPEATED EXPOSURE MAY CAUSE EFFECTS AS DESCRIBED IN ACUTE EXPOSURE.

FIRST AID- REMOVE FROM EXPOSURE AREA TO FRESH AIR IMMEDIATELY. IF BREATHING HAS STOPPED, GIVE ARTIFICIAL RESPIRATION. MAINTAIN AIRWAY AND BLOOD PRESSURE AND ADMINISTER OXYGEN IF AVAILABLE. KEEP AFFECTED PERSON WARM AND AT REST. TREAT SYMPTOMATICALLY AND SUPPORTIVELY. ADMINISTRATION OF OXYGEN SHOULD BE PERFORMED BY QUALIFIED PERSONNEL. GET MEDICAL ATTENTION IMMEDIATELY.

SKIN CONTACT: ISOLAN: HIGHLY TOXIC. ONE PERSON BECAME ILL WITH CONVULSIONS AFTER CONTACT WITH DROPS ON THE FACE AND LIPS. IN THIS CASE AND OTHER CASES OF POISONING, LIVER DAMAGE DEVELOPED AS INDICATED BY ABNORMAL LIVER FUNCTION TESTS. THESE TESTS CLEARED IN 2 TO 9 DAYS. SEE INFORMATION ON CARBAMATES.

CARBAMATES: CHOLINESTERASE INHIBITOR. **ACUTE EXPOSURE-** SOME COMPOUNDS MAY CAUSE IRRITATION. LOCALIZED SWEATING AND FASCICULATIONS MAY OCCUR AT THE SITE OF CONTACT. IF SUFFICIENT AMOUNTS ARE ABSORBED THROUGH THE SKIN, OTHER EFFECTS OF CHOLINESTERASE INHIBITION MAY OCCUR AS DESCRIBED IN ACUTE INHALATION; SYMPTOMS MAY BE DELAYED FOR 2-3 HOURS, USUALLY NO MORE THAN 8 HOURS. **CHRONIC EXPOSURE-** REPEATED OR PROLONGED EXPOSURE MAY CAUSE EFFECTS AS DESCRIBED IN ACUTE EXPOSURE.

FIRST AID- REMOVE CONTAMINATED CLOTHING IMMEDIATELY. WASH CONTAMINATED AREAS WITH SOAP AND WATER FOLLOWED BY ALCOHOL (ARENA, POISONING, 4TH ED.). EMERGENCY PERSONNEL SHOULD WEAR GLOVES AND AVOID CONTAMINATION. TREAT RESPIRATORY DIFFICULTY WITH ARTIFICIAL RESPIRATION. GET MEDICAL ATTENTION IMMEDIATELY.

EYE CONTACT: ISOLAN: SEE INFORMATION ON CARBAMATES.

CARBAMATES: CHOLINESTERASE INHIBITOR. **ACUTE EXPOSURE-** DIRECT CONTACT MAY CAUSE PAIN, HYPEREMIA, LACRIMATION, TWITCHING OF THE EYELIDS, MIOSIS, AND CILIARY MUSCLE SPASM WITH LOSS OF ACCOMODATION, BLURRED OR DIMMED VISION AND BROWACHE. SOMETIMES MYDRIASIS MAY OCCUR INSTEAD OF MIOSIS. WITH SUFFICIENT EXPOSURE, OTHER SYMPTOMS OF CHOLINESTERASE INHIBITION MAY OCCUR AS DESCRIBED IN ACUTE INHALATION. **CHRONIC EXPOSURE-** PROLONGED EXPOSURE MAY CAUSE EFFECTS AS DESCRIBED IN ACUTE EXPOSURE. SOME COMPOUNDS HAVE CAUSED TOXIC EFFECTS ON THE CRYSTALLINE LENS, CONJUNCTIVAL THICKENING AND OBSTRUCTION OF NASOLACRIMAL CANALS WHEN USED AS MIOTIC EYE DROPS.

FIRST AID- IRRIGATE EYES WITH WATER OR SALINE SOLUTION. IF SYMPTOMS OF POISONING OCCUR, TREAT RESPIRATORY DIFFICULTY WITH ARTIFICIAL RESPIRATION AND OXYGEN. OBSERVE PATIENT FOR AT LEAST 24-36 HOURS (GOSSELIN, CLINICAL TOXICOLOGY OF COMMERCIAL PRODUCTS, 5TH ED.). GET MEDICAL ATTENTION IMMEDIATELY. OXYGEN SHOULD BE ADMINISTERED BY QUALIFIED MEDICAL PERSONNEL.

INGESTION: ISOLAN: HIGHLY TOXIC. IN SEVERAL CASES OF SEVERE BUT NONFATAL POISONING, COMA DEVELOPED ALONG WITH TRANSIENT LIVER DAMAGE AS INDICATED BY ABNORMAL LIVER FUNCTION TESTS. THESE TESTS CLEARED WITHIN 2 TO 9 DAYS. SEE INFORMATION ON CARBAMATES.

CARBAMATES: CHOLINESTERASE INHIBITOR. **ACUTE EXPOSURE-** WHEN INGESTED, THE FIRST EFFECTS MAY BE NAUSEA, VOMITING, ANOREXIA, ABDOMINAL CRAMPS, AND DIARRHEA. WITH ABSORPTION FROM THE GASTROINTESTINAL TRACT, THE OTHER EFFECTS OF CHOLINESTERASE INHIBITION AS DESCRIBED IN ACUTE INHALATION MAY OCCUR; SYMPTOMS MAY BEGIN WITHIN MINUTES OR BE DELAYED SEVERAL HOURS. **CHRONIC EXPOSURE-** REPEATED INGESTION MAY CAUSE EFFECTS AS DESCRIBED IN ACUTE EXPOSURE.

FIRST AID- IF PERSON IS ALERT AND RESPIRATION IS NOT DEPRESSED, GIVE SYRUP OF IPECAC FOLLOWED BY WATER (IF VOMITING OCCURS, KEEP HEAD BELOW HIPS TO PREVENT ASPIRATION). IF CONSCIOUSNESS LEVEL DECLINES OR VOMITING HAS NOT OCCURRED IN 15 MINUTES EMPTY STOMACH BY GASTRIC LAVAGE WITH THE AID OF CUFFED ENDOTRACHEAL TUBE USING ISOTONIC SALINE OR 5% SODIUM BICARBONATE FOLLOW WITH ACTIVATED CHARCOAL. ESTABLISH AND MAINTAIN AIRWAY. TREAT RESPIRATORY DIFFICULTY WITH ARTIFICIAL RESPIRATION AND OXYGEN. DO NOT GIVE MORPHINE, AMINOPHYLLINE, PHENOTHIAZINES, RESERPINE, FUROSEMIDE, OR ETHACRYNIC ACID (MORGAN, RECOGNITION AND MANAGEMENT OF PESTICIDE POISONINGS, 3RD ED.). TREAT SYMPTOMATICALLY AND SUPPORTIVELY. ADMINISTRATION OF OXYGEN AND LAVAGE MUST BE PERFORMED BY QUALIFIED MEDICAL PERSONNEL. GET MEDICAL ATTENTION IMMEDIATELY.

ANTIDOTE: THE FOLLOWING ANTIDOTE(S) HAVE BEEN RECOMMENDED. HOWEVER, THE DECISION AS TO WHETHER THE SEVERITY OF POISONING REQUIRES ADMINISTRATION OF ANY ANTIDOTE AND ACTUAL DOSE REQUIRED SHOULD BE MADE BY QUALIFIED MEDICAL PERSONNEL.

FOR CHOLINESTERASE INHIBITORS: ESTABLISH CLEAR AIRWAY AND TISSUE OXYGENATION BY ASPIRATION OF SECRETIONS, AND IF NECESSARY, BY ASSISTED PULMONARY VENTILATION WITH OXYGEN. IMPROVE TISSUE OXYGENATION AS MUCH AS POSSIBLE BEFORE ADMINISTERING ATROPINE TO MINIMIZE THE RISK OF VENTRICULAR FIBRILLATION. ADMINISTER ATROPINE SULFATE INTRAVENOUSLY, OR INTRAMUSCULARLY IF IV INJECTION IS NOT POSSIBLE. IN MODERATELY SEVERE POISONING ADMINISTER ATROPINE SULFATE, 0.4-2.0 MG REPEATED EVERY 15 MINUTES UNTIL ATROPINIZATION IS ACHIEVED (TACHYCARDIA, FLUSHING, DRY MOUTH, MYDRIASIS). MAINTAIN ATROPINIZATION BY REPEATED DOSES FOR 2-12 HOURS, OR LONGER, DEPENDING ON THE SEVERITY OF POISONING. THE APPEARANCE OF RALES IN THE LUNG BASES, MIOSIS, SALIVATION, NAUSEA, BRADYCARDIA, ARE ALL INDICATIONS OF INADEQUATE ATROPINIZATION. SEVERELY POISONED INDIVIDUALS MAY EXHIBIT REMARKABLE TOLERANCE TO ATROPINE; TWO OR MORE TIMES THE DOSAGES SUGGESTED ABOVE MAY BE NEEDED. PERSONS NOT POISONED OR ONLY SLIGHTLY POISONED, HOWEVER, MAY DEVELOP SIGNS OF ATROPINE TOXICITY FROM SUCH LARGE DOSAGES: FEVER, MUSCLE FIBRILLATIONS, AND DELIRIUM ARE THE MAIN SIGNS OF ATROPINE TOXICITY. IF THESE SIGNS APPEAR WHILE THE PATIENT IS FULLY ATROPINIZED, ATROPINE ADMINISTRATION SHOULD BE DISCONTINUED, AT LEAST TEMPORARILY. OBSERVE TREATED PATIENTS CLOSELY AT LEAST 24 HOURS TO INSURE THAT SYMPTOMS (POSSIBLY PULMONARY EDEMA) DO NOT RECUR AS ATROPINIZATION WEARS OFF. IN VERY SEVERE POISONINGS, METABOLIC DISPOSITION OF TOXICANT MAY REQUIRE SEVERAL HOURS OR DAYS DURING WHICH ATROPINIZATION MUST BE MAINTAINED. MARKEDLY LOWER LEVELS OF URINARY METABOLITES INDICATE THAT ATROPINE DOSAGE CAN BE TAPERED OFF. AS DOSAGE IS REDUCED, CHECK THE LUNG BASES FREQUENTLY FOR RALES. IF RALES ARE HEARD OR OTHER SYMPTOMS RETURN, RE-ESTABLISH ATROPINIZATION PROMPTLY (MORGAN, RECOGNITION AND MANAGEMENT OF PESTICIDE POISONINGS, 3RD ED.). ADMINISTRATION OF ANTIDOTE MUST BE PERFORMED BY QUALIFIED MEDICAL PERSONNEL.

PRALIDOXIME (PROTOPAM-AYERST, 2-PAM) IS OF DOUBTFUL VALUE IN POISONINGS BY CARBAMATE INHIBITORS OF CHOLINESTERASE. ATROPINE ALONE IS ALMOST ALWAYS AN ADEQUATE ANTIDOTE. PRALIDOXIME IS PROBABLY CONTRAINDICATED IN POISONING BY CARBARYL SPECIFICALLY, AND OTHER MONOMETHYLATED CARBAMATES. IF A VICTIM OF DIMETHYLCARBAMATE INSECTICIDE POISONING FAILS TO RESPOND PROMPTLY AND ADEQUATELY TO ATROPINE, OR IF POISONING INVOLVES A COMBINATION OF CARBAMATE AND ORGANOPHOSPHATE, A DILUTE SOLUTION OF PRALIDOXIME (TOTAL DOSE IN 250 ML 5% GLUCOSE SOLUTION) MAY BE GIVEN CAUTIOUSLY INTRAVENOUSLY. ADULT

DOSAGE IS 1 GRAM (MORGAN, RECOGNITION AND MANAGEMENT OF PESTICIDE POISONINGS, THIRD EDITION; HAYES, PESTICIDES STUDIED IN MAN, 1982).

REACTIVITY

REACTIVITY: NO DATA AVAILABLE.
INCOMPATIBILITIES: ISOLAN: OXIDIZERS (STRONG): FIRE AND EXPLOSION HAZARD.
DECOMPOSITION: THERMAL DECOMPOSITION PRODUCTS MAY INCLUDE TOXIC OXIDES OF CARBON AND NITROGEN.
POLYMERIZATION: HAZARDOUS POLYMERIZATION HAS NOT BEEN REPORTED TO OCCUR UNDER NORMAL TEMPERATURES AND PRESSURES.

STORAGE AND DISPOSAL

OBSERVE ALL FEDERAL, STATE AND LOCAL REGULATIONS WHEN STORING OR DISPOSING OF THIS SUBSTANCE. FOR ASSISTANCE, CONTACT THE DISTRICT DIRECTOR OF THE ENVIRONMENTAL PROTECTION AGENCY.

STORAGE

STORE AWAY FROM INCOMPATIBLE SUBSTANCES.
THRESHOLD PLANNING QUANTITY (TPQ): THE SUPERFUND AMENDMENTS AND REAUTHORIZATION ACT (SARA) SECTION 302 REQUIRES THAT EACH FACILITY WHERE ANY EXTREMELY HAZARDOUS SUBSTANCE IS PRESENT IN A QUANTITY EQUAL TO OR GREATER THAN THE TPQ ESTABLISHED FOR THAT SUBSTANCE NOTIFY THE STATE EMERGENCY RESPONSE COMMISSION FOR THE STATE IN WHICH IT IS LOCATED. SECTION 303 OF SARA REQUIRES THESE FACILITIES TO PARTICIPATE IN LOCAL EMERGENCY RESPONSE PLANNING (40 CFR 355.30).

DISPOSAL

DISPOSAL MUST BE IN ACCORDANCE WITH 40 CFR 165 RECOMMENDED PROCEDURES FOR THE DISPOSAL AND STORAGE OF PESTICIDES AND PESTICIDE CONTAINERS.

CONDITIONS TO AVOID

MAY BURN BUT DOES NOT IGNITE READILY.

SPILL AND LEAK PROCEDURES

OCCUPATIONAL SPILL: DO NOT TOUCH SPILLED MATERIAL. STOP LEAK IF YOU CAN DO IT WITHOUT RISK. FOR SMALL SPILLS, TAKE UP WITH SAND OR OTHER ABSORBENT MATERIAL AND PLACE INTO CONTAINERS FOR LATER DISPOSAL. FOR SMALL DRY SPILLS, WITH A CLEAN SHOVEL PLACE MATERIAL INTO CLEAN, DRY CONTAINER AND COVER. MOVE CONTAINERS FROM SPILL AREA. FOR LARGER SPILLS, DIKE FAR AHEAD OF SPILL FOR LATER DISPOSAL. KEEP UNNECESSARY PEOPLE AWAY. ISOLATE HAZARD AREA AND DENY ENTRY.
REPORTABLE QUANTITY (RQ): 1 POUND THE SUPERFUND AMENDMENTS AND REAUTHORIZATION ACT (SARA) SECTION 304 REQUIRES THAT A RELEASE EQUAL TO OR GREATER THAN THE REPORTABLE QUANTITY FOR THIS SUBSTANCE BE IMMEDIATELY REPORTED TO THE LOCAL EMERGENCY PLANNING COMMITTEE AND THE STATE EMERGENCY RESPONSE COMMISSION (40 CFR 355.40). IF THE RELEASE OF THIS SUBSTANCE IS REPORTABLE UNDER CERCLA SECTION 103, THE NATIONAL RESPONSE CENTER MUST BE NOTIFIED IMMEDIATELY AT (800) 424-8802 OR (202) 426-2675 IN THE METROPOLITAN WASHINGTON, D.C. AREA (40 CFR 302.6).

PROTECTIVE EQUIPMENT

VENTILATION: PROCESS ENCLOSURE RECOMMENDED.
RESPIRATOR: THE FOLLOWING RESPIRATORS ARE RECOMMENDED BASED ON INFORMATION FOUND IN THE PHYSICAL DATA, TOXICITY AND HEALTH EFFECTS SECTIONS. THEY ARE RANKED IN ORDER FROM MINIMUM TO MAXIMUM RESPIRATORY PROTECTION. THE SPECIFIC RESPIRATOR SELECTED MUST BE BASED ON CONTAMINATION LEVELS FOUND IN THE WORK PLACE, MUST NOT EXCEED THE WORKING LIMITS OF THE RESPIRATOR AND BE JOINTLY APPROVED BY THE NATIONAL INSTITUTE FOR OCCUPATIONAL SAFETY AND HEALTH AND THE MINE SAFETY AND HEALTH ADMINISTRATION (NIOSH-MSHA).
TYPE 'C' SUPPLIED-AIR RESPIRATOR WITH A FULL FACEPIECE OPERATED IN PRESSURE-DEMAND OR OTHER POSITIVE PRESSURE MODE OR WITH A FULL FACEPIECE, HELMET OR HOOD OPERATED IN CONTINOUS-FLOW MODE.
SELF-CONTAINED BREATHING APPARATUS WITH A FULL FACEPIECE OPERATED IN PRESSURE-DEMAND OR OTHER POSITIVE PRESSURE MODE.
FOR FIREFIGHTING AND OTHER IMMEDIATELY DANGEROUS TO LIFE OR HEALTH CONDITIONS:
SELF-CONTAINED BREATHING APPARATUS WITH FULL FACEPIECE OPERATED IN PRESSURE-DEMAND OR OTHER POSITIVE PRESSURE MODE.
SUPPLIED-AIR RESPIRATOR WITH FULL FACEPIECE AND OPERATED IN PRESSURE-DEMAND OR OTHER POSITIVE PRESSURE MODE IN COMBINATION WITH AN AUXILIARY SELF-CONTAINED BREATHING APPARATUS OPERATED IN PRESSURE-DEMAND OR OTHER POSITIVE PRESSURE MODE.
CLOTHING: EMPLOYEE MUST WEAR APPROPRIATE PROTECTIVE (IMPERVIOUS) CLOTHING AND EQUIPMENT TO PREVENT ANY POSSIBILITY OF SKIN CONTACT WITH THIS SUBSTANCE.
GLOVES: EMPLOYEE MUST WEAR APPROPRIATE PROTECTIVE GLOVES TO PREVENT CONTACT WITH THIS SUBSTANCE.
EYE PROTECTION: EMPLOYEE MUST WEAR SPLASH-PROOF OR DUST-RESISTANT SAFETY GOGGLES AND A FACESHIELD TO PREVENT CONTACT WITH THIS SUBSTANCE.
EMERGENCY WASH FACILITIES: WHERE THERE IS ANY POSSIBILITY THAT AN EMPLOYEE'S EYES AND/OR SKIN MAY BE EXPOSED TO THIS SUBSTANCE, THE EMPLOYER SHOULD PROVIDE AN EYE WASH FOUNTAIN AND QUICK DRENCH SHOWER WITHIN THE IMMEDIATE WORK AREA FOR EMERGENCY USE.

AUTHORIZED BY- OCCUPATIONAL HEALTH SERVICES, INC.
CREATION DATE: 10/04/89 ***REVISION DATE:*** 07/10/90

MATERIAL SAFETY DATA SHEET

OCCUPATIONAL HEALTH SERVICES, INC.
AGRICULTURE AND PESTICIDE DIVISION
450 SEVENTH AVENUE, SUITE 2407
NEW YORK, NEW YORK 10123
1-800-445-MSDS OR (212) 967-1100

EMERGENCY CONTACT:
JOHN S. BRANSFORD, JR. (615) 292-1180

SUBSTANCE IDENTIFICATION

CAS-NUMBER 151-38-2
SUBSTANCE: METHOXYETHYLMERCURIC ACETATE
TRADE NAMES/SYNONYMS: (ACETATO-O)-(2-METHOXYETHYL)MERCURY; (ACETATO)(2-METHOXYETHYL)MERCURY; (2-METHOXYETHYL)MERCURY ACETATE; ACETATO(2-METHOXYETHYL)MERCURY; ACETOXY(2-METHOXYETHYL)MERCURY; MEEHG; MEMA; MERCURAN; MERKURAN; PANOGEN; PANOGEN-METOX; RADOSAN; C5H10HGO3; PST83031
CHEMICAL FAMILY: ETHER, ALIPHATIC
CARBONYL
MOLECULAR FORMULA: C5-H10-HG-O3
MOLECULAR WEIGHT: 318.74
CERCLA RATINGS (SCALE 0-3): HEALTH=3 FIRE=U REACTIVITY=U PERSISTENCE=3
NFPA RATINGS (SCALE 0-4): HEALTH=3 FIRE=U REACTIVITY=U

COMPONENTS AND CONTAMINANTS

COMPONENT: METHOXYETHYLMERCURIC ACETATE ***PERCENT:*** 100.0
CAS# 151-38-2
EXPOSURE LIMITS: MERCURY, ALL FORMS EXCEPT ALKYL (AS HG): 0.05 MG/M3 OSHA TWA (VAPOR); 0.1 MG/M3 OSHA CEILING (SKIN) 0.05 MG/M3 ACGIH TWA (VAPOR); 0.10 MG/M3 ACGIH TWA (ARYL & INORGANIC)-(SKIN) 0.05 MG/M3 NIOSH RECOMMENDED 10 HOUR TWA
SUBJECT TO SARA SECTION 313 ANNUAL TOXIC CHEMICAL RELEASE REPORTING
SUBJECT TO CALIFORNIA PROPOSITION 65 CANCER AND/OR REPRODUCTIVE TOXICITY WARNING AND RELEASE REQUIREMENTS- (JULY 1, 1990)
METHOXYETHYLMERCURIC ACETATE: 500/10,000 POUNDS SARA SECTION 302 THRESHOLD PLANNING QUANTITY 1 POUND SARA SECTION 304 REPORTABLE QUANTITY

PHYSICAL DATA

DESCRIPTION: CRYSTALS ***MELTING POINT:*** NOT AVAILABLE
SPECIFIC GRAVITY: NOT AVAILABLE ***SOLUBILITY IN WATER:*** SOLUBLE
SOLVENT SOLUBILITY: METHANOL, ETHYLENE-GLYCOL

FIRE AND EXPLOSION DATA

FIRE AND EXPLOSION HAZARD: UNKNOWN FIRE AND EXPLOSION HAZARD.
FIREFIGHTING MEDIA: DRY CHEMICAL, CARBON DIOXIDE, HALON, WATER SPRAY OR STANDARD FOAM (1987 EMERGENCY RESPONSE GUIDEBOOK, DOT P 5800.4).
FOR LARGER FIRES, USE WATER SPRAY, FOG OR STANDARD FOAM (1987 EMERGENCY RESPONSE GUIDEBOOK, DOT P 5800.4).
FIREFIGHTING: MOVE CONTAINERS FROM FIRE AREA IF POSSIBLE (1987 EMERGENCY RESPONSE GUIDEBOOK, DOT P 5800.4, GUIDE PAGE 53).
EXTINGUISH USING AGENT SUITABLE FOR TYPE OF SURROUNDING FIRE. AVOID BREATHING VAPORS AND DUSTS. KEEP UPWIND.

TRANSPORTATION DATA

DEPARTMENT OF TRANSPORTATION HAZARD CLASSIFICATION 49 CFR 172.101: POISON B
DEPARTMENT OF TRANSPORTATION LABELING REQUIREMENTS 49 CFR 172.101 AND SUBPART E: POISON

DEPARTMENT OF TRANSPORTATION PACKAGING REQUIREMENTS: 49 CFR 173.365 EXCEPTIONS: 49 CFR 173.364

TOXICITY

METHOXYETHYLMERCURIC ACETATE: TOXICITY DATA: 25 MG/KG ORAL-RAT LD50; MUTAGENIC DATA (RTECS). CARCINOGEN STATUS: NONE. LOCAL EFFECTS: IRRITANT- INHALATION, SKIN, AND EYES. ACUTE TOXICITY LEVEL: HIGHLY TOXIC BY INGESTION. TARGET EFFECTS: POISONING MAY AFFECT THE CENTRAL NERVOUS SYSTEM AND BRAIN. AT INCREASED RISK FROM EXPOSURE: PERSONS WITH SKIN, RENAL OR NEUROLOGICAL DISORDERS. ADDITIONAL DATA: ACCUMULATION OF MERCURY IN THE BODY OF WOMEN MAY AFFECT THE WELFARE OF THEIR UNBORN CHILDREN.

HEALTH EFFECTS AND FIRST AID

INHALATION: METHOXYETHYLMERCURIC ACETATE: IRRITANT. 10 MG(HG)/M3 IMMEDIATELY DANGEROUS TO LIFE OR HEALTH. **ACUTE EXPOSURE-** MAY CAUSE IRRITATION OF THE MUCOUS MEMBRANE AND UPPER RESPIRATORY TRACT. IF IS ABSORBED IN SUFFICIENT QUANTITIES IT MAY CAUSE SIGNS AND SYMPTOMS OF MERCURY POISONING, HOWEVER MOST INCIDENCES OF POISONING HAVE OCCURRED FROM THE ACCUMULATION OF MERCURY IN THE BODY AS A RESULT OF PROLONGED OR REPEATED EXPOSURE. **CHRONIC EXPOSURE-** PROLONGED OR REPEATED EXPOSURE MAY RESULT IN ABSORPTION OF A SUFFICIENT CONCENTRATION TO CAUSE POSIONING. THE ONSET OF POISONING MAY BE DELAYED FOR WEEKS OR MONTHS AFTER EXPOSURE AND INCLUDE SYMPTOMS OF A METALLIC TASTE IN MOUTH, HEADACHE, LOSS OF APPETITE, GASTROINTESTINAL DISTURBANCES, DIARRHEA, WEAKNESS, FATIGUE, INABILITY TO CONCENTRATE, TREMORS OF THE EXTREMITIES, DEAFNESS AND OTHER SENSORY LOSSES, SPEECH DISORDERS, CONSTRICTION OF THE VISUAL FIELD, SUBTLE OR DRAMATIC CHANGES IN BEHAVIOR, ATAXIA, AND ACRODYNIA WITH SCALING OF THE HANDS AND FEET. SEVERE INTOXICATION MAY PRODUCE IRREVERSIBLE BRAIN DAMAGE, STUPOR, COMA OR DEATH. RENAL DAMAGE MAY OCCUR. MERCURY MOVES READILY ACROSS THE PLACENTA INTO FETAL TISSUE. FETAL INTOXICATION BY WAY OF THE MOTHER HAS BEEN DOCUMENTED IN CASES OF METHYL MERCURY POISONING.

FIRST AID- REMOVE FROM EXPOSURE AREA TO FRESH AIR IMMEDIATELY. IF BREATHING HAS STOPPED, PERFORM ARTIFICIAL RESPIRATION. KEEP PERSON WARM AND AT REST. TREAT SYMPTOMATICALLY AND SUPPORTIVELY. GET MEDICAL ATTENTION IMMEDIATELY.

SKIN CONTACT: METHOXYETHYLMERCURIC ACETATE: IRRITANT. **ACUTE EXPOSURE-** MAY CAUSE IRRITATION OR DERMATITIS. THIS MATERIAL IS A VESICANT WHEN APPLIED IN CONCENTRATED SOLUTIONS TO THE SKIN. IT MAY CAUSE SENSITIZATION IN SOME INDIVIDUALS. ORGANIC MERCURY COMPOUNDS ARE ABSORBED THROUGH THE SKIN, HOWEVER MOST INCIDENCE OF MERCURY POISONING HAVE OCCURRED FROM ACCUMULATION OF MERCURY IN THE BODY AS RESULT OF PROLONGED OR REPEATED EXPOSURE. **CHRONIC EXPOSURE-** PROLONGED OR REPEATED EXPOSURE MAY CAUSE DERMATITIS AND SENSITIZATION DERMATITIS IN SOME INDIVIDUALS. PROLONGED OR REPEATED EXPOSURE MAY ALSO RESULT IN ABSORPTION OF A SUFFICIENT QUANTITY TO CAUSE MERCURY POISONING. THE ONSET OF POISONING MAY BE DELAYED FOR WEEKS OR MONTHS AFTER EXPOSURE AND INCLUDE SYMPTOMS OF A METALLIC TASTE IN THE MOUTH, HEADACHE, LOSS OF APPETITE, GASTROINTESTINAL DISTURBANCES, DIARRHEA, WEAKNESS, FATIGUE, INABILITY TO CONCENTRATE, TREMORS, DEAFNESS AND OTHER SENSORY LOSSES, SPEECH DISORDERS, CONSTRICTION OF THE VISUAL FIELD, SUBTLE OR DRAMATIC CHANGES IN BEHAVIOR, ATAXIA, AND ACRODYNIA WITH SCALING OF THE SKIN OF THE HANDS AND FEET. SEVERE INTOXICATION MAY PRODUCE IRREVERSIBLE BRAIN DAMAGE, STUPOR, COMA OR DEATH. RENAL DAMAGE MAY OCCUR. MERCURY MOVES READILY ACROSS THE PLACENTA INTO FETAL TISSUE. FETAL INTOXICATION BY WAY OF THE MOTHER HAS BEEN DOCUMENTED IN CASES OF METHYL MERCURY POISONING.

FIRST AID- REMOVE CONTAMINATED CLOTHING AND SHOES IMMEDIATELY. WASH AFFECTED AREA WITH SOAP OR MILD DETERGENT AND LARGE AMOUNTS OF WATER UNTIL NO EVIDENCE OF CHEMICAL REMAINS (APPROXIMATELY 15-20 MINUTES). GET MEDICAL ATTENTION IMMEDIATELY.

EYE CONTACT: METHOXYETHYLMERCURIC ACETATE: IRRITANT. **ACUTE EXPOSURE-** MAY CAUSE IRRITATION. THIS MATERIAL WAS VERY TOXIC TO RABBIT RETINA IN TISSUE CULTURE, AT CONCENTRATION OF .000006 M CAUSING GENERAL DESTRUCTION OF THE CELLS IN FOUR HOURS. **CHRONIC EXPOSURE-** PROLONGED OR REPEATED EXPOSURE MAY CAUSE CONJUNCTIVITIS.

FIRST AID- WASH EYES IMMEDIATELY WITH LARGE AMOUNTS OF WATER OR NORMAL SALINE, OCCASIONALLY LIFTING UPPER AND LOWER LIDS, UNTIL NO EVIDENCE OF CHEMICAL REMAINS (APPROXIMATELY 15-20 MINUTES). GET MEDICAL ATTENTION IMMEDIATELY.

INGESTION: METHOXYETHYLMERCURIC ACETATE: HIGHLY TOXIC. **ACUTE EXPOSURE-** A HIGHLY TOXIC DOSE WAS LETHAL IN RATS. POISONING BY VARIOUS MERCURY COMPOUNDS HAVE CAUSED ACUTE GASTROINTESTINAL INFLAMMATION WITH METALLIC TASTE, THRIST, NAUSEA, RETCHING, VOMITING, AND DIARRHEA. STOMATITIS, GASTRITIS, COLITIS AND SEVERE RENAL TUBULAR DEGENERATION MAY OCCUR. DEATH MAY OCCUR FROM IRREVERSIBLE RENAL FAILURE. **CHRONIC EXPOSURE-** REPEATED INGESTION OF SMALL DOSES OF MERCURY COMPOUNDS HAVE RESULTED IN THE ACCUMULATION OF SUFFICIENT QUANTITY OF MERCURY TO CAUSE MERCURY POISONING. THE ONSET OF POISONING MAY BE DELAYED FOR WEEKS OR MONTHS AFTER EXPOSURE AND INCLUDE SYMPTOMS OF METALLIC TASTE IN MOUTH, HEADACHE, LOSS OF APPETITE, GASTROINTESTINAL DISTURBANCES, DIARRHEA, WEAKNESS, FATIGUE, INABILITY TO CONCENTRATE, TREMORS, DEAFNESS AND OTHER SENSORY LOSSES, SPEECH DISORDERS, CONSTRICTION OF THE VISUAL FIELD, SUBTLE OR DRAMATIC CHANGES IN BEHAVIOR, ATAXIA, AND ACRODYNIA WITH SCALING OF THE SKIN OF THE HANDS AND FEET. SEVERE INTOXICATION MAY PRODUCE IRREVERSIBLE BRAIN DAMAGE, STUPOR, COMA OR DEATH. RENAL DAMAGE MAY OCCUR. MERCURY MOVES READILY ACROSS THE PLACENTA INTO FETAL TISSUE. FETAL INTOXICATION BY WAY OF THE MOTHER HAS BEEN DOCUMENTED IN CASES OF METHYL MERCURY POISONING.

FIRST AID- REMOVE INGESTED POISON BY GASTRIC LAVAGE WITH TAP WATER OR BY EMESIS AND CATHARSIS. MAINTAIN BLOOD PRESSURE, AIRWAY, AND GIVE OXYGEN IF RESPIRATION IS DEPRESSED. GET MEDICAL ATTENTION IMMEDIATELY. (DREISBACH, HANDBOOK OF POISONING, 11TH EDITION) ADMINISTRATION OF GASTRIC LAVAGE OR OXYGEN SHOLD BE PERFORMED BY QUALIFIED MEDICAL PERSONNEL.

ANTIDOTE: THE FOLLOWING ANTIDOTE HAS BEEN RECOMMENDED. HOWEVER, THE DECISION AS TO WHETHER THE SEVERITY OF POISONING REQUIRES ADMINISTRATION OF ANY ANTIDOTE AND ACTUAL DOSE REQUIRED SHOULD BE MADE BY QUALIFIED MEDICAL PERSONNEL.
POISONING FROM ORGANIC MERCURY COMPOUNDS: GIVE N-ACETYL-D,L-PENICILLAMINE (OR IF NOT AVAILABLE D-PENICILLAMINE) BY MOUTH, 250 MG, 4 TIMES DAILY FOR 5-10 DAYS. DIMERCAPROL IS LESS EFFECTIVE AND MAY BE CONTRAINDICATED (GOSSELIN, CLINICAL TOXICOLOGY OF COMMERCIAL PRODUCTS, 5TH EDITION). ANTIDOTE SHOULD BE ADMINISTERED BY QUALIFIED MEDICAL PERSONNEL.

REACTIVITY

REACTIVITY: NO DATA AVAILABLE.

INCOMPATIBILITIES: METHOXYETHYLMERCURIC ACETATE: STRONG OXIDIZERS: MAY CAUSE FIRE AND EXPLOSION HAZARD.

DECOMPOSITION: THERMAL DECOMPOSITION MAY RELEASE TOXIC FUMES OF MERCURY.

POLYMERIZATION: HAZARDOUS POLYMERIZATION HAS NOT BEEN REPORTED TO OCCUR UNDER NORMAL TEMPERATURES AND PRESSURES.

STORAGE AND DISPOSAL

OBSERVE ALL FEDERAL, STATE AND LOCAL REGULATIONS WHEN STORING OR DISPOSING OF THIS SUBSTANCE. FOR ASSISTANCE, CONTACT THE DISTRICT DIRECTOR OF THE ENVIRONMENTAL PROTECTION AGENCY.

****STORAGE****

STORE IN ACCORDANCE WITH 40 CFR 165 RECOMMENDED PROCEDURES FOR THE DISPOSAL AND STORAGE OF PESTICIDES AND PESTICIDE CONTAINERS.
STORE AWAY FROM INCOMPATIBLE SUBSTANCES.
THRESHOLD PLANNING QUANTITY (TPQ): THE SUPERFUND AMENDMENTS AND REAUTHORIZATION ACT (SARA) SECTION 302 REQUIRES THAT EACH FACILITY WHERE ANY EXTREMELY HAZARDOUS SUBSTANCE IS PRESENT IN A QUANTITY EQUAL TO OR GREATER THAN THE TPQ ESTABLISHED FOR THAT SUBSTANCE NOTIFY THE STATE EMERGENCY RESPONSE COMMISSION FOR THE STATE IN WHICH IT IS LOCATED. SECTION 303 OF SARA REQUIRES THESE FACILITIES TO PARTICIPATE IN LOCAL EMERGENCY RESPONSE PLANNING (40 CFR 355.30).

****DISPOSAL****

DISPOSAL MUST BE IN ACCORDANCE WITH 40 CFR 165 RECOMMENDED PROCEDURES FOR THE DISPOSAL AND STORAGE OF PESTICIDES AND PESTICIDE CONTAINERS.
MERCURY - REGULATORY LEVEL: 0.2 MG/L MATERIALS WHICH CONTAIN THE ABOVE SUBSTANCE AT OR ABOVE THE REGULATORY LEVEL MEET THE EPA CHARACTERISTIC OF TOXICITY, AND MUST BE DISPOSED OF IN ACCORDANCE WITH 40 CFR PART 262. EPA HAZARDOUS WASTE NUMBER D009.

CONDITIONS TO AVOID

NONE REPORTED.

SPILL AND LEAK PROCEDURES

WATER SPILL: THE CALIFORNIA SAFE DRINKING WATER AND TOXIC ENFORCEMENT ACT OF 1986 (PROPOSITION 65) PROHIBITS CONTAMINATING ANY KNOWN

SOURCE OF DRINKING WATER WITH SUBSTANCES KNOWN TO CAUSE CANCER AND/OR REPRODUCTIVE TOXICITY.

OCCUPATIONAL SPILL: DO NOT TOUCH SPILLED MATERIAL. STOP LEAK IF YOU CAN DO IT WITHOUT RISK. FOR SMALL SPILLS, TAKE UP WITH SAND OR OTHER ABSORBENT MATERIAL AND PLACE INTO CONTAINERS FOR LATER DISPOSAL. FOR SMALL DRY SPILLS, WITH A CLEAN SHOVEL PLACE MATERIAL INTO CLEAN, DRY CONTAINER AND COVER. MOVE CONTAINERS FROM SPILL AREA. FOR LARGER SPILLS, DIKE FAR AHEAD OF SPILL FOR LATER DISPOSAL. KEEP UNNECESSARY PEOPLE AWAY. ISOLATE HAZARD AREA AND DENY ENTRY.

REPORTABLE QUANTITY (RQ): 1 POUND THE SUPERFUND AMENDMENTS AND REAUTHORIZATION ACT (SARA) SECTION 304 REQUIRES THAT A RELEASE EQUAL TO OR GREATER THAN THE REPORTABLE QUANTITY FOR THIS SUBSTANCE BE IMMEDIATELY REPORTED TO THE LOCAL EMERGENCY PLANNING COMMITTEE AND THE STATE EMERGENCY RESPONSE COMMISSION (40 CFR 355.40). IF THE RELEASE OF THIS SUBSTANCE IS REPORTABLE UNDER CERCLA SECTION 103, THE NATIONAL RESPONSE CENTER MUST BE NOTIFIED IMMEDIATELY AT (800) 424-8802 OR (202) 426-2675 IN THE METROPOLITAN WASHINGTON, D.C. AREA (40 CFR 302.6).

PROTECTIVE EQUIPMENT

VENTILATION: PROCESS ENCLOSURE VENTILATION RECOMMENDED TO MEET PUBLISHED EXPOSURE LIMITS. VENTILATION EQUIPMENT MUST BE EXPLOSION-PROOF.

RESPIRATOR: THE FOLLOWING RESPIRATORS AND MAXIMUM USE CONCENTRATIONS ARE RECOMMENDATIONS BY THE U.S. DEPARTMENT OF HEALTH AND HUMAN SERVICES, NIOSH POCKET GUIDE TO CHEMICAL HAZARDS; NIOSH CRITERIA DOCUMENTS OR BY THE U.S. DEPARTMENT OF LABOR, 29 CFR 1910 SUBPART Z. THE SPECIFIC RESPIRATOR SELECTED MUST BE BASED ON CONTAMINATION LEVELS FOUND IN THE WORK PLACE, MUST NOT EXCEED THE WORKING LIMITS OF THE RESPIRATOR AND BE JOINTLY APPROVED BY THE NATIONAL INSTITUTE FOR OCCUPATIONAL SAFETY AND HEALTH AND THE MINE SAFETY AND HEALTH ADMINISTRATION (NIOSH-MSHA).

MERCURY, ALL FORMS EXCEPT ALKYL (AS HG):

0.5 MG/M3- ANY AIR-PURIFYING RESPIRATOR WITH A HIGH-EFFICIENCY PARTICULATE FILTER. ANY SUPPLIED-AIR RESPIRATOR. ANY SELF-CONTAINED BREATHING APPARATUS.

1.25 MG/M3- ANY SUPPLIED-AIR RESPIRATOR OPERATED IN A CONTINUOUS FLOW MODE. ANY POWERED AIR-PURIFYING RESPIRATOR WITH A HIGH-EFFICIENCY PARTICULATE FILTER.

2.5 MG/M3- ANY SUPPLIED-AIR RESPIRATOR WITH A FULL FACEPIECE. ANY SELF-CONTAINED BREATHING APPARATUS WITH A FULL FACEPIECE. ANY AIR-PURIFYING FULL FACEPIECE RESPIRATOR WITH A HIGH-EFFICIENCY PARTICULATE FILTER. ANY POWERED AIR-PURIFYING RESPIRATOR WITH A TIGHT-FITTING FACEPIECE AND A HIGH-EFFICIENCY PARTICULATE FILTER. ANY SUPPLIED-AIR RESPIRATOR WITH A TIGHT-FITTING FACEPIECE OPERATED IN A CONTINUOUS FLOW MODE.

28 MG/M3- ANY SUPPLIED-AIR RESPIRATOR WITH A HALF-MASK AND OPERATED IN A PRESSURE-DEMAND OR OTHER POSITIVE PRESSURE MODE.

ESCAPE- ANY AIR-PURIFYING FULL FACEPIECE RESPIRATOR WITH A HIGH-EFFICIENCY PARTICULATE FILTER. ANY APPROPRIATE ESCAPE-TYPE SELF-CONTAINED BREATHING APPARATUS.

FOR FIREFIGHTING AND OTHER IMMEDIATELY DANGEROUS TO LIFE OR HEALTH CONDITIONS:

SELF-CONTAINED BREATHING APPARATUS WITH FULL FACEPIECE OPERATED IN PRESSURE-DEMAND OR OTHER POSITIVE PRESSURE MODE.

SUPPLIED-AIR RESPIRATOR WITH FULL FACEPIECE AND OPERATED IN PRESSURE-DEMAND OR OTHER POSITIVE PRESSURE MODE IN COMBINATION WITH AN AUXILIARY SELF-CONTAINED BREATHING APPARATUS OPERATED IN PRESSURE-DEMAND OR OTHER POSITIVE PRESSURE MODE.

CLOTHING: EMPLOYEE MUST WEAR APPROPRIATE PROTECTIVE (IMPERVIOUS) CLOTHING AND EQUIPMENT TO PREVENT REPEATED OR PROLONGED SKIN CONTACT WITH THIS SUBSTANCE.

GLOVES: EMPLOYEE MUST WEAR APPROPRIATE PROTECTIVE GLOVES TO PREVENT CONTACT WITH THIS SUBSTANCE.

EYE PROTECTION: EMPLOYEE MUST WEAR SPLASH-PROOF OR DUST-RESISTANT SAFETY GOGGLES TO PREVENT EYE CONTACT WITH THIS SUBSTANCE.

EMERGENCY EYE WASH: WHERE THERE IS ANY POSSIBILITY THAT AN EMPLOYEE'S EYES MAY BE EXPOSED TO THIS SUBSTANCE, THE EMPLOYER SHOULD PROVIDE AN EYE WASH FOUNTAIN WITHIN THE IMMEDIATE WORK AREA FOR EMERGENCY USE.

AUTHORIZED BY- OCCUPATIONAL HEALTH SERVICES, INC.

CREATION DATE: 10/04/89 ***REVISION DATE:*** 07/13/90

MATERIAL SAFETY DATA SHEET

OCCUPATIONAL HEALTH SERVICES, INC.
AGRICULTURE AND PESTICIDE DIVISION
450 SEVENTH AVENUE, SUITE 2407
NEW YORK, NEW YORK 10123
1-800-445-MSDS OR (212) 967-1100

EMERGENCY CONTACT:
JOHN S. BRANSFORD, JR. (615) 292-1180

SUBSTANCE IDENTIFICATION

CAS-NUMBER 297-78-9

SUBSTANCE: ISOBENZAN

TRADE NAMES/SYNONYMS: 4,7-METHANOISOBENZOFURAN, 1,3,4,5,6,7,8,8-OCTACHLORO-1,3,3A,4,7, 7A-HEXAHYDRO-; 4,7-METHANOISOBENZOFURAN, 1,3,4,5,6,7,8,8-OCTACHLORO-3A,4,7,7A -TETRAHYDRO-; 1,3,4,5,6,7,8,8-OCTACHLORO-1,3,3A,4,7,7A-HEXAHYDRO-4,7 -METHANOISOBENZOFURAN; 1,3,4,5,6,7,10,10-OCTACHLORO-4,7-ENDOMETHYLENE-4,7,8,9 -TETRAHYDROPHTHALAN; 1,3,4,5,6,7,8,8-OCTACHLORO-3A,4,7,7A-TETRAHYDRO-4,7 -METHANOISOBENZOFURAN; SD 4402; CP 14,957; TELODRIN; OMS 206N; ENT 25,545-X; C9H4CL8O; PST83032

CHEMICAL FAMILY: BENZOFURAN DERIVATIVE
HALOGEN

MOLECULAR FORMULA: C9-H4-CL8-O

MOLECULAR WEIGHT: 411.79

CERCLA RATINGS (SCALE 0-3): HEALTH=3 FIRE=U REACTIVITY=U PERSISTENCE=3

NFPA RATINGS (SCALE 0-4): HEALTH=4 FIRE=U REACTIVITY=U

COMPONENTS AND CONTAMINANTS

COMPONENT: ISOBENZAN ***PERCENT:*** 100.0
CAS# 297-78-9

OTHER CONTAMINANTS: NONE

EXPOSURE LIMITS: ISOBENZAN: 100/10,000 POUNDS SARA SECTION 302 THRESHOLD PLANNING QUANTITY 1 POUND SARA SECTION 304 REPORTABLE QUANTITY

PHYSICAL DATA

DESCRIPTION: CRYSTALS ***MELTING POINT:*** 248-252 F (120-122 C)

SPECIFIC GRAVITY: 1.87 ***VAPOR PRESSURE:*** .00001 MMHG @ 77 F

SOLUBILITY IN WATER: INSOLUBLE

SOLVENT SOLUBILITY: SOLUBLE IN ACETONE, BENZENE, TOLUENE, ETHER, XYLENE, HEAVY AROMATIC NAPHTHA; SLIGHTLY SOLUBLE IN KEROSENE AND ETHANOL.

FIRE AND EXPLOSION DATA

FIRE AND EXPLOSION HAZARD: UNKNOWN FIRE AND EXPLOSION HAZARD.

FIREFIGHTING MEDIA: DRY CHEMICAL, CARBON DIOXIDE, HALON, WATER SPRAY OR STANDARD FOAM (1987 EMERGENCY RESPONSE GUIDEBOOK, DOT P 5800.4). FOR LARGER FIRES, USE WATER SPRAY, FOG OR STANDARD FOAM (1987 EMERGENCY RESPONSE GUIDEBOOK, DOT P 5800.4).

FIREFIGHTING: MOVE CONTAINERS FROM FIRE AREA IF POSSIBLE (1987 EMERGENCY RESPONSE GUIDEBOOK, DOT P 5800.4, GUIDE PAGE 53).

EXTINGUISH USING AGENT SUITABLE FOR TYPE OF SURROUNDING FIRE. AVOID BREATHING VAPORS AND DUSTS. KEEP UPWIND.

TRANSPORTATION DATA

DEPARTMENT OF TRANSPORTATION HAZARD CLASSIFICATION 49 CFR 172.101: POISON B

DEPARTMENT OF TRANSPORTATION LABELING REQUIREMENTS 49 CFR 172.101 AND SUBPART E: POISON

DEPARTMENT OF TRANSPORTATION PACKAGING REQUIREMENTS: 49 CFR 173.365 EXCEPTIONS: 49 CFR 173.364

TOXICITY

ISOBENZAN: TOXICITY DATA: 12 MG/KG SKIN-RABBIT LD50; 5 MG/KG SKIN-RAT LD50; 2 MG/KG SKIN-GUINEA PIG LD50; 4800 UG/KG ORAL-RAT LD50; 8400 UG/KG ORAL-MOUSE LD50; 4 MG/KG ORAL-RABBIT LD50; 2000 UG/KG ORAL-GUINEA PIG LD50; 7500 UG/KG ORAL-HAMSTER LD50; 1 MG/KG ORAL-DOG LD50; 5 MG/KG ORAL-CAT LD50; 1800 UG/KG INTRAVENOUS-RAT LD50; 2900 UG/KG INTRAVENOUS-MOUSE LD50; 3560 UG/KG INTRAPERITONEAL-RAT LD50; 8170 UG/KG INTRAPERITONEAL-MOUSE LD50; TUMORIGENIC DATA (RTECS). CARCINOGEN STATUS: NONE. ACUTE TOXICITY: HIGHLY TOXIC BY DERMAL ABSORPTION AND INGESTION. TARGET EFFECTS: CONVULSANT. ADDITIONAL DATA: ISOBENZAN IS ELIMINATED SLOWLY FROM THE BODY HAVING A HALF-LIFE IN HUMAN BLOOD OF APPROXIMATELY 2.77 YEARS. INTENSE ACTIVITY AND STARVATION MAY MOBILIZED THE PESTICIDE RESULTING IN THE REAPPEARANCE OF TOXIC SYMPTOMS. THIS CHEMICAL MAY BE EXCRETED IN THE MILK OF LACTATING WOMEN.

HEALTH EFFECTS AND FIRST AID

INHALATION: ISOBENZAN: CONVULSANT. **ACUTE EXPOSURE-** ISOBENZAN IS A CHLORINATED CYCLODIENE PESTICIDE. THESE PESTICIDES ARE ABSORBED FROM THE LUNGS AND MAY PRODUCE CENTRAL NERVOUS SYSTEM EFFECTS WITH SYMPTOMS OF MOTOR HYPEREXCITABILITY THAT MAY INCLUDE MUSCLE TWITCHING, MYOCLONIC JERKING, AND CONVULSIVE SEIZURES. THE CONVULSIONS MAY OCCUR WITH PERIODS OF UNCONSCIOUSNESS. OTHER SYMPTOMS MAY INCLUDE HEADACHE, NAUSEA, VOMITING, MALAISE, AND DIZZINESS. IN CASES OF GROSS OVEREXPOSURE, CONVULSIONS MAY OCCUR WITHOUT ANY PRIOR SYMPTOMS. ABNORMAL EEG PATTERNS MAY BE OBSERVED; THESE CHANGES IN EEG PATTERNS MAY PERSIST FOR WEEKS OR MONTHS WHILE NO OTHER OBSERVABLE SIGNS OF POISONING MAY EXIST. **CHRONIC EXPOSURE-** IN ONE CASE OF OCCUPATIONAL EXPOSURE TO ISOBENZAN, COMPLAINTS OF HEADACHE, DIZZINESS, DROWSINESS, IRRITABILITY, AND PARESTHESIAS WERE REPORTED. SOME MEN EXPERIENCED ONE OR MORE CONVULSIONS. RECOVERY WAS COMPLETE WITH SOME COMPLAINTS LASTING FOR 6 MONTHS. PROLONGED OR REPEATED EXPOSURE TO CHLORINATED CYCLODIENE PESTICIDES MAY RESULT IN THE ACCUMULATION OF THE PESTICIDE IN THE BLOOD RESULTING IN A PROGRESSION OF THE SYMPTOMS LISTED ABOVE OR IN A SUDDEN ONSET OF SYMPTOMS AFTER AN ACUTE EXPOSURE. IN ADDITION TO SYMPTOMS LISTED ABOVE, HYPERIRRITABILITY, DROWSINESS, AND ANOREXIA MAY OCCUR.

FIRST AID- REMOVE FROM EXPOSURE AREA TO FRESH AIR IMMEDIATELY. IF BREATHING HAS STOPPED, GIVE ARTIFICIAL RESPIRATION. MAINTAIN AIRWAY AND BLOOD PRESSURE AND ADMINISTER OXYGEN IF AVAILABLE. KEEP AFFECTED PERSON WARM AND AT REST. TREAT SYMPTOMATICALLY AND SUPPORTIVELY. ADMINISTRATION OF OXYGEN SHOULD BE PERFORMED BY QUALIFIED PERSONNEL. GET MEDICAL ATTENTION IMMEDIATELY.

SKIN CONTACT: ISOBENZAN: CONVULSANT/HIGHLY TOXIC. **ACUTE EXPOSURE-** A LETHAL DOSE IN RABBITS FROM DERMAL ABSORPTION WAS 12 MG/KG. CHLORINATED CYCLODIENE PESTICIDES ARE ABSORBED FROM THE SKIN AND MAY PRODUCE CENTRAL NERVOUS SYSTEM EFFECTS WITH SYMPTOMS OF MOTOR HYPEREXCITABILITY THAT MAY INCLUDE MUSCLE TWITCHING, MYOCLONIC JERKING, AND CONVULSIVE SEIZURES. THE CONVULSIONS MAY OCCUR WITH PERIODS OF UNCONSCIOUSNESS. OTHER SYMPTOMS MAY INCLUDE HEADACHE, NAUSEA, VOMITING, MALAISE, AND DIZZINESS. IN CASES OF GROSS OVEREXPOSURE, CONVULSIONS MAY OCCUR WITHOUT ANY PRIOR SYMPTOMS. ABNORMAL EEG PATTERNS MAY BE OBSERVED; THESE CHANGES IN EEG PATTERNS MAY PERSIST FOR WEEKS OR MONTHS WHILE NO OTHER OBSERVABLE SIGNS OF POISONING MAY EXIST. **CHRONIC EXPOSURE-** IN ONE CASE OF OCCUPATIONAL EXPOSURE TO ISOBENZAN, COMPLAINTS OF HEADACHE, DIZZINESS, DROWSINESS, IRRITABILITY, AND PARESTHESIAS WERE REPORTED. SOME MEN EXPERIENCED ONE OR MORE CONVULSIONS. RECOVERY WAS COMPLETE WITH SOME COMPLAINTS LASTING FOR 6 MONTHS. PROLONGED OR REPEATED EXPOSURE TO CHLORINATED CYCLODIENE PESTICIDE MAY RESULT IN THE ACCUMULATION OF THE PESTICIDE IN THE BLOOD RESULTING IN A PROGRESSION OF THE SYMPTOMS LISTED ABOVE OR IN A SUDDEN ONSET OF SYMPTOMS AFTER AN ACUTE EXPOSURE. IN ADDITION TO THE SYMPTOMS LISTED ABOVE HYPERIRRITABILITY, DROWSINESS, AND ANOREXIA MAY OCCUR.

FIRST AID- REMOVE CONTAMINATED CLOTHING AND SHOES IMMEDIATELY. WASH AFFECTED AREA WITH SOAP OR MILD DETERGENT AND LARGE AMOUNTS OF WATER UNTIL NO EVIDENCE OF CHEMICAL REMAINS (APPROXIMATELY 15-20 MINUTES). GET MEDICAL ATTENTION IMMEDIATELY.

EYE CONTACT: ISOBENZAN: **ACUTE EXPOSURE-** NO DATA AVAILABLE. **CHRONIC EXPOSURE-** NO DATA AVAILABLE.

FIRST AID- WASH EYES IMMEDIATELY WITH LARGE AMOUNTS OF WATER OR NORMAL SALINE, OCCASIONALLY LIFTING UPPER AND LOWER LIDS, UNTIL NO EVIDENCE OF CHEMICAL REMAINS (APPROXIMATELY 15-20 MINUTES). GET MEDICAL ATTENTION IMMEDIATELY.

INGESTION: ISOBENZAN: CONVULSANT/HIGHLY TOXIC. **ACUTE EXPOSURE-** A LETHAL DOSE IN RATS WAS 4800 UG/KG. SYMPTOMS OF POISONING IN RATS WERE LETHARGY, TREMORS, FROTHING AT THE MOUTH, GENERAL TWITCHING OF THE MUSCLES, LABORED BREATHING, OPISTHOTONOS, AND CONVULSIONS. **CHRONIC EXPOSURE-** CHRONIC ADMINISTRATION OF ISOBENZAN TO RATS FOR TWO YEARS IN A DOSE OF 1.5 MG/KG/DAY PRODUCED IRRITABILITY, CONVULSIONS, AND A MORTALITY RATE OF 20%. REPEATED DOSES OF 2.5 MG/KG/DAY WAS LETHAL TO RATS WITHIN A WEEK.

FIRST AID- IF THE PERSON IS CONSCIOUS AND NOT CONVULSING, REMOVE BY GIVING SYRUP OF IPECAC (IF VOMITING OCCURS, KEEP THE HEAD BELOW THE HIPS TO PREVENT ASPIRATION). GIVE ACTIVATED CHARCOAL FOLLOWED BY GASTRIC LAVAGE. FOLLOW WITH A SALINE CATHARTIC. DO NOT GIVE FATS OR OILS. INTESTINAL LAVAGE WITH 20% MANNITOL (200 ML) BY STOMACH TUBE IS ALSO USEFUL. GIVE ARTIFICIAL RESPIRATION WITH OXYGEN IF RESPIRATION IS DEPRESSED (DREISBACH, HANDBOOK OF POISONING, 12TH ED.). TREAT SYMPTOMATICALLY AND SUPPORTIVELY. LAVAGE AND ADMINISTRATION OF OXYGEN SHOULD BE PERFORMED BY QUALIFIED MEDICAL PERSONNEL. GET MEDICAL ATTENTION IMMEDIATELY.

ANTIDOTE: NO SPECIFIC ANTIDOTE. TREAT SYMPTOMATICALLY AND SUPPORTIVELY.

REACTIVITY

REACTIVITY: NO DATA AVAILABLE.

INCOMPATIBILITIES: ISOBENZAN: ACIDS: INCOMPATIBLE. CERTAIN METAL SALTS: INCOMPATIBLE.

DECOMPOSITION: THERMAL DECOMPOSITION PRODUCTS MAY INCLUDE TOXIC AND CORROSIVE FUMES OF CHLORIDES.

POLYMERIZATION: HAZARDOUS POLYMERIZATION HAS NOT BEEN REPORTED TO OCCUR UNDER NORMAL TEMPERATURES AND PRESSURES.

STORAGE AND DISPOSAL

OBSERVE ALL FEDERAL, STATE AND LOCAL REGULATIONS WHEN STORING OR DISPOSING OF THIS SUBSTANCE. FOR ASSISTANCE, CONTACT THE DISTRICT DIRECTOR OF THE ENVIRONMENTAL PROTECTION AGENCY.

****STORAGE****

STORE IN ACCORDANCE WITH 40 CFR 165 RECOMMENDED PROCEDURES FOR THE DISPOSAL AND STORAGE OF PESTICIDES AND PESTICIDE CONTAINERS.

STORE AWAY FROM INCOMPATIBLE SUBSTANCES.

THRESHOLD PLANNING QUANTITY (TPQ): THE SUPERFUND AMENDMENTS AND REAUTHORIZATION ACT (SARA) SECTION 302 REQUIRES THAT EACH FACILITY WHERE ANY EXTREMELY HAZARDOUS SUBSTANCE IS PRESENT IN A QUANTITY EQUAL TO OR GREATER THAN THE TPQ ESTABLISHED FOR THAT SUBSTANCE NOTIFY THE STATE EMERGENCY RESPONSE COMMISSION FOR THE STATE IN WHICH IT IS LOCATED. SECTION 303 OF SARA REQUIRES THESE FACILITIES TO PARTICIPATE IN LOCAL EMERGENCY RESPONSE PLANNING (40 CFR 355.30).

****DISPOSAL****

DISPOSAL MUST BE IN ACCORDANCE WITH 40 CFR 165 RECOMMENDED PROCEDURES FOR THE DISPOSAL AND STORAGE OF PESTICIDES AND PESTICIDE CONTAINERS.

CONDITIONS TO AVOID

NONE REPORTED.

SPILL AND LEAK PROCEDURES

OCCUPATIONAL SPILL: DO NOT TOUCH SPILLED MATERIAL. STOP LEAK IF YOU CAN DO IT WITHOUT RISK. FOR SMALL SPILLS, TAKE UP WITH SAND OR OTHER ABSORBENT MATERIAL AND PLACE INTO CONTAINERS FOR LATER DISPOSAL. FOR SMALL DRY SPILLS, WITH A CLEAN SHOVEL PLACE MATERIAL INTO CLEAN, DRY CONTAINER AND COVER. MOVE CONTAINERS FROM SPILL AREA. FOR LARGER SPILLS, DIKE FAR AHEAD OF SPILL FOR LATER DISPOSAL. KEEP UNNECESSARY PEOPLE AWAY. ISOLATE HAZARD AREA AND DENY ENTRY.

REPORTABLE QUANTITY (RQ): 1 POUND THE SUPERFUND AMENDMENTS AND REAUTHORIZATION ACT (SARA) SECTION 304 REQUIRES THAT A RELEASE EQUAL TO OR GREATER THAN THE REPORTABLE QUANTITY FOR THIS SUBSTANCE BE IMMEDIATELY REPORTED TO THE LOCAL EMERGENCY PLANNING COMMITTEE AND THE STATE EMERGENCY RESPONSE COMMISSION (40 CFR 355.40). IF THE RELEASE OF THIS SUBSTANCE IS REPORTABLE UNDER CERCLA SECTION 103, THE NATIONAL RESPONSE CENTER MUST BE NOTIFIED IMMEDIATELY AT (800) 424-8802 OR (202) 426-2675 IN THE METROPOLITAN WASHINGTON, D.C. AREA (40 CFR 302.6).

PROTECTIVE EQUIPMENT

VENTILATION: PROCESS ENCLOSURE RECOMMENDED.

RESPIRATOR: THE FOLLOWING RESPIRATORS ARE RECOMMENDED BASED ON INFORMATION FOUND IN THE PHYSICAL DATA, TOXICITY AND HEALTH EFFECTS SECTIONS. THEY ARE RANKED IN ORDER FROM MINIMUM TO MAXIMUM RESPIRATORY PROTECTION. THE SPECIFIC RESPIRATOR SELECTED MUST BE BASED ON CONTAMINATION LEVELS FOUND IN THE WORK PLACE, MUST NOT EXCEED THE WORKING LIMITS OF THE RESPIRATOR AND BE JOINTLY APPROVED BY THE NATIONAL INSTITUTE FOR OCCUPATIONAL SAFETY AND HEALTH AND THE MINE SAFETY AND HEALTH ADMINISTRATION (NIOSH-MSHA).

TYPE 'C' SUPPLIED-AIR RESPIRATOR WITH A FULL FACEPIECE OPERATED IN PRESSURE-DEMAND OR OTHER POSITIVE PRESSURE MODE OR WITH A FULL FACEPIECE, HELMET OR HOOD OPERATED IN CONTINOUS-FLOW MODE.

SELF-CONTAINED BREATHING APPARATUS WITH A FULL FACEPIECE OPERATED IN PRESSURE-DEMAND OR OTHER POSITIVE PRESSURE MODE.

FOR FIREFIGHTING AND OTHER IMMEDIATELY DANGEROUS TO LIFE OR HEALTH CONDITIONS:

SELF-CONTAINED BREATHING APPARATUS WITH FULL FACEPIECE OPERATED IN PRESSURE-DEMAND OR OTHER POSITIVE PRESSURE MODE.

SUPPLIED-AIR RESPIRATOR WITH FULL FACEPIECE AND OPERATED IN PRESSURE-DEMAND OR OTHER POSITIVE PRESSURE MODE IN COMBINATION WITH AN

AUXILIARY SELF-CONTAINED BREATHING APPARATUS OPERATED IN PRESSURE-DEMAND OR OTHER POSITIVE PRESSURE MODE.

CLOTHING: EMPLOYEE MUST WEAR APPROPRIATE PROTECTIVE (IMPERVIOUS) CLOTHING AND EQUIPMENT TO PREVENT ANY POSSIBILITY OF SKIN CONTACT WITH THIS SUBSTANCE.

GLOVES: EMPLOYEE MUST WEAR APPROPRIATE PROTECTIVE GLOVES TO PREVENT CONTACT WITH THIS SUBSTANCE.

EYE PROTECTION: EMPLOYEE MUST WEAR SPLASH-PROOF OR DUST-RESISTANT SAFETY GOGGLES AND A FACESHIELD TO PREVENT CONTACT WITH THIS SUBSTANCE.

EMERGENCY WASH FACILITIES: WHERE THERE IS ANY POSSIBILITY THAT AN EMPLOYEE'S EYES AND/OR SKIN MAY BE EXPOSED TO THIS SUBSTANCE, THE EMPLOYER SHOULD PROVIDE AN EYE WASH FOUNTAIN AND QUICK DRENCH SHOWER WITHIN THE IMMEDIATE WORK AREA FOR EMERGENCY USE.

AUTHORIZED BY- OCCUPATIONAL HEALTH SERVICES, INC.
CREATION DATE: 10/04/89 ***REVISION DATE:*** 05/10/90

MATERIAL SAFETY DATA SHEET

OCCUPATIONAL HEALTH SERVICES, INC.
AGRICULTURE AND PESTICIDE DIVISION
450 SEVENTH AVENUE, SUITE 2407
NEW YORK, NEW YORK 10123
1-800-445-MSDS OR (212) 967-1100

EMERGENCY CONTACT:
JOHN S. BRANSFORD, JR. (615) 292-1180

SUBSTANCE IDENTIFICATION

CAS-NUMBER 502-39-6

SUBSTANCE: METHYLMERCURIC DICYANAMIDE

TRADE NAMES/SYNONYMS: MERCURY, (CYANOGUANIDINATO-N')METHYL-; MERCURY, (CYANOGUANIDINATO)METHYL-; (CYANOGUANIDINATO-N')METHYLMERCURY; (CYANOGUANIDINATO)METHYLMERCURY; METHYL MERCURIC DICYANAMIDE; MMD; PANOGEN (FORMULATION); MERCURY, (CYANOGUANIDINE)METHYL-; (CYANOGUANIDINO)METHYLMERCURY; CYANO(METHYLMERCURI)GUANIDINE; C3H6HGN4; PST83040

CHEMICAL FAMILY: ORGANOMETALLIC GUANIDINE DERIVATIVE

MOLECULAR FORMULA: C3-H6-HG-N4

MOLECULAR WEIGHT: 298.72

CERCLA RATINGS (SCALE 0-3): HEALTH=3 FIRE=1 REACTIVITY=0 PERSISTENCE=3

NFPA RATINGS (SCALE 0-4): HEALTH=U FIRE=1 REACTIVITY=0

COMPONENTS AND CONTAMINANTS

COMPONENT: METHYLMERCURIC DICYANAMIDE ***PERCENT:*** 100.0
CAS# 502-39-6

OTHER CONTAMINANTS: NONE

EXPOSURE LIMITS: ORGANO(ALKYL)MERCURY COMPOUNDS, AS HG: 0.01 MG/M3 OSHA TWA (SKIN); 0.03 MG/M3 OSHA STEL 0.01 MG/M3 ACGIH TWA (SKIN); 0.03 MG/M3 ACGIH STEL

SUBJECT TO SARA SECTION 313 ANNUAL TOXIC CHEMICAL RELEASE REPORTING

SUBJECT TO CALIFORNIA PROPOSITION 65 CANCER AND/OR REPRODUCTIVE TOXICITY WARNING AND RELEASE REQUIREMENTS- (JULY 1, 1990)

METHYLMERCURIC DICYANAMIDE: 500/10,000 POUNDS SARA SECTION 302 THRESHOLD PLANNING QUANTITY 1 POUND SARA SECTION 304 REPORTABLE QUANTITY

PHYSICAL DATA

DESCRIPTION: CRYSTALLINE SOLID. ***MELTING POINT:*** 313 F (156 C)
SPECIFIC GRAVITY: NOT AVAILABLE ***VAPOR PRESSURE:*** 0.000065 MMHG @ 35 C
SOLUBILITY IN WATER: 2.17%

FIRE AND EXPLOSION DATA

FIRE AND EXPLOSION HAZARD: SLIGHT FIRE HAZARD WHEN EXPOSED TO HEAT OR FLAME.

FIREFIGHTING MEDIA: DRY CHEMICAL, CARBON DIOXIDE, HALON, WATER SPRAY OR STANDARD FOAM (1987 EMERGENCY RESPONSE GUIDEBOOK, DOT P 5800.4). FOR LARGER FIRES, USE WATER SPRAY, FOG OR STANDARD FOAM (1987 EMERGENCY RESPONSE GUIDEBOOK, DOT P 5800.4).

FIREFIGHTING: MOVE CONTAINERS FROM FIRE AREA IF POSSIBLE (1987 EMERGENCY RESPONSE GUIDEBOOK, DOT P 5800.4, GUIDE PAGE 53). EXTINGUISH USING AGENTS SUITABLE FOR SURROUNDING FIRE. APPLY WATER IN FLOODING QUANTITIES AS A FOG. AVOID CONTAMINATING WATER SOURCES AND SEWERS. AVOID BREATHING HAZARDOUS VAPORS; KEEP UPWIND.

TOXICITY

METHYLMERCURIC DICYANAMIDE: TOXICITY DATA: 68 MG/KG ORAL-RAT LD50; 20 MG/KG ORAL-MOUSE LD50; 13 MG/KG INTRAPERITONEAL-RAT LD50; 20 MG/KG INTRAPERITONEAL-MOUSE LD50; 45 MG/KG UNREPORTED-RAT LD50; MUTAGENIC DATA (RTECS); REPRODUCTIVE EFFECTS DATA (RTECS). CARCINOGEN STATUS: NONE. ACUTE TOXICITY LEVEL: TOXIC BY INGESTION. TARGET EFFECTS: NEUROTOXIN; TERATOGEN. POISONING MAY ALSO AFFECT THE LIVER, BRAIN, KIDNEYS AND CARDIOVASCULAR SYSTEM.* ADDITIONAL DATA: ALCOHOL MAY ENHANCE THE TOXIC EFFECTS. MAY CROSS THE PLACENTA AND BE EXCRETED IN BREAST MILK. CROSS SENSITIZATION REACTIONS MAY OCCUR WITH METALLIC OR INORGANIC MERCURY COMPOUNDS.*

* MAY BE BASED ON GENERAL INFORMATION ON ALKYL MERCURY COMPOUNDS.

HEALTH EFFECTS AND FIRST AID

INHALATION: METHYLMERCURIC DICYANAMIDE: SEE INFORMATION ON ALKYL MERCURY COMPOUNDS.

ALKYL MERCURY COMPOUNDS: NEUROTOXIN. 10 MG(HG)/M3 IMMEDIATELY DANGEROUS TO LIFE OR HEALTH. **ACUTE EXPOSURE-** DUST OR VAPORS MAY BE IRRITATING TO THE RESPIRATORY TRACT. SYSTEMIC POISONING AND DEATH, AS DESCRIBED IN CHRONIC INHALATION, MAY OCCUR. **CHRONIC EXPOSURE-** REPEATED OR PROLONGED EXPOSURE MAY CAUSE RESPIRATORY TRACT IRRITATION. SYSTEMIC SYMPTOMS, OFTEN INSIDIOUS, MAY BEGIN AFTER A LATENCY PERIOD, DEPENDING ON THE SEVERITY OF EXPOSURE, RANGING FROM WEEKS TO YEARS AFTER THE INITIAL EXPOSURE. THE ONSET MAY BEGIN WITH FATIGUE, HEADACHE, PARESTHESIAS OF THE TONGUE, AROUND THE LIPS, AND OF THE HANDS AND FEET, ATAXIA OF THE ARMS AND LEGS, FINE TREMORS IN THE HANDS, ARMS, AND FEET WHICH MAY BECOME CONVULSIVE, ATHETOSIS, ARTHRALGIA, AND AN UNSTEADY GAIT WHICH IS SPASTIC IN NATURE. VISUAL EFFECTS MAY INCLUDE TUNNEL VISION, SCOTOMATA, AND BLINDNESS WITH OPTIC NERVE ATROPHY. SLURRED SPEECH WITH DIFFICULT PRONUNCIATION AND IMPAIRED HEARING ARE ALSO COMMON. GASTROINTESTINAL DISTURBANCES MAY OCCUR WITH NAUSEA, VOMITING, DIARRHEA OR CONSTIPATION, COLIC, EPIGASTRIC PAIN, CATARRHAL GINGIVITIS, BLUE LINE ON THE GUM, AND APHTHOUS STOMATITIS. EMOTIONAL INSTABILITY, MEMORY LOSS, LOSS OF LIBIDO, DEPRESSION, HALLUCINATIONS, IRRITABILITY, ANXIETY, CONFUSION, INSOMNIA, EXCITATION, AND BOUTS OF GROANING, MOANING, SHOUTING, OR CRYING MAY OCCUR. MENTAL DETERIORATION MAY PROGRESS TO STUPOR AND COMA. OTHER EFFECTS MAY INCLUDE DIZZINESS, LACRIMATION, HYPERSALIVATION, ECZEMA, PRURITIS, EXFOLIATIVE DERMATITIS, RENAL DAMAGE, INCONTINENCE, POLYURIA, OLIGURIA, POLYDYPSIA, DEHYDRATION, WEIGHT LOSS, LIVER DAMAGE, BRADYCARDIA AND OTHER SIGNS OF CARDIAC INVOLVEMENT. WITH SEVERE INTOXICATION, CLONIC SEIZURES, PARALYSIS, COMA AND DEATH MAY OCCUR. THE DURATION OF ILLNESS IN FATAL CASES HAS RANGED FROM 1 MONTH TO 15 YEARS, WITH INFECTION, ASPIRATION PNEUMONIA OR INANITION AS THE CAUSE OF DEATH IN PROTRACTED CASES. IN MILD POISONING, SYMPTOMS MAY ALSO PERSIST FOR YEARS. REPRODUCTIVE EFFECTS MAY OCCUR AS DESCRIBED IN CHRONIC INGESTION.

FIRST AID- REMOVE FROM EXPOSURE AREA TO FRESH AIR IMMEDIATELY. IF BREATHING HAS STOPPED, PERFORM ARTIFICIAL RESPIRATION. KEEP PERSON WARM AND AT REST. TREAT SYMPTOMATICALLY AND SUPPORTIVELY. GET MEDICAL ATTENTION IMMEDIATELY.

SKIN CONTACT: METHYLMERCURIC DICYANAMIDE: SEE INFORMATION ON ALKYL MERCURY COMPOUNDS.

ALKYL MERCURY COMPOUNDS: NEUROTOXIN. **ACUTE EXPOSURE-** SYMPTOMS OF SKIN CONTACT MAY BE DELAYED FOR SEVERAL HOURS AND THEN BEGIN WITH A SENSATION OF WARMTH AND REDNESS WHICH MAY PROGRESS TO BURNS AND BLISTERING. HEALING MAY TAKE SEVERAL WEEKS. SYSTEMIC POISONING AND DEATH, AS DESCRIBED IN CHRONIC INHALATION, MAY OCCUR DUE TO SKIN ABSORPTION. **CHRONIC EXPOSURE-** REPEATED OR PROLONGED CONTACT MAY RESULT IN DERMATITIS OR EFFECTS AS DESCRIBED IN ACUTE EXPOSURE. SKIN SENSITIZATION HAS BEEN REPORTED FROM CONTACT WITH SOME ALKYL MERCURY COMPOUNDS.

FIRST AID- REMOVE CONTAMINATED CLOTHING AND SHOES IMMEDIATELY. WASH AFFECTED AREA WITH SOAP OR MILD DETERGENT AND LARGE AMOUNTS OF WATER UNTIL NO EVIDENCE OF CHEMICAL REMAINS (APPROXIMATELY 15-20 MINUTES). GET MEDICAL ATTENTION IMMEDIATELY.

EYE CONTACT: METHYLMERCURIC DICYANAMIDE: SEE INFORMATION ON ALKYL MERCURY COMPOUNDS:

ALKYL MERCURY COMPOUNDS: **ACUTE EXPOSURE-** DUSTS OR VAPORS MAY CAUSE IRRITATION. **CHRONIC EXPOSURE-** NO DATA AVAILABLE.

FIRST AID- WASH EYES IMMEDIATELY WITH LARGE AMOUNTS OF WATER OR NORMAL SALINE, OCCASIONALLY LIFTING UPPER AND LOWER LIDS, UNTIL NO EVIDENCE OF CHEMICAL REMAINS (APPROXIMATELY 15-20 MINUTES). GET MEDICAL ATTENTION IMMEDIATELY.

INGESTION: METHYLMERCURIC DICYANAMIDE: TOXIC. SEE INFORMATION ON ALKYL MERCURY COMPOUNDS. REPRODUCTIVE EFFECTS WERE REPORTED IN ANIMALS. ALKYL MERCURY COMPOUNDS: NEUROTOXIN/TERATOGEN. **ACUTE EXPOSURE**- IF A TOXIC DOSE HAS BEEN ABSORBED AND RETAINED FOR A PERIOD OF TIME, SYSTEMIC POISONING AND DEATH AS DESCRIBED IN CHRONIC INHALATION MAY OCCUR. **CHRONIC EXPOSURE**- REPEATED OR PROLONGED EXPOSURE MAY RESULT IN POISONING AS DESCRIBED IN CHRONIC INHALATION. WOMEN EXPOSED TO SOME ALKYL MERCURY COMPOUNDS WHILE PREGNANT OR PERHAPS SEVERAL YEARS BEFORE PREGNANCY HAVE HAD CHILDREN WITH IMPAIRMENT OF MOTOR AND MENTAL DEVELOPMENT OF VARIOUS DEGREES WITH FRETFULLNESS, IRRITABILITY, EXCESSIVE CRYING, DECREASED BIRTH WEIGHT AND MUSCLE TONE, CEREBRAL PALSY, DEAFNESS, BLINDNESS, MICROCEPHALY, AND MENTAL RETARDATION. POSTNATAL EXPOSURE THROUGH BREAST MILK MAY ALSO OCCUR.

FIRST AID- IF THE PERSON IS CONSCIOUS AND NOT CONVULSING, INDUCE EMESIS BY GIVING SYRUP OF IPECAC (KEEPING THE HEAD BELOW THE HIPS TO PREVENT ASPIRATION), FOLLOWED BY WATER. REPEAT IN 20 MINUTES IF NOT EFFECTIVE INITIALLY. IN PATIENTS WITH DEPRESSED RESPIRATION OR IF EMESIS IS NOT PRODUCED, PERFORM GASTRIC LAVAGE CAUTIOUSLY. FOLLOW WITH A SALINE CATHARTIC (DREISBACH, HANDBOOK OF POISONING, 12TH ED.). TREAT SYMPTOMATICALLY AND SUPPORTIVELY. GASTRIC LAVAGE SHOULD BE PERFORMED BY QUALIFIED MEDICAL PERSONNEL. GET MEDICAL ATTENTION IMMEDIATELY.

ANTIDOTE: THE FOLLOWING ANTIDOTE HAS BEEN RECOMMENDED. HOWEVER, THE DECISION AS TO WHETHER THE SEVERITY OF POISONING REQUIRES ADMINISTRATION OF ANY ANTIDOTE AND ACTUAL DOSE REQUIRED SHOULD BE MADE BY QUALIFIED MEDICAL PERSONNEL.

POISONING FROM ORGANIC MERCURY COMPOUNDS: GIVE N-ACETYL-D,L-PENICILLAMINE (OR IF NOT AVAILABLE D-PENICILLAMINE) BY MOUTH, 250 MG, 4 TIMES DAILY FOR 5-10 DAYS. DIMERCAPROL IS LESS EFFECTIVE AND MAY BE CONTRAINDICATED (GOSSELIN, CLINICAL TOXICOLOGY OF COMMERCIAL PRODUCTS, 5TH EDITION). ANTIDOTE SHOULD BE ADMINISTERED BY QUALIFIED MEDICAL PERSONNEL.

REACTIVITY

REACTIVITY: STABLE UNDER NORMAL TEMPERATURES AND PRESSURES.

INCOMPATIBILITIES: METHYLMERCURIC DICYANAMIDE: OXIDIZERS (STRONG): MAY CAUSE FIRE AND EXPLOSION HAZARD.

DECOMPOSITION: THERMAL DECOMPOSITION MAY RELEASE TOXIC FUMES OF MERCURY AND TOXIC OXIDES OF NITROGEN.

POLYMERIZATION: HAZARDOUS POLYMERIZATION HAS NOT BEEN REPORTED TO OCCUR UNDER NORMAL TEMPERATURES AND PRESSURES.

STORAGE AND DISPOSAL

OBSERVE ALL FEDERAL, STATE AND LOCAL REGULATIONS WHEN STORING OR DISPOSING OF THIS SUBSTANCE. FOR ASSISTANCE, CONTACT THE DISTRICT DIRECTOR OF THE ENVIRONMENTAL PROTECTION AGENCY.

STORAGE

STORE IN ACCORDANCE WITH 40 CFR 165 RECOMMENDED PROCEDURES FOR THE DISPOSAL AND STORAGE OF PESTICIDES AND PESTICIDE CONTAINERS.

STORE AWAY FROM INCOMPATIBLE SUBSTANCES.

THRESHOLD PLANNING QUANTITY (TPQ): THE SUPERFUND AMENDMENTS AND REAUTHORIZATION ACT (SARA) SECTION 302 REQUIRES THAT EACH FACILITY WHERE ANY EXTREMELY HAZARDOUS SUBSTANCE IS PRESENT IN A QUANTITY EQUAL TO OR GREATER THAN THE TPQ ESTABLISHED FOR THAT SUBSTANCE NOTIFY THE STATE EMERGENCY RESPONSE COMMISSION FOR THE STATE IN WHICH IT IS LOCATED. SECTION 303 OF SARA REQUIRES THESE FACILITIES TO PARTICIPATE IN LOCAL EMERGENCY RESPONSE PLANNING (40 CFR 355.30).

DISPOSAL

DISPOSAL MUST BE IN ACCORDANCE WITH 40 CFR 165 RECOMMENDED PROCEDURES FOR THE DISPOSAL AND STORAGE OF PESTICIDES AND PESTICIDE CONTAINERS.

MERCURY - REGULATORY LEVEL: 0.2 MG/L MATERIALS WHICH CONTAIN THE ABOVE SUBSTANCE AT OR ABOVE THE REGULATORY LEVEL MEET THE EPA CHARACTERISTIC OF TOXICITY, AND MUST BE DISPOSED OF IN ACCORDANCE WITH 40 CFR PART 262. EPA HAZARDOUS WASTE NUMBER D009.

CONDITIONS TO AVOID

MAY BURN BUT DOES NOT IGNITE READILY.

SPILL AND LEAK PROCEDURES

WATER SPILL: THE CALIFORNIA SAFE DRINKING WATER AND TOXIC ENFORCEMENT ACT OF 1986 (PROPOSITION 65) PROHIBITS CONTAMINATING ANY KNOWN SOURCE OF DRINKING WATER WITH SUBSTANCES KNOWN TO CAUSE CANCER AND/OR REPRODUCTIVE TOXICITY.

OCCUPATIONAL SPILL: DO NOT TOUCH SPILLED MATERIAL. STOP LEAK IF YOU CAN DO IT WITHOUT RISK. FOR SMALL SPILLS, TAKE UP WITH SAND OR OTHER ABSORBENT MATERIAL AND PLACE INTO CONTAINERS FOR LATER DISPOSAL. FOR SMALL DRY SPILLS, WITH A CLEAN SHOVEL PLACE MATERIAL INTO CLEAN, DRY CONTAINER AND COVER. MOVE CONTAINERS FROM SPILL AREA. FOR LARGER SPILLS, DIKE FAR AHEAD OF SPILL FOR LATER DISPOSAL. KEEP UNNECESSARY PEOPLE AWAY. ISOLATE HAZARD AREA AND DENY ENTRY.

REPORTABLE QUANTITY (RQ): 1 POUND THE SUPERFUND AMENDMENTS AND REAUTHORIZATION ACT (SARA) SECTION 304 REQUIRES THAT A RELEASE EQUAL TO OR GREATER THAN THE REPORTABLE QUANTITY FOR THIS SUBSTANCE BE IMMEDIATELY REPORTED TO THE LOCAL EMERGENCY PLANNING COMMITTEE AND THE STATE EMERGENCY RESPONSE COMMISSION (40 CFR 355.40). IF THE RELEASE OF THIS SUBSTANCE IS REPORTABLE UNDER CERCLA SECTION 103, THE NATIONAL RESPONSE CENTER MUST BE NOTIFIED IMMEDIATELY AT (800) 424-8802 OR (202) 426-2675 IN THE METROPOLITAN WASHINGTON, D.C. AREA (40 CFR 302.6).

PROTECTIVE EQUIPMENT

VENTILATION: PROVIDE LOCAL EXHAUST OR PROCESS ENCLOSURE VENTILATION TO MEET PUBLISHED EXPOSURE LIMITS.

RESPIRATOR: THE FOLLOWING RESPIRATORS AND MAXIMUM USE CONCENTRATIONS ARE RECOMMENDATIONS BY THE U.S. DEPARTMENT OF HEALTH AND HUMAN SERVICES, NIOSH POCKET GUIDE TO CHEMICAL HAZARDS; NIOSH CRITERIA DOCUMENTS OR BY THE U.S. DEPARTMENT OF LABOR, 29 CFR 1910 SUBPART Z.

THE SPECIFIC RESPIRATOR SELECTED MUST BE BASED ON CONTAMINATION LEVELS FOUND IN THE WORK PLACE, MUST NOT EXCEED THE WORKING LIMITS OF THE RESPIRATOR AND BE JOINTLY APPROVED BY THE NATIONAL INSTITUTE FOR OCCUPATIONAL SAFETY AND HEALTH AND THE MINE SAFETY AND HEALTH ADMINISTRATION (NIOSH-MSHA).

MERCURY, (ORGANO) ALKYL COMPOUNDS (AS HG):

0.1 MG/M3- ANY SUPPLIED-AIR RESPIRATOR. ANY SELF-CONTAINED BREATHING APPARATUS.

0.25 MG/M3- ANY SUPPLIED-AIR RESPIRATOR OPERATED IN A CONTINUOUS FLOW MODE.

0.5 MG/M3- ANY SUPPLIED-AIR RESPIRATOR WITH A FULL FACEPIECE. ANY SELF-CONTAINED BREATHING APPARATUS WITH A FULL FACEPIECE. ANY SUPPLIED-AIR RESPIRATOR WITH A TIGHT-FITTING FACEPIECE OPERATED IN A CONTINUOUS FLOW MODE.

10 MG/M3- ANY SUPPLIED-AIR RESPIRATOR WITH A HALF-MASK AND OPERATED IN A PRESSURE-DEMAND OR OTHER POSITIVE PRESSURE MODE.

ESCAPE- ANY APPROPRIATE ESCAPE-TYPE SELF-CONTAINED BREATHING APPARATUS.

FOR FIREFIGHTING AND OTHER IMMEDIATELY DANGEROUS TO LIFE OR HEALTH CONDITIONS:

SELF-CONTAINED BREATHING APPARATUS WITH FULL FACEPIECE OPERATED IN PRESSURE-DEMAND OR OTHER POSITIVE PRESSURE MODE.

SUPPLIED-AIR RESPIRATOR WITH FULL FACEPIECE AND OPERATED IN PRESSURE-DEMAND OR OTHER POSITIVE PRESSURE MODE IN COMBINATION WITH AN AUXILIARY SELF-CONTAINED BREATHING APPARATUS OPERATED IN PRESSURE-DEMAND OR OTHER POSITIVE PRESSURE MODE.

CLOTHING: EMPLOYEE MUST WEAR APPROPRIATE PROTECTIVE (IMPERVIOUS) CLOTHING AND EQUIPMENT TO PREVENT ANY POSSIBILITY OF SKIN CONTACT WITH THIS SUBSTANCE.

GLOVES: EMPLOYEE MUST WEAR APPROPRIATE PROTECTIVE GLOVES TO PREVENT CONTACT WITH THIS SUBSTANCE.

EYE PROTECTION: EMPLOYEE MUST WEAR SPLASH-PROOF OR DUST-RESISTANT SAFETY GOGGLES AND A FACESHIELD TO PREVENT CONTACT WITH THIS SUBSTANCE.

EMERGENCY WASH FACILITIES: WHERE THERE IS ANY POSSIBILITY THAT AN EMPLOYEE'S EYES AND/OR SKIN MAY BE EXPOSED TO THIS SUBSTANCE, THE EMPLOYER SHOULD PROVIDE AN EYE WASH FOUNTAIN AND QUICK DRENCH SHOWER WITHIN THE IMMEDIATE WORK AREA FOR EMERGENCY USE.

AUTHORIZED BY- OCCUPATIONAL HEALTH SERVICES, INC.

CREATION DATE: 10/04/89 ***REVISION DATE:*** 07/13/90

MATERIAL SAFETY DATA SHEET

OCCUPATIONAL HEALTH SERVICES, INC.
AGRICULTURE AND PESTICIDE DIVISION
450 SEVENTH AVENUE, SUITE 2407
NEW YORK, NEW YORK 10123
1-800-445-MSDS OR (212) 967-1100

EMERGENCY CONTACT:
JOHN S. BRANSFORD, JR. (615) 292-1180

SUBSTANCE IDENTIFICATION

CAS-NUMBER 640-15-3

SUBSTANCE: THIOMETON

TRADE NAMES/SYNONYMS: S-2-ETHYLTHIOETHYL O,O-DIMETHYL PHOSPHORODITHIOATE; O,O-DIMETHYL-S-(2-ETHYLMERCAPTOETHYL) DITHIOPHOSPHATE; O,O-DIMETHYL S-(2-(ETHYLTHIO)ETHYL)PHOSPHORDITHIOATE; S-(2-(ETHYLTHIOETHYL) O,O-DIMETHYLPHOSPHORODITHIONATE; S-(2-(ETHYLTHIOETHYL)DIMETHYL PHOSPHOROTHIOLOTHIONATE; PHOSPHORODITHIOIC ACID, O,O-DIMETHYL S-(2-ETHYLTHIO)ETHYL ESTER; EKATIN; EKATIN AEROSOL; INTRATHION; INTRATION; M 81; VELTIN; PST83056

CHEMICAL FAMILY: THIOPHOSPHATE ESTER

MOLECULAR FORMULA: C6-H15-O2-P-S3

MOLECULAR WEIGHT: 246.36

CERCLA RATINGS (SCALE 0-3): HEALTH=3 FIRE=U REACTIVITY=U PERSISTENCE=1

NFPA RATINGS (SCALE 0-4): HEALTH=3 FIRE=U REACTIVITY=U

COMPONENTS AND CONTAMINANTS

COMPONENT: THIOMETON ***PERCENT:*** 100.0
CAS# 640-15-3

OTHER CONTAMINANTS: NONE

EXPOSURE LIMITS: NO OCCUPATIONAL EXPOSURE LIMITS ESTABLISHED BY OSHA, ACGIH, OR NIOSH.

PHYSICAL DATA

DESCRIPTION: A COLORLESS OIL WITH A CHARACTERISTIC ODOR

BOILING POINT: 230 F (110 C) @ 0.1 MMHG ***SPECIFIC GRAVITY:*** 1.209 @ 20 C

VAPOR PRESSURE: 0.0003 MMHG @ 20 C ***SOLUBILITY IN WATER:*** 0.02% @ 25 C

SOLVENT SOLUBILITY: SOLUBLE IN MOST ORGANIC SOLVENTS; SLIGHTLY SOLUBLE IN LIGHT PETROLEUM

FIRE AND EXPLOSION DATA

FIRE AND EXPLOSION HAZARD: UNKNOWN FIRE AND EXPLOSION HAZARD.

FIREFIGHTING MEDIA: DRY CHEMICAL, CARBON DIOXIDE, WATER SPRAY OR FOAM FOR LARGER FIRES, USE WATER SPRAY, FOG OR ALCOHOL FOAM

FIREFIGHTING: MOVE CONTAINER FROM FIRE AREA IF POSSIBLE. DO NOT SCATTER SPILLED MATERIAL WITH MORE WATER THAN NEEDED FOR FIRE CONTROL. DIKE FIRE CONTROL WATER FOR LATER DISPOSAL
USE AGENTS SUITABLE FOR TYPE OF SURROUNDING FIRE. AVOID BREATHING HAZARDOUS VAPORS, KEEP UPWIND.

TOXICITY

THIOMETON: IRRITATION DATA: 500 MG/24 HOURS SKIN-RABBIT MILD; 750 UG/24 HOURS EYE-RABBIT SEVERE. TOXICITY DATA: 20 MG/M3/4 HOURS INHALATION-CAT LCLO; 20 MG/M3/4 HOURS INHALATION-RAT LCLO; 179 MG/KG SKIN-RAT LD50; 100 MG/KG SKIN-RABBIT LDLO; 40 MG/KG ORAL-RAT LD50; 37 MG/KG ORAL-MOUSE LD50; 38,500 UG/KG INTRAVENOUS-RAT LD50; 70 MG/KG UNREPORTED-MAMMAL LD50; MUTAGENIC DATA (RTECS). CARCINOGEN STATUS: NONE. ACUTE TOXICITY LEVEL: HIGHLY TOXIC BY DERMAL ABSORPTION AND INGESTION. TARGET EFFECTS: CHOLINESTERASE INHIBITOR. POISONING MAY AFFECT THE NERVOUS SYSTEM.* AT INCREASED RISK FROM EXPOSURE: PERSONS WITH GLAUCOMA OR OTHER OPHTHALMOLOGICAL DIFFICULTIES. ALSO, PERSONS WITH RESPIRATORY AILMENTS, RECENT EXPOSURE TO CHOLINESTERASE INHIBITORS OR IMPAIRED CHOLINESTERASE PRODUCTION, OR LIVER MALFUNCTION.* ADDITIONAL DATA: MAY CROSS THE PLACENTA. HIGH ENVIRONMENTAL TEMPERATURES OR EXPOSURE OF THE CHEMICAL TO VISIBLE OR ULTRAVIOLET LIGHT MAY ENHANCE THE TOXICITY. INTERACTIONS WITH MEDICATIONS MAY OCCUR.*
* MAY BE BASED ON GENERAL INFORMATION ON ORGANOPHOSPHATES.

HEALTH EFFECTS AND FIRST AID

INHALATION: THIOMETON: SEE INFORMATION ON ORGANOPHOSPHATES.
ORGANOPHOSPHATES: CHOLINESTERASE INHIBITOR. **ACUTE EXPOSURE-** WHEN INHALED, THE FIRST EFFECTS OF CHOLINESTERASE INHIBITORS ARE USUALLY RESPIRATORY AND MAY INCLUDE NASAL HYPEREMIA AND WATERY DISCHARGE, COUGH, CHEST DISCOMFORT, DYSPNEA, AND WHEEZING DUE TO INCREASED BRONCHIAL SECRETIONS AND BRONCHOCONSTRICTION. IF SUFFICIENT AMOUNTS ARE ABSORBED, OTHER SYSTEMIC EFFECTS MAY BEGIN WITHIN A FEW MINUTES OR BE DELAYED FOR UP TO 12 HOURS. SYMPTOMS MAY INCLUDE PALLOR, NAUSEA, VOMITING, DIARRHEA, ABDOMINAL CRAMPS, HEADACHE, DIZZINESS, OCULAR PAIN, BLURRED VISION, MIOSIS OR IN SOME CASES, ESPECIALLY INITIALLY, MYDRIASIS, LACRIMATION, SALIVATION, SWEATING, AND CONFUSION. OTHER REPORTED CENTRAL NERVOUS SYSTEM OR NEUROMUSCULAR EFFECTS MAY INCLUDE ATAXIA, SLURRED SPEECH, AREFLEXIA, WEAKNESS, FATIGUE, FASCICULATIONS, TWITCHING, TREMORS POSSIBLY OF THE TONGUE AND EYELIDS, AND EVENTUALLY PARALYSIS OF THE EXTREMITIES AND POSSIBLY OF THE RESPIRATORY MUSCLES. IN SEVERE CASES THERE MAY ALSO BE INVOLUNTARY DEFECATION AND URINATION, CYANOSIS, PSYCHOSIS, HYPERGLYCEMIA, ACUTE PANCREATITIS, CARDIAC IRREGULARITIES, PULMONARY EDEMA, UNCONSCIOUSNESS, CONVULSIONS, AND COMA. DEATH IS PRIMARILY DUE TO RESPIRATORY FAILURE, ALTHOUGH CARDIOVASCULAR EFFECTS INCLUDING CARDIAC ARREST MAY ALSO BE IMPLICATED. LONG TERM SEQUELAE ARE RARE BUT MAY INCLUDE NEUROPSYCHIATRIC DISORDERS AND MYOPATHY WITH MUSCLE TENDERNESS. SOME ORGANOPHOSPHATES MAY CAUSE A DELAYED NEUROPATHY BEGINNING 1-4 WEEKS AFTER AN ACUTE EXPOSURE WHICH MAY OR MAY NOT HAVE CAUSED ACUTE CHOLINERGIC EFFECTS. NUMBNESS, TINGLING, WEAKNESS AND CRAMPING BEGINNING SYMMETRICALLY IN THE LOWER LIMBS MAY PROGRESS TO ATAXIA AND PARALYSIS. IN SEVERE CASES, UPPER LIMB INVOLVEMENT IS POSSIBLE AND FLACCID PARALYSIS MAY PROGRESS TO SPASTIC PARALYSIS WITH EXAGGERATED REFLEXES. IMPROVEMENT MAY OCCUR OVER MONTHS TO YEARS, BUT SOME RESIDUAL IMPAIRMENT USUALLY REMAINS.
CHRONIC EXPOSURE- REPEATED OR PROLONGED EXPOSURE MAY RESULT IN THE EFFECTS OF ACUTE EXPOSURE INCLUDING THE DELAYED NEUROPATHY. OTHER EFFECTS REPORTED IN WORKERS REPEATEDLY EXPOSED INCLUDE IMPAIRED MEMORY AND CONCENTRATION, ACUTE PSYCHOSIS, SEVERE DEPRESSIONS, IRRITABILTY, CONFUSION, APATHY, EMOTIONAL LABILITY, SOCIAL WITHDRAWAL, CONFUSION, HEADACHE, SPEECH DIFFICULTIES, DELAYED REACTION TIMES, SPATIAL DISORIENTATION, NIGHTMARES, SLEEPWALKING, AND DROWSINESS OR INSOMNIA. AN INFLUENZA-LIKE CONDITION WITH HEADACHE, NAUSEA, WEAKNESS, ANOREXIA AND MALAISE HAS ALSO BEEN REPORTED.

FIRST AID- REMOVE FROM EXPOSURE AREA TO FRESH AIR IMMEDIATELY. IF BREATHING HAS STOPPED, GIVE ARTIFICIAL RESPIRATION. MAINTAIN AIRWAY AND BLOOD PRESSURE AND ADMINISTER OXYGEN IF AVAILABLE. KEEP AFFECTED PERSON WARM AND AT REST. TREAT SYMPTOMATICALLY AND SUPPORTIVELY. ADMINISTRATION OF OXYGEN SHOULD BE PERFORMED BY QUALIFIED PERSONNEL. GET MEDICAL ATTENTION IMMEDIATELY.

SKIN CONTACT: THIOMETON: HIGHLY TOXIC. MAY CAUSE IRRITATION. 500 MG APPLIED TO RABBIT SKIN PRODUCED MILD IRRITATION. PROLONGED OR REPEATED EXPOSURE MAY CAUSE DERMATITIS. SEE INFORMATION ON ORGANOPHOSPHATES.
ORGANOPHOSPHATES: CHOLINESTERASE INHIBITOR. **ACUTE EXPOSURE-** LOCALIZED SWEATING AND FASCICULATIONS MAY OCCUR AT THE SITE OF CONTACT. IF SUFFICIENT AMOUNTS ARE ABSORBED, OTHER EFFECTS OF CHOLINESTERASE INHIBITION AS DESCRIBED IN ACUTE INHALATION MAY OCCUR. SYMPTOMS MAY BE DELAYED 2-3 HOURS, BUT USUALLY NO MORE THAN 12 HOURS. THE RATE OF ABSORPTION IS INCREASED BY THE PRESENCE OF DERMATITIS OR HIGH AMBIENT TEMPERATURES. DELAYED NEUROPATHY IS ALSO POSSIBLE. **CHRONIC EXPOSURE-** REPEATED OR PROLONGED EXPOSURE MAY CAUSE EFFECTS AS DESCRIBED IN ACUTE EXPOSURE. SOME ORGANOPHOSPHATES MAY CAUSE SENSITIZATION.

FIRST AID- REMOVE CONTAMINATED CLOTHING IMMEDIATELY. WASH CONTAMINATED AREAS WITH SOAP AND WATER FOLLOWED BY ALCOHOL (ARENA, POISONING, 4TH ED.). EMERGENCY PERSONNEL SHOULD WEAR GLOVES AND AVOID CONTAMINATION. TREAT RESPIRATORY DIFFICULTY WITH ARTIFICIAL RESPIRATION. GET MEDICAL ATTENTION IMMEDIATELY.

EYE CONTACT: THIOMETON: MAY CAUSE IRRITATION. 500 UG APPLIED TO RABBIT EYES PRODUCED MILD IRRITATION. PROLONGED OR REPEATED EXPOSURE MAY CAUSE CONJUNCTIVITIS. SEE INFORMATION ON ORGANOPHOSPHATES.
ORGANOPHOSPHATES: CHOLINESTERASE INHIBITOR. **ACUTE EXPOSURE-** DIRECT CONTACT MAY CAUSE PAIN, HYPEREMIA, LACRIMATION, TWITCHING OF THE EYELIDS, MIOSIS, AND CILIARY MUSCLE SPASM WITH LOSS OF ACCOMODATION, BLURRED OR DIMMED VISION AND BROWACHE. SOMETIMES MYDRIASIS MAY OCCUR INSTEAD OF MIOSIS. WITH SUFFICIENT EXPOSURE, OTHER SYMPTOMS OF CHOLINESTERASE INHIBITION AS DESCRIBED IN ACUTE INHALATION MAY OCCUR. **CHRONIC EXPOSURE-** REPEATED OR PROLONGED EXPOSURE MAY CAUSE EFFECTS AS DESCRIBED IN ACUTE EXPOSURE. SOME COMPOUNDS HAVE CAUSED TOXIC EFFECTS ON THE CRYSTALLINE LENS, CONJUNCTIVAL THICKENING AND OBSTRUCTION OF THE NASOLACRIMAL CANALS WHEN USED AS MIOTIC EYEDROPS.

FIRST AID- IRRIGATE EYES WITH WATER OR SALINE SOLUTION. IF SYMPTOMS OF POISONING OCCUR, TREAT RESPIRATORY DIFFICULTY WITH ARTIFICIAL RESPIRATION AND OXYGEN. OBSERVE PATIENT FOR AT LEAST 24-36 HOURS (GOSSELIN, CLINICAL TOXICOLOGY OF COMMERCIAL PRODUCTS, 5TH ED.). GET

MEDICAL ATTENTION IMMEDIATELY. OXYGEN SHOULD BE ADMINISTERED BY QUALIFIED MEDICAL PERSONNEL.

INGESTION: THIOMETON: HIGHLY TOXIC. BEAGLE DOGS TREATED WITH THIOMETON AT RATES RANGING FROM ABOUT 0.5 TO 1.5 MG/KG/DAY FOR 2 YEARS DEVELOPED HISTOLOGICAL CHANGES IN THE OPTIC NERVE. IN A TWELVE MONTH STUDY OF RATS, DAILY ADMINISTRATION OF 18 MG/KG PRODUCED DEFINITE INHIBITION OF PLASMA AND RED CELL CHOLINESTERASE ACTIVITY. SEE INFORMATION ON ORGANOPHOSPHATES.
ORGANOPHOSPHATES: CHOLINESTERASE INHIBITOR. **ACUTE EXPOSURE**- WHEN INGESTED, THE FIRST EFFECTS MAY BE NAUSEA, VOMITING, ANOREXIA, ABDOMINAL CRAMPS AND DIARRHEA. GASTROINTESTINAL ABSORPTION MAY CAUSE SYMPTOMS OF CHOLINESTERASE INHIBITION AS DESCRIBED IN ACUTE INHALATION. SYMPTOMS MAY BEGIN WITHIN MINUTES OR BE DELAYED FOR HOURS. DELAYED EFFECTS INCLUDING NEUROPATHY MAY ALSO OCCUR. **CHRONIC EXPOSURE**- REPEATED INGESTION MAY CAUSE EFFECTS AS DESCRIBED IN ACUTE EXPOSURE.

FIRST AID- IF PERSON IS ALERT AND RESPIRATION IS NOT DEPRESSED, GIVE SYRUP OF IPECAC FOLLOWED BY WATER (IF VOMITING OCCURS, KEEP HEAD BELOW HIPS TO PREVENT ASPIRATION). IF CONSCIOUSNESS LEVEL DECLINES OR VOMITING HAS NOT OCCURRED IN 15 MINUTES EMPTY STOMACH BY GASTRIC LAVAGE WITH THE AID OF CUFFED ENDOTRACHEAL TUBE USING ISOTONIC SALINE OR 5% SODIUM BICARBONATE FOLLOW WITH ACTIVATED CHARCOAL. ESTABLISH AND MAINTAIN AIRWAY. TREAT RESPIRATORY DIFFICULTY WITH ARTIFICIAL RESPIRATION AND OXYGEN. DO NOT GIVE MORPHINE, AMINOPHYLLINE, PHENOTHIAZINES, RESERPINE, FUROSEMIDE, OR ETHACRYNIC ACID (MORGAN, RECOGNITION AND MANAGEMENT OF PESTICIDE POISONINGS, 3RD ED.). TREAT SYMPTOMATICALLY AND SUPPORTIVELY. ADMINISTRATION OF OXYGEN AND LAVAGE MUST BE PERFORMED BY QUALIFIED MEDICAL PERSONNEL. GET MEDICAL ATTENTION IMMEDIATELY.

ANTIDOTE: THE FOLLOWING ANTIDOTE(S) HAVE BEEN RECOMMENDED. HOWEVER, THE DECISION AS TO WHETHER THE SEVERITY OF POISONING REQUIRES ADMINISTRATION OF ANY ANTIDOTE AND ACTUAL DOSE REQUIRED SHOULD BE MADE BY QUALIFIED MEDICAL PERSONNEL.
FOR CHOLINESTERASE INHIBITORS: ESTABLISH CLEAR AIRWAY AND TISSUE OXYGENATION BY ASPIRATION OF SECRETIONS, AND IF NECESSARY, BY ASSISTED PULMONARY VENTILATION WITH OXYGEN. IMPROVE TISSUE OXYGENATION AS MUCH AS POSSIBLE BEFORE ADMINISTERING ATROPINE TO MINIMIZE THE RISK OF VENTRICULAR FIBRILLATION. ADMINISTER ATROPINE SULFATE INTRAVENOUSLY, OR INTRAMUSCULARLY IF IV INJECTION IS NOT POSSIBLE. IN MODERATELY SEVERE POISONING ADMINISTER ATROPINE SULFATE, 0.4-2.0 MG REPEATED EVERY 15 MINUTES UNTIL ATROPINIZATION IS ACHIEVED (TACHYCARDIA, FLUSHING, DRY MOUTH, MYDRIASIS). MAINTAIN ATROPINIZATION BY REPEATED DOSES FOR 2-12 HOURS, OR LONGER, DEPENDING ON THE SEVERITY OF POISONING. THE APPEARANCE OF RALES IN THE LUNG BASES, MIOSIS, SALIVATION, NAUSEA, BRADYCARDIA, ARE ALL INDICATIONS OF INADEQUATE ATROPINIZATION.
SEVERELY POISONED INDIVIDUALS MAY EXHIBIT REMARKABLE TOLERANCE TO ATROPINE; TWO OR MORE TIMES THE DOSAGES SUGGESTED ABOVE MAY BE NEEDED. PERSONS NOT POISONED OR ONLY SLIGHTLY POISONED, HOWEVER, MAY DEVELOP SIGNS OF ATROPINE TOXICITY FROM SUCH LARGE DOSAGES: FEVER, MUSCLE FIBRILLATIONS, AND DELIRIUM ARE THE MAIN SIGNS OF ATROPINE TOXICITY. IF THESE SIGNS APPEAR WHILE THE PATIENT IS FULLY ATROPINIZED, ATROPINE ADMINISTRATION SHOULD BE DISCONTINUED, AT LEAST TEMPORARILY. OBSERVE TREATED PATIENTS CLOSELY AT LEAST 24 HOURS TO INSURE THAT SYMPTOMS (POSSIBLY PULMONARY EDEMA) DO NOT RECUR AS ATROPINIZATION WEARS OFF. IN VERY SEVERE POISONINGS, METABOLIC DISPOSITION OF TOXICANT MAY REQUIRE SEVERAL HOURS OR DAYS DURING WHICH ATROPINIZATION MUST BE MAINTAINED. MARKEDLY LOWER LEVELS OF URINARY METABOLITES INDICATE THAT ATROPINE DOSAGE CAN BE TAPERED OFF. AS DOSAGE IS REDUCED, CHECK THE LUNG BASES FREQUENTLY FOR RALES. IF RALES ARE HEARD OR OTHER SYMPTOMS RETURN, RE-ESTABLISH ATROPINIZATION PROMPTLY (MORGAN, RECOGNITION AND MANAGEMENT OF PESTICIDE POISONINGS, 3RD ED.). ADMINISTRATION OF ANTIDOTE MUST BE PERFORMED BY QUALIFIED MEDICAL PERSONNEL.
IN CASES OF SEVERE POISONING BY ORGANOPHOSPHATE PESTICIDES IN WHICH RESPIRATORY DEPRESSION, MUSCLE WEAKNESS AND TWITCHINGS ARE SEVERE, GIVE PRALIDOXIME (PROTOPAM-AYERST, 2-PAM), 1.0 GRAM INTRAVENOUSLY AT NO MORE THAN 0.5 GRAM PER MINUTE. DOSAGE OF PRALIDOXIME MAY BE REPEATED IN 1-2 HOURS, THEN AT 10-12 HOUR INTERVALS IF NEEDED. IN VERY SEVERE POISONINGS, DOSAGE RATES MAY BE DOUBLED. TREATMENT WITH PRALIDOXIME WILL BE MOST EFFECTIVE IF GIVEN WITHIN THIRTY-SIX HOURS AFTER POISONING (MORGAN, RECOGNITION AND MANAGEMENT OF PESTICIDE POISONINGS, 3RD ED.). ANTIDOTE SHOULD BE ADMINISTERED BY QUALIFIED MEDICAL PERSONNEL.

REACTIVITY

REACTIVITY: THIOMETON SHOWS A POOR STABILITY IN THE FORM OF THE PURE ACTIVE INGREDIENT, WHEREAS IT IS STABLE IN NONPOLAR SOLVENTS. IT IS HYDROLYZED EASILY UNDER ALL CONDITIONS.
INCOMPATIBILITIES: THIOMETON: AQUEOUS SOLUTION: MAY HYDROLYZE ALKALINE CONDITIONS: IS UNSTABLE.
DECOMPOSITION: THERMAL DECOMPOSITION MAY RELEASE TOXIC AND/OR HAZARDOUS GASES.
POLYMERIZATION: HAZARDOUS POLYMERIZATION HAS NOT BEEN REPORTED TO OCCUR UNDER NORMAL TEMPERATURES AND PRESSURES.

STORAGE AND DISPOSAL

OBSERVE ALL FEDERAL, STATE AND LOCAL REGULATIONS WHEN STORING OR DISPOSING OF THIS SUBSTANCE. FOR ASSISTANCE, CONTACT THE DISTRICT DIRECTOR OF THE ENVIRONMENTAL PROTECTION AGENCY.

****STORAGE****

STORE IN ACCORDANCE WITH 40 CFR 165 RECOMMENDED PROCEDURES FOR THE DISPOSAL AND STORAGE OF PESTICIDES AND PESTICIDE CONTAINERS.
STORE AWAY FROM INCOMPATIBLE SUBSTANCES.

****DISPOSAL****

DISPOSAL MUST BE IN ACCORDANCE WITH 40 CFR 165 RECOMMENDED PROCEDURES FOR THE DISPOSAL AND STORAGE OF PESTICIDES AND PESTICIDE CONTAINERS.

CONDITIONS TO AVOID

AVOID CONTACT WITH ALKALI MATERIALS.

SPILL AND LEAK PROCEDURES

OCCUPATIONAL SPILL: DO NOT TOUCH SPILLED MATERIAL. STOP LEAK IF YOU CAN DO IT WITHOUT RISK. USE WATER SPRAY TO REDUCE VAPORS. FOR SMALL SPILLS, TAKE UP WITH SAND OR OTHER ABSORBENT MATERIAL AND PLACE INTO CONTAINERS FOR LATER DISPOSAL. FOR SMALL DRY SPILLS, WITH A CLEAN SHOVEL PLACE MATERIAL INTO CLEAN, DRY CONTAINERS AND COVER. MOVE CONTAINERS FROM SPILL AREA. FOR LARGER SPILLS, DIKE FAR AHEAD OF SPILL FOR LATER DISPOSAL. KEEP UNNECESSARY PEOPLE AWAY. ISOLATE HAZARD AREA AND DENY ENTRY. VENTILATE CLOSED SPACES BEFORE ENTERING.

PROTECTIVE EQUIPMENT

VENTILATION: PROCESS ENCLOSURE RECOMMENDED.
RESPIRATOR: THE FOLLOWING RESPIRATORS ARE RECOMMENDED BASED ON INFORMATION FOUND IN THE PHYSICAL DATA, TOXICITY AND HEALTH EFFECTS SECTIONS. THEY ARE RANKED IN ORDER FROM MINIMUM TO MAXIMUM RESPIRATORY PROTECTION. THE SPECIFIC RESPIRATOR SELECTED MUST BE BASED ON CONTAMINATION LEVELS FOUND IN THE WORK PLACE, MUST NOT EXCEED THE WORKING LIMITS OF THE RESPIRATOR AND BE JOINTLY APPROVED BY THE NATIONAL INSTITUTE FOR OCCUPATIONAL SAFETY AND HEALTH AND THE MINE SAFETY AND HEALTH ADMINISTRATION (NIOSH-MSHA).
TYPE 'C' SUPPLIED-AIR RESPIRATOR WITH A FULL FACEPIECE OPERATED IN PRESSURE-DEMAND OR OTHER POSITIVE PRESSURE MODE OR WITH A FULL FACEPIECE, HELMET OR HOOD OPERATED IN CONTINOUS-FLOW MODE.
SELF-CONTAINED BREATHING APPARATUS WITH A FULL FACEPIECE OPERATED IN PRESSURE-DEMAND OR OTHER POSITIVE PRESSURE MODE.
FOR FIREFIGHTING AND OTHER IMMEDIATELY DANGEROUS TO LIFE OR HEALTH CONDITIONS:
SELF-CONTAINED BREATHING APPARATUS WITH FULL FACEPIECE OPERATED IN PRESSURE-DEMAND OR OTHER POSITIVE PRESSURE MODE.
SUPPLIED-AIR RESPIRATOR WITH FULL FACEPIECE AND OPERATED IN PRESSURE-DEMAND OR OTHER POSITIVE PRESSURE MODE IN COMBINATION WITH AN AUXILIARY SELF-CONTAINED BREATHING APPARATUS OPERATED IN PRESSURE-DEMAND OR OTHER POSITIVE PRESSURE MODE.
CLOTHING: EMPLOYEE MUST WEAR APPROPRIATE PROTECTIVE (IMPERVIOUS) CLOTHING AND EQUIPMENT TO PREVENT ANY POSSIBILITY OF SKIN CONTACT WITH THIS SUBSTANCE.
GLOVES: EMPLOYEE MUST WEAR APPROPRIATE PROTECTIVE GLOVES TO PREVENT CONTACT WITH THIS SUBSTANCE.
EYE PROTECTION: EMPLOYEE MUST WEAR SPLASH-PROOF OR DUST-RESISTANT SAFETY GOGGLES AND A FACESHIELD TO PREVENT CONTACT WITH THIS SUBSTANCE.
EMERGENCY WASH FACILITIES: WHERE THERE IS ANY POSSIBILITY THAT AN EMPLOYEE'S EYES AND/OR SKIN MAY BE EXPOSED TO THIS SUBSTANCE, THE EMPLOYER SHOULD PROVIDE AN EYE WASH FOUNTAIN AND QUICK DRENCH SHOWER WITHIN THE IMMEDIATE WORK AREA FOR EMERGENCY USE.

AUTHORIZED BY- OCCUPATIONAL HEALTH SERVICES, INC.
CREATION DATE: 10/05/89 ***REVISION DATE:*** 05/18/90

MATERIAL SAFETY DATA SHEET

OCCUPATIONAL HEALTH SERVICES, INC.
AGRICULTURE AND PESTICIDE DIVISION
450 SEVENTH AVENUE, SUITE 2407
NEW YORK, NEW YORK 10123
1-800-445-MSDS OR (212) 967-1100

EMERGENCY CONTACT:
JOHN S. BRANSFORD, JR. (615) 292-1180

SUBSTANCE IDENTIFICATION

CAS-NUMBER 644-64-4

SUBSTANCE: **DIMETILAN**

TRADE NAMES/SYNONYMS: CARBAMIC ACID, DIMETHYL-, 1-((DIMETHYLAMINO)CARBONYL)-5-METHYL-1H -PYRAZOL-2-YL ESTER; CARBAMIC ACID, DIMETHYL-, ESTER WITH 3-HYDROXY-N,N,5-TRIMETHYLPYRAZOLE -1-CARBOXAMIDE; DIMETHYLCARBAMIC ACID, 1-((DIMETHYLAMINO)CARBONYL)-4-METHYL-1H -PYRAZOL-2-YL ESTER; DIMETHYLCARBAMIC ACID, ESTER WITH 3-HYDROXY-N,N,5-TRIMETHYLPYRAZOLE -1-CARBOXAMIDE; 1-DIMETHYLCARBAMOYL-5-METHYLPYRAZOL-3-YL DIMETHYLCARBAMATE; 1-((DIMETHYLAMINO)CARBONYL)-5-METHYL-1H-PYRAZOL-3-YL DIMETHYLCARBAMATE; DIMETHYLCARBAMATE ESTER OF 3-HYDROXY-N,N,5-TRIMETHYLPYRAZOLE -1-CARBOXAMIDE; 2-DIMETHYLCARBAMOYL-3-METHYL-4-PYRAZOLYL DIMETHYLCARBAMATE; 1-DIMETHYLCARBAMOYL-5-METHYL-3-PYRAZOLYL DIMETHYLCARBAMATE; DIMETILANE; GEIGY 22870; SNIP FLY; ENT 25922; C10H16N4O3; PST83057

CHEMICAL FAMILY: PYRAZOLE CARBAMATE

MOLECULAR FORMULA: C10-H16-N4-O3

MOLECULAR WEIGHT: 240.30

CERCLA RATINGS (SCALE 0-3): HEALTH=3 FIRE=U REACTIVITY=U PERSISTENCE=2

NFPA RATINGS (SCALE 0-4): HEALTH=3 FIRE=U REACTIVITY=U

COMPONENTS AND CONTAMINANTS

COMPONENT: DIMETILAN ***PERCENT:*** 100.0
CAS# 644-64-4

OTHER CONTAMINANTS: NONE

EXPOSURE LIMITS: NO OCCUPATIONAL EXPOSURE LIMITS ESTABLISHED BY OSHA, ACGIH, OR NIOSH.
DIMETILAN: 500/10,000 POUNDS SARA SECTION 302 THRESHOLD PLANNING QUANTITY 1 POUND SARA SECTION 304 REPORTABLE QUANTITY

PHYSICAL DATA

DESCRIPTION: COLORLESS SOLID

BOILING POINT: 392-410 F (200-210 C) @ 13 MMHG

MELTING POINT: 154-160 F (68-71 C) ***SPECIFIC GRAVITY:*** NOT AVAILABLE

VAPOR PRESSURE: 0.0001 @ 20 C ***SOLUBILITY IN WATER:*** SOLUBLE

SOLVENT SOLUBILITY: CHLOROFORM, DIMETHYLFORMAMIDE, ETHANOL, ACETONE, XYLENE, AND OTHER ORGANIC SOLVENTS

FIRE AND EXPLOSION DATA

FIRE AND EXPLOSION HAZARD: UNKNOWN FIRE AND EXPLOSION HAZARD.

FIREFIGHTING MEDIA: DRY CHEMICAL, CARBON DIOXIDE, HALON, WATER SPRAY OR STANDARD FOAM (1987 EMERGENCY RESPONSE GUIDEBOOK, DOT P 5800.4).
FOR LARGER FIRES, USE WATER SPRAY, FOG OR STANDARD FOAM (1987 EMERGENCY RESPONSE GUIDEBOOK, DOT P 5800.4).

FIREFIGHTING: MOVE CONTAINERS FROM FIRE AREA IF POSSIBLE. FIGHT FIRE FROM MAXIMUM DISTANCE. STAY AWAY FROM STORAGE TANK ENDS. DIKE FIRE CONTROL WATER FOR LATER DISPOSAL. DO NOT SCATTER MATERIAL (1987 EMERGENCY RESPONSE GUIDEBOOK, DOT P 5800.4, GUIDE PAGE 55).
EXTINGUISH USING AGENT SUITABLE FOR TYPE OF SURROUNDING FIRE. AVOID BREATHING VAPORS AND DUSTS. KEEP UPWIND.

TRANSPORTATION DATA

DEPARTMENT OF TRANSPORTATION HAZARD CLASSIFICATION 49 CFR 172.101: POISON B
DEPARTMENT OF TRANSPORTATION LABELING REQUIREMENTS 49 CFR 172.101 AND SUBPART E: POISON
DEPARTMENT OF TRANSPORTATION PACKAGING REQUIREMENTS: 49 CFR 173.365 EXCEPTIONS: 49 CFR 173.364

TOXICITY

DIMETILAN: TOXICITY DATA: 2000 MG/KG SKIN-RABBIT LD50; 600 MG/KG SKIN-RAT LD50; 90 MG/KG SKIN-MOUSE LD50; 25 MG/KG ORAL-RAT LD50; 60 MG/KG ORAL-MOUSE LD50; 63 MG/KG ORAL-GUINEA PIG LD50; 4 MG/KG SUBCUTANEOUS-MOUSE LD50; 12 MG/KG INTRAPERITONEAL-MOUSE LD50. CARCINOGEN STATUS: NONE. ACUTE TOXICITY LEVEL: HIGHLY TOXIC BY INGESTION: MODERATELY TOXIC BY DERMAL ABSORPTION. TARGET EFFECTS: CHOLINESTERASE INHIBITOR. AT INCREASED RISK FROM EXPOSURE: PERSONS WITH ASTHMA, DIABETES, CARDIOVASCULAR DISEASE, MECHANICAL OBSTRUCTION OF THE GASTROINTESTINAL OR UROGENITAL TRACT, AND THOSE IN VAGOTONIC STATES.*
* MAY BE BASED ON GENERAL INFORMATION ON CARBAMATES.

HEALTH EFFECTS AND FIRST AID

INHALATION: DIMETILAN: SEE INFORMATION ON CARBAMATES.
CARBAMATES: CHOLINESTERASE INHIBITOR. **ACUTE EXPOSURE-** WHEN INHALED, THE FIRST EFFECTS OF CHOLINESTERASE INHIBITION ARE USUALLY RESPIRATORY AND MAY INCLUDE NASAL HYPEREMIA AND WATERY DISCHARGE, CHEST DISCOMFORT, DYSPNEA, AND WHEEZING DUE TO INCREASED BRONCHIAL SECRETIONS AND BRONCHOCONSTRICTION. OTHER SYSTEMIC EFFECTS MAY BEGIN WITHIN A FEW MINUTES OR SEVERAL HOURS OF EXPOSURE. SYMPTOMS MAY INCLUDE NAUSEA, VOMITING, DIARRHEA, ABDOMINAL CRAMPS, HEADACHE, VERTIGO, OCULAR PAIN, CILIARY MUSCLE SPASM, BLURRING OR DIMNESS OF VISION, MIOSIS, OR IN SOME CASES MYDRIASIS, LACRIMATION, SALIVATION, SWEATING, AND CONFUSION. OTHER REPORTED CENTRAL NERVOUS SYSTEM OR NEUROMUSCULAR EFFECTS INCLUDE ATAXIA, SLURRED SPEECH, AREFLEXIA, WEAKNESS, FATIGUE, TWITCHING, FASCICULATION, TREMOR, AND EVENTUALLY PARALYSIS OF THE EXTREMITIES AND POSSIBLY OF THE RESPIRATORY MUSCLES. IN SEVERE CASES, THERE MAY ALSO BE INVOLUNTARY DEFECATION AND URINATION, BRADYCARDIA, HYPOTENSION, PULMONARY EDEMA, CONVULSIONS, COMA, AND DEATH FROM RESPIRATORY FAILURE OR CARDIAC ARREST. CARBAMATES GENERALLY DO NOT ACCUMULATE IN MAMMALIAN TISSUE AND THE CHOLINESTERASE INHIBITION REVERSES RATHER RAPIDLY. IN NON-FATAL CASES, THE ILLNESS GENERALLY LASTS LESS THAN 24 HOURS. **CHRONIC EXPOSURE-** PROLONGED OR REPEATED EXPOSURE MAY CAUSE EFFECTS AS DESCRIBED IN ACUTE EXPOSURE.

FIRST AID- REMOVE FROM EXPOSURE AREA TO FRESH AIR IMMEDIATELY. IF BREATHING HAS STOPPED, GIVE ARTIFICIAL RESPIRATION. MAINTAIN AIRWAY AND BLOOD PRESSURE AND ADMINISTER OXYGEN IF AVAILABLE. KEEP AFFECTED PERSON WARM AND AT REST. TREAT SYMPTOMATICALLY AND SUPPORTIVELY. ADMINISTRATION OF OXYGEN SHOULD BE PERFORMED BY QUALIFIED PERSONNEL. GET MEDICAL ATTENTION IMMEDIATELY.

SKIN CONTACT: DIMETILAN: SEE INFORMATION ON CARBAMATES.
CARBAMATES: CHOLINESTERASE INHIBITOR. **ACUTE EXPOSURE-** SOME COMPOUNDS MAY CAUSE IRRITATION. LOCALIZED SWEATING AND FASCICULATIONS MAY OCCUR AT THE SITE OF CONTACT. IF SUFFICIENT AMOUNTS ARE ABSORBED THROUGH THE SKIN, OTHER EFFECTS OF CHOLINESTERASE INHIBITION MAY OCCUR AS DESCRIBED IN ACUTE INHALATION; SYMPTOMS MAY BE DELAYED FOR 2-3 HOURS, USUALLY NO MORE THAN 8 HOURS. **CHRONIC EXPOSURE-** REPEATED OR PROLONGED EXPOSURE MAY CAUSE EFFECTS AS DESCRIBED IN ACUTE EXPOSURE.

FIRST AID- REMOVE CONTAMINATED CLOTHING IMMEDIATELY. WASH CONTAMINATED AREAS WITH SOAP AND WATER FOLLOWED BY ALCOHOL (ARENA, POISONING, 4TH ED.). EMERGENCY PERSONNEL SHOULD WEAR GLOVES AND AVOID CONTAMINATION. TREAT RESPIRATORY DIFFICULTY WITH ARTIFICIAL RESPIRATION. GET MEDICAL ATTENTION IMMEDIATELY.

EYE CONTACT: DIMETILAN: SEE INFORMATION ON CARBAMATES.
CARBAMATES: CHOLINESTERASE INHIBITOR. **ACUTE EXPOSURE-** DIRECT CONTACT MAY CAUSE PAIN, HYPEREMIA, LACRIMATION, TWITCHING OF THE EYELIDS, MIOSIS, AND CILIARY MUSCLE SPASM WITH LOSS OF ACCOMODATION, BLURRED OR DIMMED VISION AND BROWACHE. SOMETIMES MYDRIASIS MAY OCCUR INSTEAD OF MIOSIS. WITH SUFFICIENT EXPOSURE, OTHER SYMPTOMS OF CHOLINESTERASE INHIBITION MAY OCCUR AS DESCRIBED IN ACUTE INHALATION. **CHRONIC EXPOSURE-** PROLONGED EXPOSURE MAY CAUSE EFFECTS AS DESCRIBED IN ACUTE EXPOSURE. SOME COMPOUNDS HAVE CAUSED TOXIC EFFECTS ON THE CRYSTALLINE LENS, CONJUNCTIVAL THICKENING AND OBSTRUCTION OF NASOLACRIMAL CANALS WHEN USED AS MIOTIC EYE DROPS.

FIRST AID- IRRIGATE EYES WITH WATER OR SALINE SOLUTION. IF SYMPTOMS OF POISONING OCCUR, TREAT RESPIRATORY DIFFICULTY WITH ARTIFICIAL RESPIRATION AND OXYGEN. OBSERVE PATIENT FOR AT LEAST 24-36 HOURS (GOSSELIN, CLINICAL TOXICOLOGY OF COMMERCIAL PRODUCTS, 5TH ED.). GET MEDICAL ATTENTION IMMEDIATELY. OXYGEN SHOULD BE ADMINISTERED BY QUALIFIED MEDICAL PERSONNEL.

INGESTION: DIMETILAN: HIGHLY TOXIC. SEE INFORMATION ON CARBAMATES.
CARBAMATES: CHOLINESTERASE INHIBITOR. **ACUTE EXPOSURE-** WHEN INGESTED,

THE FIRST EFFECTS MAY BE NAUSEA, VOMITING, ANOREXIA, ABDOMINAL CRAMPS, AND DIARRHEA. WITH ABSORPTION FROM THE GASTROINTESTINAL TRACT, THE OTHER EFFECTS OF CHOLINESTERASE INHIBITION AS DESCRIBED IN ACUTE INHALATION MAY OCCUR; SYMPTOMS MAY BEGIN WITHIN MINUTES OR BE DELAYED SEVERAL HOURS. CHRONIC EXPOSURE- REPEATED INGESTION MAY CAUSE EFFECTS AS DESCRIBED IN ACUTE EXPOSURE.

FIRST AID- IF PERSON IS ALERT AND RESPIRATION IS NOT DEPRESSED, GIVE SYRUP OF IPECAC FOLLOWED BY WATER (IF VOMITING OCCURS, KEEP HEAD BELOW HIPS TO PREVENT ASPIRATION). IF CONSCIOUSNESS LEVEL DECLINES OR VOMITING HAS NOT OCCURRED IN 15 MINUTES EMPTY STOMACH BY GASTRIC LAVAGE WITH THE AID OF CUFFED ENDOTRACHEAL TUBE USING ISOTONIC SALINE OR 5% SODIUM BICARBONATE FOLLOW WITH ACTIVATED CHARCOAL. ESTABLISH AND MAINTAIN AIRWAY. TREAT RESPIRATORY DIFFICULTY WITH ARTIFICIAL RESPIRATION AND OXYGEN. DO NOT GIVE MORPHINE, AMINOPHYLLINE, PHENOTHIAZINES, RESERPINE, FUROSEMIDE, OR ETHACRYNIC ACID (MORGAN, RECOGNITION AND MANAGEMENT OF PESTICIDE POISONINGS, 3RD ED.). TREAT SYMPTOMATICALLY AND SUPPORTIVELY. ADMINISTRATION OF OXYGEN AND LAVAGE MUST BE PERFORMED BY QUALIFIED MEDICAL PERSONNEL. GET MEDICAL ATTENTION IMMEDIATELY.

ANTIDOTE: THE FOLLOWING ANTIDOTE HAS BEEN RECOMMENDED. HOWEVER, THE DECISION AS TO WHETHER THE SEVERITY OF POISONING REQUIRES ADMINISTRATION OF ANY ANTIDOTE AND ACTUAL DOSE REQUIRED SHOULD BE MADE BY QUALIFIED MEDICAL PERSONNEL.

FOR CHOLINESTERASE INHIBITORS: ESTABLISH CLEAR AIRWAY AND TISSUE OXYGENATION BY ASPIRATION OF SECRETIONS, AND IF NECESSARY, BY ASSISTED PULMONARY VENTILATION WITH OXYGEN. IMPROVE TISSUE OXYGENATION AS MUCH AS POSSIBLE BEFORE ADMINISTERING ATROPINE TO MINIMIZE THE RISK OF VENTRICULAR FIBRILLATION. ADMINISTER ATROPINE SULFATE INTRAVENOUSLY, OR INTRAMUSCULARLY IF IV INJECTION IS NOT POSSIBLE. IN MODERATELY SEVERE POISONING ADMINISTER ATROPINE SULFATE, 0.4-2.0 MG REPEATED EVERY 15 MINUTES UNTIL ATROPINIZATION IS ACHIEVED (TACHYCARDIA, FLUSHING, DRY MOUTH, MYDRIASIS). MAINTAIN ATROPINIZATION BY REPEATED DOSES FOR 2-12 HOURS, OR LONGER, DEPENDING ON THE SEVERITY OF POISONING. THE APPEARANCE OF RALES IN THE LUNG BASES, MIOSIS, SALIVATION, NAUSEA, BRADYCARDIA, ARE ALL INDICATIONS OF INADEQUATE ATROPINIZATION. SEVERELY POISONED INDIVIDUALS MAY EXHIBIT REMARKABLE TOLERANCE TO ATROPINE; TWO OR MORE TIMES THE DOSAGES SUGGESTED ABOVE MAY BE NEEDED. PERSONS NOT POISONED OR ONLY SLIGHTLY POISONED, HOWEVER, MAY DEVELOP SIGNS OF ATROPINE TOXICITY FROM SUCH LARGE DOSAGES: FEVER, MUSCLE FIBRILLATIONS, AND DELIRIUM ARE THE MAIN SIGNS OF ATROPINE TOXICITY. IF THESE SIGNS APPEAR WHILE THE PATIENT IS FULLY ATROPINIZED, ATROPINE ADMINISTRATION SHOULD BE DISCONTINUED, AT LEAST TEMPORARILY. OBSERVE TREATED PATIENTS CLOSELY AT LEAST 24 HOURS TO INSURE THAT SYMPTOMS (POSSIBLY PULMONARY EDEMA) DO NOT RECUR AS ATROPINIZATION WEARS OFF. IN VERY SEVERE POISONINGS, METABOLIC DISPOSITION OF TOXICANT MAY REQUIRE SEVERAL HOURS OR DAYS DURING WHICH ATROPINIZATION MUST BE MAINTAINED. MARKEDLY LOWER LEVELS OF URINARY METABOLITES INDICATE THAT ATROPINE DOSAGE CAN BE TAPERED OFF. AS DOSAGE IS REDUCED, CHECK THE LUNG BASES FREQUENTLY FOR RALES. IF RALES ARE HEARD OR OTHER SYMPTOMS RETURN, RE-ESTABLISH ATROPINIZATION PROMPTLY (MORGAN, RECOGNITION AND MANAGEMENT OF PESTICIDE POISONINGS, 3RD ED.). ADMINISTRATION OF ANTIDOTE MUST BE PERFORMED BY QUALIFIED MEDICAL PERSONNEL.

REACTIVITY

REACTIVITY: NO DATA AVAILABLE.

INCOMPATIBILITIES: DIMETILAN: OXIDIZERS (STRONG): FIRE AND EXPLOSION HAZARD.

DECOMPOSITION: THERMAL DECOMPOSITION PRODUCTS MAY INCLUDE TOXIC OXIDES OF NITROGEN.

POLYMERIZATION: HAZARDOUS POLYMERIZATION HAS NOT BEEN REPORTED TO OCCUR UNDER NORMAL TEMPERATURES AND PRESSURES.

STORAGE AND DISPOSAL

OBSERVE ALL FEDERAL, STATE AND LOCAL REGULATIONS WHEN STORING OR DISPOSING OF THIS SUBSTANCE. FOR ASSISTANCE, CONTACT THE DISTRICT DIRECTOR OF THE ENVIRONMENTAL PROTECTION AGENCY.

****STORAGE****

STORE IN ACCORDANCE WITH 40 CFR 165 RECOMMENDED PROCEDURES FOR THE DISPOSAL AND STORAGE OF PESTICIDES AND PESTICIDE CONTAINERS.

THRESHOLD PLANNING QUANTITY (TPQ): THE SUPERFUND AMENDMENTS AND REAUTHORIZATION ACT (SARA) SECTION 302 REQUIRES THAT EACH FACILITY WHERE ANY EXTREMELY HAZARDOUS SUBSTANCE IS PRESENT IN A QUANTITY EQUAL TO OR GREATER THAN THE TPQ ESTABLISHED FOR THAT SUBSTANCE NOTIFY THE STATE EMERGENCY RESPONSE COMMISSION FOR THE STATE IN WHICH IT IS LOCATED. SECTION 303 OF SARA REQUIRES THESE FACILITIES TO PARTICIPATE IN LOCAL EMERGENCY RESPONSE PLANNING (40 CFR 355.30).

****DISPOSAL****

DISPOSAL MUST BE IN ACCORDANCE WITH 40 CFR 165 RECOMMENDED PROCEDURES FOR THE DISPOSAL AND STORAGE OF PESTICIDES AND PESTICIDE CONTAINERS.

CONDITIONS TO AVOID

NONE REPORTED.

SPILL AND LEAK PROCEDURES

OCCUPATIONAL SPILL: DO NOT TOUCH SPILLED MATERIAL. STOP LEAK IF YOU CAN DO IT WITHOUT RISK. USE WATER SPRAY TO REDUCE VAPORS. FOR SMALL SPILLS, TAKE UP WITH SAND OR OTHER ABSORBENT MATERIAL AND PLACE INTO CONTAINERS FOR LATER DISPOSAL. FOR SMALL DRY SPILLS, WITH A CLEAN SHOVEL PLACE MATERIAL INTO CLEAN, DRY CONTAINERS AND COVER. MOVE CONTAINERS FROM SPILL AREA. FOR LARGER SPILLS, DIKE FAR AHEAD OF SPILL FOR LATER DISPOSAL. KEEP UNNECESSARY PEOPLE AWAY. ISOLATE HAZARD AREA AND DENY ENTRY. VENTILATE CLOSED SPACES BEFORE ENTERING.

REPORTABLE QUANTITY (RQ): 1 POUND THE SUPERFUND AMENDMENTS AND REAUTHORIZATION ACT (SARA) SECTION 304 REQUIRES THAT A RELEASE EQUAL TO OR GREATER THAN THE REPORTABLE QUANTITY FOR THIS SUBSTANCE BE IMMEDIATELY REPORTED TO THE LOCAL EMERGENCY PLANNING COMMITTEE AND THE STATE EMERGENCY RESPONSE COMMISSION (40 CFR 355.40). IF THE RELEASE OF THIS SUBSTANCE IS REPORTABLE UNDER CERCLA SECTION 103, THE NATIONAL RESPONSE CENTER MUST BE NOTIFIED IMMEDIATELY AT (800) 424-8802 OR (202) 426-2675 IN THE METROPOLITAN WASHINGTON, D.C. AREA (40 CFR 302.6).

PROTECTIVE EQUIPMENT

VENTILATION: PROVIDE LOCAL EXHAUST VENTILATION SYSTEM.

RESPIRATOR: THE FOLLOWING RESPIRATORS ARE RECOMMENDED BASED ON INFORMATION FOUND IN THE PHYSICAL DATA, TOXICITY AND HEALTH EFFECTS SECTIONS. THEY ARE RANKED IN ORDER FROM MINIMUM TO MAXIMUM RESPIRATORY PROTECTION. THE SPECIFIC RESPIRATOR SELECTED MUST BE BASED ON CONTAMINATION LEVELS FOUND IN THE WORK PLACE, MUST NOT EXCEED THE WORKING LIMITS OF THE RESPIRATOR AND BE JOINTLY APPROVED BY THE NATIONAL INSTITUTE FOR OCCUPATIONAL SAFETY AND HEALTH AND THE MINE SAFETY AND HEALTH ADMINISTRATION (NIOSH-MSHA).

CHEMICAL CARTRIDGE RESPIRATOR WITH AN ORGANIC VAPOR CARTRIDGE(S) IN COMBINATION WITH A DUST AND MIST FILTER.

GAS MASK WITH ORGANIC VAPOR CANISTER (CHIN-STYLE OR FRONT- OR BACK-MOUNTED CANISTER) WITH A DUST AND MIST FILTER.

GAS MASK WITH ORGANIC VAPOR CANISTER (CHIN-STYLE OR FRONT- OR BACK-MOUNTED CANISTER) WITH A PARTICULATE FILTER.

POWERED AIR-PURIFYING RESPIRATOR WITH A HIGH-EFFICIENCY FILTER.

TYPE 'C' SUPPLIED-AIR RESPIRATOR WITH A FULL FACEPIECE OPERATED IN A PRESSURE-DEMAND OR OTHER POSITIVE PRESSURE MODE.

SELF-CONTAINED BREATHING APPARATUS WITH A FULL FACEPIECE OPERATED IN PRESSURE-DEMAND OR OTHER POSITIVE PRESSURE MODE.

FOR FIREFIGHTING AND OTHER IMMEDIATELY DANGEROUS TO LIFE OR HEALTH CONDITIONS:

SELF-CONTAINED BREATHING APPARATUS WITH FULL FACEPIECE OPERATED IN PRESSURE-DEMAND OR OTHER POSITIVE PRESSURE MODE.

SUPPLIED-AIR RESPIRATOR WITH FULL FACEPIECE AND OPERATED IN PRESSURE-DEMAND OR OTHER POSITIVE PRESSURE MODE IN COMBINATION WITH AN AUXILIARY SELF-CONTAINED BREATHING APPARATUS OPERATED IN PRESSURE-DEMAND OR OTHER POSITIVE PRESSURE MODE.

CLOTHING: EMPLOYEE MUST WEAR APPROPRIATE PROTECTIVE (IMPERVIOUS) CLOTHING AND EQUIPMENT TO PREVENT REPEATED OR PROLONGED SKIN CONTACT WITH THIS SUBSTANCE.

GLOVES: EMPLOYEE MUST WEAR APPROPRIATE PROTECTIVE GLOVES TO PREVENT CONTACT WITH THIS SUBSTANCE.

EYE PROTECTION: EMPLOYEE MUST WEAR SPLASH-PROOF OR DUST-RESISTANT SAFETY GOGGLES TO PREVENT EYE CONTACT WITH THIS SUBSTANCE.

EMERGENCY EYE WASH: WHERE THERE IS ANY POSSIBILITY THAT AN EMPLOYEE'S EYES MAY BE EXPOSED TO THIS SUBSTANCE, THE EMPLOYER SHOULD PROVIDE AN EYE WASH FOUNTAIN WITHIN THE IMMEDIATE WORK AREA FOR EMERGENCY USE.

AUTHORIZED BY- OCCUPATIONAL HEALTH SERVICES, INC.

CREATION DATE: 10/04/89 ***REVISION DATE:*** 06/12/90

MATERIAL SAFETY DATA SHEET

OCCUPATIONAL HEALTH SERVICES, INC.
AGRICULTURE AND PESTICIDE DIVISION
450 SEVENTH AVENUE, SUITE 2407
NEW YORK, NEW YORK 10123
1-800-445-MSDS OR (212) 967-1100

EMERGENCY CONTACT:
JOHN S. BRANSFORD, JR. (615) 292-1180

SUBSTANCE IDENTIFICATION

CAS-NUMBER 919-86-8

SUBSTANCE: DEMETON-S-METHYL

TRADE NAMES/SYNONYMS: PHOSPHOROTHIOIC ACID, S-(2-(ETHYLTHIO)ETHYL)O,O-DIMETHYL ESTER; S-(2-(ETHYLTHIO)ETHYL)O,O-DIMETHYL PHOSPHOROTHIOATE; S-2-ETHYLTHIOETHYL O,O-DIMETHYL PHOSPHOROTHIOATE; METASYSTOX I (FORMULATION); METHYL DEMETON THIOESTER; BAYER 18.436; ISOMETASYSTOX (FORMULATION); DURATOX (FORMULATION); BAYER 25/154; C6H15O3PS2; PST83065

CHEMICAL FAMILY: ORGANOPHOSPHATE

MOLECULAR FORMULA: C2-H5-S-C2-H4-S-P-(O)-(O-C-H3)2

MOLECULAR WEIGHT: 230.30

CERCLA RATINGS (SCALE 0-3): HEALTH=3 FIRE=U REACTIVITY=0 PERSISTENCE=0

NFPA RATINGS (SCALE 0-4): HEALTH=4 FIRE=U REACTIVITY=0

COMPONENTS AND CONTAMINANTS

COMPONENT: DEMETON-S-METHYL ***PERCENT:*** 100.0
CAS# 919-86-8

OTHER CONTAMINANTS: NONE

EXPOSURE LIMITS: NO OCCUPATIONAL EXPOSURE LIMITS ESTABLISHED BY OSHA, ACGIH, OR NIOSH.
DEMETON-S-METHYL 500 POUNDS SARA SECTION 302 THRESHOLD PLANNING QUANTITY 1 POUND SARA SECTION 304 REPORTABLE QUANTITY

PHYSICAL DATA

DESCRIPTION: PALE YELLOW, OILY LIQUID.

BOILING POINT: 192 F (89 C) @ 0.15 MMHG

SPECIFIC GRAVITY: 1.207 ***VAPOR PRESSURE:*** 0.00036 MMHG @ 20 C

SOLUBILITY IN WATER: 0.33%

SOLVENT SOLUBILITY: SOLUBLE IN ORGANIC SOLVENTS.

FIRE AND EXPLOSION DATA

FIRE AND EXPLOSION HAZARD: UNKNOWN FIRE AND EXPLOSION HAZARD.

FLASH POINT: NOT AVAILABLE

FIREFIGHTING MEDIA: DRY CHEMICAL, CARBON DIOXIDE, HALON, WATER SPRAY OR STANDARD FOAM (1987 EMERGENCY RESPONSE GUIDEBOOK, DOT P 5800.4).
FOR LARGER FIRES, USE WATER SPRAY, FOG OR STANDARD FOAM (1987 EMERGENCY RESPONSE GUIDEBOOK, DOT P 5800.4).

FIREFIGHTING: MOVE CONTAINER FROM FIRE AREA IF POSSIBLE. DIKE FIRE CONTROL WATER FOR LATER DISPOSAL; DO NOT SCATTER THE MATERIAL. COOL FIRE-EXPOSED CONTAINERS WITH WATER FROM SIDE UNTIL WELL AFTER FIRE IS OUT. STAY AWAY FROM STORAGE TANK ENDS. WITHDRAW IMMEDIATELY IN CASE OF RISING SOUND FROM VENTING SAFETY DEVICE OR ANY DISCOLORATION OF STORAGE TANK DUE TO FIRE (1987 EMERGENCY RESPONSE GUIDEBOOK, DOT P 5800.4, GUIDE PAGE 28).
EXTINGUISH ONLY IF FLOW CAN BE STOPPED. USE FLOODING AMOUNTS OF WATER AS A FOG; SOLID STREAMS MAY BE INEFFECTIVE. COOL CONTAINERS WITH FLOODING AMOUNTS OF WATER FROM AS FAR A DISTANCE AS POSSIBLE. AVOID BREATHING POISONOUS VAPORS, KEEP UPWIND.

TRANSPORTATION DATA

DEPARTMENT OF TRANSPORTATION HAZARD CLASSIFICATION 49 CFR 172.101: POISON B
DEPARTMENT OF TRANSPORTATION LABELING REQUIREMENTS 49 CFR 172.101 AND SUBPART E: POISON
DEPARTMENT OF TRANSPORTATION PACKAGING REQUIREMENTS: 49 CFR 173.365 EXCEPTIONS: 49 CFR 173.364

TOXICITY

DEMETON-S-METHYL: TOXICITY DATA: 500 MG/M3/4 HOURS INHALATION-RAT LC50; 85 MG/KG SKIN-RAT LD50; 110 MG/KG ORAL-GUINEA PIG LD50; 40 MG/KG ORAL-RAT LD50; 65 MG/KG INTRAVENOUS-RAT LD50; 7500 UG/KG INTRAPERITONEAL-RAT LD50; 12,500 UG/KG INTRAPERITONEAL-GUINEA PIG LD50; 40 MG/KG UNREPORTED-MAMMAL LD50; MUTAGENIC DATA (RTECS). CARCINOGEN STATUS: NONE. ACUTE TOXICITY LEVEL: HIGHLY TOXIC BY INHALATION, DERMAL ABSORPTION, AND INGESTION. TARGET EFFECTS: CHOLINESTERASE INHIBITOR. POISONING MAY AFFECT THE NERVOUS SYSTEM.* AT INCREASED RISK FROM EXPOSURE: PERSONS WITH RESPIRATORY AILMENTS, RECENT EXPOSURE TO CHOLINESTERASE INHIBITORS OR IMPAIRED CHOLINESTERASE PRODUCTION, OR LIVER MALFUNCTION.* ADDITIONAL DATA: MAY CROSS THE PLACENTA. HIGH ENVIRONMENTAL TEMPERATURES OR EXPOSURE OF THE CHEMICAL TO VISIBLE OR ULTRAVIOLET LIGHT MAY ENHANCE THE TOXICITY. INTERACTIONS WITH MEDICATIONS MAY OCCUR.*
* MAY BE BASED ON GENERAL INFORMATION ON ORGANOPHOSPHATES.

HEALTH EFFECTS AND FIRST AID

INHALATION: DEMETON-S-METHYL: HIGHLY TOXIC. SEE INFORMATION ON ORGANOPHOSPHATES.
ORGANOPHOSPHATES: CHOLINESTERASE INHIBITOR. **ACUTE EXPOSURE-** WHEN INHALED, THE FIRST EFFECTS OF CHOLINESTERASE INHIBITORS ARE USUALLY RESPIRATORY AND MAY INCLUDE NASAL HYPEREMIA AND WATERY DISCHARGE, COUGH, CHEST DISCOMFORT, DYSPNEA, AND WHEEZING DUE TO INCREASED BRONCHIAL SECRETIONS AND BRONCHOCONSTRICTION. IF SUFFICIENT AMOUNTS ARE ABSORBED, OTHER SYSTEMIC EFFECTS MAY BEGIN WITHIN A FEW MINUTES OR BE DELAYED FOR UP TO 12 HOURS. SYMPTOMS MAY INCLUDE PALLOR, NAUSEA, VOMITING, DIARRHEA, ABDOMINAL CRAMPS, HEADACHE, DIZZINESS, OCULAR PAIN, BLURRED VISION, MIOSIS OR IN SOME CASES, ESPECIALLY INITIALLY, MYDRIASIS, LACRIMATION, SALIVATION, SWEATING, AND CONFUSION. OTHER REPORTED CENTRAL NERVOUS SYSTEM OR NEUROMUSCULAR EFFECTS MAY INCLUDE ATAXIA, SLURRED SPEECH, AREFLEXIA, WEAKNESS, FATIGUE, FASCICULATIONS, TWITCHING, TREMORS POSSIBLY OF THE TONGUE AND EYELIDS, AND EVENTUALLY PARALYSIS OF THE EXTREMITIES AND POSSIBLY OF THE RESPIRATORY MUSCLES. IN SEVERE CASES THERE MAY ALSO BE INVOLUNTARY DEFECATION AND URINATION, CYANOSIS, PSYCHOSIS, HYPERGLYCEMIA, ACUTE PANCREATITIS, CARDIAC IRREGULARITIES, PULMONARY EDEMA, UNCONSCIOUSNESS, CONVULSIONS, AND COMA. DEATH IS PRIMARILY DUE TO RESPIRATORY FAILURE, ALTHOUGH CARDIOVASCULAR EFFECTS INCLUDING CARDIAC ARREST MAY ALSO BE IMPLICATED. LONG TERM SEQUELAE ARE RARE BUT MAY INCLUDE NEUROPSYCHIATRIC DISORDERS AND MYOPATHY WITH MUSCLE TENDERNESS. SOME ORGANOPHOSPHATES MAY CAUSE A DELAYED NEUROPATHY BEGINNING 1-4 WEEKS AFTER AN ACUTE EXPOSURE WHICH MAY OR MAY NOT HAVE CAUSED ACUTE CHOLINERGIC EFFECTS. NUMBNESS, TINGLING, WEAKNESS AND CRAMPING BEGINNING SYMMETRICALLY IN THE LOWER LIMBS MAY PROGRESS TO ATAXIA AND PARALYSIS. IN SEVERE CASES, UPPER LIMB INVOLVEMENT IS POSSIBLE AND FLACCID PARALYSIS MAY PROGRESS TO SPASTIC PARALYSIS WITH EXAGGERATED REFLEXES. IMPROVEMENT MAY OCCUR OVER MONTHS TO YEARS, BUT SOME RESIDUAL IMPAIRMENT USUALLY REMAINS.
CHRONIC EXPOSURE- REPEATED OR PROLONGED EXPOSURE MAY RESULT IN THE EFFECTS OF ACUTE EXPOSURE INCLUDING THE DELAYED NEUROPATHY. OTHER EFFECTS REPORTED IN WORKERS REPEATEDLY EXPOSED INCLUDE IMPAIRED MEMORY AND CONCENTRATION, ACUTE PSYCHOSIS, SEVERE DEPRESSIONS, IRRITABILTY, CONFUSION, APATHY, EMOTIONAL LABILITY, SOCIAL WITHDRAWAL, CONFUSION, HEADACHE, SPEECH DIFFICULTIES, DELAYED REACTION TIMES, SPATIAL DISORIENTATION, NIGHTMARES, SLEEPWALKING, AND DROWSINESS OR INSOMNIA. AN INFLUENZA-LIKE CONDITION WITH HEADACHE, NAUSEA, WEAKNESS, ANOREXIA AND MALAISE HAS ALSO BEEN REPORTED.

FIRST AID- REMOVE FROM EXPOSURE AREA TO FRESH AIR IMMEDIATELY. IF BREATHING HAS STOPPED, GIVE ARTIFICIAL RESPIRATION. MAINTAIN AIRWAY AND BLOOD PRESSURE AND ADMINISTER OXYGEN IF AVAILABLE. KEEP AFFECTED PERSON WARM AND AT REST. TREAT SYMPTOMATICALLY AND SUPPORTIVELY. ADMINISTRATION OF OXYGEN SHOULD BE PERFORMED BY QUALIFIED PERSONNEL. GET MEDICAL ATTENTION IMMEDIATELY.

SKIN CONTACT: DEMETON-S-METHYL: HIGHLY TOXIC. SEE INFORMATION ON ORGANOPHOSPHATES.
ORGANOPHOSPHATES: CHOLINESTERASE INHIBITOR. **ACUTE EXPOSURE-** LOCALIZED SWEATING AND FASCICULATIONS MAY OCCUR AT THE SITE OF CONTACT. IF SUFFICIENT AMOUNTS ARE ABSORBED, OTHER EFFECTS OF CHOLINESTERASE INHIBITION AS DESCRIBED IN ACUTE INHALATION MAY OCCUR. SYMPTOMS MAY BE DELAYED 2-3 HOURS, BUT USUALLY NO MORE THAN 12 HOURS. THE RATE OF ABSORPTION IS INCREASED BY THE PRESENCE OF DERMATITIS OR HIGH AMBIENT TEMPERATURES. DELAYED NEUROPATHY IS ALSO POSSIBLE. **CHRONIC EXPOSURE-** REPEATED OR PROLONGED EXPOSURE MAY CAUSE EFFECTS AS DESCRIBED IN ACUTE EXPOSURE. SOME ORGANOPHOSPHATES MAY CAUSE SENSITIZATION.

FIRST AID- REMOVE CONTAMINATED CLOTHING IMMEDIATELY. WASH CONTAMINATED AREAS WITH SOAP AND WATER FOLLOWED BY ALCOHOL (ARENA, POISONING, 4TH ED.). EMERGENCY PERSONNEL SHOULD WEAR GLOVES AND AVOID CONTAMINATION. TREAT RESPIRATORY DIFFICULTY WITH ARTIFICIAL RESPIRATION. GET MEDICAL ATTENTION IMMEDIATELY.

EYE CONTACT: DEMETON-S-METHYL: SEE INFORMATION ON ORGANOPHOSPHATES.
ORGANOPHOSPHATES: CHOLINESTERASE INHIBITOR. **ACUTE EXPOSURE-** DIRECT CONTACT MAY CAUSE PAIN, HYPEREMIA, LACRIMATION, TWITCHING OF THE EYELIDS, MIOSIS, AND CILIARY MUSCLE SPASM WITH LOSS OF ACCOMODATION,

BLURRED OR DIMMED VISION AND BROWACHE. SOMETIMES MYDRIASIS MAY OCCUR INSTEAD OF MIOSIS. WITH SUFFICIENT EXPOSURE, OTHER SYMPTOMS OF CHOLINESTERASE INHIBITION AS DESCRIBED IN ACUTE INHALATION MAY OCCUR. **CHRONIC EXPOSURE-** REPEATED OR PROLONGED EXPOSURE MAY CAUSE EFFECTS AS DESCRIBED IN ACUTE EXPOSURE. SOME COMPOUNDS HAVE CAUSED TOXIC EFFECTS ON THE CRYSTALLINE LENS, CONJUNCTIVAL THICKENING AND OBSTRUCTION OF THE NASOLACRIMAL CANALS WHEN USED AS MIOTIC EYEDROPS.

FIRST AID- IRRIGATE EYES WITH WATER OR SALINE SOLUTION. IF SYMPTOMS OF POISONING OCCUR, TREAT RESPIRATORY DIFFICULTY WITH ARTIFICIAL RESPIRATION AND OXYGEN. OBSERVE PATIENT FOR AT LEAST 24-36 HOURS (GOSSELIN, CLINICAL TOXICOLOGY OF COMMERCIAL PRODUCTS, 5TH ED.). GET MEDICAL ATTENTION IMMEDIATELY. OXYGEN SHOULD BE ADMINISTERED BY QUALIFIED MEDICAL PERSONNEL.

INGESTION: DEMETON-S-METHYL: HIGHLY TOXIC. SEE INFORMATION ON ORGANOPHOSPHATES.

ORGANOPHOSPHATES: CHOLINESTERASE INHIBITOR. **ACUTE EXPOSURE-** WHEN INGESTED, THE FIRST EFFECTS MAY BE NAUSEA, VOMITING, ANOREXIA, ABDOMINAL CRAMPS AND DIARRHEA. GASTROINTESTINAL ABSORPTION MAY CAUSE SYMPTOMS OF CHOLINESTERASE INHIBITION AS DESCRIBED IN ACUTE INHALATION. SYMPTOMS MAY BEGIN WITHIN MINUTES OR BE DELAYED FOR HOURS. DELAYED EFFECTS INCLUDING NEUROPATHY MAY ALSO OCCUR. **CHRONIC EXPOSURE-** REPEATED INGESTION MAY CAUSE EFFECTS AS DESCRIBED IN ACUTE EXPOSURE.

FIRST AID- IF PERSON IS ALERT AND RESPIRATION IS NOT DEPRESSED, GIVE SYRUP OF IPECAC FOLLOWED BY WATER (IF VOMITING OCCURS, KEEP HEAD BELOW HIPS TO PREVENT ASPIRATION). IF CONSCIOUSNESS LEVEL DECLINES OR VOMITING HAS NOT OCCURRED IN 15 MINUTES EMPTY STOMACH BY GASTRIC LAVAGE WITH THE AID OF CUFFED ENDOTRACHEAL TUBE USING ISOTONIC SALINE OR 5% SODIUM BICARBONATE FOLLOW WITH ACTIVATED CHARCOAL. ESTABLISH AND MAINTAIN AIRWAY. TREAT RESPIRATORY DIFFICULTY WITH ARTIFICIAL RESPIRATION AND OXYGEN. DO NOT GIVE MORPHINE, AMINOPHYLLINE, PHENOTHIAZINES, RESERPINE, FUROSEMIDE, OR ETHACRYNIC ACID (MORGAN, RECOGNITION AND MANAGEMENT OF PESTICIDE POISONINGS, 3RD ED.). TREAT SYMPTOMATICALLY AND SUPPORTIVELY. ADMINISTRATION OF OXYGEN AND LAVAGE MUST BE PERFORMED BY QUALIFIED MEDICAL PERSONNEL. GET MEDICAL ATTENTION IMMEDIATELY.

ANTIDOTE: THE FOLLOWING ANTIDOTE(S) HAVE BEEN RECOMMENDED. HOWEVER, THE DECISION AS TO WHETHER THE SEVERITY OF POISONING REQUIRES ADMINISTRATION OF ANY ANTIDOTE AND ACTUAL DOSE REQUIRED SHOULD BE MADE BY QUALIFIED MEDICAL PERSONNEL.

FOR CHOLINESTERASE INHIBITORS: ESTABLISH CLEAR AIRWAY AND TISSUE OXYGENATION BY ASPIRATION OF SECRETIONS, AND IF NECESSARY, BY ASSISTED PULMONARY VENTILATION WITH OXYGEN. IMPROVE TISSUE OXYGENATION AS MUCH AS POSSIBLE BEFORE ADMINISTERING ATROPINE TO MINIMIZE THE RISK OF VENTRICULAR FIBRILLATION. ADMINISTER ATROPINE SULFATE INTRAVENOUSLY, OR INTRAMUSCULARLY IF IV INJECTION IS NOT POSSIBLE. IN MODERATELY SEVERE POISONING ADMINISTER ATROPINE SULFATE, 0.4-2.0 MG REPEATED EVERY 15 MINUTES UNTIL ATROPINIZATION IS ACHIEVED (TACHYCARDIA, FLUSHING, DRY MOUTH, MYDRIASIS). MAINTAIN ATROPINIZATION BY REPEATED DOSES FOR 2-12 HOURS, OR LONGER, DEPENDING ON THE SEVERITY OF POISONING. THE APPEARANCE OF RALES IN THE LUNG BASES, MIOSIS, SALIVATION, NAUSEA, BRADYCARDIA, ARE ALL INDICATIONS OF INADEQUATE ATROPINIZATION. SEVERELY POISONED INDIVIDUALS MAY EXHIBIT REMARKABLE TOLERANCE TO ATROPINE; TWO OR MORE TIMES THE DOSAGES SUGGESTED ABOVE MAY BE NEEDED. PERSONS NOT POISONED OR ONLY SLIGHTLY POISONED, HOWEVER, MAY DEVELOP SIGNS OF ATROPINE TOXICITY FROM SUCH LARGE DOSAGES: FEVER, MUSCLE FIBRILLATIONS, AND DELIRIUM ARE THE MAIN SIGNS OF ATROPINE TOXICITY. IF THESE SIGNS APPEAR WHILE THE PATIENT IS FULLY ATROPINIZED, ATROPINE ADMINISTRATION SHOULD BE DISCONTINUED, AT LEAST TEMPORARILY. OBSERVE TREATED PATIENTS CLOSELY AT LEAST 24 HOURS TO INSURE THAT SYMPTOMS (POSSIBLY PULMONARY EDEMA) DO NOT RECUR AS ATROPINIZATION WEARS OFF. IN VERY SEVERE POISONINGS, METABOLIC DISPOSITION OF TOXICANT MAY REQUIRE SEVERAL HOURS OR DAYS DURING WHICH ATROPINIZATION MUST BE MAINTAINED. MARKEDLY LOWER LEVELS OF URINARY METABOLITES INDICATE THAT ATROPINE DOSAGE CAN BE TAPERED OFF. AS DOSAGE IS REDUCED, CHECK THE LUNG BASES FREQUENTLY FOR RALES. IF RALES ARE HEARD OR OTHER SYMPTOMS RETURN, RE-ESTABLISH ATROPINIZATION PROMPTLY (MORGAN, RECOGNITION AND MANAGEMENT OF PESTICIDE POISONINGS, 3RD ED.). ADMINISTRATION OF ANTIDOTE MUST BE PERFORMED BY QUALIFIED MEDICAL PERSONNEL.

IN CASES OF SEVERE POISONING BY ORGANOPHOSPHATE PESTICIDES IN WHICH RESPIRATORY DEPRESSION, MUSCLE WEAKNESS AND TWITCHINGS ARE SEVERE, GIVE PRALIDOXIME (PROTOPAM-AYERST, 2-PAM), 1.0 GRAM INTRAVENOUSLY AT NO MORE THAN 0.5 GRAM PER MINUTE. DOSAGE OF PRALIDOXIME MAY BE REPEATED IN 1-2 HOURS, THEN AT 10-12 HOUR INTERVALS IF NEEDED. IN VERY SEVERE POISONINGS, DOSAGE RATES MAY BE DOUBLED. TREATMENT WITH PRALIDOXIME WILL BE MOST EFFECTIVE IF GIVEN WITHIN THIRTY-SIX HOURS AFTER POISONING (MORGAN, RECOGNITION AND MANAGEMENT OF PESTICIDE POISONINGS, 3RD ED.). ANTIDOTE SHOULD BE ADMINISTERED BY QUALIFIED MEDICAL PERSONNEL.

REACTIVITY

REACTIVITY: STABLE UNDER NORMAL TEMPERATURES AND PRESSURES.

INCOMPATIBILITIES: DEMETON-S-METHYL: OXIDIZERS (STRONG): FIRE AND EXPLOSION HAZARD.

DECOMPOSITION: THERMAL DECOMPOSITION PRODUCTS MAY INCLUDE TOXIC OXIDES OF CARBON, SULFUR, AND PHOSPHORUS.

POLYMERIZATION: HAZARDOUS POLYMERIZATION HAS NOT BEEN REPORTED TO OCCUR UNDER NORMAL TEMPERATURES AND PRESSURES.

STORAGE AND DISPOSAL

OBSERVE ALL FEDERAL, STATE AND LOCAL REGULATIONS WHEN STORING OR DISPOSING OF THIS SUBSTANCE. FOR ASSISTANCE, CONTACT THE DISTRICT DIRECTOR OF THE ENVIRONMENTAL PROTECTION AGENCY.

STORAGE

STORE IN ACCORDANCE WITH 40 CFR 165 RECOMMENDED PROCEDURES FOR THE DISPOSAL AND STORAGE OF PESTICIDES AND PESTICIDE CONTAINERS.

STORE AWAY FROM INCOMPATIBLE SUBSTANCES.

MAY SELF-REACT ON STORAGE TO GIVE A MORE TOXIC COMPOUND.

THRESHOLD PLANNING QUANTITY (TPQ): THE SUPERFUND AMENDMENTS AND REAUTHORIZATION ACT (SARA) SECTION 302 REQUIRES THAT EACH FACILITY WHERE ANY EXTREMELY HAZARDOUS SUBSTANCE IS PRESENT IN A QUANTITY EQUAL TO OR GREATER THAN THE TPQ ESTABLISHED FOR THAT SUBSTANCE NOTIFY THE STATE EMERGENCY RESPONSE COMMISSION FOR THE STATE IN WHICH IT IS LOCATED. SECTION 303 OF SARA REQUIRES THESE FACILITIES TO PARTICIPATE IN LOCAL EMERGENCY RESPONSE PLANNING (40 CFR 355.30).

DISPOSAL

DISPOSAL MUST BE IN ACCORDANCE WITH 40 CFR 165 RECOMMENDED PROCEDURES FOR THE DISPOSAL AND STORAGE OF PESTICIDES AND PESTICIDE CONTAINERS.

CONDITIONS TO AVOID

AVOID CONTACT WITH HEAT, SPARKS, FLAMES OR OTHER IGNITION SOURCES. VAPORS MAY BE EXPLOSIVE. MATERIAL IS POISONOUS; AVOID INHALATION OF VAPORS OR CONTACT WITH SKIN. DO NOT ALLOW MATERIAL TO CONTAMINATE WATER SOURCES.

SPILL AND LEAK PROCEDURES

OCCUPATIONAL SPILL: SHUT OFF IGNITION SOURCES. DO NOT TOUCH SPILLED MATERIAL. STOP LEAK IF YOU CAN DO IT WITHOUT RISK. USE WATER SPRAY TO REDUCE VAPORS. FOR SMALL SPILLS, TAKE UP WITH SAND OR OTHER ABSORBENT MATERIAL AND PLACE INTO CONTAINERS FOR LATER DISPOSAL. FOR LARGER SPILLS, DIKE FAR AHEAD OF SPILL FOR LATER DISPOSAL. NO SMOKING, FLAMES OR FLARES IN HAZARD AREA! KEEP UNNECESSARY PEOPLE AWAY; ISOLATE HAZARD AREA AND DENY ENTRY.

REPORTABLE QUANTITY (RQ): 1 POUND THE SUPERFUND AMENDMENTS AND REAUTHORIZATION ACT (SARA) SECTION 304 REQUIRES THAT A RELEASE EQUAL TO OR GREATER THAN THE REPORTABLE QUANTITY FOR THIS SUBSTANCE BE IMMEDIATELY REPORTED TO THE LOCAL EMERGENCY PLANNING COMMITTEE AND THE STATE EMERGENCY RESPONSE COMMISSION (40 CFR 355.40). IF THE RELEASE OF THIS SUBSTANCE IS REPORTABLE UNDER CERCLA SECTION 103, THE NATIONAL RESPONSE CENTER MUST BE NOTIFIED IMMEDIATELY AT (800) 424-8802 OR (202) 426-2675 IN THE METROPOLITAN WASHINGTON, D.C. AREA (40 CFR 302.6).

PROTECTIVE EQUIPMENT

VENTILATION: PROVIDE LOCAL EXHAUST OR PROCESS ENCLOSURE VENTILATION. VENTILATION EQUIPMENT MUST BE EXPLOSION-PROOF.

RESPIRATOR: THE FOLLOWING RESPIRATORS ARE RECOMMENDED BASED ON INFORMATION FOUND IN THE PHYSICAL DATA, TOXICITY AND HEALTH EFFECTS SECTIONS. THEY ARE RANKED IN ORDER FROM MINIMUM TO MAXIMUM RESPIRATORY PROTECTION. THE SPECIFIC RESPIRATOR SELECTED MUST BE BASED ON CONTAMINATION LEVELS FOUND IN THE WORK PLACE, MUST NOT EXCEED THE WORKING LIMITS OF THE RESPIRATOR AND BE JOINTLY APPROVED BY THE NATIONAL INSTITUTE FOR OCCUPATIONAL SAFETY AND HEALTH AND THE MINE SAFETY AND HEALTH ADMINISTRATION (NIOSH-MSHA).

TYPE 'C' SUPPLIED-AIR RESPIRATOR WITH A FULL FACEPIECE OPERATED IN PRESSURE-DEMAND OR OTHER POSITIVE PRESSURE MODE OR WITH A FULL FACEPIECE, HELMET OR HOOD OPERATED IN CONTINOUS-FLOW MODE.

SELF-CONTAINED BREATHING APPARATUS WITH A FULL FACEPIECE OPERATED IN PRESSURE-DEMAND OR OTHER POSITIVE PRESSURE MODE.

FOR FIREFIGHTING AND OTHER IMMEDIATELY DANGEROUS TO LIFE OR HEALTH CONDITIONS:
SELF-CONTAINED BREATHING APPARATUS WITH FULL FACEPIECE OPERATED IN PRESSURE-DEMAND OR OTHER POSITIVE PRESSURE MODE.
SUPPLIED-AIR RESPIRATOR WITH FULL FACEPIECE AND OPERATED IN PRESSURE-DEMAND OR OTHER POSITIVE PRESSURE MODE IN COMBINATION WITH AN AUXILIARY SELF-CONTAINED BREATHING APPARATUS OPERATED IN PRESSURE-DEMAND OR OTHER POSITIVE PRESSURE MODE.

CLOTHING: EMPLOYEE MUST WEAR APPROPRIATE PROTECTIVE (IMPERVIOUS) CLOTHING AND EQUIPMENT TO PREVENT ANY POSSIBILITY OF SKIN CONTACT WITH THIS SUBSTANCE.

GLOVES: EMPLOYEE MUST WEAR APPROPRIATE PROTECTIVE GLOVES TO PREVENT CONTACT WITH THIS SUBSTANCE.

EYE PROTECTION: EMPLOYEE MUST WEAR SPLASH-PROOF OR DUST-RESISTANT SAFETY GOGGLES AND A FACESHIELD TO PREVENT CONTACT WITH THIS SUBSTANCE.
EMERGENCY WASH FACILITIES: WHERE THERE IS ANY POSSIBILITY THAT AN EMPLOYEE'S EYES AND/OR SKIN MAY BE EXPOSED TO THIS SUBSTANCE, THE EMPLOYER SHOULD PROVIDE AN EYE WASH FOUNTAIN AND QUICK DRENCH SHOWER WITHIN THE IMMEDIATE WORK AREA FOR EMERGENCY USE.

AUTHORIZED BY- OCCUPATIONAL HEALTH SERVICES, INC.
CREATION DATE: 10/04/89 ***REVISION DATE:*** 04/27/90

MATERIAL SAFETY DATA SHEET

OCCUPATIONAL HEALTH SERVICES, INC.
AGRICULTURE AND PESTICIDE DIVISION
450 SEVENTH AVENUE, SUITE 2407
NEW YORK, NEW YORK 10123
1-800-445-MSDS OR (212) 967-1100

EMERGENCY CONTACT:
JOHN S. BRANSFORD, JR. (615) 292-1180

SUBSTANCE IDENTIFICATION

CAS-NUMBER 1129-41-5

SUBSTANCE: **METOLCARB**

TRADE NAMES/SYNONYMS: CARBAMIC ACID, METHYL-, 3-METHYLPHENYL ESTER; CARBAMIC ACID, METHYL-, M-TOLY ESTER; METHYL CARBAMIC ACID, 3-METHYLPHENYL ESTER; METHYL CARBAMIC ACID, M-TOLY ESTER; M-CRESYL METHYLCARBAMATE; M-METHYLPHENYL METHYLCARBAMATE; 3-METHYLPHENYL METHYLCARBAMATE; M-TOLYL METHYLCARBAMATE; 3-TOLYL-N-METHYLCARBAMATE; 3-TOLYL METHYLCARBAMATE; DRC 3341; METACRATE; 12MC; S 1065; TSUMACIDE; TSUMAUNKA; PST83074

CHEMICAL FAMILY: CARBAMATE

MOLECULAR FORMULA: C9-H11-N-O2

MOLECULAR WEIGHT: 165.21

CERCLA RATINGS (SCALE 0-3): HEALTH=3 FIRE=0 REACTIVITY=U PERSISTENCE=2

NFPA RATINGS (SCALE 0-4): HEALTH=4 FIRE=0 REACTIVITY=U

COMPONENTS AND CONTAMINANTS

COMPONENT: METOLCARB ***PERCENT:*** 100.0
CAS# 1129-41-5

OTHER CONTAMINANTS: NONE

EXPOSURE LIMITS: NO OCCUPATIONAL EXPOSURE LIMITS ESTABLISHED BY OSHA, ACGIH, OR NIOSH.
METOLCARB: 100/10,000 POUNDS SARA SECTION 302 THRESHOLD PLANNING QUANTITY 1 POUND SARA SECTION 304 REPORTABLE QUANTITY

PHYSICAL DATA

DESCRIPTION: COLORLESS CRYSTALLINE SOLID

MELTING POINT: 169-171 F (76-77 C)

SPECIFIC GRAVITY: NOT AVAILABLE ***VAPOR PRESSURE:*** 0.00001 MMHG @ 25 C

SOLUBILITY IN WATER: .26% @ 30 C

SOLVENT SOLUBILITY: SOLUBLE IN CYCLOHEXANONE, XYLENE, METHANOL, MOST POLAR SOLVENTS; HARDLY SOLUBLE IN NONPOLAR SOLVENTS

FIRE AND EXPLOSION DATA

FIRE AND EXPLOSION HAZARD: NEGLIGIBLE FIRE HAZARD WHEN EXPOSED TO HEAT OR FLAME.

FIREFIGHTING MEDIA: DRY CHEMICAL, CARBON DIOXIDE, HALON, WATER SPRAY OR STANDARD FOAM (1987 EMERGENCY RESPONSE GUIDEBOOK, DOT P 5800.4).
FOR LARGER FIRES, USE WATER SPRAY, FOG OR STANDARD FOAM (1987 EMERGENCY RESPONSE GUIDEBOOK, DOT P 5800.4).

FIREFIGHTING: MOVE CONTAINERS FROM FIRE AREA IF POSSIBLE (1987 EMERGENCY RESPONSE GUIDEBOOK, DOT P 5800.4, GUIDE PAGE 53).
EXTINGUISH USING AGENT SUITABLE FOR TYPE OF SURROUNDING FIRE. AVOID BREATHING VAPORS AND DUSTS. KEEP UPWIND.

TRANSPORTATION DATA

DEPARTMENT OF TRANSPORTATION HAZARD CLASSIFICATION 49 CFR 172.101: POISON B
DEPARTMENT OF TRANSPORTATION LABELING REQUIREMENTS 49 CFR 172.101 AND SUBPART E: POISON
DEPARTMENT OF TRANSPORTATION PACKAGING REQUIREMENTS: 49 CFR 173.365 EXCEPTIONS: 49 CFR 173.364

TOXICITY

METOLCARB: TOXICITY DATA: 3400 UG/M3/2 DAYS-INTERMITTENT INHALATION-HUMAN TCLO; 475 MG/M3 INHALATION-RAT LC50; 896 MG/KG SKIN-RAT LD50; 6 MG/KG SKIN-MOUSE LD50; 268 MG/KG ORAL-RAT LD50; 109 MG/KG ORAL-MOUSE LD50; 430 MG/KG UNREPORTED-RAT LD50; 270 MG/KG UNREPORTED-MOUSE LD50; MUTAGENIC DATA (RTECS). CARCINOGEN STATUS: NONE. ACUTE TOXICITY LEVEL: HIGHLY TOXIC BY INHALATION AND SKIN ABSORPTION; TOXIC BY INGESTION. TARGET EFFECTS: CHOLINESTERASE INHIBITOR. AT INCREASED RISK FROM EXPOSURE: PERSONS WITH ASTHMA, DIABETES, CARDIOVASCULAR DISEASE, MECHANICAL OBSTRUCTION OF THE GASTROINTESTINAL OR UROGENITAL TRACT, AND THOSE IN VAGOTONIC STATES.*
* MAY BE BASED ON GENERAL INFORMATION ON CARBAMATES.

HEALTH EFFECTS AND FIRST AID

INHALATION: METOLCARB: HIGHLY TOXIC. MAY CAUSE IRRITATION. SEE INFORMATION ON CARBAMATES.
CARBAMATES: CHOLINESTERASE INHIBITOR. **ACUTE EXPOSURE-** WHEN INHALED, THE FIRST EFFECTS OF CHOLINESTERASE INHIBITION ARE USUALLY RESPIRATORY AND MAY INCLUDE NASAL HYPEREMIA AND WATERY DISCHARGE, CHEST DISCOMFORT, DYSPNEA, AND WHEEZING DUE TO INCREASED BRONCHIAL SECRETIONS AND BRONCHOCONSTRICTION. OTHER SYSTEMIC EFFECTS MAY BEGIN WITHIN A FEW MINUTES OR SEVERAL HOURS OF EXPOSURE. SYMPTOMS MAY INCLUDE NAUSEA, VOMITING, DIARRHEA, ABDOMINAL CRAMPS, HEADACHE, VERTIGO, OCULAR PAIN, CILIARY MUSCLE SPASM, BLURRING OR DIMNESS OF VISION, MIOSIS, OR IN SOME CASES MYDRIASIS, LACRIMATION, SALIVATION, SWEATING, AND CONFUSION. OTHER REPORTED CENTRAL NERVOUS SYSTEM OR NEUROMUSCULAR EFFECTS INCLUDE ATAXIA, SLURRED SPEECH, AREFLEXIA, WEAKNESS, FATIGUE, TWITCHING, FASCICULATION, TREMOR, AND EVENTUALLY PARALYSIS OF THE EXTREMITIES AND POSSIBLY OF THE RESPIRATORY MUSCLES. IN SEVERE CASES, THERE MAY ALSO BE INVOLUNTARY DEFECATION AND URINATION, BRADYCARDIA, HYPOTENSION, PULMONARY EDEMA, CONVULSIONS, COMA, AND DEATH FROM RESPIRATORY FAILURE OR CARDIAC ARREST. CARBAMATES GENERALLY DO NOT ACCUMULATE IN MAMMALIAN TISSUE AND THE CHOLINESTERASE INHIBITION REVERSES RATHER RAPIDLY. IN NON-FATAL CASES, THE ILLNESS GENERALLY LASTS LESS THAN 24 HOURS. **CHRONIC EXPOSURE-** PROLONGED OR REPEATED EXPOSURE MAY CAUSE EFFECTS AS DESCRIBED IN ACUTE EXPOSURE.

FIRST AID- REMOVE FROM EXPOSURE AREA TO FRESH AIR IMMEDIATELY. IF BREATHING HAS STOPPED, GIVE ARTIFICIAL RESPIRATION. MAINTAIN AIRWAY AND BLOOD PRESSURE AND ADMINISTER OXYGEN IF AVAILABLE. KEEP AFFECTED PERSON WARM AND AT REST. TREAT SYMPTOMATICALLY AND SUPPORTIVELY. ADMINISTRATION OF OXYGEN SHOULD BE PERFORMED BY QUALIFIED PERSONNEL. GET MEDICAL ATTENTION IMMEDIATELY.

SKIN CONTACT: METOLCARB: HIGHLY TOXIC. MAY CAUSE IRRITATION. PROLONGED OR REPEATED EXPOSURE MAY CAUSE IRRITATION OR DERMATITIS. SEE INFORMATION ON CARBAMATES.
CARBAMATES: CHOLINESTERASE INHIBITOR. **ACUTE EXPOSURE-** SOME COMPOUNDS MAY CAUSE IRRITATION. LOCALIZED SWEATING AND FASCICULATIONS MAY OCCUR AT THE SITE OF CONTACT. IF SUFFICIENT AMOUNTS ARE ABSORBED THROUGH THE SKIN, OTHER EFFECTS OF CHOLINESTERASE INHIBITION MAY OCCUR AS DESCRIBED IN ACUTE INHALATION; SYMPTOMS MAY BE DELAYED FOR 2-3 HOURS, USUALLY NO MORE THAN 8 HOURS. **CHRONIC EXPOSURE-** REPEATED OR PROLONGED EXPOSURE MAY CAUSE EFFECTS AS DESCRIBED IN ACUTE EXPOSURE.

FIRST AID- REMOVE CONTAMINATED CLOTHING IMMEDIATELY. WASH CONTAMINATED AREAS WITH SOAP AND WATER FOLLOWED BY ALCOHOL (ARENA, POISONING, 4TH ED.). EMERGENCY PERSONNEL SHOULD WEAR GLOVES AND AVOID CONTAMINATION. TREAT RESPIRATORY DIFFICULTY WITH ARTIFICIAL RESPIRATION. GET MEDICAL ATTENTION IMMEDIATELY.

EYE CONTACT: METOLCARB: MAY CAUSE IRRITATION. SEE INFORMATION ON CARBAMATES.
CARBAMATES: CHOLINESTERASE INHIBITOR. **ACUTE EXPOSURE-** DIRECT CONTACT MAY CAUSE PAIN, HYPEREMIA, LACRIMATION, TWITCHING OF THE EYELIDS, MIOSIS, AND CILIARY MUSCLE SPASM WITH LOSS OF ACCOMODATION, BLURRED OR DIMMED VISION AND BROWACHE. SOMETIMES MYDRIASIS MAY OCCUR INSTEAD OF MIOSIS. WITH SUFFICIENT EXPOSURE, OTHER SYMPTOMS OF CHOLINESTERASE INHIBITION MAY OCCUR AS DESCRIBED IN ACUTE INHALATION. **CHRONIC EXPOSURE-** PROLONGED EXPOSURE MAY CAUSE EFFECTS AS DESCRIBED IN ACUTE EXPOSURE. SOME COMPOUNDS HAVE CAUSED TOXIC EFFECTS ON THE CRYSTALLINE LENS, CONJUNCTIVAL THICKENING AND OBSTRUCTION OF NASOLACRIMAL CANALS WHEN USED AS MIOTIC EYE DROPS.
FIRST AID- IRRIGATE EYES WITH WATER OR SALINE SOLUTION. IF SYMPTOMS OF POISONING OCCUR, TREAT RESPIRATORY DIFFICULTY WITH ARTIFICIAL RESPIRATION AND OXYGEN. OBSERVE PATIENT FOR AT LEAST 24-36 HOURS (GOSSELIN, CLINICAL TOXICOLOGY OF COMMERCIAL PRODUCTS, 5TH ED.). GET MEDICAL ATTENTION IMMEDIATELY. OXYGEN SHOULD BE ADMINISTERED BY QUALIFIED MEDICAL PERSONNEL.

INGESTION: METOLCARB: TOXIC. SEE INFORMATION ON CARBAMATES.
CARBAMATES: CHOLINESTERASE INHIBITOR. **ACUTE EXPOSURE-** WHEN INGESTED, THE FIRST EFFECTS MAY BE NAUSEA, VOMITING, ANOREXIA, ABDOMINAL CRAMPS, AND DIARRHEA. WITH ABSORPTION FROM THE GASTROINTESTINAL TRACT, THE OTHER EFFECTS OF CHOLINESTERASE INHIBITION AS DESCRIBED IN ACUTE INHALATION MAY OCCUR; SYMPTOMS MAY BEGIN WITHIN MINUTES OR BE DELAYED SEVERAL HOURS. **CHRONIC EXPOSURE-** REPEATED INGESTION MAY CAUSE EFFECTS AS DESCRIBED IN ACUTE EXPOSURE.
FIRST AID- IF PERSON IS ALERT AND RESPIRATION IS NOT DEPRESSED, GIVE SYRUP OF IPECAC FOLLOWED BY WATER (IF VOMITING OCCURS, KEEP HEAD BELOW HIPS TO PREVENT ASPIRATION). IF CONSCIOUSNESS LEVEL DECLINES OR VOMITING HAS NOT OCCURRED IN 15 MINUTES EMPTY STOMACH BY GASTRIC LAVAGE WITH THE AID OF CUFFED ENDOTRACHEAL TUBE USING ISOTONIC SALINE OR 5% SODIUM BICARBONATE FOLLOW WITH ACTIVATED CHARCOAL. ESTABLISH AND MAINTAIN AIRWAY. TREAT RESPIRATORY DIFFICULTY WITH ARTIFICIAL RESPIRATION AND OXYGEN. DO NOT GIVE MORPHINE, AMINOPHYLLINE, PHENOTHIAZINES, RESERPINE, FUROSEMIDE, OR ETHACRYNIC ACID (MORGAN, RECOGNITION AND MANAGEMENT OF PESTICIDE POISONINGS, 3RD ED.). TREAT SYMPTOMATICALLY AND SUPPORTIVELY. ADMINISTRATION OF OXYGEN AND LAVAGE MUST BE PERFORMED BY QUALIFIED MEDICAL PERSONNEL. GET MEDICAL ATTENTION IMMEDIATELY.
ANTIDOTE: THE FOLLOWING ANTIDOTE HAS BEEN RECOMMENDED. HOWEVER, THE DECISION AS TO WHETHER THE SEVERITY OF POISONING REQUIRES ADMINISTRATION OF ANY ANTIDOTE AND ACTUAL DOSE REQUIRED SHOULD BE MADE BY QUALIFIED MEDICAL PERSONNEL.
FOR CHOLINESTERASE INHIBITORS: ESTABLISH CLEAR AIRWAY AND TISSUE OXYGENATION BY ASPIRATION OF SECRETIONS, AND IF NECESSARY, BY ASSISTED PULMONARY VENTILATION WITH OXYGEN. IMPROVE TISSUE OXYGENATION AS MUCH AS POSSIBLE BEFORE ADMINISTERING ATROPINE TO MINIMIZE THE RISK OF VENTRICULAR FIBRILLATION. ADMINISTER ATROPINE SULFATE INTRAVENOUSLY, OR INTRAMUSCULARLY IF IV INJECTION IS NOT POSSIBLE. IN MODERATELY SEVERE POISONING ADMINISTER ATROPINE SULFATE, 0.4-2.0 MG REPEATED EVERY 15 MINUTES UNTIL ATROPINIZATION IS ACHIEVED (TACHYCARDIA, FLUSHING, DRY MOUTH, MYDRIASIS). MAINTAIN ATROPINIZATION BY REPEATED DOSES FOR 2-12 HOURS, OR LONGER, DEPENDING ON THE SEVERITY OF POISONING. THE APPEARANCE OF RALES IN THE LUNG BASES, MIOSIS, SALIVATION, NAUSEA, BRADYCARDIA, ARE ALL INDICATIONS OF INADEQUATE ATROPINIZATION. SEVERELY POISONED INDIVIDUALS MAY EXHIBIT REMARKABLE TOLERANCE TO ATROPINE; TWO OR MORE TIMES THE DOSAGES SUGGESTED ABOVE MAY BE NEEDED. PERSONS NOT POISONED OR ONLY SLIGHTLY POISONED, HOWEVER, MAY DEVELOP SIGNS OF ATROPINE TOXICITY FROM SUCH LARGE DOSAGES: FEVER, MUSCLE FIBRILLATIONS, AND DELIRIUM ARE THE MAIN SIGNS OF ATROPINE TOXICITY. IF THESE SIGNS APPEAR WHILE THE PATIENT IS FULLY ATROPINIZED, ATROPINE ADMINISTRATION SHOULD BE DISCONTINUED, AT LEAST TEMPORARILY. OBSERVE TREATED PATIENTS CLOSELY AT LEAST 24 HOURS TO INSURE THAT SYMPTOMS (POSSIBLY PULMONARY EDEMA) DO NOT RECUR AS ATROPINIZATION WEARS OFF. IN VERY SEVERE POISONINGS, METABOLIC DISPOSITION OF TOXICANT MAY REQUIRE SEVERAL HOURS OR DAYS DURING WHICH ATROPINIZATION MUST BE MAINTAINED. MARKEDLY LOWER LEVELS OF URINARY METABOLITES INDICATE THAT ATROPINE DOSAGE CAN BE TAPERED OFF. AS DOSAGE IS REDUCED, CHECK THE LUNG BASES FREQUENTLY FOR RALES. IF RALES ARE HEARD OR OTHER SYMPTOMS RETURN, RE-ESTABLISH ATROPINIZATION PROMPTLY (MORGAN, RECOGNITION AND MANAGEMENT OF PESTICIDE POISONINGS, 3RD ED.). ADMINISTRATION OF ANTIDOTE MUST BE PERFORMED BY QUALIFIED MEDICAL PERSONNEL.

REACTIVITY

REACTIVITY: NO DATA AVAILABLE.
INCOMPATIBILITIES: METOLCARB: NO DATA AVAILABLE.
DECOMPOSITION: THERMAL DECOMPOSITION PRODUCTS MAY INCLUDE TOXIC OXIDES OF NITROGEN.
POLYMERIZATION: HAZARDOUS POLYMERIZATION HAS NOT BEEN REPORTED TO OCCUR UNDER NORMAL TEMPERATURES AND PRESSURES.

STORAGE AND DISPOSAL

OBSERVE ALL FEDERAL, STATE AND LOCAL REGULATIONS WHEN STORING OR DISPOSING OF THIS SUBSTANCE. FOR ASSISTANCE, CONTACT THE DISTRICT DIRECTOR OF THE ENVIRONMENTAL PROTECTION AGENCY.

****STORAGE****

STORE IN ACCORDANCE WITH 40 CFR 165 RECOMMENDED PROCEDURES FOR THE DISPOSAL AND STORAGE OF PESTICIDES AND PESTICIDE CONTAINERS.
THRESHOLD PLANNING QUANTITY (TPQ): THE SUPERFUND AMENDMENTS AND REAUTHORIZATION ACT (SARA) SECTION 302 REQUIRES THAT EACH FACILITY WHERE ANY EXTREMELY HAZARDOUS SUBSTANCE IS PRESENT IN A QUANTITY EQUAL TO OR GREATER THAN THE TPQ ESTABLISHED FOR THAT SUBSTANCE NOTIFY THE STATE EMERGENCY RESPONSE COMMISSION FOR THE STATE IN WHICH IT IS LOCATED. SECTION 303 OF SARA REQUIRES THESE FACILITIES TO PARTICIPATE IN LOCAL EMERGENCY RESPONSE PLANNING (40 CFR 355.30).

****DISPOSAL****

DISPOSAL MUST BE IN ACCORDANCE WITH 40 CFR 165 RECOMMENDED PROCEDURES FOR THE DISPOSAL AND STORAGE OF PESTICIDES AND PESTICIDE CONTAINERS.

CONDITIONS TO AVOID

NONE REPORTED.

SPILL AND LEAK PROCEDURES

OCCUPATIONAL SPILL: SWEEP UP AND PLACE IN SUITABLE CLEAN, DRY CONTAINERS FOR RECLAMATION OR LATER DISPOSAL. DO NOT FLUSH SPILLED MATERIAL INTO SEWER. KEEP UNNECESSARY PEOPLE AWAY.
REPORTABLE QUANTITY (RQ): 1 POUND THE SUPERFUND AMENDMENTS AND REAUTHORIZATION ACT (SARA) SECTION 304 REQUIRES THAT A RELEASE EQUAL TO OR GREATER THAN THE REPORTABLE QUANTITY FOR THIS SUBSTANCE BE IMMEDIATELY REPORTED TO THE LOCAL EMERGENCY PLANNING COMMITTEE AND THE STATE EMERGENCY RESPONSE COMMISSION (40 CFR 355.40). IF THE RELEASE OF THIS SUBSTANCE IS REPORTABLE UNDER CERCLA SECTION 103, THE NATIONAL RESPONSE CENTER MUST BE NOTIFIED IMMEDIATELY AT (800) 424-8802 OR (202) 426-2675 IN THE METROPOLITAN WASHINGTON, D.C. AREA (40 CFR 302.6).

PROTECTIVE EQUIPMENT

VENTILATION: PROCESS ENCLOSURE RECOMMENDED.
RESPIRATOR: THE FOLLOWING RESPIRATORS ARE RECOMMENDED BASED ON INFORMATION FOUND IN THE PHYSICAL DATA, TOXICITY AND HEALTH EFFECTS SECTIONS. THEY ARE RANKED IN ORDER FROM MINIMUM TO MAXIMUM RESPIRATORY PROTECTION. THE SPECIFIC RESPIRATOR SELECTED MUST BE BASED ON CONTAMINATION LEVELS FOUND IN THE WORK PLACE, MUST NOT EXCEED THE WORKING LIMITS OF THE RESPIRATOR AND BE JOINTLY APPROVED BY THE NATIONAL INSTITUTE FOR OCCUPATIONAL SAFETY AND HEALTH AND THE MINE SAFETY AND HEALTH ADMINISTRATION (NIOSH-MSHA).
TYPE 'C' SUPPLIED-AIR RESPIRATOR WITH A FULL FACEPIECE OPERATED IN PRESSURE-DEMAND OR OTHER POSITIVE PRESSURE MODE OR WITH A FULL FACEPIECE, HELMET OR HOOD OPERATED IN CONTINOUS-FLOW MODE.
SELF-CONTAINED BREATHING APPARATUS WITH A FULL FACEPIECE OPERATED IN PRESSURE-DEMAND OR OTHER POSITIVE PRESSURE MODE.
FOR FIREFIGHTING AND OTHER IMMEDIATELY DANGEROUS TO LIFE OR HEALTH CONDITIONS:
SELF-CONTAINED BREATHING APPARATUS WITH FULL FACEPIECE OPERATED IN PRESSURE-DEMAND OR OTHER POSITIVE PRESSURE MODE.
SUPPLIED-AIR RESPIRATOR WITH FULL FACEPIECE AND OPERATED IN PRESSURE-DEMAND OR OTHER POSITIVE PRESSURE MODE IN COMBINATION WITH AN AUXILIARY SELF-CONTAINED BREATHING APPARATUS OPERATED IN PRESSURE-DEMAND OR OTHER POSITIVE PRESSURE MODE.
CLOTHING: EMPLOYEE MUST WEAR APPROPRIATE PROTECTIVE (IMPERVIOUS) CLOTHING AND EQUIPMENT TO PREVENT ANY POSSIBILITY OF SKIN CONTACT WITH THIS SUBSTANCE.
GLOVES: EMPLOYEE MUST WEAR APPROPRIATE PROTECTIVE GLOVES TO PREVENT CONTACT WITH THIS SUBSTANCE.
EYE PROTECTION: EMPLOYEE MUST WEAR SPLASH-PROOF OR DUST-RESISTANT SAFETY GOGGLES AND A FACESHIELD TO PREVENT CONTACT WITH THIS SUBSTANCE.
EMERGENCY WASH FACILITIES: WHERE THERE IS ANY POSSIBILITY THAT AN EMPLOYEE'S EYES AND/OR SKIN MAY BE EXPOSED TO THIS SUBSTANCE, THE EMPLOYER SHOULD PROVIDE AN EYE WASH FOUNTAIN AND QUICK DRENCH SHOWER WITHIN THE IMMEDIATE WORK AREA FOR EMERGENCY USE.

AUTHORIZED BY- OCCUPATIONAL HEALTH SERVICES, INC.
CREATION DATE: 10/04/89 ***REVISION DATE:*** 06/12/90

MATERIAL SAFETY DATA SHEET

OCCUPATIONAL HEALTH SERVICES, INC.
AGRICULTURE AND PESTICIDE DIVISION
450 SEVENTH AVENUE, SUITE 2407
NEW YORK, NEW YORK 10123
1-800-445-MSDS OR (212) 967-1100

EMERGENCY CONTACT:
JOHN S. BRANSFORD, JR. (615) 292-1180

SUBSTANCE IDENTIFICATION

CAS-NUMBER 1397-94-0
SUBSTANCE: **ANTIMYCIN A**
TRADE NAMES/SYNONYMS: ANTIPIRICULLIN; VIROSIN; PST83076
CHEMICAL FAMILY: ANTIBIOTIC
MOLECULAR FORMULA: C28-H40-N2-O9
MOLECULAR WEIGHT: 548.70
CERCLA RATINGS (SCALE 0-3): HEALTH=3 FIRE=U REACTIVITY=U PERSISTENCE=2
NFPA RATINGS (SCALE 0-4): HEALTH=3 FIRE=U REACTIVITY=U

COMPONENTS AND CONTAMINANTS

COMPONENT: ANTIMYCIN A ***PERCENT:*** 100.0
CAS# 1397-94-0
OTHER CONTAMINANTS: NONE
EXPOSURE LIMITS: ANTIMYCIN A: NO OCCUPATIONAL EXPOSURE LIMITS ESTABLISHED BY OSHA, ACGIH, OR NIOSH.
1000/10,000 POUNDS SARA SECTION 302 THRESHOLD PLANNING QUANTITY 1 POUND SARA SECTION 304 REPORTABLE QUANTITY

PHYSICAL DATA

DESCRIPTION: SOLID ***MELTING POINT:*** 284 F (140 C)
SOLUBILITY IN WATER: INSOLUBLE
SOLVENT SOLUBILITY: ALCOHOL, ETHER, ACETONE, CHLOROFORM

FIRE AND EXPLOSION DATA

FIRE AND EXPLOSION HAZARD: UNKNOWN FIRE AND EXPLOSION HAZARD.
FIREFIGHTING MEDIA: DRY CHEMICAL, CARBON DIOXIDE, HALON, WATER SPRAY OR STANDARD FOAM (1987 EMERGENCY RESPONSE GUIDEBOOK, DOT P 5800.4).
FOR LARGER FIRES, USE WATER SPRAY, FOG OR STANDARD FOAM (1987 EMERGENCY RESPONSE GUIDEBOOK, DOT P 5800.4).
FIREFIGHTING: MOVE CONTAINERS FROM FIRE AREA IF POSSIBLE (1987 EMERGENCY RESPONSE GUIDEBOOK, DOT P 5800.4, GUIDE PAGE 53).
EXTINGUISH USING AGENT SUITABLE FOR TYPE OF SURROUNDING FIRE. AVOID BREATHING VAPORS AND DUSTS. KEEP UPWIND.

TRANSPORTATION DATA

DEPARTMENT OF TRANSPORTATION HAZARD CLASSIFICATION 49 CFR 172.101: POISON B
DEPARTMENT OF TRANSPORTATION LABELING REQUIREMENTS 49 CFR 172.101 AND SUBPART E: POISON
DEPARTMENT OF TRANSPORTATION PACKAGING REQUIREMENTS: 49 CFR 173.365 EXCEPTIONS: 49 CFR 173.364

TOXICITY

ANTIMYCIN A: TOXICITY DATA: 28 MG/KG ORAL-RAT LD50; 55 MG/KG ORAL-MOUSE LD50; 10 MG/KG ORAL-RABBIT LD50; 1800 UG/KG ORAL-GUINEA PIG LD50; 25 MG/KG SUBCUTANEOUS-RAT LD50; 1600 UG/KG SUBCUTANEOUS-MOUSE LD50; 893 UG/KG INTRAVENOUS-MOUSE LD50; 820 UG/KG INTRAPERITONEAL-MOUSE LD50; 800 UG/KG INTRAPERITONEAL-RAT LD50; MUTAGENIC DATA (RTECS). CARCINOGEN STATUS: NONE. ACUTE TOXICITY: HIGHLY TOXIC BY INGESTION. TARGET EFFECTS: NO DATA AVAILABLE.

HEALTH EFFECTS AND FIRST AID

INHALATION: ANTIMYCIN A: **ACUTE EXPOSURE-** NO DATA AVAILABLE. **CHRONIC EXPOSURE-** NO DATA AVAILABLE.
FIRST AID- REMOVE FROM EXPOSURE AREA TO FRESH AIR IMMEDIATELY. IF BREATHING HAS STOPPED, PERFORM ARTIFICIAL RESPIRATION. KEEP PERSON WARM AND AT REST. TREAT SYMPTOMATICALLY AND SUPPORTIVELY. GET MEDICAL ATTENTION IMMEDIATELY.

SKIN CONTACT: ANTIMYCIN A: **ACUTE EXPOSURE-** NO DATA AVAILABLE. TOPICAL APPLICATION OF SOME ANTIBIOTICS HAS PRODUCED SENSITIZATION IN SOME INDIVIDUALS RESULTING IN DELAYED ECZEMATOUS, URTICARIAL, AND ANAPHYLACTIC REACTIONS. **CHRONIC EXPOSURE-** NO DATA AVAILABLE.
FIRST AID- REMOVE CONTAMINATED CLOTHING AND SHOES IMMEDIATELY. WASH AFFECTED AREA WITH SOAP OR MILD DETERGENT AND LARGE AMOUNTS OF WATER UNTIL NO EVIDENCE OF CHEMICAL REMAINS (APPROXIMATELY 15-20 MINUTES). GET MEDICAL ATTENTION IMMEDIATELY.

EYE CONTACT: ANTIMYCIN A: **ACUTE EXPOSURE-** NO DATA AVAILABLE. **CHRONIC EXPOSURE-** NO DATA AVAILABLE.
FIRST AID- WASH EYES IMMEDIATELY WITH LARGE AMOUNTS OF WATER OR NORMAL SALINE, OCCASIONALLY LIFTING UPPER AND LOWER LIDS, UNTIL NO EVIDENCE OF CHEMICAL REMAINS (APPROXIMATELY 15-20 MINUTES). GET MEDICAL ATTENTION IMMEDIATELY.

INGESTION: ANTIMYCIN A: HIGHLY TOXIC. **ACUTE EXPOSURE-** A LETHAL DOSE IN RATS WAS 28 MG/KG; NO SYMPTOMS WERE REPORTED. ANTIMYCIN A IS AN AMINOGLYCOSIDE ANTIBIOTIC. THIS GROUP OF ANTIBIOTICS HAVE PRODUCED HEADACHES, DIZZINESS, AND NAUSEA AND VOMITING DURING MOVEMENT AS EARLY SIGNS OF IMPAIRMENT OF VESTIBULAR FUNCTION. THE LOSS OF AUDITORY PERCEPTION OF HIGH-FREQUENCY SOUND INDICATES THE ONSET OF AUDITORY TOXICITY. MANY AMINOGLYCOSIDE ANTIBIOTICS HAVE THE POTENTIAL FOR PRODUCING NEPHROTOXICITY MANIFESTED BY ALBUMINURIA, HEMATURIA, CYLINDRURIA, AZOTEMIA, TUBULAR NECROSIS AND RENAL FAILURE. HYPERSENSITIVITY AS INDICATED BY RASHES, DRUG FEVER AND BLOOD DYSCRASIAS HAS OCCURRED IN SOME INDIVIDUALS. **CHRONIC EXPOSURE-** PROLONGED USE OF ANTIBIOTICS MAY INTERFERE WITH THE MICROBIAL ECOLOGY RESULTING IN THE OVERGROWTH OF ORGANISMS NOT AFFECTED BY THE ANTIBIOTIC AGENT.
FIRST AID- TREAT SYMPTOMATICALLY AND SUPPORTIVELY. GET MEDICAL ATTENTION IMMEDIATELY. IF VOMITING OCCURS, KEEP HEAD LOWER THAN HIPS TO PREVENT ASPIRATION.
ANTIDOTE: NO SPECIFIC ANTIDOTE. TREAT SYMPTOMATICALLY AND SUPPORTIVELY.

REACTIVITY

REACTIVITY: NO DATA AVAILABLE.
INCOMPATIBILITIES: ANTIMYCIN A: NO DATA AVAILABLE.
DECOMPOSITION: THERMAL DECOMPOSITION PRODUCTS MAY INCLUDE TOXIC OXIDES OF NITROGEN.
POLYMERIZATION: HAZARDOUS POLYMERIZATION HAS NOT BEEN REPORTED TO OCCUR UNDER NORMAL TEMPERATURES AND PRESSURES.

STORAGE AND DISPOSAL

OBSERVE ALL FEDERAL, STATE AND LOCAL REGULATIONS WHEN STORING OR DISPOSING OF THIS SUBSTANCE. FOR ASSISTANCE, CONTACT THE DISTRICT DIRECTOR OF THE ENVIRONMENTAL PROTECTION AGENCY.

STORAGE

STORE IN ACCORDANCE WITH 40 CFR 165 RECOMMENDED PROCEDURES FOR THE DISPOSAL AND STORAGE OF PESTICIDES AND PESTICIDE CONTAINERS.
THRESHOLD PLANNING QUANTITY (TPQ): THE SUPERFUND AMENDMENTS AND REAUTHORIZATION ACT (SARA) SECTION 302 REQUIRES THAT EACH FACILITY WHERE ANY EXTREMELY HAZARDOUS SUBSTANCE IS PRESENT IN A QUANTITY EQUAL TO OR GREATER THAN THE TPQ ESTABLISHED FOR THAT SUBSTANCE NOTIFY THE STATE EMERGENCY RESPONSE COMMISSION FOR THE STATE IN WHICH IT IS LOCATED. SECTION 303 OF SARA REQUIRES THESE FACILITIES TO PARTICIPATE IN LOCAL EMERGENCY RESPONSE PLANNING (40 CFR 355.30).

DISPOSAL

DISPOSAL MUST BE IN ACCORDANCE WITH 40 CFR 165 RECOMMENDED PROCEDURES FOR THE DISPOSAL AND STORAGE OF PESTICIDES AND PESTICIDE CONTAINERS.

CONDITIONS TO AVOID

NONE REPORTED.

SPILL AND LEAK PROCEDURES

OCCUPATIONAL SPILL: DO NOT TOUCH SPILLED MATERIAL. STOP LEAK IF YOU CAN DO IT WITHOUT RISK. FOR SMALL SPILLS, TAKE UP WITH SAND OR OTHER ABSORBENT MATERIAL AND PLACE INTO CONTAINERS FOR LATER DISPOSAL. FOR SMALL DRY SPILLS, WITH A CLEAN SHOVEL PLACE MATERIAL INTO CLEAN, DRY

CONTAINER AND COVER. MOVE CONTAINERS FROM SPILL AREA. FOR LARGER SPILLS, DIKE FAR AHEAD OF SPILL FOR LATER DISPOSAL. KEEP UNNECESSARY PEOPLE AWAY. ISOLATE HAZARD AREA AND DENY ENTRY.
REPORTABLE QUANTITY (RQ): 1 POUND THE SUPERFUND AMENDMENTS AND REAUTHORIZATION ACT (SARA) SECTION 304 REQUIRES THAT A RELEASE EQUAL TO OR GREATER THAN THE REPORTABLE QUANTITY FOR THIS SUBSTANCE BE IMMEDIATELY REPORTED TO THE LOCAL EMERGENCY PLANNING COMMITTEE AND THE STATE EMERGENCY RESPONSE COMMISSION (40 CFR 355.40). IF THE RELEASE OF THIS SUBSTANCE IS REPORTABLE UNDER CERCLA SECTION 103, THE NATIONAL RESPONSE CENTER MUST BE NOTIFIED IMMEDIATELY AT (800) 424-8802 OR (202) 426-2675 IN THE METROPOLITAN WASHINGTON, D.C. AREA (40 CFR 302.6).

PROTECTIVE EQUIPMENT

VENTILATION: PROVIDE LOCAL EXHAUST OR PROCESS ENCLOSURE VENTILATION SYSTEM.

RESPIRATOR: THE FOLLOWING RESPIRATORS AND MAXIMUM USE CONCENTRATIONS ARE RECOMMENDATIONS BY THE U.S. DEPARTMENT OF HEALTH AND HUMAN SERVICES, NIOSH POCKET GUIDE TO CHEMICAL HAZARDS; NIOSH CRITERIA DOCUMENTS OR BY THE U.S. DEPARTMENT OF LABOR, 29 CFR 1910 SUBPART Z.
THE SPECIFIC RESPIRATOR SELECTED MUST BE BASED ON CONTAMINATION LEVELS FOUND IN THE WORK PLACE, MUST NOT EXCEED THE WORKING LIMITS OF THE RESPIRATOR AND BE JOINTLY APPROVED BY THE NATIONAL INSTITUTE FOR OCCUPATIONAL SAFETY AND HEALTH AND THE MINE SAFETY AND HEALTH ADMINISTRATION (NIOSH-MSHA).
CHEMICAL CARTRIDGE RESPIRATOR WITH AN ORGANIC VAPOR CARTRIDGE(S) WITH A FULL FACEPIECE AND ORGANIC VAPOR CARTRIDGE(S) IN COMBINATION WITH A DUST AND MIST FILTER.
POWERED AIR-PURIFYING RESPIRATOR WITH A TIGHT-FITTING FACEPIECE AND ORGANIC VAPOR CARTRIDGE(S) IN COMBINATION WITH A HIGH-EFFICIENCY PARTICULATE FILTER.
TYPE 'C' SUPPLIED-AIR RESPIRATOR WITH A FULL FACEPIECE OPERATED IN A PRESSURE-DEMAND OR OTHER POSITIVE PRESSURE MODE.
SELF-CONTAINED BREATHING APPARATUS WITH A FULL FACEPIECE OPERATED IN PRESSURE-DEMAND OR OTHER POSITIVE PRESSURE MODE.
FOR FIREFIGHTING AND OTHER IMMEDIATELY DANGEROUS TO LIFE OR HEALTH CONDITIONS:
SELF-CONTAINED BREATHING APPARATUS WITH FULL FACEPIECE OPERATED IN PRESSURE-DEMAND OR OTHER POSITIVE PRESSURE MODE.
SUPPLIED-AIR RESPIRATOR WITH FULL FACEPIECE AND OPERATED IN PRESSURE-DEMAND OR OTHER POSITIVE PRESSURE MODE IN COMBINATION WITH AN AUXILIARY SELF-CONTAINED BREATHING APPARATUS OPERATED IN PRESSURE-DEMAND OR OTHER POSITIVE PRESSURE MODE.

CLOTHING: EMPLOYEE MUST WEAR APPROPRIATE PROTECTIVE (IMPERVIOUS) CLOTHING AND EQUIPMENT TO PREVENT REPEATED OR PROLONGED SKIN CONTACT WITH THIS SUBSTANCE.

GLOVES: EMPLOYEE MUST WEAR APPROPRIATE PROTECTIVE GLOVES TO PREVENT CONTACT WITH THIS SUBSTANCE.

EYE PROTECTION: EMPLOYEE MUST WEAR SPLASH-PROOF OR DUST-RESISTANT SAFETY GOGGLES TO PREVENT EYE CONTACT WITH THIS SUBSTANCE.
EMERGENCY EYE WASH: WHERE THERE IS ANY POSSIBILITY THAT AN EMPLOYEE'S EYES MAY BE EXPOSED TO THIS SUBSTANCE, THE EMPLOYER SHOULD PROVIDE AN EYE WASH FOUNTAIN WITHIN THE IMMEDIATE WORK AREA FOR EMERGENCY USE.

AUTHORIZED BY- OCCUPATIONAL HEALTH SERVICES, INC.
CREATION DATE: 10/04/89 ***REVISION DATE:*** 05/07/90

MATERIAL SAFETY DATA SHEET

OCCUPATIONAL HEALTH SERVICES, INC.
AGRICULTURE AND PESTICIDE DIVISION
450 SEVENTH AVENUE, SUITE 2407
NEW YORK, NEW YORK 10123
1-800-445-MSDS OR (212) 967-1100

EMERGENCY CONTACT:
JOHN S. BRANSFORD, JR. (615) 292-1180

SUBSTANCE IDENTIFICATION

CAS-NUMBER 50782-69-9

SUBSTANCE: **VX**

TRADE NAMES/SYNONYMS: PHOSPHONOTHIONIC ACID, METHYL-, S-(2-(BIS(1-METHYLETHYL)AMINO)ETHYL) O-ETHYL ESTER; O-ETHYL S-(2-(BIS(1-METHYLETHYL)AMINO)ETHYL METHYLPHOSPHONOTHIOATE; METHYLPHOSPHONIC ACID, S-(2-BIS(1-METHYLETHYL)AMINO)ETHYL) O-ETHYL ESTER; O-ETHYL S-(2-(DIISOPROPYLAMINO)ETHYL)METHYLPHOSPHONOTHIOATE; TX 60; MPT; C11H26NO2PS; PST83104

CHEMICAL FAMILY: PHOSPHONOTHIOATE

MOLECULAR FORMULA: C11-H26-N-O2-P-S

MOLECULAR WEIGHT: 267.37

CERCLA RATINGS (SCALE 0-3): HEALTH = 3 FIRE = 1 REACTIVITY = 0 PERSISTENCE = 3

NFPA RATINGS (SCALE 0-4): HEALTH = U FIRE = 1 REACTIVITY = 0

COMPONENTS AND CONTAMINANTS

COMPONENT: VX ***PERCENT:*** 100
CAS# 50782-69-9

OTHER CONTAMINANTS: NONE

EXPOSURE LIMITS: NO OCCUPATIONAL EXPOSURE LIMITS ESTABLISHED BY OSHA, ACGIH, OR NIOSH.
VX: 100 POUNDS SARA SECTION 302 THRESHOLD PLANNING QUANTITY. 1 POUND SARA SECTION 304 REPORTABLE QUANTITY.

PHYSICAL DATA

DESCRIPTION: NONVOLATILE, ODORLESS LIQUID. ***BOILING POINT:*** 569 F (298 C)
MELTING POINT: <-60 F (<-51 C) ***SPECIFIC GRAVITY:*** 1.0083 @ 25 C
VAPOR PRESSURE: 0.0007 MMHG @ 25 C ***SOLUBILITY IN WATER:*** NOT AVAILABLE
VAPOR DENSITY: 9.2
SOLVENT SOLUBILITY: SOLUBLE IN LIPIDS.

FIRE AND EXPLOSION DATA

FIRE AND EXPLOSION HAZARD: SLIGHT FIRE HAZARD WHEN EXPOSED TO HEAT OR FLAME.

FLASH POINT: 318 F (159 C) ***FLAMMABILITY CLASS(OSHA):*** IIIB

FIREFIGHTING MEDIA: DRY CHEMICAL, CARBON DIOXIDE, HALON, WATER SPRAY OR STANDARD FOAM (1987 EMERGENCY RESPONSE GUIDEBOOK, DOT P 5800.4).
FOR LARGER FIRES, USE WATER SPRAY, FOG OR STANDARD FOAM (1987 EMERGENCY RESPONSE GUIDEBOOK, DOT P 5800.4).

FIREFIGHTING: MOVE CONTAINERS FROM FIRE AREA IF POSSIBLE. FIGHT FIRE FROM MAXIMUM DISTANCE. STAY AWAY FROM STORAGE TANK ENDS. DIKE FIRE CONTROL WATER FOR LATER DISPOSAL. DO NOT SCATTER MATERIAL (1987 EMERGENCY RESPONSE GUIDEBOOK, DOT P 5800.4, GUIDE PAGE 55).
EXTINGUISH ONLY IF FLOW CAN BE STOPPED. EXTINGUISH USING AGENT INDICATED. USE FLOODING AMOUNTS OF WATER AS A FOG. COOL CONTAINERS WITH FLOODING AMOUNTS OF WATER FROM AS FAR A DISTANCE AS POSSIBLE. AVOID BREATHING POISONOUS VAPORS, KEEP UPWIND. CONSIDER EVACUATION OF DOWNWIND AREA IF MATERIAL IS LEAKING.

TRANSPORTATION DATA

DEPARTMENT OF TRANSPORTATION HAZARD CLASSIFICATION 49 CFR 172.101: POISON B
DEPARTMENT OF TRANSPORTATION LABELING REQUIREMENTS 49 CFR 172.101 AND SUBPART E: POISON
DEPARTMENT OF TRANSPORTATION PACKAGING REQUIREMENTS: 49 CFR 173.119 EXCEPTIONS: NONE

TOXICITY

VX: TOXICITY DATA: 86 UG/KG SKIN-HUMAN LDLO; 4 UG/KG ORAL-MAN TDLO; 30 UG/KG SUBCUTANEOUS-HUMAN TDLO; 12 UG/KG SUBCUTANEOUS-RAT LD50; 22 UG/KG SUBCUTANEOUS-MOUSE LD50; 14 UG/KG SUBCUTANEOUS-RABBIT LD50; 8400 NG/KG SUBCUTANEOUS-GUINEA PIG LD50; 1500 NG/KG INTRAVENOUS-MAN TDLO; 50 UG/KG INTRAPERITONEAL-MOUSE LD50; 66 UG/KG INTRAPERITONEAL-RABBIT LD50; 3200 NG/KG INTRAMUSCULAR-HUMAN TDLO; REPRODUCTIVE EFFECTS DATA (RTECS). CARCINOGEN STATUS: NONE. ACUTE TOXICITY LEVEL: INSUFFICIENT DATA. TARGET EFFECTS: CHOLINESTERASE INHIBITOR. POISONING MAY AFFECT THE NERVOUS SYSTEM.* AT INCREASED RISK FROM EXPOSURE: PERSONS WITH RESPIRATORY AILMENTS, RECENT EXPOSURE TO CHOLINESTERASE INHIBITORS OR IMPAIRED CHOLINESTERASE PRODUCTION, OR LIVER MALFUNCTION.* ADDITIONAL DATA: MAY CROSS THE PLACENTA. HIGH ENVIRONMENTAL TEMPERATURES OR EXPOSURE OF THE CHEMICAL TO VISIBLE OR ULTRAVIOLET LIGHT MAY ENHANCE THE TOXICITY. INTERACTIONS WITH MEDICATIONS MAY OCCUR.*
* MAY BE BASED ON GENERAL INFORMATION ON ORGANOPHOSPHATES.

HEALTH EFFECTS AND FIRST AID

INHALATION: VX: SEE INFORMATION ON ORGANOPHOSPHATES.
ORGANOPHOSPHATES: CHOLINESTERASE INHIBITOR. **ACUTE EXPOSURE-** WHEN INHALED, THE FIRST EFFECTS OF CHOLINESTERASE INHIBITORS ARE USUALLY RESPIRATORY AND MAY INCLUDE NASAL HYPEREMIA AND WATERY DISCHARGE, COUGH, CHEST DISCOMFORT, DYSPNEA, AND WHEEZING DUE TO INCREASED

BRONCHIAL SECRETIONS AND BRONCHOCONSTRICTION. IF SUFFICIENT AMOUNTS ARE ABSORBED, OTHER SYSTEMIC EFFECTS MAY BEGIN WITHIN A FEW MINUTES OR BE DELAYED FOR UP TO 12 HOURS. SYMPTOMS MAY INCLUDE PALLOR, NAUSEA, VOMITING, DIARRHEA, ABDOMINAL CRAMPS, HEADACHE, DIZZINESS, OCULAR PAIN, BLURRED VISION, MIOSIS OR IN SOME CASES, ESPECIALLY INITIALLY, MYDRIASIS, LACRIMATION, SALIVATION, SWEATING, AND CONFUSION. OTHER REPORTED CENTRAL NERVOUS SYSTEM OR NEUROMUSCULAR EFFECTS MAY INCLUDE ATAXIA, SLURRED SPEECH, AREFLEXIA, WEAKNESS, FATIGUE, FASCICULATIONS, TWITCHING, TREMORS POSSIBLY OF THE TONGUE AND EYELIDS, AND EVENTUALLY PARALYSIS OF THE EXTREMITIES AND POSSIBLY OF THE RESPIRATORY MUSCLES. IN SEVERE CASES THERE MAY ALSO BE INVOLUNTARY DEFECATION AND URINATION, CYANOSIS, PSYCHOSIS, HYPERGLYCEMIA, ACUTE PANCREATITIS, CARDIAC IRREGULARITIES, PULMONARY EDEMA, UNCONSCIOUSNESS, CONVULSIONS, AND COMA. DEATH IS PRIMARILY DUE TO RESPIRATORY FAILURE, ALTHOUGH CARDIOVASCULAR EFFECTS INCLUDING CARDIAC ARREST MAY ALSO BE IMPLICATED. LONG TERM SEQUELAE ARE RARE BUT MAY INCLUDE NEUROPSYCHIATRIC DISORDERS AND MYOPATHY WITH MUSCLE TENDERNESS. SOME ORGANOPHOSPHATES MAY CAUSE A DELAYED NEUROPATHY BEGINNING 1-4 WEEKS AFTER AN ACUTE EXPOSURE WHICH MAY OR MAY NOT HAVE CAUSED ACUTE CHOLINERGIC EFFECTS. NUMBNESS, TINGLING, WEAKNESS AND CRAMPING BEGINNING SYMMETRICALLY IN THE LOWER LIMBS MAY PROGRESS TO ATAXIA AND PARALYSIS. IN SEVERE CASES, UPPER LIMB INVOLVEMENT IS POSSIBLE AND FLACCID PARALYSIS MAY PROGRESS TO SPASTIC PARALYSIS WITH EXAGGERATED REFLEXES. IMPROVEMENT MAY OCCUR OVER MONTHS TO YEARS, BUT SOME RESIDUAL IMPAIRMENT USUALLY REMAINS. **CHRONIC EXPOSURE-** REPEATED OR PROLONGED EXPOSURE MAY RESULT IN THE EFFECTS OF ACUTE EXPOSURE INCLUDING THE DELAYED NEUROPATHY. OTHER EFFECTS REPORTED IN WORKERS REPEATEDLY EXPOSED INCLUDE IMPAIRED MEMORY AND CONCENTRATION, ACUTE PSYCHOSIS, SEVERE DEPRESSIONS, IRRITABILTY, CONFUSION, APATHY, EMOTIONAL LABILITY, SOCIAL WITHDRAWAL, CONFUSION, HEADACHE, SPEECH DIFFICULTIES, DELAYED REACTION TIMES, SPATIAL DISORIENTATION, NIGHTMARES, SLEEPWALKING, AND DROWSINESS OR INSOMNIA. AN INFLUENZA-LIKE CONDITION WITH HEADACHE, NAUSEA, WEAKNESS, ANOREXIA AND MALAISE HAS ALSO BEEN REPORTED.

FIRST AID- REMOVE FROM EXPOSURE AREA TO FRESH AIR IMMEDIATELY. IF BREATHING HAS STOPPED, GIVE ARTIFICIAL RESPIRATION. MAINTAIN AIRWAY AND BLOOD PRESSURE AND ADMINISTER OXYGEN IF AVAILABLE. KEEP AFFECTED PERSON WARM AND AT REST. TREAT SYMPTOMATICALLY AND SUPPORTIVELY. ADMINISTRATION OF OXYGEN SHOULD BE PERFORMED BY QUALIFIED PERSONNEL. GET MEDICAL ATTENTION IMMEDIATELY.

SKIN CONTACT: VX: SEE INFORMATION ON ORGANOPHOSPHATES.

ORGANOPHOSPHATES: CHOLINESTERASE INHIBITOR. **ACUTE EXPOSURE-** LOCALIZED SWEATING AND FASCICULATIONS MAY OCCUR AT THE SITE OF CONTACT. IF SUFFICIENT AMOUNTS ARE ABSORBED, OTHER EFFECTS OF CHOLINESTERASE INHIBITION AS DESCRIBED IN ACUTE INHALATION MAY OCCUR. SYMPTOMS MAY BE DELAYED 2-3 HOURS, BUT USUALLY NO MORE THAN 12 HOURS. THE RATE OF ABSORPTION IS INCREASED BY THE PRESENCE OF DERMATITIS OR HIGH AMBIENT TEMPERATURES. DELAYED NEUROPATHY IS ALSO POSSIBLE. **CHRONIC EXPOSURE-** REPEATED OR PROLONGED EXPOSURE MAY CAUSE EFFECTS AS DESCRIBED IN ACUTE EXPOSURE. SOME ORGANOPHOSPHATES MAY CAUSE SENSITIZATION.

FIRST AID- REMOVE CONTAMINATED CLOTHING IMMEDIATELY. WASH CONTAMINATED AREAS WITH SOAP AND WATER FOLLOWED BY ALCOHOL (ARENA, POISONING, 4TH ED.). EMERGENCY PERSONNEL SHOULD WEAR GLOVES AND AVOID CONTAMINATION. TREAT RESPIRATORY DIFFICULTY WITH ARTIFICIAL RESPIRATION. GET MEDICAL ATTENTION IMMEDIATELY.

EYE CONTACT: VX: SEE INFORMATION ON ORGANOPHOSPHATES.

ORGANOPHOSPHATES: CHOLINESTERASE INHIBITOR. **ACUTE EXPOSURE-** DIRECT CONTACT MAY CAUSE PAIN, HYPEREMIA, LACRIMATION, TWITCHING OF THE EYELIDS, MIOSIS, AND CILIARY MUSCLE SPASM WITH LOSS OF ACCOMODATION, BLURRED OR DIMMED VISION AND BROWACHE. SOMETIMES MYDRIASIS MAY OCCUR INSTEAD OF MIOSIS. WITH SUFFICIENT EXPOSURE, OTHER SYMPTOMS OF CHOLINESTERASE INHIBITION AS DESCRIBED IN ACUTE INHALATION MAY OCCUR. **CHRONIC EXPOSURE-** REPEATED OR PROLONGED EXPOSURE MAY CAUSE EFFECTS AS DESCRIBED IN ACUTE EXPOSURE. SOME COMPOUNDS HAVE CAUSED TOXIC EFFECTS ON THE CRYSTALLINE LENS, CONJUNCTIVAL THICKENING AND OBSTRUCTION OF THE NASOLACRIMAL CANALS WHEN USED AS MIOTIC EYEDROPS.

FIRST AID- IRRIGATE EYES WITH WATER OR SALINE SOLUTION. IF SYMPTOMS OF POISONING OCCUR, TREAT RESPIRATORY DIFFICULTY WITH ARTIFICIAL RESPIRATION AND OXYGEN. OBSERVE PATIENT FOR AT LEAST 24-36 HOURS (GOSSELIN, CLINICAL TOXICOLOGY OF COMMERCIAL PRODUCTS, 5TH ED.). GET MEDICAL ATTENTION IMMEDIATELY. OXYGEN SHOULD BE ADMINISTERED BY QUALIFIED MEDICAL PERSONNEL.

INGESTION: VX: SEE INFORMATION ON ORGANOPHOSPHATES. PERSONS INGESTING SMALL AMOUNTS OF THIS SUBSTANCE, FOLLOWED BY AN ANTIDOTE WITHIN 5-48 HOURS, EXPERIENCED NAUSEA, DIARRHEA, AND REDUCED BLOOD CHOLINESTERASE ACTIVITY.

ORGANOPHOSPHATES: CHOLINESTERASE INHIBITOR. **ACUTE EXPOSURE-** WHEN INGESTED, THE FIRST EFFECTS MAY BE NAUSEA, VOMITING, ANOREXIA, ABDOMINAL CRAMPS AND DIARRHEA. GASTROINTESTINAL ABSORPTION MAY CAUSE SYMPTOMS OF CHOLINESTERASE INHIBITION AS DESCRIBED IN ACUTE INHALATION. SYMPTOMS MAY BEGIN WITHIN MINUTES OR BE DELAYED FOR HOURS. DELAYED EFFECTS INCLUDING NEUROPATHY MAY ALSO OCCUR. **CHRONIC EXPOSURE-** REPEATED INGESTION MAY CAUSE EFFECTS AS DESCRIBED IN ACUTE EXPOSURE.

FIRST AID- IF PERSON IS ALERT AND RESPIRATION IS NOT DEPRESSED, GIVE SYRUP OF IPECAC FOLLOWED BY WATER (IF VOMITING OCCURS, KEEP HEAD BELOW HIPS TO PREVENT ASPIRATION). IF CONSCIOUSNESS LEVEL DECLINES OR VOMITING HAS NOT OCCURRED IN 15 MINUTES EMPTY STOMACH BY GASTRIC LAVAGE WITH THE AID OF CUFFED ENDOTRACHEAL TUBE USING ISOTONIC SALINE OR 5% SODIUM BICARBONATE FOLLOW WITH ACTIVATED CHARCOAL. ESTABLISH AND MAINTAIN AIRWAY. TREAT RESPIRATORY DIFFICULTY WITH ARTIFICIAL RESPIRATION AND OXYGEN. DO NOT GIVE MORPHINE, AMINOPHYLLINE, PHENOTHIAZINES, RESERPINE, FUROSEMIDE, OR ETHACRYNIC ACID (MORGAN, RECOGNITION AND MANAGEMENT OF PESTICIDE POISONINGS, 3RD ED.). TREAT SYMPTOMATICALLY AND SUPPORTIVELY. ADMINISTRATION OF OXYGEN AND LAVAGE MUST BE PERFORMED BY QUALIFIED MEDICAL PERSONNEL. GET MEDICAL ATTENTION IMMEDIATELY.

ANTIDOTE: THE FOLLOWING ANTIDOTE(S) HAVE BEEN RECOMMENDED. HOWEVER, THE DECISION AS TO WHETHER THE SEVERITY OF POISONING REQUIRES ADMINISTRATION OF ANY ANTIDOTE AND ACTUAL DOSE REQUIRED SHOULD BE MADE BY QUALIFIED MEDICAL PERSONNEL.

FOR CHOLINESTERASE INHIBITORS: ESTABLISH CLEAR AIRWAY AND TISSUE OXYGENATION BY ASPIRATION OF SECRETIONS, AND IF NECESSARY, BY ASSISTED PULMONARY VENTILATION WITH OXYGEN. IMPROVE TISSUE OXYGENATION AS MUCH AS POSSIBLE BEFORE ADMINISTERING ATROPINE TO MINIMIZE THE RISK OF VENTRICULAR FIBRILLATION. ADMINISTER ATROPINE SULFATE INTRAVENOUSLY, OR INTRAMUSCULARLY IF IV INJECTION IS NOT POSSIBLE. IN MODERATELY SEVERE POISONING ADMINISTER ATROPINE SULFATE, 0.4-2.0 MG REPEATED EVERY 15 MINUTES UNTIL ATROPINIZATION IS ACHIEVED (TACHYCARDIA, FLUSHING, DRY MOUTH, MYDRIASIS). MAINTAIN ATROPINIZATION BY REPEATED DOSES FOR 2-12 HOURS, OR LONGER, DEPENDING ON THE SEVERITY OF POISONING. THE APPEARANCE OF RALES IN THE LUNG BASES, MIOSIS, SALIVATION, NAUSEA, BRADYCARDIA, ARE ALL INDICATIONS OF INADEQUATE ATROPINIZATION. SEVERELY POISONED INDIVIDUALS MAY EXHIBIT REMARKABLE TOLERANCE TO ATROPINE; TWO OR MORE TIMES THE DOSAGES SUGGESTED ABOVE MAY BE NEEDED. PERSONS NOT POISONED OR ONLY SLIGHTLY POISONED, HOWEVER, MAY DEVELOP SIGNS OF ATROPINE TOXICITY FROM SUCH LARGE DOSAGES: FEVER, MUSCLE FIBRILLATIONS, AND DELIRIUM ARE THE MAIN SIGNS OF ATROPINE TOXICITY. IF THESE SIGNS APPEAR WHILE THE PATIENT IS FULLY ATROPINIZED, ATROPINE ADMINISTRATION SHOULD BE DISCONTINUED, AT LEAST TEMPORARILY. OBSERVE TREATED PATIENTS CLOSELY AT LEAST 24 HOURS TO INSURE THAT SYMPTOMS (POSSIBLY PULMONARY EDEMA) DO NOT RECUR AS ATROPINIZATION WEARS OFF. IN VERY SEVERE POISONINGS, METABOLIC DISPOSITION OF TOXICANT MAY REQUIRE SEVERAL HOURS OR DAYS DURING WHICH ATROPINIZATION MUST BE MAINTAINED. MARKEDLY LOWER LEVELS OF URINARY METABOLITES INDICATE THAT ATROPINE DOSAGE CAN BE TAPERED OFF. AS DOSAGE IS REDUCED, CHECK THE LUNG BASES FREQUENTLY FOR RALES. IF RALES ARE HEARD OR OTHER SYMPTOMS RETURN, RE-ESTABLISH ATROPINIZATION PROMPTLY (MORGAN, RECOGNITION AND MANAGEMENT OF PESTICIDE POISONINGS, 3RD ED.). ADMINISTRATION OF ANTIDOTE MUST BE PERFORMED BY QUALIFIED MEDICAL PERSONNEL.

IN CASES OF SEVERE POISONING BY ORGANOPHOSPHATE PESTICIDES IN WHICH RESPIRATORY DEPRESSION, MUSCLE WEAKNESS AND TWITCHINGS ARE SEVERE, GIVE PRALIDOXIME (PROTOPAM-AYERST, 2-PAM), 1.0 GRAM INTRAVENOUSLY AT NO MORE THAN 0.5 GRAM PER MINUTE. DOSAGE OF PRALIDOXIME MAY BE REPEATED IN 1-2 HOURS, THEN AT 10-12 HOUR INTERVALS IF NEEDED. IN VERY SEVERE POISONINGS, DOSAGE RATES MAY BE DOUBLED. TREATMENT WITH PRALIDOXIME WILL BE MOST EFFECTIVE IF GIVEN WITHIN THIRTY-SIX HOURS AFTER POISONING (MORGAN, RECOGNITION AND MANAGEMENT OF PESTICIDE POISONINGS, 3RD ED.). ANTIDOTE SHOULD BE ADMINISTERED BY QUALIFIED MEDICAL PERSONNEL.

REACTIVITY

REACTIVITY: STABLE UNDER NORMAL TEMPERATURES AND PRESSURES.

INCOMPATIBILITIES: VX: OXIDIZERS (STRONG): FIRE AND EXPLOSION HAZARD.

DECOMPOSITION: THERMAL DECOMPOSITION PRODUCTS MAY INCLUDE TOXIC OXIDES OF NITROGEN, CARBON, PHOSPHORUS, AND SULFUR.

POLYMERIZATION: HAZARDOUS POLYMERIZATION HAS NOT BEEN REPORTED TO OCCUR UNDER NORMAL TEMPERATURES AND PRESSURES.

STORAGE AND DISPOSAL

OBSERVE ALL FEDERAL, STATE AND LOCAL REGULATIONS WHEN STORING OR DISPOSING OF THIS SUBSTANCE. FOR ASSISTANCE, CONTACT THE DISTRICT DIRECTOR OF THE ENVIRONMENTAL PROTECTION AGENCY.

****STORAGE****

STORE AWAY FROM INCOMPATIBLE SUBSTANCES.

THRESHOLD PLANNING QUANTITY (TPQ): THE SUPERFUND AMENDMENTS AND REAUTHORIZATION ACT (SARA) SECTION 302 REQUIRES THAT EACH FACILITY WHERE ANY EXTREMELY HAZARDOUS SUBSTANCE IS PRESENT IN A QUANTITY EQUAL TO OR GREATER THAN THE TPQ ESTABLISHED FOR THAT SUBSTANCE NOTIFY THE STATE EMERGENCY RESPONSE COMMISSION FOR THE STATE IN WHICH IT IS LOCATED. SECTION 303 OF SARA REQUIRES THESE FACILITIES TO PARTICIPATE IN LOCAL EMERGENCY RESPONSE PLANNING (40 CFR 355.30).

CONDITIONS TO AVOID

MAY BURN BUT DOES NOT IGNITE READILY. CONTAINERS MAY EXPLODE IN HEAT OF FIRE.

SPILL AND LEAK PROCEDURES

OCCUPATIONAL SPILL: DO NOT TOUCH SPILLED MATERIAL. STOP LEAK IF YOU CAN DO IT WITHOUT RISK. USE WATER SPRAY TO REDUCE VAPORS. FOR SMALL SPILLS, TAKE UP WITH SAND OR OTHER ABSORBENT MATERIAL AND PLACE INTO CONTAINERS FOR LATER DISPOSAL. FOR SMALL DRY SPILLS, WITH A CLEAN SHOVEL PLACE MATERIAL INTO CLEAN, DRY CONTAINERS AND COVER. MOVE CONTAINERS FROM SPILL AREA. FOR LARGER SPILLS, DIKE FAR AHEAD OF SPILL FOR LATER DISPOSAL. KEEP UNNECESSARY PEOPLE AWAY. ISOLATE HAZARD AREA AND DENY ENTRY. VENTILATE CLOSED SPACES BEFORE ENTERING.

REPORTABLE QUANTITY (RQ): 1 POUND THE SUPERFUND AMENDMENTS AND REAUTHORIZATION ACT (SARA) SECTION 304 REQUIRES THAT A RELEASE EQUAL TO OR GREATER THAN THE REPORTABLE QUANTITY FOR THIS SUBSTANCE BE IMMEDIATELY REPORTED TO THE LOCAL EMERGENCY PLANNING COMMITTEE AND THE STATE EMERGENCY RESPONSE COMMISSION (40 CFR 355.40). IF THE RELEASE OF THIS SUBSTANCE IS REPORTABLE UNDER CERCLA SECTION 103, THE NATIONAL RESPONSE CENTER MUST BE NOTIFIED IMMEDIATELY AT (800) 424-8802 OR (202) 426-2675 IN THE METROPOLITAN WASHINGTON, D.C. AREA (40 CFR 302.6).

PROTECTIVE EQUIPMENT

VENTILATION: PROVIDE LOCAL EXHAUST OR PROCESS ENCLOSURE VENTILATION SYSTEM.

RESPIRATOR: THE FOLLOWING RESPIRATORS ARE RECOMMENDED BASED ON INFORMATION FOUND IN THE PHYSICAL DATA, TOXICITY AND HEALTH EFFECTS SECTIONS. THEY ARE RANKED IN ORDER FROM MINIMUM TO MAXIMUM RESPIRATORY PROTECTION. THE SPECIFIC RESPIRATOR SELECTED MUST BE BASED ON CONTAMINATION LEVELS FOUND IN THE WORK PLACE, MUST NOT EXCEED THE WORKING LIMITS OF THE RESPIRATOR AND BE JOINTLY APPROVED BY THE NATIONAL INSTITUTE FOR OCCUPATIONAL SAFETY AND HEALTH AND THE MINE SAFETY AND HEALTH ADMINISTRATION (NIOSH-MSHA).

CHEMICAL CARTRIDGE RESPIRATOR WITH AN ORGANIC VAPOR CARTRIDGE(S) WITH A FULL FACEPIECE.

GAS MASK WITH ORGANIC VAPOR CANISTER (CHIN-STYLE OR FRONT- OR BACK-MOUNTED CANISTER) WITH A FULL FACEPIECE.

TYPE 'C' SUPPLIED-AIR RESPIRATOR WITH A FULL FACEPIECE OPERATED IN PRESSURE-DEMAND OR OTHER POSITIVE PRESSURE MODE OR WITH A FULL FACEPIECE, HELMET OR HOOD OPERATED IN CONTINUOUS-FLOW MODE.

SELF-CONTAINED BREATHING APPARATUS WITH A FULL FACEPIECE OPERATED IN PRESSURE-DEMAND OR OTHER POSITIVE PRESSURE MODE.

FOR FIREFIGHTING AND OTHER IMMEDIATELY DANGEROUS TO LIFE OR HEALTH CONDITIONS:

SELF-CONTAINED BREATHING APPARATUS WITH FULL FACEPIECE OPERATED IN PRESSURE-DEMAND OR OTHER POSITIVE PRESSURE MODE.

SUPPLIED-AIR RESPIRATOR WITH FULL FACEPIECE AND OPERATED IN PRESSURE-DEMAND OR OTHER POSITIVE PRESSURE MODE IN COMBINATION WITH AN AUXILIARY SELF-CONTAINED BREATHING APPARATUS OPERATED IN PRESSURE-DEMAND OR OTHER POSITIVE PRESSURE MODE.

CLOTHING: EMPLOYEE MUST WEAR APPROPRIATE PROTECTIVE (IMPERVIOUS) CLOTHING AND EQUIPMENT TO PREVENT REPEATED OR PROLONGED SKIN CONTACT WITH THIS SUBSTANCE.

GLOVES: EMPLOYEE MUST WEAR APPROPRIATE PROTECTIVE GLOVES TO PREVENT CONTACT WITH THIS SUBSTANCE.

EYE PROTECTION: EMPLOYEE MUST WEAR SPLASH-PROOF OR DUST-RESISTANT SAFETY GOGGLES TO PREVENT EYE CONTACT WITH THIS SUBSTANCE.

EMERGENCY EYE WASH: WHERE THERE IS ANY POSSIBILITY THAT AN EMPLOYEE'S EYES MAY BE EXPOSED TO THIS SUBSTANCE, THE EMPLOYER SHOULD PROVIDE AN EYE WASH FOUNTAIN WITHIN THE IMMEDIATE WORK AREA FOR EMERGENCY USE.

AUTHORIZED BY- OCCUPATIONAL HEALTH SERVICES, INC.

CREATION DATE: 05/18/90 ***REVISION DATE:*** 05/18/90

MATERIAL SAFETY DATA SHEET

OCCUPATIONAL HEALTH SERVICES, INC.
AGRICULTURE AND PESTICIDE DIVISION
450 SEVENTH AVENUE, SUITE 2407
NEW YORK, NEW YORK 10123
1-800-445-MSDS OR (212) 967-1100

EMERGENCY CONTACT:
JOHN S. BRANSFORD, JR. (615) 292-1180

SUBSTANCE IDENTIFICATION

CAS-NUMBER 2058-46-0

***SUBSTANCE:* OXYTETRACYCLINE HYDROCHLORIDE**

TRADE NAMES/SYNONYMS: AQUACYCLINE; ENGEMYCIN; LIQUAMYCIN INJECTABLE; MEPATAR; OXYTETRIN; TERRAMYCIN HYDROCHLORIDE; TETRAN HYDROCHLORIDE; TM 5; 2-NAPHTHACENECARBOXAMIDE, 4-(DIMETHYLAMINO)-1,4,4A,5,5A,6,11,12A- OCTAHYDRO-3,5,6,10,12,12A-HEXAHYDROXY-6-METHYL-1,11-DIOXO, MONOHYDROCHLORIDE, (4S-(4 ALPHA,4A ALPHA,5 ALPHA,5A ALPHA,6 BETA, 12A ALPHA))-; 2-NAPHTHACENECARBOXAMIDE, 4-(DIMETHYLAMINO)-1,4,4A,5,5A,6,11,12A-; OCTAHYDRO-3,5,6,10,12,12A-HEXAHYDROXY-6-METHYL-1,11-DIOXO, MONOHYDROCHLORIDE; (4S-(4 ALPHA,4A ALPHA,5 ALPHA,5A ALPHA,6 BETA,12A ALPHA))-4-(DIMETHYLAMINO)-1,4,4A,5,5A,6,11,12A-OCTAHYDRO-3,5,6,10,12,12A-HEXAHYDROXY-6-METHYL-1,11-DIOXO-2-NAPHTHACENECARBOXAMIDE, MONOHYDROCHLORIDE; 5-HYDROXYTETRACLINE HYDROCHLORIDE; PST84045

CHEMICAL FAMILY: ANTIBIOTIC

MOLECULAR FORMULA: C22-H24-N2-O9.H-CL

MOLECULAR WEIGHT: 496.94

CERCLA RATINGS (SCALE 0-3): HEALTH=1 FIRE=0 REACTIVITY=0 PERSISTENCE=2

NFPA RATINGS (SCALE 0-4): HEALTH=1 FIRE=0 REACTIVITY=0

COMPONENTS AND CONTAMINANTS

COMPONENT: OXYTETRACYCLINE HYDROCHLORIDE ***PERCENT:*** 100
CAS# 2058-46-0

OTHER CONTAMINANTS: NONE

EXPOSURE LIMITS: NO OCCUPATIONAL EXPOSURE LIMITS ESTABLISHED BY OSHA, ACGIH, OR NIOSH.

PHYSICAL DATA

DESCRIPTION: YELLOW, ODORLESS CRYSTALLINE OR HYGROSCOPIC POWDER WITH A BITTER TASTE; CONTACT WITH MOIST AIR CAUSES DARKENING.

MELTING POINT: 356 F (180 C) DECOMPOSES ***SPECIFIC GRAVITY:*** NOT AVAILABLE

PH: 2.5 (1% SOLUTION) ***SOLUBILITY IN WATER:*** SOLUBLE

SOLVENT SOLUBILITY: SOLUBLE IN ETHANOL AND METHANOL; INSOLUBLE IN ETHER AND CHLOROFORM

FIRE AND EXPLOSION DATA

FIRE AND EXPLOSION HAZARD: NEGLIGIBLE FIRE HAZARD WHEN EXPOSED TO HEAT OR FLAME.

FIREFIGHTING MEDIA: DRY CHEMICAL, CARBON DIOXIDE, HALON, WATER SPRAY OR STANDARD FOAM (1987 EMERGENCY RESPONSE GUIDEBOOK, DOT P 5800.4). FOR LARGER FIRES, USE WATER SPRAY, FOG OR STANDARD FOAM (1987 EMERGENCY RESPONSE GUIDEBOOK, DOT P 5800.4).

FIREFIGHTING: MOVE CONTAINER FROM FIRE AREA IF POSSIBLE. DO NOT SCATTER SPILLED MATERIAL WITH HIGH PRESSURE WATER STREAMS. DIKE FIRE CONTROL WATER FOR LATER DISPOSAL (1987 EMERGENCY RESPONSE GUIDEBOOK, DOT P 5800.4, GUIDE PAGE 31).

USE AGENTS SUITABLE FOR TYPE OF SURROUNDING FIRE. AVOID BREATHING HAZARDOUS VAPORS, KEEP UPWIND.

TOXICITY

OXYTETRACYCLINE HYDROCHLORIDE: TOXICITY DATA: 6696 MG/KG ORAL-MOUSE LD50; 800 MG/KG SUBCUTANEOUS-RAT LD50; 963 MG/KG SUBCUTANEOUS-MOUSE LD50; 302 MG/KG INTRAVENOUS-RAT LD50; 100 MG/KG INTRAVENOUS-MOUSE LD50; 100 MG/KG INTRAVENOUS-DOG LDLO; 80 MG/KG INTRAVENOUS-

RABBIT LDLO; MUTAGENIC DATA (RTECS); REPRODUCTIVE EFFECTS DATA (RTECS); TUMORIGENIC DATA (RTECS). CARCINOGEN STATUS: NONE. IN 2 YEAR FEEDING STUDIES, THERE WAS EQUIVOCAL EVIDENCE OF CARCINOGENICITY FOR MALE AND FEMALE RATS AND NO EVIDENCE OF CARCINOGENICITY FOR MALE OR FEMALE MICE (NTP TR 315). ACUTE TOXICITY LEVEL: SLIGHTLY TOXIC BY INGESTION. TARGET EFFECTS: NO DATA AVAILABLE. AT INCREASED RISK FROM EXPOSURE: PERSONS WITH RENAL OR HEPATIC DYSFUNCTION. ADDITIONAL DATA: INTERACTIONS WITH MEDICATIONS HAVE BEEN REPORTED.

HEALTH EFFECTS AND FIRST AID

INHALATION: OXYTETRACYCLINE HYDROCHLORIDE: **ACUTE EXPOSURE-** NO DATA AVAILABLE. DUSTS MAY IRRITATE MUCOUS MEMBRANES. **CHRONIC EXPOSURE-** NO DATA AVAILABLE.

FIRST AID- REMOVE FROM EXPOSURE AREA TO FRESH AIR IMMEDIATELY. IF BREATHING HAS STOPPED, PERFORM ARTIFICIAL RESPIRATION. KEEP PERSON WARM AND AT REST. TREAT SYMPTOMATICALLY AND SUPPORTIVELY. GET MEDICAL ATTENTION IMMEDIATELY.

SKIN CONTACT: OXYTETRACYCLINE HYDROCHLORIDE: **ACUTE EXPOSURE-** NO DATA AVAILABLE. HOWEVER, OXYTETRACYCLINE MAY CAUSE SKIN IRRITATION IN SOME INDIVIDUALS. THERE IS A POSSIBILITY OF SENSITIZATION REACTIONS IN INDIVIDUALS WHO HAVE EXHIBITED HYPERSENSITIVITY TO TETRACYCLINES. **CHRONIC EXPOSURE-** WHEN USED TOPICALLY, OXYTETRACYCLINE HYDROCHLORIDE MAY CAUSE SENSITIZATION. HOWEVER, REPEATED ORAL EXPOSURES TO OXYTETRACYCLINE HAS PRODUCED DERMATITIS, PHOTO-ONYCHOLYSIS AND PORPHYRIA-LIKE CUTANEOUS CHANGES.

FIRST AID- REMOVE CONTAMINATED CLOTHING AND SHOES IMMEDIATELY. WASH AFFECTED AREA WITH SOAP OR MILD DETERGENT AND LARGE AMOUNTS OF WATER UNTIL NO EVIDENCE OF CHEMICAL REMAINS (APPROXIMATELY 15-20 MINUTES). GET MEDICAL ATTENTION IMMEDIATELY.

EYE CONTACT: OXYTETRACYCLINE HYDROCHLORIDE: **ACUTE EXPOSURE-** NO DATA AVAILABLE. HOWEVER 1% TETRACYCLINE IN AN OINTMENT CAUSED NO DETECTABLE INJURY TO RABBIT'S EYES. **CHRONIC EXPOSURE-** NO DATA AVAILABLE.

FIRST AID- WASH EYES IMMEDIATELY WITH LARGE AMOUNTS OF WATER OR NORMAL SALINE, OCCASIONALLY LIFTING UPPER AND LOWER LIDS, UNTIL NO EVIDENCE OF CHEMICAL REMAINS (APPROXIMATELY 15-20 MINUTES). GET MEDICAL ATTENTION IMMEDIATELY.

INGESTION: OXYTETRACYCLINE HYDROCHLORIDE: **ACUTE EXPOSURE-** A DOSE OF 6696 MG/KG WAS LETHAL IN MICE. TETRACYCLINES MAY CAUSE NAUSEA, GASTROINTESTINAL IRRITATION, VOMITING, ABDOMINAL PAIN, ESOPHAGEAL ULCERS, EPIGASTRIC PAIN AND BURNING, DIARRHEA, DYSPHAGIA, ENTEROCOLITIS, ANOREXIA, UREMIA, PANCYTOPENIA, ACIDOSIS, HYPERKALEMIA, AND CARDIAC ARRHYTHMIAS. LARGE ORAL DOSES MAY CAUSE HYPERSENSITIVITY, PHOTOTOXIC, NEPHROTOXIC, AND HEPATOTOXIC REACTIONS IN HUMANS PREVIOUSLY EXPOSED TO TETRACYCLINES. **CHRONIC EXPOSURE-** IN 14 DAY FEED STUDIES, A REDUCTION IN MEAN BODY WEIGHTS AND FEED CONSUMPTION WAS NOTED IN RATS AND MICE AT 100,000 PPM. THE STUDY INDICATED THAT MALES WERE MORE SENSITIVE THAN FEMALES TO THE EFFECTS; NO DEATHS WERE REPORTED. IN 13 WEEK STUDIES, MEAN BODY WEIGHT REDUCTION WAS NOTED IN MICE AT 50,000 PPM. NO DEATHS OCCURRED BUT A FATTY METAMORPHOSIS OF THE LIVER WAS OBSERVED IN MALE RATS. IN A 2 YEAR STUDY, NO SIGNIFICANT TOXIC EFFECT WAS NOTED, NOR WAS SURVIVAL AFFECTED. HOWEVER, PHEOCHROMOCYTOMAS OF THE ADRENAL GLAND OCCURRED WITH A POSITIVE TREND IN MALE RATS AND AN INCREASED INCIDENCE OF ADENOMAS OF THE PITUITARY GLAND IN FEMALE RATS WAS RECORDED. AN INCREASED INCIDENCE OF MAMMARY ADENOFIBROMAS WAS OBSERVED IN FEMALE RATS. THE AVERAGE SURVIVAL TIME FOR RATS RECEIVING OXYTETRACYCLINE HYDROCHLORIDE WAS 11% GREATER THAN THAT OF THE CONTROLS. REPRODUCTIVE EFFECTS HAVE BEEN REPORTED IN ANIMALS. USE OF OXYTETRACYCLINES IS ASSOCIATED WITH 3 KINDS OF RENAL DISEASE: ACUTE NON-OLIGURIC RENAL FAILURE IN PERSONS WITH PANCREATITIS OR FATTY LIVER; UREMIA, IN PERSONS WITH PREVIOUSLY IMPAIRED RENAL FUNCTION; AND A FALCONI-LIKE SYNDROME, USUALLY ASSOCIATED WITH OUTDATED OR DEGRADED TETRACYCLINES. TETRACYCLINES TEND TO BE DEPOSITED IN THE BONES AND THE TEETH AT SITES OF ACTIVE CALCIFICATION. PROLONGED USE HAS CAUSED DISCOLORATION OF THE TEETH AND A 40% DEPRESSION OF BONE GROWTH IN NEONATES, INFANTS AND CHILDREN. SENSITIZATION REACTIONS MAY OCCUR, CHARACTERIZED BY BURNING OF THE EYES, JAUNDICE, FATTY LIVER, CHEILOSIS, GLOSSITIS, PRURITUS, CONJUNCTIVITIS, DERMATITIS, EOSINOPHILIA, LEUKOCYTOSIS, THROMBOCYTOPENIC PUPPURA, AND PHOTOSENSITIVITY MANIFESTED BY EXAGGERATED SUNBURN. CROSS-SENSITIZATION IS COMMON AMONG THE VARIOUS TETRACYCLINES. IN PERSONS WITH IMPAIRED RENAL FUNCTION, HIGH SERUM LEVELS OF TETRACYCLINE MAY LEAD TO AZOTEMIA, HYPERPHOSPHATEMIA, ACIDOSIS, AND IN INFANTS TENSE BULGING OF THE FONTANELS. TETRACYCLINES MAY CAUSE BENIGN INTRACRANIAL HYPERTENSION WITH PAPILLEDEMA AND RETINAL HEMORRHAGES; THIS MAY OCCUR MORE FREQUENTLY IN CHILDREN THAN ADULTS. PREGNANT WOMEN APPEAR TO BE MORE SUSCEPTIBLE TO SEVERE HEPATIC DAMAGE. TETRACYCLINES MAY INTERFERE WITH VITAMIN K SYNTHESIS AND BLOOD COAGULATION. REPEATED USE OF ANTIBIOTICS MAY LEAD TO THE DEVELOPMENT OF VAGINAL, ORAL, PHARYNGEAL, INTESTINAL AND SYSTEMIC SUPRAINFECTIONS DUE TO OVERGROWTH OF ORGANISMS NOT AFFECTED BY THE ANTIBIOTIC AGENT. IN SOME CASES, THESE ORGANISMS PRODUCE TOXINS THAT CAUSE SEVERE VOMITING, DIARRHEA AND CIRCULATORY COLLAPSE.

FIRST AID- IN PRESENCE OF SYMPTOMS, REMOVE BY IPECAC EMESIS UNLESS PATIENT IS UNCONSCIOUS OR CONVULSING. 4-8 OUNCES OF CLEAR FLUID MAY BE GIVEN AFTER IPECAC. REPEAT IN 20-30 MINUTES IF VOMITING DOES NOT OCCUR. IN COMATOSE OR CONVULSING PATIENTS, USE GASTRIC LAVAGE WITH ENDOTRACHEAL INTUBATION. ACTIVATED CHARCOAL AND CATHARTICS MAY BE ADMINISTERED 1-1.5 HOURS AFTER EMESIS IS INDUCED OR THEY MAY BE PUT INTO THE LAVAGE TUBE AFTER THE STOMACH WASHOUT. (ELLENHORN AND BARCELOUX, MEDICAL TOXICOLOGY). MAINTAIN AIRWAY, RESPIRATION AND BLOOD PRESSURE. TREAT SYMPTOMATICALLY AND SUPPORTIVELY. GET MEDICAL ATTENTION IMMEDIATELY.

ANTIDOTE: NO SPECIFIC ANTIDOTE. TREAT SYMPTOMATICALLY AND SUPPORTIVELY.

REACTIVITY

REACTIVITY: STABLE UNDER NORMAL TEMPERATURES AND PRESSURES. STRONG SUNLIGHT IN MOIST AIR CAUSES DARKENING. TEMPERATURES EXCEEDING 90 C IN MOIST AIR CAUSES DARKENING. CONCENTRATED AQUEOUS SOLUTIONS AT NEUTRAL PH HYDROLYZE ON STANDING AND DEPOSIT CRYSTALS OF OXYTETRACYCLINE.

INCOMPATIBILITIES: OXYTETRACYCLINE HYDROCHLORIDE: SOLUTIONS HAVING PH BELOW 2: DIMINISHED POTENCY. ALKALI HYDROXIDE SOLUTIONS: RAPIDLY DESTROYED.

DECOMPOSITION: WHEN HEATED TO DECOMPOSITION IT MAY RELEASE CORROSIVE HYDROGEN CHLORIDE FUMES AND TOXIC OXIDES OF NITROGEN.

POLYMERIZATION: HAZARDOUS POLYMERIZATION HAS NOT BEEN REPORTED TO OCCUR UNDER NORMAL TEMPERATURES AND PRESSURES.

STORAGE AND DISPOSAL

OBSERVE ALL FEDERAL, STATE AND LOCAL REGULATIONS WHEN STORING OR DISPOSING OF THIS SUBSTANCE. FOR ASSISTANCE, CONTACT THE DISTRICT DIRECTOR OF THE ENVIRONMENTAL PROTECTION AGENCY.

CONDITIONS TO AVOID

MAY BURN BUT DOES NOT IGNITE READILY. AVOID CONTACT WITH STRONG OXIDIZERS, EXCESSIVE HEAT, SPARKS, OR OPEN FLAME.

SPILL AND LEAK PROCEDURES

OCCUPATIONAL SPILL: SWEEP UP AND PLACE IN SUITABLE CLEAN, DRY CONTAINERS FOR RECLAMATION OR LATER DISPOSAL. DO NOT FLUSH SPILLED MATERIAL INTO SEWER. KEEP UNNECESSARY PEOPLE AWAY.

PROTECTIVE EQUIPMENT

VENTILATION: PROVIDE LOCAL EXHAUST OR GENERAL DILUTION VENTILATION SYSTEM.

RESPIRATOR: THE FOLLOWING RESPIRATORS ARE RECOMMENDED BASED ON INFORMATION FOUND IN THE PHYSICAL DATA, TOXICITY AND HEALTH EFFECTS SECTIONS. THEY ARE RANKED IN ORDER FROM MINIMUM TO MAXIMUM RESPIRATORY PROTECTION. THE SPECIFIC RESPIRATOR SELECTED MUST BE BASED ON CONTAMINATION LEVELS FOUND IN THE WORK PLACE, MUST NOT EXCEED THE WORKING LIMITS OF THE RESPIRATOR AND BE JOINTLY APPROVED BY THE NATIONAL INSTITUTE FOR OCCUPATIONAL SAFETY AND HEALTH AND THE MINE SAFETY AND HEALTH ADMINISTRATION (NIOSH-MSHA).

DUST AND MIST RESPIRATOR WITH A FULL FACEPIECE.

AIR-PURIFYING FULL FACEPIECE RESPIRATOR WITH A HIGH-EFFICIENCY PARTICULATE FILTER.

POWERED AIR-PURIFYING RESPIRATOR WITH A TIGHT-FITTING FACEPIECE AND HIGH-EFFICIENCY PARTICULATE FILTER.

TYPE 'C' SUPPLIED-AIR RESPIRATOR WITH A FULL FACEPIECE OPERATED IN PRESSURE-DEMAND OR OTHER POSITIVE PRESSURE MODE OR WITH A FULL FACEPIECE, HELMET OR HOOD OPERATED IN CONTINUOUS-FLOW MODE.

SELF-CONTAINED BREATHING APPARATUS WITH A FULL FACEPIECE OPERATED IN PRESSURE-DEMAND OR OTHER POSITIVE PRESSURE MODE.

FOR FIREFIGHTING AND OTHER IMMEDIATELY DANGEROUS TO LIFE OR HEALTH CONDITIONS:

SELF-CONTAINED BREATHING APPARATUS WITH FULL FACEPIECE OPERATED IN PRESSURE-DEMAND OR OTHER POSITIVE PRESSURE MODE.

SUPPLIED-AIR RESPIRATOR WITH FULL FACEPIECE AND OPERATED IN PRESSURE-DEMAND OR OTHER POSITIVE PRESSURE MODE IN COMBINATION WITH AN AUXILIARY SELF-CONTAINED BREATHING APPARATUS OPERATED IN PRESSURE-DEMAND OR OTHER POSITIVE PRESSURE MODE.

CLOTHING: EMPLOYEE MUST WEAR APPROPRIATE PROTECTIVE (IMPERVIOUS) CLOTHING AND EQUIPMENT TO PREVENT REPEATED OR PROLONGED SKIN CONTACT WITH THIS SUBSTANCE.

GLOVES: EMPLOYEE MUST WEAR APPROPRIATE PROTECTIVE GLOVES TO PREVENT CONTACT WITH THIS SUBSTANCE.

EYE PROTECTION: EMPLOYEE MUST WEAR SPLASH-PROOF OR DUST-RESISTANT SAFETY GOGGLES TO PREVENT EYE CONTACT WITH THIS SUBSTANCE. EMERGENCY EYE WASH: WHERE THERE IS ANY POSSIBILITY THAT AN EMPLOYEE'S EYES MAY BE EXPOSED TO THIS SUBSTANCE, THE EMPLOYER SHOULD PROVIDE AN EYE WASH FOUNTAIN WITHIN THE IMMEDIATE WORK AREA FOR EMERGENCY USE.

AUTHORIZED BY- OCCUPATIONAL HEALTH SERVICES, INC.
CREATION DATE: 10/04/89 ***REVISION DATE:*** 05/31/90

MATERIAL SAFETY DATA SHEET

OCCUPATIONAL HEALTH SERVICES, INC.
AGRICULTURE AND PESTICIDE DIVISION
450 SEVENTH AVENUE, SUITE 2407
NEW YORK, NEW YORK 10123
1-800-445-MSDS OR (212) 967-1100

EMERGENCY CONTACT:
JOHN S. BRANSFORD, JR. (615) 292-1180

SUBSTANCE IDENTIFICATION

CAS-NUMBER 134-62-3

SUBSTANCE: DEET

TRADE NAMES/SYNONYMS: BENZAMIDE, N,N-DIETHYL-3-METHYL-; M-TOLUAMIDE, N,N-DIETHYL-; N,N-DIETHYL-3-METHYLBENZAMIDE; N,N-DIETHYL-M-TOLUAMIDE; DIETHYL-M-TOLUAMIDE; M-TOLUIC ACID DIETHYLAMIDE; DIETHYLTOLUAMIDE; DET; M-DETA; DELTA; AUTAN; M-DELPHENE; DETAMIDE; DIELTAMID; FLYPEL; METADELPHENE; OFF (FORMULATION); ENT 20218; C12H17NO; PST84230

CHEMICAL FAMILY: AMIDE, AROMATIC

MOLECULAR FORMULA: C-H3-C6-H4-C-O-N-(C2-H5)2

MOLECULAR WEIGHT: 191.27

CERCLA RATINGS (SCALE 0-3): HEALTH=3 FIRE=1 REACTIVITY=0 PERSISTENCE=1

NFPA RATINGS (SCALE 0-4): HEALTH=3 FIRE=1 REACTIVITY=0

COMPONENTS AND CONTAMINANTS

COMPONENT: DEET ***PERCENT:*** 100.0
CAS# 134-62-3

EXPOSURE LIMITS: NO OCCUPATIONAL EXPOSURE LIMITS ESTABLISHED BY OSHA, ACGIH, OR NIOSH.

PHYSICAL DATA

DESCRIPTION: COLORLESS TO AMBER, HYGROSCOPIC, OILY LIQUID WITH A MILD CHARACTERISTIC ODOR. ***BOILING POINT:*** 320 F (160 C) @ 19 MMHG

SPECIFIC GRAVITY: 0.996 @ 25 C ***VAPOR PRESSURE:*** 0.0019 MMHG @ 160 C

EVAPORATION RATE: (BUTYL ACETATE=1) <1

SOLUBILITY IN WATER: PRACTICALLY INSOLUBLE ***VAPOR DENSITY:*** 6.7

SOLVENT SOLUBILITY: SOLUBLE IN ETHANOL, ETHER, ISOPROPANOL, CHLOROFORM, CARBON DISULFIDE, ALCOHOL, BENZENE, PROPYLENE GLYCOL, COTTONSEED OIL, KETONES, PETROLEUM DISTILLATES; SPARINGLY SOLUBLE IN PETROLEUM ETHER AND GLYCERIN.

FIRE AND EXPLOSION DATA

FIRE AND EXPLOSION HAZARD: SLIGHT FIRE HAZARD WHEN EXPOSED TO HEAT OR FLAME.

FLASH POINT: 311 F (155 C) (OC) ***FLAMMABILITY CLASS(OSHA):*** IIIB

FIREFIGHTING MEDIA: DRY CHEMICAL, CARBON DIOXIDE, HALON, WATER SPRAY OR STANDARD FOAM (1987 EMERGENCY RESPONSE GUIDEBOOK, DOT P 5800.4). FOR LARGER FIRES, USE WATER SPRAY, FOG OR STANDARD FOAM (1987 EMERGENCY RESPONSE GUIDEBOOK, DOT P 5800.4).

FIREFIGHTING: MOVE CONTAINER FROM FIRE AREA IF POSSIBLE. DO NOT SCATTER SPILLED MATERIAL WITH HIGH PRESSURE WATER STREAMS. DIKE FIRE CONTROL WATER FOR LATER DISPOSAL (1987 EMERGENCY RESPONSE GUIDEBOOK, DOT P 5800.4, GUIDE PAGE 31). USE AGENTS SUITABLE FOR TYPE OF SURROUNDING FIRE. AVOID BREATHING HAZARDOUS VAPORS, KEEP UPWIND.

TOXICITY

DEET: IRRITATION DATA: 500 MG SKIN-RABBIT MODERATE; 100 MG EYE-RABBIT; 10 MG EYE-RABBIT MODERATE. TOXICITY DATA: 5950 MG/M3 INHALATION-RAT LC50; 35 MG/KG/5 DAYS SKIN-HUMAN TDLO; 3180 MG/KG SKIN-RABBIT LD50; 5000 MG/KG SKIN-RAT LD50; 3170 MG/KG SKIN-MOUSE LD50; 4750 MG/KG ORAL-CHILD TDLO; 950 MG/KG ORAL-WOMAN LDLO; 950 MG/KG ORAL-WOMAN TDLO; 679 MG/KG ORAL-MAN LDLO; 1950 MG/KG ORAL-RAT LD50; 1584 MG/KG ORAL-RABBIT LD50; 75 MG/KG INTRAVENOUS-RABBIT LDLO; 1170 UG/KG UNREPORTED-MOUSE LD50; MUTAGENIC DATA (RTECS); REPRODUCTIVE EFFECTS DATA (RTECS). CARCINOGEN STATUS: NONE. LOCAL EFFECTS: IRRITANT- EYE. ACUTE TOXICITY LEVEL: TOXIC BY INHALATION; MODERATELY TOXIC BY INGESTION; SLIGHTLY TOXIC BY DERMAL ABSORPTION. TARGET EFFECTS: POISONING MAY AFFECT THE CENTRAL NERVOUS SYSTEM. ADDITIONAL DATA: MAY BE EXCRETED IN BREAST MILK.

HEALTH EFFECTS AND FIRST AID

INHALATION: DEET: TOXIC. **ACUTE EXPOSURE-** TEMPORARY IRRITATION AND BEHAVIORAL CHANGES WERE NOTED IN ANIMALS EXPOSED TO DEET. THE LC50 REPORTED IN RATS WAS 5950 MG/M3. **CHRONIC EXPOSURE-** AN INCREASED INCIDENCE OF SPERM HEAD ABNORMALITIES AND PERIODIC NAUSEA, VOMITING, AND NASAL EXUDATE WERE OBSERVED IN ANIMALS FOLLOWING CHRONIC EXPOSURE.

FIRST AID- REMOVE FROM EXPOSURE AREA TO FRESH AIR IMMEDIATELY. IF BREATHING HAS STOPPED, PERFORM ARTIFICIAL RESPIRATION. KEEP PERSON WARM AND AT REST. TREAT SYMPTOMATICALLY AND SUPPORTIVELY. GET MEDICAL ATTENTION IMMEDIATELY.

SKIN CONTACT: DEET: **ACUTE EXPOSURE-** APPLICATION OF UNDILUTED MATERIAL AND 50% SOLUTION TO HUMAN SKIN CAUSED NO PRIMARY IRRITATION OR SENSITIZATION. CENTRAL NERVOUS SYSTEM DISORDERS OF EXCITATION, STIFFNESS OF MOVEMENT AND LACK OF COORDINATION WERE OBSERVED IN MICE FOLLOWING APPLICATION OF DEET. **CHRONIC EXPOSURE-** REPEATED APPLICATION TO HUMAN SKIN RESULTED IN SLIGHT IRRITATION AND DRYNESS OF THE FACE, DESQUAMATION AROUND THE NOSE, AND A SLIGHT TINGLING SENSATION. RARE INCIDENCES OF SPORADIC ALLERGIC REACTIONS AND DERMATITIS INCLUDING ANAPHYLAXIS AND SCARRING BULLOUS DERMATITIS HAVE OCCURRED. ENCEPHALOPATHY AND NEUROLOGICAL SYMPTOMS OF MUSCLE CRAMPS, URINARY HESITATION, INSOMIA, ABNORMAL SWEATING, IRRITABILITY, DEPRESSION, PARANOIA, EPISODES OF CONFUSION, AND AGRRESSIVE BEHAVIOR HAVE OCCURRED AMONG INDIVIDUALS REPEATEDLY EXPOSED TO DEET. THREE CASES OF POISONING IN CHILDREN RESULTED IN DEATH. MARKED HISTOPATHOLOGICAL CHANGES IN THE KIDNEY WERE OBSERVED IN RABBITS AFTER A 90-DAY EXPOSURE TO 1.3 GM/KG. EMBRYOTOXICITY FOLLOWING DERMAL APPLICATIONS OF LARGE AMOUNTS TO RABBITS WAS REPORTED IN RUSSIAN LITERATURE.

FIRST AID- REMOVE CONTAMINATED CLOTHING AND SHOES IMMEDIATELY. WASH AFFECTED AREA WITH SOAP OR MILD DETERGENT AND LARGE AMOUNTS OF WATER UNTIL NO EVIDENCE OF CHEMICAL REMAINS (APPROXIMATELY 15-20 MINUTES). GET MEDICAL ATTENTION IMMEDIATELY.

EYE CONTACT: DEET: IRRITANT. **ACUTE EXPOSURE-** UNDILUTED MATERIAL IN THE EYE MAY CAUSE MODERATE TO SEVERE IRRITATION. INSTILLATION OF DEET INTO THE EYES OF RABBITS PRODUCED EDEMA OF THE CONJUNCTIVA, LACRIMATION, CONJUNCTIVITIS, AND SOME CORNEAL INJURY; THE EYES APPEARED NORMAL AFTER FIVE DAYS. **CHRONIC EXPOSURE-** IN RABBITS, REPEATED EXPOSURE TO A 71% AEROSOL OR CONCENTRATED MATERIAL RESULTED IN IRRITATION OF THE CONJUNCTIVAL EPITHELIUM AND CORNEAL OPACIFICATION.

FIRST AID- WASH EYES IMMEDIATELY WITH LARGE AMOUNTS OF WATER OR NORMAL SALINE, OCCASIONALLY LIFTING UPPER AND LOWER LIDS, UNTIL NO EVIDENCE OF CHEMICAL REMAINS (APPROXIMATELY 15-20 MINUTES). GET MEDICAL ATTENTION IMMEDIATELY.

INGESTION: DEET: **ACUTE EXPOSURE-** EFFECTS OF IRRITABILITY, BIZARRE MOVEMENT, DEPRESSED MUSCLE STRETCH REFLEXES, HYPOTENSION, SEIZURES AND COMA WERE REPORTED FROM CASES OF HUMAN INGESTION. IN SOME INSTANCES, THESE EFFECTS WERE RAPID AND RESULTED IN DEATH. INGESTION IN ANIMALS PRODUCED LACRIMATION, CHROMODACRYORRHEA, CENTRAL NERVOUS SYSTEM DEPRESSION, LOSS OF RIGHTING REFLEXES, LABORED RESPIRATION, TREMORS, COMA AND TERMINAL CONVULSIONS. RESPIRATORY FAILURE USUALLY PRECEDED CARDIAC FAILURE. **CHRONIC EXPOSURE-** HYPERTROPHY OF THE KIDNEYS AND LIVER AND EFFECTS OF MILD CENTRAL NERVOUS SYSTEM STIMULATION INCLUDING TREMORS AND HYPERACTIVITY WERE NOTED IN ANIMALS FOLLOWING REPEATED EXPOSURE. SIGNIFICANT TESTICULAR HYPERTROPHY WAS OBSERVED

IN MALE RATS REPEATEDLY FED A DIET CONTAINING FROM 48 TO 531 MG/KG/DAY.

FIRST AID- IF THE PERSON IS CONSCIOUS AND NOT CONVULSING, REMOVE BY GASTRIC LAVAGE AND FOLLOW WITH A CATHARTIC (DREISBACH, HANDBOOK OF POISONING, 12TH ED.). TREAT SYMPTOMATICALLY AND SUPPORTIVELY. GASTRIC LAVAGE SHOULD BE PERFORMED BY QUALIFIED MEDICAL PERSONNEL. GET MEDICAL ATTENTION IMMEDIATELY.

ANTIDOTE: NO SPECIFIC ANTIDOTE. TREAT SYMPTOMATICALLY AND SUPPORTIVELY.

REACTIVITY

REACTIVITY: STABLE UNDER NORMAL TEMPERATURES AND PRESSURES. SLOWLY HYDROLYZES IN CONTACT WITH WATER.

INCOMPATIBILITIES: DEET: OXIDIZERS (STRONG): MAY CAUSE FIRE AND EXPLOSION HAZARD.

DECOMPOSITION: THERMAL DECOMPOSITION PRODUCTS MAY INCLUDE TOXIC OXIDES OF CARBON AND NITROGEN.

POLYMERIZATION: HAZARDOUS POLYMERIZATION HAS NOT BEEN REPORTED TO OCCUR UNDER NORMAL TEMPERATURES AND PRESSURES.

STORAGE AND DISPOSAL

OBSERVE ALL FEDERAL, STATE AND LOCAL REGULATIONS WHEN STORING OR DISPOSING OF THIS SUBSTANCE. FOR ASSISTANCE, CONTACT THE DISTRICT DIRECTOR OF THE ENVIRONMENTAL PROTECTION AGENCY.

****STORAGE****

STORE IN ACCORDANCE WITH 40 CFR 165 RECOMMENDED PROCEDURES FOR THE DISPOSAL AND STORAGE OF PESTICIDES AND PESTICIDE CONTAINERS.

STORE AWAY FROM INCOMPATIBLE SUBSTANCES.

****DISPOSAL****

DISPOSAL MUST BE IN ACCORDANCE WITH 40 CFR 165 RECOMMENDED PROCEDURES FOR THE DISPOSAL AND STORAGE OF PESTICIDES AND PESTICIDE CONTAINERS.

CONDITIONS TO AVOID

MAY BURN BUT DOES NOT IGNITE READILY. AVOID CONTACT WITH STRONG OXIDIZERS, EXCESSIVE HEAT, SPARKS, OR OPEN FLAME.

SPILL AND LEAK PROCEDURES

OCCUPATIONAL SPILL: STOP LEAK IF YOU CAN DO IT WITHOUT RISK. FOR SMALL SPILLS, TAKE UP WITH SAND OR OTHER ABSORBENT MATERIAL AND PLACE INTO CLEAN, DRY CONTAINERS FOR LATER DISPOSAL. KEEP UNNECESSARY PEOPLE AWAY. ISOLATE HAZARD AREA AND DENY ENTRY.

PROTECTIVE EQUIPMENT

VENTILATION: PROVIDE LOCAL EXHAUST VENTILATION SYSTEM.

RESPIRATOR: THE FOLLOWING RESPIRATORS ARE RECOMMENDED BASED ON INFORMATION FOUND IN THE PHYSICAL DATA, TOXICITY AND HEALTH EFFECTS SECTIONS. THEY ARE RANKED IN ORDER FROM MINIMUM TO MAXIMUM RESPIRATORY PROTECTION. THE SPECIFIC RESPIRATOR SELECTED MUST BE BASED ON CONTAMINATION LEVELS FOUND IN THE WORK PLACE, MUST NOT EXCEED THE WORKING LIMITS OF THE RESPIRATOR AND BE JOINTLY APPROVED BY THE NATIONAL INSTITUTE FOR OCCUPATIONAL SAFETY AND HEALTH AND THE MINE SAFETY AND HEALTH ADMINISTRATION (NIOSH-MSHA).

CHEMICAL CARTRIDGE RESPIRATOR WITH PESTICIDE CARTRIDGE.

GAS MASK WITH A PESTICIDE CANISTER (CHIN-STYLE OR FRONT- OR BACK-MOUNTED CANISTER).

TYPE 'C' SUPPLIED-AIR RESPIRATOR OPERATED IN THE PRESSURE-DEMAND OR OTHER POSITIVE PRESSURE OR CONTINUOUS-FLOW MODE.

SELF-CONTAINED BREATHING APPARATUS.

FOR FIREFIGHTING AND OTHER IMMEDIATELY DANGEROUS TO LIFE OR HEALTH CONDITIONS:

SELF-CONTAINED BREATHING APPARATUS WITH FULL FACEPIECE OPERATED IN PRESSURE-DEMAND OR OTHER POSITIVE PRESSURE MODE.

SUPPLIED-AIR RESPIRATOR WITH FULL FACEPIECE AND OPERATED IN PRESSURE-DEMAND OR OTHER POSITIVE PRESSURE MODE IN COMBINATION WITH AN AUXILIARY SELF-CONTAINED BREATHING APPARATUS OPERATED IN PRESSURE-DEMAND OR OTHER POSITIVE PRESSURE MODE.

CLOTHING: EMPLOYEE MUST WEAR APPROPRIATE PROTECTIVE (IMPERVIOUS) CLOTHING AND EQUIPMENT TO PREVENT REPEATED OR PROLONGED SKIN CONTACT WITH THIS SUBSTANCE.

GLOVES: EMPLOYEE MUST WEAR APPROPRIATE PROTECTIVE GLOVES TO PREVENT CONTACT WITH THIS SUBSTANCE.

EYE PROTECTION: EMPLOYEE MUST WEAR SPLASH-PROOF OR DUST-RESISTANT SAFETY GOGGLES TO PREVENT EYE CONTACT WITH THIS SUBSTANCE.

EMERGENCY EYE WASH: WHERE THERE IS ANY POSSIBILITY THAT AN EMPLOYEE'S EYES MAY BE EXPOSED TO THIS SUBSTANCE, THE EMPLOYER SHOULD PROVIDE AN EYE WASH FOUNTAIN WITHIN THE IMMEDIATE WORK AREA FOR EMERGENCY USE.

AUTHORIZED BY- OCCUPATIONAL HEALTH SERVICES, INC.
CREATION DATE: 10/04/89 ***REVISION DATE:*** 05/08/90

MATERIAL SAFETY DATA SHEET

OCCUPATIONAL HEALTH SERVICES, INC.
AGRICULTURE AND PESTICIDE DIVISION
450 SEVENTH AVENUE, SUITE 2407
NEW YORK, NEW YORK 10123
1-800-445-MSDS OR (212) 967-1100

EMERGENCY CONTACT:
JOHN S. BRANSFORD, JR. (615) 292-1180

SUBSTANCE IDENTIFICATION

CAS-NUMBER 15251-48-6

SUBSTANCE: CALCIUM OXYTETRACYCLINE

TRADE NAMES/SYNONYMS: CALCIUM DIOXYTETRACYCLINE; 4-(DIMETHYLAMINO)-1,4,4A,5,5A,6,11,12A-OCTAHYDRO-3,5,6,10,12,12A- HEXAHYDROXY-6-METHYL-1,11-DIOXO-2-NAPHTHACENECARBOXAMIDE, (4S-(4 ALPHA,4A ALPHA,5 ALPHA,5A ALPHA,6 BETA,12A ALPHA))-CALCIUM SALT; 4-(DIMETHYLAMINO)-1,4,4A,5,5A,6,11,12A-OCTAHYDRO-3,5,6,10,12,12A- HEXAHYDROXY-6-METHYL-1,11-DIOXO-2-NAPHTHACENECARBOXAMIDE, CALCIUM SALT; OXYTETRACYCLINE CALCIUM SALT; TERRABON; 2-NAPHTHACENECARBOXAMIDE, 4-(DIMETHYLAMINO)-1,4,4A,5,5A,6,11,12A-OCTA- HYDRO-3,5,6,10,12,12A-HEXAHYDROXY-6-METHYL-1,11-DIOXO-, CALCIUM SALT, (4S-(4 ALPHA, 4A ALPHA, 5 ALPHA, 5A ALPHA, 6 BETA, 12A ALPHA))-; 2-NAPHTHACENECARBOXAMIDE, 4-(DIMETHYLAMINO)-1,4,4A,5,5A,6,11,12A-OCTA- HYDRO-3,5,6,10,12,12A-HEXAHYDROXY-6-METHYL-1,11-DIOXO-, CALCIUM SALT; C44H48CAN4O18; PST84256

CHEMICAL FAMILY: ANTIBIOTIC

MOLECULAR FORMULA: (C22-H23-N2-O9)2.CA

MOLECULAR WEIGHT: 958.94

CERCLA RATINGS (SCALE 0-3): HEALTH=U FIRE=1 REACTIVITY=0 PERSISTENCE=2

NFPA RATINGS (SCALE 0-4): HEALTH=U FIRE=1 REACTIVITY=0

COMPONENTS AND CONTAMINANTS

COMPONENT: CALCIUM OXYTETRACYCLINE ***PERCENT:*** 100
CAS# 15251-48-6

OTHER CONTAMINANTS: NONE

EXPOSURE LIMITS: NO OCCUPATIONAL EXPOSURE LIMITS ESTABLISHED BY OSHA, ACGIH, OR NIOSH.

PHYSICAL DATA

DESCRIPTION: YELLOW TO LIGHT BROWN CRYSTALLINE POWDER.

MELTING POINT: NOT AVAILABLE ***SPECIFIC GRAVITY:*** NOT AVAILABLE

PH: 6.0-8.0 @ 25% SUSP ***SOLUBILITY IN WATER:*** INSOLUBLE

SOLVENT SOLUBILITY: SOLUBLE IN METHANOL, HYDROCHLORIC ACID

FIRE AND EXPLOSION DATA

FIRE AND EXPLOSION HAZARD: SLIGHT FIRE HAZARD WHEN EXPOSED TO HEAT OR FLAME.

FIREFIGHTING MEDIA: DRY CHEMICAL, CARBON DIOXIDE, HALON, WATER SPRAY OR STANDARD FOAM (1987 EMERGENCY RESPONSE GUIDEBOOK, DOT P 5800.4).

FOR LARGER FIRES, USE WATER SPRAY, FOG OR STANDARD FOAM (1987 EMERGENCY RESPONSE GUIDEBOOK, DOT P 5800.4).

FIREFIGHTING: MOVE CONTAINER FROM FIRE AREA IF POSSIBLE. DO NOT SCATTER SPILLED MATERIAL WITH HIGH PRESSURE WATER STREAMS. DIKE FIRE CONTROL WATER FOR LATER DISPOSAL (1987 EMERGENCY RESPONSE GUIDEBOOK, DOT P 5800.4, GUIDE PAGE 31).

USE AGENTS SUITABLE FOR TYPE OF SURROUNDING FIRE. AVOID BREATHING HAZARDOUS VAPORS, KEEP UPWIND.

TOXICITY

CALCIUM OXYTETRACYCLINE: CARCINOGEN STATUS: NONE. ACUTE TOXICITY LEVEL: NO DATA AVAILABLE. TARGET EFFECTS: NO DATA AVAILABLE. AT INCREASED RISK FROM EXPOSURE: PERSONS WITH RENAL OR HEPATIC DYSFUNCTION, ANURIA, AND AZOTEMIA. ADDITIONAL DATA: CROSS REACTIONS BETWEEN DIFFERENT TETRACYLCINES MAY OCCUR. INTERACTIONS WITH MEDICATIONS HAVE BEEN REPORTED.

HEALTH EFFECTS AND FIRST AID

INHALATION: CALCIUM OXYTETRACYCLINE: **ACUTE EXPOSURE-** INHALATION OF ANTIBIOTIC DUSTS OR AEROSOLS MAY RARELY CAUSE HYPERSENSITIVITY REACTIONS IN PREVIOUSLY EXPOSED INDIVIDUALS AS DETAILED IN CHRONIC EXPOSURE. **CHRONIC EXPOSURE-** REPEATED EXPOSURE TO ANTIBIOTICS MAY RESULT IN SENSITIZATION CHARACTERIZED BY PRONOUNCED PERSPIRATION, PALLOR, COLLAPSE PERHAPS WITH LOSS OF CONSCIOUSNESS, POSSIBLY DYSPNEA AND COUGH, SNEEZING AND URTICARIA. ANAPHYLACTIC SHOCK FROM OCCUPATIONAL EXPOSURE IS VERY RARE. TETRACYCLINE EXPOSURE MAY RARELY PRODUCE HEMORRHAGIC RHINITIS.

FIRST AID- REMOVE FROM EXPOSURE AREA TO FRESH AIR IMMEDIATELY. IF BREATHING HAS STOPPED, PERFORM ARTIFICIAL RESPIRATION. KEEP PERSON WARM AND AT REST. TREAT SYMPTOMATICALLY AND SUPPORTIVELY. GET MEDICAL ATTENTION IMMEDIATELY.

SKIN CONTACT: CALCIUM OXYTETRACYCLINE: **ACUTE EXPOSURE-** NO SPECIFIC DATA AVAILABLE. THREE CASES OF ECZEMATOUS CONTACT ALLERGY HAVE BEEN REPORTED IN PERSONS USING OXYTETRACYCLINE. **CHRONIC EXPOSURE-** NO SPECIFIC DATA AVAILABLE. REPEATED ORAL EXPOSURES TO OXYTETRACYCLINE HAS PRODUCED DERMATITIS AND PHOTO-ONYCHOLYSIS AND PORPHYRIA-LIKE CUTANEOUS CHANGES. TOPICALLY APPLIED TETRACYCLINES MAY CAUSE A YELLOW DISCOLORATION OF THE SKIN WHICH FLUORESCES UNDER BLACK OR FLUORESCENT LIGHTS.

FIRST AID- REMOVE CONTAMINATED CLOTHING AND SHOES IMMEDIATELY. WASH AFFECTED AREA WITH SOAP OR MILD DETERGENT AND LARGE AMOUNTS OF WATER UNTIL NO EVIDENCE OF CHEMICAL REMAINS (APPROXIMATELY 15-20 MINUTES). GET MEDICAL ATTENTION IMMEDIATELY.

EYE CONTACT: CALCIUM OXYTETRACYCLINE: **ACUTE EXPOSURE-** NO DATA AVAILABLE. **CHRONIC EXPOSURE-** NO SPECIFIC DATA AVAILABLE. TETRACYCLINES MAY DEPOSIT IN THE EYE AND MAY PRODUCE ABNORMAL PIGMENTATION OF THE CONJUNCTIVA. RETINAL HEMORRHAGES MAY OCCUR AS A COMPLICATION OF THE SYSTEMICALLY ADMINISTERED TETRACYCLINES.

FIRST AID- WASH EYES IMMEDIATELY WITH LARGE AMOUNTS OF WATER OR NORMAL SALINE, OCCASIONALLY LIFTING UPPER AND LOWER LIDS, UNTIL NO EVIDENCE OF CHEMICAL REMAINS (APPROXIMATELY 15-20 MINUTES). GET MEDICAL ATTENTION IMMEDIATELY.

INGESTION: CALCIUM OXYTETRACYCLINE: **ACUTE EXPOSURE-** ALL TETRACYCLINES MAY CAUSE GASTROINTESTINAL UPSET IN CERTAIN INDIVIDUALS. THERE MAY BE NAUSEA, EPIGASTRIC PAIN AND BURNING, VOMITING, ABDOMINAL PAIN, TRANSITORY YELLOWISH-BROWN DISCOLORATION OF THE TONGUE, ANOREXIA, AND DIARRHEA. LARGE ORAL DOSES MAY CAUSE NEPHROTOXIC, HEPATOTOXIC AND PHOTOTOXIC REACTIONS. HYPERSENSITIVITY MAY OCCUR IN HUMANS PREVIOUSLY EXPOSED TO TETRACYCLINES. **CHRONIC EXPOSURE-** REPEATED OR PROLONGED EXPOSURE TO TETRACYCLINES MAY CAUSE SORE THROAT, HOARSENESS, BLACK HAIRY TONGUE, BULKY LOOSE STOOLS, STEATORRHEA, STOMATITIS, DYSPHAGIA, INFLAMMATORY LESIONS IN THE ANOGENITAL REGION AND POSSIBLE ESOPHAGEAL ULCERS. THE USE OF OXYTETRACYCLINES IS ASSOCIATED WITH 3 KINDS OF RENAL DISEASE: ACUTE NON-OLIGURIC RENAL FAILURE IN PERSONS WITH PANCREATITIS OR FATTY LIVER; UREMIA, IN PERSONS WITH PREVIOUSLY IMPAIRED RENAL FUNCTION; AND A REVERSIBLE NEPHROTOXICITY ASSOCIATED WITH OUTDATED OR DEGRADED TETRACYCLINES. THE LATTER IS MANIFESTED BY NAUSEA, VOMITING, PROXIMAL TUBULAR DAMAGE WITH POLYURIA, POLYDIPSIA, PROTEINURIA, ACIDOSIS, GLYCOSURIA AND GROSS AMINOACIDURIA. ALSO A FACIAL LESION TYPICAL OF SYSTEMIC LUPUS ERYTHEMATOUS AND SENSITIVITY TO LIGHT HAS ALSO BEEN OBSERVED WITH OUTDATED OR DEGRADED TETRACYCLINES. TETRACYCLINES TEND TO BE DEPOSITED IN THE BONES AND TEETH AT SITES OF ACTIVE CALCIFICATION. SENSITIZATION REACTIONS MAY OCCUR CHARACTERIZED BY BURNING OF THE EYES, CONJUNCTIVITIS, MACULOPAPULAR AND ERTHEMATOUS RASHES, UNCOMMON EXFOLIATIVE DERMATITIS, URTICARIA, PRURITIS, CHEILOSIS, GLOSSITIS, FEVER, ASTHMA, FATTY LIVER, RARE HEPATIC CHOLESTASIS AT HIGH DOSE LEVELS, THROMBOCYTOPENIC PURPURA, LEUKOCYTOSIS, TOXIC GRANULATION OF GRANULOCYTES, ATYPICAL LEUKOCYTES, EOSINOPHILIA, IMMUNE HEMOLYTIC ANEMIA, APLASTIC ANEMIA, THROMBOCYTOPENIA, NEUTROPENIA, LEUKOPENIA, OR PANCYTOPENIA, ANGIONEUROTIC EDEMA, PERICARDITIS, EXACERBATION OF SYSTEMIC LUPUS ERYTHEMATOSUS AND SERUM SICKNESS-LIKE REACTIONS, POSSIBLE ANAPHYLAXIS AND ANAPHYLACTOID PURPURA. PULMONARY INFILTRATES, DIABETES, TRANSIENT MYOPATHY, RISE IN BLOOD UREA NITROGEN, TOXEMIA, PSYCHOTIC REACTIONS AND FATAL LIVER DAMAGE HAVE BEEN REPORTED. PHOTOSENSITIVITY REACTIONS MAY INCLUDE AN EXAGGERATED SUNBURN. RARELY, ONYCHOLYSIS AND PIGMENTATION OF THE NAILS MAY DEVELOP SIMULTANEOUSLY. TETRACYCLINES MAY CAUSE BENIGN INTRACRANIAL HYPERTENSION WITH PAPILLEDEMA, HEADACHE, IMPAIRMENT OF VISION, AND RETINAL HEMORRHAGES OCCURRING MORE FREQUENTLY IN CHILDREN THAN ADULTS. PREGNANT WOMEN APPEAR TO BE MORE SUSCEPTIBLE TO SEVERE TETRACYCLINE-INDUCED HEPATIC DAMAGE. JAUNDICE APPEARS FIRST AND AZOTEMIA, ACIDOSIS AND IRREVERSIBLE SHOCK MAY FOLLOW. PATHOLOGICALLY, THE LIVER SHOWS FINE VACUOLES, CYTOPLASMIC CHANGES AND IS DIFFUSELY INFILTRATED WITH FAT. TETRACYCLINES ARE EXCRETED IN BREAST MILK AND READILY CROSS THE PLACENTAL BARRIER. THEY MAY CAUSE RETARDATION OF SKELETAL DEVELOPMENT, ENAMEL HYPOPLASIA AND TOOTH DISCOLORATION IN THE DEVELOPING FETUS. WHEN GIVEN OVER PROLONGED PERIODS, TETRACYCLINES HAVE BEEN REPORTED TO PRODUCE BROWN-BLACK MICROSCOPIC DISCOLORATION OF THYROID GLANDS WITH NO ABNORMALITIES OF THYROID FUNCTION. TETRACYCLINES MAY INTERFERE WITH VITAMIN K SYNTHESIS AND CAUSE A DELAY IN BLOOD COAGULATION. REPEATED USE OF ANTIBIOTICS MAY LEAD TO DEVELOPMENT OF VAGINAL, ORAL, PHARYNGEAL, INTESTINAL AND SYSTEMIC SUPRAINFECTIONS DUE TO OVERGROWTH OF ORGANISMS NOT AFFECTED BY THE ANTIBIOTIC AGENT. IN SOME CASES, THESE ORGANISMS PRODUCE TOXINS THAT CAUSE SEVERE VOMITING, DIARRHEA AND CIRCULATORY COLLAPSE.

FIRST AID- IN PRESENCE OF SYMPTOMS, REMOVE BY IPECAC EMESIS UNLESS PATIENT IS UNCONSCIOUS OR CONVULSING. 4-8 OUNCES OF CLEAR FLUID MAY BE GIVEN AFTER IPECAC. REPEAT IN 20-30 MINUTES IF VOMITING DOES NOT OCCUR. IN COMATOSE OR CONVULSING PATIENTS, USE GASTRIC LAVAGE WITH ENDOTRACHEAL INTUBATION. ACTIVATED CHARCOAL AND CATHARTICS MAY BE ADMINISTERED 1-1.5 HOURS AFTER EMESIS IS INDUCED OR THEY MAY BE PUT INTO THE LAVAGE TUBE AFTER THE STOMACH WASHOUT. (ELLENHORN AND BARCELOUX, MEDICAL TOXICOLOGY). MAINTAIN AIRWAY, RESPIRATION AND BLOOD PRESSURE. TREAT SYMPTOMATICALLY AND SUPPORTIVELY. GET MEDICAL ATTENTION IMMEDIATELY.

ANTIDOTE: NO SPECIFIC ANTIDOTE. TREAT SYMPTOMATICALLY AND SUPPORTIVELY.

REACTIVITY

REACTIVITY: STABLE UNDER NORMAL TEMPERATURES AND PRESSURES.

INCOMPATIBILITIES: CALCIUM OXYTETRACYCLINE: NO DATA AVAILABLE.

DECOMPOSITION: THERMAL DECOMPOSITION MAY RELEASE TOXIC AND/OR HAZARDOUS GASES.

POLYMERIZATION: HAZARDOUS POLYMERIZATION HAS NOT BEEN REPORTED TO OCCUR UNDER NORMAL TEMPERATURES AND PRESSURES.

STORAGE AND DISPOSAL

OBSERVE ALL FEDERAL, STATE AND LOCAL REGULATIONS WHEN STORING OR DISPOSING OF THIS SUBSTANCE. FOR ASSISTANCE, CONTACT THE DISTRICT DIRECTOR OF THE ENVIRONMENTAL PROTECTION AGENCY.

CONDITIONS TO AVOID

MAY BURN BUT DOES NOT IGNITE READILY. AVOID CONTACT WITH STRONG OXIDIZERS, EXCESSIVE HEAT, SPARKS, OR OPEN FLAME.

SPILL AND LEAK PROCEDURES

OCCUPATIONAL SPILL: SWEEP UP AND PLACE IN SUITABLE CLEAN, DRY CONTAINERS FOR RECLAMATION OR LATER DISPOSAL. DO NOT FLUSH SPILLED MATERIAL INTO SEWER. KEEP UNNECESSARY PEOPLE AWAY.

PROTECTIVE EQUIPMENT

VENTILATION: PROVIDE LOCAL EXHAUST OR GENERAL DILUTION VENTILATION SYSTEM.

RESPIRATOR: THE FOLLOWING RESPIRATORS ARE RECOMMENDED BASED ON INFORMATION FOUND IN THE PHYSICAL DATA, TOXICITY AND HEALTH EFFECTS SECTIONS. THEY ARE RANKED IN ORDER FROM MINIMUM TO MAXIMUM RESPIRATORY PROTECTION. THE SPECIFIC RESPIRATOR SELECTED MUST BE BASED ON CONTAMINATION LEVELS FOUND IN THE WORK PLACE, MUST NOT EXCEED THE WORKING LIMITS OF THE RESPIRATOR AND BE JOINTLY APPROVED BY THE NATIONAL INSTITUTE FOR OCCUPATIONAL SAFETY AND HEALTH AND THE MINE SAFETY AND HEALTH ADMINISTRATION (NIOSH-MSHA).

DUST AND MIST RESPIRATOR WITH A FULL FACEPIECE.

AIR-PURIFYING FULL FACEPIECE RESPIRATOR WITH A HIGH-EFFICIENCY PARTICULATE FILTER.

POWERED AIR-PURIFYING RESPIRATOR WITH A TIGHT-FITTING FACEPIECE AND HIGH-EFFICIENCY PARTICULATE FILTER.

TYPE 'C' SUPPLIED-AIR RESPIRATOR WITH A FULL FACEPIECE OPERATED IN PRESSURE-DEMAND OR OTHER POSITIVE PRESSURE MODE OR WITH A FULL FACEPIECE, HELMET OR HOOD OPERATED IN CONTINUOUS-FLOW MODE.

SELF-CONTAINED BREATHING APPARATUS WITH A FULL FACEPIECE OPERATED IN PRESSURE-DEMAND OR OTHER POSITIVE PRESSURE MODE.

FOR FIREFIGHTING AND OTHER IMMEDIATELY DANGEROUS TO LIFE OR HEALTH CONDITIONS:

SELF-CONTAINED BREATHING APPARATUS WITH FULL FACEPIECE OPERATED IN

PRESSURE-DEMAND OR OTHER POSITIVE PRESSURE MODE.
SUPPLIED-AIR RESPIRATOR WITH FULL FACEPIECE AND OPERATED IN PRESSURE-DEMAND OR OTHER POSITIVE PRESSURE MODE IN COMBINATION WITH AN AUXILIARY SELF-CONTAINED BREATHING APPARATUS OPERATED IN PRESSURE-DEMAND OR OTHER POSITIVE PRESSURE MODE.

CLOTHING: EMPLOYEE MUST WEAR APPROPRIATE PROTECTIVE (IMPERVIOUS) CLOTHING AND EQUIPMENT TO PREVENT REPEATED OR PROLONGED SKIN CONTACT WITH THIS SUBSTANCE.

GLOVES: EMPLOYEE MUST WEAR APPROPRIATE PROTECTIVE GLOVES TO PREVENT CONTACT WITH THIS SUBSTANCE.

EYE PROTECTION: EMPLOYEE MUST WEAR SPLASH-PROOF OR DUST-RESISTANT SAFETY GOGGLES TO PREVENT EYE CONTACT WITH THIS SUBSTANCE.
EMERGENCY EYE WASH: WHERE THERE IS ANY POSSIBILITY THAT AN EMPLOYEE'S EYES MAY BE EXPOSED TO THIS SUBSTANCE, THE EMPLOYER SHOULD PROVIDE AN EYE WASH FOUNTAIN WITHIN THE IMMEDIATE WORK AREA FOR EMERGENCY USE.

AUTHORIZED BY- OCCUPATIONAL HEALTH SERVICES, INC.
CREATION DATE: 10/04/89 ***REVISION DATE:*** 05/31/90

MATERIAL SAFETY DATA SHEET

OCCUPATIONAL HEALTH SERVICES, INC.
AGRICULTURE AND PESTICIDE DIVISION
450 SEVENTH AVENUE, SUITE 2407
NEW YORK, NEW YORK 10123
1-800-445-MSDS OR (212) 967-1100

EMERGENCY CONTACT:
JOHN S. BRANSFORD, JR. (615) 292-1180

SUBSTANCE IDENTIFICATION

CAS-NUMBER 1405-10-3

SUBSTANCE: **NEOMYCIN SULFATE**

TRADE NAMES/SYNONYMS: NEOMYCIN, SULFATE (SALT); BYKOMYCIN; FRADIOMYCIN SULFATE; LIDAMYCIN CREME; MYCERIN SULFATE; MYCIFRADIN; MYCIFRADIN-N; MYCIGUENT; NEOFRACIN; NEOLATE; NEO-MANTLE CREME; NEOMIX; NEOMYCIN SULPHATE; OTOBIOTIC; QUINTESS-N; BP-916; PST84263

CHEMICAL FAMILY: ANTIBIOTIC

CERCLA RATINGS (SCALE 0-3): HEALTH=3 FIRE=0 REACTIVITY=0 PERSISTENCE=2

NFPA RATINGS (SCALE 0-4): HEALTH=3 FIRE=0 REACTIVITY=0

COMPONENTS AND CONTAMINANTS

COMPONENT: NEOMYCIN SULFATE ***PERCENT:*** 100
CAS# 1405-10-3

EXPOSURE LIMITS: NEOMYCIN SULFATE: SUBJECT TO CALIFORNIA PROPOSITION 65 CANCER AND/OR REPRODUCTIVE TOXICITY WARNING AND RELEASE REQUIREMENTS- (JULY 1, 1990)

PHYSICAL DATA

DESCRIPTION: WHITE TO TAN, AMORPHOUS POWDER WHICH IS ODORLESS OR WITH A SLIGHTLY EARTHY ODOR AND IS PRACTICALLY TASTELESS.

MELTING POINT: NOT AVAILABLE

SPECIFIC GRAVITY: NOT AVAILABLE ***SOLUBILITY IN WATER:*** COMPLETE

SOLVENT SOLUBILITY: METHANOL, ETHANOL, ISOPROPANOL, ISOAMYL ALCOHOL, CYCLOHEXANE, BENZENE; PRACTICALLY INSOLUBLE IN ACETONE, ETHER AND CHLOROFORM.

FIRE AND EXPLOSION DATA

FIRE AND EXPLOSION HAZARD: NEGLIGIBLE FIRE HAZARD WHEN EXPOSED TO HEAT OR FLAME.

FIREFIGHTING MEDIA: DRY CHEMICAL, CARBON DIOXIDE, HALON, WATER SPRAY OR STANDARD FOAM (1987 EMERGENCY RESPONSE GUIDEBOOK, DOT P 5800.4). FOR LARGER FIRES, USE WATER SPRAY, FOG OR STANDARD FOAM (1987 EMERGENCY RESPONSE GUIDEBOOK, DOT P 5800.4).

FIREFIGHTING: NO ACUTE HAZARD. MOVE CONTAINER FROM FIRE AREA IF POSSIBLE. AVOID BREATHING VAPORS OR DUSTS; KEEP UPWIND.

TOXICITY

NEOMYCIN SULFATE: IRRITATION DATA: 6 MG/3 DAYS INTERMITTENT SKIN-HUMAN MILD. TOXICITY DATA: 12,600 MG/KG/7 DAYS ORAL-WOMAN TDLO; 200 MG/KG SUBCUTANEOUS-RAT LD50; 190 MG/KG SUBCUTANEOUS-MOUSE LD50; 17,400 UG/KG INTRAVENOUS-MOUSE LD50; 300 MG/KG INTRAPERITONEAL-MOUSE LD50; 142 MG/KG INTRAMUSCULAR-MOUSE LD50. CARCINOGEN STATUS: NONE. ACUTE TOXICITY LEVEL: INSUFFICIENT DATA. TARGET EFFECTS: SENSITIZER-INHALATION, DERMAL, OCULAR; NEPHROTOXIN. POISONING MAY ALSO AFFECT THE HEARING. AT INCREASED RISK FROM EXPOSURE- PERSONS WITH IMPAIRED RENAL FUNCTION. ADDITIONAL DATA: MAY BE EXCRETED IN BREAST MILK. INTERACTIONS WITH MEDICATIONS HAVE BEEN REPORTED.

HEALTH EFFECTS AND FIRST AID

INHALATION: NEOMYCIN SULFATE: NEPHROTOXIN/SENSITIZER. **ACUTE EXPOSURE-** INHALATION OF THE DUST OR AEROSOL MAY BE IRRITATING TO THE RESPIRATORY TRACT. SENSITIZATION REACTIONS MAY OCCUR IN PREVIOUSLY EXPOSED INDIVIDUALS. **CHRONIC EXPOSURE-** NEOMYCIN BY AEROSOL EXPOSURE HAS CAUSED FEVER, DIARRHEA, TACHYCARDIA, BIOCHEMICAL ABNORMALITIES INCLUDING HYPERCALCEMIA, HYPOMAGNESIA, AND HYPOKALEMIA, RESPIRATORY DEPRESSION, SENSORINEURAL DEAFNESS AND KIDNEY FAILURE. REPEATED OR PROLONGED EXPOSURE MAY RESULT IN SENSITIZATION.

FIRST AID- REMOVE FROM EXPOSURE AREA TO FRESH AIR IMMEDIATELY. IF BREATHING HAS STOPPED, PERFORM ARTIFICIAL RESPIRATION. KEEP PERSON WARM AND AT REST. TREAT SYMPTOMATICALLY AND SUPPORTIVELY. GET MEDICAL ATTENTION IMMEDIATELY.

SKIN CONTACT: NEOMYCIN SULFATE: NEPHROTOXIN/SENSITIZER. **ACUTE EXPOSURE-** MAY CAUSE MILD IRRITATION, SENSITIZATION REACTIONS MAY OCCUR IN PREVIOUSLY EXPOSED INDIVIDUALS. **CHRONIC EXPOSURE-** REPEATED OR PROLONGED CONTACT HAS OCCASIONALLY CAUSED DERMATITIS. USE OF AEROSOLS ON BURNED SKIN HAS CAUSED DIARRHEA, TACHYCARDIA, BIOCHEMICAL ABNORMALITIES INCLUDING HYPERCALCEMIA, HYPOMAGNESIA, AND HYPOKALEMIA, KIDNEY DAMAGE, POSSIBLY REVERSIBLE, AND DEAFNESS. SIGNS OF OTOTOXICITY MAY COMMENCE WITH TINNITUS AND HIGH FREQUENCY HEARING LOSS AND PROGRESS TO TOTAL BILATERAL DEAFNESS. REPEATED OR PROLONGED CONTACT MAY CAUSE ALLERGIC REACTIONS INCLUDING REDNESS, SWELLING, DRY SCALING AND ITCHING OF THE SKIN, STOMATITIS, FEVER, EOSINOPHILIA, AND ANAPHYLACTIC SHOCK.

FIRST AID- REMOVE CONTAMINATED CLOTHING AND SHOES IMMEDIATELY. WASH AFFECTED AREA WITH SOAP OR MILD DETERGENT AND LARGE AMOUNTS OF WATER UNTIL NO EVIDENCE OF CHEMICAL REMAINS (APPROXIMATELY 15-20 MINUTES). GET MEDICAL ATTENTION IMMEDIATELY.

EYE CONTACT: NEOMYCIN SULFATE: SENSITIZER. **ACUTE EXPOSURE-** MAY CAUSE IRRITATION. SENSITIZATION REACTIONS MAY OCCUR IN PREVIOUSLY EXPOSED INDIVIDUALS. **CHRONIC EXPOSURE-** PROLONGED EXPOSURE MAY CAUSE AN ALLERGIC REACTION WITH CHARACTERISTIC KERATITIS EPITHELIALIS WITH LESIONS IN THE FORM OF TINY SNOWFLAKES, USUALLY ASSOCIATED WITH A SENSATION OF IRRITATION, WHICH MAY PERSIST FOR WEEKS AFTER EXPOSURE IS DISCONTINUED.

FIRST AID- WASH EYES IMMEDIATELY WITH LARGE AMOUNTS OF WATER OR NORMAL SALINE, OCCASIONALLY LIFTING UPPER AND LOWER LIDS, UNTIL NO EVIDENCE OF CHEMICAL REMAINS (APPROXIMATELY 15-20 MINUTES). GET MEDICAL ATTENTION IMMEDIATELY.

INGESTION: NEOMYCIN SULFATE: NEPHROTOXIN. **ACUTE EXPOSURE-** EXCESSIVE DOSES MAY CAUSE CENTRAL NERVOUS SYSTEM DISORDERS, SEIZURES, KIDNEY DAMAGE, HEARING LOSS, GASTROINTESTINAL DISORDERS, AND POSSIBLY DEATH. **CHRONIC EXPOSURE-** REPEATED INGESTION MAY CAUSE SYMPTOMS AS DESCRIBED IN ACUTE EXPOSURE. A WOMAN TAKING NEOMYCIN SULFATE FOR 7 DAYS DEVELOPED SYMPTOMS OF SOMNOLENCE, ANOREXIA, AND HALLUCINATIONS. CHRONIC USE OF THE DRUG MAY CAUSE INTESTINAL MALABSORPTION WITH DIARRHEA. OTHER SIDE EFFECTS MAY INCLUDE DERMATITIS, A TINGLING SENSATION IN THE HANDS AND FEET, DIZZINESS, RESPIRATORY DEPRESSION, AND MILD FEVER. THERE HAVE BEEN MANY REPORTED CASES OF KIDNEY DAMAGE AND SENSORINEURAL HEARING LOSS. OTOTOXICITY APPEARS INITIALLY AS A HIGH-TONE LOSS WHICH MAY PROGRESS TO BILATERAL DEAFNESS. HEARING LOSS MAY BE IMMEDIATE OR MAY PROGRESS FOR SEVERAL MONTHS AFTER DISCONTINUATION OF EXPOSURE. WHILE RENAL IMPAIRMENT IS COMMONLY A PREDISPOSING FACTOR, IT IS NOT A PREREQUISISTE TO OTOTOXICITY. THE NEPHROTOXICITY IS USUALLY REVERSIBLE, BUT THE OTOTOXICITY IS NOT.

FIRST AID- TREAT SYMPTOMATICALLY AND SUPPORTIVELY. GET MEDICAL ATTENTION IMMEDIATELY. IF VOMITING OCCURS, KEEP HEAD LOWER THAN HIPS TO PREVENT ASPIRATION.

ANTIDOTE: NO SPECIFIC ANTIDOTE. TREAT SYMPTOMATICALLY AND SUPPORTIVELY.

REACTIVITY

REACTIVITY: STABLE UNDER NORMAL TEMPERATURES AND PRESSURES.

INCOMPATIBILITIES: NEOMYCIN SULFATE: OXIDIZERS (STRONG): FIRE AND EXPLOSION HAZARD.

DECOMPOSITION: THERMAL DECOMPOSITION MAY RELEASE TOXIC AND/OR HAZARDOUS GASES.

POLYMERIZATION: HAZARDOUS POLYMERIZATION HAS NOT BEEN REPORTED TO OCCUR UNDER NORMAL TEMPERATURES AND PRESSURES.

CONDITIONS TO AVOID

NONE REPORTED.

SPILL AND LEAK PROCEDURES

WATER SPILL: THE CALIFORNIA SAFE DRINKING WATER AND TOXIC ENFORCEMENT ACT OF 1986 (PROPOSITION 65) PROHIBITS CONTAMINATING ANY KNOWN SOURCE OF DRINKING WATER WITH SUBSTANCES KNOWN TO CAUSE CANCER AND/OR REPRODUCTIVE TOXICITY.

OCCUPATIONAL SPILL: NO SPECIAL PRECAUTIONS INDICATED.

PROTECTIVE EQUIPMENT

VENTILATION: PROVIDE LOCAL EXHAUST OR PROCESS ENCLOSURE VENTILATION SYSTEM.

RESPIRATOR: THE FOLLOWING RESPIRATORS ARE RECOMMENDED BASED ON INFORMATION FOUND IN THE PHYSICAL DATA, TOXICITY AND HEALTH EFFECTS SECTIONS. THEY ARE RANKED IN ORDER FROM MINIMUM TO MAXIMUM RESPIRATORY PROTECTION. THE SPECIFIC RESPIRATOR SELECTED MUST BE BASED ON CONTAMINATION LEVELS FOUND IN THE WORK PLACE, MUST NOT EXCEED THE WORKING LIMITS OF THE RESPIRATOR AND BE JOINTLY APPROVED BY THE NATIONAL INSTITUTE FOR OCCUPATIONAL SAFETY AND HEALTH AND THE MINE SAFETY AND HEALTH ADMINISTRATION (NIOSH-MSHA).

DUST AND MIST RESPIRATOR WITH A FULL FACEPIECE.

AIR-PURIFYING FULL FACEPIECE RESPIRATOR WITH A HIGH-EFFICIENCY PARTICULATE FILTER.

POWERED AIR-PURIFYING RESPIRATOR WITH A TIGHT-FITTING FACEPIECE AND HIGH-EFFICIENCY PARTICULATE FILTER.

TYPE 'C' SUPPLIED-AIR RESPIRATOR WITH A FULL FACEPIECE OPERATED IN PRESSURE-DEMAND OR OTHER POSITIVE PRESSURE MODE OR WITH A FULL FACEPIECE, HELMET OR HOOD OPERATED IN CONTINUOUS-FLOW MODE.

SELF-CONTAINED BREATHING APPARATUS WITH A FULL FACEPIECE OPERATED IN PRESSURE-DEMAND OR OTHER POSITIVE PRESSURE MODE.

FOR FIREFIGHTING AND OTHER IMMEDIATELY DANGEROUS TO LIFE OR HEALTH CONDITIONS:

SELF-CONTAINED BREATHING APPARATUS WITH FULL FACEPIECE OPERATED IN PRESSURE-DEMAND OR OTHER POSITIVE PRESSURE MODE.

SUPPLIED-AIR RESPIRATOR WITH FULL FACEPIECE AND OPERATED IN PRESSURE-DEMAND OR OTHER POSITIVE PRESSURE MODE IN COMBINATION WITH AN AUXILIARY SELF-CONTAINED BREATHING APPARATUS OPERATED IN PRESSURE-DEMAND OR OTHER POSITIVE PRESSURE MODE.

CLOTHING: EMPLOYEE MUST WEAR APPROPRIATE PROTECTIVE (IMPERVIOUS) CLOTHING AND EQUIPMENT TO PREVENT REPEATED OR PROLONGED SKIN CONTACT WITH THIS SUBSTANCE.

GLOVES: EMPLOYEE MUST WEAR APPROPRIATE PROTECTIVE GLOVES TO PREVENT CONTACT WITH THIS SUBSTANCE.

EYE PROTECTION: EMPLOYEE MUST WEAR SPLASH-PROOF OR DUST-RESISTANT SAFETY GOGGLES TO PREVENT EYE CONTACT WITH THIS SUBSTANCE.

EMERGENCY EYE WASH: WHERE THERE IS ANY POSSIBILITY THAT AN EMPLOYEE'S EYES MAY BE EXPOSED TO THIS SUBSTANCE, THE EMPLOYER SHOULD PROVIDE AN EYE WASH FOUNTAIN WITHIN THE IMMEDIATE WORK AREA FOR EMERGENCY USE.

AUTHORIZED BY- OCCUPATIONAL HEALTH SERVICES, INC.

CREATION DATE: 10/04/89 ***REVISION DATE:*** 07/10/90

MATERIAL SAFETY DATA SHEET

OCCUPATIONAL HEALTH SERVICES, INC.
AGRICULTURE AND PESTICIDE DIVISION
450 SEVENTH AVENUE, SUITE 2407
NEW YORK, NEW YORK 10123
1-800-445-MSDS OR (212) 967-1100

EMERGENCY CONTACT:
JOHN S. BRANSFORD, JR. (615) 292-1180

SUBSTANCE IDENTIFICATION

CAS-NUMBER 3810-74-0

***SUBSTANCE:* <u>STREPTOMYCIN SULFATE (2:3) SALT</u>**

TRADE NAMES/SYNONYMS: D-STREPTAMINE, O-2-DEOXY-2-(METHYLAMINO)-ALPHA-L-GLUCOPYRANOSYL-(1->2) -O-5-DEOXY-3-C-FORMYL-ALPHA-L-LYXOFURANOSYL-(1->4)-N,N'-BIS (AMINOIMINOMETHYL)-SULFATE (2:3) (SALT); AGRIMYCIN 17; AGRI STREP; AMBISTRYN S; STREPTOMYCIN A SULFATE; STREPTOMYCIN SESQUISULPHATE; STREPTOMYCIN SULFATE; STREPTOMYCIN SULPHATE; VETSTREP; STREPTOBRETTIN; STREPTOREX; STREPTONEX; BP-910; PST84290

CHEMICAL FAMILY: ANTIBIOTIC

MOLECULAR FORMULA: C42-H78-N14-O24.H6-O12-S3

MOLECULAR WEIGHT: 1457.58

CERCLA RATINGS (SCALE 0-3): HEALTH=3 FIRE=U REACTIVITY=0 PERSISTENCE=2

NFPA RATINGS (SCALE 0-4): HEALTH=3 FIRE=U REACTIVITY=0

COMPONENTS AND CONTAMINANTS

COMPONENT: STREPTOMYCIN SULFATE (2:3) SALT ***PERCENT:*** 100
CAS# 3810-74-0

OTHER CONTAMINANTS: NONE

EXPOSURE LIMITS: NO OCCUPATIONAL EXPOSURE LIMITS ESTABLISHED BY OSHA, ACGIH, OR NIOSH.

PHYSICAL DATA

DESCRIPTION: WHITE TO LIGHT GRAY OR PALE BUFF HYGROSCOPIC POWDER WITH A FAINT AMINE-LIKE ODOR. ***MELTING POINT:*** NOT AVAILABLE

SPECIFIC GRAVITY: NOT AVAILABLE ***PH:*** 4.5-7.0 (20% SOLN)

SOLUBILITY IN WATER: SOLUBLE

SOLVENT SOLUBILITY: SOLUBLE IN METHANOL, ETHANOL, ISOPROPANOL, PETROLEUM ETHER, CARBON TETRACHLORIDE, ETHER, CHLOROFORM

FIRE AND EXPLOSION DATA

FIRE AND EXPLOSION HAZARD: UNKNOWN FIRE AND EXPLOSION HAZARD.

FIREFIGHTING MEDIA: DRY CHEMICAL, CARBON DIOXIDE, WATER SPRAY OR FOAM FOR LARGER FIRES, USE WATER SPRAY, FOG OR ALCOHOL FOAM

FIREFIGHTING: MOVE CONTAINER FROM FIRE AREA IF POSSIBLE. DO NOT SCATTER SPILLED MATERIAL WITH MORE WATER THAN NEEDED FOR FIRE CONTROL. DIKE FIRE CONTROL WATER FOR LATER DISPOSAL

USE AGENTS SUITABLE FOR TYPE OF SURROUNDING FIRE. AVOID BREATHING HAZARDOUS VAPORS, KEEP UPWIND.

TOXICITY

STREPTOMYCIN SULFATE: TOXICITY DATA: 9000 MG/KG ORAL-MAMMAL LD50; 400 MG/KG ORAL-HAMSTER LD50; 600 MG/KG SUBCUTANEOUS-RAT LD50; 500 MG/KG SUBCUTANEOUS-MOUSE LD50; 90,200 UG/KG INTRAVENOUS-MUSE LD50; 170 MG/KG INTRAPERITONEAL-INFANT TDLO; MUTAGENIC DATA (RTECS); REPRODUCTIVE EFFECTS DATA (RTECS). CARCINOGEN STATUS: NONE. ACUTE TOXICITY LEVEL: TOXIC BY INGESTION. TARGET EFFECTS: SENSITIZER-RESPIRATORY, DERMAL. AT INCREASED RISK FROM EXPOSURE: PERSONS WITH IMPAIRED KIDNEY FUNCTION. ADDITIONAL DATA: PARENTERAL ADMINISTRATION OF STREPTOMYCIN MAY AFFECT THE BLOOD, KIDNEYS AND NERVOUS SYSTEM, ESPECIALLY THE VESTIBULAR BRANCH OF THE AUDITORY NERVE. RECOVERY IS GENERALLY COMPLETE FOLLOWING DISCONTINUANCE OF THE DRUG; HOWEVER, LONG TERM THERAPY HAS RESULTED IN LOSS OF HEARING. STREPTOMYCIN IS REPORTED TO HAVE INDUCED APLASTIC ANEMIA, PANCYTOPENIA, AND HEMOLYSIS OF RED BLOOD CELLS IN SENSITIZED AND NONSENSITIZED INDIVIDUALS. MAY CROSS THE PLACENTA. INTERACTIONS WITH MEDICATIONS HAVE BEEN REPORTED.

HEALTH EFFECTS AND FIRST AID

INHALATION: STREPTOMYCIN SULFATE: SENSITIZER. **<u>ACUTE EXPOSURE</u>-** DUSTS MAY CAUSE IRRITATION OF THE MUCOUS MEMBRANES. ALLERGIC REACTIONS MAY OCCUR IN PREVIOUSLY SENSITIZED INDIVIDUALS. ABSORPTION THROUGH THE LUNGS MAY OCCUR. PALLOR, CYANOSIS, WHEEZING, COLLAPSE, FROTHY SPUTUM, PULMONARY EDEMA, AND DEATH IN RESPIRATORY FAILURE MAY OCCUR WITHIN SECONDS TO MINUTES AFTER THE APPLICATION OF STREPTOMYCIN TO THE MUCOUS MEMBRANES. DELAYED REACTIONS MAY CONSIST OF FEVER, SKIN ERUPTIONS AND PHARYNGEAL OR LARYNGEAL EDEMA. **<u>CHRONIC EXPOSURE</u>-** REPEATED OR PROLONGED EXPOSURE MAY RESULT IN SENSITIZATION.

FIRST AID- REMOVE FROM EXPOSURE AREA TO FRESH AIR IMMEDIATELY. IF BREATHING HAS STOPPED, PERFORM ARTIFICIAL RESPIRATION. KEEP PERSON WARM AND AT REST. TREAT SYMPTOMATICALLY AND SUPPORTIVELY. GET MEDICAL ATTENTION IMMEDIATELY.

SKIN CONTACT: STREPTOMYCIN SULFATE: SENSITIZER. **<u>ACUTE EXPOSURE</u>-** EXCESSIVE AMOUNTS OF DUST MAY BE IRRITATING AND MAY CAUSE CONTACT DERMATITIS, SKIN RASH, URTICARIA, AND EXFOLIATIVE DERMATITIS IN SENSITIZED INDIVIDUALS HANDLING STREPTOMYCIN WITHOUT GLOVES. INTOXICATION MAY OCCUR WHEN AMINOGLYCOSIDES ARE APPLIED TOPICALLY

TO LARGE WOUNDS, BURNS, OR CUTANEOUS ULCERS, PARTICULARLY IF THERE IS RENAL INSUFFICIENCY. **CHRONIC EXPOSURE-** TOPICALLY, STREPTOMYCIN HAS CAUSED A HIGH INCIDENCE OF SENSITIZATION. PROLONGED CONTACT IN THE SENSITIZED INDIVIDUAL MAY PRODUCE DEEP FISSURES AND HYPERKERATOSES WITH SUPERIMPOSED ECZEMATIZATION.

FIRST AID- REMOVE CONTAMINATED CLOTHING AND SHOES IMMEDIATELY. WASH AFFECTED AREA WITH SOAP OR MILD DETERGENT AND LARGE AMOUNTS OF WATER UNTIL NO EVIDENCE OF CHEMICAL REMAINS (APPROXIMATELY 15-20 MINUTES). GET MEDICAL ATTENTION IMMEDIATELY.

EYE CONTACT: STRETOMYCIN SULFATE: **ACUTE EXPOSURE-** DUSTS MAY BE IRRITATING. **CHRONIC EXPOSURE-** STREPTOMYCIN MAY CAUSE CONTACT DERMATITIS OF THE EYELID. THIS PRESUMABLY IS CAUSED FROM RUBBING THE EYES WITH CONTAMINATED FINGERS. GREEN COLOR BLINDNESS, NYSTAGMUS, OSCILLOPSIA OR OTHER VISUAL DISTURBANCES MAY OCCUR AS A SYSTEMIC EFFECT DUE TO PARENTERAL ADMINISTRATION.

FIRST AID- WASH EYES IMMEDIATELY WITH LARGE AMOUNTS OF WATER OR NORMAL SALINE, OCCASIONALLY LIFTING UPPER AND LOWER LIDS, UNTIL NO EVIDENCE OF CHEMICAL REMAINS (APPROXIMATELY 15-20 MINUTES). GET MEDICAL ATTENTION IMMEDIATELY.

INGESTION: STREPTOMYCIN SULFATE: TOXIC. **ACUTE EXPOSURE-** STREPTOMYCIN MAY BE ADMINISTERED ORALLY. HOWEVER THIS ROUTE IS INEFFECTIVE AGAINST SYSTEMIC INFECTIONS. A LOW DOSE WAS LETHAL TO HAMSTERS; HOWEVER, THERE IS SOME EVIDENCE THAT HAMSTERS MAY BE MORE SUSCEPTIBLE TO ANTIBIOTICS THAN OTHER SPECIES AND THE TOXIC EFFECTS MAY BY ASSOCIATED WITH INTESTINAL FLORA RATHER THAN ABSORPTION OF THE STREPTOMYCIN. THE AMINOGLYCOSIDES ARE HIGHLY POLAR CATIONS; THEY ARE THUS VERY POORLY ABSORBED FROM THE INTESTINAL TRACT. LESS THAN 1% OF A DOSE IS ABSORBED FOLLOWING ORAL ADMINISTRATION. AMINOGLYCOSIDES ARE NOT INACTIVATED IN THE INTESTINE, AND ARE ELIMINATED QUANTITATIVELY IN THE FECES. ORAL ADMINISTRATION OF STREPTOMYCIN CAN CAUSE ANAPHYLACTOID REACTIONS CHARACTERIZED BY NAUSEA AND VOMITING, ABDOMINAL PAIN AND CRAMPING, LOCALIZED EDEMA, CYANOSIS, RESPIRATORY DISTRESS, CONVULSIONS, SEVERE CHEST PAIN AND DEATH IN RESPIRATORY FAILURE. **CHRONIC EXPOSURE-** REPEATED ORAL ADMINISTRATION MAY RESULT IN HYPOVITAMINOSIS AND STREPTOMYCIN ACCUMULATION TO TOXIC CONCENTRATIONS IN PATIENTS WITH RENAL IMPAIRMENT. THE MOST COMMON UNTOWARD REACTION TO THE ADMINISTRATION OF ANTIBIOTICS IS THE OVERGROWTH OF ORGANISMS NOT AFFECTED BY THE ANTIBIOTIC AGENT. IN SOME CASES THESE ORGANISMS PRODUCE TOXINS THAT CAN CAUSE VOMITING, DIARRHEA AND CARDIOVASCULAR COLLAPSE. A MULTIGENERATION STUDY RESULTED IN EFFECTS ON FEMALE FERTILITY AND THE NEWBORN IN RATS ADMINISTERED STREPTOMYCIN SULFATE (2:3) SALT.

FIRST AID- IF ANAPHYLAXIS OCCURS, THE ANTIDOTE SHOULD BE ADMINISTERED BY QUALIFIED MEDICAL PERSONNEL. IF STREPTOMYCIN IS BEING GIVEN FOR THERAPEUTIC PURPOSES, DISCONTINUE USE OF THE DRUG. GET MEDICAL ATTENTION IMMEDIATELY. (DREISBACH HANDBOOK OF POISONING, 11TH ED.)

ANTIDOTE: NO SPECIFIC ANTIDOTE. TREAT SYMPTOMATICALLY AND SUPPORTIVELY.

REACTIVITY

REACTIVITY: STABLE UNDER NORMAL TEMPERATURES AND PRESSURES.

INCOMPATIBILITIES: STREPTOMYCIN SULFATE: ACIDS (STRONG): INCOMPATIBLE. OXIDIZERS (STRONG): FIRE AND EXPLOSION HAZARD.

DECOMPOSITION: THERMAL DECOMPOSITION MAY RELEASE TOXIC OXIDES OF NITROGEN, CARBON AND SULFUR.

POLYMERIZATION: HAZARDOUS POLYMERIZATION HAS NOT BEEN REPORTED TO OCCUR UNDER NORMAL TEMPERATURES AND PRESSURES.

STORAGE AND DISPOSAL

OBSERVE ALL FEDERAL, STATE AND LOCAL REGULATIONS WHEN STORING OR DISPOSING OF THIS SUBSTANCE. FOR ASSISTANCE, CONTACT THE DISTRICT DIRECTOR OF THE ENVIRONMENTAL PROTECTION AGENCY.

CONDITIONS TO AVOID

NONE REPORTED.

SPILL AND LEAK PROCEDURES

OCCUPATIONAL SPILL: SWEEP UP AND PLACE IN SUITABLE CLEAN, DRY CONTAINERS FOR RECLAMATION OR LATER DISPOSAL. DO NOT FLUSH SPILLED MATERIAL INTO SEWER. KEEP UNNECESSARY PEOPLE AWAY.

PROTECTIVE EQUIPMENT

VENTILATION: PROVIDE LOCAL EXHAUST OR PROCESS ENCLOSURE VENTILATION SYSTEM.

RESPIRATOR: THE FOLLOWING RESPIRATORS ARE RECOMMENDED BASED ON INFORMATION FOUND IN THE PHYSICAL DATA, TOXICITY AND HEALTH EFFECTS SECTIONS. THEY ARE RANKED IN ORDER FROM MINIMUM TO MAXIMUM RESPIRATORY PROTECTION. THE SPECIFIC RESPIRATOR SELECTED MUST BE BASED ON CONTAMINATION LEVELS FOUND IN THE WORK PLACE, MUST NOT EXCEED THE WORKING LIMITS OF THE RESPIRATOR AND BE JOINTLY APPROVED BY THE NATIONAL INSTITUTE FOR OCCUPATIONAL SAFETY AND HEALTH AND THE MINE SAFETY AND HEALTH ADMINISTRATION (NIOSH-MSHA).

TYPE 'C' SUPPLIED-AIR RESPIRATOR WITH A FULL FACEPIECE OPERATED IN PRESSURE-DEMAND OR OTHER POSITIVE PRESSURE MODE OR WITH A FULL FACEPIECE, HELMET OR HOOD OPERATED IN CONTINOUS-FLOW MODE.

SELF-CONTAINED BREATHING APPARATUS WITH A FULL FACEPIECE OPERATED IN PRESSURE-DEMAND OR OTHER POSITIVE PRESSURE MODE.

FOR FIREFIGHTING AND OTHER IMMEDIATELY DANGEROUS TO LIFE OR HEALTH CONDITIONS:

SELF-CONTAINED BREATHING APPARATUS WITH FULL FACEPIECE OPERATED IN PRESSURE-DEMAND OR OTHER POSITIVE PRESSURE MODE.

SUPPLIED-AIR RESPIRATOR WITH FULL FACEPIECE AND OPERATED IN PRESSURE-DEMAND OR OTHER POSITIVE PRESSURE MODE IN COMBINATION WITH AN AUXILIARY SELF-CONTAINED BREATHING APPARATUS OPERATED IN PRESSURE-DEMAND OR OTHER POSITIVE PRESSURE MODE.

CLOTHING: EMPLOYEE MUST WEAR APPROPRIATE PROTECTIVE (IMPERVIOUS) CLOTHING AND EQUIPMENT TO PREVENT REPEATED OR PROLONGED SKIN CONTACT WITH THIS SUBSTANCE.

GLOVES: EMPLOYEE MUST WEAR APPROPRIATE PROTECTIVE GLOVES TO PREVENT CONTACT WITH THIS SUBSTANCE.

EYE PROTECTION: EMPLOYEE MUST WEAR SPLASH-PROOF OR DUST-RESISTANT SAFETY GOGGLES TO PREVENT EYE CONTACT WITH THIS SUBSTANCE.

EMERGENCY EYE WASH: WHERE THERE IS ANY POSSIBILITY THAT AN EMPLOYEE'S EYES MAY BE EXPOSED TO THIS SUBSTANCE, THE EMPLOYER SHOULD PROVIDE AN EYE WASH FOUNTAIN WITHIN THE IMMEDIATE WORK AREA FOR EMERGENCY USE.

AUTHORIZED BY- OCCUPATIONAL HEALTH SERVICES, INC.

CREATION DATE: 10/05/89 ***REVISION DATE:*** 05/31/90

MATERIAL SAFETY DATA SHEET

OCCUPATIONAL HEALTH SERVICES, INC.
AGRICULTURE AND PESTICIDE DIVISION
450 SEVENTH AVENUE, SUITE 2407
NEW YORK, NEW YORK 10123
1-800-445-MSDS OR (212) 967-1100

EMERGENCY CONTACT:
JOHN S. BRANSFORD, JR. (615) 292-1180

SUBSTANCE IDENTIFICATION

CAS-NUMBER 68131-40-8

SUBSTANCE: **ETHOXYLATED ALCOHOLS (C11-C15):**

TRADE NAMES/SYNONYMS: SECONDARY ALCOHOL ETHOXYLATE; TERGITOL 15-S-5; TERGITOL(R) NONIC SURFACTANT 15-S-5; ALKYLOXYPOLYETHYLENEOXYETHANOL; ALCOHOLS, C11-15-SECONDARY, ETHOXYLATED; ETHOXYLATED ALCOHOLS, C11-15-SECONDARY; C11-15-SECONDARY, ETHOXYLATED ALCOHOLS; TERGITOL 15S; TERGITOL 15-S-3; TERGITOL 15-S-7; TERGITOL 15S9; TERGITOL 15-S-12; TERGITOL 15-S-15; TERGITOL 15-S-20; PST85315

CHEMICAL FAMILY: ALCOHOL, ALIPHATIC

CERCLA RATINGS (SCALE 0-3): HEALTH=2 FIRE=1 REACTIVITY=0 PERSISTENCE=0

NFPA RATINGS (SCALE 0-4): HEALTH=2 FIRE=1 REACTIVITY=0

COMPONENTS AND CONTAMINANTS

COMPONENT: ETHOXYLATED ALCOHOLS (C11-C15) ***PERCENT:*** 100.0
CAS# 68131-40-8

COMPONENT: ETHYLENE OXIDE ***PERCENT:*** <0.1
CAS# 75-21-8

OTHER CONTAMINANTS: NONE

EXPOSURE LIMITS: ETHYLENE OXIDE: 1 PPM OSHA TWA; 5 PPM OSHA 15 MINUTE EXCURSION LIMIT; 0.5 PPM OSHA TWA ACTION LEVEL 1 PPM ACGIH TWA ACGIH A2-SUSPECTED HUMAN CARCINOGEN. NOT TO EXCEED 0.1 PPM NIOSH RECOMMENDED 8 HOUR TWA; 5 PPM NIOSH RECOMMENDED 10 MINUTE CEILING 1000 POUNDS SARA SECTION 302 THRESHOLD PLANNING QUANTITY 1 POUND SARA SECTION 304 REPORTABLE QUANTITY 10 POUNDS CERCLA SECTION 103 REPORTABLE QUANTITY SUBJECT TO SARA SECTION 313 ANNUAL TOXIC CHEMICAL RELEASE REPORTING SUBJECT TO CALIFORNIA PROPOSITION 65

CANCER AND/OR REPRODUCTIVE TOXICITY WARNING AND RELEASE REQUIREMENTS- (FEBRUARY 27, 1987)

PHYSICAL DATA

DESCRIPTION: WHITE, WAXY SOLID WITH A MILD ODOR.
BOILING POINT: >482 F (>250 C)
MELTING POINT: 102 F (39 C) ***SPECIFIC GRAVITY:*** 1.040
EVAPORATION RATE: (BUTYL ACETATE = 1) <1.0 ***SOLUBILITY IN WATER:*** 100%
VAPOR DENSITY: >1.0
SOLVENT SOLUBILITY: SOLUBLE IN ALCOHOL, ACETONE; INSOLUBLE IN PETROLEUM ETHER.
POUR POINT: 93 F (34 C)

FIRE AND EXPLOSION DATA

FIRE AND EXPLOSION HAZARD: SLIGHT FIRE HAZARD WHEN EXPOSED TO HEAT OR FLAME.
FLASH POINT: 480 F (248 C) (COC)
FIREFIGHTING MEDIA: DRY CHEMICAL, CARBON DIOXIDE, HALON, WATER SPRAY OR STANDARD FOAM (1987 EMERGENCY RESPONSE GUIDEBOOK, DOT P 5800.4).
FOR LARGER FIRES, USE WATER SPRAY, FOG OR STANDARD FOAM (1987 EMERGENCY RESPONSE GUIDEBOOK, DOT P 5800.4).
FIREFIGHTING: MOVE CONTAINER FROM FIRE AREA IF POSSIBLE. DO NOT SCATTER SPILLED MATERIAL WITH HIGH PRESSURE WATER STREAMS. DIKE FIRE CONTROL WATER FOR LATER DISPOSAL (1987 EMERGENCY RESPONSE GUIDEBOOK, DOT P 5800.4, GUIDE PAGE 31).
USE AGENTS SUITABLE FOR TYPE OF SURROUNDING FIRE. AVOID BREATHING HAZARDOUS VAPORS, KEEP UPWIND.

TOXICITY

ETHOXYLATED ALCOHOLS (C11-C15): IRRITATION DATA: 500 MG OPEN SKIN-RABBIT MILD. TOXICITY DATA: 5660 MG/KG SKIN-RABBIT LD50; 32 GM/KG ORAL-RAT LD50. CARCINOGEN STATUS: NONE. LOCAL EFFECTS: IRRITANT- SKIN AND EYES. ACUTE TOXICITY LEVEL: SLIGHTLY TOXIC BY DERMAL ABSORPTION; RELATIVELY NONTOXIC BY INGESTION. TARGET EFFECTS: NO DATA AVAILABLE.

HEALTH EFFECTS AND FIRST AID

INHALATION: ETHOXYLATED ALCOHOLS (C11-C15): **ACUTE EXPOSURE-** DUE TO LOW VAPOR PRESSURE, NO SIGNIFICANT HEALTH HAZARD FROM INHALATION IS LIKELY TO OCCUR AT NORMAL ROOM TEMPERATURES. INHALATION OF GENERATED MIST OR VAPORS PRODUCED FROM ELEVATED TEMPERATURES MAY CAUSE IRRITATION OF THE MUCOUS MEMBRANES. **CHRONIC EXPOSURE-** NO DATA AVAILABLE.
FIRST AID- REMOVE FROM EXPOSURE AREA TO FRESH AIR IMMEDIATELY. IF BREATHING HAS STOPPED, PERFORM ARTIFICIAL RESPIRATION. KEEP PERSON WARM AND AT REST. TREAT SYMPTOMATICALLY AND SUPPORTIVELY. GET MEDICAL ATTENTION IMMEDIATELY.

SKIN CONTACT: ETHOXYLATED ALCOHOLS (C11-C15): **ACUTE EXPOSURE-** DIRECT CONTACT TO SKIN MAY CAUSE IRRITATION AND REDNESS. MAY BE ABSORBED THROUGH THE SKIN IN LETHAL AMOUNTS. **CHRONIC EXPOSURE-** PROLONGED CONTACT MAY RESULT IN THE ABSORPTION OF POTENTIALLY HARMFUL AMOUNTS.
FIRST AID- REMOVE CONTAMINATED CLOTHING AND SHOES IMMEDIATELY. WASH AFFECTED AREA WITH SOAP OR MILD DETERGENT AND LARGE AMOUNTS OF WATER UNTIL NO EVIDENCE OF CHEMICAL REMAINS (APPROXIMATELY 15-20 MINUTES). GET MEDICAL ATTENTION IMMEDIATELY.

EYE CONTACT: ETHOXYLATED ALCOHOLS (C11-C15): **ACUTE EXPOSURE-** MAY CAUSE MODERATE TO SEVERE IRRITATION WITH POSSIBLE MODERATE CORNEAL INJURY. **CHRONIC EXPOSURE-** NO DATA AVAILABLE.
FIRST AID- WASH EYES IMMEDIATELY WITH LARGE AMOUNTS OF WATER OR NORMAL SALINE, OCCASIONALLY LIFTING UPPER AND LOWER LIDS, UNTIL NO EVIDENCE OF CHEMICAL REMAINS (APPROXIMATELY 15-20 MINUTES). GET MEDICAL ATTENTION IMMEDIATELY.

INGESTION: ETHOXYLATED ALCOHOLS (C11-C15): **ACUTE EXPOSURE-** MAY CAUSE NAUSEA. **CHRONIC EXPOSURE-** NO DATA AVAILABLE.
FIRST AID- TREAT SYMPTOMATICALLY AND SUPPORTIVELY. GET MEDICAL ATTENTION IMMEDIATELY. IF VOMITING OCCURS, KEEP HEAD LOWER THAN HIPS TO PREVENT ASPIRATION.
ANTIDOTE: NO SPECIFIC ANTIDOTE. TREAT SYMPTOMATICALLY AND SUPPORTIVELY.

REACTIVITY

REACTIVITY: STABLE UNDER NORMAL TEMPERATURES AND PRESSURES.
INCOMPATIBILITIES: ETHOXYLATED ALCOHOLS (C11-C15): ACIDS (STRONG): INCOMPATIBLE. ALKALI (STRONG): INCOMPATIBLE AT HIGH TEMPERATURES. OXIDIZERS (STRONG): FIRE AND EXPLOSION HAZARD. SEE ALSO ALCOHOLS.
DECOMPOSITION: THERMAL DECOMPOSITION PRODUCTS MAY INCLUDE TOXIC OXIDES OF CARBON.
POLYMERIZATION: HAZARDOUS POLYMERIZATION HAS NOT BEEN REPORTED TO OCCUR UNDER NORMAL TEMPERATURES AND PRESSURES.

STORAGE AND DISPOSAL

OBSERVE ALL FEDERAL, STATE AND LOCAL REGULATIONS WHEN STORING OR DISPOSING OF THIS SUBSTANCE. FOR ASSISTANCE, CONTACT THE DISTRICT DIRECTOR OF THE ENVIRONMENTAL PROTECTION AGENCY.

STORAGE

STORE AWAY FROM INCOMPATIBLE SUBSTANCES.
KEEP IN A TIGHTLY CLOSED CONTAINER. STORE IN A COOL, DRY, VENTILATED AREA.

CONDITIONS TO AVOID

MAY BURN BUT DOES NOT IGNITE READILY. AVOID CONTACT WITH STRONG OXIDIZERS, EXCESSIVE HEAT, SPARKS, OR OPEN FLAME.
TRACE AMOUNTS OF ETHYLENE OXIDE, A CARCINOGEN, MAY BE PRESENT IN THIS PRODUCT. THERE IS A POTENTIAL FOR ACCUMULATION OF ETHYLENE OXIDE IN THE HEAD SPACE OF CONTAINERS OR IN ENCLOSED AREAS WHERE THE PRODUCT IS STORED, HANDLED OR USED. USERS SHOULD COMPLY WITH 29 CFR 1910.1047.

SPILL AND LEAK PROCEDURES

OCCUPATIONAL SPILL: SWEEP UP AND PLACE IN SUITABLE CLEAN, DRY CONTAINERS FOR RECLAMATION OR LATER DISPOSAL. DO NOT FLUSH SPILLED MATERIAL INTO SEWER. KEEP UNNECESSARY PEOPLE AWAY.

PROTECTIVE EQUIPMENT

VENTILATION: PROVIDE LOCAL EXHAUST VENTILATION SYSTEM.
RESPIRATOR: THE FOLLOWING RESPIRATORS ARE RECOMMENDED BASED ON INFORMATION FOUND IN THE PHYSICAL DATA, TOXICITY AND HEALTH EFFECTS SECTIONS. THEY ARE RANKED IN ORDER FROM MINIMUM TO MAXIMUM RESPIRATORY PROTECTION. THE SPECIFIC RESPIRATOR SELECTED MUST BE BASED ON CONTAMINATION LEVELS FOUND IN THE WORK PLACE, MUST NOT EXCEED THE WORKING LIMITS OF THE RESPIRATOR AND BE JOINTLY APPROVED BY THE NATIONAL INSTITUTE FOR OCCUPATIONAL SAFETY AND HEALTH AND THE MINE SAFETY AND HEALTH ADMINISTRATION (NIOSH-MSHA).
CHEMICAL CARTRIDGE RESPIRATOR WITH AN ORGANIC VAPOR CARTRIDGE(S) WITH A FULL FACEPIECE.
GAS MASK WITH ORGANIC VAPOR CANISTER (CHIN-STYLE OR FRONT- OR BACK-MOUNTED CANISTER) WITH A FULL FACEPIECE.
TYPE 'C' SUPPLIED-AIR RESPIRATOR WITH A FULL FACEPIECE OPERATED IN PRESSURE-DEMAND OR OTHER POSITIVE PRESSURE MODE OR WITH A FULL FACEPIECE, HELMET OR HOOD OPERATED IN CONTINUOUS-FLOW MODE.
SELF-CONTAINED BREATHING APPARATUS WITH A FULL FACEPIECE OPERATED IN PRESSURE-DEMAND OR OTHER POSITIVE PRESSURE MODE.
FOR FIREFIGHTING AND OTHER IMMEDIATELY DANGEROUS TO LIFE OR HEALTH CONDITIONS:
SELF-CONTAINED BREATHING APPARATUS WITH FULL FACEPIECE OPERATED IN PRESSURE-DEMAND OR OTHER POSITIVE PRESSURE MODE.
SUPPLIED-AIR RESPIRATOR WITH FULL FACEPIECE AND OPERATED IN PRESSURE-DEMAND OR OTHER POSITIVE PRESSURE MODE IN COMBINATION WITH AN AUXILIARY SELF-CONTAINED BREATHING APPARATUS OPERATED IN PRESSURE-DEMAND OR OTHER POSITIVE PRESSURE MODE.
CLOTHING: EMPLOYEE MUST WEAR APPROPRIATE PROTECTIVE (IMPERVIOUS) CLOTHING AND EQUIPMENT TO PREVENT REPEATED OR PROLONGED SKIN CONTACT WITH THIS SUBSTANCE.
GLOVES: EMPLOYEE MUST WEAR APPROPRIATE PROTECTIVE GLOVES TO PREVENT CONTACT WITH THIS SUBSTANCE.
EYE PROTECTION: EMPLOYEE MUST WEAR SPLASH-PROOF OR DUST-RESISTANT SAFETY GOGGLES TO PREVENT EYE CONTACT WITH THIS SUBSTANCE.
EMERGENCY EYE WASH: WHERE THERE IS ANY POSSIBILITY THAT AN EMPLOYEE'S EYES MAY BE EXPOSED TO THIS SUBSTANCE, THE EMPLOYER SHOULD PROVIDE AN EYE WASH FOUNTAIN WITHIN THE IMMEDIATE WORK AREA FOR EMERGENCY USE.

AUTHORIZED BY- OCCUPATIONAL HEALTH SERVICES, INC.
CREATION DATE: 10/04/89 ***REVISION DATE:*** 05/31/90

MATERIAL SAFETY DATA SHEET

OCCUPATIONAL HEALTH SERVICES, INC.
AGRICULTURE AND PESTICIDE DIVISION
450 SEVENTH AVENUE, SUITE 2407
NEW YORK, NEW YORK 10123
1-800-445-MSDS OR (212) 967-1100

EMERGENCY CONTACT:
JOHN S. BRANSFORD, JR. (615) 292-1180

SUBSTANCE IDENTIFICATION

SUBSTANCE: **RAID (R) ANT AND ROACH KILLER-LIQUID**
TRADE NAMES/SYNONYMS: PST86204
CERCLA RATINGS (SCALE 0-3): HEALTH=U FIRE=3 REACTIVITY=0 PERSISTENCE=1
NFPA RATINGS (SCALE 0-4): HEALTH=U FIRE=3 REACTIVITY=0

COMPONENTS AND CONTAMINANTS

COMPONENT: 2-(1-METHYLETHOXY)PHENOL METHYL CARBAMATE ***PERCENT:*** 0.665
CAS# 114-26-1
COMPONENT: 2,2-DICHLOROVINYL DIMETHYL PHOSPHATE (DDVP) ***PERCENT:*** 0.186
CAS# 62-73-7
COMPONENT: RELATED COMPOUNDS ***PERCENT:*** 0.014
COMPONENT: ALIPHATIC SOLVENT NAPHTHA ***PERCENT:*** 80.0-90.0
CAS# 64742-89-8
COMPONENT: ISOPROPYL ALCOHOL ***PERCENT:*** 10.0-15.0
CAS# 67-63-0
EXPOSURE LIMITS: PETROLEUM DISTILLATES: 1600 MG/M3 (400 PPM) OSHA TWA
ISOPROPYL ALCOHOL (ISOPROPANOL; 2-PROPANOL): 400 PPM (980 MG/M3) OSHA TWA; 500 PPM (1225 MG/M3) OSHA STEL 400 PPM (980 MG/M3) ACGIH TWA; 500 PPM (1225 MG/M3) ACGIH STEL 400 PPM NIOSH RECOMMENDED 10 HOUR TWA; 800 PPM NIOSH RECOMMENDED 15 MINUTE CEILING
SUBJECT TO SARA SECTION 313 ANNUAL TOXIC CHEMICAL RELEASE REPORTING

PHYSICAL DATA

DESCRIPTION: DISPENSED AS A SPRAY MIST WITH A NAPHTHA ODOR
BOILING POINT: NOT AVAILABLE ***SPECIFIC GRAVITY:*** 0.79
SOLUBILITY IN WATER: MODERATELY SOLUBLE

FIRE AND EXPLOSION DATA

FIRE AND EXPLOSION HAZARD: DANGEROUS FIRE HAZARD WHEN EXPOSED TO HEAT OR FLAME.
FLASH POINT: 58 F (29 C) (CC) ***FLAMMABILITY CLASS(OSHA):*** IC
FIREFIGHTING MEDIA: DRY CHEMICAL, CARBON DIOXIDE, HALON, WATER SPRAY OR STANDARD FOAM (1987 EMERGENCY RESPONSE GUIDEBOOK, DOT P 5800.4).
FOR LARGER FIRES, USE WATER SPRAY, FOG OR STANDARD FOAM (1987 EMERGENCY RESPONSE GUIDEBOOK, DOT P 5800.4).
FIREFIGHTING: MOVE CONTAINER FROM FIRE AREA IF POSSIBLE. COOL FIRE-EXPOSED CONTAINERS WITH WATER FROM SIDE UNTIL WELL AFTER FIRE IS OUT. STAY AWAY FROM STORAGE TANK ENDS. FOR MASSIVE FIRE IN STORAGE AREA, USE UNMANNED HOSE HOLDER OR MONITOR NOZZLES, ELSE WITHDRAW FROM AREA AND LET FIRE BURN. WITHDRAW IMMEDIATELY IN CASE OF RISING SOUND FROM VENTING SAFETY DEVICE OR ANY DISCOLORATION OF STORAGE TANK DUE TO FIRE (1987 EMERGENCY RESPONSE GUIDEBOOK, DOT P 5800.4, GUIDE PAGE 27).
EXTINGUISH ONLY IF FLOW CAN BE STOPPED; USE FLOODING AMOUNTS OF WATER AS A FOG, SOLID STREAMS MAY BE INEFFECTIVE. COOL CONTAINERS WITH FLOODING AMOUNTS OF WATER, APPLY FROM AS FAR A DISTANCE AS POSSIBLE. AVOID BREATHING VAPORS, KEEP UPWIND.

TRANSPORTATION DATA

DEPARTMENT OF TRANSPORTATION HAZARD CLASSIFICATION 49 CFR 172.101: FLAMMABLE LIQUID
DEPARTMENT OF TRANSPORTATION LABELING REQUIREMENTS 49 CFR 172.101 AND SUBPART E: FLAMMABLE LIQUID
DEPARTMENT OF TRANSPORTATION PACKAGING REQUIREMENTS: 49 CFR 173.119 EXCEPTIONS: 49 CFR 173.118

TOXICITY

ALIPHATIC SOLVENT NAPHTHA: CARCINOGEN STATUS: NONE. THERE IS INSUFFICIENT DATA TO QUANTIFY THE TOXICITY OF ALIPHATIC SOLVENT NAPHTHA. IT IS AN EYE, SKIN AND MUCOUS MEMBRANE IRRITANT AND CENTRAL NERVOUS SYSTEM DEPRESSANT.
ISOPROPYL ALCOHOL (ISOPROPANOL; 2-PROPANOL): IRRITATION DATA: 500 MG SKIN-RABBIT MILD; 16 MG EYE-RABBIT; 10 MG EYE-RABBIT MODERATE; 100 MG/24 HOURS EYE-RABBIT MODERATE. TOXICITY DATA: 12,800 PPM/3 HOURS INHALATION-MOUSE LCLO; 16,000 PPM/4 HOURS INHALATION-RAT LCLO; 12,800 MG/KG SKIN-RABBIT LD50; 5272 MG/KG ORAL-MAN LDLO; 14,432 MG/KG ORAL-MAN TDLO; 3570 MG/KG ORAL-HUMAN LDLO; 223 MG/KG ORAL-HUMAN TDLO; 5045 MG/KG ORAL-RAT LD50; 3600 MG/KG ORAL-MOUSE LD50; 6410 MG/KG ORAL-RABBIT LD50; 4797 MG/KG ORAL-DOG LD50; 6000 MG/KG SUBCUTANEOUS-MOUSE LDLO; 6 MG/KG SUBCUTANEOUS-MAMMAL LDLO; 1088 MG/KG INTRAVENOUS-RAT LD50; 1509 MG/KG INTRAVENOUS-MOUSE LD50; 1184 MG/KG INTRAVENOUS-RABBIT LD50; 2735 MG/KG INTRAPERITONEAL-RAT LD50; 4477 MG/KG INTRAPERITONEAL-MOUSE LD50; 667 MG/KG INTRAPERITONEAL-RABBIT LD50; 2770 MG/KG UNREPORTED-MAN LDLO; MUTAGENIC DATA (RTECS); REPRODUCTIVE EFFECTS DATA (RTECS). CARCINOGEN STATUS: HUMAN INADEQUATE EVIDENCE, ANIMAL INADEQUATE EVIDENCE (IARC GROUP-3). STRONG ACID MANUFACTURING PROCESS: KNOWN HUMAN CARCINOGEN (NTP); HUMAN SUFFICIENT EVIDENCE (IARC GROUP-1). WORKERS INVOLVED IN THE MANUFACTURE OF ISOPROPYL ALCOHOL BY THE STRONG-ACID PROCESS, INVOLVING THE FORMATION OF ISOPROPYL OILS, SHOWED AN INCREASE IN PARANASAL AND LARYNGEAL CANCERS. LOCAL EFFECTS: IRRITANT- INHALATION, EYE. ACUTE TOXICITY LEVEL: SLIGHTLY TOXIC BY INGESTION, DERMAL ABSORPTION. TARGET EFFECTS: CENTRAL NERVOUS SYSTEM DEPRESSANT. AT INCREASED RISK FROM EXPOSURE: PERSONS WITH PRE-EXISTING SKIN DISORDERS; IMPAIRED LIVER, RENAL AND/OR PULMONARY FUNCTION. ADDITIONAL INFORMATION: POTENTIATES THE EFFECT OF CARBON TETRACHLORIDE AND OTHER HEPATOTOXIC CHLORINATED ALIPHATIC HYDROCARBONS.

HEALTH EFFECTS AND FIRST AID

INHALATION: ALIPHATIC SOLVENT NAPHTHA: IRRITANT/NARCOTIC. **ACUTE EXPOSURE-** VAPORS MAY CAUSE PULMONARY IRRITATION. IRRITATION INCREASES AS THE NUMBER OF CARBONS INCREASES. DIRECT ASPIRATION INTO THE LUNGS MAY CAUSE CHEMICAL PNEUMONITIS, PULMONARY EDEMA, AND HEMORRHAGING. NARCOTIC POTENCY INCREASES WITH THE CHAIN LENGTH AT LEAST THROUGH OCTANE. SOME NAPHTHENES ARE NARCOTIC AND MAY CAUSE DEATH THROUGH RESPIRATORY PARALYSIS. FOR MOST NAPHTHENES THERE APPEARS TO BE A NARROW RANGE BETWEEN THE CONCENTRATIONS CAUSING DEEP NARCOSIS AND THOSE CAUSING DEATH. OTHER SYMPTOMS MAY BE THOSE OF CENTRAL NERVOUS SYSTEM DEPRESSION SUCH AS HEADACHE, DIZZINESS, LOSS OF APPETITE, WEAKNESS, AND LOSS OF COORDINATION. **CHRONIC EXPOSURE-** NO DATA AVAILABLE.
ISOPROPYL ALCOHOL (ISOPROPANOL; 2-PROPANOL): IRRITANT/NARCOTIC. 12,000 PPM IMMEDIATELY DANGEROUS TO LIFE OR HEALTH. **ACUTE EXPOSURE-** HUMAN SUBJECTS EXPOSED TO 400 PPM FOR 3-5 MINUTES HAD MILD IRRITATION OF THE NOSE AND THROAT. AT 800 PPM THE IRRITATION WAS NOT SEVERE BUT UNCOMFORTABLE. HIGHER CONCENTRATIONS MAY CAUSE EFFECTS AS DETAILED IN ACUTE INGESTION. THE LENGTH OF TIME REQUIRED TO PRODUCE DEEP NARCOSIS IN ANIMALS WAS INVERSELY PROPORTIONAL TO THE CONCENTRATION: THE ONSET OF DEEP NARCOSIS RANGED FROM 460 MINUTES AT 3250 PPM TO 100 MINUTES AT 24,500 PPM. **CHRONIC EXPOSURE-** MICE SUBJECTED TO 10900 PPM ISOPROPYL ALCOHOL IN AIR FOR ABOUT 4 HOURS/DAY UNTIL THEY HAD ACCUMULATED 123 HOURS OF EXPOSURE WERE NARCOTIZED BUT SURVIVED. REVERSIBLE FATTY CHANGES WERE OBSERVED IN THE LIVER. MALE MICE EXPOSED TO EITHER 1000 OR 5000 PPM OF ISOPROPYL ALCOHOL VAPOR FOR 6 HOURS A DAY FOR 9 EXPOSURES EXHIBITED HYALINE DROPLET NEPHROPATHY. REPRODUCTIVE EFFECTS HAVE BEEN REPORTED IN ANIMALS. THERE HAS BEEN AN INCREASED INCIDENCE OF CANCER OF THE PARANASAL SINUSES, AND POSSIBLY OF THE LARYNX, IN THE MANUFACTURE OF ISOPROPYL ALCOHOL BY THE STRONG ACID PROCESS, INVOLVING THE FORMATION OF ISOPROPYL OILS. IT IS NOT CLEAR WHICH SUBSTANCES ARE RESPONSIBLE.
FIRST AID- REMOVE FROM EXPOSURE AREA TO FRESH AIR IMMEDIATELY. IF BREATHING HAS STOPPED, PERFORM ARTIFICIAL RESPIRATION. KEEP PERSON WARM AND AT REST. TREAT SYMPTOMATICALLY AND SUPPORTIVELY. GET MEDICAL ATTENTION IMMEDIATELY.

SKIN CONTACT: ALIPHATIC SOLVENT NAPHTHA: IRRITANT. **ACUTE EXPOSURE-** LIQUID HAS A DEFATTING ACTION ON THE SKIN AND MAY CAUSE IRRITATION. DERMAL IRRITANCY INCREASES WITH THE NUMBER OF CARBONS. **CHRONIC EXPOSURE-** PROLONGED OR REPEATED CONTACT MAY CAUSE DERMATITIS.
ISOPROPYL ALCOHOL (ISOPROPANOL; 2-PROPANOL): NARCOTIC. **ACUTE EXPOSURE-** CONTACT WITH THE SKIN MAY CAUSE SLIGHT IRRITATION. CONTACT DERMATITIS HAS BEEN REPORTED IN A FEW SENSITIVE INDIVIDUALS. SUBSTANCE MAY BE DERMALLY ABSORBED RESULTING IN SYSTEMIC TOXICITY AS DETAILED IN ACUTE INGESTION. TOXIC EFFECTS MAY BECOME MORE MARKED IF ABSORPTION AND INHALATION OCCUR CONCURRENTLY. **CHRONIC EXPOSURE-** REPEATED OR PROLONGED EXPOSURE MAY CAUSE DERMATITIS DUE TO THE DEFATTING ACTION ON THE SKIN. REPEATED AND PROLONGED EXPOSURE TO THE SKIN OF RABBITS CAUSED SLIGHT ERYTHEMA, DRYING, AND SUPERFICIAL DESQUAMATION.
FIRST AID- REMOVE CONTAMINATED CLOTHING AND SHOES IMMEDIATELY. WASH AFFECTED AREA WITH SOAP OR MILD DETERGENT AND LARGE AMOUNTS OF WATER UNTIL NO EVIDENCE OF CHEMICAL REMAINS (APPROXIMATELY 15-20 MINUTES). GET MEDICAL ATTENTION IMMEDIATELY.

EYE CONTACT: ALIPHATIC SOLVENT NAPHTHA: IRRITANT. **ACUTE EXPOSURE-** MAY CAUSE IRRITATION. IN THE ANTERIOR CHAMBER OF RABBIT EYES, PARAFFINS

HAVE CAUSED SLIGHT INFLAMMATORY REACTIONS ACCOMPANIED BY CLOUDING OF THE CORNEA. **CHRONIC EXPOSURE-** MAY CAUSE CONJUNCTIVITIS.
ISOPROPYL ALCOHOL (ISOPROPANOL; 2-PROPANOL): IRRITANT. **ACUTE EXPOSURE-** 400-800 PPM MAY CAUSE IRRITATION. IN RABBIT EYES, A DROP CAUSED MILD TRANSITORY INJURY AND A 50% AQUEOUS SOLUTION AFTER 3 MINUTES CAUSED MODERATE IRRITATION. CONTACT WITH A 70% SOLUTION CAUSED CONJUNCTIVITIS, IRITIS, AND CORNEAL OPACITY. **CHRONIC EXPOSURE-** PROLONGED OR REPEATED EXPOSURE TO VAPORS MAY CAUSE CONJUNCTIVITIS.

FIRST AID- WASH EYES IMMEDIATELY WITH LARGE AMOUNTS OF WATER OR NORMAL SALINE, OCCASIONALLY LIFTING UPPER AND LOWER LIDS, UNTIL NO EVIDENCE OF CHEMICAL REMAINS (APPROXIMATELY 15-20 MINUTES). GET MEDICAL ATTENTION IMMEDIATELY.

INGESTION: ALIPHATIC SOLVENT NAPHTHA: NARCOTIC. **ACUTE EXPOSURE-** PARAFFINS, AND OTHER PETROLEUM DISTILLATES WITH BOILING POINTS ABOVE 150 C HAVE LITTLE TOXICITY BY ABSORPTION AFTER INGESTION. IF LARGE AMOUNTS ARE ABSORBED CENTRAL NERVOUS SYSTEM DEPRESSION MAY OCCUR WITH SYMPTOMS OF HEADACHE, DIZZINESS, LOSS OF APPETITE, WEAKNESS, AND LOSS OF COORDINATION. THE PRIMARY HAZARD IS ASPIRATION. DIRECT ASPIRATION OF PARAFFINS, WITH A CARBON RANGE OF 6 TO 16, INTO THE LUNGS MAY CAUSE CHEMICAL PNEUMONITIS, PULMONARY EDEMA, AND HEMORRHAGING. THE EFFECTS ARE MOST SEVERE FOR PARAFFINS CONTAINING 6 TO 8 CARBONS. ASPIRATION MAY CAUSE ASPHYXIA, CARDIAC ARREST, AND IMMEDIATE DEATH DUE TO RESPIRATORY PARALYSIS. ASPIRATION EFFECTS MAY BE LESS SEVERE FOR PARAFFINS CONTAINING 9 OR MORE CARBONS. SYMPTOMS MAY INCLUDE DYSPNEA, CYANOSIS AND NASAL HEMORRHAGING WITH A SLOW DEATH AS A RESULT OF PULMONARY EDEMA. **CHRONIC EXPOSURE-** NO DATA AVAILABLE.
ISOPROPYL ALCOHOL (ISOPROPANOL; 2-PROPANOL): NARCOTIC. **ACUTE EXPOSURE-** INGESTION MAY CAUSE ABDOMINAL PAIN, HEMATEMESIS, NAUSEA, VOMITING, AND HEMORRHAGE. CENTRAL NERVOUS SYSTEM DEPRESSION MAY OCCUR WITH HEADACHE, DIZZINESS, FLUSHING, INCOORDINATION, STUPOR, CONFUSION, HYPOTENSION, AREFLEXIA, AND REFRACTORY NARCOSIS. OLIGURIA FOLLOWED BY DIURESIS AND COMA MAY ALSO OCCUR. OTHER SYMPTOMS MAY INCLUDE HYPOGLYCEMIA, TENDERNESS AND EDEMA OF MUSCLES, AND ARRHYTHMIAS. VOMITING WITH ASPIRATION MAY CAUSE ASPIRATION PNEUMONIA. DEPRESSED RESPIRATION AND DEATH DUE TO RESPIRATORY PARALYSIS MAY OCCUR IN A FEW HOURS AFTER EXPOSURE. SEVERE AND PROLONGED SHOCK MAY LEAD TO SERIOUS OR FATAL RENAL DAMAGE AFTER SEVERAL DAYS. PATHOLOGIC FINDINGS HAVE INCLUDED EXTENSIVE HEMORRHAGIC TRACHEOBRONCHITIS, BRONCHOPNEUMONIA AND HEMORRHAGIC PULMONARY EDEMA. **CHRONIC EXPOSURE-** NO ADVERSE EFFECTS RESULTED IN HUMANS FOLLOWING DAILY INGESTION OF 2.6 AND 6.4 MG/KG FOR 6 WEEKS. RATS THAT INGESTED 0.5 TO 10.0% ISOPROPYL ALCOHOL IN DRINKING WATER FOR 27 WEEKS SHOWED DECREASED BODY WEIGHT. PROLONGED ORAL ADMINISTRATION IN RABBITS PRODUCED ANESTHESIA AND DEATH. REPRODUCTIVE EFFECTS HAVE BEEN REPORTED IN ANIMALS.

FIRST AID- TREAT SYMPTOMATICALLY AND SUPPORTIVELY. GET MEDICAL ATTENTION AND ADVICE ON WHETHER TO USE GASTRIC LAVAGE. EXTREME CARE MUST BE TAKEN TO PREVENT ASPIRATION. A CUFFED ENDOTRACHEAL TUBE USED BY QUALIFIED MEDICAL PERSONNEL MIGHT BE ADVISABLE. KEEP HEAD LOWER THAN HIPS TO PREVENT ASPIRATION SHOULD VOMITING OCCUR.

REACTIVITY

REACTIVITY: STABLE UNDER NORMAL TEMPERATURES AND PRESSURES.

INCOMPATIBILITIES: ALIPHATIC SOLVENT NAPHTHA: STRONG OXIDIZERS: INCOMPATIBLE.
ISOPROPYL ALCOHOL (ISOPROPANOL; 2-PROPANOL): ALUMINUM: DISSOLUTION IS EXOTHERMIC. BARIUM PERCHLORATE: FORMATION OF EXPLOSIVE COMPOUND. 2-BUTANONE (METHYL ETHYL KETONE): ACCELERATES THE PEROXIDATION OF THE ALCOHOL. CHROMIUM TRIOXIDE (GRANULAR): IGNITION. COATINGS: MAY BE ATTACKED. DIOXYGENYL TETRAFLUOROBORATE: IGNITION AT AMBIENT TEMPERATURES. HYDROGEN + PALLADIUM (PARTICLES): IGNITION ON EXPOSURE TO AIR. HYDROGEN PEROXIDE: FORMATION OF EXPLOSIVE COMPOUND. KETONES: MARKEDLY INCREASES THE POSSIBILITY OF PEROXIDATION. NITROFORM (TRINITROMETHANE): DISSOLVES LIBERATING HEAT AND POSSIBLY EXPLODING. OLEUM: TEMPERATURE AND PRESSURE INCREASE IN CLOSED CONTAINER. OXIDIZERS (STRONG): FIRE AND EXPLOSION HAZARD. OXYGEN (GAS): AUTOXIDATION, ON EXPOSURE TO LIGHT, RESULTS IN FORMATION OF KETONES AND POTENTIALLY EXPLOSIVE HYDROGEN PEROXIDE. PHOSGENE: IN THE PRESENCE OF IRON SALTS, MAY EXPLODE. PLASTICS: MAY BE ATTACKED. POTASSIUM TERT-BUTOXIDE: IGNITION. RUBBER: MAY BE ATTACKED. SODIUM DICHROMATE + SULFURIC ACID: EXOTHERMIC REACTION WITH POSSIBLE INCANDESCENCE. SEE ALSO ALCOHOLS.

DECOMPOSITION: THERMAL DECOMPOSITION MAY RELEASE TOXIC AND/OR HAZARDOUS GASES.

POLYMERIZATION: HAZARDOUS POLYMERIZATION HAS NOT BEEN REPORTED TO OCCUR UNDER NORMAL TEMPERATURES AND PRESSURES.

CONDITIONS TO AVOID

AVOID CONTACT WITH HEAT, SPARKS, FLAMES, OR OTHER SOURCES OF IGNITION. VAPORS MAY BE EXPLOSIVE. AVOID OVERHEATING OF CONTAINERS; CONTAINERS MAY VIOLENTLY RUPTURE IN HEAT OF FIRE. AVOID CONTAMINATION OF WATER SOURCES.

SPILL AND LEAK PROCEDURES

OCCUPATIONAL SPILL: SHUT OFF IGNITION SOURCES. STOP LEAK IF YOU CAN DO IT WITHOUT RISK. USE WATER SPRAY TO REDUCE VAPORS. FOR SMALL SPILLS, TAKE UP WITH SAND OR OTHER ABSORBENT MATERIAL AND PLACE INTO CONTAINERS FOR LATER DISPOSAL. FOR LARGER SPILLS, DIKE FAR AHEAD OF SPILL FOR LATER DISPOSAL. NO SMOKING, FLAMES OR FLARES IN HAZARD AREA. KEEP UNNECESSARY PEOPLE AWAY; ISOLATE HAZARD AREA AND RESTRICT ENTRY.

PROTECTIVE EQUIPMENT

VENTILATION: PROVIDE LOCAL EXHAUST OR GENERAL DILUTION VENTILATION TO MEET PUBLISHED EXPOSURE LIMITS. VENTILATION EQUIPMENT MUST BE EXPLOSION-PROOF.

RESPIRATOR: THE FOLLOWING RESPIRATORS ARE RECOMMENDED BASED ON INFORMATION FOUND IN THE PHYSICAL DATA, TOXICITY AND HEALTH EFFECTS SECTIONS. THEY ARE RANKED IN ORDER FROM MINIMUM TO MAXIMUM RESPIRATORY PROTECTION. THE SPECIFIC RESPIRATOR SELECTED MUST BE BASED ON CONTAMINATION LEVELS FOUND IN THE WORK PLACE, MUST NOT EXCEED THE WORKING LIMITS OF THE RESPIRATOR AND BE JOINTLY APPROVED BY THE NATIONAL INSTITUTE FOR OCCUPATIONAL SAFETY AND HEALTH AND THE MINE SAFETY AND HEALTH ADMINISTRATION (NIOSH-MSHA).
TYPE 'C' SUPPLIED-AIR RESPIRATOR WITH A FULL FACEPIECE OPERATED IN PRESSURE-DEMAND OR OTHER POSITIVE PRESSURE MODE OR WITH A FULL FACEPIECE, HELMET OR HOOD OPERATED IN CONTINOUS-FLOW MODE. SELF-CONTAINED BREATHING APPARATUS WITH A FULL FACEPIECE OPERATED IN PRESSURE-DEMAND OR OTHER POSITIVE PRESSURE MODE.
FOR FIREFIGHTING AND OTHER IMMEDIATELY DANGEROUS TO LIFE OR HEALTH CONDITIONS:
SELF-CONTAINED BREATHING APPARATUS WITH FULL FACEPIECE OPERATED IN PRESSURE-DEMAND OR OTHER POSITIVE PRESSURE MODE.
SUPPLIED-AIR RESPIRATOR WITH FULL FACEPIECE AND OPERATED IN PRESSURE-DEMAND OR OTHER POSITIVE PRESSURE MODE IN COMBINATION WITH AN AUXILIARY SELF-CONTAINED BREATHING APPARATUS OPERATED IN PRESSURE-DEMAND OR OTHER POSITIVE PRESSURE MODE.

CLOTHING: EMPLOYEE MUST WEAR APPROPRIATE PROTECTIVE (IMPERVIOUS) CLOTHING AND EQUIPMENT TO PREVENT REPEATED OR PROLONGED SKIN CONTACT WITH THIS SUBSTANCE.

GLOVES: EMPLOYEE MUST WEAR APPROPRIATE PROTECTIVE GLOVES TO PREVENT CONTACT WITH THIS SUBSTANCE.

EYE PROTECTION: EMPLOYEE MUST WEAR SPLASH-PROOF OR DUST-RESISTANT SAFETY GOGGLES TO PREVENT EYE CONTACT WITH THIS SUBSTANCE.
EMERGENCY EYE WASH: WHERE THERE IS ANY POSSIBILITY THAT AN EMPLOYEE'S EYES MAY BE EXPOSED TO THIS SUBSTANCE, THE EMPLOYER SHOULD PROVIDE AN EYE WASH FOUNTAIN WITHIN THE IMMEDIATE WORK AREA FOR EMERGENCY USE.

AUTHORIZED BY- OCCUPATIONAL HEALTH SERVICES, INC.
CREATION DATE: 10/05/89 ***REVISION DATE:*** 06/28/90

SUBSTANCE NAME	CAS #	PST #
((BENZOYLAMINO)OXY)ACETIC ACID	5251-93-4	PST72964
((DIBUTYLAMINO)THIO)METHYLCARBAMIC ACID 2,3-DIHYDRO-2,2-DIMETHYL-7-BENZOFURANYL ESTER	55285-14-8	PST72266
((DIETHOXYPHOSPHINOTHIOYL)THIO)ACETIC ACID ETHYL ESTER	919-54-0	PST00117
((DIETHOXYPHOSPHINYL)THIO)ACETIC ACID, ETHYL ESTER	2425-25-4	PST73057
((DIMETHOXYPHOSPHINOTHIOYL)THIO)BUTANEDIOATE	121-75-5	PST13540
((DIMETHOXYPHOSPHINOTHIOYL)THIO)BUTANEDIOIC ACID DIETHYL ESTER	121-75-5	PST13540
((DIMETHOXYPHOSPHINYL)THIO)BUTANEDIOIC ACID DIETHYL ESTER	1634-78-2	PST13541
((DIMETHOXYPHOSPHINYL)THIO)DIETHYL BUTANEDIOATE	1634-78-2	PST13541
((DIMETHYLARSINO)OXY)SODIUM, AS-OXIDE	124-65-2	PST21070
((1,2-ETHANEDIYLBIS(CARBAMODITHIOATO))(2-))MANGANESE	12427-38-2	PST13589
((1,2-ETHANEDIYLBIS(CARBAMODITHIOATO))(2-))MANGANESE MIXTURE WITH ((1,2-ETHANEDIYLBIS(CARBAMODITHIOATO))(2-))ZINC	8018-01-7	PST71120
((3,5,6-TRICHLORO-2-PYRIDINYL)OXY)ACETIC ACID	55335-06-3	PST72472
((3,5,6-TRICHLORO-2-PYRIDYL)OXY)ACETIC ACID	55335-06-3	PST72472
((4-AMINOPHENYL)SULFONYL)CARBAMIC ACID, METHYL ESTER	3337-71-1	PST72352
((4-CHLORO-O-TOLY)OXY) ACETIC ACID, METHYL ESTER	2436-73-9	PST27881
((4-CHLORO-O-TOLYL)OXY)METHYL ACETATE	2436-73-9	PST27881
((4-CHLORO-ORTHO-TOLYL)OXY)ACETIC ACID	94-74-6	PST27880
((4,6-DINITRO-O-TOLYL)OXY)SODIUM	2312-76-7	PST71411
(+)-(Z)-2,2-DIMETHYL-3-(2-METHYLPROPENYL)-CYCLOPROPANECARBOXYLIC ACID, ESTER WITH 2-ALLYL-4-HYDROXY-3-METHYL-2-CYCLOPENTEN-1-ONE	34624-48-1	PST00551
(+)-CIS-ALLETHRIN	34624-48-1	PST00551
(+)-CIS-RESMETHRIN	35764-59-1	PST20094
(+)-CIS-TETRAMETHRIN	51348-90-4	PST23062
(+)-TRANS-CHRYSANTHEMUMIC ACID ESTER OF (+-)-ALLETHROLONE	UNASSIGNED	PST00553
(+)-TRANS-PHTHALTHRIN	1166-46-7	PST23063
(+)-TRANS-RESMETHRIN	28434-01-7	PST20093
(+)-TRANS-TETRAMETHRIN	1166-46-7	PST23063
(+)-TRANS,CIS-RESMETHRIN	UNASSIGNED	PST20096
(+-)-ALPHA-CYANO-3-PHENOXYBENZYL-(+-)-CIS,TRANS-3-(2,2-DICHLOROVINYL)-2,2-DIMETHYLCYCLOPROPANE CARBOXYLATE	52315-07-8	PST72392
(+/-)-2-(4,5-DIHYDRO-4-METHYL-4-(1-METHYLETHYL)-5-OXO-1H-IMIDAZOL-2-YL)-5-ETHYL-3-PYRIDINECARBOXYLIC ACID	81335-77-5	PST11308
(+,-)-(ZE)-2-(1-ETHOXYIMINOBUTYL)-5-(2-(ETHYLTHIO)PROPYL)-3-HYDROXYCYCLOHEX-2-ENONE	74051-80-2	PST20577
(+,-)-ETHYL 2-(4-((6-CHLORO-2-BENZOXAZOLYL)OXY)PHENOXY)PROPANOATE	66441-23-4	PST72723
(+,-)-2-(1-(ETHOXYIMINO)BUTYL)-5-(2-(ETHYLTHIO)PROPYL)-3-HYDROXY-2-CYCLOHEXEN-1-ONE	74051-80-2	PST20577
(+,-)-2-ETHOXY-2,3-DIHYDRO-3,3-DIMETHYL-5-BENZOFURANOL METHANESULFONATE	26225-79-6	PST72404
(+,-)-2-ETHOXY-2,3-DIHYDRO-3,3-DIMETHYL-5-BENZOFURANYL METHANESULFONATE	26225-79-6	PST72404
(+,-)-2-ETHOXY-2,3-DIHYDRO-3,3-DIMETHYLBENZOFURAN-5-YL METHANESULPHONATE	26225-79-6	PST72404
(+,-)-2-ETHOXY-2,3-DIHYDRO-3,3-DIMETHYLBENZOFURAN-5-YL METHANESULFONATE	26225-79-6	PST72404
(+,-)-2-ETHOXY-2,3-DIHYDRO-3,3-DIMETHYLBENZOFURAN-5-YL-METHANE SULFONATE	26225-79-6	PST72404
(-)-CIS-RESMETHRIN	UNASSIGNED	PST20097
(-)-STRYCHNINE	57-24-9	PST22080
(-)-TRANS-RESMETHRIN	33911-28-3	PST20098
(ACETATO) PHENYLMERCURY	62-38-4	PST18560
(ACETATO)(2-METHOXYETHYL)MERCURY	151-38-2	PST83031

ALPHABETICAL INDEX

SUBSTANCE NAME	CAS #	PST #
(ACETATO)ETHYLMERCURY	109-62-6	PST71476
(ACETATO-O)-(2-METHOXYETHYL)MERCURY	151-38-2	PST83031
(ACETATO-O)ETHYLMERCURY	109-62-6	PST71476
(ACETOXY)TRIPHENYLSTANNANE	900-95-8	PST24378
(ACETYLOXY)TRIBUTYLSTANNANE	56-36-0	PST72220
(AMINOIMINOMETHYL)-SULFATE (1:3) (SALT)	298-39-5	PST71042
(AMINOIMINOMETHYL)-SULFATE (2:3) (SALT)	3810-74-0	PST84290
(BENZAMIDOOXY)ACETIC ACID	5251-93-4	PST72964
(CHLOROMERCURI) BENZENE	100-56-1	PST18570
(CYANOGUANIDINATO)METHYLMERCURY	502-39-6	PST83040
(CYANOGUANIDINATO-N')METHYLMERCURY	502-39-6	PST83040
(CYANOGUANIDINO)METHYLMERCURY	502-39-6	PST83040
(DELTA)2-1,3,4-OXADIAZOLIN-5-ONE, 2-TERT-BUTYL-4-(2,4-DICHLORO-5-ISOPROPOXYPHENYL)-	19666-30-9	PST72385
(DIHYDROGEN PHOSPHATO)ETHYLMERCURY	2235-25-8	PST71479
(DODECYLBENZYL)TRIMETHYLAMMONIUM CHLORIDE	1330-85-4	PST71854
(E)-DIMETHYL 1-METHYL-3-(METHYLAMINO)-3-OXO-1-PROPENYL PHOSPHATE	6923-22-4	PST15165
(E)-O-2-ISPROPROPOXYCARBONYL-1-METHYLVINYL O-METHYL ETHYL-PHOSPHORAMIDOTHIOATE	31218-83-4	PST72440
(E)-1-METHYLETHYL 3-(((ETHYLAMINO)METHOXYPHOSPHINOTHIOYL)OXYL)-2-BUTENOATE	31218-83-4	PST72440
(E)-1-PHENYLETHYL 3-((DIMETHOXYPHOSPHINYL)OXY)-2-BUTENOATE	7700-17-6	PST05115
(E)-2-CHLORO-1-(2,4,5-TRICHLOROPHENYL)ETHENYL DIMETHYL PHOSPHATE	22350-76-1	PST72245
(E)-2-CHLORO-1-(2,4,5-TRICHLOROPHENYL)VINYL DIMETHYL PHOSPHATE	22350-76-1	PST72245
(E)-2-DIMETHYLCARBAMOYL-1-METHYLVINYL DIMETHYL PHOSPHATE	141-66-2	PST03090
(E)-3-(((ETHYLAMINO)METHOXYPHOSPHINOTHIOYL)OXY)-2-BUTENOIC ACID 1-METHYLETHYL ESTER	31218-83-4	PST72440
(E)-3-(DIMETHYLAMINO)-1-METHYL-3-OXO-1-PROPENYL DIMETHYL PHOSPHATE	141-66-2	PST03090
(E)-3-HYDROXYCROTONIC ACID ISOPROPYL ESTER O-ESTER WITH O-METHYLETHYL -PHOSPHORAMIDOTHIOATE	31218-83-4	PST72440
(ETHYLENEBIS(DITHIOCARBAMATO))MANGANESE	12427-38-2	PST13589
(ETHYLENEBIS(DITHIOCARBAMATO))MANGANESE MIXTURE WITH (ETHYLENEBIS(DITHIOCARBAMATO))ZINC	8018-01-7	PST71120
(ETHYLENEDIAMINETETRAACETIC ACID), DISODIUM SALT	139-33-3	PST08305
(ETHYLENEDINITRILO)TETRAACETIC ACID	60-00-4	PST09570
(ETHYLENEDINITRILOENDACETIC ACID	64-02-8	PST23137
(HYDROXYMETHYL)BENZENE	100-51-6	PST02800
(MERCAPTOACETYL)METHYLCARBAMIC ACID, METHYL ESTER, S-ESTER WITH O-METHYLMETHYLPHOSPHONODITHIOATE	29173-31-7	PST73246
(MU-(HYDROGEN ORTHOBORATO)DIPHENYLDIMERCURY	6273-99-0	PST71754
(MU-(ORTHOBORATO-O:O'))DIPHENYLDIMERCURY	6273-99-0	PST71754
(O-CHLOROANILINO)DICHLOROTRIAZINE	101-05-3	PST01526
(O-METHYL O-(4-BROMO-2,5-DICHLOROPHENYL) PHENYLPHOSPHONOTHIOATE	21609-90-5	PST12780
(OC-6-11)-TRIS(DIMETHYLCARBAMODITHIOATO-S,S')IRON	14484-64-1	PST09680
(OLEATO)PHENYLMERCURY	104-60-9	PST71769
(OLEOYLOXY)PHENYLMERCURY	104-60-9	PST71769
(PHENYLAMINO)BENZENE	122-39-4	PST08100
(R*,R*)-(+/-)-DETA-((2,4-DICHLOROPHENYL)METHYL)-ALPHA-(1,1-DIMETHYLETHYL)-1H-1,2,4-TRIAZOLE-1-EHANOL	75736-33-3	PST07005
(R)-(-)-1-(ETHYLCARBAMOYL)ETHYL PHENYLCARBAMATE	16118-49-3	PST72941
(R)-N-ETHYL-2-(((PHENYLAMINO)CARBONYL)OXY)PROPANAMIDE	16118-49-3	PST72941
(R)-1-(ETHYLCARBAMOYL)ETHYL CARBANILATE	16118-49-3	PST72941
(R)-1-(ETHYLCARBAMOYL)ETHYL PHENYLCARBAMATE	16118-49-3	PST72941
(R)-2-(4-((5-(TRIFLUOROMETHYL)-2-PYRIDINYL)OXY)PHENOXY)PROPANOIC ACID	79241-46-6	PST72557

SUBSTANCE NAME	CAS #	PST #
-3-(2-METHYL-1-PROPENYL)CYCLOPROPANECARBOXYLATE		
(1,4,5,6,7,7-HEXACHLORO-8,9,10-TRINORBORN-5-EN-2,3-YLENEBISMETHYLENE) SULPHITE	115-29-7	PST08560
(1,4,5,6,7,7-HEXACHLORO-8,9,10-TRINORBORN-5-EN-2,3-YLENEBISMETHYLENE) SULFITE	115-29-7	PST08560
(1A ALPHA, 2 BETA, 2A ALPHA, 3 BETA, 6 BETA, 6A ALPHA, 7 BETA, 7A ALPHA)-3,4,5,6,9,9-HEXACHLORO-1A,2,2A,3,6,6A,7,7A-OCTAHYDRO-2,7:3,6	60-57-1	PST07080
(1A ALPHA, 2 BETA, 2A BETA, 3 ALPHA, 6 ALPHA, 6A BETA, 7 BETA, 7A ALPHA)-3,4,5,6,9,9-HEXACHLORO-1A,2,2A,3,6,6A,7,7A-OCTAHYDRO-2,7:3,6	72-20-8	PST08600
(1A ALPHA,1B BETA,2ALPHA,5ALPHA,5A BETA,6BETA,6A ALPHA)-2,3,4,5,6, 6A,7,7-OCTACHLORO-1A,1B,5,5A,6,6A-HEXAHYDRO-2,5-METHANO-2H-INDENO	27304-13-8	PST17372
(1A(ALPHA),1B(BETA),2(ALPHA),5(ALPHA),5A(BETA),6(BETA),6A(ALPHA)-2,3, 4,5,6,7,7-HEPTACHLORO-1A,1B,5,5A,6,6A-HEXAHYDRO-2,5-METHANO-2H-	1024-57-3	PST10670
(1ALPHA(S*)3ALPHA)-(+/-)-CYANO(3-PHENOXYPHENYL)METHYL 3-(2,2-DICHLOROETHENYL)-2,2-DIMETHYLCYCLOPROPANECARBOXYLATE	67375-30-8	PST06118
(1ALPHA,2ALPHA,3A ALPHA,4BETA,7BETA,7A ALPHA)-1,2,4,5,6,7,8,8-OCTACHLORO-2,3,3A,4,7,7A-HEXAHYDRO-4,7-METHANO-1H-INDENE	5103-71-9	PST00776
(1ALPHA,2ALPHA,3ALPHA,4BETA,5ALPHA,6BETA)-1,2,3,4,5,6-HEXACHLOROCYCLOHEXANE	319-86-8	PST06310
(1ALPHA,2ALPHA,3BETA,4ALPHA,5ALPHA,6BETA)-1,2,3,4,5,6-HEXACHLOROCYCLOHEXANE	58-89-9	PST12810
(1ALPHA,2ALPHA,3BETA,4ALPHA,5BETA,6BETA)-1,2,3,4,5,6-HEXACHLOROCYCLOHEXANE	319-84-6	PST00770
(1ALPHA,2BETA,3A ALPHA,4BETA,7BETA,7A ALPHA)-1,2,4,5,6,7,8,8-OCTACHLORO-2,3,3A,4,7,7A-HEXAHYDRO-4,7-METHANO-1H-INDENE	5103-74-2	PST10331
(1ALPHA,2BETA,3ALPHA,3A ALPHA,4BETA,7BETA,7A ALPHA)-1,2,3,4,5,6,7,8, 8-NONACHLORO-2,3,3A,4,7,7A-HEXAHYDRO-4,7-METHANO-1H-INDENE	39765-80-5	PST23079
(1ALPHA,2BETA,3ALPHA,4BETA,5ALPHA,6BETA)-1,2,3,4,5,6-HEXACHLOROCYCLOHEXANE	319-85-7	PST03010
(1ALPHA,3A ALPHA,4BETA,5ALPHA,6A ALPHA)-1,2,3,5,7,8-HEXACHLORO-1,3A,4, 5,6,6A-HEXAHYDRO-1,4-ETHENOPENTALENE	56534-02-2	PST04566
(1ALPHA,3A BETA,6ALPHA,7A BETA,8R*)-2,3,3A,4,5,8-HEXACHLORO-3A,6,7 7A-TETRAHYDRO-1,6-METHANO-1H-INDENE	56641-38-4	PST04567
(1R CIS S) AND (1S CIS R) ENANTIOMERIC ISOMER PAIR OF ALPHA-CYANO-3-PHENOXYBENZYL-3-(2,2-DICHLOROVINYL)-2,2-	67375-30-8	PST06118
(1R(1 ALPHA(S*), 3 BETA))-2,2-DIMETHYL-3-(2-METHYL-1-PROPENYL)-CYCLO -PROPANECARBOXYLIC ACID-2-METHYL-4-OXO-3-(2-PROPENYL)-2-CYCLOPENTEN	28434-00-6	PST71013
(1R)-CIS-TETRAMETHRIN	51348-90-4	PST23062
(1R-(1 ALPHA(S*),3 ALPHA))-CYANO(3-PHENOXYPHENYL)METHYL-3-(2,2-DIBROMOVINYL)-2,2-DIMETHYLCYCLOPROPANECARBOXYLATE	52918-63-5	PST72784
(1R-(1 ALPHA(S*),3 ALPHA))-3-(2,2-DIBROMOETHENYL)-2,2-DIMETHYLCYCLOPROPANECARBOXYLIC ACID CYANO(3-PHENOXYPHENYL)METHYL ESTER	52918-63-5	PST72784
(1R-(1ALPHA(S*(Z)),3BETA))-	121-21-1	PST19960
(1R-(1ALPHA(S*(Z)),3BETA))-2,2-DIMETHYL-3-(2-METHYL-1-PROPENYL)-CYCLOPROPANECARBOXYLIC ACID, 3-(2-BUTENYL)-2-METHYL-4-OXO-2-	25402-06-6	PST05090
(1R-(1ALPHA(S*(Z)),3BETA))-2,2-DIMETHYL-3-(2-METHYL-1-PROPENYL)-CYCLOPROPANECARBOXYLIC ACID 2-METHYL-4-OXO-3-(2,4-PENTADIENYL)-	25402-06-6	PST05090
(1R-(1ALPHA(S*(Z),3BETA(E))-3-(3-METHOXY-2-METHYL-3-OXO-1-PROPENYL)-2,2,-DIMETHYLCYCLOPROPANECARBOXYLIC ACID, 2-METHYL-4-OXO-3-	121-29-9	PST19970
(1R-CIS)-	51348-90-4	PST23062
(1R-TRANS)	1166-46-7	PST23063
(1R-TRANS)-3-(2,2-DICHLOROETHENYL)-2,2-DIMETHYL-CYCLOPROPANECARBOXYLIC ACID, (3-PHENOXYPHENYL)METHYL ESTER	51877-74-8	PST23708
(1R,4S,4AS,5R,6R,7S,8S,8AR)-1,2,3,4,10,10-HEXACHLORO-1,4,4A,5,6,7,8,8A	60-57-1	PST07080

ALPHABETICAL INDEX

ALPHABETICAL INDEX

ALPHABETICAL INDEX

ALPHABETICAL INDEX

SUBSTANCE NAME	CAS #	PST #
AGRI-SUL	7704-34-9	PST22280
AGRIMYCIN	57-92-1	PST21917
AGRIMYCIN 17	57-92-1	PST21917
AGRIMYCIN 17	3810-74-0	PST84290
AGRISIL	327-98-0	PST00478
AGRITOX	327-98-0	PST00478
AGRITOX OXON	6492-18-8	PST23871
AGROCERES	76-44-8	PST10660
AGROCIT	17804-35-2	PST02580
AGROTHION	122-14-5	PST09678
AGROXON	94-74-6	PST27880
AGROXONE	94-74-6	PST27880
AGUATHOL	129-67-9	PST08590
AI 3-29054	35367-38-5	PST07388
AIP	20859-73-8	PST00970
AITC	57-06-7	PST00680
AIZEN MALACHITE GREEN	569-64-2	PST13533
AKAR	510-15-6	PST04740
AKTICON	1912-24-9	PST02150
AKTIKON	1912-24-9	PST02150
AKTISAL	144-62-7	PST17360
AKTON	1757-18-2	PST00493
AL	7429-90-5	PST01000
AL-PHOS	20859-73-8	PST00970
ALACHLOR	15972-60-8	PST00506
ALANAP	132-66-1	PST71340
ALANAP	132-67-2	PST71341
ALANAP 3	132-67-2	PST71341
ALANEX	15972-60-8	PST00506
ALAOURIN	8006-54-0	PST12425
ALAR	1596-84-5	PST06195
ALATEX	75-99-0	PST06200
ALBOCARBON	91-20-3	PST16120
ALBONE	7722-84-1	PST11190
ALBONE DS	7722-84-1	PST11190
ALBRASS	1918-16-7	PST19686
ALCIDE	10049-04-4	PST04610
ALCL3	7446-70-0	PST00900
ALCOHOL	64-17-5	PST08700
ALCOHOL ANHYDROUS	64-17-5	PST08700
ALCOHOL C-10	112-30-1	PST06285
ALCOHOL C-6	111-27-3	PST15630
ALCOHOLS, C11-15-SECONDARY, ETHOXYLATED	68131-40-8	PST85315
ALCOHOLS, LANOLIN, ETHOXYLATED	61790-81-6	PST08741
ALDACIDE	30525-89-4	PST18000
ALDEHYDE C18	104-61-0	PST10334
ALDICARB	116-06-3	PST00500
ALDICARB SULFONE	1646-88-4	PST72406
ALDICARB SULFOXIDE	1646-87-3	PST00503
ALDIFEN	51-28-5	PST28620
ALDOXYCARB	1646-88-4	PST72406
ALDRIN	309-00-2	PST00520
ALENTISAN	21564-17-0	PST71392
ALFACRON	18181-70-9	PST73035

ALPHABETICAL INDEX

SUBSTANCE NAME	CAS #	PST #
ALFLOC 7020	2425-06-1	PST04200
ALFLOC 7046	2425-06-1	PST04200
ALFOL 10	112-30-1	PST06285
ALFOXYLATE	67375-30-8	PST06118
ALGAEDYN	7440-22-4	PST20770
ALGISTAT	117-80-6	PST06810
ALGOGRENE TYPE 2	75-71-8	PST06880
ALGRAIN	64-17-5	PST08700
ALIDOCHLORE	93-71-0	PST71155
ALIETTE	39148-24-8	PST72563
ALKARSODYL	124-65-2	PST21070
ALKRON	56-38-2	PST18040
ALKYL DIMETHYL ETHYLBENZYL AMMONIUM CHLORIDE	8001-54-5	PST00539
ALKYL DIMETHYL 3,4-DICHLOROBENZYL AMMONIUM CHLORIDE	8023-53-8	PST71839
ALKYL(ETHYLPHENYL)METHYL)DIMETHYL QUARTENARY AMMONIUM CHLORIDES	8001-54-5	PST00539
ALKYLDIMETHYLBENZYLAMMONIUM CHLORIDE	8001-54-5	PST00537
ALKYLDIMETHYLBENZYLAMMONIUM CHLORIDE (50% C14, 40% C12, 10% C16)	68424-85-1	PST71835
ALKYLDIMETHYLBENZYLAMMONIUM CHLORIDE (60% C14, 30% C16, 5% C18,	53516-76-0	PST71834
ALKYLOXYPOLYETHYLENEOXYETHANOL	68131-40-8	PST85315
ALLBRI NATURAL COPPER	7440-50-8	PST05430
ALLERON	56-38-2	PST18040
ALLETHRIN	584-79-2	PST00550
ALLETHRIN (RACEMIC MIXTURE)	UNASSIGNED	PST00554
ALLETHRIN I	28434-00-6	PST71013
ALLETHRONYL D,1-CIS,TRANS CHRYSANTHEMATE	584-79-2	PST00550
ALLIDOCHLOR	93-71-0	PST71155
ALLIE	74223-64-6	PST72546
ALLIED GC 6506	3254-63-5	PST73095
ALLISAN	99-30-9	PST28910
ALLIUM SATIVUM	8000-78-0	PST72626
ALLOPHANIC ACID, 4,4'-O-PHENYLENEBIS(3-THIO-, DIETHYL ESTER	23564-06-9	PST72322
ALLOPHANIC ACID, 4,4'-O-PHENYLENEBIS(3-THIO-, DIMETHYL ESTER	23564-05-8	PST72308
ALLOXOL S	74051-80-2	PST20577
ALLOXYDIM SODIUM	55635-13-7	PST72430
ALLOXYDIMEDON SODIUM	55635-13-7	PST72430
ALLTOX	8001-35-2	PST23640
ALLY 20DF	74223-64-6	PST72546
ALLYL ALDEHYDE	107-02-8	PST00330
ALLYL CINERIN I	584-79-2	PST00550
ALLYL HOMOLOG OF CINERIN I	UNASSIGNED	PST00553
ALLYL ISOSULFOCYANATE	57-06-7	PST00680
ALLYL ISOTHIOCYANATE	57-06-7	PST00680
ALLYL MUSTARD OIL	57-06-7	PST00680
ALLYLSENEVOL	57-06-7	PST00680
ALLYXYCARB	6392-46-7	PST72977
ALMEDERM	70-30-4	PST10780
ALODAN	2550-75-6	PST73193
ALON	34123-59-6	PST12254
ALPHA CYANO-3-PHENOXYBENZYL(+-)CIS,TRANS, 3-(,2-DICHLOROVINYL)-2,2- DIMETHYL CYCLOPROPANE CARBOXYLATE	52315-07-8	PST72392
ALPHA-(((DIETHOXYPHOSPHINOTHIOYL)OXY)IMINO)BENZENEACETONITRILE	14816-18-3	PST73292
ALPHA-((DIMETHOXYPHOSPHINOTHIOYL)THIO)BENZENEACETATE	2597-03-7	PST72337
ALPHA-((DIMETHOXYPHOSPHINOTHIOYL)THIO)BENZENEACETIC ACID, ETHYL ESTER	2597-03-7	PST72337
ALPHA-(ETHYLTHIO)-O-TOLYL METHYLCARBAMATE	29973-13-5	PST72421

ALPHABETICAL INDEX

ALPHABETICAL INDEX

ALPHABETICAL INDEX

SUBSTANCE NAME	CAS #	PST #
AMETHOPTERIN SODIUM	15475-56-6	PST14211
AMETHOPTERINE	59-05-2	PST14210
AMETHOPTERINE SODIUM	15475-56-6	PST14211
AMETREX	834-12-8	PST01006
AMETRYN	834-12-8	PST01006
AMETRYNE	834-12-8	PST01006
AMEX	33629-47-9	PST03525
AMIBEN	133-90-4	PST29084
AMIBEN AMMONIUM SALT	1076-46-6	PST71252
AMIBEN METHYL ESTER	7286-84-2	PST71255
AMIBEN SODIUM SALT	1954-81-0	PST71256
AMIBIN	133-90-4	PST29084
AMIDITHION	919-76-6	PST01007
AMIDOCYANOGEN	420-04-2	PST05760
AMIDOFOS	299-86-5	PST05550
AMIDOPHOS	299-86-5	PST05550
AMIDOSULFONIC ACID	5329-14-6	PST22200
AMIDOSULFURIC ACID	5329-14-6	PST22200
AMILFENOL	80-46-6	PST71715
AMINESULFONIC ACID	5329-14-6	PST22200
AMINO-4-PYRIDINE	504-24-5	PST02180
AMINOCARB	2032-59-9	PST71500
AMINOETHANOL	141-43-5	PST08710
AMINOPYRIDINE	504-24-5	PST02180
AMINOSULFONIC ACID	5329-14-6	PST22200
AMINOSULFURIC ACID	5329-14-6	PST22200
AMINOTRIAZOLE	61-82-5	PST01040
AMINOZIDE	1596-84-5	PST06195
AMITON	78-53-5	PST83006
AMITON OXALATE	3734-97-2	PST71642
AMITROL	61-82-5	PST01040
AMITROLE	61-82-5	PST01040
AMMATE	7773-06-0	PST01400
AMMO	52315-07-8	PST72392
AMMONIUM AMIDOSULFATE	7773-06-0	PST01400
AMMONIUM AMIDOSULFONATE	7773-06-0	PST01400
AMMONIUM AMIDOSULPHATE	7773-06-0	PST01400
AMMONIUM AMINOSULFONATE	7773-06-0	PST01400
AMMONIUM FERROUS SULFATE	10045-89-3	PST09820
AMMONIUM HYPOSULFITE	7783-18-8	PST01460
AMMONIUM IRON(II) SULFATE (2:1:2)	10045-89-3	PST09820
AMMONIUM POLYSULFIDE SOLUTION	9080-17-5	PST01380
AMMONIUM SULFAMATE	7773-06-0	PST01400
AMMONIUM SULFIDE SOLUTION, RED	9080-17-5	PST01380
AMMONIUM SULPHAMATE	7773-06-0	PST01400
AMMONIUM THIOSULFATE	7783-18-8	PST01460
AMMONIUM 3-AMINO-2,5-DICHLOROBENZOATE	1076-46-6	PST71252
AMMONIUM-DL-HOMOALANIN-4-YL(METHYL)PHOSPHINATE	77182-82-2	PST72647
AMMONIUM, (DODECYLBENZYL)TRIMETHYL-, CHLORIDE	1330-85-4	PST71854
AMMONIUM, (2-CHLOROETHYL)TRIMETHYL-, CHLORIDE 2-CHLORO-N,N,N-TRIMETHYLETHANAMINIUM CHLORIDE	999-81-5	PST71147
AMMONIUM, BENZYLDIMETHYL(2-(2-((4-(1,1,3,3-TETRAMETHYLBUTYL)TOLYL)OXY)ETHOXY)ETHYL)-, CHLORIDE	25155-18-4	PST71862
AMMONIUM, BENZYLDIMETHYL(2-(2-(P-(1,1,3,3-TETRAMETHYLBUTYL)PHENOXY)	121-54-0	PST71851

SUBSTANCE NAME	CAS #	PST #
ETHOXY)ETHYL)-, CHLORIDE		
AMMONIUM, BENZYLDIMETHYL(2-(2-(P-1,1,3,3-TETRAMETHYLBUTYLCRESOXY)ETHOXY)ETHYL)-, CHLORIDE	25155-18-4	PST71862
AMMONIUM, DIMETHYLOCTADECYL(3-TRIMETHOXYSILYL)PROPYL)-, CHLORIDE	27668-52-6	PST72370
AMOBEN	133-90-4	PST29084
AMORPHOUS SILICA DUST	7631-86-9	PST20610
AMORPHOUS, RED PHOSPHORUS	7723-14-0	PST18790
AMS	7773-06-0	PST01400
AMYL ACETATE	628-63-7	PST15270
AMYL ACETATE ETHER	628-63-7	PST15270
AMYL ACETIC ESTER	628-63-7	PST15270
AMYL ACETIC ETHER	628-63-7	PST15270
AMYLCARBINOL	111-27-3	PST15630
AMYLIN	9004-53-9	PST06363
ANACEL	136-47-0	PST72269
ANALAP-1	132-66-1	PST71340
ANALAPE	132-66-1	PST71340
ANALGIT	119-36-8	PST14720
ANATOX	8001-35-2	PST23640
ANELDA	2008-41-5	PST71474
ANESTARON	136-47-0	PST72269
ANESTHESINE	94-09-7	PST72267
ANHYDROGLUCOCHLORAL	15879-93-3	PST00775
ANHYDROL	64-17-5	PST08700
ANHYDROUS BORIC ACID	1303-86-2	PST03290
ANHYDROUS CALCIUM SULFATE	7778-18-9	PST04110
ANHYDROUS CITRIC ACID	77-92-9	PST05200
ANHYDROUS GYPSUM	7778-18-9	PST04110
ANHYDROUS HYDROCHLORIC ACID	7647-01-0	PST11150
ANHYDROUS SODIUM ACID PHOSPHATE	7558-79-4	PST08330
ANHYDROUS SODIUM SULFITE	7757-83-7	PST21660
ANHYDROUS SULFATE OF LIME	7778-18-9	PST04110
ANICON KOMBI	94-74-6	PST27880
ANICON M	94-74-6	PST27880
ANILAZIN	101-05-3	PST01526
ANILAZINE	101-05-3	PST01526
ANILINE GREEN	569-64-2	PST13533
ANILINE, N-SEC-BUTYL-4-TERT-BUTYL-2,6-DINITRO-	33629-47-9	PST03525
ANILINE, 2,6-DICHLORO-4-NITRO-	99-30-9	PST28910
ANILINE, 4-(METHYLSULFONYL)-2,6-DINITRO-N,N-DIPROPYL-	4726-14-1	PST16525
ANILINOBENZENE	122-39-4	PST08100
ANIMAL OIL	8001-85-2	PST03250
ANISE OIL	8007-70-3	PST71028
ANISEED OIL	8007-70-3	PST71028
ANISOLE, 2-SEC-BUTYL-4,6-DINITRO-	6099-79-2	PST08022
ANIYALINE	101-05-3	PST01526
ANKILOSTIN	127-18-4	PST22900
ANON	108-94-1	PST05890
ANONE	108-94-1	PST05890
ANOZOL	84-66-2	PST07210
ANSAR 138	75-60-5	PST03710
ANTABUSE	97-77-8	PST08370
ANTAK	112-30-1	PST06285
ANTERGON	123-33-1	PST13570

SUBSTANCE NAME	CAS #	PST #
ARATHANE	39300-45-3	PST71402
ARATRON	140-57-8	PST01850
ARBORSEAL	2425-06-1	PST04200
ARCANUM DUPLICATUM	7778-80-5	PST19590
ARCTON 6	75-71-8	PST06880
ARD 34/02	74051-80-2	PST20577
ARELON	34123-59-6	PST12254
ARESIN	1746-81-2	PST15174
ARETIT	2813-95-8	PST08021
AREZIN	1746-81-2	PST15174
AREZINE	1746-81-2	PST15174
ARGENTI NITRAS	7761-88-8	PST20810
ARGENTUM	7440-22-4	PST20770
ARGEROL	7761-88-8	PST20810
ARGEZIN	1912-24-9	PST02150
ARIOTOX	108-62-3	PST14090
ARISAN	3766-60-7	PST03523
ARKOTINE	50-29-3	PST06250
ARMOTAN PMO-20	9005-65-6	PST40200
ARPROCARB	114-26-1	PST02540
ARRESIN	1746-81-2	PST15174
ARSAN	75-60-5	PST03710
ARSECODILE	124-65-2	PST21070
ARSENATE	7778-39-4	PST01990
ARSENATE OF LEAD	7784-40-9	PST12540
ARSENETTE, SCHULTENITE	7784-40-9	PST12540
ARSENIC ACID	7778-39-4	PST01990
ARSENIC ACID	1303-28-2	PST02020
ARSENIC ACID ANHYDRIDE	1303-28-2	PST02020
ARSENIC ACID, CALCIUM SALT (2:3)	7778-44-1	PST03850
ARSENIC ACID, LEAD(2+) SALT	7784-40-9	PST12540
ARSENIC ACID, SODIUM SALT	7631-89-2	PST20940
ARSENIC ANHYDRIDE	1303-28-2	PST02020
ARSENIC HYDRIDE	7784-42-1	PST02100
ARSENIC OXIDE	1303-28-2	PST02020
ARSENIC OXIDE	1327-53-3	PST02070
ARSENIC OXIDE (AS2O3)	1327-53-3	PST02070
ARSENIC OXIDE (AS2O5)	1303-28-2	PST02020
ARSENIC PENTOXIDE, SOLID	1303-28-2	PST02020
ARSENIC SESQUIOXIDE	1327-53-3	PST02070
ARSENIC SESQUIOXIDE (AS2O3)	1327-53-3	PST02070
ARSENIC TRIHYDRIDE	7784-42-1	PST02100
ARSENIC TRIOXIDE	1327-53-3	PST02070
ARSENIC TRIOXIDE, SOLID	1327-53-3	PST02070
ARSENIC(III) OXIDE	1327-53-3	PST02070
ARSENIC(V) OXIDE	1303-28-2	PST02020
ARSENICUM ALBUM	1327-53-3	PST02070
ARSENIOUC OXIDE	1327-53-3	PST02070
ARSENIURETTED HYDROGEN	7784-42-1	PST02100
ARSENOUS ACID	1327-53-3	PST02070
ARSENOUS ACID ANHYDRIDE	1327-53-3	PST02070
ARSENOUS HYDRIDE	7784-42-1	PST02100
ARSENOUS OXIDE	1327-53-3	PST02070
ARSENOUS OXIDE ANHYDRIDE	1327-53-3	PST02070

ALPHABETICAL INDEX

SUBSTANCE NAME	CAS #	PST #
AVERMECTIN A1A, 5-O-DEMETHYL-	65195-55-3	PST72553
AVERMECTIN A1A, 5-O-DEMETHYL-25-DE(1-METHYLPROPYL)-25-(1-METHYLETHYL)-	65195-56-4	PST02156
AVERMECTIN B1A	65195-55-3	PST72553
AVERMECTIN B1B	65195-56-4	PST02156
AVICOL	82-68-8	PST18140
AVIROL 130	8002-33-3	PST24575
AVITROL	504-24-5	PST02180
AVOLIN	131-11-3	PST07740
AZAPLANT	61-82-5	PST01040
AZIDE	26628-22-8	PST20960
AZIDITHION	78-57-9	PST72980
AZINPHOS-ETHYL	2642-71-9	PST02205
AZINPHOS-METHYL	86-50-0	PST02210
AZINPHOSMETHYL OXON	961-22-8	PST10585
AZINPHOSMETHYL OXYGEN ANALOG	961-22-8	PST10585
AZIPROTRYN	4658-28-0	PST02216
AZIPROTRYNE	4658-28-0	PST02216
AZIUM	26628-22-8	PST20960
AZODOX	1314-13-2	PST25490
AZODRIN	6923-22-4	PST15165
AZOGEN DEVELOPER	135-19-3	PST03050
AZOLANE	61-82-5	PST01040
AZOQUIMIOL	72-14-0	PST72047
AZOSEPTALE	72-14-0	PST72047
B 10094	13067-93-1	PST05805
B 3014	1934-21-0	PST22465
B 3015	28249-77-6	PST72381
B-K POWDER	7778-54-3	PST03990
B-NINE	1596-84-5	PST06195
B-10	8007-47-4	PST04145
B-33172	3878-19-1	PST73188
B-385	7726-95-6	PST03340
B-622	101-05-3	PST01526
B-995	1596-84-5	PST06195
BACTINE	25155-18-4	PST71862
BADDELEYITE	1314-23-4	PST25635
BAKING SODA	144-55-8	PST20970
BAKTOL	59-50-7	PST29890
BAKTOLAN	59-50-7	PST29890
BALAN	1861-40-1	PST02570
BALFIN	1861-40-1	PST02570
BALSAM OF FIR	8007-47-4	PST04145
BAN-HOE	2164-08-1	PST73238
BAN-HOE (FORMULATION)	122-42-9	PST71564
BANAFINE	1861-40-1	PST02570
BANANA OIL	628-63-7	PST15270
BANEX	1918-00-9	PST02260
BANFEL	1918-00-9	PST02260
BANOL	671-04-5	PST02250
BANTEX	155-04-4	PST27776
BANTU	86-88-4	PST01830
BANVEL	1918-00-9	PST02260
BANVEL D METHYL ESTER	6597-78-0	PST73131
BARBAN	101-27-9	PST71143

ALPHABETICAL INDEX

SUBSTANCE NAME	CAS #	PST #
BARBANE	101-27-9	PST71143
BARRICADE	52315-07-8	PST72392
BARTILEX	82-68-8	PST18140
BAS 083	24307-26-4	PST72386
BAS 210311	28805-78-9	PST73199
BAS 263	51487-69-5	PST72572
BAS 290H	21267-72-1	PST73038
BAS 85559X	24307-26-4	PST72386
BAS 90520H	74051-80-2	PST20577
BASAGRAN	25057-89-0	PST02584
BASAGRAN AIBA METABOLITE	UNASSIGNED	PST02581
BASAMAIZE	21267-72-1	PST73038
BASAMID (FORMULATION)	533-74-4	PST06230
BASCILLOL	1319-77-3	PST05510
BASF 9052	74051-80-2	PST20577
BASFAPON	75-99-0	PST06200
BASFAPON B	75-99-0	PST06200
BASFAPON/BASFAPON N	75-99-0	PST06200
BASIC GREEN 4	569-64-2	PST13533
BASINEX	75-99-0	PST06200
BASINEX P	75-99-0	PST06200
BASSA	3766-81-2	PST03324
BASTA	77182-82-2	PST72647
BATASAN	900-95-8	PST24378
BAY DIC 1577	57052-04-7	PST11844
BAY HOX 1901	29973-13-5	PST72421
BAY MET-1486	30043-49-3	PST72551
BAY NTN 8629	34643-46-4	PST72655
BAY NTN 9306 OXYGEN ANALOG SULFONE	42795-00-6	PST03231
BAY 171476	86-50-0	PST02210
BAY 210974	301-12-2	PST17375
BAY 23655	2674-91-1	PST14105
BAY 25141	115-90-2	PST06210
BAY 33172	3878-19-1	PST73188
BAY 37289	327-98-0	PST00478
BAY 37289 OXYGEN ANALOG	6492-18-8	PST23871
BAY 41831	122-14-5	PST09678
BAY 45432	1113-02-6	PST17328
BAY 47531	1085-98-9	PST73026
BAY 50282	6392-46-7	PST72977
BAY 5621	14816-18-3	PST73292
BAY 5712	731-27-1	PST73030
BAY 6159H	21087-64-9	PST15006
BAY 68138	22224-92-6	PST16145
BAY 68138 SULFONE	31972-44-8	PST16144
BAY 70143	1563-66-2	PST04240
BAY 77049	13593-03-8	PST73112
BAY 77488	14816-18-3	PST73292
BAY 78418	17109-49-8	PST08555
BAY 9002	1491-41-4	PST72737
BAY 92144	25311-71-1	PST11985
BAY 94337	21087-64-9	PST15006
BAY-DRW 1139	41394-05-2	PST14095
BAY-E 6975	38083-17-9	PST05208

SUBSTANCE NAME	CAS #	PST #
BAY-FCR 1272	68359-37-5	PST72630
BAY-SYM 1500	64529-56-2	PST09111
BAYCID (FORMULATION)	55-38-9	PST02550
BAYER NTN 9306	35400-43-2	PST22387
BAYER 16259	2642-71-9	PST02205
BAYER 18.436	919-86-8	PST83065
BAYER 19639	298-04-4	PST08380
BAYER 21/116	8022-00-2	PST14438
BAYER 22/190	500-28-7	PST71379
BAYER 22190	500-28-7	PST71379
BAYER 22555	140-56-7	PST73084
BAYER 25/154	919-86-8	PST83065
BAYER 29493	55-38-9	PST02550
BAYER 33172	3878-19-1	PST73188
BAYER 37289	327-98-0	PST00478
BAYER 39007	114-26-1	PST02540
BAYER 41 367C	3766-81-2	PST03324
BAYER 44646	2032-59-9	PST71500
BAYER 5360	443-48-1	PST72529
BAYER 60618	1929-88-0	PST72971
BAYER 74283	18691-97-9	PST14108
BAYER 77049	13593-03-8	PST73112
BAYER 77488	14816-18-3	PST73292
BAYER 78418	17109-49-8	PST08555
BAYER 8169	8065-48-3	PST06320
BAYGON	114-26-1	PST02540
BAYPIVAL	38083-17-9	PST05208
BAYRUSIL	13593-03-8	PST73112
BAYSAN	38083-17-9	PST05208
BAYTEX (FORMULATION)	55-38-9	PST02550
BAYTEX OXON	6552-12-1	PST02551
BAYTEX OXON SULFONE	14086-35-2	PST02552
BAYTEX OXON SULFOXIDE	6552-13-2	PST02553
BAYTEX SULFONE	3761-42-0	PST02554
BAYTHION	14816-18-3	PST73292
BAYTHROID	68359-37-5	PST72630
BCF-BUSHKILLER	93-76-5	PST28690
BEET-KLEEN	101-42-8	PST09679
BEET-KLEEN	101-21-3	PST71148
BELGRAN	34123-59-6	PST12254
BELMARK	51630-58-1	PST19948
BENALAN	1861-40-1	PST02570
BENAZOLIN	3813-05-6	PST72725
BENAZOLINE	3813-05-6	PST72725
BENCARBATE	22781-23-3	PST02560
BENDIOCARB	22781-23-3	PST02560
BENDIOXIDE	25057-89-0	PST02584
BENE OIL	8008-74-0	PST20575
BENEFEX	1861-40-1	PST02570
BENEFIN	1861-40-1	PST02570
BENELUX	39196-18-4	PST23330
BENFLURALIN	1861-40-1	PST02570
BENFURACARB	82560-54-1	PST72562
BENI OIL	8008-74-0	PST20575

ALPHABETICAL INDEX

ALPHABETICAL INDEX

ALPHABETICAL INDEX

SUBSTANCE NAME	CAS #	PST #
BENZONITRILE, 2,6-DICHLORO-	1194-65-6	PST06800
BENZONITRILE, 3,5-DIBROMO-4-HYDROXY-	1689-84-5	PST03542
BENZONITRILE, 3,5-DIIODO-4-HYDROXY	1689-83-4	PST11468
BENZONITRILE, 4-HYDROXY-3,5-DIIODO-	1689-83-4	PST11468
BENZONITRILE, 4-HYDROXY-3,5-DIIODO-, SODIUM SALT	2961-62-8	PST73074
BENZOPHENONE,4,4'-DICHLORO-	90-98-2	PST06246
BENZOPYRAN-6(6AH)-ONE	83-79-4	PST20200
BENZOTHIAZOLE-2-THIONE	149-30-4	PST13738
BENZOXIMATE	29104-30-1	PST72988
BENZTHIAZURON	1929-88-0	PST72971
BENZYFURDINE	10453-86-8	PST20095
BENZYL ALCOHOL	100-51-6	PST02800
BENZYL BENZENECARBOXYLATE	120-51-4	PST02805
BENZYL BENZOATE	120-51-4	PST02805
BENZYL PHENYLFORMATE	120-51-4	PST02805
BENZYLCARBINYL PROPIONATE	122-70-3	PST72314
BENZYLDIMETHYL (2-(2-(P-(1,1,3,3-TETRAMETHYLBUTYL)PHENOXY)ETHOXY) ETHYL)AMMONIUM CHLORIDE	121-54-0	PST71851
BENZYLDIMETHYL(2-(2-((4-(1,1,3,3 TETRAMETHYLBUTYL)TOLYL)OXY)ETHOXY)ETHYL)AMMONIUM CHLORIDE	25155-18-4	PST71862
BENZYLDIMETHYL(2-(2-(P-1,1,3,3-TETRAMETHYLBUTYLCRESOXY)ETHOXY)ETHYL)AMMONIUM CHLORIDE	25155-18-4	PST71862
BENZYLETS	120-51-4	PST02805
BENZYTOL	88-04-0	PST72258
BERELEX	77-06-5	PST10405
BETA BUTYLENE GLYCOL	107-88-0	PST26730
BETA-(2-(3,5-DIMETHYL-2-OXOCYCLOHEXYL)-2-HYDROXYETHYL)GLUTARIMIDE	66-81-9	PST05930
BETA-ALANINE, N-(((((2,3-DIHYDRO-2,2-DIMETHYL-7-BENZOFURANYL)OXY) CARBONYL)METHYLAMINO)THIO)-N-(1-METHYLETHYL)-, ETHYL ESTER	82560-54-1	PST72562
BETA-AMINOETHANOL	141-43-5	PST08710
BETA-AMINOETHYL ALCOHOL	141-43-5	PST08710
BETA-AMINOETHYLAMINE	107-15-3	PST09560
BETA-BENZENE HEXACHLORIDE	319-85-7	PST03010
BETA-BENZOEPIN	33213-65-9	PST03040
BETA-BHC	319-85-7	PST03010
BETA-BROMO-BETA-NITROTRIMETHYLENEGLYCOL	52-51-7	PST72832
BETA-BUTOXY-BETA'-THIOCYANODIETHYL ETHER	112-56-1	PST75661
BETA-BUTOXYETHANOL	111-76-2	PST03540
BETA-CHLORDAN	5103-74-2	PST10331
BETA-CHLORDANE	5103-74-2	PST10331
BETA-CHLOROETHYL-BETA-(P-TERT-BUTYLPHENOXY)-ALPHA-METHYLETHYL SULPHITE	140-57-8	PST01850
BETA-CHLOROETHYLPHOSPHONIC ACID	16672-87-0	PST72293
BETA-ENDOSULFAN	33213-65-9	PST03040
BETA-ETHANOLAMINE	141-43-5	PST08710
BETA-HCH	319-85-7	PST03010
BETA-HEPTACHLOREPOXIDE	1024-57-3	PST10670
BETA-HEXACHLOROBENZENE	319-85-7	PST03010
BETA-HEXACHLOROCYCLOHEXANE	319-85-7	PST03010
BETA-HYD-ROXYNAPHTHALENE	135-19-3	PST03050
BETA-HYDROXYETHYLAMINE	141-43-5	PST08710
BETA-HYDROXYTRICARBALLYLIC ACID	77-92-9	PST05200
BETA-IBA	133-32-4	PST29325
BETA-INDOLEBUTYRIC ACID	133-32-4	PST29325
BETA-INDOLYLBUTRIC ACID	133-32-4	PST29325

SUBSTANCE NAME	CAS #	PST #
BETA-KETOPROPANE	67-64-1	PST00140
BETA-METHOXYETHANOL	109-86-4	PST14340
BETA-MONOXYNAPHTHALENE	135-19-3	PST03050
BETA-NAPHTHYL HYD-ROXIDE	135-19-3	PST03050
BETA-NAPHTHYLALCOHOL	135-19-3	PST03050
BETA-NAPTHOL	135-19-3	PST03050
BETA-PHENYLETHYL PROPIONATE	122-70-3	PST72314
BETA-PYRIDYL-ALPHA-N-METHYLPYRROLIDINE	54-11-5	PST16430
BETA-SELEKTONON M	94-74-6	PST27880
BETA-TERPINEOL	138-87-4	PST03075
BETA-THIODAN	33213-65-9	PST03040
BETA-THIONEX	959-98-8	PST00800
BETA-1,2,3,4,5,6-HEXACHLOROCYCLOHEXANE	319-85-7	PST03010
BETACIDE P	94-13-3	PST19941
BETANAL	13684-63-4	PST72282
BETANEX	13684-56-5	PST72336
BETASAN	741-58-2	PST02583
BETASAN OXON	UNASSIGNED	PST02582
BETHRODINE	1861-40-1	PST02570
BEXTON	1918-16-7	PST19686
BFPO	115-26-4	PST07655
BH DALAPON	75-99-0	PST06200
BHC	319-84-6	PST00770
BHC	319-85-7	PST03010
BHC	608-73-1	PST03080
BHC	319-86-8	PST06310
BH3O3	10043-35-3	PST03260
BICARBURETTED HYDROGEN	74-85-1	PST09330
BICHLORIDE OF MERCURY	7487-94-7	PST13800
BICHROMATE OF POTASH	7778-50-9	PST19370
BICYCLO(2.2.1)HEPT-2-ENE, 1,2,3,4,7,7-HEXACHLORO-5,6-BIS(CHLOROMETHYL)	2550-75-6	PST73193
BIDERON	34643-46-4	PST72655
BIDRIN	141-66-2	PST03090
BIF	7681-38-1	PST20990
BIFENOX	42576-02-3	PST72332
BIFORMYLCHLORAZIN	26644-46-2	PST24086
BILEVON	70-30-4	PST10780
BINAPACRYL	485-31-4	PST71960
BINNELL	1861-40-1	PST02570
BIOALLETHRIN	584-79-2	PST00550
BIOALLETHRIN	UNASSIGNED	PST00553
BIOALLETHRIN	28434-00-6	PST71013
BIOBAN-S	137-40-6	PST21575
BIOCALC	1305-62-0	PST03980
BIOMET	1983-10-4	PST72227
BIONEOPYNAMIN	7696-12-0	PST23061
BIONOL	8001-54-5	PST00537
BIOPERMETHRIN	51877-74-8	PST23708
BIOQUIN	148-24-3	PST30450
BIORESMETHRIN	28434-01-7	PST20093
BIOSIL	63231-67-4	PST20670
BIOSTAT	79-57-2	PST17414
BIOTETRAMETHRIN	1166-46-7	PST23063
BIOTHION	3383-96-8	PST00020

ALPHABETICAL INDEX

ALPHABETICAL INDEX

SUBSTANCE NAME	CAS #	PST #
BLACK LEAF 40	65-30-5	PST16459
BLACO-THANE (BARON-BLAKESLEE)	71-55-6	PST14370
BLADAFUM	3689-24-5	PST22470
BLADEX	21725-46-2	PST05762
BLATTANEX	114-26-1	PST02540
BLAZER	62476-59-9	PST72453
BLEACH LIQUOR	7681-52-9	PST21310
BLOTIC	31218-83-4	PST72440
BLUE COPPER	7758-98-7	PST05670
BLUE COPPER AS	7758-99-8	PST05690
BLUE SALT	10101-97-0	PST16410
BLUE VITRIOL	7758-98-7	PST05670
BLUE VITRIOL	7758-99-8	PST05690
BLUESTONE	7758-99-8	PST05690
BOLDSTAR O.A. SULFONE	42795-00-6	PST03231
BOLDSTAR OXON SULFONE (FORMULATION)	42795-00-6	PST03231
BOLERO	28249-77-6	PST72381
BOLSTAR	35400-43-2	PST22387
BOLSTAR OXYGEN ANALOG SULFONE	42795-00-6	PST03231
BOMYL	122-10-1	PST03240
BONALAN	1861-40-1	PST02570
BONAZEN	7733-02-0	PST25570
BONE OIL	8001-85-2	PST03250
BONOMOLD OP	94-13-3	PST19941
BOOSTER FUEL (HENES PRODUCT CORP.)	67-56-1	PST14280
BORACIC ACID	10043-35-3	PST03260
BORAX	1303-96-4	PST21010
BORAX (B4NA2O7.10H2O)	1303-96-4	PST21010
BORAX DECAHYDRATE	1303-96-4	PST21010
BORIC ACID	10043-35-3	PST03260
BORIC ACID (H3BO3)	10043-35-3	PST03260
BORIC ACID, DISODIUM SALT, DECAHYDRATE	1303-96-4	PST21010
BORIC ANHYDRIDE	1303-86-2	PST03290
BORIC OXIDE	1303-86-2	PST03290
BORIC OXIDE (B2O3)	1303-86-2	PST03290
BORIC TRIHYDROXIDE	10043-35-3	PST03260
BORON OXIDE	1303-86-2	PST03290
BORON OXIDE (B2O3)	1303-86-2	PST03290
BORON SESQUIOXIDE	1303-86-2	PST03290
BORON TRIOXIDE	1303-86-2	PST03290
BORTRYSAN	101-05-3	PST01526
BOTRAN	99-30-9	PST28910
BOTRILEX	82-68-8	PST18140
BOV	7664-93-9	PST22350
BP-223	108-39-4	PST13080
BP-325	124-65-2	PST21070
BP-612	100-02-7	PST17800
BP-648	9004-53-9	PST06363
BP-858	67-97-0	PST60913
BP-870	58-27-5	PST71050
BP-910	3810-74-0	PST84290
BP-916	1405-10-3	PST84263
BP-936	133-32-4	PST29325
BP-938	77-06-5	PST10405

ALPHABETICAL INDEX

SUBSTANCE NAME	CAS #	PST #
BP-942	525-79-1	PST72483
BPMC	3766-81-2	PST03324
BRASORAN	4658-28-0	PST02216
BRASSICOL	82-68-8	PST18140
BRAVO	1897-45-6	PST04890
BRELLIN	77-06-5	PST10405
BRESTAN	900-95-8	PST24378
BRESTANOL	639-58-7	PST24380
BRICK OIL	8001-58-9	PST05230
BRILLIANT BLUE	2650-18-2	PST08277
BRILLIANT BLUE FCF, DIAMMONIUM SALT	2650-18-2	PST08277
BRIMSTONE	7704-34-9	PST22280
BRITISH GUM	9004-53-9	PST06363
BRODIFACOUM	56073-10-0	PST03327
BROMACIL	314-40-9	PST03330
BROMADIOLONE	28772-56-7	PST03334
BROMAZIL	314-40-9	PST03330
BROMCHLOPHOS	300-76-5	PST06660
BROMEX	13360-45-7	PST04552
BROMEX	300-76-5	PST06660
BROMIDE SALT OF POTASSIUM	7758-02-3	PST19280
BROMIDE SALT OF SODIUM	7647-15-6	PST21060
BROMINAL	1689-84-5	PST03542
BROMINE	7726-95-6	PST03340
BROMINIL	1689-84-5	PST03542
BROMNATRIUM	7647-15-6	PST21060
BROMO SELTZER	62-44-2	PST18340
BROMOFUME (FORMULATION)	106-93-4	PST09380
BROMOGAS	74-83-9	PST14300
BROMOMETHANE	74-83-9	PST14300
BROMOPHOS	2104-96-3	PST71064
BROMOPHOS-ETHYL	4824-78-6	PST03458
BROMOPHOS-METHYL	2104-96-3	PST71064
BROMOVUR	2104-96-3	PST71064
BROMOXYNIL	1689-84-5	PST03542
BROMOXYNIL BUTYRATE	3861-41-4	PST71388
BROMOXYNIL N-OCTANOYL ESTER	1689-99-2	PST03543
BROMOXYNIL OCTANOATE	1689-99-2	PST03543
BROMOXYNIL OCTANOIC ACID ESTER	1689-99-2	PST03543
BROMOXYNILOCTANOATE	1689-99-2	PST03543
BROMPYRAZON	3042-84-0	PST72769
BROMPYRAZONE	3042-84-0	PST72769
BRONCO HERBICIDE	UNASSIGNED	PST03451
BRONOCOT	52-51-7	PST72832
BRONOPOL	52-51-7	PST72832
BRONOSOL	52-51-7	PST72832
BROWN COPPER OXIDE	1317-39-1	PST05470
BROXYNIL	1689-84-5	PST03542
BTC	53516-76-0	PST71834
BTC 471	8001-54-5	PST00539
BTC 824	8001-54-5	PST00537
BTS 40542	67747-09-5	PST72648
BUCTRIL	1689-84-5	PST03542
BUD NIP	101-21-3	PST71148

SUBSTANCE NAME	CAS #	PST #
BUFENCARB	8065-36-9	PST03480
BUFOPTO ZINC SULFATE	7733-02-0	PST25570
BULAN	117-26-0	PST71635
BUNT-CURE	118-74-1	PST10730
BUNT-NO-MORE	118-74-1	PST10730
BURIDAZOL	3878-19-1	PST73188
BURNT LIME	1305-78-8	PST04030
BUSAN	21564-17-0	PST71392
BUSAN 15	21564-17-0	PST71392
BUSAN 30	21564-17-0	PST71392
BUSAN 30-1	21564-17-0	PST71392
BUSAN 30A	21564-17-0	PST71392
BUSAN 30I	21564-17-0	PST71392
BUSAN 70	21564-17-0	PST71392
BUSAN 71	21564-17-0	PST71392
BUSAN 72	21564-17-0	PST71392
BUSAN 72A	21564-17-0	PST71392
BUSULFAN	55-98-1	PST03482
BUTACARB	2655-19-8	PST72994
BUTACARBE	2655-19-8	PST72994
BUTACHLOR	23184-66-9	PST03497
BUTACIDE	51-03-6	PST75640
BUTACLOR	23184-66-9	PST03497
BUTADIENE-FURFURAL COPOLYMER	126-15-8	PST71487
BUTALIN	33629-47-9	PST03525
BUTAM	35256-85-0	PST72852
BUTANE -1,3-DIOL	107-88-0	PST26730
BUTANE, 1,1-BIS(P-CHLOROPHENYL)-2-NITRO-	117-26-0	PST71635
BUTANEDIOIC ACID MONO(2,2-DIMETHYLHYDRAZIDE)	1596-84-5	PST06195
BUTANEDIOIC ACID, ((DIMETHOXYPHOSPHINOTHIOYL)THIO)-, DIETHYL ESTER	121-75-5	PST13540
BUTANEDIOIC ACID, ((DIMETHOXYPHOSPHINYL)THIO-, DIETHYL ESTER	1634-78-2	PST13541
BUTANEDIOIC ACID, MONO(2,2-DIMETHYLHYDRAZIDE)	1596-84-5	PST06195
BUTANEDIOIC ACID, SULFO-, 1,4-BIS(2-ETHYLHEXYL) ESTER, SODIUM SALT	577-11-7	PST00406
BUTANEX	23184-66-9	PST03497
BUTANOIC ACID, 2-AMINO-4(HYDROXYMETHYLPHOSPHINYL), MONOAMMONIUM SALT	77182-82-2	PST72647
BUTANOIC ACID, 2,2,2-TRICHLORO-1-(DIMETHOXYPHOSPHINYL)ETHYL ESTER	126-22-7	PST71399
BUTANOIC ACID, 2,6-DIBROMO-4-CYANOPHENYL ESTER	3861-41-4	PST71388
BUTANOIC ACID, 4-(2,4-DICHLOROPHENOXY)-, METHYL ESTER	18625-12-2	PST06227
BUTANOIC ACID, 4-(2,4,5-TRICHLOROPHENOXY)-	93-80-1	PST73203
BUTANONE	78-93-3	PST14460
BUTETHENOL	136-47-0	PST72269
BUTIFOS	78-48-8	PST06300
BUTILATE	2008-41-5	PST71474
BUTISAN	21267-72-1	PST73038
BUTISAN S	67129-08-2	PST14106
BUTOCARBOXIM	34681-10-2	PST73270
BUTOCIDE	51-03-6	PST75640
BUTONATE	126-22-7	PST71399
BUTOXICARBOXIM	34681-23-7	PST72434
BUTOXIDE	51-03-6	PST75640
BUTOXYCARBOXIM	34681-23-7	PST72434
BUTOXYCARBOXIME	34681-23-7	PST72434
BUTOXYPROPYL SILVEX	25537-26-2	PST72194
BUTOXYRHODANODIETHYL ETHER	112-56-1	PST75661

ALPHABETICAL INDEX

ALPHABETICAL INDEX

ALPHABETICAL INDEX

SUBSTANCE NAME	CAS #	PST #
CAPTAN	133-06-2	PST04210
CAPTANE	133-06-2	PST04210
CAPTAX	149-30-4	PST13738
CARAGARD	33693-04-8	PST72770
CARATHANE	39300-45-3	PST71402
CARBAM	137-42-8	PST71430
CARBAMIC ACID, ((DIBUTYLAMINO)THIO)METHYL-, 2,3-DIHYDRO-2,2-DIMETHYL-7-BENZOFURANYL ESTER	55285-14-8	PST72266
CARBAMIC ACID, ((4-AMINOPHENYL)SULFONYL)-, METHYL ESTER	3337-71-1	PST72352
CARBAMIC ACID, (MERCAPTOACETYL)METHYL-, ETHYL ESTER, S-ESTER WITH O,O-DIETHYL PHOSPHORODITHIOATE	2595-54-2	PST13675
CARBAMIC ACID, (MERCAPTOACETYL)METHYL-, METHYL ESTER, S-ESTER WITH O-METHYL METHYLPHOSPHONODITHIOATE	29173-31-7	PST73246
CARBAMIC ACID, (1-((BUTYLAMINO)CARBONYL)-1H-BENZIMIDAZOL-2-YL)-METHYL ESTER	17804-35-2	PST02580
CARBAMIC ACID, (1,1-DIMETHYLETHYL)-, 3-(((DIMETHYLAMINO)CARBONYL) AMINO)PHENYL ESTER	4849-32-5	PST72271
CARBAMIC ACID, (1,2-PHENYLENEBIS(IMINOCARBONOTHIOYL))BIS-, DIETHYL ESTER	23564-06-9	PST72322
CARBAMIC ACID, (1,2-PHENYLENEBIS(IMINOCARBONOTHIOYL))BIS-, DIMETHYL ESTER	23564-05-8	PST72308
CARBAMIC ACID, (2-(4-PHENOXYPHENOXY)ETHYL)-, ETHYL ESTER	72490-01-8	PST72618
CARBAMIC ACID, (3-(((PHENYLAMINO)CARBONYL)OXY)PHENYL)-, ETHYL ESTER	13684-56-5	PST72336
CARBAMIC ACID, (3-CHLOROPHENYL)-, 1-METHYL-2-PROPYNYL ESTER	1967-16-4	PST73265
CARBAMIC ACID, (3-CHLOROPHENYL)-, 1-METHYLETHYL ESTER	101-21-3	PST71148
CARBAMIC ACID, (3-CHLOROPHENYL)-, 4-CHLORO-2-BUTYNYL ESTER	101-27-9	PST71143
CARBAMIC ACID, (3-METHYL-5-(1-METHYLETHYL)PHENYL-, METHYL ESTER	2631-37-0	PST72957
CARBAMIC ACID, (3-METHYLPHENYL)-, 3-((METHOXYCARBONYL)AMINO)PHENYL ESTER	13684-63-4	PST72282
CARBAMIC ACID, (3,4-DICHLOROPHENYL)-, METHYL ESTER	1918-18-9	PST72247
CARBAMIC ACID, BUTYLETHYLTHIO-, S-PROPYL ESTER	1114-71-2	PST71472
CARBAMIC ACID, DIETHYLDITHIO, 2-CHLOROALLYL ESTER	95-06-7	PST22190
CARBAMIC ACID, DIETHYLTHIO-, S-(P-CHLOROBENZYL) ESTER	28249-77-6	PST72381
CARBAMIC ACID, DIETHYLTHIO-, S-ETHYL ESTER	2941-55-1	PST72327
CARBAMIC ACID, DIISOBUTYLTHIO-, S-ETHYL ESTER	2008-41-5	PST71474
CARBAMIC ACID, DIISOPROPYLTHIO-, S (2,3-DICHLOROALLYL) ESTER	2303-16-4	PST06480
CARBAMIC ACID, DIISOPROPYLTHIO-, S-(2,3,3-TRICHLOROALLYL) ESTER	2303-17-5	PST72050
CARBAMIC ACID, DIMETHYL-, ESTER WITH 3-HYDROXY-N,N,5-TRIMETHYLPYRAZOLE -1-CARBOXAMIDE	644-64-4	PST83057
CARBAMIC ACID, DIMETHYL-, 1-((DIMETHYLAMINO)CARBONYL)-5-METHYL-1H -PYRAZOL-2-YL ESTER	644-64-4	PST83057
CARBAMIC ACID, DIMETHYL-, 1-ISOPROPYL-3-METHYLPYRAZOL-5-YL ESTER	119-38-0	PST83027
CARBAMIC ACID, DIMETHYL-, 2-(DIMETHYLAMINO)-5,6-DIMETHYL-4-PYRIMIDINYL ESTER	23103-98-2	PST72345
CARBAMIC ACID, DIMETHYL-, 3-METHYL-1-(1-METHYLETHYL)-1H-PYRAZOL-5-YL ESTER	119-38-0	PST83027
CARBAMIC ACID, DIMETHYL-, 3-METHYL-1-PHENYL-1H-PYRAZOL-5-YL ESTER	87-47-8	PST73263
CARBAMIC ACID, DIMETHYL-, 3-METHYL-1-PHENYLPYRAZOL-5-YL ESTER	87-47-8	PST73263
CARBAMIC ACID, DIMETHYL-, 6-METHYL-2-PROPYL-4-PYRIMIDINYL ESTER	2532-49-2	PST73266
CARBAMIC ACID, DIMETHYLDITHIO-, SODIUM SALT	128-04-1	PST71383
CARBAMIC ACID, DIPROPYLTHIO-, S-ETHYL ESTER	759-94-4	PST71470
CARBAMIC ACID, DIPROPYLTHIO-, S-PROPYL ESTER	1929-77-7	PST71473
CARBAMIC ACID, ETHYLENEBIS(DITHIO , MANGANESE ZINC COMPLEX	8018-01-7	PST71120
CARBAMIC ACID, ETHYLENEBIS(DITHIO-, DISODIUM SALT	142-59-6	PST16080

SUBSTANCE NAME	CAS #	PST #
CARBAMOTHIOIC ACID, CYCLOHEXYLETHYL-, S-ETHYL ESTER	1134-23-2	PST71469
CARBAMOTHIOIC ACID, DIETHYL-, S-((4-CHLOROPHENYL)METHYL) ESTER	28249-77-6	PST72381
CARBAMOTHIOIC ACID, DIETHYL-, S-ETHYL ESTER	2941-55-1	PST72327
CARBAMOTHIOIC ACID, DIPROPYL-, S-ETHYL ESTER	759-94-4	PST71470
CARBAMOTHIOIC ACID, DIPROPYL-, S-PROPYL ESTER	1929-77-7	PST71473
CARBAMOTHIOIC ACID, S,S'-(2-(SIMETHYLAMINO)-1,3-PROPANEDIYL) ESTER, MONOHYDROCHLORIDE	15263-52-2	PST04359
CARBAMULT	2631-37-0	PST72957
CARBANILIC ACID, ISOPROPYL ESTER	122-42-9	PST71564
CARBANILIC ACID, M-CHLORO-, ISOPROPYL ESTER	101-21-3	PST71148
CARBANILIC ACID, M-CHLORO-, 1-METHYL-2-PROPYNYL ESTER	1967-16-4	PST73265
CARBANILIC ACID, M-CHLORO-, 4-CHLORO-2-BUTYNYL ESTER	101-27-9	PST71143
CARBANILIC ACID, M-HYDROXY-, ETHYL ESTER, CARBANILATE (ESTER)	13684-56-5	PST72336
CARBANILIC ACID, M-HYDROXY-, METHYL ESTER, M-METHYLCARBANILATE (ESTER)	13684-63-4	PST72282
CARBANILIC ACID, 3-ISOPROPYL-5-METHYL-, METHYL ESTER	2631-37-0	PST72957
CARBANILIC ACID, 3,4-DICHLORO, METHYL ESTER	1918-18-9	PST72247
CARBANOLATE	671-04-5	PST02250
CARBARYL	63-25-2	PST04220
CARBATENE	9006-42-2	PST71123
CARBAZINC	137-30-4	PST25397
CARBETAMEX	16118-49-3	PST72941
CARBETAMIDE	16118-49-3	PST72941
CARBETHAMIDE	16118-49-3	PST72941
CARBICRON	141-66-2	PST03090
CARBIMIDE	420-04-2	PST05760
CARBINOL	67-56-1	PST14280
CARBOFENOTHION	786-19-6	PST04340
CARBOFENOTHION SULFOXIDE	17297-40-4	PST04345
CARBOFENTHION	786-19-6	PST04340
CARBOFURAN	1563-66-2	PST04240
CARBOFURAN-3-KETO-7-PHENOL	17781-16-7	PST72799
CARBOLIC ACID	108-95-2	PST18380
CARBOMER	9003-01-4	PST04349
CARBON CHLORIDE (CCL4)	56-23-5	PST04310
CARBON ELEMENT	7440-44-0	PST04246
CARBON TETRACHLORIDE	56-23-5	PST04310
CARBON-12	7440-44-0	PST04246
CARBON, ACTIVATED	7440-44-0	PST04246
CARBONIC ACID MONOSODIUM SALT	144-55-8	PST20970
CARBONIC ACID SODIUM SALT	497-19-8	PST21080
CARBONIC ACID SODIUM SALT (1:1)	144-55-8	PST20970
CARBONIC ACID SODIUM SALT (1:2)	497-19-8	PST21080
CARBONIC ACID 1-METHYLETHYL 2-(1-METHYLPROPYL)-4,6-DINITROPHENYL ESTER	973-21-7	PST07990
CARBONIC ACID 2-SEC-BUTYL-4,6-DINITROPHENYL ISOPROPYL ESTER	973-21-7	PST07990
CARBONIC ACID, DIPOTASSIUM SALT	584-08-7	PST19290
CARBONIC ACID, DISODIUM SALT	497-19-8	PST21080
CARBONIC ACID, 1-METHYLETHYL 2-(1-METHYLPROPYL)-4,6-DINITROPHENYL ESTER	973-21-7	PST07990
CARBONIC ACID, 2-SEC-BUTYL-4,6-DINITROPHENYL ISOPROPYL ESTER	973-21-7	PST07990
CARBOPHENOTHION	786-19-6	PST04340
CARBOPHENOTHION METHYL	953-17-3	PST71647
CARBOPHENOTHION OXON	7173-84-4	PST04341
CARBOPHENOTHION OXON SULFOXIDE	16662-86-5	PST04343
CARBOPHENOTHION OXYGEN ANALOG	7173-84-4	PST04341

ALPHABETICAL INDEX

ALPHABETICAL INDEX

SUBSTANCE NAME	CAS #	PST #
CEDRUS ATLANTICA OIL	8000-27-9	PST04365
CEKUMETA	108-62-3	PST14090
CELA S 1942	2104-96-3	PST71064
CELA W 524	26644-46-2	PST24086
CELFUME	74-83-9	PST14300
CELMONE	86-87-3	PST26130
CELON ATH	60-00-4	PST09570
CELON E	64-02-8	PST23137
CELPHOS	20859-73-8	PST00970
CEPA	16672-87-0	PST72293
CEPHALON	330-55-2	PST12826
CEQUARTYL	8001-54-5	PST00539
CERCOBIN	23564-06-9	PST72322
CERCOBIN M	23564-05-8	PST72308
CERCOBIN METHYL	23564-05-8	PST72308
CERTOX	57-24-9	PST22080
CES	140-57-8	PST01850
CET	122-34-9	PST20837
CETOL	36653-82-4	PST04525
CETYL ALCOHOL	36653-82-4	PST04525
CETYLIC ALCOHOL	36653-82-4	PST04525
CEVADINE MIXTURE WITH VERATRIDINE	8051-02-3	PST71010
CF 12	75-71-8	PST06880
CFC 11	75-69-4	PST09990
CFC 12	75-71-8	PST06880
CGA 15324	41198-08-7	PST72412
CGA 15646	15545-48-9	PST04912
CGA 17020	50563-36-5	PST07677
CGA 18731	34123-59-6	PST12254
CGA 45156	59669-26-0	PST72456
CGA 72662	66215-27-8	PST72536
CGA-12223	42509-80-8	PST15035
CGA-18762	32889-48-8	PST72398
CGA-24705	51218-45-2	PST15003
CHAMELEON MINERAL	7722-64-7	PST19520
CHEELOX	60-00-4	PST09570
CHEELOX BF-12	64-02-8	PST23137
CHELAPLEX	139-33-3	PST08305
CHEM BAM	142-59-6	PST16080
CHEM-HOE (FORMULATION)	122-42-9	PST71564
CHEMAGRO B-1776	78-48-8	PST06300
CHEMAID	124-65-2	PST21070
CHEMCOLOX 200	64-02-8	PST23137
CHEMCOLOX 340	60-00-4	PST09570
CHEMFORM	57-92-1	PST21917
CHEMICAL 109	86-88-4	PST01830
CHEMOCIDE PK	94-13-3	PST19941
CHEMOX	88-85-7	PST08020
CHILE SALTPETER	7631-99-4	PST21400
CHINA GREEN	569-64-2	PST13533
CHINALPHOS	13593-03-8	PST73112
CHINESE BEAN OIL	8001-22-7	PST21765
CHINESE WHITE	1314-13-2	PST25490
CHINORTO	311-45-5	PST07200

ALPHABETICAL INDEX

SUBSTANCE NAME	CAS #	PST #
CHINUFUR	1563-66-2	PST04240
CHIP-CAL	7778-44-1	PST03850
CHIP-CAL GRANALAR	7778-44-1	PST03850
CHIPMAN R-6,199	3734-97-2	PST71642
CHLOR IPC	101-21-3	PST71148
CHLOR-O-PIC	76-06-2	PST04830
CHLORACID	103-17-3	PST71139
CHLORALLYL DIETHYLDITHIOCARBAMATE	95-06-7	PST22190
CHLORALOSANE	15879-93-3	PST00775
CHLORAMBEN	133-90-4	PST29084
CHLORAMBEN AMMONIUM SALT	1076-46-6	PST71252
CHLORAMBEN METHYL	7286-84-2	PST71255
CHLORAMBEN METHYL ESTER	7286-84-2	PST71255
CHLORAMBEN, SODIUM SALT	1954-81-0	PST71256
CHLORAMBENE	133-90-4	PST29084
CHLORANIL	118-75-2	PST72136
CHLORANOCRYL	2164-09-2	PST71378
CHLORATE OF SODA	7775-09-9	PST21100
CHLORATE SALT OF SODIUM	7775-09-9	PST21100
CHLORAZIN	580-48-3	PST72143
CHLORAZINE	580-48-3	PST72143
CHLORBENSID	103-17-3	PST71139
CHLORBENSIDE	103-17-3	PST71139
CHLORBENZYLATE	510-15-6	PST04740
CHLORBICYCLEN	2550-75-6	PST73193
CHLORBROMURON	13360-45-7	PST04552
CHLORBUFAM	1967-16-4	PST73265
CHLORBUFAME	1967-16-4	PST73265
CHLORBUPHAM	1967-16-4	PST73265
CHLORCARAGARD	5915-41-3	PST22536
CHLORCHOLINE CHLORIDE	999-81-5	PST71147
CHLORDAN	12789-03-6	PST71948
CHLORDANE	5103-71-9	PST00776
CHLORDANE	57-74-9	PST04560
CHLORDANE	5103-74-2	PST10331
CHLORDANE	12789-03-6	PST71948
CHLORDANE (COMMERCIAL)	12789-03-6	PST71948
CHLORDECONE	143-50-0	PST12330
CHLORDENE	3734-48-3	PST04565
CHLORDENE	56534-02-2	PST04566
CHLORDENE	56641-38-4	PST04567
CHLORDIMEFORM	6164-98-3	PST04570
CHLORDIMEFORM HYDROCHLORIDE	19750-95-9	PST71656
CHLORDIMEFORM MONOHYDROCHLORIDE	19750-95-9	PST71656
CHLOREAL	87-90-1	PST23860
CHLORETHEPHON	16672-87-0	PST72293
CHLORFENIDIM	150-68-5	PST15196
CHLORFENVINPHOS	470-90-6	PST04575
CHLORFLURAZOLE	3615-21-2	PST73047
CHLORFLURECOL	2536-31-4	PST72283
CHLORFLURECOL METHYL ESTER	2536-31-4	PST72283
CHLORFLURECOL-METHYL	2536-31-4	PST72283
CHLORFLURENOL	2536-31-4	PST72283
CHLORFLURENOL METHYL ESTER	2536-31-4	PST72283

ALPHABETICAL INDEX

SUBSTANCE NAME	CAS #	PST #
CHLOROTHION	500-28-7	PST71379
CHLOROTOLURON	15545-48-9	PST04912
CHLOROTRIBUTYLSTANNANE	1461-22-9	PST72222
CHLOROTRIBUTYLTIN	1461-22-9	PST72222
CHLOROTRIPHENYL-STANNANE	639-58-7	PST24380
CHLOROTRIPHENYLSTANNANE	639-58-7	PST24380
CHLOROTRIPHENYLTIN	639-58-7	PST24380
CHLOROUS ACID, SODIUM SALT	7758-19-2	PST21110
CHLOROXIFENIDIM	1982-47-4	PST04905
CHLOROXURON	1982-47-4	PST04905
CHLOROXYLENOL	88-04-0	PST72258
CHLORPARACIDE	103-17-3	PST71139
CHLORPENTAN	2307-68-8	PST71164
CHLORPHACINONE	3691-35-8	PST04826
CHLORPHENACONE	3691-35-8	PST04826
CHLORPHENAMIDINE	6164-98-3	PST04570
CHLORPHENAMIDINE MONOHYDROCHLORIDE	19750-95-9	PST71656
CHLORPROPHAM	101-21-3	PST71148
CHLORPYRIFOS	2921-88-2	PST04910
CHLORPYRIFOS OXON	5598-15-2	PST04911
CHLORPYRIFOS OXYGEN ANALOG	5598-15-2	PST04911
CHLORPYRIFOS-METHYL	5598-13-0	PST71652
CHLORPYRIFOXON	5598-15-2	PST04911
CHLORPYRIPHOS	2921-88-2	PST04910
CHLORPYRIPHOXON	5598-15-2	PST04911
CHLORSULFURON	64902-72-3	PST72504
CHLORSULPHACIDE	103-17-3	PST71139
CHLORTEN	71-55-6	PST14370
CHLORTHAL DIMETHYL	1861-32-1	PST04913
CHLORTHAL DIMETHYL ESTER	1861-32-1	PST04913
CHLORTHAL-DIMETHYL	1861-32-1	PST04913
CHLORTHAL-METHYL	1861-32-1	PST04913
CHLORTHIAMID	1918-13-4	PST73046
CHLORTHIAMIDE	1918-13-4	PST73046
CHLORTHION	500-28-7	PST71379
CHLORTHION METHYL	500-28-7	PST71379
CHLORTHIOPHOS	60238-56-4	PST64913
CHLORTOLURON	15545-48-9	PST04912
CHLORYL RADICAL	10049-04-4	PST04610
CHNAO3	144-55-8	PST20970
CHOLECALCIFEROL	67-97-0	PST60913
CHROMIC ACID	7738-94-5	PST04930
CHROMIC ACID (H2CR207), DISODIUM SALT	10588-01-9	PST21190
CHROMIC ACID, DIPOTASSIUM SALT	7778-50-9	PST19370
CHROMIC ACID, SOLUTION	7738-94-5	PST04930
CHROMIC(VI) ACID	7738-94-5	PST04930
CHROMIUM SODIUM OXIDE (CR3NA207)	10588-01-9	PST21190
CHROMIUM TRIOXIDE, SOLUTION	7738-94-5	PST04930
CHRYSANTHEMUMMONOCARBOXYLIC ACID ESTER WITH 3-(2-CYCLOPENTEN-1-YL) -2-METHYL-4-OXO-2-CYCLOPENTEN-1-OL	97-11-0	PST19949
CHRYSON	10453-86-8	PST20095
CHWASTOX F	94-74-6	PST27880
CHWASTOX 30	94-74-6	PST27880
CH2CL2	75-09-2	PST14930

ALPHABETICAL INDEX

SUBSTANCE NAME	CAS #	PST #
CH2N2	420-04-2	PST05760
CH2O	50-00-0	PST50003
CH4O	67-56-1	PST14280
CIAFOS	2636-26-2	PST72950
CIBA C 7019	4658-28-0	PST02216
CIBA 2059	2164-17-2	PST09907
CIBA 8514	6164-98-3	PST04570
CIBAZOL	72-14-0	PST72047
CIDEX	111-30-8	PST10423
CIDIAL	2597-03-7	PST72337
CINERIN	25402-06-6	PST05090
CINERIN I	25402-06-6	PST05090
CINERIN I ALLYL HOMOLOG	584-79-2	PST00550
CINNAMAL	104-55-2	PST05100
CINNAMALDEHYDE	104-55-2	PST05100
CINNAMIC ALDEHYDE	104-55-2	PST05100
CINNAMYL ALDEHYDE	104-55-2	PST05100
CIODRIN	7700-17-6	PST05115
CIPC	101-21-3	PST71148
CIS-ALLETHRIN	34624-48-1	PST00551
CIS-CHLORDAN	5103-71-9	PST00776
CIS-CHLORDANE	5103-71-9	PST00776
CIS-GARDONA	22248-79-9	PST72244
CIS-OCTADEC-9-ENOIC ACID	112-80-1	PST17305
CIS-OLEIC ACID	112-80-1	PST17305
CIS-11-HEXADECENAL	53939-28-9	PST72519
CIS-9-OCTADECENOIC	112-80-1	PST17305
CIS-9-TRICOSENE	27519-02-4	PST05185
CISMETHRIN	35764-59-1	PST20094
CITRAM	3734-97-2	PST71642
CITRAZON	29104-30-1	PST72988
CITRETTEN	77-92-9	PST05200
CITRIC ACID	77-92-9	PST05200
CITRIC ACID, COPPER SALT	10402-15-0	PST71496
CITRO	77-92-9	PST05200
CITRONELLA	8000-29-1	PST71180
CITRONELLA OIL	8000-29-1	PST71180
CKN	151-50-8	PST19350
CL 12150	34123-59-6	PST12254
CL 26691	115-93-5	PST06135
CL 47470	950-10-7	PST13735
CL 64475	21548-32-3	PST16141
CLAROSAN	886-50-0	PST22538
CLCLETHRIN	97-11-0	PST19949
CLEAR LACQUER 1830 (RAFFI AND SWANSON, INC.)	628-63-7	PST15270
CLEWAT	60-00-4	PST09570
CLH	7647-01-0	PST11150
CLHONA1	7681-52-9	PST21310
CLIMBAZOL	38083-17-9	PST05208
CLIMBAZOLE	38083-17-9	PST05208
CLNA	7647-14-5	PST21105
CLNAO3	7775-09-9	PST21100
CLOETHOCARB	51487-69-5	PST72572
CLONT	443-48-1	PST72529

ALPHABETICAL INDEX

SUBSTANCE NAME	CAS #	PST #
COPPER CITRATE	10402-15-0	PST71496
COPPER DICHLORIDE DIHYDRATE	10125-13-0	PST05625
COPPER DIHYDROXIDE	20427-59-2	PST05640
COPPER DINITRATE	3251-23-8	PST05644
COPPER DUST	7440-50-8	PST05430
COPPER FUME	7440-50-8	PST05430
COPPER HYDROXIDE	20427-59-2	PST05640
COPPER MESOSULFATE	10257-54-2	PST05675
COPPER MONOSULFATE	7758-98-7	PST05670
COPPER MONOTHIOCYANATE	1111-67-7	PST71224
COPPER MONOXIDE	1317-38-0	PST05655
COPPER NAPHTHENATE	1338-02-9	PST05460
COPPER NARDOX	1317-39-1	PST05470
COPPER OXIDE	1317-39-1	PST05470
COPPER OXIDE	1317-38-0	PST05655
COPPER OXIDE (CUO)	1317-38-0	PST05655
COPPER SLAG-AIRBORNE	7440-50-8	PST05430
COPPER SLAG-MILLED	7440-50-8	PST05430
COPPER SUBOXIDE	1317-39-1	PST05470
COPPER SULFATE	7758-98-7	PST05670
COPPER SULFATE SUPERFINE XTLS (ASHLAND CHEMICAL COMPANY)	7758-98-7	PST05670
COPPER SULPHATE	7758-99-8	PST05690
COPPER THIOCYANATE	1111-67-7	PST71224
COPPER THIOCYANATE (CU(NCS))	1111-67-7	PST71224
COPPER UVERSOL	1338-02-9	PST05460
COPPER(I) OXIDE	1317-39-1	PST05470
COPPER(II) HYDROXIDE	20427-59-2	PST05640
COPPER(II) NITRATE	3251-23-8	PST05644
COPPER(II) OXALATE	814-91-5	PST05650
COPPER(II) OXIDE	1317-38-0	PST05655
COPPER(II) OXIDE(CUO)	1317-38-0	PST05655
COPPER(II) SULFATE, PENTAHYDRATE	7758-99-8	PST05690
COPPER(II) SULFATE, PENTAHYDRATE (1:1:5)	7758-99-8	PST05690
COPPER(II)SULFATE	7758-98-7	PST05670
COPPER(1+) OXIDE	1317-39-1	PST05470
COPPER(1+) THIOCYANATE	1111-67-7	PST71224
COPPER(2+) HYDROXIDE	20427-59-2	PST05640
COPPER(2+) NITRATE	3251-23-8	PST05644
COPPER(2+) OXIDE	1317-38-0	PST05655
COPPER(2+) SULFATE, PENTAHYDRATE	7758-99-8	PST05690
COPPER(2+), BIS(1,2-ETHANEDIAMINE-N,N')-	13426-91-0	PST05710
COPPER-AIRBORNE	7440-50-8	PST05430
COPPER-BRONZE	7440-50-8	PST05430
COPPER-ETHYLENEDIAMINE COMPLEX	13426-91-0	PST05710
COPPER-MILLED	7440-50-8	PST05430
COPPER-SANDOZ	1317-39-1	PST05470
COPPERAS	7782-63-0	PST09870
COPPERFINE-ZINC	7758-99-8	PST05690
CORALOX	321-54-0	PST65468
CORBAN	2921-88-2	PST04910
CORBIT	84-65-1	PST01600
CORN DEXTRIN	9004-53-9	PST06363
CORNOX CWK	3813-05-6	PST72725
CORONA WIRE CLEANER (CANON BUSINESS MACHINES)	67-63-0	PST12090

SUBSTANCE NAME	CAS #	PST #
COROXON	321-54-0	PST65468
COROZATE	137-30-4	PST25397
CORROSIVE MERCURY CHLORIDE	7487-94-7	PST13800
CORROSIVE SUBLIMATE	7487-94-7	PST13800
CORRY'S SLUG DEATH	108-62-3	PST14090
CORTILAN-NEU	57-74-9	PST04560
CORTILAN-NEU	12789-03-6	PST71948
COSAN	7704-34-9	PST22280
COSAN T	133-07-3	PST10012
COSBAN	2655-14-3	PST25171
COTOFILM	70-30-4	PST10780
COTOFOR	4147-51-7	PST72333
COTORAN	2164-17-2	PST09907
COTTON OIL	8001-29-4	PST05475
COTTON SEED OIL	8001-29-4	PST05475
COTTONEX	2164-17-2	PST09907
COTTONSEED OIL	8001-29-4	PST05475
COTTONSEED OIL (DEODERIZED WINTERIZED)	8001-29-4	PST05475
COTTONSEED OIL REFINED	8001-29-4	PST05475
COULOMATIC (R) CONDITIONER SOLUTION	67-56-1	PST14280
COUMADIN	129-06-6	PST83008
COUMAFENE	81-81-2	PST25090
COUMAFENE SODIUM	129-06-6	PST83008
COUMAFURYL	117-52-2	PST05476
COUMAPHEN	81-81-2	PST25090
COUMAPHOS	56-72-4	PST05490
COUMAPHOS O-ANALOG	321-54-0	PST65468
COUMAPHOSOXON	321-54-0	PST65468
COUMARIN, 3-(ALPHA-(P-(P-BROMOPHENYL)-BETA-HYDROXYPHENETHYL)BENZYL)-4-HYDROXY-	28772-56-7	PST03334
COUMARIN, 3-(ALPHA-ACETONYLBENZYL)-4-HDYROXY-, SODIUM SALT	129-06-6	PST83008
COUMARIN, 3-(ALPHA-ACETONYLBENZYL)-4-HYDROXY-	81-81-2	PST25090
COUMARIN, 3-(ALPHA-ACETONYLFURFURYL)-4-HYDROXY-	117-52-2	PST05476
COUMARIN, 3-CHLORO-7-HYDROXY-4-METHYL-,O-ESTER WITH O,O-DIETHYL PHOSPHOROTHIOATE	56-72-4	PST05490
COUMARIN, 4-HYDROXY-3-(1,2,3,4-TETRAHYDRO-1-NAPHTHYL)-	5836-29-3	PST05493
COUMATETRALYL	5836-29-3	PST05493
COUMITHOATE	572-48-5	PST73073
COUNTER	13071-79-9	PST22545
COUNTER OXYGEN ANALOG SULFONE	56070-15-6	PST22537
COUTAVERM	92-84-2	PST18400
CP 14,957	297-78-9	PST83032
CP 15336	2303-16-4	PST06480
CP 17029	845-52-3	PST72212
CP 19699	13067-93-1	PST05805
CP 23426	2303-17-5	PST72050
CP 31393	1918-16-7	PST19686
CP 4,742	95-06-7	PST22190
CP 40294	2665-30-7	PST73278
CP 50144	15972-60-8	PST00506
CP 53619	23184-66-9	PST03497
CP 53926	2540-82-1	PST10081
CP 6,343	93-71-0	PST71155
CPBS	80-38-6	PST09677

ALPHABETICAL INDEX

ALPHABETICAL INDEX

ALPHABETICAL INDEX

SUBSTANCE NAME	CAS #	PST #
C10H13CLN6	32889-48-8	PST72398
C10H13CL2FN202S2	731-27-1	PST73030
C10H13NO2	62-44-2	PST18340
C10H13NO2	2655-14-3	PST25171
C10H13NO2	122-42-9	PST71564
C10H14CL2NO2PS	299-85-4	PST71236
C10H14CL2N2	19750-95-9	PST71656
C10H14CL6N402	26644-46-2	PST24086
C10H14NO5PS	56-38-2	PST18040
C10H14N2NA208	139-33-3	PST08305
C10H140	98-54-4	PST17440
C10H14ON2	UNASSIGNED	PST02581
C10H1504PS	6552-12-1	PST02551
C10H1504PS2	3761-41-9	PST02555
C10H1505PS	6552-13-2	PST02553
C10H1505PS2	3761-42-0	PST02554
C10H1506PS	14086-35-2	PST02552
C10H1503PS2	55-38-9	PST02550
C10H16NO5PS2	52-85-7	PST09675
C10H16N208	60-00-4	PST09570
C10H16N402	UNASSIGNED	PST06336
C10H16N403	644-64-4	PST83057
C10H17CL2NOS	2303-16-4	PST06480
C10H17N204PS	38260-54-7	PST73148
C10H17N205P	UNASSIGNED	PST09666
C10H17N302	55861-78-4	PST72586
C10H17N302	119-38-0	PST83027
C10H18N404S3	59669-26-0	PST72456
C10H19N204PS	3734-95-0	PST72949
C10H19N50	1610-18-0	PST19967
C10H19N204PS	26259-45-0	PST73051
C10H19N5S	7287-19-6	PST19968
C10H19N5S	886-50-0	PST22538
C10H19N50	33693-04-8	PST72770
C10H1907PS	1634-78-2	PST13541
C10H19PS206	121-75-5	PST13540
C10H20NO4PS	31218-83-4	PST72440
C10H220	112-30-1	PST06285
C10H4CL80	27304-13-8	PST17372
C10H5CL7	76-44-8	PST10660
C10H5CL70	1024-57-3	PST10670
C10H5CL9	39765-80-5	PST23079
C10H6CL404	1861-32-1	PST04913
C10H6CL6	3734-48-3	PST04565
C10H6CL6	56534-02-2	PST04566
C10H6CL6	56641-38-4	PST04567
C10H6CL8	5103-71-9	PST00776
C10H6CL8	57-74-9	PST04560
C10H6CL8	5103-74-2	PST10331
C10H6CL8	12789-03-6	PST71948
C10H7BRN30	3042-84-0	PST72769
C10H8CLN30	1698-60-8	PST71928
C10H9CL2NO	2164-09-2	PST71378
C10H9CL303	4841-20-7	PST20831

ALPHABETICAL INDEX

SUBSTANCE NAME	CAS #	PST #
C11H22N2O	2163-69-1	PST05996
C11H22O	112-12-9	PST14675
C11H26NO2PS	50782-69-9	PST83104
C11H9BR2NO2	3861-41-4	PST71388
C11H9CL2NO2	101-27-9	PST71143
C12H10O	90-43-7	PST18470
C12H10O2	86-87-3	PST26130
C12H11BHGO3	6273-99-0	PST71754
C12H11CL2NO	23950-58-5	PST19670
C12H11N	122-39-4	PST08100
C12H12CLNO	21267-72-1	PST73038
C12H12CLN5O4S	64902-72-3	PST72504
C12H12N2.2BR	85-00-7	PST08250
C12H13CLN2O	3766-60-7	PST03523
C12H13NO2S	5234-68-4	PST04348
C12H13NO4S	5259-88-1	PST17373
C12H14CL2O3	94-80-4	PST71295
C12H14CL3O3PS	1757-18-2	PST00493
C12H14CL3O4P	470-90-6	PST04575
C12H14NO4PS	5131-24-8	PST72347
C12H14N2	4685-14-7	PST71671
C12H14N2.2CL	1910-42-5	PST18020
C12H14N2O6	2813-95-8	PST08021
C12H14N4O4S2	23564-05-8	PST72308
C12H15CLNO4PS2	2310-17-0	PST25720
C12H15NO3	1563-66-2	PST04240
C12H15NO4	16655-82-6	PST72800
C12H15N2O3PS	13593-03-8	PST73112
C12H15N2O3PS	14816-18-3	PST73292
C12H16CL2N2O	555-37-3	PST16143
C12H16N2O3	16118-49-3	PST72941
C12H16N3O3PS2	2642-71-9	PST02205
C12H17NAO7	52508-35-7	PST72391
C12H17NO	134-62-3	PST84230
C12H17NO2	3766-81-2	PST03324
C12H17NO2	2631-37-0	PST72957
C12H17N3O2	17702-57-7	PST73082
C12H17O4PS2	2597-03-7	PST72337
C12H18N2O	34123-59-6	PST12254
C12H18N2O2	315-18-4	PST15010
C12H18N4O6S	19044-88-3	PST17324
C12H18O4S2	50512-35-1	PST12253
C12H19CLNO3P	299-86-5	PST05550
C12H19O5PS2	42795-00-6	PST03231
C12H20N4O2	51235-04-2	PST10994
C12H20N4OS	57052-04-7	PST11844
C12H21N2O3PS	333-41-5	PST06540
C12H21N2O4P	962-58-3	PST06541
C12H23KO2	10124-65-9	PST72072
C12H23N5O2S	845-52-3	PST72212
C12H25NAO4S	151-21-3	PST08485
C12H26O	112-53-8	PST12500
C12H26O6P2S4	78-34-2	PST08050
C12H27CLSN	1461-22-9	PST72222

ALPHABETICAL INDEX

SUBSTANCE NAME	CAS #	PST #
C12H27FSN	1983-10-4	PST72227
C12H2805P2S2	3244-90-4	PST72135
C12H4CL402	1746-01-6	PST08060
C12H6CL3N03	1836-77-7	PST23865
C12H7CL2N03	1836-75-5	PST23580
C12H8CL202S	97-24-5	PST71737
C12H8CL203S	97-16-5	PST71350
C12H8CL6	309-00-2	PST00520
C12H8CL6	465-73-6	PST11810
C12H8CL60	60-57-1	PST07080
C12H8CL60	72-20-8	PST08600
C12H9CLF3N30	27314-13-2	PST72343
C12H9CL0	85-97-2	PST71680
C12H9CL02S	80-00-2	PST71663
C12H9CL03S	80-38-6	PST09677
C13H10BRCL203P	25006-32-0	PST12776
C13H10CL2	101-76-8	PST06321
C13H10CL202	97-23-4	PST71611
C13H10CL2S	103-17-3	PST71139
C13H12N403	53558-25-1	PST72334
C13H14F3N304	55283-68-6	PST72436
C13H15N302	87-47-8	PST73263
C13H16F3N304	1861-40-1	PST02570
C13H16F3N304	1582-09-8	PST24085
C13H16N04PS	18854-01-8	PST12280
C13H1602	126-15-8	PST71487
C13H18CLN0	2307-68-8	PST71164
C13H18CLN02	50563-36-5	PST07677
C13H18N202	2164-08-1	PST73238
C13H1805S	26225-79-6	PST72404
C13H19N02	8065-36-9	PST03480
C13H19N306S	4726-14-1	PST16525
C13H22N03PS	22224-92-6	PST16145
C13H22N04PS	31972-43-7	PST16146
C13H22N05PS	31972-44-8	PST16144
C13H22N20	18530-56-8	PST71400
C13H22N20	28805-78-9	PST73199
C13H7F3N205	15457-05-3	PST72248
C13H8CL20	90-98-2	PST06246
C13N18CLN0	7287-36-7	PST72987
C14H10CL202	83-05-6	PST06232
C14H10CL4	4329-12-8	PST04752
C14H10CL4	72-54-8	PST06240
C14H12CL20	2642-82-2	PST06323
C14H12F3N04S2	37924-13-3	PST72375
C14H12N402S	59-40-5	PST72046
C14H13CL2N202PS	4104-14-7	PST71150
C14H13CL202PS	3792-59-4	PST73239
C14H14N04PS	2104-64-5	PST08650
C14H1402	2122-70-5	PST71628
C14H1403	83-26-1	PST18970
C14H1403	83-28-3	PST24738
C14H15N506S	74223-64-6	PST72546
C14H16CLN30	67129-08-2	PST14106

SUBSTANCE NAME	CAS #	PST #
C14H16CLO5PS	56-72-4	PST05490
C14H16CLO6P	321-54-0	PST65468
C14H17CLNO4PS2	10311-84-9	PST23630
C14H17N2O4PS	119-12-0	PST71604
C14H18N2O7	973-21-7	PST07990
C14H18N4O3	17804-35-2	PST02580
C14H18N4O4S2	23564-06-9	PST72322
C14H19NO	91-53-2	PST08740
C14H20CLNO2	15972-60-8	PST00506
C14H20CLNO2	34256-82-1	PST72539
C14H20N2O	1982-49-6	PST20586
C14H20N2O8S2	2074-50-2	PST71670
C14H20N3O5PS	13457-18-6	PST73169
C14H21N3O3	4849-32-5	PST72271
C14H21N3O4	33629-47-9	PST03525
C14H24NO4PS3	741-58-2	PST02583
C14H24NO5PS2	UNASSIGNED	PST02582
C14H27KO2	13429-27-1	PST72073
C14H30O2SN	56-36-0	PST72220
C14H4N2O2S2	3347-22-6	PST72290
C14H6CLF3NANO5	62476-59-9	PST72453
C14H7CLF3NO5	50594-66-6	PST72452
C14H8CL4	3424-82-6	PST06245
C14H8CL4	72-55-9	PST06247
C14H9CLF2N2O2	35367-38-5	PST07388
C14H9CL2NO5	42576-02-3	PST72332
C14H9CL3	14835-94-0	PST04753
C14H9CL3	1022-22-6	PST06322
C14H9CL5	50-29-3	PST06250
C14H9CL5O	115-32-2	PST07010
C15H11CLF3NO4	42874-03-3	PST72413
C15H11CLF3NO4	69806-34-4	PST72580
C15H11CLO3	2536-31-4	PST72283
C15H15CLN2O2	1982-47-4	PST04905
C15H16CL3N3O2	67747-09-5	PST72648
C15H16N4O5S	74222-97-2	PST72544
C15H17BR2NO2	1689-99-2	PST03543
C15H17CLN2O2	38083-17-9	PST05208
C15H17I2NO2	3861-47-0	PST73075
C15H18CL2N2O3	19666-30-9	PST72385
C15H18N2O6	485-31-4	PST71960
C15H19CL2N3O	75736-33-3	PST07005
C15H19CL3O4	3084-62-6	PST22393
C15H19N3O3	81335-77-5	PST11308
C15H20CL2O4	1928-45-6	PST71294
C15H22CLNO2	51218-45-2	PST15003
C15H23NO	35256-85-0	PST72852
C15H24NO4PS	25311-71-1	PST11985
C15H25CLN2O2	136-47-0	PST72269
C15H25HGNO6	23319-66-6	PST71768
C16H13F3CLNO4	69806-40-2	PST72579
C16H13NO3	7091-57-8	PST71657
C16H14CL2N2O2	3134-12-1	PST72972
C16H14CL2O3	510-15-6	PST04740

ALPHABETICAL INDEX

SUBSTANCE NAME	CAS #	PST #
C16H15CL2NO2	117-26-0	PST71635
C16H15CL3O2	72-43-5	PST14220
C16H16NO6P	1491-41-4	PST72737
C16H16N2O4	13684-63-4	PST72282
C16H16N2O4	13684-56-5	PST72336
C16H17NO	957-51-7	PST71406
C16H18N2O3	14214-32-5	PST07386
C16H20O7P2S3	17210-55-8	PST71651
C16H22CLNO3	38727-55-8	PST72968
C16H22N2O2	6392-46-7	PST72977
C16H25NO2	2655-19-8	PST72994
C16H30O	53939-28-9	PST72519
C16H34O	36653-82-4	PST04525
C17H14O5	117-52-2	PST05476
C17H17N2	49866-87-7	PST72349
C17H19NO4	72490-01-8	PST72618
C17H21NO2	15299-99-7	PST72319
C17H21O5PS	572-48-5	PST73073
C17H24NNAO5	55635-13-7	PST72430
C17H26CLNO2	23184-66-9	PST03497
C17H29NO3S	74051-80-2	PST20577
C18HS9NAO3S	25155-30-0	PST21220
C18H12NANO3	132-67-2	PST71341
C18H13NO3	132-66-1	PST71340
C18H16CLNO5	66441-23-4	PST72723
C18H18CLNO5	29104-30-1	PST72988
C18H20CL2	72-56-0	PST71373
C18H20N2O4S	43222-48-6	PST72348
C18H24N2O6	39300-45-3	PST71402
C18H32O2	52207-99-5	PST72448
C18H33KO3	7492-30-0	PST72074
C18H34O2	112-80-1	PST17305
C19H15NAO4	129-06-6	PST83008
C19H16O3	5836-29-3	PST05493
C19H16O4	81-81-2	PST25090
C19H17CLN2O4	76578-14-8	PST20075
C19H20F3NO4	69806-50-4	PST72554
C19H20F3NO4	79241-46-6	PST72557
C19H21CLN2O	66063-05-6	PST72622
C19H21KO6	125-67-7	PST71492
C19H26O4S	2312-35-8	PST19720
C19H26O3	28434-00-6	PST71013
C19H30O5	51-03-6	PST75640
C19H39NO	24602-86-6	PST72537
C2CL3NAO2	650-51-1	PST73307
C2CL4	127-18-4	PST22900
C2HCL3O2	76-03-9	PST23810
C2H2O4	144-62-7	PST17360
C2H3CL3	71-55-6	PST14370
C2H3NS	556-61-6	PST14950
C2H4	74-85-1	PST09330
C2H4BR2	106-93-4	PST09380
C2H4CL2	107-06-2	PST09390
C2H4N2O2	557-30-2	PST73143

ALPHABETICAL INDEX

SUBSTANCE NAME	CAS #	PST #
C2H4N4	61-82-5	PST01040
C2H4O	75-21-8	PST09520
C2H4O2	64-19-7	PST00120
C2H5CLHG	107-27-7	PST09620
C2H6CLO3	16672-87-0	PST72293
C2H6O	64-17-5	PST08700
C2H6O2	107-21-1	PST09400
C2H7ASO2	75-60-5	PST03710
C2H7HGO4P	2235-25-8	PST71479
C2H7NO	141-43-5	PST08710
C2H7O4P	813-78-5	PST07882
C2H8N2	107-15-3	PST09560
C20H14O4	84-62-8	PST08095
C20H22N8O5	59-05-2	PST14210
C20H22N8O5	15475-56-6	PST14211
C20H28O3	25402-06-6	PST05090
C20H30N2O5S	82560-54-1	PST72562
C20H32N2O3S	55285-14-8	PST72266
C20H38NAO7S	577-11-7	PST00406
C20H48O8P4S8	37333-40-7	PST18807
C21H20CL2O3	51877-74-8	PST23708
C21H22N2O2	57-24-9	PST22080
C21H28O3	121-21-1	PST19960
C22H18CL2FNO3	68359-37-5	PST72630
C22H19BR2NO3	52918-63-5	PST72784
C22H19BR4NO3	66841-25-6	PST72538
C22H19CL2NO3	67375-30-8	PST06118
C22H19CL2NO3	52315-07-8	PST72392
C22H26O3	10453-86-8	PST20095
C22H28O5	121-29-9	PST19970
C22H40CLN	1330-85-4	PST71854
C23H15CLO3	3691-35-8	PST04826
C23H22O6	83-79-4	PST20200
C23H26O3	26002-80-2	PST71954
C24H38HGO2	104-60-9	PST71769
C24H38O4	117-84-0	PST08040
C24H38O4	117-81-7	PST06440
C24H40O8	5281-13-0	PST71828
C25H24F6N4	67485-29-4	PST01009
C26H58CLNO3SI	27668-52-6	PST72370
C27H42CLNO2	121-54-0	PST71851
C28H44CLNO2	25155-18-4	PST71862
C3H3CL2NAO2	127-20-8	PST71239
C3H4CLN5	UNASSIGNED	PST06504
C3H4CL2	542-75-6	PST26820
C3H4O	107-02-8	PST00330
C3H5BR2CL	96-12-8	PST26490
C3H5O2NA	137-40-6	PST21575
C3H6BRNO4	52-51-7	PST72832
C3H6HGN4	502-39-6	PST83040
C3H6O	67-64-1	PST00140
C3H6O2	79-09-4	PST19750
C3H7C12	78-87-5	PST19860
C3H8NO5P	1071-83-6	PST10515

ALPHABETICAL INDEX

SUBSTANCE NAME	CAS #	PST #
C3H8O	67-63-0	PST12090
C3H8O2	109-86-4	PST14340
C3H8O2	57-55-6	PST19870
C3H8O3	56-81-5	PST10440
C3H9NO2	34375-28-5	PST72288
C30H23BRO4	28772-56-7	PST03334
C31H23BRO3	56073-10-0	PST03327
C31H24O3	56073-07-5	PST07385
C4H10O	75-65-0	PST22630
C4H4KO7SB	28300-74-5	PST01690
C4H5NOS	2682-20-4	PST72362
C4H5NO2	10004-44-1	PST22404
C4H6NMN2S4	12427-38-2	PST13589
C4H6N2NA2S4	142-59-6	PST16080
C4H7CL2O4P	62-73-7	PST07000
C4H7NAO4	126-96-5	PST71497
C4H8HGO2	109-62-6	PST71476
C4H8O	78-93-3	PST14460
C4H8O2	141-78-6	PST08750
C4H9NO5	126-11-4	PST24430
C44H48CAN4O18	15251-48-6	PST84256
C47H70O14	65195-56-4	PST02156
C48H72O14	65195-55-3	PST72553
C5H10HGO3	151-38-2	PST83031
C5H10N2S2	533-74-4	PST06230
C5H10N2O2S	16752-77-5	PST14200
C5H11NO4	597-09-1	PST71953
C5H12CLO2PS2	24934-91-6	PST04655
C5H13CL2N	999-81-5	PST71147
C5H15N2O4P	77182-82-2	PST72647
C5H4O2	98-01-1	PST10180
C5H6CL6N2O3	116-52-9	PST06817
C5H8CLN5	UNASSIGNED	PST01011
C6CL4O2	118-75-2	PST72136
C6CL5ONA	131-52-2	PST08506
C6HCL4NO2	117-18-0	PST71616
C6HCL5O	87-86-5	PST18150
C6H10N6	66215-27-8	PST72536
C6H10O	108-94-1	PST05890
C6H12NNAO4	139-41-3	PST71447
C6H12NO3PS2	21548-32-3	PST16141
C6H12N2O3	1596-84-5	PST06195
C6H12N2S4	137-26-8	PST23430
C6H12N5O2PS2	78-57-9	PST72980
C6H12O	108-10-1	PST14550
C6H12O7	526-95-4	PST10408
C6H14FO3P	55-91-4	PST07590
C6H14O2	111-76-2	PST03540
C6H14O4	112-27-6	PST24000
C6H15NO3	102-71-6	PST23932
C6H15O3PS2	919-86-8	PST83065
C6H15O5PS2	17040-19-6	PST06319
C6H17N2O5P	38641-94-0	PST20205
C6H18ALO9P3	39148-24-8	PST72563

SUBSTANCE NAME	CAS #	PST #
C6H2CL2	95-50-1	PST16970
C6H2CL4O	25167-83-3	PST71689
C6H3CL2NO2	1702-17-6	PST05211
C6H3CL3N2O2	1918-02-1	PST18840
C6H3CL4N	1929-82-4	PST16530
C6H4CL2	106-46-7	PST17640
C6H4CL2N2O2	99-30-9	PST28910
C6H4N2O5	51-28-5	PST28620
C6H6CL6	319-84-6	PST00770
C6H6CL6	319-85-7	PST03010
C6H6CL6	608-73-1	PST03080
C6H6CL6	319-86-8	PST06310
C6H6CL6	58-89-9	PST12810
C6H6O	108-95-2	PST18380
C6H8O7	77-92-9	PST05200
C6H9N3O3	443-48-1	PST72529
C7H11N7S	4658-28-0	PST02216
C7H12CLN5	122-34-9	PST20837
C7H12N4O3S2	30043-49-3	PST72551
C7H13N2O4PS3	2669-32-1	PST73147
C7H13N3O2S	23135-22-0	PST17370
C7H14NO4PS2	29173-31-7	PST73246
C7H14N2O2S	116-06-3	PST00500
C7H14N2O2S	34681-10-2	PST73270
C7H14N2O3S	1646-87-3	PST00503
C7H14N2O4S	1646-88-4	PST72406
C7H14N2O4S	34681-23-7	PST72434
C7H15NOS	2941-55-1	PST72327
C7H16CLN	24307-26-4	PST72386
C7H16CLN3O2S2	15263-52-2	PST04359
C7H17O2PS3	36614-38-7	PST12275
C7H17O2PS3	298-02-2	PST18640
C7H17O3PS2	2600-69-3	PST18641
C7H17O3PS3	2588-03-6	PST18646
C7H17O4PS2	2588-05-8	PST18644
C7H17O4PS3	2588-04-7	PST18643
C7H17O5PS2	2588-06-9	PST18642
C7H2CL3NAO2	2078-42-4	PST71136
C7H3BR2NO	1689-84-5	PST03542
C7H3CL2N	1194-65-6	PST06800
C7H3CL3O2	50-31-7	PST71134
C7H3I2NNAO	2961-62-8	PST73074
C7H3I2NO	1689-83-4	PST11468
C7H4CL2NANO2	1954-81-0	PST71256
C7H4CL3NO3	55335-06-3	PST72472
C7H4F3NO3	88-30-2	PST71405
C7H5CL2NO2	133-90-4	PST29084
C7H5CL2NS	1918-13-4	PST73046
C7H5NS2	149-30-4	PST13738
C7H5N2NAO5	2312-76-7	PST71411
C7H6N2O5	534-52-1	PST07910
C7H6O	100-52-7	PST02590
C7H6O2	65-85-0	PST02720
C7H6O3	69-72-7	PST20315

ALPHABETICAL INDEX

SUBSTANCE NAME	CAS #	PST #
C9H10BRCLN2O2	13360-45-7	PST04552
C9H10CL2N2O	330-54-1	PST08420
C9H10CL2N2O2	330-55-2	PST12826
C9H10NO3PS	2636-26-2	PST72950
C9H11BRN2O2	3060-89-7	PST15008
C9H11CLN2O	150-68-5	PST15196
C9H11CLN2O2	1746-81-2	PST15174
C9H11CL2FN2O2S2	1085-98-9	PST73026
C9H11CL3NO3PS	2921-88-2	PST04910
C9H11CL3NO4P	5598-15-2	PST04911
C9H11NO2	94-09-7	PST72267
C9H12CLO2PS3	953-17-3	PST71647
C9H12N2O	101-42-8	PST09679
C9H13BRN2O2	314-40-9	PST03330
C9H13CLN2O2	5902-51-2	PST71099
C9H13CLN6	21725-46-2	PST05762
C9H14CLN5	22936-86-3	PST72296
C9H15O8P	122-10-1	PST03240
C9H16CLN5	139-40-2	PST19736
C9H16CLN5	5915-41-3	PST22536
C9H16CLN9	1912-26-1	PST23927
C9H16N4OS	64529-56-2	PST09111
C9H16N4OS	34014-18-1	PST72340
C9H17CLN3O3PS	42509-80-8	PST15035
C9H17NO2S	112-56-1	PST75661
C9H17N5O	1610-17-9	PST02148
C9H17N5S	834-12-8	PST01006
C9H18N2O2S	39196-18-4	PST23330
C9H19NOS	759-94-4	PST71470
C9H21O2PS3	13071-79-9	PST22545
C9H21O5PS2	56070-15-6	PST22537
C9H4CL8O	297-78-9	PST83032
C9H5CL3N4	101-05-3	PST01526
C9H6CLNO3S	3813-05-6	PST72725
C9H6CL2N2O3	20354-26-1	PST72344
C9H6CL6O3S	959-98-8	PST00800
C9H6CL6O3S	33213-65-9	PST03040
C9H6CL6O3S	115-29-7	PST08560
C9H6CL8	2550-75-6	PST73193
C9H7CL3O3	1928-37-6	PST22392
C9H8CL2O3	1928-38-7	PST71307
C9H8CL2O3	6597-78-0	PST73131
C9H8N4OS	51707-55-2	PST23299
C9H9NO4	5251-93-4	PST72964
C9H9N3OS	1929-88-0	PST72971
C9H9N3O2S2	72-14-0	PST72047
D AND C BLUE NO. 1	2650-18-2	PST08277
D 014	2312-35-8	PST19720
D 25 ANTIMYKOTIKUM	97-24-5	PST71737
D 735	5234-68-4	PST04348
D-(-)-N-ETHYL-2-(PHENYLCARBAMOYLOXY)PROPIONAMIDE	16118-49-3	PST72941
D-ALLETHRIN	584-79-2	PST00550
D-CIS-RESMETHRIN	35764-59-1	PST20094
D-GLUCONIC ACID	526-95-4	PST10408

ALPHABETICAL INDEX

SUBSTANCE NAME	CAS #	PST #
DDA	83-05-6	PST06232
DDA (DEGRADATION PRODUCT)	83-05-6	PST06232
DDA-P,P'	83-05-6	PST06232
DDBSA	27176-87-0	PST08480
DDD	72-54-8	PST06240
DDD-M,P'	4329-12-8	PST04752
DDE	3424-82-6	PST06245
DDE	72-55-9	PST06247
DDH	118-52-5	PST26800
DDM	101-76-8	PST06321
DDMU	1022-22-6	PST06322
DDOH	2642-82-2	PST06323
DDOM	2642-82-2	PST06323
DDT	50-29-3	PST06250
DDVP	62-73-7	PST07000
DE-GREEN	78-48-8	PST06300
DEAD OIL	8001-58-9	PST05230
DECABANE	1194-65-6	PST06800
DECACHLORO-OCTAHYDRO-1,3,4-METHENO-2H-CYCLOBUTA(CD)PENTALEN-2-ONE	143-50-0	PST12330
DECACHLOROKETONE	143-50-0	PST12330
DECACHLOROOCTAHYDRO-1,3,4-METHENO-2H-CYCLOBUTA(CD)PENTALEN-2-ONE	143-50-0	PST12330
DECAMETHRIN	52918-63-5	PST72784
DECANOL	112-30-1	PST06285
DECCO SALT NO 5	7673-09-8	PST80113
DECEMTHION	732-11-6	PST11307
DECHLORANE	2385-85-5	PST09690
DECIS	52918-63-5	PST72784
DECOFOL	115-32-2	PST07010
DECYL ALCOHOL	112-30-1	PST06285
DECYLIC ALCOHOL	112-30-1	PST06285
DED-WEED	75-99-0	PST06200
DED-WEED	93-72-1	PST20830
DEDEVAP	62-73-7	PST07000
DEET	134-62-3	PST84230
DEF	78-48-8	PST06300
DEF DEFOLIANT	78-48-8	PST06300
DEFENDION	60-51-5	PST07670
DEFTOR	19937-59-8	PST15009
DEGUMMED SOYBEAN OIL	8001-22-7	PST21765
DEHP	117-81-7	PST06440
DEIQUAT	85-00-7	PST08250
DEKETON	137-40-6	PST21575
DEKRYSIL	534-52-1	PST07910
DEKSONAL	140-56-7	PST73084
DELAN	3347-22-6	PST72290
DELAN-COL	3347-22-6	PST72290
DELIA	20859-73-8	PST00970
DELICIA	20859-73-8	PST00970
DELICIA GASTOXIN	20859-73-8	PST00970
DELNATEX	78-34-2	PST08050
DELNAV	78-34-2	PST08050
DELSTEROL	67-97-0	PST60913
DELTA	134-62-3	PST84230
DELTA-BENZENE HEXACHLORIDE	319-86-8	PST06310

ALPHABETICAL INDEX

ALPHABETICAL INDEX

SUBSTANCE NAME	CAS #	PST #
DEVRINOL	15299-99-7	PST72319
DEXON	140-56-7	PST73084
DEXOXON	140-56-7	PST73084
DEXTRID	9004-53-9	PST06363
DEXTRIN	9004-53-9	PST06363
DEXTRIN, CORN	9004-53-9	PST06363
DEXTRINE	9004-53-9	PST06363
DEXTRINS	9004-53-9	PST06363
DEXTRONIC ACID	526-95-4	PST10408
DFP	55-91-4	PST07590
DI(ETHYLHEXYL)PHTHALATE	117-81-7	PST06440
DI(P-CHLOROPHENYL)ACETIC ACID	83-05-6	PST06232
DI(P-CHLOROPHENYL)KETONE	90-98-2	PST06246
DI(P-CHLOROPHENYL)TRICHLOROMETHYLCARBINOL	115-32-2	PST07010
DI(P-ETHYLPHENYL)DICHLOROETHANE	72-56-0	PST71373
DI(2-ETHYLHEXYL) PHTHALATE	117-81-7	PST06440
DI-(2-ETHYLHEXYL)PHTHALATE	117-81-7	PST06440
DI-ALLATE	2303-16-4	PST06480
DI-BETA-HYDROXYETHOXYETHANE	112-27-6	PST24000
DI-ISOPROPYL 1,3-DITHIOLAN-2-YLIDENEMALONATE	50512-35-1	PST12253
DI-N-BUTYL PHTHALATE	84-74-2	PST06740
DI-N-OCTYL PHTHALATE	117-84-0	PST08040
DI-ON	330-54-1	PST08420
DI-SYSTON	298-04-4	PST08380
DIALIFOR	10311-84-9	PST23630
DIALLATE	2303-16-4	PST06480
DIALUMINUM SULFATE	10043-01-3	PST00980
DIALUMINUM SULPHATE	10043-01-3	PST00980
DIALUMINUM TRISULFATE	10043-01-3	PST00980
DIAMIDAFOS	1754-58-1	PST72310
DIAMIDAPHOS	1754-58-1	PST72310
DIAMIDFOS	1754-58-1	PST72310
DIAMIDOFOS	1754-58-1	PST72310
DIAMIDOPHOS	1754-58-1	PST72310
DIAMINOETHANE	107-15-3	PST09560
DIAMMONIUM THIOSULFATE	7783-18-8	PST01460
DIAMOND GREEN	569-64-2	PST13533
DIANAT	1918-00-9	PST02260
DIAPADRIN	141-66-2	PST03090
DIAPARENE CHLORIDE	25155-18-4	PST71862
DIARSENIC PENTOXIDE	1303-28-2	PST02020
DIATOMIC CHLORINE	7782-50-5	PST04600
DIATOMIC IODINE	7553-56-2	PST11400
DIAZENESULFONIC ACID, (4-(DIMETHYLAMINO)PHENYL)-, SODIUM SALT	140-56-7	PST73084
DIAZIDE	333-41-5	PST06540
DIAZINON	333-41-5	PST06540
DIAZINON OXON	962-58-3	PST06541
DIAZINON OXYGEN ANALOG	962-58-3	PST06541
DIAZOXON	962-58-3	PST06541
DIBAM	128-04-1	PST71383
DIBAR	101-42-8	PST09679
DIBASIC LEAD ARSENITE	7784-40-9	PST12540
DIBENZO(B,E)(1,4)DIOXIN, 2,3,7,8-TETRACHLORO-	1746-01-6	PST08060
DIBENZO-P-DIOXIN, 2,3,7,8-TETRACHLORO-	1746-01-6	PST08060

SUBSTANCE NAME	CAS #	PST #
DIBENZO-1,4-THIAZINE	92-84-2	PST18400
DIBENZOPARATHIAZINE	92-84-2	PST18400
DIBENZOTHIAZINE	92-84-2	PST18400
DIBORON TRIOXIDE	1303-86-2	PST03290
DIBROM	300-76-5	PST06660
DIBROMFOS	300-76-5	PST06660
DIBROMOCHLOROPROPANE	96-12-8	PST26490
DIBUTALIN	33629-47-9	PST03525
DIBUTYL PHTHALATE	84-74-2	PST06740
DIBUTYLENE TETRAFURFURAL	126-15-8	PST71487
DIC 1577	57052-04-7	PST11844
DICAMBA	1918-00-9	PST02260
DICAMBA METHYL ESTER	6597-78-0	PST73131
DICAMBA SODIUM SALT	1982-69-0	PST71250
DICAPROATE	112-27-6	PST24000
DICAPTAN	2463-84-5	PST71380
DICAPTHION	2463-84-5	PST71380
DICAPTHON	2463-84-5	PST71380
DICARBASULF	59669-26-0	PST72456
DICARBOXIMIDE	113-48-4	PST15955
DICARBOXYLIC ACID	144-62-7	PST17360
DICARZOL	23422-53-9	PST10050
DICHLOBENIL	1194-65-6	PST06800
DICHLOBUTRAZOL	75736-33-3	PST07005
DICHLOFENTHION	97-17-6	PST06805
DICHLOFENTION	97-17-6	PST06805
DICHLOFLUANID	1085-98-9	PST73026
DICHLOFLUANID-M	731-27-1	PST73030
DICHLOFULANIDE	1085-98-9	PST73026
DICHLONE	117-80-6	PST06810
DICHLOPHENTHION	97-17-6	PST06805
DICHLORAL UREA	116-52-9	PST06817
DICHLORALUREA	116-52-9	PST06817
DICHLORAN	99-30-9	PST28910
DICHLORANTIN	118-52-5	PST26800
DICHLORFENIDIM	330-54-1	PST08420
DICHLORINE	7782-50-5	PST04600
DICHLORMAN	62-73-7	PST07000
DICHLORO-S-TRIAZINE TRIONE	2782-57-2	PST06975
DICHLORO-S-TRIAZINE-2,4,6(1H,3H,5H)-TRIONE POTASSIUM DERIVATIVE	2244-21-5	PST19360
DICHLORO-S-TRIAZINE-2,4,6-TRIONE	2782-57-2	PST06975
DICHLOROBENZALKONIUM CHLORIDE	8023-53-8	PST71839
DICHLOROBENZENE, PARA, SOLID	106-46-7	PST17640
DICHLOROCADMIUM	10108-64-2	PST03740
DICHLORODIFLUOROMETHANE	75-71-8	PST06880
DICHLORODIFLUOROMETHANE (CCL2F2)	75-71-8	PST06880
DICHLORODIFLUOROMETHANE(R-12)	75-71-8	PST06880
DICHLORODIMETHYLHYDANTOIN	118-52-5	PST26800
DICHLORODIPHENYL DICHLOROETHANE	72-54-8	PST06240
DICHLORODIPHENYLACETIC ACID	83-05-6	PST06232
DICHLORODIPHENYLDICHLOROETHYLENE	3424-82-6	PST06245
DICHLORODIPHENYLDICHLOROETHYLENE	72-55-9	PST06247
DICHLORODIPHENYLTRICHLOROETHANE	50-29-3	PST06250
DICHLOROISOCYANURIC ACID	2782-57-2	PST06975

ALPHABETICAL INDEX

ALPHABETICAL INDEX

SUBSTANCE NAME	CAS #	PST #
DIFONATUL	944-22-9	PST10020
DIFOS	3383-96-8	PST00020
DIHYDRO-5-PENTYL-2(3H)-FURANONE	104-61-0	PST10334
DIHYDROGEN SODIUM PHOSPHATE	7558-80-7	PST15190
DIHYDROGEN SULFATE	7664-93-9	PST22350
DIHYDROOXIRENE	75-21-8	PST09520
DIIODINE	7553-56-2	PST11400
DIIRON TRISULFATE	10028-22-5	PST09790
DIISOBUTYL KETONE	108-83-8	PST07500
DIISOBUTYLTHIOCARBAMIC ACID S-ETHYL ESTER	2008-41-5	PST71474
DIISOCARB	2008-41-5	PST71474
DIISOPROPOXYPHOSPHORYL FLUORIDE	55-91-4	PST07590
DIISOPROPYL FLUOROPHOSPHATE	55-91-4	PST07590
DIISOPROPYL PHOSPHOFLUORIDATE	55-91-4	PST07590
DIISOPROPYL PHOSPHOROFLUORIDATE	55-91-4	PST07590
DIISOPROPYLTHIOCARBAMIC ACID S-(2,3,3-TRICHLOROALLYL) ESTER	2303-17-5	PST72050
DIISOPROPYLTHIOCARBAMIC ACID, S (2,3-DICHLOROALLYL) ESTER	2303-16-4	PST06480
DIKEGULAC SODIUM	52508-35-7	PST72391
DIKEGULAC SODIUM SALT	52508-35-7	PST72391
DIKONITE	2893-78-9	PST21180
DILAN	1330-20-7	PST25150
DIMANIN	8001-54-5	PST00537
DIMANINC	2893-78-9	PST21180
DIMECRON	13171-21-6	PST18670
DIMEFOX	115-26-4	PST07655
DIMEPHENTHOATE	2597-03-7	PST72337
DIMETHACHLOR	50563-36-5	PST07677
DIMETHACHLORO	50563-36-5	PST07677
DIMETHAMETORIN	22936-75-0	PST72145
DIMETHAMETRYN	22936-75-0	PST72145
DIMETHIRIMOL	5221-53-4	PST72919
DIMETHOATE	60-51-5	PST07670
DIMETHOATE O-ANALOG	1113-02-6	PST17328
DIMETHOATE OXON	1113-02-6	PST17328
DIMETHOATE OXYGEN ANALOG	1113-02-6	PST17328
DIMETHOATE PO ISOLOGUE	1113-02-6	PST17328
DIMETHOATE-ETHYL	116-01-8	PST08723
DIMETHOXANE	828-00-2	PST28395
DIMETHOXON	1113-02-6	PST17328
DIMETHOXY-DDT	72-43-5	PST14220
DIMETHRIN	70-38-2	PST07676
DIMETHYL (E)-1-METHYL-2-(METHYLCARBAMOYL)VINYL PHOSPHATE	6923-22-4	PST15165
DIMETHYL (E)-1-METHYL-2-(1-PHENYLETHOXYCARBONYL)VINYL PHOSPHATE	7700-17-6	PST05115
DIMETHYL (1,2-PHENYLENEBIS(IMINOCARBONOTHIOYL))BIS(CARBAMATE)	23564-05-8	PST72308
DIMETHYL (2,2,2-TRICHLORO-1-HYDROXYETHYL)PHOSPHONATE	52-68-6	PST23790
DIMETHYL CIS-1-METHYL-2-(1-PHENYLETHOXYCARBONYL)VINYL PHOSPHATE	7700-17-6	PST05115
DIMETHYL HYDROGEN PHOSPHATE	813-78-5	PST07882
DIMETHYL KETONE	67-64-1	PST00140
DIMETHYL N,N'-(THIOBIS((METHYLIMINO)CARBONYLOXY)) BISETHANIMIDOTHIOATE)	59669-26-0	PST72456
DIMETHYL O-PHTHALATE	131-11-3	PST07740
DIMETHYL P-(METHYLTHIO)PHENYL ESTER PHOSPHORIC ACID	3254-63-5	PST73095
DIMETHYL P-(METHYLTHIO)PHENYL PHOSPHATE	3254-63-5	PST73095
DIMETHYL P-NITROPHENYL PHOSPHATE	950-35-6	PST14678

SUBSTANCE NAME	CAS #	PST #
DIOCTYL-MEDO FORTE	577-11-7	PST00406
DIOCTYLAL	577-11-7	PST00406
DIORTHO LEAD ARSENATE	7784-40-9	PST12540
DIOTHYL	5221-49-8	PST08049
DIOTILAN	577-11-7	PST00406
DIOVAC	577-11-7	PST00406
DIOXABENZOFOS	3811-49-2	PST20325
DIOXACARB	6988-21-2	PST73123
DIOXATHION	78-34-2	PST08050
DIOXIN	1746-01-6	PST08060
DIPAXIN	82-66-6	PST08068
DIPEL 2X	UNASSIGNED	PST08603
DIPHACIN	82-66-6	PST08068
DIPHACINON	82-66-6	PST08068
DIPHACINONE	82-66-6	PST08068
DIPHENACIN	82-66-6	PST08068
DIPHENACOUM	56073-07-5	PST07385
DIPHENADION	82-66-6	PST08068
DIPHENADIONE	82-66-6	PST08068
DIPHENAMID	957-51-7	PST71406
DIPHENAMIDE	957-51-7	PST71406
DIPHENOXURON	14214-32-5	PST07386
DIPHENYL PHTHALATE	84-62-8	PST08095
DIPHENYLAMINE	122-39-4	PST08100
DIPHENYLMETHANE, 5,5'-DICHLORO-2,2'-HYDROXY-	97-23-4	PST71611
DIPHOSPHORAMIDE, OCTAMETHYL-	152-16-9	PST20350
DIPHOSPHORIC ACID TETRAETHYL ESTER	107-49-3	PST22520
DIPHOSPHORIC ACID, TETRAPOTASSIUM SALT	7320-34-5	PST19546
DIPHOSPHORIC ACID, TETRASODIUM SALT	7722-88-5	PST23140
DIPOTASSIUM CARBONATE	584-08-7	PST19290
DIPOTASSIUM DICHROMATE	7778-50-9	PST19370
DIPOTASSIUM SALT	7778-50-9	PST19370
DIPOTASSIUM SULFATE	7778-80-5	PST19590
DIPPEL'S OIL	8001-85-2	PST03250
DIPPING ACID	7664-93-9	PST22350
DIPROPETRYN	4147-51-7	PST72333
DIPROPYLCARBAMOTHIOIC ACID S-ETHYL ESTER	759-94-4	PST71470
DIPROPYLCARBAMOTHIOIC ACID S-PROPYL ESTER	1929-77-7	PST71473
DIPROPYLTHIOCARBAMIC ACID S-ETHYL ESTER	759-94-4	PST71470
DIPROPYLTHIOCARBAMIC ACID S-PROPYL ESTER	1929-77-7	PST71473
DIPTEREX	52-68-6	PST23790
DIPTHAL	2303-17-5	PST72050
DIPYRIDO(1,2-A:2',1'-C)PYRAZINEDIIUM, 6,7-DIHYDRO-, DIBROMIDE	85-00-7	PST08250
DIQUAT	85-00-7	PST08250
DIQUAT DIBROMIDE	85-00-7	PST08250
DIRAX	86-88-4	PST01830
DIRIMAL	19044-88-3	PST17324
DIS(DIETHYLAMINO)THIOXOMETHYL DISULFIDE	97-77-8	PST08370
DISAN	741-58-2	PST02583
DISK DRIVE HEAD CLEANING KIT (DIGITAL EQUIPMENT CORPORATION)	67-63-0	PST12090
DISODIUM ACID ORTHOPHOSPHATE	7558-79-4	PST08330
DISODIUM ACID PHOSPHATE	7558-79-4	PST08330
DISODIUM CARBONATE	497-19-8	PST21080
DISODIUM DICHROMATE	10588-01-9	PST21190

ALPHABETICAL INDEX

SUBSTANCE NAME	CAS #	PST #
DISODIUM EDETATE	139-33-3	PST08305
DISODIUM EDTA	139-33-3	PST08305
DISODIUM ETHYLENE BISDITHIOCARBAMATE	142-59-6	PST16080
DISODIUM ETHYLENE-1,2-BISDITHIOCARBAMATE	142-59-6	PST16080
DISODIUM ETHYLENEBIS(DITHIOCARBAMATE)	142-59-6	PST16080
DISODIUM ETHYLENEDIAMINE TETRAACETATE	139-33-3	PST08305
DISODIUM HEXAFLUOROSILICATE	16893-85-9	PST21620
DISODIUM HYDROGEN PHOSPHATE	7558-79-4	PST08330
DISODIUM METASILICATE	6834-92-0	PST21373
DISODIUM MONOHYDROGEN PHOSPHATE	7558-79-4	PST08330
DISODIUM MONOSILICATE	6834-92-0	PST21373
DISODIUM ORTHOPHOSPHATE	7558-79-4	PST08330
DISODIUM PHOSPHATE	7558-79-4	PST08330
DISODIUM PHOSPHORIC ACID	7558-79-4	PST08330
DISODIUM SEQUESTRENE	139-33-3	PST08305
DISODIUM SILICATE	6834-92-0	PST21373
DISODIUM SULFITE	7757-83-7	PST21660
DISODIUM TETRABORATE DECAHYDRATE	1303-96-4	PST21010
DISODIUM VERSENATE	139-33-3	PST08305
DISODIUM VERSENE	139-33-3	PST08305
DISODIUM 1,2-ETHANEDIYLBIS(CARBAMODITHIOATE)	142-59-6	PST16080
DISODIUM 3,6-ENDOXOHEXAHYDROPHTHALATE	129-67-9	PST08590
DISODIUM 3,6-EPOXYCYCLOHEXANE-1,2-DICARBOXYLATE	129-67-9	PST08590
DISODIUM-7-OXABICYCLO(2.2.1)HEPTANE-2,3-DICARBOXYLATE	129-67-9	PST08590
DISODIUM-7-OXABICYCLO(2.2.1)HEPTANE-2,3-DICARBOXYLIC ACID	129-67-9	PST08590
DISONATE	577-11-7	PST00406
DISTODIN	70-30-4	PST10780
DISUGRAN	6597-78-0	PST73131
DISUL-SODIUM	136-78-7	PST05500
DISULFAN	97-77-8	PST08370
DISULFIDE, BIS(DIMETHYLTHIOCARBAMOYL)	137-26-8	PST23430
DISULFIRAM	97-77-8	PST08370
DISULFOTON	298-04-4	PST08380
DISULFOTON DIOXIDE	2497-06-5	PST08381
DISULFOTON O.A. SULFONE	2496-91-5	PST06306
DISULFOTON OXYGEN ANALOG SULFONE	2496-91-5	PST06306
DISULFOTON SULFONE	2497-06-5	PST08381
DISULFOTON SULFOXIDE	2497-07-6	PST17385
DISULPHINE LAKE BLUE EG	2650-18-2	PST08277
DISYSTON SULFONE	2497-06-5	PST08381
DISYSTON SULFOXIDE	2497-07-6	PST17385
DISYSTOX O.A. SULFONE	2496-91-5	PST06306
DITALIMFOS	5131-24-8	PST72347
DITALIMPHOS	5131-24-8	PST72347
DITHANE A 40 (FORMULATION)	142-59-6	PST16080
DITHANE M 22	12427-38-2	PST13589
DITHANE M-45	8018-01-7	PST71120
DITHANE Z-78	UNASSIGNED	PST08396
DITHIANON	3347-22-6	PST72290
DITHIANONE	3347-22-6	PST72290
DITHION	572-48-5	PST73073
DITHIONE	3689-24-5	PST22470
DITHIONE	572-48-5	PST73073
DITHIONIC ACID	7664-93-9	PST22350

ALPHABETICAL INDEX

SUBSTANCE NAME	CAS #	PST #
DOUBLE STRENGTH	93-72-1	PST20830
DOW DURSBAN L.O. INSECTICIDE	UNASSIGNED	PST08522
DOW DURSBAN 4E INSECTICIDE	UNASSIGNED	PST08521
DOW FUME	74-83-9	PST14300
DOW 1329	299-85-4	PST71236
DOWANOL EB	111-76-2	PST03540
DOWANOL EM	109-86-4	PST14340
DOWCO 132	299-86-5	PST05550
DOWCO 139	315-18-4	PST15010
DOWCO 169	1754-58-1	PST72310
DOWCO 179	2921-88-2	PST04910
DOWCO 199	5131-24-8	PST72347
DOWCO 213	13121-70-5	PST06110
DOWCO 214	5598-13-0	PST71652
DOWCO 233	55335-06-3	PST72472
DOWCO 290	1702-17-6	PST05211
DOWCO 453	69806-40-2	PST72579
DOWCO 453	69806-34-4	PST72580
DOWCO 453 METHYL ESTER	69806-40-2	PST72579
DOWCO 453ME	69806-40-2	PST72579
DOWCO-163	1929-82-4	PST16530
DOWFROST	57-55-6	PST19870
DOWFUME MC-2	74-83-9	PST14300
DOWFUME W 85 (FORMULATION)	106-93-4	PST09380
DOWICIDE A	132-27-4	PST08500
DOWICIDE B	136-32-3	PST21713
DOWICIDE G	131-52-2	PST08506
DOWICIDE 1 ANTIMICROBIAL	90-43-7	PST18470
DOWICIDE 2	95-95-4	PST28700
DOWICIDE 7	87-86-5	PST18150
DOWICIDE 9	13347-42-7	PST71731
DOWPON	75-99-0	PST06200
DOWPON	127-20-8	PST71239
DOWTHERM E	95-50-1	PST16970
DOWTHERM SR	107-21-1	PST09400
DOWTHERM SR 1	107-21-1	PST09400
DOXCIDE 50	10049-04-4	PST04610
DOXINATE	577-11-7	PST00406
DOXOL	577-11-7	PST00406
DOZER	4482-55-7	PST71389
DPA	122-39-4	PST08100
DPD 6376OH	74223-64-6	PST72546
DPX 3674	51235-04-2	PST10994
DPX 4189	64902-72-3	PST72504
DPX 6376	74223-64-6	PST72546
DPX 6774	34123-59-6	PST12254
DPX-T 6376	74223-64-6	PST72546
DRACYLIC ACID	65-85-0	PST02720
DRAPOLEX	8001-54-5	PST00539
DRAWIN 755	34681-10-2	PST73270
DRAZA	2032-65-7	PST14190
DRC 3341	1129-41-5	PST83074
DREFT	151-21-3	PST08485
DREPAMON	36756-79-3	PST72405

SUBSTANCE NAME	CAS #	PST #
DRIERITE	7778-18-9	PST04110
DRILLZID	2104-96-3	PST71064
DRINOX	76-44-8	PST10660
DROPP	51707-55-2	PST23299
DRW-1139	41394-05-2	PST14095
DS 15647	39196-18-4	PST23330
DSDP	78-53-5	PST83006
DSE	142-59-6	PST16080
DSP	7558-79-4	PST08330
DTMC761	115-32-2	PST07010
DU PONT 1991	17804-35-2	PST02580
DU PONT 326	330-55-2	PST12826
DU PONT 634	2164-08-1	PST73238
DU PONT 732	5902-51-2	PST71099
DUAL	51218-45-2	PST15003
DUATEX	72-14-0	PST72047
DULCIDOR	15879-93-3	PST00775
DUPHAR PH 60-40	35367-38-5	PST07388
DUPONOL	151-21-3	PST08485
DUPONT HERBICIDE 326	330-55-2	PST12826
DURAFUR DEVELOPER C	120-80-9	PST04360
DURATOX (FORMULATION)	919-86-8	PST83065
DURSBAN	2921-88-2	PST04910
DURSBAN (R) L.O. INSECTICIDE	UNASSIGNED	PST08522
DURSBAN (R) 4E INSECTICIDE	UNASSIGNED	PST08521
DURSBAN L.O. INSECTICIDE	UNASSIGNED	PST08522
DURSBAN METHYL	5598-13-0	PST71652
DURSBAN OXON	5598-15-2	PST04911
DURSBAN OXYGEN ANALOG	5598-15-2	PST04911
DURSBAN 4E EMULSIFIABLE INSECTICIDE	UNASSIGNED	PST08521
DURSBAN 4E INSECTICIDE	UNASSIGNED	PST08521
DURSBANOXON	5598-15-2	PST04911
DUTCH LIQUID	107-06-2	PST09390
DUTOM	2307-68-8	PST71164
DW3418	21725-46-2	PST05762
DXP 5648	74222-97-2	PST72544
DYBAR	101-42-8	PST09679
DYCARB	22781-23-3	PST02560
DYCLOMEC	1194-65-6	PST06800
DYFLOS	55-91-4	PST07590
DYFONAT	944-22-9	PST10020
DYFONATE	944-22-9	PST10020
DYKON	126-96-5	PST71497
DYLOX	52-68-6	PST23790
DYMID	957-51-7	PST71406
DYNACHEM (R) DEVELOPER DCR (THIOKOL/DYNACHEM CORPORATION)	1330-20-7	PST25150
DYNEX	330-54-1	PST08420
DYRENE	101-05-3	PST01526
DYREX	52-68-6	PST23790
DYTOL S-91	112-30-1	PST06285
D3-VIGANTOL	67-97-0	PST60913
E 1059	8065-48-3	PST06320
E 20	7440-22-4	PST20770
E 600	311-45-5	PST07200

SUBSTANCE NAME	CAS #	PST #
E 7256	27176-87-0	PST08480
E-162	84-66-2	PST07210
E-175	107-06-2	PST09390
E-182; 0-3487	109-86-4	PST14340
E-48	18854-01-8	PST12280
E-513	16423-68-0	PST08685
EARTHCIDE	82-68-8	PST18140
ECTORAL	299-84-3	PST20180
EDB	106-93-4	PST09380
EDC	107-06-2	PST09390
EDETATE DISODIUM	139-33-3	PST08305
EDETATE TETRASODIUM	64-02-8	PST23137
EDETIC ACID	60-00-4	PST09570
EDIFENPHOS	17109-49-8	PST08555
EDIPHENPHOS	17109-49-8	PST08555
EDTA	60-00-4	PST09570
EDTA (CHELATING AGENT)	60-00-4	PST09570
EDTA DISODIUM SALT	139-33-3	PST08305
EDTA TETRASODIUM SALT	64-02-8	PST23137
EDTA, DISODIUM SALT	139-33-3	PST08305
EFOSITE AL	39148-24-8	PST72563
EGG YELLOW A	1934-21-0	PST22465
EH2	116-52-9	PST06817
EI 47031	947-02-4	PST06115
EI 47470	950-10-7	PST13735
EKAGOM G	149-30-4	PST13738
EKALUX	13593-03-8	PST73112
EKAMET (FORMULATION)	38260-54-7	PST73148
EKATIN	640-15-3	PST83056
EKATIN AEROSOL	640-15-3	PST83056
EKATIN F	144-41-2	PST73096
EKATIN M	144-41-2	PST73096
EKTAFOS	141-66-2	PST03090
EKTASOLVE EB	111-76-2	PST03540
EKTASOLVE EM	109-86-4	PST14340
EL 103	34014-18-1	PST72340
EL 110	1861-40-1	PST02570
EL 119	19044-88-3	PST17324
EL 161	55283-68-6	PST72436
EL 400	2104-96-3	PST71064
ELANCOLAN	1582-09-8	PST24085
ELECTROLYTIC TOUGH PITCH (EASTERN ROLLING MILLS, INC.)	7440-50-8	PST05430
ELEMENTAL CARBON	7440-44-0	PST04246
ELEUDRON	72-14-0	PST72047
ELFAN WA SULPHONIC ACID	27176-87-0	PST08480
ELOCRON	6988-21-2	PST73123
ELOSAL	7704-34-9	PST22280
ELOZ	1934-21-0	PST22465
ELSAN	2597-03-7	PST72337
ELTESOL SX 30	1300-72-7	PST75603
ELVARON	1085-98-9	PST73026
EM 923	97-16-5	PST71350
EMAR	1314-13-2	PST25490
EMBAFUME	74-83-9	PST14300

ALPHABETICAL INDEX

SUBSTANCE NAME	CAS #	PST #
EMBARK	53780-34-0	PST72444
EMCEPAN	94-74-6	PST27880
EMERSOL 210	112-80-1	PST17305
EMP	2235-25-8	PST71479
EMPIRIN COMPOUND	62-44-2	PST18340
EMSORB 6900	9005-65-6	PST40200
ENDO-1,4,5,6,7,7-HEXACHLORO-5-NORBORNENE-2,3-DIMETHANOL CYCLIC SULFITE	959-98-8	PST00800
ENDO,ENDO-1,2,3,4,10,10-HEXACHLORO-1,4,4A,5,8,8A-HEXAHYDRO-1,4:5,8 DIMETHANONAPHTHALENE	465-73-6	PST11810
ENDO,ENDO-1,2,3,4,10,10-HEXACHLORO-6,7-EPOXY-1,4,4A,5,6,7,8,8A- -OCTAHYDRO-1,4:5,8-DIMETHANONAPHTHALENE	72-20-8	PST08600
ENDO,EXO-1,2,3,4,10,10-HEXACHLORO-1,4,4A,5,8,8A-HEXAHYDRO-1,4:5,8 -DIMETHANONAPHTHALENE	309-00-2	PST00520
ENDO,EXO-1,2,3,4,10,10-HEXACHLORO-6,7-EPOXY-1,4,4A5,6,7,8,8A-OCTAHYDRO 1,4:5,8-DIMETHANONAPHTHALENE	60-57-1	PST07080
ENDO,EXO-5-3-(HEXAHYDRO-4,7-METHANOINDAN-5-YL)-1,1-DIMETHYLUREA	18530-56-8	PST71400
ENDOCID	2778-04-3	PST73139
ENDOCIDE	2778-04-3	PST73139
ENDOSAN	485-31-4	PST71960
ENDOSULFAN	115-29-7	PST08560
ENDOSULFAN A	959-98-8	PST00800
ENDOSULFAN B	33213-65-9	PST03040
ENDOSULFAN I	959-98-8	PST00800
ENDOSULFAN II	33213-65-9	PST03040
ENDOSULFAN 1	959-98-8	PST00800
ENDOSULFAN 2	33213-65-9	PST03040
ENDOTHAL	145-73-3	PST08580
ENDOTHAL DISODIUM SALT	129-67-9	PST08590
ENDOTHAL-SODIUM	129-67-9	PST08590
ENDOTHALL	145-73-3	PST08580
ENDOTHALL DISODIUM SALT	129-67-9	PST08590
ENDOTHALL-SODIUM	129-67-9	PST08590
ENDOTHION	2778-04-3	PST73139
ENDRATE DISODIUM	139-33-3	PST08305
ENDRIN	72-20-8	PST08600
ENDROCIDE	5836-29-3	PST05493
ENERSOL 213	112-80-1	PST17305
ENGEMYCIN	2058-46-0	PST84045
ENIDE	957-51-7	PST71406
ENOVIT	23564-06-9	PST72322
ENT 1,122	88-85-7	PST08020
ENT 1,860	127-18-4	PST22900
ENT 14,250	51-03-6	PST75640
ENT 14,689	14484-64-1	PST09680
ENT 14875	12427-38-2	PST13589
ENT 15,108	56-38-2	PST18040
ENT 15,152	76-44-8	PST10660
ENT 15,349	106-93-4	PST09380
ENT 15,406	78-87-5	PST19860
ENT 1506	50-29-3	PST06250
ENT 154	534-52-1	PST07910
ENT 15949	309-00-2	PST00520
ENT 16,391	143-50-0	PST12330
ENT 16255	60-57-1	PST07080

ALPHABETICAL INDEX

SUBSTANCE NAME	CAS #	PST #
ENT 24969	470-90-6	PST04575
ENT 24988	300-76-5	PST06660
ENT 25 726	2032-65-7	PST14190
ENT 25,506	116-01-8	PST08723
ENT 25,515	13171-21-6	PST18670
ENT 25,545-X	297-78-9	PST83032
ENT 25,552-X	12789-03-6	PST71948
ENT 25,554-X	3735-23-7	PST73085
ENT 25,580	297-97-2	PST25590
ENT 25,586	953-17-3	PST71647
ENT 25,602-X	299-86-5	PST05550
ENT 25,613	2665-30-7	PST73278
ENT 25,640	115-93-5	PST06135
ENT 25,644	52-85-7	PST09675
ENT 25,671	114-26-1	PST02540
ENT 25,674	2674-91-1	PST14105
ENT 25,705	732-11-6	PST11307
ENT 25,715	122-14-5	PST09678
ENT 25,766	315-18-4	PST15010
ENT 25,776	1113-02-6	PST17328
ENT 25,784	2032-59-9	PST71500
ENT 25,793	485-31-4	PST71960
ENT 25,830	947-02-4	PST06115
ENT 25,832	13067-93-1	PST05805
ENT 25,962	15271-41-7	PST73177
ENT 25445	61-82-5	PST01040
ENT 25500	64-00-6	PST29423
ENT 25540	55-38-9	PST02550
ENT 25567	1491-41-4	PST72737
ENT 25584	1024-57-3	PST10670
ENT 25585	2275-14-1	PST18373
ENT 25647	299-85-4	PST71236
ENT 25650	919-54-0	PST00117
ENT 25670	2631-40-5	PST73231
ENT 25685	3309-87-3	PST72763
ENT 25712	327-98-0	PST00478
ENT 25719	2385-85-5	PST09690
ENT 25734	3254-63-5	PST73095
ENT 25760	78-57-9	PST72980
ENT 25922	644-64-4	PST83057
ENT 25991	950-10-7	PST13735
ENT 26,058	101-05-3	PST01526
ENT 26613	2275-23-2	PST73108
ENT 27 258	4824-78-6	PST03458
ENT 27 566	23422-53-9	PST10050
ENT 27 822	30560-19-1	PST00065
ENT 27,093	116-06-3	PST00500
ENT 27,102	1757-18-2	PST00493
ENT 27,160	919-76-6	PST01007
ENT 27,165	3383-96-8	PST00020
ENT 27,305	17702-57-7	PST73082
ENT 27,341	16752-77-5	PST14200
ENT 27,395-X	13121-70-5	PST06110
ENT 27,396	10265-92-6	PST15160

ALPHABETICAL INDEX

ALPHABETICAL INDEX

SUBSTANCE NAME	CAS #	PST #
DIMETHYL ESTER		
ETHANOIC ACID	64-19-7	PST00120
ETHANOL	64-17-5	PST08700
ETHANOL, 2-(ETHYLTHIO)-, DIETHYL PHOSPHATE	23052-51-9	PST06317
ETHANOL, 2-(HYDROXYMETHYLAMINE)-	34375-28-5	PST72288
ETHANOL, 2-(2,4-DICHLOROPHENOXY)-	120-67-2	PST06915
ETHANOL, 2-AMINO-	141-43-5	PST08710
ETHANOL, 2-BUTOXY-	111-76-2	PST03540
ETHANOL, 2-METHOXY	109-86-4	PST14340
ETHANOL, 2,2-BIS(P-CHLOROPHENYL)-	2642-82-2	PST06323
ETHANOL, 2,2',2''-NITRILOTRI-	102-71-6	PST23932
ETHANOL, 2,2',2''-NITRILOTRIS-	102-71-6	PST23932
ETHANOL,2,2'-(1,2-ETHANEDIYLBIS(OXY))BIS-,	112-27-6	PST24000
ETHANOLAMINE	141-43-5	PST08710
ETHEFON	16672-87-0	PST72293
ETHENE	74-85-1	PST09330
ETHENE OXIDE	75-21-8	PST09520
ETHENE, HOMOPOLYMER	9002-88-4	PST19119
ETHENE, TETRACHLORO-	127-18-4	PST22900
ETHEPHON	16672-87-0	PST72293
ETHER, P-NITROPHENYL ALPHA,ALPHA,ALPHA-TRIFLUORO-2-NITRO-P-TOLYL	15457-05-3	PST72248
ETHER, P-NITROPHENYL 2,4,6-TRICHLOROPHENYL	1836-77-7	PST23865
ETHER, 2,4-DICHLOROPHENYL P-NITROPHENYL	1836-75-5	PST23580
ETHIDIMURON	30043-49-3	PST72551
ETHIOFENCARB	29973-13-5	PST72421
ETHIOLAT	2941-55-1	PST72327
ETHIOLATE	2941-55-1	PST72327
ETHION	563-12-2	PST08720
ETHIOZIN	64529-56-2	PST09111
ETHIRIMOL	23947-60-6	PST08721
ETHOATE-METHYL	116-01-8	PST08723
ETHOFUMESATE	26225-79-6	PST72404
ETHOHEXADIOL	94-96-2	PST71458
ETHOL	36653-82-4	PST04525
ETHOPROP	13194-48-4	PST15080
ETHOPROPHOS	13194-48-4	PST15080
ETHOXYLAN 1685	61790-81-6	PST08741
ETHOXYLAN 1685 PEG (75) LANOLIN	61790-81-6	PST08741
ETHOXYLATED ALCOHOLS (C11-C15):	68131-40-8	PST85315
ETHOXYLATED ALCOHOLS, C11-15-SECONDARY	68131-40-8	PST85315
ETHOXYLATED LANOLIN	61790-81-6	PST08741
ETHOXYLATED LANOLIN ALCOHOLS	61790-81-6	PST08741
ETHOXYLATED NONYLPHENOL	9016-45-9	PST16835
ETHOXYLATED SORBITAN MONOOLAURATE	9005-64-5	PST80107
ETHOXYLATED WOOL WAX ALCOHOLS	61790-81-6	PST08741
ETHOXYPHAS	919-54-0	PST00117
ETHOXYPHOS	919-54-0	PST00117
ETHOXYQUIN	91-53-2	PST08740
ETHOXYQUINE	91-53-2	PST08740
ETHREL	16672-87-0	PST72293
ETHYL (((DIETHOXYPHOSPHINOTHIOYL)THIO)ACETYL)METHYLCARBAMATE	2595-54-2	PST13675
ETHYL (DIETHOXYPHOSPHINOTHIOYLTHIO)ACETYL(METHYL)CARBAMATE	2595-54-2	PST13675
ETHYL (MERCAPTOACETYL)METHYLCARBAMATE S-ESTER WITH O,O-DIETHYL PHOSPHORODITHIOATE	2595-54-2	PST13675

SUBSTANCE NAME	CAS #	PST #
ETHYL (2-(P-PHENOXY)ETHYL)CARBAMATE	72490-01-8	PST72618
ETHYL (2-(4-PHENOXYPHENOXY)ETHYL)CARBAMATE	72490-01-8	PST72618
ETHYL (3-(((PHENYLAMINO)CARBONYL)OXY)PHENYL)CARBAMATE	13684-56-5	PST72336
ETHYL ACETATE	141-78-6	PST08750
ETHYL ALCOHOL	64-17-5	PST08700
ETHYL ALCOHOL, 100%	64-17-5	PST08700
ETHYL ALPHA-((DIMETHOXYPHOSPHINOTHIOYL)THIO) BENZENEACETATE	2597-03-7	PST72337
ETHYL AMINOBENZOATE	94-09-7	PST72267
ETHYL AZINPHOS	2642-71-9	PST02205
ETHYL BROMOPHOS	4824-78-6	PST03458
ETHYL CARBINOL	67-63-0	PST12090
ETHYL CARBOPHENOTHION	786-19-6	PST04340
ETHYL DI-N-PROPYLTHIOLCARBAMATE	759-94-4	PST71470
ETHYL ETHANOATE	141-78-6	PST08750
ETHYL GUSATHION	2642-71-9	PST02205
ETHYL GUTHION	2642-71-9	PST02205
ETHYL HEXYLENE GLYCOL	94-96-2	PST71458
ETHYL HYDRATE	64-17-5	PST08700
ETHYL HYDROXIDE	64-17-5	PST08700
ETHYL M-HYDROXYCARBANILATE CARBANILATE (ESTER)	13684-56-5	PST72336
ETHYL MERCAPTOPHENYLACETATE, S-ESTER WITH O,O-DIMETHYL PHOSPHORODITHIOATE	2597-03-7	PST72337
ETHYL MERCURIC CHLORIDE	107-27-7	PST09620
ETHYL MERCURY CHLORIDE	107-27-7	PST09620
ETHYL MERCURY PHOSPHATE	2235-25-8	PST71479
ETHYL METHYL KETONE	78-93-3	PST14460
ETHYL METHYLENE PHOSPHORODITHIOATE (((ETO)2P(S)S)2CH2)	563-12-2	PST08720
ETHYL METRIBUZIN	64529-56-2	PST09111
ETHYL N-(((((2,3-DIHYDRO-2,2-DIMETHYL-7-BENZOFURANYL)OXY)CARBONYL) METHYLAMINO)THIO)-N-(1-METHYLETHYL)-BETA-ALANINATE	82560-54-1	PST72562
ETHYL N-(DIETHOXYTHIOPHOSPHORYLTHIO)ACETYL-N-METHYLCARBAMATE	2595-54-2	PST13675
ETHYL N,N-DIISOBUTYLTHIOCARBAMATE	2008-41-5	PST71474
ETHYL P-AMINOBENZENECARBOXYLATE	94-09-7	PST72267
ETHYL P-AMINOBENZOATE	94-09-7	PST72267
ETHYL P-AMINOPHENYLCARBOXYLATE	94-09-7	PST72267
ETHYL P-NITOPHENYL BENZENETHIOPHOSPHONATE	2104-64-5	PST08650
ETHYL P,P'-DICHLOROBENZILATE	510-15-6	PST04740
ETHYL PARAOXON	311-45-5	PST07200
ETHYL PARATHION	56-38-2	PST18040
ETHYL PHTHALATE	84-66-2	PST07210
ETHYL PIRIMIPHOS	23505-41-1	PST72377
ETHYL PROPYL PHOSPHORODITHIOATE	13194-48-4	PST15080
ETHYL PYRAZINYL PHOSPHATE	7359-55-9	PST71377
ETHYL PYRAZINYL PHOSPHOROTHIOATE	297-97-2	PST25590
ETHYL S-PHENYL ETHYLPHOSPHONOTHIOLOTHIONATE	944-22-9	PST10020
ETHYL SYSTOX	8065-48-3	PST06320
ETHYL THIOPHANATE	23564-06-9	PST72322
ETHYL THIOPYROPHOSPHATE	3689-24-5	PST22470
ETHYL THIURAM	97-77-8	PST08370
ETHYL 1-NAPHTHALENEACETATE	2122-70-5	PST71628
ETHYL 1-NAPHTHYLACETATE	2122-70-5	PST71628
ETHYL 2-(4-PHENOXYPHENOXY)ETHYLCARBAMATE	72490-01-8	PST72618
ETHYL 2-DIETHOXYPHOSPHINOTHIOYLOXY-5-METHYLPYRAZOLO(1,5-A)PYRIMIDINE-6 CARBOXYLATE	13457-18-6	PST73169

ALPHABETICAL INDEX

SUBSTANCE NAME	CAS #	PST #
F 139	126-22-7	PST71399
F 461	5259-88-1	PST17373
F-319	10004-44-1	PST22404
FAA	640-19-7	PST09930
FAC	2275-18-5	PST19943
FAC 20	2275-18-5	PST19943
FAK-40	2275-18-5	PST19943
FALCON DUST OFF II (FALCON SAFETY PRODUCT INC.)	75-71-8	PST06880
FALISILVAN	101-42-8	PST09679
FALTAN	133-07-3	PST10012
FAMID	6988-21-2	PST73123
FAMOPHOS	52-85-7	PST09675
FAMPHOS	52-85-7	PST09675
FAMPHUR	52-85-7	PST09675
FANAL	7681-38-1	PST20990
FANTERRIN	79-57-2	PST17414
FAP	525-79-1	PST72483
FAR-GO	2303-17-5	PST72050
FARTOX	82-68-8	PST18140
FAST GREEN	569-64-2	PST13533
FASTAC	67375-30-8	PST06118
FATSCO ANT POISON	7631-89-2	PST20940
FB/2	85-00-7	PST08250
FC 11	75-69-4	PST09990
FCR 1272	68359-37-5	PST72630
FD AND C RED NO. 3	16423-68-0	PST08685
FD[C YELLOW NO.5	1934-21-0	PST22465
FDA 0101	7681-49-4	PST21230
FDA 1541	759-94-4	PST71470
FEDONA	67375-30-8	PST06118
FEENO	92-84-2	PST18400
FEH7011S	7782-63-0	PST09870
FELAN	2212-67-1	PST71471
FELIDERM K	7773-06-0	PST01400
FENAM	957-51-7	PST71406
FENAMINOSULF	140-56-7	PST73084
FENAMIPHOS	22224-92-6	PST16145
FENAMIPHOS SULFONE	31972-44-8	PST16144
FENAMIPHOS SULFOXIDE	31972-43-7	PST16146
FENBUTATIN OXIDE	13356-08-6	PST24866
FENCAL	7778-44-1	PST03850
FENCHLOFOS	299-84-3	PST20180
FENCHLORFOS	299-84-3	PST20180
FENCHLORPHOS	299-84-3	PST20180
FENCHLORPHOS-OXON	3983-45-7	PST25082
FENDONA	52315-07-8	PST72392
FENFOSPHORIN	3811-49-2	PST20325
FENIDIM	101-42-8	PST09679
FENITROTHION	122-14-5	PST09678
FENMEDIFAM	13684-63-4	PST72282
FENOBUCARB	3766-81-2	PST03324
FENORMONE	93-72-1	PST20830
FENOVERM	92-84-2	PST18400
FENOXAPROP-ETHYL	66441-23-4	PST72723

ALPHABETICAL INDEX

SUBSTANCE NAME	CAS #	PST #
FILTRASORB	7440-44-0	PST04246
FINAVEN	43222-48-6	PST72348
FITIOS	116-01-8	PST08723
FITIOS B/77	116-01-8	PST08723
FITOSOL	327-98-0	PST00478
FLAC	7778-44-1	PST03850
FLAGYL	443-48-1	PST72529
FLAXSEED OIL	8001-26-1	PST71365
FLEXIMEL	117-81-7	PST06440
FLEXOL DOP	117-81-7	PST06440
FLO-MOR	30525-89-4	PST18000
FLORALTONE	77-06-5	PST10405
FLORDIMEX	16672-87-0	PST72293
FLOREL	16672-87-0	PST72293
FLOWERS OF SULFUR	7704-34-9	PST22280
FLOWERS OF ZINC	1314-13-2	PST25490
FLUAZIFOP-BUTYL	69806-50-4	PST72554
FLUAZIFOP-P-BUTYL	79241-46-6	PST72557
FLUBALEX	1861-40-1	PST02570
FLUCARMIT	119-36-8	PST14720
FLUOMETURON	2164-17-2	PST09907
FLUORAKIL 100	640-19-7	PST09930
FLUORENE-9-CARBOXYLIC ACID, 2-CHLORO-9-HYDROXY-, METHYL ESTER	2536-31-4	PST72283
FLUORETOXURON	27954-37-6	PST23002
FLUORIDAMID	47000-92-0	PST73184
FLUORIGARD	7681-49-4	PST21230
FLUOROACETAMIDE	640-19-7	PST09930
FLUOROACETIC ACID AMIDE	640-19-7	PST09930
FLUOROACETIC ACID, SODIUM SALT	62-74-8	PST21240
FLUOROCHLOROFORM	75-69-4	PST09990
FLUOROCID	7681-49-4	PST21230
FLUORODAY	7681-49-4	PST21230
FLUORODIFEN	15457-05-3	PST72248
FLUORODIISOPROPYL PHOSPHATE	55-91-4	PST07590
FLUORODIPHEN (FORMULATION)	15457-05-3	PST72248
FLUOROTRIBUTYLSTANNANE	1983-10-4	PST72227
FLUOROTRIBUTYLTIN	1983-10-4	PST72227
FLUOROTRICHLOROMETHANE	75-69-4	PST09990
FLUOSTIGMINE	55-91-4	PST07590
FLURSOL	7681-49-4	PST21230
FLYPEL	134-62-3	PST84230
FMC 11092	4849-32-5	PST72271
FMC 30980	52315-07-8	PST72392
FMC 35001	55285-14-8	PST72266
FMC 45498	52918-63-5	PST72784
FMC 710	8001-29-4	PST05475
FNA	7681-49-4	PST21230
FOLCID	2425-06-1	PST04200
FOLEX	150-50-5	PST10010
FOLIDOL	56-38-2	PST18040
FOLIMAT	1113-02-6	PST17328
FOLITHION	122-14-5	PST09678
FOLNIT	133-07-3	PST10012
FOLOSAN	82-68-8	PST18140

SUBSTANCE NAME	CAS #	PST #
FRUITONE N	86-87-3	PST26130
FRUITORE 1	93-72-1	PST20830
FRUMIN-AL	298-04-4	PST08380
FTALAN	133-07-3	PST10012
FTALOPHOS	732-11-6	PST11307
FUBERIDAZOL	3878-19-1	PST73188
FUBERIDAZOLE	3878-19-1	PST73188
FUCLASIN	137-30-4	PST25397
FUEL OIL NO. 1	8008-20-6	PST10090
FUJI-ONE	50512-35-1	PST12253
FUJITHION	3309-87-3	PST72763
FUKLASIN	137-30-4	PST25397
FUKLASIN ULTRA	14484-64-1	PST09680
FUMARIN	117-52-2	PST05476
FUMAZONE	96-12-8	PST26490
FUMED SILICA	7631-86-9	PST20610
FUMED SILICON DIOXIDE	7631-86-9	PST20610
FUNDAL	6164-98-3	PST04570
FUNDAZOL	17804-35-2	PST02580
FUNGCHEX	7487-94-7	PST13800
FUNGICIDE D-1991	17804-35-2	PST02580
FUNGICLOR	82-68-8	PST18140
FUNGIFEN	87-86-5	PST18150
FUNGIMAR	1317-39-1	PST05470
FUNGINEX	26644-46-2	PST24086
FUNGITOX OR	62-38-4	PST18560
FUNGITROL 11	133-07-3	PST10012
FUNGOL B	7681-49-4	PST21230
FURADAN	1563-66-2	PST04240
FURAL	98-01-1	PST10180
FURALE	98-01-1	PST10180
FURATOL	62-74-8	PST21240
FURETHRIN	17080-02-3	PST10175
FURFURAL	98-01-1	PST10180
FURFURALDEHYDE	98-01-1	PST10180
FURFUROL	98-01-1	PST10180
FURFUROLE	98-01-1	PST10180
FURIDAZOLE	3878-19-1	PST73188
FURLOE	101-21-3	PST71148
FURORE	66441-23-4	PST72723
FUSAREX	117-18-0	PST71616
FUSED BORIC ACID	1303-86-2	PST03290
FUSILADE	69806-50-4	PST72554
FUSILADE 2000	79241-46-6	PST72557
FUSILADE 5 (FORMULATION)	79241-46-6	PST72557
FUSSOL	640-19-7	PST09930
FW 925	1836-75-5	PST23580
FYRAN 206K	7773-06-0	PST01400
G 13529	5915-41-3	PST22536
G 22008	87-47-8	PST73263
G 25	76-06-2	PST04830
G 25,804	580-48-3	PST72143
G 27692	122-34-9	PST20837
G 27901	1912-26-1	PST23927

SUBSTANCE NAME	CAS #	PST #
G 28029	2275-14-1	PST18373
G 30027	1912-24-9	PST02150
G 30028	139-40-2	PST19736
G 31435	1610-18-0	PST19967
G 32293	1610-17-9	PST02148
G 32911	1014-70-6	PST02838
G 34162	834-12-8	PST01006
G 34360	1014-69-3	PST06353
G-30494	3735-23-7	PST73085
G-31; G-33	56-81-5	PST10440
G-36393	841-06-5	PST14204
GA	77-06-5	PST10405
GAFCOL EB	111-76-2	PST03540
GALECRON	6164-98-3	PST04570
GALECRON, MONOHYDROCHLORIDE	19750-95-9	PST71656
GALLOTOX	62-38-4	PST18560
GAMMA-AMINO PYRIDINE	504-24-5	PST02180
GAMMA-AMYLBUTYROLACTONE	104-61-0	PST10334
GAMMA-BENZENE HEXACHLORIDE	58-89-9	PST12810
GAMMA-BHC	58-89-9	PST12810
GAMMA-CHLORDANE	5103-74-2	PST10331
GAMMA-CHLORDENE	56641-38-4	PST04567
GAMMA-CHLOROALLYL CHLORIDE	542-75-6	PST26820
GAMMA-HCH	58-89-9	PST12810
GAMMA-HEXACHLOROBENZENE	58-89-9	PST12810
GAMMA-HEXACHLOROCYCLOHEXANE	58-89-9	PST12810
GAMMA-LACTONE-4-HYDROXY-NONANOIC ACID	104-61-0	PST10334
GAMMA-N-AMYLBUTYROLACTONE	104-61-0	PST10334
GAMMA-NONALACTONE	104-61-0	PST10334
GAMMA-NONANOLACTONE	104-61-0	PST10334
GAMMA-NONANOLIDE	104-61-0	PST10334
GAMMA-1,2,3,4,5,6-HEXACHLOROCYCLOHEXANE	58-89-9	PST12810
GAMOPHENE	70-30-4	PST10780
GARDONA	961-11-5	PST72243
GARDONA	22248-79-9	PST72244
GARDONA	22350-76-1	PST72245
GARDONA, CIS	22248-79-9	PST72244
GARDONA, TRANS-	22350-76-1	PST72245
GARDOPRIM	5915-41-3	PST22536
GARLIC OIL	8000-78-0	PST72626
GARLON	55335-06-3	PST72472
GARRATHION	786-19-6	PST04340
GARVOX	22781-23-3	PST02560
GASIL	63231-67-4	PST20670
GATNON	1929-88-0	PST72971
GA3	77-06-5	PST10405
GC 1189	143-50-0	PST12330
GC 1283	2385-85-5	PST09690
GC 2996	140-41-0	PST15197
GC 3707	122-10-1	PST03240
GC 3944-3-4	82-68-8	PST18140
GC 6506	3254-63-5	PST73095
GC 6936	900-95-8	PST24378
GC 8993	639-58-7	PST24380

ALPHABETICAL INDEX

ALPHABETICAL INDEX

SUBSTANCE NAME	CAS #	PST #
GLYPHOSATE-MONO(ISOPROPYLAMMONIUM)	38641-94-0	PST20205
GLYROL	56-81-5	PST10440
GLYSANIN	56-81-5	PST10440
GOAL	42874-03-3	PST72413
GOLD BRONZE	7440-50-8	PST05430
GOLTIX	41394-05-2	PST14095
GOMMELIN	9004-53-9	PST06363
GOOD-RITE K-700	9003-01-4	PST04349
GOPHA-RID (FORMULATION)	1314-84-7	PST25540
GOPHACIDE	4104-14-7	PST71150
GOSSYPLURE	52207-99-5	PST72448
GRAMEVIN	75-99-0	PST06200
GRAMINON	34123-59-6	PST12254
GRAMIXEL	1910-42-5	PST18020
GRAMOXONE	1910-42-5	PST18020
GRAMOXONE DICHLORIDE	1910-42-5	PST18020
GRAMOXONE METHYL SULFATE	2074-50-2	PST71670
GRANUTOX (FORMULATION)	298-02-2	PST18640
GRASLAN	34014-18-1	PST72340
GRAZON	1918-02-1	PST18840
GREEN VITRIOL	7782-63-0	PST09870
GROCEL	77-06-5	PST10405
GROCO 2	112-80-1	PST17305
GROPPER	74223-64-6	PST72546
GROSAFE	7440-44-0	PST04246
GS 12968	2669-32-1	PST73147
GS 13529	5915-41-3	PST22536
GS 14254	26259-45-0	PST73051
GS 14259	33693-04-8	PST72770
GS 14260	886-50-0	PST22538
GS 16068	4147-51-7	PST72333
GT 2041	55-98-1	PST03482
GT 41	55-98-1	PST03482
GUM CAMPHOR	76-22-2	PST04130
GUM SPIRITS OF TURPENTINE (GRUMBACHER)	8006-64-2	PST24580
GUM TURPENTINE (PARKS CORP.)	8006-64-2	PST24580
GUSATHION ETHYL	2642-71-9	PST02205
GUSATHION M	86-50-0	PST02210
GUTHION	86-50-0	PST02210
GUTHION ETHYL	2642-71-9	PST02205
GUTHION OXON	961-22-8	PST10585
GUTHION OXYGEN ANALOG	961-22-8	PST10585
GUTHOXON	961-22-8	PST10585
GUTOXON	961-22-8	PST10585
GY-BON	1014-70-6	PST02838
GYPSINE	7784-40-9	PST12540
G1V-GARD DXN	828-00-2	PST28395
G34161	7287-19-6	PST19968
H 1318	1982-49-6	PST20586
H 133	1194-65-6	PST06800
H 5727	64-00-6	PST29423
H 82	314-42-1	PST71090
H 8757	64-00-6	PST29423
H 95	3766-60-7	PST03523

ALPHABETICAL INDEX

SUBSTANCE NAME	CAS #	PST #
H 9789	27314-13-2	PST72343
H-119	1698-60-8	PST71928
HACHE UNO SUPER	69806-50-4	PST72554
HAIPEN 50	2425-06-1	PST04200
HALANE	118-52-5	PST26800
HALENOL	97-23-4	PST71611
HALIMIDE	1330-85-4	PST71854
HALITE	7647-14-5	PST21105
HALIZAN	108-62-3	PST14090
HALOFLEX 208	9003-01-4	PST04349
HALON 1001	74-83-9	PST14300
HALOXYFOP	69806-34-4	PST72580
HALOXYFOP-METHYL	69806-40-2	PST72579
HAMPSHIRE DEG	139-41-3	PST71447
HANANE	115-26-4	PST07655
HARNESS	34256-82-1	PST72539
HAVIDOTE	60-00-4	PST09570
HAVOC	56073-10-0	PST03327
HC 2072	311-45-5	PST07200
HCE	1024-57-3	PST10670
HCH	319-84-6	PST00770
HCH	319-85-7	PST03010
HCH	608-73-1	PST03080
HCH	319-86-8	PST06310
HCH	58-89-9	PST12810
HCS 3260	12789-03-6	PST71948
HEAVY OIL	8001-58-9	PST05230
HEBACID OXON SULFONE	14086-35-2	PST02552
HEBURID OXON	6552-12-1	PST02551
HEDAPUR M 52	94-74-6	PST27880
HEDONAL	94-75-7	PST28510
HELMETINA	92-84-2	PST18400
HELOTHION	35400-43-2	PST22387
HEOLITE	84-65-1	PST01600
HEPTA	76-44-8	PST10660
HEPTACHLOR	76-44-8	PST10660
HEPTACHLOR CIS-OXIDE	1024-57-3	PST10670
HEPTACHLOR EPOXIDE	1024-57-3	PST10670
HEPTENOPHOS	23560-59-0	PST10685
HEPTYL CARBINOL	111-87-5	PST17270
HERBAN	18530-56-8	PST71400
HERBATOX	330-54-1	PST08420
HERBATOXOL	1912-24-9	PST02150
HERBAZIN	122-34-9	PST20837
HERBICIDE 326	330-55-2	PST12826
HERBICIDE 976	314-40-9	PST03330
HERBICIDES, SILVEX	93-72-1	PST20830
HERBOGIL	1420-07-1	PST72921
HERCO AND YARMOR 80 PINE OIL (HERCULES, INC.)	8002-09-3	PST18900
HERCULES AC 5727	64-00-6	PST29423
HERCULES AC528	78-34-2	PST08050
HERCULES 14 503	10311-84-9	PST23630
HERCULES 22234	38727-55-8	PST72968
HERCULES 426	2550-75-6	PST73193

ALPHABETICAL INDEX

SUBSTANCE NAME	CAS #	PST #
HERCULES 5727	64-00-6	PST29423
HERCULES 7531	18530-56-8	PST71400
HEXABALM	70-30-4	PST10780
HEXACHLORO-HEXAHYDRO-ENDO,ENDO-DIMETHANONAPHTHALENE	465-73-6	PST11810
HEXACHLOROBENZENE	319-85-7	PST03010
HEXACHLOROBENZENE	608-73-1	PST03080
HEXACHLOROBENZENE	118-74-1	PST10730
HEXACHLOROCYCLOHEXANE	319-84-6	PST00770
HEXACHLOROCYCLOHEXANE	319-85-7	PST03010
HEXACHLOROCYCLOHEXANE	608-73-1	PST03080
HEXACHLOROCYCLOHEXANE	319-86-8	PST06310
HEXACHLOROCYCLOHEXANE	58-89-9	PST12810
HEXACHLOROCYCLOPENTADIENE DIMER	2385-85-5	PST09690
HEXACHLOROPHENE	70-30-4	PST10780
HEXACOL TARTRAZINE	1934-21-0	PST22465
HEXADECANOL	36653-82-4	PST04525
HEXADECYL ALCOHOL	36653-82-4	PST04525
HEXAFERB	14484-64-1	PST09680
HEXAHYDRO-1H-AZEPINE-1-CARBOTHIOIC ACID S-ETHYL ESTER	2212-67-1	PST71471
HEXAHYDROXY-6-METHYL-1,11-DIOXO-2-NAPHTHACENECARBOXAMIDE, MONOHYDROCHLORIDE	2058-46-0	PST84045
HEXAKIS(B,B-DIMETHYLPHENETHYL)-DISTANNOXANE	13356-08-6	PST24866
HEXAKIS(2-METHYL-2-PHENYLPROPYL)-DISTANNOXANE	13356-08-6	PST24866
HEXAN-1-OL	111-27-3	PST15630
HEXANEMA	97-17-6	PST06805
HEXANOL	111-27-3	PST15630
HEXANON	108-94-1	PST05890
HEXASUL	7704-34-9	PST22280
HEXATHION	786-19-6	PST04340
HEXAZINONE	51235-04-2	PST10994
HEXAZIR	137-30-4	PST25397
HEXONE	108-10-1	PST14550
HEXYL ALCOHOL	111-27-3	PST15630
HEXYLTHIOCARBAM	1134-23-2	PST71469
HHDN	309-00-2	PST00520
HI-SIL	63231-67-4	PST20670
HI-YIELD DESICCANT H-10	7778-39-4	PST01990
HILTACHLOR	23184-66-9	PST03497
HINOSAN	17109-49-8	PST08555
HIZAROCIN	66-81-9	PST05930
HKO	1310-58-3	PST19430
HKO4S	7646-93-7	PST19255
HNAO4S	7681-38-1	PST20990
HNA2O4P	7558-79-4	PST08330
HOE 16410	34123-59-6	PST12254
HOE 2747	1746-81-2	PST15174
HOE 2784	485-31-4	PST71960
HOE 2872	639-58-7	PST24380
HOE 2873	13457-18-6	PST73169
HOE 2960	24017-47-8	PST73068
HOE 2982	23560-59-0	PST10685
HOE 2991	27954-37-6	PST23002
HOE 33171	66441-23-4	PST72723
HOE 39 866	77182-82-2	PST72647

ALPHABETICAL INDEX

ALPHABETICAL INDEX

SUBSTANCE NAME	CAS #	PST #
HYDROXYACETIC ACID, SODIUM SALT	2836-32-0	PST11235
HYDROXYBENZENE	108-95-2	PST18380
HYDROXYBENZOPYRIDINE	148-24-3	PST30450
HYDROXYDIMETHYLARSINE OXIDE	75-60-5	PST03710
HYDROXYDIMETHYLARSINE OXIDE, SODIUM SALT	124-65-2	PST21070
HYDROXYDIMETHYLBENZENE	1300-71-6	PST25160
HYDROXYDIMETHYLBENZENE	105-67-9	PST28670
HYDROXYETHANOIC ACID	79-14-1	PST10500
HYDROXYISOXAZOLE	10004-44-1	PST22404
HYDROXYISOXAZOLE (PESTICIDE)	10004-44-1	PST22404
HYDROXYLATED SILICON DIOXIDE	63231-67-4	PST20670
HYDROXYPHENYL MERCURY	100-57-2	PST18580
HYDROXYPHENYLMERCURY	100-57-2	PST18580
HYDROXYTRICYCLOHEXYLSTANNANE	13121-70-5	PST06110
HYMEXAZOL	10004-44-1	PST22404
HYMEXAZOLE	10004-44-1	PST22404
HYOSAN	97-23-4	PST71611
HYPOCHLOROUS ACID, CALCIUM SALT	7778-54-3	PST03990
HYPOCHLOROUS ACID, LITHIUM SALT	13840-33-0	PST12920
HYPOCHLOROUS ACID, SODIUM SALT	7681-52-9	PST21310
HYTROL O	108-94-1	PST05890
HYVAR	314-42-1	PST71090
HYVAR X	314-40-9	PST03330
HYVAR X-WS	314-40-9	PST03330
HYVAREX	314-40-9	PST03330
H14NI010SI	10101-97-0	PST16410
H2O2	7722-84-1	PST11190
H2O4S	7664-93-9	PST22350
H3O4P	7664-38-2	PST18690
H6N2O3S	7773-06-0	PST01400
IBA	133-32-4	PST29325
IBP	26087-47-8	PST12355
ICETONE	15096-52-3	PST05560
ICHIBAN	21564-17-0	PST71392
ICI 29661	5221-49-8	PST08049
IGRAN	886-50-0	PST22538
IKURIN	7773-06-0	PST01400
IMAZETHAPYR	81335-77-5	PST11308
IMC 3950	28249-77-6	PST72381
IMIDAN	732-11-6	PST11307
IMIDAN O.A.	3735-33-9	PST18665
IMIDATHION	732-11-6	PST11307
IMIDAZOLE-1-ETHANOL, 2-METHYL-5-NITRO-	443-48-1	PST72529
IMIDAZOLE, 1-(2-HYDROXYETHYL)-2-METHYL-5-NITRO	443-48-1	PST72529
IMIDOCARBONIC ACID, PHOSPHONODITHIO-, CYCLIC METHYLENE P,P-DIETHYL ESTER	21548-32-3	PST16141
IMIDOCARBONIC ACID, PHOSPHONODITHIO-,CYCLIC ETHYLENE P,P-DIETHYL ESTER	947-02-4	PST06115
IMIDOCARBONIC ACID, PHOSPHONODITHIO-,CYCLIC PROPYLENE P,P-DIETHYL ESTER	950-10-7	PST13735
IMIDOXON	3735-33-9	PST18665
IMPEDEX	137-40-6	PST21575
INDEN-2-YL)UREA	28805-78-9	PST73199
INDENO(1,2-B)OXIRENE	1024-57-3	PST10670
INDOLE-3-BUTANOIC ACID	133-32-4	PST29325

ALPHABETICAL INDEX

SUBSTANCE NAME	CAS #	PST #
INDOLEBUTYRIC ACID	133-32-4	PST29325
INDOPOL L-50	9003-29-6	PST75671
INFERNO	78-53-5	PST83006
INHIBINE	7722-84-1	PST11190
INPC	122-42-9	PST71564
INPERON FIXER T	545-55-1	PST22510
INSECT REPELLENT-11	126-15-8	PST71487
INSECTOL	7696-12-0	PST23061
INSEGAR	72490-01-8	PST72618
INTERCIDE TMP	133-07-3	PST10012
INTEXAN LB-50	8001-54-5	PST00537
INTRATHION	640-15-3	PST83056
INTRATION	640-15-3	PST83056
INVALON OP	90-43-7	PST18470
IODINE	7553-56-2	PST11400
IODINE A.R. CRYSTALS (MALLINCKRODT)	7553-56-2	PST11400
IODINE CRYSTALS	7553-56-2	PST11400
IODINE MOLECULE (I2)	7553-56-2	PST11400
IODINE, SUBLIMED	7553-56-2	PST11400
IODOFENFOS	18181-70-9	PST73035
IODOFENPHOS	18181-70-9	PST73035
IODOPHOS	18181-70-9	PST73035
IOPEZITE	7778-50-9	PST19370
IOXYNIL	1689-83-4	PST11468
IOXYNIL OCTANOATE	3861-47-0	PST73075
IOXYNIL SODIUM	2961-62-8	PST73074
IP 50	34123-59-6	PST12254
IPC	122-42-9	PST71564
IPPC	122-42-9	PST71564
IPT	50512-35-1	PST12253
IPURON	34123-59-6	PST12254
IRON (III) DIMETHYLDITHIOCARBAMATE	14484-64-1	PST09680
IRON AMMONIUM SULFATE	10045-89-3	PST09820
IRON PERSULFATE	10028-22-5	PST09790
IRON SESQUISULFATE	10028-22-5	PST09790
IRON SULFATE	7782-63-0	PST09870
IRON SULFATE (2:3)	10028-22-5	PST09790
IRON TERSULFATE	10028-22-5	PST09790
IRON TRIS(DIMETHYLDITHIOCARBAMATE)	14484-64-1	PST09680
IRON(II) SULFATE	7782-63-0	PST09870
IRON(II) SULFATE (1:1), HEPTAHYDRATE	7782-63-0	PST09870
IRON(2+) SULFATE HEPTAHYDRATE	7782-63-0	PST09870
IRON(3+) SULFATE	10028-22-5	PST09790
IS	126-75-0	PST71646
ISAZOFOS	42509-80-8	PST15035
ISAZOPHOS	42509-80-8	PST15035
ISCOBROME	74-83-9	PST14300
ISOBENZAN	297-78-9	PST83032
ISOBUMETONE	26259-45-0	PST73051
ISOBUTYL KETONE	108-83-8	PST07500
ISOBUTYL METHYL KETONE	108-10-1	PST14550
ISOCHLOROTHION	2463-84-5	PST71380
ISOCHLORTHION	2463-84-5	PST71380
ISOCIL	314-42-1	PST71090

ALPHABETICAL INDEX

ALPHABETICAL INDEX

SUBSTANCE NAME	CAS #	PST #
ISOTHIOCYANIC ACID, ALLYL ESTER	57-06-7	PST00680
ISOTHIOCYANIC ACID, METHYL ESTER	556-61-6	PST14950
ISOTINOX	2587-90-8	PST73094
ISOTRON 11	75-69-4	PST09990
ISOURON	55861-78-4	PST72586
ISOVALERONE	108-83-8	PST07500
ISOXATHION	18854-01-8	PST12280
ISOXYL	55861-78-4	PST72586
IT 3456	2536-31-4	PST72283
IT-931	3347-22-6	PST72290
IVOSIT	2813-95-8	PST08021
I2	7553-56-2	PST11400
JALAN	2212-67-1	PST71471
JAPANESE CAMPHOR OIL	8008-51-3	PST04140
JAPANESE, OIL OF CAMPHOR	8008-51-3	PST04140
JAYSOL	64-17-5	PST08700
JODFENPHOS	18181-70-9	PST73035
JONNIX	3337-71-1	PST72352
JOXYNIL	1689-83-4	PST11468
JUDEAN PITCH	8052-42-4	PST02140
JUDEAN PITCH	8052-42-4	PST71177
JULIN'S CARBON CHLORIDE	118-74-1	PST10730
JUMBO	5329-14-6	PST22200
JURIMER AC 10H	9003-01-4	PST04349
K 22023	299-85-4	PST71236
K 6295	22936-86-3	PST72296
K-OTHRIN	52918-63-5	PST72784
K-THROMBYL	58-27-5	PST71050
K-10	8008-20-6	PST10090
KAKEN	66-81-9	PST05930
KALII	7758-02-3	PST19280
KALO	7778-44-1	PST03850
KAPTAX	149-30-4	PST13738
KARATHANE	39300-45-3	PST71402
KARBAM BLACK	14484-64-1	PST09680
KARBAM WHITE	137-30-4	PST25397
KARBOFOS	121-75-5	PST13540
KARBUTILATE	4849-32-5	PST72271
KARIDIUM	7681-49-4	PST21230
KARMEX	330-54-1	PST08420
KARPHOS	18854-01-8	PST12280
KARSTENITE	7778-18-9	PST04110
KAVADEL	78-34-2	PST08050
KAYQUINONE	58-27-5	PST71050
KAZOE	26628-22-8	PST20960
KEENATE	137-40-6	PST21575
KELTHANE	115-32-2	PST07010
KEMATE	101-05-3	PST01526
KENAPON	75-99-0	PST06200
KENCO #880-T FLUX THINNER (KENCO)	67-63-0	PST12090
KEPONE	143-50-0	PST12330
KERB	23950-58-5	PST19670
KEROSENE	8008-20-6	PST10090
KEROSINE	8008-20-6	PST10090

SUBSTANCE NAME	CAS #	PST #
KETHON CG 243	2682-20-4	PST72362
KETOHEXAMETHYLENE	108-94-1	PST05890
KI-N	7681-11-0	PST19435
KIESELGEL	63231-67-4	PST20670
KILLMASTER	2921-88-2	PST04910
KILMAG	7778-44-1	PST03850
KILRAT	1314-84-7	PST25540
KILVAL	2275-23-2	PST73108
KINETIN	525-79-1	PST72483
KITAZIN L	26087-47-8	PST12355
KITAZIN P	26087-47-8	PST12355
KITON BLUE AR	2650-18-2	PST08277
KLERAT	56073-10-0	PST03327
KLION	443-48-1	PST72529
KLOBEN	555-37-3	PST16143
KNOLLIDE	7681-11-0	PST19435
KNOX OUT 2FM INSECTICIDE	UNASSIGNED	PST12357
KNO3	7757-79-1	PST19470
KOBU	82-68-8	PST18140
KOBUTOL	82-68-8	PST18140
KODAFLEX DOP	117-81-7	PST06440
KODAK SODIUM BISULFITE,ANHYDROUS (KODAK)	7631-90-5	PST21000
KOLO 100	7704-34-9	PST22280
KOLTAR	42874-03-3	PST72413
KORIUM	97-23-4	PST71611
KORLAN	299-84-3	PST20180
KP 2	82-68-8	PST18140
KROVAR II	314-40-9	PST03330
KRYOCIDE	15096-52-3	PST05560
KRYSID	86-88-4	PST01830
KTI ACETONE (HUGHES)	67-64-1	PST00140
KUMULUS	7704-34-9	PST22280
KUPRITE	1317-39-1	PST05470
KURAN	93-72-1	PST20830
KURON	93-72-1	PST20830
KUROSAL G	93-72-1	PST20830
KVK 733059	21564-17-0	PST71392
KWIK-KIL	57-24-9	PST22080
KYLAR	1596-84-5	PST06195
KYONATE	333-20-0	PST19640
KYPFARIN	81-81-2	PST25090
K204S	7778-80-5	PST19590
K206S4	13932-13-3	PST72015
K407P2	7320-34-5	PST19546
K62-105	21609-90-5	PST12780
L 3	7440-22-4	PST20770
L 34314	957-51-7	PST71406
L 36352	1582-09-8	PST24085
L-(+)-N-(P-(((2,4-DIAMINO-6-PTERIDINYL)METHYL)METHYLAMINO)BENZOYL)-GLUTAMIC ACID	59-05-2	PST14210
L-(+)-N-(P-(((2,4-DIAMINO-6-PTERIDINYL)METHYL)METHYLAMINO)BENZOYL)-GLUTAMIC ACID, SODIUM SALT	15475-56-6	PST14211
L-GLUTAMIC ACID, N-(4-(((2,4-DIAMINO-6-PTERIDINYL)METHYL)-METHYLAMINO)BENZOYL)-	59-05-2	PST14210

SUBSTANCE NAME	CAS #	PST #
L-GLUTAMIC ACID, N-(4-(((2,4-DIAMINO-6-PTERIDINYL)METHYL)METHYLAMINO) BENZOYL)-, SODIUM SALT	15475-56-6	PST14211
L-METHOTREXATE	59-05-2	PST14210
L-METHOTREXATE SODIUM	15475-56-6	PST14211
L-3-(1-METHYL 1-2-PYRROLIDYL) PYRIDINE	54-11-5	PST16430
L-7	8006-54-0	PST12425
LACCO METHYLENE CHLORIDE (PPG INDUSTRIES INC.)	75-09-2	PST14930
LACTAMIDE, N-ETHYL-, CARBANILATE (ESTER), D-	16118-49-3	PST72941
LAKE YELLOW	1934-21-0	PST22465
LAMBAST	23184-66-9	PST03497
LAMBAST	845-52-3	PST72212
LAMPRECID	88-30-2	PST71405
LANAIN	8006-54-0	PST12425
LANALIN	8006-54-0	PST12425
LANCE	51487-69-5	PST72572
LANDRIN	12407-86-2	PST12420
LANESIN	8006-54-0	PST12425
LANEX	2164-17-2	PST09907
LANICHOL	8006-54-0	PST12425
LANIOL	8006-54-0	PST12425
LANNATE	16752-77-5	PST14200
LANOLIN	8006-54-0	PST12425
LANUM	8006-54-0	PST12425
LAPIS INFERNALIS	7761-88-8	PST20810
LAPROL	25322-69-4	PST19140
LARIAT FLOWABLE HERBICIDE	UNASSIGNED	PST12471
LARVACIDE	76-06-2	PST04830
LARVADEX	66215-27-8	PST72536
LARVAKIL	35367-38-5	PST07388
LARVIN	59669-26-0	PST72456
LASER GUARD (DYNATEX CORPORATION)	127-18-4	PST22900
LASSO	15972-60-8	PST00506
LASSO AND ATRAZINE FLOWABLE HERBICIDE	UNASSIGNED	PST12481
LAURIC ACID, POTASSIUM SALT	10124-65-9	PST72072
LAURIC ALCOHOL	112-53-8	PST12500
LAURINIC ALCOHOL	112-53-8	PST12500
LAURYL ALCOHOL	112-53-8	PST12500
LAURYL SODIUM SULFATE	151-21-3	PST08485
LAURYL SULFATE SODIUM	151-21-3	PST08485
LAURYL SULFATE SODIUM SALT	151-21-3	PST08485
LAURYLBENZENESULFONATE	27176-87-0	PST08480
LAURYLBENZENESULFONIC ACID	27176-87-0	PST08480
LAUXTOL	87-86-5	PST18150
LAZO	15972-60-8	PST00506
LB-BUTYLENE GLYCOL	107-88-0	PST26730
LEAD ARSENATE	7784-40-9	PST12540
LEAD ARSENATE, SOLID	7784-40-9	PST12540
LEBAYCID (FORMULATION)	55-38-9	PST02550
LEGURAME	16118-49-3	PST72941
LEIOCOM	9004-53-9	PST06363
LEMON YELOW A	1934-21-0	PST22465
LENACIL	2164-08-1	PST73238
LENOCYCLINE	79-57-2	PST17414
LENS CLENS #3 (GENERAL PRODUCTION SERVICES INC.)	67-63-0	PST12090

ALPHABETICAL INDEX

SUBSTANCE NAME	CAS #	PST #
LEPICRON	59669-26-0	PST72456
LEPTOPHOS	21609-90-5	PST12780
LEPTOPHOS OA	25006-32-0	PST12776
LEPTOPHOS OXON	25006-32-0	PST12776
LEPTOPHOS OXYGEN ANALOG	25006-32-0	PST12776
LETHANE	112-56-1	PST75661
LETHANE 384	112-56-1	PST75661
LETHANE 384 REGULAR	112-56-1	PST75661
LETHELMIN	92-84-2	PST18400
LEXONEEX	21087-64-9	PST15006
LEY-CORNOX	3813-05-6	PST72725
LIDAMYCIN CREME	1405-10-3	PST84263
LIGHT CAMPHOR OIL	8008-51-3	PST04140
LIGNASAN	2235-25-8	PST71479
LIME	1305-78-8	PST04030
LIME CHLORIDE	7778-54-3	PST03990
LIME WATER	1305-62-0	PST03980
LIME, UNSLAKED	1305-78-8	PST04030
LINDANE	58-89-9	PST12810
LINSEED OIL	8001-26-1	PST71365
LINSEED OIL, BLEACHED	8001-26-1	PST71365
LINSEED OIL, RAW	8001-26-1	PST71365
LINUREX	330-55-2	PST12826
LINURON	330-55-2	PST12826
LIPHADIONE	3691-35-8	PST04826
LIPOSORB L-20	9005-65-6	PST40200
LIPOSORB O-20	9005-65-6	PST40200
LIQUAMYCIN	79-57-2	PST17414
LIQUAMYCIN INJECTABLE	2058-46-0	PST84045
LIQUID PITCH OIL	8001-58-9	PST05230
LIROMATIN	900-95-8	PST24378
LIRONION	14214-32-5	PST07386
LIRONOX	94-80-4	PST71295
LIROPON	75-99-0	PST06200
LIROPREM	87-86-5	PST18150
LIROSTANOL	900-95-8	PST24378
LITHIUM HYPOCHLORITE	13840-33-0	PST12920
LITHIUM HYPOCHLORITE COMPOUND, DRY	13840-33-0	PST12920
LM 91	3691-35-8	PST04826
LOGIC	72490-01-8	PST72618
LONTREL	1702-17-6	PST05211
LOREX	330-55-2	PST12826
LOROX	330-55-2	PST12826
LORSBAN	2921-88-2	PST04910
LOSANTIN	7778-54-3	PST03990
LS 4442	639-58-7	PST24380
LS 74-783	39148-24-8	PST72563
LS-303 (POLYTECH)	75-09-2	PST14930
LUBRICATING BASE OIL	64742-52-5	PST17323
LUNAR CAUSTIC	7761-88-8	PST20810
LUPRISOL	79-09-4	PST19750
LUTROL-9	107-21-1	PST09400
LYE	1310-58-3	PST19430
LYE	1310-73-2	PST21300

ALPHABETICAL INDEX

SUBSTANCE NAME	CAS #	PST #
MERCURAN	151-38-2	PST83031
MERCURATE(2), ETHYL(PHOSPHATO(3-)-O-)-, DIHYDROGEN	2235-25-8	PST71479
MERCURIC BICHLORIDE	7487-94-7	PST13800
MERCURIC CHLORIDE	7487-94-7	PST13800
MERCURIC CHLORIDE, SOLID	7487-94-7	PST13800
MERCURIPHENYL ACETATE	62-38-4	PST18560
MERCURIPHENYL CHLORIDE	100-56-1	PST18570
MERCURY BICHLORIDE	7487-94-7	PST13800
MERCURY PERCHLORIDE	7487-94-7	PST13800
MERCURY(II) CHLORIDE	7487-94-7	PST13800
MERCURY(1+), (2,2',2''-NITRILOTRIS(ETHANOL)-N,O,O',O'') PHENYL-, SALT WITH 2-HYDROXYPROPANOIC ACID(1:1)	23319-66-6	PST71768
MERCURY, (ACETATO)ETHYL-	109-62-6	PST71476
MERCURY, (ACETATO-O)ETHYL-	109-62-6	PST71476
MERCURY, (CYANOGUANIDINATO)METHYL-	502-39-6	PST83040
MERCURY, (CYANOGUANIDINATO-N')METHYL-	502-39-6	PST83040
MERCURY, (CYANOGUANIDINE)METHYL-	502-39-6	PST83040
MERCURY, (DIHYDROGEN PHOSPHATO)ETHYL-	2235-25-8	PST71479
MERCURY, (MU-(HYDROGEN ORTHOBORATO))DIPHENYLDI-	6273-99-0	PST71754
MERCURY, (MU-(ORTHOBORATO(2-)-O:O'))DIPHENYLDI-	6273-99-0	PST71754
MERCURY, (OLEATO)PHENYL	104-60-9	PST71769
MERCURY, (OLEOYLOXY)PHENYL-	104-60-9	PST71769
MERCURY, (9-OCTADECENOATO-O)PHENYL-, (Z)-	104-60-9	PST71769
MERCURY, ACETOXYETHYL-	109-62-6	PST71476
MERCURY, CHLOROETHYL-	107-27-7	PST09620
MERFAZIN	100-56-1	PST18570
MERKAZIN	7287-19-6	PST19968
MERKON	13171-21-6	PST18670
MERKURAN	151-38-2	PST83031
MERPAFOS	35400-43-2	PST22387
MERPAN	133-06-2	PST04210
MERPHOS	150-50-5	PST10010
MERSOLITE	62-38-4	PST18560
MERSOLITE 1	100-57-2	PST18580
MERSOLITE 2	100-56-1	PST18570
MERTAX	149-30-4	PST13738
MESORANIL	4658-28-0	PST02216
MESULFENFOS	3761-41-9	PST02555
MESUROL	2032-65-7	PST14190
MESUROL SULFOXIDE	2635-10-1	PST14191
MET 1486	30043-49-3	PST72551
META	108-62-3	PST14090
META-CRESOL,6 ISO-PROPYL	89-83-8	PST23475
METABENZTHIAZURON	18691-97-9	PST14108
METABROM	2104-96-3	PST71064
METACETALDEHYDE	108-62-3	PST14090
METACETONIC ACID	79-09-4	PST19750
METACHLOR	15972-60-8	PST00506
METACIDE	298-00-0	PST14680
METACRATE	1129-41-5	PST83074
METADELPHENE	134-62-3	PST84230
METAFUME	74-83-9	PST14300
METAISOSYSTOX SULFOXIDE	301-12-2	PST17375

SUBSTANCE NAME	CAS #	PST #
METHANIMIDAMIDE, N'-(4-CHLORO-2-METHYLPHENYL) N,N-DIMETHYL-	6164-98-3	PST04570
METHANIMIDAMIDE, N'-(4-CHLORO-2-METHYLPHENYL)-N,N-DIMETHYL-, MONOHYDROCHLORIDE	19750-95-9	PST71656
METHANOL	67-56-1	PST14280
METHANOL (ELECTROKLEIN) (ROK)	67-56-1	PST14280
METHANOL, SPECTRO QUALITY (MCB MANF. CHEMIST)	67-56-1	PST14280
METHANONE, BIS(4-CHLOROPHENYL)-	90-98-2	PST06246
METHASAN	137-30-4	PST25397
METHAZOLE	20354-26-1	PST72344
METHBENZTHIAZURON	18691-97-9	PST14108
METHIDATHION	950-37-8	PST14175
METHIOCARB	2032-65-7	PST14190
METHIOCARB SULFOXIDE	2635-10-1	PST14191
METHOGAS	74-83-9	PST14300
METHOMYL	16752-77-5	PST14200
METHOPROPTRYNE	841-06-5	PST14204
METHOPROTRYN	841-06-5	PST14204
METHOPROTRYNE	841-06-5	PST14204
METHOTREXATE	59-05-2	PST14210
METHOTREXATE	15475-56-6	PST14211
METHOTREXATE SODIUM	15475-56-6	PST14211
METHOTRYNE	841-06-5	PST14204
METHOXONE	94-74-6	PST27880
METHOXY-DDT	72-43-5	PST14220
METHOXYCHLOR	72-43-5	PST14220
METHOXYDIURON	330-55-2	PST12826
METHOXYETHANOL	109-86-4	PST14340
METHOXYETHYLENE GLYCOL	109-86-4	PST14340
METHOXYETHYLMERCURIC ACETATE	151-38-2	PST83031
METHOXYHYDROXYETHANE	109-86-4	PST14340
METHOXYPROPAZINE	1610-18-0	PST19967
METHYL ((METHOXY(METHYLPHOSPHINOTHIOYL)THIO)ACETYL)METHYLCARBAMATE	29173-31-7	PST73246
METHYL ((4-AMINOPHENYL)SULFONYL)CARBAMATE	3337-71-1	PST72352
METHYL (MERCAPTOACETYL)METHYLCARBAMATE S-ESTER WITH O-METHYL METHYLPHOSPHONODITHIOATE	29173-31-7	PST73246
METHYL (1-((BUTYLAMINO)CARBONYL)-1H-BENZIMIDAZOL-2-YL)CARBAMATE	17804-35-2	PST02580
METHYL ACETIC ACID	79-09-4	PST19750
METHYL ACETONE	78-93-3	PST14460
METHYL ALCOHOL	67-56-1	PST14280
METHYL ALDEHYDE	50-00-0	PST50003
METHYL ARSONIC ACID, MONOSODIUM SALT	2163-80-6	PST15180
METHYL BROMIDE	74-83-9	PST14300
METHYL BROMIDE, LIQUID	74-83-9	PST14300
METHYL CARBAMIC ACID 1-NAPHTHYL ESTER	63-25-2	PST04220
METHYL CARBAMIC ACID 4-(DIALLYLAMINO)-3,5-XYLYL ESTER	6392-46-7	PST72977
METHYL CARBAMIC ACID, M-TOLY ESTER	1129-41-5	PST83074
METHYL CARBAMIC ACID, 3-METHYLPHENYL ESTER	1129-41-5	PST83074
METHYL CARBOPHENOTHION	953-17-3	PST71647
METHYL CELLOSOLVE	109-86-4	PST14340
METHYL CHEMOSEPT	99-76-3	PST14677
METHYL CHLORAMBEN	7286-84-2	PST71255
METHYL CHLOROFORM	71-55-6	PST14370
METHYL CHLORPYRIFOS	5598-13-0	PST71652
METHYL DEMETON	8022-00-2	PST14438

ALPHABETICAL INDEX

SUBSTANCE NAME	CAS #	PST #
METHYL DEMETON THIOESTER	919-86-8	PST83065
METHYL DURSBAN	5598-13-0	PST71652
METHYL ETHYL KETONE	78-93-3	PST14460
METHYL ETHYLENE OXIDE	75-56-9	PST19910
METHYL GLYCOL	109-86-4	PST14340
METHYL HYDROXIDE	67-56-1	PST14280
METHYL ISOBUTYL KETONE	108-10-1	PST14550
METHYL ISOTHIOCYANATE	556-61-6	PST14950
METHYL KETONE	67-64-1	PST00140
METHYL M-HYDROXYCARBANILATE M-METHYLCARBANILATE (ESTER)	13684-63-4	PST72282
METHYL MERCURIC DICYANAMIDE	502-39-6	PST83040
METHYL MUSTARD	556-61-6	PST14950
METHYL MUSTARD OIL	556-61-6	PST14950
METHYL N-(((METHYLAMINO)CARBONYL)OXY)ETHANIMIDOTHIOATE	16752-77-5	PST14200
METHYL N-((METHYLCARBOMOYL)OXY)THIOACETIMIDATE	16752-77-5	PST14200
METHYL N-(METHOXY(METHYL)THIOPHOSPHORYLTHIOACETYL)-N-METHYLCARBAMATE	29173-31-7	PST73246
METHYL N-(3,4-DICHLOROPHENYL)CARBAMATE	1918-18-9	PST72247
METHYL N-NONYL KETONE	112-12-9	PST14675
METHYL N',N'-DIMETHYL-N-((METHYLCARBAMOYL)OXY)-1-THIOOXAMIMIDATE	23135-22-0	PST17370
METHYL NONYL KETONE	112-12-9	PST14675
METHYL O-(METHYLCARBAMOYL)THIOLACETOHYDROXAMATE	16752-77-5	PST14200
METHYL O-HYDROXYBENZOATE	119-36-8	PST14720
METHYL OXIRANE	75-56-9	PST19910
METHYL OXITOL	109-86-4	PST14340
METHYL OXYDEMETON S	301-12-2	PST17375
METHYL P-HYDROXYBENZOATE	99-76-3	PST14677
METHYL P-OXYBENZOATE	99-76-3	PST14677
METHYL PARABEN	99-76-3	PST14677
METHYL PARAHYDROXYBENZOATE	99-76-3	PST14677
METHYL PARAOXON	950-35-6	PST14678
METHYL PARASEPT	99-76-3	PST14677
METHYL PARATHION	298-00-0	PST14680
METHYL PARATHION OXYGEN ANALOG	950-35-6	PST14678
METHYL PARATHION 80%	UNASSIGNED	PST14681
METHYL PHENCAPTON	3735-23-7	PST73085
METHYL PHENKAPTON	3735-23-7	PST73085
METHYL PHOSPHORAMIDOTHIOATE	10265-92-6	PST15160
METHYL PYRIMIPHOS	29232-93-7	PST72378
METHYL SALICYLATE	119-36-8	PST14720
METHYL SULFANILYLCARBAMATE	3337-71-1	PST72352
METHYL SULPHANILYLCARBAMATE	3337-71-1	PST72352
METHYL SYSTOX	8022-00-2	PST14438
METHYL THIOISOCYANATE	556-61-6	PST14950
METHYL TRITHION	953-17-3	PST71647
METHYL VIOLOGEN	1910-42-5	PST18020
METHYL VIOLOGEN (2+)	4685-14-7	PST71671
METHYL VIOLOGEN DICHLORIDE	1910-42-5	PST18020
METHYL 1-(BUTYLCARBAMOYL)-2-BENZIMIDAZOLECARBAMATE	17804-35-2	PST02580
METHYL 1-(BUTYLCARBAMOYL)BENZIMIDAZOL-2-YLCARBAMATE	17804-35-2	PST02580
METHYL 2-((((4,6-DIMETHYL-2-PYRIMIDINYL)AMINO)CARBONYL)AMINO)-SULFONYL)BENZOATE	74222-97-2	PST72544
METHYL 2-(DIMETHYLAMINO)N-(((METHYLAMINO)CARBONYL)OXYL)-2-OXOETHANIMIDOTHIOATE	23135-22-0	PST17370
METHYL 2-(3-(4,6-DIMETHYLPYRIMIDIN-2-YL)UREIDOSULPHONYL)BENZOATE	74222-97-2	PST72544

SUBSTANCE NAME	CAS #	PST #
METHYL 2-CHLORO-9-HYDROXY-9H-FLUORENE-9-CARBOXYLATE	2536-31-4	PST72283
METHYL 2-HYDROXYBENZOATE	119-36-8	PST14720
METHYL 2,4-DICHLOROPHENOXY ACETATE	1928-38-7	PST71307
METHYL 3-((DIMETHOXYPHOSPHINYL)OXY)-2-BUTENOATE	7786-34-7	PST18650
METHYL 3-(DIMETHOXYPHOSPHINOYLOXY)BUT-2-ENOATE	7786-34-7	PST18650
METHYL 3-(M-TOLYLCARBAMOYLOXY)PHENYLCARBAMATE	13684-63-4	PST72282
METHYL 3-(3-METHYLCARBANILOYLOXY)CARBANILATE	13684-63-4	PST72282
METHYL 3-AMINO-2,5-DICHLOROBENZOATE	7286-84-2	PST71255
METHYL 3-HYDROXYCROTONATE DIMETHYL PHOSPHATE ESTER	7786-34-7	PST18650
METHYL 3,4-DICHLOROCARBANILATE	1918-18-9	PST72247
METHYL 3,4-DICHLOROPHENYLCARBAMATE	1918-18-9	PST72247
METHYL 3,7-DIMETHYL-6-OXO-2-OXA-4-THIA-7-AZA-3-PHOSPHAOCTAN-8-OATE 3-SULFIDE	29173-31-7	PST73246
METHYL 4-(2,4-DICHLOROPHENOXY)BUTYRATE	18625-12-2	PST06227
METHYL 4-AMINOBENZENESULPHONYLCARBAMATE	3337-71-1	PST72352
METHYL 4-AMINOPHENYLSULPHONYLCARBAMATE	3337-71-1	PST72352
METHYL 4-CHLORO-2-METHYLPHENOXY ACETATE	2436-73-9	PST27881
METHYL 5-(2,4-DICHLOROPHENOXY)-2-NITROBENZOATE	42576-02-3	PST72332
METHYL(METHOXY(METHYL)PHOSPHINOTHIOYLTHIO)ACETYL(METHYL)CARBAMATE	29173-31-7	PST73246
METHYL(2,4,5-TRICHLOROPHENOXY) ACETATE	1928-37-6	PST22392
METHYL-NITROIMIDAZOLE-1-ETHANOL	443-48-1	PST72529
METHYL-O-DEMETON	867-27-6	PST71969
METHYL-2-(((((4-METHOXY-6-METHYL-1,3,5-TRIAZIN-2-YL)-AMINO)CARBONYL) AMINO)SULFONYL)BENZOATE	74223-64-6	PST72546
METHYL-2-(2,4,5-TRICHLOROPHENOXY)PROPIONATE	4841-20-7	PST20831
METHYL-2-METHOXY-3,6-DICHLOROBENZOATE	6597-78-0	PST73131
METHYL-3,6-DICHLORO-O-ANISATE	6597-78-0	PST73131
METHYLAMINOPTERIN	59-05-2	PST14210
METHYLAMINOPTERIN SODIUM	15475-56-6	PST14211
METHYLBEN	99-76-3	PST14677
METHYLBENZETHONIUM CHLORIDE	25155-18-4	PST71862
METHYLCARBAMIC ACID BENZO(B)THIEN-4-YL ESTER	1079-33-0	PST29855
METHYLCARBAMIC ACID ESTER WITH N'-(M-HYDROXYPHENYL)-N,N-DIMETHYLFORMAMIDINE, MONOHYDROCHLORIDE	23422-53-9	PST10050
METHYLCARBAMIC ACID ESTER WITH N'-(4-HYDROXY-O-TOLYL)-N,N-DIMETHYL FORMAMIDINE	17702-57-7	PST73082
METHYLCARBAMIC ACID M-(1-ETHYLPROPYL)PHENYL ESTER MIXTURE WITH M-(1-METHYLBUTYL)PHENYL ESTER	8065-36-9	PST03480
METHYLCARBAMIC ACID M-CUMENYL ESTER	64-00-6	PST29423
METHYLCARBAMIC ACID M-CYM-5-YL ESTER	2631-37-0	PST72957
METHYLCARBAMIC ACID O-CUMENYL ESTER	2631-40-5	PST73231
METHYLCARBAMIC ACID O-SEC-BUTYLPHENYL ESTER	3766-81-2	PST03324
METHYLCARBAMIC ACID O-1,3-DIOXOLAN-2-YLPHENYL ESTER	6988-21-2	PST73123
METHYLCARBAMIC ACID 2,3-(ISOPROPYLIDENEDIOXY)PHENYL ESTER	22781-23-3	PST02560
METHYLCARBAMIC ACID 2,3-DIHYDRO-2,2-DIMETHYL-7-BENZOFURANYL ESTER	1563-66-2	PST04240
METHYLCARBAMIC ACID 3,5-DI-TERT-BUTYLPHENYL ESTER	2655-19-8	PST72994
METHYLCARBAMIC ACID 3,5-XYLYL ESTER	2655-14-3	PST25171
METHYLCARBAMIC ACID 4-(DIMETHYLAMINO)-3,5-XYLYL ESTER	315-18-4	PST15010
METHYLCARBAMIC ACID 4-(METHYLTHIO)-3,5-XYLYL ESTER	2032-65-7	PST14190
METHYLCARBAMIC ACID-2,3-DIHYDRO-3-HYDROXY-2,2-DIMETHYL-7-BENZOFURANYL ESTER	16655-82-6	PST72800
METHYLCARBAMIC ACID, ALPHA-(ETHYLTHIO)-O-TOLYL ESTER	29973-13-5	PST72421
METHYLCARBAMIC ACID, ESTER WITH N'-(M-HYDROXYPHENYL)-N,N-DIMETHYL-FORMAMIDINE	22259-30-9	PST73187

SUBSTANCE NAME	CAS #	PST #
METHYLCARBAMIC ACID, M-(((DIMETHYLAMINO)METHYLENE)AMINO)PHENYL ESTER	22259-30-9	PST73187
METHYLCARBAMIC ACID, O((2,4-DIMETHYL-1,3-DITHIOLAN-2-YL)METHYLENE) AMINO)	26419-73-8	PST73088
METHYLCARBAMIC ACID, O-ISOPROPOXYPHENYL ESTER	114-26-1	PST02540
METHYLCARBAMIC ACID, 1-NAPHTHYL ESTER	63-25-2	PST04220
METHYLCARBAMIC ACID, 4-(DIMETHYLAMINO)-M-TOLYL ESTER	2032-59-9	PST71500
METHYLCARBAMIC 2,3,5(OR 3,4,5)-TRIMETHYLPHENYL ESTER	12407-86-2	PST12420
METHYLCARBAMODITHIOIC ACID, MONOSODIUM SALT	137-42-8	PST71430
METHYLCHLOROFORM	71-55-6	PST14370
METHYLCHLOROTHION	500-28-7	PST71379
METHYLDITHIOCARBAMIC ACID, MONOSODIUM SALT	137-42-8	PST71430
METHYLENE CHLORIDE	75-09-2	PST14930
METHYLENE DICHLORIDE	75-09-2	PST14930
METHYLENE GLYCOL	50-00-0	PST50003
METHYLENE OXIDE	50-00-0	PST50003
METHYLETHYL GLYCOL	57-55-6	PST19870
METHYLETHYLENE GLYCOL	57-55-6	PST19870
METHYLISOTHIOCYANATE	556-61-6	PST14950
METHYLMERCAPTOPHOS	8022-00-2	PST14438
METHYLMERCURIC DICYANAMIDE	502-39-6	PST83040
METHYLOL	67-56-1	PST14280
METHYLPARAOXON	950-35-6	PST14678
METHYLPHOSPHONIC ACID, S-(2-BIS(1-METHYLETHYL)AMINO)ETHYL) O-ETHYL ESTER	50782-69-9	PST83104
METHYLPHOSPHONOTHIOIC ACID, O-(PARA-NITROPHENYL) O-PHENYL ESTER	2665-30-7	PST73278
METHYLPHOSPHONOTHIOIC ACID, O-(4-NITROPHENYL) O-PHENYL ESTER	2665-30-7	PST73278
METHYLPHOSPHORAMIDIC ACID 2-CHLORO-4-(1,1-DIMETHYLETHYL)PHENYL METHYL ESTER	299-86-5	PST05550
METHYLPHOSPHORAMIDIC ACID 4-TERT-BUTYL-2-CHLOROPHENYL METHYL ESTER	299-86-5	PST05550
METHYLPIRIMIPHOS	29232-93-7	PST72378
METHYLTHIOFANATE	23564-05-8	PST72308
METHYLTHIOPHANATE	23564-05-8	PST72308
METHYLTHIOPHOS	298-00-0	PST14680
METHYLTRICHLOROMETHANE	71-55-6	PST14370
METHYLTRIMETHYLENE GLYCOL	107-88-0	PST26730
METHYLVIOLOGEN CHLORIDE	1910-42-5	PST18020
METHYRIMOL	5221-53-4	PST72919
METIRAM	9006-42-2	PST71123
METMERCAPTURON	2032-65-7	PST14190
METOBROMURON	3060-89-7	PST15008
METOLACHLOR	51218-45-2	PST15003
METOLACHLORE	51218-45-2	PST15003
METOLCARB	1129-41-5	PST83074
METOXURAN	19937-59-8	PST15009
METOXURON	19937-59-8	PST15009
METRAMAC	78-53-5	PST83006
METRIBUZIN	21087-64-9	PST15006
METRIFONATE	52-68-6	PST23790
METRIPHONATE	52-68-6	PST23790
METRONIDAZOLE	443-48-1	PST72529
METSIL	6834-92-0	PST21373
METSO BEADS, DRYMET	6834-92-0	PST21373
METSO 200	6834-92-0	PST21373
METSULFURON METHYL	74223-64-6	PST72546

SUBSTANCE NAME	CAS #	PST #
METSULFURON-METHYL	74223-64-6	PST72546
MEVINPHOS	7786-34-7	PST18650
MEXACARBATE	315-18-4	PST15010
MEXATE	59-05-2	PST14210
MEXATE SODIUM	15475-56-6	PST14211
MEZENE	137-30-4	PST25397
MEZOPUR	20354-26-1	PST72344
MEZOTOX	1836-75-5	PST23580
MEZURON	4658-28-0	PST02216
MGK DOG AND CAT REPELLENT	112-12-9	PST14675
MGK REPELLENT 11	126-15-8	PST71487
MGK 11	126-15-8	PST71487
MGK 264	113-48-4	PST15955
MGO4S	7487-88-9	PST13510
MH	123-33-1	PST13570
MH30	123-33-1	PST13570
MIBK	108-10-1	PST14550
MICRO ETCH 50 (DELTA ENTERPRISES INC.)	7722-84-1	PST11190
MICRO-CHEK 11	26530-20-1	PST72294
MICROLYSIN	76-06-2	PST04830
MIK	108-10-1	PST14550
MILCURB	5221-53-4	PST72919
MILCURB SUPER	23947-60-6	PST08721
MILDEX	39300-45-3	PST71402
MILDOTHANE	23564-05-8	PST72308
MILGO	23947-60-6	PST08721
MILLIE	5131-24-8	PST72347
MILO-PRO	139-40-2	PST19736
MILOGARD	139-40-2	PST19736
MILSTEM	23947-60-6	PST08721
MINACIDE	2631-37-0	PST72957
MINERAL PITCH	8052-42-4	PST02140
MINERAL PITCH	8052-42-4	PST71177
MINTACOL	311-45-5	PST07200
MIOTISAL	311-45-5	PST07200
MIPAFOX	371-86-8	PST15030
MIPC	2631-40-5	PST73231
MIPCIN	2631-40-5	PST73231
MIRAL	42509-80-8	PST15035
MIREX	2385-85-5	PST09690
MISSILE	13457-18-6	PST73169
MISULBAN	55-98-1	PST03482
MITOSANI	55-98-1	PST03482
MITOX	103-17-3	PST71139
MITROL G-ST	131-52-2	PST08506
MMD	502-39-6	PST83040
MO	1836-77-7	PST23865
MOBAM	1079-33-0	PST29855
MOBILE KEROSINE (MOBILE OIL CORP.)	8008-20-6	PST10090
MOCAP	13194-48-4	PST15080
MODOWN	42576-02-3	PST72332
MOHR'S SALT	10045-89-3	PST09820
MOLECULAR CHLORINE	7782-50-5	PST04600
MOLECULAR IODINE	7553-56-2	PST11400

ALPHABETICAL INDEX

SUBSTANCE NAME	CAS #	PST #
MOLINATE	2212-67-1	PST71471
MON 0139	38641-94-0	PST20205
MON 0573	1071-83-6	PST10515
MON 097	34256-82-1	PST72539
MONALIDE	7287-36-7	PST72987
MONAQUEST IA	139-41-3	PST71447
MONCEREN	66063-05-6	PST72622
MONITAN	9005-65-6	PST40200
MONITOR	10265-92-6	PST15160
MONO(2,2-DIMETHLYHYDRAZIDE)SUCCINIC ACID	1596-84-5	PST06195
MONOAMMONIUM SULFAMATE	7773-06-0	PST01400
MONOBASIC SODIUM PHOSPHATE	7558-80-7	PST15190
MONOBROMOMETHANE	74-83-9	PST14300
MONOBUTYL GLYCOL ETHER	111-76-2	PST03540
MONOCHLOROTRIBUTYLTIN	1461-22-9	PST72222
MONOCROTOPHOS	6923-22-4	PST15165
MONODODECYL SODIUM SULFATE	151-21-3	PST08485
MONOETHANOLAMINE	141-43-5	PST08710
MONOETHYLENE GLYCOL	107-21-1	PST09400
MONOFLUOROTRICHLOROMETHANE	75-69-4	PST09990
MONOHYDROCHLORIDE, (4S-(4 ALPHA,4A ALPHA,5 ALPHA,5A ALPHA,6 BETA, 12A ALPHA))-	2058-46-0	PST84045
MONOHYDROGEN DISODIUM PHOSPHATE	7558-79-4	PST08330
MONOHYDROXYBENZENE	108-95-2	PST18380
MONOHYDROXYMETHANE	67-56-1	PST14280
MONOLINURON	1746-81-2	PST15174
MONOMETHYLGLYCOL	109-86-4	PST14340
MONOPHENOL	108-95-2	PST18380
MONOPOLE OIL MDD	8002-33-3	PST24575
MONOPOTASSIUM SALT	125-67-7	PST71492
MONOPOTASSIUM SULFATE	7646-93-7	PST19255
MONOPROPYLENE GLYCOL	57-55-6	PST19870
MONOROTOX	1746-81-2	PST15174
MONOSODIUM ACID METHANE ARSONATE	2163-80-6	PST15180
MONOSODIUM ARSENITE LIQUID	7784-46-5	PST52136
MONOSODIUM CARBONATE	144-55-8	PST20970
MONOSODIUM DIHYDROGEN PHOSPHATE	7558-80-7	PST15190
MONOSODIUM HYDROGEN CARBONATE	144-55-8	PST20970
MONOSODIUM HYDROGEN PHOSPHATE	7558-80-7	PST15190
MONOSODIUM HYDROGEN SULFATE	7681-38-1	PST20990
MONOSODIUM METHANE ARSONATE	2163-80-6	PST15180
MONOSODIUM METHANEARSONATE	2163-80-6	PST15180
MONOSODIUM ORTHOPHOSPHATE	7558-80-7	PST15190
MONOSODIUM PHOSPHATE	7558-80-7	PST15190
MONOSODIUM SULFATE	7681-38-1	PST20990
MONOSODIUM SULFITE	7631-90-5	PST21000
MONSANTO CP-19699	13067-93-1	PST05805
MONTREL	299-86-5	PST05550
MONUREX	150-68-5	PST15196
MONURON	150-68-5	PST15196
MONURON TCA	140-41-0	PST15197
MONURON TRICHLOROACETATE	140-41-0	PST15197
MOROCIDE	485-31-4	PST71960
MORPHACTIN	2536-31-4	PST72283

ALPHABETICAL INDEX

SUBSTANCE NAME	CAS #	PST #
MORPHOTHION	144-41-2	PST73096
MORPHOTOX	144-41-2	PST73096
MORTON SOLAR SALT (MORTON THIOKOL)	7647-14-5	PST21105
MOTH BALLS	91-20-3	PST16120
MOTH FLAKES	91-20-3	PST16120
MOUSE TOX	57-24-9	PST22080
MOUSE-CON	1314-84-7	PST25540
MOUSE-RID	57-24-9	PST22080
MPMT	845-52-3	PST72212
MPT	50782-69-9	PST83104
MSMA	2163-80-6	PST15180
MSP	7558-80-7	PST15190
MULTIPROP	2536-31-4	PST72283
MUREX	15879-93-3	PST00775
MURFOTOX	2595-54-2	PST13675
MURIACITE	7778-18-9	PST04110
MURIATIC ACID	7647-01-0	PST11150
MURVESCO	80-38-6	PST09677
MUSCALURE	27519-02-4	PST05185
MUSCATOX	56-72-4	PST05490
MUSTARD OIL	57-06-7	PST00680
MV 119A	3347-22-6	PST72290
MYACIDE AS	52-51-7	PST72832
MYCERIN SULFATE	1405-10-3	PST84263
MYCIFRADIN	1405-10-3	PST84263
MYCIFRADIN-N	1405-10-3	PST84263
MYCIGUENT	1405-10-3	PST84263
MYCOBAN	137-40-6	PST21575
MYFUSAN	117-18-0	PST71616
MYLERAN	55-98-1	PST03482
MYLONE	533-74-4	PST06230
MYRISTIC ACID POTASSIUM SALT	13429-27-1	PST72073
MYSTOX WFA	132-27-4	PST08500
N 2790	944-22-9	PST10020
N(MERCAPTOMETHYL)PHTHALIMIDE S-(O,O-DIMETHYL)PHOSPHOROTHIOATE	3735-33-9	PST18665
N-(((((2,3-DIHYDRO-2,2-DIMETHYL-7-BENZOFURANYL)OXY)CARBONYL) METHYLAMINO)THIO)-N-(1-METHYLETHYL)-BETA-ALANINE ETHYL ESTER	82560-54-1	PST72562
N-(((METHYLAMINO)CARBONYL)OXY)ETHANIMIDOTHIOIC ACID METHYL ESTER	16752-77-5	PST14200
N-(((4-CHLOROPHENYL)AMINO)CARBONYL)-2,6-DIFLUOROBENZAMIDE	35367-38-5	PST07388
N-((DICHLOROFLUOROMETHYL)THIO)-N',N'-DIMETHYL-N-P-TOLYLSULFAMIDE	731-27-1	PST73030
N-((DICHLOROFLUOROMETHYL)THIO)-N',N'-DIMETHYL-N-PHENYLSULFAMIDE	1085-98-9	PST73026
N-((METHYLCARBAMOYL)OXYTHIOACETIMIDIC ACID METHYL ESTER	16752-77-5	PST14200
N-((TRICHLOROMETHYL)THIO)-PHTHALIMIDE	133-07-3	PST10012
N-((TRICHLOROMETHYL)THIO)-4-CYCLOHEXENE-1,2-DICARBOXIMIDE	133-06-2	PST04210
N-((TRICHLOROMETHYL)THIO)TETRAHYDROPHTHALIMIDE	133-06-2	PST04210
N-((1,1,2,2-TETRACHLOROETHYL)THIO)-4-CYCLOHEXENE-1,2-DICARBOXIMIDE	2425-06-1	PST04200
N-((4-CHLOROPHENYL)METHYL-N-CYCLOPENTYL-N'-PHENYLUREA	66063-05-6	PST72622
N-(BUTOXYMETHYL)-2-CHLORO-N-(2,6-DIETHYLPHENYL)ACETAMIDE	23184-66-9	PST03497
N-(CHLOROACETYL)-N-(2,6-DIETHYLPHENYL)GLYCINE ETHYL ESTER	38727-55-8	PST72968
N-(DIMETHOXYPHOSPHINOTHIOYLTHIOMETHYL)PHTHALIMIDE	732-11-6	PST11307
N-(DIMETHYLAMINO)SUCCINAMIC ACID	1596-84-5	PST06195
N-(MERCAPTOMETHYL)PHTHALIMIDE S-(O,O-DIMETHYL PHOSPHORODITHIOATE	732-11-6	PST11307
N-(NITROPHENYL)-N'-(3-PYRIDINYLMETHYL)UREA	53558-25-1	PST72334
N-(PHOSPHONOMETHYL)GLYCINE	1071-83-6	PST10515

SUBSTANCE NAME	CAS #	PST #
N-(PHOSPHONOMETHYL)GLYCINE COMPOUNDED WITH 2-PROPANAMINE (1:1)	38641-94-0	PST20205
N-(TRICHLOROMETHYL)THIO-4-CYCLOHEXENE-1,2-DICARBOXIMIDE	133-06-2	PST04210
N-(TRICHLOROMETHYLMERCAPTO)-DELTA(SUP 4)-TETRAHYDROPHTHALIMIDE	133-06-2	PST04210
N-(TRICHLOROMETHYLMERCAPTO)PHTHALIMIDE	133-07-3	PST10012
N-(TRICHLOROMETHYLTHIO)PHTHALIMIDE	133-07-3	PST10012
N-(1-CYANO-1-METHYLETHYL)-2-(DIETHOXYPHOSPHINOYLTHIO)ACETAMIDE	3734-95-0	PST72949
N-(1,1-DIMETHYL-2-PROPYNYL) 3,5-DICHLOROBENZAMIDE	23950-58-5	PST19670
N-(1,1-DIMETHYLETHYL)-N'-ETHYL-6-(METHYLTHIO)-1,3,5-TRIAZINE -2,4-DIAMINE	886-50-0	PST22538
N-(1,1-DIMETHYLETHYL)-N'-ETHYL-6-METHOXY-1,3,5-TRIAZINE-2,4-DIAMINE	33693-04-8	PST72770
N-(1,2-DIMETHYLPROPYL)-N'-ETHYL-6-(METHYLTHIO)-1,3,5-TRIAZINE -2,4-DIAMINE	22936-75-0	PST72145
N-(2-(O,O-DIISOPROPYLDITHIOPHOSPHORYL)ETHYL)BENZENESULFONAMIDE	741-58-2	PST02583
N-(2-CHLORO-1-(DIETHOXYPHOSPHINOTHIOYLTHIO)ETHYL)PHTHALIMIDE	10311-84-9	PST23630
N-(2-ETHYLHEXYL)-5-NORBORNENE-2,3-DICARBOXIMIDE	113-48-4	PST15955
N-(2-FURANYLMETHYL)1H-PURIN-6-AMINE	525-79-1	PST72483
N-(2-METHYLCYCLOHEXYL)-N'-PHENYLUREA	1982-49-6	PST20586
N-(2,4-DIMETHYL-5-(((TRIFLUOROMETHYL)SULFONYL)AMINO)PHENYL)ACETAMIDE	53780-34-0	PST72444
N-(3-CHLORO-P-TOLYL)-2-METHYLVALERAMIDE	2307-68-8	PST71164
N-(3-CHLORO-4-METHYLPHENYL)-2-METHYLPENTANAMIDE	2307-68-8	PST71164
N-(3-METHOXYPROPYL)-N'-(1-METHYLETHYL)-6-(METHYLTHIO)-1,3,5-TRIAZINE -2,4-DIAMINE	841-06-5	PST14204
N-(3-TRIFLUOROMETHYLPHENYL)-N',N'-DIMETHYLUREA	2164-17-2	PST09907
N-(3,4-DICHLOROPHENYL)-N-((DIMETHYLAMINO)CARBONYL)BENZAMIDE	3134-12-1	PST72972
N-(3,4-DICHLOROPHENYL)-2-METHYL-2-PROPENAMIDE	2164-09-2	PST71378
N-(4-(((2,4-DIAMINO-6-PTERIDINYL)METHYL)METHYLAMINO)BENZOYL)- L-GLUTAMIC ACID	59-05-2	PST14210
N-(4-(((2,4-DIAMINO-6-PTERIDINYL)METHYLAMINO)BENZOYL-L-GLUTAMIC ACID, SODIUM SALT	15475-56-6	PST14211
N-(4-CHLOROPHENYL)-2,2-DIMETHYLPENTANAMIDE	7287-36-7	PST72987
N-(4-CHLOROPHENYL)-2,2-DIMETHYLVALERAMIDE	7287-36-7	PST72987
N-(4-ETHOXYPHENYL) ACETAMIDE	62-44-2	PST18340
N-(4-ISOPROPYLPHENYL)-N',N'-DIMETHYLUREA	34123-59-6	PST12254
N-(4-METHYL-3-(((TRIFLUOROMETHYL)SULFONYL)AMINO)PHENYL)ACETAMIDE	47000-92-0	PST73184
N-(5-(ETHYLSULFONYL)-1,3,4-THIADIAZOL-2-YL)-N,N'-DIMETHYLUREA	30043-49-3	PST72551
N-(5-(1,1-DIMETHYLETHYL)-1,3,4-THIADIAZOL-2-YL)-N,N'-DIMETHYLUREA	34014-18-1	PST72340
N-ACETYL-P-PHENETIDINE	62-44-2	PST18340
N-ACETYL-PHOSPHORAMIDOTHIOIC ACID O,O-DIMETHYL ESTER	30560-19-1	PST00065
N-ALPHA-NAPHTHYLPHTHALAMIC ACID	132-66-1	PST71340
N-AMYL ACETATE	628-63-7	PST15270
N-BENZYL-N-(DICHLORO-3,4-PHENYL)-N',N'-DIMETHYLUREA	3134-12-1	PST72972
N-BENZYL-N-ISOPROPYL TRIMETHYLACETAMIDE	35256-85-0	PST72852
N-BENZYL-N-ISOPROPYLPIVALAMIDE	35256-85-0	PST72852
N-BUTOXYMETHYL-ALPHA-CHLORO-2',6'-DIETHYLACETANILIDE	23184-66-9	PST03497
N-BUTOXYMETHYL-2-CHLORO-2',6'-DIETHYLACETANILIDE	23184-66-9	PST03497
N-BUTYL 2,4-DICHLOROPHENOXY ACETATE	94-80-4	PST71295
N-BUTYL-N-ETHYL-ALPHA,ALPHA,ALPHA-TRIFLUORO-2,6-DINITRO-P-TOLUIDINE	1861-40-1	PST02570
N-BUTYL-N-ETHYL-2,6-DINITRO-4-(TRIFLUOROMETHYL)BENZENAMINE	1861-40-1	PST02570
N-BUTYL-N-ETHYL-2,6-DINITRO-4-TRIFLUOROMETHYLANILINE	1861-40-1	PST02570
N-BUTYL-N-ETHYLTHIOCARBAMIC ACID S-PROPYL ESTER	1114-71-2	PST71472
N-BUTYL-N'-(3,4-DICHLOROPHENYL)-N-METHYLUREA	555-37-3	PST16143
N-CETYL ALCOHOL	36653-82-4	PST04525
N-CYANOAMINE	420-04-2	PST05760
N-CYCLOPROPYL-1,3,5-TRIAZINE-2,4-6-TRIAMINE	66215-27-8	PST72536

ALPHABETICAL INDEX

SUBSTANCE NAME	CAS #	PST #
N-DECANOL	112-30-1	PST06285
N-DECATYL ALCOHOL	112-30-1	PST06285
N-DECYL ALCOHOL	112-30-1	PST06285
N-DICHLOROFLUOROMETHANESULPHENYL-N',N'-DIMETHYL-N-PHENYLSULPHAMIDE	1085-98-9	PST73026
N-DICHLOROFLUOROMETHYLTHIO-N',N'-DIMETHYL-N-PHENYLSULPHAMIDE	1085-98-9	PST73026
N-DIETHOXYPHOSPHINOTHIOYLPHTHALIMIDE	5131-24-8	PST72347
N-DIMETHYLAMINOSUCCINAMIC ACID	1596-84-5	PST06195
N-DIPHENYLANILINE	122-39-4	PST08100
N-DODECYL SULFATE SODIUM	151-21-3	PST08485
N-DODECYLBENZENESULFONIC ACID	27176-87-0	PST08480
N-ETHYL-ALPHA,ALPHA,ALPHA-TRIFLUORO-N-(2-METHYLALLYL)-2,6-DINITRO-P-TOLUIDINE	55283-68-6	PST72436
N-ETHYL-N-(2-METHYL-2-PROPENYL)-2,6-DINITRO-4-(TRIFLUOROMETHYL)-BENZENAMINE	55283-68-6	PST72436
N-ETHYL-N-(2-METHYLALLYL)-2,6-DINITRO-4-TRIFLUOROMETHYLANILINE	55283-68-6	PST72436
N-ETHYL-N-(4((4-ETHYL((3-SULFOPHENYL)METHYL)AMINO)PHENYL)(2-SULFOPHENYL)METHYLENE)-2,5-CYCLOHEXADIEN-1-YLIDENE)-3-SULFOBENZENE	2650-18-2	PST08277
N-ETHYL-N'-(1-METHYLETHYL)-6-(METHYLTHIO)-1,3,5-TRIAZINE-2,4-DIAMINE	834-12-8	PST01006
N-ETHYL-6-METHOXY-N'-(1-METHYLETHYL)-1,3,5-TRIAZINE-2,4-DIAMINE	1610-17-9	PST02148
N-ETHYL-6-METHOXY-N'-(1-METHYLPROPYL)-1,3,5-TRIAZINE-2,4-DIAMINE	26259-45-0	PST73051
N-ETHYLAMIDE OF O,O-DIMETHYL DITHIOPHOSPHORYLACETIC ACID	116-01-8	PST08723
N-ETHYLTHIOCYLCLOHEXANECARBAMIC ACID S-ETHYL ESTER	1134-23-2	PST71469
N-FURFURYLADENINE	525-79-1	PST72483
N-HEXADECANOL	36653-82-4	PST04525
N-HEXAN-1-OL	111-27-3	PST15630
N-HEXANOL	111-27-3	PST15630
N-HEXYL ALCOHOL	111-27-3	PST15630
N-HYDROXYNAPTHALIMIDE DIETHYL PHOSPHATE	1491-41-4	PST72737
N-ISOPROPYL-ALPHA-CHLOROACETANILIDE	1918-16-7	PST19686
N-METHYL-N'-(1-METHYLETHYL)-6-(METHYLTHIO)-1,3,5-TRIAZINE-2,4-DIAMINE	1014-69-3	PST06353
N-METHYL-1-NAPHTHYLCARBAMATE	63-25-2	PST04220
N-METHYL-2-ISOPROPOXYPHENYLCARBAMATE	114-26-1	PST02540
N-METHYLCARBAMIC ACID 3-METHYL-5-ISOPROPYLPHENYL ESTER	2631-37-0	PST72957
N-METHYLDITHIOCARBAMIC ACID, SODIUM SALT	137-42-8	PST71430
N-OCTANOL	111-87-5	PST17270
N-OCTYL ALCOHOL	111-87-5	PST17270
N-OCTYL BICYCLOHEPTENE DICARBOXIMIDE	113-48-4	PST15955
N-OCTYL PHTHALATE	117-84-0	PST08040
N-PARA-ETHOXYACETANILIDE	62-44-2	PST18340
N-PENTYL ACETATE	628-63-7	PST15270
N-PHENYL ISOPROPYL CARBAMATE	122-42-9	PST71564
N-PHENYL-N'-1,2,3-THIADIAZOL-5-YL UREA	51707-55-2	PST23299
N-PHENYL-N'-1,2,3-THIADIAZOL-5-YL-UREA	51707-55-2	PST23299
N-PHENYL-N',N'-DIMETHYLUREA	101-42-8	PST09679
N-PHENYLANILINE	122-39-4	PST08100
N-PHENYLBENZENAMINE	122-39-4	PST08100
N-PHOSPHOMETHYLGLYCINE	1071-83-6	PST10515
N-PHOSPHONOMETHYLGLYCINE	1071-83-6	PST10515
N-PROPYL ETHYL-N-BUTYLTHIOLCARBAMATE	1114-71-2	PST71472
N-PROPYL-N-(2-(2,4,6-TRICHLOROPHENOXY)ETHYL)-1-IMIDAZOLE-1-CARBOXAMIDE	67747-09-5	PST72648
N-SEC-BUTYL-N-ETHYL-6-METHOXY-1,3,5-TRIAZINE-2,6-DIAMINE	26259-45-0	PST73051
N-SEC-BUTYL-4-TERT-BUTYL-2,6-DINITROANILINE	33629-47-9	PST03525
N-SERVE	1929-82-4	PST16530
N-TRICHLOROMETHYLMERCAPTO-4-CYCLOHEXENE-1,2-DICARBOXIMIDE	133-06-2	PST04210

SUBSTANCE NAME	CAS #	PST #
N,N-DISECBUTYL-S-BENZYLTHIOLCARBAMATE	36756-79-3	PST72405
N,N-ETHYLENEDIAMINEDIACETIC ACID TETRASODIUM SALT	64-02-8	PST23137
N,N,N',N'-TETRAMETHYLPHOSPHORODIAMIDIC FLUORIDE	115-26-4	PST07655
N,N'-(PIPERAZINE-1,4-DIYLBIS((TRICHLOROMETHYL)METHYLENE))DIFORMAMIDE	26644-46-2	PST24086
N,N'-(1,4-PIPERAZINEDIYLBIS(2,2,2-TRICHLOROETHYLIDENE))BISFORMAMIDE	26644-46-2	PST24086
N,N'-(1,4-PIPERAZINEDIYLBIS(2,2,2-TRICHLOROETHYLIDENE)BIS(FORMAMIDE)	26644-46-2	PST24086
N,N'-BIS(1-METHYLETHYL)-6-(METHYLTHIO)-1,3-5-TRIAZINE-2,4-DIAMINE	7287-19-6	PST19968
N,N'-BIS(1-METHYLETHYL)-6-METHYLTHIO-1,3,5-TRIAZINE-2,4-DIAMINE	7287-19-6	PST19968
N,N'-BIS(1-METHYLETHYL)PHOSPHORODIAMIDIC FLUORIDE	371-86-8	PST15030
N,N'-BIS(2,2,2-TRICHLORO-1-HYDROXYETHYL)UREA	116-52-9	PST06817
N,N'-BIS(3-METHOXYPROPYL)-6-(METHYLTHIO)-1,3,5-TRIAZINE-2,4-DIAMINE	845-52-3	PST72212
N,N'-DI-ISOPROPYLPHOSPHORODIAMIDIC FLUORIDE	371-86-8	PST15030
N,N'-DIETHYL-6-(METHYLTHIO)-1,3,5-TRIAZINE-2,4-DIAMINE	1014-70-6	PST02838
N,N'-DIISOPROPYLPHOSPHORODIAMIDIC FLUORIDE	371-86-8	PST15030
N,N'-DIMETHYL-GAMMA,GAMMA'-DIPYRIDYLIUM	4685-14-7	PST71671
N,N'-1,2-ETHANEDIYLBIS(N-(CARBOXYMETHYL)GLYCINE	60-00-4	PST09570
N,N'-1,2-ETHANEDIYLBIS(N-(CARBOXYMETHYL)GLYCINE, TETRASODIUM SALT	64-02-8	PST23137
N,N'-1,2-ETHYLENEDIYLBIS(N-(CARBOXYMETHYL)GLYCINE, DISODIUM SALT	139-33-3	PST08305
N,N',N''-TRICHLORO-2,4,6-TRIAMINE-4,3,5-TRIAZINE	7673-09-8	PST80113
N,N',N"-TRI-1,2-ETHANEDIYLPHOSPHORIC TRIAMIDE	545-55-1	PST22510
N,N',N"-TRIETHYLENEPHOSPHORAMIDE	545-55-1	PST22510
N,N',N"-TRIETHYLENEPHOSPHORIC TRIAMIDE	545-55-1	PST22510
N,N'N"-TRICHLOROISOCYANURIC ACID	87-90-1	PST23860
N'-(HEXAHYDRO-4,7-METHANOINDAN-5-YL)-N,N-DIMETHYLUREA	18530-56-8	PST71400
N'-(M-HYDROXYPHENYL)-N,N-DIMETHYLFORMAMIDINE METHYLCARBAMATE ESTER	22259-30-9	PST73187
N'-(3-CHLORO-4-METHOXYPHENYL)-N,N-DIMETHYLUREA	19937-59-8	PST15009
N'-(3-CHLORO-4-METHYLPHENYL)-N,N-DIMETHYLUREA	15545-48-9	PST04912
N'-(3,4-DICHLOROPHENYL)-N-METHOXY-N-METHYLUREA	330-55-2	PST12826
N'-(3,4-DICHLOROPHENYL)-N,N-DIMETHYLUREA	330-54-1	PST08420
N'-(4-(4-CHLOROPHENOXY)PHENYL)-N,N-DIMETHYLUREA	1982-47-4	PST04905
N'-(4-(4-METHOXYPHENOXY)PHENYL)-N,N-DIMETHYLUREA	14214-32-5	PST07386
N'-(4-BROMO-3-CHLOROPHENYL)-N-METHOXY-N-METHYLUREA	13360-45-7	PST04552
N'-(4-BROMOPHENYL)-N-METHOXY-N-METHYLUREA	3060-89-7	PST15008
N'-(4-CHLOARO-2-METHYLPHENYL)-N,N-DIMETHYLFORMAMIDINE MONOHYDROCHLORIDE	19750-95-9	PST71656
N'-(4-CHLORO-O-TOLYL)-N,N-DIMETHYLFORMAMIDINE	6164-98-3	PST04570
N'-(4-CHLORO-2-METHYLPHENYL)-N,N-DIMETHYLFORMAMIDINIUMCHLORIDE	19750-95-9	PST71656
N'-(4-CHLORO-2-METHYLPHENYL)-N,N-DIMETHYLMETHANIMIDAMIDE	6164-98-3	PST04570
N'-(4-CHLORO-2-METHYLPHENYL)-N,N-DIMETHYLMETHANIMIDAMIDE MONOHYDROCHLORIDE	19750-95-9	PST71656
N'-(4-CHLOROPHENYL)-N-METHOXY-N-METHYLUREA	1746-81-2	PST15174
N'-(4-CHLOROPHENYL)-N-METHYL-N-(1-METHYL-2-PROPYNYL)UREA	3766-60-7	PST03523
N'-(4-CHLOROPHENYL)-N,N-DIMETHYLUREA	150-68-5	PST15196
N'-(4-CHLOROPHENYL)-1,1-DIMETHYLUREA TRICHLOROACETATE	140-41-0	PST15197
N'-(5-(1,1-DIMETHYLETHYL)-3-ISOXAZOLYL)-N,N-DIMETHYLUREA	55861-78-4	PST72586
N'-CYCLOOCTYL-N,N-DIMETHYLUREA	2163-69-1	PST05996
N'-2-QUINOXALINYLSULFANILAMIDE	59-40-5	PST72046
N',N'-DIMETHYL-N-((METHYLCARBAMOYL)OXY)-1-THIOOXAMIMIDIC ACID METHYL ESTER	23135-22-0	PST17370
NA 1120	75-65-0	PST22630
NA 1479	10588-01-9	PST21190
NA 1581	UNASSIGNED	PST75471
NA 1581	UNASSIGNED	PST75474
NA 1760	75-99-0	PST06200

ALPHABETICAL INDEX

ALPHABETICAL INDEX

SUBSTANCE NAME	CAS #	PST #
NAPROPION	137-40-6	PST21575
NAPTALAM	132-66-1	PST71340
NAPTALAM	132-67-2	PST71341
NAPTALAM SODIUM	132-67-2	PST71341
NAPTHALIMIDE, N-HYDROXY-, DIETHYL PHOSPHATE	1491-41-4	PST72737
NARAMYCIN	66-81-9	PST05930
NARAMYCIN A	66-81-9	PST05930
NARKOTIL	75-09-2	PST14930
NATA	650-51-1	PST73307
NATURAL ANHYDRITE	7778-18-9	PST04110
NATURAL ARCANITE	7778-80-5	PST19590
NATURAL TENORITE	1317-38-0	PST05655
NATURAL VILLIAUMITE	7681-49-4	PST21230
NAVADEL	78-34-2	PST08050
NAVRON	640-19-7	PST09930
NAXONATE	1300-72-7	PST75603
NAXONATE G	1300-72-7	PST75603
NA2SIO3	6834-92-0	PST21373
NA3O4P	7601-54-9	PST24480
NA4O7P2	7722-88-5	PST23140
NA5O10P3	7758-29-4	PST21730
NC 1667	1912-26-1	PST23927
NC 3363	3615-21-2	PST73047
NC 6897	22781-23-3	PST02560
NC 8438	26225-79-6	PST72404
NCB	118-74-1	PST10730
NCI-C00099	57-74-9	PST04560
NCI-C00099	12789-03-6	PST71948
NCI-C00180	76-44-8	PST10660
NCI-C00453	95-06-7	PST22190
NCI-C00486	115-32-2	PST07010
NCI-C02971	298-00-0	PST14680
NCI-C08640	116-06-3	PST00500
NCI-C08673	333-41-5	PST06540
NCI-C00113	62-73-7	PST07000
NCI-C00191	143-50-0	PST12330
NCI-C00204	58-89-9	PST12810
NCI-C00237	1918-02-1	PST18840
NCI-C00408	510-15-6	PST04740
NCI-C00475	72-54-8	PST06240
NCI-C00500	96-12-8	PST26490
NCI-C0054	315-18-4	PST15010
NCI-C00555	72-55-9	PST06247
NCI-C04580	127-18-4	PST22900
NCI-C08684	101-05-3	PST01526
NCI-C54831	52-68-6	PST23790
NCI-C55298	148-24-3	PST30450
NCI-C60048	84-66-2	PST07210
NCI-C60413	510-15-6	PST04740
NCI-000077	133-06-2	PST04210
NEANTINE	84-66-2	PST07210
NEBUREA	555-37-3	PST16143
NEBUREX	555-37-3	PST16143
NEBURON	555-37-3	PST16143

SUBSTANCE NAME	CAS #	PST #
NECATORINA	56-23-5	PST04310
NECTRYL	90-43-7	PST18470
NEFUSAN	533-74-4	PST06230
NEGUVON	52-68-6	PST23790
NELLITE	1754-58-1	PST72310
NEM-A-TAK	21548-32-3	PST16141
NEMA	127-18-4	PST22900
NEMACIDE	97-17-6	PST06805
NEMACUR	22224-92-6	PST16145
NEMACUR SULFONE (FORMULATION)	31972-44-8	PST16144
NEMACUR SULFOXIDE	31972-43-7	PST16146
NEMAFAX	23564-06-9	PST72322
NEMAFOS	297-97-2	PST25590
NEMAFUME	96-12-8	PST26490
NEMAGON	96-12-8	PST26490
NEMAGON SOIL FUMIGANT	96-12-8	PST26490
NEMAPAZ	96-12-8	PST26490
NEMAPHOS	297-97-2	PST25590
NEMATOCIDE GR	297-97-2	PST25590
NEMAZENE	92-84-2	PST18400
NEMAZON	96-12-8	PST26490
NEO-GERMITOL	8001-54-5	PST00537
NEO-MANTLE CREME	1405-10-3	PST84263
NEOCHLOR 59	2244-21-5	PST19360
NEOCID	50-29-3	PST06250
NEOCYCLOHEXIMIDE	66-81-9	PST05930
NEODIESTROPTOPAB	57-92-1	PST21917
NEOFRACIN	1405-10-3	PST84263
NEOGLAUCIT	55-91-4	PST07590
NEOLATE	1405-10-3	PST84263
NEOMIX	1405-10-3	PST84263
NEOMYCIN SULFATE	1405-10-3	PST84263
NEOMYCIN SULPHATE	1405-10-3	PST84263
NEOMYCIN, SULFATE (SALT)	1405-10-3	PST84263
NEOPYNAMIN	7696-12-0	PST23061
NEOSOREXA	56073-07-5	PST07385
NEOXTANOX	13356-08-6	PST24866
NEPTUNE BLUE BRA	2650-18-2	PST08277
NETAZOL	94-74-6	PST27880
NEUTRAL NICOTINE SULFATE	65-30-5	PST16460
NEXAGAN	4824-78-6	PST03458
NEXAGAN	2104-96-3	PST71064
NEXION	2104-96-3	PST71064
NF 35	23564-06-9	PST72322
NF 44	23564-05-8	PST72308
NIA 10242	1563-66-2	PST04240
NIA 11092	4849-32-5	PST72271
NIA 249	584-79-2	PST00550
NIA 5273	51-03-6	PST75640
NIA 5996	1194-65-6	PST06800
NIA 9044	485-31-4	PST71960
NIA 9102	9006-42-2	PST71123
NIA-18739	28434-01-7	PST20093
NIA-5767	2778-04-3	PST73139

ALPHABETICAL INDEX

SUBSTANCE NAME	CAS #	PST #
NIAGARA 10242	1563-66-2	PST04240
NIAGARA 4512	2307-68-8	PST71164
NIAGARA 4556	2164-09-2	PST71378
NIAGARA 5006	1194-65-6	PST06800
NIAGARA 5767	2778-04-3	PST73139
NIAGARAMITE	140-57-8	PST01850
NIAX	25322-69-4	PST19140
NICKEL MONOSULFATE HEXAHYDRATE	10101-97-0	PST16410
NICKEL SULFATE (NISO4) HEXAHYDRATE	10101-97-0	PST16410
NICKEL SULFATE, HEXAHYDRATE	10101-97-0	PST16410
NICKEL(II) SULFATE HEXAHYDRATE	10101-97-0	PST16410
NICKEL(II) SULFATE, HEXAHYDRATE (1:1:6)	10101-97-0	PST16410
NICKEL(2+) SULFATE HEXAHYDRATE	10101-97-0	PST16410
NICLOFEN	1836-75-5	PST23580
NICO-DUST	54-11-5	PST16430
NICO-FUME	54-11-5	PST16430
NICOCIDE	54-11-5	PST16430
NICOTINE	54-11-5	PST16430
NICOTINE ACID TARTRATE	65-31-6	PST16470
NICOTINE ALKALOID	54-11-5	PST16430
NICOTINE BITARTRATE	65-31-6	PST16470
NICOTINE HYDROGEN TARTRATE	65-31-6	PST16470
NICOTINE MONOSALICYLATE	29790-52-1	PST16450
NICOTINE SALICYLATE	29790-52-1	PST16450
NICOTINE SULFATE	65-30-5	PST16459
NICOTINE SULFATE (2:1)	65-30-5	PST16460
NICOTINE SULFATE SOLUTION	65-30-5	PST16459
NICOTINE SULFATE, LIQUID	65-30-5	PST16459
NICOTINE SULFATE, SOLID	65-30-5	PST16460
NICOTINE TARTRATE	65-31-6	PST16470
NICOTINE TARTRATE (1:2)	65-31-6	PST16470
NICOULINE	83-79-4	PST20200
NIFLEX N	91-53-2	PST08740
NIOMIL	22781-23-3	PST02560
NIP	1836-75-5	PST23580
NIPAGIN M	99-76-3	PST14677
NIPASOL	94-13-3	PST19941
NIPHEN	100-02-7	PST17800
NITER	7757-79-1	PST19470
NITER	7631-99-4	PST21400
NITER CAKE	7681-38-1	PST20990
NITICID	1918-16-7	PST19686
NITRADOR	534-52-1	PST07910
NITRALIN	4726-14-1	PST16525
NITRALINE	4726-14-1	PST16525
NITRAN	1582-09-8	PST24085
NITRAPYRIN	1929-82-4	PST16530
NITRAPYRINE	1929-82-4	PST16530
NITRATINE	7631-99-4	PST21400
NITRE	7757-79-1	PST19470
NITRE CAKE	7681-38-1	PST20990
NITRIC ACID POTASSIUM SALT	7757-79-1	PST19470
NITRIC ACID POTASSIUM SALT (1:1)	7757-79-1	PST19470
NITRIC ACID, COPPER(2+) SALT	3251-23-8	PST05644

SUBSTANCE NAME	CAS #	PST #
NITRIC ACID, SILVER(1+) SALT	7761-88-8	PST20810
NITRIC ACID, SODIUM SALT	7631-99-4	PST21400
NITRIC ACID, SODIUM SALT(1:1)	7631-99-4	PST21400
NITRILOTRIACETIC ACID, TRISODIUM SALT	5064-31-3	PST24475
NITRILOTRIETHANOL	102-71-6	PST23932
NITROCHLOR	1836-75-5	PST23580
NITROCHLOROFORM	76-06-2	PST04830
NITROCHLOROMETHANE	76-06-2	PST04830
NITROFEN	1836-75-5	PST23580
NITROFENE	1836-75-5	PST23580
NITROISOBUTYLGLYCEROL	126-11-4	PST24430
NITROLIME	156-62-7	PST03930
NITROPHEN	1836-75-5	PST23580
NITROPHENE	1836-75-5	PST23580
NITROPHOS	122-14-5	PST09678
NITROTRIMETHYLOLMETHANE	126-11-4	PST24430
NITROTRIS(HYDROXYMETHYL)METHANE	126-11-4	PST24430
NITROUS ACID SODIUM SALT(1:1)	7632-00-0	PST21410
NITROUS ACID, SODIUM SALT	7632-00-0	PST21410
NITTAN	7440-44-0	PST04246
NK 711	21609-90-5	PST12780
NNAO2	7632-00-0	PST21410
NNAO3	7631-99-4	PST21400
NNF 109	50512-35-1	PST12253
NO BUNT	118-74-1	PST10730
NO BUNT LIQUID	118-74-1	PST10730
NO BUNT 40	118-74-1	PST10730
NO BUNT 80	118-74-1	PST10730
NOCRACK AW	91-53-2	PST08740
NOLTRAN	5598-13-0	PST71652
NONACHLOR	39765-80-5	PST23079
NONAN-1,4-OLIDE	104-61-0	PST10334
NONOXYNOL	9016-45-9	PST16835
NONYL METHYL KETONE	112-12-9	PST14675
NONYL PHENYL POLYETHYLENE GLYCOL	9016-45-9	PST16835
NONYL PHENYL POLYETHYLENE GLYCOL ETHER	9016-45-9	PST16835
NONYLCARBINOL	112-30-1	PST06285
NONYLPHENOL ETHOXYLATE	9016-45-9	PST16835
NONYLPHENOL POLYETHYLENE OXIDE	9016-45-9	PST16835
NONYLPHENOXYPOLY(ETHYLENE OXY) ETHANOL	9016-45-9	PST16835
NONYPHENOXY POLYETHOXY ETHANOL	9016-45-9	PST16835
NOPCOCIDE N 96	1897-45-6	PST04890
NORAMETRYNE	1014-69-3	PST06353
NORBORMIDE	991-42-4	PST72254
NORCAINE	94-09-7	PST72267
NORDHADSEN ACID	7664-93-9	PST22350
NORDOX	1317-39-1	PST05470
NOREA	18530-56-8	PST71400
NOREX	1982-47-4	PST04905
NORFLURAZON	27314-13-2	PST72343
NORFLURAZONE	27314-13-2	PST72343
NORIT	7440-44-0	PST04246
NORMERSAN	137-26-8	PST23430
NOROSAC	1194-65-6	PST06800

ALPHABETICAL INDEX

SUBSTANCE NAME	CAS #	PST #
O-(6-ETHOXY-2-ETHYL-4-PYRIMIDINYL) O,O-DIMETHYL-PHOSPHOROTHIOATE	38260-54-7	PST73148
O-ACETOTOLUIDIDE, 2-CHLORO-N-(ETHOXYMETHYL)-6'-ETHYL-	34256-82-1	PST72539
O-ACETYL-2-SEC-BUTYL-4,6-DINITROPHENOL	2813-95-8	PST08021
O-ANISIC ACID, 3,6-DICHLORO-, METHYL ESTER	6597-78-0	PST73131
O-ANISIC ACID, 3,6-DICHLORO-, SODIUM SALT	1982-69-0	PST71250
O-BENZENEDICARBOXYLIC ACID DIETHYL ESTHER	84-66-2	PST07210
O-BENZENEDICARBOXYLIC ACID, DIBUTYL ESTER	84-74-2	PST06740
O-BENZENEDICARBOXYLIC ACID, DIOCTYL ESTER	117-84-0	PST08040
O-BENZENEDIOL	120-80-9	PST04360
O-BIPHENYLOL	90-43-7	PST18470
O-CARBOXYPHENOL	69-72-7	PST20315
O-CRESOL, 4,6-DINITRO-	534-52-1	PST07910
O-CRESOL, 4,6-DINITRO-, SODIUM SALT	2312-76-7	PST71411
O-CUMENYL METHYLCARBAMATE	2631-40-5	PST73231
O-DICHLOROBENZENE	95-50-1	PST16970
O-DICHLOROBENZENE, LIQUID	95-50-1	PST16970
O-DIHYDROXYBENZENE	120-80-9	PST04360
O-DIOXYBENZENE	120-80-9	PST04360
O-DIPHENOL	120-80-9	PST04360
O-DIPHENYLOL	90-43-7	PST18470
O-ETHYL O-(P-NITROPHENYL) PHENYLPHOSPHONOTHIOATE	2104-64-5	PST08650
O-ETHYL O-(2,4,5-TRICHLOROPHENYL) ETHYLPHOSPHONOTHIOATE	327-98-0	PST00478
O-ETHYL O-(4-(METHYLMERCAPTO)PHENYL)-S-N-PROPYLPHOSPHOROTHIONOTHIOLATE	35400-43-2	PST22387
O-ETHYL O-(4-(METHYLSULFONYL)PHENYL)5-PROPYL- PHOSPHOROTHIOATE	42795-00-6	PST03231
O-ETHYL O-(4-CYANOPHENYL) PHENYLPHOSPHONOTHIOATE	13067-93-1	PST05805
O-ETHYL O-(4-NITROPHENYL)PHENYLPHOSPHONOTHIOATE	2104-64-5	PST08650
O-ETHYL O-P-NITOPHENYL PHENYLPHOSPHONOTHIOATE	2104-64-5	PST08650
O-ETHYL O-2-ISOPROPOXYCARBONYLPHENYL ISOPROPYLPHOSPHORAMIDOTHIOATE	25311-71-1	PST11985
O-ETHYL O-2,4,5-TRICHLOROPHENYL ETHYLPHOSPHONOTHIOATE	327-98-0	PST00478
O-ETHYL O-4-(METHYLTHIO)PHENYL S-PROPYL PHOSPHORODITHIOATE	35400-43-2	PST22387
O-ETHYL S-(2-(BIS(1-METHYLETHYL)AMINO)ETHYL METHYLPHOSPHONOTHIOATE	50782-69-9	PST83104
O-ETHYL S-(2-(DIISOPROPYLAMINO)ETHYL)METHYLPHOSPHONOTHIOATE	50782-69-9	PST83104
O-ETHYL S-PHENYL (RS)-ETHYLPHOSPHONODITHIOATE	944-22-9	PST10020
O-ETHYL S-PHENYL ETHYLPHOSPHONOTHIOLOTHIONATE	944-22-9	PST10020
O-ETHYL S,S-DIPHENYL ESTER PHOSPHORODITHIOIC ACID	17109-49-8	PST08555
O-ETHYL S,S-DIPHENYL PHOSPHORODITHIOATE	17109-49-8	PST08555
O-ETHYL S,S-DIPROPYL PHOSPHORODITHIOATE	13194-48-4	PST15080
O-HYDROQUINONE	120-80-9	PST04360
O-HYDROXYBENZOIC ACID	69-72-7	PST20315
O-HYDROXYBENZOIC ACID METHYL ESTER	119-36-8	PST14720
O-HYDROXYBIPHENYL	90-43-7	PST18470
O-HYDROXYDIPHENYL	90-43-7	PST18470
O-HYDROXYPHENOL	120-80-9	PST04360
O-ISOPROPOXYPHENYL METHYLCARBAMATE	114-26-1	PST02540
O-ISOPROPOXYPHENYL N-METHYLCARBAMATE	114-26-1	PST02540
O-ISOPROPYL N-PHENYL CARBAMATE	122-42-9	PST71564
O-ISOPROPYLPHENOL METHYLCARBAMATE	2631-40-5	PST73231
O-ISOPROPYLPHENYL METHYLCARBAMATE	2631-40-5	PST73231
O-METHYL O-(4-BROMO-2,5-DICHLOROPHENYL)PHENYL PHOSPHONATE	25006-32-0	PST12776
O-METHYL O-2,5-DICHLORO-4-BROMOPHENYL PHENYLTHIOPHOSPHONATE	21609-90-5	PST12780
O-METHYL-O-(4-TERT-BUTYL-2-CHLOROPHENYL)METHYLPHOSPHORAMIDATE	299-86-5	PST05550
O-O-DIETHYL-O-(2-DIETHYLAMINO-6-METHYL-4-PIRIMIDINYL)PHOSPHOROTHIOATE	23505-41-1	PST72377
O-O-DIMETHYL-O-(2-DIETHYLAMINO-6-METHYL-4-PIRIMIDINYL)PHOSPHOROTHIOATE	29232-93-7	PST72378
O-P-CYANOPHENYL O,O-DIMETHYL PHOSPHOROTHIOATE	2636-26-2	PST72950

ALPHABETICAL INDEX

SUBSTANCE NAME	CAS #	PST #
O,O-DIETHYL (ETHYLSULFINYL)METHYL ESTER	2588-03-6	PST18646
O,O-DIETHYL (1,3-DIHYDRO-1,3-DIOXO-2H-ISOINDOL-2-YL)PHOSPHONOTHIOATE	5131-24-8	PST72347
O,O-DIETHYL ALPHA-CYANOBENZYLIDENEAMINO-OXYPHOSPHONOTHIOATE	14816-18-3	PST73292
O,O-DIETHYL O-(P-(METHYLSULFINYL)PHENYL) PHOSPHOROTHIOATE	115-90-2	PST06210
O,O-DIETHYL O-(P-METHYLSULFONYL)PHENYL PHOSPHOROTHIOATE	14255-72-2	PST06228
O,O-DIETHYL O-(P-NITROPHENYL) THIONOPHOSPHATE	56-38-2	PST18040
O,O-DIETHYL O-(P-NITROPHENYL)PHOSPHOROTHIOATE	56-38-2	PST18040
O,O-DIETHYL O-(1-PHENYL-1H-1,2,4-TRIAZOL-3-YL)PHOSPHOROTHIOATE	24017-47-8	PST73068
O,O-DIETHYL O-(2-(ETHYLSULFONYL)ETHYL) PHOSPHOROTHIOATE	4891-54-7	PST06309
O,O-DIETHYL O-(2-CHLORO-1-(2,5-DICHLOROPHENYL)VINYL)PHOSPHOROTHIOATE	1757-18-2	PST00493
O,O-DIETHYL O-(2-ETHTHIOETHYL) PHOSPHOROTHIOATE	298-03-3	PST71645
O,O-DIETHYL O-(2-ISOPROPYL-4-METHYL-6-PYRIMIDINYL)PHOSPHOROTHIOATE	333-41-5	PST06540
O,O-DIETHYL O-(2-ISOPROPYL-6-METHYL-4-PYRIMIDINYL)PHOSPHOROTHIOATE	333-41-5	PST06540
O,O-DIETHYL O-(3,5,6-TRICHLORO-2-PYRIDINYL) PHOSPHOROTHIOATE	2921-88-2	PST04910
O,O-DIETHYL O-(3,5,6-TRICHLORO-2-PYRIDYL) PHOSPHOROTHIOATE	2921-88-2	PST04910
O,O-DIETHYL O-(4-(METHYLSULFINYL)PHENYL) PHOSPHOROTHIOATE	115-90-2	PST06210
O,O-DIETHYL O-(4-NITROPHENYL) PHOSPHOROTHIOATE	56-38-2	PST18040
O,O-DIETHYL O-(5-PHENYL-3-ISOXAZOLYL)ESTER PHOSPHOROTHIOIC ACID	18854-01-8	PST12280
O,O-DIETHYL O-(5-PHENYL-3-ISOXAZOLYL)PHOSPHOROTHIOATE	18854-01-8	PST12280
O,O-DIETHYL O-(6-METHYL-2-(1-METHYLETHYL)-4-PYRIMIDINYL) PHOSPHOROTHIOATE	333-41-5	PST06540
O,O-DIETHYL O-(7,8,9,10-TETRAHYDRO-6-OXO-6H-DIBENZO(B,D)PYRAN-3-YL) PHOSPHOROTHIOATE	572-48-5	PST73073
O,O-DIETHYL O-NAPHTHALOXIMIDE PHOSPHATE	1491-41-4	PST72737
O,O-DIETHYL O-PYRAZINYL ESTER PHOSPHOROTHIOIC ACID	297-97-2	PST25590
O,O-DIETHYL O-PYRAZINYL THIOPHOSPHATE	297-97-2	PST25590
O,O-DIETHYL O-QUINOXALIN-2-YL PHOSPHOROTHIOATE	13593-03-8	PST73112
O,O-DIETHYL O-2 ETHYLSULFINYLETHYL PHOSPHOROTHIOATE	UNASSIGNED	PST06308
O,O-DIETHYL O-2-(ETHYLTHIO)ETHYL PHOSPHOROTHIOATE	298-03-3	PST71645
O,O-DIETHYL O-2-ETHYL-SULFONYLETHYL PHOSPHOROTHIOATE	4891-54-7	PST06309
O,O-DIETHYL O-2-ETHYLTHIOETHYL PHOSPHATE	23052-51-9	PST06317
O,O-DIETHYL O-2-ISOPROPYL-4-METHYL-6-PYRIMIDINYL THIONOPHOSPHATE	333-41-5	PST06540
O,O-DIETHYL O-2-ISOPROPYL-6-METHYLPYRIMIDIN-4-YL PHOSPHOROTHIOATE	333-41-5	PST06540
O,O-DIETHYL O-2-QUINOXALINYL PHOSPHOROTHIOATE	13593-03-8	PST73112
O,O-DIETHYL O-2,4-DICHLOROPHENYL PHOSPHOROTHIOATE	97-17-6	PST06805
O,O-DIETHYL O-3,5,6-TRICHLORO-2-PYRIDYL PHOSPHOROTHIOATE	2921-88-2	PST04910
O,O-DIETHYL O-4-NITROPHENYL PHOSPHOROTHIOATE	56-38-2	PST18040
O,O-DIETHYL O-5-PHENYLISOXAZOL-3-YL PHOSPHOROTHIOATE	18854-01-8	PST12280
O,O-DIETHYL O-7-HYDROXY-3,4-TETRAMETHYLENECOUMARINYL PHOSPHOROTHIOATE	572-48-5	PST73073
O,O-DIETHYL O,2-PYRAZINYL PHOSPHOROTHIOATE	297-97-2	PST25590
O,O-DIETHYL PHOSPHORODITHIOATE S-ESTER WITH N-(2-CHLORO-1 -MERCAPTOETHYL)PHTHALIMIDE	10311-84-9	PST23630
O,O-DIETHYL PHOSPHORODITHIOATE S-ESTER WITH N-ISOPROPYL-2-MERCAPTOACETAMIDE	2275-18-5	PST19943
O,O-DIETHYL PHOSPHORODITHIOATE S-ESTER WITH 3-(MERCAPTOMETHYL) -1,2,3-BENZOTRIAZIN-4(3H)-ONE	2642-71-9	PST02205
O,O-DIETHYL PHOSPHORODITHIOATE S-ESTER WITH 6-CHLORO-3-MERCAPTOMETHYL)-2-BENZOXAZOLINONE	2310-17-0	PST25720
O,O-DIETHYL PHOSPHOROTHIOATE S-ESTER WITH N-(1-CYANO-1-METHYLETHYL)-2 -MERCAPTOACETAMIDE	3734-95-0	PST72949
O,O-DIETHYL PHTHALIMIDOPHOSPHONOTHIOATE	5131-24-8	PST72347
O,O-DIETHYL S-(((1,1-DIMETHYLETHYL)SULFONYL)METHYL)PHOSPHOROTHIOATE	56070-15-6	PST22537
O,O-DIETHYL S-((ETHYLSULFINYL)METHYL) PHOSPHORODITHIOATE	2588-03-6	PST18646
O,O-DIETHYL S-((ETHYLSULFONYLMETHYL) PHOSPHORODITHIOATE	2588-04-7	PST18643

SUBSTANCE NAME	CAS #	PST #
O,O-DIMETHYL ESTER PHOSPHORODITHIOIC ACID S-ESTER WITH N-ETHYL-2 -MERCAPTOACDTAMIDE	116-01-8	PST08723
O,O-DIMETHYL ESTER, S-ESTER WITH 2-ETHOXY-4-(MERCATOMETHYL)-DELTA2 -1,3,4-THIADIAZOLIN-5-ONE PHOSPHOROTHIOIC ACID	2669-32-1	PST73147
O,O-DIMETHYL HYDROGEN PHOSPHATE	813-78-5	PST07882
O,O-DIMETHYL O-(P-NITROPHENYL) PHOSPHOROTHIOATE	298-00-0	PST14680
O,O-DIMETHYL O-(2-(ETHYLTHIO)ETHYL) PHOSPHOROTHIOATE	867-27-6	PST71969
O,O-DIMETHYL O-(2-(METHYLTHIO)ETHYL)PHOSPHOROTHIOATE	682-80-4	PST73093
O,O-DIMETHYL O-(2-CHLORO-4-NITROPHENYL)PHOSPHOROTHIOATE	2463-84-5	PST71380
O,O-DIMETHYL O-(2,2-DICHLOROVINYL) PHOSPHATE	62-73-7	PST07000
O,O-DIMETHYL O-(2,4,5-TRICHLOROPHENYL) PHOSPHOROTHIOATE	299-84-3	PST20180
O,O-DIMETHYL O-(2,5-DICHLORO-4-IODOPHENYL)PHOSPHORTHIOATE	18181-70-9	PST73035
O,O-DIMETHYL O-(3-CHLORO-4-NITROPHENYL) THIONOPHOSPHATE	500-28-7	PST71379
O,O-DIMETHYL O-(3-METHYL-4-(METHYLSULFINYL)PHENYL) PHOSPHOROTHIOATE	3761-41-9	PST02555
O,O-DIMETHYL O-(3-METHYL-4-(METHYLSULFONYL) PHOSPHOROTHIOATE	3761-42-0	PST02554
O,O-DIMETHYL O-(3-METHYL-4-(METHYLTHIO)PHENYL) PHOSPHOROTHIOATE	55-38-9	PST02550
O,O-DIMETHYL O-(3-METHYL-4-NITROPHENYL)PHOSPHOROTHIOATE	122-14-5	PST09678
O,O-DIMETHYL O-(3,5,6-TRICHLORO-2-PYRIDINYL) PHOSPHOROTHIOATE	5598-13-0	PST71652
O,O-DIMETHYL O-(4-(AMINOSULFONYL)PHENYL) PHOSPHOROTHIOATE	115-93-5	PST06135
O,O-DIMETHYL O-(4-(METHYLSULFINYL)M-TOLYL) PHOSPHOROTHIOATE	3761-41-9	PST02555
O,O-DIMETHYL O-(4-(METHYLTHIO)-M-TOLYL) PHOSPHOROTHIOATE	55-38-9	PST02550
O,O-DIMETHYL O-(4-METHYLSULFONYL)-M-TOLYL PHOSPHOROTHIOATE	3761-42-0	PST02554
O,O-DIMETHYL O-(4-NITRO-M-TOLYL)PHOSPHOROTHIOATE	122-14-5	PST09678
O,O-DIMETHYL O-(4-NITROPHENYL) PHOSPHOROTHIOATE	298-00-0	PST14680
O,O-DIMETHYL O-P-NITROPHENYL PHOSPHOROTHIOATE	298-00-0	PST14680
O,O-DIMETHYL O-P-NITROPHENYL THIOPHOSPHATE	298-00-0	PST14680
O,O-DIMETHYL O-P-SULFAMOYLPHENYLPHOSPHOROTHIOATE	115-93-5	PST06135
O,O-DIMETHYL O-2-(ETHYLTHIO)ETHYL PHOSPHOROTHIOATE	867-27-6	PST71969
O,O-DIMETHYL O-2-METHYLTHIOETHYL PHOSPHOROTHIOATE	682-80-4	PST73093
O,O-DIMETHYL O-2,4,5-TRICHLOROPHENYL PHOSPHOROTHIOATE	299-84-3	PST20180
O,O-DIMETHYL O-3-CHLORO-4-NITROPHENYL THIONOPHOSPHATE	500-28-7	PST71379
O,O-DIMETHYL O-3,5,6-TRICHLORO-2-PYRIDYL PHOSPHOROTHIOATE	5598-13-0	PST71652
O,O-DIMETHYL O-4-METHYLTHIO-M-TOLYL PHOSPHOROTHIOATE	55-38-9	PST02550
O,O-DIMETHYL O-4-NITRO-M-TOLYL PHOSPHOROTHIOATE	122-14-5	PST09678
O,O-DIMETHYL O-4-NITROPHENYL PHOSPHOROTHIOATE	298-00-0	PST14680
O,O-DIMETHYL O-4-SULPHAMOYLPHENYL PHOSPHOROTHIOATE	115-93-5	PST06135
O,O-DIMETHYL PHOPHORODITHIOATE S-ESTER WITH 2-MERCAPTO-N-(2 -METHOXYETHYL ACETAMIDE	919-76-6	PST01007
O,O-DIMETHYL PHOSPHATE	813-78-5	PST07882
O,O-DIMETHYL PHOSPHORODITHIOATE OF DIETHYL MERCAPTOSUCCINATE	121-75-5	PST13540
O,O-DIMETHYL PHOSPHORODITHIOATE S-ESTER WITH N-ETHYL- 2-MERCAPTOACETAMIDE	116-01-8	PST08723
O,O-DIMETHYL PHOSPHORODITHIOATE S-ESTER WITH 2-ETHOXY-4 -(MERCAPTOMETHYL)- DELTA2-1,3,4-THIADIAZOLIN-5-ONE	2669-32-1	PST73147
O,O-DIMETHYL PHOSPHORODITHIOATE S-ESTER WITH 3-(MERCAPTOMETHYL)-1,2, 3-BENZOTRIAZIN-4(3H)-ONE	86-50-0	PST02210
O,O-DIMETHYL PHOSPHORODITHIOATE S-ESTER WITH 4-(MERCAPTOACETYL) MORPHOLINE	144-41-2	PST73096
O,O-DIMETHYL PHOSPHORODITHIOATE S-ESTER WITH 4-(MERCAPTOMETHYL) -2-METHOXY-DELTA 2-1,3,4-THIADIAZOLIN-5-ONE	950-37-8	PST14175
O,O-DIMETHYL PHOSPHORODITHOATE S-ESTER WITH N-FORMYL-2-MERCAPTO -N-METHYLACETAMIDE	2540-82-1	PST10081
O,O-DIMETHYL PHOSPHOROTHIOATE O-ESTER WITH P-HYDROXY-N,N DIMETHYLBENZENESULFONAMIDE	52-85-7	PST09675

SUBSTANCE NAME	CAS #	PST #
O,O-DIMETHYL PHOSPHOROTHIOATE O-ESTER WITH P-HYDROXYBENZENESULFONAMIDE	115-93-5	PST06135
O,O-DIMETHYL PHOSPHOROTHIOATE S-ESTER WITH 2-MERCAPTO -N-METHYLACETAMIDE	1113-02-6	PST17328
O,O-DIMETHYL PHOSPHOROTHIOATE, S-ESTER WITH 2-((2-MERCAPTOETHYL)THIO) -N-METHYLPROPIONAMIDE	2275-23-2	PST73108
O,O-DIMETHYL S-((2-ISOPROPYLTHIO)ETHYL) PHOSPHORODITHIOATE	36614-38-7	PST12275
O,O-DIMETHYL S-((4-OXO-1,2,3-BENZOTRIAZIN-3(4H)-YL)METHYL) PHOSPHORODITHIOATE	86-50-0	PST02210
O,O-DIMETHYL S-((4,6-DIAMINO-S-TRIAZIN-2-YL)METHYL) PHOSPHORODITHIOATE	78-57-9	PST72980
O,O-DIMETHYL S-(ETHYLSULFINYLMETHYL) PHOSPHOROTHIOATE	2588-05-8	PST18644
O,O-DIMETHYL S-(MORPHOLINOCARBONYLMETHYL)PHOSPHORODITHIOATE	144-41-2	PST73096
O,O-DIMETHYL S-(14-OXO-1,2,3-BENZOTRIAZIN-3(4H)-YL)METHYL) PHOSPHOROTHIOATE	961-22-8	PST10585
O,O-DIMETHYL S-(2((1-METHYLETHYL)THIO)ETHYL)PHOSPHORODITHIOATE	36614-38-7	PST12275
O,O-DIMETHYL S-(2-((1-METHYL-2-(METHYLAMINO)-2-OXOETHYL)THIO)ETHYL PHOSPHOROTHIOATE	2275-23-2	PST73108
O,O-DIMETHYL S-(2-((1-METHYLETHYL)THIO)ETHYL ESTER PHOSPHORODITHIOIC ACID	36614-38-7	PST12275
O,O-DIMETHYL S-(2-(ETHYLTHIO)ETHYL)PHOSPHORDITHIOATE	640-15-3	PST83056
O,O-DIMETHYL S-(2-(METHYLAMINO)-2-OXOETHYL) PHOSPHOROTHIOATE	1113-02-6	PST17328
O,O-DIMETHYL S-(2-(METHYLAMINO)-2-OXOETHYL)PHOSPHORODITHIOATE	60-51-5	PST07670
O,O-DIMETHYL S-(2-(METHYLTHIO)ETHYL)PHOSPHOROTHIOATE	2587-90-8	PST73094
O,O-DIMETHYL S-(2-(1-METHYLCARBAMOYLETHYLTHIO)ETHYL PHOSPHOROTHIOATE	2275-23-2	PST73108
O,O-DIMETHYL S-(2-(4-MORPHOLINYL)-2-OXOETHYL)PHOSPHORODITHIOATE	144-41-2	PST73096
O,O-DIMETHYL S-(2,3-DIHYDRO-5-METHOXY-2-OXO-1,3,4-THIADIAZOL -3-YLMETHYL)PHOSPHORODITHIOATE	950-37-8	PST14175
O,O-DIMETHYL S-(5-METHOXY-4-OXO-4H-PYRAN-2-YL)PHOSPHOROTHIOATE	2778-04-3	PST73139
O,O-DIMETHYL S-(5-METHOXYPYRONYL-2-METHYL)THIOPHOSPHATE	2778-04-3	PST73139
O,O-DIMETHYL S-ALPHA-ETHOXYCARBONYLBENZYLPHOSPHORODITHIOATE	2597-03-7	PST72337
O,O-DIMETHYL S-METHYLCARBAMOYLMETHYL PHOSPHORODITHIOATE	60-51-5	PST07670
O,O-DIMETHYL S-METHYLCARBAMOYLMETHYL PHOSPHOROTHIOATE	1113-02-6	PST17328
O,O-DIMETHYL S-MORPHOLINOCARBONYLMETHYL PHOSPHORODITHIOATE	144-41-2	PST73096
O,O-DIMETHYL S-PHTHALIMIDOMETHYL PHOSPHORODITHIOATE	732-11-6	PST11307
O,O-DIMETHYL S-2-METHYLTHIOETHYL PHOSPHOROTHIOATE	2587-90-8	PST73094
O,O-DIMETHYL S-3-(MERCAPTOMETHYL)-1,2,3-BENZOTRIAZIN-4-ONE PHOSPHOROTHIOATE	961-22-8	PST10585
O,O-DIMETHYL 1-CARBOMETHOXY-1-PROPEN-2-YL PHOSPHATE	7786-34-7	PST18650
O,O-DIMETHYL 2-ETHYLMERCAPTOETHYL THIOPHOSPHATE	8022-00-2	PST14438
O,O-DIMETHYL 2-ETHYLTHIOETHYL PHOSPHOROTHIOATE	8022-00-2	PST14438
O,O-DIMETHYL 2,2,2-TRICHLORO-1-HYDROXYETHYLPHOSPHONATE	52-68-6	PST23790
O,O-DIMETHYL 2,2,2-TRICHLORO-1-N-BUTYRYLOXYETHYLPHOSPHONATE	126-22-7	PST71399
O,O-DIMETHYL(2,2,2-TRICHLORO-1-HYDROXYETHYL)PHOSPHONATE	52-68-6	PST23790
O,O-DIMETHYL-O-(PARA-(DIMETHYLSULFAMOYL)PHENYL)PHOSPHOROTHIOATE	52-85-7	PST09675
O,O-DIMETHYL-O-(PARA-(N,N-DIMETHYLSULFAMOYL)PHENYL)PHOSPHOROTHIOATE	52-85-7	PST09675
O,O-DIMETHYL-O-(2-CHLORO-2-DIETHYCARBAMOYL-1-METHYLVINYL) PHOSPHATE	13171-21-6	PST18670
O,O-DIMETHYL-O-(2-CHLORO-4-NITROPHENYL)THIONOPHOSPHATE	2463-84-5	PST71380
O,O-DIMETHYL-O-(2,5-DICHLORO-4-BROMOPHENYL)THIOPHOSPHATE	2104-96-3	PST71064
O,O-DIMETHYL-O-(3-CHLORO-4-NITROPHENYL)PHOSPHOROTHIOATE	500-28-7	PST71379
O,O-DIMETHYL-O-(4(METHYLSULFINYL)-M-TOLYL)PHOSPHATE	6552-13-2	PST02553
O,O-DIMETHYL-O-(4-(METHYLSULFONYL)-M-TOLYL)PHOSPHATE	14086-35-2	PST02552
O,O-DIMETHYL-O-(4-(METHYLTHIO)-M-TOLYL)PHOSPHATE	6552-12-1	PST02551
O,O-DIMETHYL-O-(4-CYANOPHENYL) PHOSPHOROTHIOATE	2636-26-2	PST72950
O,O-DIMETHYL-O-P-CYANOPHENOL PHOSPHOROTHIOATE	2636-26-2	PST72950
O,O-DIMETHYL-O-1,2-DIBROMO-2,2-DICHLOROETHYL PHOSPHATE	300-76-5	PST06660

ALPHABETICAL INDEX

SUBSTANCE NAME	CAS #	PST #
OLOTHORB	9005-65-6	PST40200
OLPISAN	82-68-8	PST18140
OMACIDE 24	15922-78-8	PST21420
OMADINE SODIUM	15922-78-8	PST21420
OMADINE SODIUM SALT	15922-78-8	PST21420
OMCHLOR	118-52-5	PST26800
OMETHOATE	1113-02-6	PST17328
OMEXAN	2104-96-3	PST71064
OMITE	2312-35-8	PST19720
OMPA	152-16-9	PST20350
OMS 1056	973-21-7	PST07990
OMS 1075	2597-03-7	PST72337
OMS 1078	72-54-8	PST06240
OMS 1102	6988-21-2	PST73123
OMS 115	299-85-4	PST71236
OMS 1155	5598-13-0	PST71652
OMS 1170	14816-18-3	PST73292
OMS 1206	10453-86-8	PST20095
OMS 1209	6164-98-3	PST04570
OMS 1211	18181-70-9	PST73035
OMS 123	299-84-3	PST20180
OMS 1328	470-90-6	PST04575
OMS 1344	1757-18-2	PST00493
OMS 1437	57-74-9	PST04560
OMS 1478	29173-31-7	PST73246
OMS 15	64-00-6	PST29423
OMS 1502	31218-83-4	PST72440
OMS 16	50-29-3	PST06250
OMS 162	64-00-6	PST29423
OMS 17	58-89-9	PST12810
OMS 17KO	2032-59-9	PST71500
OMS 1804	35367-38-5	PST07388
OMS 1809	26002-80-2	PST71954
OMS 186	86-50-0	PST02210
OMS 193	76-44-8	PST10660
OMS 197	72-20-8	PST08600
OMS 20	87-47-8	PST73263
OMS 206N	297-78-9	PST83032
OMS 214	2463-84-5	PST71380
OMS 217	500-28-7	PST71379
OMS 227	8065-36-9	PST03480
OMS 244	786-19-6	PST04340
OMS 32	2631-40-5	PST73231
OMS 33	114-26-1	PST02540
OMS 43	122-14-5	PST09678
OMS 466	72-43-5	PST14220
OMS 47	315-18-4	PST15010
OMS 503	78-57-9	PST72980
OMS 658	2104-96-3	PST71064
OMS 659	4824-78-6	PST03458
OMS 708	1079-33-0	PST29855
OMS 771	116-06-3	PST00500
OMS 773	6392-46-7	PST72977
OMS 870	13067-93-1	PST05805

ALPHABETICAL INDEX

SUBSTANCE NAME	CAS #	PST #
OMS 958	2669-32-1	PST73147
OMS 971	2921-88-2	PST04910
OMU	2163-69-1	PST05996
ONCOL	82560-54-1	PST72562
ONECIDE	69806-50-4	PST72554
ONYOXIDE 500	52-51-7	PST72832
ORAGULANT	82-66-6	PST08068
ORDRAM	2212-67-1	PST71471
ORIMON	92-84-2	PST18400
ORTHENE	30560-19-1	PST00065
ORTHESIN	94-09-7	PST72267
ORTHO DIQUAT	85-00-7	PST08250
ORTHO SPRAY STOCK "L"	64742-52-5	PST17323
ORTHO 5353	8065-36-9	PST03480
ORTHO 5865	2425-06-1	PST04200
ORTHO-MITE	140-57-8	PST01850
ORTHO-PHENYLPHENOL	90-43-7	PST18470
ORTHOARSENATE	7631-89-2	PST20940
ORTHOARSENIC ACID	7778-39-4	PST01990
ORTHOBORIC ACID	10043-35-3	PST03260
ORTHOBORIC ACID (B(OH)3)	10043-35-3	PST03260
ORTHOBORIC ACID (H3BO3)	10043-35-3	PST03260
ORTHOCIDE	133-06-2	PST04210
ORTHOPHALTAN	133-07-3	PST10012
ORTHOPHOSPHORIC ACID	7664-38-2	PST18690
ORTHORALTAN 50	133-07-3	PST10012
ORTRAN	30560-19-1	PST00065
ORVAGIL	443-48-1	PST72529
ORYZALIN	19044-88-3	PST17324
OS 1897	96-12-8	PST26490
OSBON AC	79-21-0	PST18310
OSMOGLYN	56-81-5	PST10440
OSSIN	7681-49-4	PST21230
OSVAN	8001-54-5	PST00537
OTC	79-57-2	PST17414
OTOBIOTIC	1405-10-3	PST84263
OTTAFACT	59-50-7	PST29890
OTTASEPT	88-04-0	PST72258
OUST	74222-97-2	PST72544
OUTFOX	22936-86-3	PST72296
OVITROL	97-24-5	PST71737
OXACYCLOPROPANE	75-21-8	PST09520
OXADIAZON	19666-30-9	PST72385
OXADIAZONE	19666-30-9	PST72385
OXAF	155-04-4	PST27776
OXALIC ACID	144-62-7	PST17360
OXALIC ACID, COPPER	814-91-5	PST05650
OXAMYL	23135-22-0	PST17370
OXANE	75-21-8	PST09520
OXICARBOXIN	5259-88-1	PST17373
OXIDOETHANE	75-21-8	PST09520
OXIME	39196-18-4	PST23330
OXINE	148-24-3	PST30450
OXINE BENZOATE	7091-57-8	PST71657

ALPHABETICAL INDEX

SUBSTANCE NAME	CAS #	PST #
P,P'-DICHLOROBENZOPHENONE	90-98-2	PST06246
P,P'-DICHLORODIPHENYLMETHANE	101-76-8	PST06321
P,P'-DMDT	72-43-5	PST14220
P,P'-DME	1022-22-6	PST06322
P,P'-METHOXYCHLOR	72-43-5	PST14220
P,P'-TDE	72-54-8	PST06240
P,P'-TDE OLEFIN	1022-22-6	PST06322
P,P'-TDEE	1022-22-6	PST06322
P'P'-DDT	50-29-3	PST06250
PAA	79-21-0	PST18310
PAC	1698-60-8	PST71928
PADAN	15263-52-2	PST04359
PADOPHENE	92-84-2	PST18400
PAKHTARAN	2164-17-2	PST09907
PALATINOL	84-66-2	PST07210
PALITINOL M	131-11-3	PST07740
PALMITOYL ALCOHOL	36653-82-4	PST04525
PANACIDE	97-23-4	PST71611
PANOGEN	151-38-2	PST83031
PANOGEN (FORMULATION)	502-39-6	PST83040
PANOGEN-METOX	151-38-2	PST83031
PANTOCAIN	136-47-0	PST72269
PANWARFIN	129-06-6	PST83008
PAPTHION	2597-03-7	PST72337
PARA-DIMETHYLAMINOBENZENEDIAZO SODIUM SULPHONATE	140-56-7	PST73084
PARA-MENTH-8-EN-1-OL	138-87-4	PST03075
PARA-NITROPHENOL	100-02-7	PST17800
PARA-NITROPHENYL PHENYL METHYLPHOSPHONOTHIONATE	2665-30-7	PST73278
PARABIS	97-23-4	PST71611
PARADI	106-46-7	PST17640
PARADICHLORBENZENE	106-46-7	PST17640
PARADOW	106-46-7	PST17640
PARAFORM	30525-89-4	PST18000
PARAFORM	50-00-0	PST50003
PARAFORMALDEHYDE	30525-89-4	PST18000
PARAMEX	2385-85-5	PST09690
PARAMOTH	106-46-7	PST17640
PARAOXON	311-45-5	PST07200
PARAOXON METHYL	950-35-6	PST14678
PARAPHOS	56-38-2	PST18040
PARAQUAT	1910-42-5	PST18020
PARAQUAT	2074-50-2	PST71670
PARAQUAT	4685-14-7	PST71671
PARAQUAT BIS(METHYL SULFATE)	2074-50-2	PST71670
PARAQUAT DICATION	4685-14-7	PST71671
PARAQUAT DICHLORIDE	1910-42-5	PST18020
PARAQUAT DIMETHOSULFATE	2074-50-2	PST71670
PARAQUAT DIMETHYL SULFATE	2074-50-2	PST71670
PARAQUAT DIMETHYL SULPHATE	2074-50-2	PST71670
PARAQUAT I	2074-50-2	PST71670
PARAQUAT ION	4685-14-7	PST71671
PARAQUAT METHOXULFATE	2074-50-2	PST71670
PARAQUAT METHYLSULFATE	2074-50-2	PST71670

SUBSTANCE NAME	CAS #	PST #
PARASEPT	99-76-3	PST14677
PARASEPT	94-13-3	PST19941
PARATHESINE	94-09-7	PST72267
PARATHION	56-38-2	PST18040
PARATHION-ETHYL	56-38-2	PST18040
PARATHION-METHYL	298-00-0	PST14680
PARATHION-METHYL HOMOLOG	298-00-0	PST14680
PARAZATE	142-59-6	PST16080
PARDNER	1689-84-5	PST03542
PARIDOL	99-76-3	PST14677
PARTISIL	63231-67-4	PST20670
PASEPTOL	94-13-3	PST19941
PATENT ALUM	10043-01-3	PST00980
PATORAN	3060-89-7	PST15008
PAXILON	20354-26-1	PST72344
PCA	1698-60-8	PST71928
PCI	80-38-6	PST09677
PCMC	59-50-7	PST29890
PCMX	88-04-0	PST72258
PCNB	82-68-8	PST18140
PCP	87-86-5	PST18150
PCP SODIUM SALT	131-52-2	PST08506
PCP-SODIUM	131-52-2	PST08506
PCPBS	80-38-6	PST09677
PDU	101-42-8	PST09679
PEACOCK BLUE X 1756	2650-18-2	PST08277
PEARL ASH	584-08-7	PST19290
PEBBLE LIME	1305-78-8	PST04030
PEBC	1114-71-2	PST71472
PEBULATE	1114-71-2	PST71472
PELARGONIUM OIL	8000-46-2	PST73283
PELT	23564-06-9	PST72322
PENCAL	7778-44-1	PST03850
PENCHLOROL	87-86-5	PST18150
PENCYCURON	66063-05-6	PST72622
PENNAC ZT	155-04-4	PST27776
PENNYROYAL OIL	8007-44-1	PST71456
PENTACHLORIN	50-29-3	PST06250
PENTACHLORONITROBENZENE	82-68-8	PST18140
PENTACHLOROPHENATE SODIUM	131-52-2	PST08506
PENTACHLOROPHENOL	87-86-5	PST18150
PENTACHLOROPHENOL SODIUM SALT	131-52-2	PST08506
PENTACHLOROPHENOXY SODIUM	131-52-2	PST08506
PENTACHLOROPHENYL CHLORIDE	118-74-1	PST10730
PENTAGEN	82-68-8	PST18140
PENTAHYDROXYCAPROIC ACID	526-95-4	PST10408
PENTANAMIDE, N-(3-CHLORO-4-METHYLPHENYL)-2-METHYL-	2307-68-8	PST71164
PENTANAMIDE, N-(4-CHLOROPHENYL)-2,2-DIMETHYL-	7287-36-7	PST72987
PENTANOCHLOR	2307-68-8	PST71164
PENTAPHEN	80-46-6	PST71715
PENTASODIUM TRIPHOSPHATE	7758-29-4	PST21730
PENTASODIUM TRIPOLYPHOSPHATE	7758-29-4	PST21730
PENTHAZINE	92-84-2	PST18400
PENTYL ACETATE	628-63-7	PST15270

SUBSTANCE NAME	CAS #	PST #
PENTYLCARBINOL	111-27-3	PST15630
PERACETIC ACID	79-21-0	PST18310
PERACTIC ACID SOLUTION	79-21-0	PST18310
PERBULATE	1929-77-7	PST71473
PERC	127-18-4	PST22900
PERCHLORIDE OF MERCURY	7487-94-7	PST13800
PERCHLOROBENZENE	118-74-1	PST10730
PERCHLOROETHENE	127-18-4	PST22900
PERCHLOROETHYLENE	127-18-4	PST22900
PERCHLOROMETHANE	56-23-5	PST04310
PERCHLOROPENTACYCLODECANE	2385-85-5	PST09690
PERCLENE	127-18-4	PST22900
PERENOX	1317-39-1	PST05470
PERFLAN	34014-18-1	PST72340
PERFLUIDONE	37924-13-3	PST72375
PERHYDROL	7722-84-1	PST11190
PERM ETHANE DG (DETREX CHEMICALS)	71-55-6	PST14370
PERMA KLEER ACID	60-00-4	PST09570
PERMANENT WHITE	1314-13-2	PST25490
PERMANGANIC ACID POTASSIUM SALT	7722-64-7	PST19520
PERMASAN	87-86-5	PST18150
PERMETHRIN	51877-74-8	PST23708
PEROXAN	7722-84-1	PST11190
PEROXOACETIC ACID	79-21-0	PST18310
PEROXYACETIC ACID	79-21-0	PST18310
PERTHANE	72-56-0	PST71373
PERUSCABIN	120-51-4	PST02805
PESTAN	2595-54-2	PST13675
PESTMASTER	74-83-9	PST14300
PESTON XV	371-86-8	PST15030
PESTON 15	371-86-8	PST15030
PESTOX	152-16-9	PST20350
PESTOX 14	115-26-4	PST07655
PETROLEUM ASPHALT	8052-42-4	PST02140
PETROLEUM ASPHALT	8052-42-4	PST71177
PETROLEUM PITCH	8052-42-4	PST02140
PETROLEUM PITCH	8052-42-4	PST71177
PETRONATE L	68608-26-4	PST18339
PF 7402	3878-19-1	PST73188
PH 60-40	35367-38-5	PST07388
PH 6040	35367-38-5	PST07388
PHALTAN	133-07-3	PST10012
PHEMERIDE	121-54-0	PST71851
PHEMEROL	121-54-0	PST71851
PHEMEROL CHLORIDE	121-54-0	PST71851
PHENACETIN	62-44-2	PST18340
PHENACIDE	8001-35-2	PST23640
PHENAMIPHOS	22224-92-6	PST16145
PHENATOX	8001-35-2	PST23640
PHENCAPTON	2275-14-1	PST18373
PHENETHYL ALCOHOL PROPIONATE	122-70-3	PST72314
PHENETHYL PROPANOATE	122-70-3	PST72314
PHENETHYL PROPANOIC ACID ESTER	122-70-3	PST72314
PHENETHYL PROPIONATE	122-70-3	PST72314

ALPHABETICAL INDEX

SUBSTANCE NAME	CAS #	PST #
PHENIC ACID	108-95-2	PST18380
PHENKAPTON	2275-14-1	PST18373
PHENKAPTONE	2275-14-1	PST18373
PHENMAD	62-38-4	PST18560
PHENMEDIPHAM	13684-63-4	PST72282
PHENO, 2-SEC-BUTYL-4,6-DINITRO, ACETATE	2813-95-8	PST08021
PHENOBENZURON	3134-12-1	PST72972
PHENOL	108-95-2	PST18380
PHENOL SODIUM	139-02-6	PST21530
PHENOL-2-CARBOXYLIC ACID	69-72-7	PST20315
PHENOL, DIMETHYL	1300-71-6	PST25160
PHENOL, METHYL-	1319-77-3	PST05510
PHENOL, P-TERT-BUTYL-	98-54-4	PST17440
PHENOL, PENTACHLORO-	87-86-5	PST18150
PHENOL, PENTACHLORO-, SODIUM SALT	131-52-2	PST08506
PHENOL, SODIUM SALT, (SOLID)	139-02-6	PST21530
PHENOL, TETRACHLORO-	25167-83-3	PST71689
PHENOL, 2-((ETHYLTHIO)METHYL)-, METHYLCARBAMATE	29973-13-5	PST72421
PHENOL, 2-(1-METHYLETHOXY)-, METHYLCARBAMATE	114-26-1	PST02540
PHENOL, 2-(1-METHYLETHYL)-, METHYLCARBAMATE	2631-40-5	PST73231
PHENOL, 2-(1-METHYLPROPYL)-, METHYLCARBAMATE	3766-81-2	PST03324
PHENOL, 2-(1-METHYLPROPYL)-4,6-DINITRO-	88-85-7	PST08020
PHENOL, 2-(1-METHYLPROPYL)-4,6-DINITRO-, ACETATE (ESTER)	2813-95-8	PST08021
PHENOL, 2-(1,1-DIMETHYLETHYL)-4,6-DINITRO-	1420-07-1	PST72921
PHENOL, 2-(1,3-DIOXOLAN-2YL)-, METHYLCARBAMATE	6988-21-2	PST73123
PHENOL, 2-(2-CHLORO-1-METHOXYETHOXY)-, METHYLCARBAMATE	51487-69-5	PST72572
PHENOL, 2-CHLORO-4,5-DIMETHYL-, METHYLCARBAMATE	671-04-5	PST02250
PHENOL, 2-METHYL-4,6-DINITRO-	534-52-1	PST07910
PHENOL, 2-METHYL-4,6-DINITRO-, SODIUM SALT	2312-76-7	PST71411
PHENOL, 2-SEC-BUTYL-4,6-DINITRO-	88-85-7	PST08020
PHENOL, 2-SEC-BUTYL-4,6-DINITRO-, ACETATE (ESTER)	2813-95-8	PST08021
PHENOL, 2-TERT-BUTYL-4,6-DINITRO-	1420-07-1	PST72921
PHENOL, 2,2'-METHYLENEBIS(4-CHLORO-	97-23-4	PST71611
PHENOL, 2,2'-THIOBIS(4-CHLORO-	97-24-5	PST71737
PHENOL, 2,3,5(OR 3,4,5)-TRIMETHYL-, METHYLCARBAMATE	12407-86-2	PST12420
PHENOL, 2,4-DICHLORO-, BENZENESULFONATE	97-16-5	PST71350
PHENOL, 2,4-DIMETHYL	105-67-9	PST28670
PHENOL, 2,4-DINITRO-	51-28-5	PST28620
PHENOL, 3-(1-ETHYLPROPYL)-, METHYLCARBAMATE, MIXTURE WITH 3-(1-METHYLBUTYL)PHENYL METHYLCARBAMATE	8065-36-9	PST03480
PHENOL, 3-(1-METHYLETHYL)-, METHYLCARBAMATE	64-00-6	PST29423
PHENOL, 3-METHYL-5-(1-METHYLETHYL)-, METHYLCARBAMATE	2631-37-0	PST72957
PHENOL, 3,5-BIS(1,1-DIMETHYLETHYL)-, METHYLCARBAMATE	2655-19-8	PST72994
PHENOL, 3,5-DIMETHYL-, METHYLCARBAMATE	2655-14-3	PST25171
PHENOL, 3,5-DIMETHYL-4-(METHYLSULFINYL)-, METHYLCARBAMATE	2635-10-1	PST14191
PHENOL, 3,5-DIMETHYL-4-(METHYLTHIO)-, METHYLCARBAMATE	2032-65-7	PST14190
PHENOL, 4-(DI-2-PROPENYLAMINO)-3,5-DIMETHYL-, METHYLCARBAMATE (ESTER)	6392-46-7	PST72977
PHENOL, 4-(DIMETHYLAMINO)-3-METHYL-, METHYLCARBAMATE (ESTER)	2032-59-9	PST71500
PHENOL, 4-(DIMETHYLAMINO)-3,5-DIMETHYL-, METHYLCARBAMATE (ESTER)	315-18-4	PST15010
PHENOL, 4-(1,1-DIMETHYLETHYL)-	98-54-4	PST17440
PHENOL, 4-CHLORO-2-CYCLOPENTYL-	13347-42-7	PST71731
PHENOL, 4-CHLORO-3-METHYL-	59-50-7	PST29890
PHENOL, 4-CHLORO-3,5-DIMETHYL-	88-04-0	PST72258
PHENOL, 4-NITRO-3-(TRIFLUOROMETHYL)-	88-30-2	PST71405

SUBSTANCE NAME	CAS #	PST #
PHENOMERCURIC ACETATE	62-38-4	PST18560
PHENOPYRIDINE	148-24-3	PST30450
PHENOTHIAZINE	92-84-2	PST18400
PHENOTHRIN	26002-80-2	PST71954
PHENOXAPROP-ETHYL	66441-23-4	PST72723
PHENTHOATE	2597-03-7	PST72337
PHENTIN ACETATE	900-95-8	PST24378
PHENUDIN	2275-14-1	PST18373
PHENUDINE	2275-14-1	PST18373
PHENVALERATE	51630-58-1	PST19948
PHENYL ALCOHOL	108-95-2	PST18380
PHENYL CARBOXYLIC ACID	65-85-0	PST02720
PHENYL CHLOROMERCURY	100-56-1	PST18570
PHENYL HYDRATE	108-95-2	PST18380
PHENYL HYDROXIDE	108-95-2	PST18380
PHENYL HYDROXYMERCURY	100-57-2	PST18580
PHENYL MERCURIC ACETATE	62-38-4	PST18560
PHENYL MERCURIC CHLORIDE	100-56-1	PST18570
PHENYL MERCURIC TRIETHANOL AMMONIUM LACTATE	23319-66-6	PST71768
PHENYL N,N'-DIMETHYL PHOSPHOROMIADATE	1754-58-1	PST72310
PHENYL PERCHLORYL	118-74-1	PST10730
PHENYL PHOSPHONOTHIOIC ACID, O-ETHYL O-(4-NITROPHENYL)ESTER	2104-64-5	PST08650
PHENYL PHTHALATE	84-62-8	PST08095
PHENYLANILINE	122-39-4	PST08100
PHENYLCARBAMIC ACID 1-METHYLETHYL ESTER	122-42-9	PST71564
PHENYLCARBINOL	100-51-6	PST02800
PHENYLCARBOXYLIC ACID	65-85-0	PST02720
PHENYLETHYL PROPIONATE	122-70-3	PST72314
PHENYLFORMIC ACID	65-85-0	PST02720
PHENYLGLYOXYLONITRILE OXIME O,O-DIETHYL PHOSPHOROTHIOATE	14816-18-3	PST73292
PHENYLIC ACID	108-95-2	PST18380
PHENYLIC ALCOHOL	108-95-2	PST18380
PHENYLMERCURIC ACETATE	62-38-4	PST18560
PHENYLMERCURIC BORATE	6273-99-0	PST71754
PHENYLMERCURIC CHLORIDE	100-56-1	PST18570
PHENYLMERCURIC HYDROXIDE	100-57-2	PST18580
PHENYLMERCURIC OLEATE	104-60-9	PST71769
PHENYLMERCURY ACETATE	62-38-4	PST18560
PHENYLMERCURY BORATE	6273-99-0	PST71754
PHENYLMERCURY CHLORIDE	100-56-1	PST18570
PHENYLMERCURY HYDROXIDE	100-57-2	PST18580
PHENYLMERCURY OLEATE	104-60-9	PST71769
PHENYLMETHANAL	100-52-7	PST02590
PHENYLMETHANOL	100-51-6	PST02800
PHENYLMETHYL ALCOHOL	100-51-6	PST02800
PHENYLPHOSPHONOTHIOIC ACID O-(4-CYANOPHENYL) O-ETHYL ESTER	13067-93-1	PST05805
PHENYLPHOSPHONOTHIOIC ACID O-ETHYL ESTER O-ESTER WITH P-HYDROXYBENZONITRILE	13067-93-1	PST05805
PHENYLPHOSPHONOTHIOIC ACID, ETHYL P-NITROPHENYL ESTER	2104-64-5	PST08650
PHENYLPHOSPHONOTHIOIC ACID, O-(2,4-DICHLOROPHENYL)-O-ETHYL ESTER	3792-59-4	PST73239
PHENYLPHOSPHONOTHIOIC ACID, O-(4-BROMO-2,5-DICHLOROPHENYL)O-METHYL ESTER	21609-90-5	PST12780
PHENYLPHOSPHONOTHIOIC ACID, O-ETHYL O-(P-NITROPHENYL)ESTER	2104-64-5	PST08650
PHILLIPS REPELLENT 11	126-15-8	PST71487

ALPHABETICAL INDEX

SUBSTANCE NAME	CAS #	PST #
PHILOSOPHER'S WOOL	1314-13-2	PST25490
PHODA-NIDE	333-20-0	PST19640
PHORATE	298-02-2	PST18640
PHORATE O.A. SULFOXIDE	2588-05-8	PST18644
PHORATE O-SULFOXIDE	2588-03-6	PST18646
PHORATE OXON	2600-69-3	PST18641
PHORATE OXON SULFONE	2588-06-9	PST18642
PHORATE OXON SULFOXIDE	2588-05-8	PST18644
PHORATE OXYGEN ANALOG	2600-69-3	PST18641
PHORATE OXYGEN ANALOG SULFONE	2588-06-9	PST18642
PHORATE OXYGEN ANALOG SULFOXIDE	2588-05-8	PST18644
PHORATE SULFONE	2588-04-7	PST18643
PHORATE SULFOXIDE	2588-03-6	PST18646
PHORATE THIOLATE ANALOG	2600-69-3	PST18641
PHORATOXON	2600-69-3	PST18641
PHORATOXON SULFONE	2588-06-9	PST18642
PHORATOXON SULFOXIDE	2588-05-8	PST18644
PHOSACETIM	4104-14-7	PST71150
PHOSALON	2310-17-0	PST25720
PHOSALONE	2310-17-0	PST25720
PHOSDRIN	7786-34-7	PST18650
PHOSETHYL AL	39148-24-8	PST72563
PHOSFOLAN	947-02-4	PST06115
PHOSMET	732-11-6	PST11307
PHOSMET OXYGEN ANALOG	3735-33-9	PST18665
PHOSMETOXON	3735-33-9	PST18665
PHOSPHACHOLE	311-45-5	PST07200
PHOSPHACOL; PHOSPHAKOL	311-45-5	PST07200
PHOSPHAMIDE	60-51-5	PST07670
PHOSPHAMIDON	13171-21-6	PST18670
PHOSPHOLAN	947-02-4	PST06115
PHOSPHONIC ACID, (2-CHLOROETHYL)-	16672-87-0	PST72293
PHOSPHONIC ACID, (2,2,2-TRICHLORO-1-HYDROXYETHYL)-, DIMETHYL ESTER	52-68-6	PST23790
PHOSPHONIC ACID, ETHYL-, ETHYL 2,4,5-TRICHLOROPHENYL ESTER	6492-18-8	PST23871
PHOSPHONIC ACID, MONOETHYL ESTER, ALUMINUM SALT	39148-24-8	PST72563
PHOSPHONIC ACID, PHENYL-, 4-BROMO-2,5-DICHLOROPHENYL METHYL ESTER	25006-32-0	PST12776
PHOSPHONIC DIAMIDE, P-(5-AMINO-3-PHENYL-1H-1,2,4-TRIAZOL-1-YL)-N,N,N', N'-TETRAMETHYL	1031-47-6	PST72937
PHOSPHONODITHIOIC ACID, ETHYL-, O-ETHYL S-PHENYL ESTER	944-22-9	PST10020
PHOSPHONODITHIOIMIDOCARBONIC ACID CYCLIC METHYLENE P,P-DIETHYL ESTER	21548-32-3	PST16141
PHOSPHONODITHIOIMIDOCARBONIC ACID CYCLIC PROPYLENE P,P-DIETHYL ESTER	950-10-7	PST13735
PHOSPHONOMETHYLGLYCINE	1071-83-6	PST10515
PHOSPHONOMETHYLIMINOACETIC ACID	1071-83-6	PST10515
PHOSPHONOTHIOIC ACID, (1,3-DIHYDRO-1,3-DIOXO-2H-ISOINDOL-2-YL)-, O,O-DIETHYL ESTER	5131-24-8	PST72347
PHOSPHONOTHIOIC ACID, ETHYL-, O-ETHYL O-(2,4,5-TRICHLOROPHENYL)ESTER	327-98-0	PST00478
PHOSPHONOTHIOIC ACID, PHENYL ETHYL P-NITROPHENYL ESTER	2104-64-5	PST08650
PHOSPHONOTHIOIC ACID, PHENYL-, O-(2,4-DICHLOROPHENYL)-O-ETHYL ESTER	3792-59-4	PST73239
PHOSPHONOTHIOIC ACID, PHENYL-, O-(4-CYANOPHENYL) O-ETHYL ESTER	13067-93-1	PST05805
PHOSPHONOTHIOIC ACID, PHENYL-, O-ETHYL ESTER, O-ESTER WITH P-HYDROXYBENZONITRILE	13067-93-1	PST05805
PHOSPHONOTHIOIC ACID, PHENYL-, O-ETHYL O-(P-NITROPHENYL)ESTER	2104-64-5	PST08650
PHOSPHONOTHIOIC ACID, PHENYL-, O-ETHYL O-(4-NITROPHENYL)ESTER	2104-64-5	PST08650
PHOSPHONOTHIOIC ACID, PHTHALIMIDO-, O,O-DIETHYL ESTER	5131-24-8	PST72347

SUBSTANCE NAME	CAS #	PST #
PHOSPHONOTHIONIC ACID, METHYL-, S-(2-(BIS(1-METHYLETHYL)AMINO)ETHYL) O-ETHYL ESTER	50782-69-9	PST83104
PHOSPHORAMIDIC ACID, (1-METHYLETHYL)-, ETHYL 3-METHYL-4-(METHYLSULFONYL)PHENYL ESTER	31972-44-8	PST16144
PHOSPHORAMIDIC ACID, (1-METHYLETHYL)-, ETHYL 3-METHYL-4-(METHYLSULFINYL)PHENYL ESTER	31972-43-7	PST16146
PHOSPHORAMIDIC ACID, (1-METHYLETHYL)-, ETHYL 3-METHYL-4-(METHYLTHIO) PHENYL ESTER	22224-92-6	PST16145
PHOSPHORAMIDIC ACID, (4-METHYL-1,3-DITHIOLAN-2-YLIDENE)-, DIETHYL ESTER	950-10-7	PST13735
PHOSPHORAMIDIC ACID, ISOPROPYL-, ETHYL 4-(ETHYLSULFINYL)-M-TOLYL ESTER	31972-43-7	PST16146
PHOSPHORAMIDIC ACID, ISOPROPYL-, ETHYL 4-(METHYLTHIO)-M-TOLYL ESTER	22224-92-6	PST16145
PHOSPHORAMIDIC ACID, ISOPROPYL-, ETHYL-4-(METHYLSULFONYL)-M-TOLYL ESTER	31972-44-8	PST16144
PHOSPHORAMIDIC ACID, METHYL-, 4-TERT-BUTYL-2-CHLOROPHENYL METHYL ESTER	299-86-5	PST05550
PHOSPHORAMIDIC ACID, METHYL-,2-CHLORO-4-(1,1-DIMETHYLETHYL)PHENYL METHYL ESTER	299-86-5	PST05550
PHOSPHORAMIDIC ACID, 1-3-DITHIOLAN-2-YLIDENE-, DIETHYL ESTER	947-02-4	PST06115
PHOSPHORAMIDIC ACID, 1,3-DITHIETAN-2-YLIDENE-, DIETHYL ESTER	21548-32-3	PST16141
PHOSPHORAMIDOTHIOIC ACID, (1-IMINOETHYL)-, O,O-BIS(P-CHLOROPHENYL) ESTER	4104-14-7	PST71150
PHOSPHORAMIDOTHIOIC ACID, (1-METHYLETHYL)-, O-(2,4-DICHLOROPHENYL) O-METHYL ESTER	299-85-4	PST71236
PHOSPHORAMIDOTHIOIC ACID, ACETIMIDOYL-, O,O-BIS(P-CHLOROPHENYL) ESTER	4104-14-7	PST71150
PHOSPHORAMIDOTHIOIC ACID, ISOPROPYL-, O-(2,4-DICHLOROPHENYL) O-METHYL ESTER	299-85-4	PST71236
PHOSPHORAMIDOTHIOIC ACID, O,S-DIMETHYL ESTER	10265-92-6	PST15160
PHOSPHORIC ACID	7664-38-2	PST18690
PHOSPHORIC ACID SODIUM SALT (1:3)	7601-54-9	PST24480
PHOSPHORIC ACID TRIETHYLENEIMINE	545-55-1	PST22510
PHOSPHORIC ACID, DIETHYL P-(METHYLSULFINYL)PHENYL ESTER	6552-21-2	PST09684
PHOSPHORIC ACID, DIETHYL P-(METHYLSULFONYL)PHENYL ESTER	6132-17-8	PST06211
PHOSPHORIC ACID, DIETHYL P-NITROPHENYL ESTER	311-45-5	PST07200
PHOSPHORIC ACID, DIETHYL PYRAZINYL ESTER	7359-55-9	PST71377
PHOSPHORIC ACID, DIETHYL 2-(ETHYLTHIO)ETHYL ESTER	23052-51-9	PST06317
PHOSPHORIC ACID, DIETHYL 2-ISOPROPYL-6-METHYL-4-PYRIMIDINYL ESTER	962-58-3	PST06541
PHOSPHORIC ACID, DIETHYL 3,5,6-TRICHLORO-2-PYRIDINYL ESTER	5598-15-2	PST04911
PHOSPHORIC ACID, DIETHYL 3,5,6-TRICHLORO-2-PYRIDYL ESTER	5598-15-2	PST04911
PHOSPHORIC ACID, DIETHYL 4-(METHYLSULFINYL)PHENYL ESTER	6552-21-2	PST09684
PHOSPHORIC ACID, DIETHYL 4-(METHYLSULFONYL)PHENYL ESTER	6132-17-8	PST06211
PHOSPHORIC ACID, DIETHYL 4-NITROPHENYL ESTER	311-45-5	PST07200
PHOSPHORIC ACID, DIETHYL 6-METHYL-2-(1-METHYLETHYL)-4-PYRIMIDINYL ESTER	962-58-3	PST06541
PHOSPHORIC ACID, DIMETHYL ESTER	813-78-5	PST07882
PHOSPHORIC ACID, DIMETHYL ESTER, ESTER WITH 2-CHLORO-N,N-DIETHYL -3-HYDROXYCROTONAMIDE	13171-21-6	PST18670
PHOSPHORIC ACID, DIMETHYL ESTER, ESTER WITH 3-HYDROXY-N-METHYL CROTONAMIDE, (E)-	6923-22-4	PST15165
PHOSPHORIC ACID, DIMETHYL ESTER, ESTER WITH 3-HYDROXY-N,N -DIMETHYLCROTONAMIDE, (E)-	141-66-2	PST03090
PHOSPHORIC ACID, DIMETHYL P-NITROPHENYL ESTER	950-35-6	PST14678
PHOSPHORIC ACID, DIMETHYL 1-METHYL-3-(METHYLAMINO)-3-OXO-1-PROPENYL ESTER, (E)	6923-22-4	PST15165
PHOSPHORIC ACID, DIMETHYL 2,4,5-TRICHLOROPHENYL ESTER	3983-45-7	PST25082

ALPHABETICAL INDEX

SUBSTANCE NAME	CAS #	PST #
PHOSPHORIC ACID, DIMETHYL 3-METHYL-4-(METHYLSULFINYL)PHENYL ESTER	14086-35-2	PST02552
PHOSPHORIC ACID, DIMETHYL 3-METHYL-4-(METHYLSULFINYL)PHENYL ESTER	6552-13-2	PST02553
PHOSPHORIC ACID, DIMETHYL 3-METHYL-4-(METHYLTHIO)PHENYL ESTER	6552-12-1	PST02551
PHOSPHORIC ACID, DIMETHYL 4-(METHYLSULFINYL)-M-TOLYL ESTER	6552-13-2	PST02553
PHOSPHORIC ACID, DIMETHYL 4-(METHYLSULFONYL)-M-TOLYL ESTER	14086-35-2	PST02552
PHOSPHORIC ACID, DIMETHYL 4-(METHYLTHIO) PHENYL ESTER	3254-63-5	PST73095
PHOSPHORIC ACID, DIMETHYL 4-(METHYLTHIO)-M-TOLYL ESTER	6552-12-1	PST02551
PHOSPHORIC ACID, DIMETHYL 4-NITROPHENYL ESTER	950-35-6	PST14678
PHOSPHORIC ACID, DISODIUM SALT	7558-79-4	PST08330
PHOSPHORIC ACID, MONOSODIUM SALT	7558-80-7	PST15190
PHOSPHORIC ACID, O,O-DIETHYL O-2 ETHYLSULFINYLETHYL ESTER	UNASSIGNED	PST06308
PHOSPHORIC ACID, SOLID	7664-38-2	PST18690
PHOSPHORIC ACID, TRISODIUM SALT	7601-54-9	PST24480
PHOSPHORIC ACID, TRISODIUM SALT (CHLORINATED)	56802-99-4	PST80117
PHOSPHORIC ACID, 1,2-DIBROMO-2,2-DICHLOROETHYL DIMETHYL ESTER	300-76-5	PST06660
PHOSPHORIC ACID, 2-CHLORO-1-(2,4-DICHLOROPHENYL)ETHENYL DIETHYL ESTER	470-90-6	PST04575
PHOSPHORIC ACID, 2-CHLORO-1-(2,4-DICHLOROPHENYL)VINYL DIETHYL ESTER	470-90-6	PST04575
PHOSPHORIC ACID, 2-CHLORO-1-(2,4,5-TRICHLOROPHENYL)ETHENYL DIMETHYL ESTER	961-11-5	PST72243
PHOSPHORIC ACID, 2-CHLORO-1-(2,4,5-TRICHLOROPHENYL)ETHENYL DIMETHYL ESTER, (Z)-	22248-79-9	PST72244
PHOSPHORIC ACID, 2-CHLORO-1-(2,4,5-TRICHLOROPHENYL)ETHENYL DIMETHYL ESTER, (E)-	22350-76-1	PST72245
PHOSPHORIC ACID, 2-CHLORO-1-(2,4,5-TRICHLOROPHENYL)VINYL DIMETHYL ESTER	961-11-5	PST72243
PHOSPHORIC ACID, 2-CHLORO-1-(2,4,5-TRICHLOROPHENYL)VINYL DIMETHYL ESTER, (Z)-	22248-79-9	PST72244
PHOSPHORIC ACID, 2-CHLORO-1-(2,4,5-TRICHLOROPHENYL)VINYL DIMETHYL ESTER, (E)-	22350-76-1	PST72245
PHOSPHORIC ACID, 2,2-DICHLOROETHENYL DIMETHYL ESTER	62-73-7	PST07000
PHOSPHORIC ACID, 2,2-DICHLOROVINYL DIMETHYL ESTER	62-73-7	PST07000
PHOSPHORIC ACID, 3-(DIMETHYLAMINO)-1-METHYL-3-OXO-1-PROPENYL DIMETHYL ESTER, (E)-	141-66-2	PST03090
PHOSPHORIC ACID, 7-CHLOROBICYCLO(3.2.0)HEPTA-2,6-DIEN-6-YL DIMETHYL ESTER	23560-59-0	PST10685
PHOSPHORODIAMIDIC ACID, N,N'-DIMETHYL-, PHENYL ESTER	1754-58-1	PST72310
PHOSPHORODIAMIDIC FLUORIDE N,N'-DIISOPROPYL	371-86-8	PST15030
PHOSPHORODIAMIDIC FLUORIDE, N,N'-BIS(1-METHYLETHYL)-	371-86-8	PST15030
PHOSPHORODITHIOIC ACID , O,O-DIISOPROPYL ESTER, S-ESTER WITH N-(2-MERCAPTOETHYL)BENZENESULFONAMIDE	741-58-2	PST02583
PHOSPHORODITHIOIC ACID, O-(2,4-DICHLOROPHENYL) O-ETHYL-S-PROPYL ESTER	34643-46-4	PST72655
PHOSPHORODITHIOIC ACID, O-ETHYL O-(4-(METHYLTHIO)PHENYL)S-PROPYL ESTER	35400-43-2	PST22387
PHOSPHORODITHIOIC ACID, O-ETHYL S,S DIPROPYL ESTER	13194-48-4	PST15080
PHOSPHORODITHIOIC ACID, O,O-BIS(1-METHYLETHYL) S-(2-((PHENYLSULFONYL)AMINO)ETHYL) ESTER	741-58-2	PST02583
PHOSPHORODITHIOIC ACID, O,O-DIETHYL (ETHYLSULFINYL)METHYL ESTER	2588-03-6	PST18646
PHOSPHORODITHIOIC ACID, O,O-DIETHYL (ETHYLSULFONYL)METHYL ESTER	2588-04-7	PST18643
PHOSPHORODITHIOIC ACID, O,O-DIETHYL ESTER, S-ESTER WITH 3-(MERCAPTOMETHYL)-1,2,3-BENZOTRIAZIN-4(3H)-ONE	2642-71-9	PST02205
PHOSPHORODITHIOIC ACID, O,O-DIETHYL ESTER, S-ESTER WITH N-ISOPROPYL -2-MERCAPTOACETAMIDE	2275-18-5	PST19943
PHOSPHORODITHIOIC ACID, O,O-DIETHYL ESTER, S-ESTER WITH 6-CHLORO -3-(MERCAPTOMETHYL)-2-BENZOXAZOLINONE	2310-17-0	PST25720
PHOSPHORODITHIOIC ACID, O,O-DIETHYL S-((ETHYLSULFINYL)METHYL) ESTER	2588-03-6	PST18646

ALPHABETICAL INDEX

SUBSTANCE NAME	CAS #	PST #
PHOSPHORODITHIOIC ACID, S-((2,4-DICHLOROPHENYL)THIO)METHYL) O,O-DIETHYL ESTER	2275-14-1	PST18373
PHOSPHORODITHIOIC ACID, S-((5-ETHOXY-2-OXO-1,3,4-THIADIAZOL-3(2H)-YL) METHYL) O,O-DIMETHYL ESTER	2669-32-1	PST73147
PHOSPHORODITHIOIC ACID, S-((5-METHOXY-2-OXO-1,3,4-THIADIAZOL-3(2H)-YL) METHYL) O,O-DIMETHYL ESTER	950-37-8	PST14175
PHOSPHORODITHIOIC ACID, S-((6-CHLORO-2-OXO-3(2H)-BENZOXAZOYL)METHYL) O,O-DIETHYL ESTER	2310-17-0	PST25720
PHOSPHORODITHIOIC ACID, S-(CHLOROMETHYL) O,O-DIETHYL ESTER	24934-91-6	PST04655
PHOSPHORODITHIOIC ACID, S-(2-((2-METHOXYETHYL)AMINO)-2-OXOETHYL) O,O-DIMETHYL ESTER	919-76-6	PST01007
PHOSPHORODITHIOIC ACID, S-(2-(FORMYLMETHYLAMINO)-2-OXOETHYL) O,O-DIMETHYL ESTER	2540-82-1	PST10081
PHOSPHORODITHIOIC ACID, S-(2-CHLORO-1-(1,3-DIHYDRO-1,3-DIOXO-2H -ISOINDOL-2-YL)ETHYL) O,O-DIETHYL ESTER	10311-84-9	PST23630
PHOSPHORODITHIOIC ACID, S,S'-METHYLENE O,O,O',O'-TETRAETHYL ESTER	563-12-2	PST08720
PHOSPHORODITHIOIC ACID, S,S'-PARA-DIOXANE-2,3-DIYL O,O,O',O' -TETRAETHYL ESTER	78-34-2	PST08050
PHOSPHORODITHIOIC ACID, S,S'-1,4-DIOXANE-2,3-DIYL O,O,O',O'-TETRAETHYL ESTER	78-34-2	PST08050
PHOSPHORODITHOIC ACID O,O-DIETHYL ESTER S-ESTER WITH N-(2-CHLORO -1-MERCAPTOETHYL)PHTHALIMIDE	10311-84-9	PST23630
PHOSPHORODITHOIC ACID, S-(((1,1-DIMETHYLETHYL)THIO)METHYL) O,O-DIETHYL ESTER	13071-79-9	PST22545
PHOSPHOROFLUORIDIC ACID, BIS(1-METHYLETHYL) ESTER	55-91-4	PST07590
PHOSPHOROFLUORIDIC ACID, DIISOPROPYL ESTER	55-91-4	PST07590
PHOSPHOROIC ACID, 2-CHLORO-3-(DIETHYLAMINO)-1-METHYL-3-OXO-1-PROPENYL DIMETHYL ESTER	13171-21-6	PST18670
PHOSPHOROTHIOIC ACID ((H3PO3S)), O,O-DIMETHYL O-4-(METHYLTHIO)-M-TOLYL ESTER	55-38-9	PST02550
PHOSPHOROTHIOIC ACID, CYCLIC O,O-(METHYLENE-O-PHENYLENE) O-METHYL ESTER	3811-49-2	PST20325
PHOSPHOROTHIOIC ACID, DIETHYL O-(P-(METHYLSULFONYL)PHENYL) ESTER	14255-72-2	PST06228
PHOSPHOROTHIOIC ACID, DIMETHYL (4-(METHYLTHIO)-M-TOLYL) ESTER	55-38-9	PST02550
PHOSPHOROTHIOIC ACID, O-(DICHLORO(METHYLTHIO)PHENYL) O,O-DIETHYL ESTER	60238-56-4	PST64913
PHOSPHOROTHIOIC ACID, O-(PARA-(DIMETHYLSULFAMOYL)PHENYL) O,O-DIMETHYL ESTER	52-85-7	PST09675
PHOSPHOROTHIOIC ACID, O-(1,6-DIHYDRO-6-OXO-1-PHENYL-3-PYRIDAZINYL) O,O-DIETHYL ESTER	119-12-0	PST71604
PHOSPHOROTHIOIC ACID, O-(2-(DIETHYLAMINO)-6-METHYL-4-PYRIMIDINYL) O,O-DIETHYL ESTER	23505-41-1	PST72377
PHOSPHOROTHIOIC ACID, O-(2-(DIETHYLAMINO)-6-METHYL-4-PYRIMIDINYL) O,O-DIMETHYL ESTER	29232-93-7	PST72378
PHOSPHOROTHIOIC ACID, O-(2-(DIMETHYLAMINO)-6-METHYL-4-PYRIDINYL) O,O-DIETHYL ESTER	5221-49-8	PST08049
PHOSPHOROTHIOIC ACID, O-(2-(ETHYLTHIO)ETHYL) O,O-DIMETHYL ESTER	867-27-6	PST71969
PHOSPHOROTHIOIC ACID, O-(2-(ETHYLTHIO)ETHYL) O,O-DIMETHYL ESTER, MIXTURE WITH S-(2-(ETHYLTHIO)ETHYL) O,O-DIMETHYL PHOSPHOROTHIOATE	8022-00-2	PST14438
PHOSPHOROTHIOIC ACID, O-(2-(ETHYLTHIO)ETHYL) O,O-DIMETHYL ESTER, MIXTURE WITH S-(2-(ETHYLTHIO)ETHYL) O,O-DIMETHYL ESTER	8022-00-2	PST14438
PHOSPHOROTHIOIC ACID, O-(2-CHLORO-1-(2,5-DICHLOROPHENYL)ETHYL O,O DIETHYL ESTER	1757-18-2	PST00493
PHOSPHOROTHIOIC ACID, O-(2-CHLORO-1-(2,5-DICHLOROPHENYL)VINYL) O,O-DIETHYL ESTER	1757-18-2	PST00493

ALPHABETICAL INDEX

ALPHABETICAL INDEX

SUBSTANCE NAME	CAS #	PST #
POLYRAM	9006-42-2	PST71123
POLYRAM M	12427-38-2	PST13589
POLYSORBATE 20	9005-64-5	PST80107
POLYSORBATE 80	9005-65-6	PST40200
POLYSORBATE 80 B.P.C.	9005-65-6	PST40200
POMARSOL	137-26-8	PST23430
PONTOCAINE HYDROCHLORIDE	136-47-0	PST72269
POSSE	55285-14-8	PST72266
POTABLAN	7287-36-7	PST72987
POTASH	584-08-7	PST19290
POTASSA	1310-58-3	PST19430
POTASSIUM ACID SULFATE	7646-93-7	PST19255
POTASSIUM ANTIMONY TARTRATE	28300-74-5	PST01690
POTASSIUM ANTIMONYL D-TARTRATE	28300-74-5	PST01690
POTASSIUM ANTIMONYL TARTRATE	28300-74-5	PST01690
POTASSIUM BICHROMATE	7778-50-9	PST19370
POTASSIUM BISULFATE	7646-93-7	PST19255
POTASSIUM BISULPHATE	7646-93-7	PST19255
POTASSIUM BROMIDE	7758-02-3	PST19280
POTASSIUM CARBONATE	584-08-7	PST19290
POTASSIUM CIS-9-OCTADECENOIC ACID	143-18-0	PST72131
POTASSIUM CYANIDE	151-50-8	PST19350
POTASSIUM CYANIDE (K(CN))	151-50-8	PST19350
POTASSIUM CYANIDE, SOLID	151-50-8	PST19350
POTASSIUM DICHLORO-S-TRIAZINETRIONE	2244-21-5	PST19360
POTASSIUM DICHLOROCYANURATE	2244-21-5	PST19360
POTASSIUM DICHLOROISOCYANURATE	2244-21-5	PST19360
POTASSIUM DICHROMATE	7778-50-9	PST19370
POTASSIUM DICHROMATE (VI)	7778-50-9	PST19370
POTASSIUM DIPHOSPHATE(K4P207)	7320-34-5	PST19546
POTASSIUM DODECANOATE	10124-65-9	PST72072
POTASSIUM GIBBERELLATE	125-67-7	PST71492
POTASSIUM HYDRATE	1310-58-3	PST19430
POTASSIUM HYDROGEN SULFATE	7646-93-7	PST19255
POTASSIUM HYDROGEN SULFATE, SOLID	7646-93-7	PST19255
POTASSIUM HYDROXIDE	1310-58-3	PST19430
POTASSIUM HYDROXIDE, SOLUTION	1310-58-3	PST19430
POTASSIUM IODIDE	7681-11-0	PST19435
POTASSIUM ISOTHIOCYANATE	333-20-0	PST19640
POTASSIUM LAURATE	10124-65-9	PST72072
POTASSIUM MYRISTATE	13429-27-1	PST72073
POTASSIUM N-DODECANOATE	10124-65-9	PST72072
POTASSIUM NITRATE	7757-79-1	PST19470
POTASSIUM NITRATE (JT BAKER)	7757-79-1	PST19470
POTASSIUM OLEATE	143-18-0	PST72131
POTASSIUM PERMANGANATE	7722-64-7	PST19520
POTASSIUM PHOSPHATE TRIBASIC	7778-53-2	PST19544
POTASSIUM PHOSPHATE(K4P207)	7320-34-5	PST19546
POTASSIUM PHOSPHATE, NEUTRAL	7778-53-2	PST19544
POTASSIUM PHOSPHATE, NORMAL	7778-53-2	PST19544
POTASSIUM PHOSPHATE, TERTIARY	7778-53-2	PST19544
POTASSIUM POLYSULFIDE	37199-66-9	PST19548
POTASSIUM PYROPHOSPHATE, ANHYDROUS	7320-34-5	PST19546
POTASSIUM PYROPHOSPHATE, NORMAL	7320-34-5	PST19546

ALPHABETICAL INDEX

ALPHABETICAL INDEX

SUBSTANCE NAME	CAS #	PST #
PROPARGITE	2312-35-8	PST19720
PROPASIN	139-40-2	PST19736
PROPAZIN	139-40-2	PST19736
PROPAZINE	139-40-2	PST19736
PROPENAL	107-02-8	PST00330
PROPENE OXIDE	75-56-9	PST19910
PROPENE, 1,3-DICHLORO-	542-75-6	PST26820
PROPENYL)CYCLOPROPANECARBOXYLATE	10453-86-8	PST20095
PROPETAMPHOS	31218-83-4	PST72440
PROPHAM	122-42-9	PST71564
PROPHOS	13194-48-4	PST15080
PROPINATE	127-20-8	PST71239
PROPIOFAR	137-40-6	PST21575
PROPION	137-40-6	PST21575
PROPIONALDEHYDE, 2-METHYL-2-(METHYLSULFINYL)-, O-(METHYLCARBAMOYL) OXIME	1646-87-3	PST00503
PROPIONALDEHYDE, 2-METHYL-2-(METHYLSULFONYL)-, O-(METHYLCARBAMOYL) OXIME	1646-88-4	PST72406
PROPIONALDEHYDE, 2-METHYL-2-(METHYLTHIO)-, O-(METHYLCARBAMOYL)OXIME	116-06-3	PST00500
PROPIONAMIDE, N,N-DIETHYL-2-(1-NAPHTHYLOXY)-	15299-99-7	PST72319
PROPIONIC ACID	79-09-4	PST19750
PROPIONIC ACID GRAIN PRESERVER	79-09-4	PST19750
PROPIONIC ACID, 2-(2,4,5-TRICHLOROPHENOXY)-, METHYL ESTER	4841-20-7	PST20831
PROPIONIC ACID, 2-(2,4,5-TRICHLOROPHENOXY)-, 3-BUTOXYPROPYL ESTER	25537-26-2	PST72194
PROPIONIC ACID, 2,2-DICHLORO-, SODIUM SALT	127-20-8	PST71239
PROPIONITRILE, 2-((4-CHLORO-6-(CYCLOPROPYLAMINO)-S-TRIAZIN-2-YL) AMINO)-2-METHYL-	32889-48-8	PST72398
PROPIONITRILE, 2-((4-CHLORO-6-(ETHYLAMINO)-S-TRIAZIN-2-YL) AMINO)-2-METHYL-	21725-46-2	PST05762
PROPISOL	137-40-6	PST21575
PROPOGON	114-26-1	PST02540
PROPON	93-72-1	PST20830
PROPOXUR	114-26-1	PST02540
PROPRIONIC ACID SODIUM SALT	137-40-6	PST21575
PROPYL ALCOHOL	67-63-0	PST12090
PROPYL ASEPTOFORM	94-13-3	PST19941
PROPYL CHEMOSEPT	94-13-3	PST19941
PROPYL DIPROPYLTHIOLCARBAMATE	1929-77-7	PST71473
PROPYL ETHYL-N-BUTYLTHIOCARBAMATE	1114-71-2	PST71472
PROPYL P-HYDROXYBENZOATE	94-13-3	PST19941
PROPYL P-OXYBENZOATE	94-13-3	PST19941
PROPYL PARABEN	94-13-3	PST19941
PROPYL PARASEPT	94-13-3	PST19941
PROPYL THIOPYROPHSOPHATE (((PRO)2P(S))2O)	3244-90-4	PST72135
PROPYLAN	25322-69-4	PST19140
PROPYLENE CHLORIDE	78-87-5	PST19860
PROPYLENE DICHLORIDE	78-87-5	PST19860
PROPYLENE EPOXIDE	75-56-9	PST19910
PROPYLENE GLYCOL	57-55-6	PST19870
PROPYLENE OXIDE	75-56-9	PST19910
PROPYZAMIDE	23950-58-5	PST19670
PROTABEN	94-13-3	PST19941
PROTASORB O-20	9005-65-6	PST40200
PROTEROXYNA	79-57-2	PST17414

SUBSTANCE NAME	CAS #	PST #
PROTHIOFOS	34643-46-4	PST72655
PROTHIOPHOS	34643-46-4	PST72655
PROTHOAT	2275-18-5	PST19943
PROTHOATE	2275-18-5	PST19943
PROTHROMADIN	129-06-6	PST83008
PROXEL EF	2425-06-1	PST04200
PROZINEX	139-40-2	PST19736
PROZOIN	79-09-4	PST19750
PRUNOLIDE	104-61-0	PST10334
PRYNACHLOR	21267-72-1	PST73038
PS	76-06-2	PST04830
PSEUDOACETIC ACID	79-09-4	PST19750
PSORISAN	118-75-2	PST72136
PURATURF	23319-66-6	PST71768
PURIVEL	19937-59-8	PST15009
PUROGENE	10049-04-4	PST04610
PURSUIT	81335-77-5	PST11308
PYDRIN	51630-58-1	PST19948
PYNAMIN	584-79-2	PST00550
PYPYRETHRIN	97-11-0	PST19949
PYRAMAT	2532-49-2	PST73266
PYRAMIN	1698-60-8	PST71928
PYRAZOLO(1,5-A)PYRIMIDINE-6-CARBOXYLIC ACID, 2-((DIETHOXYPHOSPHINOTHIOYL)OXY)-5-METHYL-, ETHYL ESTER	13457-18-6	PST73169
PYRAZOLO(1,5-A)PYRIMIDINE-6-CARBOXYLIC ACID, 2-HYDROXY-5-METHYL, ETHYL ESTER, O-ESTER WITH O,O-DIETHYLPHOSPHOROTHIOATE	13457-18-6	PST73169
PYRAZON	1698-60-8	PST71928
PYRAZOPHOS	13457-18-6	PST73169
PYRENONE	51-03-6	PST75640
PYRETHRIN	25402-06-6	PST05090
PYRETHRIN	121-21-1	PST19960
PYRETHRIN	121-29-9	PST19970
PYRETHRIN	8003-34-7	PST19980
PYRETHRIN I	121-21-1	PST19960
PYRETHRIN II	121-29-9	PST19970
PYRETHRIN 2	121-29-9	PST19970
PYRETHROID NRDC 107	28434-01-7	PST20093
PYRETHRUM	8003-34-7	PST19980
PYRIDAFENTHION	119-12-0	PST71604
PYRIDAPHENTHION	119-12-0	PST71604
PYRIDIMINE PHOSPHATE	29232-93-7	PST72378
PYRIDINE, 2-CHLORO-6-(TRICHLOROMETHYL)	1929-82-4	PST16530
PYRIDYLMETHYL-N'-PARA-NITROPHENYL UREA	53558-25-1	PST72334
PYRIMINIL	53558-25-1	PST72334
PYRIMINYL	53558-25-1	PST72334
PYRIMIPHOS METHYL	29232-93-7	PST72378
PYRIMITAL	5221-49-8	PST08049
PYRIMITHATE	5221-49-8	PST08049
PYRIMOR	23103-98-2	PST72345
PYRINURON	53558-25-1	PST72334
PYRO	7722-88-5	PST23140
PYRO POWDER	7429-90-5	PST01000
PYROACETIC ETHER	67-64-1	PST00140
PYROCATECHOL	120-80-9	PST04360

ALPHABETICAL INDEX

SUBSTANCE NAME	CAS #	PST #
PYROCATECHUIC ACID	120-80-9	PST04360
PYRODEXTRIN	9004-53-9	PST06363
PYROLAN	87-47-8	PST73263
PYROLIGNEUS ACID	64-19-7	PST00120
PYROMURIC ALDEHYDE	98-01-1	PST10180
PYROPHOSPHORAMIDE, OCTAMETHYL-	152-16-9	PST20350
PYROPHOSPHORIC ACID TETRAETHYL ESTER	107-49-3	PST22520
PYROPHOSPHORIC ACID, TETRAPOTASSIUM SALT	7320-34-5	PST19546
PYROPHOSPHORIC ACID, TETRASODIUM SALT	7722-88-5	PST23140
PYROXYLIC SPIRIT	67-56-1	PST14280
P2ZN3	1314-84-7	PST25540
Q 137	72-56-0	PST71373
QUATERNARY AMMONIUM COMPOUNDS, BENZYL-C12-C18-ALKYLDIMETHYL, CHLORIDES	53516-76-0	PST71834
QUATERNARY AMMONIUM COMPOUNDS, BENZYL-C12-16-ALKYLDIMETHYL, CHLORIDES	68424-85-1	PST71835
QUATRAMINE	8001-54-5	PST00537
QUELETOX (FORMULATION)	55-38-9	PST02550
QUESTEX	64-02-8	PST23137
QUICKLIME	1305-78-8	PST04030
QUICKPHOS	20859-73-8	PST00970
QUILAN	1861-40-1	PST02570
QUINALPHOS	13593-03-8	PST73112
QUINALPHOS-ETHYL	13593-03-8	PST73112
QUINOLINE, 6-ETHOXY-1,2-DIHYDRO-2,2,4-TRIMETHYL	91-53-2	PST08740
QUINONE TETRACHLORIDE	118-75-2	PST72136
QUINOPHENOL	148-24-3	PST30450
QUINTESS-N	1405-10-3	PST84263
QUINTOCENE	82-68-8	PST18140
QUINTOZENE	82-68-8	PST18140
QUIZALOFOP-ETHYL	76578-14-8	PST20075
R 10	56-23-5	PST04310
R 10 (REFRIGERANT)	56-23-5	PST04310
R 11	126-15-8	PST71487
R 12 (REFRIGERANT)	75-71-8	PST06880
R 1472	7173-84-4	PST04341
R 1513	2642-71-9	PST02205
R 1608	759-94-4	PST71470
R 1910	2008-41-5	PST71474
R 2061	1114-71-2	PST71472
R 2063	1134-23-2	PST71469
R 2170	301-12-2	PST17375
R 42211	23505-41-1	PST72377
R 5153	78-53-5	PST83006
R 7465	15299-99-7	PST72319
R-11	126-15-8	PST71487
R-1607	1929-77-7	PST71473
R-4572	2212-67-1	PST71471
RABON	961-11-5	PST72243
RABON	22248-79-9	PST72244
RABON	22350-76-1	PST72245
RABOND	22248-79-9	PST72244
RACRYL	9003-01-4	PST04349
RACUMIN	5836-29-3	PST05493
RACUSA	6597-78-0	PST73131
RACUZA	6597-78-0	PST73131

ALPHABETICAL INDEX

SUBSTANCE NAME	CAS #	PST #
RAD-E-CATE	75-60-5	PST03710
RADAPON	75-99-0	PST06200
RADAZIN	1912-24-9	PST02150
RADOSAN	151-38-2	PST83031
RAGADAN	23560-59-0	PST10685
RAID (R) ANT AND ROACH KILLER-LIQUID	UNASSIGNED	PST86204
RAMETIN	1491-41-4	PST72737
RAMROD	1918-16-7	PST19686
RANDOX	93-71-0	PST71155
RANGE OIL	8008-20-6	PST10090
RAT-NIP	7723-14-0	PST18800
RATAFIN	117-52-2	PST05476
RATAK	56073-07-5	PST07385
RATAK +	56073-10-0	PST03327
RATBANE 1080	62-74-8	PST21240
RATICATE	991-42-4	PST72254
RATINDAN	82-66-6	PST08068
RATOL	1314-84-7	PST25540
RATSUL SOLUBLE	129-06-6	PST83008
RATTRACK	86-88-4	PST01830
RAX	81-81-2	PST25090
RC 9485	116-52-9	PST06817
RCRA P001	81-81-2	PST25090
RCRA P001	129-06-6	PST83008
RCRA P003	107-02-8	PST00330
RCRA P004	309-00-2	PST00520
RCRA P006	20859-73-8	PST00970
RCRA P008	504-24-5	PST02180
RCRA P010	7778-39-4	PST01990
RCRA P011	1303-28-2	PST02020
RCRA P012	1327-53-3	PST02070
RCRA P020	88-85-7	PST08020
RCRA P037	60-57-1	PST07080
RCRA P039	298-04-4	PST08380
RCRA P040	297-97-2	PST25590
RCRA P041	311-45-5	PST07200
RCRA P043	55-91-4	PST07590
RCRA P044	60-51-5	PST07670
RCRA P045	39196-18-4	PST23330
RCRA P047	534-52-1	PST07910
RCRA P047	2312-76-7	PST71411
RCRA P048	51-28-5	PST28620
RCRA P050	115-29-7	PST08560
RCRA P051	72-20-8	PST08600
RCRA P057	640-19-7	PST09930
RCRA P058	62-74-8	PST21240
RCRA P059	76-44-8	PST10660
RCRA P060	465-73-6	PST11810
RCRA P066	16752-77-5	PST14200
RCRA P070	116-06-3	PST00500
RCRA P071	298-00-0	PST14680
RCRA P072	86-88-4	PST01830
RCRA P075	54-11-5	PST16430
RCRA P085	152-16-9	PST20350

ALPHABETICAL INDEX

SUBSTANCE NAME	CAS #	PST #
RCRA P088	145-73-3	PST08580
RCRA P089	56-38-2	PST18040
RCRA P092	62-38-4	PST18560
RCRA P094	298-02-2	PST18640
RCRA P097	52-85-7	PST09675
RCRA P098	151-50-8	PST19350
RCRA P105	26628-22-8	PST20960
RCRA P106	143-33-9	PST21160
RCRA P108	57-24-9	PST22080
RCRA P109	3689-24-5	PST22470
RCRA P111	107-49-3	PST22520
RCRA P122	1314-84-7	PST25540
RCRA P123	8001-35-2	PST23640
RCRA U002	67-64-1	PST00140
RCRA U011	61-82-5	PST01040
RCRA U028	117-81-7	PST06440
RCRA U029	74-83-9	PST14300
RCRA U036	57-74-9	PST04560
RCRA U036	12789-03-6	PST71948
RCRA U038	510-15-6	PST04740
RCRA U039	59-50-7	PST29890
RCRA U051	8001-58-9	PST05230
RCRA U057	108-94-1	PST05890
RCRA U060	72-54-8	PST06240
RCRA U061	50-29-3	PST06250
RCRA U062	2303-16-4	PST06480
RCRA U066	96-12-8	PST26490
RCRA U067	106-93-4	PST09380
RCRA U069	84-74-2	PST06740
RCRA U075	75-71-8	PST06880
RCRA U077	107-06-2	PST09390
RCRA U080	75-09-2	PST14930
RCRA U083	78-87-5	PST19860
RCRA U084	542-75-6	PST26820
RCRA U101	105-67-9	PST28670
RCRA U102	131-11-3	PST07740
RCRA U107	117-84-0	PST08040
RCRA U112	141-78-6	PST08750
RCRA U114	12427-38-2	PST13589
RCRA U114	8018-01-7	PST71120
RCRA U114	9006-42-2	PST71123
RCRA U115	75-21-8	PST09520
RCRA U121	75-69-4	PST09990
RCRA U122	50-00-0	PST50003
RCRA U125	98-01-1	PST10180
RCRA U127	118-74-1	PST10730
RCRA U129	58-89-9	PST12810
RCRA U136	75-60-5	PST03710
RCRA U142	143-50-0	PST12330
RCRA U148	123-33-1	PST13570
RCRA U154	67-56-1	PST14280
RCRA U159	78-93-3	PST14460
RCRA U161	108-10-1	PST14550
RCRA U170	100-02-7	PST17800

ALPHABETICAL INDEX

SUBSTANCE NAME	CAS #	PST #
RCRA U185	82-68-8	PST18140
RCRA U187	62-44-2	PST18340
RCRA U188	108-95-2	PST18380
RCRA U192	23950-58-5	PST19670
RCRA U210	127-18-4	PST22900
RCRA U211	56-23-5	PST04310
RCRA U226	71-55-6	PST14370
RCRA U233	93-72-1	PST20830
RCRA U239	1330-20-7	PST25150
RCRA U240	94-75-7	PST28510
RCRA U240	1928-45-6	PST71294
RCRA U240	1928-38-7	PST71307
RCRA U242	87-86-5	PST18150
RCRA U244	137-26-8	PST23430
RCRA U247	72-43-5	PST14220
RD 14639	2655-19-8	PST72994
RE 12420	30560-19-1	PST00065
RE 4355	300-76-5	PST06660
RED CEDARWOOD OIL	8000-27-9	PST04365
RED COPPER OXIDE	1317-39-1	PST05470
RED OIL	112-80-1	PST17305
RED OIL, DISTILLED	8002-33-3	PST24575
RED PHOSPHOROUS	7723-14-0	PST18790
RED POTASSIUM CHROMATE	7778-50-9	PST19370
REDSKIN	57-06-7	PST00680
REFRIGERANT 11	75-69-4	PST09990
REGLON	85-00-7	PST08250
REGLONE	85-00-7	PST08250
REGLOX	85-00-7	PST08250
REGULOX 36	123-33-1	PST13570
RELDAN	5598-13-0	PST71652
REMOL TRF	90-43-7	PST18470
RENEGADE	67375-30-8	PST06118
REPEL 111	126-15-8	PST71487
RERANIL	118-75-2	PST72136
RESISAN	99-30-9	PST28910
RESMETHRIN	10453-86-8	PST20095
RETARDER BA	65-85-0	PST02720
RETARDEX	65-85-0	PST02720
RH 2915	42874-03-3	PST72413
RH 315	23950-58-5	PST19670
RH 787	53558-25-1	PST72334
RHOCYN	333-20-0	PST19640
RHODIACHLOR	76-44-8	PST10660
RHODIANEBE	12427-38-2	PST13589
RHOTHANE	72-54-8	PST06240
RH6201	62476-59-9	PST72453
RICHONATE SXS	1300-72-7	PST75603
RICHONIC ACID	27176-87-0	PST08480
RICID II	26087-47-8	PST12355
RICID P	26087-47-8	PST12355
RICINOLEIC ACID, MONOPOTASSIUM SALT	7492-30-0	PST72074
RICKETON	67-97-0	PST60913
RIOMITSIN	79-57-2	PST17414

ALPHABETICAL INDEX

SUBSTANCE NAME	CAS #	PST #
RIPCORD	52315-07-8	PST72392
RO 13-5223	72490-01-8	PST72618
RO-DEX	57-24-9	PST22080
RO-NEET	1134-23-2	PST71469
ROAD ASPHALT	8052-42-4	PST02140
ROAD ASPHALT	8052-42-4	PST71177
ROAD TAR	8052-42-4	PST02140
ROAD TAR	8052-42-4	PST71177
ROCCAL	8001-54-5	PST00539
ROCK SALT	7647-14-5	PST21105
RODALON	8001-54-5	PST00539
RODANCA	333-20-0	PST19640
RODENTIN	5836-29-3	PST05493
RODEO	UNASSIGNED	PST20208
RODEO HERBICIDE	UNASSIGNED	PST20208
RODEX	640-19-7	PST09930
ROGOR	60-51-5	PST07670
ROMAN VITRIOL	7758-98-7	PST05670
ROMAN VITRIOL	7758-99-8	PST05690
RONIT	1134-23-2	PST71469
RONNEL	299-84-3	PST20180
RONNEL OXON	3983-45-7	PST25082
RONNEL OXYGEN ANALOG	3983-45-7	PST25082
RONNOXON	3983-45-7	PST25082
RONOXON	3983-45-7	PST25082
RONSTAR	19666-30-9	PST72385
ROOT BARK OIL	76-22-2	PST04130
ROOT BARK SPIRIT	76-22-2	PST04130
ROSE GERANIUM OIL ALGERIAN	8000-46-2	PST73283
ROTAX	149-30-4	PST13738
ROTENONE	83-79-4	PST20200
ROTOX	74-83-9	PST14300
ROUNDUP	UNASSIGNED	PST20207
ROUNDUP HERBICIDE	UNASSIGNED	PST20207
ROVOKIL	13194-48-4	PST15080
ROZOL	3691-35-8	PST04826
RP 11561	16118-49-3	PST72941
RP 17623	19666-30-9	PST72385
RP 8823	443-48-1	PST72529
RP11974	2310-17-0	PST25720
RS 141	6164-98-3	PST04570
RU 22974	52918-63-5	PST72784
RUBITOX	2310-17-0	PST25720
RUELENE	299-86-5	PST05550
RUMETAN	1314-84-7	PST25540
RUTGERS 612	94-96-2	PST71458
RYZELAN	19044-88-3	PST17324
S G900	2540-82-1	PST10081
S 1	76-06-2	PST04830
S 1065	1129-41-5	PST83074
S 1752	55-38-9	PST02550
S 1942	2104-96-3	PST71064
S 4084	2636-26-2	PST72950
S 4087	13067-93-1	PST05805

SUBSTANCE NAME	CAS #	PST #
S-(P-CHLOROPHENYLSULFINYLMETHYL)-O,O-DIETHYLPHOSPHORODITHIOATE	17297-40-4	PST04345
S-(P-CHLOROPHENYLTHIOMETHYL)DIETHYL PHOSPHOROTHIOLOTHIONATE	786-19-6	PST04340
S-(P-CHLOROPHENYLTHIOMETHYL)DIMETHYL PHOSPHOROTHIOLOTHIONATE	953-17-3	PST71647
S-(PHENYLMETHYL) BIS(1-METHYLPROPYL)CARBAMOTHIOATE	36756-79-3	PST72405
S-(TERT-BUTYLTHIO)METHYL O,O-DIETHYL PHOSPHORODITHIOATE	13071-79-9	PST22545
S-(1,2-DI(ETHOXYCARBONYL)ETHYL)DIMETHYL PHOSPHOROTHIOLOTHIONATE	121-75-5	PST13540
S-(2-((1-CYANO-1-METHYLETHYL)AMINO)-2-OXOETHYL) O,O-DIETHYL PHOSPHOROTHIOATE	3734-95-0	PST72949
S-(2-((2-METHOXYETHYL)AMINO-2-OXOETHYL) O,O-DIMETHYL PHOSPHORODITHIOATE	919-76-6	PST01007
S-(2-(DIETHYLAMINO)ETHYL) O,O-DIETHYL ESTER PHOSPHOROTHIOIC ACID	78-53-5	PST83006
S-(2-(DIETHYLAMINO)ETHYL)PHOSPHOROTHIOIC ACID O,O-DIETHYL ESTER	78-53-5	PST83006
S-(2-(ETHYLAMINO)-2-OXOETHYL) O,O-DIMETHYL ESTER PHOSPHORODITHIOIC ACID	116-01-8	PST08723
S-(2-(ETHYLAMINO)-2-OXOETHYL) O,O-DIMETHYL PHOSPHORODITHIOATE	116-01-8	PST08723
S-(2-(ETHYLSULFINYL)-1-METHYLETHYL) O,O-DIMETHYL PHOSPHOROTHIOATE	2674-91-1	PST14105
S-(2-(ETHYLSULFINYL)ETHYL) O,O-DIMETHYL PHOSPHOROTHIOATE	301-12-2	PST17375
S-(2-(ETHYLSULFONYL)ETHYL) O,O-DIMETHYL PHOSPHOROTHIOATE	17040-19-6	PST06319
S-(2-(ETHYLTHIO)ETHYL)O,O-DIMETHYL PHOSPHOROTHIOATE	919-86-8	PST83065
S-(2-(ETHYLTHIOETHYL) O,O-DIMETHYLPHOSPHORODITHIONATE	640-15-3	PST83056
S-(2-(ETHYLTHIOETHYL)DIMETHYL PHOSPHOROTHIOLOTHIONATE	640-15-3	PST83056
S-(2-(FORMYLMETHYLAMINO)-2-OXOETHYL) O,O-DIMETHYL PHOSPHORODITHIOATE	2540-82-1	PST10081
S-(2-CHLORO-1-(1,3-DIHYDRO-1,3-DIOXO-2H-ISOINDOL-2-YL)ETHYL) O,O -DIETHYL PHOSPHORODITHIOATE	10311-84-9	PST23630
S-(2,3-DICHLORO-2-PROPENYL) BIS(1-METHYLETHYL)CARBAMOTHIOATE	2303-16-4	PST06480
S-(2,3-DICHLOROALLYL) DIISOPROPYLTHIOCARBAMATE	2303-16-4	PST06480
S-(2,3,3-TRICHLORO-2-PROPENYL) BIS(1-METHYLETHYL)CARBAMOTHIOATE	2303-17-5	PST72050
S-(2,3,3-TRICHLOROALLYL) DIISOPROPYLTHIOCARBAMATE	2303-17-5	PST72050
S-(2,3,3-TRICHLOROALLYL)DIISOPROPYLTHIOCARBAMATE	2303-17-5	PST72050
S-(2,5-DICHLOROPHENYLTHIOMETHYL)DIETHYL PHOSPHOROTHIOLOTHIONATE	2275-14-1	PST18373
S-(2,5,-DICHLOROPHENYLTHIOMETHYL) DIMETHYL PHOSPHORODITHIOATE	3735-23-7	PST73085
S-(4-CHLOROPHENYL) O,O-DIMETHYL PHOSPHOROTHIOATE	3309-87-3	PST72763
S-(4-CHLOROPHENYL) O,O-DIMETHYL PHOSPHOROTHIOIC ACID, ESTER	3309-87-3	PST72763
S-(4-CHLOROPHENYL)METHYL DIETHYLCARBAMOTHIOATE	28249-77-6	PST72381
S-(4,6-DIAMINO-S-TRIAZIN-2-YL)METHYL) O,O-DIMETHYL PHOSPHORODITHIOATE	78-57-9	PST72980
S-(4,6-DIAMINO-1,3,5-TRIAZIN-2-YL)METHYL O,O-DIMETHYL PHOSPHORODITHIOATE	78-57-9	PST72980
S-(5-ETHOXY-2-OXO-1,3,4-THIADIAZOL-3(2H)-YLMETHYL) O,O-DIMETHYL PHOSPHORODITHIOATE	2669-32-1	PST73147
S-(5-METHOXY-4-PYRON-2-YLMETHYL) DIMETHYL PHOSPHOROTHIOLATE	2778-04-3	PST73139
S-ALPHA-ETHOXYCARBONYLBENZYL O,O-DIMETHYL PHOSPHORODITHIOATE	2597-03-7	PST72337
S-BENZYL DI-SEC-BUTYL(THIOCARBAMATE)	36756-79-3	PST72405
S-BENZYL DI-SEC-BUTYLTHIOCARBAMATE	36756-79-3	PST72405
S-BENZYL DIISOPROPYL PHOSPHOROTHIOLATE	26087-47-8	PST12355
S-BENZYL N,N-DI-SEC-BUTYLTHIOLCARBAMATE	36756-79-3	PST72405
S-BENZYL O,O-DI-ISOPROPYL PHOSPHOROTHIOATE	26087-47-8	PST12355
S-BIOALLETHRIN	28434-00-6	PST71013
S-CHLOROMETHYL O,O-DIETHYL PHOSPHORODITHIOATE	24934-91-6	PST04655
S-DIISOPROPYLACETONE	108-83-8	PST07500
S-ETHYL AZEPANE-1-CARBOTHIOATE	2212-67-1	PST71471
S-ETHYL BIS(2-METHYLPROPYL)CARBAMOTHIOATE	2008-41-5	PST71474
S-ETHYL CYCLOHEXYLETHYLCARBAMOTHIOATE	1134-23-2	PST71469
S-ETHYL DI-ISOBUTYL(THIOCARBAMATE)	2008-41-5	PST71474
S-ETHYL DI-ISOBUTYLTHIOCARBAMATE	2008-41-5	PST71474

ALPHABETICAL INDEX

ALPHABETICAL INDEX

ALPHABETICAL INDEX

ALPHABETICAL INDEX

ALPHABETICAL INDEX

ALPHABETICAL INDEX

SUBSTANCE NAME	CAS #	PST #
SODIUM FLUOACETIC ACID	62-74-8	PST21240
SODIUM FLUOALUMINATE	15096-52-3	PST05560
SODIUM FLUORACETATE	62-74-8	PST21240
SODIUM FLUORIDE	7681-49-4	PST21230
SODIUM FLUORIDE(NAF)	7681-49-4	PST21230
SODIUM FLUORIDE, SOLID	7681-49-4	PST21230
SODIUM FLUOROACETATE	62-74-8	PST21240
SODIUM FLUOROSILICATE	16893-85-9	PST21620
SODIUM FLUOSILICATE	16893-85-9	PST21620
SODIUM GLYCOLATE	2836-32-0	PST11235
SODIUM HEXAFLUOROALUMINATE	15096-52-3	PST05560
SODIUM HEXAFLUOROSILICATE	16893-85-9	PST21620
SODIUM HEXAFLUOSILICATE	16893-85-9	PST21620
SODIUM HYDRATE	1310-73-2	PST21300
SODIUM HYDROGEN CARBONATE	144-55-8	PST20970
SODIUM HYDROGEN DIACETATE	126-96-5	PST71497
SODIUM HYDROGEN SULFATE	7681-38-1	PST20990
SODIUM HYDROGEN SULFITE	7631-90-5	PST21000
SODIUM HYDROSULFATE	7681-38-1	PST20990
SODIUM HYDROXIDE	1310-73-2	PST21300
SODIUM HYDROXIDE (NA(OH))	1310-73-2	PST21300
SODIUM HYDROXIDE, DRY	1310-73-2	PST21300
SODIUM HYDROXIDE, DRY SOLID, FLAKE, BEAD, OR GRANULAR	1310-73-2	PST21300
SODIUM HYDROXIDE, FLAKE	1310-73-2	PST21300
SODIUM HYDROXIDE, SOLID	1310-73-2	PST21300
SODIUM HYDROXYACETATE	2836-32-0	PST11235
SODIUM HYPOCHLORITE	7681-52-9	PST21310
SODIUM HYPOCHLORITE (NACLO)	7681-52-9	PST21310
SODIUM HYPOCHLORITE (NAOCL)	7681-52-9	PST21310
SODIUM HYPOCHLORITE SOLUTION	7681-52-9	PST21310
SODIUM HYPOCHLORITE, PHOSPHATE	56802-99-4	PST80117
SODIUM LAURYL SULFATE	151-21-3	PST08485
SODIUM LAURYL SULPHATE	151-21-3	PST08485
SODIUM LAURYLBENZENESULFONATE	25155-30-0	PST21220
SODIUM META-ARSENITE LIQUID (SOLUTION)	7784-46-5	PST52136
SODIUM METAARSENATE	7631-89-2	PST20940
SODIUM METAM	137-42-8	PST71430
SODIUM METASILICATE	6834-92-0	PST21373
SODIUM METASILICATE (NA2SIO3)	6834-92-0	PST21373
SODIUM METASILICATE, ANHYDROUS	6834-92-0	PST21373
SODIUM METHAM	137-42-8	PST71430
SODIUM METHYLCARBAMODITHIOATE	137-42-8	PST71430
SODIUM METHYLDITHIOCARBAMATE	137-42-8	PST71430
SODIUM MONOCHLORIDE	7647-14-5	PST21105
SODIUM MONODODECYL SULFATE	151-21-3	PST08485
SODIUM MONOFLUORIDE	7681-49-4	PST21230
SODIUM MONOFLUOROACETATE	62-74-8	PST21240
SODIUM MONOHYDROGEN PHOSPHATE	7558-79-4	PST08330
SODIUM MONOLAURYL SULFATE	151-21-3	PST08485
SODIUM MONOMETHYLDITHIOCARBAMATE	137-42-8	PST71430
SODIUM N-DODECYL SULFATE	151-21-3	PST08485
SODIUM N-METHYLDITHIOCARBAMATE	137-42-8	PST71430
SODIUM N-OCTANOATE	1984-06-1	PST72105
SODIUM N-1-NAPHTHYLPHTHALAMATE	132-67-2	PST71341

ALPHABETICAL INDEX

ALPHABETICAL INDEX

SUBSTANCE NAME	CAS #	PST #
SODIUM SULFITE	7757-83-7	PST21660
SODIUM SULFITE, ANHYDROUS	7757-83-7	PST21660
SODIUM SULPHITE	7757-83-7	PST21660
SODIUM TCA	650-51-1	PST73307
SODIUM TETRABORATE DECAHYDRATE	1303-96-4	PST21010
SODIUM TRICHLOROACETATE	650-51-1	PST73307
SODIUM TRIPHOSPHATE	7758-29-4	PST21730
SODIUM TRIPHOSPHATE (NA5P3010)	7758-29-4	PST21730
SODIUM TRIPOLYPHOSPHATE	7758-29-4	PST21730
SODIUM TRIPOLYPHOSPHATE (NA5P3010)	7758-29-4	PST21730
SODIUM WARFARIN	129-06-6	PST83008
SODIUM XYLENE SULFONATE	1300-72-7	PST75603
SODIUM XYLENESULFONATE	1300-72-7	PST75603
SODIUM 2-((1-NAPHTHALENYLAMINO)CARBONYL)BENZOATE	132-67-2	PST71341
SODIUM 2-(2,4-DICHLOROPHENOXY)ETHYL SULFATE	136-78-7	PST05500
SODIUM 2,2-DICHLOROPROPIONATE	127-20-8	PST71239
SODIUM 2,2-DICHLOROPROPIONIC ACID	127-20-8	PST71239
SODIUM 2,3,6-TRICHLOROBENZOATE	2078-42-4	PST71136
SODIUM 2,3,6-TRICHLOROBENZOIC ACID	2078-42-4	PST71136
SODIUM 2,3:4,6-BIS-O-(1-METHYLETHYLIDENE)-A-L-XYOL -2-HEXULOFURANOSONATE	52508-35-7	PST72391
SODIUM 2,4-DICHLOROPHENOXYETHYL SULFATE	136-78-7	PST05500
SODIUM 2,4,5- TRICHLOROPHENOLATE	136-32-3	PST21713
SODIUM 2,4,5-TRICHLOROPHENATE	136-32-3	PST21713
SODIUM 2,4,5-TRICHLOROPHENOXIDE	136-32-3	PST21713
SODIUM 4,6-DINITRO-O-CRESYLATE	2312-76-7	PST71411
SODIUM 5-(2-CHLORO-4-(TRIFLUOROMETHYL)-PHENOXY)-2-NITROBENZOATE	62476-59-9	PST72453
SODIUM(+1) NITRATE	7631-99-4	PST21400
SODIUM(I) NITRATE	7631-99-4	PST21400
SODIUM(1-) ION	55635-13-7	PST72430
SODIUM-2-BIPHENOLATE	132-27-4	PST08500
SODIUM, ((4,6-DINITRO-O-TOLYL)OXY)-	2312-76-7	PST71411
SODIUM, (4-CYANO-2,6-DIIODOPHENOXY)-	2961-62-8	PST73074
SOK	671-04-5	PST02250
SOL 9050 XYLENE (CHEMTECH INDUSTRIES, INC.)	1330-20-7	PST25150
SOLAESTHIN	75-09-2	PST14930
SOLAN	2307-68-8	PST71164
SOLANE	2307-68-8	PST71164
SOLBROL M	99-76-3	PST14677
SOLBROL P	94-13-3	PST19941
SOLFRIL	7704-34-9	PST22280
SOLGARD	23505-41-1	PST72377
SOLICAM	27314-13-2	PST72343
SOLMETHINE	75-09-2	PST14930
SOLUDAL	144-55-8	PST20970
SOLVAN	82-66-6	PST08068
SOLVANOL	84-66-2	PST07210
SOLVENT, THINNER AND SCREEN WASH (NAZ-DAR CO.)	111-76-2	PST03540
SOLVESSO XYLENE (HUMBLE OIL AND REFINING COMPANY)	1330-20-7	PST25150
SOLVIREX	298-04-4	PST08380
SOLVO POWDER	65-85-0	PST02720
SOMIO	15879-93-3	PST00775
SONAC	7664-38-2	PST18690
SONACIDE	111-30-8	PST10423

ALPHABETICAL INDEX

ALPHABETICAL INDEX

ALPHABETICAL INDEX

ALPHABETICAL INDEX

SUBSTANCE NAME	CAS #	PST #
STCC 4941127	95-50-1	PST16970
STCC 4941128	106-46-7	PST17640
STCC 4941129	50-29-3	PST06250
STCC 4941132	75-09-2	PST14930
STCC 4941133	60-57-1	PST07080
STCC 4941141	333-41-5	PST06540
STCC 4941143	30525-89-4	PST18000
STCC 4941152	58-89-9	PST12810
STCC 4941156	121-75-5	PST13540
STCC 4941158	371-86-8	PST15030
STCC 4941163	2275-14-1	PST18373
STCC 4941170	10588-01-9	PST21190
STCC 4941176	71-55-6	PST14370
STCC 4941177	131-52-2	PST08506
STCC 4941187	137-26-8	PST23430
STCC 4941189	8001-35-2	PST23640
STCC 4941193	1300-71-6	PST25160
STCC 4941193	105-67-9	PST28670
STCC 4944148	7646-93-7	PST19255
STCC 4944150	7681-49-4	PST21230
STCC 4944155	7631-90-5	PST21000
STCC 4944173	10125-13-0	PST05625
STCC 4944515	1305-78-8	PST04030
STCC 4960140	143-50-0	PST12330
STCC 4960630	76-44-8	PST10660
STCC 4960647	72-43-5	PST14220
STCC 4961164	133-06-2	PST04210
STCC 49611665	2312-35-8	PST19720
STCC 4961316	7758-98-7	PST05670
STCC 4961316	7758-99-8	PST05690
STCC 4961380	87-86-5	PST18150
STCC 4961658	300-76-5	PST06660
STCC 4962505	10108-64-2	PST03740
STCC 4962621	330-54-1	PST08420
STCC 4963303	10043-01-3	PST00980
STCC 4963337	1918-00-9	PST02260
STCC 4963344	85-00-7	PST08250
STCC 4963354	10045-89-3	PST09820
STCC 4963374	25155-30-0	PST21220
STCC 4963394	100-02-7	PST17800
STCC 4963786	7733-02-0	PST25570
STCC 4963814	1194-65-6	PST06800
STCC 4963818	10028-22-5	PST09790
STCC 4963841	7782-63-0	PST09870
STCC 4963881	8003-34-7	PST19980
STCC 4966340	65-85-0	PST02720
STCC 4966368	10101-97-0	PST16410
STCC 4966380	7558-79-4	PST08330
STCC 4966383	7601-54-9	PST24480
STCC 4966392	16871-71-9	PST25410
STCC 4966732	7773-06-0	PST01400
STCC 4966750	7783-18-8	PST01460
STCC 4966790	7646-85-7	PST25350
STCC 4966940	115-32-2	PST07010

ALPHABETICAL INDEX

SUBSTANCE NAME	CAS #	PST #
SULFAMIC ACID	5329-14-6	PST22200
SULFAMIC ACID, MONOAMMONIUM SALT	7773-06-0	PST01400
SULFAMIDE, N-((DICHLOROFLUOROMETHYL)THIO)-N',N'-DIMETHYL-N-P-TOLYL-	731-27-1	PST73030
SULFAMIDE, N-((DICHLOROFLUOROMETHYL)THIO)-N',N'-DIMETHYL-N-PHENYL-	1085-98-9	PST73026
SULFAMIDIC ACID	5329-14-6	PST22200
SULFANILAMIDE, N'-2-QUINOXALINYL-	59-40-5	PST72046
SULFANILAMIDE, N1-2-THIAZOLYL-	72-14-0	PST72047
SULFANILAMIDE, N1-4-THIAZOLIN-2-YLIDENE-	72-14-0	PST72047
SULFANILAMIDE, 3,5-DINITRO-N4,N4-DIPROPYL-	19044-88-3	PST17324
SULFANILAMIDETHIAZOLE	72-14-0	PST72047
SULFANILYLCARBAMIC ACID METHYL ESTER	3337-71-1	PST72352
SULFAQUINOXALINE	59-40-5	PST72046
SULFATED CASTOR OIL	8002-33-3	PST24575
SULFATHIAZOLE	72-14-0	PST72047
SULFATODIALUMINUM DISULFATE	10043-01-3	PST00980
SULFENON	80-00-2	PST71663
SULFEX	7704-34-9	PST22280
SULFIDE, P-CHLOROBENZYL P-CHLOROPHENYL	103-17-3	PST71139
SULFOBUTANEDIOIC ACID 1,4-BIS(2-ETHYLHEXYL) ESTER, SODIUM SALT	577-11-7	PST00406
SULFOCARB	1646-88-4	PST72406
SULFODIAZOL	30043-49-3	PST72551
SULFOMETURON-METHYL	74222-97-2	PST72544
SULFONE, P-CHLOROPHENYL PHENYL-	80-00-2	PST71663
SULFOSUCCINIC ACID 1,4-BIS(2-ETHYLHEXYL) ESTER, SODIUM SALT	577-11-7	PST00406
SULFOTEP	3689-24-5	PST22470
SULFOTEPP	3689-24-5	PST22470
SULFRAMIN ACID 1298	27176-87-0	PST08480
SULFUR	7704-34-9	PST22280
SULFUR DIOXIDE	7446-09-5	PST22290
SULFUR DIOXIDE(SO2)	7446-09-5	PST22290
SULFUR FLOUR	7704-34-9	PST22280
SULFUR OXIDE	7446-09-5	PST22290
SULFUR OXIDE(SO2)	7446-09-5	PST22290
SULFURIC ACID	7664-93-9	PST22350
SULFURIC ACID CALCIUM SALT	7778-18-9	PST04110
SULFURIC ACID COPPER SALT, MONOHYDRATE	10257-54-2	PST05675
SULFURIC ACID DIPOTASSIUM SALT	7778-80-5	PST19590
SULFURIC ACID MAGNESIUM SALT (1:1)	7487-88-9	PST13510
SULFURIC ACID POTASSIUM SALT	7778-80-5	PST19590
SULFURIC ACID ZINC SALT	7733-02-0	PST25570
SULFURIC ACID 66 BAUME (COLLIER CARBON & CHEMICAL CORP.)	7664-93-9	PST22350
SULFURIC ACID, ALUMINUM SALT	10043-01-3	PST00980
SULFURIC ACID, AMMONIUM IRON(2+) SALT	10045-89-3	PST09820
SULFURIC ACID, AMMONIUM IRON(2+) SALT (2:2:1)	10045-89-3	PST09820
SULFURIC ACID, CALCIUM SALT (1:1)	7778-18-9	PST04110
SULFURIC ACID, COPPER(2+) SALT	7758-98-7	PST05670
SULFURIC ACID, IRON(2+) SALT (1:1), HEPTAHYDRATE	7782-63-0	PST09870
SULFURIC ACID, IRON(3+) SALT (3:2)	10028-22-5	PST09790
SULFURIC ACID, MAGNESIUM SALT	7487-88-9	PST13510
SULFURIC ACID, MONODODECYL ESTER, SODIUM SALT	151-21-3	PST08485
SULFURIC ACID, MONOPOTASSIUM SALT	7646-93-7	PST19255
SULFURIC ACID, MONOSODIUM SALT	7681-38-1	PST20990
SULFURIC ACID, NICKEL(2+) SALT(1:1), HEXAHYDRATE	10101-97-0	PST16410
SULFURIC ACID, NICKEL(2+) SALT, HEXAHYDRATE	10101-97-0	PST16410

ALPHABETICAL INDEX

ALPHABETICAL INDEX

ALPHABETICAL INDEX

SUBSTANCE NAME	CAS #	PST #
TAT	12789-03-6	PST71948
TATD	97-77-8	PST08370
TATTOO	22781-23-3	PST02560
TBPT	78-48-8	PST06300
TBTP	78-48-8	PST06300
TC 523 EPOXY DISSOLVER (TECHFORM)	75-09-2	PST14930
TCA	76-03-9	PST23810
TCA SODIUM	650-51-1	PST73307
TCB	50-31-7	PST71134
TCBA	50-31-7	PST71134
TCDBD	1746-01-6	PST08060
TCDD	1746-01-6	PST08060
TCG 7R	7440-22-4	PST20770
TCM	7673-09-8	PST80113
TCMTB	21564-17-0	PST71392
TCNB	117-18-0	PST71616
TCP	95-95-4	PST28700
TDE	72-54-8	PST06240
TDE-M,P'	4329-12-8	PST04752
TDEE	1022-22-6	PST06322
TEA	102-71-6	PST23932
TEAL OIL	8008-74-0	PST20575
TEBUTAM	35256-85-0	PST72852
TEBUTHIURON	34014-18-1	PST72340
TECNAZEN	117-18-0	PST71616
TECNAZENE	117-18-0	PST71616
TECSOL	64-17-5	PST08700
TEDP	3689-24-5	PST22470
TEEL OIL	8008-74-0	PST20575
TEG	112-27-6	PST24000
TEGOSEPT M	99-76-3	PST14677
TEGOSEPT P	94-13-3	PST19941
TEKRESOL	1319-77-3	PST05510
TEKTAMER 38	35691-65-7	PST26487
TELAR	64902-72-3	PST72504
TELODRIN	297-78-9	PST83032
TELOK	27314-13-2	PST72343
TELVAR	150-68-5	PST15196
TELVAR DIURON WEED KILLER	330-54-1	PST08420
TEMEFOS	3383-96-8	PST00020
TEMEPHOS	3383-96-8	PST00020
TEMEPHOS SULFOXIDE	17210-55-8	PST71651
TEMIK	116-06-3	PST00500
TEMIK SULFOXIDE	1646-87-3	PST00503
TENIATOL	97-23-4	PST71611
TENN-PLAS	65-85-0	PST02720
TENORAN	1982-47-4	PST04905
TENOX P GRAIN PRESERVATIVE	79-09-4	PST19750
TEPA	545-55-1	PST22510
TEPP	107-49-3	PST22520
TEPPEL'S OIL	8001-85-2	PST03250
TERAVIT	79-57-2	PST17414
TERBACIL	5902-51-2	PST71099
TERBUFOS	13071-79-9	PST22545

SUBSTANCE NAME	CAS #	PST #
TERBUFOS OXON SULFONE	56070-15-6	PST22537
TERBUFOS OXYGEN ANALOG SULFONE	56070-15-6	PST22537
TERBUFOXON SULFONE	56070-15-6	PST22537
TERBUMETON	33693-04-8	PST72770
TERBUTAZINE	5915-41-3	PST22536
TERBUTHYLAZINE	5915-41-3	PST22536
TERBUTHYLON	33693-04-8	PST72770
TERBUTONE	1912-26-1	PST23927
TERBUTONE	33693-04-8	PST72770
TERBUTREX	886-50-0	PST22538
TERBUTRYN	886-50-0	PST22538
TERBUTRYNE	886-50-0	PST22538
TERBUTYLAZINE	5915-41-3	PST22536
TERBUTYLETHYLAZINE	5915-41-3	PST22536
TEREPHTHALIC ACID, TETRACHLORO-, DIMETHYL ESTER	1861-32-1	PST04913
TERGITOL 15-S-12	68131-40-8	PST85315
TERGITOL 15-S-15	68131-40-8	PST85315
TERGITOL 15-S-20	68131-40-8	PST85315
TERGITOL 15-S-3	68131-40-8	PST85315
TERGITOL 15-S-5	68131-40-8	PST85315
TERGITOL 15-S-7	68131-40-8	PST85315
TERGITOL 15S	68131-40-8	PST85315
TERGITOL 15S9	68131-40-8	PST85315
TERGITOL(R) NONIC SURFACTANT 15-S-5	68131-40-8	PST85315
TERIDOX	50563-36-5	PST07677
TERMIL	1897-45-6	PST04890
TERPENE POLYCHLORINATE	8001-50-1	PST71162
TERR-O-GAS 100	74-83-9	PST14300
TERRABON	15251-48-6	PST84256
TERRACUR P (FORMULATION)	115-90-2	PST06210
TERRACYDIN	62-44-2	PST18340
TERRAMYCIN	79-57-2	PST17414
TERRAMYCIN HYDROCHLORIDE	2058-46-0	PST84045
TERRANEB SP	2675-77-6	PST71229
TERRAZOL	2425-06-1	PST04200
TERSAN	137-26-8	PST23430
TERSAN 1991	17804-35-2	PST02580
TERT-BUTANOL	75-65-0	PST22630
TERT-BUTYL ALCOHOL	75-65-0	PST22630
TERT-BUTYLCARBAMIC ACID ESTER WITH 3-(M-HYDROXYPHENYL) -1,1-DIMETHYLUREA	4849-32-5	PST72271
TESCOL	107-21-1	PST09400
TETRA-N-PROPYL DITHIOPYROPHOSPHATE	3244-90-4	PST72135
TETRA-SYSTAM	115-26-4	PST07655
TETRACAINE HYDROCHLORIDE	136-47-0	PST72269
TETRACAINE MONOHYDROCHLORIDE	136-47-0	PST72269
TETRACAP	127-18-4	PST22900
TETRACEMATE DISODIUM	139-33-3	PST08305
TETRACEMATE TETRASODIUM	64-02-8	PST23137
TETRACHLORMETHANE	56-23-5	PST04310
TETRACHLORO-META-PHTHALODINITRILE	1897-45-6	PST04890
TETRACHLORO-P-BENZOQUINONE	118-75-2	PST72136
TETRACHLORO-P-QUINONE	118-75-2	PST72136
TETRACHLORO-1,4-BENZOQUINONE	118-75-2	PST72136

ALPHABETICAL INDEX

SUBSTANCE NAME	CAS #	PST #
TETRACHLOROBENZOQUINONE	118-75-2	PST72136
TETRACHLORODIBENZODIOXIN	1746-01-6	PST08060
TETRACHLORODIPHENYLETHANE	72-54-8	PST06240
TETRACHLOROETHENE	127-18-4	PST22900
TETRACHLOROETHYLENE	127-18-4	PST22900
TETRACHLOROISOPHTHALONITRILE	1897-45-6	PST04890
TETRACHLORONITROBENZENE	117-18-0	PST71616
TETRACHLOROPARABENZOQUINONE	118-75-2	PST72136
TETRACHLOROPHENOL	25167-83-3	PST71689
TETRACHLOROQUINONE	118-75-2	PST72136
TETRACHLOROTEREPHTHALIC ACID DIMETHYL ESTER	1861-32-1	PST04913
TETRACHLORVINPHOS	961-11-5	PST72243
TETRACHLORVINPHOS	22248-79-9	PST72244
TETRACHLORVINPHOS	22350-76-1	PST72245
TETRADECANOIC ACID, POTASSIUM SALT	13429-27-1	PST72073
TETRAETHYL DIPHOSPHATE	107-49-3	PST22520
TETRAETHYL DITHIOPYROPHOSPHATE	3689-24-5	PST22470
TETRAETHYL PYROPHOSPHATE	107-49-3	PST22520
TETRAETHYL S,S'-METHYLENE BIS(PHOSPHOROTHIOLOTHIONATE)	563-12-2	PST08720
TETRAETHYL THIODIPHOSPHATE	3689-24-5	PST22470
TETRAETHYL THIOPYROPHOSPHATE	3689-24-5	PST22470
TETRAETHYL THIURAM	97-77-8	PST08370
TETRAETHYLTHIOPEROXYDICARBONIC DIAMIDE OHS08370	97-77-8	PST08370
TETRAFLUORON	27954-37-6	PST23002
TETRAHYDRO-3,5-DIMETHYL-2H-1,3,5-THIADIAZINE-2-THIONE	533-74-4	PST06230
TETRAHYDRO-5,5-DIMETHYL-2(1H)-PYRIMIDINONE(3-(4-(TRIFLUOROMETHYL) PHENYL)-1-(2-(4-(TRIFLUOROMETHYL)PHENYL)ETHENYL)-2-PROPENYLIDENE)	67485-29-4	PST01009
TETRAIODOFLUORESCEIN SODIUM SALT	16423-68-0	PST08685
TETRAKALIUM PYROPHOSPHATE	7320-34-5	PST19546
TETRAM	3734-97-2	PST71642
TETRAM MONOOXALATE	3734-97-2	PST71642
TETRAMETHRIN	7696-12-0	PST23061
TETRAMETHYL DIAPARA-AMINO-TRIPHENYL CARBINOL	569-64-2	PST13533
TETRAMETHYLENE BIS(METHANESULFONATE)	55-98-1	PST03482
TETRAMETHYLPHOSPHORODIAMIDIC FLUORIDE	115-26-4	PST07655
TETRAMETHYLTHIOPEROXYDICARBONIC DIAMIDE (((ME2N)C(S))2S2)	137-26-8	PST23430
TETRAMETHYLTHIURAM BISULFIDE	137-26-8	PST23430
TETRAMETHYLTHIURAM DISULFIDE	137-26-8	PST23430
TETRAMETHYLTHIURAM DISULPHIDE	137-26-8	PST23430
TETRAN HYDROCHLORIDE	2058-46-0	PST84045
TETRAOXYMETHYLENE	50-00-0	PST50003
TETRAPOTASSIUM DIPHOSPHATE	7320-34-5	PST19546
TETRAPOTASSIUM PYROPHOSPHATE	7320-34-5	PST19546
TETRAPROPYL THIODIPHOSPHATE	3244-90-4	PST72135
TETRAPROPYL THIOPYROPHOSPHATE	3244-90-4	PST72135
TETRASODIUM DIPHOSPHATE	7722-88-5	PST23140
TETRASODIUM DIPHOSPHATE (NA4P207)	7722-88-5	PST23140
TETRASODIUM EDTA	64-02-8	PST23137
TETRASODIUM PYROPHOSPHATE (HUGHES)	7722-88-5	PST23140
TETRASODIUM PYROPHOSPHATE, ANHYDROUS	7722-88-5	PST23140
TETRATHIONIC ACID, DIPOTASSIUM SALT	13932-13-3	PST72015
TETRON	107-49-3	PST22520
TETRON	7722-88-5	PST23140
TETRON (DISPERSANT)	7722-88-5	PST23140

SUBSTANCE NAME	CAS #	PST #
TETROSAN	8023-53-8	PST71839
TETROSIN OE-N	90-43-7	PST18470
TEXCRYL	9003-01-4	PST04349
TEXPADS (THE TEXWIPE COMPANY)	67-63-0	PST12090
TF 1169	69806-50-4	PST72554
TFM	88-30-2	PST71405
TH 6040	35367-38-5	PST07388
THALONIL	1897-45-6	PST04890
THIADIAZURON	51707-55-2	PST23299
THIAZON	533-74-4	PST06230
THIDIAZURON	51707-55-2	PST23299
THIMET (FORMULATION)	298-02-2	PST18640
THIMET O.A. SULFOXIDE	2588-05-8	PST18644
THIMET OXON	2600-69-3	PST18641
THIMET OXYGEN ANALOG	2600-69-3	PST18641
THIMET OXYGEN ANALOG SULFONE	2588-06-9	PST18642
THIMET OXYGEN ANALOG SULFOXIDE	2588-05-8	PST18644
THIMET SULFONE	2588-04-7	PST18643
THIMET SULFOXIDE	2588-03-6	PST18646
THINNER 2000 (KOP-COAT)	1330-20-7	PST25150
THIO-SUL	7783-18-8	PST01460
THIOALLATE	95-06-7	PST22190
THIOBENCARB	28249-77-6	PST72381
THIOCARA	333-20-0	PST19640
THIOCARBAMIC ACID, N-BUTYL-N-ETHYL, S-PROPYL ESTER	1114-71-2	PST71472
THIOCARBAZIL	36756-79-3	PST72405
THIOCRON	919-76-6	PST01007
THIOCYANIC ACID, COPPER(1+) SALT	1111-67-7	PST71224
THIODAN	115-29-7	PST08560
THIODEMETON	298-04-4	PST08380
THIODICARB	59669-26-0	PST72456
THIODIPHENYLAMINE	92-84-2	PST18400
THIODIPHOSPHORIC ACID (((HO)2-(S))2O) TETRAETHYL ESTER	3689-24-5	PST22470
THIODIPHOSPHORIC ACID (((HO)2P(S))2O), TETRAPROPYL ESTER	3244-90-4	PST72135
THIODIPHOSPHORIC ACID(HO)2P(S))2O), TETRAETHYL ESTER	3689-24-5	PST22470
THIODIPHOSPHORIC ACID, TETRAETHYL ESTER	3689-24-5	PST22470
THIOFANATE	23564-06-9	PST72322
THIOFANOX	39196-18-4	PST23330
THIOL SYSTOX SULFOXIDE	UNASSIGNED	PST06308
THIOLDEMETON	126-75-0	PST71646
THIOMETAN	2674-91-1	PST14105
THIOMETON	640-15-3	PST83056
THIONAZIN	297-97-2	PST25590
THIONAZIN OXYGEN ANALOG	7359-55-9	PST71377
THIONAZIN-O-ANALOG	7359-55-9	PST71377
THIONAZIN-OXON	7359-55-9	PST71377
THIONAZINE	297-97-2	PST25590
THIONO SYSTOX SULFONE	4891-54-7	PST06309
THIONODEMETON SULFONE	4891-54-7	PST06309
THIOPEROXYDICARBONIC DIAMIDE (((H2N)C'S))2S2), TETRAMETHYL-	137-26-8	PST23430
THIOPEROXYDIPHOSPHORIC ACID ((HO)2P(S))2S2), ETHYL TRIS(1-METHYL ETHYL) ESTER MIXTURE WITH THIOPEROXYDIPHOSPHORIC ACID (((HO)2P(S))2S2)	37333-40-7	PST18807
THIOPHANATE	23564-06-9	PST72322
THIOPHANATE-ETHYL	23564-06-9	PST72322

ALPHABETICAL INDEX

ALPHABETICAL INDEX

SUBSTANCE NAME	CAS #	PST #
TRICHLORONITROMETHANE	76-06-2	PST04830
TRICHLOROPHENE	70-30-4	PST10780
TRICHLORPHON	52-68-6	PST23790
TRICLOPYR	55335-06-3	PST72472
TRICRESOL	1319-77-3	PST05510
TRICURON	28805-78-9	PST73199
TRICYCLOHEXYLHYDROXY TIN	13121-70-5	PST06110
TRICYCLOHEXYLHYDROXYSTANNANE	13121-70-5	PST06110
TRICYCLOHEXYLHYDROXYTIN	13121-70-5	PST06110
TRICYCLOHEXYLSTANNOL	13121-70-5	PST06110
TRICYCLOHEXYLSTANNYL HYDROXIDE	13121-70-5	PST06110
TRICYCLOHEXYLTIN HYDROXIDE	13121-70-5	PST06110
TRIDEMORPH	24602-86-6	PST72537
TRIETAZINE	1912-26-1	PST23927
TRIETHANOLAMIN	102-71-6	PST23932
TRIETHANOLAMINE	102-71-6	PST23932
TRIETHAZINE	1912-26-1	PST23927
TRIETHYL 1-METHYLETHYL ESTER	37333-40-7	PST18807
TRIETHYLENE GLYCOL	112-27-6	PST24000
TRIETHYLENEPHOSPHORIC TRIAMIDE	545-55-1	PST22510
TRIETHYLENEPHOSPHOROTRIAMIDE	545-55-1	PST22510
TRIFLORAN	1582-09-8	PST24085
TRIFLURALILNE	1582-09-8	PST24085
TRIFLURALIN	1582-09-8	PST24085
TRIFOL	133-07-3	PST10012
TRIFORIN	26644-46-2	PST24086
TRIFORINE	26644-46-2	PST24086
TRIGARD	66215-27-8	PST72536
TRIGEN	112-27-6	PST24000
TRIGLYCOL	112-27-6	PST24000
TRIHYDROXYBORANE	10043-35-3	PST03260
TRIHYDROXYETHYL AMINE	102-71-6	PST23932
TRIHYDROXYMETHYLNITROMETHANE	126-11-4	PST24430
TRIHYDROXYPROPANE	56-81-5	PST10440
TRIHYDROXYTRIETHYLAMINE	102-71-6	PST23932
TRIKEPIN	1582-09-8	PST24085
TRIMAGNESIUM PHOSPHIDE	12057-74-8	PST13480
TRIMANGOL	12427-38-2	PST13589
TRIMETHACARB	12407-86-2	PST12420
TRIMETHYL METHANOL	75-65-0	PST22630
TRIMETHYLCARBINOL	75-65-0	PST22630
TRIMETHYLMETHANOL	75-65-0	PST22630
TRIMETHYLOLNITROMETHANE	126-11-4	PST24430
TRINEOPHYLTIN OXIDE	13356-08-6	PST24866
TRINIDAD PITCH	8052-42-4	PST02140
TRINIDAD PITCH	8052-42-4	PST71177
TRIOXON	93-76-5	PST28690
TRIPHENLYCHLOROTIN	639-58-7	PST24380
TRIPHENYLACETO STANNANE	900-95-8	PST24378
TRIPHENYLCHLOROSTANNANE	639-58-7	PST24380
TRIPHENYLTIN ACETATE	900-95-8	PST24378
TRIPHENYLTIN CHLORIDE	639-58-7	PST24380
TRIPHOSPHORIC ACID, PENTASODIUM SALT	7758-29-4	PST21730
TRIPOTASSIUM ORTHOPHOSPHATE	7778-53-2	PST19544

ALPHABETICAL INDEX

ALPHABETICAL INDEX

SUBSTANCE NAME	CAS #	PST #
UN 1846	56-23-5	PST04310
UN 1848	79-09-4	PST19750
UN 1894	100-57-2	PST18580
UN 1897	127-18-4	PST22900
UN 1910	1305-78-8	PST04030
UN 1915	108-94-1	PST05890
UN 1962	74-85-1	PST09330
UN 2011	12057-74-8	PST13480
UN 2015	7722-84-1	PST11190
UN 2047	542-75-6	PST26820
UN 2076	1319-77-3	PST05510
UN 2076	108-39-4	PST13080
UN 2131	79-21-0	PST18310
UN 2188	7784-42-1	PST02100
UN 2191	2699-79-8	PST22380
UN 2209	50-00-0	PST50003
UN 2213	30525-89-4	PST18000
UN 2261	1300-71-6	PST25160
UN 2261	105-67-9	PST28670
UN 2282	111-27-3	PST15630
UN 2331	7646-85-7	PST25350
UN 2369	111-76-2	PST03540
UN 2465	2782-57-2	PST06975
UN 2465	2893-78-9	PST21180
UN 2468	87-90-1	PST23860
UN 2472	83-26-1	PST18970
UN 2477	556-61-6	PST14950
UN 2491	141-43-5	PST08710
UN 2497	139-02-6	PST21530
UN 2501	545-55-1	PST22510
UN 2509	7646-93-7	PST19255
UN 2567	131-52-2	PST08506
UN 2629	62-74-8	PST21240
UN 2669	59-50-7	PST29890
UN 2674	16893-85-9	PST21620
UN 2717	76-22-2	PST04130
UN 2729	118-74-1	PST10730
UN 27617	76-44-8	PST10660
UN 2762	57-74-9	PST04560
UN 2789	64-19-7	PST00120
UN 2818	9080-17-5	PST01380
UN 2831	71-55-6	PST14370
UN 2855	16871-71-9	PST25410
UN 2872	96-12-8	PST26490
UN 2875	70-30-4	PST10780
UN 2967	5329-14-6	PST22200
UN 2968	12427-38-2	PST13589
UN 9125	7782-63-0	PST09870
UNDEN	114-26-1	PST02540
UNIMOLL DM	131-11-3	PST07740
UNION CARBIDE UC-25074	17702-57-7	PST73082
UNIROYAL D014	2312-35-8	PST19720
UNSLAKED LIME	1305-78-8	PST04030
UN2802	10125-13-0	PST05625

ALPHABETICAL INDEX

SUBSTANCE NAME	CAS #	PST #
UREA, 3-(P-CHLOROPHENYL)-1,1-DIMETHYL-	150-68-5	PST15196
UREA, 3-(3-CHLORO-P-TOLYL)-1,1-DIMETHYL-	15545-48-9	PST04912
UREA, 3-(3-CHLORO-4-METHOXYPHENYL)-1,1-DIMETHYL-	19937-59-8	PST15009
UREA, 3-(3,4-DICHLOROPHENYL)-1-METHOXY-1-METHYL-	330-55-2	PST12826
UREA, 3-(3,4-DICHLOROPHENYL)-1,1-DIMETHYL-	330-54-1	PST08420
UREA, 3-(4-BROMO-3-CHLOROPHENYL)-1-METHOXY-1-METHYL-	13360-45-7	PST04552
UREA, 3-CYCLOOCTYL-1,1-DIMETHYL-	2163-69-1	PST05996
UREA, 3-P-CUMENYL-1,1-DIMETHYL-	34123-59-6	PST12254
UROX	140-41-0	PST15197
UROX B	314-40-9	PST03330
USR 604	117-80-6	PST06810
USTILAN	30043-49-3	PST72551
UZGEN	17804-35-2	PST02580
U052	1319-77-3	PST05510
U052	108-39-4	PST13080
U088	84-66-2	PST07210
U165	91-20-3	PST16120
U230	95-95-4	PST28700
U232	93-76-5	PST28690
V 9	7440-22-4	PST20770
VACOR	53558-25-1	PST72334
VAGIMID	443-48-1	PST72529
VALERANILIDE, 4'-CHLORO-2,2-DIMETHYL-	7287-36-7	PST72987
VALERONE	108-83-8	PST07500
VALEXON	14816-18-3	PST73292
VALONE	83-28-3	PST24738
VAMIDOATE	2275-23-2	PST73108
VAMIDOTHION	2275-23-2	PST73108
VAMPIROL	60-41-3	PST22090
VAN DYKE 264	113-48-4	PST15955
VANALATE	1929-77-7	PST71473
VANZOATE	120-51-4	PST02805
VAPAM	137-42-8	PST71430
VAPONA	62-73-7	PST07000
VAPOTONE	107-49-3	PST22520
VARFINE	129-06-6	PST83008
VARITOX	650-51-1	PST73307
VC 13	97-17-6	PST06805
VC 9-104	13194-48-4	PST15080
VCS 438	20354-26-1	PST72344
VCS 506	21609-90-5	PST12780
VEGADEX	95-06-7	PST22190
VEGADEX SUPER	95-06-7	PST22190
VEGETOX	15263-52-2	PST04359
VEGIBEN	133-90-4	PST29084
VEL 3973	53780-34-0	PST72444
VELPAR	51235-04-2	PST10994
VELSICOL COMPOUND R	1918-00-9	PST02260
VELSICOL 104	76-44-8	PST10660
VELSICOL 506	21609-90-5	PST12780
VELSICOL 53-CS-17	1024-57-3	PST10670
VELSICOL 58-CS-11	1918-00-9	PST02260
VELTIN	640-15-3	PST83056
VENDEX	13356-08-6	PST24866

ALPHABETICAL INDEX

SUBSTANCE NAME	CAS #	PST #
XA 208	7440-22-4	PST20770
XEROX FILM REMOVER (UNION CARBIDE)	67-63-0	PST12090
XMC	2655-14-3	PST25171
XMC (PESTICIDE)	2655-14-3	PST25171
XPA	9003-01-4	PST04349
XYLENE	1330-20-7	PST25150
XYLENE BLUE VSG	2650-18-2	PST08277
XYLENESULFONIC ACID, SODIUM SALT	1300-72-7	PST75603
XYLENOL	1300-71-6	PST25160
XYLENOL	105-67-9	PST28670
XYLENOL (MIXED ISOMERS)	1300-71-6	PST25160
XYLOL	1330-20-7	PST25150
YALAN	2212-67-1	PST71471
YANOCK	640-19-7	PST09930
YARMOR	8002-09-3	PST18900
YELLOW CUPROCIDE	1317-39-1	PST05470
YELLOW LAKE 69	1934-21-0	PST22465
YELLOW PHOSPHOROUS	7723-14-0	PST18800
YELLOW PHOSPHORUS	7723-14-0	PST18800
YULAN	2212-67-1	PST71471
Z-31	7646-85-7	PST25350
Z-33	7646-85-7	PST25350
Z-68	297-97-2	PST25590
Z-70	297-97-2	PST25590
Z-76	297-97-2	PST25590
Z-83	1314-23-4	PST25635
ZEAZIN	1912-24-9	PST02150
ZECTANE	315-18-4	PST15010
ZECTRAN	315-18-4	PST15010
ZEPHIRAN CHLORIDE	8001-54-5	PST00537
ZEPHIRAN CHLORIDE	8001-54-5	PST00539
ZEPHIROL	8001-54-5	PST00539
ZERLATE	137-30-4	PST25397
ZETAX	155-04-4	PST27776
ZEXTRAN	315-18-4	PST15010
ZIMATE	137-30-4	PST25397
ZIMTALDEHYDE	104-55-2	PST05100
ZINC AMMONIATE ETHYLENEBIS(DITHIOCARBAMATE)-POLY(ETHYLENETHIURAM DISULPHIDE)	9006-42-2	PST71123
ZINC AMMONIATE ETHYLENEBIS(DITHIOCARBAMATE)-POLY(ETHYLENETHIURAM DISULFIDE)	9006-42-2	PST71123
ZINC BENZOTHIAZOL-2-YLTHIOLATE	155-04-4	PST27776
ZINC BIS(DIMETHYLDITHIOCARBAMATE)	137-30-4	PST25397
ZINC BUTTER	7646-85-7	PST25350
ZINC CHLORIDE	7646-85-7	PST25350
ZINC CHLORIDE, SOLID	7646-85-7	PST25350
ZINC DICHLORIDE	7646-85-7	PST25350
ZINC DIMETHYLDITHIOCARBAMATE	137-30-4	PST25397
ZINC FLUOROSILICATE	16871-71-9	PST25410
ZINC FLUOSILICATE	16871-71-9	PST25410
ZINC GELATIN	1314-13-2	PST25490
ZINC HEXAFLUOROSILICATE	16871-71-9	PST25410
ZINC HEXAFLUOROSILICATE(2-)	16871-71-9	PST25410
ZINC MONOXIDE	1314-13-2	PST25490

ALPHABETICAL INDEX

SUBSTANCE NAME	CAS #	PST #
1-(2-CHLOROPHENYLSULPHONYL)-3-(4-METHOXY-6-METHYL-1,3,5-TRIAZIN-2-YL)-UREA	64902-72-3	PST72504
1-(2-HYDROXYETHYL)-2-METHYL-5-NITROIMIDAZOLE	443-48-1	PST72529
1-(2-METHYLCYCLOHEXYL)-3-PHENYLUREA	1982-49-6	PST20586
1-(2,2-DIMETHYL-1-METHYLTHIOMETHYLPROPYLIDENEAMINO-OXY)-N-METHYLFORMAMIDE	39196-18-4	PST23330
1-(2,4-DICHLOROPHENYL)-4,4-DIMETHYL-2-(1,2,4-TRIAZOL-1-YL)PENTAN-3-OL	75736-33-3	PST07005
1-(3-PYRIDYLMETHYL)-3-(4-NITROPHENYL)UREA	53558-25-1	PST72334
1-(4-CHLOROBENZYL)-1-CYCLOPENTYL-3-PHENYLUREA	66063-05-6	PST72622
1-(4-CHLOROPHENOXY)-1-(IMIDAZOL-1-YL)-3,3-DIMETHYLBUTANONE	38083-17-9	PST05208
1-(4-CHLOROPHENOXY)-1-(IMIDAZOLE-1-YL)-3,3-DIMETHYLBUTANONE	38083-17-9	PST05208
1-(4-CHLOROPHENOXY)-1-(1H-IMIDAZOL-1-YL)-3,3-DIMETHYL-2-BUTANONE	38083-17-9	PST05208
1-(4-CHLOROPHENOXY)-1-(1H-IMIDAZOL-1-YL)-3,3-DIMETHYLBUTANONE	38083-17-9	PST05208
1-(4-CHLOROPHENYL)-3-(2,6-DIFLUOROBENZOYL)UREA	35367-38-5	PST07388
1-(4-NITROPHENYL)-3-(3-PYRIDYLMETHYL)UREA	53558-25-1	PST72334
1-(4'-HYDROXY-3'-COUMARINYL)-1-PHENYL-3-BUTANONE	81-81-2	PST25090
1-(5-(ETHYLSULFONYL)-1,3,4-THIADIAZOL-2-YL)-1,3-DIMETHYLUREA	30043-49-3	PST72551
1-(5-ETHYLSULPHONYL-1,3-4-THIADIAZOL-2-YL)-1,3-DIMETHYLUREA	30043-49-3	PST72551
1-(5-TERT-BUTYL-1,3,4-THIADIAZOL-2-YL)-1,3-DIMETHYLUREA	34014-18-1	PST72340
1-AZIRIDINYL PHOSPHINE OXIDE (TRIS)	545-55-1	PST22510
1-BENZOTHIAZOL-2-YL-1,3-DIMETHYLUREA	18691-97-9	PST14108
1-BENZOTHIAZOL-2-YL-3-METHYLUREA	1929-88-0	PST72971
1-BENZOYL-1-(3,4-DICHLOROPHENYL)-3,3-DIMETHYLUREA	3134-12-1	PST72972
1-BIS(2-(2-BUTOXYETHOXY)ETHOXY)METHYL-3,4-METHYLENEDIOXYBENZENE	5281-13-0	PST71828
1-BUTOXY-ALPHA-(2-THIOCYANOETHOXY)ETHANE	112-56-1	PST75661
1-BUTYL-3-(3,4-DICHLOROPHENYL)-1-METHYLUREA	555-37-3	PST16143
1-CHLORO-1-N,N-DIETHYLCARBAMOYL-1-PROPEN-2-YL DIMETHYL PHOSPHATE	13171-21-6	PST18670
1-CHLORO-2-(O-CHLOROPHENYL)-2-(P-CHLOROPHENYL)ETHYLENE	14835-94-0	PST04753
1-CHLORO-2-(2-CHLORO-1-(4-CHLOROPHENYL)ETHENYL)BENZENE	14835-94-0	PST04753
1-CHLORO-2-(2,2-DICHLORO-1-(4-CHLOROPHENYL)ETHENYLBENZENE	3424-82-6	PST06245
1-CHLORO-2,3-DIBROMOPROPANE	96-12-8	PST26490
1-CHLORO-3-(2,2-DICHLORO-1-(4-CHLOROPHENYL)ETHYL)BENZENE	4329-12-8	PST04752
1-CHLORO-4-(((4-CHLOROPHEYL)METHYL)THIO)BENZENE	103-17-3	PST71139
1-CHLORO-4-(PHENYLSULFONYL)BENZENE	80-00-2	PST71663
1-CYCLOHEXENE-1-CARBOXYLIC ACID, 2-(2,4-DIHYDROXYPHENYL)-, DELTA -LACTONE, O-ESTER WITH O,O-DIETHYL PHOSPHOROTHIOATE	572-48-5	PST73073
1-CYCLOHEXENE-1,2-DICARBOXIMIDOMETHYL 2,2-DIMETHYL-3-(2 -METHYLPROPENYL)CYCLOPROPANECARBOXYLATE	7696-12-0	PST23061
1-DECANOL	112-30-1	PST06285
1-DIMETHYLCARBAMOYL-5-METHYL-3-PYRAZOLYL DIMETHYLCARBAMATE	644-64-4	PST83057
1-DIMETHYLCARBAMOYL-5-METHYLPYRAZOL-3-YL DIMETHYLCARBAMATE	644-64-4	PST83057
1-DODECANOL	112-53-8	PST12500
1-DODECYL ALCOHOL	112-53-8	PST12500
1-H-BENZ(DE)ISOQUINOLINE-1,3(2H)-DIONE, 2-((DIETHOXYPHOSPHINYL)OXY)-	1491-41-4	PST72737
1-HEXADECANOL	36653-82-4	PST04525
1-HEXADECYL ALCOHOL	36653-82-4	PST04525
1-HEXANOL	111-27-3	PST15630
1-HEXYL ALCOHOL	111-27-3	PST15630
1-HYDROXY-2-(IH)-PYRIDINETHIONE, SODIUM SALT	15922-78-8	PST21420
1-HYDROXY-2,4-DINITROBENZENE	51-28-5	PST28620
1-HYDROXY-3-METHYL BENZENE	108-39-4	PST13080
1-HYDROXY-3-METHYLBENZENE	108-39-4	PST13080
1-HYDROXYDODECANE	112-53-8	PST12500
1-HYDROXYETHYL-2-METHYL-5-NITROIMIDAZOLE	443-48-1	PST72529

ALPHABETICAL INDEX

ALPHABETICAL INDEX

SUBSTANCE NAME	CAS #	PST #
-DIMETHANONAPHTHALENE		
1,2,3,4,10,10-HEXACHLORO-6,7-EPOXY-1,4,4A,5,6,7,8,8A-OCTAHYDRO-ENDO -1,4-EXO-5,8-DIMETHANONAPHTHALENE	60-57-1	PST07080
1,2,3,4,10,10-HEXACHLORO-6,7-EPOXY-1,4,4A,5,6,7,8,8A-OCTAHYDRO-ENDO ENDO-1,4:5,8-DIMETHANONAPHTHALENE	72-20-8	PST08600
1,2,3,4,10,10-HEXACHLORO-6,7-EPOXY-1,4,4A,5,6,7,8,8A-OCTAHYDRO-1, 4-ENDO-EXO-5,8-DIMETHANONAPHTHALENE	60-57-1	PST07080
1,2,3,4,5,6-HEXACHLOROCYCLOHEXANE	319-84-6	PST00770
1,2,3,4,5,6-HEXACHLOROCYCLOHEXANE	608-73-1	PST03080
1,2,3,4,5,6-HEXACHLOROCYCLOHEXANE	319-86-8	PST06310
1,2,3,4,5,6-HEXACHLOROCYCLOHEXANE	58-89-9	PST12810
1,2,3,4,5,6,-HEXACHLOROCYCLOHEXANE	319-85-7	PST03010
1,2,3,4,7,7-HEXACHLORO-5,6-BIS(CHLOROMETHYL)-BICYCLO(2.2.1)HEPT-2-ENE	2550-75-6	PST73193
1,2,3,4,7,7-HEXACHLORO-5,6-BIS(CHLOROMETHYL)-2-NORBORNENE	2550-75-6	PST73193
1,2,3,4,7,7-HEXACHLORO-5,6-BIS(CHLOROMETHYL)-8,9,10-TRINORBORN-2-ENE	2550-75-6	PST73193
1,2,3,4,7,7-HEXACHLORO-5,6-BIS-(CHLOROMETHYL)-2-NORBON-ENE	2550-75-6	PST73193
1,2,3,4,7,7-HEXACHLOROBICYCLO(2.2.1)-2-HEPTENE-5,6-BISOXYMETHYLENE SULFITE	115-29-7	PST08560
1,2,4-OXADIAZOLIDINE-3,5-DIONE, 2-(3,4-DICHLOROPHENYL)-4-METHYL-	20354-26-1	PST72344
1,2,4-TRIAZIN-5(4H)-ONE, 4-AMINO-6-(1,1-DIMETHYLETHYL)-3-(ETHYLTHIO)-	64529-56-2	PST09111
1,2,4-TRIAZIN-5(4H)-ONE, 4-AMINO-6-(1,1-DIMETHYLETHYL)-3-(METHYLTHIO)-	21087-64-9	PST15006
1,2,4-TRIAZIN-5(4H)-ONE, 6-(1,1-DIMETHYLETHYL)-4-((2-METHYLPROPYLIDENE)AMINO)-3-(METHYLTHIO)-	57052-04-7	PST11844
1,2,4-TRIAZINE-5-(4H)-ONE, 4-AMINO-3-METHYL-6-PHENYL-	41394-05-2	PST14095
1,2,4,5-TETRACHLORO-3-NITRO-BENZENE	117-18-0	PST71616
1,2,4,5,6,7,8,8-OCTACHLORO-2,3,3A,4,7,7A-HEXAHYDRO-4,7-METHANO-1H -INDENE	57-74-9	PST04560
1,2,4,5,6,7,8,8-OCTACHLORO-2,3,3A,4,7,7A-HEXAHYDRO-4,7-METHANO-1H -INDENE	12789-03-6	PST71948
1,2,4,5,6,7,8,8-OCTACHLORO-2,3,3A,4,7,7A-HEXAHYDRO-4,7-METHANOINDENE	57-74-9	PST04560
1,2,4,5,6,7,8,8-OCTACHLORO-3A,4,7,7A-TETRAHYDRO-4,7-METHANOINDAN	57-74-9	PST04560
1,2,4,5,6,7,8,8-OCTACHLORO-3A,4,7,7A-TETRAHYDRO-4,7-METHANOINDAN	12789-03-6	PST71948
1,2,4,5,6,7,8,8-OCTACHLORO-3A,4,7,7A-TETRAHYDRO-4,7-METHANOINDANE	57-74-9	PST04560
1,2,4,5,6,7,8,8-OCTACHLORO-4,7-METHANE-3A,4,7,7A-TETRAHYDROINDANE	57-74-9	PST04560
1,3-BENZENEDICARBONITRILE, 2,4,5,6-TETRACHLORO-	1897-45-6	PST04890
1,3-BENZODIOXOL-4-OL, 2,2-DIMETHYL-, METHYLCARBAMATE	22781-23-3	PST02560
1,3-BENZODIOXOLE, 5-((2-(2-BUTOXYETHOXY)ETHOXY)METHYL)-6-PROPYL-	51-03-6	PST75640
1,3-BENZODIOXOLE, 5-(BIS(2-(2-BUTOXYETHOXY)ETHOXY)METHYL)-	5281-13-0	PST71828
1,3-BIS(CARBAMOYLTHIO)-2-(N,N-DIMETHYLAMINO)PROPANE HYDROCHLORIDE	15263-52-2	PST04359
1,3-BIS(2,2,2-TRICHLORO-1-HYDROXYETHYL)UREA	116-52-9	PST06817
1,3-BUTANEDIOL	107-88-0	PST26730
1,3-BUTYLENE GLYCOL	107-88-0	PST26730
1,3-D	542-75-6	PST26820
1,3-DI(CARBAMOYLTHIO)-2-DIMETHYLAMINOPROPANE-HYDROCHLORIDE	15263-52-2	PST04359
1,3-DICHLORO-S-TRIAZINE-2,4,6(1H,3H,5H)-TRIONE POTASSIUM SALT	2244-21-5	PST19360
1,3-DICHLORO-S-TRIAZINE-2,4,6,(1H,3H,5H) -TRIONE	2782-57-2	PST06975
1,3-DICHLORO-1-PROPENE	542-75-6	PST26820
1,3-DICHLORO-1,3,5-TRIAZINE-2,4,6(1H,3H,5H)-TRIONE POTASSIUM SALT	2244-21-5	PST19360
1,3-DICHLORO-5,5-DIMETHYL-2-IMIDAZOLIDINEDIONE	118-52-5	PST26800
1,3-DICHLORO-5,5-DIMETHYLHYDANTOIN	118-52-5	PST26800
1,3-DICHLORO-5,5-METHYLHYDANTOIN	118-52-5	PST26800
1,3-DICHLOROPROPENE	542-75-6	PST26820
1,3-DICHLOROPROPYLENE	542-75-6	PST26820
1,3-DICYANOTETRACHLOROBENZENE	1897-45-6	PST04890

ALPHABETICAL INDEX

SUBSTANCE NAME	CAS #	PST #
2-((1-NAPHTHALENYLAMINO)CARBONYL)BENZOIC ACID	132-66-1	PST71340
2-((1-NAPHTHALENYLAMINO)CARBONYL)BENZOIC ACID MONOSODIUM SALT	132-67-2	PST71341
2-((1,2-DIMETHYLPROPYL)AMINO)-4-(ETHYLAMINO)-6-(METHYLTHIO)-S-TRIAZINE	22936-75-0	PST72145
2-((4-CHLORO-6-(CYCLOPROPYLAMINO)-S-TRIAZIN-2-YL)AMINO)-2-METHYL PROPIONITRILE	32889-48-8	PST72398
2-((4-CHLORO-6-(CYCLOPROPYLAMINO)-1,3,5-TRIAZIN-2-YL)AMINO)-2-METHYL PROPANENITRILE	32889-48-8	PST72398
2-((4-CHLORO-6-(ETHYLAMINO)-S-TRIAZIN-2-YL))AMINO)-2-METHYLPROPIONITRILE	21725-46-2	PST05762
2-((4-CHLORO-6-(ETHYLAMINO)-S-TRIAZIN-2-YL)AMINO-2-METHYLPROPIONITRILE	21725-46-2	PST05762
2-((4-CHLORO-6-(ETHYLAMINO)-1,3,5-TRIAZIN-2-YL)AMINO)-2-METHYLPROPANENITRILE	21725-46-2	PST05762
2-((4-CHLOROPHENYL)PHENYLACETYL)-1H-INDENE-1,3(2H)-DIONE	3691-35-8	PST04826
2-(ALPHA-NAPHTHOXY)-N,N-DIETHYLPROPIONAMIDE	15299-99-7	PST72319
2-(DIETHOXYPHOSPHINOTHIOYLOXYIMINO)-2-PHENYLACETONITRILE	14816-18-3	PST73292
2-(DIETHOXYPHOSPHINYLIMINO)-1,3-DIETHIETANE	21548-32-3	PST16141
2-(DIETHOXYPHOSPHINYLIMINO)-1,3-DITHIOLAN	947-02-4	PST06115
2-(DIETHOXYPHOSPHINYLIMINO)-1,3-DITHIOLANE	947-02-4	PST06115
2-(DIETHOXYPHOSPHINYLIMINO)-4-METHYL-1,3-DITHIOLANE	950-10-7	PST13735
2-(DIMETHYLAMINO)-N-(((METHYLAMINO)CARBONYL)OXYL)-2 -OXOETHANIMIDOTHIOIC ACID METHYL ESTER	23135-22-0	PST17370
2-(DIMETHYLAMINO)-5,6-DIMETHYL-4-PYRIMIDINYL DIMETHYLCARBAMATE	23103-98-2	PST72345
2-(DIMETHYLAMINO)ETHYL-P-(BUTYLAMINO) BENZOATE MONOHYDROCHLORIDE	136-47-0	PST72269
2-(DIPHENYLACETYL)-1,3-INDANDIONE	82-66-6	PST08068
2-(DIPHENYLACETYL)-1H-INDEND-1,3(2H)-DIONE	82-66-6	PST08068
2-(ETHYLAMINO)-4-(ISOPROPYLAMINO)-6-(METHYLTHIO)-S-TRIAZINE	834-12-8	PST01006
2-(ETHYLAMINO)-4-(ISOPROPYLAMINO)-6-METHOXY-S-TRIAZINE	1610-17-9	PST02148
2-(ETHYLTHIO)-4,6-BIS(ISOPROPYLAMINO)-S-TRIAZINE	4147-51-7	PST72333
2-(ETHYLTHIO)-4,6-BIS(ISOPROPYLAMINO)-1,3,5-TRIAZINE	4147-51-7	PST72333
2-(HYDROXYMETHYL)-2-NITRO-1,3-PROPANEDIOL	126-11-4	PST24430
2-(ISOPROPYLAMINO)-4-((3-METHOXYPROPYL)AMINO)-6-(METHYLTHIO) -S-TRIAZINE	841-06-5	PST14204
2-(ISOPROPYLAMINO)-4-(METHYLAMINO)-6-(METHYLTHIO)-S-TRIAZINE	1014-69-3	PST06353
2-(M-CHLOROPHENYL) 2-(P-CHLOROPHENYL-1,1-DICHLOROETHANE	4329-12-8	PST04752
2-(METHOXYCARBONYL)PHENOL	119-36-8	PST14720
2-(P-SULFANILAMIDO)QUINOZALINE	59-40-5	PST72046
2-(P-TERT-BUTYLPHENOXY)CYCLOHEXYL 2-PROPYNYL SULFITE	2312-35-8	PST19720
2-(P-TERT-BUTYLPHENOXY)ISOPROPYL 2-CHLOROETHYL SULPHITE	140-57-8	PST01850
2-(SEC-BUTYLAMINO)-4-(ETHYLAMINO)-6-METHOXY-S-TRIAZINE	26259-45-0	PST73051
2-(SULFANILYLAMINO)THIAZOLE	72-14-0	PST72047
2-(TERT-BUTYLAMINO)-4-(ETHYLAMINO)-6-(METHYLTHIO)-S-TRIAZINE	886-50-0	PST22538
2-(TERT-BUTYLAMINO)-4-(ETHYLAMINO)-6-METHOXY-S-TRIAZINE	33693-04-8	PST72770
2-(TERT-BUTYLAMINO)-4-CHLORO-6-(ETHYLAMINO)-S-TRIAZINE	5915-41-3	PST22536
2-(THIOCYANOMETHYLTHIO)BENZOTHIAZOLE	21564-17-0	PST71392
2-(1-(ETHOXYAMINO)BUTYLIDENE)-5-(2-(ETHYLTHIO)PROPYL)-1,3-CYCLOHEXANEDIONE	74051-80-2	PST20577
2-(1-(ETHXOYIMINOBUTYL)-5-(2-(ETHYLTHIO)PROPYL)-3-HYDROXY-2-CYCLOHEXENE-1-ONE	74051-80-2	PST20577
2-(1-METHYLETHOXY)PHENOL METHYLCARBAMATE	114-26-1	PST02540
2-(1-METHYLETHOXY)PHENYL METHYLCARBAMATE	114-26-1	PST02540
2-(1-METHYLETHYL)PHENOL METHYLCARBAMATE	2631-40-5	PST73231
2-(1-METHYLETHYL)PHENYL METHYLCARBAMATE	2631-40-5	PST73231
2-(1-METHYLPROPYL)-4,6-DINITROPHENOL	88-85-7	PST08020
2-(1-METHYLPROPYL)-4,6-DINITROPHENOL ACETATE (ESTER)	2813-95-8	PST08021

ALPHABETICAL INDEX

ALPHABETICAL INDEX

SUBSTANCE NAME	CAS #	PST #
2-ALLYL-4-HYDROXY-3-METHYL-2-CYCLOPENTEN-1-ONE ESTER OF CHRYSANTHEMUMMONOCARBOXYLIC ACID	584-79-2	PST00550
2-AMINO-N-ISOPROPYL BENZAMIDE	UNASSIGNED	PST02581
2-AMINO-4(HYDROXYMETHYLPHOSPHINYL)BUTANOIC ACID, MONOAMMONIUM SALT	77182-82-2	PST72647
2-AMINO-4-CHLORO-6-ETHYLAMINE-S-TRIAZINE	UNASSIGNED	PST01011
2-AMINOETHANOL	141-43-5	PST08710
2-AZIDO-4-(ISOPROPYLAMINO)-6-(METHYLTHIO)-S-TRIAZINE,	4658-28-0	PST02216
2-AZIDO-4-ISOPROPYLAMINO-6-METHYLTHIO-S-TRIAZINE	4658-28-0	PST02216
2-AZIDO-4-ISOPROPYLAMINO-6-METHYLTHIO-1,3,5-TRIAZINE	4658-28-0	PST02216
2-BENZIMIDAZOLECARBAMIC ACID, 1-(BUTYLCARBAMOYL)-, METHYL ESTER	17804-35-2	PST02580
2-BENZOTHIAZOLETHIOL	149-30-4	PST13738
2-BENZOTHIAZOLETHIOL, ZINC SALT	155-04-4	PST27776
2-BENZOTHIAZOLETHIOLE	149-30-4	PST13738
2-BENZOTHIAZOLETHIONE	149-30-4	PST13738
2-BENZOTHIAZOLINETHIONE	149-30-4	PST13738
2-BIPHENYLOL	90-43-7	PST18470
2-BIPHENYLOL,SODIUM SALT	132-27-4	PST08500
2-BORNANONE	76-22-2	PST04130
2-BROMO-2-BROMOMETHYLGLURATONITRILE	35691-65-7	PST26487
2-BROMO-2-NITRO-1,3-PROPANEDIOL	52-51-7	PST72832
2-BROMO-2-NITROPROPANE-1,3-DIOL	52-51-7	PST72832
2-BUTANONE	78-93-3	PST14460
2-BUTANONE, 1-(4-CHLOROPHENOXY)-1-(1H-IMIDAZOL-1-YL)-3,3-DIMETHYL-	38083-17-9	PST05208
2-BUTANONE, 3-(METHYLSULFONYL)-, O-((METHYLAMINO)CARBONYL)OXIME	34681-23-7	PST72434
2-BUTANONE, 3-(METHYLTHIO)-, O-((METHYLAMINO)CARBONYL)OXIME	34681-10-2	PST73270
2-BUTANONE, 3,3-DIMETHYL-1-(METHYLTHIO)-, O-((METHYLAMINO)CARBONYL)	39196-18-4	PST23330
2-BUTENOIC ACID, 2(OR 4)-ISOOCTYL-4,6(OR 2,6)-DINITROPHENYL ESTER	39300-45-3	PST71402
2-BUTENOIC ACID, 3-(((ETHYLAMINO)METHOXYPHOSPHINOTHIOYL)OXY)-, 1-METHYLETHYL ESTER, (E)-	31218-83-4	PST72440
2-BUTENOIC ACID, 3-((DIMETHOXYPHOSPHINYL)OXY)-, METHYL ESTER	7786-34-7	PST18650
2-BUTENOIC ACID, 3-((DIMETHOXYPHOSPHINYL)OXY)-, 1-PHENYLETHYL ESTER, (E)-	7700-17-6	PST05115
2-BUTENOIC ACID, 3-METHYL-, 2-(1-METHYLPROPYL)-4,6-DINITROPHENYL ESTER	485-31-4	PST71960
2-BUTOXYETHANOL	111-76-2	PST03540
2-CAMPHONE	76-22-2	PST04130
2-CARBOMETHOXY-1-METHYLVINYL DIMETHYL PHOSPHATE	7786-34-7	PST18650
2-CARBOXYPHENOL	69-72-7	PST20315
2-CHLORETHANEPHOSPHONIC ACID	16672-87-0	PST72293
2-CHLORO-ALPHA,ALPHA,ALPHA-TRIFLUORO-P-TOLYL-3-ETHOXY-4-NITROPHENYL ETHER	42874-03-3	PST72413
2-CHLORO-DIETHYL-N-(BUTOXYMETHYL)ACETANILIDE	23184-66-9	PST03497
2-CHLORO-N-(((4-METHOXY-6-METHYL-1,3,5-TRIAZIN-2-YL)AMINO)CARBONYL) BENZENESULFONAMIDE	64902-72-3	PST72504
2-CHLORO-N-(ETHOXYMETHYL)-N-(2-ETHYL-6-METHYLPHENYL)ACETAMIDE	34256-82-1	PST72539
2-CHLORO-N-(ETHOXYMETHYL)-6'-ETHYL-O-ACETOTOLUIDIDE	34256-82-1	PST72539
2-CHLORO-N-(ETHOXYMETHYL)-6'-ETHYLACET-O-TOLUIDIDE	34256-82-1	PST72539
2-CHLORO-N-(PYRAZOL-1-YLMETHYL)ACET-2',6'-XYLIDIDE	67129-08-2	PST14106
2-CHLORO-N-(1-METHYL-2-PROPYNYL)-N-PHENYLACETAMIDE	21267-72-1	PST73038
2-CHLORO-N-(1-METHYL-2-PROPYNYL)ACETANILIDE	21267-72-1	PST73038
2-CHLORO-N-(1-METHYLETHYL)-N-PHENYLACETAMIDE	1918-16-7	PST19686
2-CHLORO-N-(1-METHYLPROP-2-YNYL)ACETANILIDE	21267-72-1	PST73038
2-CHLORO-N-(2-ETHYL-6-METHYLPHENYL)-N-(2-METHOXY-1-METHYLETHYL) ACETAMIDE	51218-45-2	PST15003
2-CHLORO-N-(2-METHOXYETHYL)ACET-2',6'-XYLIDIDE	50563-36-5	PST07677

ALPHABETICAL INDEX

ALPHABETICAL INDEX

ALPHABETICAL INDEX

ALPHABETICAL INDEX

ALPHABETICAL INDEX

ALPHABETICAL INDEX

SUBSTANCE NAME	CAS #	PST #
3(2H)-PYRIDAZINONE, 4-CHLORO-5-(METHYLAMINO)-2-(3-(TRIFLUOROMETHYL) PHENYL)-	27314-13-2	PST72343
3(2H)-PYRIDAZINONE, 5-AMINO-4-BROMO-2-PHENYL-	3042-84-0	PST72769
3(2H)-PYRIDAZINONE, 5-AMINO-4-CHLORO-2-PHENYL-	1698-60-8	PST71928
3-(((DIMETHYLAMINO)CARBONYL)AMINO)PHENYL (1,1-DIMETHYLETHYL)CARBAMATE	4849-32-5	PST72271
3-((DIMETHOXYPHOSPHINYL)OXY-2-PENTENEDIOIC ACID DIMETHYL ESTER	122-10-1	PST03240
3-((DIMETHOXYPHOSPHINYL)OXYL-2-BUTENOIC ACID METHYL ESTER	7786-34-7	PST18650
3-((METHOXYCARBONYL)AMINO)PHENYL (3-METHYLPHENYL)CARBAMATE	13684-63-4	PST72282
3-(ALPHA-(P-(P-BROMOPHENYL)-BETA-HYDROXYPHENETHYL)BENZYL)-4-HYDROXY-COUMARIN	28772-56-7	PST03334
3-(ALPHA-(2-FURYL)-BETA-ACETYLETHYL)4-HYDROXYCOUMARIN	117-52-2	PST05476
3-(ALPHA-ACETONYLBENZYL)-4-HYDROXYCOUMARIN	81-81-2	PST25090
3-(ALPHA-ACETONYLBENZYL)-4-HYDROXYCOUMARIN, SODIUM SALT	129-06-6	PST83008
3-(ALPHA-ACETONYLFURFURYL)-4-HYDROXYCOUMARIN	117-52-2	PST05476
3-(DIMETHOXYPHOSPHINYLOXY)-N-METHYL-CIS-CROTONAMIDE	6923-22-4	PST15165
3-(DIMETHOXYPHOSPHINYLOXY)-N-METHYLISOCROTONAMIDE	6923-22-4	PST15165
3-(DIMETHOXYPHOSPHINYLOXY)-N,N-DIMETHYL-CIS-CROTONAMIDE	141-66-2	PST03090
3-(HEXAHYDRO-4,7-METHANOINDAN-1(OR 2)-YL)-1,1-DIMETHYLUREA	28805-78-9	PST73199
3-(HEXAHYDRO-4,7-METHANOINDAN-1-YL)-1,1-DIMETHYLUREA + 3-HEXAHYDRO-4,7-METHANOINDAN-2-YL)-1,1-DIMETHYLUREA	28805-78-9	PST73199
3-(HEXAHYDRO-4,7-METHANOINDAN-5-YL)-1,1-DIMETHYLUREA	18530-56-8	PST71400
3-(METHYLSULFONYL)-2-BUTANONE O-((METHYLAMINO)CARBONYL)OXIME	34681-23-7	PST72434
3-(METHYLSULFONYL)-2-BUTANONE O-(METHYLCARBAMOYL)OXIME	34681-23-7	PST72434
3-(METHYLTHIO)-2-BUTANONE O-((METHYLAMINO)CARBONYL)OXIME	34681-10-2	PST73270
3-(METHYLTHIO)-2-BUTANONE O-(METHYLCARBAMOYL)OXIME	34681-10-2	PST73270
3-(METHYLTHIO)BUTANONE O-METHYLCARBAMOYLOXIME	34681-10-2	PST73270
3-(P-(P-CHLOROPHENOXY)PHENYL)-1,1-DIMETHYLUREA	1982-47-4	PST04905
3-(P-(P-METHOXYPHENOXY)PHENYL)-1,1-DIMETHYLUREA	14214-32-5	PST07386
3-(P-BROMOPHENYL)-1-METHOXY-1-METHYLUREA	3060-89-7	PST15008
3-(P-CHLOROPHENYL)-1-METHOXY-1-METHYLUREA	1746-81-2	PST15174
3-(P-CHLOROPHENYL)-1-METHYL-1-(1-METHYL-2-PROPYNYL)UREA	3766-60-7	PST03523
3-(P-CHLOROPHENYL)-1,1-DIMETHYLUREA	150-68-5	PST15196
3-(P-CHLOROPHENYL)-1,1-DIMETHYLUREA TRICHLOROACETATE	140-41-0	PST15197
3-(PHENOXYPHENYL)METHYL-TRANS-3-(2,2-DICHLOROETHENYL)-2,2-DIMETHYLCYCLOPROPANECARBOXYLATE	51877-74-8	PST23708
3-(PHENOXYPHENYL)METHYL-TRANS-3-(2,2-DICHLOROVINYL)-2,2-DIMETHYLCYCLOPROPANECARBOXYLATE	51877-74-8	PST23708
3-(TRIMETHOXYSILYL)PROPYLDIMETHYLOCTADECYLAMMONIUM CHLORIDE	27668-52-6	PST72370
3-(1 OR 2-HEXAHYDRO-4,7-METHANOINDANLYL)-1,1-DIMETHYLUREA	28805-78-9	PST73199
3-(1-(2-FURANYL)-3-OXOBUTYL)-4-HYDROXY-2H-1-BENZOPYRAN-2-ONE	117-52-2	PST05476
3-(1-ETHYLPROPYL)PHENOL METHYLCARBAMATE MIXTURE WITH 3-(1-METHYLBUTYL) PHENYL METHYLCARBAMATE	8065-36-9	PST03480
3-(1-METHYLETHYL)-1H-2,1,3-BENZOTHIADIAZIN-4(3H)-ONE 2,2-DIOXIDE	25057-89-0	PST02584
3-(1-METHYLETHYL)PHENOL METHYLCARBAMATE	64-00-6	PST29423
3-(2-CYCLOPENTENYL)-2-METHYL-4-OXO-2-CYCLOPENTENYL ESTER OF CHRYSANTHEMUMMONOCARBOXYLIC ACID	97-11-0	PST19949
3-(2-FURANYLMETHYL)-2-METHYL-4-OXO-2-CYCLOPENTEN-1-YL 2,2-DIMETHYL -3-(2-METHYL-1-PROPENYL)CYCLOPROPANECARBOXYLATE	17080-02-3	PST10175
3-(2,2-DIBROMOETHENYL)-2,2-DIMETHYLCYCLOPROPANECARBOXYLIC ACID CYANO(3-PHENOXYPHENYL)METHYL ESTER	52918-63-5	PST72784
3-(2,2-DICHLOROETHENYL)-2,2-DIMETHYLCYCLOPROPANECARBOXYLIC ACID CYANO(3-PHENOXYPHENYL) METHYL ESTER	52315-07-8	PST72392
3-(2,4-DICHLORO-5-(1-METHYLETHOXY)PHENYL)-5-(1,1-DIMETHYLETHYL)-1,3,4-OXADIAZOL-2(3H)-ONE	19666-30-9	PST72385

SUBSTANCE NAME	CAS #	PST #
3-(3-(1,1'-BIPHENYL)-4-YL-1,2,3,4-TETRAHYDRO-1-NAPHTHALENYL)-4-HYDROXY-2H-1-BENZOPYRAN-2-ONE	56073-07-5	PST07385
3-(3-(4'-BROMO(1,1'-BIPHENYL)-4-YL)-1,2,3,4-TETRAHYDRO-1-NAPHTHALENYL)-4-HYDROXY-2H-1-BENZOPYRAN-2-ONE	56073-10-0	PST03327
3-(3-(4'-BROMO(1,1'-BIPHENYL)-4-YL)-3-HYDROXY-1-PHENYLPROPYL)-4-HYDROXY-2H-1-BENZOPYRAN-2-ONE	28772-56-7	PST03334
3-(3-(4'-BROMOBIPHENYL-4-YL)-1,2,3,4-TETRAHYDRO-1-NAPHTHYL-4-HYDROXYCOUMARIN	56073-10-0	PST03327
3-(3-(4'-BROMOBIPHENYL-4-YL)-3-HYDROXY-1-PHENYLPROPYL)-4-HYDROXY-COUMARIN	28772-56-7	PST03334
3-(3-BIPHENYL-4-YL-1,2,3,4-TETRAHYDRO-1-NAPHTHYL)-4-HYDROXYCOUMARIN	56073-07-5	PST07385
3-(3-CHLORO-P-TOLYL)-1,1-DIMETHYLUREA	15545-48-9	PST04912
3-(3-CHLORO-4-METHOXYPHENYL)-1,1-DIMETHYLUREA	19937-59-8	PST15009
3-(3,3-DIMETHYLUREIDO)PHENYL TERT-BUTYLCARBAMATE	4849-32-5	PST72271
3-(3,4-DICHLOROPHENYL)-1-METHOXY-1-METHYLUREA	330-55-2	PST12826
3-(3,4-DICHLOROPHENYL)-1-METHYL-1-N-BUTYLUREA	555-37-3	PST16143
3-(3,4-DICHLOROPHENYL)-1,1-DIMETHYLUREA	330-54-1	PST08420
3-(4-(4-CHLOROPHENOXY)PHENYL)-1,1-DIMETHYLUREA	1982-47-4	PST04905
3-(4-(4-METHOXYPHENOXY)PHENYL)-1,1-DIMETHYLUREA	14214-32-5	PST07386
3-(4-BROMO-3-CHLOROPHENYL)-1-METHOXY-1-METHYLUREA	13360-45-7	PST04552
3-(4-BROMOPHENYL)-1-METHOXY-1-METHYLUREA	3060-89-7	PST15008
3-(4-CHLOROPHENYL)-1-METHOXY-1-METHYLUREA	1746-81-2	PST15174
3-(4-CHLOROPHENYL)-1-METHYL-1-(1-METHYLPROP-2-YNYL)UREA	3766-60-7	PST03523
3-(4-CHLOROPHENYL)-1,1-DIMETHYLUREA	150-68-5	PST15196
3-(4-CHLOROPHENYL)-1,1-DIMETHYLURONIUM TRICHLOROACETATE	140-41-0	PST15197
3-(4-ISOPROPYLPHENYL)-1,1-DIMETHYLUREA	34123-59-6	PST12254
3-(5-TERT-BUTYLISOXAZOL-3-YL)-1,1-DIMETHYLUREA	55861-78-4	PST72586
3-ALPHA-PHENYL-BETA-ACETYLETHYL-4-HYDROXYCOUMARIN	81-81-2	PST25090
3-AMINO-S-TRIAZOLE	61-82-5	PST01040
3-AMINO-1,2,4-TRIAZOLE	61-82-5	PST01040
3-AMINO-1H-1,2,4-TRIAZOLE	61-82-5	PST01040
3-AMINO-2,5-DICHLOROBENZOIC ACID	133-90-4	PST29084
3-AMINO-2,5-DICHLOROBENZOIC ACID, METHYL ESTER	7286-84-2	PST71255
3-AMINO-2,5-DICHLOROBENZOIC ACID, MONOAMMONIUM SALT	1076-46-6	PST71252
3-AMINO-2,5-DICHLOROBENZOIC ACID, MONOSODIUM SALT	1954-81-0	PST71256
3-AMINOTRIAZOLE	61-82-5	PST01040
3-BENZOTHIAZOLINEACETIC ACID, 4-CHLORO-2-OXO'	3813-05-6	PST72725
3-BUTANONE	78-93-3	PST14460
3-CARBOXY-ALPHA,2-2-TRIMETHYLCYCLOPROPANEACRYLIC ACID, 1-METHYL ESTER, ESTER WITH 4-HYDROXY-3-METHYL-2-(2,4-PENTADIENYL)-2-CYCLOPENTEN-1-ONE	121-29-9	PST19970
3-CHLORO-ALPHA-ETHOXYIMINO-2,6-DIMETHOXYBENZYL BENZOATE	29104-30-1	PST72988
3-CHLORO-1,2-DIBROMOPROPANE	96-12-8	PST26490
3-CHLORO-4-METHYL-2-OXO-2H-1-BENZOPYRAN-7-YL DIETHYL ESTER PHOSPHORIC ACID	321-54-0	PST65468
3-CHLORO-4-METHYLCOUMARIN-7-YL DIETHYL PHOSPHATE	321-54-0	PST65468
3-CHLORO-4-METHYLCOUMARIN-7-YL DIETHYL PHOSPHOROTHIONATE	56-72-4	PST05490
3-CHLORO-4-NITROPHENYL DIMETHYL PHOSPHOROTHIONATE	500-28-7	PST71379
3-CHLORO-7-DIETHOXYPHOSPHINOTHIOYLOXY-4-METHYLCOUMARIN	56-72-4	PST05490
3-CHLORO-7-HYDROXY-4-METHYL-COUMARIN-O,O-DIETHYL PHOSPHOROTHIOATE	56-72-4	PST05490
3-CHLORO-7-HYDROXY-4-METHYLCOUMARIN DIETHYL PHOSPHATE	321-54-0	PST65468
3-CHLORO-7-HYDROXY-4-METHYLCOUMARIN O-ESTER WITH O,O DIETHYL PHOSPHOROTHIOATE	56-72-4	PST05490
3-CHLOROALLYL CHLORIDE	542-75-6	PST26820
3-CHLOROPROPENYL CHLORIDE	542-75-6	PST26820

SUBSTANCE NAME	CAS #	PST #
3-CRESOL	108-39-4	PST13080
3-CRESOLE	108-39-4	PST13080
3-CYCLO-OCTYL-1,1-DIMETHYLUREA	2163-69-1	PST05996
3-CYCLOHEXYL-1,5,6,7-TETRAHYDRO-2H-CYCLOPENTAPYRIMIDINE-2,4(3H)-DIONE	2164-08-1	PST73238
3-CYCLOHEXYL-1,5,6,7-TETRAHYDROCYCLOPENTAPYRIMIDINE-2,4(3H)-DIONE	2164-08-1	PST73238
3-CYCLOHEXYL-5,6-TRIMETHYLENEURACIL	2164-08-1	PST73238
3-CYCLOHEXYL-6-(DIMETHYLAMINO)-1-METHYL-S-TRIAZINE-3,4(1H,3H)-DIONE	51235-04-2	PST10994
3-CYCLOHEXYL-6-(DIMETHYLAMINO)-1-METHYL-1,3,5-TRIAZINE-2,4(1H,3H)-DIONE	51235-04-2	PST10994
3-CYCLOHEXYL-6-DIMETHYLAMINO-1-METHYL-1,3,5-TRIAZINE-2,4(1H,3H)-DIONE	51235-04-2	PST10994
3-CYCLOHEXYL-6-DIMETHYLAMINO-1-METHYL-1,3,5-TRIAZINE-2,4-DIONE	51235-04-2	PST10994
3-CYCLOHEXYL-6,7-DIHYDRO-1H-CYCLOPENTAPYRIMIDINE-2,4(3H,5H)-DIONE	2164-08-1	PST73238
3-CYCLOOCTYL-1,1-DIMETHYLUREA	2163-69-1	PST05996
3-DIETHOXYPHOSPHINOTHIOYLTHIOMETHYL-1,2,3-BENZOTRIAZIN-4(3H)-ONE	2642-71-9	PST02205
3-DIMETHOXYPHOSPHINITHIOYLTHIOMETHYL-1,2,3-BENZOTRIAZIN-4(3H)-ONE	86-50-0	PST02210
3-DIMETHOXYPHOSPHINOTHIOYLTHIOMETHYL-5-ETHOXY-1,3,4-THIADIAZOL -2(3H)-ONE	2669-32-1	PST73147
3-DIMETHOXYPHOSPHINOTHIOYLTHIOMETHYL-5-METHOXY-1,3,4-THIADIAZOL -2(3H)ONE	950-37-8	PST14175
3-DIMETHOXYPHOSPHINOYLOXY-N-METHYLISOCROTONAMIDE	6923-22-4	PST15165
3-DIMETHOXYPHOSPHINOYLOXY-N,N-DIMETHYLISOCROTONAMIDE	141-66-2	PST03090
3-DIMETHOXYPHOSPHINYLOXY-N,N-DIMETHYLISOCROTONAMIDE	141-66-2	PST03090
3-DIMETHYLAMINOMETHYLENEAMINOPHENYL METHYLCARBAMATE	22259-30-9	PST73187
3-ETHOXYCARBONYLAMINOPHENYL PHENYLCARBAMATE	13684-56-5	PST72336
3-ETHYLTHIO-4-AMINO-6-TERT-BUTYL-1,2,4-TRIAZINE-5-ONE	64529-56-2	PST09111
3-FURFURYL-2-METHYL-4-OXO-2-CYCLOPENTEN-1-YL CHRYSANTHEMUMATE	17080-02-3	PST10175
3-HYDROXY-P-CYMENE	89-83-8	PST23475
3-HYDROXY-2-PENTENEDIOIC ACID DIMETHYL ESTER DIMETHYL PHOSPHATE	122-10-1	PST03240
3-HYDROXY-5-METHYLISOXAZOLE	10004-44-1	PST22404
3-HYDROXYCARBOFURAN	16655-82-6	PST72800
3-HYDROXYCROTONIC ACID METHYL ESTER DIMETHYL PHOSPHATE	7786-34-7	PST18650
3-HYDROXYGLUTACONIC ACID DIMETHYL ESTER DIMETHYL PHOSPHATE	122-10-1	PST03240
3-HYDROXYTOLUENE	108-39-4	PST13080
3-INDOLEBUTYRIC ACID	133-32-4	PST29325
3-INDOLYLBUTRIC ACID	133-32-4	PST29325
3-ISOPROPYL-1H-BENZO-2,1,3-THIADIAZIN-4-ONE 2,2-DIOXIDE	25057-89-0	PST02584
3-ISOPROPYL-1H-2,1,3-BENZOTHIADIAZIN-4(3H)-ONE 2,2-DIOXIDE	25057-89-0	PST02584
3-ISOPROPYL-5-METHYLCARBAMIC ACID METHYL ESTER	2631-37-0	PST72957
3-ISOPROPYLL-5-METHYLPHENYL-N-METHYLCARBAMATE	2631-37-0	PST72957
3-ISOPROPYLPHENYL METHYLCARBAMATE	64-00-6	PST29423
3-ISOPROPYLPHENYL N-METHYLCARBAMATE	64-00-6	PST29423
3-ISOXAZOLOL, 5-METHYL-	10004-44-1	PST22404
3-KETO-7-CARBOFURAN PHENOL	17781-16-7	PST72799
3-KETOCARBOFURAN PHENOL	17781-16-7	PST72799
3-MESYLBUTANONE O-METHYLCARBAMOYLOXIME	34681-23-7	PST72434
3-METHOXYCARBONYLAMINOPHENYL 3'-METHYLCARBANILATE	13684-63-4	PST72282
3-METHYL-1-(1-METHYLETHYL)-1H-PYRAZOL-5-YL DIMETHYLCARBAMATE	119-38-0	PST83027
3-METHYL-1-PHENYL-1H-PYRAZOL-5-YL DIMETHYLCARBAMATE	87-47-8	PST73263
3-METHYL-1-PHENYL-5-PYRAZOLYL DIMETHYLCARBAMATE	87-47-8	PST73263
3-METHYL-1-PHENYLPYRAZOL-5-YL DIMETHYLCARBAMATE	87-47-8	PST73263
3-METHYL-2-BUTENOIC ACID-2-(1-METHYLPROPYL)-4,6-DINITROPHENYL ESTER	485-31-4	PST71960
3-METHYL-4-CHLOROPHENOL	59-50-7	PST29890
3-METHYL-5-(1-METHYLETHYL)PHENOL METHYLCARBAMATE	2631-37-0	PST72957
3-METHYL-5-(1-METHYLETHYL)PHENYL-CARBAMIC ACID METHYL ESTER	2631-37-0	PST72957

SUBSTANCE NAME	CAS #	PST #
3,5,6-TRICHLORO-2-PYRIDINYLOXYACETIC ACID	55335-06-3	PST72472
3,5,6-TRICHLORO-2-PYRIDYLOXYACETIC ACID	55335-06-3	PST72472
3,5,6-TRICHLORO-4-AMINOPICOLINIC ACID	1918-02-1	PST18840
3,6-DICHLORO-O-ANISIC ACID	1918-00-9	PST02260
3,6-DICHLORO-O-ANISIC ACID METHYL ESTER	6597-78-0	PST73131
3,6-DICHLORO-O-ANISIC ACID SODIUM SALT	1982-69-0	PST71250
3,6-DICHLORO-2-METHOXY METHYL BENZOATE	6597-78-0	PST73131
3,6-DICHLORO-2-METHOXYBENZOIC ACID	1918-00-9	PST02260
3,6-DICHLORO-2-METHOXYBENZOIC ACID METHYL ESTER	6597-78-0	PST73131
3,6-DICHLORO-2-METHOXYBENZOIC ACID SODIUM SALT	1982-69-0	PST71250
3,6-DICHLORO-2-PYRIDINECARBOXYLIC ACID	1702-17-6	PST05211
3,6-DICHLOROPICOLINIC ACID	1702-17-6	PST05211
3,6-DIHYDROXYPYRIDAZINE	123-33-1	PST13570
3,6-DIOXOPYRIDAZINE	123-33-1	PST13570
3,6-ENDOOXOHEXAHYDROPHTHALIC ACID	145-73-3	PST08580
3,6-ENDOXOHEXAHYDROPHTHALIC ACID	145-73-3	PST08580
3,6-ENDOXOHEXAHYDROPHTHALIC ACID DISODIUM SALT	129-67-9	PST08590
3,6-EPOXYCYCLOHEXANE-1,2-DICARBOXYLIC ACID	145-73-3	PST08580
3,7-BENZOFURANDIOL, 2,3-DIHYDRO-2,2-DIMETHYL-, 7-(METHYLCARBAMATE)	16655-82-6	PST72800
3,7-DIMETHYL-6-OXO-2-OXA-4-THIA-7-AZA-3-PHOSPHAOCTAN-8-OIC ACID, 3-SULFIDE, METHYL ESTER	29173-31-7	PST73246
3,7,9,13-TETRAMETHYL-5,11-DIOXA-2,8,14-TRITHIA-4,7,9,12-TETRA-AZAPENTADECA-3,12-DIENE-6,10-DIONE	59669-26-0	PST72456
3'-CHLORO-2-METHYL-P-VALEROTOLUIDIDE	2307-68-8	PST71164
3'-CHLORO-2-METHYLVALER-P-TOLUIDIDE	2307-68-8	PST71164
3',4'-DICHLORO-2-METHYLACRYLANILIDE	2164-09-2	PST71378
3',4'-DICHLOROMETHACRYLAMIDE	2164-09-2	PST71378
3',6'-DIHYDROXY-2',4',5',7'-TETRAIODOSPIRO(ISOBENZOFURAN -1(3H),9'-(9H)XANTHEN)-3-ONE	16423-68-0	PST08685
3A,4,7,7A-TETRAHYDRO-2-((TRICHLOROMETHYL)THIO)-1H-ISOINDOLE-1,3(2H)-DIONE	133-06-2	PST04210
3A,4,7,7A-TETRAHYDRO-2-((1,1,2,2-TETRACHLOROETHYL)THIO)-1H-ISOINDOLE-1,3(2H)-DIONE	2425-06-1	PST04200
3A,4,7,7A-TETRAHYDRO-5-(HYDROXYPHENYL-2-PYRIDINYLMETHYL)-8-(PHENYL -2-PYRIDINYLMETHYLENE)-4,7-METHANO-1H-ISOINDOLE-1,3(2H)-DIONE	991-42-4	PST72254
4(1H)-PYRIMIDINONE, 5-BUTYL-2-(DIMETHYLAMINO)-6-METHYL-	5221-53-4	PST72919
4(1H)-PYRIMIDINONE, 5-BUTYL-2-(ETHYLAMINO)-6-METHYL-	23947-60-6	PST08721
4(3H)-PYRIMIDINONE, 5-BUTYL-2-(ETHYLAMINO)-6-METHYL-	23947-60-6	PST08721
4-(((DIMETHYLAMINO)METHYLENE)AMINO)-M-TOLYL ESTER, METHYLCARBAMIC ACID	17702-57-7	PST73082
4-(DI-2-PROPENYLAMINO)-3,5-DIMETHYLPHENOL METHYLCARBAMATE (ESTER)	6392-46-7	PST72977
4-(DI-2-PROPENYLAMINO)-3,5-DIMETHYLPHENYL METHYLCARBAMATE	6392-46-7	PST72977
4-(DIMETHOXYPHOSPHINOTHIOYLOXY)BENZONITRILE	2636-26-2	PST72950
4-(DIMETHYLAMINO)-M-TOLYL METHYLCARBAMATE	2032-59-9	PST71500
4-(DIMETHYLAMINO)-1,4,4A,5,5A,6,11,12A-OCTAHYDRO-3,5,6,10,12,12A-HEXAHYDROXY-6-METHYL-1,11-DIOXO-2-NAPHTHACENECARBOXAMIDE, (4S-(4	15251-48-6	PST84256
4-(DIMETHYLAMINO)-1,4,4A,5,5A,6,11,12A-OCTAHDRO-3,5,6,10,12,12A-HEXAHYDROXY-6-METHYL-1,11-DIOXO-2-NAPHTHACENECARBOXAMIDE, CALCIUM SALT	15251-48-6	PST84256
4-(DIMETHYLAMINO)-3-METHYLPHENOL METHYLCARBAMATE (ESTER)	2032-59-9	PST71500
4-(DIMETHYLAMINO)-3,5-DIMETHYLPHENOL METHYLCARBAMATE (ESTER)	315-18-4	PST15010
4-(DIPROPYLAMINO)-3,5-DINITROBENZENESULFONAMIDE	19044-88-3	PST17324
4-(ETHOXYCARBONYL)ANILINE	94-09-7	PST72267
4-(HYDROXYMETHYLPHOSPHINOYL)-DL-HOMOALANINE, MONOAMMONIUM SALT	77182-82-2	PST72647
4-(METHYLSULFINYL)-3,5-XYLYL ESTER METHYLCARBAMIC ACID	2635-10-1	PST14191
4-(METHYLSULFINYL)-3,5-XYLYL METHYLCARBAMATE	2635-10-1	PST14191

ALPHABETICAL INDEX

SUBSTANCE NAME	CAS #	PST #
4-(METHYLSULFONYL)-2,6-DINITRO-N,N-DIPROPYLANILINE	4726-14-1	PST16525
4-(METHYLSULFONYL)-2,6-DINITRO-N,N-DIPROPYLBENZENAMINE	4726-14-1	PST16525
4-(METHYLTHIO)-3,5-XYLYL METHYLCARBAMATE	2032-65-7	PST14190
4-(1,1-DIMETHYLETHYL)-N-(1-METHYLPROPYL)-2,6-DINITROBENZENAMINE	33629-47-9	PST03525
4-(1,1-DIMETHYLETHYL)PHENOL	98-54-4	PST17440
4-(1,1-DIMETHYLPROPYL)PHENOL	80-46-6	PST71715
4-(2,4-DB) METHYL ESTER	18625-12-2	PST06227
4-(2,4-DICHLOROPHENOXY) METHYL BUTYRATE	18625-12-2	PST06227
4-(2,4-DICHLOROPHENOXY)BUTANOIC ACID METHYL ESTER	18625-12-2	PST06227
4-(2,4-DICHLOROPHENOXY)BUTYRIC ACID METHYL ESTER	18625-12-2	PST06227
4-(2,4-DICHLOROPHENOXY)METHYL BUTANOATE	18625-12-2	PST06227
4-(2,4,5-TB)	93-80-1	PST73203
4-(2,4,5-TRICHLOROPHENOXY) BUTANOIC ACID	93-80-1	PST73203
4-(2,4,5-TRICHLOROPHENOXY) BUTYRIC ACID	93-80-1	PST73203
4-AMINO-N-2-QUINOXALINYL-BENZENESULFONAMIDE	59-40-5	PST72046
4-AMINO-N-2-THIAZOLYLBENZENESULFONAMIDE	72-14-0	PST72047
4-AMINO-3-METHYL-6-PHENYL-1,2,4-TRIAZIN-5(4H)-ONE	41394-05-2	PST14095
4-AMINO-3-METHYL-6-PHENYL-1,2,4-TRIAZINE-5(4H)-ONE	41394-05-2	PST14095
4-AMINO-3,5,6-TRICHLORO-2-PICOLINIC ACID	1918-02-1	PST18840
4-AMINO-3,5,6-TRICHLORO-2-PYRIDINECARBOXYLIC ACID	1918-02-1	PST18840
4-AMINO-3,5,6-TRICHLOROPICOLINIC ACID	1918-02-1	PST18840
4-AMINO-3,5,6-TRICHLOROPYRIDINE-2-CARBOXYLIC ACID	1918-02-1	PST18840
4-AMINO-4,5-DIHYDRO-3-METHYL-6-PHENYL-1,2,4-TRIAZIN-5-ONE	41394-05-2	PST14095
4-AMINO-6-(1,1-DIMETHYLETHYL)-3-(ETHYLTHIO)-1,2,4-TRIAZIN-5(4H)-ONE	64529-56-2	PST09111
4-AMINO-6-(1,1-DIMETHYLETHYL)-3-(METHYLTHIO)-1,2,4-TRIAZIN-5(4H)-ONE	21087-64-9	PST15006
4-AMINO-6-TERT-BUTYL-3-(METHYLTHIO)-AS-TRIAZIN-5(4H)-ONE	21087-64-9	PST15006
4-AMINO-6-TERT-BUTYL-3-METHYLTHIO-1,2,4-TRIAZIN-5(4H)-ONE	21087-64-9	PST15006
4-AMINO-6-TERT-BUTYL-4,5-DIHYDRO-3-METHYLTHIO-1,2,4-TRIAZIN-5-ONE	21087-64-9	PST15006
4-AMINOBENZOIC ACID, ETHYL ESTER	94-09-7	PST72267
4-AMINOPYRIDINE	504-24-5	PST02180
4-AMINOTRICHLOROPICOLINIC ACID	1918-02-1	PST18840
4-AP	504-24-5	PST02180
4-AZIDO-N-(1-METHYLETHYL)-6-(METHYLTHIO)-1,3,5-TRIAZIN-2-AMINE	4658-28-0	PST02216
4-AZIDO-N-ISOPROPYL-6-METHYLTHIO-1,3,5-TRIAZIN-2-YLAMINE	4658-28-0	PST02216
4-BENZOTHIENYL METHYLCARBAMATE	1079-33-0	PST29855
4-BENZOTHIENYL-N-METHYLCARBAMATE	1079-33-0	PST29855
4-BROMO-2,5-DICHLOROPHENYL DIMETHYL PHOSPHOROTHIONATE	4824-78-6	PST03458
4-BROMO-2,5-DICHLOROPHENYL DIMETHYL PHOSPHOROTHIONATE	2104-96-3	PST71064
4-BROMO-2,5-DICHLOROPHENYL METHYL PHENYLPHOSPHONATE	25006-32-0	PST12776
4-BUTYLAMINOBENZOIC ACID, 2-(DIMETHYLAMINO)ETHYL ESTER, MONOHYDROCHLORIDE	136-47-0	PST72269
4-CARBETHOXYANILINE	94-09-7	PST72267
4-CHLORO-(ALPHA-(1-METHYLETHYL)BENZENEACETIC ACID CYANO (3-PHENOXYPHENYL)METHYL ESTER	51630-58-1	PST19948
4-CHLORO-ALPHA-(4-CHLOROPHENYL)-ALPHA(TRICHLOROMETHYL)BENZENEMETHANOL	115-32-2	PST07010
4-CHLORO-ALPHA-(4-CHLOROPHENYL)-ALPHA-HYDROXYBENZENEACETIC ACID ETHYL ESTER	510-15-6	PST04740
4-CHLORO-ALPHA-(4-CHLOROPHENYL)BENZENEACETIC ACID	83-05-6	PST06232
4-CHLORO-BETA-(4-CHLOROPHENYL)BENZENEETHANOL	2642-82-2	PST06323
4-CHLORO-M-CRESOL	59-50-7	PST29890
4-CHLORO-1-HYDROXY-3-METHYLBENZENE	59-50-7	PST29890
4-CHLORO-2-BUTYNYL M-CHLOROPHENYLCARBAMATE	101-27-9	PST71143
4-CHLORO-2-BUTYNYL N-(3-CHLOROPHENYL)CARBAMATE	101-27-9	PST71143
4-CHLORO-2-BUTYNYL 3-CHLOROPHENYLCARBAMATE	101-27-9	PST71143

SUBSTANCE NAME	CAS #	PST #
4-CHLORO-2-CYCLOPENTYLPHENOL	13347-42-7	PST71731
4-CHLORO-2-OXO-3(2H)-BENZOTHIAZOLEACETIC ACID	3813-05-6	PST72725
4-CHLORO-2-OXO-3-BENZOTHIAZOLINEACETIC ACID	3813-05-6	PST72725
4-CHLORO-2-OXOBENZOTHIAZOLIN-3-YLACETIC ACID	3813-05-6	PST72725
4-CHLORO-2,3-DIHYDRO-2-OXO-1,3-BENZOTHIAZOL-3-YLACETIC ACID	3813-05-6	PST72725
4-CHLORO-3-METHYLPHENOL	59-50-7	PST29890
4-CHLORO-3,5-DIMETHYLPHENOL	88-04-0	PST72258
4-CHLORO-3,5-XYLENOL	88-04-0	PST72258
4-CHLORO-5-(METHYLAMINO)-2-(ALPHA,ALPHA,ALPHA-TRIFLUORO-M-TOLYL)-3(2H)-PYRIDAZINONE	27314-13-2	PST72343
4-CHLORO-5-(METHYLAMINO)-2-(3-(TRIFLUOROMETHYL)PHENYL-3(2H)-PYRIDAZINONE	27314-13-2	PST72343
4-CHLORO-5-METHYLAMINO-2-(ALPHA,ALPHA,ALPHA-TRIFLUORO-M-TOLYL)-PYRIDAZIN-3(2H)-ONE	27314-13-2	PST72343
4-CHLORO-5-METHYLAMINO-2-(3-TRIFLUOROMETHYLPHENYL)PYRIDAZIN-3-ONE	27314-13-2	PST72343
4-CHLOROBENZYL 4-CHLOROPHENYL SULFIDE	103-17-3	PST71139
4-CHLOROBUT-2-YNYL 3-CHLOROCARBANILATE	101-27-9	PST71143
4-CHLOROBUT-2-YNYL 3-CHLOROPHENYLCARBAMATE	101-27-9	PST71143
4-CHLORODIPHENYL SULFONE	80-00-2	PST71663
4-CHLOROPHENYL BENZENESULFONATE	80-38-6	PST09677
4-CHLOROPHENYL BENZENESULFONIC ACID ESTER	80-38-6	PST09677
4-CHLOROPHENYL BENZENESULPHONATE	80-38-6	PST09677
4-CHLOROPHENYL PHENYL SULFONE	80-00-2	PST71663
4-CYANO-2,6-DI-IODOPHENYL OCTANOATE	3861-47-0	PST73075
4-CYANO-2,6-DIIODOPHENOL	1689-83-4	PST11468
4-CYANO-2,6-DIIODOPHENYL OCTANOATE	3861-47-0	PST73075
4-CYANOPHENYLETHYLPHENYL PHOSPHONOTHIONATE	13067-93-1	PST05805
4-DIALLYLAMINO-3,5-XYLYL METHYLCARBAMATE	6392-46-7	PST72977
4-DIMETHYLAMINO-M-CRESYL METHYLCARBAMATE	2032-59-9	PST71500
4-DIMETHYLAMINO-M-TOLYL METHYLCARBAMATE	2032-59-9	PST71500
4-DIMETHYLAMINO-3-CRESYL METHYLCARBAMATE	2032-59-9	PST71500
4-DIMETHYLAMINO-3-METHYL-PHENYL-N-METHYLCARBAMATE	2032-59-9	PST71500
4-ETHOXY-7-PHENYL-3,5-DIOXA-6-AZA-4-PHOSPHAOCT-6-ENE-8-NITRILE-4-SULFIDE	14816-18-3	PST73292
4-ETHOXYACETANILIDE	62-44-2	PST18340
4-HYDROXY-3-(1,2,3,4-TETRAHYDRO-1-NAPHTHALENYL)-2H-1-BENZOPYRAN-2-ONE	5836-29-3	PST05493
4-HYDROXY-3-(1,2,3,4-TETRAHYDRO-1-NAPHTHYL)COUMARIN	5836-29-3	PST05493
4-HYDROXY-3-(3-OXO-1-PHENYLBUTYL)-2H-1-BENZOPYRAN-2-ONE	81-81-2	PST25090
4-HYDROXY-3-(3-OXO-1-PHENYLBUTYL)-2H-1-BENZOPYRAN-2-ONE, SODIUM SALT	129-06-6	PST83008
4-HYDROXY-3-(3-OXO-1-PHENYLBUTYL)COUMARIN	81-81-2	PST25090
4-HYDROXY-3,5-DIIODOBENZONITRILE	1689-83-4	PST11468
4-HYDROXY-3,5-DIIODOBENZONITRILE, SODIUM SALT	2961-62-8	PST73074
4-HYDROXY-3,5-DIIODOPHENYL CYANIDE	1689-83-4	PST11468
4-HYDROXYBENZOIC ACID, METHYL ESTER	99-76-3	PST14677
4-HYDROXYBENZOIC ACID, PROPYL ESTER	94-13-3	PST19941
4-HYDROXYNITROBENZENE	100-02-7	PST17800
4-HYDROXYNONANOIC ACID LACTONE	104-61-0	PST10334
4-ISOTHIAZOLIN-3-ONE, 2-METHYL-	2682-20-4	PST72362
4-ISOTHIAZOLIN-3-ONE, 2-N-OCTYL-	26530-20-1	PST72294
4-ISOTHIAZOLIN-3-ONE, 2-OCTYL-	26530-20-1	PST72294
4-METHYL-2-PENTANONE	108-10-1	PST14550
4-METHYLBENZENESULFONIC ACID	104-15-4	PST67915
4-METHYLSULFONYL-2,6-DINITRO-N,N-DIPROPYLANILINE	4726-14-1	PST16525
4-METHYLSULPHONYL-2,6-DINITRO-N,N-DIPROPYLANILINE	4726-14-1	PST16525

ALPHABETICAL INDEX

ALPHABETICAL INDEX

SUBSTANCE NAME	CAS #	PST #
5-CHLORO-6-OXO-2-NORBORNANECARBONITRILE O-(METHYLCARBAMOYL)OXIME, (E)-ENDO-2-, EXO-5-	15271-41-7	PST73177
5-HYDROXYTETRACLINE HYDROCHLORIDE	2058-46-0	PST84045
5-ISOPROPYL-M-TOLYL METHYL-CARBAMATE	2631-37-0	PST72957
5-METHOXY-2-(DIMETHOXYPHOSPHINYLTHIOETHYL)PYRONE-4	2778-04-3	PST73139
5-METHYL M-CUMENYL METHYLCARBAMATE	2631-37-0	PST72957
5-METHYL-2-(1-METHYLETHYL) PHENOL	89-83-8	PST23475
5-METHYL-2-ISOPROPYL-1-PHENOL	89-83-8	PST23475
5-METHYL-3(2H)-ISOXAZOLONE	10004-44-1	PST22404
5-METHYL-3-ISOOXAZOLOL	10004-44-1	PST22404
5-METHYLISOXAZOL-3-OL	10004-44-1	PST22404
5-NORBORNENE-2,3-DIMETHANOL, 1,4,5,6,7,7-HEXACHLORO-, CYCLIC SULFITE	115-29-7	PST08560
5-NORBORNENE-2,3-DIMETHANOL,1,4,5,6,7,7-HEXACHLORO-,CYCLIC SULFITE, ENDO	959-98-8	PST00800
5-NORBORNENE-2,3-DIMETHANOL,1,4,5,6,7,7-HEXACHLORO-,CYCLIC SULFITE, EXO-	33213-65-9	PST03040
5-O-DEMETHYL-25-DE(1-METHYLPROPYL)-25-(1-METHYLETHYL)AVERMECTIN A1A	65195-56-4	PST02156
5-O-DEMETHYLAVERMECTIN A1A	65195-55-3	PST72553
5-TERT-BUTYL-3-(2,4-DICHLORO-5-ISOPROPOXYPHENYL)-1,3,4-OXADIAZOLIN-2-ONE	19666-30-9	PST72385
5-TERT-BUTYL-3-(2,4-DICHLORO-5-ISOPROPOXYPHENYL)-1,3,4-OXADIAZOL-(2(3H)ONE	19666-30-9	PST72385
5-2,3-DICHLOROALLYL DIISOPROPYLTHIOCARBAMATE	2303-16-4	PST06480
5,10-DIHYDRO-5,10-DIOXONAPHTHO(2,3-B)-P-DITHIIN-2,3-DICARBONITRILE	3347-22-6	PST72290
5,10-DIHYDRO-5,10-DIOXONAPHTHO(2,3-B)-1,4-DITHIIN-2,3-DICARBONITRILE	3347-22-6	PST72290
5,5-DIMETHYLPERHYDROPYRIMIDIN-2-ONE 4-TRIFLUOROMETHYL-ALPHA-(4-(4-TRILFLUOROMETHYLSTYRYL)CINNAMYLIDENEHYDRAZONE	67485-29-4	PST01009
5,6-BIS(CHLOROMETHYL)-1,2,3,4,7,7-HEXACHLORO-BICYCLO(2.2.1)HEPT-2-ENE	2550-75-6	PST73193
5,6-DIHYDRO-2-METHYL-N-PHENYL-1,4-OXATHIIN-3-CARBOXAMIDE	5234-68-4	PST04348
5,6-DIHYDRO-2-METHYL-N-PHENYL-1,4-OXATHIIN-3-CARBOXAMIDE 4,4-DIOXIDE	5259-88-1	PST17373
5,6-DIHYDRO-2-METHYL-1,4-OXATHI-IN-3-CARBOXANILIDE	5234-68-4	PST04348
5,6-DIHYDRO-2-METHYL-1,4-OXATHI-IN-3-CARBOXANILIDE 4,4-DIOXIDE	5259-88-1	PST17373
5,6-DIHYDRO-2-METHYL-1,4-OXATHI-INE-3-CARBOXANILIDE	5234-68-4	PST04348
5,6-DIHYDRO-2-METHYL-1,4-OXATHI-INE-3-CARBOXANILIDE 4,4-DIOXIDE	5259-88-1	PST17373
5,6-DIHYDRO-2-METHYL-1,4-OXATHIIN-3-CARBOXANILIDE	5234-68-4	PST04348
5,6-DIHYDRO-2-METHYL-1,4-OXATHIIN-3-CARBOXANILIDE 4,4-DIOXIDE	5259-88-1	PST17373
5,6-DIMETHYL-2-(METHYLAMINO)-4-PYRIMIDINYL DIMETHYLCARBAMATE	UNASSIGNED	PST06336
5,6-DIMETHYL-2-DIMETHYLAMINO-4-DIMETHYLCARBAMOYLOXYPYRIMIDINE	23103-98-2	PST72345
5'-(1,1,1-TRIFLUOROMETHANESULFONAMIDO)ACET-2',4'-XYLIDIDE	53780-34-0	PST72444
5'-(1,1,1-TRIFLUOROMETHANESULPHONAMIDO)ACET-2',4'-XYLIDIDE	53780-34-0	PST72444
6 ALPHA, 6A BETA, 7 BETA, 7A ALPHA)	72-20-8	PST08600
6(A)ALPHA,12(A)ALPHA))-	83-79-4	PST20200
6(BETA),6A(ALPHA)-	1024-57-3	PST10670
6-(ETHYLTHIO)-N,N'-BIS(1-METHYLETHYL)-1,3,5-TRIAZINE-2,4-DIAMINE	4147-51-7	PST72333
6-(1,1-DIMETHYLETHYL)-4-((2-METHYLPROPYLIDENE)AMINO)-3-(METHYLTHIO)-1,2,4-TRIAZIN-5(4H)-ONE	57052-04-7	PST11844
6-ACETOXY-2,4-DIMETHYL-M-DIOXAN-4-YL ESTER	828-00-2	PST28395
6-CHLORO-M-CRESOL	59-50-7	PST29890
6-CHLORO-N-(1,1-DIMETHYLETHYL)-N'-ETHYL-1,3,5-TRIAZINE-2,4-DIAMINE	5915-41-3	PST22536
6-CHLORO-N-CYCLOPROPYL-N'-(1-METHYLETHYL)-1,3,5-TRIAZINE-2,4-DIAMINE	22936-86-3	PST72296
6-CHLORO-N-ETHYL-N'-(1-METHYLETHYL)-1,3,5-TRIAZINE-2,4-DIAMINE	1912-24-9	PST02150
6-CHLORO-N,N,N'-TRIETHYL-1,3,5-TRIAZINE-2,4-DIAMINE	1912-26-1	PST23927
6-CHLORO-N,N,N',N'-TETRAETHYL-1,3,5-TRIAZINE-2,4-DIAMINE	580-48-3	PST72143
6-CHLORO-N,N'-BIS(1-METHYLETHYL)-1,3,5-TRIAZINE-2,4-DIAMINE	139-40-2	PST19736

SUBSTANCE NAME	CAS #	PST #
6-CHLORO-N,N'-DIETHYL-1,3,5-TRIAZINE-2,4-DIAMINE	122-34-9	PST20837
6-CHLORO-2-PHENYLPHENOL	85-97-2	PST71680
6-CHLORO-3-DIETHOXYPHOSPHINOTHIOYLTHIOMETHYL-1,3-BENZOXAZOL-2(3H)-ONE	2310-17-0	PST25720
6-CHLORO-3-HYDROXYTOLUENE	59-50-7	PST29890
6-CHLORO-3,4-XYLYL ESTER METHYLCARBAMIC ACID	671-04-5	PST02250
6-CHLORO-3,4-XYLYL METHYLCARBAMATE	671-04-5	PST02250
6-CHLOROXENOL	85-97-2	PST71680
6-ETHOXY-1,2-DIHYDRO-2,2,4-TRIMETHYLQUINOLINE	91-53-2	PST08740
6-ETHYLTHIO-N,N-DI-ISOPROPYL-1,3,5-TRIAZINE-2,4-DIAMINE	4147-51-7	PST72333
6-FURFURYLADENINE	525-79-1	PST72483
6-FURFURYLAMINO PURINE	525-79-1	PST72483
6-HYDROXY-3(2H)-PYRIDAZINONE	123-33-1	PST13570
6-METHOXY-N,N'-BIS(1-METHYLETHYL)-1,3,5-TRIAZINE-2,4-DIAMINE	1610-18-0	PST19967
6-METHYL-2-PROPYL-4-PYRIMIDINYL DIMETHYLCARBAMATE	2532-49-2	PST73266
6-TERT-BUTYL-4-ISOBUTYLIDENEAMINO-3-METHYLTHIO-1,2,4-TRIAZIN-5(4H) -ONE	57052-04-7	PST11844
6,7-DIHYDRODIPYRIDO(1,2-A:2',1'-C)PYRAZINEDIIUM DIBROMIDE	85-00-7	PST08250
6,7-DIHYDRODIPYRIDOL(1,2-A:2',1'-C)PYRAZIDIINIUM DIBROMIDE	85-00-7	PST08250
6,7,8,9,10,10-HEXACHLORO-1,5,5A,6,9,9A-HEXAHYDRO-6,9-METHANO-2,4, 3-BENZODIOXATHIEPIN 3-OXIDE	115-29-7	PST08560
6,9-METHANO-2,4,3-BENZODIOXATHIEPIN, 6, 7,8,9,10,10-HEXACHLORO-1,5, 5A,6,9,9A-HEXAHYDRO-,3-OXIDE	115-29-7	PST08560
6,9-METHANO-2,4,3-BENZODIOXATHIEPIN, 6,7,8,9,10,10-HEXACHLORO-1, 5,5A,6,9,9A-HEXAHYDRO-, 3-OXIDE, (3 ALPHA, 5A BETA, 6 ALPHA, 9 ALPHA,	959-98-8	PST00800
6,9-METHANO-2,4,3-BENZODIOXATHIEPIN, 6,7,8,9,10,10-HEXACHLORO-1, 5,5A,6,9,9A-HEXAHYDRO-, 3-OXIDE, (3 ALPHA, 5A ALPHA, 6 BETA, 9 BETA,	33213-65-9	PST03040
6A ALPHA, 7 BETA, 7A ALPHA)-	60-57-1	PST07080
6BETA,6A ALPHA)-	27304-13-8	PST17372
7-BENZOFURANOL, 2,3-DIHYDRO-2,2-DIMETHYL-, METHYLCARBAMATE	1563-66-2	PST04240
7-CHLOROBICYCLO(3.2.0)HEPTA-2.6-DIEN-6-YL DIMETHYL PHOSPHATE	23560-59-0	PST10685
7-HYDROXY-2,2-DIMETHYL-3(2H)-BENZOFURANONE	17781-16-7	PST72799
7-OXA-5-THIA-2-AZA-6-PHOSPHANONANOIC ACID, 6-ETHOXY-2-METHYL-3-, OXO-, ETHYL ESTER, 6-SULFIDE	2595-54-2	PST13675
7-OXABICYCLO(2.2.1)HEPTANE-2,3-DICARBOSYLIC ACID, DISODIUM SALT	129-67-9	PST08590
7-OXABICYCLO(2.2.1)HEPTANE-2,3-DICARBOXYLIC ACID	145-73-3	PST08580
7,11-HEXADECADIEN-1-OL, ACETATE, (Z,Z)-	52207-99-5	PST72448
8-HYDROXYQUINOLINE	148-24-3	PST30450
8-HYDROXYQUINOLINE BENZOATE (SALT)	7091-57-8	PST71657
8-OQ	148-24-3	PST30450
8-OXYQUINOLINE	148-24-3	PST30450
8-QUINOLINOL	148-24-3	PST30450
8-QUINOLINOL BENZOATE	7091-57-8	PST71657
88R	140-57-8	PST01850
9-OCTADECANOIC ACID (Z)-	112-80-1	PST17305
9-OCTADECENOIC ACID (Z)-,POTASSIUM SALT	143-18-0	PST72131
9-OCTADECENOIC ACID, 12-HYDROXY-, MONOPOTASSIUM SALT	7492-30-0	PST72074
9-OCTADECENOIC ACID, 12-HYDROXY-, MONOPOTASSIUM SALT, (R-(Z))-	7492-30-0	PST72074
9-TRICOSENE, (Z)-	27519-02-4	PST05185
9,10-ANTHRACENEDIONE	84-65-1	PST01600
9,10-ANTHRAQUINONE	84-65-1	PST01600
9,10-DIHYDRO-9,10-DIKETOANTHRACENE	84-65-1	PST01600
9,10-DIOXOANTHRACENE	84-65-1	PST01600
9A ALPHA)-	33213-65-9	PST03040
9A BETA)-	959-98-8	PST00800

CAS NUMBER INDEX

CAS NUMBER INDEX

CAS #	PST #	SUBSTANCE NAME
108-62-3	PST14090	METALDEHYDE
108-83-8	PST07500	DIISOBUTYL KETONE
108-94-1	PST05890	CYCLOHEXANONE
108-95-2	PST18380	PHENOL
1085-98-9	PST73026	DICHLOFLUANID
109-62-6	PST71476	ETHYLMERCURY ACETATE
109-86-4	PST14340	ETHYLENE GLYCOL MONOMETHYL ETHER
111-27-3	PST15630	N-HEXANOL
111-30-8	PST10423	GLUTARALDEHYDE
111-76-2	PST03540	BUTYL CELLOSOLVE
111-87-5	PST17270	N-OCTYL ALCOHOL
1111-67-7	PST71224	COPPER THIOCYANATE
1113-02-6	PST17328	OMETHOATE
1114-71-2	PST71472	PEBULATE
112-12-9	PST14675	METHYL NONYL KETONE
112-27-6	PST24000	TRIETHYLENE GLYCOL
112-30-1	PST06285	DECYL ALCOHOL
112-53-8	PST12500	LAURYL ALCOHOL
112-56-1	PST75661	LETHANE 384
112-80-1	PST17305	OLEIC ACID
1129-41-5	PST83074	METOLCARB
113-48-4	PST15955	N-OCTYL BICYCLOHEPTENE DICARBOXIMIDE
1134-23-2	PST71469	CYCLOATE
114-26-1	PST02540	O-ISOPROPOXYPHENYL METHYLCARBAMATE
115-26-4	PST07655	DIMEFOX
115-29-7	PST08560	ENDOSULFAN
115-32-2	PST07010	DICOFOL
115-90-2	PST06210	FENSULFOTHION
115-93-5	PST06135	CYTHIOATE
116-01-8	PST08723	ETHOATE-METHYL
116-06-3	PST00500	ALDICARB
116-52-9	PST06817	DICHLORALUREA
1166-46-7	PST23063	(+)-TRANS-TETRAMETHRIN
117-18-0	PST71616	TECNAZENE
117-26-0	PST71635	BULAN
117-52-2	PST05476	COUMAFURYL
117-80-6	PST06810	DICHLONE
117-81-7	PST06440	DI-(2-ETHYLHEXYL)PHTHALATE
117-84-0	PST08040	DIOCTYL PHTHALATE
118-52-5	PST26800	1,3-DICHLORO-5,5-DIMETHYLHYDANTOIN
118-74-1	PST10730	HEXACHLOROBENZENE
118-75-2	PST72136	CHLORANIL
119-12-0	PST71604	PYRIDAPHENTHION
119-36-8	PST14720	METHYL SALICYLATE
119-38-0	PST83027	ISOLAN
1194-65-6	PST06800	DICHLOBENIL
120-51-4	PST02805	BENZYL BENZOATE
120-67-2	PST06915	2,4-DICHLOROPHENOXY ETHANOL
120-80-9	PST04360	CATECHOL
12057-74-8	PST13480	MAGNESIUM PHOSPHIDE
121-21-1	PST19960	PYRETHRIN I
121-29-9	PST19970	PYRETHRIN II
121-54-0	PST71851	BENZETHONIUM CHLORIDE
121-75-5	PST13540	MALATHION

CAS NUMBER INDEX

CAS #	PST #	SUBSTANCE NAME
122-10-1	PST03240	BOMYL
122-14-5	PST09678	FENITROTHION
122-34-9	PST20837	SIMAZINE
122-39-4	PST08100	DIPHENYLAMINE
122-42-9	PST71564	PROPHAM
122-70-3	PST72314	2-PHENYLETHYL PROPIONATE
123-33-1	PST13570	MALEIC HYDRAZIDE
124-65-2	PST21070	SODIUM CACODYLATE
12407-86-2	PST12420	LANDRIN
12427-38-2	PST13589	MANEB
125-67-7	PST71492	POTASSIUM GIBBERELLATE
126-11-4	PST24430	2-(HYDROXYMETHYL)-2-NITRO-1,3-PROPANEDIOL
126-15-8	PST71487	2,3,4,5-BIS(2-BUTYLENE)TETRAHYDRO-2-FURALDEHYDE
126-22-7	PST71399	BUTONATE
126-75-0	PST71646	DEMETON-S
126-96-5	PST71497	SODIUM DIACETATE
127-18-4	PST22900	TETRACHLOROETHYLENE
127-20-8	PST71239	SODIUM DALAPON
12789-03-6	PST71948	CHLORDANE (COMMERCIAL)
128-04-1	PST71383	SODIUM DIMETHYLDITHIOCARBAMATE
129-06-6	PST83008	WARFARIN SODIUM
129-67-9	PST08590	ENDOTHALL-SODIUM
1300-71-6	PST25160	XYLENOL (MIXED ISOMERS)
1300-72-7	PST75603	SODIUM XYLENE SULFONATE
1303-28-2	PST02020	ARSENIC PENTOXIDE, SOLID
1303-86-2	PST03290	BORON OXIDE
1303-96-4	PST21010	SODIUM BORATE DECAHYDRATE
1305-62-0	PST03980	CALCIUM HYDROXIDE
1305-78-8	PST04030	CALCIUM OXIDE
13067-93-1	PST05805	CYANOFENPHOS
13071-79-9	PST22545	TERBUFOS
131-11-3	PST07740	DIMETHYL PHTHALATE
131-52-2	PST08506	SODIUM PENTACHLOROPHENATE
1310-58-3	PST19430	POTASSIUM HYDROXIDE, SOLUTION
1310-73-2	PST21300	SODIUM HYDROXIDE
13121-70-5	PST06110	CYHEXATIN
1314-13-2	PST25490	ZINC OXIDE
1314-23-4	PST25635	ZIRCONIUM OXIDE
1314-84-7	PST25540	ZINC PHOSPHIDE
1317-38-0	PST05655	CUPRIC OXIDE
1317-39-1	PST05470	CUPROUS OXIDE
13171-21-6	PST18670	PHOSPHAMIDON
1319-77-3	PST05510	CRESOL
13194-48-4	PST15080	ETHOPROP
132-27-4	PST08500	DOWICIDE A
132-66-1	PST71340	NAPTALAM
132-67-2	PST71341	NAPTALAM SODIUM
1327-53-3	PST02070	ARSENIC TRIOXIDE, SOLID
133-06-2	PST04210	CAPTAN
133-07-3	PST10012	FOLPET
133-32-4	PST29325	3-INDOLEBUTYRIC ACID
133-90-4	PST29084	CHLORAMBEN
1330-20-7	PST25150	XYLENE
1330-85-4	PST71854	DODECYLBENZYLTRIMETHYLAMMONIUM CHLORIDE

CAS NUMBER INDEX

CAS #	PST #	SUBSTANCE NAME
13347-42-7	PST71731	4-CHLORO-2-CYCLOPENTYLPHENOL
13356-08-6	PST24866	VENDEX
13360-45-7	PST04552	CHLORBROMURON
1338-02-9	PST05460	COPPER NAPHTHENATE
134-62-3	PST84230	DEET
13426-91-0	PST05710	CUPRIETHYLENEDIAMINE
13429-27-1	PST72073	POTASSIUM MYRISTATE
13457-18-6	PST73169	PYRAZOPHOS
135-19-3	PST03050	2-NAPHTHOL
13593-03-8	PST73112	QUINALPHOS
136-32-3	PST21713	2,4,5-SODIUM TRICHLOROPHENATE
136-47-0	PST72269	TETRACAINE HYDROCHLORIDE
136-78-7	PST05500	SODIUM 2,4-DICHLOROPHENOXYETHYL SULFATE
13684-56-5	PST72336	DESMEDIPHAM
13684-63-4	PST72282	PHENMEDIPHAM
137-26-8	PST23430	THIRAM
137-30-4	PST25397	ZINC DIMETHYLDITHIOCARBAMATE
137-40-6	PST21575	SODIUM PROPIONATE
137-42-8	PST71430	SODIUM METHYLDITHIOCARBAMATE
138-87-4	PST03075	BETA-TERPINEOL
13840-33-0	PST12920	LITHIUM HYPOCHLORITE
139-02-6	PST21530	SODIUM PHENOLATE
139-33-3	PST08305	ETHYLENEDIAMINETETRAACETIC ACID, DISODIUM SALT
139-40-2	PST19736	PROPAZINE
139-41-3	PST71447	SODIUM DIHYDROXYETHYLGLYCINE
13932-13-3	PST72015	POTASSIUM TETRATHIONATE
1397-94-0	PST83076	ANTIMYCIN A
140-41-0	PST15197	MONURON TCA
140-56-7	PST73084	FENAMINOSULF
140-57-8	PST01850	ARAMITE
1405-10-3	PST84263	NEOMYCIN SULFATE
14086-35-2	PST02552	FENTHION OXON SULFONE
141-43-5	PST08710	ETHANOLAMINE
141-66-2	PST03090	DICROTOPHOS
141-78-6	PST08750	ETHYL ACETATE
142-59-6	PST16080	NABAM
1420-07-1	PST72921	DINOTERB
14214-32-5	PST07386	DIFENOXURON
14255-72-2	PST06228	FENSULFOTHION SULFONE
143-18-0	PST72131	POTASSIUM OLEATE
143-19-1	PST21418	SODIUM OLEATE
143-33-9	PST21160	SODIUM CYANIDE, SOLID
143-50-0	PST12330	CHLORDECONE
144-41-2	PST73096	MORPHOTHION
144-55-8	PST20970	SODIUM BICARBONATE
144-62-7	PST17360	OXALIC ACID
14484-64-1	PST09680	FERBAM
145-73-3	PST08580	ENDOTHALL
1461-22-9	PST72222	TRIBUTYLTIN CHLORIDE
148-24-3	PST30450	8-HYDROXYQUINOLINE
14816-18-3	PST73292	PHOXIM
14835-94-0	PST04753	1-CHLORO-2-(O-CHLOROPHENYL)-2-(P-CHLOROPHENYL)ETHYLENE
149-30-4	PST13738	MERCAPTOBENZOTHIAZOLE
1491-41-4	PST72737	NAPHTHALOPHOS

CAS NUMBER INDEX

CAS #	PST #	SUBSTANCE NAME
150-50-5	PST10010	MERPHOS
150-68-5	PST15196	MONURON
15096-52-3	PST05560	SODIUM FLUOALUMINATE
151-21-3	PST08485	DODECYL SODIUM SULFATE
151-38-2	PST83031	METHOXYETHYLMERCURIC ACETATE
151-50-8	PST19350	POTASSIUM CYANIDE, SOLID
152-16-9	PST20350	SCHRADAN
15251-48-6	PST84256	CALCIUM OXYTETRACYCLINE
15263-52-2	PST04359	CARTAP HYDROCHLORIDE
15271-41-7	PST73177	EXO-3-CHLORO-ENDO-6-CYANO-2-NORBORANONE O-(METHYLCARBAMOYL)OXIME
15299-99-7	PST72319	NAPROPAMIDE
15457-05-3	PST72248	FLUORODIFEN
15475-56-6	PST14211	METHOTREXATE SODIUM
155-04-4	PST27776	2-MERCAPTOBENZOTHIAZOLE, ZINC SALT
15545-48-9	PST04912	CHLOROTOLURON
156-62-7	PST03930	CALCIUM CYANAMIDE, NOT HYDRATED
1563-66-2	PST04240	CARBOFURAN
1582-09-8	PST24085	TRIFLURALIN
15879-93-3	PST00775	ALPHA-CHLORALOSE
15922-78-8	PST21420	SODIUM PYRIDINETHIONE
1596-84-5	PST06195	DAMINOZIDE
15972-60-8	PST00506	ALACHLOR
1610-17-9	PST02148	ATRATON
1610-18-0	PST19967	PROMETON
16118-49-3	PST72941	CARBETAMIDE
1634-78-2	PST13541	MALATHION OXYGEN ANALOG
16423-68-0	PST08685	ERYTHROSIN B
1646-87-3	PST00503	ALDICARB SULFOXIDE
1646-88-4	PST72406	ALDOXYCARB
16655-82-6	PST72800	3-HYDROXYCARBOFURAN
16662-85-4	PST04344	CARBOPHENOTHION SULFONE
16662-86-5	PST04343	CARBOPHENOTHION OXYGEN ANALOG SULFOXIDE
16662-87-6	PST04342	CARBOPHENOTHION OXYGEN ANALOG SULFONE
16672-87-0	PST72293	ETHEPHON
16752-77-5	PST14200	METHOMYL
16871-71-9	PST25410	ZINC SILICOFLUORIDE
1689-83-4	PST11468	IOXYNIL
1689-84-5	PST03542	BROMOXYNIL
1689-99-2	PST03543	BROMOXYNIL OCTANOATE
16893-85-9	PST21620	SODIUM SILICOFLUORIDE
1698-60-8	PST71928	PYRAZON
1702-17-6	PST05211	CLOPYRALID
17040-19-6	PST06319	DEMETON-S-METHYL SULFONE
17080-02-3	PST10175	FURETHRIN
17109-49-8	PST08555	EDIFENPHOS
17210-55-8	PST71651	TEMEPHOS SULFOXIDE
17297-40-4	PST04345	CARBOPHENOTHION SULFOXIDE
1746-01-6	PST08060	2,3,7,8-TETRACHLORODIBENZO-P-DIOXIN
1746-81-2	PST15174	MONOLINURON
1754-58-1	PST72310	DIAMIDOFOS
1757-18-2	PST00493	AKTON
17702-57-7	PST73082	FORMPARANATE
17781-16-7	PST72799	7-HYDROXY-2,2-DIMETHYL-3(2H)-BENZOFURANONE
17804-35-2	PST02580	BENOMYL

CAS NUMBER INDEX

CAS #	PST #	SUBSTANCE NAME
18181-70-9	PST73035	IODOFENPHOS
1836-75-5	PST23580	NITROFEN
1836-77-7	PST23865	CHLORNITROFEN
18530-56-8	PST71400	NOREA
1861-32-1	PST04913	CHLORTHAL-DIMETHYL
1861-40-1	PST02570	BENFLURALIN
18625-12-2	PST06227	2,4-DB METHYL ESTER
18691-97-9	PST14108	METHABENZTHIAZURON
18854-01-8	PST12280	ISOXATHION
1897-45-6	PST04890	CHLOROTHALONIL
19044-88-3	PST17324	ORYZALIN
1910-42-5	PST18020	PARAQUAT DICHLORIDE
1912-24-9	PST02150	ATRAZINE
1912-26-1	PST23927	TRIETAZINE
1918-00-9	PST02260	DICAMBA
1918-02-1	PST18840	PICLORAM
1918-13-4	PST73046	CHLORTHIAMID
1918-16-7	PST19686	PROPACHLOR
1918-18-9	PST72247	SWEP
1928-37-6	PST22392	2,4,5-T METHYL ESTER
1928-38-7	PST71307	METHYL 2,4-DICHLOROPHENOXY ACETATE
1928-45-6	PST71294	2,4-D PROPYLENE GLYCOL BUTYL ETHER ESTER
1929-77-7	PST71473	VERNOLATE
1929-82-4	PST16530	NITRAPYRIN
1929-88-0	PST72971	BENZTHIAZURON
1934-21-0	PST22465	TARTRAZINE YELLOW DYE
1954-81-0	PST71256	CHLORAMBEN, SODIUM SALT
19666-30-9	PST72385	OXADIAZON
1967-16-4	PST73265	CHLORBUFAM
19750-95-9	PST71656	CHLORDIMEFORM HYDROCHLORIDE
1982-47-4	PST04905	CHLOROXURON
1982-49-6	PST20586	SIDURON
1982-69-0	PST71250	SODIUM DICAMBA
1983-10-4	PST72227	TRIBUTYLTIN FLUORIDE
1984-06-1	PST72105	SODIUM CAPRYLATE
19937-59-8	PST15009	METOXURON
2008-41-5	PST71474	BUTYLATE
2032-59-9	PST71500	AMINOCARB
2032-65-7	PST14190	METHIOCARB
20354-26-1	PST72344	METHAZOLE
20427-59-2	PST05640	CUPRIC HYDROXIDE
2058-46-0	PST84045	OXYTETRACYCLINE HYDROCHLORIDE
2074-50-2	PST71670	PARAQUAT DIMETHYL SULFATE
2078-42-4	PST71136	SODIUM 2,3,6-TRICHLOROBENZOIC ACID
20859-73-8	PST00970	ALUMINUM PHOSPHIDE
2104-64-5	PST08650	EPN
2104-96-3	PST71064	BROMOPHOS
21087-64-9	PST15006	METRIBUZIN
2122-70-5	PST71628	ETHYL 1-NAPHTHALENEACETATE
21267-72-1	PST73038	PRYNACHLOR
21548-32-3	PST16141	FOSTHIETAN
21564-17-0	PST71392	2-(THIOCYANOMETHYLTHIO)BENZOTHIAZOLE
21609-90-5	PST12780	LEPTOPHOS
2163-69-1	PST05996	CYCLURON

CAS #	PST #	SUBSTANCE NAME
2163-80-6	PST15180	MONOSODIUM METHANE ARSONATE
2164-08-1	PST73238	LENACIL
2164-09-2	PST71378	DICRYL
2164-17-2	PST09907	FLUOMETURON
21725-46-2	PST05762	CYANAZINE
2212-67-1	PST71471	MOLINATE
22224-92-6	PST16145	FENAMIPHOS
22248-79-9	PST72244	(Z)-2-CHLORO-1-(2,4,5-TRICHLOROPHENYL)VINYL DIMETHYL PHOSPHATE
22259-30-9	PST73187	FORMETANATE
2235-25-8	PST71479	ETHYLMERCURIC PHOSPHATE
22350-76-1	PST72245	(E)-2-CHLORO-1-(2,4,5-TRICHLOROPHENYL)VINYL DIMETHYL PHOSPHATE
2244-21-5	PST19360	POTASSIUM DICHLOROISOCYANURATE
2275-14-1	PST18373	PHENCAPTON
2275-18-5	PST19943	PROTHOATE
2275-23-2	PST73108	VAMIDOTHION
22781-23-3	PST02560	BENDIOCARB
22936-75-0	PST72145	DIMETHAMETRYN
22936-86-3	PST72296	CYPRAZINE
2303-16-4	PST06480	DIALLATE
2303-17-5	PST72050	TRIALLATE
23052-51-9	PST06317	DEMETON-O OXYGEN ANALOG
2307-68-8	PST71164	PENTANOCHLOR
2310-17-0	PST25720	PHOSALONE
23103-98-2	PST72345	PIRIMICARB
2312-35-8	PST19720	PROPARGITE
2312-76-7	PST71411	DINITRO-O-CRESOL SODIUM SALT
23135-22-0	PST17370	OXAMYL
23184-66-9	PST03497	BUTACHLOR
23319-66-6	PST71768	PHENYL MERCURIC TRIETHANOL AMMONIUM LACTATE
23422-53-9	PST10050	FORMETANATE HYDROCHLORIDE
23505-41-1	PST72377	PIRIMIFOS-ETHYL
23560-59-0	PST10685	HEPTENOPHOS
23564-05-8	PST72308	THIOPHANATE-METHYL
23564-06-9	PST72322	THIOPHANATE
2385-85-5	PST09690	MIREX
23947-60-6	PST08721	ETHIRIMOL
23950-58-5	PST19670	PRONAMIDE
24017-47-8	PST73068	TRIAZOPHOS
2425-06-1	PST04200	CAPTAFOL
2425-25-4	PST73057	ACETOXON
24307-26-4	PST72386	MEPIQUAT CHLORIDE
2436-73-9	PST27881	MCPA METHYL ESTER
24602-86-6	PST72537	2,6-DIMETHYL-4-TRIDECYLMORPHOLINE
2463-84-5	PST71380	DICAPTHON
24934-91-6	PST04655	CHLORMEPHOS
2496-91-5	PST06306	DEMETON-S-SULFONE
2496-92-6	PST06316	DEMETON-S SULFOXIDE
2497-06-5	PST08381	DISULFOTON SULFONE
2497-07-6	PST17385	OXYDISULFOTON
25006-32-0	PST12776	LEPTOPHOS OXYGEN ANALOG
25057-89-0	PST02584	BENTAZON
25155-18-4	PST71862	METHYLBENZETHONIUM CHLORIDE
25155-30-0	PST21220	SODIUM DODECYLBENZENESULFONATE
25167-83-3	PST71689	TETRACHLOROPHENOL

CAS NUMBER INDEX

CAS NUMBER INDEX

CAS #	PST #	SUBSTANCE NAME
28805-78-9	PST73199	ISONORURON
2893-78-9	PST21180	SODIUM DICHLOROISOCYANURATE
29104-30-1	PST72988	BENZOXIMATE
29173-31-7	PST73246	MECARPHON
2921-88-2	PST04910	CHLORPYRIFOS
29232-93-7	PST72378	PIRIMIFOS-METHYL
2941-55-1	PST72327	ETHIOLATE
2961-62-8	PST73074	IOXYNIL SODIUM
297-78-9	PST83032	ISOBENZAN
297-97-2	PST25590	THIONAZIN
29790-52-1	PST16450	NICOTINE SALICYLATE
298-00-0	PST14680	METHYL PARATHION
298-02-2	PST18640	PHORATE
298-03-3	PST71645	DEMETON-O
298-04-4	PST08380	DISULFOTON
298-39-5	PST71042	STREPTOMYCIN SULFATE (1:3) SALT
299-84-3	PST20180	RONNEL
299-85-4	PST71236	O-2,4-DICHLOROPHENYL O-METHYL ISOPROPYLPHOSPHORAMIDOTHIOATE
299-86-5	PST05550	CRUFOMATE
29973-13-5	PST72421	ETHIOFENCARB
300-76-5	PST06660	NALED
30043-49-3	PST72551	ETHIDIMURON
301-12-2	PST17375	OXYDEMETON-METHYL
3042-84-0	PST72769	BROMPYRAZON
30525-89-4	PST18000	PARAFORMALDEHYDE
30560-19-1	PST00065	ACEPHATE
3060-89-7	PST15008	METOBROMURON
3084-62-6	PST22393	2,4,5-T, PROPYLENE GLYCOL BUTYL ETHER ESTER
309-00-2	PST00520	ALDRIN
311-45-5	PST07200	DIETHYL P-NITROPHENYL PHOSPHATE
31218-83-4	PST72440	PROPETAMPHOS
3134-12-1	PST72972	PHENOBENZURON
314-40-9	PST03330	BROMACIL
314-42-1	PST71090	ISOCIL
315-18-4	PST15010	MEXACARBATE
319-84-6	PST00770	ALPHA-HEXACHLOROCYCLOHEXANE
319-85-7	PST03010	BETA-HEXACHLOROCYCLOHEXANE
319-86-8	PST06310	DELTA-HEXACHLOROCYCLOHEXANE
31972-43-7	PST16146	FENAMIPHOS SULFOXIDE
31972-44-8	PST16144	FENAMIPHOS SULFONE
321-54-0	PST65468	COROXON
3244-90-4	PST72135	O,O,O',O'-TETRAPROPYL DITHIOPYROPHOSPHATE
3251-23-8	PST05644	CUPRIC NITRATE
3254-63-5	PST73095	DIMETHYL P-(METHYLTHIO)PHENYL PHOSPHATE
327-98-0	PST00478	TRICHLORONATE
32889-48-8	PST72398	PROCYAZINE
330-54-1	PST08420	DIURON
330-55-2	PST12826	LINURON
3309-87-3	PST72763	S-(4-CHLOROPHENYL) O,O-DIMETHYL PHOSPHOROTHIOATE
33213-65-9	PST03040	BETA-ENDOSULFAN
333-20-0	PST19640	POTASSIUM THIOCYANATE
333-41-5	PST06540	DIAZINON
3337-71-1	PST72352	ASULAM
3347-22-6	PST72290	DITHIANON

CAS NUMBER INDEX

CAS #	PST #	SUBSTANCE NAME
33629-47-9	PST03525	BUTRALIN
33693-04-8	PST72770	TERBUMETON
3383-96-8	PST00020	TEMEPHOS
33911-28-3	PST20098	(-)-TRANS-RESMETHRIN
34014-18-1	PST72340	TEBUTHIURON
34123-59-6	PST12254	ISOPROTURON
3424-82-6	PST06245	2-(2-CHLOROPHENYL)-2-(4-CHLOROPHENYL)-1,1-DICHLOROETHENE
34256-82-1	PST72539	ACETOCHLOR
34375-28-5	PST72288	2-((HYDROXYMETHYL)AMINO)ETHANOL
34624-48-1	PST00551	CIS-ALLETHRIN
34643-46-4	PST72655	PROTHIOPHOS
34681-10-2	PST73270	BUTOCARBOXIM
34681-23-7	PST72434	BUTOXYCARBOXIM
35256-85-0	PST72852	TEBUTAM
35367-38-5	PST07388	DIFLUBENZURON
35400-43-2	PST22387	SULPROFOS
35691-65-7	PST26487	1,2-DIBROMO-2,4-DICYANOBUTANE
35764-59-1	PST20094	CISMETHRIN
3615-21-2	PST73047	CHLORFLURAZOLE
36614-38-7	PST12275	ISOTHIOATE
36653-82-4	PST04525	CETYL ALCOHOL
36756-79-3	PST72405	TIOCABAZIL
3689-24-5	PST22470	SULFOTEP
3691-35-8	PST04826	CHLOROPHACINONE
371-86-8	PST15030	MIPAFOX
37199-66-9	PST19548	POTASSIUM POLYSULFIDE
37333-40-7	PST18807	PHOSTEX
3734-48-3	PST04565	CHLORDENE
3734-95-0	PST72949	CYANTHOATE
3734-97-2	PST71642	AMITON OXALATE
3735-23-7	PST73085	METHYL PHENCAPTON
3735-33-9	PST18665	PHOSMET OXYGEN ANALOG
3761-41-9	PST02555	FENTHION SULFOXIDE
3761-42-0	PST02554	FENTHION SULFONE
3766-60-7	PST03523	BUTURON
3766-81-2	PST03324	FENOBUCARB
3792-59-4	PST73239	O-(2,4-DICHLOROPHENYL) O-ETHYL PHENYLPHOSPHONOTHIOATE
37924-13-3	PST72375	PERFLUIDONE
38083-17-9	PST05208	CLIMBAZOLE
3810-74-0	PST84290	STREPTOMYCIN SULFATE (2:3) SALT
3811-49-2	PST20325	SALITHION
3813-05-6	PST72725	BENAZOLIN
38260-54-7	PST73148	ETRIMFOS
3861-41-4	PST71388	BROMOXYNIL BUTYRATE
3861-47-0	PST73075	IOXYNIL OCTANOATE
38641-94-0	PST20205	GLYPHOSATE ISOPROPYLAMINE SALT
38727-55-8	PST72968	DIETHATYL-ETHYL
3878-19-1	PST73188	FUBERIDAZOLE
39148-24-8	PST72563	FOSETYL AL
39196-18-4	PST23330	THIOFANOX
39300-45-3	PST71402	DINOCAP
39765-80-5	PST23079	TRANS-NONACHLOR
3983-45-7	PST25082	VIOZENE OXON
4104-14-7	PST71150	PHOSACETIM

CAS NUMBER INDEX

CAS #	PST #	SUBSTANCE NAME
41198-08-7	PST72412	PROFENOFOS
41394-05-2	PST14095	METAMITRON
4147-51-7	PST72333	DIPROPETRYN
420-04-2	PST05760	CYANAMIDE
42509-80-8	PST15035	ISAZOPHOS
42576-02-3	PST72332	BIFENOX
42795-00-6	PST03231	SULPROFOS OXYGEN ANALOG SULFONE
42874-03-3	PST72413	OXYFLUORFEN
43222-48-6	PST72348	DIFENZOQUAT METHYL SULFATE
4329-12-8	PST04752	1-CHLORO-3-(2,2-DICHLORO-1-(4-CHLOROPHENYL)ETHYL)BENZENE
443-48-1	PST72529	METRONIDAZOLE
4482-55-7	PST71389	FENURON-TCA
465-73-6	PST11810	ISODRIN
4658-28-0	PST02216	AZIPROTRYN
4685-14-7	PST71671	PARAQUAT ION
470-90-6	PST04575	CHLORFENVINPHOS
47000-92-0	PST73184	FLUORIDAMID
4726-14-1	PST16525	NITRALIN
4824-78-6	PST03458	BROMOPHOS-ETHYL
4841-20-7	PST20831	SILVEX, METHYL ESTER
4849-32-5	PST72271	KARBUTILATE
485-31-4	PST71960	BINAPACRYL
4891-54-7	PST06309	DEMETON-O-SULFONE
497-19-8	PST21080	SODIUM CARBONATE
49866-87-7	PST72349	DIFENZOQUAT ION
50-00-0	PST50003	FORMALDEHYDE SOLUTION, 37%
50-29-3	PST06250	DICHLORODIPHENYLTRICHLOROETHANE
50-31-7	PST71134	2,3,6-TRICHLOROBENZOIC ACID
500-28-7	PST71379	CHLORTHION
502-39-6	PST83040	METHYLMERCURIC DICYANAMIDE
504-24-5	PST02180	AVITROL
50512-35-1	PST12253	ISOPROTHIOLANE
50563-36-5	PST07677	DIMETHACHLOR
50594-66-6	PST72452	ACIFLUORFEN
5064-31-3	PST24475	TRISODIUM NITRILOTRIACETATE
50782-69-9	PST83104	VX
51-03-6	PST75640	PIPERONYL BUTOXIDE
51-28-5	PST28620	2,4-DINITROPHENOL
510-15-6	PST04740	CHLOROBENZILATE
5103-71-9	PST00776	ALPHA-CHLORDANE
5103-74-2	PST10331	BETA-CHLORDANE
51218-45-2	PST15003	METOLACHLOR
51235-04-2	PST10994	HEXAZINONE
5131-24-8	PST72347	DITALIMFOS
51348-90-4	PST23062	(+)-CIS-TETRAMETHRIN
51487-69-5	PST72572	CLOETHOCARB
51630-58-1	PST19948	FENVALERATE
51707-55-2	PST23299	THIDIAZURON
51877-74-8	PST23708	TRANS-PERMETHRIN
52-51-7	PST72832	2-BROMO-2-NITROPROPANE-1,3-DIOL
52-68-6	PST23790	TRICHLORFON
52-85-7	PST09675	FAMPHUR
52207-99-5	PST72448	(Z,Z)-7,11-HEXADECADIEN-1-OL ACETATE
5221-49-8	PST08049	DIOTHYL

CAS #	PST #	SUBSTANCE NAME
5221-53-4	PST72919	DIMETHIRIMOL
52315-07-8	PST72392	CYPERMETHRIN
5234-68-4	PST04348	CARBOXIN
525-79-1	PST72483	KINETIN
52508-35-7	PST72391	SODIUM DIKEGULAC
5251-93-4	PST72964	BENZADOX
5259-88-1	PST17373	OXYCARBOXIN
526-95-4	PST10408	GLUCONIC ACID
5281-13-0	PST71828	PIPROTAL
52918-63-5	PST72784	DELTAMETHRIN
532-32-1	PST20965	SODIUM BENZOATE
5329-14-6	PST22200	SULFAMIC ACID
533-74-4	PST06230	DAZOMET
534-52-1	PST07910	DINITRO-ORTHO-CRESOL
53516-76-0	PST71834	ALKYLDIMETHYLBENZYLAMMONIUM CHLORIDE (60% C14, 30% C16, 5% C18,
53558-25-1	PST72334	PYRIMINIL
53780-34-0	PST72444	MEFLUIDIDE
53939-28-9	PST72519	(Z)-11-HEXADECENAL
54-11-5	PST16430	NICOTINE
542-75-6	PST26820	1,3-DICHLOROPROPENE
545-55-1	PST22510	TEPA
55-38-9	PST02550	FENTHION
55-91-4	PST07590	ISOFLUROPHATE
55-98-1	PST03482	BUSULFAN
55283-68-6	PST72436	ETHALFLURALIN
55285-14-8	PST72266	CARBOSULFAN
55335-06-3	PST72472	TRICLOPYR
555-37-3	PST16143	NEBURON
556-61-6	PST14950	METHYLISOTHIOCYANATE
55635-13-7	PST72430	SODIUM ALLOXYDIM
557-30-2	PST73143	GLYOXIME
55861-78-4	PST72586	ISOURON
5598-13-0	PST71652	CHLORPYRIFOS-METHYL
5598-15-2	PST04911	CHLORPYRIFOS OXYGEN ANALOG
56-23-5	PST04310	CARBON TETRACHLORIDE
56-36-0	PST72220	TRIBUTYLTIN ACETATE
56-38-2	PST18040	PARATHION
56-72-4	PST05490	COUMAPHOS
56-81-5	PST10440	GLYCERIN
56070-15-6	PST22537	TERBUFOS OXYGEN ANALOG SULFONE
56073-07-5	PST07385	DIFENACOUM
56073-10-0	PST03327	BRODIFACOUM
563-12-2	PST08720	ETHION
56534-02-2	PST04566	ALPHA-CHLORDENE
56641-38-4	PST04567	GAMMA-CHLORDENE
56802-99-4	PST80117	CHLORINATED TRISODIUM PHOSPHATE
569-64-2	PST13533	MALACHITE GREEN CHLORIDE
57-06-7	PST00680	ALLYL ISOTHIOCYANATE
57-24-9	PST22080	STRYCHNINE
57-55-6	PST19870	PROPYLENE GLYCOL
57-74-9	PST04560	CHLORDANE
57-92-1	PST21917	STREPTOMYCIN
57052-04-7	PST11844	ISOMETHIOZIN
572-48-5	PST73073	COUMITHOATE

CAS #	PST #	SUBSTANCE NAME
577-11-7	PST00406	DIOCTYL SODIUM SULFOSUCCINATE
58-27-5	PST71050	MENADIONE
58-36-6	PST30500	10, 10'-OXYDIPHENOXARSINE
58-89-9	PST12810	LINDANE
580-48-3	PST72143	CHLORAZINE
5836-29-3	PST05493	COUMATETRALYL
584-08-7	PST19290	POTASSIUM CARBONATE
584-79-2	PST00550	ALLETHRIN
59-05-2	PST14210	METHOTREXATE
59-40-5	PST72046	SULFAQUINOXALINE
59-50-7	PST29890	4-CHLORO-M-CRESOL
5902-51-2	PST71099	TERBACIL
5915-41-3	PST22536	TERBUTHYLAZINE
59669-26-0	PST72456	THIODICARB
597-09-1	PST71953	2-NITRO-2-ETHYL-1,3-PROPANEDIOL
60-00-4	PST09570	ETHYLENEDIAMINETETRAACETIC ACID
60-41-3	PST22090	STRYCHNINE SULFATE
60-51-5	PST07670	DIMETHOATE
60-57-1	PST07080	DIELDRIN
60238-56-4	PST64913	CHLORTHIOPHOS
608-73-1	PST03080	1,2,3,4,5,6-HEXACHLOROCYCLOHEXANE
6099-79-2	PST08022	DINOSEB METHYL ETHER
61-82-5	PST01040	AMITROLE
6132-17-8	PST06211	FENSULFOTHION OXYGEN ANALOG SULFONE
6164-98-3	PST04570	CHLORDIMEFORM
61790-81-6	PST08741	ETHOXYLAN 1685
62-38-4	PST18560	PHENYLMERCURIC ACETATE
62-44-2	PST18340	PHENACETIN
62-73-7	PST07000	DICHLORVOS
62-74-8	PST21240	SODIUM FLUOROACETATE
62476-59-9	PST72453	SODIUM ACIFLUORFEN
6273-99-0	PST71754	PHENYLMERCURIC BORATE
628-63-7	PST15270	N-AMYL ACETATE
63-25-2	PST04220	CARBARYL
63231-67-4	PST20670	SILICA GEL
639-58-7	PST24380	TRIPHENYLTIN CHLORIDE
6392-46-7	PST72977	ALLYXYCARB
64-00-6	PST29423	3-ISOPROPYLPHENYL N-METHYLCARBAMATE
64-02-8	PST23137	ETHYLENEDIAMINETETRAACETIC ACID, TETRASODIUM SALT
64-17-5	PST08700	ETHYL ALCOHOL
64-19-7	PST00120	ACETIC ACID, GLACIAL
640-15-3	PST83056	THIOMETON
640-19-7	PST09930	FLUOROACETAMIDE
644-64-4	PST83057	DIMETILAN
64529-56-2	PST09111	ETHYL METRIBUZIN
64742-52-5	PST17323	ORTHO SPRAY STOCK "L"
64902-72-3	PST72504	CHLORSULFURON
6492-18-8	PST23871	TRICHLORONATE OXYGEN ANALOG
65-30-5	PST16459	NICOTINE SULFATE, LIQUID
65-30-5	PST16460	NICOTINE SULFATE, SOLID
65-31-6	PST16470	NICOTINE TARTRATE
65-85-0	PST02720	BENZOIC ACID
650-51-1	PST73307	SODIUM TRICHLOROACETATE
65195-55-3	PST72553	AVERMECTIN B1A

CAS NUMBER INDEX

CAS #	PST #	SUBSTANCE NAME
74222-97-2	PST72544	SULFOMETURON-METHYL
74223-64-6	PST72546	METSULFURON-METHYL
7429-90-5	PST01000	ALUMINUM, METALLIC, POWDER
7440-22-4	PST20770	SILVER
7440-44-0	PST04246	CARBON, ACTIVATED
7440-50-8	PST05430	COPPER
7446-09-5	PST22290	SULFUR DIOXIDE
7446-70-0	PST00900	ALUMINUM CHLORIDE, ANHYDROUS
7487-88-9	PST13510	MAGNESIUM SULFATE
7487-94-7	PST13800	MERCURIC CHLORIDE
7492-30-0	PST72074	POTASSIUM RICINOLEATE
75-09-2	PST14930	DICHLOROMETHANE
75-21-8	PST09520	ETHYLENE OXIDE
75-56-9	PST19910	PROPYLENE OXIDE
75-60-5	PST03710	CACODYLIC ACID
75-65-0	PST22630	TERT-BUTYL ALCOHOL
75-69-4	PST09990	FLUOROTRICHLOROMETHANE
75-71-8	PST06880	DICHLORODIFLUOROMETHANE
75-99-0	PST06200	DALAPON
7553-56-2	PST11400	IODINE
7558-79-4	PST08330	SODIUM PHOSPHATE, DIBASIC
7558-80-7	PST15190	SODIUM PHOSPHATE, MONOBASIC
75736-33-3	PST07005	DICLOBUTRAZOL
759-94-4	PST71470	S-ETHYL DIPROPYLTHIOCARBAMATE
76-03-9	PST23810	TRICHLOROACETIC ACID, SOLID
76-06-2	PST04830	CHLOROPICRIN
76-22-2	PST04130	CAMPHOR
76-44-8	PST10660	HEPTACHLOR
7601-54-9	PST24480	TRISODIUM PHOSPHATE
7631-86-9	PST20610	SILICON DIOXIDE, AMORPHOUS
7631-89-2	PST20940	SODIUM ARSENATE
7631-90-5	PST21000	SODIUM BISULFITE
7631-99-4	PST21400	SODIUM NITRATE
7632-00-0	PST21410	SODIUM NITRITE
7646-85-7	PST25350	ZINC CHLORIDE, SOLID
7646-93-7	PST19255	POTASSIUM BISULFATE
7647-01-0	PST11150	HYDROGEN CHLORIDE, ANHYDROUS
7647-14-5	PST21105	SODIUM CHLORIDE
7647-15-6	PST21060	SODIUM BROMIDE
76578-14-8	PST20075	QUIZALOFOP-ETHYL
7664-38-2	PST18690	PHOSPHORIC ACID, SOLID
7664-93-9	PST22350	SULFURIC ACID
7673-09-8	PST80113	TRICHLOROMELAMINE
7681-11-0	PST19435	POTASSIUM IODIDE
7681-38-1	PST20990	SODIUM BISULFATE
7681-49-4	PST21230	SODIUM FLUORIDE, SOLID
7681-52-9	PST21310	SODIUM HYPOCHLORITE
7696-12-0	PST23061	TETRAMETHRIN
77-06-5	PST10405	GIBBERELLIC ACID
77-92-9	PST05200	CITRIC ACID
7700-17-6	PST05115	CROTOXYPHOS
7704-34-9	PST22280	SULFUR
77182-82-2	PST72647	GLUFOSINATE-AMMONIUM
7722-64-7	PST19520	POTASSIUM PERMANGANATE

CAS #	PST #	SUBSTANCE NAME
7722-84-1	PST11190	HYDROGEN PEROXIDE
7722-88-5	PST23140	TETRASODIUM PYROPHOSPHATE, ANHYDROUS
7723-14-0	PST18790	PHOSPHORUS, RED
	PST18800	PHOSPHORUS, WHITE
7726-95-6	PST03340	BROMINE
7733-02-0	PST25570	ZINC SULFATE
7738-94-5	PST04930	CHROMIC ACID
7757-79-1	PST19470	POTASSIUM NITRATE
7757-83-7	PST21660	SODIUM SULFITE
7758-02-3	PST19280	POTASSIUM BROMIDE
7758-19-2	PST21110	SODIUM CHLORITE
7758-29-4	PST21730	SODIUM TRIPOLYPHOSPHATE
7758-98-7	PST05670	CUPRIC SULFATE
7758-99-8	PST05690	CUPRIC SULFATE, PENTAHYDRATE
7761-88-8	PST20810	SILVER NITRATE
7773-06-0	PST01400	AMMONIUM SULFAMATE
7775-09-9	PST21100	SODIUM CHLORATE
7778-18-9	PST04110	CALCIUM SULFATE, ANHYDROUS
7778-39-4	PST01990	ARSENIC ACID
7778-44-1	PST03850	CALCIUM ARSENATE
7778-50-9	PST19370	POTASSIUM DICHROMATE
7778-53-2	PST19544	POTASSIUM PHOSPHATE TRIBASIC
7778-54-3	PST03990	CALCIUM HYPOCHLORITE
7778-80-5	PST19590	POTASSIUM SULFATE
7782-50-5	PST04600	CHLORINE
7782-63-0	PST09870	FERROUS SULFATE, HEPTAHYDRATE
7783-18-8	PST01460	AMMONIUM THIOSULFATE
7783-90-6	PST20787	SILVER CHLORIDE
7784-40-9	PST12540	LEAD ARSENATE
7784-42-1	PST02100	ARSINE
7784-46-5	PST52136	SODIUM ARSENITE, LIQUID
7786-30-3	PST13360	MAGNESIUM CHLORIDE
7786-34-7	PST18650	MEVINPHOS
78-34-2	PST08050	DIOXATHION
78-48-8	PST06300	DEF
78-53-5	PST83006	AMITON
78-57-9	PST72980	MENAZON
78-87-5	PST19860	PROPYLENE DICHLORIDE
78-93-3	PST14460	METHYL ETHYL KETONE
786-19-6	PST04340	CARBOPHENOTHION
79-09-4	PST19750	PROPIONIC ACID
79-14-1	PST10500	GLYCOLIC ACID
79-21-0	PST18310	PEROXYACETIC ACID
79-57-2	PST17414	OXYTETRACYCLINE
79241-46-6	PST72557	FLUAZIFOP-P-BUTYL
80-00-2	PST71663	P-CHLOROPHENYL PHENYL SULFONE
80-38-6	PST09677	FENSON
80-46-6	PST71715	4-TERT-AMYLPHENOL
8000-27-9	PST04365	CEDARWOOD OIL
8000-29-1	PST71180	OIL OF CITRONELLA
8000-46-2	PST73283	OIL OF GERANIUM
8000-48-4	PST71453	OIL OF EUCALYPTUS
8000-78-0	PST72626	GARLIC OIL
8001-22-7	PST21765	SOYBEAN OIL

CAS NUMBER INDEX

CAS #	PST #	SUBSTANCE NAME
8001-26-1	PST71365	LINSEED OIL
8001-29-4	PST05475	COTTONSEED OIL
8001-35-2	PST23640	TOXAPHENE
8001-50-1	PST71162	STROBANE
8001-54-5	PST00537	ALKYLDIMETHYLBENZYLAMMONIUM CHLORIDE
8001-54-5	PST00539	ALKYL DIMETHYL ETHYLBENZYL AMMONIUM CHLORIDE
8001-58-9	PST05230	COAL TAR CREOSOTE
8001-78-3	PST11225	CASTOR OIL, HYDROGENATED
8001-85-2	PST03250	BONE OIL
8002-09-3	PST18900	PINE OIL
8002-33-3	PST24575	TURKEY RED OIL
8003-34-7	PST19980	PYRETHRUM
8006-54-0	PST12425	LANOLIN
8006-64-2	PST24580	TURPENTINE
8007-44-1	PST71456	PENNYROYAL OIL
8007-47-4	PST04145	CANADA BALSAM
8007-70-3	PST71028	OIL OF ANISE
8008-20-6	PST10090	KEROSENE
8008-51-3	PST04140	CAMPHOR OIL
8008-74-0	PST20575	SESAME OIL
8018-01-7	PST71120	MANCOZEB
8021-39-4	PST71221	WOOD CREOSOTE
8022-00-2	PST14438	METHYL DEMETON
8023-53-8	PST71839	DICHLOROBENZALKONIUM CHLORIDE
8051-02-3	PST71010	SABADILLA ALKALOIDS
8052-42-4	PST02140	ASPHALT
8052-42-4	PST71177	BITUMEN
8065-36-9	PST03480	BUFENCARB
8065-48-3	PST06320	DEMETON
81-81-2	PST25090	WARFARIN
813-78-5	PST07882	DIMETHYL PHOSPHATE
81335-77-5	PST11308	IMAZETHAPYR
814-91-5	PST05650	CUPRIC OXALATE
82-66-6	PST08068	DIPHACINONE
82-68-8	PST18140	PENTACHLORONITROBENZENE
82560-54-1	PST72562	BENFURACARB
828-00-2	PST28395	DIMETHOXANE
83-05-6	PST06232	DDA-P,P'
83-26-1	PST18970	PIVAL
83-28-3	PST24738	VALONE
83-79-4	PST20200	ROTENONE
834-12-8	PST01006	AMETRYN
84-62-8	PST08095	DIPHENYL PHTHALATE
84-65-1	PST01600	ANTHRAQUINONE
84-66-2	PST07210	DIETHYL PHTHALATE
84-74-2	PST06740	DIBUTYL PHTHALATE
841-06-5	PST14204	METHOPROTRYNE
845-52-3	PST72212	2,4-BIS(3-METHOXYPROPYLAMINO)-6-METHYLTHIO-S-TRIAZINE
85-00-7	PST08250	DIQUAT
85-97-2	PST71680	6-CHLORO-2-PHENYLPHENOL
86-50-0	PST02210	AZINPHOS-METHYL
86-87-3	PST26130	1-NAPHTHALENEACETIC ACID
86-88-4	PST01830	ANTU
867-27-6	PST71969	DEMETON-O-METHYL

CAS NUMBER INDEX

CAS #	PST #	SUBSTANCE NAME
87-47-8	PST73263	PYROLAN
87-86-5	PST18150	PENTACHLOROPHENOL
87-90-1	PST23860	TRICHLOROISOCYANURIC ACID
88-04-0	PST72258	4-CHLORO-3,5-DIMETHYLPHENOL
88-30-2	PST71405	ALPHA, ALPHA, ALPHA-TRIFLUORO-4-NITRO-M-CRESOL
88-85-7	PST08020	DINOSEB
886-50-0	PST22538	TERBUTRYN
89-83-8	PST23475	THYMOL
90-43-7	PST18470	ORTHO-PHENYLPHENOL
90-98-2	PST06246	4,4'-DICHLOROBENZOPHENONE
900-95-8	PST24378	TRIPHENYLTIN ACETATE
9002-88-4	PST19119	POLYETHYLENE
9003-01-4	PST04349	POLYACRYLIC ACID
9003-29-6	PST75671	POLYBUTENE
9004-53-9	PST06363	DEXTRIN, CORN
9005-64-5	PST80107	POLYOXYETHYLENE (20) SORBITAN MONOLAURATE
9005-65-6	PST40200	POLYOXYETHYLENE (20) SORBITAN MONOOLEATE
9006-42-2	PST71123	METIRAM
9016-45-9	PST16835	ETHOXYLATED NONYLPHENOL
9080-17-5	PST01380	AMMONIUM POLYSULFIDE SOLUTION
91-20-3	PST16120	NAPHTHALENE
91-53-2	PST08740	ETHOXYQUIN
919-54-0	PST00117	ACETHION
919-76-6	PST01007	AMIDITHION
919-86-8	PST83065	DEMETON-S-METHYL
92-84-2	PST18400	PHENOTHIAZINE
93-71-0	PST71155	ALLIDOCHLOR
93-72-1	PST20830	SILVEX
93-76-5	PST28690	2,4,5-TRICHLOROPHENOXYACETIC ACID
93-80-1	PST73203	4-(2,4,5-TRICHLOROPHENOXY) BUTYRIC ACID
94-09-7	PST72267	BENZOCAINE
94-13-3	PST19941	PROPYL PARABEN
94-74-6	PST27880	MCPA
94-75-7	PST28510	2,4-DICHLOROPHENOXYACETIC ACID
94-80-4	PST71295	BUTYL 2,4-DICHLOROPHENOXYACETATE
94-96-2	PST71458	2-ETHYL-1,3-HEXANEDIOL
944-22-9	PST10020	FONOFOS
947-02-4	PST06115	PHOSFOLAN
95-06-7	PST22190	SULFALLATE
95-50-1	PST16970	O-DICHLOROBENZENE, LIQUID
95-95-4	PST28700	2,4,5-TRICHLOROPHENOL
950-10-7	PST13735	MEPHOSFOLAN
950-35-6	PST14678	METHYL PARAOXON
950-37-8	PST14175	METHIDATHION
953-17-3	PST71647	METHYL CARBOPHENOTHION
957-51-7	PST71406	DIPHENAMID
959-98-8	PST00800	ALPHA-ENDOSULFAN
96-12-8	PST26490	1,2-DIBROMO-3-CHLOROPROPANE
961-11-5	PST72243	TETRACHLORVINPHOS
961-22-8	PST10585	GUTHION OXYGEN ANALOG
962-58-3	PST06541	DIAZINON OXYGEN ANALOG
97-11-0	PST19949	PYPYRETHRIN
97-16-5	PST71350	GENITE
97-17-6	PST06805	DICHLOFENTHION

CAS NUMBER INDEX